PATTERSON'S

AMERICAN EDUCATION

2014 Edition
VOLUME CX

Editorial Staff
Editor Wayne Moody
Assistant Editor Rita Ostdick
Assistant Editor James Thiessen

EDUCATIONAL DIRECTORIES INC.

Educational Directories Inc.
PO Box 68097
Schaumburg IL 60168-0097
(847) 891-1250 or (800) 357-6183
www.ediusa.com

First edition published 1904. One Hundred Tenth edition 2014

ISBN 978-0-9883500-2-1
ISSN 0079-0230
Library of Congress Catalog Card Number: 04-012953
Printed in the United States of America

CONTENTS

HOW TO USE THIS DIRECTORY

Patterson's AMERICAN EDUCATION (published annually since 1904) is THE standard directory to secondary schools and is the first in a series of school directories published by Educational Directories Inc. Patterson's ELEMENTARY EDUCATION (published annually since 1989) is identical in format to Patterson's AMERICAN EDUCATION but is a directory to elementary schools. The two volumes combined fulfill the need for a single, systematized, comprehensive directory to our nation's schools from kindergarten through post-graduate studies.

Patterson's AMERICAN EDUCATION contains 10,778 public school districts, 30,979 public secondary schools, 6,159 private and Catholic secondary schools and more than 7,000 post-secondary schools in an easy-to-use and consistent format. It is an invaluable resource for anyone involved in education or educational research. School registrars, guidance counselors, principals, superintendents, directors of admissions, financial aid officers, schools of education, public libraries, government agencies, armed forces, and business people find it a welcome replacement for the multitude of other directories required for national coverage of our nation's school systems with their variation in size, content, format and publishing date.

One of the primary objectives of this directory is to make available the latest, most comprehensive information about secondary and post-secondary schools in a condensed and easily accessible format. Its general organization is geographical. Entries are arranged alphabetically, by state, then by community (post office) and then by District and School name. Each state begins with a listing of the officials in its Department of Education followed by the head of the State Board of Education. If a state has intermediate superintendents (a level of superintendent between the state superintendent of schools and the superintendents who actually supervise the schools) they appear in a table preceding the community listings. Community listings follow and include the community name, county name, community population, district name, total district student enrollment, the superintendent's name, address, telephone, fax number and website where available followed by a listing of the district schools, showing their enrollment, grade range and the principal's name, address, telephone number and fax number. A district may be responsible for schools in more than one community. To achieve consistency, the district office is listed in the community in which it is located. A cross-reference is provided to and from the schools of the district located in other communities.

A short line may appear at the end of the listing of public secondary schools. This line separates the public secondary schools from the private and Catholic secondary schools and the post-secondary schools located in the community. Private and Catholic school listings include their enrollment, grade range and the principal's name, address, telephone number and fax number. Post-secondary school listings include their name, address and telephone number. Please refer to page vi, "Guide to Editorial Style," for an example of how these elements work together to provide an easy-to-use format.

Schools Listed

Patterson's AMERICAN EDUCATION lists the following types of schools

- **Middle Schools** usually teach any combination of grades five through eight.
- **Junior High Schools** usually teach grades seven through nine.
- **Junior-Senior High Schools** usually teach any combination of grades five through eight and include nine through twelve.
- **High Schools** usually teach grades nine through twelve or ten through twelve.
- **K-12 Schools**
- **Vocational-Technical Schools**

The following are included:

- All graded state approved public secondary schools.
- All graded secondary schools belonging to the National Catholic Education Association.
- All graded, regionally accredited, private secondary schools.
- Private secondary schools belonging to the member associations of the Council of American Private Education.

Non graded, special education schools and other non-traditional secondary schools are not listed.

Patterson's ELEMENTARY EDUCATION lists Kindergarten Schools, Primary Schools, Elementary Schools, Middle Schools and K-12 Schools.

ABBREVIATIONS

ALT . . . Alternative School
AVC. . . Area Vocational Center
AVTS . . Area Vocational Technical School
CCSD. . Community Consolidated School District
CDC . . Child Development Center
CESD . . Consolidated Elementary School District
CISD . . City Independent School District
CSD. . . City School District
CUSD. . Community Unit School District
ECC. . . Early Childhood Center
ECCSD . Elementary Community Consolidated School District
EHSD . . Elementary-High School District
ES . . . Elementary School
ESD. . . Elementary School District
EVD. . . Exempted Village District
HS . . . High School
HSD. . . High School District
IS. . . . Intermediate School
ISD . . . Independent School District
JESD . . Joint Elementary School District
JHS . . . Junior High School
JSD . . . Joint School District
JSHS . . Junior-Senior High School
JUESD . Joint Unified Elementary School District
JUHSD . Joint Unified High School District
JUNESD Joint Union Elementary School District
JUNHSD Joint Union High School District
JUSD . . Joint Unified School District
JVSD . . Joint Vocational School District
K . . . . Kindergarten
MS . . . Middle School
MSHS. . Middle School High School
PS . . . Primary School
RHSD. . Rural High School District
RISD . . Rural Independent School District
ROC . . Regional Occupational Center
ROP . . Regional Occupational Program
RSD. . . Reorganized School District
S . . . . School
SAD. . . School Administrative District
SC . . . School Corporation
SD . . . School District
SHS. . . Senior High School
SSD. . . Separate School District
UESD . . Unified Elementary School District
UFD. . . Union Free District
UHSD. . Unified High School District
UNESD . Union Elementary School District
UNHSD . Union High School District
UNSD. . Union School District
USD. . . Unified School District
Vo/Tech. Vocational/Technical

GUIDE TO EDITORIAL STYLE

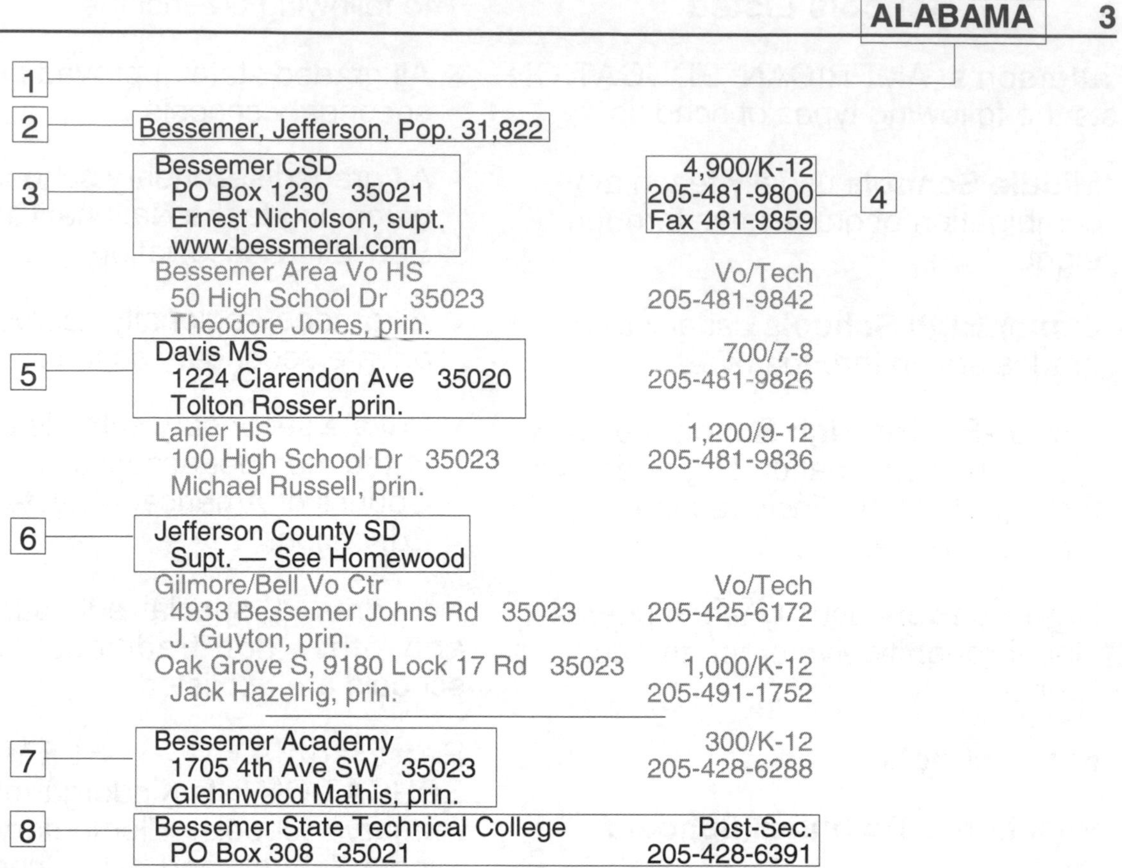

1. State.
2. City, county and city population.
3. Community school districts - school district name (refer to page v for abbreviations), address, superintendent's name and website (please enter as shown to access districts website).
4. Enrollment, grade range and phone number (fax number is included where available).
5. Community schools - school name, address and principal's name.
6. If the school district office is not located in this city, a cross-reference will show office location.
7. Private and Catholic secondary schools appear below a short line in the cities where they are located.
8. Post-secondary schools also appear below the line in the cities where they are located.

SECONDARY SCHOOL COUNTS BY STATE

	Public								
State	Districts	5-9	7-12	9-12	10-12	K-12	Private	Catholic	Total
Alabama	134	235	78	204	9	72	99	10	841
Alaska	54	35	17	36	0	175	11	3	331
Arizona	112	200	10	195	1	6	40	13	577
Arkansas	238	157	122	104	37	2	42	7	709
California	416	1,222	65	1,017	10	12	537	126	3,405
Colorado	178	255	76	218	1	11	66	9	814
Connecticut	123	167	14	160	3	2	52	25	546
Delaware	16	33	2	24	0	0	37	8	120
District Of Columbia	1	14	1	12	0	2	13	9	52
Florida	67	516	38	387	10	14	371	37	1,440
Georgia	175	448	12	382	8	6	185	12	1,228
Hawaii	1	38	6	33	0	6	44	7	135
Idaho	109	92	34	78	7	17	28	1	366
Illinois	479	663	54	583	17	0	135	78	2,009
Indiana	291	296	106	242	7	2	69	25	1,038
Iowa	316	250	101	222	8	2	23	30	952
Kansas	278	219	98	224	1	3	31	16	870
Kentucky	169	217	31	198	5	8	49	29	706
Louisiana	70	203	64	163	6	57	85	52	700
Maine	104	87	15	91	3	10	33	4	347
Maryland	24	221	13	185	1	0	103	38	585
Massachusetts	226	274	49	226	1	0	89	53	918
Michigan	518	467	109	458	19	33	176	53	1,833
Minnesota	326	199	184	156	15	21	59	28	988
Mississippi	148	164	51	157	6	33	85	9	653
Missouri	446	318	200	285	14	6	56	46	1,371
Montana	160	210	2	166	0	0	13	8	559
Nebraska	249	110	162	100	1	4	14	28	668
Nevada	16	89	10	70	5	9	31	2	232
New Hampshire	77	81	3	75	0	2	35	7	280
New Jersey	267	370	37	307	8	0	111	63	1,163
New Mexico	89	133	23	102	5	0	39	4	395
New York	639	762	255	787	23	75	352	120	3,013
North Carolina	115	456	20	452	6	5	262	7	1,323
North Dakota	148	33	109	42	5	1	6	5	349
Ohio	611	550	154	575	9	8	109	85	2,101
Oklahoma	421	266	28	395	37	3	36	6	1,192
Oregon	164	191	44	170	4	17	59	12	661
Pennsylvania	496	458	158	407	28	1	232	85	1,865
Rhode Island	32	48	0	44	0	1	18	11	154
South Carolina	81	237	20	178	8	1	92	4	621
South Dakota	149	151	5	147	1	2	11	8	474
Tennessee	120	310	33	259	8	19	153	12	914
Texas	974	1,387	148	1,084	56	124	260	56	4,089
Utah	41	129	22	32	58	2	34	4	322
Vermont	52	28	23	26	0	11	24	2	166
Virginia	132	327	39	294	16	2	148	13	971
Washington	247	340	53	271	19	24	116	17	1,087
West Virginia	55	122	18	93	0	2	30	7	327
Wisconsin	377	326	80	319	5	11	106	51	1,275
Wyoming	47	58	8	52	4	7	5	0	181
Total	10,778	14,162	3,004	12,487	495	831	4,814	1,345	47,916

SECONDARY SCHOOLS

ALABAMA

ALABAMA DEPARTMENT OF EDUCATION

PO Box 302101, Montgomery 36130-2101
Telephone 334-242-9700
Fax 334-242-9708
Website http://www.alsde.edu

State Superintendent of Education Dr. Thomas R. Bice

ALABAMA BOARD OF EDUCATION

PO Box 302101, Montgomery 36130-2101

President Governor Robert Bentley

PUBLIC, PRIVATE AND CATHOLIC SECONDARY SCHOOLS

Abbeville, Henry, Pop. 2,658
Henry County SD 2,700/PK-12
300 N Trawick St 36310 334-585-2206
Lesa Knowles, supt. Fax 585-2551
www.henrycountyboe.org
Abbeville JSHS 500/7-12
411 Graball Cutoff 36310 334-585-2065
Dale Barnes, prin. Fax 585-6562
Other Schools – See Headland

Abbeville Christian Academy 200/K-12
PO Box 9 36310 334-585-5100
Jim Arrington, head sch Fax 585-5100

Adamsville, Jefferson, Pop. 4,485
Jefferson County SD
Supt. — See Birmingham
Bottenfield MS 800/6-8
400 Hillcrest Rd 35005 205-379-2550
Jonetta Terry, prin. Fax 379-2553
Minor HS 1,100/9-12
2285 Minor Pkwy 35005 205-379-4750
Dr. Juanita Inman-Vann, prin. Fax 379-4795

Addison, Winston, Pop. 756
Winston County SD
Supt. — See Double Springs
Addison HS 300/7-12
PO Box 240 35540 256-747-2286
Micah Smothers, prin. Fax 747-6410

Akron, Hale, Pop. 355
Hale County SD
Supt. — See Greensboro
Akron Community S 200/K-12
PO Box 38 35441 205-372-3787
Jessica Tinker-Constant, prin. Fax 372-3782

Alabaster, Shelby, Pop. 29,944
Shelby County SD
Supt. — See Columbiana
Shelby County Alternative S Alt
601 1st St S 35007 205-682-5910
Dr. George Theodore, prin. Fax 682-5905
Thompson HS 1,800/9-12
100 Warrior Dr 35007 205-682-5700
Dr. Daniel Steele, prin. Fax 682-5705
Thompson MS 900/7-8
1509 Kent Dairy Rd 35007 205-682-5710
Jeff Atkins, prin. Fax 682-5715

Kingwood Christian S 400/PK-12
1351 Royalty Dr 35007 205-663-3973
Ruth Gray, prin. Fax 663-7145

Albertville, Marshall, Pop. 20,874
Albertville CSD 4,100/PK-12
107 W Main St 35950 256-891-1183
Dr. Frederic Ayer, supt. Fax 891-6303
www.albertk12.org
Albertville HS 1,000/9-12
402 E Mccord Ave 35950 256-878-6580
Paul McAbee, prin. Fax 891-6305
Albertville MS 600/7-8
600 E Alabama Ave 35950 256-878-2341
Lance Kitchens, prin. Fax 891-6334

Marshall County SD
Supt. — See Guntersville
Asbury MSHS 400/7-12
1990 Asbury Rd 35951 256-878-4068
Amy Price, prin. Fax 878-5233

Marshall Christian Academy 200/PK-12
1631 Brashers Chapel Rd 35951 256-279-0192
Rodney Cranford, admin. Fax 891-4160

Alexander City, Tallapoosa, Pop. 14,759
Alexander City SD 3,200/K-12
375 Lee St 35010 256-234-5074
Lou Ann Wagoner, supt. Fax 234-8649
www.alex.k12.al.us
Alexander City MS 500/7-8
359 State St 35010 256-234-8660
Dr. Beverly Price, prin. Fax 234-8659
Russell HS 1,000/9-12
225 Heard Blvd 35010 256-234-8611
Jose Reyes, prin. Fax 234-8680

Central Alabama Community College Post-Sec.
1675 Cherokee Rd 35010 256-234-6346

Alexandria, Calhoun, Pop. 3,872
Calhoun County SD
Supt. — See Anniston
Alexandria HS 1,000/6-12
PO Box 180 36250 256-741-4400
Anthony Holley, prin. Fax 820-7161

Aliceville, Pickens, Pop. 2,445
Pickens County SD
Supt. — See Carrollton
Aliceville HS 300/9-12
417 3rd St SE 35442 205-373-6378
Terry Sterling, prin. Fax 373-6730
Aliceville MS 300/5-8
1000 Columbus Rd NW 35442 205-373-6900
Fred Young, prin. Fax 373-8296

Alpine, Talladega
Talladega County SD
Supt. — See Talladega
Genesis Alternative Education Center Alt
22501 AL Highway 21 35014 256-315-5580
Dr. Ola Curry, admin. Fax 315-5585
Winterboro HS 300/5-12
22601 AL Highway 21 35014 256-315-5370
Michelle Head, prin. Fax 315-5380

Andalusia, Covington, Pop. 8,865
Andalusia CSD 1,700/K-12
122 6th Ave 36420 334-222-3186
Ted Watson, supt. Fax 222-8631
andalusia.schoolinsites.com
Andalusia HS 500/9-12
701 3rd St 36420 334-222-7569
Dr. Daniel Shakespeare, prin. Fax 222-5834
Andalusia MS 400/6-8
1201 C C Baker Ave, 334-222-6542
Victoria Anderson, prin. Fax 222-3875

Covington County SD 2,900/PK-12
807 C C Baker Ave, 334-222-7571
Shannon Driver, supt. Fax 222-7573
www.cov.k12.al.us
Pleasant Home S 600/K-12
12548 Falco Rd 36420 334-222-1315
Craig Nichols, prin. Fax 222-4415
Straughn HS 400/9-12
29448 Straughn School Rd, 334-222-2511
John Evers, prin. Fax 222-4010
Straughn MS 300/6-8
29324 Straughn School Rd, 334-222-4090
Cassandra Scott, prin. Fax 222-4132
Other Schools – See Florala, Red Level

Lurleen B. Wallace Community College Post-Sec.
PO Box 1418 36420 334-222-6591

Anniston, Calhoun, Pop. 22,755
Anniston CSD 2,300/PK-12
PO Box 1500 36202 256-231-5000
Joan Frazier, supt. Fax 231-5073
www.annistonschools.com/
Anniston HS 600/9-12
1301 Woodstock Ave 36207 256-231-5010
Dr. Sherron Jinadu, prin. Fax 231-5069
Anniston MS 500/6-8
4800 Mcclellan Blvd 36206 256-231-5020
Lynwood Hawkins, prin. Fax 231-5024

Calhoun County SD 9,000/K-12
PO Box 2084 36202 256-741-7400
Joe Dyar, supt. Fax 237-5332
www.ccboe.us
Saks HS 500/8-12
4401 Saks Rd 36206 256-741-7000
Jody Whaley, prin. Fax 236-5121
Wellborn HS 500/7-12
135 Pinson Rd 36201 256-741-7600
Rick Carter, prin. Fax 237-7071
White Plains HS 400/9-12
250 White Plains Rd 36207 256-741-7800
Andy Ward, prin. Fax 237-3301
White Plains MS 200/5-8
5800 AL Highway 9 36207 256-741-4700
Courtney Wilburn, prin. Fax 238-1715
Other Schools – See Alexandria, Jacksonville, Ohatchee, Weaver

---

Donoho S 400/PK-12
2501 Henry Rd 36207 256-237-5477
Janice Hurd, pres. Fax 237-6474
Faith Christian S 300/PK-12
4100 Ronnaki Rd 36207 256-236-4499
Robert Phillips, hdmstr. Fax 236-4673
Gadsden State Community College Post-Sec.
1801 Coleman Rd 36207 256-835-5400
Sacred Heart S 200/PK-12
16 Morton Rd 36205 256-237-4231
Charlie Maniscalco, prin. Fax 237-2353

Arab, Marshall, Pop. 7,960
Arab CSD 2,500/PK-12
750 Arabian Dr NE 35016 256-586-6011
John Mullins, supt. Fax 586-6013
www.arabcityschools.org
Arab HS 800/9-12
511 Arabian Dr NE 35016 256-586-6026
Dr. Michael Douglas, prin. Fax 586-1948
Arab JHS 700/6-8
911 Old Cullman Rd SW 35016 256-586-6074
John Ingram, prin. Fax 586-1348

Ardmore, Limestone, Pop. 1,178
Limestone County SD
Supt. — See Athens
Ardmore JSHS 900/6-12
30285 Ardmore Ave 35739 256-423-2685
Tommy Hunter, prin. Fax 423-4991

Ariton, Dale, Pop. 752
Dale County SD
Supt. — See Ozark
Ariton S 700/K-12
PO Box 750 36311 334-762-2371
Ben Baker, prin. Fax 762-2126

Arley, Winston, Pop. 344
Winston County SD
Supt. — See Double Springs
Meek HS 200/7-12
6615 County Road 41 35541 205-384-5825
Marla Murrah, prin. Fax 384-6825

Ashford, Houston, Pop. 2,133
Houston County SD
Supt. — See Dothan
Ashford JSHS 800/7-12
607 Church St 36312 334-899-5411
James Odom, prin. Fax 899-7450
Houston County AVC Vo/Tech
PO Box 3005 36312 334-899-3308
Glenn Maloy, prin. Fax 899-8854

Ashford Academy 200/PK-12
1100 N Broadway St 36312 334-899-3286
Tina Worley, hdmstr. Fax 899-7503

Ashland, Clay, Pop. 2,015
Clay County SD 1,600/K-12
PO Box 278 36251 256-354-5414
Garey Reynolds, supt. Fax 354-5415
www.claycoboe.org
Other Schools – See Lineville

Ashville, Saint Clair, Pop. 2,172
Saint Clair County SD 8,000/PK-12
410 Roy Dr 35953 205-594-7131
Jenny Seals, supt. Fax 594-4441
www.sccboe.org

Ashville HS 400/9-12
33215 US Highway 231 35953 205-594-7943
Patti Johnson, prin. Fax 594-4349
Ashville MS 400/5-8
PO Box 340 35953 205-594-7044
Phillip Johnson, prin. Fax 594-2241
Eden Career-Technical Center Vo/Tech
45 County Road 33 35953 205-594-7055
Ronnie McFarling, dir. Fax 594-4124
Yancy Alternative S Alt
466 10th St 35953 205-594-7492
David Gray, prin. Fax 594-3258
Other Schools – See Moody, Odenville, Ragland, Springville

Athens, Limestone, Pop. 21,523
Athens CSD 3,100/K-12
455 US Highway 31 N 35611 256-233-6600
Dr. Orman Bridges, supt. Fax 233-6640
www.acs-k12.org
Athens HS 900/9-12
PO Box 109 35612 256-233-6613
Christopher Bolen, prin. Fax 233-6617
Athens MS 500/7-8
601 S Clinton St 35611 256-233-6620
Mike Bishop, prin. Fax 233-6623

Limestone County SD 8,300/K-12
300 S Jefferson St 35611 256-232-5353
Dr. Tom Sisk, supt. Fax 233-6461
www.lcsk12.org
Clements MSHS 600/6-12
7730 US Highway 72 35611 256-729-6564
Keith Hairrell, prin. Fax 729-1029
East Limestone JSHS 1,200/6-12
15641 E Limestone Rd 35613 256-233-6660
Dennis Black, prin. Fax 230-9366
Limestone County Career Technical Center Vo/Tech
505 E Sanderfer Rd 35611 256-233-6463
Mickey Glass, prin. Fax 233-6667
Other Schools – See Ardmore, Elkmont, Lester, Tanner

Athens Bible S 300/K-12
507 Hoffman St 35611 256-232-3525
Randall L. Adams, prin. Fax 232-5417
Athens State University Post-Sec.
300 N Beaty St 35611 256-233-8100
Lindsay Lane Christian Academy 100/PK-12
1300 Lindsay Ln S 35613 256-262-5323
Stephen Murr, head sch Fax 232-0425

Atmore, Escambia, Pop. 10,046
Escambia County SD
Supt. — See Brewton
Escambia County HS 500/9-12
1215 S Presley St 36502 251-368-9181
Dennis Fuqua, prin. Fax 368-0674
Escambia County MS 600/5-8
PO Box 1236 36504 251-368-9105
Anthony Morris, prin Fax 368-0969

Escambia Academy 200/K-12
268 Cowpen Creek Rd 36502 251-368-2080
Fax 368-1950
Jefferson Davis Community College Post-Sec.
PO Box 1119 36504 251-368-8118

Attalla, Etowah, Pop. 5,935
Attalla CSD 1,400/PK-12
101 Case Ave SE 35954 256-538-8051
David Bowman, supt. Fax 538-8388
www.attalla.k12.al.us
Etowah HS 700/9-12
201 Case Ave SE 35954 256-538-8381
John Serafini, prin. Fax 538-2136
Etowah MS 500/6-8
429 4th St SW 35954 256-538-3236
Wesley Gulledge, prin. Fax 538-3232

Etowah County SD
Supt. — See Gadsden
Career Technical Center Vo/Tech
105 Burke Ave SE 35954 256-538-3312
Fax 538-1090
Etowah County Alternative S 200/Alt
106 Burke Ave SE 35954 256-538-8431
David Dixon, admin. Fax 538-8431

Auburn, Lee, Pop. 52,538
Auburn CSD 5,300/K-12
PO Box 3270 36831 334-887-2100
Dr. Karen DeLano, supt. Fax 887-2107
auburnschools.org
Auburn HS 1,400/10-12
405 Dean Rd 36830 334-887-4970
Rick Rainer, prin. Fax 887-4177
Auburn JHS 1,000/8-9
332 E Samford Ave 36830 334-887-1960
Dr. Shannon Pignato, prin. Fax 887-4160

Auburn University 36849 Post-Sec.
334-844-4000
Lee-Scott Academy 600/PK-12
1601 Academy Dr 36830 334-821-2430

Autaugaville, Autauga, Pop. 858
Autauga County SD
Supt. — See Prattville
Autaugaville S 300/K-12
PO Box 99 36003 334-365-8329
Sharon Hickmon, prin. Fax 365-8043

Axis, Mobile, Pop. 736
Mobile County SD
Supt. — See Mobile
North Mobile County MS 500/6-8
1950 Salco Rd W 36505 251-221-2000
Thomas Campbell, prin. Fax 221-2004

Bay Minette, Baldwin, Pop. 7,923
Baldwin County SD 27,800/PK-12
2600 Hand Ave 36507 251-937-0306
Alan Lee Ph.D., supt. Fax 580-1856
www.bcbe.org
Baldwin County HS 1,200/9-12
1 Tiger Dr 36507 251-937-2341
John Cabaniss, prin. Fax 937-2933
Bay Minette MS 500/7-8
1311 W 13th St 36507 251-580-2960
Kyle Nobles, prin. Fax 580-5120
North Baldwin Center for Tech Vo/Tech
505 W Hurricane Rd 36507 251-937-6751
Holly Resmondo, prin. Fax 937-4688
Other Schools – See Daphne, Elberta, Fairhope, Foley, Gulf Shores, Robertsdale, Spanish Fort

---

James H. Faulkner State Comm. College Post-Sec.
1900 S US Highway 31 36507 251-580-2100

Bayou La Batre, Mobile, Pop. 2,494
Mobile County SD
Supt. — See Mobile
Alba MS 600/6-8
14180 S Wintzell Ave 36509 251-824-4134
Rhonda Mayfield, prin. Fax 824-1324

Bear Creek, Marion, Pop. 1,062
Marion County SD
Supt. — See Hamilton
Phillips HS 200/7-12
142 School Ave 35543 205-486-3737
Daryl Weatherly, prin. Fax 486-1716

Beatrice, Monroe, Pop. 301
Monroe County SD
Supt. — See Monroeville
Shields S 200/PK-12
17688 Highway 21 N 36425 251-789-2168
Larry Turner, prin. Fax 789-2715

Berry, Fayette, Pop. 1,134
Fayette County SD
Supt. — See Fayette
Berry HS 300/7-12
18242 Highway 18 E 35546 205-689-4467
Trevor Kribbs, prin. Fax 689-8819

Bessemer, Jefferson, Pop. 27,229
Bessemer CSD 3,300/K-12
PO Box 1230 35021 205-432-3000
Dr. Fred Primm, supt. Fax 432-3085
www.bessk12.org
Bessemer Center for Technology Vo/Tech
4940 Premiere Pkwy 35022 205-432-3778
Keith Mahaffey, dir. Fax 432-0041
Bessemer City HS 9-12
4950 Premiere Pkwy 35022 205-432-3700
Jaaponica Florence Moore, prin. Fax 432-0040
Davis MS 700/7-8
1224 Clarendon Ave 35020 205-432-3600
Albert Soles, prin Fax 432-3607
New Horizon S Alt
1701 6th Ave N 35020 205-432-3036
Edith Hunter, prin Fax 432-3062

Jefferson County SD
Supt. — See Birmingham
Oak Grove HS 900/6-12
9494 Oak Grove Pkwy 35023 205-379-5000
Alan Pruden, prin. Fax 379-5045

Flint Hill Christian S 400/PK-12
1630 Powder Plant Rd 35022 205-424-2675
Bill McKelvey, admin. Fax 424-3535
ITT Technical Institute Post-Sec.
6270 Park South Dr 35022 205-497-5700
Lawson State Community College Post-Sec.
1100 9th Ave SW 35022 205-925-2515

Billingsley, Autauga, Pop. 144
Autauga County SD
Supt. — See Prattville
Billingsley S 700/K-12
PO Box 118 36006 334-365-5516
Mike Nixon, prin. Fax 755-1633

Birmingham, Jefferson, Pop. 210,274
Alabama School of Fine Arts SD 400/7-12
1800 Rev Abraham Woods Blvd 35203 205-252-9241
Dr. Michael Meeks, dir. Fax 251-9541
www.asfa.k12.al.us
Alabama S of Fine Arts JSHS 400/7-12
1800 Rev Abraham Woods Blvd 35203 205-252-9241
Dr. Michael Meeks, dir. Fax 251-9541

Birmingham CSD 22,700/PK-12
PO Box 10007 35202 205-231-4600
Dr. Craig Witherspoon, supt. Fax 231-4925
www.bhamcityschools.org/
Arrington MS 300/6-8
2101 Jefferson Ave SW 35211 205-231-1130
Mario Lumzy, prin. Fax 231-1133
Bush MS 300/6-8
1112 25th Street Ensley 35218 205-231-6000
Emeka Nzeocha, prin. Fax 231-6056
Carver HS 1,100/9-12
3900 24th St N 35207 205-231-3900
Darrell Hudson, prin. Fax 231-3973
Center Street MS 300/6-8
1832 Center Way S 35205 205-231-7190
Carolyn Denson, prin. Fax 231-7231
Gaskins MS 400/6-8
200 Dalton Dr 35215 205-231-9200
Dr. Sherene Carpenter, prin. Fax 231-9253
Green Acres MS 400/6-8
1220 67th St W 35228 205-231-1370
Etheldia Reynolds, prin. Fax 231-1414
Huffman HS 1,200/9-12
950 Springville Rd 35215 205-231-5000
John Lyons, prin. Fax 231-5056
Huffman MS 300/6-8
517 Huffman Rd 35215 205-231-5370
Milton Hopkins, prin. Fax 231-5426
Jackson-Olin HS 1,400/9-12
510 12th Street Ensley 35218 205-231-6431
Janice Drake, prin. Fax 231-6527
Kennedy Alternative S 100/Alt
125 63rd St N 35212 205-231-8740
Shirley Graham-Burrell, prin. Fax 231-8784
Mitchell MS 300/6-8
501 81st St S 35206 205-231-9400
Damita Pitts, prin. Fax 231-9464
Parker HS 900/9-12
900 4th St N 35204 205-231-2370
Cedric Tatum, prin. Fax 231-2916
Payne MS 300/6-8
1500 Daniel Payne Dr 35214 205-231-3190
Eddie Cauthen, prin. Fax 231-3236
Putnam MS 300/6-8
1757 Montclair Rd 35210 205-231-8680
Brenda Dial, prin. Fax 231-8685
Ramsay HS 700/Alt
1800 13th Ave S 35205 205-231-7000
Dr. Evelyn Nettles, prin. Fax 231-7076
Smith MS 300/6-8
1124 Five Mile Rd 35215 205-231-5675
Dr. Charles Willis, prin. Fax 231-5899
Wenonah HS 1,000/9-12
2916 Wilson Rd SW 35221 205-231-1675
Regina Carr-Hope, prin. Fax 231-1921
Wilkerson MS 400/6-8
116 11th Ct W 35204 205-231-2740
Constance Burnes, prin. Fax 231-2790
Woodlawn HS 1,100/9-12
5620 1st Ave N 35212 205-231-8000
Fred Stewart, prin. Fax 231-8084

Hoover CSD
Supt. — See Hoover
Berry MS 1,200/6-8
4500 Jaguar Dr 35242 205-439-2000
Dr. Kathleen Wheaton, prin. Fax 439-2001

Jefferson County SD 35,400/K-12
2100 18th St S 35209 205-379-2000
Stephen Nowlin, supt. Fax 379-2311
www.jefcoed.com
Center Point HS 800/9-12
1000 Eagle Dr 35215 205-379-3400
Van Phillips, prin. Fax 379-3425
Erwin MS 6-8
532 23rd Ave NW 35215 205-379-3430
Jay Gary, prin. Fax 856-6663
Fultondale JSHS 500/6-12
1450 Carson Rd N 35217 205-379-3500
Dr. Stephanie Robinson, prin. Fax 379-3545
Irondale MS 700/6-8
6200 Old Leeds Rd 35210 205-379-3800
Bobby Jackson, prin. Fax 379-3845
Jefferson Co. Counseling/Lrng Ctr-East Alt
50 Long St 35217 205-379-4250
Jason Wilson, prin. Fax 379-4295
Shades Valley Technical Academy Vo/Tech
5191 Pine Whispers Dr 35210 205-379-3300
Mary Beth Blankenship, prin. Fax 379-5397
Other Schools – See Adamsville, Bessemer, Dora, Gardendale, Hueytown, Irondale, Kimberly, Mc Calla, Pinson, Pleasant Grove, Trussville

Shelby County SD
Supt. — See Columbiana
Oak Mountain HS 1,700/9-12
5476 Caldwell Mill Rd 35242 205-682-5200
Joan Doyle, prin. Fax 682-5205
Oak Mountain MS 1,200/6-8
5650 Cahaba Valley Rd 35242 205-682-5210
Larry Haynes, prin. Fax 682-5215
Riverchase MS 700/6-8
853 Willow Oak Dr 35244 205-682-5510
Charles Smith, prin. Fax 682-5515

Altamont S 400/5-12
PO Box 131429 35213 205-879-2006
Sarah Whiteside, hdmstr. Fax 871-5666
Birmingham-Southern College Post-Sec.
900 Arkadelphia Rd 35254 800-523-5793
Briarwood Christian S 2,000/PK-12
2204 Briarwood Way 35243 205-776-5800
Dr. Barrett Mosbacker, admin. Fax 776-5815
Brown Mackie College - Birmingham Post-Sec.
105 Vulcan Rd 35209 205-909-1500
Carroll HS 600/9-12
300 Lakeshore Pkwy 35209 205-940-2400
Rev. John McDonald, prin. Fax 945-7429
Central Park Christian S 200/K-12
1900 43rd St W 35208 205-786-4811
Levan Parker, hdmstr. Fax 786-0140
Fortis Institute Post-Sec.
100 London Pkwy Ste 150 35211 205-940-7800
Herzing University Post-Sec.
280 W Valley Ave 35209 205-916-2800
Holy Family Cristo Rey HS 200/9-12
2001 19th Street Ensley 35218 205-787-9937
Sindey Moore, prin. Fax 787-8530
Hoover Christian S 50/K-12
2113 Old Rocky Ridge Rd 35216 205-987-3376
Gaylan Herr, prin. Fax 987-4428
Jefferson State Community College Post-Sec.
2601 Carson Rd 35215 205-853-1200
Lawson State Community College Post-Sec.
3060 Wilson Rd SW 35221 205-925-2515
Parkway Christian Academy 400/PK-12
959 Huffman Rd 35215 205-833-2410
Michael Gallien, prin. Fax 833-4692

Samford University Post-Sec.
800 Lakeshore Dr 35229 205-726-2011
Southeastern Bible College Post-Sec.
2545 Valleydale Rd 35244 205-970-9200
Southeastern School of Cosmetology Post-Sec.
849 Dennison Ave SW Ste 101 35211 205-925-0011
Strayer University Post-Sec.
3570 Grandview Pkwy Ste 200 35243 205-453-6300
University of Alabama at Birmingham Post-Sec.
1720 2nd Ave S 35294 205-934-4011
University of Alabama Hospital Post-Sec.
619 19th St S 35249 205-934-5490
Virginia College Post-Sec.
488 Palisades Blvd 35209 205-802-1200

Blountsville, Blount, Pop. 1,659
Blount County SD
Supt. — See Oneonta
Moore HS 600/7-12
4040 Susan Moore Rd 35031 205-466-7663
Chris Pullen, prin. Fax 466-7858
Pennington HS 600/7-12
81 College St 35031 205-429-4101
Brian Kirk, prin. Fax 429-4104

Boaz, Marshall, Pop. 9,410
Boaz CSD 2,300/PK-12
126 Newt Parker Dr 35957 256-593-8180
Dr. Mark Isley, supt. Fax 593-8181
www.boazk12.org/
Boaz HS 700/9-12
907 Brown St 35957 256-593-2401
Allen Johnson, prin. Fax 593-2403
Boaz MS 500/6-8
140 Newt Parker Dr 35957 256-593-0799
Jeff Johnson, prin. Fax 593-0729

Snead State Community College Post-Sec.
PO Box 734 35957 256-593-5120

Brantley, Crenshaw, Pop. 786
Crenshaw County SD
Supt. — See Luverne
Brantley S 600/PK-12
PO Box 86 36009 334-527-8879
Dodd Hawthorne, prin. Fax 527-3405

Bremen, Cullman
Cullman County SD
Supt. — See Cullman
Cold Springs HS 400/7-12
PO Box 130 35033 256-287-1787
Tommy Youngblood, prin. Fax 287-2841

Brewton, Escambia, Pop. 5,355
Brewton CSD 1,200/K-12
811 Belleville Ave 36426 251-867-8400
Lynn Smith, supt. Fax 867-8403
www.brewtoncityschools.org/
Brewton MS 400/5-8
1384 Old Castleberry Rd 36426 251-867-8420
Carrie Brown, prin. Fax 867-8422
Miller HS 400/9-12
1835 Douglas Ave 36426 251-867-8430
Mary Bell, prin. Fax 867-8407

Escambia County SD 4,500/K-12
PO Box 307 36427 251-867-6251
Randall Little, supt. Fax 867-6252
www.escambiak12.net
Escambia Career Readiness Center Vo/Tech
2824 Pea Ridge Rd 36426 251-867-7829
David Lanier, dir. Fax 867-7064
Other Schools – See Atmore, East Brewton, Flomaton

Jefferson Davis Community College Post-Sec.
PO Box 958 36427 251-867-4832

Bridgeport, Jackson, Pop. 2,317
Jackson County SD
Supt. — See Scottsboro
Bridgeport MS 200/5-8
620 Jacobs Ave 35740 256-495-2967
A.J. Buckner, prin. Fax 495-2850

Brilliant, Marion, Pop. 893
Marion County SD
Supt. — See Hamilton
Brilliant HS 200/7-12
PO Box 90 35548 205-465-2322
Jack Hayes, prin. Fax 465-2382

Brookwood, Tuscaloosa, Pop. 1,803
Tuscaloosa County SD
Supt. — See Tuscaloosa
Brookwood HS 1,000/9-12
15981 Highway 216 35444 205-342-2777
Laura McBride, prin. Fax 553-3390

Brundidge, Pike, Pop. 2,052
Pike County SD
Supt. — See Troy
Pike County JSHS 500/7-12
552 S Main St 36010 334-735-2389
Willie Wright, prin. Fax 735-3176

Buhl, Tuscaloosa
Tuscaloosa County SD
Supt. — See Tuscaloosa
Sipsey Valley HS 9-12
15815 Romulus Rd 35446 205-342-2850
Dennis Alvarez, prin. Fax 342-2851
Sipsey Valley MS 6-8
15817 Romulus Rd 35446 205-342-2870
Frank Kelly, prin. Fax 342-2871

Butler, Choctaw, Pop. 1,876
Choctaw County SD 1,800/K-12
107 Tom Orr Dr 36904 205-459-3031
Glenda Sue Moore, supt. Fax 459-3037
www.choctawk12.org
Choctaw County HS 400/7-12
277 Tom Orr Dr 36904 205-459-2139
Kevin Howard, prin. Fax 459-2277
Other Schools – See Gilbertown

Patrician Academy 300/PK-12
901 S Mulberry Ave 36904 205-459-3605
Michael Ethridge, hdmstr. Fax 459-4802

Calera, Shelby, Pop. 11,417
Shelby County SD
Supt. — See Columbiana
Calera HS 600/9-12
100 Calera Eagle Dr 35040 205-682-6100
Richard Bishop, prin. Fax 682-6105
Calera MS 200/6-8
8454 Highway 31 35040 205-682-6140
Brent Copes, prin. Fax 682-6145

Camden, Wilcox, Pop. 2,011
Wilcox County SD 1,900/PK-12
PO Box 160 36726 334-682-4716
Dr. Tyrone Yarbrough, supt. Fax 682-4179
www.wilcox.k12.al.us
Camden S of Arts & Technology 300/7-8
PO Box 698 36726 334-682-4514
Lashonda Dear-Rogers, prin. Fax 682-5934
Wilcox Central HS 600/9-12
PO Box 1089 36726 334-682-9239
Kim Staley, prin. Fax 682-5411
Wilcox County Alternative S Alt
PO Box 160 36726 334-682-5074
Robert Stallworth, admin. Fax 682-4769

Wilcox Academy 300/PK-12
PO Box 1149 36726 334-682-9619

Camp Hill, Tallapoosa, Pop. 1,004
Tallapoosa County SD
Supt. — See Dadeville
Bell Career Tech Center Vo/Tech
251 M L King St 36850 256-896-0160
Gerry Moses, admin. Fax 896-0170

Lyman Ward Military Academy 100/6-12
PO Box 550 36850 800-896-4127

Carbon Hill, Walker, Pop. 1,992
Walker County SD
Supt. — See Jasper
Carbon Hill HS 400/9-12
217 Bulldog Blvd 35549 205-924-8821
Dr. Gypsy Stovall, prin. Fax 924-8877

Carrollton, Pickens, Pop. 1,006
Pickens County SD 2,800/K-12
377 Ladow Center Cir 35447 205-367-2082
Jamie Chapman, supt. Fax 367-8404
pickenscountyschools.schoolinsites.com
LaDow Technology Center Vo/Tech
377 Ladow Center Cir 35447 205-367-2080
Alma Somerville, prin. Fax 367-8404
Other Schools – See Aliceville, Gordo, Reform

Pickens Academy 300/PK-12
225 Ray Bass Rd 35447 205-367-8144

Cedar Bluff, Cherokee, Pop. 1,779
Cherokee County SD
Supt. — See Centre
Cedar Bluff S 600/K-12
3655 Old Highway 9 35959 256-779-6211
Bobby Mintz, prin. Fax 779-8328

Centre, Cherokee, Pop. 3,423
Cherokee County SD 4,100/PK-12
130 E Main St 35960 256-927-3362
William Guice, supt. Fax 927-3399
www.cherokeek12.org
Centre MS 500/5-8
1920 E Main St 35960 256-927-5656
Marcia Sewell, prin. Fax 927-4656
Cherokee Co. Career & Technology Center Vo/Tech
600 Bay Springs Rd 35960 256-927-5351
Mitchell Guice, prin. Fax 927-3501
Cherokee County HS 400/9-12
910 Warrior Dr 35960 256-927-3625
Douglas Davis, prin. Fax 927-6445
Other Schools – See Cedar Bluff, Gaylesville, Sand Rock, Spring Garden

Centreville, Bibb, Pop. 2,751
Bibb County SD 2,900/K-12
157 SW Davidson Dr 35042 205-926-9881
Greg Blake, supt. Fax 926-5075
www.bibbed.org/
Bibb County HS 600/9-12
220 Birmingham Rd 35042 205-926-9071
James Alston, prin. Fax 926-6848
Centreville MS 500/5-8
1621 Montgomery Hwy 35042 205-926-9861
Ernie Cutts, prin. Fax 926-3917
Other Schools – See West Blocton

Cahawba Christian Academy 100/PK-12
2415 Montevallo Rd 35042 205-926-4676

Chatom, Washington, Pop. 1,283
Washington County SD 3,400/K-12
PO Box 1359 36518 251-847-2401
Tim Savage, supt. Fax 847-3611
www.wcbek12.org
Washington County AVC Vo/Tech
PO Box 1298 36518 251-847-2040
Harold Crouch, prin. Fax 847-3489
Washington County JSHS 600/5-12
PO Box 1329 36518 251-847-2851
David Wofford, prin. Fax 847-2825
Other Schools – See Fruitdale, Leroy, Mc Intosh, Millry

Chelsea, Shelby, Pop. 10,063
Shelby County SD
Supt. — See Columbiana
Chelsea HS 1,000/9-12
PO Box 639 35043 205-682-7200
Jay Peoples, prin. Fax 682-7205
Chelsea MS 900/6-8
2321 Highway 39 35043 205-682-7210
William Harper, prin. Fax 682-7215

Cherokee, Colbert, Pop. 1,027
Colbert County SD
Supt. — See Tuscumbia
Cherokee HS 300/7-12
850 High School Dr 35616 256-359-4434
Pam Worsham, prin. Fax 359-4060

Childersburg, Talladega, Pop. 5,086
Talladega County SD
Supt. — See Talladega
Childersburg HS 500/9-12
122 Faye S Perry Dr 35044 256-315-5475
Jesse Hooks, prin. Fax 315-5495
Childersburg MS 500/5-8
800 4th St SE 35044 256-315-5505
Jena Jones, prin. Fax 315-5520

Citronelle, Mobile, Pop. 3,830
Mobile County SD
Supt. — See Mobile
Citronelle HS 800/9-12
19325 Rowe St 36522 251-221-3444
Richard Dickson, prin. Fax 221-3418
Lott MS 500/6-8
17740 Celeste Rd 36522 251-221-2240
Deborah Altman, prin. Fax 221-2247

Clanton, Chilton, Pop. 8,519
Chilton County SD 7,800/PK-12
1705 Lay Dam Rd 35045 205-280-3000
Dave Hayden, supt. Fax 755-6549
www.chilton.k12.al.us
Chilton County HS 800/9-12
1214 7th St S 35045 205-280-2710
Dr. Cynthia Stewart, prin. Fax 755-0618
Clanton MS 600/6-8
835 Temple Rd 35045 205-280-2750
Don Finlayson, prin. Fax 755-2446
LeCroy Career Technical Center Vo/Tech
2829 4th Ave N 35045 205-280-2920
Tommy Glasscock, prin. Fax 755-2035
Other Schools – See Jemison, Maplesville, Thorsby, Verbena

Clayton, Barbour, Pop. 3,001
Barbour County SD 900/PK-12
PO Box 429 36016 334-775-3453
Jimmie Fryer, supt. Fax 775-7301
barbourschools.org
Barbour County HS 200/10-12
PO Box 339 36016 334-775-3545
Clarence Magee, prin. Fax 775-8861
Barbour County JHS 200/7-9
PO Box 549 36016 334-775-3404
Roderick Hamilton, prin. Fax 775-9447

Cleveland, Blount, Pop. 1,288
Blount County SD
Supt. — See Oneonta
Blount County Career Technology Vo/Tech
PO Box 125 35049 205-625-3424
Johnny Pullen, dir. Fax 625-3427
Cleveland HS 500/7-12
71 High School St 35049 205-274-9915
Denise Martin, prin. Fax 274-0201

Collinsville, DeKalb, Pop. 1,945
De Kalb County SD
Supt. — See Rainsville
Collinsville S 700/K-12
PO Box 269 35961 256-524-2111
Donny Jones, prin. Fax 524-7526

Columbia, Houston, Pop. 730
Houston County SD
Supt. — See Dothan
Houston County JSHS 400/7-12
200 W Church St 36319 334-696-2221
Scott Stephens, prin. Fax 696-4677

Columbiana, Shelby, Pop. 4,133
Shelby County SD 27,300/K-12
PO Box 1910 35051 205-682-7000
Randy Fuller, supt. Fax 682-7005
www.shelbyed.k12.al.us
Columbiana MS 500/6-8
222 Joiner Town Rd 35051 205-682-6610
Dr. Kerry Rush, prin. Fax 682-6615
School of Technology Vo/Tech
701 Highway 70 35051 205-682-6650
Tim Elliff, prin. Fax 682-6655
Shelby County HS 700/9-12
101 Washington St 35051 205-682-6600
Gene Rogers, prin. Fax 682-6605
Other Schools – See Alabaster, Birmingham, Calera, Chelsea, Helena, Montevallo, Pelham, Vincent

---

Cornerstone Christian S 200/PK-12
24975 Highway 25 35051 205-669-7777
Jay Adams, dir. Fax 395-8304

Cordova, Walker, Pop. 2,077
Walker County SD
Supt. — See Jasper
Bankhead MS 300/5-8
110 School Rd 35550 205-483-7245
Amber Freeman, prin. Fax 483-7244
Cordova HS 400/9-12
183 School Rd 35550 205-483-7404
Kathy Vintson, prin. Fax 483-1934

Cottondale, Tuscaloosa
Tuscaloosa CSD
Supt. — See Tuscaloosa
Bryant HS 900/9-12
6315 Mary Harmon Bryant Dr 35453 205-759-3538
Raquel Payne, prin. Fax 759-8315
Eastwood MS 700/6-8
6314 Mary Harmon Bryant Dr 35453 205-759-3613
Portia Martin, prin. Fax 759-3798

Tuscaloosa County SD
Supt. — See Tuscaloosa
Davis - Emerson MS 400/6-8
1500 Bulldog Blvd 35453 205-342-2750
Coneta Guinn, prin. Fax 247-4169

Tuscaloosa Christian S 300/PK-12
PO Box 250 35453 205-553-4303
Dan Lancaster, prin. Fax 553-4259

Cottonwood, Houston, Pop. 1,266
Houston County SD
Supt. — See Dothan
Cottonwood S 700/K-12
663 Houston St 36320 334-691-2587
Judy Fowler, prin. Fax 691-4200

Courtland, Lawrence, Pop. 595
Lawrence County SD
Supt. — See Moulton
Hubbard S 300/K-12
12905 Jessie Jackson Pkwy 35618 256-637-3010
Thomas Jones, prin. Fax 637-3006

Crossville, DeKalb, Pop. 1,821
De Kalb County SD
Supt. — See Rainsville
Crossville HS 900/6-12
5405 County Road 28 35962 256-528-7858
David Uptain, prin. Fax 528-7840

Cullman, Cullman, Pop. 14,641
Cullman CSD 3,000/PK-12
301 1st St NE 35055 256-734-2233
Janet Harris Ed.D., supt. Fax 737-9621
www.cullmancats.net
Cullman City Career Tech S Vo/Tech
301 1st St NE 35055 256-734-2233
Helen Dunn, prin. Fax 737-9621
Cullman HS 900/9-12
510 13th St NE 35055 256-734-3923
Dr. Elton Bouldin, prin. Fax 734-9570
Cullman MS 500/7-8
800 2nd Ave NE 35055 256-734-7959
Patrick Hill, prin. Fax 734-7711

Cullman County SD 9,700/PK-12
PO Box 1590 35056 256-734-2933
Billy Coleman, supt. Fax 736-2486
www.ccboe.org/
CARE Alternative S Alt
192 County Road 940 35057 256-747-6371
Deborah Peake, coord. Fax 747-7376
Cullman Area Career Center Vo/Tech
17640 US Highway 31 35058 256-734-7740
Jeff Curtis, prin Fax 734-7464
Fairview HS 500/9-12
841 Welcome Rd 35058 256-796-5106
Chris Gambrill, prin. Fax 796-9025
Fairview MS 300/6-8
841 Welcome Rd 35058 256-796-0883
Dr. Susan Creel Patterson, prin. Fax 796-0885
Good Hope HS 400/9-12
210 Good Hope School Rd 35057 256-734-3807
Dr. Anita Kilpatrick, prin. Fax 734-3427
Good Hope MS 300/6-8
216 Good Hope School Rd 35057 256-734-9600
April Tucker, prin. Fax 734-9704
West Point HS 600/9-12
4314 County Road 1141 35057 256-734-5375
Heith Yearwood, prin. Fax 775-6047
Other Schools – See Bremen, Hanceville, Holly Pond, Vinemont

Cullman Christian S 100/K-12
PO Box 2655 35056 256-734-0734
Rachael Howze, prin. Fax 734-0117
St. Bernard Prep HS 100/9-12
101 Saint Bernard Ave SE 35055 256-739-6682
Rev. Joel Martin, pres. Fax 734-2925

Dadeville, Tallapoosa, Pop. 3,198
Tallapoosa County SD 3,100/K-12
125 N Broadnax St Rm 113 36853 256-825-1020
Joseph Windle, supt. Fax 825-1003
www.tallapoosak12.org/
Councill MS 200/6-8
254 Leach St 36853 256-825-2846
Melanie McKinney, prin. Fax 825-7473
Dadeville HS 400/9-12
227 Weldon St 36853 256-825-7848
Chris Hand, prin. Fax 825-0697
Tallapoosa County Alternative S 50/Alt
254 Leach St Ste A 36853 256-825-2848
Ginger East, prin. Fax 825-7473
Other Schools – See Camp Hill, New Site, Notasulga

Daleville, Dale, Pop. 5,083
Daleville CSD 1,200/K-12
626 N Daleville Ave 36322 334-598-2456
Andrew Kelley, supt. Fax 598-9006
www.daleville.k12.al.us
Daleville JSHS 600/7-12
626 N Daleville Ave 36322 334-598-4461
Mike McDuffie, prin. Fax 598-3850

Danville, Morgan
Morgan County SD
Supt. — See Decatur
Danville HS 400/9-12
9235 Danville Rd 35619 256-773-9909
Gilmer Ellis, prin. Fax 773-5622
Danville MS 400/5-8
5933 Highway 36 W 35619 256-773-7723
Gary Walker, prin. Fax 773-7708

Daphne, Baldwin, Pop. 21,279
Baldwin County SD
Supt. — See Bay Minette
Daphne HS 1,100/9-12
9300 Lawson Rd 36526 251-626-8787
Dr. Meredith Foster, prin. Fax 626-3024
Daphne MS 500/7-8
1 Jody Davis Cir 36526 251-626-2845
Tom Hartner, prin. Fax 626-0025

Bayside Academy 700/PK-12
303 Dryer Ave 36526 251-338-6300
United States Sports Academy Post-Sec.
1 Academy Dr 36526 251-626-3303

Deatsville, Elmore, Pop. 1,131
Autauga County SD
Supt. — See Prattville
Marbury HS 500/9-12
2360 US Highway 31 N 36022 334-387-1910
William Hollon, prin. Fax 387-1920

Elmore County SD
Supt. — See Wetumpka
Holtville HS 500/9-12
10425 Holtville Rd 36022 334-569-3034
Jimmy Hull, prin. Fax 569-1013
Holtville MS 500/5-8
655 Bulldog Ln 36022 334-569-1596
Tremeca Jackson, prin. Fax 569-3258

J. F. Ingram State Technical College Post-Sec.
PO Box 220350 36022 334-285-5177

Decatur, Morgan, Pop. 54,679
Decatur CSD 9,300/PK-12
302 4th Ave NE 35601 256-552-3000
Dr. Edwin Nichols, supt. Fax 552-3981
www.dcs.edu
Austin HS 1,500/9-12
1625 Danville Rd SW 35601 256-552-3060
Dr. Donald Snow, prin. Fax 350-7802
Brookhaven MS 1,100/6-8
1302 5th Ave SW 35601 256-552-3045
Melissa Scott, prin. Fax 552-3047
Cedar Ridge MS 700/6-8
2715 Danville Rd SW 35603 256-552-4622
Tommy Davis, prin. Fax 552-4623
Decatur HS 1,000/9-12
1011 Prospect Dr SE 35601 256-552-3011
Dr. Travis Schrimsher, prin. Fax 308-2535
Horizon HS Alt
809 Church St NE 35601 256-552-3054
Linda McClain, prin. Fax 552-4691
Oak Park MS 600/6-8
1218 16th Ave SE 35601 256-552-3035
Ashley McIntyre, prin. Fax 552-3082

Morgan County SD 7,800/PK-12
1325 Point Mallard Pkwy SE 35601 256-353-6442
Bill Hopkins, supt. Fax 309-2187
www.morgank12.org
Morgan County Learning Center Alt
1325 Point Mallard Pkwy SE 35601 256-309-2171
Cliff Booth, prin. Fax 309-2158
Priceville HS 400/9-12
317 Highway 67 S 35603 256-353-1950
Mark Mason, prin. Fax 353-2802
Priceville JHS 400/6-8
317 Highway 67 S 35603 256-355-5104
Mary Speegle, prin. Fax 355-5932
Other Schools – See Danville, Falkville, Somerville, Trinity

Calhoun Community College Post-Sec.
PO Box 2216 35609 256-306-2500
Decatur Heritage Christian Academy 300/K-12
PO Box 5659 35601 256-351-4275
Scott Mayo, hdmstr. Fax 355-4738

Demopolis, Marengo, Pop. 7,436
Demopolis CSD 2,300/PK-12
PO Box 759 36732 334-289-1670
Dr. Al Griffin, supt. Fax 289-1689
www.demopoliscityschools.com
Demopolis HS 700/9-12
701 US Highway 80 W 36732 334-289-0294
Leon Clark, prin. Fax 289-8777
Demopolis MS 500/6-8
300 E Pettus St 36732 334-289-4242
Blaine Hathcock, prin. Fax 289-2670

Marengo County SD
Supt. — See Linden
Essex S 200/K-12
70 Essex Dr 36732 334-289-3504
Tiffany Davis, prin. Fax 289-3591

Dixons Mills, Marengo
Marengo County SD
Supt. — See Linden
Marengo S 300/K-12
212 Panther Dr 36736 334-992-2395
David Miller, prin. Fax 992-2197

Dora, Walker, Pop. 1,996
Jefferson County SD
Supt. — See Birmingham
Corner HS 500/9-12
4301 Warrior Jasper Rd 35062 205-379-3200
Ronald Cooper, prin. Fax 379-3245

Walker County SD
Supt. — See Jasper
Dora HS 500/9-12
330 Glenn C Gant Cir 35062 205-648-6863
Dr. Cathy James, prin. Fax 648-4709

Dothan, Houston, Pop. 64,426
Dothan CSD 9,400/PK-12
500 Dusy St 36301 334-793-1397
Tim Wilder, supt. Fax 794-1499
www.dothan.k12.al.us
Beverlye Magnet MS 500/6-8
1025 S Beverlye Rd 36301 334-794-1432
Maria Johnson, prin. Fax 792-0886
Carver Magnet MS 400/6-8
1001 Webb Rd 36303 334-794-1440
Joseph Meigs, prin. Fax 794-1587
Dothan HS 1,200/9-12
1236 S Oates St 36301 334-794-1400
Stan Eldridge, prin. Fax 677-0099
Dothan Technology Center Vo/Tech
3165 Reeves St 36303 334-794-1436
Terry Scott, prin. Fax 794-1439
Girard MS 500/6-8
600 Girard Ave 36303 334-794-1426
Charles Corbitt, prin. Fax 794-6373
Honeysuckle MS 600/6-8
1665 Honeysuckle Rd 36305 334-794-1420
Scott Faulk, prin. Fax 678-6546
Northview HS 1,300/9-12
3209 Reeves St 36303 334-794-1410
Chris Shaw, prin. Fax 702-4802
P.A.S.S. Academy Alt
201 E Wilson St 36303 334-671-1474
Edward Fleming, prin. Fax 677-7480

Houston County SD 6,300/PK-12
404 W Washington St 36301 334-792-8331
Tim Pitchford, supt. Fax 792-1016
hcboe.us/
Houston County Alternative S Alt
315 N Foster St 36303 334-671-9295
James Murrey, prin. Fax 794-1016
Rehobeth HS 700/9-12
373 Malvern Rd 36301 334-677-7002
Matt Swann, prin. Fax 677-2699
Rehobeth MS 500/6-8
5631 County Road 203 36301 334-677-5153
John Dixon, prin. Fax 677-5947
Other Schools – See Ashford, Columbia, Cottonwood, Newton

Emmanuel Christian S 500/PK-12
178 Earline Rd 36305 334-792-0935
Mark Redmond, admin. Fax 702-7410
Flowers Hospital Post-Sec.
PO Box 6907 36302 334-793-5000
Fortis College Post-Sec.
200 Vulcan Way 36303 334-677-2832
Houston Academy 600/PK-12
901 Buena Vista Dr 36303 334-794-4106
John O'Connell, hdmstr. Fax 793-4053
Providence Christian S 700/1-12
4847 Murphy Mill Rd 36303 334-702-8933
Emory Latta, head sch Fax 702-0700
Southeast Alabama Medical Center Post-Sec.
PO Box 6987 36302 334-793-8100
Wallace Community College Post-Sec.
1141 Wallace Dr 36303 334-983-3521

Double Springs, Winston, Pop. 1,073
Winston County SD 2,700/PK-12
PO Box 9 35553 205-489-5018
Gregory Pendley, supt. Fax 489-3203
www.winstonk12.org
Double Springs MS 300/5-8
PO Box 669 35553 205-489-3813
Ben Aderholt, prin. Fax 489-8832
Winston County HS 300/9-12
PO Box 549 35553 205-489-5593
Jeff Cole, prin. Fax 489-8204
Winston County Technical Center Vo/Tech
PO Box 1000 35553 205-489-2121
Shandy Porter, prin. Fax 489-2121
Other Schools – See Addison, Arley, Lynn

Douglas, Marshall, Pop. 724
Marshall County SD
Supt. — See Guntersville
Douglas HS 500/9-12
PO Box 300 35964 256-593-2810
Scott Bonds, prin. Fax 840-5489
Douglas MS 500/6-8
PO Box 269 35964 256-593-1240
Dr. Charles Edmonds, prin. Fax 593-1259

Duncanville, Tuscaloosa
Tuscaloosa County SD
Supt. — See Tuscaloosa
Duncanville MS 300/6-8
11205 Eagle Pkwy 35456 205-342-2830
Kaye Ridgway, prin. Fax 759-1998

East Brewton, Escambia, Pop. 2,446
Escambia County SD
Supt. — See Brewton
Neal HS 400/9-12
801 Andrew Jackson St 36426 251-867-4645
Patricia Frazier, prin. Fax 867-4642
Neal MS 500/5-8
703 Williamson St 36426 251-867-5035
Dennis Hadaway, prin. Fax 867-5051

Eclectic, Elmore, Pop. 979
Elmore County SD
Supt. — See Wetumpka
Eclectic MS 500/5-8
170 S Ann St 36024 334-541-2131
Dane Hawk, prin. Fax 541-3556

Elmore County HS 600/9-12
155 N College Ave 36024 334-541-3662
Wes Rogers, prin. Fax 541-4441

Eight Mile, See Prichard
Mobile County SD
Supt. — See Mobile
Blount HS 1,300/9-12
5450 Lott Rd 36613 251-221-3070
Jerome Woods, prin. Fax 221-3075

Elba, Coffee, Pop. 3,889
Coffee County SD 2,000/PK-12
400 Reddoch Hill Rd 36323 334-897-5016
Don McPherson Ph.D., supt. Fax 897-6207
www.coffeecountyschools.org
Other Schools – See Jack, Kinston, New Brockton

Elba CSD 800/K-12
131 Tiger Dr 36323 334-897-2801
Frederick Rainer, supt. Fax 897-5601
www.elbaed.com
Elba Area Vocational HS Vo/Tech
371 Tiger Dr 36323 334-897-2266
Rodney Smith, coord. Fax 897-5106
Elba HS 400/7-12
371 Tiger Dr 36323 334-897-2266
Rodney Smith, prin. Fax 897-5106

Elberta, Baldwin, Pop. 1,467
Baldwin County SD
Supt. — See Bay Minette
Elberta MS 600/4-8
13355 Main St 36530 251-986-8127
Claude Eilert, prin. Fax 986-7472

Elkmont, Limestone, Pop. 433
Limestone County SD
Supt. — See Athens
Elkmont S 1,000/K-12
25630 Evans Ave 35620 256-732-4291
Stan Davis, prin. Fax 732-3418

Enterprise, Coffee, Pop. 25,851
Enterprise CSD 6,400/PK-12
PO Box 311790 36331 334-347-9531
Dr. Aaron Milner, supt. Fax 347-5102
www.enterpriseschools.net/
Dauphin JHS 600/8-9
1271 Dauphin Street Ext 36330 334-347-1141
Trent Trawick, prin. Fax 347-0845
Enterprise JHS 500/8-9
401 W College St 36330 334-347-1733
Judy Thomas, prin. Fax 347-1009
Enterprise SHS 1,500/10-12
1801 Boll Weevil Cir 36330 334-347-2640
Matt Rodgers, prin. Fax 347-3144

Enterprise Preparatory Academy 200/PK-12
PO Box 310600 36331 334-308-0260
Judy Tucker, head sch Fax 308-0264
Enterprise State Community College Post-Sec.
PO Box 1300 36331 334-347-2623

Eufaula, Barbour, Pop. 13,021
Eufaula CSD 2,800/PK-12
333 State Docks Rd 36027 334-687-1100
Carl Tyler, supt. Fax 687-1150
www.ecs.k12.al.us
Eufaula HS 700/9-12
530 Lake Dr 36027 334-687-1110
Steve Hawkins, prin. Fax 687-1121
Hope Academy 100/Alt
333 State Docks Rd 36027 334-687-1104
Frances Person-Crews, prin. Fax 687-1150
Moorer MS 600/6-8
101 Saint Francis Rd 36027 334-687-1130
Penny Kinsey, prin. Fax 687-1138

Lakeside S 200/PK-12
1020 Lake Dr 36027 334-687-5748
Dee Bennett, hdmstr. Fax 687-6306
Wallace Community College Post-Sec.
PO Box 580 36072 334-687-3543

Eutaw, Greene, Pop. 2,918
Greene County SD 1,300/K-12
220 Main St 35462 205-372-4900
Dr. Emma Louie, supt. Fax 372-3247
www.greene.k12.al.us
Carver MS 300/4-8
PO Box 659 35462 205-372-4816
Barbara Martin, prin. Fax 372-4828
Greene County Career Center Vo/Tech
627 Mesopotamia St 35462 205-372-4636
Dr. Rhinnie Scott, prin. Fax 372-2358
Greene County HS 400/9-12
PO Box 658 35462 205-372-3789
Garry Rice, prin. Fax 372-3404

Evergreen, Conecuh, Pop. 3,925
Conecuh County SD 1,700/PK-12
100 Jackson St 36401 251-578-1752
Ronnie Brogden, supt. Fax 578-7061
www.conecuhk12.com
Hillcrest HS 500/9-12
1989 Jaguar Dr 36401 251-578-1126
Rodney Drish, prin. Fax 578-7071
Marshall MS 200/6-8
428 Reynolds Ave 36401 251-578-2866
Geneva Lyons, prin. Fax 578-7067

Reid State Technical College Post-Sec.
PO Box 588 36401 251-578-1313
Sparta Academy 300/PK-12
300 Pierce St 36401 251-578-2852
Wayne Hammonds, prin. Fax 578-2878

Excel, Monroe, Pop. 708
Monroe County SD
Supt. — See Monroeville
Excel S 1,100/PK-12
PO Box 429 36439 251-765-2351
Marty Hanks, prin. Fax 765-9153

Fairfield, Jefferson, Pop. 11,062
Fairfield CSD 1,900/K-12
6405 Avenue D 35064 205-783-6850
Walter Gonsoulin Ph.D., supt. Fax 783-6805
www.fairfieldcityschoolsystem.com
Fairfield Alternative S Alt
6405 Avenue D 35064 205-264-9501
Dr. Gordon Fears, prin. Fax 783-6810
Fairfield Area Vocational HS Vo/Tech
610 Valley Rd 35064 205-785-5176
Valerie Holmes, prin. Fax 783-6748
Fairfield Preparatory HS 700/9-12
610 Valley Rd 35064 205-785-5176
Michelle Hayes, prin. Fax 783-6748
Forest Hills MS 300/7-8
7000 Grasselli Rd 35064 205-783-6845
Shun Williams, prin. Fax 783-6753

Miles College Post-Sec.
5500 Myron Massey Blvd 35064 205-929-1000
Restoration Academy 200/K-12
PO Box 30 35064 205-785-8805
Carl Lynn, dir. Fax 785-0870

Fairhope, Baldwin, Pop. 15,206
Baldwin County SD
Supt. — See Bay Minette
Fairhope HS 1,400/9-12
1 Pirate Dr 36532 251-928-8309
Jan Cardwell, prin. Fax 990-2053
Fairhope MS 700/7-8
2 Pirate Dr 36532 251-928-2573
Angie Hall, prin. Fax 990-0403

Bayshore Christian S 200/K-10
23050 US Highway 98 36532 251-929-0011
John Howard, hdmstr. Fax 928-0149

Falkville, Morgan, Pop. 1,257
Morgan County SD
Supt. — See Decatur
Falkville JSHS 400/6-12
43 Clark Dr 35622 256-784-5248
Glenn Lang, prin. Fax 784-9438

Fayette, Fayette, Pop. 4,573
Fayette County SD 2,400/PK-12
PO Box 686 35555 205-932-4611
Wade Shipman, supt. Fax 932-7246
www.fayette.k12.al.us
Fayette County HS 400/9-12
202 Tiger Dr 35555 205-932-6313
Jeremy Madden, prin. Fax 932-8361
Fayette MS 500/5-8
418 3rd Ave NE 35555 205-932-7660
Rodney Hannah, prin. Fax 932-7661
Hubbertville S 400/PK-12
7360 County Road 49 35555 205-487-2845
Tim Dunavant, prin. Fax 487-3375
Other Schools – See Berry

Flomaton, Escambia, Pop. 1,423
Escambia County SD
Supt. — See Brewton
Escambia County Alternative S Alt
21280 Highway 31 36441 251-296-4113
Hilda Rudolph Blakely, prin. Fax 296-4075
Flomaton HS 300/9-12
21200 Highway 31 36441 251-296-2627
Scott Hammond, prin. Fax 296-2625

Florala, Covington, Pop. 1,935
Covington County SD
Supt. — See Andalusia
Florala HS 200/7-12
22114 Begonia St 36442 334-858-3765
Brent Zessin, prin. Fax 858-6925

Florence, Lauderdale, Pop. 38,649
Florence CSD 4,300/K-12
102 S Court St Ste 600 35630 256-768-3000
Dr. Janet Womack, supt. Fax 768-3006
www.florencek12.org/
Florence Career Technical Education Vo/Tech
541 Riverview Dr 35630 256-768-3021
Darrin Lett, admin. Fax 768-3010
Florence Freshman Center 300/9-9
648 N Cherry St 35630 256-768-2400
Rod Sheppard, prin. Fax 768-2405
Florence HS 1,000/10-12
1201 Bradshaw Dr 35630 256-768-2200
Lynne Hice, prin. Fax 768-2205
Florence MS 600/7-8
648 N Cherry St 35630 256-768-3100
Aimee Rainey, prin. Fax 768-3105

Lauderdale County SD 8,600/PK-12
PO Box 278 35631 256-760-1300
Jennifer Gray, supt. Fax 766-5815
www.lcschools.org
Central S 1,300/PK-12
3000 County Road 200 35633 256-764-2903
Ryan Harrison, prin. Fax 764-5409
Rogers S 1,300/K-12
300 Rogers Ln 35634 256-757-3106
Michael Stamps, prin. Fax 757-9625
Wilson S 1,300/K-12
7601 Highway 17 35634 256-764-8470
Gary Horton, prin. Fax 764-1304
Other Schools – See Killen, Lexington, Rogersville, Waterloo

Heritage Christian University Post-Sec.
PO Box HCU 35630 256-766-6610
Mars Hill Bible S 600/K-12
698 Cox Creek Pkwy 35630 256-767-1203
Shoals Christian S 200/PK-12
301 Heathrow Dr 35633 256-767-7070
Jim Koan M.A., hdmstr. Fax 766-5677
University of North Alabama Post-Sec.
1 Harrison Plz 35632 256-765-4100

Foley, Baldwin, Pop. 14,389
Baldwin County SD
Supt. — See Bay Minette
Foley HS 1,700/9-12
1 Pride Pl 36535 251-943-2221
Russ Moore, prin. Fax 943-3538
Foley MS 600/7-8
201 N Pine St 36535 251-943-1255
Danny McDuffie, prin. Fax 943-8221

Fortis College Post-Sec.
200 E Laurel Ave 36535 251-970-1460

Fort Deposit, Lowndes, Pop. 1,336
Lowndes County SD
Supt. — See Hayneville
Lowndes County MS 200/6-8
PO Box 393 36032 334-227-4206
Archie Curtis, prin. Fax 227-4125

Fort Payne, DeKalb, Pop. 13,756
Fort Payne CSD 3,100/PK-12
PO Box 681029 35968 256-845-0915
James Cunningham, supt. Fax 845-4962
www.ftpayk12.org
Fort Payne HS 800/9-12
201 45th St NE 35967 256-845-0535
Brian Jett, prin. Fax 845-7868
Fort Payne MS 900/5-8
4910 Martin Ave NE 35967 256-845-7501
Shane Byrd, prin. Fax 845-8292

Fruitdale, Washington, Pop. 184
Washington County SD
Supt. — See Chatom
Fruitdale S 400/K-12
PO Box 448 36539 251-827-6655
Curtis Stagner, prin. Fax 827-6573

Fyffe, DeKalb, Pop. 992
De Kalb County SD
Supt. — See Rainsville
Fyffe S 1,000/K-12
PO Box 7 35971 256-623-2116
Ricky Bryant, prin. Fax 623-4388

Gadsden, Etowah, Pop. 36,211
Etowah County SD 9,300/K-12
3200 W Meighan Blvd 35904 256-549-7560
Dr. Alan Cosby, supt. Fax 549-7589
www.ecboe.org/
Gaston S 600/K-12
4550 US Highway 411 35901 256-547-8828
Dr. Miria King-Garner, prin. Fax 543-7124
Hokes Bluff MS 300/6-8
3121 Appalachian Hwy 35903 256-492-1963
Dena Cook, prin. Fax 492-1950
Other Schools – See Attalla, Glencoe, Hokes Bluff, Rainbow City, Sardis City, Southside, Walnut Grove

Gadsden CSD 6,000/K-12
PO Box 184 35902 256-543-3512
Dr. Ed Miller, supt. Fax 549-2950
www.gcs.k12.al.us
Gadsden City HS 1,600/9-12
1917 Black Creek Pkwy 35904 256-543-3614
Keith Blackwell, prin. Fax 543-4251
Gadsden MS 400/6-8
612 Tracy St 35901 256-547-6341
Joel Gulledge, prin. Fax 547-6323
Litchfield MS 200/6-8
1109 Hoke St 35903 256-492-6793
Micah Cook, prin. Fax 492-4010
Sansom MS 500/6-8
2210 W Meighan Blvd 35904 256-546-4992
Sharon Maness, prin. Fax 543-1060
Secondary Alternative S 600/Alt
607 S 12th St 35901 256-547-5446
Donna Smoots, prin. Fax 547-5448

Coosa Christian S 400/PK-12
2736 Wills Creek Rd 35904 256-547-1841
Amanda Justus, admin. Fax 547-0456
Gadsden State Community College Post-Sec.
PO Box 227 35902 256-549-8200
Holy Comforter Episcopal Day S 100/PK-12
156 S 9th St 35901 256-546-9071
Laura McCartney, hdmstr. Fax 546-7912

Gardendale, Jefferson, Pop. 13,766
Jefferson County SD
Supt. — See Birmingham
Bragg MS 900/6-8
840 Ash Ave 35071 205-379-2600
Neal Underwood, prin. Fax 379-2645
Gardendale HS 1,100/9-12
800 Main St 35071 205-379-3600
Jeff Caufield, prin. Fax 379-3645

Alabama State College of Barber Styling Post-Sec.
753 Main St 35071 205-631-8898

Gaylesville, Cherokee, Pop. 143
Cherokee County SD
Supt. — See Centre
Gaylesville S 400/PK-12
760 Trojan Way 35973 256-422-3401
Scott Hays, prin. Fax 422-3165

Geneva, Geneva, Pop. 4,382
Geneva CSD 1,200/K-12
511 Panther Dr 36340 334-684-1090
Ricky Bennett, supt. Fax 684-3128
www.genevacity.schoolinsites.com
Geneva HS 400/9-12
505 Panther Dr 36340 334-684-9379
Mickey Bennett, prin. Fax 684-0303
Geneva MS 300/6-8
501 Panther Dr 36340 334-684-6431
Danny Bedsole, prin. Fax 684-0476

Geneva County SD 2,700/K-12
PO Box 250 36340 334-684-5690
Becky Birdsong, supt. Fax 684-5601
genevacounty.schoolinsites.com/
Other Schools – See Hartford, Samson, Slocomb

Georgiana, Butler, Pop. 1,722
Butler County SD
Supt. — See Greenville
Georgiana S 300/K-12
PO Box 680 36033 334-376-9130
Joseph Dean, prin. Fax 376-2956

Geraldine, DeKalb, Pop. 882
De Kalb County SD
Supt. — See Rainsville
Geraldine S 1,200/K-12
13011 AL Highway 227 35974 256-659-2142
Steven Street, prin. Fax 659-4296

Gilbertown, Choctaw, Pop. 214
Choctaw County SD
Supt. — See Butler
Southern Choctaw HS 400/7-12
10941 Highway 17 36908 251-843-5645
Leo Leddon Ed.D., prin. Fax 843-5649

Glencoe, Etowah, Pop. 5,099
Etowah County SD
Supt. — See Gadsden
Glencoe HS 400/9-12
803 Lonesome Bend Rd 35905 256-492-2250
Charlton Giles, prin. Fax 492-2265
Glencoe MS 300/5-8
809 Lonesome Bend Rd 35905 256-492-5627
Ginger Smith, prin. Fax 492-7076

Gordo, Pickens, Pop. 1,715
Pickens County SD
Supt. — See Carrollton
Gordo JSHS 500/7-12
630 4th St NW 35466 205-364-7353
Ken Holder, prin. Fax 364-6160

Goshen, Pike, Pop. 265
Pike County SD
Supt. — See Troy
Goshen JSHS 400/7-12
286 Eagle Cir 36035 334-484-3245
Dr. C. Warren Weeks, prin. Fax 484-3247

Grand Bay, Mobile, Pop. 3,617
Mobile County SD
Supt. — See Mobile
Grand Bay MS 800/6-8
12800 Cunningham Rd 36541 251-865-6511
John Poiroux, prin. Fax 221-2405

Grant, Marshall, Pop. 887
Marshall County SD
Supt. — See Guntersville
Smith DAR HS 500/9-12
6077 Main St 35747 256-728-4238
Stacy Anderton, prin. Fax 728-8900
Smith DAR MS 400/5-8
6077 Main St 35747 256-728-5950
Keith Stanfield, prin. Fax 728-8447

Greensboro, Hale, Pop. 2,483
Hale County SD 2,800/PK-12
1115 Powers St 36744 334-624-8836
Osie A. Pickens, supt. Fax 624-3415
www.halek12.org
Greensboro HS 400/9-12
620 Carver St 36744 334-624-9156
Kendrick Britford, prin. Fax 624-9157
Greensboro MS 300/6-8
620 Carver St 36744 334-624-4005
Anthony Sanders, prin. Fax 624-0308
Hale County Technology Center Vo/Tech
PO Box 517 36744 334-624-3691
James Essex, prin. Fax 624-1090
Other Schools – See Akron, Moundville, Newbern

Southern Academy 300/K-12
407 College St 36744 334-624-8111

Greenville, Butler, Pop. 8,092
Butler County SD 3,100/K-12
211 School Highlands Rd 36037 334-382-2665
Darren Douthitt, supt. Fax 382-8607
www.butlerco.k12.al.us
Butler County Area Vocational HS Vo/Tech
100 Tiger Dr 36037 334-382-0266
Joseph West, prin. Fax 382-8607
Greenville HS 800/9-12
100 Tiger Dr 36037 334-382-2608
Joseph Dean, prin. Fax 382-7202
Greenville MS 800/5-8
300 Overlook Rd 36037 334-382-3450
Ward Thigpen, prin. Fax 382-0686
Other Schools – See Georgiana, Mc Kenzie

Fort Dale Academy 400/K-12
1100 Gamble St 36037 334-382-2606
David Brantley, hdmstr. Fax 382-0912

Grove Hill, Clarke, Pop. 1,558
Clarke County SD 3,200/PK-12
PO Box 936 36451 251-275-3255
Larry Bagley, supt. Fax 275-8061
www.clarkecountyschools.org/
Clarke County HS 400/9-12
PO Box 937 36451 251-275-3368
Debra Dennis, prin. Fax 275-4132
Wilson Hall MS 400/5-8
401 Carter Dr 36451 251-275-8993
Carolyn Taite, prin. Fax 275-4688
Other Schools – See Jackson

Clarke Preparatory S 300/PK-12
20100 Highway 43 36451 251-275-8576

Guin, Marion, Pop. 2,339
Marion County SD
Supt. — See Hamilton
Marion County HS 200/7-12
PO Box 549 35563 205-468-3377
Jason Bourland, prin. Fax 468-8047

Gulf Shores, Baldwin, Pop. 9,533
Baldwin County SD
Supt. — See Bay Minette
Gulf Shores HS 800/9-12
600 E 15th Ave 36542 251-968-4747
Dr. Ernie Rosado, prin. Fax 968-4770
Gulf Shores MS 400/7-8
450 E 15th Ave 36542 251-968-8719
Phillip Fountain, prin. Fax 967-1577

Guntersville, Marshall, Pop. 8,040
Guntersville CSD 1,900/K-12
PO Box 129 35976 256-582-3159
Dale Edwards, supt. Fax 582-6158
www.guntersvilleboe.com
Guntersville HS 600/9-12
14227 US Highway 431 35976 256-582-2046
John Richey, prin. Fax 582-4742
Guntersville MS 400/6-8
901 Sunset Dr 35976 256-582-5182
Shirl Dollar, prin. Fax 582-4477

Marshall County SD 5,100/PK-12
12380 US Highway 431 35976 256-582-3171
Tim Nabors, supt. Fax 582-2998
www.marshallk12.org
Brindlee Mountain HS 400/9-12
994 Scant City Rd 35976 256-753-2800
Jeff Jones, prin. Fax 753-2802
Brindlee Mountain MS 300/6-8
1050 Scant City Rd 35976 256-753-2820
Mike Little, prin. Fax 753-2822
Marshall Technical HS Vo/Tech
12312 US Highway 431 35976 256-582-5629
Cindy Wigley, prin. Fax 582-2580
Other Schools – See Albertville, Douglas, Grant

Gurley, Madison, Pop. 783
Madison County SD
Supt. — See Huntsville
Madison County HS 600/9-12
174 Brock Rd 35748 256-776-6247
Jeremy Lowry, prin. Fax 776-4302

Hackleburg, Marion, Pop. 1,499
Marion County SD
Supt. — See Hamilton
Hackleburg HS 300/7-12
PO Box 310 35564 205-935-3223
John Hardin, prin. Fax 935-8092

Haleyville, Winston, Pop. 4,111
Haleyville CSD 1,700/PK-12
2011 20th St 35565 205-486-9231
Alan Miller, supt. Fax 486-8833
haley-k12.us
Haleyville Center of Technology Vo/Tech
2007 20th St 35565 205-486-9481
William Bishop, prin. Fax 486-8735
Haleyville HS 500/9-12
2001 20th St 35565 205-486-3122
Roger Satcher, prin. Fax 486-1660
Haleyville MS 400/6-8
2014 20th Ave 35565 205-486-9240
Russ O'Rear, prin. Fax 486-9244

Hamilton, Marion, Pop. 6,817
Marion County SD 3,600/PK-12
188 Winchester Dr 35570 205-921-9319
Ryan Hollingsworth, supt. Fax 921-7336
www.mcbe.net
Hamilton HS 500/9-12
211 Aggie Ave 35570 205-921-3281
Ronnie Miller, prin. Fax 921-2333
Hamilton MS 500/5-8
400 Military St S 35570 205-921-7030
Steven Deavours, prin. Fax 921-3821
Marion County Alternative S 50/Alt
188 Winchester Dr 35570 205-952-9083
Lynda Hall, prin. Fax 952-9083
Other Schools – See Bear Creek, Brilliant, Guin, Hackleburg

Hampton Cove, Madison
Huntsville CSD
Supt. — See Huntsville
Hampton Cove MS 600/6-8
261 Old Highway 431 35763 256-428-8380
Dr. Debi Edwards, prin. Fax 428-8383

Hanceville, Cullman, Pop. 2,928
Cullman County SD
Supt. — See Cullman
Hanceville HS 400/9-12
801 Commercial St SE 35077 256-352-6111
Tracy Hubbert, prin. Fax 352-6491
Hanceville MS 300/6-8
805 Commercial St SE 35077 256-352-6175
Cynthia Roden, prin. Fax 352-9741

Wallace State Community College Post-Sec.
PO Box 2000 35077 256-352-8000

Hartford, Geneva, Pop. 2,582
Geneva County SD
Supt. — See Geneva
Geneva County HS 200/9-12
301 Lily St 36344 334-588-2943
Harold Birge, prin. Fax 588-3650
Geneva County MS 200/6-8
301 Lily St 36344 334-588-2943
Bill Singleton, prin. Fax 588-3650

Hartselle, Morgan, Pop. 14,036
Hartselle CSD 3,100/PK-12
305 College St NE 35640 256-773-5419
Dr. Mike Reed, supt. Fax 773-5433
www.hartselletigers.org
Hartselle AVC Vo/Tech
904 Sparkman St SW 35640 256-773-5426
Jeff Hyche, prin. Fax 773-5572
Hartselle HS 900/9-12
904 Sparkman St SW 35640 256-773-5426
Jeff Hyche, prin. Fax 773-5572
Hartselle JHS 800/6-8
130 Petain St SW 35640 256-773-6094
Don Pouncey, prin. Fax 773-3499

Harvest, Madison, Pop. 5,123
Madison County SD
Supt. — See Huntsville
Sparkman HS 1,900/10-12
2616 Jeff Rd 35749 256-837-0331
Manuel Wallace, prin. Fax 837-7673
Sparkman Ninth Grade S 600/9-9
2680 Jeff Rd 35749 256-382-2030
Martin Hester, prin. Fax 382-2025

Hayden, Blount, Pop. 432
Blount County SD
Supt. — See Oneonta
Hayden HS 900/8-12
125 Atwood Rd 35079 205-647-0397
Allen Hargett, prin. Fax 647-8633

Hayneville, Lowndes, Pop. 928
Lowndes County SD 1,800/K-12
PO Box 755 36040 334-548-2131
Dr. Daniel Boyd, supt. Fax 548-2161
www.lowndesboe.org/
Central HS 300/9-12
145 Main St 36040 334-563-7311
Peggy Grant, prin. Fax 563-7299
Hayneville MS 200/6-8
PO Box 307 36040 334-548-2184
Antonio Williams, prin. Fax 548-5237
Project Success Learning Center Alt
147 Main St 36040 334-563-9869
Lorenza Smith, prin. Fax 563-9869
Other Schools – See Fort Deposit, Letohatchee

Hazel Green, Madison, Pop. 3,538
Madison County SD
Supt. — See Huntsville
Hazel Green HS 1,300/9-12
14380 Highway 231 431 N 35750 256-828-0764
Darrell Long, prin. Fax 828-6203
Meridianville MS 1,000/6-8
12975 Highway 231 431 N 35750 256-829-1165
Tom Highfield, prin. Fax 829-1104

Headland, Henry, Pop. 4,460
Henry County SD
Supt. — See Abbeville
Headland HS 400/10-12
8 Sporman St 36345 334-693-2442
Jason Bradford, prin. Fax 693-5255
Headland MS 500/6-9
1 Martin Luther King Dr 36345 334-693-3764
Kevin Sanders, prin. Fax 693-9058

Heflin, Cleburne, Pop. 3,431
Cleburne County SD 2,700/PK-12
93 Education St 36264 256-463-5624
Claire Dryden, supt. Fax 463-5709
www.cleburneschools.net
Cleburne County Career Technical S Vo/Tech
11200 Highway 46 36264 256-748-2961
Eric Lovvorn, prin. Fax 748-3904
Cleburne County HS 700/8-12
520 Evans Bridge Rd 36264 256-463-2012
Gregory Corkren, prin. Fax 463-5504
Other Schools – See Ranburne

Helena, Shelby, Pop. 16,576
Shelby County SD
Supt. — See Columbiana
Helena MS 800/6-8
1299 Hillsboro Pkwy 35080 205-682-5300
Scott Knight, prin. Fax 682-5305

Higdon, Jackson
Jackson County SD
Supt. — See Scottsboro
North Sand Mountain S 700/K-12
PO Box 129 35979 256-597-2111
Chris Davis, prin. Fax 597-2505

Highland Home, Crenshaw
Crenshaw County SD
Supt. — See Luverne
Highland Home S 800/PK-12
18434 Montgomery Hwy 36041 334-537-4379
Barry Gross, prin. Fax 537-9805

Hokes Bluff, Etowah, Pop. 4,266
Etowah County SD
Supt. — See Gadsden
Hokes Bluff HS 400/9-12
1865 Appalachian Hwy 35903 256-492-1360
Scott Calhoun, prin. Fax 492-7502

Holly Pond, Cullman, Pop. 794
Cullman County SD
Supt. — See Cullman
Holly Pond HS 300/9-12
160 New Hope Rd 35083 256-796-5169
Kim Butler, prin. Fax 796-5199
Holly Pond MS 200/6-8
91 Buckner Rd 35083 256-796-5898
Dr. Chuck Gambrill, prin. Fax 796-0680

Hollywood, Jackson, Pop. 967
Jackson County SD
Supt. — See Scottsboro
Pruett Center of Technology Vo/Tech
29490 US Highway 72 35752 256-574-6079
Shane Small, prin. Fax 259-1644

Homewood, Jefferson, Pop. 24,859
Homewood CSD 3,500/K-12
PO Box 59366 35259 205-870-4203
Dr. Bill Cleveland, supt. Fax 877-4544
www.homewood.k12.al.us
Homewood HS 1,000/9-12
1901 Lakeshore Dr S 35209 205-871-9663
Dr. Zack Barnes, prin. Fax 879-0879
Homewood MS 800/6-8
395 Mecca Ave 35209 205-870-0878
Dr. Martin Nalls, prin. Fax 877-4573

Hoover, Jefferson, Pop. 80,440
Hoover CSD 12,100/K-12
2810 Metropolitan Way 35243 205-439-1000
Andy Craig, supt. Fax 439-1003
www.hoover.k12.al.us
Bumpus MS 700/7-8
6055 Fleming Pkwy 35244 205-439-2200
Dr. Tamala Maddox, prin. Fax 439-2201
Crossroads S Alt
2826 Columbiana Rd 35216 205-439-1800
Anna Whitney, prin. Fax 439-1899
Hoover HS 1,900/9-12
1000 Buccaneer Dr 35244 205-439-1200
Don Hulin, prin. Fax 439-1201
Simmons MS 900/6-8
1575 Patton Chapel Rd 35226 205-439-2100
Brian Cain, prin. Fax 439-2101
Other Schools – See Birmingham, Vestavia Hills

Shades Mountain Christian S 400/PK-12
2290 Old Tyler Rd 35226 205-978-6001
Brian Willett, prin. Fax 978-9120

Hope Hull, Montgomery

Hooper Academy 400/PK-12
380 Fischer Rd 36043 334-288-5980

Hueytown, Jefferson, Pop. 15,960
Jefferson County SD
Supt. — See Birmingham
Hueytown HS 1,000/9-12
4881 15th Street Rd 35023 205-379-4150
Dr. Gayle Gober, prin. Fax 379-4195
Hueytown MS 800/6-8
701 Sunrise Blvd 35023 205-379-5150
Chris Anders, prin. Fax 379-5195
Jefferson Co. Counseling/Lrng Ctr-West Alt
131 Dabbs Ave 35023 205-379-4130
Jason Wilson, prin. Fax 379-4135

Huntsville, Madison, Pop. 175,870
Huntsville CSD 21,800/PK-12
PO Box 1256 35807 256-428-6800
Dr. E. Casey Wardynski, supt. Fax 428-6817
www.hsv-k12.org
Butler HS 600/9-12
3401 Holmes Ave NW 35816 256-428-7950
Sanchella Graham, prin. Fax 428-7951
Challenger MS 500/6-8
13555 Chaney Thompson Rd SE 35803
256-428-7620
Dianne Hasty, prin. Fax 428-7621
Chapman MS 300/6-8
2006 Reuben Dr NE 35811 256-428-7640
Glenn Bryant, prin. Fax 428-7641
Columbia HS 700/9-12
300 Explorer Blvd NW 35806 256-428-7576
Greg Hicks, prin. Fax 428-7579
Davis Hills MS 400/6-8
3221 Mastin Lake Rd NW 35810 256-428-7660
Jill Burwell, prin. Fax 428-7661
Grissom HS 2,000/9-12
7901 Bailey Cove Rd SE 35802 256-428-8000
June Kalange, prin. Fax 428-8001
Huntsville Center for Technology Vo/Tech
2800 Drake Ave SW 35805 256-428-7810
Shelton Cobb, prin. Fax 428-7811
Huntsville HS 1,700/9-12
2304 Billie Watkins St SW 35801 256-428-8050
Mark Mincher, prin. Fax 428-8051
Huntsville MS 700/6-8
817 Adams St SE 35801 256-428-7700
Aaron King, prin. Fax 428-7701
Johnson HS 600/9-12
6201 Pueblo Dr NW 35810 256-428-8100
Eric Jones, prin. Fax 428-8118
Lee HS 800/9-12
2500 Meridian St N 35811 256-428-8150
Kevin Wieseman, prin. Fax 428-8151
New Century Technology S 300/9-12
2500 Meridian St N 35811 256-428-7800
Stewart Thorson, prin. Fax 428-7801
Providence MS 400/6-8
10 Chalkstone St 35806 256-428-7125
Paul Bonner, prin. Fax 428-7127
Westlawn MS 500/6-8
4217 9th Ave SW 35805 256-428-7760
Presonia Alexander, prin. Fax 428-7761
White MS 400/6-8
4800 Sparkman Dr NW 35810 256-428-7680
Jo Stafford, prin. Fax 428-7681
Williams MS 200/6-8
155A Barren Fork Blvd SW 35824 256-428-7330
Lois Mays, prin. Fax 428-7331
Other Schools – See Hampton Cove

Madison County SD 18,700/PK-12
PO Box 226 35804 256-852-2557
Dr. David Copeland, supt. Fax 852-2538
www.madison.k12.al.us
Madison County Career Technical Center Vo/Tech
1275 Jordan Rd 35811 256-852-2170
Michael Romine, prin. Fax 851-9790
Monrovia MS 1,100/6-8
1216 Jeff Rd NW 35806 256-430-4499
Derrell Brown, prin. Fax 726-0230
PACE Academy Alt
1275 Jordan Rd 35811 256-859-1148
Dr. Vince Edmonds, prin. Fax 859-1033
Other Schools – See Gurley, Harvest, Hazel Green, New Hope, New Market, Toney

---

Alabama A & M University Post-Sec.
4900 Meridian St N 35810 256-372-5000
Huntsville Bible College Post-Sec.
904 Oakwood Ave NW 35811 256-539-0834
Huntsville Hospital Post-Sec.
101 Sivley Rd SW 35801 256-533-8123
J. F. Drake State Technical College Post-Sec.
3421 Meridian St N 35811 256-539-8161
Oakwood Adventist Academy 200/K-12
7000 Adventist Blvd NW 35896 256-726-7010
Sharon Lewis, prin. Fax 726-7016
Oakwood University Post-Sec.
7000 Adventist Blvd NW 35896 256-726-7000
Pope John Paul II Catholic HS 300/9-12
7301 Old Madison Pike NW 35806 256-430-1760
Vince Aquila, prin. Fax 430-1766
Providence Classical S 200/K-12
PO Box 22238 35814 256-852-8884
Pattie Steward, admin. Fax 852-8884
Randolph S 900/K-12
1005 Drake Ave SE 35802 256-799-6100
Dr. Byron Hulsey, hdmstr. Fax 881-1784
Union Chapel Christian Academy 200/K-12
315 Winchester Rd NE Ste B 35811 256-489-4728
Ted Walton, prin. Fax 489-9025
University of Alabama in Huntsville Post-Sec.
301 Sparkman Dr NW 35805 256-824-1000
Valley Fellowship Christian Academy 200/PK-12
3616 Holmes Ave NW 35816 256-533-5248
Patti Simon, admin. Fax 533-5253
Virginia College Post-Sec.
2021 Drake Ave SW 35801 256-533-7387
Westminster Christian Academy 400/6-12
237 Johns Rd NW 35806 256-705-8000
Craig Bouvier, hdmstr. Fax 705-8001
Whitesburg Christian Academy 400/K-12
6806 Whitesburg Dr SW 35802 256-704-5678
Jerry Reeder, hdmstr. Fax 880-5309

Ider, DeKalb, Pop. 708
De Kalb County SD
Supt. — See Rainsville
Ider S 800/K-12
1064 Crabapple Ln 35981 256-632-2302
Jeff Watkins, prin. Fax 632-3481

Indian Springs, Shelby, Pop. 2,352

Indian Springs S 300/8-12
190 Woodward Dr 35124 205-988-3350
Gareth Vaughan, dir. Fax 988-3797

Irondale, Jefferson, Pop. 12,191
Jefferson County SD
Supt. — See Birmingham
Shades Valley HS 1,400/9-12
6100 Old Leeds Rd 35210 205-379-5350
Mary Beth Blankenship, prin. Fax 379-5395

Jefferson Christian Academy K-12
1500 Heritage Place Dr 35210 205-956-9111
Chad Hudelson, prin. Fax 956-9508

Irvington, Mobile
Mobile County SD
Supt. — See Mobile
Bryant Career Technical S Vo/Tech
8950 Padgett Switch Rd 36544 251-957-2845
Thomas Reed, prin. Fax 957-3170
Bryant HS 1,700/9-12
14001 Hurricane Blvd 36544 251-824-3213
Doug Estle, prin. Fax 824-3221

Jack, Coffee
Coffee County SD
Supt. — See Elba
Zion Chapel S 800/K-12
29256 Highway 87 36346 334-897-6275
Joan Calhoun, prin. Fax 897-5136

Jackson, Clarke, Pop. 5,191
Clarke County SD
Supt. — See Grove Hill
Jackson HS 600/9-12
321 Stanley Dr 36545 251-246-2571
Ken Harbuck, prin. Fax 246-3190
Jackson MS 500/6-8
235 College Ave 36545 251-246-3597
Stuart Etheredge, prin. Fax 246-6017

Jackson Academy 200/K-12
PO Box 838 36545 251-246-5552
Suzanne Bailey, head sch Fax 246-0202

Jacksonville, Calhoun, Pop. 12,298
Calhoun County SD
Supt. — See Anniston
Calhoun County Alternative S Alt
1200 Church Ave SE 36265 256-741-7900
Robin Kines, dir. Fax 237-9212
Calhoun County Career Technical Center Vo/Tech
1200 Church Ave SE 36265 256-741-4600
Wayne Smart, prin. Fax 435-4221
Pleasant Valley HS 500/7-12
4141 Pleasant Valley Rd 36265 256-741-6700
Mark Proper, prin. Fax 435-0171

Jacksonville CSD 1,700/K-12
123 College St SW 36265 256-782-5682
Dr. Jon Paul Campbell, supt. Fax 782-5947
www.jacksonville.k12.al.us
Jacksonville HS 800/7-12
1000 George Douthit Dr SW 36265 256-782-8800
Mike Newell, prin. Fax 782-8801

Jacksonville Christian Academy 200/K-12
831 Alexandria Rd SW 36265 256-435-3333
Dr. Tommy Miller, prin. Fax 435-2059
Jacksonville State University Post-Sec.
700 Pelham Rd N 36265 256-782-5781

Jasper, Walker, Pop. 14,147
Jasper CSD 2,700/PK-12
PO Box 500 35502 205-384-6880
Dr. Robert Sparkman, supt. Fax 387-5213
www.jasper.k12.al.us
Maddox MS 600/6-8
201 Panther Trl 35501 205-384-3235
Patsy Stricklin, prin. Fax 387-5208
Walker HS 800/9-12
1601 Highland Ave 35501 205-221-9277
Gary Boling, prin. Fax 387-5228

Walker County SD 7,600/PK-12
PO Box 311 35502 205-387-0555
Dr. Jason Adkins, supt. Fax 221-5636
www.walkercountyschools.com
Curry HS 600/9-12
155 Yellow Jacket Dr 35503 205-384-3887
Rod Aaron, prin. Fax 221-7381
Curry MS 300/6-8
115 Yellow Jacket Dr 35503 205-384-3441
David Hendon, prin. Fax 384-1110
Walker County Alternative S Alt
1100 Viking Dr 35501 205-387-9984
Rickey Pate, prin. Fax 387-7239
Walker County Center for Tech Vo/Tech
1100 Viking Dr 35501 205-387-0561
Debra Ellis, prin. Fax 384-5170
Other Schools – See Carbon Hill, Cordova, Dora, Oakman, Parrish

---

Bevill State Community College Post-Sec.
1411 Indiana Ave 35501 205-387-0511

Jemison, Chilton, Pop. 2,561
Chilton County SD
Supt. — See Clanton
Jemison HS 700/8-12
25125 US Highway 31 35085 205-280-4860
Allen Wilson, prin. Fax 688-4761

Killen, Lauderdale, Pop. 1,097
Lauderdale County SD
Supt. — See Florence
Brooks JSHS 800/7-12
4300 Highway 72 35645 256-757-2115
Stephen Howard, prin. Fax 757-1136
Thornton Career Technical Center Vo/Tech
7275 Highway 72 35645 256-757-2101
Kelley Joiner, prin. Fax 757-8692

Kimberly, Jefferson, Pop. 2,694
Jefferson County SD
Supt. — See Birmingham
Jordan HS 800/9-12
1920 Blue Devil Dr 35091 205-379-4850
Barbara Snider, prin. Fax 379-4895
North Jefferson MS 600/6-8
8350 Warrior Kimberly Rd 35091 205-379-4000
Craig Kanaday, prin. Fax 379-4045

Kinston, Coffee, Pop. 531
Coffee County SD
Supt. — See Elba
Kinston S 500/K-12
201 College St 36453 334-565-3016
Gary Glass, prin. Fax 565-3494

Lafayette, Chambers, Pop. 2,991
Chambers County SD 4,100/PK-12
PO Box 408 36862 334-864-9343
Dr. Kelli Tucker, supt. Fax 864-0119
www.chambersk12.org
Chambers County Career Tech Center Vo/Tech
PO Box 318 36862 334-864-8863
Ken Sealy, prin. Fax 864-9394
Lafayette HS 300/9-12
214 1st Ave SE 36862 334-864-9881
Montray Thompson, prin. Fax 864-0650
Powell MS 200/6-8
621 1st St SE 36862 334-864-8876
Daron Brooks, prin. Fax 864-8169
Other Schools – See Valley

Chambers Academy 200/K-12
15048 US Highway 431 36862 334-864-9852
Jim Childers, hdmstr. Fax 864-9691

Lanett, Chambers, Pop. 6,366
Lanett CSD — 800/K-12
105 N Lanier Ave 36863 — 334-644-5900
Phillip Johnson, supt. — Fax 644-5910
www.lanettcityschools.org
Lanett HS — 200/9-12
1301 S 8th Ave 36863 — 334-644-5965
Jennifer Boyd, prin. — Fax 644-5979
Lanett JHS — 100/7-8
1301 S 8th Ave 36863 — 334-644-5950
Joan Gilbert, prin. — Fax 644-5964

Springwood S — 300/PK-12
PO Box 1030 36863 — 334-644-2191
Rick Johnson, hdmstr. — Fax 644-2194

Leeds, Jefferson, Pop. 11,579
Leeds CSD — 1,400/K-12
PO Box 1083 35094 — 205-699-5437
John Moore, supt. — Fax 699-6629
www.leedsk12.org/
Leeds HS — 400/9-12
1500 Greenwave Dr 35094 — 205-699-4510
Michael Turner, prin. — Fax 699-4515
Leeds MS — 400/5-8
1771 Whitmire St 35094 — 205-699-4505
Dr. Jason Baker, prin. — Fax 699-4509

Leighton, Colbert, Pop. 711
Colbert County SD
Supt. — See Tuscumbia
Colbert County HS — 500/7-12
2200 High School St 35646 — 256-446-8214
Melcha Satchel, prin. — Fax 446-8951

Leroy, Washington, Pop. 902
Washington County SD
Supt. — See Chatom
Leroy S — 800/K-12
PO Box 40 36548 — 251-246-2000
Danny Patterson, prin. — Fax 246-2199

Lester, Limestone, Pop. 111
Limestone County SD
Supt. — See Athens
West Limestone S — 1,000/K-12
10945 W School House Rd 35647 — 256-233-6687
Charlotte Craig, prin. — Fax 233-8034

Letohatchee, Lowndes
Lowndes County SD
Supt. — See Hayneville
Calhoun HS — 300/9-12
8213 County Road 33 36047 — 334-227-4515
Kenneth Fair, prin. — Fax 227-8335

Lexington, Lauderdale, Pop. 728
Lauderdale County SD
Supt. — See Florence
Lexington S — 900/K-12
101 School St 35648 — 256-229-6622
Willie Joiner, prin. — Fax 229-6636

Lincoln, Talladega, Pop. 6,180
Talladega County SD
Supt. — See Talladega
Drew MS — 300/7-8
78975 AL Highway 21 35096 — 256-315-5280
Dr. Rhonda Lee, prin. — Fax 315-5290
Lincoln HS — 500/9-12
78989 AL Highway 77 35096 — 256-315-5295
Fax 315-5315

Linden, Marengo, Pop. 2,103
Linden CSD — 500/PK-12
PO Box 480609 36748 — 334-295-8802
George Baldwin, supt. — Fax 295-8801
www.lindencity.org
Austin JHS — 100/6-8
PO Box 480699 36748 — 334-295-5378
Terry Gosa, prin. — Fax 295-5376
Linden HS — 200/9-12
PO Box 480729 36748 — 334-295-4287
Dr. Timothy Thurman, prin. — Fax 295-0988

Marengo County SD — 1,500/K-12
PO Box 480339 36748 — 334-295-4123
Luke Hallmark, supt. — Fax 295-2259
www.marengocounty.schoolinsites.com/
Marengo County Alternative S — Alt
PO Box 480339 36748 — 334-295-9798
Luther Hallmark, prin. — Fax 295-9797
Other Schools – See Demopolis, Dixons Mills, Sweet Water, Thomaston

---

Marengo Academy — 200/K-12
2103 S Main St 36748 — 334-295-4151
Fax 295-4159

Lineville, Clay, Pop. 2,331
Clay County SD
Supt. — See Ashland
Central HS of Clay County — 600/7-12
1 Bob Riley Dr 36266 — 256-396-1400
Bobby Vinson, prin. — Fax 396-2452

Livingston, Sumter, Pop. 3,462
Sumter County SD — 1,900/PK-12
PO Box 10 35470 — 205-652-9605
Katie Jones-Powell, supt. — Fax 652-9641
www.sumter.k12.al.us
Bell-Brown Career Technical Center — Vo/Tech
PO Box 1380 35470 — 205-652-9469
Travis Bailey, dir. — Fax 652-9487
Other Schools – See York

University of West Alabama — Post-Sec.
UWA Station 04 35470 — 205-652-3400

Loachapoka, Lee, Pop. 179
Lee County SD
Supt. — See Opelika
Loachapoka HS — 300/7-12
PO Box 187 36865 — 334-887-8038
Zelda Kitt, prin. — Fax 887-5228

Locust Fork, Blount, Pop. 1,182
Blount County SD
Supt. — See Oneonta
Locust Fork HS — 700/7-12
77 School Rd 35097 — 205-681-7846
Daniel Smith, prin. — Fax 681-6175

Lowndesboro, Lowndes, Pop. 112

Lowndes Academy — 200/K-12
PO Box 99 36752 — 334-278-3366
Darrell Self, hdmstr. — Fax 278-4476

Luverne, Crenshaw, Pop. 2,775
Crenshaw County SD — 2,300/PK-12
183 Votec Dr 36049 — 334-335-6519
Randy Wilkes, supt. — Fax 335-6510
crenshawcounty.schoolinsites.com/
Crenshaw County AVTS — Vo/Tech
183 Votec Dr 36049 — 334-335-6519
Ashley Catrett, prin. — Fax 335-6510
Luverne S — 1,000/PK-12
194 First Ave 36049 — 334-335-3331
Greg Pittman, prin. — Fax 335-2246
Other Schools – See Brantley, Highland Home

Crenshaw Christian Academy — 200/K-12
608 Country Club Dr 36049 — 334-335-5749
Roland Jones B.S., prin. — Fax 335-6422

Lynn, Winston, Pop. 651
Winston County SD
Supt. — See Double Springs
Lynn HS — 200/8-12
531 E Main St 35575 — 205-893-5471
Greg Pendley, prin. — Fax 893-2484

Mc Calla, Jefferson
Jefferson County SD
Supt. — See Birmingham
McAdory HS — 900/9-12
4800 McAdory School Rd 35111 — 205-379-4700
Samuel Staggs, prin. — Fax 481-8037
McAdory MS — 900/6-8
5450 Yellow Jacket Blvd 35111 — 205-379-4730
James McLeod, prin. — Fax 379-4745

Mc Intosh, Washington, Pop. 237
Washington County SD
Supt. — See Chatom
McIntosh HS — 300/6-12
PO Box 359 36553 — 251-944-2449
Dr. Joannee Barnes, prin. — Fax 944-8779

Mc Kenzie, Butler, Pop. 519
Butler County SD
Supt. — See Greenville
Mc Kenzie S — 400/K-12
PO Box 158 36456 — 334-374-2711
J. Randy Williams, prin. — Fax 374-8108

Madison, Madison, Pop. 41,860
Madison CSD — 7,700/PK-12
211 Celtic Dr 35758 — 256-464-8370
Dr. Dee Fowler, supt. — Fax 774-0404
www.madisoncity.k12.al.us
Academy — Alt
11306 County Line Rd 35756 — 256-216-5313
Dr. Travis Schrimsher, prin. — Fax 216-5314
Clemens HS — 9-12
11306 County Line Rd 35756 — 256-216-5313
Brian Clayton, prin. — Fax 216-5314
Discovery MS — 600/7-8
1304 Hughes Rd 35758 — 256-837-3735
Robbie Smith, prin. — Fax 837-1573
Jones HS — 2,200/9-12
650 Hughes Rd 35758 — 256-772-2547
Robert Parker, prin. — Fax 772-6698
Liberty MS — 700/7-8
281 Dock Murphy Dr 35758 — 256-430-0001
Nelson Brown, prin. — Fax 430-0282

ITT Technical Institute — Post-Sec.
9238 Madison Blvd Ste 500 35758 — 256-542-2900
Madison Academy — 900/PK-12
325 Slaughter Rd 35758 — 256-971-1620
Dr. Robert Burton, pres. — Fax 971-1436

Maplesville, Chilton, Pop. 698
Chilton County SD
Supt. — See Clanton
Isabella S — 700/K-12
11338 County Road 15 36750 — 205-280-2770
Ricky Porter, prin. — Fax 755-8549
Maplesville S — 500/K-12
1256 AL Highway 139 36750 — 205-280-4900
Maggie Hicks, prin. — Fax 366-2531

Marbury, Autauga, Pop. 1,390
Autauga County SD
Supt. — See Prattville
Marbury MS — 500/6-8
PO Box A 36051 — 334-365-3522
Julie Weston, prin. — Fax 755-3168

Marion, Perry, Pop. 3,671
Perry County SD — 1,800/PK-12
PO Box 900 36756 — 334-683-6528
John Heard, supt. — Fax 683-8427
pcschooldistrict.org/
Marion HS — 400/7-12
PO Box 150 36756 — 334-683-6741
Maxine Coley, prin. — Fax 683-8838
Other Schools – See Uniontown

Judson College — Post-Sec.
302 Bibb St 36756 — 800-447-9472
Marion Military Institute — Post-Sec.
1101 Washington St 36756 — 800-664-1842

Midfield, Jefferson, Pop. 5,311
Midfield CSD — 1,200/K-12
417 Parkwood St 35228 — 205-923-2262
Demica Sanders, supt. — Fax 929-0585
www.midfield.k12.al.us/
Midfield Area Vocational HS — Vo/Tech
1600 High School Dr 35228 — 205-923-2833
Kevin Tyson, coord. — Fax 929-0593
Midfield HS — 400/9-12
1600 High School Dr 35228 — 205-923-2833
Reginald Ware, prin. — Fax 929-0593
Rutledge MS — 400/5-8
1221 8th St 35228 — 205-780-8647
Terrell Brown, prin. — Fax 780-3664

Midland City, Dale, Pop. 2,267
Dale County SD
Supt. — See Ozark
Dale County HS — 400/9-12
PO Box 1140 36350 — 334-983-3541
Patrick Cain, prin. — Fax 983-1549

Millbrook, Elmore, Pop. 14,375
Elmore County SD
Supt. — See Wetumpka
Millbrook MS — 1,100/5-8
4228 Chapman Rd 36054 — 334-285-2100
Steve McKenzie, prin. — Fax 285-2102
Stanhope Elmore HS — 1,200/9-12
4300 Main St 36054 — 334-285-4263
Jamey McGowin, prin. — Fax 285-4575

Victory Baptist S — 200/PK-12
PO Box 1090 36054 — 334-285-5082
Daniel Todd M.A., admin. — Fax 285-0216

Millport, Lamar, Pop. 1,035
Lamar County SD
Supt. — See Vernon
South Lamar S — 500/K-12
300 Sls Rd 35576 — 205-662-4411
Craig Henson, prin. — Fax 662-4544

Millry, Washington, Pop. 541
Washington County SD
Supt. — See Chatom
Millry S — 600/K-12
PO Box 65 36558 — 251-846-2987
John Carter, prin. — Fax 846-2986

Mobile, Mobile, Pop. 192,396
Mobile County SD — 58,200/PK-12
PO Box 180069 36618 — 251-221-4000
Martha Peek, supt. — Fax 221-4399
www.mcpss.com
Baker HS — 2,200/9-12
8901 Airport Blvd 36608 — 251-221-3000
Clem Richardson, prin. — Fax 221-3004
Burns MS — 1,000/6-8
6175 Girby Rd 36693 — 251-221-2025
John Adams, prin. — Fax 221-2021
Calloway-Smith MS — 700/6-8
350 N Lawrence St 36603 — 251-221-2042
D.H. Walton, prin. — Fax 221-2041
Causey MS — 1,500/6-8
2205 McFarland Rd 36695 — 251-221-2060
James Gill, prin. — Fax 221-2062
Chastang MS — 600/6-8
2800 Berkley Ave 36617 — 251-221-2081
Sonya Floyd, prin. — Fax 221-2080
Clark-Shaw Magnet S — 700/5-8
5960 Arlberg St 36608 — 251-221-2106
Dianne McWain, prin. — Fax 221-2108
Davidson HS — 1,600/9-12
3900 Pleasant Valley Rd 36609 — 251-221-3084
Lewis Copeland, prin. — Fax 221-3083
Denton MS — 800/6-8
3800 Pleasant Valley Rd 36609 — 251-221-2148
Joe Toomey, prin. — Fax 221-2152
Dunbar Magnet S — 500/4-8
500 Saint Anthony St 36603 — 251-221-2160
Debra Smith, prin. — Fax 221-2162
Eanes MS — 400/6-8
1901 Hurtel St 36605 — 251-221-2189
Merrier Jackson, prin. — Fax 221-2191
LeFlore Magnet HS — 1,000/9-12
700 Donald St 36617 — 251-221-3125
Alvin Dailey, prin. — Fax 221-3117
Murphy HS — 2,400/9-12
100 S Carlen St 36606 — 251-221-3186
William Smith, prin. — Fax 221-3188
Pathway S — Alt
800 1/2 Whitley St 36610 — 251-221-5010
Ronald Coleman, prin. — Fax 221-6801
Phillips Preparatory S — 800/6-8
3255 Old Shell Rd 36607 — 251-221-2286
Brenda Hartzog, prin. — Fax 221-2285
Pillans MS — 600/6-8
2051 Military Rd 36605 — 251-221-2300
Ed Sanderson, prin. — Fax 221-2314
Rain HS — 600/9-12
3125 Dauphin Island Pkwy 36605 — 251-221-3233
Marlon Firle, prin. — Fax 470-7759
Scarborough MS — 500/6-8
1800 Phillips Ln 36618 — 251-221-2323
Dr. Jason Laffitte, prin. — Fax 221-2321
Washington MS — 400/6-8
1961 Andrews St 36617 — 251-221-2361
Reginald Wilson, prin. — Fax 221-2367
Williamson HS — 1,000/9-12
1567 E Dublin St 36605 — 251-221-3411
Robert Likely, prin. — Fax 221-3414

Continuous Learning Center Adult
1870 Pleasant Ave 36617 251-221-2122
Sharon Magee, prin. Fax 221-2124
Other Schools – See Axis, Bayou La Batre, Citronelle, Eight Mile, Grand Bay, Irvington, Prichard, Semmes, Theodore

---

Bishop State Community College Post-Sec.
351 N Broad St 36603 251-405-7000
Blue Cliff Career College Post-Sec.
2970 Cottage Hill Rd # 175 36606 251-473-2220
Cottage Hill Christian Academy 200/9-12
7355 Creekwood Dr 36695 251-634-2513
Jim McMillan, supt. Fax 634-2566
Faith Academy 2,100/PK-12
8650 Tanner Williams Rd 36608 251-633-7267
Tim Skelton, hdmstr. Fax 633-9133
Fortis College Post-Sec.
3590 Pleasant Valley Rd 36609 251-344-1203
Fortis College Post-Sec.
300 Azalea Rd Ste F 36609 251-342-3230
ITT Technical Institute Post-Sec.
3100 Cottage Hill Rd Bldg 3 36606 251-472-4760
McGill-Toolen HS 1,100/9-12
1501 Old Shell Rd 36604 251-445-2900
Michelle Haas, prin. Fax 433-8356
Mobile Christian S 600/PK-12
5900 Cottage Hill Rd 36609 251-661-1613
David Pahman, hdmstr. Fax 661-1396
Mobile Jr. Academy 50/K-10
1900 Cody Rd S 36695 251-633-8638
Wesley Gennick, prin. Fax 633-8639
Remington College Post-Sec.
828 Downtowner Loop W 36609 251-343-8200
St. Luke's Episcopal S 700/PK-12
3975 Japonica Ln 36693 251-666-2991
W. Palmer Kennedy, hdmstr. Fax 666-2996
St. Paul's Episcopal S 1,400/PK-12
161 Dogwood Ln 36608 251-342-6700
F. Martin Lester, hdmstr. Fax 342-1844
Spring Hill College Post-Sec.
4000 Dauphin St 36608 251-380-4000
UMS Wright Preparatory S 1,300/PK-12
65 Mobile St 36607 251-479-6551
Dr. Tony Havard, hdmstr. Fax 470-9010
University of Mobile Post-Sec.
5735 College Pkwy 36613 800-946-7267
University of South Alabama Post-Sec.
307 University Blvd N 36688 251-460-6101
Virginia College Post-Sec.
3725 Airport Blvd Ste 165 36608 251-343-7227

Monroeville, Monroe, Pop. 6,440
Monroe County SD 3,400/PK-12
PO Box 967 36461 251-575-2168
Dr. Kathy Murphy, supt. Fax 575-5818
www.monroe.k12.al.us/
Carmichael Alternative S Alt
1323 Veterans Dr 36460 251-575-4189
Larry Woolfolk, prin. Fax 575-9648
Monroe County Career Technical Center Vo/Tech
230 Tiger Dr 36460 251-575-4381
Edna Richardson, prin. Fax 575-2017
Monroe County HS 600/9-12
212 Tiger Dr 36460 251-575-3258
Larry Turner, prin. Fax 575-2019
Monroeville MS 400/5-8
201 York St 36460 251-575-4121
Valerie Stevens, prin. Fax 575-2934
Other Schools – See Beatrice, Excel, Uriah

Alabama Southern Community College Post-Sec.
PO Box 2000 36461 251-575-3156
Monroe Academy 400/PK-12
4096 S Alabama Ave 36460 251-743-3932
John Ross, hdmstr. Fax 743-4267

Montevallo, Shelby, Pop. 6,221
Shelby County SD
Supt. — See Columbiana
Montevallo HS 400/9-12
980 Oak St 35115 205-682-6400
Gary Minnick, prin. Fax 682-6405
Montevallo MS 300/6-8
235 Samford St 35115 205-682-6410
Sheila Lewis, prin. Fax 682-6415

University of Montevallo 35115 Post-Sec.
205-665-6000

Montgomery, Montgomery, Pop. 203,255
Montgomery County SD 27,400/K-12
PO Box 1991 36102 334-223-6700
Barbara Thompson, supt. Fax 269-3076
www.mps.k12.al.us
Baldwin Arts & Academics Magnet S 600/6-8
410 S McDonough St 36104 334-269-3870
Jannette Wright, prin. Fax 269-3918
Bellingrath MS 800/6-8
3488 S Court St 36105 334-269-3623
Sabrina Johnson, prin. Fax 269-6173
Brewbaker MS 600/6-8
4425 Brewbaker Dr 36116 334-284-8008
Larry McQuiston, prin. Fax 284-8052
Brewbaker Technology Magnet HS 600/9-12
4405 Brewbaker Dr 36116 334-284-7100
April Wise-Lee, prin. Fax 284-7110
Capitol Heights MS 400/6-8
116 Federal Dr 36107 334-260-1000
Bobby Abrams, prin. Fax 260-1049
Carr MS 500/6-8
1610 Ray Thorington Rd 36117 334-244-4005
John Johnston, prin. Fax 244-4009
Carver HS 1,200/9-12
2001 W Fairview Ave 36108 334-269-3636
Gary Hall, prin. Fax 262-2440
Davis HS 2,100/9-12
3420 Carter Hill Rd 36111 334-269-3712
Cheryl Fountain, prin. Fax 269-3715
Floyd MS for Math Science & Technology 500/6-8
3444 Le Bron Rd 36111 334-284-7130
Vince Johnson, prin. Fax 284-7125
Goodwyn MS 400/6-8
209 Perry Hill Rd 36109 334-260-1021
Debra Webster, prin. Fax 260-1079
Lanier HS 1,100/9-12
1756 S Court St 36104 334-269-3726
Michael Gibbs, prin. Fax 269-6180
Lee HS 2,000/9-12
225 Ann St 36107 334-269-3742
Lorenza Pharrams, prin. Fax 269-3888
Loveless Academic Magnet HS 400/9-12
921 W Jeff Davis Ave 36108 334-269-3714
Mary George Jester, prin. Fax 269-3961
McKee MS 400/6-8
4017 McInnis Dr 36116 334-284-7528
Patrick Nelson, prin. Fax 241-5308
Progressive Academy of Creative Ed 200/Alt
1015 E Jefferson St 36104 334-269-3760
Robert Price, prin. Fax 269-3989
Southlawn MS 500/6-8
5333 Mobile Hwy 36108 334-284-8086
Rafiq Vaughn, prin. Fax 284-8094
Washington Magnet HS 500/9-12
632 S Union St 36104 334-269-3617
Quesha Starks, prin. Fax 269-6140
Other Schools – See Pike Road

Alabama Christian Academy 1,000/PK-12
4700 Wares Ferry Rd 36109 334-277-1985
Alabama State University Post-Sec.
915 S Jackson St 36104 334-229-4100
Amridge University Post-Sec.
1200 Taylor Rd 36117 888-790-8080
Auburn University at Montgomery Post-Sec.
PO Box 244023 36124 334-244-3000
Baptist Medical Center Post-Sec.
301 Brown Springs Rd 36117 334-273-4400
Community College of the Air Force Post-Sec.
100 S Turner Blvd 36114 334-649-5000
Eastwood Christian S 400/K-12
1701 E Trinity Blvd 36106 334-272-8195
Evangel Christian Academy 300/PK-12
3975 Vaughn Rd 36106 334-272-3882
Rev. Scott Matthes, admin. Fax 272-5662
Faulkner University Post-Sec.
5345 Atlanta Hwy 36109 334-272-5820
Fortis College Post-Sec.
3736 Atlanta Hwy 36109 334-272-3857
Huntingdon College Post-Sec.
1500 E Fairview Ave 36106 334-833-4222
Montgomery Academy 500/5-12
3240 Vaughn Rd 36106 334-272-8210
Dave Farace, hdmstr. Fax 277-3240
Montgomery Catholic Prep HS 300/9-12
5350 Vaughn Rd 36116 334-272-7220
Chad Barwick, prin. Fax 272-2440
Montgomery Catholic Prep MS 200/7-8
5350 Vaughn Rd 36116 334-272-2465
Chad Barwick, prin. Fax 272-2330
Prince Institute - Southeast Post-Sec.
7735 Atlanta Hwy 36117 334-271-1670
St. James S 1,000/PK-12
6010 Vaughn Rd 36116 334-277-8033
Melba Richardson, hdmstr. Fax 277-2542
St. Jude Educational Institute 200/7-12
2048 W Fairview Ave 36108 334-264-5376
Wanda Twitty, prin. Fax 264-6669
South University Post-Sec.
5355 Vaughn Rd 36116 334-395-8800
The Hair Academy Post-Sec.
3150 McGeehee Rd 36111 334-281-0411
The Robert B. Adams/LabCorp CLS Program Post-Sec.
543 S Hull St 36104 334-263-5745
Trenholm State Technical College Post-Sec.
PO Box 10048 36108 334-420-4200
Trinity Presbyterian S 900/K-12
1700 E Trinity Blvd 36106 334-213-2100
Robert Neu, head sch Fax 213-2171
Virginia College Post-Sec.
6200 Atlanta Hwy 36117 334-277-3390

Moody, Saint Clair, Pop. 11,564
Saint Clair County SD
Supt. — See Ashville
Moody HS 600/9-12
714 High School Dr 35004 205-640-5127
Cheryl Kuyk, prin. Fax 640-2300
Moody JHS 300/7-8
600 High School Dr 35004 205-640-2040
Cassandra Taylor, prin. Fax 640-3036

Moulton, Lawrence, Pop. 3,330
Lawrence County SD 5,000/K-12
14131 Market St 35650 256-905-2400
Heath Grimes, supt. Fax 905-2406
www.lawrenceal.org
Jester Learning Center Alt
371 School St 35650 256-974-3258
Aaron Goode, prin.
Lawrence County Center of Technology Vo/Tech
179 College St 35650 256-974-3751
Wade Fleming, prin. Fax 905-2482
Lawrence County JSHS 700/8-12
102 College St 35650 256-905-2440
Jean Howard, prin. Fax 905-2444
Moulton MS 600/5-8
660 College St 35650 256-905-2460
Stacie Givens, prin. Fax 905-2481
Other Schools – See Courtland, Town Creek, Trinity

Moundville, Hale, Pop. 2,391
Hale County SD
Supt. — See Greensboro
Hale County HS 500/7-12
PO Box 188 35474 205-371-2514
Joseph Stegall, prin. Fax 371-6800

Mountain Brook, Jefferson, Pop. 20,299
Mountain Brook CSD 4,500/K-12
32 Vine St, Birmingham AL 35213 205-871-4608
Richard Barlow, supt. Fax 877-8303
www.mtnbrook.k12.al.us
Mountain Brook JHS 1,000/7-9
205 Overbrook Rd, Birmingham AL 35213
205-871-3516
Donald Clayton, prin. Fax 969-8113
Mountain Brook SHS 1,000/10-12
3650 Bethune Dr 35223 205-414-3800
Amanda Hood, prin. Fax 969-8113

Munford, Talladega, Pop. 1,274
Talladega County SD
Supt. — See Talladega
Munford HS 400/7-12
300 Cedars Rd 36268 256-315-5220
Anthony Wilkinson, prin. Fax 315-5240

Muscle Shoals, Colbert, Pop. 12,952
Muscle Shoals CSD 2,800/PK-12
PO Box 2610 35662 256-389-2600
Dr. Jeff Wooten, supt. Fax 389-2605
www.mscs.k12.al.us
Muscle Shoals Center for Technology Vo/Tech
PO Box 2186 35662 256-389-2660
Gary Williams, prin. Fax 389-2662
Muscle Shoals HS 800/9-12
1900 Avalon Ave 35661 256-389-2682
Dr. Brian Lindsey, prin. Fax 389-2689
Muscle Shoals MS 700/6-8
100 Trojan Dr 35661 256-389-2640
Dr. Mary Stegall, prin. Fax 389-2647

Northwest-Shoals Community College Post-Sec.
PO Box 2545 35662 256-331-5200

Newbern, Hale, Pop. 186
Hale County SD
Supt. — See Greensboro
Sunshine S 300/K-12
3125 County Road 10 36765 334-624-8747
Charlayne' Jordan, prin. Fax 624-8781

New Brockton, Coffee, Pop. 1,118
Coffee County SD
Supt. — See Elba
New Brockton HS 400/7-12
PO Box 399 36351 334-894-2350
Kevin Killingsworth, prin. Fax 894-5204

New Hope, Madison, Pop. 2,743
Madison County SD
Supt. — See Huntsville
New Hope HS 400/9-12
5216 Main Dr 35760 256-723-4226
Lavell Everett, prin. Fax 723-4063

New Market, Madison, Pop. 1,576
Madison County SD
Supt. — See Huntsville
Buckhorn HS 1,200/9-12
4123 Winchester Rd 35761 256-379-2123
Todd Markham, prin. Fax 379-5311
Buckhorn MS 7-8
4185 Winchester Rd 35761 256-379-4185
William Markham, prin. Fax 379-4183

New Site, Tallapoosa, Pop. 769
Tallapoosa County SD
Supt. — See Dadeville
Horseshoe Bend S 700/K-12
10684 Highway 22 E 36256 256-329-9110
Casey Davis, prin. Fax 329-9119

Newton, Dale, Pop. 1,478
Houston County SD
Supt. — See Dothan
Wicksburg S 900/K-12
1172 S State Highway 123 36352 334-692-5549
Cheryl Smith, prin. Fax 692-3184

Northport, Tuscaloosa, Pop. 23,073
Tuscaloosa County SD
Supt. — See Tuscaloosa
Collins-Riverside MS 500/6-8
1400 3rd St 35476 205-342-2680
Bryant Williams, prin. Fax 752-8024
Echols MS 600/6-8
2701 Echols Ave 35476 205-342-2884
Nancy Terry, prin. Fax 339-1064
Northside HS 400/9-12
19230 Northside Pkwy 35475 205-342-2755
David Patrick, prin. Fax 339-3437
Northside MS 300/6-8
19130 Northside Pkwy 35475 205-342-2740
Bobby Beasley, prin. Fax 247-4188
Tuscaloosa County HS 1,600/9-12
12500 Wildcat Dr 35475 205-342-2670
Reba Caldwell, prin. Fax 333-3197

Notasulga, Macon, Pop. 958
Macon County SD
Supt. — See Tuskegee
Notasulga S 400/K-12
PO Box 10 36866 334-724-1240
Brelinda Sullen, prin. Fax 257-4228

Tallapoosa County SD
Supt. — See Dadeville
Reeltown S 800/K-12
4085 AL Highway 120 36866 334-257-1670
Thomas Cochran, prin. Fax 257-3978

Oakman, Walker, Pop. 785
Walker County SD
Supt. — See Jasper

Oakman HS 200/9-12
PO Box 286 35579 205-622-3381
Patrick Gann, prin. Fax 622-3542

Odenville, Saint Clair, Pop. 3,535
Saint Clair County SD
Supt. — See Ashville
Odenville MS 500/6-8
100 1st Ave 35120 205-629-2280
Debra Carroll, prin. Fax 620-2282
St. Clair County HS 600/9-12
16700 US Highway 411 35120 205-629-6222
Brian Terry, prin. Fax 629-2228

Ohatchee, Calhoun, Pop. 1,146
Calhoun County SD
Supt. — See Anniston
Ohatchee HS 500/7-12
100 Cherokee Trl 36271 256-741-4900
Bobby Tittle, prin. Fax 892-9181

Oneonta, Blount, Pop. 6,492
Blount County SD 8,500/K-12
PO Box 578 35121 205-625-4102
James Carr, supt. Fax 625-4100
www.blountboe.net/
Allgood Alternative S Alt
45 Community Rd 35121 205-274-9865
Jeff Dean, prin. Fax 274-9865
Appalachian S 600/K-12
350 County Highway 12 35121 205-274-9712
Mark Hitt, prin. Fax 274-9706
Other Schools – See Blountsville, Cleveland, Hayden, Locust Fork, Remlap

Oneonta CSD 1,400/K-12
27605 State Highway 75 35121 205-625-4106
Scott Coefield, supt. Fax 274-2910
www.oneontacityschools.com
Oneonta HS 700/7-12
27605 State Highway 75 35121 205-625-3801
Keith Bender, prin. Fax 625-5015

Opelika, Lee, Pop. 26,170
Lee County SD 9,300/K-12
2410 Society Hill Rd 36804 334-705-6000
Dr. Stephen Nowlin, supt. Fax 745-9822
www.lee.k12.al.us
Beauregard HS 600/9-12
7343 AL Highway 51 36804 334-745-5916
Richard Brown, prin. Fax 749-6421
Sanford MS 700/5-8
1500 Lee Road 11 36804 334-745-5023
Michelle Rutherford, prin. Fax 745-5685
Other Schools – See Loachapoka, Smiths Station, Valley

Opelika CSD 4,300/PK-12
300 Simmons St 36801 334-745-9700
Dr. Mark Neighbors, supt. Fax 745-9706
www.opelikaschools.org
Opelika HS 1,300/9-12
1700 Lafayette Pkwy 36801 334-745-9716
Dr. Farrell Seymore, prin. Fax 745-9721
Opelika Learning Center 100/Alt
214 Jeter Ave 36801 334-741-5603
Tony Hoyett, prin. Fax 741-5604
Opelika MS 1,000/6-8
1206 Denson Dr 36801 334-745-9726
Keith York, prin. Fax 745-9730

Southern Union State Community College Post-Sec.
1701 Lafayette Pkwy 36801 334-745-6437
Trinity Christian S 300/K-12
PO Box 311 36803 334-745-2464
Carl Warmouth, hdmstr. Fax 745-4856

Opp, Covington, Pop. 6,581
Opp CSD 1,400/K-12
PO Box 840 36467 334-493-3173
Michael Smithart, supt. Fax 493-3060
www.oppcityschools.com
Opp HS 400/9-12
502 N Maloy St 36467 334-493-4561
Ron Snell, prin. Fax 493-2146
Opp MS 400/5-8
303 E Stewart Ave 36467 334-493-6332
Aaron Hightower, prin. Fax 493-1120

Lureen B. Wallace Community College Post-Sec.
PO Box 910 36467 334-493-3573

Orange Beach, Baldwin, Pop. 5,326

Columbia Southern University Post-Sec.
PO Box 3110 36561 251-981-3771

Orrville, Dallas, Pop. 204
Dallas County SD
Supt. — See Selma
Keith MSHS 300/6-12
1166 County Road 115 36767 334-996-8464
Lou Ella Guthridge, prin. Fax 996-0918

Owens Cross Roads, Madison, Pop. 1,475

Big Cove Christian Academy 50/K-10
6354 Highway 431 S 35763 256-518-9642
Rachel Wiegand, prin. Fax 725-3179

Oxford, Calhoun, Pop. 21,062
Oxford CSD 4,000/K-12
310 E 2nd St 36203 256-241-3140
Dr. Jeff Goodwin, supt. Fax 831-8620
www.oxford.k12.al.us/
Oxford Area Vo HS Vo/Tech
1 Yellow Jacket Dr 36203 256-241-3166
William Holladay, prin. Fax 241-3943
Oxford HS 1,200/9-12
1 Yellow Jacket Dr 36203 256-241-3166
William Holladay, prin. Fax 241-3943
Oxford MS 600/7-8
1750 US Highway 78 W 36203 256-241-3816
Robert McCartney, prin. Fax 241-3831

Ozark, Dale, Pop. 14,570
Dale County SD 2,900/K-12
202 S Highway 123 Ste E 36360 334-774-2355
Donny Bynum, supt. Fax 774-3503
www.dalecountyboe.org/
Other Schools – See Ariton, Midland City, Pinckard, Skipperville

Ozark CSD 2,400/K-12
1044 Andrews Ave 36360 334-774-5197
Michael Lenhart, supt. Fax 774-2685
www.ozarkcityschools.net
Carroll HS 700/9-12
315 Eagle Way 36360 334-774-4915
Patrick Brannan, prin. Fax 774-1865
Carroll HS Career Center Vo/Tech
227 Faust Ave 36360 334-774-4949
Dana Griggs, prin. Fax 774-8314
Smith MS 500/6-8
994 Andrews Ave 36360 334-774-4913
Danelle Peterman, prin. Fax 774-0568

Parrish, Walker, Pop. 961
Walker County SD
Supt. — See Jasper
Parrish JSHS 200/7-12
35 Tornado Aly 35580 205-686-7701
Eric Smith, prin. Fax 686-9350

Pelham, Shelby, Pop. 21,087
Shelby County SD
Supt. — See Columbiana
Pelham HS 1,700/9-12
2500 Panther Cir 35124 205-682-5500
Bob Lavett, prin. Fax 682-5505

Pell City, Saint Clair, Pop. 12,505
Pell City CSD 4,200/PK-12
1000 Bruce Etheredge Pkwy 35128 205-884-4440
Dr. Bobby Hathcock, supt. Fax 814-1010
www.pellcityschools.net
Duran JHS 300/8-8
309 Williamson Dr 35125 205-338-2825
Karen Davis, prin. Fax 884-6502
Pell City HS 1,300/9-12
1300 Cogswell Ave 35125 205-338-2250
Helene Bettinger, prin. Fax 338-2838

Victory Christian S 500/PK-12
PO Box 710 35125 205-338-2901

Phenix City, Russell, Pop. 32,176
Phenix City SD 6,200/K-12
PO Box 460 36868 334-298-0534
Dr. Larry DiChiara, supt. Fax 298-2674
www.pcboe.net
Central HS 1,300/10-12
2400 Dobbs Dr 36870 334-298-3626
Tommy Vickers, prin. Fax 298-7690
Central HS Freshman Academy 400/9-9
2800 Dobbs Dr 36870 334-448-8880
Jason Stamp, prin. Fax 448-8690
South Girard S 400/8-8
521 Fontaine Rd 36869 334-298-2527
Jason Bryant, prin. Fax 297-8274

Russell County SD 3,000/PK-12
PO Box 400 36868 334-298-8791
Dr. Mike Green, supt. Fax 448-8825
rcsd-al.schoolloop.com/
Other Schools – See Seale

Chattahoochee Valley Community College Post-Sec.
2602 College Dr 36869 334-291-4900

Phil Campbell, Franklin, Pop. 1,134
Franklin County SD
Supt. — See Russellville
Phil Campbell HS 400/7-12
PO Box 849 35581 256-331-2150
Gary Odom, prin. Fax 331-2151

Piedmont, Calhoun, Pop. 4,787
Piedmont CSD 1,100/K-12
502 W Hood St 36272 256-447-8831
Matthew Akin, supt. Fax 447-6486
www.piedmont.k12.al.us/
Piedmont HS 300/9-12
750 Tom Bible Memorial Hwy 36272 256-447-2829
Jerry Snow, prin. Fax 447-8722
Piedmont MS 300/6-8
401 N Main St 36272 256-447-6165
Hugh McWhorter, prin. Fax 447-8070

Pike Road, Montgomery, Pop. 5,366
Montgomery County SD
Supt. — See Montgomery
Washington MS 300/6-8
696 Georgia Washington Rd 36064 334-215-8290
Deirdre Gulley, prin. Fax 215-1304

Pinckard, Dale, Pop. 638
Dale County SD
Supt. — See Ozark
South Dale MS 400/5-8
PO Box D 36371 334-983-3077
David West, prin. Fax 983-5882

Pinson, Jefferson, Pop. 7,099
Jefferson County SD
Supt. — See Birmingham
Clay-Chalkville HS 1,300/9-12
6623 Roe Chandler Rd 35126 205-379-3050
Michael Lee, prin. Fax 680-8128
Pinson Valley HS 1,000/9-12
6895 Highway 75 35126 205-379-5100
Dr. Terrence Brown, prin. Fax 379-5145
Rudd MS 800/6-8
4526 Rudd School Rd 35126 205-379-5300
Susan Whitehurst, prin. Fax 680-8124

Pisgah, Jackson, Pop. 710
Jackson County SD
Supt. — See Scottsboro
Pisgah S 600/K-12
60 Metcalf St 35765 256-451-3241
Mark Guffey, prin. Fax 451-3457

Plantersville, Dallas
Dallas County SD
Supt. — See Selma
Dallas County HS 600/9-12
PO Box 145 36758 334-366-2232
Michael Blair, prin. Fax 366-4015

Pleasant Grove, Jefferson, Pop. 10,034
Jefferson County SD
Supt. — See Birmingham
Pleasant Grove HS 600/9-12
100 Spartan Dr 35127 205-379-5250
Wayne Byram, prin. Fax 379-5265
Pleasant Grove MS 500/6-8
805 7th Ave 35127 205-379-5280
Jarvis Watkins, prin. Fax 379-5295

Prattville, Autauga, Pop. 33,381
Autauga County SD 9,800/K-12
153 W 4th St 36067 334-365-5706
Spence Agee, supt. Fax 361-3828
www.acboe.net
Autauga County Tech Center Vo/Tech
1301 Upper Kingston Rd 36067 334-361-0258
Brock Dunn, admin. Fax 361-3839
Prattville HS 2,100/9-12
PO Box 680810 36068 334-365-8804
Richard Dennis, prin. Fax 358-0011
Prattville JHS 1,100/7-8
1089 Martin Luther King Dr 36067 334-365-6697
Kenneth Childree, prin. Fax 361-3870
Second Chance Alternative S Alt
816 Cardinal Ln 36067 334-361-3834
Darryl Pickett, prin. Fax 361-3834
Other Schools – See Autaugaville, Billingsley, Deatsville, Marbury

---

Autauga Academy 200/PK-12
497 Golson Rd 36067 334-365-4343
Gerald Carter, hdmstr. Fax 365-7713
East Memorial Christian Academy K-12
1320 Old Ridge Rd E 36066 334-358-4085
Jerry Watkins, admin. Fax 358-9226
Prattville Christian Academy 700/PK-12
322 Old Farm Ln N 36066 334-285-0077
Ron Mitchell, pres. Fax 285-1777

Prichard, Mobile, Pop. 22,453
Mobile County SD
Supt. — See Mobile
Faulkner Vocational S Vo/Tech
33 W Elm St 36610 251-221-5431
William White, prin. Fax 221-5433
Mobile County Training MS 300/6-8
800 Whitley St 36610 251-221-2267
Dr. Yulanda Clinton, prin. Fax 221-2269
Vigor HS 800/9-12
913 N Wilson Ave 36610 251-221-3045
Kenneth Edwards, prin. Fax 221-3378

Princeton, Jackson
Jackson County SD
Supt. — See Scottsboro
Paint Rock Valley S 100/K-12
PO Box 150 35766 256-776-2628
Clay Webber, prin. Fax 776-0042

Ragland, Saint Clair, Pop. 1,613
Saint Clair County SD
Supt. — See Ashville
Ragland S 600/K-12
1060 Main St 35131 205-472-2123
Roger Wilkinson, prin. Fax 472-0086

Rainbow City, Etowah, Pop. 9,471
Etowah County SD
Supt. — See Gadsden
Rainbow MS 700/6-8
454 Lumbley Rd 35906 256-442-1095
Tracy Cross, prin. Fax 442-1028

Westbrook Christian S 600/PK-12
100 Westminster Dr 35906 256-442-7457
Cynthia Greer, admin. Fax 442-7635

Rainsville, DeKalb, Pop. 4,882
De Kalb County SD 8,800/K-12
PO Box 1668 35986 256-638-6921
Hugh Taylor, supt. Fax 638-6972
www.dekalbk12.org
De Kalb Vocational S Vo/Tech
PO Box 529 35986 256-638-4421
Gelane Nelson, prin. Fax 638-4420
Plainview S 1,200/K-12
PO Box 469 35986 256-638-3510
Rita Barksdale, prin. Fax 638-6274
Other Schools – See Collinsville, Crossville, Fyffe, Geraldine, Ider, Sylvania, Valley Head

---

Northeast Alabama Community College Post-Sec.
PO Box 159 35986 256-638-4418

Ranburne, Cleburne, Pop. 406
Cleburne County SD
Supt. — See Heflin
Ranburne MSHS 500/5-12
21045 Main St 36273 256-568-3402
Tim Ward, prin. Fax 568-2605

Red Bay, Franklin, Pop. 3,100
Franklin County SD
Supt. — See Russellville
Red Bay S 800/K-12
PO Box 1518 35582 256-331-2270
Kenny Sparks, prin. Fax 331-2275

Red Level, Covington, Pop. 487
Covington County SD
Supt. — See Andalusia
Red Level HS 300/7-12
PO Box D 36474 334-469-5315
Johny Odom, prin. Fax 469-6192

Reform, Pickens, Pop. 1,691
Pickens County SD
Supt. — See Carrollton
Pickens County JSHS 300/7-12
PO Box 1239 35481 205-375-2344
Darrell Woods, prin. Fax 375-8151

Remlap, Blount
Blount County SD
Supt. — See Oneonta
Southeastern S 400/K-12
18770 State Highway 75 35133 205-681-3964
Michael Peoples, prin. Fax 681-3975

Roanoke, Randolph, Pop. 6,021
Roanoke CSD 1,600/K-12
PO Box 1367 36274 334-863-2628
Chuck Marcum, supt. Fax 863-2849
www.roanokecityschools.org/
Handley HS 500/9-12
PO Box 1393 36274 334-863-6815
Greg Foster, prin. Fax 863-6284
Handley MS 600/4-8
PO Box 725 36274 334-863-4174
Linda Crim, prin. Fax 863-6129

Robertsdale, Baldwin, Pop. 5,180
Baldwin County SD
Supt. — See Bay Minette
Central Baldwin MS 700/7-8
PO Box 930 36567 251-947-2327
Chuck Anderson, prin. Fax 947-1949
Robertsdale HS 1,300/9-12
PO Box 69 36567 251-947-4154
Craig Ross, prin. Fax 947-2666
South Baldwin Center for Tech Vo/Tech
19200 Carolina St 36567 251-947-5041
Kendall Mowdy, prin. Fax 947-4837

Central Christian S 300/PK-12
17395 State Highway 104 36567 251-947-5043
Tim Shelton, admin. Fax 947-2572

Rockford, Coosa, Pop. 477
Coosa County SD 1,300/K-12
PO Box 37 35136 256-377-4913
Dennis Sanford, supt. Fax 377-2385
www.coosaschools.k12.al.us
Central HS Coosa County 400/9-12
243 Coosa County Road 75 35136 256-377-4384
Keith Bullard, prin. Fax 377-4466
Central MS Coosa County 400/5-8
97 Coosa County Road 75 35136 256-377-1490
Todd Wingard, prin. Fax 377-1493
Coosa County Science & Technology Ctr Vo/Tech
17768 US Highway 231 35136 256-377-4678
Jocelyn Marbury, dir. Fax 377-4589

Rogersville, Lauderdale, Pop. 1,248
Lauderdale County SD
Supt. — See Florence
Lauderdale County S 1,000/K-12
PO Box 220 35652 256-247-3414
Eric Cornelius, prin. Fax 247-3444

Russellville, Franklin, Pop. 9,705
Franklin County SD 3,300/K-12
PO Box 610 35653 256-332-1360
Gary Williams, supt. Fax 331-0069
www.franklin.k12.al.us/
Belgreen S 400/K-12
14220 Highway 187 35653 256-332-1376
Myra Frederick, prin. Fax 332-7209
Franklin County Career Technical Center Vo/Tech
85 Jail Springs Rd 35653 256-332-2127
Scott Wiginton, dir. Fax 332-2219
Tharptown HS 300/7-12
255 Highway 80 35654 256-332-6485
Barry Laster, prin. Fax 332-2840
Other Schools – See Phil Campbell, Red Bay, Vina

Russellville CSD 2,400/K-12
1945 Waterloo Rd 35653 256-331-2000
Rex Mayfield, supt. Fax 332-7323
www.rcs.k12.al.us
Russellville HS 700/9-12
1865 Waterloo Rd 35653 256-332-2110
Dr. Timothy Guinn, prin. Fax 332-8447
Russellville MS 600/6-8
765 Summit St 35653 256-331-2120
Frankie Hammock, prin. Fax 332-8453

Samson, Geneva, Pop. 1,902
Geneva County SD
Supt. — See Geneva
Samson HS 200/9-12
209 N Broad St 36477 334-898-2371
Lance Mitchell, prin. Fax 898-7576
Samson MS 100/7-8
209 N Broad St 36477 334-898-2371
Jay Mikel, prin. Fax 898-7576

Sand Rock, Cherokee, Pop. 556
Cherokee County SD
Supt. — See Centre
Sand Rock S 900/K-12
1950 Sand Rock Ave 35983 256-523-3564
John East, prin. Fax 523-3507

Saraland, Mobile, Pop. 13,216
Saraland CSD 2,000/K-12
943 Saraland Blvd S 36571 251-375-5420
Dr. Wayne Vickers, supt. Fax 375-5430
www.saralandboe.org/
Saraland HS 500/9-12
1115 Industrial Pkwy 36571 251-602-8970
Beverly Spondike, prin. Fax 602-8994
Saraland MS - Nelson Adams Campus 600/6-8
401 Baldwin Rd 36571 251-679-9405
Alex Crane, prin. Fax 679-9456

Sardis City, Etowah, Pop. 1,693
Etowah County SD
Supt. — See Gadsden
Sardis JSHS 700/7-12
1420 Church St 35956 256-593-5221
Gerald Beard, prin. Fax 593-5223

Satsuma, Mobile, Pop. 6,101
Satsuma City SD 1,300/K-12
PO Box 939 36572 251-380-8200
Joe Walters, supt. Fax 380-8201
satsumacity.schoolinsites.com/
Satsuma HS 900/7-12
1 Gator Cir 36572 251-380-8190
Cliffton Maddox, prin. Fax 380-8191

Scottsboro, Jackson, Pop. 14,491
Jackson County SD 5,800/K-12
PO Box 490 35768 256-259-9500
Ken Harding, supt. Fax 259-0076
www.jackson.k12.al.us/
Jackson County Alternative S Alt
PO Box 490 35768 256-574-6446
Shane Small, prin. Fax 259-1392
Skyline S 500/K-12
897 County Road 25 35768 256-587-6561
Kevin Dukes, prin. Fax 587-6562
Other Schools – See Bridgeport, Higdon, Hollywood, Pisgah, Princeton, Section, Stevenson, Woodville

Scottsboro CSD 2,600/K-12
305 S Scott St 35768 256-218-2100
Dr. Judith Berry, supt. Fax 218-2190
www.scottsboroschools.net
Scottsboro HS 700/9-12
25053 John T Reid Pkwy 35768 256-218-2000
Kathy Hughes, prin. Fax 218-2090
Scottsboro JHS 400/7-8
1601 Jefferson St 35768 256-218-2300
Jason Hass, prin. Fax 218-2390

Seale, Russell
Russell County SD
Supt. — See Phenix City
Russell County HS 1,000/9-12
4699 Old Seale Hwy 36875 334-855-4378
Vantreise Davis, prin. Fax 855-4334
Russell County MS 500/7-8
4716 Old Seale Hwy 36875 334-855-4453
LaLanya Ramsey, prin. Fax 855-4437

Section, Jackson, Pop. 755
Jackson County SD
Supt. — See Scottsboro
Section S 600/K-12
PO Box 10 35771 256-228-6718
Gene Roberts, prin. Fax 228-6252

Selma, Dallas, Pop. 20,594
Dallas County SD 3,600/K-12
PO Box 1056 36702 334-875-3440
Dr. Fannie Major-McKenzie, supt. Fax 876-4493
www.dallask12.org
Dallas County Alternative S Alt
Craig Industrial Bldg 37 36701 334-872-6761
Don Ingram, prin. Fax 872-6761
Dallas County Career Technical Center Vo/Tech
1306 Roosevelt St 36701 334-872-8031
Jerolene Williams, dir. Fax 872-5697
Southside HS 500/9-12
7975 US Highway 80 E 36701 334-872-0518
Clarence Jackson, prin. Fax 872-0295
Tipton MS 300/7-8
2500 Tipton St 36701 334-872-8080
Jackie Averhart, prin. Fax 872-8008
Other Schools – See Orrville, Plantersville, Valley Grande

Selma CSD 4,200/PK-12
PO Box 350 36702 334-874-1600
Gerald Shirley, supt. Fax 874-1604
www.selmacityschools.org
Hudson MS 500/7-8
1701 Summerfield Rd 36701 334-874-1675
James Pope, prin. Fax 874-1679
Selma HS 1,000/9-12
2180 Broad St 36701 334-874-1680
Rev. Major Burrell, prin. Fax 874-9450

Concordia College Alabama Post-Sec.
1712 Broad St 36701 334-874-5700
George C. Wallace State Comm College Post-Sec.
PO Box 2530 36702 334-876-9227
Meadowview Christian S 200/PK-12
1512 Old Orrville Rd 36701 334-872-8448
Miriam Anderson, hdmstr. Fax 872-8443
Morgan Academy 500/K-12
PO Box 2650 36702 334-875-4464
Selma University Post-Sec.
1501 Lapsley St 36701 334-872-2533

Semmes, Mobile
Mobile County SD
Supt. — See Mobile
Montgomery HS 1,800/9-12
4275 Snow Rd N 36575 251-221-3153
Wade Whitney, prin. Fax 221-3150
Semmes MS 1,600/6-8
4566 Ed George Rd 36575 251-221-2344
Brenda Shenesey, prin. Fax 221-2347

Sheffield, Colbert, Pop. 8,895
Sheffield CSD 1,100/PK-12
300 W 6th St 35660 256-383-0400
Dr. Timothy Morgan, supt. Fax 386-5704
www.scs.k12.al.us/
Sheffield HS 300/9-12
2800 E 19th Ave 35660 256-383-6052
Laura Kelly, prin. Fax 386-5707
Sheffield JHS 200/7-8
1803 E 30th St 35660 256-386-5735
Brezofski Anderson, prin. Fax 386-5706

Skipperville, Dale
Dale County SD
Supt. — See Ozark
Long HS 400/7-12
2565 County Road 60 36374 334-774-2380
Jason Steed, prin. Fax 774-3937

Slocomb, Geneva, Pop. 1,949
Geneva County SD
Supt. — See Geneva
Slocomb HS 300/9-12
591 S County Road 9 36375 334-886-2008
Derrick Morris, prin. Fax 886-9889
Slocomb MS 300/6-8
591 S County Road 9 36375 334-886-2008
Debra Hope, prin. Fax 886-9889

Smiths, Lee, Pop. 3,456

Glenwood S 400/K-12
5801 Summerville Rd 36877 334-297-3614
Frankie Mitchum, hdmstr. Fax 214-9027

Smiths Station, Lee, Pop. 4,838
Lee County SD
Supt. — See Opelika
Smiths Station Freshman Center 9-9
1150 Lee Road 298 36877 334-664-4063
Dr. Brad Cook, prin.
Smiths Station HS 1,400/10-12
4228 Lee Road 430 36877 334-298-0969
Dr. Jason Yohn, prin. Fax 298-1304
Smiths Station JHS 7-8
1100 Lee Road 298 36877 334-664-4070
Rick Harris, prin.

Somerville, Morgan, Pop. 713
Morgan County SD
Supt. — See Decatur
Brewer HS 900/9-12
59 Eva Rd 35670 256-778-8634
Jeremy Childers, prin. Fax 778-8012
Brewer Vocational HS Vo/Tech
59 Eva Rd 35670 256-309-2119
Christal Blevins, prin. Fax 309-2180

Southside, Etowah, Pop. 8,359
Etowah County SD
Supt. — See Gadsden
Southside HS 800/9-12
2361 School Dr 35907 256-442-2172
Dr. Marguerite Early, prin. Fax 442-2183

Spanish Fort, Baldwin, Pop. 6,701
Baldwin County SD
Supt. — See Bay Minette
Spanish Fort HS 900/9-12
1 Plaza De Toros 36527 251-625-3259
Marty McRae, prin. Fax 615-5648
Spanish Fort MS 700/6-8
33899 Jimmy Faulkner Dr 36527 251-625-3271
Oliver Sinclair, prin. Fax 626-7201

Spring Garden, Cherokee, Pop. 234
Cherokee County SD
Supt. — See Centre
Spring Garden S 600/K-12
PO Box 31 36275 256-447-7045
Michael Welsh, prin. Fax 447-6947

Springville, Saint Clair, Pop. 4,042
Saint Clair County SD
Supt. — See Ashville
Springville HS 600/9-12
8295 US Highway 11 35146 205-467-7833
Dr. Robert Harris, prin. Fax 467-2734
Springville MS 500/6-8
6691 US Highway 11 35146 205-467-2740
Virgil Winslett, prin. Fax 467-2742

Stevenson, Jackson, Pop. 1,968
Jackson County SD
Supt. — See Scottsboro
North Jackson HS 500/9-12
45549 AL Highway 277 35772 256-437-2136
Sam Houston, prin. Fax 437-2400
Stevenson MS 300/5-8
701 Kentucky Ave 35772 256-437-2945
Dr. Dianne Brooks, prin. Fax 437-2747

Sulligent, Lamar, Pop. 1,890
Lamar County SD
Supt. — See Vernon
Sulligent S 800/K-12
PO Box 909 35586 205-698-9254
Mike King, prin. Fax 698-8497

Sweet Water, Marengo, Pop. 258
Marengo County SD
Supt. — See Linden
Sweet Water S 700/K-12
PO Box 127 36782 334-994-4263
Stan Stokley, prin. Fax 994-4686

Sylacauga, Talladega, Pop. 12,625
Sylacauga CSD 2,400/PK-12
605 W 4th St 35150 256-245-5256
Renee Riggins, supt. Fax 245-6665
www.sylacauga.k12.al.us
Nichols-Lawson MS 600/6-8
1550 Talladega Hwy 35150 256-245-4376
Gerald Douglass, prin. Fax 245-4071
Sylacauga HS 700/9-12
701 N Broadway Ave 35150 256-249-0911
Matt Hubbard, prin. Fax 245-1026

Talladega County SD
Supt. — See Talladega
Comer Memorial HS 600/7-12
801 Seminole Ave 35150 256-315-5400
Judson Warlick, prin. Fax 315-5420
Fayetteville S 600/K-12
170 WW Averitte Dr 35151 256-315-5550
Byron Brasher, prin. Fax 315-5575

Sylvania, DeKalb, Pop. 1,781
De Kalb County SD
Supt. — See Rainsville
Sylvania S 900/K-12
PO Box 390 35988 256-638-2030
Westley King, prin. Fax 638-7839

Talladega, Talladega, Pop. 15,505
Talladega CSD 2,100/PK-12
PO Box 946 35161 256-315-5600
Douglas Campbell, supt. Fax 315-5606
www.talladega-cs.net
Ellis JHS 300/7-8
414 Elm St 35160 256-315-5700
Scott Bailey, prin. Fax 315-5704
Talladega High Career Tech Vo/Tech
110 Picadilly Dr 35160 256-315-5688
Trisha Howell-Turner, dir. Fax 315-5690
Talladega HS 700/9-12
1177 McMillan St E 35160 256-315-5666
Darren Anglin, prin. Fax 315-5670

Talladega County SD 7,200/K-12
PO Box 887 35161 256-315-5100
Dr. Suzanne Lacey, supt. Fax 315-5126
www.tcboe.org
Talladega County Central HS 200/7-12
5104 Howell Cove Rd 35160 256-315-5340
Timothy Young, prin. Fax 315-5350
Other Schools – See Alpine, Childersburg, Lincoln, Munford, Sylacauga

---

Alabama Institute for the Deaf and Blind Post-Sec.
PO Box 698 35161 256-761-3207
Talladega College Post-Sec.
627 Battle St W 35160 256-362-0206

Tallassee, Elmore, Pop. 4,755
Tallassee CSD 1,900/K-12
308 King St 36078 334-283-6864
Kenneth Varner, supt. Fax 283-4338
www.tcschools.com
Southside MS 600/5-8
901 EB Payne Sr Dr 36078 334-283-2151
Bruce Dean, prin. Fax 283-3577
Tallassee HS 600/9-12
502 Barnett Blvd 36078 334-283-2187
Matt Coker, prin. Fax 283-6210

Tanner, Limestone
Limestone County SD
Supt. — See Athens
Tanner S 900/K-12
12060 Sommers Rd 35671 256-233-6682
Billy Owens, prin. Fax 233-6449

Tarrant, Jefferson, Pop. 6,300
Tarrant CSD 900/K-12
1318 Alabama St 35217 205-849-3700
Dr. Shelly Mize, supt. Fax 849-3728
www.tarrant.k12.al.us/
Tarrant HS 300/7-12
91 Black Creek Rd 35217 205-849-0172
Darius McKay, prin. Fax 849-3724

Theodore, Mobile, Pop. 6,002
Mobile County SD
Supt. — See Mobile
Hankins MS 1,000/6-8
5750 Katherine Hankins Dr 36582 251-221-2200
Cheryl Wittner, prin. Fax 221-2204
Theodore HS 1,700/9-12
6201 Swedetown Rd N 36582 251-221-3351
Ronald Rowell, prin. Fax 221-3355

Lighthouse Baptist Academy 100/K-12
6335 Swedetown Rd N 36582 251-653-6542
John Felt, prin. Fax 653-1196

Thomaston, Marengo, Pop. 414
Marengo County SD
Supt. — See Linden
Johnson S 200/K-12
PO Box 67 36783 334-627-3364
Lepolean Peterson, prin. Fax 627-3396

Thomasville, Clarke, Pop. 4,190
Thomasville CSD 1,500/PK-12
PO Box 458 36784 334-636-9955
Dr. Vic Adkison, supt. Fax 636-4096
www.thomasvilleschools.org/
Thomasville HS 500/9-12
777 Gates Dr 36784 334-636-4451
Kyle Ferguson, prin. Fax 636-0022
Thomasville MS 500/5-8
781 Gates Dr 36784 334-636-4928
Vickie Morris, prin. Fax 636-4924

Thorsby, Chilton, Pop. 1,968
Chilton County SD
Supt. — See Clanton
Thorsby S 900/K-12
54 Opportunity Dr 35171 205-280-4880
Russ Bryan, prin. Fax 646-2197

Toney, Madison
Madison County SD
Supt. — See Huntsville
Sparkman MS 800/6-8
2697 Carters Gin Rd 35773 256-852-0112
Ronnie Blair, prin. Fax 852-4368

Town Creek, Lawrence, Pop. 1,049
Lawrence County SD
Supt. — See Moulton
Hatton JSHS 400/7-12
6909 AL Highway 101 35672 256-685-4010
Brent Gillespie, prin. Fax 685-4007

Toxey, Choctaw, Pop. 137

South Choctaw Academy 300/K-12
5245 New Hope Rd 36921 251-843-2426
Fax 843-2088

Trinity, Morgan, Pop. 2,059
Lawrence County SD
Supt. — See Moulton
East Lawrence HS 500/9-12
55 County Road 370 35673 256-905-2430
Jacki Hall, prin. Fax 905-2424
East Lawrence MS 500/4-8
99 County Road 370 35673 256-905-2420
Jon Smith, prin. Fax 905-2477

Morgan County SD
Supt. — See Decatur
West Morgan HS 400/9-12
261 S Greenway Dr 35673 256-353-5214
Keith Harris, prin. Fax 351-0161
West Morgan MS 400/5-8
261 S Greenway Dr 35673 256-353-5214
Bruce Sparkman, prin. Fax 355-8713

Troy, Pike, Pop. 17,799
Pike County SD 2,200/K-12
101 W Love St 36081 334-566-1850
Mark Bazzell M.Ed., supt. Fax 566-2580
www.pikecountyschools.com
Troy-Pike Regional Center for Technology Vo/Tech
285 Gibbs St 36081 334-566-5395
Julie Simmons, prin. Fax 566-1690
Other Schools – See Brundidge, Goshen

Troy CSD 2,100/K-12
PO Box 529 36081 334-566-3741
Lee Hicks, supt. Fax 566-1425
www.troyschools.net
Henderson HS 600/9-12
PO Box 1006 36081 334-566-3510
Boyd English, prin. Fax 566-4940
Henderson MS 500/6-8
PO Box 925 36081 334-566-5770
Aaron Brown, prin. Fax 566-3071

Pike Liberal Arts S 500/PK-12
PO Box 329 36081 334-566-2023
Ceil Sikes, hdmstr. Fax 670-2010
Troy University 36082 Post-Sec.
334-670-3100

Trussville, Jefferson, Pop. 19,764
Jefferson County SD
Supt. — See Birmingham
Clay-Chalkville MS 1,100/6-8
6700 Trussville Clay Rd 35173 205-379-3100
Ron Tillman, prin. Fax 379-3145

Trussville City SD 4,200/K-12
113 N Chalkville Rd 35173 205-228-3018
Dr. Patricia Neill, supt. Fax 228-3001
trussvillecityschools.com/
Hewitt-Trussville HS 1,300/9-12
6450 Huskey Pkwy 35173 205-228-4000
Timothy Salem, prin. Fax 228-4001
Hewitt-Trussville MS 1,000/6-8
5275 Trussville Clay Rd 35173 205-228-3700
Phyllis Faust, prin. Fax 228-3701

Tuscaloosa, Tuscaloosa, Pop. 89,545
Tuscaloosa CSD 10,300/PK-12
PO Box 38991 35403 205-759-3700
Dr. Paul McKendrick, supt. Fax 759-3542
www.tusc.k12.al.us
Central HS 800/9-12
905 15th St 35401 205-759-3720
Clarence Sutton, prin. Fax 759-3756
Northridge HS 1,200/9-12
2901 Northridge Rd 35406 205-759-3590
Dr. Isaac Espy, prin. Fax 759-3605
Rock Quarry MS 500/6-8
2100 Rock Quarry Dr 35406 205-759-3578
Andrew Maxey, prin. Fax 759-3582
Southview MS 800/6-8
2605 Southview Dr 35405 205-752-1831
Mark Capps, prin. Fax 554-7243
Tuscaloosa Center for Technology Vo/Tech
1300 James I Harrison Jr E 35405 205-759-3649
Kathleen Hughston, coord. Fax 759-3767
Tuscaloosa Magnet MS 200/6-8
315 McFarland Blvd E 35404 205-759-3653
Kristi Thomson, prin. Fax 759-3784
University Place MS 200/6-8
1715 MI King Jr Blvd 35401 205-759-3631
Tom Danner, prin. Fax 759-3635
Westlawn MS 400/6-8
1715 ML King Jr Blvd 35401 205-759-3673
Vertis Giles-Brown, prin. Fax 759-3770

Other Schools – See Cottondale

Tuscaloosa County SD 16,900/PK-12
PO Box 2568 35403 205-758-0411
Dan Butler, supt. Fax 758-2990
www.tcss.net/
Hillcrest HS 1,200/9-12
300 Patriot Pkwy 35405 205-342-2800
Allison Mays, prin. Fax 758-3018
Hillcrest MS 800/6-8
401 Hillcrest School Rd 35405 205-342-2820
C'Kimba Hobbs, prin. Fax 247-4177
Holt HS 500/9-12
3801 Alabama Ave NE 35404 205-342-2768
Neal Guy, prin. Fax 247-4179
Other Schools – See Brookwood, Buhl, Cottondale, Duncanville, Northport, Vance

---

American Christian Academy 1,000/PK-12
2300 Veterans Memorial Pkwy 35404 205-553-5963
Dr. Dan Carden, hdmstr. Fax 553-5942
DCH Regional Medical Center Post-Sec.
809 University Blvd E 35401 205-759-7111
Holy Spirit HS 300/7-12
601 James I Harrison Jr E 35405 205-553-5606
Judy Halli, prin. Fax 566-7103
North River Christian Academy 100/K-12
1785 McFarland Blvd N 35406 205-349-4881
Daniel Habrial, admin. Fax 349-3246
Shelton State Community College Post-Sec.
9500 Old Greensboro Rd 35405 205-391-2211
Stillman College Post-Sec.
PO Box 1430 35403 205-349-4240
Tuscaloosa Academy 300/PK-12
420 Rice Valley Rd N 35406 205-758-4462
Jeffrey Mitchell, hdmstr. Fax 758-4418
University of Alabama 35487 Post-Sec.
205-348-6010

Tuscumbia, Colbert, Pop. 8,279
Colbert County SD 2,900/PK-12
PO Box 538 35674 256-386-8565
Anthony Olivis, supt. Fax 381-9375
colbert.k12.al.us/
Colbert Heights HS 500/7-12
6825 Woodmont Dr 35674 256-383-7875
James Brudgie Davis, prin. Fax 389-8319
Other Schools – See Cherokee, Leighton

Tuscumbia CSD 1,600/K-12
303 N Commons St E 35674 256-389-2900
Mary Kate Smith, supt. Fax 389-2903
www.tuscumbia.k12.al.us
Deshler Career Technical Center Vo/Tech
200 N Commons St E 35674 256-389-2900
Vickey Moon, coord. Fax 389-2903
Deshler HS 400/9-12
200 N Commons St E 35674 256-389-2910
Donny Davis, prin. Fax 389-2915
Deshler MS 400/6-8
590 N High St 35674 256-389-2920
Robert Mullen, prin. Fax 389-2921
Tuscumbia City Alternative S Alt
303 N Commons St E 35674 256-389-2900
Paul Pickett, prin. Fax 389-2903

Covenant Christian S 200/PK-12
1900 Covenant Dr 35674 256-383-4436
Bill Deegan, admin. Fax 381-4437

Tuskegee, Macon, Pop. 9,751
Macon County SD 2,600/PK-12
PO Box 830090 36083 334-727-1600
Dr. Jacqueline Brooks, supt. Fax 724-9990
www.maconk12.org
Washington HS 700/9-12
3803 W Mrtn Luther King Hwy 36083 334-727-0073
Albert Nelson, prin. Fax 724-0222
Other Schools – See Notasulga, Tuskegee Institute

Tuskegee University 36088 Post-Sec.
334-727-8011

Tuskegee Institute, See Tuskegee
Macon County SD
Supt. — See Tuskegee
Macon County Area Vocational S Vo/Tech
1902 Taylor St 36088 334-727-1600
Dr. Lelia Frank, prin.
Tuskegee Institute MS 600/6-8
1809 Franklin Rd 36088 334-727-2580
Rosemary Wright, prin. Fax 727-5089

Union Springs, Bullock, Pop. 3,959
Bullock County SD 1,200/K-12
PO Box 231 36089 334-738-2860
Keith Allen Stewart, supt. Fax 738-2802
bullockcounty.schoolinsites.com
Bullock County Career Technical Ctr Vo/Tech
304 Blackmon Ave E 36089 334-738-4370
James Foulks, dir. Fax 738-4369
Bullock County HS 500/9-12
PO Box 5108 36089 334-738-2198
Undrea Johnson, prin. Fax 738-2606
South Highlands MS 300/5-8
PO Box 111 36089 334-738-2896
Sean Dees, prin. Fax 738-5746

Uniontown, Perry, Pop. 1,770
Perry County SD
Supt. — See Marion
Hatch JSHS 400/7-12
PO Box 709 36786 334-628-4061
Leslie Turner, prin. Fax 683-4935

Uriah, Monroe, Pop. 280
Monroe County SD
Supt. — See Monroeville

Blacksher S — 700/PK-12
PO Box 430 36480 — 251-862-2130
Donald Baggett, prin. — Fax 862-2808

Valley, Chambers, Pop. 9,430
Chambers County SD
Supt. — See Lafayette
Burns MS — 700/6-8
292 Johnson St 36854 — 334-756-3567
Priscilla Holley, prin. — Fax 756-7511
Valley HS — 900/9-12
501 US Highway 29 36854 — 334-756-4105
James Davidson, prin. — Fax 756-9602

Lee County SD
Supt. — See Opelika
Beulah HS — 700/7-12
4848 Lee Road 270 36854 — 334-745-5010
Joey Biddle, prin. — Fax 749-1914

Valley Grande, Dallas, Pop. 3,989
Dallas County SD
Supt. — See Selma
Martin MS — 300/7-8
2863 County Road 81, — 334-872-6417
Queen Morrow, prin. — Fax 875-4013

Valley Head, DeKalb, Pop. 541
De Kalb County SD
Supt. — See Rainsville
Valley Head S — 500/K-12
PO Box 149 35989 — 256-635-6228
William Monroe, prin. — Fax 635-6229

Vance, Tuscaloosa, Pop. 1,508
Tuscaloosa County SD
Supt. — See Tuscaloosa
Brookwood MS — 800/6-8
17021 Brookwood Pkwy 35490 — 205-342-2748
Mark Franks, prin. — Fax 553-9910

Verbena, Chilton
Chilton County SD
Supt. — See Clanton
Verbena S — 600/K-12
202 County Road 510 36091 — 205-280-2820
Robin Cagle, prin. — Fax 755-0393

Vernon, Lamar, Pop. 1,977
Lamar County SD — 2,400/K-12
PO Box 1379 35592 — 205-695-7615
Garth Moss, supt. — Fax 695-7678
www.lamarcountyschools.net
Lamar County S — 700/4-12
8990 Highway 18 35592 — 205-695-7717
Vance Herron, prin. — Fax 695-8218
Lamar County School of Technology — Vo/Tech
43880 Highway 17 35592 — 205-695-7129
Ken Dawkins, prin. — Fax 695-6153
Other Schools – See Millport, Sulligent

Vestavia Hills, Jefferson, Pop. 33,714
Hoover CSD
Supt. — See Hoover
Spain Park HS — 1,500/9-12
4700 Jaguar Dr 35242 — 205-439-1400
Dr. Kenneth Jarnagin, prin. — Fax 439-1401

Vestavia Hills CSD — 6,300/K-12
PO Box 660826 35266 — 205-402-5100
Dr. Jamie Blair, supt. — Fax 402-5134
www.vestavia.k12.al.us
Liberty Park MS — 400/6-8
17035 Liberty Pkwy 35242 — 205-402-5450
Kacy Pierce, prin. — Fax 402-5450
Pizitz MS — 1,000/6-8
2020 Pizitz Dr 35216 — 205-402-5350
David Miles, prin. — Fax 402-5354
Vestavia Hills HS — 1,800/9-12
2235 Lime Rock Rd 35216 — 205-402-5250
Caswell Mcwaters, prin. — Fax 402-5262

Vina, Franklin, Pop. 354
Franklin County SD
Supt. — See Russellville
Vina S — 300/K-12
8250 Highway 23 35593 — 256-331-2260
James Pharr, prin. — Fax 351-4731

Vincent, Shelby, Pop. 1,969
Shelby County SD
Supt. — See Columbiana
Vincent MSHS — 500/6-12
42505 Highway 25 35178 — 205-682-7300
Joel Dixon, prin. — Fax 682-7305

Vinemont, Cullman
Cullman County SD
Supt. — See Cullman
Vinemont HS — 300/9-12
PO Box 189 35179 — 256-734-0571
Dr. Brandon Payne, prin. — Fax 739-8605
Vinemont MS — 300/6-8
170 High School Rd 35179 — 256-739-1943
Phillip Mabry, prin. — Fax 737-1664
West Point MS — 400/6-8
4545 County Road 1141 35179 — 256-734-5904
Clark Farley, prin. — Fax 736-2354

Wadley, Randolph, Pop. 735
Randolph County SD
Supt. — See Wedowee
Wadley S — 400/K-12
PO Box 49 36276 — 256-395-2286
Todd Wilson, prin. — Fax 395-4488

Southern Union State Community College — Post-Sec.
PO Box 1000 36276 — 256-395-2211

Walnut Grove, Etowah, Pop. 690
Etowah County SD
Supt. — See Gadsden
West End HS — 400/7-12
4515 Elm St 35990 — 205-589-6421
Mark Stancil, prin. — Fax 589-4782

Waterloo, Lauderdale, Pop. 203
Lauderdale County SD
Supt. — See Florence
Waterloo S — 400/K-12
PO Box 68 35677 — 256-766-3100
Regina Adams, prin. — Fax 766-3194

Weaver, Calhoun, Pop. 2,963
Calhoun County SD
Supt. — See Anniston
Weaver HS — 500/7-12
917 Clairmont Dr 36277 — 256-741-7200
Michael Allison, prin. — Fax 820-0811

Wedowee, Randolph, Pop. 821
Randolph County SD — 2,100/K-12
182 Circle Dr 36278 — 256-357-4611
Rance Kirby, supt. — Fax 357-4844
www.randolph.k12.al.us
Randolph County HS — 400/7-12
465 Woodland Ave W 36278 — 256-357-4751
Tammy Culbertson, prin. — Fax 357-2310
Randolph-Roanoke Career Tech — Vo/Tech
960 Main St S 36278 — 256-357-2839
Rance Kirby, prin. — Fax 357-4580
Other Schools – See Wadley, Woodland

West Blocton, Bibb, Pop. 1,231
Bibb County SD
Supt. — See Centreville
Bibb County Career Academy — Vo/Tech
17191 Highway 5 35184 — 205-938-7434
Dennis Duncan, prin. — Fax 938-2037
West Blocton HS — 400/9-12
4734 Truman Aldrich Pkwy 35184 — 205-938-9002
Dr. Douglas Milligan, prin. — Fax 938-9546
West Blocton MS — 500/5-8
4721 Truman Aldrich Pkwy 35184 — 205-938-2451
Terry McGee, prin. — Fax 938-3261

Wetumpka, Elmore, Pop. 6,406
Elmore County SD — 11,000/PK-12
PO Box 817 36092 — 334-567-1200
Jeffery Langham, supt. — Fax 567-1405
www.elmoreco.com
Elmore County Technical Center — Vo/Tech
800 Kelly Fitzpatrick Dr 36092 — 334-567-1218
Carl Thomas, dir. — Fax 567-1417
Wetumpka HS — 1,100/9-12
1251 Coosa River Pkwy 36092 — 334-567-5158
Cindy Veazey, prin. — Fax 567-1178
Wetumpka MS — 900/5-8
1000 Micanopy St 36092 — 334-567-1413
Bessie Robinson, prin. — Fax 567-1408
Other Schools – See Deatsville, Eclectic, Millbrook

Winfield, Marion, Pop. 4,666
Winfield CSD — 1,300/K-12
PO Box 70 35594 — 205-487-4255
Dr. Keith Davis, supt. — Fax 487-4603
www.winfield.k12.al.us
Winfield HS — 400/9-12
232 Pirate Cv 35594 — 205-487-6900
Benny Parrish, prin. — Fax 487-4257
Winfield MS — 500/5-8
481 Apple Ave 35594 — 205-487-6901
Terri Miles, prin. — Fax 487-6258

Woodland, Randolph, Pop. 182
Randolph County SD
Supt. — See Wedowee
Woodland S — 800/K-12
24574 Highway 48 36280 — 256-449-2315
Don Birchfield, prin. — Fax 449-2316

Woodville, Jackson, Pop. 730
Jackson County SD
Supt. — See Scottsboro
Woodville S — 600/K-12
290 County Road 63 35776 — 256-776-2874
Bruce Maples, prin. — Fax 776-4718

York, Sumter, Pop. 2,533
Sumter County SD
Supt. — See Livingston
Sumter Central HS — 600/9-12
13878 U S Highway 11 36925 — 205-652-1501
Eric Hines, prin. — Fax 652-1513

Sumter Academy — 200/K-12
181 Sumter Academy Rd 36925 — 205-392-5238
Judy Matlock, hdmstr. — Fax 392-5239

ALASKA

ALASKA DEPARTMENT OF EDUCATION
PO Box 110500, Juneau 99811-0500
Telephone 907-465-2800
Fax 907-465-4165
Website http://www.eed.state.ak.us/

Commissioner of Education   Mike Hanley

ALASKA BOARD OF EDUCATION
PO Box 110500, Juneau 99811-0500

Chairperson   Jim Merriner

PUBLIC, PRIVATE AND CATHOLIC SECONDARY SCHOOLS

Adak, Aleutians West, Pop. 290
Aleutian Region SD
Supt. — See Anchorage
Adak S   50/PK-12
PO Box 2083 99546   907-592-3820
Julie Plummer, lead tchr.   Fax 592-2249

Akhiok, Kodiak Island, Pop. 51
Kodiak Island Borough SD
Supt. — See Kodiak
Akhiok S   50/K-12
PO Box 5049 99615   907-836-2223
Phil Johnson, prin.   Fax 836-2206

Akiachak, Bethel, Pop. 621
Yupiit SD   500/PK-12
PO Box 51190 99551   907-825-3600
Kim Langton, supt.   Fax 825-3655
www.yupiit.org/
Akiachak S   200/K-12
PO Box 51190 99551   907-825-3616
Peggie Price, prin.   Fax 825 3640
Other Schools – See Akiak, Tuluksak

Akiak, Bethel, Pop. 339
Yupiit SD
Supt. — See Akiachak
Akiak S   100/PK-12
PO Box 52049 99552   907-765-4600
Dr. Sherry McKenzie, prin.   Fax 765-4642

Akutan, Aleutians East, Pop. 979
Aleutian East Borough SD
Supt. — See Sand Point
Akutan S   50/PK-12
PO Box 25 99553   907-698-2205
Edwin Sharpe, prin.   Fax 698-2216

Alakanuk, Wade Hampton, Pop. 660
Lower Yukon SD
Supt. — See Mountain Village
Alakanuk S   200/PK-12
PO Box 9 99554   907-238-3312
Diane Reed, prin.   Fax 238-3417

Allakaket, Yukon-Koyukuk, Pop. 101
Yukon-Koyukuk SD
Supt. — See Fairbanks
Allakaket S   50/PK-12
PO Box 69 99720   907-968-2205
Kent Hoffman, prin.   Fax 968-2250

Ambler, Northwest Arctic, Pop. 248
Northwest Arctic Borough SD
Supt. — See Kotzebue
Ambler S   100/PK-12
PO Box 109 99786   907-445-2154
Lois Ballard, prin.   Fax 445-2159

Anaktuvuk Pass, North Slope, Pop. 294
North Slope Borough SD
Supt. — See Barrow
Nunamiut S   100/PK-12
PO Box 21029 99721   907-661-3226
Shele Kinkead, prin.   Fax 661-3402

Anchorage, Anchorage, Pop. 265,438
AVTEC SD
Supt. — See Seward
AVTEC Allied Health Dept   Vo/Tech
1251 Muldoon Rd Ste 103 99504   907-334-2230
Fred Esposito, dir.   Fax 334-2287

Aleutian Region SD   50/PK-12
PO Box 92230 99509   907-277-2648
Joe Beckford, supt.   Fax 277-2649
www.aleutregion.org
Other Schools – See Adak, Atka

Anchorage SD   48,100/PK-12
5530 E Northern Lights Blvd 99504   907-742-4000
Jim Browder, supt.   Fax 742-4318
www.asdk12.org
ACE / ACT Program   Alt
3745 Community Park Loop 99508   907-742-3950
Robyn Harris, prin.   Fax 742-3988
AVAIL S   100/Alt
425 C St 99501   907-742-4930
Nichelle Mauk, prin.   Fax 742-4933
Bartlett HS   1,600/9-12
1101 N Muldoon Rd 99504   907-742-1800
Dan Gallego, prin.   Fax 742-1825
Begich MS   700/7-8
7440 Creekside Center Dr 99504   907-742-0500
Jeanne Fischer, prin.   Fax 742-0510
Benson HS / SEARCH   300/Alt
4515 Campbell Airstrip Rd 99507   907-742-2050
Natalie Burnett, prin.   Fax 742-2060
Central MS of Science   600/7-8
1405 E St 99501   907-742-5100
Lisa Prince, prin.   Fax 742-5125
Clark MS   700/7-8
150 Bragaw St 99508   907-742-4700
Cessilye Williams, prin.   Fax 742-4756
Dimond HS   1,800/9-12
2909 W 88th Ave 99502   907-742-7000
Cheryl Guyott, prin.   Fax 742-7007
East Anchorage HS   2,200/9-12
4025 E Northern Lights Blvd 99508   907-742-2100
Michael Graham, prin.   Fax 742-2134
Goldenview MS   800/7-8
15800 Golden View Dr 99516   907-348-8626
Julie Maker, prin.   Fax 742-8273
Hanshew MS   800/7-8
10121 Lake Otis Pkwy 99507   907-349-1561
Julye Neel, prin.   Fax 349-2835
King Career Center   Vo/Tech
2650 E Northern Lights Blvd 99508   907-742-8900
Lou Pondolfino, prin.   Fax 742-8907
Mears MS   800/7-8
2700 W 100th Ave 99515   907-742-6400
Michael Perkins, prin.   Fax 742-6444
Polaris S   500/Alt
6200 Ashwood St 99507   907-742-8700
Carol Bartholomew, prin.   Fax 742-8777
Romig MS   700/7-8
2500 Minnesota Dr 99503   907-742-5200
Sven Gustafson, prin.   Fax 742-5252
SAVE HS   200/Alt
410 E 56th Ave 99518   907-742-1250
Karin Parker, prin.   Fax 742-1266
Service HS   1,800/9-12
5577 Abbott Rd 99507   907-742-8100
John Gaskins, prin.   Fax 742-6615
South Anchorage HS   1,500/9-12
13400 Elmore Rd 99516   907-742-6200
K. Johnson-Struempler, prin.   Fax 742-6207
Steller JSHS   300/Alt
2508 Blueberry Rd 99503   907-742-4950
Dale Evern, prin.   Fax 742-4966
Wendler MS   500/7-8
2905 Lake Otis Pkwy 99508   907-742-7300
Brendan Wilson, prin.   Fax 742-7307
West Anchorage HS   1,800/9-12
1700 Hillcrest Dr 99517   907-742-2500
Rick Stone, prin.   Fax 742-2525
Other Schools – See Chugiak, Eagle River

Chugach SD   100/PK-12
9312 Vanguard Dr Ste 100 99507   907-522-7400
Bob Crumley, supt.   Fax 522-3399
www.chugachschools.com
Other Schools – See Chenega Bay, Fairbanks, Tatitlek, Whittier

---

Alaska Career College   Post-Sec.
1415 E Tudor Rd 99507   907-563-7575
Alaska Pacific University   Post-Sec.
4101 University Dr 99508   800-252-7528
Anchorage Christian S   700/PK-12
6575 E Northern Lights Blvd 99504   907-337-9575
Thomas Cobaugh, admin.   Fax 338-3903
Charter College   Post-Sec.
2221 E Northern Lights #120 99508   907-277-1000
Grace Christian S   600/K-12
12407 Pintail St 99516   907-868-1203
Randy Karlberg, supt.   Fax 644-2261
Holy Rosary Academy   100/K-12
1010 W Fireweed Ln 99503   907-276-5822
Catherine Neumayr, prin.   Fax 258-1055
Lumen Christi JSHS   100/7-12
8110 Jewel Lake Rd Bldg D 99502   907-245-9231
Tom Sorci, prin.   Fax 245-9232
University of Alaska Anchorage   Post-Sec.
3211 Providence Dr 99508   907-786-1800

Anderson, Denali, Pop. 234
Denali Borough SD
Supt. — See Healy
Anderson S   50/K-12
PO Box 3120 99744   907-582-2700
Tim Fraychineaud, prin.   Fax 582-2000

Angoon, Skagway-Hoonah-Angoon, Pop. 409
Chatham SD   200/K-12
PO Box 109 99820   907-788-3302
Scott Butterfield Ph.D., supt.   Fax 788-3252
www.chathamsd.org/
Angoon S   100/K-12
PO Box 209 99820   907-788-3811
Lester McCormick, prin.   Fax 788-3812
Other Schools – See Gustavus, Haines, Tenakee Springs

Aniak, Bethel, Pop. 452
Kuspuk SD   300/PK-12
PO Box 49 99557   907-675-4250
Brad Allen, supt.   Fax 675-4305
www.kuspuk.org
Aniak JSHS   50/7-12
PO Box 29 99557   907-675-4330
Amore't Allen, prin.   Fax 675-4256
Other Schools – See Chuathbaluk, Crooked Creek, Kalskag, Sleetmute, Stony River

Anvik, Yukon-Koyukuk, Pop. 82
Iditarod Area SD
Supt. — See Mc Grath
Blackwell S   50/PK-12
PO Box 90 99558   907-663-6348
Meta DeArmoun, prin.   Fax 663-6349

Arctic Village, Yukon-Koyukuk, Pop. 142
Yukon Flats SD
Supt. — See Fort Yukon
Arctic Village S   50/PK-12
PO Box 22049 99722   907-587-5211
Terry Reed, prin.   Fax 587-5210

Atka, Aleutians West, Pop. 61
Aleutian Region SD
Supt. — See Anchorage
Netsvetov S   50/K-12
PO Box 47050 99547   907-839-2210
Sally Swetzof, lead tchr.   Fax 839-2212

Atmautluak, Bethel, Pop. 277
Lower Kuskokwim SD
Supt. — See Bethel
Alexie Memorial S   100/PK-12
PO Box ATT 99559   907-553-5112
Ashley Crace, prin.   Fax 553-5129

Atqasuk, North Slope, Pop. 231
North Slope Borough SD
Supt. — See Barrow
Meade River S   100/PK-12
PO Box 91030 99791   907-633-6315
Kathy Blizard, prin.   Fax 633-6215

Barrow, North Slope, Pop. 3,772
North Slope Borough SD   1,900/PK-12
PO Box 169 99723   907-852-5311
Peggy Cowan, supt.   Fax 852-9503
www.nsbsd.org/
Barrow HS   200/9-12
PO Box 960 99723   907-852-8950
Beverly Gillaspie, prin.   Fax 852-8969
Hopson Memorial MS   200/6-8
PO Box 509 99723   907-852-3880
Carla Seavey, prin.   Fax 852-7794
Kiita Learning Community   100/Alt
PO Box 169 99723   907-852-9677
Robert Meade, prin.   Fax 852-4334
Other Schools – See Anaktuvuk Pass, Atqasuk, Kaktovik, Nuiqsut, Point Hope, Point Lay, Wainwright

Ilisagvik College Post-Sec.
PO Box 749 99723 907-852-3333

Beaver, Yukon-Koyukuk, Pop. 83
Yukon Flats SD
Supt. — See Fort Yukon
Cruikshank S 50/PK-12
PO Box 24050 99724 907-628-6313
Charlene Fisher, prin. Fax 628-6615

Bethel, Bethel, Pop. 5,648
Lower Kuskokwim SD 4,100/PK-12
PO Box 305 99559 907-543-4800
Gary Baldwin, supt. Fax 543-4904
www.lksd.org
Bethel Alternative Boarding S 50/Alt
PO Box 1949 99559 907-543-5610
Doug Bower, prin. Fax 543-5603
Bethel Regional HS 500/7-12
PO Box 700 99559 907-543-3957
Janelle Vanasse, prin. Fax 543-2327
Other Schools – See Atmautluak, Chefornak, Eek, Goodnews Bay, Kasigluk, Kipnuk, Kongiganak, Kwethluk, Kwigillingok, Mekoryuk, Napakiak, Napaskiak, Newtok, Nightmute, Nunapitchuk, Platinum, Quinhagak, Toksook Bay, Tuntutuliak, Tununak

Big Lake, Matanuska-Susitna, Pop. 3,191
Matanuska-Susitna Borough SD
Supt. — See Palmer
Houston MS 300/6-8
PO Box 520920 99652 907-892-9500
Benjamin Howard, prin. Fax 892-9560

Brevig Mission, Nome, Pop. 377
Bering Strait SD
Supt. — See Unalakleet
Brevig Mission S 100/PK-12
General Delivery 99785 907-642-4021
Hannibal Anderson, prin. Fax 642-4031

Buckland, Northwest Arctic, Pop. 408
Northwest Arctic Borough SD
Supt. — See Kotzebue
Buckland S 200/PK-12
PO Box 91 99727 907-494-2127
Terri Walker, prin. Fax 494-2106

Cantwell, Denali, Pop. 205
Denali Borough SD
Supt. — See Healy
Cantwell S 50/K-12
PO Box 29 99729 907-768-2372
Jeni Mason, prin. Fax 768-2500

Chalkyitsik, Yukon-Koyukuk, Pop. 69
Yukon Flats SD
Supt. — See Fort Yukon
Tsuk Taih S 50/PK-12
1 Marten Hill 99788 907-848-8113
John Bruce, prin. Fax 848-8312

Chefornak, Bethel, Pop. 415
Lower Kuskokwim SD
Supt. — See Bethel
Chaptnquak S 200/PK-12
PO Box 50 99561 907-867-8700
Kenton Bodily, prin. Fax 867-8727

Chenega Bay, Valdez-Cordova, Pop. 94
Chugach SD
Supt. — See Anchorage
Chenega Bay Community S 50/PK-12
PO Box 8030 99574 907-573-5123
Steve Grajewski, prin. Fax 573-5137

Chevak, Wade Hampton, Pop. 915
Kashunamiut SD 300/K-12
PO Box 345 99563 907-858-7713
Larry Parker, supt. Fax 858-7328
www.chevakschool.org/
Chevak S 300/K-12
PO Box 345 99563 907-858-7712
Matthew Good, prin. Fax 858-6150

Chignik, Lake and Peninsula, Pop. 87
Lake & Peninsula SD
Supt. — See King Salmon
Chignik Bay S 50/K-12
PO Box 9 99564 907-749-2213
Joe Ward, prin. Fax 749-2261

Chignik Lagoon, Lake and Peninsula, Pop. 69
Lake & Peninsula SD
Supt. — See King Salmon
Chignik Lagoon S 50/K-12
PO Box 50 99565 907-840-2210
Joe Ward, prin. Fax 840-2265

Chignik Lake, Lake and Peninsula, Pop. 71
Lake & Peninsula SD
Supt. — See King Salmon
Chignik Lake S 50/K-12
General Delivery 99548 907-845-2210
Joe Ward, prin. Fax 845-2254

Chuathbaluk, Bethel, Pop. 112
Kuspuk SD
Supt. — See Aniak
Crow Village Sam S 50/PK-12
PO Box CHU 99557 907-467-4229
Susan Hubbard, prin. Fax 467-4122

Chugiak, See Anchorage
Anchorage SD
Supt. — See Anchorage
Chugiak HS 1,200/9-12
16525 S Birchwood Loop Rd 99567 907-742-3050
Sam Spinella, prin. Fax 742-3148

Mirror Lake MS 700/6-8
22901 Lake Hill Dr 99567 907-742-3500
Dr. Sherry Ellers, prin. Fax 742-3545

Birchwood Christian S 100/PK-12
22208 Birchwood Loop Rd 99567 907-688-2228
Todd Clark, prin. Fax 688-2159

Circle, Yukon-Koyukuk, Pop. 98
Yukon Flats SD
Supt. — See Fort Yukon
Circle S 50/PK-12
PO Box 49 99733 907-773-1250
Kurt Schmidt, prin. Fax 773-1259

Coffman Cove, Prince of Wales-Outer Ketchikan, Pop. 173
Southeast Island SD
Supt. — See Thorne Bay
Valentine S 50/K-12
PO Box 18002 99918 907-329-2244
James Hughes, lead tchr. Fax 329-2210

Cold Bay, Aleutians East, Pop. 100
Aleutian East Borough SD
Supt. — See Sand Point
Cold Bay S 50/PK-12
PO Box 128 99571 907-532-2409
Kerry Burkhardt, prin. Fax 532-2421

Cooper Landing, Kenai Peninsula, Pop. 282
Kenai Peninsula Borough SD
Supt. — See Soldotna
Cooper Landing S 50/K-12
PO Box 990 99572 907-595-1244
Christine Ermold, prin. Fax 595-1461

Copper Center, Valdez-Cordova, Pop. 312
Copper River SD
Supt. — See Glennallen
Kenny Lake S 100/1-12
HC 60 Box 224 99573 907-822-3870
Stacey Stansell, prin. Fax 822-3794

Cordova, Valdez-Cordova, Pop. 2,067
Cordova CSD 300/PK-12
PO Box 1330 99574 907-424-3265
Theresa Keel, supt. Fax 424-3271
cordovasd.org
Cordova JSHS 200/7-12
PO Box 1330 99574 907-424-3266
Leif Jacobsen, prin. Fax 424-5215

Craig, Prince of Wales-Outer Ketchikan, Pop. 1,047
Craig CSD 300/PK-12
PO Box 800 99921 907-826-3274
Ron Erickson, supt. Fax 826-3322
www.craigschools.com
Craig Alternative HS 50/Alt
PO Box 800 99921 907-826-3274
Ron Erickson, prin. Fax 826-2974
Craig HS 100/9-12
PO Box 800 99921 907-826-2274
Josh Andrews, prin. Fax 826-3016
Craig MS 100/6-8
PO Box 800 99921 907-826-3274
Jackie Hanson, prin. Fax 826-3309

Southeast Island SD
Supt. — See Thorne Bay
Hollis S 50/K-12
PO Box 803 99921 907-530-7108
Julie Vasquez, lead tchr. Fax 530-7111

Crooked Creek, Bethel, Pop. 96
Kuspuk SD
Supt. — See Aniak
John Sr. S 50/PK-12
PO Box 20 99575 907-432-2205
Susan Hubbard, prin. Fax 432-2206

Deering, Northwest Arctic, Pop. 117
Northwest Arctic Borough SD
Supt. — See Kotzebue
Deering S 50/PK-12
PO Box 36009 99736 907-363-2121
Garrett McMullen, prin. Fax 363-2128

Delta Junction, Southeast Fairbanks, Pop. 919
Delta-Greely SD 800/PK-12
PO Box 527 99737 907-895-4657
Duncan Ware, supt. Fax 895-4781
www.dgsd.k12.ak.us/
Delta Junction HS 200/9-12
PO Box 647 99737 907-895-4460
Pat Mayer, prin. Fax 895-4049
New Horizons S 50/Alt
PO Box 527 99737 907-895-4655
Laural Jackson, prin. Fax 895-4246
Other Schools – See Fort Greely

Dillingham, Dillingham, Pop. 2,086
Dillingham CSD 500/PK-12
PO Box 170 99576 907-842-5223
William McLeod, supt. Fax 842-5634
www.dlgsd.org
Dillingham MSHS 300/6-12
PO Box 170 99576 907-842-5221
William Schwan, prin. Fax 842-4395

Southwest Region SD 600/K-12
PO Box 90 99576 907-842-5287
David Piazza, supt. Fax 842-5428
www.swrsd.org/
Other Schools – See Koliganek, Manokotak, New Stuyahok, Togiak

Diomede, Nome, Pop. 111
Bering Strait SD
Supt. — See Unalakleet
Diomede S 50/PK-12
PO Box 7099 99762 907-686-3021
Willis Ferenbaugh, prin. Fax 686-3022

Dot Lake, Southeast Fairbanks, Pop. 12
Alaska Gateway SD
Supt. — See Tok
Dot Lake S 50/K-12
PO Box 2280 99737 907-882-2663
Gordon Kron, prin. Fax 882-2112

Eagle, Southeast Fairbanks, Pop. 85
Alaska Gateway SD
Supt. — See Tok
Eagle Community S 50/K-12
PO Box 168 99738 907-547-2210
Ann Millard, prin. Fax 547-2302

Eagle River, See Anchorage
Anchorage SD
Supt. — See Anchorage
Eagle River HS 900/9-12
8701 Yosemite Dr 99577 907-742-2700
Martin Lang, prin. Fax 742-2710
Gruening MS 600/7-8
9601 Lee St 99577 907-742-3600
Bobby Jefts, prin. Fax 742-3666

Eagle River Christian S 100/K-12
10336 E Eagle River Loop Rd 99577 907-694-4602
Denny Archer, admin. Fax 694-4141

Eek, Bethel, Pop. 296
Lower Kuskokwim SD
Supt. — See Bethel
Eek S 100/PK-12
PO Box 50 99578 907-536-5227
Brett Stirling, prin. Fax 536-5628

Egegik, Lake and Peninsula, Pop. 97
Lake & Peninsula SD
Supt. — See King Salmon
Egegik S 50/K-12
PO Box 10 99579 907-233-2210
Sherry McKenzie, prin. Fax 233-2254

Eielson AFB, Fairbanks North Star, Pop. 2,496
Fairbanks-North Star Borough SD
Supt. — See Fairbanks
Eielson JSHS 500/7-12
675 Ravens Way 99702 907-372-3110
Mario Gatto, prin. Fax 372-3202

Elim, Nome, Pop. 322
Bering Strait SD
Supt. — See Unalakleet
Aniguiin S 100/PK-12
PO Box 29 99739 907-890-3041
Steve Petz, prin. Fax 890-3031

Emmonak, Wade Hampton, Pop. 759
Lower Yukon SD
Supt. — See Mountain Village
Emmonak S 200/PK-12
General Delivery 99581 907-949-1248
Thomas Gobeske, prin. Fax 949-1148

Fairbanks, Fairbanks North Star, Pop. 29,138
Chugach SD
Supt. — See Anchorage
Fairbanks Extension S Alt
2216 Penrose Ln 99709 907-457-2545
Annie Dougherty, prin. Fax 374-0466

Fairbanks-North Star Borough SD 14,000/PK-12
520 5th Ave 99701 907-452-2000
Pete Lewis, supt. Fax 451-0541
www.k12northstar.org
Hutchison HS Vo/Tech
3750 Geist Rd 99709 907-479-2261
Dan Domke, prin. Fax 479-8286
Lathrop HS 1,100/9-12
901 Airport Way 99701 907-456-7794
Dave Dershin, prin. Fax 452-6735
Ryan MS 400/7-8
951 Airport Way 99701 907-452-4751
Heather Stewart, prin. Fax 451-8834
Smith MS 300/7-8
1401 Bainbridge Blvd 99701 907-458-7600
Sandy Kowalski, prin. Fax 458-7676
Tanana MS 500/7-8
600 Trainor Gate Rd 99701 907-452-8145
Gregg Platt, prin. Fax 456-2780
West Valley HS 1,100/9-12
3800 Geist Rd 99709 907-479-4221
Shaun Kraska, prin. Fax 474-8901
Other Schools – See Eielson AFB, North Pole

Yukon-Koyukuk SD 300/PK-12
4762 Old Airport Way 99709 907-374-9400
Kerry Boyd, supt. Fax 374-9440
www.yksd.com
Other Schools – See Allakaket, Hughes, Huslia, Kaltag, Koyukuk, Manley Hot Springs, Minto, Nulato, Ruby

Fairhill Christian S 100/PK-12
101 City Lights Blvd 99712 907-457-2167
Walt Williams, prin. Fax 457-4382
Monroe Catholic JSHS 200/7-12
615 Monroe St 99701 907-452-2044
Vince Fantazzi, prin. Fax 452-5978
University of Alaska Fairbanks Post-Sec.
PO Box 757500 99775 907-474-7500

False Pass, Aleutians East, Pop. 35
Aleutian East Borough SD
Supt. — See Sand Point
False Pass S 50/PK-12
PO Box 30 99583 907-548-2224
Ward Walker, prin. Fax 548-2304

Fort Greely, Southeast Fairbanks, Pop. 513
Delta-Greely SD
Supt. — See Delta Junction
Ft. Greely S 300/4-8
Building 725, 907-869-3105
Jeff Lansing, prin. Fax 869-3382

Fort Yukon, Yukon-Koyukuk, Pop. 569
Yukon Flats SD 300/PK-12
PO Box 350 99740 907-662-2515
Lance Bowie, supt. Fax 662-2519
www.yukonflats.net
Career Technical Education Vo/Tech
PO Box 350 99740 907-662-2765
Jim Cammon, dir. Fax 662-2988
Fort Yukon S 100/PK-12
PO Box 129 99740 907-662-2352
Debra Van Dyke, prin. Fax 662-2958
Other Schools – See Arctic Village, Beaver, Chalkyitsik, Circle, Stevens Village, Venetie

Fritz Creek, Kenai Peninsula, Pop. 1,832
Kenai Peninsula Borough SD
Supt. — See Soldotna
Kachemak Selo S 100/PK-12
PO Box 15007 99603 907-235-5552
Andy Rothenberger, prin. Fax 235-5644
Voznesenka S 100/PK-12
PO Box 15336 99603 907-235-8549
Michael Wojciak, prin. Fax 235-6086

Galena, Yukon-Koyukuk, Pop. 441
Galena CSD 300/PK-12
PO Box 299 99741 907-656-1205
Chris Reitan, supt. Fax 656-2238
www.galenaalaska.org
Galena Interior Learning Academy 200/9-12
PO Box 359 99741 907-656-2053
John Riddle, prin. Fax 656-2107
Huntington JSHS 50/7-12
PO Box 299 99741 907-656-1205
Beth Buchanan, prin. Fax 656-1368

Gambell, Nome, Pop. 678
Bering Strait SD
Supt. — See Unalakleet
Gambell S 200/PK-12
PO Box 169 99742 907-985-5515
Deb Forkner, prin. Fax 985-5435

Glennallen, Valdez-Cordova, Pop. 422
Copper River SD 400/K-12
PO Box 108 99588 907-822-3234
Dr. Michael Johnson, supt. Fax 822-3949
www.crsd.us
Glennallen JSHS 100/7-12
PO Box 108 99588 907-822-5286
Jack Von Thaer, prin. Fax 822-8501
Other Schools – See Copper Center, Slana

Alaska Bible College Post-Sec.
PO Box 289 99588 907-822-3201

Golovin, Nome, Pop. 153
Bering Strait SD
Supt. — See Unalakleet
Olson S 100/PK-12
PO Box 62040 99762 907-779-3021
Margaret Koegler, prin. Fax 779-3031

Goodnews Bay, Bethel, Pop. 241
Lower Kuskokwim SD
Supt. — See Bethel
Rocky Mountain S 100/PK-12
PO Box 153 99589 907-967-8213
Christopher Carmichael, prin. Fax 967-8228

Grayling, Yukon-Koyukuk, Pop. 182
Iditarod Area SD
Supt. — See Mc Grath
David-Louis Memorial S 50/K-12
PO Box 90 99590 907-453-5135
Richard Webster, prin. Fax 453-5165

Gustavus, Skagway-Hoonah-Angoon, Pop. 422
Chatham SD
Supt. — See Angoon
Gustavus S 100/K-12
PO Box 120 99826 907-697-2248
Holly Cervin, prin. Fax 697-2378

Haines, Haines, Pop. 1,608
Chatham SD
Supt. — See Angoon
Klukwan S 50/K-12
HC 60 Box 2222 99827 907-767-5551
Cynthia McFeeters, lead tchr. Fax 767-5573

Haines Borough SD 300/PK-12
PO Box 1289 99827 907-766-6725
Michael Byer, supt. Fax 766-6794
www.hbsd.net
Haines HS 100/9-12
PO Box 1289 99827 907-766-6700
Michelle Byer, prin. Fax 766-6791

Healy, Denali, Pop. 980
Denali Borough SD 800/PK-12
PO Box 280 99743 907-683-2278
James Elliott, supt. Fax 683-2514
denali.ak.schoolwebpages.com
Denali PEAK 500/Alt
PO Box 280 99743 907-683-7325
Jeni Mason, prin. Fax 683-0329
Tri-Valley S 200/K-12
PO Box 400 99743 907-683-2267
Robyn Taylor, prin. Fax 683-2632
Other Schools – See Anderson, Cantwell

Holy Cross, Yukon-Koyukuk, Pop. 171
Iditarod Area SD
Supt. — See Mc Grath
Holy Cross S 50/PK-12
PO Box 210 99602 907-476-7131
Jeff Bader, prin. Fax 476-7161

Homer, Kenai Peninsula, Pop. 4,783
Kenai Peninsula Borough SD
Supt. — See Soldotna
Homer Flex S 50/Alt
4122 Ben Walters Ln 99603 907-235-5558
Karen Wessel, prin. Fax 235-5633
Homer HS 400/9-12
600 E Fairview Ave 99603 907-235-4600
Dr. D. Allan Gee, prin. Fax 235-8933
Homer MS 200/7-8
500 Sterling Hwy 99603 907-235-5700
Dave Larson, prin. Fax 235-2513
Razdolna S 100/K-12
PO Box 15098 99603 907-235-6870
Timothy Whip, prin. Fax 235-6485

Hoonah, Skagway-Hoonah-Angoon, Pop. 657
Hoonah CSD 100/PK-12
PO Box 157 99829 907-945-3611
Angie Lunda, supt. Fax 945-3492
www.hoonahschools.org
Hoonah JSHS 100/7-12
PO Box 157 99829 907-945-3613
Carmen Russo, prin. Fax 945-3607

Hooper Bay, Wade Hampton, Pop. 1,055
Lower Yukon SD
Supt. — See Mountain Village
Hooper Bay S 400/PK-12
General Delivery 99604 907-758-1200
Mike Jump, prin. Fax 758-1280

Hope, Kenai Peninsula, Pop. 178
Kenai Peninsula Borough SD
Supt. — See Soldotna
Hope S 50/K-12
PO Box 47 99605 907-782-3202
Michael Hanson, admin. Fax 782-3140

Houston, Matanuska-Susitna, Pop. 1,746
Matanuska-Susitna Borough SD
Supt. — See Palmer
Houston HS 400/9-12
PO Box 940315 99694 907-892-9400
William Johnson, prin. Fax 892-9460

Hughes, Yukon-Koyukuk, Pop. 77
Yukon-Koyukuk SD
Supt. — See Fairbanks
Oldman S 50/K-12
PO Box 30 99745 907-889-2204
Gina Hrinko, admin. Fax 889-2220

Huslia, Yukon-Koyukuk, Pop. 272
Yukon-Koyukuk SD
Supt. — See Fairbanks
Huntington S 100/PK-12
PO Box 110 99746 907-829-2205
Teresa Cox, prin. Fax 829-2270

Hydaburg, Prince of Wales-Outer Ketchikan, Pop. 342
Hydaburg CSD 100/K-12
PO Box 109 99922 907-285-3491
Lauren Burch, supt. Fax 285-3391
www.hydaburg.k12.ak.us
Hydaburg S 100/K-12
PO Box 109 99922 907-285-3591
Troy Heaton, prin. Fax 285-3391

Igiugig, Lake and Peninsula, Pop. 34
Lake & Peninsula SD
Supt. — See King Salmon
Igiugig S 50/K-12
PO Box 4010 99613 907-533-3220
Colter Barnes, prin. Fax 533-3221

Iliamna, Lake and Peninsula, Pop. 96
Lake & Peninsula SD
Supt. — See King Salmon
Newhalen S 100/K-12
PO Box 89 99606 907-571-1211
Ed Lester, prin. Fax 571-1466

Juneau, Juneau, Pop. 28,325
Juneau Borough SD 5,000/PK-12
10014 Crazy Horse Dr 99801 907-523-1700
Glenn Gelbrich, supt. Fax 523-1708
www.juneauschools.org
Dryden MS 600/6-8
10014 Crazy Horse Dr 99801 907-463-1850
Tom Milliron, prin. Fax 463-1828
Heeni MS 500/6-8
10014 Crazy Horse Dr 99801 907-463-1899
Molly Yerkes, prin. Fax 463-1877
Juneau-Douglas HS 800/9-12
10014 Crazy Horse Dr 99801 907-523-1500
Ryan Alsup, prin. Fax 523-1616
Thunder Mountain HS 600/9-12
10014 Crazy Horse Dr 99801 907-780-1900
Dan Larson, prin. Fax 780-1909
YaaKoosge Daakahidi Alternative HS 200/Alt
10014 Crazy Horse Dr 99801 907-523-1800
Sarah Marino, prin. Fax 523-1819

University of Alaska Southeast Post-Sec.
11120 Glacier Hwy 99801 907-796-6000

Kake, Wrangell-Petersburg, Pop. 485
Kake CSD 100/PK-12
PO Box 450 99830 907-785-3741
Kevin Shipley, supt. Fax 785-6439
www.kakeschools.com
Kake S 100/PK-12
PO Box 450 99830 907-785-3741
Kevin Shipley, prin. Fax 785-6439

Kaktovik, North Slope, Pop. 236
North Slope Borough SD
Supt. — See Barrow
Kaveolook S 100/PK-12
PO Box 20 99747 907-640-6626
Jim LeClair, prin. Fax 640-6718

Kalskag, Bethel, Pop. 186
Kuspuk SD
Supt. — See Aniak
Morgan HS 50/7-12
PO Box 30 99607 907-471-2288
Greg Wohlman, prin. Fax 471-2242

Kaltag, Yukon-Koyukuk, Pop. 185
Yukon-Koyukuk SD
Supt. — See Fairbanks
Kaltag S 50/PK-12
PO Box 30 99748 907-534-2204
Nancy Mason, prin. Fax 534-2227

Karluk, Kodiak Island, Pop. 37
Kodiak Island Borough SD
Supt. — See Kodiak
Karluk S 50/K-12
General Delivery 99608 907-241-2217
Phil Johnson, prin. Fax 241-2207

Kasaan, Prince of Wales-Outer Ketchikan, Pop. 44
Southeast Island SD
Supt. — See Thorne Bay
Kasaan S 50/K-12
1 Kasaan Rd 99901 907-542-2217
Ryan Nelson, lead tchr. Fax 542-2219

Kasigluk, Bethel, Pop. 558
Lower Kuskokwim SD
Supt. — See Bethel
Akiuk Memorial S 100/PK-12
General Delivery 99609 907-477-6829
Christina Powers, prin. Fax 477-6314
Akula Elitnaurvik S 100/K-12
PO Box 79 99609 907-477-6615
Lewis Beaver, prin. Fax 477-6715

Kenai, Kenai Peninsula, Pop. 6,541
Kenai Peninsula Borough SD
Supt. — See Soldotna
Kenai Alternative S 100/Alt
705 Frontage Rd Ste C 99611 907-335-2870
Loren Reese, prin. Fax 283-6463
Kenai Central HS 500/9-12
9583 Kenai Spur Hwy 99611 907-283-2100
Alan Fields, prin. Fax 283-3230
Kenai MS 400/6-8
201 N Tinker Ln 99611 907-283-1700
Vaughn Dosko, prin. Fax 283-3180
Marathon S 50/Alt
405 Marathon Rd 99611 907-335-3343
Randy Neill, lead tchr. Fax 335-3342

Ketchikan, Ketchikan Gateway, Pop. 7,299
Ketchikan Gateway Borough SD 2,200/PK-12
333 Schoenbar Rd 99901 907-247-2142
Robert Boyle, supt. Fax 247-3822
www.kgbsd.org
Ketchikan HS 500/9-12
2610 4th Ave 99901 907-225-9815
Sam Nelson, prin. Fax 247-5761
Revilla HS 100/7-12
3131 Baranof Ave 99901 907-225-6681
Kurt Lindemann, prin. Fax 247-6681
Schoenbar MS 300/7-8
217 Schoenbar Rd 99901 907-225-5138
Casey Robinson, prin. Fax 225-5761

Southeast Island SD
Supt. — See Thorne Bay
Edna Bay S K-12
PO Box EDB 99950 907-594-6110
Mack McDaniel, lead tchr. Fax 594-6111
Naukati S 50/K-12
PO Box NKI 99950 907-629-4121
Kim Hoover, lead tchr. Fax 629-4122
Port Protection S 50/K-12
PO Box PPV 99950 907-489-2228
Rocky Near, lead tchr. Fax 489-2235
Whale Pass S 50/PK-12
126 Bayview Rd 99950 907-846-5320
Christine Cook, lead tchr. Fax 846-5319

Kiana, Northwest Arctic, Pop. 351
Northwest Arctic Borough SD
Supt. — See Kotzebue
Kiana S 100/PK-12
PO Box 190 99749 907-475-2115
Kathy Scott, prin. Fax 475-2120

King Cove, Aleutians East, Pop. 905
Aleutian East Borough SD
Supt. — See Sand Point
King Cove S 100/PK-12
PO Box 69 99612 907-497-2354
Keri St. Jeor, prin. Fax 497-2408

King Salmon, Bristol Bay, Pop. 341
Lake & Peninsula SD 300/K-12
PO Box 498 99613 907-246-4280
Ty Mase, supt. Fax 246-4473
www.lpsd.com
Other Schools – See Chignik, Chignik Lagoon, Chignik Lake, Egegik, Igiugig, Iliamna, Kokhanok, Levelock, Nondalton, Perryville, Pilot Point, Port Alsworth, Port Heiden

Kipnuk, Bethel, Pop. 637
Lower Kuskokwim SD
Supt. — See Bethel
Chief Paul Memorial S 200/PK-12
PO Box 19 99614 907-896-5011
Jami Whedbee, prin. Fax 896-5428

Kivalina, Northwest Arctic, Pop. 368
Northwest Arctic Borough SD
Supt. — See Kotzebue
McQueen S 100/PK-12
General Delivery 99750 907-645-2125
Dr. Zoe Theoharis, prin. Fax 645-2124

Klawock, Prince of Wales-Outer Ketchikan, Pop. 670
Klawock CSD 100/PK-12
PO Box 9 99925 907-755-2917
Rich Carlson, supt. Fax 755-2320
www.klawockschool.com/
Klawock City S 100/PK-12
PO Box 9 99925 907-755-2220
Jim Holien, prin. Fax 755-2913

Kobuk, Northwest Arctic, Pop. 151
Northwest Arctic Borough SD
Supt. — See Kotzebue
Kobuk S 50/PK-12
PO Box 40 99751 907-948-2231
Jack Richards, lead tchr. Fax 948-2225

Kodiak, Kodiak Island, Pop. 5,742
Kodiak Island Borough SD 2,500/PK-12
722 Mill Bay Rd 99615 907-481-6200
Stewart McDonald, supt. Fax 481-6218
www.kibsd.org/
Kodiak HS 800/9-12
722 Mill Bay Rd 99615 907-481-2501
Bill Watkins, prin. Fax 481-2505
Kodiak MS 500/6-8
722 Mill Bay Rd 99615 907-481-2200
Ron Bryant, prin. Fax 481-2201
Other Schools – See Akhiok, Karluk, Larsen Bay, Old Harbor, Ouzinkie, Port Lions

Kokhanok, Lake and Peninsula, Pop. 153
Lake & Peninsula SD
Supt. — See King Salmon
Kokhanok S 50/K-12
PO Box 1109 99606 907-282-2210
Colter Barnes, admin. Fax 282-2247

Koliganek, Dillingham, Pop. 207
Southwest Region SD
Supt. — See Dillingham
Koliganek S 100/K-12
PO Box 5052 99576 907-596-3444
Cody McCanna, prin. Fax 596-3484

Kongiganak, Bethel, Pop. 430
Lower Kuskokwim SD
Supt. — See Bethel
Ayagina'ar Elitnaurvik S 100/PK-12
PO Box 5109, 907-557-5126
Shannon Hutson, prin. Fax 557-5639

Kotlik, Wade Hampton, Pop. 574
Lower Yukon SD
Supt. — See Mountain Village
Kotlik S 200/PK-12
PO Box 20129 99620 907-899-4415
Gerald Earley, prin. Fax 899-4515

Kotzebue, Northwest Arctic, Pop. 2,953
Northwest Arctic Borough SD 1,900/PK-12
PO Box 51 99752 907-442-1800
Norman Eck Ph.D., supt. Fax 442-2246
www.nwarctic.org/
Alaska Technical Center Vo/Tech
PO Box 51 99752 907-442-3733
Cheryl Edenshaw, dir. Fax 442-2764
Kotzebue MSHS 300/6-12
PO Box 264 99752 907-442-1876
Mike Lane, prin. Fax 442-2141
Other Schools – See Ambler, Buckland, Deering, Kiana, Kivalina, Kobuk, Noatak, Noorvik, Selawik, Shungnak

Koyuk, Nome, Pop. 308
Bering Strait SD
Supt. — See Unalakleet
Koyuk-Malemute S 100/PK-12
PO Box 53009 99753 907-963-3021
John Weemes, prin. Fax 963-2428

Koyukuk, Yukon-Koyukuk, Pop. 94
Yukon-Koyukuk SD
Supt. — See Fairbanks
Vernetti S 50/PK-10
PO Box 70 99754 907-927-2212
Josie Dayton, prin. Fax 927-2251

Kwethluk, Bethel, Pop. 696
Lower Kuskokwim SD
Supt. — See Bethel
Ket'acik Aap'alluk Memorial S 200/PK-12
PO Box 150 99621 907-757-6014
Darrell Richards, prin. Fax 757-6013

Kwigillingok, Bethel, Pop. 316
Lower Kuskokwim SD
Supt. — See Bethel
Kwigillingok S 100/PK-12
PO Box 109 99622 907-588-8629
Megan Haglund, prin. Fax 588-8613

Larsen Bay, Kodiak Island, Pop. 83
Kodiak Island Borough SD
Supt. — See Kodiak
Larsen Bay S 50/K-12
PO Box 70 99624 907-847-2252
Phil Johnson, prin. Fax 847-2260

Levelock, Lake and Peninsula, Pop. 65
Lake & Peninsula SD
Supt. — See King Salmon
Levelock S 50/K-12
PO Box 89 99625 907-287-3060
Ed Cox, admin. Fax 287-3021

Mc Grath, Yukon-Koyukuk, Pop. 277
Iditarod Area SD 300/PK-12
PO Box 90 99627 907-524-1200
Scott Ballard, supt. Fax 524-3217
www.iditarodsd.org/
Mc Grath S 100/PK-12
PO Box 290 99627 907-524-3388
S. Parker, prin. Fax 524-3751
Other Schools – See Anvik, Grayling, Holy Cross, Nikolai, Shageluk, Takotna

Manley Hot Springs, Yukon-Koyukuk, Pop. 75
Yukon-Koyukuk SD
Supt. — See Fairbanks
Manley Hart Springs Gladys Dart S 50/PK-12
PO Box 29 99756 907-672-3202
Gina Hrinko, admin. Fax 672-3201

Manokotak, Dillingham, Pop. 440
Southwest Region SD
Supt. — See Dillingham
Manokotak S 100/K-12
PO Box 30 99628 907-289-1013
Lawrence Johnson, prin. Fax 289-2050

Marshall, Wade Hampton, Pop. 404
Lower Yukon SD
Supt. — See Mountain Village
Marshall S 100/PK-12
PO Box 89 99585 907-679-6112
Randall Heinrichs, prin. Fax 679-6637

Mekoryuk, Bethel, Pop. 184
Lower Kuskokwim SD
Supt. — See Bethel
Nuniwarmiut S 50/PK-12
PO Box 49 99630 907-827-8415
Walt Betz, prin. Fax 827-8613

Mentasta Lake, Southeast Fairbanks, Pop. 111
Alaska Gateway SD
Supt. — See Tok
Mentasta Lake S 50/K-12
PO Box 6039 99780 907-291-2317
Craig Roach, prin. Fax 291-2327

Metlakatla, Prince of Wales-Outer Ketchikan, Pop. 1,313
Annette Islands SD 300/K-12
PO Box 7 99926 907-886-6332
Eugene Avey M.A., supt. Fax 886-5130
aisdk12.org/
Leask MS 100/6-8
PO Box 7 99926 907-886-6000
Taw Lindsey M.A., prin. Fax 886-5119
Metlakatla HS 100/9-12
PO Box 7 99926 907-886-6000
Taw Lindsey M.A., prin. Fax 886-5120

Minto, Yukon-Koyukuk, Pop. 200
Yukon-Koyukuk SD
Supt. — See Fairbanks
Minto S 50/PK-12
PO Box 81 99758 907-798-7212
Vicky Charlie, prin. Fax 798-7282

Mountain Village, Wade Hampton, Pop. 788
Lower Yukon SD 2,000/PK-12
PO Box 32089 99632 907-591-2411
Dr. Alex Russin, supt. Fax 591-2449
www.loweryukon.org
Beans S 200/PK-12
PO Box 32105 99632 907-591-2204
Stacey Wilson, prin. Fax 591-2819
Other Schools – See Alakanuk, Emmonak, Hooper Bay, Kotlik, Marshall, Pilot Station, Russian Mission, Scammon Bay, Sheldon Point

Naknek, Bristol Bay, Pop. 421
Bristol Bay Borough SD 200/PK-12
PO Box 169 99633 907-246-4225
Jack Walsh, supt. Fax 246-6857
www.bbbsd.net
Bristol Bay MSHS 100/7-12
PO Box 169 99633 907-246-4265
James Dube, prin. Fax 246-4447

Nanwalek, Kenai Peninsula, Pop. 231
Kenai Peninsula Borough SD
Supt. — See Soldotna
Nanwalek S 100/K-12
PO Box 8007 99603 907-281-2210
Nancy Kleine, prin. Fax 281-2211

Napakiak, Bethel, Pop. 354
Lower Kuskokwim SD
Supt. — See Bethel
Miller Memorial S 100/PK-12
PO Box 34050 99634 907-589-2420
Marlene Schmitt, prin. Fax 589-2515

Napaskiak, Bethel, Pop. 403
Lower Kuskokwim SD
Supt. — See Bethel
Qugcuun Memorial S 50/PK-12
PO Box 6199 99559 907-737-7214
Nick Straw, prin. Fax 737-7211
Williams S 200/K-12
PO Box 6089 99559 907-737-7212
Talbert Bentley, prin. Fax 737-7967

Nenana, Yukon-Koyukuk, Pop. 357
Nenana CSD 1,200/K-12
PO Box 10 99760 907-832-5464
Eric Gebhart, supt. Fax 832-5625
nenanalynx.org
Nenana City S 200/K-12
PO Box 10 99760 907-832-5464
Joe Krause, prin. Fax 832-5625

New Stuyahok, Dillingham, Pop. 495
Southwest Region SD
Supt. — See Dillingham

Chief Blunka S 100/K-12
PO Box 29 99636 907-693-3144
Brett Scott, prin. Fax 693-3163

Newtok, Bethel, Pop. 352
Lower Kuskokwim SD
Supt. — See Bethel
Ayaprun S 100/PK-12
PO Box WWT 99559 907-237-2504
Grant Kashatok, prin. Fax 237-2506

Nightmute, Bethel, Pop. 279
Lower Kuskokwim SD
Supt. — See Bethel
Nightmute S 100/PK-12
General Delivery 99690 907-647-6313
Michael Thomas, prin. Fax 647-6227

Nikiski, Kenai Peninsula, Pop. 4,284
Kenai Peninsula Borough SD
Supt. — See Soldotna
Nikiski MSHS 400/6-12
PO Box 7112 99635 907-776-9400
Dan Carstens, prin. Fax 776-3486

Nikolaevsk, Kenai Peninsula, Pop. 307
Kenai Peninsula Borough SD
Supt. — See Soldotna
Nikolaevsk S 100/K-12
PO Box 5129 99556 907-235-8972
Mike Sellers, prin. Fax 235-3617

Nikolai, Yukon-Koyukuk, Pop. 83
Iditarod Area SD
Supt. — See Mc Grath
Top of the Kuskokwim S 50/PK-12
PO Box 9190 99691 907-293-2427
Amy Cook, prin. Fax 293-2214

Ninilchik, Kenai Peninsula, Pop. 836
Kenai Peninsula Borough SD
Supt. — See Soldotna
Ninilchik S 200/K-12
15735 Sterling Hwy 99639 907-567-3301
Jeffrey Ambrosier, prin. Fax 567-3504

Noatak, Northwest Arctic, Pop. 502
Northwest Arctic Borough SD
Supt. — See Kotzebue
Napaaqtugmiut S 200/PK-12
PO Box 49 99761 907-485-2153
Stan VanAmburg, lead tchr. Fax 485-2150

Nome, Nome, Pop. 3,196
Nome SD 700/PK-12
PO Box 131 99762 907-443-2231
Steve Gast, supt. Fax 443-5144
www.nomeschools.com
Nome-Beltz JSHS 200/7-12
PO Box 131 99762 907-443-5201
Scott Handley, prin. Fax 443-3626

Nondalton, Lake and Peninsula, Pop. 130
Lake & Peninsula SD
Supt. — See King Salmon
Nondalton S 50/K-12
General Delivery 99640 907-294-2210
Ed Cox, prin. Fax 294-2265

Noorvik, Northwest Arctic, Pop. 618
Northwest Arctic Borough SD
Supt. — See Kotzebue
Aqqaluk / Noorvik S 200/PK-12
PO Box 165 99763 907-636-2178
Paul Clark, prin. Fax 636-2160

North Pole, Fairbanks North Star, Pop. 1,997
Fairbanks-North Star Borough SD
Supt. — See Fairbanks
North Pole HS 800/9-12
601 NPHS Blvd 99705 907-488-3761
Bridget Lewis, prin. Fax 488-1488
North Pole MS 600/6-8
300 E 8th Ave 99705 907-488-2271
Rich Smith, prin. Fax 488-9213

North Pole Christian S 100/PK-12
2936 Badger Rd 99705 907-488-0133
Terrance Lawrence, prin. Fax 488-8248

Northway, Southeast Fairbanks, Pop. 65
Alaska Gateway SD
Supt. — See Tok
Northway S 50/PK-12
PO Box 519 99764 907-778-2287
Frank Cook, prin. Fax 778-2221

Nuiqsut, North Slope, Pop. 391
North Slope Borough SD
Supt. — See Barrow
Nuiqsut Trapper S 100/PK-12
PO Box 89167 99789 907-480-6712
Al Strack, prin. Fax 480-6621

Nulato, Yukon-Koyukuk, Pop. 263
Yukon-Koyukuk SD
Supt. — See Fairbanks
Demoski S 50/PK-12
PO Box 65029 99765 907-898-2204
Merrill Feller, prin. Fax 898-2340

Nunapitchuk, Bethel, Pop. 487
Lower Kuskokwim SD
Supt. — See Bethel
Tobeluk Memorial S 200/K-12
PO Box 150 99641 907-527-5325
Edward Pekar, prin. Fax 527-5610

Old Harbor, Kodiak Island, Pop. 215
Kodiak Island Borough SD
Supt. — See Kodiak

Old Harbor S 50/K-12
PO Box 49 99643 907-286-2213
Phil Johnson, prin. Fax 286-2222

Ouzinkie, Kodiak Island, Pop. 146
Kodiak Island Borough SD
Supt. — See Kodiak
Ouzinkie S 50/K-12
PO Box 49 99644 907-680-2204
Phil Johnson, prin. Fax 680-2288

Palmer, Matanuska-Susitna, Pop. 5,499
Matanuska-Susitna Borough SD 16,600/PK-12
501 N Gulkana St 99645 907-746-9200
Dr. Deena Paramo, supt. Fax 746-9292
www.matsuk12.us
Beryozava S 50/K-12
501 N Gulkana St 99645 907-746-2500
Laurine Domke, prin. Fax 495-2502
Colony HS 1,200/9-12
9550 E Colony Schools Dr 99645 907-861-5500
Cydney Duffin, prin. Fax 861-5509
Colony MS 600/6-8
9250 E Colony Schools Dr 99645 907-761-1500
Mary McMahon, prin. Fax 761-1592
Mat-Su Secondary S Alt
581 Outer Springer Loop Rd 99645 907-761-7238
Jeannie Roy, prin. Fax 761-7249
Palmer HS 800/9-12
1170 W Arctic Ave 99645 907-746-8400
Reese Everett, prin. Fax 746-8481
Palmer MS 600/6-8
1159 S Chugach St 99645 907-761-4300
Thomas Lytle, prin. Fax 761-4372
Valley Pathways HS 200/9-12
PO Box 2962 99645 907-761-4650
James Wanser, prin. Fax 761-4680
Other Schools – See Big Lake, Houston, Sutton, Talkeetna, Wasilla

Pelican, Skagway-Hoonah-Angoon, Pop. 82
Pelican CSD 50/PK-12
PO Box 90 99832 907-735-2236
Martin Laster, supt. Fax 735-2263
Pelican S 50/PK-12
PO Box 90 99832 907-735-2236
Daniel Blanton, admin. Fax 735-2263

Perryville, Lake and Peninsula, Pop. 111
Lake & Peninsula SD
Supt. — See King Salmon
Perryville S 50/K-12
PO Box 103 99648 907-853-2210
Joe Ward, prin. Fax 853-2267

Petersburg, Wrangell-Petersburg, Pop. 2,720
Petersburg CSD 500/K-12
PO Box 289 99833 907-772-4271
Dr. Robert Thomason, supt. Fax 772-4719
www.pcsd.us
Mitkof MS 100/6-8
PO Box 289 99833 907-772-3860
Rick Dormer, prin. Fax 772-3617
Petersburg HS 200/9-12
PO Box 289 99833 907-772-3861
Rick Dormer, prin. Fax 772-4168

Pilot Point, Lake and Peninsula, Pop. 56
Lake & Peninsula SD
Supt. — See King Salmon
Pilot Point S 50/K-12
PO Box 467 99649 907-797-2210
Sherry McKenzie, prin. Fax 797-2267

Pilot Station, Wade Hampton, Pop. 567
Lower Yukon SD
Supt. — See Mountain Village
Pilot Station S 200/PK-12
PO Box 5090 99650 907-549-3212
Robert Shadle, prin. Fax 549-3335

Platinum, Bethel, Pop. 58
Lower Kuskokwim SD
Supt. — See Bethel
Arviq S 50/PK-12
PO Box 28 99651 907-979-8111
Linae Sanger, prin. Fax 979-8308

Point Hope, North Slope, Pop. 647
North Slope Borough SD
Supt. — See Barrow
Tikigaq S 200/PK-12
PO Box 148 99766 907-368-2662
Gregg Wilbanks, prin. Fax 368-2770

Point Lay, North Slope, Pop. 187
North Slope Borough SD
Supt. — See Barrow
Kali S 100/PK-12
PO Box 59077 99759 907-833-2311
Glenn Cole, prin. Fax 833-2315

Port Alexander, Wrangell-Petersburg, Pop. 51
Southeast Island SD
Supt. — See Thorne Bay
Port Alexander S 50/PK-12
PO Box 8170 99836 907-568-2205
Robin Griggs, lead tchr. Fax 568-2261

Port Alsworth, Lake and Peninsula, Pop. 150
Lake & Peninsula SD
Supt. — See King Salmon
Tanalian S 50/K-12
General Delivery 99653 907-781-2210
Nathan Davis, prin. Fax 781-2254

Port Graham, Kenai Peninsula, Pop. 143
Kenai Peninsula Borough SD
Supt. — See Soldotna
Port Graham S 50/K-12
PO Box 5550 99603 907-284-2210
Sheryl Hingley, prin. Fax 284-2213

Port Heiden, Lake and Peninsula, Pop. 100
Lake & Peninsula SD
Supt. — See King Salmon
Meshik S 50/K-12
General Delivery 99549 907-837-2210
Sherry McKenzie, prin. Fax 837-2265

Port Lions, Kodiak Island, Pop. 189
Kodiak Island Borough SD
Supt. — See Kodiak
Port Lions S 50/K-12
PO Box 109 99550 907-454-2237
Phil Johnson, prin. Fax 454-2377

Quinhagak, Bethel, Pop. 642
Lower Kuskokwim SD
Supt. — See Bethel
Kuinerrarmiut Elitnaurviat S 200/PK-12
General Delivery 99655 907-556-8628
Eric Pederson, prin. Fax 556-8228

Ruby, Yukon-Koyukuk, Pop. 156
Yukon-Koyukuk SD
Supt. — See Fairbanks
Kangas S 50/PK-12
PO Box 68110 99768 907-468-4465
Anne Titus, prin. Fax 468-4444

Russian Mission, Wade Hampton, Pop. 309
Lower Yukon SD
Supt. — See Mountain Village
Russian Mission S 100/PK-12
PO Box 90 99657 907-584-5615
Jason Moen, prin. Fax 584-5412

Saint Marys, Wade Hampton, Pop. 483
Saint Mary's SD 200/PK-12
PO Box 9 99658 907-438-2411
David Herbert, supt. Fax 438-2735
www.smcsd.us
Saint Mary's S 200/PK-12
PO Box 9 99658 907-438-2411
Dewayne Bahnsen, prin. Fax 438-2735

Saint Michael, Nome, Pop. 392
Bering Strait SD
Supt. — See Unalakleet
Andrews S 200/PK-12
100 Baker St 99659 907-923-3041
Carolyn Heflin, prin. Fax 923-3031

Saint Paul Island, Aleutians West, Pop. 459
Pribilof SD 100/PK-12
PO Box 905 99660 907-546-3331
Connie A. Newman M.Ed., supt. Fax 546-2327
psd-k12.org
St. Paul S 100/PK-12
PO Box 905 99660 907-546-2221
John Holcomb M.Ed., prin. Fax 546-2356

Sand Point, Aleutians East, Pop. 929
Aleutian East Borough SD 300/PK-12
PO Box 429 99661 907-383-5222
Timothy Stathis, supt. Fax 383-3496
www.aebsd.org
Sand Point S 100/PK-12
PO Box 269 99661 907-383-2393
Ralph Lindquist, prin. Fax 383-3833
Other Schools – See Akutan, Cold Bay, False Pass, King Cove

Savoonga, Nome, Pop. 668
Bering Strait SD
Supt. — See Unalakleet
Kingeekuk Memorial S 200/K-12
PO Box 200 99769 907-984-6811
Bobby Bolen, prin. Fax 984-6413

Scammon Bay, Wade Hampton, Pop. 473
Lower Yukon SD
Supt. — See Mountain Village
Scammon Bay S 200/PK-12
General Delivery 99662 907-558-5312
Lance Morton, prin. Fax 558-5320

Selawik, Northwest Arctic, Pop. 742
Northwest Arctic Borough SD
Supt. — See Kotzebue
Davis-Ramoth S 300/PK-12
PO Box 29 99770 907-484-2142
Platonida Kashatok, prin. Fax 484-2127

Seldovia, Kenai Peninsula, Pop. 230
Kenai Peninsula Borough SD
Supt. — See Soldotna
English S 100/K-12
PO Box 171 99663 907-234-7616
Sheryl Hingley, prin. Fax 234-7884

Seward, Kenai Peninsula, Pop. 2,478
AVTEC SD
PO Box 889 99664 907-224-6150
Fred Esposito, dir. Fax 224-4401
www.avtec.edu
AVTEC-Alaska's Institute of Technology Vo/Tech
PO Box 889 99664 907-224-6150
Fred Esposito, dir. Fax 224-4401
Other Schools – See Anchorage

Kenai Peninsula Borough SD
Supt. — See Soldotna
Seward HS 200/9-12
PO Box 1049 99664 907-224-3351
Trevan Walker, prin. Fax 224-3306
Seward MS 100/7-8
PO Box 1149 99664 907-224-9000
Jason Bickling, prin. Fax 224-9001

Alaska Vocational Technical School Post-Sec.
PO Box 889 99664 907-224-3322

Shageluk, Yukon-Koyukuk, Pop. 78
Iditarod Area SD
Supt. — See Mc Grath
Innoko River S 50/PK-12
PO Box 53 99665 907-473-8233
Joy Hamilton, prin. Fax 473-8268

Shaktoolik, Nome, Pop. 250
Bering Strait SD
Supt. — See Unalakleet
Shaktoolik S 100/PK-12
PO Box 40 99771 907-955-3021
Larry Cobb, prin. Fax 955-3031

Sheldon Point, Wade Hampton, Pop. 121
Lower Yukon SD
Supt. — See Mountain Village
Sheldon Point S 100/PK-12
PO Box 32, Nunam Iqua AK 99666 907-498-4112
Russell Clark, prin. Fax 498-4111

Shishmaref, Nome, Pop. 556
Bering Strait SD
Supt. — See Unalakleet
Shishmaref S 200/PK-12
1 Seaview Ln 99772 907-649-3021
Steve Sammons, prin. Fax 649-3031

Shungnak, Northwest Arctic, Pop. 262
Northwest Arctic Borough SD
Supt. — See Kotzebue
Shungnak S 100/PK-12
PO Box 79 99773 907-437-2151
Roger Franklin, prin. Fax 437-2177

Sitka, Sitka, Pop. 8,072
Mt. Edgecumbe HSD 400/9-12
1330 Seward Ave 99835 907-966-3200
Randy Hawk, supt. Fax 966-2442
www.mehs.us
Mt. Edgecumbe HS 400/9-12
1330 Seward Ave 99835 907-966-3200
Bernie Gurule, prin. Fax 966-2442

Sitka SD 1,400/PK-12
300 Kostrometinoff St 99835 907-747-8622
Steve Bradshaw, supt. Fax 966-1260
www.sitkaschools.org
Blatchley MS 300/6-8
601 Halibut Point Rd 99835 907-747-8672
Joe Robidou, prin. Fax 966-1460
Pacific HS 50/Alt
509 Lincoln St 99835 907-747-0525
Phil Burdick, prin. Fax 747-7310
Sitka HS 400/9-12
1000 Lake St 99835 907-747-3263
PJ Ford-Slack, prin. Fax 747-3229

Skagway, Skagway-Hoonah-Angoon, Pop. 884
Skagway SD 100/K-12
PO Box 497 99840 907-983-2960
Dr. Jeff Thielbar, supt. Fax 983-2964
www.skagwayschool.org
Skagway S 100/K-12
PO Box 497 99840 907-983-2960
Dr. Jeff Thielbar, prin. Fax 983-2964

Slana, Valdez-Cordova, Pop. 142
Copper River SD
Supt. — See Glennallen
Slana S 50/1-12
PO Box 870 99586 907-822-5868
Tammy Van Wyhe, prin. Fax 822-3850

Sleetmute, Bethel, Pop. 86
Kuspuk SD
Supt. — See Aniak
Egnaty Sr. S 50/K-12
PO Box 69 99668 907-449-4216
Susan Hubbard, prin. Fax 449-4217

Soldotna, Kenai Peninsula, Pop. 3,894
Kenai Peninsula Borough SD 9,200/PK-12
148 N Binkley St 99669 907-714-8888
Dr. Steve Atwater, supt. Fax 262-9645
www.kpbsd.k12.ak.us
Connections S 900/Alt
143 E Park Ave 99669 907-714-8880
Lee Young, prin. Fax 262-2859
River City Academy 100/7-12
46188 Sterling Hwy 99669 907-714-8945
Dawn Edwards-Smith, prin. Fax 714-8946
Skyview HS 300/9-12
46188 Sterling Hwy 99669 907-260-2300
Randy Neill, prin. Fax 262-6555
Soldotna HS 500/9-12
425 W Marydale Ave 99669 907-260-7000
Todd Syverson, prin. Fax 262-4288
Soldotna MS 400/7-8
426 W Redoubt Ave 99669 907-260-2500
Sarge Truesdell, prin. Fax 262-7036
Other Schools – See Cooper Landing, Fritz Creek, Homer, Hope, Kenai, Nanwalek, Nikiski, Nikolaevsk, Ninilchik, Port Graham, Seldovia, Seward, Tyonek

---

Alaska Christian College Post-Sec.
35109 Royal Pl 99669 907-260-7422
Cook Inlet Academy 200/PK-12
45872 Kalifornsky Beach Rd 99669 907-262-5101
Mary Rowley, admin. Fax 262-1541

Stebbins, Nome, Pop. 556
Bering Strait SD
Supt. — See Unalakleet
Tukurngailnguq S 200/K-12
General Delivery 99671 907-934-3041
Gerald Pickner, prin. Fax 934-3031

Sterling, Kenai Peninsula, Pop. 5,392

Academy of Higher Learning 50/K-12
32930 Fair Game Ave 99672 907-260-7741
Catherine Gibson, prin. Fax 260-7741

Stevens Village, Yukon-Koyukuk, Pop. 73
Yukon Flats SD
Supt. — See Fort Yukon
Stevens Village S 50/PK-12
355 Bridge St 99774 907-478-7116
Joe Waarvik, prin. Fax 478-7893

Stony River, Bethel, Pop. 49
Kuspuk SD
Supt. — See Aniak
Michael S 50/K-12
General Delivery 99557 907-537-3226
Susan Hubbard, prin. Fax 537-3237

Sutton, Matanuska-Susitna, Pop. 308
Matanuska-Susitna Borough SD
Supt. — See Palmer
Glacier View S 50/K-12
65975 S Wolverine Cir 99674 907-861-5650
Wendy Taylor, prin. Fax 861-5680

Takotna, Yukon-Koyukuk, Pop. 38
Iditarod Area SD
Supt. — See Mc Grath
Takotna S 50/PK-12
PO Box 90 99675 907-298-2115
Jolene Kinsland, prin. Fax 298-2316

Talkeetna, Matanuska-Susitna, Pop. 845
Matanuska-Susitna Borough SD
Supt. — See Palmer
Susitna Valley JSHS 200/7-12
HC 89 Box 8580 99676 907-733-9300
Jason Mabry, prin. Fax 733-9380

Tanana, Yukon-Koyukuk, Pop. 238
Tanana CSD 50/K-12
PO Box 89 99777 907-366-7203
M. Therese Ashton, supt. Fax 366-7201
home.tananawolves.com/
Sommer S 50/K-12
PO Box 89 99777 907-366-7203
M. Therese Ashton, supt. Fax 366-7201

Tatitlek, Valdez-Cordova, Pop. 84
Chugach SD
Supt. — See Anchorage
Tatitlek Community S 50/K-12
PO Box 167 99677 907-325-2252
Nichole Palmer, prin. Fax 325-2299

Teller, Nome, Pop. 229
Bering Strait SD
Supt. — See Unalakleet
Isabell S 100/PK-12
100 Airport Ave 99778 907-642-3041
Susette Carroll, prin. Fax 642-3031

Tenakee Springs, Skagway-Hoonah-Angoon, Pop. 127
Chatham SD
Supt. — See Angoon
Tenakee Springs S 50/K-12
PO Box 62 99841 907-736-2204
Anne Connelly, lead tchr. Fax 736-2204

Thorne Bay, Prince of Wales-Outer Ketchikan, Pop. 450
Southeast Island SD 200/PK-12
PO Box 19569 99919 907-828-8254
Lauren Burch, supt. Fax 828-8257
www.sisd.org/
Thorne Bay S 100/K-12
PO Box 19005 99919 907-828-3921
Nick Higson, prin. Fax 828-3901
Other Schools – See Coffman Cove, Craig, Kasaan, Ketchikan, Port Alexander

Togiak, Dillingham, Pop. 691
Southwest Region SD
Supt. — See Dillingham
Togiak S 200/K-12
PO Box 50 99678 907-493-5829
Sam Gosuk, prin. Fax 493-5933

Tok, Southeast Fairbanks, Pop. 1,157
Alaska Gateway SD 300/PK-12
PO Box 226 99780 907-883-5151
Todd Poage, admin. Fax 883-5154
www.agsd.us/
Tetlin S 50/PK-12
PO Box 277 99780 907-324-2104
Ed Becker, prin. Fax 324-2120
Tok S 200/K-12
PO Box 249 99780 907-883-5161
Jason Roslansky, prin. Fax 883-5165
Other Schools – See Dot Lake, Eagle, Mentasta Lake, Northway

Toksook Bay, Bethel, Pop. 578
Lower Kuskokwim SD
Supt. — See Bethel
Nelson Island S 200/PK-12
General Delivery 99637 907-427-7815
Daryl Daugaard, prin. Fax 427-7612

Tuluksak, Bethel, Pop. 370
Yupiit SD
Supt. — See Akiachak
Tuluksak S 100/PK-12
PO Box 115 99679 907-695-5600
Gene Burke, prin. Fax 695-5645

Tuntutuliak, Bethel, Pop. 403
Lower Kuskokwim SD
Supt. — See Bethel
Angapak Memorial S 100/PK-12
General Delivery 99680 907-256-2415
Michael Silverman, prin. Fax 256-2527

Tununak, Bethel, Pop. 322
Lower Kuskokwim SD
Supt. — See Bethel
Albert Memorial S 100/K-12
PO Box 49 99681 907-652-6827
Gary Stillwell, prin. Fax 652-6028

Tyonek, Kenai Peninsula, Pop. 165
Kenai Peninsula Borough SD
Supt. — See Soldotna
Tebughna S 50/K-12
PO Box 82010 99682 907-583-2291
Marilyn Johnson, prin. Fax 583-2692

Unalakleet, Nome, Pop. 644
Bering Strait SD 1,800/PK-12
PO Box 225 99684 907-624-3611
Rob Picou, supt. Fax 624-3099
www.bssd.org
Unalakleet S 200/PK-12
PO Box 130 99684 907-624-3444
Jay Thomas, prin. Fax 624-3388
Other Schools – See Brevig Mission, Diomede, Elim, Gambell, Golovin, Koyuk, Saint Michael, Savoonga, Shaktoolik, Shishmaref, Stebbins, Teller, Wales, White Mountain

Unalaska, Aleutians West, Pop. 4,083
Unalaska CSD 400/PK-12
PO Box 570 99685 907-581-3151
John Conwell, supt. Fax 581-3152
www.ucsd.net
Unalaska City HS 200/7-12
PO Box 570 99685 907-581-1222
Jim Wilson, prin. Fax 581-2428

Valdez, Valdez-Cordova, Pop. 3,714
Valdez CSD 600/PK-12
PO Box 398 99686 907-835-4357
Dr. Jacob Jensen, supt. Fax 835-4964
www.valdezcityschools.org/
Gilson MS 100/6-8
PO Box 398 99686 907-835-2244
Rodney Morrison, prin. Fax 835-2540
Valdez HS 200/9-12
PO Box 398 99686 907-835-4767
Dr. Elizabeth Balcerek, prin. Fax 835-2596

Prince William Sound Community College Post-Sec.
PO Box 97 99686 907-834-1600

Venetie, Yukon-Koyukuk, Pop. 159
Yukon Flats SD
Supt. — See Fort Yukon
Fredson S 100/PK-12
PO Box 39 99781 907-849-8415
Dan Barnett, prin. Fax 849-8630

Wainwright, North Slope, Pop. 547
North Slope Borough SD
Supt. — See Barrow
Alak S 100/PK-12
PO Box 10 99782 907-763-2541
Herman Gerving, prin. Fax 763-2565

Wales, Nome, Pop. 132
Bering Strait SD
Supt. — See Unalakleet
Wales S 50/PK-12
PO Box 490 99783 907-664-3021
Roxie Quick, prin. Fax 664-3031

Wasilla, Matanuska-Susitna, Pop. 7,351
Matanuska-Susitna Borough SD
Supt. — See Palmer
Burchell HS 300/Alt
1775 W Parks Hwy 99654 907-864-2600
Adam Mokelke, prin. Fax 864-2680
Mat-Su Career and Technical HS Vo/Tech
2472 N Seward Meridian Pkwy 99654 907-352-0400
Mark Okeson, prin. Fax 352-0480
Mat-Su Day S 100/Alt
3901 E Bogard Rd 99654 907-864-2040
Wolfgang Winter, prin. Fax 864-2083
Teeland MS 700/6-8
2788 N Seward Meridian Pkwy 99654 907-352-7500
Katherine Ellsworth, prin. Fax 352-7585
Wasilla HS 1,200/9-12
701 E Bogard Rd 99654 907-352-8200
Amy Spargo, prin. Fax 352-8280
Wasilla MS 900/6-8
650 E Bogard Rd 99654 907-352-5300
Leigh Stanton, prin. Fax 352-5380

Charter College Post-Sec.
721 W Parks Hwy 99654 907-352-1000
Cornerstone Christian S 50/K-12
4001 E Darrington Village 99654 907-357-9798
Dr. Kevin Newman, admin. Fax 357-9799
Wasilla Lake Christian S 200/PK-12
2001 Palmer Wasilla Hwy 99654 907-373-6439
Becky Stringer, admin. Fax 373-6438

White Mountain, Nome, Pop. 178
Bering Strait SD
Supt. — See Unalakleet
White Mountain S 100/PK-12
PO Box 84069 99784 907-638-3041
Andy Haviland, prin. Fax 638-3031

Whittier, Valdez-Cordova, Pop. 187
Chugach SD
Supt. — See Anchorage
Whittier Community S 50/PK-12
PO Box 638 99693 907-472-2575
Stephanie Burgoon, prin. Fax 472-2409

Wrangell, Wrangell-Petersburg, Pop. 2,153
Wrangell SD 300/K-12
PO Box 2319 99929 907-874-2347
Dr. Richard Rhodes, supt. Fax 874-3137
www.wrangellschools.org
Stikine MS 100/6-8
PO Box 1935 99929 907-874-3393
Monty Buness, prin. Fax 874-3149
Wrangell HS 100/9-12
PO Box 651 99929 907-874-3395
Monty Buness, prin. Fax 874-3143

Yakutat, Yakutat, Pop. 549
Yakutat SD 100/PK-12
PO Box 429 99689 907-784-3317
Rod Schug, supt. Fax 784-3446
www.yakutatschools.org
Yakutat S 100/PK-12
PO Box 429 99689 907-784-3317
Rod Schug, prin. Fax 784-3446

ARIZONA

ARIZONA DEPARTMENT OF EDUCATION
1535 W Jefferson St, Phoenix 85007-3280
Telephone 602-542-5393
Fax 602-542-5440
Website http://www.azed.gov

Superintendent of Public Instruction John Huppenthal

ARIZONA BOARD OF EDUCATION
1535 W Jefferson St, Phoenix 85007-3280

Executive Director Vince Yanez

COUNTY SUPERINTENDENTS OF SCHOOLS

Apache County Office of Education
R. Barry Williams, supt. 928-337-7539
PO Box 548, Saint Johns 85936 Fax 337-2033
www.acsbc.net/superintendent/

Cochise County Office of Education
Trudy Berry, supt. 520-432-8950
PO Box 208, Bisbee 85603 Fax 432-7136
www.cochise.az.gov/cochise_schools.aspx?id=462

Coconino County Office of Education
Robert Kelty, supt. 928-679-8070
110 E Cherry Ave, Flagstaff 86001 Fax 679-8077
www.coconino.az.gov/schools.aspx

Gila County Office of Education
Dr. Linda O'Dell, supt. 928-425-3231
1400 E Ash St, Globe 85501
www.gilacountyschools.org

Graham County Office of Education
Donna McGaughey, supt. 928-428-2880
921 W Thatcher Blvd Fax 428-8824
Safford 85546
www.graham.az.gov

Greenlee County Office of Education
Tom Powers, supt. 928-865-2822
PO Box 1595, Clifton 85533 Fax 865-4417
www.co.greenlee.az.us

Lapaz County Office of Education
Janice Shelton, supt. 928-669-6183
1112 S Joshua Ave Ste 205 Fax 669-4406
Parker 85344
www.lapazschools.org

Maricopa County Office of Education
Dr. Don Covey, supt. 602-506-3866
4041 N Central Ave, Phoenix 85012 Fax 506-3753
www.maricopa.gov/Schools/

Mohave County Office of Education
Michael File, supt. 928-753-0747
PO Box 7000, Kingman 86402 Fax 718-4958
www.mcss.k12.az.us/

Navajo County Office of Education
Linda Morrow, supt. 928-524-4204
PO Box 668, Holbrook 86025 Fax 524-4209
www.navajocountyaz.gov/schools/

Pima County Office of Education
Dr. Linda Arzoumanian, supt. 520-740-8451
130 W Congress St Fl 4 Fax 623-9308
Tucson 85701
www.schools.pima.gov/

Pinal County Office of Education
Jill Broussard, supt. 520-866-6565
PO Box 769, Florence Fax 866-6973
www.pinalcso.org/

Santa Cruz County Office of Education
Alfredo Velasquez, supt. 520-375-7940
2150 N Congress Dr Fax 375-7958
Nogales 85621
www.co.santa-cruz.az.us/schools/index.html

Yavapai County Office of Education
Tim Carter, supt. 928-771-3326
1015 Fair St Rm 324 Fax 771-3329
Prescott 86305
www.yavapai.us/

Yuma County Office of Education
Thomas Tyree, supt. 928-373-1006
210 S 1st Ave, Yuma 85364 Fax 329-2008
www.co.yuma.az.us/

PUBLIC, PRIVATE AND CATHOLIC SECONDARY SCHOOLS

Ajo, Pima, Pop. 3,253
Ajo USD 15 400/PK-12
PO Box 68 85321 520-387-5618
Robert Dooley Ed.D., supt. Fax 387-6545
ajoschools.org/
Ajo HS 100/9-12
PO Box 68 85321 520-387-7602
Brian MacKenzie, prin. Fax 387-7603

Anthem, Maricopa, Pop. 21,203
Deer Valley USD 97
Supt. — See Phoenix
Boulder Creek HS 2,300/9-12
40404 N Gavilan Peak Pkwy 85086 623-445-8600
Lauren Sheahan, prin. Fax 445-8680

Apache Junction, Pinal, Pop. 35,261
Apache Junction USD 43 5,000/K-12
1575 W Southern Ave, 480-982-1110
Dr. Chad Wilson, supt. Fax 982-6474
www.ajusd.org
Apache Junction HS 1,600/9-12
2525 S Ironwood Dr, 480-982-1110
Larry LaPrise, prin. Fax 982-3787
Cactus Canyon JHS 900/7-8
801 W Southern Ave, 480-982-1110
Courtney Castelhano, prin. Fax 983-4913

Central Arizona College Post-Sec.
805 S Idaho Rd, 480-677-7700

Ash Fork, Yavapai, Pop. 392
Ash Fork JUSD 31 300/K-12
PO Box 247 86320 928-637-2561
Seth Staples, admin. Fax 637-2623
www.afjusd.org/
Ash Fork HS 100/9-12
PO Box 247 86320 928-637-2561
Seth Staples, prin. Fax 637-2623
Ash Fork MS 100/6-8
PO Box 247 86320 928-637-2561
Seth Staples, prin. Fax 637-2623

Avondale, Maricopa, Pop. 74,219
Agua Fria UNHSD 216 6,700/9-12
1481 N Eliseo Felix Jr Way 85323 623-932-7000
Dr. Dennis Runyan, supt. Fax 932-2796
www.aguafria.org
Agua Fria HS 1,600/9-12
530 E Riley Dr 85323 623-932-7300
Dr. Matthew Bentz, prin. Fax 932-0650
Other Schools – See Buckeye, Goodyear

Tolleson UNHSD 214
Supt. — See Tolleson
La Joya Community HS 1,800/9-12
11650 W Whyman Ave 85323 623-478-4400
Brandi Haskins, prin. Fax 478-7225
Westview HS 2,500/9-12
10850 W Garden Lakes Pkwy, 623-478-4600
Dr. Michele Wilson, prin. Fax 478-4669

Estrella Mountain Community College Post-Sec.
3000 N Dysart Rd, 623-935-8000
Maricopa Beauty College Post-Sec.
515 W Western Ave 85323 623-932-4414
Universal Technical Institute Post-Sec.
10695 W Pierce St 85323 623-245-4600

Bagdad, Yavapai, Pop. 1,847
Bagdad USD 20 300/PK-12
PO Box 427 86321 928-633-4101
Jeffry St. Clair, supt. Fax 633-4345
bagdadschools.org
Bagdad HS 100/9-12
PO Box 427 86321 928-633-2201
Tom Finnerty, prin. Fax 633-4135

Beaver Dam, Mohave, Pop. 1,928
Littlefield USD 9 500/PK-12
3490 E Rio Virgin Rd 86432 928-347-5486
Michael Robison, supt. Fax 347-5967
www.lusd9.com/
Beaver Dam HS 100/9-12
3475 E Rio Virgin Rd 86432 928-347-5252
Mark Coleman, prin. Fax 347-5151
Beaver Dam MS 100/6-8
3436 E Rio Virgin Rd 86432 928-347-5796
Mark Coleman, prin. Fax 347 5795

Benson, Cochise, Pop. 5,014
Benson USD 9 1,200/PK-12
360 S Patagonia St 85602 520-720-6731
David Woodall, supt. Fax 720-6701
www.bensonsd.k12.az.us/
Benson HS 400/9-12
360 S Patagonia St 85602 520-720-6841
Ben Rodriguez, prin. Fax 720-6710
Benson MS 300/5-8
360 S Patagonia St 85602 520-720-6801
Shad Housley, prin. Fax 720-6709

Bisbee, Cochise, Pop. 5,464
Bisbee USD 2 900/PK-12
100 Old Douglas Rd 85603 520-432-5381
James Phillips, supt. Fax 432-7622
www.busd.k12.az.us
Bisbee HS 400/9-12
100 Old Douglas Rd 85603 520-432-5714
Lisa Holland, prin. Fax 432-6105

Lowell JHS 200/5-8
100 Old Douglas Rd 85603 520-432-5391
Mary Franco, prin. Fax 432-6106

Blue, Greenlee
Blue ESD 22 50/PK-12
PO Box 80 85922 928-339-4346
Sally Hulsey, hdmstr. Fax 339-4116
Blue S 50/PK-12
PO Box 80 85922 928-339-4346
Sally Hulsey, prin. Fax 339-4116

Bowie, Cochise, Pop. 442
Bowie USD 14 100/K-12
PO Box 157 85605 520-847-2545
Roger Studley, supt. Fax 847-2546
www.bowieschools.org
Bowie HS 50/9-12
PO Box 157 85605 520-847-2545
Roger Studley, supt. Fax 847-2546

Buckeye, Maricopa, Pop. 49,727
Agua Fria UNHSD 216
Supt. — See Avondale
Verrado HS 1,400/9-12
20050 W Indian School Rd, 623-932-7400
Thomas Huffman, prin. Fax 853-0369

Buckeye ESD 33 4,400/PK-8
25555 W Durango St 85326 623-925-3400
Allen Steen, supt. Fax 386-6063
besd.k12.az.us
Buckeye MS 300/5-8
25555 W Durango St 85326 623-386-4487
Lorrese Roer, prin. Fax 386-7901

Buckeye UNHSD 201 3,800/9-12
1000 E Narramore Ave 85326 623-386-9700
Fax 386-9705
www.buhsd.org
Buckeye Academy 100/Alt
402 E Narramore Ave 85326 623-386-1072
Bernie Garcia, prin. Fax 386-1340
Buckeye Union HS 1,200/9-12
1000 E Narramore Ave 85326 623-386-4423
Tawn Argeris, prin. Fax 386-9711
Youngker HS 1,400/9-12
3000 S Apache Rd 85326 623-474-0100
Randy Stillman, prin. Fax 474-0141
Other Schools – See Goodyear

Litchfield ESD 79
Supt. — See Litchfield Park
Verrado MS 1,000/6-8
20880 W Main St, 623-547-1300
Kim Franz, prin. Fax 853-2358

Bullhead City, Mohave, Pop. 38,810
Bullhead City ESD 15 3,000/PK-8
1004 Hancock Rd 86442 928-758-3961
Benje Hookstra, supt. Fax 758-4996
www.bullheadschools.com
Bullhead City JHS 500/6-8
1062 Hancock Rd 86442 928-758-3921
Buffy Moreno, prin. Fax 758-7428
Fox Creek JHS 600/6-8
3101 Desert Sky Blvd 86442 928-704-2500
Jon Jones, prin. Fax 704-2504

Colorado River UNHSD 2
Supt. — See Fort Mohave
Mohave HS 1,500/9-12
2251 Highway 95 86442 928-758-3916
Steve Lawrence, prin. Fax 758-7145

Camp Verde, Yavapai, Pop. 10,552
Camp Verde USD 28 1,400/PK-12
410 Camp Lincoln Rd 86322 928-567-8000
Dr. Amber Lee, admin. Fax 567-8004
www.campverdeschools.org
Camp Verde HS 400/9-12
1326 N Montezuma Castle Hwy 86322 928-567-8033
Robert Weir, prin. Fax 567-8045
Camp Verde MS 300/6-8
370 Camp Lincoln Rd 86322 928-567-8014
Danny Howe, prin. Fax 567-8022

Casa Grande, Pinal, Pop. 47,575
Casa Grande ESD 4 7,500/PK-8
220 W Kortsen Rd, 520-836-2111
Frank Davidson, supt.
www.cgelem.k12.az.us
Cactus MS 900/6-8
1220 E Kortsen Rd, 520-421-3330
Deanna Smith-Stout, prin. Fax 421-7425
Casa Grande MS 700/6-8
300 W McMurray Blvd, 520-836-7310
Sylvia Trotter, prin. Fax 836-2399
Villago MS 800/6-8
574 E Lakeside Pkwy, 520-423-0176
Jeffrey Lavender, prin. Fax 423-0177

Casa Grande UNHSD 82 3,700/9-12
1362 N Casa Grande Ave, 520-316-3360
Dr. Shannon Goodsell, supt. Fax 316-3352
www.cguhsd.org
Casa Grande Union HS 1,900/9-12
2730 N Trekell Rd, 520-836-8500
Christian Paulson, prin. Fax 316-3353
Desert Winds HS 300/Alt
1362 N Casa Grande Ave, 520-316-3361
Crystal Danzy, prin. Fax 421-1536
Vista Grande HS 1,200/9-12
1556 N Arizola Rd, 520-876-9400
Tim Hamilton, prin. Fax 876-5348

Chandler, Maricopa, Pop. 229,946
Chandler USD 80 38,100/PK-12
1525 W Frye Rd 85224 480-812-7000
Dr. Camille Casteel, supt. Fax 224-9128
ww2.chandler.k12.az.us/
Andersen JHS 1,000/7-8
1255 N Dobson Rd 85224 480-883-5300
Jim Anderson, prin. Fax 883-5320
Arizona College Prep S - Erie 300/7-12
1150 W Erie St 85224 480-424-8000
Robert Bickes, prin. Fax 224-9268
Arizona College Prep S - Oakland 300/6-8
191 W Oakland St 85225 480-224-3930
Sandy Lundberg, prin. Fax 224-3940
Basha HS 2,300/9-12
5990 S Val Vista Dr 85249 480-224-2100
Ken James, prin. Fax 224-2120
Bogle JHS 1,100/7-8
1600 W Queen Creek Rd 85248 480-883-5500
Susie Avey, prin. Fax 883-5520
Chandler HS 3,200/9-12
350 N Arizona Ave 85225 480-812-7700
Terry Williams, prin. Fax 812-7720
Hamilton HS 3,400/9-12
3700 S Arizona Ave 85248 480-883-5000
Dr. Fred DePrez, prin. Fax 883-5020
Hill Learning Academy 200/Alt
290 S Cooper Rd 85225 480-812-7150
Saunders Montague, prin. Fax 224-9066
Santan JHS 1,200/7-8
1550 E Chandler Heights Rd 85249 480-883-4600
Barbara Kowalinski, prin. Fax 883-4620
Willis JHS 900/7-8
401 S McQueen Rd 85225 480-883-5700
Jeff Delp, prin. Fax 883-5720
Other Schools – See Gilbert, Queen Creek

Kyrene ESD 28
Supt. — See Tempe
Kyrene Aprende MS 1,100/6-8
777 N Desert Breeze Blvd E 85226 480-541-6200
Jim Verrill, prin. Fax 541-6210
Kyrene Del Pueblo MS 1,000/6-8
360 S Twelve Oaks Blvd 85226 480-541-6800
Sheryl Houston, prin. Fax 541-6810

Chandler-Gilbert Community College Post-Sec.
2626 E Pecos Rd 85225 480-732-7000
Empire Beauty School Post-Sec.
2978 N Alma School Rd Ste 3 85224 480-855-7901
Golf Academy of America Post-Sec.
2031 N Arizona Ave Ste 2 85225 800-342-7342
International Baptist College Post-Sec.
2211 W Germann Rd, 480-245-7903
Quantum Helicopters Post-Sec.
2401 S Heliport Way, 480-814-8118
Seton Catholic Preparatory HS 600/9-12
1150 N Dobson Rd 85224 480-963-1900
Patricia Collins, prin. Fax 963-1974
Tri-City Christian Academy 300/PK-12
2211 W Germann Rd, 480-245-7902
Rev. Thad Todd, admin. Fax 245-7908
Valley Christian HS 400/9-12
6900 W Galveston St 85226 480-705-8888
Mark Bistricky, prin. Fax 705-8889

Chinle, Apache, Pop. 4,452
Chinle USD 24 2,900/PK-12
PO Box 587 86503 928-674-9600
Dr. Jesus de la Garza, supt. Fax 674-9608
www.chinleusd.k12.az.us/
Chinle HS 1,100/9-12
PO Box 587 86503 928-674-9407
Douglas Clauschee, prin. Fax 674-9432
Chinle JHS 400/7-8
PO Box 587 86503 928-674-9400
Tammy Smith, prin. Fax 674-9499

Chino Valley, Yavapai, Pop. 10,639
Chino Valley USD 51 2,400/PK-12
PO Box 225 86323 928-636-2458
Duane Howard, supt. Fax 636-1434
www.cvsd.k12.az.us
Chino Valley HS 800/9-12
PO Box 225 86323 928-636-2298
Grant Turley, prin. Fax 636-6219
Heritage MS 600/6-8
PO Box 225 86323 928-636-4464
Scott Muir, prin. Fax 636-6214

Clifton, Greenlee, Pop. 3,280
Clifton USD 3 100/PK-12
PO Box 1567 85533 928-865-2752
Jack Day, supt. Fax 865-2792
Clifton HS 50/9-12
PO Box 1567 85533 928-865-3262
Jack Day, prin. Fax 865-2792

Colorado City, Mohave, Pop. 4,817
Colorado City USD 14 400/PK-12
PO Box 309 86021 928-875-9000
Carol Timpson, supt. Fax 875-8066
www.elcap.us
El Capitan S 400/PK-12
PO Box 309 86021 928-875-9000
Carol Timpson, prin. Fax 875-8068

Coolidge, Pinal, Pop. 11,531
Coolidge USD 21 4,100/PK-12
450 N Arizona Blvd, 520-723-2040
Patricia Jimenez, admin. Fax 723-2442
www.coolidgeschools.org/
Coolidge HS 800/9-12
800 W Northern Ave, 520-723-2305
Steve Adolph, prin. Fax 723-2306
Hohokam MS 600/6-8
800 N 9th St, 520-723-2202
Tom Cox, prin. Fax 723-2203
Other Schools – See San Tan Valley

Central Arizona College Post-Sec.
8470 N Overfield Rd, 520-494-5444

Cornville, Yavapai, Pop. 3,217

Oak Creek Ranch S 100/7-12
1165 E Willow Point Rd 86325 928-634-5571
David Wick, hdmstr. Fax 634-4915

Corona, Pima, Pop. 5,546
Vail USD 20
Supt. — See Vail
Corona Foothills MS 400/6-8
16705 S Houghton Rd 85641 520-879-3500
Margaret Steuer, prin. Fax 879-3501

Cottonwood, Yavapai, Pop. 11,102
Cottonwood-Oak Creek ESD 6 1,800/PK-8
1 N Willard St 86326 928-634-2288
Barbara U'Ren, supt. Fax 634-2309
www.cocsd.k12.az.us
Cottonwood MS 700/6-8
1 N Willard St 86326 928-634-2231
Denise Kennedy, prin. Fax 634-2874

Mingus UNHSD 4 1,300/9-12
1801 E Fir St 86326 928-634-8901
Paul Tighe, supt. Fax 649-4399
www.mingusunion.com
Mingus Union HS 1,300/9-12
1801 E Fir St 86326 928-634-7531
Jennifer Chilton, prin. Fax 639-4236

Dewey, Yavapai, Pop. 3,640
Humboldt USD 22
Supt. — See Prescott Valley
Bradshaw Mountain MS 300/7-8
12255 E Turquoise Cir 86327 928-759-4900
Jessica Bennett, prin. Fax 759-4920

Dolan Springs, Mohave, Pop. 1,994
Kingman USD 20
Supt. — See Kingman
Mt. Tipton S 300/K-12
PO Box 248 86441 928-767-3350
Starr Jensen, prin. Fax 767-4330

Douglas, Cochise, Pop. 17,315
Douglas USD 27 4,100/PK-12
PO Box 1237 85608 520-364-2447
Sheila Rogers, supt. Fax 224-2470
www.dusd.k12.az.us
Borane MS 300/6-8
PO Box 1237 85608 520-364-2461
Ana Samaniego, prin. Fax 364-5537
Douglas HS 1,400/9-12
PO Box 1237 85608 520-364-3462
Ralph Schneider, prin. Fax 805-4171
Huber JHS 600/6-8
PO Box 1237 85608 520-364-2840
Andrea Overman, prin. Fax 364-2421

Cochise College Post-Sec.
4190 W Highway 80 85607 800-966-7943

Duncan, Greenlee, Pop. 683
Duncan USD 2 400/K-12
PO Box 710 85534 928-359-2472
Eldon Merrell, supt. Fax 359-2807
duncanschools.org
Duncan ES 200/3-8
PO Box 710 85534 928-359-2471
Kent Baldwin, prin. Fax 359-1105
Duncan HS 100/9-12
PO Box 710 85534 928-359-2474
Toni Corona, dean Fax 359-1141

Eagar, Apache, Pop. 4,784
Round Valley USD 10
Supt. — See Springerville
Round Valley HS 400/9-12
550 N Butler St 85925 928-333-6800
John Allen, prin. Fax 333-6819
Round Valley MS 300/6-8
126 W 2nd St 85925 928-333-6700
Darwin Rhoton, prin. Fax 333-5252

Elfrida, Cochise, Pop. 454
Valley UNHSD 22 200/9-12
PO Box 158 85610 520-642-3492
Ron Aguallo, supt. Fax 642-3523
www.vuhs.net
Valley Union HS 200/9-12
PO Box 158 85610 520-642-3492
Steve Yoder, prin. Fax 642-3523

El Mirage, Maricopa, Pop. 30,983
Dysart USD 89
Supt. — See Surprise
Dysart HS 1,600/9-12
11425 N Dysart Rd 85335 623-876-7500
Roberta Lockhart, prin. Fax 876-7521

Eloy, Pinal, Pop. 15,495
Eloy ESD 11 900/PK-8
1011 N Sunshine Blvd, 520-466-2100
Ruby James, supt. Fax 466-2101
www.eloyesd.org
Eloy JHS 200/7-8
1011 N Sunshine Blvd, 520-466-2140
Ernest Montijo, prin. Fax 466-2150

Pinal County Office of Education
Supt. — See Florence
Villa Oasis Interscholastic Center 100/Alt
3740 N Toltec Rd, 520-464-8960
Justin DeMello, prin. Fax 466-3752

Santa Cruz Valley UNHSD 840 400/9-12
900 N Main St, 520-466-2220
Charie Wallace, supt. Fax 466-2222
www.scvuhs.org/
Santa Cruz Valley Union HS 400/9-12
900 N Main St, 520-466-2200
Orante Jenkins, prin. Fax 466-2222

Toltec ESD 22 1,300/PK-8
3315 N Toltec Rd, 520-466-2360
Dr. Bryan McCleney, supt. Fax 466-2398
www.toltec.k12.az.us
Toltec MS 500/5-8
3315 N Toltec Rd, 520-466-2350
Dee Dee Ivanoff, prin. Fax 466-2399

Flagstaff, Coconino, Pop. 64,141
Flagstaff USD 1 10,000/PK-12
3285 E Sparrow Ave 86004 928-527-6000
Barbara Hickman, supt. Fax 527-6015
www.fusd1.org
Coconino HS 1,500/9-12
2801 N Izabel St 86004 928-773-8200
Stacie Zanzucchi, prin. Fax 773-8247
Flagstaff HS 1,600/9-12
400 W Elm Ave 86001 928-773-8100
Tony Cullen, prin. Fax 773-8146
Mount Elden MS 1,000/6-8
3223 N 4th St 86004 928-773-8250
Steven Boadway, prin. Fax 773-8269
New Start Alternative S 100/Alt
4000 N Cummings St 86004 928-773-8198
Chris Koenker, prin. Fax 773-8427
Sinagua MS 1,000/6-8
3950 E Butler Ave 86004 928-527-5500
Tari Popham, prin. Fax 527-5561

Coconino Community College Post-Sec.
2800 S Lone Tree Rd, 928-527-1222
CollegeAmerica Post-Sec.
3012 E Route 66 86004 928-213-6060
Empire Beauty School Post-Sec.
1790 E Route 66 86004 928-774-7146
Montessori S of Flagstaff - Cedar 50/7-8
2212 E Cedar Ave 86004 928-774-1600
Marlane Spencer, prin. Fax 774-0424
Northern Arizona University Post-Sec.
S San Francisco St 86011 928-523-9011

Florence, Pinal, Pop. 25,223
Florence USD 1 8,100/PK-12
PO Box 2850, 520-866-3500
Dr. Gary Nine, supt. Fax 868-2302
www.fusdaz.org
Florence HS 800/9-12
PO Box 2850, 520-866-3560
Chris Knutsen, prin. Fax 868-2329
Other Schools – See Queen Creek

Pinal County Office of Education 200/
PO Box 769 85132 520-866-6565
Jill Broussard, supt. Fax 866-6973
www.pinalcso.org/
Other Schools – See Eloy

Fort Defiance, Apache, Pop. 3,530
Window Rock USD 8 2,500/K-12
PO Box 559 86504 928-729-6705
Dr. Deborah Jackson-Dennison, supt. Fax 729-5780
www.wrschool.net
Tse Ho Tso MS 500/6-8
PO Box 559 86504 928-729-6802
Kay Rochester, prin. Fax 729-6814
Window Rock HS 700/9-12
PO Box 559 86504 928-729-7004
Donna Manuelito, prin. Fax 729-7661

Fort Huachuca, See Sierra Vista
Fort Huachuca Accommodation SD 00 1,000/K-8
PO Box 12954 85670 520-458-5082
Dr. Ronda Frueauff, supt. Fax 515-5972
www.fthuachuca.k12.az.us
Smith MS 300/6-8
PO Box 12954 85670 520-459-8892
Dr. Nancy Nicholson, prin. Fax 459-8939

Fort Mohave, Mohave, Pop. 14,105
Colorado River UNHSD 2 2,400/9-12
5221 S Highway 95 Ste 5 86426 928-768-1665
Riley Frei, supt. Fax 768-1702
www.cruhsd.org
Other Schools – See Bullhead City, Mohave Valley

Fort Thomas, Graham, Pop. 360
Fort Thomas USD 7 500/K-12
PO Box 300 85536 928-485-9423
Dr. Leon Ben, supt. Fax 485-3019
www.ftthomas.k12.az.us
Fort Thomas JSHS 200/7-12
PO Box 28 85536 928-485-2427
Shane Hawkins, prin. Fax 485-2834

Fountain Hills, Maricopa, Pop. 22,214
Fountain Hills USD 98 1,900/PK-12
16000 E Palisades Blvd 85268 480-664-5011
Tom Lawrence, supt. Fax 664-5099
www.fhusd.org
Fountain Hills HS 700/9-12
16100 E Palisades Blvd 85268 480-664-5500
Tom Brennan, prin. Fax 837-5699
Fountain Hills MS 500/6-8
15414 N McDowell Mountain R 85268 480-664-5400
Anita Gomez, prin. Fax 664-5499

American Institute of Interior Design Post-Sec.
13014 N Saguaro Blvd # 206 85268 480-946-9601

Fredonia, Coconino, Pop. 1,295
Fredonia-Moccasin USD 6 300/PK-12
PO Box 247 86022 928-643-7333
Nicholas Bartlett, supt. Fax 643-7044
www.fredonia.org/
Fredonia-Moccasin HS 100/7-12
PO Box 247 86022 928-643-7333
Nick Bartlett, prin. Fax 643-7044

Ganado, Apache, Pop. 1,188
Ganado USD 20 1,600/K-12
PO Box 1757 86505 928-755-1000
William L. Allsbrooks, supt. Fax 755-1012
www.ganado.k12.az.us/
Ganado HS 600/9-12
PO Box 1757 86505 928-755-1511
Robin Pete, prin. Fax 755-1502
Ganado MS 200/7-8
PO Box 1757 86505 928-755-1411
Loretta Eltsosie, prin. Fax 755-1402

Gila Bend, Maricopa, Pop. 1,896
Gila Bend USD 24 500/PK-12
PO Box V 85337 928-683-2225
Lynnette Michalski, supt. Fax 683-2671
gilabendusd.org
Gila Bend HS 100/9-12
PO Box V 85337 928-683-2225
Rachele Reese, prin. Fax 683-2671

Gilbert, Maricopa, Pop. 202,881
Chandler USD 80
Supt. — See Chandler
Perry HS 2,100/9-12
1919 E Queen Creek Rd 85297 480-224-2800
Dan Serrano, prin. Fax 224-2820

Gilbert Unified SD 37,800/PK-12
140 S Gilbert Rd 85296 480-497-3300
Dave Allison Ed.D., supt. Fax 497-3398
www.gilbertschools.net
Campo Verde HS 1,300/9-12
3870 S Quartz St 85297 480-545-3100
Jared Ryan, prin. Fax 545-3111
Gilbert Classical Academy 200/7-12
55 N Greenfield Rd 85234 480-497-4034
Jodie Dean, prin. Fax 507-1645
Gilbert HS 2,700/9-12
1101 E Elliot Rd 85234 480-497-0177
Christopher Stroud, prin. Fax 497-5673
Gilbert JHS 700/7-8
1016 N Burk St 85234 480-892-6908
Kevin Rainey, prin. Fax 813-8240
Greenfield JHS 1,000/7-8
101 S Greenfield Rd 85296 480-813-1770
Brian Yee, prin. Fax 813-7279
Highland HS 3,000/9-12
4301 E Guadalupe Rd 85234 480-813-0051
Domonic Salce, prin. Fax 813-0258
Mesquite HS 2,500/9-12
500 S McQueen Rd 85233 480-632-4750
Ken Fetter, prin. Fax 632-4777
Mesquite JHS 900/7-8
130 W Mesquite St 85233 480-926-1433
Ron Izzett, prin. Fax 813-9002
South Valley JHS 1,200/7-8
2034 S Lindsay Rd, 480-855-0015
Brian Jaeger, prin. Fax 855-3542
Other Schools – See Mesa

Higley USD 60 10,000/PK-12
2935 S Recker Rd, 480-279-7000
Dr. Denise Birdwell, supt. Fax 279-7500
www.husd.org
Higley HS 1,400/9-12
4068 E Pecos Rd, 480-279-7300
Larry Rother, prin. Fax 279-7305
Williams Field HS 1,400/9-12
2076 S Higley Rd, 480-279-8000
Shawn Lynch, prin. Fax 279-8005

Bios Christian Academy 200/K-12
1249 N Lindsay Rd 85234 480-440-9203
Tim Ihms, admin. Fax 303-0578
Conservatory of Recording Arts/Sciences Post-Sec.
1205 N Fiesta Blvd 85233 480-858-9400
Gilbert Christian S 600/PK-12
3632 E Jasper Dr 85296 480-699-1215
Jim Desmarchais, supt. Fax 809-6677

Glendale, Maricopa, Pop. 221,458
Alhambra ESD 68
Supt. — See Phoenix
Barcelona MS 800/4-8
6530 N 44th Ave 85301 623-842-8616
Melissa White, prin. Fax 842-1384

Deer Valley USD 97
Supt. — See Phoenix
Deer Valley Crossroads S Alt
18400 N 51st Ave 85308 602-467-5100
Rob Archer, admin. Fax 467-5110
Deer Valley HS 1,900/9-12
18424 N 51st Ave 85308 602-467-6700
Barbara Dobbs, prin. Fax 467-6780
Desert Sky MS 800/7-8
5130 W Grovers Ave 85308 602-467-6500
Kim Crooks, prin. Fax 467-6580
Hillcrest MS 1,100/7-8
22833 N 71st Ave 85310 623-376-3300
Estela Hazelton, prin. Fax 376-3380
Mountain Ridge HS 2,300/9-12
22800 N 67th Ave 85310 623-376-3000
Debra Poulson, prin. Fax 376-3080

Glendale ESD 40 12,700/PK-8
7301 N 58th Ave 85301 623-237-7100
Dr. Joe Quintana, supt. Fax 237-7291
www.gesd40.org/
Bicentennial North S 800/4-8
7237 W Missouri Ave 85303 623-237-4009
Dr. Kenneth Fleming, prin. Fax 237-4915
Challenger MS 700/4-8
6905 W Maryland Ave 85303 623-237-4011
Tiffany Molina, prin. Fax 237-5115
Mensendick IS 800/4-8
5535 N 67th Ave 85301 623-237-4006
Jeff Vilardi, prin. Fax 237-4615

Glendale UNHSD 205 14,700/9-12
7650 N 43rd Ave 85301 623-435-6000
Eugene Dudo, supt. Fax 435-6078
guhsdaz.org
Apollo HS 1,800/9-12
8045 N 47th Ave 85302 623-435-6300
Allison Mattingly, prin. Fax 435-6369
Glendale HS 1,600/9-12
6216 W Glendale Ave 85301 623-435-6200
Kevin Cashatt, prin. Fax 435-6270
Independence HS 1,900/9-12
6602 N 75th Ave 85303 623-435-6100
Rob Ambrose, prin. Fax 435-6157
Other Schools – See Phoenix

Peoria USD 11 36,400/PK-12
6330 W Thunderbird Rd 85306 623-486-6000
Dr. Denton Santarelli, supt. Fax 486-6009
www.peoriaud.k12.az.us
Cactus HS 1,400/9-12
6330 W Greenway Rd 85306 623-412-5000
Tad Bloss, prin. Fax 412-5020
Ironwood HS 2,000/9-12
6051 W Sweetwater Ave 85304 623-486-6400
Vance Setka, prin. Fax 486-6424
Kellis HS 1,800/9-12
8990 W Orangewood Ave 85305 623-412-5425
Jeffrey Wooten, prin. Fax 412-5447
Other Schools – See Peoria

Tolleson UNHSD 214
Supt. — See Tolleson
Copper Canyon HS 1,700/9-12
9126 W Camelback Rd 85305 623-478-4800
Alan Potts, prin. Fax 478-4802

Washington ESD 6 22,000/PK-8
4650 W Sweetwater Ave 85304 602-347-2600
Dr. Susan Cook, supt. Fax 347-2720
www.wesdschools.org
Other Schools – See Phoenix

Arizona College of Allied Health Post-Sec.
4425 W Olive Ave Ste 300 85302 602-222-9300
Glendale Community College Post-Sec.
6000 W Olive Ave 85302 623-845-3000
Joy Christian S 500/PK-12
21000 N 75th Ave 85308 623-561-2000
Patrick Bennett, prin. Fax 362-3202
Midwestern University Post-Sec.
19555 N 59th Ave 85308 623-572-3200
Thunderbird School of Global Management Post-Sec.
1 Global Pl 85306 602-978-7100

Globe, Gila, Pop. 7,446
Globe USD 1 1,800/PK-12
460 N Willow St 85501 928-402-6000
Jerry Jennex, supt. Fax 425-8912
www.globeschools.org
Globe HS 500/9-12
460 N Willow St 85501 928-402-6000
Bobby Armenta, prin. Fax 425-8909
High Desert MS 500/5-8
460 N Willow St 85501 928-402-5900
Steve Estatico, prin. Fax 402-5905

Goodyear, Maricopa, Pop. 63,699
Agua Fria UNHSD 216
Supt. — See Avondale
Desert Edge HS 1,500/9-12
15778 W Yuma Rd 85338 623-932-7500
Bob Grey, prin. Fax 932-7502
Millennium HS 2,200/9-12
14802 W Wigwam Blvd, 623-932-7200
Tamee Gressett, prin. Fax 932-7204

Buckeye UNHSD 201
Supt. — See Buckeye
Estrella Foothills HS 1,000/9-12
13033 S Estrella Pkwy 85338 623-327-2470
Dr. Leslie Standerfer, prin. Fax 327-2499

Litchfield ESD 79
Supt. — See Litchfield Park
Western Sky MS 900/6-8
4905 N 144th Ave, 623-535-6300
Tami Garrett, prin. Fax 935-9536

Grand Canyon, Coconino
Grand Canyon USD 4 200/K-12
PO Box 519 86023 928-638-2461
Sharyl Allen, supt. Fax 638-2045
www.grandcanyonschool.org
Grand Canyon S 200/K-12
PO Box 519 86023 928-638-2461
Toby Melster, prin. Fax 638-2045

Heber, Navajo, Pop. 1,581
Heber-Overgaard USD 6 400/PK-12
PO Box 547 85928 928-535-4622
Ken VanWinkle, supt. Fax 535-5146
www.heberovergaardschools.org
Mogollon JSHS 100/7-12
PO Box 279 85928 928-535-4622
Rick Honsinger, prin. Fax 535-3933

Holbrook, Navajo, Pop. 4,904
Holbrook USD 3 2,000/PK-12
PO Box 640 86025 928-524-6144
Dr. Robbie Koerperich, supt. Fax 524-3073
www.holbrook.k12.az.us
Holbrook HS 700/9-12
PO Box 640 86025 928-524-2815
Lance Phaturos, prin. Fax 524-3537
Holbrook JHS 400/6-8
PO Box 640 86025 928-524-3959
Charles Gover, prin. Fax 524-3766

Holbrook SDA Indian S 100/1-12
PO Box 910 86025 928-524-6845
Pedro Ojeda, prin. Fax 524-3190
Northland Pioneer College Post-Sec.
PO Box 610 86025 928-524-7311

Joseph City, Navajo, Pop. 1,364
Joseph City USD 2 400/PK-12
PO Box 8 86032 928-288-3307
Robert Klein, supt. Fax 288-3309
josephcityschools.org
Joseph City JSHS 200/7-12
PO Box 8 86032 928-288-3361
Bryan Fields, prin. Fax 288-3825

Kayenta, Navajo, Pop. 5,074
Kayenta USD 27 1,400/PK-12
PO Box 337 86033 928-697-3251
Harry Martin, supt. Fax 697-2014
www.kayenta.k12.az.us
Kayenta IS 200/5-8
PO Box 337 86033 928-697-2371
David Hawley, prin. Fax 697-2371
Monument Valley HS 800/9-12
PO Box 337 86033 928-697-2177
Jack Gilmore, prin. Fax 697-2177

Keams Canyon, Navajo, Pop. 299
Cedar USD 25 300/PK-12
PO Box 367 86034 928-738-2366
Kimberly Randall, supt. Fax 738-5404
www.cedarusd.org
White Cone HS 100/9-12
PO Box 367 86034 928-654-3950
George Mattice, prin. Fax 654-3552

Kearny, Pinal, Pop. 1,932
Ray USD 3 500/PK-12
PO Box 427, 520-363-5515
Dr. Robert Dunn, supt. Fax 363-5642
www.rayusd.org
Ray HS 200/9-12
PO Box 427, 520-363-5515
James Simmons, prin. Fax 363-5517
Ray MS 200/5-8
PO Box 427, 520-363-5511
Curt Cook, prin. Fax 363-5005

Kingman, Mohave, Pop. 27,434
Kingman USD 20 6,700/PK-12
3033 McDonald Ave 86401 928-753-5678
Roger Jacks, supt. Fax 753-6910
www.kusd.org

Kingman HS 1,500/10-12
4182 N Bank St, 928-692-6480
Patrick Carey, prin. Fax 692-6418
Kingman JHS 700/6-8
1969 Detroit Ave 86401 928-753-3588
Jerry Arave, prin. Fax 753-1336
White Cliffs MS 700/6-8
3550 Prospector St 86401 928-753-6238
Cliff Angle, prin. Fax 753-4042
Williams HS 9-9
400 Grandview Ave 86401 928-718-6000
Steven Elwood, prin. Fax 718-1058
Other Schools – See Dolan Springs

Mohave Community College Post-Sec.
1971 E Jagerson Ave, 928-757-4331

Lake Havasu City, Mohave, Pop. 51,709
Lake Havasu USD 1 5,100/PK-12
2200 Havasupai Blvd 86403 928-505-6900
Gail Malay, supt. Fax 505-6999
www.havasu.k12.az.us/
Lake Havasu HS 1,900/9-12
2675 Palo Verde Blvd S 86403 928-854-5001
Denise Miner, prin. Fax 854-5499
Thunderbolt MS 1,000/7-8
695 Thunderbolt Ave 86406 928-854-7224
Marijo Mulligan, prin. Fax 854-7482

Charles of Italy Beauty College Post-Sec.
1987 McCulloch Blvd #205 86403 928-453-6666

Lakeside, Navajo, Pop. 4,210
Blue Ridge USD 32 2,100/PK-12
1200 W White Mountain Blvd 85929 928-368-6126
Greg Schalow, supt. Fax 368-5570
www.brusd.k12.az.us/
Blue Ridge HS 900/9-12
1200 W White Mountain Blvd 85929 928-368-6328
Eric Harmon, prin. Fax 368-9572
Blue Ridge JHS 400/7-8
1200 W White Mountain Blvd 85929 928-368-2350
Loren Webb, prin. Fax 368-2399

Laveen, Maricopa
Phoenix UNHSD 210
Supt. — See Phoenix
Chavez HS 2,100/9-12
3921 W Baseline Rd 85339 602-764-4000
Scott Gayman, prin. Fax 764-4054
Fairfax HS, 8225 S 59th Ave 85339 1,800/9-12
Dr. Zack Munoz, prin. 602-764-9000

Litchfield Park, Maricopa, Pop. 5,366
Litchfield ESD 79 9,000/PK-8
272 E Sagebrush St 85340 623-535-6000
Dr. Julianne Lein, supt. Fax 935-1448
www.lesd.k12.az.us
Heck MS 100/6-8
272 E Sagebrush St 85340 623-547-1700
Dr. Ron Sterr, prin. Fax 536-5955
Wigwam Creek MS 900/6-8
272 E Sagebrush St 85340 623-547-1100
John Scudder, prin. Fax 547-0873
Other Schools – See Buckeye, Goodyear

Marana, Pima, Pop. 34,148
Marana USD 6 12,900/K-12
11279 W Grier Rd Ste 106 85653 520-682-4774
Dr. Doug Wilson, supt. Fax 682-2421
www.maranausd.org
ACE 50/Alt
13650 N McDuff Rd 85653 520-682-1014
Lynne Prouty, dir. Fax 682-1016
Marana Career and Technical HS 100/Alt
13650 N McDuff Rd 85653 520-682-4773
Lynne Prouty, dir. Fax 682-4106
Marana MS 1,100/7-8
11279 W Grier Rd Ste 105 85653 520-682-4730
Kristin Reidy, prin. Fax 682-4790
Other Schools – See Tucson

Maricopa, Pinal, Pop. 42,031
Maricopa USD 20 5,900/PK-12
44150 W Maricopa Casa Grand,
520-568-5100
Dr. Steve Chestnut, supt. Fax 568-5110
maricopausd.org/
Desert Wind MS 700/6-8
44150 W Maricopa Casa Grand,
520-568-7110
Joe Veres, prin. Fax 568-7119
Maricopa HS 1,600/9-12
44150 W Maricopa Casa Grand,
520-568-8100
June Celaya, prin. Fax 568-8119
Maricopa Wells MS 600/6-8
44150 W Maricopa Casa Grand,
520-568-7100
Rick Abel, prin. Fax 568-7104

Mayer, Yavapai, Pop. 1,462
Mayer USD 43 500/PK-12
PO Box 1059 86333 928-642-1000
Dean Slaga, supt. Fax 632-4005
www.mayerschools.org
Mayer HS 200/9-12
PO Box 1059 86333 928-642-1201
Jeff Duncan, prin. Fax 632-5714

Orme S 100/7-12
HC 63 Box 3040 86333 928-632-7601
Dr. Michael Gemma, hdmstr. Fax 632-7605

Mesa, Maricopa, Pop. 428,892
East Valley Institute of Tech. SD 401
1601 W Main St 85201 480-461-4000
Sally Downey Ed.D., supt. Fax 461-4089
evit.com
East Valley Institute of Technology Vo/Tech
1601 W Main St 85201 480-461-4000
Sally Downey Ed.D., supt. Fax 461-4169

Gilbert Unified SD
Supt. — See Gilbert
Canyon Valley S 200/Alt
7007 E Guadalupe Rd 85212 480-507-0519
Chad Fitzgerald, prin. Fax 507-3978
Desert Ridge HS 2,500/9-12
10045 E Madero Ave, 480-984-8947
Dan Coombs, prin. Fax 354-5090
Desert Ridge JHS 1,300/7-8
10211 E Madero Ave, 480-635-2025
Jean Woods, prin. Fax 635-2044
Highland JHS 1,300/7-8
6915 E Guadalupe Rd 85212 480-632-4739
Marcie Taylor, prin. Fax 632-4729

Mesa USD 4 60,400/PK-12
63 E Main St Ste 101 85201 480-472-0000
Dr. Michael Cowan, supt. Fax 472-0204
www.mpsaz.org
Carson JHS 800/7-8
525 N Westwood 85201 480-472-2900
Ray Chavez, prin. Fax 472-2899
Crossroads S 100/Alt
855 W 8th Ave 85210 480-308-7330
Dr. Tiffany Uhlik, prin. Fax 308-7338
Dobson HS 3,000/9-12
1501 W Guadalupe Rd 85202 480-472-3000
Matthew Gehrman, prin. Fax 472-3075
East Valley Academy 200/Alt
855 W 8th Ave 85210 480-472-9350
Tim Keilty, prin. Fax 472-9393
Franklin JHS 100/7-8
4949 E Southern Ave 85206 480-472-2600
Jeffrey Abrams, prin. Fax 472-2698
Fremont JHS 900/7-8
1001 N Power Rd 85205 480-472-8300
Patricia Christie, prin. Fax 472-8333
Kino JHS 700/7-8
848 N Horne 85203 480-472-2400
Susan O'Brien, prin. Fax 472-2549
Mesa Academy for Advanced Studies 400/4-8
6919 E Brown Rd 85207 480-308-7400
Bob Crispin, prin. Fax 308-7428
Mesa HS 2,700/9-12
1630 E Southern Ave 85204 480-472-5900
Jim Souder, prin. Fax 472-5995
Mountain View HS 2,500/9-12
2700 E Brown Rd 85213 480-472-6900
Craig Luketich, prin. Fax 472-6983
Poston JHS 900/7-8
2433 E Adobe St 85213 480-472-2100
Allen Flax, prin. Fax 472-2105
Red Mountain HS 2,500/9-12
7301 E Brown Rd 85207 480-472-8000
Gerald Slemmer, prin. Fax 472-8008
Rhodes JHS 1,000/7-8
1860 S Longmore 85202 480-472-2300
Matt Devlin, prin. Fax 472-2299
Riverview HS 100/Alt
1731 N Country Club Dr 85201 480-472-5350
Raul Ruiz, prin. Fax 472-5355
Shepherd JHS 700/7-8
1407 N Alta Mesa Dr 85205 480-472-1800
Eileen Cahoon, prin. Fax 472-1888
Skyline HS 2,600/9-12
845 S Crismon Rd 85208 480-472-9400
Dr. Steve Green, prin. Fax 472-9406
Smith JHS 900/7-8
10100 E Adobe Rd 85207 480-472-9900
Casey Eagleburger, prin. Fax 472-9999
Stapley JHS 700/7-8
3250 E Hermosa Vista Dr 85213 480-472-2700
Ken Erickson, prin. Fax 472-2828
Taylor JHS 900/7-8
705 S 32nd St 85204 480-472-1500
Gina Piraino, prin. Fax 472-1616
Westwood HS 2,900/9-12
945 W Rio Salado Pkwy 85201 480-472-4400
Tim Richard, prin. Fax 472-4509

Arizona Sch of Dentistry & Oral Health Post-Sec.
5850 E Still Cir 85206 866-626-2878
Arizona School of Health Sciences Post-Sec.
5850 E Still Cir 85206 866-626-2878
Avalon School of Cosmetology Post-Sec.
2111 S Alma School Rd #21 85210 480-897-1688
Carrington College Post-Sec.
1001 W Southern Ave Ste 130 85210 480-212-1600
DeVry University - Mesa Center Post-Sec.
1201 S Alma School Rd #5450 85210 480-827-1511
Everest College Post-Sec.
5416 E Baseline Rd Ste 200 85206 480-830-5151
Faith Christian S 100/K-12
7464 E Main St 85207 480-833-1983
Dick Buckingham, admin. Fax 325-1096
International Academy of Hair Design Post-Sec.
1445 W Southern Ave # 2006 85202 480-820-9422
Mesa Community College Post-Sec.
1833 W Southern Ave 85202 480-461-7000
Pima Medical Institute Post-Sec.
957 S Dobson Rd 85202 480-644-0267
Redeemer Christian S 100/PK-12
719 N Stapley Dr 85203 480-962-5003
Denise Monroe Ed.D., prin. Fax 833-7502
Sch of Osteopathic Medicine - AT Still U Post-Sec.
5850 E Still Cir 85206 866-626-2878

Miami, Gila, Pop. 1,817
Miami USD 40 700/K-12
PO Box 2070 85539 928-425-3271
Dr. Sherry Dorathy, supt. Fax 425-7419
miami.az.schoolwebpages.com
Miami JSHS 300/7-12
PO Box 2070 85539 928-425-3271
Rob Bueche, prin. Fax 425-7027

Mohave Valley, Mohave, Pop. 2,530
Colorado River UNHSD 2
Supt. — See Fort Mohave
River Valley HS 900/9-12
2250 E Laguna Rd 86440 928-768-2300
Bud Scully, prin. Fax 768-6156

Mohave Valley ESD 16 1,800/PK-8
8450 S Olive Ave 86440 928-768-2507
Whitney Crow, supt. Fax 768-2510
www.mvesd16.org
Mohave Valley JHS 400/7-8
6565 S Girard Ave 86440 928-768-9196
Christina Stahl, prin. Fax 768-1129

Morenci, Greenlee, Pop. 1,476
Morenci USD 18 1,500/PK-12
PO Box 1060 85540 928-865-2081
Dr. Javier Abrego, supt. Fax 865-3130
www.morenci.k12.az.us/
Morenci JSHS 500/7-12
PO Box 1060 85540 928-865-3631
Bryan Boling, prin. Fax 865-3614

Nogales, Santa Cruz, Pop. 20,797
Nogales USD 1 5,600/K-12
PO Box 5000 85628 520-287-0800
Steve Zimmerman, supt. Fax 287-3586
www.nusd.k12.az.us
Carpenter Middle Academy 600/6-8
595 W Kino St 85621 520-287-0820
Liza Montiel, prin. Fax 287-0817
Desert Shadows MS 800/6-8
340 Boulevard Del Rey David 85621 520-377-2646
Joan Molera, prin. Fax 377-2674
Nogales HS 1,700/9-12
1905 N Apache Blvd 85621 520-377-2021
Judith Mendoza Jimenez, prin. Fax 281-4448
Pierson Vocational HS Vo/Tech
451 N Arroyo Blvd 85621 520-287-0915
Joel Kramer, lead tchr. Fax 287-0918

Santa Cruz County Office of Education
2150 N Congress Dr 85621 520-375-7940
Alfredo Velasquez, supt. Fax 375-7958
www.co.santa-cruz.az.us/schools/index.html
Pimeria Alta Accommodation S Alt
3231 N Grand Ave 85621 520-281-9179
Vanessa Rothstein, lead tchr. Fax 281-9713

Lourdes HS 100/9-12
555 E Patagonia Hwy 85621 520-287-5659
Sr. Barbara Monsegur, prin. Fax 287-2910

Oro Valley, Pima, Pop. 40,283
Amphitheater USD 10
Supt. — See Tucson
Ironwood Ridge HS 1,900/9-12
2475 W Naranja Dr, 520-696-3900
Michael Bejarano, prin. Fax 696-3999

Page, Coconino, Pop. 6,933
Page USD 8 2,200/K-12
PO Box 1927 86040 928-608-4100
Jim Walker, supt. Fax 645-2805
pageusd.org
Page HS 1,000/9-12
PO Box 1927 86040 928-608-4138
Paul Gagnon, prin. Fax 645-9243
Page MS 700/6-8
PO Box 1927 86040 928-608-4300
Christy Rodriguez, prin. Fax 645-9285

Paradise Valley, Maricopa, Pop. 12,621

Phoenix Country Day S 700/PK-12
3901 E Stanford Dr 85253 602-955-8200
Andrew Rodin, hdmstr. Fax 955-1286
Tesseract S 400/PK-12
4800 E Doubletree Ranch Rd 85253 480-991-1770
Nigel Taplin, head sch Fax 991-1954

Parker, LaPaz, Pop. 2,994
Parker USD 27 1,800/PK-12
PO Box 1090 85344 928-669-9244
James Lotts, supt. Fax 669-2515
www.parkerusd.k12.az.us
Parker HS 500/9-12
PO Box 1090 85344 928-669-2202
Dr. Le Roy Shontz, prin. Fax 669-2315
Wallace JHS 200/7-8
PO Box 1090 85344 928-669-2141
Amanda Maxwell, prin. Fax 669-2515

Patagonia, Santa Cruz, Pop. 909
Patagonia SD 100/PK-12
PO Box 295 85624 520-394-3000
Denise Blake, supt. Fax 394-3001
www.patagonia.k12.az.us
Patagonia Union HS 100/9-12
PO Box 254 85624 520-394-3050
Denise Blake, prin. Fax 394-3051

Payson, Gila, Pop. 15,087
Payson USD 10 2,500/PK-12
PO Box 919 85547 928-474-2070
Ron Hitchcock, supt. Fax 472-2013
www.pusd.k12.az.us/
Center for Success HS Alt
PO Box 919 85547 928-472-2011
Linda Gibson, lead tchr. Fax 472-2039
Payson HS 800/9-12
PO Box 919 85547 928-474-2233
Anna VanZile, prin. Fax 472-2010
Rim Country MS 600/6-8
PO Box 919 85547 928-474-4511
Will Dunman, prin. Fax 472-2044

Payson Community Christian S 100/PK-12
213 S Colcord Rd 85541 928-474-8050
Patricia Fleeger, admin. Fax 474-3252

Peoria, Maricopa, Pop. 150,709

Peoria USD 11
Supt. — See Glendale
Centennial HS 2,100/9-12
14388 N 79th Ave 85381 623-412-4400
Christine Lopezlira, prin. Fax 412-4420
Liberty HS 1,700/9-12
9621 W Speckled Gecko Dr 85383 623-773-6525
John Croteau, prin. Fax 773-6540
Peoria HS 1,700/9-12
11200 N 83rd Ave 85345 623-486-6300
Paul Bower, prin. Fax 486-6330
Peoria Transition Center 100/Alt
7565 W Peoria Ave Ste A 85345 623-412-5475
Marla Morrison, prin. Fax 412-5480
Sunrise Mountain HS 1,600/9-12
21200 N 83rd Ave 85382 623-487-5125
Dale Nicol, prin. Fax 487-5140

Phoenix, Maricopa, Pop. 1,416,459

Alhambra ESD 68 13,900/PK-8
4510 N 37th Ave 85019 602-336-2920
Dr. Karen Williams, supt. Fax 336-2270
www.alhambraesd.org/
Andalucia MS 1,100/4-8
4730 W Campbell Ave 85031 623-848-8646
Monique Martinez-Ortiz, prin. Fax 846-6044
Cordova MS 900/4-8
5631 N 35th Ave 85017 602-841-0704
Dr. Sharon Spearman, prin. Fax 973-8416
Granada East MS 1,100/4-8
3022 W Campbell Ave 85017 602-589-0110
Sandra Kennedy, prin. Fax 589-0140
Sevilla West S 1,100/4-8
3851 W Missouri Ave 85019 602-347-0232
Karen Stengel, prin. Fax 347-9906
Simpson MS 1,000/4-8
5330 N 23rd Ave 85015 602-246-0699
Cynthia Nicholas, prin. Fax 246-4305
Other Schools – See Glendale

Balsz ESD 31 2,800/PK-8
4825 E Roosevelt St 85008 602-629-6400
Dr. Jeffrey Smith, supt. Fax 629-6470
www.balsz.k12.az.us
Orangedale JHS Prep Academy 400/7-8
5048 E Oak St 85008 602-629-6800
Michael Halpert, prin. Fax 629-6804

Cartwright ESD 83 17,500/K-8
3401 N 67th Ave 85033 623-691-4000
Dr. Jacob Chavez, supt. Fax 691-5920
www.csd83.org/
Atkinson MS 1,200/6-8
4315 N Maryvale Pkwy 85031 623-691-1700
Scott Wintero, prin. Fax 691-1720
Castro MS 800/6-8
2730 N 79th Ave 85035 623-691-5300
Sarah Hernandez, prin. Fax 691-5320
Desert Sands MS 1,100/6-8
6308 W Campbell Ave 85033 623-691-4900
Dr. Randy Mahlerwein, prin. Fax 691-4920
Estrella MS 1,200/6-8
3733 N 75th Ave 85033 623-691-5400
Nick Radavich, prin. Fax 691-5420

Cave Creek USD 93
Supt. — See Scottsdale
Sonoran Trails MS 800/7-8
5555 E Pinnacle Vista Dr 85085 480-272-8600
Bill Dolezal, prin. Fax 272-8699

Deer Valley USD 97 35,000/PK-12
20402 N 15th Ave 85027 623-445-5000
Dr. James R. Veitenheimer, supt. Fax 445-5086
www.dvusd.org
Deer Valley MS 800/7-8
21100 N 27th Ave 85027 623-445-3300
Dr. Lynn Miller, prin. Fax 445-3380
Goldwater HS 1,900/9-12
2820 W Rose Garden Ln 85027 623-445-3000
Dr. Mike Andersen, prin. Fax 445-3080
O'Connor HS 2,400/9-12
25250 N 35th Ave, 623-445-7100
Dr. Bryce Anderson, prin. Fax 445-7180
Other Schools – See Anthem, Glendale

Fowler ESD 45 4,600/PK-8
1617 S 67th Ave 85043 623-707-4500
Marvene Lobato, supt. Fax 707-4560
www.fesd.org
Santa Maria MS 700/6-8
7250 W Lower Buckeye Rd 85043 623-707-1100
Desiree Castillo, prin. Fax 707-1110
Western Valley MS 800/6-8
6250 W Durango St 85043 623-707-2200
Trent Lyon, prin. Fax 707-2204

Glendale UNHSD 205
Supt. — See Glendale
Cortez HS 1,200/9-12
8828 N 31st Ave 85051 623-915-8200
Reid Chitwood, prin. Fax 915-8244
Greenway HS 1,600/9-12
3930 W Greenway Rd 85053 623-915-8500
Edward Barnes, prin. Fax 915-8560
Moon Valley HS 1,500/9-12
3625 W Cactus Rd 85029 623-915-8000
Craig Mussi, prin. Fax 915-8070
Sunnyslope HS 1,800/9-12
35 W Dunlap Ave 85021 623-915-8760
Steven Ducey, prin. Fax 915-8762
Thunderbird HS 1,600/9-12
1750 W Thunderbird Rd 85023 623-915-8900
Jeannie Paparella, prin. Fax 915-8971

Washington HS 1,700/9-12
2217 W Glendale Ave 85021 623-915-8400
Carol Lippert, prin. Fax 915-8437

Isaac ESD 5 6,600/PK-8
3348 W McDowell Rd 85009 602-455-6700
Mario Ventura, supt. Fax 278-1693
www.isaacschools.org
Isaac MS 800/6-8
3402 W McDowell Rd 85009 602-455-6800
Daniel Salaz, prin. Fax 455-6868
Pueblo Del Sol MS 600/6-8
3449 N 39th Ave 85019 602-455-6900
Armando Chavez, prin. Fax 484-4118

Kyrene ESD 28
Supt. — See Tempe
Kyrene Akimel A-al MS 1,100/6-8
2720 E Liberty Ln 85048 480-541-5800
Michael Deignan, prin. Fax 541-5810
Kyrene Altadena MS 1,100/6-8
14620 S Desert Fthills Pkwy 85048 480-541-6000
Nancy Corner, prin. Fax 541-6010
Kyrene Centennial MS 1,100/6-8
13808 S 36th St 85044 480-541-6400
Jocelyn Sims, prin. Fax 541-6410

Madison ESD 38 5,600/PK-8
5601 N 16th St 85016 602-664-7900
Tim Ham Ed.D., supt. Fax 664-7999
www.msd38.org
Madison # 1 MS 800/5-8
5525 N 16th St 85016 602-664-7100
Casey George, prin. Fax 664-7199
Madison Meadows MS 800/5-8
225 W Ocotillo Rd 85013 602-664-7600
Susan Doyle, prin. Fax 664-7699
Madison Park MS 500/5-8
1431 E Campbell Ave 85014 602-664-7500
Kevin Sotomayor, prin. Fax 664-7599

Osborn ESD 8 2,700/PK-8
1226 W Osborn Rd 85013 602-707-2000
Dr. Wilma Basnett, supt. Fax 707-2040
www.osbornnet.org
Osborn MS 600/7-8
1102 W Highland Ave 85013 602-707-2400
Marty Makar, prin. Fax 707-2440

Paradise Valley USD 69 32,600/PK-12
15002 N 32nd St 85032 602-449-2000
James Lee Ed.D., supt. Fax 449-2005
www.pvschools.net
Explorer MS 800/7-8
22401 N 40th St 85050 602-449-4200
Barbara Newman, prin. Fax 449-4205
Greenway MS 500/7-8
3002 E Nisbet Rd 85032 602-449-2400
Dr. Ibi Haghighat, prin. Fax 449-2405
Mountain Trail MS 800/7-8
2323 E Mountain Gate Pass 85024 602-449-4600
Craig Lahlum, prin. Fax 449-4605
North Canyon HS 2,400/9-12
1700 E Union Hills Dr 85024 602-449-5000
Elaine Jacobs, prin. Fax 449-5005
Paradise Valley HS 1,600/9-12
3950 E Bell Rd 85032 602-449-7000
Ian Deonise, prin. Fax 449-7005
Pinnacle HS 2,400/9-12
3535 E Mayo Blvd 85050 602-449-4000
Dr. Troy Bales, prin. Fax 449-4205
Polaris HS 100/Alt
15002 N 32nd St 85032 602-449-2300
Jean Scharrer, prin. Fax 449-2305
Prospect S 50/Alt
15002 N 32nd St 85032 602-449-2300
Jean Scharrer, prin. Fax 449-2305
Shadow Mountain HS 1,700/9-12
2902 E Shea Blvd 85028 602-449-3000
David Appleman, prin. Fax 449-3005
Shea MS 700/7-8
2728 E Shea Blvd 85028 602-449-3500
Dan Knak, prin. Fax 449-3505
Star Tech Professional Center Vo/Tech
3950 E Bell Rd 85032 602-449-7036
Tony Maldonado, dir. Fax 449-2333
Vista Verde MS 800/7-8
2826 E Grovers Ave 85032 602-449-5300
Andrea Hoffler, prin. Fax 449-5305
Other Schools – See Scottsdale

Phoenix UNHSD 210 24,900/9-12
4502 N Central Ave 85012 602-764-1100
Kent Scribner Ph.D., supt. Fax 271-3593
www.phoenixunion.org
Alhambra HS 2,700/9-12
3839 W Camelback Rd 85019 602-764-6022
Claudio Coria, prin. Fax 271-3497
Bostrom Alternative Center 300/Alt
3535 N 27th Ave 85017 602-764-1700
Alvin Watson, prin. Fax 271-2923
Browne HS 2,800/9-12
7402 W Catalina Dr 85033 602-764-8500
Dr. Gabriel Trujillo, prin. Fax 440-6803
Camelback HS 1,900/9-12
4612 N 28th St 85016 602-764-7000
Dr. Chad Gestson, prin. Fax 271-2295
Central HS 2,200/9-12
4525 N Central Ave 85012 602-764-7500
Christopher Jones, prin. Fax 271-2385
Franklin Police and Fire HS 300/9-12
1645 W McDowell Rd 85007 602-764-0200
Lorenzo Cabrera, prin. Fax 258-2868
Hayden Community HS 2,200/9-12
3333 W Roosevelt St 85009 602-764-3000
Ricardo Cordova, prin. Fax 229-8387
Maryvale HS 2,600/9-12
3415 N 59th Ave 85033 602-764-2000
Phillip Verdugo, prin. Fax 271-2597

Metro Tech HS Vo/Tech
1900 W Thomas Rd 85015 602-764-8000
Kate McDonald, prin. Fax 452-5302
North HS 2,400/9-12
1101 E Thomas Rd 85014 602-764-6500
Juan Nunez, prin. Fax 271-2765
Phoenix Union Bioscience HS 300/9-12
512 E Pierce St 85004 602-764-5600
Quintin Boyce, prin. Fax 253-9013
South Mountain HS 1,800/9-12
5401 S 7th St 85040 602-764-5000
LaCresha Williams, prin. Fax 271-2880
Suns-Diamondbacks Education Academy 200/Alt
2920 N 7th St 85014 602-764-0050
Dr. Lisa Scinto, prin. Fax 744-1221
Other Schools – See Laveen

Riverside ESD 2 700/PK-8
1414 S 51st Ave 85043 602-477-8900
Jaime Rivera Ed.D., supt. Fax 272-8378
resdonline.org/
Kings Ridge MS 300/5-8
3650 S 64th Ln 85043 602-477-8960
Rochelle Elliott, prin. Fax 936-5531

Roosevelt ESD 66 9,900/PK-8
6000 S 7th St 85042 602-243-4800
Jacqueline Jackson, supt. Fax 243-2637
www.rsd.k12.az.us
Greenfield MS 600/4-8
7009 S 10th St 85042 602-232-4240
Stuart Starky, prin. Fax 243-4973

Scottsdale USD 48 26,200/PK-12
3811 N 44th St 85018 480-484-6100
Dr. David Peterson, supt. Fax 484-6287
www.susd.org/
Arcadia HS 1,700/9-12
4703 E Indian School Rd 85018 480-484-6300
John Biera, prin. Fax 484-6301
Ingleside MS 700/6-8
5402 E Osborn Rd 85018 480-484-4900
Tanya Beckwith, prin. Fax 484-4901
Other Schools – See Scottsdale

Tempe UNHSD 213
Supt. — See Tempe
Desert Vista HS 2,900/9-12
16440 S 32nd St 85048 480-706-7900
Dr. Anna Battle, prin. Fax 706-7976
Mountain Pointe HS 2,600/9-12
4201 E Knox Rd 85044 480-759-8449
Bruce Kipper, prin. Fax 759-8458

Tolleson UNHSD 214
Supt. — See Tolleson
Sierra Linda HS 9-12
3434 S 67th Ave 85043 623-474-7700
Tim Madrid, prin. Fax 474-7790

Washington ESD 6
Supt. — See Glendale
Cholla MS 800/7-8
3120 W Cholla St 85029 602-896-5400
Phil Garitson, prin. Fax 896-5420
Desert Foothills JHS 700/7-8
3333 W Banff Ln 85053 602-896-5500
James Hall, prin. Fax 896-5520
Mountain Sky JHS 800/7-8
16225 N 7th Ave 85023 602-896-6100
Perry Mason, prin. Fax 896-6120
Palo Verde MS 900/7-8
7502 N 39th Ave 85051 602-347-2500
Carol Patterson, prin. Fax 347-2520
Royal Palm MS 600/6-8
8520 N 19th Ave 85021 602-347-3200
Leonard Hoover, prin. Fax 347-3220

Wilson ESD 7 1,100/PK-8
3025 E Fillmore St 85008 602-681-2200
Antonio Sanchez, supt. Fax 275-7517
www.wsd.k12.az.us
Wilson MS 600/4-8
2929 E Fillmore St 85008 602-683-2400
Cindy Campton, prin. Fax 275-8677

American Indian Coll of Assemblies/God Post-Sec.
10020 N 15th Ave 85021 602-944-3335
American Institute of Technology Post-Sec.
440 S 54th Ave 85043 602-457-3294
Anthem College Post-Sec.
1515 E Indian School Rd 85014 602-279-9700
Argosy University/Phoenix Post-Sec.
2233 W Dunlap Ave 85021 602-216-2600
Arizona Christian University Post-Sec.
2625 E Cactus Rd 85032 800-247-2697
Arizona Lutheran Academy 200/9-12
6036 S 27th Ave 85041 602-268-8686
Kurt Rosenbaum, prin. Fax 243-1353
Bourgade Catholic HS 400/9-12
4602 N 31st Ave 85017 602-973-4000
Kathy Rother, prin. Fax 973-5854
Brookline College Post-Sec.
2445 W Dunlap Ave Ste 100 85021 602-242-6265
Brophy College Prep HS 1,300/9-12
4701 N Central Ave 85012 602-264-5291
Bob Ryan, prin. Fax 234-1669
Brown Mackie College - Phoenix Post-Sec.
13430 N Black Canyon # 190 85029 602-337-3044
Bryman School Post-Sec.
2250 W Peoria Ave Ste A100 85029 602-274-4300
Carrington College Post-Sec.
8503 N 27th Ave 85051 877-206-2106
Carrington College - Phoenix Westside Post-Sec.
2701 W Bethany Home Rd 85017 602-433-1333
Chamberlain College of Nursing Post-Sec.
2149 W Dunlap Ave 85021 602-331-2720
CollegeAmerica Post-Sec.
9801 N Metro Pkwy E 85051 602-257-7522

Collins College Post-Sec.
4750 S 44th Pl 85040 480-966-3000
DeVry University - Phoenix Campus Post-Sec.
2149 W Dunlap Ave 85021 602-870-9222
Dunlap-Stone University Post-Sec.
19820 N 7th St Ste 100 85024 800-474-8013
Empire Beauty School Post-Sec.
2727 W Glendale Ave Ste 200 85051 623-939-8364
Everest College Post-Sec.
10400 N 25th Ave Ste 190 85021 602-942-4141
Fortis College Post-Sec.
555 N 18th St Ste 110 85006 602-254-3099
Gateway Community College Post-Sec.
108 N 40th St 85034 602-286-8000
Grand Canyon University Post-Sec.
3300 W Camelback Rd 85017 602-639-7500
ITT Technical Institute Post-Sec.
10220 N 25th Ave Ste 100 85021 602-749-7900
ITT Technical Institute Post-Sec.
1840 N 95th Ave Ste 132 85037 623-474-7900
Motorcycle Mechanics Institute Post-Sec.
2844 W Deer Valley Rd 85027 623-869-9644
National Paralegal College Post-Sec.
717 E Maryland Ave 85014 800-371-6105
91st Psalm Christian S 100/PK-12
2020 E Baseline Rd 85042 602-243-1900
Scott Ranney, prin. Fax 243-5919
Northwest Christian S 1,300/PK-12
16401 N 43rd Ave 85053 602-978-5134
Geoffrey Brown, supt. Fax 978-5804
Ottawa University Arizona Post-Sec.
10020 N 25th Ave 85021 602-371-1188
Paradise Valley Christian Preparatory S 300/PK-12
11875 N 24th St 85028 602-992-8140
Fax 992-8152
Paradise Valley Community College Post-Sec.
18401 N 32nd St 85032 602-787-6500
Phoenix Christian JSHS 300/6-12
1751 W Indian School Rd 85015 602-265-4707
Dr. Phil Adams, prin. Fax 277-7170
Phoenix College Post-Sec.
1202 W Thomas Rd 85013 602-285-7800
Phoenix Institute of Herbal Medicine Post-Sec.
301 E Bethany Home Rd #A100 85012
602-274-1885
Phoenix School of Law Post-Sec.
1 N Central Ave Ste 1400 85004 602-682-6800
Phoenix Seminary Post-Sec.
4222 E Thomas Rd Ste 400 85018 602-850-8000
Refrigeration School Post-Sec.
4210 E Washington St 85034 602-275-7133
Roberto-Venn School of Luthiery Post-Sec.
1012 Grand Ave 85007 602-243-1179
St. Marys Catholic HS 700/9-12
2525 N 3rd St 85004 602-251-2500
Suzanne Fessler, prin. Fax 251-2595
Sanford-Brown College Post-Sec.
9630 N 25th Ave 85021 480-444-1112
Scottsdale Christian Academy 900/PK-12
14400 N Tatum Blvd 85032 602-992-5100
Peter Laugen, supt. Fax 992-0575
South Mountain Community College Post-Sec.
7050 S 24th St 85042 602-243-8000
The Art Institute of Phoenix Post-Sec.
2233 W Dunlap Ave 85021 602-331-7500
University of Phoenix Post-Sec.
4615 E Elwood St 85040 866-766-0766
Valley Lutheran HS 200/9-12
5199 N 7th Ave 85013 602-230-1600
Robert Koehne M.A., prin. Fax 230-1602
West Coast Ultrasound Institute Post-Sec.
4250 E Camelback Rd 85018 602-954-3834
Western International University Post-Sec.
9215 N Black Canyon Hwy 85021 602-943-2311
Xavier College Prep HS 1,200/9-12
4710 N 5th St 85012 602-277-3772
Sr. Joan Fitzgerald, prin. Fax 279-1346

Pima, Graham, Pop. 2,335
Pima USD 6 800/K-12
PO Box 429 85543 928-387-8000
Sean Rickert, supt. Fax 485-2343
www.pima.k12.az.us/
Pima HS 200/9-12
PO Box 429 85543 928-387-8150
Kalem Norton, prin. Fax 387-8023
Pima JHS 100/7-8
PO Box 429 85543 928-387-8100
Mark Squires, prin. Fax 387-8021

Pinon, Navajo, Pop. 897
Pinon USD 4 1,200/PK-12
PO Box 839 86510 928-725-3450
Larry Wallen, supt. Fax 725-2123
www.pusdatsa.org
Pinon HS 400/9-12
PO Box 839 86510 928-725-2489
Slade Morgan, prin. Fax 725-2470
Pinon MS 300/6-8
PO Box 839 86510 928-725-2300
Rae Thompson, prin. Fax 725-2370

Prescott, Yavapai, Pop. 39,213
Prescott USD 1 5,300/K-12
146 S Granite St 86303 928-445-5400
Dave Smucker, supt. Fax 713-3207
www.prescottschools.com
Granite Mountain MS 600/6-8
1800 N Williamson Valley Rd 86305 928-717-3253
Stephanie Hillig, prin. Fax 717-3284
Prescott HS 1,800/9-12
1050 Ruth St 86301 928-445-2322
Totsy McCraley, prin. Fax 778-6106
Prescott Mile High MS 700/6-8
300 S Granite St 86303 928-717-3241
Jim Wells, prin. Fax 717-3298

Yavapai Accommodation SD 200/7-12
2970 Centerpointe East Dr 86301 928-759-8126
Jim Taylor, dir. Fax 759-8136
www.yavapaicountyhs.org/
Aspire JSHS 200/Alt
2970 Centerpointe East Dr 86301 928-759-8126
Jim Taylor, dir. Fax 759-8136
Other Schools – See Prescott Valley

Embry-Riddle Aeronautical University Post-Sec.
3700 Willow Creek Rd 86301 800-888-3728
Empire Beauty School Post-Sec.
410 W Goodwin St 86303 928-778-5064
Prescott College Post-Sec.
220 Grove Ave 86301 877-350-2100
Trinity Christian S 200/K-12
1077 Mogollon Rd 86301 928-445-6306
Kyle Maestri, hdmstr. Fax 445-7210
Yavapai College Post-Sec.
1100 E Sheldon St 86301 928-445-7300

Prescott Valley, Yavapai, Pop. 38,121
Humboldt USD 22 6,000/PK-12
6411 N Robert Rd 86314 928-759-4000
Dr. Paul Stanton, supt. Fax 759-4020
www.humboldtunified.com/
Bradshaw Mountain HS 1,700/9-12
6000 E Long Look Dr 86314 928-759-4100
Kort Miner, prin. Fax 759-4120
Glassford Hill MS 400/7-8
6901 Panther Path 86314 928-759-4600
Dr. Theresa Matteson, prin. Fax 759-4620
Other Schools – See Dewey

Yavapai Accommodation SD
Supt. — See Prescott
Yavapai County HS 100/Alt
6325 Baja Cir 86314 928-759-8126
Jim Taylor, dir. Fax 759-8136

Northcentral University Post-Sec.
10000 E University Dr 86314 928-541-7777

Queen Creek, Maricopa, Pop. 25,755
Chandler USD 80
Supt. — See Chandler
Payne JHS 1,200/7-8
7655 S Higley Rd, 480-224-2400
Paul Bollard, prin. Fax 224-2420

Florence USD 1
Supt. — See Florence
Poston Butte HS 1,300/9-12
32375 N Gantzel Rd, 480-474-6100
Dr. Bob Pappalardo, prin. Fax 882-1390

Queen Creek USD 95 5,400/PK-12
20217 E Chandler Heights Rd, 480-987-5935
Tom Lindsey, supt. Fax 987-9714
www.qcusd.org/
Barney JHS 800/7-8
24937 S Sossaman Rd, 480-474-6700
Denise Johnson, prin. Fax 882-3181
Queen Creek HS 1,700/9-12
22149 E Ocotillo Rd, 480-987-5973
Dr. Joseph Farnsworth, prin. Fax 882-1276

Freedom Christian Academy 50/PK-12
39731 N Kennedy Dr, 480-987-5488
Keather Healy, prin. Fax 987-9344

Red Valley, Apache, Pop. 30
Red Mesa USD 27
Supt. — See Teec Nos Pos
Red Valley/Cove HS 100/9-12
Navaho Route 13 86544 928-653-4200
Laurethena Kady, prin. Fax 653-4204

Rio Rico, Santa Cruz, Pop. 18,904
Santa Cruz Valley USD 35 3,500/PK-12
1374 W Frontage Rd 85648 520-375-8261
Rodney K. Rich, supt. Fax 281-7093
www.santacruz.k12.az.us
Calabasas MS 500/6-8
1374 W Frontage Rd 85648 520-375-8600
David Verdugo, prin. Fax 375-8690
Coatimundi MS 400/6-8
1374 W Frontage Rd 85648 520-375-8800
John Fanning, prin. Fax 761-4669
Rio Rico HS 1,100/9-12
1374 W Frontage Rd 85648 520-375-8700
Shelly Vroegh, prin. Fax 377-9556

Sacaton, Pinal, Pop. 2,641
Sacaton ESD 18 500/PK-12
PO Box 98, 520-562-8600
Dr. James Christensen, supt. Fax 763-4410
sacatonschools.org
Sacaton MS 200/5-8
PO Box 98, 520-562-8600
Philip Bonds, prin. Fax 763-4410

Safford, Graham, Pop. 9,405
Safford USD 1 3,200/PK-12
734 W 11th St 85546 928-348-7000
Dr. Mark Tregaskes, supt. Fax 348-7001
www.saffordusd.k12.az.us
Mt. Graham HS 100/Alt
300 W Discovery Park Blvd 85546 928-348-7060
Lori VanScyoc, prin. Fax 348-7061
Safford HS 700/9-12
1400 W 11th St 85546 928-348-7050
Rich DeRidder, prin. Fax 348-7051
Safford MS 500/7-8
612 W 11th St 85546 928-348-7040
Clay Emery, prin. Fax 348-7041

Safford College of Beauty Culture Post-Sec.
1550 W Thatcher Blvd 85546 928-428-0331

Sahuarita, Pima, Pop. 24,638
Sahuarita USD 30 6,300/PK-12
350 W Sahuarita Rd 85629 520-625-3502
Dr. Manuel Valenzuela, supt. Fax 625-4609
www.sahuarita.net/
Sahuarita HS 1,500/9-12
350 W Sahuarita Rd 85629 520-625-3502
Kent Thompson, prin. Fax 399-1223
Sahuarita MS 700/6-8
350 W Sahuarita Rd 85629 520-625-3502
Stephanie Silman, prin. Fax 393-7043
Walden Grove HS 700/9-12
350 W Sahuarita Rd 85629 520-625-3502
Teresa Hill, prin. Fax 393-7048

Saint David, Cochise, Pop. 1,668
Saint David USD 21 400/PK-12
PO Box 70 85630 520-720-4781
Mark Goodman, supt. Fax 720-4783
www.stdavidschools.org/
Saint David HS 100/9-12
PO Box 70 85630 520-720-4781
Dan Cover, prin. Fax 720-4783

Saint Johns, Apache, Pop. 3,399
Saint Johns USD 1 900/PK-12
PO Box 3030 85936 928-337-2255
Larry Heap, supt. Fax 337-2263
www.sjusd.net
Saint Johns HS 300/9-12
PO Box 429 85936 928-337-2221
Roger Heap, prin. Fax 337-2263
Saint Johns Learning Center 50/Alt
PO Box 3030 85936 928-337-2221
Kim Fejes, dir.
Saint Johns MS 300/4-8
PO Box 3060 85936 928-337-2132
Ed Burgoyne, prin. Fax 337-3147

Saint Michaels, Apache, Pop. 1,404

St. Michael HS 200/9-12
PO Box 650 86511 928-871-4443
Susan Clement, prin. Fax 871-3191

Salome, LaPaz, Pop. 1,511
Bicentennial UNHSD 76 100/9-12
PO Box 519 85348 928-859-3453
Fax 859-3875
www.salomehs.org
Salome HS 100/9-12
PO Box 519 85348 928-859-3453
Byron Maynes, prin. Fax 859-3875

San Carlos, Gila, Pop. 4,011
San Carlos USD 20 800/PK-12
PO Box 207 85550 928-475-2315
Catherine Steele, supt. Fax 475-2301
www.sancarlosbraves.org
San Carlos Alternative S Alt
PO Box 207 85550 928-475-5538
Carol Slim, prin. Fax 475-2301
San Carlos JSHS 300/7-12
PO Box 207 85550 928-475-2378
LaRonda Lugo, prin. Fax 475-2697

Sanders, Apache, Pop. 600
Sanders USD 18 1,000/K-12
PO Box 250 86512 928-688-4750
Marilinda Porter, supt. Fax 688-4723
www.sandersusd.net/
Sanders MS 300/6-8
PO Box 250 86512 928-688-4770
Josh Kervin, prin. Fax 688-4773
Valley HS 400/9-12
PO Box 250 86512 928-688-4200
Kenneth Poppino, prin. Fax 688-4202

San Luis, Yuma, Pop. 25,496
Gadsden ESD 32 5,000/PK-8
PO Box 6870 85349 928-627-6540
Raymond Aguilera, supt. Fax 627-3635
www.gesd32.org/
San Luis MS 600/7-8
PO Box 6870 85349 928-627-6920
Rafael Sanchez, prin. Fax 627-9339
Southwest JHS 700/7-8
PO Box 6870 85349 928-627-6580
Richard West, prin. Fax 627-9266

Yuma UNHSD 70
Supt. — See Yuma
San Luis HS 2,600/9-12
PO Box 7380 85349 928-502-6100
Fran Rodriguez, prin. Fax 502-6222

San Manuel, Pinal, Pop. 3,491
Mammoth-San Manuel USD 8 800/PK-12
PO Box 406 85631 520-385-2337
John Ryan, supt. Fax 385-2621
www.msmusd.org
San Manuel JSHS 300/7-12
PO Box 406 85631 520-385-2336
John Ryan, prin. Fax 385-3035

San Simon, Cochise, Pop. 160
San Simon USD 18 100/K-12
PO Box 38 85632 520-845-2275
Curry Donaldson, supt. Fax 845-2480
www.sansimon.k12.az.us
San Simon S 100/K-12
PO Box 38 85632 520-845-2275
Joe Guthrie, admin. Fax 845-2480

San Tan Valley, Pinal, Pop. 79,014
Coolidge USD 21
Supt. — See Coolidge
Mountain Vista MS 400/6-8
33622 N Mountain Vista Blvd, 480-677-4400
Denise Taylor, prin. Fax 677-4406

San Tan Foothills HS 500/9-12
1255 W Silverdale Rd, 480-677-4405
Alison Bruening, prin. Fax 888-2611

J.O. Combs USD 44 2,600/K-12
301 E Combs Rd, 480-987-5300
Dr. Gayle A. Blanchard, supt. Fax 987-3487
www.jocombs.org/
Combs HS 9-12
2505 E Germann Rd, 480-882-3540
Brenda Mayberry, prin. Fax 987-0837
Combs MS 300/7-8
37611 N Pecan Crk, 480-882-3510
Mark Mauro, prin. Fax 888-8049

Scottsdale, Maricopa, Pop. 213,310
Cave Creek USD 93 5,800/PK-12
33606 N 60th St 85266 480-575-2000
Dr. Debbi Burdick, supt. Fax 488-7055
www.ccusd93.org
Cactus Shadows HS 1,800/9-12
5802 E Dove Valley Rd 85266 480-575-2400
Steve Bebee, prin. Fax 488-6701
Other Schools – See Phoenix

Paradise Valley USD 69
Supt. — See Phoenix
Desert Shadows MS 700/7-8
5858 E Sweetwater Ave 85254 602-449-6800
Patrick Clancy, prin. Fax 449-6805
Horizon HS 2,100/9-12
5601 E Greenway Rd 85254 602-449-6000
Linda Ihnat, prin. Fax 449-6005
Sunrise MS 600/7-8
4960 E Acoma Dr 85254 602-449-6100
Gregory Martin, prin. Fax 449-6105

Scottsdale USD 48
Supt. — See Phoenix
Chaparral HS 2,100/9-12
6935 E Gold Dust Ave 85253 480-484-6500
Gayle Holland, prin. Fax 484-6501
Cocopah MS 900/6-8
6615 E Cholla St 85254 480-484-4400
Susan Thomas, prin. Fax 484-4401
Coronado HS 1,300/9-12
7501 E Virginia Ave 85257 480-484-6800
Alyssa Tarkington, prin. Fax 484-6801
Desert Canyon MS 700/6-8
10203 E McDowell Mntn Ranch 85255 480-484-4600
Eileen Nilson, prin. Fax 484-4601
Desert Mountain HS 2,300/9-12
12575 E Via Linda 85259 480-484-7000
Greg Milbrandt, prin. Fax 484-7001
Mohave MS 600/7-8
8490 E Jackrabbit Rd 85250 480-484-5200
Chris Asmussen, prin. Fax 484-5201
Mountainside MS 900/6-8
11256 N 128th St 85259 480-484-5500
Terri Kellen, prin. Fax 484-5501
Saguaro HS 1,400/9-12
6250 N 82nd St 85250 480-484-7100
Brian Corto, prin. Fax 484-7101
Sierra Vista Academy 100/Alt
7501 E Oak St 85257 480-484-7900
Rhonda Rickard, prin. Fax 484-7901
Supai MS 500/7-8
6720 E Continental Dr 85257 480-484-5800
Sheryl Rednor, prin. Fax 484-5801

Arizona Culinary Institute Post-Sec.
10585 N 114th St Ste 401 85259 480-603-1066
Arizona International Academy 50/5-9
12430 N Scottsdale Rd 85254 480-948-3419
Fax 948-8884
Automotive Dealership Institute Post-Sec.
6613 N Scottsdale Rd 85250 480-998-7200
Brighton College Post-Sec.
7332 E Butherus Dr Ste 102 85260 800-354-1254
Cortiva Institute - Scottsdale Post-Sec.
8010 E McDowell Rd Ste 214 85257 480-684-1275
Devereux-Arizona Treatment Network Post-Sec.
11000 N Scottsville Rd #260 85254 480-998-2920
Empire Beauty School Post-Sec.
7730 E McDowell Rd 85257 480-949-7557
Frank Lloyd Wright Sch of Architecture Post-Sec.
PO Box 4430 85261 480-860-2700
Le Cordon Bleu College of Culinary Arts Post-Sec.
8100 E Camelback Rd # 1001 85251 480-990-3773
Notre Dame Preparatory HS 900/9-12
9701 E Bell Rd 85260 480-634-8200
David Gonsalves, prin. Fax 634-8299
Penn Foster College Post-Sec.
14300 N Northsight Ste 120 85260 480-947-6644
Penrose Academy Post-Sec.
13402 N Scottsdale Rd #B160 85254 480-222-9540
Schwartz College Prep S 100/9-12
12701 N Scottsdale Rd 85254 480-219-9097
Fax 634-4588
Scott Cole Academy Post-Sec.
7201 E Camelback Rd Ste 100 85251 480-994-4222
Scottsdale Community College Post-Sec.
9000 E Chaparral Rd 85256 480-423-6000
Sonoran Desert Institute Post-Sec.
10245 E Via Linda Ste 110 85258 480-314-2102
The Paralegal Institute Post-Sec.
7332 E Butherus Dr Ste 102 85260 800-354-1254
Thunderbird Adventist Academy 100/9-12
7410 E Sutton Dr 85260 480-948-3300
Rick Maloon, prin. Fax 443-4944

Sedona, Coconino, Pop. 9,896
Sedona-Oak Creek JUSD 9 1,200/K-12
221 Brewer Rd Ste 100 86336 928-204-6800
David Lykins, supt. Fax 282-0232
www.sedona.k12.az.us/
Sedona Red Rock HS 500/9-12
995 Upper Red Rock Loop Rd 86336 928-204-6700
David Lykins, prin. Fax 282-5992

Verde Valley S 100/9-12
3511 Verde Valley School Rd 86351 928-284-2272
Graham Frey, hdmstr. Fax 284-0432

Seligman, Yavapai, Pop. 428
Seligman USD 40 100/K-12
PO Box 650 86337 928-422-3233
Kristen Rex, supt. Fax 422-3642
www.seligmanschools.org/
Seligman HS 100/9-12
PO Box 650 86337 928-422-3233
Fax 422-3642

Sells, Pima, Pop. 2,459
Baboquivari USD 40 1,100/K-12
PO Box 248 85634 520-383-6746
Alberto Siqueiros, supt. Fax 383-5441
busd40.org
Baboquivari MS 200/6-8
PO Box 248 85634 520-383-6950
Toni Allen, prin. Fax 383-5930
Indian Oasis JSHS 100/Alt
PO Box 248 85634 520-383-6746
Gregory Copeland, prin. Fax 383-5441
Other Schools – See Topawa

Tohono O'odham Community College Post-Sec.
PO Box 3129 85634 520-383-8401

Show Low, Navajo, Pop. 10,473
Show Low USD 10 2,400/PK-12
500 W Old Linden Rd 85901 928-537-6000
Kevin Brackney, supt. Fax 537-6009
www.show-low.k12.az.us
Show Low HS 800/9-12
500 W Old Linden Rd 85901 928-537-6200
Farrell Adams, prin. Fax 537-6299
Show Low JHS 600/6-8
500 W Old Linden Rd 85901 928-537-6100
Kevin Bortin, prin. Fax 537-6149
White Mountain Institute 50/Alt
500 W Old Linden Rd 85901 928-537-6201
Farrell Adams, prin. Fax 537-6299

American Indian Christian S 50/3-8
924 Mission Ln Lot 1 85901 928-537-5912
Angela Solliday, prin. Fax 537-5620

Sierra Vista, Cochise, Pop. 41,754
Sierra Vista USD 68 5,100/PK-12
3555 E Fry Blvd 85635 520-515-2714
Brett Agenbroad, supt. Fax 515-2721
www.svusd68.org
Buena HS 2,200/9-12
3555 E Fry Blvd 85635 520-515-2800
John Schreur, prin. Fax 515-2877
Clark MS 7-8
3555 E Fry Blvd 85635 520-515-2930
Jim Sprigg, prin. Fax 515-2941

DeVoe College of Beauty Post-Sec.
PO Box 1571 85636 520-458-8660
Veritas Christian Community S 100/K-12
215 Taylor Dr 85635 520-417-1113
Karen Bolton, head sch Fax 417-0180

Snowflake, Navajo, Pop. 5,508
Snowflake USD 5 2,600/K-12
682 W School Bus Ln 85937 928-536-4156
Hollis Merrell, supt. Fax 536-2634
www.snowflake.k12.az.us
Snowflake HS 700/9-12
682 W School Bus Ln 85937 928-536-4156
Larry Titus, prin. Fax 536-4240
Snowflake JHS 400/7-8
682 W School Bus Ln 85937 928-536-4156
Kim Lewis, prin. Fax 536-3007

Somerton, Yuma, Pop. 14,249
Somerton ESD 11 2,600/PK-8
PO Box 3200 85350 928-341-6000
Dr. Frank Reed, supt. Fax 341-6090
www.somerton.k12.az.us
Somerton MS 800/6-8
PO Box 3200 85350 928-341-6100
Elizabeth Garza, prin. Fax 341-6190

Springerville, Apache, Pop. 1,931
Round Valley USD 10 1,100/K-12
PO Box 610 85938 928-333-6580
Travis Udall, supt. Fax 333-2823
www.elks.net
White Mountain Academy Alt
PO Box 610 85938 928-333-6563
Scott Patton, lead tchr. Fax 333-6895
Other Schools – See Eagar

Sun City, Maricopa, Pop. 37,274

Walter Boswell Memorial Hospital Post-Sec.
10401 W Thunderbird Blvd 85351 623-977-7211

Superior, Pinal, Pop. 2,804
Superior USD 15 400/PK-12
1500 W Sunset Dr Ste 101, 520-689-3000
Pete Guzman, supt. Fax 689-3009
www.superior.k12.az.us/
Superior HS 100/9-12
100 W Mary Dr, 520-689-3100
Pete Guzman, prin. Fax 689-3197
Superior JHS 100/7-8
100 W Mary Dr, 520-689-3100
Pete Guzman, prin. Fax 689-3197

Surprise, Maricopa, Pop. 114,476
Dysart USD 89 24,000/K-12
15802 N Parkview Pl 85374 623-876-7000
Dr. Gail Pletnick, supt. Fax 876-7042
www.dysart.org

Shadow Ridge HS 900/9-12
10909 N Perryville Rd, 623-523-5100
Michael Hawkins, prin. Fax 523-5111
Sundown Mountain Alternative Program Alt
10909 N Perryville Rd, 623-876-7250
Jim Grieshaber, coord. Fax 876-7261
Valley Vista HS 2,200/9-12
15550 N Parkview Pl 85374 623-523-8800
Dannene Truett, prin. Fax 523-8811
Willow Canyon HS 2,000/9-12
17901 W Lundberg St, 623-523-8000
Anthony Capuano, prin. Fax 523-8011
Other Schools – See El Mirage

Teec Nos Pos, Apache, Pop. 721
Red Mesa USD 27 800/K-12
HC 61 Box 40 86514 928-656-4100
Dr. Tommie Yazzie, supt. Fax 656-4106
www.rmusd.net
Red Mesa HS 300/9-12
HC 61 Box 40 86514 928-656-4177
Don Lawrence, prin. Fax 656-4178
Other Schools – See Red Valley

Immanuel Mission S 100/K-12
PO Box 1080 86514 830-200-0351
John Bloom, prin. Fax 435-7041

Tempe, Maricopa, Pop. 156,729
Kyrene ESD 28 17,700/PK-8
8700 S Kyrene Rd 85284 480-541-1000
David Schauer Ed.D., supt. Fax 541-1860
www.kyrene.org
Kyrene MS 1,100/6-8
1050 E Carver Rd 85284 480-541-6600
Jama Nacke, prin. Fax 541-6610
Other Schools – See Chandler, Phoenix

Tempe ESD 3 10,600/K-8
PO Box 27708 85285 480-730-7100
Christine Busch, supt. Fax 730-7177
www.tempeschools.org
Connolly MS 800/6-8
2002 E Concorda Dr 85282 480-967-8933
Kathryn Mullery, prin. Fax 929-9695
Fees College Preparatory Academy 800/6-8
1600 E Watson Dr 85283 480-897-6063
Kacy Tomason, prin. Fax 838-0853
Gililland MS 800/6-8
1025 S Beck Ave 85281 480-966-7114
Brady Wald, prin. Fax 829-6178
Tempe Academy of International Studies 6-8
2250 S College Ave 85282 480-730-7101
Marianne McMurrin, prin.

Tempe UNHSD 213 13,800/9-12
500 W Guadalupe Rd 85283 480-839-0292
Kenneth Baca, supt. Fax 413-0605
www.tuhsd.k12.az.us
Compadre Academy 600/Alt
500 W Guadalupe Rd 85283 480-752-3560
Sean McDonald, prin. Fax 752-3569
Compadre Academy North Alt
4525 S College Ave 85282 480-345-3560
George Barnes, prin. Fax 491-8540
Corona Del Sol HS 2,400/9-12
1001 E Knox Rd 85284 480-752-8888
Brent Brown, prin. Fax 820-3632
Marcos De Niza HS 1,900/9-12
6000 S Lakeshore Dr 85283 480-838-3200
Frank Mirizio, prin. Fax 730-7665
McClintock HS 1,900/9-12
1830 E Del Rio Dr 85282 480-839-4222
Derek Hoffland, prin. Fax 752-8661
Tempe HS 1,400/9-12
1730 S Mill Ave 85281 480-967-1661
Mark Yslas, prin. Fax 736-4096
Other Schools – See Phoenix

Acacia University Post-Sec.
7665 S Research Dr 85284 480-428-6034
Arizona State University Post-Sec.
PO Box 870112 85287 480-965-9011
Brookline College Post-Sec.
1140 S Priest Dr 85281 480-545-8755
Carsten Aveda Institute Post-Sec.
3345 S Rural Rd 85282 480-491-0449
Conservatory of Recording Arts/Sciences Post-Sec.
2300 E Broadway Rd 85282 480-858-9400
Harrison Middleton University Post-Sec.
1105 E Broadway Rd 85282 877-248-6724
International Academy of Hair Post-Sec.
4812 S Mill Ave 85282 480-964-8675
ITT Technical Institute Post-Sec.
5005 S Wendler Dr 85282 602-437-7500
Lamson College Post-Sec.
875 W Elliot Rd Ste 206 85284 480-898-7000
Rio Salado College Post-Sec.
2323 W 14th St 85281 480-517-8000
Sessions College of Professional Design Post-Sec.
398 S Mill Ave Ste 300 85281 480-212-1704
Southwest Coll of Naturopathic Medicine Post-Sec.
2140 E Broadway Rd 85282 480-858-9100
Southwest Institute of Healing Arts Post-Sec.
1100 E Apache Blvd 85281 480-994-9244
University of Advancing Technology Post-Sec.
2625 W Baseline Rd 85283 800-658-5744

Thatcher, Graham, Pop. 4,760
Thatcher USD 4 1,400/K-12
PO Box 610 85552 928-348-7200
Paul Nelson, supt. Fax 348-7220
www.thatcherud.k12.az.us
Thatcher HS 400/9-12
601 N 3rd Ave 85552 928-348-7272
Carol McAtee, prin. Fax 348-7273

Thatcher MS 200/7-8
1300 N 4th Ave 85552 928-348-7262
Matt Petersen, prin. Fax 348-7263

Eastern Arizona College Post-Sec.
615 N Stadium Ave 85552 800-678-3808

Tolleson, Maricopa, Pop. 6,455
Tolleson UNHSD 214 8,300/9-12
9801 W Van Buren St 85353 623-478-4000
Dr. Lexi Cunningham, supt. Fax 936-5048
www.tuhsd.org
Tolleson Union HS 1,800/9-12
9419 W Van Buren St 85353 623-478-4200
Ernie Molina, prin. Fax 478-4226
University HS 500/9-12
9419 W Van Buren St 85353 623-478-4212
Courtney Stevens, prin. Fax 478-4226
Other Schools – See Avondale, Glendale, Phoenix

Tombstone, Cochise, Pop. 1,359
Tombstone USD 1 900/PK-12
PO Box 1000 85638 520-457-2217
Karl Uterhardt, supt. Fax 457-3270
www.tombstone.k12.az.us/
Tombstone HS 400/9-12
PO Box 1000 85638 520-457-2215
Robert Devere, prin. Fax 457-3643

Tonalea, Coconino, Pop. 542
San Juan SD
Supt. — See Blanding, UT
Navajo Mountain HS 50/9-12
PO Box 10040 86044 435-678-1287
Gary Rock, admin. Fax 678-1289

Tonopah, Maricopa, Pop. 60
Saddle Mountain USD 90 1,600/K-12
38201 W Indian School Rd 85354 623-474-5115
Dr. Mark Joraanstad, supt. Fax 474-5190
www.smusd90.org
Tonopah Valley HS 400/9-12
38201 W Indian School Rd 85354 623-474-5201
Edgar Garcia, prin. Fax 474-5214

Topawa, Pima, Pop. 298
Baboquivari USD 40
Supt. — See Sells
Baboquivari HS 300/9-12
Indian Rte 10 85639 520-383-6800
Dawn Maddock, prin. Fax 383-4852

Tsaile, Apache, Pop. 1,179

Din College Post-Sec.
1 Circle Dr 86556 928-724-6600

Tuba City, Coconino, Pop. 8,486
Tuba City USD 15 1,700/PK-12
PO Box 67 86045 928-283-1000
Fax 283-1200
www.tcusd.org
Tuba City Alternative S 50/Alt
PO Box 67 86045 928-283-1070
Charles Henderson, prin. Fax 283-1226
Tuba City HS 700/9-12
PO Box 67 86045 928-283-1050
Ralph Navarre, prin. Fax 283-1204
Tuba City JHS 200/7-8
PO Box 67 86045 928-283-1042
Harriett Sloan-Carter, prin. Fax 283-1218

Tucson, Pima, Pop. 507,980
Altar Valley ESD 51 700/PK-8
10105 S Sasabe Rd 85736 520-822-1484
Nathan McCann, supt. Fax 822-1798
altarvalleyschools.org/
Altar Valley MS 300/5-8
10105 S Sasabe Rd 85736 520-822-9343
Josh Peebles, prin. Fax 822-5801

Amphitheater USD 10 14,800/PK-12
701 W Wetmore Rd 85705 520-696-5000
Patrick Nelson, supt. Fax 696-5015
www.amphi.com
Amphitheater HS 1,300/9-12
125 W Yavapai Rd 85705 520-696-5340
Jon Lansa, prin. Fax 696-5410
Amphitheater MS 700/6-8
315 E Prince Rd 85705 520-696-6230
Tassi Call, prin. Fax 696-6236
Canyon Del Oro HS 1,700/9-12
25 W Calle Concordia 85704 520-696-5560
Marcia Volpe, prin. Fax 696-5590
Cross MS 800/6-8
1000 W Chapala Dr 85704 520-696-5920
Shannon Chandler, prin. Fax 696-5996
La Cima MS 600/6-8
5600 N La Canada Dr 85704 520-696-6730
Christine Sullivan, prin. Fax 696-6792
Other Schools – See Oro Valley

Catalina Foothills USD 16 4,900/PK-12
2101 E River Rd 85718 520-209-7500
Mary Kamerzell, supt. Fax 209-7570
www.cfsd16.org/
Catalina Foothills HS 1,700/9-12
4300 E Sunrise Dr 85718 520-209-8300
Angela Chomokos, prin. Fax 209-8520
Esperero Canyon MS 600/6-8
5801 N Sabino Canyon Rd 85750 520-209-8100
Brian Lorimer, prin. Fax 209-8170
Orange Grove MS 600/6-8
1911 E Orange Grove Rd 85718 520-209-8200
Susan Rosenthal, prin. Fax 209-8275

Flowing Wells USD 8 5,600/PK-12
1556 W Prince Rd 85705 520-696-8800
Dr. Nicholas Clement, supt. Fax 690-2330
www.flowingwellsschools.org
Flowing Wells HS 1,800/9-12
3725 N Flowing Wells Rd 85705 520-696-8150
Jim Brunenkant, prin. Fax 690-2379
Flowing Wells JHS 800/7-8
4545 N La Cholla Blvd 85705 520-696-8550
Pete Wells, prin. Fax 690-2420
Sentinel Peak HS 100/Alt
4125 W Aerie 85705 520-696-8900
Kim Parkinson, prin. Fax 690-2329

Marana USD 6
Supt. — See Marana
Marana HS 1,900/9-12
12000 W Emigh Rd 85743 520-616-6400
Dr. Allison Murphy, prin. Fax 616-6426
Mountain View HS 1,900/9-12
3901 W Linda Vista Blvd 85742 520-579-4400
Patricia Cadigan, prin. Fax 579-4505
Tortolita MS 1,000/7-8
4101 W Hardy Rd 85742 520-579-4600
Barbara Kohl, prin. Fax 579-4646

Sunnyside USD 12 17,300/PK-12
2238 E Ginter Rd 85706 520-545-2000
Dr. Manuel Isquierdo, supt. Fax 545-2120
www.susd12.org
Apollo MS 800/6-8
265 W Nebraska St 85706 520-545-4500
Rosemary Rosas, prin. Fax 545-4516
Challenger MS 900/6-8
100 E Elvira Rd, 520-545-4600
Roxana Rico, prin. Fax 545-4616
Chaparral MS 700/6-8
3700 E Alvord Rd 85706 520-545-4700
John Benavidez, prin. Fax 545-4716
Desert View HS 2,100/9-12
4101 E Valencia Rd 85706 520-545-5100
Jose Gastelum, prin. Fax 545-5116
Lauffer MS 600/6-8
5385 E Littletown Rd, 520-545-4900
Robert Miranda, prin. Fax 545-4916
S.T.A.R. Academic Center 300/Alt
5093 S Liberty Ave 85706 520-545-2300
Art Menchaca, prin. Fax 545-2316
Sierra MS 1,000/6-8
5801 S Del Moral Blvd 85706 520-545-4800
Donna Samorano, prin. Fax 545-4816
Sunnyside HS 2,300/9-12
1725 E Bilby Rd 85706 520-545-5300
Steve Ybarra, prin. Fax 545-5316

Tanque Verde USD 13 1,700/PK-12
2300 N Tanque Verde Loop Rd 85749 520-749-5751
Dr. Doug Price, supt. Fax 749-5400
www.tanqueverdeschools.org/
Gray JHS 300/7-8
11150 E Tanque Verde Rd 85749 520-749-3838
Greg Miller, prin. Fax 749-9668
Tanque Verde HS 300/9-12
4201 N Melpomene Way 85749 520-760-0801
Greg Anderson, prin. Fax 749-9668

Tucson USD 1 51,800/PK-12
1010 E 10th St 85719 520-225-6000
John Pedicone Ph.D., supt. Fax 225-6174
www.tusd.k12.az.us
Carson MS 500/6-8
7777 E Stella Rd 85730 520-584-4700
John Howe, prin. Fax 584-4701
Catalina Magnet HS 1,400/9-12
3645 E Pima St 85716 520-232-8400
Rex Scott, prin. Fax 232-8401
Cholla Magnet HS 1,700/9-12
2001 W Starr Pass Blvd 85713 520-225-4000
Frank Armenta, prin. Fax 225-4001
Dodge Magnet MS 400/6-8
5831 E Pima St 85712 520-731-4100
Daniel Schulter, prin. Fax 731-4101
Doolen MS 700/6-8
2400 N Country Club Rd 85716 520-232-6900
Martha Taylor, prin. Fax 232-6901
Gridley MS 700/6-8
350 S Harrison Rd 85748 520-731-4600
Kathleen Scheppe, prin. Fax 731-4601
Hohokam MS 500/6-8
7400 S Settler Ave 85746 520-908-3700
Theresa Leal-Holmes, prin. Fax 908-3701
Howenstine Magnet HS 200/9-12
555 S Tucson Blvd 85716 520-232-7300
Maritza Nunez, prin. Fax 232-7301
Lawrence IS 200/3-8
4850 W Jeffrey Rd, 520-908-3900
Mary Mercado, prin. Fax 908-3901
Life Skills/Core Plus 50/Alt
6855 S Mark Rd, 520-908-3976
Israel Macias-Reyes, prin. Fax 908-3978
Magee MS 700/6-8
8300 E Speedway Blvd 85710 520-731-5000
Daniel Erickson, prin. Fax 731-5001
Mansfeld MS 700/6-8
1300 E 6th St 85719 520-225-1800
Paul DeWeerdt, prin. Fax 225-1801
Maxwell MS 400/6-8
2802 W Anklam Rd 85745 520-225-2000
Mary Quinnan, prin. Fax 225-2001
Palo Verde Magnet HS 1,200/9-12
1302 S Avenida Vega 85710 520-584-7400
Janna Acevedo, prin. Fax 584-7441
Pistor MS 1,100/6-8
5455 S Cardinal Ave 85746 520-908-5400
Kathryn Manley-Crockett, prin. Fax 908-5411
Project M.O.R.E. HS 100/Alt
440 S Park Ave 85719 520-225-2600
Charlotte Patterson, prin. Fax 225-2601

Pueblo Magnet HS 1,800/9-12
3500 S 12th Ave 85713 520-225-4300
Vivi Watt, prin. Fax 225-4301
Rincon HS 1,200/9-12
421 N Arcadia Ave 85711 520-232-5600
Catherine Comstock, prin. Fax 232-5601
Sabino HS 1,200/9-12
5000 N Bowes Rd 85749 520-584-7700
Valerie Payne, prin. Fax 584-7701
Sahuaro HS 1,800/9-12
545 N Camino Seco 85710 520-731-7100
Sam Giangardella, prin. Fax 731-7101
Santa Rita HS 1,100/9-12
3951 S Pantano Rd 85730 520-731-7500
Christopher Bonn, prin. Fax 731-7501
Secrist MS 500/6-8
3400 S Houghton Rd 85730 520-731-5300
Sunshine Turner, prin. Fax 731-5301
Southwest Alternative HS 50/Alt
6855 S Mark Rd, 520-908-3980
Roxanne Begay, prin. Fax 908-3978
Tucson Magnet HS 3,000/9-12
400 N 2nd Ave 85705 520-225-5000
Clarice Clash, prin. Fax 225-5221
University HS 900/9-12
421 N Arcadia Ave 85711 520-232-5900
Elizabeth Moll, prin. Fax 235-5901
Utterback Magnet MS 800/6-8
3233 S Pinal Vls 85713 520-225-3500
Cindy Shephard-Mady, prin. Fax 225-3501
Vail MS 700/6-8
5350 E 16th St 85711 520-584-5400
Robert Vinyard, prin. Fax 584-5401
Valencia MS 700/6-8
4400 W Irvington Rd 85746 520-908-4500
Patricia Acosta, prin. Fax 908-4501
Wakefield MS 500/6-8
101 W 44th St 85713 520-225-3800
Ruben Diaz, prin. Fax 225-3801

Vail USD 20
Supt. — See Vail
Andrada Polytechnic HS 600/9-12
12960 S Houghton Rd 85747 520-879-3300
Darcy Mentone, prin. Fax 879-3301
Desert Sky MS 700/6-8
9850 E Rankin Loop 85747 520-879-2700
Micah Mortensen, prin. Fax 879-2701
Empire HS 800/9-12
10701 E Mary Ann Cleveland 85747 520-879-3000
Matt Donaldson, prin. Fax 879-3001
Pantano HS 100/Alt
13010 S Houghton Rd 85747 520-879-1200
Monica Wright, prin. Fax 879-1201
Rincon Vista MS 500/6-8
10770 E Bilby Rd 85747 520-879-3200
Lydia Crain, prin. Fax 879-3201

Arizona Academy of Beauty Post-Sec.
5631 E Speedway Blvd 85712 520-885-4120
Arizona Academy of Beauty - North Post-Sec.
4066 N Oracle Rd 85705 520-888-0170
AZ School of Acupuncture & Oriental Med Post-Sec.
4646 E Ft Lowell Rd Ste 103 85712 520-795-0787
AZ State School for the Deaf & Blind Post-Sec.
PO Box 85000 85754 520-770-3719
Asian Institute of Medical Studies Post-Sec.
3131 N Country Club Rd #100 85716 520-322-6330
Brookline College Post-Sec.
5441 E 22nd St Ste 125 85711 520-748-9799
Brown Mackie College - Tucson Post-Sec.
4585 E Speedway Blvd # 204 85712 520-319-3300
Carondelet Saint Marys Hospital Post-Sec.
1601 W Saint Marys Rd 85745 520-622-5833
Carrington College Post-Sec.
3550 N Oracle Rd 85705 520-888-5885
Cortiva Institute - Tucson Post-Sec.
6390 E Broadway Blvd 85710 520-407-5160
Desert Christian HS 200/9-12
7525 E Speedway Blvd 85710 520-298-5817
Jon Self, prin. Fax 298-9312
Empire Beauty School Post-Sec.
3030 E Speedway Blvd 85716 520-327-6544
Fenster S 50/6-12
8505 E Ocotillo Dr 85750 520-749-3340
Tony Tsang, hdmstr. Fax 749-3349
Green Fields Country Day S 200/K-12
6000 N Camino De La Tierra 85741 520-297-2288
Rebecca Cordier M.Ed., head sch Fax 297-2072
HDS Truck Driving Institute Post-Sec.
PO Box 17600 85731 520-721-5825
Imago Dei MS 100/5-8
PO Box 3056 85702 520-882-4008
Rev. Anne Sawyer, hdmstr. Fax 882-4011
Immaculate Heart HS 400/9-12
625 E Magee Rd 85704 520-297-2851
Dan Ethridge, prin. Fax 797-7374
ITT Technical Institute Post-Sec.
1455 W River Rd 85704 520-408-7488
Pima Community College Post-Sec.
4905 E Broadway Blvd 85709 520-206-4500
Pima Medical Institute Post-Sec.
3350 E Grant Rd 85716 520-326-1600
Pusch Ridge Christian Academy 500/6-12
9500 N Oracle Rd 85704 520-797-0107
Dennis O'Reilly, head sch Fax 797-0598
St. Augustine Catholic HS 100/9-12
8800 E 22nd St 85710 520-751-8300
Lynn Cuffari, prin. Fax 751-8304
St. Gregory College Preparatory S 300/6-12
3231 N Craycroft Rd 85712 520-327-6395
Dr. Julie Sherrill, head sch Fax 327-8276
Salpointe Catholic HS 1,200/9-12
1545 E Copper St 85719 520-327-6581
Sr. Helen Timothy, prin. Fax 327-8477

San Miguel HS — 300/9-12
6601 S San Fernando Rd, — 520-294-6403
Richard Reyes, prin. — Fax 294-6417
Southwest University of Visual Arts — Post-Sec.
2525 N Country Club Rd 85716 — 520-325-0123
The Art Institute of Tucson — Post-Sec.
5099 E Grant Rd Ste 100 85712 — 520-318-2700
Tucson College — Post-Sec.
5151 E Broadway Blvd # 155 85711 — 800-915-2096
Tucson Waldorf S — 100/3-8
3605 E River Rd 85718 — 520-529-1032
University of Arizona 85721 — Post-Sec.
520-621-2211

Vail, Pima, Pop. 9,882
Vail USD 20 — 10,500/K-12
PO Box 800 85641 — 520-879-2000
Calvin Baker, supt. — Fax 879-2001
www.vail.k12.az.us
Cienega HS — 2,000/9-12
12775 Mary Ann Cleveland 85641 — 520-879-2800
Dr. Tricia Pena, prin. — Fax 879-2801
Old Vail MS — 700/6-8
13299 E Colossal Cave Rd 85641 — 520-879-2400
Dr. Laurie Emery, prin. — Fax 879-2401
Other Schools – See Corona, Tucson

Wellton, Yuma, Pop. 2,851
Antelope UNHSD 50 — 300/9-12
9168 S Avenue 36 E 85356 — 928-785-4041
Andrew Smith, supt. — Fax 785-4588
www.antelopeunion.org/
Antelope Union HS — 300/9-12
9168 S Avenue 36 E 85356 — 928-785-3344
Randall O'Donnell, prin. — Fax 785-9566

Whiteriver, Navajo, Pop. 4,055
Whiteriver USD 20 — 2,200/PK-12
PO Box 190 85941 — 928-338-4842
Jeffrey Fuller, supt. — Fax 338-5124
www.wusd.us
Alchesay HS — 600/9-12
PO Box 190 85941 — 928-338-4848
Richard Swearengin, prin. — Fax 338-4840
Canyon Day JHS — 200/6-8
PO Box 190 85941 — 928-338-1040
Jay Cox, prin. — Fax 338-4850

Wickenburg, Maricopa, Pop. 6,301
Wickenburg USD 9 — 1,500/PK-12
40 W Yavapai St 85390 — 928-668-5350
Dr. Howard Carlson, supt. — Fax 668-5390
www.wickenburgschools.org/
Vulture Peak MS — 200/6-8
920 S Vulture Mine Rd 85390 — 928-684-6700
Marcia Hespen, prin. — Fax 684-6746
Wickenburg HS — 600/9-12
1090 S Vulture Mine Rd 85390 — 928-684-6600
Jacquelyn Jacobson, prin. — Fax 684-6628

Gospel Outreach Christian S — 50/PK-12
515 W Wickenburg Way 85390 — 928-684-5227
Victor Bedoian, supt. — Fax 684-2878
Wickenburg Christian Academy — 100/PK-12
260 W Yavapai St 85390 — 928-684-5916
Fax 684-6104

Willcox, Cochise, Pop. 3,704
Willcox USD 13 — 1,300/PK-12
480 N Bisbee Ave 85643 — 520-384-8600
Dr. Richard Rundhaug, supt. — Fax 384-4401
wusd13.org
Willcox HS — 400/9-12
240 N Bisbee Ave 85643 — 520-384-8601
Doris Jones, prin. — Fax 384-4006
Willcox MS — 400/4-8
360 N Bisbee Ave 85643 — 520-384-8602
Mike Patterson, prin. — Fax 384-6322

Williams, Coconino, Pop. 2,960
Williams USD 2 — 700/PK-12
PO Box 427 86046 — 928-635-4473
Rachel Savage, supt. — Fax 635-4767
www.wusd2.org
Williams HS — 200/9-12
PO Box 427 86046 — 928-635-4474
Tristan Heisley, prin. — Fax 635-2796

Winkelman, Gila, Pop. 352
Hayden-Winkelman USD 41 — 400/PK-12
PO Box 409, — 520-356-7876
Jeff Gregorich, supt. — Fax 356-7303
www.hwusd.k12.az.us/
Hambly MS — 100/6-8
PO Box 409, — 520-356-7876
Paul Hatch, prin. — Fax 356-7303
Hayden HS — 100/9-12
PO Box 409, — 520-356-7876
Paul Hatch, prin. — Fax 356-7303

Winslow, Navajo, Pop. 9,382
Winslow USD 1 — 2,300/PK-12
PO Box 580 86047 — 928-288-8101
Douglas Watson, supt. — Fax 288-8292
www.wusd1.org
Winslow HS — 800/9-12
PO Box 580 86047 — 928-288-8100
Chris Gilmore, prin. — Fax 288-8290
Winslow JHS — 400/7-8
PO Box 580 86047 — 928-288-8300
Justin Hartman, prin. — Fax 288-8303

Young, Gila, Pop. 657
Young ESD 5 — 50/PK-12
PO Box 390 85554 — 928-462-3244
Linda Cheney, supt. — Fax 462-3283
www.youngschool.org/

Young S — 50/PK-12
PO Box 390 85554 — 928-462-3244
Linda Cheney, prin. — Fax 462-3283

Yuma, Yuma, Pop. 91,424
Crane ESD 13 — 6,000/PK-8
4250 W 16th St 85364 — 928-373-3403
Robert Klee, supt. — Fax 782-6831
www.craneschools.org/
Centennial MS — 700/7-8
2650 W 20th St 85364 — 928-373-3300
Helen Coffeen, prin. — Fax 376-7742
Crane MS — 700/7-8
4450 W 32nd St 85364 — 928-373-3200
Laurie Doering, prin. — Fax 344-6821

Yuma ESD 1 — 9,500/PK-8
450 W 6th St 85364 — 928-502-4300
Darwin Stiffler, supt. — Fax 502-4442
www.yuma.org
Castle Dome MS — 800/6-8
2353 S Otondo Dr 85365 — 928-502-7300
Lori Sheffield, prin. — Fax 341-1700
Fourth Avenue JHS — 500/6-8
450 S 4th Ave 85364 — 928-502-7000
Jose Cazares, prin. — Fax 783-2195
Gila Vista JHS — 500/6-8
2245 S Arizona Ave 85364 — 928-502-7100
Rusty Tyndall, prin. — Fax 782-1483
Watson MS — 400/6-8
9851 E 28th St 85365 — 928-502-7400
Donna Franklin, prin. — Fax 502-7403
Woodard JHS — 800/6-8
2250 S 8th Ave 85364 — 928-502-7200
Andy Wait, prin. — Fax 782-4596

Yuma UNHSD 70 — 11,100/9-12
3150 S Avenue A 85364 — 928-502-4600
Toni Badone, supt. — Fax 344-9157
www.yumaunion.org/
Cibola HS — 2,500/9-12
4100 W 20th St 85364 — 928-502-5700
Tim Brienza, prin. — Fax 502-6046
Gila Ridge HS — 1,800/9-12
7150 E 24th St 85365 — 928-502-6400
Suzanne Alka, prin. — Fax 502-6749
Kofa HS — 2,200/9-12
3100 S Avenue A 85364 — 928-502-5400
Mike Sharp, prin. — Fax 502-5693
Vista Alternative S — 300/Alt
2350 S Virginia Dr 85364 — 928-343-2521
Lisa Anderson, prin. — Fax 343-2582
Yuma HS — 1,600/9-12
400 S 6th Ave 85364 — 928-502-5000
Faith Klostreich, prin. — Fax 502-5338
Other Schools – See San Luis

Arizona Western College — Post-Sec.
PO Box 929 85366 — 928-317-6000
Yuma Catholic HS — 300/9-12
2100 W 28th St 85364 — 928-317-7000
Danny Garcia, prin. — Fax 317-8558

ARKANSAS

ARKANSAS DEPARTMENT OF EDUCATION

4 State Capitol Rm 304A, Little Rock 72201
Telephone 501-682-4475
Fax 501-682-1079
Website http://www.arkansased.org/

Commissioner of Education Dr. Tom Kimbrell

ARKANSAS BOARD OF EDUCATION

4 State Capitol, Little Rock 72201

Chairperson Jim Cooper

EDUCATION SERVICE COOPERATIVES (ESC)

Arch Ford ESC
Phillip Young, dir. 501-354-2269
101 Bulldog Dr, Plumerville 72127 Fax 354-0167
www.afsc.k12.ar.us/

Arkansas River ESC
Barbara Warren, dir. 870-534-6129
912 W 6th Ave, Pine Bluff 71601 Fax 534-2847
genie.arsc.k12.ar.us

Crowley's Ridge ESC
John Manning, dir. 870-578-5426
1606 Pine Grove Ln Fax 578-5896
Harrisburg 72432
crowleys.crsc.k12.ar.us/

Dawson ESC
Ron Wright, dir. 870-246-3077
711 Clinton St Ste 201 Fax 246-5892
Arkadelphia 71923
www.dawson.dsc.k12.ar.us

De Queen/Mena ESC
John Ponder, dir. 870-386-2251
PO Box 110, Gillham 71841 Fax 386-7731
nexus.dmsc.k12.ar.us/

Great Rivers ESC
Suzann McCommon, dir. 870-338-6461
PO Box 2837, West Helena 72390 Fax 338-7905
www.grsc.k12.ar.us/

Northcentral Arkansas ESC
Dr. Dennis Martin, dir. 870-368-7955
99 Haley St, Melbourne 72556 Fax 368-4920
naesc.k12.ar.us/

Northeast Arkansas ESC
Donna Harris, dir., 211 W Hickory St 870-886-7717
Walnut Ridge 72476 Fax 886-7719
nea.k12.ar.us

Northwest Arkansas ESC
Mike Van Dyke, dir. 479-267-7450
4 N Double Springs Rd Fax 267-7456
Farmington 72730
www.starfishnw.org

Ozarks Unlimited Resource Cooperative
Rick Nance, dir. 870-429-9100
5823 Resource Dr, Harrison 72601 Fax 429-9099
www.oursc.k12.ar.us/

South Central ESC
Marsha Daniels, dir. 870-836-1600
2235 California Ave SW Fax 836-1600
Camden 71701
www.scsc.k12.ar.us/

Southeast Arkansas ESC
Karen Eoff, dir. 870-367-6848
1022 Scogin Dr, Monticello 71655 Fax 367-9877
se.sesc.k12.ar.us/

Southwest Arkansas ESC
Phoebe Bailey, dir. 870-777-3076
2502 S Main St, Hope 71801 Fax 777-5793
www.swaec.org

Western Arkansas ESC
Guy Fenter, dir. 479-965-2191
3010 Highway 22 E Ste A Fax 965-2723
Branch 72928
www.wsc.k12.ar.us

Wilbur D. Mills ESC
Jeff Williams, dir. 501-882-5467
PO Box 850, Beebe 72012 Fax 882-2155
www.wilbur.k12.ar.us

PUBLIC, PRIVATE AND CATHOLIC SECONDARY SCHOOLS

Alexander, Saline, Pop. 2,843
Bryant SD
Supt. — See Bryant
Bethel MS 800/6-8
5415 Northlake Rd 72002 501-316-0937
Todd Sellers, prin. Fax 316-0338

Avilla Christian Academy 200/PK-10
302 Avilla E 72002 501-316-0922
Ross Chiles, prin. Fax 316-5053

Alma, Crawford, Pop. 5,279
Alma SD 3,400/K-12
PO Box 2359 72921 479-632-4791
David Woolly, supt. Fax 632-4793
almasd.net
Alma HS 1,100/9-12
PO Box 2139 72921 479-632-2162
Jerry Valentine, prin. Fax 632-5070
Alma MS 800/6-8
PO Box 2229 72921 479-632-2168
Pat Whorton, prin. Fax 632-2160

Alpena, Boone, Pop. 380
Alpena SD 600/K-12
PO Box 270 72611 870-437-2220
James Trammell, supt. Fax 437-2133
alpenaschools.k12.ar.us/
Alpena JSHS 200/7-12
PO Box 270 72611 870-437-2228
David Bennett, prin. Fax 437-5638

Amity, Clark, Pop. 719
Centerpoint SD 1,000/PK-12
755 Highway 8 E 71921 870-356-2912
Anne Butcher, supt. Fax 356-4637
www.centerpoint.dsc.k12.ar.us/
Centerpoint HS 300/9-12
755 Highway 8 E 71921 870-356-3612
Deric Owens, prin. Fax 356-4519
Centerpoint JHS 300/6-8
755 Highway 8 E 71921 870-356-3612
Michael Jackson, prin. Fax 356-4519

Arkadelphia, Clark, Pop. 10,545
Arkadelphia SD 2,000/K-12
235 N 11th St 71923 870-246-5564
Donnie Whitten, supt. Fax 246-1144
www.arkadelphiaschools.org
Arkadelphia HS 600/9-12
401 High School Rd 71923 870-246-7373
David Maxwell, prin. Fax 246-1154
Goza MS 400/6-8
1305 Caddo St 71923 870-246-4291
Angela Garner, prin. Fax 246-1153

Arkadelphia Beauty College Post-Sec.
203 S 26th St 71923 870-246-6726
Henderson State University Post-Sec.
1100 Henderson St 71999 870-230-5000
Ouachita Baptist University Post-Sec.
410 Ouachita St 71998 870-245-5000

Armorel, Mississippi
Armorel SD 500/K-12
PO Box 99 72310 870-763-6639
Sally Bennett, supt. Fax 763-0028
armorel.k12.ar.us/
Armorel JSHS 200/7-12
PO Box 99 72310 870-763-7121
Scott Smith, prin. Fax 763-7020

Ashdown, Little River, Pop. 4,622
Ashdown SD 1,500/K-12
511 N 2nd St 71822 870-898-3208
Mike Walker, supt. Fax 898-3709
www.ashdownschools.org
Ashdown HS 500/9-12
171 S Locust St 71822 870-898-3562
Tim Erwin, prin. Fax 898-4452
Ashdown JHS 400/6-8
600 S Ellen Dr 71822 870-898-5138
James Jones, prin. Fax 898-4472
Ashdown New Traditions S Alt
751 Rankin St 71822 870-898-4413
Susan Fleming, dir. Fax 898-4489

Atkins, Pope, Pop. 2,978
Atkins SD 1,000/K-12
307 N Church St 72823 479-641-7871
Boyce Watkins, supt. Fax 641-7569
atkinspublic.schoolinsites.com
Atkins HS 300/9-12
403 Avenue 3 NW 72823 479-641-7872
Margaret Robinson, prin. Fax 641-1306
Atkins MS 300/5-8
611 NW 4th St 72823 479-641-2032
Darrell Webb, prin. Fax 641-5504

Augusta, Woodruff, Pop. 2,163
Augusta SD 500/PK-12
320 Sycamore St 72006 870-347-2241
Scott Jones, supt. Fax 347-5423
www.augustasd.org/
Augusta HS 200/8-12
320 Sycamore St 72006 870-347-2515
Thomas Garner, prin. Fax 347-8113

Bald Knob, White, Pop. 2,847
Bald Knob SD 1,300/K-12
103 W Park Ave 72010 501-724-3273
Dr. Kieth Williams, supt. Fax 724-6621
www.baldknobschools.org/
Bald Knob HS 400/9-12
901 N Hickory St 72010 501-724-3843
Brad Roberts, prin. Fax 724-8323
Bald Knob MS 400/5-8
103 W Park Ave 72010 501-724-5652
Jake Smith, prin. Fax 724-2062

Batesville, Independence, Pop. 10,067
Batesville SD 3,000/K-12
955 Water St 72501 870-793-6831
Dr. Randy Willison, supt. Fax 793-6760
www.batesvilleschools.com
Batesville HS 600/10-12
1 Pioneer Dr 72501 870-793-6846
David Campbell, prin. Fax 793-0607
Batesville JHS 700/7-9
2 Pioneer Dr 72501 870-793-7533
Brent Bogy, prin. Fax 793-0626
Other Schools – See Cushman

Southside SD 1,600/PK-12
70 Scott Dr 72501 870-251-2341
Roger Rich, supt. Fax 251-3316
southside.k12.ar.us/
Southside HS 500/9-12
70 Scott Dr 72501 870-251-2662
Roger Reid, prin. Fax 251-3316
Southside MS 500/5-8
70 Scott Dr 72501 870-251-2332
Dion Stevens, prin. Fax 251-3316

Bee-Jay's Hairstyling Academy Post-Sec.
130 W Main St 72501 870-793-3898
Lyon College Post-Sec.
PO Box 2317 72503 870-307-7000
University of Arkansas Community College Post-Sec.
PO Box 3350 72503 870-612-2000

Bauxite, Saline, Pop. 486
Bauxite SD 1,000/PK-12
800 School St 72011 501-557-5453
Jerrod Williams, supt. Fax 557-2235
www.edline.net/pages/Bauxite_SD
Bauxite HS 400/9-12
800 School St 72011 501-557-5303
Ann Webb, prin. Fax 557-2274
Bauxite MS 5-8
6725 Benton Rd 72011 501-557-5491
Susan Blockburger, prin. Fax 557-5509

Eaton Barber College — Post-Sec.
8333 Sagebrush Cir 72011 — 501-375-0211

Bay, Craighead, Pop. 1,780
Bay SD — 600/K-12
PO Box 39 72411 — 870-781-[illegible]
Oliver Layne, supt. — Fax 781-3712
www.edline.net/pages/bay
Bay JSHS — 300/7-12
PO Box 39 72411 — 870-781-3297
Jodi Cobb, prin. — Fax 781-3837

Bearden, Ouachita, Pop. 942
Bearden SD — 600/K-12
100 Oak Ave 71720 — 870-687-2236
Denny Rozenberg, supt. — Fax 687-3683
www.beardenschools.org/
Bearden JSHS — 300/7-12
635 N Plum St 71720 — 870-687-2913
John Goodman, prin. — Fax 687-2514

Beebe, White, Pop. 7,140
Beebe SD — 3,300/PK-12
1201 W Center St 72012 — 501-882-5463
Dr. Belinda Shook, supt. — Fax 882-5465
beebebadgers.org
Beebe HS — 900/9-12
1201 W Center St 72012 — 501-882-5463
Scott Jennings, prin. — Fax 882-8404
Beebe JHS — 500/7-8
1201 W Center St 72012 — 501-882-5463
Chris Ellis, prin. — Fax 882-8416

Arkansas State University - Beebe — Post-Sec.
PO Box 1000 72012 — 501-882-3600

Bee Branch, Van Buren
South Side SD — 500/K-12
334 Southside Rd 72013 — 501-654-2633
Billy Jackson, supt. — Fax 654-2336
ssbb.k12.ar.us/
South Side JSHS — 200/7-12
334 Southside Rd 72013 — 501-654-2242
Travis Love, prin. — Fax 654-2331

Benton, Saline, Pop. 30,248
Benton SD — 4,700/K-12
PO Box 939 72018 — 501-778-4861
Jeff Collum, supt. — Fax 776-5777
ww2.bentonschools.org
Benton HS — 1,000/10-12
211 N Border St 72015 — 501-778-3288
John Dedman, prin. — Fax 776-5783
Benton JHS — 700/8-9
411 N Border St 72015 — 501-778-7698
Mike Hudgeons, prin. — Fax 776-5744

Harmony Grove SD — 1,100/K-12
2621 N Highway 229 72015 — 501-778-6271
Daniel Henley, supt. — Fax 778-6271
cardinals.dsc.k12.ar.us
Harmony Grove HS — 300/9-12
2621 N Highway 229 72015 — 501-776-2337
Timothy Hollicer, prin. — Fax 776-2337
Harmony Grove MS — 400/5-8
2621 N Highway 229 72015 — 501-860-6796
Sarah Gober, prin. — Fax 860-6796

Bentonville, Benton, Pop. 34,453
Bentonville SD — 13,500/PK-12
500 Tiger Blvd 72712 — 479-254-5000
Michael Poore, supt. — Fax 271-1159
bentonvillek12.org
Bentonville HS — 3,500/9-12
1801 SE J St 72712 — 479-254-5100
Kimberly Garrett, prin. — Fax 271-1184
Fulbright JHS — 7-8
5303 SW Bright Rd 72712 — 479-802-7000
Kathy Murry, prin.
Lincoln JHS — 1,000/7-8
1206 Leopard Ln 72712 — 479-254-5250
Jonathon Guthrie, prin. — Fax 271-1128
Washington JHS — 1,000/7-8
1501 NE Wildcat Way 72712 — 479-254-5345
Tim Sparacino, prin. — Fax 271-1191

Ambassadors For Christ Academy — 100/PK-12
PO Box 924 72712 — 479-273-5635
David Welshenbaugh, admin. — Fax 273-0684
Northwest Arkansas Community College — Post-Sec.
1 College Dr 72712 — 479-636-9222

Bergman, Boone, Pop. 427
Bergman SD — 1,100/K-12
PO Box 1 72615 — 870-741-5213
Joe Couch, supt. — Fax 741-6701
bergman.oursc.k12.ar.us
Bergman HS — 300/9-12
PO Box 1 72615 — 870-741-1414
Bryan Pruitt, prin. — Fax 741-6701
Bergman MS — 400/5-8
PO Box 1 72615 — 870-741-8557
Sarah Alexander, prin. — Fax 741-3490

Berryville, Carroll, Pop. 5,283
Berryville SD — 1,900/K-12
902 W Trimble Ave 72616 — 870-423-7065
Dr. Randy Byrd, supt. — Fax 423-6824
bobcat.k12.ar.us
Berryville HS — 500/9-12
902 W Trimble Ave 72616 — 870-480-4632
Owen Powell, prin. — Fax 480-4635
Berryville MS — 500/6-8
902 W Trimble Ave 72616 — 870-480-4633
David Gilmore, prin. — Fax 480-4634

Bigelow, Perry, Pop. 315
East End SD — 600/K-12
PO Box 360 72016 — 501-759-2808
Eric Saunders, supt. — Fax 759-2667
eastendpanthers.com
Bigelow JSHS — 300/7-12
PO Box 360 72016 — 501-759-2602
Dewayne Wammack, prin. — Fax 759-3081

Bismarck, Hot Spring
Bismarck SD — 1,000/K-12
11636 Highway 84 71929 — 501-865-4888
Susan Stewart-Harper, supt. — Fax 865-3626
www.bismarcklions.net/
Bismarck HS — 300/9-12
11636 Highway 84 71929 — 501-865-4541
Larry Newsom, prin. — Fax 865-4542
Bismarck MS — 300/5-8
11636 Highway 84 71929 — 501-865-4543
Dan Breshears, prin. — Fax 865-4505

Black Rock, Lawrence, Pop. 659
Lawrence County SD
Supt. — See Walnut Ridge
Black Rock JSHS — 100/7-12
PO Box 240 72415 — 870-878-6461
Lori McKenzie, prin. — Fax 878-6051

Blevins, Hempstead, Pop. 310
Blevins SD — 600/K-12
PO Box 98 71825 — 870-874-2801
Billy Lee, supt. — Fax 874-2889
blevinshornets.weebly.com/
Blevins JSHS — 300/7-12
PO Box 98 71825 — 870-874-2281
Jeffrey Steed, prin. — Fax 874-2450

Blytheville, Mississippi, Pop. 15,417
Blytheville SD — 2,100/PK-12
PO Box 1169 72316 — 870-762-2053
Richard Atwill, supt. — Fax 762-0141
www.blythevilleschools.com
Blytheville HS - A New Tech S — 800/9-12
600 N 10th St 72315 — 870-762-2772
Bobby Ashley, prin. — Fax 762-0175
Blytheville MS — 400/6-8
700 Chickasawba St 72315 — 870-762-2983
Mike Wallace, prin. — Fax 762-0174

Arkansas Northeastern College — Post-Sec.
2501 S Division St 72315 — 870-762-1020

Bonnerdale, Hot Spring, Pop. 50

Ewing Jr Academy — 50/K-10
709 Adventist Church Rd 71933 — 870-356-2780

Booneville, Logan, Pop. 3,888
Booneville SD — 1,400/K-12
381 W 7th St 72927 — 479-675-3504
John Parrish, supt. — Fax 675-3106
www.booneville.k12.ar.us/
Booneville HS — 300/10-12
945 N Plum St 72927 — 479-675-3277
Michael Johnson, prin. — Fax 675-3214
Booneville JHS — 300/7-9
835 E 8th St 72927 — 479-675-5247
Scotty Pierce, prin. — Fax 675-0793

Bradford, White, Pop. 744
Bradford SD — 500/K-12
PO Box 60 72020 — 501-344-2707
Arthur Dunn, supt. — Fax 344-2706
bradford.k12.ar.us
Bradford JSHS — 200/7-12
PO Box 60 72020 — 501-344-2607
Rick Wood, prin. — Fax 344-2706

Bradley, Lafayette, Pop. 627
Bradley SD — 400/K-12
521 School Dr 71826 — 870-894-3313
Oscar Gammye Moore, supt. — Fax 894-3344
bradleyweb.swsc.k12.ar.us/
Bradley HS — 200/7-12
521 School Dr 71826 — 870-894-3316
Amanda Jones, prin. — Fax 894-3344

Branch, Franklin, Pop. 358
County Line SD — 500/PK-12
12092 W State Highway 22 72928 — 479-635-2222
Joan Jones, supt. — Fax 635-2087
indians.wsc.k12.ar.us/
County Line JSHS — 200/7-12
12092 W State Highway 22 72928 — 479-635-2441
Taylor Gattis, prin. — Fax 635-2452

Brinkley, Monroe, Pop. 3,151
Brinkley SD — 600/K-12
200 Tigers Dr 72021 — 870-734-5000
Dr. Arthur Tucker, supt. — Fax 734-5187
www.brinkleyschools.com
Brinkley JSHS — 300/7-12
100 Tigers Dr 72021 — 870-734-5005
Samuel White, prin. — Fax 734-1354

Brockwell, Izard
Izard County Consolidated SD — 500/K-12
PO Box 115 72517 — 870-258-7700
Fred Walker, supt. — Fax 258-3140
icc.k12.ar.us/
Izard County Consolidated HS — 200/9-12
PO Box 115 72517 — 870-258-7788
David Harmon, prin. — Fax 258-3140
Izard County Consolidated MS — 200/5-8
PO Box 115 72517 — 870-258-7788
Billy McBride, prin. — Fax 258-3140

Brookland, Craighead, Pop. 1,612
Brookland SD — 1,600/PK-12
200 W School St 72417 — 870-932-2080
Kevin McGaughey, supt. — Fax 932-2088
www.brooklandbearcats.org
Brookland HS — 400/9-12
100 W School St 72417 — 870-932-2080
Steven Hovis, prin. — Fax 932-1251
Brookland JHS — 300/7-9
100 W School St 72417 — 870-932-8610
Keith McDaniel, prin. — Fax 974-9762

Bryant, Saline, Pop. 16,446
Bryant SD — 7,900/K-12
200 NW 4th St 72022 — 501-847-5600
Randy Rutherford, supt. — Fax 847-5603
www.bryantschools.org
Bryant HS — 2,300/9-12
200 NW 4th St 72022 — 501-847-5605
Jay Pickering, prin. — Fax 847-5612
Bryant MS — 1,200/6-8
200 NW 4th St 72022 — 501-847-5651
Sue Reeves, prin. — Fax 847-5654
Other Schools – See Alexander

Arkansas Christian Academy — 200/PK-12
PO Box 150 72089 — 501-847-1559
Fax 847-3692

Burdette, Mississippi, Pop. 191

Cotton Boll Technical Institute — Post-Sec.
PO Box 36 72321 — 870-763-1486

Cabot, Lonoke, Pop. 23,349
Cabot SD — 10,100/PK-12
602 N Lincoln St 72023 — 501-843-3363
Dr. Tony Thurman, supt. — Fax 843-0576
cabot.k12.ar.us
Cabot HS — 2,000/10-12
401 N Lincoln St 72023 — 501-843-3562
Henry Hawkins, prin. — Fax 843-4231
Cabot JHS North — 1,200/7-9
38 Spirit Dr 72023 — 501-743-3572
Roger Tonnessen, prin. — Fax 605-8472
Cabot JHS South — 1,100/7-9
38 Panther Trl 72023 — 501-743-3573
John West, prin. — Fax 941-7746

Calico Rock, Izard, Pop. 1,531
Calico Rock SD — 400/K-12
PO Box 220 72519 — 870-297-8339
Jerry Skidmore, supt. — Fax 297-4233
pirates.k12.ar.us/
Calico Rock JSHS — 200/7-12
PO Box 220 72519 — 870-297-3745
Anita Cook, prin. — Fax 297-3168

Camden, Ouachita, Pop. 11,970
Camden Fairview SD — 2,400/K-12
625 Clifton St 71701 — 870-836-4193
Robert Davis, supt. — Fax 836-6039
cfsd.k12.ar.us/
Camden Fairview HS — 800/9-12
1750 Cash Rd SW 71701 — 870-837-1300
Peggy Burton, prin. — Fax 837-2330
Camden Fairview MS — 500/6-8
647 J A Dooley Womack Dr 71701 — 870-836-9361
Andre Toney, prin. — Fax 836-3717

Harmony Grove SD — 1,000/K-12
401 Ouachita 88 71701 — 870-574-0971
Harold Davidson, supt. — Fax 574-2765
harmonygrovesd.org
Harmony Grove JSHS — 400/7-12
401 Ouachita 88 71701 — 870-574-0867
Walton Pigott, prin. — Fax 574-2765
Other Schools – See Sparkman

Camden Christian Academy — 50/PK-12
1245 California Ave SW 71701 — 870-836-3716
Kathy Wells, admin. — Fax 836-4511
Southern Arkansas University Tech — Post-Sec.
100 Carr Rd 71701 — 870-574-4500

Carlisle, Lonoke, Pop. 2,193
Carlisle SD — 800/PK-12
520 Center St 72024 — 870-552-3931
Jason Clark, supt. — Fax 552-7967
bison.wmsc.k12.ar.us
Carlisle JSHS — 400/7-12
520 Center St 72024 — 870-552-3931
Brad Horn, prin. — Fax 552-3032

Cave City, Sharp, Pop. 1,876
Cave City SD — 1,200/K-12
PO Box 600 72521 — 870-283-5391
Steven Green, supt. — Fax 283-6887
www.cavecity.k12.ar.us
Cave City HS — 400/9-12
PO Box 600 72521 — 870-283-3333
Marc Walling, prin. — Fax 283-3322
Cave City MS — 200/5-8
PO Box 600 72521 — 870-283-5392
Mark Smith, prin. — Fax 266-3258

Cedarville, Crawford, Pop. 1,339
Cedarville SD — 900/K-12
PO Box 97 72932 — 479-474-7021
Dr. Dan Foreman, supt. — Fax 410-1804
www.edline.net/pages/Cedarville_School_District
Cedarville HS — 300/9-12
PO Box 97 72932 — 479-474-7021
Randal Betts, prin. — Fax 410-1804
Cedarville MS — 300/5-8
PO Box 97 72932 — 479-474-5847
Dr. Jim Cox, prin. — Fax 471-7036

Center Ridge, Conway, Pop. 385
Nemo Vista SD 400/PK-12
5690 Highway 9 72027 501-893-2925
Cody Beene, supt. Fax 893-2367
socs.nemo.k12.ar.us
Nemo Vista HS 100/9-12
5690 Highway 9 72027 501-893-2811
Jeff Andrews, prin. Fax 893-6472
Nemo Vista MS 6-8
5690 Highway 9 72027 501-893-6494
Tresa Virden, prin.

Centerton, Benton, Pop. 9,305

Life Way Christian S 500/PK-12
PO Box 220 72719 479-795-9322
Dr. Luke Bowers, admin. Fax 795-9399

Charleston, Franklin, Pop. 2,451
Charleston SD 800/PK-12
PO Box 188 72933 479-965-7160
Jeff Stubblefield, supt. Fax 965-9989
tigers.wsc.k12.ar.us/
Charleston HS 300/9-12
PO Box 188 72933 479-965-7150
Shane Storey, prin. Fax 965-7140
Charleston MS 200/5-8
PO Box 188 72933 479-965-7170
Melissa Moore, prin. Fax 965-9989

Clarendon, Monroe, Pop. 1,643
Clarendon SD 500/K-12
PO Box 248 72029 870-747-3351
Lee Vent, supt. Fax 747-5963
lions.grsc.k12.ar.us
Clarendon HS 300/7-12
PO Box 248 72029 870-747-3326
Douglas Caldwell, prin. Fax 747-5963

Clarksville, Johnson, Pop. 9,041
Clarksville SD 2,500/K-12
1701 W Clark Rd 72830 479-705-3200
Dr. David Hopkins, supt. Fax 754-3748
www.csdar.org/
Clarksville JHS 600/7-9
1801 W Clark Rd 72830 479-705-3224
Paul Dean, prin. Fax 754-7431
Clarksville SHS 400/10-12
1703 W Clark Rd 72830 479-705-3212
John Burke, prin. Fax 754-2492

University of the Ozarks Post-Sec.
415 N College Ave 72830 479-979-1000

Clinton, Van Buren, Pop. 2,548
Clinton SD 1,300/K-12
683 Poplar St 72031 501-745-6000
Scott Jones, supt. Fax 745-2475
clinton.k12.ar.us/
Clinton HS 300/10-12
489 Yellowjacket Ln 72031 501-745-6035
Frank McMurry, prin. Fax 745-2450
Clinton JHS 300/7-9
443 Yellowjacket Ln 72031 501-745-6079
Mark Gammill, prin. Fax 745-6065

Concord, Cleburne, Pop. 243
Concord SD 500/K-12
PO Box 10 72523 870-668-3844
Mike Davidson Ed.D., supt. Fax 668-3380
concord.k12.ar.us
Concord JSHS 200/7-12
PO Box 358 72523 870-668-3522
Scott Whillock, prin. Fax 668-3600

Conway, Faulkner, Pop. 57,689
Conway SD 8,100/PK-12
2220 Prince St 72034 501-450-4800
Dr. Greg Murry, supt. Fax 450-4898
www.conwayschools.org
Conway Area Career Center Vo/Tech
2300 Prince St 72034 501-450-4888
Jason Lawrence, prin. Fax 450-6658
Conway HS 1,300/10-12
2300 Prince St 72034 501-450-4880
Joel Linn, prin. Fax 450-4884
Conway JHS 800/8-9
1815 Prince St 72034 501-450-4860
Todd Edwards, prin. Fax 450-6651

Arkansas Beauty School - Conway Post-Sec.
1061 Markham St 72032 501-329-8303
Central Baptist College Post-Sec.
1501 College Ave 72034 501-329-6872
Conway Christian S 500/PK-12
500 E German Ln S 72032 501-336-9067
Gloria Massey, supt. Fax 336-9251
Hendrix College Post-Sec.
1600 Washington Ave 72032 501-329-6811
St. Joseph S 500/K-12
502 Front St 72032 501-327-1204
Joe Mallett, prin. Fax 513-6805
University of Central Arkansas Post-Sec.
201 Donaghey Ave 72035 501-450-5000

Corning, Clay, Pop. 3,348
Corning SD 1,000/K-12
PO Box 479 72422 870-857-6818
Kellee Smith, supt. Fax 857-5086
www.corningschools.k12.ar.us/
Corning JSHS 500/7-12
PO Box 479 72422 870-857-3041
Andrew Eubanks, prin. Fax 857-6797

Cotter, Baxter, Pop. 947
Cotter SD 700/K-12
PO Box 70 72626 870-435-6171
Don Sharp, supt. Fax 435-1300
www.cotterschools.net
Cotter JSHS 300/7-12
PO Box 70 72626 870-435-6323
Amanda Britt, prin. Fax 435-1300

Cove, Polk, Pop. 372
Cossatot River SD
Supt. — See Wickes
Cossatot River HS 500/7-12
6330 Highway 71 S 71937 870-387-4200
Terry Thompson, prin. Fax 387-4250

Crossett, Ashley, Pop. 5,460
Crossett SD 2,000/PK-12
219 Main St 71635 870-364-3112
Tommy Tyler, supt. Fax 304-2525
www.crossettschools.org
Crossett HS 600/9-12
301 W 9th Ave 71635 870-364-2625
Jenny Graves, prin. Fax 364-4792
Crossett MS 600/5-8
100 Petersburg Rd 71635 870-364-4712
Lou Gregorio, prin. Fax 364-3771

University of Arkansas - Monticello Post-Sec.
1326 Highway 52 W 71635 870-364-6414

Cushman, Independence, Pop. 440
Batesville SD
Supt. — See Batesville
White River Academy Alt
PO Box 370 72526 870-698-1145
Gary Anderson, dir. Fax 698-1455

Danville, Yell, Pop. 2,373
Danville SD 700/K-12
PO Box 939 72833 479-495-4800
Mike Hernandez, supt. Fax 495-4803
www.dps-littlejohns.net/
Danville JSHS 300/6-12
PO Box 939 72833 479-495-4810
Kenny Holland, prin. Fax 495-4832

Dardanelle, Yell, Pop. 4,680
Dardanelle SD 2,000/K-12
209 Cedar St 72834 479-229-4111
John Thompson, supt. Fax 229-1387
www.dardanelle.k12.ar.us/
Dardanelle HS 500/9-12
1079 N State Highway 28 72834 479-229-4655
Marcia Lawrence, prin. Fax 229-4687
Dardanelle MS 300/7-8
2032 State Highway 7 N 72834 479-229-4550
John David Keeling, prin. Fax 229-1697

Decatur, Benton, Pop. 1,637
Decatur SD 500/PK-12
1498 Stadium Ave 72722 479-752-3986
Dr. Larry Ben, supt. Fax 752-2490
www.edline.net/pages/decatur_sd
Decatur JSHS 200/7-12
1498 Stadium Ave 72722 479-752-3983
Deborah Coffer, prin. Fax 752-2491

Deer, Newton
Deer / Mt. Judea SD 400/K-12
PO Box 56 72628 870-428-5433
Richard Denniston, supt. Fax 428-5901
deermtjudea.k12.ar.us
Deer JSHS 100/7-12
PO Box 56 72628 870-428-5288
Elvis Middleton, prin. Fax 428-5901
Other Schools – See Mount Judea

De Queen, Sevier, Pop. 6,482
De Queen SD 2,400/K-12
PO Box 950 71832 870-584-4312
Bruce Hill, supt. Fax 642-8881
www.dequeenleopards.org
De Queen HS 400/10-12
1803 W Coulter Ave 71832 870-642-2426
Roger Busse, prin. Fax 642-4931
De Queen JHS 400/8-9
1803 W Coulter Ave 71832 870-642-3077
Bill Huddleston, prin. Fax 642-3355

Beacon Hill Adventist Junior Academy 50/K-10
1446 Red Bridge Rd 71832 870-642-4876
Cossatot Community College Univ. of AR Post-Sec.
PO Box 960 71832 870-584-4471

Dermott, Chicot, Pop. 2,294
Dermott SD 400/K-12
PO Box 380 71638 870-538-1000
Kelvin Gragg, supt. Fax 538-1005
dermott.k12.ar.us
Dermott JSHS 200/7-12
PO Box 380 71638 870-538-1030
Terry Murry, prin. Fax 538-1005

Des Arc, Prairie, Pop. 1,696
Des Arc SD 600/K-12
600 Main St 72040 870-256-4164
Rick Burns, supt. Fax 256-3701
desarc.wmsc.k12.ar.us/
Des Arc JSHS 300/7-12
600 Main St 72040 870-256-4166
Nick Hill, prin. Fax 256-3701

De Witt, Arkansas, Pop. 3,250
De Witt SD 1,400/PK-12
PO Box 700 72042 870-946-3576
Gary Wayman, supt. Fax 946-1491
www.dewittschooldistrict.net
De Witt HS 400/9-12
1614 S Grandview Dr 72042 870-946-4661
Marty Weaver, prin. Fax 946-2746
De Witt MS 300/6-8
301 N Jackson St 72042 870-946-3708
Julie Blevins, prin. Fax 946-1301

Dierks, Howard, Pop. 1,118
Dierks SD 600/K-12
PO Box 124 71833 870-286-2191
Donnie Davis, supt. Fax 286-2450
www.edline.net/pages/dierks_school_district
Dierks JSHS 300/7-12
PO Box 124 71833 870-286-3234
Holly Cothren, prin. Fax 286-2450

Donaldson, Hot Spring, Pop. 298
Ouachita SD 500/K-12
166 Schoolhouse Rd 71941 501-384-2318
Ronnie Kissire, supt. Fax 384-5615
www.ouachita.dsc.k12.ar.us/
Ouachita JSHS 200/7-12
258 Schoolhouse Rd 71941 501-384-2323
David Thigpen, prin. Fax 384-5614

Dover, Pope, Pop. 1,350
Dover SD 1,400/K-12
PO Box 325 72837 479-331-2916
Jerry Owens, supt. Fax 331-2205
www.doverschools.net/
Dover HS 400/9-12
PO Box 325 72837 479-331-2120
Jo Lynn Taverner, prin. Fax 331-3286
Dover MS 400/5-8
PO Box 325 72837 479-331-4814
Verna Boxnick, prin. Fax 331-4965

Dumas, Desha, Pop. 4,687
Dumas SD 1,500/PK-12
213 Adams St 71639 870-382-4571
Dr. David Rainey, supt. Fax 382-4874
dpsd.k12.ar.us
Dumas HS 300/10-12
709 Dan Gill Dr 71639 870-382-4151
Paul Morara, prin. Fax 382-8904
Dumas JHS 300/7-9
315 S College St 71639 870-382-4476
Edgar Montgomery, prin. Fax 382-2162

Earle, Crittenden, Pop. 2,397
Earle SD 700/K-12
PO Box 637 72331 870-792-8486
Rickey Nicks, supt. Fax 792-8897
www.earle.crsc.k12.ar.us/
Earle JSHS 300/7-12
PO Box 637 72331 870-792-8716
Phylistia Stanley, prin. Fax 792-1004

Edmondson, Crittenden, Pop. 415
West Memphis SD
Supt. — See West Memphis
West Memphis Learning Center 100/Alt
200 B J Taylor St 72332 870-735-5113
Mike Hardage, dir. Fax 732-8653

El Dorado, Union, Pop. 18,658
El Dorado SD 4,700/K-12
200 W Oak St 71730 870-864-5001
Bob Watson, supt. Fax 864-5015
www.eldoradopublicschools.com
Barton JHS 700/7-8
400 W Faulkner St 71730 870-864-5051
Sherry Hill, prin. Fax 864-5064
El Dorado HS 1,300/9-12
2000 Wild Cat Dr 71730 870-864-5100
Alva Reibe, prin. Fax 863-3309
Murmil Heights Educational Center 200/Alt
2000 Ripley St 71730 870-864-5021
Doyle Woodall, prin.

Parkers Chapel SD 700/K-12
401 Parkers Chapel Rd 71730 870-862-4641
John Gross, supt. Fax 881-5092
www.parkerschapelschool.com
Parkers Chapel JSHS 300/7-12
401 Parkers Chapel Rd 71730 870-862-2360
Mike LaRue, prin. Fax 881-5092

South Arkansas Community College Post-Sec.
PO Box 7010 71731 870-862-8131
West Side Christian S 100/PK-12
2400 W Hillsboro St 71730 870-863-5636
Bob Templeton, admin. Fax 863-3529

Elkins, Washington, Pop. 2,568
Elkins SD 1,100/K-12
349 N Center St 72727 479-643-2172
Dan Jordan, supt. Fax 643-3605
www.elkinsdistrict.org
Elkins HS 400/9-12
349 N Center St 72727 479-643-3381
Paula Wheeler, prin. Fax 643-2726
Elkins MS 200/6-8
349 N Center St 72727 479-643-2552
Steve Denzer, prin. Fax 643-4272

Emerson, Columbia, Pop. 368
Emerson - Taylor SD 600/K-12
PO Box 129 71740 870-547-2218
Gary Hines, supt. Fax 547-2077
emersontaylor.k12.ar.us
Emerson HS 200/7-12
212 Grayson St 71740 870-547-2862
Jim Deloach, prin. Fax 547-2011
Other Schools – See Taylor

England, Lonoke, Pop. 2,789
England SD 800/K-12
501 Pine Bluff Hwy 72046 501-842-2996
Paula Henderson, supt. Fax 842-3698
england.k12.ar.us
England JSHS 300/7-12
501 Pine Bluff Hwy 72046 501-842-2031
Stephen Delaney, prin. Fax 842-3263

Eureka Springs, Carroll, Pop. 2,008
Eureka Springs SD 700/K-12
147 Greenwood Hollow Rd 72632 479-253-5999
David Kellogg, supt. Fax 253-5955
eurekaspringsschools.k12.ar.us
Eureka Springs HS 200/9-12
44 Kingshighway 72632 479-253-8875
Kathryn Lavender, prin. Fax 253-8390
Eureka Springs MS 200/5-8
142 Greenwood Hollow Rd 72632 479-253-7716
Cindy Holt, prin. Fax 253-7809

Clear Spring S 100/PK-12
PO Box 511 72632 479-253-7888
Debbie Hartsell, hdmstr. Fax 253-0768

Everton, Marion, Pop. 128
Ozark Mountain SD
Supt. — See Saint Joe
Bruno-Pyatt JSHS 100/7-12
4754 Highway 125 S 72633 870-427-5227
Bob Ricketts, prin. Fax 427-5255

Farmington, Washington, Pop. 5,772
Farmington SD 2,200/K-12
42 S Double Springs Rd 72730 479-266-1800
Bryan Law, supt. Fax 267-6030
www.farmcards.org/
Farmington HS 600/9-12
278 W Main St 72730 479-266-1860
Bob Echols, prin. Fax 267-6065
Lynch MS 600/6-8
359 Rheas Mill Rd 72730 479-266-1840
Terry Lakey, prin. Fax 267-6051

Fayetteville, Washington, Pop. 71,413
Fayetteville SD 8,800/K-12
PO Box 849 72702 479-444-3000
Vicki Thomas, supt. Fax 973-8670
www.fayar.net
Fayetteville SHS 1,800/10-12
994 W Martin Luther King Bl 72701 479-444-3050
John Jacoby, prin. Fax 444-3056
Ramay JHS 600/8-9
401 S Sang Ave 72701 479-444-3064
Matt Saferite, prin. Fax 444-3013
Woodland JHS 700/8-9
15 E Poplar St 72703 479-444-3067
Dr. Anita Lawson, prin. Fax 444-3039

Blue Cliff College Post-Sec.
3448 N College Ave 72703 479-521-2914
Fayetteville Christian S 200/PK-12
2006 E Mission Blvd 72703 479-442-2565
Brad Jones, supt. Fax 444-6156
Paul Mitchell The School Post-Sec.
2167 W 6th St 72701 479-442-5181
University of Arkansas at Fayetteville Post-Sec.
1 University of Arkansas 72701 479-575-2000

Flippin, Marion, Pop. 1,337
Flippin SD 800/K-12
210 Alford St 72634 870-453-2270
Dale Query, supt. Fax 453-5059
www.flippinschools.com
Flippin HS 300/9-12
103 Alford St 72634 870-453-2233
Cassie Gilley, prin. Fax 453-7380
Flippin MS 200/6-8
308 N 1st St 72634 870-453-6464
Kelvin Hudson, prin. Fax 453-6465

Fordyce, Dallas, Pop. 4,245
Fordyce SD 700/PK-12
PO Box 706 71742 870-352-3005
Donny Collins, supt. Fax 352-7187
www.fordyceschools.org/
Fordyce HS 300/7-12
PO Box 706 71742 870-352-2126
Dale Stokes, prin. Fax 352-3953

Foreman, Little River, Pop. 984
Foreman SD 500/K-12
PO Box 480 71836 870-542-7211
Jason Sanders, supt. Fax 542-7225
www.foremanschools.org
Foreman JSHS 200/7-12
PO Box 480 71836 870-542-7212
Curt Barger, prin. Fax 542-7227

Forrest City, Saint Francis, Pop. 15,183
Forrest City SD 3,000/K-12
625 Irving St 72335 870-633-1485
Joye Hughes, supt. Fax 633-1415
mustang.grsc.k12.ar.us/
Forrest City HS 1,000/9-12
467 Victoria St 72335 870-633-1464
Patti Long, prin. Fax 261-1844
Forrest City JHS 500/7-8
1133 N Division St 72335 870-633-3230
Reginald Murphy, prin. Fax 633-6066

Calvary Christian S 200/K-12
1611 N Washington St 72335 870-633-5333
Suzanne Hess, prin. Fax 633-6238
Crowley's Ridge Technical Institute Post-Sec.
1620 New Castle Rd 72335 870-633-5411
East Arkansas Community College Post-Sec.
1700 New Castle Rd 72335 870-633-4480

Fort Smith, Sebastian, Pop. 83,397
Fort Smith SD 14,000/PK-12
PO Box 1948 72902 479-785-2501
Ben Gooden Ed.D., supt. Fax 785-1722
www.fortsmithschools.org
Belle Point Alternative Center 100/Alt
1501 Dodson Ave 72901 479-783-7034
Brad Ray, dir. Fax 784-8161
Chaffin JHS 800/7-9
3025 Massard Rd 72903 479-452-2226
Todd Marshell, prin. Fax 478-3103
Darby JHS 600/7-9
616 N 14th St 72901 479-783-4159
Darren McKinney Ed.D., prin. Fax 784-8165
Kimmons JHS 800/7-9
2201 N 50th St 72904 479-785-2451
David Watkins, prin. Fax 784-8177
Northside SHS 1,400/10-12
2301 N B St 72901 479-783-1171
Ginni McDonald, prin. Fax 784-8144
Ramsey JHS 1,000/7-9
3201 Jenny Lind Rd 72901 479-783-5115
Dennis Siebenmorgen, prin. Fax 784-8178
Southside SHS 1,500/10-12
4100 Gary St 72903 479-646-7371
Wayne Haver, prin. Fax 648-8204
Adult Education Adult
501 S 20th St 72901 479-785-1232
Gary Udouj, dir. Fax 784-8184

Academy of Salon and Spa Post-Sec.
311 S 16th St 72901 479-782-5059
Trinity JHS 300/7-9
1205 S Albert Pike Ave 72903 479-782-2451
Dr. Jim Hattabaugh, prin. Fax 782-7263
Union Christian Academy 200/7-12
4201 Windsor Dr 72904 479-783-7327
Paul Bridges, supt. Fax 783-9342
University of Arkansas at Fort Smith Post-Sec.
PO Box 3649 72913 479-788-7000

Fouke, Miller, Pop. 849
Fouke SD 1,100/PK-12
PO Box 20 71837 870-653-4311
Forrest Mulkey, supt. Fax 653-2856
fouke.schoolfusion.us
Fouke HS 300/9-12
PO Box 20 71837 870-653-4551
Julie Sheppard, prin. Fax 653-3313
Smith MS 300/6-8
PO Box 20 71837 870-653-2304
Amanda Whitehead, prin. Fax 653-7840

Fox, Stone
Mountain View SD
Supt. — See Mountain View
Rural Special HS 100/7-12
13237 Highway 263 72051 870-363-4365
Junior Barham, prin. Fax 363-4222

Gentry, Benton, Pop. 3,064
Gentry SD 1,400/K-12
201 S Giles Ave 72734 479-736-2253
Dr. Randy C. Barrett, supt. Fax 736-2245
www.gentrypioneers.com/
Gentry HS 400/9-12
201 S Giles Ave 72734 479-736-2666
Brae Harper, prin. Fax 736-5202
Gentry MS 400/6-8
201 S Giles Ave 72734 479-736-2251
Larry Cozens, prin. Fax 736-3414

Ozark Adventist Academy 200/9-12
20997 Dawn Hill East Rd 72734 479-736-2221
Mike Dale, prin. Fax 736-2224

Gosnell, Mississippi, Pop. 3,483
Gosnell SD 1,400/K-12
600 N State Highway 181 72315 870-532-4000
Bonard Mace, supt. Fax 532-4002
www.gosnellschool.net
Gosnell JSHS 700/7-12
600 N State Highway 181 72315 870-532-4010
Len Whitehead, prin. Fax 532-4031

Gravette, Benton, Pop. 2,243
Gravette SD 1,800/PK-12
609 Birmingham St SE 72736 479-787-4100
Richard Page, supt. Fax 787-4108
gravetteschools.net
Gravette HS 500/9-12
325 Lion Dr S 72736 479-787-4180
Jo Ellen Hastings, prin. Fax 787-4188
Gravette MS 500/6-8
607 Dallas St SE 72736 479-787-4160
Duane Thomas, prin. Fax 787-4178

Greenbrier, Faulkner, Pop. 4,616
Greenbrier SD 3,100/PK-12
4 School Dr 72058 501-679-4808
Scott Spainhour, supt. Fax 679-1024
www.greenbrierschools.org
Greenbrier HS 600/10-12
72 Green Valley Dr 72058 501-679-4236
Susan Jackson, prin. Fax 679-5765
Greenbrier JHS 500/8-9
10 School Dr 72058 501-679-3433
John Ashworth, prin. Fax 679-3658

Green Forest, Carroll, Pop. 2,720
Green Forest SD 1,200/K-12
PO Box 1950 72638 870-438-5201
Matt Summers, supt. Fax 438-6214
www.gf.k12.ar.us
Green Forest HS 300/9-12
PO Box 1950 72638 870-438-5203
Bill Lange, prin. Fax 438-4588
Green Forest MS 300/6-8
PO Box 1950 72638 870-438-5242
Rebeca Brasel, prin. Fax 438-6343

Greenland, Washington, Pop. 1,236
Greenland SD 800/K-12
PO Box 57 72737 479-521-2366
Dr. Charles Cudney, supt. Fax 521-1480
greenlandschools.k12.ar.us/
Greenland HS 300/9-12
PO Box 57 72737 479-521-2366
Hope Dorman, prin. Fax 521-1350
Greenland MS 300/5-8
PO Box 57 72737 479-521-2366
Phil Costner, prin. Fax 251-1203

Greenwood, Sebastian, Pop. 8,785
Greenwood SD 3,400/K-12
420 N Main St 72936 479-996-4142
Dr. Kay Johnson, supt. Fax 996-4143
www.greenwoodk12.com/
Greenwood HS 800/10-12
440 E Gary St 72936 479-996-4141
Jerry Efurd, prin. Fax 996-6548
Greenwood JHS 500/8-9
300 E Gary St 72936 479-996-7440
Kevin Hesslen, prin. Fax 996-7469

Greers Ferry, Cleburne, Pop. 887
West Side SD 500/K-12
7295 Greers Ferry Rd 72067 501-825-6258
Dr. Ray Nassar, supt. Fax 825-6258
westside.afsc.k12.ar.us/
West Side JSHS 200/7-12
7295 Greers Ferry Rd 72067 501-825-7241
Rick Waters, prin. Fax 825-7241

Gurdon, Clark, Pop. 2,184
Gurdon SD 800/K-12
1 Go Devil Dr 71743 870-353-4454
Allen Blackwell, supt. Fax 353-4455
gurdon.sharpschool.net/
Cabe MS 300/5-8
7780 Highway 67 S 71743 870-353-4311
Jeremy Bell, prin. Fax 353-5149
Gurdon HS 200/9-12
7777 Highway 67 S 71743 870-353-5123
Tommie Campbell, prin. Fax 353-5131

Guy, Faulkner, Pop. 699
Guy-Perkins SD 400/K-12
492 Highway 25 N 72061 501-679-7224
Brian Cossey, supt. Fax 679-3508
thunderbird.k12.ar.us/
Guy-Perkins HS 200/7-12
492 Highway 25 N 72061 501-679-3507
Damon Teas, prin. Fax 679-3508

Hackett, Sebastian, Pop. 782
Hackett SD 600/K-12
102 N Oak St 72937 479-638-8822
William Pittman, supt. Fax 638-7106
hackett.wsc.k12.ar.us/
Hackett JSHS 300/7-12
102 N Oak St 72937 479-638-7003
Kenneth Perrin, prin. Fax 638-8210

Hamburg, Ashley, Pop. 2,843
Hamburg SD 1,600/PK-12
202 E Parker St 71646 870-853-9851
Max Dyson, supt. Fax 853-2842
www.hsdlions.org
Hamburg HS 500/9-12
1119 S Main St 71646 870-853-9856
Donald Rosen, prin. Fax 853-2850
Hamburg MS 400/6-8
1109 Cub Dr 71646 870-853-2811
Kent Broughton, prin. Fax 853-2835

Hampton, Calhoun, Pop. 1,315
Hampton SD 600/K-12
PO Box 1176 71744 870-798-2742
Jimmy Cunningham, supt. Fax 798-2239
www.edline.net/pages/Hampton_Public_Schools
Hampton JSHS 300/7-12
PO Box 1176 71744 870-798-2742
Glenn Johnston, prin. Fax 798-2239

Hardy, Sharp, Pop. 755
Highland SD 1,600/K-12
PO Box 419 72542 870-856-3275
James Floyd, supt. Fax 856-2765
highlandrebels.k12.ar.us/
Highland JSHS 600/8-12
1 Rebel Cir 72542 870-856-3273
Clint Shackelford, prin. Fax 856-2768

Harrisburg, Poinsett, Pop. 2,253
Harrisburg SD 1,400/K-12
207 W Estes St 72432 870-578-2416
Danny Sample, supt. Fax 578-9366
www.hbgsd.org/
Harrisburg HS 300/9-12
207 W Estes St 72432 870-578-2417
Steve Rorex, prin. Fax 578-2338
Harrisburg MS 300/5-8
207 W Estes St 72432 870-578-2410
Karli Saracini, prin. Fax 578-2338
Other Schools – See Weiner

Harrison, Boone, Pop. 12,739
Harrison SD 2,800/PK-12
110 S Cherry St 72601 870-741-7600
Dr. Melinda Moss, supt. Fax 741-4520
harrison.k12.ar.us/
Harrison JHS 600/7-9
515 S Pine St 72601 870-741-3496
Mike Stokes, prin. Fax 741-0101
Harrison SHS 600/10-12
925 Goblin Dr 72601 870-741-8223
Bill Keaster, prin. Fax 741-2606

Harrison Christian Academy 50/PK-12
PO Box 7 72602 870-741-8505
Lou Ketchum, admin. Fax 741-6605
North Arkansas College Post-Sec.
1515 Pioneer Dr 72601 870-743-3000

Hartford, Sebastian, Pop. 634
Hartford SD 400/PK-12
508 W Main St 72938 479-639-5002
Teresa Ragsdale, supt. Fax 639-2158
www.hartfordhustlers.net/
Hartford HS 200/7-12
508 W Main St 72938 479-639-2239
David Lee, prin. Fax 639-2158

Hartman, Johnson, Pop. 516
Westside SD 600/K-12
1535 Rabbit Hill Rd 72840 479-497-1991
Lucas Skaggs, supt. Fax 497-9037
www.westsiderebels.net
Westside JSHS 300/7-12
400 Highway 164 72840 479-497-1171
Chase Carter, prin. Fax 497-1537

Hattieville, Conway
Wonderview SD 400/K-12
2436 Highway 95 72063 501-354-0211
J. Carroll Purtle, supt. Fax 354-6071
www.edline.net/pages/wonderview_sd
Wonderview JSHS 200/7-12
2436 Highway 95 72063 501-354-8668
Jason Reynolds, prin. Fax 354-8602

Havana, Yell, Pop. 375
Western Yell County SD 500/K-12
PO Box 214 72842 479-476-4116
Brad Spikes, supt. Fax 476-4115
wolverines.k12.ar.us
Western Yell County JSHS 200/7-12
PO Box 214 72842 479-476-4100
Andy Chisum, prin. Fax 476-4111

Hazen, Prairie, Pop. 1,454
Hazen SD 700/PK-12
477 N Hazen Ave 72064 870-255-4549
Matt Donaghy, supt. Fax 255-4508
sites.google.com/a/hazen.k12.ar.us/hazen-school-dist
Hazen HS 200/9-12
477 N Hazen Ave 72064 870-255-4546
Roxanne Bradow, prin. Fax 255-4559

Heber Springs, Cleburne, Pop. 7,068
Heber Springs SD 1,800/K-12
1100 W Pine St 72543 501-362-6712
Russell Hester, supt. Fax 362-0613
hssd.k12.ar.us/
Heber Springs HS 500/9-12
1100 W Pine St 72543 501-362-3141
Justin Johnston, prin. Fax 362-9931
Heber Springs MS 400/6-8
1100 W Pine St 72543 501-362-2488
Connie Moody, prin. Fax 362-2193

Hector, Pope, Pop. 441
Hector SD 600/K-12
11520 SR 27 72843 479-284-2021
Walt Davis, supt. Fax 284-2350
wildcats.afsc.k12.ar.us/
Hector JSHS 300/7-12
11601 SR 27 72843 479-284-3536
Jordan Price, prin. Fax 284-5023

Helena, Phillips, Pop. 5,687
Helena/West Helena SD 1,500/PK-12
PO Box 369 72342 870-338-4425
Suzanne McCommon, supt. Fax 338-4434
hwh.grsc.k12.ar.us/
Other Schools – See West Helena

Phillips Comm. Coll. of the Univ. of AR Post-Sec.
PO Box 785 72342 870-338-6474

Hermitage, Bradley, Pop. 823
Hermitage SD 500/PK-12
PO Box 38 71647 870-463-2246
Richard Rankin, supt. Fax 463-8520
se.sesc.k12.ar.us/pages/SE_Coop/148366133676555 0802
Hermitage HS 200/7-12
PO Box 190 71647 870-463-2235
Mark Price, prin. Fax 463-2122

Hope, Hempstead, Pop. 9,935
Hope SD 2,500/K-12
117 E 2nd St 71801 870-722-2700
Bobby Hart, supt. Fax 777-4087
hpsdistrict.org
Garland Learning Center 50/Alt
601 W 6th St 71801 870-777-3454
Angela Brewster, prin. Fax 722-2745
Hope HS 600/9-12
1701 S Main St 71801 870-777-3451
Sammy Bray, prin. Fax 722-2736
Yerger MS 400/7-8
400 E 9th St 71801 870-722-2770
Vanessa McCraw, prin. Fax 722-2707

Spring Hill SD 500/K-12
633 Highway 355 W 71801 870-777-8236
Angie Raney, supt. Fax 777-9200
sites.google.com/a/springhill.k12.ar.us/web/home
Spring Hill JSHS 300/7-12
633 Highway 355 W 71801 870-722-7430
Steve Britton, prin. Fax 722-7425

Garrett Memorial Christian S 200/PK-10
1 Genesis Dr 71801 870-777-3256
Fax 722-5639
University of Arkansas Community College Post-Sec.
PO Box 140 71802 870-777-5722

Horatio, Sevier, Pop. 1,021
Horatio SD 900/PK-12
204 Lawson Ln 71842 870-832-2343
John Ward, supt. Fax 832-4465
www.horatioschools.org/
Horatio JSHS 400/7-12
1101 Metcalf 71842 870-832-1900
James Dobbins, prin. Fax 832-2174

Hot Springs National Park, Garland, Pop. 34,276
Cutter-Morning Star SD 600/K-12
2801 Spring St 71901 501-262-2414
Nancy Anderson, supt. Fax 262-0670
eaglesnest.dsc.k12.ar.us/
Cutter-Morning Star JSHS 300/7-12
2801 Spring St 71901 501-262-1220
David Tollett, prin. Fax 262-3771

Fountain Lake SD 800/K-12
4207 Park Ave 71901 501-701-1700
Darin Beckwith, supt. Fax 623-6447
www.edline.net/pages/Fountain_Lake_SD
Fountain Lake HS 400/9-12
4207 Park Ave 71901 501-701-1706
Stephen Campbell, prin. Fax 623-6447
Fountain Lake MS 5-8
4207 Park Ave 71901 501-701-1730
Frank Janaskie, prin. Fax 318-6922

Hot Springs SD 3,500/PK-12
400 Linwood Ave 71913 501-624-3372
Joyce Craft, supt. Fax 620-7829
www.hssd.net
Hot Springs HS 800/9-12
701 Emory St 71913 501-624-5286
Lloyd Jackson, prin. Fax 620-7820
Hot Springs MS 500/7-8
700 Main St 71913 501-624-5228
George Wilson, prin. Fax 620-7828
Summit S Alt
220 Tom Ellsworth Dr 71901 501-620-7830
Kelly Deardorff, dir. Fax 620-7833

Lakeside SD 3,100/PK-12
2837 Malvern Ave 71901 501-262-1880
Shawn Cook, supt. Fax 262-2732
lakeside.ar.schoolwebpages.com/
Lakeside JHS 500/8-9
2865 Malvern Ave 71901 501-262-1316
Bruce Orr, prin. Fax 262-6232
Lakeside SHS 700/10-12
2871 Malvern Ave 71901 501-262-1530
Bruce Orr, prin. Fax 262-6205

Christian Ministries Academy 100/K-12
PO Box 8500 71910 501-624-1952
David Pate, prin. Fax 318-2624
Hot Springs Beauty College Post-Sec.
100 Cones Rd 71901 501-624-0203
Hot Springs SDA S 50/PK-10
401 Weston Rd 71913 501-760-3336
National Park Community College Post-Sec.
101 College Dr 71913 501-760-4222

Hoxie, Lawrence, Pop. 2,716
Hoxie SD 900/PK-12
PO Box 240 72433 870-886-2401
Dennis Truxler, supt. Fax 886-4252
hoxieschools.com
Hoxie HS 400/7-12
PO Box 240 72433 870-886-4254
Bart Hyde, prin. Fax 886-4255

Hughes, Saint Francis, Pop. 1,433
Hughes SD 400/K-12
PO Box 9 72348 870-339-2570
Jimmy Wilkins, supt. Fax 339-3317
hsd4.org/
Hughes JSHS 200/7-12
PO Box 9 72348 870-339-2580
Gheric Bruce, prin. Fax 339-3317

Huntsville, Madison, Pop. 2,295
Huntsville SD 2,300/K-12
PO Box F 72740 479-738-2011
Dr. Robert Allen, supt. Fax 738-2563
eagle.nwsc.k12.ar.us/
Huntsville HS 700/9-12
PO Box 1377 72740 479-738-2500
Michael Gray, prin. Fax 738-2849
Huntsville MS 500/6-8
PO Box G 72740 479-738-6520
Mike Cain, prin. Fax 738-6259
Other Schools – See Saint Paul

Imboden, Lawrence, Pop. 668
Sloan-Hendrix SD 700/K-12
PO Box 1080 72434 870-869-2384
Mitch Walton, supt. Fax 869-2380
shsd.k12.ar.us
Sloan-Hendrix HS 300/8-12
PO Box 1080 72434 870-869-2361
Clifford Rorex, prin. Fax 869-2362

Jacksonville, Pulaski, Pop. 27,377
Pulaski County Special SD
Supt. — See Little Rock
Jacksonville HS 900/9-12
2400 Linda Ln 72076 501-982-2128
Henry Anderson, prin. Fax 982-1692
Jacksonville MS 700/6-8
1320 School Dr 72076 501-982-1587
Don Booth, prin. Fax 241-2139
North Pulaski HS 800/9-12
718 Harris Rd 72076 501-982-9436
Jeff Senn, prin. Fax 241-2256

Arthur's Beauty College Post-Sec.
2600 John Harden Dr 72076 501-982-8987

Jasper, Newton, Pop. 462
Jasper SD 900/K-12
PO Box 446 72641 870-446-2223
Kerry Saylors, supt. Fax 446-2305
jasper.k12.ar.us
Jasper JSHS 200/7-12
PO Box 446 72641 870-446-2223
Jeff Lewis, prin. Fax 446-5549
Other Schools – See Kingston, Oark

Jessieville, Garland
Jessieville SD 900/K-12
PO Box 4 71949 501-984-5381
George Foshee, supt. Fax 984-4200
jsdlions.net/jessieville/lions/
Jessieville HS 300/9-12
PO Box 4 71949 501-984-5011
Toby Packard, prin. Fax 984-4200
Jessieville MS 200/6-8
PO Box 4 71949 501-984-5610
Janis Bremer, prin. Fax 984-4211

Jonesboro, Craighead, Pop. 66,085
Jonesboro SD 5,500/PK-12
2506 Southwest Sq 72401 870-933-5800
Dr. Kim Wilbanks, supt. Fax 933-5838
www.jonesboroschools.net
Area Technical Center Vo/Tech
1727 S Main St 72401 870-933-5891
Lisa Trotter, prin. Fax 933-5890
Camp JHS 600/7-9
1814 W Nettleton Ave 72401 870-933-5820
William Cheatham, prin. Fax 933-5837
Jonesboro SHS 1,100/10-12
301 Hurricane Dr 72401 870-933-5881
Dr. David Clark, prin. Fax 933-5812
MacArthur JHS 600/7-9
1615 Wilkins Ave 72401 870-933-5840
Dr. Brad Faught, prin. Fax 933-5848
SUCCESS Alt
613 N Fisher St 72401 870-931-9647
Todd Rhoades, dir. Fax 934-3555

Nettleton SD 2,800/K-12
3300 One Pl 72404 870-910-7800
James Dunivan, supt. Fax 910-7854
nettleton.ar.schoolwebpages.com
Nettleton JHS 500/7-9
4208 Chieftan Ln 72401 870-910-7819
Grace McElrath, prin. Fax 910-6984
Nettleton SHS 600/10-12
4201 Chieftan Ln 72401 870-910-7805
Brian Carter, prin. Fax 910-7804

Valley View SD 2,600/PK-12
2131 Valley View Dr 72404 870-935-6200
Dr. Radius Baker, supt. Fax 972-0373
blazers.k12.ar.us
Valley View HS 600/9-12
2118 Valley View Dr 72404 870-935-4602
Roland Popejoy, prin. Fax 935-6202
Valley View JHS 600/7-9
2115 Valley View Dr 72404 870-935-4602
Barry Jones, prin. Fax 932-2291
Adult Education Center Adult
2311 E Nettleton Ave 72401 870-935-6205
Steve Clayton, dir. Fax 935-6208

Westside Consolidated SD 1,600/K-12
1630 Highway 91 W 72404 870-935-7503
Dr. Bryan Duffie, supt. Fax 935-2123
www.westsideschools.org
Westside HS 600/8-12
1630 Highway 91 W 72404 870-935-7501
Freddy Bowen, prin. Fax 268-9119

Ridgefield Christian S 300/PK-12
3824 Casey Springs Rd 72404 870-932-7540

Judsonia, White, Pop. 1,987
White County Central SD 700/PK-12
3259 Highway 157 72081 501-729-3992
Sheila Whitlow, supt. Fax 729-3992
www.edline.net/pages/White_County_Central_SD
White County Central JSHS 300/7-12
3259 Highway 157 72081 501-729-3947
Jackwlyn Underwood, prin. Fax 729-3947

Junction City, Union, Pop. 576
Junction City SD 500/K-12
PO Box 790 71749 870-924-4575
Danny Thomas, supt. Fax 924-4565
junctioncity.k12.ar.us/
Junction City JSHS 300/7-12
PO Box 790 71749 870-924-4576
William Lowe, prin. Fax 924-4565

Kingston, Madison
Jasper SD
Supt. — See Jasper
Kingston JSHS 100/7-12
PO Box 149 72742 479-665-2835
Marsha Shaver, prin. Fax 665-2577

Kirby, Pike, Pop. 768
Kirby SD 400/K-12
PO Box 9 71950 870-398-4212
Jeff Alexander, supt. Fax 398-4442
www.kirbytrojans.net/
Kirby HS 200/7-12
PO Box 9 71950 870-398-4211
Jarrod Bray, prin. Fax 398-5413

Lake City, Craighead, Pop. 2,050
Riverside SD 600/K-12
PO Box 178 72437 870-237-4329
Tommy Knight, supt. Fax 237-4867
riverside.k12.ar.us
Riverside HS 200/7-12
PO Box 178 72437 870-237-4328
Chad Jordan, prin. Fax 237-9929

Lake Village, Chicot, Pop. 2,553
Lakeside SD 1,300/PK-12
1110 S Lakeshore Dr 71653 870-265-7300
Joyce Vaught, supt. Fax 265-5466
lakeside.k12.ar.us
Lakeside HS 300/9-12
1110 S Lakeshore Dr 71653 870-265-2232
Linda Armour, prin. Fax 265-7302
Lakeside MS 300/6-8
1110 S Lakeshore Dr 71653 870-265-2970
Arthur Gray, prin. Fax 265-7309

Lamar, Johnson, Pop. 1,567
Lamar SD 1,100/K-12
301 Elberta St 72846 479-885-3907
Roy Hester, supt. Fax 885-2380
lamarwarriors.org
Lamar HS 300/9-12
301 Elberta St 72846 479-885-3344
Charles Harris, prin. Fax 885-3842
Lamar MS 300/5-8
301 Elberta St 72846 479-885-6511
Lance Spence, prin. Fax 885-3920

Lavaca, Sebastian, Pop. 2,248
Lavaca SD 900/PK-12
PO Box 8 72941 479-674-5611
Steve Rose, supt. Fax 674-2271
www.lavacaschools.com
Lavaca HS 300/9-12
PO Box 8 72941 479-674-5612
Chris Watson, prin. Fax 674-0087
Lavaca MS 300/5-8
PO Box 8 72941 479-674-5618
Melissa Braddy, prin. Fax 674-2271

Leachville, Mississippi, Pop. 1,967
Buffalo Island Central SD
Supt. — See Monette
Buffalo Island Central JHS 200/7-9
PO Box 110 72438 870-539-6883
Mark Hurst, prin. Fax 539-6696

Lead Hill, Boone, Pop. 266
Lead Hill SD 400/K-12
PO Box 20 72644 870-436-5249
Regina Brown, supt. Fax 436-5946
leadhill.ar.schoolwebpages.com
Lead Hill JSHS 200/7-12
PO Box 20 72644 870-436-5677
Steve Williams, prin. Fax 436-6827

Lepanto, Poinsett, Pop. 1,866
East Poinsett County SD 700/PK-12
502 McClellan St 72354 870-475-2472
Michael Pierce, supt. Fax 475-3531
epc.k12.ar.us/
East Poinsett County JSHS 300/7-12
502 McClellan St 72354 870-475-2472
Gary Williams, prin. Fax 475-2206

Leslie, Searcy, Pop. 431
Searcy County SD
Supt. — See Marshall
North Central Career Center Vo/Tech
402 Oak St 72645 870-447-6111
Fax 447-2872

Lewisville, Lafayette, Pop. 1,260
Lafayette County SD 800/K-12
PO Box 950 71845 870-921-5500
Mark Keith, supt. Fax 921-4277
www.lcscougars.org
Other Schools – See Stamps

South Arkansas Christian S K-12
1429 Highway 82 71845 870-921-5050
Andy Hawkins, hdmstr.

Lexa, Phillips, Pop. 285
Barton-Lexa SD 800/K-12
9546 Highway 85 72355 870-572-7294
Tom Wilson, supt. Fax 572-4713
Barton JSHS 400/7-12
9546 Highway 85 72355 870-572-6867
David Bagley, prin. Fax 572-4713

Lincoln, Washington, Pop. 2,196
Lincoln Consolidated SD 1,100/PK-12
107 E School St 72744 479-824-7300
Mary Ann Spears, supt. Fax 824-3045
www.lincolncsd.com
Lincoln Academic Center of Excellence 100/Alt
1392 E Pridemore Dr 72744 479-824-7490
Courtney Jones, prin. Fax 824-3057
Lincoln HS 400/8-12
1392 E Pridemore Dr 72744 479-824-7450
Courtney Jones, prin. Fax 824-3042

Little Rock, Pulaski, Pop. 190,562
Little Rock SD 26,000/PK-12
810 W Markham St 72201 501-447-1000
Dr. Dexter Suggs, supt. Fax 447-1159
www.lrsd.org
Accelerated Learning Center 200/Alt
7701 Scott Hamilton Dr 72209 501-447-1370
Brenda Allen, prin. Fax 447-1371
Central HS 2,500/9-12
1500 S Park St 72202 501-447-1400
Nancy Rousseau, prin. Fax 447-1401
Dunbar Magnet MS 800/6-8
1100 Wright Ave 72206 501-447-2600
Eunice Thrasher, prin. Fax 447-2601
Fair Magnet HS 900/9-12
13420 David O Dodd Rd 72210 501-447-1700
Jeremy Owoh, prin. Fax 447-1701
Forest Heights MS 600/6-8
5901 Evergreen Dr 72205 501-447-2700
Connie Green, prin. Fax 447-2701
Hall HS 1,300/9-12
6700 H St 72205 501-447-1900
Larry Schleicher, prin. Fax 447-1901
Hamilton Learning Academy 300/Alt
3301 S Bryant St 72204 501-447-3400
Willie Vinson, prin. Fax 447-3401
Henderson Magnet MS 700/6-8
401 John Barrow Rd 72205 501-447-2800
Steve Geurin, prin. Fax 447-2801
Mann Magnet MS 800/6-8
1000 E Roosevelt Rd 72206 501-447-3100
Keith McGee, prin. Fax 447-3101
McClellan Magnet HS 900/9-12
9417 Geyer Springs Rd 72209 501-447-2100
Henry Anderson, prin. Fax 447-2101
Metropolitan Career-Tech Center Vo/Tech
7701 Scott Hamilton Dr 72209 501-447-1370
Cassandra Norm-McGhee, prin. Fax 447-1371
Parkview Magnet HS 1,100/9-12
2501 John Barrow Rd 72204 501-447-2300
Dr. Dexter Booth, prin. Fax 447-2301
Pulaski Heights MS 900/6-8
401 N Pine St 72205 501-447-3200
Dr. Suzanne Ross, prin. Fax 447-3201
Adult Education Center Adult
4800 W 26th St 72204 501-447-1850
Linda Kindy, coord. Fax 447-1897
Other Schools – See Mabelvale

Pulaski County Special SD 16,600/PK-12
925 E Dixon Rd 72206 501-490-2000
Dr. Jerry Guess, supt. Fax 490-0483
www.pcssd.org
Fuller MS 500/6-8
808 E Dixon Rd 72206 501-490-5730
Brent Mitchell, prin. Fax 490-5736
Mills HS 800/9-12
1205 E Dixon Rd 72206 501-490-5700
Dr. Veronica Perkins, prin. Fax 490-5709
PCSSD Learning Academy Alt
708 E Dixon Rd 72206 501-490-5742
Ken Clark, prin. Fax 490-5757
Robinson HS 500/9-12
21501 Highway 10 72223 501-868-2400
Dr. Yolaundra Williams, prin. Fax 868-2405
Robinson MS 400/6-8
21001 Highway 10 72223 501-868-2410
Kimala Forrest, prin. Fax 868-2441
Other Schools – See Jacksonville, Maumelle, North Little Rock, Sherwood

---

Arkansas Baptist College Post-Sec.
1621 Dr Martin Luther King 72202 501-370-4000
Arkansas Baptist JSHS 400/7-12
8400 Ranch Blvd 72223 501-868-5121
Arthur Bennett, hdmstr. Fax 868-5403
Arkansas Beauty School Post-Sec.
5108 Baseline Rd 72209 501-562-5673
AR College of Barbering & Hair Design Post-Sec.
2500 S State St 72206 501-376-9696
Arkansas School for the Blind Post-Sec.
PO Box 668 72203 [illegible]
Arkansas School for the Deaf Post-Sec.
2400 W Markham St 72205 501-324-9506
Baptist Schools of Allied Health Post-Sec.
11900 Colonel Glenn Rd 72210 501-202-6200
Catholic HS for Boys 700/9-12
6300 Father Tribou St 72205 501-664-3939
Steve Straessle, prin. Fax 664-6549
Central Arkansas Radiation Therapy Inst. Post-Sec.
PO Box 55050 72215 501-664-8573
Eastern College of Health Vocations Post-Sec.
200 S University Ave 72205 501-568-0211
Episcopal Collegiate S 800/PK-12
1701 Cantrell Rd 72201 501-372-1194
Stephen Hickman, hdmstr. Fax 372-2160
Heritage College Post-Sec.
1309 Old Forge Dr 72227 501-708-0909
ITT Technical Institute Post-Sec.
12200 Westhaven Dr 72211 501-565-5550
Little Rock Adventist Academy 50/K-10
8708 N Rodney Parham Rd 72205 501-225-6183
Little Rock Christian Academy 1,300/K-12
19010 Cantrell Rd 72223 501-868-9822
Dr. Gary Arnold, hdmstr. Fax 868-8766
Mt. St. Mary Academy 500/9-12
3224 Kavanaugh Blvd 72205 501-664-8006
Diane Wolfe, prin. Fax 666-4382
Philander Smith College Post-Sec.
900 W Daisy L Gatson Bates 72202 501-375-9845
Pulaski Academy 1,400/PK-12
12701 Hinson Rd 72212 501-604-1910
Dr. Joe Hatcher, pres. Fax 225-1974
Remington College Post-Sec.
19 Remington Dr 72204 501-312-0007
St. Vincent Infirmary Medical Center Post-Sec.
2 Saint Vincent Cir 72205 501-660-3910
Southwest Christian Academy 400/PK-12
11301 Geyer Springs Rd 72209 501-565-3276
Sharon Stewart, prin. Fax 394-4967
University of Arkansas at Little Rock Post-Sec.
2801 S University Ave 72204 501-569-3000
University of Arkansas/Medical Sciences Post-Sec.
4301 W Markham St 72205 501-686-5000
Velvatex College of Beauty Culture Post-Sec.
1520 Dr Martin Luther King 72202 501-372-9678
Washington Barber College Post-Sec.
5300 W 65th St 72209 501-568-8800

Lonoke, Lonoke, Pop. 4,204
Lonoke SD 1,800/K-12
401 W Holly St 72086 501-676-2042
Suzanne Bailey, supt. Fax 676-7074
lonokeschools.org/
Lonoke HS 600/9-12
501 W Academy St 72086 501-676-2476
Phynaus Wilson, prin. Fax 676-3716
Lonoke MS 500/6-8
1100 W Palm St 72086 501-676-6670
Jeannie Holt, prin. Fax 676-7013

Mabelvale, Pulaski
Little Rock SD
Supt. — See Little Rock
Mabelvale Magnet MS 700/6-8
10811 Mabelvale West Rd 72103 501-447-3000
Rhonda Hall, prin. Fax 447-3001

Mc Crory, Woodruff, Pop. 1,707
Mc Crory SD 700/K-12
PO Box 930 72101 870-731-2535
Barry Scott, supt. Fax 731-2536
mccrory.k12.ar.us/
Mc Crory JSHS 300/7-12
PO Box 930 72101 870-731-2851
Lincoln Daniels, prin. Fax 731-2574

Mc Gehee, Desha, Pop. 4,181
McGehee SD 1,100/K-12
PO Box 767 71654 870-222-3670
Thomas Gathen, supt. Fax 222-6957
owls.k12.ar.us/
McGehee JSHS 500/7-12
PO Box 767 71654 870-222-5026
Derrell Thompson, prin. Fax 222-5838

Baptist School of Nursing-SE Post-Sec.
Highway 1 NE 71654

Magazine, Logan, Pop. 835
Magazine SD 600/PK-12
485 E Priddy St 72943 479-969-2566
Sandra Beck, supt. Fax 969-8740
magazinerattlers.k12.ar.us
Leftwich HS 300/7-12
292 E Priddy St 72943 479-969-2640
Randy Bryan, prin. Fax 969-2610

Magnolia, Columbia, Pop. 11,431
Magnolia SD 2,900/PK-12
PO Box 649 71754 870-234-4933
Dr. John Moore, supt. Fax 901-2508
www.magnoliaschools.net
Magnolia JHS 700/7-9
PO Box 649 71754 870-234-2206
Gwen Carter, prin. Fax 234-1293
Magnolia SHS 600/10-12
PO Box 649 71754 870-234-2610
Roger Loper, prin. Fax 901-2509

Columbia Christian S 500/PK-12
250 Warnock Springs Rd 71753 870-234-2831
Dr. Marla Strecker, dir. Fax 234-1497
Southern Arkansas University Post-Sec.
100 E University 71753 870-235-4000

Malvern, Hot Spring, Pop. 10,082
Glen Rose SD 1,000/PK-12
14334 Highway 67 72104 501-332-3694
Nathan Gills, supt. Fax 332-3031
www.grbeavers.org
Glen Rose HS 300/9-12
14334 Highway 67 72104 501-332-3694
Vic Gandolph, prin. Fax 332-3902
Glen Rose MS 300/5-8
14334 Highway 67 72104 501-332-3694
Shawn Pilgrim, prin. Fax 332-3799

Magnet Cove SD 700/K-12
472 Magnet School Rd 72104 501-332-5468
Gail McClure, supt. Fax 337-4119
magnetcove.k12.ar.us
Magnet Cove HS 300/7-12
472 Magnet School Rd 72104 501-332-5466
Brad Sullivan, prin. Fax 337-8711

Malvern Special SD 2,100/K-12
1517 S Main St 72104 501-332-7500
Brian Golden, supt. Fax 332-7501
malvernleopards.org
Malvern MS 300/7-8
339 E Donnelly St 72104 501-332-7530
Velda Keeney, prin. Fax 332-7532
Malvern SHS 600/9-12
525 E Highland Ave 72104 501-332-6905
Stephen Barber, prin. Fax 332-7523

College of the Ouachitas Post-Sec.
1 College Cir 72104 501-337-5000

Mammoth Spring, Fulton, Pop. 962
Mammoth Spring SD 500/K-12
410 Goldsmith Ave 72554 870-625-3612
David Turnbough, supt. Fax 625-3609
www.mammothspringschools.com
Mammoth Spring HS 200/7-12
410 Goldsmith Ave 72554 870-625-7212
Brian Davis, prin. Fax 625-3609

Manila, Mississippi, Pop. 3,321
Manila SD 1,000/PK-12
PO Box 670 72442 870-561-4419
Pamela Castor, supt. Fax 561-4410
mps.crsc.k12.ar.us
Manila HS 300/9-12
PO Box 670 72442 870-561-4417
Robin Baugher, prin. Fax 561-4243
Manila MS 300/5-8
PO Box 670 72442 870-561-4815
LeAnn Helms, prin. Fax 561-4828

Mansfield, Scott, Pop. 1,119
Mansfield SD 1,000/K-12
402 Grove St 72944 479-928-4006
Robert Ross, supt. Fax 928-4482
www.mansfieldtigers.com

Mansfield HS 300/9-12
2500 Highway 71 S 72944 479-928-1105
Tina Smith, prin. Fax 928-1108
Mansfield MS 300/5-8
400 Grove St 72944 479-928-4451
Cindy Coleman, prin. Fax 928-4323

Marianna, Lee, Pop. 4,065
Lee County SD 1,100/PK-12
188 W Chestnut St 72360 870-295-7100
Willie Murdock, supt. Fax 295-7125
lcsd1.grsc.k12.ar.us/
Lee HS 300/9-12
523 Forest Ave 72360 870-295-7130
Clyde Noel, prin. Fax 295-7313
Strong MS 300/5-8
214 S Alabama St 72360 870-295-7140
Carolyn Love, prin. Fax 295-7314

Marion, Crittenden, Pop. 12,214
Marion SD 4,200/K-12
200 Manor St 72364 870-739-5100
Don Johnston, supt. Fax 739-5156
www.msd3.org/
Crittenden Prep Academy Alt
200 Manor St 72364 870-739-5153
Connie Steele, prin. Fax 739-5130
Marion JHS 700/8-9
801 Carter Dr 72364 870-739-5140
Elmer West, prin. Fax 739-5142
Marion SHS 900/10-12
1 Patriot Dr 72364 870-739-5130
Stephen Landers, prin. Fax 739-5135

Marked Tree, Poinsett, Pop. 2,530
Marked Tree SD 500/PK-12
406 Saint Francis St 72365 870-358-2913
Annesa Thompson, supt. Fax 358-3953
mtree.k12.ar.us
Marked Tree JSHS 200/7-12
406 Saint Francis St 72365 870-358-2891
Matt Wright, prin. Fax 358-3953

Delta Technical Institute Post-Sec.
PO Box 280 72365 870-358-2117

Marmaduke, Greene, Pop. 1,093
Marmaduke SD 700/K-12
1010 Greyhound Dr 72443 870-597-2723
Tim Gardner, supt. Fax 597-4693
www.mhs.nesc.k12.ar.us
Marmaduke JSHS 300/7-12
1010 Greyhound Dr 72443 870-597-4693
Bill Muse, prin. Fax 597-4693

Marshall, Searcy, Pop. 1,315
Searcy County SD 800/K-12
952 Highway 65 N 72650 870-448-3011
Andrew Vining, supt. Fax 448-3012
searcycounty.ar.schoolwebpages.com
Marshall MSHS 400/7-12
950 Highway 65 N 72650 870-448-3331
Jimmy Yarbrough, prin. Fax 448-5306
Other Schools – See Leslie

Marvell, Phillips, Pop. 1,170
Marvell-Elaine SD 500/PK-12
PO Box 1870 72366 870-829-2101
Ruth Bowles Denson, supt. Fax 829-2044
marvell.grsc.k12.ar.us/
Marvell-Elaine HS 200/6-12
PO Box 1870 72366 870-829-1351
Adrian Watkins, prin. Fax 829-3150

Marvell Academy 200/K-12
PO Box 277 72366 870-829-2931
Brad Foster, hdmstr. Fax 829-2931

Maumelle, Pulaski, Pop. 16,888
Pulaski County Special SD
Supt. — See Little Rock
Maumelle HS 9-12
100 Victory Ln 72113 501-851-5350
Becky Guthrie, prin. Fax 851-5356
Maumelle MS 800/6-8
1000 Carnahan Dr 72113 501-851-8990
Charlotte Wallace, prin. Fax 851-8988

Mayflower, Faulkner, Pop. 2,195
Mayflower SD 1,100/PK-12
15 Old Sandy Rd 72106 501-470-0506
John Gray, supt. Fax 470-1343
mayflowerschools.info
Mayflower HS 300/9-12
10 Leslie King N 72106 501-470-0388
Jeff Cagle, prin. Fax 470-2106
Mayflower MS 300/5-8
18 Eagle Circle 72106 501-470-2111
John Pipkins, prin. Fax 470-2116

Maynard, Randolph, Pop. 421
Maynard SD 500/K-12
74 Campus Dr 72444 870-647-3500
Larry Sullinger, supt. Fax 647-2301
maynard.nesc.k12.ar.us/
Maynard JSHS 300/7-12
74 Campus Dr 72444 870-647-3500
Cindy Dauck, prin. Fax 647-2301

Melbourne, Izard, Pop. 1,832
Melbourne SD 900/K-12
PO Box 250 72556 870-368-7070
Gerald Cooper, supt. Fax 368-7071
bearkatz.k12.ar.us/
Melbourne JSHS 400/7-12
PO Box 250 72556 870-368-4345
Kelly Powell, prin. Fax 368-4349

Ozarka College Post-Sec.
PO Box 10 72556 870-368-7371

Mena, Polk, Pop. 5,622
Mena SD 1,800/K-12
501 Hickory Ave 71953 479-394-1710
Benny Weston, supt. Fax 394-1713
www.menaschools.org
Mena HS 600/9-12
PO Box 1810 71953 479-394-1144
Mark Shumate, prin. Fax 394-1145
Mena MS 300/6-8
700 Morrow St S 71953 479-394-2572
Mike Hobson, prin. Fax 394-0258

Ouachita River SD 700/K-12
143 Polk Road 96 71953 479-394-2348
Steve Crumpler, supt. Fax 394-6687
orsd.k12.ar.us
Acorn JSHS 200/7-12
143 Polk Road 96 71953 479-394-5544
Sean Couch, prin. Fax 394-1041
Other Schools – See Oden

Rich Mountain Community College Post-Sec.
1100 College Dr 71953 479-394-7622

Mineral Springs, Howard, Pop. 1,190
Mineral Springs SD 500/PK-12
PO Box 189 71851 870-287-4748
Bill Blackwood, supt. Fax 287-5301
mssd2.k12.ar.us/
Mineral Springs JSHS 200/7-12
PO Box 189 71851 870-287-4747
Davey Jones, prin. Fax 287-5300

Monette, Craighead, Pop. 1,489
Buffalo Island Central SD 900/PK-12
PO Box 730 72447 870-486-5411
George Holland, supt. Fax 486-2657
www.buffaloislandcentral.com
Buffalo Island Central SHS 200/10-12
PO Box 730 72447 870-486-5512
Randy Rose, prin. Fax 486-2657
Other Schools – See Leachville

Monticello, Drew, Pop. 9,357
Drew Central SD 800/K-12
250 University Dr 71655 870-367-5369
Mike Johnston, supt. Fax 367-1932
www.drewcentral.org/
Drew Central HS 300/9-12
250 University Dr 71655 870-367-6076
Steve Noble, prin. Fax 460-5501
Drew Central MS 100/5-8
250 University Dr 71655 870-367-5235
Joy Graham, prin. Fax 460-5502

Monticello SD 2,100/K-12
935 Scogin Dr 71655 870-367-4000
Bobby Harper, supt. Fax 367-1531
www.billies.org
Monticello HS 600/9-12
390 Clyde Ross Dr 71655 870-367-4050
Jim Lucas, prin. Fax 367-3699
Monticello MS 500/6-8
180 Clyde Ross Dr 71655 870-367-4040
Jerry Martens, prin. Fax 367-5437
Occupational Education Center Vo/Tech
741 Scogin Dr 71655 870-367-4060
Randy Lay, dir. Fax 367-1385

University of Arkansas at Monticello Post-Sec.
346 University Dr 71656 870-460-1026

Morrilton, Conway, Pop. 6,618
South Conway County SD 2,200/K-12
100 Baramore St 72110 501-354-9400
Dr. Annette Henderson, supt. Fax 354-9464
www.sccsd.org
Morrilton HS 600/9-12
701 E Harding St 72110 501-354-9430
Danny Ketcherside, prin. Fax 354-9468
Morrilton JHS 300/7-8
1400 Poor Farm Rd 72110 501-354-9437
Robert Hogan, prin. Fax 354-9429

Sacred Heart S 200/PK-12
106 N Saint Joseph St 72110 501-354-8113
Brian Bailey, prin. Fax 354-2001
University of Arkansas Community College Post-Sec.
1537 University Blvd 72110 501-354-2465

Mountainburg, Crawford, Pop. 624
Mountainburg SD 700/K-12
129 Highway 71 SW 72946 479-369-2121
Dennis Copeland, supt. Fax 369-2138
www.mountainburg.org
Mountainburg HS 200/9-12
129 Highway 71 SW 72946 479-369-2146
Jason Rutherford, prin. Fax 369-2845
Mountainburg MS 200/5-8
129 Highway 71 SW 72946 479-369-4506
Jason Rutherford, prin. Fax 369-4355

Mountain Home, Baxter, Pop. 12,291
Mountain Home SD 3,000/K-12
2465 Rodeo Dr 72653 870-425-1201
Dr. Lonnie Myers, supt. Fax 425-1316
bombers.k12.ar.us/
Mountain Home HS Career Academies 1,200/9-12
500 Bomber Blvd 72653 870-425-1215
Dana Brown, prin. Fax 508-6097
Mountain Home JHS 300/8-8
2301 Rodeo Dr 72653 870-425-1231
Ron Czanstkowski, prin. Fax 424-4797

Arkansas State University Mountain Home Post-Sec.
1600 S College St 72653 870-508-6100
Marsha Kay Beauty College Post-Sec.
408 Highway 201 N 72653 870-425-7575

Mountain Home Christian Academy 100/PK-12
1989 Glenbriar Dr 72653 870-424-6622
Lori Mathis, prin.

Mountain Pine, Garland, Pop. 749
Mountain Pine SD 600/PK-12
PO Box 1 71956 501-767-1540
Robert Gray, supt. Fax 767-1589
www.edline.net/pages/Mountain_Pine_SD
Mountain Pine JSHS 300/7-12
PO Box 1 71956 501-767-6917
Doug Booker, prin. Fax 767-0170

Mountain View, Stone, Pop. 2,714
Mountain View SD 1,700/PK-12
210 High School Rd 72560 870-269-3443
Rowdy Ross, supt. Fax 269-3446
mountainviewschooldistrict.k12.ar.us/
Mountain View HS 400/9-12
210 High School Rd 72560 870-269-3943
George Lucas, prin. Fax 269-2372
Mountain View MS 300/6-8
210 High School Rd 72560 870-269-4335
Robert Ross, prin. Fax 269-4447
Other Schools – See Fox, Timbo

Mount Ida, Montgomery, Pop. 1,049
Mount Ida SD 500/K-12
PO Box 1230 71957 870-867-2323
Jeanne Smith, supt. Fax 867-3734
www.dmsc.k12.ar.us/~mountida/cms/
Mount Ida JSHS 300/7-12
PO Box 1230 71957 870-867-2771
Hal Landrith, prin. Fax 867-3734

Mount Judea, Newton
Deer / Mt. Judea SD
Supt. — See Deer
Mount Judea JSHS 100/7-12
PO Box 40 72655 870-434-5362
Sammie Dye, prin. Fax 434-5359

Mount Vernon, Faulkner, Pop. 139
Mount Vernon-Enola SD 500/K-12
PO Box 43 72111 501-849-2220
Larry Walters, supt. Fax 849-3076
mve.k12.ar.us/
Mount Vernon-Enola JSHS 200/7-12
PO Box 43 72111 501-849-2221
Rudy Beavers, prin. Fax 849-3302

Mulberry, Crawford, Pop. 1,638
Mulberry/Pleasant View Bi-County SD 400/K-12
424 Alma Ave 72947 479-997-1715
Dana Higdon, supt. Fax 997-1897
www.edline.net/pages/Mulberry_SD
Mulberry HS 100/10-12
424 Alma Ave 72947 479-997-1363
Melvin Williams, prin. Fax 997-1491
Other Schools – See Ozark

Murfreesboro, Pike, Pop. 1,612
South Pike County SD 700/K-12
PO Box 339 71958 870-285-2201
Roger Featherston, supt. Fax 285-2276
mboro.k12.ar.us/
Murfreesboro JSHS 200/7-12
PO Box 339 71958 870-285-2184
Kathaleen Cole, prin. Fax 285-2276

Nashville, Howard, Pop. 4,566
Nashville SD 2,000/K-12
600 N 4th St 71852 870-845-3425
Douglas Graham, supt. Fax 845-7344
www.nashvillesd.com
Nashville JHS 400/7-9
1000 N 8th St 71852 870-845-3418
Deb Tackett, prin. Fax 845-7334
Nashville SHS 400/10-12
1301 Mount Pleasant Dr 71852 870-845-3261
Tate Gordon, prin. Fax 845-7345

Newark, Independence, Pop. 1,165
Cedar Ridge SD 800/PK-12
1502 N Hill St 72562 870-799-8691
Dr. Ann Webb, supt. Fax 799-8647
www.crsd.k12.ar.us/
Cedar Ridge JSHS 400/7-12
1500 N Hill St 72562 870-799-8691
Danny Davis, prin. Fax 799-3225

Newport, Jackson, Pop. 7,757
Newport SD 700/PK-12
406 Wilkerson Dr 72112 870-523-1312
Dr. Larry Bennett, supt. Fax 523-1388
newportschools.org
Newport HS 400/9-12
406 Wilkerson Dr 72112 870-523-1321
Becky Watkins, prin. Fax 523-1383
Newport JHS 200/7-8
406 Wilkerson Dr 72112 870-523-1346
Kenneth Black, prin. Fax 523-1334

Arkansas State University - Newport Post-Sec.
7648 Victory Blvd 72112 870-512-7800

Norfork, Baxter, Pop. 502
Norfork SD 500/K-12
44 Fireball Ln 72658 870-499-5228
Mike Seay, supt. Fax 499-5109
norfork.k12.ar.us
Norfork JSHS 200/7-12
136 Mildred Simpson Dr 72658 870-499-7191
Bob Hulse, prin. Fax 499-5659

Norman, Montgomery, Pop. 367
Caddo Hills SD 600/PK-12
2268 Highway 8 E 71960 870-356-5700
Paul Shelton, supt. Fax 356-3426
www.caddohills.org

Caddo Hills JSHS 300/7-12
2268 Highway 8 E 71960 870-356-5701
James Vines, prin. Fax 356-3444

Norphlet, Union, Pop. 829
Norphlet SD 400/K-12
PO Box 50 71759 870-546-2781
Albert Snow Ed.D., supt. Fax 546-2345
www.norphlet.k12.ar.us
Norphlet JSHS 200/7-12
PO Box 50 71759 870-546-2781
Raymond Coleman, prin. Fax 546-9554

North Little Rock, Pulaski, Pop. 61,111
North Little Rock SD 6,900/PK-12
PO Box 687 72115 501-771-8000
Kelly Rodgers, supt. Fax 771-8067
www.nlrsd.org
Lakewood MS 700/6-8
2400 Lakeview Rd 72116 501-771-8200
Lee Tackett, prin. Fax 771-8206
North Little Rock HS 1,500/9-12
101 W 22nd St 72114 501-771-8100
Brian Brown, prin. Fax 771-8123
Ridgeroad MS 500/6-8
4601 Ridge Rd 72116 501-771-8155
Bill Bowers, prin. Fax 771-8159

Pulaski County Special SD
Supt. — See Little Rock
Northwood MS 600/6-8
10200 Bamboo Ln 72120 501-833-1170
Dr. Kirk Freeman, prin. Fax 833-1178

AR College of Barbering & Hair Design Post-Sec.
200 E Washington Ave 72114 501-376-9696
Central Arkansas Christian S 1,000/PK-12
1 Windsong Dr 72113 501-758-3160
Lee's School of Cosmetology Post-Sec.
2700 W Pershing Blvd 72114 501-758-2800
New Tyler Barber College Post-Sec.
1221 Bishop Lindsey Ave 72114 501-375-0377
Pulaski Technical College Post-Sec.
3000 W Scenic Dr 72118 501-812-2200
Shorter College Post-Sec.
604 N Locust St 72114 501-374-6305

Oark, Johnson
Jasper SD
Supt. — See Jasper
Oark JSHS 100/7-12
370 Highway 215 72852 479-292-3353
Geary Brown, prin. Fax 292-3435

Oden, Montgomery, Pop. 227
Ouachita River SD
Supt. — See Mena
Oden JSHS 100/7-12
PO Box 150 71961 870-326-4311
William Edwards, prin. Fax 326-5552

Ola, Yell, Pop. 1,269
Two Rivers SD 700/K-12
17727 E State Highway 28 72853 479-272-3113
Jim Loyd, supt. Fax 272-3125
www.trgators.org/
Two Rivers JSHS 400/5-12
17727 E State Highway 28 72853 479-272-3150
Barry Fisher, prin. Fax 272-3149

Omaha, Boone, Pop. 159
Omaha SD 400/K-12
522 College Rd 72662 870-426-3366
Jerry Parrett, supt. Fax 426-3355
omaha.k12.ar.us/
Omaha JSHS 200/7-12
522 College Rd 72662 870-426-3373
Nathan White, prin. Fax 426-3360

Osceola, Mississippi, Pop. 7,648
Osceola SD 1,200/PK-12
2750 W Semmes Ave 72370 870-563-2561
Michael Cox, supt. Fax 563-2181
www.osd1.org/
Osceola HS 300/9-12
2800 W Semmes Ave 72370 870-563-2192
Zrano Bowles, prin. Fax 622-1003
Osceola STEM Academy 200/5-8
112 N School St 72370 870-563-2150
Ellouise Tubbs, prin. Fax 622-1025

Ozark, Franklin, Pop. 3,615
Mulberry/Pleasant View Bi-County SD
Supt. — See Mulberry
Pleasant View JHS 100/7-9
5750 Hornet Ln 72949 479-997-8469
Rodney Finley, prin. Fax 997-1667

Ozark SD 1,800/K-12
PO Box 135 72949 479-667-4118
Jim Ford, supt. Fax 667-4092
www.ozarkhillbillies.org/
Ozark JHS 300/8-9
1301 Walden Dr 72949 479-667-4747
Jerrod Burns, prin. Fax 667-0898
Ozark SHS 400/10-12
1631 Hillbilly Dr 72949 479-667-4118
Jody Jenkins, prin. Fax 667-5921

Arkansas Technical University Ozark Cmps Post-Sec.
1700 Helberg Ln 72949 866-225-2884

Palestine, Saint Francis, Pop. 671
Palestine-Wheatley SD 700/PK-12
PO Box 790 72372 870-581-2646
Richard Jon Estes, supt. Fax 581-4420
www.edline.net/pages/Palestine-Wheatley_School_Dist/
Palestine-Wheatley HS 200/9-12
PO Box 790 72372 870-581-2425
Randy Cannon, prin. Fax 581-4421

Other Schools – See Wheatley

Pangburn, White, Pop. 587
Pangburn SD 800/K-12
1100 Short St 72121 501-728-4511
Dr. Kathy Berryhill, supt. Fax 728-4514
pangburnschools.org
Pangburn MSHS 400/7-12
1100 Short St 72121 501-728-3513
David Rolland, prin. Fax 728-4514

Paragould, Greene, Pop. 25,788
Greene County Technical SD 3,300/PK-12
5413 W Kingshighway 72450 870-236-2762
Jerry Noble, supt. Fax 236-7333
www.gctsd.k12.ar.us/
Greene County Technical HS 700/10-12
4601 Linwood Dr 72450 870-215-4460
Scott Gerrish, prin. Fax 239-6976
Greene County Technical JHS 500/8-9
5201 W Kingshighway 72450 870-215-4450
Michael Todd, prin. Fax 239-2148

Paragould SD 2,900/PK-12
1501 W Court St 72450 870-239-2105
Debbie Smith, supt. Fax 239-4697
paragould.k12.ar.us/
Paragould HS 800/9-12
1701 W Court St 72450 870-236-7744
Scott Gauntt, prin. Fax 239-2934
Paragould JHS 400/7-8
1713 W Court St 72450 870-236-7744
James Brittingham, prin. Fax 239-0185

Crowleys Ridge Academy 300/PK-12
606 Academy Dr 72450 870-236-6909
Perry Gates, pres. Fax 236-6988
Crowley's Ridge College Post-Sec.
100 College Dr 72450 870-236-6901

Paris, Logan, Pop. 3,477
Paris SD 1,200/PK-12
602 N 10th St 72855 479-963-3243
Wayne Fawcett, supt. Fax 963-3620
www.parisschools.org
Paris HS 300/9-12
2000 E Wood St 72855 479-963-2247
Britt Bauer, prin. Fax 963-8018
Paris MS 400/5-8
602 N 10th St 72855 479-963-6995
Martha Dodson, prin. Fax 963-8052

Pearcy, Garland
Lake Hamilton SD 4,100/K-12
205 Wolf St 71964 501-767-2306
Steve Anderson, supt. Fax 767-5573
wolves.dsc.k12.ar.us
Lake Hamilton JHS 700/8-9
281 Wolf St 71964 501-767-2731
Jerald Humphries, prin. Fax 767-1711
Lake Hamilton SHS 900/10-12
280 Wolf St 71964 501-767-9311
Kirk Nance, prin. Fax 767-9318

Pea Ridge, Benton, Pop. 4,709
Pea Ridge SD 1,600/K-12
781 W Pickens Rd 72751 479-451-8181
Rick Neal, supt. Fax 451-8235
www.prs.k12.ar.us/
Pea Ridge HS 500/9-12
781 W Pickens Rd 72751 479-451-8182
Jon Laffoon, prin. Fax 451-0323
Pea Ridge MS 400/6-8
1391 Weston St 72751 479-451-0620
Sue McElroy, prin. Fax 451-0624

Perryville, Perry, Pop. 1,437
Perryville SD 1,000/K-12
614 S Fourche Ave 72126 501-889-2327
Dr. Ron Wilson, supt. Fax 889-5191
mustangs.k12.ar.us/
Perryville JSHS 500/7-12
325 Houston Ave 72126 501-889-2326
Kevin Campbell, prin. Fax 889-5006

Piggott, Clay, Pop. 3,820
Piggott SD 1,000/K-12
PO Box 387 72454 870-598-2572
Charnelsa Powell, supt. Fax 598-5283
piggottths.k12.ar.us/
Piggott HS 500/7-12
PO Box 387 72454 870-598-3815
Barry DeHart, prin. Fax 598-1560

Pine Bluff, Jefferson, Pop. 48,534
Dollarway SD 1,700/PK-12
4900 Dollarway Rd 71602 870-534-7003
Frank Anthony, supt. Fax 534-7859
dollarway.k12.ar.us
Dollarway HS 500/9-12
4900 Dollarway Rd 71602 870-534-3878
Arnold Robertson, prin. Fax 534-1455
Morehead MS 400/6-8
2602 W Fluker Ave 71601 870-534-5243
Yolanda Prim, prin. Fax 535-1215

Pine Bluff SD 4,900/PK-12
PO Box 7678 71611 870-543-4200
Dr. Linda Watson, supt. Fax 543-4208
www.pinebluffschools.k12.ar.us/
First Ward Learning Center Alt
1300 E 5th Ave 71601 870-543-4389
Ronald Laurent, dir. Fax 850-2028
Pine Bluff SHS 1,000/10-12
711 W 11th Ave 71601 870-543-4300
Dr. Michael Nellums, prin. Fax 543-4302
Robey JHS 700/8-9
4101 S Olive St 71603 870-543-4290
Dr. Jerry Bell, prin. Fax 850-2027

Watson Chapel SD 3,100/K-12
4100 Camden Rd 71603 870-879-0220
Danny Hazelwood, supt. Fax 879-0588
watson2.arsc.k12.ar.us
Watson Chapel JHS 800/7-9
3900 Camden Rd 71603 870-879-4420
Henry Webb, prin. Fax 879-4426
Watson Chapel SHS 700/10-12
4000 Camden Rd 71603 870-879-3230
Leydel Willis, prin. Fax 879-1842

Jefferson Regional Medical Center Post-Sec.
1600 W 40th Ave 71603 870-541-7858
St. Joseph JSHS 100/5-12
1501 W 73rd Ave 71603 870-540-0413
Alexandra Pritchett, prin. Fax 540-0345
Southeast Arkansas College Post-Sec.
1900 S Hazel St 71603 870-543-5900
University of Arkansas at Pine Bluff Post-Sec.
1200 University Dr 71601 870-543-8000

Pleasant Plains, Independence, Pop. 344
Midland SD 500/K-12
PO Box 630 72568 501-345-8844
Dean Stanley, supt. Fax 345-2086
www.midland.k12.ar.us
Midland JSHS 200/7-12
PO Box 630 72568 501-345-2610
Donna Clark, prin. Fax 345-3355

Pocahontas, Randolph, Pop. 6,538
Pocahontas SD 1,800/K-12
2300 N Park St 72455 870-892-4573
Daryl Blaxton, supt. Fax 892-8857
www.nesc.k12.ar.us/
Pocahontas HS 400/10-12
2312 Stadium Dr 72455 870-892-4573
Ivy Pfeffer, prin. Fax 892-8857
Pocahontas JHS 400/7-9
2405 N Park St 72455 870-892-4573
Byron Busby, prin. Fax 892-8857

Black River Technical College Post-Sec.
PO Box 468 72455 870-248-4000

Pottsville, Pope, Pop. 2,791
Pottsville SD 1,600/K-12
7000 SR 247 72858 479-968-8101
Larry Dugger, supt. Fax 968-6339
apache.afsc.k12.ar.us
Pottsville HS 400/10-12
500 Apache Dr 72858 479-968-6334
Jonathan Bradley, prin. Fax 968-3442
Pottsville JHS 400/7-9
250 Apache Dr 72858 479-968-6574
Kenneth Bell, prin. Fax 498-2345

Poyen, Grant, Pop. 289
Poyen SD 600/PK-12
PO Box 209 72128 501-332-8884
Jerry Newton, supt. Fax 332-8886
www.poyenschool.com
Poyen JSHS 300/7-12
PO Box 209 72128 501-332-2939
Dennis Emerson, prin. Fax 332-7809

Prairie Grove, Washington, Pop. 4,291
Prairie Grove SD 1,800/K-12
110 School St 72753 479-846-4242
Allen Williams, supt. Fax 846-2015
pgtigers.org
Prairie Grove HS 500/9-12
500 Cole Dr 72753 479-846-4212
Ron Bond, prin. Fax 846-4207
Prairie Grove MS 600/5-8
806 N Mock St 72753 479-846-4221
Reba Holmes, prin. Fax 846-4275

Prescott, Nevada, Pop. 3,248
Prescott SD 900/K-12
762 Martin St 71857 870-887-3016
Robert Poole, supt. Fax 887-5021
www.prescott.k12.ar.us/
Prescott HS 300/7-12
736 Martin St 71857 870-887-3123
Bobby Joe Applegate, prin. Fax 887-3682

Quitman, Cleburne, Pop. 754
Quitman SD 600/PK-12
PO Box 178 72131 501-589-3156
Rhonda Bradford, supt. Fax 589-3523
www.quitman.k12.ar.us
Quitman JSHS 300/7-12
PO Box 178 72131 501-589-2554
Brett Bunch, prin. Fax 589-3524

Rector, Clay, Pop. 1,960
Rector SD 600/K-12
PO Box 367 72461 870-595-3151
Johnny Fowler, supt. Fax 595-9067
rector.k12.ar.us
Rector HS 300/7-12
PO Box 367 72461 870-595-3553
Wade Williams, prin. Fax 595-9067

Redfield, Jefferson, Pop. 1,264
White Hall SD
Supt. — See White Hall
Redfield JHS 100/7-9
PO Box 350 72132 501-397-2253
James Kight, prin. Fax 397-6534

Rison, Cleveland, Pop. 1,329
Cleveland County SD 800/K-12
PO Box 600 71665 870-325-6344
Johnnie Johnson, supt. Fax 325-7094
rison.k12.ar.us/
Rison JSHS 400/7-12
PO Box 600 71665 870-325-6241
Jeffrey Baggett, prin. Fax 325-6799

Woodlawn SD 600/K-12
6760 Highway 63 71665 870-357-8108
Billy Williams, supt. Fax 357-8718
bears.k12.ar.us
Woodlawn JSHS 300/7-12
6760 Highway 63 71665 870-357-8171
Jeff Wylie, prin. Fax 357-8022

Rogers, Benton, Pop. 54,921
Rogers SD 14,000/K-12
500 W Walnut St 72756 479-636-3910
Dr. Janie Darr, supt. Fax 631-3504
www.rogersschools.net/
Annex Alternative Center Alt
2922 S 1st St 72758 479-631-3690
Cindy Ford, prin. Fax 631-3612
Elmwood MS 800/6-8
1610 S 13th St 72758 479-631-3600
Bob White, prin. Fax 631-3603
Kirksey MS 900/6-8
2930 S 1st St 72758 479-631-3625
Mel Ahart, prin. Fax 631-3624
Lingle MS 800/6-8
901 N 13th St 72756 479-631-3590
Mary Elmore, prin. Fax 631-3594
Oakdale MS 800/6-8
511 N Dixieland Rd 72756 479-631-3615
Donna Charlton, prin. Fax 631-3617
Rogers Heritage HS 2,100/9-12
1114 S 5th St 72756 479-631-3579
Karen Steen, prin. Fax 631-3580
Rogers HS 2,000/9-12
2300 S Dixieland Rd 72758 479-636-2202
Robert Moore, prin. Fax 631-3554

Bryan University Post-Sec.
3704 W Walnut St 72756 479-899-6644
Providence Classical Christian Academy 300/K-12
4911 W Pleasant Grove Rd 72758 479-263-8861
Jason Ross M.Ed., hdmstr. Fax 439-8149

Rose Bud, White, Pop. 462
Rose Bud SD 800/PK-12
124 School Rd 72137 501-556-5815
Curtis Spann, supt. Fax 556-6000
rosebudschools.com
Rose Bud JSHS 400/7-12
124 School Rd 72137 501-556-5404
Danny Starkey, prin. Fax 556-6005

Rosston, Nevada, Pop. 259
Nevada SD 400/K-12
PO Box 50 71858 870-871-2418
Rick McAfee, supt. Fax 871-2419
www.nevadaschooldistrict.net/
Nevada JSHS 200/7-12
PO Box 50 71858 870-871-2478
Atwell Bradley, prin. Fax 871-2419

Russellville, Pope, Pop. 27,404
Russellville SD 5,100/K-12
PO Box 928 72811 479-968-1306
Randall Williams, supt. Fax 968-6381
www.russellvilleschools.net/
Russellville JHS 800/8-9
2000 W Parkway Dr 72802 479-968-1599
Al Harpenau, prin. Fax 890-6419
Russellville SHS 1,100/10-12
2203 S Knoxville Ave 72802 479-968-3151
Sammy Ussery, prin. Fax 968-4264

Arkansas Beauty College Post-Sec.
109 N Commerce Ave 72801 479-968-3075
Arkansas Tech University Post-Sec.
1509 N Boulder Ave 72801 479-968-0389
Community Christian S 100/K-12
PO Box 1786 72811 479-968-1429
Rebecca Partain, admin. Fax 968-1436

Saint Joe, Searcy, Pop. 132
Ozark Mountain SD 700/K-12
250 S Highway 65 72675 870-439-2213
Joe Hulsey, supt. Fax 439-2604
www.omsd.k12.ar.us
Saint Joe JSHS 100/7-12
250 S Highway 65 72675 870-439-2213
Karen Greening, prin. Fax 439-2604
Other Schools – See Everton, Western Grove

Saint Paul, Madison, Pop. 113
Huntsville SD
Supt. — See Huntsville
Saint Paul JSHS 100/7-12
PO Box 125 72760 479-677-2711
Daisy Dyer-Duerr, prin. Fax 677-2210

Salem, Fulton, Pop. 1,613
Salem SD 700/K-12
313 Highway 62 E Ste 1 72576 870-895-2516
Ken Rich, supt. Fax 895-4062
www.salemschools.net/
Salem JSHS 300/7-12
313 Highway 62 E Ste 2 72576 870-895-3293
Wayne Guiltner, prin. Fax 895-5937

Scranton, Logan, Pop. 220
Scranton SD 400/K-12
103 N 10th St 72863 479-938-7121
James Bridges, supt. Fax 938-7564
www.scrantonrockets.net
Scranton JSHS 200/7-12
103 N 10th St 72863 479-938-7121
Mark Siebenmorgen, prin. Fax 938-7564

Searcy, White, Pop. 22,441
Riverview SD 1,300/K-12
800 Raider Dr 72143 501-279-0540
Howard Morris, supt. Fax 279-0737
riverview.k12.ar.us
Riverview HS 400/9-12
810 Raider Dr 72143 501-279-7700
Bill Mullins, prin. Fax 279-2848
Riverview JHS 200/7-8
820 Raider Dr 72143 501-279-7111
Pat Falcinelli, prin. Fax 279-7166

Searcy SD 3,700/K-12
801 N Elm St 72143 501-268-3517
Diane Barrett, supt. Fax 278-2220
www.searcyschools.org/
Ahlf JHS 600/7-8
308 W Vine Ave 72143 501-268-3158
Steve Garrison, prin. Fax 278-2212
Searcy HS 1,100/9-12
301 N Ella St 72143 501-268-8315
Claude Smith, prin. Fax 267-2249

Arkansas State University Searcy Campus Post-Sec.
PO Box 909 72145 501-207-4014
Harding Academy 700/PK-12
PO Box 10775 72149 501-279-7200
James Simmons, supt. Fax 279-7213
Harding University Post-Sec.
915 E Market Ave 72149 501-279-4000
Searcy Beauty College Post-Sec.
1004 S Main St 72143 501-268-6300

Sheridan, Grant, Pop. 4,558
Sheridan SD 4,200/K-12
400 N Rock St 72150 870-942-3135
Brenda Haynes, supt. Fax 942-2931
www.sheridanschools.org/
Sheridan HS 1,200/9-12
700 W Vine St 72150 870-942-3137
Rodney Williams, prin. Fax 942-7546
Sheridan MS 900/6-8
500 N Rock St 72150 870-942-3813
Peggy West, prin. Fax 942-3034

Sherwood, Pulaski, Pop. 28,899
Pulaski County Special SD
Supt. — See Little Rock
Sylvan Hills HS 800/9-12
484 Bear Paw Rd 72120 501-833-1100
Tracy Allen, prin. Fax 833-1104
Sylvan Hills MS 700/6-8
10001 Johnson Dr 72120 501-833-1120
Jo Wilcox, prin. Fax 833-1137

Abundant Life S 300/K-12
9200 Highway 107 72120 501-835-3120
Justin Moseley, supt. Fax 835-4428

Shirley, Van Buren, Pop. 283
Shirley SD 500/K-12
199 School Dr 72153 501-723-8191
Betty McGruder, supt. Fax 723-4020
www.shirley.k12.ar.us/
Shirley JSHS 200/7-12
201 Blue Devil Dr 72153 501-723-8192
Randy Moore, prin. Fax 723-8114

Siloam Springs, Benton, Pop. 14,431
Siloam Springs SD 4,000/PK-12
PO Box 798 72761 479-524-3191
Kendall Ramey, supt. Fax 524-8002
sssd.k12.ar.us/
Siloam Springs HS 1,200/9-12
700 N Progress Ave 72761 479-524-5134
Charles Abernathy, prin. Fax 524-8211
Siloam Springs MS 900/6-8
1500 N Mount Olive St 72761 479-524-6184
Teresa Morgan, prin. Fax 524-3228

John Brown University Post-Sec.
2000 W University St 72761 479-524-9500

Smackover, Union, Pop. 1,823
Smackover SD 900/K-12
112 E 8th St 71762 870-725-3132
Don Smeltzer, supt. Fax 725-2385
smackover.k12.ar.us/
Smackover HS 400/7-12
1 Buckaroo Ln 71762 870-725-3101
Jan Henderson, prin. Fax 725-2540

Sparkman, Dallas, Pop. 421
Harmony Grove SD
Supt. — See Camden
Sparkman HS 100/7-12
PO Box 37 71763 870-678-9312
Robert McAdoo, prin. Fax 678-2917

Springdale, Washington, Pop. 64,520
Springdale SD 18,800/PK-12
PO Box 8 72765 479-750-8800
Dr. Jim Rollins, supt. Fax 750-8812
www.springdaleschools.org/
Alternative Learning Center 300/Alt
500 E Meadow Ave 72764 479-750-8773
Paul Greip, admin. Fax 750-8778
Central JHS 800/8-9
2811 W Huntsville Ave 72762 479-750-8854
Dr. Tamekia Brown, prin. Fax 750-8700
George JHS 1,000/8-9
3200 Powell St 72764 479-750-8750
Don Hoover, prin. Fax 750-8756
Har-Ber HS 1,600/10-12
300 Jones Rd 72762 479-750-8777
Dr. Danny Brackett, prin. Fax 306-4250
Sonora MS 6-8
17051 E Highway 412 72764 479-750-8821
Dr. Shawna Lyons, prin. Fax 750-8823
Southwest JHS 900/8-9
1807 Princeton Ave 72762 479-750-8849
Brice Wagner, prin. Fax 750-8704
Springdale HS 1,800/10-12
101 S Pleasant St 72764 479-750-8832
Peter Joenks, prin. Fax 750-8811

Baptist School of Nursing-NW Post-Sec.
610 E Emma Ave 72764 479-750-6200
Ecclesia College Post-Sec.
9653 Nations Dr 72762 479-248-7236
Northwest Technical Institute Post-Sec.
PO Box 2000 72765 479-751-8824
Shiloh Christian S 800/PK-12
1707 Johnson Rd 72762 479-756-1140
Ben Mayes, pres. Fax 756-7229

Stamps, Columbia, Pop. 1,678
Lafayette County SD
Supt. — See Lewisville
Lafayette County HS 400/7-12
1209 Alexander Ln 71860 870-533-4464
Opal Anderson, prin. Fax 533-2367

Star City, Lincoln, Pop. 2,243
Star City SD 1,700/K-12
206 Cleveland St 71667 870-628-4237
Richard Montgomery, supt. Fax 628-4228
www.starcityschools.com
Star City HS 500/9-12
206 Cleveland St 71667 870-628-4111
Mike Walker, prin. Fax 628-4165
Star City MS 400/6-8
206 Cleveland St 71667 870-628-5125
Susan White, prin. Fax 628-1393

State University, Craighead

Arkansas State University Post-Sec.
PO Box 600 72467 870-972-2100

Stephens, Ouachita, Pop. 880
Stephens SD 400/K-12
315 W Chert St 71764 870-786-5443
Mary Thomas, supt. Fax 786-5095
stephens.k12.ar.us
Stephens JSHS 200/7-12
315 W Chert St 71764 870-786-5442
Mary Thomas, prin. Fax 786-5095

Strawberry, Lawrence, Pop. 295
Hillcrest SD 400/K-12
PO Box 50 72469 870-528-3856
Greg Crabtree, supt. Fax 528-3383
hillcrest.k12.ar.us
Hillcrest JSHS 200/7-12
PO Box 50 72469 870-528-3856
Mike Smith, prin. Fax 528-3383

Strong, Union, Pop. 548
Strong-Huttig SD 500/K-12
PO Box 735 71765 870-797-3040
Saul Lusk, supt. Fax 797-3012
strong.k12.ar.us
Strong HS 200/7-12
PO Box 735 71765 870-797-7322
Jerry Langston, prin. Fax 797-2257

Stuttgart, Arkansas, Pop. 9,196
Stuttgart SD 1,800/K-12
2501 S Main St 72160 870-673-8701
Dr. Melvin Bryant, supt. Fax 673-7337
www.stuttgartschools.org/
Stuttgart HS 600/9-12
2501 S Main St 72160 870-674-1341
Donnie Boothe, prin. Fax 673-7337
Stuttgart JHS 300/7-8
2501 S Main St 72160 870-674-1368
Cedric Hawkins, prin. Fax 673-7337

Grand Prairie Evangelical Methodist S 100/K-12
PO Box 728 72160 870-830-0601
Thomas Bormann, prin. Fax 673-4718

Subiaco, Logan, Pop. 567

Subiaco Academy 200/7-12
405 N Subiaco Ave 72865 479-934-1005
Robert Loia, hdmstr. Fax 934-1033

Taylor, Columbia, Pop. 562
Emerson - Taylor SD
Supt. — See Emerson
Taylor JSHS 100/7-12
506 E Pine St 71861 870-694-2251
Mike Lyons, prin. Fax 694-2901

Texarkana, Miller, Pop. 29,379
Genoa Central SD 1,000/PK-12
12472 Highway 196 71854 870-653-4343
Albert Murphy, supt. Fax 653-2624
dragons1.k12.ar.us/dragons/
Cobb MS 300/5-8
11986 Highway 196 71854 870-653-2132
Deloris Coe, prin. Fax 653-6944
Genoa Central HS 300/9-12
12472 Highway 196 71854 870-653-2272
Bobby Hart, prin. Fax 653-6967

Texarkana Arkansas SD 4,300/K-12
3512 Grand Ave 71854 870-772-3371
Russell Sapaugh, supt. Fax 773-2602
www.tasd7.net/
Arkansas Magnet HS 1,100/9-12
1500 Jefferson Ave 71854 870-774-7641
Robin Stover, prin. Fax 772-2613
North Heights Magnet JHS 600/7-8
2118 E 35th St 71854 870-773-1091
Theresa Cowling, prin. Fax 772-2722
Texarkana Area Vocational Center Vo/Tech
3512 Grand Ave 71854 870-774-7641

Washington 4-A Academy 100/Alt
3512 Grand Ave 71854 870-774-8861
Fax 774-2185

Trinity Christian S 400/PK-12
3107 Trinity Blvd 71854 870-779-1009
Ron Fellers, head sch Fax 772-1258

Tillar, Desha, Pop. 224

Cornerstone Christian Academy 100/K-12
PO Box 129 71670 870-392-2482
Fax 392-2328

Timbo, Stone
Mountain View SD
Supt. — See Mountain View
Timbo S 100/K-12
23747 Highway 263 72680 870-746-4303
Jimmy Lowery, prin. Fax 746-4844

Trumann, Poinsett, Pop. 7,174
Trumann SD 1,300/K-12
221 N Pine Ave 72472 870-483-6444
Myra Graham, supt. Fax 483-2602
www.trumannwildcat.com
Trumann HS 400/9-12
1620 W Main St 72472 870-483-5301
Wanda Van Dyke, prin. Fax 483-0227
Trumann IS 200/5-8
221 N Pine Ave 72472 870-483-5356
Bobby Benson, prin. Fax 483-2602

Tuckerman, Jackson, Pop. 1,848
Jackson County SD 800/K-12
PO Box 1070 72473 870-349-2232
Chester Shannon, supt. Fax 349-2355
bulldogs.k12.ar.us/
Tuckerman HS 300/8-12
PO Box 1070 72473 870-349-2657
Michael Holland, prin. Fax 349-2294

Umpire, Howard
Cossatot River SD
Supt. — See Wickes
Umpire S 100/PK-12
PO Box 60 71971 870-583-2141
Ladonna White, prin. Fax 583-6264

Valley Springs, Boone, Pop. 182
Valley Springs SD 1,000/K-12
PO Box 640 72682 870-429-9200
Charles Trammell, supt. Fax 429-5551
valley.k12.ar.us
Valley Springs HS 300/9-12
PO Box 640 72682 870-429-9200
Ronnie Ruff, prin. Fax 429-8160
Valley Springs MS 300/5-8
PO Box 640 72682 870-429-9200
Tony Mincer, prin. Fax 429-8121

Van Buren, Crawford, Pop. 22,172
Van Buren SD 4,400/K-12
2221 E Pointer Trl 72956 479-474-7942
Dr. Merle Dickerson, supt. Fax 471-3146
www.vbsd.us
Butterfield Trail MS 500/6-8
310 N 11th St 72956 479-474-6838
Karen Endel, prin. Fax 471-3101
Northridge MS 300/6-8
120 Northridge Dr 72956 479-471-3126
Lonnie Mitchell, prin. Fax 471-3129
Van Buren Freshman Academy 200/9-9
821 E Pointer Trl 72956 479-471-3160
Lisa Miller, prin. Fax 471-0249
Van Buren HS 1,300/10-12
2001 E Pointer Trl 72956 479-474-6821
Becky Guthrie, prin. Fax 471-3199

Vilonia, Faulkner, Pop. 3,760
Vilonia SD 2,900/K-12
PO Box 160 72173 501-796-2113
Dr. Frank Mitchell, supt. Fax 796-3134
www.viloniaschools.org/
Vilonia JHS 500/8-9
PO Box 160 72173 501-796-2037
Rick Kelley, prin. Fax 796-4326
Vilonia SHS 700/10-12
PO Box 160 72173 501-796-2111
Andy Ashley, prin. Fax 796-8895

Viola, Fulton, Pop. 326
Viola SD 400/K-12
PO Box 380 72583 870-458-2323
John May, supt. Fax 458-2214
violaschool.k12.ar.us
Viola JSHS 200/7-12
PO Box 380 72583 870-458-2213
Bryan Russell, prin. Fax 458-4049

Waldron, Scott, Pop. 3,541
Waldron SD 1,600/PK-12
1560 W 6th St 72958 479-637-3179
Dr. Barbara Wood, supt. Fax 637-3177
www.edline.net/pages/Waldron_SD
Waldron HS 500/9-12
736 W Highway 80 72958 479-637-3405
Paulette Crouthers, prin. Fax 637-5624
Waldron MS 500/5-8
2075 Rice St 72958 479-637-4549
Kim Solomon, prin. Fax 637-3165

Walnut Ridge, Lawrence, Pop. 4,854
Lawrence County SD 1,100/K-12
508 E Free St 72476 870-886-6634
Terry Belcher, supt. Fax 886-6635
www.bobcats.k12.ar.us
Walnut Ridge JSHS 300/7-12
508 E Free St 72476 870-886-6623
Jacob Kersey, prin. Fax 819-0403
Other Schools – See Black Rock

Williams Baptist College Post-Sec.
60 W Fulbright St 72476 870-886-6741

Warren, Bradley, Pop. 5,957
Warren SD 1,500/K-12
PO Box 1210 71671 870-226-8500
Marilyn Johnson, supt. Fax 226-8531
www.edline.net/pages/Warren_SD
Warren HS 400/9-12
PO Box 1210 71671 870-226-6736
Gary Jackson, prin. Fax 226-8527
Warren MS 400/6-8
PO Box 1210 71671 870-226-2484
Glenetta Burks, prin. Fax 226-8511

Weiner, Poinsett, Pop. 712
Harrisburg SD
Supt. — See Harrisburg
Weiner JSHS 200/7-12
313 N Garfield St 72479 870-684-2250
Pam Hogue, prin. Fax 684-2254

Western Grove, Newton, Pop. 373
Ozark Mountain SD
Supt. — See Saint Joe
Western Grove JSHS 100/7-12
300 School St 72685 870-429-5215
James Jones, prin. Fax 429-5276

West Fork, Washington, Pop. 2,246
West Fork SD 1,200/K-12
359 School Ave 72774 479-839-2231
John Karnes, supt. Fax 839-8412
www.edline.net/pages/West_Fork_Public_Schools
West Fork HS 400/9-12
359 School Ave 72774 479-839-3131
John Crowder, prin. Fax 839-3374
West Fork MS 400/5-8
333 School Ave 72774 479-839-3342
Becky Ramsey, prin. Fax 839-2555

West Helena, Phillips, Pop. 7,876
Helena/West Helena SD
Supt. — See Helena
Central HS 700/7-12
103 School Rd 72390 870-572-6744
Monica McMurray, prin. Fax 572-4504

De Soto S 300/K-12
PO Box 2807 72390 870-572-6717
E.G. Morris, hdmstr. Fax 572-9531

West Memphis, Crittenden, Pop. 26,012
West Memphis SD 5,700/K-12
301 S Avalon St 72301 870-735-1915
Jon Collins, supt. Fax 732-8643
www.wmsd.net
East JHS 400/7-9
1151 Goodwin Ave 72301 870-735-2081
Arther Quarrels, prin. Fax 732-8583
West JHS 500/7-9
331 W Barton Ave 72301 870-735-3161
Charlie Tyler, prin. Fax 732-8566
West Memphis SHS 1,200/10-12
501 W Broadway St 72301 870-735-3660
Dan Henderson, prin. Fax 732-8510
Wonder JHS 500/7-9
1401 Madison Ave 72301 870-735-8522
Dr. Palmer Quarrels, prin. Fax 732-8584
Other Schools – See Edmondson

Mid-South Community College Post-Sec.
2000 W Broadway St 72301 870-733-6722
West Memphis Christian S 100/K-12
PO Box 996 72303 870-400-4000
Mary Anne Pike, hdmstr. Fax 400-4001

Wheatley, Saint Francis, Pop. 354
Palestine-Wheatley SD
Supt. — See Palestine
Palestine-Wheatley MS 200/5-8
PO Box 109 72392 870-457-2121
Zenna Smith, prin. Fax 457-4840

White Hall, Jefferson, Pop. 5,470
White Hall SD 3,000/K-12
1020 W Holland Ave 71602 870-247-2002
Dr. Larry Smith, supt. Fax 247-3707
www.whitehallsd.org/
White Hall JHS 600/7-9
8106 Dollarway Rd 71602 870-247-2711
Douglas Dorris, prin. Fax 247-4689
White Hall SHS 700/10-12
700 Bulldog Dr 71602 870-247-3255
Don Stringer, prin. Fax 247-2756
Other Schools – See Redfield

Wickes, Polk, Pop. 743
Cossatot River SD 1,100/PK-12
130 School Dr 71973 870-385-7101
David Kellogg, supt. Fax 385-2238
www.cossatot.us
Other Schools – See Cove, Umpire

Wilson, Mississippi, Pop. 888
South Mississippi County SD 1,400/PK-12
22 N Jefferson St 72395 870-655-8633
Gary Masters, supt. Fax 655-8841
www.smccolts.com/
Rivercrest JSHS 600/7-12
1700 W State Highway 14 72395 870-655-8111
Mike Smith, prin. Fax 655-8507

Wynne, Cross, Pop. 8,285
Wynne SD 2,900/K-12
PO Box 69 72396 870-238-5020
Carl Easley, supt. Fax 238-5011
wynneschools.org
Wynne HS 900/9-12
PO Box 69 72396 870-238-5070
Keith Watson, prin. Fax 238-5009
Wynne JHS 600/6-8
PO Box 69 72396 870-238-5040
David Stepp, prin. Fax 238-5043

Caldwell Christian Academy 50/PK-12
1699 Falls Blvd S 72396 870-238-2244
Dorma Huffstuttler, admin. Fax 238-2244

Yellville, Marion, Pop. 1,190
Yellville-Summit SD 800/K-12
1124 N Panther Ave 72687 870-449-4061
Larry Ivens, supt. Fax 449-5003
yellvillesummitschools.com/
Yellville-Summit HS 300/9-12
1124 N Panther Ave 72687 870-449-4066
David Wyatt, prin. Fax 449-4773
Yellville-Summit MS 300/5-8
1124 N Panther Ave 72687 870-449-6533
Calvin Mallett, prin. Fax 449-4330

CALIFORNIA

CALIFORNIA DEPARTMENT OF EDUCATION
1430 N St, Sacramento 95814-5901
Telephone 916-319-0800
Fax 916-319-0100
Website http://www.cde.ca.gov

Superintendent of Public Instruction Tom Torlakson

CALIFORNIA BOARD OF EDUCATION
1430 N St, Sacramento 95814-5901

President Dr. Michael Kirst

COUNTY SUPERINTENDENTS OF SCHOOLS

Alameda County Office of Education
Sheila Jordan, supt. 510-887-0152
313 W Winton Ave, Hayward 94544 Fax 670-4146
www.acoe.org

Alpine County Office of Education
Lisa Fontana Ph.D., supt. 530-694-2230
43 Hawkside Dr Fax 694-2379
Markleeville 96120
www.alpinecoe.k12.ca.us

Amador County Office of Education
Dick Glock, supt. 209-257-5353
217 Rex Ave, Jackson 95642 Fax 257-5360
www.amadorcoe.org/

Butte County Office of Education
Tim Taylor, supt. 530-532-5650
1859 Bird St, Oroville 95965 Fax 532-5762
www.bcoe.org

Calaveras County Office of Education
Kathy Northington, supt. 209-736-4662
PO Box 760, Angels Camp 95221 Fax 736-2138
www.ccoe.k12.ca.us

Colusa County Office of Education
Kay Spurgeon, supt. 530-458-0350
146 7th St, Colusa 95932 Fax 458-8054
www.ccoe.net

Contra Costa County Office of Education
Dr. Joseph Ovick, supt. 925-942-3388
77 Santa Barbara Rd Fax 472-0875
Pleasant Hill 94523
www.cocoschools.org

Del Norte County Office of Education
Don Olson, supt. 707-464-0200
301 W Washington Blvd Fax 464-0238
Crescent City 95531
www.delnorte.k12.ca.us

El Dorado County Office of Education
Vicki Barber Ed.D., supt. 530-622-7130
6767 Green Valley Rd Fax 621-2543
Placerville 95667
www.edcoe.org

Fresno County Office of Education
Larry Powell, supt. 559-265-3000
1111 Van Ness Ave, Fresno 93721 Fax 265-4005
www.fcoe.org

Glenn County Office of Education
Tracey Quarne, supt. 530-934-6575
311 S Villa Ave, Willows 95988 Fax 934-6576
www.glenncoe.org

Humboldt County Office of Education
Garry Eagles Ph.D., supt. 707-445-7000
901 Myrtle Ave, Eureka 95501 Fax 445-7143
www.humboldt.k12.ca.us

Imperial County Office of Education
Anne Mallory, supt. 760-312-6464
1398 Sperber Rd, El Centro Fax 312-6568
www.icoe.org

Inyo County Office of Education
Dr. Terence McAteer, supt. 760-878-2426
PO Box G, Independence 93526 Fax 878-2279
www.inyo.k12.ca.us

Kern County Office of Education
Christine Frazier, supt. 661-636-4000
1300 17th St, Bakersfield 93301 Fax 636-4130
www.kern.org/

Kings County Office of Education
Tim Bowers, supt. 559-584-1441
1144 W Lacey Blvd, Hanford 93230 Fax 589-7000
www.kings.k12.ca.us

Lake County Office of Education
Wally Holbrook, supt. 707-262-4100
1152 S Main St, Lakeport 95453 Fax 263-0197
www.lake-coe.k12.ca.us

Lassen County Office of Education
Richard DuVarney, supt. 530-257-2196
472-013 Johnstonville Rd Fax 257-2518
Susanville 96130
www.lcoe.org

Los Angeles County Office of Education
Dr. Arturo Delgado, supt. 562-922-6111
9300 Imperial Hwy, Downey 90242 Fax 922-6768
www.lacoe.edu

Madera County Office of Education
Cecilia Massetti Ed.D., supt. 559-673-6051
1105 S Madera Ave, Madera 93637 Fax 673-5569
www.maderacoe.k12.ca.us

Marin County Office of Education 415-472-4110
, PO Box 4925, San Rafael 94913 Fax 491-6625
www.marinschools.org/

Mariposa County Office of Education
Aaron Rosander, supt. 209-742-0250
PO Box 8, Mariposa 95338 Fax 966-4549
www.mariposa.k12.ca.us

Mendocino County Office of Education
Paul Tichinin, supt. 707-467-5000
2240 Old River Rd, Ukiah 95482 Fax 462-0379
www.mcoe.us

Merced County Office of Education
Steven Gomes Ed.D., supt. 209-381-6600
632 W 13th St, Merced 95341 Fax 381-6767
www.mcoe.org

Modoc County Office of Education
Gary Jones, supt. 530-233-7100
139 Henderson St, Alturas 96101 Fax 233-5531
www.modoccoe.k12.ca.us

Mono County Office of Education
Stacey Adler, supt. 760-932-7311
PO Box 477, Bridgeport 93517 Fax 932-7278
www.monocoe.org

Monterey County Office of Education
Dr. Nancy Kotowski, supt. 831-755-0300
PO Box 80851, Salinas 93912 Fax 753-6473
www.monterey.k12.ca.us

Napa County Office of Education
Barbara Nemko, supt. 707-253-6800
2121 Imola Ave, Napa 94559 Fax 253-6841
www.napacoe.org

Nevada County Office of Education
Holly Hermansen, supt. 530-478-6400
112 Nevada City Hwy Fax 478-6410
Nevada City 95959
www.nevco.org/

Orange County Office of Education
Al Mijares, supt. 714-966-4000
PO Box 9050, Costa Mesa 92628 Fax 662-3570
www.ocde.us

Placer County Office of Education
Gayle Garbolino-Mojica, supt. 530-889-8020
360 Nevada St, Auburn 95603 Fax 888-1367
www.placercoe.k12.ca.us

Plumas County Office of Education
Bruce Williams, admin. 530-283-6500
50 Church St, Quincy 95971 Fax 283-6509
www.pcoe.k12.ca.us

Riverside County Office of Education
Kenneth Young, supt. 951-826-6530
PO Box 868, Riverside 92502 Fax 826-6199
www.rcoe.us

Sacramento County Office of Education
David Gordon, supt. 916-228-2500
10474 Mather Blvd, Mather 95655 Fax 228-2403
www.scoe.net

San Benito County Office of Education
Mike Sanchez, supt. 831-637-5393
460 5th St, Hollister 95023 Fax 637-0140
www.sbcoe.org

San Bernardino Co. Office of Education
Gary Thomas, supt. 909-888-3228
601 N E St, San Bernardino 92415 Fax 386-2478
www.sbcss.k12.ca.us

San Diego County Office of Education
Randolph Ward, supt. 858-292-3500
6401 Linda Vista Rd Fax 292-3653
San Diego 92111
www.sdcoe.net

San Francisco County Office of Education
Richard Carranza, supt. 415-241-6000
555 Franklin St Fax 241-6012
San Francisco 94102
www.sfusd.edu

San Joaquin County Office of Education
Dr. Mick Founts, supt. 209-468-4800
PO Box 213030, Stockton 95213 Fax 468-4819
www.sjcoe.org

San Luis Obispo Co. Office of Education
Julian Crocker, supt. 805-543-7732
3350 Education Dr Fax 541-1105
San Luis Obispo 93405
www.slocoe.org

San Mateo County Office of Education
Anne Campbell, supt. 650-802-5550
101 Twin Dolphin Dr Fax 802-5564
Redwood City 94065
www.smcoe.k12.ca.us

Santa Barbara County Office of Education
William Cirone, supt. 805-964-4711
PO Box 6307, Santa Barbara 93160 Fax 964-4712
www.sbceo.org

Santa Clara County Office of Education
Xavier De La Torre Ed.D., supt. 408-453-6500
1290 Ridder Park Dr Fax 453-6601
San Jose 95131
www.sccoe.org

Santa Cruz County Office of Education
Michael Watkins, supt. 831-466-5600
400 Encinal St, Santa Cruz 95060 Fax 466-5607
www.santacruz.k12.ca.us

Shasta County Office of Education
Tom Armelino, supt. 530-225-0200
1644 Magnolia Ave Fax 225-0329
Redding 96001
www.shastacoe.org

Sierra County Office of Education
Stan Hardeman, supt. 530-994-1044
PO Box 157, Sierraville 96126 Fax 994-1045
www.sierracountyofficeofeducation.org/

Siskiyou County Office of Education
Kermith Walters, dir. 530-842-8400
609 S Gold St, Yreka 96097 Fax 842-8436
www.siskiyoucoe.net/

Solano County Office of Education
Jay Speck, supt. 707-399-4400
5100 Business Center Dr Fax 863-4174
Fairfield
www.solanocoe.net/

Sonoma County Office of Education
Steven D. Herrington Ph.D., supt. 707-524-2600
5340 Skylane Blvd Fax 578-0220
Santa Rosa 95403
www.scoe.org/

Stanislaus County Office of Education
Tom Changnon, supt. 209-238-1700
1100 H St, Modesto 95354 Fax 238-4201
www.stancoe.org/

Sutter County Office of Education
Bill Cornelius, supt. 530-822-2900
970 Klamath Ln, Yuba City 95993 Fax 671-3422
www.sutter.k12.ca.us

Tehama County Office of Education
Larry Champion, supt. 530-527-5811
PO Box 689, Red Bluff 96080 Fax 529-4120
www.tehamaschools.org/

Trinity County Office of Education
Bettina Blackwell, supt. 530-623-2861
PO Box 1256, Weaverville 96093 Fax 623-4489
www.tcoek12.org/

Tulare County Office of Education
Jim Vidak, supt. 559-733-6300
PO Box 5091, Visalia 93278 Fax 737-4378
www.tcoe.org/

Tuolumne County Office of Education
Joseph Silva, supt. 209-536-2000
175 Fairview Ln, Sonora 95370 Fax 536-2003
www.tuolcoe.k12.ca.us

Ventura County Office of Education
Stan Mantooth, supt. 805-383-1900
5189 Verdugo Way Fax 383-1908
Camarillo 93012
www.vcoe.org

Yolo County Office of Education
Jorge Ayala, supt. 530-668-6700
1280 Santa Anita Ct Ste 100 Fax 668-3848
Woodland 95776
www.ycoe.org

Yuba County Office of Education
Scotia Holmes Sanchez, supt. 530-749-4900
935 14th St, Marysville 95901 Fax 741-6500
www.yuba.net/

PUBLIC, PRIVATE AND CATHOLIC SECONDARY SCHOOLS

Acton, Los Angeles, Pop. 7,398
Acton-Agua Dulce USD 1,700/K-12
32248 Crown Valley Rd 93510 661-269-5999
Dr. Brent Woodard, supt. Fax 269-0849
aadusd.k12.ca.us/
High Desert MS 400/6-8
3620 Antelope Woods Rd 93510 661-269-0310
Stephanie Najar, prin. Fax 269-9336
Vasquez HS 600/9-12
33630 Red Rover Mine Rd 93510 661-269-0410
Ty Devoe, prin. Fax 269-5325

Adelanto, San Bernardino, Pop. 30,727
Adelanto ESD 8,200/K-12
PO Box 70 92301 760-246-8691
Richard Bray, supt. Fax 246-8259
www.aesd.net
Columbia International Sci/Math/Tech S 500/7-8
PO Box 70 92301 760-530-1950
Mike McGirr, prin. Fax 530-1953
Other Schools – See Victorville

Agoura Hills, Los Angeles, Pop. 19,692
Las Virgenes USD
Supt. — See Calabasas
Agoura HS 2,100/9-12
28545 Driver Ave 91301 818-889-1262
Larry Misel, prin. Fax 597-0816
Indian Hills Continuation HS - West 100/Alt
28545 Driver Ave 91301 818-880-4828
Larry Misel, prin. Fax 878-9864
Lindero Canyon MS 1,000/6-8
5844 Larboard Ln 91301 818-889-2134
Dr. Abbe Irshay, prin. Fax 889-9432

Alameda, Alameda, Pop. 69,145
Alameda City USD 10,000/PK-12
2060 Challenger Dr 94501 510-337-7000
Kirsten Vital, supt. Fax 522-6926
www.alameda.k12.ca.us
Alameda HS 1,900/9-12
2201 Encinal Ave 94501 510-337-7022
Robert Ithurburn, prin. Fax 521-4740
Alameda Science & Technical Institute 200/9-12
2200 Central Ave 94501 510-337-7059
Fax 337-7163
Encinal HS 1,000/6-12
210 Central Ave 94501 510-748-4023
Kirsten Zazo, prin. Fax 521-4956
Island Continuation HS 200/Alt
1900 3rd St 94501 510-748-4024
Fax 769-7417
Lincoln MS 900/6-8
1250 Fernside Blvd 94501 510-748-4018
Michael Hans, prin. Fax 523-6217
Wood MS 600/6-8
420 Grand St 94501 510-748-4015
Cammie Harris, prin. Fax 523-8829
Alameda Adult S Adult
1900 3rd St 94501 510-522-3858
Joy Chua, prin. Fax 522-0846

Regional Occupational Center & Program
Supt. — None
East Bay ROP Vo/Tech
1900 3rd St Rm 23 94501 510-879-3037
Brigitte Marshall, dir.

Alameda Beauty College Post-Sec.
2318 Central Ave 94501 510-523-1050
Argosy University San Francisco Campus Post-Sec.
1005 Atlantic Ave 94501 510-217-4700
College of Alameda Post-Sec.
555 Ralph Appezzato Mem Pky 94501
510-522-7221
St. Joseph Notre Dame HS 400/9-12
1011 Chestnut St 94501 510-523-1526
Simon Chiu, prin. Fax 523-2181

Alamo, Contra Costa, Pop. 14,161
San Ramon Valley USD
Supt. — See Danville
Stone Valley MS 700/6-8
3001 Miranda Ave 94507 925-855-5800
Shaun McElroy, prin. Fax 838-5680

Albany, Alameda, Pop. 17,446
Albany City USD 3,900/PK-12
1051 Monroe St 94706 510-558-3750
Marla Stephenson, supt. Fax 559-6560
www.ausdk12.org
Albany HS 1,200/9-12
603 Key Route Blvd 94706 510-558-2500
Theodore Barone, prin. Fax 559-6584
Albany MS 900/6-8
1259 Brighton Ave 94706 510-558-3600
Peter Parenti, prin. Fax 559-6547
MacGregor Continuation HS 50/Alt
601 San Gabriel Ave 94706 510-559-6570
Alexia Ritchie, prin. Fax 559-6572
Albany Adult S Adult
603 Key Route Blvd 94706 510-558-2516
Alexia Ritchie, prin.

Tilden Preparatory S 50/6-12
1231 Solano Ave 94706 510-525-5506
Dr. Karen Hobbs, dir. Fax 525-5508

Alhambra, Los Angeles, Pop. 81,736
Alhambra USD 18,200/K-12
1515 W Mission Rd 91803 626-943-3000
Laura Tellez-Gagliano Ed.D., supt. Fax 943-8050
www.alhambra.k12.ca.us
Alhambra HS 3,100/9-12
101 S 2nd St 91801 626-308-2342
Duane Russell, prin. Fax 308-2344
Century Continuation HS 200/Alt
20 S Marengo Ave 91801 626-943-6681
Lindsey Ma, prin. Fax 308-2299
Keppel HS 2,500/9-12
501 E Hellman Ave 91801 626-943-6710
Jacinth Cisneros, prin. Fax 572-2217
Other Schools – See San Gabriel

Alhambra Beauty College Post-Sec.
200 W Main St 91801 626-282-7765
Alhambra Medical University Post-Sec.
25 S Raymond Ave Ste 201 91801 626-289-7719
Alliant International University Post-Sec.
1000 S Fremont Ave Unit 5 91803 626-270-3300
Everest College Post-Sec.
2215 W Mission Rd 91803 626-979-4940
Platt College Alhambra Post-Sec.
1000 S Fremont Ave Ste A9W 91803 626-300-5444
Ramona Convent Secondary S 400/7-12
1701 W Ramona Rd 91803 626-282-4151
Tina Bonacci, prin. Fax 281-0797

Aliso Viejo, Orange, Pop. 45,578
Capistrano USD
Supt. — See San Juan Capistrano
Aliso Niguel HS 3,000/9-12
28000 Wolverine Way 92656 949-831-5590
Chris Carter, prin. Fax 448-9854
Aliso Viejo MS 1,100/6-8
111 Park Ave 92656 949-831-2622
Jennifer Smalley, prin. Fax 643-2784
Avila MS 1,300/6-8
26278 Wood Canyon Dr 92656 949-362-0348
Josh Wellikson, prin. Fax 362-9076

Soka University of America Post-Sec.
1 University Dr 92656 949-480-4000

Alpaugh, Tulare, Pop. 1,021
Alpaugh USD 500/K-12
PO Box 9 93201 559-949-8413
Robert Hudson, supt. Fax 949-8173
www.tcoe.org/districts/alpaugh.shtm
Alpaugh JSHS 100/7-12
PO Box 9 93201 559-949-8413
Robert Hudson, admin. Fax 949-8679
Tule Continuation HS 50/Alt
PO Box 9 93201 559-949-8644
Robert Hudson, dir. Fax 949-8679

Alpine, San Diego, Pop. 13,892
Alpine UNESD 2,000/PK-8
1323 Administration Way 91901 619-445-3236
Tom Pellegrino, supt. Fax 445-7045
www.alpineschools.net/
MacQueen MS 700/6-8
2001 Tavern Rd 91901 619-445-3245
Katy Andersen, prin. Fax 445-6503

Day-McKellar Preparatory S 100/K-12
2710 Alpine Blvd 91901 619-415-4144

Altadena, Los Angeles, Pop. 40,865
Pasadena USD
Supt. — See Pasadena
Eliot MS 800/6-8
2184 Lake Ave 91001 626-396-5680
Lorena Martinez, prin. Fax 794-7238
Focus Point Academy Alt
2126 N Glen Rose Ave 91001 626-398-3371
James Albanese, prin.

Renaissance Academy 100/K-12
536 E Mendocino St 91001 626-765-9358
Sandra Staffer, dir.
Sahag-Mesrob Armenian Christian S 300/PK-12
2501 Maiden Ln 91001 626-798-5020
Hovsep Injejikian, prin. Fax 798-0062

Alta Loma, San Bernardino
Alta Loma ESD 6,400/K-8
9390 Baseline Rd 91701 909-484-5151
Michael Whisenand, supt. Fax 484-5155
www.alsd.k12.ca.us
Alta Loma JHS 800/7-8
9000 Lemon Ave 91701 909-484-5100
Melinda Early, prin. Fax 484-5105
Vineyard JHS 800/7-8
6440 Mayberry Ave 91737 909-484-5120
Catharine Perry, prin. Fax 484-5125

Chaffey JUNHSD
Supt. — See Ontario
Alta Loma HS 2,700/9-12
8880 Baseline Rd 91701 909-989-5511
James Cronin, prin. Fax 987-8321

Alturas, Modoc, Pop. 2,746
Modoc County Office of Education 50/
139 Henderson St 96101 530-233-7100
Gary Jones, supt. Fax 233-5531
www.modoccoe.k12.ca.us
Modoc County Community S 50/Alt
139 Henderson St 96101 530-230-7103
Marian Hall, prin.

Modoc JUSD 800/K-12
906 W 4th St 96101 530-233-7201
Mike Martin, supt. Fax 233-4362
www.modoc.k12.ca.us
High Desert Community Day S 50/Alt
802 N East St 96101 530-233-7201
Tom O'Malley, prin. Fax 233-5158
Modoc HS 300/9-12
900 N Main St 96101 530-233-7201
Tom O'Malley, prin. Fax 233-7306
Modoc MS 200/6-8
906 W 4th St 96101 530-233-7201
Barry Barnhart, prin. Fax 233-7503
Warner Continuation HS 50/Alt
802 N East St 96101 530-233-7201
Tom O'Malley, prin. Fax 233-5158

Regional Occupational Center & Program
Supt. — None
Modoc County ROP Vo/Tech
139 Henderson St 96101 530-233-7102
Marian Hall, dir.

American Canyon, Napa, Pop. 18,364
Napa Valley USD
Supt. — See Napa
American Canyon HS 700/9-12
3000 Newell Dr 94503 707-267-2710
Mark Brewer, prin. Fax 644-1139
American Canyon MS 900/6-8
300 Benton Way 94503 707-259-8592
Dan Scudero, prin. Fax 259-8800

Anaheim, Orange, Pop. 327,991
Anaheim UNHSD 33,100/7-12
501 N Crescent Way 92801 714-999-3511
Dr. Elizabeth Novack, supt. Fax 535-1706
www.auhsd.us
Anaheim HS 3,500/9-12
811 W Lincoln Ave 92805 714-999-3717
Ben Sanchez, prin. Fax 772-6537
Ball JHS 1,200/7-8
1500 W Ball Rd 92802 714-999-3663
Jaron Fried Ed.D., prin. Fax 563-9214
Brookhurst JHS 1,300/7-8
601 N Brookhurst St 92801 714-999-3613
Darrick Garcia, prin. Fax 999-1764
Community Day S 100/Alt
1800 W Ball Rd 92804 714-999-7754
Marilyn Miller Ed.D., prin. Fax 780-9730
Dale JHS 1,300/7-8
900 S Dale Ave 92804 714-220-4210
Daphne Hammer, prin. Fax 220-4076
Gilbert HS 700/Alt
1800 W Ball Rd 92804 714-999-3738
Kelly Wilson, prin. Fax 999-5651
Katella HS 2,700/9-12
2200 E Wagner Ave 92806 714-999-3621
Luis Lopez, prin. Fax 535-3991
Loara HS 2,700/9-12
1765 W Cerritos Ave 92804 714-999-3677
John Briquelet, prin. Fax 999-3703
Magnolia HS 2,200/9-12
2450 W Ball Rd 92804 714-220-4221
Robert Cunard Ed.D., prin. Fax 220-4233
Orangeview JHS 1,000/7-8
3715 W Orange Ave 92804 714-220-4205
Yousef Nasouf, prin. Fax 220-3023
Polaris HS 200/Alt
1800 W Ball Rd 92804 714-999-3738
Kelly Wilson, prin. Fax 999-5651
Savanna HS 2,300/9-12
301 N Gilbert St 92801 714-220-4262
Manuel Colon, prin. Fax 995-2544
South JHS 1,500/7-8
2320 E South St 92806 714-999-3667
Carlos Hernandez, prin. Fax 999-3721
Sycamore JHS 1,600/7-8
1801 E Sycamore St 92805 714-999-3616
Joe Carmona, prin. Fax 776-3879
Western HS 2,300/9-12
501 S Western Ave 92804 714-220-4040
Daniel Lunt, prin. Fax 220-4027
Other Schools – See Cypress, La Palma

Orange USD
Supt. — See Orange
Canyon HS 2,400/9-12
220 S Imperial Hwy 92807 714-532-8000
Greg Bowden, prin. Fax 921-0278

Placentia-Yorba Linda USD
Supt. — See Placentia
Esperanza HS 2,200/9-12
1830 N Kellogg Dr 92807 714-985-7540
Ken Fox, prin. Fax 693-7527

Regional Occupational Center & Program
Supt. — None
North Orange County ROP Vo/Tech
385 N Muller St 92801 714-502-5800
Dr. Michael Worley, supt. Fax 766-3880

Acaciawood S 100/1-12
2530 W La Palma Ave 92801 714-995-1800
Michio Miyake, prin. Fax 876-0723
American Career College Orange County Post-Sec.
1200 N Magnolia Ave 92801 714-763-9066
Anaheim University Post-Sec.
1240 S State College # 110 92806 714-772-3330
Bethesda University of California Post-Sec.
730 N Euclid St 92801 714-517-1945
Bristol University Post-Sec.
2390 E Orangewood Ave # 485 92806 714-542-8086
Brownson Technical School Post-Sec.
1110 S Technology Cir Ste D 92805 714-774-9443
California Career School Post-Sec.
1100 S Technology Cir 92805 714-635-6585
CA University of Management and Sciences Post-Sec.
721 N Euclid St 92801 714-533-3946
Connelly HS 300/9-12
2323 W Broadway 92804 714-776-1717
Sr. Francine Gunther, hdmstr. Fax 776-2534
Evangelia University Post-Sec.
2660 W Woodland Dr Ste 200 92801 714-527-0691
Everest College Post-Sec.
511 N Brookhurst St Ste 300 92801 714-953-6500

Fairmont Preparatory Academy 500/9-12
2200 W Sequoia Ave 92801 714-999-5055
Robert Mendoza, hdmstr. Fax 999-0150
Integrity Christian S 100/1-12
4905 E La Palma Ave 92807 714-693-2022
Shelly Kitada, prin.
Orange County Christian S 200/PK-12
641 S Western Ave 92804 714-821-6227
Elaine Findley M.Ed., prin. Fax 952-8823
Saints of Glory S 50/K-12
1210 W Park Ave 92801 714-875-9387
Y. Yasuma, pres. Fax 817-0612
Servite HS 1,000/9-12
1952 W La Palma Ave 92801 714-774-7575
Michael Brennan, prin. Fax 774-1404
South Baylo University Post-Sec.
1126 N Brookhurst St 92801 714-533-1495
Southern California Institute of Tech Post-Sec.
222 S Harbor Blvd Ste 200 92805 714-300-0300
Vineyard Christian S 400/PK-12
5340 E La Palma Ave 92807 714-777-5462
Jim Wilkinson, prin. Fax 777-5422
West Coast University Post-Sec.
1477 S Manchester Ave 92802 714-782-1700
Westwood College - Anaheim Post-Sec.
1551 S Douglass Rd 92806 714-704-2720

Anderson, Shasta, Pop. 9,521

Anderson UNHSD 2,100/9-12
1469 Ferry St 96007 530-378-0568
Tim Azevedo, supt. Fax 378-0834
www.auhsd.net
Anderson HS 700/9-12
1471 Ferry St 96007 530-365-2741
Rebecca Evers, prin. Fax 365-5446
North Valley HS 100/Alt
20083 Olinda Rd 96007 530-365-6054
Brandt Shriner, prin. Fax 378-1264
Oakview HS 100/Alt
20111 Olinda Rd 96007 530-378-6895
Brandt Shriner, prin. Fax 365-0801
Other Schools – See Cottonwood

Cascade UNESD 800/K-8
1645 Mill St 96007 530-378-7000
Harley North, supt. Fax 378-7001
www.cuesd.com/
Anderson MS 400/5-8
1646 Ferry St 96007 530-378-7060
Carol Koppes, prin. Fax 378-7061

Happy Valley UNESD 400/K-8
17480 Palm Ave 96007 530-357-2134
Janet Tufts, supt. Fax 357-4143
www.shastalink.k12.ca.us/happyvalley/
Happy Valley MS 200/5-8
17480 Palm Ave 96007 530-357-2111
Janet Tufts, prin. Fax 357-4193

Pacheco UNESD
Supt. — See Redding
Pacheco Community Day S 50/Alt
1645 Mill St 96007 530-365-1801
Jason Provence, prin.

Angels Camp, Calaveras, Pop. 2,997

Bret Harte UNHSD 800/9-12
PO Box 7000 95221 209-736-8340
Michael Chimente, supt. Fax 736-8367
www.bhuhsd.k12.ca.us
Bret Harte Union HS 800/9-12
364 Murphys Grade Rd 95222 209-736-2507
Michael Chimente, prin. Fax 736-8383
Vierra HS 50/Alt
364 Murphys Grade Rd 95222 209-736-8327
Michael Chimente, prin. Fax 736-0598
Other Schools – See Vallecito

Calaveras County Office of Education 500/
PO Box 760 95221 209-736-4662
Kathy Northington, supt. Fax 736-2138
www.ccoe.k12.ca.us
Other Schools – See San Andreas

Regional Occupational Center & Program
Supt. — None
Calaveras County ROP Vo/Tech
PO Box 760 95221 209-736-6033
Patrick Miller, dir. Fax 736-2138

Angwin, Napa, Pop. 2,912

Pacific Union College Post-Sec.
1 Angwin Ave 94508 707-965-6311
Pacific Union College Prep S 100/9-12
1 Angwin Ave 94508 707-965-7272
Peter Fackenthall, prin. Fax 965-6689

Antelope, Sacramento, Pop. 42,966

Center JUSD 4,700/K-12
8408 Watt Ave 95843 916-338-6330
Scott Loehr, supt. Fax 338-6411
www.centerusd.k12.ca.us
Center HS 1,400/9-12
3111 Center Court Ln 95843 916-338-6420
Mike Jordan, prin. Fax 338-6370
McClellan Continuation HS 100/Alt
8725 Watt Ave 95843 916-338-6440
David DeArcos, prin. Fax 338-6535
Other Schools – See Roseville

Dry Creek JESD
Supt. — See Roseville
Antelope Crossing MS 900/6-8
9200 Palmerson Dr 95843 916-745-2100
Greg O'Meara, prin. Fax 745-2135

Roseville JUNHSD
Supt. — See Roseville
Antelope HS 1,300/9-12
7801 Titan Dr 95843 916-726-1400
John Becker, prin. Fax 726-0700

Antioch, Contra Costa, Pop. 96,748

Antioch USD 18,900/K-12
510 G St 94509 925-779-7500
Donald Gill Ed.D., supt. Fax 779-7509
www.antioch.k12.ca.us
Antioch HS 2,200/9-12
700 W 18th St 94509 925-706-5300
Louie Rocha, prin. Fax 706-1875
Antioch MS 800/6-8
1500 D St 94509 925-779-7400
Andy Cannon, prin. Fax 779-7414
Bidwell HS 200/Alt
800 Gary Ave 94509 925-776-5565
Amy Farias, prin. Fax 776-5566
Black Diamond MS 900/6-8
4730 Sterling Hill Dr 94531 925-776-5500
Ivanna Huthman, prin. Fax 779-2600
Dallas Ranch MS 1,400/6-8
1401 Mount Hamilton Dr 94531 925-706-4491
Ed Dacus, prin. Fax 706-1933
Deer Valley HS 2,800/9-12
4700 Lone Tree Way 94531 925-776-5555
Kenneth Gardner, prin. Fax 754-8094
Dozier-Libbey Medical HS 500/9-12
4900 Sand Creek Rd 94531 925-779-7540
Nancie Castro, prin. Fax 779-7542
Live Oak Continuation HS 200/Alt
1708 F St 94509 925-706-5206
Amy Farias, prin. Fax 776-7857
Park MS 1,000/6-8
1 Spartan Way 94509 925-706-5314
John Jimno, prin. Fax 706-2376
Prospects HS 300/Alt
820 W 2nd St 94509 925-706-5310
Amy Farias, prin. Fax 779-1976
Antioch Adult S Adult
820 W 2nd St 94509 925-706-5365
Amy Farias, prin. Fax 778-5843

Carrington College California Post-Sec.
2157 Country Hills Dr 94509 925-522-7777
Cornerstone Christian S 500/PK-12
1745 E 18th St 94509 925-779-2010
Logan Heyer, prin. Fax 754-0769
Heritage Baptist Academy 100/K-12
5200 Heidorn Ranch Rd 94531 925-778-2234
Paideia Academy 50/K-12
320 Worrell Rd 94509 925-628-4033
John Crowder, admin.

Anza, Riverside, Pop. 2,927

Hemet USD
Supt. — See Hemet
Hamilton HS 400/9-12
57430 Mitchell Rd 92539 951-763-1865
Jim Allured, prin. Fax 763-5420

Apple Valley, San Bernardino, Pop. 66,794

Apple Valley USD 13,700/PK-12
12555 Navajo Rd 92308 760-247-8001
Thomas Hoegerman, supt. Fax 247-4103
www.avusd.org
Apple Valley HS 2,100/9-12
11837 Navajo Rd 92308 760-247-7206
Dustin Conrad, prin. Fax 247-2092
Granite Hills HS 1,900/9-12
22900 Esaws Rd 92307 760-961-2290
Mike Kincaid, prin. Fax 961-8755
Willow Park HS 100/Alt
12555 Navajo Rd 92308 760-240-4252
Matt Pollack, prin. Fax 240-1261

San Bernardino Co. Office of Education
Supt. — See San Bernardino
Desert Mountain Community S 100/Alt
17800 US Highway 18 92307 760-242-6322
Bernadine Hollingsworth, dir. Fax 242-6338

AVFC Prep S 50/PK-12
19923 Bear Valley Rd 92308 760-247-2933
Mary Ann Beaumont, prin. Fax 247-4903

Aptos, Santa Cruz, Pop. 6,003

Pajaro Valley USD
Supt. — See Watsonville
Aptos HS 1,400/9-12
100 Mariner Way 95003 831-688-6565
Casey O'Brien, prin. Fax 688-6430
Aptos JHS 700/7-8
1001 Huntington Dr 95003 831-688-3234
Brian Saxton, prin. Fax 728-8139

Cabrillo College Post-Sec.
6500 Soquel Dr 95003 831-479-6100

Arbuckle, Colusa, Pop. 2,990

Pierce JUSD 1,300/K-12
PO Box 239 95912 530-476-2892
Ernest C. Sopp, supt. Fax 476-2289
www.pierce.k12.ca.us
Arbuckle Alternative HS 50/Alt
960 Wildwood Rd 95912 530-476-2173
George Griffin, prin. Fax 476-2674
Johnson JHS 300/6-8
938 Wildwood Rd 95912 530-476-3261
Blake Kitchen, prin. Fax 476-2017
Pierce HS 400/9-12
960 Wildwood Rd 95912 530-476-2277
George Griffin, prin. Fax 476-3285

Arcadia, Los Angeles, Pop. 55,191

Arcadia USD 9,700/K-12
234 Campus Dr 91007 626-821-8300
Dr. Joel Shawn, supt. Fax 821-8647
site.ausd.net
Arcadia HS 3,700/9-12
180 Campus Dr 91007 626-821-8370
Dr. Brent Forsee, prin. Fax 821-1712
Dana MS 700/6-8
1401 S 1st Ave 91006 626-821-8361
Dr. Daniel Hacking, prin. Fax 447-1965
First Avenue MS 800/6-8
301 S 1st Ave 91006 626-821-8362
Jeffrey Wilson, prin. Fax 446-1660
Foothills MS 800/6-8
171 E Sycamore Ave 91006 626-821-8363
Dr. Nadia Hillman, prin. Fax 303-7983
Rancho Learning Center 100/Alt
150 S 3rd Ave 91006 626-821-8371
Dr. David Munoz, prin. Fax 574-3806

Arroyo Pacific Academy 200/9-12
41 W Santa Clara St 91007 626-294-0661
Philip Clarke, pres. Fax 294-0677
Immaculate Conception/Annunciation S 100/5-8
1307 E Longden Ave 91006 626-447-8262
Norma Moreno, prin. Fax 358-3933
Rio Hondo Preparatory S 200/6-12
PO Box 662080 91066 626-444-9531
Leslie Orsburn, prin. Fax 442-1113

Arcata, Humboldt, Pop. 16,233

Arcata ESD 900/K-8
1435 Buttermilk Ln 95521 707-822-0351
Pamela Jones, supt. Fax 822-6589
www.humboldt.k12.ca.us/arcata_sd/
Sunny Brae MS 200/6-8
1430 Buttermilk Ln 95521 707-822-5988
Lynda Yeoman, prin. Fax 822-7002

Northern Humboldt UNHSD
Supt. — See Mc Kinleyville
Arcata HS 800/9-12
1720 M St 95521 707-825-2400
Dave Navarre, prin. Fax 825-2407
Pacific Coast HS 100/Alt
1720 M St 95521 707-825-2443
Jon Larson, prin. Fax 825-2130

Humboldt State University Post-Sec.
1 Harpst St 95521 707-826-3011

Arleta, See Los Angeles

Los Angeles USD
Supt. — See Los Angeles
Arleta HS 1,900/9-12
14200 Van Nuys Blvd 91331 818-686-4100
Linda Calvo, prin. Fax 890-1040

Armona, Kings, Pop. 4,080

Armona UNESD 1,300/PK-12
PO Box 368 93202 559-583-5000
Steve Bogan, supt. Fax 583-5004
www.auesd.com/
Parkview MS 400/5-8
PO Box 368 93202 559-583-5020
Dr. Xavier Pina, prin. Fax 583-5030

Armona Union Academy 100/K-12
PO Box 397 93202 559-582-4468
Erik Borges, prin. Fax 582-6609

Arroyo Grande, San Luis Obispo, Pop. 16,717

Lucia Mar USD 10,600/K-12
602 Orchard Ave 93420 805-474-3000
James Hogeboom, supt. Fax 481-1398
www.lmusd.org/
Arroyo Grande HS 2,200/9-12
495 Valley Rd 93420 805-474-3200
Tom Butler, prin. Fax 473-4222
Lopez HS 200/Alt
1055 Mesa View Dr 93420 805-474-3750
Charlissa Boaz-Skinner, prin. Fax 473-5518
Mesa MS 500/7-8
2555 S Halcyon Rd 93420 805-474-3400
Paul Jarvis, prin. Fax 473-4396
Paulding MS 600/7-8
600 Crown Hill St 93420 805-474-3500
Chuck Fiorentino, prin. Fax 473-5525
Other Schools – See Nipomo, Pismo Beach

Regional Occupational Center & Program
Supt. — None
Santa Lucia ROP Vo/Tech
602 Orchard Ave 93420 805-474-3000
James Souza, dir. Fax 473-5593

Coastal Christian S 200/K-12
1220 Farroll Ave 93420 805-489-1213
Dr. Bob McLaughlin, prin. Fax 489-5394
Valley View Adventist Academy 100/K-10
230 Vernon St 93420 805-489-2687
Philip Ermshar, prin. Fax 489-2704

Artesia, Los Angeles, Pop. 16,099

ABC USD
Supt. — See Cerritos
Ross MS 700/7-8
17707 Elaine Ave 90701 562-924-8331
Ricardo Brown, prin. Fax 402-6145

Angeles Institute Post-Sec.
11688 South St Ste 205 90701 562-531-4100

Arvin, Kern, Pop. 19,155
Arvin UNSD 3,300/PK-8
737 Bear Mountain Blvd 93203 661-854-6500
Michelle McLean Ed.D., supt. Fax 854-2362
www.arvinschools.com
Haven Drive MS 700/7-8
737 Bear Mountain Blvd 93203 661-854-6540
Tammie Hollis-Prime Ed.D., prin. Fax 854-1440

Kern UNHSD
Supt. — See Bakersfield
Arvin HS 2,500/9-12
900 Varsity Rd 93203 661-854-5561
Carlos Sardo, prin. Fax 854-5943

Atascadero, San Luis Obispo, Pop. 27,543
Atascadero USD 4,900/K-12
5601 West Mall 93422 805-462-4200
Deborah Bowers Ed.D., supt. Fax 462-4421
www.atasusd.org/
Atascadero Fine Arts Academy 300/4-8
6100 Olmeda Ave 93422 805-460-2500
Kirk Smith, prin. Fax 460-2522
Atascadero HS 1,500/9-12
1 High School Hill Rd 93422 805-462-4300
E.J. Rossi, prin. Fax 462-4387
Atascadero JHS 600/7-8
6501 Lewis Ave 93422 805-462-4360
Lori Thomas-Hicks, prin. Fax 462-4373
Del Rio Continuation HS 100/Alt
5601 West Mall 93422 805-462-4350
D.J. Pittenger, prin. Fax 462-0837
West Mall Alternative S 50/Alt
5601 West Mall 93422 805-462-4238
D.J. Pittenger, prin. Fax 462-0837

Laurus College Post-Sec.
8693 El Camino Real 93422 805-267-1690
North County Christian S 200/PK-12
PO Box 6017 93423 805-466-4457
Jennifer Clayton, admin. Fax 466-7948

Atherton, San Mateo, Pop. 6,660
Menlo Park City ESD 2,600/K-8
181 Encinal Ave 94027 650-321-7140
Maurice Ghysels Ed.D., supt. Fax 321-7184
www.mpcsd.org
Other Schools – See Menlo Park

Sequoia UNHSD
Supt. — See Redwood City
Menlo-Atherton HS 2,000/9-12
555 Middlefield Rd 94027 650-322-5311
Matthew Zito, prin. Fax 323-1411

Menlo College Post-Sec.
1000 El Camino Real 94027 650-543-3753
Menlo S 800/6-12
50 Valparaiso Ave 94027 650-330-2001
Norman Colb, head sch Fax 330-2002
Sacred Heart Prep HS 600/9-12
150 Valparaiso Ave 94027 650-322-7151
Dr. James Everitt, prin.

Atwater, Merced, Pop. 27,459
Atwater ESD 4,500/K-8
1401 Broadway Ave 95301 209-357-6100
Dr. Sandy Schiber, supt. Fax 357-6163
www.aesd.edu
Mitchell Senior ES 800/7-8
1753 5th St 95301 209-357-6124
Andrew Kersten, prin. Fax 357-6506

Merced County Office of Education
Supt. — See Merced
Valley Atwater Community Day S 100/Alt
1800 Matthews Ave 95301 209-381-4550
Carrie Harkreader, prin. Fax 385-5380

Merced UNHSD 10,400/9-12
3430 A St 95301 209-385-6413
Scott Scambray, supt. Fax 385-6442
muhsd.k12.ca.us
Atwater HS 1,900/9-12
PO Box 835 95301 209-357-6000
Alan Peterson, prin. Fax 357-6067
Buhach Colony HS 1,900/9-12
PO Box 753 95301 209-357-6600
Stacy McAfee, prin. Fax 357-6602
Other Schools – See Livingston, Merced

Sierra Academy of Aeronautics Post-Sec.
3515 Hardstand Ave Ste B 95301 209-722-7522

Auburn, Placer, Pop. 12,869
Placer UNHSD 4,500/9-12
13000 New Airport Rd 95603 530-886-4400
Dave Horsey, supt. Fax 886-4439
sites.google.com/a/puhsd.k12.ca.us/puhsd-us/
Chana Continuation HS 200/Alt
3775 Richardson Dr 95602 530-885-8401
Stan Parker, prin. Fax 885-1657
Maidu HS 100/Alt
3775 Richardson Dr 95602 530-885-8401
Stan Parker, prin. Fax 885-1657
Placer HS 1,400/9-12
275 Orange St 95603 530-885-4581
Peter Efstathiu, prin. Fax 823-5770
Placer S for Adults Adult
390 Finley St 95603 530-885-8585
Bill Bettencourt, prin. Fax 823-1406
Other Schools – See Colfax, Foresthill, Loomis

Regional Occupational Center & Program
Supt. — None
Forty-Niner ROP Vo/Tech
360 Nevada St 95603 530-889-5940
Ward Andrus, dir. Fax 887-1704

Forest Lake Christian S 400/K-12
12515 Combie Rd 95602 530-269-1535
Dr. Jean Schoellerman, dir. Fax 269-1541
Pine Hills Adventist Academy 100/K-12
13500 Richards Ln 95603 530-885-9447
Victor Anderson, prin. Fax 885-5237

Avalon, Los Angeles, Pop. 3,671
Long Beach USD
Supt. — See Long Beach
Avalon S 600/K-12
PO Box 557 90704 310-510-0790
Angelica Gonzalez, prin. Fax 510-2986

Avenal, Kings, Pop. 15,241
Reef-Sunset USD 2,400/K-12
205 N Park Ave 93204 559-386-9083
Dr. David East, supt. Fax 386-5303
www.rsusd.net
Avenal HS 600/9-12
601 E Mariposa St 93204 559-386-5253
Juan Ruiz, prin. Fax 386-9413
Reef-Sunset MS 300/7-8
608 N 1st Ave 93204 559-386-4128
Steve Betteridge, prin. Fax 386-4918
Reef Sunset Sec Community Day S 50/Alt
205 N Park Ave 93204 559-386-0460
Suzy VanDerMolen, prin. Fax 386-5303
Sunrise Continuation HS 50/Alt
209 N Park Ave 93204 559-386-4162
Suzy VanDerMolen, prin. Fax 386-4937
Other Schools – See Kettleman City

Avery, Calaveras, Pop. 622
Vallecito UNSD 700/K-8
PO Box 329 95224 209-795-8500
Christine Cearley, supt. Fax 795-8505
www.vusd.wikispaces.net/
Avery MS 200/6-8
PO Box 329 95224 209-795-8520
Christine Cearley, prin. Fax 795-8539

Azusa, Los Angeles, Pop. 45,586
Azusa USD 10,300/PK-12
PO Box 500 91702 626-967-6211
Linda Kaminski, supt. Fax 858-6123
www.azusausd.k12.ca.us
Azusa HS 1,400/9-12
PO Box 500 91702 626-815-3400
John Coke, prin. Fax 815-3430
Center MS 700/6-8
PO Box 500 91702 626-815-5184
Lynne Jorgensen, prin. Fax 815-2601
Foothill MS 700/6-8
PO Box 500 91702 626-815 6600
Jane Ostrowski, prin. Fax 815-1027
Slauson MS 800/6-8
PO Box 500 91702 626-815-5144
Ann Somers, prin Fax 815-5147
Other Schools – See Covina, Glendora

Azusa Pacific University Post-Sec.
901 E Alosta Ave 91702 626-969-3434

Baker, San Bernardino, Pop. 711
Baker Valley USD 200/K-12
PO Box 460 92309 760-733-4567
Ronda Tremblay, supt. Fax 733-4605
www.baker.k12.ca.us
Baker HS 100/9-12
PO Box 460 92309 760-733-4567
Ronda Tremblay, supt. Fax 733-4605
Baker JHS 50/6-8
PO Box 460 92309 760-733-4567
Ronda Tremblay, supt. Fax 733-4605
Baker Valley Adult S Adult
PO Box 460 92309 760-733-4567
Ronda Tremblay, supt. Fax 733-4605

Bakersfield, Kern, Pop. 338,954
Bakersfield CSD 27,500/K-8
1300 Baker St 93305 661-631-4600
Robert Arios Ed.D., supt. Fax 631-4623
www.bcsd.com
Chipman JHS 900/7-8
2905 Eissler St 93306 661-631-5210
Russell Taylor, prin. Fax 631-3229
Compton JHS 600/7-8
3211 Pico Ave 93306 661-631-5230
Alex Soriano, prin. Fax 631-3166
Curran MS 900/6-8
1116 Lymric Way 93309 661-631-5240
Jason Brannen, prin. Fax 631-4538
Emerson MS 800/6-8
801 4th St 93304 661-631-5260
Kempton Coman, prin. Fax 327-8505
Sequoia MS 1,000/6-8
900 Belle Ter 93304 661-631-5940
Gary McCloskey, prin. Fax 631-3236
Sierra MS 800/6-8
3017 Center St 93306 661-631-5470
Tomas Prieto, prin. Fax 631-4541
Stiern MS 1,400/6-8
2551 Morning Dr 93306 661-631-5480
Julie Short, prin. Fax 631-3241
Washington MS 600/6-8
1101 Noble Ave 93305 661-631-5810
Jeff Fenske, prin. Fax 631-3172

Beardsley ESD 1,700/K-8
1001 Roberts Ln 93308 661-393-8550
Paul Miller, supt. Fax 393-5965
www.beardsleyschool.org/
Beardsley JHS 300/7-8
1001 Roberts Ln 93308 661-392-9254
David Hilton, prin. Fax 399-3925

Edison ESD 1,100/K-8
11518 School St 93307 661-363-5394
Erica Andrews, supt. Fax 363-4631
www.edline.net/pages/Edison_Elementary
Edison MS 500/5-8
721 S Edison Rd 93307 661-366-8216
Loreda Clevenger, prin. Fax 366-0922

Fairfax ESD 2,200/K-8
1500 S Fairfax Rd 93307 661-366-7221
Michael Coleman, supt. Fax 366-1901
www.fairfax.k12.ca.us
Fairfax MS 700/6-8
1500 S Fairfax Rd 93307 661-366-4461
Alice Pacheco, prin. Fax 366-5831

Fruitvale SD 3,300/K-8
7311 Rosedale Hwy 93308 661-589-3830
Dr. Mary Westendorf, supt. Fax 589-3674
www.fruitvale.k12.ca.us
Fruitvale JHS 700/7-8
2114 Calloway Dr 93312 661-589-3933
Leslie Roberts, prin. Fax 588-3259

Greenfield UNESD 8,200/K-8
1624 Fairview Rd 93307 661-837-6000
Chris Crawford, supt. Fax 832-2873
www.gfusd.k12.ca.us/
Greenfield MS 700/6-8
1109 Pacheco Rd 93307 661-837-6110
Sandra Welch, prin. Fax 832-7431
McKee MS 900/6-8
205 McKee Rd 93307 661-837-6060
Bethany Ferguson, prin. Fax 834-7566
Ollivier MS 800/6-8
7310 Monitor St 93307 661-837-6120
Sheila Johnson, prin. Fax 396-0963

Kern County Office of Education 3,800/
1300 17th St 93301 661-636-4000
Christine Frazier, supt. Fax 636-4130
www.kern.org/
Kern County Community S 1,700/Alt
1300 17th St 93301 661-636-4346
Warcester Williams, dir. Fax 636-4127

Kern UNHSD 36,600/9-12
5801 Sundale Ave 93309 661-827-3154
Donald Carter, supt. Fax 827-3302
www.khsd.k12.ca.us/
Bakersfield HS 2,800/9-12
1241 G St 93301 661-324-9841
David Reese, prin. Fax 324-3401
Centennial HS 1,800/9-12
8601 Hageman Rd 93312 661-588-8601
Steve Wedel, prin. Fax 588-8608
East Bakersfield HS 2,300/9-12
2200 Quincy Dr 93306 661-871-7221
Librado Vasquez, prin. Fax 872-6980
Foothill HS 2,000/9-12
501 Park Dr 93306 661-366-4491
Brenda Lewis, prin. Fax 363-6223
Frontier HS 2,500/9-12
6401 Allen Rd, 661-829-1107
Dan Shannon, prin. Fax 829-1185
Golden Valley HS 2,600/9-12
801 Hosking Ave 93307 661-827-0800
Paul Helman, prin. Fax 827-0480
Highland HS 1,900/9-12
2900 Royal Scots Way 93306 661-872-2777
Debra Vigstrom, prin. Fax 871-6052
Independence HS 1,300/9-12
8001 Old River Rd 93311 661-834-8001
Willie Sandoval, prin. Fax 398-0899
Liberty HS 1,800/9-12
925 Jewetta Ave 93312 661-587-0925
Libby Wyatt, prin. Fax 587-1299
Mira Monte HS 1,600/9-12
1800 S Fairfax Rd 93307 661-366-1800
Jamie Quinonez, prin. Fax 363-6475
North HS 2,000/9-12
300 Galaxy Ave 93308 661-399-3351
Alan Paradise, prin. Fax 393-5918
Ridgeview HS 2,200/9-12
8501 Stine Rd 93313 661-398-3100
Steve Holmes, prin. Fax 398-9758
Ruggenberg Career Center Vo/Tech
610 Ansol Ln 93306 661-366-4401
Carissa Krizo, coord. Fax 363-0828
Schuetz Career Center Vo/Tech
8600 Shannon Dr 93307 661-827-4800
Jim Bennett, coord. Fax 827-4804
South HS 1,900/9-12
1101 Planz Rd 93304 661-831-3680
Connie Grumling, prin. Fax 837-2756
Stockdale HS 2,100/9-12
2800 Buena Vista Rd 93311 661-665-2800
Ramon Hendrix, prin. Fax 665-0914
Tierra Del Sol Continuation HS Alt
3700 E Belle Ter 93307 661-832-3700
Chris Dutton, admin. Fax 832-9807
Vista Continuation HS 300/Alt
200 P St 93304 661-327-8561
Tracey Lozano, admin. Fax 631-0558
Vista West Continuation HS 300/Alt
7115 Rosedale Hwy 93308 661-589-4242
Mike Mullings, admin. Fax 588-1627
West HS 2,100/9-12
1200 New Stine Rd 93309 661-832-2822
Dean McGee, prin. Fax 831-5606
Bakersfield Adult HS Adult
501 S Mount Vernon Ave 93307 661-835-1855
Mark Wyatt, prin. Fax 835-9612
Other Schools – See Arvin, Lake Isabella, Lamont, Shafter

Lamont ESD
Supt. — See Lamont
Mountain View MS 500/7-8
8001 Weedpatch Hwy 93307 661-845-2291
Jonathan Martinez, prin. Fax 845-1839

Norris SD 3,600/K-8
6940 Calloway Dr 93312 661-387-7000
Steve Shelton, supt. Fax 399-9750
www.norris.k12.ca.us/
Norris MS 1,200/6-8
6940 Calloway Dr 93312 661-387-7060
Jon Boles, prin. Fax 399-9356

Panama-Buena Vista UNSD 16,600/K-8
4200 Ashe Rd 93313 661-831-8331
Kip Hearron, supt. Fax 398-2141
www.pbvusd.k12.ca.us
Actis JHS 700/7-8
2400 Westholme Blvd 93309 661-833-1250
Patrick Spears, prin. Fax 833-9656
Stonecreek JHS 800/7-8
8000 Akers Rd 93313 661-834-4521
Matthew Kennedy, prin. Fax 834-6908
Tevis JHS 700/7-8
3901 Pin Oak Park Blvd 93311 661-664-7211
Robert Machado, prin. Fax 664-9659
Thompson JHS 800/7-8
4200 Planz Rd 93309 661-832-8011
Darryl Pope, prin. Fax 832-5165
Warren JHS 800/7-8
4615 Mountain Vista Dr 93311 661-665-9210
George Thornburgh, prin. Fax 665-9507

Regional Occupational Center & Program
Supt. — None
Kern HSD ROC Vo/Tech
501 S Mount Vernon Ave 93307 661-831-3327
Sandra Banducci, prin. Fax 398-8239

Rio Bravo-Greeley UNESD 1,000/K-8
6521 Enos Ln, 661-589-2696
Ernie Unruh, supt. Fax 589-2218
www.rbgusd.k12.ca.us
Rio Bravo-Greeley MS 500/5-8
6601 Enos Ln, 661-589-2505
Charles Coleman, prin. Fax 588-7204

Rosedale UNESD 5,200/K-8
2553 Old Farm Rd 93312 661-588-6000
John Mendiburu Ed.D., supt. Fax 588-6009
www.ruesd.net
Freedom MS 600/7-8
11445 Noriega Rd 93312 661-588-6044
Charles Monaco, prin. Fax 588-6048
Rosedale MS 600/7-8
12463 Rosedale Hwy 93312 661-588-6030
Becky Devahl, prin. Fax 588-6039

Standard ESD 2,900/K-8
1200 N Chester Ave 93308 661-392-2110
Kevin Silberberg Ed.D., supt. Fax 392-0681
district.standard.k12.ca.us
Standard MS 900/6-8
1222 N Chester Ave 93308 661-392-2130
Jason Hodgson, prin. Fax 392-2134

Vineland ESD 900/K-8
14713 Weedpatch Hwy 93307 661-845-3713
Danny Whetton, supt. Fax 845-8449
vineland.k12.ca.us
Sunset S 400/5-8
8301 Sunset Blvd 93307 661-845-1320
Rocio Munoz, prin. Fax 845-3952

Bakersfield Adventist Academy 200/K-12
3333 Bernard St 93306 661-871-1591
Mike Schwartz, prin. Fax 871-1594
Bakersfield Christian HS 400/9-12
12775 Stockdale Hwy, 661-410-7000
Gregory Root M.Ed., admin. Fax 410-7007
Bakersfield College Post-Sec.
1801 Panorama Dr 93305 661-395-4011
California State University-Bakersfield Post-Sec.
9001 Stockdale Hwy 93311 661-654-2782
DeVry University Post-Sec.
3000 Ming Ave 93304 661-833-7120
Eternity Preparatory Academy 50/K-12
PO Box 13158 93389 661-834-0948
Mike Kirkland, hdmstr.
Garces Memorial HS 700/9-12
2800 Loma Linda Dr 93305 661-327-2578
Kathleen Bears, prin. Fax 327-5427
Kaplan College Post-Sec.
1914 Wible Rd 93304 661-836-6300
Lyle's College of Beauty Post-Sec.
2935 F St 93301 661-327-9784
Milan Institute Post-Sec.
2822 F St 93301 661-325-8900
San Joaquin Valley College Post-Sec.
201 New Stine Rd 93309 661-834-0126
Santa Barbara Business College Post-Sec.
5300 California Ave 93309 866-749-7222

Baldwin Park, Los Angeles, Pop. 74,883
Baldwin Park USD 15,600/PK-12
3699 Holly Ave 91706 626-962-3311
Mark M. Skvarna, supt. Fax 856-4901
www.bpusd.net
Baldwin Park HS 2,400/9-12
3900 Puente Ave 91706 626-960-5431
Anthony Ippolito, prin. Fax 856-4059
Holland MS 600/6-8
4733 Landis Ave 91706 626-962-8412
Michael Rust, prin. Fax 813-6148
Jones JHS 600/7-8
14250 Merced Ave 91706 626-962-8312
Elizabeth Cox, prin. Fax 856-4291
North Park Continuation HS 300/Alt
4600 Bogart Ave 91706 626-337-4407
Harris Vincent Pratt, prin. Fax 856-4402
Olive MS 600/6-8
13701 Olive St 91706 626-962-8416
Richard Noblett, prin. Fax 856-4568
Santa Fe S 400/3-8
4650 Baldwin Park Blvd 91706 626-856-1525
Margie Clark, prin. Fax 813-0614
Sierra Vista HS 2,000/9-12
3600 Frazier St 91706 626-960-7741
Jackie White, prin. Fax 856-4050
Sierra Vista JHS 800/7-8
13400 Foster Ave 91706 626-962-1300
Christine Simmons, prin. Fax 856-4577
Baldwin Park Adult & Community Education Adult
4640 Maine Ave 91706 626-939-4456
John Kerr, prin. Fax 856-4384

Ballico, Merced, Pop. 398
Ballico-Cressey ESD 300/K-8
11818 Gregg Ave 95303 209-632-5371
Bryan Ballenger, supt. Fax 632-8929
www.ballicocressey.com
Ballico MS 200/4-8
11818 Gregg Ave 95303 209-632-5371
Bryan Ballenger, prin. Fax 632-8929

Banning, Riverside, Pop. 28,937
Banning USD 4,500/K-12
161 W Williams St 92220 951-922-0200
Robert Guillen, supt. Fax 922-0227
www.banning.k12.ca.us
Banning HS 1,100/9-12
100 W Westward Ave 92220 951-922-0285
Douglas Newton, prin. Fax 922-2137
New Horizons Continuation HS 100/Alt
1151 W Wilson St 92220 951-922-0250
Sean McMurray, prin. Fax 922-2750
Nicolet MS 700/7-8
101 E Nicolet St 92220 951-922-0280
Robert Meteau, prin. Fax 922-2748

Barstow, San Bernardino, Pop. 21,497
Barstow USD 6,100/K-12
551 S Avenue H 92311 760-255-6000
Jeff Malan, supt. Fax 255-8965
www.barstow.k12.ca.us
Barstow HS 1,500/9-12
551 S Avenue H 92311 760-255-6105
Derrick Delton, prin. Fax 256-4076
Barstow JHS 800/7-8
551 S Avenue H 92311 760-255-6200
Oron Jackson, prin. Fax 255-6205
Central Continuation HS 300/Alt
551 S Avenue H 92311 760-255-6063
Carolyn Norman, prin. Fax 256-2125

Barstow Community College Post-Sec.
2700 Barstow Rd 92311 760-252-2411

Bay Point, Contra Costa, Pop. 20,582
Mount Diablo USD
Supt. — See Concord
Gateway HS 50/Alt
235 Pacifica Ave 94565 925-458-1316
Rachelle Buckner, admin. Fax 458-1487
Riverview MS 700/6-8
205 Pacifica Ave 94565 925-458-3216
Thom Kwiatkowski, prin. Fax 458-0875

Beaumont, Riverside, Pop. 35,877
Beaumont USD 8,500/K-12
PO Box 187 92223 951-845-1631
Dr. Maureen Latham, supt. Fax 845-2039
www.beaumont-ca.schoolloop.com
Beaumont HS 2,400/9-12
PO Box 187 92223 951-845-3171
Marilyn Saucedo, prin. Fax 769-9289
Glen View HS 100/Alt
PO Box 187 92223 951-845-6012
Matthew Russo, prin. Fax 769-8760
Mountain View MS 1,000/6-8
PO Box 187 92223 951-845-1627
Tyson Lingenfelter, prin. Fax 845-8679
San Gorgonio MS 1,000/6-8
PO Box 187 92223 951-769-4391
Drew Scherrer, prin. Fax 769-8750
Beaumont Adult S Adult
PO Box 187 92223 951-845-6012
David Williams, prin. Fax 769-8760

Bell, Los Angeles, Pop. 35,263
Los Angeles USD
Supt. — See Los Angeles
Bell HS 4,300/9-12
4328 Bell Ave 90201 323-832-4700
Rafael Balderas, prin. Fax 560-7874
Orchard Academy #2B 200/6-8
6411 Orchard Ave 90201 323-826-3951
David Manzo, prin. Fax 826-3951
Orchard Academy #2C 100/6-8
6411 Orchard Ave 90201 323-826-3975
Mirian Rubalcava, prin. Fax 826-3976

Bellflower, Los Angeles, Pop. 74,379
Bellflower USD 13,900/K-12
16703 Clark Ave 90706 562-866-9011
Brian Jacobs Ed.D., supt. Fax 866-7713
www.busd.k12.ca.us/
Bellflower MSHS 3,000/7-12
15301 Mcnab Ave 90706 562-920-1801
Michael Lundgren, prin. Fax 804-2387
Somerset Continuation HS 300/Alt
9242 Laurel St 90706 562-804-6548
Mark Kailiponi, prin. Fax 804-6587
Other Schools – See Lakewood

St. John Bosco HS 800/9-12
13640 Bellflower Blvd 90706 562-920-1734
Casey Yeazel, prin. Fax 867-5322

Bell Gardens, Los Angeles, Pop. 41,928
Montebello USD
Supt. — See Montebello
Bell Gardens HS 3,400/9-12
6119 Agra St 90201 323-826-5151
Juan Herrera, prin. Fax 887-7959
Bell Gardens IS 1,200/6-8
5841 Live Oak St 90201 562-927-1319
Rick Mendez, prin. Fax 806-5131
Suva IS 900/6-8
6660 Suva St 90201 562-927-2679
Teresa Alonzo, prin. Fax 806-5132
Bell Gardens Adult Education Adult
6119 Agra St 90201 323-887-7955
Kathy Brendzal, prin. Fax 887-7958
Ford Park Adult S Adult
7800 Scout Ave 90201 562-927-7750
Daniel Garcia, prin. Fax 806-5133

Belmont, San Mateo, Pop. 24,354
Belmont-Redwood Shores ESD 3,200/K-8
2960 Hallmark Dr 94002 650-637-4800
Nellie Hungerford, supt. Fax 637-4811
www.brssd.org
Ralston IS 900/6-8
2675 Ralston Ave 94002 650-637-4880
Scott Carson, prin. Fax 637-4888

Sequoia UNHSD
Supt. — See Redwood City
Carlmont HS 2,100/9-12
1400 Alameda De Las Pulgas 94002 650-595-0210
Raul Zamora, prin. Fax 591-6067

Notre Dame de Namur University Post-Sec.
1500 Ralston Ave 94002 650-508-3500
Notre Dame HS 500/9-12
1540 Ralston Ave 94002 650-595-1913
Rita Gleason, prin. Fax 593-9330

Benicia, Solano, Pop. 25,504
Benicia USD 5,000/K-12
350 E K St 94510 707-747-8300
Janice Adams Ph.D., supt. Fax 748-0146
www.beniciaunified.org
Benicia HS 1,700/9-12
1101 Military W 94510 707-747-8325
Damon Wright, prin. Fax 745-6769
Benicia MS 1,200/6-8
1100 Southampton Rd 94510 707-747-8340
Michael Minahen, prin. Fax 747-8349
Liberty Continuation HS 100/Alt
351 E J St 94510 707-747-8323
JoAnn Severson, prin. Fax 748-2684

Ben Lomond, Santa Cruz, Pop. 6,022
San Lorenzo Valley USD 4,000/K-12
325 Marion Ave 95005 831-336-5194
Julie Haff, supt. Fax 336-9531
www.slvusd.org
Other Schools – See Felton

Berkeley, Alameda, Pop. 106,371
Berkeley USD 9,300/PK-12
2020 Bonar St 94702 510-644-4500
Javetta Cleveland, supt. Fax 540-5358
www.berkeleyschools.net
Berkeley HS 3,400/9-12
1980 Allston Way 94704 510-644-6120
Pasquale Scuderi, prin. Fax 548-4221
Berkeley Technology Academy 100/Alt
2701 Martin Luther King Jr 94703 510-644-6159
Sheila Quintana, prin. Fax 644-4597
King MS 1,000/6-8
1781 Rose St 94703 510-644-6280
Janet Levenson, prin. Fax 644-8783
Longfellow Arts & Technology MS 400/6-8
1500 Derby St 94703 510-644-6360
Patricia Saddler, prin. Fax 644-8707
Willard MS 500/6-8
2425 Stuart St 94705 510-644-6330
Robert Ithurburn, prin. Fax 548-4219
Berkeley Adult S Adult
1701 San Pablo Ave 94702 510-644-6130
Burr Guthrie, prin. Fax 644-6784

Acupuncture & Integrative Medicine Coll. Post-Sec.
2550 Shattuck Ave 94704 510-666-8248
American Baptist Seminary of the West Post-Sec.
2606 Dwight Way 94704 510-841-1905
Archway S 5-8
1940 Virginia St 94709 510-849-4747
Johanna McCormack, head sch Fax 849-4740
Berkeley City College Post-Sec.
2050 Center St 94704 510-981-2800
Church Divinity School of the Pacific Post-Sec.
2451 Ridge Rd 94709 510-204-0700
Dominican School of Philosophy/Theology Post-Sec.
2301 Vine St 94708 510-849-2030
Franciscan School of Theology Post-Sec.
1712 Euclid Ave 94709 510-848-5232
Graduate Theological Union Post-Sec.
2400 Ridge Rd 94709 510-649-2400
Maybeck HS 100/9-12
2727 College Ave 94705 510-841-8489
Trevor Cralle, dir. Fax 704-0473
Pacific Lutheran Theological Seminary Post-Sec.
2770 Marin Ave 94708 510-524-5264
Pacific School of Religion Post-Sec.
1798 Scenic Ave 94709 510-849-8200
St. Marys College HS 600/9-12
1294 Albina Ave 94706 510-526-9242
Peter Imperial, prin. Fax 559-6277

Starr King School for the Ministry Post-Sec.
2441 Le Conte Ave 94709 510-845-6232
University of California Post-Sec.
110 Sproul Hall 94720 510-642-6000
Wright Institute Post-Sec.
2728 Durant Ave 94704 510-841-9230

Bermuda Dunes, Riverside, Pop. 7,164

Desert Christian Academy 400/PK-12
40700 Yucca Ln, 760-345-2848
David Fulton, head sch Fax 345-8173

Beverly Hills, Los Angeles, Pop. 32,498
Beverly Hills USD 4,600/PK-12
255 S Lasky Dr 90212 310-551-5100
Dr. Gary W. Woods, supt. Fax 286-2138
www.bhusd.org/
Beverly Hills HS 2,100/9-12
241 S Moreno Dr 90212 310-229-3685
Carter Paysinger, prin. Fax 286-7446

Academy of Couture Art Post-Sec.
8484 Wilshire Blvd Ste 730 90211 310-360-8888
West Coast Ultrasound Institute Post-Sec.
291 S La Cienega Blvd # 500 90211 310-289-5123

Bieber, Lassen, Pop. 307
Big Valley JUSD 200/K-12
PO Box 157 96009 530-294-5266
Larry Todd, supt. Fax 294-5396
www.bigvalleyschool.org
Big Valley Community Day S 50/Alt
PO Box 157 96009 530-294-5266
Larry Robins, lead tchr. Fax 294-5396
Big Valley JSHS 100/8-12
PO Box 157 96009 530-294-5231
Larry Robins, prin. Fax 294-5100
Gateway High S 50/Alt
PO Box 157 96009 530-294-5214
Phil Pirkle, lead tchr. Fax 294-5109

Big Bear Lake, San Bernardino, Pop. 4,883
Bear Valley USD 2,700/K-12
PO Box 1529 92315 909-866-4631
Kurt Madden, supt. Fax 866-2040
www.bigbear.k12.ca.us
Big Bear MS 400/7-8
PO Box 1607 92315 909-866-4634
Tina Fulmer, prin. Fax 866-5679
Other Schools – See Sugarloaf

Biggs, Butte, Pop. 1,654
Biggs USD 500/PK-12
300 B St 95917 530-868-1281
Doug Kaelin, supt. Fax 868-1615
www.biggs.org/
Biggs HS, 300 B St 95917 200/9-12
Doug Kaelin, prin. 530-868-5825
Biggs Secondary Community Day S 50/Alt
300 B St 95917 – Doug Kaelin, prin. 530-868-1281

Big Pine, Inyo, Pop. 1,716
Big Pine USD 200/K-12
PO Box 908 93513 760-938-2005
Pamela Jones, supt. Fax 938-2310
www.bp.k12.ca.us
Big Pine HS 50/9-12
PO Box 908 93513 760-938-2222
Katie Kolker, prin. Fax 938-2310

Bishop USD
Supt. — See Bishop
Palisade Glacier Continuation HS 50/Alt
PO Box 938 93513 760-938-2001
Randy Cook, prin. Fax 938-2310

Big Sur, Monterey
Big Sur USD 100/PK-12
69325 Highway 1 93920 805-927-4507
Raeanna Thomasson, supt. Fax 927-8123
www.pacificvalleyschool.com
Pacific Valley S 50/PK-12
69325 Highway 1 93920 805-927-4507
Raeanna Thomasson, admin. Fax 927-8123

Bishop, Inyo, Pop. 3,811
Bishop USD 1,600/K-12
301 N Fowler St 93514 760-872-3680
Barry Simpson, supt. Fax 872-6016
bishop-ca.schoolloop.com
Bishop Union HS 700/9-12
301 N Fowler St 93514 760-873-4275
Allen Van Velzen, prin. Fax 873-3065
Home Street MS 400/6-8
201 Home St 93514 760-872-1381
Patrick Twomey, prin. Fax 872-1877
Other Schools – See Big Pine

Inyo County Office of Education
Supt. — See Independence
Boothe S 50/Alt
166 Grandview Dr 93514 760-873-3262
Dr. Terence McAteer, prin. Fax 873-3324
Phoenix Community S 50/Alt
166 Grandview Dr 93514 760-873-3262
Dr. Terence McAteer, prin. Fax 873-3324

Regional Occupational Center & Program
Supt. — None
Inyo County ROP Vo/Tech
166 Grandview Dr 93514 760-873-3262
Sophie Kenn, dir. Fax 873-3324

Bloomington, San Bernardino, Pop. 23,603
Colton JUSD
Supt. — See Colton
Baca MS 800/7-8
1640 S Lilac Ave 92316 909-580-5014
Joda Murphy, prin. Fax 876-4195
Bloomington HS 2,800/9-12
10750 Laurel Ave 92316 909-580-5004
Ignacio Cabrera, prin. Fax 876-6326
Harris MS 900/7-8
11150 Alder Ave 92316 909-580-5020
Sandy Torres, prin. Fax 820-2238
Slover Mountain Continuation HS 300/Alt
18829 Orange St 92316 909-580-5013
Kristi Richardson, prin. Fax 876-6363

Bloomington Christian S 900/PK-12
955 Bloomington Ave 92316 909-877-1239
Yvonna Williams, supt. Fax 873-3160

Blue Jay, San Bernardino
Rim of the World USD 4,500/K-12
27315 N Bay Rd 92317 909-336-2031
Donna Kellogg, supt. Fax 337-4527
www.rimsd.k12.ca.us
Other Schools – See Crestline, Lake Arrowhead

Blue Lake, Humboldt, Pop. 1,210

Dell'Arte International School Post-Sec.
PO Box 816 95525 707-668-5663

Blythe, Riverside, Pop. 20,420
Palo Verde USD 3,500/K-12
295 N 1st St 92225 760-922-4164
Bob Bilek, supt. Fax 922-5942
www.pvusd.us
Blythe MS 500/7-8
825 N Lovekin Blvd 92225 760-922-1300
Douglas Ferber, prin. Fax 922-3748
Palo Verde HS 900/9-12
667 N Lovekin Blvd 92225 760-922-7148
Bonita Bradshaw, prin. Fax 922-8916
Twin Palms Continuation S Adult
811 W Chanslor Way 92225 760-922-4884
Meliton Sanchez, prin. Fax 922-1177

Palo Verde College Post-Sec.
1 College Dr 92225 760-921-5500

Bonsall, San Diego, Pop. 3,866
Bonsall UNESD 2,000/K-8
31505 Old River Rd 92003 760-631-5200
Justin Cunningham Ed.D., supt. Fax 941-4409
www.bonsallusd.com
Sullivan MS 500/6-8
7350 W Lilac Rd 92003 760-631-5210
Janet Whiddon, prin. Fax 631-5230

Boonville, Mendocino, Pop. 1,016
Anderson Valley USD 500/PK-12
PO Box 457 95415 707-895-3774
James Collins, supt. Fax 895-2665
www.avusd.k12.ca.us
Anderson Valley JSHS 200/7-12
PO Box 130 95415 707-895-3496
James Tomlin, prin. Fax 895-3150
Rancheria Continuation S 50/Alt
PO Box 457 95415 707-895-3151
James Tomlin, lead tchr. Fax 895-2665
Anderson Valley Adult S Adult
PO Box 457 95415 707-895-2953
James Collins, prin. Fax 895-2665

Boron, Kern, Pop. 2,180
Muroc JUSD
Supt. — See North Edwards
Boron JSHS 300/7-12
26831 Prospect St 93516 760-762-5121
S. Nat Adams, prin. Fax 762-5040

Borrego Springs, San Diego, Pop. 3,399
Borrego Springs USD 600/PK-12
1315 Palm Canyon Dr 92004 760-767-5357
Martha Deichler, supt. Fax 767-0494
www.bsusd.com
Borrego Springs HS 100/9-12
1315 Palm Canyon Dr 92004 760-767-5335
Martha Deichler, prin. Fax 767-5999
Borrego Springs MS 100/6-8
1315 Palm Canyon Dr 92004 760-767-5335
Martha Deichler, prin. Fax 767-5999
Santa Rosa Community Day S 50/Alt
1315 Palm Canyon Dr 92004 760-767-5335
Martha Deichler, prin. Fax 767-5999

Brawley, Imperial, Pop. 24,758
Brawley ESD 3,800/K-8
261 D St 92227 760-344-2330
Ronald Garcia, supt. Fax 344-8928
www.besd.org
Worth JHS 800/7-8
385 W D St 92227 760-344-2153
Bryan O'Donnell, prin. Fax 351-5043

Brawley UNHSD 1,900/9-12
480 N Imperial Ave 92227 760-312-5819
Hasmik Danielian Ed.D., supt. Fax 344-9520
www.brawleyhigh.org
Brawley HS 1,700/9-12
480 N Imperial Ave 92227 760-312-6073
Simon Canalez, prin. Fax 344-9520
BUHS Renaissance Community Day S 50/Alt
480 N Imperial Ave 92227 760-312-5109
Antonio Munguia, admin. Fax 344-9520
Desert Valley Continuation HS 200/Alt
480 N Imperial Ave 92227 760-312-5110
Antonio Munguia, prin. Fax 344-7425

Brawley Christian Academy 100/K-12
430 N 2nd St 92227 760-344-3911
Antonio Flores, prin. Fax 344-5864

Brea, Orange, Pop. 38,164
Brea-Olinda USD 5,900/K-12
PO Box 300 92822 714-990-7800
Arthur Roland, supt. Fax 529-2137
www.bousd.k12.ca.us
Brea Canyon HS 100/Alt
689 Wildcat Way 92821 714-990-7882
Carol Christman, prin. Fax 990-7587
Brea JHS 900/7-8
400 N Brea Blvd 92821 714-990-7500
Pam Gallarda, prin. Fax 990-7585
Brea-Olinda HS 2,000/9-12
789 Wildcat Way 92821 714-990-7850
Jerry Halpin, prin. Fax 990-7547

Brea School of Exceptional Children Post-Sec.
875 N Brea Blvd 92821

Brentwood, Contra Costa, Pop. 49,001
Brentwood UNESD 8,700/K-8
255 Guthrie Ln 94513 925-513-6300
Dana Eaton, supt. Fax 634-8583
www.brentwood.k12.ca.us
Adams MS 1,100/6-8
401 American Ave 94513 925-513-6450
Kelly Manke, prin. Fax 513-3470
Bristow MS 1,000/6-8
855 Minnesota Ave 94513 925-513-6460
Russ Cornell, prin. Fax 516-8725
Hill MS 900/6-8
140 Birch St 94513 925-513-6440
Kirsten Jobb, prin. Fax 513-0696

Liberty UNHSD 7,400/9-12
20 Oak St 94513 925-634-2166
Eric Volta, supt. Fax 634-1687
www.libertyuhsd.k12.ca.us
Heritage HS 2,200/9-12
101 American Ave 94513 925-634-0037
Larry Oshodi, prin. Fax 240-0662
Independence HS 400/Alt
929 2nd St 94513 925-634-2589
Colleen Sanchez, dir. Fax 634-5317
La Paloma Continuation HS 200/Alt
400 Ghiggeri Dr 94513 925-634-2888
Regina Greene, prin. Fax 634-6578
Liberty HS 2,100/9-12
850 2nd St 94513 925-634-3521
Patrick Walsh, prin. Fax 513-2739
Liberty Adult Education S Adult
929 2nd St 94513 925-634-2565
Colleen Sanchez, dir. Fax 634-5317
Other Schools – See Oakley

Bridgeport, Mono, Pop. 560
Eastern Sierra USD 500/K-12
PO Box 575 93517 760-932-7443
Don Clark, supt. Fax 932-7140
www.esusd.org
Other Schools – See Coleville, Lee Vining

Mono County Office of Education 300/
PO Box 477 93517 760-932-7311
Stacey Adler, supt. Fax 932-7278
www.monocoe.org
Sawtooth Ridge Community S 100/7-12
PO Box 477 93517 760-934-0031
Janet Hunt, prin.
Other Schools – See Mammoth Lakes

Regional Occupational Center & Program
Supt. — None
Mono County ROP Vo/Tech
PO Box 477 93517 760-932-7311
Rhea Kerby, dir. Fax 932-7278

Brisbane, San Mateo, Pop. 4,026
Brisbane ESD 500/K-8
1 Solano St 94005 415-467-0550
Toni Presta, supt. Fax 467-2914
brisbane.ca.campusgrid.net/home
Lipman MS 200/6-8
1 Solano St 94005 415-467-9541
Jolene Heckerman, prin. Fax 467-5073

Buellton, Santa Barbara, Pop. 4,686
Buellton UNESD 700/PK-8
595 2nd St 93427 805-686-2767
Bryan McCabe, supt. Fax 686-2719
www.buelltonusd.org
Jonata MS 200/6-8
301 2nd St 93427 805-688-4222
Kathy Fayram, prin. Fax 688-6611

Buena Park, Orange, Pop. 78,169
Buena Park ESD 5,300/K-8
6885 Orangethorpe Ave 90620 714-522-8412
Greg Magnuson, supt. Fax 994-1506
www.bpsd.k12.ca.us/
Buena Park JHS 1,100/7-8
6931 Orangethorpe Ave 90620 714-522-8491
Luisa Rogers, prin. Fax 523-1602

Fullerton JUNHSD
Supt. — See Fullerton
Buena Park HS 1,900/9-12
8833 Academy Dr 90621 714-992-8601
Jim Coombs, prin. Fax 992-8619

Bethel Baptist Academy 200/K-12
8433 Philodendron Way 90620 714-521-5586
Sharon Wallace, admin.

Burbank, Los Angeles, Pop. 99,967
Burbank USD 15,300/K-12
1900 W Olive Ave 91506 818-729-4400
Dr. Jan Britz, supt. Fax 729-4483
www.burbankusd.org

Burbank HS 2,700/9-12
902 N 3rd St 91502 818-558-4700
Michael Bertram, prin. Fax 845-6122
Burbank MS 1,000/6-8
3700 W Jeffries Ave 91505 818-558-4646
Dr. Brian O'Rourke, prin. Fax 842-3727
Burroughs HS 2,800/9-12
1920 W Clark Ave 91506 818-558-4777
John Paramo, prin. Fax 846-9268
Jordan MS 1,200/6-8
420 S Mariposa St 91506 818-558-4622
Stacy Cashman, prin. Fax 843-3509
Monterey Continuation HS 200/Alt
1915 W Monterey Ave 91506 818-558-5455
Ann Brooks, prin. Fax 841-2446
Muir MS 1,400/6-8
1111 N Kenneth Rd 91504 818-558-5320
Dr. Greg Miller, prin. Fax 841-4637
Burbank Adult S Adult
3811 W Allan Ave 91505 818-558-4611
Joseph Stark, dir. Fax 558-4620

Bellarmine-Jefferson HS 400/9-12
465 E Olive Ave 91501 818-972-1400
John Matheus, prin. Fax 559-6387
Elegante Beauty College Post-Sec.
200 N San Fernando Blvd 91502 818-954-8894
Intercoast Colleges Post-Sec.
175 E Olive Ave Fl 3 91502 818-500-8400
Make-up Designory Post-Sec.
129 S San Fernando Blvd 91502 818-729-9420
Providence HS 400/9-12
511 S Buena Vista St 91505 818-846-8141
Joe Sciuto, hdmstr. Fax 843-8421
Woodbury University Post-Sec.
7500 N Glenoaks Blvd 91504 818-767-0888

Burlingame, San Mateo, Pop. 27,534
Burlingame ESD 2,800/K-8
1825 Trousdale Dr 94010 650-259-3800
Maggie MacIsaac Ed.D., supt. Fax 259-3820
www.bsd.k12.ca.us
Burlingame IS 800/6-8
1715 Quesada Way 94010 650-259-3830
Pamela Scott, prin. Fax 259-3843

San Mateo UNHSD
Supt. — See San Mateo
Burlingame HS 1,400/9-12
1 Mangini Way 94010 650-558-2899
Christopher Holleran, prin. Fax 558-2852

Mercy HS 500/9-12
2750 Adeline Dr 94010 650-343-3631
Lisa Tortorich, prin. Fax 343-3358
Mills Peninsula Health Services Post-Sec.
1783 El Camino Real 94010 650-696-5678

Burney, Shasta, Pop. 3,044
Fall River JUSD 1,100/K-12
20375 Tamarack Ave 96013 530-335-4538
Greg Hawkins, supt. Fax 335-3115
www.frjusd.org
Burney Community Day S 50/Alt
20375 Tamarack Ave 96013 530-335-5189
Greg Hawkins, prin. Fax 335-3115
Burney JSHS 200/7-12
37571 Mountain View Rd 96013 530-335-4576
Ray Guerrero, prin. Fax 335-3554
Mountain View Continuation HS 50/Alt
20375 Tamarack Ave 96013 530-335-5189
Greg Hawkins, prin. Fax 335-3115
Other Schools – See Mc Arthur

Byron, Contra Costa, Pop. 1,236
Byron UNESD 1,700/PK-8
14301 Byron Hwy 94514 925-809-7500
Ken Jacopetti, supt. Fax 634-9421
www.byronusd.com
Excelsior MS 600/6-8
14301 Byron Hwy 94514 925-809-7530
Kelly Basmagian, prin. Fax 634-5120

Calabasas, Los Angeles, Pop. 22,176
Las Virgenes USD 11,400/K-12
4111 Las Virgenes Rd 91302 818-880-4000
Dan Stepenosky Ed.D., supt. Fax 880-4200
www.lvusd.org
Calabasas HS 1,900/9-12
22855 Mulholland Hwy 91302 818-222-7177
C.J. Foss, prin. Fax 223-8477
Indian Hills Continuation HS - East 50/Alt
22855 Mulholland Hwy 91302 818-222-7177
C.J. Foss, prin. Fax 223-8477
Stelle MS 900/6-8
22450 Mulholland Hwy 91302 818-224-4107
Mary Sistrunk, prin. Fax 224-4989
Wright MS 900/6-8
4029 Las Virgenes Rd 91302 818-880-4614
Kimmarie Taylor, prin. Fax 878-0453
Other Schools – See Agoura Hills

Mesivta of Greater Los Angeles S 100/9-12
25115 Mureau Rd 91302 818-876-0550
Rabbi Shlomo Gottesman, dir. Fax 876-0537
Viewpoint S 1,200/K-12
23620 Mulholland Hwy 91302 818-340-2901
Dr. Robert Dworkoski, hdmstr. Fax 591-0834

Calexico, Imperial, Pop. 38,495
Calexico USD 8,100/K-12
901 Andrade Ave 92231 760-768-3888
Richard Fragale, supt. Fax 768-3856
www.calexico.k12.ca.us/
Aurora HS 200/Alt
641 Rockwood Ave 92231 760-768-3940
John Moreno, prin. Fax 768-1459
Calexico HS 2,100/10-12
1030 Encinas Ave 92231 760-768-3980
Sergio Pesqueira, prin. Fax 357-9640
Camarena JHS 700/7-8
800 E Rivera Ave 92231 760-768-3808
Carlos Gonzales, prin. Fax 768-3807
De Anza 9th Grade Academy 800/9-9
824 Blair Ave 92231 760-768-3950
Sergio Pesqueira, prin. Fax 357-8251
Moreno JHS 700/7-8
1202 Kloke Ave 92231 760-768-3960
Gabrielle Williams, prin. Fax 768-1905
Morales Adult Education Center Adult
1201 Kloke Ave 92231 760-768-3914
John Moreno, admin. Fax 768-3916

Calexico Mission S 300/K-12
601 E 1st St 92231 760-357-3711
Susan Smith, prin. Fax 357-3713
Vincent Memorial HS 200/9-12
525 Sheridan St 92231 760-357-3461
Sr. Guadalupe Hernandez, prin. Fax 357-0902

California City, Kern, Pop. 13,467
Mojave USD
Supt. — See Mojave
California City HS 400/9-12
8567 Raven Way 93505 760-373-5263
Harold Roney, prin. Fax 373-9028
California City MS 300/7-8
9736 Redwood Blvd 93505 760-373-3241
Suresh Bajnath, prin. Fax 373-1355

Calimesa, Riverside, Pop. 7,727
Yucaipa-Calimesa JUSD
Supt. — See Yucaipa
Mesa View MS 600/6-8
800 Mustang Way 92320 909-790-8008
Jim Stolze, prin. Fax 795-6810

Mesa Grande Academy 300/K-12
975 Fremont St 92320 909-795-1112
Alfred Riddle, prin. Fax 795-1653

Calipatria, Imperial, Pop. 7,613
Calipatria USD 1,100/K-12
501 W Main St 92233 760-348-2892
Douglas Kline, supt. Fax 344-8926
www.calipat.com
Calipatria HS 300/9-12
601 W Main St 92233 760-348-2254
Joe Derma, prin. Fax 348-2431
Young MS 400/5-8
220 S International Blvd 92233 760-348-2842
Virginia Calsada-Medina, prin. Fax 348-2848

Calistoga, Napa, Pop. 5,085
Calistoga JUSD 900/K-12
1520 Lake St 94515 707-942-4703
Dr. Esmeralda Mondragon, supt. Fax 942-6589
www.calistoga.k12.ca.us
Calistoga JSHS 400/7-12
1608 Lake St 94515 707-942-6278
Richard Savage, prin. Fax 942-6592
Palisades HS 50/Alt
1507 Grant St 94515 707-942-5255
Richard Savage, prin. Fax 942-5255

Camarillo, Ventura, Pop. 63,018
Oxnard UNHSD
Supt. — See Oxnard
Camarillo HS 2,400/9-12
4660 Mission Oaks Blvd 93012 805-389-6407
Glenn Lipman, prin. Fax 484-8087
Frontier HS 400/Alt
545 Airport Way 93010 805-389-6450
Wayne Lamas, prin. Fax 389-6466

Pleasant Valley SD 7,000/K-8
600 Temple Ave 93010 805-482-2763
Dr. Luis Villegas, supt. Fax 987-5511
www.pvsd.k12.ca.us
Las Colinas MS 1,000/6-8
5750 Fieldcrest Dr 93012 805-484-0461
Pam Gonzalez, prin. Fax 482-2443
Monte Vista MS 900/6-8
888 Lantana St 93010 805-482-8891
Joseph Herzog, prin. Fax 987-8951

Regional Occupational Center & Program
Supt. — None
Ventura County ROP Vo/Tech
465 Horizon Way 93010 805-388-4423
Peggy Velarde, dir. Fax 388-4428

California State University-Channel Isle Post-Sec.
1 University Dr 93012 805-437-8400
Saint John's Seminary Post-Sec.
5012 Seminary Rd 93012 805-482-2755

Cambria, San Luis Obispo, Pop. 5,934
Coast USD 800/K-12
1350 Main St 93428 805-927-3880
Chris Adams, supt. Fax 927-0312
www.coastusd.org
Coast Union HS 200/9-12
2950 Santa Rosa Creek Rd 93428 805-927-3889
Wade Lawrence, prin. Fax 924-2933
Leffingwell Continuation HS 50/Alt
2820 Santa Rosa Creek Rd 93428 805-927-7148
Wade Lawrence, prin. Fax 927-6741
Santa Lucia MS 200/6-8
2850 Schoolhouse Ln 93428 805-927-3693
John Calandro, prin. Fax 927-4615

Cameron Park, El Dorado, Pop. 17,664
Buckeye UNSD
Supt. — See Shingle Springs
Camerado Springs MS 600/6-8
2480 Merrychase Dr 95682 530-677-1658
Meg Enns, prin. Fax 677-9537

Campbell, Santa Clara, Pop. 37,545
Campbell UNESD 7,500/K-8
155 N 3rd St 95008 408-364-4200
Dr. Eric Andrew, supt. Fax 341-7280
www.campbellusd.org
Campbell MS 700/5-8
295 Cherry Ln 95008 408-364-4222
April Mouton, prin. Fax 341-7150
Other Schools – See Los Gatos, San Jose

Campbell UNHSD
Supt. — See San Jose
Westmont HS 1,700/9-12
4805 Westmont Ave 95008 408-626-3406
Fax 379-1720

The International Culinary Center Post-Sec.
700 W Hamilton Ave 95008 866-318-2433

Canoga Park, See Los Angeles
Los Angeles USD
Supt. — See Los Angeles
Canoga Park HS 1,800/9-12
6850 Topanga Canyon Blvd 91303 818-673-1300
Luis Rodriguez, prin. Fax 702-8942
Columbus MS 900/6-8
22250 Elkwood St 91304 818-702-1200
Anne Allocca, prin. Fax 348-2894
Owensmouth Continuation HS 100/Alt
6921 Jordan Ave 91303 818-340-7663
Matthew Klinefelter, prin. Fax 340-2947
Sutter MS 1,400/6-8
7330 Winnetka Ave 91306 818-773-5800
David Gonzalez, prin. Fax 341-3039

AGBU Manoogian-Demirdjian S 800/PK-12
6844 Oakdale Ave 91306 818-883-2428
Hagop Hagopian, prin. Fax 883-8353
Faith Baptist S 1,300/PK-12
7644 Farralone Ave 91304 818-340-6131
Dr. Stephania Rasmussen, prin. Fax 592-0279

Canyon Country, See Santa Clarita
William S. Hart UNHSD
Supt. — See Santa Clarita
Canyon HS 2,500/9-12
19300 Nadal St 91351 661-252-6110
Mike Kuhlman, prin. Fax 251-1419
Sierra Vista JHS 1,200/7-8
19425 Stillmore St 91351 661-252-3113
Mark Crawford, prin. Fax 250-8157

Charter College Canyon Country Post-Sec.
27125 Sierra Hwy Ste 329 91351 661-252-1864
Santa Clarita Christian S 600/K-12
27249 Luther Dr 91351 661-252-7371
Kirk Huckabone, admin. Fax 252-4354

Capitola, Santa Cruz, Pop. 9,578
Regional Occupational Center & Program
Supt. — None
Santa Cruz County ROP Vo/Tech
809 Bay Ave Ste H 95010 831-479-5335
Brian Wall, dir. Fax 479-5333

Soquel UNESD 1,900/K-8
620 Monterey Ave 95010 831-464-5633
Henry Castaniada, supt. Fax 475-5196
www.soqueldo.santacruz.k12.ca.us/
New Brighton MS 700/6-8
250 Washburn Ave 95010 831-464-5660
Craig Broadhurst, prin. Fax 475-8236

Carlsbad, San Diego, Pop. 101,706
Carlsbad USD 11,000/K-12
6225 El Camino Real 92009 760-331-5000
Suzette Lovely, supt. Fax 431-6707
www.carlsbadusd.k12.ca.us
Aviara Oaks MS 1,000/6-8
6225 El Camino Real 92009 760-331-6100
Megan Coelho, prin. Fax 729-3040
Calavera Hills MS 600/6-8
6225 El Camino Real 92009 760-331-6400
Kimberly Huesing, prin. Fax 729-3040
Carlsbad HS 3,000/9-12
6225 El Camino Real 92009 760-331-5100
Matthew Steitz, prin. Fax 729-6830
Carlsbad Seaside Academy 50/Alt
6225 El Camino Real 92009 760-331-5100
Matthew Steitz, prin. Fax 729-1791
Carlsbad Village Academy 100/Alt
6225 El Camino Real 92009 760-331-5100
Matthew Steitz, prin. Fax 729-1791
Valley MS 1,000/6-8
6225 El Camino Real 92009 760-331-5300
Thomas Bloomquist, prin. Fax 720-2326

San Dieguito UNHSD
Supt. — See Encinitas
La Costa Canyon HS 2,400/9-12
1 Maverick Way 92009 760-436-6136
Kyle Ruggles, prin. Fax 943-3539

Applied Professional Training Post-Sec.
PO Box 131717 92013 800-431-8488
Army and Navy Academy 300/7-12
PO Box 3000 92018 760-729-2385
Stephen Bliss, pres. Fax 434-5948
Gemological Institute of America Post-Sec.
5345 Armada Dr 92008 760-603-4000
Golf Academy of America Post-Sec.
1950 Camino Vida Roble #125 92008 760-734-1208
Pacific Ridge S 400/7-12
6269 El Fuerte St 92009 760-448-9820
Dr. Eileen Mullady, head sch

Carmel, Monterey, Pop. 3,645
Carmel USD 2,300/K-12
PO Box 222700 93922 831-624-1546
Marvin Biasotti, supt. Fax 626-4052
www.carmelunified.org
Carmel HS 700/9-12
PO Box 222780 93922 831-624-1821
Rick Lopez, prin. Fax 626-4313
Carmel MS 500/6-8
PO Box 222740 93922 831-624-2785
Ken Griest, prin. Fax 624-0839
Carmel Valley HS 50/Alt
PO Box 222700 93922 831-624-4462
Tom Stewart, prin. Fax 624-4487
Carmel Adult Education Adult
PO Box 222700 93922 831-624-1714
Craig Beller, prin. Fax 624-8747

Carmichael, Sacramento, Pop. 58,920
San Juan USD 43,900/PK-12
PO Box 477 95609 916-971-7700
Glynn Thompson, supt. Fax 971-7758
www.sanjuan.edu
Barrett MS 900/6-8
4243 Barrett Rd 95608 916-971-7842
Lisa Herstrom-Smith, prin. Fax 971-7839
Churchill MS 1,000/6-8
4900 Whitney Ave 95608 916-971-7324
Michael Dolan, prin. Fax 971-7856
Other Schools – See Citrus Heights, Fair Oaks, Orangevale, Sacramento

---

Jesuit HS 1,100/9-12
1200 Jacob Ln 95608 916-482-6060
Brianna Latko, prin. Fax 482-2310
Sacramento Adventist Academy 200/PK-12
5601 Winding Way 95608 916-481-2300
John Soule M.A., prin. Fax 481-7426
Victory Christian S 200/K-12
3045 Garfield Ave 95608 916-488-5601
John Huffman, prin. Fax 488-2589

Carpinteria, Santa Barbara, Pop. 12,835
Carpinteria USD 2,300/K-12
1400 Linden Ave 93013 805-684-4511
Paul Cordeiro, supt. Fax 684-0218
www.cusd.net
Carpinteria HS 700/9-12
4810 Foothill Rd 93013 805-684-4107
Gerardo Cornejo, prin. Fax 566-5952
Carpinteria MS 500/6-8
5351 Carpinteria Ave 93013 805-684-4544
John Merritt, prin. Fax 566-3839
Foothill Alternative HS 50/Alt
4698 Foothill Rd 93013 805-684-3277
Kristin Mayville, prin. Fax 566 9707
Rincon Continuation S 50/Alt
4698 Foothill Rd 93013 805-684-3277
Kristin Mayville, prin. Fax 566-9707

Cate S 300/9-12
1960 Cate Mesa Rd 93013 805-684-4127
Benjamin Williams, hdmstr. Fax 684-8940
International Sports Sciences Post-Sec.
1015 Mark Ave 93013 805-745-8111
Pacifica Graduate Institute Post-Sec.
249 Lambert Rd 93013 805-969-3626

Carson, Los Angeles, Pop. 87,081
Long Beach USD
Supt. — See Long Beach
California Academy of Math & Science 600/9-12
1000 E Victoria St 90747 310-243-2025
Janice Filer, prin. Fax 516-4041

Los Angeles USD
Supt. — See Los Angeles
Academy of Education and Empowerment 9-12
22328 Main St 90745 310-847-6000
Michelle Bryant, prin.
Academy of Medical Arts at Carson HS 9-12
22328 Main St 90745 310-847-6000
Leah Levy, prin.
Carnegie MS 1,400/6-8
21820 Bonita St 90745 310-952-5700
Verna Stroud, prin. Fax 830-9015
Carson HS 3,300/9-12
22328 Main St 90745 310-847-6000
Windy Warren, prin. Fax 518-5817
Curtiss MS 800/6-8
1254 E Helmick St 90746 310-661-4500
Gina Russell-Williams, prin. Fax 537-2115
Eagle Tree Continuation S 100/Alt
22628 Main St 90745 310-549-0970
Edmund Johnson, prin. Fax 518-5746
White MS 1,800/6-8
22102 Figueroa St 90745 310-783-4900
Edna Burems, prin. Fax 782-8954

Bethel Baptist S 50/K-12
1361 E Carson St 90745 310-522-4450
Rudolph Abrot, admin. Fax 522-4404
California State Univ.-Dominguez Hills Post-Sec.
1000 E Victoria St 90747 310-243-3300

Caruthers, Fresno, Pop. 2,460
Caruthers USD 1,300/K-12
PO Box 127 93609 559-864-6500
Orin Hirschkorn, supt. Fax 864-8857
www.caruthers.k12.ca.us
Caruthers HS 500/9-12
PO Box 545 93609 559-864-6500
Mark Fowler, prin. Fax 864-8303
MARC HS, PO Box 545 93609 50/Alt
Tyson Lowry, dir. 559-495-6443

Castaic, Los Angeles, Pop. 18,337
Castaic UNESD
Supt. — See Valencia
Castaic MS 1,100/6-8
28900 Hillcrest Pkwy 91384 661-257-4550
Ellen Edeburn, prin. Fax 294-9714

Castro Valley, Alameda, Pop. 58,286
Castro Valley USD 9,000/K-12
PO Box 2146 94546 510-537-3000
Jim Negri, supt. Fax 886-8962
www.cv.k12.ca.us
Canyon MS 1,300/6-8
19600 Cull Canyon Rd 94552 510-538-8833
Mark Croghan, prin. Fax 247-9439
Castro Valley HS 3,000/9-12
19400 Santa Maria Ave 94546 510-537-5910
Mary Ann Valles, prin. Fax 582-3924
Creekside MS 800/6-8
19722 Center St 94546 510-247-0665
Mary Ann DeGrazia, prin. Fax 581-6617
Redwood HS 100/Alt
18400 Clifton Way 94546 510-537-3193
Suzanne Williams, prin. Fax 247-3397
Castro Valley Adult S Adult
4430 Alma Ave 94546 510-886-1000
Jerry Green, dir. Fax 537-8537

Castroville, Monterey, Pop. 6,411
North Monterey County USD
Supt. — See Moss Landing
North Monterey County HS 1,300/9-12
13990 Castroville Blvd 95012 831-633-5221
Antonio Vela, prin. Fax 633-2520
North Monterey County MS 600/7-8
10301 Seymour St 95012 831-633-3391
David Burke, prin. Fax 633-3680

Cathedral City, Riverside, Pop. 50,401
Palm Springs USD
Supt. — See Palm Springs
Cathedral City HS 2,800/9-12
69250 Dinah Shore Dr 92234 760-770-0100
Guillermo Chavez, prin. Fax 770-0149
Coffman MS 1,100/6-8
34603 Plumley Rd 92234 760-770-8617
Lucinda Killebrew, prin. Fax 770-8623
Mt. San Jacinto Continuation HS 500/Alt
30800 Landau Blvd 92234 760-770-8563
Milt Jones, prin. Fax 770-8568
Workman MS 1,500/6-8
69300 30th Ave 92234 760-770-8540
Brad Sauer, prin. Fax 770-8545

Mayfield College Post-Sec.
35325 Date Palm Dr Ste 101 92234 760-328-5554

Cedarville, Modoc, Pop. 502
Surprise Valley JUSD 100/K-12
PO Box 100 96104 530-279-6141
Don Demsher, supt. Fax 279-2210
www.svjusd.org
Surprise Valley HS 50/9-12
PO Box 100 96104 530-279-6141
Michael Ray, prin. Fax 279-2210

Central Valley, Shasta, Pop. 4,340
Gateway USD
Supt. — See Redding
Central Valley HS 800/9-12
4066 La Mesa Ave 96019 530-275-7075
Ryan Johnson, prin. Fax 275-7065

Ceres, Stanislaus, Pop. 43,964
Ceres USD 11,600/K-12
PO Box 307 95307 209-556-1500
Scott Siegel, supt. Fax 556-1090
www.ceres.k12.ca.us
Argus HS 300/Alt
PO Box 307 95307 209-556-1800
Jan Gordon, prin. Fax 538-1027
Blaker-Kinser JHS 800/7-8
PO Box 307 95307 209-556-1810
Kristi Britton, prin. Fax 541-0174
Central Valley HS 1,700/9-12
PO Box 307 95307 209-556-1900
Amy Peterman, prin. Fax 531-2748
Ceres HS 1,400/9-12
PO Box 307 95307 209-556-1920
Linda Stubbs, prin. Fax 538-8978
Chavez JHS 7-8
PO Box 307 95307 209-556-1830
Jose Beltran, prin. Fax 538-3970
Hensley JHS 900/7-8
PO Box 307 95307 209-556-1820
Carol Lubinsky, prin. Fax 538-9428

Central Valley Christian Academy 300/PK-12
2020 Academy Pl 95307 209-537-4521
Wayne Dunbar, prin. Fax 538-0706

Cerritos, Los Angeles, Pop. 47,521
ABC USD 20,500/K-12
16700 Norwalk Blvd 90703 562-926-5566
Mary Sieu, supt. Fax 404-1092
www.abcusd.k12.ca.us
Carmenita MS 700/7-8
13435 166th St 90703 562-926-4405
Kester Song, prin. Fax 404-7807
Cerritos HS 2,100/9-12
12500 183rd St 90703 562-926-5566
Janice Peterson, prin. Fax 924-3187
Gahr HS 2,100/9-12
11111 Artesia Blvd 90703 562-926-5566
Gina Zietlow, prin. Fax 924-8136
Haskell MS 600/7-8
11525 Del Amo Blvd 90703 562-860-6529
Camille Lewis, prin. Fax 809-7250
Tetzlaff MS 600/7-8
12351 Del Amo Blvd 90703 562-865-9539
Crechena Wise, prin. Fax 402-6412
Tracy Continuation HS 500/Alt
12222 Cuesta Dr 90703 562-926-7136
Jeff Green, prin. Fax 926-8740
Whitney JSHS 1,000/7-12
16800 Shoemaker Ave 90703 562-229-7745
Rhonda Buss Ed.D., prin. Fax 926-2751
ABC Adult HS Adult
12254 Cuesta Dr 90703 562-229-7960
Pao-Ling Guo, prin. Fax 921-9958
Other Schools – See Artesia, Hawaiian Gardens, Lakewood

Fremont College Post-Sec.
18000 Studebaker Rd # 900A 90703 800-373-6668
PCI College Post-Sec.
17215 Studebaker Rd Ste 310 90703 562-916-5055
Valley Christian HS 600/9-12
17700 Dumont Ave 90703 562-865-0281
Jeffrey Hoogeveen, prin. Fax 865-0082
Valley Christian MS 200/7-8
18100 Dumont Ave 90703 562-865-6519
Paul Theule, prin. Fax 403-3159

Chatsworth, See Los Angeles
Los Angeles USD
Supt. — See Los Angeles
Aggeler Community Day S 100/Alt
21050 Plummer St 91311 818-341-1232
Odus Caldwell, prin. Fax 349-1404
Chatsworth HS 2,900/9-12
10027 Lurline Ave 91311 818-678-3400
Timothy Guy, prin. Fax 709-6952
Lawrence MS 1,700/6-8
10100 Variel Ave 91311 818-678-7900
Danford Schar, prin. Fax 349-4539
Stoney Point Continuation HS 100/Alt
10010 De Soto Ave 91311 818-678-3491
George Padgett, prin. Fax 773-1796

Chaminade College Prep MS 700/6-8
19800 Devonshire St 91311 818-363-8127
Mike Valentine, prin. Fax 363-1219
Phillips Graduate Institute Post-Sec.
19900 Plummer St 91311 818-386-5600
Sierra Canyon HS 300/7-12
20801 Rinaldi St 91311 818-882-8121
James Skrumbis, hdmstr. Fax 534-2398
Univ of West Los Angeles School of Law Post-Sec.
9201 Oakdale Ave Ste 201 91311 818-775-4500

Chester, Plumas, Pop. 2,075
Plumas USD
Supt. — See Quincy
Almanor HS 50/Alt
PO Box 797 96020 530-258-2126
Aurora Westwood, prin. Fax 258-2306
Chester JSHS 200/7-12
PO Box 797 96020 530-258-2126
Jeff James, prin. Fax 258-2306

Chico, Butte, Pop. 82,892
Chico USD 12,900/K-12
1163 E 7th St 95928 530-891-3000
Kelly Staley, supt. Fax 891-3220
www.chicousd.org
Academy for Change 100/Alt
290 East Ave 95926 530-895-4047
David McKay, prin. Fax 895-4048
Bidwell JHS 700/7-8
2376 North Ave 95926 530-891-3080
Judi Roth, prin. Fax 891-3082
Chico HS 1,800/9-12
901 Esplanade 95926 530-891-3026
Jim Hanlon, prin. Fax 891-3284
Chico JHS 600/7-8
280 Memorial Way 95926 530-891-3066
Pedro Caldera, prin. Fax 891-3264
Fair View HS 200/Alt
290 East Ave 95926 530-891-3092
David McKay, prin. Fax 891-3232
Marsh JHS 600/7-8
2253 Humboldt Rd 95928 530-895-4110
Jay Marchant, prin. Fax 895-4111
Pleasant Valley HS 1,900/9-12
1475 East Ave 95926 530-879-5100
John Shepherd, prin. Fax 879-5263

Regional Occupational Center & Program
Supt. — None
Butte County ROP Vo/Tech
2491 Carmichael Dr Ste 100 95928 530-879-7457
Paul Watters, dir. Fax 879-7458

California State University-Chico Post-Sec.
400 W 1st St 95929 530-898-6116

Chino, San Bernardino, Pop. 76,369
Chino Valley USD 30,000/K-12
5130 Riverside Dr 91710 909-628-1201
Wayne Joseph, supt. Fax 548-6096
www.chino.k12.ca.us
Buena Vista Continuation HS 200/Alt
13509 Ramona Ave 91710 909-628-9903
Rigoberto Vasquez, prin. Fax 548-6027
Chino HS 2,700/9-12
5472 Park Pl 91710 909-627-7351
Felix Melendez, prin. Fax 548-6004
Lugo HS 2,300/9-12
13400 Pipeline Ave 91710 909-591-3902
Don Jones, prin. Fax 548-6020
Magnolia JHS 800/7-8
13150 Mountain Ave 91710 909-627-9263
Melody Kohn, prin. Fax 627-2165

Ramona JHS 800/7-8
4575 Walnut Ave 91710 909-627-9144
Fax 548-6055

Chino Community Adult Adult
5130 Riverside Dr 91710 909-628-1201
Rick Landorf, prin. Fax 548-6016
Other Schools – See Chino Hills, Ontario

Chino Valley Christian S 300/PK-12
4166 Riverside Dr 91710 909-613-1381
Dr. Eugene Huang, pres. Fax 613-1383

Chino Hills, San Bernardino, Pop. 72,538
Chino Valley USD
Supt. — See Chino
Ayala HS 2,500/9-12
14255 Peyton Dr 91709 909-627-3584
Diana Yarboi, prin. Fax 464-9239
Boy's Republic HS 100/Alt
1907 Boys Republic Dr 91709 909-628-1217
Rick Landorf, prin. Fax 628-9847
Canyon Hills JHS 1,100/7-8
2500 Madrugada Dr 91709 909-464-9938
Mike Finkbiner, prin. Fax 548-6058
Chino Hills HS 2,900/9-12
16150 Pomona Rincon Rd 91709 909-606-7540
Jacqueline Perez, prin. Fax 548-6041
Townsend JHS 1,200/7-8
15359 Ilex Dr 91709 909-591-2161
Sharyn MacCharles, prin. Fax 548-6057

Chowchilla, Madera, Pop. 17,893
Alview-Dairyland UNESD 400/K-8
12861 Avenue 18 1/2 93610 559-665-2394
Lori Flanagan, supt. Fax 665-7347
www.adusd.k12.ca.us
Dairyland MS 200/4-8
12861 Avenue 18 1/2 93610 559-665-2394
Lori Flanagan, prin. Fax 665-7347

Chowchilla ESD 2,100/K-8
PO Box 910 93610 559-665-8000
Dr. Charles Martin, supt. Fax 665-3036
www.chowchillaelem.k12.ca.us
Wilson MS 400/7-8
PO Box 910 93610 559-665-8070
Jennifer Euker, prin. Fax 665-8004

Chowchilla UNHSD 1,000/9-12
805 Humboldt Ave 93610 559-665-1331
Ronald Seals, supt. Fax 665-4659
www.chowchillahigh.k12.ca.us
Chowchilla HS 1,000/9-12
805 Humboldt Ave 93610 559-665-1331
Fred Cogan, prin. Fax 665-1074
Gateway Continuation HS 50/Alt
805 Humboldt Ave 93610 559-665-1331
Michelle Irwin, prin. Fax 665-2220
Chowchilla Adult/ISP Adult
805 Humboldt Ave 93610 559-665-5683
Michelle Irwin, prin.

Madera County Office of Education
Supt. — See Madera
Discovery Secondary S 50/Alt
345 S 11th St 93610 559-665-3204
Steve Carney, prin. Fax 674-8737

Chula Vista, San Diego, Pop. 235,860
Sweetwater UNHSD 38,800/7-12
1130 5th Ave 91911 619-691-5500
Dr. Edward Brand, supt. Fax 498-1997
www.sweetwaterschools.org
Bonita Vista HS 2,300/9-12
751 Otay Lakes Rd 91913 619-397-2000
Bettina Batista, prin. Fax 656-1203
Bonita Vista MS 1,100/7-8
650 Otay Lakes Rd 91910 619-397-2200
V. Sandoval-Johnson, prin. Fax 482-9356
Castle Park HS 1,600/9-12
1395 Hilltop Dr 91911 619-585-2000
Thomas Glover, prin. Fax 427-5967
Castle Park MS 1,100/7-8
160 Quintard St 91911 619-498-6000
Robert Bleisch, prin. Fax 427-8045
Chula Vista HS 2,700/9-12
820 4th Ave 91911 619-476-3300
Steven Lizarraga, prin. Fax 427-5824
Chula Vista MS 1,200/7-8
415 5th Ave 91910 619-498-6800
Viky Mitrovich, prin. Fax 427-5723
Eastlake HS 2,500/9-12
1120 Eastlake Pkwy 91915 619-397-3800
Maria Esther Lizarraga, prin. Fax 656-9736
Eastlake MS 1,600/7-8
900 Duncan Ranch Rd 91914 619-591-4000
Juan Ulloa, prin. Fax 482-0553
Hilltop HS 2,200/9-12
555 Claire Ave 91910 619-476-4200
Ernesto Zamudio, prin. Fax 425-3284
Hilltop MS 1,100/7-8
44 E J St 91910 619-498-2700
Maribel Gavin, prin. Fax 585-3576
Olympian HS 1,700/9-12
1925 Magdalena Ave 91913 619-656-2400
Elaine Elefante-Leano, prin. Fax 216-0650
Options Secondary S 300/Alt
467 Moss St 91911 619-585-7896
Fax 420-5663
Otay Ranch HS 2,700/9-12
1250 Olympic Pkwy 91913 619-591-5000
Jose Brosz, prin. Fax 591-5010
Palomar Continuation HS 400/Alt
480 Palomar St 91911 619-407-4800
Griselda Delgado, prin. Fax 585-6232
Rancho del Rey MS 1,600/7-8
1174 E J St 91910 619-397-2500
William Walsh, prin. Fax 656-3810

Chula Vista Adult S Adult
1034 4th Ave 91911 619-796-7000
Jan Godfrey Ed.D., prin. Fax 425-5447
Other Schools – See Imperial Beach, National City, San Diego, San Ysidro

---

Calvary Christian Academy 500/PK-12
1771 E Palomar St 91913 619-591-2260
Dr. Richard Andujo, hdmstr. Fax 591-2261
Covenant Christian S 100/K-12
505 E Naples St 91911 619-421-8822
Thomas McManus, admin. Fax 216-9846
Kaplan College Post-Sec.
555 Broadway Ste 144 91910 619-498-4100
Lutheran HS of San Diego 100/9-12
810 Buena Vista Way 91910 619-262-4444
Scott Dufresne M.A., dir. Fax 691-0424
Mater Dei Catholic HS 700/9-12
PO Box 210760 91921 619-423-2121
George Milke, prin. Fax 423-6910
Pima Medical Institute Post-Sec.
780 Bay Blvd Ste 101 91910 619-425-3200
Southwestern College Post-Sec.
900 Otay Lakes Rd 91910 619-421-6700
United States University Post-Sec.
830 Bay Blvd 91911 619-477-6310

Citrus Heights, Sacramento, Pop. 79,798
San Juan USD
Supt. — See Carmichael
Mesa Verde HS 1,100/9-12
7501 Carriage Dr 95621 916-971-5288
Rick Messer, prin. Fax 971-5215
New San Juan HS 600/9-12
7551 Greenback Ln 95610 916-971-5112
Gloria Ervin, prin. Fax 971-5111
Sylvan MS 500/7-8
7137 Auburn Blvd 95610 916-971-7873
Kristen Schnepp, prin. Fax 971-7896
Sunrise Tech Center Adult
7322 Sunrise Blvd 95610 916-971-7654
Bill Bettencourt, prin. Fax 971-7695

Carrington College California Post-Sec.
7301 Greenback Ln Bldg A 95621 916-722-8200
Institute of Technology - Citrus Heights Post-Sec.
6249 Sunrise Blvd 95610 877-887-8007

City of Industry, Los Angeles, Pop. 217
Bassett USD
Supt. — See La Puente
Torch MS 800/6-8
904 Willow Ave 91746 626-931-2700
Berenice Rios, prin. Fax 931-2702

Hacienda La Puente USD 20,700/K-12
PO Box 60002 91716 626-933-1000
Dr. Barbara Nakaoka, supt. Fax 855-3505
www.hlpschools.org
Workman HS 1,200/9-12
16303 Temple Ave 91744 626-933-8800
Yvette Meneses, prin. Fax 855-3148
Other Schools – See Hacienda Heights, La Puente

Regional Occupational Center & Program
Supt. — None
La Puente Valley ROP Vo/Tech
18501 Gale Ave Ste 100 91748 626-810-3300
Esperanza Fernandez, supt. Fax 581-9108

Elegante Beauty College Post-Sec.
1600 S Azusa Ave Unit 244 91748 626-965-2532
Everest College Post-Sec.
12801 Crossroads Pkwy S 91746 562-908-2500

Claremont, Los Angeles, Pop. 33,627
Claremont USD 7,100/K-12
170 W San Jose Ave 91711 909-398-0609
James Elsasser Ed.D., supt. Fax 398-0690
www.cusd.claremont.edu
Claremont HS 2,400/9-12
1601 N Indian Hill Blvd 91711 909-624-9053
Brett O'Connor, prin. Fax 624-2128
Community Day S 50/Alt
125 W San Jose Ave 91711 909-398-0316
Steven Boyd, prin. Fax 398-0384
El Roble IS 1,100/7-8
665 N Mountain Ave 91711 909-398-0343
Scott Martinez, prin. Fax 398-0399
San Antonio HS 100/Alt
125 W San Jose Ave 91711 909-398-0316
Steven Boyd, prin. Fax 398-0384
Claremont Adult S Adult
170 W San Jose Ave Ste 100 91711 909-398-0609
Steven Boyd, prin. Fax 626-5109

Claremont Graduate University Post-Sec.
150 E 10th St 91711 909-621-8000
Claremont McKenna College Post-Sec.
500 E 9th St 91711 909-621-8000
Claremont School of Theology Post-Sec.
1325 N College Ave 91711 909-447-2500
Harvey Mudd College Post-Sec.
301 Platt Blvd 91711 909-621-8000
Keck Graduate Institute Post-Sec.
535 Watson Dr 91711 909-607-7855
Pitzer College Post-Sec.
1050 N Mills Ave 91711 909-621-8219
Pomona College Post-Sec.
333 N College Way 91711 909-621-8000
Scripps College Post-Sec.
1030 Columbia Ave 91711 909-621-8000
Webb S 400/9-12
1175 W Baseline Rd 91711 909-626-3587
Taylor Stockdale, head sch Fax 621-4582

Clarksburg, Yolo, Pop. 410
River Delta USD
Supt. — See Rio Vista
Clarksburg MS 100/7-9
PO Box 99 95612 916-744-1717
Laura Uslan, prin. Fax 744-5704
Delta HS 100/10-12
PO Box 100 95612 916-744-1714
Laura Uslan, prin. Fax 744-1673

Clayton, Contra Costa, Pop. 10,503
Mount Diablo USD
Supt. — See Concord
Diablo View MS 600/6-8
300 Diablo View Ln 94517 925-672-0898
Patti Bannister, prin. Fax 672-4327

Clearlake, Lake, Pop. 14,540
Konocti USD
Supt. — See Lower Lake
Highlands Academy 100/Alt
15850 Dam Road Ext 95422 707-994-6447
James Burger, prin. Fax 994-5047

Lake County Office of Education
Supt. — See Lakeport
Clearlake Community S 50/Alt
6945 Old Highway 53 95422 707-995-9523
Andrew Goodwin, dir. Fax 995-9059
Hance Community S 50/Alt
6945 Old Highway 53 95422 707-995-9523
Andrew Goodwin, lead tchr. Fax 263-6262

Cloverdale, Sonoma, Pop. 8,447
Cloverdale USD 1,500/PK-12
97 School St 95425 707-894-1920
Steven L. Jorgensen, supt. Fax 894-1922
www.cusd.org/
Cloverdale HS 500/9-12
509 N Cloverdale Blvd 95425 707-894-1900
Theresa Burke, prin. Fax 894-4804
Echols-Hansen Continuation HS 50/Alt
322 N Washington St 95425 707-894-1925
Theresa Burke, prin.
Washington MS 500/4-8
129 S Washington St 95425 707-894-1940
Ashley Tatman, prin. Fax 894-1946

Clovis, Fresno, Pop. 92,614
Clovis USD 37,200/K-12
1450 Herndon Ave 93611 559-327-9000
Janet Young Ed.D., supt. Fax 327-9109
www.cusd.com
Alta Sierra IS 1,400/7-8
380 W Teague Ave, 559-327-3500
Steve Pagani, prin. Fax 327-3590
Buchanan HS 2,500/9-12
1560 N Minnewawa Ave, 559-327-3000
Ricci Ulrich, prin. Fax 327-3090
Clark IS 1,400/7-8
902 5th St 93612 559-327-1500
Scott Steele, prin. Fax 327-1556
Clovis Community Day Secondary S 50/Alt
1715 David E Cook Way 93611 559-327-1980
Tom Judd, prin. Fax 327-1989
Clovis East HS 2,200/9-12
2940 Leonard Ave, 559-327-4000
Darin Tockey, prin. Fax 327-4190
Clovis HS 2,800/9-12
1055 Fowler Ave 93611 559-327-1000
Pam Winter, prin. Fax 327-1010
Enterprise S Alt
1550 Herndon Ave 93611 559-327-1800
Rees Warne, prin.
Gateway HS 300/Alt
1550 Herndon Ave 93611 559-327-1800
Rees Warne, prin. Fax 327-1890
Reyburn IS 1,100/7-8
2901 De Wolf Ave, 559-327-4500
Darin Tockey, prin. Fax 327-4791
Clovis Adult S Adult
1452 David E Cook Way 93611 559-327-2800
Kevin Cookingham, prin. Fax 327-2889
Other Schools – See Fresno

Fresno USD
Supt. — See Fresno
C.A.R.T 11-12
2555 Clovis Ave 93612 559-248-7400
Devin Blizzard, prin. Fax 248-7423

Institute of Technology - Clovis Campus Post-Sec.
564 W Herndon Ave 93612 559-297-4500
ITT Technical Institute Post-Sec.
362 N Clovis Ave 93612 559-325-5400
Kaplan College Post-Sec.
44 Shaw Ave 93612 559-325-5101
Milan Institute Post-Sec.
731 W Shaw Ave 93612 559-323-2800
San Joaquin College of Law Post-Sec.
901 5th St 93612 559-323-2100
Tower Christian S 100/K-12
8753 Chickadee Ln, 559-298-2772
Ann Raber, admin. Fax 297-4348

Coachella, Riverside, Pop. 40,549
Coachella Valley USD
Supt. — See Thermal
Cahuilla Desert Academy 900/7-8
82489 Avenue 52 92236 760-398-0097
Encarnacion Becerra, prin. Fax 398-0088
Duke MS 700/7-8
85358 Bagdad Ave 92236 760-398-0139
Maria McLeod, prin. Fax 398-5399
Coachella Valley Adult Education Adult
1099 Orchard Ave 92236 760-398-6302
Jereme Weischedel, prin. Fax 398-0436

Coalinga, Fresno, Pop. 13,188
Coalinga - Huron JUSD 4,300/K-12
657 Sunset St 93210 559-935-7500
Roger Campbell, supt. Fax 935-5329
www.chjusd.org
Cambridge HS 100/Alt
516 Baker St 93210 559-935-7578
Royal Cash, prin. Fax 935-1692
Coalinga HS 1,100/9-12
750 Van Ness St 93210 559-935-7520
Margo Fisher, prin. Fax 935-3571
Coalinga MS 700/6-8
265 Cambridge Ave 93210 559-935-7550
Sabrina Greiten, prin. Fax 934-1311
Culwell Community Day S 50/Alt
275 Cambridge Ave 93210 559-935-7660
Royal Cash, prin. Fax 935-5601
Other Schools – See Huron

Faith Christian Academy 100/PK-12
450 W Elm Ave 93210 559-935-9209
Tara Davis, prin. Fax 935-0745
West Hills College Coalinga Post-Sec.
300 W Cherry Ln 93210 559-935-2000

Coarsegold, Madera, Pop. 1,773
Yosemite USD
Supt. — See Oakhurst
Foothill HS 50/Alt
43875 Patrick Ave 93614 559-658-8616
Dr. Randy Haggard, prin. Fax 658-2034
Meadowbrook Community Day S 50/Alt
45426 Road 415 93614 559-683-3533
Dr. Randy Haggard, prin. Fax 683-3533
Yosemite Falls Education Center 50/Alt
35572 Highway 41 93614 559-658-8801
Dr. Randy Haggard, prin. Fax 658-2359

Cobb, Lake, Pop. 1,722
Kelseyville USD
Supt. — See Kelseyville
Intermountain HS 50/Alt
13412 Bottle Rock Rd 95426 707-928-4831
Dave McQueen, prin. Fax 928-4653

Coleville, Mono, Pop. 479
Eastern Sierra USD
Supt. — See Bridgeport
Coleville HS 100/9-12
111591 US Highway 395 96107 530-495-2231
Steve Childs, prin. Fax 495-2730
Walker River HS 50/Alt
111591 US Highway 395 96107 530-495-2231
Jason Reid, prin. Fax 495-2730

Colfax, Placer, Pop. 1,892
Placer UNHSD
Supt. — See Auburn
Colfax HS 900/9-12
24995 Ben Taylor Rd 95713 530-346-2204
Rick Spears, prin. Fax 346-6476

Colma, San Mateo, Pop. 1,713
Jefferson ESD
Supt. — See Daly City
Franklin IS 400/7-8
700 Stewart Ave, Daly City CA 94015 650-991-1200
James Parrish, prin. Fax 756-5475

Colton, San Bernardino, Pop. 51,046
Colton JUSD 23,300/PK-12
1212 Valencia Dr 92324 909-580-5000
Jerry Almendarez, supt. Fax 433-9471
www.cjusd.net
Colton HS 3,400/9-12
777 W Valley Blvd 92324 909-580-5005
Amanda Corridan, prin. Fax 876-4093
Colton MS 1,000/7-8
670 W Laurel St 92324 909-580-5009
Chris Marin, prin. Fax 876-4095
Washington Alternative HS 200/Alt
900 E C St 92324 909-580-5011
Pete Tasaka, prin. Fax 876-6352
Other Schools – See Bloomington, Grand Terrace

Rialto USD
Supt. — See Rialto
Jehue MS 1,400/6-8
1500 N Eucalyptus Ave 92324 909-421-7377
Armando Urteaga, prin. Fax 421-7376

San Bernardino Co. Office of Education
Supt. — See San Bernardino
East Valley Community S 200/Alt
1060 E Cooley Dr 92324 909-433-4622
Bernadine Hollingsworth, dir. Fax 433-4823

Coast Career Institute Post-Sec.
1250 E Cooley Dr 92324 877-277-7170
DeVry University Post-Sec.
1090 E Washington St Ste H 92324 909-514-1808
Four-D College Post-Sec.
1020 E Washington St 92324 909-783-9331

Colusa, Colusa, Pop. 5,849
Colusa County Office of Education 100/
146 7th St 95932 530-458-0350
Kay Spurgeon, supt. Fax 458-8054
www.ccoe.net
Colusa County Community S 50/Alt
345 5th St Ste D 95932 530-458-0332
Ben Flores, admin. Fax 458-0339
Colusa County Opportunity S 50/Alt
345 5th St Ste D 95932 530-458-0330
Ben Flores, admin. Fax 458-0345

Colusa USD 1,300/K-12
745 10th St 95932 530-458-7791
Dwayne Newman, supt. Fax 458-4030
www.colusa.k12.ca.us
Colusa Alternative HS 50/Alt
817 Colus Ave 95932 530-458-2232
Darren Brown, prin. Fax 458-4070
Colusa HS 300/9-12
901 Colus Ave 95932 530-458-2156
Darren Brown, prin. Fax 458-5783
Egling MS 500/4-8
813 Webster St 95932 530-458-7631
Jody Johnston, prin. Fax 458-8107

Commerce, Los Angeles, Pop. 12,764

National Polytechnic College Post-Sec.
6630 Telegraph Rd 90040 866-800-0672

Compton, Los Angeles, Pop. 94,840
Compton USD 23,500/PK-12
501 S Santa Fe Ave 90221 310-639-4321
Dr. Carmella Franco, supt. Fax 632-3014
www.compton.k12.ca.us
Bunche MS 700/6-8
12338 S Mona Blvd 90222 310-898-6010
Dr. Michael Nkemnji, prin. Fax 638-4935
Centennial HS 1,200/9-12
2600 N Central Ave 90222 310-635-2715
Jesse Jones, prin. Fax 631-9164
Chavez Continuation HS 300/Alt
12501 S Wilmington Ave 90222 310-898-6340
Rudolph Washington, prin. Fax 763-4186
Community Day S 50/Alt
417 W Alondra Blvd 90220 310-898-6154
Rudolph Washington, prin. Fax 632-7304
Compton HS 2,400/9-12
601 S Acacia Ave 90220 310-635-3881
Letitia Bradley, prin. Fax 898-6402
Davis MS 1,000/6-8
621 W Poplar St 90220 310-898-6020
Senida Wade, prin. Fax 631-5725
Dominguez HS 2,100/9-12
15301 S San Jose Ave 90221 562-630-0142
Rigoberto Roman, prin. Fax 408-2367
Enterprise MS 500/6-8
2600 W Compton Blvd 90220 310-898-6030
Dr. Yvonne Smith, prin. Fax 632-4183
Marshall Alternative S 50/Alt
12501 S Wilmington Ave 90222 310-604-2780
Rudolph Washington, prin. Fax 223-0970
Roosevelt MS 1,000/6-8
1200 E Alondra Blvd 90221 310-898-6040
Dr. Edd Bond, prin. Fax 631-3298
Tubman Continuation HS 50/Alt
12501 S Wilmington Ave 90222 310-898-6340
Rudolph Washington, prin. Fax 763-4186
Walton MS 500/6-8
900 W Greenleaf Dr 90220 310-898-6060
Mark Jones, prin. Fax 631-3409
Whaley MS 800/6-8
14401 S Gibson Ave 90221 310-898-6070
Gipson Lyles, prin. Fax 638-7079
Willowbrook MS 400/6-8
2601 N Wilmington Ave 90222 310-898-6080
Fax 537-2932
Compton Adult S Adult
1104 E 148th St 90220 310-898-6490
Melanie Prince, admin. Fax 898-6477
Other Schools – See Los Angeles

Regional Occupational Center & Program
Supt. — None
Compton Unified ROP Vo/Tech
700 N Bullis Rd 90221 310-898-6000
Reena Singh, dir. Fax 763-3871

El Camino College Compton Center Post-Sec.
1111 E Artesia Blvd 90221 310-900-1600
St. Albert the Great MS 200/6-8
823 E Compton Blvd 90220 310-515-3891
Tina Johnson, prin. Fax 515-1413
Universal College of Beauty Post-Sec.
718 W Compton Blvd 90220 310-635-6969

Concord, Contra Costa, Pop. 116,303
Mount Diablo USD 31,200/PK-12
1936 Carlotta Dr 94519 925-682-8000
Steven Lawrence, supt. Fax 689-1649
www.mdusd.org
Concord HS 1,600/9-12
4200 Concord Blvd 94521 925-687-2030
Gary McAdam, prin. Fax 682-4613
Crossroads HS 100/Alt
2701 Willow Pass Rd 94519 925-689-6852
Pam Neudecker, admin. Fax 603-1771
Diablo Community Day S 50/Alt
1026 Mohr Ln 94518 925-676-6862
Linda Pete, admin. Fax 682-9352
El Dorado MS 900/6-8
1750 West St 94521 925-682-5700
Robert Humphrey, prin. Fax 685-1460
Mount Diablo HS 1,500/9-12
2450 Grant St 94520 925-682-4030
Kate McClatchy, prin. Fax 687-9658
Nueva Vista HS / Summit/TLC 50/Alt
4200 Concord Blvd 94521 925-689-1487
Edward Penca, prin. Fax 689-2134
Oak Grove MS 600/6-8
2050 Minert Rd 94518 925-682-1843
Lisa Oates, prin. Fax 682-2083
Olympic Continuation HS 400/Alt
2730 Salvio St 94519 925-687-0363
Mark Lopes, prin. Fax 798-6317
Pine Hollow MS 700/6-8
5522 Pine Hollow Rd 94521 925-672-5444
Shelley Bain, prin. Fax 672-9751

Summit HS 50/Alt
4200 Concord Blvd 94521 925-687-0991
Edward Penca, prin. Fax 603-1770
Ygnacio Valley HS 1,300/9-12
755 Oak Grove Rd 94518 925-685-8414
Susan Brothers, prin. Fax 685-1435
Mount Diablo Adult Center Adult
1266 San Carlos Ave 94518 925-685-7340
Joanne Durkee, dir. Fax 687-8217
Other Schools – See Bay Point, Clayton, Pleasant Hill, Walnut Creek

Carondelet HS 800/9-12
1133 Winton Dr 94518 925-686-5353
Nancy Libby, prin. Fax 671-9429
De La Salle HS 1,100/9-12
1130 Winton Dr 94518 925-288-8100
Br. Robert Wickman, prin. Fax 686-3474
Heald College Post-Sec.
5130 Commercial Cir 94520 925-288-5800
ITT Technical Institute Post-Sec.
1140 Galaxy Way Ste 400 94520 925-674-8200
Paris Beauty College Post-Sec.
1655 Willow Pass Rd 94520 925-685-7600

Corcoran, Kings, Pop. 24,292
Corcoran JUSD 3,200/PK-12
1520 Patterson Ave 93212 559-992-8888
Rich Merlo, supt. Fax 992-3957
www.corcoranunified.com/
Corcoran HS 1,000/9-12
1520 Patterson Ave 93212 559-992-8884
Chuck Gent, prin. Fax 992-5066
Kings Lake Education Center 50/Alt
1520 Patterson Ave 93212 559-992-8885
Mary Taylor, prin. Fax 992-4858
Muir MS 700/6-8
1520 Patterson Ave 93212 559-992-8886
Ken Spencer, prin. Fax 992-4423

Corning, Tehama, Pop. 7,468
Corning UNESD 1,700/K-8
1590 South St 96021 530-824-7700
Catherine Reimer Ed.D., supt. Fax 824-2493
www.corningelementary.org
Columbia Academy 50/Alt
1785 Columbia Ave 96021 530-824-7730
Diane Bailey, admin. Fax 824-7742
Maywood MS 400/7-8
1666 Marguerite Ave 96021 530-824-7730
Dave Cory, prin. Fax 824-7742

Corning UNHSD 900/9-12
643 Blackburn Ave 96021 530-824-8000
Bruce Cole, supt. Fax 824-8005
www.corninghs.org/
Centennial Continuation HS 100/Alt
250 E Fig Ln 96021 530-824-7400
Andrea Nilsen, prin. Fax 824-7405
Corning Community Day S 50/Alt
823 North St 96021 530-824-7140
Andrea Nilsen, prin. Fax 824-8005
Corning HS 900/9-12
643 Blackburn Ave 96021 530-824-8000
Charlie Troughton, prin. Fax 824-8005

Corona, Riverside, Pop. 147,939
Corona-Norco USD
Supt. — See Norco
Auburndale IS 800/7-8
1255 River Rd 92880 951-736-3231
Rob Ibbetson, prin. Fax 736-3360
Centennial HS 3,000/9-12
1820 Rimpau Ave 92881 951-739-5670
Ben Roberts, prin. Fax 739-5693
Citrus Hills IS 1,500/7-8
3211 S Main St 92882 951-736-4600
Andrew Roberts, prin. Fax 736-4623
Corona Fundamental IS 1,200/7-8
1230 S Main St 92882 951-736-3321
Dr. Gina Boster, prin. Fax 736-3417
Corona HS 3,200/9-12
1150 W 10th St 92882 951-736-3211
Dr. Danny Kim, prin. Fax 736-3408
El Cerrito MS 1,000/6-8
7610 El Cerrito Rd 92881 951-736-3216
Shelly Yarbrough, prin. Fax 736-3286
Orange Grove HS 200/Alt
300 S Buena Vista Ave 92882 951-736-3339
Joe Almasy, prin. Fax 736-3435
Pollard HS 800/Alt
185 Magnolia Ave 92879 951-736-3367
Mike Ridgway, prin. Fax 736-7104
Raney IS 1,400/6-8
1010 W Citron St 92882 951-736-3221
Elizabeth Moore, prin. Fax 736-3439
Santiago HS 3,800/9-12
1395 Foothill Pkwy 92881 951-739-5600
Reginald Thompkins, prin. Fax 739-5639
Corona-Norco Adult Education Adult
300 S Buena Vista Ave 92882 951-736-3325
JoDee Guerard, prin. Fax 736-7159

Christian Heritage S 300/K-12
PO Box 1780 92878 951-736-3033
Arleen Morris, admin.
Crossroads Christian S 1,000/PK-12
2380 Fullerton Ave 92881 951-278-3199
Doug Husen, supt. Fax 493-2169
ITT Technical Institute Post-Sec.
4160 Temescal Canyon # 100 92883 951-277-5400
JEM College Post-Sec.
271 Ott St Ste 23 92882 951-549-0693

Coronado, San Diego, Pop. 18,310
Coronado USD 3,100/PK-12
201 6th St 92118 619-522-8900
Jeffrey Felix, supt. Fax 437-6570
www.coronado.k12.ca.us
Coronado HS 1,100/9-12
650 D Ave 92118 619-522-8907
Karl Mueller, prin. Fax 437-0236
Coronado MS 700/6-8
550 F Ave 92118 619-522-8921
Jay Marquand, prin. Fax 522-6948
Palm Academy, 555 D Ave 92118 50/Alt
Kevin Nicolls, prin. 619-437-7256

Costa Mesa, Orange, Pop. 106,497
Newport - Mesa USD 21,700/K-12
2985 Bear St 92626 714-424-5000
Frederick Navarro Ed.D., supt. Fax 424-5018
www.nmusd.us
Back Bay HS 100/Alt
390 Monte Vista Ave 92627 949-515-6900
Debbie Lucker-Davis, prin. Fax 515-3380
Costa Mesa JSHS 1,700/7-12
2650 Fairview Rd 92626 714-424-8700
Phil D'Agostino, prin. Fax 424-8770
Early College HS 300/9-12
2990 Mesa Verde Dr E 92626 714-241-6108
Kathy Slawson, prin. Fax 241-6185
Estancia HS 1,300/9-12
2323 Placentia Ave 92627 949-515-6500
Kirk Bauermeister, prin. Fax 515-6571
Monte Vista HS 100/Alt
390 Monte Vista Ave 92627 949-515-6900
Debbie Lucker-Davis, prin. Fax 515-3380
TeWinkle MS 700/7-8
3224 California St 92626 714-424-7965
Rich Rodriguez, prin. Fax 424-5680
Other Schools – See Newport Beach

Regional Occupational Center & Program
Supt. — None
Coastline ROP Vo/Tech
1001 Presidio Sq 92626 714-979-1955
Darlene LeFort, supt. Fax 557-6812

James Albert School of Cosmetology Post-Sec.
1835 Newport Blvd 92627 949-642-0606
Orange Coast College Post-Sec.
PO Box 5005 92628 714-432-5072
Pacific College Post-Sec.
3160 Red Hill Ave 92626 714-662-4402
Paul Mitchell The School Post-Sec.
3309 Hyland Ave Ste J 92626 714-546-8786
Vanguard University of Southern CA Post-Sec.
55 Fair Dr 92626 714-556-3610
Waldorf S of Orange County 300/PK-12
2350 Canyon Dr 92627 949-574-7775
Fax 574-7740

Cottonwood, Shasta, Pop. 3,202
Anderson UNHSD
Supt. — See Anderson
West Valley HS 900/9-12
3805 Happy Valley Rd 96022 530-347-7171
Emmett Koerperich, prin. Fax 347-0481

Cottonwood UNESD 700/K-8
20512 1st St 96022 530-347-3165
Robert Lowden, supt. Fax 347-0247
cwusd.com
West Cottonwood JHS 400/5-8
20512 1st St 96022 530-347-3123
Douglas Geren, prin. Fax 347-0247

Evergreen UNSD 1,000/K-8
19500 Learning Way 96022 530-347-3411
Brad Mendenhall, supt. Fax 347-7954
www.evergreenusd.org
Evergreen MS 500/5-8
19500 Learning Way 96022 530-347-3411
Felicia Ross, prin. Fax 347-7953

Coulterville, Mariposa, Pop. 195
Mariposa County USD
Supt. — See Mariposa
Coulterville HS 50/9-12
PO Box 480 95311 209-878-3955
Ron Henderson, prin. Fax 878-3816

Courtland, Sacramento, Pop. 350
River Delta USD
Supt. — See Rio Vista
Mokelumne HS 50/Alt
PO Box 574 95615 916-775-9160
David Nelson, prin. Fax 775-1797
River Delta Community Day S 50/Alt
160 Courtland High School 95615 916-775-9160
David Nelson, prin. Fax 775-1797

Covelo, Mendocino, Pop. 1,175
Round Valley USD 400/K-12
PO Box 276 95428 707-983-6171
Christine Thomas, supt. Fax 983-6655
www.roundvalleyschools.org/
Round Valley Continuation HS 50/Alt
PO Box 276 95428 707-983-6171
Nikki Arvantis, prin. Fax 983-6179
Round Valley HS 100/9-12
PO Box 276 95428 707-983-6174
Nikki Arvantis, prin. Fax 983-6179

Covina, Los Angeles, Pop. 46,744
Azusa USD
Supt. — See Azusa
Gladstone HS 1,500/9-12
1340 N Enid Ave 91722 626-815-3600
Scott Magnusson, prin. Fax 815-3655

Charter Oak USD 5,900/K-12
20240 E Cienega Ave 91724 626-966-8331
Michael Hendricks Ed.D., supt. Fax 967-9580
www.cousd.net
Charter Oak HS 1,900/9-12
1430 E Covina Blvd 91724 626-915-5841
Kathleen Wiard, prin. Fax 915-3398
Royal Oak MS 900/7-8
303 S Glendora Ave 91724 626-967-6354
Maria Thompson, prin. Fax 331-2074
Other Schools – See Glendora

Covina-Valley USD 13,900/K-12
519 E Badillo St 91723 626-974-7000
Dr. Catherine Nichols, supt. Fax 974-7032
www.cvusd.k12.ca.us
Covina HS 1,500/9-12
463 S Hollenbeck Ave 91723 626-974-6020
Claudia Karnoski, prin. Fax 974-6045
Fairvalley HS 200/Alt
231 E Stephanie Dr 91722 626-974-6420
Daniel Gribbon, prin. Fax 974-6415
Las Palmas MS 1,000/6-8
641 N Lark Ellen Ave 91722 626-974-7200
Nicole Higuera, prin. Fax 974-7215
Northview HS 1,600/9-12
1016 W Cypress St 91722 626-974-6120
Dr. Josie Paredes, prin. Fax 974-6145
Sierra Vista MS 1,100/6-8
777 E Puente St 91723 626-974-7300
Tanina Barbagallo, prin. Fax 974-7315
Business Center Adult
342 S 4th Ave 91723 626-974-6800
Bruce Krall, dir. Fax 974-6814
Tri Community Adult Ed.-Griswold Center Adult
342 S 4th Ave 91723 626-472-7680
Bruce Krall, dir. Fax 472-7681
Other Schools – See West Covina

American Graduate University Post-Sec.
733 N Dodsworth Ave 91724 626-966-4576
Firm Foundation Christian Academy 100/1-12
541 S Aldenville Ave 91723 626-938-1199
Mary Carnighan, head sch

Crescent City, Del Norte, Pop. 7,317
Del Norte County Office of Education 500/
301 W Washington Blvd 95531 707-464-0200
Don Olson, supt. Fax 464-0238
www.delnorte.k12.ca.us
Del Norte Community Day S 50/Alt
400 W Harding Ave 95531 707-464-0750
Tony Fabricus, prin. Fax 464-5116
McCarthy Center 50/Alt
301 W Washington Blvd 95531 707-464-0399
Tony Fabricus, prin. Fax 465-5116
Paragon/Avalon S 50/Alt
400 W Harding Ave 95531 707-464-0750
Tony Fabricus, prin. Fax 465-5116

Del Norte County USD 3,700/K-12
301 W Washington Blvd 95531 707-464-6141
Don Olson, supt. Fax 464-0238
www.delnorte.k12.ca.us
Crescent Elk MS 600/6-8
994 G St 95531 707-464-0320
Billy Hartwick, prin. Fax 464-0326
Del Norte County HS 1,100/9-12
1301 El Dorado St 95531 707-464-0260
Coleen Parker, prin. Fax 464-0785
Educational Options Alt
400 W Harding Ave 95531 707-464-0750
Tony Fabricius, prin. Fax 465-5116
Sunset Continuation HS 100/Alt
2500 Elk Valley Cross Rd 95531 707-464-0380
Tony Fabricius, prin. Fax 465-5346

Regional Occupational Center & Program
Supt. — None
Del Norte County ROP Vo/Tech
1301 El Dorado St 95531 707-464-0274
Colleen Parker, dir. Fax 465-6923

Foursquare Christian S 100/PK-12
144 Butte St 95531 707-464-9501
George Olson, prin. Fax 465-3254

Crestline, San Bernardino, Pop. 10,356
Rim of the World USD
Supt. — See Blue Jay
Mountain HS 200/Alt
24740 San Mortiz Way 92325 909-589-0041
Debra Wogen, prin.

Crockett, Contra Costa, Pop. 2,949
John Swett USD
Supt. — See Rodeo
Carquinez MS 400/6-8
1099 Pomona St 94525 510-787-1081
Quiauna Scott, prin. Fax 787-2359
Swett HS 500/9-12
1098 Pomona St 94525 510-787-1088
Jeff Brauning, prin. Fax 787-1930
Willow Continuation HS 50/Alt
1650 Crockett Blvd 94525 510-787-1286
Joanne Clark, prin. Fax 787-4770

Crows Landing, Stanislaus, Pop. 352
Chatom UNESD
Supt. — See Turlock
Mountain View MS 200/6-8
10001 Crows Landing Rd 95313 209-664-8515
Cherise Olvera, prin. Fax 669-1733

Cudahy, Los Angeles, Pop. 23,704
Los Angeles USD
Supt. — See Los Angeles

Elizabeth Learning Center 1,800/K-12
4811 Elizabeth St 90201 323-271-3600
Sharon Sweet, prin. Fax 560-8412

Culver City, Los Angeles, Pop. 36,982
Culver City USD 6,800/K-12
4034 Irving Pl 90232 310-842-4220
David LaRose, supt. Fax 842-4205
www.ccusd.org
Culver City HS 2,300/9-12
4401 Elenda St 90230 310-842-4200
Dylan Farris, prin. Fax 842-4303
Culver City MS 1,600/6-8
4601 Elenda St 90230 310-842-4200
Jon Pearson, prin. Fax 842-4304
Culver Park Continuation HS 100/Alt
4601 Elenda St 90230 310-390-8886
Veronica Montes, prin. Fax 390-3796
Culver City Adult S Adult
4909 Overland Ave 90230 310-842-4300
Veronica Montes, prin. Fax 842-4343

Antioch University Los Angeles Post-Sec.
400 Corporate Pointe 90230 310-578-1080
ITT Technical Institute Post-Sec.
6101 W Centinela Ave 90230 310-417-5800
West Los Angeles College Post-Sec.
9000 Overland Ave 90230 310-287-4200

Cupertino, Santa Clara, Pop. 56,415
Cupertino UNSD 18,400/PK-8
10301 Vista Dr 95014 408-252-3000
Dr. Wendy Gudalewicz, supt. Fax 343-2801
www.edline.net/pages/Cupertino_Union_SD
Hyde MS 1,000/6-8
19325 Bollinger Rd 95014 408-252-6290
Todd Shimada, prin. Fax 255-3288
Kennedy MS 1,300/6-8
821 Bubb Rd 95014 408-253-1525
Nicole Johnston, prin. Fax 257-5777
Lawson MS 1,000/6-8
10401 Vista Dr 95014 408-255-7500
Jeff Bowman, prin. Fax 446-4987
Other Schools – See San Jose, Sunnyvale

Fremont UNHSD
Supt. — See Sunnyvale
Cupertino HS 1,800/9-12
10100 Finch Ave 95014 408-366-7300
Kami Tomberlain, prin. Fax 255-8466
Homestead HS 2,300/9-12
21370 Homestead Rd 95014 408-522-2500
Graham Clark, prin. Fax 738-8631
Monta Vista HS 2,500/9-12
21840 McClellan Rd 95014 408-366-7600
April Scott, prin. Fax 252-1519

DeAnza College Post-Sec.
21250 Stevens Creek Blvd 95014 408-864-5678

Cutler, Tulare, Pop. 4,971
Cutler-Orosi JUSD
Supt. — See Orosi
Lovell HS 100/Alt
12724 Avenue 392 93615 559-528-4703
Martha Calderon, prin. Fax 528-0102

Cypress, Orange, Pop. 46,012
Anaheim UNHSD
Supt. — See Anaheim
Cypress HS 2,600/9-12
9801 Valley View St 90630 714-220-4144
Ben Carpenter Ed.D., prin. Fax 220-4174
Lexington JHS 1,300/7-8
4351 Orange Ave 90630 714-220-4201
Jodie Wales Ed.D., prin. Fax 761-4989
Oxford Academy 1,100/7-12
5172 Orange Ave 90630 714-220-3055
Kathy Scott, prin. Fax 527-7128

Cypress College Post-Sec.
9200 Valley View St 90630 714-484-7000
Trident University International Post-Sec.
5757 Plaza Dr Ste 100 90630 800-579-3197

Daggett, San Bernardino
Silver Valley USD
Supt. — See Yermo
Calico Continuation HS 50/Alt
33525 Ponnay St 92327 760-254-2715
Stefan Cvijanovich, prin. Fax 254-2194
Silver Valley Academy 50/Alt
33525 Ponnay St 92327 760-254-2715
Stefan Cvijanovich, prin. Fax 254-2194
Silver Valley Community Day S 50/Alt
33525 Ponnay 92327 760-254-2715
Stefan Cvijanovich, prin. Fax 254-2194
Silver Valley Adult S Adult
33525 Ponnay 92327 760-254-2715
Stefan Cvijanovich, prin. Fax 254-2194

Daly City, San Mateo, Pop. 97,070
Bayshore ESD 400/K-8
1 Martin St 94014 415-467-5443
Toni Presta, supt. Fax 467-1542
www.bayshore.k12.ca.us
Robertson IS 200/5-8
1 Martin St 94014 415-467-5443
Sergio Nesterov, prin. Fax 467-1542

Jefferson ESD 5,900/K-8
101 Lincoln Ave 94015 650-991-1000
Bernardo Vidales, supt. Fax 992-2265
www.jsd.k12.ca.us/
Pollicita MS 600/6-8
550 E Market St 94014 650-991-1216
Brent Marquez-Valenti, prin. Fax 755-2170

Rivera IS 500/7-8
1255 Southgate Ave 94015 650-991-1225
Sibane Parcels, prin. Fax 755-6273
Other Schools – See Colma

Jefferson UNHSD 5,000/9-12
699 Serramonte Blvd Ste 100 94015 650-550-7900
Thomas H. Minshew, supt. Fax 550-7888
www.juhsd.net
Jefferson HS 1,200/9-12
6996 Mission St 94014 650-550-7700
Jason Brockmeyer, prin. Fax 550-7790
Thornton HS 200/Alt
115 1st Ave 94014 650-550-7840
Monica Casey, prin. Fax 758-2092
Westmoor HS 1,700/9-12
131 Westmoor Ave 94015 650-550-7400
Allan Reyes, prin. Fax 550-7490
Adult Education Divison Adult
699 Serramonte Blvd Ste 111 94015 650-550-7890
Diana Rumney, prin. Fax 550-7889
Other Schools – See Pacifica

Bridgemont HS 50/9-12
444 E Market St 94014 650-991-1211
Peter Tropper, dir.
DeVry University Post-Sec.
2001 Junipero Serra Ste 161 94014 650-991-3520
Hilltop Beauty School Post-Sec.
6317 Mission St 94014 650-756-2720

Dana Point, Orange, Pop. 32,532
Capistrano USD
Supt. — See San Juan Capistrano
Dana Hills HS 2,900/9-12
33333 Golden Lantern St 92629 949-496-6666
Jason Allemann, prin. Fax 489-8317

Danville, Contra Costa, Pop. 40,475
San Ramon Valley USD 28,400/K-12
699 Old Orchard Dr 94526 925-552-5500
Mary Shelton, supt. Fax 838-3147
www.srvusd.net/
Del Amigo Continuation HS 100/Alt
189 Del Amigo Rd 94526 925-552-5571
Joseph Ianora, prin. Fax 838-5372
Diablo Vista MS 800/6-8
4100 Camino Tassajara 94506 925-648-8560
Becky Ingram, prin. Fax 648-7167
Los Cerros MS 600/6-8
968 Blemer Rd 94526 925-552-5620
Phyllis Roach, prin. Fax 837-3512
Monte Vista HS 2,200/9-12
3131 Stone Valley Rd 94526 925-552-5530
Janet Terranova, prin. Fax 743-1744
San Ramon Valley HS 2,000/9-12
501 Danville Blvd 94526 925-552-3000
Ruth Steele, prin. Fax 552-3060
Wood MS 1,000/6-8
600 El Capitan Dr 94526 925-552-5600
Christopher George, prin. Fax 820-1057
Other Schools – See Alamo, San Ramon

Athenian S 500/6-12
2100 Mount Diablo Scenic 94506 925-837-5375
Eric Niles, head sch Fax 362-7292

Davis, Yolo, Pop. 62,607
Davis JUSD 8,500/K-12
526 B St 95616 530-757-5300
Winfred Roberson, supt. Fax 757-5323
www.djusd.net
Davis S for Independent Study 100/Alt
526 B St 95616 530-757-5333
Kimberly Wallace, prin. Fax 757-5382
Davis SHS 1,700/10-12
315 W 14th St 95616 530-757-5400
Jacqui Moore, prin. Fax 757-5492
Emerson JHS 400/7-9
2121 Calaveras Ave 95616 530-757-5430
Alicia Cummings, prin. Fax 757-5434
Harper JHS 700/7-9
4000 E Covell Blvd 95618 530-757-5330
Zena Ingles, prin. Fax 757-5350
Holmes JHS 700/7-9
1220 Drexel Dr 95616 530-757-5445
Derek Brothers, prin. Fax 757-5435
King Continuation HS 100/Alt
635 B St 95616 530-757-5425
Kimberly Wallace, prin. Fax 757-5440
Davis Adult S Adult
315 W 14th St 95616 530-757-5380
Laurel Clumpner, prin. Fax 757-5381

D-Q University Post-Sec.
PO Box 409 95617 530-758-0470
University of California Post-Sec.
1 Shields Ave 95616 530-752-1011

Delano, Kern, Pop. 52,490
Delano JUNHSD 4,200/9-12
1720 Norwalk St 93215 661-725-4000
Rosalina Rivera, supt. Fax 721-9390
www.djuhsd.org/
Chavez HS 1,400/9-12
1720 Norwalk St 93215 661-720-4502
Ben DeLeon, prin. Fax 725-8875
Delano HS 1,700/9-12
1720 Norwalk St 93215 661-720-4121
April Gregerson, prin. Fax 720-4119
Kennedy HS 800/9-12
1720 Norwalk St 93215 661-720-5102
Jason Garcia, prin. Fax 721-0833
Valley HS 200/Alt
1720 Norwalk St 93215 661-720-4374
Paul Chavez, prin. Fax 725-7611
Delano Adult S Adult
1720 Norwalk St 93215 661-720-4173
Dr. Terri Nuckols, dir. Fax 725-5852

Delano UNESD 7,200/K-8
1405 12th Ave 93215 661-721-5000
Robert Aguilar, supt. Fax 725-2201
www.duesd.org
Almond Tree MS 700/6-8
200 W 15th Ave 93215 661-721-3641
Mike Havens, prin. Fax 721-3649
La Vina MS 700/6-8
1331 Browning Rd 93215 661-721-3601
Jennifer Townson, prin. Fax 721-3662

Sequoia Christian Academy 50/K-12
PO Box 1876 93216 661-721-2721
Roberta Hunter, admin. Fax 721-2722

Delhi, Merced, Pop. 10,554
Delhi USD 2,600/K-12
9716 Hinton Ave 95315 209-656-2000
Brian Stephens, supt. Fax 668-6133
www.delhi.k12.ca.us
Delhi HS 700/9-12
9716 Hinton Ave 95315 209-656-2050
Anthony Arista, prin. Fax 669-3168
Shattuck Educational Park HS 50/Alt
9716 Hinton Ave 95315 209-656-2012
Francisca Briones, prin. Fax 669-6165
Delhi Adult S Adult
9716 Hinton Ave 95315 209-656-2012
Francisca Briones, prin. Fax 669-6165

Del Mar, San Diego, Pop. 4,073

Cal Coast Academy 50/6-12
445 Marine View Ave Ste 105 92014 858-481-0882
Jan Dunning, prin. Fax 481-8583

Denair, Stanislaus, Pop. 4,321
Denair USD 1,600/PK-12
3460 Lester Rd 95316 209-632-7514
Dr. Walt Hanline, supt. Fax 632-9194
dusd.k12.ca.us
Denair HS 400/9-12
3460 Lester Rd 95316 209-632-9911
Aaron Delworth, prin. Fax 632-8153
Denair MS 300/6-8
3460 Lester Rd 95316 209-632-2510
Aaron Delworth, prin. Fax 632-0269

Desert Hot Springs, Riverside, Pop. 25,289
Palm Springs USD
Supt. — See Palm Springs
Desert Hot Springs Alternative Center Alt
11555 Palm Dr Ste A 92240 760-251-7226
Milt Jones, prin. Fax 251-7226
Desert Hot Springs HS 1,900/9-12
65850 Pierson Blvd 92240 760-288-7000
Anne Kalisek, prin. Fax 288-7010
Desert Springs MS 1,600/6-8
66755 Two Bunch Palms Trl 92240 760-251-7200
Kiela Snider, prin. Fax 251-7206
Painted Hills MS 6-8
9250 Sonora Dr 92240 760-251-1551
Ryan Saunders, prin. Fax 251-5330

Diamond Bar, Los Angeles, Pop. 54,094
Pomona USD
Supt. — See Pomona
Lorbeer MS 700/7-8
501 S Diamond Bar Blvd 91765 909-397-4527
Krystana Walks-Harper, prin. Fax 396-9022

Walnut Valley USD
Supt. — See Walnut
Chaparral MS 1,300/6-8
1405 Spruce Tree Dr 91765 909-861-6227
Ronald Thibodeaux, prin. Fax 396-0749
Diamond Bar HS 3,100/9-12
21400 Pathfinder Rd 91765 909-594-1405
Catherine Real, prin. Fax 595-8301

California Intercontinental University Post-Sec.
1470 Valley Vista Dr # 150 91765 909-396-6090

Diamond Springs, El Dorado, Pop. 10,676
El Dorado UNHSD
Supt. — See Placerville
Community Day S 50/Alt
385 Pleasant Valley Rd 95619 530-622-7090
Alison Gennai, prin. Fax 642-2291
Independence HS 100/Alt
385 Pleasant Valley Rd 95619 530-622-7090
Alison Gennai, prin. Fax 642-2291

Dinuba, Tulare, Pop. 21,288
Dinuba USD 6,000/K-12
1327 E El Monte Way 93618 559-595-7200
Joe Hernandez Ed.D., supt. Fax 591-3334
dusd.dinuba.k12.ca.us
Dinuba HS 1,800/9-12
1327 E El Monte Way 93618 559-595-7220
Chris Meyer, prin. Fax 591-3655
Reagan Academy 200/Alt
1327 E El Monte Way 93618 559-595-7295
Suzanne Rodriguez, prin. Fax 595-7248
Sierra Vista HS 100/Alt
1327 E El Monte Way 93618 559-595-7240
Suzanne Rodriguez, prin. Fax 595-8198
Washington IS 900/7-8
1327 E El Monte Way 93618 559-595-7252
Mike Roberts, prin. Fax 595-8158
Dinuba Adult S Adult
1327 E El Monte Way 93618 559-595-7242
Suzanne Rodriguez, prin. Fax 595-7248

Kings Canyon JUSD
Supt. — See Reedley
Kings Canyon Continuation HS 100/Alt
10026 S Crawford Ave 93618 559-305-7393
Keith Merrihew, dir. Fax 591-8511

Dixon, Solano, Pop. 17,699
Dixon USD 3,700/K-12
180 S 1st St 95620 707-693-6300
Brian Dolan, supt. Fax 678-0726
www.dixonusd.org
Dixon Community Day S 50/Alt
180 S 1st St 95620 707-678-4061
Yvette Ramos, prin.
Dixon HS 1,200/9-12
555 College Way 95620 707-693-6330
Nick Girimonte, prin. Fax 678-9318
Jacobs IS 600/7-8
200 N Lincoln St 95620 707-678-9222
Cindy Moody-Perkins, prin. Fax 678-1245
Maine Prairie HS 100/Alt
305 E C St 95620 707-678-4560
Yvette Ramos, prin. Fax 678-4892

Dorris, Siskiyou, Pop. 895
Butte Valley USD 300/K-12
PO Box 709 96023 530-397-4000
Edward Brown, supt. Fax 397-3999
www.bvalusd.org/
Butte Valley HS 100/9-12
PO Box 709 96023 530-397-3990
Edward Brown, prin. Fax 397-3989
Cascade Continuation HS 50/Alt
PO Box 709 96023 530-397-3363
Edward Brown, prin. Fax 397-3360
Mahogany Community Day HS 50/Alt
PO Box 709 96023 530-397-3406
Edward Brown, prin. Fax 397-3360
Butte Valley Adult S Adult
PO Box 709 96023 530-397-3363
Edward Brown, prin. Fax 397-3360
Other Schools – See Macdoel

Dos Palos, Merced, Pop. 4,873
Dos Palos Oro Loma JUSD 2,300/K-12
2041 Almond St 93620 209-392-0200
Brian Walker, supt. Fax 392-3347
www.dpol.net
Bryant MS 500/6-8
16695 Bryant Ave 93620 209-392-0240
Laura Andrews, prin. Fax 392-2636
Dos Palos HS 700/9-12
1701 E Blossom St 93620 209-392-0300
Heather Ruiz, prin. Fax 392-2705
Other Schools – See South Dos Palos

Downey, Los Angeles, Pop. 110,312
Downey USD 22,800/K-12
PO Box 7017 90241 562-469-6500
John Garcia Ph.D., supt. Fax 469-6515
www.dusd.net
Columbus Continuation HS 400/Alt
12330 Woodruff Ave 90241 562-904-3552
Kathleen Succa, prin. Fax 469-7320
Doty MS 1,400/6-8
10301 Woodruff Ave 90241 562-904-3586
Brent Shubin, prin. Fax 469-7240
Downey HS 4,200/9-12
11040 Brookshire Ave 90241 562-869-7301
Tom Houts, prin. Fax 469-7340
Griffiths MS 1,400/6-8
9633 Tweedy Ln 90240 562-904-3580
Gregg Stapp, prin. Fax 469-7260
Sussman MS 1,300/6-8
12500 Birchdale Ave 90242 562-904-3572
Joe Webster, prin. Fax 469-7280
Warren HS 3,800/9-12
8141 De Palma St 90241 562-869-7306
John Harris, prin. Fax 469-7360
West MS 1,400/6-8
11985 Old River School Rd 90242 562-904-3565
Alyda Mir, prin. Fax 469-7300
Downey Adult S Adult
12340 Woodruff Ave 90241 562-940-6200
Phil Davis, dir. Fax 940-6221

Los Angeles County Office of Education 6,700/
9300 Imperial Hwy 90242 562-922-6111
Dr. Arturo Delgado, supt. Fax 922-6768
www.lacoe.edu
Alternative Opportunity Programs 400/Alt
9300 Imperial Hwy 90242 562-803-8203
Perry Wiseman, dir. Fax 401-5742
Other Schools – See Hawthorne, Lancaster, Los Angeles, Monterey Park, Pomona, Whittier

Regional Occupational Center & Program
Supt. — None
Los Angeles County ROP Vo/Tech
9300 Imperial Hwy 90242 562-922-6850
Jimmy Benavides, dir. Fax 940-1672

Calvary Chapel Christian S 800/PK-12
12808 Woodruff Ave 90242 562-803-4076
Yuri Escandon, admin. Fax 803-9916
Keystone Academy 200/K-12
8615 Florence Ave Ste 207 90240 562-862-7134
Philip Troutt, hdmstr.
Los Amigos Research & Education Inst. Post-Sec.
PO Box 3500 90242 562-401-8111
St. Pius X / St. Matthias Academy 200/9-12
7851 Gardendale St 90242 562-861-2271
Erick Rubalcava, prin. Fax 869-8652

Downieville, Sierra, Pop. 276
Sierra-Plumas JUSD
Supt. — See Loyalton
Downieville JSHS 50/7-12
PO Box B 95936 530-289-3473
Derek Cooper, prin. Fax 289-3693

Duarte, Los Angeles, Pop. 20,755
Duarte USD 4,000/K-12
1620 Huntington Dr 91010 626-599-5000
Terry Nichols, supt. Fax 599-5069
www.duarte.k12.ca.us
Duarte HS 1,200/9-12
1620 Huntington Dr 91010 626-599-5700
Robin Nelson, prin. Fax 599-5784
Mt. Olive Alternative Education S 100/Alt
1620 Huntington Dr 91010 626-599-5900
Kevin Morris, prin. Fax 599-5984
Northview IS 600/7-8
1620 Huntington Dr 91010 626-599-5600
Michael Chavez, prin. Fax 599-5684

Irell & Manella Grad Sch of Biological Post-Sec.
1500 Duarte Rd 91010 626-256-4673

Dublin, Alameda, Pop. 43,591
Dublin USD 6,400/K-12
7471 Larkdale Ave 94568 925-828-2551
Dr. Stephen Hanke, supt. Fax 829-6532
www.dublinusd.org
Dublin HS 1,500/9-12
8151 Village Pkwy 94568 925-833-3300
Carol Shimizu, prin. Fax 833-3322
Valley Continuation HS 100/Alt
6901 York Dr 94568 925-829-4322
Rinda Bartley, prin. Fax 833-7609
Wells MS 700/6-8
6800 Penn Dr 94568 925-828-6227
Kevin Grier, prin. Fax 829-8851
Dublin Adult Education Adult
6901 York Dr 94568 925-829-4322
Rinda Bartley, prin. Fax 833-7609

Golden State College of Court Reporting Post-Sec.
6543 Regional St 94568 925-829-0115
Quarry Lane S 500/PK-12
6363 Tassajara Rd 94568 925-829-8000
Sabri Arac Ph.D., hdmstr. Fax 829-4928
Valley Christian S 900/PK-12
7500 Inspiration Dr 94568 925-560-6200
Roger Valci, supt. Fax 828-6725

Dunsmuir, Siskiyou, Pop. 1,565
Dunsmuir JUNHSD 100/9-12
5805 High School Way 96025 530-235-4835
Emily Houck, supt. Fax 235-2224
www.dunsmuirhigh.k12.ca.us/
Dunsmuir Community Day S 50/Alt
5805 High School Way 96025 530-235-2225
Ray Kellar, prin. Fax 235-2224
Dunsmuir HS 100/9-12
5805 High School Way 96025 530-235-4835
Ray Kellar, prin. Fax 235-2224

Durham, Butte, Pop. 5,377
Durham USD 1,000/K-12
PO Box 300 95938 530-895-4675
Mary von Rotz Sakuma, supt. Fax 895-4692
www.durhamunified.org/
Durham HS 400/9-12
PO Box 600 95938 530-895-4685
Bill Frey, prin. Fax 895-4688
Durham IS 300/6-8
PO Box 310 95938 530-895-4690
Greg Blake, prin. Fax 895-4305

Earlimart, Tulare, Pop. 8,499
Earlimart ESD 2,000/K-8
PO Box 11970 93219 661-849-3386
Sandra Rivera, supt. Fax 849-2352
www.earlimart.org
Earlimart Community Day S 50/Alt
PO Box 11970 93219 661-849-4841
Raylene Welch, lead tchr. Fax 849-2352
Earlimart MS 600/6-8
PO Box 11970 93219 661-849-2611
Phillip Nystrom, prin. Fax 849-4214

East Palo Alto, San Mateo, Pop. 25,414
Ravenswood City ESD 4,100/PK-12
2120 Euclid Ave 94303 650-329-2800
Maria De La Vega, supt. Fax 323-1072
www.ravenswood.k12.ca.us
Chavez Academy 300/6-8
2450 Ralmar Ave 94303 650-329-6700
Amika Guillaume, prin. Fax 326-8902
McNair Academy 300/6-8
2033 Pulgas Ave 94303 650-329-2888
Jocelyn Lee, prin. Fax 473-9247
San Francisco 49er Academy 100/6-8
2695 Fordham St 94303 650-614-4300
Michele Sharky, dir. Fax 614-4310

Sequoia UNHSD
Supt. — See Redwood City
Sequoia Community Day S Alt
763 Green St 94303 650-323-1985
Marshall Burgamy, admin. Fax 566-1198

Eastside College Preparatory S 300/6-12
1041 Myrtle St 94303 650-688-0850
Chris Bischof, prin.

Eastvale, Riverside, Pop. 51,943
Corona-Norco USD
Supt. — See Norco
Ramirez IS 100/7-8
6905 Harrison Ave, 951-736-8241
Ryan Lewis, prin. Fax 273-3145
River Heights IS 1,800/7-8
7227 Scholar Way, 951-738-2155
Teri Dudley, prin. Fax 738-2175
Roosevelt HS 3,200/9-12
7447 Scholar Way, 951-738-2100
Mark Lenoir, prin. Fax 738-2104

Edwards, Kern
Muroc JUSD
Supt. — See North Edwards
Desert JSHS 600/7-12
1575 Payne Ave 93523 661-258-4411
David Ellms, prin. Fax 258-5029

El Cajon, San Diego, Pop. 94,267
Cajon Valley UNESD 15,100/K-8
PO Box 1007 92022 619-588-3000
Janice Cook Ed.D., supt. Fax 588-7653
www.cajonvalley.net/
Cajon Valley MS 800/6-8
505 E Park Ave 92020 619-588-3092
Don Hohimer, prin. Fax 579-4817
Emerald MS 700/6-8
1221 Emerald Ave 92020 619-588-3097
Kathy Skube, prin. Fax 588-3225
Greenfield MS 700/6-8
1495 Greenfield Dr 92021 619-588-3103
Froylan Villanueva, prin. Fax 588-3648
Hillsdale MS 1,500/6-8
1301 Brabham St 92019 619-441-6156
Marietta Minjares, prin. Fax 441-6185
Los Coches Creek MS 6-8
9669 Dunbar Ln 92021 619-441-5741
Chona Killeen, prin. Fax 938-1850
Montgomery MS 800/6-8
1570 Melody Ln 92019 619-588-3107
Jacqueline Luzak, prin. Fax 441-6122

Grossmont UNHSD
Supt. — See La Mesa
Chaparral HS 300/Alt
1600 N Cuyamaca St 92020 619-956-4600
Randy Reid, prin. Fax 596-7815
El Cajon Valley HS 2,300/9-12
1035 E Madison Ave 92021 619-401-4700
Erin Richison, prin. Fax 447-3943
Granite Hills HS 2,800/9-12
1719 E Madison Ave 92019 619-593-5500
Georgette Torres, prin. Fax 588-9389
Grossmont HS 2,600/9-12
1100 Murray Dr 92020 619-668-6000
Dan Barnes, prin. Fax 463-7108
Grossmont Middle College HS 100/11-12
8800 Grossmont College Dr 92020 619-644-7524
Kathy Burton, prin. Fax 644-7011
Valhalla HS 2,100/9-12
1725 Hillsdale Rd 92019 619-593-5300
Mary Kastan, prin. Fax 588-9713
Grossmont Adult S Adult
1550 Melody Ln 92019 619-401-4200
Gary Schwartzwald, dir. Fax 579-9291

Advanced Training Associates Post-Sec.
1810 Gillespie Way Ste 104 92020 619-596-2766
Bellus Academy Post-Sec.
1073 E Main St 92021 619-442-3407
Christian JSHS 500/7-12
2100 Greenfield Dr 92019 619-201-8800
Scott Meadows, prin. Fax 201-8898
Cuyamaca College Post-Sec.
900 Rancho San Diego Pkwy 92019 619-660-4000
Foothills Christian HS 200/9-12
2321 Dryden Rd 92020 619-303-8035
Tom Edelen, prin. Fax 741-2648
Grossmont College Post-Sec.
8800 Grossmont College Dr 92020 619-644-7000
San Diego Christian College Post-Sec.
2100 Greenfield Dr 92019 619-201-8700
Southern California Seminary Post-Sec.
2075 E Madison Ave 92019 888-389-7244

El Centro, Imperial, Pop. 42,253
Central UNHSD 5,000/9-12
351 W Ross Ave, 760-336-4500
C. Thomas Budde Ph.D., supt. Fax 353-3606
www.cuhsd.net
Central Union HS 1,800/9-12
1001 W Brighton Ave, 760-336-4300
Michael Sterner, prin. Fax 353-3570
Desert Oasis HS 200/Alt
1302 S 3rd St, 760-336-4555
Tracie Baughn, prin. Fax 337-3952
Southwest HS 2,000/9-12
2001 Ocotillo Dr, 760-336-4100
Dannette Morrell, prin. Fax 353-0467
Central Union Adult Education Adult
1302 S 3rd St, 760-336-4544
Tish Thompson, dir. Fax 336-4547

El Centro ESD 5,300/K-8
1256 Broadway St, 760-352-5712
Jon LeDoux, supt. Fax 312-9522
www.ecesd.com
Kennedy MS 400/7-8
900 N 6th St, 760-352-0444
Spencer Wavra, prin. Fax 353-0325
Wilson JHS 700/7-8
600 S Wilson St, 760-352-5341
Matt Phillips, prin. Fax 337-3800

Regional Occupational Center & Program
Supt. — None
Imperial Valley ROP Vo/Tech
687 W State St, 760-482-2600
Mary Camacho, supt. Fax 482-2751

El Cerrito, Contra Costa, Pop. 22,213
West Contra Costa USD
Supt. — See Richmond
El Cerrito HS 1,000/9-12
540 Ashbury Ave 94530 510-231-1437
David Luongo, prin. Fax 525-1810
Portola MS 300/6-8
1021 Navellier St 94530 510-524-0405
Matthew Burnham, prin. Fax 559-8784

Prospect Sierra MS 300/5-8
960 Avis Dr 94530 510-528-5800
Katherine Dinh, head sch Fax 527-3728

El Dorado, El Dorado
El Dorado UNHSD
Supt. — See Placerville
Mountain View HS 50/Alt
6530 Koki Ln 95623 530-621-4003
Jennifer Myers, prin. Fax 622-6034
Union Mine HS 1,000/9-12
6530 Koki Ln 95623 530-621-4003
Tony DeVille, prin. Fax 622-6034

El Dorado Hills, El Dorado, Pop. 40,513
Buckeye UNSD
Supt. — See Shingle Springs
Rolling Hills MS 1,000/6-8
7141 Silva Valley Pkwy 95762 916-933-9290
Debra Bowers, prin. Fax 939-7454

El Dorado UNHSD
Supt. — See Placerville
Oak Ridge HS 2,200/9-12
1120 Harvard Way 95762 916-933-6980
Paul Burke, prin. Fax 933-6987

Rescue UNESD
Supt. — See Rescue
Marina Village MS 800/6-8
1901 Francisco Dr 95762 916-933-3993
Jeff Warshaw, prin. Fax 933-3995

Guiding Hands S 100/PK-12
4900 Windplay Dr 95762 916-939-0553
Cindy Keller, dir. Fax 939-0563

Elk Creek, Glenn, Pop. 158
Stony Creek JUSD 100/K-12
3430 County Road 309 95939 530-968-5361
Tracey Quarne, supt. Fax 968-5102
www.scjusd.org
Bidwell Point HS 50/Alt
3430 County Road 309 95939 530-968-5177
Tim Drury, prin. Fax 968-5535
Elk Creek JSHS 100/7-12
3430 County Road 309 95939 530-968-5361
Tim Drury, prin. Fax 968-5102
Stony Creek Community Day S 50/Alt
3430 County Road 309 95939 530-968-5177
Tim Drury, prin. Fax 968-5102

Elk Grove, Sacramento, Pop. 142,334
Elk Grove USD 61,500/PK-12
9510 Elk Grove Florin Rd 95624 916-686-5085
Steven Ladd Ed.D., supt. Fax 686-7787
www.egusd.net/
Albiani MS 1,400/7-8
9140 Bradshaw Rd 95624 916-686-5210
Melanie Dopson, prin. Fax 686-5538
Cosumnes Oaks HS 1,100/9-12
8350 Lotz Pkwy, 916-683-7670
Patrick McDougall, prin. Fax 683-4522
Eddy MS 800/7-8
9329 Soaring Oaks Dr 95758 916-683-1302
William Del Bonta, prin. Fax 684-6142
Elk Grove HS 1,800/9-12
9800 Elk Grove Florin Rd 95624 916-686-7741
Catherine Guy, prin. Fax 685-5515
Franklin HS 2,800/9-12
6400 Whitelock Pkwy, 916-714-8150
Michael Reed, prin. Fax 714-8155
Harris MS 1,200/7-8
8691 Power Inn Rd 95624 916-688-0075
Felicia Bessent, prin. Fax 688-0084
Johnson MS 1,400/7-8
10099 Franklin High Rd, 916-714-8181
Dawnelle Maffei, prin. Fax 714-8177
Kerr MS 900/7-8
8865 Elk Grove Blvd 95624 916-686-7728
Cecil Duke, prin. Fax 685-2952
Laguna Creek HS 1,900/9-12
9050 Vicino Dr 95758 916-683-1339
Douglas Craig, prin. Fax 683-3128
Monterey Trail HS 2,200/9-12
8661 Power Inn Rd 95624 916-688-0050
David Byrd, prin. Fax 688-0058
Pinkerton MS 1,000/7-8
8365 Whitelock Pkwy, 916-683-7680
Kim Doyle, prin. Fax 685-5703
Pleasant Grove HS 2,500/9-12
9531 Bond Rd 95624 916-686-0230
Hank Meyer, prin. Fax 686-0239
Other Schools – See Sacramento

DeVry University Post-Sec.
2216 Kausen Dr 95758 916-478-2847
Lutheran HS 100/9-12
9270 Bruceville Rd 95758 916-691-2277
James Maddock, prin. Fax 691-2292

El Monte, Los Angeles, Pop. 112,772
El Monte UNHSD 10,000/9-12
3537 Johnson Ave 91731 626-444-9005
Nick Salerno, supt. Fax 350-1095
www.emuhsd.k12.ca.us
Arroyo HS 2,300/9-12
4921 Cedar Ave 91732 626-444-9201
Oscar Cisneros, prin. Fax 443-1175
El Monte HS 1,900/9-12
3048 Tyler Ave 91731 626-444-7701
Keith Richardson, prin. Fax 442-6594
Ledesma Continuation HS 400/Alt
12347 Ramona Blvd 91732 626-442-0481
Fred Arteaga, prin. Fax 442-7260
Mountain View HS 1,800/9-12
2900 Parkway Dr 91732 626-443-6181
Keith Wheeler, prin. Fax 442-7284

El Monte-Rosemead Adult Education — Adult
10807 Ramona Blvd 91731 — 626-258-5800
Robin Torres, prin. — Fax 258-5809
Other Schools – See Rosemead, South El Monte

Mountain View ESD — 8,000/K-8
3320 Gilman Rd 91732 — 626-652-4000
Lillian Maldonado-French, supt. — Fax 652-4052
www.mtviewschools.com/
Kranz IS — 1,000/7-8
12460 Fineview St 91732 — 626-652-4200
Raymond Andry, prin. — Fax 652-4215
Madrid MS — 1,100/6-8
3300 Gilman Rd 91732 — 626-652-4300
Bonnie Tanaka, prin. — Fax 652-4315
Magnolia Learning Center — Alt
11919 Magnolia St 91732 — 626-652-4938
Terri Thomas, admin. — Fax 652-4939

International Theological Seminary — Post-Sec.
3225 Tyler Ave 91731 — 626-448-0023
Logos Evangelical Seminary — Post-Sec.
9358 Telstar Ave 91731 — 626-571-5110
Palladium Technical Academy — Post-Sec.
10503 Valley Blvd 91731 — 626-444-0880
Professional Institute of Beauty — Post-Sec.
10801 Valley Mall 91731 — 626-443-9401

El Segundo, Los Angeles, Pop. 15,912
El Segundo USD — 3,200/K-12
641 Sheldon St 90245 — 310-615-2650
Geoff Yantz Ed.D., supt. — Fax 322-0231
elsegundousd.org/
Arena HS — 50/Alt
641 Sheldon St 90245 — 310-615-2650
Janice Hickey, prin. — Fax 322-7939
El Segundo HS — 1,200/9-12
641 Sheldon St 90245 — 310-615-2662
Jim Garza, prin. — Fax 640-8079
El Segundo MS — 800/6-8
641 Sheldon St 90245 — 310-615-2690
Dr. Jack Plotkin, prin. — Fax 640-9634

Vistamar S — 300/9-12
737 Hawaii St 90245 — 310-643-7377
Karen Eshoo, head sch — Fax 643-7371

El Sobrante, Contra Costa, Pop. 11,868
West Contra Costa USD
Supt. — See Richmond
Crespi MS — 300/7-8
1121 Allview Ave 94803 — 510-223-8611
Patrick Martin, prin. — Fax 243-2090

El Sobrante Christian JSHS — 100/7-12
5070 Appian Way 94803 — 510-223-1966
C. Scott Wells, prin. — Fax 223-5344

Elverta, Sacramento, Pop. 5,268
Elverta JESD — 300/K-8
7900 Eloise Ave 95626 — 916-991-2244
Michael Borgaard, supt. — Fax 991-0271
www.ejesd.net
Alpha Technology MS — 100/6-8
7900 Eloise Ave 95626 — 916-991-2244
Michael Borgaard, prin. — Fax 991-0271

Emeryville, Alameda, Pop. 9,492
Emery USD — 700/K-12
1275 61st St 94608 — 510-601-4000
Dr. Debbra Lindo, supt. — Fax 601-4913
www.emeryusd.org/
Emery HS — 200/9-12
915 54th St 94608 — 510-601-4000
William Chavarin, prin. — Fax 601-4988

Carrington College California — Post-Sec.
6001 Shellmound St Ste 200 94608 — 510-964-3084
Expression College for Digital Arts — Post-Sec.
6601 Shellmound St 94608 — 510-654-2934

Encinitas, San Diego, Pop. 57,785
San Dieguito UNHSD — 12,500/7-12
710 Encinitas Blvd 92024 — 760-753-6491
Rick Schmitt, supt. — Fax 943-3501
www.sduhsd.net
Diegueno MS — 800/7-8
710 Encinitas Blvd 92024 — 760-944-1892
Bryan Marcus, prin. — Fax 944-3717
North Coast Alternative HS — 100/Alt
710 Encinitas Blvd 92024 — 760-753-3860
Rick Ayala, prin. — Fax 633-3170
Oak Crest MS — 900/7-8
710 Encinitas Blvd 92024 — 760-753-6241
Anna Pedroza, prin. — Fax 942-0520
San Dieguito HS Academy — 1,600/9-12
710 Encinitas Blvd 92024 — 760-753-1121
Tim Hornig, prin. — Fax 753-8142
Sunset HS — 100/Alt
710 Encinitas Blvd 92024 — 760-753-3860
Rick Ayala, prin. — Fax 753-8469
San Dieguito Adult HS — Adult
710 Encinitas Blvd 92024 — 760-753-7073
Denise Stanley, prin. — Fax 436-8376
Other Schools – See Carlsbad, San Diego, Solana Beach

Encinitas Country Day — 200/K-12
3616 Manchester Ave 92024 — 760-942-1111
Graeg Lehmunn, prin.
Grauer S — 200/6-12
1500 S El Camino Real 92024 — 760-944-6777
Dr. Stuart Grauer, head sch — Fax 944-6784

Encino, See Los Angeles

Crespi Carmelite HS — 600/9-12
5031 Alonzo Ave 91316 — 818-345-1672
Fr. Paul Henson, prin. — Fax 705-0209
Ferrahian HS — 300/6-12
5300 White Oak Ave 91316 — 818-784-6228
Westmark S — 200/3-12
5461 Louise Ave 91316 — 818-986-5045
T. Muir Meredith, head sch — Fax 986-2605

Escalon, San Joaquin, Pop. 7,002
Escalon USD — 2,900/K-12
1520 Yosemite Ave 95320 — 209-838-3591
Ron Costa, supt. — Fax 838-6703
www.escalonusd.org/
El Portal MS — 700/6-8
805 1st St 95320 — 209-838-7095
Mark Vos, prin. — Fax 838-3017
Escalon HS — 900/9-12
1528 Yosemite Ave 95320 — 209-838-7073
David Lattig, prin. — Fax 838-6127
Vista HS — 50/Alt
1520 Yosemite Ave 95320 — 209-838-1450
David Lattig, admin. — Fax 838-1922

Escondido, San Diego, Pop. 140,582
Escondido UNHSD — 9,300/9-12
302 N Midway Dr 92027 — 760-291-3200
Ed Nelson, supt. — Fax 480-3163
www.euhsd.k12.ca.us
Escondido HS — 2,700/9-12
1535 N Broadway 92026 — 760-291-4000
Rich Watkins, prin. — Fax 739-7313
Orange Glen HS — 2,300/9-12
2200 Glenridge Rd 92027 — 760-291-5000
Tom Allison, prin. — Fax 739-7314
San Pasqual HS — 2,600/9-12
3300 Bear Valley Pkwy S 92025 — 760-291-6000
Dr. Tom McCoy, prin. — Fax 739-7315
Valley HS — 400/9-12
410 Hidden Trails Rd 92027 — 760-291-2240
Saundra Uribe-Silverman, prin. — Fax 741-7605
Escondido Adult S — Adult
220 W Crest St 92025 — 760-739-7300
Dom Gagliardi, prin. — Fax 739-7310

Escondido Union SD — 19,200/PK-8
2310 Aldergrove Ave 92029 — 760-432-2400
Jennifer Walters, supt. — Fax 735-2874
www.eusd.org
Bear Valley MS — 1,100/6-8
3003 Bear Valley Pkwy S 92025 — 760-432-4060
Angel Gotay, prin. — Fax 504-0158
Del Dios MS — 900/6-8
1400 W 9th Ave 92029 — 760-432-2439
Suzanne Adkins, prin. — Fax 432-0728
Hidden Valley MS — 1,300/6-8
2700 Reed Rd 92027 — 760-432-2457
Trent Smith, prin. — Fax 480-0845
Mission MS — 1,000/6-8
939 E Mission Ave 92025 — 760-432-2452
Jon Centofranchi, prin. — Fax 737-9085
Nicolaysen Community Day S — 50/Alt
420 Falconer Rd 92027 — 760-432-2474
Randy Garcia, prin. — Fax 745-2739
Rincon MS — 1,200/6-8
925 Lehner Ave 92026 — 760-432-2491
Beth Crooks, prin. — Fax 743-6713

Calvin Christian JSHS — 300/6-12
2000 N Broadway 92026 — 760-489-6430
Frank Steidl, prin. — Fax 489-7055
Escondido Adventist Academy — 200/K-12
1301 Deodar Rd 92026 — 760-746-1800
Kristine Fuentes, prin. — Fax 743-3499
Westminster Seminary California — Post-Sec.
1725 Bear Valley Pkwy 92027 — 760-480-8474

Esparto, Yolo, Pop. 3,053
Esparto USD — 1,100/K-12
26675 Plainfield St 95627 — 530-787-3446
Aida Buelna, supt. — Fax 787-3033
www.espartok12.org
Esparto HS — 300/9-12
26675 Plainfield St 95627 — 530-787-3405
Aida Buelna, prin. — Fax 787-4850
Other Schools – See Madison

Etiwanda, See Rancho Cucamonga
Chaffey JUNHSD
Supt. — See Ontario
Etiwanda HS — 3,200/9-12
PO Box 447 91739 — 909-899-2531
Dr. Brian Joseph, prin. — Fax 899-3661

Etiwanda SD — 12,800/K-8
6061 East Ave 91739 — 909-899-2451
Shawn Judson Ed.D., supt. — Fax 899-1235
www.etiwanda.k12.ca.us
Day Creek IS — 1,200/6-8
12345 Coyote Dr 91739 — 909-803-3300
Alicia Lyon, prin. — Fax 803-3309
Etiwanda Community Day S — Alt
5959 East Ave 91739 — 909-899-1704
Lori Arita, prin. — Fax 899-7596
Etiwanda IS — 1,300/6-8
6925 Etiwanda Ave 91739 — 909-899-1701
Janella Cantu-Myricks, prin. — Fax 899-5676
Summit IS — 900/6-8
5959 East Ave 91739 — 909-899-1704
Lori Arita, prin. — Fax 899-7596
Other Schools – See Fontana

Etna, Siskiyou, Pop. 666
Scott Valley USD
Supt. — See Fort Jones
Etna HS — 200/9-12
PO Box 721 96027 — 530-467-3244
Bruce Bishop, prin. — Fax 467-5763
Scott River HS — 50/Alt
PO Box 59 96027 — 530-467-5279
Bruce Bishop, prin. — Fax 467-3459
Scott Valley Community Day S — 50/Alt
PO Box 59 96027 — 530-467-5279
Allan Carver, admin. — Fax 467-3459
Adult S — Adult
PO Box 721 96027 — 530-467-3244
Bruce Bishop, admin. — Fax 467-5763

Eureka, Humboldt, Pop. 25,748
Eureka City SD — 3,600/K-12
2100 J St 95501 — 707-441-2400
Fred Van Vleck Ed.D., supt. — Fax 441-3326
www.eurekacityschools.org
Barnum Continuation HS — 100/Alt
216 W Harris St 95503 — 707-441-2467
Sheri Jensen, prin. — Fax 441-0299
Eureka HS — 1,400/9-12
1915 J St 95501 — 707-441-2508
Rick Jordan, prin. — Fax 445-1956
Winship MS, 2500 Cypress Ave 95503 — 6-8
Kathy Cloney-Gardiner, prin. — 707-441-2488
Zane MS — 700/6-8
2155 S St 95501 — 707-441-2470
Jan Schmidt, prin. — Fax 441-0286
Eureka Adult Education — Adult
2100 J St 95501 — 707-441-2448
Laurie Alexander, prin. — Fax 442-1403

Fortuna UNHSD
Supt. — See Fortuna
Academy of the Redwoods — 200/9-12
7351 Tompkins Hill Rd 95501 — 707-476-4203
Matt Malkus, prin. — Fax 476-4439

Humboldt County Office of Education — 300/
901 Myrtle Ave 95501 — 707-445-7000
Garry Eagles Ph.D., supt. — Fax 445-7143
www.humboldt.k12.ca.us
Eureka Community S — 100/Alt
1820 6th St 95501 — 707-445-7108
Jennifer Fairbanks, prin. — Fax 445-7071
Other Schools – See Fortuna, Garberville

Regional Occupational Center & Program
Supt. — None
Humboldt County ROP — Vo/Tech
901 Myrtle Ave 95501 — 707-445-7018
Lori Breyer, dir. — Fax 445-7143

College of the Redwoods — Post-Sec.
7351 Tompkins Hill Rd 95501 — 707-476-4100
Frederick and Charles Beauty College — Post-Sec.
831 F St 95501 — 707-443-2733
Gospel Outreach S — 50/K-12
2845 Saint James Pl 95503 — 707-445-2214
David Sczepanski, prin. — Fax 445-2212
St. Bernard S — 300/PK-12
222 Dollison St 95501 — 707-443-2735
Paul Shanahan, dean — Fax 443-4723

Exeter, Tulare, Pop. 10,133
Exeter USD — 3,100/K-12
134 S E St 93221 — 559-592-9421
Tim Hire, supt. — Fax 592-9445
www.exeter.k12.ca.us/
Exeter Union HS — 1,000/9-12
505 Rocky Hill Dr 93221 — 559-592-2127
Frank Silveira, prin. — Fax 592-3539
Kaweah Continuation HS — 100/Alt
1107 Rocky Hill Dr 93221 — 559-592-4420
Darin Pace, prin. — Fax 592-5246
Wilson MS — 700/6-8
710 W Maple St 93221 — 559-592-2144
Sonia Wilson, prin. — Fax 592-5536

Sierra View Junior Academy — 100/K-10
19933 Avenue 256 93221 — 559-592-3689
Jeri Hoag, prin. — Fax 592-5615

Fairfax, Marin, Pop. 7,179
Ross Valley ESD
Supt. — See San Anselmo
White Hill MS — 600/6-8
101 Glen Dr 94930 — 415-454-8390
David Finnane, prin. — Fax 454-3980

Fairfield, Solano, Pop. 97,586
Fairfield-Suisun USD — 20,400/K-12
2490 Hilborn Rd, — 707-399-5000
Jacki Cottingim-Dias Ph.D., supt. — Fax 399-5154
www.fsusd.k12.ca.us
Armijo HS — 2,400/9-12
824 Washington St 94533 — 707-422-7500
Eric Tretten, prin. — Fax 438-3390
Fairfield HS — 1,700/9-12
205 E Atlantic Ave 94533 — 707-438-3000
Tim Halloran, prin. — Fax 422-0178
Garcia Learning Center — 2-12
1100 Civic Center Dr 94533
Amy Oss, prin.
Grange MS — 900/6-8
1975 Blossom Ave 94533 — 707-421-4175
Christine Harrison, prin. — Fax 422-4004
Green Valley MS — 900/6-8
1350 Gold Hill Rd, — 707-646-7000
Greg Hubbs, prin. — Fax 864-1503
Public Safety Academy — Vo/Tech
230 Atlantic Ave 94533 — 707-421-4100
Kathleen Frazer, prin.
Rodriguez HS — 2,200/9-12
5000 Red Top Rd, — 707-863-7950
Marie Williams, prin. — Fax 863-7974

Sem Yeto Continuation HS 200/Alt
301 E Alaska Ave 94533 707-421-4271
Amy Oss, prin. Fax 421-3232
Fairfield-Suisun Adult Education Adult
900 Travis Blvd 94533 707-421-4155
Kay Hartley, prin. Fax 421-4158
Other Schools – See Suisun City

Regional Occupational Center & Program
Supt. — None
Solano County ROP Vo/Tech
2460 Clay Bank Rd 94533 707-399-4800
Janet Harden, dir. Fax 429-1360

Travis USD 5,300/K-12
2751 De Ronde Dr 94533 707-437-4604
Kate Wren Gavlak, supt. Fax 437-8122
www.travisusd.k12.ca.us
Golden West MS 800/7-8
2651 De Ronde Dr 94533 707-437-8240
Jackie Tretten, prin. Fax 437-3416
Travis Community Day S 50/Alt
2785 De Ronde Dr 94533 707-437-8265
Allyson Rude Azevedo, prin.
Travis Education Center HS 100/Alt
2775 De Ronde Dr 94533 707-437-8265
Allyson Rude Azevedo, prin. Fax 437-0141
Vanden HS 1,600/9-12
2951 Markeley Ln 94533 707-437-7333
Sandra Reese, prin. Fax 437-7220

Fairfield Christian S 100/K-12
PO Box 2172 94533 707-427-2665
Rev. Jason Yarbrough, prin. Fax 402-6450
Mars Hill Christian S 100/K-12
PO Box 2172 94533 707-427-2665
Rev. Jason Yarbrough, admin. Fax 402-6450
Milan Institute of Cosmetology Post-Sec.
934 Missouri St 94533 707-425-2288
Solano Community College Post-Sec.
4000 Suisun Valley Rd, 707-864-7000

Fair Oaks, Sacramento, Pop. 29,764
San Juan USD
Supt. — See Carmichael
Bella Vista HS 2,000/9-12
8301 Madison Ave 95628 916-971-5052
Peggy Haskins, prin. Fax 971-5011
Del Campo HS 2,000/9-12
4925 Dewey Dr 95628 916-971-5664
Brett Wolfe, prin. Fax 971-5640
El Sereno Independent Study S 200/Alt
10700 Fair Oaks Blvd 95628 916-971-5060
Amy Slavensky, prin. Fax 971-5070
Rogers MS 600/6-8
4924 Dewey Dr 95628 916-971-7889
Gabriel Cooper, prin. Fax 971-7903

Freedom Christian S 100/K-12
7736 Sunset Ave 95628 916-962-3247
Annette Coller, admin. Fax 962-0783
Rudolf Steiner College Post-Sec.
9200 Fair Oaks Blvd 95628 916-961-8727
Sacramento Waldorf S 400/K-12
3750 Bannister Rd 95628 916-961-3900
Fax 961-3970

Fallbrook, San Diego, Pop. 29,874
Fallbrook UNESD 5,800/K-8
321 Iowa St 92028 760-731-5420
Candace Singh, supt. Fax 723-3895
www.fuesd.org
Potter IS 900/7-8
1743 Reche Rd 92028 760-731-4150
Leonard Rodriguez, prin. Fax 723-5740

Fallbrook UNHSD 3,000/9-12
2234 S Stage Coach Ln 92028 760-723-6332
Dale Mitchell Ed.D., supt. Fax 723-1795
www.fuhsd.net
Fallbrook HS 2,700/9-12
2400 S Stage Coach Ln 92028 760-723-6300
Rod King, prin. Fax 723-6343
Ivy HS 200/Alt
1056 Winter Haven Rd 92028 760-723-6395
Melissa Marovich, prin. Fax 723-6392
Oasis Alternative HS 100/Alt
2208 S Stage Coach Ln 92028 760-723-1886
Melissa Marovich, prin. Fax 723-6411

Farmersville, Tulare, Pop. 10,466
Farmersville USD 2,400/K-12
571 E Citrus Dr 93223 559-592-2010
Christina Luna Ed.D., supt. Fax 592-2203
www.farmersville.k12.ca.us
Deep Creek Academy 100/Alt
281 S Farmersville Blvd 93223 559-747-6205
Randy DeGraw, prin. Fax 747-0591
Farmersville HS 700/9-12
631 E Walnut Ave 93223 559-594-4567
Ernie Flores, prin. Fax 594-5287
Farmersville JHS 400/7-8
650 N Virginia Ave 93223 559-747-0764
Loretta Aragon, prin. Fax 747-2704

Felton, Santa Cruz, Pop. 3,909
San Lorenzo Valley USD
Supt. — See Ben Lomond
San Lorenzo Valley HS 800/9-12
7105 Highway 9 95018 831-335-4425
Karen van Putten, prin. Fax 335-1531
San Lorenzo Valley MS 500/6-8
7179 Hacienda Way 95018 831-335-4452
Jeff Calden, prin. Fax 335-3812

Ferndale, Humboldt, Pop. 1,343
Ferndale USD 500/K-12
1231 Main St 95536 707-786-5900
Jack Lakin, supt. Fax 786-4865
www.ferndalek12.org/
Ferndale HS 200/9-12
1231 Main St 95536 707-786-5900
Jack Lakin, prin. Fax 786-4865

Fillmore, Ventura, Pop. 14,823
Fillmore USD 3,800/K-12
PO Box 697 93016 805-524-6000
Alan Nishino, supt. Fax 524-6060
www.fillmore.k12.ca.us
Fillmore HS 1,100/9-12
PO Box 697 93016 805-524-6100
Russom Mesfun, prin. Fax 524-6121
Fillmore MS 800/6-8
PO Box 697 93016 805-524-6055
Bobbi Roderick, prin. Fax 524-6063
Sierra HS 100/Alt
PO Box 697 93016 805-524-8202
Cynthia Frutos, prin. Fax 524-6080

Firebaugh, Fresno, Pop. 7,529
Firebaugh-Las Deltas JUSD 2,200/PK-12
1976 Morris Kyle Dr 93622 559-659-1476
Russell Freitas, supt. Fax 659-2355
www.fldusd.org/
El Puente Continuation HS 50/Alt
1976 Morris Kyle Dr 93622 559-659-3899
Susan Lopez, admin. Fax 659-1511
Firebaugh HS 700/9-12
1976 Morris Kyle Dr 93622 559-659-1415
Terry Anderson, prin. Fax 659-2636
Firebaugh MS 500/6-8
1976 Morris Kyle Dr 93622 559-659-1481
Howard Yamagiwa, admin. Fax 659-7106
Firebaugh-Las Deltas Adult S Adult
1976 Morris Kyle Dr 93622 559-659-3899
Susan Lopez, admin. Fax 659-1511

Folsom, Sacramento, Pop. 69,359
Folsom-Cordova USD
Supt. — See Rancho Cordova
Folsom HS 1,900/9-12
1655 Iron Point Rd 95630 916-355-1115
Kathryn Allaman, prin. Fax 355-1110
Folsom Lake HS 100/Alt
955 Riley St 95630 916-294-9809
Leane Linson, prin. Fax 294-9728
Folsom MS 1,200/6-8
500 Blue Ravine Rd 95630 916-983-4466
Chris Aland, prin. Fax 983-3462
Sutter MS 1,200/6-8
715 Riley St 95630 916-985-3644
Keri Phillips, prin. Fax 985-7044
Vista Del Lago HS 1,400/9-12
1970 Broadstone Pkwy 95630 916-294-2410
John Dixon, prin. Fax 294-2411

Folsom Lake College Post-Sec.
10 College Pkwy 95630 916-608-6500

Fontana, San Bernardino, Pop. 192,303
Etiwanda SD
Supt. — See Etiwanda
Heritage IS 1,300/6-8
13766 S Heritage Cir 92336 909-357-1345
Laura Rowland, prin. Fax 357-8945

Fontana USD 39,700/PK-12
9680 Citrus Ave 92335 909-357-7600
Cali Olsen-Binks, supt. Fax 357-5012
www.fusd.net
Alder MS 1,200/6-8
7555 Alder Ave 92336 909-357-5330
Erik Swanson, prin. Fax 357-5348
Almeria MS 1,000/6-8
7723 Almeria Ave 92336 909-357-5350
Douglas Bergquist, prin. Fax 357-5360
Birch HS 400/Alt
7930 Locust Ave 92336 909-357-5310
Fax 357-5319
Citrus Continuation HS 400/Alt
9820 Citrus Ave 92335 909-357-5300
Eric Groeber, prin. Fax 357-5302
Fontana HS 3,400/9-12
9453 Citrus Ave 92335 909-357-5500
Ofelia Hinojosa, prin. Fax 357-5629
Fontana MS 1,100/6-8
8425 Mango Ave 92335 909-357-5370
Sergio Chavez, prin. Fax 357-5391
Jurupa Hills HS 9-12
10700 Oleander Ave 92337 909-357-6300
Victor Uribe, prin. Fax 357-7540
Kaiser HS 2,400/9-12
11155 Almond Ave 92337 909-357-5900
Terry Abernathy, prin. Fax 357-5997
Miller HS 2,800/9-12
6821 Oleander Ave 92336 909-357-5800
Fax 357-7680
Ruble MS 1,300/6-8
6762 Juniper Ave 92336 909-357-5530
Crystal Whitley, prin. Fax 357-5539
Sequoia MS 1,200/7-8
9452 Hemlock Ave 92335 909-357-5400
Gorge Santiago, prin. Fax 357-5419
Southridge MS 1,200/6-8
14500 Live Oak Ave 92337 909-357-5420
Gerald Mullins, prin. Fax 822-4609
Summit HS 2,600/9-12
15551 Summit Ave 92336 909-357-5950
Delia Fant, prin. Fax 357-5959
Truman MS 1,300/6-8
16224 Mallory Dr 92335 909-357-5190
Kim Hall, prin. Fax 357-5199

Fontana Adult S Adult
10755 Oleander Ave 92337 909-357-5490
Tracie Zerpoli, prin. Fax 357-5556

American Institute of Technology Post-Sec.
14235 Slover Ave 92337 909-498-4250

Foresthill, Placer, Pop. 1,441
Foresthill UNESD 500/K-8
24750 Main St 95631 530-367-2966
Jim Roberts, supt. Fax 367-2470
www.fusd.org
Foresthill Divide MS 200/5-8
22888 Foresthill Rd 95631 530-367-3782
Shannon Jacinto, prin. Fax 367-4526

Placer UNHSD
Supt. — See Auburn
Foresthill HS 300/9-12
23319 Foresthill Rd 95631 530-367-5244
Sue Lunsford, prin. Fax 367-4623

Forestville, Sonoma, Pop. 3,212
West Sonoma CUHSD
Supt. — See Sebastopol
El Molino HS 800/9-12
7050 Covey Rd 95436 707-824-6570
Doria Trombetta, prin. Fax 887-0448

Fort Bragg, Mendocino, Pop. 7,053
Fort Bragg USD 1,900/PK-12
312 S Lincoln St 95437 707-961-2850
Dr. Donald Armstrong, supt. Fax 964-5002
www.fbusd.us
Fort Bragg HS 500/9-12
300 Dana St 95437 707-961-2880
Rebecca Walker, prin. Fax 961-2884
Fort Bragg MS 400/6-8
500 N Harold St 95437 707-961-2870
Donna Miller, prin. Fax 964-9416
Lighthouse Community Day S 50/Alt
250 S Sanderson Way 95437 707-964-1017
Coni Belli, prin.
Noyo HS 50/Alt
250 S Sanderson Way 95437 707-961-2889
Coni Belli, prin. Fax 964-1017
Shelter Cove S 50/Alt
310 S Lincoln St 95437 707-961-2889
Coni Belli, prin. Fax 964-1017
Coastal Adult S Adult
250 S Sanderson Way 95437 707-961-2889
Coni Belli, prin. Fax 964-1017

Fort Irwin, San Bernardino, Pop. 8,282
Silver Valley USD
Supt. — See Yermo
Fort Irwin MS 300/6-8
1700 Pork Chop Hill St 92310 760-386-1133
Michael Sullivan, prin. Fax 386-2448

Fort Jones, Siskiyou, Pop. 789
Scott Valley USD 700/K-12
PO Box 687 96032 530-468-2727
Dr. Bryan Caples, supt. Fax 468-2729
www.svusd.us/
Scott Valley JHS 100/6-9
PO Box 249 96032 530-468-5565
Allan Carver, prin. Fax 468-5658
Other Schools – See Etna

Fortuna, Humboldt, Pop. 11,506
Fortuna ESD 1,300/K-8
500 9th St 95540 707-725-2293
Dr. Patti Hafner, supt. Fax 725-2228
www.humboldt.k12.ca.us/fortuna_un/
Fortuna MS 200/5-8
843 L St 95540 707-725-3415
Oscar Mendez, prin. Fax 725-6240
Thomas MS 300/5-8
2800 Thomas St 95540 707-725-5197
Julie Johansen, prin. Fax 725-8637

Fortuna UNHSD 1,100/9-12
379 12th St 95540 707-725-4461
Glen Senestraro, supt. Fax 725-6085
www.fuhsdistrict.org
East HS 100/Alt
379 12th St 95540 707-725-4461
Brian Schoenfield, dir. Fax 725-9746
Fortuna Union HS 800/9-12
379 12th St 95540 707-725-4461
Clint Duey, admin. Fax 725-5511
Strongs Creek Community Day S 50/Alt
379 12th St 95540 707-725-5303
Stephanie Bennett, dir. Fax 725-5313
Fortuna Adult Education Adult
379 12th St 95540 707-725-4482
Glen Senestraro, coord. Fax 726-0347
Other Schools – See Eureka

Humboldt County Office of Education
Supt. — See Eureka
Eel River Community S 100/Alt
2292 Newburg Rd 95540 707-725-0209
Jennifer Fairbanks, prin. Fax 725-0326

New Life Christian S 100/PK-12
1202 Ross Hill Rd 95540 707-725-9136
Karen Johnson, prin. Fax 725-1638

Foster City, San Mateo, Pop. 29,077
San Mateo-Foster City ESD 10,900/K-8
1170 Chess Dr 94404 650-312-7700
Cynthia Simms Ph.D., supt. Fax 312-7348
www.smfc.k12.ca.us
Bowditch MS 900/6-8
1450 Tarpon St 94404 650-312-7680
Judy Ross, prin. Fax 312-7639
Other Schools – See San Mateo

Fountain Valley, Orange, Pop. 53,408
Fountain Valley ESD 5,900/K-8
10055 Slater Ave 92708 714-843-3200
Marc Ecker Ph.D., supt. Fax 841-0356
www.fvsd.k12.ca.us
Fulton MS 800/6-8
8778 El Lago Cir 92708 714-375-2816
Jennifer Perkins, prin. Fax 375-2825
Masuda MS 900/6-8
17415 Los Jardines W 92708 714-378-4250
Chris Mullin, prin. Fax 378-4259
Other Schools – See Huntington Beach

Garden Grove USD
Supt. — See Garden Grove
Los Amigos HS 2,200/9-12
16566 Newhope St 92708 714-663-6288
Robin Patterson, prin. Fax 663-6518

Huntington Beach UNHSD
Supt. — See Huntington Beach
Fountain Valley HS 3,400/9-12
17816 Bushard St 92708 714-962-3301
Chris Herzfeld, prin. Fax 964-0491
Valley Vista HS 300/Alt
9600 Dolphin St 92708 714-964-7766
Kerry Clitheroe, prin. Fax 964-3045

Ocean View SD
Supt. — See Huntington Beach
Vista View MS 800/6-8
16250 Hickory St 92708 714-842-0626
Robert Miller, prin. Fax 843-9156

Coastline Community College Post-Sec.
11460 Warner Ave 92708 714-546-7600
Modern Technology School Post-Sec.
16560 Harbor Blvd Ste K 92708 714-418-9100

Fowler, Fresno, Pop. 5,491
Fowler USD 2,300/K-12
658 E Adams Ave 93625 559-834-6080
Eric Cederquist, supt. Fax 834-3390
www.fowlerusd.org
Fowler HS 600/9-12
701 E Main St 93625 559-834-6160
Henry Gutierrez, prin. Fax 834-3284
Fowler Unified Alternative Education 50/Alt
658 E Adams Ave 93625 559-834-6098
Jonathan Farley, prin. Fax 834-6721
Sutter MS 500/6-8
701 E Walter Ave 93625 559-834-6180
Gary Geringer, prin. Fax 834-4739

Fremont, Alameda, Pop. 203,344
Fremont USD 32,500/K-12
PO Box 5008 94537 510-657-2350
James Morris Ed.D., supt. Fax 659-2597
www.fremont.k12.ca.us
American HS 2,000/9-12
36300 Fremont Blvd 94536 510-796-1776
Greg Bailey, prin. Fax 791-5331
Centerville JHS 900/7-8
37720 Fremont Blvd 94536 510-797-2072
Sherry Strausbaugh, prin. Fax 794-7588
Hopkins JHS 1,100/7-8
600 Driscoll Rd 94539 510-656-3500
Mary Miller, prin. Fax 656-3731
Horner JHS 1,000/7-8
41365 Chapel Way 94538 510-656-4000
Steve Musto, prin. Fax 656-2793
Irvington HS 2,100/9-12
41800 Blacow Rd 94538 510-656-5711
Sarah Smoot, prin. Fax 623-9805
Kennedy HS 1,400/9-12
39999 Blacow Rd 94538 510-657-4070
Eddie Velez, prin. Fax 438-9287
Mission San Jose HS 2,200/9-12
41717 Palm Ave 94539 510-657-3600
Zack Larsen, prin. Fax 657-2302
Robertson Continuation HS 300/Alt
4455 Seneca Park Ave 94538 510-657-9155
Sal Herrera, prin. Fax 657-5535
Thornton JHS 1,000/7-8
4357 Thornton Ave 94536 510-793-9090
Stan Hicks, prin. Fax 793-9756
Vista Alternative S 100/Alt
4455 Seneca Park Ave 94538 510-657-7028
Sal Herrera, prin. Fax 657-0733
Walters JHS 800/7-8
39600 Logan Dr 94538 510-656-7211
Brian Weems, prin. Fax 656-4056
Washington HS 2,000/9-12
38442 Fremont Blvd 94536 510-505-7300
Rob Moran, prin. Fax 794-8437
Fremont Adult S Adult
4700 Calaveras Ave 94538 510-793-6465
Steve Giudici, prin. Fax 793-2271

Regional Occupational Center & Program
Supt. — None
Mission Valley ROP Vo/Tech
5019 Stevenson Blvd 94538 510-657-1865
Pete Murchison, supt. Fax 438-0378

Alsion Montessori MSHS 100/7-12
PO Box 3296 94539 510-445-1127
Michael Leahy, admin.
California School for the Blind Post-Sec.
500 Walnut Ave 94536
California School for the Deaf Post-Sec.
39350 Gallaudet Dr 94538 510-794-3684
DeVry University Post-Sec.
6600 Dumbarton Cir 94555 510-574-1200
Fremont Christian S 800/PK-12
4760 Thornton Ave 94536 510-744-2249
Dr. Tricia Meyer, supt. Fax 744-2255
Northwestern Polytechnic University Post-Sec.
47671 Westinghouse Dr 94539 510-592-9688
Ohlone College Post-Sec.
43600 Mission Blvd 94539 510-659-6000
Queen of the Holy Rosary College Post-Sec.
43326 Mission Blvd 94539 510-657-2468
Unitek College Post-Sec.
4670 Auto Mall Pkwy 94538 888-735-4355
Wyotech Post-Sec.
420 Whitney Pl 94539 510-490-6900

Fresno, Fresno, Pop. 482,604
Central USD 14,800/K-12
4605 N Polk Ave 93722 559-274-4700
Michael A. Berg, supt. Fax 271-8200
www.centralunified.org/
Central HS East Campus 4,000/9-12
3535 N Cornelia Ave 93722 559-276-0280
Jack Kelejian, prin. Fax 276-5653
Central HS West Campus 9-12
2045 N Dickenson Ave, 559-276-5276
Jack Kelejian, prin. Fax 276-6380
Central Unified Alternative S 300/Alt
2698 N Brawley Ave 93722 559-276-5230
Patrick Flattley, prin. Fax 276-8204
El Capitan MS 900/7-8
4443 W Weldon Ave 93722 559-276-5270
Jeff Wimp, prin. Fax 276-3121
Glacier Point MS 7-8
4055 N Bryan Ave, 559-276-3105
Eliseo Cuellar, prin. Fax 276-3105
Pathway Community Day School 50/Alt
11 S Teilman Ave 93706 559-487-1201
Wayne Morris, prin. Fax 487-1204
Pershing Continuation HS 100/Alt
855 W Nielsen 93706 559-268-2272
Wayne Morris, prin. Fax 268-2279
Rio Vista MS 1,300/7-8
6240 W Palo Alto Ave 93722 559-276-3185
Lori Hamada, prin. Fax 276-3199
Central Unified Adult Education Adult
2698 N Brawley Ave 93722 559-276-5230
Patrick Flattley, prin. Fax 276-8204

Clovis USD
Supt. — See Clovis
Clovis North HS 1,300/9-12
2770 E International Ave, 559-327-5000
Scott Dille, prin. Fax 327-5290
Clovis West HS 2,300/9-12
1070 E Teague Ave 93720 559-327-2000
Eimear O'Farrell, prin. Fax 327-2490
Granite Ridge IS 1,100/7-8
2770 E International Ave, 559-327-5000
Scott Dille, prin. Fax 327-5090
Kastner IS 1,100/7-8
7676 N 1st St 93720 559-327-2500
Johnny Alvarado, prin. Fax 327-2790

Fresno County Office of Education 1,800/
1111 Van Ness Ave 93721 559-265-3000
Larry Powell, supt. Fax 265-4005
www.fcoe.org
Fresno County Community Day S 100/Alt
1320 N Mariposa St 93703 559-443-4863
Bill Johnson, prin. Fax 264-6398
Fresno County Community S 100/Alt
4939 E Yale Ave 93727 559-443-4863
Bill Johnson, prin. Fax 443-4856

Fresno USD 74,600/PK-12
2309 Tulare St 93721 559-457-3000
Michael Hanson, supt. Fax 457-3786
www.fresnounified.org
Ahwahnee MS 700/7-8
1127 E Escalon Ave 93710 559-451-4300
Jose Guzman, prin. Fax 439-1808
Baird MS 600/5-8
5500 N Maroa Ave 93704 559-451-4310
Janetta McGensy, prin. Fax 432-4075
Bullard HS 2,600/9-12
5445 N Palm Ave 93704 559-451-4320
Brian Beck, prin. Fax 451-4339
Cambridge Continuation HS 400/Alt
1001 S Chestnut Ave 93702 559-253-6560
Yolanda Jimenez-Ruiz, prin. Fax 266-9776
Carver Academy 100/5-8
2463 Martin L King Jr Blvd 93706 559-457-2620
Steve Gonzalez, prin. Fax 497-5336
Computech MS 800/7-8
555 E Belgravia Ave 93706 559-457-2640
Jeremy Ward, prin. Fax 457-2643
Cooper MS 500/7-8
2277 W Bellaire Way 93705 559-248-7050
Kristine Belcher, prin. Fax 224-7255
Design Science HS 200/9-12
2004 E Cambridge Ave 93703 559-248-7353
Roy Exum, prin.
Dewolf Continuation HS 300/Alt
2021 N Clark St 93703 559-248-7350
Frank Duran, prin. Fax 224-2840
Duncan Polytechnical HS Vo/Tech
4330 E Garland Ave 93726 559-248-7080
Carol Hansen, prin. Fax 222-6186
Edison HS 2,200/9-12
540 E California Ave 93706 559-457-2650
Lindsay Sanders, prin. Fax 457-2742
Ft. Miller MS 900/7-8
1302 E Dakota Ave 93704 559-248-7100
Debbie Buckman, prin. Fax 221-7548
Fresno HS 2,600/9-12
1839 N Echo Ave 93704 559-457-2780
John Forbes, prin. Fax 457-2801
Hoover HS, 5550 N 1st St 93710 2,000/9-12
Lori Grace, prin. 559-451-4000
Kings Canyon MS 900/7-8
5117 E Tulare Ave 93727 559-253-6470
Clark Mello, prin. Fax 253-1005
McLane HS 2,400/9-12
2727 N Cedar Ave 93703 559-248-5100
Scott Lamm, prin. Fax 255-5253
Phoenix Secondary Academy Alt
2445 W Dakota Ave 93705 559-457-2990
Brian Radtke, prin.
Roosevelt HS 2,300/9-12
4250 E Tulare St 93702 559-253-5200
Bryan Wells, prin. Fax 253-5319
Scandinavian MS 600/7-8
3216 N Sierra Vista Ave 93726 559-253-6510
Julie Goorabian-Ellis, prin. Fax 252-7608
Sequoia MS 900/7-8
4050 E Hamilton Ave 93702 559-457-3210
Matt Ward, prin. Fax 497-1745
Sunnyside HS 3,200/9-12
1019 S Peach Ave 93727 559-253-6700
Tim Liles, prin. Fax 253-6799
Tehipite MS 500/7-8
630 N Augusta St 93701 559-457-3420
Yvonne Zysling, prin. Fax 457-3423
Tenaya MS 900/7-8
1239 W Mesa Ave 93711 559-451-4570
Heather Garcia, prin. Fax 431-0771
Terronez MS 800/7-8
2300 S Willow Ave 93725 559-253-6570
Virginia Mendez-Buelna, prin. Fax 253-6572
Tioga MS 800/7-8
3232 E Fairmont Ave 93726 559-248-7280
Curtis Shamlin, prin. Fax 226-1296
Wawona MS 800/7-8
4524 N Thorne Ave 93704 559-248-7310
Mike Darling, prin. Fax 227-5206
Yosemite MS 600/7-8
1292 N 9th St 93703 559-457-3450
Ed Gomes, prin. Fax 264-0933
Young Academic Center 1,400/Alt
822 N Abby St 93701 559-457-3190
Janice Trimble, prin. Fax 457-3193
Chavez Adult S Adult
2500 Stanislaus St 93721 559-457-6000
Sally Fowler, prin. Fax 457-6001
Other Schools – See Clovis

Regional Occupational Center & Program
Supt. — None
Fresno ROP Vo/Tech
1318 E Shaw Ave Ste 420 93710 559-497-3850
Valerie Vuicich, admin. Fax 497-3806

Washington USD 3,000/K-12
6041 S Elm Ave 93706 559-485-8805
John Pestorich, supt. Fax 485-4435
www.wusd.ws
Easton Community S 50/Alt
6041 S Elm Ave 93706 559-485-9350
Glen Freeman, prin. Fax 237-0270
Easton Continuation HS 50/Alt
5865 S Clara Ave 93706 559-485-9350
Glen Freeman, prin. Fax 237-0270
Washington Union HS 1,100/9-12
6041 S Elm Ave 93706 559-485-8805
Derek Cruz, prin. Fax 485-4435
West Fresno MS 300/6-8
2888 S Ivy Ave 93706 559-495-5607
Alan Macedo, prin. Fax 485-3006

Advanced Career Institute Post-Sec.
2953 S East Ave 93725 559-441-4345
Alliant International University Post-Sec.
5130 E Clinton Way 93727 559-253-2200
California Christian College Post-Sec.
4881 E University Ave 93703 559-251-4215
California State University-Fresno Post-Sec.
5241 N Maple Ave 93740 559-278-4240
Central Valley Christian Academy 50/K-12
4147 E Dakota Ave 93726 559-226-4644
Timothe Addelsee, prin. Fax 248-2775
DeVry University Post-Sec.
7575 N Fresno St 93720 559-439-8595
Fresno Adventist Academy 200/K-12
5397 E Olive Ave 93727 559-251-5548
Dr. Marvin Mitchell, prin. Fax 456-1735
Fresno Christian S - Peoples Campus 300/7-12
7280 N Cedar Ave 93720 559-299-1695
Todd Bennett, prin. Fax 299-1051
Fresno City College Post-Sec.
1101 E University Ave 93741 559-442-4600
Fresno Pacific Biblical Seminary Post-Sec.
1717 S Chestnut Ave 93702 559-453-2310
Fresno Pacific University Post-Sec.
1717 S Chestnut Ave 93702 559-453-2000
Galen College Medical & Dental Assts. Post-Sec.
1325 N Wishon Ave 93728 559-264-9700
Heald College Post-Sec.
255 W Bullard Ave 93704 559-438-4222
Lyle's College of Beauty Post-Sec.
6735 N 1st St Ste 112 93710 559-431-6060
Manchester Beauty College Post-Sec.
3756 N Blackstone Ave 93726 559-224-4242
San Joaquin Memorial HS 600/9-12
1406 N Fresno St 93703 559-268-9251
Edward Borges, prin. Fax 268-1351
San Joaquin Valley College Post-Sec.
295 E Sierra Ave 93710 559-448-8282
San Joaquin Valley College Post-Sec.
4985 E Andersen Ave 93727 559-453-0123
Sierra Valley College of Court Reporting Post-Sec.
4747 N 1st St # D 93726 559-222-0947
UEI College Post-Sec.
2002 N Gateway Blvd 93727 559-456-0623

Fullerton, Orange, Pop. 131,685
Fullerton JUNHSD 14,700/9-12
1051 W Bastanchury Rd 92833 714-870-2800
George Giokaris Ed.D., supt. Fax 870-2807
www.fjuhsd.net
Fullerton Union HS 2,100/9-12
201 E Chapman Ave 92832 714-626-3801
Cathy Gach, prin. Fax 626-3839

La Sierra HS 600/Alt
951 N State College Blvd 92831 714-447-7820
Sandi Layana, prin.
La Vista HS 600/Alt
909 N State College Blvd 92831 714-447-7821
Sandi Layana, prin. Fax 773-0644
Sunny Hills HS 2,500/9-12
1801 Warburton Way 92833 714-626-4201
Judy Fancher, prin. Fax 738-3728
Troy HS 2,600/9-12
2200 Dorothy Ln 92831 714-626-4401
Maggie Buchan, prin. Fax 626-4492
Other Schools – See Buena Park, La Habra

Fullerton SD 13,600/K-8
1401 W Valencia Dr 92833 714-447-7400
Bob Pletka Ed.D., supt. Fax 447-7414
fsd.k12.ca.us
Ladera Vista JHS 900/7-8
1700 E Wilshire Ave 92831 714-447-7765
John Albert, prin. Fax 447-7554
Nicolas JHS 800/7-8
1100 W Olive Ave 92833 714-447-7775
Dr. Mathew Barnett, prin. Fax 447-7586
Parks JHS 1,000/7-8
1710 Rosecrans Ave 92833 714-447-7785
Sherry Dustin, prin. Fax 447-7753

California State University-Fullerton Post-Sec.
PO Box 34080 92834 657-278-2011
Eastside Christian S 200/K-12
1701 W Valencia Dr 92833 714-525-7200
Kim Van Geloof, head sch Fax 525-7200
Fullerton College Post-Sec.
321 E Chapman Ave 92832 714-992-7000
Grace Christian Academy 100/K-12
1619 W Louise Pl 92833 714-871-5278
Sydney Christy, admin.
Grace Mission University Post-Sec.
1645 W Valencia Dr 92833 714-525-0088
Hope International University Post-Sec.
2500 Nutwood Ave 92831 714-879-3901
Rosary HS 600/9-12
1340 N Acacia Ave 92831 714-879-6302
Annette Zaleski, prin. Fax 879-0853
Southern California College of Optometry Post-Sec.
2575 Yorba Linda Blvd 92831 714-870-7226
Western State University College of Law Post-Sec.
1111 N State College Blvd 92831 714-738-1000

Galt, Sacramento, Pop. 22,880
Galt JUNESD 4,000/K-8
1018 C St Ste 210 95632 209-744-4545
Karen Schauer, supt. Fax 744-4553
www.galt.k12.ca.us
McCaffrey MS 1,000/7-8
997 Park Terrace Dr 95632 209-745-5462
Cleo Del Toro-Anguiano, prin. Fax 745-5465

Galt JUNHSD 2,300/9-12
12945 Marengo Rd 95632 209-745-0249
Dr. Matthew Roberts, supt. Fax 745-0881
www.ghsd.k12.ca.us
Estrellita Continuation HS 200/Alt
12935 Marengo Rd 95632 209-745-2167
Tony Lara, prin. Fax 745-7026
Galt HS 1,200/9-12
145 N Lincoln Way 95632 209-745-3081
Maria Orr, prin. Fax 745-4786
Liberty Ranch HS 900/9-12
12945 Marengo Rd 95632 209-744-4250
Brian Deis, prin. Fax 745-2601
Adult Education Adult
150 Camellia Way 95632 209-745-5852
Karin Liu, dir. Fax 745-7026

Garberville, Humboldt, Pop. 894
Humboldt County Office of Education
Supt. — See Eureka
Southern Humboldt Community S 50/Alt
390 Lake Benbow Dr Ste A 95542 707-923-2550
Jennifer Fairbanks, prin.

Gardena, Los Angeles, Pop. 56,918
Los Angeles USD
Supt. — See Los Angeles
Gardena HS 2,300/9-12
1301 W 182nd St 90248 310-354-5000
Russell Thompson, prin. Fax 366-6943
Moneta Continuation HS 50/Alt
1230 W 177th St 90248 310-354-4951
Antonio Morreale, prin. Fax 352-4027
Peary MS 1,900/6-8
1415 W Gardena Blvd 90247 310-225-4200
Marva Patton, prin. Fax 329-3957
Kiriyama Community Adult S Adult
18120 S Normandie Ave 90248 310-354-4900
Wanda Chang, prin. Fax 323-8981

American Institute of Technology Post-Sec.
18010 S Figueroa St 90248 310-594-8971
Everest College Post-Sec.
1045 W Rdnd Bch Blvd #275 90247 310-527-7105
Junipero Serra HS 600/9-12
14830 Van Ness Ave 90249 310-324-6675
De Larkin, prin. Fax 352-4953
UEI College Post-Sec.
661 W Redondo Beach Blvd 90247 888-202-2485

Garden Grove, Orange, Pop. 166,793
Garden Grove USD 48,600/K-12
10331 Stanford Ave 92840 714-663-6000
Laura Schwalm Ph.D., supt. Fax 663-6100
www.ggusd.us/
Alamitos IS 900/7-8
12381 Dale St 92841 714-663-6101
Bill Gates, prin. Fax 663-6277
Bell IS 700/7-8
11852 Knott St 92841 714-663-6466
Frank Mackay, prin. Fax 663-6238
Bolsa Grande HS 2,000/9-12
9401 Westminster Ave 92844 714-663-6424
Louise Milner, prin. Fax 663-6029
Doig IS 900/7-8
12752 Trask Ave 92843 714-663-6241
Michael Kennedy, prin. Fax 663-6845
Garden Grove HS 2,400/9-12
11271 Stanford Ave 92840 714-663-6115
Steve Osborne, prin. Fax 663-6030
Hare HS 600/Alt
12012 Magnolia St 92841 714-663-6508
Mark Nguien, prin. Fax 663-6510
Irvine IS 900/7-8
10552 Hazard Ave 92843 714-663-6551
Vicki Braddock, prin. Fax 663-6013
Jordan IS 700/7-8
9821 Woodbury Ave 92844 714-663-6124
Christina Pflughoft, prin. Fax 663-6123
Lake IS 700/7-8
10801 Orangewood Ave 92840 714-663-6506
Dave Biniasz, prin. Fax 663-6065
Lincoln Continuation HS 50/Alt
11262 Garden Grove Blvd 92843 714-663-6532
Nancy Fyson Ed.D., dir. Fax 530-4105
Pacifica HS 1,900/9-12
6851 Lampson Ave 92845 714-663-6515
Jason Bevacqua, prin. Fax 663-6037
Ralston IS 600/7-8
10851 Lampson Ave 92840 714-663-6366
Jan Cody, prin. Fax 638-7155
Rancho Alamitos HS 2,000/9-12
11351 Dale St 92841 714-663-6415
Mary Hibbard, prin. Fax 663-6439
Santiago HS 2,300/9-12
12342 Trask Ave 92843 714-663-6215
Lila Jenkins, prin. Fax 530-0764
Walton IS 700/7-8
12181 Buaro St 92840 714-663-6040
John Marsh, prin. Fax 534-4814
Lincoln Education Center Adult
11262 Garden Grove Blvd 92843 714-663-6291
Nancy Fyson Ed.D., dir.
Other Schools – See Fountain Valley, Santa Ana, Westminster

Career Academy of Beauty Post-Sec.
12471 Valley View St 92845 714-897-3010
Concorde Career Institute Post-Sec.
12951 Euclid St Ste 101 92840 714-703-1900
Crystal Cathedral Academy 300/K-12
13280 Chapman Ave 92840 714-971-4159
Mike DeMaster, prin. Fax 971-4028
Hope Christian Academy 300/K-12
12211 Magnolia St 92841 714-373-4673
Deborah Haller, prin. Fax 589-2766
Lola Beauty College Post-Sec.
11883 Valley View St 92845 714-894-3366
Orangewood Academy 200/PK-12
13732 Clinton St 92843 714-534-4694
Datha Tickner, prin. Fax 534-5931
Stanton University Post-Sec.
12666 Brookhurst St 92840 714-539-6561
Thanh Le College School of Cosmetology Post-Sec.
12875 Chapman Ave 92840 714-971-5844

Garden Valley, El Dorado
Black Oak Mine USD
Supt. — See Georgetown
Golden Sierra JSHS 500/7-12
5101 Garden Valley Rd 95633 530-333-8330
Kevin Ahern, prin. Fax 333-8333

Georgetown, El Dorado, Pop. 2,308
Black Oak Mine USD 1,300/K-12
PO Box 4510 95634 530-333-8300
Robert Williams Ed.D., supt. Fax 333-8303
www.bomusd.org/
Black Oak Mine Independent Study 50/Alt
PO Box 4510 95634 530-333-8350
Kevin Ahern, admin. Fax 333-8353
Other Schools – See Garden Valley, Greenwood

Gerber, Tehama, Pop. 1,047
Gerber UNESD 400/K-8
23014 Chard Ave 96035 530-385-1041
Rod Stone, supt. Fax 385-1451
www.gerberschool.org
Gerber Community Day S 50/Alt
23014 Chard Ave 96035 530-385-1041
Rod Stone, prin. Fax 385-1451

Geyserville, Sonoma, Pop. 841
Geyserville USD 200/K-12
1300 Moody Ln 95441 707-857-3592
Joseph Carnation, supt. Fax 857-3071
www.gusd.com
Buena Vista HS 50/Alt
1300 Moody Ln 95441 707-433-3208
Katherine Hadden, prin.
Geyserville HS 100/9-12
1300 Moody Ln 95441 707-857-3592
Katherine Hadden, prin. Fax 857-3071
Geyserville MS 100/6-8
1300 Moody Ln 95441 707-857-3592
Katherine Hadden, prin. Fax 857-3071

Gilroy, Santa Clara, Pop. 47,703
Gilroy USD 11,000/K-12
7810 Arroyo Cir 95020 408-847-2700
Deborah Flores, supt. Fax 847-4717
www.gusd.k12.ca.us
Brownell MS 600/6-8
7800 Carmel St 95020 408-847-3377
Greg Camacho-Light, prin. Fax 846-7521
Christopher HS 1,000/9-12
850 Day Rd 95020 408-848-7171
John Perales, prin. Fax 847-7256
Gilroy HS 1,800/9-12
750 W 10th St 95020 408-847-2424
Marco Sanchez, prin. Fax 842-3311
Mt. Madonna HS 300/Alt
8750 Hirasaki Ct 95020 408-842-4313
Jennifer del Bono, prin. Fax 842-2918
Owens-Gilroy Early College Academy 200/9-12
5055 Santa Teresa Blvd 95020 408-846-4909
MaryAnn Boylan, prin. Fax 848-4730
Solorsano MS 1,200/6-8
7121 Grenache Way 95020 408-848-4121
Maria Walker, prin. Fax 848-7121
South Valley MS 700/6-8
385 I O O F Ave 95020 408-847-2828
Anisha Munshi, prin. Fax 847-5708
Gilroy Adult Education Adult
7881 Murray Ave 95020 408-848-7149
Alma Quintana, prin.

Regional Occupational Center & Program
Supt. — None
Santa Clara County ROP South Vo/Tech
700 W 6th St Ste L 95020 408-842-0361
Dr. David Matuszak, dir. Fax 842-0653

Anchorpoint Christian HS 50/9-12
2220 Pacheco Pass Hwy 95020 408-846-6642
Steve White, pres. Fax 848-4426
Gavilan College Post-Sec.
5055 Santa Teresa Blvd 95020 408-848-4800

Glendale, Los Angeles, Pop. 184,933
Glendale USD 26,200/K-12
223 N Jackson St 91206 818-241-3111
Richard Sheehan Ed.D., supt. Fax 548-9041
www.gusd.net/
Daily Continuation HS 300/Alt
220 N Kenwood St 91206 818-247-4805
Chris Coulter Ed.D., prin. Fax 547-3081
Glendale HS 2,900/9-12
1440 E Broadway 91205 818-242-3161
Monica Makiewicz Ed.D., prin. Fax 244-6309
Hoover HS 2,000/9-12
651 Glenwood Rd 91202 818-242-6801
Jennifer Earl Ed.D., prin. Fax 247-8825
Jewel City Community Day S 50/Alt
223 N Jackson St 91206 818-241-3111
Chris Coulter Ed.D., dir. Fax 547-0213
Roosevelt MS 800/6-8
1017 S Glendale Ave 91205 818-242-6845
Mary Mason Ed.D., prin. Fax 552-5188
Toll MS 1,300/6-8
700 Glenwood Rd 91202 818-244-8414
Bill Card Ed.D., prin. Fax 500-1487
Wilson MS 1,500/6-8
1221 Monterey Rd 91206 818-244-8145
Richard Lucas, prin. Fax 244-2050
Other Schools – See La Crescenta

Brand College Post-Sec.
529 Hahn Ave Ste 101 91203 818-550-0770
Glendale Adventist Academy 600/K-12
700 Kimlin Dr 91206 818-244-8671
Dr. Mario Negrete, prin. Fax 546-1180
Glendale Community College Post-Sec.
1500 N Verdugo Rd 91208 818-240-1000
Holy Family HS 300/9-12
400 E Lomita Ave 91205 818-241-3178
Nancy O'Sullivan, prin. Fax 241-7753
Integrated Digital Technologies Post-Sec.
130 N Brand Blvd Ste 300 91203 818-396-3500
Moro Beauty College Post-Sec.
124 N Brand Blvd 91203 818-246-7376
North-West College Post-Sec.
221 N Brand Blvd 91203 818-242-0205
Uni Health America/Glendale Mem Hospital Post-Sec.
1420 S Central Ave 91204 818-502-2334

Glendora, Los Angeles, Pop. 48,747
Azusa USD
Supt. — See Azusa
Sierra HS 300/Alt
1134 S Barranca Ave 91740 626-852-8300
Mari Bordona, prin. Fax 914-3797
Azusa Adult Educ Center Adult
1134 S Barranca Ave 91740 626-852-8400
Mary Ketza, prin. Fax 852-8407

Charter Oak USD
Supt. — See Covina
Arrow Continuation HS 100/Alt
1505 Sunflower Ave 91740 626-914-3961
Lisa Raigosa, prin. Fax 852-7685
Bridges Community Day S 50/Alt
1507 Sunflower Ave 91740 626-914-3961
Lisa Raigosa, prin. Fax 852-7685

Glendora USD 6,700/PK-12
500 N Loraine Ave 91741 626-963-1611
Dr. Robert Voors, supt. Fax 335-2196
www.glendora.k12.ca.us
Glendora HS 2,000/9-12
1600 E Foothill Blvd 91741 626-963-5731
Paul Lopez, prin. Fax 963-2880
Goddard MS 900/6-8
859 E Sierra Madre Ave 91741 626-852-4500
Brock Jacobsen, prin. Fax 852-4520
Sandburg MS 800/6-8
819 W Bennett Ave 91741 626-852-4530
Scott Bell, prin. Fax 852-4521
Whitcomb Continuation HS 100/Alt
350 W Mauna Loa Ave 91740 626-852-4550
Rebecca Summers, prin. Fax 852-4519

Glendora Adult S Adult
350 W Mauna Loa Ave 91740 626-852-4550
Rebecca Summers, prin. Fax 852-4519

Citrus College Post-Sec.
1000 W Foothill Blvd 91741 626-963-0323
Grace Communion Seminary Post-Sec.
PO Box 5005 91740 626-650-2306
St. Lucy's Priory HS 800/9-12
655 W Sierra Madre Ave 91741 626-335-3322
Sr. Monica Collins, prin. Fax 335-4373

Gold River, Sacramento, Pop. 7,625

Bryan College Post-Sec.
2317 Gold Meadow Way 95670 866-649-2400

Goleta, Santa Barbara, Pop. 29,028
Santa Barbara SD
Supt. — See Santa Barbara
Dos Pueblos HS 2,300/9-12
7266 Alameda Ave 93117 805-968-2541
Shawn Carey, prin. Fax 968-2891
Goleta Valley JHS 800/7-8
6100 Stow Canyon Rd 93117 805-967-3486
Veronica Rogers, prin. Fax 967-8176

Gonzales, Monterey, Pop. 8,098
Gonzales USD 2,300/K-12
PO Box G 93926 831-675-0100
Elizabeth Modena, supt. Fax 675-2763
www.gonzales.k12.ca.us
Fairview MS 700/5-8
PO Box G 93926 831-675-3704
Al Velasquez, prin. Fax 675-3274
Gonzales HS 700/9-12
PO Box G 93926 831-675-2495
Barbara Lawrence-Emanuel, prin. Fax 675-8054
Somavia HS 50/Alt
PO Box G 93926 831-675-1081
Patrick O'Donnell, admin. Fax 675-1084

Granada Hills, See Los Angeles
Los Angeles USD
Supt. — See Los Angeles
Addams Continuation HS 200/Alt
16341 Donmetz St 91344 818-271-2946
James Kilroy, prin. Fax 271-2569
Frost MS 1,600/6-8
12314 Bradford Pl 91344 818-332-6900
Jose Ayala, prin. Fax 360-9584
Henry MS 1,200/6-8
17340 San Jose St 91344 818-832-3870
Jose Castelo, prin. Fax 368-7333
Kennedy HS 3,000/9-12
11254 Gothic Ave 91344 818-271-2900
Suzanne Blake, prin. Fax 368-9527
Porter MS 1,700/6-8
15960 Kingsbury St 91344 818-920-2050
Alfredo Tarin, prin. Fax 891-7826
Valley Academy of Arts & Sciences 9-12
10445 Balboa Blvd 91344 818-832-7750
Debra McIntyre-Sciarrino, prin. Fax 368-5140
Kennedy-San Fernando Adult Education Adult
11254 Gothic Ave 91344 818-271-2550
Kathleen Javaheri, prin. Fax 271-2559

Newberry School of Beauty Post-Sec.
16852 Devonshire St 91344 818-366-3211

Grand Terrace, San Bernardino, Pop. 11,712
Colton JUSD
Supt. — See Colton
Grand Terrace HS 9-12
21810 Main St 92313 909-580-5006
Angela Dischinger, prin. Fax 876-4001
Terrace Hills MS 900/7-8
22579 De Berry St 92313 909-580-5022
Claudia Harris, prin. Fax 783-3836

Granite Bay, Placer, Pop. 19,714
Eureka UNSD 3,400/PK-8
5455 Eureka Rd 95746 916-791-4939
Linda Rooney, supt. Fax 791-5527
www.eureka-usd.k12.ca.us
Cavitt JHS 400/7-8
7200 Fuller Dr 95746 916-791-4152
Jennifer Platt, prin. Fax 791-7414
Other Schools – See Roseville

Roseville JUNHSD
Supt. — See Roseville
Granite Bay HS 2,200/9-12
1 Grizzly Way 95746 916-786-8676
Michael McGuire, prin. Fax 786-0766

Grass Valley, Nevada, Pop. 12,474
Grass Valley ESD 1,400/PK-8
10840 Gilmore Way 95945 530-273-4483
Eric Fredrickson, supt. Fax 273-0248
www.gvsd.k12.ca.us
Gilmore MS 500/5-8
10837 Rough and Ready Hwy 95945 530-273-8479
Christopher Roberts, prin. Fax 273-1675

Nevada County Office of Education
Supt. — See Nevada City
Jamieson HS 50/Alt
12338 McCourtney Rd 95949 530-272-5464
Lisa Sanford, admin. Fax 272-5870

Nevada JUNHSD 3,400/9-12
11645 Ridge Rd 95945 530-273-3351
Marianne Cartan, supt. Fax 273-3372
www.njuhsd.com
Bear River HS 900/9-12
11130 Magnolia Rd 95949 530-268-3700
Jim Nieto, prin. Fax 268-8372
Ghidotti Early College HS 9-12
250 Sierra College Dr 95945 530-274-5270
Melissa Madigan, prin. Fax 274-5272
Nevada Union HS 2,200/9-12
11761 Ridge Rd 95945 530-273-4431
Michael Blake, prin. Fax 477-9317
Nevada Union Technical HS Vo/Tech
11761 Ridge Rd 95945 530-273-4431
Bruce Kinseth, admin. Fax 477-9317
Pioneer HS 50/Alt
11130 Magnolia Rd 95949 530-268-3700
Cathy Peterson, prin. Fax 268-8372
Sierra Foothill HS 50/Alt
140 Park Ave 95945 530-272-2635
Marty Mathiesen, prin. Fax 272-8564
Sierra Mountain HS 100/Alt
12338 McCourtney Rd 95949 530-477-1225
Anita Bagwell, prin. Fax 272-8564
Silver Springs HS 100/Alt
130 Park Ave 95945 530-272-2635
Marty Mathiesen, prin. Fax 272-2687
Nevada Adult Education Adult
12338 McCourtney Rd 95949 530-272-2643
Anita Bagwell, admin. Fax 272-3422

Pleasant Ridge UNESD 1,500/K-8
22580 Kingston Ln 95949 530-268-2800
Rusty Clark, supt. Fax 268-2804
www.pleasantridge.k12.ca.us
Magnolia IS 600/6-8
22431 Kingston Ln 95949 530-268-2815
Gene Morgan, prin. Fax 268-2819

Graton, Sonoma, Pop. 1,648

Pacific Christian Academy 100/K-12
PO Box 369 95444 707-823-2880
Carla Peterson, prin. Fax 829-4736

Greenfield, Monterey, Pop. 16,188
Greenfield UNSD 2,500/K-8
493 El Camino Real 93927 831-674-2840
Trevor McDonald, supt. Fax 674-3712
www.greenfield.k12.ca.us
Vista Verde MS 800/6-8
1199 Elm Ave 93927 831-674-1420
Scott Smith, prin. Fax 674-1425

South Monterey JUNHSD
Supt. — See King City
Greenfield HS 900/9-12
225 S El Camino Real 93927 831-674-2751
Lisa Mazza, prin. Fax 674-2646

Greenville, Plumas, Pop. 1,068
Plumas USD
Supt. — See Quincy
Greenville JSHS 100/7-12
117 Grand St 95947 530-284-7107
Gary Miller, prin. Fax 284-6710

Greenwood, El Dorado
Black Oak Mine USD
Supt. — See Georgetown
Divide HS 50/Alt
4405 State Highway 193 95635 530-333-8315
Drew Woodall, admin. Fax 333-8317

Grenada, Siskiyou, Pop. 348
Grenada ESD 200/K-8
PO Box 10 96038 530-436-2233
GingerLee Charles, supt. Fax 436-2235
www.grenada.k12.ca.us
Grenada Community Day S 50/Alt
PO Box 10 96038 530-436-2233
GingerLee Charles, supt. Fax 436-2235

Gridley, Butte, Pop. 6,408
Gridley USD 2,100/K-12
429 Magnolia St 95948 530-846-4721
Rick Rubino, supt. Fax 846-4595
www.gridley.k12.ca.us/
Esperanza Continuation HS 50/Alt
581 Jackson St 95948 530-846-4383
Cindy Kershaw, prin. Fax 846-2435
Gridley HS 700/9-12
300 E Spruce St 95948 530-846-4791
Joan Zappettini, prin. Fax 846-3412
Gridley Unified Community Day S 50/Alt
581 Jackson St 95948 530-846-4721
Cindy Kershaw, prin. Fax 846-2435
Sycamore MS 500/6-8
1125 Sycamore St 95948 530-846-3636
Christine McCormick, prin. Fax 846-6796

Groveland, Tuolumne, Pop. 585
Big Oak Flat-Groveland USD 50/K-12
PO Box 1397 95321 209-962-5765
Dave Urquhart, supt. Fax 962-6108
www.bofg.k12.ca.us
Moccasin Community Day S 50/Alt
PO Box 1397 95321 209-962-7160
Kay Brick, lead tchr. Fax 962-7160
Tioga HS 50/9-12
19304 Ferretti Rd 95321 209-962-4763
Dave Urquhart, prin. Fax 962-4507
Other Schools – See La Grange

Guadalupe, Santa Barbara, Pop. 6,975
Guadalupe UNESD 1,200/K-8
PO Box 788 93434 805-343-2114
Ed Cora, supt. Fax 343-6155
www.guadusd.org
McKenzie JHS 400/6-8
PO Box 788 93434 805-343-1951
Gabriel Solorio, prin. Fax 343-6931

Guerneville, Sonoma, Pop. 4,341
Guerneville ESD 300/K-8
14630 Armstrong Woods Rd 95446 707-869-2864
Elaine Carlson, supt. Fax 869-3149
www.guernevilleschool.org
Guerneville Community Day S 50/Alt
14630 Armstrong Woods Rd 95446 707-869-2864
Elaine Carlson, prin. Fax 869-3149

Gustine, Merced, Pop. 5,420
Gustine USD 1,700/K-12
1500 Meredith Ave 95322 209-854-3784
Gail McWilliams, supt. Fax 854-9164
www.gustine.k12.ca.us
Gustine HS 500/9-12
501 North Ave 95322 209-854-6414
John Petrone, prin. Fax 854-1955
Gustine MS 300/7-8
28075 Sullivan Rd 95322 209-854-5030
Manuel Bettencourt, prin. Fax 854-9592
Pioneer HS 50/Alt
501 North Ave 95322 209-854-6414
John Petrone, prin. Fax 854-9581

Hacienda Heights, Los Angeles, Pop. 53,234
Hacienda La Puente USD
Supt. — See City of Industry
Los Altos HS 2,100/9-12
15325 Los Robles Ave 91745 626-934-5400
Cheli McReynolds, prin. Fax 855-3145
Newton MS 600/6-8
15616 Newton St 91745 626-933-2400
Dr. Stephen Lee, prin. Fax 855-3832
Orange Grove MS 700/6-8
14505 Orange Grove Ave 91745 626-933-7000
Erika Terrazas, prin. Fax 855-3837
Valley Alternative S 100/Alt
15430 Shadybend Dr 91745 626-933-3400
Priscilla Tam, prin. Fax 933-3412
Wilson HS 1,700/9-12
16455 Wedgeworth Dr 91745 626-934-4400
Elena Paul, prin. Fax 855-3792

Half Moon Bay, San Mateo, Pop. 11,097
Cabrillo USD 3,300/K-12
498 Kelly Ave 94019 650-712-7100
Tony Roehrick Ed.D., supt. Fax 726-0279
www.cabrillo.k12.ca.us/
Cunha IS 800/6-8
498 Kelly Ave 94019 650-712-7190
Ladilao Lopez, prin. Fax 712-7195
Half Moon Bay HS 1,000/9-12
498 Kelly Ave 94019 650-712-7200
Allison Silvestri, prin. Fax 712-7232
Pilarcitos Continuation HS 50/Alt
498 Kelly Ave 94019 650-712-7224
Rajan Bechar, prin. Fax 712-7225
Cabrillo Adult S Adult
498 Kelly Ave 94019 650-712-7224
John Corry, prin. Fax 712-7225

Hamilton City, Glenn, Pop. 1,746
Hamilton USD 800/K-12
PO Box 488 95951 530-826-3261
Charles Tracy, supt. Fax 826-0440
www.hamiltonusd.org
Barkley HS 50/Alt
PO Box 488 95951 530-826-3331
Charles Tracy, prin. Fax 826-3929
Hamilton Community Day S 50/Alt
PO Box 488 95951 530-826-0504
Charles Tracy, prin. Fax 826-3929
Hamilton HS 300/9-12
PO Box 488 95951 530-826-3261
Cris Oseguera, prin. Fax 826-0440
Hamilton Adult S Adult
PO Box 488 95951 530-826-3331
Jeanne Robinson, dir. Fax 826-3929

Hanford, Kings, Pop. 52,527
Hanford ESD 6,100/K-8
PO Box 1067 93232 559-585-3601
Paul Terry, supt. Fax 584-7833
www.hesd.k12.ca.us/
Kennedy JHS 600/7-8
PO Box 1067 93232 559-585-3850
Jason Strickland, prin. Fax 585-2374
Wilson JHS 600/7-8
PO Box 1067 93232 559-585-3870
Kenneth Eggert, prin. Fax 585-2336

Hanford JUNHSD 4,500/9-12
823 W Lacey Blvd 93230 559-583-5901
William Fishbough, supt. Fax 589-9769
www.hjuhsd.k12.ca.us
Hanford Community Day S 50/Alt
120 E Grangeville Blvd 93230 559-583-5902
Scott Pickle, prin. Fax 582-5229
Hanford HS 1,600/9-12
120 E Grangeville Blvd 93230 559-583-5902
Scott Pickle, prin. Fax 582-5229
Hanford Night Continuation HS 100/Alt
1201 N Douty St 93230 559-583-5904
Stacey Broussard, prin. Fax 583-6580
Hanford West HS 1,500/9-12
1150 W Lacey Blvd 93230 559-583-5903
Darin Parson, prin. Fax 583-6708
Johnson HS 200/Alt
1201 N Douty St 93230 559-583-5904
Gary Marr, prin. Fax 583-6580
Sierra Pacific HS 500/9-12
1259 13th Ave 93230 559-583-5912
Michele Borges, prin. Fax 583-5914
Hanford Adult S Adult
905 Campus Dr 93230 559-583-5905
Gary Marr, prin. Fax 589-9564

Kings County Office of Education 300/
1144 W Lacey Blvd 93230 559-584-1441
Tim Bowers, supt. Fax 589-7000
www.kings.k12.ca.us
Kings County Community S 100/Alt
146 W Highland St 93230 559-582-0784
Janet Schales, prin. Fax 582-0731

Regional Occupational Center & Program
Supt. — None
Kings County ROP Vo/Tech
1144 W Lacey Blvd 93230 559-589-7026
Glenda Woolley, dir. Fax 589-7007

Happy Camp, Siskiyou, Pop. 1,130
Siskiyou UNHSD
Supt. — See Mount Shasta
Happy Camp HS 100/9-12
PO Box 437 96039 530-493-2697
Angelika Brown, prin. Fax 493-2605

Harbor City, See Los Angeles
Los Angeles USD
Supt. — See Los Angeles
Narbonne HS 3,500/9-12
24300 Western Ave 90710 310-257-7100
Gerald Kobata, prin. Fax 326-1805
Patton Continuation HS 100/Alt
24514 Western Ave 90710 310-257-4740
Kenneth Martinez, prin. Fax 257-4742

Hawaiian Gardens, Los Angeles, Pop. 14,073
ABC USD
Supt. — See Cerritos
Fedde MS 400/7-8
21409 Elaine Ave 90716 562-924-2309
Carol Castro, prin. Fax 809-6895

Hawthorne, Los Angeles, Pop. 81,457
Centinela Valley UNHSD
Supt. — See Lawndale
Hawthorne HS 2,100/9-12
4859 W El Segundo Blvd 90250 310-263-4400
Dr. Mark Newell, prin. Fax 675-7017

Hawthorne SD 8,900/K-12
14120 Hawthorne Blvd 90250 310-676-2276
Helen Morgan Ed.D., supt. Fax 675-9464
www.hawthorne.k12.ca.us
Carson MS 700/6-8
13838 Yukon Ave 90250 310-676-1908
Patricia Jordan, prin. Fax 676-0634
Hawthorne MS 1,000/6-8
4366 W 129th St 90250 310-676-0167
Rudy Salas, prin. Fax 675-0924
Prairie Vista MS 1,000/6-8
13600 Prairie Ave 90250 310-679-1003
Christine Fagnano, prin. Fax 679-1142

Los Angeles County Office of Education
Supt. — See Downey
Renaissance Community Day S 100/Alt
14600 Cerise Ave 90250 310-970-9914
Peggy Dunn, prin. Fax 679-8106

Wiseburn ESD 3,200/K-12
13530 Aviation Blvd 90250 310-643-3025
Dr. Tom Johnstone, supt. Fax 643-7659
www.wiseburn.k12.ca.us
Dana MS 1,000/6-8
5504 W 135th St 90250 310-725-4700
Aileen Harbeck, prin. Fax 536-9091

Hayfork, Trinity, Pop. 2,231
Mountain Valley USD 400/K-12
PO Box 339 96041 530-628-5265
Ed Traverso, supt. Fax 628-5267
www.mvusd.us
Hayfork HS 100/9-12
PO Box 10 96041 530-628-5261
Ed Traverso, prin. Fax 628-3091
Mountain Valley Community Day S 50/Alt
PO Box 339 96041 530-628-9225
Ed Traverso, prin. Fax 628-5267
Valley Continuation HS 50/Alt
PO Box 339 96041 530-628-4690
Ed Traverso, prin. Fax 628-5018

Hayward, Alameda, Pop. 133,787
Alameda County Office of Education 2,900/
313 W Winton Ave 94544 510-887-0152
Sheila Jordan, supt. Fax 670-4146
www.acoe.org
Alameda County Community S 200/K-12
313 W Winton Ave 94544 510-670-6619
Mary Fisher, prin. Fax 293-9201
Alameda County Opportunity S 100/7-12
313 W Winton Ave 94544 510-670-4558
Carolyn Hobbs, prin. Fax 670-4577

Hayward USD 21,300/PK-12
PO Box 5000 94540 510-784-2600
Donald Evans, supt. Fax 784-2641
www.husd.us
Brenkwitz Alternative HS 200/Alt
PO Box 5000 94540 510-723-3160
Edward Brown, prin. Fax 582-6376
Chavez MS 600/7-8
PO Box 5000 94540 510-723-3110
Jeffrey James, prin. Fax 538-8478
Harte MS 700/7-8
PO Box 5000 94540 510-723-3100
Lisa Davies-Gomez, prin. Fax 886-5926
Hayward HS 1,700/9-12
PO Box 5000 94540 510-723-3170
George Bullis, prin. Fax 581-3145
King MS 600/7-8
PO Box 5000 94540 510-723-3120
Estella Santos, prin. Fax 786-4139

Mt. Eden HS 1,900/9-12
PO Box 5000 94540 510-723-3180
Benjamin Schmookler, prin. Fax 786-2269
Ochoa MS 700/7-8
PO Box 5000 94540 510-723-3130
Ariel Dolowich, prin. Fax 786-0559
Tennyson HS 1,300/9-12
PO Box 5000 94540 510-723-3190
Lori Villanueva, prin. Fax 582-0964
Winton MS 600/7-8
PO Box 5000 94540 510-723-3140
George Porter, prin. Fax 733-9043
Hayward Adult Education Center Adult
PO Box 5000 94540 510-293-8595
Ryan Whetstone, prin. Fax 727-1139

New Haven USD
Supt. — See Union City
Conley-Caraballo HS 50/Alt
541 Blanche St 94544 510-471-5126
Ramon Camacho, prin. Fax 475-3949

Regional Occupational Center & Program
Supt. — None
Eden Area ROP Vo/Tech
26316 Hesperian Blvd 94545 510-293-2900
Irene Fujii, dir. Fax 783-2955

San Lorenzo USD
Supt. — See San Lorenzo
East Bay Arts HS 300/9-12
20450 Royal Ave 94541 510-317-4471
Abigail Kotzin, prin. Fax 317-4495
Royal Sunset HS 200/Alt
20450 Royal Ave 94541 510-317-4400
Abigail Kotzin, prin. Fax 317-4495

California State University-East Bay Post-Sec.
25800 Carlos Bee Blvd 94542 510-885-3000
Chabot College Post-Sec.
25555 Hesperian Blvd 94545 510-723-6600
Everest College Post-Sec.
22336 Main St Fl 1 94541 510-582-9500
Heald College Post-Sec.
25500 Industrial Blvd 94545 510-783-2100
Life Chiropractic College West Post-Sec.
25001 Industrial Blvd 94545 800-788-4476
Moreau HS 900/9-12
27170 Mission Blvd 94544 510-881-4300
Lauren Lek, prin. Fax 581-5669
NCP College of Nursing Post-Sec.
21615 Hesperian Blvd Ste A 94541 510-785-0454

Healdsburg, Sonoma, Pop. 11,079
Healdsburg USD 2,600/K-12
1028 Prince Ave 95448 707-431-3488
Jeff Harding Ed.D., supt. Fax 433-8403
www.husd.com
Healdsburg HS 800/9-12
1024 Prince Ave 95448 707-431-3420
Chris VandenHeuvel, prin. Fax 431-3467
Healdsburg JHS 400/6-8
315 Grant St 95448 707-431-3410
Deborah Hall, prin. Fax 431-3593
Marce Becerra Academy 50/Alt
1024 Prince Ave 95448 707-431-3449
Chris VandenHeuvel, prin. Fax 431-3595

Rio Lindo Adventist Academy 200/9-12
3200 Rio Lindo Ave 95448 707-431-5100
Doug Schmidt, admin. Fax 431-5115

Heber, Imperial, Pop. 4,270
Heber ESD 700/K-8
1052 Heber Ave 92249 760-337-6530
Jaime Silva, supt. Fax 353-3421
hesdk8.org
Heber ES 600/4-8
1052 Heber Ave 92249 760-337-6530
Patty Marcial, prin. Fax 353-3421

Helendale, San Bernardino
Helendale ESD 600/K-12
PO Box 249 92342 760-952-1180
Ross Swearingen, supt. Fax 952-1178
www.helendalesd.org
Riverview MS 100/7-8
PO Box 249 92342 760-952-1266
Diana Green, prin. Fax 952-1178

Hemet, Riverside, Pop. 76,330
Hemet USD 21,900/K-12
1791 W Acacia Ave 92545 951-765-5100
Fax 765-5115
www.hemetusd.k12.ca.us
Acacia MS 1,000/6-8
1200 E Acacia Ave 92543 951-765-1620
Derek Jindra, prin. Fax 765-5149
AdvancePath Academics Alt
831 E Devonshire Ave 92543 951-663-4244
Tara O'Malley, prin.
Alessandro HS 400/Alt
831 E Devonshire Ave 92543 951-765-5182
Tara O'Malley, prin. Fax 925-7548
Dartmouth MS 900/6-8
41535 Mayberry Ave 92544 951-765-2550
Eric Dahlstrom, prin. Fax 765-2559
Diamond Valley MS 1,200/6-8
291 W Chambers Ave 92543 951-925-2899
David Howland, prin. Fax 925-6297
Hemet HS 2,500/9-12
41701 Stetson Ave 92544 951-765-5150
Dr. Emily Shaw, prin. Fax 765-5177
Jackson S 400/Alt
258 N Thompson St 92543 951-765-5193
Sharleen Rainville, prin. Fax 765-5195
Rancho Viejo MS 1,300/6-8
985 N Cawston Ave 92545 951-765-6287
Fax 925-5244

Tahquitz HS 1,600/9-12
4425 Titan Trl 92545 951-765-6300
Dr. Michael Roe, prin. Fax 765-6344
West Valley HS 1,900/9-12
3401 Mustang Way 92545 951-765-1600
Alex Ballard, prin. Fax 765-1607
Hemet Adult Education Adult
831 E Devonshire Ave 92543 951-765-5190
Tara O'Malley, prin. Fax 925-7478
Other Schools – See Anza

Baptist Christian S 300/PK-12
26089 Girard St 92544 951-658-3203
Mark Best, admin. Fax 658-0723
Community Christian S 200/PK-12
41762 Stetson Ave 92544 951-929-2135
Cynthia Henninger, prin. Fax 765-6696

Hercules, Contra Costa, Pop. 22,834
West Contra Costa USD
Supt. — See Richmond
Hercules MSHS 800/6-12
1900 Refugio Valley Rd 94547 510-231-1429
Guy Zakrevsky, prin. Fax 245-1089

Herlong, Lassen, Pop. 264
Fort Sage USD 200/K-12
PO Box 35 96113 530-827-2129
Bryan Young, supt. Fax 827-2019
www.fortsage.org
Fort Sage MS 50/7-8
PO Box 35 96113 530-827-2101
Bryan Young, prin. Fax 827-3362
Herlong HS 100/9-12
PO Box 97 96113 530-827-2101
Bryan Young, prin. Fax 827-3362
Render Continuation HS 50/Alt
PO Box 910 96113 530-827-2101
Bryan Young, prin.

Hermosa Beach, Los Angeles, Pop. 18,753
Hermosa Beach City ESD 1,300/K-8
1645 Valley Dr 90254 310-937-5877
Patricia Escalante, supt. Fax 376-4974
www.hbcsd.org
Hermosa Valley ES 800/3-8
1645 Valley Dr 90254 310-937-5888
Kimberly Taylor, prin. Fax 798-4365

Hope Chapel Academy 100/K-12
2420 Pacific Coast Hwy 90254 310-374-4673
Kevin Bryan, prin.

Hesperia, San Bernardino, Pop. 88,087
Hesperia USD 22,900/K-12
15576 Main St 92345 760-244-4411
Mark McKinney, supt. Fax 244-2806
www.hesperiausd.org
Canyon Ridge HS 200/Alt
12850 Muscatel St, 760-244-6530
Mary Porras, prin. Fax 244-7210
Cedar MS 1,200/7-8
13565 Cedar St, 760-244-6093
Michelle Estrada, prin. Fax 244-5439
Hesperia Community Day S 50/Alt
16527 1/2 Lemon St 92345 760-244-1771
Nate Lambdin, prin. Fax 948-0691
Hesperia HS 2,000/9-12
9898 Maple Ave 92345 760-244-9898
Bob Schnebeck, prin. Fax 244-0939
Hesperia JHS 1,000/7-8
10275 Cypress Ave 92345 760-244-9386
Robert McCollum, prin. Fax 244-0595
Mojave HS 400/Alt
16633 Lemon St 92345 760-948-3999
Nate Lambdin, prin. Fax 948-0508
Ranchero MS 1,100/7-8
17607 Ranchero Rd 92345 760-948-0175
Cindy Costa, prin. Fax 948-0381
Sultana HS 2,200/9-12
17311 Sultana St 92345 760-947-6777
Lawrence Bird, prin. Fax 947-6788
Other Schools – See Oak Hills

Apple Valley Christian S 200/PK-12
9608 I Ave Ste E 92345 760-995-3516
John Richart, admin. Fax 995-3524
Hesperia Christian S 300/PK-12
16775 Olive St 92345 760-244-6164
Cindy Harmon, admin. Fax 244-9756
San Joaquin Valley College Post-Sec.
9331 Mariposa Rd, 760-948-1947

Highland, San Bernardino, Pop. 51,532
Redlands USD
Supt. — See Redlands
Beattie MS 1,300/6-8
7800 Orange St 92346 909-307-2400
Angela Neuhaus, prin. Fax 307-2416

San Bernardino City USD
Supt. — See San Bernardino
San Andreas SHS 700/Alt
3232 Pacific St 92346 909-388-6521
Hector Murrieta, prin. Fax 425-0523
San Bernadino Alternative Learning Ctr. 100/Alt
3236 Pacific St 92346 909-388-6221
Robyn Eberhardt, coord. Fax 388-6223
Serrano MS 800/7-8
3131 Piedmont Dr 92346 909-388-6530
Arwyn Wild, prin. Fax 864-6232

Hillsborough, San Mateo, Pop. 10,401
Hillsborough CSD 1,500/K-8
300 El Cerrito Ave 94010 650-342-5193
Anthony Ranii, supt. Fax 342-6964
www.hcsd.k12.ca.us

Crocker MS 500/6-8
2600 Ralston Ave 94010 650-342-6331
Catherine Mikes, prin. Fax 579-5943

Crystal Springs Uplands S 400/6-12
400 Uplands Dr 94010 650-342-4175
Amy Richards, head sch Fax 342-7623

Hilmar, Merced, Pop. 3,392
Hilmar USD 2,300/K-12
7807 Lander Ave 95324 209-667-5701
Isabel Cabral-Johnson, supt. Fax 667-1721
www.hilmar.k12.ca.us
Colony HS 50/Alt
7807 Lander Ave 95324 209-667-0276
Darlene Carvalho, prin. Fax 667-1532
Hilmar HS 700/9-12
7807 Lander Ave 95324 209-667-5903
Bret Theodozio, prin. Fax 667-7628
Hilmar MS 500/6-8
7807 Lander Ave 95324 209-632-8847
Eric Hixson, prin. Fax 667-7018
Irwin HS 50/Alt
7807 Lander Ave 95324 209-667-0276
Darlene Carvalho, prin. Fax 667-1532

Hollister, San Benito, Pop. 34,317
Hollister SD 4,800/K-8
2690 Cienega Rd 95023 831-630-6300
Gary McIntire Ed.D., supt. Fax 634-2080
www.hesd.org
Maze MS 400/7-8
900 Meridian St 95023 831-636-4480
Cindy Cordova, prin. Fax 636-4488
Rancho San Justo MS 600/7-8
1201 Rancho Dr 95023 831-636-4450
Barbara Nakasone, prin. Fax 634-4952

San Benito County Office of Education 50/
460 5th St 95023 831-637-5393
Mike Sanchez, supt. Fax 637-0140
www.sbcoe.org
San Benito County Opportunity S 50/Alt
460 5th St 95023 831-637-9269
Angel Rivera, dir. Fax 636-7769

San Benito HSD 3,100/9-12
1220 Monterey St 95023 831-637-5831
Stan Rose Ed.D., supt. Fax 637-6524
www.sbhsd.k12.ca.us
San Andreas Continuation HS 200/Alt
191 Alvarado St 95023 831-637-9269
Angel Rivera, prin. Fax 636-0376
San Benito HS 2,900/9-12
1220 Monterey St 95023 831-637-5831
Krystal Lomanto, prin. Fax 637-6524

Hollywood, See Los Angeles
Los Angeles USD
Supt. — See Los Angeles
Bernstein HS 1,300/9-12
1309 N Wilton Pl 90028 323-817-6400
Angela Hewlett, prin. Fax 860-9711
Le Conte MS 1,100/6-8
1316 N Bronson Ave 90028 323-308-1700
Rosemary Hindinger, prin. Fax 856-3053

American Academy of Dramatic Arts Post-Sec.
1336 N La Brea Ave 90028 800-463-8990
Elegance International Post-Sec.
1622 N Highland Ave 90028 323-871-8318
Los Angeles Film School Post-Sec.
6363 W Sunset Blvd 90028 323-860-0789
Musicians Institute Post-Sec.
6752 Hollywood Blvd 90028 323-462-1384

Holtville, Imperial, Pop. 5,905
Holtville USD 1,600/K-12
621 E 6th St 92250 760-356-2974
Jon LeDoux, supt. Fax 356-4936
www.holtville.k12.ca.us
Holtville HS 500/9-12
755 Olive Ave 92250 760-356-2926
Jeff Magin, prin. Fax 356-1206
Holtville JHS 300/6-8
800 Beale Ave 92250 760-356-2811
Mario Garcia, prin. Fax 356-5741
Webb Continuation HS 50/Alt
522 W 8th St 92250 760-356-1304
Celso Ruiz, prin. Fax 356-5621

Homeland, Riverside, Pop. 5,870
Romoland ESD 3,000/K-8
25900 Leon Rd 92548 951-926-9244
Hilda Swain, supt. Fax 926-2170
www.romoland.k12.ca.us
Other Schools – See Romoland

Honeydew, Humboldt
Mattole USD 1,000/K-12
29289 Chambers Rd 95545 707-629-3311
Richard Graey, supt. Fax 629-3575
www.humboldt.k12.ca.us/mattole_usd
Other Schools – See Petrolia

Hoopa, Humboldt
Klamath-Trinity JUSD 1,000/PK-12
PO Box 1308 95546 530-625-5600
Michael A. Reid, supt. Fax 625-5611
www.ktjusd.k12.ca.us/
Hoopa Valley HS 300/9-12
PO Box 1308 95546 530-625-5600
Martin Wilkes, prin. Fax 625-5619
John Continuation HS 50/Alt
PO Box 1308 95546 530-625-5600
Mike Gorman, prin. Fax 625-4840
Two Rivers Community Day S 50/Alt
PO Box 1308 95546 530-625-5600
Mike Gorman, prin. Fax 625-4840

Hughson, Stanislaus, Pop. 6,490
Hughson USD 2,200/K-12
PO Box 189 95326 209-883-4428
Brian Beck, supt. Fax 883-4639
www.hughson.k12.ca.us
Dickens HS 50/Alt
6937 Fox Rd 95326 209-883-4182
Debra Davis, admin. Fax 883-4726
Hughson Community Day S 50/Alt
6937 Fox Rd 95326 209-883-4428
Jim Schuller, admin. Fax 883-4726
Hughson HS 800/9-12
PO Box 99 95326 209-883-0469
Debra Davis, prin. Fax 883-0870
Ross MS 500/6-8
7448 Fox Rd 95326 209-883-4425
Ryan Smith, prin. Fax 883-2017
Valley Community Day S 50/Alt
PO Box 99 95326 209-883-0469
Jim Schuller, admin. Fax 883-0870

Keyes UNESD
Supt. — See Keyes
Spratling MS 200/6-8
5277 Washington Rd 95326 209-664-3833
Karen Redfield, prin. Fax 656-2384

Huntington Beach, Orange, Pop. 183,010
Fountain Valley ESD
Supt. — See Fountain Valley
Talbert MS 600/6-8
9101 Brabham Dr, 714-378-4220
Cara Robinson, prin. Fax 378-4229

Huntington Beach City ESD 7,000/K-12
20451 Craimer Ln, 714-964-8888
Gregg Haulk, supt. Fax 963-9565
www.hbcsd.us
Dwyer MS 1,300/6-8
1502 Palm Ave, 714-536-7507
Morgan Smith, prin. Fax 960-0955
Sowers MS 1,200/6-8
9300 Indianapolis Ave, 714-962-7738
Cynthia Guerrero, prin. Fax 968-5580
Other Schools – See Los Angeles

Huntington Beach UNHSD 16,100/9-12
5832 Bolsa Ave 92649 714-903-7000
Greg Plutko, supt. Fax 892-5750
www.hbuhsd.edu
Coast HS, 17231 Gothard St, 200/Alt
Steve Curiel, prin. 714-842-4227
Edison HS 2,600/9-12
21400 Magnolia St, 714-962-1356
D'Liese Melendrez, prin. Fax 963-4280
Huntington Beach HS 2,700/9-12
1905 Main St, 714-536-2514
Rocky Murray, prin. Fax 960-7042
Marina HS 2,800/9-12
15871 Springdale St, 714-893-6571
Paul Morrow, prin. Fax 892-7855
Ocean View HS 1,500/9-12
17071 Gothard St, 714-848-0656
Dan Bryan, prin. Fax 843-0541
Huntington Beach Adult Education Adult
17231 Gothard St, 714-901-8106
Steve Curiel, prin. Fax 373-5245
Other Schools – See Fountain Valley, Westminster

Ocean View SD 9,500/PK-8
17200 Pinehurst Ln 92647 714-847-2551
William Loose Ed.D., supt. Fax 847-1430
www.ovsd.org
Marine View MS 900/6-8
5682 Tilburg Dr, 714-846-0624
Roni Ellis, prin. Fax 846-2074
Mesa View MS 700/6-8
17601 Avilla Ln, 714-842-6608
Leona Olson, prin. Fax 842-8798
Spring View MS 800/6-8
16662 Trudy Ln, 714-846-2891
Jason Blade, prin. Fax 377-9821
Other Schools – See Fountain Valley

Westminster ESD
Supt. — See Westminster
Stacey MS 900/6-8
6311 Larchwood Dr, 714-894-7212
Heidi DeBritton, prin. Fax 373-0478

Apollos University Post-Sec.
17011 Beach Blvd Ste 900, 714-375-6697
Brethren Christian HS 400/6-12
21141 Strathmoor Ln, 714-962-6617
Rick Niswonger, prin. Fax 962-3171
Golden West College Post-Sec.
15744 Goldenwest St, 714-892-7711
Hebrew Academy 300/PK-12
14401 Willow Ln, 714-898-0051
Dr. Megan Carlson, prin. Fax 898-0633
Liberty Christian S 200/PK-12
7661 Warner Ave, 714-842-5992
Teri Yates M.Ed., prin. Fax 848-7484

Huntington Park, Los Angeles, Pop. 57,940
Los Angeles USD
Supt. — See Los Angeles
Gage MS 2,700/6-8
2880 E Gage Ave 90255 323-826-1500
Cesar Quezada, prin. Fax 589-6925
Huntington Park HS 4,100/9-12
6020 Miles Ave 90255 323-826-2300
Lupe Hernandez, prin. Fax 583-0463
Marquez HPIAM HS 9-12
6361 Cottage St 90255 323-584-3800
Jonathan Chaikittirattan, prin. Fax 583-1305
Marquez LIBRA Academy 9-12
6361 Cottage St 90255 323-584-3800
Lisa Davis, prin. Fax 583-1305
Marquez School of Social Justice HS 9-12
6361 Cottage St 90255 323-584-3800
Michael Hammond, prin. Fax 583-1305
Nimitz MS 2,100/6-8
6021 Carmelita Ave 90255 323-887-5400
Onofre Di'Stefano, prin. Fax 773-5201
San Antonio Continuation HS 100/Alt
2861 Randolph St 90255 323-826-2420
Allan Maciel, prin. Fax 826-2427
Huntington Park-Bell Community Adult S Adult
2945 Belgrave Ave 90255 323-826-2400
Clifton DeCordoba, prin. Fax 826-2413

ICDC College Post-Sec.
6812 Pacific Blvd 90255 323-277-0240
United Education Institute Post-Sec.
6055 Pacific Blvd 90255 323-319-9500

Huron, Fresno, Pop. 6,708
Coalinga - Huron JUSD
Supt. — See Coalinga
Huron MS 400/6-8
PO Box 99 93234 559-945-2926
Javier Gonzalez, prin. Fax 945-8482

Idyllwild, Riverside, Pop. 2,853

Idyllwild Arts Academy 300/9-12
PO Box 38 92549 951-659-2171
Brian Cohen, hdmstr. Fax 659-2323

Imperial, Imperial, Pop. 14,611
Imperial USD 3,600/K-12
219 N E St 92251 760-355-3200
Lisa Tabarez, supt. Fax 355-4511
iusd.imperial.k12.ca.us/
Imperial Avenue Holbrook S 100/Alt
322 N Imperial Ave 92251 760-355-3207
Kerry Legarra, prin. Fax 355-3258
Imperial HS 900/9-12
517 W Barioni Blvd 92251 760-355-3220
Roger Ruvalcaba, prin. Fax 355-0869
Wright MS 900/6-8
885 N Imperial Ave 92251 760-355-3240
Diego Lopez, prin. Fax 355-3256

Imperial Valley College Post-Sec.
380 E Aten Rd 92251 760-352-8320

Imperial Beach, San Diego, Pop. 25,203
Sweetwater UNHSD
Supt. — See Chula Vista
Mar Vista HS 1,700/9-12
505 Elm Ave 91932 619-628 5700
Wes Braddock, prin. Fax 424-6232
Sweetwater Community Day MS 100/Alt
505 1/2 Elm Ave 91932 619-628-3056
Fax 628-3060

Independence, Inyo, Pop. 646
Inyo County Office of Education 50/
PO Box G 93526 760-878-2426
Dr. Terence McAteer, supt. Fax 878-2279
www.inyo.k12.ca.us
Opportunity S 50/Alt
PO Box G 93526 760-878-2426
Dr. Terence McAteer, prin. Fax 878-2279
Other Schools – See Bishop, Lone Pine

Owens Valley USD 50/K-12
PO Box E 93526 760-878-2405
Joel Hampton, supt. Fax 878-2626
www.ovusd.org
Owens Valley HS 50/9-12
PO Box E 93526 760-878-2405
Joel Hampton, prin. Fax 878-2626

Indio, Riverside, Pop. 75,249
Desert Sands USD
Supt. — See La Quinta
Amistad Continuation HS 500/Alt
44801 Golf Center Pkwy 92201 760-775-3570
Robert Blinkinsop, prin. Fax 775-3575
Desert Ridge Academy 900/6-8
79767 Avenue 39 92203 760-393-5500
Dan Borgen, prin. Fax 393-5502
Glenn MS of International Studies 1,300/6-8
79655 Miles Ave 92201 760-200-3700
Majid Salehi, prin. Fax 200-3709
Indio HS 2,300/9-12
81750 Avenue 46 92201 760-775-3550
Rudy Ramirez, prin. Fax 775-3565
Indio MS 900/6-8
81195 Miles Ave 92201 760-775-3800
Jesus Jimenez, prin. Fax 775-3807
Jefferson MS 700/6-8
83089 US Highway 111 92201 760-863-3660
Esther Lopez, prin. Fax 775-3597
Shadow Hills HS 900/9-12
39225 Jefferson St 92203 760-393-5400
Marcus Wood, prin. Fax 200-1967

Milan Institute Post-Sec.
45691 Monroe St Ste 2 92201 760-347-5000

Inglewood, Los Angeles, Pop. 107,237
Inglewood USD 12,600/K-12
401 S Inglewood Ave 90301 310-419-2700
Dr. Donald Brann, admin. Fax 680-5144
www.inglewood.k12.ca.us
Crozier MS 900/6-8
120 W Regent St 90301 310-680-5280
Davina Mills, prin. Fax 680-5299
Inglewood HS 1,600/9-12
231 S Grevillea Ave 90301 310-680-5200
Fax 680-5201
Monroe MS 600/6-8
10711 S 10th Ave 90303 310-680-5310
Franklin Tilley, prin. Fax 680-5317

Morningside HS 1,300/9-12
10500 Yukon Ave 90303 310-680-5230
Reginald Sirls, prin. Fax 680-5257

Crimson Technical College Post-Sec.
8911 Aviation Blvd 90301 866-451-0818
Daniel Freeman Mem. Hospital Post-Sec.
333 N Prairie Ave 90301 310-674-7050
Marinello School of Beauty Post-Sec.
240 S Market St 90301 310-674-8100
St. Marys Academy 400/9-12
701 Grace Ave 90301 310-674-8470
Dr. Yvonne McNeal, prin. Fax 674-6255
Univ of West Los Angeles School of Law Post-Sec.
9800 S La Cienega Blvd 90301 310-342-5200

Ione, Amador, Pop. 7,650
Amador County USD
Supt. — See Jackson
Ione JHS 400/6-8
450 S Mill St 95640 209-257-5500
Dr. William Murray, prin. Fax 274-0671

Irvine, Orange, Pop. 201,858
Irvine USD 27,200/PK-12
5050 Barranca Pkwy 92604 949-936-5000
Terry Walker, supt. Fax 936-5259
www.iusd.org
Creekside HS 200/9-12
3387 Barranca Pkwy 92606 949-936-7400
Mark Miller, prin. Fax 936-7409
Irvine HS 1,900/9-12
4321 Walnut Ave 92604 949-936-7000
Monica Colunga, prin. Fax 936-7009
Lakeside MS 700/7-8
3 Lemongrass 92604 949-559-1601
Gina Cuneo, prin. Fax 936-6109
Northwood HS 1,900/9-12
4515 Portola Pkwy 92620 949-936-7200
Leslie Roach, prin. Fax 936-7209
Rancho San Joaquin MS 800/7-8
4861 Michelson Dr 92612 949-936-6500
Scott Bowman, prin. Fax 936-6509
San Joaquin Alternative Education 100/Alt
3387 Barranca Pkwy 92606 949-936-7440
Mark Miller, dir. Fax 936-7409
Sierra Vista MS 1,100/7-8
2 Liberty 92620 949-936-6600
Lynn Matassarin, prin. Fax 936-6609
South Lake MS 600/7-8
655 W Yale Loop 92614 949-936-6700
Bruce Baron, prin. Fax 936-6709
University HS 2,400/9-12
4771 Campus Dr 92612 949-936-7600
John Pehrson, prin. Fax 936-7609
Venado MS 700/7-8
4 Deerfield Ave 92604 949-936-6800
Robert Valdez, prin. Fax 936-6809
Woodbridge HS 2,200/9-12
2 Meadowbrook 92604 949-786-1104
Jason Viloria, prin.
Irvine Adult S Adult
3387 Barranca Pkwy 92606 949-936-7400
Linda O'Neal, dir. Fax 936-7459

Tustin USD
Supt. — See Tustin
Beckman HS 2,400/9-12
3588 Bryan 92602 714-734-2900
Adele Heuer, prin. Fax 505-9676

Alliant International University Post-Sec.
2855 Michelle Ste 300 92606 949-833-2651
Brandman University Post-Sec.
16355 Laguna Canyon Rd 92618 949-341-9800
California Southern University Post-Sec.
930 Roosevelt 92620 714-882-7800
Chicago Sch of Professional Psychology Post-Sec.
4199 Campus Dr 92612 949-737-5460
Concordia University Post-Sec.
1530 Concordia 92612 949-854-8002
Crean Lutheran South HS 300/9-12
12500 Sand Canyon Ave 92618 949-916-0897
Jeffrey Beavers, prin. Fax 387-1200
FIDM Fashion Institute of Design Post-Sec.
17590 Gillette Ave 92614 949-851-6200
Irvine Valley College Post-Sec.
5500 Irvine Center Dr 92618 949-451-5100
Stanbridge College Post-Sec.
2041 Business Center Dr 107 92612 949-794-9090
Tarbut V'Torah Day MSHS 300/6-12
5 Federation Way 92603 949-509-9500
Larry Acheatel, head sch Fax 509-7866
University of California 92697 Post-Sec.
949-824-5011

Irwindale, Los Angeles, Pop. 1,410

Premiere Career College Post-Sec.
12901 Ramona Blvd Ste D 91706 626-814-2080
Public Health Foundation Enterprises Post-Sec.
12781 Schabarum Ave 91706 626-856-6376

Jackson, Amador, Pop. 4,513
Amador County Office of Education 300/
217 Rex Ave 95642 209-257-5353
Dick Glock, supt. Fax 257-5360
www.amadorcoe.org/
Other Schools – See Plymouth

Amador County USD 3,900/K-12
217 Rex Ave 95642 209-223-1750
Richard Glock, supt. Fax 296-3133
www.amadorcoe.org
Argonaut HS 600/9-12
501 Argonaut Ln 95642 209-257-7700
David Vicari, prin. Fax 223-3149
Jackson JHS 300/6-8
747 Sutter St 95642 209-257-5700
Janet Pabst, prin. Fax 257-5757
Other Schools – See Ione, Sutter Creek

Regional Occupational Center & Program
Supt. — None
Amador County ROP Vo/Tech
217 Rex Ave 95642 209-259-5339
Elizabeth Chapin-Pinotti, dir.

Jacumba, San Diego, Pop. 550
Mountain Empire USD
Supt. — See Pine Valley
Jacumba MS 100/6-8
44343 Old Highway 80 91934 619-766-4464
Bill Dennett, prin. Fax 766-4532

Jamul, San Diego, Pop. 5,990
Jamul-Dulzura UNSD 1,200/K-12
14581 Lyons Valley Rd 91935 619-669-7700
Nadine Bennett, supt. Fax 669-0254
www.jdusd.net
Oak Grove MS 300/6-8
14344 Olive Vista Dr 91935 619-669-2700
Liz Bystedt, prin. Fax 669-7632

Joshua Tree, San Bernardino, Pop. 7,144

Copper Mountain College Post-Sec.
PO Box 1398 92252 760-366-3791

Julian, San Diego, Pop. 1,474
Julian UNESD 2,400/K-12
PO Box 337 92036 760-765-0661
Kevin Ogden, supt. Fax 765-0220
www.juesd.net
Julian JHS 100/6-8
PO Box 337 92036 760-765-0575
Brian Duffy, prin. Fax 765-3340

Julian UNHSD 200/9-12
PO Box 417 92036 760-765-0606
David Schlottman, supt. Fax 765-2926
www.juhsd.org
Julian HS 200/9-12
PO Box 417 92036 760-765-0606
David Schlottman, prin. Fax 765-2926
Redding Continuation HS 50/Alt
PO Box 417 92036 760-765-0620
David Schlottman, prin. Fax 765-0889

Kelseyville, Lake, Pop. 3,286
Kelseyville USD 1,700/K-12
4410 Konocti Rd 95451 707-279-1511
Dave McQueen, supt. Fax 279-9221
www.kusd.lake.k12.ca.us
Donaldson Continuation HS 50/Alt
4410 Konocti Rd 95451 707-279-8414
Dave McQueen, prin. Fax 279-4404
Kelseyville Community Day S 50/Alt
3980 Gard St 95451 707-279-2415
Dave McQueen, prin. Fax 279-4404
Kelseyville HS 500/9-12
5480 Main St 95451 707-279-4923
Matt Cockerton, prin. Fax 279-9173
Mountain Vista MS 400/6-8
5081 Konocti Rd 95451 707-279-4060
John Berry, prin. Fax 279-8835
Other Schools – See Cobb

Kentfield, Marin, Pop. 6,290
Kentfield ESD 1,100/K-8
750 College Ave 94904 415-458-5130
Elizabeth Schott, supt. Fax 458-5137
www.kentfieldschools.org/
Kent MS 500/5-8
800 College Ave 94904 415-458-5970
Skip Kniesche, prin. Fax 458-5973

College of Marin Post-Sec.
835 College Ave 94904 415-457-8811
Marin Catholic HS 700/9-12
675 Sir Francis Drake Blvd 94904 415-464-3800
Chris Valdez, prin. Fax 461-6943

Kerman, Fresno, Pop. 13,348
Kerman USD 5,400/K-12
151 S 1st St 93630 559-846-5383
Robert Frausto, supt. Fax 846-5941
www.kermanusd.com
Enterprise HS 50/Alt
15405 W Sunset Ave 93630 559-842-3500
Eric Paolinelli, admin. Fax 846-5371
Kerman HS 1,200/9-12
205 S 1st St 93630 559-842-2500
Jim Volkoff, dir. Fax 846-4229
Kerman MS 700/7-8
601 S 1st St 93630 559-842-3000
Amanda Guizar, prin. Fax 846-5217

Kettleman City, Kings, Pop. 1,426
Reef-Sunset USD
Supt. — See Avenal
Adelante Continuation HS 50/Alt
PO Box 149 93239 559-386-9081
Suzy VanDerMolen, prin. Fax 386-0207

Keyes, Stanislaus, Pop. 5,468
Keyes UNESD 1,100/K-12
PO Box 310 95328 209-669-2921
Cynthia Schaefer, supt. Fax 669-2923
www.keyes.k12.ca.us/
Other Schools – See Hughson

King City, Monterey, Pop. 12,778
King City UNSD 2,400/K-8
435 Pearl St 93930 831-385-2940
Theresa Rouse, supt. Fax 386-0372
www.kcusd.org
Chalone Peaks MS 700/6-8
667 Meyer St 93930 831-385-4400
Mike Barbree, prin. Fax 385-4422

South Monterey JUNHSD 1,900/9-12
800 Broadway St 93930 831-385-0606
Daniel Moirao, supt. Fax 385-0695
www.kingcity.k12.ca.us
King City HS 900/9-12
720 Broadway St 93930 831-385-5461
Janet Sanchez Matos, prin. Fax 385-0901
Portola-Butler Continuation HS 100/Alt
760 Broadway St 93930 831-385-4661
Bruce Corbett, prin. Fax 385-0643
Other Schools – See Greenfield

Kingsburg, Fresno, Pop. 11,129
Kingsburg JUNHSD 1,200/9-12
1900 18th Ave 93631 559-897-7721
Randy Morris, supt. Fax 897-7759
www.kjuhsd.k12.ca.us
Kingsburg HS 1,100/9-12
1900 18th Ave 93631 559-897-5156
Randy Morris, prin. Fax 897-7759
Oasis Continuation HS 50/Alt
1900 18th Ave 93631 559-897-3880
Randy Morris, prin. Fax 897-0458

La Canada Flintridge, Los Angeles, Pop. 19,647
La Canada USD 4,000/K-12
4490 Cornishon Ave 91011 818-952-8300
Wendy Sinnette, supt. Fax 952-8309
www.lcusd.net
La Canada JSHS 2,100/7-12
4463 Oak Grove Dr 91011 818-952-4200
Ian McFeat, prin. Fax 952-4214

Flintridge Preparatory S 500/7-12
4543 Crown Ave 91011 818-790-1178
Peter Bachmann, hdmstr. Fax 952-6247
Flintridge Sacred Heart Academy 400/9-12
440 Saint Katherine Dr 91011 626-685-8300
Sr. Celeste Botello, prin. Fax 685-8305
St. Francis HS 700/9-12
200 Foothill Blvd 91011 818-790-0325
Thomas Moran, prin. Fax 790-5542

La Crescenta, Los Angeles, Pop. 19,112
Glendale USD
Supt. — See Glendale
Clark Magnet HS 1,100/9-12
4747 New York Ave 91214 818-248-8324
Douglas Dall, prin. Fax 957-2954
Crescenta Valley HS 2,900/9-12
2900 Community Ave 91214 818-249-5871
Michele Doll Ed.D., prin. Fax 541-9531
Rosemont MS 1,400/7-8
4725 Rosemont Ave 91214 818-248-4224
Cynthia Livingston Ed.D., prin. Fax 248-3790

Ladera Ranch, Orange, Pop. 21,970
Capistrano USD
Supt. — See San Juan Capistrano
Ladera Ranch MS 1,200/6-8
29551 Sienna Pkwy 92694 949-234-5922
George Duarte, prin. Fax 364-1149

Stoneybrooke Christian JHS 100/7-8
26122 ONeill Dr 92694 949-429-3812
Lloyd Grim, prin. Fax 429-3820

Lafayette, Contra Costa, Pop. 22,962
Acalanes UNHSD 5,600/9-12
1212 Pleasant Hill Rd 94549 925-280-3900
John Nickerson, supt. Fax 932-2336
www.acalanes.k12.ca.us
Acalanes HS 1,400/9-12
1200 Pleasant Hill Rd 94549 925-280-3970
Aida Glimme, prin. Fax 280-3971
Other Schools – See Moraga, Orinda, Walnut Creek

Lafayette SD 3,200/K-8
3477 School St 94549 925-927-3500
Fred Brill Ed.D., supt. Fax 284-1525
www.lafsd.k12.ca.us
Stanley MS 1,100/6-8
3455 School St 94549 925-927-3530
David Schrag, prin. Fax 283-1797

Bentley Upper S - Lafayette Campus 300/9-12
1000 Upper Happy Valley Rd 94549 510-283-2101
Arlene Hogan, head sch Fax 299-0469

La Grange, Stanislaus
Big Oak Flat-Groveland USD
Supt. — See Groveland
Pedro HS 50/9-12
3090 Merced Falls Rd 95329 209-852-2864
Dave Urquhart, prin. Fax 852-2125

Laguna Beach, Orange, Pop. 22,111
Laguna Beach USD 3,000/K-12
550 Blumont St 92651 949-497-7700
Sherine Smith, supt. Fax 497-6021
www.lbusd.org
Laguna Beach HS 1,000/9-12
625 Park Ave 92651 949-497-7750
Dr. Joanne Culverhouse, prin. Fax 497-7766
Thurston MS 700/6-8
2100 Park Ave 92651 949-497-7785
Jennifer Salberg, prin. Fax 497-7798

Laguna College of Art and Design Post-Sec.
2222 Laguna Canyon Rd 92651 949-376-6000

Laguna Hills, Orange, Pop. 29,183
Saddleback Valley USD
Supt. — See Mission Viejo

Laguna Hills HS 1,800/9-12
25401 Paseo De Valencia 92653 949-770-5447
Sean Boulton, prin. Fax 830-0295

Allied American University Post-Sec.
22952 Alcalde Dr 92653 888-384-0849
Lake Forest Beauty College Post-Sec.
23565 Moulton Pkwy Ste A 92653 949-951-8883

Laguna Niguel, Orange, Pop. 60,641
Capistrano USD
Supt. — See San Juan Capistrano
Niguel Hills MS 1,300/6-8
29070 Paseo De La Escuela 92677 949-234-5360
Tim Reece, prin. Fax 249-2069

Laguna Niguel Jr. Academy 100/K-10
29702 Kensington Dr 92677 949-495-3428
David Tripp, prin. Fax 495-3438

La Habra, Orange, Pop. 59,112
Fullerton JUNHSD
Supt. — See Fullerton
La Habra HS 2,300/9-12
801 Highlander Ave 90631 562-266-5200
Karl Zener, prin. Fax 691-8280
Sonora HS 2,100/9-12
401 S Palm St 90631 562-266-2003
John Oldenburg, prin. Fax 266-2040

La Habra City ESD 5,400/K-8
PO Box 307 90633 562-690-2305
Susan Belenardo Ed.D., supt. Fax 690-4154
www.lhcsd.k12.ca.us
Imperial MS 900/6-8
PO Box 307 90633 562-690-2344
Cathy Seighman, prin. Fax 526-3678
Washington MS 900/6-8
PO Box 307 90633 562-690-2374
Mario Carlos, prin. Fax 690-7834

Whittier Christian HS 600/9-12
501 N Beach Blvd 90631 562-694-3803
Carl Martinez, head sch Fax 697-1673

La Jolla, See San Diego
San Diego USD
Supt. — See San Diego
La Jolla HS 1,600/9-12
750 Nautilus St 92037 858-454-3081
Dana Shelburne, prin. Fax 459-2188
Muirlands MS 1,100/6-8
1056 Nautilus St 92037 858-459-4211
Christine Hargrave, prin. Fax 459-8075

Bishop's S 800/6-12
7607 La Jolla Blvd 92037 858-459-4021
Aimeclaire Roche, head sch Fax 459-3914
La Jolla Country Day S 1,100/PK-12
9490 Genesee Ave 92037 858-453-3440
Christopher Schuck, head sch Fax 453-8210
National University Post-Sec.
11255 N Torrey Pines Rd 92037 858-642-8000
Sanford-Burnham Graduate School Post-Sec.
10901 N Torrey Pines Rd 92037 858-646-3100
Scripps Memorial Hospital Post-Sec.
9888 Genesee Ave 92037 858-457-6100
Scripps Research Institute Post-Sec.
10550 N Torrey Pines Rd 92037 858-784-8469
University of California Post-Sec.
9500 Gilman Dr 92093 858-534-2230

Lake Almanor, Plumas, Pop. 353

Lake Almanor Christian S 50/K-12
2610 State Route A13 96137 530-596-4100
Floren Suetos, prin. Fax 596-4682

Lake Arrowhead, San Bernardino, Pop. 12,063
Rim of the World USD
Supt. — See Blue Jay
Henck IS 1,000/6-8
PO Box 430 92352 909-336-0360
Ken Decroo, prin. Fax 336-3449
Lake Gregory Education Center 100/Alt
PO Box 430 92352 909-336-3474
Debra Wogen, prin. Fax 336-3450
Rim of the World HS 1,400/9-12
PO Box 430 92352 909-336-2038
Catherine Obregon, prin. Fax 336-0254

Lake Elsinore, Riverside, Pop. 50,250
Lake Elsinore USD 21,600/K-12
545 Chaney St 92530 951-253-7000
Doug Kimberly, supt. Fax 253-7084
www.leusd.k12.ca.us
Canyon Lake MS 1,200/6-8
33005 Canyon Hills Rd 92532 951-244-2123
Preston Perez, prin. Fax 244-2103
Elsinore MS 800/6-8
1203 W Graham Ave 92530 951-674-2118
James Judziewicz, prin. Fax 674-6302
Lakeside HS 2,000/9-12
32593 Riverside Dr 92530 951-253-7300
Peter Hopping Ed.D., prin. Fax 253-7335
McCarthy Academy 200/Alt
520 Chaney St 92530 951-253-7065
Amy Campbell, prin. Fax 245-1988
Ortega Continuation HS 300/Alt
520 Chaney St 92530 951-253-7065
Amy Campbell, prin. Fax 245-1988
Temescal Canyon HS 2,100/9-12
28755 El Toro Rd 92532 951-253-7250
Whitney D'Amico Ed.D., prin. Fax 253-7266
Terra Cotta MS 1,500/6-8
29291 Lake St 92530 951-253-7380
Sarah Arredondo, prin. Fax 674-5191
Valley Adult S Adult
520 Chaney St 92530 951-253-7093
Amy Campbell, prin. Fax 253-7039
Other Schools – See Wildomar

Lake Forest, Orange, Pop. 74,539
Saddleback Valley USD
Supt. — See Mission Viejo
El Toro HS 2,800/9-12
25255 Toledo Way 92630 949-586-6333
Terri Gusiff, prin. Fax 380-9874
Serrano IS 1,400/7-8
24642 Jeronimo Rd 92630 949-586-3221
Robert Sherlock, prin. Fax 586-3773

Elegante Beauty College Post-Sec.
23635 El Toro Rd Ste K 92630 949-586-4900
Heritage Christian S 200/PK-12
22882 Loumont Dr 92630 949-598-9166
George Gay, prin. Fax 598-1892

Lake Isabella, Kern, Pop. 3,311
Kern UNHSD
Supt. — See Bakersfield
Kern Valley HS 600/9-12
3340 Erskine Creek Rd 93240 760-379-2611
John Meyers, prin. Fax 379-8314
Summit Continuation HS 50/Alt
2811 Pasadena Ln 93240 760-379-3997
Carr Wheat, admin. Fax 379-6234

Kernville UNESD 700/K-8
3240 Erskine Creek Rd 93240 760-379-3651
Robin Shive, supt. Fax 379-3812
www.kernvilleusd.org
Rio Vista Community Day S 50/Alt
3240 Erskine Creek Rd 93240 760-379-4863
Jill Shaw, prin. Fax 379-1324
Wallace MS 300/5-8
3240 Erskine Creek Rd 93240 760-379-4646
Jill Shaw, prin. Fax 379-1322

Lakeport, Lake, Pop. 4,650
Lake County Office of Education 50/
1152 S Main St 95453 707-262-4100
Wally Holbrook, supt. Fax 263-0197
www.lake-coe.k12.ca.us
Other Schools – See Clearlake

Lakeport USD 1,500/K-12
2508 Howard Ave 95453 707-262-3000
Erin Smith-Hagberg, supt. Fax 263-7332
www.lakeport.k12.ca.us
Clear Lake HS 500/9-12
2508 Howard Ave 95453 707-262-3010
Steve Gentry, prin. Fax 262-3026
Lakeport Alternative S 50/Alt
2508 Howard Ave 95453 707-262-3013
Erin Smith-Hagberg, admin. Fax 263-6304
Lakeport Community Day S 50/Alt
2508 Howard Ave 95453 707-262-3013
Erin Smith-Hagberg, admin. Fax 263-6304
Natural Continuation HS 50/Alt
2508 Howard Ave 95453 707-262-3013
Erin Smith-Hagberg, admin. Fax 263-6304
Terrace MS 600/4-8
2508 Howard Ave 95453 707-262-3007
Jill Falconer, prin. Fax 262-5532

Regional Occupational Center & Program
Supt. — None
Lake County ROP Vo/Tech
1152 S Main St 95453 707-262-4162
Brock Falkenberg, dir. Fax 262-0197

Lakeside, San Diego, Pop. 20,041
Grossmont UNHSD
Supt. — See La Mesa
El Capitan HS 1,800/9-12
10410 Ashwood St 92040 619-938-9100
Laura Whitaker, prin. Fax 390-8503

Lakeside UNSD 4,500/K-12
12335 Woodside Ave 92040 619-390-2600
Brian Bristol Ed.D., supt. Fax 561-7929
www.lsusd.net
East County Academy of Learning 50/Alt
11838 Valle Vista Rd 92040 619-390-2634
Keven Bowers, prin. Fax 390-2575
Lakeside MS 600/6-8
11833 Woodside Ave 92040 619-390-2636
Stephen Mull, prin. Fax 390-2643
Tierra Del Sol MS 600/6-8
9611 Petite Ln 92040 619-390-2670
Scott Goergens, prin. Fax 390-2518

Lakewood, Los Angeles, Pop. 76,583
ABC USD
Supt. — See Cerritos
Artesia HS 1,500/9-12
12108 Del Amo Blvd 90715 562-229-7700
Sergio Garcia, prin. Fax 809-5604

Bellflower USD
Supt. — See Bellflower
Mayfair MSHS 3,500/7-12
6000 Woodruff Ave 90713 562-925-9981
Matt Eeles, prin. Fax 804-1656

Long Beach USD
Supt. — See Long Beach
Hoover MS 1,000/6-8
3501 Country Club Dr 90712 562-421-1213
Dr. Avery Hall, prin. Fax 421-8063
Lakewood HS 4,100/9-12
4400 Briercrest Ave 90713 562-425-1281
Mario Jimenez, prin. Fax 421-9616

Paramount USD
Supt. — See Paramount
Buena Vista HS Alt
3717 Michelson St 90712 562-602-8090
Jean Law, admin. Fax 602-8091

St. Joseph HS 800/9-12
5825 Woodruff Ave 90713 562-925-5073
Dr. Terri Mendoza, prin. Fax 925-3315

La Mesa, San Diego, Pop. 54,494
Grossmont UNHSD 23,600/9-12
PO Box 1043 91944 619-644-8000
Ralf Swenson, supt. Fax 465-1349
www.guhsd.net
Other Schools – See El Cajon, Lakeside, Santee, Spring Valley

La Mesa-Spring Valley SD 11,100/K-8
4750 Date Ave 91942 619-668-5700
Brian Marshall, supt. Fax 668-5809
www.lmsvsd.k12.ca.us
La Mesa MS 700/7-8
4200 Parks Ave 91941 619-668-5730
Beth Thomas, prin. Fax 668-8303
Parkway MS 800/7-8
9009 Park Plaza Dr 91942 619-668-5810
Mary Beason, prin. Fax 668-5779
Other Schools – See Spring Valley

California Hair Design Academy Post-Sec.
8011 University Ave Ste A2 91942 619-461-8600

La Mirada, Los Angeles, Pop. 47,368
Norwalk-La Mirada USD
Supt. — See Norwalk
Benton MS 500/6-8
15709 Olive Branch Dr 90638 562-943-1553
Michelle Green, prin. Fax 947-3861
Hutchinson MS 600/6-8
13900 Estero Rd 90638 562-944-3268
Sara Siemens, prin. Fax 944-3269
La Mirada HS 2,200/9-12
13520 Adelfa Dr 90638 562-868-0431
Bill Seals, prin. Fax 943-7872
Los Coyotes MS 700/6-8
14640 Mercado Ave 90638 714-523-2051
Christina Stanley, prin. Fax 739-2368
Norwalk Adult S Adult
15920 Barbata Rd 90638 562-670-9279
Sharon Todd, dir. Fax 670-1654

Biola University Post-Sec.
13800 Biola Ave 90639 562-903-6000
Heights Christian JHS 200/6-8
12900 Bluefield Ave 90638 562-947-3309
Nicholas Damico, prin. Fax 947-1001

Lamont, Kern, Pop. 15,088
Kern UNHSD
Supt. — See Bakersfield
Nueva Continuation HS 100/Alt
8600 Palm Ave 93241 661-845-1532
Mike Bhone, admin. Fax 845-9523

Lamont ESD 2,800/K-8
7915 Burgundy Ave 93241 661-845-0751
Ricardo Robles, supt. Fax 845-0689
www.lamontschooldistrict.org
Other Schools – See Bakersfield

Lancaster, Los Angeles, Pop. 151,168
Antelope Valley UNHSD 26,000/7-12
44811 Sierra Hwy 93534 661-948-7655
David Vierra, supt. Fax 942-8744
www.avdistrict.org
Antelope Valley HS 1,800/9-12
44900 Division St 93535 661-948-8552
Matt Anderson, prin. Fax 945-8867
Desert Winds Continuation HS 1,000/Alt
45030 3rd St E 93535 661-948-7555
Susan McDougal, prin. Fax 948-5947
Eastside HS 2,500/9-12
3200 E Avenue J8 93535 661-946-3800
Joe Kelly, prin. Fax 946-3850
Lancaster HS 2,500/9-12
44701 Eagle Way 93536 661-726-7649
Steve Radford, prin. Fax 726-7694
SOAR HS 300/9-12
3041 W Avenue K 93536 661-722-6509
Michael Dutton, prin. Fax 722-6583
Antelope Valley Adult HS Adult
45110 3rd St E 93535 661-942-3042
Terry O'Connor, prin. Fax 948-0846
Other Schools – See Littlerock, Palmdale, Quartz Hill

Eastside UNSD 3,300/K-8
45006 30th St E 93535 661-952-1200
Mark Marshall Ed.D., supt. Fax 952-1220
www.eastside.k12.ca.us
Cole MS 900/6-8
3126 E Avenue I 93535 661-946-1041
Francisco Pinto, prin. Fax 946-0166

Lancaster ESD 16,900/PK-8
44711 Cedar Ave 93534 661-948-4661
Michele Bowers Ed.D., supt. Fax 948-9398
www.lancsd.org
Amargosa Creek MS 1,100/6-8
44333 27th St W 93536 661-729-6064
Kymberlee Cochran, prin. Fax 729-6858
Endeavour MS 800/6-8
43755 45th St W 93536 661-723-0351
David Denning, prin. Fax 723-1362
Lancaster Virtual Alternative Academy 100/Alt
44310 Hardwood Ave 93534 661-726-4354
Gary Keyes, coord. Fax 726-5457

New Vista MS 1,200/6-8
753 E Avenue K2 93535 661-726-4271
Kathy Lee, prin. Fax 726-4278
Piute MS 1,300/6-8
425 E Avenue H11 93535 661-942-9508
Michael David, prin. Fax 940-6676

Los Angeles County Office of Education
Supt. — See Downey
Westside Community Day S 50/Alt
5506 W Avenue L8 93536 661-974-8659
Michael Jaurequi, prin. Fax 945-4196

Westside UNESD 8,600/K-8
41914 50th St W 93536 661-722-0716
Regina Rossall, supt. Fax 206-3645
www.westside.k12.ca.us
Other Schools – See Palmdale, Quartz Hill

Wilsona SD
Supt. — See Palmdale
Challenger MS 700/5-8
41725 170th St E 93535 661-264-1790
Janice Stowers, prin. Fax 264-1793
Wilsona Achievement Academy 50/Alt
41725 170th St E 93535 661-264-1790
Janice Stowers, prin. Fax 264-1793

Antelope Valley Christian S 300/PK-12
3700 W Avenue L 93536 661-943-0044
Douglas McKenzie, dir. Fax 943-6774
Antelope Valley College Post-Sec.
3041 W Avenue K 93536 661-722-6300
Bethel Christian S 400/PK-12
3100 W Avenue K 93536 661-943-2224
Matt Konnerth, prin. Fax 943-6574
Charter College Lancaster Post-Sec.
43141 Business Ctr Pkwy 102 93535 661-341-3500
Desert Christian HS 400/9-12
2340 W Avenue J8 93536 661-723-7441
Cecil Swetland, dir. Fax 723-7437
Desert Christian MS 300/6-8
44662 15th St W 93534 661-723-0665
Cecil Swetland, dir. Fax 723-6774
Lancaster Beauty School Post-Sec.
44646 10th St W 93534 661-948-1672
Paraclete HS 800/9-12
42145 30th St W 93536 661-943-3255
John Anson, prin. Fax 722-9455
University of Antelope Valley Post-Sec.
44055 Sierra Hwy 93534 661-726-1911

La Palma, Orange, Pop. 15,047
Anaheim UNHSD
Supt. — See Anaheim
Kennedy HS 2,400/9-12
8281 Walker St 90623 714-220-4101
Russell Earnest, prin. Fax 995-1833
Walker JHS 1,100/7-8
8132 Walker St 90623 714-220-4051
Kirsten Levitin Ed.D., prin. Fax 220-2237

La Palma Christian S 100/PK-12
8082 Walker St 90623 714-527-3231
Karen Bland, dir. Fax 995-8046

La Puente, Los Angeles, Pop. 39,527
Bassett USD 4,500/K-12
904 Willow Ave 91746 626-931-3000
Jose Reynoso, supt. Fax 918-5105
www.bassett.k12.ca.us
Bassett HS 1,200/9-12
904 Willow Ave 91746 626-931-2800
Robert Reyes, prin. Fax 931-2850
Nueva Vista Continuation HS 100/Alt
904 Willow Ave 91746 626-931-3177
Salvador Flores, prin. Fax 931-3145
Bassett Adult S Adult
904 Willow Ave 91746 626-931-3102
Jorge Seccia, prin. Fax 931-3168
Other Schools – See City of Industry

Hacienda La Puente USD
Supt. — See City of Industry
La Puente HS 1,600/9-12
15615 Nelson Ave 91744 626-934-6700
Ava Smalley, prin. Fax 855-3798
Puente Hills HS 100/Alt
14162 Lomitas Ave 91746 626-933-3400
Priscilla Tam, prin. Fax 855-3719
Sierra Vista MS 400/7-8
15801 Sierra Vista Ct 91744 626-933-4000
Maria Ceja, prin. Fax 855-3817
Sparks MS 500/7-8
15100 Giordano St 91744 626-933-5000
Collin Miller, prin. Fax 855-3848

Rowland USD
Supt. — See Rowland Heights
Nogales HS 2,200/9-12
401 Nogales St 91744 626-965-3437
Fax 965-4587

Bishop Amat HS 1,400/9-12
14301 Fairgrove Ave 91746 626-962-2495
Dr. Merritt Hemenway, prin. Fax 960-0994
Hacienda LaPuente Valley Adult Education Post-Sec.
14101 Nelson Ave 91746 626-934-2800

La Quinta, Riverside, Pop. 36,785
Desert Sands USD 29,100/K-12
47950 Dune Palms Rd 92253 760-777-4200
Dr. Sharon McGehee, supt. Fax 771-8505
www.dsusd.us
Horizon S 400/Alt
43330 Palm Royale Dr 92253 760-238-9720
Cara Prentiss, prin. Fax 360-2182
La Quinta HS 3,000/9-12
79255 Blackhawk Way 92253 760-772-4150
Donna Salazar, prin. Fax 772-4166
La Quinta MS 700/6-8
78900 Avenue 50 92253 760-777-4220
Janet Seto, prin. Fax 777-4216
Paige MS 1,000/6-8
43495 Palm Royale Dr 92253 760-238-9710
Derrick Lawson, prin. Fax 345-1202
Summit HS 300/Alt
43330 Palm Royale Dr 92253 760-238-9760
Cara Prentiss, prin. Fax 238-9751
Other Schools – See Indio, Palm Desert

Larkspur, Marin, Pop. 11,461
Larkspur-Corte Madera SD 1,300/K-8
230 Doherty Dr 94939 415-927-6960
Valerie Pitts, supt. Fax 927-6964
www.larkspurschools.org
Hall MS 600/5-8
200 Doherty Dr 94939 415-927-6978
Tom Utic, prin. Fax 927-6985

Tamalpais UNHSD 3,800/9-12
PO Box 605 94977 415-945-3600
Laurie Kimbrel, supt. Fax 945-3719
www.tamdistrict.org
Redwood HS 1,500/9-12
395 Doherty Dr 94939 415-924-6200
David Sondheim, prin. Fax 945-3675
San Andreas HS 100/Alt
599 William Ave 94939 415-945-3770
Gerald Austin, prin. Fax 945-3754
Tamiscal HS 100/Alt
PO Box 605 94977 415-945-3750
Corbett Elsen, prin. Fax 945-3752
Other Schools – See Mill Valley, San Anselmo

La Selva Beach, Santa Cruz, Pop. 2,748
Pajaro Valley USD
Supt. — See Watsonville
Renaissance HS 200/Alt
11 Spring Valley Rd 95076 831-728-6344
Artemisa Cortez, prin. Fax 728-6419

Monterey Bay Academy 200/9-12
783 San Andreas Rd 95076 831-728-1481
Tim Kubrock, prin. Fax 728-1485

Lathrop, San Joaquin, Pop. 17,283
Manteca USD
Supt. — See Manteca
Lathrop HS 700/9-12
647 Spartan Way 95330 209-938-6350
Michael Horwood, prin. Fax 938-6390

ITT Technical Institute Post-Sec.
16916 S Harlan Rd 95330 209-858-0077

Laton, Fresno, Pop. 1,814
Laton USD 600/K-12
PO Box 248 93242 559-922-4015
Terry Hirschfield, supt. Fax 923-4791
www.laton.k12.ca.us
Conejo MS 6-8
PO Box 7 93242 559-922-4030
Terry Hirschfield, prin. Fax 923-9651
Laton HS 200/9-12
PO Box 278 93242 559-922-4080
James Reed, prin. Fax 923-4072

La Verne, Los Angeles, Pop. 30,232
Bonita USD
Supt. — See San Dimas
Bonita HS 2,000/9-12
3102 D St 91750 909-971-8220
Robert Ketterling, prin. Fax 971-8229
Ramona MS 1,400/6-8
3490 Ramona Ave 91750 909-971-8260
Anne Neal, prin. Fax 971-8269

Calvary Baptist S 100/PK-12
2990 Damien Ave 91750 909-593-4672
Taylora Dial, prin. Fax 392-9533
Damien HS 1,100/9-12
2280 Damien Ave 91750 909-596-1946
Dr. Merritt Hemenway, prin. Fax 596-1946
Lutheran HS 1,100/9-12
3960 Fruit St 91750 909-593-4494
Dr. Lance Ebel, prin. Fax 596-3744
University of La Verne Post-Sec.
1950 3rd St 91750 909-593-3511

Lawndale, Los Angeles, Pop. 31,604
Centinela Valley UNHSD 6,500/9-12
14901 Inglewood Ave 90260 310-263-3200
Jose Fernandez, supt. Fax 675-8286
www.centinela.k12.ca.us/
Centinela Valley Independent Study HS 100/Alt
4951 Marine Ave 90260 310-263-3264
Dr. James Tarouilly, prin. Fax 978-3995
Lawndale HS 1,900/9-12
14901 Inglewood Ave 90260 310-263-3100
Joseph Guidetti, prin. Fax 675-8174
Leuzinger HS 2,200/9-12
4118 Rosecrans Ave 90260 310-263-2200
Michael Ono, prin. Fax 675-7023
Lloyde Continuation HS 200/Alt
4951 Marine Ave 90260 310-263-3264
James Tarouilly, prin. Fax 978-3995
Centinela Valley Adult S Adult
4953 Marine Ave 90260 310-263-3165
Dr. James Tarouilly, prin. Fax 644-6142
Other Schools – See Hawthorne

Lawndale ESD 6,300/K-12
4161 W 147th St 90260 310-973-1300
Ellen Dougherty Ed.D., supt. Fax 675-6462
www.lawndalesd.org/
Addams MS 900/6-8
4161 W 147th St 90260 310-676-4806
Frank Noyes, prin. Fax 676-8621
Rogers MS 1,000/6-8
4161 W 147th St 90260 310-676-1197
Maurita De La Torre Ed.D., prin. Fax 675-0489

ICDC College Post-Sec.
4415 Redondo Beach Blvd 90260 310-793-4100

Laytonville, Mendocino, Pop. 1,182
Laytonville USD 400/K-12
PO Box 868 95454 707-984-6414
Joan Potter, supt. Fax 984-8223
layt.k12.ca.us
Laytonville Community Day S 50/Alt
PO Box 868 95454 707-984-6414
Lorre Stange, prin. Fax 984-8761
Laytonville Continuation HS 50/Alt
PO Box 868 95454 707-984-6811
Daniel Regelbrugge, prin. Fax 984-8066
Laytonville HS 100/9-12
PO Box 868 95454 707-984-6108
Daniel Regelbrugge, prin. Fax 984-8066

Lebec, Kern, Pop. 1,432
El Tejon USD 1,000/K-12
PO Box 876 93243 661-248-6247
Katherine Kleier, supt. Fax 248-6714
www.el-tejon.k12.ca.us
El Tejon Continuation HS Alt
PO Box 876 93243 661-248-0310
Sara Haflich, admin. Fax 248-6460
El Tejon MS 300/5-8
PO Box 876 93243 661-248-6680
Fax 248-5203
Frazier Mountain HS 400/9-12
PO Box 876 93243 661-248-0310
Sara Haflich, prin. Fax 248-0403

Lee Vining, Mono, Pop. 220
Eastern Sierra USD
Supt. — See Bridgeport
Lee Vining HS 100/9-12
PO Box 268 93541 760-647-6366
Roger Yost, prin. Fax 647-6695

Leggett, Mendocino, Pop. 105
Leggett Valley USD 100/K-12
PO Box 186 95585 707-925-6230
Tom Puskarich, supt. Fax 925-6396
www.leggett.k12.ca.us
Leggett Valley HS 50/9-12
PO Box 186 95585 707-925-6230
Tom Puskarich, prin. Fax 925-6396
Redwood HS Alt
PO Box 100 95585 707-925-6285
Tom Puskarich, prin. Fax 925-6396
Other Schools – See Whitethorn

Le Grand, Merced, Pop. 1,644
Le Grand UNHSD 500/9-12
12961 Le Grand Rd 95333 209-389-9403
Donna Alley M.A., supt. Fax 389-9414
www.lghs.k12.ca.us/
Le Grand Union HS 500/9-12
12961 Le Grand Rd 95333 209-389-9400
Javier Martinez, admin. Fax 389-4065
Other Schools – See Planada

Lemon Grove, San Diego, Pop. 24,153
Lemon Grove ESD 3,800/PK-8
8025 Lincoln St 91945 619-825-5600
Ernest Anastos, supt. Fax 462-7959
www.lgsd.k12.ca.us
Lemon Grove MS 700/7-8
7866 Lincoln St 91945 619-825-5628
Rick Oser, prin. Fax 825-5781

Lemoore, Kings, Pop. 23,462
Lemoore ESD 3,300/K-8
100 Vine St 93245 559-924-6800
Richard Rayburn, supt. Fax 924-6809
www.luesd.k12.ca.us
Liberty MS 600/7-8
100 Vine St 93245 559-924-6860
Ben Luis, prin. Fax 924-6869

Lemoore UNHSD 2,200/9-12
5 Powell Ave 93245 559-924-6610
Debbie Muro, supt. Fax 924-9212
www.luhsd.k12.ca.us/
Jamison Alternative Education HS 100/Alt
351 E Bush St 93245 559-924-6620
Sandi Lowe, prin. Fax 924-6637
Lemoore HS 1,900/9-12
101 E Bush St 93245 559-924-6600
Rodney Brumit, prin. Fax 924-5086

Kings Christian S 300/PK-12
900 E D St 93245 559-924-8301
Steven Reynolds, admin. Fax 924-0607
West Hills College Lemoore Post-Sec.
555 College Dr 93245 559-925-3000

Lennox, Los Angeles, Pop. 22,462
Lennox ESD 7,200/K-12
10319 Firmona Ave 90304 310-695-4000
Dr. Barbara Flores, supt. Fax 695-4000
www.lennox.k12.ca.us
Lennox MS 1,200/7-8
11033 Buford Ave 90304 310-419-1800
Debra Johnson, prin. Fax 677-4635

Lincoln, Placer, Pop. 41,451
Western Placer USD 7,800/PK-12
600 6th St Ste 400 95648 916-645-6350
Scott Leaman, supt. Fax 645-6356
www.wpusd.k12.ca.us
Edwards MS 700/6-8
204 L St 95648 916-645-6370
Shelly Hoover, prin. Fax 645-6379
Lincoln HS 1,500/9-12
790 J St 95648 916-645-6360
Jay Berns, prin. Fax 645-6349
Phoenix Continuation HS 100/Alt
870 J St 95648 916-645-6395
Michael Doherty, prin. Fax 645-6347
Twelve Bridges MS 800/6-8
770 Westview Dr 95648 916-434-5270
Stacey Brown, prin. Fax 434-5240

Linden, San Joaquin, Pop. 1,741
Linden USD 2,300/K-12
18527 E Highway 26 95236 209-887-3894
Michael Gonzales, supt. Fax 887-2250
www.lindenusd.com
Linden HS 800/9-12
18527 E Front St 95236 209-887-3073
Richard Schmidig, prin. Fax 887-3815
Other Schools – See Stockton

Lindsay, Tulare, Pop. 11,716
Lindsay USD 5,000/PK-12
371 E Hermosa St 93247 559-562-5111
Thomas L. Rooney, supt. Fax 562-4637
www.lindsay.k12.ca.us
Cairns Continuation HS 100/Alt
467 E Honolulu St 93247 559-562-5913
Dennis Doane, prin. Fax 562-1753
Lindsay HS 1,100/9-12
1849 E Tulare Rd 93247 559-562-5911
Jaime Robles, prin. Fax 562-4291

Littlerock, Los Angeles, Pop. 1,327
Antelope Valley UNHSD
Supt. — See Lancaster
Littlerock HS 1,800/9-12
10833 E Avenue R 93543 661-944-5209
Karen Parker, prin. Fax 944-5191

Keppel UNESD
Supt. — See Pearblossom
Keppel Academy 400/5-8
9330 E Avenue U 93543 661-944-2152
Dr. Richie Romero, prin. Fax 944-0694

Live Oak, Sutter, Pop. 8,180
Live Oak USD 1,800/K-12
2201 Pennington Rd 95953 530-695-5400
Tom Pritchard, supt. Fax 695-5460
www.lousd.k12.ca.us
Live Oak Alternative S 50/Alt
2207 Pennington Rd 95953 530-695-5400
Mat Gulbrandsen, prin. Fax 695-5432
Live Oak HS 500/9-12
2351 Pennington Rd 95953 530-695-5415
Mat Gulbrandsen, prin. Fax 695-5422
Live Oak MS 500/5-8
2082 Pennington Rd 95953 530-695-5435
Parm Virk, prin. Fax 695-5443

Livermore, Alameda, Pop. 77,773
Livermore Valley JUSD 12,800/K-12
685 E Jack London Blvd 94551 925-606-3200
Kelly Bowers, supt. Fax 606-3329
www.livermoreschools.com
Christensen MS 600/6-8
5757 Haggin Oaks Ave 94551 925-606-4702
Pat Avilla, prin. Fax 606-4705
Del Valle Continuation HS 100/Alt
2253 5th St 94550 925-606-4709
Darrel Avilla, prin. Fax 606-3371
East Avenue MS 700/6-8
3951 East Ave 94550 925-606-4711
Josh Swerdlow, prin. Fax 606-4763
Granada HS 2,200/9-12
400 Wall St 94550 925-606-4800
Philomena Rambo, prin. Fax 606-4808
Livermore HS 2,000/9-12
600 Maple St 94550 925-606-4812
Alberto Solorzano, prin. Fax 606-4851
Mendenhall MS 900/6-8
1701 El Padro Dr 94550 925-606-4731
Susan Sambuceti, prin. Fax 606-4737
Phoenix Continuation HS 50/Alt
2253 5th St 94550 925-606-4709
Darrel Avilla, prin. Fax 606-3371
Vineyard Alternative S 200/Alt
1401 Almond Ave 94550 925-606-4722
Sheryl Howser, prin. Fax 606-4799
Livermore Adult Community Education Adult
1401 Almond Ave 94550 925-606-4722
Sheryl Howser, prin Fax 606-3389

Regional Occupational Center & Program
Supt. — None
Tri-Valley ROP Vo/Tech
1040 Florence Rd 94550 925-455-4800
Julie Duncan, supt. Fax 449-9126

Las Positas College Post-Sec.
3000 Campus Hill Dr 94551 925-424-1000

Livingston, Merced, Pop. 12,876
Livingston UNESD 2,500/K-8
922 B St 95334 209-394-5400
Andres Zamora, supt. Fax 394-5401
www.lusd.k12.ca.us
Livingston MS 800/6-8
101 F St 95334 209-394-5450
Filomena Sousa, prin. Fax 394-5451

Merced County Office of Education
Supt. — See Merced
Schelby S 50/Alt
6738 Sultana Dr 95334 209-394-1800
Jennifer Slatten, coord. Fax 394-7818

Merced UNHSD
Supt. — See Atwater
Livingston HS 1,200/9-12
1617 Main St 95334 209-394-7961
Ralph Calderon, prin. Fax 358-1093

Lodi, San Joaquin, Pop. 60,610
Lodi USD 29,900/PK-12
1305 E Vine St 95240 209-331-7000
Cathy Nichols-Washer, supt. Fax 331-7256
www.lodiusd.net/
Henderson Community Day S 100/Alt
13451 N Extension Rd 95242 209-331-7331
Allen Dosty, prin. Fax 331-7601
Independence S North 300/Alt
660 W Walnut St 95240 209-331-7622
Carol Owens, prin. Fax 331-7624
Liberty Continuation HS 100/Alt
660 W Walnut St 95240 209-331-7633
Tami Somera, prin. Fax 331-7624
Lincoln Technical Academy Vo/Tech
542 E Pine St 95240 209-331-7616
William Atterberry, prin. Fax 331-7526
Lodi HS 2,100/9-12
3 S Pacific Ave 95242 209-331-7819
Bob Lofsted, prin. Fax 331-7779
Lodi MS 900/7-8
945 S Ham Ln 95242 209-331-7540
Scott McGregor, prin. Fax 331-7550
Millswood MS 800/7-8
233 N Mills Ave 95242 209-331-8332
Sheree Flemmer, prin. Fax 331-8347
Tokay HS 2,100/9-12
1111 W Century Blvd 95240 209-331-7990
Erik Sandstrom, prin. Fax 331-7168
Lodi Adult S Adult
542 E Pine St 95240 209-331-7605
William Atterberry, prin. Fax 331-7167
Other Schools – See Stockton

Elliot Christian HS 200/9-12
2695 W Vine St 95242 209-368-2800
David Couchman, admin. Fax 333-5208
Lodi Academy 100/9-12
1230 S Central Ave 95240 209-368-2781
Doug Brown, prin. Fax 368-6142
Vineyard Christian MS 100/6-8
2301 W Lodi Ave 95242 209-333-8300
Karen Hale, prin. Fax 339-4327

Loma Linda, San Bernardino, Pop. 22,264

Loma Linda Academy 1,400/K-12
10656 Anderson St 92354 909-796-0161
Dr. Doug Herrmann, prin. Fax 799-8049
Loma Linda University 92350 Post-Sec.
909-558-1000

Lomita, Los Angeles, Pop. 19,339
Los Angeles USD
Supt. — See Los Angeles
Fleming MS 1,800/6-8
25425 Walnut St 90717 310-257-4500
Janice Hackett, prin. Fax 326-9071

Coastal Academy 100/K-12
25501 Oak St 90717 310-644-0433
Grace DiPasquale, prin.

Lompoc, Santa Barbara, Pop. 41,015
Lompoc USD 9,800/K-12
PO Box 8000 93438 805-742-3300
Gregory Kampf, supt. Fax 735-8452
www.lusd.org
Cabrillo HS 1,500/9-12
PO Box 8000 93438 805-742-2900
Lore Desmond, prin. Fax 733-4156
Lompoc HS 1,400/9-12
PO Box 8000 93438 805-742-3000
Paul Bommersbach, prin. Fax 742-3004
Lompoc Valley MS 700/7-8
PO Box 8000 93438 805-742-2600
Larry Boone, prin. Fax 737-9480
Maple HS 200/Alt
PO Box 8000 93438 805-742-3150
Kim McCollum, prin. Fax 742-3163
Mission Valley S Alt
PO Box 8000 93438 805-742-3252
Mary Coggins, prin. Fax 742-3159
Lompoc Adult Education Adult
PO Box 8000 93438 805-742-3100
Greg Halfman, prin Fax 742-3085
Other Schools – See Vandenberg AFB

Lone Pine, Inyo, Pop. 1,990
Inyo County Office of Education
Supt. — See Independence
Alabama Hills Community Day S 50/Alt
301 E Locust St 93545 760-876-5006
Dr. Terence McAteer, dir.

Lone Pine USD 400/K-12
PO Box 159 93545 760-876-5579
Victor Hopper, supt. Fax 876-5438
lpusd-ca.schoolloop.com
Lone Pine HS 100/9-12
PO Box 159 93545 760-876-5577
Victor Hopper, prin. Fax 876-1037
Sierra Alternative Learning Academy Alt
PO Box 159 93545 760-876-5577
Victor Hopper, prin.
Lone Pine Adult S Adult
PO Box 159 93545 760-876-5579
Victor Hopper, prin. Fax 876-5438

Long Barn, Tuolumne, Pop. 153
Summerville UNHSD
Supt. — See Tuolumne
Cold Springs HS 50/Alt
25910 Long Barn Rd 95335 209-586-3011
David Johnstone, prin. Fax 928-1422
Long Barn HS 50/Alt
25910 Long Barn Dr 95335 209-586-3011
Mitch Heldstab, prin. Fax 928-1422

Long Beach, Los Angeles, Pop. 443,652
Long Beach USD 82,300/PK-12
1515 Hughes Way 90810 562-997-8000
Christopher Steinhauser, supt. Fax 997-8280
www.lbschools.net/
Bancroft MS 1,100/6-8
5301 E Centralia St 90808 562-425-7461
Kimberly Dalton, prin. Fax 425-9741
Beach HS, 3701 E Willow St 90815 Alt
Matthew Saldana, prin. 562-595-8893
Cabrillo HS 3,400/9-12
2001 Santa Fe Ave 90810 562-951-7700
Elio Mendoza, prin. Fax 951-7797
Franklin Classical MS 1,000/6-8
540 Cerritos Ave 90802 562-435-4952
Maria Perossio, prin. Fax 432-6308
Hamilton MS 1,100/6-8
1060 E 70th St 90805 562-602-0302
Pamela Sawyer, prin. Fax 602-1354
Hill Classical MS 1,100/6-8
1100 Iroquois Ave 90815 562-598-7611
Sophia Griffieth, prin. Fax 598-6329
Hughes MS 1,600/6-8
3846 California Ave 90807 562-595-0831
Sally Gregory, prin. Fax 595-9221
Jefferson Leadership Academies 900/6-8
750 Euclid Ave 90804 562-438-9904
Brian Moskovitz, prin. Fax 439-3718
Jordan HS 3,800/9-12
6500 Atlantic Ave 90805 562-423-1471
Shawn Ashley, prin. Fax 422-9091
Lindbergh MS 800/6-8
1022 E Market St 90805 562-422-2845
Connie Magee, prin. Fax 423-8176
Lindsey Academy 900/6-8
5075 Daisy Ave 90805 562-423-6451
Stephanie Dunn, prin. Fax 422-3800
Marshall Academy of the Arts 900/6-8
5870 E Wardlow Rd 90808 562-429-7013
Michael Navia, prin. Fax 429-6973
Millikan HS 4,200/9-12
2800 Snowden Ave 90815 562-425-7441
Jeferey Cornejo, prin. Fax 425-1151
PAAL Academy Alt
1545 Long Beach Blvd 90813 562-591-1381
Ernest Chavez, admin.
Polytechnic HS Vo/Tech
1600 Atlantic Ave 90813 562-591-0581
Joe Carlson, prin. Fax 591-0631
Reid Continuation HS 400/Alt
2153 W Hill St 90810 562-989-2098
Barbara Lindholm, prin. Fax 989-2097
Renaissance HS for the Arts 500/9-12
235 E 8th St 90813 562-901-0168
Quentin Brown, prin. Fax 435-7147
Rogers MS 900/6-8
365 Monrovia Ave 90803 562-434-7411
Kimberly Holland, prin. Fax 434-0581
Stanford MS 1,300/6-8
5871 E Los Arcos St 90815 562-594-9793
Kathleen Cruz, prin. Fax 594-8591
Stephens MS 1,000/6-8
1830 W Columbia St 90810 562-595-0841
Diane Prince, prin. Fax 426-5631
Washington MS 1,000/6-8
1450 Cedar Ave 90813 562-591-2434
Shivaun Williams, prin. Fax 591-6888
Wilson HS 4,300/9-12
4400 E 10th St 90804 562-433-0481
Sandy Blazer, prin. Fax 433-2731
Long Beach School for Adults Adult
3701 E Willow St 90815 562-595-8893
Matthew Saldana, prin. Fax 988-1486
Other Schools – See Avalon, Carson, Lakewood, Signal Hill

Los Angeles USD
Supt. — See Los Angeles
Rancho Dominguez Preparatory S 6-12
4110 Santa Fe Ave 90810 310-847-6400
Keri Lew, prin. Fax 518-1022

Regional Occupational Center & Program
Supt. — None
Long Beach USD ROP Vo/Tech
3701 E Willow St Ste B 90815 562-595-8893
Matt Saldana, dir. Fax 424-8976

California State University-Long Beach Post-Sec.
1250 N Bellflower Blvd 90840 562-985-4111
Charter College Long Beach Post-Sec.
100 W Broadway Ste 3000 90802 562-216-7500
DeVry University Post-Sec.
3880 Kilroy Airport Way 90806 562-427-0861
First Baptist Church S 200/K-12
1000 Pine Ave 90813 562-432-8447
Dr. James Allen, admin. Fax 499-6847
John Wesley Intl. Barber/Beauty Coll Post-Sec.
717 Pine Ave 90813 562-435-7060
Long Beach City College Post-Sec.
4901 E Carson St 90808 562-938-4111
Newbridge College Post-Sec.
3799 E Burnett St 90815 562-498-4500

Pacific Baptist S 200/K-12
3332 Magnolia Ave 90806 562-426-5214
Dr. Joseph Esposito, dir.
St. Anthony HS 300/9-12
620 Olive Ave 90802 562-435-4496
Mike Schabert, prin. Fax 437-3055
WyoTech Post-Sec.
2161 Technology Pl 90810 562-624-9530

Loomis, Placer, Pop. 6,199
Placer UNHSD
Supt. — See Auburn
Del Oro HS 1,700/9-12
3301 Taylor Rd 95650 916-652-7243
Dan Gayaldo, prin. Fax 652-3706

Los Alamitos, Orange, Pop. 10,908
Los Alamitos USD 9,600/PK-12
10293 Bloomfield St 90720 562-799-4700
Sherry Kropp Ed.D., supt. Fax 799-4730
www.losal.org
Laurel HS 100/Alt
3591 Cerritos Ave 90720 562-799-4820
Heidi Olshan, prin. Fax 799-4822
Los Alamitos HS 3,200/9-12
3591 Cerritos Ave 90720 562-799-4780
Joshua Arnold Ed.D., prin. Fax 799-4798
McAuliffe MS 1,300/6-8
4112 Cerritos Ave 90720 714-816-3320
Ann Allen, prin. Fax 816-3362
Oak MS 1,000/6-8
10821 Oak St 90720 562-799-4740
Sally Neiser, prin. Fax 799-4773

Los Altos, Santa Clara, Pop. 27,727
Los Altos ESD 4,400/K-8
201 Covington Rd 94024 650-947-1150
Jeffrey Baier, supt. Fax 947-0118
www.lasdschools.org/
Blach IS 500/7-8
1120 Covington Rd 94024 650-934-3800
Sandra McGonagle, prin. Fax 968-3918
Egan IS 500/7-8
100 W Portola Ave 94022 650-917-2200
Brenda Dyckman, prin. Fax 949-3748

Mountain View-Los Altos UNHSD
Supt. — See Mountain View
Los Altos HS 1,700/9-12
201 Almond Ave 94022 650-968-6571
Wynne Satterwhite, prin. Fax 948-8672

Pinewood S 600/K-12
327 Fremont Ave 94024 650-209-3030

Los Altos Hills, Santa Clara, Pop. 7,599

Foothill College Post-Sec.
12345 S El Monte Rd 94022 650-949-7777

Los Angeles, Los Angeles, Pop. 3,699,911
Compton USD
Supt. — See Compton
Vanguard Learning Center 300/6-8
13305 S San Pedro St 90061 310-898-6050
Lori Body, prin. Fax 327-7180

Huntington Beach City ESD
Supt. — See Huntington Beach
Academy for Multilingual Arts & Science 9-12
8800 S San Pedro St 90003 323-565-4600
Simone Charles, prin. Fax 750-1084
Technology Arts and Design HS 9-12
8800 S San Pedro St 90003 323-565-4600
Candace Lee, prin. Fax 750-1084

Los Angeles County Office of Education
Supt. — See Downey
Los Angeles County HS for the Arts 600/Alt
5151 State University Dr 90032 323-343-2787
George Simpson, prin. Fax 343-2549

Los Angeles USD 642,400/PK-12
333 S Beaudry Ave 90017 213-241-1000
John Deasy, supt. Fax 241-8442
www.lausd.net
Academic Leadership Community S 400/9-12
322 Lucas Ave 90017 213-240-3815
Tadeo Climaco, prin. Fax 482-0232
Academy of Environmental & Social Policy 9-12
3921 Selig Pl 90031 323-224-5991
Bruce Bivins, prin. Fax 224-5992
Adams MS 1,200/6-8
151 W 30th St 90007 213-745-3700
Evelyn Wesley, prin. Fax 749-8542
Alonzo Community Day S 7-12
5755 Fountain Ave 90028 323-817-6500
Victorio Gutierrez, prin. Fax 817-6599
Ambassador School of Global Leadership 100/6-12
701 S Catalina St 90005 213-480-4540
John Samaniego, prin. Fax 480-4599
Apex Academy 300/7-12
1309 N Wilton Pl 90028 323-817-6550
Cesar Lopez, prin. Fax 817-6555
ArtLAB HS 9-12
2050 N San Fernando Rd 90065 323-276-5515
Annick Draghi, prin. Fax 276-5524
Audubon MS 800/6-8
4120 11th Ave 90008 323-290-6300
Charmain Young, prin. Fax 296-2433
Bancroft MS 1,100/6-8
929 N Las Palmas Ave 90038 323-993-3400
Maria Rico, prin. Fax 461-8246
Belmont HS 1,200/9-12
1575 W 2nd St 90026 213-241-4300
Felipe Caceres, prin. Fax 250-9706
Belvedere MS 1,600/6-8
312 N Record Ave 90063 323-266-5400
Maricela Ramirez, prin. Fax 269-6769
Berendo MS 1,400/6-8
1157 S Berendo St 90006 213-739-5600
Rosa Trujillo, prin. Fax 382-8599
Bethune MS 1,400/6-8
155 W 69th St 90003 323-541-1800
Carlos Gonzalez, prin. Fax 759-1271
Boyle Heights Continuation S 100/Alt
544 S Mathews St 90033 323-264-8070
Bonnie Sadrpour, prin. Fax 266-7177
Bravo Medical Magnet HS 1,900/9-12
1200 Cornwell St 90033 323-227-4400
Maria Flores, prin. Fax 342-9139
Burbank MS 900/6-8
6460 N Figueroa St 90042 323-340-4400
Arturo Valdez, prin. Fax 257-7420
Burroughs MS 2,000/6-8
600 S McCadden Pl 90005 323-549-5000
Steve Martinez, prin. Fax 934-9051
Business and Technology S 6-8
1420 E Adams Blvd 90011 323-846-2235
Hugo Carlos, prin.
Carver MS 1,600/6-8
4410 McKinley Ave 90011 323-846-2900
Luz Cotto, prin. Fax 232-5344
Castro MS 6-8
1575 W 2nd St 90026 213-241-4415
Erick Mitchell, prin. Fax 241-4418
Cheviot Hills Continuation S 100/Alt
9200 Cattaraugus Ave 90034 310-838-8462
Rhea Turek, prin. Fax 839-4051
City of Angels Independent Study 1,900/Alt
1449 S San Pedro St 90015 213-745-1100
Alex Placencio Ed.D., prin. Fax 746-7175
CIVITAS Leadership 300/9-12
1200 Colton St 90026 213-580-6430
Gregory Jackson, prin. Fax 580-6499
Clinton MS 1,000/6-8
3500 S Hill St 90007 323-235-7200
Sissi O'Reilly, prin. Fax 846-0054
Cochran MS 1,300/6-8
4066 W Johnnie Cochran Vst 90019 323-730-4300
Scott Schmerelson, prin. Fax 733-9106
Communication and Technology S 9-12
6100 S Central Ave 90001 323-846-2118
Alexander Contreras, prin.
Contreras Learning Complex 900/9-12
322 Lucas Ave 90017 213-240-3800
Nova Meza, prin. Fax 482-0232
Cortines S of Visual & Performing Arts 1,400/9-12
450 N Grand Ave 90012 213-217-8600
Norman Isaacs, prin. Fax 928-0933
Crenshaw HS 1,700/9-12
5010 11th Ave 90043 323-290-7800
Lenalda Corley, prin. Fax 292-6712
Dorsey HS 1,600/9-12
3537 Farmdale Ave 90016 323-298-8400
Reginald Sample, prin. Fax 298-8501
Downtown Business HS 1,000/9-12
1081 W Temple St 90012 213-481-0371
Brandon Cohen, prin. Fax 482-0792
Drew MS 1,300/6-8
8511 Compton Ave 90001 323-826-1700
Karen O'Riley, prin. Fax 583-6030
Eagle Rock JSHS 3,100/7-12
1750 Yosemite Dr 90041 323-340-3500
Salvador Velasco, prin. Fax 255-3398
Edison MS 1,200/6-8
6500 Hooper Ave 90001 323-826-2500
Pedro Garcia, prin. Fax 581-8389
Ellington Continuation HS 100/Alt
1541 W 110th St 90047 323-418-4130
Cecil McLinn, prin. Fax 754-1281
El Sereno MS 1,500/6-8
2839 N Eastern Ave 90032 323-224-4700
Frances Gipson, prin. Fax 223-9024
Emerson MS 900/6-8
1650 Selby Ave 90024 310-234-3100
Dimone Watson, prin. Fax 474-6517
Fairfax HS 2,500/9-12
7850 Melrose Ave 90046 323-370-1200
Carmina Nacorda, prin. Fax 651-5803
Fine and Performing Arts Academy 9-12
300 E 53rd St 90011 323-846-4700
Abigail Nunez, prin. Fax 846-4714
Foshay Learning Center 2,200/Alt
3751 S Harvard Blvd 90018 323-373-2700
Yvonne Garrison, prin. Fax 733-2120
Franklin HS 2,300/9-12
820 N Avenue 54 90042 323-550-2000
Deborah Madrigal, prin. Fax 258-5940
Fremont HS 4,300/9-12
7676 S San Pedro St 90003 323-565-1200
Rafael Gaeta, prin. Fax 971-5890
Garfield HS 2,900/9-12
5101 E 6th St 90022 323-981-5500
Jose Huerta, prin. Fax 268-4957
Global Issues Academy 9-12
300 E 53rd St 90011 323-846-4740
Jonathan Sison, prin.
Gompers MS 1,200/6-8
234 E 112th St 90061 323-241-4000
Traci Gholar, prin. Fax 418-0778
Green Design S 9-12
6100 S Central Ave 90001 323-846-2108
William Lupejkis, prin.
Griffith MS 1,500/6-8
4765 E 4th St 90022 323-266-7400
Teresa Hurtado, prin. Fax 268-6375
Hamilton HS 3,000/9-12
2955 S Robertson Blvd 90034 310-280-1400
Gary Garcia, prin. Fax 842-8663
Harte Prep MS 1,100/6-8
9301 S Hoover St 90044 323-242-5400
Luz Cortes, prin. Fax 757-0408
Hawkins Community Health Advocates S 9-12
825 W 60th St 90044 323-789-1282
Claudia Rojas, prin.
Hawkins Critical Design and Gaming S 9-12
825 W 60th St 90044 323-789-1282
Andre Hargunani, prin.
Hawkins RISE S, 825 W 60th St 90044 9-12
Anthony Terry, prin. 323-789-1282
Highland Park Continuation S 100/Alt
928 N Avenue 53 90042 323-254-3421
Enrique Gonzalez, prin. Fax 340-8132
Hollenbeck MS 1,500/6-8
2510 E 6th St 90023 323-780-3000
Christina Rico, prin. Fax 269-8137
Hollywood HS 1,700/9-12
1521 N Highland Ave 90028 323-993-1700
Alejandra Sanchez, prin. Fax 957-0238
Hope Continuation S 100/Alt
7840 Towne Ave 90003 323-565-1292
Tipawan McGee, prin. Fax 565-1319
Irving MS 800/6-8
3010 Estara Ave 90065 323-259-3700
Kirk Roskam, prin. Fax 254-6447
Jefferson HS 2,100/9-12
1319 E 41st St 90011 323-521-1200
Michael Taft, prin. Fax 231-4755
Kahlo Continuation HS 200/Alt
1924 S Los Angeles St 90011 213-763-1090
Sandra Washington, prin. Fax 763-1092
Kim Academy 900/6-8
615 Shatto Pl 90005 213-739-6500
Edward Colacion, prin. Fax 384-3083
King-Drew Medical Magnet HS 1,600/9-12
1601 E 120th St 90059 323-566-0420
Juanita Woods, prin. Fax 567-1429
King MS 1,500/6-8
4201 Fountain Ave 90029 323-644-6700
Mark Naulls, prin. Fax 913-3594
LACES Magnet S 1,600/6-12
5931 W 18th St 90035 323-549-5900
Harold Boger, prin. Fax 938-8737
Leadership in Entertainment & Media Arts 9-12
3501 N Broadway 90031 323-441-7614
Scott Petri, prin. Fax 441-7688
Liechty MS 1,500/6-8
650 S Union Ave 90017 213-989-1200
Helen Carrillo, prin. Fax 484-2700
Lincoln HS 2,500/9-12
3501 N Broadway 90031 323-441-4600
Jose Torres, prin. Fax 223-1291
Los Angeles Academy 2,100/6-8
644 E 56th St 90011 323-238-1800
Maria Borges, prin. Fax 231-0136
Los Angeles HS 2,200/9-12
4650 W Olympic Blvd 90019 323-900-2700
Helena Yoon-Fontamillas, prin. Fax 936-8455
Los Angeles HS For The Arts 400/9-12
701 S Catalina St 90005 213-480-4600
Esther Soliman, prin. Fax 480-4650
Los Angeles River S 9-12
2050 N San Fernando Rd 90065 323-276-5535
Kristine Puich, prin. Fax 276-5544
Los Angeles S of Global Studies 300/9-12
322 Lucas Ave 90017 213-240-3850
Christian Quintero, prin. Fax 240-3875
Los Angeles Teacher Prep Academy 200/9-12
1575 W 2nd St 90026 213-241-4360
Carlos Rodriguez-Penuela, prin. Fax 241-4321
Los Angeles Technology Center Vo/Tech
3721 W Washington Blvd 90018 323-732-0153
Maxine Hammond, prin. Fax 731-1568
Mann JHS 800/6-8
7001 S St Andrews Pl 90047 323-541-1900
Deborah Gayle, prin. Fax 758-8203
Manual Arts HS 3,500/9-12
4131 S Vermont Ave 90037 323-846-7300
Robert Whitman, prin. Fax 232-0837
Marina Del Rey MS 800/6-8
12500 Braddock Dr 90066 310-578-2700
Miranda Conston-Raoof, prin. Fax 821-3248
Markham MS 1,200/6-8
1650 E 104th St 90002 323-568-5500
Paul Hernandez, prin. Fax 569-6066
Marlton S 300/Alt
4000 Santo Tomas Dr 90008 323-296-7680
Robert Eiseman, prin. Fax 290-1794
Marshall HS 3,400/9-12
3939 Tracy St 90027 323-671-1400
Daniel Harrison, prin. Fax 665-8682
McAlister JSHS 200/Alt
611 S Carondelet St 90057 213-381-2823
Maxcine Donadelle, prin. Fax 384-8947
Metropolitan Continuation S 200/Alt
727 Wilson St 90021 213-623-4272
Raul Aguilar, prin. Fax 629-1069
Middle College HS 400/9-12
1600 W Imperial Hwy Bldg 16 90047 323-418-4700
Wanda Moats, prin. Fax 242-2449
Monterey Continuation HS 100/Alt
466 Fraser Ave 90022 323-269-0786
Douglas Franklin, prin. Fax 526-0795
Muir MS 1,400/6-8
5929 S Vermont Ave 90044 323-565-2200
Nisha Dugal, prin. Fax 778-9824
Newmark Continuation HS 100/Alt
134 Witmer St 90026 213-250-9675
Justin Lauer, prin. Fax 482-3697
New Open World Academy 900/K-12
3201 W 8th St 90005 213-480-3700
Charles Flores, prin. Fax 389-1559
New Technology HS @ Jefferson 400/9-12
1319 E 41st St 90011 323-521-1290
Brenda Pensamiento, prin. Fax 521-1294
Nightingale MS 1,200/6-8
3311 N Figueroa St 90065 323-224-4800
Patricia Heideman, prin. Fax 222-4506
Obama Global Preparation Academy 1,200/6-8
1700 W 46th St 90062 323-421-1700
Herbert Jones, prin. Fax 293-2003

Palms MS 1,700/6-8
10860 Woodbine St 90034 310-253-7600
Derek Moriuchi, prin. Fax 559-0397
Partnership Academy for the Arts 9-12
2265 E 103rd St 90002 323-568-4100
Sherri Williams, prin. Fax 249-4709
Performing Arts Community S 9-12
6100 S Central Ave 90001 323-846-2136
Richard Alvarez, prin.
Phoenix Continuation HS 100/Alt
12971 Zanja St 90066 310-306-8775
Nancy Huerta, prin. Fax 827-3876
Pio Pico MS 700/6-8
1512 Arlington Ave 90019 323-733-8801
Robert Hinojosa, prin. Fax 735-2665
Public Service Community S 9-12
6100 S Central Ave 90001 323-846-2128
Angela Brathwaite, prin. Fax 846-2122
Pueblo de los Angeles Continuation HS 100/Alt
2506 Alta St 90031 323-223-3258
Michael Olivo, prin. Fax 223-4537
Ramona Opportunity HS 100/Alt
231 S Alma Ave 90063 323-266-7600
Anna Carrasco, prin. Fax 415-8077
Riley HS - Cyesis 200/Alt
1524 E 103rd St 90002 323-563-6692
Linda Roussel, prin. Fax 566-6379
Rodia Continuation HS 100/Alt
2315 E 103rd St 90002 323-568-4191
Reginald Obiamalu, prin. Fax 566-4346
Roosevelt Acad of Medical & Health Sci 9-12
456 S Mathews St 90033 323-780-6500
Maura Crossin, prin. Fax 269-5473
Roosevelt Communication/Media/Tech HS 500/9-12
456 S Mathews St 90033 323-780-6500
Benjamin Gertner, prin. Fax 269-5473
Roosevelt Humanitas Arts S 9-12
456 S Mathews St 90033 323-780-6500
Alvin Lewis, prin. Fax 269-5473
Roosevelt Math/Science/Tech Magnet HS 9-12
456 S Mathews St 90033 323-780-4551
Randy Romero, prin. Fax 269-5473
Roosevelt S of Law & Government 9-12
456 S Mathews St 90033 323-780-6503
Cynthia Gonzalez, admin. Fax 269-5473
Roybal Learning Center 1,700/9-12
1200 Colton St 90026 213-580-6400
Scott Braxton, prin. Fax 482-0775
Santee Education Complex 2,800/9-12
1921 Maple Ave 90011 213-763-1000
Martin Gomez, prin. Fax 742-9883
School for Visual Arts & Humanities 9-12
701 S Catalina St 90005 213-480-4700
Eftihia Danellis, prin. Fax 480-4750
School of Arts and Culture 6-8
1420 E Adams Blvd 90011 323-846-2245
Tommy Welch, prin.
School of Engineering and Technology 500/9-12
1200 Plaza Del Sol St 90033 323-981-5400
Alex Avila, prin.
School of History & Dramatic Arts 9-12
2050 N San Fernando Rd 90065 323-276-5500
Irene Narvaez, prin. Fax 276-5514
School of Math & Science 500/9-12
1200 Plaza Del Sol St 90033 323-981-6100
Mauro Bautista, prin.
School of Sci/Tech/ Engineering/Math 9-12
456 S Mathews St 90033 323-780-6537
Silvia Tovar, prin. Fax 269-5473
Solis Learning Academy 9-12
319 N Humphreys Ave 90022 323-729-1700
Jose Rodriguez, prin. Fax 264-2002
STEM @ Bernstein S 9-12
1309 N Wilton Pl 90028 323-817-6461
Lupe Sonnie, prin. Fax 817-6465
Stevenson MS 2,000/6-8
725 S Indiana St 90023 323-780-6400
Leo Gonzalez, prin. Fax 265-3952
32nd Street / USC MaST S 1,100/K-12
822 W 32nd St 90007 213-748-0126
Ezequiel Gonzalez, prin. Fax 744-1608
Torres Engineering and Technology Acad 100/9-12
4211 Dozier St 90063 323-265-6795
Alex Fuentes, prin. Fax 265-6796
Torres Humanitas Visual Arts & Tech 100/9-12
4211 Dozier St 90063 323-265-6830
Debbie Thompson, prin. Fax 265-6831
Torres Performing Arts Academy 200/9-11
4211 Dozier St 90063 323-265-6725
Carolyn McKnight, prin. Fax 265-6726
Torres Renaissance Academy 100/9-12
4211 Dozier St 90063 323-265-6760
Douglas Waybright, prin. Fax 265-6761
Torres Social Justice Leadership Academy 100/9-12
4211 Dozier St 90063 323-265-6665
Roseann Cazares, prin. Fax 265-6866
Twain MS 700/6-8
2224 Walgrove Ave 90066 310-305-3100
Rex Patton, prin. Fax 398-1627
UCLA Community S 800/K-12
700 S Mariposa Ave 90005 213-480-3750
Robert Bilovsky, prin. Fax 480-3759
University HS 2,200/9-12
11800 Texas Ave 90025 310-914-3500
Eric Davidson, prin. Fax 478-6535
USC Hybrid HS 9-12
350 S Figueroa St Ste 100 90071 213-929-1046
Dr. Stephanie McClay, prin. Fax 929-1047
Venice HS 2,600/9-12
13000 Venice Blvd 90066 310-577-4200
Elsa Mendoza, prin. Fax 306-3249
View Park Continuation HS 100/Alt
4701 Rodeo Rd 90016 323-292-0331
Eddie Rambo, prin. Fax 292-7920
Virgil MS 1,400/6-8
152 N Vermont Ave 90004 213-368-2800
James Kodani, prin. Fax 383-8774

Washington Preparatory HS 1,900/9-12
10860 S Denker Ave 90047 323-418-4000
Athaur Ullah Ed.D., prin. Fax 754-3517
Webster MS 700/6-8
11330 Graham Pl 90064 310-235-4600
Liam Joyce, prin. Fax 477-0146
WESM Health/Sports Medicine HS 1,500/9-12
7400 W Manchester Ave 90045 310-338-2400
Robert Canosa-Carr, prin. Fax 410-1067
West Adams Preparatory HS 2,600/9-12
1500 W Washington Blvd 90007 323-373-2500
Jose Iniguez, prin. Fax 373-2518
Whitman Continuation HS 100/Alt
7795 Rosewood Ave 90036 323-651-0645
Conrado Tiu, prin. Fax 653-9214
Widney JSHS 200/Alt
2302 S Gramercy Pl 90018 323-731-8633
Carrie Delisle, prin. Fax 734-8048
Wilson HS 2,300/9-12
4500 Multnomah St 90032 323-276-1600
Ursula Rosin, prin. Fax 223-7936
Wright MS 900/6-8
6550 W 80th St 90045 310-258-6600
Stephen Rochelle, prin. Fax 568-8942
Young Continuation HS 100/Alt
3051 W 52nd St 90043 323-296-3258
Wanda Robinson, prin. Fax 292-6595
Belmont Community Adult Education Adult
1575 W 2nd St 90026 213-241-8500
Fax 241-8525
East Los Angeles Occupational Center Adult
2100 Marengo St 90033 323-223-1283
Rosario Galvan, prin. Fax 223-6365
East Los Angeles Skills Center Adult
3921 Selig Pl 90031 323-224-5970
Donna Brashear, prin. Fax 222-2351
Evans Community Adult Education Adult
717 N Figueroa St 90012 213-626-7151
Danette Roe, prin. Fax 626-4487
Franklin Community Adult S Adult
820 N Avenue 54 90042 323-550-2100
Karen Kuser, prin. Fax 550-2011
Fremont-Washington Community Adult S Adult
7676 S San Pedro St 90003 323-565-1300
Michael Wada, prin. Fax 565-1301
Friedman Occupational Center Adult
1646 S Olive St 90015 213-765-2400
Howard Saxe, prin. Fax 748-7406
Garfield Community Adult S Adult
4343 New York Ave 90022 323-262-9115
Penny Kunitani, prin. Fax 262-9765
Hollywood Community Adult Education Adult
1521 N Highland Ave 90028 323-993-1800
Fax 993-1801
Jefferson Community Adult S Adult
1319 E 41st St 90011 323-235-8120
Anna Carrasco, prin. Fax 233-9658
Los Angeles Adult Education Adult
4650 W Olympic Blvd 90019 323-900-3500
Celia Dominguez, prin. Fax 900-2796
Manual Arts-Crenshaw Community Adult S Adult
4131 S Vermont Ave 90037 323-846-3000
Joanna McConaghy, prin. Fax 234-1310
Metropolitan Skills Center Adult
2801 W 6th St 90057 213-386-7269
Candace Lee, prin. Fax 386-4554
Roosevelt Community Adult S Adult
456 S Mathews St 90033 323-780-6650
Penny Kunitani, prin. Fax 780-6668
Venice Community Adult S Adult
13000 Venice Blvd 90066 310-577-4230
Cynthia Tollette, prin. Fax 577-4238
Waters Employment Preparation Center Adult
10925 S Central Ave 90059 323-564-1431
Janet Clark, prin. Fax 566-0147
Westchester-Emerson Community Adult S Adult
8810 Emerson Ave 90045 310-258-2000
Cynthia Tollette, prin. Fax 645-8043
Westside Community Adult S Adult
7850 Melrose Ave 90046 323-370-1040
James Chacon, prin. Fax 370-1055
Wilson-Lincoln Community Adult S Adult
4500 Multnomah St 90032 323-276-1700
Fax 276-1710

Other Schools – See Arleta, Bell, Canoga Park, Carson, Chatsworth, Cudahy, Gardena, Granada Hills, Harbor City, Hollywood, Huntington Park, Lomita, Long Beach, Maywood, Mission Hills, North Hills, North Hollywood, Northridge, Pacoima, Panorama City, Rancho Palos Verdes, Reseda, San Fernando, San Pedro, Sherman Oaks, South Gate, Sunland, Sun Valley, Sylmar, Tarzana, Tujunga, Van Nuys, Venice, Walnut Park, Wilmington, Woodland Hills

Regional Occupational Center & Program
Supt. — None
Los Angeles USD ROC/P Vo/Tech
333 S Beaudry Ave 90017 213-241-3162
Isabel Vazquez, dir.

Abraham Lincoln University Post-Sec.
3530 Wilshire Blvd Ste 1430 90010 213-252-5100
Academy for Jewish Religion Post-Sec.
574 Hilgard Ave 90024 310-824-1586
Advanced Computing Institute Post-Sec.
3470 Wilshire Blvd Ste 1100 90010 213-383-8999
AMDA College and Conservatory Post-Sec.
6305 Yucca St 90028 323-469-3300
American Career College - Los Angeles Post-Sec.
4021 Rosewood Ave 90004 323-668-7555
American Evangelical University Post-Sec.
1818 S Western Ave Ste 409 90006 323-643-0301
American Film Institute Conservatory Post-Sec.
2021 N Western Ave 90027 323-856-7628
American Jewish University Post-Sec.
15600 Mulholland Dr 90077 310-476-9777

Archer S for Girls 400/6-12
11725 W Sunset Blvd 90049 310-873-7000
Elizabeth English, hdmstr. Fax 873-7077
Arete Preparatory Academy 50/9-12
11500 W Olympic Blvd # 318 90064 310-478-9900
Jim Hahn, hdmstr. Fax 478-9901
Argosy University Los Angeles Post-Sec.
5230 Pacific Concourse #200 90045 310-531-9700
Associated Technical College Post-Sec.
1670 Wilshire Blvd 90017 213-353-1845
Bais Chana Chabad HS 100/9-12
9017 W Pico Blvd 90035 310-777-7700
Rabbi Aron Begun, dean Fax 385-9170
Bais Yaakov S 300/9-12
7353 Beverly Blvd 90036 323-938-3231
Rabbi Joel Bursztyn, dir. Fax 930-0477
Bishop Conaty-Our Lady Loretto HS 300/9-12
2900 W Pico Blvd 90006 323-737-0012
Richard Spicer, prin. Fax 737-1749
Bishop Mora Salesian HS 400/9-12
960 S Soto St 90023 323-261-7124
Sam Robles, prin. Fax 261-7600
Bnos Devorah HS 9-12
461 N La Brea Ave 90036 323-930-0047
Shulamith May, head sch Fax 930-1901
Brentwood S 700/7-12
100 S Barrington Pl 90049 310-476-9633
Dr. Michael Riera, hdmstr. Fax 476-4087
Bryan University Post-Sec.
3580 Wilshire Blvd Ste 400 90010 213-484-8850
California Healing Arts College Post-Sec.
12217 Santa Monica Blvd 90025 310-826-7622
California State University-Los Angeles Post-Sec.
5151 State University Dr 90032 323-343-3000
Cathedral HS 700/9-12
1253 Bishops Rd 90012 323-225-2438
Br. John Montgomery, prin. Fax 222-7223
CBD College Post-Sec.
3699 Wilshire Blvd Ste 400 90010 213-427-2200
Charles R. Drew Univ. of Med. & Science Post-Sec.
1731 E 120th St 90059 323-563-4800
Chicago Sch. of Professional Psychology Post-Sec.
617 W 7th St 90017 800-721-8072
Chicago Sch of Professional Psychology Post-Sec.
1145 Gayley Ave 90024 310-208-4240
Children's Hospital of Los Angeles Post-Sec.
4650 W Sunset Blvd 90027 323-669-2301
Coast Career Institute Post-Sec.
1354 S Hill St 90015 213-235-0606
Colburn School Post-Sec.
200 S Grand Ave 90012 213-621-2200
Concord Law School of Kaplan University Post-Sec.
10866 Wilshire Blvd # 1200 90024 310-689-3200
Dongguk University Post-Sec.
440 Shatto Pl 90020 213-487-0110
East Los Angeles Occupational Center Post-Sec.
2100 Marengo St 90033 323-223-1283
Episcopal S of Los Angeles 6-12
6325 Santa Monica Blvd 90038 323-720-7075
Rev. Maryetta Anschutz, prin.
Everest College Post-Sec.
3460 Wilshire Blvd Ste 500 90010 213-388-9950
Everest College Post-Sec.
3000 S Robertson Blvd # 300 90034 310-840-5777
FIDM Fashion Institute of Design Post-Sec.
919 S Grand Ave 90015 213-624-1200
Fremont College Post-Sec.
3440 Wilshire Blvd Fl 10 90010 800-373-6668
Gnomon School of Visual Effects Post-Sec.
1015 N Cahuenga Blvd 90038 323-466-6663
Harvard-Westlake MS 700/7-9
700 N Faring Rd 90077 310-274-7281
Jeanne Huybrechts, hdmstr. Fax 288-3331
Hebrew Union College Post-Sec.
3077 University Ave 90007 213-749-3424
ICDC College Post-Sec.
5422 W Sunset Blvd 90027 323-468-0404
Immaculate Heart HS 500/9-12
5515 Franklin Ave 90028 323-461-3651
Virginia Hurst, prin. Fax 461-7182
Immaculate Heart MS 200/6-8
5515 Franklin Ave 90028 323-461-3651
Ann Phelps, dir. Fax 462-0610
International Christian Education Coll. Post-Sec.
3807 Wilshire Blvd Ste 730 90010 213-368-0316
John Tracy Clinic Post-Sec.
806 W Adams Blvd 90007 213-748-5481
Kabbaz HS 200/9-12
10309 National Blvd 90034 310-836-3464
Ladera Career Paths Training Centers Post-Sec.
6820 La Tijera Blvd Ste 217 90045 310-568-0244
Learnet Academy Post-Sec.
3251 W 6th St 90020 213-387-4242
Los Angeles Adventist Academy 300/PK-12
846 E El Segundo Blvd 90059 323-321-2585
Lorenzo Paytee, prin. Fax 324-3207
Los Angeles City College Post-Sec.
855 N Vermont Ave 90029 323-953-4000
Los Angeles Co. Coll. Nursing/Alld Hlth Post-Sec.
1237 N Mission Rd 90033 323-226-4911
Los Angeles ORT College Post-Sec.
6435 Wilshire Blvd 90048 323-966-5444
Los Angeles Southwest College Post-Sec.
1600 W Imperial Hwy 90047 323-241-5225
Los Angeles Trade-Technical College Post-Sec.
400 W Washington Blvd 90015 213-763-7000
Loyola HS 1,200/9-12
1901 Venice Blvd 90006 213-381-5121
Frank Kozakowski, prin. Fax 368-3819
Loyola Marymount University Post-Sec.
1 LMU Dr 90045 310-338-2700
Lycee International de Los Angeles 500/PK-12
4155 Russell Ave 90027 323-665-4526
Stephane Plancke, dir. Fax 665-2607
Marinello School of Beauty Post-Sec.
1241 S Soto St Ste 101 90023 323-980-9253
Marinello School of Beauty Post-Sec.
6111 Wilshire Blvd 90048 323-938-2005

Marlborough S — 500/7-12
250 S Rossmore Ave 90004 — 323-935-1147
Barbara Wagner, head sch — Fax 933-0542
Marymount HS — 400/9-12
10643 W Sunset Blvd 90077 — 310-472-1205
Jacqueline Landry, head sch — Fax 476-0910
Mesivta Birkas Yitzchok — 100/9-12
6022 W Pico Blvd 90035 — 323-937-4748
Rabbi Sholom Tendler, prin. — Fax 937-4782
Milken Community HS of Wise Temple — 700/7-12
15800 Zeldins Way 90049 — 310-440-3500
Jason Ablin, head sch — Fax 471-5139
Mt. St. Mary's College — Post-Sec.
12001 Chalon Rd 90049 — 310-954-4000
Mt. St. Mary's College - Doheny Campus — Post-Sec.
10 Chester Pl 90007 — 213-477-2500
New Covenant Academy — 100/1-12
3119 W 6th St 90020 — 213-487-5437
Jason Song, prin. — Fax 487-5430
New York Film Academy — Post-Sec.
3801 Barham Blvd 90068 — 818-733-2600
Notre Dame Academy for Girls — 400/9-12
2851 Overland Ave 90064 — 310-839-5289
Lilliam Paetzold, prin. — Fax 839-7957
Occidental College — Post-Sec.
1600 Campus Rd 90041 — 323-259-2500
Ohr Haemet Institute for Girls — 50/9-12
1030 S Robertson Blvd 90035 — 310-854-3006
Shira Shapiro, prin. — Fax 854-6689
Optimist HS — 100/7-12
PO Box 411076 90041 — 310-443-3100
Alan Eskot, dir. — Fax 443-3262
Otis College of Art and Design — Post-Sec.
9045 Lincoln Blvd 90045 — 310-665-6800
Pacific States University — Post-Sec.
3450 Wilshire Blvd Fl 5 90010 — 323-731-2383
Pacific Union College — Post-Sec.
1720 E Cesar E Chavez Ave 90033 — 323-268-5000
Pilgrim S — 300/PK-12
540 S Commonwealth Ave 90020 — 213-385-7351
Mark Brooks, head sch — Fax 386-7264
Pilibos Armenian S — 600/K-12
1615 N Alexandria Ave 90027 — 323-668-2661
Dr. Alina Dorian, prin. — Fax 662-0332
Price S — 200/PK-12
7901 S Vermont Ave 90044 — 323-758-3777
Harges Pittman, prin. — Fax 753-6770
Ribet Academy — 300/PK-12
2911 N San Fernando Rd 90065 — 323-344-4330
Ronald Dauzat, head sch — Fax 344-4339
Sacred Heart HS — 300/9-12
2111 Griffin Ave 90031 — 323-225-2209
Sr. Janice Wellington, prin. — Fax 225-5046
SAE Institute of Technology — Post-Sec.
6565 W Sunset Blvd Ste 100 90028 — 323-466-6323
St. Mary Magdalen S — 100/5-8
1223 S Corning St 90035 — 310-652-4723
Nuria Gordillo, prin. — Fax 933-7453
Samra University of Oriental Medicine — Post-Sec.
3545 Wilshire Blvd Ste 355 90010 — 213-381-1700
Shalhevet S — 200/9-12
910 S Fairfax Ave 90036 — 323-930-9333
Rabbi Ari Segal, hdmstr. — Fax 930-9444
Shepherd University School of Theology — Post-Sec.
1111 W Sunset Blvd 90012 — 213-481-1313
Southern California Inst. Architecture — Post-Sec.
960 E 3rd St 90013 — 213-613-2200
Southern CA Univ School of Oriental Med. — Post-Sec.
1541 Wilshire Blvd Fl 3 90017 — 213-413-9500
Southwestern Law School — Post-Sec.
3050 Wilshire Blvd 90010 — 213-738-6700
Summit View S - Westside — 100/1-12
12101 W Washington Blvd 90066 — 310-751-1100
Nancy Rosenfelt, dir.
SUTECH School of Voc/Tech Training — Post-Sec.
3455 E Olympic Blvd 90023 — 323-262-3210
T.C.A. Arshag Dickranian Armenian S — 300/PK-12
1200 N Cahuenga Blvd 90038 — 323-461-4377
Vartkes Kourouyan, prin. — Fax 461-4247
Theatre of Arts — Post-Sec.
6755 Hollywood Blvd Fl 2 90028 — 323-463-2500
Union Institute & University — Post-Sec.
6701 Center Dr W Ste 1200 90045 — 310-417-3500
Universal College of Beauty — Post-Sec.
8619 S Vermont Ave 90044 — 323-750-5750
Universal College of Beauty — Post-Sec.
3419 W 43rd Pl 90008 — 323-298-0045
University of California — Post-Sec.
1147 Murphy Hall # 951436 90095 — 310-825-4321
University of Philosophical Research — Post-Sec.
3910 Los Feliz Blvd 90027 — 323-663-2167
University of Southern California — Post-Sec.
University Park 90089 — 213-740-2311
Verbum Dei HS — 300/9-12
11100 S Central Ave 90059 — 323-564-6651
Dr. Daniel O'Connell, prin. — Fax 564-9009
Village Glen S - Westside — 300/K-12
4160 Grand View Blvd 90066 — 310-751-1101
Pamela Clark, dir.
Virginia School Center — Post-Sec.
1033 S Broadway 90015 — 213-747-8292
West Los Angeles VA Medical Center — Post-Sec.
Wilshire & Sawtelle Blvds 90073 — 310-824-3132
Westwood College - Los Angeles — Post-Sec.
3250 Wilshire Blvd Fl 400 90010 — 213-739-9999
Wildwood Secondary S — 400/6-12
11811 W Olympic Blvd 90064 — 310-478-7189
Landis Green, hdmstr. — Fax 478-6875
Windward S — 500/7-12
11350 Palms Blvd 90066 — 310-391-7127
Tom Gilder, head sch — Fax 397-5655
Wise Temple S — 400/K-12
15500 Stephen S Wise Dr 90077 — 310-476-8561
Jason Ablin, hdmstr. — Fax 476-3587
World Mission University — Post-Sec.
500 Shatto Pl Ste 600 90020 — 213-385-2322
Yeshiva Gedola of Los Angeles HS — 100/9-12
5444 W Olympic Blvd 90036 — 323-938-2071
Rabbi Shlomo Zalman Hauer, prin. — Fax 938-4650
Yeshiva Ohr Elchonon Chabad — Post-Sec.
7215 Waring Ave 90046 — 323-937-3763
Yeshiva Ohr Elchonon Chabad West Coast — 100/9-12
7215 Waring Ave 90046 — 323-937-3763
Rabbi Ezra Schochet, dean — Fax 937-9456
Yeshiva University Boys HS — 200/9-12
9760 W Pico Blvd 90035 — 310-203-3180
Rabbi Heshy Glass Ed.D., head sch — Fax 203-3199
Yeshiva University Girls HS — 200/9-12
1619 S Robertson Blvd 90035 — 310-203-0755
Rabbi Abraham Lieberman, head sch — Fax 551-0312
Yo San Univ. of Traditional Chinese Med. — Post-Sec.
13315 W Washington Blvd 90066 — 310-577-3000

Los Banos, Merced, Pop. 35,167
Los Banos USD — 8,500/K-12
1717 S 11th St 93635 — 209-826-3801
Dr. Steve Tietjen, supt. — Fax 826-6810
www.losbanosusd.k12.ca.us
Crossroads Alternative Education Center — 100/Alt
265 Mercey Springs Rd Ste C 93635 — 209-826-4013
John Lupini, prin. — Fax 826-4104
Los Banos Community Day S — 50/Alt
715 W H St 93635 — 209-827-5600
Janette Alvarado, prin.
Los Banos HS — 1,700/9-12
1966 S 11th St 93635 — 209-826-6033
Dan Sutton, prin. — Fax 827-4156
Los Banos JHS — 1,400/7-8
1750 San Luis St 93635 — 209-826-0867
Deo Brasil, prin. — Fax 826-8532
Pacheco HS — 9-12
200 Ward Rd 93635 — 209-827-4506
Brett Lee, prin. — Fax 827-4715
San Luis HS — 100/Alt
125 7th St 93635 — 209-826-8410
John Lupini, prin. — Fax 826-2252

Merced County Office of Education
Supt. — See Merced
Valley Los Banos Community S — 100/Alt
715 W H St 93635 — 209-827-5600
Trucker Clark, prin. — Fax 827-1486

Merced College-Los Banos Campus — Post-Sec.
22240 Highway 152 93635 — 209-826-3495

Los Gatos, Santa Clara, Pop. 28,259
Campbell UNESD
Supt. — See Campbell
Rolling Hills MS — 900/5-8
1585 More Ave 95032 — 408-364-4235
Cynthia Dodd, prin. — Fax 341-7070

Loma Prieta JUNESD — 400/K-8
23800 Summit Rd 95033 — 408-353-1101
Corey Kidwell, supt. — Fax 353-8051
www.loma.k12.ca.us
English MS — 200/6-8
23800 Summit Rd 95033 — 408-353-1123
Denee Signorelli, prin. — Fax 353-5024

Los Gatos UNESD — 3,000/K-8
17010 Roberts Rd 95032 — 408-335-2000
Diana Abbati, supt. — Fax 395-6481
www.lgusd.k12.ca.us
Fisher MS — 1,000/6-8
19195 Fisher Ave 95032 — 408-335-2300
Lisa Fraser, prin. — Fax 356-7616

Los Gatos-Saratoga JUNHSD — 3,100/9-12
17421 Farley Rd W 95030 — 408-354-2520
Bob Mistele, supt. — Fax 354-3375
www.lgsuhsd.org
Los Gatos HS — 1,800/9-12
20 High School Ct 95030 — 408-354-2730
Markus Autrey, prin. — Fax 354-3742
Other Schools – See Saratoga

Los Molinos, Tehama, Pop. 1,963
Los Molinos USD — 600/K-12
7851 State Highway 99E 96055 — 530-384-7826
Charles Ward, supt. — Fax 384-7832
www.lmusd.net
Los Molinos Community Day S — 50/Alt
7851 State Highway 99E 96055 — 530-384-7900
Cliff Curry, coord.
Los Molinos HS — 200/9-12
PO Box 609 96055 — 530-384-7900
Cliff Curry, prin. — Fax 384-1534

Los Nietos, Los Angeles, Pop. 24,164
Los Nietos ESD — 1,900/K-8
8324 Westman Ave 90606 — 562-692-0271
Jonathan Vasquez, supt. — Fax 699-0082
www.losnietos.k12.ca.us
Los Nietos MS — 400/7-8
11425 Rivera Rd 90606 — 562-695-0637
Jacqueline Cardenas, prin. — Fax 695-3805

Los Olivos, Santa Barbara, Pop. 1,116

Dunn S — 200/6-12
PO Box 98 93441 — 805-688-6471
Tom Holmes, prin. — Fax 686-2078
Midland S — 100/9-12
PO Box 8 93441 — 805-688-5114
William Graham, head sch — Fax 686-2470

Los Osos, San Luis Obispo, Pop. 13,912
San Luis Coastal USD
Supt. — See San Luis Obispo
Los Osos MS — 400/6-8
1555 El Morro Ave 93402 — 805-534-2835
Kyle Pruitt, prin. — Fax 528-5133

Lost Hills, Kern, Pop. 2,409
Lost Hills Union ESD — 600/K-8
PO Box 158 93249 — 661-797-2626
Harrison Favereaux, supt. — Fax 797-2580
Thomas MS — 200/6-8
PO Box 158 93249 — 661-797-2626
Veronica Sanchez-Gregory, prin. — Fax 797-3015

Lower Lake, Lake, Pop. 1,225
Konocti USD — 3,100/K-12
PO Box 759 95457 — 707-994-6475
Donna Becnel, supt. — Fax 994-0210
www.konoctiusd.org
Carle Continuation HS — 100/Alt
PO Box 309 95457 — 707-994-1033
James Burger, prin. — Fax 994-4121
Lewis Alternative S — 50/Alt
PO Box 5000 95457 — 707-994-2045
Rick Evans, prin. — Fax 994-6807
Lower Lake HS — 800/9-12
PO Box 799 95457 — 707-994-6471
Jeff Dixon, prin. — Fax 994-4050
Other Schools – See Clearlake

Loyalton, Sierra, Pop. 752
Sierra-Plumas JUSD — 400/K-12
PO Box 955 96118 — 530-993-1660
Merrill Grant Ed.D., supt. — Fax 993-0828
www.sierracountyofficeofeducation.org
Loyalton JSHS — 100/7-12
PO Box 37 96118 — 530-993-4454
Marla Stock, prin. — Fax 993-4667
Sierra Pass HS, PO Box 37 96118 — 50/Alt
Marla Stock, prin. — 530-993-1325
Other Schools – See Downieville

Lucerne Valley, San Bernardino, Pop. 5,647
Lucerne Valley USD — 2,400/K-12
8560 Aliento Rd 92356 — 760-248-6108
Suzette Davis, supt. — Fax 248-6677
www.lvsd.k12.ca.us/
Community Day S — 50/Alt
8560 Aliento Rd 92356 — 760-248-2408
Suzette Davis, prin. — Fax 248-6677
Lucerne Valley JSHS — 300/7-12
8560 Aliento Rd 92356 — 760-248-2124
Patricia Countney, prin. — Fax 248-2162
Mountain View HS — 50/Alt
8560 Aliento Rd 92356 — 760-248-2408
Suzette Davis, prin. — Fax 248-6677

Lynwood, Los Angeles, Pop. 69,209
Lynwood USD — 15,800/K-12
11321 Bullis Rd 90262 — 310-886-1600
Paul Gothold, supt. — Fax 763-0959
www.lynwood.k12.ca.us
Chavez MS — 800/6-8
3898 Abbott Rd 90262 — 310-886-7300
Larry Reed, prin. — Fax 603-2048
Firebaugh HS — 1,500/10-12
5246 Martin Luther King Blv 90262 — 310-886-5200
Tony Hua, prin. — Fax 637-8041
Hosler MS — 500/7-8
11300 Spruce St 90262 — 310-603-1447
Hector Marquez, prin. — Fax 764-4124
Lynwood HS — 4,100/9-12
4050 E Imperial Hwy 90262 — 310-603-1582
Carlos Zaragoza, prin. — Fax 638-9253
Lynwood MS — 700/7-9
12124 Bullis Rd 90262 — 310-603-1466
Hector Preciado, prin. — Fax 638-2156
Vista Continuation HS — 300/Alt
11300 Wright Rd 90262 — 310-603-1516
Maribel Martinez, prin. — Fax 537-7295
Lynwood Adult S — Adult
4050 E Imperial Hwy 90262 — 310-604-3096
Dr. Jean Jones, prin. — Fax 635-9107

St. Francis Career College — Post-Sec.
3680 E Imperial Hwy Ste 500 90262 — 310-900-8050

Mc Arthur, Shasta, Pop. 335
Fall River JUSD
Supt. — See Burney
Fall River Community Day HS — 50/Alt
44144 A St 96056 — 530-336-7154
Greg Hawkins, prin. — Fax 336-7071
Fall River JSHS — 200/7-12
PO Box 340 96056 — 530-336-5515
Jeanne Utterback, prin. — Fax 336-6256
Soldier Mountain Continuation HS — 50/Alt
44144 A St 96056 — 530-336-7159
Greg Hawkins, prin. — Fax 336-7071

Mc Clellan, Sacramento
Twin Rivers USD — 28,900/PK-12
5115 Dudley Blvd Bay A 95652 — 916-566-1600
Fax 566-1784
www.twinriversusd.org/
Keema HS — 700/Alt
5201 Arnold Ave 95652 — 916-286-5149
Harjinder Mattu, prin. — Fax 570-0171
Other Schools – See North Highlands, Rio Linda, Sacramento

Mc Cloud, Siskiyou, Pop. 1,075
Siskiyou UNHSD
Supt. — See Mount Shasta
McCloud HS — 50/9-12
PO Box 1530 96057 — 530-964-2181
Ed Stokes, prin. — Fax 964-2011

Macdoel, Siskiyou, Pop. 132
Butte Valley USD
Supt. — See Dorris
Butte Valley MS — 100/7-9
13001 Old State Hwy 96058 — 530-398-4415
Jason Allen, lead tchr. — Fax 398-4401

Mc Farland, Kern, Pop. 12,620
McFarland USD 3,300/K-12
601 2nd St 93250 661-792-3081
Gabriel McCurtis, supt. Fax 792-2447
www.mcfarlandusd.com
Mc Farland HS 900/9-12
259 W Sherwood Ave 93250 661-792-3126
Ty Bryson, prin. Fax 792-2315
McFarland Independent S 100/Alt
599 5th St 93250 661-792-6312
Lori Schultz, admin. Fax 792-6758
Mc Farland MS 700/6-8
405 Mast Ave 93250 661-792-3340
Louie Gomez, prin. Fax 792-5681
San Joaquin HS 100/Alt
599 5th St 93250 661-792-6312
Lorie Schultz, prin. Fax 792-6758

Mc Kinleyville, Humboldt, Pop. 14,503
McKinleyville UNESD 1,100/K-8
2275 Central Ave 95519 707-839-1549
Michael Davies-Hughes, supt. Fax 839-1540
www.nohum.k12.ca.us/msd
McKinleyville MS 400/6-8
2285 Central Ave 95519 707-839-1508
Wendy Pearcy, prin. Fax 839-2548

Northern Humboldt UNHSD 1,600/9-12
2755 McKinleyville Ave 95519 707-839-6470
Chris Hartley, supt. Fax 839-6457
www.nohum.k12.ca.us
Mc Kinleyville HS 600/9-12
1300 Murray Rd 95519 707-839-6400
Roger Macdonald, prin. Fax 839-6407
Northern Humboldt Community Day S 50/Alt
1300 Murray Rd 95519 707-267-9403
Tom Pender, admin. Fax 839-6407
Tsurai HS 50/Alt
1300 Murray Rd 95519 707-839-6480
Sam Razo, prin. Fax 839-6494
Other Schools – See Arcata

Madera, Madera, Pop. 60,700
Golden Valley USD 1,900/K-12
37479 Avenue 12, 559-645-7500
Andy Alvarado, supt. Fax 645-7144
www.gvusd.k12.ca.us
Independence Continuation HS 50/Alt
12150 Road 36, 559-645-3580
Kristi Fisher, prin.
Liberty HS 600/9-12
12220 Road 36, 559-645-3500
Kuljeet Mann, prin. Fax 645-4769
Ranchos MS 300/7-8
12455 Road 35 1/2, 559-645-3550
Kevin Hatch, prin. Fax 645-3565

Madera County Office of Education 800/
1105 S Madera Ave 93637 559-673-6051
Cecilia Massetti Ed.D., supt. Fax 673-5569
www.maderacoe.k12.ca.us
Enterprise Secondary S 100/Alt
1105 S Madera Ave 93637 559-661-3570
Alyson Crafton, prin. Fax 673-5569
Other Schools – See Chowchilla

Madera USD 19,500/K-12
1902 Howard Rd 93637 559-675-4500
Gustavo Balderas, supt. Fax 661-7764
www.madera.k12.ca.us
Desmond MS 900/7-8
26490 Martin St 93638 559-664-1775
Marvin Baker, prin. Fax 664-1308
Eastin-Arcola HS Alt
29551 Avenue 8 93637 559-674-8841
John Denno, prin. Fax 674-2566
Furman HS 200/Alt
955 W Pecan Ave 93637 559-675-4482
David Raygoza, prin. Fax 675-3811
Jefferson MS 1,000/7-8
1407 Sunset Ave 93637 559-673-9286
Jesse Carrasco, prin. Fax 673-6930
King MS 700/7-8
601 Lilly St 93638 559-674-4681
Sabrina Rodriquez, prin. Fax 674-4261
Madera HS North Campus 2,100/9-12
200 S L St 93637 559-675-4444
Kent Albertson, prin. Fax 675-4531
Madera HS South Campus 2,700/9-12
705 W Pecan Ave 93637 559-675-4450
Sandon Schwartz, prin. Fax 675-9985
Madera Adult S Adult
955 W Pecan Ave 93637 559-675-4425
David Raygoza, prin. Fax 675-4562

Madera Beauty College Post-Sec.
325 N Gateway Dr 93637 559-673-9201

Madison, Yolo, Pop. 493
Esparto USD
Supt. — See Esparto
Madison Community HS 50/Alt
17923 Stephens St 95653 530-787-3165
Richard Radcliffe, prin. Fax 662-1521

Mad River, Trinity, Pop. 402
Southern Trinity JUSD 100/K-12
680 Van Duzen Rd, 707-574-6237
Peggy Canale, supt. Fax 574-6538
www.southerntrinityusd.org
Mt. Lassic HS 50/Alt
600 Van Duzen Rd, 707-574-6239
Peggy Canale, prin. Fax 574-6538
Southern Trinity HS 50/9-12
600 Van Duzen Rd, 707-574-6239
Peggy Canale, prin. Fax 574-1067

Magalia, Butte, Pop. 10,902
Paradise USD
Supt. — See Paradise

Ridgeview HS 100/Alt
13665 Skyway 95954 530-872-6478
Michael Lerch, prin. Fax 872-6481

Malibu, Los Angeles, Pop. 12,292
Santa Monica-Malibu USD
Supt. — See Santa Monica
Malibu MSHS 1,200/6-12
30215 Morning View Dr 90265 310-457-6801
Fax 457-4984

New Roads MS 50/6-8
3504 Las Flores Canyon Rd 90265 310-456-1977
Dr. David Bryan, head sch Fax 456-8027
Pepperdine University Post-Sec.
24255 Pacific Coast Hwy 90263 310-506-4000

Mammoth Lakes, Mono, Pop. 8,104
Mammoth USD 1,100/K-12
PO Box 3509 93546 760-934-6802
Rich Boccia, supt. Fax 934-6803
www.mammothusd.org
Mammoth HS 300/9-12
PO Box 3149 93546 760-934-8541
Gabe Solorio, prin. Fax 934-3008
Mammoth MS 300/6-8
PO Box 2429 93546 760-934-7072
Annie Rinaldi, prin. Fax 934-7073
Sierra Continuation HS 50/Alt
PO Box 3509 93546 760-934-3702
Rich Boccia, prin. Fax 924-0062

Mono County Office of Education
Supt. — See Bridgeport
Mammoth Community Day S 200/Alt
451 Sierra Park Rd 93546 760-934-0031
Janet Hunt, prin. Fax 934-1443
Mono County Adult S Adult
451 Sierra Park Rd 93546 760-934-0031
Janet Hunt, prin. Fax 934-1443

Manhattan Beach, Los Angeles, Pop. 33,631
Manhattan Beach USD 7,100/PK-12
325 S Peck Ave 90266 310-318-7345
Dr. Michael Matthews, supt. Fax 303-3822
www.mbusd.org
Manhattan Beach MS 1,400/6-8
325 S Peck Ave 90266 310-545-4878
John Jackson, prin. Fax 303-3829
Mira Costa HS 2,400/9-12
325 S Peck Ave 90266 310-318-7337
Ben Dale, prin. Fax 303-3814

Manteca, San Joaquin, Pop. 64,370
Manteca USD 23,000/K-12
PO Box 32 95336 209-825-3200
Jason Messer, supt. Fax 858-7570
www.mantecausd.net/
Calla Continuation HS 200/Alt
130 S Austin Rd 95336 209-858-7230
Kathy Crouse, prin. Fax 858-7505
East Union HS 1,500/9-12
1700 N Union Rd 95336 209-858-7270
John Alba, prin. Fax 825-3148
Manteca Community Day S 50/Alt
737 W Yosemite Ave 95337 209-858-7380
Rupinder Bhatti, prin. Fax 858-7526
Manteca HS 1,600/9-12
450 E Yosemite Ave 95336 209-858-7340
Frank Gonzales, prin. Fax 825-3158
Manteca Unified Vocational Academy Vo/Tech
2271 W Louise Ave 95337 209-858-7460
Diane Medeiros, prin. Fax 858-7524
McParland S 800/3-8
1601 Northgate Dr 95336 209-858-7290
Dale Borgeson, prin. Fax 858-7510
Sierra HS 1,400/9-12
1700 Thomas St 95337 209-858-7410
Steve Clark, prin. Fax 825-3198
Manteca Adult S Adult
2271 W Louise Ave 95337 209-858-7330
Diane Medeiros, prin. Fax 858-7524
Other Schools – See Lathrop, Stockton

Maricopa, Kern, Pop. 1,126
Maricopa USD 1,000/K-12
955 Stanislaus St 93252 661-769-8231
Scott Meier, supt. Fax 769-8168
www.maricopaschools.org
Maricopa HS 100/9-12
955 Stanislaus St 93252 661-769-8231
Scott Meier, prin. Fax 769-8168

Marina, Monterey, Pop. 17,783
Monterey Peninsula USD
Supt. — See Monterey
Los Arboles MS 700/6-8
294 Hillcrest Ave 93933 831-384-3550
Rebecca Tyson, prin. Fax 384-6353
Marina HS 600/9-12
298 Patton Pkwy 93933 831-583-2060
Sean Roach, prin. Fax 384-2288

Mariposa, Mariposa, Pop. 2,123
Mariposa County Office of Education 100/
PO Box 8 95338 209-742-0250
Aaron Rosander, supt. Fax 966-4549
www.mariposa.k12.ca.us
Fremont Community Day 50/Alt
4802 State Highway 140 95338 209-742-0290
Mark Molina, prin. Fax 742-0292

Mariposa County USD 1,600/K-12
PO Box 8 95338 209-742-0250
Aaron Rosander, supt. Fax 966-4549
www.mariposa.k12.ca.us/
Fremont Community S 50/Alt
PO Box 8 95338 209-742-0290
Celeste Azevedo, admin. Fax 742-0292

Mariposa County HS 600/9-12
PO Box 127 95338 209-742-0260
David Naranjo, prin. Fax 742-0264
Other Schools – See Coulterville, Yosemite National Park

Summit Christian S 50/2-10
PO Box 1445 95338 209-966-7636
Lauri Phillips, dir.

Markleeville, Alpine, Pop. 204
Alpine County Office of Education 50/
43 Hawkside Dr 96120 530-694-2230
Lisa Fontana Ph.D., supt. Fax 694-2379
www.alpinecoe.k12.ca.us
Alpine County Opportunity S 50/Alt
43 Hawkside Dr 96120 530-694-2230
Lisa Fontana Ph.D., prin. Fax 694-2379

Alpine County USD 100/K-12
43 Hawkside Dr 96120 530-694-2230
Lisa Fontana Ph.D., supt. Fax 694-2379
www.alpinecoe.k12.ca.us
Alpine County Community Day S Alt
43 Hawkside Dr 96120 530-694-9423
Laura Parks, prin.

Martinez, Contra Costa, Pop. 34,098
Contra Costa County Office of Education
Supt. — See Pleasant Hill
Golden Gate Community S 200/Alt
222 Glacier Dr 94553 925-313-2950
Rebecca Corrigan, prin. Fax 313-2955

Martinez USD 4,000/K-12
921 Susana St 94553 925-335-5800
Rami Muth, supt. Fax 335-5960
www.martinez.k12.ca.us/
Alhambra HS 1,300/9-12
150 E St 94553 925-313-0440
Nermin Kamel, prin. Fax 229-2097
Briones S 100/K-12
614 F St 94553 925-228-9232
Carol Adams, prin. Fax 313-9890
Martinez Continuation HS 100/Alt
614 F St 94553 925-228-9232
Carol Adams, prin. Fax 313-9989
Martinez JHS 900/6-8
1600 Court St 94553 925-313-0414
Helen Rossi, prin. Fax 370-0143
Martinez Adult Center Adult
600 F St 94553 925-228-3276
Kathy Farwell, dir. Fax 228-6989

Martinez Adult Education Post-Sec.
600 F St 94553 925-228-3276
New Vistas Christian S 50/5-12
68 Morello Ave 94553 925-370-7767
Maria Zablah, admin. Fax 370-6395

Marysville, Yuba, Pop. 11,483
Marysville JUSD 9,700/PK-12
1919 B St 95901 530-741-6000
Gay Todd Ed.D., supt. Fax 741-7894
www.mjusd.com
Foothill IS 200/7-8
5351 Fruitland Rd 95901 530-741-6130
Kathleen Hansen, prin. Fax 741-6017
Lincoln Alternative S 100/Alt
1919 B St 95901 530-741-6918
Rocco Greco, prin. Fax 741-7886
Marysville HS 1,000/9-12
12 E 18th St 95901 530-741-6180
Gary Cena, prin. Fax 741-7828
McKenney IS 500/6-8
1904 Huston St 95901 530-741-6187
Gina Lanphier, prin. Fax 741-6004
North Marysville Continuation HS 100/Alt
1919 B St 95901 530-741-6128
Rocco Greco, prin. Fax 741-7886
Other Schools – See Olivehurst

Yuba County Office of Education 600/
935 14th St 95901 530-749-4900
Scotia Holmes Sanchez, supt. Fax 741-6500
www.yuba.net/
Yuba County Opportunity S 50/Alt
131 F St 95901 – Pete Seiler, prin. 530-741-6349

Yuba College Post-Sec.
2088 N Beale Rd 95901 530-741-6700

Mather, Sacramento, Pop. 4,082
Folsom-Cordova USD
Supt. — See Rancho Cordova
Mather Youth Academy 100/Alt
4420 Monhegan Way 95655 916-363-5019
Rolando Rosas, coord. Fax 364-1637

Regional Occupational Center & Program
Supt. — None
Sacramento County ROP Vo/Tech
10474 Mather Blvd 95655 916-228-2500
Tim Taylor, admin. Fax 228-2459

Sacramento County Office of Education 500/
10474 Mather Blvd 95655 916-228-2500
David Gordon, supt. Fax 228-2403
www.scoe.net
Other Schools – See Sacramento

Maxwell, Colusa, Pop. 1,095
Maxwell USD 300/K-12
PO Box 788 95955 530-438-2291
Ron Turner, supt. Fax 438-2693
www.maxwell.k12.ca.us
Maxwell HS 100/7-12
PO Box 788 95955 530-438-2291
Ron Turner, prin. Fax 438-2693

Maywood, Los Angeles, Pop. 27,328
Los Angeles USD
Supt. — See Los Angeles
Maywood Academy 1,300/9-12
6125 Pine Ave 90270 323-838-6000
Cristopher Ziegel, prin. Fax 560-9206

Meadow Vista, Placer, Pop. 3,116
Placer Hills UNESD 700/K-8
16801 Placer Hills Rd 95722 530-878-2606
Fred Adam, supt. Fax 878-2663
www.phusd.k12.ca.us/
Other Schools – See Weimar

Mendocino, Mendocino, Pop. 866
Mendocino USD 500/K-12
PO Box 1154 95460 707-937-5868
Jason Morse, supt. Fax 937-0714
www.mendocinousd.org/
Mendocino Alternative S 50/Alt
PO Box 1154 95460 707-937-3703
Gail Dickenson, prin. Fax 937-6806
Mendocino HS 200/9-12
PO Box 226 95460 707-937-5871
Gail Dickenson, prin. Fax 937-1552
Mendocino Sunrise HS 50/Alt
PO Box 226 95460 707-937-9232
Gail Dickenson, prin. Fax 937-5629

Mendota, Fresno, Pop. 10,983
Mendota USD 2,800/K-12
115 McCabe Ave 93640 559-655-4942
Michael Crass, supt. Fax 655-4944
www.musdaztecs.com
Mendota Community Day S 50/Alt
115 McCabe Ave 93640 559-655-4471
Rebecca Gamez, prin. Fax 655-2440
Mendota Continuation HS 50/Alt
115 McCabe Ave 93640 559-655-4471
Rebecca Gamez, prin. Fax 655-2440
Mendota HS 700/9-12
115 McCabe Ave 93640 559-655-1993
Silvia Delgado, prin. Fax 655-0223
Mendota JHS 400/7-8
115 McCabe Ave 93640 559-655-4301
Manuel Bautista, prin. Fax 655-1229

Menifee, Riverside, Pop. 75,080
Menifee UNESD 9,000/PK-12
30205 Menifee Rd 92584 951-672-1851
Steve Kennedy Ed.D., supt. Fax 672-9832
www.menifeeusd.org
Bell Mountain MS 1,100/6-8
28525 La Piedra Rd 92584 951-301-8496
Ernie Lizzarraga, prin. Fax 301-5286
Christensen MS 900/6-8
27625 Sherman Rd, 951-679-8356
Ed Resnick, prin. Fax 679-4090
Menifee Valley MS 900/6-8
26255 Garbani Rd 92584 951-672-6400
Robert Voelkel, prin. Fax 672-6415

Perris UNHSD
Supt. — See Perris
Paloma Valley HS 2,700/9-12
31375 Bradley Rd 92584 951-672-6030
Brian Morris, prin. Fax 672-6037

Revival Christian Academy 100/K-12
29220 Scott Rd 92584 951-672-3157
Diana Miller, dir. Fax 672-9187

Menlo Park, San Mateo, Pop. 30,400
Las Lomitas ESD 1,300/K-8
1011 Altschul Ave 94025 650-854-2880
Lisa Cesario, supt. Fax 854-0882
www.llesd.k12.ca.us
La Entrada MS 700/4-8
2200 Sharon Rd 94025 650-854-3962
Larry Thomas, prin. Fax 854-5947

Menlo Park City ESD
Supt. — See Atherton
Hillview MS 700/6-8
1100 Elder Ave 94025 650-326-4341
Erik Burmeister, prin. Fax 325-3861

Sequoia UNHSD
Supt. — See Redwood City
Sequoia District Adult S Adult
3247 Middlefield Rd 94025 650-306-8866
Lionel de Maine, admin. Fax 365-2420

Mid-Peninsula HS 100/9-12
1340 Willow Rd 94025 650-321-1991
Dr. Douglas Thompson, hdmstr. Fax 321-9921
St. Patrick's Seminary & University Post-Sec.
320 Middlefield Rd 94025 650-325-5621

Merced, Merced, Pop. 76,840
Merced City ESD 10,800/K-8
444 W 23rd St 95340 209-385-6600
Rosemary Duran Ed.D., supt. Fax 385-6316
www.mcsd.k12.ca.us
Cruickshank MS 900/6-8
601 Mercy Ave 95340 209-385-6330
Elena Castro, prin. Fax 385-6338
Hoover MS 900/6-8
800 E 26th St 95340 209-385-6631
Doug Collins, prin. Fax 385-6799
Rivera MS 900/6-8
945 Buena Vista Dr 95348 209-385-6680
Sergio Mendez, prin. Fax 385-6702
Tenaya MS 900/6-8
760 W 8th St 95341 209-385-6687
Tara Bright, prin. Fax 385-6365

Merced County Office of Education 1,500/
632 W 13th St 95341 209-381-6600
Steven Gomes Ed.D., supt. Fax 381-6767
www.mcoe.org
Valley Community S 700/Alt
632 W 13th St 95341 209-381-4500
Kurt Kollmann, prin. Fax 385-8308
Other Schools – See Atwater, Livingston, Los Banos

Merced UNHSD
Supt. — See Atwater
El Capitan HS 9-12
100 W Farmland Ave 95348 209-384-5500
Anthony Johnson, prin.
Golden Valley HS 2,200/9-12
PO Box 2188 95344 209-385-8000
Constantino Aguilar, prin. Fax 385-8002
Independence HS 200/Alt
1900 G St 95340 209-385-6515
Torrin Johnson, dir. Fax 385-6435
Merced HS 2,600/9-12
PO Box 2167 95344 209-385-6465
John Olson, prin. Fax 385-6556
Sequoia HS 100/Alt
123 E 18th St 95340 209-385-8950
Jon Schaefer, prin. Fax 385-6535
Yosemite Continuation HS 300/Alt
1900 G St 95340 209-385-6425
Torrin Johnson, prin. Fax 385-6435
Merced Adult S Adult
50 E 20th St 95340 209-385-6524
Debbie Glass, prin. Fax 385-6430

Regional Occupational Center & Program
Supt. — None
Merced County ROP Vo/Tech
632 W 13th St 95341 209-381-6677
Holly Newlon, supt. Fax 381-6766

Weaver UNSD 2,600/K-8
3076 E Childs Ave 95341 209-723-7606
John Curry, supt. Fax 725-7128
www.weaverusd.k12.ca.us
Weaver MS 800/6-8
3076 E Childs Ave 95341 209-723-2174
Mike Weber, prin. Fax 725-7116

Merced College Post-Sec.
3600 M St 95348 209-384-6000
Sierra College of Beauty Post-Sec.
1340 W 18th St 95340 209-723-2989
Stone Ridge Christian HS 100/9-12
500 Buena Vista Dr 95348 209-386-0322
Sandra Mobley, admin. Fax 386-0334
University of California Post-Sec.
5200 N Lake Rd 95343 209-228-4400
WestMed College-Merced Post-Sec.
330 E Yosemite Ave 95340 209-386-6300

Middletown, Lake, Pop. 1,281
Middletown USD 1,700/K-12
20932 Big Canyon Rd 95461 707-987-4100
Korby Olson Ed.D., supt. Fax 987-4105
www.middletownusd.org
Loconoma Vally HS 50/Alt
20932 Big Canyon Rd 95461 707-987-4170
John Phelps, prin. Fax 987-4171
Middletown Community Day S 50/Alt
20932 Big Canyon Rd 95461 707-987-4185
John Phelps, prin. Fax 987-4171
Middletown HS 500/9-12
20932 Big Canyon Rd 95461 707-987-4140
Bill Roderick, prin. Fax 987-4146
Middletown MS 300/7-8
20932 Big Canyon Rd 95461 707-987-4160
Thad Owens, prin. Fax 987-4162
Middletown Adult S Adult
20932 Big Canyon Rd 95461 707-987-4175
Fax 987-4171

Middletown Christian S 100/K-12
PO Box 989 95461 707-987-2556
Anna Mayfield, prin.

Midway City, Orange, Pop. 8,289

Huntington College of Dental Technology Post-Sec.
14848 Monroe St 92655 - -

Millbrae, San Mateo, Pop. 20,615
Millbrae ESD 2,200/K-8
555 Richmond Dr 94030 650-697-5693
Linda Luna, supt. Fax 697-6865
www.millbraeschooldistrict.org
Taylor MS 800/6-8
850 Taylor Blvd 94030 650-697-4096
Lesley Martin, prin. Fax 697-8435

San Mateo UNHSD
Supt. — See San Mateo
Mills HS 1,400/9-12
400 Murchison Dr 94030 650-558-2599
Paul Belzer, prin. Fax 558-2552

Mill Valley, Marin, Pop. 13,420
Mill Valley ESD 2,800/K-8
411 Sycamore Ave 94941 415-389-7700
Paul Johnson, supt. Fax 389-7773
www.mvschools.org
Mill Valley MS 800/6-8
425 Sycamore Ave 94941 415-389-7711
Anna Lazzarini, prin. Fax 389-7780

Tamalpais UNHSD
Supt. — See Larkspur
Tamalpais HS 1,200/9-12
700 Miller Ave 94941 415-388-3292
Tom Drescher, prin. Fax 380-3526

Golden Gate Baptist Theological Seminary Post-Sec.
201 Seminary Dr 94941 415-380-1300

Milpitas, Santa Clara, Pop. 64,272
Milpitas USD 10,000/PK-12
1331 E Calaveras Blvd 95035 408-635-2600
Cary Matsuoka, supt. Fax 635-2616
www.musd.org
Calaveras Hills HS 200/Alt
1331 E Calaveras Blvd 95035 408-635-2690
Alecia Myers, prin. Fax 635-2615
Milpitas HS 3,000/9-12
1285 Escuela Pkwy 95035 408-635-2800
Ken Schlaff, prin. Fax 635-2851
Rancho Milpitas MS 700/7-8
1915 Yellowstone Ave 95035 408-635-2656
Leticia Villa-Gascon, prin. Fax 635-2661
Russell MS 800/7-8
1500 Escuela Pkwy 95035 408-635-2864
Laura Foegal, prin. Fax 635-2869
Milpitas Adult S Adult
1331 E Calaveras Blvd 95035 408-635-2692
Kathleen Pearson, prin. Fax 635-2611

Heald College Post-Sec.
341 Great Mall Pkwy 95035 408-934-4900

Mira Loma, Riverside, Pop. 21,582
Jurupa USD
Supt. — See Riverside
Jurupa Valley HS 1,900/9-12
10551 Bellegrave Ave 91752 951-360-2600
Ilsa Garza-Gonzalez, prin. Fax 360-2612

Miranda, Humboldt, Pop. 496
Southern Humbolt JUSD 800/K-12
PO Box 650 95553 707-943-1789
Catherine Scott, supt. Fax 943-1921
internet.humboldt.k12.ca.us/sohumb_usd/school/
Osprey Learning Center 50/Alt
PO Box 188 95553 707-943-3144
Jim Stewart, prin. Fax 943-3627
South Fork HS 300/8-12
PO Box 188 95553 707-943-3144
Lisa Gray, prin. Fax 943-3129

Mission Hills, Los Angeles, Pop. 3,460
Los Angeles USD
Supt. — See Los Angeles
North Valley Occupational Center Vo/Tech
11450 Sharp Ave 91345 818-365-9645
Carlynn Huddleston, prin. Fax 365-2695

Bishop Alemany HS 1,600/9-12
11111 Alemany Dr 91345 818-365-3925
Frank Ferry, prin. Fax 365-2064

Mission Viejo, Orange, Pop. 89,770
Capistrano USD
Supt. — See San Juan Capistrano
Capistrano Valley HS 2,700/9-12
26301 Via Escolar 92692 949-364-6100
Kevin Astor, prin. Fax 347-0514
Newhart MS 1,500/6-8
25001 Veterans Way 92692 949-855-0162
Jeff Jones, prin. Fax 770-1262

Saddleback Valley USD 31,300/K-12
25631 Peter A Hartman Way 92691 949-586-1234
Clint Harwick Ed.D., supt. Fax 951-0994
www.svusd.k12.ca.us
La Paz IS 1,000/7-8
25151 Pradera Dr 92691 949-830-1720
Jean Carroll, prin. Fax 830-3320
Los Alisos IS 900/7-8
25171 Moor Ave 92691 949-830-9700
Bill Hinds, prin. Fax 472-3968
Mira Monte Alternative HS 100/Alt
25632 Peter A Hartman Way 92691 949-830-8857
David Gordon, prin. Fax 462-0352
Mission Viejo HS 2,700/9-12
25025 Chrisanta Dr 92691 949-837-7722
Ray Gatfield, prin. Fax 830-0782
Silverado Continuation HS 300/Alt
25632 Peter A Hartman Way 92691 949-586-8800
David Gordon, prin. Fax 583-9865
Trabuco Hills HS 3,300/9-12
27501 Mustang Run 92691 949-768-1934
Craig Collins, prin. Fax 588-0763
Adult Education Center Adult
25598 Peter A Hartman Way 92691 949-837-8830
David Gordon, dean Fax 837-1921
Other Schools – See Laguna Hills, Lake Forest, Rancho Santa Margarita

---

Agape Academy 50/K-12
26861 Trabuco Rd Ste E 92691 949-701-9086
Denise Justiniano, admin.
Halstrom HS-Mission Viejo 100/7-12
26440 La Alameda Ste 150 92691 949-348-0608
Wendy Jones, dir. Fax 348-0610
Master's Academy 100/K-12
23052 Alicia Pkwy Ste H107 92692 949-459-5293
Helen Martinez, admin. Fax 459-5293
Saddleback College Post-Sec.
28000 Marguerite Pkwy 92692 949-582-4500

Modesto, Stanislaus, Pop. 192,307
Empire UNESD 3,000/K-8
116 N McClure Rd 95357 209-521-2800
David Garcia, supt. Fax 526-6421
www.empire.k12.ca.us
Glick MS 500/7-8
400 Frazine Rd 95357 209-577-3945
C.W. Smith, prin. Fax 577-3975

Modesto CSD 30,000/K-12
426 Locust St 95351 209-576-4011
Pamela Able, supt. Fax 576-4184
www.monet.k12.ca.us
Beyer HS 2,000/9-12
1717 Sylvan Ave 95355 209-576-4311
Dan park, prin. Fax 576-4352
Davis HS 2,000/9-12
1200 W Rumble Rd 95350 209-576-4500
Lynn Lysko, prin. Fax 576-4028
Downey HS 2,000/9-12
1000 Coffee Rd 95355 209-576-4211
Richard Baum, prin. Fax 576-4258
Elliott Alternative & Continuing Educ 800/Alt
1440 Sunrise Ave 95350 209-569-2890
Julie Beebe, prin. Fax 576-4863
Enochs HS 2,600/9-12
3201 Sylvan Ave 95355 209-550-3400
Deborah Rowe, prin. Fax 550-3413
Gregori HS, 3701 Pirrone Rd 95356 900/9-12
Jeff Albritton, prin. 209-550-3420
Hanshaw MS 800/7-8
1725 Las Vegas St 95358 209-576-4847
Lupe Robles, prin. Fax 576-4723
Johansen HS 2,000/9-12
641 Norseman Dr 95357 209-576-4702
Julie Moore, prin. Fax 576-4752
La Loma JHS 700/7-8
1800 Encina Ave 95354 209-576-4627
Ronna Rutishauser, prin. Fax 576-4631
Modesto HS 2,600/9-12
18 H St 95351 209-576-4401
Jason Manning, prin. Fax 576-4434
Roosevelt JHS 800/7-8
1330 College Ave 95350 209-576-4871
Nathan Schar, prin. Fax 569-2713
Twain JHS 800/7-8
707 S Emerald Ave 95351 209-576-4814
Mike Berhorst, prin. Fax 576-4843

Regional Occupational Center & Program
Supt. — None
Yosemite ROP, 1100 H St 95354 Vo/Tech
Cindy Young, admin. 209-238-1500

Stanislaus County Office of Education 1,400/
1100 H St 95354 209-238-1700
Tom Changnon, supt. Fax 238-4201
www.stancoe.org/
Petersen Alternative Center 300/Alt
715 13th St 95354 209-238-6716
Fax 238-6796

Stanislaus UNESD 3,100/K-8
2410 Janna Ave 95350 209-529-9546
Wayne Brown, supt. Fax 529-0243
www.stanunion.k12.ca.us
Prescott JHS 700/7-8
2243 W Rumble Rd 95350 209-529-9892
John Rastatter, prin. Fax 529-4406

Sylvan Union ESD 8,200/K-8
605 Sylvan Ave 95350 209-574-5000
Debra Hendricks, supt. Fax 524-2672
www.sylvan.k12.ca.us
Savage MS 1,000/6-8
1900 Maid Mariane Ln 95355 209-552-3300
Mitch Wood, prin. Fax 552-3305
Somerset MS 900/6-8
1037 Floyd Ave 95350 209-574-5300
Patricia Lingerfelt, prin. Fax 529-1110
Ustach MS 900/6-8
2701 Kodiak Dr 95355 209-552-3000
Nick Stever, prin. Fax 552-3010

Adrian's Beauty College Post-Sec.
124 Floyd Ave 95350 209-526-2040
Big Valley Christian S 700/PK-12
4040 Tully Rd Ste D 95356 209-527-3481
Marsha Holbrook, admin. Fax 569-0138
Brethren Heritage S 100/K-12
3549 Dakota Ave 95358 209-543-7860
James Shuman, prin. Fax 543-7862
California Beauty College Post-Sec.
1115 15th St 95354 209-524-5184
Central Catholic HS 400/9-12
200 S Carpenter Rd 95351 209-524-9611
Melissa Bengtson, prin. Fax 524-4913
Community Business College Post-Sec.
3800 McHenry Ave 95356 209-529-3648
Computer Tutor Business & Technical Inst Post-Sec.
4306 Sisk Rd 95356 209-545-5200
Institute of Technology - Modesto Campus Post-Sec.
5601 Stoddard Rd 95356 209-545-3100
Modesto Christian HS 300/9-12
5755 Sisk Rd 95356 209-343-2330
Cynthia Jewell, prin. Fax 545-0584
Modesto Christian MS 100/6-8
5901 Sisk Rd 95356 209-529-5510
Cynthia Jewell, prin. Fax 545-1369
Modesto Junior College Post-Sec.
435 College Ave 95350 209-575-6550
Western Pacific Truck School Post-Sec.
2316 Nickerson Dr 95358 209-531-9226

Mojave, Kern, Pop. 4,110
Mojave USD 2,300/K-12
3500 Douglas Ave 93501 661-824-4001
Dr. Aaron Haughton, supt. Fax 824-2686
www.mojave.k12.ca.us/
Douglas S Alt
3200 Pat Ave 93501 661-824-2411
Tim Shelby, prin. Fax 824-5251
Mojave JSHS 400/7-12
15732 O St 93501 661-824-4088
Scott Small, prin. Fax 824-3406
Mountain View HS 9-12
3200 Pat Ave 93501 661-824-2411
Tim Shelby, prin. Fax 824-5251

Other Schools – See California City

Regional Occupational Center & Program
Supt. — None
Kern County ROP Vo/Tech
15926 K St 93501 661-824-9313
Tom Anspach, admin. Fax 824-9316

National Test Pilot Institute Post-Sec.
PO Box 658 93502 661-824-2977

Monrovia, Los Angeles, Pop. 35,498
Monrovia USD 5,900/PK-12
325 E Huntington Dr 91016 626-471-2000
Dr. Katherine F. Thorossian, supt. Fax 471-2077
www.monroviaschools.net
Canyon Oaks HS 100/Alt
930 Royal Oaks Dr 91016 626-471-3000
Flint Fertig, dir. Fax 471-3033
Clifton MS 700/6-8
226 S Ivy Ave 91016 626-471-2600
Jennifer Gates, prin. Fax 471-2610
Monrovia HS 1,700/9-12
845 W Colorado Blvd 91016 626-471-2800
Kirk McGinnis, prin. Fax 471-2810
Mountain Park S 100/Alt
950 S Mountain Ave 91016 626-471-3029
Flint Fertig, dir. Fax 471-3077
Quest Academy Community Day S 50/Alt
1831 Santa Fe Pl 91016 626-471-2044
Susan Hirsch, dir. Fax 471-2076
Santa Fe MS 600/6-8
148 W Duarte Rd 91016 626-471-2700
Ron Letourneau, prin. Fax 471-2710
Monrovia Community Adult Education Adult
920 S Mountain Ave 91016 626-471-3035
Flint Fertig, dir. Fax 471-3036

Mt. Sierra College Post-Sec.
101 E Huntington Dr 91016 626-873-2144

Montclair, San Bernardino, Pop. 36,107
Chaffey JUNHSD
Supt. — See Ontario
Montclair HS 3,300/9-12
4725 Benito St 91763 909-621-6781
Martin Alvarado, prin. Fax 621-1882

Ontario-Montclair ESD
Supt. — See Ontario
Serrano MS 700/7-8
4725 San Jose St 91763 909-624-0029
Ursula Estrada-Reveles, prin. Fax 445-1687
Vernon MS 800/7-8
9775 Vernon Ave 91763 909-624-5036
Sarah Niemann, prin. Fax 445-1720

Montebello, Los Angeles, Pop. 62,028
Montebello USD 31,300/K-12
123 S Montebello Blvd 90640 323-887-7900
Cleve Pell, supt. Fax 887-5890
www.montebello.k12.ca.us
Eastmont IS 1,100/6-8
400 Bradshawe St 90640 323-721-5133
Cecilia Ramirez, prin. Fax 887-3058
La Merced IS 1,400/6-8
215 E Avenida De La Merced 90640 323-722-7262
Michael Ladjevic, prin. Fax 887-5816
Montebello Community Day S 100/Alt
123 S Montebello Blvd 90640 323-887-7900
Ayele Dodoo, dir. Fax 887-5895
Montebello HS 3,500/9-12
2100 W Cleveland Ave 90640 323-728-0121
Jeffrey Schwartz, prin. Fax 887-7848
Montebello IS 1,200/6-8
1600 W Whittier Blvd 90640 323-721-5111
Susan Donnelly, prin. Fax 887-3192
Schurr HS 3,500/9-12
820 N Wilcox Ave 90640 323-887-3090
Stacey Honda, prin. Fax 887-3097
Vail Continuation HS 400/Alt
1230 S Vail Ave 90640 323-728-1940
Suzette Montano, prin. Fax 887-3004
Montebello Adult Education Adult
149 N 21st St 90640 323-887-7844
Joe Torres, prin. Fax 724-8175
Schurr Adult Education Adult
820 N Wilcox Ave 90640 323-887-3088
Joe Torres, prin. Fax 887-3098
Other Schools – See Bell Gardens, Monterey Park

Cantwell-Sacred Heart of Mary HS 600/9-12
329 N Garfield Ave 90640 323-887-2066
David Chambers, prin. Fax 724-4332
Montebello Beauty College Post-Sec.
2201 W Whittier Blvd 90640 323-727-7851

Monterey, Monterey, Pop. 26,593
Monterey Peninsula USD 10,700/PK-12
PO Box 1031 93942 831-645-1203
Dr. Marilyn Shepherd, supt. Fax 649-4175
www.mpusd.k12.ca.us
Colton MS 600/6-8
100 Toda Vis 93940 831-649-1951
Kim Cooper, prin. Fax 649-4692
Monterey HS 1,300/9-12
101 Herrmann Dr 93940 831-392-3801
Marcie Plummer, prin. Fax 649-1154
Vocational Educ/ROP Vo/Tech
700 Pacific St 93940 831-645-1203
Sharon Albert, dir.
Other Schools – See Marina, Seaside

Monterey Institute of Intl. Studies Post-Sec.
460 Pierce St 93940 831-647-4100
Monterey Peninsula College Post-Sec.
980 Fremont St 93940 831-646-4000
Santa Catalina S 500/PK-12
1500 Mark Thomas Dr 93940 831-655-9300
Sr. Claire Barone, hdmstr. Fax 649-3056
Trinity Christian HS 100/9-12
601 E Franklin St 93940 831-656-9434
Timothy Wong, dir. Fax 656-9670
York S 200/8-12
9501 York Rd 93940 831-372-7338
Chuck Harmon, head sch Fax 372-8055

Monterey Park, Los Angeles, Pop. 59,435
Los Angeles County Office of Education
Supt. — See Downey
East Los Angeles Community Day S 300/Alt
1260 Monterey Pass Rd 91754 323-262-2263
Teresa Merino, prin.

Montebello USD
Supt. — See Montebello
Macy IS 1,000/6-8
2101 Lupine Ave 91755 323-722-0260
Sterling Schubert, prin. Fax 887-3068

East Los Angeles College Post-Sec.
1301 Avenida Cesar Chavez 91754 323-265-8650

Montrose, See La Crescenta

Holy Redeemer/St James S 100/6-8
2361 Del Mar Rd 91020 818-541-9005
Susan Romero, prin. Fax 541-9006

Moorpark, Ventura, Pop. 33,338
Moorpark USD 7,200/K-12
5297 Maureen Ln 93021 805-378-6300
Teresa Williams, supt. Fax 529-8592
www.mrpk.org
Chaparral MS 800/6-8
280 Poindexter Ave 93021 805-378-6302
Ruby Delery, prin. Fax 378-6324
Community Continuation HS 100/Alt
5700 Condor Dr 93021 805-378-6304
Jorge Espinoza, prin. Fax 531-6448
Mesa Verde MS 800/6-8
14000 Peach Hill Rd 93021 805-378-6309
Mike Winters, prin. Fax 531-6622
Moorpark HS 2,300/9-12
4500 Tierra Rejada Rd 93021 805-378-6305
Carrie Pentis, prin. Fax 531-6498
HS at Moorpark College 100/Alt
7075 Campus Rd 93021 805-378-1444
Patricia Birckhead, prin. Fax 378-1440

Moorpark College Post-Sec.
7075 Campus Rd 93021 805-378-1400

Moraga, Contra Costa, Pop. 15,277
Acalanes UNHSD
Supt. — See Lafayette
Campolindo HS 1,300/9-12
300 Moraga Rd 94556 925-280-3950
John Walker, prin. Fax 280-3951

Moraga ESD 1,700/K-8
1540 School St 94556 925-376-5943
Bruce K. Burns, supt. Fax 376-8132
www.moraga.k12.ca.us
Moraga IS 600/6-8
1010 Camino Pablo 94556 925-376-7206
Joan Danilson, prin. Fax 376-6836

St. Mary's College Post-Sec.
1928 Saint Marys Rd 94556 925-631-4000

Moreno Valley, Riverside, Pop. 186,933
Moreno Valley USD 36,500/K-12
25634 Alessandro Blvd 92553 951-571-7500
Dr. Judy White, supt. Fax 571-7550
www.mvusd.net
Alessandro S 100/Alt
23311 Dracaea Ave 92553 951-571-4510
Karen Tomei, admin. Fax 571-4515
Badger Springs MS 1,300/6-8
24750 Delphinium Ave 92553 951-571-4200
Jason Barney, prin. Fax 571-4205
Canyon Springs HS 2,600/9-12
23100 Cougar Canyon Dr 92557 951-571-4760
Dr. Tammy Guzzetta, prin. Fax 571-4765
Landmark MS 1,300/6-8
15261 Legendary Dr 92555 951-571-4220
Doug Murphy, prin. Fax 571-4225
March Mountain HS 500/Alt
24551 Dracaea Ave 92553 951-571-4800
Sean McMurray, prin. Fax 571-4805
March Valley HS 100/Alt
24551 Dracaea Ave 92553 951-571-4800
Sean McMurray, prin. Fax 571-4805
Moreno Valley HS 2,500/9-12
23300 Cottonwood Ave 92553 951-571-4820
Robert Brough, prin. Fax 571-4825
Mountain View MS 1,300/6-8
13130 Morrison St 92555 951-571-4240
Deborah Fay, prin. Fax 571-4245
Palm MS 1,300/6-8
11900 Slawson Ave 92557 951-571-4260
Richard Rideout, prin. Fax 571-4265
Sunnymead MS 1,600/6-8
23996 Eucalyptus Ave 92553 951-571-4280
Jennifer Castillo, prin. Fax 571-4285
Valley View HS 2,900/9-12
13135 Nason St 92555 951-571-4850
Kristen Hunter, prin. Fax 571-4855
Vista Del Lago HS 2,700/9-12
15150 Lasselle St 92551 951-571-4880
Patricia Bazanos, prin. Fax 571-4885
Vista Heights MS 1,500/6-8
23049 Old Lake Dr 92557 951-571-4300
Mark Hasson, prin. Fax 571-4305

Moreno Valley Community Adult S Adult
13350 Indian St 92553 951-571-4790
Dulce Leyva-Hall, prin. Fax 571-4795

Val Verde USD
Supt. — See Perris
March MS 800/6-8
15800 Indian St 92551 951-490-0430
Jim Owen, prin. Fax 490-0435
Rancho Verde HS 3,300/9-12
17750 Lasselle St 92551 951-485-6200
Olivier Wong, prin. Fax 485-6218
Val Verde/Student Success Academy 50/Alt
25100 Red Maple Ln 92551 951-443-2450
Tracy Bunz, prin.
Vista Verde MS 1,000/6-8
25777 Krameria St 92551 951-485-6270
Rick Aleksak, prin. Fax 485-6278

Calvary Chapel Christian S 400/K-12
11960 Pettit St 92555 951-485-6088
Tim Hamilton, prin. Fax 485-6718
Elegante Beauty College Post-Sec.
24741 Alessandro Blvd 92553 951-247-2047
Moreno Valley College Post-Sec.
16130 Lasselle St 92551 951-571-6100
Sage College Post-Sec.
12125 Day St Ste L 92557 951-781-2727
Westech College Post-Sec.
22515 Alessandro Blvd 92553 877-714-6669

Morgan Hill, Santa Clara, Pop. 36,440
Morgan Hill USD 9,500/K-12
15600 Concord Cir 95037 408-201-6000
Dr. Wesley Smith, supt. Fax 201-6007
www.mhu.k12.ca.us
Britton MS 700/7-8
80 W Central Ave 95037 408-201-6160
Glen Webb, prin. Fax 201-6175
Central HS 200/Alt
17960 Monterey St 95037 408-201-6300
Irene Macias-Morriss, prin. Fax 201-6310
Live Oak HS 1,200/9-12
1505 E Main Ave 95037 408-201-6100
Lloyd Webb, prin. Fax 201-6143
Sobrato HS 1,500/9-12
401 Burnett Ave 95037 408-201-6200
Debbie Padilla, prin. Fax 201-6241
Community Adult Education Adult
17940 Monterey St 95037 408-201-6520
Dennis Browne, prin. Fax 201-6525
Other Schools – See San Jose

Oakwood S 400/PK-12
105 John Wilson Way 95037 408-782-7177
Patty Crone, prin. Fax 782-7138

Morro Bay, San Luis Obispo, Pop. 10,002
San Luis Coastal USD
Supt. — See San Luis Obispo
Morro Bay HS 800/9-12
235 Atascadero Rd 93442 805-771-1845
Dan Andrus, prin. Fax 772-5944

Moss Landing, Monterey, Pop. 194
North Monterey County USD 4,400/K-12
8142 Moss Landing Rd 95039 831-633-3343
Kari Yeater, supt. Fax 633-2937
www.nmcusd.org
Other Schools – See Castroville, Salinas

Mountain View, Santa Clara, Pop. 70,771
Mountain View Whisman SD 4,800/K-8
750A San Pierre Way 94043 650-526-3500
Craig Goldman, supt. Fax 964-8907
www.mvwsd.org/
Crittenden MS 600/6-8
1701 Rock St 94043 650-903-6945
Geoffrey Chang, prin. Fax 967-1707
Graham MS 700/6-8
1175 Castro St 94040 650-526-3570
Kim Thompson, prin. Fax 965-9278

Mountain View-Los Altos UNHSD 3,600/9-12
1299 Bryant Ave 94040 650-940-4650
Dr. Barry Groves, supt. Fax 961-7008
www.mvla.net/
Alta Vista HS 200/Alt
1325 Bryant Ave 94040 650-691-2433
Bill Pierce, prin. Fax 691-2469
Mountain View HS 1,800/9-12
3535 Truman Ave 94040 650-940-4600
Keith Moody, prin. Fax 961-6349
Mountain View/Los Altos Adult Education Adult
333 Moffett Blvd 94043 650-940-1333
Laura Stefanski, dir. Fax 967-4699
Other Schools – See Los Altos

German International S of Silicon Valley 500/PK-12
310 Easy St 94043 650-254-0748
Andrea Spiegelberg, admin. Fax 254-0749
Mountain View Academy 200/9-12
360 S Shoreline Blvd 94041 650-967-2324
Dan Meidinger, prin. Fax 967-6886
St. Francis HS 1,700/9-12
1885 Miramonte Ave 94040 650-968-1213
Patricia Tennant, prin. Fax 968-1706

Mount Madonna, Santa Cruz

Mount Madonna S 200/PK-12
491 Summit Rd, 408-847-2717
Mary McDonald, head sch Fax 847-5633

Mount Shasta, Siskiyou, Pop. 3,264
Mount Shasta UNSD 600/K-8
595 E Alma St 96067 530-926-6007
Kathi Emerson, supt. Fax 926-6103
www.mtshastaandweedschooldistricts.com/

Sisson S 300/4-8
601 E Alma St 96067 530-926-3846
Kale Riccomini, prin. Fax 926-2152

Siskiyou UNHSD 700/9-12
624 Everitt Memorial Hwy 96067 530-926-3006
Michael Matheson, supt. Fax 926-3113
www.sisuhsd.net/
Jefferson Continuation HS 50/Alt
720 Rockfellow Dr 96067 530-926-0425
Ed Stokes, prin. Fax 926-0586
Mount Shasta HS 400/9-12
710 Everitt Memorial Hwy 96067 530-926-2614
Jennifer McKinnon, prin. Fax 926-5162
South County Community Day S 50/Alt
720 Rockfellow Dr 96067 530-926-0425
Ed Stokes, prin. Fax 926-0586
Siskiyou Adult S Adult
720 Rockfellow Dr 96067 530-926-0425
Ed Stokes, prin. Fax 926-0586
Other Schools – See Happy Camp, Mc Cloud, Weed

Murrieta, Riverside, Pop. 99,237
Murrieta Valley USD 20,600/K-12
41870 McAlby Ct 92562 951-696-1600
Patrick Kelley, supt. Fax 304-1523
www.murrieta.k12.ca.us
Creekside HS 200/Alt
24150 Hayes Ave 92562 951-696-1409
Jared Rogers, dir. Fax 304-1665
McElhinney MS 1,000/6-8
35125 Briggs Rd 92563 951-304-1885
Garrett Corduan, prin. Fax 304-1889
Murrieta Mesa HS 9-12
24801 Monroe Ave 92562 951-677-0568
Mary Walters, prin. Fax 304-1895
Murrieta Valley HS 2,500/9-12
42200 Nighthawk Way 92562 951-696-1408
Renate Jefferson, prin. Fax 304-1803
Shivela MS 1,500/6-8
24515 Lincoln Ave 92562 951-696-1406
Marcie Kea, prin. Fax 304-1643
Tenaja Canyon Academy 100/Alt
24150 Hayes Ave 92562 951-304-1661
Jared Rogers, dir. Fax 304-1665
Thompson MS 1,700/6-8
24040 Hayes Ave 92562 951-696-1410
Dale Velk, prin. Fax 304-1691
Vista Murrieta HS 3,400/9-12
28251 Clinton Keith Rd 92563 951-894-5750
Darren Daniel, prin. Fax 304-1832
Warm Springs MS 1,100/6-8
39245 Calle de Fortuna 92563 951-696-3503
Mick Wager, prin. Fax 304-1611
Murrieta Valley Adult S Adult
24150 Hayes Ave 92562 951-696-3805
Tom Petrich, dir. Fax 304-1664

Temecula Valley USD
Supt. — See Temecula
Bella Vista MS 1,300/6-8
31650 Browning St 92563 951-294-6600
Shery Stewart, prin. Fax 294-6624

Calvary Murrieta Christian S 1,200/PK-12
24225 Monroe Ave 92562 951-834-9190
Desmond Starr, supt. Fax 698-4896
Murrieta Springs Adventist Christian Acd 100/K-10
32477 Starbuck Cir 92562 951-461-2243
Darena Shetler, prin. Fax 461-9565
Veritas Evangelical Seminary Post-Sec.
39407 Murrieta Hot Springs 92563 951-698-6389

Napa, Napa, Pop. 75,253
Napa County Office of Education 200/
2121 Imola Ave 94559 707-253-6800
Barbara Nemko, supt. Fax 253-6841
www.napacoe.org
Napa County Community S 200/Alt
2121 Imola Ave 94559 707-253-6817
Sandy Leveque, dir. Fax 253-6983

Napa Valley USD 17,900/K-12
2425 Jefferson St 94558 707-253-3511
Patrick Sweeney, supt. Fax 253-3855
www.nvusd.k12.ca.us
Harvest MS 800/6-8
2449 Old Sonoma Rd 94558 707-259-8866
Linda Beckstrom, prin. Fax 253-4013
Napa HS 2,200/9-12
2475 Jefferson St 94558 707-253-3711
Barb Franco, prin. Fax 253-3906
New Technology HS Vo/Tech
920 Yount St 94559 707-259-8557
Michelle Spencer, prin. Fax 253-8558
Redwood MS 1,000/6-8
3600 Oxford St 94558 707-253-3415
Drew Herron, prin. Fax 259-0718
Silverado MS 800/6-8
1133 Coombsville Rd 94558 707-253-3688
Mike Mansuy, prin. Fax 253-3830
Valley Oak HS 200/Alt
1600 Myrtle Ave 94558 707-253-3791
Maria Cisneros, prin. Fax 253-3437
Vintage HS 2,100/9-12
1375 Trower Ave 94558 707-253-3601
Mike Pearson, prin. Fax 253-3604
Napa Valley Adult Education Adult
1600 Lincoln Ave 94558 707-253-3594
Rhonda Slota, prin. Fax 253-3828
Other Schools – See American Canyon

Regional Occupational Center & Program
Supt. — None
Napa County ROP Vo/Tech
2121 Imola Ave 94559 707-253-6830
Tammie Holloway, dir. Fax 253-6917

Justin-Siena HS 600/9-12
4026 Maher St 94558 707-255-0950
Noel Hesser, prin. Fax 255-0334
Kolbe Academy Trinity Prep PK-12
2055 Redwood Rd 94558 707-258-9030
Brian Muth, prin. Fax 258-9031
Napa Christian S 100/K-12
2201 Pine St 94559 707-255-5233
Greg Coryell, prin. Fax 255-8530
Napa State Hospital Post-Sec.
2100 Napa Vallejo Hwy 94558 707-253-5428
Napa Valley College Post-Sec.
2277 Napa Vallejo Hwy 94558 707-253-3000

National City, San Diego, Pop. 57,012
Sweetwater UNHSD
Supt. — See Chula Vista
Granger JHS 1,000/7-9
2101 Granger Ave 91950 619-472-6000
Mary Rose Peralta, prin. Fax 267-4107
National City MS 700/7-8
1701 D Ave 91950 619-336-2600
Arturo Montano, prin. Fax 474-1756
Sweetwater HS 2,400/9-12
2900 Highland Ave 91950 619-474-9700
Roman Del Rosario, prin. Fax 474-7635
National City Adult S Adult
517 Mile of Cars Way 91950 619-336-9400
Bernard Balanay, prin. Fax 336-0641

Bellus Academy Post-Sec.
1520 E Plaza Blvd 91950 619-474-6607
Faithful Ambassadors Bible Baptist Acad 100/K-12
2432 E 18th St 91950 619-434-2265
Ireneo Austria, prin.
Kuyper Preparatory HS 50/7-12
2400 Euclid Ave 91950 877-458-9737
Brian Hendry, pres. Fax 458-9737
San Diego Academy 300/K-12
2800 E 4th St 91950 619-267-9550
Winston Morgan, prin. Fax 267-8662

Needles, San Bernardino, Pop. 4,672
Needles USD 1,000/K-12
1900 Erin Dr 92363 760-326-3891
Fax 326-4218
www.needles.k12.ca.us
Educational Training Center 50/Alt
1900 Erin Dr 92363 760-326-2092
Jeff Ritchley, prin. Fax 326-2191
Needles HS 200/9-12
1900 Erin Dr 92363 760-326-2191
Jeff Ritchley, prin. Fax 326-1212
Needles MS 200/6-8
1900 Erin Dr 92363 760-326-3894
Jeff Ritchley, prin. Fax 326-4052

Nevada City, Nevada, Pop. 2,983
Nevada City ESD 800/K-8
800 Hoover Ln 95959 530-265-1820
Roxanne Gilpatric, supt. Fax 265-1822
www.ncsd.k12.ca.us
Seven Hills IS 500/5-8
700 Hoover Ln 95959 530-265-1840
Joe Limov, prin. Fax 265-1846

Nevada County Office of Education 3,400/
112 Nevada City Hwy 95959 530-478-6400
Holly Hermansen, supt. Fax 478-6410
www.nevco.org/
Other Schools – See Grass Valley

Ananda Living Wisdom S 100/PK-12
14618 Tyler Foote Rd 95959 530-478-7640
Diane Atwell, dir. Fax 478-7646
Woolman Semester 50/11-12
13075 Woolman Ln 95959 530-273-3183
Dorothy Henderson, hdmstr. Fax 273-9028

Newark, Alameda, Pop. 40,127
Newark USD 6,600/K-12
5715 Musick Ave 94560 510-818-4100
Dr. Dave Marken, supt. Fax 794-2199
www.nusd.k12.ca.us
Bridgepoint Continuation HS 100/Alt
35753 Cedar Blvd 94560 510-818-3200
Tom Orput, prin. Fax 818-3255
Crossroads HS 100/Alt
35753 Cedar Blvd 94560 510-818-3720
Tom Orput, prin. Fax 818-3255
Newark JHS 1,000/7-8
6201 Lafayette Ave 94560 510-818-3050
Mark Neal, prin. Fax 794-2079
Newark Memorial HS 1,900/9-12
39375 Cedar Blvd 94560 510-818-4350
Edward Marquez, prin. Fax 794-2120
Newark Adult S Adult
35753 Cedar Blvd 94560 510-818-3700
Tom Orput, prin. Fax 818-3738

Newbury Park, See Thousand Oaks
Conejo Valley USD
Supt. — See Thousand Oaks
Conejo Valley HS Alt/Continuation 200/Alt
1872 Newbury Rd 91320 805-498-6646
Martin Manzer, prin. Fax 498-1423
Newbury Park HS 2,600/9-12
456 N Reino Rd 91320 805-498-3676
Athol Wong, prin. Fax 499-3549
Sequoia MS 1,100/6-8
2855 Borchard Rd 91320 805-498-3617
Vivian Vina-Hunt, prin. Fax 375-5605

Newbury Park Adventist Academy 200/9-12
180 Academy Dr 91320 805-498-2191
Jacob Perrin, prin. Fax 499-1165

New Cuyama, Santa Barbara, Pop. 510
Cuyama JUSD 200/K-12
2300 Highway 166 93254 661-766-2482
Roland Maier, supt. Fax 766-2255
www.cuyamaunified.org
Cuyama Valley HS 100/9-12
2300 Highway 166 93254 661-766-2293
Roland Maier, prin. Fax 766-2593
Sierra Madre Continuation HS 50/Alt
2300 Highway 166 93254 661-766-2293
Roland Maier, prin. Fax 766-2593

Newhall, See Santa Clarita
William S. Hart UNHSD
Supt. — See Santa Clarita
Hart HS 2,100/9-12
24825 Newhall Ave 91321 661-259-7575
Dr. Collyn Nielsen, prin. Fax 254-6436
Placerita JHS 1,000/7-8
25015 Newhall Ave 91321 661-259-1551
Jan Hayes-Rennels, prin. Fax 287-9748

Master's College and Seminary Post-Sec.
21726 Placerita Canyon Rd 91321 661-259-3540

Newman, Stanislaus, Pop. 10,029
Newman-Crows Landing USD 2,800/PK-12
1162 Main St 95360 209-862-2933
Ed Felt, supt. Fax 862-0113
www.nclusd.k12.ca.us/
Foothill Community Day S 50/Alt
890 Main St 95360 209-862-2309
John Luis, prin. Fax 862-2316
Newman Independent Study 50/Alt
890 Main St 95360 209-862-2309
John Luis, prin. Fax 862-2316
Orestimba HS 800/9-12
707 Hardin Rd 95360 209-862-2916
Randy Fillpot, prin. Fax 862-0259
Westside Valley Continuation HS 50/Alt
890 Main St 95360 209-862-2309
John Luis, prin. Fax 862-2316
Yolo MS 700/6-8
901 Hoyer Rd 95360 209-862-2984
John Stuart, prin. Fax 862-3734

Newport Beach, Orange, Pop. 82,964
Newport - Mesa USD
Supt. — See Costa Mesa
Corona Del Mar JSHS 2,500/7-12
2101 Eastbluff Dr 92660 949-515-6000
Tim Bryan, prin. Fax 515-6070
Ensign IS 1,100/7-8
2000 Cliff Dr 92663 949-515-6910
Gloria Duncan, prin. Fax 515-3370
Newport Harbor HS 2,500/9-12
600 Irvine Ave 92663 949-515-6300
Michael Vossen, prin. Fax 515-6370

Interior Designers Institute Post-Sec.
1061 Camelback St 92660 949-675-4451
Southern States University Post-Sec.
1601 Dove St Ste 105 92660 949-833-8868

Newport Coast, Orange

Sage Hill S 400/9-12
20402 Newport Coast Dr 92657 949-219-0100
Gordon McNeill, head sch Fax 219-1399

Nicolaus, Sutter, Pop. 204
East Nicolaus JUNHSD 300/9-12
2454 Nicolaus Ave 95659 530-656-2255
Karen Villalobos, supt. Fax 656-1065
www.eastnicolaus.k12.ca.us
East Nicolaus HS 300/9-12
2454 Nicolaus Ave 95659 530-656-2255
Karen Villalobos, prin. Fax 656-1065
Three Rivers HS 50/Alt
2454 Nicolaus Ave 95659 530-656-2255
Pamela Ogren, prin. Fax 656-1065

Nipomo, San Luis Obispo, Pop. 16,314
Lucia Mar USD
Supt. — See Arroyo Grande
Central Coast New Tech HS 9-12
525 N Thompson Ave 93444
Dan Neff, prin.
Nipomo HS 1,100/9-12
525 N Thompson Ave 93444 805-474-3300
Michelle Johnson, prin. Fax 929-2551

Norco, Riverside, Pop. 26,516
Corona-Norco USD 53,200/K-12
2820 Clark Ave 92860 951-736-5000
Michael H. Lin Ed.D., supt. Fax 736-5016
www.cnusd.k12.ca.us
Kennedy HS 800/10-12
1951 3rd St 92860 951-738-2200
Dr. April Moore, prin. Fax 738-2212
Norco HS 2,200/9-12
2065 Temescal Ave 92860 951-736-3241
Lisa Simon, prin. Fax 736-3282
Norco IS 800/7-8
2711 Temescal Ave 92860 951-736-3206
Fax 736-3208
Other Schools – See Corona, Eastvale

Norco College Post-Sec.
2001 3rd St 92860 951-372-7000

Norden, Nevada

Sugar Bowl Academy 50/6-12
PO Box 68 95724 530-426-1844
Tracy Keller, head sch Fax 426-1860

North Edwards, Kern, Pop. 1,016
Muroc JUSD 2,100/PK-12
17100 Foothill Ave 93523 760-769-4821
Loretta Gibson, supt. Fax 769-4241
www.muroc.k12.ca.us
Other Schools – See Boron, Edwards

North Fork, Madera
Chawanakee USD 800/K-12
PO Box 400 93643 559-877-6209
Robert Nelson, supt. Fax 877-2065
www.chawanakee.k12.ca.us
Chawanakee Culinary Arts Institute 9-12
PO Box 505 93643 559-877-6209
Paul Griffin, prin. Fax 877-2065
Cougar Springs Community Day S 50/Alt
PO Box 339 93643 559-877-6209
Robert Nelson, prin. Fax 877-4430
Manzanita Community Day S 50/Alt
PO Box 339 93643 559-877-6209
Robert Nelson, prin. Fax 877-4430
Mountain Oaks HS 50/9-12
PO Box 339 93643 559-877-4440
Paul Griffin, prin. Fax 877-4430
Other Schools – See O Neals

North Highlands, Sacramento, Pop. 40,275
Twin Rivers USD
Supt. — See Mc Clellan
Highlands HS 900/9-12
6601 Guthrie St 95660 916-566-3465
Darryl Hawthrone, prin. Fax 263-6985
Pacific Career & Technology HS Vo/Tech
6560 Melrose Dr 95660 916-566-2715
Harjinder Mattu, prin. Fax 263-6404
Winona Adult S Adult
3222 Winona Way 95660 916-286-3836
Kirk Williams, prin. Fax 286-3885

North Hills, Los Angeles
Los Angeles USD
Supt. — See Los Angeles
Einstein Continuation HS 100/Alt
15938 Tupper St 91343 818-892-4367
Flor Ayala, prin. Fax 893-3423
Monroe HS 2,700/9-12
9229 Haskell Ave 91343 818-830-4200
Christopher Rosas, prin. Fax 892-5622
Sepulveda MS 1,800/6-8
15330 Plummer St 91343 818-920-2130
Kimberly Noble, prin. Fax 891-5754

Centers of Learning 100/PK-12
PO Box 2037 91393 818-894-3213
Debra Grill, prin. Fax 893-8074
Heritage Christian S South Campus 800/7-12
9825 Woodley Ave 91343 818-894-5742
Lance Haliday, prin. Fax 892-5018

North Hollywood, See Los Angeles
Los Angeles USD
Supt. — See Los Angeles
Earhart Continuation S 100/Alt
5355 Colfax Ave 91601 818-769-4877
John Berns, prin. Fax 980-1794
East Valley HS 1,100/9-12
5525 Vineland Ave 91601 818-753-4400
Carrie Allen, prin. Fax 487-6922
Madison MS 1,500/6-8
13000 Hart St 91605 818-255-5200
Estelle Baptiste, prin. Fax 765-4692
North Hollywood HS 3,200/9-12
5231 Colfax Ave 91601 818-753-6200
Randall Delling, prin. Fax 508-7124
Reed MS 1,700/6-8
4525 Irvine Ave 91602 818-487-7600
Donna Tobin, prin. Fax 766-9069
Romer MS 1,400/6-8
6501 Laurel Canyon Blvd 91606 818-505-2200
John McLaughlin, prin. Fax 761-9343

Anderson Medical Career College Post-Sec.
10752 Burbank Blvd 91601 818-762-7095
Art Institute of California - Hollywood Post-Sec.
5250 Lankershim Blvd 91601 818-299-5100
Campbell Hall S 1,100/K-12
4533 Laurel Canyon Blvd 91607 818-980-7280
Rev. Julian Bull, hdmstr. Fax 505-5362
Concorde Career College Post-Sec.
12412 Victory Blvd 91606 818-766-8151
Harvard-Westlake HS 900/10-12
3700 Coldwater Canyon Ave 91604 818-980-6692
Jeanne Huybrechts, hdmstr. Fax 487-6631
Kaplan College Post-Sec.
6180 Laurel Canyon Ste 101 91606 818-763-2563
Marinello School of Beauty Post-Sec.
6219 Laurel Canyon Blvd 91606 818-980-1300
Oakwood S 500/7-12
11600 Magnolia Blvd 91601 818-732-3000
Dr. James Astman, hdmstr.
Southern California Health Institute Post-Sec.
5200 Lankershim Blvd 91601 818-980-8990
Valley Torah Girls' HS 200/9-12
12003 Riverside Dr 91607 818-755-1697
Rabbi Avrohom Stulberger, head sch Fax 755-1694
West Coast University Post-Sec.
12215 Victory Blvd 91606 818-299-5500

Northridge, See Los Angeles
Los Angeles USD
Supt. — See Los Angeles
Holmes MS 1,600/6-8
9351 Paso Robles Ave 91325 818-678-4100
Blanca Hernandez, prin. Fax 886-3358
Northridge Academy HS 1,100/9-12
9601 Zelzah Ave 91325 818-700-2222
Karen Matsui, prin. Fax 718-2239
Northridge MS 900/6-8
17960 Chase St 91325 818-678-5100
Deborah Wiltz, prin. Fax 885-1461

CA National University Advanced Studies Post-Sec.
8550 Balboa Blvd Ste 210 91325 800-782-2422
California State University-Northridge Post-Sec.
18111 Nordhoff St 91330 818-677-1200
Highland Hall Waldorf S 200/PK-12
17100 Superior St 91325 818-349-1394
Lynn Kern, admin. Fax 349-2390
San Fernando Valley Academy 100/PK-12
17601 Lassen St 91325 818-349-1373
David Branum, prin. Fax 773-6353

Norwalk, Los Angeles, Pop. 103,851
Little Lake City SD
Supt. — See Santa Fe Springs
Lakeside MS 800/6-8
11000 Kenney St 90650 562-868-9422
David Grant, prin. Fax 863-9252

Norwalk-La Mirada USD 20,000/PK-12
12820 Pioneer Blvd 90650 562-868-0431
Ruth Perez Ed.D., supt. Fax 864-9857
www.nlmusd.k12.ca.us
Corvallis MS 800/6-8
11032 Leffingwell Rd 90650 562-868-2678
Bob Easton, prin. Fax 863-4755
Glenn HS 1,800/9-12
13520 Shoemaker Ave 90650 562-868-0431
Thomas Puccia, prin. Fax 802-1596
Los Alisos MS 1,000/6-8
14800 Jersey Ave 90650 562-868-0865
Gloria Jimenez, prin. Fax 864-2967
Norwalk HS 2,300/9-12
11356 Leffingwell Rd 90650 562-868-0431
Rick Ronquillo, prin. Fax 864-0796
Waite MS 900/6-8
14320 Norwalk Blvd 90650 562-921-7981
Willie Norman, prin. Fax 921-8114
Norwalk Adult S Adult
15711 Pioneer Blvd 90650 562-868-9858
Sharon Todd, dir. Fax 863-2159
Other Schools – See La Mirada, Whittier

Regional Occupational Center & Program
Supt. — None
Southeast ROP Vo/Tech
12940 Foster Rd 90650 562-860-1927
Gilbert Montano, prin. Fax 929-2474

ATI College Post-Sec.
12440 Firestone Blvd # 2001 90650 562-864-0506
Cerritos College Post-Sec.
11110 Alondra Blvd 90650 562-860-2451
New Harvest Christian S 200/PK-12
PO Box 529 90651 562-929-6034
Sergio Romo, dir. Fax 484-3260
NTMA Training Center of Southern CA Post-Sec.
14926 Bloomfield Ave 90650 562-921-3722

Novato, Marin, Pop. 49,983
Novato USD 7,400/K-12
1015 7th St 94945 415-897-4201
Shalee Cunningham Ph.D., supt. Fax 898-5790
www.nusd.org
Marin Oaks HS 100/Alt
720 Diablo Ave 94947 415-892-8733
Kessa Early, prin. Fax 897-4229
Nova Education Center/Adult Education 100/Alt
740 Diablo Ave 94947 415-897-7653
Kessa Early, prin. Fax 897-5603
Novato HS 1,300/9-12
625 Arthur St 94947 415-898-2125
Rey Mayoral, prin. Fax 897-4242
San Jose MS 400/6-8
1000 Sunset Pkwy 94949 415-883-7831
Justin Mori, prin. Fax 883-0624
San Marin HS 900/9-12
15 San Marin Dr 94945 415-898-2121
Adam Littlefield, prin. Fax 892-8284
Sinaloa MS 700/6-8
2045 Vineyard Rd 94947 415-897-2111
Mary Pritchard, prin. Fax 892-1201

College of Marin Post-Sec.
1800 Ignacio Blvd 94949 415-457-8811
North Bay Christian Academy 100/K-12
6965 Redwood Blvd 94945 415-892-8921
Pamela Carraher, prin. Fax 893-1750

Nuevo, Riverside, Pop. 6,326
Nuview UNESD 2,000/K-12
29780 Lakeview Ave 92567 951-928-0066
David Pyle, supt. Fax 928-0324
www.nuview.k12.ca.us
Mountain Shadows MS 400/7-8
30401 Reservoir Ave 92567 951-928-3836
Michelle Walsh, prin. Fax 928-3015

Oakdale, Stanislaus, Pop. 20,174
Oakdale JUSD 5,300/K-12
168 S 3rd Ave 95361 209-848-4884
Marc Malone, supt. Fax 847-0155
www.oakdale.k12.ca.us
East Stanislaus HS 100/Alt
250 Hinkley Ave 95361 209-847-1735
Dennis Hitch, prin. Fax 847-9627
Oakdale HS 1,600/9-12
739 W G St 95361 209-847-3007
Michael Moore, prin. Fax 848-0314
Oakdale JHS 800/7-8
400 S Maag Ave 95361 209-847-2294
John Simons, prin. Fax 847-8521
Valley Oak JSHS 100/Alt
200 Hinkley Ave 95361 209-847-3097
Dennis Hitch, prin. Fax 848-4359

Oak Hills, San Bernardino, Pop. 8,716
Hesperia USD
Supt. — See Hesperia
Oak Hills HS 2,200/9-12
7625 Cataba Rd, 760-244-2283
Larry Porras, prin. Fax 244-0351

Oakhurst, Madera, Pop. 2,743
Bass Lake JUNESD 900/K-8
40096 Indian Springs Rd 93644 559-642-1555
Glenn Reid, supt. Fax 642-1556
www.basslakeschooldistrict.com/
Oak Creek IS 200/6-8
40094 Indian Springs Rd 93644 559-642-1570
Nicole White, prin. Fax 683-7279

Yosemite USD 2,300/K-12
50200 Road 427 93644 559-683-8801
James Sargent, supt. Fax 683-4160
www.yosemiteusd.com/
Ahwahnee Continuation HS 50/Alt
50200 Road 427 93644 559-683-8801
Dr. Randy Haggard, prin. Fax 658-2034
Campbell High Community Day S 50/Alt
50200 Road 427 93644 559-683-8801
Dr. Randy Haggard, prin. Fax 658-2359
Evergreen HS 50/Alt
50200 Road 427 93644 559-683-5544
Dr. Randy Haggard, prin. Fax 658-2359
Yosemite HS 800/9-12
50200 Road 427 93644 559-683-4667
Ed VanHoose, prin. Fax 683-8392
Yosemite Adult HS Adult
50200 Road 427 93644 559-683-8801
Dr. Randy Haggard, prin. Fax 642-4334
Other Schools – See Coarsegold, Raymond

Oakland, Alameda, Pop. 373,354
Oakland USD 39,500/PK-12
2111 International Blvd 94606 510-434-7790
Anthony Smith Ph.D., supt.
www.ousd.k12.ca.us
Alliance Academy 400/6-8
1800 98th Ave 94603 510-639-2893
Cheryl Lana, prin. Fax 639-3387
Brewer MS 800/6-8
3748 13th Ave 94610 510-531-6600
Sam Pasarow, prin. Fax 531-6626
Bunche Continuation S 50/Alt
1240 18th St 94607 510-874-3300
Betsye Steele, prin. Fax 874-3305
Castlemont HS 9-12
8601 MacArthur Blvd 94605 510-639-1466
John Lynch, prin. Fax 639-4271
Claremont MS 500/6-8
5750 College Ave 94618 510-654-7337
Reginald Richardson, prin. Fax 654-7341
Coliseum College Prep Academy 400/6-12
1390 66th Ave 94621 510-639-3201
Amy Carozza, prin. Fax 639-3214
Community Day MSHS 50/Alt
4917 Mountain Blvd 94619 510-531-6800
Michael Johnson, prin. Fax 482-7144
Dewey Academy 300/Alt
1111 2nd Ave 94606 510-874-3660
Robin Glover, prin. Fax 874-3661
Elmhurst Community Prep S 400/6-8
1800 98th Ave 94603 510-639-2888
Kilian Betlach, prin. Fax 639-2891
Fremont HS 9-12
4610 Foothill Blvd 94601 510-434-5257
Daniel Hurst, prin. Fax 434-2018
Frick MS 400/6-8
2845 64th Ave 94605 510-729-7736
Jerome Gourdine, prin. Fax 729-7739
Gateway to College S Alt
900 Fallon St 94607 510-986-6941
Anthony Flores, prin. Fax 464-3231
Harte MS 700/6-8
3700 Coolidge Ave 94602 510-531-6400
Tom Hughes, prin. Fax 482-7272
LIFE Academy 300/6-12
2101 35th Ave 94601 510-534-0282
Preston Thomas, prin. Fax 534-0283
Madison MS 300/6-8
400 Capistrano Dr 94603 510-879-2150
Lucinda Taylor, prin.
McClymonds HS 9-12
2608 Myrtle St 94607 510-879-3033
Kevin Taylor, prin. Fax 874-3796
MetWest HS 200/Alt
1100 3rd Ave 94606 510-451-5902
Sean McClung, prin. Fax 451-5903
Montera MS 900/6-8
5555 Ascot Dr 94611 510-531-6070
Tina Tranzor, prin. Fax 531-6354
Oakland HS 1,800/9-12
1023 MacArthur Blvd 94610 510-874-3676
Jeff Rogers, prin. Fax 874-3675
Oakland International HS 300/Alt
4521 Webster St 94609 510-879-2142
Carmelita Welsh-Reyes, prin.
Oakland Technical HS Vo/Tech
4351 Broadway 94611 510-879-3050
Sheilagh Andujar, prin. Fax 879-3059
Roosevelt MS 700/6-8
1926 E 19th St 94606 510-879-2120
Clifford Hong, prin. Fax 879-2129
ROOTS International Academy 400/6-8
1390 66th Ave 94621 510-639-3226
Gina Hill, prin. Fax 639-3214
Rudsdale Continuation S 200/Alt
8251 Fontaine St 94605 510-636-7992
Willie Thompson, prin.
Skyline HS, 12250 Skyline Blvd 94619 1,900/9-12
Troy Johnston, prin. 510-879-3060
Sojourner Truth S 100/Alt
8251 Fontaine St 94605 510-729-4308
Willie Thompson, prin. Fax 636-4701
Street Academy 100/Alt
417 29th St 94609 510-874-3630
Patricia Williams-Myrick, prin. Fax 874-3633
United for Success Academy 400/6-8
2101 35th Ave 94601 510-879-1494
Elia Bustamante, prin.
Urban Promise Academy 300/6-8
3031 E 18th St 94601 510-436-3636
Mark Triplett, prin. Fax 436-3638
Westlake MS 600/6-8
2629 Harrison St 94612 510-879-2130
Misha Karigica, prin. Fax 835-7170
West Oakland MS, 991 14th St 94607 200/6-8
Ron Smith, prin. 510-879-2093
Neighborhood Centers Adult S Adult
750 International Blvd 94606 510-451-7300
Brigitte Marshall, prin. Fax 451-7320

Academy of Chinese Culture & Health Sci. Post-Sec.
1601 Clay St 94612 510-763-7787
American University of Armenia Post-Sec.
300 Lakeside Dr Fl 12 94612 510-987-9452
Bayhill HS 100/9-12
521 Boden Way 94610 510-268-1500
Shelley Lobell, dir. Fax 268-1503
Bishop O'Dowd HS 1,200/9-12
9500 Stearns Ave 94605 510-577-9100
Pamela Shay, prin. Fax 638-3259
California College of the Arts Post-Sec.
5212 Broadway 94618 510-594-3600
College Preparatory S 400/9-12
6100 Broadway 94618 510-652-0111
Monique DeVane, head sch Fax 652-7467
DeVry University Post-Sec.
505 14th St Ste 100 94612 510-267-1340
Head-Royce S 800/K-12
4315 Lincoln Ave 94602 510-531-1300
Robert Lake, head sch Fax 531-2649
Holy Names HS 200/9-12
4660 Harbord Dr 94618 510-450-1110
Colleen Curran, prin. Fax 547-3111
Holy Names University Post-Sec.
3500 Mountain Blvd 94619 510-436-1000
ITT Technical Institute Post-Sec.
7901 Oakport St Ste 3000 94621 510-553-2800
Laney College Post-Sec.
900 Fallon St 94607 510-834-5740
Lincoln University Post-Sec.
401 15th St 94612 510-628-8010
Merritt College Post-Sec.
12500 Campus Dr 94619 510-531-4911
Mills College Post-Sec.
5000 MacArthur Blvd 94613 510-430-2255
Moler Barber College Post-Sec.
3815 Telegraph Ave 94609 510-652-4177
Morgan S for Girls 200/6-8
PO Box 9966 94613 510-632-6000
Sandra Luna, head sch Fax 632-6301
Muhammad University of Islam 100/K-12
5277 Foothill Blvd 94601 510-436-0206
Salamah Muhammad, admin.
Patten Academy of Christian Education 100/K-12
2433 Coolidge Ave 94601 510-533-3121
Dr. Sharon Anderson, prin. Fax 535-9381
Patten University Post-Sec.
2433 Coolidge Ave 94601 510-261-8500
St. Elizabeth HS 200/9-12
1530 34th Ave 94601 510-532-8947
Martin Procaccio, prin. Fax 532-9754
St. Martin de Porres S 100/6-8
1630 10th St 94607 510-832-1757
Ann Magovern, pres. Fax 832-6481
Samuel Merritt University Post-Sec.
3100 Telegraph Ave Ste 1000 94609 510-869-6511
SUM Bible College & Theological Seminary Post-Sec.
735 105th Ave 94603 510-567-6174

Oakley, Contra Costa, Pop. 33,914
Liberty UNHSD
Supt. — See Brentwood
Freedom HS 2,500/9-12
1050 Neroly Rd 94561 925-625-5900
Erik Faulkner, prin. Fax 625-0396

Oakley UNESD 4,600/K-8
91 Mercedes Ln 94561 925-625-0700
Richard Rogers Ed.D., supt. Fax 625-1863
www.ouesd.k12.ca.us
Delta Vista MS 900/6-8
4901 Frank Hengel Way 94561 925-625-6840
Greg Hetrick, prin. Fax 625-6850
O'Hara Park MS 800/6-8
1100 OHara Ave 94561 925-625-5060
Colleen Creswell, prin. Fax 625-5096

Oak Park, Ventura, Pop. 13,435
Oak Park USD 3,900/PK-12
5801 Conifer St 91377 818-735-3200
Dr. Anthony Knight, supt. Fax 879-0372
www.oakparkusd.org/
Medea Creek MS 1,100/6-8
1002 Doubletree Rd 91377 818-707-7922
Brad Benioff, prin. Fax 865-8641
Oak Park HS 1,400/9-12
899 Kanan Rd 91377 818-735-3300
Kevin Buchanan, prin. Fax 707-7970
Oak View HS 50/Alt
5701 Conifer St 91377 818-735-3217
Stewart McGugan, prin. Fax 735-3290

Oceanside, San Diego, Pop. 159,148
Oceanside USD 21,100/K-12
2111 Mission Ave 92058 760-966-4000
Larry Perondi, supt. Fax 433-8620
www.oside.us
Chavez MS 800/6-8
202 Oleander Dr 92057 760-966-4900
Eileen Frazier, prin. Fax 945-4665
El Camino HS 3,100/9-12
400 Rancho Del Oro Dr 92057 760-757-8550
Bob Rowe, prin. Fax 757-5321
Jefferson MS 1,100/6-8
823 Acacia Ave 92058 760-757-6060
Marie Higareda de Ochoa, prin. Fax 757-5791
King MS 1,500/6-8
1290 Ivey Ranch Rd 92057 760-901-8800
Dr. Ron Pirayoff, prin. Fax 967-4154
Lincoln MS 900/6-8
2000 California St 92054 760-901-8900
Steve Bessant, prin. Fax 433-2035
Ocean Shores HS 200/Alt
3131 Oceanside Blvd 92056 760-901-8600
Barbara Perez, prin. Fax 439-5588
Oceanside HS 2,400/9-12
1 Pirates Cove Way 92054 760-722-8201
Chris Hurst, prin. Fax 757-2419

Vista USD
Supt. — See Vista
Madison MS 1,300/6-8
4930 Lake Blvd 92056 760-940-0176
Susan Ford, prin. Fax 940-2081
Mission Vista HS 9-12
1306 Melrose Dr 92057 760-758-6800
Craig Wiblemo, prin. Fax 758-6832
Roosevelt MS 1,100/6-8
850 Sagewood Dr 92057 760-726-8003
Courtney Goode, prin. Fax 726-8596

MediaTech Institute Post-Sec.
302 Oceanside Blvd 92054 760-231-5368
MiraCosta College Post-Sec.
1 Barnard Dr 92056 760-757-2121
Oceanside College of Beauty Post-Sec.
1575 S Coast Hwy 92054 760-757-6161

Ojai, Ventura, Pop. 7,310
Ojai USD 3,000/K-12
PO Box 878 93024 805-640-4300
Dr. Henry Bangser, supt. Fax 640-4419
www.ojai.k12.ca.us
Chaparral Continuation HS 100/Alt
PO Box 878 93024 805-640-4330
Linus Raibys, lead tchr. Fax 640-4341
Matilija JHS 500/7-8
703 El Paseo Rd 93023 805-640-4355
Bill Rosen, prin. Fax 640-4398
Nordhoff HS 900/9-12
1401 Maricopa Hwy 93023 805-640-4343
Greg Bayless, prin. Fax 640-4336

Besant Hill S 100/9-12
PO Box 850 93024 805-646-4343
Randy Bertin, head sch Fax 646-4371
Laurel Springs S 1,600/K-12
302 El Paseo Rd 93023 805-646-2473
Marilyn Gordanier, dir. Fax 646-0186
Oak Grove S 200/PK-12
220 W Lomita Ave 93023 805-646-8236
Meredy Benson Rice, hdmstr. Fax 646-6509
Ojai Valley S 300/PK-12
723 El Paseo Rd 93023 805-646-1423
Michael Hall-Mounsey, pres. Fax 646-0362
Thacher S 300/9-12
5025 Thacher Rd 93023 805-646-4377
Michael Mulligan, head sch Fax 646-9490
Villanova Preparatory HS 300/9-12
12096 N Ventura Ave 93023 805-646-1464
Carol Hoffer, hdmstr. Fax 646-4430

Olivehurst, Yuba, Pop. 13,017
Marysville JUSD
Supt. — See Marysville
Lindhurst HS 1,300/9-12
4446 Olive Ave 95961 530-741-6150
Bob Eckardt, prin. Fax 741-6171
South Lindhurst Continuation HS 100/Alt
4446 Olive Ave 95961 530-741-6918
Rocco Greco, prin. Fax 741-7875
Yuba Gardens IS 700/7-8
1964 11th Ave 95961 530-741-6194
Kari Ylst, prin. Fax 741-7847

New Life Christian S 200/PK-12
5736 Arboga Rd 95961 530-742-3033
John Lewallen, admin. Fax 741-8221

Olympic Valley, Placer

Squaw Valley Academy 100/9-12
PO Box 2667 96146 530-583-9393
Fax 581-1111

O Neals, Madera
Chawanakee USD
Supt. — See North Fork
Chawanakee Academy 200/Alt
PO Box 210 93645 559-868-4200
Jessica Fairbanks, prin. Fax 868-4222
Minarets HS 300/9-12
PO Box 186 93645 559-868-8689
Michael Niehoff, prin. Fax 868-3407
Chawanakee Adult Education Adult
PO Box 186 93645 559-868-4200
Mike Niehoff, prin. Fax 868-4222

Ontario, San Bernardino, Pop. 161,020
Chaffey JUNHSD 25,400/9-12
211 W 5th St 91762 909-988-8511
Mathew Holton, supt. Fax 984-1164
www.cjuhsd.k12.ca.us
Chaffey Community Day S 50/Alt
1802 E 7th St 91764 909-460-5663
Bart Goldstein, prin.

Chaffey HS 3,700/9-12
1245 N Euclid Ave 91762 909-988-5560
Dawn Buboltz, prin. Fax 988-0146
Colony HS 2,300/9-12
3850 E Riverside Dr 91761 909-930-2929
Dr. Kern Oduro, prin. Fax 460-5856
Ontario HS 2,900/9-12
901 W Francis St 91762 909-988-7411
Cary Willborn, prin. Fax 986-2181
Valley View Continuation HS 700/Alt
1801 E 6th St 91764 909-985-0966
Bart Goldstein, prin. Fax 946-5586
Chaffey Adult S Adult
211 W 5th St 91762 909-988-8511
Todd Haag, prin. Fax 983-9916
Other Schools – See Alta Loma, Etiwanda, Montclair, Rancho Cucamonga

Chino Valley USD
Supt. — See Chino
Woodcrest JHS 400/7-8
2725 S Campus Ave 91761 909-923-3455
Sue Pederson, prin. Fax 548-6059

Mountain View ESD 2,800/K-8
2585 S Archibald Ave 91761 909-947-2992
Dr. Rick Carr, supt. Fax 947-1605
www.mtnview.k12.ca.us
Yokley MS, 2947 S Turner Ave 91761 1,000/6-8
Lisa Alcala, prin. 909-947-6774

Ontario-Montclair ESD 22,500/PK-8
950 W D St 91762 909-459-2500
Dr. James Hammond, supt. Fax 459-2542
www.omsd.k12.ca.us
Danks MS 1,000/6-8
1020 N Vine Ave 91762 909-983-2691
Timothy Sullivan, prin. Fax 459-2959
De Anza MS 600/7-8
1450 S Sultana Ave 91761 909-986-8577
Michael Gomez, prin. Fax 459-2673
Oaks MS 900/7-8
1221 S Oaks Ave 91762 909-988-2050
Dave Foley, prin. Fax 988-2081
Wiltsey MS 700/6-8
1450 E G St 91764 909-986-5838
William Corrette, prin. Fax 459-2834
Other Schools – See Montclair

American Career College Post-Sec.
3130 Sedona Ct 91764 909-218-3253
Argosy University Inland Empire Post-Sec.
3401 Centre Lake Dr Ste 200 91761 909-472-0800
Everest College Post-Sec.
1460 S Milliken Ave 91761 909-984-5027
Everest College Post-Sec.
1819 Excise Ave 91761 909-484-4311
Franklin Career College Post-Sec.
1274 Slater Cir 91761 909-937-9007
Marinollo School of Beauty Post-Sec.
940 N Mountain Ave 91762 909-984-5884
NTMA Training Center of Southern CA Post-Sec.
1717 S Grove Ave 91761 909-947-9363
Ontario Christian HS 500/9-12
931 W Philadelphia St 91762 909-984-1756
Tim Hoekstra, prin. Fax 460-0176
Platt College Post-Sec.
3700 Inland Empire Ste 400 91764 909-941-9410
Richard's Beauty College Post-Sec.
200 N Euclid Ave 91762 909-988-7584
San Antonio Christian S 100/K-10
1722 E 8th St 91764 909-982-2301
Brianna Perry, prin. Fax 982-0921
West Coast University Post-Sec.
2855 E Guasti Rd 91761 909-467-6100
Westech College Post-Sec.
3491 Concours 91764 909-980-4474

Orange, Orange, Pop. 133,187
Orange USD 29,700/PK-12
PO Box 11022 92856 714-628-4040
Michael Christenson Ed.D., supt. Fax 628-4041
www.orangeusd.org/
Career Education Center Vo/Tech
250 S Yorba St 92869 714-997-6066
Dennis McCuistion, coord. Fax 997-6035
El Modena HS 2,200/9-12
3920 E Spring St 92869 714-997-6331
Rebecca Martinez, prin. Fax 997-0705
Orange HS 2,200/9-12
525 N Shaffer St 92867 714-997-6211
Ernest Gonzalez, prin. Fax 633-6460
Portola MS 800/6-8
270 N Palm Dr 92868 714-997-6361
Debra Backstrom, prin. Fax 978-0274
Richland Continuation HS 400/Alt
615 N Lemon St 92867 714-997-6167
Ed Madrid, prin. Fax 771-5967
Yorba MS 500/7-8
935 N Cambridge St 92867 714-997-6161
Kerrie Torres, prin. Fax 532-4759
Other Schools – See Anaheim, Villa Park

Argosy University Orange County Post-Sec.
601 S Lewis St 92868 714-620-3700
Chapman University Post-Sec.
1 University Dr 92866 714-997-6815
CNI College Post-Sec.
702 W Town and Country Rd 92868 714-437-9697
COBA Academy Post-Sec.
102 N Glassell St 92866 714-633-5950
Eldorado S for the Gifted Child 200/PK-12
4100 E Walnut Ave 92869 714-633-4774
Dr. Glory Ludwick, dir. Fax 744-3304
ITT Technical Institute Post-Sec.
4000 W Metropolitan Dr #100 92868 714-941-2400

Lutheran HS of Orange County 1,300/9-12
2222 N Santiago Blvd 92867 714-998-5151
Leslie Smith, prin. Fax 998-1371
St. Joseph Hospital Post-Sec.
1100 W Stewart Dr 92868 714-771-8111
Santiago Canyon College Post-Sec.
8045 E Chapman Ave 92869 714-628-4900
South Coast College Post-Sec.
2011 W Chapman Ave 92868 866-266-8779

Orange Cove, Fresno, Pop. 9,005
Kings Canyon JUSD
Supt. — See Reedley
Citrus MS 600/6-8
1400 Anchor Ave 93646 559-305-7370
Patricia Ledesma, prin. Fax 626-7255
Orange Cove HS 600/9-12
1700 Anchor Ave 93646 559-626-5900
Roberto Gutierrez, prin. Fax 626-7217

Orangevale, Sacramento, Pop. 32,766
San Juan USD
Supt. — See Carmichael
Carnegie MS 900/6-8
5820 Illinois Ave 95662 916-971-7853
Trish Baldwin, prin. Fax 971-7849
Casa Roble Fundamental HS 1,600/9-12
9151 Oak Ave 95662 916-971-5452
Jim Shoemake, prin. Fax 971-5495
Pasteur MS 700/6-8
8935 Elm Ave 95662 916-971-7891
Janet Deal, prin. Fax 971-7893

Orcutt, Santa Barbara, Pop. 28,086
Orcutt UNESD 4,500/K-12
500 Dyer St 93455 805-938-8900
Robert Bush, supt. Fax 938-8919
www.orcutt-schools.net
Orcutt JHS 400/7-8
608 Pinal Ave 93455 805-938-8700
Susan Salucci, prin. Fax 938-8749
Other Schools – See Santa Maria

Orinda, Contra Costa, Pop. 16,885
Acalanes UNHSD
Supt. — See Lafayette
Miramonte HS 1,300/9-12
750 Moraga Way 94563 925-280-3930
Adam Clark, prin. Fax 280-3931

Orinda UNESD 2,400/K-8
8 Altarinda Rd 94563 925-254-4901
Joe Jaconette Ed.D., supt. Fax 254-5261
www.orindaschools.org/
Orinda IS 800/6-8
80 Ivy Dr 94563 925-258-3090
Michael Randall, prin. Fax 631-7985

Orinda Academy 100/6-12
19 Altarinda Rd 94563 925-254-7553
Ronald Graydon, hdmstr. Fax 254-4768

Orland, Glenn, Pop. 7,173
Orland JUSD 2,200/K-12
1320 6th St 95963 530-865-1200
Chris von Kleist, supt. Fax 865-1202
www.orlandusd.net
North Valley HS 50/Alt
1320 6th St 95963 530-865-1285
Dr. Armand Brett, prin. Fax 865-1285
Orland Community Day S 50/Alt
1320 6th St 95963 530-865-1264
Dr. Armand Brett, prin.
Orland HS 700/9-12
1320 6th St 95963 530-865-1210
Nicole Newman, prin. Fax 865-1215
Price IS 500/6-8
1320 6th St 95963 530-865-1225
Steven Hiscock, prin. Fax 865-1227

North Valley Christian S 100/K-12
1148 E Walker St 95963 530-865-4924
Gordon Wiens, supt. Fax 865-4926

Orosi, Tulare, Pop. 8,702
Cutler-Orosi JUSD 4,100/K-12
12623 Avenue 416 93647 559-528-4763
Carolyn Kehrli Ed.D., supt. Fax 528-3132
www.cojusd.org
Cutler-Orosi Community Day S 50/Alt
12623 Avenue 416 93647 559-528-4703
Martha Calderon, prin. Fax 528-0102
El Monte MS 900/6-8
12623 Avenue 416 93647 559-528-3017
Antonio Rivera, prin. Fax 528-2822
Esperanza S 100/Alt
12623 Avenue 416 93647 559-528-4703
Martha Calderon, prin. Fax 528-0102
Orosi HS 1,000/9-12
12623 Avenue 416 93647 559-528-4731
Tanya Goosev, prin. Fax 528-4930
Cutler-Orosi Adult S Adult
12623 Avenue 416 93647 559-528-4763
Melissa Calvero, dir.
Other Schools – See Cutler

Oroville, Butte, Pop. 14,775
Oroville City ESD 2,600/K-8
2795 Yard St 95966 530-532-3000
Penny Chennell-Carter, supt. Fax 532-3050
www.ocesd.org
Central MS 300/7-8
2565 Mesa Ave 95966 530-532-3002
Don Phillips, prin. Fax 532-3042
Ishi Hills MS 400/6-8
1 Ishi Hills Way 95966 530-532-3078
Kathy Myszka, prin. Fax 532-3040

Oroville UNHSD 2,700/9-12
2211 Washington Ave 95966 530-538-2300
Dr. Corey Willenberg, supt. Fax 538-2308
www.ouhsd.org
Las Plumas HS 1,300/9-12
2380 Las Plumas Ave 95966 530-538-2310
Dana Ramos, prin. Fax 534-5974
Oroville Community Day S 50/Alt
2120 2nd St 95965 530-538-2330
Jeff Ochs, dir. Fax 533-2338
Oroville HS 1,300/9-12
1535 Bridge St 95966 530-538-2320
Jeff Peek, prin. Fax 534-6203
Prospect Continuation HS 200/Alt
2060 2nd St 95965 530-538-2330
Jeff Ochs, dir. Fax 533-2338
Oroville Adult Education Adult
2750 Mitchell Ave 95966 530-538-5350
Jeff Ochs, dir. Fax 538-5396

Thermalito UNESD 1,300/K-8
400 Grand Ave 95965 530-538-2900
Julian Diaz, supt. Fax 538-2908
www.thermalito.org/
Heritage Community Day S 50/Alt
2080 6th St 95965 530-532-4376
Jim Walters, prin. Fax 538-2949
Nelson Avenue MS 500/6-8
2255 6th St 95965 530-538-2940
Jim Walters, prin. Fax 538-2949

Butte College Post-Sec.
3536 Butte Campus Dr 95965 530-895-2511
Northwest Lineman College Post-Sec.
2009 Challenger Ave 95965 530-534-7260

Oxnard, Ventura, Pop. 194,223
Hueneme ESD
Supt. — See Port Hueneme
Blackstock JHS 1,300/6-8
701 E Bard Rd 93033 805-488-3644
Tom Beneke, prin. Fax 488-1250
Green JHS 1,000/6-8
3739 S C St 93033 805-986-8750
Heidi Haines, prin. Fax 986-8756

Ocean View ESD 2,500/PK-8
4200 Olds Rd 93033 805-488-4441
Craig Helmstedter Ed.D., supt. Fax 986-6797
www.oceanviewsd.org
Ocean View JHS 800/6-8
4300 Olds Rd 93033 805-488-6421
Heather Hendrix, prin. Fax 488-4132

Oxnard SD 15,900/K-8
1051 S A St 93030 805-487-3918
Jeff Chancer, supt. Fax 483-7426
www.oxnardsd.org
Frank IS 1,200/7-8
701 N Juanita Ave 93030 805-385-1536
Maria Elena Plaza, prin. Fax 981-1754
Fremont IS 1,200/7-8
1130 N M St 93030 805-385-1539
Pam Morrison, prin. Fax 485-2486
Haydock IS 800/7-8
647 Hill St 93033 805-385-1545
Amelia Sugden, prin. Fax 487-7159

Oxnard UNHSD 16,600/K-12
309 S K St 93030 805-385-2500
Gabe Soumakian Ed.D., supt. Fax 483-3069
www.ouhsd.k12.ca.us
Channel Islands HS 2,700/9-12
1400 Raiders Way 93033 805-385-2787
Maricruz Hernandez, prin. Fax 385-2748
Hueneme HS 2,100/9-12
500 W Bard Rd 93033 805-385-2667
Oscar Hernandez Ed.D., prin. Fax 385-2817
Oxnard HS 3,000/9-12
3400 W Gonzales Rd, 805-278-2907
Eric Riegert, prin. Fax 278-2912
Pacifica HS 3,300/9-12
600 E Gonzales Rd, 805-278-5000
Bijou Beltran, prin. Fax 278-7187
Rio Mesa HS 2,100/9-12
545 Central Ave, 805-278-5500
Ray Gonzales, prin. Fax 278-5525
Oxnard Adult S Adult
1101 W 2nd St 93030 805-385-2584
Judy Perkins, prin. Fax 385-2581
Other Schools – See Camarillo

Rio SD 4,500/PK-8
2500 E Vineyard Ave, 805-485-3111
John Puglisi, supt. Fax 981-7736
www.rio.k12.ca.us
Rio Del Valle MS 700/6-8
2500 E Vineyard Ave, 805-485-3119
Joanne Davidson, prin. Fax 981-7737
Rio Vista MS 700/6-8
2500 E Vineyard Ave, 805-981-1507
Brasilia Perez, prin. Fax 981-6791

Charter College - Oxnard Post-Sec.
2000 Outlet Center Dr # 150, 805-973-1240
ITT Technical Institute Post-Sec.
2051 Solar Dr Ste 150, 805-988-0143
Laurus College Post-Sec.
2351 Lockwood St, 805-267-1691
Modern Beauty Academy Post-Sec.
699 S C St 93030 805-483-4994
Modern Institute of Technology Post-Sec.
2550 E Vineyard Ave Ste 220, 888-983-2444
Oxnard College Post-Sec.
4000 S Rose Ave 93033 805-986-5800
Pacific Coast Trade School Post-Sec.
1690 Universe Cir 93033 805-487-9260
St. John's Regional Medical Center Post-Sec.
1600 N Rose Ave 93030 805-988-2500

Santa Clara HS 400/9-12
2121 Saviers Rd 93033 805-483-9502
Dr. Edward Robillard, prin. Fax 483-1588

Pacifica, San Mateo, Pop. 35,016
Jefferson UNHSD
Supt. — See Daly City
Oceana HS 600/9-12
401 Paloma Ave 94044 650-550-7300
Caro Pemberton, prin. Fax 550-7310
Terra Nova HS 1,200/9-12
1450 Terra Nova Blvd 94044 650-550-7600
Dorene Basuino, prin. Fax 550-7690

Pacifica SD 3,100/K-8
375 Reina Del Mar Ave 94044 650-738-6600
Wendy Tukloff, supt. Fax 557-9672
www.pacificasd.org/
Lacy MS 600/6-8
1427 Palmetto Ave 94044 650-738-6665
Donald West, prin. Fax 738-6669

Alma Heights Christian S 300/K-12
1295 Seville Dr 94044 650-359-0555
David Gross, admin. Fax 359-5020

Pacific Grove, Monterey, Pop. 14,485
Pacific Grove USD 1,600/K-12
435 Hillcrest Ave 93950 831-646-6520
Ralph Porras, supt. Fax 646-6500
pgusd.org
Community HS 50/Alt
435 Hillcrest Ave 93950 831-646-6535
Matt Bell, prin. Fax 648-8417
Pacific Grove HS 400/9-12
615 Sunset Dr 93950 831-646-6590
Matt Bell, prin. Fax 646-6660
Pacific Grove MS 300/6-8
835 Forest Ave 93950 831-646-6568
Buck Roggeman, prin. Fax 646-6652
Pacific Grove Adult Education Adult
1025 Lighthouse Ave 93950 831-646-6580
Craig Beller, prin. Fax 646-6578

Stanford University Hopkins Marine Post-Sec.
120 Ocean View Blvd 93950 831-655-6200

Pacoima, See Los Angeles
Los Angeles USD
Supt. — See Los Angeles
MacLay MS 900/6-8
12540 Pierce St 91331 818-686-3800
Veronica Arreguin, prin. Fax 834-1012
Pacoima MS 1,700/6-8
9919 Laurel Canyon Blvd 91331 818-686-4200
Marsha Hamm, prin. Fax 834-2021
Pacoima Skills Center Adult
13545 Van Nuys Blvd 91331 818-896-9558
Juan Jimenez, admin. Fax 899-7087

Palermo, Butte, Pop. 5,130
Palermo UNESD 1,300/K-8
7390 Bulldog Way 95968 530-533-4842
Dr. Jacqueline Dolar, supt. Fax 532-1047
www.palermoschools.org
Palermo MS 400/6-8
7350 Bulldog Way 95968 530-533-4708
Kathleen Andoe, prin. Fax 532-7801

Palmdale, Los Angeles, Pop. 148,782
Antelope Valley UNHSD
Supt. — See Lancaster
Highland HS 3,100/9-12
39055 25th St W 93551 661-538-0304
Laura Herman, prin. Fax 538-0405
Knight HS 3,400/9-12
37423 70th St E 93552 661-533-9000
Will Laird, prin. Fax 533-0111
Palmdale HS 3,000/9-12
2137 E Avenue R 93550 661-273-3181
Greg Nehen, prin. Fax 273-1093
Parris Continuation HS 400/Alt
38801 Clock Tower Plaza Dr 93550 661-274-1230
Susan McDougal, prin. Fax 274-1168
Phoenix HS Community Day 200/Alt
2270 E Avenue Q 93550 661-274-4619
Dan Brown, prin.

Palmdale ESD 20,500/K-9
39139 10th St E 93550 661-947-7191
Roger Gallizzi, supt. Fax 273-5137
www.palmdalesd.org/
Cactus IS 300/7-8
3243 E Avenue R8 93550 661-273-0847
Ruth James, prin. Fax 273-5514
Desert Willow IS 1,000/7-8
36555 Sunny Ln 93550 661-285-5866
Kim Shaw, prin. Fax 456-1145
Juniper IS 800/7-8
39066 Palm Tree Way 93551 661-947-0181
Annette Heins, prin. Fax 456-1576
Shadow Hills IS 1,100/7-8
37315 60th St E 93552 661-533-7400
Barbara Gaines, prin. Fax 533-7445

Regional Occupational Center & Program
Supt. — None
Antelope Valley ROP Vo/Tech
1156 E Avenue S 93550 661-575-1026
Betsy McKinstry, dir. Fax 575-1037

Westside UNESD
Supt. — See Lancaster
Hillview MS 1,000/7-8
40525 Peonza Ln 93551 661-722-9993
Robert Garza, prin. Fax 722-9483

Wilsona SD 1,500/K-8
18050 E Avenue O 93591 661-264-1111
Teresa Grey, supt. Fax 261-3259
www.wilsonasd.net
Other Schools – See Lancaster

DeVry University Post-Sec.
39115 Trade Center Dr # 100 93551 866-986-9388

Palm Desert, Riverside, Pop. 47,665
Desert Sands USD
Supt. — See La Quinta
Palm Desert HS 2,000/9-12
74910 Aztec Rd 92260 760-862-4300
Bob Hicks, prin. Fax 862-4390

College of the Desert Post-Sec.
43500 Monterey Ave 92260 760-346-8041
Oasis Preparatory S 50/K-12
39605 Entrepreneur Ln 92211 760-772-8255
Susan Roberts, head sch Fax 772-7446
Xavier College Preparatory S 100/9-12
34200 Cook St 92211 760-601-3900
Chris Alling, prin. Fax 601-3901

Palm Springs, Riverside, Pop. 43,639
Palm Springs USD 23,600/PK-12
980 E Tahquitz Canyon Way 92262 760-416-6000
Dr. Christine Anderson, supt. Fax 416-6015
www.psusd.us
Cree MS 1,000/6-8
1011 E Vista Chino 92262 760-416-8283
Tracy Piper, prin. Fax 416-8287
Independent Study Alt
2248 E Ramon Rd 92264 760-416-8206
Milt Jones, prin. Fax 416-8210
Palm Springs HS 2,200/9-12
2401 E Baristo Rd 92262 760-778-0400
Ricky Wright, prin. Fax 778-0481
Ramon Alternative Center 50/Alt
2248 E Ramon Rd 92264 760-778-0487
Milt Jones, prin. Fax 778-0497
Palm Springs Adult Education Adult
2248 E Ramon Rd 92264 760-778-0494
Milt Jones, prin. Fax 778-0497
Other Schools – See Cathedral City, Desert Hot Springs

California Nurses Educational Institute Post-Sec.
5200 E Ramon Rd Ste I1 92264 760-416-5955
Desert Chapel Christian S 400/K-12
630 S Sunrise Way 92264 760-327-2772
Frank Marshall, admin. Fax 325-7048
Kaplan College Post-Sec.
2475 E Tahquitz Canyon Way 92262 760-778-3540

Palo Alto, Santa Clara, Pop. 61,626
Palo Alto USD 11,800/K-12
25 Churchill Ave 94306 650-329-3700
Kevin Skelly Ph.D., supt. Fax 329-3803
www.pausd.org
Gunn HS 1,900/9-12
780 Arastradero Rd 94306 650-354-8200
Katya Villalobos, prin. Fax 493-7801
Jordan MS 1,000/6-8
750 N California Ave 94303 650-494-8120
Gregory Barnes, prin. Fax 858-1310
Palo Alto HS 1,900/9-12
50 Embarcadero Rd 94301 650-329-3701
Phil Winston, prin. Fax 329-3753
Stanford MS 1,000/6-8
480 E Meadow Dr 94306 650-856-5188
Sharon Ofek, prin. Fax 856-3248
Terman MS 700/6-8
655 Arastradero Rd 94306 650-856-9810
Katherine Baker, prin. Fax 856-9878
Palo Alto Adult S Adult
50 Embarcadero Rd 94301 650-329-3752
Kara Rosenberg, prin. Fax 329-8515

Castilleja S 400/6-12
1310 Bryant St 94301 650-328-3160
Nanci Kauffman, head sch Fax 326-8036
Girls' MS 200/6-8
3400 W Bayshore Rd 94303 650-968-8338
Laura Reeve, head sch Fax 968-4775
Kehillah Jewish HS 100/9-12
3900 Fabian Way 94303 650-213-9600
Lillian Howard, head sch Fax 213-9601
Palo Alto University Post-Sec.
1791 Arastradero Rd 94304 800-818-6136
Sofia University Post-Sec.
1069 E Meadow Cir 94303 650-493-4430

Palo Cedro, Shasta, Pop. 1,232
Junction ESD 300/K-8
9087 Deschutes Rd 96073 530-547-3274
Deidra Hoffman, supt. Fax 547-4829
www.junctionesd.net
Junction IS 100/6-8
9019 Deschutes Rd 96073 530-547-5494
Jim Boesiger, prin. Fax 547-4829

Shasta UNHSD
Supt. — See Redding
Foothill HS 1,400/9-12
9733 Deschutes Rd 96073 530-547-1700
Jim Bartow, prin. Fax 245-2700
Foothill Plus HS 50/Alt
9733 Deschutes Rd 96073 530-245-2715
Elsbeth Prigmore, prin. Fax 245-2700

Redding Christian S 500/PK-12
21945 Old 44 Dr 96073 530-547-5600
Erika Piper, prin. Fax 547-5655

Palos Verdes Estates, Los Angeles, Pop. 12,975
Palos Verdes Peninsula USD 11,900/PK-12
375 Via Almar 90274 310-378-9966
Walker Williams, supt. Fax 378-0732
www.pvpusd.k12.ca.us
Palos Verdes HS 1,800/9-12
600 Cloyden Rd 90274 310-378-8471
Dr. Nick Stephany, prin. Fax 378-0311
Palos Verdes IS 1,000/6-8
2161 Via Olivera 90274 310-544-4816
Frank Califano, prin. Fax 265-5944
Other Schools – See Rancho Palos Verdes, Rolling Hills

Palos Verdes Peninsula, See Rolling Hills Estates

Chadwick S 900/K-12
26800 Academy Dr 90274 310-377-1543
Frederick Hill, hdmstr. Fax 377-0380

Panorama City, See Los Angeles
Los Angeles USD
Supt. — See Los Angeles
Burke HS 200/Alt
14630 Lanark St 91402 818-781-7665
Susan Garcia Phillips, prin. Fax 781-3226
Panorama HS 2,200/9-12
8015 Van Nuys Blvd 91402 818-909-4500
Elias De La Torre, prin. Fax 786-6991

St. Genevieve HS 600/9-12
13967 Roscoe Blvd 91402 818-894-6417
Daniel Horn, prin. Fax 892-9853
Western Beauty Institute Post-Sec.
8700 Van Nuys Blvd 91402 818-894-9550

Paradise, Butte, Pop. 25,494
Paradise USD 4,400/K-12
6696 Clark Rd 95969 530-872-6400
Roger Bylund, supt. Fax 872-6409
www.pusdk12.org
Honey Run Academy Alt
622 Pearson Rd 95969 530-872-6461
Dena Kapsalis, prin. Fax 872-9708
Paradise HS 1,300/9-12
5911 Maxwell Dr 95969 530-872-6425
Michelle John, prin. Fax 872-6427
Paradise IS 500/6-8
5657 Recreation Dr 95969 530-872-6465
Frederick Light, prin. Fax 876-1852
Paradise Adult S Adult
622 Pearson Rd 95969 530-872-6424
Dena Kapsalis, dir. Fax 872-9708
Other Schools – See Magalia

Champion Christian JSHS 100/7-12
5850 Clark Rd 95969 530-413-9802
John Pease, prin. Fax 345-5405
Paradise Adventist Academy 200/K-12
PO Box 2169 95967 530-877-6540
Lance Taggart, prin. Fax 877-0870

Paramount, Los Angeles, Pop. 53,159
Paramount USD 15,700/K-12
15110 California Ave 90723 562-602-6000
Herman Mendez, supt. Fax 602-8123
www.paramount.k12.ca.us
Alondra MS 900/6-8
16200 Downey Ave 90723 562-602-8004
Lynn Butler, prin. Fax 602-8005
Jackson MS 800/4-8
7220 Jackson St 90723 562-602-8020
Lisa Nunley, prin. Fax 602-8021
Paramount Community Day S 50/Alt
14507 Paramount Blvd 90723 562-602-8084
Richard Morgan, prin. Fax 602-8085
Paramount HS 3,600/10-12
14429 Downey Ave 90723 562-602-6064
Greg Buckner Ed.D., prin. Fax 602-6099
Paramount HS - West Campus 1,300/9-9
14708 Paramount Blvd 90723 562-602-8073
Morrie Kosareff, prin. Fax 602-8075
Paramount Park MS 800/6-8
14608 Paramount Blvd 90723 562-602-8052
Topekia Jones, prin. Fax 602-8053
Zamboni MS 900/6-8
15733 Orange Ave 90723 562-602-8048
Elizabeth Salcido, prin. Fax 602-8049
Paramount Adult Education Adult
14507 Paramount Blvd 90723 562-602-8080
Richard Morgan, prin. Fax 602-8081
Other Schools – See Lakewood

Infotech Career College Post-Sec.
8527 Alondra Blvd Ste 174 90723 562-804-1239
Marinello School of Beauty Post-Sec.
8527 Alondra Blvd Ste 129 90723 714-998-7461

Parlier, Fresno, Pop. 14,454
Parlier USD 3,200/K-12
900 S Newmark Ave 93648 559-646-2731
Esperanza Zendejas, supt. Fax 646-0626
www.parlierunified.org
Parlier HS 700/9-12
603 3rd St 93648 559-646-3573
Alberto Corrales, prin. Fax 646-2610
Parlier JHS 500/7-8
1200 E Parlier Ave 93648 559-646-1660
Homar Garza, prin. Fax 646-1633

Pasadena, Los Angeles, Pop. 132,725
Pasadena USD 18,900/K-12
351 S Hudson Ave 91101 626-396-3600
Jon Gundry, supt. Fax 795-5309
www.pusd.us/
Advance Path Academy Alt
325 S Oak Knoll Ave 91101 626-389-3855
Eric Sahakian, prin. Fax 683-9309

Blair HS 1,000/7-12
1201 S Marengo Ave 91106 626-396-5820
Trudell Skinner, prin. Fax 441-6148
Center for Independent Study 200/Alt
2925 E Sierra Madre Blvd 91107 626-396-5883
Jack Loos, dir. Fax 398-8793
Marshall Fundamental JSHS 1,900/6-12
990 N Allen Ave 91104 626-396-5810
Dr. Mark Anderson, prin. Fax 798-0643
Muir HS 1,100/9-12
1905 Lincoln Ave 91103 626-396-5600
Timothy Sippel, prin. Fax 791-3499
Pasadena HS 2,100/9-12
2925 E Sierra Madre Blvd 91107 626-798-8901
Dr. Gilbert Barraza, prin. Fax 798-1875
Roosevelt S 300/K-12
315 N Pasadena Ave 91103 626-396-5770
Juan Ruelas, prin. Fax 795-5180
Rose City HS 300/Alt
351 S Hudson Ave 91101 626-396-5620
Eric Sahakian, prin. Fax 683-9309
Washington MS 600/6-8
1505 N Marengo Ave 91103 626-396-5830
Dr. Merian Stewart, prin. Fax 798-2844
Wilson MS 700/6-8
300 Madre St 91107 626-396-5800
Sarah Rudchenko, prin. Fax 584-9895
Other Schools – See Altadena, Sierra Madre

AGBU Vatche & Tamar Manoukian HS 200/9-12
2495 E Mountain St 91104 626-794-0363
Dr. Talin Kargodorian, prin. Fax 240-0818
Art Center College of Design Post-Sec.
1700 Lida St 91103 626-396-2200
California Institute of Technology Post-Sec.
1200 E California Blvd 91125 626-395-6811
Fuller Theological Seminary Post-Sec.
135 N Oakland Ave 91182 626-584-5200
Huntington Memorial Hospital Post-Sec.
100 W California Blvd 91105 626-397-5000
LA Music Academy Post-Sec.
370 S Fair Oaks Ave 91105 626-568-8850
La Salle HS 700/9-12
3880 E Sierra Madre Blvd 91107 626-351-8951
Christopher Brady, prin. Fax 351-0275
Le Cordon Bleu College of Culinary Arts Post-Sec.
530 E Colorado Blvd 91101 626-229-1300
Maranatha HS 700/9-12
169 S Saint John Ave 91105 626-817-4000
Dr. Michelle Purghart, prin. Fax 817-4040
Mayfield Senior S 300/9-12
500 Bellefontaine St 91105 626-799-9121
Rita McBride, hdmstr. Fax 799-8576
North-West College Post-Sec.
530 E Union St 91101 626-796-5815
Pacific Oaks College Post-Sec.
55 Eureka St 91103 626-529-8061
Pasadena City College Post-Sec.
1570 E Colorado Blvd 91106 626-585-7123
Peace & Justice Academy 50/6-12
PO Box 51061 91115 626-345-0504
Randy Christopher, dir.
Polytechnic S 900/K-12
1030 E California Blvd 91106 626-396-6300
Deborah Reed, head sch Fax 796-2249
Providence Christian College Post-Sec.
1539 E Howard St 91104 866-323-0233
St. Monica Academy 200/1-12
301 N Orange Grove Blvd 91103 626-229-0351
Marguerite Grimm, hdmstr. Fax 229-0343
Westridge S 500/4-12
324 Madeline Dr 91105 626-799-1153
Elizabeth McGregor, head sch Fax 799-9236

Paso Robles, San Luis Obispo, Pop. 20,187
Paso Robles JUSD 6,700/K-12
PO Box 7010 93447 805-769-1000
Kathleen McNamara Ed.D., supt. Fax 237-3339
www.pasoschools.org/
Culinary Arts Academy Vo/Tech
PO Box 7010 93447 805-769-1133
Rodney Blackner, dir. Fax 237-3449
Flamson MS 700/6-8
PO Box 7010 93447 805-769-1400
Gene Miller, prin. Fax 237-3427
Independence HS 200/Alt
PO Box 7010 93447 805-769-1620
Wendy Nielsen, prin. Fax 237-3374
Lewis MS 700/6-8
PO Box 7010 93447 805-769-1450
Dr. Rick Oyler, prin. Fax 237-3458
Liberty Continuation HS 100/Alt
PO Box 7010 93447 805-769-1600
Wendy Nielsen, prin. Fax 237-3466
Paso Robles HS 2,000/9-12
PO Box 7010 93447 805-769-1500
Randall Nelson, prin. Fax 237-3424

ACTS Advanced Christian Training S 100/K-12
3025 Adelaida Rd 93446 805-239-0707
Dr. William Thompson, supt. Fax 238-1133

Patterson, Stanislaus, Pop. 19,584
Patterson JUSD 5,800/K-12
510 Keystone Blvd 95363 209-895-7700
Philip M. Alfano, supt. Fax 892-5803
www.patterson.k12.ca.us/
Creekside MS 1,100/6-8
535 Peregrine Dr 95363 209-892-4710
Shawn Posey, prin. Fax 892-7101
Del Puerto HS 100/Alt
640 M St 95363 209-892-4720
Tonya Bibbins, prin. Fax 892-3533
Patterson HS 1,700/9-12
200 N 7th St 95363 209-892-4750
David Stubbs, prin. Fax 892-7093

Patton, San Bernardino, Pop. 1,000

Patton State Hospital Post-Sec.
3102 E Highland Ave 92369 909-425-7297

Pearblossom, Los Angeles
Keppel UNESD 2,700/K-8
PO Box 186 93553 661-944-2155
Steve Doyle, supt. Fax 944-2933
www.keppel.k12.ca.us
Other Schools – See Littlerock

Pebble Beach, Monterey, Pop. 3,600

Stevenson Upper S 500/9-12
3152 Forest Lake Rd 93953 831-625-8300
Greg Foster, hdmstr. Fax 625-5208

Penn Valley, Nevada, Pop. 1,545
Pleasant Valley ESD 500/K-8
14806 Pleasant Valley Rd 95946 530-432-7311
Debra Sandoval, supt. Fax 432-7314
www.pennvalleyschools.k12.ca.us
Pleasant Valley S 300/4-8
14685 Pleasant Valley Rd 95946 530-432-7333
Teena Corker, prin. Fax 432-7338

Perris, Riverside, Pop. 66,780
Perris UNHSD 10,600/6-12
155 E 4th St 92570 951-943-6369
Dr. Jonathan Greenberg, supt. Fax 940-5378
www.puhsd.org
Academy Community Day S 100/Alt
515 E 7th St 92570 951-657-2174
Narciso Iglesias, prin. Fax 657-8102
Perris HS 2,500/9-12
175 E Nuevo Rd 92571 951-657-2171
Lynne Sheffield, prin. Fax 940-5717
Perris Lake HS 400/Alt
418 W Ellis Ave 92570 951-657-7357
Narciso Iglesias, prin. Fax 940-5305
Pinacate MS 1,200/7-8
1990 S A St 92570 951-943-6441
Charles Newman, prin. Fax 940-5344
Other Schools – See Menifee, Sun City

Val Verde USD 19,000/PK-12
975 Morgan St 92571 951-940-6100
Juan M. Lopez, supt. Fax 940-6121
www.valverde.edu
Citrus Hill HS 2,200/9-12
18150 Wood Rd 92570 951-490-0400
Juan Cabral, prin. Fax 490-0405
Lakeside MS 1,000/7-8
27720 Walnut St 92571 951-443-2440
John Parker, prin. Fax 443-2445
Rivera MS 1,100/6-8
21675 Martin St 92570 951-940-8570
Joshua Workman, prin Fax 940 6133
Val Verde Continuation HS 500/Alt
972 Morgan St 92571 951-940-6155
Dan Flower, prin Fax 940 6158
Other Schools – See Moreno Valley

Temple Christian S 100/PK-12
745 N Perris Blvd 92571 951-657-7326
Jim Carter, admin. Fax 657-5838

Pescadero, San Mateo, Pop. 633
La Honda-Pescadero USD 300/PK-12
PO Box 189 94060 650-879-0286
Amy Wooliever, supt. Fax 879-0816
www.lhpusd.com
Pescadero MSHS 100/6-12
PO Box 730 94060 650-879-0274
Patricia Talbot, prin. Fax 879-0589

Petaluma, Sonoma, Pop. 56,146
Petaluma SD 7,800/K-12
200 Douglas St 94952 707-778-4604
Steve Bolman, supt. Fax 778-4736
www.petalumacityschools.org
Carpe Diem HS 50/Alt
199 Fair St 94952 707-778-4796
Greg Stevenson, prin. Fax 762-7099
Casa Grande HS 1,800/9-12
333 Casa Grande Rd 94954 707-778-4677
Linda Scheele, prin. Fax 778-4687
Crossroads S 50/Alt
700 Bantam Way 94952 707-778-4793
Kenilworth JHS 1,000/7-8
800 Riesling Rd 94954 707-778-4710
Emily Dunnagan, prin. Fax 766-8231
Petaluma HS 1,300/9-12
201 Fair St 94952 707-778-4651
David Stirrat, prin. Fax 778-4767
Petaluma JHS 600/7-8
700 Bantam Way 94952 707-778-4724
Renee Semik, prin. Fax 778 4600
San Antonio HS 100/Alt
500 Vallejo St 94952 707-778-4758
Rusty Sims, prin. Fax 778-4899
Sonoma Mountain HS 50/Alt
299 Casa Grande Rd 94954 707-778-4738
Greg Stevenson, prin. Fax 778-1350
Valley Oaks Alternative S 100/Alt
540 Vallejo St 94952 707-778-4794
Rusty Sims, prin. Fax 778-4898
Petaluma Adult S Adult
200 Douglas St 94952 707-778-4633
Carol Waxman, prin. Fax 778-4785

St. Vincent de Paul HS 400/9-12
849 Keokuk St 94952 707-763-1032
John Walker, prin. Fax 763-9448
Santa Rosa Junior College Post-Sec.
680 Sonoma Mountain Pkwy 94954 707-778-2415

Petrolia, Humboldt
Mattole USD
Supt. — See Honeydew
Mattole Triple Junction HS 50/9-12
PO Box 211 95558 707-629-3250
Gail Dube, prin. Fax 629-3575

Phelan, San Bernardino, Pop. 13,933
Snowline JUSD 8,300/K-12
PO Box 296000 92329 760-868-5817
Eric Johnston, supt. Fax 868-5309
www.snowlineschools.com/
Chaparral HS 200/Alt
PO Box 296000 92329 760-868-5400
Dave Smith, prin. Fax 868-4725
Eagle Summit Community S 100/Alt
PO Box 296000 92329 760-868-3442
Dave Smith, coord. Fax 868-6402
Pinon Mesa MS 800/6-8
PO Box 296000 92329 760-868-3126
Burt Umstead, prin. Fax 868-3033
Quail Valley MS 1,000/6-8
PO Box 296000 92329 760-949-4888
Dennis Zimmerman, prin. Fax 949-3663
Serrano HS 2,500/9-12
PO Box 296000 92329 760-868-3222
Sharon Schlegel, prin. Fax 868-3803
Snowline Virtual S 100/Alt
PO Box 296000 92329 760-868-6277
Dave Smith, prin. Fax 868-4024

Pico Rivera, Los Angeles, Pop. 62,624
El Rancho USD 10,300/K-12
9333 Loch Lomond Dr 90660 562-942-1500
Norbert Genis, supt. Fax 949-2821
erusd.org
Burke MS 600/6-8
8101 Orange Ave 90660 562-801-5059
Elias Vargas, prin. Fax 801-5067
El Rancho HS 3,200/9-12
6501 Passons Blvd 90660 562-801-5295
Sam Genis, prin. Fax 801-5293
North Park MS 900/6-8
4450 Durfee Ave 90660 562-801-5137
Priscilla Rodriguez, prin. Fax 801-5143
Rivera MS 900/6-8
7200 Citronell Ave 90660 562-801-5088
Andrew Alvidrez, prin. Fax 801-9158
Salazar Continuation HS 200/Alt
9115 Balfour St 90660 562-801-5021
Reynaldo Reyes, prin. Fax 942-9458
El Rancho Education Center Adult
9515 Haney St 90660 562-801-5009
Charles Collings, prin. Fax 948-2041

Armenian Mesrobian S 200/PK-12
8420 Beverly Rd 90660 562-699-2057
David Ghoogasian, prin. Fax 699 0757

Piedmont, Alameda, Pop. 10,117
Piedmont City USD 2,600/K-12
760 Magnolia Ave 94611 510-594-2600
Constance Hubbard, supt. Fax 654-7374
www.piedmont.k12.ca.us
Millennium HS 100/Alt
760 Magnolia Ave 94611 510-594-2703
Ting Hsu Engelman, prin. Fax 594-2791
Piedmont HS 800/9-12
800 Magnolia Ave 94611 510-594-2626
Rich Kitchens, prin. Fax 450-0425
Piedmont MS 600/6-8
740 Magnolia Ave 94611 510-594-2660
Jeanne Donovan, prin. Fax 595-3523
Piedmont Adult S Adult
740 Magnolia Ave 94611 510-594-2655
Michael Brady, dir. Fax 595-8173

Pinecrest, Tuolumne
Summerville UNHSD
Supt. — See Tuolumne
Mountain HS 50/Alt
2 Pinecrest School Rd 95364 209-965-4046
David Johnstone, prin. Fax 928-1422

Pine Valley, San Diego, Pop. 1,469
Mountain Empire USD 2,000/PK-12
3291 Buckman Springs Rd 91962 619-473-9022
Steve VanZant, supt. Fax 473-9728
www.meusd.net
Mountain Empire HS 400/9-12
3305 Buckman Springs Rd 91962 619-473-8601
Ken Edwards, prin. Fax 473-8038
Pine Valley MS 100/6-8
PO Box 571 91962 619-473-8693
Barbara Cowling, prin. Fax 473-8026
Other Schools – See Jacumba

Pinole, Contra Costa, Pop. 17,432
West Contra Costa USD
Supt. — See Richmond
Pinole MS 400/7-8
1575 Mann Dr 94564 510-231-1436
Denise Van Hook, prin. Fax 724-9583
Pinole Valley HS 1,200/9-12
2900 Pinole Valley Rd 94564 510-758-4664
Sue Kahn, prin. Fax 758-6054

Pismo Beach, San Luis Obispo, Pop. 7,494
Lucia Mar USD
Supt. — See Arroyo Grande
Judkins MS 500/7-8
680 Wadsworth Ave 93449 805-474-3600
Ian Penton, prin. Fax 473-4376

Pittsburg, Contra Costa, Pop. 60,137
Pittsburg USD 10,800/PK-12
2000 Railroad Ave 94565 925-473-2300
Linda K. Rondeau, supt. Fax 473-4274
www.pittsburg.k12.ca.us

Black Diamond HS 300/Alt
1131 Stoneman Ave 94565 925-473-2510
Joseph Alvarez, prin.
Hillview JHS 1,200/6-8
333 Yosemite Dr 94565 925-473-2380
Anthony Molina, prin. Fax 473-4406
King JHS, 2012 Carion Ct 94565 800/6-8
Angela Stevenson, prin. 925-473-2500
Pittsburg HS 2,500/9-12
1750 Harbor St 94565 925-473-2390
Todd Whitmire, prin. Fax 473-4183
Rancho Medanos JHS 1,100/6-8
2301 Range Rd 94565 925-473-2490
Eric Peyko, prin. Fax 473-1060
Pittsburg Adult Education Center Adult
1151 Stoneman Ave 94565 925-473-4460
Robert Beck, prin. Fax 473-4470

Christian Center S 100/PK-12
1210 Stoneman Ave 94565 925-439-2552
Edward Marquardt, prin. Fax 439-2555
Los Medanos College Post-Sec.
2700 E Leland Rd 94565 925-439-2181

Pixley, Tulare, Pop. 3,289
Pixley UNESD 1,000/K-8
300 N School St 93256 559-757-5207
Dr. Keith Tomes, supt. Fax 757-0705
www.pixley.k12.ca.us/
Pixley MS 300/6-8
1520 E Court Ave 93256 559-757-3018
Monty Dunbar, prin. Fax 757-3507

Placentia, Orange, Pop. 49,404
Placentia-Yorba Linda USD 25,600/K-12
1301 E Orangethorpe Ave 92870 714-996-2550
Doug Domene, supt. Fax 524-3034
www.pylusd.org/
El Camino Real Continuation HS 300/Alt
1351 E Orangethorpe Ave 92870 714-986-7060
Gordon Chamberlin, prin. Fax 996-0294
El Dorado HS 2,200/9-12
1651 Valencia Ave 92870 714-986-7580
Cary Johnson, prin. Fax 524-2458
Kraemer MS 900/6-8
645 N Angelina Dr 92870 714-996-1551
Keith Carmona, prin. Fax 996-8407
Tuffree MS 800/7-8
2151 N Kraemer Blvd 92870 714-986-7480
Rosie Baldwin-Shirey, prin. Fax 993-6359
Valadez MS Academy 700/6-8
161 E La Jolla St 92870 714-986-7440
Minerva Gandara, prin. Fax 238-9159
Valencia HS 2,500/9-12
500 N Bradford Ave 92870 714-996-4970
Jim Bell, prin. Fax 996-3159
Other Schools – See Anaheim, Yorba Linda

Placerville, El Dorado, Pop. 10,089
El Dorado County Office of Education 800/
6767 Green Valley Rd 95667 530-622-7130
Vicki Barber Ed.D., supt. Fax 621-2543
www.edcoe.org
Golden Ridge S 50/Alt
6767 Green Valley Rd 95667 530-622-7130
Sue Roth, prin.
El Dorado COE Adult Education Adult
6767 Green Valley Rd 95667 530-295-0007
David Publicover, dir. Fax 621-1395
Other Schools – See South Lake Tahoe

El Dorado UNHSD 6,800/9-12
4675 Missouri Flat Rd 95667 530-622-5081
Christopher Hoffman, supt. Fax 642-0806
www.eduhsd.k12.ca.us
El Dorado HS 1,400/9-12
561 Canal St 95667 530-622-3634
Matthew Barnes, prin. Fax 622-1802
Vista HS 100/Alt
561 Canal St 95667 530-622-3634
Lara Clickner, prin. Fax 622-1802
Other Schools – See Diamond Springs, El Dorado, El Dorado Hills, Shingle Springs

Gold Oak UNESD 500/K-8
3171 Pleasant Valley Rd 95667 530-626-3150
Wendy Neade, supt. Fax 626-3145
www.gousd.org
Pleasant Valley MS 100/6-8
4120 Pleasant Valley Rd 95667 530-644-9620
Wendy Neade, prin. Fax 644-9622

Gold Trail UNESD 500/K-8
1575 Old Ranch Rd 95667 530-626-3194
Joe Murchison, supt. Fax 626-3199
www.gtusd.org
Gold Trail MS 300/4-8
889 Cold Springs Rd 95667 530-626-2595
Scott Lyons, head sch Fax 626-3289

Mother Lode UNESD 1,200/K-8
3783 Forni Rd 95667 530-622-6464
Tim Smith, supt. Fax 622-6163
www.mlusd.net
Green MS 600/5-8
3781 Forni Rd 95667 530-622-4668
Jason Harm, prin. Fax 622-4680

Placerville UNSD 1,300/K-8
1032 Thompson Way 95667 530-622-7216
Eric Bonniksen, supt. Fax 622-0336
www.pusdk8.us/
Markham MS 400/6-8
2800 Moulton Dr 95667 530-622-0403
Terry Edinger, prin. Fax 622-5584

Regional Occupational Center & Program
Supt. — None
Central Sierra ROP Vo/Tech
4675 Missouri Flat Rd 95667 530-621-0123
Carolyn Zachary, dir.

El Dorado Adventist S 200/K-12
1900 Broadway 95667 530-622-3560
Larry Ballew, prin. Fax 622-2604

Planada, Merced, Pop. 4,571
Le Grand UNHSD
Supt. — See Le Grand
Granada HS 50/Alt
PO Box 984 95365 209-382-0202
Randall Lapin M.A., prin. Fax 382-1443

Planada ESD 700/K-8
PO Box 236 95365 209-382-0756
Jose Gonzalez, supt. Fax 382-1750
www.planada.k12.ca.us/
Chavez MS 200/6-8
PO Box 236 95365 209-382-0768
Ildefonso Nava, prin. Fax 382-0775

Playa Del Rey, See Los Angeles

St. Bernard HS 300/9-12
9100 Falmouth Ave 90293 310-823-4651
Dr. Cynthia Hoepner, prin. Fax 827-3365

Pleasant Hill, Contra Costa, Pop. 31,678
Contra Costa County Office of Education 900/
77 Santa Barbara Rd 94523 925-942-3388
Dr. Joseph Ovick, supt. Fax 472-0875
www.cocoschools.org
Other Schools – See Martinez, Richmond

Mount Diablo USD
Supt. — See Concord
College Park HS 2,000/9-12
201 Viking Dr 94523 925-682-7670
Paul Gengler, prin. Fax 676-7892
Horizons 200/Alt
1 Santa Barbara Rd 94523 925-938-2564
Leyla Benson, admin. Fax 937-6271
Pleasant Hill MS 800/6-8
1 Santa Barbara Rd 94523 925-256-0791
Terry McCormick, prin. Fax 937-6271
Prospect HS 50/Alt
1 Santa Barbara Rd 94523 925-945-7902
Leyla Benson, admin. Fax 937-6271
Sequoia MS 900/6-8
265 Boyd Rd 94523 925-934-8174
Connie Cirimeli, prin. Fax 946-9063
Valley View MS 700/6-8
181 Viking Dr 94523 925-686-6136
Ean Ainsworth, prin. Fax 687-5381

Regional Occupational Center & Program
Supt. — None
Contra Costa County ROP Vo/Tech
77 Santa Barbara Rd 94523 925-942-3368
Janet Haun, dir. Fax 934-1057

Carrington College California Post-Sec.
380 Civic Dr Ste 300 94523 925-298-6299
Diablo Valley College Post-Sec.
321 Golf Club Rd 94523 925-685-1230
John F. Kennedy University Post-Sec.
100 Ellinwood Way 94523 925-969-3300
Pleasant Hill Adventist Academy 200/K-12
796 Grayson Rd 94523 925-934-9261
Alex Emmerson, prin. Fax 934-5871

Pleasanton, Alameda, Pop. 67,470
Pleasanton USD 14,900/K-12
4665 Bernal Ave 94566 925-462-5500
Parvin Ahmadi, supt. Fax 484-3591
www.pleasanton.k12.ca.us
Amador Valley HS 2,600/9-12
1155 Santa Rita Rd 94566 925-461-6100
Jim Hansen, prin. Fax 461-6133
Foothill HS 2,300/9-12
4375 Foothill Rd 94588 925-461-6650
John Dwyer, prin. Fax 461-6633
Hart MS 1,100/6-8
4433 Willow Rd 94588 925-426-3102
Terry Conde, prin. Fax 460-0799
Harvest Park MS 1,200/6-8
4900 Valley Ave 94566 925-426-4444
Ken Rocha, prin. Fax 426-9613
Pleasanton MS 1,200/6-8
5001 Case Ave 94566 925-426-4390
John Whitney, prin. Fax 426-1382
Village Continuation HS 200/Alt
4645 Bernal Ave 94566 925-426-4260
Greg Giglio, prin. Fax 426-8394

Plumas Lake, Yuba, Pop. 5,494
Plumas Lake ESD 1,000/K-8
2743 Plumas School Rd, 530-743-4428
Jeff Roberts, supt. Fax 743-1408
www.plusd.org
Riverside Meadows IS 300/6-8
1751 Cimarron Dr, 530-743-1271
Jason Hofhenke, prin. Fax 743-8970

Plymouth, Amador, Pop. 952
Amador County Office of Education
Supt. — See Jackson
County Community S 100/Alt
10010 Shenandoah Rd 95669 209-245-4284
Frank Wagner, prin. Fax 245-3864

Point Arena, Mendocino, Pop. 438
Point Arena SD 500/K-12
PO Box 87 95468 707-882-2803
Colleen Cross Ed.D., supt. Fax 882-2848
www.pointarenaschools.org
Point Arena HS 200/9-12
PO Box 7 95468 707-882-2134
Warren Galletti, prin. Fax 882-3453
South Coast Continuation HS 50/Alt
PO Box 87 95468 707-882-2307
Leah Martini, prin. Fax 882-2309

Pollock Pines, El Dorado, Pop. 6,676
Pollock Pines ESD 700/K-8
2701 Amber Trl 95726 530-644-5416
Kevin Monsma, supt. Fax 644-5483
www.ppesd.org
Sierra Ridge MS 300/5-8
2700 Amber Trl 95726 530-644-2031
Rich Callaghan, prin. Fax 644-0198

Pomona, Los Angeles, Pop. 146,537
Los Angeles County Office of Education
Supt. — See Downey
International Polytechnic HS 500/Alt
3801 W Temple Ave 91768 909-869-4567
Bruce Petersen, prin. Fax 869-2202

Pomona USD 26,100/PK-12
PO Box 2900 91769 909-397-4800
Richard Martinez, supt. Fax 397-4881
www.pusd.org
Diamond Ranch HS 1,800/9-12
100 Diamond Ranch Rd 91766 909-397-4715
S. Steinsefer-Ripley, prin. Fax 591-9374
Emerson MS 700/6-8
635 Lincoln Ave 91767 909-397-4516
Jesus Altamirano, prin. Fax 397-5280
Fremont Academy of Engineeing & Design 600/7-12
725 W Franklin Ave 91766 909-397-4521
Elizabeth Harper, prin. Fax 620-6229
Ganesha HS 1,400/9-12
1151 Fairplex Dr 91768 909-397-4400
Jennifer Francev, prin. Fax 629-4069
Garey HS 1,800/9-12
321 W Lexington Ave 91766 909-397-4451
Stacey Wilkins, prin. Fax 620-1575
Marshall MS 700/6-8
1921 Arroyo Ave 91768 909-397-4532
Silvestre Maravilla, prin. Fax 629-8275
Palomares Academy of Health Sciences 300/7-12
2211 N Orange Grove Ave 91767 909-397-4539
Reedy Wade, prin. Fax 625-0337
Park West HS 300/Alt
1460 E Holt Ave Ste 100 91767 909-397-4900
Neville Brown, prin. Fax 865-2423
Pomona Alternative S 50/Alt
1460 E Holt Ave Ste 100 91767 909-397-4900
Neville Brown, prin. Fax 865-2423
Pomona HS 1,500/9-12
475 Bangor St 91767 909-397-4498
Roger Fasting, prin. Fax 629-1410
Pueblo MS 200/8-8
1460 E Holt Ave Ste 100 91767 909-397-4900
Victor Torres, prin. Fax 622-4301
Simons MS 700/6-8
900 E Franklin Ave 91766 909-397-4544
Cristine Goens, prin. Fax 623-4691
Village Academy Vo/Tech
1444 E Holt Ave 91767 909-397-4900
Victor Torres, prin. Fax 865-9250
Pomona Adult & Career Education Adult
1515 W Mission Blvd 91766 909-469-2333
Enrique Medina, dir. Fax 623-3841
Other Schools – See Diamond Bar

Regional Occupational Center & Program
Supt. — None
San Antonio ROP Vo/Tech
1425 E Holt Ave Ste 101 91767 909-469-2304
Donna Clark, dir.

California State Polytechnic University Post-Sec.
3801 W Temple Ave 91768 909-869-7659
Carrington College California Post-Sec.
901 Corporate Center Dr 125 91768 877-206-2106
City of Knowledge S 200/K-12
3285 N Garey Ave 91767 909-392-0251
Dr. Haleema Shaikley, prin. Fax 392-0295
DeVry University Post-Sec.
901 Corporate Center Dr 91768 909-622-8866
North-West College Post-Sec.
134 W Holt Ave 91768 909-623-1552
Pomona Catholic HS 200/6-12
533 W Holt Ave 91768 909-623-5297
Samuel Torres, prin. Fax 620-6057
Western University of Health Sciences Post-Sec.
309 E 2nd St 91766 909-623-6116
Young People Corporation Academy 100/K-12
101 W Mission Blvd Ste 110 91766 909-802-2800
Candace Dean, dir. Fax 802-2031

Porterville, Tulare, Pop. 53,236
Burton ESD 4,400/K-12
264 N Westwood St 93257 559-781-8020
Dr. Sharon Kamberg, supt. Fax 781-1403
www.burtonschools.org
Burton Community Day S Alt
264 N Westwood St 93257 559-781-8020
Sergio Mendoza, dir.
Burton MS 600/7-8
1155 N Elderwood St 93257 559-781-2671
Dr. Michelle Pengilly, prin. Fax 788-6424

Pleasant View ESD 800/K-8
14004 Road 184 93257 559-784-6769
Mark Odsather, supt. Fax 784-6819
www.pleasant-view.k12.ca.us
Pleasant View West S 400/3-8
14004 Road 184 93257 559-784-6769
Mark Odsather, supt. Fax 784-6819

Porterville USD 13,700/K-12
600 W Grand Ave 93257 559-793-2400
John Snavely Ed.D., supt. Fax 793-1088
www.portervilleschools.org
Bartlett MS 500/7-8
600 W Grand Ave 93257 559-782-7100
Mike Tsuboi, prin. Fax 784-3432

Citrus Continuation HS 200/Alt
600 W Grand Ave 93257 559-782-7130
Magdalena Sanchez Ph.D., prin. Fax 782-3643
Granite Hills HS 1,100/9-12
600 W Grand Ave 93257 559-782-7075
Apolinar Marroquin, prin. Fax 789-9357
Monache HS 1,900/9-12
600 W Grand Ave 93257 559-782-7150
Richard Smithey, prin. Fax 781-3377
Pioneer MS 500/7-8
600 W Grand Ave 93257 559-782-7200
Angel Valdez, prin. Fax 784-3507
Porterville HS 1,800/9-12
600 W Grand Ave 93257 559-782-7210
Jose Valdez, prin. Fax 782-7215
Prospect Education Center 200/Alt
600 W Grand Ave 93257 559-782-7095
Jim Tyler, dir. Fax 781-6846
Sequoia MS 600/7-8
600 W Grand Ave 93257 559-788-0925
Joe Santos Ed.D., prin. Fax 788-0927
Vine Street Community Day S 50/Alt
600 W Grand Ave 93257 559-782-6650
Monty Newkirk, prin. Fax 782-6652
Porterville Adult S Adult
600 W Grand Ave 93257 559-782-7030
Fernando Carrera, dir. Fax 781-4943
Other Schools – See Strathmore

Regional Occupational Center & Program
Supt. — None
Tulare Co. Organization/Vocational Educ Vo/Tech
600 W Grand Ave 93257 559-793-2406
Melinda Brown, dir.

Porterville College Post-Sec.
100 E College Ave 93257 559-791-2200

Port Hueneme, Ventura, Pop. 20,969
Hueneme ESD 8,100/K-8
205 N Ventura Rd 93041 805-488-3588
Dr. Jerry Dannenberg, supt. Fax 986-8755
www.huensd.k12.ca.us
Other Schools – See Oxnard

Portola, Plumas, Pop. 2,059
Plumas USD
Supt. — See Quincy
Beckwourth HS 50/Alt
155 6th Ave 96122 530-832-4284
Aurora Westwood, prin. Fax 832-5582
Portola JSHS 200/7-12
155 6th Ave 96122 530-832-4284
Sara Sheridan, prin. Fax 832-5582

Portola Valley, San Mateo, Pop. 4,271
Portola Valley ESD 700/K-8
4575 Alpine Rd 94028 650-851-1777
Lisa Gonzales, supt. Fax 851-3700
www.pvsd.net
Corte Madera MS 400/4-8
4575 Alpine Rd 94028 650-851-1777
Michael Corritone, prin. Fax 529-8553

Woodside Priory HS 300/9-12
302 Portola Rd 94028 650-851-8221
Tim Molak, prin. Fax 851-2839
Woodside Priory MS 100/6-8
302 Portola Rd 94028 650-851-8221
Caitha Ambler, prin. Fax 851-2839

Potter Valley, Mendocino, Pop. 628
Potter Valley Community USD 200/K-12
PO Box 219 95469 707-743-2101
Nicole Glentzer, supt. Fax 743-1930
www.pottervalleyschools.us/
Centerville HS 50/Alt
PO Box 219 95469 707-743-1762
Yareli Macias, prin. Fax 743-2879
Potter Valley Community Day S 50/Alt
PO Box 219 95469 707-743-1115
Nicole Glentzer, prin. Fax 743-2879
Potter Valley JSHS 100/7-12
PO Box 219 95469 707-743-1142
Yareli Macias, prin. Fax 743-2879

Poway, San Diego, Pop. 46,170
Poway USD
Supt. — See San Diego
Abraxas Continuation HS 200/Alt
12450 Glenoak Rd 92064 858-748-5900
Ron Garrett, prin. Fax 679-1739
Meadowbrook MS 1,300/6-8
12320 Meadowbrook Ln 92064 858-748-0802
Miguel Carrillo, prin. Fax 679-0149
Poway HS 2,600/9-12
15500 Espola Rd 92064 858-748-0245
Scott Fisher, prin. Fax 679-6879
Twin Peaks MS 1,200/6-8
14640 Tierra Bonita Rd 92064 858-748-5131
Kelly Burke, prin. Fax 679-6823
Poway Adult S Adult
13626 Twin Peaks Rd 92064 858-668-4024
Kathleen Porter, dir. Fax 748-7423

Poway Academy of Hair Design Post-Sec.
13266 Poway Rd 92064 858-748-1490

Princeton, Colusa, Pop. 299
Princeton JUSD 200/K-12
PO Box 8 95970 530-439-2261
John Greene, supt. Fax 439-2113
www.pjusd.org
Princeton Community Day HS 50/Alt
PO Box 8 95970 530-439-2261
John Greene, prin. Fax 439-2113
Princeton JSHS 100/7-12
PO Box 8 95970 530-439-2261
John Greene, prin. Fax 439-2113

Prunedale, Monterey, Pop. 16,965

Prunedale Christian Academy 100/PK-12
8145 Prunedale North Rd 93907 831-663-2211
Dr. E.L. Moon, admin. Fax 663-1663

Quartz Hill, Los Angeles, Pop. 10,599
Antelope Valley UNHSD
Supt. — See Lancaster
Quartz Hill HS 3,200/9-12
6040 W Avenue L 93536 661-718-3100
Cheri Kreitz, prin. Fax 943-8203

Westside UNESD
Supt. — See Lancaster
Walker MS 800/7-8
5632 W Avenue L8 93536 661-943-3258
Christine Fitzgerald, prin. Fax 943-2969

Quincy, Plumas, Pop. 1,652
Plumas County Office of Education 50/
50 Church St 95971 530-283-6500
Bruce Williams, admin. Fax 283-6509
www.pcoe.k12.ca.us
Plumas County Community S 50/Alt
50 Church St 95971 530-283-6500
Bruce Williams, prin. Fax 283-6509
Plumas County Opportunity S 50/Alt
50 Church St 95971 530-283-6500
Bruce Williams, prin. Fax 283-6509

Plumas USD 2,000/K-12
50 Church St 95971 530-283-6500
Micheline Miglis, supt. Fax 283-6509
www.pcoe.k12.ca.us
Quincy JSHS 300/7-12
6 Quincy Junction Rd 95971 530-283-6510
Dr. Sue Segura, prin. Fax 283-6519
Other Schools – See Chester, Greenville, Portola

Regional Occupational Center & Program
Supt. — None
Plumas County ROP Vo/Tech
50 Church St Ste B 95971 530-283-6500
Terry Oestreich, dir. Fax 283-6509

Feather River College Post-Sec.
570 Golden Eagle Ave 95971 530-283-0202
Plumas Christian S 100/K-12
49 S Lindan Ave 95971 530-283-0415
John Sturley, prin. Fax 283-2933

Ramona, San Diego, Pop. 19,844
Ramona USD 6,100/K-12
720 9th St 92065 760-787-2000
Bob Graeff, supt. Fax 789-9168
www.ramonausd.net/
Montecito HS 100/Alt
720 9th St 92065 760-787-4300
Dave Lohman, prin. Fax 789-0928
Peirce MS 800/7-8
1521 Hanson Ln 92065 760-787-2400
Linda Solis, prin. Fax 788-5014
Ramona Community S 600/Alt
1010 Ramona St 92065 760-788-5130
Carol Tennebaum, prin. Fax 788-5918
Ramona HS 1,900/9-12
1401 Hanson Ln 92065 760-787-4000
Tony Newman, prin. Fax 789-4596

Rancho Cordova, Sacramento, Pop. 60,932
Folsom-Cordova USD 18,900/PK-12
1965 Birkmont Dr 95742 916-294-9000
Debbie Bettencourt, supt. Fax 294-9020
www.fcusd.org
Cordova HS 1,800/9-12
2239 Chase Dr 95670 916-294-2450
Dan Anklam, prin. Fax 294-9080
Kinney Continuation HS 200/Alt
2710 Kilgore Rd 95670 916-635-1292
Dana Carrigan, prin. Fax 635-0719
Mills MS 800/6-8
10439 Coloma Rd 95670 916-363-6544
Peter Maroon, prin. Fax 361-3744
Mitchell MS 800/6-8
2100 Zinfandel Dr 95670 916-635-8460
Mike Shepherd, prin. Fax 635-8979
Walnutwood Independent Study HS 200/Alt
10850 Gadsten Way 95670 916-638-2598
Charlie Linebarger, prin. Fax 635-6147
Folsom-Cordova Adult Education Adult
10850 Gadsten Way 95670 916-635-6810
Charlie Linebarger, prin. Fax 635-0905
Other Schools – See Folsom, Mather

California Northstate Coll of Pharmacy Post-Sec.
10811 International Dr 95670 916-631-8108
Heald College Post-Sec.
2910 Prospect Park Dr 95670 916-638-1616
ITT Technical Institute Post-Sec.
10863 Gold Center Dr 95670 916-851-3900
National Career Education Post-Sec.
11080 White Rock Rd Ste 100 95670 800-915-3593
San Joaquin Valley College Post-Sec.
11050 Olson Dr Ste 210 95670 916-638-7582

Rancho Cucamonga, San Bernardino, Pop. 159,896
Central ESD 4,800/K-8
10601 Church St Ste 112 91730 909-989-8541
Donna Libutti, supt. Fax 941-1732
www.csd.k12.ca.us/
Cucamonga MS 900/6-8
7611 Hellman Ave 91730 909-987-1788
Jeff Koenig, prin. Fax 483-3201
Musser MS 1,000/5-8
10789 Terra Vista Pkwy 91730 909-980-1230
Mary Kate Perez, prin. Fax 980-3042

Chaffey JUNHSD
Supt. — See Ontario
Los Osos HS 3,400/9-12
6001 Milliken Ave 91737 909-477-6900
Susan Petrocelli, prin. Fax 460-5872
Rancho Cucamonga HS 3,200/9-12
11801 Lark Dr 91701 909-989-1600
Dr. Virginia Kelsen, prin. Fax 945-5355

Cucamonga ESD 2,700/K-8
8776 Archibald Ave 91730 909-987-8942
Janet Temkin, supt. Fax 980-3628
www.cuca.k12.ca.us
Rancho Cucamonga MS 900/6-8
8776 Archibald Ave 91730 909-980-0969
Bruce LaVallee, prin. Fax 481-5381

Regional Occupational Center & Program
Supt. — None
Baldy View ROP Vo/Tech
8265 Aspen St Ste 100 91730 909-980-6490
Jose Castro, supt. Fax 980-8364

San Bernardino Co. Office of Education
Supt. — See San Bernardino
West End Community S 200/Alt
8265 Aspen St 91730 909-433-4621
Bernadine Hollingsworth, dir.

Chaffey College Post-Sec.
5885 Haven Ave 91737 909-652-6000
San Joaquin Valley College Post-Sec.
10641 Church St 91730 909-948-7582
Universal Technical Institute Post-Sec.
9494 Haven Ave 91730 909-484-1929
Upland Christian Academy 400/K-12
10900 Civic Center Dr 91730 909-758-8747
Tim Hoy, supt. Fax 204-4555

Rancho Mirage, Riverside, Pop. 16,964

Eisenhower Memorial Hospital Post-Sec.
39000 Bob Hope Dr 92270 760-340-3911
Marywood-Palm Valley S 400/PK-12
35525 Da Vall Dr 92270 760-328-0861
Robert Graves, head sch Fax 770-4541
Santa Barbara Business College Post-Sec.
34275 Monterey Ave 92270 866-749-7222

Rancho Palos Verdes, Los Angeles, Pop. 39,919
Los Angeles USD
Supt. — See Los Angeles
Dodson MS 1,800/6-8
28014 S Montereina Dr 90275 310-241-1900
John Vladovic, prin. Fax 832-4709

Palos Verdes Peninsula USD
Supt. — See Palos Verdes Estates
Miraleste IS 900/6-8
29323 Palos Verdes Dr E 90275 310-732-0900
Beth Hadley, prin. Fax 521-8915
Ridgecrest IS 1,000/6-8
28915 Northbay Rd 90275 310-544-2747
Brent Kuykendall, prin. Fax 265-1716

Marymount College Post-Sec.
30800 Palos Verdes Dr E 90275 310-377-5501
Salvation Army College Officer Training Post-Sec.
30840 Hawthorne Blvd 90275 310 377-0481

Rancho Santa Fe, San Diego, Pop. 3,061
Rancho Sante Fe ESD 700/K-8
PO Box 809 92067 858-756-1141
Lindy Delaney, supt. Fax 756-0912
www.rsfschool.net/
Rowe MS 200/7-8
PO Box 809 92067 858-756-1141
Lindy Delaney, prin. Fax 759-0712

Rancho Santa Margarita, Orange, Pop. 46,094
Capistrano USD
Supt. — See San Juan Capistrano
Las Flores MS 1,200/6-8
25862 Antonio Pkwy 92688 949-589-6543
Robert Miller, prin. Fax 589-9286
Tesoro HS 2,500/9-12
1 Tesoro Creek Rd 92688 949-234-5310
Marc Patterson, prin. Fax 766-3370

Saddleback Valley USD
Supt. — See Mission Viejo
Rancho Santa Margarita IS 1,600/7-8
21931 Alma Aldea 92688 949-459-8253
Rick Jameson, prin. Fax 459-8258

Rancho Viejo Montessori S 100/PK-10
29782 Ave De Las Banderas 92688 949-459-0199
Deborah Warkentien, head sch Fax 459-0299
Santa Margarita HS 1,600/9-12
22062 Antonio Pkwy 92688 949-766-6000
Ray Dunne, prin. Fax 766-6005

Raymond, Madera
Yosemite USD
Supt. — See Oakhurst
Raymond Granite HS 50/Alt
PO Box 228 93653 559-689-3490
Dr. Randy Haggard, prin.

Red Bluff, Tehama, Pop. 13,607
Antelope ESD 600/K-8
22630 Antelope Blvd 96080 530-527-1272
Todd Brose, supt. Fax 527-2931
www.antelopeschools.org/
Berrendos MS 200/6-8
401 Chestnut Ave 96080 530-527-6700
Steve Prinz, prin. Fax 527-2506

Red Bluff JUNHSD 1,800/7-12
PO Box 1507 96080 530-529-8700
Lisa Escobar, supt. Fax 529-8709
www.rbuhsd.k12.ca.us/district/
Rebound S 50/Alt
PO Box 1507 96080 530-529-8987
Patrick Gleason, prin. Fax 529-8739
Red Bluff HS 1,600/9-12
1260 Union St 96080 530-529-8710
Patrick Gleason, prin. Fax 529-8739
Salisbury HS 100/Alt
1050 Kimball Rd 96080 530-529-8766
Barbara Thomas, prin. Fax 529-8840

Red Bluff UNESD 2,200/K-8
1755 Airport Blvd 96080 530-527-7200
William McCoy, supt. Fax 527-9308
www.rbuesd.org
Vista MS 400/7-8
1770 S Jackson St 96080 530-527-7840
Isaac Scharaga, prin. Fax 527-9374

Regional Occupational Center & Program
Supt. — None
Tehama County ROP Vo/Tech
PO Box 689 96080 530-528-7341
Larry Champion, admin. Fax 529-4120

Mercy HS 100/9-12
233 Riverside Way 96080 530-527-8314
Paul Weber, prin. Fax 527-3058

Redding, Shasta, Pop. 86,489
Columbia ESD 900/PK-8
10140 Old Oregon Trl 96003 530-223-1915
Clay Ross, supt. Fax 223-4168
www.columbiasd.com
Mountain View MS 400/5-8
675 Shasta View Dr 96003 530-221-6224
Shannon Angstadt, prin. Fax 221-5620

Enterprise ESD 3,500/PK-8
1155 Mistletoe Ln 96002 530-224-4100
Brian Winstead Ed.D., supt. Fax 224-4101
www.eesd.net/
Parsons JHS 600/6-8
750 Hartnell Ave 96002 530-224-4190
Cheryl Olson, prin. Fax 224-4191

Gateway USD 3,800/K-12
4411 Mountain Lakes Blvd 96003 530-245-7900
James Harrell, supt. Fax 245-7920
www.gateway-schools.org
Gateway Educational Options 100/Alt
3500 Tamarack Dr 96003 530-245-7960
Ryan Johnson, prin. Fax 245-7963
Other Schools – See Central Valley, Shasta Lake

Pacheco UNESD 600/K-8
7424 Pacheco School Rd 96002 530-224-4585
Jason Provence, supt. Fax 224-4588
www.pacheco.k12.ca.us
Pacheco MS 400/4-8
7430 Pacheco School Rd 96002 530-224-4585
Jason Provence, prin. Fax 224-4588
Other Schools – See Anderson

Redding ESD 3,300/K-12
5885 E Bonnyview Rd 96001 530-225-0011
Rick Fauss, supt. Fax 225-0015
www.reddingschools.net/
Sequoia MS 800/4-8
5885 E Bonnyview Rd 96001 530-225-0020
Cass Ditzler, prin. Fax 225-0029

Regional Occupational Center & Program
Supt. — None
Shasta-Trinity ROP Vo/Tech
4659 Eastside Rd 96001 530-246-3302
Charlie Hoffman, supt. Fax 246-3306

Shasta County Office of Education 200/
1644 Magnolia Ave 96001 530-225-0200
Tom Armelino, supt. Fax 225-0329
www.shastacoe.org
Magnolia Independent Learning Center 7-12
1524 Magnolia Ave 96001 530-225-0163
Debbie Livingston, prin. Fax 225-0216
Oasis Community S Alt
3711 Oasis Rd 96003 530-225-0360
Debbie Livingston, prin. Fax 225-0366
Shasta County Opportunity S 50/Alt
1644 Magnolia Ave 96001 530-225-0361
Debbie Livingston, prin. Fax 225-0391

Shasta UNHSD 5,900/6-12
2200 Eureka Way Ste B 96001 530-241-3261
Jim Cloney, supt. Fax 225-8499
www.suhsd.net
Enterprise HS 1,300/9-12
3411 Churn Creek Rd 96002 530-222-6601
Eric Peterson, prin. Fax 222-5138
Enterprise Plus HS 50/Alt
3411 Churn Creek Rd 96002 530-245-2714
Elsbeth Prigmore, prin. Fax 222-5138
Freedom HS 50/Alt
590 Mary St 96001 530-245-2660
Guy Malain, prin. Fax 245-2661
North State Independence HS 200/Alt
2200 Eureka Way Ste B 96001 530-245-2760
Kyle Turner, admin. Fax 245-2761
Pioneer Continuation HS 200/Alt
2650 8th St 96001 530-243-1880
Elsbeth Prigmore, prin. Fax 243-0753
Shasta HS 1,600/9-12
2500 Eureka Way 96001 530-241-4161
Milan Woollard, prin. Fax 241-9571
Shasta Plus HS 50/Alt
2500 Eureka Way 96001 530-245-2716
Elsbeth Prigmore, prin. Fax 241-9571

Shasta Adult S Adult
590 Mary St 96001 530-245-2626
Guy Malain, prin. Fax 245-2682
Other Schools – See Palo Cedro

Institute of Technology - Redding Campus Post-Sec.
1755 Hilltop Dr 96002 530-224-1000
Liberty Christian S 200/PK-12
3782 Churn Creek Rd 96002 530-222-2232
Daniel Curry, supt. Fax 222-1784
Redding Adventist Academy 100/K-12
1356 E Cypress Ave 96002 530-222-1018
Wayne Gungl, prin. Fax 222-4260
Shasta Bible College & Graduate School Post-Sec.
2951 Goodwater Ave 96002 530-221-4275
Shasta College Post-Sec.
PO Box 496006 96049 530-242-7500
Simpson University Post-Sec.
2211 College View Dr 96003 530-224-5600

Redlands, San Bernardino, Pop. 66,575
Redlands USD 21,400/K-12
PO Box 3008 92373 909-307-5300
Lori Rhodes, supt. Fax 748-6711
www.redlands.k12.ca.us
Citrus Valley HS 1,700/9-12
PO Box 3008 92373 909-799-2300
Bernie Cavanagh, prin. Fax 799-2349
Clement MS 1,000/6-8
501 E Pennsylvania Ave 92374 909-307-5400
Robert Clarey, prin. Fax 307-5414
Cope MS 1,300/6-8
1000 W Cypress Ave 92373 909-307-5420
Kate Pearne, prin. Fax 307-5436
Moore MS 1,200/6-8
1550 E Highland Ave 92374 909-307-5440
Jamie Cortz, prin. Fax 307-5453
Orangewood HS 300/Alt
515 Texas St 92374 909-307-5380
Carol Ruhm, prin. Fax 307-5384
Redlands East Valley HS 2,600/9-12
31000 Colton Ave 92374 909-389-2500
John Maloney, prin. Fax 389-2517
Redlands HS 2,800/9-12
840 E Citrus Ave 92374 909-307-5500
Christina Rivera, prin. Fax 307-5524
Other Schools – See Highland

Regional Occupational Center & Program
Supt. — None
Colton-Redlands-Yucaipa ROP Vo/Tech
1214 Indiana Ct 92374 909-793-3115
Stephanie Houston, supt. Fax 793-6901

Arrowhead Christian Academy 400/7-12
105 Tennessee St 92373 909-793-0601
Daniel Cole, head sch Fax 792-5691
Citrus Valley Christian Academy 100/1-12
PO Box 8037 92375 909-556-7201
Cheryl Van Gelder, admin.
Community Christian College Post-Sec.
251 Tennessee St 92373 909-335-8863
Hands-On Medical Massage School Post-Sec.
2015 W Park Ave Ste 7 92373 909-793-4263
Packinghouse Christian Academy 200/K-12
27165 San Bernardino Ave 92374 909-793-4984
Steve Hicok, prin. Fax 307-1852
Redlands Adventist Academy 400/K-12
130 Tennessee St 92373 909-793-1000
Linda Woolley, prin. Fax 793-9862
University of Redlands Post-Sec.
PO Box 3080 92373 909-793-2121

Redondo Beach, Los Angeles, Pop. 63,466
Redondo Beach Unified SD 8,400/K-12
1401 Inglewood Ave 90278 310-379-5449
Steven Keller Ed.D., supt. Fax 798-8610
www.rbusd.org
Adams MS 900/6-8
2600 Ripley Ave 90278 310-798-8636
Anthony Taranto, prin. Fax 318-3064
Parras MS 900/6-8
200 N Lucia Ave 90277 310-798-8616
Dr. Lars Nygren, prin. Fax 798-8620
Redondo Shores HS 100/Alt
1000 Del Amo St 90277 310-798-8690
Dr. Erin Simon, prin. Fax 798-5287
Redondo Union HS 2,500/9-12
1 Sea Hawk Way 90277 310-798-8665
Dr. Nicole Wesley, prin. Fax 798-4685
South Bay Adult S Adult
3401 Inglewood Ave 90278 310-937-3340
Vivian Ibarra, dir. Fax 937-3345

South Bay Faith Academy 500/K-12
PO Box 7000 90277 310-379-8242
Clifford Constable, pres.

Redwood City, San Mateo, Pop. 73,481
Redwood City ESD 9,100/PK-8
750 Bradford St 94063 650-423-2200
Jan Christensen, supt. Fax 423-2204
www.rcsdk8.net
Kennedy MS 800/6-8
2521 Goodwin Ave 94061 650-365-4611
Charles Krause, prin. Fax 367-4362
McKinley Institute of Technology 400/6-8
400 Duane St 94062 650-366-3827
Ray Dawley, prin. Fax 367-4363
North Star Academy 500/3-8
400 Duane St 94062 650-482-5973
Leslie Crane, prin. Fax 482-5980

Regional Occupational Center & Program
Supt. — None
San Mateo County ROP Vo/Tech
101 Twin Dolphin Dr 94065 650-802-5411
Ken San Filippo, dir. Fax 802-5414

San Mateo County Office of Education 200/
101 Twin Dolphin Dr 94065 650-802-5550
Anne Campbell, supt. Fax 802-5564
www.smcoe.k12.ca.us
Other Schools – See San Mateo

Sequoia UNHSD 8,700/9-12
480 James Ave 94062 650-369-1411
James Lianides, supt. Fax 306-8870
www.seq.org
Middle College HS 11-12
4200 Farm Hill Blvd 94061 650-306-3120
Fax 306-3128
Redwood HS 400/Alt
1968 Old County Rd 94063 650-369-1411
Frank Wells, prin. Fax 261-0213
Sequoia HS 1,900/9-12
1201 Brewster Ave 94062 650-367-9780
Bonnie Hansen, prin. Fax 368-5180
Other Schools – See Atherton, Belmont, East Palo Alto, Menlo Park, Woodside

Canada College Post-Sec.
4200 Farm Hill Blvd 94061 650-306-3100

Redwood Valley, Mendocino, Pop. 1,695
Ukiah USD
Supt. — See Ukiah
Eagle Peak MS 400/5-8
8601 West Rd 95470 707-485-8154
Dan Stearns, prin. Fax 485-9542

Deep Valley Christian S 100/PK-12
PO Box 9 95470 707-485-8778
Euline Olinger, admin. Fax 485-9362

Reedley, Fresno, Pop. 23,944
Kings Canyon JUSD 9,900/PK-12
675 W Manning Ave 93654 559-305-7010
Juan Garza, supt. Fax 637-1292
www.kcusd.com
Grant MS 500/6-8
360 N East Ave 93654 559-305-7330
Monica Benner, prin. Fax 638-6772
Mountain View S 400/Alt
477 W Manning Ave 93654 559-305-7080
Keith Merrihew, dir. Fax 637-7778
Navelencia MS 300/6-8
22620 Wahtoke Ave 93654 559-305-7350
Victor Martinez, prin. Fax 637-1316
Reedley HS 1,900/9-12
740 W North Ave 93654 559-305-7100
Rodney Cisneros, prin. Fax 637-0458
Reedly Middle College HS 9-12
675 W Manning Ave 93654 559-305-7010
Lori Botkin, prin. Fax 637-1292
Kings Canyon Adult S Adult
675 W Manning Ave 93654 559-305-7085
Keith Merrihew, dir. Fax 637-9486
Other Schools – See Dinuba, Orange Cove

Immanuel S 500/K-12
1128 S Reed Ave 93654 559-638-2529
Phil Goertzen, prin. Fax 638-7030
Reedley College Post-Sec.
995 N Reed Ave 93654 559-638-3641

Rescue, El Dorado
Rescue UNESD 4,100/K-8
2390 Bass Lake Rd 95672 530-677-4461
David Swart, supt. Fax 677-0719
www.rescueusd.org
Pleasant Grove MS 600/6-8
2540 Green Valley Rd 95672 530-672-4400
Dave Scroggins, prin. Fax 677-5829
Other Schools – See El Dorado Hills

Reseda, See Los Angeles
Los Angeles USD
Supt. — See Los Angeles
Cleveland HS 3,900/9-12
8140 Vanalden Ave 91335 818-885-2300
Herman Clay, prin. Fax 727-0964
Grey Continuation S 200/Alt
18230 Kittridge St 91335 818-758-3769
Harold Starr, prin. Fax 758-3714
Reseda HS 2,000/9-12
18230 Kittridge St 91335 818-758-3600
Jose Rodriguez, prin. Fax 776-0452
Sherman Oaks Ctr for Enriched Studies 2,100/4-12
18605 Erwin St 91335 818-758-5600
Judith Anderson-Henderso, prin. Fax 344-5909
Wooden HS 100/Alt
18741 Elkwood St 91335 818-345-0203
Jason Garrison, prin. Fax 996-9008
Reseda Adult Education Adult
18230 Kittridge St 91335 818-758-3700
Andrea Rodriguez, prin. Fax 758-3719

Everest College Post-Sec.
18040 Sherman Way Ste 400 91335 818-774-0550
Marinello School of Beauty Post-Sec.
18442 Sherman Way 91335 818-881-2521

Rialto, San Bernardino, Pop. 97,244
Rialto USD 27,000/K-12
182 E Walnut Ave 92376 909-820-7700
Dr. Harold Cebrun, supt. Fax 873-0448
www.rialto.k12.ca.us
Carter HS 2,500/9-12
2630 N Linden Ave 92377 909-854-4100
Christine Foote, prin. Fax 574-7313
Eisenhower HS 2,400/9-12
1321 N Lilac Ave 92376 909-820-7777
Arthur Sanchez, prin. Fax 421-7640
Frisbie MS 1,100/6-8
1442 N Eucalyptus Ave 92376 909-820-7887
Akinlana Osonduagwuike, prin. Fax 820-7885

Kolb MS 1,000/6-8
2351 N Spruce Ave 92377 909-820-7849
Dr. Monique Means, prin. Fax 875-0374
Kucera MS 1,300/6-8
2140 W Buena Vista Dr 92377 909-421-7662
Monique Conway, prin. Fax 421-7681
Milor Continuation HS 400/Alt
266 W Randall Ave 92376 909-820-7785
Amanda McLeod-Weiser, prin. Fax 421-7617
Rialto HS 3,000/9-12
595 S Eucalyptus Ave 92376 909-421-7500
Albert Castillo, prin. Fax 421-7584
Rialto MS 1,500/6-8
1262 W Rialto Ave 92376 909-879-7308
Arnie Ayala, prin. Fax 877-4893
Zupanic HS 200/Alt
266 W Randall Ave 92376 909-820-7955
Amanda McLeod-Weiser, admin. Fax 421-7617
Rialto Adult S Adult
595 S Eucalyptus Ave 92376 909-879-6010
Peggy Wheeler, dir. Fax 879-6011
Other Schools – See Colton

San Bernardino Co. Office of Education
Supt. — See San Bernardino
Murphy County Community S 100/Alt
149 N Arrowhead Ave 92376 909-421-7814
Bernadine Hollingsworth, dir.

Richmond, Contra Costa, Pop. 99,595
Contra Costa County Office of Education
Supt. — See Pleasant Hill
Contra Costa Adult S Adult
5555 Giant Hwy 94806 510-262-4340
Tom Scruggs, prin. Fax 262-4343

West Contra Costa USD 25,700/PK-12
1108 Bissell Ave 94801 510-231-1100
Bruce Harter, supt. Fax 236-6784
www.wccusd.net
De Anza HS 600/9-12
5000 Valley View Rd 94803 510-223-3811
Robert Evans, prin. Fax 223-7984
DeJean MS 300/7-8
3400 MacDonald Ave 94805 510-231-1430
Sylvia Greenwood, prin. Fax 236-6680
Gompers Continuation HS 100/Alt
715 Chanslor Ave 94801 510-231-1402
Latoya Williams, prin. Fax 234-8128
Kennedy HS 700/9-12
4300 Cutting Blvd 94804 510-231-1433
Roxanne Brown-Garcia, prin. Fax 235-1915
Richmond HS 1,300/9-12
1250 23rd St 94804 510-237-8770
Julio Franco, prin. Fax 235-0316
West CC Adult Ed - Serra Adult
6028 Ralston Ave 94805 510-215-4666
Raul Ramirez, prin. Fax 215-0430
West Contra Costa Adult Educ - Alvarado Adult
5626 Suttor Ave 94804 510-559-2660
Raul Ramirez, prin. Fax 559-2664
Other Schools – See El Cerrito, El Sobrante, Hercules, Pinole, San Pablo

---

Kaiser Permanente Medical Center Post-Sec.
901 Nevin Ave 94801 510-307-2412
Salesian HS 600/9-12
2851 Salesian Ave 94804 510-234-4434
Tim Chambers, prin. Fax 236-4636

Ridgecrest, Kern, Pop. 26,434
Sierra Sands USD 5,200/K-12
113 W Felspar Ave 93555 760-499-1600
Joanna Rummer, supt. Fax 375-3338
www.ssusdschools.org
Burroughs HS 1,500/9-12
500 E French Ave 93555 760-499-1800
Dave Ostash, prin. Fax 375-1735
Mesquite Continuation HS 100/Alt
140 Drummond Ave 93555 760-499-1810
Shirley Kennedy, prin. Fax 446-3328
Monroe MS 500/6-8
340 W Church Ave 93555 760-499-1830
Clara Finneran, prin. Fax 375-8781
Murray MS 600/6-8
921 E Inyokern Rd 93555 760-446-5525
Kirsti Smith, prin. Fax 446-3838
Sierra Sands Adult S Adult
1327 N Norma St Ste 143 93555 760-499-1725
Ernie Bell, prin. Fax 446-1391

Cerro Coso Community College Post-Sec.
3000 College Heights Blvd 93555 760-384-6100
Immanuel Christian S 200/PK-12
201 W Graaf Ave 93555 760-446-6114
Scott Johnson, prin. Fax 446-7035

Rio Dell, Humboldt, Pop. 3,219
Rio Dell ESD 300/K-8
95 Center St 95562 707-764-5694
Mary Varner, supt. Fax 764-2656
riodell.schoolwires.com
Monument MS 100/6-8
95 Center St 95562 707-764-3783
Chris Byrne, prin. Fax 764-2656

Rio Linda, Sacramento, Pop. 14,536
Twin Rivers USD
Supt. — See Mc Clellan
Rio Linda HS 1,900/9-12
6309 Dry Creek Rd 95673 916-566-2725
Ed Delgado, prin. Fax 263-6462
Rio Linda Preparatory Academy 600/5-8
1101 G St 95673 916-566-2720
Maria Sevilla, prin. Fax 263-4674

Rio Vista, Solano, Pop. 7,140
River Delta USD 1,600/K-12
445 Montezuma St 94571 707-374-1700
Richard Hennes, supt. Fax 374-2995
riverdelta.org
Rio Vista HS 300/9-12
410 S 4th St 94571 707-374-6336
Vicky Turk, prin. Fax 374-6810
River Delta S 50/Alt
525 S 2nd St 94571 707-374-1730
Pierre Laleau, prin. Fax 374-5623
Riverview MS 200/6-8
525 S 2nd St 94571 707-374-2345
Pierre Laleau, prin. Fax 374-5623
Wind River Adult S Adult
445 Montezuma St Ste B 94571 707-374-1723
Pierre Laleau, prin. Fax 374-1723
Other Schools – See Clarksburg, Courtland

Ripon, San Joaquin, Pop. 13,864
Ripon USD 3,100/K-12
304 N Acacia Ave 95366 209-599-2131
Dr. Louise Johnson, supt. Fax 599-6271
www.riponusd.net
Ripon HS 900/9-12
301 N Acacia Ave 95366 209-599-4287
Lance Morrow, prin. Fax 599-6410
Ripon Adult S Adult
304 N Acacia Ave 95366 209-599-2131
Kathy Coleman, prin.

Ripon Christian HS 200/9-12
435 Maple Ave 95366 209-599-2155
Kerry Manus, supt. Fax 599-2170

Riverbank, Stanislaus, Pop. 22,058
Riverbank USD 2,200/K-12
6715 7th St 95367 209-869-2538
Dr. Daryl Camp, supt. Fax 869-1487
www.riverbank.k12.ca.us
Adelante Continuation HS 100/Alt
6200 Claus Rd 95367 209-869-2383
Karen Young, prin. Fax 869-7433
Cardozo MS 500/6-8
3525 Santa Fe St 95367 209-869-2591
Kevin Bizzini, prin. Fax 869-2714
Riverbank HS 700/9-12
6200 Claus Rd 95367 209-869-1891
Diana Jimenez, prin. Fax 869-2116

Riverdale, Fresno, Pop. 3,092
Riverdale JUSD 1,500/K-12
PO Box 1058 93656 559-867-8200
Pete Faragia, supt. Fax 867-6722
www.rjusd.org
Horizon HS 50/Alt
PO Box 726 93656 559-867-3614
Jeff Moore, prin. Fax 867-4575
Riverdale ES 500/4-8
PO Box 338 93656 559-867-3589
Mark Allein, prin. Fax 867-3393
Riverdale HS 500/9-12
PO Box 726 93656 559-867-3562
Jeff Moore, prin. Fax 867-4750

Riverside, Riverside, Pop. 295,499
Alvord USD 20,200/K-12
10365 Keller Ave 92505 951-509-5070
Nicolas Ferguson, supt. Fax 509-6070
www.alvord.k12.ca.us
Alvord Continuation HS 200/Alt
10365 Keller Ave 92505 951-358-1715
Laura Roy, prin. Fax 358-1716
Arizona MS 1,200/6-8
10365 Keller Ave 92505 951-358-1675
Traci Matela, prin. Fax 358-1676
Hillcrest HS 500/9-12
10365 Keller Ave 92505 951-358-1755
Scott Wilbur, prin. Fax 358-1756
La Sierra HS 3,300/9-12
10365 Keller Ave 92505 951-358-1725
Will Mynster, prin. Fax 358-1726
Loma Vista MS 1,100/6-8
10365 Keller Ave 92505 951-358-1685
Sherri Duckworth-Kemp, prin. Fax 358-1686
Norte Vista HS 2,300/9-12
10365 Keller Ave 92505 951-358-1740
Susan Boyd, prin. Fax 358-1741
Villegas MS 1,400/6-8
10365 Keller Ave 92505 951-358-1695
Julie Koehler-Mount, prin. Fax 358-1696
Wells MS 1,000/6-8
10365 Keller Ave 92505 951-358-1705
David Ferguson, prin. Fax 358-1706

Jurupa USD 20,100/K-12
4850 Pedley Rd 92509 951-360-4100
Elliott Duchon, supt. Fax 360-4194
www.jusd.k12.ca.us
Jurupa MS 1,200/7-8
8700 Galena St 92509 951-360-2846
Josh Lewis, prin. Fax 360-8928
Mira Loma MS 900/7-8
5051 Steve Ave 92509 951-360-2883
Andrew Huben, prin. Fax 685-7405
Mission MS 1,000/7-8
5961 Mustang Ln 92509 951-222-7842
Jose Araux, prin. Fax 369-1407
Nueva Vista Continuation HS 300/Alt
6836 34th St 92509 951-360-2802
Mike Chalmers, prin. Fax 360-0928
Patriot HS 2,400/9-12
4355 Camino Real 92509 951-361-6500
Roberta Pace, prin. Fax 361-6526
Rio Vista Continuation HS 50/Alt
6836 34th St 92509 951-360-2818
Mike Chalmers, prin. Fax 360-2723

Rubidoux HS 1,700/9-12
4250 Opal St 92509 951-222-7700
Trenton Hansen, prin. Fax 275-0079
Steps Community Day S 100/Alt
4041 Pacific Ave 92509 951-222-7739
Michael West, prin. Fax 788-8689
Adult Education Adult
4041 Pacific Ave 92509 951-222-7739
Mike West, prin. Fax 788-8689
Other Schools – See Mira Loma

Regional Occupational Center & Program
Supt. — None
Riverside County ROP Vo/Tech
PO Box 868 92502 951-826-6797
Nancy Pavelsky, dir. Fax 826-6440

Riverside County Office of Education 5,700/
PO Box 868 92502 951-826-6530
Kenneth Young, supt. Fax 826-6199
www.rcoe.us
Riverside County Opportunity S 200/Alt
PO Box 868 92502 951-826-6464
Richard Collins, dir. Fax 826-6906

Riverside USD 42,200/K-12
PO Box 2800 92516 951-788-7135
Rick Miller, supt. Fax 778-5668
www.rusd.k12.ca.us
Arlington HS 2,200/9-12
2951 Jackson St 92503 951-352-8316
Antonio Garcia, prin. Fax 328-7311
Central MS 700/7-8
4795 Magnolia Ave 92506 951-788-7282
Pablo Sanchez, prin. Fax 328-2580
Chemawa MS 1,000/7-8
8830 Magnolia Ave 92503 951-352-8244
Sean Curtin, prin. Fax 328-2980
Earhart MS 1,100/7-8
20202 Aptos St 92508 951-697-5700
Coleman Kells, prin. Fax 328-7580
Educational Options Center 200/Alt
6401 Lincoln Ave 92506 951-276-7670
David Haglund, dir. Fax 778-5623
Gage MS 1,100/7-8
6400 Lincoln Ave 92506 951-788-7350
Chuck Hiroto, prin. Fax 328-5680
King HS 3,100/9-12
9301 Wood Rd 92508 951-789-5690
Darel Hansen, prin. Fax 778-5680
Lincoln HS 300/Alt
4341 Victoria Ave 92507 951-788-7371
Elton Ross, prin. Fax 328-2931
Miller MS 800/7-8
17925 Kramoria Ave 92504 951-789-8181
Janelle Woodward, prin. Fax 328-2912
North HS 2,500/9-12
1550 3rd St 92507 951-788-7311
Trevor Painton, prin. Fax 328-2581
Polytechnic HS 2,800/9-12
5450 Victoria Ave 92506 951-788-7203
Wade Coe, prin. Fax 328-2901
Raincross HS 100/Alt
6401 Lincoln Ave 92506 951-276-7670
David Haglund, dir. Fax 778-5623
Ramona HS 2,100/9-12
7675 Magnolia Ave 92504 951-352-8429
Jamie Angulo, prin. Fax 328-2532
Sierra MS 900/7-8
4950 Central Ave 92504 951-788-7501
Steven Ybarra, prin. Fax 328-2552
Summit View S 700/Alt
6401 Lincoln Ave 92506 951-276-7670
David Haglund, dir. Fax 276-7685
University Heights MS 800/7-8
1155 Massachusetts Ave 92507 951-788-7388
Isabelle Hayes-Grice, prin. Fax 328-2566
Riverside Adult S Adult
6735 Magnolia Ave 92506 951-788-7185
James Dawson, prin. Fax 328-2523

Bethel Christian S 300/PK-12
2425 Van Buren Blvd 92503 951-359-1123
Michael Crites, supt. Fax 359-1719
California Baptist University Post-Sec.
8432 Magnolia Ave 92504 951-689-5771
Kaplan College Post-Sec.
4040 Vine St 92507 951-276-1704
La Sierra Academy 700/K-12
4900 Golden Ave 92505 951-351-1445
Walter Lancaster, prin. Fax 689-3708
La Sierra University Post-Sec.
4500 Riverwalk Pkwy 92505 951-785-2000
North-West College Post-Sec.
4550 La Sierra Ave 92505 951-351-7750
Notre Dame HS 500/9-12
7085 Brockton Ave 92506 951-275-5896
Matt Luttringer, prin. Fax 781-9020
Platt College Post-Sec.
6465 Sycamore Canyon # 100 92507 888-807-5288
Riverside Christian S 600/PK-12
3532 Monroe St 92504 951-687-0077
John Moran, supt. Fax 687-3340
Riverside City College Post-Sec.
4800 Magnolia Ave 92506 951-222-8000
Somerset Academy 100/K-12
17241 Van Buren Blvd 92504 951-789-4405
Cory Darrington, dir.
The Fab School Post-Sec.
2001 3rd St Ste E 92507 951-782-0567
UEI College Post-Sec.
1860 University Ave 92507 888-202-2485
University of California Post-Sec.
900 University Ave 92521 951-827-1012
Woodcrest Christian S 500/7-12
18401 Van Buren Blvd 92508 951-780-2010
Jim Sullivan, supt. Fax 780-2079

Rocklin, Placer, Pop. 54,666
Rocklin USD 11,100/K-12
2615 Sierra Meadows Dr 95677 916-624-2428
Kevin Brown, supt. Fax 630-2229
www.rocklin.k12.ca.us
Granite Oaks MS 900/7-8
2600 Wyckford Blvd 95765 916-315-9009
Jay Holmes, prin. Fax 315-9885
Rocklin Alternative Education Center 100/Alt
3250 Victory Dr 95765 916-632-3195
Mark Williams, prin. Fax 632-8630
Rocklin HS 1,800/9-12
5301 Victory Ln 95765 916-632-1600
David Bills, prin. Fax 632-0305
Spring View MS 800/7-8
5040 5th St 95677 916-624-3381
Marty Flowers, prin. Fax 624-5737
Victory HS 100/Alt
3250 Victory Dr 95765 916-632-3195
Mark Williams, prin. Fax 632-8630
Whitney HS 1,600/9-12
701 Wildcat Blvd 95765 916-632-6500
Debra Hawkins, prin. Fax 435-2542

Sierra College Post-Sec.
5000 Rocklin Rd 95677 916-624-3333
William Jessup University Post-Sec.
333 Sunset Blvd 95765 916-577-2200

Rodeo, Contra Costa, Pop. 8,152
John Swett USD 1,700/K-12
400 Parker Ave 94572 510-245-4300
Fax 245-4312
www.jsusd.org
Other Schools – See Crockett

Rohnert Park, Sonoma, Pop. 39,217
Cotati-Rohnert Park USD 5,600/K-12
7165 Burton Ave 94928 707-792-4722
Robert Haley, supt. Fax 792-4537
www.crpusd.org
El Camino HS 200/Alt
7165 Burton Ave 94928 707-588-5700
Erin Lane, prin. Fax 588-5704
Jones MS 1,000/6-8
5154 Snyder Ln 94928 707-588-5600
Laurie Mason, prin. Fax 588-5607
Phoenix HS 50/Alt
7165 Burton Ave 94928 707-284-3494
Erin Lane, prin. Fax 284-3495
Rancho Cotate HS 1,500/9-12
5450 Snyder Ln 94928 707-792-4750
Robert Steffen, prin. Fax 792-4758
Technology HS Vo/Tech
1801 E Cotati Ave 94928 707-792-4825
Bruce Mims, prin. Fax 792-4727

Bergin University of Canine Studies Post-Sec.
5860 Labath Ave 94928 707-545-3647
Sonoma State University Post-Sec.
1801 E Cotati Ave 94928 707-664-2880

Rolling Hills, Los Angeles, Pop. 1,810
Palos Verdes Peninsula USD
Supt. — See Palos Verdes Estates
Palos Verdes Peninsula HS 2,400/9-12
27118 Silver Spur Rd 90274 310-377-4888
Mitzi Cress, prin. Fax 544-4378
Rancho Del Mar HS 100/Alt
38 Crest Rd W 90274 310-377-6691
Rosemary Humphrey, prin. Fax 544-5526
PVPUSD Adult Education Adult
38 Crest Rd W 90274 310-541-7626
Rosemary Humphrey, prin. Fax 265-5967

Romoland, Riverside, Pop. 1,639
Romoland ESD
Supt. — See Homeland
Boulder Ridge MS 900/6-8
27327 Junipero Rd 92585 951-723-8931
Fax 723-8929

Rosamond, Kern, Pop. 17,416
Southern Kern USD 3,200/K-12
PO Box CC 93560 661-256-5000
Jeffrey Weinstein, supt. Fax 256-1247
www.skusd.k12.ca.us
Lincoln Alternative Education 100/Alt
PO Box CC 93560 661-256-5090
Alice Prindle, lead tchr. Fax 256-6868
Rare Earth Continuation HS 100/Alt
PO Box CC 93560 661-256-5090
Alice Prindle, lead tchr. Fax 256-6868
Rosamond HS 800/9-12
PO Box CC 93560 661-256-5020
Vern Folley, prin. Fax 256-6880
Tropico MS 700/6-8
PO Box CC 93560 661-256-5040
Julio Hernandez, prin. Fax 256-0630

Rosemead, Los Angeles, Pop. 53,367
El Monte UNHSD
Supt. — See El Monte
Rosemead HS 1,900/9-12
9063 Mission Dr 91770 626-286-3141
Larry Cecil, prin. Fax 286-6396

Garvey ESD 5,300/K-8
2730 Del Mar Ave 91770 626-307-3400
Sandra Johnson Ed.D., supt. Fax 307-1964
www.garvey.k12.ca.us
Garvey IS 800/7-8
2720 Jackson Ave 91770 626-307-3385
Gema Macias, prin. Fax 307-3443
Temple IS 500/7-8
8470 Fern Ave 91770 626-307-3360
C.P. Cheung, prin. Fax 307-8162

Rosemead ESD 2,900/PK-8
3907 Rosemead Blvd 91770 626-312-2900
Amy Enomoto-Perez Ed.D., supt. Fax 312-2906
www.rosemead.k12.ca.us
Muscatel MS 700/7-8
4201 Ivar Ave 91770 626-287-1139
Dawn Rock, prin. Fax 307-6185

Don Bosco Technical Institute Post-Sec.
1151 San Gabriel Blvd 91770 626-307-6500
Don Bosco Technical Institute 600/9-12
1151 San Gabriel Blvd 91770 626-940-2000
Xavier Jimenez, prin. Fax 940-2001
Rosemead Beauty School Post-Sec.
8531 Valley Blvd 91770 626-286-2147
University of the West Post-Sec.
1409 Walnut Grove Ave 91770 626-571-8811

Roseville, Placer, Pop. 114,218
Center JUSD
Supt. — See Antelope
Riles MS 800/7-8
4747 PFE Rd 95747 916-787-8100
Joyce Frisch, prin. Fax 773-4131

Dry Creek JESD 7,100/K-8
9707 Cook Riolo Rd 95747 916-770-8800
Mark Geyer, supt. Fax 771-0650
www.drycreek.k12.ca.us
Creekview Ranch MS 700/6-8
8779 Cook Riolo Rd 95747 916-770-8845
Marty Alberti, prin. Fax 772-4145
Silverado MS 1,000/6-8
2525 Country Club Dr 95747 916-780-2620
Priscilla Rasanen, prin. Fax 780-2635
Other Schools – See Antelope

Eureka UNSD
Supt. — See Granite Bay
Olympus JHS 500/7-8
2625 La Croix Dr 95661 916-782-1667
Kelly Graham, prin. Fax 782-1339

Roseville City ESD 9,800/K-8
1050 Main St 95678 916-771-1600
Richard Pierucci, supt. Fax 771-1620
www.rcsdk8.org
Buljan MS 1,200/6-8
100 Hallissy Dr 95678 916-771-1720
Greg Gunn, prin. Fax 773-2696
Cooley MS 1,000/6-8
9300 Prairie Woods Way 95747 916-771-1740
Karen Calkins, prin. Fax 786-3003
Eich IS 500/7-8
1509 Sierra Gardens Dr 95661 916-771-1770
Marc Buljan, prin. Fax 783-7292

Roseville JUNHSD 9,600/9-12
1750 Cirby Way 95661 916-786-2051
Tony Monetti, supt. Fax 786-2681
www.rjuhsd.us
Adelante HS 200/Alt
350 Atlantic St 95678 916-782-3155
Suzanne Laughrea, prin. Fax 782-4064
Independence HS 200/Alt
125 Berry St 95678 916-786-0793
Debbie Latteri, prin. Fax 786-3389
Oakmont HS 1,600/9-12
1710 Cirby Way 95661 916-782-3781
Rob Hasty, prin. Fax 782-4943
Roseville HS 2,000/9-12
1 Tiger Way 95678 916-782-3753
Brad Basham, prin. Fax 786-3846
Woodcreek HS 2,100/9-12
2551 Woodcreek Oaks Blvd 95747 916-771-6565
Jess Borjon, prin. Fax 771-6596
Roseville Adult S Adult
200 Branstetter St 95678 916-782-3952
Joyce Lude, dir. Fax 782-4361
Other Schools – See Antelope, Granite Bay

Christian Life Academy 100/K-12
1301 Coloma Way 95661 916-956-4662
Gary Gubitz, prin. Fax 786-7916
Cornerstone Christian S 100/K-12
143 Clinton Ave 95678 916-783-7779
Richard Batista, hdmstr. Fax 783-1856
Heald College Post-Sec.
7 Sierra Gate Plz 95678 916-789-8600
Valley Christian Academy 300/PK-12
301 W Whyte Ave 95678 916-728-5500
Chris Crowe, prin. Fax 721-3305

Ross, Marin, Pop. 2,341

Branson S 300/9-12
PO Box 887 94957 415-454-3612
Dr. Thomas Price, hdmstr. Fax 454-2327

Rowland Heights, Los Angeles, Pop. 48,135
Rowland USD 15,200/K-12
1830 Nogales St 91748 626-965-2541
Ruben P. Frutos, supt. Fax 854-8302
www.rowlandschools.org
Alvarado IS 1,000/7-8
1901 Desire Ave 91748 626-964-2358
Karen Magana, prin. Fax 810-5579
Community Day S 50/Alt
1928 Nogales St 91748 626-935-8210
Dr. Melissa Neal, prin. Fax 964-6450
Rowland HS 2,400/9-12
2000 Otterbein Ave 91748 626-965-3448
Mitch Brunyer, prin. Fax 810-4859
Santana Alternative Education Center 300/Alt
1006 Otterbein Ave 91748 626-965-5971
Guillermo Munoz, prin. Fax 854-2225
Rowland Adult & Continuing Education Adult
2100 Lerona Ave 91748 626-965-5975
Rocky Bettar, dir. Fax 854-1191

Other Schools – See La Puente, West Covina

Sacramento, Sacramento, Pop. 437,732
Elk Grove USD
Supt. — See Elk Grove
Calvine HS 300/Alt
8333 Vintage Park Dr 95828 916-689-7502
Joe Airoso, prin. Fax 689-7546
Daylor HS 200/Alt
6131 Orange Ave 95823 916-427-5428
Fax 391-2017
Florin HS 1,700/9-12
7956 Cottonwood Ln 95828 916-689-8600
Don Ross, prin. Fax 689-7430
Jackman MS 1,000/7-8
7925 Kentwall Dr 95823 916-393-2352
Paul Burke, prin. Fax 393-4053
Las Flores Independent Study 400/Alt
5900 Bamford Dr 95823 916-422-5604
Ralph Robles, admin. Fax 428-8307
Rio Cazadero HS 300/Alt
7825 Grandstaff Dr 95823 916-422-3058
Douglas Wendle, prin. Fax 422-0604
Rutter MS 1,000/7-8
7350 Palmer House Dr 95828 916-422-7590
Yuri Penermon, prin. Fax 422-8354
Sheldon HS 2,400/9-12
8333 Kingsbridge Dr 95829 916-681-7500
Paula Duncan, prin. Fax 681-7505
Smedberg MS 1,200/7-8
8239 Kingsbridge Dr 95829 916-681-7525
Sharon Douglas, prin. Fax 681-7530
Valley HS 1,600/9-12
6300 Ehrhardt Ave 95823 916-689-6500
Chelsea Bowler-Shelton, prin. Fax 682-1528
Adult/Community Education Adult
8401 Gerber Rd 95828 916-686-7717
Fax 689-5752

Natomas USD 12,300/PK-12
1901 Arena Blvd 95834 916-567-5400
Chris Evans, supt. Fax 567-5405
www.natomas.k12.ca.us
Discovery HS 100/Alt
3401 Fong Ranch Rd 95834 916-928-5200
Julius Lockett, prin. Fax 928-5222
Inderkum HS 1,600/9-12
2500 New Market Dr 95835 916-567-5640
George Tapanes, prin. Fax 567-5649
Natomas HS 1,300/9-12
3301 Fong Ranch Rd 95834 916-641-4960
John Eick, prin. Fax 641-5455
Natomas MS 900/7-8
3200 N Park Dr 95835 916-567-5540
Carla Najera-Kunsemiller, prin. Fax 567-5549

Sacramento City USD 45,300/K-12
PO Box 246870 95824 916-643-9000
Jonathan Raymond, supt. Fax 643-9480
www.scusd.edu
American Legion HS 300/Alt
3801 Broadway 95817 916-277-6600
Stan Echols, prin. Fax 277-6800
Bacon MS 600/7-8
4140 Cuny Ave 95823 916-433-5000
Nancy Purcell, prin. Fax 433-5166
Benjamin Health Professions HS 400/9-12
451 McClatchy Way 95818 916-264-3262
Ann Curtis, prin. Fax 264-3245
Brannan MS 700/7-8
5301 Elmer Way 95822 916-264-4350
Greg Purcell, prin. Fax 264-4481
Burbank HS 1,900/9-12
3500 Florin Rd 95823 916-433-5100
Ted Appel, prin. Fax 433-5199
California MS 700/7-8
1600 Vallejo Way 95818 916-264-4550
Elizabeth Vigil, prin. Fax 264-4477
Capital City Independent Study 700/Alt
7222 24th St 95822 916-433-5187
Michael Salman, prin. Fax 433-5195
Carson MS 300/7-8
5301 N St 95819 916-277-6750
Charles Watters, prin. Fax 277-6550
Einstein MS 800/7-8
9325 Mirandy Dr 95826 916-228-5800
Garrett Kirkland, prin. Fax 228-5813
Johnson HS 1,900/9-12
6879 14th Ave 95820 916-277-6300
Felisberto Cedros, prin. Fax 277-6740
Kennedy HS 2,100/9-12
6715 Gloria Dr 95831 916-433-5200
Chad Sweitzer, prin. Fax 433-5511
McClatchy HS 2,200/9-12
3066 Freeport Blvd 95818 916-264-4400
Peter Lambert, prin. Fax 264-4499
Parks MS 500/7-8
2250 68th Ave 95822 916-433-5400
Robert Sullivan, prin. Fax 433-5518
Rosemont HS 1,600/9-12
9594 Kiefer Blvd 95827 916-228-5844
Leise Martinez, prin. Fax 228-5733
School of Engineering and Sciences 400/7-12
7345 Gloria Dr 95831 916-433-2960
Matt Turkie, prin. Fax 433-2959
Still MS 400/6-8
2250 John Still Dr 95832 916-433-5375
Sara Morabito, prin. Fax 433-2716
Success Academy Alt
5601 47th Ave 95824 916-643-2338
Kathy Whiteside, prin. Fax 433-5301
Sutter MS 1,300/7-8
3150 I St 95816 916-264-4150
Dave Rodriguez, prin. Fax 264-3436
West Campus HS 900/9-12
5022 58th St 95820 916-277-6400
Greg Thomas, prin. Fax 277-6593

Wood MS 700/7-8
6201 Lemon Hill Ave 95824 916-382-5900
Mary DeSplinter, prin. Fax 382-5914
Jones Skills Center Adult
5451 Lemon Hill Ave 95824 916-433-2600
Donna Philp, dir. Fax 433-2640
McClaskey Adult Education Center Adult
5241 J St 95819 916-277-6625
Susan Gilmore, prin. Fax 277-6810

Sacramento County Office of Education
Supt. — See Mather
El Centro JSHS Alt
PO Box 269003 95826 916-228-2525
Marc Nigel, prin. Fax 228-2532
Gerber JSHS 200/Alt
PO Box 269003 95826 916-228-2329
Sharon Douglas, contact Fax 689-3730
Hickey JSHS 100/Alt
PO Box 269003 95826 916-566-2074
Lisa Alcala, prin. Fax 566-2018
Morgan JSHS Alt
PO Box 269003 95826 916-228-2317
Marc Nigel, prin. Fax 596-4222
North Area Community S 100/Alt
PO Box 269003 95826 916-566-1302
Lisa Alcala, prin. Fax 566-1304

San Juan USD
Supt. — See Carmichael
Arcade Fundamental MS 600/6-8
3500 Edison Ave 95821 916-971-7300
Steve Hunt, prin. Fax 971-7821
Arden MS 800/6-8
1640 Watt Ave 95864 916-971-7306
Jamey Schrey, prin. Fax 971-7830
El Camino Fundamental HS 1,700/9-12
4300 El Camino Ave 95821 916-971-7430
Jill Spears, prin. Fax 971-7429
Encina Preparatory HS 800/6-12
1400 Bell St 95825 916-971-7538
Will Jarrell, prin. Fax 971-7555
La Entrada Continuation HS 100/Alt
5320 Hemlock St 95841 916-971-7590
Tony Oddo, prin. Fax 971-7302
Mira Loma HS 1,600/9-12
4000 Edison Ave 95821 916-971-7465
Rich Nichols, prin.
Palos Verde Continuation HS 50/Alt
5320 Hemlock St 95841 916-971-5291
Jose Reyes, prin. Fax 971-5367
Rio Americano HS 1,700/9-12
4540 American River Dr 95864 916-971-7494
Brian Ginter, prin. Fax 971-7513
Orange Grove Adult Education Adult
4640 Orange Grove Ave 95841 916-971-7399
Paige Ashley, prin. Fax 482-3540

Twin Rivers USD
Supt. — See Mc Clellan
Foothill HS 1,300/9-12
5000 McCloud Dr 95842 916-566-3445
Joseph Williams, prin. Fax 566-3526
Foothill Ranch MS 600/5-8
5001 Diablo Dr 95842 916-566-3440
Roxanne Mitchell, prin. Fax 263-3756
Grant Union HS 2,100/9-12
1400 Grand Ave 95838 916-566-3450
Craig Murray, prin. Fax 286-1084
Grant West HS 9-12
1221 South Ave 95838 916-566-3455
Wesley Marshall, prin. Fax 286-1240
King Technology Academy 500/7-8
3051 Fairfield St 95815 916-566-3490
Danny Williams, prin. Fax 263-6701
Norwood JHS 700/6-8
4601 Norwood Ave 95838 916-566-2710
Brent Givens, prin. Fax 566-3529
NOVA Community Day S 50/Alt
2035 North Ave 95838 916-566-2765
Shant Hagopian, prin. Fax 289-1110
Rio Tierra JHS 600/6-8
3201 Northstead Dr 95833 916-566-2730
Paul Orlando, prin. Fax 263-6971
Vista Nueva Career & Tech HS Vo/Tech
2035 North Ave 95838 916-566-2750
Harjinder Mattu, prin. Fax 263-6498

Al-Arqam Islamic S 300/K-12
6990 65th St 95823 916-391-3333
A.M. Fain, prin. Fax 391-3334
Aldar Academy K-12
4436 Engle Rd 95821 916-485-9685
Daniel Ramirez, prin. Fax 485-1569
Alliant International University Post-Sec.
2030 W El Camino Ave # 200 95833 916-565-2955
American River College Post-Sec.
4700 College Oak Dr 95841 916-484-8011
Anthem College Post-Sec.
9738 Lincoln Village # 100 95827 916-929-9700
Art Institute of California - Sacramento Post-Sec.
2850 Gateway Oaks Dr # 100 95833 800-477-1957
Bradshaw Christian S 1,300/PK-12
8324 Bradshaw Rd 95829 916-688-0521
Michelle Reynolds, supt. Fax 688-0502
California State University-Sacramento Post-Sec.
6000 J St 95819 916-278-6011
Capital Christian S 1,100/PK-12
9470 Micron Ave 95827 916-856-5600
Todd Jacobs, supt. Fax 856-5951
Carrington College California Post-Sec.
8909 Folsom Blvd 95826 916-361-1660
Christian Brothers HS 1,100/9-12
4315 Mrtn Lthr King Jr Blvd 95820 916-733-3600
Mary Hesser, prin. Fax 733-3657
Cornerstone Christian S 200/PK-12
5073 Andrea Blvd 95842 916-334-6236
Richard Batista, hdmstr.

Cosumnes River College Post-Sec.
8401 Center Pkwy 95823 916-691-7344
Cristo Rey HS 300/9-12
6200 McMahon Dr 95824 916-733-2660
Joanne Castronovo, prin. Fax 739-1310
Emergency Medical Sciences Training Inst Post-Sec.
3105 Fite Cir Ste 108 95827 800-500-0711
Epic Bible College Post-Sec.
4330 Auburn Blvd 95841 916-348-4689
Federico College of Hairstyling Post-Sec.
1515 Sports Dr 95834 916-929-4242
Intnl Academy of Design & Technology Post-Sec.
2450 Del Paso Rd 95834 916-285-9468
Kaplan College Post-Sec.
4330 Watt Ave Ste 400 95821 916-649-8168
Le Cordon Bleu Academy of Culinary Arts Post-Sec.
2450 Del Paso Rd 95834 888-807-8222
MTI College Post-Sec.
5221 Madison Ave 95841 916-339-1500
My-Le's Beauty College Post-Sec.
5972 Stockton Blvd 95824 916-422-0223
Sacramento City College Post-Sec.
3835 Freeport Blvd 95822 916-558-2111
Sacramento Country Day S 500/PK-12
2636 Latham Dr 95864 916-481-8811
Stephen Repsher, hdmstr. Fax 481-6016
St. Francis HS 1,100/9-12
5900 Elvas Ave 95819 916-452-3461
Patrick O'Neill, prin. Fax 452-1591
Truck Driving Academy Post-Sec.
3100 Fite Cir Ste 105 95827 916-381-2285
Union Institute & University Post-Sec.
160 Promenade Cir Ste 115 95834 916-564-3100
Unitek College Post-Sec.
1111 Howe Ave Ste 300 95825 888-518-6601
Universal Technical Institute Post-Sec.
4100 Duckhorn Dr 95834 916-263-9100
Western Pacific Truck School Post-Sec.
8720 Fruitridge Rd 95826 800-333-1233

Saint Helena, Napa, Pop. 5,723
St. Helena USD 1,400/K-12
465 Main St 94574 707-967-2708
Bill McGuire, supt. Fax 963-1335
www.sthelena.k12.ca.us
St. Helena HS 500/9-12
1401 Grayson Ave 94574 707-967-2740
Ben Scinto, prin. Fax 967-2735
Stevenson MS 300/6-8
1316 Hillview Pl 94574 707-967-2725
Mary Allen, prin. Fax 967-2734

Culinary Institute of America Greystone Post-Sec.
2555 Main St 94574 707-967-1100

Salida, Stanislaus, Pop. 13,232
Salida UNESD 2,800/K-8
4801 Sisk Rd 95368 209-545-0339
Twila Tosh, supt. Fax 545-2002
www.salida.k12.ca.us/
Salida MS - Vella Campus 1,000/6-8
5041 Toomes Rd 95368 209-545-1033
Doan Way, prin. Fax 545-0831

Heald College Modesto Post-Sec.
5260 Pirrone Ct 95368 209-416-3700
Kaplan College Post-Sec.
5172 Kiernan Ct 95368 209-543-7000
San Joaquin Valley College Post-Sec.
5380 Pirrone Rd 95368 209-543-8800

Salinas, Monterey, Pop. 147,570
Monterey County Office of Education 1,400/
PO Box 80851 93912 831-755-0300
Dr. Nancy Kotowski, supt. Fax 753-6473
www.monterey.k12.ca.us
Salinas Community S 300/Alt
1420 Natividad Rd 93906 831-755-3790
Crystal Beget, prin. Fax 753-1042

North Monterey County USD
Supt. — See Moss Landing
Central Bay Continuation HS 100/Alt
17500 Pesante Rd 93907 831-663-2997
Aida Ramirez, prin. Fax 663-1151
N Monterey Co. Ctr for Independent Study 100/K-12
17500 Pesante Rd 93907 831-663-7050
Aida Ramirez, prin. Fax 663-6184

Regional Occupational Center & Program
Supt. — None
Mission Trails ROP Vo/Tech
867 E Laurel Dr 93905 831-753-4209
Randy Bangs, dir. Fax 422-5115

Salinas UNHSD 13,500/7-12
431 W Alisal St 93901 831-796-7000
Tim Vanoli, supt. Fax 796-7005
www.salinas.k12.ca.us
Alisal HS 2,500/9-12
777 Williams Rd 93905 831-796-7600
Ernesto Garcia, prin. Fax 796-7605
Carr Lake Community Day S Alt
10 Sherwood Pl 93906 831-796-7770
Michael Romero, prin.
El Puente S, 20 Sherwood Dr 93901 Alt
August Caresani, prin. 831-796-7770
El Sausal MS 900/7-8
1155 E Alisal St 93905 831-796-7200
Francisco Huerta, prin. Fax 796-7205
Everret Alvarez HS 2,100/9-12
1900 Independence Blvd 93906 831-796-7800
Jacqui Axtell, prin. Fax 796-7805
Harden MS 1,200/7-8
1561 McKinnon St 93906 831-796-7300
Alberto Verduzco, prin. Fax 796-7305
La Paz MS 900/7-8
1300 N Sanborn Rd 93905 831-796-7900
Arturo Rodriguez, prin. Fax 796-7905

Mount Toro HS 300/Alt
10 Sherwood Pl 93906 831-796-7700
Michael Romero, prin. Fax 424-7325
North Salinas HS 2,100/9-12
55 Kip Dr 93906 831-796-7500
Steve Oliver, prin. Fax 796-7505
Salinas HS 2,500/9-12
726 S Main St 93901 831-796-7400
Judith Peterson, prin. Fax 796-7405
Washington MS 1,000/7-8
560 Iverson St 93901 831-796-7100
Robert Cannon, prin. Fax 796-7105
Salinas Adult S Adult
20 Sherwood Pl 93906 831-796-6900
Todd Farr, prin. Fax 796-6905

Santa Rita UNSD 3,000/K-8
57 Russell Rd 93906 831-443-7200
Michael Brusa, supt. Fax 442-1729
www.santaritaschools.org
Bolsa Knolls MS 300/6-8
1031 Rogge Rd 93906 831-443-3300
John Gutierrez, prin. Fax 443-4766
Gavilan View MS 700/6-8
18250 Van Buren Ave 93906 831-443-7212
Carissa Edeza, prin. Fax 443-0908

Spreckels UNESD
Supt. — See Spreckels
Buena Vista MS 400/6-8
18250 Tara Dr 93908 831-455-8936
Eric Tarallo, prin. Fax 455-8832

Washington UNESD 1,000/K-8
43 San Benancio Rd 93908 831-484-2166
Dee Baker, supt. Fax 484-2828
www.washingtonusd.org
San Benancio MS 300/6-8
43 San Benancio Rd 93908 831-484-1172
Gina Uccelli, prin. Fax 484-6509

Hartnell College Post-Sec.
411 Central Ave 93901 831-755-6700
Heald College Post-Sec.
1450 N Main St 93906 831-443-1700
Notre Dame HS 300/9-12
455 Palma Dr 93901 831-751-1850
Andy Bedell, prin. Fax 757-5749
Palma HS 600/7-12
919 Iverson St 93901 831-422-6391
David Sullivan, prin. Fax 422-5065
Soaring Eagles Christian Academy 50/PK-12
298 E Market St 93901 831-274-6717
Anna Musumeci, dir.

Salton City, Imperial, Pop. 3,695
Coachella Valley USD
Supt. — See Thermal
West Shores HS 400/7-12
2381 Shore Hawk Ave 92275 760-394-4331
Rudy Wilson, prin. Fax 394-0971

San Andreas, Calaveras, Pop. 2,665
Calaveras County Office of Education
Supt. — See Angels Camp
Calaveras River Academy 100/Alt
PO Box 249 95249 209-754-1996
Scott Nanik, prin. Fax 754-4261
Oakendell S 50/Alt
PO Box 249 95249 209-754-1961
Scott Nanik, prin. Fax 754-1659
Calaveras County Adult Education Adult
PO Box 249 95249 209-754-1996
Scott Nanik, prin. Fax 754-4261

Calaveras USD, PO Box 788 95249 3,300/K-12
Mark Campbell, supt. 209-754-2300
www.calaveras.k12.ca.us
Calaveras Educational Transitions S 50/Alt
PO Box 788 95249 209-754-2123
Fred Mier, prin. Fax 754-2144
Calaveras HS 1,000/9-12
PO Box 607 95249 209-754-1811
Michael Merrill, prin. Fax 754-0276
Gold Strike Continuation HS 100/Alt
PO Box 788 95249 209-754-2123
Fred Mier, prin. Fax 754-2144
Other Schools – See Valley Springs

San Anselmo, Marin, Pop. 11,931
Ross Valley ESD 2,300/K-8
110 Shaw Dr 94960 415-454-2160
Eileen Rohan, supt. Fax 454-6840
rossvalleyschools.org
Other Schools – See Fairfax

Tamalpais UNHSD
Supt. — See Larkspur
Sir Francis Drake HS 1,000/9-12
1327 Sir Francis Drake Blvd 94960 415-453-8770
Liz Seabury, prin. Fax 458-3429

San Domenico HS 100/9-12
1500 Butterfield Rd 94960 415-258-1939
Alyce Brownridge, prin. Fax 258-1940
San Domenico MS 100/6-8
1500 Butterfield Rd 94960 415-258-1900
Cecily Stock, prin. Fax 258-1901
San Francisco Theological Seminary Post-Sec.
105 Seminary Rd 94960 415-451-2800

San Bernardino, San Bernardino, Pop. 204,762
Regional Occupational Center & Program
Supt. — None
San Bernadino County ROP Vo/Tech
601 N E St 92415 909-386-2449
Kit Alvarez, admin. Fax 386-2479

San Bernardino City USD 52,000/K-12
777 N F St 92410 909-381-1100
Dr. Dale Marsden, supt. Fax 885-6392
www.sbcusd.k12.ca.us/
Arrowview MS 800/7-8
2299 N G St 92405 909-881-8109
Hector Vasquez, prin. Fax 881-8119
Arroyo Valley HS 2,900/9-12
1881 W Base Line St 92411 909-381-4295
Gordon Amerson, prin. Fax 386-2577
Cajon HS 2,900/9-12
1200 W Hill Dr 92407 909-881-8120
Toni Miller, prin. Fax 881-8141
Chavez MS 1,100/6-8
6650 Magnolia Ave 92407 909-386-2050
Karen Strong, prin. Fax 473-8443
Curtis MS 1,000/6-8
1050 Del Rosa Ave 92410 909-388-6332
Marlene Bicondova, prin. Fax 388-6339
Del Vallejo MS 900/6-8
1885 E Lynwood Dr 92404 909-881-8280
Charles McWilliams, prin. Fax 881-8285
Golden Valley MS 1,100/6-8
3800 N Waterman Ave 92404 909-881-8168
Kristen Vicondova, prin. Fax 881-5196
Indian Springs HS 9-12
650 N Del Rosa Dr 92410 909-383-1360
Dr. Alan Kay, prin. Fax 383-1750
King MS 900/6-8
1250 Medical Center Dr 92411 909-388-6350
Maria Jauregui, prin. Fax 388-6361
Middle College HS 200/9-12
701 S Mount Vernon Ave 92410 909-824-3218
James Espinoza, prin. Fax 824-3187
Pacific HS 2,300/9-12
1020 Pacific St 92404 909-388-6419
Tex Acosta, prin. Fax 388-6427
Richardson Prep MS 600/6-8
455 S K St 92410 909-388-6438
Natalie Raymundo, prin. Fax 383-0368
Rodriguez Prep MS 500/6-8
1985 Guthrie St 92404 909-884-6030
Teenya Bishop, prin. Fax 863-7869
San Bernardino HS 2,400/9-12
1850 N E St 92405 909-881-8217
Sandra Rodriguez, prin. Fax 881-8245
San Gorgonio HS 2,900/9-12
2299 Pacific St 92404 909-388-6524
Fax 388-6498
Shandin Hills MS 1,100/6-8
4301 Little Mountain Dr 92407 909-880-6666
Carmen Beck, prin. Fax 880-6672
Sierra HS 600/Alt
570 E 9th St 92410 909-388-6478
Ken Martinez, prin. Fax 889-4188
San Bernardino Adult S Adult
1200 N E St 92405 909-388-6000
Karen Bautista, prin. Fax 381-2887
Other Schools – See Highland

San Bernardino Co. Office of Education 2,200/
601 N E St 92415 909-888-3228
Gary Thomas, supt. Fax 386-2478
www.sbcss.k12.ca.us
Other Schools – See Apple Valley, Colton, Rancho Cucamonga, Rialto

---

Aquinas HS 400/9-12
2772 Sterling Ave 92404 909-886-4659
Christopher Barrows, prin. Fax 886-7717
California State Univ.-San Bernadino Post-Sec.
5500 University Pkwy 92407 909-537-5000
Concorde Career College Post-Sec.
201 E Airport Dr # A 92408 909-884-8891
Dikaios Christian Academy 200/K-12
PO Box 9067 92427 909-881-8310
Von Sommerville, admin. Fax 881-8315
Everest College Post-Sec.
217 E Club Center Dr Ste A 92408 909-777-3300
Hair Masters University of Beauty Post-Sec.
208 W Highland Ave 92405 909-882-2987
ITT Technical Institute Post-Sec.
670 Carnegie Dr 92408 909-806-4600
Marinello School of Beauty Post-Sec.
721 W 2nd St Ste E 92410 909-884-8747
San Bernardino Valley College Post-Sec.
701 S Mount Vernon Ave 92410 909-384-4400
The Art Institute of CA - Inland Empire Post-Sec.
674 E Brier Dr 92408 909-915-2100

San Bruno, San Mateo, Pop. 37,955
San Bruno Park ESD 2,300/K-8
500 Acacia Ave 94066 650-624-3100
David Hutt, supt. Fax 266-9626
sbpsd.k12.ca.us
Parkside MS 500/6-8
1801 Niles Ave 94066 650-624-3180
Angela Addiego, prin. Fax 877-8195

San Mateo UNHSD
Supt. — See San Mateo
Capuchino HS 1,100/9-12
1501 Magnolia Ave 94066 650-558-2799
Shamar Shanks, prin. Fax 558-2752
Peninsula Continuation HS 300/Alt
300 Piedmont Ave 94066 650-558-2499
Donald Scatena, prin. Fax 866-4120

Skyline College Post-Sec.
3300 College Dr 94066 650-738-4100

San Carlos, San Mateo, Pop. 27,121
San Carlos ESD 3,200/K-8
1200 Industrial Rd Ste 9 94070 650-508-7333
Craig Baker, supt. Fax 508-7340
www.sancarlos.k12.ca.us
Central MS 600/5-8
828 Chestnut St 94070 650-508-7321
Steven Kaufman, prin. Fax 508-7342

San Clemente, Orange, Pop. 61,767
Capistrano USD
Supt. — See San Juan Capistrano
Ayer MS 900/6-8
1271 Calle Sarmentoso 92673 949-366-9607
Holly Feldt, prin. Fax 366-1519
San Clemente HS 3,100/9-12
700 Avenida Pico 92673 949-492-4165
Michael Halt, prin. Fax 361-5175
Shorecliffs MS 1,100/6-8
240 Via Socorro 92672 949-498-1660
Heidi Crowley, prin. Fax 498-0826
Vista del Mar MS 500/6-8
1130 Avenida Talega 92673 949-234-5955
Sandra McKinney, prin. Fax 940-0262

San Diego, San Diego, Pop. 1,256,111
Poway USD 34,000/K-12
15250 Avenue of Science 92128 858-521-2800
Dr. John Collins, supt. Fax 485-1075
www.powayusd.com
Bernardo Heights MS 1,400/6-8
12990 Paseo Lucido 92128 858-485-4850
Tim Biland, prin. Fax 485-4865
Black Mountain MS 1,300/6-8
9353 Oviedo St 92129 858-484-1300
Greg Magno, prin. Fax 538-9440
Del Norte HS 1,200/9-12
16601 Nighthawk Ln 92127 858-487-0877
Greg Mizel, prin. Fax 487-2443
Mesa Verde MS 1,300/6-8
8375 Entreken Way 92129 858-538-5478
Cliff Mitchell, prin. Fax 538-8636
Mt. Carmel HS 2,100/9-12
9550 Carmel Mountain Rd 92129 858-484-1180
Dawn Kastner, prin. Fax 538-9426
Oak Valley MS 1,300/6-8
16055 Winecreek Rd 92127 858-487-2939
Casey Currigan, prin. Fax 457-0991
Rancho Bernardo HS 2,400/9-12
13010 Paseo Lucido 92128 858-485-4800
David LeMaster, prin. Fax 485-4822
Westview HS 2,400/9-12
13500 Camino Del Sur 92129 858-780-2000
Todd Cassen, prin. Fax 780-2054
Other Schools – See Poway

Regional Occupational Center & Program
Supt. — None
San Diego County ROP Vo/Tech
6401 Linda Vista Rd Ste 408 92111 858-292-3500
Steve Pinning, dir. Fax 268-9726

San Diego County Office of Education 1,100/
6401 Linda Vista Rd 92111 858-292-3500
Randolph Ward, supt. Fax 292-3653
www.sdcoe.net
Other Schools – See San Marcos

San Diego USD 130,600/PK-12
4100 Normal St 92103 619-725-8000
William Kowba, supt. Fax 291-7182
www.sandi.net
A. L. B. A. S, 4041 Oregon St 92104 50/Alt
Richard Moore, prin. 619-293-4468
Bell MS 1,100/6-8
620 Briarwood Rd 92139 619-479-7111
Michael Dodson, prin. Fax 470-6054
Challenger MS 1,100/6-8
10810 Parkdale Ave 92126 858-586-7001
Sheelagh Moran, prin. Fax 271-5203
Clairemont HS 1,400/9-12
4150 Ute Dr 92117 858-273-0201
Lenora Smith, prin. Fax 272-4219
Clark MS 1,100/6-8
4388 Thorn St 92105 619-563-6801
Thomas Liberto, prin. Fax 563-9653
Community Health and Medical Practices S 400/9-12
4191 Colts Way 92115 619-583-2501
Reashon Villery, prin. Fax 229-9088
Correia MS 900/7-8
4302 Valeta St 92107 619-222-0476
Patricia Ladd, prin. Fax 221-0147
Crawford HS 300/9-12
4191 Colts Way 92115 619-583-2504
Diego Gutierrez, dir. Fax 229-9225
Creative Performing & Media Arts S 1,000/6-8
5050 Conrad Ave 92117 858-278-5917
Scott Thomason, prin. Fax 293-7235
De Portola MS 1,000/6-8
11010 Clairemont Mesa Blvd 92124 858-496-8080
Listy Gillingham, prin. Fax 576-4419
Farb MS 700/6-8
4880 La Cuenta Dr 92124 858-496-8090
Susan Levy, prin. Fax 576-0931
Foster Construction Tech Academy 500/9-12
7651 Wellington Way 92111 858-496-8370
Laura Bellofatto, dir. Fax 496-4907
Garfield HS 300/Alt
1255 16th St 92101 619-525-2059
Jolie Pickett, prin. Fax 525-2063
Henry HS 2,500/9-12
6702 Wandermere Dr 92120 619-286-7700
Patricia Crowder, prin. Fax 229-0370
Hoover HS 2,100/9-12
4474 El Cajon Blvd 92115 619-283-6281
Chuck Podhorsky, prin. Fax 280-5837
Innovation MS 500/7-8
5095 Arvinels Ave 92117 858-278-5948
Harlan Klein, prin.
Invention & Design Educational Academy 300/9-12
4191 Colts Way 92115 619-583-2502
Diego Gutierrez, dir. Fax 582-4173
Kearny Digital Media and Design HS 500/9-12
7651 Wellington Way 92111 858-496-8370
Cheryl Hibbeln, prin. Fax 278-6349
Kearny HS of International Business 500/9-12
7651 Wellington Way 92111 858-496-8370
Ana Diaz-Booz, prin. Fax 496-8379
Kearny Science Connections & Tech HS 500/9-12
7651 Wellington Way 92111 858-496-8370
V. Derek Morris, dir. Fax 715-9504
Lewis MS 1,100/6-8
5170 Greenbrier Ave 92120 619-583-3233
Brad Callahan, prin. Fax 229-1338
Lincoln HS, 4777 Imperial Ave 92113 2,000/9-12
Esther Omogbehin, prin. 619-266-6500
Madison HS 1,300/9-12
4833 Doliva Dr 92117 858-496-8410
Richard Nash, prin. Fax 496-8421
Mann MS 800/6-8
4345 54th St 92115 619-582-8990
Courtney Young, prin. Fax 583-2637
Marcy Center Alt
2716 Marcy Ave 92113 619-525-7372
Marshall MS 1,500/6-8
9700 Avenue of Nations 92131 858-549-5400
Michelle Irwin, prin. Fax 549-5490
Marston MS 800/6-8
3799 Clairemont Dr 92117 858-273-2030
Dr. Elizabeth Cook, prin. Fax 272-3460
Memorial Prep for Scholars & Athletes 500/6-8
2850 Logan Ave 92113 619-231-8581
Georgina Barajas-Aguirre, prin.
Millennial Tech MS 500/6-8
1110 Carolina Ln 92102 619-527-6933
Helen Griffith, prin.
Mira Mesa HS 2,600/9-12
10510 Reagan Rd 92126 858-566-2262
Scott Giusti, prin. Fax 549-9541
Mission Bay HS 1,600/9-12
2475 Grand Ave 92109 858-273-1313
Fred Hilgers, prin. Fax 270-8294
Montgomery MS 400/6-8
2470 Ulric St 92111 858-496-8330
Jonathan Ton, prin. Fax 292-0125
Morse HS 2,100/9-12
6905 Skyline Dr 92114 619-262-0763
Harry Shelton, prin. Fax 262-6835
Mt. Everest Academy 100/Alt
4350 Mount Everest Blvd 92117 858-496-8778
Michael Rood, prin. Fax 496-8797
Muir S 400/Alt
4431 Mount Herbert Ave 92117 858-268-1954
Nancy Johnson, prin. Fax 627-9289
New Dawn Alt
5650 Mount Ackerly Dr 92111 858-496-1655
Danielle Clark, prin. Fax 496-1655
Pacific Beach MS 700/6-8
4676 Ingraham St 92109 858-273-9070
Ernest Remillard, prin. Fax 270-8063
Pershing MS 900/6-8
8204 San Carlos Dr 92119 619-465-3234
Sarah Sullivan, prin. Fax 461-5447
Point Loma HS 2,100/9-12
2335 Chatsworth Blvd 92106 619-223-3121
Barbara Samilson, prin. Fax 225-1298
Roosevelt International MS 800/6-8
3366 Park Blvd 92103 619-293-4450
Dr. Arturo Cabello, prin. Fax 497-0918
San Diego Early College S 100/Alt
1425 Russ Blvd Ste T-112D 92101 619-525-2000
Elizabeth Larkin, prin.
San Diego HS of Business 500/9-12
1405 Park Blvd 92101 619-525-7455
Consuelo Manriquez, prin. Fax 525-7337
San Diego HS of Communications 300/9-12
1405 Park Blvd 92101 619-525-7455
Dianne Cordero, prin. Fax 525-7259
San Diego HS of LEADS 500/9-12
1405 Park Blvd 92101 619-525-7456
Consuelo Manriquez, prin. Fax 744-7676
San Diego International Studies HS 600/9-12
1405 Park Blvd 92101 619-525-7464
Kirk Ankeney, prin. Fax 744-7651
San Diego Media Visual & Prfrmng Arts HS 500/9-12
1405 Park Blvd 92101 619-525-7457
Kirk Ankeney, prin. Fax 744-7680
San Diego Metro Career & Tech HS Vo/Tech
7250 Mesa College Dr 92111 619-388-2299
Mildred Phillips, prin.
San Diego Science & Technology HS 500/9-12
1405 Park Blvd 92101 619-525-7459
Dianne Cordero, prin. Fax 744-7677
School of Creative & Performing Arts 1,400/6-12
2425 Dusk Dr 92139 619-470-0555
Mitzi Lizarraga, prin. Fax 470-9430
School of Law and Business 300/9-12
4191 Colts Way 92115 619-583-2503
Reashon Villery, prin. Fax 229-2005
Scripps Ranch HS 2,500/9-12
10410 Treena St 92131 858-621-9020
Ann Menna, prin. Fax 621-0646
Serra HS 2,000/9-12
5156 Santo Rd 92124 858-496-8342
Michael Jimenez, prin. Fax 571-3457
Standley MS 1,100/6-8
6298 Radcliffe Dr 92122 858-455-0550
Heidi Eastcott, prin. Fax 546-7627
Taft MS 600/6-8
9191 Gramercy Dr 92123 858-496-8245
Michael George, prin. Fax 496-8138
TRACE S 500/Alt
2555 Camino del Rio S 92108 619-574-1073
Bob Morris, prin.
Twain HS 300/Alt
6402 Linda Vista Rd 92111 858-496-8260
Cesar Alcantar, prin. Fax 576-9514
University City HS 1,900/9-12
6949 Genesee Ave 92122 858-457-3040
Jeff Olivero, prin. Fax 458-9432

Wangenheim MS 1,100/6-8
9230 Gold Coast Dr 92126 858-578-1400
Matthew Fallon, prin. Fax 578-9481
Whittier S, 3401 Clairemont Dr 92117 300/Alt
Cathie Whitley, prin. 858-490-2770
Wilson MS 600/6-8
3838 Orange Ave 92105 619-280-1661
David Downey, prin. Fax 280-6437
Other Schools – See La Jolla

San Dieguito UNHSD
Supt. — See Encinitas
Canyon Crest Academy 1,900/9-12
5951 E Village Center Loop 92130 858-350-0253
Brian Kohn, prin. Fax 350-0280
Carmel Valley MS 1,500/7-8
3800 Mykonos Ln 92130 858-481-8221
Laurie Francis, prin. Fax 481-8256
Torrey Pines HS 2,600/9-12
3710 Del Mar Heights Rd 92130 858-755-0125
Brett Killeen, prin. Fax 481-0098

Sweetwater UNHSD
Supt. — See Chula Vista
Mar Vista MS 1,100/7-8
1267 Thermal Ave 92154 619-628-5100
Thomas Winters, prin. Fax 423-8431
Montgomery HS 1,600/9-12
3250 Palm Ave 92154 619-628-3800
Tom Rodrigo, prin. Fax 424-6473
Montgomery MS 900/7-8
1051 Picador Blvd 92154 619-662-8200
Victor Tapia-Sanchez, prin. Fax 428-6517
San Ysidro HS 2,500/9-12
5353 Airway Rd 92154 619-710-2300
Hector Espinoza, prin. Fax 710-2318
Southwest HS 1,700/9-12
1685 Hollister St 92154 619-628-3600
Lee Romero, prin. Fax 423-8253
Southwest MS 600/7-8
2710 Iris Ave 92154 619-628-4000
Oscar Medina, prin. Fax 423-1151
Montgomery Adult S Adult
3240 Palm Ave 92154 619-600-3800
Adriana Sanchez-Aldana, prin. Fax 423-7876

Academy of Our Lady of Peace 700/9-12
4860 Oregon St 92116 619-297-2266
Lauren Lek, prin. Fax 297-2473
Alliant International University Post-Sec.
10455 Pomerado Rd 92131 858-635-4772
Argosy University San Diego Post-Sec.
1615 Murray Canyon Ste 100 92108 619-321-3000
Art Institute of California - San Diego Post-Sec.
7650 Mission Valley Rd 92108 858-598-1200
Associated Technical College Post-Sec.
707 Broadway Ste 300 92101 619-234-2181
Avance Beauty College Post-Sec.
750 Beyer Way Ste B 92154 619-575-1511
Balboa City S 100/K-12
525 Hawthorn St 92101 619-298-2990
Dr. Stephen Parker, dir. Fax 295-8886
Bethel Seminary Post-Sec.
6116 Arosa St 92115 619-325-5200
California College San Diego Post-Sec.
2820 Camino Del Rio S # 300 92108 619-680-4430
CA International Business University Post-Sec.
520 W Ash St 92101 619-702-9400
California Miramar University Post-Sec.
9750 Miramar Rd Ste 180 92126 858-653-3000
California Western School of Law Post-Sec.
225 Cedar St 92101 619-239-0391
Career College of San Diego Post-Sec.
3350 Market St 92102 619-338-0813
Cathedral Catholic HS 9-12
5555 Del Mar Heights Rd 92130 858-523-4000
Michael Deely, prin. Fax 523-4097
Childrens Creative/Performing Arts Acad. 200/PK-12
3051 El Cajon Blvd 92104 619-584-2454
Janet Cherif, prin. Fax 584-2422
Coleman University Post-Sec.
8888 Balboa Ave 92123 858-499-0202
Concorde Career Institute Post-Sec.
4393 Imperial Ave Ste 100 92113 619-688-0800
Design Institute of San Diego Post-Sec.
8555 Commerce Ave 92121 858-566-1200
DeVry University Post-Sec.
2655 Camino Del Rio N #350 92108 619-683-2446
Fashion Careers College Post-Sec.
1923 Morena Blvd 92110 619-275-4700
FIDM Fashion Institute of Design Post-Sec.
350 10th Ave Fl 3 92101 619-235-2049
Halstrom HS 50/7-12
9988 Hibert St Ste 210 92131 619-549-6290
Kimberly Haagan, dir. Fax 549-6292
High Tech High Graduate School of Educ Post-Sec.
2855 Farragut Rd 92106 619-398-4902
Horizon College of San Diego Post-Sec.
5331 Mount Alifan Dr 92111 858-695-8587
Horizon JSHS 400/7-12
5331 Mount Alifan Dr 92111 858-244-0333
Chris Johnson, prin. Fax 654-3054
International Prof School of Body Work Post-Sec.
9025 Balboa Ave Ste 130 92123 858-505-1000
ITT Technical Institute Post-Sec.
9680 Granite Ridge Dr 92123 858-571-8500
John Paul the Great Catholic University Post-Sec.
10174 Old Grove Rd Ste 200 92131 858-653-6740
Kaplan College Post-Sec.
9055 Balboa Ave 92123 800-935-1857
Maranatha Christian S 600/PK-12
9050 Maranatha Dr 92127 858-759-9737
Glen Goldie, supt. Fax 759-4001
Marinello School of Beauty Post-Sec.
7550 Miramar Rd Ste 440 92126 858-547-9260
Maritime Institute Post-Sec.
1310 Rosecrans St Ste G 92106 619-225-1783

Mueller College Post-Sec.
123 Camino De La Reina 92108 619-291-9811
Newschool of Architecture & Design Post-Sec.
1249 F St 92101 619-684-8800
Ocean View Christian Academy 200/PK-12
2460 Palm Ave 92154 619-424-7875
Stephen Johnson, prin. Fax 424-9204
Pacific College of Oriental Medicine Post-Sec.
7445 Mission Valley Rd #105 92108 619-574-6909
Parker S 700/6-12
6501 Linda Vista Rd 92111 858-569-7900
Kevin Yaley, head sch Fax 569-0621
Platt College Post-Sec.
6250 El Cajon Blvd 92115 619-265-0107
Point Loma Nazarene University Post-Sec.
3900 Lomaland Dr 92106 619-849-2200
Rock Academy 400/PK-12
2277 Rosecrans St 92106 619-764-5200
Dr. Richard Andujo, head sch Fax 764-5201
Sage College Post-Sec.
2820 Camino Del Rio S # 100 92108 619-683-2727
St. Augustine HS 700/9-12
3266 Nutmeg St 92104 619-282-2184
Jim Horne, prin. Fax 282-1203
San Diego City College Post-Sec.
1313 Park Blvd 92101 619-388-3400
San Diego Jewish Academy 600/K-12
11860 Carmel Creek Rd 92130 858-704-3700
Chaim Heller, head sch Fax 704-3850
San Diego Mesa College Post-Sec.
7250 Mesa College Dr 92111 619-388-2600
San Diego Miramar College Post-Sec.
10440 Black Mountain Rd 92126 619-388-7800
San Diego State University Post-Sec.
5500 Campanile Dr 92182 619-594-5200
Southern States University Post-Sec.
123 Camino De La Reina #100 92108 619-298-1829
Thomas Jefferson School of Law Post-Sec.
1155 Island Ave 92101 619-297-9700
Torah HS of San Diego 50/9-12
9001 Towne Centre Dr 92122 858-558-6880
Rabbi Michoel Peikes, dir. Fax 558-6835
Travel University International Post-Sec.
3625 Ruffin Rd Ste 308 92123 858-292-9755
United Truck Driving School Post-Sec.
2425 Camino Del Rio S 92108 619-296-2020
University of San Diego Post-Sec.
5998 Alcala Park 92110 619-260-4600
Veterans Affairs Medical Center Post-Sec.
3350 La Jolla Village Dr 92161 858-552-8585
Waldorf S of San Diego 300/PK-12
3547 Altadena Ave 92105 619-280-8016
Johannes Lasthaus, admin. Fax 280-8071

San Dimas, Los Angeles, Pop. 32,412
Bonita USD 9,800/K-12
115 W Allen Ave 91773 909-971-8200
Dr. Gary Rapkin, supt. Fax 971-8329
www.bonita.k12.ca.us
Chaparral HS 100/Alt
115 W Allen Ave 91773 909-971-8240
Maureen Williams, prin. Fax 971-8249
Lone Hill MS 900/6-8
115 W Allen Ave 91773 909-971-8270
Sean Grycel, prin. Fax 971-8279
San Dimas HS 1,300/9-12
115 W Allen Ave 91773 909-971-8230
Michael Kelly, prin. Fax 971-8239
Vista Alternative S 100/Alt
115 W Allen Ave 91773 909-971-8242
Maureen Williams, prin. Fax 971-8249
Other Schools – See La Verne

Canyon View S, 762 Cypress St 91773 100/K-12
John Mann, prin. 909-599-1227
ITT Technical Institute Post-Sec.
650 W Cienega Ave 91773 909-971-2300
Life Pacific College Post-Sec.
1100 W Covina Blvd 91773 800-356-0001

San Fernando, Los Angeles, Pop. 23,530
Los Angeles USD
Supt. — See Los Angeles
Academy of Scientific Exploration 9-12
1001 Arroyo St 91340 818-838-3926
Maria Padilla, prin. Fax 838-3945
Arts, 1001 Arroyo St 91340 9-12
John Lawler, prin. 818-837-6428
Mission Continuation HS 100/Alt
11015 Omelveny Ave 91340 818-361-1777
Santiago Vides, prin. Fax 365-2592
San Fernando HS 3,200/9-12
11133 Omelveny Ave 91340 818-898-7600
Kenneth Lee, prin. Fax 365-7255
San Fernando MS 1,600/6-8
130 N Brand Blvd 91340 818-837-5400
Olivia Robledo, prin. Fax 365-8911
Social Justice Humanities Academy 9-12
1001 Arroyo St 91340 818-838-3915
Jose Navarro, prin. Fax 838-6759
Teacher Preparation Academy 9-12
1001 Arroyo St 91340 818-838-3946
Elizabeth Beltran, prin.

San Francisco, San Francisco, Pop. 773,534
Regional Occupational Center & Program
Supt. — None
San Francisco County ROP Vo/Tech
1098 Harrison St 94103 415-355-7711
Linda Wells, coord. Fax 355-7744

San Francisco County Office of Education 100/
555 Franklin St 94102 415-241-6000
Richard Carranza, supt. Fax 241-6012
www.sfusd.edu
Civic Center Secondary S Alt
727 Golden Gate Ave 94102 415-241-3000
Elisa Villafuerte, prin. Fax 241-6192

San Francisco USD 54,900/PK-12
555 Franklin St 94102 415-241-6000
Richard Carranza, supt. Fax 241-6012
www.sfusd.edu
Academy of Arts & Sciences 400/9-12
555 Portola Dr 94131 415-695-5700
Carmelo Sgarlato, prin. Fax 695-5326
Aptos MS 1,000/6-8
105 Aptos Ave 94127 415-469-4520
Doug Dent, prin. Fax 333-9038
Asawa San Francisco S of the Arts 600/9-12
555 Portola Dr 94131 415-695-5700
Carmelo Sgarlato, prin. Fax 695-5326
Balboa HS 1,400/9-12
1000 Cayuga Ave 94112 415-469-4090
Kevin Kerr, prin. Fax 469-0859
Burton Academic HS 700/9-12
400 Mansell St 94134 415-469-4550
William Kappenhagen, prin. Fax 239-6806
Carmichael MS 200/6-8
824 Harrison St 94107 415-291-7983
Lawrence Gotanco, prin. Fax 291-7985
Civic Center Secondary S 50/Alt
727 Golden Gate Ave 94102 415-241-3000
Elisa Villafuerte, prin. Fax 241-6192
Denman MS 600/6-8
241 Oneida Ave 94112 415-469-4535
Teresa Kohler, prin. Fax 585-8402
Downtown HS 200/9-12
693 Vermont St 94107 415-695-5860
Ellen Wong, prin. Fax 695-5863
Everett MS 300/6-8
450 Church St 94114 415-241-6344
Richard Curci, prin. Fax 241-6361
Francisco MS 600/6-8
2190 Powell St 94133 415-291-7900
Kenneth Lee, prin. Fax 291-7910
Galileo Academy of Science & Technology 2,100/9-12
1150 Francisco St 94109 415-749-3430
Marcus Blacksher, prin. Fax 771-2322
Giannini MS 1,200/6-8
3151 Ortega St 94122 415-759-2770
Michael Reichle, prin. Fax 664-8541
Hoover MS 1,100/6-8
2290 14th Ave 94116 415-759-2783
Thomas Graven, prin. Fax 759-2881
Independence HS 300/Alt
3045 Santiago St 94116 415-242-2528
Robert Maass, prin. Fax 242-2533
International Studies Academy 400/Alt
655 De Haro St 94107 415-695-5866
Paul Koh, prin. Fax 695-5864
Jordan S for Equity 200/Alt
325 La Grande Ave 94112 415-452-4922
Matt Alexander, admin. Fax 452-4927
King Academic MS 500/6-8
350 Girard St 94134 415-330-1500
Natalie Eberhard, prin. Fax 468-7295
Lick MS 600/6-8
1220 Noe St 94114 415-695-5675
Rita Nazarian, prin. Fax 695-5360
Lilienthal S Winifred Scott Campus 400/Alt
3630 Divisadero St 94123 415-749-3516
William Hack, prin. Fax 749-3431
Lincoln HS 2,100/9-12
2162 24th Ave 94116 415-759-2700
Barnaby Payne, prin. Fax 566-2224
Lowell HS 2,600/9-12
1101 Eucalyptus Dr 94132 415-759-2730
Andrew Ishibashi, prin. Fax 759-2742
Marina MS 900/6-8
3500 Fillmore St 94123 415-749-3495
Joanna Fong, prin. Fax 921-7539
Marshall HS 800/9-12
45 Conkling St 94124 415-695-5612
Martha Torres, prin. Fax 695-5438
Mission HS 800/9-12
3750 18th St 94114 415-241-6240
Eric Guthertz, prin. Fax 626-1641
O'Connell HS 600/9-12
2355 Folsom St 94110 415-695-5370
Mark Alvarado, prin. Fax 695-5379
Presidio MS 1,200/6-8
450 30th Ave 94121 415-750-8435
Tony Payne, prin. Fax 750-8445
Rooftop Alternative S - Mayeda Campus Alt
500 Corbett Ave 94114 415-522-6757
Jeff Burgos, prin. Fax 522-6763
Roosevelt MS 700/6-8
460 Arguello Blvd 94118 415-750-8446
Michael Reimer, prin. Fax 750-8455
San Francisco International HS 100/9-12
1050 York St 94110 415-695-5781
Sophia Geerdes, prin. Fax 695-5402
Visitacion Valley MS 300/6-8
450 Raymond Ave 94134 415-469-4590
Gloria Minjares, prin. Fax 469-4703
Wallenberg HS 700/9-12
40 Vega St 94115 415-749-3469
Cheryl Foster, prin. Fax 346-7303
Washington HS 2,300/9-12
600 32nd Ave 94121 415-750-8400
Ericka Lovrin, prin. Fax 750-8417
Wells HS 200/Alt
1099 Hayes St 94117 415-241-6315
Richard Duber, prin. Fax 241-6317

Academy of Art University Post-Sec.
79 New Montgomery St Fl 4 94105 415-274-2200
Alliant International University Post-Sec.
1 Beach St Ste 100 94133 415-955-2100
Alliant International University Post-Sec.
20 Haight St 94102 415-626-5550
American Coll of Traditional Chinese Med Post-Sec.
455 Arkansas St 94107 415-282-7600
American Conservatory Theater Post-Sec.
30 Grant Ave Fl 6 94108 415-439-2350

Archbishop Riordan HS 600/9-12
175 Phelan Ave 94112 415-586-8200
Kevin Asbra, prin. Fax 587-1310

Art Institute of California - San Fran Post-Sec.
1170 Market St 94102 888-493-3261

Bay S of San Francisco 300/9-12
35 Keyes Ave 94129 415-561-5800
Timothy Johnson, head sch Fax 561-5808

California College of the Arts Post-Sec.
1111 8th St 94107 415-703-9500

California Culinary Academy Post-Sec.
350 Rhode Island St 94103 415-771-3500

California Institute of Integral Studies Post-Sec.
1453 Mission St 94103 415-575-6100

City College of San Francisco Post-Sec.
50 Phelan Ave 94112 415-239-3000

Convent of the Sacred Heart HS 200/9-12
2222 Broadway St 94115 415-563-2900
Mary Forsyth, prin. Fax 929-0553

Cornerstone Academy 400/5-12
501 Cambridge St 94134 415-585-5183
Derrick Wong, prin. Fax 469-9600

De Marillac Academy 100/4-8
175 Golden Gate Ave 94102 415-552-5220
Christopher Giangregorio, prin. Fax 621-5632

Drew S 200/9-12
2901 California St 94115 415-409-3739
Samuel Cuddeback, head sch Fax 346-0720

Everest College Post-Sec.
814 Mission St Ste 500 94103 415-777-2500

FIDM Fashion Institute of Design Post-Sec.
55 Stockton St 94108 415-675-5200

French-American International S 1,000/PK-12
150 Oak St 94102 415-558-2000
Jane Camblin, head sch Fax 558-2024

Golden Gate University Post-Sec.
536 Mission St 94105 415-442-7000

Heald College Post-Sec.
875 Howard St Ste 100 94103 415-808-3000

Immaculate Conception Academy 200/9-12
3625 24th St 94110 415-824-2052
Lisa Graham, prin. Fax 821-4677

Jewish Community HS of the Bay 200/9-12
1835 Ellis St 94115 415-345-9777
Rabbi Howard Ruben, head sch Fax 345-1888

Kampner Hebrew Academy 100/PK-12
645 14th Ave 94118 415-752-7333
Katheryn Schopp, prin. Fax 752-5851

Lick-Wilmerding HS 400/9-12
755 Ocean Ave 94112 415-333-4021
Eric Temple, head sch Fax 586-0737

Lycee Francais de San Francisco 400/6-12
1201 Ortega St 94122 415-661-5232
Marc Rossano, hdmstr. Fax 661-0246

Mercy HS 500/9-12
3250 19th Ave 94132 415-334-0525
Dr. Dorothy McCrea, prin. Fax 334-9726

New Charter University Post-Sec.
543 Howard St Fl 5 94105 415-813-5970

Olivet University Post-Sec.
250 4th St 94103 415-371-0002

Sacred Heart Cathedral Prep S 1,300/9-12
1055 Ellis St 94109 415-775-6626
Gary Cannon, prin. Fax 931-6941

St. Ignatius College Prep S 1,400/9-12
2001 37th Ave 94116 415-731-7500
Patrick Ruff, prin. Fax 731-2227

St. John Orthodox Academy 100/K-12
6210 Geary Blvd 94121 415-221-3484
Hieromonk Irenei, admin. Fax 386-4368

San Francisco Art Institute Post-Sec.
800 Chestnut St 94133 415-771-7020

San Francisco Christian S 200/K-12
25 Whittier St 94112 415-586-1117
Mark Asire, admin. Fax 841-0833

San Francisco Conservatory of Music Post-Sec.
50 Oak St 94102 800-899-7326

San Francisco State University Post-Sec.
1600 Holloway Ave 94132 415-338-1111

San Francisco University HS 400/9-12
3065 Jackson St 94115 415-447-3100
Dr. Michael Diamonti, hdmstr. Fax 447-5801

San Francisco Waldorf S 400/PK-12
2938 Washington St 94115 415-931-2750
Dan Ingoglia, admin. Fax 931-0590

Saybrook University Post-Sec.
747 Front St Fl 3 94111 800-825-4480

Stuart Hall HS 200/9-12
1715 Octavia St 94109 415-345-5811
Anthony Farrell, prin. Fax 931-9161

University of California Post-Sec.
PO Box 244 94143 415-476-9000

University of CA Hastings College of Law Post-Sec.
200 McAllister St 94102 415-565-4600

University of San Francisco Post-Sec.
2130 Fulton St 94117 415-422-5555

Urban S of San Francisco 400/9-12
1563 Page St 94117 415-626-2919
Mark Salkind, head sch Fax 626-1125

Woodside International S 100/6-12
1555 Irving St 94122 415-564-1063
John Edwards, hdmstr. Fax 564-2511

San Gabriel, Los Angeles, Pop. 39,114

Alhambra USD
Supt. — See Alhambra

San Gabriel HS 2,400/9-12
801 S Ramona St 91776 626-308-2352
James Schofield, prin. Fax 308-2332

San Gabriel USD 5,400/K-12
408 Junipero Serra Dr 91776 626-451-5400
David Yoshihara Ed.D., supt. Fax 451-5494
www.sgusd.k12.ca.us

Del Mar HS 100/Alt
312 S Del Mar Ave 91776 626-291-5723
Lon Sellers, prin. Fax 291-2540

Gabrielino HS 1,800/9-12
1327 S San Gabriel Blvd 91776 626-573-2453
Sharron Heinrich, prin. Fax 573-5089

Jefferson MS 1,200/6-8
1372 E Las Tunas Dr 91776 626-287-5260
Dr. Kaivan Yuen, prin. Fax 285-5387

San Gabriel Academy 400/PK-12
8827 E Broadway 91776 626-292-1156
Paul Negrete, prin. Fax 285-4949

San Gabriel Mission HS 300/9-12
254 S Santa Anita Ave 91776 626-282-3181
Jamie Collins M.A., prin. Fax 282-4209

Sanger, Fresno, Pop. 24,008

Regional Occupational Center & Program
Supt. — None

Valley ROP Vo/Tech
1305 Q St 93657 559-646-3591
Debbe Marvin, dir. Fax 646-3593

Sanger USD 10,800/K-12
1905 7th St 93657 559-524-6521
Marcus Johnson, supt. Fax 875-0311
www.sanger.k12.ca.us/

Community Day S 100/Alt
818 L St 93657 559-524-6630
Nick Taylor, prin. Fax 875-6379

Kings River Continuation HS 100/Alt
1801 7th St 93657 559-524-6490
Rick Church, prin. Fax 875-0676

Sanger HS 2,800/9-12
1045 Bethel Ave 93657 559-524-7121
Dan Chacon, prin. Fax 875-5721

Taft Independent Study 100/Alt
1801 7th St 93657 559-524-6490
Rick Church, prin. Fax 875-0676

Washington Academic MS 1,600/6-8
1705 10th St 93657 559-524-7015
Jamie Nino, prin. Fax 875-6365

Sanger Adult S Adult
1045 Bethel Ave 93657 559-524-7203
Nancy Penny, prin. Fax 875-1820

San Jacinto, Riverside, Pop. 42,978

San Jacinto USD 9,100/K-12
2045 S San Jacinto Ave 92583 951-929-7700
Fax 658-3574
www.sanjacinto.k12.ca.us/

Monte Vista MS 1,000/6-8
181 N Ramona Blvd 92583 951-654-9361
Dr. Sharon Raffiee, prin. Fax 654-0173

Mountain View HS Mountain Heights Acad 300/Alt
1000 N Ramona Blvd 92582 951-487-7710
Cliff Weaver, prin. Fax 487-7718

North Mountain MS 1,000/6-8
1202 E 7th St 92583 951-487-7797
Sandra Penaloza, prin. Fax 487-7799

San Jacinto HS 2,100/9-12
500 Idyllwild Dr 92583 951-654-7374
Garry Packham, prin. Fax 654-7702

San Jacinto Leadership Academy 6-8
1599 Malaga Dr 92583 951-929-1954
Col. Francis Sick, prin.

Mt. San Jacinto College Post-Sec.
1499 N State St 92583 951-487-6752

San Joaquin, Fresno, Pop. 3,985

Golden Plains USD 1,900/K-12
PO Box 937 93660 559-693-1115
Jesus Cruz, supt. Fax 693-4366
www.gpusd.org
Other Schools – See Tranquillity

San Jose, Santa Clara, Pop. 914,803

Alum Rock UNESD 12,900/K-8
2930 Gay Ave 95127 408-928-6800
Stephen Fiss, supt. Fax 928-6416
www.arusd.org/

Fischer MS 600/6-8
1720 Hopkins Dr 95122 408-928-7500
Howard Greenfield, prin. Fax 928-7501

George MS 600/6-8
277 Mahoney Dr 95127 408-928-7600
Melissa Howell, prin. Fax 928-7601

Mathson MS 700/6-8
2050 Kammerer Ave 95116 408-928-7950
Jackie Montejano, prin. Fax 928-7951

Ocala MS 600/6-8
2800 Ocala Ave 95148 408-928-8350
Oscar Leon, prin. Fax 928-8351

Renaissance Academy 300/6-8
1720 Hopkins Dr 95122 408-928-1950
Doug Kleinhenz, prin. Fax 928-1951

Sheppard MS 800/6-8
480 Rough and Ready Rd 95133 408-928-8800
Imee Almazan, prin. Fax 928-8801

Berryessa UNESD 8,200/K-8
1376 Piedmont Rd 95132 408-923-1800
Will Ector, supt. Fax 923-0623
www.berryessa.k12.ca.us

Morrill MS 900/6-8
1970 Morrill Ave 95132 408-923-1930
Anjanette Winckler, prin. Fax 946-0776

Piedmont MS 900/6-8
955 Piedmont Rd 95132 408-923-1945
Steve Hamm, prin. Fax 251-2392

Sierramont MS 1,000/6-8
3155 Kimlee Dr 95132 408-923-1955
Chris Mosley, prin. Fax 729-5840

Campbell UNESD
Supt. — See Campbell

Monroe MS 900/5-8
1055 S Monroe St 95128 408-556-0360
Dawnel Sonntag, prin. Fax 341-7020

Campbell UNHSD 7,600/9-12
3235 Union Ave 95124 408-371-0960
Fax 558-3006
www.cuhsd.org/

Boynton Alternative HS 200/Alt
901 Boynton Ave 95117 408-626-3404
Fax 984-8917

Branham HS 1,400/9-12
1570 Branham Ln 95118 408-626-3407
Fax 267-2676

Camden Community Day S 50/Alt
2223 Camden Ave 95124 408-626-3409
Fax 558-3000

Del Mar HS 1,300/9-12
1224 Del Mar Ave Ste A 95128 408-626-3403
Fax 295-9476

Leigh HS 1,700/9-12
5210 Leigh Ave 95124 408-626-3405
Fax 265-7525

Campbell Adult & Community Education Adult
1224 Del Mar Ave 95128 408-371-0960
Fax 947-2342

Other Schools – See Campbell, Saratoga

Cupertino UNSD
Supt. — See Cupertino

Miller MS 1,200/6-8
6151 Rainbow Dr 95129 408-252-3755
Steven Burrell, prin. Fax 255-5269

East Side UNHSD 25,500/K-12
830 N Capitol Ave 95133 408-347-5000
Chris Funk, supt. Fax 347-5045
www.esuhsd.org

Apollo Continuation HS 200/Alt
1835 Cunningham Ave 95122 408-928-5400
Vito Chiala, dir.

Evergreen Valley HS 2,700/9-12
3300 Quimby Rd 95148 408-347-7000
Ana Lomas, prin. Fax 347-7175

Foothill HS 300/Alt
230 Pala Ave 95127 408-928-9100
Lynne Murray, prin. Fax 928-9115

Hill HS 2,300/9-12
3200 Senter Rd 95111 408-347-4100
Bettina Lopez, prin. Fax 347-4115

Independence HS 3,400/9-12
1776 Educational Park Dr 95133 408-928-9500
Grettel Castro-Stanley, prin. Fax 928-9515

Lick HS 1,300/9-12
57 N White Rd 95127 408-347-4400
Glenn Vanderzee, prin. Fax 347-4415

Mt. Pleasant HS 1,700/9-12
1750 S White Rd 95127 408-937-2800
Teresa Marquez, prin. Fax 937-2815

Oak Grove HS 2,100/9-12
285 Blossom Hill Rd 95123 408-347-6500
Martha Brazil, prin. Fax 347-6515

Overfelt HS 1,500/9-12
1835 Cunningham Ave 95122 408-347-5900
Vito Chiala, prin. Fax 347-5915

Pegasus HS 100/Alt
1776 Educational Park Dr 95133 408-928-9597
Grettel Castro-Stanley, coord. Fax 928-9535

Phoenix HS 100/Alt
6150 Snell Ave 95123 408-347-6291
Greg Louie, prin. Fax 347-6295

Piedmont Hills HS 2,200/9-12
1377 Piedmont Rd 95132 408-347-3800
Traci Williams, prin. Fax 347-3805

Santa Teresa HS 2,200/9-12
6150 Snell Ave 95123 408-347-6200
Greg Louie, prin. Fax 347-6215

Silver Creek HS 2,500/9-12
3434 Silver Creek Rd 95121 408-347-5600
Adolfo Laguna, prin. Fax 347-5615

Yerba Buena HS 1,600/9-12
1855 Lucretia Ave 95122 408-347-4700
Tom Huynh, prin. Fax 347-4715

East Side Adult Center Adult
625 Educational Park Dr 95133 408-928-9300
Richard Uribe, dir. Fax 928-9309

Evergreen ESD 13,400/K-8
3188 Quimby Rd 95148 408-270-6800
Kathy Gomez, supt. Fax 274-3894
www.eesd.org/

Chaboya MS 1,000/7-8
3276 Fowler Rd 95135 408-270-6900
Derrick Watkins, prin. Fax 270-6916

LeyVa IS 900/7-8
1865 Monrovia Dr 95122 408-270-4993
Dolores Garcia, prin. Fax 270-5462

Quimby Oak MS 1,000/7-8
3190 Quimby Rd 95148 408-270-6735
Phil Bond, prin. Fax 223-4533

Franklin-McKinley ESD 10,500/K-8
645 Wool Creek Dr 95112 408-283-6000
Dr. John Porter, supt. Fax 283-6022
www.fmsd.org

Sylvandale MS 800/7-8
653 Sylvandale Ave 95111 408-363-5700
Dan Fowler, prin. Fax 363-5649

Fremont UNHSD
Supt. — See Sunnyvale

Lynbrook HS 1,800/9-12
1280 Johnson Ave 95129 408-366-7700
Gail Davidson, prin. Fax 257-0551

Moreland ESD 4,200/K-8
4711 Campbell Ave 95130 408-874-2900
Mark Barmore, supt. Fax 374-8863
www.moreland.org

Moreland MS 900/6-8
4600 Student Ln 95130 408-875-3300
Karen Allard, prin. Fax 379-3622

Morgan Hill USD
Supt. — See Morgan Hill
Murphy MS 600/7-8
141 Avenida Espana 95139 408-201-6260
Joey Adame, prin. Fax 201-6270

Mount Pleasant ESD 2,600/PK-8
3434 Marten Ave 95148 408-223-3700
Mariann Engle, supt. Fax 223-3715
www.mountpleasant.k12.ca.us
Boeger MS 800/6-8
1944 Flint Ave 95148 408-223-3770
Diane Haywood, prin. Fax 223-6959

Oak Grove ESD 11,500/K-8
6578 Santa Teresa Blvd 95119 408-227-8300
Jose Manzo, supt. Fax 629-7183
www.ogsd.k12.ca.us
Academy 50/Alt
6578 Santa Teresa Blvd 95119 408-226-2350
Oscar Ortiz, prin. Fax 227-2719
Bernal IS 900/7-8
6610 San Ignacio Ave 95119 408-578-5731
Jeannette McCuller, prin. Fax 578-7367
Davis IS 800/7-8
5035 Edenview Dr 95111 408-227-0616
Derek Grasty, prin. Fax 224-8957
Herman IS 900/5-8
5955 Blossom Ave 95123 408-226-1886
Laura Meusel, prin. Fax 226-1897

Regional Occupational Center & Program
Supt. — None
Metropolitan Education District Vo/Tech
760 Hillsdale Ave 95136 408-723-6464
Paul Hay, supt. Fax 723-7266

San Jose USD 33,000/K-12
855 Lenzen Ave 95126 408-535-6000
Dr. Vincent Matthews, supt. Fax 535-2362
www.sjusd.org
Broadway HS 200/Alt
4825 Speak Ln 95118 408-535-6285
Stephanie Ogden, prin. Fax 264-6392
Burnett Academy 900/6-8
850 N 2nd St 95112 408-535-6267
Lisa Aguerria-Lewis, prin. Fax 298-1675
Castillero MS 1,300/6-8
6384 Leyland Park Dr 95120 408-535-6385
Katrina Johnson, prin. Fax 268-4489
Gunderson HS 1,100/9-12
622 Gaundabert Ln 95136 408-535-6340
Domenic Bejarano, prin. Fax 224-2209
Gunderson Plus Continuation HS 50/Alt
622 Gaundabert Ln 95136 408-972-8629
Dane Caldwell-Holden, prin.
Harte MS 1,200/6-8
7050 Bret Harte Dr 95120 408-535-6270
Cyndi Maijala, prin. Fax 927-0698
Hoover MS 1,000/6-8
1635 Park Ave 95126 408-535-6274
Mary Martinez, prin. Fax 286-4864
Leland HS 1,800/9-12
6677 Camden Ave 95120 408-535-6290
Deepa Mukherjee, prin. Fax 927-6448
Leland Plus Continuation HS 50/Alt
6677 Camden Ave 95120 408-535-6100
Dane Caldwell-Holden, prin.
Liberty MSHS 400/Alt
5845 Allen Ave 95123 408-229-0722
Dane Caldwell-Holden, prin. Fax 225-5348
Lincoln HS 1,700/9-12
555 Dana Ave 95126 408-535-6300
Matt Hewitson, prin. Fax 535-2352
Lincoln Plus S, 1999 Olive Ave 95128 50/Alt
Dane Caldwell-Holden, prin. 408-292-3794
Middle College HS 50/Alt
2100 Moorpark Ave 95128 408-288-3100
Dane Caldwell-Holden, prin.
Muir MS 1,100/6-8
1260 Branham Ln 95118 408-535-6281
Gloria Marchant, prin. Fax 535-2319
O'Connor Career Academy Vo/Tech
2105 Forest Ave 95128 408-947-2852
Dane Caldwell-Holden, prin.
Pioneer HS 1,600/9-12
1290 Blossom Hill Rd 95118 408-535-6310
Stefani Garino, prin. Fax 535-2357
Pioneer Plus Continuation HS 50/Alt
1290 Blossom Hill Rd 95118 408-264-4428
Dane Caldwell-Holden, prin.
San Jose Community Day S 50/Alt
1155 E Julian St 95116 408-279-2550
Rosa Nieto, prin. Fax 280-7306
San Jose High Academy Plus 50/Alt
275 N 24th St 95116 408-287-1631
Dane Caldwell-Holden, prin.
San Jose HS Academy 1,200/9-12
275 N 24th St 95116 408-535-6320
Cary Catching, prin. Fax 535-2355
Willow Glen HS 1,500/9-12
2001 Cottle Ave 95125 408-535-6330
Kaia Hamilton, prin. Fax 535-2353
Willow Glen MS 1,300/6-8
2105 Cottle Ave 95125 408-535-6277
Shannon McGee, prin. Fax 535-2353
Willow Glen Plus HS 50/Alt
2001 Cottle Ave 95125 408-264-4422
Dane Caldwell-Holden, prin.

Santa Clara County Office of Education 3,300/
1290 Ridder Park Dr 95131 408-453-6500
Xavier De La Torre Ed.D., supt. Fax 453-6601
www.sccoe.org
EDGE S 50/Alt
258 Sunol St 95126 408-573-3250
Carey Johnson, prin. Fax 226-5419

Union ESD 4,800/K-8
5175 Union Ave 95124 408-377-8010
Jacqueline Horejs Ed.D., supt. Fax 377-7182
www.unionsd.org
Dartmouth MS 700/6-8
5575 Dartmouth Dr 95118 408-264-1122
Randy Martino, prin. Fax 264-9332
Union MS 800/6-8
2130 Los Gatos Almaden Rd 95124 408-371-0366
Todd Feinberg, prin. Fax 371-1217

Apostles Lutheran S 200/PK-10
5828 Santa Teresa Blvd 95123 408-578-4800
Ben Washburn, prin. Fax 225-0720
Archbishop Mitty HS 1,700/9-12
5000 Mitty Way 95129 408-252-6610
Timothy Brosnan, prin. Fax 252-6967
Bellarmine College Prep S 1,600/9-12
960 W Hedding St 95126 408-294-9224
Chris Meyercord, prin. Fax 297-5585
Carrington College California Post-Sec.
6201 San Ignacio Ave 95119 408-360-0840
Center of Employment Training Post-Sec.
701 Vine St 95110 408-287-7924
DeVry University Post-Sec.
2160 Lundy Ave Ste 250 95131 408-571-3760
Everest College Post-Sec.
1245 S Wnchstr Blvd #102 95128 408-246-4171
Evergreen Valley College Post-Sec.
3095 Yerba Buena Rd 95135 408-274-7900
Five Branches University Post-Sec.
3031 Tisch Way Ste 507 95128 408-260-0208
Harker MS 500/6-8
3800 Blackford Ave 95117 408-248-2510
Christopher Nikoloff, hdmstr. Fax 248-2502
Harker Upper S 700/9-12
500 Saratoga Ave 95129 408-249-2510
Christopher Nikoloff, hdmstr. Fax 984-2325
International Technological University Post-Sec.
355 W San Fernando St 95110 888-488-4968
Liberty Baptist S 200/K-12
2790 S King Rd 95122 408-274-5613
Russel Barnes, prin. Fax 274-1363
National Hispanic University Post-Sec.
14271 Story Rd 95127 408-254-6900
Notre Dame HS 600/9-12
596 S 2nd St 95112 408-294-1113
Mary Beth Riley, prin. Fax 293-9779
Palmer College of Chiropractic West Cmps Post-Sec.
90 E Tasman Dr 95134 408-944-6000
Presentation HS 800/9-12
2281 Plummer Ave 95125 408-264-1664
Mary Miller, prin. Fax 266-3028
Sacred Heart Nativity Schools 100/6-8
310 Edwards Ave 95110 408-993-1293
Jeff Cunjak, prin. Fax 292-0172
Saint Francis Career College Post-Sec.
749 Story Rd Ste 50 95122 408-286-8903
San Jose City College Post-Sec.
2100 Moorpark Ave 95128 408-298-2181
San Jose State University Post-Sec.
1 Washington Sq 95192 408-924-1000
Silicon Valley University Post-Sec.
2160 Lundy Ave Ste 110 95131 408-435-8989
Stratford MS, 1718 Andover Ln 95124 100/6-8
Maggie Schwartz, prin. 408-626-0001
Valley Christian HS 1,400/9-12
100 Skyway Dr Ste 110 95111 408-513-2400
Mark Lodewyk, prin. Fax 513-2424
Valley Christian JHS 600/6-8
100 Skyway Dr Ste 140 95111 408-513-2460
Lisa Arnett, prin. Fax 513-2466
WestMed College-San Jose Post-Sec.
3031 Tisch Way 95128 408-236-1170

San Juan Bautista, San Benito, Pop. 1,810
Aromas/San Juan USD 1,200/PK-12
2300 San Juan Hwy 95045 831-623-4500
Willard McCabe, supt. Fax 623-4907
www.asjusd.k12.ca.us
Anzar HS 400/9-12
2000 San Juan Hwy 95045 831-623-7660
Charlene McKowen, prin. Fax 623-7676

San Juan Capistrano, Orange, Pop. 33,954
Capistrano USD 51,400/K-12
33122 Valle Rd 92675 949-234-9200
Joseph Farley Ed.D., supt. Fax 493-8729
capousd.ca.schoolloop.com/
Forster MS 1,400/6-8
25601 Camino Del Avion 92675 949-234-5907
Carrie Bertini, prin. Fax 488-3567
Junipero Serra HS 200/Alt
31422 Camino Capistrano 92675 949-489-7216
Joshua Hill, prin. Fax 496-2007
San Juan Hills HS 1,500/9-12
29211 Vista Montana 92675 949-234-5900
Tom Ressler, prin. Fax 488-9727
Capistrano Unified Adult Education Adult
31431 El Camino Real 92675 949-493-0658
Jolene Dougherty, prin. Fax 489-1421
Other Schools – See Aliso Viejo, Dana Point, Ladera Ranch, Laguna Niguel, Mission Viejo, Rancho Santa Margarita, San Clemente

Regional Occupational Center & Program
Supt. — None
Capistrano-Laguna Beach ROP Vo/Tech
31522 El Camino Real 92675 949-496-3118
Richard Bogart, dir. Fax 496-1850

Capistrano Valley Christian S 400/PK-12
32032 Del Obispo St 92675 949-493-5683
Dr. Ronald Sipus, head sch Fax 493-6057
JSerra HS 1,000/9-12
26351 Junipero Serra Rd 92675 949-493-9307
Dr. John Freeh, prin. Fax 493-9308

Saddleback Valley Christian S 800/PK-12
26333 Oso Rd 92675 949-443-4050
Edward Carney, admin. Fax 443-3941
St. Margaret Episcopal S 1,200/PK-12
31641 La Novia Ave 92675 949-661-0108
William Moseley, head sch Fax 661-8637

San Leandro, Alameda, Pop. 81,465
San Leandro USD 8,800/K-12
14735 Juniper St 94579 510-667-3500
Dr. Mike McLaughlin, supt. Fax 667-3569
www.sanleandro.k12.ca.us
Bancroft MS 1,000/6-8
1150 Bancroft Ave 94577 510-618-4380
Jonathan Ferrer, prin. Fax 895-4113
Lincoln HS 100/Alt
2600 Teagarden St 94577 510-618-4460
Fax 614-2018
Muir MS 1,000/6-8
1444 Williams St 94577 510-618-4400
Belen Magers, prin. Fax 667-3545
San Leandro HS 2,800/9-12
2200 Bancroft Ave 94577 510-618-4600
Linda Granger, prin. Fax 347-1064
San Leandro Adult S Adult
2255 Bancroft Ave 94577 510-618-4420
Bradley Frazier, prin. Fax 352-2183

San Lorenzo USD
Supt. — See San Lorenzo
Washington Manor MS 900/6-8
1170 Fargo Ave 94579 510-317-5500
James Gray, prin. Fax 317-5597

Carrington College California Post-Sec.
15555 E 14th St Ste 500 94578 510-276-3888
Chinese Christian S 600/K-12
750 Fargo Ave 94579 510-351-4957
Robin Hom, supt. Fax 351-1789

San Lorenzo, Alameda, Pop. 22,527
San Lorenzo USD 11,900/K-12
15510 Usher St 94580 510-317-4600
Dennis Byas, supt. Fax 278-4344
www.slzusd.org
Arroyo HS 1,800/9-12
15701 Lorenzo Ave 94580 510-317-4000
Larry Smith, prin. Fax 278-9067
Bohannon MS 1,000/6-8
800 Bockman Rd 94580 510-317-3800
Margaret Arman, prin. Fax 278-7794
Edendale MS 500/6-8
16160 Ashland Ave 94580 510-317-5100
John Shimko, prin. Fax 317-5190
San Lorenzo HS 1,400/9-12
50 E Lewelling Blvd 94580 510-317-3000
Tovi Scruggs, prin. Fax 278-0547
San Lorenzo Adult S Adult
820 Bockman Rd 94580 510-317-4200
John Kelly, prin. Fax 317-4291
Other Schools – See Hayward, San Leandro

Redwood Christian MSHS 400/6-12
1000 Paseo Grande 94580 510-317-8990
Al Hearne, prin. Fax 278-5064

San Luis Obispo, San Luis Obispo, Pop. 43,697
San Luis Coastal USD 7,100/PK-12
1500 Lizzie St 93401 805-549-1200
Dr. Eric Prater, supt. Fax 549-9074
www.slcusd.org
Laguna MS 700/7-8
11050 Los Osos Valley Rd 93405 805-596-4055
John Calandro, prin. Fax 544-2449
Pacific Beach HS 100/Alt
11950 Los Osos Valley Rd 93405 805-596-4023
Andrew Marinello, prin.
San Luis Obispo HS 1,500/9-12
1499 San Luis Dr 93401 805-596-4040
Leslie O'Connor, prin. Fax 542-9075
Adult S Adult
1500 Lizzie St Bldg G 93401 805-549-1222
Sally Ames, prin. Fax 544-0638
Other Schools – See Los Osos, Morro Bay

California Polytechnic State University Post-Sec.
1 Grand Ave 93407 805-756-1111
Central CA School of Continuing Educ. Post-Sec.
3195 McMillan Ave Ste F 93401 805-543-9123
Cuesta College Post-Sec.
PO Box 8106 93403 805-546-3100
Laurus College Post-Sec.
81 Higuera St Ste 110 93401 805-267-1690
Mission College Preparatory Catholic HS 300/9-12
682 Palm St 93401 805-543-2131
James Childs, prin. Fax 543-4359

San Marcos, San Diego, Pop. 80,807
San Diego County Office of Education
Supt. — See San Diego
North Coastal Consortium S PK-12
255 Pico Ave 92069 760-761-5110
John Kramer, prin.

San Marcos USD 18,600/K-12
255 Pico Ave Ste 250 92069 760-752-1299
Kevin Holt Ed.D., supt. Fax 471-4928
www.smusd.org/
Foothills HS 100/Alt
158 Cassou Rd 92069 760-290-2544
Mary Bunker, prin. Fax 736-2221
Mission Hills HS 2,500/9-12
1 E Mission Hills Ct 92069 760-290-2700
Courtney Goode, prin. Fax 290-2680
San Elijo MS 1,400/6-8
1600 Schoolhouse Way 92078 760-290-2800
Doug Hall, prin. Fax 290-2828

San Marcos HS 2,200/9-12
1615 W San Marcos Blvd 92078 760-290-2200
Julie Mottershaw, prin. Fax 736-8275
San Marcos MS 1,300/6-8
650 W Mission Rd 92069 760-290-2500
Tiffany Campbell, prin. Fax 744-0893
Twin Oaks HS 200/Alt
158 Cassou Rd 92069 760-290-2555
Mary Bunker, prin. Fax 736-2221
Woodland Park MS 1,300/6-8
1270 Rock Springs Rd 92069 760-290-2455
Brian Randall, prin. Fax 741-6178

California State University-San Marcos Post-Sec.
333 S Twin Oaks Valley Rd 92096 760-750-4000
Coleman University Post-Sec.
1284 W San Marcos Blvd 92078 760-747-3990
Palomar College Post-Sec.
1140 W Mission Rd 92069 760-744-1150
Palomar Institute of Cosmetology Post-Sec.
355 Via Vera Cruz Ste 3 92078 760-744-7900
Univ of St. Augustine for Health Science Post-Sec.
700 Windy Point Dr 92069 800-241-1027

San Marino, Los Angeles, Pop. 12,791
San Marino USD 3,200/K-12
1665 West Dr 91108 626-299-7000
Loren Kleinrock, supt. Fax 299-7010
www.smusd.us
Huntington MS 800/6-8
1700 Huntington Dr 91108 626-299-7060
David Murray, prin. Fax 299-7064
San Marino HS 1,100/9-12
2701 Huntington Dr 91108 626-299-7020
Keith Derrick, prin. Fax 299-7037

Southwestern Academy 100/6-12
2800 Monterey Rd 91108 626-799-5010
Kenneth R. Veronda, hdmstr. Fax 799-0407

San Mateo, San Mateo, Pop. 91,447
San Mateo County Office of Education
Supt. — See Redwood City
Gateway Center 8-12
35 Tower Rd 94402 650-598-2150
Melinda Fore, prin. Fax 598-2191

San Mateo UNHSD 8,400/9-12
650 N Delaware St 94401 650-558-2299
Scott Laurence, supt. Fax 762-0249
www.smuhsd.org
Aragon HS 1,600/9-12
900 Alameda De Las Pulgas 94402 650-558-2999
Patricia Kurtz, prin. Fax 558-2952
Hillsdale HS 1,300/9-12
3115 Del Monte St 94403 650-558-2699
Jeff Gilbert, prin. Fax 574-4173
San Mateo HS 1,300/9-12
506 N Delaware St 94401 650-558-2399
Yvonne Shiu, prin. Fax 558-2352
San Mateo Adult S Adult
789 E Poplar Ave 94401 650-558-2100
Lawrence Teshara, dir. Fax 762-0232
Other Schools – See Burlingame, Millbrae, San Bruno

San Mateo-Foster City ESD
Supt. — See Foster City
Abbott MS 800/6-8
600 36th Ave 94403 650-312-7600
Cathy Ennon, prin. Fax 312-7605
Bayside S.T.E.M. Academy 500/6-8
2025 Kehoe Ave 94403 650-312-7660
Jeanne Elliot, prin. Fax 312-7634
Borel MS 900/6-8
425 Barneson Ave 94402 650-312-7670
John Cosmos, prin. Fax 312-7644

Alpha Beacon Christian S 100/PK-12
525 42nd Ave 94403 650-212-4222
Chris Chu, prin. Fax 212-1026
College of San Mateo Post-Sec.
1700 W Hillsdale Blvd 94402 650-574-6161
Junipero Serra HS 1,000/9-12
451 W 20th Ave 94403 650-345-8207
Barry Thornton, prin. Fax 573-6638
Pacific Rim International S 100/PK-12
454 Peninsula Ave 94401 650-685-1881

San Pablo, Contra Costa, Pop. 28,206
West Contra Costa USD
Supt. — See Richmond
Helms MS 500/7-8
2500 Road 20 94806 510-233-3988
Jose DeLeon, prin. Fax 234-5977
Middle College HS 200/9-12
2600 Mission Bell Dr 94806 510-235-7800
Hattie Smith, prin. Fax 215-7927
North Campus Continuation HS 100/Alt
2465 Dolan Way 94806 510-231-1438
Paul Shatswell, prin. Fax 724-4795
Vista S 200/Alt
2625 Barnard St 94806 510-231-1431
Sherry Bell, prin. Fax 222-8357

Contra Costa College Post-Sec.
2600 Mission Bell Dr 94806 510-235-7800

San Pedro, See Los Angeles
Los Angeles USD
Supt. — See Los Angeles
Angels Gate Continuation S 100/Alt
3607 S Gaffey St 90731 310-221-4600
Joan D'Amore, prin. Fax 221-4629
Dana MS 1,600/6-8
1501 S Cabrillo Ave 90731 310-241-1100
Jesus Nunez, prin. Fax 514-9925

Johnston Community Day S 200/7-12
2210 N Taper Ave 90731 310-832-0376
Barbara Politz, prin. Fax 832-7914
San Pedro HS 3,100/9-12
1001 W 15th St 90731 310-241-5800
Jeanette Stevens, prin. Fax 547-3183
Harbor Community Adult S Adult
950 W Santa Cruz St 90731 310-547-4425
Lanny Nelms, prin. Fax 832-3489
Harbor Occupational Center Adult
740 N Pacific Ave 90731 310-547-5551
Gertrude Hawkins, prin. Fax 547-4979

Mary Star of the Sea HS 500/9-12
2500 N Taper Ave 90731 310-547-1138
Rita Dever, prin. Fax 547-1827
Rolling Hills Preparatory S 300/6-12
1 Rolling Hills Prep Way 90732 310-791-1101
Peter McCormack, head sch Fax 373-4931

San Rafael, Marin, Pop. 55,927
Dixie ESD 1,800/K-8
380 Nova Albion Way 94903 415-492-3700
Dr. Thomas Lohwasser, supt. Fax 492-3707
dixieschooldistrict.org
Miller Creek MS 600/6 8
2255 Las Gallinas Ave 94903 415-492-3760
Patricia Elliott, prin. Fax 492-3765

Marin County Office of Education 300/
PO Box 4925 94913 415-472-4110
Fax 491-6625
www.marinschools.org/
Marin County Community S 100/Alt
PO Box 4925 94913 415-491-0581
Raquel Rose, dir. Fax 491-0981

Regional Occupational Center & Program
Supt. — None
Marin County ROP Vo/Tech
PO Box 4925 94913 415-499-5892
Gene Abbott, coord. Fax 491-6622

San Rafael CSD 6,000/K-12
310 Nova Albion Way 94903 415-492-3233
Dr. Michael Watenpaugh, supt. Fax 492-3245
www.srcs.org
Davidson MS 800/6-8
280 Woodland Ave 94901 415-485-2400
Harriet MacLean, prin. Fax 485-2476
Madrone Continuation HS 100/Alt
185 Mission Ave 94901 415-485-2435
Jane Songer, prin. Fax 485-2438
San Rafael HS 900/9-12
185 Mission Ave 94901 415-485-2330
Kit Pappenheimer, prin. Fax 485-2345
Terra Linda HS 1,100/9-12
320 Nova Albion Way 94903 415-492-3100
Lars Christensen, prin. Fax 492-3105

Dominican University of California Post-Sec.
50 Acacia Ave 94901 415-457-4440
Marin Academy 400/9-12
1600 Mission Ave 94901 415-453-4550
Travis Brownley, head sch Fax 453-8538
Marin S 100/9-12
PO Box 4368 94913 415-339-9336
Barbara Brown, head sch Fax 339-9337

San Ramon, Contra Costa, Pop. 68,811
San Ramon Valley USD
Supt. — See Danville
California HS 2,500/9-12
9870 Broadmoor Dr 94583 925-803-3200
Mark Corti, prin. Fax 803-9341
Dougherty Valley HS 1,800/9-12
10550 Albion Rd, 925-479-6400
Jason Reimann, prin. Fax 479-6597
Gale Ranch MS 700/6-8
6400 Main Branch Rd, 925-479-1500
Lisa Ward, prin. Fax 479-1595
Iron Horse MS 1,000/6-8
12601 Alcosta Blvd 94583 925-824-2820
Joe Nguyen, prin. Fax 824-2830
Pine Valley MS 900/6-8
3000 Pine Valley Rd 94583 925-479-7700
Jason Law, prin. Fax 828-1972
Venture Independent Study S 300/Alt
10540 Albion Rd, 925-479-1200
Matt Hermann, prin. Fax 479-1297
Windemere Ranch MS 900/6-8
11611 E Branch Pkwy, 925-479-7400
David Bolin, prin. Fax 479-7469
San Ramon Adult Education Adult
10540 Albion Rd, 925-479-1200
Matt Hermann, prin.

Santa Ana, Orange, Pop. 321,180
Garden Grove USD
Supt. — See Garden Grove
Fitz IS 800/7-8
4600 W McFadden Ave 92704 714-663-6351
Mischelle Repsher, prin. Fax 663-6527

Regional Occupational Center & Program
Supt. — None
Central Orange County CTE Partnership Vo/Tech
2323 N Broadway Ste 301 92706 714-541-5537
Diana Schneider, dir. Fax 541-5214

Santa Ana USD 57,200/PK-12
1601 E Chestnut Ave 92701 714-558-5501
T. Melendez de Santa Ana Ph.D., supt. Fax 558-5610
www.sausd.us
Carr IS 1,700/6-8
2120 W Edinger Ave 92704 714-480-4100
Edward Bustamante, prin. Fax 957-8766

Century HS 2,200/9-12
1401 S Grand Ave 92705 714-568-7000
Lucinda Pueblos, prin. Fax 568-7038
Chavez HS 300/Alt
2128 Cypress Ave 92707 714-430-5700
Lisa Hinshaw, prin. Fax 430-5799
Community Day S 100/Alt
804 N Fairview St 92703 714-796-9000
Lisa Hinshaw, prin. Fax 796-9099
Godinez Fundamental HS 2,500/9-12
3002 W Centennial Rd 92704 714-433-6600
Cindy Landsiedel, prin. Fax 433-6731
Lathrop IS 1,300/6-8
1111 S Broadway 92707 714-567-3300
Adrian Ayala, prin. Fax 567-3399
MacArthur Fundamental IS 1,300/6-8
600 W Alton Ave 92707 714-513-9800
David Casper, prin. Fax 513-9899
McFadden IS 1,400/6-8
2701 S Raitt St 92704 714-435-3700
Ignacio Muniz, prin. Fax 435-3799
Mendez Fundamental IS 1,400/5-8
2000 N Bristol St 92706 714-972-7800
Dennis Cole, prin. Fax 972-7899
Middle College HS 300/9-12
1530 W 17th St 92706 714-953-3900
Claudia Flint, prin. Fax 953-3999
Saddleback HS 2,100/9-12
2802 S Flower St 92707 714-513-2900
Robert Laxton Ed.D., prin. Fax 513-2911
Santa Ana HS 3,200/9-12
520 W Walnut St 92701 714-567-4900
Julie Infante, prin. Fax 567-4952
Segerstrom HS 2,500/9-12
2301 W MacArthur Blvd 92704 714-241-5000
Amy Avina Ed.D., prin. Fax 241-5099
Sierra Preparatory Academy 900/6-8
2021 N Grand Ave 92705 714-567-3500
Jeff Bishop, prin. Fax 567-3591
Spurgeon IS 1,200/5-8
2701 W 5th St 92703 714-480-2200
Lillian Soto, prin. Fax 480-2215
Valley HS 2,400/9-12
1801 S Greenville St 92704 714-241-6410
Pat Yrarrazaval-Correa, prin. Fax 241-6547
Villa Fundamental IS 1,400/6-8
1441 E Chestnut Ave 92701 714-558-5100
Jonathan Swanson, prin. Fax 558-5103
Willard IS 1,000/5-8
1342 N Ross St 92706 714-480-4800
Lisa Hinshaw, prin. Fax 480-4899

Tustin USD
Supt. — See Tustin
Foothill HS 2,300/9-12
19251 Dodge Ave 92705 714-730-7464
Al Marzilli, prin. Fax 573-9376
Hewes MS 1,100/6-8
13232 Hewes Ave 92705 714-730-7348
Michele Boudreaux, prin. Fax 730-7315

Art Institute of California - Orange Co. Post-Sec.
3601 W Sunflower Ave 92704 714-830-0200
ATI College Post-Sec.
1125 E 17th St Ste N251 92701 714-730-7080
Bethel Baptist S 200/PK-12
901 S Euclid St 92704 714-839-3600
Fax 839-4953
California Coast University Post-Sec.
925 N Spurgeon St 92701 888-228-8648
Calvary Chapel S 1,600/K-12
3800 S Fairview St 92704 714-662-7485
Colleen O'Hara's Beauty Academy Post-Sec.
109 W 4th St Fl 2 92701 714-568-5399
Everest College Post-Sec.
500 W Santa Ana Blvd 92701 714-656-1000
Mater Dei HS 2,200/9-12
1202 W Edinger Ave 92707 714-754-7711
Frances Clare, prin. Fax 754-1880
Newbridge College Post-Sec.
1840 E 17th St Ste 140 92705 714-550-8000
Santa Ana College Post-Sec.
1530 W 17th St 92706 714-564-6000
Taft Law School Post-Sec.
3700 S Susan St Ste 200 92704 714-850-4800

Santa Barbara, Santa Barbara, Pop. 86,425
Regional Occupational Center & Program
Supt. — None
Santa Barbara County ROP Vo/Tech
PO Box 6307 93160 805-937-8427
Tony Bauer, dir. Fax 569-2507

Santa Barbara County Office of Education 300/
PO Box 6307 93160 805-964-4711
William Cirone, supt. Fax 964-4712
www.sbceo.org
Santa Barbara County Community S 7-12
PO Box 6307 93160 805-964-4711
Fred Razo, prin. Fax 967-0088
Summit HS 9-12
PO Box 6307 93160 805-965-7490
Mark Leufkens, prin. Fax 965-1460

Santa Barbara SD 15,100/PK-12
720 Santa Barbara St 93101 805-963-4331
David Cash, supt. Fax 962-3146
www.sbsdk12.org/
Alta Vista Alternative HS 100/Alt
215 E Ortega St 93101 805-965-1916
Kathleen Abney, prin.
La Colina JHS 800/7-8
4025 Foothill Rd 93110 805-967-4506
David Ortiz, prin. Fax 967-3056
La Cuesta Continuation HS 100/Alt
710 Santa Barbara St 93101 805-966-0883
Kathleen Abney, prin. Fax 963-8006

La Cumbre JHS 500/7-8
2255 Modoc Rd 93101 805-687-0761
Jo Ann Caines, prin. Fax 563-4636
San Marcos HS 1,900/9-12
4750 Hollister Ave 93110 805-967-4581
Ed Behrens, prin. Fax 967-8358
Santa Barbara HS 2,200/9-12
700 E Anapamu St 93103 805-966-9101
John Becchio, prin. Fax 965-6872
Santa Barbara JHS 800/7-8
721 E Cota St 93103 805-963-7751
Lito Garcia, prin. Fax 962-7196
Other Schools – See Goleta

Anacapa S 100/7-12
814 Santa Barbara St 93101 805-965-0228
Sheryn Sears, admin. Fax 899-2758
Antioch University Santa Barbara Post-Sec.
602 Anacapa St 93101 805-962-8179
Avalon Beauty College Post-Sec.
504 N Milpas St 93103 805-966-1931
Bishop Garcia Diego HS 300/9-12
4000 La Colina Rd 93110 805-967-1266
Dr. Paul Harrington, prin. Fax 964-3178
Brooks Institute Post-Sec.
27 E Cota St 93101 888-276-4999
Fielding Graduate University Post-Sec.
2112 Santa Barbara St 93105 805-687-1099
Garden Street Academy 100/K-12
2300 Garden St 93105 805-687-3717
Mike Hagan, dir. Fax 456-1897
Laguna Blanca S 300/K-12
4125 Paloma Dr 93110 805-687-1752
Paul Slocombe, hdmstr. Fax 682-2553
Providence Hall S 100/7-12
630 E Canon Perdido St 93103 805-962-4400
David O'Neil, head sch Fax 962-0132
Santa Barbara Business College Post-Sec.
506 Chapala St 93101 866-749-7222
Santa Barbara City College Post-Sec.
721 Cliff Dr 93109 805-965-0581
Santa Barbara Cottage & Gen. Hosp. Post-Sec.
PO Box 689 93102 805-569-7290
Santa Barbara MS 100/6-9
1321 Alameda Padre Serra 93103 805-682-2989
Brian McWilliams, hdmstr. Fax 682-0893
University of California 93106 Post-Sec.
805-893-8000
Westmont College Post-Sec.
955 La Paz Rd 93108 805-565-6000

Santa Clara, Santa Clara, Pop. 111,315
Santa Clara USD 15,200/K-12
PO Box 397 95052 408-423-2000
Dr. Bobbie Plough, supt. Fax 423-2285
www.santaclarausd.org
Buchser MS 1,000/6-8
1111 Bellomy St 95050 408-423-3000
Kyle Eaton, prin. Fax 423-3080
Cabrillo MS 800/6-8
2550 Cabrillo Ave 95051 408-423-3700
Stan Garber, prin. Fax 423-3780
New Valley Continuation HS 200/Alt
1875 Lawrence Rd 95051 408-423-2300
Robert Griffin, prin. Fax 423-2380
Santa Clara HS 1,900/9-12
3000 Benton St 95051 408-423-2600
David Grissom, prin. Fax 423-2681
Wilcox HS 1,900/9-12
3250 Monroe St 95051 408-423-2400
Bonnie Billings, prin. Fax 423-2480
Wilson Alternative S 300/Alt
1840 Benton St 95050 408-423-3600
Daniene Marciano, prin. Fax 423-3580
Santa Clara Adult Comm Education Center Adult
1840 Benton St 95050 408-423-3500
Rochelle Kelly, dir. Fax 423-3580
Other Schools – See Sunnyvale

California College of Communication Post-Sec.
1265 El Camino Real Ste 250 95050 408-374-5066
California Cosmetology College Post-Sec.
955 Monroe St 95050 408-247-2200
Henley-Putnam University Post-Sec.
2804 Mission Coll Blvd #240 95054 408-453-9900
Institute for Business and Technology Post-Sec.
2400 Walsh Ave 95051 800-915-3562
Mission College Post-Sec.
3000 Mission College Blvd 95054 408-988-2200
North Valley Baptist S 200/K-12
941 Clyde Ave 95054 408-988-8883
Dan Azzarello, prin.
St. Lawrence Academy 300/9-12
2000 Lawrence Ct 95051 408-296-3013
Christie Filios, prin. Fax 296-3794
Santa Clara University Post-Sec.
500 El Camino Real 95053 408-554-4000

Santa Clarita, Los Angeles, Pop. 171,060
Regional Occupational Center & Program
Supt. — None
Hart District ROP Vo/Tech
21515 Centre Pointe Pkwy 91350 661-259-0033
Dave LeBarron, coord. Fax 260-1909

William S. Hart UNHSD 26,100/K-12
21515 Centre Pointe Pkwy 91350 661-259-0033
Robert Challinor, supt. Fax 254-8653
www.hartdistrict.org
Academy of the Canyons 400/Alt
26455 Rockwell Canyon Rd 91355 661-362-3056
Jill Shenberger, prin. Fax 255-2954
Bowman Continuation HS 500/Alt
21508 Centre Pointe Pkwy 91350 661-253-4400
Robin Geissler, prin. Fax 253-4125
Golden Valley HS 2,200/9-12
27051 Robert C Lee Pkwy 91350 661-298-8140
Sal Frias, prin. Fax 250-8362

La Mesa JHS 1,200/7-8
26623 May Way 91351 661-250-0022
Pete Fries, prin. Fax 252-3326
Learning Post HS 100/Alt
26455 Rockwell Canyon Rd 91355 661-255-8338
Jill Shenberger, prin. Fax 255-3801
Rio Norte JHS 1,200/7-8
28771 Rio Norte Dr 91354 661-295-3700
John Costanzo, prin. Fax 257-1413
Golden Oak Adult S Adult
23201 Dalbey Dr 91355 661-253-0583
Ron Rudzinski, admin. Fax 260-1371
Other Schools – See Canyon Country, Newhall, Saugus, Stevenson Ranch, Valencia

---

Advantage Preparatory S 200/K-12
PO Box 802274 91380 661-296-5466
Cyndee Grant, admin.
College of the Canyons Post-Sec.
26455 Rockwell Canyon Rd 91355 661-259-7800

Santa Cruz, Santa Cruz, Pop. 57,302
Live Oak SD 2,100/K-12
984 Bostwick Ln Ste 1 95062 831-475-6333
Tamra Taylor, supt. Fax 475-2638
www.losd-ca.schoolloop.com/
Shoreline MS 600/6-8
855 17th Ave 95062 831-475-6565
Colleen Martin, prin. Fax 462-1653

Santa Cruz CSD
Supt. — See Soquel
Alternative Family Education 200/Alt
840 N Branciforte Ave 95062 831-429-3898
Lysa Tabachnick, prin. Fax 429-3912
ARK Independent S 100/Alt
840 N Branciforte Ave 95062 831-429-3432
Daniel Denton, prin. Fax 429-3912
Branciforte MS 500/6-8
315 Poplar Ave 95062 831-429-3883
Kristin Pfotenhauer, prin. Fax 429-3962
Costanoa Continuation HS 100/Alt
840 N Branciforte Ave 95062 831-429-3898
Daniel Denton, prin. Fax 429-3912
Harbor HS 1,000/9-12
300 La Fonda Ave 95062 831-429-3810
Richard Davis, prin. Fax 429-3982
Mission Hill MS 600/6-8
425 King St 95060 831-429-3860
Valerie Quandt, prin. Fax 427-4846
Santa Cruz HS 1,100/9-12
415 Walnut Ave 95060 831-429-3960
Karen Edmonds, prin. Fax 429-3944
Santa Cruz Adult Education Adult
319 La Fonda Ave 95062 831-429-3966
Lysa Tabachnick, prin. Fax 429-3061

Santa Cruz County Office of Education 1,000/
400 Encinal St 95060 831-466-5600
Michael Watkins, supt. Fax 466-5607
www.santacruz.k12.ca.us
Santa Cruz County Community S 700/Alt
400 Encinal St 95060 831-466-5728
Sandy Mast, dir. Fax 466-5730

Five Branches University Post-Sec.
200 7th Ave 95062 831-476-9424
Kirby Preparatory S 200/6-12
425 Encinal St 95060 831-423-0658
Joshua Karter Ph.D., head sch Fax 423-0679
University of California Post-Sec.
1156 High St 95064 831-459-0111

Santa Fe Springs, Los Angeles, Pop. 16,058
Little Lake City SD 4,800/K-8
10515 Pioneer Blvd 90670 562-868-8241
Phillip Perez Ed.D., supt. Fax 868-1192
www.littlelake.k12.ca.us
Lake Center MS 1,000/6-8
10503 Pioneer Blvd 90670 562-868-4977
William Crean Ed.D., prin. Fax 929-4527
Other Schools – See Norwalk

Whittier UNHSD
Supt. — See Whittier
Santa Fe HS 2,800/9-12
10400 Orr and Day Rd 90670 562-698-8121
Kevin Jamero, prin. Fax 868-8277

Presbyterian Theological Seminary Post-Sec.
15605 Carmenita Rd 90670 562-926-1023
St. Paul HS 600/9-12
9635 Greenleaf Ave 90670 562-698-6246
Kate Aceves, prin. Fax 696-8396

Santa Maria, Santa Barbara, Pop. 97,930
Orcutt UNESD
Supt. — See Orcutt
Lakeview JHS 600/7-8
3700 Orcutt Rd 93455 805-938-8600
Alan Majewski, prin. Fax 938-8649

Santa Maria JUNHSD 7,800/9-12
2560 Skyway Dr 93455 805-922-4573
Mark Richardson Ed.D., supt. Fax 928-9916
www.smjuhsd.k12.ca.us
Delta HS 500/Alt
4893 Bethany Ln 93455 805-937-6356
Esther Prieto-Chavez, prin. Fax 934-4743
Pioneer Valley HS 2,600/9-12
675 Panther Dr 93454 805-922-1305
Shanda Herrera, prin. Fax 928-9916
Righetti HS 2,300/9-12
941 E Foster Rd 93455 805-937-2051
Steve Molina, prin. Fax 934-0819
Santa Maria HS 2,400/9-12
901 S Broadway 93454 805-925-2567
Joseph Domingues, prin. Fax 922-0215

Santa Maria-Bonita ESD 14,200/K-8
708 S Miller St 93454 805-928-1783
Phillip Alvarado, supt. Fax 928-7874
www.smbsd.org/
Arellanes JHS 600/7-8
1890 Sandalwood Dr 93455 805-361-6820
Stacie Rivera, prin. Fax 346-8535
El Camino JHS 600/7-8
219 W El Camino St 93458 805-361-7800
Ann Orton, prin. Fax 346-1851
Fesler JHS 800/7-8
1100 E Fesler St 93454 805-361-7880
Brian Zimmerman, prin. Fax 346-1849
Kunst JHS 800/7-8
930 Hidden Pines Way 93458 805-361-5800
Sharon Shell, prin. Fax 925-8239

Allan Hancock College Post-Sec.
800 S College Dr 93454 805-922-6966
Laurus College Post-Sec.
325 E Betteravia Rd Ste B8 93454 805-267-1690
St. Joseph HS 600/9-12
4120 S Bradley Rd 93455 805-937-2038
Joanne Poloni, prin. Fax 937-4248
Santa Barbara Business College Post-Sec.
303 Plaza Dr 93454 866-749-7222
Valley Christian Academy 300/K-12
2970 Santa Maria Way 93455 805-937-6317
Charles Mason, admin. Fax 934-2563

Santa Monica, Los Angeles, Pop. 86,130
Santa Monica-Malibu USD 11,600/PK-12
1651 16th St 90404 310-450-8338
Sandra Lyon, supt. Fax 450-1667
www.smmusd.org
Adams MS 1,000/6-8
2425 16th St 90405 310-452-2326
Eva Mayoral, prin. Fax 452-5352
Lincoln MS 1,100/6-8
1501 California Ave 90403 310-393-9227
Suzanne Webb, prin. Fax 393-4297
Off Campus Learning Center Alt
1401 Olympic Blvd 90404 310-581-5739
Dr. Janie Gates, prin. Fax 450-1667
Olympic Continuation HS 100/Alt
721 Ocean Park Blvd 90405 310-392-2494
Dr. Janie Gates, prin. Fax 392-9741
Santa Monica HS 3,100/9-12
601 Pico Blvd 90405 310-395-3204
Laurel Fretz, prin. Fax 395-5842
Santa Monica-Malibu Adult Education Adult
2510 Lincoln Blvd 90405 310-664-6222
Dr. Janie Gates, prin. Fax 664-6220
Other Schools – See Malibu

Art Institute of California-Los Angeles Post-Sec.
2900 31st St 90405 310-752-4700
Concord Prep HS 100/9-12
1238 Lincoln Blvd 90401 424-999-8870
Marissa DeSiena, dir.
Crossroads S for Arts & Sciences 1,200/K-12
1714 21st St 90404 310-829-7391
Bob Riddle, head sch Fax 828-5636
Emperor's Coll. of Trad. Oriental Med. Post-Sec.
1807 Wilshire Blvd Ste 200 90403 310-453-8300
Lighthouse Christian Academy 50/9-12
1424 Yale St 90404 310-829-2522
Jack Mefford, prin. Fax 829-5544
New Roads HS 400/9-12
3131 Olympic Blvd 90404 310-828-5582
Dr. David Bryan, head sch Fax 828-2582
New Roads MS 200/6-8
3131 Olympic Blvd 90404 310-828-5582
Dr. David Bryan, head sch Fax 828-2582
Pacifica Christian HS 200/9-12
1730 Wilshire Blvd 90403 310-828-7015
Jim Knight, head sch Fax 829-2063
Pardee RAND Grad Sch of Policy Studies Post-Sec.
1776 Main St 90401 310-393-0411
St. Monica HS 600/9-12
1030 Lincoln Blvd 90403 310-394-3701
Alex Chacon, prin. Fax 458-1353
Santa Monica College Post-Sec.
1900 Pico Blvd 90405 310-434-4000

Santa Paula, Ventura, Pop. 29,121
Briggs ESD 600/PK-8
12465 Foothill Rd 93060 805-525-7540
Deborah Cuevas, supt. Fax 933-1111
www.briggsesd.org
Briggs MS 300/5-8
14438 W Telegraph Rd 93060 805-525-7151
Brandon Gallagher, prin. Fax 933-3565

Santa Paula USD 3,700/K-12
201 S Steckel Dr 93060 805-933-8800
Alfonso Gamino, supt. Fax 933-3023
www.spuhsd.k12.ca.us
Isbell MS 1,100/6-8
221 S 4th St 93060 805-933-8880
George Alessi, prin. Fax 933-5582
Renaissance Continuation HS 100/Alt
325 N Palm Ave 93060 805-525-4407
Fax 525-2294
Santa Paula HS 1,500/9-12
404 N 6th St 93060 805-525-4406
Elizabeth Garcia, prin. Fax 525-1690

Thomas Aquinas College Post-Sec.
10000 Ojai Rd 93060 800-634-9797

Santa Rosa, Sonoma, Pop. 161,788
Regional Occupational Center & Program
Supt. — None
Sonoma County ROP Vo/Tech
5340 Skylane Blvd 95403 707-524-2720
Stephen Jackson, dir. Fax 524-2789

Santa Rosa CSD 16,800/K-12
211 Ridgway Ave 95401 707-528-5388
Sharon Liddell Ed.D., supt. Fax 528-5440
www.srcs.k12.ca.us
Allen HS 1,100/9-12
599 Bellevue Ave 95407 707-528-5020
Mary Gail Stablein, prin. Fax 528-5023
Carillo HS 1,600/9-12
6975 Montecito Blvd 95409 707-528-5790
Rand VanDyke, prin. Fax 528-5789
Comstock MS 300/7-8
2750 W Steele Ln 95403 707-528-5266
Laura Hendrickson, prin. Fax 528-5480
Cook MS 400/7-8
2480 Sebastopol Rd 95407 707-528-5156
Patricia Turner, prin. Fax 528-5163
Grace Necessary Small HS 100/Alt
1702 Fulton Rd 95403 707-528-5756
Tony Negri, prin. Fax 528-5246
Lewis Opportunity S 50/Alt
2230 Lomitas Ave 95404 707-284-8225
Cal Morgan, prin. Fax 284-8232
Mesa Necessary Small HS 100/Alt
1237 Mendocino Ave 95401 707-528-5227
Tony Negri, prin. Fax 528 5724
Midrose Necessary Small HS 100/Alt
597 Bellevue Ave 95407 707-528-5041
Tony Negri, prin. Fax 528-5027
Montgomery HS 1,700/9-12
1250 Hahman Dr 95405 707-528-5191
Laurie Fong, prin. Fax 528-5056
Nueva Vista Necessary Small HS 50/Alt
2232 Lomitas Ave 95404 707-522-3291
Cal Morgan, prin. Fax 522-3293
Piner HS 1,100/9-12
1700 Fulton Rd 95403 707-528-5245
Sally Bimrose, prin. Fax 528-5246
Ridgway Continuation HS 300/Alt
325 Ridgway Ave 95401 707-528-5325
Robert Hucek, prin. Fax 528-5717
Rincon Valley MS 900/7-8
4650 Badger Rd 95409 707-528-5255
Matt Marshall, prin. Fax 528-5644
Santa Rosa HS 2,000/9-12
1235 Mendocino Ave 95401 707-528-5291
Brad Coscarelli, prin. Fax 528-5724
Santa Rosa MS 600/7-8
500 E St 95404 707-528-5281
Kathy Coker, prin. Fax 528-5283
Slater MS 900/7-8
3500 Sonoma Ave 95405 707-528-5241
Jason Lea, prin. Fax 528-5733

Cardinal Newman HS 400/9-12
50 Ursuline Rd 95403 707-546-6470
Graham Rutherford, prin. Fax 544-8502
Empire College Post-Sec.
3035 Cleveland Ave 95403 707-546-4000
Lytle's Redwood Empire Beauty College Post-Sec.
186 Wikiup Dr 95403 707-545-8490
Redwood Adventist Academy 100/K-12
385 Mark West Springs Rd 95404 707-545-1697
Rob Fenderson, prin. Fax 545-8020
Rincon Valley Christian S 300/PK-12
4585 Badger Rd 95409 707-539-1486
Brent Mitten, admin. Fax 539-1493
Santa Rosa Junior College Post-Sec.
1501 Mendocino Ave 95401 707-527-4011
Sonoma Academy 200/9-12
2500 Farmers Ln 95404 707-545-1770
Janet Durgin, admin. Fax 636-2474
Summerfield Waldorf S 400/PK-12
655 Willowside Rd 95401 707-575-7194
Jefferson Buller, pres. Fax 575-3217

Santa Ynez, Santa Barbara, Pop. 4,319
Santa Ynez Valley UNHSD 1,100/9-12
PO Box 398 93460 805-688-6487
Paul Turnbull, supt. Fax 686-4454
www.syvuhsd.org
Refugio HS 50/Alt
PO Box 398 93460 805-688-6487
Paul Turnbull, prin. Fax 686-5627
Santa Ynez Valley Union HS 1,000/9-12
PO Box 398 93460 805-688-6487
Mark Swanitz, prin. Fax 688-1913

Santee, San Diego, Pop. 51,246
Grossmont UNHSD
Supt. — See La Mesa
Santana HS 1,500/9-12
9915 N Magnolia Ave 92071 619-956-0200
Tim Schwuchow, prin. Fax 449-3119
West Hills HS, 8756 Mast Blvd 92071 2,000/9-12
Paul Dautremont, prin. 619-956-0400

San Ysidro, See San Diego
San Ysidro ESD 4,900/PK-8
4350 Otay Mesa Rd 92173 619-428-4476
Manuel Paul, supt. Fax 428-1505
www.sysd.k12.ca.us
San Ysidro MS 900/7-8
4345 Otay Mesa Rd 92173 619-428-5551
David Torres, prin. Fax 690-2837

Sweetwater UNHSD
Supt. — See Chula Vista
San Ysidro Adult S Adult
4220 Otay Mesa Rd 92173 619-428-7200
Linda Carlton, prin. Fax 428-0295

Saratoga, Santa Clara, Pop. 28,911
Campbell UNHSD
Supt. — See San Jose
Prospect HS 1,300/9-12
18900 Prospect Rd 95070 408-626-3408
Fax 973-1759

Los Gatos-Saratoga JUNHSD
Supt. — See Los Gatos
Saratoga HS 1,400/9-12
20300 Herriman Ave 95070 408-867-3411
Paul Robinson, prin. Fax 867-3577

Saratoga UNESD 2,200/K-8
20460 Forrest Hills Dr 95070 408-867-3424
Lane Weiss, supt. Fax 867-2312
www.saratogausd.org
Redwood MS 900/6-8
13925 Fruitvale Ave 95070 408-867-3042
Kelly Green, prin. Fax 867-3195

West Valley College Post-Sec.
14000 Fruitvale Ave 95070 408-867-2200

Saugus, See Santa Clarita
William S. Hart UNHSD
Supt. — See Santa Clarita
Saugus HS 2,400/9-12
21900 Centurion Way 91350 661-297-3900
Bill Bolde, prin. Fax 297-7491

Sausalito, Marin, Pop. 6,877
Sausalito Marin CSD 400/K-8
200 Phillips Dr 94965 415-332-3190
Valerier Pitts, supt. Fax 332-9643
smcsd.org
King Jr Academy 50/5-8
200 Phillips Dr 94965 415-332-3573
Daniel Norbutas, prin. Fax 332-2492

Scotts Valley, Santa Cruz, Pop. 11,122
Scotts Valley USD 2,600/K-12
4444 Scotts Valley Dr Ste 5 95066 831-438-1820
Penny Weaver, supt. Fax 438-2314
www.svusd.santacruz.k12.ca.us
Scotts Valley HS 800/9-12
555 Glenwood Dr 95066 831-439-9555
Valerie Bariteau, prin. Fax 439-9501
Scotts Valley MS 600/6-8
8 Bean Creek Rd 95066 831-438-0610
Mary Lonhart, prin. Fax 439-8935

Seaside, Monterey, Pop. 30,879
Monterey Peninsula USD
Supt. — See Monterey
Central Coast HS 200/Alt
200 Coe Ave 93955 831-392-3560
Kevin McClelland, dir. Fax 392-3561
Monterey Peninsula Community Day S 50/Alt
200 Coe Ave 93955 831-392-3822
Kevin McClelland, dir. Fax 649-6621
Seaside HS 1,000/9-12
2200 Noche Buena St 93955 831-392-3530
Dr. Mary White, prin. Fax 899-0212
Seaside MS 800/6-8
999 Coe Ave 93955 831-899-7080
Joan Nugent, prin. Fax 899-0663
Adult Education - GED/HS Diploma Adult
200 Coe Ave 93955 831-392-3560
Kevin McClelland, dir.
Adult Education - Spanish/GED/ESL Adult
1713 Broadway Ave 93955 831-392-3565
Kevin McClelland, admin.

California State University-Monterey Bay Post-Sec.
100 Campus Ctr 93955 831-582-3000
Chartwell S 100/K-12
2511 Numa Watson Rd 93955 831-394-3468
Douglas Atkins, dir. Fax 394-7991

Sebastopol, Sonoma, Pop. 7,156
Gravenstein UNESD 600/PK-8
3840 Twig Ave 95472 707-823-7008
Linda LaMarre, supt. Fax 823-2108
www.grav.k12.ca.us/
Hillcrest MS 300/6-8
725 Bloomfield Rd 95472 707-823-7653
David Fichera, prin. Fax 823-4630

West Sonoma CUHSD 2,200/9-12
462 Johnson St 95472 707-824-6403
Keller McDonald, supt. Fax 824-6499
wscuhsd.k12.ca.us
Analy HS 1,300/9-12
6950 Analy Ave 95472 707-824-2300
Chris Heller, prin. Fax 827-7936
Laguna Continuation HS 100/Alt
445 Taft St 95472 707-824-6485
Kent Cromwell, prin. Fax 829-7910
Other Schools – See Forestville

Selma, Fresno, Pop. 22,943
Selma USD 6,300/K-12
3036 Thompson Ave 93662 559-898-6500
Mark Sutton, supt. Fax 896-7147
www.selma.k12.ca.us
Heartland Alternative HS 100/Alt
2269 Sylvia St 93662 559-898-6670
Drew Sylvia, prin. Fax 896-4635
Lincoln MS 1,000/7-8
1239 Nelson Blvd 93662 559-898-6600
Wayne Dixon, prin. Fax 896-0733
Selma HS 1,700/9-12
3125 Wright St 93662 559-898-6550
Mark Babiarz, prin. Fax 896-1110
Selma Adult S Adult
3125 Wright St 93662 559-898-6590
Drew Sylvia, coord. Fax 896-4333

Shafter, Kern, Pop. 16,846
Kern UNHSD
Supt. — See Bakersfield
Central Valley Continuation HS 100/Alt
526 Mannel Ave 93263 661-746-4281
Anthony Ransick, admin. Fax 746-0521

Shafter HS 1,500/9-12
526 Mannel Ave 93263 661-746-4961
Connie Sack, prin. Fax 746-6743

Richland UNESD 3,200/PK-8
331 N Shafter Ave 93263 661-746-8600
Kenneth Bergevin, supt. Fax 746-8614
www.richland.k12.ca.us
Richland JHS 500/7-8
331 N Shafter Ave 93263 661-746-8630
Jason Hutchison, prin. Fax 746-8614

Shandon, San Luis Obispo, Pop. 1,278
Shandon JUSD 300/K-12
PO Box 79 93461 805-238-0286
Rod Wallace, supt. Fax 238-0777
shandon.echalk.com
Shandon Community Day S 50/Alt
101 S 1st St 93461 805-238-0286
Rod Wallace, prin. Fax 238-0777
Shandon HS 100/9-12
PO Box 79 93461 805-238-0286
Rod Wallace, prin. Fax 238-0777

Shasta Lake, Shasta, Pop. 9,765
Gateway USD
Supt. — See Redding
Mountain Lakes HS 100/Alt
17752 Shasta Dam Blvd 96019 530-275-7000
Mark Telles, prin. Fax 275-7006

Sherman Oaks, See Los Angeles
Los Angeles USD
Supt. — See Los Angeles
Millikan MS 2,100/6-8
5041 Sunnyslope Ave 91423 818-528-1600
John Plevack, prin. Fax 990-7651

Buckley S 800/K-12
3900 Stansbury Ave 91423 818-783-1610
Dr. Larry Dougherty, head sch Fax 461-6714
DeVry University Post-Sec.
15301 Ventura Blvd Ste 100 91403 818-713-8111
Notre Dame HS 1,200/9-12
13645 Riverside Dr 91423 818-933-3600
Stephanie Connelly, prin. Fax 501-0507

Shingle Springs, El Dorado, Pop. 4,277
Buckeye UNSD 4,700/K-8
PO Box 547 95682 530-677-2261
Dr. David Roth, supt. Fax 677-1015
www.buckeyeusd.org/
Other Schools – See Cameron Park, El Dorado Hills

El Dorado UNHSD
Supt. — See Placerville
Ponderosa HS 1,900/9-12
3661 Ponderosa Rd 95682 530-677-2281
Lisa Garrett, prin. Fax 676-1401

Latrobe SD 200/K-8
7900 S Shingle Rd 95682 530-677-0260
Jean Pinotti, supt. Fax 672-0463
www.latrobeschool.com
Miller's Hill S 100/4-8
7900 S Shingle Rd 95682 530-677-0260
Jean Pinotti, prin. Fax 672-0463

Shingletown, Shasta, Pop. 2,210
Black Butte UNESD 200/K-8
7752 Ponderosa Way 96088 530-474-3125
Don Aust, supt. Fax 474-3118
www.blackbutteschool.org
Black Butte JHS 100/6-8
7946 Ponderosa Way 96088 530-474-3441
Don Aust, prin. Fax 474-1361

Shoshone, Inyo, Pop. 30
Death Valley USD 100/K-12
PO Box 217 92384 760-852-4303
James Copeland, supt. Fax 852-4395
www.inyo.k12.ca.us
Death Valley Academy 50/7-12
PO Box 217 92384 760-852-4303
James Copeland, prin. Fax 852-4395
Shoshone Continuation HS 50/Alt
PO Box 217 92384 760-852-4303
James Copeland, prin. Fax 852-4395

Sierra Madre, Los Angeles, Pop. 10,555
Pasadena USD
Supt. — See Pasadena
Sierra Madre MS 200/6-8
160 N Canon Ave 91024 626-836-2947
Garret Newson, prin. Fax 836-2964

Alverno HS 200/9-12
200 N Michillinda Ave 91024 626-355-3463
Ann Gillick, prin. Fax 355-3153

Sierraville, Sierra, Pop. 200
Regional Occupational Center & Program
Supt. — None
Rouse ROP Vo/Tech
PO Box 157 96126 530-994-1044
Stan Hardeman, supt. Fax 994-1045

Signal Hill, Los Angeles, Pop. 10,477
Long Beach USD
Supt. — See Long Beach
Nelson Academy 6-8
1951 Cherry Ave, 562-591-6041
Sparkle Peterson, prin. Fax 591-8690

American University of Health Science Post-Sec.
1600 E Hill St Bldg 1, 562-988-2278

Silverado, Orange

St. Michaels Preparatory S 100/9-12
19292 El Toro Rd 92676 949-858-0222
Fr. Victor Szczurek, hdmstr. Fax 858-7365

Simi Valley, Ventura, Pop. 120,233
Simi Valley USD 19,900/K-12
875 Cochran St 93065 805-520-6500
Kathryn Scroggin Ed.D., supt. Fax 520-6504
www.simivalleyusd.org
Apollo HS 300/Alt
3150 School St 93065 805-520-6150
Dean May, prin. Fax 520-6655
Hillside MS 900/6-8
2222 Fitzgerald Rd 93065 805-520-6810
Laura Wellington, prin. Fax 520-6156
Monte Vista S 100/Alt
1755 Blackstock Ave 93065 805-579-6326
Elizabeth Brown, prin. Fax 579-6329
Royal HS 2,500/9-12
1402 Royal Ave 93065 805-306-4875
Deborah Salgado, prin. Fax 520-6644
Santa Susana HS 1,200/9-12
3570 Cochran St 93063 805-520-6800
Jason Peplinski, prin. Fax 579-6385
Simi Valley HS 2,600/9-12
5400 Cochran St 93063 805-577-1400
Stephen Pietrolungo, prin. Fax 520-6633
Sinaloa MS 1,100/6-8
601 Royal Ave 93065 805-520-6830
Diana Janke, prin. Fax 520-6835
Valley View MS 1,300/6-8
3347 Tapo St 93063 805-520-6820
Terry Webb, prin. Fax 520-6157
Simi Valley Adult Education Adult
1880 Blackstock Ave 93065 805-579-6200
William Waxman, dir. Fax 522-8902

Eternity Bible College Post-Sec.
2136 Winifred St 93063 805-581-1233
Grace Brethren JSHS 400/7-12
1350 Cherry Ave 93065 805-522-4667
John Hynes, prin. Fax 522-5617
Heritage Christian Academy 100/K-12
1559 Rosita Dr 93065 805-428-2511
Robert Neher, prin.
Simi Valley Adult Education Post-Sec.
1880 Blackstock Ave 93065 805-579-6200
Stoneridge Preparatory S 50/6-12
1625 Tierra Rejada Rd 93065 805-581-9110
Maria Arnold, dir. Fax 581-2864

Solana Beach, San Diego, Pop. 12,580
San Dieguito UNHSD
Supt. — See Encinitas
Warren MS 700/7-8
155 Stevens Ave 92075 858-755-1558
MaryAnne Nuskin, prin. Fax 755-0891

Santa Fe Christian S 900/PK-12
838 Academy Dr 92075 858-755-8900
Dr. Tom Bennett, head sch Fax 755-2480

Soledad, Monterey, Pop. 25,398
Soledad USD 4,500/PK-12
1261 Metz Rd 93960 831-678-3987
Rupi Boyd Ed.D., supt. Fax 678-2866
www.soledad.k12.ca.us
Chalone HS/Pinnacles HS 100/Alt
690 Main St 93960 831-678-6300
Jeffrey Lopez, prin. Fax 678-0162
Main Street MS 700/PK-PK, 7-
441 Main St 93960 831-678-6460
Dr. Amelia Jimenez, prin. Fax 678-0797
Soledad HS 1,200/9-12
425 Gabilan Dr 93960 831-678-6400
Elizabeth Austin, prin. Fax 678-0449

Liberty Christian S 50/K-12
274 Kidder St 93960 831-678-2885
Erika Schumacher, dir. Fax 678-2889

Somerset, El Dorado
Pioneer UNESD 400/K-8
6862 Mount Aukum Rd 95684 530-620-3556
Elizabeth Haines, supt. Fax 620-4932
www.pioneer.k12.ca.us
Mountain Creek MS 100/5-8
6862 Mount Aukum Rd 95684 530-620-4393
Richard Williams, prin. Fax 620-6509

Sonoma, Sonoma, Pop. 10,444
Sonoma Valley USD 4,600/K-12
17850 Railroad Ave 95476 707-935-6000
Louann Carlomagno Ph.D., supt. Fax 939-2235
svusdca.org/
Altimira MS 500/6-8
17805 Arnold Dr 95476 707-935-6020
William Deeths, prin. Fax 935-6027
Creekside HS 100/Alt
20000 Broadway 95476 707-933-4046
Paul Tuohy, prin. Fax 933-4095
Gateway S 50/Alt
17878 Railroad Ave 95476 707-935-4264
Nanci Mathison J.D., prin. Fax 939-2239
Harrison MS 500/6-8
1150 Broadway 95476 707-935-6080
Karla Conroy, prin. Fax 935-6083
Sonoma Valley HS 1,300/9-12
20000 Broadway 95476 707-933-4010
Dino Battaglini, prin. Fax 935-4205
Sonoma Valley Adult S Adult
20000 Broadway 95476 707-933-4033
Pam Garramone, prin. Fax 933-4205

Sonora, Tuolumne, Pop. 4,736
Sonora UNHSD 1,300/9-12
100 School St 95370 209-533-8510
Michael McCoy, supt. Fax 532-4513
www.sonorahs.k12.ca.us/
Bird HS 100/Alt
251 Barretta St 95370 209-532-2923
Roy Morlan, prin. Fax 533-0980
Cassina Continuation HS 100/Alt
251 Barretta St 95370 209-532-1587
Roy Morlan, prin. Fax 533-0980
Sonora HS 1,100/9-12
430 N Washington St 95370 209-532-5511
Todd Dearden, prin. Fax 533-1158

Columbia College Post-Sec.
11600 Columbia College Dr 95370 209-588-5100
Mother Lode Adventist Junior Academy 100/K-10
80 N Forest Rd 95370 209-532-2855
Emily Villeda, prin. Fax 532-7757

Soquel, Santa Cruz, Pop. 9,255
Santa Cruz CSD 7,000/K-12
405 Old San Jose Rd 95073 831-429-3410
Gary Bloom, supt. Fax 429-3439
www.sccs.santacruz.k12.ca.us
Soquel HS 1,000/9-12
401 Old San Jose Rd 95073 831-429-3909
Ken Lawrence-Emanuel, prin. Fax 429-3311
Other Schools – See Santa Cruz

South Dos Palos, Merced, Pop. 1,600
Dos Palos Oro Loma JUSD
Supt. — See Dos Palos
Westside HS 50/Alt
22369 6th St 93665 209-392-0280
Brian Walker, prin. Fax 392-1043

South El Monte, Los Angeles, Pop. 19,998
El Monte UNHSD
Supt. — See El Monte
South El Monte HS 1,600/9-12
1001 Durfee Ave 91733 626-442-0218
Angelita Gonzales-Hernan, prin. Fax 442-4794

Valle Lindo ESD 1,100/K-8
1431 Central Ave 91733 626-580-0610
Dr. Mary Labrucherie, supt. Fax 575-1534
www.vallelindo.k12.ca.us
Shively MS 600/4-8
1431 Central Ave 91733 626-580-0610
Lynn Bulgin, prin. Fax 575-1534

South Gate, Los Angeles, Pop. 94,017
Los Angeles USD
Supt. — See Los Angeles
International Studies Learning Center 800/6-12
2701 Sequoia Dr 90280 323-357-7521
Guillermina Jauregui, prin. Fax 569-7139
Odyssey Continuation HS 100/Alt
8693 Dearborn Ave 90280 323-567-5536
Julieta Badgley, prin. Fax 563-3468
Science Tech English Arts & Math HS 9-12
5225 Tweedy Blvd 90280 323-357-7500
Carla Barrera-Ortiz, prin. Fax 564-8371
South East HS 3,100/9-12
2720 Tweedy Blvd 90280 323-568-3400
Maria Sotomayor, prin. Fax 566-7918
Southeast MS 1,400/6-8
2560 Tweedy Blvd 90280 323-568-3100
Wanda Sequeira, prin. Fax 564-9398
South Gate HS 3,300/9-12
3351 Firestone Blvd 90280 323-568-5600
German Cerda, prin. Fax 249-0237
South Gate MS 2,600/6-8
4100 Firestone Blvd 90280 323-568-4000
Musetta Malone, prin. Fax 564-7434
Visual and Performing Arts HS 9-12
5225 Tweedy Blvd 90280 323-357-7500
Alison Miller, prin. Fax 564-8371
South Gate Adult Education Adult
2525 Firestone Blvd 90280 323-568-5700
Anna Madrid, prin. Fax 568-5716

Advanced College Post-Sec.
13180 Paramount Blvd 90280 562-408-6969
Career College of America Post-Sec.
5612 Imperial Hwy 90280 562-861-8702
GDS Institute Post-Sec.
7916 Long Beach Blvd 90280 323-585-5577

South Lake Tahoe, El Dorado, Pop. 20,898
El Dorado County Office of Education
Supt. — See Placerville
Blue Ridge S 50/Alt
1041 Al Tahoe Blvd 96150 530-626-0007
Sue Roth, prin.

Lake Tahoe USD 3,900/PK-12
1021 Al Tahoe Blvd 96150 530-541-2850
Dr. James Tarwater, supt. Fax 541-5930
www.ltusd.org/
Mt. Tallac Continuation HS 100/Alt
1735 Lake Tahoe Blvd 96150 530-543-2245
Karen Tinlin, prin. Fax 542-1036
South Tahoe HS 1,100/9-12
1735 Lake Tahoe Blvd 96150 530-541-4111
Ivone Larson, prin. Fax 541-4157
South Tahoe MS 900/6-8
2940 Lake Tahoe Blvd 96150 530-541-6404
Beth Delacour, prin. Fax 541-4624
Transition Learning Center 50/Alt
1735 Lake Tahoe Blvd 96150 530-543-2264
Ivone Larson, prin. Fax 542-1036

Lake Tahoe Community College Post-Sec.
1 College Dr 96150 530-541-4660

South Pasadena, Los Angeles, Pop. 24,612
South Pasadena USD 4,400/PK-12
1020 El Centro St 91030 626-441-5810
Joel Shapiro, supt. Fax 441-5815
www.spusd.net
South Pasadena HS 1,500/9-12
1401 Fremont Ave 91030 626-441-5820
Janet Anderson, prin. Fax 441-5825
South Pasadena MS 1,100/6-8
1500 Fair Oaks Ave 91030 626-441-5830
Dave Kubela, prin. Fax 441-5835

South San Francisco, San Mateo, Pop. 60,202
South San Francisco USD 9,300/K-12
398 B St 94080 650-877-8700
Alejandro Hogan, supt. Fax 583-4717
www.ssfusd.org
Alta Loma MS 700/6-8
116 Romney Ave 94080 650-877-8797
Lou Delorio, prin. Fax 877-8824
Baden HS 100/Alt
825 Southwood Dr 94080 650-877-8769
Jim Murphy, prin. Fax 737-9072
El Camino HS 1,500/9-12
1320 Mission Rd 94080 650-877-8806
David Putney, prin. Fax 589-2343
Parkway Heights MS 500/6-8
650 Sunset Ave 94080 650-877-8788
Stephen Redmond, prin. Fax 225-9427
South San Francisco HS 1,500/9-12
400 B St 94080 650-877-8754
Anthony Limoges, prin. Fax 871-7943
Westborough MS 700/6-8
2570 Westborough Blvd 94080 650-877-8848
Ed Colucci, prin. Fax 871-5356
South San Francisco Adult Adult
825 Southwood Dr 94080 650-877-8844
Jim Murphy, prin. Fax 877-8786

NCP College of Nursing Post-Sec.
257 Longford Dr Ste 5 94080 650-871-0701

Spreckels, Monterey, Pop. 663
Spreckels UNESD 1,000/K-8
PO Box 7362 93962 831-455-2550
Eric Tarallo Ed.D., supt. Fax 455-1871
Other Schools – See Salinas

Spring Valley, San Diego, Pop. 26,795
Grossmont UNHSD
Supt. — See La Mesa
Monte Vista HS 1,900/9-12
3230 Sweetwater Springs Blv 91977 619-660-3000
Randy Montesanto, prin. Fax 670-9749
Mt. Miguel HS 1,700/9-12
8585 Blossom Ln 91977 619-667-6400
Steve Coover, prin. Fax 697-0794

La Mesa-Spring Valley SD
Supt. — See La Mesa
La Presa MS 500/7-8
1001 Leland St 91977 619-668-5720
Mike Allmann, prin. Fax 668-8305
Spring Valley MS 700/7-8
3900 Conrad Dr 91977 619-668-5750
Dana Wright, prin. Fax 668-8302

Heartland Christian S 100/PK-12
3327 Kenora Dr 91977 619-461-7220
Lynda Hansen, prin. Fax 461-0962

Stanford, Santa Clara, Pop. 12,819

EPGY Online HS at Stanford 50/7-12
220 Panama St 94305 800-372-3749
Dr. Jan Keating, hdmstr. Fax 618-1929
Stanford University Post-Sec.
450 Serra Mall 94305 650-723-2300

Stevenson Ranch, Los Angeles, Pop. 16,902
William S. Hart UNHSD
Supt. — See Santa Clarita
Rancho Pico JHS 1,000/7-8
26250 Valencia Blvd 91381 661-284-3260
Erum Jones, prin. Fax 255-7523
West Ranch HS 2,800/9-12
26255 Valencia Blvd 91381 661-222-1220
Bob Vincent, prin. Fax 290-2676

Stockton, San Joaquin, Pop. 279,493
Lincoln USD 8,900/PK-12
2010 W Swain Rd 95207 209-953-8700
Thomas Uslan, supt. Fax 474-7817
www.lusd.net
Independent Learning Center Alt
6844 Alexandria Pl 95207 209-953-8432
Debbi Holmerud, prin.
Larsson HS 200/Alt
1813 McClellan Way 95207 209-953-8687
Phyllis Kahl, prin. Fax 953-8741
Lincoln HS 2,700/9-12
6844 Alexandria Pl 95207 209-953-8920
Debbi Holmerud, prin. Fax 952-4646
McCandless S Alt
2020 W Swain Rd 95207 209-953-8740
Phyllis Kahl, prin.
Sierra MS 600/7-8
6768 Alexandria Pl 95207 209-953-8749
Terry Asplund, prin. Fax 953-8747

Linden USD
Supt. — See Linden
Linden Unified Community Day S 50/Alt
100 N Jack Tone Rd 95215 209-931-4131
Sheri Griffith, coord. Fax 946-0457
Pride Continuation HS 100/Alt
100 N Jack Tone Rd 95215 209-887-3894
Jane Steinkamp, prin.

Waterloo MS 400/5-8
7007 Pezzi Rd 95215 209-931-0818
Stephanie Hitchcock, prin. Fax 931-2915

Lodi USD
Supt. — See Lodi
Bear Creek HS 2,000/9-12
10555 Thornton Rd 95209 209-953-8234
Shirley McNichols, prin. Fax 953-8247
Delta Sierra MS 500/7-8
2255 Wagner Heights Rd 95209 209-953-8510
Jacquelyn Ollison, prin. Fax 953-8139
Elkhorn MS 300/4-8
10505 Davis Rd 95209 209-953-8312
Pierre Kirby, prin. Fax 953-8319
Independence S South Alt
9434 Thornton Rd 95209 209-953-8065
Carol Owens, prin. Fax 953-9484
McAuliffe MS 900/7-8
3880 Iron Canyon Cir 95209 209-953-9431
Randy Malandro, prin. Fax 953-9430
McNair HS 1,900/9-12
9550 Ronald E McNair Way 95210 209-953-9245
Jim Davis, prin. Fax 953-9261
Middle College HS 200/9-12
5151 Pacific Ave 95207 209-954-5790
Sherry Balian, prin. Fax 954-5875
Morada MS 800/7-8
5001 Eastview Dr 95212 209-953-8490
Janet Perez, prin. Fax 953-8502
Plaza Robles Continuation HS 200/Alt
9434 Thornton Rd 95209 209-953-8068
Bill Toledo, prin. Fax 953-8064

Manteca USD
Supt. — See Manteca
Great Valley Annex S 400/6-8
4550 Star Way 95206 209-938-6310
Patricia Boutte, prin. Fax 938-6383
New Vision HS 200/Alt
4726 McCuen Ave 95206 209-938-6225
Katie Peters, prin. Fax 938-6394
Weston Ranch HS 1,200/9-12
4606 McCuen Ave 95206 209-938-6245
Jose Fregoso, prin. Fax 938-6397

Regional Occupational Center & Program
Supt. — None
San Joaquin County ROC/P Vo/Tech
PO Box 213030 95213 209-468-5930

Stockton USD 35,300/K-12
701 N Madison St 95202 209-933-7000
Dr. Steven Lowder, supt. Fax 933-7071
www.stockton.k12.ca.us
Chavez HS 2,200/9-12
2929 Windflower Ln 95212 209-933-7480
William Nelson, prin. Fax 475-9097
Edison HS 2,100/9-12
1425 S Center St 95206 209-933-7425
Brian Biedermann, prin. Fax 942-2106
Franklin HS 2,200/9-12
300 N Gertrude Ave 95215 209-933-7435
Reyes Gauna, prin. Fax 464-4708
Frederick Continuation S 300/Alt
1141 E Weber Ave 95205 209-933-7340
Elena Molina, prin. Fax 933-7341
Merlo Institute of Environmental Tech 200/9-12
1670 E 6th St 95206 209-933-7190
Yanik Ruley, prin. Fax 469-3740
Stagg HS 1,700/9-12
1621 Brookside Rd 95207 209-933-7445
Bill Parks, prin. Fax 954-9037
Weber Institute Vo/Tech
302 W Weber Ave 95203 209-933-7330
Nancy Zoepfl, dir. Fax 464-4917
School for Adults Adult
1525 Pacific Ave 95204 209-933-7455
Carol Hirota, prin. Fax 464-4917

Brookside Christian HS 100/7-12
915 Rosemarie Ln 95207 209-954-7651
Dennis Gibson, prin. Fax 954-7677
Carrington College California Post-Sec.
1313 W Robinhood Dr Ste B 95207 209-956-1240
Heald College Post-Sec.
1605 E March Ln 95210 209-473-5200
Humphreys College Post-Sec.
6650 Inglewood Ave 95207 209-478-0800
Kaplan College Post-Sec.
722 W March Ln 95207 209-462-8777
MTI Business College of Stockton Post-Sec.
6006 N El Dorado St 95207 209-957-3030
St. Mary HS 1,100/9-12
PO Box 7247 95267 209-957-3340
Peter Morelli, prin. Fax 957-0861
San Joaquin Delta College Post-Sec.
5151 Pacific Ave 95207 209-954-5151
San Joaquin General Hospital Post-Sec.
PO Box 1020 95201 209-468-6600
Stockton Christian S 300/K-12
9021 West Ln 95210 209-957-3043
Manny DeLaRosa, prin. Fax 957-4120
Teachers College of San Joaquin Post-Sec.
2857 Transworld Dr 95206 209-468-9155
University of the Pacific Post-Sec.
3601 Pacific Ave 95211 209-946-2285
Western Pacific Truck School Post-Sec.
1002 N Broadway Ave 95205 209-465-1191

Strathmore, Tulare, Pop. 2,793
Porterville USD
Supt. — See Porterville
Strathmore HS 300/9-12
22568 Avenue 196 93267 559-568-1731
John Buckley, prin. Fax 568-0091

Strathmore UNESD 800/K-8
PO Box 247 93267 559-568-1283
Shelly Long Ed.D., supt. Fax 568-1262
www.suesd.k12.ca.us
Strathmore MS 300/5-8
PO Box 247 93267 559-568-9293
Evelyn Erquhart, prin. Fax 568-2944

Studio City, See Los Angeles

Bridges Academy 100/5-12
3921 Laurel Canyon Blvd 91604 818-506-1091
Carl Sabatino M.A., head sch Fax 506-8094

Sugarloaf, San Bernardino
Bear Valley USD
Supt. — See Big Bear Lake
Big Bear HS 800/9-12
351 N Maple Ln 92386 909-585-6892
Mike Ghelber, prin. Fax 585-6809
Chautauqua HS 100/Alt
525 Maple Ln 92386 909-585-2521
Dr. Steve Schour, prin. Fax 585-3311

Suisun City, Solano, Pop. 25,805
Fairfield-Suisun USD
Supt. — See Fairfield
Crystal MS 900/6-8
400 Whispering Bay Ln 94585 707-435-5800
Kristin Witt, prin. Fax 435-5806

Sun City, Riverside, Pop. 14,930
Perris UNHSD
Supt. — See Perris
Heritage HS 2,700/9-12
26001 Briggs Rd 92585 951-940-5447
Julie Zierold, prin. Fax 325-5449

Sunland, See Los Angeles
Los Angeles USD
Supt. — See Los Angeles
Mt. Gleason MS 1,200/6-8
10965 Mount Gleason Ave 91040 818-951-2580
Deborah Acosta, prin. Fax 352-6209

Sunnyvale, Santa Clara, Pop. 134,677
Cupertino UNSD
Supt. — See Cupertino
Cupertino MS 1,200/6-8
1650 S Bernardo Ave 94087 408-245-0303
Kara Butler, prin. Fax 732-4152

Fremont UNHSD 10,300/9-12
589 W Fremont Ave 94087 408-522-2200
Polly Bove, supt. Fax 245-5325
www.fuhsd.org
Fremont HS 2,000/9-12
1279 Sunnyvale Saratoga Rd 94087 408-522-2400
Bryan Emmert, prin. Fax 522-2401
Adult & Community Education Adult
591 W Fremont Ave 94087 408-522-2700
Peggy Raun-Linde, prin. Fax 522-2799
Other Schools – See Cupertino, San Jose

Regional Occupational Center & Program
Supt. — None
North County ROP Vo/Tech
589 W Fremont Ave 94087 408-522-2200
Adrienne Moberly, coord. Fax 733-0894

Santa Clara USD
Supt. — See Santa Clara
Peterson MS 900/6-8
1380 Rosalia Ave 94087 408-423-2800
Susan Harris, prin. Fax 423-2880

Sunnyvale ESD 6,400/K-8
PO Box 3217 94088 408-522-8200
Benjamin Picard Ed.D., supt. Fax 522-8221
www.sesd.org
Columbia MS 800/6-8
739 Morse Ave 94085 408-522-8247
Mary Beth Allmann, prin. Fax 522-8254
Sunnyvale MS 1,100/6-8
1080 Mango Ave 94087 408-522-8288
Dorothy Abreu-Coito, prin. Fax 522-8296

Art Institute of California - Sunnyvale Post-Sec.
1120 Kifer Rd 94086 408-962-6400
Catholic Academy St. Martin Campus 100/5-8
597 Central Ave 94086 408-736-5534
Marie Bordeleau, dir. Fax 736-1034
Cogswell Polytechnical College Post-Sec.
1175 Bordeaux Dr 94089 408-541-0100
King's Academy 800/6-12
562 N Britton Ave 94085 408-481-9900
Bob Kellogg, prin. Fax 481-9932
University of East West Medicine Post-Sec.
595 Lawrence Expy 94085 408-733-1878

Sun Valley, See Los Angeles
Los Angeles USD
Supt. — See Los Angeles
Byrd MS 1,800/6-8
8501 Arleta Ave 91352 818-394-4300
Sondra Reynolds, prin. Fax 768-1837
Francis Polytechnic HS 3,000/9-12
12431 Roscoe Blvd 91352 818-394-3600
Ari Bennett, prin. Fax 771-0452
Lewis Continuation S 100/Alt
12508 Wicks St 91352 818-394-3980
Laura Hale, prin. Fax 394-3981
Sun Valley HS 1,100/9-12
9171 Telfair Ave 91352 818-394-4600
Paul Del Rosario, prin. Fax 767-8125
Sun Valley MS 1,400/6-8
7330 Bakman Ave 91352 818-255-5100
Roberto Lee, prin. Fax 503-9846

N Hollywood/Poly Cas Adult
12431 Roscoe Blvd 91352 818-394-3950
Carl Badeau, prin. Fax 394-3961

Village Christian HS 400/9-12
8930 Village Ave 91352 818-768-5540
Bruce Osgood, prin. Fax 768-5618
Village Christian MS 200/6-8
8930 Village Ave 91352 818-768-1588
Bruce Osgood, prin. Fax 504-0982

Susanville, Lassen, Pop. 17,110
Lassen County Office of Education 100/
472-013 Johnstonville Rd 96130 530-257-2196
Richard DuVarney, supt. Fax 257-2518
www.lcoe.org
Lassen County Opportunity S 50/Alt
472-103 Johnstonville Rd 96130 530-257-2196
Richard DuVarney, admin.
Rocky Ridge HS 50/Alt
477-060 Sheriff Cady Ln 96130 530-257-7214
Richard DuVarney, dir. Fax 257-0535

Lassen UNHSD 1,000/9-12
1000 Main St 96130 530-257-5134
Roy Casey, supt. Fax 251-0473
www.lassenhigh.org
Credence HS 50/Alt
1110 Main St 96130 530-257-2141
Robbin Pedrett, prin. Fax 251-1173
Lassen HS 900/9-12
1110 Main St 96130 530-257-2141
Robbin Pedrett, prin. Fax 251-1173
Diploma Gold Adult S Adult
1000 Main St 96130 530-257-5134
Robbin Pedrett, prin. Fax 251-0473

Regional Occupational Center & Program
Supt. — None
Lassen County ROP Vo/Tech
472-013 Johnstonville Rd 96130 530-257-2196
Rich Duvarney, dir. Fax 257-2518

Susanville ESD 1,100/K-8
109 S Gilman St 96130 530-257-8200
Jason Waddell, supt. Fax 257-8246
www.susanvillesd.org
Diamond View MS 400/6-8
850 Richmond Rd 96130 530-257-5144
Holly Theobald, prin. Fax 257-7232

Lassen Christian Academy 50/K-12
2545 Riverside Dr 96130 530-257-4643
Melanie Clement, prin. Fax 257-4295
Lassen Community College Post-Sec.
PO Box 3000 96130 530-257-6181

Sutter, Sutter, Pop. 2,803
Sutter UNHSD 700/9-12
PO Box 498 95982 530-822-5161
Ryan Robison, supt. Fax 822-5168
www.sutterhigh.k12.ca.us/
Butte View HS 50/Alt
PO Box 498 95982 530-822-5161
Ryan Robison, prin. Fax 822-5168
Sutter HS 700/9-12
PO Box 498 95982 530-822-5161
Ryan Robison, prin. Fax 822-5168

Sutter Creek, Amador, Pop. 2,442
Amador County USD
Supt. — See Jackson
Amador HS 600/9-12
330 Spanish St 95685 209-257-7300
Jared Critchfield, prin. Fax 267-5942
Independence HS 100/Alt
525 Independence Dr 95685 209-257-5100
Butch Wagner, prin. Fax 267-5497
North Star S Alt
525 Independence Dr 95685 209-257-5150
Dr. Thomas Littlefair, prin. Fax 267-5847

Sylmar, See Los Angeles
Los Angeles USD
Supt. — See Los Angeles
Evergreen Continuation S 100/Alt
13101 Dronfield Ave 91342 818-367-5989
Robinson Acosta, prin. Fax 367-2796
Olive Vista MS 1,500/6-8
14600 Tyler St 91342 818-833-3900
Pamela Damonte, prin. Fax 367-8273
Sylmar HS 3,500/9-12
13050 Borden Ave 91342 818-833-3700
James Lee, prin. Fax 364-1037

Concordia JSHS 200/6-12
13570 Eldridge Ave 91342 818-362-5861
Edward Amey, dir. Fax 367-0043
ITT Technical Institute Post-Sec.
12669 Encinitas Ave 91342 818-364-5151
Los Angeles Mission College Post-Sec.
13356 Eldridge Ave 91342 818-364-7600
Olive View/UCLA Medical Centers Post-Sec.
14445 Olive View Dr 91342 818-364-4224

Taft, Kern, Pop. 9,099
Regional Occupational Center & Program
Supt. — None
West Side ROP, PO Box 1337 93268 Vo/Tech
Dale Countryman, dir. 661-763-2390

Taft CSD 2,100/K-8
820 6th St 93268 661-763-1521
Ron Bryant, supt. Fax 763-1495
www.taftcity.org
Lincoln JHS 700/6-8
810 6th St 93268 661-765-2127
Brandi Swearengin, prin. Fax 763-3970

Taft Community Day S 50/Alt
623 Rose Ave 93268 661-765-4117
Brandi Swearengin, prin. Fax 765-2065

Taft UNHSD 1,100/9-12
1 Wildcat Way 93268 661-763-2300
Dr. Mark Richardson, supt. Fax 763-1445
www.taft.k12.ca.us/
Buena Vista Continuation HS 100/Alt
1 Wildcat Way 93268 661-763-2383
Carolyn Wilson, prin. Fax 763-2393
Taft Union HS 900/9-12
1 Wildcat Way 93268 661-763-2300
Dr. Mark Richardson, prin. Fax 763-4736

Taft College Post-Sec.
29 Emmons Park Dr 93268 661-763-7700

Tahoe City, Placer, Pop. 1,643
Tahoe-Truckee JUSD
Supt. — See Truckee
Cold Stream Alternative S 50/Alt
740 Timberland Ln 96145 530-582-2640
Jane Loomis, prin. Fax 581-3457
North Tahoe HS 300/9-12
PO Box 5099 96145 530-581-7000
Joanna Mitchell, prin. Fax 581-3252
North Tahoe MS 400/5-8
PO Box 794 96145 530-581-7050
Teresa Rensch, prin. Fax 581-1237

Tarzana, See Los Angeles
Los Angeles USD
Supt. — See Los Angeles
Portola MS 1,900/6-8
18720 Linnet St 91356 818-654-3300
Adrienne Shaha, prin. Fax 996-0292

Columbia College Hollywood Post-Sec.
18618 Oxnard St 91356 800-785-0585
Hypnosis Motivation Institute Post-Sec.
18607 Ventura Blvd Ste 310 91356 800-600-0464

Tecate, San Diego

Tecate Christian S 100/1-12
PO Box 1000 91980 619-468-3355
Rick Rowe, prin. Fax 478-5910

Tehachapi, Kern, Pop. 14,166
Tehachapi USD 4,700/K-12
300 S Robinson St 93561 661-822-2100
Lisa Gilbert, supt. Fax 822-2159
www.teh.k12.ca.us
Jacobsen MS 1,100/6-8
711 Anita Dr 93561 661-822-2150
Paul Kaminski, prin. Fax 822-2156
Monroe HS 100/Alt
126 S Snyder Ave 93561 661-822-2124
Paul Press, prin. Fax 822-2188
Tehachapi HS 1,400/9-12
801 S Dennison Rd 93561 661-822-2130
Scott Heitman, prin. Fax 822-1854
Tehachapi Adult S Adult
126 S Snyder Ave 93561 661-822-2112
Paul Press, prin. Fax 822-2188

Heritage Oak S 100/K-12
20915 Schout Rd 93561 661-823-0885
Lori Gohr, prin. Fax 823-0863

Temecula, Riverside, Pop. 95,946
Temecula Valley USD 30,200/K-12
31350 Rancho Vista Rd 92592 951-676-2661
Timothy Ritter, supt. Fax 695-7121
www.tvusd.k12.ca.us
Chaparral HS 3,200/9-12
27215 Nicolas Rd 92591 951-695-4200
Gil Compton, prin. Fax 695-4219
Day MS 1,000/6-8
40775 Camino Campos Verde 92591 951-699-8138
Tina Miller, prin. Fax 699-4198
Gardner MS 1,000/6-8
45125 Via Del Coronado 92592 951-699-0080
Kristen Larson, prin. Fax 699-0081
Great Oak HS 3,300/9-12
32555 Deer Hollow Way 92592 951-294-6450
Joe Balleweg, prin. Fax 294-6477
Margarita MS 1,000/6-8
30600 Margarita Rd 92591 951-695-7370
Karen Hayes, prin. Fax 695-7378
Nelson S 100/Alt
32225 Pio Pico Rd 92592 951-695-7360
Greg Cooke, prin. Fax 294-6303
Rancho Vista HS 300/Alt
32225 Pio Pico Rd 92592 951-695-7320
Greg Cooke, prin. Fax 294-6304
Temecula MS 1,300/6-8
42075 Meadows Pkwy 92592 951-302-5151
Rob Sousa, prin. Fax 302-5160
Temecula Valley HS 2,800/9-12
31555 Rancho Vista Rd 92592 951-695-7300
Dr. Richard Lawrence, prin. Fax 695-7311
Vail Ranch MS 1,300/6-8
33340 Camino Piedra Rojo 92592 951-302-5188
Kevin Groepper, prin. Fax 302-5195
Temecula Valley Adult S Adult
43000 Margarita Rd 92592 951-294-6512
Greg Cooke, prin. Fax 294-6521
Other Schools – See Murrieta

Health Staff Training Institute Post-Sec.
28671 Calle Cortez Ste F 92590 951-694-4784
Linfield Christian S 700/PK-12
31950 Pauba Rd 92592 951-676-8111
Karen Raftery, pres. Fax 695-1291
Professional Golfers Career College Post-Sec.
26109 Ynez Rd 92591 800-877-4380
Rancho Christian S 700/PK-12
31300 Rancho Community Way 92592
951-303-1408
Dan Saatzer, prin. Fax 302-1580
Royale College of Beauty Post-Sec.
27485 Commerce Center Dr 92590 951-676-0833

Temple City, Los Angeles, Pop. 34,921
Temple City USD 5,600/K-12
9700 Las Tunas Dr 91780 626-548-5000
Chelsea Kang-Smith Ed.D., supt. Fax 548-5022
www.tcusd.net
Oak Avenue IS 900/7-8
6623 Oak Ave 91780 626-548-5060
Lawton Gray, prin. Fax 548-5170
Sears Learning Center 100/Alt
9229 Pentland St 91780 626-548-5113
Chris Sewell, prin. Fax 548-5118
Temple City HS 2,000/9-12
9501 Lemon Ave 91780 626-548-5040
Mary Jo Fosselman-King, prin. Fax 548-5045
Temple City Adult Education Adult
9229 Pentland St 91780 626-548-5050
Chris Sewell, prin. Fax 548-5118

United Beauty College Post-Sec.
10229 Lower Azusa Rd 91780 626-443-0900

Templeton, San Luis Obispo, Pop. 7,486
Templeton USD 2,200/K-12
960 Old County Rd 93465 805-434-5800
Joe Koski, supt. Fax 434-5879
tusd.ca.schoolloop.com/
Eagle Canyon HS 50/9-12
964 Old County Rd 93465 805-434-5833
Joe Koski, prin. Fax 434-3879
Templeton HS 700/9-12
1200 S Main St 93465 805-434-5888
Andrew Cherry, prin. Fax 434-0743
Templeton Independent Study HS 100/Alt
950 Old County Rd 93465 805-434-5846
Cheryl London, prin. Fax 434-5848
Templeton MS 500/6-8
925 Old County Rd 93465 805-434-5813
Kristina Benson, prin. Fax 434-5812

Terra Bella, Tulare, Pop. 3,287
Terra Bella UNESD 900/K-8
9121 Road 240 93270 559-535-4451
Frank Betry, supt. Fax 535-0314
www.tbuesd.org
Smith MS 300/6-8
23825 Avenue 92 93270 559-535-4451
Guadalupe Roman, prin. Fax 535-0829

Thermal, Riverside, Pop. 2,856
Coachella Valley USD 18,400/K-12
PO Box 847 92274 760-399-5137
Darryl Adams, supt. Fax 399-1052
www.cvusd.us
Coachella Valley HS 2,700/9-12
83800 Airport Blvd 92274 760-399-5183
Mary Velasco, prin. Fax 399-0089
Desert Mirage HS 1,900/9-12
86150 Avenue 66 92274 760-397-2255
Dr. Marrio Walker, prin. Fax 397-8760
La Familia Continuation HS 100/Alt
56-615 Olive St 92274 760-399-5929
Charles Housewright, prin. Fax 399-5169
Toro Canyon MS 1,000/7-8
86150 Avenue 66 92274 760-397-2244
Gabriel Fajardo, prin. Fax 397-8760
Other Schools – See Coachella, Salton City

Thousand Oaks, Ventura, Pop. 122,978
Conejo Valley USD 20,800/K-12
1400 E Janss Rd 91362 805-497-9511
Jeffrey Baarstad Ph.D., supt. Fax 371-9170
www.conejousd.org
Century Academy 50/Alt
1025 Old Farm Rd 91360 805-496-0286
Martin Manzer, prin. Fax 496-5169
Colina MS 1,100/6-8
1500 E Hillcrest Dr 91362 805-495-7429
Shane Frank, prin. Fax 374-1163
Los Cerritos MS 1,000/6-8
2100 E Ave De Las Flores 91362 805-492-3538
Jason Branham, prin. Fax 493-8854
Redwood MS 1,100/6-8
233 W Gainsborough Rd 91360 805-497-7264
Steve Lepire, prin. Fax 497-3734
Thousand Oaks HS 2,500/9-12
2323 N Moorpark Rd 91360 805-495-7491
Lou Lichtl, prin. Fax 374-1165
Conejo Valley Adult Education Adult
1025 Old Farm Rd 91360 805-497-2761
Mike Waters, prin. Fax 374-1167
Other Schools – See Newbury Park, Westlake Village

California Lutheran University Post-Sec.
60 W Olsen Rd 91360 805-492-2411
Hillcrest Christian S 400/PK-12
384 Erbes Rd 91362 805-497-7501
Kathy Horan J.D., prin. Fax 494-9355
La Reina HS 600/7-12
106 W Janss Rd 91360 805-495-6494
Shannon Gomez Ed.D., prin. Fax 494-4966
Trinity Pacific Christian S 400/K-12
3389 Camino Calandria 91360 805-492-0863
Barbara Richert, prin.

Tiburon, Marin, Pop. 8,606
Reed UNESD 1,300/K-8
277 Karen Way Ste A 94920 415-381-1112
Dr. Steven Herzog, supt. Fax 384-0890
www.reedschools.org
Del Mar MS 400/6-8
105 Avenida Miraflores 94920 415-435-1468
Dr. Alan Vann Gardner, prin. Fax 435-6190

Tollhouse, Fresno
Sierra USD 1,000/K-12
33326 Lodge Rd 93667 559-855-3662
Michael Gardner Ph.D., supt. Fax 855-3585
www.sierra.k12.ca.us
Oak Meadow Community Day S 50/Alt
33411 Lodge Rd 93667 559-855-4347
Larry Silva, prin. Fax 855-4348
Sandy Bluffs Alternative Education Ctr. 50/Alt
33280 Lodge Rd 93667 559-855-3020
Larry Silva, prin. Fax 855-3081
Sierra HS 600/7-12
33326 Lodge Rd 93667 559-855-8311
Melissa Ireland, prin. Fax 855-2162

Tomales, Marin, Pop. 200
Shoreline USD 600/K-12
PO Box 198 94971 707-878-2266
Tom Stubbs, supt. Fax 878-2554
www.shorelineunified.org
Tomales HS 200/9-12
PO Box 25 94971 707-878-2286
Dr. Stephen Rosenthal, prin. Fax 878-2787

Torrance, Los Angeles, Pop. 138,782
Regional Occupational Center & Program
Supt. — None
Southern California ROC Vo/Tech
2300 Crenshaw Blvd 90501 310-224-4220
Christine Hoffman, supt. Fax 320-1029

Torrance USD 24,200/K-12
2335 Plaza Del Amo 90501 310-972-6500
George Mannon Ed.D., supt. Fax 972-6012
www.tusd.org
Calle Mayor MS 800/6-8
4800 Calle Mayor 90505 310-533-4548
David Mosley, prin. Fax 972-6389
Casimir MS 700/6-8
17220 Casimir Ave 90504 310-533-4498
Susan Holmes, prin. Fax 972-6391
Hull MS 600/6-8
2080 W 231st St 90501 310-533-4516
Barry Lafferty, prin. Fax 972-6397
Jefferson MS 600/6-8
21717 Talisman St 90503 310-533-4794
Lee Chou, prin. Fax 972-6398
Lynn MS 800/6-8
5038 Halison St 90503 310-533-4495
Leroy Jackson, prin. Fax 972-6401
Madrona MS 800/6-8
21364 Madrona Ave 90503 310-533-4562
Ron Richardson, prin. Fax 972-6402
Magruder MS 700/6-8
4100 W 185th St 90504 310-533-4527
Chris Shek, prin. Fax 972-6403
North HS 2,200/9-12
3620 W 182nd St 90504 310-533-4412
Matthew Horvath, prin. Fax 972-6404
Richardson MS 700/6-8
23751 Nancylee Ln 90505 310-533-4790
Chad Mabery, prin. Fax 972-6405
Shery Continuation HS 100/Alt
2600 Vine Ave 90501 310-533-4440
Jamie Jimenez, prin. Fax 972-6408
South HS 2,200/9-12
4801 Pacific Coast Hwy 90505 310-533-4352
Scott McDowell, prin. Fax 972-6454
Torrance Community Day S 50/Alt
2291 Washington Ave 90501 310-972-6962
Jamie Jimenez, prin. Fax 972-6964
Torrance HS 2,100/9-12
2200 W Carson St 90501 310-533-4396
Karim Girgis, prin. Fax 972-6455
West HS 2,100/9-12
20401 Victor St 90503 310-533-4299
Ben Egan, prin. Fax 972-6483
Griffith Adult Education Center Adult
2291 Washington Ave 90501 310-533-4454
James Jones, prin. Fax 972-6394
Hamilton Adult Education Center Adult
2606 W 182nd St 90504 310-533-4459
Wayne Diulio, dir. Fax 972-6395
Levy Adult Education Center Adult
3420 W 229th Pl 90505 310-533-4689
Fax 972-6399

Ambassador HS 9-12
540 Maple Ave 90503 310-356-0950
Michael Barker Ed.D., head sch
Bishop Montgomery HS 1,100/9-12
5430 Torrance Blvd 90503 310-540-2021
Rosemary Libbon, prin. Fax 792-1273
El Camino College Post-Sec.
16007 Crenshaw Blvd 90506 310-532-3670
Everest College Post-Sec.
1231 Cabrillo Ave Ste 201 90501 310 320-3200
ITT Technical Institute Post-Sec.
2555 W 190th St Ste 125 90504 310-965-5900
Los Angeles Co. Harbor UCLA Medical Ctr. Post-Sec.
1000 W Carson St 90502 310-533-2101
Pacific Lutheran HS 100/9-12
PO Box 3295 90510 310-530-1231
Lucas Fitzgerald, prin. Fax 530-1215
South Bay Junior Academy 200/PK-10
4400 Del Amo Blvd 90503 310-370-6215
Susan Vlach, prin. Fax 793-8665
Westwood College - South Bay Campus Post-Sec.
19700 S Vermont Ave Ste 100 90502 310-965-0888

Tracy, San Joaquin, Pop. 78,298
Jefferson ESD 2,600/K-8
1219 Whispering Wind Dr 95377 209-836-3388
James W. Bridges Ed.D., supt. Fax 836-2930
www.jeffersonschooldistrict.com
Jefferson S 500/5-8
7500 W Linne Rd 95304 209-835-3053
Jim Bridges, prin. Fax 835-4419

Tracy JUSD 17,300/K-12
1875 W Lowell Ave 95376 209-830-3200
James Franco, supt. Fax 830-3204
www.tracy.k12.ca.us
Duncan-Russell Continuation S 50/Alt
164 W Grant Line Rd 95376 209-830-3357
Dave Pickering, prin. Fax 830-3358
Kimball HS 1,500/9-12
3200 Jaguar Run 95377 209-832-6600
Cheryl Domenichelli, prin. Fax 832-6601
Monte Vista MS 800/6-8
751 W Lowell Ave 95376 209-830-3340
Susan O'Hara-Jones, prin. Fax 830-3341
Stein Continuation HS 200/Alt
650 W 10th St 95376 209-830-3395
Cynthia Johannes, prin. Fax 830-3396
Tracy HS 2,100/9-12
315 E 11th St 95376 209-830-3360
Jason Noll, prin. Fax 830-3361
West HS 2,500/9-12
1775 W Lowell Ave 95376 209-830-3370
Jeff Frase, prin. Fax 830-3371
Williams MS 1,200/6-8
1600 Tennis Ln 95376 209-830-3345
Barbara Montgomery, prin. Fax 830-3346
Willow Community Day S 50/Alt
164 W Grant Line Rd 95376 209-830-3357
Dave Pickering, admin. Fax 830-3358
Tracy Adult S Adult
1895 W Lowell Ave 95376 209-830-3384
Dave Pickering, prin. Fax 830-3385

Tranquillity, Fresno, Pop. 794
Golden Plains USD
Supt. — See San Joaquin
Rio Del Rey Continuation HS 50/Alt
PO Box 457 93668 559-866-5900
Espi Sandoval, prin. Fax 866-5711
Tranquillity HS 500/9-12
PO Box 457 93668 559-698-7205
Espi Sandoval, prin. Fax 698-7632
Golden Plains Adult Educ-San Joaquin Adult
PO Box 457 93668 559-693-2401
Jesus Cruz, prin. Fax 693-2519

Trona, San Bernardino, Pop. 18
Trona JUSD 300/K-12
83600 Trona Rd 93562 760-372-2861
David Olney, supt. Fax 372-4534
www.trona.k12.ca.us/
Trona Community Day S 50/Alt
83600 Trona Rd 93562 760-372-2895
David Olney, prin. Fax 372-4534
Trona JSHS 100/7-12
83600 Trona Rd 93562 760-372-2824
David Olney, prin. Fax 372-4504

Truckee, Nevada, Pop. 15,914
Tahoe-Truckee JUSD 4,100/K-12
11603 Donner Pass Rd 96161 530-582-2500
Robert Leri, supt. Fax 582-7606
www.ttusd.org
Alder Creek MS 600/6-8
10931 Alder Dr 96161 530-582-2750
Susan Phebus, prin. Fax 582-7640
Sierra HS 50/Alt
11661 Donner Pass Rd 96161 530-582-2640
Jane Loomis, prin. Fax 582-7687
Tahoe-Truckee HS 700/9-12
11725 Donner Pass Rd 96161 530-582-2600
Grant Steunenberg, prin. Fax 582-7636
Other Schools – See Tahoe City

Tujunga, See Los Angeles
Los Angeles USD
Supt. — See Los Angeles
Mt. Lukens Continuation HS 100/Alt
7705 Summitrose St 91042 818-352-4039
Allan Tamshen, prin. Fax 352-2499
Verdugo Hills HS 2,000/9-12
10625 Plainview Ave 91042 818-951-5400
Edward Trimis, prin. Fax 352-3577

Smart Academy 50/K-12
7754 McGroarty St 91042 818-951-7182
Brandon Moore, prin. Fax 951-7183

Tulare, Tulare, Pop. 58,086
Tulare CSD 9,300/K-8
600 N Cherry St 93274 559-685-7200
Clare Gist Ed.D., supt. Fax 685-7287
www.tcsdk8.org/
Cherry Avenue MS 700/6-8
540 N Cherry St 93274 559-685-7320
Greg Anderson, prin. Fax 685-5621
Live Oak MS 700/6-8
980 N Laspina St 93274 559-685-7310
Tracey Jenkins, prin. Fax 685-7313
Los Tules MS 600/6-8
801 W Gail Ave 93274 559-687-3156
Gary Yentes, prin. Fax 685-7374
Mulcahy MS 600/5-8
1001 W Sonora Ave 93274 559-685-7250
Terri Martindale, prin. Fax 687-6412

Tulare JUNHSD 4,900/9-12
426 N Blackstone St 93274 559-688-2021
Sarah Koligian, supt. Fax 687-7317
www.tulare.k12.ca.us
Countryside HS Community Day School 50/Alt
1084 S Pratt St 93274 559-687-7384
Steve Ramirez, prin. Fax 687-7388
Mission Oak HS 1,000/9-12
3442 E Bardsley Ave 93274 559-687-7308
Isidro Carrasco, prin. Fax 687-7383
Sierra Vista HS Independent Study 200/Alt
1070 S Pratt St 93274 559-687-7384
Steve Ramirez, prin. Fax 687-7388
Tulare Technical Preparatory S Vo/Tech
737 W Bardsley Ave 93274 559-687-7400
Steve Ramirez, prin. Fax 687-7414
Tulare Union HS 1,800/9-12
755 E Tulare Ave 93274 559-686-4761
Michelle Nunley, prin. Fax 687-7367
Tulare Western HS 1,700/9-12
824 W Maple Ave 93274 559-686-8751
Lucy Van Scyoc, prin. Fax 687-7341
Valley Continuation HS 50/Alt
737 W Bardsley Ave 93274 559-687-7400
Steve Ramirez, prin. Fax 687-7414
Tulare Adult S Adult
575 W Maple Ave 93274 559-686-0225
Bill Edminster, dir. Fax 687-7447

Tulare Beauty College Post-Sec.
1400 W Inyo Ave 93274 559-688-2901

Tulelake, Siskiyou, Pop. 985
Tulelake Basin JUSD 400/K-12
PO Box 640 96134 530-667-2295
Lane Bates, supt. Fax 667-4298
www.tulelake.k12.ca.us
Tulelake Continuation HS 50/Alt
PO Box 640 96134 530-667-2280
Paul Keegan, prin. Fax 667-4298
Tulelake HS 200/7-12
PO Box 640 96134 530-667-2292
Paul Keegan, prin. Fax 667-4298
Tulelake Adult S Adult
PO Box 640 96134 530-667-3152
Terry Steiner, dir. Fax 667-4298

Tuolumne, Tuolumne
Summerville UNHSD 800/K-12
17555 Tuolumne Rd 95379 209-928-3498
Robert Griffith, supt. Fax 928-1321
www.summbears.k12.ca.us
Summerville HS 500/9-12
17555 Tuolumne Rd 95379 209-928-4228
David Johnstone, prin. Fax 928-1422
Tuolumne HS 50/Alt
17555 Tuolumne Rd 95379 209-928-4228
Mitch Heldstab, prin. Fax 928-1422
Other Schools – See Long Barn, Pinecrest, Twain Harte

Turlock, Stanislaus, Pop. 66,239
Chatom UNESD 700/K-8
7201 Clayton Rd 95380 209-664-8505
Cherise Olvera, supt. Fax 664-8508
www.chatom.k12.ca.us
Other Schools – See Crows Landing

Turlock USD 13,500/K-12
PO Box 819013 95381 209-667-0632
Sonny H. Da Marto Ed.D., supt. Fax 667-6520
www.turlock.k12.ca.us
Dutcher MS 700/7-8
1441 Colorado Ave 95380 209-667-8817
Scott Lucas, prin. Fax 667-1332
Pitman HS 2,200/9-12
2525 W Christoffersen Pkwy 95382 209-656-1592
Rodney Hollars, prin. Fax 656-1639
Roselawn HS 200/Alt
312 S Roselawn Ave 95380 209-634-9311
Felipe Meraz, prin. Fax 634-8730
Turlock HS 2,200/9-12
1600 E Canal Dr 95380 209-667-2055
Dana Trevethan, prin. Fax 634-2698
Turlock JHS 1,300/7-8
3951 N Walnut Rd 95382 209-667-0881
Dave Kline, prin. Fax 668-3985
Turlock Adult Education Adult
1574 E Canal Dr 95380 209-667-0643
Alice Pollard, prin. Fax 667-0695

Adrian's Beauty College of Turlock Post-Sec.
1340 W Main St 95380 209-632-2233
California State University-Stanislaus Post-Sec.
1 University Cir 95382 209-667-3122
Turlock Christian JSHS 200/7-12
PO Box 1540 95381 209-632-2337
Kyle Fast, prin. Fax 632-5859

Tustin, Orange, Pop. 73,165
Tustin USD 22,600/K-12
300 S C St 92780 714-730-7305
Dr. Gregory Franklin, supt. Fax 730-7436
www.tustin.k12.ca.us
Columbus Tustin MS 900/6-8
17952 Beneta Way 92780 714-730-7352
Dean Crow, prin. Fax 730-7512
Currie MS 700/6-8
1402 Sycamore Ave 92780 714-730-7360
Christine Matos, prin. Fax 730-7593
Hillview HS 200/Alt
15400 Lansdowne Rd 92782 714-730-7356
Tim O'Donoghue, prin. Fax 730-7584
Pioneer MS 1,300/6-8
2700 Pioneer Rd 92782 714-730-7534
Tracey VanderHayden, prin. Fax 730-5405
Sycamore HS 50/Alt
13780 Orange St 92780 714-730-7395
Betty Sarell, prin. Fax 730-4895
Tustin HS 2,100/9-12
1171 El Camino Real 92780 714-730-7414
Jonathan Blackmore, prin. Fax 730-7568
Utt MS 900/6-8
13601 Browning Ave 92780 714-730-7573
Tom Giebe, prin. Fax 750-7576
Other Schools – See Irvine, Santa Ana

Spirit Academy 200/K-12
1372 Irvine Blvd 92780 714-731-2630
Joe Rispoli, admin. Fax 731-2639

Twain Harte, Tuolumne, Pop. 2,173
Summerville UNHSD
Supt. — See Tuolumne
South Fork HS 50/Alt
25611 Lyons Dam Rd 95383 209-586-5672
David Johnstone, prin. Fax 928-1422

Twain Harte-Long Barn UNSD 300/K-8
18995 Twain Harte Dr 95383 209-586-3772
Jeff Winfield, supt. Fax 586-9938
www.thsd.k12.ca.us
Twain Harte MS 100/5-8
18995 Twain Harte Dr 95383 209-586-3266
Dan Mayers, prin. Fax 586-3975

Twentynine Palms, San Bernardino, Pop. 23,540
Morongo USD 9,100/K-12
PO Box 1209 92277 760-367-9191
James Majchrzak, supt. Fax 367-7189
www.morongo.k12.ca.us
Twentynine Palms HS 900/9-12
72750 Wild Cat Way 92277 760-367-9591
Amy Woods, prin. Fax 367-2106
Twentynine Palms JHS 500/7-8
5798 Utah Trl 92277 760-367-9507
Justin Monical, prin. Fax 367-0742
Other Schools – See Yucca Valley

Twin Peaks, San Bernardino

Lake Arrowhead Christian S 100/K-12
PO Box 870 92391 909-337-3739
Linda Huffman M.Ed., prin. Fax 337-4550

Ukiah, Mendocino, Pop. 15,561
Mendocino County Office of Education 100/
2240 Old River Rd 95482 707-467-5000
Paul Tichinin, supt. Fax 462-0379
www.mcoe.us
Mendocino County Community S 100/Alt
2240 Old River Rd 95482 707-467-5155
Merry Catron, dir. Fax 467-5164
Orr Creek S 50/Alt
2240 Old River Rd 95482 707-467-2517
Barbara Bloom, dir. Fax 467-2531
Talmage Community MS 50/Alt
2240 Old River Rd 95482 707-467-5155
Merry Catron, dir. Fax 467-6022

Regional Occupational Center & Program
Supt. — None
Mendocino County ROP Vo/Tech
2240 Old River Rd 95482 707-467-5123
Non Olsen, dir. Fax 468-8212

Ukiah USD 6,200/K-12
925 N State St 95482 707-463-5200
Lois Nash Ed.D., supt. Fax 463-2120
www.uusd.net/
Pomolita MS 700/6-8
740 N Spring St 95482 707-463-5224
Bryan Barrett, prin. Fax 463-5203
South Valley Continuation HS 100/Alt
429 S Dora St 95482 707-463-5220
Antonio Lopez, prin. Fax 462-9654
Ukiah HS 1,600/9-12
1000 Low Gap Rd 95482 707-463-5253
Dennis Willeford, prin. Fax 463-4859
Ukiah Adult Education Adult
1056 N Bush St 95482 707-463-5217
Tracy Anderson, prin. Fax 463-0718
Other Schools – See Redwood Valley

Developing Virtue S 100/9-12
2001 Talmage Rd 95482 707-468-3847
Mendocino College Post-Sec.
1000 Hensley Creek Rd 95482 707-468-3000
Ukiah Junior Academy 100/K-10
180 Stipp Ln 95482 707-462-6350
Ken Nelson, prin. Fax 462-4026

Union City, Alameda, Pop. 65,266
New Haven USD 12,600/K-12
34200 Alvarado Niles Rd 94587 510-471-1100
Kari McVeigh, supt. Fax 471-7108
www.nhusd.k12.ca.us
Alvarado MS 1,400/6-8
31604 Alvarado Blvd 94587 510-489-0700
Jesus Varela, prin. Fax 475-3936
Chavez MS 1,500/6-8
2801 Hop Ranch Rd 94587 510-487-1700
Mireya Casarez, prin. Fax 475-3938
Logan HS 4,100/9-12
1800 H St 94587 510-471-2520
Amy McNamara, prin. Fax 471-0514
New Haven Adult S Adult
600 G St 94587 510-489-2185
Jessica Wilder, prin. Fax 471-0554
Other Schools – See Hayward

Upland, San Bernardino, Pop. 71,871
Upland USD 12,100/K-12
390 N Euclid Ave 91786 909-985-1864
Nancy Kelly Ed.D., supt. Fax 949-7872
www.upland.k12.ca.us
Hillside HS 300/Alt
1558 W 9th St 91786 909-949-8400
Brad Cuff, prin. Fax 949-7840
Pioneer JHS 1,000/7-8
245 W 18th St 91784 909-949-7770
Aaron Dover, prin. Fax 949-7778
Upland HS 3,700/9-12
565 W 11th St 91786 909-949-7880
Ivan Ayro, prin. Fax 949-7895
Upland JHS 1,000/7-8
444 E 11th St 91786 909-949-7810
Pam Chavira, prin. Fax 949-7817

Western Christian HS 400/9-12
100 W 9th St 91786 909-920-5858
Robert Yovino, prin. Fax 985-3449
Westwood College - Inland Empire Post-Sec.
20 W 7th St 91786 909-931-7550

Upper Lake, Lake, Pop. 1,026
Upper Lake UNESD 500/K-8
PO Box 36 95485 707-275-2357
Valerie Gardner, supt. Fax 275-2205
www.uluesd.lake.k12.ca.us/
Grove S, PO Box 36 95485 50/Alt
Tony Loumena, prin. 707-275-0327
Upper Lake Union MS 200/6-8
PO Box 36 95485 707-275-0223
Tony Loumena, prin. Fax 275-2911

Upper Lake UNHSD 400/9-12
675 Clover Valley Rd 95485 707-275-2655
Patrick Iaccino, supt. Fax 275-0239
www.ulhs.k12.ca.us
Clover Valley HS 50/Alt
682 Clover Valley Rd 95485 707-275-0840
Don Boyd, lead tchr. Fax 275-0208
Upper Lake Community Day HS 50/Alt
675 Clover Valley Rd 95485 707-275-0840
Don Boyd, lead tchr. Fax 275-0208
Upper Lake HS 300/9-12
675 Clover Valley Rd 95485 707-275-2338
Patrick Iaccino, prin. Fax 275-0239

Vacaville, Solano, Pop. 87,007
Vacaville USD 12,200/K-12
401 Nut Tree Rd 95687 707-453-6100
John Niederkorn, supt. Fax 453-7114
www.vacavilleusd.org
Country HS 200/Alt
100 McClellan St Ste B 95688 707-453-6215
Bill Ewing, prin. Fax 451-3875
Jepson MS 1,000/7-8
580 Elder St 95688 707-453-6280
Kelley Birch, prin. Fax 447-7128
Vaca Pena MS 900/7-8
200 Keith Way 95687 707-453-6270
Janet Dietrich, prin. Fax 451-9501
Vacaville HS 2,100/9-12
100 W Monte Vista Ave 95688 707-453-6011
Ed Santopadre, prin. Fax 447-5604
Wood HS 1,700/9-12
998 Marshall Rd 95687 707-453-6900
Cliff DeGraw, prin. Fax 451-3656
Adult Education Adult
100 McClellan St Ste A 95688 707-453-6018
Mark Frazier, prin. Fax 453-6959

Blake Austin College Post-Sec.
611 Orange Dr Ste K 95687 707-455-0557
Vacaville Christian S 1,200/PK-12
1117 Davis St 95687 707-446-1776
Paul Harrell, hdmstr. Fax 446-1538

Valencia, See Santa Clarita
Castaic UNESD 3,000/K-8
28131 Livingston Ave 91355 661-257-4500
James Gibson, supt. Fax 257-3596
www.castaic.k12.ca.us
Other Schools – See Castaic

William S. Hart UNHSD
Supt. — See Santa Clarita
Arroyo Seco JHS 1,200/7-8
27171 Vista Delgado Dr 91354 661-296-0991
Rhondi Durand, prin. Fax 296-3436
Valencia HS 3,000/9-12
27801 Dickason Dr 91355 661-294-1188
Dr. Paul Priesz, prin. Fax 294-3828

California Institute of the Arts Post-Sec.
24700 McBean Pkwy 91355 661-255-1050
Trinity Classical Academy 200/K-12
28310 Kelly Johnson Pkwy 91355 661-296-2601
Liz Caddow, head sch Fax 607-0664

Vallecito, Calaveras, Pop. 425
Bret Harte UNHSD
Supt. — See Angels Camp
Vallecito Continuation HS 50/Alt
PO Box 247 95251 209-736-8327
Michael Chimente, prin. Fax 736-0598

Vallejo, Solano, Pop. 108,826
Vallejo City USD 13,300/K-12
665 Walnut Ave 94592 707-556-8921
Ramona Bishop, supt. Fax 649-3907
www.vallejo.k12.ca.us
Bethel HS 1,600/9-12
1800 Ascot Pkwy 94591 707-556-5700
Lloyd Cartwright, prin. Fax 556-5703
Franklin MS 700/6-8
501 Starr Ave 94590 707-556-8470
Michelle Jordan-Faucett, prin. Fax 556-8475
Hogan MS 800/6-8
850 Rosewood Ave 94591 707-556-8510
Jocelyn Hendrix, prin. Fax 556-8529
Peoples Continuation HS 200/Alt
233 Hobbs Ave 94589 707-556-8670
Edison Kelly, prin. Fax 556-8674
Solano MS 600/6-8
1025 Corcoran Ave 94589 707-556-8600
Robert Russell, prin. Fax 556-8615
Vallejo HS 1,700/9-12
840 Nebraska St 94590 707-556-1700
Clarence Isadore, prin. Fax 556-8729
Vallejo Adult Education Adult
2833 Tennessee St 94591 707-556-8680
Paul Jacobs, prin. Fax 556-8686

California Maritime Academy Post-Sec.
200 Maritime Academy Dr 94590 707-654-1000
North Hills Christian S 300/PK-12
200 Admiral Callaghan Ln 94591 707-644-5284
Andrew Robinson M.S., admin. Fax 644-5295
St. Patrick-St. Vincent HS 600/9-12
1500 Benicia Rd 94591 707-644-4425
Mary Ellen Ryan, prin. Fax 644-3107
Touro University - California Post-Sec.
1310 Club Dr 94592 707-638-5200

Valley Center, San Diego, Pop. 9,007
Valley Center-Pauma USD 4,100/K-12
28751 Cole Grade Rd 92082 760-749-0464
Dr. Lou Obermeyer, supt. Fax 749-1208
www.vcpusd.net
Oak Glen HS 100/Alt
28751 Cole Grade Rd 92082 760-751-0455
Mike Schanze, prin. Fax 749-0767
Valley Center HS 1,300/9-12
28751 Cole Grade Rd 92082 760-751-5500
Ron McCowan, prin. Fax 751-5509
Valley Center MS 900/6-8
28751 Cole Grade Rd 92082 760-751-4295
Jon Peterson, prin. Fax 751-4259

Valley Glen, Los Angeles

Los Angeles Valley College Post-Sec.
5800 Fulton Ave, 818-947-2600
Summit View S 100/1-12
6455 Coldwater Canyon Ave, 818-623-6300
Nancy Rosenfelt, dir.

Valley Springs, Calaveras, Pop. 3,427
Calaveras USD
Supt. — See San Andreas
Lind HS 50/Alt
11618 School St 95252 209-754-2123
Fred Mier, prin. Fax 786-0500
Toyon MS 500/7-8
PO Box 1510 95252 209-754-2137
Lisa McInturf, prin. Fax 754-5327

Valley Village, See Los Angeles

Valley Torah Boys HS 300/9-12
12517 Chandler Blvd 91607 818-505-7999
Rabbi Avrohom Stulberger, head sch Fax 505-7997

Vandenberg AFB, Santa Barbara, Pop. 3,111
Lompoc USD
Supt. — See Lompoc
Vandenberg MS 800/7-8
Mountain View Blvd 93437 805-742-2700
Kathi Froemming, prin. Fax 742-2759

Van Nuys, See Los Angeles
Los Angeles USD
Supt. — See Los Angeles
Fulton College Prep S 2,200/6-12
7477 Kester Ave 91405 818-947-2100
Raquel George, prin. Fax 994-2284
Grant HS 2,600/9-12
13000 Oxnard St 91401 818-756-2700
Linda Ibach, prin. Fax 908-0774
Independence Continuation HS 100/Alt
6501 Balboa Blvd 91406 818-881-7737
Deborah Smith, prin. Fax 609-0764
London HS 100/Alt
12924 Oxnard St 91401 818-756-2794
Angela Cleveland, prin. Fax 902-9671
Mulholland MS 1,700/6-8
17120 Vanowen St 91406 818-609-2500
Gregory Vallone, prin. Fax 345-1933
Pearl Journalism & Communications HS 300/9-12
6649 Balboa Blvd 91406 818-654-3775
Janet Kiddo, prin. Fax 654-3701
Rogers Continuation HS 200/Alt
14711 Gilmore St 91411 818-778-6895
Sunshine Sepulveda-Klus, prin. Fax 904-0675
Valley Alternative S 600/Alt
6701 Balboa Blvd 91406 818-342-6133
Bennet Blum, prin. Fax 342-8645
Van Nuys HS 2,900/9-12
6535 Cedros Ave 91411 818-778-6800
Judith Vanderbok, prin. Fax 781-5181
Van Nuys MS 1,400/6-8
5435 Vesper Ave 91411 818-267-5900
Manuel Diaz, prin. Fax 909-7274
Vista MS 1,600/6-8
15040 Roscoe Blvd 91402 818-901-2727
Nidia Castro, prin. Fax 901-2740
Van Nuys Community Adult S Adult
6535 Cedros Ave 91411 818-778-6000
Bernadine Gonzalez, prin. Fax 778-6015

American Pacific College Post-Sec.
14435 Sherman Way Ste 210 91405 818-781-0001
California Institute of Locksmithing Post-Sec.
14719 1/2 Oxnard St 91411 818-994-7425
Casa Loma College Post-Sec.
6725 Kester Ave 91405 818-785-2726
Help Group's North Hills Prep S 100/4-12
15339 Saticoy St 91406 818-267-2600
Elin Bradley, dir. Fax 988-9143
ICDC College Post-Sec.
14434 Sherman Way 91405 818-787-0008
Montclair College Preparatory S 300/6-12
8071 Sepulveda Blvd 91402 818-787-5290
Walt Steele, prin. Fax 786-3382
Nick Harris Detective Academy Post-Sec.
14721 Oxnard St 91411 818-343-6611
The Kings University Post-Sec.
14800 Sherman Way 91405 818-779-8040

Venice, See Los Angeles
Los Angeles USD
Supt. — See Los Angeles
Venice Adult Skills Center Adult
611 5th Ave 90291 310-664-5820
Janice Brittain, prin. Fax 392-3461

Ventura, Ventura, Pop. 103,287
Ventura USD 17,300/K-12
255 W Stanley Ave Ste 100 93001 805-641-5000
Dr. Trudy Tuttle Arriaga, supt. Fax 653-7855
www.venturausd.org
Anacapa MS 1,000/6-8
100 S Mills Rd 93003 805-289-7900
Soledad Molinar, prin. Fax 289-7909
Balboa MS 1,300/6-8
247 S Hill Rd 93003 805-289-1800
Teresa Gern, prin. Fax 289-1806
Buena HS 2,200/9-12
5670 Telegraph Rd 93003 805-289-1826
Jesus Vaca, prin. Fax 289-1854
Cabrillo MS 1,000/6-8
1426 E Santa Clara St 93001 805-641-5155
Peggy Kroener, prin. Fax 641-5377
De Anza Academy 500/6-8
2060 Cameron St 93001 805-641-5165
Hector Guerrero, prin. Fax 641-5282
El Camino HS 300/9-12
61 Day Rd 93003 805-289-7955
Cheryl Burns, prin. Fax 658-6315
Foothill Technology HS Vo/Tech
100 Day Rd 93003 805-289-0023
Joe Bova, prin. Fax 289-0029
Pacific HS 200/Alt
501 College Dr 93003 805-289-7950
Barbara Boggio, prin. Fax 289-7962
Ventura HS 2,100/9-12
2 N Catalina St 93001 805-641-5116
Val Wyatt, prin. Fax 641-5310
Ventura Adult and Continuing Education Adult
5200 Valentine Rd 93003 805-289-7925
Teresa Johnson, prin. Fax 289-7931

Brooks Institute Post-Sec.
5301 N Ventura Ave 93001 805-585-8000
St. Augustine Academy 100/K-12
PO Box 4506 93007 805-672-0411
Michael Van Hecke, hdmstr. Fax 672-2365
St. Bonaventure HS 600/9-12
3167 Telegraph Rd 93003 805-648-6836
Marc Groff, prin. Fax 648-4903
Santa Barbara Business College Post-Sec.
4839 Market St 93003 866-749-7222
Santa Barbara Business College - Online Post-Sec.
1834 Palma Dr 93003 805-339-6370
Ventura College Post-Sec.
4667 Telegraph Rd 93003 805-654-6400
Ventura County Christian S 100/K-12
96 MacMillan Ave 93001 805-641-0187
Tanja Geue, admin. Fax 641-0252

Victorville, San Bernardino, Pop. 111,837
Adelanto ESD
Supt. — See Adelanto
Mesa Linda MS 1,000/7-8
13001 Mesa Linda Ave 92392 760-246-6363
Matthew Pollack, prin. Fax 956-7456

Victor Valley UNHSD 13,000/7-12
16350 Mojave Dr, 760-955-3200
Elvin Momon, supt. Fax 245-3128
www.vvuhsd.org
Adelanto HS 1,200/9-12
13853 Seneca Rd 92392 760-955-3201
Jerry Cradduck, prin. Fax 245-4634
Cobalt MS 600/7-8
13801 Cobalt Rd 92392 760-955-2530
Dr. Melda Gaskins, prin. Fax 955-2437
Goodwill Education Center 600/Alt
14045 Topaz Rd 92392 760-955-3440
Kevan Loyd, prin. Fax 245-3512
Hook JHS 900/7-8
15000 Hook Blvd 92394 760-955-3360
Daryl Bell, prin. Fax 245-5839
Lakeview MS 900/7-8
12484 Tamarisk Rd, 760-955-3400
Lonnie Keeter, prin. Fax 955-1992
Silverado HS 3,800/9-12
14048 Cobalt Rd 92392 760-955-3353
Sergio White, prin. Fax 955-3439
University Preparatory S 1,100/Alt
16925 Forrest Ave, 760-243-5940
Valerie Hatcher, prin. Fax 951-2803
Victor Valley HS 2,700/9-12
16500 Mojave Dr, 760-955-3300
Chris Douglass, prin. Fax 955-3319
Victor Valley Adult Education Adult
13853 Seneca Rd 92392 760-955-3440
Gloria McGee, coord. Fax 241-0115

Four-D College Post-Sec.
16534 Victor St, 760-962-1325
Victor Valley Beauty College Post-Sec.
16515 Mojave Dr, 760-245-2522
Victor Valley Christian S 400/PK-12
15260 Nisqually Rd, 760-241-8827
Deb Clarkson, admin. Fax 243-0654
Victor Valley College Post-Sec.
18422 Bear Valley Rd, 760-245-4271
Westech College Post-Sec.
14554 7th St, 760-951-5050

Villa Park, Orange, Pop. 5,691
Orange USD
Supt. — See Orange
Cerro Villa MS 1,000/7-8
17852 Serrano Ave 92861 714-997-6251
Kenneth Miller Ed.D., prin. Fax 921-9331

Villa Park HS 2,500/9-12
18042 Taft Ave 92861 714-532-8020
Ed Howard, prin. Fax 628-4302

Visalia, Tulare, Pop. 121,741
Visalia USD 27,200/K-12
5000 W Cypress Ave 93277 559-730-7300
Craig Wheaton, supt. Fax 730-7508
www.vusd.org/
Divisadero MS 900/7-8
1200 S Divisadero St 93277 559-730-7661
Matt Shin, prin. Fax 730-7908
El Diamante HS 1,900/9-12
5100 W Whitendale Ave 93277 559-735-3501
Drew Sorensen, prin. Fax 735-3579
Golden West HS 1,800/9-12
1717 N McAuliff St 93292 559-730-7801
Rick Hamilton, prin. Fax 730-7408
Green Acres MS 1,200/7-8
1147 N Mooney Blvd 93291 559-730-7671
Angela Sanchez, prin. Fax 730-7918
La Joya MS 1,000/7-8
4711 W La Vida Ave 93277 559-730-7921
Melanie Stringer, prin. Fax 730-7505
Mt. Whitney HS 1,600/9-12
900 S Conyer St 93277 559-730-7602
Jeff Hohne, prin. Fax 730-7679
Redwood HS 1,900/9-12
1001 W Main St 93291 559-730-7367
Fernie Marroquin, prin. Fax 730-7741
Sequoia HS 300/Alt
901 N Mooney Blvd 93291 559-730-7649
Yolanda Luoma, prin. Fax 730-7487
Valley Oak MS 900/7-8
2000 N Lovers Ln 93292 559-730-7681
Michael Hernandez, prin. Fax 730-7822
Visalia Adult Education Adult
3110 E Houston Ave 93292 559-730-7655
Jill Rojas, prin. Fax 635-0372

Advanced Career Institute Post-Sec.
1728 N Kelsey St 93291 559-651-1978
Central Valley Christian S 1,000/PK-12
5600 W Tulare Ave 93277 559-734-9481
Dr. John DeLeeuw, supt. Fax 734-7963
College of the Sequoias Post-Sec.
915 S Mooney Blvd 93277 559-730-3700
Estes Inst. Cosmetology Arts & Sciences Post-Sec.
324 E Main St 93291 559-733-3617
Milan Institute of Cosmetology Post-Sec.
6500 S Mooney Blvd Unit A 93277 559-735-3829
San Joaquin Valley College Post-Sec.
8400 W Mineral King Ave 93291 559-651-2500

Vista, San Diego, Pop. 90,562
Vista USD 24,500/K-12
1234 Arcadia Ave 92084 760-726-2170
Devin Vodicka, supt. Fax 758-7838
www.vusd.k12.ca.us
Alta Vista HS 200/Alt
1575 Bonair Rd 92084 760-724-3775
JoAnn Jones, prin. Fax 724-0410
Murray Continuation S 200/Alt
215 N Melrose Dr 92083 760-631-2502
Chuck Hoover, prin. Fax 643-2685
Rancho Buena Vista HS 2,900/9-12
1601 Longhorn Dr, 760-727-7284
Chuck Schindler, prin. Fax 598-7062
Rancho Minerva MS 900/6-8
2245 Foothill Dr 92084 760-631-4500
Steve Riehle, prin. Fax 643-2490
Vista HS 2,800/9-12
1 Panther Way 92084 760-726-5611
Steve James, prin. Fax 630-9738
Vista Magnet MS 600/6-8
151 Civic Center Dr 92084 760-726-5766
Jose Villarreal, prin. Fax 945-4273
Vista Visions Academy Alt
305 E Bobier Dr 92084 760-724-4785
JoAnn Jones, prin. Fax 630-4206
Washington MS 700/6-8
740 Olive Ave 92083 760-724-7115
Adalia Lavado, prin. Fax 941-6912
Vista Adult S Adult
510 Sunset Dr, 760-758-7122
Ebon Brown, prin. Fax 726-3277
Other Schools – See Oceanside

Calvary Christian S 200/K-12
885 E Vista Way 92084 760-724-4590
Cindy Barger, prin. Fax 560-0607
Kaplan College Post-Sec.
2022 University Dr 92083 760-630-1555
Tri City Christian S 700/PK-12
302 N Emerald Dr 92083 760-724-3016
Clark Gilbert, supt. Fax 724-6643

Walnut, Los Angeles, Pop. 28,480
Walnut Valley USD 14,700/K-12
880 S Lemon Ave 91789 909-595-1261
Dr. Dean Conklin, supt. Fax 444-3435
www.wvusd.k12.ca.us
Hockwalt Academies 50/Alt
476 S Lemon Ave 91789 909-594-0776
Jose Annicchiarico, prin. Fax 594-1272
South Pointe MS 1,000/6-8
20671 Larkstone Dr 91789 909-595-8171
Susan Arzola, prin. Fax 468-5201
Suzanne MS 1,400/6-8
525 Suzanne Rd 91789 909-594-1657
Lester Ojeda, prin. Fax 598-6741
Walnut HS 2,900/9-12
400 Pierre Rd 91789 909-594-1333
Jeffrey Jordan, prin. Fax 598-7282
Other Schools – See Diamond Bar

Mt. San Antonio College Post-Sec.
1100 N Grand Ave 91789 909-594-5611
Southlands Christian S 600/PK-12
1920 Brea Canyon Cut Off Rd 91789 909-598-9733
Glenn Duncan, supt. Fax 468-9943

Walnut Creek, Contra Costa, Pop. 61,759
Acalanes UNHSD
Supt. — See Lafayette
Acalanes Center for Independent Study 100/9-12
1963 Tice Valley Blvd 94595 925-280-3945
Mark Uhrenholt, dir. Fax 280-3947
Las Lomas HS 1,500/9-12
1460 S Main St 94596 925-280-3920
Matt Campbell, prin. Fax 280-3921
Acalanes Adult S & Center Adult
1963 Tice Valley Blvd 94595 925-280-3980
Mark Uhrenholt, dir. Fax 395-3981

Mount Diablo USD
Supt. — See Concord
Foothill MS 1,000/6-8
2775 Cedro Ln 94598 925-939-8600
April Bush, prin. Fax 256-4281
Northgate HS 1,500/9-12
425 Castle Rock Rd 94598 925-938-0900
John McMorris, prin. Fax 945-6429

Walnut Creek ESD 3,500/K-8
960 Ygnacio Valley Rd 94596 925-944-6850
Patricia Wool Ed.D., supt. Fax 944-1768
www.walnutcreeksd.org
Walnut Creek IS 1,100/6-8
2425 Walnut Blvd 94597 925-944-6840
Michael Cannon, prin. Fax 933-1922

Berean Christian HS 400/9-12
245 El Divisadero Ave 94598 925-945-6464
Dr. Nelson Noriega, prin. Fax 945-7473
Contra Costa Christian S 300/PK-12
2721 Larkey Ln 94597 925-934-4964
Darren Price, hdmstr. Fax 934-4966

Walnut Park, Los Angeles, Pop. 15,927
Los Angeles USD
Supt. — See Los Angeles
Science Tech English & Math Academy 6-8
7500 Marbrisa Ave 90255 323-277-2600
Venkatesan Sudha, prin. Fax 589-1529
S of Social Justice and Service Learning 6-8
7500 Marbrisa Ave 90255 323-277-2600
Aida Coronado-Delon, prin. Fax 589-1529

Warner Springs, San Diego
Warner USD 300/PK-12
PO Box 8 92086 760-782-3517
Melissa Brown Ph.D., supt. Fax 782-9117
www.warnerusd.net
San Jose Valley Continuation HS 50/Alt
PO Box 8 92086 760-782-3517
Melissa Brown Ph.D., admin. Fax 782-9117
Warner JSHS 100/7-12
PO Box 8 92086 760-782-3517
Melissa Brown Ph.D., admin. Fax 782-0605

Wasco, Kern, Pop. 25,343
Regional Occupational Center & Program
Supt. — None
North Kern Vocational Training Center Vo/Tech
2150 7th St 93280 661-758-3045
Gary Garcia, dir. Fax 758-5956

Wasco UNESD 3,300/K-8
639 Broadway St 93280 661-758-7100
Elizabeth McCray, supt. Fax 758-7110
www.wuesd.org
Jefferson MS 700/7-8
639 Broadway St 93280 661-758-7140
Rafaela Lopez, prin. Fax 758-9366

Wasco UNHSD 1,700/9-12
2100 7th St 93280 661-758-8447
Elizabeth McCray, supt. Fax 758-4946
www.wasco.k12.ca.us/
Independence HS 100/Alt
1445 Poso Dr 93280 661-758-7450
Martin Lonza, prin. Fax 758-7451
Wasco HS 1,600/9-12
1900 7th St 93280 661-758-7400
Joseph Elwood, prin. Fax 758-9201

Waterford, Stanislaus, Pop. 8,248
Waterford USD 3,600/K-12
219 N Reinway Ave 95386 209-874-1809
Don Davis, supt. Fax 874-3109
www.waterford.k12.ca.us
Sentinel HS 50/Alt
121 S Reinway Ave 95386 209-874-9017
Peggy Herndon, prin. Fax 874-9065
Waterford HS 600/9-12
121 S Reinway Ave 95386 209-874-9060
Don Davis, prin. Fax 874-9065
Waterford MS 300/7-8
12916 Bentley St 95386 209-874-2382
Paul Patterson, prin. Fax 874-3652

Watsonville, Santa Cruz, Pop. 50,582
Pajaro Valley USD 16,900/K-12
294 Green Valley Rd 95076 831-786-2100
Dorma Baker, supt. Fax 728-4288
www.pvusd.net
Hall MS 600/6-8
201 Brewington Ave 95076 831-728-6270
Olga de Santa Anna, prin. Fax 761-6150
Lakeview MS 600/6-8
2350 E Lake Ave 95076 831-728-6454
Ken Woods, prin. Fax 728-6480
New S 50/Alt
165 Harkins Slough Rd 95076 831-761-6140
Victoria Sorensen, prin. Fax 761-6188
Pajaro MS 400/6-8
250 Salinas Rd 95076 831-728-6238
Jean Gottlob, prin. Fax 728-6219
Rolling Hills MS 600/6-8
130 Herman Ave 95076 831-728-6341
Rick Ito, prin. Fax 724-7323
Watsonville HS 2,100/9-12
250 E Beach St 95076 831-728-6390
Elaine Legorreta, prin. Fax 761-6013
Adult Education Downtown Center Adult
280 Main St 95076 831-728-6330
Dr. Nancy Bilicich, dir. Fax 728-6245
Adult Education Green Valley Center Adult
294 Green Valley Rd 95076 831-786-2160
Dr. Nancy Bilicich, dir. Fax 786-2193
Other Schools – See Aptos, La Selva Beach

Green Valley Christian S 300/PK-12
376 S Green Valley Rd 95076 831-724-6505
Sharon Harris, admin. Fax 724-1002
Monte Vista Christian S 800/6-12
2 School Way 95076 831-722-8178
Stephen Sharp, supt. Fax 722-6003
St. Francis Central Coast Catholic HS 200/9-12
PO Box 2649 95077 831-724-5933
Patrick Lee, prin. Fax 724-5995

Weaverville, Trinity, Pop. 3,455
Trinity Alps USD 800/K-12
PO Box 1227 96093 530-623-6104
Tom Barnett, supt. Fax 623-3418
www.tausd.org
Alps View HS 50/Alt
PO Box 1227 96093 530-623-6104
Tom Barnett, supt. Fax 623-3418
Trinity HS 400/9-12
PO Box 1060 96093 530-623-6127
Christine Camara, prin. Fax 623-6661
Trinity Adult S Adult
PO Box 1227 96093 530-623-6104
Tom Barnett, supt. Fax 623-3418

Weed, Siskiyou, Pop. 2,802
Siskiyou UNHSD
Supt. — See Mount Shasta
Weed HS 200/9-12
909 Hillside Dr 96094 530-938-4774
Mike Matheson, prin. Fax 938-1319

College of the Siskiyous Post-Sec.
800 College Ave 96094 530-938-5555

Weimar, Placer, Pop. 1,300
Placer Hills UNESD
Supt. — See Meadow Vista
Weimar Hills MS 200/4-8
PO Box 255 95736 530-637-4121
Steve Schaumleffel, prin. Fax 637-4054

Weldon, Kern, Pop. 2,564
South Fork UNSD 300/PK-8
5225 S Kelso Valley Rd 93283 760-378-4000
Robin Shive, supt. Fax 378-3046
www.southforkschool.org
South Fork MS 100/5-8
5225 S Kelso Valley Rd 93283 760-378-1300
Robin Shive, supt. Fax 378-9113

West Covina, Los Angeles, Pop. 103,993
Covina-Valley USD
Supt. — See Covina
South Hills HS 2,000/9-12
645 S Barranca St 91791 626-974-6220
Chad Smith, prin. Fax 974-6245
Traweek MS 1,000/6-8
1941 E Rowland Ave 91791 626-974-7400
Rodney Zerbel, prin. Fax 974-7415
Tri Community Adult Ed.-Pioneer Center Adult
1651 E Rowland Ave 91791 626-974-6821
Julie Caston-Hicks, prin. Fax 974-6830

Regional Occupational Center & Program
Supt. — None
East San Gabriel Valley ROP Vo/Tech
1501 Del Norte St 91790 626-962-5080
Dr. Laurel Adler, supt. Fax 472-5145

Rowland USD
Supt. — See Rowland Heights
Giano IS 600/7-8
3223 S Giano Ave 91792 626-965-2461
Fax 854-2212

West Covina USD 10,100/K-12
1717 W Merced Ave 91790 626-939-4600
Debra Kaplan, supt. Fax 939-4701
www.wcusd-ca.schoolloop.com/
Coronado Alternative HS 200/Alt
1500 E Francisquito Ave 91791 626-931-1810
Armando Marentes, prin. Fax 931-1819
Edgewood HS 200/9-12
1301 Trojan Way 91790 626-939-4900
Marc Trovatore, prin. Fax 939-0800
Edgewood MS 600/6-8
1625 W Durness St 91790 626-939-4900
Marc Trovatore, prin. Fax 939-4999
Hollencrest MS 700/6-8
2101 E Merced Ave 91791 626-931-1760
Hector Galicia, prin. Fax 931-1762
Walnut Grove IS 500/7-8
614 W Vine Ave 91790 626-919-7018
Rich Nambu, prin. Fax 919-7207
West Covina HS 2,900/9-12
1609 E Cameron Ave 91791 626-859-2900
Alejandro Ruvalcaba, prin. Fax 859-3950

American Beauty College Post-Sec.
646 S Sunset Ave 91790 - -

Marinello School of Beauty Post-Sec.
118 Plaza Dr 91790 626-962-1021
North-West College Post-Sec.
2121 W Garvey Ave N 91790 626-960-5046

West Hills, Los Angeles

Chaminade College Prep HS 1,300/9-12
7500 Chaminade Ave 91304 818-347-8300
Br. Tom Fahy, prin. Fax 348-8374
New Community Jewish HS 400/9-12
7353 Valley Circle Blvd 91304 818-348-0048
Dr. Bruce Powell, head sch Fax 348-0092

West Hollywood, Los Angeles, Pop. 33,330

Cedars-Sinai Graduate Program Post-Sec.
8700 Beverly Blvd Atrium 90048 310-423-8294
Pacific Hills S 200/6-12
8628 Holloway Dr 90069 310-276-3068
Dr. Peter Temes, head sch Fax 657-3831
Touro College Los Angeles Post-Sec.
1317 N Crescent Hts Blvd 90046 323-822-9700

Westlake Village, Los Angeles, Pop. 8,064
Conejo Valley USD
Supt. — See Thousand Oaks
Westlake HS 2,400/9-12
100 N Lakeview Canyon Rd 91362 805-497-6711
Ronald Lipari, prin. Fax 497-2606

Malibu Cove Private S 100/K-12
860 Hampshire Rd 91361 805-267-4818
Joanne Alfonso, admin.
Oaks Christian S 1,400/6-12
31749 La Tienda Rd 91362 818-575-9900
Jeffrey Woodcock, hdmstr. Fax 575-9951

Westminster, Orange, Pop. 87,394
Garden Grove USD
Supt. — See Garden Grove
La Quinta HS 2,200/9-12
10372 McFadden Ave 92683 714-663-6315
Denise Halstead, prin. Fax 775-7307
McGarvin IS 700/7-8
9802 Bishop Pl 92683 714-663-6218
Margaret Feliciani, prin. Fax 663-6163

Huntington Beach UNHSD
Supt. — See Huntington Beach
Westminster HS 2,700/9-12
14325 Goldenwest St 92683 714-893-1381
Owen Crosby, prin. Fax 898-4721

Westminster ESD 9,700/PK-8
14121 Cedarwood St 92683 714-894-7311
Richard Tauer, supt. Fax 899-2781
www.wsd.k12.ca.us
Johnson MS 800/6-8
13603 Edwards St 92683 714-894-7244
Shane Vinagupta, prin. Fax 379-0784
Warner MS 900/6-8
14171 Newland St 92683 714-894-7281
Matthew Skoll, prin. Fax 895-2378
Other Schools – See Huntington Beach

Asian American Intl Beauty College Post-Sec.
7871 Westminster Blvd 92683 714-891-0508
Covenant Christian Academy 50/K-12
10101 Cunningham Ave 92683 714-531-9950
Joe LoGiudice, prin. Fax 531-9926

West Sacramento, Yolo, Pop. 45,910
Washington USD 7,300/K-12
930 Westacre Rd 95691 916-375-7600
Dayton Gilleland Ed.D., supt. Fax 375-7619
www.wusd.k12.ca.us
River City HS 1,900/9-12
1 Raider Ln 95691 916-375-7800
Katie Nemer, prin. Fax 375-7809
West Sacramento S for Independent Study 100/Alt
1200 Anna St 95605 916-375-7650
Kerry Koerwitz, dir. Fax 375-7771
Yolo HS 100/Alt
919 Westacre Rd 95691 916-375-7740
Stan Mojsich, prin. Fax 375-0928
Washington Adult S Adult
919 Westacre Rd 95691 916-375-7740
Stan Mojsich, prin. Fax 375-7744

WyoTech Post-Sec.
980 Riverside Pkwy 95605 916-376-8888

Westwood, Lassen, Pop. 1,610
Westwood USD 600/K-12
PO Box 1225 96137 530-256-2311
Adele Emershaw, supt. Fax 256-3539
www.westwoodusd.org/
Westwood HS 100/8-12
PO Box 1510 96137 530-256-3235
Adele Emershaw, prin. Fax 256-3693

Wheatland, Yuba, Pop. 3,292
Wheatland ESD 800/K-8
111 Main St 95692 530-633-3130
Craig Guensler, supt. Fax 633-4807
www.wheatlandsd.com/
Bear River S 300/4-8
100 Wheatland Park Dr 95692 530-633-3135
Angela Gouker, prin. Fax 633-3142

Wheatland UNHSD 700/9-12
1010 Wheatland Rd 95692 530-633-3100
Vic Ramos, supt. Fax 633-3109
www.wheatlandhigh.org
Wheatland Union HS 700/9-12
1010 Wheatland Rd 95692 530-633-3100
Vic Ramos, prin. Fax 633-3109

Whitethorn, Humboldt
Leggett Valley USD
Supt. — See Leggett
Whale Gulch HS 50/9-12
76811 Usal Rd 95589 707-925-6285
Tom Puskarich, prin.

Whittier, Los Angeles, Pop. 84,209
East Whittier City ESD 8,900/K-8
14535 Whittier Blvd 90605 562-907-5959
Mary Branca, supt. Fax 696-9256
www.ewcsd.org/
East Whittier MS 1,100/6-8
14421 Whittier Blvd 90605 562-789-7220
Tim Strand, prin. Fax 945-3542
Granada MS 1,000/6-8
15337 Lemon Dr 90604 562-464-2330
Justin Mayernik, prin. Fax 943-5413
Hillview MS 900/6-8
10931 Stamy Rd 90604 562-789-2000
Genny Cadena, prin. Fax 946-3066

Los Angeles County Office of Education
Supt. — See Downey
Eastern Community Day S 200/Alt
5777 Lockheed Ave 90606 562-692-1497
Seema Gaur, dir. Fax 908-0332

Lowell JSD 3,100/PK-8
11019 Valley Home Ave 90603 562-943-0211
Dr. Patricia Howell, supt. Fax 947-7874
www.ljsd.org
Rancho-Starbuck IS 700/7-8
16430 Woodbrier Dr 90604 562-902-4261
Linda Takacs, prin. Fax 947-9911

Norwalk-La Mirada USD
Supt. — See Norwalk
El Camino HS 400/Alt
14625 Keese Dr 90604 562-868-0431
Darryl Brown, prin. Fax 944-1843

Regional Occupational Center & Program
Supt. — None
Tri-Cities ROP Vo/Tech
12519 Washington Blvd 90602 562-698-9571
Norm Kirschenbaum, supt. Fax 696-5352

South Whittier ESD 3,600/K-8
11200 Telechron Ave 90605 562-944-6231
Dr. Erich Kwek, supt. Fax 944-9659
www.swhittier.k12.ca.us
Graves MS 800/7-8
13243 Los Nietos Rd 90605 562-944-0135
Dr. Matthew Fraijo, prin. Fax 944-9433

Whittier City ESD 6,500/K-8
7211 Whittier Ave 90602 562-789-3075
Dr. Ron Carruth, supt. Fax 698-6534
www.whittiercity.net
Dexter MS 1,200/6-8
11532 Floral Dr 90601 562-789-3090
Diane Kinnart, prin. Fax 789-3095
Edwards MS 900/6-8
6812 Norwalk Blvd 90606 562-789-3120
Maria Ruiz, prin. Fax 789-3133

Whittier UNHSD 13,500/9-12
9401 Painter Ave 90605 562-698-8121
Sandra Thorstenson, supt. Fax 693-0221
www.wuhsd.org
California HS 3,000/9-12
9800 Mills Ave 90604 562-698-8121
Bill Schloss, prin. Fax 946-6094
Frontier HS 600/Alt
9401 Painter Ave 90605 562-698-8121
Margie Moriarty, prin. Fax 945-7451
La Serna HS 2,500/9-12
15301 Youngwood Dr 90605 562-698-8121
Ann Fitzgerald, prin. Fax 698-6918
Pioneer HS 1,500/9-12
10800 Ben Avon St 90606 562-698-8121
Monica Oviedo, prin. Fax 692-9194
Sierra Vista Alternative HS 400/Alt
9401 Painter Ave 90605 562-698-8121
Nicki Buchholz, dir. Fax 698-0004
Whittier HS 2,600/9-12
12417 Philadelphia St 90601 562-698-8121
Lori Eshilian, prin. Fax 698-8925
Adult Education Center Adult
9401 Painter Ave 90605 562-698-8121
Debbie Roberts, dir. Fax 693-5354
Other Schools – See Santa Fe Springs

Marinello School of Beauty Post-Sec.
6538 Greenleaf Ave 90601 562-698-0068
Remnant Christian S 50/8-12
7346 Painter Ave 90602 562-464-2554
James Turnbough, admin. Fax 464-2556
Rio Hondo College Post-Sec.
3600 Workman Mill Rd 90601 562-692-0921
Southern CA University of Health Science Post-Sec.
16200 Amber Valley Dr 90604 562-947-8755
Whittier Christian JHS 100/7-8
6548 Newlin Ave 90601 562-698-0527
Robert Sowell, prin. Fax 698-2859
Whittier College Post-Sec.
PO Box 634 90608 562-907-4200

Wildomar, Riverside, Pop. 31,160
Lake Elsinore USD
Supt. — See Lake Elsinore
Brown MS 1,000/6-8
21861 Grand Ave 92595 951-253-7430
Karen Gaither, prin. Fax 253-7437
Elsinore HS 2,400/9-12
21800 Canyon Dr 92595 951-253-7200
Jon Hurst Ed.D., prin. Fax 253-7209

California Lutheran HS 100/9-12
PO Box 1570 92595 951-678-7000
Andrew Aguilar, supt. Fax 678-0172
Cornerstone Christian S 300/PK-12
34570 Monte Vista Dr 92595 951-674-9381
Sharon Privett, hdmstr. Fax 674-8462
Faith Baptist Academy 200/K-12
PO Box 1030 92595 951-245-8748
Greg Beil, admin.

Williams, Colusa, Pop. 5,073
Williams USD 1,300/K-12
PO Box 7 95987 530-473-2550
Dr. Judith Rossi, supt. Fax 473-5894
www.williamsusd.net
Mid Valley HS 50/Alt
PO Box 7 95987 530-473-5369
Nicholas Richter, prin. Fax 473-5540
Williams HS 400/9-12
PO Box 7 95987 530-473-5369
Nicholas Richter, prin. Fax 473-5540
Williams JHS 200/7-8
PO Box 7 95987 530-473-3029
Nicholas Richter, prin. Fax 473-5540

Willits, Mendocino, Pop. 4,738
Willits USD 1,800/K-12
120 Pearl St 95490 707-459-5314
Patricia Johnson, supt. Fax 459-7862
www.willitsunified.net
Baechtel Grove MS 400/6-8
1150 Magnolia St 95490 707-459-2417
Maria Mungia, prin. Fax 459-7881
New Horizons S 100/Alt
120 N Main St 95490 707-459-4801
Tawny Fernandez, prin. Fax 459-6580
Sanhedrin Continuation HS 50/Alt
120 N Main St 95490 707-459-4801
Tawny Fernandez, prin. Fax 459-6580
Willits HS 500/9-12
299 N Main St 95490 707-459-7700
Jeffrey Ritchley, prin. Fax 459-7741
Willits Secondary Community Day S 50/Alt
371 E Commercial St 95490 707-459-7640
Tawny Fernandez, prin. Fax 459-6580

Willows, Glenn, Pop. 6,043
Glenn County Office of Education 300/
311 S Villa Ave 95988 530-934-6575
Tracey Quarne, supt. Fax 934-6576
www.glenncoe.org
Glenn County Opportunity S 50/Alt
311 S Villa Ave 95988 530-934-6575
Susan Domenighini, prin. Fax 934-6576
Glenn Adult Program Adult
451 S Villa Ave 95988 530-934-6320
Jess Modesto, dir. Fax 934-6325

Regional Occupational Center & Program
Supt. — None
Glenn County ROP Vo/Tech
311 S Villa Ave 95988 530-934-6575
Jess Modesto, dir. Fax 934-6576

Willows USD 1,400/K-12
823 W Laurel St 95988 530-934-6600
Dr. Mort Geivett, supt. Fax 934-6609
www.willowsunified.org
Willows Community HS 50/Alt
823 W Laurel St 95988 530-934-6605
Dr. Mort Geivett, prin. Fax 934-6609
Willows HS 500/9-12
203 N Murdock Ave 95988 530-934-6611
Jerry Smith, prin. Fax 934-6619
Willows IS 300/6-8
1145 W Cedar St 95988 530-934-6633
Steve Sailsbery, prin. Fax 934-6697

Wilmington, See Los Angeles
Los Angeles USD
Supt. — See Los Angeles
Avalon Continuation HS 100/Alt
1425 N Avalon Blvd 90744 310-549-2112
Monica Fiello, prin. Fax 549-3287
Banning HS 3,400/9-12
1527 Lakme Ave 90744 310-847-3700
Rudy Mendoza, prin. Fax 830-5515
Harbor Teacher Preparation Academy 400/Alt
1111 Figueroa Pl 90744 310-834-3932
Mattie Adams, admin. Fax 834-4194
Wilmington MS 2,000/6-8
1700 Gulf Ave 90744 310-847-1500
Myrna Brutti, prin. Fax 549-5307

Los Angeles Harbor College Post-Sec.
1111 Figueroa Pl 90744 310-233-4000
Pacific Harbor Christian S 200/PK-12
1530 N Wilmington Blvd 90744 310-835-5665
Amie Gray, prin. Fax 835-6316

Windsor, Sonoma, Pop. 26,016
Windsor USD 5,700/K-12
9291 Old Redwood Hwy 95492 707-837-7700
Tammy Gabel Ed.D., supt. Fax 838-4031
www.wusd.org
Windsor HS 1,700/9-12
8695 Windsor Rd 95492 707-837-7767
Marc Elin, prin. Fax 837-7773
Windsor MS 900/6-8
9500 Brooks Rd S 95492 707-837-7737
Lisa Saxon, prin. Fax 837-7743
Windsor Oaks Academy 100/Alt
8681 Windsor Rd 95492 707-837-7771
Marc Elin, prin. Fax 837-7770

Winterhaven, Imperial, Pop. 381
San Pasqual Valley USD 800/K-12
676 Base Line Rd 92283 760-572-0222
Dr. David Bealer, supt. Fax 572-0711
www.spvusd.org/
Manes HS 50/Alt
676 Base Line Rd 92283 760-572-0095
Paul Keegan, prin. Fax 572-0829
San Pasqual Valley HS 100/9-12
676 Base Line Rd 92283 760-572-0222
Paul Keegan, prin. Fax 572-0881
San Pasqual Valley MS 200/6-8
676 Base Line Rd 92283 760-572-0222
Jeralyn Shaw, prin. Fax 572-0829

Winters, Yolo, Pop. 6,490
Winters JUSD 1,600/K-12
909 Grant Ave 95694 530-795-6100
Brent Cushenbery, supt. Fax 795-6114
www.wintersjusd.org
Winters HS 500/9-12
101 Grant Ave 95694 530-795-6140
Paul Fawcett, prin. Fax 795-6147
Winters MS 400/6-8
425 Anderson Ave 95694 530-795-6130
Sandra Ayon, prin. Fax 795-6137
Wolfskill HS 50/Alt
200 Baker St 95694 530-795-6154
Tecera Philbrook, admin. Fax 795-6162

Winton, Merced, Pop. 10,450
Merced River UNESD 200/PK-8
4402 Oakdale Rd 95388 209-358-5679
Dr. Helio Brasil, supt. Fax 358-2855
www.mercedriver.k12.ca.us
Washington MS 100/4-8
4402 Oakdale Rd 95388 209-358-5679
Dr. Helio Brasil, supt. Fax 358-2855

Winton SD 1,800/PK-8
PO Box 8 95388 209-357-6175
Randall Heller, supt. Fax 357-1994
www.winton.k12.ca.us
Winton MS 600/6-8
PO Box 1299 95388 209-357-6189
Kristie Warner, prin. Fax 358-5889

Woodlake, Tulare, Pop. 7,217
Woodlake USD 2,400/K-12
300 W Whitney Ave 93286 559-564-8081
Drew Sorensen, supt. Fax 564-3831
www.w-usd.org
Bravo Lake HS 50/Alt
450 W Sequoia Ave 93286 559-564-8716
Tony Casares, prin. Fax 564-2695
Woodlake Community Day S 50/Alt
36220 Millwood Dr 93286 559-564-8716
Tony Casares, dir. Fax 564-2695
Woodlake Union HS 800/9-12
400 W Whitney Ave 93286 559-564-3307
Lisa Castillo, prin. Fax 564-3320
Woodlake Valley MS 500/6-8
497 N Palm St 93286 559-564-8061
Lou Saephan, prin. Fax 564-0702

Woodland, Yolo, Pop. 54,082
Regional Occupational Center & Program
Supt. — None
Yolo County ROP Vo/Tech
1280 Santa Anita Ct Ste 100 95776 530-668-3770
Ronda Adams, coord. Fax 668-3850

Woodland JUSD 10,600/K-12
435 6th St 95695 530-662-0201
Dr. Debra LaVoi, supt. Fax 662-6956
www.wjusd.org
Douglass MS 900/7-8
525 Granada Dr 95695 530-666-2191
Jonathon Brunson, prin. Fax 668-9217
Independent Learning Center Alt
1400 Pioneer Ave 95776 530-666-0264
Kerry Callahan, admin. Fax 662-3228
Lee MS 700/7-8
520 West St 95695 530-662-0251
Kathleen Leehane, prin. Fax 662-9423
Pioneer HS 1,700/9-12
1400 Pioneer Ave 95776 530-406-1148
Kerry Callahan, prin. Fax 662-3661
Woodland HS 1,400/9-12
21 N West St 95695 530-662-4678
Michelle Seijas, prin. Fax 662-7464
Woodland Adult Education Adult
575 Hays St 95695 530-662-0798
Susan Moylan, prin. Fax 662-8039
Other Schools – See Yolo

Yolo County Office of Education 300/
1280 Santa Anita Ct Ste 100 95776 530-668-6700
Jorge Ayala, supt. Fax 668-3848
www.ycoe.org
Einstein Education Center 100/Alt
1280 Santa Anita Ct Ste 100 95776 530-668-5408
Debra Wellbrock, dir. Fax 662-6873

Cambridge Junior College Post-Sec.
501 Main St 95695 530-662-0100
Woodland Christian HS 100/6-12
1787 Matmor Rd 95776 530-406-8800
Justin Smith, admin. Fax 406-0900
Woodland Community College Post-Sec.
2300 E Gibson Rd 95776 530-661-5700

Woodland Hills, See Los Angeles
Los Angeles USD
Supt. — See Los Angeles
Leonis Continuation HS 100/Alt
5445 Manton Ave 91367 818-888-7050
Lisa Ring, prin. Fax 716-0810
Taft HS 2,600/9-12
5461 Winnetka Ave 91364 818-227-3600
Delia Estrada, prin. Fax 592-0877
Thoreau Continuation HS 100/Alt
5429 Quakertown Ave 91364 818-340-4395
Charles Masterson, prin. Fax 347-4235
Woodland Hills Academy 1,300/6-8
20800 Burbank Blvd 91367 818-226-2900
Edwin Hayek, prin. Fax 716-0649
El Camino Real Adult Education Adult
5440 Valley Circle Blvd 91367 818-595-8000
Andrea Rodriguez, prin. Fax 888-6714
West Valley Occupational Center Adult
6200 Winnetka Ave 91367 818-346-3540
Fax 346-3858

Los Angeles Pierce College Post-Sec.
6201 Winnetka Ave 91371 818-347-0551
Louisville HS 400/9-12
22300 Mulholland Dr 91364 818-346-8812
Kathleen Vercillo, prin. Fax 346-9483

Woodside, San Mateo, Pop. 5,153
Sequoia UNHSD
Supt. — See Redwood City
Woodside HS 1,800/9-12
199 Churchill Ave 94062 650-367-9750
Diane Burbank, prin. Fax 367-7263

Yermo, San Bernardino
Silver Valley USD 2,500/PK-12
PO Box 847 92398 760-254-2916
Dr. Marc Jackson, supt. Fax 254-2091
www.svusdk12.net
Silver Valley HS 400/9-12
PO Box 847 92398 760-254-2963
Cameron Smart, prin. Fax 254-3043
Other Schools – See Daggett, Fort Irwin

Yolo, Yolo, Pop. 447
Woodland JUSD
Supt. — See Woodland
Cache Creek HS 200/Alt
PO Box 298 95697 530-662-4331
Olga Nevarez, prin. Fax 666-9082

Yorba Linda, Orange, Pop. 62,269
Placentia-Yorba Linda USD
Supt. — See Placentia
La Entrada HS 100/Alt
4175 Fairmont Blvd 92886 714-779-4170
Elizabeth Moore, prin. Fax 779-6825
Yorba Linda HS 1,400/9-12
4175 Fairmont Blvd 92886 714-986-7500
Dave Flynn, prin. Fax 986-7501
Yorba Linda MS 900/6-8
4777 Casa Loma Ave 92886 714-986-7080
James Hardin, prin. Fax 996-2752
Yorba MS 800/7-8
5350 Fairmont Blvd 92886 714-986-7400
Cameron Malotte, prin. Fax 970-1647

Friends Christian MS 400/5-8
4231 Rose Dr 92886 714-524-5240
Dave Hamman, prin. Fax 524-5784

Yosemite National Park, Mariposa
Mariposa County USD
Supt. — See Mariposa
Yosemite Park HS 50/9-12
9670 Rancheria Flat Rd 95389 209-372-2382
Sean Jacobs, lead tchr. Fax 379-9138

Yreka, Siskiyou, Pop. 7,387
Regional Occupational Center & Program
Supt. — None
Siskiyou County ROP Vo/Tech
431 Knapp St 96097 530-842-6155
Kim Greene, dir. Fax 842-1759

Yreka UNESD 800/K-8
309 Jackson St 96097 530-842-1168
Dave Parsons, supt. Fax 842-4576
www.yrekausd.net
Jackson Street ES 400/4-8
405 Jackson St 96097 530-842-3561
Chris Harris, prin. Fax 842-1716

Yreka UNHSD 700/9-12
400 Preece Way 96097 530-842-2521
Mark Greenfield, supt. Fax 842-1759
www.yuhsd.net
Discovery HS 50/9-12
400 Preece Way 96097 530-842-1659
Randy Baker, prin. Fax 841-1057
Yreka HS 700/9-12
400 Preece Way 96097 530-842-6151
Marie Caldwell, prin. Fax 841-0740
Yreka Union Community Day S Alt
400 Preece Way 96097 530-842-1659
Randy Baker, prin.
Yreka Union HS Adult Education Adult
400 Preece Way 96097 530-842-7829
Randy Baker, dir. Fax 842-1759

Yreka Adventist Christian S 50/K-10
346 Payne Ln 96097 530-842-7071
Marilee Dalton, prin. Fax 842-7463

Yuba City, Sutter, Pop. 62,225
Regional Occupational Center & Program
Supt. — None
Tri-County ROP Vo/Tech
970 Klamath Ln 95993 530-822-2952
Randy Page, dir. Fax 822-3003

Sutter County Office of Education 400/
970 Klamath Ln 95993 530-822-2900
Bill Cornelius, supt. Fax 671-3422
www.sutter.k12.ca.us
Feather River Academy 100/Alt
1895 Lassen Blvd 95993 530-822-2400
Gayelynn Gerhart, prin. Fax 822-3267

Yuba City USD 13,200/K-12
750 N Palora Ave 95991 530-822-5200
Nancy Aaberg, supt. Fax 671-2454
www.ycusd.k12.ca.us
Gray Avenue MS 700/6-8
808 Gray Ave 95991 530-822-5240
Brian Gault, prin. Fax 822-5057
Powell Continuation HS 200/Alt
1875 Clark Ave 95991 530-822-5210
Chuck Whitecotton, prin. Fax 822-5053
River Valley HS 1,800/9-12
801 El Margarita Rd 95993 530-822-2500
Tom Reusser, prin. Fax 822-2589
Yuba City HS 1,700/9-12
850 B St 95991 530-674-4900
Martin Ramirez, prin. Fax 671-7814
Yuba City Unified Alternative S 100/Alt
984 B St 95991 530-822-5244
Bruce Morton, prin. Fax 822-5096

Cambridge Junior College Post-Sec.
990 Klamath Ln Ste A 95993 530-674-9199
Faith Christian JSHS 200/7-12
PO Box 1690 95992 530-674-5474
Steve Finlay, prin. Fax 674-0194

Yucaipa, San Bernardino, Pop. 50,145
Yucaipa-Calimesa JUSD 8,700/K-12
12797 3rd St 92399 909-797-0174
Sherry Kendrick, supt. Fax 797-5751
www.yucaipaschools.com
Green Valley Continuation HS 100/Alt
35948 Susan St 92399 909-790-8580
Christina Pierce, prin. Fax 790-8584
Green Valley Independent Study 100/Alt
35948 Susan St 92399 909-790-8580
Christina Pierce, prin.
Oak View HS & Education Center 100/Alt
12358 6th St 92399 909-797-7931
Sam Spencer, prin. Fax 797-7962
Park View MS 800/7-8
34875 Tahoe Dr 92399 909-790-3285
Frank Tucci, prin. Fax 790-3295
Yucaipa HS 3,000/9-12
33000 Yucaipa Blvd 92399 909-797-0106
Sherry Smith, prin. Fax 790-3200
Yucaipa Adult S Adult
35948 Susan St 92399 909-797-0121
Christina Pierce, prin. Fax 790-6115
Other Schools – See Calimesa

Crafton Hills College Post-Sec.
11711 Sand Canyon Rd 92399 909-794-2161

Yucca Valley, San Bernardino, Pop. 20,139
Morongo USD
Supt. — See Twentynine Palms
Black Rock HS 100/Alt
59273 Sunnyslope Dr 92284 760-369-6310
Vonda Viland, prin. Fax 365-3366
La Contenta MS 900/7-8
7050 La Contenta Rd 92284 760-228-1802
Garrett Gruwell, prin. Fax 369-6324
Yucca Valley HS 1,500/9-12
7600 Sage Ave 92284 760-365-3391
Carl Phillips, prin. Fax 365-1845

Joshua Springs Christian S 300/PK-12
57373 Joshua Ln 92284 760-365-3599
Fern Ontiveros, admin. Fax 369-0315

COLORADO

COLORADO DEPARTMENT OF EDUCATION
201 E Colfax Ave, Denver 80203-1704
Telephone 303-866-6646
Fax 303-830-0793
Website http://www.cde.state.co.us

Commissioner of Education Robert Hammond

COLORADO BOARD OF EDUCATION
201 E Colfax Ave, Denver 80203-1704

Chairperson Bob Schaffer

BOARDS OF COOPERATIVE EDUCATIONAL SERVICES (BOCES)

Adams County BOCES
Eric Wiant, dir. 303-286-7294
1400 W 122nd Ave Ste 110 Fax 286-9079
Denver 80234
www.adamsboces.org/
Centennial BOCES
Dr. Randy Zila, dir. 970-352-7404
2020 Clubhouse Dr, Greeley 80634 Fax 352-7350
www.cboces.org
East Central BOCES
Don Anderson, dir. 719-775-2342
PO Box 910, Limon 80828 Fax 775-9714
www.ecboces.org
Expeditionary BOCES
Chad Burns, dir. 303-759-2076
1700 S Holly St, Denver 80222 Fax 757-7442
www.rmsel.org/
Front Range BOCES
Hi Howard, dir. 303-561-5096
6500 Arapahoe Rd, Boulder 80303 Fax 375-5813
www.frontrangeboces.org
Grand Valley BOCES
Bridgitte Sunderman, dir. 970-255-2700
2508 Blichman Ave Fax 255-2626
Grand Junction 81505

Mountain BOCES
Troy Lange, dir. 719-486-2603
1713 Mount Lincoln Dr W Fax 486-2109
Leadville 80461
www.mtnboces.org/
Mount Evans BOCES
Lynn Gentry, dir. 303-567-4467
PO Box 3399, Idaho Springs 80452 Fax 567-2208
Northeast Colorado BOCES
Tim Sanger, dir. 970-774-6152
PO Box 98, Haxtun 80731 Fax 774-6157
www.neboces.com
Northwest Colorado BOCES
Jane Toothaker, dir., PO Box 773390 970-879-0391
Steamboat Springs 80477 Fax 879-0442
www.nwboces.org/
Pikes Peak BOCES
Jerry Stremel, dir., 4825 Lorna Pl 719-570-7474
Colorado Springs 80915 Fax 380-9685
www.ppboces.org
Rio Blanco BOCES
Teresa Schott, dir. 970-675-2064
402 W Main St Ste 219 Fax 675-5738
Rangely 81648
www.rioblancoboces.org/

San Juan BOCES
Randy Boyer, dir. 970-247-3261
201 E 12th St, Durango 81301 Fax 247-8333
www.sjbocs.org/
San Luis Valley BOCES
Nita McAuliffe, dir. 719-589-5851
2261 Enterprise Dr, Alamosa 81101 Fax 589-5007
www.slvbocs.org
Santa Fe Trail BOCES
Sandy Malouff, dir. 719-383-2623
PO Box 980, La Junta 81050 Fax 383-2627
South Central BOCES
Cynthia Seidel, dir. 719-647-0023
323 S Purcell Blvd, Pueblo 81007 Fax 647-0136
www.sc-boces.org/
Southeastern BOCES
Matt Snyder, dir. 719-336-9046
PO Box 1137, Lamar 81052 Fax 336-9679
www.seboces.k12.co.us/
Uncompahgre BOCS
Lyndell Copeland, dir. 970-626-2977
PO Box 728, Ridgway 81432 Fax 626-2978
www.unbocs.org/
Ute Pass BOCES
Marcy Palmer, dir., 405 El Monte Pl 719-685-2640
Manitou Springs 80829 Fax 685-4536
www.upboces.org/

PUBLIC, PRIVATE AND CATHOLIC SECONDARY SCHOOLS

Agate, Elbert, Pop. 100
Agate SD 300 50/PK-12
PO Box 118 80101 719-764-2741
Kendra Ewing, supt. Fax 764-2751
www.agateschools.net/
Agate JSHS 50/6-12
PO Box 118 80101 719-764-2741
Kendra Ewing, prin. Fax 764-2751

Aguilar, Las Animas, Pop. 527
Aguilar RSD 6 100/PK-12
PO Box 567 81020 719-941-4188
Dr. Stacy Houser, supt. Fax 941-4279
www.aguilarschools.org
Aguilar JSHS 50/7-12
PO Box 567 81020 719-941-4188
Dennis Hoyt, prin. Fax 941-4279

Akron, Washington, Pop. 1,685
Akron SD R-1 300/K-12
PO Box 429 80720 970-345-2053
Brian Christensen, supt. Fax 345-6508
akronrams.schoolwires.net
Akron JSHS 100/7-12
600 Elm Ave 80720 970-345-2268
Ed Lundquist, prin. Fax 345-6508

Alamosa, Alamosa, Pop. 8,620
Alamosa SD RE-11J 1,000/K-12
209 Victoria Ave 81101 719-587-1600
Rob Alejo, supt. Fax 587-1712
www.alamosa.k12.co.us/
Alamosa HS 600/9-12
805 Craft Dr 81101 719-587-6000
Glen Hodges, prin. Fax 587-6069
Ortega MS 500/6-8
401 Victoria Ave 81101 719-587-1650
Susie Paulson, prin. Fax 587-1721

Adams State University Post-Sec.
208 Edgemont Blvd 81101 719-587-7011

Anton, Washington, Pop. 40
Arickaree SD R-2 100/PK-12
12155 County Road NN 80801 970-383-2202
Leslie Lindauer, supt. Fax 383-2205
www.arickaree.org
Arickaree JSHS 50/7-12
12155 County Road NN 80801 970-383-2202
Leslie Lindauer, admin. Fax 383-2205

Antonito, Conejos, Pop. 772
South Conejos SD RE-10 200/K-12
PO Box 398 81120 719-376-5512
Michael Moore, supt. Fax 376-5425
sc-sd.org
Antonito HS 100/9-12
PO Box 398 81120 719-376-5468
Virginia Goddard, prin. Fax 376-5425
Antonito MS 50/6-8
PO Box 398 81120 719-376-5407
Emily Romero, prin. Fax 376-5425

Arvada, Jefferson, Pop. 104,595
Jefferson County SD R-1
Supt. — See Golden
Arvada HS 1,000/9-12
7951 W 65th Ave 80004 303-982-0162
Kathleen Norton, prin. Fax 982-0163
Arvada West HS 1,700/9-12
11595 Allendale Dr 80004 303-982-1303
Robert Bishop, prin. Fax 982-1304
Drake MS 700/7-8
12550 W 52nd Ave 80002 303-982-1510
Rod Pugnetti, prin. Fax 982-1511
Moore MS 500/7-8
8455 W 88th Ave 80005 303-982-0400
Michelle McAteer, prin. Fax 982-0462
North Arvada MS 400/7-8
7285 Pierce St 80003 303-982-0528
Dana Ellis, prin. Fax 982-0529
Oberon MS 700/7-8
7300 Quail St 80005 303-982-2020
Tara Pena, prin. Fax 982-2021
Pomona HS 1,500/9-12
8101 W Pomona Dr 80005 303-982-0710
Andy Geise, prin. Fax 982-0709
Ralston Valley HS 1,700/9-12
13355 W 80th Ave 80005 303-982-5600
Jim Ellis, prin. Fax 982-5601

Faith Christian Academy 300/6-8
6250 Wright St 80004 303-424-7310
Terrie Simmons, prin. Fax 403-2720
Faith Christian Academy 300/9-12
4890 Carr St 80002 303-424-7310
Andrew Hasz, prin. Fax 403-2730

Aspen, Pitkin, Pop. 6,573
Aspen SD RE-1 1,700/PK-12
235 High School Rd 81611 970-925-3760
Dr. John Maloy, supt. Fax 925-5721
www.aspenk12.net/

Aspen HS 500/9-12
235 High School Rd 81611 970-925-3760
Kimberly Martin, prin. Fax 925-1205
Aspen MS 500/5-8
235 High School Rd 81611 970-925-3760
Tom Heald, prin. Fax 925-8374

Ault, Weld, Pop. 1,488
Ault-Highland SD RE-9 800/K-12
PO Box 68 80610 970-834-1345
Robert Ring, supt. Fax 834-1347
www.weldre9.k12.co.us
Highland HS 300/9-12
PO Box 68 80610 970-834-2816
Randy Yaussi, prin. Fax 834-2858
Highland MS 200/6-8
PO Box 68 80610 970-834-2829
Clay Naughton, prin. Fax 834-2663

Aurora, Arapahoe, Pop. 313,203
Aurora SD 37,700/PK-12
15701 E 1st Ave 80011 303-344-8060
John Barry, supt. Fax 326-1280
www.aps.k12.co.us
Aurora Central HS 2,300/9-12
11700 E 11th Ave 80010 303-340-1600
Lynn Fair, prin. Fax 326-1270
Aurora Hills MS 900/6-8
1009 S Uvalda St 80012 303-341-7450
Darla Stumpp, prin. Fax 326-1250
Aurora West College Preparatory S 800/6-12
10100 E 13th Ave 80010 303-366-2671
Dale Krueger, prin. Fax 326-1260
Columbia MS 800/6-8
17600 E Columbia Ave 80013 303-690-6570
Steve Hamilton, prin. Fax 326-1251
East MS 900/6-8
1275 Fraser St 80011 303-340-0660
Fred Quinonez, prin. Fax 326-1252
Fletcher IS of Science & Technology 4-8
10455 E 25th Ave 80010 303-326-2800
Celi Leggett, prin. Fax 326-1993
Gateway HS 1,700/9-12
1300 S Sable Blvd 80012 303-755-7160
William Hedges, prin. Fax 326-1272
Hinkley HS 2,100/9-12
1250 Chambers Rd 80011 303-340-1500
Jinger Haberer, prin. Fax 326-1275
Mrachek MS 1,000/6-8
1955 S Telluride St 80013 303-750-2836
Edward Snyder, prin. Fax 326-1254

North MS 700/6-8
12095 Montview Blvd 80010 303-364-7411
Gerardo de la Garza, prin. Fax 326-1256
Options S 1,900/Alt
11351 Montview Blvd 80010 303-340-0666
Thomas Synnott, prin. Fax 326-1281
Rangeview HS 2,300/9-12
17599 E Iliff Ave 80013 303-695-6848
Ron Fay, prin. Fax 326-1276
Smith HS 300/9-12
400 Airport Blvd 80011 303-364-8715
Jane Shirley, prin. Fax 326-1278
South MS 700/6-8
12310 E Parkview Dr 80011 303-364-7623
Yvonne Davis, prin. Fax 326-1258
Vista PEAK S 900/PK-12
24551 E 1st Pl 80018 303-364-3757
Marisol Enriquez, dir. Fax 326-1966

Cherry Creek SD 5
Supt. — See Greenwood Village
Cherokee Trail HS 2,400/9-12
25901 E Arapahoe Rd 80016 720-886-1900
Kim Rauh, prin. Fax 886-1989
Eaglecrest HS 2,400/9-12
5100 S Picadilly St 80015 720-886-1000
Gwen Hansen-Vigil, prin. Fax 886-1097
Falcon Creek MS 1,100/6-8
6100 S Genoa St 80016 720-886-7700
John Kennedy, prin. Fax 886-7788
Fox Ridge MS 800/6-8
26301 E Arapahoe Rd 80016 720-886-4400
Tracey Grant, prin. Fax 886-4488
Grandview HS 2,600/9-12
20500 E Arapahoe Rd 80016 720-886-6500
Kurt Wollenweber, prin. Fax 886-6698
Horizon Community MS 1,000/6-8
3981 S Reservoir Rd 80013 720-886-6100
Dr. Jeanette Patterson, prin. Fax 886-6253
I Team - Estate Alt
4360 S Pitkin St 80015 720-886-5850
William Keup, lead tchr. Fax 886-5865
I Team - Manor Alt
1820 S Joliet St 80012 720-747-2955
Susan Hickey, lead tchr. Fax 747-2951
I Team - The Ranch Alt
7250 S Gartrell Rd 80016 720-886-6880
Orvin Breningstall, lead tchr. Fax 886-6888
Laredo MS 1,200/6-8
5000 S Laredo St 80015 720-886-5000
Mike Giles, prin. Fax 886-5298
Liberty MS 1,100/6-8
21500 E Dry Creek Rd 80016 720-886-2400
Carla Stearns, prin. Fax 886-2688
Overland HS 2,200/9-12
12400 E Jewell Ave 80012 720-747-3700
Leon Lundie, prin. Fax 747-3895
Prairie MS 1,600/6-8
12600 E Jewell Ave 80012 720-747-3000
David Gonzales, prin. Fax 747-3113
Sky Vista MS 800/6-8
4500 S Himalaya St 80015 720-886-4700
Dr. Tony Poole, prin. Fax 886-4788
Smoky Hill HS 2,300/9-12
16100 E Smoky Hill Rd 80015 720-886-5300
Randy Karr, prin. Fax 886-5408
Thunder Ridge MS 1,200/6-8
5250 S Picadilly St 80015 720-886-1500
Mark Sneden, prin. Fax 886-1582

American Sentinel University Post-Sec.
2260 S Xanadu Way Ste 310 80014 303-991-1575
Anthem College Post-Sec.
350 Blackhawk St 80011 720-859-7900
CedarWood Christian Academy 100/K-12
PO Box 111389 80042 303-361-6456
Gene Oborny, admin. Fax 340-0971
Colorado Technical University Post-Sec.
3151 S Vaughn Way 80014 303-632-2300
Community College of Aurora Post-Sec.
16000 E Centretech Pkwy 80011 303-360-4700
Concorde Career College Post-Sec.
111 Havana St 80010 303-861-1151
Ecotech Institute Post-Sec.
1400 S Abilene St 80012 877-326-5576
Everest College Post-Sec.
14280 E Jewell Ave Ste 100 80012 303-745-6244
Excelsior Youth Center 200/7-12
15001 E Oxford Ave 80014 303-693-1550
Joan Gabrielson, dir. Fax 693-8309
ITT Technical Institute Post-Sec.
12500 E Iliff Ave Ste 100 80014 303-695-6317
Pickens Technical Center Post-Sec.
500 Airport Blvd 80011 303-344-4910
Platt College Post-Sec.
3100 S Parker Rd 80014 303-369-5151
Regis Jesuit HS for Boys 900/9-12
6400 S Lewiston Way 80016 303-269-8000
Alan Carruthers, prin. Fax 766-2240
Regis Jesuit HS for Girls 700/9-12
6300 S Lewiston Way 80016 303-269-8100
Gretchen Kessler, prin. Fax 221-4772
Xenon International Post-Sec.
2231 S Peoria St 80014 303-752-1560

Bailey, Park, Pop. 150
Platte Canyon SD 1 1,200/PK-12
PO Box 1069 80421 303-838-7666
Jim Walpole Ed.D., supt. Fax 679-7504
www.plattecanyonschools.org
Fitzsimmons MS 200/6-8
PO Box 1069 80421 303-838-7666
Rim Watson, prin. Fax 679-7506
Platte Canyon HS 400/9-12
PO Box 1069 80421 303-838-7666
Michael Schmidt, prin. Fax 679-7497

Basalt, Pitkin, Pop. 3,792
Roaring Fork SD RE-1
Supt. — See Glenwood Springs
Basalt HS 400/9-12
600 Southside Dr 81621 970-384-5959
David Schmid, prin. Fax 384-5955
Basalt MS 400/5-8
51 School St 81621 970-384-5900
Jeremy Voss, prin. Fax 384-5905

Bayfield, LaPlata, Pop. 2,294
Bayfield SD 10 JT-R 1,400/PK-12
24 S Clover Ln 81122 970-884-2496
Troy Zabel, supt. Fax 884-4284
www.bayfield.k12.co.us
Bayfield HS 400/9-12
24 S Clover Ln 81122 970-884-9521
Scott Story, prin. Fax 884-4226
Bayfield MS 300/6-8
24 S Clover Ln 81122 970-884-9592
Karen Lunceford, prin. Fax 884-4110

Bennett, Adams, Pop. 2,268
Bennett SD 29J 1,200/PK-12
615 7th St 80102 303-644-3234
Dennis Veal, supt. Fax 644-4121
www.bennett29j.k12.co.us
Bennett HS 300/9-12
610 7th St 80102 303-644-3234
Greg Biga, prin. Fax 644-3894
Bennett MS 200/6-8
455 8th St 80102 303-644-3234
Jeff Casey, prin. Fax 644-4398

Berthoud, Larimer, Pop. 5,034
Thompson SD R-2J
Supt. — See Loveland
Berthoud HS 600/9-12
850 Spartan Ave 80513 970-613-7700
Chris Garcia, prin. Fax 613-7728
Turner MS 400/6-8
950 Massachusetts Ave 80513 970-613-7400
Bill Siebers, prin. Fax 613-7420

Bethune, Kit Carson, Pop. 236
Bethune SD R-5 100/PK-12
PO Box 127 80805 719-346-7513
Shila Adolf, supt. Fax 346-5048
bethuneschool.com/
Bethune JSHS 100/7-12
PO Box 127 80805 719-343-7513
Shila Adolf, prin. Fax 346-5048

Black Hawk, Gilpin, Pop. 118
Gilpin County SD RE-1 400/PK-12
10595 Highway 119 80422 303-582-3444
Dr. Morris Ververs, supt. Fax 582-3346
www.gilpin.k12.co.us
Gilpin County JSHS 200/6-12
10595 Highway 119 80422 303-582-3444
Alexis Donaldson, prin. Fax 582-3346

Blanca, Costilla, Pop. 380
Sierra Grande SD R-30 300/PK-12
17523 E Highway 160 81123 719-379-3259
Darren Edgar, supt. Fax 379-2572
www.sierragrandeschool.net
Sierra Grande HS 100/9-12
17523 E Highway 160 81123 719-379-3257
Brandon Mizokami, prin. Fax 379-2572
Sierra Grande MS 100/6-8
17523 E Highway 160 81123 719-379-3257
Lauren Sheldrake, prin. Fax 379-2572

Boulder, Boulder, Pop. 95,063
Boulder Valley SD RE-2 29,200/PK-12
PO Box 9011 80301 303-447-1010
Bruce Messinger Ph.D., supt. Fax 561-5134
www.bvsd.org
Arapahoe Campus 200/9-12
6600 Arapahoe Rd 80303 720-561-5220
Joan Bludorn, prin. Fax 561-5258
Boulder HS 1,800/9-12
1604 Arapahoe Ave 80302 720-561-2200
Kevin Braney, prin. Fax 561-5317
Casey MS 400/6-8
1301 High St 80304 720-561-2700
Alison Boggs, prin. Fax 561-2701
Centennial MS 600/6-8
2205 Norwood Ave 80304 720-561-5441
Cheryl Scott, prin. Fax 561-2090
Fairview HS 2,000/9-12
1515 Greenbriar Blvd 80305 720-561-3100
Don Stensrud, prin. Fax 561-5353
Manhattan S of Arts and Academics 500/6-8
290 Manhattan Dr 80303 720-561-6300
Robbyn Fernandez, prin. Fax 561-6301
New Vista HS 300/9-12
700 20th St 80302 720-561-8700
Kirk Quitter, prin. Fax 561-8701
Platt MS 500/6-8
6096 Baseline Rd 80303 720-561-5536
Kevin Gates, prin. Fax 561-6898
Southern Hills MS 500/6-8
1500 Knox Dr 80305 720-561-3400
Terry Gillach, prin. Fax 561-3401
Other Schools – See Broomfield, Lafayette, Louisville, Nederland

---

Boulder College of Massage Therapy Post-Sec.
6255 Longbow Dr 80301 303-530-2100
Naropa University Post-Sec.
2130 Arapahoe Ave 80302 303-444-0202
Rolf Institute of Structural Integration Post-Sec.
5055 Chaparral Ct Ste 103 80301 303-449-5903
September HS 50/9-12
1902 Walnut St 80302 303-443-9933
John Dunn, head sch Fax 444-5027
Shining Mountain Waldorf S 300/PK-12
999 Violet Ave 80304 303-444-7697
Susan Levine, dir. Fax 444-7701
Southwest Acupuncture College Post-Sec.
6620 Gunpark Dr 80301 303-581-9955
Tara Performing Arts HS 50/9-12
4180 19th St 80304 303-440-4510
Greg Fisher, admin. Fax 448-0090
University of Colorado Boulder 80309 Post-Sec.
303-492-1411

Branson, Las Animas, Pop. 73
Branson RSD 82 500/PK-12
PO Box 128 81027 719-946-5531
Brad Caldwell, supt. Fax 946-5619
www.bransonschoolonline.com
Branson JSHS 50/7-12
PO Box 128 81027 719-946-5531
Brad Caldwell, prin. Fax 946-5620
Branson S Online 400/Alt
PO Box 128 81027 719-946-5531
Leanna Christians, prin. Fax 946-5619

Briggsdale, Weld, Pop. 225
Briggsdale SD RE-10 200/PK-12
PO Box 129 80611 970-656-3417
Rick Mondt, supt. Fax 656-3479
www.briggsdaleschool.org/
Briggsdale JSHS 100/6-12
PO Box 129 80611 970-656-3417
Rick Mondt, prin. Fax 656-3479

Brighton, Adams, Pop. 32,801
Brighton SD 27J 14,500/PK-12
18551 E 160th Ave 80601 303-655-2900
Chris Fiedler Ed.D., supt. Fax 655-2870
www.sd27j.org/
Brighton Heritage Academy 100/Alt
830 E Bridge St 80601 303-655-2850
Cyndra Foster, prin. Fax 655-2886
Brighton HS 1,600/9-12
270 S 8th Ave 80601 303-655-4200
John Biner, prin. Fax 655-2883
Overland Trail MS 700/6-8
455 N 19th Ave 80601 303-655-4000
Eric Lambright, prin. Fax 655-2880
Vikan MS 600/6-8
879 Jessup St 80601 303-655-4050
Trina Norris-Buck, prin. Fax 655-2881
Other Schools – See Commerce City, Henderson

Brighton Adventist Academy 100/PK-10
820 S 5th Ave 80601 303-659-1223
Fax 558-8837
Elmwood Baptist Academy 100/PK-12
13100 E 144th Ave 80601 303-659-3818
Fax 685-9005

Broomfield, Boulder, Pop. 54,716
Adams 12 Five Star SD
Supt. — See Thornton
Legacy HS 2,000/9-12
2701 W 136th Ave, 720-972-6700
Lee Peters, prin. Fax 972-6897
Westlake MS 900/6-8
2800 W 135th Ave 80020 720-972-5200
Jessica Fiedler, prin. Fax 972-5239

Boulder Valley SD RE-2
Supt. — See Boulder
Broomfield Heights MS 500/6-8
1555 Daphne St 80020 720-561-8400
Chris Meyer, prin. Fax 561-8401
Broomfield HS 1,400/9-12
1 Eagle Way 80020 720-561-8100
Ginger Ramsey, prin. Fax 561-5390

Holy Family HS 500/9-12
5195 W 144th Ave, 303-410-1411
Tim Gallic, prin. Fax 466-1935
Redstone College Post-Sec.
10851 W 120th Ave 80021 303-466-1714
Westwood College - Online Post-Sec.
10249 Church Ranch Way 80021 720-887-8888

Brush, Morgan, Pop. 5,401
Brush SD RE-2(J) 1,500/PK-12
PO Box 585 80723 970-842-5176
Dr. Michelle Johnstone, supt. Fax 842-4481
www.brushschools.org
Brush HS 400/9-12
PO Box 585 80723 970-842-5171
Dave Vondy, prin. Fax 842-2804
Brush MS 300/6-8
PO Box 585 80723 970-842-5035
Sherry Kyle, prin. Fax 842-3009

Buena Vista, Chaffee, Pop. 2,579
Buena Vista SD R-31 1,000/PK-12
PO Box 2027 81211 719-395-7000
Robert Crowther, supt. Fax 395-7007
www.bvschools.org
Buena Vista HS 300/9-12
PO Box 2027 81211 719-395-7100
Brian Yates, prin. Fax 395-7106
Chaffee County HS 50/Alt
PO Box 2027 81211 719-395-4064
Mike Post, prin. Fax 395-8267
McGinnis MS 200/6-8
PO Box 2027 81211 719-395-7060
John Emilsson, prin. Fax 395-7090

Patterson Christian Academy 100/PK-12
PO Box 1243 81211 719-395-6046
Erik Ritschard, admin. Fax 395-2055

Burlington, Kit Carson, Pop. 4,206
Burlington SD RE-6J 800/PK-12
PO Box 369 80807 719-346-8737
Tom Satterly, supt. Fax 346-8541
www.burlingtonk12.org/
Burlington HS 200/9-12
380 Mike Lounge Dr 80807 719-346-8455
Michael Clark, prin. Fax 346-5599

Burlington MS 200/5-8
2600 Rose Ave 80807 719-346-5440
Mitzi Swiatkowski, prin. Fax 346-7900

Byers, Arapahoe, Pop. 1,139
Byers SD 32J 500/PK-12
444 E Front St 80103 303-822-5292
Tom Turrell, supt. Fax 822-9592
www.byers32j.k12.co.us
Byers HS 200/7-12
444 E Front St 80103 303-822-5292
Terrell Price, prin. Fax 822-8616

Calhan, El Paso, Pop. 759
Calhan SD RJ-1 600/PK-12
780 8th St 80808 719-347-2541
Linda Miller, supt. Fax 347-2144
calhanschool.org/
Calhan HS 200/9-12
780 8th St 80808 719-347-2766
David Slothower, prin. Fax 347-2108
Calhan MS 100/6-8
780 8th St 80808 719-347-2766
David Slothower, prin. Fax 347-2108

Campo, Baca, Pop. 109
Campo SD RE-6 100/PK-12
PO Box 70 81029 719-787-2226
Nikki Johnson, supt. Fax 787-0140
www.campo.k12.co.us
Campo JSHS 50/6-12
PO Box 70 81029 719-787-2226
Kim Jenkins, prin. Fax 787-0140

Canon City, Fremont, Pop. 16,140
Canon City SD RE-1 3,600/K-12
101 N 14th St 81212 719-276-5700
Dr. Robin Gooldy, supt. Fax 276-5739
www.canoncityschools.org/
Canon City HS 1,100/9-12
1313 College Ave 81212 719-276-5870
Bret Meuli, prin. Fax 276-5950
Canon City MS 400/6-8
1215 Main St 81212 719-276-5740
Ken Trujillo, prin. Fax 276-5795

Colorado Institute of Taxidermy Post-Sec.
708 Royal Gorge Blvd 81212 719-276-2883

Carbondale, Garfield, Pop. 6,354
Roaring Fork SD RE-1
Supt. — See Glenwood Springs
Bridges HS 100/Alt
455 S 3rd St 81623 970-384-6160
Lyn Blair, prin. Fax 384-6165
Carbondale MS 300/5-8
180 Snowmass Dr 81623 970-384-5700
Jennifer Lamont, prin. Fax 384-5705
Roaring Fork HS 300/9-12
2270 Highway 133 81623 970-384-5757
Drew Adams, prin. Fax 384-5755

Colorado Rocky Mountain S 200/9-12
1493 County Road 106 81623 970-963-2562
Jeff Leahy, hdmstr. Fax 963-9865

Castle Rock, Douglas, Pop. 47,126
Douglas County SD RE-1 59,500/PK-12
620 Wilcox St 80104 303-387-0100
Dr. Elizabeth Celania-Fagen, supt. Fax 387-0107
www.dcsdk12.org
Castle Rock MS 800/7-8
2575 Meadows Pkwy, 303-387-1300
Terry Olson, prin. Fax 387-1301
Castle View HS 1,600/9-12
5254 Meadows Dr, 303-387-9000
James Calhoun, prin. Fax 387-9001
Douglas County HS 1,800/9-12
2842 Front St 80104 303-387-1000
Tony Kappas, prin. Fax 387-1001
Mesa MS 900/7-8
365 N Mitchell St 80104 303-387-4750
Karmen Smith, prin. Fax 387-4751
Oakes HS 200/Alt
961 S Plum Creek Blvd 80104 303-387-0650
Mark Morgan, prin. Fax 387-0651
Other Schools – See Highlands Ranch, Littleton, Lonetree, Parker

Cedaredge, Delta, Pop. 2,222
Delta County SD 50(J)
Supt. — See Delta
Cedaredge HS 300/9-12
575 SE Deer Creek Dr 81413 970-856-6882
Kevin Gardner, prin. Fax 856-6616
Cedaredge MS 200/6-8
845 SE Deer Creek Dr 81413 970-856-3118
Randy Brown, prin. Fax 856-3235

Centennial, Arapahoe, Pop. 97,891
Cherry Creek SD 5
Supt. — See Greenwood Village
Endeavor Academy Alt
14076 E Briarwood Ave 80112 720-886-7200
Debra Lewis, prin. Fax 886-7288

Littleton SD 6
Supt. — See Littleton
Arapahoe HS 2,200/9-12
2201 E Dry Creek Rd 80122 303-347-6000
Natalie Pramenko, prin. Fax 347-6004
Newton MS 700/6-8
4001 E Arapahoe Rd 80122 303-347-7900
James O'Tremba, prin. Fax 347-3945

Jones International University Post-Sec.
9697 E Mineral Ave 80112 303-784-8904

Center, Saguache, Pop. 2,207
Center Consolidated SD 26JT 600/PK-12
550 Sylvester Ave 81125 719-754-3442
George Welsh, supt. Fax 754-3952
www.center.k12.co.us
Academic Recovery Center 50/Alt
550 Sylvester Ave 81125 719-251-3334
Joy Werner, dir. Fax 754-3952
Center HS 100/9-12
550 Sylvester Ave 81125 719-754-2232
Kevin Jones, prin. Fax 754-2856
Skoglund MS 100/6-8
550 Sylvester Ave 81125 719-754-2232
Carrie Zimmerman, prin. Fax 754-2856

Cheraw, Otero, Pop. 245
Cheraw SD 31 200/PK-12
PO Box 160 81030 719-853-6655
Rick Lovato, supt. Fax 853-6322
cheraw.k12.co.us
Cheraw HS 50/9-12
PO Box 160 81030 719-853-6655
Ryan Nesselhuf, prin. Fax 853-6322
Cheraw MS 100/6-8
PO Box 160 81030 719-853-6655
Ryan Nesselhuf, prin. Fax 853-6322

Cheyenne Wells, Cheyenne, Pop. 839
Cheyenne County SD RE-5 200/PK-12
PO Box 577 80810 719-767-5866
Glen Bradshaw, supt. Fax 767-8773
www.cheyennesd.net/
Cheyenne Wells HS 100/9-12
PO Box 577 80810 719-767-5612
Mike Miller, prin. Fax 767-5749
Cheyenne Wells MS 50/7-8
PO Box 577 80810 719-767-5656
Mike Miller, prin. Fax 767-5136

Clifton, Mesa, Pop. 19,453
Mesa County Valley SD 51
Supt. — See Grand Junction
Mt. Garfield MS 600/6-8
3475 Front St 81520 970-254-4720
Terrie Requa, prin. Fax 464-0536

Christian Community S 200/K-12
PO Box 349 81520 970-434-0205
Debbie Childs, admin. Fax 434-3847

Collbran, Mesa, Pop. 699
Plateau Valley SD 50 500/PK-12
56600 Highway 330 81624 970-487-3547
Gregory Randall, supt. Fax 487-3876
www.pvsd50.org
Grand Mesa HS 100/Alt
56600 Highway 330 81624 970-487-3576
Gary Winkleblack, prin. Fax 487-3405
Plateau Valley HS 100/9-12
56600 Highway 330 81624 970-487-3547
Leroy Gutierrez, prin. Fax 487-3876
Plateau Valley MS 50/6-8
56600 Highway 330 81624 970-487-3547
Leroy Gutierrez, prin. Fax 487-3876

Colorado City, Pueblo, Pop. 2,165
Pueblo County SD 70
Supt. — See Pueblo
Craver MS 200/6-8
PO Box 19369 81019 719-676-3030
Alexandra Strunk, prin. Fax 676-3511

Colorado Springs, El Paso, Pop. 400,464
Academy SD 20 25,100/PK-12
1110 Chapel Hills Dr 80920 719-234-1200
Dr. Mark Hatchell, supt. Fax 234-1299
www.asd20.org/
Aspen Valley HS 100/9-12
1450 Chapel Hills Dr 80920 719-234-6000
George Stone, prin. Fax 234-6099
Challenger MS 700/6-8
10215 Lexington Dr 80920 719-234-3000
Tony Scott, prin. Fax 234-3199
Discovery Canyon Campus 2,200/PK-12
1810 N Gate Blvd 80921 719-234-1800
Jim Bailey, prin. Fax 234-1899
Eagleview MS 1,000/6-8
1325 Vindicator Dr 80919 719-234-3400
Jim Smith, prin. Fax 234-3599
Liberty HS 1,500/9-12
8720 Scarborough Dr 80920 719-234-2200
Alan Thimmig, prin. Fax 234-2399
Mountain Ridge MS 1,100/6-8
9150 Lexington Dr 80920 719-234-3200
Jeff Sterk, prin. Fax 234-3399
Pine Creek HS 1,400/9-12
10750 Thunder Mountain Ave 80908 719-234-2600
Kolette Back, prin. Fax 234-2799
Rampart HS 1,600/9-12
8250 Lexington Dr 80920 719-234-2000
Pete Alvarez, prin. Fax 234-2199
Timberview MS 1,000/6-8
8680 Scarborough Dr 80920 719-234-3600
Brett Smith, prin. Fax 234-3799
Other Schools – See USAF Academy

Cheyenne Mountain SD 12 4,600/PK-12
1775 LaClede St 80905 719-475-6100
Dr. Walter Cooper, supt. Fax 475-6106
www.cmsd.k12.co.us
Cheyenne Mountain HS 1,300/9-12
1200 Cresta Rd 80906 719-475-6110
Dr. John Weishaar, prin. Fax 475-6116
Cheyenne Mountain JHS 600/7-8
1200 W Cheyenne Rd 80906 719-475-6120
Dr. Lori Smith, prin. Fax 475-6123

Colorado Springs SD 11 29,300/PK-12
1115 N El Paso St 80903 719-520-2000
Dr. Nicholas Gledich, supt. Fax 577-4546
www.d11.org/
Bijou S 100/Alt
2904 W Kiowa St 80904 719-328-7900
Kathryn Presnal, dir. Fax 630-3379
Coronado HS 1,500/9-12
1590 W Fillmore St 80904 719-328-3600
David Engstrom, prin. Fax 328-3601
Digital HS Alt
1702 N Murray Blvd 80915 719-328-3000
John Bailey, prin. Fax 328-3071
Doherty HS 2,100/9-12
4515 Barnes Rd 80917 719-328-6400
Dennis Vigil, prin. Fax 328-6401
Galileo S of Math & Science 700/6-8
1600 N Union Blvd 80909 719-328-2200
Richard Law, prin. Fax 448-0498
Holmes MS 700/6-8
2455 Mesa Rd 80904 719-328-3800
Robert Utter, prin. Fax 448-0358
Jenkins MS 1,000/6-8
6410 Austin Bluffs Pkwy, 719-328-5300
Darren Joiner, prin. Fax 266-5276
Mann MS 600/6-8
1001 E Van Buren St 80907 719-328-2300
Peggy Layh, prin. Fax 488-0354
Mitchell HS 1,100/9-12
1205 Potter Dr 80909 719-328-6600
Rusty Moomey, prin. Fax 328-6601
North MS 600/6-8
612 E Yampa St 80903 719-328-2400
Judy Hawkins, prin. Fax 448-0268
Palmer HS 2,000/9-12
301 N Nevada Ave 80903 719-328-5000
Lara Disney, prin. Fax 328-5001
Russell MS 700/6-8
3825 Montebello Dr W 80918 719-328-5200
Julie Williams, prin. Fax 531-5520
Sabin MS 800/6-8
3605 N Carefree Cir 80917 719-328-7000
Sherry Kalbach, prin. Fax 573-4960
Swigert Aerospace Academy 600/6-8
4220 E Pikes Peak Ave 80909 719-328-6900
James Nason, prin. Fax 573-5094
Tesla Educational Opportunity Center 200/Alt
2560 International Cir 80910 719-520-2701
Glen Stull, prin. Fax 630-0243
Wasson HS 1,000/9-12
2115 Afton Way 80909 719-328-2000
Darryl Bonds, prin. Fax 520-2966
West MS 300/6-8
1920 W Pikes Peak Ave 80904 719-328-3900
Clay Gomez, prin. Fax 448-0141
Adult Education Center Adult
1702 N Murray Blvd 80915 719-328-3000
M. Burkhardt-Shields, prin. Fax 630-2286
Springs Community Night S at Mitchell Adult
1205 Potter Dr 80909 719-328-6700
Tanya Nash, prin.

Falcon SD 49
Supt. — See Falcon
Horizon MS 700/6-8
1750 Piros Dr 80915 719-495-5210
Greg Moles, prin. Fax 495-5201
Sand Creek HS 1,200/9-12
7005 N Carefree Cir 80922 719-495-1160
Sean Dorsey, prin. Fax 495-1196
Skyview MS 1,100/6-8
6350 Windom Peak Blvd, 719-495-5566
Catherine Tinucci, prin. Fax 495-5569
Vista Ridge HS 1,100/9-12
6888 Black Forest Rd, 719-494-8800
Bruce Grose, prin. Fax 494-8838

Fountain-Fort Carson SD 8
Supt. — See Fountain
Carson MS 700/6-8
6200 Prussman Blvd, 719-382-1610
Josh Hobgood, prin. Fax 382-8526

Hanover SD 28 200/PK-12
17050 S Peyton Hwy 80928 719-683-2247
Paul McCarty, supt. Fax 683-2299
www.hanoverhornets.org
Hanover JSHS 100/5-12
17050 S Peyton Hwy 80928 719-683-2247
Paul McCarty, admin. Fax 683-3805

Harrison SD 2 10,700/PK-12
1060 Harrison Rd 80905 719-579-2000
David MacKenzie, supt. Fax 579-2019
www.hsd2.org
Carmel MS 400/6-8
1740 Pepperwood Dr 80910 719-579-3210
Ted Knight, prin. Fax 579-2695
Fox Meadow MS 500/6-8
1450 Cheyenne Meadows Rd 80906 719-527-7100
John Rogerson, prin. Fax 576-0918
Gorman Education Center 200/Alt
2883 S Circle Dr 80906 719-579-2600
Fax 579-2599
Harrison HS 1,000/9-12
2755 Janitell Rd 80906 719-579-2080
Cheri Martinez, prin. Fax 579-2454
Panorama MS 600/6-8
2145 S Chelton Rd 80916 719-579-3220
Tina Hackett, prin. Fax 579-2756
Sierra HS 900/9-12
2250 Jet Wing Dr 80916 719-579-2090
Zach Craddock, prin. Fax 579-2536

Widefield SD 3 8,600/PK-12
1820 Main St 80911 719-391-3000
Joe Royer, supt. Fax 390-4372
www.wsd3.org
Discovery HS 100/Alt
701 Widefield Dr 80911 719-391-3121
Charles Poncelow, prin. Fax 391-3091

Mesa Ridge HS 1,300/9-12
6070 Mesa Ridge Pkwy 80911 719-391-3600
Kathi Mata, prin. Fax 390-9697
Sproul JHS 600/6-8
235 Sumac Dr 80911 719-391-3215
Maureen di Stasio, prin. Fax 391-3215
Watson JHS 600/6-8
136 Fontaine Blvd 80911 719-391-3255
Justin Lee, prin. Fax 392-3419
Widefield HS 1,300/9-12
615 Widefield Dr 80911 719-391-3200
Kevin Duren, prin. Fax 391-8072
Other Schools – See Fountain

CollegeAmerica - Colorado Springs Post-Sec.
3645 Citadel Dr S 80909 719-227-0170
Colorado Acad of Veterinary Technology Post-Sec.
2766 Janitell Rd 80906 719-219-9636
Colorado College Post-Sec.
14 E Cache La Poudre St 80903 719-389-6000
Colorado School for the Deaf and Blind Post-Sec.
33 N Institute St 80903 719-578-2100
Colorado Springs Christian S 900/PK-12
4855 Mallow Rd 80907 719-599-3553
Dr. Roland DeRenzo, supt. Fax 268-2184
Colorado Springs S 500/PK-12
21 Broadmoor Ave 80906 719-475-9747
Kevin Reel, hdmstr. Fax 475-9864
Colorado Technical University Post-Sec.
4435 N Chestnut St 80907 719-598-0200
DeVry University Post-Sec.
1175 Kelly Johnson Blvd 80920 719-632-3000
Evangelical Christian Academy 200/7-12
4052 S Nonchalant Cir 80917 719-597-3675
Jim Johnson, supt. Fax 597-6983
Everest College Post-Sec.
1815 Jet Wing Dr 80916 719-638-6580
Fountain Valley S of Colorado 200/9-12
6155 Fountain Valley School 80911 719-390-7035
Craig Larimer, hdmstr. Fax 391-9039
IntelliTec College Post-Sec.
2315 E Pikes Peak Ave 80909 719-632-7626
IntelliTec Medical Institute Post-Sec.
6805 Corporate Dr Ste 100 80919 866-749-2608
International Salon and Spa Academy Post-Sec.
5705 N Academy Blvd 80918 719-597-1413
Memorial Health System Sch of Rad Tech Post-Sec.
1400 E Boulder St 80909 719-365-8291
National American University Post-Sec.
1915 Jamboree Dr Ste 185 80920 719-590-8300
Nazarene Bible College Post-Sec.
1111 Academy Park Loop 80910 719-884-5000
Pikes Peak Christian S 400/PK-12
5905 Flintridge Dr 80918 719-598-8610
Matt Johns, dir. Fax 598-1491
Pikes Peak Community College Post-Sec.
5675 S Academy Blvd 80906 719-502-2000
St. Mary HS 300/9-12
2501 E Yampa St 80909 719-635-7540
Michael Biondini, prin. Fax 471-7623
Toni & Guy Hairdressing Academy Post-Sec.
332 Main St 80911 719-390-9898
University of Colorado Colorado Springs Post-Sec.
1420 Austin Bluffs Pkwy 80918 719-255-8227
University of the Rockies Post-Sec.
555 E Pikes Peak Ave # 108 80903 719-442-0505

Commerce City, Adams, Pop. 45,019
Adams County SD 14 6,900/PK-12
5291 E 60th Ave 80022 303-853-3333
Pat Sanchez, supt. Fax 286-9753
www.adams14.org/
Adams City HS 1,700/9-12
7200 Quebec Pkwy 80022 303-289-3111
Bryan Wright, prin. Fax 288-6113
Adams City MS 700/6-8
4451 E 72nd Ave 80022 303-289-5881
Jennifer Skrobela, prin. Fax 288-8574
Arnold HS 200/9-12
6500 E 72nd Ave 80022 303-289-2983
Gionni Thompson, prin. Fax 289-7167
Kearney MS 500/6-8
6160 Kearney St 80022 303-287-0261
Kathy Heronema, prin. Fax 287-0432

Brighton SD 27J
Supt. — See Brighton
Stuart MS 500/6-8
15955 E 101st Way 80022 720-685-5500
Martin Pearson, prin. Fax 685-5506

Conifer, Jefferson, Pop. 600
Jefferson County SD R-1
Supt. — See Golden
Conifer HS 900/9-12
10441 Highway 73 80433 303-982-5255
Dr. Michael Musick, prin. Fax 982-5256
West Jefferson MS 600/6-8
9449 Barnes Ave 80433 303-982-3056
Becky Brown, prin. Fax 982-3057

Cortez, Montezuma, Pop. 8,328
Montezuma-Cortez SD RE-1 2,900/PK-12
PO Box R 81321 970-565-7282
Alex Carter, supt. Fax 565-2161
www.cortez.k12.co.us
Cortez MS 600/6-8
450 W 2nd St 81321 970-565-7824
Jamie Haukeness, prin. Fax 565-5120
Montezuma-Cortez HS 700/9-12
206 W 7th St 81321 970-565-3722
Jason Wayman, prin. Fax 565-5118

Cotopaxi, Fremont, Pop. 45
Cotopaxi SD RE-3 100/PK-12
PO Box 385 81223 719-942-4131
Chuck McKenna, supt. Fax 942-4134
www.cotopaxire3.org/
Cotopaxi S 100/PK-12
PO Box 385 81223 719-942-4131
Jackie Crabtree, prin. Fax 942-4134

Craig, Moffat, Pop. 9,327
Moffat County SD RE-1 2,400/PK-12
775 Yampa Ave 81625 970-824-3268
Dr. Joe Petrone, supt. Fax 824-6655
moffatsd.org/
Craig MS 500/6-8
915 Yampa Ave 81625 970-824-3289
Julie Baker, prin. Fax 824-3858
Moffat County HS 600/9-12
900 Finley Ln 81625 970-824-7036
Thom Schnellinger, prin. Fax 824-3130

Creede, Mineral, Pop. 412
Creede Consolidated SD 1 100/PK-12
PO Box 429 81130 719-658-2220
Buck Stroh, supt. Fax 658-2942
www.creedek12.net
Creede JSHS 50/6-12
PO Box 429 81130 719-658-2220
John Goss, prin. Fax 658-2942

Crested Butte, Gunnison, Pop. 1,477
Gunnison Watershed SD RE 1J
Supt. — See Gunnison
Crested Butte S 600/K-12
PO Box 339 81224 970-641-7720
Stephanie Niemi, prin. Fax 641-7729

Cripple Creek, Teller, Pop. 1,167
Cripple Creek-Victor SD RE-1 400/PK-12
PO Box 897 80813 719-689-2685
Susan Holmes, supt. Fax 689-2256
www.ccvschools.com/
Cripple Creek-Victor JSHS 200/7-12
PO Box 897 80813 719-689-2661
Trudy Vader, prin. Fax 389-2256

De Beque, Mesa, Pop. 499
De Beque SD 49JT 100/PK-12
PO Box 70 81630 970-283-5418
Stephen Strong, supt. Fax 283-5213
www.dbschools.org
De Beque JSHS 50/7-12
PO Box 70 81630 970-283-5596
Stephen Strong, prin. Fax 283-5598

Deer Trail, Arapahoe, Pop. 538
Deer Trail SD 26J 200/PK-12
PO Box 129 80105 303-769-4421
Robin Purdy, supt. Fax 769-4600
www.dt26j.org
Deer Trail JSHS 100/6-12
PO Box 129 80105 303-769-4421
Robin Purdy, prin. Fax 769-4600

Del Norte, Rio Grande, Pop. 1,670
Del Norte SD C-7 400/K-12
770 11th St 81132 719-657-4040
Nathan Smith, supt. Fax 657-2546
delnorte.schoolfusion.us
Del Norte HS 200/9-12
770 11th St 81132 719-657-4020
Brian Herman, prin. Fax 657-4024
Del Norte MS 100/5-8
770 11th St 81132 719-657-4030
Wendy O'Rourke, prin. Fax 657-9087

Delta, Delta, Pop. 8,798
Delta County SD 50(J) 4,700/PK-12
7655 2075 Rd 81416 970-874-4438
Caryn Gibson, supt. Fax 874-5744
www.deltaschools.com
Delta Academy of Applied Learning 50/Alt
PO Box 224 81416 970-874-0835
Al Williams, prin. Fax 874-8684
Delta County Opportunity S 100/Alt
822 Grand Ave 81416 970-874-2753
Delaine Hudson, prin. Fax 874-6852
Delta HS 700/9-12
1400 Pioneer Rd 81416 970-874-8031
Derek Carlson, prin. Fax 874-8034
Delta MS 500/6-8
910 Grand Ave 81416 970-874-8046
Adam Truitt, prin. Fax 874-8049
Other Schools – See Cedaredge, Hotchkiss, Paonia

Denver, Denver, Pop. 585,815
Adams County SD 50
Supt. — See Westminster
Carpenter MS 600/6-8
7001 Lipan St 80221 303-428-8583
Kelly Williams, prin. Fax 657-3962
Ranum MS 800/6-8
2401 W 80th Ave 80221 303-428-9577
Alan Kaylor, prin. Fax 657-3952

Denver County SD 1 76,100/PK-12
900 Grant St 80203 720-423-3200
Tom Boasberg, supt. Fax 423-3413
www.dpsk12.org/
CEC Middle College of Denver Vo/Tech
2650 Eliot St 80211 720-423-6600
Scott Springer, prin. Fax 423-6604
Collegiate Preparatory Academy 9-12
5000 Crown Blvd 80239 720-423-5800
Karen Alexander, prin.
Contemporary Learning Academy Alt HS 200/Alt
2211 W 27th Ave 80211 720-423-6900
Deborah Staten, prin. Fax 423-6999
Crittenton HS 200/Alt
96 S Zuni St 80223 303-733-7686
Shirley Algiene, admin. Fax 733-4119
DCIS at Montbello 6-8
5000 Crown Blvd 80239 720-423-5900
Trent Sharp, prin.
Denver Center for 21st Century Learning Alt
1690 Williams St 80218 720-424-2980
Christian DeLaOliva, prin. Fax 424-3005
Denver Center for International Studies 600/6-12
574 W 6th Ave 80204 720-423-9000
Stephen Parce, prin. Fax 423-9075

Denver Montessori JSHS 6-12
2949 California St 80205 720-424-2600
Katy Myers, prin.
Denver S of the Arts 1,000/6-12
7111 Montview Blvd 80220 720-424-1700
William Kohut, prin. Fax 424-1845
East HS 2,200/9-12
1600 City Park Esplanade 80206 720-423-8300
Andy Mendelsberg, prin. Fax 423-8306
Escuela Tlatelolco 100/Alt
2949 Federal Blvd 80211 303-964-8993
Betty deBaca, prin. Fax 964-9795
Gilliam S 50/Alt
2844 Downing St 80205 303-291-8929
Kim Ortiz, dir. Fax 292-9348
Grant Beacon MS 400/6-8
1751 S Washington St 80210 720-423-9360
Alex Magana, prin. Fax 423-9385
Griffith HS, 1250 Welton St 80204 500/Alt
David Daves, prin. 720-423-4757
Hamilton MS 1,000/6-8
8600 E Dartmouth Ave 80231 720-423-9500
Reina Gutierrez, prin. Fax 423-9445
Henry World MS 900/6-8
3005 S Golden Way 80227 720-423-9560
Dackri Davis, prin. Fax 423-9585
High Tech Early College 9-12
11200 E 45th Ave 80239 720-424-2450
John Fry, prin.
Hill MS 800/6-8
451 Clermont St 80220 720-423-9680
Don Roy, prin. Fax 423-9705
Jefferson HS 1,100/9-12
3950 S Holly St 80237 720-423-7000
Sandra Just, prin. Fax 423-7047
Kennedy HS 1,100/9-12
2855 S Lamar St 80227 720-423-4300
Jeannie Peppel, prin. Fax 423-4309
Kepner MS 1,100/6-8
911 S Hazel Ct 80219 720-424-0000
Stephen Linkous, prin. Fax 424-0023
King Early College HS 1,200/6-12
19535 E 46th Ave 80249 720-424-0420
Anthony Smith, prin. Fax 424-0496
Kunsmiller Creative Arts Academy 600/K-12
2250 S Quitman Way 80219 720-424-0200
Peter Castillo, prin. Fax 424-0145
Lake International MS 600/6-8
1820 Lowell Blvd 80204 720-424-0260
Amy Highsmith, prin. Fax 424-0380
Lincoln HS 1,900/9-12
2285 S Federal Blvd 80219 720-423-5000
Josefina Higa, prin. Fax 423-5098
Manual HS 300/9-12
1700 E 28th Ave 80205 720-423-6300
Brian Dale, prin. Fax 423-6301
McAuliffe International MS 6-8
3480 Syracuse St 80238 720-424-4790
Kurt Dennis, prin.
Merrill MS 500/6-8
1551 S Monroe St 80210 720-424-0600
Amy Bringedahl, prin. Fax 424-0625
Montbello HS 1,600/9-12
5000 Crown Blvd 80239 720-423-5700
Larry Irvin, prin. Fax 423-5801
Morey MS 800/6-8
840 E 14th Ave 80218 720-424-0700
Doris Claunch, prin. Fax 424-0727
Noel Community Arts S 6-12
5290 Kittredge St 80239 720-424-0920
Stacy Miller, prin. Fax 424-0925
Noel MS 700/6-8
5290 Kittredge St 80239 720-424-0800
Robert Thomas, prin. Fax 424-0945
North HS 900/9-12
2960 N Speer Blvd 80211 720-423-2700
Nicole Veltze, prin. Fax 423-2708
P.R.E.P. Center 200/Alt
2727 Columbine St 80205 720-424-8451
Jamie Lafaro, prin. Fax 424-8477
Randolph MSHS 900/6-12
3955 Steele St 80205 720-424-1080
Cesar Cedillo, prin. Fax 424-1241
Skinner MS 300/6-8
3435 W 40th Ave 80211 720-424-1420
Michelle Koyama, prin. Fax 424-1446
Smiley MS 300/6-8
2540 Holly St 80207 720-424-1540
Gwendolyn Victor, prin. Fax 424-1565
South HS 1,400/9-12
1700 E Louisiana Ave 80210 720-423-6000
Kristin Waters, prin. Fax 423-6280
Summit Academy 100/Alt
3001 S Federal Blvd 80236 720-424-2400
Annette Zambrano, prin.
Vista Academy 6-12
4800 Telluride St 80249 720-423-7650
Rhonda Juett, prin. Fax 423-7667
Washington HS 1,600/9-12
655 S Monaco Pkwy 80224 720-423-8600
Michael Johnson, prin. Fax 423-8614
West Generation Academy 6-12
951 Elati St 80204 720-423-5347
Domonic Martinez, prin.
West HS 800/9-12
951 Elati St 80204 720-423-5300
Santiago Grado, prin. Fax 423-5410
West Leadership Academy 6-12
951 Elati St 80204 720-423-5342
Teresa Klava, prin.

Jefferson County SD R-1
Supt. — See Golden
D'Evelyn JSHS 1,000/7-12
10359 W Nassau Ave 80235 303-982-2600
Terry Elliott, prin. Fax 982-2601

Mapleton SD 1 7,200/PK-12
591 E 80th Ave 80229 303-853-1000
Charlotte Ciancio, supt. Fax 853-1087
www.mapleton.us
Global Leadership Academy 400/K-12
7480 Conifer Rd 80221 303-853-1930
Dave Sauer, dir. Fax 853-1956
Other Schools – See Thornton

Sheridan SD 2
Supt. — See Sheridan
S.O.A.R. Academy Alt
3201 W Oxford Ave 80236 720-833-6796
Michael Granderson, dir.
Sheridan HS 500/9-12
3201 W Oxford Ave 80236 720-833-6987
Michele Kelley, prin. Fax 833-6833

Accelerated Schools 50/K-12
2160 S Cook St 80210 303-758-2003
Jane Queen, dir. Fax 757-4336
American Pathways University Post-Sec.
2227 Franklin St 80205 303-839-2551
American University of Paris Post-Sec.
700 Colorado Blvd # 502 80206 303-993-4326
Argosy University / Denver Post-Sec.
7600 E Eastman Ave 80231 303-923-4110
Arrupe Jesuit HS 300/9-12
4343 Utica St 80212 303-455-7449
Michael O'Hagan, prin. Fax 455-7453
Art Institute of Colorado Post-Sec.
1200 Lincoln St 80203 303-837-0825
Aspen University Post-Sec.
720 S Colorado Blvd #1150N 80246 800-441-4746
Bel-Rea Institute of Animal Technology Post-Sec.
1681 S Dayton St, 303-751-8700
Beth Jacob HS of Denver 100/9-12
5100 W 14th Ave 80204 303-893-1333
Rabbi Myer Schwab, dean Fax 573-4932
Bishop Machebeuf Catholic HS 400/9-12
458 Uinta Way 80230 303-344-0082
Jessie Skipwith, prin. Fax 344-1582
Centura-St. Anthony Hospital Post-Sec.
4231 W 16th Ave 80204 303-629-4350
CollegeAmerica - Denver Post-Sec.
1385 S Colorado Blvd Fl 5 80222 303-534-0226
Colorado Academy 900/PK-12
3800 S Pierce St 80235 303-986-1501
Michael Davis Ph.D., hdmstr. Fax 914-2583
Colorado Ctr for Medical Laboratory Sci. Post-Sec.
1719 E 19th Ave 80218 303-839-6485
Colorado Heights University Post-Sec.
3001 S Federal Blvd 80236 303-937-4225
CO Sch of Traditional Chinese Medicine Post-Sec.
1441 York St Ste 202 80206 303-329-6355
Community College of Denver Post-Sec.
PO Box 173363 80217 303-556-2600
Denver Academy 400/1-12
4400 E Iliff Ave 80222 303-777-5870
Kevin Smith, hdmstr. Fax 777-5893
Denver Academy of Torah 100/PK-12
6825 E Alameda Ave 80224 720-859-6806
Rabbi Daniel Alter, hdmstr. Fax 859-6847
Denver Christian HS 100/9-12
2135 S Pearl St 80210 303-733-2421
Dr. Steven Kortenhoeven, prin. Fax 733-7734
Denver Health Medical Center Post-Sec.
660 Bannock St 80204 303-436-6611
Denver Jewish Day School 400/K-12
2450 S Wabash St 80231 303-369-0663
Avi Halzel, pres. Fax 369-0664
Denver School of Nursing Post-Sec.
1401 19th St 80202 303-292-0015
Denver Waldorf S 300/PK-12
940 Fillmore St 80206 303-777-0531
Judy Lucas, admin. Fax 744-1216
Emily Griffith Opportunity School Post-Sec.
1250 Welton St 80204 720-423-4700
Heritage College Post-Sec.
12 Lakeside Ln 80212 303-477-7240
Iliff School of Theology Post-Sec.
2201 S University Blvd 80210 303-744-1287
Johnson & Wales University-Denver Campus Post-Sec.
7150 Montview Blvd 80220 303-256-9300
Lincoln College of Technology Post-Sec.
11194 E 45th Ave 80239 303-722-5724
Metropolitan State University Post-Sec.
PO Box 173362 80217 303-556-2400
Mile High Academy 200/PK-12
711 E Yale Ave 80210 303-744-1069
Kase Vunileva, prin. Fax 744-1060
Mullen HS 900/9-12
3601 S Lowell Blvd 80236 303-761-1764
Janell Kloostermann, prin. Fax 761-0502
National American University Post-Sec.
1325 S Colorado Blvd #100 80222 303-876-7100
National Theatre Conservatory Post-Sec.
1101 13th St 80204 303-446-4855
Phlebotomy Learning Center Post-Sec.
1780 S Bellaire St Ste 780 80222 303-584-0575
Pima Medical Institute Post-Sec.
7475 Dakin St 80221 303-426-1800
Regis University Post-Sec.
3333 Regis Blvd 80221 303-458-4100
Rocky Mountain College of Art & Design Post-Sec.
1600 Pierce St 80214 800-888-2787
Rocky Mountain Lutheran HS 100/9-12
2300 W 90th Ave 80260 303-346-1947
Frederick Lohmiller, prin. Fax 451-0817
St. John Vianney Theological Seminary Post-Sec.
1300 S Steele St 80210 303-282-3427
University of Colorado Denver Post-Sec.
1250 14th St 80202 303-556-2400
University of Denver Post-Sec.
2199 S University Blvd 80210 303-871-2000
Westwood College - Denver North Post-Sec.
7350 Broadway 80221 303-650-5050
Westwood College - Denver South Post-Sec.
3150 S Sheridan Blvd 80227 303-934-1122

William Howard Taft University Post-Sec.
600 S Cherry St Ste 525 80246 303-867-1155
Yeshiva Toras Chaim 100/9-12
PO Box 40067 80204 303-629-8200
Yeshiva Toras Chaim Talmudical Seminary Post-Sec.
1555 Stuart St 80204 303-629-8200

Dolores, Montezuma, Pop. 903
Dolores SD RE-4A 700/PK-12
PO Box 727 81323 970-882-7255
Scott Cooper, supt. Fax 882-7685
www.dolores.k12.co.us
Dolores HS 200/9-12
PO Box 727 81323 970-882-7288
Brandon Thurston, prin. Fax 882-7289
Dolores MS 200/6-8
PO Box 727 81323 970-882-7288
Jimmie Lankford, admin. Fax 882-7289

Dove Creek, Dolores, Pop. 714
Dolores County SD RE-2J 300/PK-12
PO Box 459 81324 970-677-2522
Bruce Hankins, supt. Fax 677-2712
www.dc2j.org
Dove Creek HS 100/6-12
PO Box 459 81324 970-677-2237
Ty Gray, prin. Fax 677-2927

Durango, LaPlata, Pop. 16,541
Durango SD 9-R 4,700/PK-12
201 E 12th St 81301 970-247-5411
Dan Snowberger, supt. Fax 247-9581
www.durangoschools.org
Durango HS 1,400/9-12
2390 Main Ave 81301 970-259-1630
LeAnne Garcia, prin. Fax 385-1493
Escalante MS 500/6-8
141 Baker Ln 81303 970-247-9490
Tim Arnold, prin. Fax 385-1194
Miller MS 500/6-8
2608 Junction St 81301 970-247-1418
Tam Smith, prin. Fax 385-1191

Colorado Timberline Academy 50/9-12
35554 Highway 550 81301 970-247-5898
Daniel Coey, dir. Fax 259-8067
Fort Lewis College Post-Sec.
1000 Rim Dr 81301 970-247-7010
Grace Preparatory Academy of Durango 50/6-12
PO Box 3354 81302 970-385-7544
Louise Powers-Ackley, admin. Fax 259-9917

Eads, Kiowa, Pop. 605
Eads SD RE-1 200/PK-12
210 W 10th St 81036 719-438-2218
Glenn Smith, supt. Fax 438-5499
www.eadseaglee.com
Eads HS 100/9-12
210 W 10th St 81036 719-438-2214
Betsy Barnett, prin. Fax 438-2272
Eads JHS 50/6-8
900 Maine St 81036 719-438-2216
Glenn Smith, prin. Fax 438-2090

Eagle, Eagle, Pop. 6,436
Eagle County SD RE-50 5,900/PK-12
PO Box 740 81631 970-328-6321
Sandra Smyser Ph.D., supt. Fax 328-1024
www.eagleschools.net
Eagle Valley MS 300/6-8
PO Box 1019 81631 970-328-6224
Katie Jarnot, prin. Fax 328-8915
Other Schools – See Edwards, Gypsum

Eaton, Weld, Pop. 4,298
Eaton SD RE-2 1,700/K-12
200 Park Ave 80615 970-454-3402
Randy Miller Ed.D., supt. Fax 454-5193
www.eaton.k12.co.us
Eaton HS 500/9-12
114 Park Ave 80615 970-454-3374
Mark Naill, prin. Fax 454-5190
Eaton MS 400/6-8
225 Juniper Ave 80615 970-454-3358
Jim Orth, prin. Fax 454-1337

Edgewater, Jefferson, Pop. 5,086
Jefferson County SD R-1
Supt. — See Golden
Jefferson HS 600/9-12
2305 Pierce St 80214 303-982-6056
Mike Little, prin. Fax 982-6057

Edwards, Eagle, Pop. 10,187
Eagle County SD RE-50
Supt. — See Eagle
Battle Mountains HS 700/9-12
151 Miller Ranch Rd 81632 970-328-2930
Philip Qualman, prin. Fax 328-2935
Berry Creek MS 300/6-8
PO Box 1416 81632 970-328-2960
Amy Vanwel, prin. Fax 926-4137
Red Canyon HS 100/Alt
1002 Miller Ranch Rd 81632 970-328-2852
Wade Hill, prin. Fax 328-6976

Vail Christian HS 100/9-12
31621 Highway 6 81632 970-926-3015
Jeremy Lowe, prin. Fax 766-3016

Elbert, Elbert, Pop. 225
Elbert SD 200 200/PK-12
PO Box 38 80106 303-648-3030
Kelli Loflin, supt. Fax 648-3652
elbertschool.org
Elbert JSHS 100/7-12
PO Box 38 80106 303-648-3030
Mike Epright, prin. Fax 648-3652

Elizabeth, Elbert, Pop. 1,335
Elizabeth SD C-1 2,500/PK-12
PO Box 610 80107 303-646-4441
Douglas Bissonette, supt. Fax 646-0337
elizabeth.k12.co.us/
Elizabeth HS 800/9-12
PO Box 660 80107 303-646-4616
Greg Wieman, prin. Fax 646-6030
Elizabeth MS 500/6-8
PO Box 369 80107 303-646-4520
Steve Thiessen, prin. Fax 646-0980
Frontier HS 100/Alt
PO Box 610 80107 303-646-1798
Robert McMullen, dir. Fax 646-1329

Ellicott, El Paso, Pop. 1,094
Ellicott SD 22 1,000/PK-12
395 S Ellicott Hwy 80808 719-683-2700
Patrick Cullen Ed.D., supt. Fax 683-4442
www.ellicottschools.org
Ellicott HS 300/9-12
375 S Ellicott Hwy 80808 719-683-2700
Danielle VanEsselstine, prin. Fax 683-2705
Ellicott MS 200/6-8
350 S Ellicott Hwy 80808 719-683-2700
Chris Smith, prin. Fax 683-5430

Englewood, Arapahoe, Pop. 29,512
Cherry Creek SD 5
Supt. — See Greenwood Village
Campus MS 1,400/6-8
4785 S Dayton St 80111 720-554-2677
Jane Miller, prin. Fax 554-2782
Career & Technical Education Vo/Tech
9150 E Union Ave 80111 720-554-4553
Fax 554-4531
Cherry Creek HS 3,400/9-12
9300 E Union Ave 80111 720-554-2000
Ryan Silva, prin. Fax 554-2239

Englewood SD 1 2,800/PK-12
4101 S Bannock St 80110 303-761-7050
Brian Ewert, supt. Fax 806-2064
www.englewood.k12.co.us
Colorado's Finest Alternative HS 400/Alt
2323 W Baker Ave 80110 303-934-5786
Bobbie Skaggs, prin. Fax 934-9183
Englewood HS 600/9-12
3800 S Logan St, 303-806-2266
Jon Fore, prin. Fax 806-2298
Englewood Leadership Academy 100/6-8
3800 S Logan St, 303-806-2266
Jon Fore, prin.
Englewood MS 300/7-8
300 W Chenango Ave 80110 303-781-7817
Mandy Braun, prin. Fax 806-2399

Columbia HealthOne Post-Sec.
501 E Hampden Ave, 303-788-6484
Elliot Christian S 100/6-12
8505 S Valley Hwy 80112 303-922-0011
Michael Eaves, admin. Fax 922-0159
Kent Denver S 700/6-12
4000 E Quincy Ave, 303-770-7660
Todd Horn, hdmstr. Fax 770-7137
St. Mary's Academy 700/PK-12
4545 S University Blvd, 303-762-8300
Deirdre Cryor, pres. Fax 783-6201

Erie, Weld, Pop. 17,723
St. Vrain Valley SD RE-1J
Supt. — See Longmont
Erie HS 800/9-12
3180 County Road 5 80516 303-828-4213
Steven Payne, prin. Fax 494-3869
Erie MS 500/6-8
650 Main St 80516 303-828-3391
Todd Bissell, prin. Fax 828-3817

Vista Ridge Academy 100/K-12
3100 Ridgeview Dr 80516 303-828-4944
Deborah de Trevino, prin. Fax 828-1525

Estes Park, Larimer, Pop. 5,792
Estes Park SD R-3 1,100/PK-12
1605 Brodie Ave 80517 970-586-2361
Dr. Patrick Hickey, supt. Fax 586-1108
www.psdr3.k12.co.us/
Estes Park HS 400/9-12
1600 Manford Ave 80517 970-586-5321
Charles Scott, prin. Fax 586-1102
Estes Park MS 200/6-8
1500 Manford Ave 80517 970-586-4439
Ruby Bode, prin. Fax 586-1100

Eagle Rock S 100/9-12
2750 Notaiah Rd 80517 970-586-0600
Robert Burkhardt, hdmstr. Fax 586-4805

Evergreen, Jefferson, Pop. 8,923
Clear Creek SD RE-1
Supt. — See Idaho Springs
Clear Creek HS 200/9-12
185 Beaver Brook Canyon Rd 80439 303-679-4600
Elizabeth Gardner, prin. Fax 679-4603
Clear Creek MS 100/7-8
185 Beaver Brook Canyon Rd 80439 303-670-4600
Roslin Marshall, prin. Fax 670-4690

Jefferson County SD R-1
Supt. — See Golden
Evergreen HS 1,000/9-12
29300 Buffalo Park Rd 80439 303-982-5140
Matthew Walsh, prin. Fax 982-5141
Evergreen MS 700/6-8
2059 Hiwan Dr 80439 303-982-5020
Kristopher Schuh, prin. Fax 982-5021

Fairplay, Park, Pop. 659
Park County SD RE-2 600/PK-12
PO Box 189 80440 719-836-3114
Becky Minnis, supt. Fax 836-2275
www.parkcountyre2.org/
South Park HS 100/9-12
PO Box 189 80440 719-836-4406
Jane Newman, prin. Fax 836-2275
South Park MS 100/6-8
PO Box 189 80440 719-836-4406
Jane Newman, prin. Fax 836-2275

Falcon, El Paso, Pop. 200
Falcon SD 49 14,000/PK-12
10850 E Woodmen Rd 80831 719-495-1100
Don Begier, admin. Fax 494-8900
www.d49.org
Falcon HS 1,300/9-12
10255 Lambert Rd 80831 719-495-5520
Susan Thomas, prin. Fax 495-5521
Falcon MS 900/6-8
9755 Towner Ave 80831 719-495-5232
Brian Smith, prin. Fax 495-5237
Patriot Learning Center Alt
11990 Swingline Rd 80831 719-495-5505
Thomas Wilke, prin.
Other Schools – See Colorado Springs

Firestone, Weld, Pop. 9,981
St. Vrain Valley SD RE-1J
Supt. — See Longmont
Coal Ridge MS 800/6-8
6201 Booth Dr 80504 303-833-4176
Brian Young, prin. Fax 833-4192

Flagler, Kit Carson, Pop. 558
Arriba-Flagler SD C-20 100/PK-12
PO Box 218 80815 719-765-4684
Thomas Arensdorf, supt. Fax 765-4418
flaglerschools.co.afs.schoolinsites.com
Flagler HS 50/9-12
PO Box 218 80815 719-765-4684
Tom Arensdorf, supt. Fax 765-4418

Fleming, Logan, Pop. 408
Frenchman SD RE-3 200/PK-12
506 N Fremont Ave 80728 970-265-2111
Jim Copeland, supt. Fax 265-2815
www.flemingschools.org
Fleming HS 100/7-12
506 N Fremont Ave 80728 970-265-2022
Dustin Seger, prin. Fax 265-2029

Florence, Fremont, Pop. 3,816
Florence SD RE-2 1,600/K-12
403 W 5th St 81226 719-784-6312
Rhonda Vendetti, supt. Fax 784-4140
www.re-2.org/
Florence HS 500/9-12
2006 Highway 67 81226 719-784-6414
Brian Schipper, prin. Fax 784-3821
Fremont MS 400/6-8
215 Maple St 81226 719-784-4856
Andy Fieth, prin. Fax 784-4060

Fort Collins, Larimer, Pop. 140,582
Poudre SD R-1 26,600/PK-12
2407 Laporte Ave 80521 970-490-3607
Dr. Nancy Wright, supt. Fax 490-3514
www.psdschools.org
Blevins MS 500/6-8
2101 S Taft Hill Rd 80526 970-488-4000
David Linehan, prin. Fax 488-4011
Boltz MS 600/6-8
720 Boltz Dr 80525 970-472-3700
Penny Stires, prin. Fax 472-3730
Centennial Alternative HS 200/Alt
330 E Laurel St 80524 970-488-4940
Mike Roberts, prin. Fax 488-4942
Fort Collins HS 1,700/9-12
3400 Lambkin Way 80525 970-488-8021
Mark Eversole, prin. Fax 488-8008
Fossil Ridge HS 1,900/9-12
5400 Ziegler Rd 80528 970-488-6260
Dierdre Cook, prin. Fax 488-6263
Kinard MS 800/6-8
3002 E Trilby Rd 80528 970-488-5400
Joe Cuddemi, prin. Fax 488-5402
Lesher MS 700/6-8
1400 Stover St 80524 970-472-3800
Thomas Dodd, prin. Fax 472-3880
Lincoln MS 500/6-8
1600 Lancer Dr 80521 970-488-5700
Don Rangel, prin. Fax 488-5752
Polaris Expeditionary Learning S 200/6-12
1905 Orchard Pl 80521 970-488-8260
Joe Gawronski, prin. Fax 488-8262
Poudre Community Academy 100/Alt
2540 LaPorte Ave 80521 970-490-3295
Troy Krotz, prin. Fax 490-3402
Poudre HS 1,900/9-12
201 S Impala Dr 80521 970-488-6000
George Osborne, prin. Fax 488-6060
Preston MS 800/6-8
4901 Corbett Dr 80528 970-488-7300
Scott Nielsen, prin. Fax 488-7307
Rocky Mountain HS 2,000/9-12
1300 W Swallow Rd 80526 970-488-7023
Tom Lopez, prin. Fax 488-7001
Webber MS 800/6-8
4201 Seneca St 80526 970-488-7800
Sandra Bickel, prin. Fax 488-7811
Other Schools – See Laporte, Wellington

At-Home Professions Post-Sec.
2001 Lowe St 80525 970-225-6300
CollegeAmerica - Fort Collins Post-Sec.
4601 S Mason St 80525 970-221-2769
Colorado State University Post-Sec.
1062 Campus Delivery 80523 970-491-6909
Front Range Baptist Academy 100/PK-12
625 E Harmony Rd 80525 970-223-2173
Fax 223-5826
Front Range Community College Post-Sec.
4616 S Shields St 80526 970-226-2500
Hair Dynamics Education Center Post-Sec.
PO Box 272389 80527 970-223-9943
Heritage Christian Academy 200/PK-12
2506 Zurich Dr 80524 970-494-1022
Mike Cuckler, admin. Fax 494-1025
Institute of Business & Medical Careers Post-Sec.
3842 S Mason St 80525 970-223-2669
McKinley College Post-Sec.
2001 Lowe St 80525 970-207-4550
US Career Institute Post-Sec.
2001 Lowe St 80525 800-347-7899

Fort Lupton, Weld, Pop. 7,284
Weld County SD RE-8 2,400/PK-12
301 Reynolds St 80621 303-857-3200
Mark Payler, supt. Fax 857-3219
www.ftlupton.k12.co.us
Fort Lupton HS 600/9-12
530 Reynolds St 80621 303-857-7100
Alan Kaylor, prin. Fax 857-7179
Fort Lupton MS 500/6-8
201 S McKinley Ave 80621 303-857-7200
Candace Kensinger, prin. Fax 857-7287

Fort Morgan, Morgan, Pop. 11,188
Ft. Morgan SD RE-3 3,200/PK-12
715 W Platte Ave 80701 970-867-5633
Ron Echols, supt. Fax 867-0262
www.morgan.k12.co.us
Fort Morgan HS 900/9-12
709 E Riverview Ave 80701 970-867-5648
Ben Bauman, prin. Fax 867-3347
Fort Morgan MS 500/7-8
300 Deuel St 80701 970-867-8253
Jason Frasco, prin. Fax 867-4876
Lincoln HS 50/9-12
230 Walnut St 80701 970-867-2924
Vicki Davis, prin. Fax 867-4958

Morgan Community College Post-Sec.
920 Barlow Rd 80701 970-542-3100

Fountain, El Paso, Pop. 24,314
Fountain-Fort Carson SD 8 7,500/PK-12
10665 Jimmy Camp Rd 80817 719-382-1300
Cheryl Serrano, supt. Fax 382-7338
www.ffc8.org
Fountain-Fort Carson HS 1,600/9-12
900 Jimmy Camp Rd 80817 719-382-1640
Burnie Hibbard, prin. Fax 382-3228
Fountain MS 900/6-8
515 N Santa Fe Ave 80817 719-382-1580
Deb Keiley, prin. Fax 382-9065
Welte Education Center 100/Alt
330 Lyckman Pl 80817 719-382-1550
Cheryl Lassota, prin. Fax 382-5782
Other Schools – See Colorado Springs

Widefield SD 3
Supt. — See Colorado Springs
Janitell JHS 700/6-8
7635 Fountain Mesa Rd 80817 719-391-3295
Aaron Hoffman, prin. Fax 390-7869

Fowler, Otero, Pop. 1,170
Fowler SD R-4J 400/K-12
PO Box 218 81039 719-263-4224
Steven Grasmick, supt. Fax 263-4625
www.fowler.k12.co.us/
Fowler HS 100/9-12
PO Box 218 81039 719-263-4279
Russell Bates, prin. Fax 263-4625
Fowler JHS 100/7-8
PO Box 218 81039 719-263-4224
Russell Bates, prin. Fax 263-4625

Frederick, Weld, Pop. 8,509
St. Vrain Valley SD RE-1J
Supt. — See Longmont
Frederick HS 800/9-12
5690 Tipple Pkwy 80530 303-833-3533
Peter Vargas, prin. Fax 833-4488

Frisco, Summit, Pop. 2,654
Summit SD RE-1 3,100/PK-12
PO Box 7 80443 970-368-1000
Dr. Heidi Pace, supt. Fax 368-1049
summit.k12.co.us
Snowy Peaks HS Alt
PO Box 7 80443 970-368-1108
Brett Tomlinson, admin. Fax 368-1199
Summit HS 800/9-12
PO Box 7 80443 970-368-1100
Drew Adkins, prin. Fax 368-1199
Summit MS 600/6-8
PO Box 7 80443 970-368-1200
Joel Rivera, prin. Fax 368-1299

Fruita, Mesa, Pop. 12,442
Mesa County Valley SD 51
Supt. — See Grand Junction
Fruita 8th & 9th Grade S 800/8-9
1835 J Rd 81521 970-254-6720
Jason Plantiko, prin. Fax 858-7751
Fruita Monument HS 1,300/10-12
1102 Wildcat Ave 81521 970-254-6600
Janelle Keirns, prin. Fax 858-9661

Gateway, Mesa, Pop. 7,510
Mesa County Valley SD 51
Supt. — See Grand Junction
Gateway S 50/K-12
PO Box 240 81522 970-254-7080
Yogi Cherp, prin. Fax 931-2883

Gilcrest, Weld, Pop. 1,023
Weld County SD RE-1 2,000/PK-12
PO Box 157 80623 970-737-2403
Dr. Jo Barbie, supt. Fax 737-2516
www.weld-re1.k12.co.us
Valley HS 500/9-12
PO Box 156 80623 970-737-2494
Rich Dalgliesh, prin. Fax 737-2203
Other Schools – See La Salle, Platteville

Glenwood Springs, Garfield, Pop. 9,485
Roaring Fork SD RE-1 5,200/PK-12
1405 Grand Ave 81601 970-384-6000
Diana Sirko, supt. Fax 384-6005
www.rfsd.k12.co.us
Glenwood Springs HS 800/9-12
1521 Grand Ave 81601 970-384-5555
Paul Freeman, prin. Fax 384-5556
Glenwood Springs MS 500/6-8
120 Soccer Field Rd 81601 970-384-5500
Sandy DeCrow, prin. Fax 384-5505
Other Schools – See Basalt, Carbondale

Colorado Mountain College Post-Sec.
802 Grand Ave 81601 970-945-8691
Glenwood Beauty Academy Post-Sec.
51241 Highway 6 Ste 1 81601 970-945-0485

Golden, Jefferson, Pop. 18,494
Jefferson County SD R-1 83,500/PK-12
PO Box 4001 80402 303-982-6500
Dr. Cindy Stevenson, supt. Fax 982-6814
www.jeffcopublicschools.org/
Bell MS 500/7-8
1001 Ulysses St 80401 303-982-4280
Bridget Jones, prin. Fax 982-4281
Golden HS 1,300/9-12
701 24th St 80401 303-982-4200
Brian Conroy, prin. Fax 982-4201
Manning S 400/Alt
13200 W 32nd Ave 80401 303-982-6340
Barb Goings, prin. Fax 982-6341
Other Schools – See Arvada, Conifer, Denver, Edgewater, Evergreen, Lakewood, Littleton, Westminster, Wheat Ridge

---

Colorado School of Mines Post-Sec.
1500 Illinois St 80401 303-273-3000
Holmes Institute Post-Sec.
573 Park Point Dr 80401 720-496-1370

Granada, Prowers, Pop. 515
Granada SD RE-1 200/PK-12
PO Box 259 81041 719-734-5492
Leo Laprarie, supt. Fax 734-5495
www.granadaschool.com
Granada JSHS 100/7-12
PO Box 259 81041 719-734-5492
Ty Kemp, prin. Fax 734-5495

Granby, Grand, Pop. 1,839
East Grand SD 2 1,300/PK-12
PO Box 125 80446 970-887-2581
Nancy Karas, supt. Fax 887-2635
www.egsd.org
East Grand MS 300/6-8
PO Box 2210 80446 970-887-3382
Jenny Rothboeck, prin. Fax 887-9234
Middle Park HS 300/9-12
PO Box 130 80446 970-887-2104
Scott Eldred, prin. Fax 887-9454

Grand Junction, Mesa, Pop. 57,510
Mesa County Valley SD 51 21,700/PK-12
2115 Grand Ave 81501 970-254-5100
Steven Schultz, supt. Fax 254-5282
www.d51schools.org
Bookcliff MS 600/6-8
540 29 1/4 Rd 81504 970-254-6220
Catherine Drake, prin. Fax 245-7812
Career Center Vo/Tech
2935 North Ave 81504 970-254-6000
Pat Chapin, prin. Fax 255-8465
Central HS 1,600/9-12
550 Warrior Way 81504 970-254-6200
Jody Diers, prin. Fax 254-6169
East MS 400/6-8
830 Gunnison Ave 81501 970-254-5020
Leah Gonyeau, prin. Fax 242-0513
Grand Junction HS 1,800/9-12
1400 N 5th St 81501 970-254-6900
Jon Bilbo, prin. Fax 241-5154
Grand Mesa MS 700/6-8
585 31 1/2 Rd 81504 970-254-6270
Mark Vana, prin. Fax 523-5938
Orchard Mesa MS 500/6-8
2736 C Rd 81503 970-254-6320
John Murtell, prin. Fax 245-7343
R-5 HS 400/Alt
310 N 7th St 81501 970-254-6880
Anna Goetz, prin. Fax 242-4465
Redlands MS 600/6-8
2200 Broadway, 970-254-7000
Kelly Reed, prin. Fax 245-1985
Valley S West Alt
2508 Blichmann Ave 81505 970-255-2708
Brenda Witte, prin. Fax 255-2711
West MS 400/6-8
123 W Orchard Ave 81505 970-254-5090
Vernon Walker, prin. Fax 243-0574
Other Schools – See Clifton, Fruita, Gateway, Palisade

Colorado Mesa University Post-Sec.
1100 North Ave 81501 970-248-1020
Grand Valley Christian HS 50/8-12
402 Grand Ave 81501 970-241-4126
Rebecca Daniels, admin.
IntelliTec College Post-Sec.
772 Horizon Dr 81506 970-245-8101

Greeley, Weld, Pop. 91,409
Weld County SD 6 19,000/PK-12
1025 9th Ave 80631 970-348-6000
Dr. Ranelle Lang, supt. Fax 348-6231
www.greeleyschools.org
Brentwood MS 700/6-8
2600 24th Avenue Ct 80634 970-348-3000
Shelly Lantz, prin. Fax 348-3030
Evans MS 700/6-8
2900 15th Ave 80631 970-348-3600
Dawn Hillman, prin. Fax 348-3630
Franklin MS 700/6-8
818 35th Ave 80634 970-348-3200
John Diebold, prin. Fax 348-3230
Greeley Central HS 1,400/9-12
1515 14th Ave 80631 970-348-5000
Mark Cousins, prin. Fax 348-5030
Greeley-Evans Alternative Program Alt
1113 10th Ave 80631 970-348-4900
Dave Shaffer, admin. Fax 348-4930
Greeley West HS 1,500/9-12
2401 35th Ave 80634 970-348-5400
Shelli Robins, prin. Fax 348-5430
Heath MS 800/6-8
2223 16th St 80631 970-348-3400
Dr. Blakley Wallace, prin. Fax 348-3430
Jefferson HS 9-12
1315 4th Ave 80631 970-348-1600
Larry Green, prin. Fax 348-1630
Northridge HS 1,000/9-12
100 N 71st Ave 80634 970-348-5200
Wesley Paxton, prin. Fax 348-5230

Aims Community College Post-Sec.
5401 W 20th St 80634 970-330-8008
Cheeks Intl Academy of Beauty Culture Post-Sec.
2547 11th Ave Ste B 80631 970-352-4500
Dayspring Christian Academy 300/PK-12
3734 W 20th St 80634 970-330-1151
Weston Kurz, dir. Fax 330-0565
Institute of Business & Medical Careers Post-Sec.
5400 W 11th St Ste D 80634 970-356-4733
University of Northern Colorado Post-Sec.
501 20th St 80639 970-351-1890

Greenwood Village, Arapahoe, Pop. 13,663
Cherry Creek SD 5 50,900/PK-12
4700 S Yosemite St 80111 303-773-1184
Mary Chesley, supt. Fax 773-9370
www.cherrycreekschools.org
Other Schools – See Aurora, Centennial, Englewood, Littleton

College for Financial Planning Post-Sec.
8000 E Maplewood Ave # 200 80111 303-220-1200
Colorado State University Global Campus Post-Sec.
8000 E Maplewood Bldg 5 #250 80111
720-279-0159
DeVry University Post-Sec.
6312 S Fiddlers Green #150E 80111 303-329-3000
Tri-County Health Nutrition Services Post-Sec.
6162 S Willow Dr Ste 100 80111 303-220-9200

Grover, Weld, Pop. 137
Pawnee SD RE-12 100/PK-12
PO Box 220 80729 970-895-2222
Bret Robinson, supt. Fax 895-2221
www.pawneeschool.org
Pawnee JSHS 50/7-12
PO Box 220 80729 970-895-2222
Bret Robinson, prin. Fax 895-2221

Gunnison, Gunnison, Pop. 5,730
Gunnison Watershed SD RE 1J 1,800/PK-12
800 N Boulevard St 81230 970-641-7760
Jon Nelson, supt. Fax 641-7777
www.gunnisonschools.net/
Gunnison HS 300/9-12
800 W Ohio Ave 81230 970-641-7700
Andy Hanks, prin. Fax 641-7709
Gunnison MS 200/6-8
1099 N 11th St 81230 970-641-7710
Doug Tredway, prin. Fax 641-7739
Other Schools – See Crested Butte

Western State Colorado University Post-Sec.
600 N Adams St 81231 970-943-0120

Gypsum, Eagle, Pop. 6,422
Eagle County SD RE-50
Supt. — See Eagle
Eagle Valley HS 700/9-12
PO Box 188 81637 970-328-8960
Greg Doan, prin. Fax 328-8965
Gypsum Creek MS 300/6-8
PO Box 5129 81637 970-328-8980
David Russell, prin. Fax 524-7393

Haxtun, Phillips, Pop. 937
Haxtun SD RE-2J 300/PK-12
201 W Powell St 80731 970-774-6111
Darcy Garretson, supt. Fax 774-7568
www.haxtunschools.com
Haxtun HS 100/9-12
201 W Powell St 80731 970-774-6111
Darcy Garretson, prin. Fax 774-7568

Hayden, Routt, Pop. 1,785
Hayden SD RE-1 400/PK-12
PO Box 70 81639 970-276-3864
Mike Luppes, supt. Fax 276-4217
www.haydenschools.org/
Hayden HS 100/9-12
PO Box 70 81639 970-276-3761
Regina Zabel, prin. Fax 276-4374
Hayden MS 100/6-8
PO Box 70 81639 970-276-3762
Regina Zabel, prin. Fax 276-7235

Henderson, Adams, Pop. 500
Brighton SD 27J
Supt. — See Brighton
Prairie View HS 1,500/9-12
12909 E 120th Ave 80640 303-655-8800
Ana Mendoza, prin. Fax 655-8920
Prairie View MS 800/6-8
12915 E 120th Ave 80640 720-685-5400
Tom Delgado, prin. Fax 685-5404

American Institute of Technology Post-Sec.
9239 Brighton Rd Unit 201 80640 303-558-3152

Highlands Ranch, Douglas, Pop. 94,597
Douglas County SD RE-1
Supt. — See Castle Rock
Cresthill MS 900/7-8
9195 Cresthill Ln 80130 303-387-2800
Sid Rundle, prin. Fax 387-2801
Highlands Ranch HS 1,700/9-12
9375 Cresthill Ln 80130 303-387-2500
Jerry Goings, prin. Fax 387-2501
Mountain Ridge MS 1,100/7-8
10590 Mountain Vista Rdg 80126 303-387-1800
Shannon Clarke, prin. Fax 387-1801
Mountain Vista HS 2,000/9-12
10585 Mountain Vista Rdg 80126 303-387-1500
Mike Weaver, prin. Fax 387-1501
Ranch View MS 1,000/7-8
1731 W Wildcat Reserve Pkwy 80129 303-387-2300
James McMurphy, prin. Fax 387-2301
STEM S 6-10
8773 Ridgeline Blvd 80129 303-683-7836
Penny Eucker, prin. Fax 452-4519
Thunderridge HS 1,800/9-12
1991 W Wildcat Reserve Pkwy 80129 303-387-2000
Carole Jennings, prin. Fax 387-2001
Eagle Academy Adult
9375 Cresthill Ln 80130 303-387-2700
Doug Seligman, prin. Fax 387-2701

Valor Christian S 800/9-12
3775 Grace Blvd 80126 303-471-3000
Kurt Unruh, head sch Fax 471-3001

Hoehne, Las Animas, Pop. 111
Hoehne RSD 3 200/K-12
PO Box 91 81046 719-846-4457
Christine Barela, supt. Fax 846-2208
www.hoehnesd.org/
Hoehne S 200/K-12
PO Box 91 81046 719-846-4457
Jenifer Hufman, prin. Fax 846-2208

Holly, Prowers, Pop. 799
Holly SD RE-3 300/PK-12
PO Box 608 81047 719-537-6616
Carlyn Yokum, supt. Fax 537-0315
www.hollyschools.org
Holly JSHS 100/7-12
PO Box 608 81047 719-537-6512
Randy Holmen, prin. Fax 537-6519

Holyoke, Phillips, Pop. 2,299
Holyoke SD RE-1J 500/K-12
435 S Morlan Ave 80734 970-854-3634
Bret Miles, supt. Fax 854-4049
holyoke.schoolfusion.us
Holyoke Alternative HS Alt
545 E Hale St 80734 970-854-2284
Cindi Beavers, dir. Fax 854-4578
Holyoke JSHS 200/7-12
545 E Hale St 80734 970-854-2284
Susan Ortner, prin. Fax 854-4578

Hotchkiss, Delta, Pop. 933
Delta County SD 50(J)
Supt. — See Delta
Hotchkiss HS 300/9-12
438 Bulldog St 81419 970-872-3882
Mike Beard, prin. Fax 872-2390

Hugo, Lincoln, Pop. 718
Genoa-Hugo SD C113 200/PK-12
PO Box 247 80821 719-743-2428
Frank Reeves, supt. Fax 743-2194
www.genoahugo.org/
Genoa-Hugo HS 100/9-12
PO Box 247 80821 719-743-2428
Shari Humphrey, prin. Fax 743-2194
Genoa-Hugo MS 50/6-8
PO Box 247 80821 719-743-2428
Shari Humphrey, prin. Fax 743-2194

Idaho Springs, Clear Creek, Pop. 1,695
Clear Creek SD RE-1 1,000/PK-12
PO Box 3399 80452 303-567-3850
Todd Lancaster, supt. Fax 567-3861
www.ccsdre1.org/
Other Schools – See Evergreen

Idalia, Yuma, Pop. 88
Idalia SD RJ-3 200/PK-12
PO Box 40 80735 970-354-7298
Tim Krause, supt. Fax 354-7416
www.idaliaco.us
Idalia JSHS 50/6-12
PO Box 40 80735 970-354-7298
Tim Krause, admin. Fax 354-7416

Ignacio, LaPlata, Pop. 652
Ignacio SD 11 JT 700/K-12
PO Box 460 81137 970-563-0500
Rocco Fuschetto Ed.D., supt. Fax 563-4524
www.ignacioschools.org
Ignacio HS 200/9-12
PO Box 460 81137 970-563-0515
Melanie Taylor, prin. Fax 563-9463
Ignacio JHS 100/7-8
PO Box 460 81137 970-563-0600
Chris deKay, prin. Fax 563-1030

Iliff, Logan, Pop. 261
Valley SD RE-1
Supt. — See Sterling
Caliche JSHS 100/7-12
26308 County Road 65 80736 970-522-8200
Doug Stutzman, prin. Fax 522-9400

Joes, Yuma, Pop. 78
Liberty SD J-4 100/PK-12
PO Box 112 80822 970-358-4288
Doris Lessing, supt. Fax 358-4282
www.libertyschoolj4.com
Liberty JSHS 50/7-12
PO Box 112 80822 970-358-4288
Doris Lessing, prin. Fax 358-4282

Johnstown, Weld, Pop. 9,738
Weld County SD RE-5J
Supt. — See Milliken
Roosevelt HS 700/9-12
616 N 2nd St 80534 970-587-6000
Trevor Long, prin. Fax 587-2608

Julesburg, Sedgwick, Pop. 1,216
Julesburg SD RE-1 300/PK-12
102 W 6th St 80737 970-474-3365
Shawn Ehnes, supt. Fax 474-3742
www.julesburg.org
Julesburg JSHS 100/7-12
102 W 6th St 80737 970-474-3364
Shawn Ehnes, prin. Fax 474-3592

Karval, Lincoln, Pop. 50
Karval SD RE-23 200/PK-12
PO Box 5 80823 719-446-5311
Todd Werner, supt. Fax 446-5332
www.karvalschool.org
Karval JSHS 50/6-12
PO Box 5 80823 719-446-5311
Fax 446-5332

Keenesburg, Weld, Pop. 1,112
Weld County SD RE-3J 2,100/PK-12
PO Box 269 80643 303-536-2000
Greg Rabenhorst, supt. Fax 536-2010
www.re3j.com
Weld Central HS 600/9-12
4715 County Road 59 80643 303-536-2100
Dale Fleming, prin. Fax 536-2110
Weld Central MS 300/6-8
4977 County Road 59 80643 303-536-2700
Karla Schriner, prin. Fax 536-2710

Kersey, Weld, Pop. 1,432
Weld County SD RE-7 1,100/PK-12
PO Box 485 80644 970-336-8500
E. Glenn McClain Ed.D., supt. Fax 336-8511
www.plattevalley.k12.co.us
Platte Valley HS 300/9-12
PO Box 487 80644 970-336-8700
Brad Joens, prin. Fax 336-8794
Platte Valley MS 300/6-8
PO Box 515 80644 970-336-8610
George Clear, prin. Fax 336-8635

Kim, Las Animas, Pop. 73
Kim RSD 88 100/PK-12
PO Box 100 81049 719-643-5295
Monica Johnson, supt. Fax 643-5299
www.kim.k12.co.us/
Kim JSHS 50/7-12
PO Box 100 81049 719-643-5295
Monica Johnson, prin. Fax 643-5299

Kiowa, Elbert, Pop. 708
Kiowa SD C-2 400/PK-12
PO Box 128 80117 303-621-2220
Jason Westfall, supt. Fax 621-2239
www.kiowaschool.org
Kiowa HS 100/9-12
PO Box 128 80117 303-621-2115
Amy Smith, prin. Fax 621-2566
Kiowa MS 100/6-8
PO Box 128 80117 303-621-2785
Amy Smith, prin. Fax 621-2239

Kit Carson, Cheyenne, Pop. 230
Kit Carson SD R-1 100/K-12
PO Box 185 80825 719-962-3219
Gerald Keefe, supt. Fax 962-3317
www.kcsdr1.org
Carson JSHS 100/6-12
PO Box 185 80825 719-962-3219
Gerald Keefe, prin. Fax 962-3317

Kremmling, Grand, Pop. 1,417
West Grand SD 1-JT 400/K-12
PO Box 515 80459 970-724-3217
Terry Vanderpan, supt. Fax 724-9373
www.westgrand.k12.co.us/
West Grand HS 100/9-12
PO Box 515 80459 970-724-3425
Kyle York, prin. Fax 724-3450
West Grand MS 100/6-8
PO Box 515 80459 970-724-1000
Kyle York, prin. Fax 724-9052

Lafayette, Boulder, Pop. 23,902
Boulder Valley SD RE-2
Supt. — See Boulder
Angevine MS 500/6-8
1150 W South Boulder Rd 80026 720-561-7100
Mike Medina, prin. Fax 561-7101
Centaurus HS 1,000/9-12
10300 E South Boulder Rd 80026 720-561-7500
Rhonda Haniford, prin. Fax 561-5368

Dawson S 400/K-12
10455 Dawson Dr 80026 303-665-6679
George Moore, head sch Fax 665-0757

La Jara, Conejos, Pop. 805
North Conejos SD RE-1J 1,000/PK-12
PO Box 72 81140 719-274-5174
Kevin Schott, supt. Fax 274-5621
www.northconejos.com
Centauri HS 300/9-12
17889 US Highway 285 81140 719-274-5178
Curt Wilson, prin. Fax 274-5637
Centauri MS 200/6-8
17891 US Highway 285 81140 719-274-4301
Michael Cadicamo, prin. Fax 274-4306
New Horizons HS 100/Alt
PO Box 72 81140 719-274-4220
Susan Hamilton, admin. Fax 274-3809

La Junta, Otero, Pop. 6,961
East Otero SD R-1 1,100/K-12
1802 Colorado Ave Ste 200 81050 719-384-6900
Carol Noll, supt. Fax 384-6910
www.lajunta.k12.co.us
La Junta JSHS 400/7-12
1817 Smithland Ave 81050 719-384-4467
Paul Jebe, prin. Fax 384-9160

Otero Junior College Post-Sec.
1802 Colorado Ave 81050 719-384-6831

Lake City, Hinsdale, Pop. 393
Hinsdale County SD RE 1 100/PK-12
PO Box 39 81235 970-944-2314
Dr. Karen Thormalen, supt. Fax 944-2662
www.lakecityschool.org/
Lake City Community S 100/PK-12
PO Box 39 81235 970-944-2314
Dr. Karen Thormalen, prin. Fax 944-2662

Lakewood, Jefferson, Pop. 140,229
Jefferson County SD R-1
Supt. — See Golden
Alameda HS 700/9-12
1255 S Wadsworth Blvd 80232 303-982-8160
Susie VanScoyk, prin. Fax 982-8161
Bear Creek HS 1,900/9-12
9800 W Dartmouth Pl 80227 303-982-8855
Kevin Carroll, prin. Fax 982-8856
Brady Exploration S 300/Alt
5220 W Ohio Ave 80226 303-982-6722
Troy Braley, prin. Fax 982-6723
Carmody MS 700/7-8
2050 S Kipling St 80227 303-982-8930
Scott Allensworth, prin. Fax 982-8931
Creighton MS 700/7-8
50 S Kipling St 80226 303-982-6282
Nick Kemmer, prin. Fax 982-6283
Dunstan MS 600/7-8
1855 S Wright St 80228 303-982-9270
Cheryl Hensley, prin. Fax 982-9269
Green Mountain HS 1,300/9-12
13175 W Green Mountain Dr 80228 303-982-9500
Colleen Owens, prin. Fax 982-9501
Jefferson County Open JSHS 300/7-12
7655 W 10th Ave 80214 303-982-7045
Scott Bain, prin. Fax 982-7046
Lakewood HS 2,000/9-12
9700 W 8th Ave 80215 303-982-7096
Ron Castagna, prin. Fax 982-7097
Long View HS 50/Alt
13301 W 2nd Pl 80228 303-982-8523
Deborah Gard, prin. Fax 982-8568
McClain Community HS 200/Alt
13600 W 2nd Pl 80228 303-982-7460
Deborah Gard, prin. Fax 982-7494
O'Connell MS 500/7-8
1275 S Teller St 80232 303-982-8370
Marc Nesteorick, prin. Fax 982-8371
Warren Tech S Vo/Tech
13300 W 2nd Pl 80228 303-982-8600
Joe Shaw, prin. Fax 982-8622

Colorado Christian University Post-Sec.
8787 W Alameda Ave 80226 303-963-3000
Colorado School of Healing Arts Post-Sec.
7655 W Mississippi #100 80226 303-986-2320
Colorado School of Trades Post-Sec.
1575 Hoyt St 80215 303-233-4697
Ohio Center for Broadcasting - Colorado Post-Sec.
404 S Upham St 80226 303-937-7070
Red Rocks Community College Post-Sec.
13300 W 6th Ave 80228 303-914-6600

Lamar, Prowers, Pop. 7,721
Lamar SD RE-2 1,500/PK-12
210 W Pearl St 81052 719-336-3251
Dave Tecklenburg, supt. Fax 336-2817
www.lamar.k12.co.us
Lamar HS 400/9-12
1900 S 11th St 81052 719-336-3488
Rocky Robbins, prin. Fax 336-3026
Lamar MS 200/6-8
104 W Park St 81052 719-336-7436
Steve Banker, prin. Fax 336-5457

Lamar Community College Post-Sec.
2401 S Main St 81052 719-336-2248

Laporte, Larimer, Pop. 2,391
Poudre SD R-1
Supt. — See Fort Collins
Cache La Poudre MS 300/6-8
3515 W County Road 54G 80535 970-488-7400
Alicia Bono, prin. Fax 488-7433

La Salle, Weld, Pop. 1,932
Weld County SD RE-1
Supt. — See Gilcrest
North Valley MS 300/6-8
300 2nd Ave 80645 970-284-5508
Richard Dufault, prin. Fax 284-6595

Las Animas, Bent, Pop. 2,388
Las Animas SD RE-1 500/PK-12
1021 2nd St 81054 719-456-0161
Jerry Nickell, supt. Fax 456-1117
www.lasanimas.k12.co.us
Las Animas HS 100/9-12
300 Grove Ave 81054 719-456-0211
Elsie Goines, prin. Fax 456-0932
Las Animas JHS 100/7-8
1021 2nd St 81054 719-456-0228
Elsie Goines, prin. Fax 456-0241

La Veta, Huerfano, Pop. 774
La Veta SD RE-2 200/PK-12
PO Box 85 81055 719-742-3562
Bree Lessar, supt. Fax 742-3959
www.laveta.k12.co.us
La Veta JSHS 100/7-12
PO Box 85 81055 719-742-3662
Bree Lessar, prin. Fax 742-5799

Leadville, Lake, Pop. 2,564
Lake County SD R-1 1,200/PK-12
107 Spruce St 80461 719-486-6800
Wendy Wyman, supt. Fax 486-2048
www.lakecountyschools.net/
Lake County HS 300/9-12
1000 W 4th St 80461 719-486-6950
Christina Gosselin, prin. Fax 486-3767
Lake County MS 300/5-8
1000 W 6th St 80461 719-486-6830
Lacey Dahl, prin. Fax 486-6880

Limon, Lincoln, Pop. 1,854
Limon SD RE-4J 400/K-12
PO Box 249 80828 719-775-2350
Dave Marx, supt. Fax 775-9052
www.limonbadgers.com/
Limon JSHS 300/5-12
PO Box 249 80828 719-775-2350
Traci Weisensee, prin. Fax 775-9052

Littleton, Arapahoe, Pop. 40,946
Cherry Creek SD 5
Supt. — See Greenwood Village
West MS 1,100/6-8
5151 S Holly St 80121 720-554-5180
David Strohfus, prin. Fax 554-5181

Douglas County SD RE-1
Supt. — See Castle Rock
Rocky Heights MS 1,300/6-8
11033 Monarch Blvd 80124 303-387-3300
Mike Loitz, prin. Fax 387-3301

Jefferson County SD R-1
Supt. — See Golden
Chatfield HS 1,900/9-12
7227 S Simms St 80127 303-982-3670
Wendy Rubin, prin. Fax 982-3671
Columbine HS 1,600/9-12
6201 S Pierce St 80123 303-982-4400
Frank DeAngelis, prin. Fax 982-4401
Dakota Ridge HS 1,500/9-12
13399 W Coal Mine Ave 80127 303-982-1970
Dr. James Jelinek, prin. Fax 982-1971
Deer Creek MS 500/7-8
9201 W Columbine Dr 80128 303-982-3820
Rob Hoover, prin. Fax 982-3821
Falcon Bluffs MS 700/6-8
8449 S Garrison St 80128 303-982-9900
Ryan West, prin. Fax 982-9901
Ken Caryl MS 600/7-8
6509 W Ken Caryl Ave 80128 303-982-4710
Patrick Sandos, prin. Fax 982-4711
Summit Ridge MS 800/7-8
11809 W Coal Mine Ave 80127 303-982-9013
Ari Goldberg, prin. Fax 982-8998

Littleton SD 6 15,700/PK-12
5776 S Crocker St 80120 303-347-3300
Scott Murphy, supt. Fax 347-3439
www.littletonpublicschools.net
Euclid MS 700/6-8
777 W Euclid Ave 80120 303-347-7800
Gary Hein, prin. Fax 347-7830
Goddard MS 800/6-8
3800 W Berry Ave 80123 303-347-7850
Kathleen Ambron, prin. Fax 347-7880
Heritage HS 1,800/9-12
1401 W Geddes Ave 80120 303-347-7600
Stacey Riendeau, prin. Fax 347-7604
Littleton HS 1,500/9-12
199 E Littleton Blvd 80121 303-347-7700
Amy Oaks, prin. Fax 347-3772
Powell MS 900/6-8
8000 S Corona Way 80122 303-347-7950
Steve Wolf, prin. Fax 347-3975
Other Schools – See Centennial

Arapahoe Community College Post-Sec.
5900 S Santa Fe Dr 80120 303-797-4222
Denver Seminary Post-Sec.
6399 S Santa Fe Dr 80120 303-762-6982
Front Range Christian ES 100/PK-12
6657 W Ottawa Ave Ste A17 80128 303-922-3269
David Cooper, head sch Fax 922-3296
Truth Christian Academy 100/PK-12
PO Box 621961 80162 303-670-3360
Stanley Silverman, admin. Fax 670-8069

Lonetree, See Littleton
Douglas County SD RE-1
Supt. — See Castle Rock
Rock Canyon HS 1,600/9-12
5810 McArthur Ranch Rd 80124 303-387-3000
Andrew Abner, prin. Fax 387-3001

University of Phoenix Post-Sec.
10004 Park Meadows Dr 80124 303-755-9090

Longmont, Boulder, Pop. 84,733
St. Vrain Valley SD RE-1J 27,400/PK-12
395 S Pratt Pkwy 80501 303-776-6200
Don Haddad Ed.D., supt. Fax 682-7396
www.svvsd.org
Altona MS 600/6-8
4600 Clover Basin Dr 80503 720-494-3980
Joe Mehsling, prin. Fax 494-3989
Career Development Center Vo/Tech
1200 S Sunset St 80501 303-772-3333
Deniece Cook, prin. Fax 651-7446
Heritage MS 400/6-8
233 E Mountain View Ave 80504 303-772-7900
Karrie Borski, prin. Fax 776-4376
Longmont HS 1,200/9-12
1040 Sunset St 80501 303-776-6014
Rick Olsen, prin. Fax 678-7583
Longs Peak MS 500/6-8
1500 14th Ave 80501 303-776-5611
Matt Buchler, prin. Fax 651-3144
Mead HS 400/9-10
12750 County Road 7 80504 720-494-3940
Dr. Troy Snyder, prin. Fax 494-3959
Olde Columbine HS 100/Alt
1200 S Sunset St 80501 720-494-3961
Deniece Cook, prin. Fax 494-3968
Silver Creek HS 1,100/9-12
4901 Nelson Rd 80503 720-494-3721
Erick Finnestead, prin. Fax 494-1848
Skyline HS 1,200/9-12
600 E Mountain View Ave 80504 720-494-3741
Patty Quinones, prin. Fax 682-7382
Sunset MS 600/6-8
1300 S Sunset St 80501 303-776-3963
Dr. Dawn Macy, prin. Fax 772-2875
Trail Ridge MS 600/6-8
1000 Button Rock Dr 80504 720-494-3820
Eddie Cloke, prin. Fax 494-3829
Westview MS 600/6-8
1651 Airport Rd 80503 303-772-3134
Mark Spencer, prin. Fax 772-0596
Adult Education Lincoln Center Adult
820 Main St 80501 303-678-5662
Deniece Cook, admin. Fax 776-7426
Other Schools – See Erie, Firestone, Frederick, Lyons, Mead, Niwot

---

Faith Baptist S 1,100/PK-12
833 15th Ave 80501 303-776-5677
Rick Cross, supt. Fax 682-5359
Institute of Business & Medical Careers Post-Sec.
2315 Main St 80501 303-651-6819
Longmont Christian S 200/PK-12
550 Coffman St 80501 303-776-3254
Donnie Bennett, prin. Fax 485-6937

Louisville, Boulder, Pop. 17,982
Boulder Valley SD RE-2
Supt. — See Boulder
Louisville MS 600/6-8
1341 Main St 80027 720-561-7400
Adam Fels, prin. Fax 561-7401
Monarch HS 1,500/9-12
329 Campus Dr 80027 720-561-4200
Jerry Anderson, prin. Fax 561-5650

Institute of Taoist Educ & Acupuncture Post-Sec.
325 W South Boulder Rd # 2 80027 720-890-8922

Loveland, Larimer, Pop. 65,828
Thompson SD R-2J 14,400/K-12
800 S Taft Ave 80537 970-613-5000
Judy Skupa, supt. Fax 613-5095
www.thompson.k12.co.us
Ball MS 600/6-8
2660 Monroe Ave 80538 970-613-7300
Scott Elias, prin. Fax 613-7341
Clark MS 600/6-8
2605 Carlisle Dr 80537 970-613-5400
Martha Gustafson, prin. Fax 613-5420
Erwin MS 900/6-8
4700 Lucerne Ave 80538 970-613-7600
Diane Worner, prin. Fax 613-7619
Ferguson HS 100/Alt
1101 Hilltop Dr 80537 970-613-5300
Sheila Pottorff, prin. Fax 613-5395
Loveland HS 1,600/9-12
920 W 29th St 80538 970-613-5200
Todd Ball, prin. Fax 613-7191
Mountain View HS 1,100/9-12
3500 Mountain Lion Dr 80537 970-613-7800
Kim Young, prin. Fax 613-7820
Reed MS 700/6-8
370 W 4th St 80537 970-613-7200
Arnold Jahnke, prin. Fax 613-7287
Thompson Valley HS 1,300/9-12
1669 Eagle Dr 80537 970-613-7900
Mark Johnson, prin. Fax 613-7909
Other Schools – See Berthoud

Campion Academy 200/9-12
300 42nd St SW 80537 970-667-5592
Resurrection Christian S 900/PK-12
6508 E Crossroads Blvd 80538 970-612-0674
Rev. Allen Howlett M.A., supt. Fax 612-0975

Lyons, Boulder, Pop. 2,004
St. Vrain Valley SD RE-1J
Supt. — See Longmont
Lyons MSHS 400/6-12
100 McConnell Dr 80540 303-823-6631
Greg Winger, prin. Fax 823-5492

Mc Clave, Bent, Pop. 150
McClave SD RE-2 300/PK-12
PO Box 1 81057 719-829-4517
Terry Webber, supt. Fax 829-4430
www.mcclaveschools.org/

Mc Clave JSHS 100/7-12
PO Box 1 81057 719-829-4517
Rachel Dunning, prin. Fax 829-4430

Mancos, Montezuma, Pop. 1,302
Mancos SD RE-6 400/PK-12
395 Grand Ave 81328 970-533-7748
Brian Hanson, supt. Fax 533-7954
www.mancosre6.edu
Mancos HS 100/9-12
355 Grand Ave 81328 970-533-7746
Jeanette Allen, prin. Fax 533-7537
Mancos MS 100/6-8
100 S Beech St 81328 970-533-9143
Jeanette Allen, prin. Fax 533-1463

San Juan Basin Technical College Post-Sec.
33057 Highway 160 81328 970-565-8457

Manitou Springs, El Paso, Pop. 4,882
Manitou Springs SD 14 1,400/PK-12
405 El Monte Pl 80829 719-685-2024
Ed Longfield, supt. Fax 685-4536
www.mssd14.org/
Manitou Springs HS 500/9-12
401 El Monte Pl 80829 719-685-2074
Glenn Hard, prin. Fax 685-4755
Manitou Springs MS 300/6-8
415 El Monte Pl 80829 719-685-2127
Chris Burr, prin. Fax 685-4552

Manzanola, Otero, Pop. 429
Manzanola SD 3J 200/K-12
PO Box 148 81058 719-462-5527
Steve Sanchez, supt. Fax 462-5708
www.manzanola.k12.co.us/
Manzanola JSHS 100/7-12
PO Box 148 81058 719-462-5528
Howard Disney, prin. Fax 462-5115

Mead, Weld, Pop. 3,346
St. Vrain Valley SD RE-1J
Supt. — See Longmont
Mead MS 400/6-8
620 Welker Ave 80542 970-535-4446
Joshua Barnett, prin. Fax 535-4434

Meeker, Rio Blanco, Pop. 2,417
Meeker SD RE-1 700/PK-12
PO Box 1089 81641 970-878-9040
Mark Meyer, supt. Fax 878-3682
www.meeker.k12.co.us
Barone MS 100/6-8
PO Box 690 81641 970-878-9060
Jim Hanks, prin. Fax 878-4291
Meeker HS 200/9-12
PO Box 159 81641 970-878-9070
Dr. Kimberly Ibach, prin. Fax 878-3633

Merino, Logan, Pop. 281
Merino SD RE-4J 300/K-12
PO Box 198 80741 970-522-7424
Robert Sanders, supt. Fax 522-1541
www.merino-sd.schoolfusion.us/
Merino JSHS 200/7-12
PO Box 198 80741 970-522-7424
Lonnie Brungardt, prin. Fax 522-1541

Milliken, Weld, Pop. 5,520
Weld County SD RE-5J 3,100/PK-12
110 Centennial Dr Ste A 80543 970-587-6050
Dr. Martin Foster, supt. Fax 587-2607
www.weldre5j.k12.co.us
Milliken MS 600/6-8
PO Box 339 80543 970-587-6300
Ron Hruby, prin. Fax 587-5749
Other Schools – See Johnstown

Moffat, Saguache, Pop. 116
Moffat SD 2 200/PK-12
PO Box 127 81143 719-256-4710
Kirk Banghart, supt. Fax 256-4730
www.moffat.csd.schoolfusion.us
Moffat HS 50/9-12
PO Box 127 81143 719-256-4710
Michelle Hashbarger, prin. Fax 256-4730
Moffat MS 50/6-8
PO Box 127 81143 719-256-4710
Michelle Hashbarger, prin. Fax 256-4730

Monte Vista, Rio Grande, Pop. 4,392
Monte Vista SD C-8 1,000/PK-12
349 E Prospect Ave 81144 719-852-5996
Robert Webb, supt. Fax 852-6184
www.monte.k12.co.us
Byron Syring Delta Center 100/Alt
345 E Prospect Ave 81144 719-852-2212
Dirk Oden, dir. Fax 852-6184
Monte Vista HS 300/9-12
295 E Prospect Ave 81144 719-852-3586
Scott Wiedeman, prin. Fax 852-6121
Monte Vista MS 200/6-8
3720 Sherman Ave 81144 719-852-5984
Tom Tichy, prin. Fax 852-6199

Sargent SD RE-33J 400/K-12
7090 N County Road 2 E 81144 719-852-4023
Steven Marantino, supt. Fax 852-9890
www.sargent.k12.co.us
Sargent JSHS 100/7-12
7090 N County Road 2 E 81144 719-852-4025
Philip Compton, prin. Fax 852-9672

Montrose, Montrose, Pop. 18,812
Montrose County SD RE-1J 6,400/PK-12
PO Box 10000 81402 970-249-7726
Mark MacHale, supt. Fax 249-7173
www.mcsd.org
Centennial MS 600/6-8
PO Box 10000 81402 970-249-2576
Nancy Alex, prin. Fax 240-6461
Columbine MS 500/6-8
PO Box 10000 81402 970-249-2581
Ben Stephenson, prin. Fax 240-6404
Montrose HS 1,300/9-12
PO Box 10000 81402 970-249-6636
James Barnhill, prin. Fax 240-6414
Other Schools – See Olathe

Monument, El Paso, Pop. 5,337
Lewis-Palmer SD 38 5,300/PK-12
PO Box 40 80132 719-488-4700
John Borman, supt. Fax 488-4704
www.lewispalmer.org
Lewis-Palmer HS 900/9-12
1300 Higby Rd 80132 719-488-4720
Sandi Brandl, prin. Fax 488-4723
Lewis-Palmer MS 800/7-8
1776 Woodmoor Dr 80132 719-488-4776
Seann O'Connor, prin. Fax 488-4780
Palmer Ridge HS 1,100/9-12
19255 Monument Hill Rd 80132 719-867-8600
Gary Gabel, prin. Fax 867-8605

Mosca, Alamosa, Pop. 180
Sangre De Cristo SD RE-22J 300/PK-12
8751 Lane 7 N 81146 719-378-2321
Brady Stagner, supt. Fax 378-2327
www.sangreschools.org/
Sangre De Cristo JSHS 100/7-12
8751 Lane 7 N 81146 719-378-2321
John Stephens, prin. Fax 378-2327

Nederland, Boulder, Pop. 1,417
Boulder Valley SD RE-2
Supt. — See Boulder
Nederland MSHS 400/6-12
597 County Road 130 80466 720-561-4900
Lynn Donnelly, prin. Fax 561-4901

New Castle, Garfield, Pop. 4,478
Garfield SD RE-2
Supt. — See Rifle
Coal Ridge HS 500/9-12
35947 Highway 6 81647 970-665-6710
David Morgan, prin. Fax 665-6701
Riverside MS 700/5-8
215 Alder Ave 81647 970-665-7800
Lacey Moser, prin. Fax 665-7846

New Raymer, Weld, Pop. 95
Prairie SD RE-11 200/PK-12
PO Box 68 80742 970-437-5351
R. Joe Kimmel, supt. Fax 437-5732
www.prairieschool.org/
Prairie JSHS 100/7-12
PO Box 68 80742 970-437-5351
Tabitha Piel, prin. Fax 437-5732

Niwot, Boulder, Pop. 3,929
St. Vrain Valley SD RE-1J
Supt. — See Longmont
Niwot HS 1,300/9-12
8989 Niwot Rd 80503 303-652-2550
Dennis Daly, prin. Fax 652-1592

Rocky Mountain Christian Academy 300/PK-12
9447 Niwot Rd 80503 303-652-9162
Dr. Sylvia Robinson, prin. Fax 652-8072

Northglenn, Adams, Pop. 35,024
Adams 12 Five Star SD
Supt. — See Thornton
Crossroads Alternative S 100/Alt
10900 Huron St 80234 720-972-5900
Alan Hollenbeck, dir. Fax 972-5919
Northglenn HS 1,700/9-12
601 W 100th Pl 80260 720-972-4600
Mary Lindimore, prin. Fax 972-4739
Northglenn MS 700/6-8
1123 Muriel Dr 80233 720-972-5080
Jennifer Ederley, prin. Fax 972-5119
Vantage Point HS 400/Alt
10900 Huron St 80234 720-972-5800
Alan Hollenbeck, prin. Fax 972-5814

Community Christian S 200/PK-12
11980 Irma Dr 80233 303-452-7514
Tim Shaffer, admin. Fax 452-4904

Norwood, San Miguel, Pop. 505
Norwood SD R-2J 200/PK-12
PO Box 448 81423 970-327-4336
David Crews, supt. Fax 327-4116
www.npsmavs.com
Norwood HS 100/9-12
PO Box 448 81423 970-327-4336
Bill Nickell, prin. Fax 327-4116

Nucla, Montrose, Pop. 704
West End SD RE-2 300/PK-12
PO Box 570 81424 970-864-7350
Thomas Taucher, supt. Fax 864-7269
www.westendschools.org
Nucla HS 100/9-12
PO Box 570 81424 970-864-7350
Thomas Taucher, prin. Fax 864-7269

Oak Creek, Routt, Pop. 865
South Routt SD RE-3 400/PK-12
PO Box 158 80467 970-736-2313
Scott Mader, supt. Fax 736-2458
www.southroutt.k12.co.us
Soroco HS 100/9-12
PO Box 158 80467 970-736-2531
Dennis Alt, prin. Fax 736-0211
Soroco MS 100/6-8
PO Box 158 80467 970-736-8531
Dennis Alt, prin. Fax 736-0182

Olathe, Montrose, Pop. 1,821
Montrose County SD RE-1J
Supt. — See Montrose
Olathe HS 400/9-12
410 Highway 50 81425 970-252-7950
Scot Brown, prin. Fax 323-5947
Olathe MS 300/6-8
410 Highway 50 81425 970-252-7950
Scot Brown, prin. Fax 323-5947

Ordway, Crowley, Pop. 1,058
Crowley County SD RE-1-J 500/K-12
1001 Main St 81063 719-267-3117
Scott Cuckow, supt. Fax 267-3130
www.cck12.net/
Crowley County HS 100/9-12
602 Main St 81063 719-267-3582
Lisa Bauer, prin. Fax 267-3585
Crowley County MS 100/6-8
1001 Main St 81063 719-267-9880
Scott Cuckow, prin. Fax 267-9881

Otis, Washington, Pop. 462
Lone Star SD 101 100/K-12
44940 County Road 54 80743 970-848-2778
Susan Sonnenberg, supt. Fax 848-0340
www.lonestar.k12.co.us/
Lone Star JSHS 50/6-12
44940 County Road 54 80743 970-848-2778
Michael Bowers, prin. Fax 848-0340

Otis SD R-3 200/PK-12
518 Dungan St 80743 970-246-3413
Mike Warren, supt. Fax 246-0518
www.osdco.com
Otis JSHS 100/7-12
301 Work St 80743 970-246-3486
Fax 246-3487

Ouray, Ouray, Pop. 990
Ouray SD R-1 200/PK-12
PO Box N 81427 970-325-4505
Scott Pankow, supt. Fax 325-7343
www.ouray.k12.co.us/
Ouray HS 100/9-12
PO Box N 81427 970-325-4505
Scott Pankow, prin. Fax 325-7343
Ouray MS 50/7-8
PO Box N 81427 970-325-4505
Scott Pankow, prin. Fax 325-7343

Ovid, Sedgwick, Pop. 314
Platte Valley SD RE-3 100/PK-12
PO Box 369 80744 970-463-5414
Sharon Green, supt. Fax 463-5493
www.plattevalley.schoolfusion.us
Revere JSHS 50/7-12
PO Box 369 80744 970-463-5477
Jennifer Knipp, prin. Fax 463-5669

Pagosa Springs, Archuleta, Pop. 1,685
Archuleta SD 50 JT 1,500/K-12
PO Box 1498 81147 970-264-2228
Mark DeVoti, supt. Fax 264-4631
www.mypagosaschools.com
Pagosa Springs HS 500/9-12
PO Box 1498 81147 970-264-2231
David Hamilton, prin. Fax 264-2239
Pagosa Springs MS 500/5-8
PO Box 1498 81147 970-264-2794
Chris Hinger, prin. Fax 264-6112

Palisade, Mesa, Pop. 2,644
Mesa County Valley SD 51
Supt. — See Grand Junction
Palisade HS 1,000/9-12
3679 G Rd 81526 970-254-4800
Matthew Diers, prin. Fax 464-5102

Paonia, Delta, Pop. 1,427
Delta County SD 50(J)
Supt. — See Delta
Paonia JSHS 300/7-12
846 Grand Ave 81428 970-527-4882
Randal Palmer, prin. Fax 527-4080

Parachute, Garfield, Pop. 1,062
Garfield County SD 16 900/PK-12
PO Box 68 81635 970-285-5701
Dr. Ken Haptonstall, supt. Fax 285-5711
www.garcoschools.org
Grand Valley HS 300/9-12
PO Box 68 81635 970-285-5705
Ryan Frink, prin. Fax 285-5715
Grand Valley MS 200/6-8
PO Box 68 81635 970-285-5707
Jory Sorensen, prin. Fax 285-5717

Parker, Douglas, Pop. 44,230
Douglas County SD RE-1
Supt. — See Castle Rock
Chaparral HS 2,100/9-12
15655 Brookstone Dr 80134 303-387-3500
Ron Peterson, prin. Fax 387-3501
Cimarron MS 900/7-8
12130 Canterberry Pkwy 80138 303-433-0120
Karen Tarbell, prin. Fax 433-0121
Legend HS 1,300/9-12
22219 Hilltop Rd 80138 303-387-4500
Corey Wise, prin. Fax 805-4501
Ponderosa HS 1,400/9-12
7007 Bayou Gulch Rd 80134 303-387-4000
Chuck Puga, prin. Fax 387-4001
Sagewood MS 900/6-8
4725 Fox Sparrow Rd 80134 303-387-4300
Julie Jaeger, prin. Fax 387-4301
Sierra MS 1,000/7-8
6651 E Pine Ln 80138 303-387-3800
Michelle Davis, prin. Fax 387-3801

Lutheran HS 200/9-12
11249 Newlin Gulch Blvd 80134 303-841-5551
David Ness, prin. Fax 842-1015
Rocky Vista University Post-Sec.
8401 S Chambers Rd 80134 303-373-2008

Peetz, Logan, Pop. 237
Peetz Plateau SD RE-5 — 200/PK-12
PO Box 63 80747 — 970-334-2435
Ben Dutton, supt. — Fax 334-2360
www.peetzschool.org
Peetz JSHS — 100/7-12
PO Box 63 80747 — 970-334-2361
Dean Koester, prin. — Fax 334-2360

Peyton, El Paso, Pop. 247
Peyton SD 23 JT — 700/PK-12
13990 Bradshaw Rd 80831 — 719-749-2330
Tim Kistler, supt. — Fax 749-2368
www.peyton.k12.co.us/
Peyton HS — 300/7-12
13885 Bradshaw Rd 80831 — 719-749-0417
Brian Rea, prin. — Fax 749-0150

Platteville, Weld, Pop. 2,448
Weld County SD RE-1
Supt. — See Gilcrest
South Valley MS — 200/6-8
1004 Main St 80651 — 970-785-2205
Jeff Angus, prin. — Fax 785-2180

Pritchett, Baca, Pop. 140
Pritchett SD RE-3 — 100/PK-12
PO Box 7 81064 — 719-523-4045
Don Beard, supt. — Fax 523-6991
www.pritchettschool.com/
Pritchett HS — 50/9-12
PO Box 7 81064 — 719-523-4045
Kyle Boydstun, lead tchr. — Fax 523-6991
Pritchett JHS — 50/6-8
PO Box 7 81064 — 719-523-4045
Kyle Boydstun, lead tchr. — Fax 523-6991

Pueblo, Pueblo, Pop. 104,988
Pueblo CSD 60 — 17,100/PK-12
315 W 11th St 81003 — 719-549-7100
Dr. Maggie Lopez, supt. — Fax 549-7112
pueblocityschools.us/
Centennial HS — 1,000/9-12
2525 Mountview Dr 81008 — 719-549-7335
Tharyn Mulberry, prin. — Fax 549-7634
Central HS — 1,000/9-12
216 E Orman Ave 81004 — 719-549-7300
Lynn Seifert, prin. — Fax 549-7306
Corwin International Magnet MS — 700/4-8
1500 Lakeview Ave 81004 — 719-549-7400
Julie Shue, prin. — Fax 253-5264
East HS — 900/9-12
9 MacNeil Rd 81001 — 719-549-7222
Chris Tabeling, prin. — Fax 253-5248
Freed MS — 300/6-8
715 W 20th St 81003 — 719-549-7410
Michelle Mann, prin. — Fax 253-5262
Heaton MS — 700/6-8
6 Adair Rd 81001 — 719-549-7420
Mario Romero, prin. — Fax 549-7838
Pitts MS — 300/7-8
29 Lehigh Ave 81005 — 719-549-7430
Karen Ortiz, prin. — Fax 549-7878
Risley MS — 300/6-8
625 N Monument Ave 81001 — 719-549-7440
Charlotte Macaluso, prin. — Fax 549-7926
Roncalli MS — 600/6-8
4202 W State Highway 78 81005 — 719-549-7450
Michael Kovac, prin. — Fax 549-7469
South HS — 1,400/9-12
1801 Hollywood Dr 81005 — 719-549-7255
Aaron Bravo, prin. — Fax 549-7759

Pueblo County SD 70 — 8,500/PK-12
24951 E US Highway 50 81006 — 719-542-0220
C. Edward Smith, supt. — Fax 542-0225
www.district70.org
Pleasant View MS — 300/6-8
23600 Everett Rd 81006 — 719-542-7813
Ronda Rein, prin. — Fax 545-6291
Pueblo County HS — 800/9-12
1050 35th Ln 81006 — 719-948-3351
Terrie Tafoya, prin. — Fax 948-0196
Vineland MS — 200/6-8
1132 36th Ln 81006 — 719-948-3336
Sandy Gibbs, prin. — Fax 948-2323
Other Schools – See Colorado City, Pueblo West, Rye

Colorado State University - Pueblo — Post-Sec.
2200 Bonforte Blvd 81001 — 719-549-2100
IntelliTec College — Post-Sec.
3673 Parker Blvd Ste 250 81008 — 719-542-3181
Parkview Medical Center — Post-Sec.
400 W 16th St 81003 — 719-584-4573
Pueblo Community College — Post-Sec.
900 W Orman Ave 81004 — 719-549-3200
St. Therese Catholic S — 100/PK-10
320 Goodnight Ave 81004 — 719-561-1121
John Brainard, prin. — Fax 561-2252

Pueblo West, Pueblo, Pop. 29,092
Pueblo County SD 70
Supt. — See Pueblo
Liberty Point International S — 500/6-8
484 S Maher Dr 81007 — 719-547-3752
Brian Dilka, prin. — Fax 547-0499
Pueblo West HS — 1,300/9-12
661 W Capistrano Ave 81007 — 719-547-8050
Martha Nogare, prin. — Fax 547-8041
Sky View MS — 600/6-8
1047 S Camino De Bravo 81007 — 719-547-1175
Robert DiPietro, prin. — Fax 647-9667

Rangely, Rio Blanco, Pop. 2,325
Rangely SD RE-4 — 500/PK-12
402 W Main St 81648 — 970-675-2207
Todd Cordrey, supt. — Fax 675-5023
www.rangelyk12.org/
Rangely JSHS — 200/6-12
234 S Jones Ave 81648 — 970-675-2253
Berry Swenson, prin. — Fax 675-5403

Colorado Northwestern Community College — Post-Sec.
500 Kennedy Dr 81648 — 800-562-1105

Ridgway, Ouray, Pop. 910
Ridgway SD R-2 — 400/PK-12
1115 Clinton St 81432 — 970-626-4320
Cheryl Gomez, supt. — Fax 626-4337
www.ridgway.k12.co.us/
Ridgway HS — 100/9-12
1200 Green St 81432 — 970-626-5788
Jim Hobbs, prin. — Fax 626-3249
Ridgway MS — 100/6-8
1200 Green St 81432 — 970-626-5788
Jim Hobbs, prin. — Fax 626-3249

Rifle, Garfield, Pop. 9,029
Garfield SD RE-2 — 4,600/PK-12
839 Whiteriver Ave 81650 — 970-665-7600
Susan Birdsey, supt. — Fax 665-7623
www.garfieldre2.org/
Rifle HS — 600/9-12
1350 Prefontaine Ave 81650 — 970-665-7725
Todd Ellis, prin. — Fax 665-7785
Rifle MS — 800/5-8
753 Railroad Ave 81650 — 970-665-7900
Kevin Marlatt, prin. — Fax 665-7930
Other Schools – See New Castle

Rocky Ford, Otero, Pop. 3,914
Rocky Ford SD R-2 — 900/PK-12
601 S 8th St 81067 — 719-254-7423
Kermit Snyder, supt. — Fax 254-7425
www.rockyfordk12.org
Rocky Ford JSHS — 300/7-12
601 S 8th St 81067 — 719-254-7431
Cindy Cowan, prin. — Fax 254-7436

Rush, El Paso, Pop. 100
Miami-Yoder SD 60 JT — 200/PK-12
420 S Rush Rd 80833 — 719-478-2186
Rick Walter, supt. — Fax 478-5380
www.miamiyoder.org
Miami-Yoder JSHS — 100/6-12
420 S Rush Rd 80833 — 719-478-2186
Sharon Webb, prin. — Fax 478-5380

Rye, Pueblo, Pop. 153
Pueblo County SD 70
Supt. — See Pueblo
Rye HS — 200/9-12
PO Box 10 81069 — 719-489-2271
T.J. Vinci, prin. — Fax 489-2278

Saguache, Saguache, Pop. 479
Mountain Valley SD RE-1 — 100/PK-12
PO Box 127 81149 — 719-655-0268
Corey Doss, supt. — Fax 655-0269
www.valley.k12.co.us
Mountain Valley HS — 50/9-12
PO Box 127 81149 — 719-655-2578
Laura Kelso, prin. — Fax 655-2875
Mountain Valley MS — 50/6-8
PO Box 127 81149 — 719-655-2578
Laura Kelso, prin. — Fax 655-2875

Salida, Chaffee, Pop. 5,163
Salida SD R-32 — 1,100/PK-12
349 E 9th St 81201 — 719-530-5200
Darryl Webb, supt. — Fax 539-6220
www.salida.k12.co.us/
Horizons Exploratory Academy — 50/Alt
349 E 9th St 81201 — 719-530-5252
Rob Thessler, prin. — Fax 539-6220
Salida HS — 300/9-12
26 Jones Ave 81201 — 719-530-5400
Tami Thompson, prin. — Fax 539-2407
Salida MS — 300/5-8
520 Milford St 81201 — 719-530-5300
Rose Ley, prin. — Fax 530-5364

Sanford, Conejos, Pop. 874
Sanford SD 6J — 300/PK-12
PO Box 39 81151 — 719-274-5167
Kevin Edgar M.Ed., supt. — Fax 274-5830
www.sanfordschools.org/
Sanford JSHS — 100/7-12
PO Box 39 81151 — 719-274-5167
David Judd, prin. — Fax 274-5830

San Luis, Costilla, Pop. 618
Centennial SD R-1 — 200/PK-12
PO Box 350 81152 — 719-672-3322
Brian Crowther, supt. — Fax 672-3345
www.centennialschool.net
Centennial HS — 100/9-12
PO Box 350 81152 — 719-672-3322
Curtis Garcia, prin. — Fax 672-3345
Centennial JHS — 50/7-8
PO Box 350 81152 — 719-672-3322
Curtis Garcia, prin. — Fax 672-3345

Seibert, Kit Carson, Pop. 178
Hi-Plains SD R-23
Supt. — See Vona
Hi-Plains JSHS — 100/7-12
PO Box 238 80834 — 970-664-2616
Dale Oliver, prin. — Fax 664-2622

Sheridan, Arapahoe, Pop. 5,532
Sheridan SD 2 — 1,700/PK-12
4000 S Lowell Blvd 80110 — 720-833-6616
Michael Clough, supt. — Fax 833-6650
www.ssd2.org
Sheridan MS — 300/6-8
4107 S Federal Blvd 80110 — 720-833-6988
Ian Wells, prin. — Fax 833-6903
Other Schools – See Denver

Sheridan Lake, Kiowa, Pop. 88
Plainview SD RE-2 — 100/K-12
13997 County Road 71 81071 — 719-729-3331
Jeff Bollinger, supt. — Fax 727-3451
www.plainview.k12.co.us
Plainview JHSH — 50/6-12
13997 County Road 71 81071 — 719-729-3331
Fax 727-4471

Silverton, San Juan, Pop. 625
Silverton SD 1 — 100/K-12
PO Box 128 81433 — 970-387-5543
Kim White, supt. — Fax 387-5791
www.silvertonschool.org
Silverton HS — 50/9-12
PO Box 128 81433 — 970-387-5543
Kim White, admin. — Fax 387-5791
Silverton MS — 50/6-8
PO Box 128 81433 — 970-387-5543
Kim White, prin. — Fax 387-5791

Simla, Elbert, Pop. 614
Big Sandy SD 100J — 300/PK-12
PO Box 68 80835 — 719-541-2292
Steve Wilson, supt. — Fax 541-2186
bigsandy.ppboces.org
Simla JSHS — 100/6-12
PO Box 68 80835 — 719-541-2291
Sammi Swennes, prin. — Fax 541-2443

Springfield, Baca, Pop. 1,423
Springfield SD RE-4 — 300/PK-12
389 Tipton St 81073 — 719-523-6654
Michael Page, supt. — Fax 523-4192
www.springfield.k12.co.us/
Springfield HS — 100/9-12
389 Tipton St 81073 — 719-523-6522
Richard Hargrove, prin. — Fax 523-4361
Springfield JHS — 100/7-8
389 Tipton St 81073 — 719-523-6522
Richard Hargrove, prin. — Fax 523-4361

Steamboat Springs, Routt, Pop. 11,946
Northwest Colorado BOCES — 50/
PO Box 773390 80477 — 970-879-0391
Jane Toothaker, dir. — Fax 879-0442
www.nwboces.org/
Yampa Valley HS — 50/Alt
PO Box 773390 80477 — 970-879-0391
Jane Toothaker, dir.

Steamboat Springs SD RE-2 — 2,200/K-12
325 7th St 80487 — 970-871-3199
Dr. Brad Meeks, supt. — Fax 879-3943
www.sssd.k12.co.us
Steamboat Springs HS — 600/9-12
45 Maple St 80487 — 970-879-1562
Kevin Taulman, prin. — Fax 879-8039
Steamboat Springs MS — 500/6-8
39510 Amethyst St 80487 — 970-879-1058
Tim Bishop, prin. — Fax 870-0368
Yampa Valley HS — Alt
325 7th St 80487 — 970-871-3299
Dan Juba, lead tchr. — Fax 871-3943

Heritage Christian S — 100/K-12
27285 Brandon Cir 80487 — 970-879-1760
David Entwistle, admin. — Fax 879-5511
Whiteman S — 100/9-12
42605 County Road 36 80487 — 970-879-1350
Chris Taylor, head sch — Fax 879-0506

Sterling, Logan, Pop. 14,616
Valley SD RE-1 — 2,400/PK-12
301 Hagen St 80751 — 970-522-0792
Betty Summers M.Ed., supt. — Fax 522-0525
www.re1valleyschools.org/
Sterling HS — 600/9-12
407 W Broadway St 80751 — 970-522-2944
Dianna Chrisman, prin. — Fax 522-1540
Sterling MS — 500/6-8
1177 Pawnee Ave 80751 — 970-522-1041
Robert Hall, prin. — Fax 522-0209
Other Schools – See Iliff

Northeastern Junior College — Post-Sec.
100 College Ave 80751 — 970-521-7000

Strasburg, Adams, Pop. 2,413
Strasburg SD 31J — 1,000/PK-12
56729 Colorado Ave 80136 — 303-622-9211
Edward Vandertook, supt. — Fax 622-9224
www.strasburg31j.com
Hemphill MS — 300/6-8
2100 Wagner St 80136 — 303-622-9213
Skip Harrison, prin. — Fax 622-2613
Strasburg HS — 300/9-12
56729 Colorado Ave 80136 — 303-622-9211
Jeffrey Rasp, prin. — Fax 622-6921

Stratton, Kit Carson, Pop. 658
Stratton SD R-4 — 200/PK-12
219 Illinois Ave 80836 — 719-348-5369
Jeff Durbin, supt. — Fax 348-5555
www.strattonschools.org
Stratton HS — 100/9-12
219 Illinois Ave 80836 — 719-348-5369
Dave Gottmann, prin. — Fax 348-5555
Stratton MS — 50/6-8
219 Illinois Ave 80836 — 719-348-5369
Dave Gottmann, prin. — Fax 348-5555

Swink, Otero, Pop. 607
Swink SD 33 — 400/K-12
PO Box 487 81077 — 719-384-8103
Libby Hiza, supt. — Fax 384-5471
www.swink.k12.co.us/
Swink JSHS — 200/7-12
PO Box 487 81077 — 719-384-8103
Randy Bohlander, prin. — Fax 384-5471

Telluride, San Miguel, Pop. 2,291
Telluride SD R-1 — 500/PK-12
725 W Colorado Ave 81435 — 970-728-6617
Kyle Schumacher, supt. — Fax 728-9490
www.tellurideschool.org

Telluride MSHS 200/7-12
725 W Colorado Ave 81435 970-728-4377
Mike Conran, prin. Fax 728-0257

Telluride Mountain S 100/PK-12
200 San Miguel River Dr 81435 970-728-1969
Joseph Stefani, head sch Fax 369-4412

Thornton, Adams, Pop. 116,276
Adams 12 Five Star SD 42,000/PK-12
1500 E 128th Ave 80241 720-972-4000
Chris Gdowski, supt. Fax 972-4169
www.adams12.org
Bollman Technical Education Center Vo/Tech
9451 Washington St 80229 720-972-5820
Jeff Lund, prin. Fax 972-5869
Century MS 1,100/6-8
13000 Lafayette St 80241 720-972-5240
Howard Holbrook, prin. Fax 972-5279
Horizon HS 1,800/9-12
5321 E 136th Ave 80602 720-972-4400
Pam Smiley, prin. Fax 972-4598
International S at Thornton MS 700/6-8
9451 Hoffman Way 80229 720-972-5160
Jami Miller, prin. Fax 972-5199
Rocky Top MS 1,100/6-8
14150 York St 80602 720-972-2200
Chelsea Behana, prin. Fax 972-2303
Shadow Ridge MS 1,100/6-8
12551 Holly St 80241 720-972-5040
Susie Wickham, prin. Fax 972-5079
Thornton HS 1,800/9-12
9351 Washington St 80229 720-972-4800
Johnny Terrell, prin. Fax 972-4999
Other Schools – See Broomfield, Northglenn, Westminster

Mapleton SD 1
Supt. — See Denver
Academy HS 300/9-12
8970 York St 80229 303-853-1730
Sheri Kangas, dir. Fax 853-1779
Mapleton Early College HS 200/9-12
8980 York St 80229 303-853-1960
James Long, dir. Fax 853-1996
Mapleton Expeditionary S of the Arts 500/7-12
8980 York St 80229 303-853-1270
Doug Seligman, dir. Fax 853-1296
York International S 700/K-12
9200 York St 80229 303-853-1600
Laura Nelson, dir. Fax 853-1656
North Valley S for Young Adults Adult
8990 York St 80229 303-853-1790
Chris Byrd, dir. Fax 853-1798

Empire Beauty School Post-Sec.
3811 E 120th Ave 80233 303-451-5808
Everest College Post-Sec.
9065 Grant St 80229 303-457-2757
HealthONE North Suburban Medical Center Post-Sec.
9191 Grant St 80229 303-451-7800

Trinidad, Las Animas, Pop. 8,973
Trinidad SD 1 1,400/PK-12
215 S Maple St 81082 719-846-3324
Dr. Manuel Rodriguez, supt. Fax 846-2957
www.tsd1.org/
Trinidad HS 400/9-12
816 West St 81082 719-846-2971
Olivia Bachicha, prin. Fax 846-7488
Trinidad MS 300/6-8
614 Park St 81082 719-846-4411
Deana Vachelli, prin. Fax 846-4740

Grace Christian Center S 50/K-12
1001 Obregon St 81082 719-846-6133
Jean Griffis, prin. Fax 846-6133
Trinidad State Junior College Post-Sec.
600 Prospect St 81082 719-846-5011

USAF Academy, El Paso, Pop. 9,062
Academy SD 20
Supt. — See Colorado Springs
Air Academy HS 1,400/9-12
6910 Carlton Dr, 719-234-2400
Toria McGill, prin. Fax 234-2599

United States Air Force Academy Post-Sec.
2304 Cadet Dr Ste 2300, 800-443-9266

Vail, Eagle, Pop. 5,245

Vail Mountain S 300/K-12
3000 Booth Falls Rd 81657 970-476-3850
Fax 476-3860

Vilas, Baca, Pop. 112
Vilas SD RE-5 400/PK-12
PO Box 727 81087 719-523-6738
Reid Straabe, supt. Fax 523-4818
www.vilasschools.org
Vilas Undivided HS 50/7-12
PO Box 727 81087 719-523-6738
Reid Straabe, admin. Fax 523-4818

Vona, Kit Carson, Pop. 104
Hi-Plains SD R-23 100/PK-12
PO Box 9 80861 970-664-2636
Steven McCracken, supt. Fax 664-2283
www.hp-patriots.com/
Other Schools – See Seibert

Walden, Jackson, Pop. 599
North Park SD R-1 200/PK-12
PO Box 798 80480 970-723-3300
Jim Anderson, supt. Fax 723-8486
npsd.schoolfusion.us
North Park JSHS 100/6-12
PO Box 798 80480 970-723-3300
Amy Ward, prin. Fax 723-4702

Walsenburg, Huerfano, Pop. 3,036
Huerfano SD RE-1 600/PK-12
201 E 5th St 81089 719-738-1520
Dawn Olson, supt. Fax 738-3148
huerfanosd.schoolinsites.com
Mall HS 100/9-12
335 W Pine St 81089 719-738-1610
George Purnell, prin. Fax 738-2541

Walsh, Baca, Pop. 543
Walsh SD RE-1 200/PK-12
PO Box 68 81090 719-324-5632
Kyle Hebberd, supt. Fax 324-5426
www.walsheagles.com
Walsh JSHS 100/7-12
PO Box 68 81090 719-324-5221
Tom Meardon, prin. Fax 324-5734

Weldona, Morgan, Pop. 139
Weldon Valley SD RE-20(J) 200/PK-12
911 North Ave 80653 970-645-2411
Robert Petterson M.S., supt. Fax 645-2377
www.weldonvalley.org/
Weldon Valley HS 100/9-12
911 North Ave 80653 970-645-2411
Doug Pfau, prin. Fax 645-2377
Weldon Valley JHS 50/7-8
911 North Ave 80653 970-645-2411
Doug Pfau, prin. Fax 645-2377

Wellington, Larimer, Pop. 6,177
Poudre SD R-1
Supt. — See Fort Collins
Wellington MS 400/6-8
4001 Wilson Ave 80549 970-488-6600
Alicia Durand, prin. Fax 488-6602

Westcliffe, Custer, Pop. 555
Custer County SD 1 500/PK-12
PO Box 730 81252 719-783-2357
Chris Selle, supt. Fax 783-2334
www.custercountyschools.org
Custer County HS 200/9-12
PO Box 730 81252 719-783-2291
Barb Jones, prin. Fax 783-4944
Custer County JHS 100/6-8
PO Box 730 81252 719-783-2291
Barb Jones, prin. Fax 783-4944

Westminster, Adams, Pop. 103,933
Adams 12 Five Star SD
Supt. — See Thornton
Mountain Range HS 2,000/9-12
12500 Huron St 80234 720-972-6300
Julie Enger, prin. Fax 972-6529
Silver Hills MS 1,100/6-8
12400 Huron St 80234 720-972-5000
Julie Evans, prin. Fax 972-5039

Adams County SD 50 10,000/PK-12
6933 Raleigh St 80030 303-428-3511
Dr. Pamela Swanson, supt. Fax 428-2810
www.adams50.org
Hidden Lake HS 300/Alt
7300 Lowell Blvd 80030 303-428-2600
James Steward, prin. Fax 428-2142
Shaw Heights MS 600/6-8
8780 Circle Dr 80031 303-428-9533
Christopher Benisch, prin. Fax 657-3973
Westminster HS 2,300/9-12
6933 Raleigh St 80030 303-657-3980
Michael Lynch, prin. Fax 657-3989
Other Schools – See Denver

Jefferson County SD R-1
Supt. — See Golden
Carle MS 300/7-8
10200 W 100th Ave 80021 303-982-9070
John White, prin. Fax 982-9071
Mandalay MS 400/7-8
9651 Pierce St 80021 303-982-9802
John Schalk, prin. Fax 982-9813
Standley Lake HS 1,500/9-12
9300 W 104th Ave 80021 303-982-3311
Jeff Pierson, prin. Fax 982-3312

Belleview Christian S 300/PK-12
3455 W 83rd Ave 80031 303-427-5459
Dr. Peggy Polson, prin. Fax 426-6768
Cornerstone Christian Academy 300/PK-12
12000 Zuni St 80234 303-451-1421
Larry Zimbelman, prin. Fax 280-0361
DeVry University Post-Sec.
1870 W 122nd Ave 80234 303-280-7400
Front Range Community College Post-Sec.
3645 W 112th Ave 80031 303-404-5000
Hyland Christian S 100/K-12
5255 W 98th Ave 80020 303-466-1673
ITT Technical Institute Post-Sec.
8620 Wolff Ct Ste 100 80031 303-288-4488
LIFE Christian Academy 200/PK-12
11500 Sheridan Blvd 80020 303-438-1260
Bill Strong, admin. Fax 438-1866

Prince Institute Post-Sec.
9051 Harlan St Ste 20 80031 303-427-5292

Weston, Las Animas, Pop. 54
Primero RSD RE-2 200/PK-12
20200 State Highway 12 81091 719-868-2715
Jeff Bollinger, supt. Fax 868-2241
www.primeroschool.org/
Primero JSHS 100/6-12
20200 State Highway 12 81091 719-868-2715
Jeff Bollinger, prin. Fax 868-2241

Wheat Ridge, Jefferson, Pop. 29,601
Jefferson County SD R-1
Supt. — See Golden
Everitt MS 500/7-8
3900 Kipling St 80033 303-982-1580
Jeff Gomez, prin. Fax 982-1581
Wheat Ridge HS 1,300/9-12
9505 W 32nd Ave 80033 303-982-7695
Griff Wirth, prin. Fax 982-7696
Wheat Ridge MS 400/5-8
7101 W 38th Ave 80033 303-982-2833
Warren Blair, prin. Fax 982-2834

Beth Eden Baptist S 200/K-12
2600 Wadsworth Blvd 80033 303-232-2313
Ed Francis, admin. Fax 233-3027

Wiggins, Morgan, Pop. 888
Wiggins SD RE-50(J) 400/PK-12
320 Chapman St 80654 970-483-7762
Steven Neel, supt. Fax 483-6205
www.wiggins50.k12.co.us/
Wiggins MSHS 200/6-12
320 Chapman St 80654 970-483-7762
Trent Kerr, prin. Fax 483-7796

Wiley, Prowers, Pop. 402
Wiley SD RE-13 JT 100/PK-12
PO Box 247 81092 719-829-4806
Dave Eastin, supt. Fax 829-4422
www.wiley.k12.co.us
Wiley S 100/PK-12
PO Box 247 81092 719-829-4806
Michelle Wallace, prin. Fax 829-4805

Windsor, Weld, Pop. 18,391
Weld County SD RE-4 3,900/PK-12
PO Box 609 80550 970-686-8000
Karen Trusler, supt. Fax 686-8001
www.weldre4.k12.co.us/
Severance MS 400/6-8
1801 Avery Plaza St 80550 970-674-5200
Jay Tapia, prin. Fax 674-5201
Windsor HS 1,100/9-12
1100 Main St 80550 970-686-8100
Michelle Scallon, prin. Fax 686-0935
Windsor MS 600/6-8
900 Main St 80550 970-686-8200
Eric Johnson, prin. Fax 686-7122

Woodland Park, Teller, Pop. 7,047
Woodland Park SD RE-2 2,800/PK-12
PO Box 99 80866 719-686-2000
Jed Bowman Ph.D., supt. Fax 687-8408
www.wpsdk12.org/
Woodland Park HS 900/9-12
PO Box 6820 80866 719-686-2067
Del Garrick, prin. Fax 687-3880
Woodland Park MS 600/6-8
PO Box 6790 80866 719-686-2200
John Jamison, prin. Fax 687-8458

Woodrow, Washington, Pop. 20
Woodlin SD R-104 100/PK-12
15400 County Road L 80757 970-386-2223
Rose Cronk, supt. Fax 386-2241
www.woodlinschool.com
Woodlin Undivided HS 50/7-12
15400 County Road L 80757 970-386-2223
Debbie Atwater, prin. Fax 386-2241

Wray, Yuma, Pop. 2,328
Wray SD RD-2 700/PK-12
30222 County Road 35 80758 970-332-5764
Richard Spencer, supt. Fax 332-5773
www.wrayschools.org
Buchanan MS 200/5-8
620 W 7th St 80758 970-332-3600
Kirk Salmela, prin. Fax 332-3356
Wray HS 200/9-12
30074 County Road 35 80758 970-332-3767
Julie Sumpter, prin. Fax 332-4476

Yoder, El Paso, Pop. 40
Edison SD 54 JT 200/PK-12
14550 Edison Rd 80864 719-478-2125
Patrick Bershinsky, supt. Fax 478-3000
www.edison54jt.schoolfusion.us
Edison JSHS 100/6-12
14550 Edison Rd 80864 719-478-2125
Rachel Paul, prin. Fax 478-3000

Yuma, Yuma, Pop. 3,498
Yuma SD - 1 800/PK-12
PO Box 327 80759 970-848-5831
Robert Stannard, supt. Fax 848-2256
www.yumaschools.org
Yuma HS 300/9-12
1000 S Albany St 80759 970-848-5488
Carl Rice, prin. Fax 848-0314
Yuma MS 100/7-8
500 S Elm St 80759 970-848-2000
Jess Buller, prin. Fax 848-4261

CONNECTICUT

CONNECTICUT DEPARTMENT OF EDUCATION
165 Capitol Ave, Hartford 06106-1659
Telephone 860-713-6500
Fax 860-713-7001
Website http://www.sde.ct.gov

Commissioner of Education Stefan Pryor

CONNECTICUT BOARD OF EDUCATION
165 Capitol Ave, Hartford 06106-1659

Chairperson Allan Taylor

REGIONAL EDUCATIONAL SERVICE CENTERS

Area Coop. Educational Services RESC
Craig Edmondson Ed.D., dir. 203-498-6800
350 State St, North Haven 06473 Fax 498-6890
www.aces.org

Capitol Region Education Council RESC
Dr. Bruce Douglas, dir. 860-524-4063
111 Charter Oak Ave Fax 548-9924
Hartford 06106
www.crec.org

Cooperative Educational Services RESC
Evan Pitkoff, dir. 203-365-8803
40 Lindeman Dr, Trumbull 06611 Fax 365-8804
www.ces.k12.ct.us

Eastconn RESC
Paula Colen, dir. 860-455-0707
376 Hartford Tpke, Hampton 06247 Fax 455-8026
www.eastconn.org

Education Connection RESC
Danuta Thibodeau Ph.D., dir. 860-567-0863
PO Box 909, Litchfield 06759 Fax 567-3381
www.educationconnection.org

Learn RESC
Dr. Virginia Seccombe, dir. 860-434-4800
44 Hatchetts Hill Rd Fax 434-4820
Old Lyme 06371
www.learn.k12.ct.us

PUBLIC, PRIVATE AND CATHOLIC SECONDARY SCHOOLS

Ansonia, New Haven, Pop. 18,821

Ansonia SD 2,500/K-12
42 Grove St 06401 203-736-5095
Carol Merlone, supt. Fax 736-5098
www.ansonia.org

Ansonia HS 700/9-12
20 Pulaski Hwy 06401 203-736-5060
Joseph Dobbins, prin. Fax 736-5068

Ansonia MS 400/7-8
115 Howard Ave 06401 203-736-5070
Amy O'Brien, prin. Fax 736-1044

Connecticut Technical HS System
Supt. — See Middletown

O'Brien Technical HS Vo/Tech
141 Prindle Ave 06401 203-732-1800
Lorella Lebouthillier, prin. Fax 735-6236

Avon, Hartford

Avon SD 3,600/PK-12
34 Simsbury Rd 06001 860-404-4700
Gary Mala, supt. Fax 404-4702
www.avon.k12.ct.us

Avon HS 1,100/9-12
510 W Avon Rd 06001 860-404-4740
Jason Beaudin, prin. Fax 404-4743

Avon MS 600/7-8
375 W Avon Rd 06001 860-404-4770
Marco Famiglietti, prin. Fax 404-4773

Avon Old Farms S 400/9-12
500 Old Farms Rd 06001 860-404-4100
Kenneth LaRocque, hdmstr. Fax 404-4135

Baltic, New London, Pop. 1,192

Academy of the Holy Family 100/9-12
PO Box 691 06330 860-822-9272
Sr. Loreto Beckstein, prin. Fax 822-1318

Beacon Falls, New Haven

Regional SD 16
Supt. — See Prospect

Woodland Regional HS 800/9-12
135 Back Rimmon Rd 06403 203-881-5551
Kurt Ogren, prin. Fax 881-2015

Berlin, Hartford

Berlin SD 3,100/PK-12
238 Kensington Rd 06037 860-828-6581
David B. Erwin, supt. Fax 829-0832
www.berlinschools.org

Berlin HS 1,000/9-12
139 Patterson Way 06037 860-828-6577
Francis Kennedy, prin. Fax 829-2169

McGee MS 700/6-8
899 Norton Rd 06037 860-828-0323
Scott Ratchford Ph.D., prin. Fax 828-0676

Bethany, New Haven

Regional SD 5
Supt. — See Woodbridge

Amity Regional MS 400/7-8
190 Luke Hill Rd 06524 203-393-3102
Richard Dellinger, prin. Fax 393-0583

Bethel, Fairfield, Pop. 9,266

Bethel SD 2,900/PK-12
PO Box 253 06801 203-794-8601
Dr. Kevin Smith, supt. Fax 794-8723
www.bethel.k12.ct.us

Bethel HS 1,000/9-12
300 Whittlesey Dr 06801 203-794-8600
Christopher Troetti, prin. Fax 778-7448

Bethel MS 700/6-8
600 Whittlesey Dr 06801 203-794-8670
Derek Muharem, prin. Fax 830-7318

Bethlehem, Litchfield

Woodhall S 50/9-12
PO Box 550 06751 203-266-7788
Matthew Woodhall, head sch Fax 266-5896

Bloomfield, Hartford, Pop. 7,200

Bloomfield SD 1,700/PK-12
1133 Blue Hills Ave 06002 860-769-4200
James Thompson, supt. Fax 769-4215
www.blmfld.org

Arace MS 300/7-8
390 Park Ave 06002 860-286-2622
Trevor Ellis, prin. Fax 242-0347

Bloomfield HS 600/9-12
5 Huckleberry Ln 06002 860-286-2630
Sam Galloway, prin. Fax 242-9491

Global Experience Magnet S 100/6-12
44 Griffin Rd S 06002 860-769-6600
Sabin Loveland, prin. Fax 769-6605

Capitol Region Education Council RESC
Supt. — See Hartford

Academy of Aerospace & Engineering 6-8
1289 Blue Hills Ave 06002 860-243-0857
Delores Bolton, prin. Fax 286-2842

Metropolitan Learning Center 700/6-12
1551 Blue Hills Ave 06002 860-242-7834
Sasha Douglas, prin. Fax 242-0732

Bolton, Tolland

Bolton SD 900/PK-12
72 Brandy St 06043 860-643-1569
Joseph Wood, supt. Fax 647-8452
www.boltonpublicschools.com/

Bolton HS 300/9-12
72 Brandy St 06043 860-643-2768
Joseph Maselli, prin. Fax 645-8374

Holy Seed Christian Academy 50/K-12
104 Notch Rd 06043 860-533-9483
Henrietta Creighton, admin. Fax 649-8391

Branford, New Haven, Pop. 27,603

Branford SD 3,400/PK-12
1111 Main St 06405 203-488-7276
Hamlet Hernandez, supt. Fax 315-3505
www.branfordschools.org/

Branford HS 1,100/9-12
185 E Main St 06405 203-488-7291
Lee Panagoulias, prin. Fax 315-6740

Walsh IS 1,000/5-8
185 Damascus Rd 06405 203-488-8317
Robin Goeler, prin. Fax 481-2785

Branford Hall Career Institute Post-Sec.
1 Summit Pl 06405 203-488-2525

Porter and Chester Institute Post-Sec.
221 W Main St 06405 203-315-1060

Bridgeport, Fairfield, Pop. 139,433

Bridgeport SD 18,100/PK-12
45 Lyon Ter Rm 203 06604 203-275-1000
Paul Vallas, supt. Fax 576-8488
www.bridgeportedu.com

Bassick HS 1,200/9-12
1181 Fairfield Ave 06605 203-576-7350
Wayne Alexander, prin. Fax 576-7736

Bridgeport Learning Center 50/Alt
280 Tesiny Ave 06606 203-576-8460
Marilyn Earle, prin. Fax 576-7229

Bridgeport Regional-Aquaculture S Vo/Tech
60 Saint Stephens Rd 06605 203-576-7608
John Curtis, dir. Fax 337-0168

Central HS 2,300/9-12
1 Lincoln Blvd 06606 203-576-7377
Stephen Anderson, prin. Fax 337-0173

Harding HS 1,400/9-12
1734 Central Ave 06610 203-275-2751
Dr. Victor Black, prin. Fax 337-0177

Make the Grade Opportunity S 50/Alt
160 Iranistan Ave 06604 203-275-2192
Eric Graf, prin. Fax 339-5987

Connecticut Technical HS System
Supt. — See Middletown

Bullard-Havens Technical HS Vo/Tech
500 Palisade Ave 06610 203-579-6333
Viviana Santana, prin. Fax 579-6904

Bridgeport Hospital Post-Sec.
267 Grant St 06610 203-384-3464

Bridgeport Hospital School of Nursing Post-Sec.
200 Mill Hill Ave 06610 203-384-3022

Housatonic Community College Post-Sec.
900 Lafayette Blvd 06604 203-332-5000

Kolbe Cathedral HS 300/9-12
33 Calhoun Pl 06604 203-335-2554
Jo Anne Jakab, prin. Fax 335-2556

Leon Institute of Hair Design Post-Sec.
111 Wall St 06604 203-333-1465

New England Tractor Trailer Training Sch Post-Sec.
510 Barnum Ave Ste 4 06608 203-368-9069

St. Vincent's College Post-Sec.
2800 Main St 06606 203-576-5235

University of Bridgeport Post-Sec.
126 Park Ave 06604 800-392-3582

Bristol, Hartford, Pop. 59,288

Bristol SD 7,400/PK-12
PO Box 450 06011 860-584-7000
Ellen W. Solek Ed.D., supt. Fax 584-7611
www.bristol.k12.ct.us

Bristol Central HS 1,300/9-12
PO Box 700 06011 860-584-7732
Peter Wininger, prin. Fax 584-7713

Bristol Eastern HS 1,400/9-12
PO Box 580 06011 860-584-7856
Steven Wysowski, prin. Fax 584-3897

Chippins Hill MS 900/6-8
551 Peacedale St 06010 860-584-3881
Catherine Carbone, prin. Fax 584-4833

Northeast MS 600/6-8
530 Stevens St 06010 860-584-7839
Robert Garry, prin. Fax 584-7837

Bristol Adult Education Adult
210 Redstone Hill Rd 06010 860-584-7865
Maria Groody, dir. Fax 584-4898

Connecticut Technical HS System
Supt. — See Middletown
Bristol Technical Education Center Vo/Tech
431 Minor St 06010 860-584-8433
Joyce Mowery, dir. Fax 584-0795

St. Paul Catholic HS 300/9-12
1001 Stafford Ave 06010 860-584-0911
Cary Dupont, pres. Fax 585-8815

Broad Brook, Hartford, Pop. 3,997
East Windsor SD
Supt. — See East Windsor
East Windsor MS 400/5-8
38 Main St 06016 860-623-4488
James Slattery, prin. Fax 654-1915

Brookfield, Fairfield
Brookfield SD 2,900/PK-12
PO Box 5194 06804 203-775-7620
Anthony Bivona, supt. Fax 740-9008
www.brookfield.k12.ct.us
Brookfield HS 1,000/9-12
45 Long Meadow Hill Rd 06804 203-775-7725
Joseph Palumbo, prin. Fax 775-7773
Whisconier MS 900/5-8
17 W Whisconier Rd 06804 203-775-7710
Deane Renda, prin. Fax 775-7615

Brooklyn, Windham, Pop. 976
Brooklyn SD 900/PK-8
119 Gorman Rd 06234 860-774-9153
Louise Berry J.D., supt. Fax 774-6938
www.brooklynschools.org/
Brooklyn MS 400/5-8
119 Gorman Rd 06234 860-774-9153
Alan Yanku, prin. Fax 774-6938

Burlington, Hartford
Regional SD 10 2,800/PK-12
24 Lyon Rd 06013 860-673-2538
Alan Beitman, supt. Fax 673-7534
www.region10ct.org
Har-Bur MS 900/5-8
26 Lyon Rd 06013 860-673-6163
Kenneth Smith, prin. Fax 673-3481
Mills HS 800/9-12
26 Lyon Rd 06013 860-673-0423
Pamela Lazaroski, prin. Fax 673-9128

Canterbury, Windham
Canterbury SD 500/PK-8
45 Westminster Rd 06331 860-546-6950
Richard Paskiewicz, supt. Fax 546-6423
www.canterburypublicschools.org/
Baldwin MS 200/5-8
45 Westminster Rd 06331 860-546-9421
Brian Tedeschi, prin. Fax 546-6289

Central Village, Windham
Plainfield SD
Supt. — See Plainfield
Plainfield HS 800/9-12
PO Box 218 06332 860-564-6422
James Worth, prin. Fax 564-2116

Chaplin, Windham
Regional SD 11 300/7-12
304 Parish Hill Rd 06235 860-455-9306
Keneth Henrici, supt. Fax 455-1263
www.parishhill.org/
Parish Hill JSHS 300/7-12
304 Parish Hill Rd 06235 860-455-9584
Dori Smith, prin. Fax 455-9081

Cheshire, New Haven, Pop. 25,684
Cheshire SD 4,800/PK-12
29 Main St 06410 203-250-2420
Greg Florio Ed.D., supt. Fax 250-2453
www.cheshire.k12.ct.us/
Cheshire HS 1,500/9-12
525 S Main St 06410 203-250-2511
Jeffrey Solan, prin. Fax 250-2563
Dodd MS 800/7-8
100 Park Pl 06410 203-272-3249
Donald Wailonis, prin. Fax 250-7614

Cheshire Academy 400/8-12
10 Main St 06410 203-272-5396
Dr. Gerald Larson, admin. Fax 250-7209

Clinton, Middlesex, Pop. 3,326
Clinton SD 2,000/PK-12
137B Glenwood Rd 06413 860-664-6500
Jack Cross, supt. Fax 664-6580
www.clintonpublic.org
Eliot MS 500/6-8
69 Fairy Dell Rd 06413 860-664-6503
Linda Tucker, prin. Fax 664-6583
Morgan S 600/9-12
27 Killingworth Tpke 06413 860-664-6504
Keri Hagness, prin. Fax 664-6584

Colchester, New London, Pop. 4,696
Colchester SD 3,100/PK-12
127 Norwich Ave Ste 202 06415 860-537-7260
Jeffry Mathieu, supt. Fax 537-1252
www.colchesterct.org/
Bacon Academy 1,000/9-12
611 Norwich Ave 06415 860-537-2378
Jeffry Mathieu, prin. Fax 537-5410
Johnston MS 700/6-8
360 Norwich Ave 06415 860-537-2313
Christopher Bennett, prin. Fax 537-6258

Collinsville, Hartford, Pop. 3,705
Canton SD 1,800/PK-12
4 Market St Ste 100 06019 860-693-7704
Kevin Case, supt. Fax 693-7706
www.cantonschools.org
Canton HS 500/9-12
76 Simonds Ave 06019 860-693-7707
Gary Gula, prin. Fax 693-7812
Canton MS 300/7-8
76 Simonds Ave 06019 860-693-7712
Joseph Scheideler, prin. Fax 693-7812

Coventry, Tolland, Pop. 10,063
Coventry SD 1,800/PK-12
1700 Main St 06238 860-742-7317
David Petrone Ph.D., supt. Fax 742-4567
www.coventrypublicschools.org/
Coventry HS 600/9-12
78 Ripley Hill Rd 06238 860-742-7346
Michele Mullaly, prin. Fax 742-4591
Hale MS 500/6-8
1776 Main St 06238 860-742-7334
Dena DeJulius, prin. Fax 742-4565

Cromwell, Middlesex
Cromwell SD 2,000/PK-12
9 Mann Memorial Dr 06416 860-632-4830
Dr. Matt Bisceglia, supt. Fax 632-4865
www.cromwell.k12.ct.us/
Cromwell HS 600/9-12
1 Donald Harris Dr 06416 860-632-4841
Frances DiFiore, prin. Fax 613-3363
Cromwell MS 500/6-8
6 Mann Memorial Dr 06416 860-632-4853
John Maloney, prin. Fax 632-4863

Holy Apostles College and Seminary Post-Sec.
33 Prospect Hill Rd 06416 860-632-3010
Lincoln Technical Institute Post-Sec.
106 Sebethe Dr 06416 860-613-3350

Danbury, Fairfield, Pop. 77,029
Connecticut Technical HS System
Supt. — See Middletown
Abbott Technical HS Vo/Tech
21 Hayestown Ave 06811 203-797-4460
Jerry Salese, prin. Fax 797-4382

Danbury SD 10,200/PK-12
63 Beaver Brook Rd 06810 203-797-4701
Sal Pascavella Ed.D., supt. Fax 830-6560
www.danbury.k12.ct.us
Alternative Center for Excellence 100/Alt
26 Locust Ave 06810 203-797-4786
Linda Schreiner, prin. Fax 830-6544
Broadview MS 1,100/6-8
72 Hospital Ave 06810 203-797-4861
Edward Robbs, prin. Fax 790-2856
Danbury HS 2,900/9-12
43 Clapboard Ridge Rd 06811 203-797-4803
Gary Bocaccio, prin. Fax 797-4730
Rogers Park MS 1,100/6-8
21 Memorial Dr 06810 203-797-4880
Patricia Joaquim, prin. Fax 790-2029

Danbury Hospital Post-Sec.
24 Hospital Ave 06810 203-797-7210
Immaculate HS 300/9-12
73 Southern Blvd 06810 203-744-1510
Joe Carmen, prin. Fax 744-1275
Paul Mitchell the School Post-Sec.
109 South St 06810 203-744-0900
Ridley-Lowell Business & Technical Inst Post-Sec.
44 Shelter Rock Rd 06810 203-797-0551
Western Connecticut State University Post-Sec.
181 White St 06810 203-837-8200
Wooster S 400/PK-12
91 Miry Brook Rd 06810 203-830-3900
Matt Byrnes, head sch Fax 790-7147

Danielson, Windham, Pop. 3,941
Connecticut Technical HS System
Supt. — See Middletown
Ellis Technical HS Vo/Tech
613 Upper Maple St 06239 860-774-8511
Dr. Brian Mignault, prin. Fax 779-1563

Killingly SD 2,700/PK-12
PO Box 210 06239 860-779-6600
Kevin Farr, supt. Fax 779-3798
www.killinglyschools.org
Other Schools – See Dayville

Quinebaug Valley Community College Post-Sec.
742 Upper Maple St 06239 860-412-7200

Darien, Fairfield, Pop. 20,500
Darien SD 4,800/PK-12
PO Box 1167 06820 203-656-7412
Dr. Stephen Falcone, supt. Fax 656-3052
www.darienps.org/boe/default.php
Darien HS 1,300/9-12
80 High School Ln 06820 203-655-3981
Dan Haron, prin. Fax 656-3631
Middlesex MS 1,200/6-8
204 Hollow Tree Ridge Rd 06820 203-655-2518
Debi Boccanfuso, prin. Fax 655-1627

Dayville, Windham
Killingly SD
Supt. — See Danielson
Killingly HS 800/9-12
226 Putnam Pike 06241 860-779-6620
Fax 774-0846
Killingly IS 800/5-8
1599 Upper Maple St 06241 860-779-6700
Steve Rioux, prin. Fax 779-9639

Deep River, Middlesex, Pop. 2,444
Regional SD 4 1,000/7-12
PO Box 187 06417 860-526-2417
Dr. Ruth Levy, supt. Fax 526-5469
www.reg4.k12.ct.us
Valley Regional HS 600/9-12
256 Kelsey Hill Rd 06417 860-526-5328
Ian Neviaser, prin. Fax 526-8123
Winthrop MS 400/7-8
PO Box 187 06417 860-526-9546
David Russell, prin. Fax 526-3721

Derby, New Haven, Pop. 12,664
Derby SD 1,400/PK-12
PO Box 373 06418 203-736-5027
Matthew Conway, supt. Fax 736-5031
www.derbyps.org/
Derby HS 400/9-12
8 Nutmeg Ave 06418 203-736-5032
Francis Thompson, prin. Fax 736-5031
Derby MS 200/6-8
10 Nutmeg Ave 06418 203-736-1426
Sally Bonina, prin. Fax 736-3234

Durham, Middlesex, Pop. 2,900
Regional SD 13 2,000/PK-12
135A Pickett Ln 06422 860-349-7200
Susan Viccaro, supt. Fax 349-7203
www.rsd13ct.org/
Coginchaug Regional HS 600/9-12
PO Box 280 06422 860-349-7215
Andre Hauser, prin. Fax 349-7136
Strong MS 400/7-8
PO Box 435 06422 860-349-7222
Scott Sadinsky, prin. Fax 349-7225

Lake Grove School at Durham Post-Sec.
459R Wallingford Rd 06422 860-349-3467

East Granby, Hartford
East Granby SD 900/PK-12
PO Box 674 06026 860-653-6486
Dr. Christine Mahoney, supt. Fax 413-9075
www.eastgranby.k12.ct.us/
East Granby HS 300/9-12
95 S Main St 06026 860-653-2541
Melissa Bavaro-Grande, prin. Fax 413-9092
East Granby MS 200/6-8
95 S Main St 06026 860-653-7113
Fax 413-9126

East Hampton, Middlesex, Pop. 2,637
East Hampton SD 2,000/PK-12
94 Main St 06424 860-365-4000
Diane Dugas, supt. Fax 365-4004
www.easthamptonps.org
East Hampton HS 600/9-12
15 N Maple St 06424 860-365-4030
Linda Berry, prin. Fax 365-4034
East Hampton MS 500/6-8
19 Childs Rd 06424 860-365-4060
Tracy Barber, prin. Fax 365-4064

East Hartford, Hartford, Pop. 50,077
Capitol Region Education Council RESC
Supt. — See Hartford
Two Rivers Magnet MS 700/6-8
337 E River Dr 06108 860-290-5320
Jean Privitera, prin. Fax 509-3609

East Hartford SD 7,100/PK-12
1110 Main St 06108 860-622-5107
Nathan Quesnel M.A., supt. Fax 622-5119
www.easthartford.org
CT International Baccalaureate Academy 200/9-12
857 Forbes St 06118 860-622-5560
Art Arpin, prin. Fax 622-5555
East Hartford HS 1,700/9-12
869 Forbes St 06118 860-622-5200
Matt Ryan, prin. Fax 622-5223
East Hartford MS 1,000/6-8
777 Burnside Ave 06108 860-622-5600
Anthony Menard, prin. Fax 622-5619
Stevens Alternative HS 200/Alt
40 Butternut Dr 06118 860-622-5999
John Karzar, prin. Fax 622-5990

Connecticut Training Center Post-Sec.
1137 Main St 06108 860-291-0250
Goodwin College Post-Sec.
1 Riverside Dr 06118 860-528-4111
New Testament Baptist Church S 200/PK-12
111 Ash St 06108 860-290-6696
Dr. Michael Stoddard, prin. Fax 290-6698
Stone Academy Post-Sec.
745 Burnside Ave 06108 860-569-0618

East Haven, New Haven, Pop. 28,923
East Haven SD 3,200/K-12
35 Wheelbarrow Ln 06513 203-468-3261
Anthony Serio, supt. Fax 468-3918
www.east haven.k12.ct.us
East Haven Academy 300/3-8
67 Hudson St 06512 203-468-3219
Marianne Johnson, prin. Fax 468-3961
East Haven HS 900/9-12
35 Wheelbarrow Ln 06513 203-468-3267
Vincent DeNuzzo, prin. Fax 468-3818
Melillo MS 700/6-8
67 Hudson St 06512 203-468-3227
Matthew Espinosa, prin. Fax 468-3866

East Lyme, New London
East Lyme SD 3,000/PK-12
PO Box 176 06333 860-739-3966
James Lombardo Ed.D., supt. Fax 739-1215
www.eastlymeschools.org
East Lyme HS 1,200/9-12
PO Box 210 06333 860-739-6946
Dr. John Sullivan, prin. Fax 739-1241
Other Schools – See Niantic

Easton, Fairfield
Easton SD 1,100/PK-8
PO Box 500 06612 203-261-2513
Bernard Josefsberg Ed.D., supt. Fax 261-7936
www.er9.org
Keller MS 400/6-8
360 Sport Hill Rd 06612 203-268-8651
Susan Kaplan, prin. Fax 268-6105

Redding SD 1,200/K-8
PO Box 500 06612 203-261-2513
Bernard Josefsberg Ed.D., supt. Fax 261-4549
www.er9.org
Other Schools – See West Redding

Regional SD 9 1,000/9-12
PO Box 500 06612 203-261-2513
Bernard Josefsberg Ed.D., supt. Fax 261-4549
www.er9.org
Other Schools – See Redding

East Windsor, Hartford
East Windsor SD 1,300/PK-12
70 S Main St 06088 860-623-3346
Dr. Teresa Kane, supt. Fax 292-6817
www.eastwindsorschools.org
East Windsor HS 400/9-12
76 S Main St 06088 860-623-3361
Liam O'Reilly, prin. Fax 623-7197
Other Schools – See Broad Brook

Lincoln Technical Institute Post-Sec.
97 Newberry Rd 06088 800-243-4242

Ellington, Tolland
Ellington SD 2,700/PK-12
PO Box 179 06029 860-896-2300
Stephen Cullinan, supt. Fax 896-2312
www.ellingtonschools.org
Ellington HS 800/9-12
PO Box 149 06029 860-896-2352
Neil Rinaldi, prin. Fax 896-2366
Ellington MS 400/7-8
46 Middle Butcher Rd 06029 860-896-2339
David Pearson, prin. Fax 896-2351

Enfield, Hartford, Pop. 45,500
Capitol Region Education Council RESC
Supt. — See Hartford
Public Safety Academy 300/6-12
117 Post Office Rd 06082 860-253-0274
Dr. Leslie Torres-Rodriguez, prin. Fax 741-0841

Enfield SD 3,800/PK-12
27 Shaker Rd 06082 860-253-6500
Dr. Jeffrey Schumann, supt. Fax 253-6510
www.enfieldschools.org
Enfield HS 800/9-12
1264 Enfield St 06082 860-253-5540
Jill Krieger, prin. Fax 253-5555
Fermi HS 1,100/9-12
124 N Maple St 06082 860-763-8800
Paul Newton, prin. Fax 763-8810
Kennedy MS 800/6-8
155 Raffia Rd 06082 860-763-8855
Sarah Collins, prin. Fax 763-8888

Asnuntuck Community College Post-Sec.
170 Elm St 06082 860-253-3000
Porter and Chester Institute Post-Sec.
132 Weymouth Rd 06082 860-741-2561

Fairfield, Fairfield, Pop. 54,400
Fairfield SD 10,100/PK-12
PO Box 320189, 203-255-8371
David Title, supt. Fax 255-8245
www.fairfield.k12.ct.us
Fairfield Ludlowe HS 1,500/9-12
785 Unquowa Rd, 203-255-7201
Greg Hatzis, hdmstr. Fax 255-7213
Fairfield Warde HS 1,300/9-12
755 Melville Ave, 203-255-8449
James Coyne, hdmstr. Fax 255-8284
Fairfield Woods MS 700/6-8
1115 Fairfield Woods Rd, 203-255-8334
Gary Rosato, prin. Fax 255-8210
Ludlowe MS 1,000/6-8
689 Unquowa Rd, 203-255-8345
Glenn Mackno, prin. Fax 255-8214
Tomlinson MS 800/6-8
200 Unquowa Rd, 203-255-8336
Connee Dawson, prin. Fax 255-8211

Fairfield College Prep S 900/9-12
1073 N Benson Rd, 203-254-4200
Dr. Robert Perrotta, prin. Fax 254-4108
Fairfield University Post-Sec.
1073 N Benson Rd, 203-254-4000
Notre Dame HS 500/9-12
220 Jefferson St, 203-372-6521
Christopher Cipriano, prin. Fax 374-4167
Sacred Heart University Post-Sec.
5151 Park Ave, 203-371-7999

Falls Village, Litchfield, Pop. 534
Regional SD 1 500/9-12
246 Warren Tpke 06031 860-824-0855
Patricia Chamberlain, supt. Fax 824-1271
www.region1schools.org
Housatonic Valley Regional HS 500/9-12
246 Warren Tpke 06031 860-824-5123
Dr. Gretchen Foster-Mosca, prin. Fax 824-5419

Farmington, Hartford, Pop. 2,500
Farmington SD 4,100/PK-12
1 Monteith Dr 06032 860-673-8268
Kathleen Greider, supt. Fax 673-8224
www.fpsct.org
Farmington HS 1,300/9-12
10 Monteith Dr 06032 860-673-2514
Dr. Timothy Breslin, prin. Fax 673-7284
Robbins MS 700/7-8
20 Wolf Pit Rd 06032 860-677-2683
Ted Donahue, prin. Fax 676-0697

Miss Porter's S 300/9-12
60 Main St 06032 860-409-3500
Katherine Windsor, hdmstr. Fax 409-3525
Tunxis Community College Post-Sec.
271 Scott Swamp Rd 06032 860-255-3500
University of Connecticut Health Center Post-Sec.
263 Farmington Ave 06030 860-679-2000

Gales Ferry, New London, Pop. 1,137
Ledyard SD
Supt. — See Ledyard
Ledyard MS 400/7-8
1860 Route 12 06335 860-464-0200
Joseph Chella, prin. Fax 464-2155

Glastonbury, Hartford, Pop. 27,901
Glastonbury SD 6,800/PK-12
PO Box 191 06033 860-652-7961
Dr. Alan Bookman, supt. Fax 652-7982
www.glastonburyus.org
Glastonbury HS 2,200/9-12
330 Hubbard St 06033 860-652-7200
Matthew Dunbar, prin. Fax 652-7267
Smith MS 1,100/7-8
216 Addison Rd 06033 860-652-7040
Donna Schilke, prin. Fax 652-4450

Granby, Hartford
Granby SD 2,200/PK-12
15B N Granby Rd 06035 860-844-5250
Alan Addley, supt. Fax 844-6081
www.granby.k12.ct.us
Granby Memorial HS 800/9-12
315 Salmon Brook St 06035 860-844-3014
Mary Jocelyn-Gadd, prin. Fax 844-3026
Granby Memorial MS 400/7-8
321 Salmon Brook St 06035 860-844-3029
Dr. Mark Foley, prin. Fax 844-3039

Greens Farms, Fairfield

Greens Farms Academy 700/K-12
PO Box 998, 203-256-0717
Janet Hartwell, hdmstr. Fax 256-7501

Greenwich, Fairfield, Pop. 12,646
Greenwich SD 8,900/K-12
290 Greenwich Ave 06830 203-625-7400
Dr. William McKersie, supt. Fax 618-9379
www.greenwich.k12.ct.us
Central MS 600/6-8
9 Indian Rock Ln 06830 203-661-8500
Shelley Somers, prin. Fax 661-2576
Greenwich HS 2,700/9-12
10 Hillside Rd 06830 203-625-8000
Chris Winters, hdmstr. Fax 863-8888
Western MS 500/6-8
1 Western Junior Hwy 06830 203-531-5700
Terry Starr-Klein, prin. Fax 531-5220
Other Schools – See Riverside

Brunswick S 900/PK-12
100 Maher Ave 06830 203-625-5800
Thomas Philip, hdmstr. Fax 625-5889
Convent of Sacred Heart S 700/PK-12
1177 King St 06831 203-531-6500
Pamela Hayes, hdmstr. Fax 531-5206
Eagle Hill S 300/K-12
45 Glenville Rd 06831 203-622-9240
Marjorie Castro, head sch Fax 622-0914
Greenwich Academy 800/PK-12
200 N Maple Ave 06830 203-625-8900
Molly King, head sch Fax 869-4921
Stanwich S 400/PK-10
257 Stanwich Rd 06830 203-542-0000
Patricia Young, hdmstr. Fax 542-0025

Griswold, See Jewett City
Griswold SD 2,000/PK-12
211 Slater Ave 06351 860-376-7600
Paul Smith, supt. Fax 376-2071
www.griswoldpublicschools.org/
Griswold Alternative S Alt
1553 Glasgo Rd 06351 860-376-9129
Madeline Illinger, prin. Fax 376-7669
Griswold HS 700/9-12
267 Slater Ave 06351 860-376-7640
Mark Frizzell Ph.D., prin. Fax 376-7684
Griswold MS 600/5-8
211 Slater Ave 06351 860-376-7630
Paul Berkel, prin. Fax 376-7631

Groton, New London, Pop. 9,886
Connecticut Technical HS System
Supt. — See Middletown
Grasso Technical HS Vo/Tech
189 Fort Hill Rd 06340 860-448-0220
Scott Zito, prin. Fax 446-9895

Groton SD
Supt. — See Mystic
Fitch HS 1,300/9-12
101 Groton Long Point Rd 06340 860-449-7200
Joseph Arcarese, prin. Fax 449-7255
Fitch MS 400/6-8
PO Box K 06340 860-449-5620
Robert Pendolphi, prin. Fax 449-5623
West Side MS 200/6-8
250 Brandegee Ave 06340 860-449-5630
John Jones, prin. Fax 449-5628

Connecticut Center for Massage Therapy Post-Sec.
1154 Poquonnock Rd 06340 877-295-2268
University of Connecticut Post-Sec.
1084 Shennecossett Rd 06340 860-405-9000

Guilford, New Haven, Pop. 19,848
Guilford SD 3,700/PK-12
PO Box 367 06437 203-453-8200
Paul Freeman Ed.D., supt. Fax 453-8211
www.guilford.k12.ct.us/
Adams MS 600/7-8
233 Church St 06437 203-453-2755
Catherine Walker, prin. Fax 453-8446
Guilford HS 1,100/9-12
605 New England Rd 06437 203-453-2741
Rick Misenti, prin. Fax 453-6768

Hamden, New Haven, Pop. 52,600
Connecticut Technical HS System
Supt. — See Middletown
Whitney Technical HS Vo/Tech
71 Jones Rd 06514 203-397-4031
Bridget Heston, prin. Fax 397-4129

Hamden SD 6,100/PK-12
60 Putnam Ave 06517 203-407-2000
Fran Rabinowitz, supt. Fax 407-2001
www.hamden.org
Hamden HS 1,900/9-12
2040 Dixwell Ave 06514 203-407-2040
Gary Highsmith, prin. Fax 407-2041
Hamden MS 900/7-8
2623 Dixwell Ave 06518 203-407-3140
Dan Levy, prin. Fax 407-3141
Peck Alternative S 200/PK-PK, 7-
35 Hillfield Rd 06518 203-407-2010
Valerie Coppola, admin. Fax 407-5861

Eli Whitney Tech. High School Post-Sec.
71 Jones Rd 06514 203-397-4031
Hamden Hall Country Day S 600/PK-12
1108 Whitney Ave 06517 203-752-2600
Robert Izzo, hdmstr. Fax 752-2651
Lincoln Technical Institute Post-Sec.
109 Sanford St 06514 203-287-7300
Paier College of Art Post-Sec.
20 Gorham Ave 06514 203-287-3031
Quinnipiac University Post-Sec.
275 Mount Carmel Ave 06518 203-582-8200
Sacred Heart Academy 500/9-12
265 Benham St 06514 203-288-2309
Sr. Maureen Flynn, prin. Fax 230-9680
Sawyer School Post-Sec.
1125 Dixwell Ave 06514 203-865-2900
West Woods Christian Academy 100/PK-12
2105 State St 06517 203-562-9922
William Kane, prin. Fax 786-4730

Hartford, Hartford, Pop. 121,829
Capitol Region Education Council RESC 3,700/
111 Charter Oak Ave 06106 860-524-4063
Dr. Bruce Douglas, dir. Fax 548-9924
www.crec.org
Academy of Aerospace & Engineering 9-12
15 Vernon St 06106 860-757-6300
Paul Brenton, prin. Fax 757-6399
Greater Hartford Academy of Math/Science 100/9-12
15 Vernon St 06106 860-757-6300
Paul Benton, prin. Fax 757-6399
Greater Hartford Academy of the Arts 400/9-12
15 Vernon St 06106 860-757-6300
Jeffrey Ostroff, prin. Fax 757-6382
Greater Hartford Academy of the Arts MS 6-8
140 Huyshope Ave 06106 860-724-0685
Bo Ryan, prin.
Two Rivers Magnet HS 9-12
160 Huyshope Ave 06106 860-422-7095
Robert McCain, prin.
Other Schools – See Bloomfield, East Hartford, Enfield, Windsor

Connecticut Technical HS System
Supt. — See Middletown
Aero Tech HS Vo/Tech
500 Lindbergh Dr 06114 860-566-1234
Prince Technical HS Vo/Tech
401 Flatbush Ave 06106 860-951-7112
William Chaffin, prin. Fax 951-1529

Hartford SD 20,200/PK-12
960 Main St 06103 860-695-8000
Dr. Christina Kishimoto, supt. Fax 722-6161
www.hartfordschools.org
Asian Studies Academy 300/3-8
215 South St 06114 860-695-3400
Stacy McCann, prin. Fax 956-9993
Bulkeley Lower HS 700/9-10
300 Wethersfield Ave 06114 860-695-1000
Oscar Padua, prin. Fax 247-3491
Bulkeley Upper HS 600/11-12
300 Wethersfield Ave 06114 860-695-1000
Gayle Allen-Greene, prin. Fax 247-3491
Capital Preparatory Magnet S 300/PK-12
1304 Main St 06103 860-695-9800
Steven Perry, prin. Fax 722-8520
Culinary Arts Academy 200/9-12
415 Granby St 06112 860-695-1733
Dr. Matthew Conway, prin.
Fox CommPact Upper S 200/5-8
395 Lyme St 06112 860-695-3600
Marjorie Jackson, prin.
Greater Hartford Classical Magnet S 700/6-12
85 Woodland St 06105 860-695-9100
James Motes, prin. Fax 722-6449
Hartford Journalism and Media Academy 200/9-12
415 Granby St 06112 860-695-1818
Elaine Papas, prin. Fax 722-6432

Hartford Magnet Trinity College Academy 600/6-12
53 Vernon St 06106 860-695-7201
Sally Biggs, prin. Fax 722-6954
High School Inc. 300/9-12
275 Asylum St 06103 860-695-7100
Terrell Hill, prin. Fax 768-1487
HPHS Engineering & Green Technology Acad 400/9-12
55 Forest St 06105 860-695-1315
Michael Maziarz, prin. Fax 722-8765
HPHS Law and Government Academy 400/9-12
55 Forest St 06105 860-695-1320
Adam Johnson, prin. Fax 722-8768
HPHS Nursing Academy 400/9-12
55 Forest St 06105 860-695-1325
David Chambers, prin. Fax 722-8764
Kinsella Sch of Performing Arts 700/PK-10
65 Van Block Ave 06106 860-695-4140
Irene Coe, prin. Fax 522-0004
McDonough S 400/6-8
111 Hillside Ave 06106 860-695-4260
Dr. Stacy Chambers, prin. Fax 722-8825
Opportunity HS 100/Alt
110 Washington St 06106 860-695-5980
Venitia Richardson, prin. Fax 722-8529
Renzulli Gifted & Talented Academy 4-8
121 Cornwall St 06112 860-695-2140
Ruth Lyons, lead tchr.
Sport & Medical Sciences Academy 700/6-12
280 Huyshope Ave 06106 860-695-6900
John Laverty, prin. Fax 722-8017
University HS of Science & Engineering 400/9-12
351 Mark Twain Dr 06112 860-695-9020
Martin Folam, prin. Fax 722-6408
Other Schools – See Manchester, Windsor

Capital Community College Post-Sec.
950 Main St 06103 860-906-5000
Connecticut Childrens Medical Center Post-Sec.
282 Washington St 06106 860-545-8514
Connecticut Institute for the Blind Post-Sec.
120 Holcomb St 06112 860-242-2274
Hartford Area SDA S 100/K-10
474 Woodland St 06112 860-724-5777
Hanoc Philippe, prin. Fax 548-9252
Hartford Hospital Post-Sec.
PO Box 5037 06102 860-545-2100
Hartford Seminary Post-Sec.
77 Sherman St 06105 860-509-9500
Institute of Living Schools Post-Sec.
400 Washington St 06106
Lincoln Technical Institute Post-Sec.
85 Sigourney St 06105 800-762-4337
Prince Regional Vocational Tech School Post-Sec.
500 Brookfield St 06106 860-246-8594
Rensselaer at Hartford Post-Sec.
275 Windsor St 06120 860-548-2400
Sawyer School Post-Sec.
141 Washington St 06106 860-947-4440
Trinity College Post-Sec.
300 Summit St 06106 860-297-2000
Watkinson S 200/6-12
180 Bloomfield Ave 06105 860-236-5618
John Bracker, head sch Fax 233-8295

Hebron, Tolland
Regional SD 8 1,800/7-12
PO Box 1438 06248 860-228-2115
Robert Siminski Ed.D., supt. Fax 228-4346
www.reg8.k12.ct.us/
RHAM HS 1,200/9-12
85 Wall St 06248 860-228-9474
Scott Leslie, prin. Fax 228-5312
RHAM MS 600/7-8
25 RHAM Rd 06248 860-228-9423
Michael Seroussi, prin. Fax 228-5316

Higganum, Middlesex, Pop. 1,666
Regional SD 17 2,500/PK-12
PO Box 568 06441 860-345-4534
Howard Thiery, supt. Fax 345-2817
rsd17.org
Haddam-Killingworth HS 700/9-12
PO Box 569 06441 860-345-8541
Charles Macunas, prin. Fax 345-8252
Other Schools – See Killingworth

Kent, Litchfield

Kent S 600/9-12
PO Box 2006 06757 860-927-6000
Rev. Richardson Schell, hdmstr. Fax 927-6014
Marvelwood S 200/9-12
PO Box 3001 06757 860-927-0047
Arthur Goodearl, head sch Fax 927-5325

Killingworth, Middlesex
Regional SD 17
Supt. — See Higganum
Haddam-Killingworth MS 800/5-8
451 Route 81 06419 860-663-1241
Miriam Wagner, prin. Fax 663-2071

Lakeville, Litchfield, Pop. 909

Hotchkiss S 600/9-12
11 Interlaken Rd 06039 860-435-2591
Malcolm McKenzie, hdmstr. Fax 435-8056

Lebanon, New London
Lebanon SD 1,400/PK-12
891 Exeter Rd 06249 860-642-3560
Janet Tyler, supt. Fax 642-4589
www.lebanonct.org/
Lebanon MS 400/5-8
891 Exeter Rd 06249 860-642-4702
Robert Laskarzewski, prin. Fax 642-3534
Lyman Memorial HS 500/9-12
917 Exeter Rd 06249 860-642-7567
Stephen Salisbury, prin. Fax 642-3521

Ledyard, New London
Ledyard SD 2,600/PK-12
4 Blonder Blvd 06339 860-464-9255
Michael Graner, supt. Fax 464-8589
ledyard.net/
Ledyard HS 900/9-12
24 Gallup Hill Rd 06339 860-464-9600
Louis Gabordi, prin. Fax 464-1990
Other Schools – See Gales Ferry

Litchfield, Litchfield, Pop. 1,239
Litchfield SD 1,200/PK-12
PO Box 110 06759 860-567-7500
Dr. Deborah Wheeler, supt. Fax 567-7508
www.litchfieldschools.org
Litchfield JSHS 600/7-12
PO Box 110 06759 860-567-7530
Kristen Della Volpe, prin. Fax 567-7538

Regional SD 6 1,100/PK-12
98 Wamogo Rd 06759 860-567-7400
Edward Drapp, supt. Fax 567-6652
www.rsd6.org
Wamogo Regional JSHS 500/7-12
98 Wamogo Rd 06759 860-567-7410
William Egan, prin. Fax 567-6651

Connecticut Junior Republic Post-Sec.
PO Box 161 06759

Madison, New Haven, Pop. 15,485
Madison SD 3,600/K-12
PO Box 71 06443 203-245-6300
Thomas Scarice, supt. Fax 245-6336
www.madison.k12.ct.us
Hand HS 1,300/9-12
286 Green Hill Rd 06443 203-245-6350
Anthony Salutari, prin. Fax 245-6356
Polson MS 600/7-8
302 Green Hill Rd 06443 203-245-6480
Frank Henderson, prin. Fax 245-6494

Manchester, Hartford, Pop. 29,743
Connecticut Technical HS System
Supt. — See Middletown
Cheney Technical HS Vo/Tech
791 Middle Tpke W 06040 860-649-5396
Robert Sartoris, prin. Fax 649-5263

Hartford SD
Supt. — See Hartford
Great Path Academy 300/10-12
PO Box 1046 06045 860-512-3700
Tory Niles-Outler, prin. Fax 512-3701

Manchester SD 6,100/PK-12
45 N School St, 860-647-3441
Fax 647-5042

boe.townofmanchester.org/
Bentley Alternative Education S Alt
134 Middle Tpke E 06040 860-647-3342
Matthew Geary, prin. Fax 647-5038
Illing MS 900/7-8
229 Middle Tpke E 06040 860-647-3400
David Welch, prin. Fax 647-5008
Manchester HS 1,900/9-12
134 Middle Tpke E 06040 860-647-3530
Matthew Geary, prin. Fax 646-3727

Cornerstone Christian S 200/PK-12
236 Main St, 860-643-0792
Tonya Snyder, prin. Fax 647-9291
East Catholic HS 700/9-12
115 New State Rd, 860-649-5336
Jason Hartling, prin. Fax 649-7191
Manchester Community College Post-Sec.
PO Box 1046 06045 860-512-3000

Meriden, New Haven, Pop. 59,747
Area Coop. Educational Services RESC
Supt. — See North Haven
Edison MS 700/6-8
1355 N Broad St 06450 203-639-8403
Karen Habegger, prin. Fax 639-8323

Connecticut Technical HS System
Supt. — See Middletown
Wilcox Technical HS Vo/Tech
298 Oregon Rd 06451 203-238-6260
Richard Cavallaro, prin. Fax 238-6602

Meriden SD 8,300/PK-12
22 Liberty St 06450 203-630-4171
Dr. Mark Benigni, supt. Fax 630-0110
www.meridenk12.org
Lincoln MS 700/6-8
164 Centennial Ave 06451 203-238-2381
Dianne Vumback, prin. Fax 238-7258
Maloney HS 1,200/9-12
121 Gravel St 06450 203-238-2334
Fax 630-7011
Platt HS 1,100/9-12
220 Coe Ave 06451 203-235-7963
Robert Montemurro, prin. Fax 630-4011
Washington MS 900/6-8
1225 N Broad St 06450 203-235-6606
Raymond Southland, prin. Fax 235-6040

Marinello School of Beauty Post-Sec.
1231 E Main St 06450 203-237-6683

Middlebury, New Haven, Pop. 4,100
Regional SD 15 4,400/PK-12
PO Box 395 06762 203-758-8259
Dr. Frank Sippy, supt. Fax 758-1908
www.region15.org
Memorial MS 500/6-8
PO Box 903 06762 203-758-2496
John Sieller, prin. Fax 758-9594
Other Schools – See Southbury

Westover S 200/9-12
PO Box 847 06762 203-758-2423
Ann Pollina, head sch Fax 577-4585

Middletown, Middlesex, Pop. 46,173
Connecticut Technical HS System
25 Industrial Park Rd 06457 860-807-2200
Patricia Ciccone, supt. Fax 807-2196
www.cttech.org
Vinal Technical HS Vo/Tech
60 Daniels St 06457 860-344-7100
Kerry Parker, prin. Fax 344-2622
Other Schools – See Ansonia, Bridgeport, Bristol, Danbury, Danielson, Groton, Hamden, Hartford, Manchester, Meriden, Milford, New Britain, Norwich, Torrington, Waterbury, Willimantic

Middletown SD 5,200/PK-12
311 Hunting Hill Ave 06457 860-638-1401
David Larson Ph.D., supt. Fax 638-1495
www.middletownschools.org
Middletown HS 1,400/9-12
200 La Rosa Ln 06457 860-704-4500
Robert Fontaine, prin. Fax 347-2044
Wilson MS 700/7-8
370 Hunting Hill Ave 06457 860-347-8594
Eugene Nocera, prin. Fax 347-2158

Mercy HS 700/9-12
1740 Randolph Rd 06457 860-346-6659
Sr. Mary McCarthy, prin. Fax 344-9887
Middlesex Community College Post-Sec.
100 Training Hill Rd 06457 860-343-5800
Wesleyan University 06459 Post-Sec.
860-685-2000
Xavier HS 900/9-12
181 Randolph Rd 06457 860-346-7735
Br. Brian Davis, prin. Fax 346-6859

Milford, New Haven, Pop. 50,507
Connecticut Technical HS System
Supt. — See Middletown
Platt Technical HS Vo/Tech
600 Orange Ave, 203-783-5300
Gene LaPorta, prin. Fax 783-3970

Milford SD 6,900/K-12
70 W River St 06460 203-783-3402
Dr. Elizabeth E. Feser, supt. Fax 783-3475
www.milforded.org
Academy 100/Alt
140 Gulf St 06460 203-783-3652
Annaleise Spaziano, dir. Fax 783-3679
East Shore MS 500/6-8
240 Chapel St 06460 203-783-3559
Catherine Williams, prin. Fax 301-5060
Foran HS 1,000/9-12
80 Foran Rd 06460 203-783-3502
John Barile, prin. Fax 783-3635
Harborside MS 600/6-8
175 High St 06460 203-783-3523
Gordon Beinstein, prin. Fax 783-3687
Law HS 1,000/9-12
20 Lansdale Ave 06460 203-783-3574
Francis Thompson, prin. Fax 783-3586
West Shore MS 600/6-8
70 Kay Ave 06460 203-783-3553
Vince Scarpetti, prin. Fax 783-3696

Academy of Our Lady of Mercy 400/9-12
200 High St 06460 203-877-2786
Ann Pratson, prin. Fax 876-9760

Monroe, Fairfield
Monroe SD 3,500/PK-12
375 Monroe Tpke 06468 203-452-2860
James Agostine, supt. Fax 452-5818
www.monroeps.org
Jockey Hollow S 600/6-8
365 Fan Hill Rd 06468 203-452-2905
John Ceccolini, prin. Fax 452-2444
Masuk HS 1,300/9-12
1014 Monroe Tpke 06468 203-452-5823
Joe Kobza, prin. Fax 452-5835

Montville, New London
Montville SD
Supt. — See Oakdale
Palmer Academy 50/Alt
PO Box 27 06353 860-848-7816
Sheila Reagan, prin. Fax 848-9159

Moodus, Middlesex, Pop. 1,397
East Haddam SD 1,300/PK-12
PO Box 401 06469 860-873-5090
Dr. Ellen Solek, supt. Fax 873-5092
www.easthaddamschools.org
Hale-Ray HS 400/9-12
PO Box 404 06469 860-873-5065
Linda Dadona, prin. Fax 873-5074
Hale-Ray MS 500/4-8
PO Box 363 06469 860-873-5081
Jason Peacock, prin. Fax 873-5086

Mystic, New London, Pop. 4,136
Groton SD 4,900/PK-12
1300 Flanders Rd 06355 860-572-2100
Dr. John Ramos, supt. Fax 572-2107
www.groton.k12.ct.us
Cutler MS 400/6-8
160 Fishtown Rd 06355 860-572-5830
Monson Lane, prin. Fax 572-5834
Other Schools – See Groton

Stonington SD
Supt. — See Old Mystic
Mystic MS 400/5-8
204 Mistuxet Ave 06355 860-536-9613
Stafford Thomas, prin. Fax 536-4508

Naugatuck, New Haven, Pop. 31,134
Naugatuck SD 4,200/PK-12
380 Church St 06770 203-720-5265
John Tindall-Gibson Ph.D., supt. Fax 720-5272
www.naugy.net
City Hill MS 800/7-8
441 City Hill St 06770 203-720-5246
Christine Blanchard, prin. Fax 720-5256
Naugatuck HS 1,400/9-12
543 Rubber Ave 06770 203-720-5400
Francis Serratore, prin. Fax 720-5444

New Britain, Hartford, Pop. 71,606
Connecticut Technical HS System
Supt. — See Middletown
Goodwin Regional Technical HS Vo/Tech
735 Slater Rd 06053 860-827-7736
Mary Moran, prin. Fax 827-7862

New Britain SD 10,000/PK-12
PO Box 1960 06050 860-827-2203
Kelt Cooper, supt. Fax 612-1533
www.csdnb.org/
HALS Academy 200/6-8
30 Pendleton Rd 06053 860-826-1866
Leona Clerkin, prin. Fax 826-1867
New Britain HS 2,600/9-12
110 Mill St 06051 860-225-6300
Mike Foran, prin. Fax 225-6350
Pulaski MS 600/6-8
757 Farmington Ave 06053 860-225-7665
Wanda Lickwar, prin. Fax 223-3840
Roosevelt MS 400/6-8
40 Goodwin St 06051 860-612-3334
Rachel Young, prin. Fax 826-1162
Slade MS 700/6-8
183 Steele St 06052 860-225-6395
Richard Reyes, prin. Fax 826-7894

Central Connecticut State University Post-Sec.
1615 Stanley St 06053 860-832-3200
Charter Oak State College Post-Sec.
55 Paul Manafort Dr 06053 860-515-3800
Lincoln Technical Institute Post-Sec.
200 John Downey Dr 06051 860-225-8641

New Canaan, Fairfield, Pop. 17,864
New Canaan SD 4,100/PK-12
39 Locust Ave 06840 203-594-4000
Dr. Mary M. Kolek, supt. Fax 594-4035
www.newcanaan.k12.ct.us
New Canaan HS 1,300/9-12
11 Farm Rd 06840 203-594-4600
Dr. Bryan Luizzi, prin. Fax 972-4700
Saxe MS 1,200/5-8
468 South Ave 06840 203-594-4500
Greg Macedo, prin. Fax 594-4565

St. Luke's S 500/5-12
377 N Wilton Rd 06840 203-966-5612
Mark Davis, hdmstr. Fax 972-3450

New Fairfield, Fairfield, Pop. 12,911
New Fairfield SD 2,900/PK-12
3 Brush Hill Rd 06812 203-312-5770
Dr. Alicia Roy, supt. Fax 312-5609
www.newfairfieldschools.org
New Fairfield HS 1,000/9-12
54 Gillotti Rd 06812 203-312-5800
Mariana Coelho, prin. Fax 312-5803
New Fairfield MS 700/6-8
56 Gillotti Rd 06812 203-312-5885
Christine Baldelli, prin. Fax 312-5887

New Haven, New Haven, Pop. 126,396
Area Coop. Educational Services RESC
Supt. — See North Haven
Educational Center for the Arts 300/9-12
55 Audubon St 06510 203-777-5451
Alice Schilling, prin. Fax 782-3596

New Haven SD 19,000/PK-12
54 Meadow St 06519 203-946-8888
Dr. Reginald Mayo, supt. Fax 946-7300
www.nhps.net
Brennan/Rogers S 200/3-8
200 Wilmot Rd 06515 203-946-8640
Karen Lott, prin. Fax 946-7516
Cooperative Arts & Humanities HS 600/9-12
177 College St 06510 203-691-2400
Frank Costanzo, prin. Fax 691-2404
Cross HS 1,300/9-12
181 Mitchell Dr 06511 203-497-7400
Peggy Moore, prin. Fax 946-6932
Dixwell New Light HS 50/Alt
192 Dixwell Ave 06511 203-946-5617
Michael Patterson, prin. Fax 946-5821
DOMUS Academy 50/Alt
560 Ella T Grasso Blvd 06519 203-492-0750
William Johnson, prin. Fax 946-2343
Engineering & Science University School 200/6-10
804 State St 06511 203-946-6610
Medria Blue-Ellis, prin. Fax 946-6376
High School in the Community 300/9-12
175 Water St 06511 203-946-7022
Erik Good, admin. Fax 946-7132
Hillhouse HS 1,000/9-12
480 Sherman Pkwy 06511 203-497-7500
Kermit Carolina, prin. Fax 946-8487
Hill Regional Career HS 700/9-12
140 Legion Ave 06519 203-946-5845
Madeline Negron, prin. Fax 946-5949
Hooker MS 300/3-8
691 Whitney Ave 06511 203-497-7200
Sheryl Hershonik, prin. Fax 497-7205
Hyde Leadership Academy 200/9-12
60 Sargent Dr 06511 203-946-8121
John Russell, prin. Fax 946-6161
McCabe Center 50/Alt
21 Wooster Pl 06511 203-946-8758
Bernadette Strode, prin. Fax 946-5374
Metropolitan Business HS 300/9-12
115 Water St 06511 203-497-7700
Judy Puglisi, prin. Fax 497-7705
New Haven Academy 300/9-12
444 Orange St 06511 203-946-8995
Greg Baldwin, prin. Fax 946-8428
New Horizons HS Alt
103 Hallock Ave 06519 203-946-7342
Maureen Bransfield, prin. Fax 946-7317
Riverside Educational Academy 200/9-12
560 Ella T Grasso Blvd 06519 203-492-0700
Wanda Gibbs, prin. Fax 946-2380
Ross Arts MS 400/5-8
150 Kimberly Ave 06519 203-946-8974
Shawn True, prin. Fax 946-5824
Sound HS 300/9-12
60 S Water St 06519 203-946-6937
Rebecca Gratz, prin. Fax 946-6874
Adult & Continuing Education Center Adult
580 Ella T Grasso Blvd 06519 203-492-0213
Alicia Caraballo, prin. Fax 492-6384

Albertus Magnus College Post-Sec.
700 Prospect St 06511 203-773-8550
Berkeley Divinity School Post-Sec.
409 Prospect St 06511 203-432-9285
Gateway Community College Post-Sec.
60 Sargent Dr 06511 203-285-2000
Hopkins S 700/7-12
986 Forest Rd 06515 203-397-1001
Barbara Riley, hdmstr. Fax 389-3506
St. Martin dePorres Academy 100/PK-PK, 5-
208 Columbus Ave 06519 203-772-2424
Kelly O'Leary, prin. Fax 772-2425
Southern Connecticut State University Post-Sec.
501 Crescent St 06515 203-392-5200
Yale-New Haven Hospital Post-Sec.
20 York St 06510 203-785-5074
Yale University Post-Sec.
38 Hillhouse Ave 06511 203-432-4771
Yeshiva of New Haven 50/9-12
765 Elm St 06511 203-777-7199

Newington, Hartford, Pop. 30,076
Newington SD 4,400/PK-12
131 Cedar St 06111 860-665-8610
Dr. William C. Collins, supt. Fax 665-8616
www.npsct.org
Kellogg MS 600/5-8
155 Harding Ave 06111 860-666-5418
Jason Lambert, prin. Fax 666-5925
Newington HS 1,500/9-12
605 Willard Ave 06111 860-666-5611
James Wenker, prin. Fax 666-8224
Wallace MS 700/5-8
71 Halleran Dr 06111 860-667-5888
David Milardo, prin. Fax 667-5893

Connecticut Center for Massage Therapy Post-Sec.
75 Kitts Ln 06111 860-667-1886
Hanger Orthopedic Group Post-Sec.
181 Patricia M Genova Dr 06111 860-667-5304

New London, New London, Pop. 26,373
New London SD 2,600/PK-12
134 Williams St 06320 860-447-6000
Nicholas Fischer, supt. Fax 447-6016
www.newlondon.org
Jackson MS 600/6-8
36 Waller St 06320 860-437-6480
Alison Ryan, prin. Fax 437-6494
New London HS 1,000/9-12
490 Jefferson Ave 06320 860-437-6400
Tommy Thompson, prin. Fax 271-4321
Science & Technology Magnet HS 9-12
490 Jefferson Ave 06320 860-437-6496
Louis Allen, dir. Fax 439-7774
New London Adult Education Adult
3 Shaws Cv 06320 860-437-2385
Maria Pukas, dir. Fax 437-6460

Connecticut College Post-Sec.
270 Mohegan Ave 06320 860-447-1911
Mitchell College Post-Sec.
437 Pequot Ave 06320 860-701-5000
Ridley-Lowell Business & Technical Inst. Post-Sec.
470 Bank St 06320 860-443-7441
United States Coast Guard Academy Post-Sec.
31 Mohegan Ave 06320 800-883-8724
Williams S 200/7-12
182 Mohegan Ave 06320 860-443-5333
Mark Fader, hdmstr. Fax 439-2796

New Milford, Litchfield, Pop. 6,408
New Milford SD 4,700/PK-12
50 East St 06776 860-355-8406
JeanAnn Paddyfote Ph.D., supt. Fax 210-4132
www.newmilfordps.org
New Milford HS 1,500/9-12
388 Danbury Rd 06776 860-350-6647
Greg Shugrue, prin. Fax 210-2256
Schaghticoke MS 700/7-8
23 Hipp Rd 06776 860-354-2204
Dana Ford, prin. Fax 210-2217

Canterbury S 400/9-12
PO Box 5000 06776 860-210-3800
Thomas Sheehy, hdmstr. Fax 350-4425
Faith Preparatory S 200/K-12
600 Danbury Rd Ste 2 06776 860-210-3677
Josephine DuBois, prin. Fax 210-3685

Newtown, Fairfield, Pop. 1,929
Newtown SD 4,900/PK-12
8 Primrose St 06470 203-426-7621
Janet Robinson, supt. Fax 270-6199
www.newtown.k12.ct.us
Newtown MS 900/7-8
11 Queen St 06470 203-426-7638
Diane Sherlock, prin. Fax 270-6102
Other Schools – See Sandy Hook

Niantic, New London, Pop. 3,074
East Lyme SD
Supt. — See East Lyme
East Lyme MS 900/5-8
31 Society Rd 06357 860-739-4491
Dr. Judy DeLeeuw, prin. Fax 691-5400

North Branford, New Haven, Pop. 12,996
North Branford SD
Supt. — See Northford
North Branford HS 700/9-12
49 Caputo Rd 06471 203-484-1465
Todd Stoeffler, prin. Fax 484-1233
North Branford IS 600/6-8
654 Foxon Rd 06471 203-484-1500
Alan Davis, prin. Fax 484-1505

Northford, New Haven, Pop. 3,200
North Branford SD 2,300/PK-12
PO Box 129 06472 203-484-1440
Scott Schoonmaker, supt. Fax 484-1445
www.northbranfordschools.org
Other Schools – See North Branford

North Grosvenordale, Windham, Pop. 1,481
Thompson SD 1,300/PK-12
785 Riverside Dr 06255 860-923-9581
Michael Jolin Ph.D., supt. Fax 923-9638
www.thompsonpublicschools.org/
Thompson MS 400/5-8
785 Riverside Dr 06255 860-923-9380
Ronald Springer, prin. Fax 923-9638
Tourtellotte Memorial HS 400/9-12
785 Riverside Dr 06255 860-923-9303
Dr. Penny Hebert, prin. Fax 923-3752

North Haven, New Haven, Pop. 23,822
Area Coop. Educational Services RESC 1,800/
350 State St 06473 203-498-6800
Craig Edmondson Ed.D., dir. Fax 498-6890
www.aces.org
Other Schools – See Meriden, New Haven

North Haven SD 3,600/PK-12
5 Linsley St 06473 203-239-2581
Robert Cronin Ph.D., supt. Fax 234-9811
www.north-haven.k12.ct.us/
North Haven HS 1,200/9-12
221 Elm St 06473 203-239-1641
Russell Dallai Ph.D., prin. Fax 234-2602
North Haven MS 800/6-8
55 Bailey Rd 06473 203-239-1683
Philip Piazza, prin. Fax 234-2846

Gal Mar Academy of Hairdressing Post-Sec.
97 Washington Ave Ste 8 06473 203-281-4477

North Stonington, New London
North Stonington SD 800/PK-12
297 Norwich Westerly Rd 06359 860-535-2800
Peter Nero, supt. Fax 535-1470
www.northstonington.k12.ct.us
Wheeler HS 200/9-12
298 Norwich Westerly Rd 06359 860-535-0377
Christopher Sandford, prin. Fax 535-2536
Wheeler MS 200/6-8
298 Norwich Westerly Rd 06359 860-535-0377
Christopher Sandford, prin. Fax 535-2536

North Stonington Christian Academy 100/PK-12
12 Stillman Rd 06359 860-599-5071
Pamela Wilkinson, dir. Fax 599-2815

Norwalk, Fairfield, Pop. 84,099
Norwalk SD 11,200/PK-12
PO Box 6001 06852 203-854-4001
Anthony Daddona, supt. Fax 838-3299
norwalkpublicschools.org
Briggs HS 100/Alt
350 Main Ave 06851 203-899-2820
Marie Allan, prin. Fax 899-2824
Center for Global Studies 200/9-12
300 Highland Ave 06854 203-852-9488
Roslynne McCarthy, dir. Fax 854-0832
Hale MS 600/6-8
176 Strawberry Hill Ave 06851 203-899-2910
Hugh McKiernan, prin. Fax 899-2914
McMahon HS 1,700/9-12
300 Highland Ave 06854 203-852-9488
Suzanne Koroshetz, prin. Fax 899-2814
Norwalk HS 1,500/9-12
23 Calvin Murphy Dr 06851 203-838-4481
Reginald Roberts, prin. Fax 899-2815
Ponus Ridge MS 700/6-8
21 Hunters Ln 06850 203-847-3557
Linda Sumpter, prin. Fax 899-2924
Roton MS 400/6-8
201 Highland Ave 06853 203-899-2930
Joseph Vellucci, prin. Fax 899-2934
West Rocks MS 700/6-8
81 W Rocks Rd 06851 203-899-2970
Lynne Moore, prin. Fax 899-2974

Norwalk Community College Post-Sec.
188 Richards Ave 06854 203-857-7000

Norwalk Hospital Post-Sec.
24 Stevens St 06850 203-852-2211

Norwich, New London, Pop. 38,601
Connecticut Technical HS System
Supt. — See Middletown
Norwich Technical HS Vo/Tech
7 Mahan Dr 06360 860-889-8453
Nikitoula Menounos, prin. Fax 886-4632

Endowed & Incorporated Academies 2,400/9-12
305 Broadway 06360 860-425-5500
David Klein, supt. Fax 887-2004
www.norwichfreeacademy.com
Norwich Free Academy 2,400/9-12
305 Broadway 06360 860-425-5501
David Klein, hdmstr. Fax 887-2004

Norwich SD 3,900/PK-8
90 Town St 06360 860-823-4245
Abby Dolliver, supt. Fax 823-1880
www.norwichpublicschools.org
Kelly MS 600/6-8
25 Mahan Dr 06360 860-823-4211
William Peckrul, prin. Fax 892-4302
Teachers Memorial MS 500/6-8
15 Teachers Dr 06360 860-823-4212
Alexandria Lazzari, prin. Fax 823-4277

Three Rivers Community College Post-Sec.
574 New London Tpke 06360 860-886-0177

Oakdale, New London
Montville SD 2,700/PK-12
800 Old Colchester Rd 06370 860-848-1228
Pamela Aubin, supt. Fax 848-0589
www.montvilleschools.org
Montville HS 800/9-12
800 Old Colchester Rd 06370 860-848-9208
Jeffrey Theodoss, prin. Fax 848-3872
Tyl MS 600/6-8
166 Chesterfield Rd 06370 860-848-2822
Mary Jane Dix, prin. Fax 848-8854
Other Schools – See Montville

St. Thomas More S 200/8-12
45 Cottage Rd 06370 860-859-1900
James Hanrahan, hdmstr. Fax 823-3863

Oakville, Litchfield, Pop. 8,924
Watertown SD
Supt. — See Watertown
Swift MS 800/6-8
250 Colonial St 06779 860-945-4830
Marylu Lerz, prin. Fax 945-6449

Old Lyme, New London
Regional SD 18 1,400/PK-12
53 Lyme St 06371 860-434-7238
Ian Neviaser, supt. Fax 434-9959
www.region18.org
Lyme-Old Lyme HS 400/9-12
69 Lyme St 06371 860-434-1651
James Wygonik, prin. Fax 434-8234
Lyme-Old Lyme MS 300/6-8
53 Lyme St 06371 860-434-2568
Christopher Pomroy, prin. Fax 434-0717

Lyme Academy College of Fine Arts Post-Sec.
84 Lyme St 06371 860-434-5232

Old Mystic, New London, Pop. 3,422
Stonington SD 2,400/PK-12
PO Box 479 06372 860-572-0506
Dr. Van Riley, supt. Fax 572-1470
www.stoningtonschools.org
Other Schools – See Mystic, Pawcatuck

Old Saybrook, Middlesex, Pop. 9,552
Old Saybrook SD 1,600/PK-12
50 Sheffield St 06475 860-395-3157
Heston Sutman, supt. Fax 395-3162
www.oldsaybrook.k12.ct.us
Old Saybrook HS 500/9-12
1111 Boston Post Rd 06475 860-395-3175
Scott Schoonmaker, prin. Fax 395-3179
Old Saybrook MS 600/4-8
60 Sheffield St 06475 860-395-3168
Michael Rafferty, prin. Fax 395-3350

Orange, New Haven, Pop. 13,774
Regional SD 5
Supt. — See Woodbridge
Amity Regional MS 400/7-8
100 Ohman Ave 06477 203-392-3200
Kathleen Fuller-Cutler, prin. Fax 387-7603

Southern Connecticut Hebrew Academy 100/K-12
261 Derby Ave 06477 203-795-5261
Rabbi Sheya Hecht, hdmstr. Fax 891-9719

Oxford, New Haven
Oxford SD 2,200/PK-12
1 Great Hill Rd 06478 203-888-7754
Dr. John Reed, supt. Fax 888-5955
www.oxfordpublicschools.org
Great Oak MS 500/6-8
50 Great Oak Rd 06478 203-888-5418
Brian Murphy, prin. Fax 888-7798
Oxford HS 600/9-12
61 Quaker Farms Rd 06478 203-888-2468
Frank Savo, prin. Fax 881-5250

Pawcatuck, New London, Pop. 5,474
Stonington SD
Supt. — See Old Mystic
Pawcatuck MS 300/5-8
40 Field St 06379 860-599-5696
Jane Giulini, prin. Fax 599-8948

Stonington HS 800/9-12
176 S Broad St 06379 860-599-5781
Dr. Stephen Murphy, prin. Fax 599-5784

Plainfield, Windham, Pop. 14,363
Plainfield SD 2,600/PK-12
651 Norwich Rd 06374 860-564-6403
Kenneth DiPietro, supt. Fax 564-6412
www.plainfieldschools.org
Plainfield Central MS 600/6-8
75 Canterbury Rd 06374 860-564-6437
Scott Gagnon, prin. Fax 564-1147
Other Schools – See Central Village

Plainville, Hartford, Pop. 17,932
Plainville SD 2,400/PK-12
1 Central Sq 06062 860-793-3200
Jeffrey Kitching, supt. Fax 747-6790
www.plainvilleschools.org
Plainville HS 800/9-12
47 Robert Holcomb Way 06062 860-793-3220
Steven LePage, prin. Fax 793-3224
MS of Plainville 600/6-8
150 Northwest Dr 06062 860-793-3250
Matthew Guarino, prin. Fax 793-3265

Plantsville, Hartford, Pop. 7,000
Southington SD
Supt. — See Southington
Kennedy MS 800/6-8
1071 S Main St 06479 860-628-3275
Steven Madancy, prin. Fax 628-3404

Pomfret, Windham

Pomfret S 400/9-12
398 Pomfret St 06258 860-963-6100
Timothy Richards, hdmstr. Fax 963-2086

Portland, Middlesex, Pop. 5,757
Portland SD 1,400/PK-12
33 E Main St 06480 860-342-6790
Dr. Sally Doyen, supt. Fax 342-6791
www.portlandctschools.org
Portland HS 400/9-12
95 High St 06480 860-342-1720
Andrea Lavery, prin. Fax 342-2906
Portland MS 200/7-8
93 High St 06480 860-342-1880
Scott Giegerich, prin. Fax 342-3934

Preston, New London
Preston SD 400/PK-8
325 Shetucket Tpke 06365 860-889-6098
Dr. John Welch, supt. Fax 889-8685
www.prestonschools.org/
Preston Plains MS 100/6-8
1 Route 164 06365 860-889-3831
Raymond Bernier, prin. Fax 204-0126

Prospect, New Haven, Pop. 7,775
Regional SD 16 2,500/PK-12
207 New Haven Rd 06712 203-758-6671
Tim James, supt. Fax 758-5797
www.region16ct.org
Long River MS 600/6-8
38 Columbia Ave 06712 203-758-4421
Jayne Lanphear, prin. Fax 758-6948
Other Schools – See Beacon Falls

Putnam, Windham, Pop. 7,034
Putnam SD 1,300/PK-12
126 Church St 06260 860-963-6900
William Hull, supt. Fax 963-6903
www.putnam.k12.ct.us/
Putnam HS 300/9-12
152 Woodstock Ave 06260 860-963-6905
Joseph Ptaszynski, prin. Fax 963-6911
Putnam MS 300/6-8
35 Wicker St 06260 860-963-6920
Teri Bruce, prin. Fax 963-6921

Redding, Fairfield
Regional SD 9
Supt. — See Easton
Barlow HS 1,000/9-12
100 Black Rock Tpke 06896 203-938-2508
Thomas McMorran Ed.D., prin. Fax 938-0327

Ridgefield, Fairfield, Pop. 7,542
Ridgefield SD 5,400/PK-12
70 Prospect St 06877 203-431-2800
Deborah Low, supt. Fax 431-2811
www.ridgefield.org
East Ridge MS 700/6-8
10 E Ridge Rd 06877 203-438-3744
Martin Fiedler, prin. Fax 431-2843
Ridgefield HS 1,800/9-12
700 N Salem Rd 06877 203-438-3785
Dr. Stacey Gross, prin. Fax 431-2891
Scotts Ridge MS 600/6-8
750 N Salem Rd 06877 203-894-3400
Tim Salem, prin. Fax 894-3411

Riverside, Fairfield, Pop. 8,283
Greenwich SD
Supt. — See Greenwich
Eastern MS 800/6-8
51 Hendrie Ave 06878 203-637-1744
Ralph Mayo, prin. Fax 637-3567

Rocky Hill, Hartford, Pop. 16,554
Rocky Hill SD 2,500/PK-12
PO Box 627 06067 860-258-7701
Dr. Mark Zito, supt. Fax 258-7710
www.rockyhillps.com
Griswold MS 600/6-8
144 Bailey Rd 06067 860-258-7741
Richard Watson, prin. Fax 258-7746
Rocky Hill HS 800/9-12
50 Chapin Ave 06067 860-258-7721
Mario Almeida, prin. Fax 258-7735

Porter and Chester Institute Post-Sec.
30 Waterchase Dr 06067 860-529-2519

Salisbury, Litchfield

Salisbury S 300/9-12
251 Canaan Rd 06068 860-435-5700
Chisholm Chandler, hdmstr. Fax 435-5750

Sandy Hook, Fairfield
Newtown SD
Supt. — See Newtown
Newtown HS 1,700/9-12
12 Berkshire Rd 06482 203-426-7646
Charles Dumais, prin. Fax 426-6573

Seymour, New Haven, Pop. 14,288
Seymour SD 2,100/PK-12
98 Bank St 06483 203-888-4565
Christine Syriac, supt. Fax 888-1704
www.seymourschools.org
Seymour HS 600/9-12
2 Botsford Rd 06483 203-888-2561
Glenn Lungarini, prin. Fax 888-7476
Seymour MS 600/6-8
211 Mountain Rd 06483 203-888-4513
Bernadette Hamad, prin. Fax 881-7535

Shelton, Fairfield, Pop. 39,118
Shelton SD 5,200/K-12
382 Long Hill Ave 06484 203-924-1023
Freeman Burr, supt. Fax 924-5894
www.sheltonpublicschools.org
Shelton HS 1,500/9-12
120 Meadow St 06484 203-922-3004
Dr. Beth Smith, hdmstr. Fax 924-8236
Shelton IS 900/7-8
675 Constitution Blvd N 06484 203-926-2000
Kenneth Saranich, hdmstr. Fax 926-2017

Lincoln Technical Institute Post-Sec.
8 Progress Dr 06484 203-929-0592

Simsbury, Hartford, Pop. 22,023
Simsbury SD 4,700/PK-12
933 Hopmeadow St 06070 860-651-3361
Dr. Diane Ullman, supt. Fax 651-4343
www.simsbury.k12.ct.us
James Memorial MS 800/7-8
155 Firetown Rd 06070 860-651-3341
Sue Homrok-Lemke, prin. Fax 658-3629
Simsbury HS 1,600/9-12
34 Farms Village Rd 06070 860-658-0451
Neil Sullivan, prin. Fax 658-2439

Walker S 300/6-12
230 Bushy Hill Rd 06070 860-408-4200
Elizabeth Speers, hdmstr. Fax 408-4201
Westminster S 400/9-12
995 Hopmeadow St 06070 860-408-3000
William Philip, hdmstr. Fax 408-3001

Somers, Tolland, Pop. 1,774
Somers SD 1,600/PK-12
1 Vision Blvd 06071 860-749-2270
Dr. Maynard Suffredini, supt. Fax 763-0748
www.somers.k12.ct.us
Avery MS 400/6-8
1 Vision Blvd 06071 860-749-2270
Susan Muirhead, prin. Fax 763-2073
Somers HS 600/9-12
5 Vision Blvd 06071 860-749-2270
Gary Cotzin, prin. Fax 749-9264

New England Tractor Trailer Training Post-Sec.
32 Field Rd 06071 860-749-0711

Southbury, New Haven, Pop. 15,818
Regional SD 15
Supt. — See Middlebury
Pomperaug Regional HS 1,400/9-12
234 Judd Rd 06488 203-262-3200
Lorrie Rodrigue, prin. Fax 262-6806
Rochambeau MS 600/6-8
100 Peter Rd 06488 203-264-2711
Michael Bernardi, prin. Fax 264-6638

Southington, Hartford, Pop. 39,200
Southington SD 6,800/PK-12
49 Beecher St 06489 860-628-3202
Dr. Joseph Erardi, supt. Fax 821-8056
www.southingtonschools.org
ALTA at Pyne Center Alt
242 N Main St 06489 860-628-3379
Jess Levin, dir. Fax 628-3458
DePaolo MS 700/6-8
385 Pleasant St 06489 860-628-3260
Frank Pepe, prin. Fax 628-3403
Southington HS 2,100/9-12
720 Pleasant St 06489 860-628-3229
Dr. Martin Semmel, prin. Fax 628-3397
Other Schools – See Plantsville

Branford Hall Career Institute Post-Sec.
35 N Main St 06489 860-276-0600
Lincoln College of New England Post-Sec.
2279 Mount Vernon Rd 06489 860-628-4751

South Kent, Litchfield

South Kent S 200/9-12
40 Bulls Bridge Rd 06785 860-927-3539
Andrew Vadnais, head sch Fax 803-0040

South Windsor, Hartford, Pop. 22,090
South Windsor SD 4,600/PK-12
1737 Main St 06074 860-291-1200
Kate Carter Ed.D., supt. Fax 291-1291
www.southwindsorschools.org
Edwards MS 1,100/6-8
100 Arnold Way 06074 860-648-5030
Kristin Heckt, prin. Fax 648-5029
South Windsor HS 1,500/9-12
161 Nevers Rd 06074 860-648-5000
Daniel Sullivan, prin. Fax 648-5013

Stafford Springs, Tolland, Pop. 4,869
Stafford SD 1,900/PK-12
263 East St 06076 860-684-4211
Dr. Patricia Collin, supt. Fax 684-5172
www.stafford.k12.ct.us
Stafford HS 600/9-12
PO Box 87 06076 860-684-4233
Francis Kennedy, prin. Fax 684-0424
Stafford MS 400/6-8
21 Levinthal Run 06076 860-684-2785
Kenneth Valentine, prin. Fax 684-4671

Stamford, Fairfield, Pop. 120,428
Stamford SD 15,300/PK-12
888 Washington Blvd Fl 5 06901 203-977-4543
Dr. Winifred Hamilton, supt. Fax 977-5964
www.stamfordpublicschools.org/
Academy of Info Technology & Engineering 700/9-12
411 High Ridge Rd 06905 203-977-4336
Paul Gross, prin. Fax 977-6638
Cloonan MS 600/6-8
11 W North St 06902 203-977-4544
David Tate, prin. Fax 977-4867
Dolan MS 600/6-8
51 Toms Rd 06906 203-977-4441
Charmaine Tourse, prin. Fax 977-4880
Rippowam MS 600/6-8
381 High Ridge Rd 06905 203-977-5255
George Giberti, prin. Fax 977-5154
Scofield Magnet MS 600/6-8
641 Scofieldtown Rd 06903 203-977-2750
Scott Clayton, prin. Fax 977-2766
Stamford HS 1,800/9-12
55 Strawberry Hill Ave 06902 203-977-4223
Dr. Donna Valentine, prin. Fax 356-1720
Turn of River MS 600/6-8
117 Vine Rd 06905 203-977-4284
Dr. Michael Fernandes, prin. Fax 977-5037
Westhill HS 2,300/9-12
125 Roxbury Rd 06902 203-977-4477
Camille Figluizzi, prin. Fax 977-4996

Beth Benjamin Academy of Connecticut Post-Sec.
132 Prospect St 06901 203-325-4351
King Low Heywood Thomas S 700/PK-12
1450 Newfield Ave 06905 203-322-3496
Thomas Main, hdmstr. Fax 329-0291
St. Basil College Seminary Post-Sec.
195 Glenbrook Rd 06902 203-324-4578
Stamford Hospital Post-Sec.
PO Box 9317 06904 203-276-7877
Trinity Catholic HS 500/9-12
926 Newfield Ave 06905 203-322-3401
Tony Pavia, prin. Fax 322-5330
Trinity Catholic MS 200/6-8
948 Newfield Ave 06905 203-322-7383
Richard Fox, prin. Fax 324-4435
Yeshiva Bais Binyomin 100/9-12
132 Prospect St 06901 203-325-4351
Meyer Hershkowitz, pres. Fax 323-6073

Storrs, Tolland, Pop. 14,985
Mansfield SD 1,300/PK-8
4 S Eagleville Rd 06268 860-429-3350
Frederick Baruzzi, supt. Fax 429-3379
www.mansfieldct.org/mboe/index.php
Mansfield MS 600/5-8
205 Spring Hill Rd 06268 860-429-9341
Jeffrey Cryan, prin. Fax 429-1020

Regional SD 19 1,200/9-12
1235 Storrs Rd 06268 860-487-1862
Bruce Silva, supt. Fax 429-0085
www.eosmith.org
Smith HS 1,200/9-12
1235 Storrs Rd 06268 860-487-0877
Louis DeLoreto, prin. Fax 429-7892

University of Connecticut 06269 Post-Sec.
860-486-2000

Stratford, Fairfield, Pop. 50,391
Stratford SD 7,500/PK-12
1000 E Broadway 06615 203-385-4210
Dr. Janet Robinson, supt. Fax 381-2012
stratfordk12.org
Bunnell HS 1,200/9-12
1 Bulldog Blvd 06614 203-385-4250
Dr. Dudley Orr, prin. Fax 381-2014
Flood MS 600/7-8
490 Chapel St 06614 203-385-4280
John Dellapiano, prin. Fax 381-2033
Stratford HS 1,100/9-12
45 N Parade St 06615 203-385-4230
Joseph Corso, prin. Fax 381-2021
Wooster MS 600/7-8
150 Lincoln St 06614 203-385-4275
Jack Lynch, prin. Fax 381-6918

Porter and Chester Institute Post-Sec.
670 Lordship Blvd 06615 203-375-4463

Suffield, Hartford
Suffield SD 2,500/PK-12
350 Mountain Rd 06078 860-668-3800
Karen Baldwin, supt. Fax 668-3805
www.suffield.org
Suffield MS 600/6-8
350 Mountain Rd 06078 860-668-3820
John Warrington, prin. Fax 668-3088
Other Schools – See West Suffield

Lincoln Technical Institute Post-Sec.
1760 Mapleton Ave 06078 866-672-4337
Suffield Academy 400/9-12
185 N Main St 06078 860-668-7315
Charles Cahn, hdmstr. Fax 668-2966

Terryville, Litchfield, Pop. 5,299
Plymouth SD 1,700/PK-12
77 Main St 06786 860-314-8005
Anthony Distasio Ph.D., supt. Fax 314-2766
www.plymouth.k12.ct.us/
Terry MS 400/6-8
21 N Main St 06786 860-314-2790
Gary Travers, prin. Fax 314-2768
Terryville HS 500/9-12
33 N Harwinton Ave 06786 860-314-2777
Brian Falcone, prin. Fax 314-2785

Thomaston, Litchfield, Pop. 1,888
Thomaston SD 1,100/PK-12
PO Box 166 06787 860-283-4796
Francine Coss, supt. Fax 283-6708
www.thomastonschools.net/
Thomaston HS 500/7-12
185 Branch Rd 06787 860-283-3030
John Perrucci, prin. Fax 283-3040

Thompson, Windham

Marianapolis Prep S 300/9-12
PO Box 304 06277 860-923-9565
Joseph Hanrahan, hdmstr. Fax 923-3730

Tolland, Tolland
Tolland SD 3,100/PK-12
51 Tolland Grn 06084 860-870-6850
William D. Guzman, supt. Fax 870-7737
www.tolland.k12.ct.us
Tolland HS 900/9-12
1 Eagle Hill Dr 06084 860-870-6818
Domonique Fox, prin. Fax 870-8168
Tolland MS 700/6-8
1 Falcon Way 06084 860-870-6860
Walter Willett, prin. Fax 870-5737

Torrington, Litchfield, Pop. 35,694
Connecticut Technical HS System
Supt. — See Middletown
Wolcott Technical HS Vo/Tech
75 Oliver St 06790 860-496-5300
Robert Axon, prin. Fax 496-9022

Torrington SD 4,500/PK-12
355 Migeon Ave 06790 860-489-2327
Cheryl Kloczko, supt. Fax 489-0726
www.torrington.org
Alternative Education Programs Alt
Major Besse Rd 06790 860-489-2298
Beth Robin, dir. Fax 489-2367
Torrington HS 1,100/9-12
50 Major Besse Dr 06790 860-489-2294
Joanne Creedon, prin. Fax 489-2853
Torrington MS 1,100/6-8
200 Middle School Dr 06790 860-496-4050
Steven Gottlieb, prin. Fax 496-1089

Trumbull, Fairfield, Pop. 35,588
Trumbull SD 7,000/PK-12
6254 Main St 06611 203-452-4301
Gary Cialfi, supt. Fax 452-4305
www.trumbullps.org
Hillcrest MS 700/6-8
530 Daniels Farm Rd 06611 203-452-4466
Rosemary Seaman, prin. Fax 452-4479
Madison MS 900/6-8
4630 Madison Ave 06611 203-452-4499
Valerie Forshaw, prin. Fax 452-4490
Trumbull HS 2,200/9-12
72 Strobel Rd 06611 203-452-4555
Robert Tremaglio, prin. Fax 452-4593

Christian Heritage S 400/K-12
575 White Plains Rd 06611 203-261-6230
Brian Modarelli, head sch Fax 452-1531
St. Joseph HS 800/9-12
2320 Huntington Tpke 06611 203-378-9378
Kenneth Mayo, prin. Fax 378-7306

Uncasville, New London, Pop. 2,975

St. Bernard S 400/6-12
1593 Norwich New London Tpk 06382
860-848-3007
Thomas Doherty, hdmstr. Fax 848-0261

Vernon Rockville, Tolland, Pop. 28,900
Vernon SD 3,500/PK-12
PO Box 600 06066 860-870-6000
Dr. Mary Conway, supt. Fax 870-6005
vernonpublicschools.org
Rockville HS 1,100/9-12
70 Loveland Hill Rd 06066 860-870-6050
Brian Levesque, prin. Fax 870-6314
Vernon Center MS 800/6-8
777 Hartford Tpke 06066 860-870-6070
Dr. Beth Katz, prin. Fax 870-6318

Wallingford, New Haven, Pop. 41,700
Wallingford SD 6,500/PK-12
142 Hope Hill Rd 06492 203-949-6500
Dr. Salvatore Menzo, supt. Fax 949-6550
www.wallingford.k12.ct.us
Hall HS 1,100/9-12
70 Pond Hill Rd 06492 203-294-5350
David Bryant, prin. Fax 294-5353
Hammarskjold MS 700/6-8
106 Pond Hill Rd 06492 203-294-3700
Ann Cocchiola, prin. Fax 294-3749
Moran MS 800/6-8
141 Hope Hill Rd 06492 203-741-2900
Joseph Piacentini, prin. Fax 741-2939
Sheehan HS 1,000/9-12
142 Hope Hill Rd 06492 203-294-5900
Rosemary Duthie, prin. Fax 294-5980

Choate Rosemary Hall S 900/9-12
333 Christian St 06492 203-697-2000
Alex Curtis, hdmstr. Fax 697-2720

Washington, Litchfield
Regional SD 12
Supt. — See Washington Depot
Shepaug Valley HS 300/9-12
159 South St 06793 860-868-7326
Kimberly Gallo, prin. Fax 868-0260
Shepaug Valley MS 200/6-8
159 South St 06793 860-868-6208
Kimberly Gallo, prin. Fax 868-0622

Devereux Center in Connecticut Post-Sec.
81 Sabbaday Ln 06793 860-868-7377
Gunnery 300/9-12
99 Green Hill Rd 06793 860-868-7334
Susan Graham, head sch Fax 868-1614

Washington Depot, Litchfield
Regional SD 12 900/PK-12
PO Box 386 06794 860-868-6100
Patricia Cosentino Ed.D., supt. Fax 868-6103
www.region-12.org
Other Schools – See Washington

Waterbury, New Haven, Pop. 106,427
Connecticut Technical HS System
Supt. — See Middletown
Kaynor Technical HS Vo/Tech
43 Tompkins St 06708 203-596-4302
Lisa Hylwa, prin. Fax 596-4308

Waterbury SD 17,400/PK-12
236 Grand St 06702 203-574-8000
Dr. Kathleen Ouellette, supt. Fax 574-8010
www.waterbury.k12.ct.us/
Crosby HS 1,400/9-12
300 Pierpont Rd 06705 203-574-8061
Antonio Musto, prin. Fax 574-8072
Enlightenment S 100/Alt
30 Church St 06702 203-574-8050
Michele Buerkle, prin. Fax 573-6634
Kennedy HS 1,400/9-12
422 Highland Ave 06708 203-574-8153
Robert Johnston, prin. Fax 574-8154
North End MS 1,200/6-8
534 Bucks Hill Rd 06704 203-574-8097
Michael LoRusso, prin. Fax 574-8203
Wallace MS 1,300/6-8
3465 E Main St 06705 203-574-8140
Donald Rapuano, prin. Fax 574-8141
Waterbury Arts Magnet S 500/6-12
16 S Elm St 06706 203-573-6300
Leo Lavallee, prin. Fax 573-6325
Waterbury Career Academy HS Vo/Tech
175 Birch St 06704 203-574-8023
Dr. Louis Padua, prin.
West Side MS 1,100/6-8
483 Chase Pkwy 06708 203-574-8120
Maria Burns, prin. Fax 574-8130
Wilby HS 1,300/9-12
568 Bucks Hill Rd 06704 203-574-8100
Robyn Apicella, prin. Fax 574-6896

Chase Collegiate S 500/PK-12
565 Chase Pkwy 06708 203-236-9500
John Fixx, hdmstr. Fax 236-9494
Holy Cross HS 800/9-12
587 Oronoke Rd 06708 203-757-9248
Margaret Leger, prin. Fax 757-3423
Industrial Management and Training Post-Sec.
233 Mill St 06706 203-753-7910
Mesivta of Waterbury 9-12
359 Cooke St 06710 203-756-1800
Fax 756-1200
Naugatuck Valley Community College Post-Sec.
750 Chase Pkwy 06708 203-575-8040
Post University Post-Sec.
PO Box 2540 06723 203-596-4500
Sacred Heart HS 400/9-12
142 S Elm St 06706 203-753-1605
Anthony Azzara, prin. Fax 597-1686
St. Mary's Hospital Post-Sec.
56 Franklin St 06706 203-574-6300
Stone Academy Post-Sec.
101 Pierpont Rd 06705 203-756-5500
University of Connecticut Post-Sec.
99 E Main St 06702 203-236-9800

Waterford, New London, Pop. 2,818
Waterford SD 2,700/K-12
15 Rope Ferry Rd 06385 860-444-5801
Jerome Belair, supt. Fax 444-5870
www.waterfordschools.org
Clark Lane MS 700/6-8
105 Clark Ln 06385 860-443-2837
Michael Lovetere, prin. Fax 437-6985

Waterford HS 1,000/9-12
20 Rope Ferry Rd 06385 860-437-6956
Donald Macrino, prin. Fax 447-7928

Watertown, Litchfield, Pop. 6,000
Watertown SD 3,200/PK-12
10 Deforest St 06795 860-945-4801
Dr. Gail Gilmore, supt. Fax 945-2775
www.watertownps.org/
Watertown HS 1,000/9-12
324 French St 06795 860-945-4810
Matthew Geary, prin. Fax 945-3348
Other Schools – See Oakville

Porter and Chester Institute Post-Sec.
320 Sylvan Lake Rd 06779 860-274-9294
Taft S 600/9-12
110 Woodbury Rd 06795 860-945-7777
William MacMullen, hdmstr. Fax 945-7720

Westbrook, Middlesex, Pop. 2,342
Westbrook SD 900/PK-12
158 McVeagh Rd 06498 860-399-6432
Patricia Charles, supt. Fax 399-8817
www.westbrookctschools.org/
Westbrook HS 300/9-12
156 McVeagh Rd 06498 860-399-6214
Robert Hale, prin. Fax 399-2007
Westbrook MS 300/5-8
154 McVeagh Rd 06498 860-399-2010
Cori DiMaggio, prin. Fax 399-2006

Oxford Academy 50/8-12
1393 Boston Post Rd 06498 860-399-6247
Philip Cocchiola, head sch Fax 399-6805

West Hartford, Hartford, Pop. 61,804
West Hartford SD 10,200/PK-12
50 S Main St, 860-561-6600
Karen List, supt. Fax 561-6910
www.whps.org
Bristow MS 400/6-8
34 Highland St, 860-231-2100
Andrew Morrow, prin. Fax 231-2107
Conard HS 1,600/9-12
110 Beechwood Rd, 860-521-1350
Peter Cummings, prin. Fax 521-6699
Hall HS 1,600/9-12
975 N Main St, 860-232-4561
Tom Einhorn, prin. Fax 236-0366
King Philip MS 900/6-8
100 King Philip Dr, 860-233-8236
Michael Renkawitz, prin. Fax 233-0812
Sedgwick MS 900/6-8
128 Sedgwick Rd, 860-521-0610
Roszena Haskins, prin. Fax 521-7502

American Institute Post-Sec.
99 South St, 860-947-2299
American School for the Deaf Post-Sec.
139 N Main St, 860-570-2309
Kingswood Oxford S 500/6-12
170 Kingswood Rd, 860-233-9631
Dennis Bisgaard, head sch Fax 232-3843
Northwest Catholic HS 700/9-12
29 Wampanoag Dr, 860-236-4221
Margaret Williamson, prin. Fax 586-0911
St. Timothy MS 100/6-8
225 King Philip Dr, 860-236-0614
Tara Bellefleur M.Ed., prin. Fax 920-0293
University of Hartford Post-Sec.
200 Bloomfield Ave, 860-768-4100
University of Saint Joseph Post-Sec.
1678 Asylum Ave, 860-232-4571

West Haven, New Haven, Pop. 54,140
West Haven SD 6,200/PK-12
PO Box 26010 06516 203-937-4310
Neil Cavallaro, supt. Fax 937-4315
www.whschools.org
Bailey MS 1,000/7-8
106 Morgan Ln 06516 203-937-4380
Anthony Cordone Ed.D., prin. Fax 937-4385
West Haven HS 1,500/9-12
1 McDonough Plz 06516 203-937-4360
Ronald Stancil, prin. Fax 934-4370

Notre Dame HS 600/9-12
24 Ricardo St 06516 203-933-1673
Patrick Clifford, prin. Fax 933-2474
Stone Academy Post-Sec.
560 Saw Mill Rd 06516 203-288-7474
University of New Haven Post-Sec.
300 Boston Post Rd 06516 203-932-7000

Weston, Fairfield
Weston SD 2,500/PK-12
24 School Rd 06883 203-291-1401
Colleen Palmer Ph.D., supt. Fax 291-1415
www.westonps.org
Weston HS 800/9-12
115 School Rd 06883 203-291-1600
Lisa Wolak, prin. Fax 291-1603
Weston MS 600/6-8
135 School Rd 06883 203-291-1500
Amy Watkins, prin. Fax 291-1516

Westport, Fairfield, Pop. 25,982
Westport SD 5,800/PK-12
110 Myrtle Ave 06880 203-341-1010
Dr. Elliott Landon, supt. Fax 341-1029
www.westport.k12.ct.us/
Bedford MS 800/6-8
88 North Ave 06880 203-341-1510
Adam Rosen, prin. Fax 341-1508
Coleytown MS 500/6-8
255 North Ave 06880 203-341-1600
Kris Szabo, prin. Fax 341-1614
Staples HS 1,800/9-12
70 North Ave 06880 203-341-1200
John Dodig, prin. Fax 341-1202

Connecticut Center for Massage Therapy Post-Sec.
25 Sylvan Rd S 06880 203-221-7325

West Redding, Fairfield
Redding SD
Supt. — See Easton
Read MS 600/5-8
486 Redding Rd 06896 203-938-2533
Diane Martin, prin. Fax 938-8667

West Simsbury, Hartford, Pop. 2,411

Master's S 300/PK-12
36 Westledge Rd 06092 860-651-9361
Brian Meek, hdmstr. Fax 651-9363

West Suffield, Hartford
Suffield SD
Supt. — See Suffield
Suffield HS 900/9-12
1060 Sheldon St 06093 860-668-3810
Donna Hayward, prin. Fax 668-3037

Wethersfield, Hartford, Pop. 26,301
Wethersfield SD 3,700/PK-12
127 Hartford Ave 06109 860-571-8110
Michael Emmett, supt. Fax 571-8130
www.wethersfield.k12.ct.us/
Deane MS 600/7-8
551 Silas Deane Hwy 06109 860-571-8300
Steven Cook, prin. Fax 563-0563
Wethersfield HS 1,200/9-12
411 Wolcott Hill Rd 06109 860-571-8200
Thomas Moore, prin. Fax 571-8240

Connecticut Childrens Medical Center Post-Sec.
170 Ridge Rd 06109 860-545-8551

Willimantic, Windham, Pop. 17,404
Connecticut Technical HS System
Supt. — See Middletown
Windham Technical HS Vo/Tech
210 Birch St 06226 860-456-3879
Kirk Murad, prin. Fax 450-0630

Windham SD 2,600/PK-12
322 Prospect St 06226 860-465-2310
Ana Ortiz, supt. Fax 456-2311
www.windham.k12.ct.us/
Arts and Humanities Academy 9-10
355 High St 06226 860-465-2417
Carey Edwards, hdmstr.
STEM Academy, 355 High St 06226 9-10
Dorothy Potter, hdmstr. 860-465-2481
Windham HS 400/11-12
355 High St 06226 860-465-2480
Albert Harris, prin. Fax 465-2463
Windham MS 700/6-8
123 Quarry St 06226 860-465-2351
Bryan Olkowski, prin. Fax 465-2353

Eastern Connecticut State University Post-Sec.
83 Windham St 06226 860-456-5000
Windham Community Memorial Hospital Post-Sec.
112 Mansfield Ave 06226 860-456-6800
Windham Tech High School Post-Sec.
210 Birch St 06226 860-456-3879

Willington, Tolland
Willington SD 500/PK-8
40 Old Farms Rd Ste A 06279 860-487-3130
David Harding, supt. Fax 487-3132
www.willingtonpublicschools.org
Hall Memorial MS 300/4-8
111 River Rd 06279 860-429-9391
Deborah Sullivan, prin. Fax 429-5682

Wilton, Fairfield, Pop. 7,200
Wilton SD 4,300/PK-12
PO Box 277 06897 203-762-3381
Gary Richards, supt. Fax 762-2177
www.edline.net/pages/Wilton_School_District
Middlebrook MS 1,000/6-8
131 School Rd 06897 203-762-8388
Julia Harris, prin. Fax 762-1716
Wilton HS 1,300/9-12
395 Danbury Rd 06897 203-762-0381
Robert O'Donnell, prin. Fax 834-0164

Windsor, Hartford, Pop. 27,817
Capitol Region Education Council RESC
Supt. — See Hartford
Medical Professions & Teacher Prep Acad PK-PK, 6-
10 Univac Ln 06095 860-298-0602
Andrew Skarzynski, prin. Fax 298-0668

Hartford SD
Supt. — See Hartford
Pathways to Technology Magnet S 400/9-12
184 Windsor Ave 06095 860-695-9450
Steven Dellinger-Pate, contact Fax 722-6439

Windsor SD 2,700/PK-12
601 Matianuck Ave 06095 860-687-2000
Jeffrey Villar Ph.D., supt. Fax 687-2009
www.windsorct.org
Sage Park MS 800/6-8
25 Sage Park Rd 06095 860-687-2030
Paul Cavaliere, prin. Fax 687-2039
Windsor HS 1,300/9-12
50 Sage Park Rd 06095 860-687-2020
Russell Sills, prin. Fax 687-2029

Branford Hall Career Institute Post-Sec.
995 Day Hill Rd 06095 860-683-4900
Loomis Chaffee S 700/9-12
4 Batchelder Rd 06095 860-687-6000
Sheila Culbert, hdmstr. Fax 687-6552
Praise Power & Prayer Christian S 100/K-12
PO Box 474 06095 860-285-8898
Rev. Raymond McMahon, prin.

Windsor Locks, Hartford, Pop. 12,219
Windsor Locks SD 1,800/PK-12
58 S Elm St 06096 860-292-5000
Wayne Sweeney, supt. Fax 292-5003
www.wlps.org
Windsor Locks HS 500/9-12
58 S Elm St 06096 860-292-5032
Susan Bell, prin. Fax 292-5039
Windsor Locks MS 400/6-8
7 Center St 06096 860-292-5012
Gregory Blanchfield, prin. Fax 292-5017

Winsted, Litchfield, Pop. 7,586
Endowed & Incorporated Academies 300/7-12
200 Williams Ave 06098 860-379-8521
Anthony Serio Ed.D., supt. Fax 379-6163
gilbertschool.org
Gilbert S 300/7-12
200 Williams Ave 06098 860-379-8521
Alan Strauss, prin. Fax 379-6163

Regional SD 7 1,100/7-12
PO Box 656 06098 860-379-1084
Dr. Judith Palmer, supt. Fax 379-0618
www.nwr7.com
Northwestern Regional HS 800/9-12
100 Battistoni Rd 06098 860-379-8525
Kenneth Chichester, prin. Fax 738-6059
Northwestern Regional MS 300/7-8
100 Battistoni Rd 06098 860-379-7243
Candy Perez, prin. Fax 738-6205

Northwestern CT Comm. Technical College Post-Sec.
2 Park Pl 06098 860-738 6300

Wolcott, New Haven, Pop. 13,700
Wolcott SD 2,700/PK-12
154 Center St 06716 203-879-8183
Joseph Macary, supt. Fax 879-8182
www.wolcottps.org
Tyrrell MS 700/6-8
500 Todd Rd 06716 203-879-8151
Arline Tansley, prin. Fax 879-8419
Wolcott HS 900/9-12
457 Bound Line Rd 06716 203-879-8164
Dr. Robert Eberle, prin. Fax 879-8167

Connecticut Institute of Hair Design Post-Sec.
1681 Meriden Rd 06716 203-879-4247

Woodbridge, New Haven, Pop. 7,924
Regional SD 5 2,500/7-12
25 Newton Rd 06525 203-392-2106
Dr. John Brady, supt. Fax 397-4864
www.amityregion5.org
Amity Regional HS 1,600/9-12
25 Newton Rd 06525 203-397-4830
Charles Britton, prin. Fax 397-4866
Other Schools – See Bethany, Orange

Jewish HS of Connecticut 9-12
360 Amity Rd 06525 203-275-8448
Rabbi Yonatan Yussman Ed.D., head sch

Woodbury, Litchfield, Pop. 8,131
Regional SD 14 2,100/PK-12
PO Box 469 06798 203-263-4330
Jody Goeler, supt. Fax 263-0372
www.ctreg14.org
Nonnewaug HS 900/9-12
5 Minortown Rd 06798 203-263-2186
Lori Ferreira, prin. Fax 263-3570
Woodbury MS 400/6-8
67 Washington Ave 06798 203-263-4306
Alice Jones, prin. Fax 263-0825

Woodstock, Windham
Endowed & Incorporated Academies 1,100/9-12
57 Academy Rd 06281 860-928-6575
Kim Caron, hdmstr. Fax 963-7222
www.woodstockacademy.org
Woodstock Academy 1,100/9-12
57 Academy Rd 06281 860-928-6575
Kim Caron, hdmstr. Fax 963-7222

Woodstock SD 900/PK-8
147A Route 169 06281 860-928-7453
Dr. Francis Baran, supt. Fax 928-0206
www.woodstockschools.net
Woodstock MS 400/5-8
147B Route 169 06281 860-963-6575
Paul Gamache, prin. Fax 963-6577

Hyde S - Woodstock 100/9-12
PO Box 237 06281 860-963-9096
Laura Gauld, dir. Fax 963-0164

DELAWARE

DELAWARE DEPARTMENT OF EDUCATION

401 Federal St Ste 2, Dover 19901-3639
Telephone 302-735-4000
Fax 302-739-4654
Website http://www.doe.k12.de.us

Secretary of Education Mark Murphy

DELAWARE BOARD OF EDUCATION

1006 Tulip Tree Ln, Newark 19713-1128

President Teri Quinn Gray

PUBLIC, PRIVATE AND CATHOLIC SECONDARY SCHOOLS

Bear, New Castle, Pop. 18,842

Academy of Massage & Bodywork Post-Sec.
1218 Pulaski Hwy Ste 324 19701 302-392-6768
Caravel Academy 1,100/PK-12
2801 Del Laws Rd 19701 302-834-8938
Fairwinds Christian S 200/PK-12
801 Seymour Rd 19701 302-328-7404
J. Mulholland, prin. Fax 328-0190
Red Lion Christian Academy 700/PK-12
1390 Red Lion Rd 19701 302-834-2526
Dr. Chuck Betters, admin. Fax 836-6346

Bridgeville, Sussex, Pop. 1,988
Woodbridge SD 2,200/PK-12
16359 Sussex Hwy 19933 302-337-7990
Heath Chasanov, supt. Fax 337-7998
www.wsd.k12.de.us
Wheatley MS 700/5-8
48 Church St 19933 302-337-3469
Delores Tunstall, prin. Fax 337-6016
Woodbridge HS 600/9-12
307 S Laws St 19933 302-337-8289
Robert Adams, prin. Fax 337-0631

Camden, Kent, Pop. 3,311
Caesar Rodney SD
Supt. — See Wyoming
Fifer MS 900/6-8
109 E Camden Wyoming Ave 19934 302-698-8400
Dr. Jessilene Corbett, prin. Fax 698-8409
Postlethwait MS 800/6-8
2841 S State St 19934 302-698-8410
Jason Payne, prin. Fax 698-8419
Rodney HS 2,100/9-12
239 Old North Rd 19934 302-697-2161
Elvina Knight, prin. Fax 697-6888

Claymont, New Castle, Pop. 8,108

Archmere Academy 500/9-12
3600 Philadelphia Pike 19703 302-798-6632
Dr. William Doyle, prin. Fax 798-7290

Dagsboro, Sussex, Pop. 782
Indian River SD
Supt. — See Selbyville
Indian River HS 900/9-12
29772 Armory Rd 19939 302-732-1500
Bennett Murray, prin. Fax 732-1514

Delmar, Sussex, Pop. 1,524
Delmar SD 1,300/5-12
200 N 8th St 19940 302-846-9544
David Ring Ed.D., supt. Fax 846-2793
www.delmar.k12.de.us
Delmar HS 600/9-12
200 N 8th St 19940 302-846-9544
Ashley Giska, prin. Fax 846-5056
Delmar MS 700/5-8
200 N 8th St 19940 302-846-9544
Jason Macrides, prin. Fax 846-5056

Dover, Kent, Pop. 34,742
Caesar Rodney SD
Supt. — See Wyoming
Dover AFB MS 200/6-8
3100 Hawthorne Dr 19901 302-674-3284
David Santore Ed.D., prin. Fax 730-4283

Capital SD 6,300/PK-12
198 Commerce Way 19904 302-672-1500
Michael Thomas Ed.D., supt. Fax 672-1714
www.capital.k12.de.us/
Central MS 900/7-8
211 Delaware Ave 19901 302-672-1772
Shan Green, prin. Fax 672-1733
Dover HS 1,500/9-12
1 Patrick Lynn Dr 19904 302-672-1526
Kenneth Garvey, prin. Fax 672-1565
Kent County Alternative S 100/Alt
631 Ridgely St 19904 302-736-5355
Robert Harris, prin. Fax 736-5263

Bayhealth Medical Center Post-Sec.
640 S State St 19901 302-674-7001
Calvary Christian Academy 300/PK-12
1143 E Lebanon Rd 19901 302-697-7860
Aaron Coon, admin. Fax 697-0284
Delaware State University Post-Sec.
1200 N Dupont Hwy 19901 302-857-6060
Delaware Technical & Community College Post-Sec.
100 Campus Dr 19904 302-857-1000
Harris School of Business Post-Sec.
97 Commerce Way Ste 105 19904 302-674-8060
Wesley College Post-Sec.
120 N State St 19901 302-736-2300

Felton, Kent, Pop. 1,251
Lake Forest SD 3,800/PK-12
5423 Killens Pond Rd 19943 302-284-3020
Dr. Daniel Curry, supt. Fax 284-4491
www.lf.k12.de.us
Lake Forest HS 900/9-12
5407 Killens Pond Rd 19943 302-284-9291
John Fillicicchia, prin. Fax 284-5833
Other Schools – See Harrington

Frankford, Sussex, Pop. 835
Indian River SD
Supt. — See Selbyville
Carver Educational Center Alt
30207 Frankford School Rd 19945 302-732-3800
Walter Smith, prin. Fax 732-3790

Georgetown, Sussex, Pop. 6,322
Indian River SD
Supt. — See Selbyville
Georgetown MS 500/6-8
301 W Market St 19947 302-856-1900
Mike Williams, prin. Fax 856-1915
Sussex Central HS 1,300/9-12
26026 Patriots Way 19947 302-934-3166
Jay Owens, prin. Fax 934-3234

Sussex Technical SD
PO Box 351 19947 302-856-2541
A.J. Lathbury Ed.D., supt. Fax 856-7078
www.sussexvt.k12.de.us
Sussex Technical HS Vo/Tech
PO Box 351 19947 302-856-0961
John Demby Ed.D., prin. Fax 856-1760

Delaware Technical & Community College Post-Sec.
PO Box 610 19947 302-856-5400
Delmarva Christian HS 200/9-12
21150 Airport Rd 19947 302-856-4040
Mike Vonhof, prin. Fax 856-6878

Greenville, New Castle, Pop. 2,293
Red Clay Consolidated SD
Supt. — See Wilmington
DuPont HS 1,400/9-12
50 Hillside Rd 19807 302-651-2626
Kevin Palladinetti, prin. Fax 651-2757
DuPont MS 500/6-8
3130 Kennett Pike 19807 302-651-2690
Theodore Boyer, prin. Fax 425-4585

Greenwood, Sussex, Pop. 943

Greenwood Mennonite S 200/PK-12
12802 Mennonite School Rd 19950 302-349-4131
Duane Miller, admin. Fax 349-5076

Harrington, Kent, Pop. 3,428
Lake Forest SD
Supt. — See Felton
Chipman MS 1,000/6-8
101 W Center St 19952 302-398-8197
Douglas Brown, prin. Fax 398-8375

Hockessin, New Castle, Pop. 13,327
Red Clay Consolidated SD
Supt. — See Wilmington
DuPont MS 800/6-8
735 Meeting House Rd 19707 302-239-3420
Aaron Selekman, prin. Fax 239-3450

Sanford S 600/PK-12
PO Box 888 19707 302-239-5263
Mark Anderson, hdmstr. Fax 239-5389
Towle Institute 200/K-12
PO Box 580 19707 302-993-1408
Kathleen Todd, prin. Fax 993-1409
Wilmington Christian S 500/PK-12
825 Loveville Rd 19707 302-239-2121
William Stevens, head sch Fax 239-2778

Laurel, Sussex, Pop. 3,540
Laurel SD 2,200/PK-12
1160 S Central Ave 19956 302-875-6100
John Ewald, supt. Fax 875-6106
www.laurel.k12.de.us
Laurel HS 500/9-12
1133 S Central Ave 19956 302-875-6120
Amber Deiter, prin. Fax 875-6123
Laurel MS 300/7-8
801 S Central Ave 19956 302-875-6110
Ann Lewis, prin. Fax 875-6148
Western Sussex Academy 50/Alt
815 S Central Ave 19956 302-875-6196
Richard Gaskill, prin. Fax 875-6106

Lewes, Sussex, Pop. 2,714
Cape Henlopen SD 4,600/K-12
1270 Kings Hwy 19958 302-645-6686
Robert S. Fulton M.Ed., supt. Fax 645-6684
www.capehenlopenschools.com/
Beacon MS 500/6-8
19483 John J Williams Hwy 19958 302-645-6288
David Frederick, prin. Fax 644-6118
Cape Henlopen HS 1,300/9-12
1250 Kings Hwy 19958 302-645-7711
Brian Donahue, prin. Fax 645-1356
Other Schools – See Milton

Beebe Medical Center School of Nursing Post-Sec.
424 Savannah Rd 19958 302-645-3251

Magnolia, Kent, Pop. 218

St. Thomas More Academy 200/9-12
133 Thomas More Dr 19962 302-697-8100
Fr. James Lentini, prin. Fax 697-8122

Middletown, New Castle, Pop. 18,350
Appoquinimink SD
Supt. — See Odessa
Appoquinimink HS 1,400/9-12
1080 Bunker Hill Rd 19709 302-449-3840
Gayle Rutter, prin. Fax 378-5130
Meredith MS 700/6-8
504 S Broad St 19709 302-378-5001
T.J. Vari, prin. Fax 378-5008
Middletown HS 1,200/9-12
120 Silver Lake Rd 19709 302-376-4141
Matt Donovan, prin. Fax 378-5268
Redding MS 700/6-8
201 New St 19709 302-378-5030
Chris Beck, prin. Fax 378-5080
Waters MS 800/6-8
1235 Cedar Lane Rd 19709 302-449-3490
Victoir Cahoon, prin.

New Castle County Voc-Tech SD
Supt. — See Wilmington
St. Georges Technical HS Vo/Tech
555 Hyetts Corner Rd 19709 302-449-3360
Shanta Reynolds, prin. Fax 376-6796

St. Andrew's S 300/9-12
350 Noxontown Rd 19709 302-285-4231
Daniel Roach, hdmstr. Fax 378-7120

Milford, Sussex, Pop. 9,349
Milford SD 2,900/PK-12
906 Lakeview Ave 19963 302-422-1600
Dr. Phyllis Kohel, supt. Fax 422-1608
www.milfordschooldistrict.org/

Milford Central Academy 300/6-8
1021 N Walnut St 19963 302-424-7900
Tricia Martin Ed.D., prin. Fax 424-4163
Milford HS 900/9-12
1019 N Walnut St 19963 302-422-1610
Dr. David Carter, prin. Fax 424-5463

Cross Christian Academy 50/K-12
PO Box 24 19963 302-542-4266
Donald Porter, dir.
Milford Christian S 100/PK-12
6062 Old Shawnee Rd 19963 302-422-4263
Dr. David Perdue, admin. Fax 422-6379

Millsboro, Sussex, Pop. 3,755
Indian River SD
Supt. — See Selbyville
Millsboro MS 600/6-8
302 E State St 19966 302-934-3200
Renee Jerns, prin. Fax 934-3215

Milton, Sussex, Pop. 2,504
Cape Henlopen SD
Supt. — See Lewes
Mariner MS 500/6-8
16391 Harbeson Rd 19968 302-684-8516
Fred Best, prin. Fax 684-5606

Newark, New Castle, Pop. 30,774
Christina SD
Supt. — See Wilmington
Christiana HS 1,100/9-12
190 Salem Church Rd 19713 302-631-2400
Kris Diviny, prin. Fax 454-3490
Gauger/Cobbs MS 1,300/6-8
50 Gender Rd 19713 302-454-2358
Harold Shaw, prin. Fax 454-3482
Glasgow HS 1,200/9-12
1901 S College Ave 19702 302-631-5600
Dr. Sherry Gross, prin. Fax 454-5453
Kirk MS 900/6-8
140 Brennen Dr 19713 302-454-2164
Saliyah Cruz, prin. Fax 454-3491
Newark HS 1,600/9-12
750 E Delaware Ave 19711 302-631-4700
Curtis Bedford, prin. Fax 454-2155
Shue-Medill MS 1,100/6-8
1500 Capitol Trl 19711 302-454-2171
Jason de Jonghe, prin. Fax 454-3492

New Castle County Voc-Tech SD
Supt. — See Wilmington
Hodgson Vocational-Technical HS Vo/Tech
2575 Glasgow Ave 19702 302-834-0990
Jerry Lamey Ed.D., prin. Fax 834-0598

Delaware Technical & Community College Post-Sec.
400 Stanton Christiana Rd 19713 302-454-3900
Schilling Douglas School of Hair Design Post-Sec.
70 Amstel Ave 19711 302-737-5100
University of Delaware Post-Sec.
210 S College Ave 19716 302-831-2792

New Castle, New Castle, Pop. 5,184
Colonial SD 9,700/K-12
318 E Basin Rd 19720 302-323-2700
Dorothy Linn Ed.D., supt. Fax 323-2748
www.colonial.k12.de.us
Bedford MS 1,100/6-8
801 Cox Neck Rd 19720 302-832-6280
Andrew Moffett, prin. Fax 834-6729
McCullough MS 800/6-8
20 Chase Ave 19720 302-429-4000
Elizabeth Fleetwood, prin. Fax 429-4005
New Castle Alternative S Alt
903 Delaware St 19720 302-323-2880
Dr. Ige Purnell, prin. Fax 323-2897
Penn HS 2,000/9-12
713 E Basin Rd 19720 302-323-2800
Jeffrey Menzer, prin. Fax 323-2955
Read MS 700/6-8
314 E Basin Rd 19720 302-323-2760
Holly Sage, prin. Fax 323-2763

Tall Oaks Classical S 200/K-12
903 E Basin Rd 19720 302-738-3337
Donald Post, hdmstr. Fax 328-7886
Wilmington University Post-Sec.
320 N Dupont Hwy 19720 302-356-4636

Odessa, New Castle, Pop. 353
Appoquinimink SD 8,900/PK-12
PO Box 4010 19730 302-376-4128
Matthew Burrows, supt. Fax 378-5016
www.apposchooldistrict.com
Other Schools – See Middletown

Seaford, Sussex, Pop. 6,739
Seaford SD 3,400/K-12
390 N Market St 19973 302-629-4587
Dr. Shawn Joseph, supt. Fax 629-2619
www.seafordbluejays.org/
Seaford HS 800/9-12
399 N Market St 19973 302-629-4587
Todd Fishburn, prin. Fax 628-4417
Seaford Intensive Learning Center Alt
1 Delaware Pl 19973 302-629-4587
Robin Andrus Ed.D., dir. Fax 629-2619
Seaford MS 700/6-8
500 E Stein Hwy 19973 302-629-4587
Kim Simmons, prin. Fax 628-4485

Seaford Christian Academy 50/PK-12
110 Holly St 19973 302-629-7161
Rev. Michael Hopkins, supt. Fax 629-7726

Selbyville, Sussex, Pop. 2,147
Indian River SD 8,700/PK-12
31 Hosier St 19975 302-436-1000
Susan Bunting Ed.D., supt. Fax 436-1034
www.irsd.net/
Selbyville MS 600/6-8
80 Bethany Rd 19975 302-436-1020
Mike King, prin. Fax 436-1035
Other Schools – See Dagsboro, Frankford, Georgetown, Millsboro

Smyrna, Kent, Pop. 9,689
Smyrna SD 5,400/PK-12
82 Monrovia Ave 19977 302-653-8585
Deborah Wicks, supt. Fax 653-3149
www.smyrna.k12.de.us
Smyrna HS 1,400/9-12
500 Duck Creek Pkwy 19977 302-653-8581
Stacy Cook, prin. Fax 653-3139
Smyrna MS 800/7-8
700 Duck Creek Pkwy 19977 302-653-8584
Steven Gott, prin. Fax 653-3424

Smyrna Christian S 100/K-12
PO Box 159 19977 302-653-2538
William Kidwell, admin. Fax 653-8467

Wilmington, New Castle, Pop. 69,534
Brandywine SD 10,100/K-12
1311 Brandywine Blvd 19809 302-793-5000
Mark Holodick Ed.D., supt. Fax 792-3823
www.brandywineschools.org
Brandywine Community S Alt
720 W 37th St 19802 302-762-1838
Dr. Kim Allen, dir.
Brandywine HS 1,000/9-12
1400 Foulk Rd 19803 302-479-1600
Michael Gliniak, prin. Fax 479-1604
Concord HS 1,400/9-12
2501 Ebright Rd 19810 302-475-3951
Anne Lambert, prin. Fax 529-3094
DuPont MS 900/6-8
701 W 34th St 19802 302-762-7146
Lewis Cheatwood, prin. Fax 762-7196
Mt. Pleasant HS 900/9-12
5201 Washington Blvd 19809 302-762-7125
James Simmons, prin. Fax 762-7042
Springer MS 900/6-8
2220 Shipley Rd 19803 302-479-1621
Jacquelyn Biggs, prin. Fax 479-1628
Talley MS 700/6-8
1110 Cypress Rd 19810 302-475-3976
Dr. Richard Carter, prin. Fax 475-3998

Christina SD 17,000/PK-12
600 N Lombard St 19801 302-552-2600
Freeman Williams, supt. Fax 429-4109
www.christina.k12.de.us/
Bayard MS 700/6-8
200 S Dupont St 19805 302-429-4118
Donald Patton, prin. Fax 429-4153
Pyle Academy 100/Alt
501 N Lombard St 19801 302-429-4158
Dr. Malvine Richard, prin. Fax 429-3959
Other Schools – See Newark

New Castle County Voc-Tech SD
1417 Newport Rd 19804 302-995-8050
Victoria Gehrt Ed.D., supt. Fax 995-8038
www.nccvotech.com
Delcastle Technical HS Vo/Tech
1417 Newport Rd 19804 302-995-8100
Clifton Hayes, prin. Fax 995-8197
Howard HS of Technology Vo/Tech
401 E 12th St 19801 302-571-5400
Stanley Spoor Ed.D., prin. Fax 571-5843
Delaware Skills Center Adult
13th & Clifford Brown Walk 19801 302-654-5392
Eric Wells, head sch Fax 654-9418

Other Schools – See Middletown, Newark

Red Clay Consolidated SD 18,100/K-12
1502 Spruce Ave 19805 302-552-3700
Dr. Mervin Daugherty, supt. Fax 992-7820
www.redclay.k12.de.us
Calloway S of Arts 800/6-12
100 N Dupont Rd 19807 302-651-2700
Julie Rumschlag, prin. Fax 425-4594
Central S 200/Alt
1621 Telegraph Rd 19804 302-992-5550
Michael Simmonds, prin. Fax 992-5591
Conrad S of Science 800/6-12
201 Jackson Ave 19804 302-992-5545
Mark Pruitt, prin. Fax 992-5585
Dickinson HS 600/9-12
1801 Milltown Rd 19808 302-992-5500
Byron Murphy, prin. Fax 992-5506
McKean HS 900/9-12
301 Mckennans Church Rd 19808 302-992-5520
Lisa Ueltzhoffer, prin. Fax 992-5525
Skyline MS 800/6-8
2900 Skyline Dr 19808 302-454-3410
Janet Basara, prin. Fax 454-3541
Stanton MS 700/6-8
1800 Limestone Rd 19804 302-992-5540
John Kennedy, prin. Fax 992-5586
Groves Adult Education Adult
1621 Telegraph Rd 19804 302-651-2709
Les Henry, prin. Fax 658-7137
Other Schools – See Greenville, Hockessin

Christiana Care Health Services Post-Sec.
PO Box 1668 19899 302-428-2571
Concord Christian Academy 200/PK-12
2510 Marsh Rd 19810 302-475-3247
Jeffrey Bergey, admin. Fax 475-6462
Dawn Career Institute Post-Sec.
3700 Lancaster Pike 19805 302-633-9075
Delaware College of Art and Design Post-Sec.
600 N Market St 19801 302-622-8000
Delaware Technical & Community College Post-Sec.
333 N Shipley St 19801 302-571-5300
Goldey-Beacom College Post-Sec.
4701 Limestone Rd 19808 302-998-8814
Harris School of Business Post-Sec.
1413 Foulk Rd 19803 302-478-8890
National Massage Therapy Institute Post-Sec.
1601 Concord Pike 19803 800-509-5058
Nativity Preparatory S 50/5-8
1515 Linden St 19805 302-777-1015
Michael Hassler, prin. Fax 777-1225
Padua Academy 600/9-12
905 N Broom St 19806 302-421-3739
Cindy Hayes-Mann, prin. Fax 421-3748
St. Elizabeth HS 400/9-12
1500 Cedar St 19805 302-656-3360
Shirley Bounds, prin. Fax 656-7513
St. Marks HS 1,400/9-12
2501 Pike Creek Rd 19808 302-738-3300
Carol Ripken, prin. Fax 738-5132
Salesianum S 1,000/9-12
1801 N Broom St 19802 302-654-2495
Rev. Christian Beretta, prin. Fax 654-7767
Tatnall S 600/PK-12
1501 Barley Mill Rd 19807 302-998-2292
Dr. Eric Ruoss, hdmstr. Fax 892-4389
Tower Hill S 700/PK-12
2813 W 17th St 19806 302-575-0550
Christopher Wheeler Ph.D., hdmstr. Fax 657-8366
Ursuline Academy 600/PK-12
1106 Pennsylvania Ave 19806 302-658-7158
Cathie Field-Lloyd, pres. Fax 658-4297
Widener University School of Law Post-Sec.
PO Box 7474 19803 302-477-2162
Wilmington Friends S 800/PK-12
101 School Rd 19803 302-576-2900
Bryan Garman, hdmstr. Fax 576-2939

Woodside, Kent, Pop. 178
POLYTECH SD, PO Box 22 19980
Dr. Deborah Zych, supt. 302-697-2170
www.polytechpanthers.com
POLYTECH HS, PO Box 97 19980 Vo/Tech
Dr. Jason Peel, prin. 302-697-3255
POLYTECH Adult Education Adult
PO Box 102 19980 302-697-4545
Elizabeth Jones, dir.

Wyoming, Kent, Pop. 1,263
Caesar Rodney SD 7,600/K-12
7 Front St 19934 302-697-2173
Kevin Fitzgerald Ed.D., supt. Fax 697-3406
www.cr.k12.de.us
Other Schools – See Camden, Dover

DISTRICT OF COLUMBIA

DISTRICT OF COLUMBIA PUBLIC SCHOOLS
1200 1st St NE, Washington 20002-3361
Telephone 202-442-5885
Fax 202-442-5026
Website dcps.dc.gov/

Chancellor Kaya Henderson

DISTRICT OF COLUMBIA BOARD OF EDUCATION
441 4th St NW Ste 723N, Washington 20002

President Laura Slover

PUBLIC, PRIVATE AND CATHOLIC SECONDARY SCHOOLS

Washington, District of Columbia, Pop. 587,406

District of Columbia SD 43,900/PK-12
1200 1st St NE 20002 202-442-5885
Kaya Henderson, chncllr. Fax 442-5026
dcps.dc.gov

Anacostia HS 800/9-12
1601 16th St SE 20020 202-698-2155
Ian Roberts, prin. Fax 698-2188

Ballou HS 1,200/9-12
3401 4th St SE 20032 202-645-3400
Rahman Branch, prin. Fax 645-3397

Banneker HS 400/9-12
800 Euclid St NW 20001 202-671-6320
Anita Berger, prin. Fax 673-2231

Brown MS 200/6-8
4800 Meade St NE 20019 202-724-4632
Darrin Slade, prin. Fax 724-4635

Cardozo HS 600/9-12
2501 11th St NW 20001 202-673-7385
Tanya Roane, prin. Fax 673-2232

CHOICE Academy 300/Alt
1401 Brentwood Pkwy NE 20002 202-939-4350
William Chiselom, dir. Fax 673-8123

Columbia Heights Education Campus 1,300/6-12
3101 16th St NW 20010 202-939-7700
Maria Tukeva, prin. Fax 576-9147

Coolidge HS 700/9-12
6315 5th St NW 20011 202-671-6080
Thelma Jarrett, prin. Fax 576-3147

Deal MS 900/6-8
3815 Fort Dr NW 20016 202-939-2010
James Albright, prin. Fax 282-1116

Dunbar HS 800/9-12
1301 New Jersey Ave NW 20001 202-698-3762
Stephen Jackson, prin. Fax 673-2233

Eastern HS 300/9-10
1700 E Capitol St NE 20003 202-698-4500
Rachel Skerritt, prin. Fax 698-4800

Eliot-Hine MS 300/6-8
1830 Constitution Ave NE 20002 202-939-5380
Tynika Young, prin. Fax 698-0808

Ellington HS of the Arts 500/9-12
3500 R St NW 20007 202-282-0123
Rory Pullens, prin. Fax 337-7847

Fillmore Arts Center-East K-12
915 Spring Rd NW Fl 3 20010 202-576-9709
Katherine Latterner, prin. Fax 576-7387

Fillmore Arts Center-West K-12
1819 35th St NW 20007 202-729-3794
Katherine Latterner, prin. Fax 724-3680

Hardy MS 400/6-8
1819 35th St NW 20007 202-729-4350
Mary Stefanus, prin. Fax 673-8123

Hart MS 400/7-8
601 Mississippi Ave SE 20032 202-671-6426
Billy Kearney, prin. Fax 645-3426

Jefferson MS 300/6-8
801 7th St SW 20024 202-729-3270
Natalie Gordon, prin. Fax 724-2459

Johnson MS 300/6-8
1400 Bruce Pl SE 20020 202-939-3140
Carol Campbell-Fullard, prin. Fax 645-5882

Kramer MS 300/6-8
1700 Q St SE 20020 202-939-3150
Kwame Simmons, prin. Fax 698-1169

MacFarland MS 200/6-8
4400 Iowa Ave NW 20011 202-576-6207
Andre Samuels, prin. Fax 576-6212

McKinley Technology HS Vo/Tech
151 T St NE 20002 202-281-3950
David Pinder, prin. Fax 576-6279

Miller MS 400/6-8
301 49th St NE 20019 202-388-6870
Abdullah Zaki, prin. Fax 727-8330

Moore Academy 300/Alt
1001 Monroe St NE 20017 202-281-3600
Azalia Hunt-Speight, prin. Fax 526-5022

Oyster-Adams Bilingual MS 300/4-8
2020 19th St NW 20009 202-673-7311
Monica Aguirre, prin. Fax 673-7500

Phelps Architecture Construction & Eng S 300/9-12
704 26th St NE 20002 202-729-4360
Willie Jackson, prin. Fax 442-8438

Roosevelt HS 700/9-12
4301 13th St NW 20011 202-576-6130
Ivor Mitchell, prin. Fax 541-6449

School Without Walls HS 400/Alt
2130 G St NW 20037 202-645-9690
Richard Trogisch, prin. Fax 724-8536

Shaw MS 200/6-8
2001 10th St NW 20001 202-673-7329
Guillaume Gendre, prin. Fax 673-6543

Sousa MS 300/6-8
3650 Ely Pl SE 20019 202-729-3260
Clarence Humes, prin. Fax 645-0456

Stuart-Hobson MS 300/6-8
410 E St NE 20002 202-671-6010
Dawn Clemens, prin. Fax 698-4720

Washington Metropolitan HS 200/Alt
300 Bryant St NW 20001 202-939-3610
Carlos Perkins, prin. Fax 698-3443

Wilson HS 1,500/9-12
3950 Chesapeake St NW 20016 202-282-0120
Peter Cahall, prin. Fax 282-0077

Woodson SHS 700/9-12
540 55th St NE 20019 202-939-2030
Richard Jackson, prin. Fax 645-4193

Youth Services Center 100/Alt
1000 Mount Olivet Rd NE 20002 202-576-8388
Arthur Linder, prin. Fax 576-9073

Ballou STAY S Adult
3401 4th St SE 20032 202-645-3390
Cara Fuller, prin. Fax 645-3935

Roosevelt STAY HS Adult
4301 13th St NW 20011 202-576-8399
Sean Yisrael, prin. Fax 576-8478

Academia de la Recta Porta Christian S 100/K-12
7614 Georgia Ave NW 20012 202-726-8737
Annette Miles M.A., admin. Fax 726-8759

American University Post-Sec.
4400 Massachusetts Ave NW 20016 202-885-1000

Archbishop Carroll HS 600/9-12
4300 Harewood Rd NE 20017 202-529-0900
Mary Blaufuss, prin. Fax 526-8879

Bennett Career Institute Post-Sec.
700 Monroe St NE 20017 202-526-1400

Burke S 300/6-12
4101 Connecticut Ave NW 20008 202-362-8882
Kaianasa George, admin. Fax 362-1914

Catholic University of America Post-Sec.
620 Michigan Ave NE 20064 202-319-5000

Chicago Sch of Professional Psychology Post-Sec.
901 15th St NW 20005 202-706-5052

Corcoran College of Art & Design Post-Sec.
500 17th St NW 20006 202-639-1800

Cornerstone S of Washington 200/PK-12
3742 Ely Pl SE 20019 202-575-0027
Anika Prather, head sch Fax 575-0669

Dudley Beauty College Post-Sec.
2031 Rhode Island Ave NE 20018 202-269-3666

Dupont Park Adventist S 200/PK-10
3942 Alabama Ave SE 20020 202-583-8500
Beverly Donovan, prin. Fax 583-0650

Field S 300/6-12
2301 Foxhall Rd NW 20007 202-295-5800
Dale Johnson, hdmstr. Fax 295-5858

Gallaudet University Post-Sec.
800 Florida Ave NE 20002 202-651-5000

Georgetown Day HS 500/9-12
4200 Davenport St NW 20016 202-274-3200
Russell Shaw, head sch Fax 364-9603

Georgetown University Post-Sec.
37th and O St NW 20057 202-687-0100

Georgetown Visitation Prep HS 500/9-12
1524 35th St NW 20007 202-337-3350
Daniel Kerns, hdmstr. Fax 342-5733

George Washington University Post-Sec.
2121 I St NW 20052 202-994-1000

Gonzaga College HS 900/9-12
19 I St NW 20001 202-336-7100
Rev. Vincent Conti, hdmstr. Fax 336-7164

Graduate School Post-Sec.
600 Maryland Ave SW 20024 202-314-3300

Howard University Post-Sec.
2400 6th St NW 20059 202-806-6100

Howard University School of Divinity Post-Sec.
1400 Shepherd St NE 20017 202-806-0500

Johns Hopkins University Post-Sec.
1740 Massachusetts Ave NW 20036 202-663-5600

Lab S of Washington 300/1-12
4759 Reservoir Rd NW 20007 202-965-6600
Katherine Schantz, head sch Fax 965-5015

Levine School of Music Post-Sec.
2801 Upton St NW 20008 202-686-8000

Maret S 600/K-12
3000 Cathedral Ave NW 20008 202-939-8800
Marjo Talbott, hdmstr. Fax 939-8884

Medtech College Post-Sec.
529 14th St NW 20045 202-872-4700

Model Secondary School for the Deaf Post-Sec.
800 Florida Ave NE 20002 202-651-5031

National Cathedral S 600/4-12
3612 Woodley Rd NW 20016 202-537-6300
Kathleen Jamieson, head sch Fax 537-5743

National Conservatory of Dramatic Arts Post-Sec.
1556 Wisconsin Ave NW 20007 202-333-2202

Pontifical Faculty Immaculate Conception Post-Sec.
487 Michigan Ave NE 20017 202-495-3820

Pontifical John Paul II Institute Post-Sec.
620 Michigan Ave NE 20064 202-526-3799

Potomac College Post-Sec.
4000 Chesapeake St NW 20016 202-686-0876

Preparatory S of DC 100/PK-12
209 Upshur St NW 20011 202-722-5080
Betty North, dir. Fax 722-5060

Radians College Post-Sec.
1025 Vermont Ave NW Ste 200 20005 202-291-9020

St. Albans S 600/4-12
Mount Saint Alban 20016 202-537-6435
Vance Wilson, hdmstr. Fax 537-6434

St. Anselms Abbey S 200/6-12
4501 S Dakota Ave NE 20017 202-269-2350
Bill Crittenberger, hdmstr. Fax 269-2373

St. Johns College HS 1,000/9-12
2607 Military Rd NW 20015 202-363-2316
Br. Michael Andrejko, prin. Fax 380-1754

San Miguel MS 100/6-8
7705 Georgia Ave NW 20012 202-232-8345
Br. Francis Eells, prin. Fax 232-3987

Sidwell Friends S 1,100/PK-12
3825 Wisconsin Ave NW 20016 202-537-8100
Thomas Farquhar, hdmstr. Fax 537-8138

Strayer University Post-Sec.
1133 15th St NW Ste 200 20005 202-408-2400

Technical Learning Center Post-Sec.
1720 I St NW Ste 200 20006 202-223-3500

The Institute of World Politics Post-Sec.
1521 16th St NW 20036 202-462-2101

Trinity University Post-Sec.
125 Michigan Ave NE 20017 202-884-9000

University of the District of Columbia Post-Sec.
4200 Connecticut Ave NW 20008 202-274-5000

Walter Reed Medical Center Post-Sec.
6825 16th St NW 20307 202-782-6104

Washington International S 400/6-12
3100 Macomb St NW 20008 202-243-1800
Clayton Lewis, hdmstr. Fax 243-1802

Washington Jesuit Academy 100/6-8
900 Varnum St NE 20017 202-832-7679
Marcus Washington, hdmstr. Fax 832-8098

Washington MS for Girls 6-8
1901 Mississippi Ave SE 20020 202-678-1113
Sr. Mary Bourdon, prin. Fax 678-1114

Washington Theological Union Post-Sec.
1600 Webster St NE 20017 202-726-8800

Wesley Theological Seminary Post-Sec.
4500 Massachusetts Ave NW 20016 202-885-8600

FLORIDA

FLORIDA DEPARTMENT OF EDUCATION
325 W Gaines St, Tallahassee 32399-0400
Telephone 850-245-0505
Fax 850-245-9667
Website http://www.fldoe.org/

Commissioner of Education Pam Stewart

FLORIDA BOARD OF EDUCATION
325 W Gaines St, Tallahassee 32399-0400

Chairperson Kathleen Shanahan

PUBLIC, PRIVATE AND CATHOLIC SECONDARY SCHOOLS

Alachua, Alachua, Pop. 8,873
Alachua County SD
Supt. — See Gainesville
Mebane MS 400/6-8
16401 NW 140th St 32615 386-462-1648
Manda Bessner, prin. Fax 462-9094
Santa Fe HS 1,100/9-12
16213 NW US Highway 441 32615 386-462-1125
Dr. Beth LeClear, prin. Fax 462-1711

Forest Grove Christian Academy K-12
22575 NW 94th Ave 32615 386-462-3921
Warren Chesser, admin. Fax 462-2808

Altamonte Springs, Seminole, Pop. 40,483
Seminole County SD
Supt. — See Sanford
Lake Brantley HS 2,900/9-12
991 Sand Lake Rd 32714 407-746-3450
Mary Williams-Young, prin. Fax 746-3600
Teague MS 1,400/6-8
1350 Mcneil Rd 32714 407-320-1550
Adrienne DeRienzo, prin. Fax 320-1545

Altamonte Christian S 200/K-12
601 Palm Springs Dr 32701 407-831-0950
Rev. Scott Carlson, dir. Fax 831-6840
City College Post-Sec.
177 Montgomery Rd 32714 407-831-9816
Everglades University Post-Sec.
887 E Altamonte Dr 32701 407-277-0311

Altha, Calhoun, Pop. 529
Calhoun County SD
Supt. — See Blountstown
Altha S 600/PK-12
25793 N Main St 32421 850-762-3121
Ladonna Kelley, prin. Fax 762-9502

Alva, Lee, Pop. 2,582
Lee County SD
Supt. — See Fort Myers
Alva MS 500/6-8
PO Box 128 33920 239-728-2525
Stephen Hutnik, prin. Fax 728-2835

Apopka, Orange, Pop. 40,626
Orange County SD
Supt. — See Orlando
Apopka HS 2,600/9-12
555 Martin St 32712 407-905-5500
Douglas Guthrie, prin. Fax 814-6130
Apopka MS 900/6-8
425 N Park Ave 32712 407-884-2208
Kelly Pelletier, prin. Fax 884-2217
Piedmont Lakes MS 1,200/6-8
2601 Lakeville Rd 32703 407-884-2265
David Magee, prin. Fax 884-2287
Wekiva HS 2,400/9-12
2501 N Hiawassee Rd 32703 407-297-4900
Dr. Doreen Gruber, prin. Fax 297-4970
Wolf Lake MS 1,100/6-8
1725 W Ponkan Rd 32712 407-464-3317
Dr. Cathy Thornton, prin. Fax 464-3336

Champion Preparatory Academy 300/PK-12
1935 S Orange Blossom Trl 32703 407-788-0018
Vicki Falco, admin. Fax 788-7625
Forest Lake Academy 400/9-12
500 Education Loop 32703 407-862-8411
David Denton, prin. Fax 862-7050
Golf Academy of America Post-Sec.
510 S Hunt Club Blvd 32703 800-342-7342

Arcadia, DeSoto, Pop. 7,533
De Soto County SD 4,600/PK-12
PO Box 2000 34265 863-494-4222
Dr. Karyn Gary, supt. Fax 494-0389
www.desotoschools.com
DeSoto HS 1,100/9-12
1710 E Gibson St 34266 863-494-3434
Nelson Stephenson, prin. Fax 494-7867
DeSoto MS 1,000/6-8
420 E Gibson St 34266 863-494-4133
Gary White, prin. Fax 494-6263
DeSoto County Adult Education Center Adult
310 W Whidden St 34266 863-993-1333
Kathy Severson, prin. Fax 993-9181

Atlantic Beach, Duval, Pop. 12,332
Duval County SD
Supt. — See Jacksonville
Marine Science Education Center Vo/Tech
1347 Palmer St 32233 904-247-5973
Donald Nelson, prin. Fax 247-5976
Mayport MS 800/6-8
2600 Mayport Rd 32233 904-247-5977
Katrina McCray, prin. Fax 247-5987

Auburndale, Polk, Pop. 13,305
Polk County SD
Supt. — See Bartow
Auburndale HS 1,500/9-12
1 Bloodhound Trl 33823 863-965-6200
John Hill, prin. Fax 965-6245
Stambaugh MS 900/6-8
226 N Main St 33823 863-965-5494
Robert Hartley, prin. Fax 965-5496
East Area Adult & Community S Adult
300 E Bridgers Ave 33823 863-965-5475
Loretta Cameron, prin. Fax 965-5477

Southern Technical College Post-Sec.
298 Havendale Blvd 33823 863-551-1112

Ave Maria, Collier

Ave Maria University Post-Sec.
5050 Ave Maria Blvd 34142 877-283-8648

Avon Park, Highlands, Pop. 8,676
Highlands County SD
Supt. — See Sebring
Avon Park HS 1,000/9-12
700 E Main St 33825 863-452-4311
Tealy Williams, prin. Fax 452-4324
Avon Park MS 700/6-8
401 S Lake Ave 33825 863-452-4333
Katina Kramer, prin. Fax 452-4341
Career Academy Vo/Tech
600 W College Dr 33825 863-784-7209
Jennifer Westergom, lead tchr. Fax 471-7211

South Florida State College Post-Sec.
600 W College Dr 33825 863-453-6661
Walker Memorial Academy 200/PK-12
1525 W Avon Blvd 33825 863-453-3131

Babson Park, Polk, Pop. 1,321

Webber International University Post-Sec.
PO Box 96 33827 863-638-1431

Baker, Okaloosa
Okaloosa County SD
Supt. — See Fort Walton Beach
Baker S 1,300/PK-12
1369 14th St 32531 850-689-7279
Tom Shipp, prin. Fax 689-7416

Baldwin, Duval, Pop. 1,376
Duval County SD
Supt. — See Jacksonville
Baldwin MSHS 1,100/6-12
291 Mill St W 32234 904-266-1200
Rhonda Motley, prin. Fax 266-1220

Bartow, Polk, Pop. 17,008
Polk County SD 94,800/PK-12
PO Box 391 33831 863-534-0500
Dr. Sherrie Nickell, supt. Fax 519-8231
www.polk-fl.net/
Bartow HS 1,900/9-12
1270 S Broadway Ave 33830 863-534-7400
Ron Pritchard, prin. Fax 534-0077
Bartow MS 800/6-8
550 E Clower St 33830 863-534-7415
Angela Gordan, prin. Fax 534-7418
Gause Academy of Leadership 300/6-12
1395 Polk St 33830 863-534-7425
Mark Thomas, prin. Fax 519-3716
International Baccalaureate HS at Bartow 200/9-12
1270 S Broadway Ave 33830 863-534-0194
Ed Vetter, prin. Fax 534-0077
Summerlin Academy 9-12
1500 S Jackson Ave 33830 863-519-7504
Fax 519-8774
Union Academy 400/6-8
1795 E Wabash St 33830 863-534-7435
Steve Petrie, prin. Fax 534-7487
Other Schools – See Auburndale, Davenport, Dundee, Eagle Lake, Fort Meade, Frostproof, Haines City, Lake Alfred, Lakeland, Lake Wales, Mulberry, Winter Haven

Bell, Gilchrist, Pop. 456
Gilchrist County SD
Supt. — See Trenton
Bell HS 700/6-12
930 S Main St 32619 352-463-3232
Rick Reed, prin. Fax 463-3294

Belle Glade, Palm Beach, Pop. 17,323
Palm Beach County SD
Supt. — See West Palm Beach
Crossroads Academy 200/Alt
225 SW 12th St 33430 561-993-8408
Diane Howard, prin. Fax 993-8451
Glades Central Community HS 1,100/9-12
1001 SW Avenue M 33430 561-993-4400
Anthony Anderson, prin. Fax 993-9462
Lake Shore MS 700/6-8
425 W Canal St N 33430 561-829-1100
Shundra Dowers, prin. Fax 829-1130

Glades Day S 400/PK-12
400 Gator Blvd 33430 561-996-6769
Dr. Robert Egley, head sch Fax 992-9274

Belleview, Marion, Pop. 4,408
Marion County SD
Supt. — See Ocala
Belleview HS 1,500/9-12
10400 SE 36th Ave 34420 352-671-6210
Jim Wohrley, prin. Fax 671-6212
Belleview MS 1,100/6-8
10500 SE 36th Ave 34420 352-671-6235
Lisa Krysalka, prin. Fax 671-6239

Taylor College Post-Sec.
5190 SE 125th St 34420 352-245-4119

Blountstown, Calhoun, Pop. 2,466
Calhoun County SD 2,200/PK-12
20859 Central Ave E Ste G20 32424 850-674-5927
Ralph Yoder, supt. Fax 674-5814
www.calhounflschools.org
Blountstown HS 400/9-12
18597 NE State Road 69 32424 850-674-5724
Debbie Williams, prin. Fax 674-8865
Blountstown MS 300/6-8
17586 Main St N 32424 850-674-8234
Neva Miller, prin. Fax 674-6480
Calhoun County Adult Education Center Adult
17283 NW Charlie Johns St 32424 850-674-8661
Jana Whithead, prin. Fax 237-2355
Other Schools – See Altha

Boca Raton, Palm Beach, Pop. 83,145
Palm Beach County SD
Supt. — See West Palm Beach
Boca Raton Community HS 2,900/9-12
1501 NW 15th Ct 33486 561-338-1400
Geoffrey McKee, prin. Fax 338-1440
Boca Raton Community MS 1,300/6-8
1251 NW 8th St 33486 561-416-8700
Peter Slack, prin. Fax 416-8777
Eagles Landing MS 1,300/6-8
19500 Coral Ridge Dr 33498 561-470-7000
Cynthia Chiapetta, prin. Fax 470-7030

Estridge High Tech MS 1,200/6-8
1798 NW Spanish River Blvd 33431 561-989-7800
David Benson, prin. Fax 989-7810
Loggers Run Community MS 1,100/6-8
11584 W Palmetto Park Rd 33428 561-883-8000
Francis Giblin, prin. Fax 883-8027
Olympic Heights Community HS 1,900/9-12
20101 Lyons Rd 33434 561-852-6900
Dave Clark, prin. Fax 852-6974
Omni MS 1,600/6-8
5775 Jog Rd 33496 561-989-2800
Gerald Riopelle, prin. Fax 989-2851
Spanish River Community HS 2,300/9-12
5100 Jog Rd 33496 561-241-2200
William Latson, prin. Fax 241-2236
West Boca Raton Community HS 2,100/9-12
12811 Glades Rd 33498 561-672-2001
Mark Stenner, prin. Fax 672-2014

Boca Raton Christian S 500/PK-12
315 NW 4th St 33432 561-391-2727
Robert Tennies Ed.D., hdmstr. Fax 226-0617
Boca Raton Prep International S 200/PK-12
10333 Diego Dr S 33428 561-852-1410
Stan Daniel, admin. Fax 479-1731
Digital Media Arts College Post-Sec.
5400 Broken Sound Blvd NW 33487 561-391-1148
Everglades University Post-Sec.
5002 T Rex Ave Ste 100 33431 561-912-1211
Florida Atlantic University Post-Sec.
PO Box 3091 33431 561-297-3000
Klein Jewish Academy 700/K-12
9701 Donna Klein Blvd 33428 561-852-3300
Karen Feller, head sch Fax 852-3327
Lynn University Post-Sec.
3601 N Military Trl 33431 561-237-7000
PC Professor Post-Sec.
7056 Beracasa Way 33433 561-750-7879
Pope John Paul II HS 500/9-12
4001 N Military Trl 33431 561-314-2100
Mark Freund, prin. Fax 989-8582
St. Andrew's S 1,300/PK-12
3900 Jog Rd 33434 561-210-2000
William Moseley, head sch Fax 210-2007
Weinbaum Yeshiva HS 300/9-12
7902 Montoya Cir N 33433 561-417-7422
Shimmie Kaminetsky, admin. Fax 417-7028
West Boca Medical Center Post-Sec.
21644 State Road 7 33428 561-488-8000

Bonifay, Holmes, Pop. 2,723
Holmes County SD 3,300/PK-12
701 E Pennsylvania Ave 32425 850-547-9341
Eddie Dixon, supt. Fax 547-0381
www.hdsb.org
Bethlehem S 500/PK-12
2767 Highway 160 32425 850-547-3621
Stacey Thompson, prin. Fax 547-4856
Bonifay MS 500/5-8
401 Mclaughlin Ave 32425 850-547-2754
Donald Etheridge, prin. Fax 547-3685
Graduate Alternative S Alt
401 McLaughlin Ave 32425 850-547-0470
Jean West, prin. Fax 547-0474
Holmes County HS 500/9-12
825 W Highway 90 32425 850-547-9000
Mickey Hudson, prin. Fax 547-6694
Other Schools – See Graceville, Ponce de Leon

Bonita Springs, Lee, Pop. 43,637
Lee County SD
Supt. — See Fort Myers
Bonita Springs MS 600/6-8
10141 W Terry St 34135 239-992-4422
Linda Mitchell, prin. Fax 992-9157

Boynton Beach, Palm Beach, Pop. 66,992
Palm Beach County SD
Supt. — See West Palm Beach
Boynton Beach Community HS 1,500/9-12
4975 Park Ridge Blvd 33426 561-752-1200
Karen Whetsell, prin. Fax 752-1205
Congress MS 1,000/6-8
101 S Congress Ave 33426 561-374-5600
Kathy Harris, prin. Fax 374-5642
McAuliffe MS 1,100/6-8
6500 Le Chalet Blvd, 561-374-6600
Jeff Silverman, prin. Fax 374-6636
Odyssey MS 1,000/6-8
6161 W Woolbright Rd 33437 561-752-1300
Bonnie Fox, prin. Fax 752-1305

Bethesda Memorial Hospital Post-Sec.
2815 S Seacrest Blvd 33435 561-737-7733
Florida Career College Post-Sec.
1743 N Congress Ave 33426 561-634-7400
Lake Worth Christian S 400/PK-12
7592 High Ridge Rd 33426 561-493-3100
Robert Hook, supt. Fax 493-3848
St. Vincent DePaul Regional Seminary Post-Sec.
10701 S Military Trl 33436 561-732-4424

Bradenton, Manatee, Pop. 48,642
Manatee County SD 43,000/PK-12
PO Box 9069 34206 941-708-8770
Tim McGonegal, supt. Fax 708-8686
www.manateeschools.net
Bayshore HS 1,500/9-12
5401 34th St W 34210 941-751-7004
David Underhill, prin. Fax 753-0953
Braden River HS 1,900/9-12
6545 State Road 70 E 34203 941-751-8230
Jennifer Gilray, prin. Fax 751-8250
Braden River MS 1,000/6-8
6215 River Club Blvd 34202 941-751-7080
Randy Petrilla, prin. Fax 751-7085
Central HS 200/Alt
5603 34th St W 34210 941-751-7900
Carl Auckerman, dir. Fax 751-7927
Haile MS 1,000/6-8
9501 E State Road 64 34212 941-714-7240
Janet Kerley, prin. Fax 714-7245
Harllee MS 600/6-8
6423 9th St E 34203 941-751-7027
James Hird, prin. Fax 751-7030
Horizons Academy 400/Alt
1910 27th St E 34208 941-714-7470
Jeff Harris, dir. Fax 708-6417
Johnson MS 500/6-8
2121 26th Ave E 34208 941-741-3344
Omar Edwards, prin. Fax 741-3345
King MS 1,100/6-8
600 75th St NW 34209 941-798-6820
Robin Hardy, prin. Fax 798-6835
Lakewood Ranch HS 1,900/9-12
5500 Lakewood Ranch Blvd 34211 941-727-6100
Linda Nesselhauf, prin. Fax 727-6099
Lee MS 900/6-8
4000 53rd Ave W 34210 941-727-6500
Scot Boice, prin. Fax 727-6513
Manatee HS 2,200/9-12
902 33rd Street Ct W 34205 941-714-7300
Don Sauer, prin. Fax 741-3443
Manatee Technical Institute Vo/Tech
5603 34th St W 34210 941-751-7900
Mary Cantrell, dir. Fax 751-7927
Manatee Technical Institute East Vo/Tech
5520 Lakewood Ranch Blvd 34211 941-752-8100
Mary Cantrell, dir. Fax 727-6254
Nolan MS 900/6-8
6615 Greenbrook Blvd 34202 941-751-8200
Nancy High, prin. Fax 751-8210
Southeast HS 1,400/9-12
1200 37th Ave E 34208 941-741-3366
Catherine Smith, prin. Fax 741-3372
Sugg MS 800/6-8
3801 59th St W 34209 941-741-3157
Sharon Scarbrough, prin. Fax 741-3514
Other Schools – See Palmetto

Bradenton Christian S 600/PK-12
3304 43rd St W 34209 941-792-5454
Dan van der Kooy, supt. Fax 795-7190
Community Christian S 200/PK-12
5500 18th St E 34203 941-756-8748
Curtis Tomlin, admin. Fax 753-7057
Florida College of Natural Health Post-Sec.
616 67th Street Cir E 34208 941-744-1244
Gulfcoast Christian Academy 50/K-12
1700 51st Ave E 34203 941-755-0332
Carol Pope, admin. Fax 981-1564
GUTI - Bradenton Post-Sec.
4212 Cortez Rd W 34210 941-761-4400
IMG Academy 600/PK-12
5500 34th St W 34210 941-739-3964
Richard Odell, hdmstr. Fax 739-6483
ITT Technical Institute Post-Sec.
8039 Cooper Creek Blvd 34201 941-309-9200
Lake Erie College\Osteopathic Medicine Post-Sec.
5000 Lakewood Ranch Blvd 34211 941-756-0690
Manatee Technical Institute Post-Sec.
5603 34th St W 34210 941-751-7900
Providence Community S 100/PK-12
5512 26th St W 34207 941-727-6860
Barry Batson, admin. Fax 766-7269
St. Stephen's Episcopal S 700/PK-12
315 41st St W 34209 941-746-2121
Jan Pullen, hdmstr. Fax 746-5699
State College of FL Manatee-Sarasota Post-Sec.
PO Box 1849 34206 941-752-5000

Brandon, Hillsborough, Pop. 100,869
Hillsborough County SD
Supt. — See Tampa
Brandon HS 2,000/9-12
1101 Victoria St 33510 813-744-8120
Carl Green, prin. Fax 744-8129
Burns MS 1,400/6-8
615 Brooker Rd 33511 813-744-8383
Susan Burkett, prin. Fax 740-3623
Mann MS 1,000/6-8
409 E Jersey Ave 33510 813-744-8400
Barbara Fillhart, prin. Fax 744-6707
McLane MS 1,000/6-8
306 N Knights Ave 33510 813-744-8100
Frank Oliver, prin. Fax 744-8135
Brandon Adult Education Adult
1101 Victoria St 33510 813-744-8131
Edward Cristiano, admin. Fax 664-8393

Central Baptist Christian S 200/PK-12
402 E Windhorst Rd 33510 813-689-6133
Steve Lindquist, prin. Fax 689-0011
Faith Baptist Christian S 100/PK-12
1118 N Parsons Ave 33510 813-654-4936
Gene Reynolds, admin. Fax 654-7239
Southern Technical College Post-Sec.
608 E Bloomingdale Ave 33511 813-654-8800

Branford, Suwannee, Pop. 686
Suwannee County SD
Supt. — See Live Oak
Branford HS 600/6-12
405 Reynolds St NE 32008 386-935-5600
Jimmy Wilkerson, prin. Fax 935-3867

Bristol, Liberty, Pop. 982
Liberty County SD 1,400/PK-12
PO Box 429 32321 850-643-2275
Gloria Uzzell, supt. Fax 643-2533
www.lcsbonline.org/
Liberty County HS 300/9-12
PO Box 519 32321 850-643-2241
Aaron Day, prin. Fax 643-4153
Liberty County Adult S Adult
PO Box 429 32321 850-643-2275

Bronson, Levy, Pop. 1,084
Levy County SD 5,700/PK-12
PO Box 129 32621 352-486-5231
Robert Hastings, supt. Fax 486-5237
www.levy.k12.fl.us
Bronson MSHS 600/6-12
351 Ishie Ave 32621 352-486-5260
John Lott, prin. Fax 486-5263
Hilltop S 100/Alt
1 Eagle Dr 32621 352-486-5388
Robert Turnipseed, prin. Fax 486-5388
Other Schools – See Cedar Key, Chiefland, Williston

Brooksville, Hernando, Pop. 7,591
Hernando County SD 22,000/PK-12
919 N Broad St 34601 352-797-7000
Bryan Blavatt Ed.D., supt. Fax 797-7101
www.hernandoschools.org
Central HS 1,600/9-12
14075 Ken Austin Pkwy 34613 352-797-7020
Marvin Gordon, prin. Fax 797-7120
Endeavor Academy 100/Alt
1036 Varsity Dr 34601 352-797-7013
Robert Dill, prin. Fax 797-7113
Hernando HS 1,400/9-12
700 Bell Ave 34601 352-797-7015
Leechele Booker, prin. Fax 797-7115
Nature Coast Technical HS Vo/Tech
4057 California St 34604 352-797-7088
Tony-Ann Noyes, prin. Fax 797-7188
Parrott MS 800/6-8
19220 Youth Dr 34601 352-797-7075
Brent Gaustad, prin. Fax 797-7175
Powell MS 1,000/6-8
4100 Barclay Ave 34609 352-797-7095
Jamie Young, prin. Fax 797-7195
West Hernando MS 1,000/6-8
14325 Ken Austin Pkwy 34613 352-797-7035
Carmine Rufa, prin. Fax 797-7135
Other Schools – See Spring Hill, Weeki Wachee

Hernando Christian Academy 200/PK-12
7200 Emerson Rd 34601 352-796-0616
Ken Alvarez, supt. Fax 799-3400
Pasco-Hernando Community College Post-Sec.
11415 Ponce De Leon Blvd 34601 352-796-6726

Bunnell, Flagler, Pop. 2,615
Flagler County SD 12,700/PK-12
PO Box 755 32110 386-437-7526
Janet Valentine, supt. Fax 586-2351
www.flaglerschools.com
Other Schools – See Palm Coast

Bushnell, Sumter, Pop. 2,367
Sumter County SD 7,400/PK-12
2680 W C 476 33513 352-793-2315
Richard Shirley, supt. Fax 793-4180
www.sumter.k12.fl.us
South Sumter HS 1,100/9-12
706 N Main St 33513 352-793-3131
Dr. Preston Morgan, prin. Fax 793-2992
Other Schools – See Sumterville, Webster, Wildwood

Callahan, Nassau, Pop. 1,111
Nassau County SD
Supt. — See Fernandina Beach
Callahan MS 800/6-8
450121 Old Dixie Hwy 32011 904-491-7935
Ellen Ryan, prin. Fax 879-2860
West Nassau County HS 1,000/9-12
1 Warrior Dr 32011 904-491-7942
Curtis Gaus, prin. Fax 879-5843

Sonshine Christian Academy 300/PK-12
PO Box 5026 32011 904-879-1260
Lorie Johnson, hdmstr. Fax 879-2640

Cantonment, Escambia, Pop. 4,500
Escambia County SD
Supt. — See Pensacola
Ransom MS 1,300/6-8
1000 W Kingsfield Rd 32533 850-937-2220
Brent Brummet, prin. Fax 937-2232
Tate HS 2,000/9-12
1771 Tate Rd 32533 850-937-2300
Rick Shackle, prin. Fax 937-2328

Cape Coral, Lee, Pop. 151,800
Lee County SD
Supt. — See Fort Myers
Alternative Learning Center West 100/Alt
380 Santa Barbara Blvd N 33993 239-574-1678
Ken Burns, prin. Fax 574-4751
Baker HS 1,700/9-12
3500 Agualinda Blvd 33914 239-458-6690
Melissa Robery, prin. Fax 458-6691
Caloosa MS 900/6-8
610 Del Prado Blvd S 33990 239-574-3232
Dr. Ann Cole, prin. Fax 574-2660
Cape Coral HS 1,600/9-12
2300 Santa Barbara Blvd 33991 239-574-6766
Matthew Mederios, prin. Fax 574-7799
Challenger MS 1,100/6-8
624 SW Trafalgar Pkwy 33991 239-242-4341
Teri Cannady, prin. Fax 242-7217
Diplomat MS 800/6-8
1039 NE 16th Ter 33909 239-574-5257
Angela Roles, prin. Fax 574-4008
Gulf MS 800/6-8
1809 SW 36th Ter 33914 239-549-0606
William Lane, prin. Fax 549-2806
Island Coast HS 1,600/9-12
2125 De Navarra Pkwy 33909 239-458-0362
Kristin Bueno, prin. Fax 772-8405

Lee County HS Tech Center North Vo/Tech
360 Santa Barbara Blvd N 33993 239-574-4440
Michael Schiffer, prin. Fax 458-3721
Mariner HS 1,400/9-12
701 Chiquita Blvd N 33993 239-772-3324
Robert Butz, prin. Fax 772-4880
Mariner MS 900/6-8
425 Chiquita Blvd N 33993 239-772-1848
Rachel Gould, prin. Fax 242-1256
Trafalgar MS 800/6-8
2120 SW Trafalgar Pkwy 33991 239-283-2001
Dr. Angela Pruitt, prin. Fax 283-5620

Cape Coral Christian S 200/PK-12
811 Santa Barbara Blvd 33991 239-574-3707
Christopher Roy, prin. Fax 574-0947
Lee County High Tech Center North Post-Sec.
360 Santa Barbara Blvd N 33993 239-574-4440

Casselberry, Seminole, Pop. 25,625
Seminole County SD
Supt. — See Sanford
South Seminole MS 1,200/6-8
101 S Winter Park Dr 32707 407-746-1350
Mia Coleman-Baker, prin. Fax 746-1420

Aviation Institute of Maintenance Post-Sec.
2725 S US Highway 17/92 32707 888-349-5387

Cedar Key, Levy, Pop. 698
Levy County SD
Supt. — See Bronson
Cedar Key S 200/PK-12
951 Whiddon Ave 32625 352-543-5223
Daniel Faircloth, prin. Fax 543-5988

Celebration, Osceola, Pop. 7,281
Osceola County SD
Supt. — See Kissimmee
Celebration HS 1,900/9-12
1809 Celebration Blvd 34747 321-939-6600
Mytron Lisby, prin. Fax 939-6658

Century, Escambia, Pop. 1,651
Escambia County SD
Supt. — See Pensacola
Northview HS 500/9-12
4100 W Highway 4 32535 850-327-6681
Gayle Weaver, prin. Fax 327-6106

Chiefland, Levy, Pop. 2,173
Levy County SD
Supt. — See Bronson
Chiefland HS 500/9-12
808 N Main St 32626 352-493-6000
Matt McLelland, prin. Fax 493-6018
Chiefland MS 300/6-8
811 NW 4th Dr 32626 352-493-6025
Darby Allen, prin. Fax 493-6048
Adult HS Adult
114 Rodgers Blvd 32626 352-493-9533
Fax 493-9994

Chipley, Washington, Pop. 3,525
Washington County SD 3,500/PK-12
652 3rd St 32428 850-638-6222
Dr. Sandra Cook, supt. Fax 638-6226
washingtoncountyflschools.us/
Chipley HS 600/9-12
1545 Brickyard Rd 32428 850-638-6100
Steven Griffin, prin. Fax 638-6017
Roulhac MS 600/5-8
1535 Brickyard Rd 32428 850-638-6170
Debbie Bush, prin. Fax 638-6319
Washington-Holmes Tech Center Vo/Tech
757 Hoyt St 32428 850-638-1180
Martha Compton, dir. Fax 638-6177
Washington Inst for Specialized Educ 50/Alt
680 2nd St 32428 850-638-6020
Sam Cox, lead tchr.
Other Schools – See Vernon

Washington County Christian S 200/PK-12
1405 Brickyard Rd 32428 850-638-9227
Jason Haddock, admin. Fax 638-9234

Citra, Marion
Marion County SD
Supt. — See Ocala
North Marion HS 1,300/9-12
151 W Highway 329 32113 352-671-6010
Mike Kelly, prin. Fax 671-6011
North Marion MS 800/6-8
2085 W Highway 329 32113 352-671-6035
John Williams, prin. Fax 671-6044

Citrus Springs, Citrus, Pop. 8,462
Citrus County SD
Supt. — See Inverness
Citrus Springs MS 800/6-8
150 W Citrus Springs Blvd 34434 352-344-2244
David Roland, prin. Fax 249-2111

Clearwater, Pinellas, Pop. 105,537
Pinellas County SD
Supt. — See Largo
Bayside HS 400/Alt
14405 49th St N 33762 727-507-4730
Patricia Fuller, prin. Fax 507-4735
Clearwater Fundamental MS 900/6-8
1660 Palmetto St 33755 727-298-1609
David Rosenberger, prin. Fax 298-1614
Clearwater HS 2,100/9-12
540 S Hercules Ave 33764 727-298-1620
Keith Mastorides, prin. Fax 469-5981
Clearwater IS 400/Alt
1220 Palmetto St 33755 727-298-1616
Philip Wirth, prin. Fax 469-4189
Countryside HS 2,200/9-12
3000 State Road 580 33761 727-725-7956
Gerald Schlereth, prin. Fax 725-7990
Oak Grove MS 1,300/6-8
1370 S Belcher Rd 33764 727-524-4430
Dr. Dawn Coffin, prin. Fax 524-4416
PTEC Clearwater Vo/Tech
6100 154th Ave N 33760 727-538-7167
Mark Ericksen, dir. Fax 507-4423
Clearwater Adult Education Center Adult
540 S Hercules Ave 33764 727-469-4190
Christy Richards, admin. Fax 469-4193

Allendale Academy 1,000/K-12
2655 Ulmerton Rd Ste 402 33762 727-531-2481
Ray Collins, dir. Fax 362-6208
Calvary Christian HS 300/9-12
110 N McMullen Booth Rd 33759 727-449-2247
David Kilgore, admin. Fax 461-5421
Clearwater Academy International 300/PK-12
801 Drew St 33755 727-446-1722
Jim Zwers, dir. Fax 443-5252
Clearwater Central Catholic HS 500/9-12
2750 Haines Bayshore Rd 33760 727-531-1449
James Deputy, prin. Fax 535-7034
Clearwater Christian College Post-Sec.
3400 Gulf To Bay Blvd 33759 727-726-1153
Fasttrain of Clearwater Post-Sec.
2414 Enterprise Rd 33763 866-400-3278
Florida Career College Post-Sec.
410 Park Place Blvd 33759 727-724-1037
Lakeside Christian S 300/K-12
1897 Sunset Point Rd 33765 727-461-3311
Jim Jensen, head sch Fax 445-1835
National Aviation Academy Post-Sec.
6225 Ulmerton Rd 33760 727-531-2080
Pinellas Technical Education Center Post-Sec.
6100 154th Ave N 33760 727-538-7167
St. Petersburg Theological Seminary Post-Sec.
3190 Gulf to Bay Blvd 33759 727-399-0276
Sunstate Academy Post-Sec.
2525 Drew St 33765 727-538-3827
Ultimate Medical Academy Post-Sec.
1255 Cleveland St 33755 727-298-8685

Clermont, Lake, Pop. 27,603
Lake County SD
Supt. — See Tavares
Clermont MS 700/6-8
301 East Ave 34711 352-243-2460
Steven Benson, prin. Fax 243-1407
East Ridge HS 3,100/9-12
13322 Excalibur Rd 34711 352-242-2080
Julie Robinson-Louallen, prin. Fax 242-2090
East Ridge MS 1,100/6-8
13201 Excalibur Rd 34711 352-536-8020
Charlie McDaniel, prin. Fax 536-8039
Windy Hill MS 1,100/6-8
3575 Hancock Rd 34711 352-394-2123
Janice Boyd, prin. Fax 394-7901

Real Life Christian Academy 300/PK-12
1501 Steves Rd 34711 352-394-5575
Dr. Steven Long, admin. Fax 394-7860

Clewiston, Hendry, Pop. 7,087
Hendry County SD
Supt. — See LaBelle
Clewiston HS 800/9-12
1501 S Francisco St 33440 863-983-1520
Janice Lee, prin. Fax 983-2168
Clewiston MS 800/6-8
601 W Pasadena Ave 33440 863-983-1530
Garry Ensor, prin. Fax 983-1541
Clewiston Adult S Adult
475 E Osceola Ave 33440 863-983-1511
Gary Breakfield, prin. Fax 983-1517

Cocoa, Brevard, Pop. 16,719
Brevard County SD
Supt. — See Melbourne
Clearlake MS 400/7-8
1225 Clearlake Rd 32922 321-633-3660
Catherine Halbuer, prin. Fax 617-7731
Cocoa HS 1,000/9-12
2000 Tiger Trl 32926 321-632-5300
Dr. Stephanie Soliven, prin. Fax 636-1218
Space Coast JSHS 1,700/7-12
6150 Banyan St 32927 321-638-0750
Robert Spinner, prin. Fax 638-0766

Brevard Community College Post-Sec.
1519 Clearlake Rd 32922 321-632-1111
Space Coast Christian Academy 100/PK-12
1950 Michigan Ave 32922 321-636-0883
Chad Perdue, prin. Fax 634-5318

Cocoa Beach, Brevard, Pop. 11,096
Brevard County SD
Supt. — See Melbourne
Cocoa Beach JSHS 1,400/7-12
1500 Minutemen Cswy 32931 321-783-1776
Tim Cool, prin. Fax 868-6602

Coconut Creek, Broward, Pop. 51,291
Broward County SD
Supt. — See Fort Lauderdale
Atlantic Technical Center HS Vo/Tech
4700 Coconut Creek Pkwy 33063 754-321-5300
Robert Crawford, prin. Fax 321-5384
Coconut Creek HS 2,000/9-12
1400 NW 44th Ave 33066 754-322-0350
Scott Fiske, prin. Fax 322-0480
Lyons Creek MS 2,100/6-8
4333 Sol Press Blvd 33073 754-322-3700
Dr. Ted Toomer, prin. Fax 322-3785
Monarch HS 2,100/9-12
5050 Wiles Rd 33073 754-322-1400
James Neer, prin. Fax 322-1530
Thomas Education Center West Alt
4690 Coconut Creek Pkwy 33063 754-321-6800
Tracy Lockhart-Talley, prin. Fax 321-6840

Atlantic Technical Center Post-Sec.
4700 Coconut Creek Pkwy 33063 754-321-5100
Broward College Post-Sec.
1000 Coconut Creek Blvd 33066 954-201-2240
North Broward Preparatory S 1,400/PK-12
7600 Lyons Rd 33073 954-247-0011
Randazzo S 200/PK-12
2251 NW 36th Ave 33066 954-968-1750
Dr. Ronald Simon, hdmstr. Fax 968-1857

Coconut Grove, See Miami

Carrollton S of the Sacred Heart 800/PK-12
3747 Main Hwy 33133 305-446-5673
Sr. Suzanne Cooke, hdmstr. Fax 592-6533
Ransom Everglades S 1,100/6-12
3575 Main Hwy 33133 305-460-8800
Ellen Moceri, hdmstr. Fax 854-1846

Cooper City, Broward, Pop. 28,003
Broward County SD
Supt. — See Fort Lauderdale
Cooper City HS 2,200/9-12
9401 Stirling Rd 33328 754-323-0200
Wendy Doll, prin. Fax 323-0330
Pioneer MS 1,400/6-8
5350 SW 90th Ave 33328 754-323-4100
Michael Consaul, prin. Fax 323-4185

Nur Ul-Islam Academy 300/PK-12
10600 SW 59th St 33328 954-434-3288
Dr. Kem Hussain, pres. Fax 434-9333

Coral Gables, Miami-Dade, Pop. 46,270
Miami-Dade County SD
Supt. — See Miami
Carver MS 1,000/6-8
4901 Lincoln Dr 33133 305-444-7388
Shelley Stroleny, prin. Fax 529-5148
Coral Gables HS 3,200/9-12
450 Bird Rd 33146 305-443-4871
Adolfo Costa, prin. Fax 441-8094
International Studies Preparatory Acad 9-12
1570 Madruga Ave 33146 305-663-7200
Alejandro Perez, prin. Fax 661-0196
Ponce De Leon MS 1,200/6-8
5801 Augusto St 33146 305-661-1611
Martha Chang, prin. Fax 666-3140
Coral Gables SHS Adult Education Center Adult
450 Bird Rd 33146 305-443-4871
Alexis Cazanes, prin. Fax 446-2507

New Professions Technical Institute Post-Sec.
4000 W Flagler St 33134 305-461-2223
Riviera Day S and Riveiera Preparatory S 600/PK-10
6800 Nervia St 33146 305-666-1856
Lawrence Cohen, dir. Fax 661-5437
SABER Post-Sec.
3990 W Flagler St Ste 103 33134 305-443-9170
University of Miami Post-Sec.
PO Box 248006 33124 305-284-2211

Coral Springs, Broward, Pop. 117,909
Broward County SD
Supt. — See Fort Lauderdale
Coral Glades HS 2,300/9-12
2700 Sportsplex Dr 33065 754-322-1250
Steven Carruth, prin. Fax 322-1380
Coral Springs HS 2,300/9-12
7201 W Sample Rd 33065 754-322-0500
Susan Leon-Leigh, prin. Fax 322-0630
Coral Springs MS 1,700/6-8
10300 Wiles Rd 33076 754-322-3000
Ian Murray, prin. Fax 322-3085
Forest Glen MS 1,500/6-8
6501 Turtle Run Blvd 33067 754-322-3400
James McDermott, prin. Fax 322-3485
Ramblewood MS 1,600/6-8
8505 W Atlantic Blvd 33071 754-322-4300
Christine Recchi, prin. Fax 322-4385
Sawgrass Springs MS 1,300/6-8
12500 W Sample Rd 33065 754-322-4500
James Cecil, prin. Fax 322-4585
Taravella HS 3,000/9-12
10600 Riverside Dr 33071 754-322-2300
Shawn Cerra, prin. Fax 322-2430

Coral Springs Christian Academy 800/PK-12
2251 Riverside Dr 33065 954-752-2870
Robert Clampett, hdmstr. Fax 346-1112
Florida Medical Training Institute Post-Sec.
7451 Wiles Rd Ste 105 33067 954-752-1414

Cottondale, Jackson, Pop. 899
Jackson County SD
Supt. — See Marianna
Cottondale JSHS 500/6-12
2680 Levy St 32431 850-482-9821
Jennifer See, prin. Fax 482-9827

Crawfordville, Wakulla, Pop. 3,618
Wakulla County SD 4,800/PK-12
PO Box 100 32326 850-926-0065
Robert Pearce, supt. Fax 926-0123
wakulla.fl.schoolwebpages.com/
Riversprings MS 500/6-8
800 Spring Creek Hwy 32327 850-926-2300
Dod Walker, prin. Fax 926-2111
Wakulla County HS 1,200/9-12
3237 Coastal Hwy 32327 850-926-7125
Mike Crouch, prin. Fax 926-8571

Wakulla MS 600/6-8
22 Jean Dr 32327 850-926-7143
Michael Barwick, prin. Fax 926-3752

Crescent City, Putnam, Pop. 1,539
Putnam County SD
Supt. — See Palatka
Crescent City JSHS 900/7-12
2201 S US Highway 17 32112 386-698-1629
Randy Hedstrom, prin. Fax 698-3073

Crestview, Okaloosa, Pop. 20,112
Okaloosa County SD
Supt. — See Fort Walton Beach
Crestview HS 1,900/9-12
1250 N Ferdon Blvd 32536 850-689-7177
Bob Jones, prin. Fax 689-7332
Davidson MS 900/6-8
6261 Old Bethel Rd 32536 850-683-7500
Beth Walthall, prin. Fax 683-7523
Richbourg S 50/PK-12
500 Alabama St 32536 850-689-5089
Christy Corbin, prin. Fax 689-7817
Shoal River MS 800/6-8
3200 E Redstone Ave 32539 850-689-7229
Paul Whiddon, prin. Fax 689-7245

Cross City, Dixie, Pop. 1,699
Dixie County SD 2,000/PK-12
16077 SE Highway 19 32628 352-498-6131
Mark Rains, supt. Fax 498-1308
www.dixie.k12.fl.us/
Dixie County HS 500/9-12
16077 SE Highway 19 32628 352-498-6410
Diana Locke, prin. Fax 498-1287
Rains MS 400/6-8
981 SE Highway 351 32628 352-498-1346
Roger Storey, prin. Fax 498-1283
Dixie County Adult Center Adult
16077 NE Highway 19 32628 352-498-6151
Charlotte Lord, dir. Fax 498-1308

Crystal River, Citrus, Pop. 3,056
Citrus County SD
Supt. — See Inverness
Crystal River HS 1,200/9-12
3195 Crystal River High Dr 34428 352-795-4641
Mark McCoy, prin. Fax 249-2106
Crystal River MS 900/6-8
344 NE Crystal St 34428 352-795-2116
Gloria Bishop, prin. Fax 249-2108

Cutler Bay, Miami-Dade, Pop. 39,453
Miami-Dade County SD
Supt. — See Miami
Centennial MS 800/6-8
8601 SW 212th St, 305-235-1581
Yamila Carballo, prin. Fax 234-8071
Cutler Ridge MS 700/6-8
19400 Gulfstream Rd, 305-235-4761
Eduardo Alonso, prin. Fax 254-3746

College of Business & Technology Post-Sec.
19151 S Dixie Hwy, 305-274-4499
Fortis College Post-Sec.
19600 S Dixie Hwy Ste B, 786-345-5300

Dade City, Pasco, Pop. 6,339
Pasco County SD
Supt. — See Land O Lakes
Centennial MS 700/6-8
38505 Centennial Rd 33525 352-524-9700
Rick Saylor, prin. Fax 524-9791
Irvin Education Center 100/Alt
35830 State Road 52 33525 352-524-5700
Nancy Guss, prin. Fax 524-5791
Pasco HS 1,300/9-12
36850 State Road 52 33525 352-524-5500
Pat Reedy, prin. Fax 524-5591
Pasco MS 700/6-8
13925 14th St 33525 352-524-8400
Kimberly Anderson, prin. Fax 524-8491
Moore-Mickens Education Center Adult
38301 Martin Luther King Bl 33525 352-524-9000
Jackson Johnson, prin. Fax 524-9091

East Pasco Adventist Academy 100/PK-10
38434 Centennial Rd 33525 352-567-3646
Stephen Herr, prin. Fax 567-1907
Pasco-Hernando Community College Post-Sec.
36727 Blanton Rd 33523 352-567-6701

Dania, Broward, Pop. 14,456
Broward County SD
Supt. — See Fort Lauderdale
Olsen MS 1,100/6-8
330 SE 11th Ter 33004 754-323-3800
Valerie Thomas, prin. Fax 323-3885

Dania Beach, Broward, Pop. 29,112

Key College Post-Sec.
225 E Dania Beach Blvd 33004 800-581-8292

Davenport, Polk, Pop. 2,854
Polk County SD
Supt. — See Bartow
Ridge Community HS 2,100/9-12
500 Orchid Dr 33837 863-419-3315
Sherry Wells, prin. Fax 419-3321

Davie, Broward, Pop. 90,050
Broward County SD
Supt. — See Fort Lauderdale
College Academy 300/11-12
3501 Davie Rd 33314 754-321-6900
Deborah Davey, prin. Fax 321-6940
McFatter Tech Center Vo/Tech
6500 Nova Dr 33317 754-321-5700
Jeanette Johnson, prin. Fax 321-5980
Nova HS 2,200/9-12
3600 College Ave 33314 754-323-1650
John LaCasse, prin. Fax 323-1780
Nova MS 1,300/6-8
3602 College Ave 33314 754-323-3700
Jermaine Fleming, prin. Fax 323-3785
Western HS 3,000/9-12
1200 SW 136th Ave 33325 754-323-2400
David Jones, prin. Fax 323-2530

ASM Beauty World Academy Post-Sec.
6423 Stirling Rd 33314 954-321-8411
Broward College Post-Sec.
3501 Davie Rd 33314 954-201-6800
Nova Southeastern University Post-Sec.
3301 College Ave 33314 954-262-7300
Posnack Jewish Day S 500/K-12
5890 S Pine Island Rd 33328 954-583-6100
Dr. Richard Cuenca, hdmstr. Fax 791-5463
Trinity International University Post-Sec.
8190 W State Road 84 33324 954-382-6400
Westlake Preparatory S & Academy 100/K-12
4188 S University Dr 33328 954-236-2300
Robyn Pepitone, pres. Fax 473-0770

Daytona Beach, Volusia, Pop. 59,727
Volusia County SD
Supt. — See De Land
Campbell MS, 625 S Keech St 32114 700/6-8
Craig Zablo, prin. 386-258-4661
Hinson MS 1,100/6-8
1860 N Clyde Morris Blvd 32117 386-258-4682
Lesly Sileo-Robinson, prin. Fax 506-5064
Mainland HS 1,700/9-12
1255 W Intl Speedway Blvd 32114 386-258-4665
Dr. Cheryl Salerno, prin. Fax 506-5069
Riverview Learning Center 100/Alt
801 N Wild Olive Ave 32118 386-258-4673
Kevin Tucker, prin. Fax 239-6218
Seabreeze HS 1,800/9-12
2700 N Oleander Ave 32118 386-258-4674
Bob Wallace, prin. Fax 506-5071

Bethune-Cookman University Post-Sec.
640 Dr Mary Mcld Bthn Blvd 32114 386-481-2000
Daytona State College Post-Sec.
PO Box 2811 32120 386-506-3000
Embry-Riddle Aeronautical University Post-Sec.
600 S Clyde Morris Blvd 32114 800-222-3728
Embry-Riddle Aeronautical Univ-Worldwide Post-Sec.
600 S Clyde Morris Blvd 32114 800-522-6787
Father Lopez HS 300/9-12
3918 LPGA Blvd 32124 386-253-5213
Lee Sayago, prin. Fax 252-6101
Halifax Medical Center Post-Sec.
PO Box 2830 32120 386-254-4065
Keiser University Post-Sec.
1800 Business Park Blvd 32114 386-274-5060
Phoenix East Aviation Post-Sec.
561 Pearl Harbor Dr 32114 386-258-0703

De Bary, Volusia, Pop. 19,046
Volusia County SD
Supt. — See De Land
Highbanks Learning Center Alt
336 E Highbanks Rd 32713 386-822-7896
Kevin Tucker, prin.

Deerfield Beach, Broward, Pop. 72,542
Broward County SD
Supt. — See Fort Lauderdale
Deerfield Beach HS 2,400/9-12
910 SW 15th St 33441 754-322-0650
Jon Marlow, prin. Fax 322-0780
Deerfield Beach MS 1,200/6-8
701 SE 6th Ave 33441 754-322-3300
Francine Baugh, prin. Fax 322-3385

ITT Technical Institute Post-Sec.
700 W Hillsboro Blvd 33441 954-360-4701
South Florida Bible College Post-Sec.
1100 S Federal Hwy 33441 954-545-4500
Zion Lutheran Christian S 500/PK-12
959 SE 6th Ave 33441 954-421-3146
Joe Kemp, prin. Fax 421-4250

De Funiak Springs, Walton, Pop. 5,054
Walton County SD 7,000/PK-12
145 S Park St Ste 2 32435 850-892-1100
Carlene Anderson, supt. Fax 892-1191
www.walton.k12.fl.us
Walton Career Development Center Vo/Tech
761 N 20th St 32433 850-892-1240
Mike Davis, dir. Fax 892-1249
Walton HS 800/9-12
449 Walton Rd 32433 850-892-1270
Russell Hughes, prin. Fax 892-1279
Walton MS 700/6-8
625 Park Ave 32435 850-892-1280
Tripp Hope, prin. Fax 892-1289
Other Schools – See Freeport, Paxton, Santa Rosa Beach

De Land, Volusia, Pop. 26,549
Volusia County SD 58,100/PK-12
PO Box 2118 32721 386-734-7190
Dr. Margaret Smith, supt. Fax 822-6790
blackboard.volusia.k12.fl.us/
DeLand HS 2,700/9-12
800 N Hill Ave 32724 386-822-6909
Mitch Moyer, prin. Fax 626-0556
DeLand MS 1,100/6-8
1400 Aquarius Ave 32724 386-822-5678
William Dunnigan, prin. Fax 822-6583
Southwestern MS 600/6-8
605 W New Hampshire Ave 32720 386-822-6815
Mamie Oatis, prin. Fax 822-6708
Other Schools – See Daytona Beach, De Bary, Deltona, New Smyrna Beach, Orange City, Ormond Beach, Pierson, Port Orange

---

Florida Technical College Post-Sec.
1199 S Woodland Blvd 32720 386-734-3303
Lighthouse Christian Academy 200/PK-12
126 S Ridgewood Ave 32720 386-734-5380
Paul Bryan, admin. Fax 734-5627
Stetson University Post-Sec.
421 N Woodland Blvd 32723 386-822-7000

Delray Beach, Palm Beach, Pop. 59,547
Palm Beach County SD
Supt. — See West Palm Beach
Atlantic Community HS 2,300/9-12
2455 W Atlantic Ave 33445 561-243-1500
Anthony Lockhart, prin. Fax 243-1532
Carver Community MS 900/6-8
101 Barwick Rd 33445 561-638-2100
Lena Roundtree-Wallace, prin. Fax 638-2181
Village Academy 800/K-12
400 SW 12th Ave 33444 561-243-6100
Guarn Sims, prin. Fax 243-6150
Delray Full Service Center Adult
301 SW 14th Ave 33444 561-266-1200
Sandra Caruso, prin. Fax 266-1254

American Heritage S of Boca/Delray 900/PK-12
6200 Linton Blvd 33484 561-495-7272
Cambridge Institute Allied Health/Tech Post-Sec.
5150 Linton Blvd Ste 340 33484 561-381-4990

Deltona, Volusia, Pop. 83,518
Volusia County SD
Supt. — See De Land
Deltona HS 1,900/9-12
100 Wolf Pack Run 32725 386-575-4153
Susan Freeman, prin. Fax 968-0014
Deltona MS 1,200/6-8
250 Enterprise Rd 32725 386-575-4150
James Bambrick, prin. Fax 968-0015
Galaxy MS 1,100/6-8
2400 Eustace Ave 32725 386-575-4144
Julian Jones, prin. Fax 968-0016
Heritage MS 1,200/6-8
1001 Parnell Ct 32738 386-575-4113
Carolyn Carbonell, prin. Fax 708-0020
Pine Ridge HS 1,800/9-12
926 Howland Blvd 32738 386-575-4195
John Atkinson, prin. Fax 688-9502

Deltona Christian S 200/PK-12
1200 Providence Blvd 32725 386-574-1971
Fax 574-1771
Trinity Christian Academy 600/PK-12
875 Elkcam Blvd 32725 386-789-4515
Dr. Dennis Robinson, hdmstr. Fax 789-0210

Destin, Okaloosa, Pop. 11,900
Okaloosa County SD
Supt. — See Fort Walton Beach
Destin MS 700/5-8
4608 Legendary Marina Dr 32541 850-833-7655
Dr. Diane Kelley, prin. Fax 833-7677

Doral, Miami-Dade, Pop. 45,331
Miami-Dade County SD
Supt. — See Miami
Doral MS 800/6-8
5005 NW 112th Ave, 305-592-2822
Marie Caceres, prin. Fax 597-3853
Reagan/Doral HS 2,300/9-12
8600 NW 107th Ave, 305-805-1900
Jacques Bentolila, prin. Fax 805-1901

Divine Savior Lutheran Academy 500/PK-12
10311 NW 58th St, 305-597-4545
Benjamin Troge, prin. Fax 597-4077
Miami-Dade College Post-Sec.
3800 NW 115th Ave, 305-237-8000
Millenia Atlantic University Post-Sec.
3801 NW 97th Ave, 786-331-1000
Polytechnic University of Puerto Rico Post-Sec.
8180 NW 36th St Ste 401 33166 305-418-4220

Dover, Hillsborough, Pop. 3,664
Hillsborough County SD
Supt. — See Tampa
Strawberry Crest HS 1,900/9-12
4691 Gallagher Rd 33527 813-707-7522
David Brown, prin. Fax 707-7526

Dundee, Polk, Pop. 3,628
Polk County SD
Supt. — See Bartow
Dundee Ridge MS 900/6-8
5555 Lake Trask Rd 33838 863-419-3088
Stacy Gideons, prin. Fax 419-3157

Dunedin, Pinellas, Pop. 34,705
Pinellas County SD
Supt. — See Largo
Dunedin Highland MS 1,300/6-8
70 Patricia Ave 34698 727-469-4112
Chris Bates, prin. Fax 469-4115
Dunedin HS 1,500/9-12
1651 Pinehurst Rd 34698 727-469-4100
Reuben Hepburn, prin. Fax 469-4143

Cornerstone Christian S 100/PK-12
317 Milwaukee Ave 34698 727-733-1438
Maureen Wyns, prin. Fax 733-1438

Dunnellon, Marion, Pop. 1,711
Marion County SD
Supt. — See Ocala

Dunnellon HS 1,300/9-12
10055 SW 180th Avenue Rd 34432 352-465-6745
Ken McAteer, prin. Fax 465-6746
Dunnellon MS 700/6-8
21005 Chestnut St 34431 352-465-6720
Delbert Smallridge, prin. Fax 465-6721

Dunnellon Christian Academy 100/PK-12
20831 Powell Rd 34431 352-489-7716
Kristy Nelson, admin. Fax 489-5760

Eagle Lake, Polk, Pop. 2,207
Polk County SD
Supt. — See Bartow
Lake Region HS 1,900/9-12
1995 Thunder Rd 33839 863-297-3099
Joel McGuire, prin. Fax 297-3097

Eastpoint, Franklin, Pop. 2,298
Franklin County SD 1,300/K-12
85 School Rd Ste 1 32328 850-670-2810
Nina Marks, supt. Fax 670-2811
www.franklincountyschools.org/
Franklin County S 900/K-12
1250 US Highway 98 32328 850-670-2800
George Oehlert, prin. Fax 670-2801
Franklin Learning Center 50/Alt
85 School Rd 32328 850-670-2810
Nick O'Grady, dir. Fax 670-2811
Franklin County Adult S Adult
85 School Rd 32328 850-670-2810
Nick O'Grady, dir. Fax 670-2811

Eatonville, Orange, Pop. 2,147

Life Academy of Excellence 100/PK-12
107 Wymore Rd 32751 407-622-1330
Cheryl Thomas, prin. Fax 622-1329

El Portal, Miami-Dade, Pop. 2,243
Miami-Dade County SD
Supt. — See Miami
Academy for Community Education 100/Alt
8950 NW 2nd Ave 33150 305-460-2946
Carlos Cambo, prin. Fax 460-2944

Englewood, Sarasota, Pop. 14,723
Charlotte County SD
Supt. — See Port Charlotte
Lemon Bay HS 1,300/9-12
2201 Placida Rd 34224 941-629-4552
Bob Bedford, prin. Fax 475-5260

Estero, Lee, Pop. 22,447
Lee County SD
Supt. — See Fort Myers
Estero HS 1,500/9-12
21900 River Ranch Rd 33928 239-947-9400
George Clover, prin. Fax 947-5017

Eustis, Lake, Pop. 18,227
Lake County SD
Supt. — See Tavares
Eustis HS - Curtright Campus 400/9-9
1801 Bates Ave 32726 352-589-1510
Nancy Velez, prin. Fax 589-1605
Eustis MS 1,000/6-8
18725 Bates Ave 32736 352-357-3366
David Cunningham, prin. Fax 357-5963
Eustis SHS 900/10-12
1300 E Washington Ave 32726 352-357-4147
Nancy Velez, prin. Fax 357-7449

Lake Technical Center Post-Sec.
2001 Kurt St 32726 352-589-2250

Everglades City, Collier
Collier County SD
Supt. — See Naples
Everglades City S 200/PK-12
PO Box 170 34139 239-377-9800
Robert Spano, prin. Fax 377-9801

Fernandina Beach, Nassau, Pop. 11,315
Nassau County SD 11,100/PK-12
1201 Atlantic Ave 32034 904-491-9900
Dr. John Ruis, supt. Fax 277-9042
www.nassau.k12.fl.us
Fernandina Beach HS 800/9-12
435 Citrona Dr 32034 904-491-7937
Jane Arnold, prin. Fax 277-3754
Fernandina Beach MS 600/6-8
315 Citrona Dr 32034 904-491-7938
Dr. John Mazzella, prin. Fax 261-8919
Nassau County Adult S Adult
1201 Atlantic Ave 32034 904-491-9899
Brent Lemond, prin. Fax 548-4499
Other Schools – See Callahan, Hilliard, Yulee

Fern Park, Seminole, Pop. 7,563

Lincoln Tech Fern Park Campus Post-Sec.
7275 Estapona Cir 32730 407-673-7406

Florahome, Putnam
Putnam County SD
Supt. — See Palatka
Roberts MS 300/6-8
901 State Road 100 32140 386-659-1737
Debra Buckles, prin. Fax 659-1986

Florida City, Miami-Dade, Pop. 11,104

Barrington Christian Academy 300/PK-12
1013 N Redland Rd 33034 305-242-4343
Fax 242-4341

Fort Lauderdale, Broward, Pop. 162,648
Broward County SD 248,500/PK-12
600 SE 3rd Ave 33301 754-321-0000
Robert Runcie, supt. Fax 321-2701
www.browardschools.com
Ashe MS 600/6-8
1701 NW 23rd Ave 33311 754-322-2800
Wendy Bernstein, prin. Fax 322-2880
Dandy MS 1,000/6-8
2400 NW 26th St 33311 754-322-3200
Shernette Davis, prin. Fax 322-3285
Dillard HS 1,500/9-12
2501 NW 11th St 33311 754-322-0800
Cassandra Robinson, prin. Fax 322-0930
Fort Lauderdale HS 1,800/9-12
1600 NE 4th Ave 33305 754-322-1100
Priscila Ribeiro, prin. Fax 322-1230
New River MS 1,300/6-8
3100 Riverland Rd 33312 754-323-3600
Melinda Wessinger, prin. Fax 323-3685
Parkway MS 1,100/6-8
3600 NW 5th Ct 33311 754-322-4000
Bradford Mattair, prin. Fax 322-4085
Pine Ridge Alternative Center 100/Alt
1251 SW 42nd Ave 33317 754-321-7250
Belinda Hope, prin. Fax 321-7290
Stranahan HS 1,700/9-12
1800 SW 5th Pl 33312 754-323-2100
Deborah Owens, prin. Fax 323-2230
Sunrise MS 1,100/6-8
1750 NE 14th St 33304 754-322-4700
Michael Walker, prin. Fax 322-4785
Whiddon-Rodgers Education Center 700/Alt
700 SW 26th St 33315 754-321-7550
David Watkins, prin. Fax 321-7590
Whiddon-Rodgers Education Center Annex Alt
1300 SW 32nd Ct 33315 754-321-7600
Mary McGinnis, prin. Fax 321-7640
Other Schools – See Coconut Creek, Cooper City, Coral Springs, Dania, Davie, Deerfield Beach, Hallandale Beach, Hollywood, Lauderdale Lakes, Lauderhill, Margate, Miramar, North Lauderdale, Oakland Park, Parkland, Pembroke Pines, Plantation, Pompano Beach, Sunrise, Tamarac, Weston

Alternative Education Foundation Prep S 200/1-12
4650 SW 61st Ave 33314 954-581-8222
Lynette Vanheyzen, prin. Fax 797-0700
Archbishop Edward McCarthy HS 1,400/9-12
5451 S Flamingo Rd 33330 954-434-8820
Richard Jean, prin. Fax 680-4835
Art Institute of Fort Lauderdale Post-Sec.
1799 SE 17th St 33316 954-463-3000
ATI Career Training Center Post-Sec.
2890 NW 62nd St 33309 888-209-8264
Atlantic Institute of Oriental Medicine Post-Sec.
100 E Broward Blvd Ste 100 33301 954-763-9840
Calvary Christian Academy 1,700/PK-12
2401 W Cypress Creek Rd 33309 954-905-5100
Chapin Marsh, head sch Fax 556-4480
Cardinal Gibbons HS 1,100/9-12
2900 NE 47th St 33308 954-491-2900
Paul Ott, prin. Fax 772-1025
City College Post-Sec.
2000 W Commercial Blvd #200 33309 954-492-5353
Coral Ridge Training School Post-Sec.
2121 W Oakland Park Blvd 33311 954-714-0061
DeVry University Post-Sec.
600 Corporate Dr Ste 200 33334 954-938-3083
Fort Lauderdale Preparatory S 200/PK-12
3275 W Oakland Park Blvd 33311 954-485-7500
ITT Technical Institute Post-Sec.
3401 S University Dr 33328 954-476-9300
Keiser University Post-Sec.
1500 NW 49th St 33309 954-776-4456
Knox Theological Seminary Post-Sec.
5554 N Federal Hwy 33308 954-771-0376
MedVance Institute Post-Sec.
4850 W Oakland Park Ste 200 33313 954-587-7100
Pine Crest S 1,700/PK-12
1501 NE 62nd St 33334 954-492-4100
Dr. Dana Markham, pres. Fax 492-4177
St. Thomas Aquinas HS 2,200/9-12
2801 SW 12th St 33312 954-581-0700
Tina Jones, prin. Fax 581-8263
Sanford-Brown College Post-Sec.
1201 W Cypress Creek Rd 33309 954-308-7400
Strayer University Post-Sec.
2307 W Broward Blvd Ste 100 33312 954-745-6960
University S of Nova Southeastern Univ 1,900/PK-12
3375 SW 75th Ave 33314 954-262-4506
Dr. Jerome Chermak, hdmstr.
Westminster Academy 900/PK-12
5601 N Federal Hwy 33308 954-771-4600
Dr. Leo Orsino, hdmstr. Fax 491-3021

Fort Meade, Polk, Pop. 5,552
Polk County SD
Supt. — See Bartow
Fort Meade MSHS 700/6-12
700 Edgewood Dr N 33841 863-285-1180
Arthur Martinez, prin. Fax 285-1186

Fort Myers, Lee, Pop. 60,807
Lee County SD 79,300/PK-12
2855 Colonial Blvd 33966 239-337-8300
Joseph Burke Ed.D., supt. Fax 337-8378
www.leeschools.net
Alternative Learning Center Central 100/Alt
3650 Michigan Ave 33916 239-334-3416
Edwin Carter, prin. Fax 332-7772
Cypress Lake HS 1,600/9-12
6750 Panther Ln 33919 239-481-2233
Tracy Perkins, prin. Fax 481-9838
Cypress Lake MS 700/6-8
8901 Cypress Lake Dr 33919 239-481-1533
Jean Folaros, prin. Fax 481-3121
Dunbar HS 900/9-12
3800 Edison Ave 33916 239-461-5322
Carl Burnside, prin. Fax 461-5110
Dunbar MS 800/6-8
4750 Winkler Avenue Ext, 239-334-1357
Cherise Trent, prin. Fax 334-7633
Fort Myers HS 1,900/9-12
2635 Cortez Blvd 33901 239-334-2167
David LaRosa, prin. Fax 334-3095
Fort Myers Middle Academy 600/6-8
3050 Central Ave 33901 239-936-1759
Donald Bryant, prin. Fax 936-4350
Lexington MS 900/6-8
16351 Summerlin Rd 33908 239-454-6130
Linda Caprarotta, prin. Fax 489-3419
Oak Hammock MS 1,200/6-8
5321 Tice St 33905 239-693-0469
Clayton Simmons, prin. Fax 694-4089
Riverdale HS 1,600/6-12
2600 Buckingham Rd 33905 239-694-4141
Gerald Demming, prin. Fax 694-3527
South Fort Myers HS 1,700/9-12
14020 Plantation Rd 33912 239-561-0060
Tommy O'Connell, prin. Fax 561-3612
Three Oaks MS 800/6-8
18500 3 Oaks Pkwy, 239-267-5757
Mike Carson, prin. Fax 267-4007
Adult & Community Education Adult
2855 Colonial Blvd, 239-939-6310
Sue Roshon, dir. Fax 334-4568
Dunbar Community S Adult
1857 High St 33916 239-334-2941
Charles Dailey, admin. Fax 334-3519
Other Schools – See Alva, Bonita Springs, Cape Coral, Estero, Lehigh Acres, North Fort Myers

Bishop Verot Catholic HS 700/9-12
5598 Sunrise Dr 33919 239-274-6700
John Cavell, prin. Fax 274-6798
Canterbury S 600/PK-12
8141 College Pkwy 33919 239-481-4323
Anthony Paulus, hdmstr. Fax 481-8339
Edison State College Post-Sec.
8099 College Pkwy 33919 239-489-9300
Evangelical Christian S 1,000/PK-12
8237 Beacon Blvd 33907 239-936-3319
Florida Gulf Coast University Post-Sec.
10501 FGCU Blvd 33965 239-590-1000
Fort Myers Institute of Technology Post-Sec.
3800 Michigan Ave 33916 239-334-4544
Heritage Institute Post-Sec.
6630 Orion Dr Ste 200 33912 239-936-5822
Hodges University Post-Sec.
4501 Colonial Blvd, 800-466-0019
ITT Technical Institute Post-Sec.
13500 Powers Ct Ste 100 33912 239-603-8700
Keiser University Post-Sec.
9100 Forum Corporate Pkwy 33905 239-277-1336
Rasmussen College Post-Sec.
9160 Forum Corporate # 100 33905 239-477-2100
Sonshine Christian Academy 200/PK-12
12925 Palm Beach Blvd 33905 239-694-8882
Loretta Dezarn, dir. Fax 694-8885
Southwest Florida Christian Academy 500/K-12
3750 Colonial Blvd, 239-936-8865
Eric Munn, hdmstr. Fax 936-7095
Southwest Florida Christian Community S 50/PK-12
6900 Daniels Pkwy Ste 29 33912 239-225-1502
Debbi Coe, admin. Fax 225-1502
Southwest Florida College Post-Sec.
1685 Medical Ln 33907 239-939-4766
Sunstate Academy Post-Sec.
2040 Colonial Blvd 33907 239-278-1311

Fort Pierce, Saint Lucie, Pop. 40,874
St. Lucie County SD 39,800/PK-12
4204 Okeechobee Rd 34947 772-429-3600
Michael Lannon, supt. Fax 429-3916
www.stlucieschools.org
Delaware Avenue S 200/Alt
2909 Delaware Ave 34947 772-468-5220
Pam Christofori, admin. Fax 468-5254
Forest Grove MS 700/6-8
3201 S 25th St 34981 772-468-5885
Terrance Davis, prin. Fax 595-1187
Fort Pierce Central HS 1,900/9-12
4101 S 25th St 34981 772-468-5888
Todd Smith, prin. Fax 468-5761
Fort Pierce Westwood HS 1,300/9-12
1801 Panther Ln 34947 772-468-5400
Mallissa Hamilton, prin. Fax 468-5465
Lincoln Park Academy 1,800/6-12
1806 Avenue I 34950 772-468-5474
Alan Cox, prin. Fax 468-5485
McCarty MS 800/3-8
1201 Mississippi Ave 34950 772-468-5700
Mimi Hoffman, prin. Fax 468-5737
Other Schools – See Port Saint Lucie

Aviator College of Aeronautical Sci/Tech Post-Sec.
3800 Saint Lucie Blvd 34946 772-466-4822
Faith Baptist S 200/PK-12
3607 Oleander Ave 34982 772-461-3607
Fort Pierce Beauty Academy Post-Sec.
3028 S US 1 34982 772-464-4885
Indian River State College Post-Sec.
3209 Virginia Ave 34981 772-462-4772
John Carroll HS 400/9-12
3402 Delaware Ave 34947 772-464-5200
Ben Hopper, prin. Fax 464-5233
Liberty Baptist Academy 400/PK-12
3660 W Midway Rd 34981 772-461-2731
Katherine Johnson, admin. Fax 461-2542

Fort Walton Beach, Okaloosa, Pop. 18,836
Okaloosa County SD 28,100/PK-12
120 Lowery Pl SE 32548 850-833-3100
Dr. Alexis Tibbetts, supt. Fax 833-3436
www.okaloosaschools.com/
Bruner MS 800/6-8
322 Holmes Blvd NW 32548 850-833-3266
John Spolski, prin. Fax 833-3434
Choctawhatachee HS 1,600/9-12
110 Racetrack Rd NW 32547 850-833-3614
Cindy Gates, prin. Fax 833-3410
CHOICE HS & Technical Center Vo/Tech
1976 Lewis Turner Blvd 32547 850-833-3500
Al Gardner, admin. Fax 833-3466
Fort Walton Beach HS 1,800/9-12
400 Hollywood Blvd SW 32548 850-833-3300
Charlene Couvillon, prin. Fax 833-3311
Pryor MS 600/6-8
201 Racetrack Rd NW 32547 850-833-3613
Jeff Palmer, prin. Fax 833-4276
Other Schools – See Baker, Crestview, Destin, Laurel Hill, Niceville, Shalimar

---

Calvary Christian Academy 300/PK-12
535 Clifford St 32547 850-862-1414

Fort White, Columbia, Pop. 554
Columbia County SD
Supt. — See Lake City
Fort White HS 1,200/6-12
17828 SW State Road 47 32038 386-497-5952
Keith Hatcher, prin. Fax 497-5951

Freeport, Walton, Pop. 1,743
Walton County SD
Supt. — See De Funiak Springs
Freeport HS 300/9-12
12615 331 Business 32439 850-892-1200
Shirley Foster, prin. Fax 892-1209
Freeport MS 300/5-8
360 Kylea Laird Dr 32439 850-892-1221
Charlie Morse, prin. Fax 892-1229

Frostproof, Polk, Pop. 2,965
Polk County SD
Supt. — See Bartow
Frostproof MSHS 1,100/6-12
1000 N Palm Ave 33843 863-635-7809
Kyle Windham, prin. Fax 635-7812

Fruitland Park, Lake, Pop. 3,984

Holy Trinity Episcopal S 50/6-12
2201 Spring Lake Rd 34731 352-787-8855
Keith Wagner, hdmstr. Fax 787-8063

Gainesville, Alachua, Pop. 121,031
Alachua County SD 26,700/PK-12
620 E University Ave 32601 352-955-7300
Dr. W. Daniel Boyd, supt. Fax 955-6700
www.sbac.edu/
Bishop MS 700/6-8
1901 NE 9th St 32609 352-955-6701
Mike Gamble, prin. Fax 955-6966
Buchholz HS 2,200/9-12
5510 NW 27th Ave 32606 352-955-6702
Vince Perez, prin. Fax 955-7285
Eastside HS 1,400/9-12
1201 SE 43rd St 32641 352-955-6704
Jeff Charbonnet, prin. Fax 955-7291
Ft. Clarke MS 800/6-8
9301 NW 23rd Ave 32606 352-333-2800
Donna Kidwell, prin. Fax 333-2806
Gainesville HS 1,900/9-12
1900 NW 13th St 32609 352-955-6707
David Shelnutt, prin. Fax 955-7283
Horizon Center 100/Alt
2802 NE 8th Ave 32641 352-955-7250
James Spear, prin. Fax 955-7122
Kanapaha MS 900/6-8
5005 SW 75th St 32608 352-955-6960
Jennifer Wise, prin. Fax 955-6858
Lincoln MS 700/6-8
1001 SE 12th St 32641 352-955-6711
Don Lewis, prin. Fax 955-7133
Professional Academies Magnet at Loften Vo/Tech
3000 E University Ave 32641 352-955-6839
Dr. Chet Sanders, prin. Fax 955-6999
Westwood MS 1,000/6-8
3215 NW 15th Ave 32605 352-955-6718
James Tenbieg, prin. Fax 955-6897
Other Schools – See Alachua, Hawthorne, Newberry

Academy for Five Element Acupuncture Post-Sec.
305 SE 2nd Ave 32601 352-335-2332
City College Post-Sec.
7001 NW 4th Blvd 32607 352-335-4000
Cornerstone Academy 200/PK-12
PO Box 357430 32635 352-378-9337
Countryside Christian S 100/PK-12
10926 NW 39th Ave 32606 352-332-9731
Dragon Rises College Oriental Medicine Post-Sec.
1000 NE 16th Ave Bldg F 32601 352-371-2833
Florida School of Massage Post-Sec.
6421 SW 13th St 32608 352-378-7891
Oak Hall Upper S 400/6-12
8009 SW 14th Ave 32607 352-332-3609
Richard Gehman, hdmstr. Fax 332-4975
Rock S 200/PK-12
9818 SW 24th Ave 32607 352-331-7625
Bob Carter, hdmstr. Fax 331-9760
St. Francis HS 300/9-12
4100 NW 115th Ter 32606 352-376-6545
Ernest Herrington, prin. Fax 248-0418
Santa Fe College Post-Sec.
3000 NW 83rd St 32606 352-395-5000
Sung SDA S 50/K-12
2115 NW 39th Ave 32605 352-376-6040
Fax 376-6040
University of Florida Post-Sec.
PO Box 114000 32611 352-392-3261

Gibsonton, Hillsborough, Pop. 13,940
Hillsborough County SD
Supt. — See Tampa
East Bay HS 2,000/9-12
7710 Old Big Bend Rd 33534 813-671-5134
Maria Gsell, prin. Fax 671-5139
Eisenhower MS 1,400/6-8
7620 Old Big Bend Rd 33534 813-671-5121
Danielle Shotwell, prin. Fax 671-5039

Glen Saint Mary, Baker, Pop. 430
Baker County SD
Supt. — See Macclenny
Baker County HS 1,400/9-12
1 Wildcat Dr 32040 904-259-6286
Tom Hill, prin. Fax 259-5617

Gotha, Orange, Pop. 1,873

Central Florida Preparatory S 400/PK-12
1450 Citrus Oaks Ave 34734 407-290-8073
Rowena Flanders-Ramos, dir. Fax 298-6443

Goulds, Miami-Dade, Pop. 9,967
Miami-Dade County SD
Supt. — See Miami
Mays Conservatory of the Arts 500/6-8
11700 SW 216th St 33170 305-233-2300
Martin Reid, prin. Fax 251-5462

Graceville, Jackson, Pop. 2,229
Holmes County SD
Supt. — See Bonifay
Poplar Springs S 300/PK-12
3726 Atomic Dr 32440 850-263-6260
Gordon Wells, prin. Fax 263-1252

Jackson County SD
Supt. — See Marianna
Graceville JSHS 400/6-12
5539 Brown St 32440 850-263-4451
Chris Franklin, prin. Fax 263-3605

The Baptist College of Florida Post-Sec.
5400 College Dr 32440 800-328-2660

Greenacres, Palm Beach, Pop. 36,906
Palm Beach County SD
Supt. — See West Palm Beach
Leonard HS 2,500/9-12
4701 10th Ave N 33463 561-641-1200
Terry Costa, prin. Fax 491-8350
Swain MS 1,000/6-8
5332 Lake Worth Rd 33463 561-649-6900
Edward Harris, prin. Fax 649-6906
Tradewinds MS 1,200/6-8
5090 S Haverhill Rd 33463 561-493-6400
Rebecca Subin, prin. Fax 493-6410

Greenacres Christian Academy 100/PK-12
4982 Cambridge St 33463 561-965-0363
Billy Fritsch, prin. Fax 439-7149
Southeastern College Post-Sec.
6812 Forest Hill Blvd # D1 33413 561-433-2330

Green Cove Springs, Clay, Pop. 6,779
Clay County SD 34,400/PK-12
900 Walnut St 32043 904-284-6500
Charlie Van Zant, supt. Fax 284-6525
www.clay.k12.fl.us
Bannerman Learning Center 100/Alt
608 Mill St 32043 904-529-2100
Mike Elia, prin. Fax 529-1025
Clay HS 1,400/9-12
2025 State Road 16 W 32043 904-529-3000
Pete McCabe, prin. Fax 529-3214
Green Cove Springs JHS 900/7-8
1220 Bonaventure Ave 32043 904-529-2140
Jeff Umbaugh, prin. Fax 529-2144
Lake Asbury JHS 1,100/7-8
2851 Sandridge Rd 32043 904-291-5582
Cathy Richardson, prin. Fax 291-5593
Other Schools – See Keystone Heights, Middleburg, Orange Park, Starke

Greensboro, Gadsden, Pop. 596
Gadsden County SD
Supt. — See Quincy
West Gadsden HS 400/7-12
PO Box 10 32330 850-442-9500
Ida Walker, prin. Fax 442-6126

Groveland, Lake, Pop. 8,373
Lake County SD
Supt. — See Tavares
Gray MS 1,000/6-8
205 E Magnolia St 34736 352-429-3322
Dean Haack, prin. Fax 429-0133
South Lake HS 2,200/9-12
15600 Silver Eagle Rd 34736 352-394-2100
Rob McCue, prin. Fax 394-1972

Gulf Breeze, Santa Rosa, Pop. 5,682
Santa Rosa County SD
Supt. — See Milton
Gulf Breeze HS 1,500/9-12
675 Gulf Breeze Pkwy 32561 850-916-4100
Jason Weeks, prin. Fax 916-4109
Gulf Breeze MS 900/6-8
649 Gulf Breeze Pkwy 32561 850-934-4080
Richard Cobb, prin. Fax 934-4085
Woodlawn Beach MS 1,000/6-8
1500 Woodlawn Way 32563 850-934-4010
Victor Lowrimore, prin. Fax 934-4015

Gulfport, Pinellas, Pop. 11,800
Pinellas County SD
Supt. — See Largo
Boca Ciega HS 1,600/9-12
924 58th St S 33707 727-893-2780
Michael Vigue, prin. Fax 893-1382

Haines City, Polk, Pop. 20,261
Polk County SD
Supt. — See Bartow
Boone MS 800/6-8
225 S 22nd St 33844 863-421-3302
Eileen Killebrew, prin. Fax 421-3305
Haines City HS 2,000/9-12
2800 Hornet Dr 33844 863-421-3281
Trish Butler, prin. Fax 421-3283
International Baccalaureate East HS 200/9-12
2800 Hornet Dr 33844 863-419-3371
Trish Butler, prin. Fax 419-3373
Jenkins Academy of Technology Vo/Tech
701 Ledwith Ave 33844 863-421-3267
Telay Kendrick, prin. Fax 421-3269

Landmark Christian S 200/PK-12
2020 E Hinson Ave 33844 863-422-2037
Tim Vanderveer, admin. Fax 419-1256
NorthRidge Christian Academy 200/K-12
2250 State Road 17 S 33844 863-422-3473
Dr. David Myers, admin. Fax 421-5584

Hallandale Beach, Broward, Pop. 36,609
Broward County SD
Supt. — See Fort Lauderdale
Gulfstream MS 300/6-8
120 SW 4th Ave, 754-323-4700
Brian Kingsley, prin. Fax 323-4785
Hallandale HS 1,500/9-12
720 NW 9th Ave, 754-323-0900
Estrella Eckhardt, prin. Fax 323-1030
Lanier-James Education Center 100/Alt
1050 NW 7th Ct, 754-321-7350
Kelvin Lee, prin. Fax 321-7390
Hallandale Adult & Comm Ctr Adult
1000 SW 3rd St, 754-321-7050
Dr. Linda Lopez, prin. Fax 321-7135

Havana, Gadsden, Pop. 1,746
Gadsden County SD
Supt. — See Quincy
East Gadsden HS 900/9-12
27001 Blue Star Hwy 32333 850-539-2882
Kimball Thomas, prin. Fax 539-2863
Havana MS 200/6-8
1210 Kemp Rd 32333 850-539-2822
Willie Jackson, prin. Fax 539-2866

Tallavana Christian S 200/PK-12
5840 Havana Hwy 32333 850-539-5300

Hawthorne, Alachua, Pop. 1,398
Alachua County SD
Supt. — See Gainesville
Hawthorne MSHS 400/6-12
21403 SE 69th Ave 32640 352-481-1900
Veita Jackson-Carter, prin. Fax 481-4859

Hialeah, Miami-Dade, Pop. 224,295
Miami-Dade County SD
Supt. — See Miami
American HS 2,100/9-12
18350 NW 67th Ave 33015 305-557-3770
Luis Diaz, prin. Fax 828-7380
Filer MS 1,200/6-8
531 W 29th St 33012 305-822-6601
Giovanna Blanco, prin. Fax 822-2063
Goleman HS 2,000/9-12
14100 NW 89th Ave 33018 305-362-0676
Joaquin Hernandez, prin. Fax 827-0249
Hialeah HS 3,000/9-12
251 E 47th St 33013 305-822-1500
Dr. Verena Cabrera, prin. Fax 828-5513
Hialeah-Miami Lakes HS 1,900/9-12
7977 W 12th Ave 33014 305-823-1330
Jose Bueno, prin. Fax 362-4188
Hialeah MS 900/6-8
6027 E 7th Ave 33013 305-681-3527
Lourdes Diaz, prin. Fax 681-6225
Marti MAST 6-12 Academy 700/6-12
5701 W 24th Ave 33016 305-557-5931
Jose Enriquez, prin. Fax 556-6917
Miami Lakes MS 800/6-8
6425 Miami Lakeway N 33014 305-557-3900
Dr. Manuel Sanchez, prin. Fax 828-6753
Palm Springs MS 1,100/6-9
1025 W 56th St 33012 305-821-2460
Eric Acosta, prin. Fax 828-3987
Westland Hialeah SHS 1,900/9-12
4000 W 18th Ave 33012 305-818-3000
Guillermo Munoz, prin. Fax 818-3002
American SHS Adult Education Adult
18350 NW 67th Ave 33015 305-557-3770
Alan Bashaw, prin. Fax 827-7935
Hialeah-Miami Lakes HS Adult Ed Center Adult
7977 W 12th Ave 33014 305-823-1330
Dr. Nilda Diaz, prin. Fax 828-8929
Hialeah SHS Adult Education Center Adult
251 E 47th St 33013 305-822-1500
James Bishop, prin. Fax 821-6018

Advance Science Institute Post-Sec.
3750 W 12th Ave 33012 305-827-5452
Beauty Academy of South Florida Post-Sec.
1305 W 49th St 33012 305-817-3577
Beauty Schools of America Post-Sec.
1060 W 49th St 33012 305-362-9003
Champagnat Catholic S 300/PK-12
369 E 10th St 33010 305-888-3760
Fax 883-1174

College of Business & Technology — Post-Sec.
935 W 49th St 33012 — 305-225-5228
Compu-Med Vocational Careers — Post-Sec.
2900 W 12th Ave 3rd Flr 33012 — 305-888-9200
Dade Medical College — Post-Sec.
5875 NW 163rd St Ste 101 33014 — 786-363-3340
Edison Private S — 400/PK-12
3720 E 4th Ave 33013 — 305-824-0303
Margarita Jimenez, prin. — Fax 822-4205
Everest Institute — Post-Sec.
530 W 49th St 33012 — 305-558-9500
Florida Career College — Post-Sec.
3750 W 18th Ave 33012 — 305-825-3231
Florida National University — Post-Sec.
4425 W 20th Ave 33012 — 305-821-3333
Florida National University — Post-Sec.
4206 W 12th Ave 33012 — 305-231-3326
Florida National University Online — Post-Sec.
4425 W 20th Ave 33012 — 305-821-3333
Futura Career Institute — Post-Sec.
4512 W 12th Ave 33012 — 305-825-7660
Horeb Christian S — 200/PK-12
795 W 68th St 33014 — 305-557-6811
Alex Gispert, prin. — Fax 821-5048
La Belle Beauty School — Post-Sec.
1495 W 49th St 33012 — 305-558-0562
Lincoln-Marti S #17 — 300/K-12
1750 E 4th Ave 33010 — 305-884-1570
Miami-Dade College — Post-Sec.
1780 W 49th St 33012 — 305-237-8700
Nouvelle Institute — Post-Sec.
500 W 49th St Fl 2 33012 — 305-557-3017
Total International Career Institute — Post-Sec.
3060 W 12th Ave 33012 — 305-681-6622
Trinity Christian Academy — 100/PK-12
1498 W 84th St 33014 — 305-819-8999
Joseph Jimenez, dir. — Fax 819-2554

Hialeah Gardens, Miami-Dade, Pop. 21,719
Miami-Dade County SD
Supt. — See Miami
Hialeah Gardens HS — 2,400/9-12
11700 Hialeah Gardens Blvd 33018 — 305-698-5000
Dr. Louis Algaze, prin. — Fax 698-5001
Hialeah Gardens MS — 1,700/6-8
11690 NW 92nd Ave 33018 — 305-817-0017
Maritza Jimenez, prin. — Fax 817-0018

Hilliard, Nassau, Pop. 3,050
Nassau County SD
Supt. — See Fernandina Beach
Hilliard MSHS — 800/6-12
1 Flashes Ave 32046 — 904-491-7940
Dr. Brent Tilley, prin. — Fax 845-7662

Hobe Sound, Martin, Pop. 11,387

Hobe Sound Bible College — Post-Sec.
11298 SE Gomez Ave 33455 — 772-546-5534
Hobe Sound Christian Academy — 200/PK-12
PO Box 1065 33475 — 772-545-1455
Dr. Randall McElwain, prin. — Fax 545-1454
Pine S — 200/7-12
12350 SE Federal Hwy 33455 — 772-675-7005
Stephen Mandell M.Ed., hdmstr. — Fax 675-7006

Holiday, Pasco, Pop. 21,981
Pasco County SD
Supt. — See Land O Lakes
Anclote HS — 1,200/9-12
1540 Sweetbriar Dr 34691 — 727-246-3000
Monica Ilse, prin. — Fax 246-3091
Smith MS — 1,000/6-8
1410 Sweetbriar Dr 34691 — 727-246-3200
Dr. Chris Dunning, prin. — Fax 246-3291

Hollywood, Broward, Pop. 137,985
Broward County SD
Supt. — See Fort Lauderdale
Apollo MS — 900/6-8
6800 Arthur St 33024 — 754-323-2900
Shawn Aycock, prin. — Fax 323-2985
Attucks MS — 900/6-8
3500 N 22nd Ave 33020 — 754-323-3000
Errol Evans, prin. — Fax 323-3085
Driftwood MS — 1,600/6-8
2751 NW 70th Ter 33024 — 754-323-3100
Steven Williams, prin. — Fax 323-3185
Hollywood Hills HS — 1,900/9-12
5400 Stirling Rd 33021 — 754-323-1050
Lourdes Gonzalez, prin. — Fax 323-1180
McArthur HS — 2,100/9-12
6501 Hollywood Blvd 33024 — 754-323-1200
Todd LaPace, prin. — Fax 323-1330
McNicol MS — 700/6-8
1602 S 27th Ave 33020 — 754-323-3400
Horace Hamm, prin. — Fax 323-3485
Sheridan Technical Center — Vo/Tech
5400 Sheridan St 33021 — 754-321-5400
Robert Boegli, prin. — Fax 321-5680
South Broward HS — 2,100/9-12
1901 N Federal Hwy 33020 — 754-323-1800
Olayemi Awofadeju, prin. — Fax 323-1930

Aukela Christian Military Academy — 100/PK-12
2835 Madison St 33020 — 954-929-7010
Audrey Rodriguez, prin. — Fax 927-2523
Chaminade-Madonna College Prep HS — 700/9-12
500 E Chaminade Dr 33021 — 954-989-5150
Teresita Wardlow, prin. — Fax 983-4663
City College — Post-Sec.
6565 Taft St Ste 200 33024 — 954-744-1777
Dade Medical College — Post-Sec.
6837 Taft St 33024 — 954-843-7930
Hollywood Christian S — 300/PK-12
1708 N State Road 7 33021 — 954-322-4375
Susan Robinson, head sch — Fax 322-4383
Sheridan Hills Christian S — 400/PK-12
3751 Sheridan St 33021 — 954-966-7995
Wendy Talpesh, hdmstr. — Fax 961-1359
Sheridan Technical Center — Post-Sec.
5400 Sheridan St 33021 — 754-321-5400

Homestead, Miami-Dade, Pop. 59,655
Miami-Dade County SD
Supt. — See Miami
Campbell Drive MS — 800/6-8
900 NE 23rd Ave 33033 — 305-248-7911
Paul Pfeiffer, prin. — Fax 248-3518
Homestead HS — 1,800/9-12
2351 SE 12th Ave 33034 — 305-245-7000
Cory Rodriguez, prin. — Fax 247-5757
Homestead MS — 700/6-8
650 NW 2nd Ave 33030 — 305-247-4221
Rachelle Surrancy, prin. — Fax 247-1098
Medical Academy for Science & Technology — 9-12
1220 NW 1st Ave 33030 — 305-257-4500
Lisa Noffo, prin. — Fax 257-4501
Redland MS — 600/6-8
16001 SW 248th St 33031 — 305-247-6112
Beverley Salomatoff, prin. — Fax 248-0628
School for Advanced Studies - Homestead — 100/9-12
500 College Ter 33030 — 305-237-5062
Dr. Omar Monteagudo, prin. — Fax 237-5232
South Dade HS — 3,500/9-12
28401 SW 167th Ave 33030 — 305-247-4244
Alicia Hidalgo, prin. — Fax 248-3867
South Dade MS — 1,400/4-8
29100 SW 194th Ave 33030 — 305-224-5200
Brian Hamilton, prin. — Fax 224-5201
South Dade Skill Ctr — Vo/Tech
28300 SW 152nd Ave 33033 — 305-247-7839
Doris Granberry, prin. — Fax 247-2375
South Dade Adult Education Center — Adult
109 NE 8th St 33030 — 305-248-5723
Doris Granberry, prin. — Fax 248-9164

Colonial Christian S — 200/PK-12
17105 SW 296th St 33030 — 305-246-8608
Terri Morrissey, admin. — Fax 246-1542
Dade Medical College — Post-Sec.
381 N Krome Ave 33030 — 786-454-9070
Miami-Dade College — Post-Sec.
500 College Ter 33030 — 305-237-5000
Redland Christian Academy — 200/PK-12
17700 SW 280th St 33031 — 305-247-7399
Julie Bergman, admin. — Fax 247-1147

Hudson, Pasco, Pop. 12,006
Pasco County SD
Supt. — See Land O Lakes
Fivay HS — 100/9-12
12115 Chicago Ave 34669 — 727-246-4000
Angela Stone, prin. — Fax 246-4091
Hudson HS — 1,200/9-12
14410 Cobra Way 34669 — 727-774-4200
David LaRoche, prin. — Fax 774-4291
Hudson MS — 900/6-8
14540 Cobra Way 34669 — 727-774-8200
Terry Holback, prin. — Fax 774-8291

Grace Christian S — 100/K-12
9403 Scot St 34669 — 727-863-1825
Glenwood Pratt, prin. — Fax 862-4484

Immokalee, Collier, Pop. 23,830
Collier County SD
Supt. — See Naples
Immokalee HS — 1,400/9-12
701 Immokalee Dr 34142 — 239-377-1800
Dr. Mary Murrray, prin. — Fax 377-1801
Immokalee MS — 800/6-8
401 N 9th St 34142 — 239-377-4200
Abel Jaimes, prin. — Fax 377-4201
Immokalee Technical Center — Vo/Tech
508 N 9th St 34142 — 239-377-9900
Fax 377-9901

Indialantic, Brevard, Pop. 2,676
Brevard County SD
Supt. — See Melbourne
Hoover MS — 500/7-8
2000 Hawk Haven Dr 32903 — 321-727-1611
Mollie Vega, prin. — Fax 725-0076

Indiantown, Martin, Pop. 6,057
Martin County SD
Supt. — See Stuart
Indiantown MS — 400/5-8
16303 SW Farm Rd 34956 — 772-597-2146
Jeff Raimann, prin. — Fax 597-5854

Interlachen, Putnam, Pop. 1,381
Putnam County SD
Supt. — See Palatka
Interlachen HS — 900/9-12
126 N County Road 315 32148 — 386-684-2116
Thomas Bolling, prin. — Fax 684-3915
Price MS — 500/6-8
140 N County Road 315 32148 — 386-684-2113
Leah Lundy, prin. — Fax 684-3908

Inverness, Citrus, Pop. 7,057
Citrus County SD — 15,400/PK-12
1007 W Main St 34450 — 352-726-1931
Sandra Himmel, supt. — Fax 726-4418
www.citrus.k12.fl.us
Citrus HS — 1,600/9-12
600 W Highland Blvd 34452 — 352-726-2241
Dale Johns, prin. — Fax 249-2102
Inverness MS — 1,100/6-8
1950 Highway 41 N 34450 — 352-726-1471
Patricia Douglas, prin. — Fax 249-2133
Withlachoochee Technical Institute — Vo/Tech
1201 W Main St 34450 — 352-726-2430
Denise Willis, dir. — Fax 249-2157
Other Schools – See Citrus Springs, Crystal River, Lecanto

Inverness Christian Academy — 100/PK-12
4222 S Florida Ave 34450 — 352-726-3759
Dan Riley, prin. — Fax 726-0782

Islamorada, Monroe, Pop. 1,220

Island Christian S — 200/PK-12
83400 Overseas Hwy 33036 — 305-664-4933
Dr. Chris Price, hdmstr. — Fax 664-8170

Jacksonville, Duval, Pop. 800,944
Duval County SD — 119,300/PK-12
1701 Prudential Dr 32207 — 904-390-2000
Ed Pratt-Dannals, supt. — Fax 390-2586
www.duvalschools.org/
Anderson HS of the Arts — 1,200/9-12
2445 San Diego Rd 32207 — 904-346-5620
Jackie Cornelius, prin. — Fax 346-5636
Arlington MS — 800/6-8
8141 Lone Star Rd 32211 — 904-720-1680
Dr. Linda Lisella, prin. — Fax 720-1702
Atlantic Coast HS — Vo/Tech
9735 R G Skinner Pkwy 32256 — 904-538-5120
Debra Lynch, prin. — Fax 538-5159
Butler MS — 300/6-8
900 Acorn St 32209 — 904-630-6900
Maurice Nesmith, prin. — Fax 630-6913
Darnell-Cookman MSHS — 1,100/6-12
1701 N Davis St 32209 — 904-630-6805
Mark Ertel, prin. — Fax 630-6811
Davis MS — 1,300/6-8
7050 Melvin Rd 32210 — 904-573-1060
Shilene Singleton, prin. — Fax 573-1066
DuPont MS — 900/6-8
2710 Dupont Ave 32217 — 904-739-5200
Marilyn Barnwell, prin. — Fax 739-5321
Englewood HS — 1,900/9-12
4412 Barnes Rd 32207 — 904-739-5212
Corey Wright, prin. — Fax 739-5324
First Coast HS — 2,100/9-12
590 Duval Station Rd 32218 — 904-757-0080
Vincent Hall, prin. — Fax 696-8721
Forrest HS — 1,400/9-12
5530 Firestone Rd 32244 — 904-573-1170
Al Brennan, prin. — Fax 573-1177
Ft. Caroline MS — 800/6-8
3787 University Club Blvd 32277 — 904-745-4927
Shawn Shackelford, prin. — Fax 745-4937
Gilbert MS — 500/6-8
1424 Franklin St 32206 — 904-630-6700
Evan Daniels, prin. — Fax 630-6713
Grand Park Education Center — 100/Alt
2335 W 18th St 32209 — 904-630-6894
Jackie Simmons, prin. — Fax [illegible]
Highlands MS — 900/6-8
10913 Pine Estates Rd E 32218 — 904-696-8771
Tyrone Blue, prin. — Fax 696-0782
Jackson HS — 1,000/9-12
3816 N Main St 32206 — 904-630-6950
Iranetta Wright, prin. — Fax 630-6955
Johnson MS — 1,000/6-8
3276 Norman E Thagard Blvd 32254 — 904-693-7600
Sharwonda Peek, prin. — Fax 693-7661
Kernan MS — 1,300/6-8
2271 Kernan Blvd S 32246 — 904-220-1350
Kathy Kassees, prin. — Fax 220-1355
Kirby-Smith MS — 900/6-8
2034 Hubbard St 32206 — 904-630-6600
June Marshall, prin. — Fax 630-6605
Lake Shore MS — 1,200/6-8
2519 Bayview Rd 32210 — 904-381-7440
Ronda Cotter, prin. — Fax 381-7437
Landmark MS — 1,400/6-8
101 Kernan Blvd N 32225 — 904-221-7125
David Gilmore, prin. — Fax 221-8847
Landon MS — 700/6-8
1819 Thacker Ave 32207 — 904-346-5650
Sarah Bravo, prin. — Fax 346-5657
LaVilla S of the Arts — 1,100/6-8
501 N Davis St 32202 — 904-633-6069
Janelle Wagoner, prin. — Fax 633-8089
Lee HS — 1,800/9-12
1200 McDuff Ave S 32205 — 904-381-3930
Denise Hall, prin. — Fax 381-3945
Mandarin HS — 2,800/9-12
4831 Greenland Rd 32258 — 904-260-3911
Donna Richardson, prin. — Fax 260-5439
Mandarin MS — 1,600/6-8
5100 Hood Rd 32257 — 904-292-0555
Debbie Smith, prin. — Fax 260-5415
Northwestern MS — 400/6-8
2100 W 45th St 32209 — 904-924-3100
Arvin Johnson, prin. — Fax 924-3284
Oceanway MS — 1,200/6-8
143 Oceanway Ave 32218 — 904-714-4680
Terry Connor, prin. — Fax 714-4685
Parker HS — 1,500/9-12
7301 Parker School Rd 32211 — 904-720-1650
Scott Schneider, prin. — Fax 720-1700
Paxon HS for Advanced Studies — 1,600/9-12
3239 Norman E Thagard Blvd 32254 — 904-693-7583
Royce Turner, prin. — Fax 693-7597
Peterson Academy of Technology — Vo/Tech
7450 Wilson Blvd 32210 — 904-573-1150
Cathy Barnes, prin. — Fax 573-3206
Raines HS — 1,000/9-12
3663 Raines Ave 32209 — 904-924-3049
Shateena Brown, prin. — Fax 924-3058
Randolph Academies of Technology — Vo/Tech
1157 Golfair Blvd 32209 — 904-924-3011
Robert Lewis, prin. — Fax 924-3125
Ribault HS — 1,000/9-12
3701 Winton Dr 32208 — 904-924-3092
Edward Robinson, prin. — Fax 924-3154

Ribault MS 600/6-8
3610 Ribault Scenic Dr 32208 904-924-3062
Tiffany Torrence, prin. Fax 924-3167
Rutherford Alternative Education Center 100/Alt
1514 Hubbard St 32206 904-630-6782
Sadie Milliner-Smith, prin. Fax 630-6789
Sandalwood HS 2,800/9-12
2750 John Prom Blvd 32246 904-646-5100
Dean Ledford, prin. Fax 646-5126
Southside MS 1,000/6-8
2948 Knights Ln E 32216 904-739-5238
Dr. Darrell Perry, prin. Fax 739-5244
Stanton College Preparatory HS 1,600/9-12
1149 W 13th St 32209 904-630-6760
Nongongoma Majova-Seane, prin. Fax 630-6758
Stilwell MS 1,000/6-8
7840 Burma Rd 32221 904-693-7523
Brenda Jordan, prin. Fax 693-7539
Stuart MS 800/6-8
4815 Wesconnett Blvd 32210 904-573-1000
Gregory Bostic, prin. Fax 573-3213
Twin Lakes Academy 1,500/6-8
8050 Point Meadows Dr 32256 904-538-0825
Jennifer Bridwell, prin. Fax 538-0840
White HS 2,000/9-12
1700 Old Middleburg Rd N 32210 904-693-7620
Christopher Jackson, prin. Fax 693-7639
Wolfson HS 1,600/9-12
7000 Powers Ave 32217 904-739-5265
David Garner, prin. Fax 739-5272
Other Schools – See Atlantic Beach, Baldwin, Jacksonville Beach, Neptune Beach

St. Johns County SD
Supt. — See Saint Augustine
Bartram Trail HS 1,600/9-12
7399 Longleaf Pine Pkwy 32259 904-547-8340
Dawn Sapp, prin. Fax 547-8359
Creekside HS 1,500/9-12
100 Knights Ln 32259 904-547-7300
Randy Johnson, prin. Fax 547-7305

Arlington Country Day S 400/PK-12
5725 Fort Caroline Rd 32277 904-762-0123
Deborah Condit, head sch Fax 762-0125
Art Institute of Jacksonville Post-Sec.
8775 Baypine Rd 32256 904-486-3000
Baptist Medical Centers Post-Sec.
800 Prudential Dr 32207 904-393-2001
Baptist/St. Vincent's Health System Post-Sec.
1 Shircliff Way 32204 904-387-7300
Bishop John J. Snyder HS 500/9-12
5001 Samaritan Way 32210 904-771-1029
David Yazdiya, prin. Fax 908-8988
Bishop Kenny HS 1,400/9-12
1055 Kingman Ave 32207 904-398-7545
Todd Orlando, prin. Fax 398-5728
Bolles S 1,800/PK-12
7400 San Jose Blvd 32217 904-733-9292
Bradford Reed, hdmstr. Fax 739-9363
Bolles S - Bartrum Campus 400/6-8
2264 Bartram Rd 32207 904-724-8850
Bradford Reed, head sch Fax 724-8862
Cedar Creek Christian S 300/PK-12
1372 Lane Ave S 32205 904-781-9151
Fax 781-9182
Chamberlain College of Nursing Post-Sec.
5200 Belfort Rd 32256 904-251-8100
Christ's Church Academy 600/K-12
10850 Old Saint Augustine 32257 904-268-8667
Dr. Steven Blinder, head sch Fax 880-3251
Concorde Career Institute Post-Sec.
7259 Salisbury Rd 32256 904-725-0525
Cornerstone Christian S 300/PK-12
4000 Spring Park Rd 32207 904-730-5500
Ken Brockington, admin. Fax 730-5502
DeVry University Post-Sec.
5200 Belfort Rd Ste 175 32256 904-367-4942
Eagle's View Academy 400/K-12
7788 Ramona Blvd W 32221 904-786-1411
Scott Kinlaw, admin. Fax 786-1445
Edward Waters College Post-Sec.
1658 Kings Rd 32209 904-470-8000
Episcopal S of Jacksonville 900/6-12
4455 Atlantic Blvd 32207 904-396-5751
Charley Zimmer, head sch Fax 396-7209
Esprit De Corps Center for Learning 100/K-12
9840 Wagner Rd 32219 904-924-2000
Dr. Jeannette Holmes-Vann, admin. Fax 766-8870
Everest University - Jacksonville Campus Post-Sec.
8226 Philips Hwy 32256 904-731-4949
Fasttrain of Jacksonville Post-Sec.
10752 Deerwood Park Ste 201 32256 904-265-3278
First Coast Academy 1,000/9-12
2725 College St 32205 904-381-1935
First Coast Christian S 600/PK-12
7587 Blanding Blvd 32244 904-777-3040
Morry Kemple, admin. Fax 777-3045
Florida Career College Post-Sec.
6600 Youngerman Cir 32244 904-573-1900
Florida Coastal School of Law Post-Sec.
8787 Baypine Rd 32256 904-680-7700
Florida State College Post-Sec.
3939 Roosevelt Blvd 32205 904-381-3400
Florida State College Post-Sec.
4501 Capper Rd 32218 904-766-6500
Florida State College Post-Sec.
11901 Beach Blvd 32246 904-646-2111
Florida State College - Jacksonville Post-Sec.
101 State St W 32202 904-633-8100
Fortis Institute Post-Sec.
5995 University Blvd W #2 32216 904-443-6300
Foundation Academy 300/PK-12
3675 San Pablo Rd S 32224 904-493-7300
Nadia Hionides, prin. Fax 821-1247

Greenwood S 200/6-12
9920 Regency Square Blvd 32225 904-726-5000
Beverly Connell, head sch Fax 726-5056
Harvest Community S 300/PK-12
2360 Saint Johns Bluff Rd S 32246 904-997-1882
Patty Wilcox, admin. Fax 997-1862
Heritage Institute Post-Sec.
4130 Salisbury Rd Ste 1100 32216 904-332-0910
ITT Technical Institute Post-Sec.
7011 A C Skinner Pkwy #140 32256 904-573-9100
Jacksonville University Post-Sec.
2800 University Blvd N 32211 904-256-8000
Jones College Post-Sec.
5353 Arlington Expy 32211 904-743-1122
Jones College Post-Sec.
1195 Edgewood Ave S 32205 904-743-1122
Joshua Christian Academy 200/K-10
924 Saint Clair St 32254 904-388-2227
Kaplan College Post-Sec.
7450 Beach Blvd 32216 904-855-2400
Keiser University Post-Sec.
6430 Southpoint Pkwy 32216 904-296-3440
Normandy Beauty School of Jacksonville Post-Sec.
5373 Lenox Ave 32205 904-786-6250
Parsons Christian Academy 200/PK-12
5705 Fort Caroline Rd 32277 904-745-4588
Grace Williams, prin. Fax 745-6366
Providence S 1,500/PK-12
2701 Hodges Blvd 32224 904-223-5270
David Patterson, head sch Fax 223-3028
St. Luke's Hospital/Mayo Clinic Post-Sec.
4201 Belfort Rd 32216 904-296-3733
Sanford-Brown Institute Post-Sec.
10255 Fortune Pkwy Ste 501 32256 904-363-6221
Seacoast Christian Academy 500/6-12
8057 Arlington Expy 32211 904-722-1738
Dr. Elton Brooke, prin. Fax 725-5085
Shands Jacksonville Medical Center Post-Sec.
655 W 8th St 32209 904-244-0411
Shekinah Christian Academy 100/K-12
10551 Beach Blvd 32246 904-421-1015
Southeastern College Post-Sec.
6700 Southpoint Pkwy # 400 32216 904-448-9499
Stenotype Institute Post-Sec.
3563 Phillips Hwy Ste 501 32207 904-398-4141
Success Academy 200/PK-12
2103 Grand St 32208 904-766-6212
Trinity Baptist College Post-Sec.
800 Hammond Blvd 32221 800-786-2206
Trinity Christian Academy 1,600/PK-12
800 Hammond Blvd 32221 904-596-2400
Tulsa Welding School Post-Sec.
3500 Southside Blvd 32216 904-646-9353
University Christian S 700/PK-12
5520 University Blvd W 32216 904-737-6330
Beverly Bandy, prin. Fax 739-7403
University of North Florida Post-Sec.
1 U N F Dr 32224 904-620-1000
University of Southernmost Florida Post-Sec.
9550 Regency Square Blvd 32225 877-722-3381
Victory Christian Academy 300/PK-12
10613 Lem Turner Rd 32218 904-764-7781
Sandra Effler, admin. Fax 764-7297
Virginia College Post-Sec.
5940 Beach Blvd 32207 904-520-7400

Jacksonville Beach, Duval, Pop. 20,925
Duval County SD
Supt. — See Jacksonville
Fletcher MS 1,200/6-8
2000 3rd St N 32250 904-247-5929
Teresa Mowbray, prin. Fax 247-5940

Jasper, Hamilton, Pop. 4,513
Hamilton County SD 1,700/PK-12
4280 SW County Road 152 32052 386-792-1228
Thomas Moffses, supt. Fax 792-3681
www.hamiltonfl.com
Hamilton County HS 700/7-12
5683 US Highway 129 S 32052 386-792-6540
Kip McLeod, prin. Fax 792-6594

Corinth Christian Academy 100/PK-12
7042 SW 41st Ave 32052 386-938-2270

Jay, Santa Rosa, Pop. 529
Santa Rosa County SD
Supt. — See Milton
Jay JSHS 500/7-12
13863 Alabama St 32565 850-675-4507
Brad Marcilliat, prin. Fax 675-8573

Jensen Beach, Martin, Pop. 11,571
Martin County SD
Supt. — See Stuart
Jensen Beach HS 1,600/9-12
2875 NW Goldenrod Rd 34957 772-232-3500
Ginger Featherstone, prin. Fax 232-3699

Jupiter, Palm Beach, Pop. 54,490
Palm Beach County SD
Supt. — See West Palm Beach
Independence MS 1,300/6-8
4001 Greenway Dr 33458 561-799-7500
Lori Bonino, prin. Fax 799-7505
Jupiter Community HS 2,900/9-12
500 Military Trl 33458 561-744-7900
Cheryl Alligood, prin. Fax 744-7978
Jupiter MS 1,400/6-8
15245 Military Trl 33458 561-745-7200
Faith Ann Cheek, prin. Fax 745-7246

Jupiter Christian S 500/PK-12
700 S Delaware Blvd 33458 561-746-7800
Dr. James P. Colman, pres. Fax 746-1955

Key Biscayne, Miami-Dade, Pop. 12,269
Miami-Dade County SD
Supt. — See Miami

Maritime & Science Technology Academy 600/9-12
3979 Rickenbacker Cswy 33149 305-365-6278
Jane Garraux, prin. Fax 361-0996

Keystone Heights, Clay, Pop. 1,326
Clay County SD
Supt. — See Green Cove Springs
Keystone Heights JSHS 1,300/7-12
900 Orchid Ave, 352-473-2761
Dr. Susan Sailor, prin. Fax 473-5920

Key West, Monroe, Pop. 24,199
Monroe County SD 8,200/PK-12
241 Trumbo Rd 33040 305-293-1400
Mark Porter, supt. Fax 293-1407
keysschools.schoolfusion.us/
Key West HS 1,300/9-12
2100 Flagler Ave 33040 305-293-1549
Amber Bosco, prin. Fax 293-1547
O'Bryant MS 700/6-8
1105 Leon St 33040 305-296-5628
Mike Henriquez, prin. Fax 293-1644
Other Schools – See Marathon, Tavernier

Florida Keys Community College Post-Sec.
5901 College Rd 33040 305-296-9081

Kissimmee, Osceola, Pop. 58,578
Osceola County SD 52,800/PK-12
817 Bill Beck Blvd 34744 407-870-4600
Melba Luciano, supt. Fax 870-4010
www.osceola.k12.fl.us
Challenger Learning Center 200/Alt
2320 New Beginnings Rd 34744 407-518-8140
Beth Rattie, dir. Fax 518-8141
Denn John MS 1,100/6-8
2001 Denn John Ln 34744 407-935-3560
Anna Campbell, prin. Fax 935-3572
Discovery IS 1,400/6-8
5350 San Miguel Rd 34758 407-343-7300
Alan Ramos, prin. Fax 343-7310
Endeavor HS 50/Alt
2320 New Beginnings Rd 34744 407-518-8140
Beth Rattie, dir. Fax 518-8141
Gateway HS 2,300/9-12
93 Panther Paws Trl 34744 407-935-3600
Larry Meadows, prin. Fax 935-3609
Horizon MS 1,200/6-8
2020 Ham Brown Rd 34746 407-943-7240
Michelle Henninger, prin. Fax 943-7250
Kissimmee MS 1,200/6-8
2410 Dyer Blvd 34741 407-870-0857
Gary Weeden, prin. Fax 870-5669
Liberty HS 2,200/9-12
4250 Pleasant Hill Rd 34746 407-933-3910
Robert Studly, prin. Fax 933-9990
Neptune MS 1,300/6-8
2727 Neptune Rd 34744 407-935-3500
Cindy Mohen, prin. Fax 935-3519
New Beginnings Educational Center 300/Alt
2599 W Vine St 34741 407-348-4466
Nina Wehmeyer, prin. Fax 348-4069
Osceola County S for the Arts 800/6-12
3151 N Orange Blossom Trl 34744 407-931-4803
Jonathan Rasmussen, prin. Fax 931-3019
Osceola HS 2,000/9-12
420 S Thacker Ave 34741 407-518-5400
Jim DiGiacomo, prin. Fax 943-7909
Parkway MS 900/6-8
857 Florida Pkwy 34743 407-344-7000
Evelith Olmeda-Garcia, prin. Fax 348-2797
PATHS @ TECO Vo/Tech
501 Simpson Rd 34744 407-518-5407
Paula Evans, prin. Fax 344-2467
Poinciana HS 1,200/9-12
2300 S Poinciana Blvd 34758 407-870-4860
Pete Hodges, prin. Fax 870-0382
Technical Education Center Vo/Tech
501 Simpson Rd 34744 407-344-5080
Jeanette Eddy, dir. Fax 344-5089
Zenith MS 100/Alt
2218 E Irlo Bronson Mem Hwy 34744 407-846-3976
Sheryl Alexander, prin. Fax 933-9920
Adult Learning Center Adult
2320 New Beginnings Rd 34744 407-518-8140
Beth Rattie, dir. Fax 518-8141
Other Schools – See Celebration, Saint Cloud

American Inst Coll of Health Professions Post-Sec.
420 Celebration Blvd # 309 34747 888-283-5214
American Institute Post-Sec.
1420 Celebration Blvd # 101 34747 888-387-5260
City of Life Christian Academy 400/PK-12
2874 E Irlo Bronson Mem Hwy 34744 407-847-5184
Kathy Harkema, prin. Fax 870-2679
Florida Christian College Post-Sec.
1011 Bill Beck Blvd 34744 407-847-8966
Florida Technical College Post-Sec.
3831 W Vine St 34741 407-483-5700
Heritage Christian S 600/K-12
1500 E Vine St 34744 407-847-4087
Karla Beaver, admin. Fax 932-2806
Life Christian Academy 200/K-12
2269 Partin Settlement Rd 34744 407-847-8222
Marla Butler, prin. Fax 932-4431
North Kissimmee Christian S 200/PK-12
425 W Donegan Ave 34741 407-847-2877
Yvonne Johnson, prin. Fax 847-5372
Pleasant Hill Academy 300/PK-12
2525 Trafalgar Blvd 34758 407-350-5974
Fax 350-5984
Southland Christian S 300/PK-12
2440 Fortune Rd 34744 407-201-7999
Rob Ennis, prin. Fax 350-5929

LaBelle, Hendry, Pop. 4,611
Hendry County SD 6,700/PK-12
PO Box 1980 33975 863-674-4642
Paul K. Puletti, supt. Fax 674-4090
www.hendry-schools.org
La Belle HS 1,000/9-12
4050 E Cowboy Way 33935 863-674-4120
Lucinda Kelley, prin. Fax 674-4571
La Belle MS 700/6-8
8000 E Cowboy Way 33935 863-674-4646
Gary White, prin. Fax 674-4645
Labelle Community Adult S Adult
1100 Forestry Division Rd 33935 863-612-0706
Gary Breakfield, prin. Fax 983-1511
Other Schools – See Clewiston

Lake Alfred, Polk, Pop. 4,919
Polk County SD
Supt. — See Bartow
Lake Alfred-Addair MS 700/6-8
925 N Buena Vista Dr 33850 863-295-5988
Linda Ray, prin. Fax 295-5989

Lake Butler, Union, Pop. 1,869
Union County SD 2,300/PK-12
55 SW 6th St 32054 386-496-2045
Carlton Faulk, supt. Fax 496-2580
www.union.k12.fl.us
Lake Butler MS 800/5-8
150 SW 6th St 32054 386-496-3046
David Campbell, prin. Fax 496-4352
Outpost 50/Alt
208 SE 6th St 32054 386-496-1300
Barry Sams, dir. Fax 496-4919
Union County HS 600/9-12
1000 S Lake Ave 32054 386-496-3040
Mike Ripplinger, prin. Fax 496-4187
Union County Adult HS Adult
208 SE 6th St 32054 386-496-1300
Barry Sams, prin. Fax 496-4919

Lake City, Columbia, Pop. 11,774
Columbia County SD 9,700/PK-12
372 W Duval St 32055 386-755-8000
Terry Huddleston, supt. Fax 755-8008
www.columbia.k12.fl.us
Challenge Learning Center 100/Alt
1301 NW LaBonte Ln 32055 386-755-8296
Deborah Hill, prin. Fax 755-8291
Columbia HS 1,800/9-12
469 SE Fighting Tiger Dr 32025 386-755-8080
Terry Huddleston, prin. Fax 755-8082
Lake City MS 1,100/6-8
843 SW Arlington Blvd 32025 386-758-4800
Sonja Judkins, prin. Fax 758-4839
Richardson MS 600/6-8
646 SE Pennsylvania St 32025 386-755-8130
Lex Carswell, prin. Fax 755-8154
Vocational Adult & Community Education Vo/Tech
409 SW Saint Johns St 32025 386-755-8190
Mary Keen, prin. Fax 755-8191
Other Schools – See Fort White

Florida Gateway College Post-Sec.
149 SE College Pl 32025 386-752-1822
Lake City Christian Academy 100/PK-12
3035 SW Pinemount Rd 32024 386-758-0055
Tana Norris, dir. Fax 758-3018

Lakeland, Polk, Pop. 95,497
Polk County SD
Supt. — See Bartow
Chiles MS Academy 700/6-8
400 N Florida Ave 33801 863-499-2742
Sharon Neuman, prin. Fax 499-2774
Crystal Lake MS 700/6-8
2410 N Crystal Lake Dr 33801 863-499-2970
Christopher Canning, prin. Fax 603-6267
Drop Back In Academy 500/Alt
302 E Memorial Blvd 33801 863-687-9222
Timothy James, prin. Fax 687-9220
Harrison S for the Arts 400/9-12
750 Hollingsworth Rd 33801 863-499-2855
Dr. Craig Collins, prin. Fax 499-2938
Jenkins HS 2,200/9-12
6000 Lakeland Highlands Rd 33813 863-648-3566
Buddy Thomas, prin. Fax 648-3573
Kathleen HS 1,800/9-12
1100 Red Devil Way 33815 863-499-2655
Fax 499-2726
Kathleen MS 800/6-8
3627 Kathleen Pnes 33810 863-853-6040
Brett Butler, prin. Fax 853-6037
Lake Gibson HS 1,900/9-12
7007 N Socrum Loop Rd 33809 863-853-6100
Tami Dawson, prin. Fax 853-6108
Lake Gibson MS 1,200/6-8
6901 N Socrum Loop Rd 33809 863-853-6151
Kathy Conely, prin. Fax 853-6171
Lakeland Highlands MS 1,300/6-8
740 Lake Miriam Dr 33813 863-648-3500
Donna Drisdom, prin. Fax 648-3580
Lakeland HS 2,000/9-12
726 Hollingsworth Rd 33801 863-499-2900
Tracy Collins, prin. Fax 499-2917
Sleepy Hill MS 900/6-8
2215 Sleepy Hill Rd 33810 863-815-6577
Kathryn Blackburn, prin. Fax 815-6586
Southwest MS 900/6-8
2815 Eden Pkwy 33803 863-499-2840
John Wilson, prin. Fax 499-2762
Tenoroc HS 1,400/9-12
4905 Saddle Creek Rd 33801 863-614-9183
Jason Looney, prin. Fax 614-9192
Traviss Career Center Vo/Tech
3225 Winter Lake Rd 33803 863-499-2700
Wayne Dickens, prin. Fax 499-2706
West Area Adult & Community S Adult
604 S Central Ave 33815 863-499-2835
Loretta Cameron, prin. Fax 499-2727

Everest University - Lakeland Campus Post-Sec.
995 E Memorial Blvd Ste 110 33801 863-686-1444
Excel Christian Academy 200/PK-12
6505 Odom Rd 33809 863-853-9235
Amy Kretzer, prin. Fax 853-1835
Florida Southern College Post-Sec.
111 Lake Hollingsworth Dr 33801 863-680-4111
Florida Technical College Post-Sec.
4715 S Florida Ave Ste 4 33813 863-619-6200
Geneva Classical Academy 100/PK-12
4204 Lakeland Highlands Rd 33813 863-644-1408
Rich Cali, hdmstr. Fax 619-5841
Highlands Christian Academy 100/PK-12
4210 Lakeland Highlands Rd 33813 863-646-5031
Fax 646-2267
Keiser University Post-Sec.
2400 Interstate Dr 33805 863-682-6020
Lakeland Christian S 1,000/PK-12
1111 Forest Park St 33803 863-688-2771
Dr. Michael Sligh, hdmstr. Fax 682-5637
Lakeland Regional Medical Center Post-Sec.
1324 Lakeland Hills Blvd 33805 863-687-1100
Santa Fe Catholic HS 300/9-12
3110 US Highway 92 E 33801 863-665-4188
Matthew Franzino, prin. Fax 665-4151
Sonrise Christian S 200/PK-12
3151 Hardin Combee Rd 33801 863-665-4187
Steve Burton, admin. Fax 665-6065
Southeastern University Post-Sec.
1000 Longfellow Blvd 33801 863-667-5000
Traviss Career Center Post-Sec.
3225 Winter Lake Rd 33803 863-499-2700
Victory Christian Academy 300/PK-12
1401 Griffin Rd 33810 863-858-5614
Karla Collins, admin. Fax 858-4268

Lake Mary, Seminole, Pop. 13,545
Seminole County SD
Supt. — See Sanford
Greenwood Lakes MS 1,000/6-8
601 Lake Park Dr 32746 407-320-7650
Debra Abbott, prin. Fax 320-7699
Lake Mary HS 2,600/9-12
655 Longwood Lake Mary Rd 32746 407-320-9550
Michael Kotkin, prin. Fax 320-9512
Markham Woods MS 1,100/6-8
6003 Markham Woods Rd 32746 407-871-1750
James Kubis, prin. Fax 871-1799

ITT Technical Institute Post-Sec.
1400 S International Pkwy 32746 407-660-2900
Lake Mary Preparatory S 600/PK-12
650 Rantoul Ln 32746 407-805-0095
Remington College of Nursing Post-Sec.
660 Century Pt Ste 1050 32746 800-294-4434
Remington College - Online Post-Sec.
500 International Pkwy #200 32746 800-560-6192

Lake Park, Palm Beach, Pop. 7,949

Palm Beach Academy of Health & Beauty Post-Sec.
1220 10th St Ste A 33403 561-845-1400

Lake Placid, Highlands, Pop. 2,195
Highlands County SD
Supt. — See Sebring
Lake Placid HS 800/9-12
202 Green Dragon Dr 33852 863-699-5010
Toni Stivender, prin. Fax 699-5094
Lake Placid MS 600/6-8
201 S Tangerine Ave 33852 863-699-5030
Julia Burnett, prin. Fax 699-5029

Lake Wales, Polk, Pop. 13,989
Polk County SD
Supt. — See Bartow
McLaughlin MS 800/6-8
800 S 4th St 33853 863-678-4233
Sharon Chipman, prin. Fax 678-4033
Roosevelt Academy 200/6-12
115 E St 33853 863-678-4252
Debra Edwards, prin. Fax 678-4250

Endtime Christian S of Excellence 50/PK-12
200 S 3rd St 33853 863-676-8299
Betty Hill, prin. Fax 678-1193
Warner University Post-Sec.
13895 Hwy 27 33859 863-638-1426

Lakewood Ranch, Manatee

Out of Door Academy 400/6-12
5950 Deer Dr, 941-907-1159
David Mahler, hdmstr. Fax 907-1251

Lake Worth, Palm Beach, Pop. 34,358
Palm Beach County SD
Supt. — See West Palm Beach
Lake Worth Community HS 2,000/9-12
1701 Lake Worth Rd 33460 561-533-6300
George Lockhart, prin. Fax 493-0888
Lake Worth MS 900/6-8
1300 Barnett Dr 33461 561-540-5500
Tanya Daniel, prin. Fax 540-5559
Park Vista Community HS 2,900/9-12
7900 S Jog Rd 33467 561-491-8400
Reginald Myers, prin. Fax 493-6854
South Intensive Transition S 100/Alt
1509 Barton Rd 33460 561-202-0600
Dr. Voncia Haywood, prin. Fax 202-0650
Woodlands MS 1,200/6-8
5200 Lyons Rd 33467 561-357-0300
Jeffrey Eassa, prin. Fax 357-0307

Academy of Palm Beach Post-Sec.
3141 S Military Trl 33463 561-965-5550
Palm Beach State College Post-Sec.
4200 S Congress Ave 33461 561-967-7222
Trinity Christian Academy 700/PK-12
7259 S Military Trl 33463 561-967-1900
Cindy Ansell, prin. Fax 965-4347

Land O Lakes, Pasco, Pop. 31,370
Pasco County SD 63,500/PK-12
7227 Land O Lakes Blvd 34638 813-794-2000
Heather Fiorentino Ph.D., supt. Fax 794-2716
www.pasco.k12.fl.us
Land O'Lakes HS 1,600/9-12
20325 Gator Ln, 813-794-9400
Ric Mellin, prin. Fax 794-9491
Pine View MS 800/6-8
5334 Parkway Blvd 34639 813-794-4800
Jennifer Crosby, prin. Fax 794-4891
Rushe MS 1,300/6-8
18654 Mentmore Blvd, 813-346-1200
David Salerno, prin. Fax 346-1291
Sunlake HS 1,600/9-12
3023 Sunlake Blvd, 813-346-1000
Garry Walthall, prin. Fax 346-1091
Other Schools – See Dade City, Holiday, Hudson, New Port Richey, Port Richey, Spring Hill, Wesley Chapel, Zephyrhills

---

Academy at the Lakes - McCormick 200/5-12
2331 Collier Pkwy 34639 813-948-7600
Mark Heller, hdmstr. Fax 949-0563
Land O' Lakes Christian S 200/PK-12
5105 School Rd, 813-995-9040
Rev. David Nichols, admin. Fax 996-6106

Lantana, Palm Beach, Pop. 10,206
Palm Beach County SD
Supt. — See West Palm Beach
Lantana Community MS 800/6-8
1225 W Drew St 33462 561-540-3400
Edward Burke, prin. Fax 540-3435
Santaluces Community HS 2,200/9-12
6880 Lawrence Rd 33462 561-642-6200
Kathleen Weigel, prin. Fax 642-6255

Kentwood Preparatory S 100/1-12
6210 S Congress Ave 33462 561-649-6141
Gary Fein, admin. Fax 649-6142

Largo, Pinellas, Pop. 76,001
Pinellas County SD 102,800/PK-12
301 4th St SW 33770 727-588-6000
Dr. John Stewart, supt. Fax 588-6200
www.pcsb.org
Fitzgerald MS 1,400/6-8
6410 110th Ave 33773 727-547-4526
Teresa Anderson, prin. Fax 549-6631
Largo HS 1,800/9-12
410 Missouri Ave N 33770 727-588-3758
Bradley Finkbiner, prin. Fax 588-4037
Largo MS 900/6-8
155 8th Ave SE 33771 727-588-4600
Alisa Gatlin, prin. Fax 588-3720
Pinellas Park HS 2,100/9-12
6305 118th Ave 33773 727-538-7410
John Johnston, prin. Fax 507-4563
Other Schools – See Clearwater, Dunedin, Gulfport, Palm Harbor, Pinellas Park, Safety Harbor, Saint Petersburg, Seminole, Tarpon Springs

---

ATA Career Education Post-Sec.
12360 66th St 33773 727-576-9597
Everest University - Largo Campus Post-Sec.
1199 E Bay Dr 33770 727-725-2688
Fortis College Post-Sec.
6565 Ulmerton Rd 33771 727-531-5900
Indian Rocks Christian S 700/PK-12
12685 Ulmerton Rd 33774 727-596-4342
Dr. Don Mayes, supt. Fax 593-8778
Schiller International University Post-Sec.
8560 Ulmerton Rd 33771 800-261-9751
Veritas Academy 100/K-12
12685 Ulmerton Rd 33774 727-593-8791
Kira Wilson, admin. Fax 593-8793
Westside Christian S 100/K-12
11633 137th St 33774 727-517-2153
Rev. Huey Davis, prin. Fax 593-7700

Lauderdale Lakes, Broward, Pop. 31,785
Broward County SD
Supt. — See Fort Lauderdale
Anderson HS 2,100/9-12
3050 NW 41st St 33309 754-322-0200
Angel Almanzar, prin. Fax 322-0330
Lauderdale Lakes MS 900/6-8
3911 NW 30th Ave 33309 754-322-3500
James Griffin, prin. Fax 322-3585

Florida Career College Post-Sec.
3383 N State Road 7 33319 954-535-8700

Lauderhill, Broward, Pop. 65,234
Broward County SD
Supt. — See Fort Lauderdale
Lauderhill MS 600/6-8
1901 NW 49th Ave 33313 754-322-3600
Jeannie Floyd, prin. Fax 322-3685

Intl School of Health Beauty and Tech Post-Sec.
5950 W Oakland Park Blvd 33313 954-741-0088
University of Fort Lauderdale Post-Sec.
4093 NW 16th St 33313 954-486-7728

Laurel Hill, Okaloosa, Pop. 532
Okaloosa County SD
Supt. — See Fort Walton Beach

Laurel Hill S 400/PK-12
8078 4th St 32567 850-652-4111
Susan Lowrey, prin. Fax 652-4659

Lecanto, Citrus, Pop. 5,799
Citrus County SD
Supt. — See Inverness
Citrus County Renaissance Center 100/Alt
3630 W Educational Path 34461 352-527-4567
Danita Eatman, prin. Fax 249-2144
Lecanto HS 1,800/9-12
3810 W Educational Path 34461 352-746-2334
Jeff Davis, prin. Fax 249-2136
Lecanto MS 700/6-8
3800 W Educational Path 34461 352-746-2050
William Farrell, prin. Fax 249-2138

Seven Rivers Christian S 300/PK-12
4221 W Gulf to Lake Hwy 34461 352-746-5696
Dana James, admin. Fax 746-5520

Leesburg, Lake, Pop. 19,677
Lake County SD
Supt. — See Tavares
Carver MS 900/6-8
1200 Beecher St 34748 352-787-7868
Mollie Cunningham, prin. Fax 787-1339
Leesburg HS 1,700/9-12
1401 Yellow Jacket Way 34748 352-787-5047
Bill Miller, prin. Fax 787-9040
Oak Park MS 600/6-8
2101 South St 34748 352-787-3232
Dale Delpit, prin. Fax 326-2177

Beacon College Post-Sec.
105 E Main St 34748 352-787-7660
First Academy-Leesburg 300/PK-12
219 N 13th St 34748 352-787-7762
Gregory Frescoln, admin. Fax 323-1773
Lake-Sumter Community College Post-Sec.
9501 US Highway 441 34788 352-787-3747

Lehigh Acres, Lee, Pop. 85,066
Lee County SD
Supt. — See Fort Myers
East Lee County HS 1,600/9-12
715 Thomas Sherwin Ave S, 239-369-2932
Brian Mangan, prin. Fax 369-3213
Harns Marsh MS 6-8
1820 Unice Ave N 33971 239-690-2025
Eric McFee, prin. Fax 690-2028
Lehigh Acres MS 1,000/6-8
104 Arthur Ave 33936 239-369-6108
Joe Pitura, prin. Fax 369-8808
Lehigh HS 1,500/9-12
901 Gunnery Rd N 33971 239-693-5353
Jackie Corey, prin. Fax 693-6702
Varsity Lakes MS 1,000/6-8
801 Gunnery Rd N 33971 239-694-3464
Scott Cook, prin. Fax 694-7093

Lithia, Hillsborough
Hillsborough County SD
Supt. — See Tampa
Barrington MS 1,000/6-8
5925 Village Center Dr 33547 813-657-7266
Maribeth Franklin, prin.
Newsome HS 2,200/9-12
16550 Fishhawk Blvd 33547 813-740-4600
Carla Bruning, prin. Fax 740-4604
Randall MS 1,300/6-8
16510 Fishhawk Blvd 33547 813-740-3900
Fredda Johnson, prin. Fax 740-3910

Live Oak, Suwannee, Pop. 6,744
Suwannee County SD 6,100/PK-12
702 2nd St NW 32064 386-647-4600
Jerry Scarborough, supt. Fax 364-2635
suwannee.schooldesk.net
Suwannee-Hamilton Technical Ctr Vo/Tech
415 Pinewood Dr SW 32064 386-647-4200
Walter Boatright, prin. Fax 364-4698
Suwannee HS 1,200/9-12
1314 Pine Ave SW 32064 386-647-4000
Ted Roush, prin. Fax 364-2794
Suwannee MS 1,100/6-8
1730 Walker Ave SW 32064 386-647-4500
Jay Jolicoeur, prin. Fax 208-1474
Other Schools – See Branford

Melody Christian Academy 200/PK-12
PO Box 100 32064 386-364-4800
Amanda Davis, prin. Fax 364-1889

Longwood, Seminole, Pop. 13,382
Seminole County SD
Supt. — See Sanford
Lyman HS 2,300/9-12
865 S Ronald Reagan Blvd 32750 407-746-2050
Brian Urichko, prin. Fax 746-2024
Milwee MS 1,100/6-8
1341 S Ronald Reagan Blvd 32750 407-746-3850
Michelle Walsh, prin. Fax 746-3899
Rock Lake MS 1,000/6-8
250 Slade Dr 32750 407-746-9350
Pamela Shellman-Ross, prin. Fax 746-9399

Loxahatchee, Palm Beach
Palm Beach County SD
Supt. — See West Palm Beach
Osceola Creek MS 900/6-8
6775 180th Ave N 33470 561-422-2500
Daniel Frank, prin. Fax 422-2510
Seminole Ridge Community HS 2,500/9-12
4601 Seminole Pratt Whitney 33470 561-422-2600
James Campbell, prin. Fax 422-2623

Lutz, Hillsborough, Pop. 19,035
Hillsborough County SD
Supt. — See Tampa
Martinez MS 1,100/6-8
5601 W Lutz Lake Fern Rd 33558 813-558-1190
Dallas Jackson, prin. Fax 558-1226
Steinbrenner HS 2,000/9-12
5575 W Lutz Lake Fern Rd 33558 813-792-5131
Brenda Grasso, prin. Fax 792-5135

Lynn Haven, Bay, Pop. 18,004
Bay County SD
Supt. — See Panama City
Mosley HS 1,800/9-12
501 Mosley Dr 32444 850-767-4400
Sandy Harrison, prin. Fax 872-4453
Mowat MS 900/6-8
1903 W Highway 390 32444 850-767-4040
Ed Sheffield, prin. Fax 265-2179

Macclenny, Baker, Pop. 6,242
Baker County SD 5,000/PK-12
392 South Blvd E 32063 904-259-6251
Sherrie Raulerson, supt. Fax 259-1387
www.baker.k12.fl.us
Baker County MS 1,100/6-8
211 E Jonathan St 32063 904-259-2226
Sherry Barrett, prin. Fax 259-7955
Baker County Adult Center Adult
270 South Blvd E 32063 904-259-6251
Ann Watts, prin. Fax 259-0378
Other Schools – See Glen Saint Mary

Madison, Madison, Pop. 2,801
Madison County SD 2,600/PK-12
210 NE Duval Ave 32340 850-973-5022
Doug Brown, supt. Fax 973-5027
www.madison.k12.fl.us
Madison Co. Excel Alternative Ed. Center 50/Alt
2523 W US 90 32340 850-973-5054
Fax 973-5047
Madison County HS 700/9-12
2649 W US 90 32340 850-973-5061
Ben Killingsworth, prin. Fax 973-5066

North Florida Community College Post-Sec.
325 NW Turner Davis Dr 32340 850-973-2288

Maitland, Orange, Pop. 15,449
Orange County SD
Supt. — See Orlando
Maitland MS 1,000/6-8
1901 Choctaw Trl 32751 407-623-1462
Ronald Maxwell, prin. Fax 623-1474

Florida College of Natural Health Post-Sec.
2600 Lake Lucien Dr Ste 140 32751 407-261-0319
Orangewood Christian S 700/K-12
1300 W Maitland Blvd 32751 407-339-0223
LuAnne Schendel, hdmstr. Fax 339-4148

Malone, Jackson, Pop. 2,054
Jackson County SD
Supt. — See Marianna
Malone S 500/PK-12
PO Box 68 32445 850-482-9950
Doug Powell, prin. Fax 482-9981

Marathon, Monroe, Pop. 8,204
Monroe County SD
Supt. — See Key West
Marathon HS 600/6-12
350 Sombrero Beach Rd 33050 305-289-2480
Hammond Gracy, prin. Fax 289-2486

Margate, Broward, Pop. 51,792
Broward County SD
Supt. — See Fort Lauderdale
Margate MS 1,000/6-8
500 NW 65th Ave 33063 754-322-3800
Ernest Toliver, prin. Fax 322-3885

American Institute Post-Sec.
5000 Coconut Creek Pkwy # C 33063 888-283-1671
Florida Career College Post-Sec.
3271 N State Road 7 33063 954-862-7260
Margate School of Beauty Post-Sec.
5281 Coconut Creek Pkwy 33063 954-972-9630

Marianna, Jackson, Pop. 5,957
Jackson County SD 6,900/PK-12
PO Box 5958 32447 850-482-1200
Lee Miller, supt. Fax 482-1299
www.jcsb.org
Jackson Alternative S 100/Alt
2701 Technology Cir 32448 850-482-9666
Laurence Pender, prin. Fax 482-9800
Marianna HS 800/9-12
3546 Caverns Rd 32446 850-482-9605
Sarieta Russ, prin. Fax 482-1247
Marianna MS 600/6-8
4144 South St 32448 850-482-9609
Eddie Ellis, prin. Fax 482-9795
Adult Education Adult
2971 Guyton St 32446 850-482-9617
Beth Westmoreland, prin. Fax 482-1201
Other Schools – See Cottondale, Graceville, Malone, Sneads

Chipola College Post-Sec.
3094 Indian Cir 32446 850-526-2761

Mayo, Lafayette, Pop. 1,208
LaFayette County SD 1,200/PK-12
363 NE Crawford St 32066 386-294-1351
Roberts Edwards, supt. Fax 294-3072
lafayette.schooldesk.net
LaFayette JSHS 600/6-12
160 NE Hornet Ln 32066 386-294-1701
Ray Hancock, prin. Fax 294-4197
Adult Education Adult
363 NE Crawford St 32066 386-294-4120
Debra Land, admin. Fax 294-3072

Lighthouse Christian Academy 100/PK-12
772 N State Road 51 32066 386-294-2994
Jennifer Roberts, prin. Fax 294-3449

Melbourne, Brevard, Pop. 74,011
Brevard County SD 69,000/PK-12
2700 Judge Fran Jamieson 32940 321-633-1000
Dr. Brian Binggeli, supt. Fax 633-3432
www.brevard.k12.fl.us
Eau Gallie HS 1,600/9-12
1400 Commodore Blvd 32935 321-242-6400
Jeremy Salmon, prin. Fax 242-6427
Johnson MS 900/7-8
2155 Croton Rd 32935 321-242-6430
Robert Fish, prin. Fax 242-6436
Melbourne HS 2,000/9-12
74 Bulldog Blvd 32901 321-952-5880
James Willcoxon, prin. Fax 952-5898
Palm Bay HS 1,900/9-12
101 Pirate Ln 32901 321-952-5900
John Thomas, prin. Fax 676-2891
South Area Alternative Learning Center 100/Alt
2175 N Wickham Rd 32935 321-242-4770
Michael Smith, prin. Fax 242-4772
Stone MS 800/7-8
1101 E University Blvd 32901 321-723-0741
Andrew Johnson, prin. Fax 951-1497
Viera HS 2,100/9-12
6103 Stadium Pkwy 32940 321-632-1770
James Hickey, prin. Fax 433-4338
West Shore JSHS 1,000/7-12
250 Wildcat Aly 32935 321-242-4730
Eric Fleming, prin. Fax 242-4740
Palm Bay HS Adult/Community Ed Adult
101 Pirate Ln 32901 321-952-5914
Karen D'Arceuil, prin.
South Area Adult/Community Education Ctr Adult
1362 S Babcock St 32901 321-952-5977
Rebecca Camp, prin. Fax 952-5831
Other Schools – See Cocoa, Cocoa Beach, Indialantic, Merritt Island, Palm Bay, Rockledge, Satellite Beach, Titusville, West Melbourne

Community Christian S 100/K-12
1616 Ferndale Ave 32935 321-259-1590
Laurel Earls, prin. Fax 259-5301
Everest University - Melbourne Campus Post-Sec.
2401 N Harbor City Blvd 32935 321-253-2929
Florida Air Academy 300/6-12
1950 Academy Dr 32901 321-723-3211
James Dwight, pres. Fax 676-9548
Florida Institute of Technology Post-Sec.
150 W University Blvd 32901 321-674-8000
Holy Trinity Episcopal Academy 900/7-12
5625 Holy Trinity Dr 32940 321-723-8323
Nancy Giangrisostomi, head sch Fax 308-9077
Keiser University Post-Sec.
900 S Babcock St 32901 321-409-4800
Melbourne Central Catholic HS 400/9-12
100 E Florida Ave 32901 321-727-0793
Thomas Armstrong, prin. Fax 727-1134
New Covenant Christian S 100/K-12
1990 W New Haven Ave # 306 32904 321-724-9603
Sandra Hancock, prin. Fax 724-6932
R.F.M Christian Academy 100/7-12
777 S Apollo Blvd 32901 321-952-3787
Ezella Parker, prin. Fax 473-8914
West Melbourne Christian Academy 200/PK-12
3150 Milwaukee Ave 32904 321-725-3743
Mark Siler, prin. Fax 725-6661

Merritt Island, Brevard, Pop. 33,904
Brevard County SD
Supt. — See Melbourne
Edgewood JSHS 900/7-12
180 E Merritt Ave 32953 321-454-1030
Dr. Kenneth Winn, prin. Fax 452-1176
Jefferson MS 700/7-8
1275 S Courtenay Pkwy 32952 321-453-5154
Sherri Bowman, prin. Fax 459-2854
Merritt Island HS 1,500/9-12
100 Mustang Way 32953 321-454-1000
Gary Shiffrin, prin. Fax 454-1013

Avalon School of Cosmetology Post-Sec.
2088 N Courtenay Pkwy 32953 321-452-8490
Merritt Island Christian S 500/PK-12
140 Magnolia Ave 32952 321-453-2710
Dr. Nanci Dettra, supt. Fax 452-6580

Miami, Miami-Dade, Pop. 396,081
Miami-Dade County SD 337,800/PK-12
1450 NE 2nd Ave 33132 305-995-1000
Alberto Carvalho, supt. Fax 995-1488
www.dadeschools.net/
Allapattah MS 700/6-8
1331 NW 46th St 33142 305-634-9787
Bridget McKinney, prin. Fax 638-8254
Ammons MS 1,200/6-8
17990 SW 142nd Ave 33177 305-971-0158
Maria Costa, prin. Fax 971-0179
Andover MS 1,100/6-8
121 NE 207th St 33179 305-654-2727
Rennina Turner, prin. Fax 654-2728
Arvida MS 1,300/6-8
10900 SW 127th Ave 33186 305-385-7144
Nancy Aragon, prin. Fax 383-9472
Baker Aviation S Vo/Tech
3275 NW 42nd Ave 33142 305-871-3143
Sean Gallagan, prin. Fax 871-5840

Bell MS 800/6-8
11800 NW 2nd St 33182 305-220-2075
Ingrid Soto, prin. Fax 229-0798
Braddock HS 3,400/9-12
3601 SW 147th Ave 33185 305-225-9729
Manuel Garcia, prin. Fax 221-3312
Brownsville MS 500/7-9
4899 NW 24th Ave 33142 305-633-1481
Dr. Edward Robinson, prin. Fax 635-8702
Canosa MS 1,900/6-8
15735 SW 144th St 33196 305-252-5900
Juan Silva, prin. Fax 252-5901
Chiles MS 1,000/6-8
8190 NW 197th St 33015 305-816-9101
Nelson Izquierdo, prin. Fax 816-9248
Citrus Grove MS 1,000/6-8
2153 NW 3rd St 33125 305-642-5055
Emirce Ladaga, prin. Fax 642-9349
C.O.P.E. Center North 100/Alt
9950 NW 19th Ave 33147 305-836-3300
Dr. Lillian Cooper, prin. Fax 835-8818
Coral Reef HS 3,100/9-12
10101 SW 152nd St 33157 305-232-2044
Adrianne Leal, prin. Fax 252-3454
Country Club MS 1,400/6-8
18305 NW 75th Pl 33015 305-820-8800
Jose Fernandez, prin. Fax 820-8801
Curry MS 1,100/6-8
15750 SW 47th St 33185 305-222-2775
Wandarece Ruan, prin. Fax 229-1521
Dario MS 800/6-8
350 NW 97th Ave 33172 305-226-0179
Dr. Verona McCarthy, prin. Fax 559-0919
De Diego MS 600/6-8
3100 NW 5th Ave 33127 305-573-7229
Yaset Fernandez, prin. Fax 573-6415
Design & Architectural Magnet HS Vo/Tech
4001 NE 2nd Ave 33137 305-573-7135
Dr. Stacy Mancuso, prin. Fax 573-8253
Drew MS 500/6-8
1801 NW 60th St 33142 305-633-6057
Reginald Lee, prin. Fax 638-1307
Ferguson HS 4,300/9-12
15900 SW 56th St 33185 305-408-2700
Dr. Lisa Robertson, prin. Fax 408-6487
Glades MS 1,200/6-8
9451 SW 64th Ter 33173 305-271-3342
Elio Falcon, prin. Fax 271-0402
Glazer MS 1,400/6-8
15015 SW 24th St 33185 305-485-2323
Melba Brito, prin. Fax 485-2324
Hammocks MS 1,200/6-8
9889 Hammocks Blvd 33196 305-385-0896
Deborah Leal, prin. Fax 382-0861
Hopkins Technical Center Vo/Tech
750 NW 20th St 33127 305-324-6070
Rosa Borgen, prin. Fax 545-6397
iPreparatory Academy 11-12
1500 Biscayne Blvd 33132 305-995-1928
Alberto Carvalho, prin. Fax 523-0736
Jefferson MS 400/7-9
525 NW 147th St 33168 305-681-7481
Maria Fernandez, prin. Fax 688-5912
Kinloch Park MS 1,200/6-8
4340 NW 3rd St 33126 305-445-5467
Scott Weiner, prin. Fax 445-3110
Krop HS 3,100/9-12
1410 NE 215th St 33179 305-652-6808
Dawn Baglos, prin. Fax 651-8043
Law Enforcement Officers Memorial HS 200/9-12
300 NW 2nd Ave 33128 305-371-0400
Christopher Shinn, prin. Fax 371-0401
Madison MS 600/6-8
3400 NW 87th St 33147 305-836-2610
Renny Neyra, prin. Fax 696-5249
Mann MS 700/6-8
8950 NW 2nd Ave 33150 305-757-9537
Carmen Jones-Carey, prin. Fax 754-0724
McMillan MS 900/6-8
13100 SW 59th St 33183 305-385-6877
Hilca Thomas, prin. Fax 387-9641
Miami Central HS 1,800/9-12
1781 NW 95th St 33147 305-696-4161
Gregory Bethune, prin. Fax 836-2872
Miami Coral Park HS 3,200/9-12
8865 SW 16th St 33165 305-226-6565
Dr. Nicholas Jacangelo, prin. Fax 553-4658
Miami Edison HS 900/9-12
6161 NW 5th Ct 33127 305-751-7337
Trynegwa Diggs, prin. Fax 759-4561
Miami Edison MS 500/6-8
6101 NW 2nd Ave 33127 305-754-4683
Keith Anderson, prin. Fax 757-2219
Miami HS 2,800/9-12
2450 SW 1st St 33135 305-649-9800
Benny Valdes, prin. Fax 649-9475
Miami Jackson HS 1,200/9-12
1751 NW 36th St 33142 305-634-2621
Carlos Rios, prin. Fax 634-7477
Miami Killian HS 2,900/9-12
10655 SW 97th Ave 33176 305-271-3311
Thomas Ennis, prin. Fax 270-9142
Miami Norland HS 1,500/9-12
1050 NW 195th St 33169 305-653-1416
Luis Solano, prin. Fax 651-6175
Miami Northwestern HS 1,800/9-12
1100 NW 71st St 33150 305-836-0991
Wallace Aristide, prin. Fax 691-4955
Miami Palmetto HS 3,000/9-12
7460 SW 118th St 33156 305-235-1360
Dr. Allison Harley, prin. Fax 235-7169
Miami Southridge HS 2,300/9-12
19355 SW 114th Ave 33157 305-238-6110
Bianca Calzadilla, prin. Fax 253-4456
Miami Sunset HS 2,600/9-12
13125 SW 72nd St 33183 305-385-4255
Dr. Lucia Cox, prin. Fax 385-6458

New World S of the Arts 500/9-12
25 NE 2nd St 33132 305-237-3135
Evonne Alvarez, prin. Fax 237-3794
Norland MS 800/6-8
1235 NW 192nd Ter 33169 305-653-1210
Ronald Redmon, prin. Fax 654-1237
Outreach Programs 100/Alt
5120 NW 24th Ave 33142 305-636-6160
Fax 636-6198
Palmetto MS 800/7-9
7351 SW 128th St 33156 305-238-3911
John Lux, prin. Fax 233-4849
Richmond Heights MS 800/6-8
15015 SW 103rd Ave 33176 305-238-2316
Kristal Hickmon, prin. Fax 251-3712
Riviera MS 800/6-8
10301 SW 48th St 33165 305-226-4286
Dr. Winston Whyte, prin. Fax 226-1025
Rockway MS 1,300/6-8
9393 SW 29th Ter 33165 305-221-8212
Melanie Megias, prin. Fax 221-5940
School for Advanced Studies - North 100/11-12
11380 NW 27th Ave Ste 1111 33167 305-237-1089
Dr. Omar Monteagudo, prin. Fax 237-1610
School for Advanced Studies-South 200/11-12
11011 SW 104th St Ste 706 33176 305-237-0510
Dr. Omar Monteagudo, prin. Fax 237-0511
School for Advanced Studies-Wolfson 100/11-12
25 NE 2nd St 33132 305-237-7270
Dr. Omar Monteagudo, prin. Fax 237-7271
Shenandoah MS 1,100/6-8
1950 SW 19th St 33145 305-856-8282
Humberto Miret, prin. Fax 856-7049
South Miami HS 2,400/9-12
6856 SW 53rd St 33155 305-666-5871
Gilberto Bonce, prin. Fax 666-6359
Southwest Miami HS 3,000/9-12
8855 SW 50th Ter 33165 305-274-0181
Carlos Diaz, prin. Fax 596-7370
TERRA Environmental Research Institute 900/9-12
11005 SW 84th St 33173 305-412-5800
Caridad Montano, prin. Fax 412-5801
Thomas MS 600/6-8
13001 SW 26th St 33175 305-995-3800
Lisa Pizzimenti, prin. Fax 995-3537
Turner Technical Arts HS Vo/Tech
10151 NW 19th Ave 33147 305-691-8324
Lavette Hunter, prin. Fax 693-9463
Varela HS 3,100/9-12
15255 SW 96th St 33196 305-752-7900
Nery Fins, prin. Fax 386-8987
Wallace C.O.P.E. Center 100/Alt
10225 SW 147th Ter 33176 305-233-1044
Karen Webb, prin. Fax 256-8604
Washington HS 1,000/9-12
1200 NW 6th Ave 33136 305-324-8900
William Aristide, prin. Fax 324-4676
West Miami MS 1,100/6-8
7525 SW 24th St 33155 305-261-8383
Colleen Del Terzo, prin. Fax 267-8204
Westview MS 600/6-8
1901 NW 127th St 33167 305-681-6647
Robin Atkins, prin. Fax 685-3192
Young Mens Preparatory Academy 100/9-12
3001 NW 2nd Ave 33127 305-571-1111
Leonard Ruan, prin. Fax 571-1112
Young Women's Preparatory Academy 400/6-12
1150 SW 1st St 33130 305-575-1200
Concepcion Martinez, prin. Fax 325-8071
Dorsey Education Center Adult
7100 NW 17th Ave 33147 305-693-2490
Gloria Evans, prin. Fax 691-7492
English Center Adult
3501 SW 28th St 33133 305-445-7731
Chely Rayjoy-Tarpin, prin. Fax 441-2150
Miami Coral Park HS Adult Education Ctr. Adult
8865 SW 16th St 33165 305-226-6565
Robert Novak, prin. Fax 559-7415
Miami Jackson HS Adult Education Center Adult
1751 NW 36th St 33142 305-634-2621
Judy Hunter, prin. Fax 633-8191
Miami Palmetto HS Adult Education Center Adult
7460 SW 118th St 33156 305-235-1360
Eunice Soto, prin. Fax 253-3898
Miami Senior Adult Education Center Adult
2450 SW 1st St 33135 305-649-9800
Gilda Santalla, prin. Fax 643-2395
Miami Sunset HS Adult Education Center Adult
13125 SW 72nd St 33183 305-385-4255
Dr. Dulce de Villa, prin. Fax 386-9218
Southwest Miami HS Adult Education Ctr. Adult
8855 SW 50th Ter 33165 305-274-0181
Steve Rummel, prin. Fax 274-3351
Turner Tech Arts Adult Ed Center Adult
10151 NW 19th Ave 33147 305-691-8324
Valmarie Rhoden, prin. Fax 693-9463
Other Schools – See Coral Gables, Cutler Bay, Doral, El Portal, Goulds, Hialeah, Hialeah Gardens, Homestead, Key Biscayne, Miami Beach, Miami Gardens, Miami Lakes, Miami Springs, Naranja, North Miami, North Miami Beach, Opa Locka, Palmetto Bay, Perrine, South Miami

---

Acupuncture & Massage College Post-Sec.
10506 N Kendall Dr 33176 305-595-9500
American HS Academy 400/6-12
10300 SW 72nd St Ste 427 33173 305-270-1440
Archbishop Coleman Carroll HS 600/9-12
10300 SW 167th Ave 33196 305-388-6700
Sr. Rosalie Nagy, prin. Fax 388-4371
Archbishop Curley-Notre Dame HS 300/9-12
4949 NE 2nd Ave 33137 305-751-8367
Douglas Romanik, prin. Fax 751-3517
ATI Career Training Center Post-Sec.
7265 NW 25th St 33122 888-209-8264
Beis Chana S for Girls 500/PK-12
17330 NW 7th Ave 33169 305-653-8770

Belen Jesuit Preparatory HS 1,500/6-12
500 SW 127th Ave 33184 305-223-8600
Rev. Guillermo Garcia-Tunon, prin. Fax 227-2565
Brito Miami Private S 300/PK-12
2732 SW 32nd Ave 33133 305-448-1463
Beatriz Brito-Ferrer, dir. Fax 448-0181
Brother Rice Academy 6-8
4949 NE 2nd Ave 33137 305-751-8367
Douglas Romanik, prin. Fax 751-3517
Brown Mackie College - Miami Post-Sec.
1 Herald Plz 33132 305-341-6600
Calusa Preparatory S 200/K-12
12515 SW 72nd St 33183 305-596-3787
Ben Darlington, prin. Fax 596-7589
Carlos Albizu University Post-Sec.
2173 NW 99th Ave 33172 305-593-1223
Center of Cinematography Art & TV Post-Sec.
1637 NW 27th Ave 33125 305-634-0550
Champagnat Catholic S 200/PK-12
2609 NW 7th St 33125 305-642-4132
Dr. Reinaldo Alonso, prin. Fax 642-8624
City College Post-Sec.
9300 S Dadeland Blvd # 200 33156 305-666-9242
College of Business & Technology Post-Sec.
8230 W Flagler St 33144 305-225-5228
College of Business & Technology Post-Sec.
8765 SW 165th Ave Ste 114 33193 888-281-4330
Columbus HS 1,400/9-12
3000 SW 87th Ave 33165 305-223-5650
Br. Michael Brady, prin. Fax 559-4306
Compu-Med Vocational Careers Post-Sec.
9738 SW 24th St 33165 305-553-2898
Dade Christian S 900/PK-12
6601 NW 167th St 33015 305-827-8702
Stan Stone, hdmstr. Fax 827-8706
Dade Medical College Post-Sec.
3721 NW 7th St Ste 1 33126 786-363-4910
DeVry University Post-Sec.
8700 W Flagler St Ste 100 33174 305-229-4833
Ebenezer Christian Academy 200/PK-12
3901 NW 2nd Ave 33127 305-573-2867
Educating Hands School of Massage Post-Sec.
3883 Biscayne Blvd 33137 305-285-6991
Eureka Institute of Health and Beauty Post-Sec.
11373 W Flagler St Ste 209 33174 305-480-1005
Everest Institute Post-Sec.
9020 SW 137th Ave 33186 305-386-9900
Everest Institute Post-Sec.
111 NW 183rd St Ste 200 33169 305-949-9500
Fasttrain of Kendall Post-Sec.
10100 SW 107th Ave 33176 305-630-4400
Fasttrain of Miami Post-Sec.
5555 W Flagler St 33134 305-262-4748
Florida Career College Post-Sec.
1321 SW 107th Ave Ste 201B 33174 305-553-6065
Florida Career College Post-Sec.
11731 Mills Dr Bldg 2 33183 888-852-7272
Florida Christian S 1,400/PK-12
4200 SW 89th Ave 33165 305-226-8152
Florida College of Natural Health Post-Sec.
7925 NW 12th St Ste 201 33126 305-597-9599
Florida International University Post-Sec.
11200 SW 8th St 33199 305-348-2000
Florida National University Post-Sec.
11865 SW 26th St Ste H3 33175 305-266-9999
Fortis College Post-Sec.
7757 W Flagler St 33144 305-717-7000
Future Tech Institute Post-Sec.
3446 SW 8th St Ste 213 33135 305-774-0227
George T. Baker Aviation School Post-Sec.
3275 NW 42nd Ave 33142 305-871-3143
Greater Miami Adventist Academy 300/PK-12
500 NW 122nd Ave 33182 305-220-5955
Luis Cortes Ph.D., prin. Fax 220-5970
Hope Center Post-Sec.
1411 NW 14th Ave 33125 305-545-7572
Immaculata - La Salle HS 700/9-12
3601 S Miami Ave 33133 305-854-2334
Sr. Kim Keraitis, prin. Fax 858-5971
International Training Careers Post-Sec.
7360 Coral Way 33155 800-649-8139
ITT Technical Institute Post-Sec.
7955 NW 12th St Ste 119 33126 305-477-3080
Jackson Memorial Medical Center Post-Sec.
1611 NW 12th Ave 33136 305-585-6754
Keiser University Post-Sec.
2101 NW 117th Ave 33172 305-596-2226
Keystone National HS 800/9-12
12840 NW 1st Ct 33168 866-257-6011
Clarence Watson Ph.D., dir. Fax 257-6013
Killian Oaks Academy 100/PK-12
10545 SW 97th Ave 33176 305-274-2221
Mercedes Ricon, prin. Fax 279-5460
La Belle Beauty Academy Post-Sec.
2960 SW 8th St 33135 305-649-2800
La Progressiva Presbyterian S 300/PK-12
2480 NW 7th St 33125 305-642-8600
Lincoln-Marti S #1 1,100/PK-12
931 SW 1st St 33130 305-324-4060
Lindsey Hopkins Technical Education Ctr Post-Sec.
750 NW 20th St 33127 305-324-6070
Management Resources Institute Post-Sec.
10 NW 42nd Ave Ste 400 33126 305-442-9223
Miami Christian S 300/PK-12
200 NW 109th Ave 33172 305-221-7754
Lorena Morrison Ed.D., hdmstr. Fax 221-7783
Miami Country Day S 1,000/PK-12
601 NE 107th St 33161 305-759-2843
Dr. John Davies, head sch Fax 759-4871
Miami-Dade College Post-Sec.
300 NE 2nd Ave 33132 305-237-3000
Miami-Dade College Post-Sec.
950 NW 20th St 33127 305-237-4160
Miami-Dade College Post-Sec.
11380 NW 27th Ave 33167 305-237-1000
Miami-Dade College Post-Sec.
11011 SW 104th St 33176 305-237-2000

Miami-Dade College Post-Sec.
627 SW 27th Ave 33135 305-237-6000
Miami International Univ of Art & Design Post-Sec.
1501 Biscayne Blvd Ste 100 33132 305-428-5700
New Concept Massage & Beauty School Post-Sec.
2022 SW 1st St 33135 305-642-3020
New Testament Church Transfiguration S 50/K-12
1320 NW 196th Ter 33169 305-333-3763
Cora Cato, pres. Fax 249-0537
New World School of the Arts Post-Sec.
300 NE 2nd Ave 33132 305-237-7007
Northwest Christian Academy 400/PK-12
951 NW 136th St 33168 305-685-8734
Lionel Nelson, admin. Fax 685-5341
Nouvelle Institute Post-Sec.
3271 NW 7th St Ste 106 33125 305-643-3360
Our Lady of Lourdes Academy 800/9-12
5525 SW 84th St 33143 305-667-1623
Sr. Kathryn Donze, prin. Fax 663-3121
Professional Training Center Post-Sec.
13926 SW 47th St 33175 305-220-4120
St. Brendan HS 1,100/9-12
2950 SW 87th Ave 33165 305-223-5181
Dr. Jose Rodelgo-Bueno, prin. Fax 220-7434
St. John Vianney College Seminary Post-Sec.
2900 SW 87th Ave 33165 305-223-4561
South Florida Institute of Technology Post-Sec.
720 NW 27th Ave Fl 2 33125 305-649-2050
The Praxis Institute Post-Sec.
1850 SW 8th St 33135 305-642-4104
Universal Beauty School Post-Sec.
10720 W Flagler St Ste 21 33174 305-485-7700
Westwood Christian S 500/PK-12
5801 SW 120th Ave 33183 305-274-3380
Dr. Edwin Oksanen, hdmstr. Fax 595-7519
World Hope Academy 200/PK-12
15190 SW 136th St Ste 26 33196 786-592-2384
Alan Goldstein, prin. Fax 359-5172
Worshipers House of Prayer Academy 100/K-12
8350 NW 7th Ave 33150 305-200-3245
Marie Zizi, prin. Fax 460-8045

Miami Beach, Miami-Dade, Pop. 86,463
Miami-Dade County SD
Supt. — See Miami
Miami Beach HS 2,300/9-12
2231 Prairie Ave 33139 305-532-4515
John Donohue, prin. Fax 531-9209
Nautilus MS 800/7-8
4301 N Michigan Ave 33140 305-532-3481
Dr. Allyn Sachtle, prin. Fax 532-8906
Miami Beach Adult Center Adult
1424 Drexel Ave 33139 305-531-0451
Shirley Velasco, prin. Fax 531-2352

Klurman Mesivta HS 100/7-12
1140 Alton Rd 33139 305-653-8770
Benzion Korf, prin. Fax 653-6790
Mechina HS of South Florida 100/7-12
4000 Alton Rd 33140 305-534-7050
Rabbi Eliyohu Kutoff, prin. Fax 534-8444
Miami Ad School Post-Sec.
955 Alton Rd 33139 305-538-3193
Mt. Sinai Medical Center Post-Sec.
4300 Alton Rd 33140 305-674-2222
RASG Hebrew Academy 600/PK-12
2400 Pine Tree Dr 33140 305-532-6421
Talmudic University Post-Sec.
4000 Alton Rd 33140 305-534-7050
Yeshiva Gedolah Rabbinical College Post-Sec.
1140 Alton Rd 33139 305-653-8770

Miami Gardens, Miami-Dade, Pop. 105,806
Miami-Dade County SD
Supt. — See Miami
Carol City MS 800/6-8
3737 NW 188th St, 305-624-2652
Joyce Jones, prin. Fax 623-2955
Lake Stevens MS 600/6-8
18484 NW 48th Pl, 305-620-1294
Dr. Mark Soffian, prin. Fax 620-1345
Miami Carol City HS 1,900/9-12
3301 Miami Gardens Dr, 305-621-5681
Jamarv Dunn, prin. Fax 620-8862
Parkway MS 400/6-8
2349 NW 175th St, 305-624-9613
Fabrice Laguerre, prin. Fax 623-9756

Azure College Post-Sec.
871 NW 167th St 33159 305-751-0001
Florida Memorial University Post-Sec.
15800 NW 42nd Ave, 305-626-3600
North Dade Christian S 100/PK-12
20295 NW 2nd Ave Ste 110, 305-769-0455
St. Thomas University Post-Sec.
16401 NW 37th Ave, 305-628-6546

Miami Lakes, Miami-Dade, Pop. 29,182
Miami-Dade County SD
Supt. — See Miami
Miami Lakes Educational Center Vo/Tech
5780 NW 158th St 33014 305-557-1100
James Parker, prin. Fax 827-9317

Southeastern College Post-Sec.
17395 NW 59th Ave 33015 305-820-5003

Miami Shores, Miami-Dade, Pop. 10,271

Barry University Post-Sec.
11300 NE 2nd Ave 33161 305-899-3000

Miami Springs, Miami-Dade, Pop. 13,739
Miami-Dade County SD
Supt. — See Miami
Miami Springs HS 1,900/9-12
751 Dove Ave 33166 305-885-3585
Anna Rodriguez, prin. Fax 884-2632
Miami Springs MS 1,600/6-8
150 S Royal Poinciana Blvd 33166 305-888-6457
Javier Perez, prin. Fax 887-5281
Miami Springs HS Adult Education Center Adult
751 Dove Ave 33166 305-885-3585
Miguel Veloso, prin. Fax 884-2632

Middleburg, Clay, Pop. 12,797
Clay County SD
Supt. — See Green Cove Springs
Middleburg HS 1,800/9-12
3750 County Road 220 32068 904-213-2100
John O'Brian, prin. Fax 291-5462
Wilkinson JHS 800/7-8
5025 County Road 218 32068 904-291-5500
Dr. David McDonald, prin. Fax 291-5510

Milton, Santa Rosa, Pop. 8,470
Santa Rosa County SD 25,100/PK-12
5086 Canal St 32570 850-983-5000
Tim Wyrosdick, supt. Fax 983-5013
www.santarosa.k12.fl.us/
Avalon MS 800/6-8
5445 King Arthurs Way 32583 850-983-5540
David Sigurnjak, prin. Fax 983-5545
Central S 500/K-12
6180 Central School Rd 32570 850 983 5640
Farcia King, prin. Fax 983-5645
Hobbs MS 700/6-8
5317 Glover Ln 32570 850-983-5630
Buddy Powell, prin. Fax 983-5635
King MS 600/6-8
5928 Stewart St 32570 850-983-5660
David Gunter, prin. Fax 983-5665
Learning Academy 100/Alt
5880 Stewart St 32570 850-983-3495
Ray Sansom, dir. Fax 983-8098
Locklin Technical Center Vo/Tech
5330 Berryhill Rd 32570 850-983-5700
Charlin Knight, prin. Fax 983-5715
Milton HS 1,700/9-12
5445 Stewart St 32570 850-983-5600
Mike Thorpe, prin. Fax 983-5610
Santa Rosa County Adult HS Adult
5330 Berryhill Rd 32570 850-983-5710
Donna Christopher, prin. Fax 983-5345
Other Schools – See Gulf Breeze, Jay, Navarre, Pace

Radford M. Locklin Technical Center Post-Sec.
5330 Berryhill Rd 32570 850-983-5700
Santa Rosa Christian S 200/PK-12
6331 Chestnut St 32570 850-623-4671
Doris Peppard, prin. Fax 623-9559
West Florida Baptist Academy 300/K-12
5621 Highway 90 32583 850-623-9307
Alan Stewart, admin. Fax 623-9306

Minneola, Lake, Pop. 9,082
Lake County SD
Supt. — See Tavares
Lake Minneola HS 9-12
101 N Hancock Rd, 352-394-9600
Linda Shepherd-Miller, prin. Fax 394-9601

Miramar, Broward, Pop. 118,644
Broward County SD
Supt. — See Fort Lauderdale
Everglades HS 2,800/9-12
17100 SW 48th Ct 33027 754-323-0500
Haleh Darbar, prin. Fax 323-0640
Glades MS 1,800/6-8
16700 SW 48th Ct 33027 754-323-4600
Krista Herrera, prin. Fax 323-4685
Miramar HS 2,700/9-12
3601 SW 89th Ave 33025 754-323-1350
Brian Faso, prin. Fax 323-1480
New Renaissance MS 1,400/6-8
10701 Miramar Blvd 33025 754-323-3500
Janet Morales, prin. Fax 323-3585
Perry MS 800/6-8
3400 Wildcat Way 33023 754-323-3900
Davida Johnson, prin. Fax 323-3985

Chamberlain College of Nursing Post-Sec.
2300 SW 145th Ave 33027 954-885-3510
Concorde Career Institute Post-Sec.
10933 Marks Way 33025 954-731-8880
DeVry University Post-Sec.
2300 SW 145th Ave 33027 954-499-9700
Le Cordon Bleu College of Culinary Arts Post-Sec.
3221 Enterprise Way 33025 954-438-8882

Monticello, Jefferson, Pop. 2,477
Jefferson County SD 1,000/PK-12
575 S Water St 32344 850-342-0100
Al Cooksey, supt. Fax 342-0108
www.jeffersonschooldistrict.org
Jefferson County MSHS 500/6-12
50 David Rd 32344 850-997-3555
Fax 997-4773
Jefferson County Adult Center Adult
1145 Second St 32344 850-342-0140
Dr. Sherman Stroman, prin. Fax 342-0402

Aucilla Christian Academy 400/PK-12
7803 Aucilla Rd 32344 850-997-3597
Richard Finlayson, dir. Fax 997-3598

Montverde, Lake, Pop. 1,436

Montverde Academy 1,000/PK-12
17235 7th St 34756 407-469-2561
Dr. Kasey Kesselring, hdmstr. Fax 469-3711

Moore Haven, Glades, Pop. 1,667
Glades County SD 1,300/K-12
PO Box 459 33471 863-946-0202
Scott Bass, supt. Fax 946-1529
www.glades-schools.org
Moore Haven JSHS 400/7-12
PO Box 99 33471 863-946-0811
George Coates, prin. Fax 946-1532

Mount Dora, Lake, Pop. 12,205
Lake County SD
Supt. — See Tavares
Mount Dora HS 1,100/9-12
700 N Highland St 32757 352-383-2177
Pamela Chateauneuf, prin. Fax 383-6466
Mount Dora MS 800/6-8
1405 Lincoln Ave 32757 352-383-6101
Albert Larry, prin. Fax 383-4949

Christian Home & Bible S 600/PK-12
301 W 13th Ave 32757 352-383-2155
Solid Rock Christian S 100/PK-12
21951 US Highway 441 32757 352-735-5777
Rachel Jones, prin. Fax 735-1084
Southern Technical College Post-Sec.
2799 W Old US Highway 441 32757 352-383-4242

Mulberry, Polk, Pop. 3,765
Polk County SD
Supt. — See Bartow
Mulberry HS 1,000/9-12
1 NE 4th Cir 33860 863-701-1104
Patricia Barnes, prin. Fax 701-1109
Mulberry MS 900/6-8
500 Dr MLK Jr Ave 33860 863-701-1066
Michael Young, prin. Fax 701-1068
New Horizons S 50/Alt
6980 State Road 37 S 33860 863-428-1520
Katherine Caldwell, prin. Fax 428-2204

Calvary Academy 50/7-12
5400 Bethlehem Rd 33860 863-428-2071
Robert Wasser, dir. Fax 428-2584
Fortis Institute Post-Sec.
5925 Imperial Pkwy Ste 200 33860 863-646-1400

Naples, Collier, Pop. 19,366
Collier County SD 41,600/PK-12
5775 Osceola Trl 34109 239-377-0001
Dr. Kamela Patton, supt. Fax 377-0206
www.collier.k12.fl.us
Beacon HS 300/Alt
3710 Estey Ave 34104 239-377-1050
Fax 377-1051
Collier HS 1,800/9-12
5600 Cougar Dr 34109 239-377-1200
Tim Kutz, prin. Fax 377-1201
Corkscrew MS 700/6-8
1165 County Road 858 34120 239-377-3400
Dennis Snider, prin. Fax 377-3401
Cypress Palm MS 800/6-8
4255 18th Ave NE 34120 239-377-5200
John Kasten, prin. Fax 377-5201
East Naples MS 1,100/6-8
4100 Estey Ave 34104 239-377-3600
Joe Mikulski, prin. Fax 377-3601
Golden Gate HS 1,300/9-12
2925 Titan Way 34116 239-377-1600
Jose Hernandez, prin. Fax 377-1601
Golden Gate MS 900/6-8
2701 48th Ter SW 34116 239-377-3800
Jon Bremseth, prin. Fax 377-3801
Gulf Coast HS 2,000/9-12
7878 Shark Way 34119 239-377-1400
Ken Fairbanks, prin. Fax 377-1401
Gulfview MS 700/6-8
255 6th St S 34102 239-377-4000
Kevin Huelsman, prin. Fax 377-4001
Lely HS 1,500/9-12
1 Lely High School Blvd 34113 239-377-2000
Dr. Leslie Ricciardelli, prin. Fax 377-2001
Manatee MS 700/6-8
1920 Manatee Rd 34114 239-377-4400
Peggy Aune, prin. Fax 377-4401
Naples HS 1,700/9-12
1100 Golden Eagle Cir 34102 239-377-2200
Dr. Nancy Graham, prin. Fax 377-2201
New Beginnings S - Naples 100/Alt
3710 Estey Ave 34104 239-377-1050
Eric Peltz, lead tchr. Fax 377-1051
North Naples MS 900/6-8
16165 Learning Ln 34110 239-377-4600
Margaret Jackson, prin. Fax 377-4601
Oakridge MS 1,100/6-8
14975 Collier Blvd 34119 239-377-4800
Kevin Saba, prin. Fax 377-4801
Palmetto Ridge HS 1,800/9-12
1655 Victory Ln 34120 239-377-2400
Tammy Caraker, prin. Fax 377-2401
Pine Ridge MS 1,000/6-8
1515 Pine Ridge Rd 34109 239-377-5000
George Brenco, prin. Fax 377-5001
Walker Technical HS Vo/Tech
3702 Estey Ave 34104 239-377-3300
Yolanda Flores, prin. Fax 377-3301
Other Schools – See Everglades City, Immokalee

Ave Maria School of Law Post-Sec.
1025 Commons Cir 34119 239-687-5300
Community S of Naples 700/PK-12
13275 Livingston Rd 34109 239-597-7575
John Zeller, hdmstr. Fax 598-2973
First Baptist Academy 500/PK-12
3000 Orange Blossom Dr 34109 239-597-2233
Thomas Rider, admin. Fax 597-4187
Hodges University Post-Sec.
2655 Northbrooke Dr 34119 239-513-1122

Lorenzo Walker Institute of Technology Post-Sec.
3702 Estey Ave 34104 239-377-0900
Nicaea Academy 100/PK-12
14785 Collier Blvd 34119 239-353-9099
Rev. Barton McIntyre, hdmstr. Fax 353-2645
St. John Neumann Catholic HS 200/9-12
3000 53rd St SW 34116 239-455-3044
Sr. Patricia Roche, prin. Fax 455-2966
Seacrest Country Day S 600/PK-12
7100 Davis Blvd 34104 239-793-1986
John Watson Ph.D., hdmstr. Fax 793-1460
Wolford College Post-Sec.
1336 Creekside Blvd Ste 2 34108 239-513-1135

Naranja, Miami-Dade, Pop. 8,180
Miami-Dade County SD
Supt. — See Miami
Miami MacArthur South HS 100/Alt
13990 SW 264th St 33032 305-258-7200
Steve Rummel, prin. Fax 258-7201

Navarre, Santa Rosa, Pop. 30,113
Santa Rosa County SD
Supt. — See Milton
Holley-Navarre MS 700/6-8
1976 Williams Creek Dr 32566 850-936-6040
Joie DeStefano, prin. Fax 936-6049
Navarre HS 1,900/9-12
8600 High School Blvd 32566 850-936-6080
Brian Noack, prin. Fax 936-6088

Neptune Beach, Duval, Pop. 6,907
Duval County SD
Supt. — See Jacksonville
Fletcher HS 2,200/9-12
700 Seagate Ave 32266 904-247-5905
Donald Nelson, prin. Fax 247-5920

Beaches Chapel Christian S 200/K-12
610 Florida Blvd 32266 904-241-4211
Vicki McDonald, prin. Fax 249-2046

Newberry, Alachua, Pop. 4,851
Alachua County SD
Supt. — See Gainesville
Newberry HS 600/9-12
400 SW 258th St 32669 352-472-1101
Shane Andrew, prin. Fax 472-1116
Oak View MS 600/5-8
1203 SW 250th St 32669 352-472-1102
Kevin Purvis, prin. Fax 472-1131

New Port Richey, Pasco, Pop. 14,612
Pasco County SD
Supt. — See Land O Lakes
Bayonet Point MS 800/6-8
11125 Little Rd 34654 727-774-7400
Michael Asbell, prin. Fax 774-7491
Gulf HS 1,400/9-12
5355 School Rd 34652 727-774-3300
Kim Davis, prin. Fax 774-3391
Gulf MS 900/6-8
6419 Louisiana Ave 34653 727-774-8000
Stan Trapp, prin. Fax 774-8091
Marchman Tech Education Center Vo/Tech
7825 Campus Dr 34653 727-774-1700
Sheila Bryan, prin. Fax 774-1791
Mitchell HS 1,800/9-12
2323 Little Rd 34655 727-774-9200
James Michaels, prin. Fax 774-9291
Ridgewood HS 1,300/9-12
7650 Orchid Lake Rd 34653 727-774-3900
Andy Frelick, prin. Fax 774-3991
River Ridge HS 1,600/9-12
11646 Town Center Rd 34654 727-774-7200
Maria Swanson, prin. Fax 774-7291
River Ridge MS 1,100/6-8
11646 Town Center Rd 34654 727-774-7000
Jason Joens, prin. Fax 774-7290
Seven Springs MS 1,300/6-8
2441 Little Rd 34655 727-774-6700
Phillip Kupczyk, prin. Fax 774-6791
Schwettman Adult Education Center Adult
5520 Grand Blvd 34652 727-774-0000
Randy Koenigsfeld, prin. Fax 774-0091

Benes International School of Beauty Post-Sec.
7027 US Highway 19 34652 727-848-8415
Elfers Christian S 200/PK-12
5630 Olympia St 34652 727-845-0235
Fax 848-5135
Genesis Preparatory S 100/6-12
7710 Osteen Rd 34653 727-846-8407
Dr. Christoph Leibrecht, hdmstr. Fax 844-3601
Pasco-Hernando Community College Post-Sec.
10230 Ridge Rd 34654 727-847-2727
Rasmussen College Post-Sec.
7660 Little Rd Ste 300 34654 727-942-0069
Southeastern College Post-Sec.
6014 US Highway 19 Ste 250 34652 727-847-6855

New Smyrna Beach, Volusia, Pop. 22,191
Volusia County SD
Supt. — See De Land
New Smyrna Beach HS 1,900/9-12
1015 10th St 32168 386-424-2555
James Tager, prin. Fax 424-2505
New Smyrna Beach MS 1,300/6-8
1200 S Myrtle Ave 32168 386-424-2550
Joe Rawlings, prin. Fax 424-2504

Niceville, Okaloosa, Pop. 12,288
Okaloosa County SD
Supt. — See Fort Walton Beach
Niceville HS 1,900/9-12
800 John Sims Pkwy E 32578 850-833-4114
Marcus Chambers, prin. Fax 833-4267
Ruckel MS 800/6-8
201 Partin Dr N 32578 850-833-4142
Dr. Debbie Collins-Goolsby, prin. Fax 833-3291

Northwest Florida State College Post-Sec.
100 College Blvd E 32578 850-678-5111
Rocky Bayou Christian S 600/PK-12
2101 Partin Dr N 32578 850-729-7227
Michael Mosley Ph.D., supt. Fax 729-2513

North Fort Myers, Lee, Pop. 39,050
Lee County SD
Supt. — See Fort Myers
North Fort Myers HS 1,600/9-12
5000 Orange Grove Blvd 33903 239-995-2117
Jeff Spiro, prin. Fax 995-1243

North Lauderdale, Broward, Pop. 39,771
Broward County SD
Supt. — See Fort Lauderdale
Silver Lakes MS 400/6-8
7600 Tam Oshanter Blvd 33068 754-322-4600
Kathryn Sullivan, prin. Fax 322-4685

North Miami, Miami-Dade, Pop. 57,562
Miami-Dade County SD
Supt. — See Miami
Mourning HS 1,200/9-12
2601 NE 151st St, 305-919-2000
Sally Alayon, prin. Fax 919-2001
North Miami HS 2,800/9-12
13110 NE 8th Ave 33161 305-891-6590
Michael Lewis, prin. Fax 895-1788
North Miami MS 800/7-9
700 NE 137th St 33161 305-891-5611
Alberto Iber, prin. Fax 891-4057
North Miami HS Adult Education Center Adult
13110 NE 8th Ave 33161 305-981-6774
Jean Ridore, prin. Fax 895-6248

Johnson & Wales University Post-Sec.
1701 NE 127th St 33181 305-892-7000
Miami Union Academy 300/PK-12
12600 NW 4th Ave 33168 305-953-9907
Renee Hodge, prin. Fax 953-3602

North Miami Beach, Miami-Dade, Pop. 40,525
Miami-Dade County SD
Supt. — See Miami
Highland Oaks MS 1,200/6-8
2375 NE 203rd St, Miami FL 33180 305-932-3810
Cheryl Kushi, prin. Fax 932-0676
Kennedy MS 1,400/6-8
1075 NE 167th St 33162 305-947-1451
Karen Robinson, prin. Fax 949-0046
North Miami Beach HS 2,300/9-12
1247 NE 167th St 33162 305-949-8381
Randy Milliken, prin. Fax 949-0491

Bais Yaakov S for Girls 300/6-12
1110 NE 163rd St 33162 305-957-1670
Hillel Community Day S 900/PK-12
19000 NE 25th Ave, Miami FL 33180 305-931-2831
Pinchos Hecht, hdmstr. Fax 932-7463
Rohr MS 100/6-8
1051 N Miami Beach Blvd 33162 305-947-7779
SAE Institute of Technology Post-Sec.
16051 W Dixie Hwy Ste 200 33160 305-944-7494
Sha'arei Bina Torah Academy for Girls 100/6-12
1557 NE 164th St Ste 206 33162 305-956-3755
Rabbi Elchonon Abramchik, admin. Fax 956-3758
Union Institute & University Post-Sec.
16853 NE 2nd Ave Ste 102 33162 305-653-7141
Yeshiva Toras Chaim 100/9-12
1025 NE Miami Gardens Dr 33179 305-944-5344

North Palm Beach, Palm Beach, Pop. 11,885

Benjamin S 1,300/PK-12
11000 Ellison Wilson Rd 33408 561-472-3405
Robert Goldberg, hdmstr. Fax 626-8752

North Port, Sarasota, Pop. 56,337
Sarasota County SD
Supt. — See Sarasota
Heron Creek MS 1,100/6-8
6501 W Price Blvd, 941-480-3371
Michael James, prin. Fax 480-3398
North Port HS 2,500/9-12
6400 W Price Blvd, 941-423-8558
David Jones, prin. Fax 480-3199
Woodland MS 700/6-8
2700 Panacea Blvd 34289 941-240-8590
Cindy Hall, prin. Fax 240-8589

Oakland Park, Broward, Pop. 40,410
Broward County SD
Supt. — See Fort Lauderdale
Northeast HS 2,200/9-12
700 NE 56th St 33334 754-322-1550
Jonathan Williams, prin. Fax 322-1680
Rickards MS 900/6-8
6000 NE 9th Ave 33334 754-322-4400
Ronald Forsman, prin. Fax 322-4485

ATI Career Training Center Post-Sec.
3501 NW 9th Ave 33309 888-209-8264

Ocala, Marion, Pop. 55,278
Marion County SD 40,500/PK-12
PO Box 670 34478 352-671-7700
James Yancey, supt. Fax 671-7581
www.marion.k12.fl.us/
Forest HS 2,200/9-12
5000 SE Maricamp Rd 34480 352-671-4700
Chester Gregory, prin. Fax 671-4702
Fort King MS 1,200/6-8
545 NE 17th Ave 34470 352-671-4725
Wayne Livingston, prin. Fax 671-4726
Horizon Academy - Marion Oak 900/5-8
365 Marion Oaks Dr 34473 352-671-6290
Troy Sanford, prin. Fax 671-6291
Howard MS 1,000/6-8
1655 NW 10th St 34475 352-671-7225
Robert Hensel, prin. Fax 671-7226
Lake Weir HS 1,600/9-12
10351 SE Maricamp Rd 34472 352-671-4820
Cynthia Saunders, prin. Fax 671-4829
Liberty MS 1,100/6-8
4773 SW 95th St 34476 352-291-7930
Michelle Lewis, prin. Fax 291-7931
Marion Technical Institute 400/9-12
1614 E Fort King St 34471 352-671-4765
Isaac Burgess, prin. Fax 671-4766
Osceola MS 900/6-8
526 SE Tuscawilla Ave 34471 352-671-7100
John McCollum, prin. Fax 671-7101
Vanguard HS 1,700/9-12
7 NW 28th St 34475 352-671-4900
Rick Lankford, prin. Fax 671-4903
West Port HS 2,000/9-12
3733 SW 80th Ave 34481 352-291-4000
Jane Ellspermann, prin. Fax 291-4001
Comm Adult Education Center Adult
1014 SW 7th Rd 34471 352-671-7200
Debbie Jenkins, dir. Fax 629-1117
Other Schools – See Belleview, Citra, Dunnellon, Summerfield

College of Central Florida Post-Sec.
3001 SW College Rd 34474 352-873-5800
Marion Co. School Radiologic Technology Post-Sec.
1014 SW 7th Rd 34471 352-671-7200
Ocala Christian Academy 400/PK-12
1714 SE 36th Ave 34471 352-694-4178
Rev. Tim Rowe, admin. Fax 694-7192
Rasmussen College Post-Sec.
4755 SW 46th Ct 34474 352-629-1941
St. John Lutheran S 400/PK-12
1915 SE Lake Weir Ave 34471 352-622-7275
Jeff Knutson, prin. Fax 433-2540
Trinity Catholic HS 600/9-12
2600 SW 42nd St 34471 352-622-9025
Jacquelyn Gehrsitz, prin. Fax 861-8164

Ocoee, Orange, Pop. 34,484
Orange County SD
Supt. — See Orlando
Ocoee HS 2,400/9-12
1925 Ocoee Crown Point Pkwy 34761 407-905-3000
William Floyd, prin. Fax 905-3099
Ocoee MS 1,600/6-8
300 S Bluford Ave 34761 407-877-5035
Sharyn Gabriel, prin. Fax 877-5045

Victory Christian Academy 200/PK-12
1601 A D Mims Rd 34761 407-656-1295
Dr. Bradley Phillips, admin. Fax 656-6895

Odessa, Hillsborough, Pop. 7,133
Hillsborough County SD
Supt. — See Tampa
Walker MS 600/6-8
8282 N Mobley Rd 33556 813-631-4726
Anthony Jones, prin. Fax 631-4738

Odessa Christian S 100/K-12
19521 Michigan Ave 33556 813-792-1825
Erin Ciulla, hdmstr. Fax 749-6690

Okeechobee, Okeechobee, Pop. 5,542
Okeechobee County SD 6,500/PK-12
700 SW 2nd Ave 34974 863-462-5000
Ken Kenworthy, supt. Fax 462-5151
www.okee.k12.fl.us/
Okeechobee Achievement Academy 200/Alt
1000 NW 34th St 34972 863-462-5125
Randal Weigum, prin. Fax 462-5295
Okeechobee Freshman Campus 500/9-9
610 SW 2nd Ave 34974 863-462-5288
Carol Revels, prin. Fax 462-5258
Okeechobee HS 1,300/10-12
2800 US Highway 441 N 34972 863-462-5025
Toni Wiersma, prin. Fax 462-5037
Osceola MS 900/5-8
825 SW 28th St 34974 863-462-5070
Sean Downing, prin. Fax 462-5076
Yearling MS 700/6-8
925 NW 23rd Ln 34972 863-462-5056
Andy Brewer, prin. Fax 462-5062

Okeechobee Christian Academy 200/PK-12
701 S Parrott Ave 34974 863-763-3072
Sabina Perera, prin. Fax 213-1339

Oldsmar, Pinellas, Pop. 13,296

Oldsmar Christian S 200/PK-12
650 Burbank Rd 34677 813-855-5746

Old Town, Dixie

Dixie County Learning Academy 100/K-12
1357 NE 82nd Ave 32680 352-542-3306
Dr. Sylvia Lamenta, prin. Fax 542-7291

Opa Locka, Miami-Dade, Pop. 15,115
Miami-Dade County SD
Supt. — See Miami
Mann Opportunity S 100/Alt
16101 NW 44th Ct 33054 305-625-0855
Kim Cox, prin. Fax 625-1605

North Dade MS 600/6-8
1840 NW 157th St 33054 305-624-8415
Dr. Tonya Dillard, prin. Fax 628-2954

Betesda Christian S 100/K-12
PO Box 540392 33054 305-685-8255
Rev. Jose Bello, hdmstr. Fax 685-5338
Monsignor Edward Pace HS 1,000/9-12
15600 NW 32nd Ave 33054 305-624-8534
Ana Garcia, prin. Fax 521-0185

Orange City, Volusia, Pop. 10,438
Volusia County SD
Supt. — See De Land
eLearning West 100/Alt
1000 W Rhode Island Ave 32763 386-968-0037
Melissa Carr, dir. Fax 968-0033
River Springs MS 1,300/6-8
900 W Ohio Ave 32763 386-968-0011
Stacy Gotlib, prin. Fax 456-5355
University HS 9-12
1000 W Rhode Island Ave 32763 386-968-0013
Dennis Neal, prin. Fax 968-0019

Orange Park, Clay, Pop. 8,196
Clay County SD
Supt. — See Green Cove Springs
Fleming Island HS 2,100/9-12
2233 Village Square Pkwy 32003 904-541-2100
Tom Pittman, prin. Fax 541-2085
Lakeside JHS 900/7-8
2750 Moody Ave 32073 904-213-2980
John Green, prin. Fax 213-2987
Oakleaf HS 1,300/9-12
4035 Plantation Oaks Blvd 32065 904-218-1900
David Broskie, prin. Fax 272-8599
Oakleaf JHS 800/7-8
4085 Plantation Oaks Blvd 32065 904-213-5500
Janice Tucker, prin. Fax 291-2549
Orange Park HS 2,000/9-12
2300 Kingsley Ave 32073 904-272-8110
Treasure Pickett, prin. Fax 272-8181
Orange Park JHS 700/7-8
1500 Gano Ave 32073 904-278-2000
Joyce Orsi, prin. Fax 278-2009
Ridgeview HS 1,800/9-12
466 Madison Ave 32065 904-213-5203
Debbie Segreto, prin. Fax 213-3033
Clay Co. Center for Community Education Adult
2306 Kingsley Ave 32073 904-272-8170
Shannah Kosek, admin. Fax 272-8149

Everest University Post-Sec.
805 Wells Rd 32073 904-264-9122
Fortis College Post-Sec.
560 Wells Rd 32073 904-269-7086
National Heavy Equipment Operator School Post-Sec.
PO Box 65789 32065 904-272-4000
R. Webber Institute for Worship Studies Post-Sec.
151 Kingsley Ave 32073 904-264-2172
St. Johns Country Day S 700/PK-12
3100 Doctors Lake Dr 32073 904-264-9572
Edward Ellison, hdmstr. Fax 264-0375

Orlando, Orange, Pop. 231,839
Orange County SD 173,100/PK-12
445 W Amelia St 32801 407-317-3200
Barbara Jenkins, supt. Fax 317-3401
www.ocps.net
Acceleration Academy 400/Alt
2274 S Semoran Blvd 32822 407-992-0917
Dr. Elvis Epps, prin. Fax 207-4961
Acceleration Academy West Alt
2751 Lake Stanley Rd 32818 407-521-2358
George Morse, prin. Fax 521-2369
Avalon MS 1,500/6-8
13914 Mailer Blvd 32828 407-207-7839
Judith Frank, prin. Fax 207-7872
Boone HS 2,900/9-12
1000 E Kaley St 32806 407-893-7200
Dr. Margaret McMillen, prin. Fax 897-2466
Carver MS 800/6-8
4500 Columbia St 32811 407-296-5110
Wesley Trimble, prin. Fax 296-6407
Chain of Lakes MS 1,300/6-8
8720 Conroy Windermere Rd 32835 407-909-5400
Karen Furno, prin. Fax 909-5410
Colonial 9th Grade Center 1,000/9-9
7775 Valencia College Ln 32807 407-249-6369
Douglas Loftus, prin. Fax 249-6297
Colonial HS 2,500/10-12
6100 Oleander Dr 32807 407-482-6300
Douglas Loftus, prin. Fax 737-1450
Conway MS 1,100/6-8
4600 Anderson Rd 32812 407-249-6420
Michael Hanson, prin. Fax 249-6429
Corner Lake MS 1,300/6-8
1700 Chuluota Rd 32820 407-568-0510
Enrique Vela, prin. Fax 568-0920
Cypress Creek HS 3,200/9-12
1101 Bear Crossing Dr 32824 407-852-3400
Susan Storch, prin. Fax 850-5160
Discovery MS 1,000/6-8
601 Woodbury Rd 32828 407-384-1555
Gloria Fernandez, prin. Fax 384-1580
Drop Back In 600/Alt
228 N Semoran Blvd 32807 407-658-9555
Fax 658-9559
East Orlando Education Center 50/Alt
2510 Gulfstream Rd 32805 407-245-1555
William Tovine, prin. Fax 245-1561
East River HS 2,000/9-12
654 Columbia School Rd 32833 407-956-8550
Eric Lundman, prin. Fax 956-8565
Edgewater HS 1,700/9-12
3100 Edgewater Dr 32804 407-835-4900
Michele Erickson, prin. Fax 245-2758

Evans HS 1,900/9-12
4949 Silver Star Rd 32808 407-522-3400
Jenny Gibson-Linkh, prin. Fax 522-3458
Freedom HS 2,900/9-12
2500 W Taft Vineland Rd 32837 407-816-5600
Harold Border, prin. Fax 816-5616
Freedom MS 1,000/6-8
2850 W Taft Vineland Rd 32837 407-858-6130
Douglas Szcinski, prin. Fax 858-6132
Glenridge MS 1,400/6-8
2900 Upper Park Rd 32814 407-623-1415
Heather Hilton, prin. Fax 623-1427
Howard MS 600/6-8
800 E Robinson St 32801 407-245-1780
Dr. Carl Cartwright, prin. Fax 245-1785
Hunters Creek MS 1,100/6-8
13400 Town Loop Blvd 32837 407-858-4620
Dr. Anne Carcara, prin. Fax 858-4621
Jackson MS 1,200/6-8
6000 Stonewall Jackson Rd 32807 407-249-6430
Eddie Ruiz, prin. Fax 249-6438
Jones HS 1,000/9-12
801 S Rio Grande Ave 32805 407-835-2300
Valeria Maxwell, prin. Fax 245-2765
Lake Nona HS 1,700/9-12
12500 Narcoossee Rd 32832 407-956-8300
Margaret Nampon, prin. Fax 956-8315
Lake Nona MS 1,100/6-8
13700 Narcoossee Rd 32832 407-858-5522
Dr. Jennifer Cupid-McCoy, prin. Fax 858-5530
Lee MS 1,000/6-8
1201 Maury Rd 32804 407-245-1800
Howard Hepburn, prin. Fax 245-1809
Legacy MS 900/6-8
11398 Lake Underhill Rd 32825 407-658-5330
Dr. Joseph Miller, prin. Fax 658-5334
Liberty MS 1,200/6-8
3405 S Chickasaw Trl 32829 407-249-6440
Rolando Bailey, prin. Fax 249-6449
Lockhart MS 800/6-8
3411 Dr Love Rd 32810 407-296-5120
Alison Kirby, prin. Fax 296-6549
Meadowbrook MS 1,000/6-8
6000 North Ln 32808 407-296-5130
Johnny Nash, prin. Fax 296-5139
Meadow Woods MS 1,200/6-8
1800 Rhode Island Woods Cir 32824 407-850-5180
Dr. Isom Rivers, prin. Fax 850-5190
Memorial MS 700/6-8
2220 29th St 32805 407-245-1810
Dr. Shelia Windom, prin. Fax 245-1820
Mid Florida Tech Vo/Tech
2900 W Oak Ridge Rd 32809 407-251-6000
Adelina Brann, prin. Fax 251-6197
Oak Ridge HS 1,900/9-12
700 W Oak Ridge Rd 32809 407-852-3200
Dr. Leigh Bradshaw, prin. Fax 850-5152
Odyssey MS 900/6-8
9290 Lee Vista Blvd 32829 407-207-3850
Dr. Suzanne Knight, prin. Fax 207-3871
Olympia HS 3,000/9-12
4301 S Apopka Vineland Rd 32835 407-905-6400
Guy Swenson, prin. Fax 905-6465
Orlando Tech Ctr Vo/Tech
301 W Amelia St 32801 407-246-7060
Alex Heidelberg, dir. Fax 317-3372
Phillips HS 3,600/9-12
6500 Turkey Lake Rd 32819 407-355-3200
Eugene Trochinski, prin. Fax 370-7232
Robinswood MS 1,200/6-8
6305 Balboa Dr 32818 407-296-5140
Marcia Newsome, prin. Fax 296-5148
South Creek MS 1,000/6-8
3801 Wetherbee Rd 32824 407-251-2413
Dr. Stefanie Shames, prin. Fax 251-2464
Southwest MS 1,300/6-8
6450 Dr Phillips Blvd 32819 407-370-7200
Matthew Arnold, prin. Fax 370-7210
Timber Creek HS 3,000/9-12
1001 Avalon Park South Blvd 32828 321-235-7800
Gabriel Berrio, prin. Fax 253-7821
Union Park MS 1,000/6-8
1844 Westfall Dr 32817 407-249-6309
Kris Viles, prin. Fax 249-4404
University HS 2,800/9-12
2450 Cougar Way 32817 407-482-8700
Michael Armbruster, prin. Fax 737-1455
Walker MS 900/6-8
150 Amidon Ln 32809 407-858-3210
Dr. Ana Gonzalez, prin. Fax 858-3218
Westridge MS 1,000/6-8
3800 W Oak Ridge Rd 32809 407-354-2640
Christopher Camacho, prin. Fax 354-2637
Avalon Center for Tech Excellence Adult
2201 Crown Hill Blvd 32828 407-281-5100
Tom Tankson, prin. Fax 281-5127
Other Schools – See Apopka, Maitland, Ocoee, Windermere, Winter Garden, Winter Park

---

Adventist University of Health Sciences Post-Sec.
671 Winyah Dr 32803 407-303-9798
Agape Christian Academy 400/PK-12
2425 N Hiawassee Rd 32818 407-298-1111
Anthem College Post-Sec.
3710 Maguire Blvd 32803 407-893-7400
Asbury Theological Seminary Post-Sec.
8401 Valencia College Ln 32825 407-482-7500
Bishop Moore HS 1,200/9-12
3901 Edgewater Dr 32804 407-293-7561
Scott Brogan, prin. Fax 296-8135
Central Florida Blood Bank Post-Sec.
8669 Commodity Cir 32819 407-849-6100
Central Florida Christian Academy 200/PK-12
700 Good Homes Rd 32818 407-850-2322
Dr. Clayton Cloer, pres. Fax 293-6914
Central Florida Institute Post-Sec.
6000 Cinderlane Pkwy 32810 407-253-5354

Centura Institute Post-Sec.
6359 Edgewater Dr 32810 407-275-9696
Christian Victory Academy 100/K-12
PO Box 721436 32872 407-281-6244
Paula Williamson, pres. Fax 281-6610
Concorde Career Institute Post-Sec.
3444 McCrory Pl 32803 407-812-3060
Conrad Academy 200/K-12
9580 Curry Ford Rd 32825 407-243-2211
Tawanda Mills, supt. Fax 243-2213
DAVE School Post-Sec.
2500 Universal Studios # 25 32819 855-328-3839
Devereux-Florida Treatment Network Post-Sec.
5850 T G Lee Blvd Ste 400 32822 407-812-4555
DeVry University Post-Sec.
4000 Millenia Blvd 32839 407-345-2800
DeVry University Post-Sec.
1800 Pembrook Dr Ste 160 32810 407-659-0900
Downey Christian S 300/PK-12
10201 E Colonial Dr 32817 407-275-0340
Dr. Charles Dees, prin. Fax 275-1481
Eastland Christian S 300/PK-12
9000 Lake Underhill Rd 32825 407-277-5858
Everest University - North Orlando Cmps Post-Sec.
5421 Diplomat Cir 32810 407-628-5870
Everest University-South Orlando Campus Post-Sec.
9200 Southpark Center Loop 32819 407-851-2525
Faith Christian Academy 600/PK-12
9307 Curry Ford Rd 32825 407-275-8031
Dr. Andrew Rumbaugh, admin. Fax 281-3710
First Academy 1,000/PK-12
2667 Bruton Blvd 32805 407-206-8600
Dr. Steve Whitaker, head sch
Florida College of Integrative Medicine Post-Sec.
7100 Lake Ellenor Dr 32809 407-888-8689
Florida Technical College Post-Sec.
12900 Challenger Pkwy 32826 407-447-7300
Heritage Prep S 200/PK-12
6000 W Colonial Dr 32808 407-293-6000
Lloyd Elliott, prin. Fax 292-7246
Ibn Seena Academy 100/PK-12
12908 S Orange Blossom Trl 32837 407-238-7600
International Academy of Design & Tech Post-Sec.
6039 S Rio Grande Ave 32809 407-857-2300
ITT Technical Institute Post-Sec.
8301 Southpark Cir Ste 100 32819 407-371-6000
Keiser University Post-Sec.
5600 Lake Underhill Rd 32807 407-273-5800
Lake Highland Preparatory S 2,000/PK-12
901 Highland Ave 32803 407-206-1900
Warren Hudson, pres. Fax 206-1933
Leaders Preparatory S 200/PK-12
1021 N Goldenrod Rd 32807 407-382-9900
Le Cordon Bleu College of Culinary Arts Post-Sec.
8511 Commodity Cir # 100 32819 407-888-4000
Motorcycle Mechanics Institute Post-Sec.
9751 Delegates Dr 32837 407-240-2422
Orlando Christian Prep S 400/PK-12
500 S Semoran Blvd 32807 407-823-9744
Pine Castle Christian Academy 500/PK-12
7101 Lake Ellenor Dr 32809 407-313-7222
Brenda Oliver, prin. Fax 313-7226
Southern Technical College Post-Sec.
1485 Florida Mall Ave 32809 407-438-6000
South Orlando Christian Academy 200/PK-12
5815 Makoma Dr 32839 407-859-9511
Stenotype Institute Post-Sec.
1636 W Oak Ridge Rd 32809 407-816-5573
Strayer University Post-Sec.
2200 N Alafaya Trl Ste 500 32826 407-926-2000
Universal Technical Institute Post-Sec.
2202 W Taft Vineland Rd 32837 321-281-9810
University of Central Florida Post-Sec.
PO Box 160000 32816 407-823-2000
Valencia College Post-Sec.
PO Box 3028 32802 407-299-5000
Victory Christian Academy 100/K-10
240 N Ivey Ln 32811 407-295-3332
Fax 296-7582
West Oaks Academy 200/PK-12
8624 A D Mims Rd 32818 407-292-8481
Fax 292-8838

Ormond Beach, Volusia, Pop. 37,607
Volusia County SD
Supt. — See De Land
Ormond Beach MS 900/6-8
151 Domicilio Ave 32174 386-258-4667
Matt Krajewski, prin. Fax 676-1258

Calvary Christian Academy 400/PK-12
1687 W Granada Blvd 32174 386-672-2081
Dr. Aaron Gonzalez, hdmstr. Fax 615-3736
Daytona College Post-Sec.
425 S Nova Rd 32174 386-267-0565
Harry Wendelstedt Umpire School Post-Sec.
88 S Saint Andrews Dr 32174 800-818-1690
Riverbend Academy 100/PK-12
2080 W Granada Blvd 32174 386-615-0986
Jason Karr, hdmstr. Fax 672-7945
WyoTech Post-Sec.
470 Destination Daytona Ln 32174 386-255-0295

Osprey, Sarasota, Pop. 6,031

Victory Baptist Academy 50/PK-12
241 Burney Rd 34229 941-966-4716
Rene Kelly, admin. Fax 966-4716

Oviedo, Seminole, Pop. 32,607
Seminole County SD
Supt. — See Sanford
Chiles MS 1,300/6-8
1240 Sanctuary Dr 32766 407-871-7050
Maggie Gunderson, prin. Fax 871-7099
Hagerty HS 2,300/9-12
3225 Lockwood Blvd 32765 407-871-0750
Sam Momary, prin. Fax 871-0749

Jackson Heights MS 1,300/6-8
41 Academy Ave 32765 407-320-4550
Winston Bailey, prin. Fax 320-4599
Oviedo HS 2,200/9-12
601 King St 32765 407-320-4050
Robert Lundquist, prin. Fax 320-4000
Tuskawilla MS 1,100/6-8
1801 Tuskawilla Rd 32765 407-746-8550
Michael Mizwicki, prin. Fax 746-8599

Master's Academy 900/PK-12
1500 Lukas Ln 32765 407-971-2221
Dr. William Harris, supt. Fax 706-0254
Reformed Theological Seminary Post-Sec.
1231 Reformation Dr 32765 407-366-9493

Pace, Santa Rosa, Pop. 19,523
Santa Rosa County SD
Supt. — See Milton
Pace HS 1,900/9-12
4065 Norris Rd 32571 850-995-3600
Stephen Shell, prin. Fax 995-3620
Sims MS 800/6-8
5500 Education Dr 32571 850-995-3676
Wanda Knowles, prin. Fax 995-3696

Pahokee, Palm Beach, Pop. 5,609
Palm Beach County SD
Supt. — See West Palm Beach
Pahokee HS 500/9-12
900 Larrimore Rd 33476 561-924-6400
Ariel Alejo, prin. Fax 924-6457
Pahokee MS 400/7-8
850 Larrimore Rd 33476 561-924-6500
Lavoise Smith, prin. Fax 924-6550

Palatka, Putnam, Pop. 10,395
Putnam County SD 11,200/PK-12
200 S 7th St 32177 386-329-0510
Tom Townsend, supt. Fax 329-0520
www.putnamschools.org
Beasley MS 500/6-8
1100 S 18th St 32177 386-329-0569
Sandra Gilyard, prin. Fax 329-0670
Jenkins MS 700/6-8
1100 N 19th St 32177 386-329-0588
Dr. Richard Surrency, prin. Fax 329-0636
Palatka HS 1,400/9-12
302 Mellon Rd 32177 386-329-0577
Fax 329-0624
Other Schools – See Crescent City, Florahome, Interlachen

Hillcrest Academy K-12
2009 President St 32177 386-328-6514
Nancy Jones, prin.
Peniel Baptist Academy 300/PK-12
110 Peniel Church Rd 32177 386-328-1707
Lester Jenkins, prin. Fax 328-0950
St. John's River State College Post-Sec.
5001 Saint Johns Ave 32177 386-312-4200

Palm Bay, Brevard, Pop. 100,267
Brevard County SD
Supt. — See Melbourne
Bayside HS 1,900/9-12
1901 Degroodt Rd SW 32908 321-956-5000
Robin Novelli, prin. Fax 956-5021
Heritage HS 1,300/9-12
2351 Malabar Rd NW 32907 321-722-4178
John Tuttle, prin. Fax 722-4198
Southwest MS 1,000/7-8
451 Eldron Blvd SE 32909 321-952-5800
Todd Scheuerer, prin. Fax 952-5819

Covenant Christian S 300/PK-12
720 Emerson Dr NE 32907 321-727-2661
Ken Ingraham, hdmstr. Fax 728-9574
Darlyne McGee's Academy of Cosmetology Post-Sec.
1975 Palm Bay Rd NE Ste 106 32905 321-951-0595

Palm Beach, Palm Beach, Pop. 8,309

Palm Beach Day Academy 200/4-9
241 Seaview Ave 33480 561-655-1188
Dr. Becky van der Bogert, hdmstr. Fax 655-5794

Palm Beach Gardens, Palm Beach, Pop. 47,764
Palm Beach County SD
Supt. — See West Palm Beach
Duncan MS 1,300/6-8
5150 117th Ct N 33418 561-776-3500
Adrian Ocampo, prin. Fax 776-3550
Dwyer HS 2,300/9-12
13601 N Military Trl 33410 561-625-7800
Glenda Sheffield, prin. Fax 625-7870
Palm Beach Gardens Community HS 2,600/9-12
4245 Holly Dr 33410 561-694-7300
Larry Clawson, prin. Fax 691-0515
Watkins MS 600/6-8
9480 MacArthur Blvd 33403 561-776-3600
Don Hoffman, prin. Fax 776-3603

Strayer University Post-Sec.
11025 RCA Center Dr Ste 200 33410 561-904-3000

Palm City, Martin, Pop. 22,880
Martin County SD
Supt. — See Stuart
Hidden Oaks MS 1,100/6-8
2801 SW Martin Hwy 34990 772-219-1655
Jenny Lambdin, prin. Fax 219-1663

Palm Coast, Flagler, Pop. 73,538
Flagler County SD
Supt. — See Bunnell
Everest Alternative S 100/Alt
5400 E Highway 100 32164 386-586-2124
Winnie Oden, prin. Fax 586-2301
Flagler Palm Coast HS 2,300/9-12
5500 E Highway 100 32164 386-437-7540
Lynette Shott, prin. Fax 437-7546
Flagler Technical Institute Vo/Tech
1 Corporate Dr Ste 1B 32137 386-446-7612
Virginia Giaramita M.S., dir. Fax 446-7620
Indian Trails MS 900/7-8
5505 Belle Terre Pkwy 32137 386-446-6732
Paul Peacock, prin. Fax 446-7662
Matanzas HS 1,500/9-12
3535 Old Kings Rd N 32137 386-447-1575
Dr. Chris Pryor, prin. Fax 447-1597
Taylor MS 1,000/7-8
4500 Belle Terre Pkwy 32164 386-446-6700
Stephen Hinson M.Ed., prin. Fax 446-6711

Palmetto, Manatee, Pop. 12,420
Manatee County SD
Supt. — See Bradenton
Buffalo Creek MS 900/6-8
7320 69th St E 34221 941-721-2260
Matthew Gruhl, prin. Fax 721-2275
Lincoln MS 600/6-8
305 17th St E 34221 941-721-6840
Ronnie King, prin. Fax 721-6853
Palmetto HS 1,700/9-12
1200 17th St W 34221 941-723-4848
Willie Clark, prin. Fax 723-4952

Palmetto Bay, Miami-Dade
Miami-Dade County SD
Supt. — See Miami
Southwood MS 1,500/6-8
16301 SW 80th Ave, 305-251-5361
Magda Pereira, prin. Fax 251-7464

Palmer Trinity S 700/6-12
7900 SW 176th St, 305-251-2230
Sean Murphy, hdmstr. Fax 254-8812
Westminster Christian HS 400/9-12
6855 SW 152nd St, 305-233-2030
David Medder, prin. Fax 238-2259
Westminster Christian MS 300/6-8
6855 SW 152nd St, 305-233-2030
John Manoogian, prin. Fax 233-5737

Palm Harbor, Pinellas, Pop. 56,551
Pinellas County SD
Supt. — See Largo
Carwise MS 1,300/6-8
3301 Bentley Dr 34684 727-724-1442
Garrison Linder, prin. Fax 724-1446
Palm Harbor MS 1,400/6-8
1800 Tampa Rd 34683 727-669-1146
Victoria Hawkins, prin. Fax 669-1244
Palm Harbor University HS 2,500/9-12
1000 Omaha St 34683 727-669-1131
Christen Tonry, prin. Fax 725-7936
Palm Harbor Community S Adult
1900 Omaha St 34683 727-669-1140
Christine Lowry, prin. Fax 725-7936

Central Florida Institute Post-Sec.
30522 US Highway 19 N # 300 34684 727-786-4707

Panama City, Bay, Pop. 35,536
Bay County SD 25,400/PK-12
1311 Balboa Ave 32401 850-767-4100
Bill Husfelt, supt.
www.bay.k12.fl.us
Arnold HS 1,400/9-12
550 N Alf Coleman Rd 32407 850-767-3700
Keith Bland, prin. Fax 236-3068
Bay HS 1,200/9-12
1200 Harrison Ave 32401 850-767-4600
Billy May, prin. Fax 767-4651
Bozeman S 1,300/K-12
13410 Highway 77 32409 850-767-1300
Josh Balkom, prin. Fax 265-5377
Brown MS 800/6-8
5044 Merritt Brown Way 32404 850-767-3976
Charlotte Marshall, prin. Fax 872-7625
Everitt MS 900/6-8
608 School Ave 32401 850-767-3776
Shirley Baker, prin. Fax 872-7721
Haney Technical Center Vo/Tech
3016 Highway 77 32405 850-767-5500
Michael Heptinstall, prin. Fax 747-5555
Jinks MS 700/6-8
600 W 11th St 32401 850-767-4695
Samuel Jackson, prin. Fax 872-7612
Rosenwald HS 300/9-12
924 Bay Ave 32401 850-767-4580
Chandra Tyson, prin. Fax 872-7615
Rutherford HS 1,300/9-12
1000 School Ave 32401 850-767-4500
L. Coy Pilson, prin. Fax 872-4827
Surfside MS 1,000/6-8
300 Nautilus St 32413 850-767-5180
Dr. Sue Harrell, prin. Fax 233-5193
Washington Academy 100/Alt
924 Bay Ave 32401 850-767-5576
Darnita Rivers, prin. Fax 914-6429
Other Schools – See Lynn Haven

Covenant Christian S 300/PK-12
2350 Frankford Ave 32405 850-769-7448
Glenda Delmar, prin. Fax 763-2104
Gooding Institute of Nurse Anesthesia Post-Sec.
615 N Bonita Ave 32401 850-747-6918
Gulf Coast State College Post-Sec.
5230 W Highway 98 32401 850-769-1551

Parkland, Broward, Pop. 23,535
Broward County SD
Supt. — See Fort Lauderdale
Stoneman HS 3,200/9-12
5901 Pine Island Rd 33076 754-322-2150
Washington Collado, prin. Fax 322-2280
Westglades MS 1,500/6-8
11000 Holmberg Rd 33076 754-322-4800
John Vesey, prin. Fax 322-4885

Paxton, Walton, Pop. 626
Walton County SD
Supt. — See De Funiak Springs
Paxton S 600/PK-12
21893 US Highway 331 N 32538 850-892-1230
Beth Tucker, prin. Fax 892-1239

Pembroke Pines, Broward, Pop. 151,189
Broward County SD
Supt. — See Fort Lauderdale
Flanagan HS 3,200/9-12
12800 Taft St 33028 754-323-0650
Michelle Kefford, prin. Fax 323-0780
Pines MS 1,700/6-8
200 N Douglas Rd 33024 754-323-4000
Carlton Campbell, prin. Fax 323-4085
West Broward HS 2,700/9-12
500 NW 209th Ave 33029 754-323-2600
Teresa Hall, prin. Fax 323-2730
Young Resource Center MS 1,500/6-8
901 NW 129th Ave 33028 754-323-4500
Harold Osborn, prin. Fax 323-4585

Broward College Post-Sec.
7200 Pines Blvd 33024 954-201-8100
Fasttrain of Pembroke Pines Post-Sec.
15800 Pines Blvd Ste 301 33027 954-392-7080
Florida Career College Post-Sec.
7891 Pines Blvd 33024 954-965-7272
Florida Technical College Post-Sec.
12520 Pines Blvd 33027 954-556-1900
Jose Maria Vargas University Post-Sec.
8300 S Palm Dr 33025 954-322-4460
Kaplan College Post-Sec.
10131 Pines Blvd 33026 954-885-3500
Keiser University Post-Sec.
1640 SW 145th Ave 33027 954-431-4300
Pelican Flight Training Center Post-Sec.
1601 SW 75th Ave 33023 954-966-9750

Pensacola, Escambia, Pop. 50,807
Escambia County SD 38,800/PK-12
75 N Pace Blvd 32505 850-432-6121
Malcolm Thomas, supt. Fax 469-6379
www.escambia.k12.fl.us
Bailey MS 1,500/6-8
4110 Bauer Rd 32506 850-492-6136
Dr. Judy Pippin, prin. Fax 492-9860
Bellview MS 1,100/6-8
6201 Mobile Hwy 32526 850-941-6080
David Thompson, prin. Fax 941-6089
Brown-Barge MS 500/6-8
201 Hancock Ln 32503 850-494-5640
Dr. Joy McMichael, prin. Fax 494-5699
Escambia HS 1,900/9-12
1310 N 65th Ave 32506 850-453-3221
Mike Sherrill, prin. Fax 453-9381
Ferry Pass MS 1,000/6-8
8355 Yancey Ave 32514 850-494-5650
Reggie Lipnick, prin. Fax 494-5653
PACE Center 50/Alt
1201 College Blvd 32504 850-478-7060
Laurie Rodgers, prin.
Pensacola HS 1,600/9-12
500 W Maxwell St 32501 850-595-1500
David Williams, prin. Fax 595-1519
Pine Forest HS 1,800/9-12
2500 Longleaf Dr 32526 850-941-6150
Frank Murphy, prin. Fax 941-6163
Stone Career Center Vo/Tech
2400 Longleaf Dr 32526 850-941-6200
Thomas Rollins, prin. Fax 941-6215
Washington HS 1,600/9-12
6000 College Pkwy 32504 850-475-5257
Dr. Michael Roberts, prin. Fax 494-7297
West Florida HS of Advanced Technology 1,300/9-12
2400 Longleaf Dr 32526 850-941-6221
Eric Smith, prin. Fax 941-6210
Woodham MS 900/6-8
150 E Burgess Rd 32503 850-494-7140
Marsha Higgins, prin. Fax 494-7484
Workman MS 900/6-8
6299 Lanier Dr 32504 850-494-5665
Juanita Edwards, prin. Fax 494-5697
Andrews Center Adult
129 N Merritt St 32507 850-453-7462
Daniel Busse, prin.
Other Schools – See Cantonment, Century, Walnut Hill, Warrington

---

Aletheia Christian Academy 200/PK-12
PO Box 10568 32524 850-969-0088
Jeff Caulfield-James, admin. Fax 969-0906
East Hill Christian S 200/PK-12
1301 E Gonzalez St 32501 850-438-7746
Jack Exum, hdmstr. Fax 434-7384
Florida Institute of Ultrasound Post-Sec.
8800 University Pkwy Ste A4 32514 850-478-7300
Fortis Institute Post-Sec.
4081 E Olive Rd Ste B 32514 850-476-7607
George Stone Vocational Technical Ctr. Post-Sec.
2400 Longleaf Dr 32526 850-941-6200
Pensacola Catholic HS 600/9-12
3043 W Scott St 32505 850-436-6400
Sr. Kierstin Martin, prin. Fax 436-6405
Pensacola Christian Academy 2,600/PK-12
10 Brent Ln 32503 850-478-8483

Pensacola Christian College | Post-Sec.
PO Box 18000 32523 | 850-478-8496
Pensacola School of Massage Therapy | Post-Sec.
2409 Creighton Rd 32504 | 850-474-1330
Pensacola State College | Post-Sec.
1000 College Blvd 32504 | 850-484-1000
Trinitas Christian S | 200/PK-12
3301 E Johnson Ave 32514 | 850-484-3515
University of West Florida | Post-Sec.
11000 University Pkwy 32514 | 850-474-2000
Virginia College | Post-Sec.
19 W Garden St 32502 | 850-436-8444

Perrine, Miami-Dade, Pop. 15,576
Miami-Dade County SD
Supt. — See Miami
Morgan Education Center | Vo/Tech
18180 SW 122nd Ave 33177 | 305-253-9920
Kimberly Davis, prin. | Fax 259-1495

Perry, Taylor, Pop. 6,889
Taylor County SD | 3,100/PK-12
318 N Clark St 32347 | 850-838-2500
Paul Dyal, supt. | Fax 838-2501
www.taylor.k12.fl.us
Taylor County HS | 700/9-12
900 N Johnson Stripling Rd 32347 | 850-838-2525
Michael Thompson, prin. | Fax 838-2521
Taylor County MS | 600/6-8
601 E Lafayette St 32347 | 850-838-2516
Kiki Puhl, prin. | Fax 838-2559
Taylor Technical Institute | Vo/Tech
3233 S Byron Butler Pkwy 32348 | 850-838-2545
Jim Brannan, coord. | Fax 838-2546

Taylor Technical Institute | Post-Sec.
3233 S Byron Butler Pkwy 32348 | 850-838-2545

Pierson, Volusia, Pop. 1,725
Volusia County SD
Supt. — See De Land
Taylor MSHS | 1,000/6-12
100 E Washington Ave 32180 | 386-749-6800
Ron Pagano, prin. | Fax 626-0051

Pinecrest, Miami-Dade

Gulliver Academy - Montgomery Dr Campus | 100/5-8
7500 SW 120th St 33156 | 305-238-3424
John Krutulis, head sch | Fax 255-0537
Gulliver Preparatory S | 900/9-12
6575 SW 88th St 33156 | 305-666-7937
John Krutulis, hdmstr. | Fax 665-3791

Pinellas Park, Pinellas, Pop. 47,904
Pinellas County SD
Supt. — See Largo
Pinellas Park MS | 1,100/6-8
6940 70th Ave N 33781 | 727-545-6400
Robyn Witcher, prin. | Fax 547-7894
Pinellas Secondary S | 100/Alt
8570 66th St N 33781 | 727-549-6550
Darren Hammond, prin. | Fax 549-6555

Center Academy - Pinellas Park | 100/4-12
6710 86th Ave N 33782 | 727-541-5716
Classical Christian S for the Arts | 100/K-12
PO Box 1455 33780 | 727-547-6820
Rev. Daniel Baker, pres. | Fax 545-3579
Cortiva Institute-Florida | Post-Sec.
4045 Park Blvd N 33781 | 727-865-4940
National University of Health Sciences | Post-Sec.
9200 113th St 33781 | 800-826-6285

Plantation, Broward, Pop. 82,808
Broward County SD
Supt. — See Fort Lauderdale
Plantation HS | 2,100/9-12
6901 NW 16th St 33313 | 754-322-1850
Susan Bruining, prin. | Fax 322-1980
Plantation MS | 900/6-8
6600 W Sunrise Blvd 33313 | 754-322-4100
Patricia Hague, prin. | Fax 322-4185
Seminole MS | 1,300/6-8
6200 SW 16th St 33317 | 754-323-4200
Kathryn Marlow, prin. | Fax 323-4285
South Plantation HS | 2,400/9-12
1300 SW 54th Ave 33317 | 754-323-1950
Dr. David Basile, prin. | Fax 323-2080

American Heritage S | 2,400/PK-12
12200 W Broward Blvd 33325 | 954-472-0022
Fasttrain of Fort Lauderdale | Post-Sec.
51 N State Road 7 33317 | 954-730-8711

Plant City, Hillsborough, Pop. 34,205
Hillsborough County SD
Supt. — See Tampa
Durant HS | 2,300/9-12
4748 Cougar Path 33567 | 813-757-9075
Pamela Bowden, prin. | Fax 707-7079
Marshall MS | 900/6-8
18 S Maryland Ave, | 813-757-9360
Daphne Blanton, prin. | Fax 707-7385
Plant City HS | 2,100/9-12
1 Raider Pl, | 813-757-9370
Colleen Richardson, prin. | Fax 757-9135
Simmons Career Center | Vo/Tech
1202 W Grant St, | 813-707-7430
Cleto Chazares, prin. | Fax 707-7435
Tomlin MS | 1,500/6-8
501 N Woodrow Wilson St, | 813-757-9400
Susan Sullivan, prin. | Fax 707-7024
Turkey Creek MS | 1,000/6-8
5005 Turkey Creek Rd 33567 | 813-757-9442
Dennis Mayo, prin. | Fax 757-9451
Plant City Adult Education | Adult
1 Raider Pl, | 813-707-7147
Guy Frazier, prin. | Fax 707-7149

Hillsborough Community College | Post-Sec.
1206 N Park Rd, | 813-757-2100

Pompano Beach, Broward, Pop. 97,655
Broward County SD
Supt. — See Fort Lauderdale
Blanche Ely HS | 1,900/9-12
1201 NW 6th Ave 33060 | 754-322-0950
Karlton Johnson, prin. | Fax 322-1080
Crystal Lake Community MS | 1,400/6-8
3551 NE 3rd Ave 33064 | 754-322-3100
Sabine Phillips, prin. | Fax 322-3185
Cypress Run Education Center | 100/Alt
2800 NW 30th Ave 33069 | 754-321-6500
Vincent Alessi, prin. | Fax 321-6540
Pompano Beach HS | 1,300/9-12
600 NE 13th Ave 33060 | 754-322-2000
Hudson Thomas, prin. | Fax 322-2130
Pompano Beach MS | 1,100/6-8
310 NE 6th St 33060 | 754-322-4200
Sonja Braziel, prin. | Fax 322-4285
Thomas Education Center East | Adult
180 SW 2nd St 33060 | 754-321-6750
Wade Edmond, prin. | Fax 321-6790

Everest University-Pompano Beach Campus | Post-Sec.
225 N Federal Hwy 33062 | 954-783-7339
Florida Barber Academy | Post-Sec.
3269 N Federal Hwy 33064 | 954-781-6066
Florida College of Natural Health | Post-Sec.
2001 W Sample Rd Ste 100 33064 | 954-975-6400
Highlands Christian Academy | 600/PK-12
501 NE 48th St 33064 | 954-421-1747
Progressive Training Center | Post-Sec.
98 E McNab Rd Ste 98 33060 | 954-946-2022

Ponce de Leon, Holmes, Pop. 585
Holmes County SD
Supt. — See Bonifay
Ponce De Leon JSHS | 400/6-12
1477 Ammons Rd 32455 | 850-836-4242
Buddy Brown, prin. | Fax 836-5388

Ponte Vedra Beach, Saint Johns
St. Johns County SD
Supt. — See Saint Augustine
Landrum MS | 1,200/6-8
230 Landrum Ln 32082 | 904-547-8410
Emily Harrison, prin. | Fax 547-8415
Nease HS | 1,500/9-12
10550 Ray Rd, | 904-547-8300
Kyle Dresback, prin. | Fax 547-8305
Ponte Vedra HS | 1,500/9-12
460 Davis Park Rd, | 904-547-7350
Craig Speziale, prin. | Fax 547-7355

Port Charlotte, Charlotte, Pop. 53,337
Charlotte County SD | 16,600/PK-12
1445 Education Way 33948 | 941-255-0808
Dr. Doug Whittaker, supt. | Fax 255-7571
yourcharlotteschools.net
Academy | Alt
18300 Cochran Blvd 33948 | 941-255-7545
Karen LaPorte, prin. | Fax 255-7548
Charlotte Technical Center | Vo/Tech
18150 Murdock Cir 33948 | 941-255-7500
Barney Duffy, dir. | Fax 255-7509
Murdock MS | 800/6-8
17325 Mariner Way 33948 | 941-255-7525
Maria Gifford, prin. | Fax 255-7533
Port Charlotte HS | 2,000/9-12
18200 Cochran Blvd 33948 | 941-255-7485
Steve Dionisio, prin. | Fax 255-7493
Port Charlotte MS | 800/6-8
23000 Midway Blvd 33952 | 941-255-7460
Demetrius Revelas, prin. | Fax 255-7469
Adult & Community Education | Adult
1441 Tamiami Trl Unit 365 33948 | 941-255-7430
Mike Riley, dir. | Fax 255-7433
Other Schools – See Englewood, Punta Gorda, Rotonda West

Community Christian S | 300/PK-12
20035 Quesada Ave 33952 | 941-625-8977
Kris Schottleutner, admin. | Fax 625-1735
Port Charlotte Adventist S | 100/K-12
2100 Loveland Blvd 33980 | 941-625-5237
Kathy Trumper, prin. | Fax 625-8460
Port Charlotte Christian S | 50/K-12
3279 Sherwood Rd 33980 | 941-625-4450
Elizabeth Kolenda, prin. | Fax 243-0586
Southwest Florida College | Post-Sec.
950 Tamiami Trl Unit 109 33953 | 877-270-9786

Port Orange, Volusia, Pop. 55,114
Volusia County SD
Supt. — See De Land
Atlantic HS | 1,100/9-12
1250 Reed Canal Rd 32129 | 386-322-6100
Teresa Marcks, prin. | Fax 506-0001
Creekside MS | 1,100/6-8
6801 Airport Rd 32128 | 386-322-6155
John Cash, prin. | Fax 506-0002
eLearning East | 50/Alt
1250 Reed Canal Rd 32129 | 386-506-0014
Melissa Carr, dir. | Fax 506-5048
Silver Sands MS | 1,300/6-8
1300 Herbert St 32129 | 386-322-6175
Rose Roland, prin. | Fax 322-7574
Spruce Creek HS | 2,800/9-12
801 Taylor Rd 32127 | 386-322-6272
Todd Sparger, prin. | Fax 506-5045

Palmer College of Chiropractic FL Campus | Post-Sec.
4777 City Center Pkwy 32129 | 386-763-2709

Port Richey, Pasco, Pop. 2,626
Pasco County SD
Supt. — See Land O Lakes
Chasco MS | 800/6-8
7702 Ridge Rd 34668 | 727-774-1300
David Huyck, prin. | Fax 774-1391

Millennium Academy | 100/K-12
5844 Pine Hill Rd 34668 | 727-845-8150
Lori Ekblad, hdmstr. | Fax 844-5424

Port Saint Joe, Gulf, Pop. 3,399
Gulf County SD | 1,500/PK-12
150 Middle School Dr 32456 | 850-229-8256
Jim Norton, supt. | Fax 229-6089
www.gulf.k12.fl.us
Port Saint Joe JSHS | 300/7-12
100 Shark Dr 32456 | 850-229-8251
Jeremy Knapp, prin. | Fax 227-1803
Gulf County Adult S | Adult
2853 Long Ave 32456 | 850-227-1744
Melodie Nelson, prin. | Fax 229-2724
Other Schools – See Wewahitchka

Port Saint Lucie, Saint Lucie, Pop. 160,756
St. Lucie County SD
Supt. — See Fort Pierce
Port Saint Lucie HS | 2,000/9-12
1201 SE Jaguar Ln 34952 | 772-337-6770
Bridgette Hargadine, prin. | Fax 337-6780
St. Lucie West Centennial HS | 2,500/9-12
1485 SW Cashmere Blvd 34986 | 772-785-6660
Kim Stephanic, prin. | Fax 785-6679
Southern Oaks MS | 900/6-8
5500 NE Saint James Dr 34983 | 772-785-5640
Lisa Sullivan, prin. | Fax 785-5660
Southport MS | 1,000/6-8
2420 SE Morningside Blvd 34952 | 772-337-5900
Lydia Martin, prin. | Fax 337-5903
Treasure Coast HS | 2,400/9-12
1000 SW Darwin Blvd 34953 | 772-807-4300
Denise Rodriguez, prin. | Fax 807-4320

Keiser University | Post-Sec.
10330 S US Highway 1 34952 | 772-398-9990
Morningside Academy | 200/6-12
1631 SE Greendon Ave 34952 | 772-335-2096
Helen Klassen, admin. | Fax 335-2095
Port St. Lucie Beauty Academy | Post-Sec.
7644 S US 1 34983 | 772-340-3540

Princeton, Miami-Dade, Pop. 21,761

Princeton Christian S | 300/PK-12
PO Box 924916 33092 | 305-257-3644
Pam Armstrong, prin. | Fax 257-5799

Punta Gorda, Charlotte, Pop. 16,453
Charlotte County SD
Supt. — See Port Charlotte
Charlotte HS | 2,000/9-12
1250 Cooper St 33950 | 941-575-5450
Richard Shafer, prin. | Fax 575-5464
Punta Gorda MS | 1,100/6-8
1001 Education Ave 33950 | 941-575-5485
Cathy Corsaletti, prin. | Fax 575-5491

Quincy, Gadsden, Pop. 7,889
Gadsden County SD | 6,000/PK-12
35 Martin Luther King Jr Bl 32351 | 850-627-9651
Reginald James, supt. | Fax 627-2760
www.gcps.k12.fl.us
Carter-Paramore Academy | 300/Alt
631 S Stewart St 32351 | 850-627-6030
Pauline West, prin. | Fax 875-8697
Gadsden Central Academy | 50/Alt
655 S Stewart St 32351 | 850-875-7249
William Blitch, prin. | Fax 627-1802
Gadsden Technical Institute | Vo/Tech
201 Martin Luther King Jr B 32351 | 850-875-8324
Debra Rackley, dir. | Fax 875-7297
Shanks MS | 600/6-8
1400 W King St 32351 | 850-875-8737
Lamar Kirkland, prin. | Fax 875-8775
Gadsden Adult Education Center | Adult
201 Martin Luther King Jr B 32351 | 850-875-8324
Debra Rackley, prin. | Fax 875-7269
Other Schools – See Greensboro, Havana

Community Learning Institute | 200/PK-12
523 S Pat Thomas Pkwy 32351 | 850-627-8150
Munroe Day S | 200/PK-12
91 Old Mt Pleasant Rd 32352 | 850-856-5500
Suzanne Johnson, head sch | Fax 856-5856

Riverview, Hillsborough, Pop. 68,857
Hillsborough County SD
Supt. — See Tampa
Giunta MS | 1,100/6-8
4202 S Falkenburg Rd, | 813-740-4888
Arlene Castelli, prin. | Fax 740-4892
Riverview HS | 2,200/9-12
11311 Boyette Rd 33569 | 813-671-5011
Robert Heilmann, prin. | Fax 671-5012
Rodgers MS | 1,000/6-8
11910 Tucker Rd 33569 | 813-671-5288
Sharon Tumicki, prin. | Fax 671-5245
Spoto HS | 1,300/9-12
8538 Eagle Palm Dr, | 813-672-5405
Phillip Carr, prin. | Fax 672-5423

East Bay Christian S | 100/PK-12
10102 Old Big Bend Rd, | 813-677-5236

Florida Career College Post-Sec.
2662 S Falkenburg Rd, 813-621-5775
Providence Christian S 200/PK-12
5416 Providence Rd, 813-661-0588

Riviera Beach, Palm Beach, Pop. 31,825
Palm Beach County SD
Supt. — See West Palm Beach
Kennedy MS 700/6-8
1901 Avenue S 33404 561-845-4500
Corey Brooks, prin. Fax 845-4537
Riviera Beach Prep & Achievement Academy 200/Alt
7071 Garden Rd 33404 561-881-4740
Jeff Pollard, prin. Fax 881-4731
Suncoast HS 1,400/9-12
1717 Avenue S 33404 561-882-3400
Linda Cartlidge, prin. Fax 882-3443

North Technical Education Center Post-Sec.
7071 Garden Rd 33404 561-881-4600

Rockledge, Brevard, Pop. 24,317
Brevard County SD
Supt. — See Melbourne
Central Area Alternative Learning Center 50/Alt
1535 Cogswell St Ste D28 32955 321-633-3489
Dr. Ronald Bove, prin. Fax 633-3515
Kennedy MS 700/7-8
2100 S Fiske Blvd 32955 321-633-3500
Richard Myers, prin. Fax 633-3509
McNair Magnet MS 500/7-8
1 Challenger Dr 32955 321-633-3630
Rosette Brown, prin. Fax 633-3639
Rockledge HS 1,200/9-12
220 Raider Rd 32955 321-636-3711
Anthony Hines, prin. Fax 632-6064
Central Area Adult Education Adult
1535 Cogswell St Ste D29 32955 321-633-3575
Jose Marlasca, prin.

Rotonda West, Charlotte
Charlotte County SD
Supt. — See Port Charlotte
Ainger MS 900/6-8
245 Cougar Way 33947 941-697-5800
Marcia Louden, prin. Fax 697-5470

Royal Palm Beach, Palm Beach, Pop. 33,307
Palm Beach County SD
Supt. — See West Palm Beach
Crestwood MS 1,200/6-8
64 Sparrow Dr 33411 561-753-5000
Stephanie Nance, prin. Fax 753-5035
Royal Palm Beach Community HS 2,100/9-12
10600 Okeechobee Blvd 33411 561-753-4000
Jesus Armas, prin. Fax 753-4015

South University Post-Sec.
9801 Belvedere Rd 33411 561-273-6500

Ruskin, Hillsborough, Pop. 16,985
Hillsborough County SD
Supt. — See Tampa
Lennard HS 1,500/9-12
2342 E Shell Point Rd 33570 813-641-5611
Craig Horstman, prin.
Shields MS 1,400/6-8
15732 Beth Shields Way 33573 813-672-5338
Anna Voida, prin. Fax 672-5342
South County Career Center Vo/Tech
2810 John Sherman Way 33570 813-233-3335
Sandra Bailey, prin. Fax 233-3339
Lennard Adult Education Adult
2342 E Shell Point Rd 33570 813-658-2075
Pam Elles, prin. Fax 658-2078

Hillsborough Community College Post-Sec.
551 24th St NE 33570 813-253-7000
Ruskin Christian S 300/PK-12
820 W College Ave 33570 813-645-6441
Tim Vanderveer, admin. Fax 641-2073

Safety Harbor, Pinellas, Pop. 16,579
Pinellas County SD
Supt. — See Largo
Safety Harbor MS 1,400/6-8
901 1st Ave N 34695 727-724-1400
Alison Kennedy, prin. Fax 724-1407

Saint Augustine, Saint Johns, Pop. 12,760
St. Johns County SD 29,900/PK-12
40 Orange St 32084 904-547-7500
Joseph Joyner Ed.D., supt. Fax 547-7515
www.stjohns.k12.fl.us
Gaines Alternative Center 50/Alt
1 Christopher St 32084 904-547-8560
Tish McMahon, prin. Fax 547-7145
Menendez HS 1,400/9-12
600 State Road 206 W 32086 904-547-8660
Dr. Clay Carmichael, prin. Fax 547-8675
Murray MS 700/6-8
150 N Holmes Blvd 32084 904-547-8470
Tom Schwarm, prin. Fax 547-8475
Pacetti Bay MS 900/6-8
245 Meadowlark Ln 32092 904-547-8760
Sue Sparkman, prin. Fax 547-8765
Rogers MS 900/6-8
6250 US Highway 1 S 32086 904-547-8700
Greg Bergamasco, prin. Fax 547-8705
Saint Augustine HS 1,700/9-12
3205 Varella Ave 32084 904-547-8530
Cathy Mittelstadt, prin. Fax 547-8535
St. Johns Technical HS Vo/Tech
2980 Collins Ave 32084 904-547-8500
Wayne King, prin. Fax 547-8505
Sebastian MS 600/6-8
2955 Lewis Speedway 32084 904-547-3840
Kelly Battel, prin. Fax 547-3845

Other Schools – See Jacksonville, Ponte Vedra Beach, Saint Johns

---

Beacon of Hope Christian S 200/K-12
1230 Kings Estate Rd 32086 904-797-6996
Fax 797-6997
First Coast Technical College Post-Sec.
2980 Collins Ave 32084 904-547-3282
Flagler College Post-Sec.
74 King St 32084 904-829-6481
Florida School for the Deaf and Blind Post-Sec.
207 San Marco Ave 32084 904-827-2200
St. Joseph Academy 300/9-12
155 State Road 207 32084 904-824-0431
Tom McGlinn, prin. Fax 826-4477
Univ. of St. Augustine for Health Sci. Post-Sec.
1 University Blvd 32086 904-826-0084

Saint Cloud, Osceola, Pop. 34,423
Osceola County SD
Supt. — See Kissimmee
Harmony HS 1,800/9-12
3601 Arthur Gallagher Blvd 34771 407-933-9900
Grover Butler, prin. Fax 933-9901
Narcoossee MS 900/6-8
2700 N Narcoossee Rd 34771 407-891-6600
Matt Phillips, prin. Fax 891-6610
Saint Cloud HS 1,800/9-12
2000 Bulldog Ln 34769 407-891-3100
Nathaniel Fancher, prin. Fax 891-3114
Saint Cloud MS 1,400/6-8
1975 Michigan Ave 34769 407-891-3200
Cynthia Chiavini, prin. Fax 891-3206

Saint Johns, Saint Johns
St. Johns County SD
Supt. — See Saint Augustine
Fruit Cove MS 1,400/6-8
3180 Race Track Rd, 904-547-7880
Steve McCormick, prin. Fax 547-7885
Switzerland Point MS 1,000/6-8
777 Greenbriar Rd, 904-547-8650
Lisa Kunze, prin. Fax 547-8645

Saint Leo, Pasco, Pop. 1,297

St. Leo University Post-Sec.
33701 State Road 52 33574 352-588-8200

Saint Petersburg, Pinellas, Pop. 239,351
Pinellas County SD
Supt. — See Largo
Azalea MS 1,100/6-8
7855 22nd Ave N 33710 727-893-2606
Connie Kolosey, prin. Fax 893-2624
Bay Point MS 1,200/6-8
2151 62nd Ave S 33712 727-893-1153
Jason Shedrick, prin. Fax 893-1181
Gibbs HS 1,600/9-12
850 34th St S 33711 727-893-5452
Stephanie Adkinson, prin. Fax 893-5461
Hollins HS 1,800/9-12
4940 62nd St N 33709 727-547-7876
Dan Evans, prin. Fax 547-7727
Hopkins MS 1,000/6-8
701 16th St S 33705 727-893-2400
Barry Brown, prin. Fax 893-1600
Lakewood HS 1,400/9-12
1400 54th Ave S 33705 727-893-2916
Robert Vicari, prin. Fax 893-1387
Lealman IS 400/Alt
4900 28th St N 33714 727-528-5802
Busara Pitts, prin. Fax 528-5807
Marshall Fundamental MS 900/6-8
3901 22nd Ave S 33711 727-552-1737
Dr. Solomon Lowery, prin. Fax 552-1741
Meadowlawn MS 1,200/6-8
6050 16th St N 33703 727-570-3097
Claudius Effiom, prin. Fax 570-3396
Northeast HS 2,000/9-12
5500 16th St N 33703 727-570-3138
Kevin Hendrick, prin. Fax 217-7318
PTEC St. Petersburg Vo/Tech
901 34th St S 33711 727-893-2500
Arlene Corbin, dir. Fax 893-2776
St. Petersburg HS 2,200/9-12
2501 5th Ave N 33713 727-893-1842
Albert Bennett, prin. Fax 893-1399
Tyrone MS 800/6-8
6421 22nd Ave N 33710 727-893-1819
Robin Mobley, prin. Fax 893-1946
Lakewood Community S Adult
1400 54th Ave S 33705 727-893-2955
Sharon Snow, admin. Fax 893-1375
Northeast Community S Adult
1717 54th Ave N 33714 727-570-3193
Dr. Kathy Gregg, admin. Fax 217-7449
Tomlinson Adult Learning Center Adult
296 Mirror Lake Dr N 33701 727-893-2723
Dr. Debby VanderWoude, dir. Fax 893-2782

Admiral Farragut Academy 400/PK-12
501 Park St N 33710 727-384-5500
Robert Fine, hdmstr. Fax 347-5160
Bayfront Medical Center Post-Sec.
701 6th St S 33701 727-893-6604
Canterbury S of Florida - Knowlton Cmps 200/5-12
990 62nd Ave NE 33702 727-525-1419
Mac Hall, head sch Fax 525-2545
Eckerd College Post-Sec.
4200 54th Ave S 33711 727-867-1166
ITT Technical Institute Post-Sec.
877 Executive Ctr Dr W #100 33702 727-209-4700
Keswick Christian S 500/PK-12
10101 54th Ave N 33708 727-393-9100
Nick Stratis, supt. Fax 397-5378
Loraine's Academy Post-Sec.
1012 58th St N 33710 727-347-4247
Northside Christian S 600/PK-12
7777 62nd Ave N 33709 727-541-7593
Dr. Don James, hdmstr. Fax 546-5836
Pinellas Technical Education Center Post-Sec.
901 34th St S 33711 727-893-2500
Poynter Institute for Media Studies Post-Sec.
801 3rd St S 33701 888-769-6837
St. Petersburg Catholic HS 600/9-12
6333 9th Ave N 33710 727-344-4065
John McMahon, prin. Fax 343-9311
St. Petersburg College Post-Sec.
PO Box 13489 33733 727-341-4772
Shorecrest Preparatory S 1,000/PK-12
5101 1st St NE 33703 727-522-2111
Michael Murphy, hdmstr. Fax 527-4191
Southeastern College Post-Sec.
11208 Blue Heron Blvd Ste A 33716 727-576-6500
University of South Florida Post-Sec.
140 7th Ave S 33701 727-873-4873

Sanford, Seminole, Pop. 52,277
Seminole County SD 63,200/PK-12
400 E Lake Mary Blvd 32773 407-320-0000
Walt Griffin, supt. Fax 320-0281
www.scps.k12.fl.us
Crooms Academy of Information Technology 600/9-12
2200 W 13th St 32771 407-320-5750
Dr. Connie Collins, prin. Fax 320-5798
Journeys Academy 300/Alt
1722 W Airport Blvd 32771 407-320-7850
Mike Icardi, prin. Fax 320-7849
Millennium MS 1,700/6-8
21 Lakeview Ave 32773 407-320-6550
Kate Egloff, prin. Fax 320-6599
Sanford MS 1,500/6-8
1700 S French Ave 32771 407-320-6150
Mark Russi, prin. Fax 320-6265
Seminole HS 3,200/9-12
2701 Ridgewood Ave 32773 407-320-5050
Mike Gaudreau, prin. Fax 320-5024
Other Schools – See Altamonte Springs, Casselberry, Lake Mary, Longwood, Oviedo, Winter Park, Winter Springs

---

Aerosim Flight Academy Post-Sec.
2700 Flightline Ave 32773 407-330-7020
Liberty Christian S 200/PK-12
2626 S Palmetto Ave 32773 407-323-1583
Rev. William Simpson, dir. Fax 323-1588
Seminole State College of Florida Post-Sec.
100 Weldon Blvd 32773 407-708-4722
Southern Technical College Post-Sec.
2910 S Orlando Dr 32773 407-323-4141

Santa Rosa Beach, Walton
Walton County SD
Supt. — See De Funiak Springs
Emerald Coast MS 400/5-8
6604 W County Highway 30A 32459 850-622-5025
Charlie Marello, prin. Fax 622-5027
South Walton HS 600/9-12
645 Greenway Trl 32459 850-622-5020
David Preast, prin. Fax 622-5039

Sarasota, Sarasota, Pop. 51,038
Sarasota County SD 40,000/PK-12
1960 Landings Blvd 34231 941-927-9000
Lori White, supt. Fax 927-4009
sarasotacountyschools.net/
Booker HS 1,100/9-12
3201 N Orange Ave 34234 941-355-2967
Dr. Rachel Shelley, prin. Fax 359-5757
Booker MS 900/6-8
2250 Myrtle St 34234 941-359-5824
LaShawn Houston, prin. Fax 359-5898
Brookside MS 1,000/6-8
3636 S Shade Ave 34239 941-361-6472
Kristine Lawrence, prin. Fax 361-6508
McIntosh MS 900/6-8
701 McIntosh Rd 34232 941-361-6520
Dr. Harriet Moore, prin. Fax 361-6340
Riverview HS 2,700/9-12
1 Ram Way 34231 941-923-1484
Linda Nook, prin. Fax 361-6175
Sarasota County Technical Institute Vo/Tech
4748 Beneva Rd 34233 941-924-1365
Todd Bowden, dir. Fax 921-7902
Sarasota HS 2,000/9-12
1000 S School Ave 34237 941-955-0181
Jeff Hradek, prin. Fax 361-6380
Sarasota MS 1,100/6-8
4826 Ashton Rd 34233 941-361-6464
Karen Rose, prin. Fax 361-6798
Suncoast Polytechnical HS Vo/Tech
4650 Beneva Rd 34233 941-921-3981
Trent Terry, dir. Fax 921-9900
YMCA Triad 100/Alt
4430 Beneva Rd 34233 941-925-6693
Margaret King, dir. Fax 925-6696
Other Schools – See North Port, Venice

Argosy University/Sarasota Post-Sec.
5250 17th St 34235 941-379-0404
Cardinal Mooney Catholic HS 500/9-12
4171 Fruitville Rd 34232 941-371-4917
Stephen Christie, prin. Fax 371-6924
East West College of Natural Medicine Post-Sec.
3808 N Tamiami Trl 34234 941-355-9080
Everglades University Post-Sec.
6001 Lake Osprey Dr Ste 110 34240 941-907-2262
Fashion Focus Hair Academy Post-Sec.
2184 Gulf Gate Dr 34231 941-921-4877
Keiser University Post-Sec.
6151 Lake Osprey Dr 34240 941-907-3900
Meridian College Post-Sec.
7020 Professional Pkwy E 34240 941-377-4880
New College of Florida Post-Sec.
5800 Bay Shore Rd 34243 941-487-5000

New Gate S 100/PK-12
5237 Ashton Rd 34233 941-922-4949
Tim Seldin, hdmstr. Fax 922-7660
Potter's Wheel Academy 100/K-12
PO Box 50203 34232 941-284-4076
Reed Palmer, dir. Fax 605-7024
Ringling College of Art & Design Post-Sec.
2700 N Tamiami Trl 34234 941-351-5100
Sarasota Christian S 400/PK-12
5415 Bahia Vista St 34232 941-371-6481
Jeffrey Shank, supt. Fax 371-0898
Sarasota County Technical Institute Post-Sec.
4748 Beneva Rd 34233 941-924-1365
Sarasota Memorial Hospital Post-Sec.
1700 S Tamiami Trl 34239 941-917-1080
Sarasota School of Massage Therapy Post-Sec.
5899 Whitfield Ave Ste 301 34243 941-957-0577
University of S Florida Sarasota-Manatee Post-Sec.
8350 N Tamiami Trl 34243 941-359-4200

Satellite Beach, Brevard, Pop. 9,911
Brevard County SD
Supt. — See Melbourne
DeLaura MS 700/7-8
300 Jackson Ave 32937 321-773-7581
Claudia Shirley, prin. Fax 773-0702
Satellite HS 1,100/9-12
300 Scorpion Ct 32937 321-779-2000
Mark Elliott, prin. Fax 773-0703

Sebastian, Indian River, Pop. 21,634
Indian River County SD
Supt. — See Vero Beach
Sebastian River HS 1,900/9-12
9001 90th Ave 32958 772-564-4170
Todd Racine, prin. Fax 564-4182
Sebastian River MS 1,000/6-8
9400 State Road 512 32958 772-564-5111
Dave Kramek, prin. Fax 564-5225

Sebring, Highlands, Pop. 10,311
Highlands County SD 11,500/PK-12
426 School St 33870 863-471-5555
Wally Cox, supt. Fax 471-5600
www.highlands.k12.fl.us
Hill-Gustat MS 700/6-8
4700 Schumacher Rd 33872 863-471-5437
Chris Doty, prin. Fax 314-5245
Sebring HS 1,600/9-12
3514 Kenilworth Blvd 33870 863-471-5500
Anne Lindsay, prin. Fax 471-5507
Sebring MS 800/6-8
500 E Center Ave 33870 863-471-5700
Sandi Whidden, prin. Fax 471-5710
Other Schools – See Avon Park, Lake Placid

Highlands University Preparatory S 200/PK-12
1160 Persimmon Ave 33870 863-385-3850
Dr. Wes Johnston, head sch Fax 385-5752

Seffner, Hillsborough, Pop. 7,410
Hillsborough County SD
Supt. — See Tampa
Alternative Education East 50/Alt
1009 N Parsons Ave 33584 813-651-2165
Nancy Lind, prin. Fax 651-2173
Armwood HS 1,700/9-12
12000 E US Highway 92 33584 813-744-8040
Michael Ippolito, prin. Fax 744-8048
Brandon Alternative S 200/Alt
1009 N Parsons Ave 33584 813-651-2165
Nancy Lind, admin. Fax 651-2173
Burnett MS 1,000/6-8
1010 N Kingsway Rd 33584 813-744-6745
Herbert Peeples, prin. Fax 744-8973
Jennings MS 900/6-8
9325 Governors Run Dr 33584 813-740-4575
Joann Johnson, prin. Fax 740-4579

Hillsborough Baptist S 100/PK-12
6021 Williams Rd 33584 813-620-0683
Jessica Brockett, prin. Fax 663-9776
Seffner Christian Academy 600/PK-12
11605 E US Highway 92 33584 813-626-0001
Roger Duncan, admin. Fax 627-0330

Seminole, Pinellas, Pop. 17,030
Pinellas County SD
Supt. — See Largo
Osceola Fundamental HS 1,700/9-12
9751 98th St 33777 727-547-7717
Michael Bohnet, prin. Fax 545-6412
Osceola MS 1,300/6-8
9301 98th St 33777 727-547-7689
Susan Arsenault, prin. Fax 547-7667
Seminole HS 2,100/9-12
8401 131st St 33776 727-547-7536
Walt Weller, prin. Fax 547-7503
Seminole MS 1,300/6-8
8701 131st St 33776 727-547-4520
Thomas Lechner, prin. Fax 547-7741
Seminole Vocational Education Center Vo/Tech
12611 86th Ave 33776 727-545-6405
Barbara Clare, prin. Fax 545-6408

Shalimar, Okaloosa, Pop. 699
Okaloosa County SD
Supt. — See Fort Walton Beach
Meigs MS 600/6-8
150 Richbourg Ave 32579 850-833-4301
Lee Hale, prin. Fax 833-9392

Sneads, Jackson, Pop. 1,817
Jackson County SD
Supt. — See Marianna
Sneads HS 400/9-12
8066 Old Spanish Trl 32460 850-482-9007
Faye Parker, prin. Fax 482-9058

South Daytona, Volusia, Pop. 12,013

International Academy Post-Sec.
2550 S Ridgewood Ave 32119 386-767-4600
Warner Christian Academy 700/PK-12
1730 S Ridgewood Ave 32119 386-767-5451
Mark Tress, supt. Fax 760-6834

South Miami, Miami-Dade, Pop. 11,508
Miami-Dade County SD
Supt. — See Miami
South Miami MS 700/7-8
6750 SW 60th St 33143 305-661-3481
Juan Boue, prin. Fax 665-6728

Spring Hill, Hernando, Pop. 96,871
Hernando County SD
Supt. — See Brooksville
Fox Chapel MS 700/6-8
9412 Fox Chapel Ln 34606 352-797-7025
Ray Pinder, prin. Fax 797-7125
Springstead HS 1,900/9-12
3300 Mariner Blvd 34609 352-797-7010
Susan Duval, prin. Fax 797-7110

Pasco County SD
Supt. — See Land O Lakes
Crews Lake MS 800/6-8
15144 Shady Hills Rd 34610 727-246-1600
Chris Christoff, prin. Fax 246-1691

ATA Career Education Post-Sec.
7355 Spring Hill Dr 34606 352-684-3007
Bene's International School of Beauty Post-Sec.
1486 Pinehurst Dr 34606 352-263-2744
Bishop McLaughlin HS 200/9-12
13651 Hays Rd 34610 727-857-2600
Sarah Regan, prin. Fax 857-2610
Spring Hill Christian Academy 300/PK-12
3140 Mariner Blvd 34609 352-683-8485
Michael Willis, prin. Fax 683-5087
West Hernando Christian S 300/PK-12
2250 Osowaw Blvd 34607 352-688-9918
Marti Covert, admin. Fax 683-1184
Wider Horizons S 200/PK-12
4060 Castle Ave 34609 352-686-1934
Dr. Domenick Maglio, prin. Fax 688-4371

Starke, Bradford, Pop. 5,317
Bradford County SD 3,300/PK-12
501 W Washington St 32091 904-966-6018
Chad Farnsworth, supt. Fax 966-6030
www.mybradford.us/
Bradford HS 900/9-12
581 N Temple Ave 32091 904-966-6075
Rick Stephens, prin. Fax 966-6020
Bradford MS 700/6-8
527 N Orange St 32091 904-966-6705
Earnest Williams, prin. Fax 966-6714
Bradford Union Career Technical Center Vo/Tech
609 N Orange St 32091 904-966-6766
Christy Reddish, dir. Fax 966-6786

Clay County SD
Supt. — See Green Cove Springs
Florida Youth Challenge Academy 200/Alt
5629 State Road 16 W 32091 904-272-8100
Mike Wingate, dir. Fax 682-3990

Bradford-Union Area Vo-Tech Center Post-Sec.
609 N Orange St 32091 904-966-6764
Hope Christian Academy 300/PK-12
3900 SE State Road 100 32091 352-473-4040
Angie Davis, prin. Fax 473-2024
Northside Christian Academy 200/PK-12
7415 NW County Road 225 32091 904-964-7124
Tobias Roehm, admin. Fax 964-7141

Stuart, Martin, Pop. 15,329
Martin County SD 17,500/PK-12
500 SE Ocean Blvd 34994 772-219-1200
Laurie Gaylord, supt. Fax 219-1231
www.martinschools.org/
Anderson MS 1,000/6-8
7000 SE Atlantic Ridge Dr 34997 772-221-7100
Patricia Schmoyer, prin. Fax 221-7149
Martin County HS 1,900/9-12
2801 S Kanner Hwy 34994 772-219-1800
Al Fabrizio, prin. Fax 219-1821
Murray MS 800/6-8
4400 SE Murray St 34997 772-219-1670
Doug Peterson, prin. Fax 219-1677
South Fork HS 1,800/9-12
10205 SW Pratt Whitney Rd 34997 772-219-1840
Dave Hall, prin. Fax 219-1860
Spectrum JSHS 100/Alt
800 SE Bahama Ave 34994 772-219-1870
Steve Carswell, prin. Fax 219-1873
Stuart MS 900/6-8
575 SE Georgia Ave 34994 772-219-1685
Sigrid George, prin. Fax 219-1229
Stuart Community Adult HS Adult
1050 E 10th St 34996 772-219-1296
Elia Parsons, coord. Fax 219-1299
Other Schools – See Indiantown, Jensen Beach, Palm City

Chapman School of Seamanship Post-Sec.
4343 SE Saint Lucie Blvd 34997 772-283-8130
Community Christian Academy 200/PK-12
777 SE Salerno Rd 34997 772-288-7227
Fax 600-2728
Star Academy for Pet Stylists Post-Sec.
2201 SE Indian St Unit C6 34997 772-221-9330

Summerfield, Marion
Marion County SD
Supt. — See Ocala
Lake Weir MS 1,200/6-8
10220 SE Sunset Harbor Rd 34491 352-671-6120
Kathy Quelland, prin. Fax 671-6121

Sumterville, Sumter
Sumter County SD
Supt. — See Bushnell
Sumter Alternative S Alt
709 N West St 33585 352-568-1113
Rodney Rocker, prin. Fax 793-6508
Sumter County Adult Center Adult
1425 CR 526A 33585 352-793-5719
Chuck Sullivan, prin. Fax 793-6508

Sunrise, Broward, Pop. 82,120
Broward County SD
Supt. — See Fort Lauderdale
Bair MS 1,000/6-8
9100 NW 21st Mnr 33322 754-322-2900
Clarissa Coddington, prin. Fax 322-2985
Piper HS 2,700/9-12
8000 NW 44th St 33351 754-322-1700
Enid Valdez, prin. Fax 322-1830
Westpine MS 1,400/6-8
9393 NW 50th St 33351 754-322-4900
Paula Meadows, prin. Fax 322-4985

Tallahassee, Leon, Pop. 177,584
Leon County SD 32,300/PK-12
2757 W Pensacola St 32304 850-487-7100
Jackie Pons, supt. Fax 487-7141
www.leonschools.net
Chiles HS 2,000/9-12
7200 Lawton Chiles Ln 32312 850-488-1756
Alan Cox, prin. Fax 488-1218
Cobb MS 800/6-8
915 Hillcrest Ave 32308 850-488-3364
Tonja Fitzgerald, prin. Fax 922-2452
Deerlake MS 900/6-8
9902 Deer Lk W 32312 850-922-6545
Shane Syfrett, prin. Fax 488-3275
Fairview MS 900/6-8
3415 Zillah St 32305 850-488-6880
Scott Hansen, prin. Fax 922-6326
Godby HS 1,100/9-12
1717 W Tharpe St 32303 850-617-4700
Shelly Bell, prin. Fax 922-4162
Griffin MS 600/6-8
800 Alabama St 32304 850-488-8436
Gwendolyn Lynn, prin. Fax 922-4226
Leon HS 1,900/9-12
550 E Tennessee St 32308 850-617-5700
Billy Epting, prin. Fax 922-5311
Lincoln HS 1,900/9-12
3838 Trojan Trl 32311 850-487-2110
Allen Burch, prin. Fax 922-4173
Lively-Technical Center Vo/Tech
500 Appleyard Dr 32304 850-487-7555
Woody Hildebrandt, prin. Fax 922-3880
Mehrdad Ghazvini Learning Center 100/Alt
860 Blountstown St 32304 850-488-2087
Joe Pons, prin. Fax 410-1531
Montford MS 1,100/6-8
5789 Pimlico Dr 32309 850-922-6011
Lewis Blessing, prin. Fax 922-7974
Nims MS 500/6-8
723 W Orange Ave 32310 850-488-5960
Desmond Cole, prin. Fax 922-0203
Raa MS 900/6-8
401 W Tharpe St 32303 850-488-6287
Donna Callaway, prin. Fax 922-5835
Rickards HS 1,200/9-12
3013 Jim Lee Rd 32301 850-488-1783
Doug Cook, prin. Fax 922-7104
SAIL HS 400/9-12
2006 Jackson Bluff Rd 32304 850-488-2468
Tiffany Thomas, prin. Fax 922-8483
Swift Creek MS 700/6-8
2100 Pedrick Rd 32317 850-414-2670
Sue Rishell, prin. Fax 414-2650
Leon Countywide Adult Education Adult
283 Trojan Trl 32311 850-922-5343
Barbara Van Camp, prin. Fax 922-5352

Christ Classical Academy 100/K-12
1983 Mahan Dr 32308 850-656-2373
Paul Shackelford, hdmstr. Fax 656-6373
Community Christian S 300/PK-12
4859 Kerry Forest Pkwy 32309 850-893-6628
Tom Argersinger, hdmstr. Fax 668-3966
Core Institute Post-Sec.
223 W Carolina St 32301 866-830-0108
Florida A&M University Post-Sec.
1601 Martin Luther King Jr 32307 850-599-3000
Florida State University Post-Sec.
600 W College Ave 32306 850-644-2525
ITT Technical Institute Post-Sec.
2639 N Monroe St Ste 100 32303 850-422-6300
John Paul II HS 100/9-12
5100 Terrebonne Dr 32311 850-201-5744
Sr. Maureen Martin, prin. Fax 205-3299
Keiser University Post-Sec.
1700 Halstead Blvd Ste 2 32309 850-906-9494
Lively Area Vocational Technical School Post-Sec.
500 Appleyard Dr 32304 850-487-7555
Maclay S 1,000/PK-12
3737 N Meridian Rd 32312 850-893-2138
William Jablon, hdmstr. Fax 893-7434
North Florida Christian S 800/PK-12
3000 N Meridian Rd 32312 850-386-6327
North Florida Cosmetology Institute Post-Sec.
2424 Allen Rd 32312 850-878-5269
Seven Hills Academy 100/K-12
2205 Thomasville Rd 32308 850-656-9211
Duwayne Baum, hdmstr. Fax 656-9602
Tallahassee Community College Post-Sec.
444 Appleyard Dr 32304 850-201-6200

Tallahassee Memorial Hospital Post-Sec.
1300 Miccosukee Rd 32308 850-681-5385

Tamarac, Broward, Pop. 59,173
Broward County SD
Supt. — See Fort Lauderdale
Millennium MS 1,700/6-8
5803 NW 94th Ave 33321 754-322-3900
Dr. Cheryl Cendan, prin. Fax 322-3985

Tampa, Hillsborough, Pop. 328,173
Hillsborough County SD 192,400/PK-12
PO Box 3408 33601 813-272-4000
MaryEllen Elia, supt. Fax 272-4510
www.sdhc.k12.fl.us/
Adams MS 1,300/6-8
10201 N Boulevard 33612 813-975-7665
Heath Beauregard, prin. Fax 632-6889
Alonso HS 2,400/9-12
8302 Montague St 33635 813-356-1525
Louis Diaz, prin. Fax 356-1529
Bartels MS 900/6-8
9020 Imperial Oak Blvd 33647 813-907-6801
Dr. Tim Binder, prin. Fax 907-6805
Benito MS 1,100/6-8
10101 Cross Creek Blvd 33647 813-631-4694
John Sanders, prin. Fax 631-4706
Blake HS 1,500/9-12
1701 N Boulevard 33607 813-272-3422
Jackie Haynes, prin. Fax 272-3715
Bowers/Whitley Career Center Vo/Tech
13609 N 22nd St 33613 813-558-1750
Dr. Anthony Colucci, prin. Fax 558-1761
Buchanan MS 800/6-8
1001 W Bearss Ave 33613 813-975-7600
Scott Hilgenberg, prin. Fax 975-7610
Chamberlain HS 2,000/9-12
9401 N Boulevard 33612 813-975-7677
Thomas Morrill, prin. Fax 975-7687
Coleman MS 900/6-8
1724 S Manhattan Ave 33629 813-872-5335
Michael Hoskinson, prin. Fax 872-5338
Davidsen MS 1,100/6-8
10501 Montague St 33626 813-558-5300
Brent McBrien, prin. Fax 558-5299
Dowdell MS 600/6-8
1208 Wishing Well Way 33619 813-744-8322
Roger Stanley, prin. Fax 740-3616
Farnell MS 1,200/6-8
13912 Nine Eagles Dr 33626 813-356-1640
John Cobb, prin. Fax 356-1644
Ferrell Girls Prep Academy 300/6-8
4302 N 24th St 33610 813-276-5608
Karen French, prin. Fax 276-5615
Franklin Boys Prep Academy 600/6-8
3915 E 21st Ave 33605 813-744-8108
John Haley, prin. Fax 744-8579
Freedom S 2,100/Alt
17410 Commerce Park Blvd 33647 813-558-1105
David Sheppard, prin. Fax 558-1189
Gaither HS 2,000/9-12
16200 N Dale Mabry Hwy 33618 813-975-7340
Marie Whelan, prin. Fax 975-7349
Hill MS 1,000/6-8
5200 Ehrlich Rd 33624 813-975-7325
Dr. Jackie Scaglione, prin. Fax 975-4819
Hillsborough HS 1,900/9-12
5000 N Central Ave 33603 813-276-5620
Dr. William Orr, prin. Fax 276-5629
Jefferson HS 1,700/9-12
4401 W Cypress St 33607 813-872-5241
Van Ayres, prin. Fax 872-5250
King HS 1,700/9-12
6815 N 56th St 33610 813-744-8333
Michael Rowan, prin. Fax 744-8343
Leto HS 1,700/9-12
4409 W Sligh Ave 33614 813-872-5300
Victor Fernandez, prin. Fax 872-5314
Liberty MS 1,200/6-8
17400 Commerce Park Blvd 33647 813-558-1180
James Ammirati, prin. Fax 558-1184
Madison MS 800/6-8
4444 W Bay Vista Ave 33611 813-272-3050
Joseph Brown, prin. Fax 233-2796
Memorial MS 800/6-8
4702 N Central Ave 33603 813-872-5230
Arthur Atkins, prin. Fax 872-5238
Middleton Magnet HS 1,200/9-12
4801 N 22nd St 33610 813-233-3360
Owen Young, prin. Fax 233-3364
Monroe MS 600/6-8
4716 W Montgomery Ave 33616 813-272-3020
Kenneth Hart, prin. Fax 272-3027
North Tampa Alternative S 200/Alt
8602 N Armenia Ave 33604 813-631-4426
Theophilus Hill, prin. Fax 631-4429
Orange Grove Magnet MS 500/6-8
3415 N 16th St 33605 813-276-5717
Dr. Scott Rudes, prin. Fax 276-5857
Pierce MS 1,100/6-8
5511 N Hesperides St 33614 813-872-5344
Henry Lefler, prin. Fax 871-7978
Plant HS 2,300/9-12
2415 S Himes Ave 33629 813-272-3033
Robert Nelson, prin. Fax 272-0624
Progress Village MS 800/6-8
8113 Zinnia Dr 33619 813-671-5110
Michael Miranda, prin. Fax 671-5240
Robinson HS 1,400/9-12
6311 S Lois Ave 33616 813-272-3006
Johnny Bush, prin. Fax 272-3014
Sickles HS 1,800/9-12
7950 Gunn Hwy 33626 813-631-4742
Jake Russell, prin. Fax 631-4754
Sligh MS 600/6-8
2011 E Sligh Ave 33610 813-276-5596
Dr. Angela Vickers, prin. Fax 276-5606
Smith MS 1,100/6-8
14303 Citrus Pointe Dr 33625 813-792-5125
Raymond Padgett, prin. Fax 792-5129
Stewart MS 900/6-8
1125 W Spruce St 33607 813-276-5691
Baretta Wilson, prin. Fax 276-5698
Tampa Bay Technical HS 2,100/9-12
6410 Orient Rd 33610 813-744-8360
Warren Brooks, prin. Fax 744-8368
Van Buren MS 600/6-8
8715 N 22nd St 33604 813-975-7652
JoAnn Redden, prin. Fax 631-4312
Waters Career Center Vo/Tech
2704 N Highland Ave 33602 813-233-2655
Veronica Knight, admin. Fax 233-2659
Webb MS 800/6-8
6035 Hanley Rd 33634 813-872-5351
Marcos Murillo, prin. Fax 872-5359
Wharton HS 2,500/9-12
20150 Bruce B Downs Blvd 33647 813-631-4710
Bradley Woods, prin. Fax 631-4722
Williams MS 800/6-8
5020 N 47th St 33610 813-744-8600
Patricia Harrell, prin. Fax 744-8665
Wilson MS 600/6-8
1005 W Swann Ave 33606 813-276-5682
Colleen Faucett, prin. Fax 233-2540
Young Magnet MS 700/6-8
1807 E Dr Martn Lthr King 33610 813-276-5739
Nadine Johnson, prin. Fax 276-5893
Adult Education Center Central Region Adult
5103 N 40th St 33610 813-744-7750
Ed Wickham, prin. Fax 247-8349
Aparicio/Levy Tech Center Adult
10119 E Ellicott St 33610 813-740-4884
AnnMarie Courtney, prin. Fax 740-4885
Bowers/Whitley Adult Education Adult
13609 N 22nd St 33613 813-463-9528
Barbara Ragin, prin.
Brewster Tech Center Adult
2222 N Tampa St 33602 813-276-5448
Paula Clark, prin. Fax 276-5756
Chamberlain Adult Education Adult
9401 N Boulevard 33612 813-631-4500
Michelle Loango, prin. Fax 631-4513
Erwin Tech Center Adult
2010 E Hillsborough Ave 33610 813-231-1800
James Rich, prin. Fax 231-1820
Gary Adult S Adult
5101 N 40th St 33610 813-740-7660
Dr. Simon Earle, prin. Fax 740-7674
Jefferson Adult & Community Center Adult
4401 W Cypress St 33607 813-356-1288
Georgene Diaz, prin. Fax 356-1291
Learey Technical Center Adult
5410 N 20th St 33610 813-231-1907
AnnMarie Courtney, prin. Fax 231-1855
Leto Adult Education Adult
4409 W Sligh Ave 33614 813-872-5314
Dr. Olaniyio Popoola, prin. Fax 872-5314
Middleton Adult Education Adult
4801 N 22nd St 33610 813-233-3360
Michelle Loango, prin. Fax 233-3364
Tampa Bay Technical Adult Ed Adult
6410 Orient Rd 33610 813-744-8360
Shirley Robbins, admin. Fax 744-8368
Other Schools – See Brandon, Dover, Gibsonton, Lithia, Lutz, Odessa, Plant City, Riverview, Ruskin, Seffner, Temple Terrace, Valrico

---

Academy of the Holy Names HS 300/9-12
3319 Bayshore Blvd 33629 813-839-5371
Camille Jowanna, prin. Fax 839-1486
Academy Prep Center of Tampa 100/5-8
1407 E Columbus Dr 33605 813-248-5600
American Youth Academy 300/PK-12
5905 E 130th Ave 33617 813-987-9282
Sr. Magda Saleh, head sch Fax 987-9262
Argosy University/Tampa Post-Sec.
1403 N Howard Ave 33607 813-393-5290
Art Institute of Tampa Post-Sec.
4401 N Himes Ave Ste 150 33614 813-873-2112
Bayshore Christian S 200/PK-12
3909 S MacDill Ave 33611 813-839-4297
Melanie Humenansky, head sch Fax 835-1404
Berkeley Preparatory S 1,300/PK-12
4811 Kelly Rd 33615 813-885-1673
Joseph Seivold, hdmstr. Fax 886-6933
Cambridge Christian S 500/PK-12
6101 N Habana Ave 33614 813-872-6744
Boyd Chitwood, hdmstr. Fax 872-6013
Carrollwood Day S 800/PK-12
1515 W Bearss Ave 33613 813-920-2288
Mary Kanter, hdmstr. Fax 960-9269
Citrus Park Christian S 300/PK-12
7705 Gunn Hwy 33625 813-920-3960
Karen Jeffers, prin. Fax 926-1240
Concorde Career Institute Post-Sec.
4202 W Spruce St 33607 813-874-0094
DeVry University Post-Sec.
5540 W Executive Dr Ste 100 33609 813-287-6700
DeVry University Post-Sec.
6700 Lakeview Center # 150 33619 813-664-4260
Everest University - Brandon Campus Post-Sec.
3924 Coconut Palm Dr 33619 813-621-0041
Everest University - Tampa Campus Post-Sec.
3319 W Hillsborough Ave 33614 813-879-6000
Faith Outreach Academy 200/PK-12
7607 Sheldon Rd 33615 813-887-5546
Julie Sierra, prin. Fax 249-6896
Fasttrain of Tampa Post-Sec.
2200 E Fowler Ave 33612 813-874-0660
Fortis College Post-Sec.
3910 N US Highway 301 # 200 33619 813-620-1446
Gateway Christian Academy 100/PK-12
14205 N Florida Ave 33613 813-964-9800
Debra Cahl, prin. Fax 964-9808
Harvest Time Christian S 100/PK-12
1511 S US Highway 301 33619 813-626-4600
Judith Thompson M.Ed., prin. Fax 622-8085
Henry W. Brewster Technical Center Post-Sec.
2222 N Tampa St 33602 813-276-5448
Hillsborough Community College Post-Sec.
10414 E Columbus Dr 33619 813-253-7802
Hillsborough Community College Post-Sec.
PO Box 30030 33630 813-253-7000
Hillsborough Community College Ybor Camp Post-Sec.
2112 N 15th St 33605 813-253-7601
International Academy of Design & Tech Post-Sec.
5104 Eisenhower Blvd 33634 813-881-0007
ITT Technical Institute Post-Sec.
4809 Memorial Hwy 33634 813-885-2244
James Haley Veteran's Hospital Post-Sec.
13000 Bruce B Downs Blvd 33612 813-972-2000
Jesuit HS 700/9-12
4701 N Himes Ave 33614 813-877-5344
Barry Neuburger, prin. Fax 872-1853
Keiser University Post-Sec.
5002 W Waters Ave 33634 813-885-4900
Manhattan Beauty School Post-Sec.
2317 E Fletcher Ave 33612 813-264-3535
Manhattan Hairstyling Academy Post-Sec.
1906 W Platt St 33606 813-837-2525
Meridian College Post-Sec.
9503 Princess Palm Ave 33619 813-402-4974
Rasmussen College Post-Sec.
4042 Park Oaks Blvd Ste 100 33610 813-246-7600
Remington College Post-Sec.
6302 E ML King Blvd Ste 400 33619 813-935-5700
Sanford-Brown Institute Post-Sec.
5701 E Hillsbrgh Ave 33610 813-393-4250
Southeastern College Post-Sec.
5225 Memorial Hwy 33634 813-961-2837
Southwest Florida College Post-Sec.
3910 Riga Blvd 33619 813-630-4401
Strayer University Post-Sec.
6302 E M L King Blvd # 450 33619 813-663-0100
Strayer University Post-Sec.
4902 Eisenhower Blvd # 100 33634 813-882-0100
Tampa Adventist Academy 100/PK-10
3205 N Boulevard 33603 813-228-7950
Tampa Bay Christian Academy 300/PK-12
300 E Sligh Ave 33604 813-238-3229
Rev. William Brown, prin. Fax 237-3426
Tampa Catholic HS 700/9-12
4630 N Rome Ave 33603 813-870-0860
Thomas Reidy, prin. Fax 877-9136
Tampa General Hospital Post-Sec.
PO Box 1289 33601 813-844-7985
Tampa Preparatory S 600/6-12
727 W Cass St 33606 813-251-8481
Kevin Plummer, hdmstr. Fax 254-2106
The Salon Professional Academy Post-Sec.
4802 Gunn Hwy Ste 144 33624 813-908-8020
Ultimate Medical Academy Post-Sec.
9309 N Florida Ave 33612 813-386-6350
Universal Academy of Florida 500/PK-12
6801 Orient Rd 33610 813-664-0695
May Khdeir, admin. Fax 664-4506
University of South Florida Post-Sec.
4202 E Fowler Ave 33620 813-974-2011
University of Tampa Post-Sec.
401 W Kennedy Blvd 33606 813-253-3333
West Gate Christian S 100/PK-12
5121 Kelly Rd 33615 813-884-5147
Justin R. Raymond, admin. Fax 888-5368

Tarpon Springs, Pinellas, Pop. 23,056
Pinellas County SD
Supt. — See Largo
East Lake HS 2,300/9-12
1300 Silver Eagle Dr 34688 727-942-5419
Robert Poth, prin. Fax 942-5441
Tarpon Springs HS 1,800/9-12
1411 Gulf Rd 34689 727-943-4900
Clint Herbic, prin. Fax 943-4907
Tarpon Springs MS 1,100/6-8
501 N Florida Ave 34689 727-943-5511
Dr. Susan Keller, prin. Fax 943-5519

St. Petersburg College Post-Sec.
600 E Klosterman Rd 34689 727-791-2400

Tavares, Lake, Pop. 13,762
Lake County SD 39,900/PK-12
201 W Burleigh Blvd 32778 352-253-6500
Susan Moxley Ed.D., supt. Fax 343-0198
www.lake.k12.fl.us/
Tavares HS 1,300/9-12
603 N New Hampshire Ave 32778 352-343-3007
June Dalton, prin. Fax 343-0892
Tavares MS 1,000/6-8
1335 Lane Park Cutoff 32778 352-343-4545
Trella Mott, prin. Fax 343-7212
Other Schools – See Clermont, Eustis, Groveland, Leesburg, Minneola, Mount Dora, Umatilla

---

Adventure Christian Academy 100/PK-12
3800 State Road 19 32778 352-742-4543
Gary Johnson, admin. Fax 343-3820
Liberty Christian Academy 200/PK-12
2451 Dora Ave 32778 352-343-0061
Debra Zischke, admin. Fax 343-2424

Tavernier, Monroe, Pop. 2,111
Monroe County SD
Supt. — See Key West
Coral Shores HS 800/9-12
89901 Old Hwy 33070 305-853-3222
Dave Murphy, prin. Fax 853-3228

Temple Terrace, Hillsborough, Pop. 23,889
Hillsborough County SD
Supt. — See Tampa

Greco MS 900/6-8
6925 E Fowler Ave 33617 813-987-6926
Yinka Alege, prin. Fax 987-6863

Florida College Post-Sec.
119 N Glen Arven Ave 33617 813-988-5131

Titusville, Brevard, Pop. 42,761
Brevard County SD
Supt. — See Melbourne
Astronaut HS 1,200/9-12
800 War Eagle Blvd 32796 321-264-3000
Terry Humphrey, prin. Fax 264-3013
Jackson MS 600/7-8
1515 Knox Mcrae Dr 32780 321-269-1812
Dr. John Harris, prin. Fax 269-7811
Madison MS 500/7-8
3375 Dairy Rd 32796 321-264-3120
Sherry Tomlinson, prin. Fax 264-3124
North Area Alternative Learning Center 50/Alt
800 Lane Ave 32780 321-264-3145
Brandy Douglas, prin. Fax 264-3068
Titusville HS 1,400/9-12
150 Terrier Trl S 32780 321-264-3100
Dr. Lori Spinner, prin. Fax 264-3103
North Area Adult Education Adult
800 Lane Ave 32780 321-264-3088
Brandy Douglas, prin.

Bristow Academy Post-Sec.
365 Golden Knights Blvd 32780 321-567-0382
Melbourne Beauty School Post-Sec.
106 Julia St 32796 - -
Temple Christian S 100/PK-12
1400 N Washington Ave 32780 321-269-2837
Marty Braemer, admin. Fax 383-9101

Trenton, Gilchrist, Pop. 1,949
Gilchrist County SD 2,500/PK-12
310 NW 11th Ave 32693 352-463-3200
Robert G. Rankin, supt. Fax 463-3276
www.gilchristschools.org
Trenton HS 600/6-12
1013 N Main St 32693 352-463-3210
Cheri Langford, prin. Fax 463-3264
Other Schools – See Bell

Trinity, Pasco, Pop. 10,776

Trinity College of Florida Post-Sec.
2430 Welbilt Blvd 34655 727-376-6911

Umatilla, Lake, Pop. 3,433
Lake County SD
Supt. — See Tavares
Umatilla HS 900/9-12
320 N Trowell Ave 32784 352-669-3131
Mike Elchenko, prin. Fax 669-6606
Umatilla MS 700/6-8
305 E Lake St 32784 352-669-3171
Thomas Sanders, prin. Fax 669-5424

Valrico, Hillsborough, Pop. 34,795
Hillsborough County SD
Supt. — See Tampa
Bloomingdale HS 2,400/9-12
1700 Bloomingdale Ave, 813-744-8018
Mark West, prin. Fax 744-8026
Mulrennan MS 1,200/6-8
4215 Durant Rd, 813-651-2100
Tim Ducker, prin. Fax 651-2104

Foundation Christian Academy PK-12
3955 Lithia Pinecrest Rd, 813-654-2969
Jonathan Smith, prin. Fax 655-4780
Grace Christian S 200/PK-12
1425 N Valrico Rd 33594 813-689-8815
Fax 681-7396
Manhattan Hairstyling Academy Post-Sec.
3244 Lithia Pinecrest #103 33594 813-655-4545

Venice, Sarasota, Pop. 20,602
Sarasota County SD
Supt. — See Sarasota
Venice HS 2,000/9-12
1 Indian Ave 34285 941-488-6726
Jack Turgeon, prin. Fax 486-2034
Venice MS 700/6-8
1900 Center Rd 34292 941-486-2100
Dr. Karin Schmidt, prin. Fax 486-2108

Venice Christian S 200/PK-12
1200 Center Rd 34292 941-496-4411
Jerry Frimmel, admin. Fax 408-8362

Vernon, Washington, Pop. 673
Washington County SD
Supt. — See Chipley
Vernon HS 400/9-12
3232 Moss Hill Rd 32462 850-535-2046
Brian Riviere, prin. Fax 535-6244
Vernon MS 500/5-8
3206 Moss Hill Rd 32462 850-535-2807
Kimberly Register, prin. Fax 535-1683

Vero Beach, Indian River, Pop. 15,009
Indian River County SD 16,700/PK-12
1990 25th St 32960 772-564-3000
Frances Adams Ed.D., supt. Fax 564-3128
www.indianriverschools.org
Gifford MS 1,000/6-8
4530 28th Ct 32967 772-564-3550
Roxanne Decker, prin. Fax 564-3561
Indian River Alternative Education 100/Alt
4680 28th Ct 32967 772-564-6240
Dr. Bud Gill, prin. Fax 564-6265

Oslo MS 900/6-8
480 20th Ave SW 32962 772-564-3980
Eric Seymour, prin. Fax 564-4029
Storm Grove MS 800/6-8
6400 57th St 32967 772-564-6400
Jen Idlette-Williams, prin. Fax 564-6321
Vero Beach Freshman Learning Center 9-9
1507 19th St 32960 772-564-5800
Shawn O'Keefe, prin. Fax 564-4928
Vero Beach HS 1,900/10-12
1707 16th St 32960 772-564-5400
Shawn O'Keefe, prin. Fax 564-5553
Indian River Adult Education Adult
1426 19th St 32960 772-564-5001
Ruth Shaw, prin. Fax 564-4977
Other Schools – See Sebastian

FlightSafety Academy Post-Sec.
2805 Airport Dr 32960 772-564-7600
Glendale Christian S 100/PK-12
790 27th Ave 32968 772-569-1095
Dr. Mark Richardson, hdmstr. Fax 562-4919
Master's Academy 300/PK-12
1105 58th Ave 32966 772-794-4655
Dr. H. Grant Powell, hdmstr. Fax 562-9808
St. Edward's S 500/PK-12
1895 Saint Edwards Dr 32963 772-231-4136
Michael Mersky, head sch Fax 231-2427

Walnut Hill, Escambia
Escambia County SD
Supt. — See Pensacola
Ward MS 500/6-8
7650 Highway 97 32568 850-327-4283
Nancy Perry, prin. Fax 327-4991

Warrington, Escambia, Pop. 14,034
Escambia County SD
Supt. — See Pensacola
Warrington MS 700/6-8
450 S Old Corry Field Rd, Pensacola FL 32507
850-453-7440
Sandra Rush-Riley, prin. Fax 453-7572

Wauchula, Hardee, Pop. 4,954
Hardee County SD 5,000/PK-12
PO Box 1678 33873 863-773-9058
David Durastanti, supt. Fax 773-0069
www.hardee.k12.fl.us
Hardee HS 1,200/9-12
830 Altman Rd 33873 863-773-3181
Michele Polk, prin. Fax 773-4390
Hardee JHS 1,100/6-8
2401 US Highway 17 N 33873 863-773-3147
Doug Herron, prin. Fax 773-3167
Family Service Center Adult
901 W Main St 33873 863-773-3173
Mike Wilkinson, dir. Fax 773-3127
Other Schools – See Zolfo Springs

Sonhaven Preparatory Academy 100/PK-12
1121 Louisiana St 33873 941-360-2000
Dr. Thomas Hilt, admin. Fax 355-6127

Webster, Sumter, Pop. 770
Sumter County SD
Supt. — See Bushnell
South Sumter MS 800/6-8
773 NW 10th Ave 33597 352-793-2232
Allen Shirley, prin. Fax 793-3976

Weeki Wachee, Hernando, Pop. 12
Hernando County SD
Supt. — See Brooksville
Weeki Wachee HS 9-12
12150 Vespa Way 34614 352-797-7029
Troy LaBarbara, prin. Fax 797-7129

Wellington, Palm Beach, Pop. 55,375
Palm Beach County SD
Supt. — See West Palm Beach
Emerald Cove MS 1,100/6-8
9950 Stribling Way 33414 561-803-8000
Nancy Lucas, prin. Fax 803-8050
Palm Beach Central HS 2,900/9-12
8499 Forest Hill Blvd, 561-304-1000
Burley Mondy, prin. Fax 304-1017
Polo Park MS 1,100/6-8
11901 Lake Worth Rd, 561-333-5500
Ann Clark, prin. Fax 333-5505
Wellington Community HS 2,300/9-12
2101 Greenview Shores Blvd 33414 561-795-4900
Mario Crocetti, prin. Fax 795-4948
Wellington Landings MS 1,300/6-8
1100 Aero Club Dr 33414 561-792-8100
Blake Bennett, prin. Fax 792-8106

#1 Education Place 100/1-12
12785 Forest Hill Blvd 33414 561-753-6563
Wellington Christian S 600/PK-12
1000 Wellington Trce 33414 561-793-1017
Dr. Timothy Sansbury, hdmstr. Fax 798-9622

Wesley Chapel, Pasco, Pop. 42,858
Pasco County SD
Supt. — See Land O Lakes
Long MS 1,800/6-8
2025 Mansfield Blvd 33543 813-346-6200
Christine Wolff, prin. Fax 346-6291
Weightman MS 1,100/6-8
30649 Wells Rd, 813-794-0200
Brandon Bracciale, prin. Fax 794-0291
Wesley Chapel HS 1,300/9-12
30651 Wells Rd, 813-794-8700
Carin Nettles, prin. Fax 794-8791
Wiregrass Ranch HS 2,100/9-12
2909 Mansfield Blvd 33543 813-346-6000
Ray Bonti, prin. Fax 346-6091

Saddlebrook Preparatory S 100/3-12
5700 Saddlebrook Way 33543 813-907-4500
Larry Robison, hdmstr. Fax 991-4713

West Melbourne, Brevard, Pop. 17,945
Brevard County SD
Supt. — See Melbourne
Central MS 1,100/7-8
2600 Wingate Blvd 32904 321-722-4150
James Kirk, prin. Fax 722-4165

Brevard Christian S 200/PK-12
1100 Dorchester Ave 32904 321-727-2038
Dr. Grant Endicott, admin. Fax 729-4212

West Miami, Miami-Dade, Pop. 5,942

Florida Education Institute Post-Sec.
5818 SW 8th St 33144 305-263-9990

Weston, Broward, Pop. 64,228
Broward County SD
Supt. — See Fort Lauderdale
Cypress Bay HS 4,100/9-12
18600 Vista Park Blvd 33332 754-323-0350
Charles Neely, prin. Fax 323-0363
Falcon Cove MS 2,500/6-8
4251 Bonaventure Blvd 33332 754-323-3200
Dr. Mark Kaplan, prin. Fax 323-3285
Tequesta Trace MS 1,500/6-8
1800 Indian Trce 33326 754-323-4400
Paul Micensky, prin. Fax 323-4485

American InterContinental University Post-Sec.
2250 N Commerce Pkwy 33326 954-446-6100
Sagemont S - Upper School Campus 500/6-12
2585 Glades Cir 33327 954-389-2454
Gayle Iacono, prin. Fax 389-8106

West Palm Beach, Palm Beach, Pop. 98,081
Palm Beach County SD 170,600/PK-12
3300 Forest Hill Blvd 33406 561-434-8000
Bill Malone, supt. Fax 434-8571
www.palmbeachschools.org/
Bak MS of the Arts 1,400/6-8
1725 Echo Lake Dr 33407 561-882-3870
Elizabeth Kennedy, prin. Fax 882-3879
Bear Lakes MS 800/6-8
3505 Shenandoah Rd 33409 561-615-7700
Kirk Howell, prin. Fax 615-7756
Conniston Community MS 1,000/6-8
3630 Parker Ave 33405 561-802-5400
Oscar Otero, prin. Fax 802-5409
Dreyfoos S of the Arts 1,300/9-12
501 S Sapodilla Ave 33401 561-802-6000
Susan Atherley, prin. Fax 802-6059
Forest Hill Community HS 1,900/9-12
6901 Parker Ave 33405 561-540-2400
Mary Stratos, prin. Fax 540-2440
Gold Coast Community S 100/Alt
4260 Westgate Ave 33409 561-687-6300
Willie Jo Young, prin. Fax 687-6350
Jeaga MS 1,300/6-8
3777 N Jog Rd 33411 561-242-8000
Kevin Gatlin, prin. Fax 242-8005
Okeeheelee MS 1,300/6-8
2200 Pinehurst Dr 33413 561-434-3200
David Samore, prin. Fax 434-3244
Palm Beach Lakes Community HS 1,900/9-12
3505 Shiloh Dr 33407 561-640-5000
Dr. Anthony Hamlet, prin. Fax 688-5340
Palm Springs Community MS 1,500/6-8
1560 Kirk Rd 33406 561-434-3300
Sandra Jinks, prin. Fax 434-3303
Roosevelt Community MS 1,200/6-8
1900 N Australian Ave 33407 561-822-0200
JoAnne Rogers, prin. Fax 882-0222
Turning Points Academy 100/Alt
1950 Benoist Farms Rd 33411 561-681-3700
Anthony Allen Ph.D., prin. Fax 681-3752
Western Pines MS 1,200/6-8
5949 140th Ave N 33411 561-792-2500
Robert Hatcher, prin. Fax 792-2530
Adult Education Center of Palm Beach Adult
2161 N Military Trl 33409 561-616-7800
Rickey Swearingen, prin. Fax 616-7850
Other Schools – See Belle Glade, Boca Raton, Boynton Beach, Delray Beach, Greenacres, Jupiter, Lake Worth, Lantana, Loxahatchee, Pahokee, Palm Beach Gardens, Riviera Beach, Royal Palm Beach, Wellington

Academy for Practical Nursing/Health Occ Post Sec.
5154 Okechobee Blvd #201 33417 561-683-1400
Berean Christian S 700/PK-12
8350 Okeechobee Blvd 33411 561-798-9300
William Dupere, admin. Fax 792-3073
Cardinal Newman HS 700/9-12
512 Spencer Dr 33409 561-683-6266
Dr. Christine Higgins, prin. Fax 683-7307
Florida Career College Post-Sec.
6058 Okeechobee Blvd 33417 561-689-0550
Health Career Institute Post-Sec.
1764 N Congress Ave 33409 561-586-0121
ITT Technical Institute Post-Sec.
1756 N Congress Ave 33409 561-233-4900
Keiser University Post-Sec.
2085 Vista Pkwy 33411 561-471-6000
King's Academy 1,100/PK-12
8401 Belvedere Rd 33411 561-686-4244
Jeffrey Loveland, pres. Fax 686-8017
Lincoln College of Technology Post-Sec.
2410 Metrocentre Blvd 33407 561-842-8324
MCI Institute of Technology Post-Sec.
3650 Shawnee Ave Ste 12 33409 888-318-9310
Northwood University Post-Sec.
2600 N Military Trl 33409 800-458-8325

Palm Beach Atlantic University — Post-Sec.
901 S Flagler Dr 33401 — 888-468-6722
PC Professor — Post-Sec.
6080 Okeechobee Blvd #200 33417 — 561-684-3333
Summit Christian S — 600/PK-12
4900 Summit Blvd 33415 — 561-686-8081
Rich Anderson, dir. — Fax 640-7613

Wewahitchka, Gulf, Pop. 1,928
Gulf County SD
Supt. — See Port Saint Joe
Wewahitchka JSHS — 200/7-12
1 Gator Cir 32465 — 850-639-2228
Debbie Baxley, prin. — Fax 639-5394

Wildwood, Sumter, Pop. 6,607
Sumter County SD
Supt. — See Bushnell
Wildwood MSHS — 700/6-12
700 Huey St 34785 — 352-748-1314
James Presley, prin. — Fax 748-7668

Williston, Levy, Pop. 2,726
Levy County SD
Supt. — See Bronson
Williston HS — 700/9-12
427 W Noble Ave 32696 — 352-528-3542
Eulin Gibbs, prin. — Fax 528-2723
Williston MS — 500/6-8
20550 NE 42nd Pl 32696 — 352-528-2941
Pam Asbell, prin. — Fax 528-2941

Windermere, Orange, Pop. 2,437
Orange County SD
Supt. — See Orlando
Gotha MS — 1,200/6-8
9155 Gotha Rd 34786 — 407-521-2360
Cheri Godek, prin. — Fax 521-2361

Windermere Preparatory S — 1,200/PK-12
6189 Winter Garden Vineland 34786 — 407-905-7737
Dr. Tom Marcy, hdmstr. — Fax 905-7710

Winter Garden, Orange, Pop. 33,427
Orange County SD
Supt. — See Orlando
Bridgewater MS — 1,400/6-8
5660 Tiny Rd 34787 — 407-905-3710
Dr. Athena Adams, prin. — Fax 905-3858
Lakeview MS — 1,300/6-8
1200 W Bay St 34787 — 407-877-5010
Dr. Shirley Fox, prin. — Fax 877-5019
Sunridge MS — 6-8
14955 Sun Ridge Blvd 34787 — 407-656-0794
Patricia Bowen-Painter, prin. — Fax 656-0806
West Orange HS — 3,200/9-12
1625 Beulah Rd 34787 — 407-905-2400
James Larsen, prin. — Fax 656-4970
Westside Tech Ctr — Vo/Tech
955 E Story Rd 34787 — 407-905-2000
Anita Gentz, dir. — Fax 656-3970

Foundation Academy - South Campus — 400/6-12
15304 Tilden Rd 34787 — 407-877-2744
Shawn Minks, hdmstr. — Fax 877-1985

Professional Golfers Career College — Post-Sec.
16349 Phil Ritson Way 34787 — 407-905-2200

Winter Haven, Polk, Pop. 33,292
Polk County SD
Supt. — See Bartow
Denison MS — 1,000/6-8
400 Avenue A SE 33880 — 863-291-5353
Sheila Gregory, prin. — Fax 291-5347
Jewett Middle Academy — 600/6-8
601 Avenue T NE 33881 — 863-291-5320
Jacquelyn Moore, prin. — Fax 297-3049
Ridge Career Center — Vo/Tech
7700 State Road 544 33881 — 863-419-3060
Lisa Harden, prin. — Fax 419-3062
Westwood MS — 1,000/6-8
3520 Avenue J NW 33881 — 863-965-5484
Benita Pierce, prin. — Fax 965-5585
Wilcox Center — 50/Alt
611 Post Ave SW 33880 — 863-291-5355
Audrey Kelley, prin. — Fax 291-5723
Winter Haven HS — 1,600/9-12
600 6th St SE 33880 — 863-291-5330
Gina Williams, prin. — Fax 297-3024

All Saints' Academy — 600/PK-12
5001 State Road 540 W 33880 — 863-293-5980
Carolyn Baldwin, hdmstr. — Fax 294-2819
Heritage Christian Academy — 100/PK-10
244 Avenue D SW 33880 — 863-293-0690
John Scott, admin. — Fax 299-4146
Oasis Christian Academy — 200/PK-12
151 King Rd 33880 — 863-293-0930
Matt Wiggins, admin. — Fax 293-0429
Polk Community College — Post-Sec.
999 Avenue H NE 33881 — 863-297-1000
Ridge Career Center — Post-Sec.
7700 State Road 544 33881 — 863-419-3060

Winter Park, Orange, Pop. 27,399
Orange County SD
Supt. — See Orlando
Winter Park 9th Grade Center — 800/9-9
528 Huntington Ave 32789 — 407-623-1476
Timothy Smith, prin. — Fax 623-1485
Winter Park HS — 2,400/10-12
2100 Summerfield Rd 32792 — 407-622-3200
Timothy Smith, prin. — Fax 975-2434
Winter Park Tech Center — Vo/Tech
901 W Webster Ave 32789 — 407-622-2900
Tom Tankson, prin. — Fax 975-2435

Seminole County SD
Supt. — See Sanford
Lake Howell HS — 2,300/9-12
4200 Dike Rd 32792 — 407-746-9050
Frank Casillo, prin. — Fax 746-9025

Central Christian Academy — 600/1-12
7212 Sandscove Ct 32792 — 407-332-6988
Leslie Rawle, dir. — Fax 332-4413
Florida Institute of Animal Arts — Post-Sec.
3776 Howell Branch Rd 32792 — 407-869-7387
Fortis College — Post-Sec.
1573 W Fairbanks Ave #100 32789 — 407-843-3984
Full Sail University — Post-Sec.
3300 University Blvd 32792 — 407-679-0100
Geneva S — 500/PK-12
2025 State Road 436 32792 — 407-332-6363
Robert Ingram, hdmstr. — Fax 332-1664
Herzing University — Post-Sec.
1865 State Road 436 32792 — 407-478-0500
International Community S — 400/PK-12
4800 Howell Branch Rd 32792 — 407-645-2343
Robyn Terwillegar, prin. — Fax 645-2366
Rollins College — Post-Sec.
1000 Holt Ave 32789 — 407-646-2000
Teacher Education University — Post-Sec.
1079 W Morse Blvd Ste B 32789 — 800-523-1578
Trinity Preparatory S — 900/6-12
5700 Trinity Prep Ln 32792 — 407-671-4140
Craig Maughan, hdmstr. — Fax 671-6935

Winter Springs, Seminole, Pop. 32,650
Seminole County SD
Supt. — See Sanford
Indian Trails MS — 1,100/6-8
415 Tuskawilla Rd 32708 — 407-320-4350
Lois Chavis, prin. — Fax 320-4399
Winter Springs HS — 2,000/9-12
130 Tuskawilla Rd 32708 — 407-320-8750
Mickey Reynolds, prin. — Fax 320-8700

Yulee, Nassau, Pop. 11,311
Nassau County SD
Supt. — See Fernandina Beach
Yulee HS — 1,000/9-12
85375 Miner Rd 32097 — 904-491-7949
Natasha Drake, prin. — Fax 225-8658
Yulee MS — 900/6-8
85439 Miner Rd 32097 — 904-491-7944
Jeremy Boatright, prin. — Fax 225-0104

Zellwood, Orange, Pop. 2,799

Hampden DuBose Academy & Legacy HS — 100/K-12
PO Box 639 32798 — 407-880-4321
Rev. Michael Jackson, admin. — Fax 886-2297

Zephyrhills, Pasco, Pop. 13,107
Pasco County SD
Supt. — See Land O Lakes
Stewart MS — 900/6-8
38505 10th Ave, — 813-794-6500
Shae Davis, prin. — Fax 794-6591
Zephyrhills HS — 1,500/9-12
6335 12th St, — 813-794-6100
Steve Van Gorden, prin. — Fax 794-6191

Zephyrhills Christian Academy — 100/PK-12
34927 Eiland Blvd 33541 — 813-779-1648
Dr. Michael Smith, prin. — Fax 799-9829

Zolfo Springs, Hardee, Pop. 1,811
Hardee County SD
Supt. — See Wauchula
Pioneer Career Academy — 50/Alt
2630 Academy Dr 33890 — 863-735-2300
Gilbert Vasquez, dir. — Fax 735-2155

GEORGIA

GEORGIA DEPARTMENT OF EDUCATION
2066 Twin Towers E, Atlanta 30334-9050
Telephone 404-656-2800
Fax 404-651-8737
Website http://www.doe.k12.ga.us

State Superintendent of Schools John Barge

GEORGIA BOARD OF EDUCATION
2053 Twin Towers East, Atlanta 30334

Chief Executive Officer John Barge

REGIONAL EDUCATIONAL SERVICE AGENCIES (RESA)

Central Savannah River Area RESA
Gene Sullivan, dir. 706-556-6225
4683 Augusta Hwy, Dearing 30808 Fax 556-8891
www.csraresa.org/

Chattahoochee-Flint RESA
Norman Carter, dir. 229-937-5341
PO Box 1150, Ellaville 31806 Fax 937-5754
www.cfresa.org/

Coastal Plains RESA
Harold Chambers, dir. 229-546-4094
245 N Robinson St, Lenox 31637 Fax 546-4167
www.cpresa.org

First District RESA
Lisa Burkhalter, dir. 912-842-5000
PO Box 780, Brooklet 30415 Fax 842-5161
www.fdresa.org/

Griffin RESA
Dr. Stephanie Gordy, dir. 770-229-3247
PO Box H, Griffin 30224 Fax 228-7316
www.griffinresa.net/

Heart of Georgia RESA
Beauford Hicks, dir. 478-374-2240
1141 Cochran Hwy Fax 374-1524
Eastman 31023
www.hgresa.org/

Metro RESA
Leigh Ann Putman, dir. 770-432-2404
1870 Teasley Dr SE, Smyrna 30080 Fax 432-6105
www.ciclt.net/mresa

Middle Georgia RESA
Carolyn Williams, dir. 478-988-7170
80 Cohen Walker Dr Fax 988-7176
Warner Robins 31088
www.mgresa.org/

Northeast Georgia RESA
Dr. Russell Cook, dir. 706-742-8292
375 Winter St, Winterville 30683 Fax 742-8928
www.negaresa.org

North Georgia RESA
Larry Harmon, dir. 706-276-1111
4731 Old Highway 5 S Fax 276-1114
Ellijay 30540
www.ngresa.org/

Northwest Georgia RESA
Dexter Mills, dir. 706-295-6189
3167 Cedartown Hwy SE Fax 295-6098
Rome 30161
www.nwgaresa.com/

Oconee RESA
Dr. Hayward Cordy, dir. 478-552-5178
206 S Main St, Tennille 31089 Fax 552-6499
www.oconeeresa.org

Okefenokee RESA
Dr. Peggy Stovall, dir. 912-285-6151
1450 N Augusta Ave Fax 287-6650
Waycross 31503
www.okresa.org

Pioneer RESA
Dr. Sandy Addis, dir. 706-865-2141
PO Box 1789, Cleveland 30528 Fax 865-6748
www.pioneerresa.org/

Southwest Georgia RESA
Tim Helms, dir. 229-207-0600
570 Martin Luther King Jr Fax 336-2888
Camilla 31730
www.ciclt.net/sn/clt/swresa/default.aspx?ClientCode=swresa

West Georgia RESA
Rachel Spates, dir. 770-583-2528
99 Brown School Dr Fax 583-3223
Grantville 30220
www.garesa.org/

PUBLIC, PRIVATE AND CATHOLIC SECONDARY SCHOOLS

Abbeville, Wilcox, Pop. 2,863
Wilcox County SD 1,300/PK-12
395 College St W 31001 229-467-2141
Steve Smith, supt. Fax 467-2302
www.wilcox.k12.ga.us/
Other Schools – See Rochelle

Acworth, Cobb, Pop. 19,875
Cobb County SD
Supt. — See Marietta
Allatoona HS 1,600/9-12
3300 Dallas Acworth Hwy NW 30101 770-975-6503
Scott Bursmith, prin. Fax 529-7744
Barber MS 1,000/6-8
4222 Cantrell Rd NW 30101 770-975-6764
Lisa Williams, prin. Fax 529-0325
Durham MS 1,100/6-8
2891 Mars Hill Rd NW 30101 770-975-6641
Susan Galante, prin. Fax 975-6643

Chattahoochee Technical College Post-Sec.
5198 Ross Rd SE 30102 770-975-4000
Cornerstone Preparatory Academy 400/K-12
1720 Mars Hill Rd NW Ste 8 30101 770-529-7077
Jeanne Borders, admin. Fax 529-7477

Adairsville, Bartow, Pop. 4,584
Bartow County SD
Supt. — See Cartersville
Adairsville HS 1,000/9-12
519 Old Highway 41 NW 30103 770-606-5841
Bruce Mulkey, prin. Fax 773-2722
Adairsville MS 700/6-8
100 College St 30103 770-606-5842
Brian Knuchel, prin. Fax 773-9260

Adel, Cook, Pop. 5,286
Cook County SD 3,400/PK-12
1109 N Parrish Ave 31620 229-896-2294
Lance Heard, supt. Fax 896-3443
www.cook.k12.ga.us/
Cook HS 900/9-12
9900 Highway 37 31620 229-896-2213
Keith Croft, prin. Fax 896-3423
Other Schools – See Sparks

Ailey, Montgomery, Pop. 429
Montgomery County SD
Supt. — See Mount Vernon
Montgomery County MS 300/6-8
900 Martin Luther King Dr 30410 912-583-2351
Brittany Deen, prin. Fax 583-4469

Alamo, Wheeler, Pop. 2,788
Wheeler County SD 1,000/PK-12
18 McRae St 30411 912-568-7198
Dr. Mark Davidson, supt. Fax 568-1985
www.wheelercountyschools.org
Wheeler County MSHS 500/6-12
50 Snowhill Rd 30411 912-568-7166
Hal Ford, prin. Fax 568-7141
Other Schools – See Glenwood

Albany, Dougherty, Pop. 76,579
Dougherty County SD 15,100/PK-12
PO Box 1470 31702 229-431-1285
Dr. Joshua Murfree, supt. Fax 431-1276
www.docoschools.org
Albany HS 800/9-12
801 W Residence Ave 31701 229-431-3300
Dr. Angela Shumate, prin. Fax 431-3481
Albany MS 500/6-8
1700 Cordell Ave 31705 229-431-3325
Horace Reid, prin. Fax 431-3474
Cross MS 600/6-8
324 Lockett Station Rd, 229-431-3362
Dr. Sammie Pringle, prin. Fax 431-3476
Dougherty HS 900/9-12
1800 Pearce Ave 31705 229-431-3310
Jose Roquemore, prin. Fax 431-1302
Dougherty MS 600/6-8
1800 Massey Dr 31705 229-431-3328
Thelma Chunn, prin. Fax 431-3475
Merry Acres MS 800/6-8
1601 Florence Dr 31707 229-431-3338
Dr. Ufot Inyang, prin. Fax 431-1204
Monroe HS 1,200/9-12
900 Lippitt Dr 31701 229-431-3316
Dr. Valerie Thomas, prin. Fax 431-3380
Radium Springs MS 700/6-8
2600 Radium Springs Rd 31705 229-431-3346
Vinson Davis, prin. Fax 431-3552
South GA Regional Achievement Center Alt
1001 W Highland Ave 31701 229-431-1218
Dr. John Davis, prin. Fax 431-3478
Southside MS 500/6-8
1615 Newton Rd 31701 229-431-3351
Dr. Johnny Scott, prin. Fax 431-1209
Westover HS 1,200/9-12
2600 Partridge Dr 31707 229-431-3320
William Chunn, prin. Fax 431-3349

Albany State University Post-Sec.
504 College Dr 31705 229-430-4600
Albany Technical College Post-Sec.
1704 S Slappey Blvd 31701 229-430-3500
Byne Christian S 100/K-12
2832 Ledo Rd 31707 229-436-0173
David Bess, hdmstr. Fax 434-0039
Darton College Post-Sec.
2400 Gillionville Rd 31707 229-317-6000
Deerfield-Windsor S 800/PK-12
PO Box 71149 31708 229-435-1301
David Davies, hdmstr. Fax 435-4118
Sherwood Christian Academy 500/PK-12
1418 Old Pretoria Rd, 229-883-5677
Glen Schultz, hdmstr. Fax 883-5794

Alma, Bacon, Pop. 3,400
Bacon County SD 2,000/PK-12
102 W 4th St 31510 912-632-7363
Dr. Laine Reichert, supt. Fax 632-2454
www.bcraiders.com/
Bacon County HS 500/9-12
901 N Pierce St 31510 912-632-4414
Teresa Sermons, prin. Fax 632-6603
Bacon County MS 400/6-8
901 N Pierce St 31510 912-632-4662
Stephanie Deen Cooks, prin. Fax 632-6603

Alpharetta, Fulton, Pop. 56,130
Fulton County SD
Supt. — See Atlanta
Alpharetta HS 2,300/9-12
3595 Webb Bridge Rd 30005 770-521-7640
Shannon Kersey, prin. Fax 521-7653
Haynes Bridge MS 600/6-8
10665 Haynes Bridge Rd 30022 770-740-7030
Lauren Seidman, prin. Fax 667-2842
Holcomb Bridge MS 700/6-8
2700 Holcomb Bridge Rd 30022 770-594-5280
Joy Schroerlucke, prin. Fax 643-3333
Independence HS Alt
86 School Dr 30009 770-521-7611
Tabatha Taylor, prin. Fax 521-7621
Milton HS 2,600/9-12
13025 Birmingham Hwy 30004 770-740-7000
Cliff Jones, prin. Fax 667-2844
Webb Bridge MS 1,300/6-8
4455 Webb Bridge Rd 30005 770-667-2940
Susan Opferman, prin. Fax 667-2948

DeVry University Post-Sec.
2555 Northwinds Pkwy 30009 770-619-3600
King's Ridge Christian S 700/PK-12
2765 Bethany Bnd 30004 770-754-5738
David Rhodes, hdmstr. Fax 754-5544

Mill Springs Academy 300/1-12
13660 New Providence Rd 30004 770-360-1336
Robert Moore, hdmstr. Fax 360-1341

Americus, Sumter, Pop. 16,892
Sumter County SD 4,400/PK-12
100 Learning Ln, 229-931-8500
Donnie Smith, supt. Fax 931-8555
www.sumterschools.org
Americus Sumpter HS South Campus 900/10-12
805 Harrold Ave 31709 229-924-3653
Walter Knighton, prin. Fax 924-1556
Americus Sumter HS North Campus 300/9-9
200 Industrial Blvd, 229-924-5914
Stacy Mack, prin. Fax 928-2827
Staley MS 500/6-8
915 N Lee St, 229-924-3168
Victoria Harris, prin. Fax 928-2135
Sumter County MS 700/6-8
439 Bumphead Rd, 229-924-1010
Kimothy Hadley, prin. Fax 928-5571

Georgia Southwestern State University Post-Sec.
800 GSW State University Dr 31709 229-928-1273
South Georgia Technical College Post-Sec.
900 S Georgia Tech Pkwy 31709 229-931-2394
Southland Academy 500/PK-12
PO Box 1127 31709 229-924-4406

Armuchee, Floyd
Floyd County SD
Supt. — See Rome
Armuchee MS 500/6-8
471 Floyd Springs Rd NE 30105 706-378-7924
Steve Turrentine, prin. Fax 378-7983

Ashburn, Turner, Pop. 4,108
Turner County SD 1,600/PK-12
423 N Cleveland St 31714 229-567-3338
Ray Jordan, supt. Fax 567-3285
www.turner.k12.ga.us/
Turner County HS 400/9-12
316 Lamar St 31714 229-567-4377
Dr. Timothy Huff, prin. Fax 567-9243
Turner County MS 300/6-8
316 Lamar St 31714 229-567-4343
David Wheeler, prin. Fax 567-9243
Turner County Specialty S 200/Alt
330 Gilmore St 31714 229-567-3412
Patricia Hargress, prin. Fax 567-2877

Athens, Clarke, Pop. 113,262
Clarke County SD 11,800/PK-12
PO Box 1708 30603 706-546-7721
Dr. Philip Lanoue, supt. Fax 208-9124
www.clarke.k12.ga.us
Burney-Harris-Lyons MS 600/6-8
1600 Tallassee Rd 30606 706-548-7208
Melanie Sigler, prin. Fax 357-5263
Cedar Shoals HS 1,500/9-12
1300 Cedar Shoals Dr 30605 706-546-5375
Dr. Tony Price, prin. Fax 357-5291
Clarke Central HS 1,500/9-12
350 S Milledge Ave 30605 706-357-5200
Dr. Robbie Hooker, prin. Fax 357-5269
Clarke MS 600/6-8
1235 Baxter St 30606 706-543-6547
Theodore MacMillan, prin. Fax 548-0257
Classic City Performance Learning Center 100/Alt
440 Dearing Ext Bldg 3 30606 706-353-2323
Kelly Girtz, dir. Fax 353-3877
Coile MS 600/6-8
110 Old Elberton Rd 30601 706-357-5318
Dwight Manzy, prin. Fax 357-5321
Hilsman MS 700/6-8
870 Gaines School Rd 30605 706-548-7281
Selena Blankenship, prin. Fax 357-5295

Jackson County SD
Supt. — See Jefferson
Kings Bridge MS 400/6-8
1630 New Kings Bridge Rd 30607 706-208-3552
Howard McGlennen, prin. Fax 208-3555

Athens Academy 1,000/PK-12
PO Box 6548 30604 706-549-9225
Robert Chambers, hdmstr. Fax 354-3775
Athens Christian S 800/PK-12
1270 Highway 29 N 30601 706-549-7586
Steve Cummings, hdmstr. Fax 549-2899
Athens Technical College Post-Sec.
800 Highway 29 N 30601 706-355-5000
Georgia Institute of Cosmetology Post-Sec.
3529 Atlanta Hwy 30606 706-549-6400
Msgr. Walter J. Donovan HS 100/9-12
590 Lavender Rd 30606 706-433-0223
Patrick Yuran, prin. Fax 433-0229
University of Georgia Post-Sec.
0 UGA 30602 706-542-3000

Atlanta, Fulton, Pop. 412,360
Atlanta CSD 45,800/PK-12
130 Trinity Ave SW 30303 404-802-3500
Erroll Davis, supt. Fax 802-1803
www.atlantapublicschools.us
B.E.S.T. Academy HS 100/9-12
1890 D L Hollowell Pkwy NW 30318 404-802-4944
Gary Cantrell, prin.
B.E.S.T. Academy MS 400/6-8
1890 D L Hollowell Pkwy NW 30318 404-802-4944
Hajj Womack, prin.
Brown MS, 765 Peeples St SW 30310 600/6-8
Joyce Thomas, prin. 404-802-6800
Bunche MS 800/6-8
1925 Niskey Lake Rd SW 30331 404-802-6700
Mario Watkins, prin.
Carver Early College HS 300/9-12
55 McDonough Blvd SE 30315 404-802-4405
Marcene Thornton, prin.
Coan MS 300/6-8
145 4th Ave SE 30317 404-802-6600
Dr. Betsy Bockman, prin. Fax 371-7135
Crim Open Campus HS 500/Alt
256 Clifton St SE 30317 404-802-5800
Saundra Windom, prin.
Douglass Business & Entrepreneurship HS 100/9-12
225 Hamilton E Holmes Dr NW 30318 404-802-3100
Dr. Mary Harris, admin. Fax 799-8022
Douglass CFEAT 100/9-12
225 Hamilton E Holmes Dr NW 30318 404-802-3100
Fax 799-8022
Douglass Communication & Journalism HS 100/9-12
225 Hamilton E Holmes Dr NW 30318 404-802-3100
Webster Langhorne, admin. Fax 799-8022
Douglass Hospitality Tourism & Marketing 100/9-12
225 Hamilton E Holmes Dr NW 30318 404-802-3100
Stephanie Bailey, admin. Fax 799-8022
Engineering Early College Academy 800/9-12
1550 Hosea L Williams Dr NE 30317 404-802-5200
Dr. Richard Williams, prin.
Fine Arts & Media Communications 9-12
1550 Hosea L Williams Dr NE 30317 404-802-5200
Leah Ervin, admin.
Forrest Hills Academy 200/Alt
2930 Forrest Hills Dr SW 30315 404-802-6950
Dr. Robert Robbins, prin.
Grady Bio Medical Science Academy 100/9-12
929 Charles Allen Dr NE 30309 404-802-3001
Grady Business & Entrepreneurship Acad 100/9-12
929 Charles Allen Dr NE 30309 404-802-3001
Willie Vincent, admin.
Grady Communication & Journalism Academy 1,500/9-12
929 Charles Allen Dr NE 30309 404-802-3001
Carrie MacBrien, admin. Fax 853-4099
Grady Law Govt. & Public Policy Academy 100/9-12
929 Charles Allen Dr NE 30309 404-802-3001
Russell Plasczyk, admin.
Harper-Archer MS 600/6-8
3399 Collier Dr NW 30331 404-802-6500
Jermaine Dawson, prin. Fax 699-4569
Information Technology Academy 9-12
1550 Hosea L Williams Dr NE 30317 404-802-5200
Inman MS 900/6-8
774 Virginia Ave NE 30306 404-802-3200
Paula Herrema, prin. Fax 853-4085
International Baccalaureate Academy 9-12
1550 Hosea L Williams Dr NE 30317 404-802-5200
Sharonda Murrelll, prin.
Kennedy MS 300/6-8
225 James P Brawley Dr SW 30314 404-802-3600
Dr. Shirlene Carter, prin.
King HS 100/9-12
1190 Northwest Dr NW 30318 404-802-4900
Termerion McCrary, prin.
King MS, 545 Hill St SE 30312 500/6-8
Paul Brown, prin. 404-802-5400
King Young Womens Leadership Academy 400/6-8
1190 Northwest Dr NW 30318 404-802-4962
Dr. Dione Simon, prin.
Long MS 600/6-8
3200 Latona Dr SW 30354 404-802-4800
Lisa Hill, prin. Fax 802-4899
Mays Business & Entrepreneurship Academy 1,500/9-12
3450 Benjamin E Mays Dr SW 30331
Shermaine Jennings, admin. 404-802-5100
Mays Eagle Academy of Leadership 100/9-12
3450 Benjamin E Mays Dr SW 30331
Casey Landsman, admin. 404-802-5100
Mays - Height Academy of Leadership 100/9-12
3450 Benjamin E Mays Dr SW 30331
Sharon Gay, admin. 404-802-5100
Mays Mass Communications Academy 100/9-12
3450 Benjamin E Mays Dr SW 30331
Jane Martin, admin. 404-802-5100
Mays Tech./Engineering/Math & Science 100/9-12
3450 Benjamin E Mays Dr SW 30331
Dante Edwards, admin. 404-802-5100
N. Atlanta Center - Broadcast Journalism 100/9-12
2875 Northside Dr NW 30305 404-802-4700
Laura Brazil, admin.
North Atlanta Center for Intl Business 100/9-12
2875 Northside Dr NW 30305 404-802-4700
Mona Nelson, prin.
North Atlanta Center for Intl Studies 100/9-12
2875 Northside Dr NW 30305 404-802-4700
John Denine, prin.
North Atlanta Center for the Arts 300/9-12
2875 Northside Dr NW 30305 404-802-4700
Reginald Colbert, admin.
Parks MS, 1090 Windsor St SW 30310 500/6-8
Sherri Bennett, prin. 404-802-6400
Price MS 600/6-8
1670 B W Bickers Dr SE 30315 404-802-6300
Sterling Christy, prin. Fax 624-2118
School of Computer Animation & Design 300/9-12
800 Hutchens Rd SE 30354 404-802-5034
Jarod Scott, prin.
School of Health & Medical Science 300/9-12
800 Hutchens Rd SE 30354 404-802-5025
Dr. Patricia Ford, prin.
School of Health Science & Research 300/9-12
3099 Panther Trl SW 30311 404-802-5355
Shelly Powell, prin.
School of Health Sciences & Research 400/9-12
55 McDonough Blvd SE 30315 404-802-4420
Dr. Darien Jones, prin.
School of Law & Government Policy 300/9-12
3099 Panther Trl SW 30311 404-802-5345
Libra Royster, prin.
School of Law & Social Justice 300/9-12
800 Hutchens Rd SE 30354 404-802-5045
Peter McKnight, prin.
School of Technology 300/9-12
55 McDonough Blvd SE 30315 404-802-4410
Tiauna Crooms, prin.
School of the Arts 300/9-12
55 McDonough Blvd SE 30315 404-802-4415
Dr. Marvin Pryor, prin.
School / Tech Engineering Math & Science 400/9-12
3099 Panther Trl SW 30311 404-802-5360
Esmie Gaynor, prin.
Sutton MS 1,200/6-8
4360 Powers Ferry Rd 30327 404-802-5600
Audrey Sofianos, prin.
Sylvan Hills MS 400/6-8
1461 Sylvan Rd SW 30310 404-802-6200
Artesa Portee, prin.
Washington Banking Finance & Investment 600/9-12
45 Whitehouse Dr SW 30314 404-802-4604
Dr. Charcia Nichols, prin. Fax 752-6063
Washington Early College HS 200/9-12
45 Whitehouse Dr SW 30314 404-802-4603
Washington Health Science & Nutrition HS 200/9-12
45 Whitehouse Dr SW 30314 404-802-4602
Dr. Samuel Scavella, prin.
West End Academy Alt
1445 Maynard Rd NW 30331 404-802-2900
Dr. Evelyn Mobley, prin.
Young MS 700/6-8
3116 Benjamin E Mays Dr SW 30311
Dr. Kelvin Griffin, prin. 404-802-5900

DeKalb County SD
Supt. — See Stone Mountain
Cross Keys HS 1,000/9-12
1626 N Druid Hills Rd NE 30319 678-874-6102
Dr. Tasharah Wilson, prin. Fax 874-6110
Druid Hills HS 1,500/9-12
1798 Haygood Dr NE 30307 678-874-6302
Mindee Adamson, prin. Fax 874-6310
International Student Center 200/3-12
2383 N Druid Hills Rd NE 30329 678-676-0902
Terry Segovis, prin. Fax 676-6608
Lakeside HS 1,800/9-12
3801 Briarcliff Rd NE 30345 678-874-6702
Joe Reed, prin. Fax 874-6710
McNair HS 900/9-12
1804 Bouldercrest Rd SE 30316 678-874-4902
Glynis Jordan, prin. Fax 874-4910

Fulton County SD 87,300/PK-12
786 Cleveland Ave SW 30315 404-768-3600
Robert Avossa Ed.D., supt. Fax 667-2806
www.fultonschools.org
Sandtown MS 1,100/6-8
5400 Campbellton Rd SW 30331 404-346-6500
Kine Geathers, prin. Fax 346-6510
Westlake HS 2,100/9-12
2400 Union Rd SW 30331 404-346-6400
Grant Rivera, prin. Fax 346-6410
Other Schools – See Alpharetta, College Park, East Point, Fairburn, Johns Creek, Milton, Roswell, Union City

---

American InterContinental University Post-Sec.
6600 Peachtree Dunwoody Rd 30328 404-965-6500
Anthem College Post-Sec.
2450 Piedmont Rd NE 30324 678-279-7000
Argosy University/Atlanta Post-Sec.
980 Hammond Dr Ste 100 30328 770-671-1200
Art Institute of Atlanta Post-Sec.
6600 Peachtree Dunwoody Rd 30328 770-394-8300
Atlanta Girls' S 200/6-12
3254 Northside Pkwy NW 30327 404-845-0900
Joan King, hdmstr. Fax 869-9718
Atlanta International S 1,100/PK-12
2890 N Fulton Dr NE 30305 404-841-3840
Kevin Glass, hdmstr. Fax 841-3896
Atlanta Medical Center Post-Sec.
303 Parkway Dr NE 30312 404-265-4203
Atlanta Metro State College Post-Sec.
1630 Metropolitan Pkwy SW 30310 404-756-4000
Atlanta School of Massage Post-Sec.
2 Dunwoody Park 30338 877-291-4485
Atlanta's John Marshall Law School Post-Sec.
1422 W Peachtree St NW 30309 404-872-3593
Atlanta Technical College Post-Sec.
1560 Metropolitan Pkwy SW 30310 404-225-4400
Bauder College Post-Sec.
384 Northyards Blvd NW #190 30313 404-237-7573
Beulah Heights University Post-Sec.
PO Box 18145 30316 404-627-2681
Brandon Hall S 100/6-12
1701 Brandon Hall Dr 30350 770-394-8177
John Singleton, pres. Fax 868-1444
Brown College of Court Reporting Post-Sec.
1900 Emery St NW Ste 200 30318 404-876-1227
Brown Mackie College Post-Sec.
4370 Peachtree Rd NE 30319 404-799-4500
Carver College Post-Sec.
3870 Cascade Rd SW 30331 404-527-4520
Chamberlain College of Nursing Post-Sec.
5775 Peachtree Dunwdy A100 30342 404-250-8500
Clark Atlanta University Post-Sec.
223 James P Brawley Dr 30314 404-880-8000
DeVry University Post-Sec.
5775 Peachtree Dunwoody NE 30342 770-391-6200
DeVry University Post-Sec.
100 Galleria Pkwy SE #100 30339 770-916-3704
Emory University Post-Sec.
201 Dowman Dr 30322 404-727-6123
Everest College Post-Sec.
2841 Greenbriar Pkwy SW 30331 678-500-3400
Franklin Academy 100/9-12
1585 Clifton Rd NE 30329 404-633-7404

Galloway S 700/PK-12
215 W Wieuca Rd NW 30342 404-252-8389
Suzanna Jemsby, head sch Fax 252-7770
Georgia Christian University Post-Sec.
6789 Peachtree Industrial 30360 770-279-0507
Georgia Institute of Technology Post-Sec.
225 North Ave NW 30332 404-894-2000
Georgia State University Post-Sec.
PO Box 3965 30302 404-413-2000
Grady Health System Post-Sec.
PO Box 26189 30303 404-616-4252
Greater Atlanta Adventist Academy 200/9-12
401 Hamilton E Holmes Dr NW 30318 404-799-0337
Johnny Holliday, prin. Fax 799-0977
Herzing University Post-Sec.
3393 Peachtree Rd NE # 1003 30326 404-816-4533
Holy Innocents' Episcopal S 1,400/PK-12
805 Mount Vernon Hwy 30327 404-255-4026
Eugene Bratek, hdmstr. Fax 250-0815
Holy Spirit College Post-Sec.
4465 Northside Dr NW 30327 678-904-4959
Holy Spirit Preparatory S 800/PK-12
4449 Northside Dr NW 30327 678-904-2811
Kyle Pietrantonio, head sch Fax 904-4983
Interdenominational Theological Center Post-Sec.
700 Mrtn Lthr King Jr Dr SW 30314 404-527-7700
International School Skin Nail Massage Post-Sec.
5600 Roswell Rd 30342 404-843-1005
ITT Technical Institute Post-Sec.
485 Oak Pl Ste 800 30349 770-765-4600
Keller Graduate School of Management Post-Sec.
3575 Piedmont Rd NE Lvl 100 30305 404-760-1400
Lovett S 1,600/K-12
4075 Paces Ferry Rd NW 30327 404-262-3032
William Peebles, hdmstr. Fax 261-1967
Marist S 1,100/7-12
3790 Ashford Dunwoody Rd NE 30319
770-457-7201
Fr. Joel Konzen, prin. Fax 457-8402
Medtech Institute Post-Sec.
4501 Circle 75 Pkwy SE 30339 770-859-9779
Mercer University - Day Grad/Prof Campus Post-Sec.
3001 Mercer University Dr 30341 678-547-6000
Mohammed Schools of Atlanta 200/PK-12
735 Fayetteville Rd SE 30316 404-378-4219
Qur'an Shakir, prin. Fax 378-4600
Morehouse College Post-Sec.
830 Westview Dr SW 30314 404-681-2800
Morehouse School of Medicine Post-Sec.
720 Westview Dr SW 30310 404-752-1500
Mt. Vernon Presbyterian S 800/PK-12
471 Mount Vernon Hwy NE 30328 404-252-3448
Dr. Brett Jacobsen, hdmstr. Fax 252-6777
North Peachtree Academy 100/PK-12
4805 Tilly Mill Rd 30360 770-457-8963
Michele Braswell, dir. Fax 457-2387
Oglethorpe University Post-Sec.
4484 Peachtree Rd NE 30319 404-261-1441
Pace Academy 1,000/K-12
966 W Paces Ferry Rd NW 30327 404-262-1345
Fred Assaf, hdmstr. Fax 264-9376
Paideia S 1,000/PK-12
1509 Ponce De Leon Ave NE 30307 404-377-3491
Paul Bianchi, hdmstr. Fax 377-0032
Portfolio Center Post-Sec.
125 Bennett St NW 30309 404-351-5055
Richmont Graduate University Post-Sec.
2055 Mount Paran Rd NW 30327 404-233-3949
SAE Institute Post-Sec.
215 Peachtree St NE Ste 300 30303 404-526-9366
St. Joseph's Hospital Post-Sec.
5665 Pchtree Dunwoody Rd 30342 404-851-7120
St. Pius X HS 1,100/9-12
2674 Johnson Rd NE 30345 404-636-3023
Steven Spellman, prin. Fax 633-8387
Sanford-Brown College Post-Sec.
1140 Hammond Dr Ste A1150 30328 770-576-4498
Savannah College of Art & Design Post-Sec.
PO Box 77300 30357 404-253-2700
Southwest Atlanta Christian Academy 200/PK-12
PO Box 310750 31131 404-346-2080
Geraldine Thompson, hdmstr. Fax 346-2085
Spelman College Post-Sec.
350 Spelman Ln SW 30314 404-681-3643
Strayer University Post-Sec.
3355 Northeast Expy NE #100 30341 770-454-9270
Strayer University Post-Sec.
3101 TowerCreek Pkwy SE 700 30339 770-612-2170
Temima HS 100/9-12
1985B Lavista Rd NE Ste B 30329 404-315-0507
Miriam Feldman, prin. Fax 634-2111
University of Atlanta Post-Sec.
6685 Peachtree Industrial 30360 770-744-0370
Weber Jewish Community HS 200/9-12
6751 Roswell Rd 30328 404-917-2500
Dr. Simcha Pearl, head sch Fax 917-2501
Westminster S 1,800/K-12
1424 W Paces Ferry Rd NW 30327 404-355-8673
William Clarkson, pres. Fax 355-6606
Westwood College Post-Sec.
1100 Spring St NW Ste 102 30309 404-745-9862
Westwood College Post-Sec.
2309 Parklake Dr NE 30345 404-962-2999
Yeshiva Atlanta HS 100/9-12
3130 Raymond Dr 30340 770-451-5299
Dr. Paul Oberman, head sch Fax 451-5571
Yeshiva Ohr Yisrael 50/9-12
1458 Holly Ln NE 30329 404-320-1444
Rabbi Mayer Neuberger, hdmstr. Fax 320-1609

Augusta, Richmond, Pop. 193,101
Richmond County SD 32,000/PK-12
864 Broad St 30901 706-826-1000
Dr. Frank Roberson, supt. Fax 826-4613
www.rcboe.org
Academy of Richmond County Comp. HS 1,300/9-12
910 Russell St 30904 706-737-7152
Tim Spivey, prin. Fax 737-7155
Butler Comprehensive HS 900/9-12
2011 Lumpkin Rd 30906 706-796-4959
Gregory Thompson, prin. Fax 796-4780
Cross Creek HS 1,300/9-12
3855 Old Waynesboro Rd 30906 706-772-8140
Dr. Jason Moore, prin. Fax 772-8153
Davidson Magnet JSHS 700/6-12
615 12th St 30901 706-823-6924
Vicky Addison, prin. Fax 823-4373
Glenn Hills HS 1,100/9-12
2840 Glenn Hills Dr 30906 706-796-4924
Charles Givens, prin. Fax 796-4932
Glenn Hills MS 700/6-8
2941 Glenn Hills Dr 30906 706-796-4705
Glenn Andrews, prin. Fax 796-4716
Johnson Health Professions HS 600/7-12
1324 Laney Walker Blvd 30901 706-823-6933
Dr. LaMonica Lewis, prin. Fax 823-6931
Josey Comprehensive HS 800/9-12
1701 15th St 30901 706-737-7360
Dr. Ronald Wiggins, prin. Fax 737-7363
Laney Comprehensive HS 700/9-12
1339 Laney Walker Blvd 30901 706-823-6900
Dr. Tonia Mason, prin. Fax 823-6918
Langford MS 600/6-8
3019 Walton Way Ext 30909 706-737-7301
Victoria Reese, prin. Fax 737-7302
Richmond Co. Technical Career Magnet S Vo/Tech
3200 Augusta Tech Dr 30906 706-823-5580
Mylinthia Renee-Kelly, prin. Fax 737-1178
Sego MS 800/6-8
3420 Julia Ave 30906 706-796-4944
Dr. Sonya Jefferson, prin. Fax 796-4670
Tubman Education Center Alt
1740 Walton Way 30904 706-796-4965
Wayne Frazier, prin. Fax 796-4643
Tutt MS 600/6-8
495 Boy Scout Rd 30909 706-737-7288
Nathan Benedict, prin. Fax 481-1620
Westside HS 800/9-12
1002 Patriots Way 30907 706-868-4030
Dr. Debbie Alexander, prin. Fax 868-4005
Evening S Adult
2216 Bungalow Rd 30906 706-796-4880
Natalie Robinson, admin. Fax 796-4750
Other Schools – See Hephzibah

Alleluia Community S 200/K-12
2819 Peach Orchard Rd 30906 706-793-9663
C. Hornsby, supt. Fax 560-2759
Aquinas HS 300/9-12
1920 Highland Ave 30904 706-736-5516
Shannon Williams, admin. Fax 736-2678
Augusta State University Post-Sec.
2500 Walton Way 30904 706-737-1400
Augusta Technical College Post-Sec.
3200 Augusta Tech Dr 30906 706-771-4000
Curtis Baptist S 400/PK-12
1326 Broad St 30901 706-828-6624
Francine Burroughs, admin. Fax 828-6627
Georgia Health Sciences University Post-Sec.
1120 15th St 30912 706-721-0211
Miller-Motte Technical College Post-Sec.
621 NW Frontage Rd 30907 706-396-8000
Paine College Post-Sec.
1235 15th St 30901 706-821-8200
University Hospital Health System Post-Sec.
1350 Walton Way 30901 706-722-9011
Virginia College Post-Sec.
2807 Wylds Road Ext 30909 205-329-7903
Westminster S of Augusta 500/PK-12
3067 Wheeler Rd 30909 706-731-5260
Stephen O'Neil, hdmstr. Fax 731-5274

Austell, Cobb, Pop. 6,416
Cobb County SD
Supt. — See Marietta
Cooper MS 800/6-8
4605 Ewing Rd 30106 770-819-2438
Vanessa Watkins, prin. Fax 819-2440
Garrett MS 900/6-8
5235 Austell Pwdr Sprgs Rd 30106 770-819-2466
Dr. Fredrick Harris, prin. Fax 819-2468
South Cobb HS 2,000/9-12
1920 Clay Rd 30106 770-819-2611
Ashley Hosey, prin. Fax 819-2613

Avondale Estates, DeKalb, Pop. 2,893
DeKalb County SD
Supt. — See Stone Mountain
DeKalb S of the Arts 300/8-12
1192 Clarendon Ave 30002 678-676-2502
Susan McCauley, prin. Fax 676-2510

Bainbridge, Decatur, Pop. 12,559
Decatur County SD 5,600/PK-12
100 S West St, 229-248-2200
Dr. Fred Rayfield, supt. Fax 248-2252
www.dcboe.com
Bainbridge HS 1,500/9-12
1 Bearcat Blvd, 229-248-2230
Tommie Howell, prin. Fax 248-2260
Bainbridge MS 800/7-8
1301 E College St, 229-248-2206
Dr. Van Thomas, prin. Fax 248-2817

Bainbridge College Post-Sec.
PO Box 990, 229-248-2500
Grace Christian Academy 300/PK-12
1302 Lake Douglas Rd, 229-243-8851
Joan Shiver, admin. Fax 243-0515

Barnesville, Lamar, Pop. 6,625
Lamar County SD 2,600/PK-12
100 Victory Ln 30204 770-358-5891
Dr. Bill Truby, supt. Fax 358-5858
www.lamar.k12.ga.us
Lamar County HS 700/9-12
1 Trojan Way 30204 770-358-8641
Derick Austin, prin. Fax 358-8649
Lamar County MS 600/6-8
100 Burnette Rd 30204 770-358-8652
Dr. Julie Steele, prin. Fax 358-8657

Gordon State College Post-Sec.
419 College Dr 30204 678-359-5555

Baxley, Appling, Pop. 4,360
Appling County SD 3,600/PK-12
249 Blackshear Hwy 31513 912-367-8600
Scarlett Copeland, supt. Fax 367-1011
www.appling.k12.ga.us
Appling County HS 900/9-12
482 Blackshear Hwy 31513 912-367-8610
Dr. Gene Starr, prin. Fax 366-9877
Appling County MS 800/6-8
2997 Blackshear Hwy 31513 912-367-8630
Chris Roppe, prin. Fax 367-8803

Bellville, Evans, Pop. 123

Pinewood Christian Academy 600/K-12
PO Box 7 30414 912-739-1272

Bethlehem, Barrow, Pop. 594
Barrow County SD
Supt. — See Winder
CCPA/PLC Alt
54 Star St W 30620 770-868-1072
Dr. Chris Wood, prin. Fax 307-4080

Bethlehem Christian Academy 300/PK-12
PO Box 187 30620 770-307-1574
Rhonda Whiting, head sch Fax 307-1589

Blackshear, Pierce, Pop. 3,390
Pierce County SD 3,600/PK-12
PO Box 349 31516 912-449-2044
Terri DeLoach, supt. Fax 449-2046
www.pierce.k12.ga.us/
Pierce County HS 900/9-12
4850 County Farm Rd 31516 912-449-2055
Dara Bennett, prin. Fax 449-2061
Pierce County MS 900/6-8
5216 County Farm Rd 31516 912-449-2077
Perry Tison, prin. Fax 449-2075

Blairsville, Union, Pop. 642
Union County SD 2,500/K-12
124 Hughes St 30512 706-745-2322
Gary Steppe, supt. Fax 745-5025
www.ucschools.org
Union County HS 700/9-12
153 Panther Cir 30512 706-745-2216
Ed Rohrbaugh, prin. Fax 745-4122
Union County MS 600/6-8
367 Wellborn St 30512 706-745-2483
Donnie Kelley, prin. Fax 781-6200
Other Schools – See Suches

Lighthouse Christian Academy 50/K-12
772 John Smith Rd E 30512 706-745-1606
Fax 745-1606
North Georgia Technical College Post-Sec.
121 Meeks Ave 30512 706-439-6300

Blakely, Early, Pop. 5,032
Early County SD 2,300/PK-12
11927 Columbia St, 229-723-4337
Bronwyn Ragan-Martin Ed.D., supt. Fax 723-8183
www.early.k12.ga.us
Early County HS 700/9-12
12020 Columbia St, 229-723-3006
David Ferry, prin. Fax 723-8690
Early County MS 500/6-8
12053 Columbia St, 229-723-3746
Anthony Yarbrough, prin. Fax 723-3942
Learning and Opportunity Academy Alt
544 Howell St, 229-723-3943
James McCoy, prin. Fax 723-6385

Blue Ridge, Fannin, Pop. 1,269
Fannin County SD 3,000/K-12
2290 E First St 30513 706-632-3771
Mark Henson, supt. Fax 632-7583
www.fannin.k12.ga.us
Fannin County HS 900/9-12
360 Rebels Cir 30513 706-632-2081
Erik Cioffi, prin. Fax 632-6908
Fannin County MS 700/6-8
4560 Old Highway 76 30513 706-632-6100
Lori Chastain, prin. Fax 632-0461

Bogart, Clarke, Pop. 1,021
Oconee County SD
Supt. — See Watkinsville
Malcom Bridge MS 800/6-8
2500 Malcom Bridge Rd 30622 706-310-1992
Amy Perry, prin. Fax 310-1993
North Oconee HS 1,000/9-12
1081 Rocky Branch Rd 30622 706-769-7760
Philip Brown, prin. Fax 310-2002

Prince Avenue Christian S 800/PK-12
2201 Ruth Jackson Rd 30622 678-753-3000
Danny Howell, head sch Fax 753-3028

Bonaire, Houston
Houston County SD
Supt. — See Perry
Bonaire MS 900/6-8
125 GA Highway 96 E 31005 478-929-6236
Cindy Randall, prin. Fax 929-6245

Bowdon, Carroll, Pop. 1,987
Carroll County SD
Supt. — See Carrollton
Bowden MS 300/6-8
129 N Jonesville Rd 30108 770-258-1778
Scott Estes, prin. Fax 258-4374
Bowdon HS 500/9-12
504 W College St 30108 770-258-5408
Travis Thomas, prin. Fax 258-7278

Braselton, Jackson, Pop. 7,379

Braselton Christian Academy 50/K-12
1215 Tuscany Dr Ste C 30517 678-425-1231
Penney Smith, dir.
Heritage Academy 200/K-12
2001 Cherry Dr 30517 770-658-3020
Ken Gossage, admin. Fax 658-3039

Bremen, Haralson, Pop. 6,130
Bremen CSD 2,000/PK-12
501 Pacific Ave 30110 770-537-5508
Dr. David Hicks, supt. Fax 537-0610
www.bremencs.com
Bremen Crossroad Academy Alt
608 Cantrell Dr 30110 770-537-5524
Beth Garrett, dir.
Bremen HS 600/9-12
504 Georgia Ave S 30110 770-537-2592
Duane McManus, prin. Fax 537-0714
Bremen MS 500/6-8
2440 Crosstown Pkwy 30110 770-537-4874
Christa Smith, prin. Fax 537-5043

Brooklet, Bulloch, Pop. 1,369
Bulloch County SD
Supt. — See Statesboro
Southeast Bulloch HS 900/9-12
9184 Brooklet Denmark Rd 30415 912-842-8440
Dr. Trey Robertson, prin. Fax 842-9411
Southeast Bulloch MS 700/6-8
9124 Brooklet Denmark Rd 30415 912-842-8400
Donna Clifton, prin. Fax 842-9559

Brunswick, Glynn, Pop. 15,115
Glynn County SD, PO Box 1677 31521 13,100/PK-12
Howard Mann, supt. 912-267-4100
www.glynn.k12.ga.us
Brunswick HS 1,800/9-12
3920 Habersham St 31520 912-267-4200
Toriano Gilbert, prin. Fax 261-4433
Coastal Education HS 50/All
4404 Glynco Pkwy 31525 912-280-4030
Terry Graff, prin. Fax 280-4035
Glynn Academy 1,800/9-12
1001 Mansfield St 31520 912-267-4210
Dr. Scott Spence, prin. Fax 267-4246
Glynn MS 1,000/6-8
635 Lanier Blvd 31520 912-267-4150
Matthew Blackstone, prin. Fax 267-4158
Jackson Learning Center 9-12
1405 H St 31520 912-280-4300
Fax 261-7917
Macon MS 900/6-8
201 McKenzie Dr 31523 912-265-3337
Michele Seals, prin. Fax 267-4118
Needwood MS 700/6-8
669 Harry Driggers Blvd 31525 912-261-4488
Jim Pulos, prin. Fax 261-4491
Risley MS, 707 S Port Pkwy 31523 500/6-8
Lori Joiner, prin. 912-280-4020

Brunswick Christian Academy 100/PK-12
4231 US Highway 17 N 31525 912-264-4546
Fax 264-0851
College of Coastal Georgia Post-Sec.
1 College Dr 31520 912-279-5700
Heritage Christian Academy 200/PK-12
4265 Norwich Street Ext 31520 912-264-5491
Cindy Zangla, admin. Fax 264-0799

Buena Vista, Marion, Pop. 2,149
Marion County SD 1,400/PK-12
PO Box 391 31803 229-649-2234
Richard McCorkle, supt. Fax 649-7423
www.marion.k12.ga.us/
Marion County MSHS 700/6-12
PO Box 177 31803 229-649-7520
Glenn Tidwell, prin. Fax 649-5945

Buford, Gwinnett, Pop. 12,025
Buford CSD 3,200/K-12
2625 Sawnee Ave 30518 770-945-5035
Dr. Geye Hamby, supt. Fax 945-4629
www.bufordcityschools.org
Buford HS 900/9-12
2750 Sawnee Ave 30518 770-945-6768
Dr. Banks Bitterman, prin. Fax 932-7570
Buford MS 700/6-8
2700 Robert Bell Pkwy 30518 770-904-3690
Rachel Adams, prin. Fax 904-3689

Gwinnett County SD
Supt. — See Suwanee
Jones MS 1,300/6-8
3575 Ridge Rd 30519 770-904-5450
Dr. Richard Holland, prin. Fax 904-5452
Lanier MS 1,100/6-8
6482 Suwanee Dam Rd 30518 770-945-8419
Jaime Espinosa, prin. Fax 271-5108

Twin Rivers MS 1,400/6-8
2300 Braselton Hwy 30519 678-407-7550
Linda Boyd, prin. Fax 407-7560

Butler, Taylor, Pop. 1,959
Taylor County SD 1,500/PK-12
PO Box 1930 31006 478-862-5224
Wayne Smith, supt. Fax 862-5818
www.taylor.k12.ga.us
Taylor County HS 500/9-12
24 Oak St 31006 478-862-3314
Clarence Mathis, prin. Fax 862-3099
Taylor County MS 200/7-8
PO Box 580 31006 478-862-5285
LaTonja Turner, prin. Fax 862-5368

Byron, Peach, Pop. 4,436
Peach County SD
Supt. — See Fort Valley
Byron MS 400/6-8
201 Linda Dr 31008 478-825-9660
Dr. Jeff Bell, prin. Fax 956-3916

Cairo, Grady, Pop. 9,480
Grady County SD 4,500/PK-12
122 N Broad St, 229-377-3701
Tommy Pharis, supt. Fax 377-3437
www.grady.k12.ga.us
Cairo HS 1,100/9-12
455 5th St SE, 229-377-2222
David McCurry, prin. Fax 377-2812
Washington MS 600/6-8
1277 Martin Luther King Jr, 229-377-2106
Dr. Kermit Gilliard, prin. Fax 377-7779

Calhoun, Gordon, Pop. 15,378
Calhoun CSD 3,500/PK-12
380 Barrett Rd 30701 706-629-2900
Dr. Michele Taylor, supt. Fax 629-3235
www.calhounschools.org
Calhoun HS 900/9-12
315 S River St 30701 706-602-6770
Greg Green, prin. Fax 602-6652
Calhoun MS 800/6-8
399 S River St 30701 706-629-3340
Michelle Knight, prin. Fax 629-0236

Gordon County SD 6,900/PK-12
PO Box 12001 30703 706-629-7366
Dr. Susan Remillard, supt. Fax 625-5671
www.gcbe.org
Ashworth MS 600/6-8
PO Box 12001 30703 706-625-9545
Marc Feuerbach, prin. Fax 625-0114
Gordon Central HS 800/9-12
PO Box 12001 30703 706-629-7391
Scott McClanahan, prin. Fax 625-5376
Sonoraville HS 1,100/9-12
PO Box 12001 30703 706-602-0320
Bruce Potts, prin. Fax 602-0321
Sonoraville MS 800/6-8
PO Box 12001 30703 706-629-0793
Allen Bowen, prin. Fax 629-2983

Georgia Cumberland Academy 200/9-12
397 Academy Dr SW 30701 706-629-4591
Greg Gerard, prin. Fax 629-1272
Georgia Northwestern Technical College Post-Sec.
1151 Highway 53 Spur SW 30701 706-624-1100

Camilla, Mitchell, Pop. 5,311
Mitchell County SD 1,800/PK-12
108 S Harney St 31730 229-336-4543
Victor Hill, supt. Fax 336-1615
www.mitchell.k12.ga.us
Mitchell County HS 400/9-12
1000 Newton Rd 31730 229-336-0970
Robert Adams, prin. Fax 336-2171
Mitchell County MS 400/6-8
55 Griffin Rd 31730 229-336-0980
Patricia English, prin. Fax 336-2139

Westwood S 400/PK-12
PO Box 528 31730 229-336-7992
Ross Worsham, hdmstr. Fax 336-0982

Canton, Cherokee, Pop. 22,432
Cherokee County SD 37,800/PK-12
221 W Main St 30114 770-479-1871
Dr. Frank Petruzielo, supt. Fax 479-7758
www.cherokee.k12.ga.us
Cherokee HS 2,100/9-12
930 Marietta Hwy 30114 770-479-4112
Debra Murdock, prin. Fax 479-8421
Creekland MS 1,300/6-8
1555 Owens Store Rd 30115 770-479-3200
Dr. Deborah Wiseman, prin. Fax 479-3210
Creekview HS 1,700/9-12
1550 Owens Store Rd 30115 770-720-7600
Dr. Adrian Thomason, prin. Fax 720-7644
Freedom MS 1,100/6-8
10550 Bells Ferry Rd 30114 770-345-4100
Sheila Grimes, prin. Fax 345-4140
Rusk MS 800/7-8
4695 Hickory Rd 30115 770-345-2832
Cindy Cooper, prin. Fax 345-5073
Sequoyah HS 1,700/9-12
4485 Hickory Rd 30115 770-345-1474
Elliott Berman, prin. Fax 345-5498
Teasley MS 800/7-8
8871 Knox Bridge Hwy 30114 770-479-7077
Dr. Susan Zinkil, prin. Fax 479-3275
Other Schools – See Holly Springs, Woodstock

Carnesville, Franklin, Pop. 574
Franklin County SD 3,700/K-12
280 Busha Rd 30521 706-384-4554
Dr. Ruth O'Dell, supt. Fax 384-7472
www.franklin.k12.ga.us
Franklin County HS 1,100/9-12
6570 Highway 145 30521 706-384-4525
Dr. Wayne Randall, prin. Fax 384-2201
Franklin County MS 800/6-8
485 Turkey Creek Rd 30521 706-384-4581
Lucy Floyd, prin. Fax 384-2284

Carrollton, Carroll, Pop. 23,838
Carroll County SD 14,500/PK-12
164 Independence Dr 30116 770-832-3568
Scott Cowart, supt. Fax 834-6399
www.carrollcountyschools.com/
Central HS 1,100/9-12
113 Central High Rd 30116 770-834-3386
Dana Harman, prin. Fax 832-0103
Central MS 900/6-8
155 Whooping Creek Rd 30116 770-832-8114
Glen Harding, prin. Fax 836-2782
GOAL Program Alt
1095 Newnan Rd 30116 770-830-5012
John Jacobs, prin. Fax 830-8634
Mount Zion HS 400/9-12
280 Eureka Church Rd 30117 770-834-6654
Tracey Barrow, prin. Fax 832-9497
Open Campus HS Adult
113 Central High Rd 30116 770-254-5970
Bonnie Robinson, prin. Fax 254-5971
Other Schools – See Bowdon, Mount Zion, Temple, Villa Rica

Carrollton CSD 4,300/PK-12
106 Trojan Dr 30117 770-832-9633
Dr. Kent Edwards, supt. Fax 836-9950
www.carrolltoncityschools.net/
Carrollton HS 1,300/9-12
202 Trojan Dr 30117 770-834-7726
Dr. Mark Albertus, prin. Fax 834-8714
Carrollton JHS 700/7-8
510 Ben Scott Blvd 30117 770-832-6535
Dr. Todd Simpson, prin. Fax 832-7003
New Horizons Alternative S Alt
101 Pearl St 30117 770-830-9630
Marvell McKelphin, prin. Fax 836-2840

Oak Mountain Academy 200/PK-12
222 Cross Plains Rd 30116 770-834-6651
Paula Gillispie, head sch Fax 834-6785
University of West Georgia Post-Sec.
1601 Maple St 30118 678-839-5000
West Georgia Technical College Post-Sec.
997 Newnan Rd 30116 770-836-6800

Cartersville, Bartow, Pop. 19,341
Bartow County SD 14,400/PK-12
PO Box 200007 30120 770-606-5800
John Harper Ed.D., supt. Fax 606-5855
www.bartow.k12.ga.us
Cass MS 1,000/6-8
195 Fire Tower Rd NW 30120 770-606-5846
Kristy Arnold, prin. Fax 606-3835
Woodland HS 1,700/9-12
800 Old Alabama Rd SE 30120 770-606-5870
Dr. Melissa Williams, prin. Fax 606-2080
Other Schools – See Adairsville, Emerson, Euharlee, White

Cartersville CSD 4,000/PK-12
PO Box 3310 30120 770-382-5880
Dr. J. Howard Hinesley, supt. Fax 387-7476
www.cartersville.k12.ga.us
Cartersville HS 1,100/9-12
320 E Church St 30120 770-382-3200
Steve Butler, prin. Fax 382-0701
Cartersville MS 900/6-8
825 Douthit Ferry Rd 30120 770-382-3666
Jeff Hogan, prin. Fax 387-7495

Excel Christian Academy 300/K-12
325 Old Mill Rd 30120 770-382-9488
Wesley Roach, prin. Fax 606-9884

Cave Spring, Floyd, Pop. 1,186

Georgia School for the Deaf Post-Sec.
232 Perry Farm Rd SW 30124 706-777-2200

Cedartown, Polk, Pop. 9,595
Polk County SD 7,200/PK-12
612 S College St 30125 770-748-3821
Marvin Williams, supt. Fax 748-5131
www.polk.k12.ga.us/
Cedartown HS 1,100/9-12
167 Frank Lott Dr 30125 770-748-0490
Hal David, prin. Fax 749-1872
Cedartown MS 900/6-8
1664 Syble W Brannon Pkwy 30125 770-749-8850
Dr. Dawn Williams, prin. Fax 749-2795
Other Schools – See Rockmart

Centerville, Houston, Pop. 6,978
Houston County SD
Supt. — See Perry
Thomson MS 800/6-8
301 Thomson St 31028 478-953-0489
Dr. Walter Stephens, prin. Fax 953-0484

Chamblee, DeKalb, Pop. 9,782
DeKalb County SD
Supt. — See Stone Mountain
Chamblee MS 900/6-8
3601 Sexton Woods Dr 30341 678-874-8202
Cynthia Jackson, prin. Fax 874-8210

Henderson MS 1,500/6-8
2830 Henderson Mill Rd 30341 678-874-2902
Terese Allen, prin. Fax 874-2910

Interactive College of Technology Post-Sec.
5303 New Peachtree Rd 30341 770-216-2960
Iverson Institute Post-Sec.
5522 New Peachtree Rd # 114 30341 770-446-1333

Chatsworth, Murray, Pop. 4,251
Murray County SD 7,700/PK-12
PO Box 40 30705 706-695-4531
Dr. Vickie Reed, supt. Fax 695-8425
www.murray.k12.ga.us
Bagley MS 600/7-8
4600 Highway 225 N 30705 706-695-1115
Spencer Gazaway, prin. Fax 695-7289
Gladden MS 600/7-8
700 Old Dalton Ellijay Rd 30705 706-695-7448
Dr. Ardith Bates, prin. Fax 517-2479
Murray County HS 1,200/9-12
1001 Green Rd 30705 706-695-1414
Gina Linder, prin. Fax 517-2625
North Murray HS 800/9-12
2568 Mount Carmel Church Rd 30705 706-695-7760
Dr. Maria Bradley, prin. Fax 517-5526
Other Schools – See Eton

Chickamauga, Walker, Pop. 3,044
Chickamauga CSD 1,400/K-12
402 Cove Rd 30707 706-382-3100
Melody Day, supt. Fax 375-5364
chickamaugacityschools.org
Lee HS 500/9-12
105 Lee Cir 30707 706-382-3100
Clay Crowder, prin. Fax 375-5881
Lee MS 400/6-8
300 Crescent Ave 30707 706-382-3100
Benny Ashley, prin. Fax 375-1020

Clarkesville, Habersham, Pop. 1,712
Habersham County SD 6,900/PK-12
PO Box 70 30523 706-754-2118
Matthew Cooper, supt. Fax 754-1549
www.habershamschools.com/
North Habersham MS 800/6-8
1500 Wall Bridge Rd 30523 706-754-2915
Elizabeth Tuck, prin. Fax 754-8218
Other Schools – See Cornelia, Demorest, Mount Airy

North Georgia Technical College Post-Sec.
PO Box 65 30523 706-754-7700

Clarkston, DeKalb, Pop. 7,202
DeKalb County SD
Supt. — See Stone Mountain
Clarkston HS 1,100/9-12
618 N Indian Creek Dr 30021 678-676-5302
Michelle Jones, prin. Fax 676-5310

Atlanta Area School for the Deaf Post-Sec.
890 N Indian Creek Dr 30021 404-296-7101
Georgia Perimeter College Post-Sec.
555 N Indian Creek Dr 30021 678-891-3200
Georgia Piedmont Technical College Post-Sec.
495 N Indian Creek Dr 30021 404-297-9522

Claxton, Evans, Pop. 2,710
Evans County SD 1,700/PK-12
613 W Main St 30417 912-739-3544
Dr. Joy Collins, supt. Fax 739-2492
www.evans.k12.ga.us
Claxton HS 400/9-12
102 N Clark St 30417 912-739-3993
Justin Russell, prin. Fax 739-2029
Claxton MS 300/6-8
600 Hendrix St 30417 912-739-3646
Dr. Diane Holland, prin. Fax 739-7217

Clayton, Rabun, Pop. 2,003
Rabun County SD 2,300/PK-12
41 Education St 30525 706-746-5376
Matt Arthur, supt. Fax 746-3084
www.rabun.k12.ga.us
Other Schools – See Tiger

Cleveland, White, Pop. 3,334
White County SD 3,500/PK-12
136 Warriors Path 30528 706-865-2315
Jeffrey Wilson, supt. Fax 865-7784
www.white.k12.ga.us
White County HS 800/10-12
2600 Highway 129 N 30528 706-865-2312
John Osborne, prin. Fax 865-5981
White County MS 600/6-8
283 Old Blairsville Rd 30528 706-865-4060
Stephen Gill, prin. Fax 865-1947
White County Ninth Grade Academy 300/9-9
328 Old Blairsville Rd 30528 706-865-0727
John Osborne, prin. Fax 865-0737

Truett McConnell College Post-Sec.
100 Alumni Dr 30528 706-865-2134

Cochran, Bleckley, Pop. 5,096
Bleckley County SD 2,300/PK-12
PO Box 516 31014 478-934-2821
Dr. Charlotte Pipkin, supt. Fax 934-9595
www.bleckley.k12.ga.us
Bleckley County HS 700/9-12
155 Highway 87 Byp S 31014 478-934-6258
Anthony Jenkins, prin. Fax 934-9707
Bleckley County MS 500/6-8
590 GA Highway 26 E 31014 478-934-7270
Trey Belflower, prin. Fax 934-6502

Middle Georgia College Post-Sec.
1100 2nd St SE 31014 478-934-6221

College Park, Fulton, Pop. 13,682
Clayton County SD
Supt. — See Jonesboro
North Clayton HS 1,100/9-12
1525 Norman Dr, 770-994-4035
Derrick Dalton, prin. Fax 994-4038
North Clayton MS 900/6-8
5517 W Fayetteville Rd, 770-994-4025
Shakira Rice, prin. Fax 994-4028

Fulton County SD
Supt. — See Atlanta
Banneker HS 1,300/9-12
5935 Feldwood Rd, 770-969-3410
Will Bradley, prin. Fax 969-3418
Camp Creek MS 800/6-8
4345 Welcome All Rd SW, 404-669-8030
DeMarcos Holland, prin. Fax 669-8228
McClarin Alternative HS 300/Alt
3605 Main St 30337 404-669-8080
Anita Lee, prin. Fax 669-8089
McNair MS 800/6-8
2800 Burdett Rd, 770-991-4160
Lori Bolds, prin. Fax 991-4165

Woodward Academy 2,800/PK-12
1662 Rugby Ave 30337 404-765-4000
Ron McCollum, hdmstr. Fax 765-4009

Colquitt, Miller, Pop. 1,979
Miller County SD 1,100/PK-12
96 Perry St, 229-758-5592
Dr. Larry Green, supt. Fax 758-6040
www.millercountyschools.schoolinsites.com
Miller County HS 300/9-12
996 Phillipsburg Rd, 229-758-4130
Frank Killingsworth, prin. Fax 758-2686
Miller County MS 200/6-8
996 Phillipsburg Rd, 229-758-4130
Robert Melton, prin. Fax 758-2686

Columbus, Muscogee, Pop. 184,779
Muscogee County SD 32,000/PK-12
PO Box 2427 31902 706-748-2000
Dr. John Phillips, supt. Fax 748-2001
www.muscogee.k12.ga.us
Academic Success Center Alternative S Alt
1042 Manchester Expy 31904 706-748-2399
Dr. Marietta Webb, prin. Fax 748-2402
Arnold Magnet Academy 800/6-8
2011 51st St 31904 706-748-2436
Lura Reed, prin. Fax 748-2435
Baker MS 300/6-8
1830 Shepherd Dr 31906 706-683-8721
Tamura Magwood, prin. Fax 683-8731
Blackmon Road MS 800/6-8
7251 Blackmon Rd 31909 706-565-2998
Marty Richburg, prin. Fax 565-3006
Carver HS 1,000/9-12
3100 8th St 31906 706-748-2499
Chris Lindsey, prin. Fax 748-2512
Columbus HS 1,400/9-12
1700 Cherokee Ave 31906 706-748-2534
Dr. Marvin Crumbs, prin. Fax 748-2546
Double Churches MS 400/6-8
7611 Whitesville Rd 31904 706-748-2678
Chris Cox, prin. Fax 748-2682
Early College Academy 200/9-12
2701 11th Ave 31904 706-565-2965
Susan Willard, dean Fax 565-2971
East Columbus Magnet Academy 600/6-8
6100 Georgetown Dr 31907 706-565-3026
Kevin Scott, prin. Fax 565-3031
Eddy MS 400/6-8
2100 S Lumpkin Rd 31903 706-683-8782
Roslyn Tymes, prin. Fax 683-8789
Fort MS 600/6-8
2900 Woodruff Farm Rd 31907 706-569-3740
Sonja Coaxum, prin. Fax 569-3616
Hardaway HS 1,700/9-12
2901 College Dr 31906 706-748-2766
Matt Bell, prin. Fax 748-2776
Jordan Vocational HS 800/9-12
3200 Howard Ave 31904 706-748-2819
Alton White, prin. Fax 748-2829
Kendrick HS 800/9-12
6015 Georgetown Dr 31907 706-565-2960
Dr. Alonzo James, prin. Fax 565-2971
Marshall MS 200/6-8
1830 Shepherd Dr 31906 706-748-2900
Dr. Michael Forte, prin. Fax 748-2908
Northside HS 1,600/9-12
2002 American Way 31909 706-748-2920
James Wilson, prin. Fax 748-2931
Richards MS 800/6-8
2892 Edgewood Rd 31906 706-569-3697
Dawn Grantham, prin. Fax 569-3704
Rose Hill Center Alt
435 21st St 31904 706-748-3093
Johnny Freeman, prin. Fax 748-3095
Rose Hill Center at Daniel 50/Alt
1042 Manchester Expy 31904 706-748-2590
Johnny Freeman, prin. Fax 748-2594
Rothschild MS 600/6-8
1136 Hunt Ave 31907 706-569-3709
Reginald Williamson, prin. Fax 569-3717
St. Elmo Center for Gifted Education K-12
2101 18th Ave 31901 706-748-3115
Paula Cash, prin. Fax 748-3118
Shaw HS 1,200/9-12
7579 Raider Way 31909 706-569-3638
Michael Barden, prin. Fax 569-3648
Spencer HS 900/9-12
4340 Victory Dr 31903 706-683-8701
Reginald Griffin, prin. Fax 683-8716
Veterans Memorial MS 700/6-8
2008 Old Guard Rd 31909 706-748-3203
Melanie Knight, prin. Fax 748-3211
Tillinghurst Adult Education Adult
514 Morris Rd 31906 706-683-8741
Tamika Phillips, dir. Fax 683-8743
Other Schools – See Midland

Brookstone S 800/PK-12
440 Bradley Park Dr 31904 706-324-1392
Dr. Brian Kennerly, hdmstr. Fax 571-0178
Calvary Christian S 600/PK-12
7556 Old Moon Rd 31909 706-323-0467
Len McWilliams, hdmstr. Fax 323-1941
Columbus State University Post-Sec.
4225 University Ave 31907 706-507-8800
Columbus Technical College Post-Sec.
928 Manchester Expy 31904 706-649-1800
Grace Christian S 100/PK-12
2915 14th Ave 31904 706-323-9161
James Horton, prin. Fax 323-8554
Medical Center Post-Sec.
PO Box 951 31902 706-571-1200
Miller-Motte Technical College Post-Sec.
1800 Box Rd 31907 706-225-5002
Rivertown School of Beauty Post-Sec.
4747 Hamilton Rd Ste B 31904 706-653-8032
St. Anne Pacelli S 500/PK-12
2020 Kay Cir 31907 706-561-8232
Danni Harris, pres. Fax 563-0211
Southeastern Beauty School Post-Sec.
PO Box 12483 31917 706-687-1054
Virginia College Post-Sec.
5601 Veterans Pkwy 31904 762-207-1600

Comer, Madison, Pop. 1,110
Madison County SD
Supt. — See Danielsville
Madison County MS 1,100/6-8
3215 Highway 172 30629 706-783-2400
Chuck Colquitt, prin. Fax 783-4390

Commerce, Jackson, Pop. 6,437
Commerce CSD 1,500/PK-12
PO Box 29 30529 706-335-5500
Dr. James McCoy, supt. Fax 335-5214
www.commerce-city.k12.ga.us
Commerce HS 400/9-12
272 Lakeview Dr 30529 706-335-5942
Donald Drew, prin. Fax 336-6955
Commerce MS 400/5-8
7690 Jefferson Rd 30529 706-335-5594
Bill Ruma, prin. Fax 335-6222

Jackson County SD
Supt. — See Jefferson
East Jackson Comprehensive HS 1,000/9-12
1435 Hoods Mill Rd 30529 706-336-8900
Tim Stowers, prin. Fax 335-2928
East Jackson MS 400/6-8
1880 Hoods Mill Rd 30529 706-335-2083
Heidi Hill, prin. Fax 335-0935

Conyers, Rockdale, Pop. 14,890
Rockdale County SD 15,800/PK-12
PO Box 1199 30012 770-860-4211
Richard Autry, supt. Fax 860-4285
www.rockdale.k12.ga.us
Alpha Alternative S Alt
1045 North St NW 30012 770-922-8636
Gregory Brown, prin. Fax 918-0248
Conyers MS 1,000/6-8
400 Sigman Rd NW 30012 770-483-3371
Torian White, prin. Fax 483-9448
Edwards MS 900/6-8
2633 Stanton Rd SE 30094 770-483-3255
Fred Middleton, prin. Fax 483-3676
Heritage HS 1,700/9-12
2400 Granade Rd SW 30094 770-483-5428
Greg Fowler, prin. Fax 483-9435
Magnet S for Science/Technology 9-12
1174 Bulldog Cir NE 30012 770-483-8737
Mary Ann Suddeth, dir. Fax 483-7379
Memorial MS 900/6-8
3205 Underwood Rd SE 30013 770-922-0139
Andrea McMahan, prin. Fax 922-6192
Open Campus S Alt
1115 West Ave SW 30012 770-388-5727
Frank Daniels, prin. Fax 388-5728
Rockdale County HS 1,800/9-12
1174 Bulldog Cir NE 30012 770-483-8754
Georgi Nour, prin. Fax 483-8708
Salem HS 1,500/9-12
3551 Underwood Rd SE 30013 770-929-0176
Tonya Bloodworth, prin. Fax 922-1292
Other Schools – See Stockbridge

Eastminster S 200/K-12
2450 Lennox Rd SE 30094 770-785-6780
Roy Alexander, hdmstr. Fax 922-8197
GDA Inc Post-Sec.
1448 V F W Dr SW 30012 770-918-8501
Georgia Career Institute Post-Sec.
1820 Highway 20 SE Ste 208 30013 770-922-7653
Peachtree Academy 400/PK-12
1801 Ellington Rd SE 30013 770-860-8900
Wendy Hughes, hdmstr. Fax 761-0883
Victory Christian S 200/PK-12
1151 Flat Shoals Rd SE 30013 770-929-3758
Fax 929-8848
Young Americans Christian S 500/PK-12
1701 Honey Creek Rd SE 30013 770-760-7902
David Taylor, admin. Fax 760-7981

Cordele, Crisp, Pop. 11,020
Crisp County SD 4,000/PK-12
PO Box 729 31010 229-276-3400
Dr. Rhonda Hayes, supt. Fax 276-3406
www.crispschools.org
Crisp County HS 1,100/9-12
2402 Cougar Aly 31015 229-276-3430
Rusty Sowell, prin. Fax 276-3436
Crisp County MS 900/6-8
1116 E 24th Ave 31015 229-276-3460
Brandon Williams, prin. Fax 276-3466

Crisp Academy 200/PK-12
150 Crisp Academy Dr 31015 229-273-6330
Kip Stevens, hdmstr. Fax 273-4141
South Georgia Technical College Post-Sec.
402 N Midway Rd 31015 229-271-4040

Cornelia, Habersham, Pop. 4,030
Habersham County SD
Supt. — See Clarkesville
South Habersham MS 800/6-8
237 Old Athens Hwy 30531 706-778-7121
Constance Franklin, prin. Fax 778-2110

Covington, Newton, Pop. 12,895
Newton County SD 18,700/PK-12
PO Box 1469 30015 770-787-1330
Samantha Fuhrey, supt. Fax 784-2950
www.newtoncountyschools.org
Alcovy HS 1,900/9-12
14567 Highway 36 30014 770-784-4995
Sandra Owens, prin. Fax 625-6117
Clements MS 700/6-8
66 Jack Neely Rd 30016 770-784-2934
Joy Scavella, prin. Fax 784-2992
Cousins MS 900/6-8
8187 Carlton Trl NW 30014 770-786-7311
Scott Sauls, prin. Fax 784-2991
Eastside HS 1,400/9-12
10245 Eagle Dr 30014 770-784-2920
Jeff Cher, prin. Fax 784-2918
Indian Creek MS 1,000/6-8
11051 By Pass Ave 30014 770-385-6453
Dr. Renee Mallard, prin. Fax 385-6456
Liberty MS 1,000/6-8
5225 Salem Rd 30016 678-625-6617
Keisa Taylor, prin. Fax 625-6200
Newton HS 2,000/9-12
1 Ram Way 30014 770-787-2250
Eclan David, prin. Fax 784-2957
Veterans Memorial MS 800/6-8
13357 Brown Bridge Rd 30016 770-385-6893
James Peek, prin. Fax 385-6899

Peachtree Academy 200/PK-12
14101 Highway 278 E 30014 678-729-9111
Wendy Hughes, hdmstr. Fax 729-9118
Woodloo's Christian Academy 100/PK-12
3915 Highway 162 30016 770-788-2770
Terri Knight, dir. Fax 788-1883

Crawford, Oglethorpe, Pop. 804
Oglethorpe County SD
Supt. — See Lexington
Oglethorpe County MS 600/6-8
270 Buddy Faust Rd 30630 706-743-8146
Beverley Levine, prin. Fax 743-3536

Cumming, Forsyth, Pop. 5,371
Forsyth County SD 35,500/PK-12
1120 Dahlonega Hwy 30040 770-887-2461
Dr. L.C. Evans, supt. Fax 781-6632
www.forsyth.k12.ga.us
Forsyth Central HS 1,400/9-12
520 Tribble Gap Rd 30040 770-887-8151
Rudy Hampton, prin. Fax 781-2289
Gateway Academy Alt
1130 Dahlonega Hwy 30040 770-781-2299
Todd Shirley, dir. Fax 888-1193
Lakeside MS 900/6-8
2565 Echols Rd 30041 678-965-5080
Debbie Sarver, prin. Fax 965-5081
Liberty MS 800/6-8
7465 Wallace Tatum Rd 30028 770-781-4889
Connie Stovall, prin. Fax 513-3877
Little Mill MS 800/6-8
6800 Little Mill Rd 30041 678-965-5000
Connie McCrary, prin. Fax 965-5001
North Forsyth HS 2,200/9-12
3635 Coal Mountain Dr 30028 770-781-6637
Dr. Beth Hebert, prin. Fax 781-2273
North Forsyth MS 900/6-8
3645 Coal Mountain Dr 30028 770-889-0743
Jeff Hunt, prin. Fax 888-1210
Otwell MS 800/6-8
605 Tribble Gap Rd 30040 770-887-5248
Steve Miller, prin. Fax 888-1214
Piney Grove MS 1,000/6-8
8135 Majors Rd 30041 678-965-5010
Terri North, prin. Fax 965-5011
South Forsyth HS 1,600/9-12
585 Peachtree Pkwy 30041 770-781-2264
Jeff Cheney, prin. Fax 888-1224
South Forsyth MS 800/6-8
4670 Windermere Pkwy 30041 770-888-3170
Sandy Tinsley, prin. Fax 888-3175
Vickery Creek MS 1,200/6-8
6240 Post Rd 30040 770-667-2580
Kathy Rohacek, prin. Fax 667-2593
West Forsyth HS 2,000/9-12
4155 Drew Rd 30040 770-888-3470
Betty Pope, prin. Fax 888-3471
Other Schools – See Suwanee

Covenant Christian Academy 200/PK-12
6905 Post Rd 30040 770-674-2990
Johnathan Arnold, hdmstr. Fax 674-2989
Fideles Christian S 200/K-12
1390 Weber Industrial Dr 30041 770-888-6705
Jonny Whisenant, dir. Fax 888-9720
Horizon Christian Academy 300/K-12
PO Box 2715 30028 678-947-3583
Gary Bennett, admin. Fax 947-0721
Pinecrest Academy 900/PK-12
955 Peachtree Pkwy 30041 770-888-4477
Edward Lindekugel, dir. Fax 888-0404

Cusseta, Chattahoochee, Pop. 1,258
Chattahoochee County SD 900/PK-12
326 Broad St 31805 706-989-3774
Jimmy Martin, supt. Fax 989-3776
www.chattco.org
ACE Academy Alternative S Alt
326 Broad St 31805 706-989-3243
Fax 989-3776
Chattahoochee County HS 500/9-12
360 GA Highway 26 31805 706-989-3678
James Sims, prin. Fax 989-0649
Chattahoochee County MS 100/6-8
360 GA Highway 26 31805 706-989-3678
Lane Lindsay, prin. Fax 989-0649

Cuthbert, Randolph, Pop. 3,851
Randolph County SD 1,300/PK-12
98 School Dr, 229-732-3601
Dianne Watkins, supt. Fax 732-3840
www.sowegak12.org/
Randolph-Clay HS 400/9-12
3451 GA Highway 266, 229-732-2101
Ronald Gadson, prin. Fax 732-5633
Randolph-Clay MS 300/6-8
3451 GA Highway 266, 229-732-2101
Ronald Gadson, prin. Fax 732-5633

Andrew College Post-Sec.
501 College St, 229-732-2171

Dacula, Gwinnett, Pop. 4,365
Gwinnett County SD
Supt. — See Suwanee
Dacula HS 1,900/9-12
123 Broad St 30019 770-963-6664
Dr. Bryan Long, prin. Fax 338-4665
Dacula MS 1,600/6-8
137 Dacula Rd 30019 770-963-1110
Dr. Kellye Riggins, prin. Fax 338-4632

Hebron Christian Academy 600/6-12
570 Dacula Rd 30019 770-963-9250
Tim Anderson, prin. Fax 277-3581

Dahlonega, Lumpkin, Pop. 5,151
Lumpkin County SD 3,900/PK-12
56 Indian Dr 30533 706-864-3611
Dewey Moyo, supt. Fax 864-3755
lumpkincounty.schoolinsites.com
Lumpkin County HS 1,100/9-12
2001 Indian Dr 30533 706-864-6186
Rick Conner, prin. Fax 864-4929
Lumpkin County MS 900/6-8
44 School Dr 30533 706-864-6189
Dr. Michael Tinney, prin. Fax 864-0199

North Georgia College & State University Post-Sec.
82 College Cir 30597 706-864-1400

Dallas, Paulding, Pop. 11,233
Paulding County SD 28,100/PK-12
3236 Atlanta Hwy 30132 770-443-8000
Cliff Cole, supt. Fax 443-8089
www.paulding.k12.ga.us
East Paulding HS 1,600/9-12
3320 E Paulding Dr 30157 770-445-5100
Dr. Kim Fraker, prin. Fax 443-6357
East Paulding MS 900/6-8
2945 Hiram Acworth Hwy 30157 770-443-7000
Brett Taylor, prin. Fax 443-0116
Jones MS 700/6-8
100 Stadium Dr 30132 770-443-8024
Craig Wilcox, prin. Fax 443-8026
McClure MS 1,100/6-8
315 Bob Grogan Dr 30132 770-505-3700
Jaynath Hayes, prin. Fax 505-7253
Moses MS 900/6-8
1066 Old County Farm Rd 30132 770-443-8727
Penny Tarallo, prin. Fax 443-8078
North Paulding HS 1,700/9-12
300 N Paulding Dr 30132 770-443-9400
Dr. Mark Crowe, prin. Fax 505-7253
Paulding County HS 1,400/9-12
1297 Villa Rica Hwy 30157 770-443-8008
Eddie Fincher, prin. Fax 443-7030
Ritch MS, 60 Old Country Trl 30157 6-8
Cassandra Dobbs, prin. 770-443-1449
Scoggins MS 700/6-8
1663 Mulberry Rock Rd 30157 770-456-4188
Tammy Allen, prin. Fax 456-4189
South Paulding MS 600/6-8
592 Nebo Rd 30157 770-445-8500
Sandra Webb, prin. Fax 445-9989
Other Schools – See Douglasville, Hiram, Powder Springs

Dalton, Whitfield, Pop. 32,710
Dalton CSD 7,000/PK-12
PO Box 1408 30722 706-876-4000
Jim Hawkins Ph.D., supt. Fax 226-4583
www.daltonpublicschools.com/
Dalton HS 1,500/9-12
1500 Manly St 30720 706-278-8757
Steve Bartoo, prin. Fax 226-2430
Dalton MS 1,500/6-8
1250 Cross Plains Trl 30721 706-278-3903
Brian Suits, prin. Fax 428-7852
Morris Innovative HS 200/Alt
104 Fort Hill Ter 30721 706-278-6297
Jennifer Phinney, prin. Fax 278-4998

Whitfield County SD 13,400/PK-12
PO Box 2167 30722 706-217-6780
Dr. Judy Gilreath, supt. Fax 217-6755
www.whitfield.k12.ga.us
Coahulla Creek HS 9-12
3361 Crow Rd NE 30721 706-694-4900
Dr. Stan Stewart, prin. Fax 694-5033
Crossroads Academy Alt
2818 Airport Rd 30721 706-271-2495
Donna Harris, prin. Fax 271-2496
Eastbrook MS 600/6-8
1382 Eastbrook Rd SE 30721 706-278-6135
Wanda Storey, prin. Fax 226-9859
New Hope MS 600/6-8
1111 New Hope Rd NW 30720 706-673-2295
Joe Barnett, prin. Fax 673-2086
North Whitfield MS 800/6-8
3264 Cleveland Rd 30721 706-259-3381
Andrea Bradley, prin. Fax 259-8168
Southeast Whitfield County HS 1,300/9-12
1954 Riverbend Rd 30721 706-876-7000
Denise Pendley, prin. Fax 278-3433
Valley Point MS 500/6-8
3796 S Dixie Rd 30721 706-277-9662
Robyn Baggett, prin. Fax 277-7035
Phoenix HS Adult
2300 Maddox Chapel Rd NE 30721 706-260-2206
Fred Toney, dir. Fax 260-2200
Other Schools – See Rocky Face, Tunnel Hill

Christian Heritage S 400/K-12
1600 Martin Luther King Jr 30721 706-277-1198
Gerald Porter, hdmstr. Fax 277-2300
Dalton State College Post-Sec.
650 College Dr 30720 706-272-4436
Georgia Beauty Academy Post-Sec.
PO Box 3516 30719 866-418-4522

Damascus, Early, Pop. 251

Southwest Georgia Academy 400/PK-12
14105 GA Highway 200, 229-725-4792
Matt Dalrymple, hdmstr. Fax 725-5476

Danielsville, Madison, Pop. 548
Madison County SD 4,800/PK-12
800 Madison St 30633 706-795-2191
Dr. Allen McCannon, supt. Fax 795-5029
www.madison.k12.ga.us
Madison County HS 1,400/9-12
600 Madison St 30633 706-795-2197
George Bullock, prin. Fax 795-3116
Other Schools – See Comer

Darien, McIntosh, Pop. 1,951
McIntosh County SD 1,800/PK-12
200 Pine St SE 31305 912-437-6645
Dr. Tina Kirby, supt. Fax 437-2140
www.mcintosh.k12.ga.us/
McIntosh County Academy 500/9-12
8945 US Highway 17 31305 912-437-6691
Terrance Haywood, prin. Fax 437-3077
McIntosh County MS 400/6-8
500 Greene St 31305 912-437-6685
Kathy Wade, prin. Fax 437-5676

Dawson, Terrell, Pop. 4,502
Terrell County SD 1,500/PK-12
955 Forrester Dr SE, 229-995-4425
Robert Aaron, supt. Fax 995-4632
www.terrell.k12.ga.us
Terrell County HS 400/9-12
201 Greenwave Blvd, 229-995-2544
Douglas Bell, prin. Fax 995-4523
Terrell County MS 300/6-8
201 Greenwave Blvd, 229-995-2544
Valencia Gardner, prin. Fax 995-4523

Terrell Academy 300/K-12
602 Academy Dr SE, 229-995-4242
Bill Murdock, hdmstr. Fax 995-6149

Dawsonville, Dawson, Pop. 2,501
Dawson County SD 3,500/PK-12
517 Allen St 30534 706-265-3246
Keith Porter, supt. Fax 265-1226
www.dawsoncountyschools.org/
Dawson County HS 1,000/9-12
PO Box 129 30534 706-265-6555
Jute Wilson, prin. Fax 265-3936
Dawson County MS 500/6-8
332 Highway 9 N 30534 706-216-5801
Dr. Mark Merges, prin. Fax 265-7252
Riverview MS 400/6-8
5126 Highway 9 S 30534 706-216-4849
William Zadernak, prin. Fax 265-1426

Decatur, DeKalb, Pop. 18,866
City Schools of Decatur 3,100/PK-12
758 Scott Blvd 30030 404-370-4400
Dr. Phyllis Edwards, supt. Fax 370-3844
www.csdecatur.net
Decatur HS 700/9-12
310 N McDonough St 30030 404-370-4420
Lauri McKain, prin. Fax 370-4434

Renfroe MS 700/6-8
220 W College Ave 30030 404-370-4440
Derrick Thomas, prin. Fax 370-4449

DeKalb County SD
Supt. — See Stone Mountain
Bethune MS 900/6-8
5200 Covington Hwy 30035 678-875-0302
Dr. Triscilla Weaver, prin. Fax 875-0310
Cedar Grove MS 900/6-8
2300 Wildcat Rd 30034 678-874-4202
Patricia May, prin. Fax 874-4210
Chapel Hill MS 1,000/6-8
3535 Dogwood Farm Rd 30034 678-676-8502
Debra Phillips, prin. Fax 676-8510
Columbia HS 1,200/9-12
2106 Columbia Dr 30032 678-874-0802
Stephanie Amey, prin. Fax 874-0810
Columbia MS 1,000/6-8
3001 Columbia Dr 30034 678-875-0502
Carlous Daniel, prin. Fax 875-0510
DeKalb HS of Technology South Vo/Tech
3303 Panthersville Rd 30034 678-874-4502
Dr. Vikki Williams, prin. Fax 874-4510
DeKalb Transition Academy 50/Alt
2670 Old Wesley Chapel Rd 30034 678-874-1002
Annette Williams, prin. Fax 874-1010
Druid Hills MS 1,100/6-8
3100 Mount Olive Dr 30033 678-874-7602
Robert Thorpe, prin. Fax 874-7610
McNair MS 800/6-8
2190 Wallingford Dr 30032 678-874-5102
Annette Williams, prin. Fax 874-5110
Miller Grove MS 1,000/6-8
2215 Miller Rd 30035 678-676-8902
Thaddeus Dixon, prin. Fax 676-8910
Southwest DeKalb HS 1,700/9-12
2863 Kelley Chapel Rd 30034 678-874-1902
Carolyn Williams, prin. Fax 874-1910
Towers HS 900/9-12
3919 Brookcrest Cir 30032 678-874-2202
Donevin Hoskins, prin. Fax 874-2210

Academe of the Oaks 50/9-12
146 New St 30030 404-405-2173
Fax 377-7178
Agnes Scott College Post-Sec.
141 E College Ave 30030 404-471-6000
American Professional Institute Post-Sec.
141 Sams St 30030 404-371-3338
Columbia Theological Seminary Post-Sec.
PO Box 520 30031 404-378-8821
DeKalb Medical Center Post-Sec.
2701 N Decatur Rd 30033 404-501-5206
DeVry University Post-Sec.
1 W Court Sq Ste 100 30030 404-270-2706
Georgia Perimeter College Post-Sec.
3251 Panthersville Rd 30034 678-891-2300
Greenforest/McCalep Christian Academy 500/PK-12
3250 Rainbow Dr 30034 404-486-6737
Julius Cawthon, prin. Fax 486-1127
Gupton-Jones College of Funeral Service Post-Sec.
5141 Snapfinger Woods Dr 30035 770-593-2257
Laurus Technical Institute Post-Sec.
523 Church St 30030 404-303-2929

Demorest, Habersham, Pop. 1,780
Habersham County SD
Supt. — See Clarkesville
Wilbanks MS 6-8
3115 Demorest Mt Airy Hwy 30535 706-894-1341
Marybeth Thomas, prin. Fax 894-1342

Piedmont College Post-Sec.
PO Box 10 30535 706-778-3000

Dexter, Laurens, Pop. 568
Laurens County SD
Supt. — See Dublin
West Laurens HS 1,200/9-12
3692 GA Highway 257 31019 478-875-1000
Clifford Garnto, prin. Fax 875-2860

Donalsonville, Seminole, Pop. 2,610
Seminole County SD 1,600/PK-12
800 S Woolfork Ave, 229-524-2433
Monroe Bonner, supt. Fax 524-2212
www.seminole.k12.ga.us
Seminole County MSHS 800/6-12
5582 GA Highway 39, 229-524-5135
Dr. H. Brinson Register, prin. Fax 524-5178

Doraville, DeKalb, Pop. 8,200
DeKalb County SD
Supt. — See Stone Mountain
Sequoyah MS 900/6-8
3456 Aztec Rd 30340 678-676-7902
Brittany Cunningham, prin. Fax 676-7910

Douglas, Coffee, Pop. 11,434
Coffee County SD 7,500/PK-12
1311 Peterson Ave S 31533 912-384-2086
Dr. Morris Leis, supt. Fax 383-5333
coffee.k12.ga.us
Carver HS Freshman Campus 600/9-9
1020 Gaskin Ave S 31533 912-384-1342
Dr. James Banks, prin. Fax 383-4160
Coffee Alternative Education Center Alt
1303 Peterson Ave S 31533 912-383-4100
James Sirmans, dir. Fax 383-4124
Coffee HS 1,400/10-12
159 Trojan Way 31533 912-384-2094
Rowland Cummings, prin. Fax 383-4142
Coffee MS 1,700/6-8
901 Connector 206 N 31533 912-720-1001
Sherri Berry, dir. Fax 720-1032

Citizens Christian Academy 200/PK-12
PO Box 1064 31534 912-384-8862
William Rish, hdmstr. Fax 384-8426
South Georgia State College Post-Sec.
100 College Park Dr W 31533 912-260-4200

Douglasville, Douglas, Pop. 30,224
Douglas County SD 24,400/K-12
PO Box 1077 30133 770-651-2000
Dr. Gordon Pritz, supt. Fax 920-4159
www.douglas.k12.ga.us
Alexander HS 1,800/9-12
6500 Alexander Pkwy 30135 770-651-6000
Nathan Hand, prin. Fax 920-4514
Chapel Hill HS 1,800/9-12
4899 Chapel Hill Rd 30135 770-651-6200
Sean Kelly, prin. Fax 947-7512
Chapel Hill MS 1,100/6-8
3989 Chapel Hill Rd 30135 770-651-5000
Dr. Jolene Morris, prin. Fax 920-4242
Chestnut Log MS 700/6-8
2544 Pope Rd 30135 770-651-5100
Dr. Nicole Hayes, prin. Fax 651-5103
Douglas County HS 2,200/9-12
8705 Campbellton St 30134 770-651-6500
Dr. Tim Scott, prin. Fax 920-4456
Factory Shoals MS 800/6-8
3301 Shoals School Rd 30135 770-651-5800
James Allen, prin. Fax 920-4356
Fairplay MS 500/6-8
8311 Highway 166 30135 770-651-5300
Yvonne Kidney, prin. Fax 920-4599
Stewart MS 300/6-8
8138 Malone St 30134 770-651-5400
Dewayne Jackson, prin. Fax 920-4229
Yeager MS 600/6-8
4000 Kings Hwy 30135 770-651-5600
Dr. Fred Ervin, prin. Fax 947-7374
Other Schools – See Lithia Springs, Winston

Paulding County SD
Supt. — See Dallas
Austin MS 900/6-8
3490 Ridge Rd 30134 770-942-0316
Gary Plunkett, prin. Fax 942-0548
South Paulding HS 1,900/9-12
1364 Winn Rd 30134 770-949-9221
Dr. Keith Rowland, prin. Fax 949-9239

Harvester Christian Academy 400/PK-12
4241 Central Church Rd 30135 770-942-1583
Joel Satterly, hdmstr. Fax 942-9332
Heirway Christian Academy 200/PK-12
6758 Spring St 30134 770-489-4392
Timothy Thomas, hdmstr. Fax 489-4318
Kings Way Christian S 300/PK-12
6456 The Kings Way 30135 770-949-0812
Strayer University Post-Sec.
4655 Timber Ridge Dr 30135 678-715-2200
West Georgia Technical College Post-Sec.
4600 Timber Ridge Dr 30135 770-947-7200

Dublin, Laurens, Pop. 16,025
Dublin CSD 2,300/PK-12
207 Shamrock Dr 31021 478-272-3440
Dr. Chuck Ledbetter, supt. Fax 272-1249
www.dublincityschools.us/
Dublin HS 700/9-12
1127 Hillcrest Pkwy 31021 478-272-4727
Robert Hunter, prin. Fax 277-9829
Dublin MS 500/6-8
1501 N Jefferson St 31021 478-272-8122
Dr. Fred Williams, prin. Fax 277-9828
Moore Street S 50/Alt
1405 W Moore St 31021 478-272-4727
Emory Bostic, prin. Fax 277-9829

Laurens County SD 6,600/PK-12
467 Firetower Rd 31021 478-272-4767
Rob Johnson, supt. Fax 277-2619
www.lcboe.net
East Laurens HS 600/9-12
920 US Highway 80 E 31027 478-272-3144
Eddie Morris, prin. Fax 274-1032
East Laurens MS 500/6-8
920 US Highway 80 E 31027 478-272-1201
Dr. Christopher Watkins, prin. Fax 609-2176
West Laurens MS 1,000/6-8
332 W Laurens School Rd 31021 478-272-8452
Tim Franks, prin. Fax 609-2202
Other Schools – See Dexter, Rentz

Oconee Fall Line Technical College Post-Sec.
560 Pinehill Rd 31021 478-275-6589
Trinity Christian S 400/K-12
200 Trinity Rd 31021 478-272-7699

Duluth, Gwinnett, Pop. 25,917
Gwinnett County SD
Supt. — See Suwanee
Duluth HS 2,400/9-12
3737 Brock Rd 30096 770-476-5206
Jason Lane, prin. Fax 232-3332
Duluth MS 1,800/6-8
3200 Pleasant Hill Rd 30096 770-476-3372
Deborah Fusi, prin. Fax 232-3295
Hull MS 2,400/6-8
1950 Old Peachtree Rd 30097 770-232-3200
Denise Showell, prin. Fax 232-3203
Radloff MS 1,500/6-8
3939 Shackleford Rd 30096 678-245-3400
Al Taylor, prin. Fax 245-3403

Atlanta Adventist Academy 100/9-12
PO Box 4088 30096 404-699-1400
Atlanta Institute of Music Post-Sec.
2875 Breckinridge Blvd #700 30096 770-242-7717
Aviation Institute of Maintenance Post-Sec.
2025 Satellite Pointe 30096 678-377-5600
Childcare Education Institute Post-Sec.
3059 Peachtree Indstrl #100 30097 800-499-9907
DeVry University Post-Sec.
3505 Koger Blvd Ste 170 30096 770-381-4400
ITT Technical Institute Post-Sec.
10700 Abbotts Bridge # 190 30097 678-957-8510

Dunwoody, DeKalb, Pop. 45,357
DeKalb County SD
Supt. — See Stone Mountain
Dunwoody HS 1,500/9-12
5035 Vermack Rd 30338 678-874-8502
Noel Maloof, prin. Fax 874-8510

Empire Beauty School Post-Sec.
4719 Ashford-Dunwoody #205 30338 770-672-2448

Eastman, Dodge, Pop. 4,921
Dodge County SD 3,400/PK-12
720 College St 31023 478-374-3783
Dr. Melinda Dennis, supt. Fax 374-6697
www.dodge.k12.ga.us
Dodge County HS 1,000/9-12
350 Pearl Bates Ave 31023 478-374-7711
Dr. Susan Long, prin. Fax 374-6987
Dodge County MS 700/6-8
5911 Oak St 31023 478-374-6492
Davey Sheffield, prin. Fax 374-6484

East Point, Fulton, Pop. 33,152
Fulton County SD
Supt. — See Atlanta
Tri-Cities HS 1,800/9-12
2575 Harris St 30344 404-669-8200
Dan Sims, prin. Fax 669-8158
West MS 800/6-8
2376 Headland Dr 30344 404-669-8130
LaRoyce Sublett, prin. Fax 669-8121
Woodland MS 1,100/6-8
2745 Stone Rd 30344 404-305-2182
Richard Fowler, prin. Fax 305-2190

Eatonton, Putnam, Pop. 6,410

Gatewood S 400/PK-12
139 Phillips Dr 31024 706-485-8231
Christopher Charles, hdmstr. Fax 485-2455

Edison, Calhoun, Pop. 1,517
Calhoun County SD
Supt. — See Morgan
Calhoun County MSHS 300/6-12
700 Manry St, 229-835-2435
C. Butler, prin. Fax 835-3040

Elberton, Elbert, Pop. 4,600
Elbert County SD 2,000/PK-12
50 Laurel Dr 30635 706-213-4000
Chuck Bell, supt. Fax 283-6674
www.elbert.k12.ga.us
Elbert County Comprehensive HS 900/9-12
600 Abernathy Cir 30635 706-213-4100
Renee Padgett, prin. Fax 283-1183
Elbert County MS 700/5-8
1108 Athens Tech Rd 30635 706-213-4200
Jon Jarvis, prin. Fax 283-1117
Elberton Education Center Alt
50 Laurel Dr 30635 706-283-2294
Sonya Barnett, admin. Fax 283-1111

Ellaville, Schley, Pop. 1,796
Schley County SD 1,400/PK-12
PO Box 66 31806 229-937-2405
Larry Stubbs, supt. Fax 937-5180
www.schleyk12.org/
Schley County MSHS 700/6-12
PO Box 1350 31806 229-937-0560
Rusty Tondee, prin. Fax 937-0565

Ellenwood, Clayton
DeKalb County SD
Supt. — See Stone Mountain
Cedar Grove HS 1,100/9-12
2360 River Rd 30294 678-874-4002
Pamela Benford, prin. Fax 874-4010

Anointed Word Christian S International 100/PK-12
3800 Linecrest Rd 30294 404-241-8200
Chrislyn Davis-Haynes, admin. Fax 328-9801

Ellijay, Gilmer, Pop. 1,600
Gilmer County SD 3,100/PK-12
134 Industrial Blvd 30540 706-276-5000
Bryan Dorsey, supt. Fax 276-5005
www.gilmerschools.com/
Clear Creek MS 400/7-8
1020 Clear Creek Rd, 706-276-5150
Jason Kouns, prin. Fax 276-5151
Gilmer HS 1,200/9-12
408 Bobcat Trl 30540 706-276-5080
Adam Hathaway, prin. Fax 276-5088

North Georgia Christian Academy 100/PK-12
191 Harold Pritchett Rd 30540 706-635-6422
Mary Pierce, admin. Fax 635-6425

Emerson, Bartow, Pop. 1,449
Bartow County SD
Supt. — See Cartersville
South Central MS 700/6-8
224 Old Alabama Rd SE 30137 770-606-5865
Donald Rucker, prin. Fax 606-5168

Eton, Murray, Pop. 907
Murray County SD
Supt. — See Chatsworth
Mountain Creek Academy | 100/Alt
273 Harris St 30724 | 706-517-5355
Paula Martin, prin. | Fax 517-5339
Adult Education | Adult
273 Harris St 30724 | 706-695-4641
Joe Jackson, prin. | Fax 695-9103

Euharlee, Bartow, Pop. 4,058
Bartow County SD
Supt. — See Cartersville
Woodland MS | 900/6-8
1061 Euharlee Rd, | 770-606-5871
Lamar Barnes, prin. | Fax 606-2092

Evans, Columbia, Pop. 28,398
Columbia County SD | 23,700/PK-12
4781 Hereford Farm Rd 30809 | 706-541-0650
Charles Nagle, supt. | Fax 541-2723
www.ccboe.net
Evans HS | 1,800/9-12
4550 Cox Rd 30809 | 706-863-1198
Don Brigdon, prin. | Fax 854-5807
Evans MS | 900/6-8
4785 Hereford Farm Rd 30809 | 706-863-2275
Michael Johnson, prin. | Fax 854-5810
Greenbrier HS | 1,700/9-12
5114 Riverwood Pkwy 30809 | 706-650-6040
Chris Segraves, prin. | Fax 855-3886
Greenbrier MS | 600/6-8
5120 Riverwood Pkwy 30809 | 706-650-6080
Chip Fulmer, prin. | Fax 854-5800
Lakeside HS | 1,700/9-12
533 Blue Ridge Dr 30809 | 706-863-0027
Dr. Steven Rhodes, prin. | Fax 854-5802
Lakeside MS | 700/6-8
527 Blue Ridge Dr 30809 | 706-855-6900
Felicia Turner, prin. | Fax 854-5805
Riverside MS | 700/6-8
1095 Furys Ferry Rd 30809 | 706-868-3712
Yvette Foster-Williams, prin. | Fax 854-5824
Other Schools – See Grovetown, Harlem, Martinez

Augusta School of Massage | Post-Sec.
608 Ponder Place Dr 30809 | 706-863-4799

Fairburn, Fulton, Pop. 12,742
Fulton County SD
Supt. — See Atlanta
Bear Creek MS | 1,000/6-8
7415 Herndon Rd 30213 | 770-969-6080
Darron Franklin, prin. | Fax 306-3584
Creekside HS | 1,300/9-12
7405 Herndon Rd 30213 | 770-306-4300
Brian Jones, prin. | Fax 306-4313
Hughes HS | 9-12
7510 Hall Rd 30213 | 770-774-3620
Eric Hollinhead, prin. | Fax 774-3633
Renaissance MS | 1,100/6-8
7155 Hall Rd 30213 | 770-306-4330
Maureen Wheeler, prin. | Fax 306-4338

Arlington Christian S | 300/K-12
4500 Ridge Rd 30213 | 770-964-9871
Romeo Brinkley, head sch | Fax 306-3630
Landmark Christian S | 800/PK-12
50 SE Broad St 30213 | 770-306-0647
Mike Titus, hdmstr. | Fax 969-6551

Fayetteville, Fayette, Pop. 15,530
Fayette County SD | 21,300/PK-12
PO Box 879 30214 | 770-460-3535
Dr. Jeff Bearden, supt. | Fax 460-8191
www.fcboe.org
Bennetts Mill MS | 600/6-8
210 Lester Rd 30215 | 770-716-3982
Rae Presley-King, prin. | Fax 716-3983
Fayette County Alternative S | Alt
205 Lafayette Ave 30214 | 770-460-3990
Tim Carder, prin. | Fax 460-3905
Fayette County HS | 1,500/9-12
1 Tiger Trl 30214 | 770-460-3540
Charles Warr, prin. | Fax 460-3410
Fayette MS | 800/6-8
450 Grady Ave 30214 | 770-460-3550
Sharlene Patterson, prin. | Fax 460-3882
Rising Starr MS | 1,000/6-8
183 Panther Path 30215 | 770-486-2721
Len Patton, prin. | Fax 486-2727
Starr's Mill HS | 1,600/9-12
193 Panther Path 30215 | 770-486-2710
Audrey Toney, prin. | Fax 486-2716
Whitewater HS | 1,600/9-12
100 Wildcat Way 30215 | 770-460-3935
Roy Rabold, prin. | Fax 716-3973
Whitewater MS | 800/6-8
1533 Highway 85 S 30215 | 770-460-3450
Connie Baldwin, prin. | Fax 460-0362
Fayette County Open Campus | Adult
205 LaFayette Ave 30214 | 770-460-3990
Ed Steil, prin. | Fax 460-0482
Other Schools – See Peachtree City, Tyrone

Fayette Beauty Academy | Post-Sec.
386 Glynn St N 30214 | 770-461-4669
GRACE Christian Academy | 200/PK-12
355 McDonough Rd 30214 | 770-461-0137
Rev. Wayne Turner, supt. | Fax 461-1190
Our Lady of Mercy Catholic HS | 300/9-12
861 Evander Holyfield Hwy 30214 | 770-461-2202
Brian Newhall, prin. | Fax 461-9353

Fitzgerald, Ben Hill, Pop. 8,940
Ben Hill County SD | 3,200/PK-12
509 W Palm St 31750 | 229-409-5500
Nancy Whidden, supt. | Fax 409-5513
www.ben-hill.k12.ga.us
Ben Hill County MS | 800/6-8
134 JC Hunter Rd 31750 | 229-409-5578
Tommie Dopson, prin. | Fax 409-5580
Fitzgerald HS | 800/9-12
601 W Cypress St 31750 | 229-409-5530
Stacey Bell, prin. | Fax 409-5534

Flintstone, Walker
Walker County SD
Supt. — See La Fayette
Chattanooga Valley MS | 500/6-8
847 Allgood Rd 30725 | 706-820-0735
Eugene Ward, prin. | Fax 820-0736

Flowery Branch, Hall, Pop. 5,590
Hall County SD
Supt. — See Gainesville
Davis MS | 1,200/6-8
4450 Hog Mountain Rd 30542 | 770-965-3020
Eddie Millwood, prin. | Fax 965-3025
South Hall MS | 1,200/6-8
4335 Falcon Pkwy 30542 | 770-532-4416
Paula Stubbs, prin. | Fax 967-5852

North Georgia Christian S | 200/PK-12
5285 Strickland Rd 30542 | 678-828-8350
Carol Cox, hdmstr.

Folkston, Charlton, Pop. 2,443
Charlton County SD | 1,500/PK-12
1259 Third St 31537 | 912-496-2596
Dr. John Lairsey, supt. | Fax 496-2595
www.charlton.k12.ga.us
Bethune MS | 400/4-8
285 Little Phoebe Church Rd 31537 | 912-496-2360
Nora Nettles, prin. | Fax 496-3766
Charlton County HS | 500/9-12
994 Indian Trl 31537 | 912-496-2501
Dr. Joshua Howard, prin. | Fax 496-3732

Forest Park, Clayton, Pop. 18,177
Clayton County SD
Supt. — See Jonesboro
Babb MS | 800/6-8
5500 Reynolds Rd 30297 | 404-362-3880
Felicia Brown, prin. | Fax 362-4087
Forest Park HS | 1,600/9-12
5452 Phillips Dr 30297 | 404-362-3890
Derrick Manning, prin. | Fax 608-7563
Forest Park MS | 700/6-8
930 Finley Dr 30297 | 404 362-3840
Monique Drewry, prin. | Fax 362-8899

Arnold/Padrick's Univ of Cosmetology | Post-Sec.
4971 Courtney Dr 30297 | 404-361-5641
Beauty College of America | Post-Sec.
1171 Main St 30297 | 404-361-4098

Forsyth, Monroe, Pop. 3,748
Monroe County SD | 4,000/PK-12
PO Box 1308 31029 | 478-994-2031
Anthony Pack, supt. | Fax 994-3364
www.monroe.k12.ga.us
Monroe County Achievement Ctr | Alt
25 Brooklyn Ave 31029 | 478-994-7072
Michelle Collier, coord. | Fax 994-7074
Monroe County MS - Banks Stephens Campus | 500/7-8
66 Thornton Rd 31029 | 478-994-6186
Jay Johnston, prin. | Fax 994-7061
Persons HS | 1,200/9-12
300 Montpelier Ave 31029 | 478-994-2812
Jim Finch, prin. | Fax 994-7065

Fort Gaines, Clay, Pop. 1,094
Clay County SD | 300/PK-8
PO Box 219, | 229-768-2232
Johnnie M. Grimsley, supt. | Fax 768-3654
www.clay.k12.ga.us
Clay County MS | 100/6-8
100 Hobbs Ln, | 229-768-2234
Michelle Oliver, coord. | Fax 768-2363

Fort Oglethorpe, Catoosa, Pop. 9,051
Catoosa County SD
Supt. — See Ringgold
Lakeview-Fort Oglethorpe HS | 1,000/9-12
1850 Battlefield Pkwy 30742 | 706-866-0342
Terri Vandiver, prin. | Fax 861-6645
Performance Learning Center | Alt
2 Barnhardt Cir 30742 | 706-866-1540
Lamar Brown, prin. | Fax 861-6643

Fort Valley, Peach, Pop. 9,695
Peach County SD | 4,000/K-12
523 Vineville St 31030 | 478-825-5933
Joe Ann Denning, supt. | Fax 825-9970
www.peachschools.org
Fort Valley MS | 500/6-8
712 Peggy Dr 31030 | 478-825-2413
Clemon Chester, prin. | Fax 825-1332
Peach County HS | 1,100/9-12
900 Campus Dr 31030 | 478-825-8258
Bruce Mackey, prin. | Fax 825-2290
Other Schools – See Byron

Fort Valley State University | Post-Sec.
1005 State University Dr 31030 | 478-825-6211

Franklin, Heard, Pop. 969
Heard County SD | 2,100/PK-12
PO Box 1330 30217 | 706-675-3320
Jerry Prince, supt. | Fax 675-3357
www.heard.k12.ga.us
Heard County Comprehensive HS | 600/9-12
545 Main St 30217 | 706-675-3656
Russell Sowell, prin. | Fax 675-8729
Heard County MS | 500/6-8
269 Old Field Rd 30217 | 706-675-9247
Mike Roberts, prin. | Fax 675-9255

Franklin Springs, Franklin, Pop. 938

Emmanuel College | Post-Sec.
PO Box 129 30639 | 800-860-8800

Gainesville, Hall, Pop. 33,306
Gainesville CSD | 7,000/PK-12
508 Oak St 30501 | 770-536-5275
Dr. Merrianne Dyer, supt. | Fax 287-2019
www.gcssk12.net/
Gainesville HS | 1,500/9-12
830 Century Pl 30501 | 770-536-4441
LaCrisia Larkin, prin. | Fax 287-2031
Gainesville MS | 1,400/6-8
1581 Community Way 30501 | 770-534-4237
Ken Martin, prin. | Fax 287-2022
Wood's Mill HS | 100/Alt
715 Woodsmill Rd 30501 | 770-287-2021
Dr. Lisa Sheehy, dir. | Fax 287-8639

Hall County SD | 25,800/PK-12
711 Green St NW 30501 | 770-534-1080
Will Schofield, supt. | Fax 535-7404
www.hallco.org
Chestatee HS | 1,100/9-12
3005 Sardis Rd 30506 | 770-532-1162
Suzanne Jarrard, prin. | Fax 532-2202
East Hall HS | 1,000/9-12
3534 E Hall Rd 30507 | 770-536-9921
Jeff Cooper, prin. | Fax 535-1184
East Hall MS | 900/6-8
4120 E Hall Rd 30507 | 770-531-9457
Dr. Vickie Tribble, prin. | Fax 531-2327
Johnson HS | 1,200/9-12
3305 Poplar Springs Rd 30507 | 770-536-2394
Stan Lewis, prin. | Fax 531-3046
Lanier Career Academy ALC | Alt
2723 Tumbling Creek Rd 30504 | 770-531-2330
Dr. Cindy Blakley, prin. | Fax 450-5978
North Hall HS | 1,100/9-12
4885 Mount Vernon Rd 30506 | 770-983-7331
Joe Gheesling, prin. | Fax 983-7941
North Hall MS | 900/6-8
4856 Rilla Rd 30506 | 770-983-9749
Dr. Brad Brown, prin. | Fax 983-9993
Other Schools – See Flowery Branch, Oakwood

Brenau University | Post-Sec.
500 Washington St SE 30501 | 800-252-5119
Gainesville State College | Post-Sec.
PO Box 1358 30503 | 678-717-3639
Interactive College of Technology | Post-Sec.
2323 Browns Bridge Rd 30504 | 678-450-0550
Lakeview Academy | 500/PK-12
796 Lakeview Dr 30501 | 770-532-4383
John Kennedy Ed.D., head sch | Fax 536-6142
Riverside Military Academy | 400/7-12
2001 Riverside Dr 30501 | 800-462-2338
Dr. James Benson, hdmstr. | Fax 291-3364

Garden City, Chatham, Pop. 8,628
Savannah-Chatham County SD
Supt. — See Savannah
Savannah Early College HS | 100/9-12
101 Priscilla D Thomas Way 31408 | 912-395-2535
Caroline Gordon-Jelks, admin. | Fax 201-7585

Georgetown, Quitman, Pop. 912
Quitman County SD | 400/PK-12
PO Box 248, | 229-334-4189
Allen Fort, supt. | Fax 334-2109
www.quitman.k12.ga.us/
Quitman HS | 100/9-12
173 Kaigler Rd, | 229-334-4298
Jon-Erik Jones, prin. | Fax 334-4700

Gibson, Glascock, Pop. 653
Glascock County SD | 700/PK-12
PO Box 205 30810 | 706-598-2291
James Holton, supt. | Fax 598-2611
www.glascock.k12.ga.us
Glascock County Consolidated S | 700/PK-12
1230 Panther Way 30810 | 706-598-2121
Danny Lovering, prin. | Fax 598-2611

Glennville, Tattnall, Pop. 3,528
Tattnall County SD
Supt. — See Reidsville
Glennville MS | 400/6-8
721 E Barnard St 30427 | 912-654-1467
Cindy Boyett, prin. | Fax 654-1300

Glenwood, Wheeler, Pop. 737
Wheeler County SD
Supt. — See Alamo
Transitional Alternative Prep S | Alt
PO Box 840 30428 | 912-523-5169
Benji Hartley, prin. | Fax 523-5269

Gray, Jones, Pop. 3,239
Jones County SD | 4,900/PK-12
125 Stewart Ave 31032 | 478-986-3032
William Mathews, supt. | Fax 986-4412
www.jones.k12.ga.us
Califf Learning Complex | 400/9-9
110 Maggie Califf St 31032 | 478-986-3046
Chuck Gibson, prin. | Fax 986-1504
Gray Station MS | 800/6-8
324 GA Highway 18 E 31032 | 478-986-2090
Wes Cavender, prin. | Fax 986-2099

Jones County SHS 1,100/10-12
339 Railroad St 31032 478-986-5444
Chuck Gibson, prin. Fax 986-1589
Other Schools – See Macon

Grayson, Gwinnett, Pop. 2,619
Gwinnett County SD
Supt. — See Suwanee
Bay Creek MS 1,000/6-8
821 Cooper Rd 30017 678-344-7570
Dana Pugh, prin. Fax 736-6908
Couch MS 1,000/6-8
1777 Grayson Hwy 30017 678-407-7272
Devon Williams, prin. Fax 407-7326

Greensboro, Greene, Pop. 3,310
Greene County SD 1,800/PK-12
101 E Third St 30642 706-453-7688
Dr. Barbara Pulliam-Davis, supt. Fax 454-1058
www.greene.k12.ga.us
Carson International Baccalaureate MS 400/6-8
1010 S Main St 30642 706-453-3308
Brock Miller, prin. Fax 453-4674
Greene County HS 500/9-12
1002 S Main St 30642 706-453-2271
Dr. Ray Hill, prin. Fax 453-3311

Greenville, Meriwether, Pop. 862
Meriwether County SD 3,300/PK-12
PO Box 70 30222 706-672-4297
Carol Lane, supt. Fax 672-1618
www.mcssga.org
Greenville HS 400/9-12
17656 Roosevelt Hwy 30222 706-672-4930
Thaddeus Jackson, prin. Fax 672-1424
Greenville MS 300/6-8
1250 Terrell St 30222 706-672-3115
Lashanda Acres, prin. Fax 672-3119
Other Schools – See Manchester

Griffin, Spalding, Pop. 23,259
Griffin Spalding County School System 10,700/PK-12
PO Box N 30224 770-229-3700
Dr. Curtis Jones, supt. Fax 229-3708
www.spalding.k12.ga.us
Achievement Center Alt
200 A Z Kelsey Ave 30223 770-229-9758
Jamie Cassaday, prin. Fax 229-9250
Carver Road MS 500/6-8
2185 Carver Rd 30224 770-229-3739
Eclan David, prin. Fax 229-3712
Cowan Road MS 600/6-8
1185 Cowan Rd 30223 770-229-3722
Rachelle Holloway, prin. Fax 227-8583
Griffin HS 1,400/9-12
1617 W Poplar St 30224 770-229-3752
Keith Simmons, prin. Fax 229-3752
Kennedy Road MS 600/6-8
280 Kennedy Rd 30223 770-229-3760
Dexter Sands, prin. Fax 467-4626
Rehoboth Road MS 700/6-8
1500 Rehoboth Rd 30224 770-229-3727
Lindy Pruitt, prin. Fax 229-3770
Spalding HS 1,300/9-12
433 Wilson Rd 30224 770-229-3775
Derrell Jeffcoat, prin. Fax 227-6899

Southern Crescent Technical College Post-Sec.
501 Varsity Rd 30223 770-228-7348

Grovetown, Columbia, Pop. 10,773
Columbia County SD
Supt. — See Evans
CCBOE Alternative S Alt
112 Ford Ave 30813 706-868-5715
Dr. Janet Bishop, prin. Fax 854-5819
Columbia MS 800/6-8
6000 Columbia Rd 30813 706-541-1252
Steve Cummings, prin. Fax 854-5820
Grovetown HS 1,300/9-12
2010 Warrior Way 30813 706-541-2723
Penny Jackson, prin. Fax 447-2109
Grovetown MS 800/6-8
5463 Harlem Grovetown Rd 30813 706-855-2514
Tom Smallwood, prin. Fax 854-5822

Guyton, Effingham, Pop. 1,661
Effingham County SD
Supt. — See Springfield
Effingham County MS 700/6-8
1659 GA Highway 119 S 31312 912-772-7001
Billy Hughes, prin. Fax 772-7005
South Effingham HS 1,500/9-12
1220 Noel C Conaway Rd 31312 912-728-7511
Dr. Mark Winters, prin. Fax 728-7529
South Effingham MS 900/6-8
1200 Noel C Conaway Rd 31312 912-728-7500
April Hodges, prin. Fax 728-7508

Hahira, Lowndes, Pop. 2,695
Lowndes County SD
Supt. — See Valdosta
Hahira MS 800/6-8
101 S Nelson St 31632 229-794-2838
Janet Hendley, prin. Fax 794-3564

Valwood S 400/PK-12
4380 Old US 41 N 31632 229-242-8491
Darren Pascavage, hdmstr. Fax 245-7894

Hamilton, Harris, Pop. 1,001
Harris County SD 5,000/PK-12
132 Barnes Mill Rd 31811 706-628-4206
Dr. Craig Dowling, supt. Fax 628-5609
www.harris.k12.ga.us
Educational Opportunity Center Alt
PO Box 388 31811 706-628-7452
Sanders Denham, prin. Fax 628-7480
Harris County - Carver MS 700/7-8
11696 US Highway 27 E 31811 706-628-4951
Stacey Carlisle, prin. Fax 628-5737
Harris County HS 1,500/9-12
8281 GA Highway 116 31811 706-628-4278
Roger Couch, prin. Fax 628-4335

Hampton, Henry, Pop. 6,827
Clayton County SD
Supt. — See Jonesboro
Lovejoy HS 1,900/9-12
1587 Mcdonough Rd 30228 770-473-2920
Keith Colbert, prin. Fax 473-2928
Lovejoy MS 600/6-8
1588 Lovejoy Rd 30228 770-473-2933
April Madden, prin. Fax 603-5777

Henry County SD
Supt. — See Mc Donough
Dutchtown HS 1,400/9-12
149 Mitchell Rd 30228 770-515-7510
Dr. Terry Oatts, prin. Fax 515-7515
Dutchtown MS 1,100/6-8
155 Mitchell Rd 30228 770-515-7500
Dr. Cynthia McCray, prin. Fax 515-7505
Hampton MS 800/6-8
799 Hampton Locust Grove Rd 30228 770-707-2130
Dr. Carolyn Flemister-Bell, prin. Fax 946-3545

Bible Baptist Christian S 200/PK-12
2780 Mount Carmel Rd 30228 770-946-4700
Tim Lee, admin. Fax 946-4715

Harlem, Columbia, Pop. 2,608
Columbia County SD
Supt. — See Evans
Harlem HS 700/9-12
1070 Appling Harlem Rd 30814 706-556-5980
Dietmar Perez, prin. Fax 854-5813
Harlem MS 500/6-8
375 W Forrest St 30814 706-556-5990
Carla Shelton, prin. Fax 854-5816

Hartwell, Hart, Pop. 4,400
Hart County SD 3,400/K-12
PO Box 696 30643 706-376-5141
Jerry Bell, supt. Fax 376-7046
www.hart.k12.ga.us
Hart County Academy 50/Alt
59 Fifth St 30643 706-856-7346
Mark Burns, prin. Fax 856-7288
Hart County HS 1,000/9-12
59 Fifth St 30643 706-376-5461
Kevin Gaines, prin. Fax 856-7237
Hart County MS 700/6-8
176 Powell Rd 30643 706-376-5431
Dr. Veronica Johnson, prin. Fax 376-2207

Hawkinsville, Pulaski, Pop. 4,540
Pulaski County SD 1,300/PK-12
72 Warren St 31036 478-783-7200
Jane Williams, supt. Fax 783-7204
www.pulaski.k12.ga.us
Alternative Learning Center Alt
Warren St 31036 478-783-7265
Marvin Hill, dir. Fax 783-7204
Hawkinsville HS 400/9-12
1 Red Devil Dr 31036 478-783-7210
Rosemary Wright, prin. Fax 783-7251
Pulaski County MS 300/6-8
8 Red Devil Dr 31036 478-892-7215
Larry Faulk, prin. Fax 783-7297

Hazlehurst, Jeff Davis, Pop. 4,181
Jeff Davis County SD 3,000/PK-12
PO Box 1780 31539 912-375-6700
Rob Brown, supt. Fax 375-6703
www.jeff-davis.k12.ga.us
Davis HS 700/9-12
156 Collins St 31539 912-375-6760
Cecelia McLoon, prin. Fax 375-0945
Davis MS 700/6-8
93 Collins St 31539 912-375-6750
Richard Stone, prin. Fax 375-6756

Hephzibah, Richmond, Pop. 3,910
Richmond County SD
Supt. — See Augusta
Hephzibah Comprehensive HS 1,200/9-12
4558 Brothersville Rd 30815 706-592-2089
Dr. Walter Reeves, prin. Fax 592-3975
Hephzibah MS 500/6-8
PO Box 70 30815 706-592-4534
Dr. Larina Thomas, prin. Fax 592-3979
Morgan Road MS 600/6-8
3635 Hiers Blvd 30815 706-796-4992
Dr. Shontier Barnes, prin. Fax 560-3947
Pine Hill MS 600/6-8
2147 McElmurray Rd 30815 706-592-3730
Glenda Collingsworth, prin. Fax 592-3741
Spirit Creek MS 500/6-8
115 Dolphin Way 30815 706-592-3987
Mary Braswell, prin. Fax 592-3999

Hiawassee, Towns, Pop. 877
Towns County SD 1,200/PK-12
67 Lakeview Cir Ste C 30546 706-896-2279
Melissa Williams, supt. Fax 896-2632
www.towns.k12.ga.us
Towns County HS 300/9-12
1400 Highway 76 E 30546 706-896-4131
Roy Perren, prin. Fax 896-6628
Towns County MS 300/6-8
1400 Highway 76 E 30546 706-896-4131
Dr. Darren Berrong, prin. Fax 896-6628

Hinesville, Liberty, Pop. 31,826
Liberty County SD 10,100/PK-12
200 Bradwell St 31313 912-876-2161
Dr. Judy Scherer, supt. Fax 368-6201
www.liberty.k12.ga.us/
Bradwell Institute HS 1,800/9-12
100 Pafford St 31313 912-876-6121
Scott Carrier, prin. Fax 876-6914
Frasier MS 900/6-8
910 Long Frasier Dr 31313 912-877-5367
Jermaine Williams, prin. Fax 877-3291
Liberty County HS 1,200/9-12
3216 E Oglethorpe Hwy 31313 912-876-4316
Paula Scott, prin. Fax 876-4303
Snelson-Golden MS 800/6-8
465 Coates Rd 31313 912-877-3112
Katrina Byers, prin. Fax 368-5342
Other Schools – See Midway

Hiram, Paulding, Pop. 3,455
Paulding County SD
Supt. — See Dallas
Hiram HS 1,700/9-12
702 Ballentine Dr 30141 770-443-1182
Jason Freeman, prin. Fax 439-5053

Grace Baptist Christian S 300/PK-12
5790 Powder Springs/Dallas 30141 770-222-8955
Dr. Ken Martin, admin. Fax 222-3321
Vogue Beauty School Post-Sec.
3655 Macland Rd 30141 770-943-6811

Hogansville, Troup, Pop. 3,003
Troup County SD
Supt. — See LaGrange
Callaway HS 800/9-12
221 Whitfield Rd 30230 706-845-2070
Dr. Janet Greer, prin. Fax 845-2071

Holly Springs, Cherokee, Pop. 9,005
Cherokee County SD
Supt. — See Canton
ACE Academy Alt
3921 Holly Springs Pkwy 30142 770-345-2005
Richard Landolt, prin. Fax 345-2214

Homer, Banks, Pop. 1,123
Banks County SD 2,900/K-12
102 Highway 51 S 30547 706-677-2224
Christopher Erwin, supt. Fax 677-2223
www.banks.k12.ga.us
Banks County HS 800/9-12
1486 Historic Homer Hwy # A 30547 706-677-2221
Dr. Joseph Goodroe, prin. Fax 677-2688
Banks County MS 700/6-8
712 Thompson St 30547 706-677-2277
Nancy Bentley, prin. Fax 677-5227

Homerville, Clinch, Pop. 2,408
Clinch County SD 1,400/PK-12
46 S College St 31634 912-487-5321
Dr. Gayle Hughes, supt. Fax 487-5068
www.clinchcounty.com/
Clinch County HS 400/8-12
863 Carswell St 31634 912-487-5366
Denise Brown, prin. Fax 487-3272

Hoschton, Jackson, Pop. 1,352
Gwinnett County SD
Supt. — See Suwanee
Mill Creek HS 3,500/9-12
4400 Braselton Hwy 30548 678-714-5850
Dr. Jim Markham, prin. Fax 714-5852
Osborne MS 1,600/6-8
4404 Braselton Hwy 30548 770-904-5400
John Campbell, prin. Fax 904-5408

Irwinton, Wilkinson, Pop. 587
Wilkinson County SD 1,600/PK-12
PO Box 206 31042 478-946-5521
Dr. Aaron Geter, supt. Fax 946-5565
www.wilkinson.k12.ga.us/
Wilkinson County HS 400/9-12
PO Box 547 31042 478-946-2441
Jerome Miles, prin. Fax 946-7134
Wilkinson County MS 300/6-8
PO Box 527 31042 478-946-2541
Dr. Angela Smith, prin. Fax 946-8981

Jackson, Butts, Pop. 4,955
Butts County SD 3,600/PK-12
181 N Mulberry St 30233 770-504-2300
Robert Costley, supt. Fax 504-2305
www.butts.k12.ga.us
Henderson MS 900/6-8
494 George Tate Dr 30233 770-504-2310
Renee Burgdorf, prin. Fax 504-2315
Jackson HS 1,000/9-12
717 S Harkness St 30233 770-504-2340
Jay Homan, prin. Fax 504-2341

Jasper, Pickens, Pop. 3,647
Pickens County SD 4,500/K-12
100 D B Carrol 30143 706-253-1700
Dr. Ben Desper, supt. Fax 253-1705
www.pickens.k12.ga.us/
Jasper MS 600/6-8
339 W Church St 30143 706-253-1760
Neil Howell, prin. Fax 253-1765
Pickens County MS 500/6-8
1802 Refuge Rd 30143 706-253-1830
Dr. Chris LeMieux, prin. Fax 253-1835
Pickens HS 1,200/9-12
500 Dragon Dr 30143 706-253-1800
Eddie McDonald, prin. Fax 253-1815

Chattahoochee Technical College Post-Sec.
100 Campus Dr 30143 706-253-4500

Jefferson, Jackson, Pop. 9,285
Jackson County SD 7,400/PK-12
1660 Winder Hwy 30549 706-367-5151
April Howard Ed.D., supt. Fax 367-9457
www.jackson.k12.ga.us
Gordon Street Center Alt
441 Gordon St 30549 706-367-2341
Malissa Hill, prin. Fax 367-1647
Jackson County Comprehensive HS 1,000/9-12
1668 Winder Hwy 30549 706-367-5003
Scott Smith, prin. Fax 367-5007
West Jackson MS 800/6-8
400 Gum Springs Church Rd 30549 706-654-2775
Mary Hale, prin. Fax 824-1969
Other Schools – See Athens, Commerce

Jefferson CSD 2,800/PK-12
345 Storey Ln 30549 706-367-2880
Dr. John Jackson, supt. Fax 367-2291
www.jeffcityschools.org/
Jefferson HS 800/9-12
575 Washington St 30549 706-367-2881
Dr. Kevin Smith, prin. Fax 367-1884
Jefferson MS 600/6-8
100 Dragon Dr 30549 706-367-2882
Brandy Corbett, prin. Fax 367-5207

Jeffersonville, Twiggs, Pop. 1,016
Twiggs County SD 1,000/PK-12
PO Box 232 31044 478-945-3127
Benjamin Roundtree, supt. Fax 945-3078
www.twiggs.k12.ga.us
Twiggs County HS 300/9-12
375 Watson Dr 31044 478-945-3112
Dr. Norman Hart, prin. Fax 945-3140
Twiggs County MS 300/5-8
375 Watson Dr 31044 478-945-3113
Lindsey Napier, prin. Fax 945-3140

Twiggs Academy 100/PK-12
961 Hamlin Floyd Rd 31044 478-945-3175
Fax 945-3275

Jesup, Wayne, Pop. 10,029
Wayne County SD 5,400/PK-12
555 Sunset Blvd 31545 912-427-1000
Dr. Daryl Fineran, supt. Fax 427-1004
www.wayne.k12.ga.us
Puckett MS 600/6-8
475 Durrence Rd 31545 912-427-1061
Dr. Pam Shuman, prin. Fax 427-1069
Wayne County HS 1,400/9-12
1 Jacket Dr 31545 912-427-1088
Jay Brinson, prin. Fax 427-1081
Williams MS 500/6-8
1175 S US Highway 301 31546 912-427-1025
Dr. Reggie Burgess, prin. Fax 427-1032

Altamaha Technical College Post-Sec.
1777 W Cherry St 31545 912-427-5800

Johns Creek, Fulton, Pop. 74,864
Fulton County SD
Supt. — See Atlanta
Autrey Mill MS 1,300/6-8
4110 Old Alabama Rd, 770-521-7622
Jimmy Zoll, prin. Fax 521-7630
Chattahoochee HS 1,700/9-12
5230 Taylor Rd, 770-521-7600
Tim Duncan, prin. Fax 521-7659
Johns Creek HS 1,600/9-12
5575 State Bridge Rd, 770-623-2138
Buck Greene, prin. Fax 623-2139
Northview HS 1,900/9-12
10625 Parsons Rd, 770-497-3828
Paul Brannon, prin. Fax 497-3844
River Trail MS 1,500/6-8
10795 Rogers Cir, 770-497-3860
Dawn Melin, prin. Fax 497-3866
Taylor Road MS 900/6-8
5150 Taylor Rd, 770-740-7090
Ed Williamson, prin. Fax 619-5609

Mt. Pisgah Christian S 700/PK-12
9820 Nesbit Ferry Rd, 678-336-3443

Jonesboro, Clayton, Pop. 4,639
Clayton County SD 50,200/PK-12
1058 5th Ave 30236 770-473-2700
Edmond Heatley Ed.D., supt. Fax 473-2706
www.clayton.k12.ga.us/
Fine Arts HS 9-12
2530 Mount Zion Pkwy 30236 770-473-2875
Monika Wiley, admin.
Jonesboro HS 1,200/9-12
7728 Mount Zion Blvd 30236 770-473-2855
Stephanie Johnson, prin. Fax 603-5177
Jonesboro MS 800/6-8
1308 Arnold St 30236 678-610-4331
Lisa Hightower, prin. Fax 610-4347
Kendrick MS 800/6-8
7971 Kendrick Rd 30238 770-472-8400
Marcus Jackson, prin. Fax 472-8413
Mt. Zion HS 1,600/9-12
2535 Mount Zion Pkwy 30236 770-473-2940
Melvin Blocker, prin. Fax 473-2784
Mundy's Mill HS 1,700/9-12
9652 Fayetteville Rd 30238 678-817-3000
William Greene, prin. Fax 817-3007
Mundy's Mill MS 800/6-8
1251 Mundys Mill Rd 30238 770-473-2880
William Greene, prin. Fax 603-5779
Perry Learning Center Vo/Tech
137 Spring St 30236 770-515-7601
Terry Young, dir. Fax 515-7689

Pointe South MS 800/6-8
8495 Thomas Rd 30238 770-473-2890
Dean Lillard, prin. Fax 477-4603
Roberts MS 700/6-8
1905 Walt Stephens Rd 30236 678-479-0100
Charmine Johnson, prin. Fax 479-0114
Other Schools – See College Park, Forest Park, Hampton, Morrow, Rex, Riverdale

Everest Institute Post-Sec.
6431 Tara Blvd 30236 770-603-0000
Laurus Technical Institute Post-Sec.
9540 Tara Blvd 30236 770-477-2799

Kathleen, Houston
Houston County SD
Supt. — See Perry
Mossy Creek MS 700/6-8
200 Danny Carpenter Dr 31047 478-988-6171
Dr. Andy Gentry, prin. Fax 218-7538
Veterans HS 9-12
340 Piney Grove Rd 31047 478-218-7537
Dr. Lionel Brown, prin. Fax 217-7570

Kennesaw, Cobb, Pop. 28,907
Cobb County SD
Supt. — See Marietta
Awtrey MS 900/6-8
3601 Nowlin Rd NW 30144 770-975-6615
Jeffrey Crawford, prin. Fax 975-6617
Harrison HS 2,100/9-12
4500 Due West Rd NW 30152 678-594-8104
Donald Griggers, prin. Fax 594-8106
Kennesaw Mountain HS 2,000/9-12
1898 Kennesaw Due West Rd 30152 678-594-8190
Dr. Kevin Daniel, prin. Fax 594-8192
Lost Mountain MS 1,100/6-8
700 Old Mountain Rd NW 30152 678-594-8224
Candace Wilkes, prin. Fax 594-8226
McClure MS 1,200/6-8
3660 Old Stilesboro Rd NW 30152 678-331-8131
Kelly Metcalfe, prin. Fax 331-8132
North Cobb HS 2,600/9-12
3400 Highway 293 N 30144 770-975-6685
Dr. Phillip Page, prin. Fax 975-6687
Palmer MS 1,000/6-8
690 N Booth Rd NW 30144 770-591-5020
Cathy Wentworth, prin. Fax 591-5032
Pine Mountain MS 700/6-8
2720 Pine Mountain Cir NW 30152 678-594-8252
Lisa Jackson, prin. Fax 594-8254

Cobb Beauty College Post-Sec.
3096 Cherokee St NW 30144 770-424-6915
Devereux-Georgia Treatment Network Post-Sec.
PO Box 1688 30156 800-342-3357
Empire Beauty School Post-Sec.
425 Ernest Barrett Pkwy #H2 30144 770-419-2303
ITT Technical Institute Post-Sec.
2065 ITT Tech Way NW 30144 770-426-2300
Kennesaw State University Post-Sec.
1000 Chastain Rd NW 30144 770-423-6000
Mount Paran Christian S 1,100/PK-12
1275 Stanley Rd NW 30152 770-578-0182
Dr. David Tilley, hdmstr. Fax 977-9284
North Cobb Christian S 700/PK-12
4500 Lakeview Dr NW 30144 770-975-0252
Todd Clingman, hdmstr. Fax 975-8446
Shiloh Hills Christian S 300/PK-12
260 Hawkins Store Rd NE 30144 770-926-7729
John Ward, admin. Fax 926-3762

Kingsland, Camden, Pop. 15,425
Camden County SD 9,400/PK-12
311 S East St 31548 912-729-5687
Dr. William Hardin, supt. Fax 729-1489
www.camden.k12.ga.us
Camden County HS 2,800/9-12
6300 Laurel Island Pkwy 31548 912-729-7318
Dr. John Tucker, prin. Fax 729-7627
Camden MS 1,100/6-8
1300 Middle School Rd 31548 912-729-3113
Mark Durham, prin. Fax 729-7489
Other Schools – See Saint Marys

La Fayette, Walker, Pop. 6,986
Walker County SD 9,200/PK-12
201 S Duke St 30728 706-638-1240
Damon Raines, supt. Fax 638-7827
www.walkerschools.org
La Fayette HS 1,200/9-12
100 Rambler Dr 30728 706-638-2342
Mike Culberson, prin. Fax 638-4767
La Fayette MS 1,000/6-8
419 Roadrunner Blvd 30728 706-638-6440
Karen Hughes, prin. Fax 638-7616
Other Schools – See Flintstone, Rossville

LaGrange, Troup, Pop. 29,111
Troup County SD 12,000/PK-12
100 N Davis Rd 30241 706-812-7900
Dr. Cole Pugh, supt. Fax 812-7904
www.troup.org/
Callaway MS 700/6-8
2244 Hammett Rd 30241 706-845-2080
Tina Johnson, prin. Fax 845-2081
Gardner-Newman MS 1,000/6-8
101 Shannon Dr 30241 706-883-1535
Anne Cook, prin. Fax 883-1562
Hope Academy Alt
200 Mooty Bridge Rd 30240 706-812-7988
Karla Fagg, prin. Fax 812-7927
La Grange HS 1,400/9-12
516 N Greenwood St 30240 706-883-1590
Dr. Penny Johnson, prin. Fax 812-7976

Long Cane MS 900/6-8
326 Long Cane Rd 30240 706-845-2085
Chip Giles, prin. Fax 845-2086
Troup County Comprehensive HS 1,300/9-12
1920 Hamilton Rd 30241 706-812-7957
Chip Medders, prin. Fax 812-7960
Other Schools – See Hogansville

Lafayette Christian S 400/PK-12
1904 Hamilton Rd 30241 706-884-6684
John Cipolla, hdmstr. Fax 882-2515
LaGrange Academy 200/K-12
1501 Vernon Rd 30240 706-882-8097
Carl Parke, head sch Fax 882-8640
LaGrange College Post-Sec.
601 Broad St 30240 706-880-8000
West Georgia Technical College Post-Sec.
1 College Cir 30240 706-845-4323

Lakeland, Lanier, Pop. 3,308
Lanier County SD 1,700/PK-12
247 S Highway 221 31635 229-482-3966
Dr. Keith Humphrey, supt. Fax 482-3020
www.lanier.k12.ga.us/
Lanier County HS 400/9-12
52 W Patten Ave 31635 229-482-3868
Gene Culpepper, prin. Fax 482-3368
Lanier County MS 400/6-8
52 W Patten Ave 31635 229-482-8247
Reada Hamm, prin. Fax 482-3643

Lawrenceville, Gwinnett, Pop. 27,847
Gwinnett County SD
Supt. — See Suwanee
Archer HS 1,700/9-12
2255 New Hope Rd 30045 678-407-7700
Ken Johnson, prin. Fax 407-7725
Central Gwinnet HS 2,600/9-12
564 W Crogan St 30046 770-963-8041
Maryanne Grimes, prin. Fax 338-4879
Creekland MS 2,300/6-8
170 Russell Rd 30043 770-338-4700
Dr. Eddie Maresh, prin. Fax 338-4703
Crews MS 1,200/6-8
1000 Old Snellville Hwy 30044 770-982-6940
Dr. Vince Botta, prin. Fax 982-6942
Five Forks MS 1,100/6-8
3250 River Dr 30044 770-972-1506
Peggy Goodman, prin. Fax 736-4547
Gwinnett InterVention Education Ctr East 300/Alt
723 Hi Hope Rd 30043 770-338-4855
Jay Paschall, prin. Fax 338-4899
Moore MS 6-8
1221 Lawrenceville Hwy 30046 678-226-7100
Lamont Mays, prin. Fax 226-7103
Mountain View HS 1,700/9-12
2351 Sunny Hill Rd 30043 678-407-7600
Keith Chaney, prin. Fax 407-7605
Phoenix HS 400/9-12
501 W Pike St 30046 770-513-6862
Donna Scott, prin. Fax 513-6864
Richards MS 2,200/6-8
3555 Sugarloaf Pkwy 30044 770-995-7133
Mark McCain, prin. Fax 338-4791
Sweetwater MS 1,800/6-8
3500 Cruse Rd 30044 770-923-4131
Georgann Eaton, prin. Fax 931-7077

Empire Beauty School Post-Sec.
1455 Pleasant Hill Rd #105 30044 770-564-0725
Georgia Gwinnett College Post-Sec.
1000 University Center Ln 30043 678-407-5000
Gerard Preparatory S 100/PK-12
1288 Braselton Hwy 30043 770-277-4722
J.G. Sinclair, admin. Fax 277-4365
Gwinnett Technical College Post-Sec.
5150 Sugarloaf Pkwy 30043 770-962-7580
Strong Wall Academy 100/PK-12
PO Box 1647 30046 678-679-3070
Anthony Knight, hdmstr. Fax 679-3075

Leesburg, Lee, Pop. 2,853
Lee County SD 5,600/PK-12
PO Box 399 31763 229-903-2100
Dr. Lawrence Walters, supt. Fax 903-2130
www.lee.k12.ga.us
Lee County 9th Grade Campus 400/9-9
370 Leslie Hwy 31763 229-903-3590
Dr. Jamie Horne, prin. Fax 903-3595
Lee County HS 1,300/10-12
1 Trojan Way 31763 229-903-2260
Kevin Dowling, prin. Fax 903-2291
Lee County MS 1,100/7-8
190 Smithville Rd N 31763 229-903-2140
Susan Manry, prin. Fax 903-2160
Transitional Learning Center Alt
185 Firetower Rd 31763 229-903-3920
Tim Mears, dir. Fax 903-3925

Lexington, Oglethorpe, Pop. 225
Oglethorpe County SD 2,400/PK-12
735 Athens Rd 30648 706-743-8128
Dr. Veta New, supt. Fax 743-3211
www.oglethorpe.k12.ga.us
Oglethorpe County HS 700/9-12
749 Athens Rd 30648 706-743-8124
Dr. Darrell Wetherington, prin. Fax 743-3536
Other Schools – See Crawford

Lilburn, Gwinnett, Pop. 11,365
Gwinnett County SD
Supt. — See Suwanee
Berkmar HS 3,000/9-12
405 Pleasant Hill Rd NW 30047 770-921-3636
Dr. Michael Zinn, prin. Fax 806-3715

Berkmar MS 1,000/6-8
4355 Lawrenceville Hwy NW 30047 770-638-2300
Kenney Wells, prin. Fax 638-2309
Lilburn MS 1,300/6-8
4994 Lawrenceville Hwy NW 30047 770-921-1776
Dr. Gene Taylor, prin. Fax 806-3866
Parkview HS 2,700/9-12
998 Cole Dr SW 30047 770-921-2874
David Smith, prin. Fax 806-3797
Trickum MS 1,900/6-8
130 Killian Hill Rd SW 30047 770-921-2705
Kay Sands, prin. Fax 806-3742

Gwinnett College Post-Sec.
4230 Lawrencevll Hwy NW #11 30047 770-381-7200
Killian Hill Christian S 500/K-12
151 Arcado Rd SW 30047 770-921-3224
Providence Christian Academy 600/K-12
4575 Lawrenceville Hwy NW 30047 770-279-7200
Dr. James Vaught, hdmstr. Fax 279-8258

Lincolnton, Lincoln, Pop. 1,557
Lincoln County SD 1,100/PK-12
PO Box 39 30817 706-359-3742
Dr. Jeff Carney, supt. Fax 359-7938
www.lincolncountyschools.org
Lincoln County HS 400/9-12
200 Charles Ward Elam Dr 30817 706-359-3121
Howie Gunby, prin. Fax 359-3552
Lincoln County MS 200/6-8
343 Ward Ave 30817 706-359-3069
Pam Carmichael, prin. Fax 359-2200

Lindale, Floyd, Pop. 4,135
Floyd County SD
Supt. — See Rome
Pepperell HS 900/9-12
3 Dragon Dr SE 30147 706-236-1844
Phil Ray, prin. Fax 236-1846
Pepperell MS 700/6-8
200 Hughes Dairy Rd SE 30147 706-236-1849
Becky McCoy, prin. Fax 802-6776

Lithia Springs, Douglas, Pop. 15,167
Douglas County SD
Supt. — See Douglasville
Lithia Springs HS 1,800/9-12
2520 E County Line Rd 30122 770-651-6700
Dr. Garrick Askew, prin. Fax 732-2644
Turner MS 600/6-8
7101 Turner Dr 30122 770-651-5500
Kwame Carr, prin. Fax 651-5503

Colonial Hills Christian S 300/PK-12
7131 Mount Vernon Rd 30122 770-941-6342
David Hicks, admin. Fax 941-2090
Lithia Christian Academy 100/PK-12
2548 Vulcan Dr 30122 770-941-5406
Lanier Motes, admin. Fax 941-9599

Lithonia, DeKalb, Pop. 1,901
DeKalb County SD
Supt. — See Stone Mountain
Arabia Mountain HS 1,500/9-12
6610 Browns Mill Rd 30038 678-875-3602
Rodney Swanson, prin. Fax 875-3610
King HS 1,700/9-12
3991 Snapfinger Rd 30038 678-874-5402
Vivian Terry, prin. Fax 874-5410
Lithonia HS 1,400/9-12
2440 Phillips Rd 30058 678-676-2902
Angela Moten, prin. Fax 676-2910
Lithonia MS 1,200/6-8
2451 Randall Ave 30058 678-875-0702
Lisa McGhee, prin. Fax 875-0710
Miller Grove HS 1,600/9-12
2645 DeKalb Medical Pkwy 30058 678-875-1102
Matthew Priester, prin. Fax 875-1110
Redan MS 900/6-8
1775 Young Rd 30058 678-874-7902
Donald Mason, prin. Fax 874-7910
Salem MS 1,100/6-8
5333 Salem Rd 30038 678-676-9402
Shelia Johnson-Reese, prin. Fax 676-9410

Luther Rice Seminary and University Post-Sec.
3038 Evans Mill Rd 30038 770-484-1204

Locust Grove, Henry, Pop. 5,279
Henry County SD
Supt. — See Mc Donough
Locust Grove HS 1,100/9-12
3275 S Ola Rd 30248 770-898-1452
Lisa Gugino, prin. Fax 898-7076
Locust Grove MS 900/6-8
3315 S Ola Rd 30248 770-957-6055
Tony Townsend, prin. Fax 957-7160
Luella HS 2,000/9-12
603 Walker Dr 30248 770-898-9822
Jerry Smith, prin. Fax 898-9625
Luella MS 800/6-8
2075 Hmpton Locust Grove Rd 30248 678-583-8919
Walter Buttler, prin. Fax 583-8920

Strong Rock Christian S 800/PK-12
4200 Strong Rock Pkwy 30248 678-833-1200
Patrick Stuart M.A., head sch Fax 833-1396

Loganville, Walton, Pop. 10,219
Gwinnett County SD
Supt. — See Suwanee
Grayson HS 2,700/9-12
50 Hope Hollow Rd 30052 770-554-1071
David Hopson, prin. Fax 554-1074
McConnell MS 1,400/6-8
550 Ozora Rd 30052 770-554-1000
Clent Chatham, prin. Fax 554-1003
Snell MS 1,200/6-8
3800 Brushy Fork Rd 30052 770-554-7750
Joyce Spraggs, prin. Fax 554-7749

Walton County SD
Supt. — See Monroe
Loganville HS 1,500/9-12
100 Trident Trl 30052 678-684-2880
Mike Robison, prin. Fax 684-2955
Loganville MS 1,100/6-8
152 Clark McCullers Dr 30052 678-684-2960
Christy Bowman, prin. Fax 684-2983
Walnut Grove HS 1,000/9-12
4863 Guthrie Cemetery Rd 30052 678-507-3900
Thomas Boutwell, prin. Fax 507-3901
Walton County Alternative Education Alt
152 Clark McCullers Dr 30052 678-684-2980
Meredith Cannon, prin. Fax 684-2983
Youth MS 1,100/6-8
1804 Highway 81 30052 678-684-2710
David Todd, prin. Fax 466-8596

Covenant Christian Academy 300/PK-12
3425 Loganville Hwy 30052 770-466-7890
Emmaline McKinnon, admin. Fax 466-2833
Faith Academy 500/9-12
2571 Highway 78 30052 770-466-7872
Loganville Christian Academy 500/PK-12
2575 Highway 81 30052 770-554-9888
Christy Monda, admin. Fax 554-9881

Lookout Mountain, Walker, Pop. 1,588

Covenant College Post-Sec.
14049 Scenic Hwy 30750 706-820-1560

Louisville, Jefferson, Pop. 2,485
Jefferson County SD 3,000/PK-12
1001 Peachtree St 30434 478-625-7626
Dr. Molly Howard, supt. Fax 625-7459
www.jefferson.k12.ga.us
Hi Tech S Alt
1200 School St 30434 478-625-7764
Teresa Brooks, prin. Fax 625-3120
Jefferson County HS 900/9-12
1157 Warrior Trl 30434 478-625-9991
Dr. Alan Long, prin. Fax 625-8988
Louisville MS 300/6-8
1200 School St 30434 478-625-7764
Ken Hildebrant, prin. Fax 625-3120
Other Schools – See Wrens

Jefferson Academy 200/K-12
2264 US Highway 1 N 30434 478-625-8861
Chuck Wimberley, hdmstr. Fax 625-9196

Ludowici, Long, Pop. 1,650
Long County SD 2,600/PK-12
PO Box 428 31316 912-545-2367
Dr. Robert Waters, supt. Fax 545-2380
www.longcountyps.com
Long County HS 600/9-12
PO Box 579 31316 912-545-2135
Scotty Hattaway, prin. Fax 545-2136
Walker MS 1,000/4-8
PO Box 729 31316 912-545-2069
Heath Crane, prin. Fax 545-2775

Lumpkin, Stewart, Pop. 2,722
Stewart County SD 500/PK-12
PO Box 547 31815 229-838-4329
Floyd Fort, supt. Fax 838-6984
www.stewart.k12.ga.us/
Stewart County HS 100/9-12
PO Box 706 31815 229-838-4301
John Hamilton, admin. Fax 838-4352
Stewart County MS 100/6-8
PO Box 706 31815 229-838-4301
Viola Fedd, prin. Fax 838-4352

Lyons, Toombs, Pop. 4,285
Toombs County SD 3,000/PK-12
117 E Wesley Ave 30436 912-526-3141
Dr. Kim Corley, supt. Fax 526-3291
www.toombs.k12.ga.us
Toombs County HS 800/9-12
600 Bulldog Rd 30436 912-526-6068
Dr. Tosha Middlebrooks, prin. Fax 526-4612
Toombs County MS 700/6-8
701 Bulldog Rd 30436 912-526-8363
Pam Sears, prin. Fax 526-0240

Toombs Christian Academy 300/PK-12
PO Box 227 30436 912-526-8938
Jon Dorminey, hdmstr. Fax 526-0571

Mableton, Cobb, Pop. 36,289
Cobb County SD
Supt. — See Marietta
Floyd MS 800/6-8
4803 Floyd Rd SW 30126 770-819-2453
Teresa Hargrett, prin. Fax 819-2455
Lindley MS 1,300/7-8
50 Veterans Memorial Hwy SE 30126 770-819-2496
Mike Bivens, prin. Fax 819-2498
Pebblebrook HS 2,100/9-12
991 Old Alabama Rd SW 30126 770-819-2521
Zinta Perkins, prin. Fax 819-2523

Cumberland Christian Academy 100/6-8
4900 Floyd Rd SW 30126 770-819-9942
Dr. Lee Campbell, hdmstr. Fax 819-9091
Whitefield Academy 700/PK-12
1 Whitefield Dr SE 30126 678-305-3000
Kevin Bracher Ph.D., hdmstr. Fax 305-3010

Mc Donough, Henry, Pop. 21,578
Henry County SD 40,700/PK-12
33 N Zack Hinton Pkwy 30253 770-957-6601
Dr. Ethan Hildreth, supt. Fax 914-6178
www.henry.k12.ga.us
Eagle's Landing HS 1,200/9-12
301 Tunis Rd 30253 770-954-9515
Gabriel Crerie, prin. Fax 914-9789
Eagle's Landing MS 900/6-8
295 Tunis Rd 30253 770-914-8189
Dr. Earlene Crump, prin. Fax 914-2989
Henry County HS 1,100/9-12
401 Tomlinson St 30253 770-957-3943
Scott John, prin. Fax 957-0368
Henry County MS 800/6-8
166 Holly Smith Dr 30253 770-957-3945
Dr. Kimberly Anderson, prin. Fax 957-0368
Mainstay Academy Alt
354 N Ola Rd 30252 678-432-2310
George Eckerle, prin. Fax 432-3190
Ola HS 1,500/9-12
357 N Ola Rd 30252 770-288-3222
Ross Iddings, prin. Fax 288-3230
Ola MS 1,200/6-8
353 N Ola Rd 30252 770-288-2108
Kathleen Truitt, prin. Fax 288-2114
Union Grove HS 1,600/9-12
120 E Lake Rd 30252 678-583-8502
Tom Smith, prin. Fax 583-8850
Union Grove MS 1,200/6-8
210 E Lake Rd 30252 678-583-8978
Tom Moreland, prin. Fax 583-8580
Other Schools – See Hampton, Locust Grove, Stockbridge

Creekside Christian Academy 600/PK-12
175 Foster Dr 30253 770-961-9300
Rodney Knox, hdmstr. Fax 960-1875
Eagle's Landing Christian Academy 1,100/PK-12
2400 Highway 42 N 30253 770-957-2927
Marshall Chambers, hdmstr. Fax 957-2290

Macon, Bibb, Pop. 90,157
Bibb County SD 24,900/PK-12
484 Mulberry St 31201 478-765-8711
Dr. Stephen Smith, supt. Fax 765-8549
www.bibb.k12.ga.us
Appling MS 600/6-8
1210 Shurling Dr 31211 478-779-2200
Steven Jones, prin. Fax 779-2202
Ballard-Hudson MS 500/6-8
1070 Anthony Rd 31204 478-779-3400
Kenneth Lanier, prin. Fax 779-3396
Bloomfield MS 500/6-8
4375 Bloomfield Drive Ext 31206 478-779-4800
Dr. Shannon Norfleet, prin. Fax 779-4760
Central HS 1,100/9-12
2155 Napier Ave 31204 478-779-2300
Dr. Efrem Yarber, prin. Fax 779-2307
Howard HS 1,100/9-12
6400 Forsyth Rd 31210 478-779-4850
Matt Adams, prin. Fax 779-4860
Howard MS 1,000/6-8
6600 Forsyth Rd 31210 478-779-3500
Dr. Eric Carlyle, prin. Fax 779-3458
Hutchings Career Center Vo/Tech
2011 Riverside Dr 31204 478-779-2550
Darrick McCray, prin. Fax 779-2540
Miller MS 800/6-8
751 Hendley St 31204 478-779-4050
Dr. Sherri Flagg, prin. Fax 779-4032
Neel Academy Alt
2840 Hollis Rd 31206 478-779-3700
Dr. Beverly Glover, prin. Fax 779-3711
Northeast HS 800/9-12
1646 Upper River Rd 31211 478-779-4100
Dr. Quintin Green, prin. Fax 779-4136
Rutland HS 1,100/9-12
6250 Skipper Rd 31216 478-779-3100
Dr. Jerri Hall, prin. Fax 779-3045
Rutland MS 1,000/6-8
6260 Skipper Rd 31216 478-779-4400
Dr. Richard Key, prin. Fax 779-4373
Southwest HS 1,000/9-12
1775 Williamson Rd 31206 478-779-4500
Dr. Tanzy Kilcrease, prin. Fax 779-4484
Weaver MS 900/6-8
2570 Heath Rd 31206 478-779-4650
Jim Montgomery, prin. Fax 779-4627
Westside HS 1,100/9-12
2851 Heath Rd 31206 478-779-3800
Dr. Julia Daniely, prin. Fax 779-3832

Jones County SD
Supt. — See Gray
Clifton Ridge MS 500/6-8
169 Dusty Ln 31211 478-743-5182
Charles Lundy, prin. Fax 743-8282

American Professional Institute Post-Sec.
1667 Eisenhower Pkwy 31206 478-314-4444
Central Fellowship Christian Academy 300/PK-12
8460 Hawkinsville Rd 31216 478-788-6909
Jeremiah Sattazahn, hdmstr. Fax 788-1614
Central Georgia Technical College Post-Sec.
3300 Macon Tech Dr 31206 478-757-3400
Covenant Academy 400/PK-12
4652 Ayers Rd 31210 478-471-0285
Dr. Jake Walters, hdmstr. Fax 471-8884
First Presbyterian Day S 900/PK-12
5671 Calvin Dr 31210 478-477-6505
Gregg Thompson, hdmstr. Fax 477-2804

Georgia Academy for the Blind Post-Sec.
2895 Vineville Ave 31204 478-751-6083
Macon State College Post-Sec.
100 College Station Dr 31206 478-471-2700
Medical Center of Central Georgia Post-Sec.
777 Hemlock St 31201 478-633-1234
Mercer University in Macon Post-Sec.
1400 Coleman Ave 31207 478-301-2700
Middle Georgia Christian S 100/PK-12
5859 Thomaston Rd 31220 478-757-9585
Miller-Motte Technical College Post-Sec.
175 Tom Hill Sr Blvd 31210 478-803-4800
Montessori of Macon 100/PK-12
855 Tolliver Pl 31210 478-757-8927
Elizabeth Irwin, dir. Fax 846-7314
Mount de Sales Academy 700/6-12
851 Orange St 31201 478-751-3240
David Held, pres. Fax 751-3241
Stratford Academy 1,000/PK-12
6010 Peake Rd 31220 478-477-8073
Dr. Robert Veto, head sch Fax 477-0299
Tattnall Square Academy 600/PK-12
111 Trojan Trl 31210 478-477-6760
Dr. Brenda Shuman-Riley, head sch Fax 474-7887
Virginia College Post-Sec.
1901 Paul Walsh Dr 31206 478-803-4600
Wesleyan College Post-Sec.
4760 Forsyth Rd 31210 800-447-6610
Windsor Academy 300/PK-12
4150 Jones Rd 31216 478-781-1621
Dr. John Cranford, admin. Fax 781-0757

Mc Rae, Telfair, Pop. 5,685
Telfair County SD 1,800/PK-12
PO Box 240 31055 229-868-5661
Lenard Harrelson, supt. Fax 868-5549
www.telfairschools.org
Telfair County HS 400/9-12
PO Box 240 31055 229-868-6096
Daymond Ray, prin. Fax 868-7221
Telfair County MS 300/6-8
PO Box 240 31055 229-868-7465
Christopher Ellis, prin. Fax 868-2616

Madison, Morgan, Pop. 3,935
Morgan County SD 3,400/PK-12
1065 East Ave 30650 706-752-4600
Dr. Ralph Bennett, supt. Fax 752-4601
www.morgan.k12.ga.us
Morgan County Crossroads Alternative S Alt
1551 Bethany Rd 30650 706-342-5041
Dr. Jannie Broadnax, prin. Fax 343-1015

Manchester, Meriwether, Pop. 4,197
Meriwether County SD
Supt. — See Greenville
Manchester HS 500/9-12
405 N 5th Ave 31816 706-846-8445
Dr. Michael Lehr, prin. Fax 846-5001
Manchester MS 400/6-8
231 W Perry St 31816 706-846-2846
Josette Brown, prin. Fax 846-0111

Marietta, Cobb, Pop. 54,999
Cobb County SD 105,800/PK-12
514 Glover St SE 30060 770-426-3300
Dr. Michael Hinojosa, supt. Fax 426-3329
www.cobb.k12.ga.us
Daniell MS 1,000/6-8
2900 Scott Rd 30066 678-594-8048
David Nelson, prin. Fax 594-8050
Dickerson MS 1,100/6-8
855 Woodlawn Dr NE 30068 770-578-2710
Carole Brink, prin. Fax 578-2712
Dodgen MS 1,100/6-8
1725 Bill Murdock Rd 30062 770-578-2726
Robin Lattizori, prin. Fax 578-2728
East Cobb MS 1,300/6-8
380 Holt Rd NE 30068 770-578-2740
Tiffany Honore, prin. Fax 578-2742
Hightower Trail MS 1,000/6-8
3905 Post Oak Tritt Rd 30062 770-578-7225
Laura Montgomery, prin. Fax 578-7227
Kell HS 1,700/9-12
4770 Lee Waters Rd 30066 678-494-7844
Ed Wagner, prin. Fax 494-7846
Lassiter HS 2,000/9-12
2601 Shallowford Rd 30066 678-494-7863
Dr. Chris Richie, prin. Fax 494-7865
Mabry MS 900/6-8
2700 Jims Rd NE 30066 770-928-5546
Merrilee Heflin, prin. Fax 928-5548
McCleskey MS 700/6-8
4080 Maybreeze Rd 30066 770-928-5560
Claire Lyons, prin. Fax 928-5562
Oakwood Digital Academy 100/Alt
1560 Joyner Ave SE 30060 678-594-8240
David Pearce, prin. Fax 594-8241
Osborne HS 1,700/9-12
2451 Favor Rd SW 30060 770-437-5900
Josh Morreale, prin. Fax 437-5902
Performance Learning Center Alt
1560 Joyner Ave SE 30060 678-331-1098
Elaine Bush, prin. Fax 331-1058
Pope HS 1,800/9-12
3001 Hembree Rd NE 30062 770-578-7900
Dr. Robert Downs, prin. Fax 578-7902
Simpson MS 800/6-8
3340 Trickum Rd NE 30066 770-971-4711
Andrew Bristow, prin. Fax 971-4507
Smitha MS 900/6-8
2025 Powder Springs Rd SW 30064 678-594-8267
Clint Terza, prin. Fax 594-8269
Sprayberry HS 1,800/9-12
2525 Sandy Plains Rd 30066 770-578-3200
Hilda Wilkins, prin. Fax 578-3202

Wheeler HS 2,100/9-12
375 Holt Rd NE 30068 770-578-3266
David Chiprany, prin. Fax 578-3268
Adult Education Center Adult
240 Barber Rd SE 30060 678-594-8011
Cherry Gipson, prin. Fax 594-8015
Other Schools – See Acworth, Austell, Kennesaw, Mableton, Powder Springs, Smyrna

Marietta CSD 7,800/K-12
250 Howard St NE 30060 770-422-3500
Dr. Emily Lembeck, supt. Fax 425-4095
www.marietta-city.org
Marietta HS 2,000/9-12
1171 Whitlock Ave SW 30064 770-428-2631
Leigh Colburn, prin. Fax 429-3151
Marietta MS 1,100/7-8
121 Winn St NW 30064 770-422-0311
Dr. Timothy Jones, prin. Fax 429-3162
Woods-Wilkins Center Alt
353 Lemon St NE Ste B 30060 770-429-3188
Tammie Roach, admin. Fax 429-3189

Chattahoochee Technical College Post-Sec.
980 S Cobb Dr SE 30060 770-528-4545
Covenant Christian Ministries Academy 100/PK-12
PO Box 4065 30061 770-919-0022
Vanessa Anderson, supt. Fax 919-2098
Cumberland Christian Academy 100/9-12
2115 Pair Rd SW 30008 770-423-0404
Dr. Lee Campbell, hdmstr. Fax 423-0366
Dominion Christian HS 200/6-12
4607 Burnt Hickory Rd NW 30064 770-420-2153
Joe Bradley, hdmstr. Fax 420-2510
Everest Institute Post-Sec.
1600 Terrell Rd Ste G 30067 770-303-7997
Life University Post-Sec.
1269 Barclay Cir SE 30060 770-426-2600
Lincoln College of Technology Post-Sec.
2359 Windy Hill Rd Ste 100 30067 770-226-0056
Southern Polytech State University Post-Sec.
1100 S Marietta Pkwy SE 30060 678-915-7778
Toni & Guy Hairdressing Academy Post-Sec.
1355 Roswell Rd Ste 150 30062 770-565-3285
Walker S 1,000/PK-12
700 Cobb Pkwy N 30062 770-427-2689
Jack Hall, head sch Fax 514-8122

Martinez, Columbia, Pop. 34,798
Columbia County SD
Supt. — See Evans
Stallings Island MS 600/6-8
3830 Blackstone Camp Rd 30907 706-447-2106
Don Putnam, prin. Fax 447-2103

Augusta Christian S 500/PK-12
313 Baston Rd 30907 706-863-2905
Dr. David Piccolo, head sch Fax 860-6618
Augusta Preparatory Day S 600/PK-12
285 Flowing Wells Rd 30907 706-863-1006
Rebecca Gilmore, head sch Fax 863-6198

Metter, Candler, Pop. 4,108
Candler County SD 2,100/PK-12
210 S College St 30439 912-685-5713
Dr. Thomas Bigwood, supt. Fax 685-3068
www.metter.org
Metter HS 500/9-12
34905 GA Highway 129 S 30439 912-685-2134
John Jordan, prin. Fax 685-2897
Metter MS 400/6-8
431 W Vertia St 30439 912-685-5580
Ralph Carlyle, prin. Fax 685-4970

Midland, Muscogee
Muscogee County SD
Supt. — See Columbus
Midland MS 800/6-8
6990 Warm Springs Rd 31820 706-569-3673
Richard Green, prin. Fax 569-3678

Midway, Liberty, Pop. 2,059
Liberty County SD
Supt. — See Hinesville
Midway MS 700/6-8
425 Edgewater Dr 31320 912-884-6677
Debra Frazier, prin. Fax 884-5944

Milledgeville, Baldwin, Pop. 17,451
Baldwin County SD 5,800/PK-12
PO Box 1188 31059 478-453-4176
Geneva Braziel, supt. Fax 457-3327
www.baldwin-county-schools.com
Baldwin HS 1,400/9-12
155 GA Highway 49 W 31061 478-453-6429
Dr. Jessica Swain, prin. Fax 451-3032
Oak Hill MS 1,100/6-8
356 Blandy Rd NW 31061 478-457-3370
Dr. Linda Ramsey, prin. Fax 457-2422

American Professional Institute Post-Sec.
2485 N Columbia St Ste 114 31061 478-452-3900
Central Georgia Technical College Post-Sec.
54 GA Highway 22 W 31061
Georgia College & State University Post-Sec.
231 W Hancock St 31061 478-445-5004
Georgia Military College Post-Sec.
201 E Greene St 31061 478-445-2700
Milledge Academy 500/PK-12
197 Log Cabin Rd NE 31061 478-452-5570

Millen, Jenkins, Pop. 3,092
Jenkins County SD 1,500/PK-12
1152 E Winthrope Ave 30442 478-982-6000
Tara Cooper, supt. Fax 982-6002
www.jchs.com/

Jenkins County HS 400/9-12
433 Barney Ave 30442 478-982-4791
Rob Gray, prin. Fax 982-6015
Jenkins County MS 300/6-8
409 Barney Ave 30442 478-982-1063
Randy Dailey, prin. Fax 982-6015
Millen Alternative S Alt
Old Sylvania Rd 30442 478-982-6023
Ray Miller, prin. Fax 982-6002

Milton, Fulton, Pop. 31,916
Fulton County SD
Supt. — See Atlanta
Hopewell MS 1,200/6-8
13060 Cogburn Rd, 678-297-3240
Lenora Patterson, prin. Fax 297-3250
Northwestern MS 1,300/6-8
12805 Birmingham Hwy, 770-667-2870
Jasmine Kullar, prin. Fax 667-2878

Monroe, Walton, Pop. 12,993
Walton County SD 13,200/PK-12
200 Double Spring Church SW 30656 770-266-4417
Gary Hobbs, supt. Fax 266-4420
www.walton.k12.ga.us
Carver MS 800/6-8
1095 Good Hope Rd 30655 770-207-3333
Dr. Dawn Spruill, prin. Fax 207-3332
Monroe Area HS 1,200/9-12
300 Double Springs Church 30656 770-266-4599
Bryan Hicks, prin. Fax 266-4598
Other Schools – See Loganville

Walton Academy 1,000/PK-12
1 Bulldog Dr 30655 770-267-7578

Montezuma, Macon, Pop. 3,439
Macon County SD
Supt. — See Oglethorpe
Macon County HS 500/9-12
611 Vienna Rd 31063 478-472-8579
Rickey Edmond, prin. Fax 472-6206
Macon County MS 400/6-8
615 Vienna Rd 31063 478-472-7045
Issiah Ross, prin. Fax 472-2549

Monticello, Jasper, Pop. 2,623
Jasper County SD 2,200/PK-12
1411 College St 31064 706-468-6350
Dr. Mike Newton, supt. Fax 468-0045
www.jasper.k12.ga.us
Jasper County HS 600/9-12
14477 GA Highway 11 N 31064 706-468-5016
Robyn Mullis, prin. Fax 468-5021
Jasper County MS 500/6-8
1289 College St 31064 706-468-2227
Dianna Blizzard, prin. Fax 468-1847

Piedmont Academy 300/PK-12
PO Box 231 31064 706-468-8818
Tony Tanner, hdmstr. Fax 468-2409

Morgan, Calhoun, Pop. 236
Calhoun County SD 600/PK-12
PO Box 39 39866 229-849-2765
Danny Ellis, supt. Fax 849-2113
www.calhoun.k12.ga.us/
Other Schools – See Edison

Morganton, Union, Pop. 300

Mountain Area Christian Academy 200/PK-12
14090 Old Highway 76 30560 706-374-6222
Barbara Brooker, admin. Fax 374-4831

Morrow, Clayton, Pop. 6,303
Clayton County SD
Supt. — See Jonesboro
Morrow HS 1,800/9-12
2299 Old Rex Morrow Rd 30260 404-362-3865
Pam Pitts, prin. Fax 362-2044
Morrow MS 700/6-8
5934 Trammell Rd 30260 770-210-4001
Rasheen Booker, prin. Fax 210-4002

Clayton State University Post-Sec.
2000 Clayton State Blvd 30260 678-466-4000
Interactive College of Technology Post-Sec.
1580 Southlake Pkwy Ste C 30260 770-960-1298

Moultrie, Colquitt, Pop. 14,082
Colquitt County SD 9,400/PK-12
PO Box 2708 31776 229-890-6200
Dr. Samuel A. DePaul, supt. Fax 890-6246
www.colquitt.k12.ga.us/
Achievement Center 100/Alt
1800 Park Ave SE 31768 229-890-6197
Todd Hall, prin. Fax 890-6181
Colquitt County HS 1,700/10-12
1800 Park Ave SE 31768 229-890-6141
Stephanie Terrell, prin. Fax 890-6166
Gray JHS 1,200/8-9
812 11th Ave NW 31768 229-890-6189
Dr. Thelma Jackson, prin. Fax 890-6123

Moultrie Technical College Post-Sec.
800 Veterans Pkwy N, 229-891-7000

Mount Airy, Habersham, Pop. 1,271
Habersham County SD
Supt. — See Clarkesville
Habersham Central SHS 1,300/10-12
2059 Highway 197 30563 706-778-7161
Jim Van Hooser, prin. Fax 778-1258
Habersham County Alternative S Alt
171 Raider Cir 30563 706-894-3056
Doug Westmoreland, prin.

Habersham Ninth Grade Academy 500/9-9
171 Raider Cir 30563 706-778-0830
Jim Van Hooser, prin. Fax 778-0848

Mount Berry, Floyd

Berry College Post-Sec.
2277 Martha Berry Hwy NW 30149 706-232-5374

Mount Vernon, Montgomery, Pop. 2,411
Montgomery County SD 1,100/PK-12
PO Box 315 30445 912-583-2301
Dr. Randy Rodgers, supt. Fax 583-4822
www.montgomery.k12.ga.us
Montgomery County HS 300/9-12
701C Dobbins St 30445 912-583-2296
Dr. Henry Walding, prin. Fax 583-2302
Other Schools – See Ailey

Brewton-Parker College Post-Sec.
PO Box 197 30445 912-583-2241

Mount Zion, Carroll, Pop. 1,655
Carroll County SD
Supt. — See Carrollton
Mount Zion MS 300/6-8
132 Eagle Dr 30150 770-834-3389
Connie Robison, prin. Fax 214-7794

Nahunta, Brantley, Pop. 1,033
Brantley County SD 3,600/PK-12
272 School Cir 31553 912-462-6176
Anthony Smith, supt. Fax 462-6731
www.brantley.k12.ga.us/
Brantley County HS 900/9-12
10804 Highway 82 31553 912-462-5121
Randy Yonz, prin. Fax 462-5123
Brantley County MS 600/7-8
10990 Highway 82 31553 912-462-7092
Angela Haney, prin. Fax 462-6785

Nashville, Berrien, Pop. 4,886
Berrien County SD 3,200/PK-12
810 S Dogwood Dr 31639 229-686-2081
Danny Hayes, supt. Fax 686-9002
www.berrien.k12.ga.us
Berrien HS 800/9-12
500 E Smith Ave 31639 229-686-7428
Angie Lovein, prin. Fax 686-6251
Berrien MS 700/6-8
800 Tifton Hwy 31639 229-686-2021
Jamie Taylor, prin. Fax 686-6546

Newborn, Newton, Pop. 690

Shiloh Christian Academy K-12
9595 Highway 142 30056 706-468-2606
Susan Jackson, dir. Fax 468-2181

Newnan, Coweta, Pop. 32,285
Coweta County SD 22,500/PK-12
PO Box 280 30264 770-254-2800
Dr. Steve Barker, supt. Fax 254-2807
www.cowetaschools.org
Arnall MS 900/6-8
700 Lora Smith Rd 30265 770-254-2765
Dr. Jan Franks, prin. Fax 254-2770
Brown MS Alt
32 Clark St 30263 770-304-5930
Derek Pitts, prin. Fax 254-2806
Dowdell Academy Alt
1 Dowdell St 30263 770-254-2870
Vern Mamon, prin. Fax 304-5919
Evans MS 700/6-8
41 Evans Dr 30263 770-254-2780
Melissa Wimbish, prin. Fax 254-2783
Madras MS 1,000/6-8
240 Edgeworth Rd 30263 770-254-2744
Lorraine Johnson, prin. Fax 304-5928
Newnan HS 2,300/9-12
190 Lagrange St 30263 770-254-2880
Dr. Doug Moore, prin. Fax 254-2797
Northgate HS 1,800/9-12
3220 Fischer Rd 30265 770-463-5585
Dr. Therese Reddekopp, prin. Fax 463-4982
Smokey Road MS 800/6-8
965 Smokey Rd 30263 770-254-2840
Dr. Laurie Barron, prin. Fax 304-5933
Other Schools – See Senoia, Sharpsburg

Heritage S 400/PK-12
2093 Highway 29 N 30263 770-253-9898
Judith Griffith, head sch Fax 253-4850
West Georgia Technical College Post-Sec.
160 Martin Luther King Dr 30263 770-755-7440

Newton, Baker, Pop. 647
Baker County SD 400/PK-12
PO Box 40, 229-734-5346
Freddie Thompson, supt. Fax 734-3064
www.baker.k12.ga.us/
Baker County S 400/PK-12
260 GA Highway 37 SW, 229-734-5274
Torrance Choates, prin. Fax 734-3071

Norcross, Gwinnett, Pop. 8,915
Gwinnett County SD
Supt. — See Suwanee
Gwinnett InterVention Education Ctr West 300/Alt
2595 Beaver Ruin Rd 30071 770-326-8000
Todd Marschke, prin. Fax 326-8033
Meadowcreek HS 2,700/9-12
4455 Steve Reynolds Blvd 30093 770-381-9680
Tommy Welch, prin. Fax 806-2230
Norcross HS 3,100/9-12
5300 Spalding Dr 30092 770-448-3674
William Bishop, prin. Fax 447-2664
Pinckneyville MS 1,300/6-8
5440 W Jones Bridge Rd 30092 770-263-0860
Wanda Yeargin, prin. Fax 447-2617
Summerour MS 1,200/6-8
585 Mitchell Rd 30071 770-448-3045
Dorothy Parker-Jarrett, prin. Fax 417-2476

Ashworth College Post-Sec.
6625 the Corners Pkwy # 500 30092 770-729-8400
Everest Institute Post-Sec.
1750 Beaver Ruin Rd Ste 500 30093 770-921-1085
Greater Atlanta Christian S 1,900/PK-12
1575 Indian Trail Lilburn 30093 770-243-2000
Dr. David Fincher, pres. Fax 243-2213
Hopewell Christian Academy 100/PK-12
182 Hunter St 30071 770-903-3387
Beauty Baldwin, admin. Fax 449-8316
Professional Career Development Inst Post-Sec.
6625 the Corners Pkey # 500 30092 800-957-5412
Wesleyan S 1,100/K-12
5405 Spalding Dr 30092 770-448-7640
Zach Young, hdmstr. Fax 448-3699

Oakwood, Hall, Pop. 3,904
Hall County SD
Supt. — See Gainesville
West Hall HS 1,100/9-12
5500 McEver Rd 30566 770-967-9826
Dr. Greg Williams, prin. Fax 967-4864
West Hall MS 800/6-8
5470 Mcever Rd 30566 770-967-4871
Dr. Karla Swafford, prin. Fax 967-4874

Lanier Technical College Post-Sec.
2990 Landrum Education Dr 30566 770-531-6300

Ocilla, Irwin, Pop. 3,380
Irwin County SD 1,700/PK-12
PO Box 225 31774 229-468-7485
Bobby Conner, supt. Fax 468-7220
www.irwin.k12.ga.us/
Irwin County HS 400/9-12
149 Chieftain Cir 31774 229-468-9421
Kerry Billingsley, prin. Fax 468-9423
Irwin County MS 400/6-8
149 Chieftain Cir 31774 229-468-5517
Heather Purvis, prin. Fax 468-3134

Oglethorpe, Macon, Pop. 1,323
Macon County SD 1,800/PK-12
PO Box 488 31068 478-472-8188
Dr. Carolyn Medlock, supt. Fax 472-2042
www.macon.k12.ga.us/
Other Schools – See Montezuma

Oxford, Newton, Pop. 2,073

Providence Christian S 100/PK-12
252 Byrd Rd 30054 770-788-6618
Ty Hensley, hdmstr. Fax 385-4988

Peachtree City, Fayette, Pop. 33,616
Fayette County SD
Supt. — See Fayetteville
Booth MS 1,000/6-8
250 S Peachtree Pkwy 30269 770-631-3240
Ted Lombard, prin. Fax 631-3245
McIntosh HS 1,700/9-12
201 Walt Banks Rd 30269 770-631-3232
Lisa Fine, prin. Fax 631-3278

Pearson, Atkinson, Pop. 2,082
Atkinson County SD 1,500/PK-12
98 Roberts Ave E 31642 912-422-7373
Tim Cochran, supt. Fax 422-7369
www.atkinson.k12.ga.us/
Atkinson County HS 400/9-12
145 Rebel Ln 31642 912-422-3267
Dr. Al Pollard, prin. Fax 422-7889
Atkinson County MS 100/6-8
145 Rebel Ln 31642 912-422-3267
Anthony Davis, prin. Fax 422-7889

Pelham, Mitchell, Pop. 3,877
Pelham CSD 1,500/PK-12
203 Mathewson Ave SW 31779 229-294-8715
Dr. James Arnold, supt. Fax 294-2760
www.pelham-city.k12.ga.us/
Pelham City MS 400/6-8
209 Mathewson Ave SW 31779 229-294-6063
Laron Smith, prin. Fax 294-6046
Pelham HS 400/9-12
720 Barrow Ave SW 31779 229-294-8623
Ben Wiggins, prin. Fax 294-6069

Pembroke, Bryan, Pop. 2,165
Bryan County SD
Supt. — See Black Creek
Bryan County MS 400/6-8
600 Payne Dr 31321 912-626-5050
Dr. Dawn Hadley, prin. Fax 653-2705
Byran County HS 500/9-12
1234 Camellia Dr 31321 912-626-5060
Dr. Dawn Hadley, prin. Fax 653-2858

Perry, Houston, Pop. 13,635
Houston County SD 25,900/PK-12
PO Box 1850 31069 478-988-6200
James Hines, supt. Fax 988-6259
www.hcbe.net
Perry HS 1,200/9-12
1307 North Ave 31069 478-988-6298
Dr. Darryl Albritton, prin. Fax 988-6381
Perry MS 800/6-8
495 Perry Pkwy 31069 478-988-6285
Thomas Moore, prin. Fax 988-6345
Other Schools – See Bonaire, Centerville, Kathleen, Warner Robins

---

Westfield S 600/PK-12
PO Box 2300 31069 478-987-0547

Pinehurst, Dooly, Pop. 452
Dooly County SD
Supt. — See Vienna
Dooly County MS 300/6-8
11949 US Highway 41 31070 229-645-3421
Dr. Daniel Sturdivant, prin. Fax 645-3840

Fullington Academy 300/PK-12
PO Box B 31070 229-645-3383

Pooler, Chatham, Pop. 18,668
Savannah-Chatham County SD
Supt. — See Savannah
West Chatham MS 1,000/6-8
800 Pine Barren Rd 31322 912-395-3650
Dr. Troy Brown, prin. Fax 748-3669

Portal, Bulloch, Pop. 637
Bulloch County SD
Supt. — See Statesboro
Portal MSHS 500/6-12
27245 US Highway 80 W 30450 912-842-8360
Dr. Shawn Haralson, prin. Fax 865-5659

Powder Springs, Cobb, Pop. 13,580
Cobb County SD
Supt. — See Marietta
Hillgrove HS 2,100/9-12
4165 Luther Ward Rd 30127 678-331-3961
Robert Shaw, prin. Fax 331-8128
Lovinggood MS 1,200/6-8
3825 Luther Ward Rd 30127 678-331-3015
Angela Stewart, prin. Fax 331-3016
McEachern HS 2,200/9-12
2400 New Macland Rd 30127 770-222-3710
Regina Montgomery, prin. Fax 222-3712
Tapp MS 600/6-8
3900 Macedonia Rd 30127 770-222-3758
Dr. Jeanne Walker, prin. Fax 222-3760

Paulding County SD
Supt. — See Dallas
Dobbins MS 900/6-8
637 Williams Lake Rd 30127 770-443-4835
Cartess Ross, prin. Fax 439-1672

Powder Springs Beauty College Post-Sec.
4114 Austell Powder Springs 30127 770-439-9432
Praise Academy 300/PK-12
4052 Hiram Lithia Springs 30127 770-943-2484
Joe White M.Ed., admin. Fax 943-9458
Youth Christian S 200/PK-12
4967 Brownsville Rd 30127 770-943-1394

Quitman, Brooks, Pop. 3,809
Brooks County SD 2,300/PK-12
1081 Barwick Rd 31643 229-263-7531
Debra Folsom, supt. Fax 263-5206
www.brookscountyschools.com/
Brooks County HS 600/9-12
1801 Moultrie Hwy 31643 229-263-8923
Howard Akers, prin. Fax 263-7049
Brooks County MS 500/6-8
2171 Moultrie Hwy 31643 229-263-7521
Ervin Sloan, prin. Fax 263-9038

Rabun Gap, Rabun

Rabun Gap-Nacoochee S 300/6-12
339 Nacoochee Dr 30568 706-746-7467
Dr. Anthony Sgro, head sch Fax 746-2594

Reidsville, Tattnall, Pop. 4,920
Tattnall County SD 3,500/PK-12
PO Box 157 30453 912-557-4726
Gina Williams, supt. Fax 557-3036
www.tattnallschools.org/
Reidsville MS 300/6-8
148 W Brazell St 30453 912-557-3993
Gwenda Johnson, prin. Fax 557-4124
Tattnall County HS 900/9-12
1 Battle Creek Warrior Blvd 30453 912-557-4374
Glenn Stewart, prin. Fax 557-4542
Other Schools – See Glennville

Rentz, Laurens, Pop. 289
Laurens County SD
Supt. — See Dublin
Crossroads Alternative S Alt
1046 Emily Currie Rd 31075 478-984-4253
Jim Rowland, prin. Fax 984-4831

Rex, Clayton
Clayton County SD
Supt. — See Jonesboro
Adamson MS 600/6-8
3187 Rex Rd 30273 770-968-2925
Timothy Guiney, prin. Fax 968-2949
Rex Mill MS 1,000/6-8
6380 Evans Dr 30273 770-474-0702
Karen Murner, prin. Fax 474-5812

Richmond Hill, Bryan, Pop. 8,989
Bryan County SD
Supt. — See Black Creek
Richmond Hill HS 1,600/9-12
1 Wildcat Dr 31324 912-459-5151
Debi McNeal, prin. Fax 756-4958
Richmond Hill MS 1,300/6-8
503 Warren Hill Rd 31324 912-459-5130
Dr. William McGrath, prin. Fax 756-5369

Rincon, Effingham, Pop. 8,590
Effingham County SD
Supt. — See Springfield

Ebenezer MS 1,000/6-8
1100 Ebenezer Rd 31326 912-754-7757
Arnie Dickerson, prin. Fax 754-4012

Ringgold, Catoosa, Pop. 3,500
Catoosa County SD 10,800/PK-12
PO Box 130 30736 706-965-2297
Denia Reese, supt. Fax 965-8913
www.catoosa.k12.ga.us
Heritage HS 1,300/9-12
3960 Poplar Springs Rd 30736 706-937-6464
Ronnie Bradford, prin. Fax 937-6477
Heritage MS 1,000/6-8
4005 Poplar Springs Rd 30736 706-937-3568
Chris Lusk, prin. Fax 937-2583
Ringgold HS 1,000/9-12
29 Tiger Trl 30736 706-935-2254
Sharon Vaughn, prin. Fax 965-8910
Ringgold MS 700/6-8
217 Tiger Trl 30736 706-935-3381
Mike Sholl, prin. Fax 965-8908
Other Schools – See Fort Oglethorpe, Rossville

Riverdale, Clayton, Pop. 14,852
Clayton County SD
Supt. — See Jonesboro
Drew HS 1,200/9-12
6237 Garden Walk Blvd 30274 770-472-2820
Gary Townsend, prin. Fax 472-2825
Riverdale HS 1,400/9-12
160 Roberts Dr 30274 770-473-2905
Jamille Miller-Brown, prin. Fax 473-2913
Riverdale MS 800/6-8
400 Roberts Dr 30274 770-994-4045
Adrian Courtland, prin. Fax 994-4467
Sequoyah MS 800/6-8
95 Valley Hill Rd SW 30274 770-515-7524
Lonnie White, prin. Fax 515-7540

Owens Christian Preparatory Academy 50/5-12
8455 Highway 85 Ste 100 30274 770-991-2334
Dr. Cecelia Owens, prin. Fax 210-3356
Southern Regional Medical Center Post-Sec.
11 Upper Riverdale Rd SW 30274 770-991-8053

Roberta, Crawford, Pop. 993
Crawford County SD 1,900/PK-12
PO Box 8 31078 478-836-3131
John Douglas, supt. Fax 836-3114
crawfordcounty.schoolinsites.com
Crawford County Comprehensive HS 600/9-12
PO Box 98 31078 478-836-3126
Mike Campbell, prin. Fax 836-4853
Crawford County MS 400/6-8
401 Lowe Rd 31078 478-836-3181
Anthony English, prin. Fax 836-3795

Rochelle, Wilcox, Pop. 1,171
Wilcox County SD
Supt. — See Abbeville
Wilcox County HS 400/9-12
186 7th Ave 31079 229-365-7231
Chad Davis, prin. Fax 365-7461
Wilcox County MS 300/6-8
114 7th Ave 31079 229-365-2331
Valentina Sutton, prin. Fax 365-2641

Rockmart, Polk, Pop. 4,119
Polk County SD
Supt. — See Cedartown
Rockmart HS 800/9-12
990 Cartersville Hwy 30153 770-684-5432
DeAnna Williams, prin. Fax 684-4768
Rockmart MS 800/6-8
60 Knox Mountain Rd 30153 678-757-1479
Shannon Hulsey, prin. Fax 757-9868

Georgia Northwestern Technical College Post-Sec.
466 Brock Rd 30153 770-684-5696

Rock Spring, Walker

Georgia Northwestern Technical College Post-Sec.
265 Bicentennial Trl 30739 706-764-3510

Rocky Face, Whitfield
Whitfield County SD
Supt. — See Dalton
Westside MS 500/6-8
580 Lafayette Rd 30740 706-673-2611
Angela Hargis, prin. Fax 673-5349

Rome, Floyd, Pop. 35,635
Floyd County SD 10,500/PK-12
600 Riverside Pkwy NE 30161 706-234-1031
Lynn Plunkett Ed.D., supt. Fax 236-1824
www.floydboe.net
Armuchee HS 600/9-12
4203 Martha Berry Hwy NW 30165 706-236-1886
Dr. James Burris, prin. Fax 802-6757
Coosa HS 700/9-12
4454 Alabama Hwy NW 30165 706-236-1870
Trevor Hubbard, prin. Fax 290-8142
Coosa MS 600/6-8
212 Eagle Dr NW 30165 706-236-1856
Dr. Lisa Landrum, prin. Fax 802-6766
Floyd County Education Center Alt
1910 Morrison Campground Rd 30161
706-236-1884
Dr. Melinda Strickland, prin. Fax 802-6780
Model HS 700/9-12
3252 Calhoun Rd NE 30161 706-236-1895
Dr. Glenn White, prin. Fax 802-6750
Model MS 500/6-8
164 Barron Rd NE 30161 706-290-8150
David Tucker, prin. Fax 802-6775
Other Schools – See Armuchee, Lindale

Rome CSD 5,600/PK-12
508 E 2nd St 30161 706-236-5050
Dr. Gayland Cooper, supt. Fax 802-4311
www.rcs.rome.ga.us
Rome HS 1,500/9-12
1000 Veterans Memorial NE 30161 706-235-9653
Dr. J. Tygar Evans, prin. Fax 236-5078
Rome MS 800/7-8
1020 Veterans Memorial NE 30161 706-235-4695
Greg Christian, prin. Fax 234-5903
Rome Transitional Academy Alt
1162 Spider Webb Dr SE 30161 706-802-4326
Jennifer Perkins, prin. Fax 802-4327

Darlington S 800/PK-12
1014 Cave Spring Rd SW 30161 706-235-6051
Thomas Whitworth, hdmstr. Fax 232-3600
Georgia Highlands College Post-Sec.
3175 Cedartown Hwy SE 30161 706-802-5000
Georgia Northwestern Technical College Post-Sec.
1 Maurice Culberson Dr SW 30161 706-295-6963
Shorter University Post-Sec.
315 Shorter Ave SW 30165 800-868-6980
Unity Christian S 400/PK-12
2960 New Calhoun Hwy NE 30161 706-292-0700
Glenn Getchell, hdmstr. Fax 292-0772

Rossville, Walker, Pop. 4,039
Catoosa County SD
Supt. — See Ringgold
Lakeview MS 700/6-8
416 Cross St 30741 706-866-1040
Steve McClure, prin. Fax 861-6644

Walker County SD
Supt. — See La Fayette
Ridgeland HS 1,400/9-12
2478 Happy Valley Rd 30741 706-820-9361
Glen Brown, prin. Fax 820-1342
Rossville MS 600/6-8
316 Bull Dog Trl 30741 706-820-0638
Jason Pelham, prin. Fax 820-0696

Roswell, Fulton, Pop. 86,448
Fulton County SD
Supt. — See Atlanta
Centennial HS 1,900/9-12
9310 Scott Rd 30076 770-650-4230
Steven Miletto, prin. Fax 650-4250
Crabapple MS 800/6-8
10700 Crabapple Rd 30075 770-552-4520
Nathan Buhl, prin. Fax 552-4524
Crossroads 2nd Chance North Alt HS 300/Alt
791 Mimosa Blvd 30075 770-552-6334
Scott O'Prey, prin. Fax 643-6353
Elkins Pointe MS 900/6-8
11290 Elkins Rd 30076 770-667-2892
Melinda Springman, prin. Fax 667-2898
Roswell HS 2,500/9-12
11595 King Rd 30075 770-552-4500
Jerome Huff, prin. Fax 552-4509

Blessed Trinity Catholic HS 900/9-12
11320 Woodstock Rd 30075 678-277-9083
Frank Moore, prin. Fax 277-9756
Fellowship Christian S 700/PK-12
10965 Woodstock Rd 30075 770-993-1650
Kathy Teston, admin. Fax 993-9262
Strayer University Post-Sec.
100 Mansell Ct E 30076 770-650-3000

Saint Marys, Camden, Pop. 16,595
Camden County SD
Supt. — See Kingsland
Saint Marys MS 900/6-8
205 Martha Dr 31558 912-882-8626
Michael Wooden, prin. Fax 882-5473

Ablaze Academy 100/1-12
300 N Julia St 31558 877-899-9985
Robert Zeige-Cullins, pres. Fax 471-6478

Saint Simons Island, Glynn, Pop. 12,646

Frederica Academy 400/PK-12
200 Murray Way 31522 912-638-9981
Greg Griffeth, head sch Fax 638-1442

Sandersville, Washington, Pop. 5,844
Washington County SD 3,200/PK-12
PO Box 716 31082 478-552-3981
Dr. Donna Hinton, supt. Fax 552-3128
www.washington.k12.ga.us/
Elder MS 700/6-8
902 Linton Rd 31082 478-552-2007
Manzie Broxton, prin. Fax 552-7388
Washington County Alternative S Alt
446 Riddleville Rd 31082 478-553-1243
Dr. Vincent Jackson, prin. Fax 553-1245
Washington County HS 1,000/9-12
420 Riddleville Rd 31082 478-552-2324
Dr. Al Gray, prin. Fax 552-3140

Brentwood S 400/PK-12
PO Box 955 31082 478-552-5136
Jackie W. Holton, head sch Fax 552-2947
Oconee Fall Line Technical College Post-Sec.
1189 Deepstep Rd 31082 478-553-2050

Sandy Springs, Fulton, Pop. 91,346

Gwinnett College - Sandy Springs Post-Sec.
6690 Roswell Rd Ste 2200 30328 770-457-2021

Savannah, Chatham, Pop. 133,567
Savannah-Chatham County SD 33,200/PK-12
208 Bull St 31401 912-395-5600
Dr. Thomas Lockamy, supt. Fax 201-9073
www.savannah.chatham.k12.ga.us/
Bartlett MS 900/6-8
207 E Montgomery Xrd 31406 912-395-3500
James Heater, prin. Fax 961-3515
Beach HS 1,100/9-12
3001 Hopkins St 31405 912-395-5330
Derrick Muhammad, prin. Fax 201-5335
Coastal MS 700/6-8
4595 US Highway 80 E 31410 912-395-3950
Kerry Coursey, prin. Fax 898-3951
DeRenne MS 700/6-8
1009 Clinch St 31405 912-395-5900
Carol Mobley, prin. Fax 201-5903
Groves HS 1,500/9-12
100 Priscilla D Thomas Way 31408 912-395-2520
Dr. Ellis Duncan, prin. Fax 201-5840
Hubert MS 600/6-8
768 Grant St 31401 912-395-5235
Dr. Gequetta Jenkins, prin. Fax 201-5238
Islands HS 9-12
170 Whitemarsh Island Rd 31410 912-395-2000
Danielle Pinkerton, prin.
Jenkins HS 1,400/9-12
1800 E De Renne Ave 31406 912-395-6300
William Brannen, prin. Fax 303-6331
Johnson HS 1,100/9-12
3012 Sunset Blvd 31404 912-395-6400
Bernadette Ball-Oliver, prin. Fax 303-6418
Mercer MS 700/6-8
201 Rommel Ave 31408 912-395-6700
Stascia Hardy, prin. Fax 965-6719
Myers MS 600/6-8
2025 E 52nd St 31404 912-395-6600
Dora Myles, prin. Fax 303-6604
New Hampstead HS 9-12
2451 Little Neck Rd 31402 912-395-6789
Jennifer Topper, prin. Fax 201-7699
Savannah Arts Academy 800/9-12
500 Washington Ave 31405 912-395-5000
Gif Lockley, prin. Fax 201-4160
School of Liberal Studies 700/9-12
400 Pennsylvania Ave 31404 912-395-5050
Dr. Toney Jordan, prin. Fax 201-5054
Southwest MS 700/6-8
6030 Ogeechee Rd 31419 912-395-3540
Kimsherion Reid, prin. Fax 201-5831
Windsor Forest HS 1,300/9-12
12419 Largo Dr 31419 912-395-3400
Joe Brasfield, prin. Fax 961-3422
Woodville-Tompkins Tech & Career HS Vo/Tech
151 Coach Joe Turner St 31408 912-395-6750
Alfred McGuire, prin. Fax 965-6760
Other Schools – See Garden City, Pooler

Armstrong Atlantic State University Post-Sec.
11935 Abercorn St 31419 912-344-2576
Benedictine Military S 300/9-12
6502 Seawright Dr 31406 912-644-7000
Rev. Frank Ziemkiewicz, hdmstr. Fax 356-3527
Bethesda Academy 100/6-12
PO Box 13039 31416 912-351-2055
Kelly Burke, prin. Fax 351-2062
Bible Baptist S 400/PK-12
4700 Skidaway Rd 31404 912-352-3067
Calvary Day S 700/PK-12
4625 Waters Ave 31404 912-351-2299
Ralph Finnegan, hdmstr. Fax 351-2280
Memorial Day S 200/PK-12
6500 Habersham St 31405 912-352-4535
Michalle Quarles, head sch Fax 352-4536
St. Andrew's S on the Marsh 500/PK-12
601 Penn Waller Rd 31410 912-897-4941
Mark Toth, hdmstr. Fax 897-4943
St. Vincent's Academy 300/9-12
207 E Liberty St 31401 912-236-5508
Mary Hogan, prin. Fax 236-7877
Savannah Christian Preparatory S 1,600/PK-12
PO Box 2848 31402 912-234-1653
Savannah College of Art & Design Post-Sec.
PO Box 3146 31402 912-525-5100
Savannah Country Day S 900/PK-12
824 Stillwood Dr 31419 912-925-8800
Dr. Jim Hendrix, hdmstr. Fax 920-7800
Savannah State University Post-Sec.
3219 College St 31404 912-358-4778
Savannah Technical College Post-Sec.
5717 White Bluff Rd 31405 912-443-5700
South University Post-Sec.
709 Mall Blvd 31406 912-201-8000
Virginia College Post-Sec.
14045 Abercorn St Ste 1503 31419 912-721-5600

Senoia, Coweta, Pop. 3,245
Coweta County SD
Supt. — See Newnan
East Coweta MS 700/6-8
6291 Highway 16 30276 770-599-6607
Dr. Schwanda Jackson, prin. Fax 599-1051

Sharpsburg, Coweta, Pop. 336
Coweta County SD
Supt. — See Newnan
East Coweta HS 2,700/9-12
400 McCollum-Sharpsburg Rd 30277 770-254-2850
Evan Horton, prin. Fax 254-2857
Lee MS 1,000/6-8
370 Willis Rd 30277 770-251-1547
Dr. Bob Heaberlin, prin. Fax 253-8381

Heritage Christian S 200/K-12
3613 Highway 34 E 30277 770-252-1234
Ronald McCurry, admin. Fax 304-9576

Shellman, Randolph, Pop. 1,079

Randolph Southern S — 200/K-12
PO Box 300, — 229-679-5324
Wendy Lamb, hdmstr. — Fax 679-5325

Siloam, Greene, Pop. 278

Greene Academy — 200/PK-12
PO Box 109 30665 — 706-467-2147
Laura Greene, head sch — Fax 467-2147

Smyrna, Cobb, Pop. 49,900
Cobb County SD
Supt. — See Marietta
Campbell HS — 2,300/9-12
5265 Ward St SE 30080 — 678-842-6850
Denise Magee, prin. — Fax 842-6852
Campbell MS — 1,200/6-8
3295 Atlanta Rd SE 30080 — 678-842-6873
Gail Johnson, prin. — Fax 842-6875
Griffin MS — 1,000/6-8
4010 King Springs Rd SE 30082 — 678-842-6917
Dr. Mark Trachtenbroit, prin. — Fax 842-6919
Hawthorne Center — Alt
1595 Hawthorne Ave SE 30080 — 678-842-6930
Marianne Weidner, prin. — Fax 842-6943

Medix School — Post-Sec.
2108 Cobb Pkwy SE 30080 — 770-980-0002

Snellville, Gwinnett, Pop. 17,762
Gwinnett County SD
Supt. — See Suwanee
Brookwood HS — 3,400/9-12
1255 Dogwood Rd 30078 — 770-972-7642
Debra Dees, prin. — Fax 978-5075
Shiloh HS — 2,100/9-12
4210 Shiloh Rd 30039 — 770-972-8471
Dr. Eric Parker, prin. — Fax 736-4345
Shiloh MS — 1,600/6-8
4285 Shiloh Rd 30039 — 770-972-3224
Dr. Eli Welch, prin. — Fax 736-4563
Snellville MS — 800/6-8
3155 Pate Rd 30078 — 770-972-1530
Eric Thigpen, prin. — Fax 736-4444
South Gwinnett HS — 2,400/9-12
2288 Main St E 30078 — 770-972-4840
Fax 736-4329

Gwinnett Christian Academy — 100/K-12
2306 Bethany Church Rd 30039 — 770-982-3773
Wyatt Bozeman, hdmstr. — Fax 982-3773
Integrity Christian Academy — 100/PK-12
3005 Lenora Church Rd 30078 — 770-978-0101
Djuana Ferguson, admin. — Fax 978-0202

Social Circle, Walton, Pop. 4,199
Social Circle CSD — 1,800/PK-12
147 Alcova Dr 30025 — 770-464-2731
Dr. Todd McGhee, supt. — Fax 464-4920
www.socialcircleschools.com/
Social Circle HS — 500/9-12
154 Alcova Dr 30025 — 770-464-2611
Dr. Keith Everson, prin. — Fax 464-2612
Social Circle MS — 400/6-8
154 Alcova Dr 30025 — 770-464-1932
Theodoris Gibbs, prin. — Fax 464-2612

Soperton, Treutlen, Pop. 3,093
Treutlen County SD — 1,200/PK-12
5040 S Third St 30457 — 912-529-4228
Charles Ellington, supt. — Fax 529-4226
www.treutlen.net
Treutlen MSHS — 600/6-12
7892 GA Highway 29 30457 — 912-529-4536
David Avery, prin. — Fax 529-6121

Sparks, Cook, Pop. 2,024
Cook County SD
Supt. — See Adel
Cook MS — 700/6-8
1601 N Elm St 31647 — 229-549-5999
Dr. David Boland, prin. — Fax 549-5986

Sparta, Hancock, Pop. 1,390
Hancock County SD — 1,200/PK-12
PO Box 488 31087 — 706-444-5775
Gwendolyn Reeves, supt. — Fax 444-7026
www.hancockcountyschools.net/
CrossRoads Alternative S — Alt
PO Box 488 31087 — 706-444-7009
Dr. Shirley Harper, dir. — Fax 444-7026
Hancock Central HS — 400/9-12
11311 GA Highway 15 31087 — 706-444-7009
Willie Gibson, prin. — Fax 444-9918
Hancock Central MS — 300/6-8
11311 GA Highway 15 31087 — 706-444-6652
Willie Gibson, prin. — Fax 444-4344

Springfield, Effingham, Pop. 2,815
Effingham County SD — 11,500/PK-12
405 N Ash St 31329 — 912-754-2537
Dr. Randy Shearouse, supt. — Fax 754-8899
www.effingham.k12.ga.us
Effingham County HS — 1,800/9-12
1589 GA Highway 119 S 31329 — 912-754-6404
Yancy Ford, prin. — Fax 754-6893
Other Schools – See Guyton, Rincon

Statenville, Echols, Pop. 1,016
Echols County SD — 400/PK-12
216 US Highway 129 N 31648 — 229-559-5734
Tim Ragan, admin. — Fax 559-0484
www.echols.k12.ga.us
Echols County HS — 200/9-12
PO Box 40 31648 — 229-559-5437
Dave Rosser, prin. — Fax 559-3491

Statesboro, Bulloch, Pop. 27,883
Bulloch County SD — 9,500/PK-12
150 Williams Rd Ste A 30458 — 912-212-8500
Dr. Charles Wilson, supt. — Fax 764-8436
www.bulloch.k12.ga.us
James MS — 600/6-8
18809 US Highway 80 W 30458 — 912-212-8820
Mike Yawn, prin. — Fax 489-5916
Langston Chapel MS — 600/6-8
156 Langston Chapel Rd 30458 — 912-212-8720
Dr. Evelyn Gamble-Hilton, prin. — Fax 681-6416
Statesboro HS — 1,300/9-12
10 Lester Rd 30458 — 912-212-8860
Dr. Marty Waters, prin. — Fax 489-5965
Transitions Learning Center — Alt
150 Williams Rd Ste B 30458 — 912-212-8610
Tim Rountree, admin. — Fax 489-9978
Other Schools – See Brooklet, Portal

Bulloch Academy — 500/PK-12
873 Westside Rd 30458 — 912-764-6297
Loica Houghton, hdmstr. — Fax 764-3165
Georgia Southern University — Post-Sec.
PO Box 8024 30460 — 912-478-5391
Ogeechee Technical College — Post-Sec.
1 Joseph E Kennedy Blvd 30458 — 912-681-5500
Trinity Christian S — 200/PK-12
571 E Main St 30461 — 912-489-1375
David Lattner, hdmstr. — Fax 764-3136

Stillmore, Emanuel, Pop. 530

Emanuel Academy — 200/K-12
PO Box 400 30464 — 912-562-4405
Em Hubbard, hdmstr. — Fax 562-3465

Stockbridge, Henry, Pop. 24,827
Henry County SD
Supt. — See Mc Donough
Austin Road MS — 700/6-8
100 Austin Rd 30281 — 770-507-5407
Gabriel Wiley, prin. — Fax 507-5413
Henry Academy North — 300/Alt
109 S Lee St 30281 — 770-507-6414
George Eckerle, prin. — Fax 507-6259
Stockbridge HS — 1,300/9-12
1151 Old Conyers Rd 30281 — 770-474-8747
Eric Watson, prin. — Fax 474-4727
Stockbridge MS — 700/6-8
533 Old Conyers Rd 30281 — 770-474-5710
Purvis Jackson, prin. — Fax 507-8406
Woodland HS — 1,600/9-12
800 Moseley Dr 30281 — 770-389-2784
Bret Cook, prin. — Fax 389-2790
Woodland MS — 800/6-8
820 Moseley Dr 30281 — 770-389-2774
Legena Williams, prin. — Fax 389-2780

Rockdale County SD
Supt. — See Conyers
Davis MS — 900/6-8
3375 E Fairview Rd SW 30281 — 770-388-5675
Michael Mauriello, prin. — Fax 388-5676

Community Christian S — 900/PK-12
2001 Jodeco Rd 30281 — 678-432-0191
DeVry University — Post-Sec.
675 Southcrest Pkwy Ste 100 30281 — 678-284-4700

Stone Mountain, DeKalb, Pop. 5,717
DeKalb County SD — 95,500/PK-12
1701 Mountain Industrial Bl 30083 — 678-676-1200
Dr. Cheryl Atkinson, supt. — Fax 676-0785
www.dekalb.k12.ga.us
Andrews HS — 500/Alt
1701 Mountain Industrial 30083 — 678-676-2602
Merlon Jones, prin. — Fax 676-2610
Champion MS — 600/6-8
5265 Mimosa Dr 30083 — 678-875-1502
Angelique Smith-Hunt, prin. — Fax 875-1510
DeKalb Alternative S — 200/Alt
5855 Memorial Dr 30083 — 678-676-2302
Margie Smith, prin. — Fax 676-2310
DeKalb Early College Academy — 200/9-12
1701 Mountain Industrial Bl 30083 — 678-875-2402
Dr. Sharon Ordu, dir.
Freedom MS — 900/6-8
505 S Hairston Rd 30088 — 678-874-8702
Corey Davidsons, prin. — Fax 874-8710
Redan HS — 1,400/9-12
5247 Redan Rd 30088 — 678-676-3602
Greg Goodwin, prin. — Fax 676-3610
Stephenson HS — 1,700/9-12
701 Stephenson Rd 30087 — 678-676-4202
Michael Jones, prin. — Fax 676-4210
Stephenson MS — 1,200/6-8
922 Stephenson Rd 30087 — 678-676-4402
Obelia Hall, prin. — Fax 676-4410
Stone Mountain HS — 1,200/9-12
4555 Central Dr 30083 — 678-676-6302
Dr. James Jones, prin. — Fax 676-6310
Stone Mountain MS — 1,100/6-8
4301 Sarr Pkwy 30083 — 678-676-4802
Vincent Hinton, prin. — Fax 676-4810
Other Schools – See Atlanta, Avondale Estates, Chamblee, Clarkston, Decatur, Doraville, Dunwoody, Ellenwood, Lithonia, Tucker

---

Pro Way Hair School — Post-Sec.
5684 Memorial Dr 30083 — 404-299-5156

Suches, Union
Union County SD
Supt. — See Blairsville
Woody Gap S — 100/K-12
2331 State Highway 60 30572 — 706-747-2401
Jinjer Taylor, prin. — Fax 747-1419

Sugar Hill, Gwinnett, Pop. 18,185
Gwinnett County SD
Supt. — See Suwanee
Lanier HS — 900/9-12
918 Buford Hwy 30518 — 678-765-4040
Kerensa Wing, prin. — Fax 765-4049
North Gwinnett MS — 1,900/6-8
170 Peachtree Industrial Bl 30518 — 678-745-2300
Wanda Law, prin. — Fax 745-2348

Summerville, Chattooga, Pop. 4,440
Chattooga County SD — 2,300/PK-12
33 Middle School Rd 30747 — 706-857-3447
Jimmy Lenderman, supt. — Fax 857-3440
www.chattooga.k12.ga.us
Chattooga CrossRoads Academy — 100/Alt
989 Highway 114 30747 — 706-857-1112
Billy Martin, dir. — Fax 857-6644
Chattooga HS — 700/9-12
989 Highway 114 30747 — 706-857-2402
Jeff Martin, prin. — Fax 857-2565
Summerville MS — 400/6-8
200 Middle School Rd 30747 — 706-857-2444
Kevin Muskett, prin. — Fax 857-7769

Suwanee, Gwinnett, Pop. 15,041
Forsyth County SD
Supt. — See Cumming
Lambert HS — 1,900/9-12
805 Nichols Rd 30024 — 678-965-5050
Dr. Gary Davison, prin. — Fax 965-5051
Riverwatch MS — 1,200/6-8
610 James Burgess Rd 30024 — 678-455-7311
Kathy Carpenter, prin. — Fax 455-7316

Gwinnett County SD — 166,000/PK-12
437 Old Peachtree Rd NW 30024 — 678-301-6000
J. Alvin Wilbanks, supt. — Fax 301-6030
www.gwinnett.k12.ga.us/
Collins Hill HS — 3,300/9-12
50 Taylor Rd 30024 — 770-682-4100
Glenn McFall, prin. — Fax 682-4105
North Gwinnett HS — 2,700/9-12
20 Level Creek Rd 30024 — 770-945-9558
Ed Shaddix, prin. — Fax 271-5185
Peachtree Ridge HS — 3,200/9-12
1555 Old Peachtree Rd NW 30024 — 678-957-3100
Dr. Kevin Tashlein, prin. — Fax 957-3108
Other Schools – See Buford, Dacula, Duluth, Grayson, Hoschton, Lawrenceville, Lilburn, Loganville, Norcross, Snellville, Sugar Hill

---

Friendship Christian S — 200/PK-12
3160 Old Atlanta Rd 30024 — 678-845-0418
Rev. Vasily Lantukh, prin. — Fax 845-0417

Swainsboro, Emanuel, Pop. 7,222
Emanuel County SD — 4,300/PK-12
PO Box 130 30401 — 478-237-6674
Erma Jenkins, supt. — Fax 419-1102
www.emanuel.k12.ga.us
Swainsboro HS — 800/9-12
689 S Main St 30401 — 478-237-2267
Denise Warnock, prin. — Fax 419-1134
Swainsboro MS — 700/6-8
200 Tiger Trl 30401 — 478-237-8047
Gail Greenway, prin. — Fax 419-1148
Other Schools – See Twin City

East Georgia State College — Post-Sec.
131 College Cir 30401 — 478-289-2000
Swainsboro Technical College — Post-Sec.
346 Kite Rd 30401 — 478-289-2200

Sylvania, Screven, Pop. 2,925
Screven County SD — 2,500/PK-12
PO Box 1668 30467 — 912-451-2000
William Bland, supt. — Fax 451-2001
www.screven.k12.ga.us
Screven County HS — 800/9-12
110 Halcyondale Rd 30467 — 912-451-2300
Brett Warren, prin. — Fax 451-2301
Screven County MS — 600/6-8
126 Friendship Rd 30467 — 912-451-2200
Brian Scott, prin. — Fax 451-2201

Sylvester, Worth, Pop. 6,122
Worth County SD — 3,200/PK-12
103 Eldridge St 31791 — 229-776-8600
Dr. Barbara Thomas, supt. — Fax 776-8603
www.worth.k12.ga.us/
Worth County Comprehensive HS — 1,000/9-12
406 W King St 31791 — 229-776-8625
Dr. Russ Chesser, prin. — Fax 776-8614
Worth County MS — 900/6-8
1305 N Isabella St 31791 — 229-776-8620
Tiffany Sevier, prin. — Fax 776-8624

Talbotton, Talbot, Pop. 965
Talbot County SD — 600/K-12
PO Box 308 31827 — 706-665-8528
Dr. James Catrett, supt. — Fax 665-3620
www.talbot.k12.ga.us/
Central S — 600/K-12
PO Box 308 31827 — 706-665-8577
Kenneth Bonaparte, prin. — Fax 665-3946

Tallapoosa, Haralson, Pop. 3,111
Haralson County SD 3,700/PK-12
299 Robertson Ave 30176 770-574-2500
Brett Stanton, supt.
www.haralson.k12.ga.us
Haralson County HS 1,000/9-12
1655 Georgia Highway 120 30176 770-574-7647
Topher Byrnes, prin. Fax 574-7648
Haralson County MS 900/6-8
2633 Georgia Highway 120 30176 770-646-8600
Dr. Brian Ridley, prin. Fax 646-0108

Tallulah Falls, Rabun, Pop. 164

Tallulah Falls S 300/6-12
PO Box 249 30573 706-754-0400
Larry Peevy, pres. Fax 754-3595

Temple, Paulding, Pop. 4,145
Carroll County SD
Supt. — See Carrollton
Temple HS 600/9-12
589 Sage St 30179 770-562-3218
Karen Suddeth, prin. Fax 562-1510
Temple MS 500/6-8
275 Rainey Rd 30179 770-562-6001
Gail Parmer, prin. Fax 562-6002
Villa Rica MS 500/6-8
614 Tumlin Lake Rd 30179 770-459-0407
Dr. Rochelle Hopson-Lamar, prin.

Thomaston, Upson, Pop. 9,037
Thomaston-Upson County SD 4,500/PK-12
205 Civic Center Dr 30286 706-647-9621
Dr. Maggie Shook, supt. Fax 647-7154
www.upson.k12.ga.us
Upson-Lee Alternative S Alt
300 Adams St 30286 706-647-5738
Cristina Cunningham, prin. Fax 646-3160
Upson-Lee HS 1,400/9-12
268 Knight Trl 30286 706-647-8171
Tracy Caldwell, prin. Fax 647-3708
Upson-Lee MS 1,000/6-8
101 Holston Dr 30286 706-647-6256
Patsy Dean, prin. Fax 647-3631

Thomasville, Thomas, Pop. 18,212
Thomas County SD 5,200/PK-12
200 N Pinetree Blvd 31792 229-225-4380
Dr. George Kornegay, supt. Fax 225-5012
www.thomas.k12.ga.us
Thomas County Central HS 1,500/9-12
4686 US Highway 84 Byp W 31792 229-225-5050
Kenneth Harper, prin. Fax 227-2422
Thomas County MS 1,600/5-8
4681 US Highway 84 Byp W 31792 229-225-4394
Kathy Keown, prin. Fax 225-4378

Thomasville CSD 3,100/PK-12
915 E Jackson St 31792 229-225-2600
Sabrina Boykins-Everett, supt. Fax 225-2696
www.tcitys.org
MacIntyre Park MS 700/6-8
117 Glenwood Dr 31792 229-225-2628
William Settle, prin. Fax 225-3502
Thomasville HS 700/9-12
315 S Hansell St 31792 229-225-2634
Todd Mobley, prin. Fax 225-2663

Brookwood S 500/PK-12
301 Cardinal Ridge Rd 31792 229-226-8070
Mike Notaro Ed.D., hdmstr. Fax 227-0326
Southwest Georgia Technical College Post-Sec.
15689 US Highway 19 N 31792 229-225-4096
Thomas University Post-Sec.
1501 Millpond Rd 31792 229-226-1621

Thomson, McDuffie, Pop. 6,688
McDuffie County SD 4,200/PK-12
716 Lee St 30824 706-986-4000
Jim LeBrun, supt. Fax 986-4001
www.mcduffie.k12.ga.us
McDuffie Achievement Center Alt
614 Martin Luther King St 30824 706-986-4070
Claude Powell, prin. Fax 595-4733
Thomson HS 1,100/9-12
PO Box 1077 30824 706-986-4200
Cecil Strong, prin. Fax 986-4201
Thomson-McDuffie MS 900/6-8
1191 White Oak Rd 30824 706-986-4300
Neal Tam, prin. Fax 986-4301

Tifton, Tift, Pop. 16,154
Tift County SD 7,500/PK-12
PO Box 389 31793 229-387-2400
Patrick Atwater, supt. Fax 386-1020
www.tiftschools.com
Eighth Street MS 1,300/7-8
700 8th St W 31794 229-387-2445
Chad Stone, prin. Fax 386-1036
Sixth Street Academy Alt
805 6th St W 31794 229-387-2485
Tom Mark, prin. Fax 386-1066
Tift County HS 1,400/10-12
1 Blue Devil Way 31794 229-387-2475
Kim Seigler, prin. Fax 386-1022
Tift County HS Northeast Campus 600/9-9
3021 Fulwood Rd 31794 229-387-2450
Scott Haskins, prin. Fax 386-1038

Abraham Baldwin Agriculture College Post-Sec.
2802 Moore Hwy 31793 229-391-5001
Moultrie Technical College Post-Sec.
52 Tech Dr 31794 229-391-2600

Tiger, Rabun, Pop. 402
Rabun County SD
Supt. — See Clayton
Rabun County HS 700/9-12
230 Wildcat Hill Dr 30576 706-782-4526
Mark Earnest, prin. Fax 782-7550
Rabun County MS 400/7-8
95 Wildcat Pride Way 30576 706-782-5470
Shane Purdy, prin. Fax 782-4520

Toccoa, Stephens, Pop. 8,279
Stephens County SD 4,100/PK-12
2332 Mize Rd 30577 706-886-9415
Sherrie Whiten, supt. Fax 886-3882
www.stephens.k12.ga.us/
Crossroads Success Academy Alt
191 Old Big A School Rd 30577 706-886-3114
Jerry Brown, dir. Fax 886-3127
Stephens County HS 1,200/9-12
638 White Pine Rd 30577 706-886-6825
Felton Stephens, prin. Fax 886-8765
Stephens County MS 900/6-8
1315 Rose Ln 30577 706-886-2880
Donna Collins, prin. Fax 886-2882

North Georgia Technical College Post-Sec.
8989 Highway 17 30577 706-779-8100

Toccoa Falls, Stephens

Toccoa Falls College Post-Sec.
107 N Chapel Dr 30598 706-886-6831

Trenton, Dade, Pop. 2,264
Dade County SD 2,500/PK-12
PO Box 188 30752 706-657-4361
Shawn Tobin, supt. Fax 657-4572
www.dadecountyschools.org/
Dade County HS 700/9-12
300 Tradition Ln 30752 706-657-7517
Josh Ingle, prin. Fax 657-4854
Dade MS 600/6-8
250 Pace Dr 30752 706-657-6491
Karen deMarche, prin. Fax 657-3055

Trion, Chattooga, Pop. 1,797
Trion CSD 1,400/PK-12
239 Simmons St 30753 706-734-2363
Phil Williams, supt. Fax 734-3397
www.trionschools.org/
Trion HS 400/9-12
919 Allgood St Ste 3 30753 706-734-7316
Bryan Edge, prin. Fax 734-7692
Trion MS 300/6-8
919 Allgood St Ste 2 30753 706-734-7433
Cindy Anderson, prin. Fax 734-7517

Tucker, DeKalb, Pop. 26,961
DeKalb County SD
Supt. — See Stone Mountain
Tucker HS 1,500/9-12
5036 Lavista Rd 30084 678-874-3700
James Jackson, prin. Fax 874-3746
Tucker MS 1,300/6-8
2160 Idlewood Rd 30084 678-875-0902
Dr. Kathy Cunningham, prin. Fax 875-0910

Le Cordon Bleu College of Culinary Arts Post-Sec.
1927 Lakeside Pkwy 30084 770-938-4711
Medtech Institute Post-Sec.
4053 Lavista Rd 30084 678-218-0600
Omnitech Institute Post-Sec.
1728 Montreal Cir 30084 404-284-8121

Tunnel Hill, Whitfield, Pop. 854
Whitfield County SD
Supt. — See Dalton
Northwest Whitfield County HS 1,800/9-12
1651 Tunnel Hill Varnell Rd 30755 706-516-2200
Britt Adams, prin. Fax 673-7098

Twin City, Emanuel, Pop. 1,730
Emanuel County SD
Supt. — See Swainsboro
Emanuel County Institute 600/6-12
PO Box 218 30471 478-763-2673
Barry Joiner, prin. Fax 763-3834

Tyrone, Fayette, Pop. 6,701
Fayette County SD
Supt. — See Fayetteville
Flat Rock MS 800/6-8
325 Jenkins Rd 30290 770-969-2830
Oatha Mann, prin. Fax 969-2835
Sandy Creek HS 1,200/9-12
360 Jenkins Rd 30290 770-969-2840
Darrell Evans, prin. Fax 969-2838

Union City, Fulton, Pop. 19,078
Fulton County SD
Supt. — See Atlanta
Crossroads 2nd Chance South Alt HS 200/Alt
4025 Flat Shoals Rd 30291 770-306-3535
David Whitfield, prin. Fax 306-3540

Valdosta, Lowndes, Pop. 53,506
Lowndes County SD 10,700/PK-12
1592 Norman Dr 31601 229-245-2250
Wes Taylor, supt. Fax 245-2255
www.lowndes.k12.ga.us
Lowndes HS 3,000/9-12
1606 Norman Dr 31601 229-245-2260
Jay Floyd, prin. Fax 245-2468
Lowndes MS 900/6-8
2379 Copeland Rd 31601 229-245-2280
Dr. Derald Jones, prin. Fax 245-2470
Mathis Learning Center 400/Alt
1500 Lankford Dr 31601 229-245-2271
Sol Summerlin, dir. Fax 259-2273
Pine Grove MS 600/6-8
4159 River Rd 31605 229-219-3234
Ken Overman, prin. Fax 219-3233
Other Schools – See Hahira

Valdosta CSD 7,500/PK-12
PO Box 5407 31603 229-333-8500
Dr. Bill Cason, supt. Fax 247-7757
www.gocats.org
Newbern MS 500/6-8
PO Box 5407 31603 229-333-8566
Dr. Dan Altman, prin. Fax 245-5655
Pinevale Learning Center 300/Alt
PO Box 5407 31603 229-333-8597
Michael Roberts, prin. Fax 333-0313
Valdosta Early College Academy 6-10
PO Box 5407 31603 229-671-8455
Ingrid Hall, prin.
Valdosta HS 1,700/9-12
PO Box 5407 31603 229-333-8540
Dr. Janice Richardson, prin. Fax 333-8584
Valdosta MS 1,000/6-8
PO Box 5407 31603 229-333-8555
Dr. David Cole, prin. Fax 245-5656

Georgia Christian S 200/PK-12
4359 Dasher Rd 31601 229-559-5131
Burt Copeland, prin. Fax 559-7401
Highland Christian Academy 200/K-12
2206 E Hill Ave 31601 229-245-8111
Jackie Noble, prin. Fax 245-8110
Open Bible Christian S 300/PK-12
3992 N Oak Street Ext 31605 229-244-6694
Peter Smith, prin. Fax 244-1687
Valdosta State University Post-Sec.
1500 N Patterson St 31698 229-333-5800
Wiregrass Georgia Technical College Post-Sec.
4089 Val Tech Rd 31602 229-333-2100

Vidalia, Toombs, Pop. 10,364
Vidalia CSD 2,600/PK-12
301 Adams St 30474 912-537-3088
Dr. J. Garrett Wilcox, supt. Fax 538-0938
www.vidaliacity.schoolinsites.com
Trippe MS 600/6-8
2200 McIntosh St 30474 912-537-3813
Gwen Warren, prin. Fax 537-3223
Vidalia Comprehensive HS 700/9-12
1001 North St W 30474 912-537-7931
John Sharpe, prin. Fax 537-3006

Southeastern Technical College Post-Sec.
3001 E 1st St 30474 912-538-3100
Vidalia Heritage Academy 100/PK-12
PO Box 2005 30475 912-537-6679
Jeff McCormick, admin.

Vienna, Dooly, Pop. 3,989
Dooly County SD 1,400/PK-12
202 E Cotton St 31092 229-268-4761
Dr. Grady Miles, supt. Fax 268-6148
www.doolyschools.org
Dooly County HS 400/9-12
712 N 3rd St 31092 229-268-8181
Arney Bryant, prin. Fax 268-1916
Other Schools – See Pinehurst

Villa Rica, Carroll, Pop. 13,578
Carroll County SD
Supt. — See Carrollton
Bay Springs MS 800/6-8
122 Bay Springs Rd 30180 770-459-2098
Bruce Tidaback, prin. Fax 459-2097
Villa Rica HS 1,400/9-12
600 Rocky Branch Rd 30180 770-459-5185
Adam Herring, prin. Fax 459-2119

Waco, Haralson, Pop. 513

West Georgia Technical College Post-Sec.
176 Murphy Campus Blvd 30182 770-537-6000

Waleska, Cherokee, Pop. 623

Reinhardt University Post-Sec.
7300 Reinhardt Cir 30183 770-720-5600

Warner Robins, Houston, Pop. 64,686
Houston County SD
Supt. — See Perry
Feagin Mill MS 700/6-8
1200 Feagin Mill Rd 31088 478-953-0430
Dr. Jesse Davis, prin. Fax 953-0438
Houston County Crossroads Center Alt
401 Dover Dr 31088 478-929-7828
Dr. Ronnie Walker, prin. Fax 929-7118
Houston County HS 1,900/9-12
920 GA Highway 96 31088 478-988-6360
Dr. Michelle Masters, prin. Fax 988-6341
Huntington MS 800/6-8
206 Wellborn Rd 31088 478-988-7200
Dr. Gwen Taylor, prin. Fax 542-2247
Northside HS 1,800/9-12
926 Green St 31093 478-929-7858
Dr. Greg Peavy, prin. Fax 929-7813
Northside MS 600/6-8
500 Johnson Rd 31093 478-929-7845
Jan Melnick, prin. Fax 929-7124
Warner Robins HS 1,900/9-12
401 S Davis Dr 31088 478-929-7877
Steve Monday, prin. Fax 929-7769
Warner Robins MS 700/6-8
425 Mary Ln 31088 478-929-7832
Dr. Donald Warren, prin. Fax 929-7834

Middle Georgia Technical College — Post-Sec.
80 Cohen Walker Dr 31088 — 478-988-6800
Westside Christian Academy — 100/PK-12
1101 Dunbar Rd 31093 — 478-784-9153
Ricky McInnis, head sch — Fax 785-1099

Warrenton, Warren, Pop. 1,925
Warren County SD — 800/PK-12
PO Box 228 30828 — 706-465-3383
Carole Carey, supt. — Fax 465-9141
www.warren.k12.ga.us/
Warren County HS — 200/9-12
1253 Atlanta Hwy 30828 — 706-465-3742
Dr. Kaveous Preston, prin. — Fax 465-0901
Warren County MS — 100/6-8
1253 Atlanta Hwy 30828 — 706-465-3742
Truett Abbott, prin. — Fax 465-0901

Briarwood Academy — 300/PK-12
4859 Thomson Hwy 30828 — 706-595-5641
Clayton Parish, hdmstr. — Fax 595-0097

Washington, Wilkes, Pop. 4,057
Wilkes County SD — 1,700/PK-12
313 N Alexander Ave Ste A 30673 — 706-678-2718
Dr. Rosemary Caddell, supt. — Fax 678-3799
www.wilkes.k12.ga.us
Washington-Wilkes Comprehensive HS — 500/9-12
1182 Tignall Rd 30673 — 706-678-2426
Mark Ward, prin. — Fax 678-2628
Washington-Wilkes MS — 400/6-8
1180 Tignall Rd 30673 — 706-678-7131
Deleki Lee, prin. — Fax 678-3546

Watkinsville, Oconee, Pop. 2,786
Oconee County SD — 6,400/K-12
PO Box 146 30677 — 706-769-5130
Dr. Jason Branch, supt. — Fax 769-3500
www.oconeeschools.org/
Oconee County HS — 1,000/9-12
2721 Hog Mountain Rd 30677 — 706-769-6655
Sheila Beckham, prin. — Fax 310-2003
Oconee County MS — 800/6-8
1101 Mars Hill Rd 30677 — 706-769-3575
Dr. Suzanne Miller, prin. — Fax 310-2001
Other Schools – See Bogart

Westminster Christian Academy — 300/PK-12
PO Box 388 30677 — 706-769-9372
Judy Childs, prin. — Fax 769-2050

Waycross, Ware, Pop. 14,397
Ware County SD — 5,600/PK-12
1301 Bailey St 31501 — 912-283-8656
Dr. Joseph Barrow, supt. — Fax 283-8698
www.ware.k12.ga.us
Ware County HS — 1,500/9-12
700 Victory Dr 31503 — 912-287-2351
Dr. Tim Dixon, prin. — Fax 287-2358
Ware County MS — 700/6-8
2301 Cherokee St 31503 — 912-287-2341
Dr. Darlene Tanner, prin. — Fax 287-2353
Waycross MS — 600/6-8
700 Central Ave 31501 — 912-287-2333
David Hitt, prin. — Fax 287-2352

Okefenokee Technical College — Post-Sec.
1701 Carswell Ave 31503 — 912-287-6584
South Georgia State College — Post-Sec.
2100 S Georgia Pkwy W 31503 — 912-449-7600

Southside Christian S — 200/PK-12
3439 Knight Ave 31503 — 912-285-5438
Joan Clark, admin. — Fax 285-2565

Waynesboro, Burke, Pop. 5,700
Burke County SD — 4,700/PK-12
789 Burke Veterans Pkwy 30830 — 706-554-5101
Rudy Falana, supt. — Fax 554-8051
www.burke.k12.ga.us
Burke County Alternative S — Alt
PO Box 1005 30830 — 706-554-8046
Earl Ishmal, prin. — Fax 554-8081
Burke County HS — 1,300/9-12
1057 Burke Veterans Pkwy 30830 — 706-554-6691
Sam Adkins, prin. — Fax 554-8070
Burke County MS — 1,000/6-8
356 Southside Dr 30830 — 706-554-3532
Dr. Mona Reynolds, prin. — Fax 554-8063

Burke Academy — 500/PK-12
PO Box 787 30830 — 706-554-4479
Brent Cribb, hdmstr. — Fax 554-7582

West Point, Troup, Pop. 3,435

Point University — Post-Sec.
507 W 10th St 31833 — 706-385-1000

White, Bartow, Pop. 658
Bartow County SD
Supt. — See Cartersville
Cass HS — 1,500/9-12
1000 Colonel Way NE 30184 — 770-606-5845
Mike Nelson, prin. — Fax 606-5467

Winder, Barrow, Pop. 13,757
Barrow County SD — 12,600/PK-12
179 W Athens St 30680 — 770-867-4527
Dr. Wanda Creel, supt. — Fax 867-4540
www.barrow.k12.ga.us
Apalachee HS — 1,600/9-12
940 Haymon Morris Rd 30680 — 770-586-5111
Glenn Wilson, prin. — Fax 307-3726
Haymon Morris MS — 800/6-8
1008 Haymon Morris Rd 30680 — 678-963-0602
Dr. Sheila Kahrs, prin. — Fax 867-1854
Russell MS — 700/6-8
84 W Midland Ave 30680 — 770-867-8181
Leigh Sears, prin. — Fax 868-1215
Westside MS — 500/6-8
240 Matthews School Rd 30680 — 770-307-2972
Valorie Rolader, prin. — Fax 307-2976
Winder-Barrow HS — 1,800/9-12
272 N 5th Ave 30680 — 770-867-4519
Dr. Al Darby, prin. — Fax 867-6412
Winder-Barrow MS — 800/6-8
163 King St 30680 — 770-867-2116
Dr. Jennifer Wood, prin. — Fax 868-1421
Adult Learning Center — Adult
89 E Athens St 30680 — 770-307-1190
Dr. Ron Saunders, dir. — Fax 867-8018
Other Schools – See Bethlehem

Winston, Douglas
Douglas County SD
Supt. — See Douglasville
Mason Creek MS — 800/6-8
7777 Mason Creek Rd 30187 — 770-651-2500
Eric Collins, prin. — Fax 920-4278

Woodbury, Meriwether, Pop. 960

Flint River Academy — 300/PK-12
11556 Highway 85 E 30293 — 706-553-2541
Michele Purvis, head sch — Fax 553-9777

Woodstock, Cherokee, Pop. 23,245
Cherokee County SD
Supt. — See Canton
Booth MS — 1,200/7-8
6550 Putnam Ford Dr 30189 — 770-926-5707
Dawn Weinbaum, prin. — Fax 928-2908
Etowah HS — 2,100/9-12
6565 Putnam Ford Dr 30189 — 770-926-4411
Keith Ball, prin. — Fax 926-4157
Mill Creek MS — 1,100/6-8
442 Arnold Mill Rd 30188 — 770-924-5489
Elaine Daniel, prin. — Fax 926-5439
River Ridge HS — 9-12
400 Arnold Mill Rd 30188 — 770-591-8450
Darrell Herring, prin. — Fax 721-6590
Woodstock HS — 2,000/9-12
2010 Towne Lake Hills S Dr 30189 — 770-592-3500
Dr. Paul Weir, prin. — Fax 592-3509
Woodstock MS — 1,100/6-8
2000 Towne Lake Hills S Dr 30189 — 770-592-3516
Mark Smith, prin. — Fax 591-8054
Polaris Evening Program — Adult
2010 Towne Lake Hls S Dr 30189 — 770-926-1662
Curt Ashley, admin. — Fax 592-3509

Cherokee Christian S — 400/K-12
3075 Trickum Rd 30188 — 678-494-5464

Wrens, Jefferson, Pop. 2,160
Jefferson County SD
Supt. — See Louisville
Wrens MS — 300/6-8
PO Box 585 30833 — 706-547-6580
Julia Wells, prin. — Fax 547-6224

Wrightsville, Johnson, Pop. 2,174
Johnson County SD — 1,200/PK-12
PO Box 110 31096 — 478-864-3302
Rebecca Thomas, supt. — Fax 864-4053
www.johnson.k12.ga.us/
Johnson County HS — 300/9-12
150 Trojan Way 31096 — 478-864-2222
John Shapre, prin. — Fax 864-4054
Johnson County MS — 300/6-8
150 Trojan Way 31096 — 478-864-2222
John Sharpe, prin. — Fax 864-4054

Young Harris, Towns, Pop. 891

Young Harris College — Post-Sec.
PO Box 68 30582 — 706-379-3111

Zebulon, Pike, Pop. 1,154
Pike County SD — 3,600/PK-12
PO Box 386 30295 — 770-567-8489
Dr. Michael Duncan, supt. — Fax 567-8349
www.pike.k12.ga.us/
Pike County Alternative Program — Alt
PO Box 405 30295 — 770-567-2915
John Welch, admin.
Pike County HS — 1,000/9-12
331 Pirate Dr 30295 — 770-567-8770
Michael Maddox, prin. — Fax 567-3303
Pike County MS — 900/6-8
406 Hughley Rd 30295 — 770-567-3353
Dr. Vickie Smith, prin. — Fax 567-5054

Black Creek, Bryan
Bryan County SD — 7,600/PK-12
8810 US Highway 280 E 31308 — 912-851-4000
Dr. Paul Brooksher, supt. — Fax 851-4093
www.bryan.k12.ga.us/
Other Schools – See Pembroke, Richmond Hill

HAWAII

HAWAII DEPARTMENT OF EDUCATION
PO Box 2360, Honolulu 96804-2360
Telephone 808-586-3230
Fax 808-586-3234
Website doe.k12.hi.us

Superintendent of Education   Kathryn Matayoshi

HAWAII BOARD OF EDUCATION
PO Box 2360, Honolulu 96804-2360

Chairperson   Donald Horner

PUBLIC, PRIVATE AND CATHOLIC SECONDARY SCHOOLS

Aiea, Honolulu, Pop. 7,258
Hawaii SD
Supt. — See Honolulu
Aiea HS 1,200/9-12
98-1276 Ulune St 96701 808-483-7300
Michael Tokioka, prin. Fax 483-7303
Aiea IS 600/7-8
99-600 Kulawea St 96701 808-483-7230
Tom Kurashige, prin. Fax 483-7235

Calvary Chapel Christian S 200/K-12
98-1016 Komo Mai Dr 96701 808-524-0846
Rev. Edwin Arcalas, dir. Fax 275-5193

Ewa Beach, Honolulu, Pop. 10,071
Hawaii SD
Supt. — See Honolulu
Campbell HS 2,600/9-12
91-980 North Rd 96706 808-689-1200
Naomi Takamari, prin. Fax 689-1242
Ewa Makai MS 7-8
91-6291 Kapolei Pkwy 96706 808-687-9500
Edward Oshiro, prin. Fax 685-2052
Ilima IS 800/7-8
91-884 Fort Weaver Rd 96706 808-687-9300
Jon Lee, prin. Fax 689-1250

Friendship Christian S 300/PK-12
91-1207 Renton Rd 96706 808-681-8838
Lanakila Baptist HS 100/7-12
91-1219 Renton Rd 96706 808-681-3146
Rick Denham, dir. Fax 681-0704

Hana, Maui, Pop. 446
Hawaii SD
Supt. — See Honolulu
Hana S 300/K-12
PO Box 128 96713 808-248-4815
Richard Paul, prin. Fax 248-4819

Hilo, Hawaii, Pop. 26,125
Hawaii SD
Supt. — See Honolulu
Hilo HS 1,200/9-12
556 Waianuenue Ave 96720 808-974-4021
Robert Dircks, prin. Fax 974-4036
Hilo IS 500/7-8
587 Waianuenue Ave 96720 808-974-4955
Esther Kanehailua, prin. Fax 974-6184
Waiakea HS 1,200/9-12
155 W Kawili St 96720 808-974-4888
Kelcy Koga, prin. Fax 974-4880
Waiakea IS 800/6-8
200 W Puainako St 96720 808-981-7231
Lloyd Matsunami, prin. Fax 981-7237
Hilo Community S Adult
155 W Kawili St # P27 96720 808-974-4100
Chad Okinaka, prin. Fax 974-6170

Hawaii College or Oriental Medicine Post-Sec.
93 Banyan Dr Rm 504 96720 808-981-2790
Hawaii Community College Post-Sec.
200 W Kawili St 96720 808-934-2500
St. Joseph JSHS 100/7-12
1000 Ululani St 96720 808-935-4936
Victoria Torcolini, prin. Fax 969-9019
University of Hawaii at Hilo Post-Sec.
200 W Kawili St 96720 808-974-7414

Holualoa, Hawaii, Pop. 6,646

Makua Lani Christian S 100/8-12
74-4947 Mamalahoa Hwy 96725 808-329-4898
Thaddea Pitts, admin. Fax 334-0969

Honokaa, Hawaii, Pop. 1,529
Hawaii SD
Supt. — See Honolulu
Honoka'a HS 700/7-12
45-527 Pakalana St 96727 808-775-8800
Glenn Gray, prin. Fax 775-8803

Honolulu, Honolulu, Pop. 378,155
Hawaii SD 177,700/PK-12
PO Box 2360 96804 808-586-3230
Kathryn Matayoshi, supt. Fax 586-3234
doe.k12.hi.us/
Aliamanu MS 700/7-8
3271 Salt Lake Blvd 96818 808-421-4100
Robert Eggleston, prin. Fax 421-4103
Anuenue S 400/K-12
2528 10th Ave 96816 808-733-8465
Charles Naumu, prin. Fax 733-8467
Central MS 400/6-8
1302 Queen Emma St 96813 808-587-4400
Cindy Yun-Kim, prin. Fax 587-4409
Dole MS 800/6-8
1803 Kamehameha IV Rd 96819 808-832-3340
Arnie Kikkawa, prin. Fax 832-3349
Farrington HS 2,500/9-12
1564 N King St 96817 808-832-3600
Alfredo Carganilla, prin. Fax 832-3587
Jarrett MS 200/6-8
1903 Palolo Ave 96816 808-733-4888
Eleanor Gonsalves, prin. Fax 733-4894
Kaimuki HS 1,100/9-12
2705 Kaimuki Ave 96816 808-733-4900
Wade Araki, prin. Fax 733-4929
Kaimuki MS 900/6-8
631 18th Ave 96816 808-733-4800
Frank Fernandes, prin. Fax 733-4810
Kaiser HS 1,100/9-12
511 Lunalilo Home Rd 96825 808-394-1200
John Sosa, prin. Fax 394-1201
Kalakaua MS 1,000/6-8
821 Kalihi St 96819 808-832-3130
Lorelei Karasaki, prin. Fax 832-3140
Kalani HS 1,100/9-12
4680 Kalanianaole Hwy 96821 808-377-7744
Mitchell Otani, prin. Fax 377-2483
Kawananakoa MS 900/6-8
49 Funchal St 96813 808-587-4430
Sandra Ishihara-Shibata, prin. Fax 587-4443
McKinley HS 1,800/9-12
1039 S King St 96814 808-594-0400
Ron Okamura, prin. Fax 594-0407
Moanalua HS 2,100/9-12
2825 Ala Ilima St 96818 808-837-8455
Darrel Galera, prin. Fax 831-7919
Moanalua MS 900/7-8
1289 Mahiole St 96819 808-831-7850
Lisa Nagamine, prin. Fax 831-7859
Niu Valley MS 800/6-8
310 Halemaumau St 96821 808-377-2440
Justin Mew, prin. Fax 377-2444
Radford HS 1,300/9-12
4361 Salt Lake Blvd 96818 808-421-4200
Elias Ali, prin. Fax 421-4210
Roosevelt HS 1,400/9-12
1120 Nehoa St 96822 808-531-9500
Jeanette Uyeda, prin. Fax 587-4637
Stevenson MS 600/6-8
1202 Prospect St 96822 808-587-4520
Linell Dilwith, prin. Fax 587-4523
Washington MS 800/6-8
1633 S King St 96826 808-973-0177
Michael Harano, prin. Fax 973-0181
Farrington Community S Adult
1101 Kalihi St 96819 808-832-3595
Kenneth Furukawa, prin. Fax 832-3598
Kaimuki Community S Adult
2705 Kaimuki Ave 96816 808-733-8460
Randal Tanaka, prin. Fax 733-8463
McKinley Community S Adult
634 Pensacola St Ste 216 96814 808-594-0540
Helen Sanpei, prin. Fax 594-0544
Moanalua/Aiea Community S Adult
2825 Ala Ilima St Ste A 96818 808-837-8466
Calvin Shimomura, prin. Fax 831-7926
Other Schools – See Aiea, Ewa Beach, Hana, Hilo, Honokaa, Hoolehua, Kahuku, Kahului, Kailua, Kailua Kona, Kaneohe, Kapaa, Kapaau, Kapolei, Keaau, Kealakekua, Kihei, Lahaina, Lanai City, Laupahoehoe, Lihue, Makawao, Mililani, Pahala, Pahoa, Pearl City, Wahiawa, Waialua, Waianae, Wailuku, Waimea, Waipahu

Academy of the Pacific 100/6-12
913 Alewa Dr 96817 808-595-6359
Lou Young, hdmstr. Fax 595-4235
Argosy University/Hawaii Post-Sec.
1001 Bishop St Ste 400 96813 808-536-5555
Assets S 300/K-12
1 Ohana Nui Way 96818 808-423-1356
Paul Singer, hdmstr. Fax 422-1920
Babel University Professional School Post-Sec.
1833 Kalakaua Ave 96815 808-946-3773
Chaminade University of Honolulu Post-Sec.
3140 Waialae Ave 96816 808-735-4711
Christian Academy 300/PK-12
3400 Moanalua Rd 96819 808-836-0233
Linda Kim, prin. Fax 836-4415
Damien Memorial S 500/6-12
1401 Houghtailing St 96817 808-841-0195
Bernard Ho, pres. Fax 847-1401
Hawaiian Mission Academy 100/9-12
1438 Pensacola St 96822 808-536-2207
Roland Graham, prin. Fax 524-3294
Hawaii Baptist Academy 700/7-12
420 Wyllie St 96817 808-595-6301
Richard Bento, pres. Fax 595-6354
Hawaii Institute of Hair Design Post-Sec.
1128 Nuuanu Ave Ste 102 96817 808-533-6596
Hawaii Pacific University Post-Sec.
1164 Bishop St 96813 808-544-0200
Hawaii School for the Deaf and the Blind Post-Sec.
3440 Leahi Ave 96815 808-733-4999
Hawaii Technology Institute Post-Sec.
629 Pohukaina St 96813 808-522-2700
Hawaii Tokai International College Post-Sec.
2241 Kapiolani Blvd 96826 808-983-4100
Heald College Post-Sec.
1500 Kapiolani Blvd 96814 808-955-1600
Honolulu Community College Post-Sec.
874 Dillingham Blvd 96817 808-845-9211
Honolulu Waldorf HS 100/9-12
5257 Kalanianaole Hwy 96821 808-735-9311
Connie Stokes, dir. Fax 373-4982
Institute of Clinical Acupuncture Post-Sec.
100 N Beretania St Ste 203B 96817 808-521-2288
Iolani S 1,900/K-12
563 Kamoku St 96826 808-949-5355
Timothy Cottrell Ph.D., hdmstr. Fax 943-2297
Kamehameha S - Kapalama Campus 3,200/K-12
1887 Makuakane St 96817 808-842-8211
Michael Chun Ph.D., pres. Fax 842-8411
Kapiolani Community College Post-Sec.
4303 Diamond Head Rd 96816 808-734-9000
La Pietra - Hawaii S for Girls 200/6-12
2933 Poni Moi Rd 96815 808-922-2744
Mahina Hugo, head sch Fax 923-4514
Lutheran HS of Hawaii 100/9-12
1404 University Ave 96822 808-949-5302
Arthur Gundell, dean Fax 947-3701
Maryknoll HS 600/9-12
1526 Alexander St 96822 808-952-7200
James Meyer, prin. Fax 952-7201
Medical Assisting School of Hawaii Post-Sec.
33 S King St Ste 223 96813 808-524-3363
Mid-Pacific Institute 1,600/PK-12
2445 Kaala St 96822 808-973-5001
Joe Rice, pres. Fax 973-5099
New Hope Christian College - Hawaii Post-Sec.
290 Sand Island Access Rd 96819 808-853-1040
Punahou S 3,700/K-12
1601 Punahou St 96822 808-944-5711
Betsy Hata, admin. Fax 944-5762
Remington College Post-Sec.
1111 Bishop St Ste 400 96813 808-942-1000
Sacred Hearts Academy 1,100/7-12
3253 Waialae Ave 96816 808-734-5058
Betty White, prin. Fax 737-7067
St. Andrew's Priory S for Girls 400/K-12
224 Queen Emma Sq 96813 808-536-6102
Sandra Theunick, hdmstr. Fax 538-1035
St. Francis JSHS 300/7-12
2707 Pamoa Rd 96822 808-988-4111
Sr. Joan of Arc Souza, prin. Fax 988-5497
St. Louis S 600/6-12
3142 Waialae Ave 96816 808-739-7777
Judge Walter Kirimitsu, pres. Fax 739-4853
Travel Institute of the Pacific Post-Sec.
1314 S King St Ste 1164 96814 808-591-2708
University of Hawaii at Manoa Post-Sec.
2500 Campus Rd 96822 808-956-8111
World Medicine Institute Post-Sec.
PO Box 11130 96828 808-373-2849

Hoolehua, Maui
Hawaii SD
Supt. — See Honolulu
Moloka'i HS 300/9-12
PO Box 158 96729 808-567-6950
Stan Hao, prin. Fax 567-6960

Moloka'i MS 200/7-8
PO Box 443 96729 808-567-6940
Gary Davidson, prin. Fax 567-6939

Kahuku, Honolulu, Pop. 995
Hawaii SD
Supt. — See Honolulu
Kahuku JSHS 1,600/7-12
56-490 Kamehameha Hwy 96731 808-293-8950
Donna Lindsey, prin. Fax 293-8960

Kahului, Maui, Pop. 18,567
Hawaii SD
Supt. — See Honolulu
Maui HS 1,800/9-12
660 Lono Ave 96732 808-873-3000
Desiree Anderson, prin. Fax 873-3010
Maui Waena IS 1,100/6-8
795 Onehee Ave 96732 808-873-3070
Jamie Yap, prin. Fax 873-3066
Maui Community S for Adults Adult
179 W Kaahumanu Ave 96732 808-873-3082
Norma Barroga, prin. Fax 873-3046

Ka'ahumanu Hou Christian Schools of Maui 100/PK-12
777 Mokulele Hwy 96732 808-871-2477
Joni Uemura, prin. Fax 871-5668
Maui College Post-Sec.
310 W Kaahumanu Ave 96732 808-984-3500

Kailua, Honolulu, Pop. 26,779
Hawaii SD
Supt. — See Honolulu
Kailua HS 900/9-12
451 Ulumanu Dr 96734 808-266-7900
Francine Honda, prin. Fax 266-7915
Kailua IS 700/7-8
145 S Kainalu Dr 96734 808-263-1500
Lisa DeLong, prin. Fax 266-7984
Kalaheo HS 800/9-12
730 Iliaina St 96734 808-254-7900
Susan Hummel, prin. Fax 254-7907
Olomana JSHS 100/7-12
42-522 Kalanianaole Hwy 96734 808-266-7866
Stacy Oshio, prin. Fax 266-7873
Windward School for Adults Adult
730 Iliaina St 96734 808-254-7955
John Vannatta, prin. Fax 254-7958

Le Jardin Academy 800/PK-12
917 Kalanianaole Hwy 96734 808-261-0707
Adrian Allan, hdmstr. Fax 262-9339
Trinity Christian S 300/PK-12
875 Auloa Rd 96734 808-262-8501
Nancy Shaw, head sch Fax 261-3916

Kailua Kona, Hawaii, Pop. 7,780
Hawaii SD
Supt. — See Honolulu
Kealakehe HS 1,500/9-12
74-5000 Puohulihuli St 96740 808-327-4300
Wilfred Murakami, prin. Fax 327-4307
Kealakehe IS 800/6-8
74-5062 Onipaa St 96740 808-327-4314
Donald Merwin, prin. Fax 327-4315
Kona Community S Adult
74-5000 Puohulihuli St 96740 808-327-4692
John Vannatta, prin. Fax 327-4693

Hualalai Academy 100/K-12
74-4966 Kealakaa St 96740 808-326-9866
Robert Whiting, hdmstr. Fax 329-9542
Mauna Loa Helicopter Post-Sec.
73-310 UU St 96740 808-334-0234

Kamuela, Hawaii, Pop. 5,972

Hawaii Preparatory Academy 600/K-12
65-1692 Kohala Mountain Rd 96743 808-885-7321
Lindsay Barnes, hdmstr. Fax 881-4003
Parker S 300/K-12
65-1224 Lindsey Rd 96743 808-885-7933
Carl Sturges Ph.D., prin. Fax 885-6233

Kaneohe, Honolulu, Pop. 22,238
Hawaii SD
Supt. — See Honolulu
Castle HS 1,300/9-12
45-386 Kaneohe Bay Dr 96744 808-233-5600
Meredith Maeda, prin. Fax 233-5623
King IS 700/7-8
46-155 Kamehameha Hwy 96744 808-233-5727
Sheena Alaiasa, prin. Fax 233-5747

Koolau Baptist Academy 200/K-12
PO Box 1642 96744 808-233-2900
John Goodale, prin. Fax 233-2903
Windward Community College Post-Sec.
45-720 Keaahala Rd 96744 808-235-7400

Kapaa, Kauai, Pop. 7,352
Hawaii SD
Supt. — See Honolulu
Kapaa HS 1,000/9-12
4695 Mailihuna Rd 96746 808-821-4400
Daniel Hamada, prin. Fax 821-4420
Kapaa MS 600/6-8
4867 Olohena Rd 96746 808-821-4460
Nathan Aiwohi, prin. Fax 821-6967

Kapaau, Hawaii, Pop. 1,135
Hawaii SD
Supt. — See Honolulu
Kohala HS 300/9-12
PO Box 279 96755 808-889-7117
Jannette Snelling, prin. Fax 889-7120
Kohala MS 200/6-8
PO Box 777 96755 808-889-7119
Patricia Champagne, prin. Fax 889-7121

Kapolei, Honolulu, Pop. 8,781
Hawaii SD
Supt. — See Honolulu
Kapolei HS 2,100/9-12
91-5007 Kapolei Pkwy 96707 808-692-8200
Elden Esmeralda, prin. Fax 692-8255
Kapolei MS 1,400/6-8
91-5335 Kapolei Pkwy 96707 808-693-7025
Bruce Naguwa, prin. Fax 693-7030

American Renaissance Academy 100/PK-12
PO Box 75357 96707 808-682-7337
Kelly Tanizaki, head sch Fax 682-7336
Island Pacific Academy 600/PK-12
909 Haumea St 96707 808-674-3523
Dr. Daniel White, hdmstr. Fax 674-3575

Keaau, Hawaii, Pop. 1,591
Hawaii SD
Supt. — See Honolulu
Kea'au HS 900/9-12
16-725 Keaau Pahoa Rd 96749 808-982-4220
Dean Cervallos, prin. Fax 982-4224
Kea'au MS 600/6-8
16-565 Keaau Pahoa Rd 96749 808-982-4200
Ken Watanabe, prin. Fax 982-4219

Christian Liberty S 300/PK-12
16-675 Milo St 96749 808-966-8445
Troy Rimel, dir. Fax 966-8446
Kamehameha S - Hawaii Campus 1,100/K-12
16-716 Volcano Rd 96749 808-982-0000
Dr. Stan Fortuna, hdmstr. Fax 982-0010

Kealakekua, Hawaii, Pop. 1,317
Hawaii SD
Supt. — See Honolulu
Konawaena HS 700/9-12
81-1043 Konawaena School Rd 96750
808-323-4500
Shawn Suzuki, prin. Fax 323-4515
Konawaena MS 500/6-8
81-1045 Konawaena School Rd 96750
808-323-4566
Teddy Burgess, prin. Fax 323-4574

Kihei, Maui, Pop. 16,763
Hawaii SD
Supt. — See Honolulu
Lokelani IS 600/6-8
1401 Liloa Dr 96753 808-875-6800
Donna Whitford, prin. Fax 875-6835

Koloa, Kauai, Pop. 1,524

Kahili Adventist S 50/PK-12
2-4035 Kaumualii Hwy 96756 808-742-9294
Fax 742-6628

Lahaina, Maui, Pop. 8,745
Hawaii SD
Supt. — See Honolulu
Lahaina IS 700/6-8
871 Lahainaluna Rd 96761 808-662-3965
Marsha Nakamura, prin. Fax 662-3968
Lahainaluna HS 1,000/9-12
980 Lahainaluna Rd 96761 808-662-4000
Emily DeCosta, prin. Fax 662-3997

Maui Preparatory Academy 200/PK-12
PO Box 186 96767 808-665-9966
George Baker, prin. Fax 665-1075

Laie, Honolulu, Pop. 2,912

Brigham Young University Post-Sec.
55-220 Kulanui St 96762 808-675-3211

Lanai City, Maui, Pop. 2,317
Hawaii SD
Supt. — See Honolulu
Lanai S 500/K-12
PO Box 630630 96763 808-565-7900
Pierce Myers, prin. Fax 565-7904

Laupahoehoe, Hawaii, Pop. 416
Hawaii SD
Supt. — See Honolulu
Laupahoehoe S 200/K-12
PO Box 189 96764 808-962-2200
Jim Denight, prin. Fax 962-2202

Lihue, Kauai, Pop. 4,702
Hawaii SD
Supt. — See Honolulu
Kamakahelei MS 900/6-8
4431 Nuhou St 96766 808-241-3200
Debra Badua, prin. Fax 241-3210
Kauai HS 1,200/9-12
3577 Lala Rd 96766 808-274-3160
Deborah Lindsey, prin. Fax 274-3170
Kauai Community S for Adults Adult
3607A Lala Rd Ste P-12 96766 808-274-3390
Lisa McDonald, prin. Fax 274-3393

Island S 300/PK-12
3-1875 Kaumualii Hwy 96766 808-246-0233
Robert Springer M.A., head sch Fax 245-6053
Kauai Community College Post-Sec.
3-1901 Kaumualii Hwy 96766 808-245-8311

Makawao, Maui, Pop. 4,664
Hawaii SD
Supt. — See Honolulu
Kalama IS 800/6-8
120 Makani Rd 96768 808-573-8735
John Costales, prin. Fax 573-8748
Kekaulike HS 1,100/9-12
121 Kula Hwy 96768 808-573-8710
Susan Scofield, prin. Fax 573-2231

Seabury Hall S 400/6-12
480 Olinda Rd 96768 808-572-7235
Joseph Schmidt, hdmstr. Fax 572-7196

Mililani, Honolulu, Pop. 19,872
Hawaii SD
Supt. — See Honolulu
Mililani HS 2,400/9-12
95-1200 Meheula Pkwy 96789 808-627-7747
Jamie Oshiro, prin. Fax 627-7375
Mililani MS 1,700/6-8
95-1140 Lehiwa Dr 96789 808-626-7355
Elynne Chung, prin. Fax 626-7358

Hanalani S 800/PK-12
94-294 Anania Dr 96789 808-625-0737
Mark Sugimoto, supt. Fax 625-0691

Pahala, Hawaii, Pop. 832
Hawaii SD
Supt. — See Honolulu
Ka'u HS & Pahala ES 500/K-12
PO Box 100 96777 808-928-2088
Sharon Beck, prin. Fax 928-2092

Pahoa, Hawaii, Pop. 606
Hawaii SD
Supt. — See Honolulu
Pahoa JSHS 700/7-12
15-3038 Puna Rd 96778 808-965-2150
Darlene Bee, prin. Fax 965-2153

Pearl City, Honolulu, Pop. 36,969
Hawaii SD
Supt. — See Honolulu
Highlands IS 1,000/7-8
1460 Hoolaulea St 96782 808-453-6480
Amy Martinson, prin. Fax 453-6484
Pearl City HS 1,800/9-12
2100 Hookiekie St 96782 808-454-5500
Carlyn Fujimoto, prin. Fax 453-6521

Leeward Community College Post-Sec.
96-045 Ala Ike St 96782 808-455-0011
University of Hawaii - West Oahu Post-Sec.
96-129 Ala Ike St 96782 808-454-4700

Pukalani, Maui, Pop. 4,987

Kamehemaha Schools Maui 1,100/K-12
270 Aapueo Pkwy, 808-572-3100
Lee Ann DeLima, hdmstr. Fax 573-7062

Wahiawa, Honolulu, Pop. 11,315
Hawaii SD
Supt. — See Honolulu
Leilehua HS 2,000/9-12
1515 California Ave 96786 808-622-6550
Aloha Coleman, prin. Fax 622-6554
Wahiawa MS 800/6-8
275 Rose St 96786 808-622-6500
Gayle Yamaguchi, prin. Fax 622-6506
Wheeler MS 800/6-8
2 Wheeler Army Airfield 96786 808-622-6525
Brenda Vierra-Chun, prin. Fax 622-6529
Wahiawa Community S Adult
1515 California Ave 96786 808-622-1634
John Vannatta, prin. Fax 621-7765

Waialua, Honolulu, Pop. 2,839
Hawaii SD
Supt. — See Honolulu
Waialua JSHS 600/7-12
67-160 Farrington Hwy 96791 808-637-8200
Randiann Porras-Tang, prin. Fax 637-8209

Waianae, Honolulu, Pop. 4,907
Hawaii SD
Supt. — See Honolulu
Nanakuli JSHS 1,000/7-12
89-980 Nanakuli Ave 96792 808-668-5823
Darin Pilialoha, prin. Fax 668-5828
Waianae HS 1,900/9-12
85-251 Farrington Hwy 96792 808-697-9400
Nelson Shigeta, prin. Fax 697-7018
Waianae IS 800/7-8
85-626 Farrington Hwy 96792 808-697-7121
Raechelle Fabrao, prin. Fax 697-7124

Wailuku, Maui, Pop. 10,085
Hawaii SD
Supt. — See Honolulu
Baldwin HS 1,600/9-12
1650 Kaahumanu Ave 96793 808-984-5656
Jacquelyn Davis, prin. Fax 984-5674
Iao IS 900/6-8
260 S Market St 96793 808-984-5610
Catherine Kilborn, prin. Fax 984-5617

St. Anthony JSHS 200/7-12
1618 Lower Main St 96793 808-244-4190
Patricia Rickard, prin. Fax 242-8081

Waimea, Kauai, Pop. 1,080
Hawaii SD
Supt. — See Honolulu
Niihau S 50/K-12
PO Box 339 96796 808-338-6800
Nely Caberto, prin. Fax 338-6807
Waimea Canyon MS 400/6-8
PO Box 518 96796 808-338-6830
Glenda Miyazaki, prin. Fax 338-6832
Waimea HS 700/9-12
PO Box 339 96796 808-338-6800
Nely Caberto, prin. Fax 338-6807

Waipahu, Honolulu, Pop. 28,747
Hawaii SD
Supt. — See Honolulu
Waipahu HS 2,400/9-12
94-1211 Farrington Hwy 96797 808-528-9555
Keith Hayashi, prin. Fax 675-0257
Waipahu IS 1,200/7-8
94-455 Farrington Hwy 96797 808-675-0177
Randell Dunn, prin. Fax 675-0181
Waipahu Community S Adult
94-1211 Farrington Hwy 96797 808-528-9577
John Vannatta, prin. Fax 675-0259

IDAHO

IDAHO DEPARTMENT OF EDUCATION
PO Box 83720, Boise 83720-0003
Telephone 208-332-6800
Fax 208-334-2228
Website http://www.sde.idaho.gov

Superintendent of Public Instruction Tom Luna

IDAHO BOARD OF EDUCATION
PO Box 83720, Boise 83720-0003

President Kenneth Edmunds

PUBLIC, PRIVATE AND CATHOLIC SECONDARY SCHOOLS

Aberdeen, Bingham, Pop. 1,945
Aberdeen SD 58 — 800/PK-12
PO Box 610 83210 — 208-397-4113
Jane Ward, supt. — Fax 397-4114
aberdeen58.org/
Aberdeen HS — 200/9-12
PO Box 610 83210 — 208-397-4152
Travis Pincock, prin. — Fax 397-4439
Aberdeen MS — 200/6-8
PO Box 610 83210 — 208-397-3280
Ann Mennear, prin. — Fax 397-3281

American Falls, Power, Pop. 4,393
American Falls JSD 381 — 1,300/PK-12
827 Fort Hall Ave 83211 — 208-226-5173
Dr. Ron Bolinger, supt. — Fax 226-5754
www.sd381.k12.id.us
American Falls Academy — 50/Alt
598 Lincoln St 83211 — 208-226-5008
Cliff Hart, admin. — Fax 226-3194
American Falls HS — 400/9-12
2966 S Frontage Rd 83211 — 208-226-2531
Jeff Read, prin. — Fax 226-5853
Thomas MS — 300/6-8
355 Bannock Ave 83211 — 208-226-5203
Randy Jensen, prin. — Fax 226-5274

Ammon, Bonneville, Pop. 13,621
Bonneville JSD 93
Supt. — See Idaho Falls
Hillcrest HS — 1,300/9-12
2800 Owen St 83406 — 208-525-4429
Doug McLaren, prin. — Fax 525-4437
Sandcreek MS — 700/7-8
2955 Owen St 83406 — 208-525-4416
Lyndon Oswald, prin. — Fax 525-4438

Arco, Butte, Pop. 974
Butte County JSD 111 — 400/PK-12
PO Box 89 83213 — 208-527-8235
Spencer Larsen, supt. — Fax 527-8950
www.butteschooldistrict.org/
Butte County HS — 100/9-12
PO Box 655 83213 — 208-527-8237
Robert Chambers, prin. — Fax 527-8246
Butte County MS — 100/6-8
PO Box 695 83213 — 208-527-8237
Robert Chambers, prin. — Fax 527-8246

Arimo, Bannock, Pop. 334
Marsh Valley JSD 21 — 1,300/PK-12
PO Box 180 83214 — 208-254-3306
Marvin Hansen, supt. — Fax 254-9243
www.mvsd21.org
Marsh Valley Alternative S — 50/Alt
12655 S Old Highway 91 83214 — 208-254-3711
Mike Welch, prin. — Fax 254-9230
Marsh Valley HS — 400/9-12
12655 S Old Highway 91 83214 — 208-254-3711
Mike Welch, prin. — Fax 254-9230
Marsh Valley MS — 200/7-8
12805 S Old Highway 91 83214 — 208-254-3260
Jason Brower, prin. — Fax 254-3631

Ashton, Fremont, Pop. 1,114
Fremont County JSD 215
Supt. — See Saint Anthony
North Fremont JSHS — 300/6-12
3581 E 1300 N 83420 — 208-652-7468
David Marotz, prin. — Fax 652-7784

Bancroft, Caribou, Pop. 366
North Gem SD 149 — 200/PK-12
PO Box 70 83217 — 208-648-7848
Jamie Holyoak, supt. — Fax 648-7895
www.sd149.com
North Gem JSHS — 100/7-12
PO Box 70 83217 — 208-648-7848
Jamie Holyoak, admin. — Fax 648-7895

Blackfoot, Bingham, Pop. 11,732
Blackfoot SD 55 — 4,400/K-12
270 E Bridge St 83221 — 208-785-8800
Chad R. Struhs, supt. — Fax 785-8809
www.d55.k12.id.us
Blackfoot HS — 1,100/9-12
870 S Fisher Ave 83221 — 208-785-8810
John Pearce, prin. — Fax 785-2329
Independence Alternative HS — 200/Alt
155 E Francis St 83221 — 208-785-8825
Mark Kartchner, prin. — Fax 785-8893
Mountain View MS — 600/7-8
645 Mitchell Ln 83221 — 208-785-8820
Todd Lauritsen, prin. — Fax 785-8823

Snake River SD 52 — 1,700/PK-12
103 S 900 W 83221 — 208-684-3001
Mark Gabrylczyk, supt. — Fax 684-3003
www.snakeriver.org
Snake River HS — 500/9-12
922 W Highway 39 83221 — 208-684-3061
Dean Bonney, prin. — Fax 684-3074
Snake River JHS — 300/7-8
918 W Highway 39 83221 — 208-684-3018
Roger Thomas, prin. — Fax 684-3047

Bliss, Gooding, Pop. 316
Bliss JSD 234 — 200/K-12
PO Box 115 83314 — 208-352-4447
Kevin Lancaster, supt. — Fax 352-4649
www.bliss.k12.id.us
Bliss S — 200/K-12
601 E Highway 30 83314 — 208-352-4445
Kevin Lancaster, prin. — Fax 352-4649

Boise, Ada, Pop. 200,322
ISD of Boise City — 24,900/PK-12
8169 W Victory Rd 83709 — 208-854-4000
Dr. Don Coberly, supt. — Fax 854-4003
www.boiseschools.org
Boise SHS — 1,400/10-12
1010 W Washington St 83702 — 208-854-4270
Amy Kohlmeier, prin. — Fax 854-4271
Borah SHS — 1,400/10-12
6001 W Cassia St 83709 — 208-854-4370
Bonita Hammer, prin. — Fax 854-4371
Capital SHS — 1,300/10-12
8055 W Goddard Rd 83704 — 208-854-4490
Jon Ruzicka, prin. — Fax 854-4491
Church HS — 400/Alt
8051 W Salt Creek Dr 83709 — 208-854-5650
Cedric Minter, prin. — Fax 854-5651
East JHS — 500/7-9
5600 E Warm Springs Ave 83716 — 208-854-4730
Dave Roberts, prin. — Fax 854-4731
Fairmont JHS — 800/7-9
2121 N Cole Rd 83704 — 208-854-4790
Brian Walker, prin. — Fax 854-4791
Hillside JHS — 500/7-9
3536 W Hill Rd 83703 — 208-854-5120
Ted Hettinga, prin. — Fax 854-5121
Les Bois JHS — 700/7-9
4150 E Grand Forest Dr 83716 — 208-854-5340
Nate Dennis, prin. — Fax 854-5341
North JHS — 800/7-9
1105 N 13th St 83702 — 208-854-5740
Dr. Teri Thaemert, prin. — Fax 854-5741
Professional-Technical Education Center — Vo/Tech
8201 W Victory Rd 83709 — 208-854-5810
Kyle Kallmeyer, prin. — Fax 854-5811
Riverglen JHS — 600/7-9
6801 Gary Ln 83714 — 208-854-5910
David Greene, prin. — Fax 854-5911
South JHS — 600/7-9
3101 W Cassia St 83705 — 208-854-6110
Betty Olson, prin. — Fax 854-6111
Timberline SHS — 1,100/10-12
701 E Boise Ave 83706 — 208-854-6230
Rich Webb, prin. — Fax 854-6232
Treasure Valley Math & Science Center — 100/7-12
6801 Gary Ln 83714 — 208-854-6800
Dr. Holly MacLean, prin. — Fax 854-6801
West JHS — 800/7-9
8371 W Salt Creek Dr 83709 — 208-854-6450
Tim Standlee, prin. — Fax 854-6451
Boise Evening S — Adult
8051 W Salt Creek Dr 83709 — 208-854-6700
Tim Ellinghouse, prin. — Fax 854-5676

Meridian JSD 2
Supt. — See Meridian
Centennial HS — 1,800/9-12
12400 W Mcmillan Rd 83713 — 208-855-4250
David Moser, prin. — Fax 855-4273
Lake Hazel MS — 1,100/6-8
11625 W La Grange St 83709 — 208-855-4375
Bret Heller, prin. — Fax 855-4399
Scott MS — 1,100/6-8
13600 W Mcmillan Rd 83713 — 208-350-4060
Linda Ventura, prin. — Fax 350-4074

Bishop Kelly HS — 600/9-12
7009 W Franklin Rd 83709 — 208-375-6010
Robert Wehde, prin. — Fax 375-3626
Boise Bible College — Post-Sec.
8695 W Marigold St 83714 — 800-893-7755
Boise State University — Post-Sec.
1910 University Dr 83725 — 208-426-1000
Brown Mackie College - Boise — Post-Sec.
9050 W Overland Rd Ste 100 83709 — 208-321-8800
Carrington College — Post-Sec.
1122 N Liberty St 83704 — 877-206-2106
ITT Technical Institute — Post-Sec.
12302 W Explorer Dr 83713 — 208-322-8844
Milan Institute — Post-Sec.
8590 W Fairview Ave 83704 — 208-672-9500
Riverstone International School — 300/PK-12
5521 E Warm Springs Ave 83716 — 208-424-5000
Bob Carignan, hdmstr. — Fax 424-0033
St. Alphonsus Regional Medical Center — Post-Sec.
1055 N Curtis Rd 83706 — 208-378-2000
Stevens-Henager College — Post-Sec.
1444 S Entertainment Ave 83709 — 208-336-7671

Bonners Ferry, Boundary, Pop. 2,493
Boundary County SD 101 — 1,500/PK-12
6577 Main St Ste 101 83805 — 208-267-3146
Dick Conley, supt. — Fax 267-7217
www.bcsd101.com
Bonners Ferry HS — 500/9-12
6485 Tamarack Ln 83805 — 208-267-3149
Fax 267-5171
Boundary County MS — 300/6-8
6577 Main St Ste 100 83805 — 208-267-5852
Dick Behrens, prin. — Fax 267-8099

Boulder Creek Academy — 300/9-12
378 Emerson Ln 83805 — 208-267-7522
Claude Bisson, dir. — Fax 267-3232

Bruneau, Owyhee
Bruneau-Grand View JSD 365
Supt. — See Grand View
Rimrock JSHS — 100/7-12
39678 State Highway 78 83604 — 208-834-2260
Dennis Wilson, prin. — Fax 834-2516

Buhl, Twin Falls, Pop. 4,067
Buhl JSD 412 — 1,300/PK-12
920 Main St 83316 — 208-543-6436
Byron Stutzman, supt. — Fax 543-6360
www.buhlschools.org
Buhl HS — 400/9-12
1 Indian Territory 83316 — 208-543-8262
Roger Keller, prin. — Fax 543-8705
Buhl MS — 300/6-8
525 Sawtooth Ave 83316 — 208-543-8292
Suzanne Wilkin, prin. — Fax 543-5137

Burley, Cassia, Pop. 10,210
Cassia County JSD 151 — 5,100/PK-12
3650 Overland Ave 83318 — 208-878-6600
Gaylen Smyer Ph.D., supt. — Fax 878-4231
www.cassiaschools.org
Burley HS — 900/9-12
1 Bobcat Blvd 83318 — 208-878-6606
Dr. Carolyn Hondo, prin. — Fax 878-6647
Burley JHS — 500/7-8
700 W 16th St 83318 — 208-878-6613
Steve Copmann, prin. — Fax 878-6624
Cassia JSHS — 100/Alt
1010 W 17th St 83318 — 208-878-6630
Lauri Heward, prin. — Fax 878-0822
Cassia Regional Technical Center — Vo/Tech
1143 W 16th St 83318 — 208-878-6610
Carl Voigt, prin. — Fax 878-6641
Other Schools – See Declo, Malta, Oakley

Caldwell, Canyon, Pop. 45,339
Caldwell SD 132 — 6,000/K-12
1502 Fillmore St 83605 — 208-455-3300
Tim Rosandick, supt. — Fax 455-3302
www.caldwellschools.org/
Caldwell HS — 1,300/9-12
3401 S Indiana Ave 83605 — 208-455-3304
Anita Wilson, prin. — Fax 455-3256
Canyon Springs HS — 400/Alt
516 N 11th Ave 83605 — 208-455-3325
Anthony Richard, prin. — Fax 455-3341

Jefferson MS 700/6-8
3311 S 10th Ave 83605 208-455-3309
Moss Strong, prin. Fax 459-6773
Syringa MS 700/6-8
1100 Willow St 83605 208-455-3305
Shay Swan, prin. Fax 455-3353

Vallivue SD 139 7,200/PK-12
5207 S Montana Ave 83607 208-454-0445
Dr. Pat Charlton, supt. Fax 454-0293
www.vallivue.org
Rivervue MS Alt
21985 Dixie River Rd 83607 208-454-8899
Mary Ann VandeBrake, prin. Fax 454-8261
Vallivue Academy 100/Alt
6123 Timbre Pl 83607 208-455-1917
Mark Layne, prin. Fax 455-3567
Vallivue HS 1,700/9-12
1407 E Homedale Rd 83607 208-454-9253
Dick Brulotte, prin. Fax 459-7114
Vallivue MS 600/6-8
16412 S 10th Ave 83607 208-454-1426
Rod Lowe, prin. Fax 454-7846
Other Schools – See Nampa

Gem State Academy 100/9-12
16115 S Montana Ave 83607 208-459-1627
Peter McPherson, prin. Fax 454-9079
The College of Idaho Post-Sec.
2112 Cleveland Blvd 83605 208-459-5011

Cambridge, Washington, Pop. 325
Cambridge JSD 432 100/PK-12
PO Box 39 83610 208-257-3321
Ed Schumacher, supt. Fax 257-3323
www.cambridge432.org/
Cambridge MSHS 100/7-12
PO Box 39 83610 208-257-3311
Angie Lakey-Campbell, prin. Fax 257-3323

Carey, Blaine, Pop. 598
Blaine County SD 61
Supt. — See Hailey
Carey S 300/K-12
PO Box 266 83320 208-823-4391
John Peck, prin. Fax 823-4310

Cascade, Valley, Pop. 926
Cascade SD 422 300/PK-12
PO Box 291 83611 208-382-4227
Vic Koshuta, supt. Fax 382-3797
www.cascadeschools.org
Cascade JSHS 100/7-12
PO Box 291 83611 208-382-4227
Pal Sartori, prin. Fax 382-3797

Castleford, Twin Falls, Pop. 224
Castleford JSD 417 300/PK-12
500 Main St 83321 208-537-6511
Andy Wiseman, supt. Fax 537-6855
www.castlefordschools.com
Castleford S 300/PK-12
500 Main St 83321 208-537-6511
Andy Wiseman, prin. Fax 537-6855

Challis, Custer, Pop. 1,066
Challis JSD 181 400/K-12
PO Box 304 83226 208-879-4231
Fax 879-5473
www.d181.k12.id.us
Challis JSHS 200/7-12
PO Box 304 83226 208-879-2255
Russ Bradshaw, prin. Fax 879-5801

Chubbuck, Bannock, Pop. 13,624

The School of Hairstyling Post-Sec.
141 E Chubbuck Rd 83202 208-232-9170

Clark Fork, Bonner, Pop. 519
Lake Pend Oreille SD 84
Supt. — See Ponderay
Clark Fork JSHS 100/7-12
PO Box 129 83811 208-266-1131
Phil Kemink, prin. Fax 266-1692

Coeur d Alene, Kootenai, Pop. 43,078
Coeur D'Alene SD 271 10,000/PK-12
1400 N Northwood Center Ct 83814 208-664-8241
Hazel Bauman, supt. Fax 664-1748
www.cdaschools.org
Canfield MS 800/6-8
1800 E Dalton Ave 83815 208-664-9188
Nick Lilyquist, prin. Fax 769-2951
Coeur D'Alene HS 1,400/9-12
5530 N 4th St 83815 208-667-4507
Warren Olson, prin. Fax 664-5785
Lake City HS 1,600/9-12
6101 N Ramsey Rd 83815 208-769-0769
Deanne Clifford, prin. Fax 769-2944
Lakes Magnet MS 600/6-8
930 N 15th St 83814 208-667-4544
Jeff Bengtson, prin. Fax 769-2982
Project CDA/Bridge Academy 50/Alt
1619 N 9th St 83814 208-667-7460
Rosie Astorquia, prin. Fax 667-7253
Woodland MS 800/6-8
2101 W Saint Michelle 83815 208-667-5996
Chris Hammons, prin. Fax 667-5997

Lake City Junior Academy 100/PK-10
111 E Locust Ave 83814 208-667-0877
Ron Jacaban, prin. Fax 665-1462
North Idaho College Post-Sec.
1000 W Garden Ave 83814 208-769-3300
SAGE Technical Service Truck Driving Sch Post-Sec.
3448 N Huetter Rd 83814 800-400-0779
The Headmasters School of Hair Design Post-Sec.
317 Coeur DAlene Lake Dr 83814 208-664-0541

Cottonwood, Idaho, Pop. 891
Cottonwood JSD 242 300/PK-12
PO Box 158 83522 208-962-3971
Rene' Forsmann, supt. Fax 962-7780
www.sd242.k12.id.us/
Prairie JSHS 200/7-12
PO Box 540 83522 208-962-3901
Carrie Nygaard, prin. Fax 962-7702

Council, Adams, Pop. 826
Council SD 13 200/PK-12
PO Box 468 83612 208-253-4217
Murray Dalgleish, supt. Fax 253-4297
www.csd13.org/
Council JSHS 100/7-12
PO Box 468 83612 208-253-4217
Murray Dalgleish, prin. Fax 253-4297

Craigmont, Lewis, Pop. 493
Highland JSD 305 200/PK-12
PO Box 130 83523 208-924-5211
Cynthia Orr, supt. Fax 924-5614
www.sd305.k12.id.us/
Highland S 200/PK-12
PO Box 130 83523 208-924-5211
Bill Gehring, prin. Fax 924-5614

Culdesac, Nez Perce, Pop. 380
Culdesac JSD 342 100/PK-12
600 Culdesac Ave 83524 208-843-5413
Alan Felgenhauer, supt. Fax 843-2719
pass.culsch.org
Culdesac S 100/PK-12
600 Culdesac Ave 83524 208-843-5413
Shannon Morris M.A., prin. Fax 843-2719

Dayton, Franklin, Pop. 454
West Side JSD 202 600/PK-12
PO Box 39 83232 208-747-3502
Spencer Barzee, supt. Fax 747-3705
www.wssd.k12.id.us
Lee MS 100/6-8
PO Box 140 83232 208-747-3303
Spencer Barzee, prin. Fax 747-3637
West Side HS 200/9-12
PO Box 89 83232 208-747-3411
Spencer Barzee, prin. Fax 747-3990

Deary, Latah, Pop. 490
Whitepine JSD 288 300/K-12
PO Box 249 83823 208-877-1408
Tera Reeves, supt. Fax 877-1570
www.sd288.k12.id.us/
Deary S 200/4-12
PO Box 9 83823 208-877-1151
Darrah Eggers, prin. Fax 877-1366

Declo, Cassia, Pop. 341
Cassia County JSD 151
Supt. — See Burley
Declo HS 300/9-12
505 E Main St 83323 208-654-2030
Roland Bott, prin. Fax 654-2404
Declo JHS 300/6-8
205 E Main St 83323 208-654-9960
Scott Muir, prin. Fax 654-2070

Dietrich, Lincoln, Pop. 330
Dietrich SD 314 200/PK-12
406 N Park St 83324 208-544-2158
Neal Hollingshead, supt. Fax 544-2832
www.sd314.k12.id.us/
Dietrich S 200/PK-12
406 N Park St 83324 208-544-2158
Neal Hollingshead, prin. Fax 544-2832

Driggs, Teton, Pop. 1,636
Teton County SD 401 1,700/K-12
PO Box 775 83422 208-354-2207
Monte Woolstenhulme, supt. Fax 354-2250
tsd401.org
Basin JSHS Alt
510 N 1st E 83422 208-354-4800
LeaAnn Gomez, prin. Fax 354-2250
Teton HS 400/9-12
555 E Ross Ave 83422 208-354-2952
Frank Mello, prin. Fax 354-2907
Teton MS 300/6-8
935 N 5th E 83422 208-354-2971
Steve Burch, prin. Fax 354-8685

Dubois, Clark, Pop. 673
Clark County SD 161 200/PK-12
PO Box 237 83423 208-374-5215
Daniel Lantis, supt. Fax 374-5234
www.clarkcountyschools161.org/
Clark County JSHS 100/6-12
PO Box 237 83423 208-374-5215
Daniel Lantis, admin. Fax 374-5234

Eagle, Ada, Pop. 19,545
Meridian JSD 2
Supt. — See Meridian
Eagle Academy 200/Alt
100 S Academy Ave 83616 208-350-4220
James Buschine, prin. Fax 350-4234
Eagle HS 1,500/9-12
574 Park Ln 83616 208-939-2189
Terry Beck, prin. Fax 350-4254
Eagle MS 1,200/6-8
1000 W Floating Feather Rd 83616 208-350-4255
Tony Nelson, prin. Fax 350-4269

Emmett, Gem, Pop. 6,420
Emmett ISD 221 1,400/K-12
400 S Pine St Ste 1 83617 208-365-6301
Wayne Rush, supt. Fax 365-2961
emmettschools.org
Black Canyon Alternative HS 100/Alt
400 S Pine St Ste 2 83617 208-365-5552
Stephen Joyner, prin. Fax 365-5085
Emmett HS 500/9-12
721 W 12th St 83617 208-365-6323
Wade Carter, prin. Fax 365-6100
Emmett MS 400/5-8
301 E 4th St 83617 208-365-2921
Bob Hyde, prin. Fax 365-2427

Fairfield, Camas, Pop. 404
Camas County SD 121 100/K-12
PO Box 370 83327 208-764-2625
Jim Cobble, supt. Fax 764-9218
www.camascountyschools.org/
Camas County HS 50/9-12
PO Box 370 83327 208-764-2472
Jeff Rast, prin. Fax 764-2018

Filer, Twin Falls, Pop. 2,469
Filer SD 413 1,400/PK-12
700B Stevens Ave 83328 208-326-5981
John Graham, supt. Fax 326-3350
www.filer.k12.id.us
Filer HS 400/9-12
3915 Wildcat Way 83328 208-326-5945
Leon Madsen, prin. Fax 326-3419
Filer MS 200/7-8
299 Highway 30 83328 208-326-5906
Gary Moon, prin. Fax 326-3385

Firth, Bingham, Pop. 462
Firth SD 59 700/PK-12
319 Lincoln St 83236 208-346-6815
Sid Tubbs, supt. Fax 346-6814
www.firthschools.org
Firth HS 200/9-12
329 Lincoln St 83236 208-346-6812
Jeff Gee, prin. Fax 346-6987
Firth MS 200/5-8
410 Roosevelt St 83236 208-346-6240
David Mecham, prin. Fax 346-4306

Fruitland, Payette, Pop. 4,599
Fruitland SD 373 1,500/PK-12
PO Box A 83619 208-452-3595
Teresa Fabricius, supt. Fax 452-6430
www.fsd.k12.id.us/
Fruitland Alternative S Alt
PO Box A 83619 208-452-3360
Gayle VanWeerdhuizen, admin.
Fruitland HS 500/9-12
PO Box A 83619 208-452-4411
Mike Fitch, prin. Fax 452-4485
Fruitland MS 400/6-8
PO Box A 83619 208-452-3350
Kimi Fitch, prin. Fax 452-4063

Garden Valley, Boise, Pop. 390
Garden Valley SD 71 200/PK-12
PO Box 710 83622 208-462-3756
Randy Schrader, supt. Fax 462-3570
www.gvsd.net
Garden Valley S 200/PK-12
PO Box 710 83622 208-462-3756
Randy Schrader, supt. Fax 462-3570

Genesee, Latah, Pop. 930
Genesee JSD 282 300/K-12
PO Box 98 83832 208-285-1161
Wendy Moore, supt. Fax 285-1495
www.sd282.org/
Genesee S 300/K-12
PO Box 98 83832 208-285-1162
Kelly Caldwell, prin. Fax 285-1495

Glenns Ferry, Elmore, Pop. 1,301
Glenns Ferry JSD 192 500/PK-12
800 Old Highway 30 83623 208-366-7436
Matt Murray, supt. Fax 366-7455
www.glennsferryschools.org/
Glenns Ferry HS 100/9-12
639 N Bannock St 83623 208-366-7434
Cody Fisher, prin. Fax 366-2056
Glenns Ferry MS 100/6-8
639 N Bannock St 83623 208-366-7438
Cody Fisher, prin. Fax 366-2056

Gooding, Gooding, Pop. 3,514
Gooding JSD 231 1,200/PK-12
507 Idaho St 83330 208-934-4321
Dr. Heather Williams, supt. Fax 934-4403
www.goodingschools.org
Gooding HS 300/9-12
1050 7th Ave W 83330 208-934-4831
Chris Comstock, prin. Fax 934-4347
Gooding MS 300/6-8
1047 7th Ave W 83330 208-934-8443
Benjamin Hardcastle, prin. Fax 934-4898

Idaho State School for the Deaf/Blind Post-Sec.
1450 Main St 83330 208-934-4457

Grace, Caribou, Pop. 908
Grace JSD 148 400/PK-12
PO Box 347 83241 208-425-3984
Jamie Holyoak, supt. Fax 425-3809
www.sd148.org/
Grace JSHS 200/7-12
PO Box 348 83241 208-425-3731
Stephen Brady, prin. Fax 425-3063

Grand View, Owyhee, Pop. 441
Bruneau-Grand View JSD 365 300/PK-12
PO Box 310 83624 208-834-2253
Dennis Wilson, supt. Fax 834-2293
www.sd365.us
Other Schools – See Bruneau

Grangeville, Idaho, Pop. 3,096
Mountain View SD 244 1,200/PK-12
714 Jefferson St 83530 208-983-0990
Kent Stokes, supt. Fax 983-1245
www.sd244.org
Grangeville HS 300/9-12
910 S D St 83530 208-983-0580
Steve Higgins, prin. Fax 983-3786
Other Schools – See Kooskia

Greenleaf, Canyon, Pop. 835

Greenleaf Friends Academy 200/PK-12
PO Box 368 83626 208-459-6346
Jeff Metcalf, prin. Fax 459-7700

Hagerman, Gooding, Pop. 864
Hagerman JSD 233 400/K-12
324 N 2nd Ave 83332 208-837-6344
Ty Jones, supt. Fax 837-6380
www.hagerman.k12.id.us
Hagerman JSHS 200/7-12
150 Lake St W 83332 208-837-4572
Mark Kress, prin. Fax 837-6502

Hailey, Blaine, Pop. 7,880
Blaine County SD 61 — 3,200/K-12
118 W Bullion St 83333 — 208-578-5000
Lonnie Barber, supt. — Fax 578-5110
www.blaineschools.org/
Silver Creek Alternative S — 50/Alt
1060 Fox Acres Rd Ste 1000 83333 — 208-578-5060
Mike Glenn, admin. — Fax 578-5160
Wood River HS — 800/9-12
1250 Fox Acres Rd 83333 — 208-578-5020
Peter Jurovich, prin. — Fax 578-5120
Wood River MS — 700/6-8
900 N 2nd Ave 83333 — 208-578-5030
Fritz Peters, prin. — Fax 578-5130
Other Schools – See Carey

Hansen, Twin Falls, Pop. 1,129
Hansen SD 415 — 400/PK-12
550 Main St S 83334 — 208-423-6387
Susan Scherz, supt. — Fax 423-6808
www.hansen.k12.id.us
Hansen JSHS — 200/7-12
550 Main St S 83334 — 208-423-5593
Bert Hursh, prin. — Fax 423-6808

Harrison, Kootenai, Pop. 203
Kootenai SD 274 — 200/K-12
13030 E Ogara Rd 83833 — 208-689-3631
Lynette Ferguson, supt. — Fax 689-3641
www.sd274.com
Kootenai JSHS — 100/6-12
13030 E Ogara Rd 83833 — 208-689-3311
Tim Schultz, prin. — Fax 689-9072

Hayden, Kootenai, Pop. 13,034

North Idaho Christian S — 200/1-12
251 W Miles Ave 83835 — 208-772-7546
Cal Booth, admin. — Fax 762-2749

Hazelton, Jerome, Pop. 738
Valley SD 262 — 600/PK-12
882 Valley Rd 83335 — 208-829-5333
Dennis Coulter, supt. — Fax 829-5548
www.valleyvikings.org
Valley S — 600/PK-12
882 Valley Rd 83335 — 208-829-5353
Dennis Coulter, admin. — Fax 829-5548

Heyburn, Minidoka, Pop. 3,058
Minidoka County JSD 331
Supt. — See Rupert
Mt. Harrison JSHS — 200/Alt
1431 17th St 83336 — 208-436-6252
Dan Rogers, prin. — Fax 436-4746

Homedale, Owyhee, Pop. 2,586
Homedale JSD 370 — 1,200/K-12
116 E Owyhee Ave 83628 — 208-337-4611
Rob Sauer, supt. — Fax 337-4911
www.homedaleschools.org
Homedale HS — 400/9-12
203 E Idaho Ave 83628 — 208-337-4613
Luci Asumendi-Mereness, prin. — Fax 337-4933
Homedale MS — 400/5-8
3437 Johnstone Rd 83628 — 208-337-5780
Amy Winters, prin. — Fax 337-5782

Horseshoe Bend, Boise, Pop. [illegible]
Horseshoe Bend SD 73 — 200/PK-12
398 School Dr 83629 — 208-793-2225
Vickie Renfro, supt. — Fax 793-2449
www.hsbschools.org
Horseshoe Bend HS — 100/9-12
398 School Dr 83629 — 208-793-2225
Dennis Chesnut, prin. — Fax 793-2449

Idaho City, Boise, Pop. 473
Basin SD 72 — 400/PK-12
PO Box 227 83631 — 208-392-4183
John McFarlane, supt. — Fax 392-9954
www.idahocityschools.net/
Idaho City MSHS — 200/7-12
PO Box 227 83631 — 208-392-4183
John McFarlane, prin. — Fax 392-9954

Idaho Falls, Bonneville, Pop. 55,872
Bonneville JSD 93 — 9,400/PK-12
3497 N Ammon Rd 83401 — 208-525-4400
Dr. Charles Shackett, supt. — Fax 529-0104
www3.d93.k12.id.us/
Bonneville HS — 1,200/9-12
3165 E Iona Rd 83401 — 208-525-4406
John Pymm, prin. — Fax 523-7014
Lincoln Alternative HS — 100/Alt
3175 E Lincoln Rd 83401 — 208-525-4447
Gordon Howard, prin. — Fax 525-4446
Rocky Mountain MS — 700/7-8
3443 N Ammon Rd 83401 — 208-525-4403
Jason Lords, prin. — Fax 525-4469
Technical Careers HS — Vo/Tech
3497 N Ammon Rd 83401 — 208-525-4433
Craig Miller, prin.
Telford Academy — 50/Alt
2017 E 49th N 83401 — 208-542-0283
Joseph Weber, prin. — Fax 524-2429
Other Schools – See Ammon

Idaho Falls SD 91 — 9,200/PK-12
690 John Adams Pkwy 83401 — 208-525-7500
George Boland, supt. — Fax 525-7596
www.d91.k12.id.us
Compass Academy — 300/9-12
955 Garfield St 83401 — 208-525-7720
Matthew Bertasso, dir.
Eagle Rock MS — 600/7-8
2020 Pancheri Dr 83402 — 208-525-7700
Vince Howard, prin. — Fax 525-7703
Emerson Alternative HS — 100/Alt
335 5th St 83401 — 208-524-7800
Robin Busch, prin. — Fax 525-7795
Idaho Falls HS — 1,200/9-12
601 S Holmes Ave 83401 — 208-525-7740
Randy Hurley, prin. — Fax 525-7768
Skyline HS — 1,000/9-12
1767 Blue Sky Dr 83402 — 208-525-7770
Scott Miller, prin. — Fax 525-7778

Taylorview MS — 500/7-8
350 Castlerock Ln 83404 — 208-524-7850
Chad Martin, prin. — Fax 524-7851

Calvary Chapel Christian S — 300/PK-12
4250 S 25th E 83404 — 208-542-6250
Bob Peck, prin. — Fax 542-0697
Eastern Idaho Technical College — Post-Sec.
1600 S 25th E 83404 — 208-524-3000
Stevens-Henager College — Post-Sec.
901 Pier View Dr Ste 105 83402 — 208-522-0887

Jerome, Jerome, Pop. 10,745
Jerome JSD 261 — 3,500/PK-12
125 4th Ave W 83338 — 208-324-2392
Dale Layne, supt. — Fax 324-7609
jeromeschools.org
Jerome HS — 900/9-12
104 Tiger Dr 83338 — 208-324-8137
Eric Anderson, prin. — Fax 324-1266
Jerome MS — 800/6-8
520 10th Ave W 83338 — 208-324-8134
Ryan Ellsworth, prin. — Fax 324-7458
Northside Alternative JSHS — 50/Alt
125 4th Ave W 83338 — 208-324-8137
Dale Layne, prin. — Fax 324-1266

Juliaetta, Latah, Pop. 565
Kendrick JSD 283 — 200/PK-12
305 4th St 83535 — 208-289-4211
Calvin Spangler, supt. — Fax 289-4201
www.dist283.org/
Other Schools – See Kendrick

Kamiah, Lewis, Pop. 1,246
Kamiah JSD 304 — 600/PK-12
1102 Hill St 83536 — 208-935-2991
Fred Mercer, supt. — Fax 935-4005
www.kamiah.org/
Kamiah HS — 200/9-12
1102 Hill St 83536 — 208-935-4067
Rollie Sullivan, prin. — Fax 935-4068
Kamiah MS — 200/5-8
1102 Hill St 83536 — 208-935-4040
Marcus Scheibe, prin. — Fax 935-4041

Kellogg, Shoshone, Pop. 2,083
Kellogg JSD 391 — 1,300/K-12
800 Bunker Ave 83837 — 208-784-1348
Woody Woodford, supt. — Fax 786-3331
www.kelloggschools.org
Kellogg HS — 400/9-12
2 Jacobs Gulch Rd 83837 — 208-784-1371
Wayne Pfeifer, prin. — Fax 783-0741
Kellogg MS — 300/6-8
810 Bunker Ave 83837 — 208-784-1311
Curt-Randall Bayer, prin. — Fax 784-0134

Silver Valley Christian Academy — 50/PK-12
514 W Brown Ave 83837 — 208-783-3791
Mandi Martinez, admin. — Fax 783-3791

Kendrick, Latah, Pop. 297
Kendrick JSD 283
Supt. — See Juliaetta
Kendrick JSHS — 100/7-12
2001 Highway 3 83537 — 208-289-[illegible]
Steven Kirkland, prin. — Fax 289-4213

Kimberly, Twin Falls, Pop. 3,233
Kimberly SD 414 — 1,400/K-12
141 Center St W 83341 — 208-423-4170
Luke Schroeder, supt. — Fax 423-6155
www.kimberly.edu/
Kimberly HS — 400/9-12
141 Center St W 83341 — 208-423-4170
Megan Garner, prin. — Fax 423-5181
Kimberly MS — 300/6-8
141 Center St W 83341 — 208-423-4170
Mathew Schvaneveldt, prin. — Fax 423-6155

Kooskia, Idaho, Pop. 590
Mountain View SD 244
Supt. — See Grangeville
Clearwater Valley JSHS — 200/6-12
PO Box 130 83539 — 208-926-4511
Randall Miskin, prin. — Fax 926-4807

Kuna, Ada, Pop. 14,851
Kuna JSD 3 — 4,900/PK-12
711 E Porter St 83634 — 208-922-1000
Jay Hummel, supt. — Fax 922-5646
www.kunaschools.org
Initial Point HS — 100/Alt
1080 N Ten Mile Rd 83634 — 208-472-9721
Lora Seabaugh, prin. — Fax 472-9730
Kuna HS — 1,300/9-12
637 E Deer Flat Rd 83634 — 208-955-0200
Karla Reynolds, prin. — Fax 922-2178
Kuna MS — 700/7-8
1360 Boise St 83634 — 208-922-1002
Deb McGrath, prin. — Fax 922-1030

Lapwai, Nez Perce, Pop. 1,098
Lapwai SD 341 — 500/PK-12
PO Box 247 83540 — 208-843-2622
David Aiken, supt. — Fax 843-7746
www.lapwaidistrict.org/
Lapwai JSHS — 300/6-12
PO Box 247 83540 — 208-843-2241
Jen Shubert, prin. — Fax 843-5289

Leadore, Lemhi, Pop. 105
South Lemhi SD 292 — 100/PK-12
PO Box 119 83464 — 208-768-2441
Erica J. Kemery, supt. — Fax 768-2797
www.leadoreschool.org
Leadore S — 100/PK-12
PO Box 119 83464 — 208-768-2441
Erica J. Kemery, prin. — Fax 768-2797

Lewiston, Nez Perce, Pop. 31,213
Lewiston ISD 1 — 4,800/PK-12
3317 12th St 83501 — 208-748-3000
Dr. Joy Rapp, supt. — Fax 748-3059
www.lewistonschools.net
Jenifer JHS — 600/7-9
1213 16th St 83501 — 208-748-3300
JoAnne Greear, prin. — Fax 748-3349

Lewiston SHS — 1,000/10-12
1114 9th Ave 83501 — 208-748-3100
Lance Hansen, prin. — Fax 748-3149
Sacajawea JHS — 600/7-9
3610 12th St 83501 — 208-748-3400
Phil Uhlorn, prin. — Fax 748-3449
Tammany Alternative Learning Center — 100/Alt
1982 Tammany Creek Rd 83501 — 208-748-3270
Susan Scully, admin. — Fax 748-3299

Confluence Christian HS — 50/9-12
PO Box 1852 83501 — 208-731-6320
Ross Carlton, admin.
Lewis-Clark State College — Post-Sec.
500 8th Ave 83501 — 208-792-5272
Mr. Leon's School of Hair Design — Post-Sec.
205 10th St 83501 — 208-743-6822
The Headmasters School of Hair Design — Post-Sec.
602 Main St 83501 — 208-743-1512

Mc Call, Valley, Pop. 2,959
McCall-Donnelly JSD 421 — 900/PK-12
120 Idaho St 83638 — 208-634-2161
Glen Szymoniak, supt. — Fax 634-4075
www.mdsd.org
Heartland Alternative S — 50/Alt
124 Idaho St 83638 — 208-634-3686
Glen Szymoniak, prin. — Fax 634-1512
McCall-Donnelly HS — 300/9-12
401 N Mission St 83638 — 208-634-2218
Tim Thomas, prin. — Fax 634-7505
Payette Lakes MS — 200/6-8
111 N Samson Trl 83638 — 208-634-5994
Susan Buescher, prin. — Fax 634-5231

Mackay, Custer, Pop. 515
Mackay JSD 182 — 200/PK-12
PO Box 390 83251 — 208-588-2896
Karen Pyron, supt. — Fax 588-2269
Mackay JSHS — 100/7-12
PO Box 390 83251 — 208-588-2262
Jess Johnson, prin. — Fax 588-2549

Malad City, Oneida, Pop. 2,070
Oneida County SD 351 — 900/PK-12
25 E 50 S Ste A 83252 — 208-766-4701
David Risenmay, supt. — Fax 766-2930
www.oneidaschooldistrict.org
Malad HS — 300/9-12
181 Jenkins Ave 83252 — 208-766-4728
John Cockett, prin. — Fax 766-4538
Malad MS — 200/6-8
175 Jenkins Ave 83252 — 208-766-9235
Sheldon Vaughan, prin. — Fax 766-9236
Oneida Alternative HS — 50/Alt
300 W 450 N 83252 — 208-766-2255
Terri Sorrensen, prin. — Fax 766-4538

Malta, Cassia, Pop. 193
Cassia County JSD 151
Supt. — See Burley
Raft River JSHS — 100/7-12
PO Box 60 83342 — 208-645-2220
Eric Boden, prin. — Fax 645-2640

Marsing, Owyhee, Pop. 1,018
Marsing JSD 363 — 800/K-12
PO Box 340 83639 — 208-896-4111
Norm Stewart, supt. — Fax 896-4790
www.marsingschools.org/
Marsing HS — 200/9-12
PO Box 340 83639 — 208-896-4111
Tim Little, prin. — Fax 896-4457
Marsing MS — 200/6-8
PO Box 340 83639 — 208-896-4111
Allen Duby, prin. — Fax 896-5128

Melba, Canyon, Pop. 503
Melba JSD 136 — 600/PK-12
PO Box 185 83641 — 208-495-1141
Andrew Grover, supt. — Fax 495-1142
www.melbaschools.org
Melba JSHS — 200/7-12
PO Box 185 83641 — 208-495-2221
Todd Shumway, prin. — Fax 495-2188

Menan, Jefferson, Pop. 728
Jefferson County JSD 251
Supt. — See Rigby
Jefferson Alternative HS — 50/Alt
529 N 3470 E 83434 — 208-754-4550
Richard Young, prin. — Fax 754-4581

Meridian, Ada, Pop. 73,335
Meridian JSD 2 — 35,000/PK-12
1303 E Central Dr 83642 — 208-855-4500
Dr. Linda Clark, supt. — Fax 350-5962
www.meridianschools.org
Central Academy — 200/Alt
6075 N Locust Grove Rd, — 208-855-4325
Randy Yadon, prin. — Fax 855-4324
Crossroads MS — 100/Alt
650 N Nola Rd 83642 — 208-855-4275
Karen Harr, prin. — Fax 855-4284
Heritage MS — 1,000/6-8
4990 N Meridian Rd, — 208-350-4130
Susan McInerney, prin. — Fax 350-4139
Lewis & Clark MS — 1,000/6-8
4141 E Pine Ave 83642 — 208-350-4270
Kelly Davies, prin. — Fax 350-4284
Meridian Academy — 200/Alt
2311 E Lanark St 83642 — 208-855-4315
Dustin Barrett, prin. — Fax 855-4326
Meridian HS — 1,500/9-12
1900 W Pine Ave 83642 — 208-350-4160
Geoff Stands, prin. — Fax 350-4179
Meridian MS — 1,000/6-8
1507 W 8th St 83642 — 208-855-4225
Lisa Austin, prin. — Fax 888-3038
Mountain View HS — 2,100/9-12
2000 S Millenium Way 83642 — 208-855-4050
Aaron Maybon, prin. — Fax 855-4074
Pathways MS — 100/Alt
1855 E Heritage Park Ln, — 208-350-4040
Eric Eschen, prin. — Fax 350-4059
Rebound School of Opportunity — Alt
1450 E Watertower St 83642 — 208-350-5232
Eric Eschen, prin. — Fax 350-5179

Renaissance HS 300/9-12
1307 E Central Dr 83642 208-350-4380
Penny Andrew, prin. Fax 350-4394
Rocky Mountain HS 2,000/9-12
5450 N Linder Rd, 208-350-4340
Mike Hirano, prin. Fax 350-4369
Sawtooth MS 900/6-8
3730 N Linder Rd, 208-855-4200
Kevin Leishman, prin. Fax 855-4224
Other Schools – See Boise, Eagle

Ambrose S 500/K-12
6100 N Locust Grove Rd, 208-323-3888
David Goodwin, hdmstr. Fax 672-0522
Broadview College Post-Sec.
2750 E Gala St 83642 208-577-2900
Cole Valley Christian HS 400/7-12
200 E Carlton Ave 83642 208-947-1212
Kimberly DeMain, prin. Fax 898-9016
Covenant Academy 50/K-12
2400 E Fairview Ave 83642 208-890-0881
David Barrett, admin. Fax 362-8061
Guardian College Post-Sec.
2150 E Fairview Ave Ste 100 83642 208-321-4744
Northwest Lineman College Post-Sec.
7600 S Meridian Rd 83642 208-888-4817

Middleton, Canyon, Pop. 5,406
Middleton SD 134 3,000/PK-12
5 S 3rd Ave W 83644 208-585-3027
Dr. Rich Bauscher, supt. Fax 585-3028
www.msd134.org
Middleton HS 1,000/9-12
1538 Emmett Rd 83644 208-585-6657
Mike Williams, prin. Fax 585-3362
Middleton MS 600/6-8
511 W Main St 83644 208-585-3251
Andrew Horning, prin. Fax 585-2098

Midvale, Washington, Pop. 169
Midvale SD 433 100/K-12
PO Box 130 83645 208-355-2234
James Warren, supt. Fax 355-2347
www.midvalerangers.org
Midvale Alternative S 50/Alt
PO Box 130 83645 208-355-2234
James Warren, prin. Fax 355-2347
Midvale S 100/K-12
PO Box 130 83645 208-355-2234
James Warren, prin. Fax 355-2347

Montpelier, Bear Lake, Pop. 2,578
Bear Lake County SD 33
Supt. — See Paris
Bear Lake HS 300/9-12
330 Boise St 83254 208-847-0294
Alan Schwab, prin. Fax 847-0144
Bear Lake MS 200/6-8
633 Washington St 83254 208-847-2255
Steve Heeder, prin. Fax 847-3626
Clover Creek HS 50/Alt
697 Jackson St 83254 208-847-2516
Alan Schwab, prin. Fax 847-2906

Moscow, Latah, Pop. 23,195
Moscow SD 281 2,000/PK-12
650 N Cleveland St 83843 208-882-1120
Dale Kleinert, supt. Fax 883-4440
www.msd281.org/
Moscow HS 600/9-12
402 E 5th St 83843 208-882-2591
Robert Celebrezze, prin. Fax 892-1136
Moscow MS 400/6-8
1410 E D St 83843 208-882-3577
Kevin Hill, prin. Fax 892-1182
Paradise Creek Regional HS 50/Alt
1314 S Main St 83843 208-882-3687
Edward Norman, prin. Fax 882-6815

Mr. Leon's School of Hair Design Post-Sec.
618 S Main St 83843 208-882-2923
New Saint Andrews College Post-Sec.
PO Box 9025 83843 208-882-1566
University of Idaho Post-Sec.
PO Box 444264 83844 208-885-6111

Mountain Home, Elmore, Pop. 13,628
Mountain Home SD 193 3,200/PK-12
PO Box 1390 83647 208-587-2580
Tim McMurtrey, supt. Fax 587-9896
www.mtnhomesd.org
Mountain Home JHS 300/8-9
1600 E 6th S 83647 208-587-2590
Albert Longhurst, prin. Fax 587-2597
Mountain Home SHS 700/10-12
300 S 11th E 83647 208-587-2570
Jeff Johnson, prin. Fax 587-2579

Mullan, Shoshone, Pop. 674
Mullan SD 392 100/K-12
345 Park Ave 83846 208-744-1118
Robin Stanley, supt. Fax 744-1119
www.mullanschools.com
Mullan JSHS 100/7-12
325 Park Ave 83846 208-744-1126
Tom Durbin, prin. Fax 744-1128

Murtaugh, Twin Falls, Pop. 114
Murtaugh JSD 418 200/PK-12
PO Box 117 83344 208-432-5451
Michelle Capps, supt. Fax 432-5477
www.murtaugh.k12.id.us/
Murtaugh HS 50/9-12
PO Box 117 83344 208-432-5451
Tom Stanley, prin. Fax 432-5477
Murtaugh MS 100/6-8
PO Box 117 83344 208-432-5451
Tom Stanley, prin. Fax 432-5477

Nampa, Canyon, Pop. 79,667
Nampa SD 131 14,400/PK-12
619 S Canyon St 83686 208-468-4600
Gary Larsen, supt. Fax 468-4638
www.nsd131.org/
Alpha One Alternative HS 50/Alt
141 Smith Ave 83651 208-468-4775
Carleen Schnitker, prin. Fax 468-4776
Columbia HS 1,300/9-12
301 S Happy Valley Rd 83687 208-498-0571
Cory Woolstenhulme, prin. Fax 498-0573
East Valley MS 1,000/6-8
4085 E Greenhurst Rd 83686 208-468-4760
Matt Crist, prin. Fax 461-4069
Lone Star MS 800/6-8
11055 Lone Star Rd 83651 208-468-4745
Greg Wiles, prin. Fax 442-4763
Nampa HS 1,200/9-12
203 Lake Lowell Ave 83686 208-498-0551
Pete Koehler, prin. Fax 466-1240
Parkview Alternative HS 50/Alt
609 15th Ave N 83687 208-498-0558
Carleen Schnitker, prin. Fax 465-6777
Ridgeline Alternative HS 100/Alt
94 N Canyon St 83651 208-498-0559
Carleen Schnitker, prin. Fax 465-6767
Skyview HS 1,100/9-12
1303 E Greenhurst Rd 83686 208-498-0561
Kim Bekkedahl, prin. Fax 468-7822
South MS 900/6-8
229 W Greenhurst Rd 83686 208-468-4740
Stuart Vickers, prin. Fax 465-2779
West MS 700/6-8
28 S Midland Blvd 83651 208-468-4750
Stefanie Duby, prin. Fax 465-2776

Vallivue SD 139
Supt. — See Caldwell
Sage Valley MS 800/6-8
18070 Santa Ana Ave 83687 208-468-4919
Sean Smith, prin. Fax 468-4904

College of Western Idaho Post-Sec.
5500 Opportunity Dr 83687 208-562-3000
Milan Institute Post-Sec.
1021 W Hemingway Blvd 83651 208-461-0616
Nampa Christian HS 300/8-12
11920 W Flamingo Ave 83651 208-466-8451
Eric Forseth Ph.D., supt. Fax 475-1739
Northwest Nazarene University Post-Sec.
623 S University Blvd 83686 208-467-8011
Razzle Dazzle College of Hair Design Post-Sec.
721 E Roosevelt Ave 83686 208-465-7660

New Meadows, Adams, Pop. 492
Meadows Valley SD 11 200/PK-12
PO Box F 83654 208-347-2411
Mike Howard, supt. Fax 347-2624
www.mvsd11.org
Meadows Valley S 200/PK-12
PO Box F 83654 208-347-2118
Mike Howard, supt. Fax 347-2624

New Plymouth, Payette, Pop. 1,508
New Plymouth SD 372 900/PK-12
103 SE Avenue 83655 208-278-5740
Ryan Kerby, supt. Fax 278-3069
www.npschools.us
New Plymouth HS 300/9-12
207 S Plymouth Ave 83655 208-278-5311
Kevin Barker, prin. Fax 278-5313
New Plymouth MS 200/6-8
4400 SW 2nd Ave 83655 208-278-5788
Christine Collins, prin. Fax 278-3773

Nezperce, Lewis, Pop. 463
Nezperce JSD 302 100/K-12
PO Box 279 83543 208-937-2551
Doug Flaming, supt. Fax 937-2136
www.nezpercesd.us/
Nezperce S 100/K-12
PO Box 279 83543 208-937-2551
Les Wells, prin. Fax 937-2136

Notus, Canyon, Pop. 520
Notus SD 135 400/K-12
PO Box 256 83656 208-459-7442
Craig Woods, supt. Fax 455-2439
www.notusschools.org
Notus JSHS 200/7-12
PO Box 256 83656 208-459-4633
Craig Woods, prin. Fax 459-6304

Oakley, Cassia, Pop. 762
Cassia County JSD 151
Supt. — See Burley
Oakley JSHS 200/7-12
455 W Main St 83346 208-862-3328
Brandell Bedke, prin. Fax 862-3330

Oldtown, Bonner, Pop. 183

House of the Lord Christian Academy 100/PK-12
754 Silver Birch Ln 83822 208-437-2184
Candace Craddick, admin. Fax 437-0441

Orofino, Clearwater, Pop. 3,071
Orofino JSD 171 1,100/PK-12
PO Box 2259 83544 208-476-5593
Robert Vian, supt. Fax 476-7293
www.sd171.k12.id.us
Orofino HS 400/7-12
300 Dunlap Rd 83544 208-476-5557
Dan Hull, prin. Fax 476-0147
Other Schools – See Weippe

Paris, Bear Lake, Pop. 510
Bear Lake County SD 33 1,100/PK-12
PO Box 300 83261 208-945-2891
Dr. Gary Brogan, supt. Fax 945-2893
blsd.net
Other Schools – See Montpelier

Parma, Canyon, Pop. 1,955
Parma SD 137 1,100/K-12
805 E McConnell Ave 83660 208-722-5115
Jim Norton, supt. Fax 722-7937
www.parmaschools.org
Parma HS 300/9-12
137 Panther Way 83660 208-722-5115
David Carson, prin. Fax 722-7153
Parma MS 300/5-8
905 E McConnell Ave 83660 208-722-5115
Peggy Sharkey, prin. Fax 722-6913

Paul, Minidoka, Pop. 1,146
Minidoka County JSD 331
Supt. — See Rupert
West Minico MS 400/6-8
155 S 600 W 83347 208-438-5018
Tim Perrigot, prin. Fax 438-8513

Payette, Payette, Pop. 7,244
Payette JSD 371 1,600/PK-12
20 N 12th St 83661 208-642-9366
Pauline King, supt. Fax 642-9006
www.payetteschools.org/
McCain MS 300/6-8
400 N Iowa Ave 83661 208-642-4122
Rick Hale, prin. Fax 642-2171
Payette HS 500/9-12
1500 6th Ave S 83661 208-642-3327
Mark Heleker, prin. Fax 642-3368

Plummer, Benewah, Pop. 956
Plummer/Worley JSD 44 300/PK-12
PO Box 130 83851 208-686-1621
Judi Sharrett, supt. Fax 686-2108
www.pwsd44.com
Lakeside JSHS 100/7-12
PO Box 130 83851 208-686-1937
John Brumley, prin. Fax 686-2207

Pocatello, Bannock, Pop. 53,083
Pocatello/Chubbuck SD 25 12,100/PK-12
3115 Pole Line Rd 83201 208-232-3563
Mary Vagner, supt. Fax 235-3280
www.sd25.us
Century HS 1,100/9-12
7801 W Diamond Back Dr 83204 208-478-6863
Sheryl Brocket, prin. Fax 478-6870
Franklin MS 700/7-8
2271 E Terry St 83201 208-233-5590
Patrick Vereecken, prin. Fax 233-1024
Hawthorne MS 500/7-8
1025 W Eldredge Rd 83201 208-237-1680
Christine Stevens, prin. Fax 237-1682
Highland HS 1,300/9-12
1800 Bench Rd 83201 208-237-1300
Dian Swanson, prin. Fax 237-1350
Irving MS 600/7-8
911 N Grant Ave 83204 208-232-3039
Susan Pettit, prin. Fax 232-0379
Kinport Academy 50/Alt
955 W Alameda Rd 83201 208-237-2233
Keith Barnes, prin. Fax 238-3635
New Horizon HS 100/Alt
955 W Alameda Rd 83201 208-237-2233
Keith Barns, prin. Fax 238-3635
Pocatello HS 1,100/9-12
325 N Arthur Ave 83204 208-233-2056
Don Cotant, prin. Fax 232-0365

Idaho State University Post-Sec.
921 S 8th Ave 83209 208-282-0211

Ponderay, Bonner, Pop. 1,102
Lake Pend Oreille SD 84 3,800/PK-12
901 N Triangle Dr 83852 208-263-2184
Shawn Woodward, supt. Fax 263-5053
www.lposd.org/
Other Schools – See Clark Fork, Sandpoint

Sandpoint Christian S 100/PK-12
477954 Highway 95 83852 208-265-8624
Elizabeth Page, prin. Fax 263-6504

Post Falls, Kootenai, Pop. 26,948
Post Falls SD 273 5,600/PK-12
PO Box 40 83877 208-773-1658
Jerry Keane, supt. Fax 773-3218
www.pfsd.com
New Vision Alternative S 100/Alt
PO Box 40 83877 208-773-3541
Dawn Mackesy, prin. Fax 773-3542
Post Falls HS 1,500/9-12
PO Box 40 83877 208-773-0581
Dena Naccarato, prin. Fax 773-0587
Post Falls MS 700/6-8
PO Box 40 83877 208-773-7554
Debbi Davis, prin. Fax 773-0884
River City MS 500/6-8
PO Box 40 83877 208-457-0933
Mike Yovetich, prin. Fax 457-1673

American Institute of Clinical Massage Post-Sec.
4365 E Inverness Dr 83854 208-773-5890
Classical Christian Academy 200/PK-12
2289 W Seltice Way 83854 208-777-4400
Dan Hopper, hdmstr. Fax 777-2544
Genesis Preparatory Academy 100/K-12
PO Box 1237 83877 208-691-0712
Chris Finch, prin. Fax 777-8853
Post Falls Christian Academy 300/PK-12
PO Box 2306 83877 208-777-0457

Potlatch, Latah, Pop. 786
Potlatch SD 285 400/PK-12
130 6th St 83855 208-875-0327
Jeffrey A. Cirka, supt. Fax 875-1028
www.potlatchschools.org
Potlatch JSHS 200/7-12
130 6th St 83855 208-875-1231
Cheryl Riedinger, prin. Fax 875-1028

Preston, Franklin, Pop. 5,154
Preston JSD 201 2,500/PK-12
120 E 2nd S 83263 208-852-0283
Joel Wilson, supt. Fax 852-3976
www.preston.k12.id.us
Franklin County HS 100/Alt
594 N State St 83263 208-852-2272
Wynn Costley, admin. Fax 852-3976
Preston HS 700/9-12
151 E 2nd S 83263 208-852-0280
Jeff Lords, prin. Fax 852-0080
Preston JHS 600/6-8
450 E Valley View Dr 83263 208-852-0751
Lance Harrison, prin. Fax 852-3510

Priest River, Bonner, Pop. 1,684
West Bonner County SD 83 1,300/PK-12
134 Main St 83856 208-448-4439
Dr. Elen Perconti, supt. Fax 448-4629
www.sd83.org
PREP Alternative HS 50/Alt
134 Main St 83856 208-448-2860
Gary Go, prin. Fax 448-0630
Priest River JHS 200/7-8
5709 Highway 2 83856 208-448-1118
Gary Go, prin. Fax 448-1119
Priest River Lamanna HS 400/9-12
596 Highway 57 83856 208-448-1211
Paul Kubena, prin. Fax 448-1212

Rathdrum, Kootenai, Pop. 6,685
Lakeland SD 272 4,400/PK-12
PO Box 39 83858 208-687-0431
Dr. Mary Ann Rannells, supt. Fax 687-1884
www.lakeland272.org/
Lakeland HS 800/9-12
PO Box 69 83858 208-687-0181
Conrad Underdahl, prin. Fax 687-1313
Lakeland JHS 400/7-8
PO Box 98 83858 208-687-0661
Todd Spear, prin. Fax 687-1510
Mountain View Alternative HS 100/Alt
PO Box 39 83858 208-687-0025
John Klingaman, admin. Fax 687-2843
Other Schools – See Spirit Lake

Rexburg, Madison, Pop. 25,087
Madison SD 321 4,700/PK-12
PO Box 830 83440 208-359-3300
Dr. Geoffrey Thomas, supt. Fax 359-3345
www.d321.k12.id.us
Central HS 100/Alt
379 S 2nd E 83440 208-359-2337
Rex Fullmer, prin. Fax 359-2521
Madison Academy 50/Alt
379 S 2nd E 83440 208-359-2337
Rex Fullmer, admin. Fax 359-2521
Madison JHS 700/7-9
134 Madison Ave 83440 208-359-3310
Randy Lords, prin. Fax 372-0105
Madison SHS 1,000/10-12
2300 University Blvd 83440 208-359-3305
Rodger Hampton, prin. Fax 359-3346

Brigham Young University - Idaho Post-Sec.
525 S Center St 83460 208-496-1411

Richfield, Lincoln, Pop. 478
Richfield SD 316 200/PK-12
555 N Tiger Dr 83349 208-487-2241
Mike Smith, supt. Fax 487-2240
sites.google.com/site/richfieldtigers/
Richfield S 200/PK-12
555 N Tiger Dr 83349 208-487-2790
Travis Jensen, prin. Fax 487-2055

Rigby, Jefferson, Pop. 3,876
Jefferson County JSD 251 4,100/PK-12
PO Box 150 83442 208-745-6693
Dr. Ron Tolman, supt. Fax 745-0848
www.sd251.org/
Rigby HS 900/9-12
3833 Rigby High Ln 83442 208-745-7701
Dr. Yvonne Thurber, prin. Fax 745-7707
Rigby MS 400/6-8
290 N 3800 E 83442 208-745-6674
Sherry Simmons, prin. Fax 745-6675
Other Schools – See Menan

Riggins, Idaho, Pop. 415
Salmon River JSD 243 100/PK-12
PO Box 50 83549 208-628-3143
Jim Doramus, supt. Fax 628-3380
www.jsd243.org
Salmon River JSHS 100/6-12
PO Box 872 83549 208-628-3431
Debra Richerson, prin. Fax 628-3840

Ririe, Jefferson, Pop. 653
Ririe JSD 252 400/PK-12
PO Box 508 83443 208-538-7482
Dr. Ron Perrenoud, supt. Fax 538-7363
www.ririeschools.org
Ririe S 200/PK-12
PO Box 568 83443 208-538-7311
Chad Williams, prin. Fax 538-7860

Rockland, Power, Pop. 294
Rockland SD 382 200/K-12
PO Box 119 83271 208-548-2221
James Woodworth, supt. Fax 548-2224
www.rbulldogs.org
Rockland S 200/K-12
PO Box 119 83271 208-548-2221
James Woodworth, prin. Fax 548-2224

Rupert, Minidoka, Pop. 5,482
Minidoka County JSD 331 3,900/K-12
310 10th St 83350 208-436-4727
Sandra Miller, supt. Fax 436-6593
www.minidokaschools.org
East Minico MS 500/6-8
310 10th St 83350 208-436-3178
John Fennell, prin. Fax 436-3235
Minico HS 1,100/9-12
310 10th St 83350 208-436-4721
Suzette Miller, prin. Fax 436-3266
Other Schools – See Heyburn, Paul

Saint Anthony, Fremont, Pop. 3,512
Fremont County JSD 215 2,100/PK-12
945 W 1st N 83445 208-624-7542
Dr. Garry Parker, supt. Fax 624-3385
www.sd215.net/
South Fremont Alternative HS 50/Alt
599 N 1st W 83445 208-624-3416
Benjamin Garcia, admin. Fax 624-4386
South Fremont HS 500/9-12
855 N Bridge St 83445 208-624-3416
Larry Bennett, prin. Fax 624-4898
South Fremont JHS 400/6-8
550 N 1st W 83445 208-624-7880
Jaci Hill, prin. Fax 624-4386
Other Schools – See Ashton

Saint Maries, Benewah, Pop. 2,361
Saint Maries JSD 41 1,000/PK-12
PO Box 384 83861 208-245-2579
Joseph Kren, supt. Fax 245-3970
www.sd41.org
Saint Maries Community Education Center 50/Alt
422 Hells Gulch Rd 83861 208-245-2152
John Cordell, prin. Fax 245-0212
Saint Maries HS 300/9-12
424 Hells Gulch Rd 83861 208-245-2142
John Cordell, prin. Fax 245-5650
Saint Maries MS 200/6-8
1315 W Jefferson Ave 83861 208-245-3495
Jeffrey Andersen, prin. Fax 245-0506

Salmon, Lemhi, Pop. 3,067
Salmon SD 291 900/PK-12
907 Sharkey St 83467 208-756-4271
Joey Foote, supt. Fax 756-6695
www.salmonschools.com
Salmon Alternative HS 50/Alt
1401 S Bean Ln 83467 208-756-6277
Joe Steele, prin. Fax 756-6695
Salmon HS 300/9-12
401 S Warpath 83467 208-756-2415
Dan Hull, prin. Fax 756-3484
Salmon MS 200/5-8
310 S Daisy St 83467 208-756-2207
Shawn Hendrickson, prin. Fax 756-2099

Sandpoint, Bonner, Pop. 7,221
Lake Pend Oreille SD 84
Supt. — See Ponderay
Lake Pend Oreille Alternative HS 100/Alt
1005 N Boyer Ave 83864 208-263-6121
Rick Dalessio, prin. Fax 265-5734
Sandpoint HS 1,000/9-12
410 S Division Ave 83864 208-263-3034
Dr. Becky Meyer, prin. Fax 263-5321
Sandpoint MS 500/7-8
310 S Division Ave 83864 208-265-4169
Kim Keaton, prin. Fax 263-5525

Shelley, Bingham, Pop. 4,332
Shelley JSD 60 1,800/PK-12
545 Seminary Ave 83274 208-357-3411
Dr. Bryan Jolley, supt. Fax 357-5741
www.shelleyschools.org/
Hobbs MS 300/7-8
350 E Pine St 83274 208-357-7667
John Crawford, prin. Fax 357-3003
Shelley HS 600/9-12
570 W Fir St 83274 208-357-7400
Dale Clark, prin. Fax 357-5585

Shoshone, Lincoln, Pop. 1,444
Shoshone JSD 312 400/PK-12
61 E Highway 24 83352 208-886-2381
Rob Waite, supt. Fax 886-2038
www.shoshone.k12.id.us
Shoshone Alternative HS Alt
409 S Apple St 83352 208-886-2381
Kelly Chapman, prin. Fax 886-2742
Shoshone JSHS 200/6-12
61 E Highway 24 83352 208-886-2381
Kelly Chapman, prin. Fax 886-2742

Soda Springs, Caribou, Pop. 3,009
Soda Springs JSD 150 800/K-12
250 E 2nd S 83276 208-547-3371
Dr. Molly Stein, supt. Fax 547-4878
www.sodaschools.org
Soda Springs HS 200/9-12
300 E 1st N 83276 208-547-4308
Doug Owen, prin. Fax 547-3327
Tigert MS 300/5-8
250 E 2nd S Ste B 83276 208-547-4922
Robert Daniel, prin. Fax 547-2619

Spirit Lake, Kootenai, Pop. 1,910
Lakeland SD 272
Supt. — See Rathdrum
Timberlake HS 500/9-12
PO Box 909 83869 208-623-6303
Kurt Hoffman, prin. Fax 623-6203
Timberlake JHS 300/7-8
PO Box 1080 83869 208-623-2582
Chris McDougall, prin. Fax 623-2750

Sugar City, Madison, Pop. 1,499
Sugar-Salem JSD 322 1,500/PK-12
PO Box 150 83448 208-356-8802
Alan Dunn, supt. Fax 356-7237
www.sd322.k12.id.us/
Sugar-Salem HS 400/9-12
1 S Digger Dr 83448 208-356-0274
Jared Jenks, prin. Fax 359-3167
Sugar-Salem JHS 200/7-8
PO Box 180 83448 208-356-4437
Kevin Schultz, prin. Fax 358-9717
Valley View Alt HS 50/Alt
1 S Digger Dr 83448 208-356-6845
Jay Miller, prin. Fax 356-3167

Sun Valley, Blaine, Pop. 1,392

Community S 300/PK-12
PO Box 2118 83353 208-622-3955
David Holmes, hdmstr. Fax 622-3962

Terreton, Jefferson
West Jefferson SD 253 600/PK-12
1256 E 1500 N 83450 208-663-4542
Dwight Richins, supt. Fax 663-4543
www.wjsd.org
West Jefferson HS 200/9-12
1260 E 1500 N 83450 208-663-4391
Marianna Taylor, prin. Fax 663-4390

Troy, Latah, Pop. 841
Troy SD 287 300/K-12
PO Box 280 83871 208-835-3791
Christy Castro, supt. Fax 835-3790
www.sd287.k12.id.us
Troy JSHS 200/7-12
101 Trojan Dr 83871 208-835-2361
Brad Malm, prin. Fax 835-2441

Twin Falls, Twin Falls, Pop. 43,303
Twin Falls SD 411 7,600/PK-12
201 Main Ave W 83301 208-733-6900
Wiley Dobbs, supt. Fax 733-6987
www.tfsd.org
Canyon Ridge HS 1,100/9-12
300 N College Rd W 83301 208-732-7555
Kasey Teske, prin. Fax 732-7556
Magic Valley HS 100/Alt
512 Main Ave N 83301 208-733-8823
Roger Keller, prin. Fax 733-8505
O'Leary JHS 900/6-8
2350 Elizabeth Blvd 83301 208-733-2155
John Hyatt, prin. Fax 733-8666
Stuart JHS 700/6-8
644 Caswell Ave W 83301 208-733-4875
Amy McBride, prin. Fax 733-4949
Twin Falls HS 1,100/9-12
1615 Filer Ave E 83301 208-733-6551
Ben Allen, prin. Fax 733-8192

College of Southern Idaho Post-Sec.
PO Box 1238 83303 208-733-9554
Lighthouse Christian S 300/PK-12
960 Eastland Dr 83301 208-737-1425
Kevin Newbry, supt. Fax 737-4671
Mr. Juan's College of Hair Design Post-Sec.
586 Blue Lakes Blvd N 83301 208-733-7777
Twin Falls Christian Academy 100/K-12
798 Eastland Dr N 83301 208-733-1452
Brent Walker, prin. Fax 734-1417

Wallace, Shoshone, Pop. 769
Wallace SD 393 500/PK-12
405 7th St 83873 208-753-4515
Dr. Robert Ranells, supt. Fax 753-4151
www.wsd393.org/
Wallace JSHS 200/7-12
1 Miners Aly 83873 208-753-5315
Don Almquist, prin. Fax 753-7105

Weippe, Clearwater, Pop. 439
Orofino JSD 171
Supt. — See Orofino
Timberline S 300/PK-12
22869 Highway 11 83553 208-435-4411
Shaun Ball, prin. Fax 435-4846

Weiser, Washington, Pop. 5,415
Weiser SD 431 1,600/PK-12
925 Pioneer Rd 83672 208-414-0616
Wil Overgaard, supt. Fax 414-1265
www.weiserschools.org
Weiser HS 500/9-12
690 W Indianhead Rd 83672 208-414-2595
Dave Davies, prin. Fax 414-1795
Weiser MS 400/6-8
320 E Galloway Ave 83672 208-414-2620
Jason Hunter, prin. Fax 414-2094

Wendell, Gooding, Pop. 2,752
Wendell SD 232 1,100/PK-12
PO Box 300 83355 208-536-2418
Greg Lowe, supt. Fax 536-2629
www.wendellschools.org
Wendell HS 300/9-12
750 E Main St 83355 208-536-2100
Jon Goss, prin. Fax 536-2124
Wendell MS 300/5-8
800 E Main St Ste A 83355 208-536-5531
Luke Kelsey, prin. Fax 536-5957

Wilder, Canyon, Pop. 1,528
Wilder SD 133 300/K-12
210 A Ave 83676 208-482-6228
Jeff Dillon, supt. Fax 482-6980
www.wilderschools.org
Wilder MSHS 100/6-12
419 Huff Rd 83676 208-482-6229
Joseph Youren, prin. Fax 482-7421

ILLINOIS

ILLINOIS DEPARTMENT OF EDUCATION
100 N 1st St, Springfield 62777-0002
Telephone 866-262-6663
Fax 217-524-8585
Website http://www.isbe.state.il.us

Superintendent of Education Dr. Christopher Koch

ILLINOIS BOARD OF EDUCATION
100 N 1st St, Springfield 62777-0002

Chairperson Gery Chico

REGIONAL OFFICES OF EDUCATION (ROE)

Adams/Pike ROE
Deborah Niederhauser, supt. 217-277-2080
507 Vermont St, Quincy 62301 Fax 277-2092
www.wc4.org

Alxndr/Jhnsn/Massac/Pulaski/Union ROE
Janet Ulrich, supt. 618-634-2292
17 Rustic Campus Dr, Ullin 62992 Fax 634-2294
www.roe02.k12.il.us/

Bond/Effingham/Fayette ROE
Julie Wollerman, supt. 618-283-5011
300 S 7th St, Vandalia 62471 Fax 283-5013
www.fayette.k12.il.us/roeweb/

Boone/Winnebago ROE
Lori Fanello, supt. 815-636-3060
300 Heart Blvd, Loves Park 61111 Fax 636-3069
www.4roe.org/

Brown/Cass/Morgan/Scott ROE
Jeff Stephens, supt. 217-243-1804
110 N West St, Jacksonville 62650 Fax 243-5354
www.roe46.net/

Bureau/Henry/Stark ROE
Angie Zarvell, supt. 309-936-7890
107 S State St, Atkinson 61235 Fax 936-1111
www.bhsroe.org

Calhoun/Greene/Jersey/Macoupin ROE
Larry Pfeiffer, supt. 217-854-4016
826 N Broad St, Carlinville 62626 Fax 854-2032
www.roe40.com

Carroll/Jo Daviess/Stephenson ROE
Aaron Mercier, supt. 815-947-3810
500 N Rush St, Stockton 61085 Fax 947-2717
www.roe8.com

Champaign/Ford ROE
Jane Quinlan, supt. 217-893-3219
200 S Fredrick St, Rantoul 61866 Fax 893-0024
www.roe9.k12.il.us/

Christian/Montgomery ROE
Marchelle Kassebaum, supt. 217-532-9591
203 S Main St, Hillsboro 62049 Fax 532-5756
www.montgomery.k12.il.us

Clay/Crawford/Jspr/Lwrnce/Rchlnd ROE
Monte Newlin, supt. 618-392-4631
103 W Main St Ste 23, Olney 62450 Fax 392-3993
www.roe12.net

Clinton/Marion/Washington ROE
Keri Jo Garrett, supt. 618-594-2432
930 Fairfax St Ste B, Carlyle 62231 Fax 594-7192
www.roe13.k12.il.us

Clk/Cls/Cumb/Dglas/Edg/Mlt/Shlb ROE
Dr. Bobbi Mattingly, supt. 217-348-0151
730 7th St, Charleston 61920 Fax 348-0171
www.roe11.k12.il.us/

DeKalb ROE
Gil Morrison, supt. 815-217-0460
2500 N Annie Glidden Rd Fax 217-0467
DeKalb 60115
www.dekalbcounty.org/ROE/roe.html

DeWitt/Livingston/McLean ROE
Mark Jontry, supt. 309-888-5120
905 N Main St Ste 1, Normal 61761 Fax 862-0420
www.roe17.org

Dupage ROE
Darlene Ruscitti, supt. 630-407-5800
421 N County Farm Rd Fax 407-5801
Wheaton 60187
www.dupage.k12.il.us/

Edwds/Gtn/Hdn/Pope/Sln/Wbsh/Wyn/Wt ROE
Lawrence Fillingim, supt. 618-253-5581
512 N Main St, Harrisburg 62946 Fax 252-8472
www.roe20.k12.il.us/

Franklin/Williamson ROE
Matt Donkin, supt. 618-438-9711
202 W Main St, Benton 62812 Fax 435-2861
www.roe21.org

Fulton/Schuyler ROE
Dave Demler, supt. 309-518-8029
257 W Lincoln Ave Fax 518-8024
Lewistown 61542
www.roe22.net

Grundy/Kendall ROE
Paul Nordstrom, supt. 815-941-3247
1320 Union St, Morris 60450 Fax 942-5384
www.roe24.org/

Hamilton/Jefferson ROE
Ron Daniels, supt. 618-244-8040
1714 Broadway St Fax 244-8073
Mount Vernon 62864
www.roe25.com

Hancock/McDonough ROE
John Meixner, supt. 309-837-4821
130 S Lafayette St Ste 200 Fax 837-2887
Macomb 61455
www.roe26.net

Henderson/Mercer/Warren ROE
Jodi Scott, supt. 309-734-6822
105 N E St Ste 1, Monmouth 61462 Fax 734-2452
www.hmwroe27.com

Iroquois/Kankakee ROE
Greg Murphy, supt. 815-937-2950
189 E Court St Ste 600 Fax 937-2921
Kankakee 60901
www.i-kan.org

Jackson/Perry ROE
Donna Boros, supt., 1001 Walnut St 618-687-7290
Murphysboro 62966 Fax 687-7296
www.roe30.k12.il.us/

Kane ROE
Patricia Dal Santo, supt. 630-232-5955
210 S 6th St, Geneva 60134 Fax 208-5115
www.kaneroe.org/

Knox ROE
Bonnie Harris, supt. 309-345-3828
PO Box 430, Galesburg 61402 Fax 345-6735
www.roe33.net

Lake ROE
Roycealee Wood, supt. 847-543-7833
800 Lancer Ln Ste E128 Fax 543-7832
Grayslake 60030
www.lake.k12.il.us

LaSalle ROE
James E. Carlson, supt. 815-434-0780
119 W Madison St, Ottawa 61350 Fax 434-2453
www.roe35.k12.il.us

Lee/Ogle ROE
Amy Jo Clemens, supt. 815-652-2054
7772 Clinton St, Dixon 61021 Fax 652-2053
www.leeogle.org/

Logan/Mason/Menard ROE
Jean Anderson, supt. 217-732-8388
122 N McLean St, Lincoln 62656 Fax 735-1569
logan.k12.il.us/roe38

Macon/Piatt ROE 39
Matthew Snyder, supt. 217-872-3721
1690 Huston Dr, Decatur 62526 Fax 872-0239
www.maconpiattroe.com/

Madison County ROE
Dr. Robert Daiber, supt. 618-296-4530
PO Box 600, Edwardsville 62025 Fax 692-7018
www.madison.k12.il.us/

Marshall/Putnam/Woodford ROE
Ronda Bangert-Cross, supt. 309-248-8212
PO Box 340, Washburn 61570 Fax 248-7983
www.roe43.org

McHenry ROE
Leslie Schermerhorn, supt. 815-334-4475
2200 N Seminary Ave Fax 338-0475
Woodstock 60098
www.mchenryroe.org/

Monroe-Randolph ROE
Marc Kiehna, supt. 618-939-5650
107 E Mill St, Waterloo 62298 Fax 939-5332
www.roe45.org

North Cook Intermediate Service Center
Robert Ingraffia, dir. 847-824-8300
2340 S River Rd Fax 824-1033
Des Plaines 60018
www.ncisc.org

Peoria ROE
Gerald Brookhart, supt. 309-672-6906
324 Main St Ste 401, Peoria 61602 Fax 672-6053
www.co.peoria.il.us/roe

Rock Island ROE
Tammy Muerhoff, supt. 309-736-1111
3430 Avenue of the Cities Fax 736-1127
Moline 61265
www.riroe.com/

Saint Clair ROE
Susan Sarfaty, supt. 618-825-3900
1000 S Illinois St, Belleville 62220 Fax 825-3999
www.stclair.k12.il.us/

Sangamon ROE
Jeff Vose, supt. 217-753-6620
200 S 9th St Ste 303 Fax 535-3166
Springfield 62701
www.roe51.org

South Cook Intermediate Service Center
Dr. Vanessa Kinder, supt. 708-754-6600
253 W Joe Orr Rd Fax 754-8687
Chicago Heights 60411
www.s-cook.org

Tazewell ROE
Gail Owen, supt. 309-477-2290
414 Court St Ste 104, Pekin 61554 Fax 347-3735
www.roe53.net

Vermilion ROE
Cheryl Reifsteck, supt. 217-431-2668
200 S College St Ste B Fax 431-2671
Danville 61832
www.roe54.k12.il.us/

West Suburb Intermediate Service Center
Kay Poyner Brown, dir. 708-544-4890
2701 Washington Blvd Fax 544-4891
Bellwood 60104
www.west40.org

Whiteside ROE
Robert Sondgeroth, supt. 815-625-1495
1001 W 23rd St, Sterling 61081 Fax 625-1625
www.whitesideroe.org

Will ROE
Jennifer Bertino-Tarrant, supt. 815-740-8360
702 W Maple St, New Lenox 60451 Fax 740-4788
www.willroe.org

PUBLIC, PRIVATE AND CATHOLIC SECONDARY SCHOOLS

Abingdon, Knox, Pop. 3,272
Abingdon CUSD 217 700/PK-12
401 W Latimer St 61410 309-462-2301
David Black, supt. Fax 462-3870
www.abingdon.k12.il.us/

Abingdon HS 200/9-12
600 W Martin St 61410 309-462-2338
Jay Hurder, prin. Fax 462-2492

Abingdon MS 200/6-8
600 W Martin St 61410 309-462-2336
Jay Hurder, prin. Fax 462-2207

Addison, DuPage, Pop. 36,491
Addison SD 4 4,100/PK-8
222 N JF Kennedy Dr Rear 2 60101 630-628-2500
John Langton, supt. Fax 628-8829
www.asd4.org

Indian Trail JHS 1,400/6-8
222 N JF Kennedy Dr Frnt 1 60101 630-458-2600
Craig Bennett, prin. Fax 628-2841

DAOES
301 S Swift Rd 60101 — 630-691-7590
Jim Thorne, dir. — Fax 691-7592
www.tcdupage.org
Technology Center of Dupage — Vo/Tech
301 S Swift Rd Ste B 60101 — 630-620-8770
Steven Carr, prin. — Fax 691-7592

DuPage HSD 88 — 4,000/9-12
2 Friendship Plz 60101 — 630-530-3980
Dr. Scott Helton, supt. — Fax 832-0198
www.dupage88.net/
Addison Trail HS — 1,900/9-12
213 N Lombard Rd 60101 — 630-628-3302
Adam Cibulka, prin. — Fax 628-0177
Other Schools – See Villa Park

Chamberlain College of Nursing — Post-Sec.
1221 N Swift Rd 60101 — 630-953-3680
DeVry University — Post-Sec.
1221 N Swift Rd 60101 — 630-953-1300

Albion, Edwards, Pop. 1,965
Edwards County CUSD 1 — 1,000/PK-12
361 W Main St Ste 100 62806 — 618-445-2814
David Cowger, supt. — Fax 445-2272
www.echs.edwrds.k12.il.us
Edwards County HS — 300/9-12
361 W Main St 62806 — 618-445-2325
Brent Julian, prin. — Fax 445-3154

Aledo, Mercer, Pop. 3,626
Mercer County SD 404 — 1,300/PK-12
1002 SW 6th St 61231 — 309-582-2238
Alan Boucher, supt. — Fax 582-7428
www.mercerschools.org
Mercer County HS — 400/9-12
1500 S College Ave 61231 — 309-582-2223
Gavin Sronce, prin. — Fax 582-5920
Other Schools – See Joy

Alexander, Morgan
Franklin CUSD 1 — 300/PK-12
PO Box 140 62601 — 217-478-3011
Andy Stremlau, supt. — Fax 478-4921
www.franklinhigh.com
Other Schools – See Franklin

Algonquin, McHenry, Pop. 29,616
CUSD 300
Supt. — See Carpentersville
Algonquin MS — 600/6-8
520 Longwood Dr 60102 — 847-658-2545
Peggy Thurow, prin. — Fax 658-2547
Jacobs HS — 2,300/9-12
2601 Bunker Hill Dr 60102 — 847-658-7500
Ami Engel, prin. — Fax 658-3203

Consolidated SD 158 — 8,900/PK-12
650 Academic Dr 60102 — 847-659-6158
Dr. John Burkey, supt. — Fax 659-6122
www.district158.org/
Heineman MS — 800/6-8
725 Academic Dr 60102 — 847-659-4300
Jim Stotz, prin. — Fax 659-4320
Other Schools – See Huntley, Lake in the Hills

Alorton, Saint Clair, Pop. 1,977
East St. Louis SD 189
Supt. — See East Saint Louis
Miller Alternative HS — 300/Alt
4400 Grand St 62207 — 618-646-3790
James Edmond, prin. — Fax 646-3798

Alsip, Cook, Pop. 19,017
Alsip-Hazelgreen-Oaklawn SD 126 — 1,600/PK-8
11900 S Kostner Ave 60803 — 708-389-1900
Craig Gwaltney, supt. — Fax 396-3793
www.dist126.org
Prairie JHS — 400/7-8
11910 S Kostner Ave 60803 — 708-371-3080
Maureen Paulmeyer, prin. — Fax 396-3798

Atwood Heights SD 125 — 700/PK-8
12150 S Hamlin Ave 60803 — 708-371-0080
Dr. Thomas Livingston, supt. — Fax 371-7847
www.ahsd125.org
Hamlin Upper Grade Center — 200/6-8
12150 S Hamlin Ave 60803 — 708-597-1550
Lisa West, prin. — Fax 396-0515

Altamont, Effingham, Pop. 2,313
Altamont CUSD 10 — 800/PK-12
7 S Ewing St 62411 — 618-483-6195
Jeff Fritchtnitch, supt. — Fax 483-6303
www.altamontschools.org/
Altamont HS — 300/9-12
7 S Ewing St 62411 — 618-483-6194
Jerry Tkachuk, prin. — Fax 483-5399

Alton, Madison, Pop. 26,887
Alton CUSD 11 — 6,400/PK-12
PO Box 9028 62002 — 618-474-2600
Dr. Kenneth Spells, supt. — Fax 463-2126
www.altonschools.org
Alton HS — 2,000/9-12
4200 Humbert Rd 62002 — 618-474-2700
Dr. Russell Tepen, prin. — Fax 463-2000
Alton MS — 1,400/6-8
2200 College Ave 62002 — 618-474-2200
David Schwartz, prin. — Fax 463-2127

CALC Institute of Technology — Post-Sec.
200 N Center Dr Ste A 62002 — 618-474-0616
Marquette HS — 300/9-12
219 E 4th St 62002 — 618-463-0580
Michael Slaughter, prin. — Fax 465-4029
Mississippi Valley Christian S — 100/PK-12
2009 Seminary St 62002 — 618-462-1071
Jerry Fair, prin. — Fax 462-9877

Amboy, Lee, Pop. 2,480
Amboy CUSD 272 — 800/PK-12
11 E Hawley St 61310 — 815-857-2164
Jeff Thake, supt. — Fax 857-4434
www.amboy.net/
Amboy HS — 300/9-12
11 E Hawley St 61310 — 815-857-3632
Ron Gruber, prin. — Fax 857-3631
Amboy JHS — 300/5-8
140 S Appleton Ave 61310 — 815-857-3528
Joyce Schamberger, prin. — Fax 857-4603

Anna, Union, Pop. 4,407
Anna CCSD 37 — 700/K-8
301 S Green St 62906 — 618-833-6812
Charles Goforth, supt. — Fax 833-3205
anna37.com/
Anna JHS — 300/5-8
301 S Green St 62906 — 618-833-6812
Mark Laster, prin. — Fax 833-6535

Anna-Jonesboro Community HSD 81 — 500/9-12
608 S Main St 62906 — 618-833-8421
James Woodward, supt. — Fax 833-4239
Anna-Jonesboro HS — 500/9-12
608 S Main St 62906 — 618-833-8502
Brett Detering, prin. — Fax 833-5931

Annawan, Henry, Pop. 875
Annawan CUSD 226 — 400/PK-12
501 W South St 61234 — 309-935-6781
Joe Buresh, supt. — Fax 935-6065
annawan226.org
Annawan HS — 100/9-12
501 W South St 61234 — 309-935-6781
Joe Buresh, prin. — Fax 935-6065

Antioch, Lake, Pop. 14,166
Antioch CCSD 34 — 3,000/PK-8
964 Spafford St 60002 — 847-838-8400
Dr. Greg Buchanan, supt. — Fax 838-8404
www.antioch34.com
Antioch Upper Grade S — 1,000/6-8
800 Highview Dr 60002 — 847-838-8310
Stacy Graff, prin. — Fax 838-8304

Community HSD 117
Supt. — See Lake Villa
Antioch Community HS — 1,400/9-12
1133 Main St 60002 — 847-395-1421
John Whitehurst, prin. — Fax 395-2435

Arcola, Douglas, Pop. 2,899
Arcola CUSD 306 — 700/PK-12
351 W Washington St 61910 — 217-268-4963
Donald Burton, supt. — Fax 268-3809
www.arcola.k12.il.us
Arcola JSHS — 300/7-12
351 W Washington St 61910 — 217-268-4962
Lisa Sigrist, prin. — Fax 268-4483

Argenta, Macon, Pop. 935
Argenta-Oreana CUSD 1 — 1,000/PK-12
PO Box 440 62501 — 217-795-2313
Damian Jones, supt. — Fax 795-2174
www.argenta-oreana.org/
Argenta-Oreana HS — 300/9-12
PO Box 469 62501 — 217-795-4821
Sean German, prin. — Fax 795-4550
Argenta-Oreana MS — 200/6-8
PO Box 439 62501 — 217-795-2163
Patrick Blair, prin. — Fax 795-4502

Arlington Heights, Cook, Pop. 74,142
Arlington Heights SD 25 — 5,100/PK-8
1200 S Dunton Ave 60005 — 847-758-4900
Dr. Sarah Jerome, supt. — Fax 758-4907
www.sd25.org
South MS — 900/6-8
400 S Highland Ave 60005 — 847-398-4250
Jake Chung, prin. — Fax 394-6260
Thomas MS — 800/6-8
1430 N Belmont Ave 60004 — 847-398-4260
Brian Kaye, prin. — Fax 394-6843

CCSD 59 — 6,200/PK-8
2123 S Arlington Heights Rd 60005 — 847-593-4300
Art Fessler, supt. — Fax 593-4409
www.ccsd59.org
Other Schools – See Des Plaines, Elk Grove Village, Mount Prospect

Township HSD 214 — 12,000/9-12
2121 S Goebbert Rd 60005 — 847-718-7600
David Schuler Ph.D., supt. — Fax 718-7609
www.d214.org
Forest View Alternative S — 100/Alt
2121 S Goebbert Rd 60005 — 847-718-7771
John Rekas, dir. — Fax 718-7773
Hersey HS — 2,000/9-12
1900 E Thomas St 60004 — 847-718-4800
Gordon Sisson, prin. — Fax 718-4817
Vanguard S — 100/Alt
2121 S Goebbert Rd 60005 — 847-718-7888
Sharyn Marsh, dir. — Fax 718-7869
Other Schools – See Buffalo Grove, Elk Grove Village, Mount Prospect, Rolling Meadows, Wheeling

---

Chicago Futabakai Japanese S — 200/K-12
2550 N Arlington Heights Rd 60004 — 847-590-5700
Nobuyuki Ozaki, prin. — Fax 590-9759
Christian Liberty Academy — 900/PK-12
502 W Euclid Ave 60004 — 847-259-4444
Dr. Philip Bennett, hdmstr. — Fax 259-9972
Northwest Community Hospital — Post-Sec.
800 W Central Rd 60005 — 847-618-1000
Robert Morris University — Post-Sec.
2123 S Goebbert Rd 60005 — 800-762-5960
St. Viator HS — 1,100/9-12
1213 E Oakton St 60004 — 847-392-4050
Eileen Manno, prin. — Fax 392-4329

Armstrong, Vermilion
Armstrong Twp. HSD 225 — 200/9-12
PO Box 37 61812 — 217-569-2122
Bill Mulvaney, supt. — Fax 569-2171
www.armstrong.k12.il.us
Armstrong HS — 200/9-12
PO Box 37 61812 — 217-569-2122
Darren Loschen, prin. — Fax 569-2171

Arthur, Douglas, Pop. 2,280
Arthur CUSD 305 — 800/PK-12
301 E Columbia St 61911 — 217-543-2511
Travis Wilson, supt. — Fax 543-2210
www.arthur.k12.il.us
Arthur JHS — 100/7-8
301 E Columbia St 61911 — 217-543-2146
Brian Hatfield, prin. — Fax 543-2174
Arthur-Lovington HS — 100/9-12
301 E Columbia St 61911 — 217-543-2146
Brandon Stone, prin. — Fax 543-2174

Arthur Christian S — 100/K-12
1710 State Highway 133 61911 — 217-543-2397
Greg Mast, prin. — Fax 543-3781

Ashland, Cass, Pop. 1,324
A-C Central CUSD 262 — 500/PK-12
PO Box 260 62612 — 217-476-8112
Rebecca Canty, supt. — Fax 476-8100
a-ccentral.com
A-C Central HS — 100/9-12
PO Box 260 62612 — 217-476-3312
Robert Sanders, prin. — Fax 476-3730
Other Schools – See Chandlerville

Ashton, Lee, Pop. 967
Ashton-Franklin Center CUSD 275 — 600/PK-12
611 Western Ave 61006 — 815-453-7461
John Zick, supt. — Fax 453-7462
www.afcschools.net
Ashton-Franklin Center HS — 200/9-12
611 Western Ave 61006 — 815-453-7461
Tammy Harvey, prin. — Fax 453-7462
Other Schools – See Franklin Grove

Assumption, Christian, Pop. 1,158
Central A & M CUSD 21 — 900/PK-12
105 N College St 62510 — 217-226-4042
Kyle VonSchnase, supt. — Fax 226-4133
www.cam.k12.il.us
Central A & M MS — 200/6-8
404 Colegrove St 62510 — 217-226-4241
Kent Stauder, prin. — Fax 226-4442
Other Schools – See Moweaqua

Astoria, Fulton, Pop. 1,131
Astoria CUSD 1 — 400/PK-12
402 N Jefferson St 61501 — 309-329-2111
Doug Daugherty, supt. — Fax 329-2214
www.astoria.fulton.k12.il.us
Astoria HS — 100/9-12
402 N Jefferson St 61501 — 309-329-2156
Doug Daugherty, prin. — Fax 329-2246
Astoria JHS — 100/6-8
402 N Jefferson St 61501 — 309-329-2158
Dave Crouse, prin. — Fax 329-2963

Athens, Menard, Pop. 1,956
Athens CUSD 213 — 1,100/PK-12
1 Warrior Way 62613 — 217-636-8761
Scott Laird, supt. — Fax 636-8851
www.athens-213.org
Athens HS — 300/9-12
1 Warrior Way 62613 — 217-636-8314
Bill Reed, prin. — Fax 636-8851
Athens JHS — 200/7-8
1 Warrior Way 62613 — 217-636-8380
Matt Rhoades, prin. — Fax 636-8851

Atwood, Douglas, Pop. 1,215
Atwood-Hammond CUSD 39 — 400/K-12
PO Box 890 61913 — 217-578-3111
Kenneth Schwengel, supt. — Fax 578-3531
www.ah.k12.il.us
Atwood-Hammond HS — 100/9-12
PO Box 890 61913 — 217-578-2226
Ed Coller, prin. — Fax 578-3355

Auburn, Sangamon, Pop. 4,722
Auburn CUSD 10 — 1,200/PK-12
606 W North St 62615 — 217-438-6164
Darren Root, supt. — Fax 438-6483
auburn.k12.il.us
Auburn HS — 400/9-12
511 N 7th St 62615 — 217-438-6817
Nathan Essex, prin. — Fax 438-6153
Other Schools – See Divernon

Augusta, Hancock, Pop. 586
Southeastern CUSD 337 — 500/PK-12
PO Box 215 62311 — 217-392-2172
Todd Fox, supt. — Fax 392-2174
www.southeastern337.com/
Southeastern JSHS — 200/7-12
PO Box 155 62311 — 217-392-2125
Cyle Rigg, prin. — Fax 392-2229

Aurora, Kane, Pop. 194,432
Aurora East Unit SD 131 — 13,700/PK-12
417 5th St 60505 — 630-299-5550
Jerome Roberts Ed.D., supt. — Fax 299-5500
www.d131.org
Cowherd MS — 1,000/6-8
441 N Farnsworth Ave 60505 — 630-299-5900
Crystal England, prin. — Fax 299-5901
East Aurora MS — 100/Alt
501 College Ave 60505 — 630-978-9482
Angela Rowley, prin.
East HS — 3,100/9-12
500 Tomcat Ln 60505 — 630-299-8000
Sheila Conrad, prin. — Fax 299-8199

Simmons MS 1,000/6-8
1130 Sheffer Rd 60505 630-299-4150
Mechelle Patterson, prin. Fax 299-4151
Waldo MS 1,000/6-8
56 Jackson St 60505 630-299-8400
Joseph Talluto, prin. Fax 299-8401

Aurora West Unit SD 129 12,400/PK-12
80 S River St 60506 630-301-5000
Dr. James Rydland, supt. Fax 844-5710
www.sd129.org/
Herget MS 800/6-8
1550 Deerpath Rd 60506 630-301-5006
Rachel Hattendorf, prin. Fax 301-5222
Jefferson MS 800/6-8
1151 Plum St 60506 630-301-5009
Patricia Cross, prin. Fax 844-5711
Washington MS 700/6-8
231 S Constitution Dr 60506 630-301-5017
Gail Wronski, prin. Fax 844-5712
West Aurora HS 3,400/9-12
1201 W New York St 60506 630-301-5600
Dr. Chuck Hiscock, prin. Fax 844-4505
Other Schools – See North Aurora

Indian Prairie CUSD 204 28,700/PK-12
780 Shoreline Dr 60504 630-375-3000
Kathryn Birkett, supt. Fax 375-3009
ipsdweb.ipsd.org/
Fischer MS 1,000/6-8
1305 Long Grove Dr 60504 630-375-3100
Jennifer Nonnemacher, prin. Fax 375-3101
Granger MS 900/6-8
2721 Stonebridge Blvd, 630-375-1010
Mary Kelly, prin. Fax 375-1110
Indian Plains HS 100/Alt
1322 N Eola Rd, 630-375-3375
Cecilia Tobin, prin. Fax 375-3361
Metea Valley HS 1,900/9-12
1801 N Eola Rd, 630-375-5900
Jim Schmid, prin. Fax 375-5901
Still MS 800/6-8
787 Meadowridge Dr 60504 630-375-3900
Kimberly Cornish, prin. Fax 375-3901
Waubonsie Valley HS 2,200/10-12
2590 Ogden Ave 60504 630-375-3300
Jason Stipp, prin. Fax 375-3301
Other Schools – See Naperville

Oswego CUSD 308
Supt. — See Oswego
Bednarcik JHS 1,000/6-8
3025 Heggs Rd, 630-636-2500
Pam Jensen, prin. Fax 636-2591

Aurora Central Catholic HS 500/9-12
1255 N Edgelawn Dr 60506 630-907-0095
Rev. F. William Etheredge, admin. Fax 907-1076
Aurora Christian S 600/PK-12
2255 Sullivan Rd 60506 630-892-1551
Collette House, supt. Fax 892-1692
Aurora University Post-Sec.
347 S Gladstone Ave 60506 630-892-6431
Marmion Academy 500/9-12
1000 Butterfield Rd, 630-897-6936
Anthony Tinerella, head sch Fax 897-7086
Rasmussen College Post-Sec.
2363 Sequoia Dr Ste 131 60506 630-888-3500
Robert Morris University Post-Sec.
905 Meridian Lake Dr 60504 800-762-5960
Rosary HS 500/9-12
901 N Edgelawn Dr 60506 630-896-0831
Sr. Ann Brummel, prin. Fax 896-8372

Avon, Fulton, Pop. 778
Avon CUSD 176 200/PK-12
320 E Woods St 61415 309-465-3708
Dan Oakley, supt. Fax 465-9030
avonschools.us
Avon HS 100/9-12
320 E Woods St 61415 309-465-3621
Tina Stier, prin. Fax 465-7194

Barrington, Cook, Pop. 10,188
Barrington CUSD 220 9,100/PK-12
310 James St 60010 847-381-6300
Tom Leonard, supt. Fax 381-6337
www.barrington220.org
Barrington HS 3,000/9-12
616 W Main St 60010 847-381-1400
Steve McWilliams, prin. Fax 304-3937
Barrington MS Prairie Campus 1,200/6-8
40 E Dundee Rd 60010 847-304-3990
Travis Lobbins, prin. Fax 304-3986
Barrington MS Station Campus 1,000/6-8
215 Eastern Ave 60010 847-756-6400
Dr. Craig Winkelman, prin. Fax 842-1343

Barry, Pike, Pop. 1,297
Western CUSD 12 600/PK-12
401 McDonough St 62312 217-335-2323
Carol Frericks, supt. Fax 335-2211
www.westerncusd12.org/
Western HS 200/9-12
401 McDonough St 62312 217-335-2323
Constance Thomas, prin. Fax 335-2211
Other Schools – See Kinderhook

Bartlett, Cook, Pop. 40,574
SD U-46
Supt. — See Elgin
Bartlett HS 2,700/9-12
701 W Schick Rd 60103 630-372-4700
Dr. Richard Lebron, prin. Fax 372-4682
Eastview MS 1,000/7-8
321 N Oak Ave 60103 630-213-5550
Donald Donner, prin. Fax 213-5563

Bartonville, Peoria, Pop. 6,361
Limestone Community HSD 310 1,100/9-12
4201 Airport Rd 61607 309-697-6271
Allan Gresham, supt. Fax 697-9635
www.limestone.k12.il.us
Limestone Community HS 1,100/9-12
4201 Airport Rd 61607 309-697-6271
Jill Warren, admin. Fax 697-9635

Oak Grove SD 68 400/PK-8
4812 Pfeiffer Rd 61607 309-697-3367
Chad Wagner, supt. Fax 633-2381
www.oakgrove.peoria.k12.il.us/
Oak Grove West JHS 100/6-8
6018 W Lancaster Rd 61607 309-697-0621
Shannon Dudek, prin. Fax 697-0721

Batavia, Kane, Pop. 25,733
Batavia Unit SD 101 6,200/PK-12
335 W Wilson St 60510 630-937-8800
Dr. Lisa Hichens, supt. Fax 937-8801
www.bps101.net
Batavia HS 1,800/9-12
1200 Main St 60510 630-937-8600
JoAnne Smith, prin. Fax 937-8601
Rotolo MS 1,500/6-8
1501 S Raddant Rd 60510 630-937-8700
Stephen Maciejewski, prin. Fax 937-8701

Beach Park, Lake, Pop. 13,341
Beach Park CCSD 3 2,400/PK-8
11315 W Wadsworth Rd 60099 847-599-5070
Dr. Robert Di Virgilio, supt. Fax 263-2133
www.bpd3.org/
Beach Park MS 900/6-8
40667 N Green Bay Rd 60099 847-596-5860
Ray Ruiz, prin. Fax 731-2402

Beardstown, Cass, Pop. 6,084
Beardstown CUSD 15 1,500/PK-12
500 E 15th St 62618 217-323-3099
Reggie Clinton, supt. Fax 323-5190
www.beardstown.com/
Beardstown JSHS 700/6-12
500 E 15th St 62618 217-323-3665
Scott Riddle, prin. Fax 323-3667

Bedford Park, Cook, Pop. 575

Fox College Post-Sec.
6640 S Cicero Ave 60638 708-444-4500

Beecher, Will, Pop. 4,314
Beecher CUSD 200U 1,100/K-12
PO Box 338 60401 708-946-2266
Tami Roskamp, supt. Fax 946-3404
www.beecher200u.org/
Beecher HS 400/9-12
PO Box 338 60401 708-946-2266
Nathan Schilling, prin. Fax 946-3403
Beecher JHS 300/6-8
101 E Church Rd 60401 708-946-3412
Michael Meyer, prin. Fax 946-2763

Beecher City, Effingham, Pop. 461
Beecher City CUSD 20 400/PK-12
438 E State Highway 33 62414 618-487-5100
Scott Cameron, supt. Fax 487-5242
www.bcity.efingham.k12.il.us/
Beecher City JSHS 200/7-12
438 E State Highway 33 62414 618-487-5117
Phil Lark, prin.

Belle Rive, Jefferson, Pop. 354
Opdyke-Belle-Rive CCSD 5 100/K-8
601 S Gum St 62810 618-756-2486
John Ashby, supt. Fax 756-2792
opdykebelle5.sharpschool.net
Other Schools – See Opdyke

Belleville, Saint Clair, Pop. 43,276
Belle Valley SD 119 800/PK-8
2465 Amann Dr 62220 618-236-5200
Louis Obernuefemann Ph.D., supt. Fax 236-4550
www.bv119.org/
Belle Valley S 400/5-8
2465 Amann Dr 62220 618-236-5200
Tamara Leib Ed.D., prin. Fax 236-4550

Belleville SD 118 3,600/PK-8
105 W A St 62220 618-233-2830
Matt Klosterman, supt. Fax 233-8355
www.belleville118.org
Central JHS 400/7-8
1801 Central School Rd 62220 618-233-5377
Rocky Horrighs, prin. Fax 233-5440
West JHS 400/7-8
840 Royal Heights Rd 62226 618-234-8200
Pam Knobeloch, prin. Fax 234-8220

Belleville Township HSD 201 5,100/9-12
2600 W Main St 62226 618-222-8241
Dr. Jeff Dosier, supt. Fax 233-7586
bths201.org/
Belleville HS East 2,700/9-12
2555 West Blvd 62221 618-222-3700
Stephanie Posey, prin. Fax 222-3799
Belleville HS West 2,300/9-12
4063 Frank Scott Pkwy W 62223 618-222-7500
Rich Mertens, prin. Fax 235-2484
Belleville Night/Alternative S 100/Alt
4063 Frank Scott Pkwy W 62223 618-222-7660
Scott Baer, admin. Fax 235-2484

Harmony Emge SD 175 800/PK-8
7401 Westchester Dr 62223 618-397-8444
Pam Leonard, supt. Fax 397-8446
www.harmony175.org/
Emge JHS 400/5-8
7401 Westchester Dr 62223 618-397-6557
Fax 397-3011

Whiteside SD 115 1,400/PK-8
111 Warrior Way 62221 618-239-0000
Peggy Burke, supt. Fax 239-9240
www.whiteside.stclair.k12.il.us
Whiteside MS 600/5-8
111 Warrior Way 62221 618-239-0000
Ron Trelow, prin. Fax 239-9240

Althoff Catholic HS 500/9-12
5401 W Main St 62226 618-235-1100
David Harris, prin. Fax 235-9535
Alvareita's College of Cosmetology Post-Sec.
5400 W Main St 62226 618-257-9193
French Academy 200/PK-12
219 W Main St 62220 618-233-7542
Phillip Paeltz, hdmstr. Fax 233-0541
St. Elizabeth Hospital Post-Sec.
211 S 3rd St 62220 618-234-2120
Southwestern Illinois College Post-Sec.
2500 Carlyle Ave 62221 618-235-2700

Bellwood, Cook, Pop. 18,875
Bellwood SD 88 2,900/PK-8
640 Eastern Ave 60104 708-344-9344
Phylistine Murphy Ph.D., supt. Fax 344-9416
www.sd88.org
Roosevelt MS 600/7-8
2500 Oak St 60104 708-544-3318
Verna Jordan, prin. Fax 544-0192

Belvidere, Boone, Pop. 25,242
Belvidere CUSD 100 8,600/PK-12
1201 5th Ave 61008 815-544-0301
Michael Houselog, supt. Fax 544-4260
www.district100.com
Belvidere Central MS 1,100/6-8
8787 Beloit Rd 61008 815-544-0190
Janelle Raine, prin. Fax 544-1128
Belvidere HS 1,200/9-12
1500 East Ave 61008 815-547-6345
Todd Martens, prin. Fax 547-7304
Belvidere North HS 1,500/9-12
9393 Beloit Rd 61008 815-544-2636
Marc Eckmann, prin. Fax 547-2916
Belvidere South MS 900/6-8
919 E 6th St 61008 815-544-3175
Ben Commore, prin. Fax 544-2780

Bement, Piatt, Pop. 1,710
Bement CUSD 5 400/PK-12
201 S Champaign St 61813 217-678-4200
Daniel Brue, supt. Fax 678-4251
www.bement.k12.il.us
Bement HS 100/9-12
201 S Champaign St 61813 217-678-4200
Douglas Kepley, prin. Fax 678-4251
Bement MS 100/6-8
201 S Champaign St 61813 217-678-4200
Douglas Kepley, prin. Fax 678-4251

Bensenville, DuPage, Pop. 18,131
Bensenville SD 2 1,400/PK-8
210 S Church Rd 60106 630-766-5940
James Stelter Ed.D., supt. Fax 766-6099
www.bsd2.org
Blackhawk MS 700/6-8
250 S Church Rd 60106 630-766-2601
Perry Finch, prin. Fax 766-7612

Fenton Community HSD 100 1,400/9-12
1000 W Green St 60106 630-860-6257
Dr. Kathleen Pierce, supt. Fax 766-3178
www.fenton100.org
Fenton HS 1,400/9-12
1000 W Green St 60106 630-766-2500
Todd Leden, prin. Fax 766-3178

Robert Morris University Post-Sec.
1000 Tower Ln # 200 60106 630-787-7800

Benson, Woodford, Pop. 423
Roanoke-Benson CUSD 60
Supt. — See Roanoke
Roanoke-Benson JHS 200/5-8
PO Box 137 61516 309-394-2233
Bill Zeman, dean Fax 394-2612

Benton, Franklin, Pop. 7,012
Benton CCSD 47 1,100/PK-8
1403 S Main St 62812 618-439-3136
Dr. Jay Goble, supt. Fax 435-4840
www.benton47.org/
Benton MS 400/5-8
1000 Forrest St 62812 618-438-4011
Tammy McCollum, prin. Fax 435-2152

Benton Consolidated HSD 103 600/9-12
511 E Main St 62812 618-439-6415
Dr. Kelly Stewart, supt. Fax 438-8091
www.bentonhighschool.org
Benton Consolidated HS 600/9-12
511 E Main St 62812 618-439-3103
Mark Miller, prin. Fax 438-2915

Berkeley, Cook, Pop. 5,108
Berkeley SD 87 2,800/PK-8
1200 N Wolf Rd 60163 708-449-3350
Dr. Eva Smith, supt. Fax 547-3341
www.berkeley87.org
MacArthur MS 500/6-8
1310 N Wolf Rd 60163 708-449-3185
Scott Savage, prin. Fax 649-3780
Other Schools – See Northlake

Berwyn, Cook, Pop. 56,069
Berwyn North SD 98 3,300/PK-8
6633 16th St 60402 708-484-6200
Dr. Carmen Ayala, supt. Fax 795-2482
www.nb98.org/
Lincoln MS 1,100/6-8
6432 16th St 60402 708-795-2475
Mike Zarco, prin. Fax 795-2880

Berwyn South SD 100 3,800/PK-8
3401 Gunderson Ave 60402 708-795-2300
Dr. Stanley Fields, supt. Fax 795-2317
www.bsd100.org
Freedom MS 600/6-8
3016 Ridgeland Ave 60402 708-795-5800
James Calabrese, prin. Fax 795-5806
Heritage MS 600/6-8
6850 31st St 60402 708-749-6110
Laura LaSalle, prin. Fax 749-6124

J. S. Morton HSD 201
Supt. — See Cicero
Morton West HS 3,300/9-12
2400 Home Ave 60402 708-780-4100
Joe Gunty, prin. Fax 222-5903

Bethalto, Madison, Pop. 9,426
Bethalto CUSD 8 2,000/PK-12
610 Texas Blvd 62010 618-377-7200
Dr. Cindy Blasa, supt. Fax 377-2845
www.bethalto.org
Civic Memorial HS 800/9-12
200 School St 62010 618-377-7220
Debra Pitts, prin. Fax 377-7001
Trimpe MS 600/6-8
910 2nd St 62010 618-377-7240
Kimberly Wilks, prin. Fax 377-7218

Bethany, Moultrie, Pop. 1,345
Okaw Valley CUSD 302 400/PK-12
PO Box 97 61914 217-665-3232
Kent Stauder, supt. Fax 665-3601
www.okawvalley.org
Okaw Valley HS 200/9-12
PO Box 249 61914 217-665-3631
Matthew Shoaff, prin. Fax 665-3863
Other Schools – See Findlay

Biggsville, Henderson, Pop. 300
West Central CUSD 235 1,000/PK-12
RR 1 Box 72 61418 309-627-2371
Ralph Grimm, supt. Fax 627-2453
www.wc235.k12.il.us/
West Central HS 300/9-12
RR 1 Box 72 61418 309-627-2377
Scott Schneider, prin. Fax 627-2120
Other Schools – See Stronghurst

Big Rock, Kane, Pop. 710
Hinckley-Big Rock CUSD 429
Supt. — See Hinckley
Hinckley-Big Rock MS 200/6-8
PO Box 247 60511 630-556-4180
Jeff Strouss, prin. Fax 556-4181

Bismarck, Vermilion, Pop. 578
Bismarck-Henning CUSD 1 900/K-12
PO Box 350 61814 217-759-7261
Scott Watson, supt. Fax 759-7942
www.bismarck.k12.il.us
Bismarck-Henning HS 400/9-12
PO Box 350 61814 217-759-7291
Brent Rademacher, prin. Fax 759-7815
Bismarck-Henning JHS 300/5-8
PO Box 350 61814 217-759-7301
Rusty Campbell, prin. Fax 759-7313

Bloomingdale, DuPage, Pop. 21,714
Bloomingdale SD 13 1,200/K-8
164 Euclid Ave 60108 630-893-9590
Dr. Jon Bartelt, supt. Fax 893-1818
www.sd13.org
Westfield MS 400/6-8
149 Fairfield Way 60108 630-529-6211
Debbie Kling, prin. Fax 893-9336

CCSD 93 3,900/PK-8
230 Covington Dr 60108 630-893-9393
William Shields Ed.D., supt. Fax 539-3450
www.ccsd93.com
Stratford MS 700/6-8
251 Butterfield Dr 60108 630-980-9898
James Doyle, prin. Fax 980-9914
Other Schools – See Carol Stream

Pivot Point International Academy Post-Sec.
144 E Lake St Ste C 60108 847-985-5900

Bloomington, McLean, Pop. 74,597
Bloomington Area Career Center
PO Box 5187 61702 309-829-8671
Tom Frazier, dir. Fax 828-3546
www.district87.org/avc/
Bloomington Area Career Center Vo/Tech
PO Box 5187 61702 309-829-8671
Tom Frazier, dir. Fax 828-3546

Bloomington SD 87 5,500/PK-12
300 E Monroe St 61701 309-827-6031
Dr. Barry Reilly, supt. Fax 827-5717
www.district87.org
Bloomington HS 1,500/9-12
1202 E Locust St 61701 309-828-5201
Tim Moore, prin. Fax 829-1078
Bloomington JHS 1,200/6-8
901 Colton Ave 61701 309-827-0086
Sherri Thomas, prin. Fax 829-0084

McLean County Unit SD 5
Supt. — See Normal
Evans JHS 6-8
2901 Morrissey Dr 61704 309-557-4406
Vincent Turner, prin. Fax 557-4507

Central Catholic HS 400/9-12
1201 Airport Rd 61704 309-661-7000
Joy Allen, prin. Fax 661-7001
Cornerstone Christian Academy 400/PK-12
PO Box 1608 61702 309-662-9900
Becky Shamess, hdmstr. Fax 662-9904

Hairmasters Institute of Cosmetology Post-Sec.
506 S McClun St 61701 309-827-6971
Illinois Wesleyan University Post-Sec.
1312 Park St 61701 309-556-1000

Blue Island, Cook, Pop. 23,417
Community HSD 218
Supt. — See Oak Lawn
Eisenhower HS 2,000/9-12
12700 Sacramento Ave 60406 708-597-6300
Dr. Gary Rauch, prin. Fax 597-9958

Cook County SD 130 3,900/PK-12
12300 Greenwood Ave 60406 708-385-6800
Dr. Raymond Lauk, supt. Fax 385-8467
www.district130.org/
Greenbriar S 100/Alt
12015 Maple Ave 60406 708-385-2915
Michael McLaughlin, prin. Fax 385-8467
Kerr MS 400/6-8
12915 Maple Ave 60406 708-385-5959
Bridgette McNeal, prin. Fax 371-6812
Veterans Memorial MS 400/6-8
12320 Greenwood Ave 60406 708-489-6630
Carrie Tisch, prin. Fax 489-3522
Other Schools – See Crestwood

Cannella School of Hair Design Post-Sec.
12840 Western Ave 60406 708-388-4949
Environmental Technical Institute Post-Sec.
13010 Division St 60406 708-385-0707

Blue Mound, Macon, Pop. 1,145
Meridian CUSD 15
Supt. — See Macon
Meridian MS 200/6-8
PO Box 320 62513 217-692-2148
Andrew Pygott, prin. Fax 692-2039

Bluffs, Scott, Pop. 708
Scott-Morgan CUSD 2 300/PK-12
PO Box 230 62621 217-754-3351
Kevin Blankenship, supt. Fax 754-3908
www.bluffs-school.com/
Bluffs HS 100/9-12
PO Box 230 62621 217-754-3815
Joseph Kuhlmann, prin. Fax 754-3908
Bluffs JHS 100/6-8
PO Box 230 62621 217-754-3815
Joseph Kuhlmann, prin. Fax 754-3908

Bluford, Jefferson, Pop. 685
Webber Township HSD 204 100/9-12
310 S Elm St 62814 618-732-6121
Scott Porter, supt. Fax 732-8784
Webber Township HS 100/9-12
310 S Elm St 62814 618-732-6121
Jennifer Martin, prin. Fax 732-8784

Bolingbrook, Will, Pop. 71,637
Valley View CUSD 365U
Supt. — See Romeoville
Addams MS 700/6-8
905 Lily Cache Ln 60440 630-759-7200
Chris Schaeflein, prin. Fax 759-6362
Bolingbrook HS 3,500/9-12
365 Raider Way 60440 630-759-6400
Michael White, prin. Fax 759-2650
Brooks MS 1,300/6-8
350 Blair Ln 60440 630-759-6340
Keith Wood, prin. Fax 759-6360
Humphrey MS 700/6-8
777 Falconridge Way 60440 630-972-9240
Dan Laverty, prin. Fax 739-8521

Bourbonnais, Kankakee, Pop. 18,268
Bourbonnais ESD 53 2,600/PK-8
281 W John Casey Rd 60914 815-929-5100
Daniel R. Hollowell, supt. Fax 939-0481
www.besd53.org
Bourbonnais Upper Grade Center 600/7-8
200 W John Casey Rd 60914 815-929-5200
Dan Chamernik, prin. Fax 935-7849

Kankakee Area Career Center
PO Box 570 60914 815-939-4971
Donald Fay, supt. Fax 939-7598
kacc-il.org/
Kankakee Area Career Center Vo/Tech
PO Box 570 60914 815-939-4971
Bosa Goodale, prin. Fax 939-7598

Olivet Nazarene University Post-Sec.
1 University Ave 60914 815-939-5011

Bradford, Stark, Pop. 767
Bradford CUSD 1 200/PK-8
115 High St 61421 309-897-2801
Ellin Lotspeich Ed.D., supt. Fax 897-4451
www.edline.net/pages/bradford_schools_1
Bradford JHS 100/6-8
115 High St 61421 309-897-2801
Ellin Lotspeich Ed.D., admin. Fax 897-4451

Bradley, Kankakee, Pop. 15,644
Bradley SD 61 1,600/PK-8
111 N Crosswell Ave 60915 815-933-3371
Scott Goselin, supt. Fax 939-6601
www.bradleyschools.com/
Bradley Central MS 500/6-8
260 N Wabash Ave 60915 815-939-3564
Mark Kohl, prin. Fax 939-6603

Bradley-Bourbonnais Comm. HSD 307 2,000/9-12
700 W North St 60915 815-937-3707
Michael Hogan, supt. Fax 937-0156
www.bbchs.org
Bradley-Bourbonnais Community HS 2,000/9-12
700 W North St 60915 815-937-3707
Dr. Brian Wright, prin. Fax 937-0156

Paul Mitchell The School Post-Sec.
605 E North St 60915 815-932-5049

Braidwood, Will, Pop. 6,143
Reed-Custer CUSD 255U 1,800/PK-12
255 Comet Dr 60408 815-458-2307
Dr. John Butts, supt. Fax 458-4106
www.rc255.net
Reed-Custer HS 500/9-12
249 Comet Dr 60408 815-458-2166
Tim Ricketts, prin. Fax 458-4138
Reed-Custer MS 400/6-8
407 Comet Dr 60408 815-458-2868
Pam Surprenant, prin. Fax 458-4118

Breese, Clinton, Pop. 4,414
Central Community HSD 71 600/9-12
7740 Old US Highway 50 62230 618-526-4510
Kevin Meyer, supt. Fax 526-2521
www.centralcougars.org/
Central Community HS 600/9-12
7740 Old US Highway 50 62230 618-526-4578
B. Kent Jones, prin. Fax 526-7647

Mater Dei HS 500/9-12
900 Mater Dei Dr 62230 618-526-7216
Dennis Litteken, prin. Fax 526-8310

Bridgeport, Lawrence, Pop. 1,874
Red Hill CUSD 10 1,100/PK-12
1250 Judy Ave 62417 618-945-2061
Matthew Seaton, supt. Fax 945-7607
www.red.lawrnc.k12.il.us
Red Hill JSHS 400/7-12
908 Church St 62417 618-945-2521
Clarence Gross, prin. Fax 945-7151

Bridgeview, Cook, Pop. 16,102

Northwestern Business College Post-Sec.
7725 S Harlem Ave 60455 888-205-2283
Universal S 600/PK-12
7350 W 93rd St 60455 708-599-4100
Hanan Abdallah M.Ed., admin. Fax 599-1588

Brighton, Macoupin, Pop. 2,236
Southwestern CUSD 9 1,700/PK-12
201 E City Limits Rd 62012 618-729-3221
Mark B. Skertich, supt. Fax 729-3764
www.piasabirds.net
Other Schools – See Piasa

Brimfield, Peoria, Pop. 851
Brimfield CUSD 309 700/PK-12
PO Box 380 61517 309-446-3378
Dennis McNamara, supt. Fax 446-3716
www.brimfield309.com/
Brimfield HS 200/9-12
PO Box 380 61517 309-446-3349
Joseph Blessman, prin. Fax 446-3716

Broadlands, Champaign, Pop. 347
Heritage CUSD 8
Supt. — See Homer
Heritage HS 200/9-12
PO Box 260 61816 217-834-3392
Thomas Davis, prin. Fax 834-3016

Brookfield, Cook, Pop. 18,709
Brookfield Lagrange Park SD 95 1,000/K-8
3524 Maple Ave 60513 708-485-0606
Dr. Mark Kuzniewski, supt. Fax 485-8066
www.district95.org
Gross MS 400/6-8
3524 Maple Ave 60513 708-485-0600
Kevin Nicholson, prin. Fax 485-0638

Brownstown, Fayette, Pop. 753
Brownstown CUSD 201 300/PK-12
421 S College Ave 62418 618-427-3355
Adam Bussard, supt. Fax 427-3704
bcusd201.com/
Brownstown JSHS 100/7-12
421 S College Ave 62418 618-427-3839
Michael Shackelford, prin. Fax 427-3704

Brussels, Calhoun, Pop. 140
Brussels CUSD 42 100/K-12
PO Box 128 62013 618-883-2131
Dr. Mark Martin, supt. Fax 883-2514
Brussels HS 100/7-12
PO Box 128 62013 618-883-2131
Marla Palmer, prin. Fax 883-2514

Buckley, Iroquois, Pop. 593

Christ Lutheran HS 50/9-12
PO Box 8 60918 217-394-2547
Sandy Spitz, prin. Fax 394-2097

Buda, Bureau, Pop. 531
Bureau Valley CUSD 340
Supt. — See Manlius
Bureau Valley South S 200/3-8
PO Box 277 61314 309-895-2037
Kristal LeRette, prin. Fax 895-2200

Buffalo, Sangamon, Pop. 499
Tri-City CUSD 1 600/PK-12
PO Box 290 62515 217-364-4811
David Bruno, supt. Fax 364-4896
www.tricityschools.org
Tri-City HS 200/9-12
PO Box 290 62515 217-364-4530
Dustin Day, prin. Fax 364-4812
Tri-City JHS 100/6-8
PO Box 290 62515 217-364-4530
Dustin Day, prin. Fax 364-4812

Buffalo Grove, Cook, Pop. 40,915
Aptakisic-Tripp CCSD 102 2,000/PK-8
1231 Weiland Rd 60089 847-353-5660
Dr. Theresa Dunkin, supt. Fax 634-5334
www.d102.org
Aptakisic JHS 500/7-8
1231 Weiland Rd 60089 847-353-5500
Jessica McIntyre, prin. Fax 634-5347

Kildeer Countryside CCSD 96 3,200/PK-8
1050 Ivy Hall Ln 60089 847-459-4260
Julie Schmidt, supt. Fax 459-2344
www.kcsd96.org
Twin Groves MS 600/6-8
2600 N Buffalo Grove Rd 60089 847-821-8946
Heather Friziellie, prin. Fax 821-8949
Other Schools – See Long Grove

Township HSD 214
Supt. — See Arlington Heights
Buffalo Grove HS 2,100/9-12
1100 W Dundee Rd 60089 847-718-4000
Carol Burlinski, prin. Fax 718-4122

Wheeling CCSD 21
Supt. — See Wheeling
Cooper MS 700/6-8
1050 Plum Grove Cir 60089 847-520-2750
Dr. Pamela Kibbons, prin. Fax 419-3071

Bunker Hill, Macoupin, Pop. 1,760
Bunker Hill CUSD 8 500/PK-12
504 E Warren St 62014 618-585-3116
Dr. Victor Buehler, supt. Fax 585-3212
bhschools.org
Bunker Hill HS 200/9-12
314 S Meissner St 62014 618-585-3232
Matthew Smith, prin. Fax 585-3241

Burbank, Cook, Pop. 28,566
Burbank SD 111 3,300/PK-8
7600 Central Ave 60459 708-496-0500
Dr. Franzy Fleck, supt. Fax 496-0510
www.bsd111.org
Liberty JHS 800/7-8
5900 W 81st St 60459 708-952-3255
Mark Antkiewicz, prin. Fax 229-0659

Reavis Township HSD 220 1,900/9-12
6034 W 77th St 60459 708-599-7200
Dr. Daniel Riordan, supt. Fax 599-8751
www.reavisd220.org
Reavis HS 1,900/9-12
6034 W 77th St 60459 708-599-7200
Dr. Daniel Riordan, prin. Fax 599-8751

Queen of Peace HS 500/9-12
7659 Linder Ave 60459 708-458-7600
Mary Nickels, prin. Fax 458-5734
St. Laurence HS 600/9-12
5556 W 77th St 60459 708-458-6900
Jim Muting, prin. Fax 458-7898

Burlington, Kane, Pop. 618
Central CUSD 301 3,100/PK-12
PO Box 396 60109 847-464-6005
Dr. Todd Stirn, supt. Fax 464-6021
www.burlington.k12.il.us/
Central HS 1,100/9-12
PO Box 68 60109 847-464-6030
Matthew Haug, prin. Fax 464-6039
Central MS 100/8-8
PO Box 397 60109 847-464-6000
Carie Walter, prin. Fax 464-0233

Burr Ridge, DuPage, Pop. 10,371
CCSD 180 700/PK-8
15W451 91st St 60527 630-734-6600
Dr. Thomas Schneider, supt. Fax 325-6450
www.ccsd180.org
Burr Ridge MS 300/5-8
15W451 91st St 60527 630-325-5454
Julie Bartell, prin. Fax 325-6450

CCSD 181 4,000/PK-8
6010 S Elm St 60527 630-887-1070
Dr. Renee Schuster, supt. Fax 887-1079
www.d181.org
Other Schools – See Clarendon Hills, Hinsdale

Gower SD 62
Supt. — See Willowbrook
Gower MS 400/5-8
7941 S Madison St 60527 630-323-8275
Tracy Murphy, prin. Fax 323-2055

Pleasantdale SD 107 800/PK-8
7450 Wolf Rd 60527 708-784-2013
Dr. Mark Fredisdorf, supt. Fax 246-0161
www.d107.org
Pleasantdale MS 300/5-8
7450 Wolf Rd 60527 708-246-3210
John Glimco, prin. Fax 352-0092

Everest College Post-Sec.
6880 N Frontage Rd 60527 630-920-1102

Bushnell, McDonough, Pop. 3,074
Bushnell-Prairie City CUSD 170 800/PK-12
845 Walnut St 61422 309-772-9461
Mike Dickson, supt. Fax 772-9462
www.bushnell-pc.k12.il.us/
Bushnell-Prairie City HS 200/9-12
845 Walnut St 61422 309-772-2113
Jon Lamb, prin. Fax 772-2104
Bushnell-Prairie City JHS 200/6-8
847 Walnut St 61422 309-772-3123
Mike Snowden, prin. Fax 772-2666

Byron, Ogle, Pop. 3,700
Byron CUSD 226 1,600/PK-12
696 N Colfax St 61010 815-234-5491
Dr. James Hammack, supt. Fax 234-4106
leeogle.org/byron/
Byron HS 600/9-12
696 N Colfax St 61010 815-234-5491
Peter J. Verona Ed.D., prin. Fax 234-4106
Byron MS 400/6-8
850 N Colfax St 61010 815-234-5491
Steve Herkert, prin. Fax 234-4225

Cahokia, Saint Clair, Pop. 14,938
Cahokia CUSD 187 2,800/K-12
1700 Jerome Ln 62206 618-332-3700
Art Ryan, supt. Fax 332-3706
www.cusd187.org
Cahokia HS 1,000/9-12
800 Range Ln 62206 618-332-3730
Kevin Bement, prin. Fax 332-3747
8th Grade Center 8-8
1900 Mousette Ln 62206 618-332-3722
Felicia Rush-Taylor, prin. Fax 332-3725

Cairo, Alexander, Pop. 2,772
Cairo Unit SD 1 500/PK-12
4201 Sycamore St 62914 618-734-4102
Andrea Evers, supt. Fax 734-4047
Cairo JSHS 200/7-12
4201 Sycamore St 62914 618-734-2187
Zena Madison, prin. Fax 734-2189

Calumet City, Cook, Pop. 36,556
Calumet City SD 155 1,200/K-8
540 Superior Ave 60409 708-862-7665
Dr. Troy Paraday, supt. Fax 868-7555
www.calumetcity155.org/
Wentworth JHS 400/6-8
560 Superior Ave 60409 708-862-0750
Ermetra Olawumi, prin. Fax 862-1194

Dolton SD 149 2,300/PK-8
292 Torrence Ave 60409 708-868-7861
Shelly Davis-Jones, supt. Fax 868-7850
www.schooldistrict149.org/
Creative Communications Academy 6-8
1650 Pulaski Rd 60409 708-868-7585
Gerald Scott, prin. Fax 868-7589
School of Fine Arts 6-8
1650 Pulaski Rd 60409 708-868-7565
Karen Slate, prin. Fax 868-7589
STEM Academy 6-8
1650 Pulaski Rd 60409 708-868-7595
John Johnson, prin. Fax 868-7589

Hoover-Schrum Memorial SD 157 900/PK-8
1255 Superior Ave 60409 708-868-7500
Dr. Michele Morris, supt. Fax 868-7511
www.hsdist157.org
Schrum Memorial MS 300/6-8
485 165th St 60409 708-862-4236
Dr. Bennie Knott, prin. Fax 862-4580

Thornton Fractional Township HSD 215 3,700/9-12
1601 Wentworth Ave 60409 708-585-2309
Dr. Creg Williams, supt. Fax 585-2318
www.tfd215.org/
Center for Academics & Technology Vo/Tech
1605 Wentworth Ave 60409 708-585-2353
Kent Farlow, prin. Fax 585-2356
Thornton Fractional North HS 1,700/9-12
755 Pulaski Rd 60409 708-585-1000
Dwayne Evans, prin. Fax 585-1010
Other Schools – See Lansing

Westwood College Post-Sec.
80 River Oaks Ctr Ste 111 60409 708-832-1988

Calumet Park, Cook, Pop. 7,781
Calumet Public SD 132 1,100/PK-8
1440 W Vermont Ave 60827 708-388-8920
Dr. Elizabeth Reynolds, supt. Fax 388-2138
www.sd132.org
Calumet MS 300/6-8
1440 W Vermont Ave 60827 708-388-8820
Dr. Terrina Ellerson, prin. Fax 388-8557

Cambridge, Henry, Pop. 2,137
Cambridge CUSD 227 500/PK-12
300 S West St 61238 309-937-2144
Thomas Akers, supt. Fax 937-5128
cambridge.il.schoolwebpages.com/
Cambridge Community JSHS 200/7-12
300 S West St 61238 309-937-2051
Robert Reagan, prin. Fax 937-5128

Campbell Hill, Jackson, Pop. 333
Trico CUSD 176 1,000/PK-12
PO Box 220 62916 618-426-1111
Jackie L. Smith, supt. Fax 426-3625
www.trico176.org
Trico HS 300/9-12
PO Box 336 62916 618-426-1111
Mike Denault, prin. Fax 426-3701
Trico JHS 200/6-8
PO Box 335 62916 618-426-1111
Mike Denault, prin. Fax 426-3712

Camp Point, Adams, Pop. 1,120
Central CUSD 3 900/K-12
2110 Highway 94 N 62320 217-593-7116
Martin Cook, supt. Fax 593-7026
www.cusd3.com/
Central HS 300/9-12
2110 Highway 94 N 62320 217-593-7731
Jeff Waggener, prin. Fax 593-7025
Central JHS 300/5-8
2110 Highway 94 N 62320 217-593-7741
Erica Smith, prin. Fax 593-7028

Canton, Fulton, Pop. 14,563
Canton Union SD 66 2,600/PK-12
20 W Walnut St 61520 309-647-9411
Roy Webb, supt. Fax 649-5036
www.cantonusd.org
Canton HS 700/9-12
1001 N Main St 61520 309-647-1820
Robin Tonkin, prin. Fax 649-5039
Ingersoll MS 800/5-8
1605 E Ash St 61520 309-647-6951
Wayne Krus, prin. Fax 647-6959

Graham Hospital Post-Sec.
210 W Walnut St 61520 309-647-4086
Spoon River College Post-Sec.
23235 N County Highway 22 61520 309-647-4645

Carbondale, Jackson, Pop. 25,058
Carbondale Community HSD 165 1,100/9-12
330 S Giant City Rd 62902 618-457-4722
Stephen Murphy, supt. Fax 457-3353
www.cchs165.jacksn.k12.il.us/
Carbondale Community HS 1,100/9-12
1301 E Walnut St 62901 618-457-3371
Daniel Booth, prin. Fax 549-1686

Carbondale ESD 95 1,300/PK-8
925 S Giant City Rd 62902 618-457-3591
Michael Shimshak, supt. Fax 457-2043
www.ces95.org
Carbondale MS 400/6-8
1150 E Grand Ave 62901 618-457-2174
Charles Goforth, prin. Fax 457-2176

Southern Illinois University 62901 Post-Sec.
618-453-2121
Trinity Christian S 100/PK-12
1218 W Freeman St 62901 618-529-3733
Dr. Betsy George, prin. Fax 549-8252

Carlinville, Macoupin, Pop. 5,852
Carlinville CUSD 1 1,400/PK-12
829 W Main St 62626 217-854-9823
Mike Kelly, supt. Fax 854-2777
www.carlinvilleschools.net/
Carlinville HS 400/9-12
829 W Main St 62626 217-854-3104
Patrick Drew, prin. Fax 854-5260
Carlinville MS 300/6-8
110 Illinois Ave 62626 217-854-3106
Roy Kulenkamp, prin. Fax 854-4503

Blackburn College Post-Sec.
700 College Ave 62626 217-854-3231

Carlyle, Clinton, Pop. 3,259
Carlyle CUSD 1 1,200/PK-12
1400 13th St 62231 618-594-8283
Joe Novsek, supt. Fax 594-8285
www.carlyle.k12.il.us
Carlyle HS 400/9-12
1461 12th St 62231 618-594-2453
Joe Wilkerson, prin. Fax 594-8286
Carlyle JHS 400/5-8
1631 12th St 62231 618-594-8292
Jay Smith, prin. Fax 594-8294

Carmi, White, Pop. 5,196
Carmi-White County CUSD 5 1,400/PK-12
301 W Main St 62821 618-382-2341
Brad Lee, supt. Fax 384-3207
www.carmi.white.k12.il.us
Carmi-White County HS 400/9-12
800 W Main St 62821 618-382-4661
Jarrod Newell, prin. Fax 382-2453
Carmi-White County MS 300/6-8
205 W Main St 62821 618-382-4631
Terry Gholson, prin. Fax 384-2076

Carol Stream, DuPage, Pop. 38,894
CCSD 93
Supt. — See Bloomingdale
Stream MS 700/6-8
283 El Paso Ln 60188 630-462-8940
Peter LaChance, prin. Fax 462-9224

Glenbard Township HSD 87
Supt. — See Glen Ellyn
Glenbard North HS 2,600/9-12
990 Kuhn Rd 60188 630-653-7000
Dr. John Mensik, prin. Fax 653-7259

Carpentersville, Kane, Pop. 37,150
CUSD 300 19,800/PK-12
300 Cleveland Ave 60110 847-551-8300
Michael Bregy, supt. Fax 551-8310
www.d300.org
Carpentersville MS 700/7-8
100 Cleveland Ave 60110 847-426-1380
Stephanie Ramstad, prin. Fax 426-1404
Dundee-Crown HS 2,500/9-12
1500 Kings Rd 60110 847-426-1415
Lynn McCarthy, prin. Fax 426-1245
Oak Ridge S 100/Alt
229 Lake Marian Rd 60110 847-426-4052
Nathan Jarot, prin. Fax 426-4474
Other Schools – See Algonquin, Hampshire, West Dundee

Carrier Mills, Saline, Pop. 1,618
Carrier Mills-Stonefort CUSD 2 500/PK-12
7071 US 45 S 62917 618-994-2392
Richard Morgan, supt. Fax 994-2929
Carrier Mills-Stonefort HS 100/9-12
7071 US 45 S 62917 618-994-2392
Richard Morgan, prin. Fax 994-2929

Carrollton, Greene, Pop. 2,475

Carrollton CUSD 1 600/PK-12
950A 3rd St 62016 217-942-5314
Dr. Kerry L. Cox, supt. Fax 942-9259
www.c-hawks.net/

Carrollton HS 200/9-12
950 3rd St 62016 217-942-6913
Leslee Frazier, prin. Fax 942-6835

Carterville, Williamson, Pop. 5,368

Carterville CUSD 5 1,900/K-12
306 Virginia Ave 62918 618-985-2940
Robert Prusator, supt. Fax 985-2041
www.c-ville.wilmsn.k12.il.us/

Carterville HS 500/9-12
1415 W Grand Ave 62918 618-985-2940
Keith Liddell, prin. Fax 985-2741

Carterville IS 500/5-8
300 School St 62918 618-985-2940
Jeff Hartford, prin. Fax 985-2492

John A. Logan College Post-Sec.
700 Logan College Dr 62918 618-985-3741

Carthage, Hancock, Pop. 2,577

Carthage ESD 317 500/PK-8
210 S Adams St 62321 217-357-3922
Vicki Hardy, supt. Fax 357-6793
carthageschools.k12.il.us

Carthage MS 200/5-8
210 S Adams St 62321 217-357-3914
Diane Pepple, prin. Fax 357-3755

Illini West HSD 307 400/9-12
641 Buchanan St 62321 217-357-9607
Kim Schilson, supt. Fax 357-9609
www.illiniwest.org

Illini West HS 400/9-12
600 Miller St 62321 217-357-2136
Brad Gooding, prin. Fax 357-3569

Cary, McHenry, Pop. 17,990

Cary CCSD 26 2,300/PK-8
2115 Crystal Lake Rd 60013 847-639-7788
Brian Coleman, supt. Fax 639-3898
www.cary26.k12.il.us

Cary JHS 800/6-8
2109 Crystal Lake Rd 60013 847-639-2148
Linda Goeglein, prin. Fax 516-5507

Community HSD 155
Supt. — See Crystal Lake

Cary-Grove HS 1,800/9-12
2208 3 Oaks Rd 60013 847-639-3825
Jay Sargeant, prin. Fax 639-3873

Haber Oaks Campus 100/Alt
400 Haber Rd 60013 847-462-1856
Debbi Cleary, coord. Fax 462-1894

Trinity Oaks Christian Academy 200/PK-10
233 Trinity Oaks Way 60013 847-462-5971
Dr. Paul Wrobbel, head sch Fax 462-5972

Casey, Clark, Pop. 2,756

Casey-Westfield CUSD C4 1,000/PK-12
502 E Delaware Ave 62420 217-932-2184
Dee Scott, supt. Fax 932-5553
www.cw.k12.il.us/education/district/district.php?sect

Casey-Westfield HS 300/9-12
306 E Edgar Ave 62420 217-932-2175
Clyde Frankie, prin. Fax 932-2004

Casey-Westfield JHS 100/7-8
401 E Main St 62420 217-932-2177
Carol Wetherell, prin. Fax 932-2753

Catlin, Vermilion, Pop. 2,025

Catlin CUSD 5 500/PK-12
701 1/2 W Vermilion St 61817 217-427-2116
Gary Lewis, supt. Fax 427-2117
catlin.il.schoolwebpages.com

Catlin HS 200/9-12
701 W Vermilion St 61817 217-427-5331
Kevin Thomas, prin. Fax 427-2468

Centralia, Marion, Pop. 12,732

Centralia HSD 200 1,000/9-12
2100 E Calumet St 62801 618-532-7391
Chuck Lane, supt. Fax 532-8952
www.centraliahs.org

Centralia HS 1,000/9-12
2100 E Calumet St 62801 618-532-7391
Reid Shipley, prin. Fax 532-8952

Centralia SD 135 1,100/PK-8
400 S Elm St 62801 618-532-1907
David Rademacher, supt. Fax 532-4986
www.ccs135.com

Centralia JHS 400/5-8
900 S Pine St 62801 618-533-7130
Lance Marcum, prin. Fax 533-7123

Christ Our Rock Lutheran HS 100/9-12
9545 Shatuc Rd 62801 618-226-3315
Don Duensing, prin. Fax 226-3312

Kaskaskia College Post-Sec.
27210 College Rd 62801 618-545-3000

Cerro Gordo, Piatt, Pop. 1,398

Cerro Gordo CUSD 100 600/K-12
PO Box 79 61818 217-763-5221
Brett Robinson, supt. Fax 763-6562
www.cerrogordo.k12.il.us

Cerro Gordo HS 200/9-12
PO Box 79 61818 217-763-2711
Gary Page, prin. Fax 763-6287

Cerro Gordo MS 100/6-8
PO Box 79 61818 217-763-6411
Steve Cline, prin. Fax 763-6287

Chadwick, Carroll, Pop. 548

Chadwick-Milledgeville CUSD 399 500/PK-12
15 School St 61014 815-684-5191
Timothy Schurman, supt. Fax 684-5241
www.dist399.net

Chadwick JHS 100/6-8
19 School St 61014 815-684-5191
Timothy Schurman, prin. Fax 684-5241

Other Schools – See Milledgeville

Champaign, Champaign, Pop. 78,771

Champaign CUSD 4 9,200/PK-12
703 S New St 61820 217-351-3800
Dr. Judy Wiegand, supt. Fax 352-3590
www.champaignschools.org

Centennial HS 1,400/9-12
913 Crescent Dr 61821 217-351-3954
Gregory Johnson, prin. Fax 351-3730

Central HS 1,200/9-12
610 W University Ave 61820 217-351-3914
Joe Williams, prin. Fax 351-3919

Edison MS 700/6-8
306 W Green St 61820 217-351-3771
Justin Uppinghouse, prin. Fax 355-2564

Franklin MS 600/6-8
817 N Harris Ave 61820 217-351-3819
Angela Smith, prin. Fax 351-3729

Jefferson MS 700/6-8
1115 Crescent Dr 61821 217-351-3790
Dr. Susan Zola, prin. Fax 351-3754

High School of St. Thomas More 400/9-12
3901 N Mattis Ave 61822 217-352-7210
Ryan Bustle, prin. Fax 352-7213

Judah Christian S 600/PK-12
908 N Prospect Ave 61820 217-359-1701
Mike Chitty, admin. Fax 359-0214

Parkland College Post-Sec.
2400 W Bradley Ave 61821 217-351-2200

Chandlerville, Cass, Pop. 551

A-C Central CUSD 262
Supt. — See Ashland

A-C Central MS 100/5-8
191 S Bluff St 62627 217-476-3312
Robert Sanders, prin. Fax 476-3730

Channahon, Will, Pop. 12,437

Channahon SD 17 1,500/PK-8
24920 S Sage St 60410 815-467-4315
Dr. Karin Evans, supt. Fax 467-4343
www.channahon.will.k12.il.us

Channahon JHS 400/7-8
24917 W Sioux Dr 60410 815-467-4314
Dr. Chad Uphoff, prin. Fax 467-2188

Minooka Community HSD 111 2,500/9-12
26655 W Eames St 60410 815-467-2557
James Colyott, supt. Fax 467-9733
www.mchs.net/

Minooka Community HS South Campus 1,300/9-10
26655 W Eames St 60410 815-521-4001
Darcie Kubinski, prin.

Other Schools – See Minooka

Families of Faith Christian Academy 100/PK-12
24466 W Eames St 60410 815-521-1381
Rev. Clark Llewellyn, prin. Fax 467-4476

Charleston, Coles, Pop. 21,496

Charleston CUSD 1 2,800/PK-12
410 W Polk Ave 61920 217-639-1000
Jim Littleford, supt. Fax 639-1005
www.charleston.k12.il.us

Charleston HS 800/9-12
1615 Lincoln Ave 61920 217-639-5000
Diane Hutchins, prin. Fax 639-5005

Charleston MS 400/7-8
920 Smith Dr 61920 217-639-6000
Trevor Doughty, prin. Fax 639-6005

Charleston Christian Academy 50/K-12
2605 University Dr 61920 217-345-4479
John Best, admin.

Eastern Illinois University Post-Sec.
600 Lincoln Ave 61920 217-581-5000

Chatham, Sangamon, Pop. 11,317

Ball Chatham CUSD 5 4,100/PK-12
201 W Mulberry St 62629 217-483-2416
Carrie Hruby, supt. Fax 483-2940
www.chathamschools.org

Glenwood HS 1,300/9-12
1501 E Plummer Blvd 62629 217-483-2424
Jim Lee, prin. Fax 483-5402

Glenwood MS 600/7-8
595 Chatham Rd 62629 217-483-2481
Christina Root, prin. Fax 483-4940

Chester, Randolph, Pop. 8,526

Chester CUSD 139 1,000/PK-12
1940 Swanwick St 62233 618-826-4509
Christopher Diddlebock, supt. Fax 826-4500
www.chester139.com

Chester HS 300/9-12
1901 Swanwick St 62233 618-826-2302
Tim Keefe, prin. Fax 826-3723

Chicago, Cook, Pop. 2,654,865

City of Chicago SD 299 397,500/PK-12
125 S Clark St 60603 773-553-1000
Barbara Byrd-Bennett, supt. Fax 535-1502
www.cps.edu

Air Force Academy HS 200/9-12
3630 S Wells St 60609 773-535-1590
Yashika Eggleston, prin. Fax 535-1847

Albany Park Multicultural MS 300/7-8
4929 N Sawyer Ave 60625 773-534-5108
Eileen O'Toole, prin. Fax 534-5178

Alcott HS 200/9-12
2957 N Hoyne Ave 60618 773-534-5979
Elias Estrada, prin. Fax 534-5789

Ames MS 600/7-8
1920 N Hamlin Ave 60647 773-534-4970
Turon Ivy, prin. Fax 534-4975

Amundsen HS 1,600/9-12
5110 N Damen Ave 60625 773-534-2320
Anna Pavichevich, prin. Fax 534-2330

Austin Polytechnical Academy 400/9-12
231 N Pine Ave 60644 773-534-6300
Ali Muhammad, prin. Fax 534-6046

Banner North Academy HS Alt
2755 N Marshfield Ave 60614 773-549-8070
Byron Stingily, prin.

Banner South Academy HS Alt
2330 E 99th St 60617 773-356-9988
Tara Lawrence, prin. Fax 356-9987

Banner West Academy HS Alt
5035 W North Ave 60639 773-622-6954
Gershon Jackson, prin. Fax 622-6909

Bogan Computer Tech HS 1,800/9-12
3939 W 79th St 60652 773-535-2180
Alahrie Aziz-Sims, prin. Fax 535-2165

Bowen HS 300/9-12
2710 E 89th St 60617 773-535-7650
Jennifer Kirmes, prin. Fax 535-6489

Bronzeville Scholastic Institute 600/9-12
4934 S Wabash Ave 60615 773-535-1150
Leeandra Khan, prin. Fax 535-1228

Brooks College Prep Academy 800/9-12
250 E 111th St 60628 773-535-9930
Andre Weaver, prin. Fax 535-9939

Canter MS 200/7-8
4959 S Blackstone Ave 60615 773-535-1410
Dr. Colleen Conlan, prin. Fax 535-1047

Carver Military Academy 600/9-12
13100 S Doty Ave 60827 773-535-5250
Steven Rouse, prin. Fax 535-5037

Castellanos MS 500/4-8
2524 S Central Park Ave 60623 773-534-1620
Virginia Jimenez, prin. Fax 534-1611

Chicago Academy for Advanced Technology 200/9-12
1301 W 14th St 60608 773-534-7755
Jade Sipic, prin. Fax 534-7757

Chicago Academy HS 500/9-12
3400 N Austin Ave 60634 773-534-0146
Erin Galfer, prin. Fax 534-0192

Chicago HS for Agricultural Sciences 600/9-12
3857 W 111th St 60655 773-535-2500
William Hook, prin. Fax 535-2507

Chicago HS for the Arts 300/9-12
521 E 35th St 60616 773-534-9710
Terri Milsap, prin. Fax 534-9720

Chicago Military Academy 500/9-12
3519 S Giles Ave 60653 773-534-9750
Richard Miller, prin. Fax 534-9760

Chicago Vocational Career Academy Vo/Tech
2100 E 87th St 60617 773-535-6100
Douglas Maclin, prin. Fax 535-6975

Clark Academic Prep HS 1,000/7-12
5101 W Harrison St 60644 773-534-6250
Beulah McLoyd, prin. Fax 534-6292

Clemente Community Academy 1,400/9-12
1147 N Western Ave 60622 773-534-4000
Marcey Sorensen, prin. Fax 534-4012

Collins Academy HS 400/9-12
1313 S Sacramento Dr 60623 773-534-1840
Andre Cowling, prin. Fax 542-6471

Community Services West Academy Vo/Tech
1239 S Pulaski Rd 60623 773-522-5133
Bertha Buchanan, prin. Fax 522-5250

Corliss HS 800/9-12
821 E 103rd St 60628 773-535-5115
Leonard Harris, prin. Fax 535-5511

Crane Technical Preparatory HS 600/9-12
2245 W Jackson Blvd 60612 773-534-7550
Richard Smith, prin. Fax 534-7557

Curie Metropolitan HS 3,700/9-12
4959 S Archer Ave 60632 773-535-2100
Phillip Perry, prin. Fax 535-2049

DeVry Advantage Academy 200/11-12
3300 N Campbell Ave 60618 773-697-2216
Dr. Arlana Bedard, prin. Fax 327-4262

Douglass Academy 400/9-12
543 N Waller Ave 60644 773-534-6176
Venessa Perry, prin. Fax 534-6172

Dunbar Vocational Career Academy Vo/Tech
3000 S King Dr 60616 773-534-9000
Dr. Camilla Covington, prin. Fax 534-9250

Dyett Academic Center 400/9-12
555 E 51st St 60615 773-535-1825
Charles Campbell, prin. Fax 535-1036

Evergreen Academy MS 400/6-8
3537 S Paulina St 60609 773-535-4836
Marian Strok, prin. Fax 535-4853

Farragut Career Academy Vo/Tech
2345 S Christiana Ave 60623 773-534-1300
Tonya Hammaker, prin. Fax 534-1336

Fenger Academy HS 800/9-12
11220 S Wallace St 60628 773-535-5430
Elizabeth Dozier, prin. Fax 535-5444

Field ES 400/4-8
7019 N Ashland Blvd 60626 773-534-2030
Brian Metcalf, prin. Fax 534-2189

Foreman HS 1,800/9-12
3235 N Leclaire Ave 60641 773-534-3400
Daniel Zimmerman, prin. Fax 534-3684

Gage Park HS 1,300/9-12
5630 S Rockwell St 60629 773-535-9230
Safiya Karimah, prin. Fax 535-9411

Gary ES 1,200/PK-PK, 3-
3740 W 31st St 60623 773-534-1455
Alberto Juarez, prin. Fax 534-1435

Gompers Fine Arts Option MS 300/4-8
12302 S State St 60628 773-535-5475
Melody Seaton, prin. Fax 535-5483

Goode STEM Academy 200/9-12
7651 S Homan Ave 60652 773-535-7875
Matsuo Marti, prin. Fax 535-7877
Hancock College Prep HS 1,000/9-12
4034 W 56th St 60629 773-535-2410
Dr. Karen Boran, prin. Fax 535-2434
Harlan Community Academy HS 1,300/9-12
9652 S Michigan Ave 60628 773-535-5400
Reginald Evans, prin. Fax 535-5061
Harper HS 700/9-12
6520 S Wood St 60636 773-535-9150
Leonetta Sanders, prin. Fax 535-9090
Hernandez MS for Advancement of Sciences 1,000/6-8
3510 W 55th St 60632 773-535-8850
Clarisa Bravo-Ruiz, prin. Fax 535-8851
Hirsch Metro HS 500/9-12
7740 S Ingleside Ave 60619 773-535-3100
Afina Lockhart, prin. Fax 535-3240
Hope College Prep HS 700/9-12
5515 S Lowe Ave 60621 773-535-3160
Michael Durr, prin. Fax 535-3444
Hubbard HS 1,700/9-12
6200 S Hamlin Ave 60629 773-535-2200
Bessie Karvelas, prin. Fax 535-2218
Hyde Park Academy HS 1,600/9-12
6220 S Stony Island Ave 60637 773-535-0880
Thomas Trotter, prin. Fax 535-0633
Infinity Math/Science Tech HS 400/9-12
3120 S Kostner Ave 60623 773-535-4225
Patricia Barrera-Brekke, prin. Fax 535-4270
Jones College Prep HS 800/9-12
606 S State St 60605 773-534-8600
Dr. Joseph Powers, prin. Fax 534-8625
Juarez Community Academy 1,700/9-12
2150 S Laflin St 60608 773-534-7030
Juan Ocon, prin. Fax 534-7058
Julian HS 1,200/9-12
10330 S Elizabeth St 60643 773-535-5170
Careda Taylor, prin. Fax 535-5230
Kelly HS 3,100/9-12
4136 S California Ave 60632 773-535-4900
James Coughlin, prin. Fax 535-4841
Kelvyn Park HS 1,400/9-12
4343 W Wrightwood Ave 60639 773-534-4200
Susan Mekarshi, prin. Fax 534-4507
Kennedy HS 1,600/9-12
6325 W 56th St 60638 773-535-2325
George Szkapiak, prin. Fax 535-2485
Kenwood Academy HS 1,800/7-12
5015 S Blackstone Ave 60615 773-535-1350
Gregory Jones, prin. Fax 535-1360
King College Prep HS 900/9-12
4445 S Drexel Blvd 60653 773-535-1180
Shontae Higginbottom, prin. Fax 535-1658
Lake View HS 1,600/9-12
4015 N Ashland Ave 60613 773-534-5440
Lilith Werner, prin. Fax 534-5585
Lane Tech HS 4,200/9-12
2501 W Addison St 60618 773-534-5400
Christopher Dignam, prin. Fax 534-5544
Lincoln Park HS 2,200/9-12
2001 N Orchard St 60614 773-534-8130
Michael Boraz, prin. Fax 534-8218
Lindblom Math/Science Academy 900/7-12
6130 S Wolcott Ave 60636 773-535-9300
Alan Mather, prin. Fax 535-9314
Madero MS 300/6-8
3202 W 28th St 60623 773-535-4466
Nancy Hanks, prin. Fax 535-4469
Manley Career Academy Vo/Tech
2935 W Polk St 60612 773-534-6900
Warren Morgan, prin. Fax 534-6924
Marine Math and Science Academy 400/9-12
145 S Campbell Ave 60612 773-534-7818
Fred Aguirre, prin. Fax 534-0877
Marshall Metro HS 800/9-12
3250 W Adams St 60624 773-534-6455
Angel Johnson, prin. Fax 534-6409
Marshall MS 500/7-8
3900 N Lawndale Ave 60618 773-534-5200
Paul Flaherty, prin. Fax 534-5292
Mason HS 50/9-12
4217 W 18th St 60623 773-534-1530
Tonya Tolbert, prin. Fax 534-1544
Mather HS 1,600/9-12
5835 N Lincoln Ave 60659 773-534-2350
Christie Jones, prin. Fax 534-2424
Morgan Park JSHS 1,700/7-12
1744 W Pryor Ave 60643 773-535-2550
Dr. Everett Edwards, prin. Fax 535-2706
Multicultural Academy of Scholarship HS 300/9-12
3120 S Kostner Ave 60623 773-535-4242
Patricia Gonzalez, prin. Fax 535-4273
North-Grand HS 900/9-12
4338 W Wabansia Ave 60639 773-534-8520
Jason Nault, prin. Fax 534-8535
Northside College Prep HS 1,100/9-12
5501 N Kedzie Ave 60625 773-534-3954
Barry Rodgers, prin. Fax 534-3964
Ogden International HS 500/6-12
1250 W Erie St, 773-534-0866
Kenneth Staral, prin. Fax 534-0869
Orr Community Academy HS 1,000/9-12
730 N Pulaski Rd 60624 773-534-6500
Tyese Sims, prin. Fax 534-6504
Pathways in Education HS 10-12
3270 W 87th St 60652 773-434-6300
Brett Craycraft, prin.
Payton College Prep HS 900/9-12
1034 N Wells St 60610 773-534-0034
Timothy Devine, prin. Fax 534-0035
Phillips Academy HS 800/9-12
244 E Pershing Rd 60653 773-535-1603
Devon Horton, prin. Fax 535-1605
Phoenix Military Academy 400/9-12
145 S Campbell Ave 60612 773-534-7275
Ferdinand Wipachit, prin. Fax 534-7273

Prosser Career Academy Vo/Tech
2148 N Long Ave 60639 773-534-3200
Kenneth Hunter, prin. Fax 534-3382
Raby HS 600/9-12
3545 W Fulton Blvd 60624 773-534-6755
Femi Worrill-Spearman, prin. Fax 534-6938
Richards Career Academy Vo/Tech
5009 S Laflin St 60609 773-535-4945
Mary Dolan, prin. Fax 535-4883
Rickover Naval Academy HS 500/9-12
5900 N Glenwood Ave 60660 773-534-2890
Michael Biela, prin. Fax 534-2895
Robeson HS 800/9-12
6835 S Normal Blvd 60621 773-535-3800
Gerald Morrow, prin. Fax 535-3620
Roosevelt HS 1,400/9-12
3436 W Wilson Ave 60625 773-534-5000
Ricardo Trujillo, prin. Fax 534-5044
School of Leadership HS 200/11-12
7627 S Constance Ave 60649 773-535-6190
Noreen Harris, prin. Fax 535-6960
School of Social Justice 400/9-12
3120 S Kostner Ave 60623 773-535-4300
Kathy Farr, prin. Fax 535-4271
Schurz HS 2,200/9-12
3601 N Milwaukee Ave 60641 773-534-3420
Daniel Kramer, prin. Fax 534-3573
Senn HS 1,000/9-12
5900 N Glenwood Ave 60660 773-534-2365
Susan Lofton, prin. Fax 534-2369
Shields MS 800/5-8
2611 W 48th St 60632 773-535-7115
Peter Auffant, prin. Fax 535-7296
Simeon Career Academy Vo/Tech
8147 S Vincennes Ave 60620 773-535-3200
Dr. Sheldon House, prin. Fax 535-3465
Solorio Academy HS 300/9-12
5400 S Saint Louis Ave 60632 773-535-9070
Victor Iturralde, prin. Fax 535-9073
South Shore International S 400/9-12
1955 E 75th St 60649 773-535-8351
Janice Elaine Wells, prin.
Spry Community Links HS 200/9-12
2400 S Marshall Blvd 60623 773-534-1997
Francisco Borras, prin. Fax 534-0354
Steinmetz Academic Centre 1,900/9-12
3030 N Mobile Ave 60634 773-534-3030
Stephen Ngo, prin. Fax 534-3151
Sullivan HS 800/9-12
6631 N Bosworth Ave 60626 773-534-2000
Carolyn Eggert, prin. Fax 534-2141
Summers Alternative S Alt
30 E 112th Pl 60628 773-468-2908
Sean Smith, prin.
Taft HS 2,800/7-12
6530 W Bryn Mawr Ave 60631 773-534-1000
Mary Kay Cappitelli, prin. Fax 534-1027
TEAM Englewood Academy 500/9-12
6201 S Stewart Ave 60621 773-535-3530
Matthew Heller, prin. Fax 535-3586
Tilden Career Community HS 500/9-12
4747 S Union Ave 60609 773-535-1625
Maurice Swinney, prin. Fax 535-1866
Uplift Community HS 500/9-12
900 W Wilson Ave 60640 773-534-2875
Stephanie Moore, prin. Fax 534-2876
VOISE Academy HS 400/9-12
231 N Pine Ave 60644 773-534-0660
Todd Yarch, prin. Fax 534-0667
Von Steuben Metro HS 1,700/9-12
5039 N Kimball Ave 60625 773-534-5100
Pedro Alonso, prin. Fax 534-5210
Washington HS 1,400/9-12
3535 E 114th St 60617 773-535-5725
Kevin Gallick, prin. Fax 535-5038
Wells Community Academy HS 700/9-12
936 N Ashland Ave 60622 773-534-7010
Ernesto Matias, prin. Fax 534-7078
Westinghouse College Prep HS 600/9-12
3223 W Franklin Blvd 60624 773-534-6400
Dr. Janice Jackson, prin. Fax 534-6422
Williams Prep S of Medicine 300/7-12
4934 S Wabash Ave 60615 773-535-1120
Diann Weston, prin. Fax 535-1023
World Language HS 400/9-12
3120 S Kostner Ave 60623 773-535-4334
Brian Rogers, prin. Fax 254-8470
Young Magnet JSHS 2,200/7-12
211 S Laflin St 60607 773-534-7500
Dr. Joyce Kenner, prin. Fax 534-7261

Adler School of Professional Psychology Post-Sec.
17 N Dearborn St 60602 312-662-4000
Advocate Illinois Masonic Post-Sec.
836 W Wellington Ave 60657 773-296-8950
Advocate Trinity Hospital Post-Sec.
2320 E 93rd St 60617 773-978-2000
American Academy of Art Post-Sec.
332 S Michigan Ave Ste 3 60604 312-461-0600
American Floral Art School Post-Sec.
2519 W Altgeld St Ste 100 60647 312-922-9328
American Health Information Management Post-Sec.
233 N Michigan Ave Ste 2150 60601 312-233-1100
Argosy University/Chicago Post-Sec.
225 N Michigan Ave Ste 1300 60601 312-777-7600
Bais Yaakov HS for Girls 100/9-12
3333 W Peterson Ave 60659 773-267-1494
Shulamis Keller, prin. Fax 267-4798
Bnos Rabbeinu HS 50/9-12
6237 N Whipple St 60659 773-267-0770
Tsyrl Turen, prin. Fax 772-1688
Brother Rice HS 1,000/9-12
10001 S Pulaski Rd 60655 773-429-4300
James Antos, prin. Fax 779-5239
Cain's Barber College Post-Sec.
365 E 51st St 60615 773-536-4441
Cannella School of Hair Design Post-Sec.
9012 S Commercial Ave 60617 773-221-4700

Cannella School of Hair Design Post-Sec.
4269 S Archer Ave 60632 773-890-0412
Cannella School of Hair Design Post-Sec.
4217 W North Ave 60639 773-278-4477
Capri Beauty College Post-Sec.
2653 W 63rd St 60629 773-778-1077
Catholic Theological Union Post-Sec.
5401 S Cornell Ave 60615 773-371-5400
Chamberlain College of Nursing Post-Sec.
3300 N Campbell Ave 60618 773-961-3000
Chicago Academy for the Arts 200/9-12
1010 W Chicago Ave, 312-421-0202
Pamela Jordan, hdmstr. Fax 421-3816
Chicago Hope Academy 200/9-12
2189 W Bowler St 60612 312-491-1600
Bob Muzikowski, pres. Fax 491-1616
Chicago Jesuit Academy 100/5-8
5058 W Jackson Blvd 60644 773-638-6103
Thomas Beckley, prin. Fax 638-6107
Chicago Sch. of Professional Psychology Post-Sec.
325 N Wells St 60654 312-329-6600
Chicago State University Post-Sec.
9501 S King Dr 60628 773-995-2000
Chicago Theological Seminary Post-Sec.
1407 E 60th St 60637 773-896-2400
Chicago Waldorf S 400/PK-12
1300 W Loyola Ave 60626 773-465-2662
Leukos Goodwin, admin. Fax 465-6648
Christ the King Jesuit College Prep S 9-12
5088 W Jackson Blvd 60644 773-261-7505
Temple Payne, prin. Fax 261-7507
College of Office Technology Post-Sec.
1520 W Division St, 773-278-0042
Columbia College Post-Sec.
600 S Michigan Ave 60605 312-369-1000
Computer Systems Institute Post-Sec.
318 W Adams St Fl 10 60606 312-346-6774
Cook County Hospital Post-Sec.
1825 W Harrison St 60612 312-633-8533
Cortiva Institute-School of Massage Thpy Post-Sec.
17 N State St Fl 5 60602 312-753-7900
Coyne College Post-Sec.
330 N Green St 60607 800-999-5220
Coyne College Post-Sec.
230 W Monroe St Ste 400 60606 800-699-5958
Cristo Rey Jesuit HS 500/9-12
1852 W 22nd Pl 60608 773-890-6800
Patricia Garrity, prin. Fax 890-6801
De La Salle Institute - Institute Campus 1,200/9-12
3455 S Wabash Ave 60616 312-842-7355
James Krygier, prin. Fax 842-5640
De La Salle Institute - Lourdes Campus 500/9-12
1040 W 32nd Pl 60608 773-650-6800
Diane Brown, prin. Fax 650-9722
De Paul University Post-Sec.
1 E Jackson Blvd 60604 312-362-8000
DeVry University Post-Sec.
3300 N Campbell Ave 60618 773-929-8500
DeVry University Post-Sec.
225 W Washington St Ste 100 60606 312-372-4900
DeVry University Post-Sec.
8550 W Bryn Mawr Ave # 450 60631 773-695-1000
Eagles' Wings Urban Academy 100/PK-12
3919 N Monticello Ave 60618 773-297-6326
East-West University Post-Sec.
816 S Michigan Ave 60605 312-939-0111
Ellis University Post-Sec.
111 N Canal St Ste 380 60606 877-355-4762
Erikson Institute Post-Sec.
451 N La Salle Dr 60654 312-755-2250
Everest College Post-Sec.
247 S State St Ste 400 60604 312-913-1616
Everest College Post-Sec.
7414 S Cicero Ave 60629 708-793-4600
Global Citizenship Experience HS 50/9-12
1535 N Dayton St, 312-643-0991
Eric Davis, dir. Fax 643-0975
Gordon Tech HS 500/9-12
3633 N California Ave 60618 773-539-3600
Fax 539-9158
Greater West Comm Development Project Post-Sec.
500 N Sacramento Blvd 60612 312-432-9595
Hales Franciscan HS 200/9-12
4930 S Cottage Grove Ave 60615 773-285-8400
Erica Brownfield, prin. Fax 285-7025
Hanna Sacks Girls HS 100/9-12
3021 W Devon Ave 60659 773-338-9222
Hanna Belsky, prin. Fax 338-2405
Harold S. Washington College Post-Sec.
30 E Lake St 60601 312-553-5600
Harrington College of Design Post-Sec.
200 W Madison St Lbby 2 60606 312-939-4975
Harry S. Truman College Post-Sec.
1145 W Wilson Ave 60640 773-907-4000
Holy Trinity HS 300/9-12
1443 W Division St, 773-278-4212
Anne Rog, prin. Fax 278-0144
Ida Crown Jewish Academy 300/9-12
2828 W Pratt Blvd 60645 773-973-1450
Rabbi Leonard Matanky, prin. Fax 973-6131
Illinois Center for Broadcasting Post-Sec.
530 S State St 60605 312-884-8000
Illinois College of Optometry Post-Sec.
3241 S Michigan Ave 60616 312-225-1700
Illinois Institute of Technology Post-Sec.
3300 S Federal St 60616 312-567-3000
Illinois School of Health Careers Post-Sec.
11 E Adams St Ste 200 60603 312-913-1230
Institute for Clinical Social Work Post-Sec.
401 S State St Ste 822 60605 312-935-4232
International Academy of Design & Tech Post-Sec.
1 N State St Ste 500 60602 312-980-9200
John Marshall Law School Post-Sec.
315 S Plymouth Ct 60604 312-427-2737
Josephinum Academy 100/6-12
1501 N Oakley Blvd 60622 773-276-1261
Lourdes Weber, prin. Fax 292-3963
Kendall College Post-Sec.
900 N North Branch St, 888-905-3632

Kennedy-King College Post-Sec.
6301 S Halsted St 60621 773-602-5000
Latin S of Chicago 1,100/PK-12
59 W North Blvd 60610 312-582-6000
Randall Dunn, head sch Fax 582-6011
Le Cordon Bleu College of Culinary Arts Post-Sec.
361 W Chestnut St 60610 312-944-0882
Leo HS 200/9-12
7901 S Sangamon St 60620 773-224-9600
Philip Mesina, prin. Fax 224-3856
Lexington College Post-Sec.
310 S Peoria St 60607 312-226-6294
Loyola University Chicago Post-Sec.
1032 W Sheridan Rd 60660 773-274-3000
Lubavitch Girls HS 100/9-12
6350 N Whipple St 60659 773-743-7716
Kreindel Pinkhus, prin. Fax 743-7735
Lubavitch Mesivta of Chicago 100/9-12
2756 W Morse Ave 60645 773-262-0430
Rabbi Moshe Perlstein, dean Fax 338-2209
Lutheran School of Theology at Chicago Post-Sec.
1100 E 55th St 60615 773-256-0700
Luther North College Prep S 200/9-12
5700 W Berteau Ave 60634 773-286-3600
Joy Mullaney, prin. Fax 286-0304
Lycee Francais de Chicago 600/PK-12
613 W Bittersweet Pl 60613 773-665-0066
Alain Weber, pres. Fax 665-1725
MacCormac College Post-Sec.
29 E Madison St 60602 312-922-1884
Malcolm X College Post-Sec.
1900 W Van Buren St 60612 312-850-7000
Maria HS 300/9-12
6727 S California Ave 60629 773-925-8686
Margaret Hayes, prin. Fax 925-8885
Marist HS 1,800/9-12
4200 W 115th St 60655 773-881-5300
Larry Tucker, prin. Fax 881-0595
McCormick Theological Seminary Post-Sec.
5460 S University Ave 60615 800-228-4687
Meadville Lombard Theological School Post-Sec.
610 S Michigan Ave 60605 773-256-3000
Midwest College of Oriental Medicine Post-Sec.
4334 N Hazel St Ste 206 60613 773-975-1295
Moody Bible Institute Post-Sec.
820 N La Salle Dr 60610 312-329-4000
Morgan Park Academy 400/PK-12
2153 W 111th St 60643 773-881-6700
Catherine Raaflaub, hdmstr. Fax 881-8409
Mother McAuley Liberal Arts HS 1,400/9-12
3737 W 99th St 60655 773-881-6500
Claudia Woodruff, prin. Fax 881-6562
Mt. Carmel HS 900/9-12
6410 S Dante Ave 60637 773-324-1020
John Stimler, prin. Fax 324-2468
National Latino Education Institute Post-Sec.
2011 W Pershing Rd 60609 773-247-0707
National-Louis University Post-Sec.
122 S Michigan Ave 60603 888-658-8632
Northeastern Illinois University Post-Sec.
5500 N Saint Louis Ave 60625 773-583-4050
North Park University Post-Sec.
3225 W Foster Ave 60625 773-244-6200
North Shore SDA Jr. Academy 100/PK-10
5220 N California Ave 60625 773-769-0733
Helen Bacchus, prin. Fax 769-0928
Northside Catholic Academy 100/6-8
5525 N Magnolia Ave 60640 773-271-2008
Debra Sullivan, prin. Fax 271-3101
Northwestern College Post-Sec.
4829 N Lipps Ave 60630 888-205-2283
Northwestern Memorial Hospital Post-Sec.
514 N Fairbanks 9th Floor 60611 312-926-2215
Northwestern University Post-Sec.
303 E Chicago Ave 60611 312-503-8649
Notre Dame HS 100/9-12
3115 N Mason Ave 60634 773-622-9494
Dr. Lucine Mastalerz, prin. Fax 622-2807
Olive-Harvey College Post-Sec.
10001 S Woodlawn Ave 60628 773-291-6100
Our Lady of Tepeyac HS 200/9-12
2228 S Whipple St 60623 773-522-0023
Becca Noonan, prin. Fax 522-0508
Pacific College of Oriental Medicine Post-Sec.
65 E Wacker Pl Fl 21 60601 773-477-4822
Parker S 900/PK-12
330 W Webster Ave 60614 773-353-3000
Daniel Frank Ph.D., prin. Fax 549-4669
Providence-St. Mel S 500/PK-12
119 S Central Park Blvd 60624 773-722-4600
Jeanette DiBella, prin. Fax 722-9004
Pyramid Career Institute Post-Sec.
3051 N Lincoln Ave 60657 773-975-9898
Ravenswood Baptist Christian S 100/K-12
4437 N Seeley Ave 60625 773-561-6576
Karl Engle, prin. Fax 561-3080
Resurrection HS 700/9-12
7500 W Talcott Ave 60631 773-775-6616
Dr. Lynne Sacarro, prin. Fax 775-0611
Richard J. Daley College Post-Sec.
7500 S Pulaski Rd 60652 773-838-7500
Robert Morris University Post-Sec.
401 S State St 60605 312-935-6800
Roosevelt University Post-Sec.
430 S Michigan Ave 60605 312-341-3500
Rosel School of Cosmetology Post-Sec.
2446 W Devon Ave 60659 773-508-5600
Rush University Post-Sec.
600 S Paulina St # 440 60612 312-942-7100
St. Augustine College Post-Sec.
1333 W Argyle St 60640 773-878-8756
St. Benedict HS 200/9-12
3900 N Leavitt St 60618 773-539-0066
Ericka Mickelburgh, hdmstr. Fax 539-3397
St. Francis De Sales HS 300/9-12
10155 S Ewing Ave 60617 773-731-7272
Mary Ramirez, prin. Fax 731-7888

St. Ignatius College Prep HS 1,400/9-12
1076 W Roosevelt Rd 60608 312-421-5900
Dr. Catherine Karl, prin. Fax 421-7124
St. Mary of Providence School Post-Sec.
4200 N Austin Ave 60634 773-545-8300
St. Patrick HS 800/9-12
5900 W Belmont Ave 60634 773-282-8844
Dr. Joseph Schmidt, prin. Fax 282-2361
St. Rita of Cascia HS 700/9-12
7740 S Western Ave 60620 773-925-6600
Brendan Conroy, prin. Fax 925-2451
St. Xavier University Post-Sec.
3700 W 103rd St 60655 773-298-3000
San Miguel MS 100/6-8
1954 W 48th St 60609 773-890-1481
Thaddeus Smith, prin. Fax 254-3382
School of the Art Institute of Chicago Post-Sec.
37 S Wabash Ave 60603 312-629-6100
Seabury-Western Theological Seminary Post-Sec.
8765 W Higgins Rd 60631 800-275-8235
Shimer College Post-Sec.
3424 S State St 60616 312-235-3500
Spertus College Post-Sec.
610 S Michigan Ave 60605 312-922-9012
Steven Papageorge Hair Academy Post-Sec.
1113 W Belmont Ave # 15 60657 773-883-5100
Taylor Business Institute Post-Sec.
318 W Adams St Fl 5 60606 312-658-5100
Telshe HS 100/9-12
3535 W Foster Ave 60625 773-463-7738
Rabbi Shmuel Adler, dir. Fax 463-2849
Telshe Yeshiva-Chicago Post-Sec.
3535 W Foster Ave 60625 773-463-7738
The Illinois Institute of Art Post-Sec.
350 N Orleans St Lbby 136 60654 312-280-3500
Toyota Technological Inst at Chicago Post-Sec.
6045 S Kenwood Ave 60637 773-834-2500
Tribeca Flashpoint Media Arts Academy Post-Sec.
28 N Clark St Ste 500 60602 312-332-0707
University of Chicago Post-Sec.
5801 S Ellis Ave 60637 773-702-1234
University of Chicago Lab S 1,800/PK-12
1362 E 59th St 60637 773-702-9450
Dr. David Magill, dir. Fax 702-7455
University of Illinois at Chicago Post-Sec.
1200 W Harrison St 60607 312-996-7000
Univ. of Chicago Hospital/Roosevelt U. Post-Sec.
5841 S Maryland Ave 60637 773-702-6240
VanderCook College of Music Post-Sec.
3140 S Federal St 60616 800-448-2655
Warde S - Holy Name Cathedral 300/4-8
751 N State St 60654 312-466-0700
D. Michael Veitch, hdmstr. Fax 337-7180
Westwood College Post-Sec.
8501 W Higgins Rd Ste 100 60631 773-380-6800
Westwood College Post-Sec.
1 N State St Ste 1000 60602 312-739-0890
Wilbur Wright College North Post-Sec.
4300 N Narragansett Ave 60634 773-777-7900
Yeshivas Meor HaTorah of Chicago 50/9-12
3635 W Devon Ave 60659 773-465-0419
Rabbi Eliyahu Millen, dean Fax 465-0520

Chicago Heights, Cook, Pop. 29,817
Bloom Township HSD 206 3,400/9-12
100 W 10th St 60411 708-755-7010
Lenell Navarre Ed.D., supt. Fax 755-1149
www.sd206.org
Bloom HS 1,700/9-12
101 W 10th St 60411 708-755-1122
Micheal Campbell, prin. Fax 755-1149
Bloom Trail HS 1,700/9-12
22331 Cottage Grove Ave 60411 708-758-7000
Debra Graham Ed.D., prin. Fax 758-8372
District 206 Alternative HS 100/Alt
100 W 10th St 60411 708-754-4095
Wanda Murphy-Fulford, prin. Fax 754-4099

Flossmoor SD 161 2,400/PK-8
41 E Elmwood Dr 60411 708-647-7000
Craig Doster, supt. Fax 754-2153
www.sd161.org
Other Schools – See Flossmoor

Marian Catholic HS 1,500/9-12
700 Ashland Ave 60411 708-755-7565
Sr. Kathleen Tait, pres. Fax 756-9758
Prairie State College Post-Sec.
202 S Halsted St 60411 708-709-3500

Chicago Ridge, Cook, Pop. 13,978
Chicago Ridge SD 127-5 1,300/PK-8
6135 108th St 60415 708-636-2000
Joyce Kleinaitis, supt. Fax 636-0916
www.crsd1275.org
Finley JHS 400/6-8
10835 Lombard Ave 60415 708-636-2005
Laura Hamacher, prin. Fax 636-0045

Chillicothe, Peoria, Pop. 6,048
Illinois Valley Central Unit SD 321 1,800/PK-12
1300 W Sycamore St 61523 309-274-5418
Dr. Nick Polyak, supt. Fax 274-5046
www.ivcschools.com/
Chillicothe S 200/4-8
914 W Truitt Ave 61523 309-274-6266
Kelli Brabson, prin. Fax 274-2010
Illinois Valley Central HS 700/9-12
1300 W Sycamore St 61523 309-274-5481
Kenton Bergman, prin. Fax 274-8613

Chrisman, Edgar, Pop. 1,339
Edgar County CUSD 6 300/K-12
23231 IL Highway 1 61924 217-269-2513
Norman Tracy, supt. Fax 269-3231
www.chrisman.k12.il.us
Chrisman HS 100/9-12
23231 IL Highway 1 61924 217-269-2823
Nancy Dalenberg, prin. Fax 269-2329

Chrisman-Scottland JHS 100/6-8
23231 IL Highway 1 61924 217-269-3980
Nancy Dalenberg, prin. Fax 269-3231

Christopher, Franklin, Pop. 2,363
Christopher Unit SD 99 700/PK-12
1 Bearcat Dr 62822 618-724-9461
Richard Towers, supt. Fax 724-9400
www.cpher.frnkln.k12.il.us
Christopher HS 300/9-12
1 Bearcat Dr 62822 618-724-9461
Jeff Johnston, prin. Fax 724-9400

Cicero, Cook, Pop. 83,518
Cicero SD 99 13,200/PK-8
5110 W 24th St 60804 708-863-4856
Donna Adamic, supt. Fax 652-8105
cicd99.edu/
Unity JHS 2,700/7-8
2115 S 54th Ave 60804 708-863-8268
Donatа Heppner, prin. Fax 656-5652

J. S. Morton HSD 201 8,200/9-12
5041 W 31st St 60804 708-780-2110
Dr. Michael Kuzniewski, supt. Fax 780-2111
morton201.org
Morton Alternative S 100/Alt
1874 S 54th Ave 60804 708-222-3080
Rodolfo Hernandez, dir. Fax 222-3070
Morton East HS 3,500/10-12
2423 S Austin Blvd 60804 708-222-5700
Frank Zarate, prin. Fax 222-3090
Morton Freshman Center 1,300/9-9
1801 S 55th Ave 60804 708-863-7900
Mayra Barahona-Arroyo, prin. Fax 863-2244
Other Schools – See Berwyn

Morton College Post-Sec.
3801 S Central Ave 60804 708-656-8000

Cisne, Wayne, Pop. 671
North Wayne CUSD 200 400/PK-12
PO Box 235 62823 618-673-2151
Joyce Carson, supt. Fax 673-2152
Cisne HS 100/9-12
1456 US Highway 45 62823 618-673-2154
Kevin Bowen, prin. Fax 673-2155
Cisne MS 200/5-8
PO Box 69 62823 618-673-2156
Joyce Carson, prin. Fax 673-2152

Cissna Park, Iroquois, Pop. 841
Cissna Park CUSD 6 300/K-12
511 N 2nd St 60924 815-457-2171
Dr. Daniel Hylbert, supt. Fax 457-3033
www.cissnapark.k12.il.us
Cissna Park HS 100/9-12
511 N 2nd St 60924 815-457-2171
Mark Portwood, prin. Fax 457-3033
Cissna Park JHS 100/6-8
511 N 2nd St 60924 815-457-2171
Mark Portwood, prin. Fax 457-3033

Clarendon Hills, DuPage, Pop. 8,292
CCSD 181
Supt. — See Burr Ridge
Clarendon Hills MS 600/6-8
301 Chicago Ave 60514 630-887-4260
Griffin Sonntag, prin. Fax 887-4267

Clay City, Clay, Pop. 956
Clay City CUSD 10 300/PK-12
PO Box 542 62824 618-676-1431
James Jones, supt. Fax 676-1430
www.claycityschools.org
Clay City HS 100/9-12
PO Box 542 62824 618-676-1522
Ben Borries, prin. Fax 676-1481
Clay City JHS 100/6-8
PO Box 542 62824 618-676-1431
Ben Borries, prin. Fax 676-1537

Clifton, Iroquois, Pop. 1,441
Central CUSD 4 1,100/PK-12
PO Box 637 60927 815-694-2231
Tonya Evans, supt. Fax 694-2844
www.clifton-u4.k12.il.us
Central HS 400/9-12
1134 E 3100 North Rd 60927 815-694-2321
Marty Felesena, prin. Fax 694-2709
Nash MS 300/5-8
1134 E 3100 North Rd 60927 815-694-2323
Victoria Marquis, prin. Fax 694-2830

Clinton, DeWitt, Pop. 7,123
Clinton CUSD 15 2,000/PK-12
1210 State Route 54 W 61727 217-935-8321
Dr. Jeff Holmes, supt. Fax 935-2300
www.cusd15.org
Clinton HS 600/9-12
1200 State Route 54 W 61727 217-935-8337
Dr. Candice Swift, prin. Fax 935-4029
Clinton JHS 400/6-8
701 Illini Dr 61727 217-935-2103
John Pine, prin. Fax 937-1918

Coal City, Grundy, Pop. 5,546
Coal City CUSD 1 2,100/PK-12
100 S Baima St 60416 815-634-2287
Dr. Kent Bugg, supt. Fax 634-8775
www.coalcity.k12.il.us
Coal City HS 600/9-12
655 W Division St 60416 815-634-2396
Mitch Hamann, prin. Fax 634-2313
Coal City MS 500/6-8
500 S Carbon Hill Rd 60416 815-634-5039
Frank Perucca, prin. Fax 634-5049

Cobden, Union, Pop. 1,130
Cobden Unit SD 17 — 600/K-12
413 N Appleknocker St 62920 — 618-893-2313
Karl Sweitzer, supt. — Fax 893-4772
www.cobdenappleknockers.com
Cobden HS — 200/9-12
413 N Appleknocker St 62920 — 618-893-4031
Crystal Housman, prin. — Fax 893-2138
Cobden JHS — 100/7-8
413 N Appleknocker St 62920 — 618-893-4031
Crystal Housman, prin. — Fax 893-2138

Colchester, McDonough, Pop. 1,398
West Prairie CUSD 103 — 700/PK-12
204 S Hun St 62326 — 309-776-3180
Dr. Jonathan Heerboth, supt. — Fax 776-3194
www.westprairie.org/
West Prairie MS — 200/5-8
600 S Hun St 62326 — 309-776-3220
Caitlin Watson, prin. — Fax 776-3115
Other Schools – See Sciota

Colfax, McLean, Pop. 1,054
Ridgeview CUSD 19 — 500/PK-12
300 S Harrison St 61728 — 309-723-5111
Guy Gradert, supt. — Fax 723-6395
www.ridgeview19.org
Ridgeview JSHS — 200/6-12
202 E Wood St 61728 — 309-723-2951
Jim Campbell, prin. — Fax 723-4851

Collinsville, Madison, Pop. 25,082
Collinsville CUSD 10 — 6,500/PK-12
201 W Clay St 62234 — 618-346-6350
Robert Green, supt. — Fax 343-3673
www.kahoks.org
Collinsville HS — 2,000/9-12
2201 S Morrison Ave 62234 — 618-346-6320
Eric Flohr, prin. — Fax 346-6341
Collinsville MS — 900/7-8
9649 Collinsville Rd 62234 — 618-343-2100
Kimberly Jackson, prin. — Fax 343-2102

Collinsville Christian Academy — 100/K-12
1203 Vandalia St 62234 — 618-345-4224
Bob Lane, prin. — Fax 345-4470

Columbia, Monroe, Pop. 9,637
Columbia CUSD 4 — 2,000/PK-12
5 Veterans Pkwy 62236 — 618-281-4772
Dr. Gina Segobiano, supt. — Fax 281-4570
www.chseagles.com
Columbia HS — 600/9-12
77 Veterans Pkwy 62236 — 618-281-5001
Jason Dandurand, prin. — Fax 281-8081
Columbia MS — 600/5-8
100 Eagle Dr 62236 — 618-281-4993
Brian Reeves, prin. — Fax 281-4964

Concord, Morgan, Pop. 167
Triopia CUSD 27 — 400/PK-12
2204 Concord Arenzville Rd 62631 — 217-457-2283
Steve Eisenhauer, supt. — Fax 457-2277
www.triopiacusd27.org/
Triopia JSHS — 200/7-12
2204 Concord Arenzville Rd 62631 — 217-457-2281
Cheri Madson, prin. — Fax 457-2277

Coulterville, Randolph, Pop. 930
Coulterville Unit SD 1 — 200/K-12
PO Box 396 62237 — 618-758-2881
Karyn Albers, supt. — Fax 758-2330
Coulterville HS — 100/9-12
PO Box 396 62237 — 618-758-2881
Patti Berry, prin. — Fax 758-2330
Coulterville JHS — 50/6-8
PO Box 396 62237 — 618-758-2881
Patti Berry, prin. — Fax 758-2330

Country Club Hills, Cook, Pop. 16,299
Bremen Community HSD 228
Supt. — See Midlothian
Hillcrest HS — 1,300/9-12
17401 Crawford Ave 60478 — 708-799-7000
Renee Simms, prin. — Fax 799-0402

Country Club Hills SD 160 — 1,400/PK-8
4411 185th St 60478 — 708-957-6200
Dr. Earline Scott, supt. — Fax 957-8686
www.cch160.org
Southwood MS — 400/7-8
18635 Lee St 60478 — 708-957-6230
Dr. Millicent Borishade, prin. — Fax 799-4033

Cowden, Shelby, Pop. 628
Cowden-Herrick Community USD 3A — 400/PK-12
PO Box 188 62422 — 217-783-2126
Darrell Gordon, supt. — Fax 783-2126
www.cowden-herrick.k12.il.us/
Cowden-Herrick HS — 100/9-12
PO Box 188 62422 — 217-783-2125
Jerry Phillips, prin. — Fax 783-2124

Crest Hill, Will, Pop. 20,552
Chaney-Monge SD 88 — 500/PK-8
400 Elsie Ave, — 815-722-6673
Andy Siegfried, supt. — Fax 722-7814
www.chaneymonge.us
Monge JHS — 200/6-8
400 Elsie Ave, — 815-722-6673
Jacelynn Hall, prin. — Fax 722-7814

Richland SD 88A — 900/PK-8
1919 Caton Farm Rd, — 815-744-7288
Dr. Michael Early, supt. — Fax 744-6196
www.d88a.org
Richland JHS — 400/5-8
1919 Caton Farm Rd, — 815-744-6166
Kelly Whyte, prin. — Fax 745-8491

Crestwood, Cook, Pop. 10,823
Cook County SD 130
Supt. — See Blue Island
Hale MS — 300/6-8
5220 135th St 60445 — 708-385-6690
John Dudzik, prin. — Fax 385-2417

Crete, Will, Pop. 8,098
Crete-Monee CUSD 201U — 5,100/PK-12
1500 S Sangamon St 60417 — 708-367-8300
Dr. John Rodgers, supt. — Fax 672-2698
www.cm201u.org
Crete-Monee HS — 1,700/9-12
1515 W Exchange St 60417 — 708-367-8200
Michael Dugan, prin. — Fax 672-2888
Other Schools – See University Park

Illinois Lutheran HS — 100/7-12
1610 Main St 60417 — 708-672-3262
Joe Archer, prin. — Fax 672-0512

Creve Coeur, Tazewell, Pop. 5,361
Creve Coeur SD 76 — 700/PK-8
300 N Highland St 61610 — 309-698-3600
Jeanne Davis, supt. — Fax 698-9827
www.cc76.k12.il.us
Parkview JHS — 300/5-8
800 Groveland St 61610 — 309-698-3610
Brad Jockisch, prin. — Fax 698-3902

Crystal Lake, McHenry, Pop. 40,164
Community HSD 155 — 7,100/9-12
1 Virginia Rd 60014 — 815-455-8500
Johnnie Thomas, supt. — Fax 459-5022
www.d155.org
Crystal Lake Central HS — 1,600/9-12
45 W Franklin Ave 60014 — 815-459-2505
Steve Olson, prin. — Fax 459-2536
Crystal Lake South HS — 1,900/9-12
1200 S McHenry Ave 60014 — 815-455-3860
Scott Shepard, prin. — Fax 455-5706
Prairie Ridge HS — 1,700/9-12
6000 Dvorak Dr 60012 — 815-479-0404
Steven Koch, prin. — Fax 459-8993
Other Schools – See Cary

Crystal Lake CCSD 47 — 8,300/PK-8
300 Commerce Dr 60014 — 815-459-6070
Dr. Donn Mendoza, supt. — Fax 459-0263
www.d47.org
Beardsley MS — 1,000/6-8
515 E Crystal Lake Ave 60014 — 815-477-5897
Ron Ludwig, prin. — Fax 479-5119
Bernotas MS — 1,000/6-8
170 N Oak St 60014 — 815-459-9210
Lori Sorensen, prin. — Fax 479-5116
Lundahl MS — 1,000/6-8
560 Nash Rd 60014 — 815-459-5971
Matt Grubbs, prin. — Fax 479-5113

Prairie Grove Consolidated SD 46 — 1,000/K-8
3223 IL Route 176 60014 — 815-459-3023
Dr. Lynette Zimmer, supt. — Fax 356-0519
www.dist46.org/
Prairie Grove JHS — 400/6-8
3225 IL Route 176 60014 — 815-459-3557
Victor Wight, prin. — Fax 459-3785

Cosmetology & Spa Institute — Post-Sec.
700 E Terra Cotta Ave 60014 — 815-455-5900
Faith Lutheran HS — 100/9-12
174 S McHenry Ave 60014 — 815-479-9305
Chris Schoenleb, prin. — Fax 479-9300
McHenry County College — Post-Sec.
8900 US Highway 14 60012 — 815-455-3700

Cuba, Fulton, Pop. 1,288
CUSD 3 Fulton County — 500/PK-12
PO Box 79 61427 — 309-785-5021
Brad Kenser, supt. — Fax 785-5432
www.cusd3.net
Cuba HS — 200/9-12
20325 N State Route 97 61427 — 309-785-5023
Chad Willis, prin. — Fax 785-5102
Cuba MS — 100/7-8
20325 N State Route 97 61427 — 309-785-5023
Chad Willis, prin. — Fax 785-5102

Cullom, Livingston, Pop. 554
Tri-Point CUSD 6-J
Supt. — See Kempton
Tri-Point HS — 200/9-12
PO Box 316 60929 — 815-689-2110
William Geasa, prin. — Fax 689-2377

Dakota, Stephenson, Pop. 499
Dakota CUSD 201 — 900/PK-12
400 Campus Dr 61018 — 815-449-2832
Mike Schiffman, supt. — Fax 449-2459
www.dakota201.com
Dakota JSHS — 400/7-12
300 Campus Dr 61018 — 815-449-2812
Debra Keith, prin. — Fax 449-2322

Danville, Vermilion, Pop. 32,053
Danville CCSD 118 — 6,100/PK-12
516 N Jackson St 61832 — 217-444-1004
Mark Denman, supt. — Fax 444-1006
www.danville.k12.il.us
Bailey Academy — Alt
502 E Main St 61832 — 217-477-0300
Tracy Cherry, prin. — Fax 799-0399
Danville HS — 1,700/9-12
202 E Fairchild St 61832 — 217-444-1500
Mark Neil, prin. — Fax 444-1529
North Ridge MS — 700/6-8
1619 N Jackson St 61832 — 217-444-3400
Jason Bletzinger, prin. — Fax 444-3488
South View MS — 600/6-8
133 E 9th St 61832 — 217-444-1800
Brenda Yoho, prin. — Fax 444-1882

Oakwood CUSD 76
Supt. — See Oakwood
Oakwood JHS — 200/7-8
21600 N 900 East Rd 61834 — 217-443-2883
Sam Erwin, prin. — Fax 776-2228

Vermilion Vocational Education Delivery
2000 E Main St 61832 — 217-443-8742
Nick Chatterton, dir.
College Express — Vo/Tech
2000 E Main St 61832 — 217-443-8742
Nick Chatterton, prin. — Fax 431-5891

Concept College of Cosmetology — Post-Sec.
2500 Georgetown Rd 61832 — 217-442-9329
Danville Area Community College — Post-Sec.
2000 E Main St 61832 — 217-443-3222
First Baptist Christian S — 100/PK-12
1211 N Vermilion St 61832 — 217-442-2434
Robert Lazzell, prin. — Fax 442-8731
Lakeview College of Nursing — Post-Sec.
903 N Logan Ave 61832 — 217-709-0920
Schlarman Academy — 200/PK-12
2112 N Vermilion St 61832 — 217-442-2725
Gail Lewis, prin. — Fax 442-0293

Darien, DuPage, Pop. 21,762
Cass SD 63 — 800/PK-8
8502 Bailey Rd 60561 — 630-985-2000
Dr. Kerry Foderaro, supt. — Fax 985-0225
www.cassd63.org
Cass JHS — 400/5-8
8502 Bailey Rd 60561 — 630-985-1900
Christine Marcinkewicz, prin. — Fax 985-2881

Darien SD 61 — 1,600/PK-8
7414 S Cass Ave 60561 — 630-968-7505
Dr. Robert Carlo, supt. — Fax 968-0872
www.darien61.org
Eisenhower JHS — 600/6-8
1410 75th St 60561 — 630-964-5200
Mike Fitzgerald, prin. — Fax 968-8002

Hinsdale Township HSD 86
Supt. — See Hinsdale
Hinsdale South HS — 1,800/9-12
7401 Clarendon Hills Rd 60561 — 630-468-4000
Dr. Brian Waterman, prin. — Fax 920-8649

Decatur, Macon, Pop. 73,849
Decatur SD 61 — 8,800/PK-12
101 W Cerro Gordo St 62523 — 217-424-3000
Gloria Davis, supt. — Fax 424-3009
www.dps61.org/
Decatur MS — 500/7-8
300 E Eldorado St 62523 — 217-424-3014
Howard Edwards, prin. — Fax 424-3169
Eisenhower HS — 1,000/9-12
1 Educational Park 62526 — 217-876-8021
Charles Hoots, prin. — Fax 876-8003
Jefferson MS — 400/7-8
4735 E Cantrell St 62521 — 217-424-3190
Nathan Sheppard, prin. — Fax 424-3037
MacArthur HS — 1,200/9-12
1155 N Fairview Ave 62522 — 217-424-3156
Dr. Rhonda Key, prin. — Fax 424-3167
Phoenix Academy — 100/Alt
1900 E Cleveland Ave 62521 — 217-424-3090
Edwin Wilson, prin. — Fax 424-3092
Other Schools – See Forsyth

Lutheran School Association — 600/K-12
2001 E Mound Rd 62526 — 217-233-2001
Kyle Karsten, dir. — Fax 233-2002
Millikin University — Post-Sec.
1184 W Main St 62522 — 800-373-7733
Mr. John's School of Cosmetology — Post-Sec.
1745 E Eldorado St 62521 — 217-423-8173
Northwest Christian Campus S — 50/PK-12
1306 N Stanley Ave 62526 — 217-429-0563
Sue Fouts, admin. — Fax 429-0612
Richland Community College — Post-Sec.
1 College Park 62521 — 217-875-7200
St. Teresa HS — 300/9-12
2710 N Water St 62526 — 217-875-2431
Dr. Ken Henriksen, prin. — Fax 875-2436

Deerfield, Lake, Pop. 18,034
Deerfield SD 109 — 3,200/PK-8
517 Deerfield Rd 60015 — 847-945-1844
Dr. Renee Goier, supt. — Fax 945-1853
www.dps109.org
Caruso MS — 500/6-8
1801 Montgomery Rd 60015 — 847-945-8430
Brian Bullis, prin. — Fax 945-1963
Shepard MS — 500/6-8
440 Grove Ave 60015 — 847-948-0620
Michael Shapiro, prin. — Fax 948-8589

Township HSD 113
Supt. — See Highland Park
Deerfield HS — 1,700/9-12
1959 Waukegan Rd 60015 — 224-632-3000
Audris Griffith, prin. — Fax 632-3700

Chicagoland Jewish HS — 200/9-12
1095 Lake Cook Rd 60015 — 847-470-6700
Tony Frank, hdmstr. — Fax 324-3701
Trinity International University — Post-Sec.
2065 Half Day Rd 60015 — 847-945-8800

DeKalb, DeKalb, Pop. 43,053
DeKalb CUSD 428 — 5,900/PK-12
901 S 4th St 60115 — 815-754-2350
Dr. James Briscoe, supt. — Fax 758-6933
dist428.org
DeKalb HS — 1,700/9-12
501 W Dresser Rd 60115 — 815-754-2100
Tamra Ropeter, prin. — Fax 758-0931

Huntley MS 600/6-8
1515 S 4th St 60115 815-754-2241
Dr. Roger Scott, prin. Fax 758-6062
Rosette MS 700/6-8
650 N 1st St 60115 815-754-2226
Tim Vincent, prin. Fax 758-1097

Northern Illinois University 60115 Post-Sec.
815-753-1000

De Land, Piatt, Pop. 442
Deland-Weldon CUSD 57 200/PK-12
304 E IL Route 10 61839 217-736-2311
Gary Brashear, supt. Fax 736-2654
www.dwschools.org
Deland-Weldon HS 50/9-12
304 E IL Route 10 61839 217-664-3314
Russ Corey, prin. Fax 736-2654
Other Schools – See Weldon

Delavan, Tazewell, Pop. 1,679
Delavan CUSD 703 500/PK-12
907 Locust St 61734 309-244-8283
Dr. Mary Parker, supt. Fax 244-7696
www.delavanschools.com/
Delavan HS 100/9-12
907 Locust St 61734 309-244-8285
Matt Gordon, prin. Fax 244-8694
Delavan JHS 100/7-8
907 Locust St 61734 309-244-8285
Matt Gordon, prin. Fax 244-8694

De Pue, Bureau, Pop. 1,815
DePue Unit SD 103 500/PK-12
PO Box 800 61322 815-447-2121
Randall Otto, supt. Fax 447-2067
depueschools.org
DePue HS 100/9-12
PO Box 800 61322 815-447-2121
Randall Otto, supt. Fax 447-2067

Des Plaines, Cook, Pop. 57,381
CCSD 59
Supt. — See Arlington Heights
Friendship JHS 700/6-8
550 Elizabeth Ln 60018 847-593-4350
Jane Paterala, prin. Fax 593-7182

CCSD 62 4,700/PK-8
777 E Algonquin Rd 60016 847-824-1136
Dr. Jane Westerhold, supt. Fax 824-0612
www.d62.org
Algonquin MS 700/6-8
767 E Algonquin Rd 60016 847-824-1205
John Swanson, prin. Fax 824-1270
Chippewa MS 600/6-8
123 N 8th Ave 60016 847-824-1503
Dr. Leah Kimmelman, prin. Fax 824-1514

East Maine SD 63 3,500/PK-8
10150 Dee Rd 60016 847-299-1900
Dr. Scott Clay, supt. Fax 299-9963
www.emsd63.org
Other Schools – See Niles

Maine Township HSD 207
Supt. — See Park Ridge
Maine West HS 2,300/9-12
1755 S Wolf Rd 60018 847-827-6176
Dr. Audrey Haugan, prin. Fax 296-4916

Oakton Community College Post-Sec.
1600 E Golf Rd 60016 847-635-1600
Willows Academy 200/6-12
1012 E Thacker St 60016 847-824-6900
Jeanne Petros, dir. Fax 824-7089

Dieterich, Effingham, Pop. 615
Dieterich CUSD 30 400/K-12
PO Box 187 62424 217-925-5249
Cary Jackson, supt. Fax 925-5447
www.dieterich.k12.il.us/
Dieterich JSHS 200/7-12
PO Box 187 62424 217-925-5247
Kevin Haarman, prin. Fax 925-5447

Divernon, Sangamon, Pop. 1,159
Auburn CUSD 10
Supt. — See Auburn
Auburn JHS 200/6-8
303 E Kenney St 62530 217-628-3414
Mark Dudley, prin. Fax 628-3814

Dixmoor, Cook, Pop. 3,616
West Harvey-Dixmoor SD 147
Supt. — See Harvey
Parks MS 400/6-8
14700 Robey Ave 60426 708-371-9575
Abigail Phillips, prin. Fax 371-1412

Dixon, Lee, Pop. 15,509
Dixon Unit SD 170 2,800/PK-12
1335 Franklin Grove Rd 61021 815-284-7722
Michael Juenger, supt. Fax 284-8576
www.dixonschools.org
Dixon HS 900/9-12
300 Lincoln Statue Dr 61021 815-284-7723
Dr. Michael Grady, prin. Fax 284-4297
Reagan MS 700/PK-PK, 6-
620 Division St 61021 815-284-7725
Andrew Bullock, prin. Fax 284-1711

Faith Christian S 100/K-12
7571 S Ridge Rd 61021 815-652-4806
Liandro Arellano, supt. Fax 652-4871
Jack Mabley Development Center Post-Sec.
1120 Washington Ave 61021 815-288-8300
Sauk Valley Community College Post-Sec.
173 IL Route 2 61021 815-288-5511

Dolton, Cook, Pop. 22,862
Dolton SD 148
Supt. — See Riverdale
Roosevelt JHS 200/7-8
111 W 146th St 60419 708-201-2071
Shalonda Randle, prin. Fax 849-1285

Thornton Township HSD 205
Supt. — See South Holland
Thornridge HS 1,500/9-12
15000 Cottage Grove Ave 60419 708-271-4401
Kim Waller, prin. Fax 271-5028

Dongola, Union, Pop. 707
Dongola Unit SD 66 200/PK-12
PO Box 190 62926 618-827-3841
Dr. Janet Gladu, supt. Fax 827-4641
Dongola HS 100/9-12
PO Box 190 62926 618-827-3524
John Goddard, prin. Fax 827-4422
Dongola JHS 50/7-8
PO Box 190 62926 618-827-3524
John Goddard, prin. Fax 827-4422

Donovan, Iroquois, Pop. 304
Donovan CUSD 3 400/PK-12
PO Box 186 60931 815-486-7397
Jerome Pankey, supt. Fax 486-7060
www.donovan.k12.il.us/
Donovan HS 100/9-12
PO Box 186 60931 815-486-7395
Jason Bauer, prin. Fax 486-7060
Donovan JHS 100/7-8
PO Box 186 60931 815-486-7395
Jason Bauer, prin. Fax 486-7060

Downers Grove, DuPage, Pop. 47,147
Center Cass SD 66 1,100/PK-8
699 Plainfield Rd 60516 630-783-5000
Timothy Arnold, supt. Fax 910-0980
www.ccsd66.org/
Lakeview JHS 400/6-8
701 Plainfield Rd 60516 630-985-2700
Paul Windsor, prin. Fax 985-1545

Community HSD 99 5,300/9-12
6301 Springside Ave 60516 630-795-7100
Dr. Mark McDonald, supt. Fax 795-7199
www.csd99.org
Downers Grove North HS 2,100/9-12
4436 Main St 60515 630-795-8400
Scott Kasik, prin. Fax 795-8499
Downers Grove South HS 3,100/9-12
1436 Norfolk St 60516 630-795-8500
Stephan Bild, prin. Fax 795-8599

Downers Grove SD 58 5,000/PK-8
1860 63rd St 60516 630-719-5800
Dr. Kari Cremascoli, supt. Fax 719-9857
www.dg58.org
Herrick MS 600/7-8
4435 Middaugh Ave 60515 630-719-5810
Jason Lynde, prin. Fax 719-1628
O'Neill MS 500/7-8
635 59th St 60516 630-719-5815
Matthew Durbala, prin. Fax 719-1436

DeVry University Post-Sec.
3005 Highland Pkwy Ste 100 60515 630-515-3000
DeVry University Online Education Center Post-Sec.
3005 Highland Pkwy Ste 100 60515 630-515-3000
Marquette Manor Baptist Academy 200/PK-12
333 75th St 60516 630-964-5363
Timothy Wampler, prin. Fax 964-5385
Midwestern University Post-Sec.
555 31st St 60515 630-969-4400

Downs, McLean, Pop. 986
Tri-Valley CUSD 3 1,100/PK-12
410 E Washington St 61736 309-378-2351
Curt Simonson, supt. Fax 378-2223
tri-valley3.org
Tri-Valley HS 300/9-12
503 E Washington St 61736 309-378-2911
Dave Mouser, prin. Fax 378-3202
Tri-Valley MS 400/4-8
505 E Washington St 61736 309-378-3414
Doug Roberts, prin. Fax 378-3214

Dunlap, Peoria, Pop. 1,372
Dunlap CUSD 323
Supt. — See Peoria
Dunlap HS 1,100/9-12
PO Box 365 61525 309-243-7751
Thomas Welsh, prin. Fax 243-9565
Dunlap MS 400/6-8
5200 W Cedar Hills Dr 61525 309-243-7778
Zac Chatterton, prin. Fax 243-1136
Dunlap Valley MS 400/6-8
PO Box 366 61525 309-243-1034
Jason Holmes, prin. Fax 243-9829

Dupo, Saint Clair, Pop. 4,069
Dupo CUSD 196 1,100/PK-12
600 Louisa Ave 62239 618-286-3812
Dr. Terry Milt, supt. Fax 286-5554
www.dupo196.org
Dupo HS, 600 Louisa Ave 62239 300/9-12
Matt Hickam, prin. 618-286-3214
Dupo JHS, 600 Louisa Ave 62239 200/7-8
William Harris, prin. 618-286-3214

Du Quoin, Perry, Pop. 5,956
Du Quoin CUSD 300 1,500/PK-12
845 E Jackson St 62832 618-542-3856
Dr. Gary Kelly, supt. Fax 542-6614
dqud300.perry.k12.il.us
Du Quoin HS 400/9-12
500 E South St 62832 618-542-4744
Matt Hickam, prin. Fax 542-8822

Du Quoin MS 400/5-8
845 E Jackson St 62832 618-542-2646
Aaron Hill, prin. Fax 542-4373

Christian Fellowship S 100/PK-12
PO Box 227 62832 618-542-6800
Stuart Davis, prin. Fax 542-6806

Durand, Winnebago, Pop. 1,423
Durand CUSD 322 700/PK-12
200 W South St 61024 815-248-2171
Michael Duffy, supt. Fax 248-2599
www.durandbulldogs.com
Durand HS 200/9-12
200 W South St 61024 815-248-2171
Jeff Pinker, prin. Fax 248-2599
Durand JHS 100/7-8
200 W South St 61024 815-248-2171
Jeff Pinker, prin. Fax 248-2599

Dwight, Livingston, Pop. 4,231
Dwight Common SD 232 600/PK-8
801 S Columbia St 60420 815-584-6216
Richard Jancek, supt. Fax 584-2950
www.dwight.k12.il.us
Dwight Common MS 200/6-8
801 S Columbia St 60420 815-584-6220
Ben Bailey, prin. Fax 584-3771

Dwight Township HSD 230 300/9-12
801 S Franklin St 60420 815-584-6200
Dr. Richard Jancek, supt. Fax 584-2950
www.dwight.k12.il.us
Dwight Township HS 300/9-12
801 S Franklin St 60420 815-584-6200
Dr. Richard Jancek, supt. Fax 584-2950

Earlville, LaSalle, Pop. 1,691
Earlville CUSD 9 500/PK-12
PO Box 539 60518 815-246-8361
Wade Winekauf, supt. Fax 246-8672
Earlville HS 100/9-12
PO Box 539 60518 815-246-8361
Rich Faivre, prin. Fax 246-8672

East Alton, Madison, Pop. 6,171
East Alton SD 13 800/PK-8
210 E Saint Louis Ave 62024 618-433-2051
Virgil Moore, supt. Fax 433-2054
www.easd13.org/
East Alton MS 200/6-8
1000 3rd St 62024 618-433-2201
Clyde McGill, prin. Fax 433-2203

East Dubuque, Jo Daviess, Pop. 1,681
East Dubuque Unit SD 119 700/PK-12
100 N School Rd 61025 815-747-2111
Greg Herbst, supt. Fax 747-3516
www.edbqhs.org
East Dubuque HS 200/9-12
200 Parklane Dr 61025 815-747-3188
Darren Sirianni, prin. Fax 747-3516

East Moline, Rock Island, Pop. 20,814
East Moline SD 37 2,600/PK-8
3555 19th St 61244 309-792-2887
Kristin Humphries, supt. Fax 792-6010
www.emsd37.org
Glenview MS 1,100/5-8
3100 7th St 61244 309-755-1919
Perry Hill, prin. Fax 752-2551

Silvis SD 34
Supt. — See Silvis
Northeast JHS 200/6-8
4280 4th Ave 61244 309-203-1300
Jim Widdop, prin. Fax 203-1322

United Township Area Career Center
1275 Avenue of the Cities 61244 309-752-1691
Larry Shimmin, admin. Fax 752-1692
uths.revealed.net/
United Township Area Career Center Vo/Tech
1275 Avenue of the Cities 61244 309-752-1691
Larry Shimmin, dir. Fax 752-1692

United Township HSD 30 1,700/9-12
1275 Avenue of the Cities 61244 309-752-1611
Jay Morrow Ed.D., supt. Fax 752-1615
uths.net/hs
United Township HS 1,700/9-12
1275 Avenue of the Cities 61244 309-752-1633
Carl Johnson, prin. Fax 752-1608

East Moline Christian S 300/PK-12
900 46th Ave 61244 309-796-1485
Rev. James Patrick, prin. Fax 796-1152
La' James College of Hairstyling Post-Sec.
485 Avenue of the Cities 61244 888-880-2106

East Peoria, Tazewell, Pop. 23,021
East Peoria Community HSD 309 1,200/9-12
1401 E Washington St 61611 309-694-8300
Dr. Chuck Nagel, supt. Fax 694-8322
www.ep309.org
East Peoria Community HS 1,200/9-12
1401 E Washington St 61611 309-694-8300
Dr. Chuck Nagel, admin. Fax 694-8322

East Peoria SD 86 1,800/PK-8
601 Taylor St 61611 309-427-5100
Tony Ingold, supt. Fax 698-1364
www.epd86.org
Central JHS 600/6-8
601 Taylor St 61611 309-427-5200
Jason Warner, prin. Fax 699-2595

Illinois Central College Post-Sec.
1 College Dr, Peoria IL 61635 309-694-5422
Midwest Technical Institute Post-Sec.
280 High Point Ln 61611 800-814-5124

Oehrlein School of Cosmetology — Post-Sec.
100 Meadow Ave 61611 — 309-699-1561

East Saint Louis, Saint Clair, Pop. 26,776
East St. Louis SD 189 — 5,600/PK-12
1005 State St 62201 — 618-646-3000
Arthur Culver, supt. — Fax 583-7186
www.estl189.com
East Saint Louis 9th Grade Center — 500/9-9
3939 Caseyville Ave 62204 — 618-646-3760
Demario Bell, prin. — Fax 646-3768
East Saint Louis HS — 1,000/10-12
4901 State St 62205 — 618-646-3700
Anthony Smith, prin. — Fax 646-3708
Lincoln MS — 600/6-8
12 S 10th St 62201 — 618-646-3770
Anson Mitchell, prin. — Fax 646-3778
Mason-Clark MS — 500/6-8
5510 State St 62203 — 618-646-3750
Lelon Seaberry, prin. — Fax 646-3758
Williams Learning Center — 100/Alt
401 Katherine Dunham Pl 62201 — 618-646-3980
Edwin Newbern, prin.
Other Schools – See Alorton

Vee's School of Beauty Culture — Post-Sec.
2701 State St 62205 — 618-274-1751

Edinburg, Christian, Pop. 1,060
Edinburg CUSD 4 — 300/PK-12
100 E Martin St 62531 — 217-623-5603
Patty Hilliard-Wood, supt. — Fax 623-5604
www.edinburgschools.net
Edinburg HS — 100/9-12
100 E Martin St 62531 — 217-623-5733
Michael McCormick, prin. — Fax 623-5604
Edinburg JHS — 50/7-8
100 E Martin St 62531 — 217-623-5733
Michael McCormick, prin. — Fax 623-5604

Edwardsville, Madison, Pop. 23,810
Edwardsville CUSD 7 — 7,500/PK-12
PO Box 250 62025 — 618-656-1182
Dr. Ed Hightower, supt. — Fax 692-7423
www.ecusd7.org
Edwardsville HS — 2,300/9-12
6161 Center Grove Rd 62025 — 618-656-7100
Dennis Cramsey, prin. — Fax 655-1037
EHS South — 100/Alt
6148 Center Grove Rd 62025 — 618-692-7466
Dennis Cramsey, admin. — Fax 656-4859
Liberty MS — 900/6-8
1 District Dr 62025 — 618-655-6800
Hillary Stanifer, prin. — Fax 655-6801
Lincoln MS — 800/6-8
145 West St 62025 — 618-656-0485
Steve Stuart, prin. — Fax 659-1268

Alvareita's College of Cosmetology — Post-Sec.
333 S Kansas St 62025 — 618-656-2593
Metro East Lutheran HS — 200/9-12
6305 Center Grove Rd 62025 — 618-656-0043
Curtis Wudtke, prin. — Fax 656-3315
Southern Illinois Univ. Edwardsville — Post-Sec.
State Route 157 62026 — 800-447-7483

Effingham, Effingham, Pop. 12,212
Effingham CUSD 40 — 2,700/PK-12
PO Box 130 62401 — 217-540-1500
Mark Doan, supt. — Fax 540-1510
www.effingham.k12.il.us
Effingham HS — 900/9-12
1301 W Grove Ave 62401 — 217-540-1100
Jason Fox, prin. — Fax 540-1102
Effingham JHS — 700/6-8
600 S Henrietta St 62401 — 217-540-1300
Bill Myers, prin. — Fax 540-1362

St. Anthony of Padua HS — 200/9-12
304 E Roadway Ave 62401 — 217-342-6969
Greg Fearday, prin. — Fax 342-6997

Eldorado, Saline, Pop. 4,079
Eldorado CUSD 4 — 1,300/PK-12
2200A Illinois Ave 62930 — 618-273-6394
Gary Siebert, supt. — Fax 273-9311
www.eldorado.k12.il.us/
Eldorado HS — 300/9-12
2200 Illinois Ave 62930 — 618-273-2881
Ryan Hobbs, prin. — Fax 273-8153
Eldorado MS — 200/6-8
1907 1st St 62930 — 618-273-8056
Chris Morris, prin. — Fax 273-2943

Elgin, Kane, Pop. 106,496
SD U-46 — 40,400/PK-12
355 E Chicago St 60120 — 847-888-5000
Jose Torres Ph.D., supt. — Fax 608-4173
www.u-46.org/
Abbott MS — 500/7-8
949 Van St 60123 — 847-888-5160
Kathy Davis, prin. — Fax 608-2740
Elgin HS — 2,400/9-12
1200 Maroon Dr 60120 — 847-888-5100
Jerry Cook, prin. — Fax 888-6997
Ellis MS — 600/7-8
225 S Liberty St 60120 — 847-888-5151
Perry Hayes, prin. — Fax 608-2744
Gifford Street HS — 100/Alt
46 S Gifford St 60120 — 847-888-5000
Morris Mallory, prin. — Fax 888-5087
Kimball MS — 600/7-8
451 N Mclean Blvd 60123 — 847-888-5290
Alan Tamburrino, prin. — Fax 608-2749
Larkin HS — 2,100/9-12
1475 Larkin Ave 60123 — 847-888-5200
Dr. Jon Tuin, prin. — Fax 888-6996
Larsen MS — 700/7-8
665 Dundee Ave 60120 — 847-888-5250
Lorie Fuller, prin. — Fax 888-7172

Other Schools – See Bartlett, South Elgin, Streamwood

Cannella School of Hair Design — Post-Sec.
117 W Chicago St 60123 — 847-742-6611
DeVry University — Post-Sec.
2250 Point Blvd Ste 250 60123 — 847-649-3980
Elgin Academy — 500/PK-12
350 Park St 60120 — 847-695-0303
Dr. John Cooper, hdmstr. — Fax 695-5017
Elgin Community College — Post-Sec.
1700 Spartan Dr 60123 — 847-697-1000
Harvest Christian Academy — 600/PK-12
1000 N Randall Rd 60123 — 847-214-3500
Marc Abbatacola, dir. — Fax 214-3501
Judson University — Post-Sec.
1151 N State St 60123 — 847-628-2500
Robert Morris University — Post-Sec.
1707 N Randall Rd Ste 180 60123 — 800-762-5960
St. Edward Central Catholic HS — 400/9-12
335 Locust St 60123 — 847-741-7535
Rich Thomas, prin. — Fax 695-4682
Westminster Christian S — 500/PK-12
2700 W Highland Ave, — 847-695-0310
Patrick Bertsche, supt. — Fax 695-0135

Elizabeth, Jo Daviess, Pop. 746
Jo Daviess-Carroll AVC
950 US Highway 20 W 61028 — 815-858-2203
Kevin Kleckner, dir. — Fax 858-2316
www.jdcavc.org
Jo Daviess-Carroll AVC — Vo/Tech
950 US Highway 20 W 61028 — 815-858-2203
Kevin Kleckner, dir. — Fax 858-2316

Elizabethtown, Hardin, Pop. 296
Hardin County CUSD 1 — 600/PK-12
PO Box 218 62931 — 618-287-2411
Dr. Keith Reinhardt, supt. — Fax 287-2421
www.hardin.k12.il.us/
Hardin County HS — 200/9-12
RR 2 62931 — 618-287-2141
Janice Winters, prin. — Fax 287-8381
Hardin County JHS — 100/7-8
RR 2 62931 — 618-287-2141
Janice Winters, prin. — Fax 287-8381

Elk Grove Village, Cook, Pop. 32,640
CCSD 59
Supt. — See Arlington Heights
Grove JHS — 800/6-8
777 W Elk Grove Blvd 60007 — 847-593-4367
Enza Papeck, prin. — Fax 472-3001

Schaumburg CCSD 54
Supt. — See Schaumburg
Mead JHS — 600/7-8
1765 Biesterfield Rd 60007 — 847-357-6000
Dr. Pete Hannigan, prin. — Fax 357-6001

Township HSD 214
Supt. — See Arlington Heights
Elk Grove HS — 2,000/9-12
500 W Elk Grove Blvd 60007 — 847-718-4400
Dr. Nancy Holman, prin. — Fax 718-4417

Elkville, Jackson, Pop. 899
Elverado CUSD 196 — 500/PK-12
PO Box 130 62932 — 618-568-1321
Kevin Spain, supt. — Fax 568-1152
www.elv196.com
Elverado HS — 200/9-12
PO Box 217 62932 — 618-568-1104
Jeremy Pierce, prin. — Fax 568-1551
Other Schools – See Vergennes

Elmhurst, DuPage, Pop. 43,533
Elmhurst SD 205 — 8,200/PK-12
162 S York St 60126 — 630-834-4530
David Pruneau, supt. — Fax 617-2345
www.elmhurst205.org/
Bryan MS — 600/6-8
111 W Butterfield Rd 60126 — 630-617-2350
Melissa Couch, prin. — Fax 617-2232
Churchville MS — 400/6-8
155 E Victory Pkwy 60126 — 630-832-8682
Gina Pogue Reeder, prin. — Fax 617-2387
Sandburg MS — 700/6-8
345 E Saint Charles Rd 60126 — 630-834-4534
Amy Read, prin. — Fax 617-2380
York Community HS — 2,600/9-12
355 W Saint Charles Rd 60126 — 630-617-2400
Diana Smith, prin. — Fax 617-2399

Elmhurst College — Post-Sec.
190 S Prospect Ave 60126 — 630-279-4100
Immaculate Conception HS — 300/9-12
217 S Cottage Hill Ave 60126 — 630-530-3460
Pamela Levar, prin. — Fax 530-2290
Timothy Christian HS — 400/9-12
1061 S Prospect Ave 60126 — 630-833-7575
Brad Mitchell, prin. — Fax 833-9821

Elmwood, Peoria, Pop. 2,079
Elmwood CUSD 322 — 700/PK-12
301 W Butternut St 61529 — 309-742-8464
Dr. Roger Alvey, supt. — Fax 742-8812
elmwood322.com
Elmwood HS — 200/9-12
301 W Butternut St 61529 — 309-742-2851
Stan Matheny, prin. — Fax 742-8350
Elmwood JHS — 100/7-8
301 W Butternut St 61529 — 309-742-2851
Stan Matheny, prin. — Fax 742-8350

Elmwood Park, Cook, Pop. 24,650
Elmwood Park CUSD 401 — 2,900/PK-12
8201 W Fullerton Ave 60707 — 708-452-7292
Kevin Anderson, supt. — Fax 452-9504
www.epcusd401.org/
Elm MS — 400/7-8
7607 W Cortland St 60707 — 708-452-3550
Dr. Kathleen Porreca, prin. — Fax 452-0662
Elmwood Park HS — 1,000/9-12
8201 W Fullerton Ave 60707 — 708-452-7272
James Jennings, prin. — Fax 452-0732

El Paso, Woodford, Pop. 2,782
El Paso-Gridley CUSD 11 — 1,200/PK-12
97 W 5th St 61738 — 309-527-4410
Leo Johnson, supt. — Fax 527-4040
www.unit11.org/
El Paso-Gridley HS — 300/9-12
600 N Elm St 61738 — 309-527-4415
Karen Krug, prin. — Fax 527-4411
Other Schools – See Gridley

Elsah, Jersey, Pop. 651

Principia College — Post-Sec.
1 Maybeck Pl 62028 — 618-374-2131

Erie, Whiteside, Pop. 1,588
Erie CUSD 1 — 700/PK-12
520 5th Ave 61250 — 309-659-2239
Bradley Cox, supt. — Fax 659-2230
www.erie1.info
Erie HS — 200/9-12
435 6th Ave 61250 — 309-659-2239
Tim McConnell, prin. — Fax 659-2514
Erie MS — 200/5-8
500 5th Ave 61250 — 309-659-2239
Keith Morgan, prin. — Fax 659-7254

Eureka, Woodford, Pop. 5,225
Eureka CUSD 140 — 1,600/PK-12
109 W Cruger Ave 61530 — 309-467-3737
Robert Gold, supt. — Fax 467-2377
www.district140.org
Eureka HS — 500/9-12
200 W Cruger Ave 61530 — 309-467-2361
Richard Wherley, prin. — Fax 467-2648
Eureka MS — 500/5-8
2005 S Main St 61530 — 309-467-3771
Robert Bardwell, prin. — Fax 467-2052

Eureka College — Post-Sec.
300 E College Ave 61530 — 309-467-3721

Evanston, Cook, Pop. 71,880
Evanston CCSD 65 — 7,000/PK-8
1500 McDaniel Ave 60201 — 847-859-8000
Hardy Murphy Ph.D., supt. — Fax 859-8707
www.district65.net
Chute MS — 500/6-8
1400 Oakton St 60202 — 847-859-8600
James McHolland, prin. — Fax 492-7956
Haven MS — 600/6-8
2417 Prairie Ave 60201 — 847-859-8200
Kathleen Roberson, prin. — Fax 492-9983
Nichols MS — 500/6-8
800 Greenleaf St 60202 — 847-859-8660
Sarah Mendez, prin. — Fax 492-7880

Evanston Township HSD 202 — 2,900/9-12
1600 Dodge Ave 60201 — 847-424-7000
Dr. Eric Witherspoon, supt. — Fax 424-7220
www.eths.k12.il.us
Evanston Township HS — 2,900/9-12
1600 Dodge Ave 60201 — 847-424-7000
Oscar Hawthorne, prin. — Fax 424-7200

Garrett Evangelical Theological Seminary — Post-Sec.
2121 Sheridan Rd 60201 — 847-866-3900
Northwestern University — Post-Sec.
633 Clark St 60208 — 847-491-3741
Pivot Point International — Post-Sec.
1560 Sherman Ave Ste 700 60201 — 847-866-0500
Roycemore S — 200/PK-12
1200 Davis St 60201 — 847-866-6055
Joseph Becker, hdmstr. — Fax 866-6545
St. Francis Hospital — Post-Sec.
355 Ridge Ave 60202 — 847-492-4000

Evansville, Randolph, Pop. 690

Christ our Savior Lutheran HS — 50/9-12
810 Soldiers Way 62242 — 618-853-7300
John Christman, admin. — Fax 853-7361

Evergreen Park, Cook, Pop. 19,576
Evergreen Park Community HSD 231 — 900/9-12
9901 S Kedzie Ave 60805 — 708-424-7400
Dr. Beth Hart, supt. — Fax 424-7497
www.evergreenpark.org
Evergreen Park HS — 900/9-12
9901 S Kedzie Ave 60805 — 708-424-7400
Bill Sanderson, prin. — Fax 424-3045

Evergreen Park ESD 124 — 1,800/PK-8
9400 S Sawyer Ave 60805 — 708-423-0950
Dr. Robert Machak, supt. — Fax 423-4292
www.d124.org
Central JHS — 400/7-8
9400 S Sawyer Ave 60805 — 708-424-0148
Rita Sparks, prin. — Fax 229-8406

Fairbury, Livingston, Pop. 3,720
Prairie Central CUSD 8 — 2,100/PK-12
605 N 7th St 61739 — 815-692-2504
Dr. John Capasso, supt. — Fax 692-3195
www.prairiecentral.org
Prairie Central HS — 600/9-12
411 N 7th St 61739 — 815-692-2355
Dan Casillas, prin. — Fax 692-2438
Other Schools – See Forrest

Fairfield, Wayne, Pop. 5,118
Fairfield Community HSD 225 — 400/9-12
300 W King St 62837 — 618-842-2649
David Savage M.Ed., supt. — Fax 842-4465
www.fchsmules.com/
Fairfield Community HS — 400/9-12
300 W King St 62837 — 618-842-2649
Jill Fulkerson, prin. — Fax 842-5187

Fairfield SD 112 — 600/PK-8
806 N 1st St 62837 — 618-842-6501
Diana Zurliene, supt. — Fax 842-2932
fairfield.d112.wayne.k12.il.us
Center Street S — 300/4-8
200 W Center St 62837 — 618-842-2679
Bill Wrenn, prin. — Fax 842-4719

Frontier Community College — Post-Sec.
2 Frontier Dr 62837 — 618-842-3711

Fairview Heights, Saint Clair, Pop. 16,671
Grant CCSD 110 — 800/PK-8
10110 Old Lincoln Trl 62208 — 618-398-5577
Matt Stines, supt. — Fax 398-5578
www.dist110.com
Grant MS — 400/5-8
10110 Old Lincoln Trl 62208 — 618-397-2764
Carla Lasley, prin. — Fax 397-7809

Pontiac-William Holliday SD 105 — 700/PK-8
400 Ashland Ave 62208 — 618-233-2320
Julie Brown, supt. — Fax 233-0918
www.pwh105.org
Pontiac JHS — 200/6-8
400 Ashland Ave 62208 — 618-233-6004
Joanna Luehmann, prin. — Fax 233-0918

Vatterott College — Post-Sec.
110 Commerce Ln 62208 — 618-489-2400

Farina, Fayette, Pop. 518
South Central CUSD 401
Supt. — See Kinmundy
South Central HS — 200/9-12
800 W Washington St 62838 — 618-245-3363
Steve Phillips, prin. — Fax 245-6165

Farmer City, DeWitt, Pop. 2,018
Blue Ridge CUSD 18 — 800/PK-12
411 N John St 61842 — 309-928-9141
Susan Wilson, supt. — Fax 928-5478
www.blueridge18.org
Blue Ridge HS — 200/9-12
411 N John St 61842 — 309-928-2622
John Lawrence, prin. — Fax 928-5301
Other Schools – See Mansfield

Farmington, Fulton, Pop. 2,424
Farmington Central CUSD 265 — 1,500/PK-12
212 N Lightfoot Rd 61531 — 309-245-1000
Dr. John Asplund, supt. — Fax 245-9161
www.dist265.com/
Farmington Central JHS — 300/6-8
300 N Lightfoot Rd 61531 — 309-245-1000
Perry Miller, prin. — Fax 245-9162
Farmington HS — 400/9-12
310 N Lightfoot Rd 61531 — 309-245-1000
Perry Miller, prin. — Fax 245-9163

Findlay, Shelby, Pop. 676
Okaw Valley CUSD 302
Supt. — See Bethany
Okaw Valley MS — 100/5-8
501 W Division St 62534 — 217-756-8521
Mike Cummins, prin. — Fax 756-8599

Fisher, Champaign, Pop. 1,871
Fisher CUSD 1 — 600/K-12
PO Box 700 61843 — 217-897-6125
Barbara Thompson, supt. — Fax 897-6676
www.fisher.k12.il.us
Fisher JSHS — 300/7-12
PO Box 670 61843 — 217-897-1225
Tom Shallenberger, prin. — Fax 897-1708

Fithian, Vermilion, Pop. 480
Oakwood CUSD 76
Supt. — See Oakwood
Oakwood HS — 300/9-12
5870 US Route 150 61844 — 217-354-2358
Brenda Ludwig, prin. — Fax 354-2603

Flanagan, Livingston, Pop. 1,105
Flanagan-Cornell Unit SD 74 — 400/PK-12
202 E Falcon Hwy 61740 — 815-796-2233
Jerry Farris, supt. — Fax 796-2856
fc74.org/
Flanagan-Cornell HS — 100/9-12
202 E Falcon Hwy 61740 — 815-796-2291
Jerry Farris, prin. — Fax 796-2856

Flora, Clay, Pop. 5,018
Flora CUSD 35 — 1,300/PK-12
444 S Locust St 62839 — 618-662-2412
Bob Pierson, supt. — Fax 662-4587
floraschools.com
Flora HS — 400/9-12
600 S Locust St 62839 — 618-662-8316
Darrell Gummert, prin. — Fax 662-2725
Henson JHS — 300/6-8
609 N Stanford Rd 62839 — 618-662-8394
Janette Schade, prin. — Fax 662-8395

Flossmoor, Cook, Pop. 9,246
Flossmoor SD 161
Supt. — See Chicago Heights
Parker JHS — 900/6-8
2810 School St 60422 — 708-647-5400
Dr. Vanessa Atkins, prin. — Fax 799-9207

Homewood-Flossmoor Community HSD 233 — 2,800/9-12
999 Kedzie Ave 60422 — 708-799-3000
Dr. Von Mansfield, supt. — Fax 799-8552
www.hfhighschool.org
Homewood-Flossmoor HS — 2,800/9-12
999 Kedzie Ave 60422 — 708-799-3000
Dr. Ryan Pitcock, prin. — Fax 335-6995

Ford Heights, Cook, Pop. 2,726
Ford Heights SD 169 — 500/PK-8
910 Woodlawn Ave 60411 — 708-758-1370
Dr. Gregory Jackson, supt. — Fax 758-1372
www.fordheights169.org
Cottage Grove Upper Grade Center — 200/5-8
800 E 14th St 60411 — 708-758-1400
Stephanie Stephen, prin. — Fax 758-0711

Forest Park, Cook, Pop. 13,818
Forest Park SD 91 — 900/PK-8
424 Des Plaines Ave 60130 — 708-366-5700
Dr. Louis Cavallo, supt. — Fax 366-5761
www.forestparkschools.org
Forest Park MS — 300/6-8
925 Beloit Ave 60130 — 708-366-5703
Karen Bukowski, prin. — Fax 366-2091

Proviso Township HSD 209 — 5,000/9-12
8601 Roosevelt Rd 60130 — 708-338-5912
Dr. Nettie Collins-Hart, supt. — Fax 338-5999
www.pths209.org
Proviso Math & Science Academy — 800/9-12
8601 Roosevelt Rd 60130 — 708-338-4100
Kim Echols, prin. — Fax 338-4199
Other Schools – See Hillside, Maywood

Forrest, Livingston, Pop. 1,217
Prairie Central CUSD 8
Supt. — See Fairbury
Prairie Central JHS — 300/7-8
800 N Wood St 61741 — 815-657-8660
Tonya Dieken, prin. — Fax 657-8677

Forreston, Ogle, Pop. 1,426
Forrestville Valley CUSD 221 — 900/PK-12
PO Box 665 61030 — 815-938-2036
Lowell Taylor, supt. — Fax 938-9028
Forreston JSHS — 500/6-12
PO Box 665 61030 — 815-938-2175
Travis Heinz, prin. — Fax 938-2546

Forsyth, Macon, Pop. 3,456
Decatur SD 61
Supt. — See Decatur
Adult Education & Training Center — Adult
1415 Hickory Point Mall 62535 — 217-875-0061
Fax 875-0062

Decatur Christian S — 300/PK-12
137 S Grant St 62535 — 217-877-5636
Randy Grigg, supt. — Fax 877-7627

Fox Lake, Lake, Pop. 10,448
Fox Lake Grade SD 114
Supt. — See Spring Grove
Stanton MS — 300/6-8
101 Hawthorne Ln 60020 — 847-973-4200
Jeff Sefcik, prin. — Fax 973-4210

Grant Community HSD 124 — 1,700/9-12
285 E Grand Ave 60020 — 847-587-2561
Dr. Christine Sefcik, supt. — Fax 587-2991
www.grant.lake.k12.il.us/
Grant Community HS — 1,700/9-12
285 E Grand Ave 60020 — 847-587-2561
John Barbini, prin. — Fax 587-2991

Fox River Grove, McHenry, Pop. 4,788
Fox River Grove SD 3 — 500/PK-8
403 Orchard St 60021 — 847-516-5100
Dr. Tim Mahaffy, supt. — Fax 516-9169
www.dist3.org
Fox River Grove MS — 200/5-8
401 Orchard St 60021 — 847-516-5105
Eric Runck, prin. — Fax 516-5104

Frankfort, Will, Pop. 17,612
Frankfort CCSD 157C — 2,400/PK-8
10482 Nebraska St 60423 — 815-469-5922
Dr. Thomas Hurlburt, supt. — Fax 469-8988
www.fsd157c.org
Hickory Creek MS — 800/6-8
22150 116th Ave 60423 — 815-469-4474
Dr. Kevin Suchinski, prin. — Fax 469-7930

Lincoln-Way Community HSD 210
Supt. — See New Lenox
Lincoln-Way East HS — 2,300/9-12
201 Colorado Ave 60423 — 815-464-4000
Dr. Scott Tingley, prin. — Fax 464-4132
Lincoln-Way North HS — 1,800/9-12
19900 S Harlem Ave 60423 — 815-534-3000
Dr. Michael Gardner, prin. — Fax 534-3009

Summit Hill SD 161 — 3,100/PK-8
20100 S Spruce Dr 60423 — 815-469-9103
Barbara Rains, supt. — Fax 469-0566
www.summithill.org/
Summit Hill JHS — 800/7-8
7260 W North Ave 60423 — 815-469-4330
Pam Hodgson, prin. — Fax 464-1596

Franklin, Morgan, Pop. 598
Franklin CUSD 1
Supt. — See Alexander
Franklin JSHS — 200/6-12
110 State 62638 — 217-675-2395
Jason Courier, prin. — Fax 675-2396

Franklin Grove, Lee, Pop. 1,012
Ashton-Franklin Center CUSD 275
Supt. — See Ashton
Ashton-Franklin Center MS — 200/5-8
318 E South St 61031 — 815-456-2323
Trina Dillon, prin. — Fax 456-3211

Franklin Park, Cook, Pop. 18,209
Franklin Park SD 84 — 1,300/PK-8
2915 Maple St 60131 — 847-455-4230
Dr. David H. Katzin, supt. — Fax 455-9094
www.d84.org/
Hester JHS — 400/6-8
2836 Gustav St 60131 — 847-455-2150
Giffen Trotter, prin. — Fax 455-0945

Leyden Community HSD 212 — 3,400/9-12
3400 Rose St 60131 — 847-451-3020
Dr. Kathryn Robbins, supt. — Fax 671-9079
www.leyden212.org
East Leyden HS — 1,700/9-12
3400 Rose St 60131 — 847-451-3023
Jason Markey, prin. — Fax 233-9928
Other Schools – See Northlake

Mannheim SD 83 — 2,500/K-8
10401 Grand Ave 60131 — 847-455-4413
Kim Petrasek, supt. — Fax 451-8290
www.d83.org/
Other Schools – See Melrose Park

Freeburg, Saint Clair, Pop. 4,312
Freeburg CCSD 70 — 800/PK-8
408 S Belleville St 62243 — 618-539-3188
Tomi Diefenbach, supt. — Fax 539-5795
www.frg70.org
Freeburg ES — 500/3-8
408 S Belleville St 62243 — 618-539-3188
Theresa Goscinski, prin. — Fax 539-5795

Freeburg Community HSD 77 — 700/9-12
401 S Monroe St 62243 — 618-539-5533
Andrew Lehman, supt. — Fax 539-4887
www.fchs77.org/district.cfm
Freeburg HS — 700/9-12
401 S Monroe St 62243 — 618-539-5533
Benjamin Howes, prin. — Fax 539-4887

Freeport, Stephenson, Pop. 24,738
Freeport SD 145 — 3,800/K-12
501 E South St 61032 — 815-232-0300
Dr. Roberta Selleck, supt. — Fax 232-6717
www.freeport.k12.il.us
Freeport HS — 1,200/9-12
701 W Moseley St 61032 — 815-232-0400
Dr. Beth Summers, prin. — Fax 232-0629
Freeport MS — 800/5-8
701 W Empire St 61032 — 815-232-0500
Nick Swords, prin. — Fax 232-0536
Sandburg MS — 400/5-8
1717 W Eby St 61032 — 815-232-0340
Stacey Kleindl, prin. — Fax 232-1241
Sleezer Home — 50/Alt
302 W Exchange St 61032 — 815-232-8336
Karen Sanders, prin.

Aquin Central Catholic HS — 200/7-12
1419 S Galena Ave 61032 — 815-235-3154
Kathy Runte, prin. — Fax 235-3185
Highland Community College — Post-Sec.
2998 W Pearl City Rd 61032 — 815-235-6121

Fulton, Whiteside, Pop. 3,442
River Bend CUSD 2 — 900/K-12
1110 3rd St 61252 — 815-589-2711
Chuck Holliday Ph.D., supt. — Fax 589-4630
www.riverbendschools.org
Fulton HS — 300/9-12
1207 12th St 61252 — 815-589-3511
Loren Beswick, prin. — Fax 589-3412
River Bend MS — 200/6-8
415 12th St 61252 — 815-589-2611
Kathleen Schipper, prin. — Fax 589-3130

Unity Christian HS — 100/7-12
711 10th St 61252 — 815-589-3912
Chris Pluister, supt. — Fax 589-4430

Galatia, Saline, Pop. 925
Galatia CUSD 1 — 400/PK-12
200 N Hickory St 62935 — 618-268-6371
Dr. Beth Rister, supt. — Fax 268-4196
www.galatiak12.org
Galatia HS — 100/9-12
200 N McKinley St 62935 — 618-268-4194
John Cummins, prin. — Fax 268-4196
Galatia JHS — 100/7-8
200 N McKinley St 62935 — 618-268-4194
John Cummins, prin. — Fax 268-4196

Galena, Jo Daviess, Pop. 3,404
Galena Unit SD 120 — 800/PK-12
1206 Franklin St 61036 — 815-777-3086
Dr. Sharon Olds, supt. — Fax 777-0303
www.gusd120.k12.il.us
Galena HS — 200/9-12
1206 Franklin St 61036 — 815-777-0917
Elizabeth Murphy, prin. — Fax 777-2089
Galena MS — 200/5-8
1230 Franklin St 61036 — 815-777-2413
Ben Soat, prin. — Fax 777-4259

Tri-State Christian S — 200/PK-12
11084 W US Highway 20 61036 — 815-777-3800
Tad Nuce, prin. — Fax 777-2991

Galesburg, Knox, Pop. 31,321
Galesburg AVC
1135 W Fremont St 61401 — 309-343-3733
Jeff Houston, dir. — Fax 343-1305
Galesburg AVC — Vo/Tech
1135 W Fremont St 61401 — 309-343-3733
Jeff Houston, dir. — Fax 343-1305

Galesburg CUSD 205 — 4,800/PK-12
PO Box 1206 61402 — 309-343-1151
Bart Arthur, supt. — Fax 343-7757
www.galesburg205.org/
Churchill JHS — 500/6-8
905 Maple Ave 61401 — 309-342-3129
Jim Wilson, prin. — Fax 342-6384
Galesburg HS — 1,400/9-12
1135 W Fremont St 61401 — 309-343-4146
Roy VanMeter, prin. — Fax 343-7122
Galesburg HS North — Alt
1017 W Dayton St 61401 — 309-344-7807
Jason Spring, prin. — Fax 343-1237
Lombard JHS — 500/6-8
1220 E Knox St 61401 — 309-342-9171
Neal Thompson, prin. — Fax 342-7135

Carl Sandburg College — Post-Sec.
2400 Tom L Wilson Blvd 61401 — 309-344-2518
Galesburg Christian S — 100/PK-12
1881 E Fremont St 61401 — 309-343-8008
Robert Nutzhorn, admin. — Fax 343-8006
Knox College — Post-Sec.
2 E South St 61401 — 309-341-7000

Galva, Henry, Pop. 2,565
Galva CUSD 224 — 600/PK-12
224 Morgan Rd 61434 — 309-932-2108
Doug O'Riley, supt. — Fax 932-8326
www.galva224.org
Galva JSHS — 300/7-12
224 Morgan Rd 61434 — 309-932-2151
Jerry Becker, prin. — Fax 932-2152

Gardner, Grundy, Pop. 1,442
Gardner-South Wilmington Twp. HSD 73 — 200/9-12
500 E Main St 60424 — 815-237-2176
Michael Perrott, supt. — Fax 237-2842
www.gswhs.grundy.k12.il.us
Gardner-South Wilmington Twp. HS — 200/9-12
500 E Main St 60424 — 815-237-2176
Michael Perrott, prin. — Fax 237-2842

Geneseo, Henry, Pop. 6,533
Geneseo CUSD 228 — 2,700/PK-12
648 N Chicago St 61254 — 309-945-0450
Scott Kuffel, supt. — Fax 945-0445
www.dist228.org
Geneseo HS — 900/9-12
700 N State St 61254 — 309-945-0399
Michael Haugse, prin. — Fax 945-0374
Geneseo MS — 600/6-8
333 E Ogden Ave 61254 — 309-945-0599
Matthew DeBaene, prin. — Fax 945-0580
Rock River Coop Alternative S — 50/Alt
20965 E 900th St 61254 — 309-949-2937
Jack Schlindwein, prin. — Fax 949-2939

Geneva, Kane, Pop. 21,261
Geneva CUSD 304 — 5,900/PK-12
227 N 4th St 60134 — 630-463-3000
Dr. Kent Mutchler, supt. — Fax 463-3009
www.geneva304.org
Geneva Community HS — 1,900/9-12
416 McKinley Ave 60134 — 630-463-3800
Thomas Rogers, prin. — Fax 232-9077
Geneva MS North — 700/6-8
1357 Viking Dr 60134 — 630-463-3700
Lawrence Bidlack, prin. — Fax 463-3709
Geneva MS South — 700/6-8
1415 Viking Dr 60134 — 630-463-3600
Terry Bleau, prin. — Fax 208-7172

Genoa, DeKalb, Pop. 5,138
Genoa-Kingston CUSD 424 — 2,000/PK-12
980 Park Ave 60135 — 815-784-6222
Joe Burgess, supt. — Fax 784-6059
www.gkschools.org
Genoa-Kingston HS — 700/9-12
980 Park Ave 60135 — 815-784-5111
Don Billington, prin. — Fax 784-3124
Genoa-Kingston MS — 500/6-8
941 W Main St 60135 — 815-784-5222
Brett McPherson, prin. — Fax 784-4323

Georgetown, Vermilion, Pop. 3,408
Georgetown-Ridge Farm CUSD 4 — 1,100/PK-12
400 W West St 61846 — 217-662-8488
Jean Neal, supt. — Fax 662-3402
www.grf.k12.il.us
Georgetown-Ridge Farm HS — 300/9-12
500 W Mulberry St 61846 — 217-662-6716
Brad Russell, prin. — Fax 662-3404
Miller JHS — 300/6-8
414 W West St 61846 — 217-662-6606
Lisa Gocken, prin. — Fax 662-6345

Germantown Hills, Woodford, Pop. 3,399
Germantown Hills SD 69 — 900/K-8
103 Warrior Way, — 309-383-2121
Dan Mair, supt. — Fax 383-2123
ghills.metamora.k12.il.us
Germantown Hills JHS — 300/6-8
103 Warrior Way, — 309-383-2121
Dave Raffel, prin. — Fax 383-4739

Gibson City, Ford, Pop. 3,366
Gibson City-Melvin-Sibley CUSD 5 — 1,000/PK-12
307 N Sangamon Ave 60936 — 217-784-8296
Anthony Galindo, supt. — Fax 784-8558
www.gcms.k12.il.us
GCMS HS — 300/9-12
815 N Church St 60936 — 217-784-4292
Christopher Garard, prin. — Fax 784-8293
GCMS MS — 200/6-8
316 E 19th St 60936 — 217-784-8731
Jeremy Darnell, prin. — Fax 784-8726

Gillespie, Macoupin, Pop. 3,280
Gillespie CUSD 7 — 1,300/PK-12
510 W Elm St 62033 — 217-839-2464
Paul Skeans, supt. — Fax 839-3353
www.gillespie.k12.il.us
Gillespie HS — 400/9-12
612 Broadway St 62033 — 217-839-2114
Dennis Tiburzi, prin. — Fax 839-4302
Gillespie MS, 412 Oregon St 62033 — 300/6-8
Lori Emmons, prin. — 217-839-2116

Gilman, Iroquois, Pop. 1,793
Iroquois West CUSD 10 — 1,000/PK-12
PO Box 67 60938 — 815-265-4642
Dr. Linda Dvorak, supt. — Fax 265-7008
www.iwest.k12.il.us/
Iroquois West HS — 300/9-12
PO Box 67 60938 — 815-265-4229
Brian Dukes, prin. — Fax 265-8108
Other Schools – See Onarga

Girard, Macoupin, Pop. 2,085
North Mac CUSD 34 — 1,100/PK-12
525 N 3rd St 62640 — 217-627-2915
Marica Cullen, supt. — Fax 627-3519
www.northmacschools.org
North Mac MS — 100/6-8
525 N 3rd St 62640 — 217-627-2136
Dennis McMillin, prin. — Fax 627-3503
Other Schools – See Virden

Glasford, Peoria, Pop. 1,015
Illini Bluffs CUSD 327 — 1,000/PK-12
9611 S Hanna City Glsfrd Rd 61533 — 309-389-2231
Dr. Samuel Light, supt. — Fax 389-2251
www.illinibluffs.com
Illini Bluffs HS — 300/9-12
9611 S Hanna City Glsfrd Rd 61533 — 309-389-5681
Julie Traenkenschuh, prin. — Fax 389-4681
Illini Bluffs MS — 200/6-8
9611 S Hanna City Glsfrd Rd 61533 — 309-389-3451
Karen Peterson, prin. — Fax 389-3454

Glen Carbon, Madison, Pop. 12,692

Gateway Legacy Christian Academy — 100/PK-12
97 Oaklawn Dr 62034 — 618-288-0452
Candice Seidler M.A., prin. — Fax 288-0453

Glencoe, Cook, Pop. 8,600
Glencoe SD 35 — 1,300/K-8
620 Greenwood Ave 60022 — 847-835-7800
Dr. Cathlene Crawford, supt. — Fax 835-7805
www.glencoeschools.org/
Central S — 700/5-8
620 Greenwood Ave 60022 — 847-835-7600
Dr. Ryan Mollet, prin. — Fax 835-7605

Glendale Heights, DuPage, Pop. 33,478
Marquardt SD 15 — 2,700/PK-8
1860 Glen Ellyn Rd 60139 — 630-469-7615
Dr. Loren May, supt. — Fax 790-1650
www.d15.us/
Marquardt MS — 900/6-8
1912 Glen Ellyn Rd 60139 — 630-858-3850
Marie Cimaglia, prin. — Fax 790-5042

Queen Bee SD 16 — 2,400/PK-8
1560 Bloomingdale Rd 60139 — 630-260-6100
Victoria Tabbert, supt. — Fax 260-6103
www.queenbee16.org
Glenside MS — 600/6-8
1560 Bloomingdale Rd 60139 — 630-260-6112
Christopher Collins, prin. — Fax 510-8568

Universal Technical Institute — Post-Sec.
601 Regency Dr 60139 — 630-529-2662

Glen Ellyn, DuPage, Pop. 27,048
CCSD 89 — 2,000/PK-8
22W600 Butterfield Rd 60137 — 630-469-8900
Dr. John Perdue, supt. — Fax 469-8936
www.ccsd89.org
Glen Crest MS — 700/6-8
725 Sheehan Ave 60137 — 630-469-5220
Todd Schrage, prin. — Fax 469-5250

Glen Ellyn SD 41 — 3,600/PK-8
793 N Main St 60137 — 630-790-6400
Ann Riebock Ed.D., supt. — Fax 790-1867
www.d41.org
Hadley JHS — 1,200/6-8
240 Hawthorne Blvd 60137 — 630-790-6450
Dr. Christopher Dransoff, prin. — Fax 790-6469

Glenbard Township HSD 87 — 8,800/9-12
596 Crescent Blvd 60137 — 630-469-9100
Dr. David Larson, supt. — Fax 469-9107
glenbard87.org/
Glenbard South HS — 1,400/9-12
23w200 Butterfield Rd 60137 — 630-469-6500
Terri Hanrahan, prin. — Fax 469-6572
Glenbard West HS — 2,300/9-12
670 Crescent Blvd 60137 — 630-469-8600
Dr. Jane Thorsen, prin. — Fax 469-8615
Other Schools – See Carol Stream, Lombard

College of DuPage — Post-Sec.
425 Fawell Blvd 60137 — 630-942-2800

Glenview, Cook, Pop. 44,009
Glenview CCSD 34 — 4,800/PK-8
1401 Greenwood Rd 60026 — 847-998-5000
Mike Nicholson, supt. — Fax 998-1629
www.glenview34.org
Attea MS — 700/6-8
2500 Chestnut Ave 60026 — 847-486-7700
James Woell, prin. — Fax 729-6251
Springman MS — 800/6-8
2701 Central Rd 60025 — 847-998-5020
Dr. Heather Hopkins, prin. — Fax 998-4032

Northfield Township HSD 225 — 4,700/9-12
3801 W Lake Ave 60026 — 847-486-4700
Dr. Michael Riggle, supt. — Fax 486-4733
www.glenbrook225.org
Glenbrook South HS — 2,600/9-12
4000 W Lake Ave 60026 — 847-486-4559
Dr. Brian Wegley, prin. — Fax 486-4462
Other Schools – See Northbrook

Glenview New Church S — 100/PK-10
74 Park Dr 60025 — 847-724-0057
Erik Synnestvedt, prin. — Fax 724-3042

Glenwood, Cook, Pop. 8,797
Brookwood SD 167 — 1,200/PK-8
201 E Glenwood Dyer Rd 60425 — 708-758-5190
Dr. Valorie Moore, supt. — Fax 757-2104
www.brookwood167.org
Brookwood JHS — 300/7-8
201 E Glenwood Lansing Rd 60425 — 708-758-5252
Bethany Lindsay, prin. — Fax 758-3954

Godfrey, Madison, Pop. 17,742

Alvareita's College of Cosmetology — Post-Sec.
3048 Godfrey Rd 62035 — 618-466-8952
Lewis & Clark Community Collogo — Post-Sec.
5800 Godfrey Rd 62035 — 618-468-7000

Golconda, Pope, Pop. 665
Pope County CUSD 1 — 600/PK-12
125 State Highway 146 W 62938 — 618-683-2301
Rob Wright, supt. — Fax 683-5181
www.pope.k12.il.us/
Pope County HS — 100/9-12
125 State Highway 146 W 62938 — 618-633-3071
Judy Kaegi, prin. — Fax 683-9956

Goreville, Johnson, Pop. 1,046
Goreville CUSD 1 — 600/PK-12
201 S Ferne Clyffe Rd 62939 — 618-995-9831
Dr. Steve Webb, supt. — Fax 995-9831
www.gorevilleschools.com
Goreville HS — 200/9-12
201 S Ferne Clyffe Rd 62939 — 618-995-2142
Jeri Miller, prin. — Fax 995-1188

Granite City, Madison, Pop. 29,332
Granite City CUSD 9 — 6,700/PK-12
1947 Adams St 62040 — 618-451-5800
Harry Briggs Ph.D., supt. — Fax 451-6135
www.gcsd9.net
Coolidge MS — 900/6-8
3231 Nameoki Rd 62040 — 618-451-5826
Curt Watters, prin. — Fax 876-5154
Granite City HS — 1,900/9-12
3101 Madison Ave 62040 — 618-451-5808
Jim Greenwald, prin. — Fax 451-6296
Grigsby MS — 600/6-8
3801 Cargill Rd 62040 — 618-931-5544
Kristen Novacich, prin. — Fax 931-5689

Grant Park, Kankakee, Pop. 1,318
Grant Park CUSD 6 — 600/PK-12
PO Box 549 60940 — 815-465-6013
John Palan, supt. — Fax 465-2505
www.grantpark.k12.il.us
Grant Park HS — 200/9-12
PO Box 549 60940 — 815-465-2181
Tom Sanidas, prin. — Fax 465-2505

Granville, Putnam, Pop. 1,410
Putnam County CUSD 535 — 900/PK-12
400 E Silverspoon Ave 61326 — 815-882-2800
Jay McCracken, supt. — Fax 882-2802
www.pcschools535.org/
Putnam County HS — 300/9-12
402 E Silverspoon Ave 61326 — 815-882-2800
Bob Peterson, prin. — Fax 339-2628
Other Schools – See Mc Nabb

Grayslake, Lake, Pop. 20,539
CCSD 46 — 3,700/PK-8
565 Frederick Rd 60030 — 847-223-3650
Ellen Correll, supt. — Fax 223-3695
www.d46.k12.il.us
Grayslake MS — 800/7-8
440 Barron Blvd 60030 — 847-223-3680
Marcus Smith, prin. — Fax 223-3526

Grayslake Community HSD 127 — 2,900/9-12
400 N Lake St 60030 — 847-986-3400
Dr. Catherine Finger, supt. — Fax 231-6838
www.d127.org/
Grayslake Community HS - Central Campus — 1,300/9-12
400 N Lake St 60030 — 847-986-3300
John Bolger, prin. — Fax 223-8690
Grayslake Community HS - North Campus — 1,500/9-12
1925 N Route 83 60030 — 847-986-3100
Dr. James Roscoe, prin. — Fax 986-3023

Lake County HS Technology Campus — 847-223-6681
19525 W Washington St 60030 — Fax 223-7363
Steve Clark, dir.
www.techcampus.org
Lake County HS Technology Campus — Vo/Tech
19525 W Washington St 60030 — 847-223-6681
Steve Clark, dir. — Fax 223-7363

College of Lake County — Post-Sec.
19351 W Washington St 60030 — 847-543-2000
Westlake Christian Academy — 200/PK-12
275 S Lake St 60030 — 847-548-6209
Dr. Michael Healan, prin. — Fax 548-6481

Grayville, White, Pop. 1,656
Grayville CUSD 1 — 300/PK-12
728 W North St 62844 — 618-375-7214
Sarah Emery, supt. — Fax 375-5202
www.grayville.white.k12.il.us

Grayville JSHS 200/6-12
728 W North St 62844 618-375-7114
Sarah Emery, prin. Fax 375-6521

Greenfield, Greene, Pop. 1,063
Greenfield CUSD 10 500/PK-12
311 Mulberry St 62044 217-368-2447
Kevin Bowman, supt. Fax 368-2724
www.greenfieldschools.org/
Greenfield HS 200/9-12
502 East St 62044 217-368-2219
Beth Bettis, prin. Fax 368-2230

Green Valley, Tazewell, Pop. 698
Midwest Central CUSD 191
Supt. — See Manito
Midwest Central MS 300/6-8
121 N Church St 61534 309-352-2300
Jeff Thompson, prin. Fax 352-2903

Greenview, Menard, Pop. 765
Greenview CUSD 200 200/PK-12
PO Box 320 62642 217-968-2295
Gary DePatis, supt. Fax 968-2297
www.menard.k12.il.us/greenviewhs
Greenview JSHS 100/7-12
PO Box 320 62642 217-968-2295
Steve Plaeger, prin. Fax 968-2297

Greenville, Bond, Pop. 6,851
Bond County CUSD 2 2,000/PK-12
1008 N Hena St 62246 618-664-0170
Jeff Stricker, supt. Fax 664-5000
www.bccu2.k12.il.us
Bond City Comm Unit 2 HS 500/9-12
1000 E State Route 140 62246 618-664-1370
Wendy Porter, prin. Fax 664-4786
Greenville JHS 300/6-8
1200 Junior High Dr 62246 618-664-1226
Gary Brauns, prin. Fax 664-5071

Greenville College Post-Sec.
315 E College Ave 62246 618-664-2800

Gridley, McLean, Pop. 1,415
El Paso-Gridley CUSD 11
Supt. — See El Paso
El Paso-Gridley JHS 300/6-8
403 McLean St 61744 309-747-2156
Robby Tomlinson, prin. Fax 747-2938

Griggsville, Pike, Pop. 1,219
Griggsville-Perry CUSD 4 400/PK-12
PO Box 439 62340 217-833-2352
Andrea Allen, supt. Fax 833-2354
griggsvilleperry.org
Griggsville-Perry HS 100/9-12
PO Box 439 62340 217-833-2352
Mark Cheatum, prin. Fax 833-2354
Other Schools – See Perry

Gurnee, Lake, Pop. 30,557
Gurnee SD 56 2,100/PK-8
3706 Florida Ave 60031 847-336-0800
Dr. John Hutton, supt. Fax 336-1110
www.d56.org
Viking MS 600/6-8
4460 Old Grand Ave 60031 847-336-2108
Patrick Jones, prin. Fax 249-0719

Warren Township HSD 121 4,400/9-12
34090 N Almond Rd 60031 847-548-6855
Mary Bates, supt. Fax 548-0564
www.wths.net
Warren Township HS 2,200/9-10
500 N OPlaine Rd 60031 847-662-1400
Greg Meyer, prin. Fax 599-4848
Warren Township HS 2,200/11-12
34090 N Almond Rd 60031 847-662-1400
Patrick Keeley, prin. Fax 548-6444

Woodland CCSD 50 9,000/PK-8
1105 N Hunt Club Rd 60031 847-596-5600
Joy Swoboda, supt. Fax 856-0311
www.dist50.net
Woodland MS 2,300/6-8
7000 Washington St 60031 847-856-3400
Scott Snyder, prin. Fax 856-1306

DeVry University Post-Sec.
1075 Tri State Pkwy Ste 800 60031 847-855-2649

Hamilton, Hancock, Pop. 2,918
Hamilton CCSD 328 600/PK-12
270 N 10th St 62341 866-332-3880
Joe Yurko, supt. Fax 847-3915
www.hhs328.com
Hamilton HS 200/9-12
1100 Keokuk St 62341 866-332-3880
Shelli Jennings, prin. Fax 847-3474
Hamilton JHS 100/7-8
1100 Keokuk St 62341 866-332-3880
Shelli Jennings, prin. Fax 847-3915

Hampshire, Kane, Pop. 5,507
CUSD 300
Supt. — See Carpentersville
Hampshire HS 1,100/9-12
1600 Big Timber Rd 60140 847-792-3500
Chuck Bumbales, prin. Fax 792-3515
Hampshire MS 700/6-8
560 S State St 60140 847-683-2522
Kurt Rohlwing, prin. Fax 683-1030

Hanover, Jo Daviess, Pop. 828
River Ridge CUSD 210 500/PK-12
4141 IL Route 84 S 61041 815-858-9005
Bradley Albrecht, supt. Fax 858-9006
www.riverridge210.org
River Ridge HS 200/9-12
4141 IL Route 84 S 61041 815-858-9005
Michael Foltz, prin. Fax 858-9006
River Ridge MS 100/6-8
4141 IL Route 84 S 61041 815-858-9005
Michael Foltz, prin. Fax 858-9006

Hanover Park, Cook, Pop. 37,237
Keeneyville SD 20 1,600/PK-8
5540 Arlington Dr E 60133 630-894-2250
Dr. Michael Connolly, supt. Fax 894-5187
www.esd20.org
Spring Wood MS 500/6-8
5540 Arlington Dr E 60133 630-893-8900
Craig Barringer, prin. Fax 894-9658

Hanover Park College of Beauty Culture Post-Sec.
1166 E Lake St 60133 630-830-6560

Hardin, Calhoun, Pop. 960
Calhoun CUSD 40 500/K-12
PO Box 387 62047 618-576-2722
Terry Strauch, supt. Fax 576-2641
www.calhoun.k12.il.us
Calhoun HS 200/9-12
PO Box 387 62047 618-576-2229
Kate Seivers, prin. Fax 576-8031

Harrisburg, Saline, Pop. 8,789
Harrisburg CUSD 3 2,200/PK-12
40 S Main St 62946 618-253-7637
Dennis Smith, supt. Fax 253-2095
www.hbg.saline.k12.il.us
Harrisburg HS 600/9-12
333 W College St 62946 618-253-7637
Karen Crank, prin. Fax 252-0994
Harrisburg MS 500/6-8
312 Bulldog Blvd 62946 618-253-7637
John Crabb, prin. Fax 253-2093

Southeastern Illinois College Post-Sec.
3575 College Rd 62946 618-252-5400

Hartsburg, Montgomery, Pop. 309
Hartsburg-Emden CUSD 21 200/PK-12
400 W Front St 62643 217-642-5244
Donald Beard, supt. Fax 642-5333
www.logan.k12.il.us/hartsem.html
Hartsburg-Emden JSHS 200/5-12
400 W Front St 62643 217-642-5244
Terry Wisniewski, prin. Fax 642-5333

Harvard, McHenry, Pop. 9,314
Harvard CUSD 50 2,300/PK-12
401 N Division St 60033 815-943-4022
Dr. Lauri Tobias, supt. Fax 943-4282
www.cusd50.org
Harvard HS 700/9-12
1103 N Jefferson St 60033 815-943-6461
Rob Zielinski, prin. Fax 943-8506
Harvard JHS 500/6-8
1301 Garfield St 60033 815-943-6466
Margaret Segersten, prin. Fax 943-8521

Harvey, Cook, Pop. 24,990
Harvey SD 152 2,500/PK-8
16001 Lincoln Ave 60426 708-333-0300
Dr. Denean Adams, supt. Fax 333-0349
www.harvey152.org
Brooks MS 500/7-8
14741 Wallace St 60426 708-333-6390
Frank Kuzniewski, prin. Fax 333-3177

Thornton Township HSD 205
Supt. — See South Holland
Thornton Township HS 2,200/9-12
15001 Broadway Ave 60426 708-225-4100
Tony Ratliff, prin. Fax 225-5014

West Harvey-Dixmoor SD 147 1,400/PK-8
191 W 155th Pl 60426 708-339-9500
Lela Bridges, supt. Fax 339-9533
www.whd147.org
Other Schools – See Dixmoor

Ingalls Memorial Hospital Post-Sec.
1 Ingalls Dr 60426 708-333-2300

Havana, Mason, Pop. 3,277
Havana CUSD 126 1,100/PK-12
501 S McKinley St 62644 309-543-3384
Dr. Patrick Twomey, supt. Fax 543-3385
mason.k12.il.us/havana126
Havana HS 300/9-12
501 S McKinley St 62644 309-543-3337
Don Willett, prin. Fax 543-6721
Havana JHS 300/5-8
801 E Laurel Ave 62644 309-543-6677
Chris Snider, prin. Fax 543-6678

Hawthorn Woods, Lake, Pop. 7,541
Lake Zurich CUSD 95
Supt. — See Lake Zurich
Lake Zurich MS North Campus 700/6-8
95 Hubbard Ln 60047 847-719-3600
Mark Richter, prin. Fax 719-3620

Hazel Crest, Cook, Pop. 13,848
Hazel Crest SD 152-5 1,100/PK-8
1910 170th St 60429 708-335-0790
Dr. Sheila Harrison-Williams, supt. Fax 335-3520
www.sd1525.org
Other Schools – See Markham

Hebron, McHenry, Pop. 1,203
Alden Hebron SD 19 500/PK-12
9604 Illinois St 60034 815-648-2886
Dr. Debbie Ehlenburg, supt. Fax 648-2339
www.alden-hebron.org
Alden-Hebron HS 100/9-12
9604 Illinois St 60034 815-648-2442
Tim Hayunga, prin. Fax 648-2339
Alden-Hebron MS 100/6-8
9604 Illinois St 60034 815-648-2442
Tim Hayunga, prin. Fax 648-2339

Henry, Marshall, Pop. 2,442
Henry-Senachwine CUSD 5 600/PK-12
1023 College St 61537 309-364-3614
Michael Miller, supt. Fax 364-2990
www.hscusd5.org
Henry-Senachwine Consolidated HS 200/9-12
1023 College St 61537 309-364-2829
Weston Wolven, prin. Fax 364-2990

Herrin, Williamson, Pop. 12,262
Herrin CUSD 4 2,400/PK-12
500 N 10th St 62948 618-988-8024
Dr. Mark Collins, supt. Fax 942-6998
www.herrinunit.org
Herrin HS 700/9-12
700 N 10th St 62948 618-942-6606
Dr. Terry Ryker, prin. Fax 942-7562
Herrin MS 500/6-8
700 S 14th St 62948 618-942-7461
Steve Robinson, prin. Fax 988-8821

Herscher, Kankakee, Pop. 1,577
Herscher CUSD 2 2,000/PK-12
PO Box 504 60941 815-426-2162
Dr. Richard Decman, supt. Fax 426-2872
www.hsd2.k12.il.us
Herscher HS 600/9-12
PO Box 504 60941 815-426-2103
Ron Oloffson, prin. Fax 426-2957

Heyworth, McLean, Pop. 2,807
Heyworth CUSD 4 900/PK-12
522 E Main St 61745 309-473-3727
Dr. Ty Wolf, supt. Fax 473-2220
www.husd4.k12.il.us/
Heyworth JSHS 400/7-12
308 W Cleveland St 61745 309-473-2322
Jeff Asmus, prin. Fax 473-2323

Hickory Hills, Cook, Pop. 13,836
North Palos SD 117
Supt. — See Palos Hills
Conrady JHS 900/6-8
7950 W 97th St 60457 708-233-4500
Andy Anderson, prin. Fax 430-8964

Highland, Madison, Pop. 9,807
Highland CUSD 5 3,100/PK-12
400 Broadway 62249 618-654-2106
Michael Sutton, supt. Fax 654-5424
www.highlandcusd5.org
Highland HS 1,000/9-12
400 Broadway 62249 618-654-7131
Dr. Karen Gauen, prin. Fax 654-6548
Highland MS 500/7-8
400 Broadway 62249 618-651-8800
Erick Baer, prin. Fax 654-1551

Highland Park, Lake, Pop. 29,398
North Shore SD 112 4,500/PK-8
1936 Green Bay Rd 60035 224-765-3000
Dr. David L. Behlow, supt. Fax 765-3083
www.nssd112.org
Edgewood MS 600/6-8
929 Edgewood Rd 60035 224-765-3200
Matt Eriksen, prin. Fax 765-3208
Elm Place MS 500/6-8
2031 Sheridan Rd 60035 224-765-3300
Richard Schroeder, prin. Fax 765-3308
Northwood JHS 500/6-8
945 North Ave 60035 224-765-3600
Jennifer Ferrari, prin. Fax 765-3608

Township HSD 113 3,700/9-12
1040 Park Ave W 60035 224-765-1000
Dr. George Fornero, supt. Fax 765-1060
www.dist113.org
Highland Park HS 2,000/9-12
433 Vine Ave 60035 224-765-2000
Brad Swanson, prin. Fax 765-2700
Other Schools – See Deerfield

Hillsboro, Montgomery, Pop. 6,176
Hillsboro CUSD 3 1,900/PK-12
1311 Vandalia Rd 62049 217-532-2942
David Powell, supt. Fax 532-3137
www.hillsboroschools.net
Hillsboro HS 500/9-12
522 E Tremont St 62049 217-532-2841
Janet Ward, prin. Fax 532-5142
Hillsboro JHS 400/6-8
909 Rountree St 62049 217-532-3742
Mark Fenske, prin. Fax 532-6211

Hillside, Cook, Pop. 8,034
Proviso Township HSD 209
Supt. — See Forest Park
Proviso West HS 2,500/9-12
4701 Harrison St 60162 708-449-6400
Dr. Roudell Kirkwood, prin. Fax 449-3636

Hinckley, DeKalb, Pop. 2,046
Hinckley-Big Rock CUSD 429 700/PK-12
700 E Lincoln Ave 60520 815-286-7578
Travis McGuire, supt. Fax 286-7577
www.hbr429.org
Hinckley-Big Rock HS 200/9-12
700 E Lincoln Ave 60520 815-286-7500
Jay Brickman, prin. Fax 286-7505
Other Schools – See Big Rock

Hines, Cook

Edward Hines Veterans Admin. Hospital Post-Sec.
PO Box 5000 60141 708-216-2153

Hinsdale, DuPage, Pop. 16,548
CCSD 181
Supt. — See Burr Ridge
Hinsdale MS 800/6-8
100 S Garfield Ave 60521 630-887-1370
Ruben Pena, prin. Fax 655-9754

Hinsdale Township HSD 86 | 4,500/9-12
5500 S Grant St 60521 | 630-655-6100
Dr. Nicholas Wahl, supt. | Fax 325-9153
www.hinsdale86.org
Hinsdale Central HS | 2,700/9-12
5500 S Grant St 60521 | 630-570-8000
Michael McGrory, prin. | Fax 887-1362
Other Schools – See Darien

Hinsdale Adventist Academy | 300/PK-12
631 E Hickory St 60521 | 630-323-9211
George Babcock Ed.D., prin. | Fax 323-9237

Hoffman Estates, Cook, Pop. 50,808
Schaumburg CCSD 54
Supt. — See Schaumburg
Eisenhower JHS | 600/7-8
800 Hassell Rd, | 847-357-5500
Kara Prusko, prin. | Fax 357-5501

Township HSD 211
Supt. — See Palatine
Conant HS | 2,000/9-12
700 E Cougar Trl, | 847-755-3600
Timothy Cannon, prin. | Fax 755-3623
Hoffman Estates HS | 1,700/9-12
1100 W Higgins Rd, | 847-755-5600
James Britton, prin. | Fax 755-5623

Valeo Academy | 100/K-12
2500 Beverly Rd 60192 | 847-645-9300
Susan Kennedy, prin. | Fax 645-3986

Homer, Champaign, Pop. 1,182
Heritage CUSD 8 | 400/K-12
512 W 1st St 61849 | 217-896-2041
Dr. Allen Hall, supt. | Fax 896-2338
www.heritage.k12.il.us
Other Schools – See Broadlands

Homer Glen, Will
Homer CCSD 33C | 3,600/PK-8
15733 S Bell Rd, | 708-226-7600
Dr. J. Michel Morrow, supt. | Fax 226-7616
www.homerschools.org
Homer JHS | 800/7-8
15711 S Bell Rd, | 708-226-7800
Troy Mitchell, prin. | Fax 226-7859

Homewood, Cook, Pop. 18,862
Homewood SD 153 | 1,900/PK-8
18205 Aberdeen St 60430 | 708-799-5661
Dr. Dale Mitchell, supt. | Fax 799-1377
www.hsd153.org
Hart JHS | 500/7-8
18220 Morgan St 60430 | 708-799-5544
Michael Klein, prin. | Fax 799-8360

Hoopeston, Vermilion, Pop. 5,322
Hoopeston Area CUSD 11 | 1,300/PK-12
615 E Orange St 60942 | 217-283-6668
Hank Hornbeck, supt. | Fax 283-5431
www.hoopeston.k12.il.us
Hoopeston Area HS | 400/9-12
615 E Orange St 60942 | 217-283-6662
Larry Maynard, prin. | Fax 283-5431
Hoopeston Area MS | 200/7-8
615 E Orange St 60942 | 217-283-6664
Anne Burton, prin. | Fax 283-5431

Hume, Edgar, Pop. 377
Shiloh CUSD 1 | 400/PK-12
21751 N 575th St 61932 | 217-887-2364
Dr. John Wheatley, supt. | Fax 887-2448
www.shiloh1.us
Shiloh JSHS | 200/7-12
21751 N 575th St 61932 | 217-887-2364
Dr. John Wheatley, prin. | Fax 887-2448

Huntley, McHenry, Pop. 23,973
Consolidated SD 158
Supt. — See Algonquin
Huntley HS | 2,200/9-12
13719 Harmony Rd 60142 | 847-659-6600
Scott Rowe, prin. | Fax 659-6620

Hutsonville, Crawford, Pop. 551
Hutsonville CUSD 1 | 400/PK-12
PO Box 218 62433 | 618-563-4912
Julie Kraemer, supt. | Fax 563-9122
hutsonvilletigers.net/
Hutsonville HS | 100/9-12
PO Box 218 62433 | 618-563-4913
Julie Kraemer, prin. | Fax 563-9122

Illiopolis, Sangamon, Pop. 880
Sangamon Valley CUSD 9
Supt. — See Niantic
Sangamon Valley MS | 200/6-8
341 Matilda St 62539 | 217-486-2241
Nancy Dale, prin. | Fax 486-6038

Ina, Jefferson, Pop. 2,329

Rend Lake College | Post-Sec.
468 N Ken Gray Pkwy 62846 | 618-437-5321

Ingleside, See Fox Lake
Big Hollow SD 38 | 1,700/PK-8
26051 W Nippersink Rd 60041 | 847-740-1490
Dr. Christine Demory, supt. | Fax 587-2663
www.bighollow.us
Big Hollow MS | 500/6-8
26051 W Nippersink Rd 60041 | 847-740-5322
Bill Schufreider, prin. | Fax 740-9021

Gavin SD 37 | 900/PK-8
25775 W IL Route 134 60041 | 847-546-2916
Dr. John Ahlemeyer, supt. | Fax 546-9584
www.gavin37.org
Gavin South JHS | 500/PK-K, 6-8
25775 W IL Route 134 60041 | 847-546-9336
Dr. John Ahlemeyer, prin. | Fax 546-9338

Island Lake, McHenry, Pop. 7,988
Wauconda CUSD 118
Supt. — See Wauconda
Matthews MS | 500/6-8
PO Box 920 60042 | 847-526-6210
Robert Taterka, prin. | Fax 526-8918

Itasca, DuPage, Pop. 8,539
Itasca SD 10 | 900/PK-8
200 N Maple St 60143 | 630-773-1232
Dr. Marcia Tornatore, supt. | Fax 773-1342
www.itasca.k12.il.us
Peacock MS | 300/6-8
301 E North St 60143 | 630-773-0335
Brian Faulkner, prin. | Fax 285-7460

Environmental Technical Institute | Post-Sec.
1101 W Thorndale Ave 60143 | 630-285-9100

Jacksonville, Morgan, Pop. 19,003
Jacksonville SD 117 | 3,200/PK-12
516 Jordan St 62650 | 217-243-9411
Dr. Barbara Suelter, supt. | Fax 243-6844
www.jsd117.org
Jacksonville HS | 1,000/9-12
1211 N Diamond St 62650 | 217-243-4384
Mike McGiles, prin. | Fax 245-0445
Turner JHS | 500/7-8
664 Lincoln Ave 62650 | 217-243-3383
Beth Brockschmidt, prin. | Fax 243-3459

Illinois College | Post-Sec.
1101 W College Ave 62650 | 217-245-3000
Illinois School for the Deaf | Post-Sec.
125 S Webster Ave 62650 | 217-479-4200
Illinois School for Visually Impaired | Post-Sec.
658 E State St 62650 | 217-479-4400
MacMurray College | Post-Sec.
447 E College Ave 62650 | 217-479-7000
Mr. John's School of Cosmetology & Nails | Post-Sec.
1429 S Main St 62650 | 217-243-1744
Routt HS | 100/9-12
500 E College Ave 62650 | 217-243-8563
Gale Thoroman, prin. | Fax 243-3138

Jerseyville, Jersey, Pop. 8,349
Jersey CUSD 100 | 2,000/PK-12
100 Lincoln Ave 62052 | 618-498-5561
Lori Franke-Hopkins, supt. | Fax 498-5265
www.jersey100.k12.il.us/
Jersey Community HS | 900/8-12
801 N State St 62052 | 618-498-5521
Lisa Schuenke, prin. | Fax 498-5332

Johnsburg, McHenry, Pop. 6,290
Johnsburg CUSD 12 | 2,300/PK-12
2222 Church St, | 815-385-6916
Dr. Dan Johnson, supt. | Fax 385-4715
www.johnsburg12.org
Johnsburg HS | 800/9-12
2002 W Ringwood Rd, | 815-385-9233
Kevin Shelton, prin. | Fax 344-0451
Johnsburg JHS | 700/5-8
2220 Church St, | 815-385-6210
Nancy Hurckes, prin. | Fax 344-7106

Johnston City, Williamson, Pop. 3,492
Johnston City CUSD 1 | 1,200/PK-12
1103 Monroe Ave 62951 | 618-983-8021
Terry Milt, supt. | Fax 983-6034
www.jcindians.org
Johnston City HS | 400/9-12
1500 Jefferson Ave 62951 | 618-983-4700
Danielle Barter, prin. | Fax 983-6812

Joliet, Will, Pop. 145,165
Joliet SD 86 | 10,800/PK-8
420 N Raynor Ave 60435 | 815-740-3196
Charles Coleman Ed.D., supt. | Fax 740-6520
www.joliet86.org
Dirksen JHS | 600/6-8
203 S Midland Ave 60436 | 815-729-1566
Kimberly Pfoutz, prin. | Fax 744-2346
Gompers JHS | 800/6-8
1501 Copperfield Ave 60432 | 815-727-5276
Constance Russell, prin. | Fax 726-5341
Hufford JHS | 1,000/6-8
1125 N Larkin Ave 60435 | 815-725-3540
Anna White, prin. | Fax 744-5974
Washington JHS & Academy | 700/6-8
402 Richards St 60433 | 815-727-5271
Michael Latting, prin. | Fax 740-5451

Joliet Township HSD 204 | 5,700/9-12
300 Caterpillar Dr 60436 | 815-727-6970
Dr. Cheryl McCarthy, supt. | Fax 727-1277
www.jths.org
Joliet Central HS | 2,900/9-12
201 E Jefferson St 60432 | 815-727-6740
John Randich, prin. | Fax 727-6824
Joliet Township Alternative HS | 100/Alt
110 Collins St 60432 | 815-727-6810
LaTanya Harris, prin.
Joliet West HS | 2,700/9-12
401 N Larkin Ave 60435 | 815-727-6940
Teresa Gibson, prin. | Fax 744-3070

Plainfield CCSD 202
Supt. — See Plainfield
Aux Sable MS | 1,200/6-8
2001 Wildspring Pkwy 60431 | 815-439-7092
Sharon Alexander, prin. | Fax 577-9476

Joliet Catholic Academy | 900/9-12
1200 N Larkin Ave 60435 | 815-741-0500
Jeffrey Budz, prin. | Fax 741-9530
Joliet Junior College | Post-Sec.
1215 Houbolt Rd 60431 | 815-729-9020
Professional Choice Hair Design Academy | Post-Sec.
2719 W Jefferson St 60435 | 815-741-8224
University of St. Francis | Post-Sec.
500 Wilcox St 60435 | 800-735-7500

Joppa, Massac, Pop. 354
Joppa-Maple Grove CUSD 38 | 300/PK-12
PO Box 10 62953 | 618-543-9023
Steven Ptacek, supt. | Fax 543-9264
joppa38.com
Joppa JSHS | 100/7-12
PO Box 10 62953 | 618-543-7589
Vickie Artman, prin. | Fax 543-9264

Joy, Mercer, Pop. 416
Mercer County SD 404
Supt. — See Aledo
Mercer County JHS | 200/7-8
203 N Washington St 61260 | 309-584-4174
Robert Reed, prin. | Fax 584-4257

Junction, Gallatin, Pop. 129
Gallatin CUSD 7 | 800/PK-12
5175 Highway 13 62954 | 618-272-3821
Lucinda Schmitt, supt. | Fax 272-4101
Gallatin HS | 200/9-12
5175 Highway 13 62954 | 618-272-5141
Jeff Herrmann, prin. | Fax 272-4101
Gallatin JHS | 200/5-8
5175 Highway 13 62954 | 618-272-7341
Chris Fromm, prin. | Fax 272-4101

Justice, Cook, Pop. 12,733
Indian Springs SD 109 | 2,800/PK-8
7540 S 86th Ave 60458 | 708-496-8700
Dr. Jon Nebor, supt. | Fax 496-8641
www.isd109.org
Wilkins JHS | 600/7-8
8001 S 82nd Ave 60458 | 708-496-8708
Joseph Porrey, prin. | Fax 728-3114

Kankakee, Kankakee, Pop. 26,896
Kankakee SD 111 | 5,200/PK-12
240 Warren Ave 60901 | 815-802-7700
Dr. Linda Mitchell, supt. | Fax 936-8944
www.k111.k12.il.us
Kankakee HS | 1,200/9-12
1200 W Jeffery St 60901 | 815-802-5500
Matthew Glenn, prin. | Fax 933-9149
Kankakee JHS | 700/7-8
2250 E Crestwood St 60901 | 815-802-5700
Charles Hensley, prin. | Fax 935-7272

Bishop McNamara HS | 400/9-12
550 W Brookmont Blvd 60901 | 815-932-7413
Terry Granger, prin. | Fax 932-0926
Grace Baptist Academy | 200/PK-12
2499 Waldron Rd 60901 | 815-939-4579
Stephen Bull, admin. | Fax 939-1334
Kankakee Community College | Post-Sec.
100 College Dr 60901 | 815-802-8100
Kankakee Trinity Academy | 200/PK-12
1580 Butterfield Trl 60901 | 815-935-8080
Brad Prairie, prin. | Fax 935-0280

Kansas, Edgar, Pop. 784
Kansas CUSD 3 | 300/PK-12
PO Box 350 61933 | 217-948-5174
Chris Long, supt. | Fax 948-5577
www.kansas.k12.il.us
Kansas JSHS | 100/7-12
PO Box 350 61933 | 217-948-5175
Dwight Stricklin, prin. | Fax 948-5577

Kempton, Ford, Pop. 229
Tri-Point CUSD 6-J | 500/PK-12
PO Box 128 60946 | 815-253-6299
Steve Fink, supt. | Fax 253-6298
www.tripointschools.org
Other Schools – See Cullom, Piper City

Kewanee, Henry, Pop. 12,667
Kewanee CUSD 229 | 1,700/PK-12
210 Lyle St 61443 | 309-853-3341
Christopher Sullens Ed.D., supt. | Fax 852-5504
www.kcud229.org/
Central JHS | 400/4-8
215 E Central Blvd 61443 | 309-853-4290
Jason Anderson, prin. | Fax 853-3195
Kewanee HS | 500/9-12
1211 E 3rd St 61443 | 309-853-3328
James Bryan, prin. | Fax 854-0210

Wethersfield CUSD 230 | 700/PK-12
439 Willard St 61443 | 309-853-4860
Shane Kazubowski, supt. | Fax 856-7976
go-geese.net
Wethersfield JSHS | 300/7-12
439 Willard St 61443 | 309-853-4205
Jeremiah Johnston, prin. | Fax 856-7976

Kincaid, Christian, Pop. 1,483
South Fork SD 14 | 400/PK-12
PO Box 20 62540 | 217-237-4333
Ron Graham, supt. | Fax 237-4370
www.southforkschools.com/
South Fork JSHS | 200/5-12
PO Box 20 62540 | 217-237-4333
Chris Clark, prin. | Fax 237-4370

Kinderhook, Pike, Pop. 216
Western CUSD 12
Supt. — See Barry
Western JHS | 100/6-8
PO Box 189 62345 | 217-432-8324
Martin Hull, prin. | Fax 432-8003

Kinmundy, Marion, Pop. 794
South Central CUSD 401 700/PK-12
PO Box 189 62854 618-547-3414
Rick Batchelor, supt. Fax 547-7790
southcentralschools.org/
South Central MS 200/5-8
PO Box 40 62854 618-547-7734
Greg Grinestaff, prin. Fax 547-7441
Other Schools – See Farina

Kirkland, DeKalb, Pop. 1,732
Hiawatha CUSD 426 400/PK-12
PO Box 428 60146 815-522-6676
Dr. Sarah Willey, supt. Fax 522-6619
www.hiawatha426.k12.il.us
Hiawatha HS 100/9-12
PO Box 428 60146 815-522-3335
Mark Zych, prin. Fax 522-9918

Knoxville, Knox, Pop. 2,888
Knoxville CUSD 202 1,100/PK-12
809 E Main St 61448 309-289-2328
Steve Wilder, supt. Fax 289-9614
knoxville202.bluebullets.org/
Knoxville HS 300/9-12
600 E Main St 61448 309-289-2324
Chad Bahnks, prin. Fax 289-9466
Knoxville JHS 300/5-8
701 E Mill St 61448 309-289-4126
S. Matt Graham, prin. Fax 289-4128

La Grange, Cook, Pop. 15,333
La Grange SD 105 1,200/PK-8
701 7th Ave 60525 708-482-2700
Glenn Schlichting Ph.D., supt. Fax 482-2727
www.d105.net
Gurrie MS 300/7-8
1001 S Spring Ave 60525 708-482-2720
Edmond Hood, prin. Fax 482-2724

Lyons Township HSD 204 3,800/9-12
100 S Brainard Ave 60525 708-579-6451
Timothy Kilrea, supt. Fax 579-6768
www.lths.net
Lyons Township HS North Campus 1,900/11-12
100 S Brainard Ave 60525 708-579-6300
Dave Franson, prin. Fax 579-3187
Other Schools – See Western Springs

Lagrange Hlds, Cook
La Grange Highlands SD 106 900/PK-8
1750 W Plainfield Rd 60525 708-246-3085
Dr. Robert Dyer, supt. Fax 246-0220
www.district106.net
Highlands MS 300/6-8
1850 W Plainfield Rd 60525 708-579-6890
Michael Papierski, prin. Fax 485-3593

Acacia Academy 100/3-12
6425 Willow Springs Rd 60525 708-579-9040
Kathryn Fouks, prin.

La Grange Park, Cook, Pop. 13,395
La Grange SD 102 3,000/PK-8
333 N Park Rd 60526 708-482-2400
Dr. Warren Shillingburg, supt. Fax 482-2402
www.dist102.k12.il.us
Park JHS 600/7-8
325 N Park Rd 60526 708-482-2500
Phil Abraham, prin. Fax 352-1170

Nazareth Academy 800/9-12
1209 W Ogden Ave 60526 708-354-0061
Deborah Tracy, prin. Fax 354-0109

La Harpe, Hancock, Pop. 1,230
La Harpe Community SD 347 200/PK-8
404 W Main St 61450 217-659-7739
Jo Campbell, supt. Fax 659-7730
laharpeeagles.org/
La Harpe JHS 100/6-8
404 W Main St 61450 217-659-3713
Lila McKeown, prin. Fax 659-7730

Lake Bluff, Lake, Pop. 5,647
Lake Bluff ESD 65 900/K-8
900 W North Shore Dr # 220 60044 847-234-9400
Jean Sophie, supt. Fax 234-6237
www.lb65.org/
Lake Bluff MS 300/6-8
31 E Sheridan Pl 60044 847-234-9407
Nathan Blackmer, prin. Fax 615-9144

Lake Forest, Lake, Pop. 19,130
Lake Forest Community HSD 115 1,700/9-12
300 S Waukegan Rd 60045 847-604-7401
Michael Simeck, supt. Fax 234-2372
www.lfhs.org/
Lake Forest HS 1,700/9-12
1285 N McKinley Rd 60045 847-582-7315
Jay Hoffmann, prin. Fax 582-7797

Lake Forest SD 67 2,000/K-8
300 S Waukegan Rd 60045 847-235-9657
Michael Simeck, supt. Fax 234-5132
www.lf67.org
Deer Path MS - West 500/7-8
155 W Deerpath 60045 847-604-7400
Renee DeVore, prin. Fax 234-2389

Lake Forest Academy 400/9-12
1500 W Kennedy Rd 60045 847-234-3210
Dr. John Strudwick, head sch Fax 615-3202
Lake Forest College Post-Sec.
555 N Sheridan Rd 60045 847-234-3100
Lake Forest Graduate Sch. of Management Post-Sec.
1905 W Field Ct 60045 847-234-5005
School of St. Mary MS 300/4-8
185 E Illinois Rd 60045 847-234-0371
Dr. Venette Biancalana, admin. Fax 234-9593

Woodlands Academy Sacred Heart 200/9-12
760 E Westleigh Rd 60045 847-234-4300
Madonna Edmunds, hdmstr. Fax 234-4348

Lake in the Hills, McHenry, Pop. 28,527
Consolidated SD 158
Supt. — See Algonquin
Marlowe MS 1,300/6-8
9625 Haligus Rd 60156 847-659-4700
Adam Zehr, prin. Fax 659-4720

Lake Villa, Lake, Pop. 8,603
Community HSD 117 2,700/9-12
1625 Deep Lake Rd Ste A 60046 847-838-7100
Jim McKay, supt. Fax 395-7553
www.d117.org
Lakes Community HS 1,400/9-12
1600 Eagle Way 60046 847-838-7100
Stephen Plank, prin. Fax 395-7553
Other Schools – See Antioch

Lake Villa CCSD 41 3,200/PK-8
131 McKinley Ave 60046 847-356-2385
Dr. John VanPelt, supt. Fax 356-2670
www.district41.org
Palombi MS 800/7-8
133 McKinley Ave 60046 847-356-2118
Mary Jordan, prin. Fax 356-0833

Lake Zurich, Lake, Pop. 19,359
Lake Zurich CUSD 95 6,100/PK-12
400 S Old Rand Rd 60047 847-438-2831
Dr. Mike Egan, supt. Fax 438-6702
www.lz95.org
Lake Zurich HS 2,200/9-12
300 Church St 60047 847-438-5155
Kim Kolze, prin. Fax 438-5989
Lake Zurich MS South Campus 700/6-8
435 W Cuba Rd 60047 847-540-7070
Dave Gardner, prin. Fax 540-9438
Other Schools – See Hawthorn Woods

Quentin Road Christian S 200/PK-12
60 Quentin Rd 60047 847-438-4494
Karen Scudder, admin.

La Moille, Bureau, Pop. 722
La Moille CUSD 303 300/PK-12
PO Box 470 61330 815-638-2018
Colette Sutton, supt. Fax 638-2392
www.orgsites.com/il/lamoilleschools
Allen JHS 100/4-8
PO Box 470 61330 815-638-2233
James Brandau, prin. Fax 638-2886
La Moille HS 100/9-12
PO Box 440 61330 815-638-2144
Colette Sutton, prin. Fax 638-2392

Lanark, Carroll, Pop. 1,444
Eastland CUSD 308 700/PK-12
200 S School St 61046 815-493-6301
Dr. Mark Hansen, supt. Fax 493-6303
www.eastland308.com
Eastland HS 200/9-12
500 S School Dr 61046 815-493-6341
Monica Burkholder, prin. Fax 493-6343
Other Schools – See Shannon

Lansing, Cook, Pop. 27,924
Lansing SD 158 2,400/PK-8
18300 Greenbay Ave 60438 708-474-6700
Cecilia Heiberger, supt. Fax 474-9976
www.d158.net
Memorial JHS 800/6-8
2721 Ridge Rd 60438 708-474-2383
Duane Schupp, prin. Fax 474-9976

Sunnybrook SD 171 1,000/PK-8
19266 Burnham Ave 60438 708-895-0750
Dr. Barbara West, supt. Fax 895-8580
www.sd171.org
Heritage MS 500/5-8
19250 Burnham Ave 60438 708-895-0790
Michael Keelan, prin. Fax 895-8580

Thornton Fractional Township HSD 215
Supt. — See Calumet City
Thornton Fractional South HS 2,000/9-12
18500 Burnham Ave 60438 708-585-2000
Judy Whalen, prin. Fax 585-2009

American School Post-Sec.
2200 E 170th St 60438 708-418-2800
Illiana Christian HS 600/9-12
2261 Indiana Ave 60438 708-474-0515
Peter Boonstra, prin. Fax 474-0581
Luther East HS 100/9-12
2750 Glenwood Lansing Rd 60438 708-895-8441
Dale Cooper M.Ed., prin. Fax 895-5220

La Salle, LaSalle, Pop. 9,462
La Salle ESD 122 1,000/PK-8
1165 Saint Vincents Ave 61301 815-223-0786
Daniel Marenda, supt. Fax 223-8740
www.lasalleschools.net
Lincoln JHS 300/6-8
1165 Saint Vincents Ave 61301 815-223-0786
Brian DeBernardi, prin. Fax 223-8740

La Salle-Peru Township HSD 120 1,200/9-12
541 Chartres St 61301 815-223-1721
Steven Wrobleski, supt. Fax 223-3444
www.lphs.net
La Salle-Peru Township HS 1,200/9-12
541 Chartres St 61301 815-223-1721
Deb Nelson, prin. Fax 223-3444

Educators of Beauty Post-Sec.
122 Wright St 61301 815-223-7326

Lawrenceville, Lawrence, Pop. 4,300
Lawrence County CUSD 20 1,200/PK-12
1802 Cedar St 62439 618-943-2326
Charles Stegall, supt. Fax 943-4092
www.cusd20.com
Lawrenceville HS 400/9-12
503 8th St 62439 618-943-3389
Paul Higginbotham, prin. Fax 943-4925
Parkview JHS 300/6-8
1802 Cedar St 62439 618-943-2327
Jeremy Brush, prin. Fax 943-4092

Lebanon, Saint Clair, Pop. 4,302
Lebanon CUSD 9 500/PK-12
200 W Schuetz St 62254 618-537-4611
Patrick Keeney, supt. Fax 537-9588
lcusd9.org/
Lebanon HS 200/6-12
200 W Schuetz St 62254 618-537-4423
Leigh Jackson, prin. Fax 537-9588

McKendree University Post-Sec.
701 College Rd 62254 618-537-4481

Leland, LaSalle, Pop. 971
Leland CUSD 1 300/PK-12
370 N Main St 60531 815-495-3821
Colette Sutton, supt. Fax 495-4611
leland1.org
Leland HS 100/9-12
370 N Main St 60531 815-495-3231
Jodi Moore, prin. Fax 495-4611

Lemont, DuPage, Pop. 15,866
Lemont Township HSD 210 1,400/9-12
800 Porter St 60439 630-257-5838
Dr. Mary Ticknor, supt. Fax 257-7603
www.lhs210.net
Lemont HS 1,400/9-12
800 Porter St 60439 630-257-5838
Dr. Tom Trengove, prin. Fax 243-0310

Lemont-Bromberek Combined SD 113A 2,000/K-8
16100 W 127th St 60439 630-257-2286
Dr. Susan Birkenmaier, supt. Fax 243-3005
www.sd113a.org/
Old Quarry MS 900/5-8
16100 W 127th St 60439 630-257-2286
Dr. William Caron, prin. Fax 243-3004

Mt. Assisi Academy 200/9-12
13860 Main St 60439 630-257-7844
Sr. Mary Werner, prin. Fax 257-6362

Lena, Stephenson, Pop. 2,887
Lena Winslow CUSD 202 900/PK-12
401 Fremont St 61048 815-369-3100
Dr. Tom Chiles, supt. Fax 369-3102
www.le-wln.net
Lena-Winslow HS 300/9-12
516 Fremont St 61048 815-369-3115
Mark Kuehl, prin. Fax 369-3165
Lena-Winslow JHS 200/6-8
517 Fremont St 61048 815-369-3114
Andrew Lobdell, prin. Fax 369-3162

Le Roy, McLean, Pop. 3,530
Le Roy CUSD 2 800/PK-12
600 E Pine St 61752 309-962-4211
Gary Tipsord, supt. Fax 962-9312
www.leroy.k12.il.us/
Le Roy HS 300/9-12
505 E Center St 61752 309-962-2911
Steve Reschke, prin. Fax 962-8421
Le Roy JHS 100/7-8
505 E Center St 61752 309-962-2911
Steve Reschke, prin. Fax 962-8421

Lewistown, Fulton, Pop. 2,366
Lewistown SD 97 700/PK-12
15501 E Avenue L 61542 309-547-5826
Bill King, supt. Fax 547-5235
www.cusd97.fulton.k12.il.us
Central MS, 15501 E Avenue L 61542 300/4-8
Jan Braun, prin. 309-547-2231
Lewistown Community HS 200/9-12
15205 N State 100 Hwy 61542 309-547-2288
Nick Roscetti, prin. Fax 547-9870

Lexington, McLean, Pop. 2,036
Lexington CUSD 7 500/PK-12
202 E Greenwich St 61753 309-365-4141
Curt Nettles, supt. Fax 365-7381
www.lexington.k12.il.us
Lexington HS 200/9-12
202 E Greenwich St 61753 309-365-2711
Jim Allen, prin. Fax 365-5032
Lexington JHS 100/7-8
202 E Greenwich St 61753 309-365-2711
Jim Allen, prin.

Liberty, Adams, Pop. 512
Liberty CUSD 2 700/PK-12
505 N Park St 62347 217-645-3433
Kelle Bunch, supt. Fax 645-3241
Liberty HS 300/7-12
505 N Park St 62347 217-645-3433
Karen Carper, prin. Fax 645-3389

Libertyville, Lake, Pop. 20,013
Community HSD 128
Supt. — See Vernon Hills
Libertyville HS 2,000/9-12
708 W Park Ave 60048 847-327-7000
Dr. Marina Scott, prin. Fax 367-2573

Libertyville SD 70 | 2,500/PK-8
1381 Lake St 60048 | 847-362-9695
Dr. Guy Schumacher, supt. | Fax 362-3003
www.d70schools.org
Highland MS | 900/6-8
310 W Rockland Rd 60048 | 847-362-9020
Jon Hallmark, prin. | Fax 362-0870

Lincoln, Logan, Pop. 14,271
Lincoln Community HSD 404 | 900/9-12
1000 Primm Rd 62656 | 217-732-4131
Robert Bagby, supt. | Fax 735-3963
www.lchs.k12.il.us
Lincoln Community HS | 900/9-12
1000 Primm Rd 62656 | 217-732-4131
Todd Poelker, prin. | Fax 735-3963

Lincoln ESD 27 | 1,300/PK-8
304 8th St 62656 | 217-732-2522
Dr. Mary Ahillen, supt. | Fax 732-2198
lincoln27.homestead.com/
Lincoln JHS | 400/6-8
208 Broadway St 62656 | 217-732-3535
Kent Froebe, prin. | Fax 732-2685

Lincolnland Technical Education Center
1000 Primm Rd 62656 | 217-732-4131
Bret Hitchings, dir. | Fax 735-3963
Lincolnland Technical Education Center | Vo/Tech
1000 Primm Rd 62656 | 217-732-4131
Bret Hitchings, dir. | Fax 735-3963

Lincoln Christian University | Post-Sec.
100 Campus View Dr 62656 | 217-732-3168
Lincoln College | Post-Sec.
300 Keokuk St 62656 | 217-732-3155

Lincolnshire, Lake, Pop. 7,186
Adlai E. Stevenson HSD 125 | 4,200/9-12
2 Stevenson Dr 60069 | 847-415-4000
Dr. Eric Twadell, supt. | Fax 634-0239
www.d125.org/
Stevenson HS | 4,200/9-12
1 Stevenson Dr 60069 | 847-415-4106
Troy Gobble, prin. | Fax 634-7309

Lincolnshire-Prairieview SD 103 | 1,600/PK-8
1370 N Riverwoods Rd 60069 | 847-295-4030
Scott Warren, supt. | Fax 295-9196
www.district103.k12.il.us
Wright JHS | 800/5-8
1370 N Riverwoods Rd 60069 | 847-295-1560
Margaret St. Claire, prin. | Fax 295-7136

Lincolnwood, Cook, Pop. 12,270
Lincolnwood SD 74 | 1,200/PK-8
6950 N East Prairie Rd 60712 | 847-675-8234
Dr. Joseph F. Bailey, supt. | Fax 675-8244
www.sd74.org
Lincoln Hall MS | 400/6-8
6855 N Crawford Ave 60712 | 847-675-8240
James Parker, prin. | Fax 675-8124

Lindenhurst, Lake, Pop. 14,182
Millburn CCSD 24
Supt. — See Wadsworth
Millburn West MS | 200/6-8
640 Freedom Way 60046 | 847-245-1600
Jake Jorgenson, prin. | Fax 265-8198

Lisle, DuPage, Pop. 21,980
Lisle CUSD 202 | 1,600/PK-12
5211 Center Ave 60532 | 630-493-8000
Keith Filipiak, supt. | Fax 971-4054
www.lisle.dupage.k12.il.us/
Lisle HS | 500/9-12
1800 Short St 60532 | 630-493-8300
Pete Sullivan, prin. | Fax 968-0182
Lisle JHS | 300/6-8
5207 Center Ave 60532 | 630-493-8200
Timothy Pociask, prin. | Fax 493-8209

Naperville CUSD 203
Supt. — See Naperville
Kennedy JHS | 1,000/6-8
2929 Green Trails Dr 60532 | 630-420-3220
Brian Valek, prin. | Fax 420-6960

Benedictine University | Post-Sec.
5700 College Rd 60532 | 630-829-6000
Benet Academy | 1,300/9-12
2200 Maple Ave 60532 | 630-719-2782
Stephen Marth, prin. | Fax 719-2849

Litchfield, Montgomery, Pop. 6,861
Litchfield CUSD 12 | 1,500/PK-12
1702 N State St 62056 | 217-324-2157
Chad Allison, supt. | Fax 324-2158
www.litchfield.k12.il.us
Litchfield HS | 500/9-12
1705 N State St 62056 | 217-324-3955
Mark Hunt, prin. | Fax 324-5851
Litchfield MS | 300/6-8
1701 N State St 62056 | 217-324-4668
Andrea Lee, prin. | Fax 324-5693

Tri-County Beauty Academy | Post-Sec.
219 N State St 62056 | 217-324-9062

Lockport, Will, Pop. 24,568
Lockport SD 91 | 600/K-8
808 Adams St 60441 | 815-838-0737
Donna Gray, supt. | Fax 834-4339
www.d91.net/
Kelvin Grove MS | 400/4-8
808 Adams St 60441 | 815-838-0737
John Jennings, prin. | Fax 834-4339

Lockport Township HSD 205 | 2,800/9-12
1323 E 7th St 60441 | 815-588-8100
Dr. Todd Wernet, supt. | Fax 588-8109
www.lths.org
Lockport Township HS Central Campus | 9-9
1222 S Jefferson St 60441 | 815-588-8200
Kerri Green, prin. | Fax 588-8209
Lockport Township HS East Campus | 2,800/10-12
1333 E 7th St 60441 | 815-588-8300
Dennis Hicks, prin. | Fax 588-8309

Will County SD 92 | 1,800/PK-8
708 N State St 60441 | 815-838-8031
Dr. Gary Peck, supt. | Fax 838-8034
www.d92.org
Oak Prairie JHS | 600/6-8
15161 S Gougar Rd, | 815-836-2724
Mark Murray, prin. | Fax 834-2178

Lombard, DuPage, Pop. 42,433
Glenbard Township HSD 87
Supt. — See Glen Ellyn
Glenbard East HS | 2,500/9-12
1014 S Main St 60148 | 630-627-9250
Josh Chambers, prin. | Fax 627-9264

Lombard SD 44 | 3,000/PK-8
150 W Madison St 60148 | 630-827-4400
James Blanche, supt. | Fax 620-3798
www.sd44.org/
Glenn Westlake MS | 1,000/6-8
1514 S Main St 60148 | 630-827-4500
Philip Wieczorek, prin. | Fax 620-3791

College Preparatory S of America | 500/PK-12
331 W Madison St 60148 | 630-889-8000
Farhat Siddiqui, prin. | Fax 889-8012
Illinois Center for Broadcasting | Post-Sec.
455 Eisenhower Ln S Ste 200 60148 | 630-916-1700
Montini Catholic HS | 700/9-12
19W070 16th St 60148 | 630-627-6930
Maryann O'Neill, prin. | Fax 627-0537
National University of Health Sciences | Post-Sec.
200 E Roosevelt Rd 60148 | 630-629-2000
Northern Seminary | Post-Sec.
660 E Butterfield Rd 60148 | 630-620-2180

London Mills, Fulton, Pop. 391
Spoon River Valley CUSD 4 | 400/PK-12
35265 N IL Route 97 61544 | 309-778-2204
K. Scot Reynolds, supt. | Fax 778-2655
www.spoon-river.k12.il.us
Spoon River Valley HS | 100/9-12
35265 N IL Route 97 61544 | 309-778-2201
Chris Janssen, prin. | Fax 778-2655
Spoon River Valley JHS | 100/7-8
35265 N IL Route 97 61544 | 309-778-2201
Chris Janssen, prin. | Fax 778-2655

Long Grove, Lake, Pop. 7,912
Kildeer Countryside CCSD 96
Supt. — See Buffalo Grove
Woodlawn MS | 600/6-8
6362 Gilmer Rd 60047 | 847-353-8500
Greg Grana, prin. | Fax 949-8237

Louisville, Clay, Pop. 1,135
North Clay CUSD 25 | 700/PK-12
PO Box C 62858 | 618-665-3358
Monty Aldrich, supt. | Fax 665-3893
members.wabash.net/~northclay/
North Clay Community HS | 200/9-12
PO Box 220 62858 | 618-665-3102
Julie Healy, prin. | Fax 665-4270

Lovejoy, Saint Clair, Pop. 732
Brooklyn Unit SD 188 | 200/PK-12
PO Box 250 62059 | 618-271-1028
Dr. Raelynn Parks, supt. | Fax 271-9108
www.lovejoy.stclair.k12.il.us
Lovejoy MS | 50/6-8
PO Box 250 62059 | 618-271-1014
Dr. Raelynn Parks, prin. | Fax 271-9108
Lovejoy Technology Academy | 50/9-12
PO Box 250 62059 | 618-271-1014
Dr. Raelynn Parks, prin. | Fax 271-9108

Loves Park, Winnebago, Pop. 23,555
Harlem Unit SD 122
Supt. — See Machesney Park
Harlem MS | 1,100/7-8
735 Windsor Rd 61111 | 815-654-4510
John Cusimano, prin. | Fax 654-4540

Lyons, Cook, Pop. 10,580
Lyons SD 103 | 2,300/K-8
4100 Joliet Ave 60534 | 708-783-4100
Dr. Mary Jo Vladika, supt. | Fax 780-9725
www.sd103.com/
Washington MS | 700/6-8
8101 Ogden Ave 60534 | 708-783-4200
Johnny Billingsley, prin. | Fax 780-9757

Mc Henry, McHenry, Pop. 26,740
McHenry CCSD 15 | 4,900/PK-8
1011 N Green St 60050 | 815-385-7210
R. Alan Hoffman Ed.D., supt. | Fax 344-7121
www.d15.org
McHenry MS | 800/6-8
2120 W Lincoln Rd 60051 | 815-385-2522
Mike Glover, prin. | Fax 578-2101
Parkland S | 800/6-8
1802 N Ringwood Rd 60050 | 815-385-8810
Mike Adams, prin. | Fax 363-5023

McHenry Community HSD 156 | 2,500/9-12
4716 W Crystal Lake Rd 60050 | 815-385-7900
Gina Swinney, supt. | Fax 344-7153
www.dist156.org
McHenry HS - East | 900/9-12
1012 N Green St 60050 | 815-385-1145
Lynn Schnelker, prin. | Fax 363-8435
McHenry HS - West | 1,600/9-12
4724 W Crystal Lake Rd 60050 | 815-385-7077
Dr. Michael Roberts, prin. | Fax 363-8651

Montini MS | 200/4-8
1405 N Richmond Rd 60050 | 815-385-1022
Sheila Murphy, prin. | Fax 363-7536

Machesney Park, Winnebago, Pop. 23,071
Harlem Unit SD 122 | 7,300/PK-12
8605 N 2nd St 61115 | 815-654-4500
Dr. Julie Morris, supt. | Fax 654-4600
www.harlem122.org
Harlem HS | 2,500/9-12
1 Huskie Cir 61115 | 815-654-4511
Joe Hazen, prin. | Fax 654-4525
Other Schools – See Loves Park

Mackinaw, Tazewell, Pop. 1,936
Deer Creek-Mackinaw CUSD 701 | 1,100/PK-12
401 E 5th St 61755 | 309-359-8965
Scott Dearman, supt. | Fax 359-5291
www.deemack.org/
Deer Creek-Mackinaw HS | 300/9-12
401 E 5th St 61755 | 309-359-4421
Mary Lanier, prin. | Fax 359-3125
Deer Creek-Mackinaw JHS | 200/7-8
102 E 5th St 61755 | 309-359-4321
Michele Jacobs, prin. | Fax 359-4015

Mc Leansboro, Hamilton, Pop. 2,863
Hamilton County CUSD 10 | 1,300/PK-12
PO Box 369 62859 | 618-643-2328
Jeff Fetcho, supt. | Fax 643-2015
www.unit10.com
Hamilton County JSHS | 500/7-12
1 Fox Ln 62859 | 618-643-2328
Jason Ronna, prin. | Fax 643-2307

Mc Nabb, Putnam, Pop. 278
Putnam County CUSD 535
Supt. — See Granville
Putnam County JHS | 200/6-8
13183 N 350th Ave 61335 | 815-882-2800
Carl Carlson, prin. | Fax 882-2299

Macomb, McDonough, Pop. 18,862
Macomb CUSD 185 | 1,900/PK-12
323 W Washington St 61455 | 309-833-4161
Dr. Alene Reuschel, supt. | Fax 836-2133
macomb185.org/
Macomb HS | 600/9-12
1525 S Johnson St 61455 | 309-837-2331
John Rumley, prin. | Fax 836-1034
Macomb JHS | 300/7-8
1525 S Johnson St 61455 | 309-833-2074
Dana Isackson, prin. | Fax 836-1034

McDonough District Hospital | Post-Sec.
525 E Grant St 61455 | 309-833-4101
Western Illinois University | Post-Sec.
1 University Cir 61455 | 309-295-1414

Macon, Macon, Pop. 1,126
Meridian CUSD 15 | 1,100/PK-12
PO Box 347 62544 | 217-764-5269
Dr. Frank Meyer, supt. | Fax 764-5291
www.meridian.k12.il.us
Meridian HS | 300/9-12
PO Box 380 62544 | 217-764-5233
Jack Blickensderfer, prin. | Fax 764-5282
Other Schools – See Blue Mound

Madison, Madison, Pop. 3,816
Madison CUSD 12 | 500/PK-12
602 Farrish St 62060 | 618-877-1712
Evelyn Kelly, supt. | Fax 877-2690
www.madisoncusd12.org/
Madison HS | 200/9-12
600 Farrish St 62060 | 618-876-7010
Rob Miller, prin. | Fax 877-2694
Madison JHS | 100/6-8
600 Farrish St 62060 | 618-876-6409
Rob Miller, prin. | Fax 877-2693
Madison Student Support Center | 50/Alt
1003 Farrish St 62060 | 618-876-6409
Tracy Brown, dir. | Fax 877-2693

Mahomet, Champaign, Pop. 7,188
Mahomet-Seymour CUSD 3 | 2,900/PK-12
PO Box 229 61853 | 217-586-4995
Rick Johnston, supt. | Fax 586-5834
www.ms.k12.il.us
Mahomet-Seymour HS | 900/9-12
PO Box 1098 61853 | 217-586-4962
Shannon Cheek, prin. | Fax 586-6844
Mahomet-Seymour JHS | 700/6-8
PO Box 560 61853 | 217-586-4415
Heather Landrus, prin. | Fax 586-5869

Malta, DeKalb, Pop. 1,142

Kishwaukee College | Post-Sec.
21193 Malta Rd 60150 | 815-825-2086

Manhattan, Will, Pop. 6,984
Manhattan SD 114 | 1,200/PK-8
25440 S Gougar Rd 60442 | 815-478-6093
Howard Butters, supt. | Fax 478-7660
www.manhattan114.org
Manhattan JHS | 400/6-8
15606 W Smith Rd 60442 | 815-478-6090
Ron Pacheco, prin. | Fax 478-6094

Community Christian S | 100/PK-12
22811 S Cedar Rd 60442 | 815-485-2379
Pat Quinn, dean

Manito, Mason, Pop. 1,628
Midwest Central CUSD 191 — 1,100/PK-12
1010 S Washington St 61546 — 309-968-6868
Todd Hellrigel, supt. — Fax 968-7916
www.midwestcentral.org/
Midwest Central HS — 300/9-12
910 S Washington St 61546 — 309-968-6766
Jay Blair, prin. — Fax 968-6340
Other Schools – See Green Valley

Manlius, Bureau, Pop. 356
Bureau Valley CUSD 340 — 1,200/PK-12
PO Box 289 61338 — 815-445-3101
James Whitmore, supt. — Fax 445-2802
bv340.com
Bureau Valley HS — 400/9-12
PO Box 329 61338 — 815-445-4004
Eric Lawson, prin. — Fax 445-3017
Other Schools – See Buda

Mansfield, Piatt, Pop. 902
Blue Ridge CUSD 18
Supt. — See Farmer City
Blue Ridge JHS — 100/7-8
247 S McKinley St 61854 — 217-489-5201
John Weaver, prin. — Fax 489-9051

Manteno, Kankakee, Pop. 9,119
Manteno CUSD 5 — 2,100/K-12
84 N Oak St 60950 — 815-928-7000
Dawn Russert, supt. — Fax 468-6439
www.manteno5.org/
Manteno HS — 700/9-12
443 N Maple St 60950 — 815-928-7101
Roger Schnitzler, prin. — Fax 468-2344
Manteno MS — 700/5-8
250 N Poplar St 60950 — 815-928-7154
David Conrad, prin. — Fax 468-8082

Maple Park, Kane, Pop. 1,296
Fox Valley Career Center
47W326 Keslinger Rd 60151 — 630-365-5113
Rick Burchell, dir. — Fax 365-9088
www.kaneland.org/shared/fvcc
Fox Valley Career Center — Vo/Tech
47W326 Keslinger Rd 60151 — 630-365-5113
Rick Burchell, dir — Fax 365-9088

Kaneland CUSD 302 — 4,800/PK-12
47W326 Keslinger Rd 60151 — 630-365-5111
Dr. Jeff Schuler, supt. — Fax 365-9428
www.kaneland.org
Kaneland HS — 1,300/9-12
47W326 Keslinger Rd 60151 — 630-365-5100
Jill Maras, prin. — Fax 365-8421
Other Schools – See Sugar Grove

Marengo, McHenry, Pop. 7,571
Marengo Community HSD 154 — 800/9-12
110 Franks Rd 60152 — 815-568-6511
Dr. Dan Bertrand, supt. — Fax 568-6510
www.mchs154.org
Marengo HS — 800/9-12
110 Franks Rd 60152 — 815-568-6511
Angela Fink, prin. — Fax 568 6610

Marengo-Union Consolidated ESD 165 — 1,100/PK-8
816 E Grant Hwy 60152 — 815-568-8323
Lea Damisch, supt. — Fax 568-8367
www.marengo.k12.il.us/
Marengo Community MS — 500/PK-PK, 5-
816 E Grant Hwy 60152 — 815-568-5720
Tracy Beam, prin. — Fax 568-7572

Marion, Williamson, Pop. 16,859
Crab Orchard CUSD 3 — 500/PK-12
19189 Bailey St 62959 — 618-982-2181
Derek Hutchins, supt. — Fax 982-2080
www.cocusd3.org/
Crab Orchard HS — 100/9-12
19189 Bailey St 62959 — 618-982-2181
William McSparin, prin. — Fax 982-2080

Marion CUSD 2 — 4,000/PK-12
1700 W Cherry St 62959 — 618-993-2321
Dr. Keith Oates, supt. — Fax 997-0943
www.marionunit2.org
Marion HS — 1,100/9-12
1501 S Carbon St 62959 — 618-993-8196
Dr. Stephen Smith, prin. — Fax 997-8749
Marion JHS — 800/6-8
1609 W Main St 62959 — 618-997-1317
Rebecca Moss, prin. — Fax 997-0477

Agape Christian HS — 100/9-12
5208 Meadowland Pkwy Ste A 62959 — 618-997-9302
Seth Knox, prin. — Fax 997-9304

Marissa, Saint Clair, Pop. 1,970
Marissa CUSD 40 — 600/PK-12
5 E Marissa St 62257 — 618-295-2313
Dr. Kevin Cogdill, supt. — Fax 295-2609
www.marissa40.org
Marissa JSHS — 200/7-12
300 School View Dr 62257 — 618-295-2393
Mark Heuring, prin. — Fax 295-2276

Markham, Cook, Pop. 12,287
Hazel Crest SD 152-5
Supt. — See Hazel Crest
Frost MS — 200/7-8
2206 W 167th St, — 708-210-9929
Marcus Baker, prin. — Fax 210-9582

Prairie-Hills ESD 144 — 2,300/PK-8
3015 W 163rd St, — 708-210-2888
Dr. Kimako Patterson, supt. — Fax 210-9925
phsd144.net/
Prairie-Hills JHS — 600/6-8
3035 W 163rd St, — 708-210-2860
Michael Moore, prin. — Fax 210-9208

Maroa, Macon, Pop. 1,775
Maroa-Forsyth CUSD 2 — 1,200/PK-12
PO Box 738 61756 — 217-794-3488
Mike Williams, supt. — Fax 794-3878
www.mfschools.org
Maroa-Forsyth HS — 300/9-12
PO Box 738 61756 — 217-794-3463
Scott Adreon, prin. — Fax 794-5459
Maroa-Forsyth MS — 300/6-8
PO Box 738 61756 — 217-794-5115
Brice Stewart, prin. — Fax 794-3351

Marquette Heights, Tazewell, Pop. 2,798
North Pekin & Marquette Hts SD 102 — 700/PK-8
51 Yates Rd 61554 — 309-382-2172
Byron Sondgeroth, supt. — Fax 382-2122
www.dist102.org/
Georgetowne MS — 200/6-8
51 Yates Rd 61554 — 309-382-3456
Bob Ketcham, prin. — Fax 382-2122

Marshall, Clark, Pop. 3,915
Marshall CUSD 2C — 1,300/PK-12
503 Pine St 62441 — 217-826-5912
Kevin Ross, supt. — Fax 826-5170
www.marshall.k12.il.us/
Marshall HS — 400/9-12
806 N 6th St 62441 — 217-826-2395
Tim Pearison, prin. — Fax 826-5511
Marshall JHS — 200/7-8
806 N 6th St 62441 — 217-826-2812
John Ritchey, prin. — Fax 826-6065

Martinsville, Clark, Pop. 1,153
Martinsville CUSD 3C — 400/PK-12
PO Box K 62442 — 217-382-4321
Jill Rogers, supt. — Fax 382-4183
www.martinsville.k12.il.us/
Martinsville JSHS — 200/7-12
PO Box K 62442 — 217-382-4132
Ray Schollenbruch, prin. — Fax 382-4761

Maryville, Madison, Pop. 7,376

McGivney Catholic HS — 9-12
142 Wilma Dr 62062 — 618-223-9708
Mike Scholz, prin. — Fax 344-5536

Mascoutah, Saint Clair, Pop. 7,258
Mascoutah CUSD 19 — 3,500/PK-12
622 S Jefferson St 62258 — 618-566-7414
Craig Fiegel, supt. — Fax 566-4507
www.mascoutah19.k12.il.us
Mascoutah HS — 1,000/9-12
1313 W Main St 62258 — 618-566-8523
Sandra Jouglard, prin. — Fax 566-8693
Mascoutah MS — 700/6-8
846 N 6th St 62258 — 618-566-2305
Bob Stone, prin. — Fax 566-2307

Mason City, Mason, Pop. 2,332
Illini Central CUSD 189 — 900/PK-12
208 N West Ave 62664 — 217-482-5180
Lori Harrison, supt. — Fax 482-3121
www.illinicentral.org
Illini Central HS — 300/9-12
208 N West Ave 62664 — 217-482-3252
Ed Jodlowski, prin. — Fax 482-3323
Illini Central MS — 200/6-8
208 N West Ave 62664 — 217-482-3252
Ed Jodlowski, prin. — Fax 482-3323

Matteson, Cook, Pop. 18,630
ESD 159 — 2,000/PK-8
6202 Vollmer Rd 60443 — 708-720-1300
Barbara Suggs-Mason, supt. — Fax 720-3218
www.dist159.com
Powell MS — 800/6-8
20600 Matteson Ave 60443 — 708-283-9600
Kimberly Johnson, prin. — Fax 283-1885

Matteson ESD 162
Supt. — See Richton Park
Huth MS — 600/7-8
3718 213th Pl 60443 — 708-748-0470
Corey Levy, prin. — Fax 503-1119

Mattoon, Coles, Pop. 18,262
Mattoon CUSD 2 — 3,400/K-12
1701 Charleston Ave 61938 — 217-238-8850
Larry Lilly, supt. — Fax 238-8855
www.mattoon.k12.il.us
Mattoon HS — 1,000/9-12
2521 Walnut Ave 61938 — 217-238-7800
Michele Sinclair, prin. — Fax 238-7805
Mattoon MS — 800/6-8
1200 S 9th St 61938 — 217-238-5800
Jeremie Smith, prin. — Fax 238-5805

Lake Land College — Post-Sec.
5001 Lake Land Blvd 61938 — 217-234-5253

Maywood, Cook, Pop. 23,814
Proviso Township HSD 209
Supt. — See Forest Park
Proviso East HS — 1,800/9-12
807 S 1st Ave 60153 — 708-344-7000
Tony Valente, prin. — Fax 344-5942

Mazon, Grundy, Pop. 1,011
Mazon-Verona-Kinsman ESD 2C — 300/PK-8
1013 North St 60444 — 815-448-2200
Nancy Dillow, supt. — Fax 448-3005
www.mvkmavericks.org
Mazon-Verona-Kinsman MS — 200/5-8
1013 North St 60444 — 815-448-2127
Debra Paulsen, prin. — Fax 448-3005

Melrose Park, Cook, Pop. 25,229
Mannheim SD 83
Supt. — See Franklin Park
Mannheim JHS — 800/6-8
2600 Hyde Park Ave 60164 — 847-455-5020
Timothy Daley, prin. — Fax 455-2038

Everest College — Post-Sec.
1101 W North Ave Ste 1 60160 — 708-731-4400
Lincoln College of Technology — Post-Sec.
8317 W North Ave 60160 — 708-344-4700
Walther Lutheran HS — 400/9-12
900 Chicago Ave 60160 — 708-344-0404
Jim Craven, hdmstr. — Fax 344-0525

Mendon, Adams, Pop. 949
CUSD 4 — 600/K-12
PO Box 200 62351 — 217-936-2111
Brian Kurz, supt. — Fax 936-2643
www.cusd4.com
Unity HS — 200/9-12
PO Box 200 62351 — 217-936-2116
William Dorethy, prin. — Fax 936-2117
Unity MS — 200/5-8
PO Box 200 62351 — 217-936-2727
Seth Klusmeyer, prin. — Fax 936-2730

Mendota, LaSalle, Pop. 7,312
Mendota CCSD 289 — 1,300/PK-8
1806 Guiles Ave 61342 — 815-539-7631
Kristen School, supt. — Fax 538-2927
www.mendota289.org/
Northbrook S — 600/PK-PK, 5-
1804 Guiles Ave 61342 — 815-539-6237
Beth Wackerlin, prin. — Fax 538-3090

Mendota Township HSD 280 — 600/9-12
2300 W Main St 61342 — 815-539-7446
Jeff Prusator, supt. — Fax 539-3103
mendotahs.org/
Mendota Township HS — 600/9-12
2300 W Main St 61342 — 815-539-7446
Denise Aughenbaugh, prin. — Fax 539-3103

Meredosia, Morgan, Pop. 1,040
Meredosia-Chambersburg CUSD 11 — 300/PK-12
PO Box 440 62665 — 217-584-1744
Michael Davies, supt. — Fax 584-1129
www.mcsd11.net
Meredosia-Chambersburg HS — 100/9-12
PO Box 440 62665 — 217-584-1291
Daniel Carie, prin. — Fax 584-1741
Meredosia-Chambersburg JHS — 100/6-8
PO Box 440 62665 — 217-584-1291
Daniel Carie, prin. — Fax 584-1741

Merrionette Park, Cook, Pop. 1,874

Everest College — Post-Sec.
11560 S Kedzie Ave 60803 — 708-239-0055

Metamora, Woodford, Pop. 3,585
Metamora Township HSD 122 — 900/9-12
PO Box 109 61548 — 309-367-4151
Randall G. Toepke, supt. — Fax 367-4351
mths.metamora.k12.il.us/
Metamora Twp HS — 900/9-12
PO Box 109 61548 — 309-367-4151
Randall Toepke, supt. — Fax 367-4154

Metropolis, Massac, Pop. 6,368
Massac Unit SD 1 — 2,200/PK-12
PO Box 530 62960 — 618-524-9376
William Hatfield, supt — Fax 524-4432
www.massac.org
Massac County HS — 600/9-12
2841 Old Marion Rd 62960 — 618-524-3440
Jason Hayes, prin. — Fax 524-3131
Massac JHS — 300/7-8
3028 Old Marion Rd 62960 — 618-524-2645
J.R. Conkle, prin. — Fax 524-2765

Midlothian, Cook, Pop. 14,581
Bremen Community HSD 228 — 5,500/9-12
15233 Pulaski Rd 60445 — 708-389-1175
Bill Kendall, supt. — Fax 389-2552
www.bhsd228.com
Bremen HS — 1,400/9-12
15203 Pulaski Rd 60445 — 708-371-3600
David Kibelkis, prin. — Fax 371-7194
Other Schools – See Country Club Hills, Oak Forest, Tinley Park

Milford, Iroquois, Pop. 1,300
Milford Township HSD 233 — 200/9-12
PO Box 304 60953 — 815-889-5176
Dr. Dale Hastings, supt. — Fax 889-5221
www.milford.k12.il.us
Milford Township HS — 200/9-12
PO Box 257 60953 — 815-889-4184
Stephen Totheroh, prin. — Fax 889-4871

Millbrook, Kendall, Pop. 329
Newark CCSD 66
Supt. — See Newark
Millbrook JHS — 100/5-8
PO Box 214 60536 — 630-553-5435
Richard Sjolund, prin. — Fax 553-1027

Milledgeville, Carroll, Pop. 1,027
Chadwick-Milledgeville CUSD 399
Supt. — See Chadwick
Milledgeville HS — 100/9-12
100 E 8th St 61051 — 815-225-7141
Paula Rademacher, prin. — Fax 225-7847

Millstadt, Saint Clair, Pop. 3,983
Millstadt CCSD 160 — 900/PK-8
211 W Mill St 62260 — 618-476-1803
Jonathan Green, supt. — Fax 476-1893
www.millstadt.stclair.k12.il.us
Millstadt S — 600/3-8
211 W Mill St 62260 — 618-476-1681
Josh Lane, prin. — Fax 476-3401

Minonk, Woodford, Pop. 2,068
Fieldcrest CUSD 6 1,200/PK-12
1 Dornbush Dr 61760 309-432-2177
Josh Olsen, supt. Fax 432-3377
www.fieldcrest.k12.il.us
Fieldcrest HS 400/9-12
1 Dornbush Dr 61760 309-432-2529
William Lapp, prin. Fax 432-2064

Minooka, Grundy, Pop. 10,784
Minooka CCSD 201 3,600/PK-8
PO Box 467 60447 815-467-6121
Al Gegenheimer, supt. Fax 467-9544
www.min201.org
Minooka JHS 800/7-8
333 W McEvilly Rd 60447 815-467-2136
Shane Trager, prin. Fax 467-5087

Minooka Community HSD 111
Supt. — See Channahon
Minooka Community HS 1,200/11-12
301 S Wabena Ave 60447 815-467-2140
Darcie Kubinski, prin. Fax 467-2431

Mokena, Will, Pop. 18,589
Mokena SD 159 2,000/PK-8
11244 Willow Crest Ln 60448 708-342-4900
Dr. Omar Castillo, supt. Fax 479-3143
www.mokena159.org
Mokena JHS 700/6-8
19815 Kirkstone Way 60448 708-342-4870
Mike Rolinitis, prin. Fax 479-3122

Rasmussen College Post-Sec.
8650 Spring Lake Dr 60448 815-534-3300

Moline, Rock Island, Pop. 42,701
Moline Unit SD 40 6,800/PK-12
1619 11th Ave 61265 309-743-1600
Dr. David Moyer, supt. Fax 757-3476
www.molineschools.org
Deere MS 500/6-8
2035 11th St 61265 309-743-1622
Scott Verstraete, prin. Fax 757-3668
Moline HS 2,100/9-12
3600 Avenue of the Cities 61265 309-743-1624
Dan McGuire, prin. Fax 757-3667
Moline HS - Coolidge Campus 100/Alt
3432 Avenue of the Cities 61265 309-743-8587
Lyle Goldensoph, prin. Fax 757-3536
Wilson MS 600/6-8
1301 48th St 61265 309-743-1623
Robert Beem, prin. Fax 757-3586

Black Hawk College Post-Sec.
6600 34th Ave 61265 309-796-5000
Midwest Technical Institute Post-Sec.
3620 Avenue of the Cities 61265 800-814-5124
Quad Cities Christian S 100/6-12
4000 11th St 61265 309-762-3800
William Olmstead, prin. Fax 762-8150

Momence, Kankakee, Pop. 3,244
Momence CUSD 1 1,300/PK-12
415 N Dixie Hwy 60954 815-472-3501
Dr. Phillip Smith, supt. Fax 472-3516
www.momence.k12.il.us
Momence HS 400/9-12
101 N Franklin St 60954 815-472-6477
Shannon Anderson, prin. Fax 472-2055
Momence JHS 400/5-8
801 W 2nd St 60954 815-472-4184
Sheila Brown, prin. Fax 472-3517

Monmouth, Warren, Pop. 9,279
Monmouth-Roseville CUSD 238 1,800/PK-12
105 N E St 61462 309-734-4712
Edward Fletcher, supt. Fax 734-4755
www.mr238.org
Monmouth-Roseville HS 500/9-12
325 W 1st Ave 61462 309-734-5118
Jeff Bryan, prin. Fax 734-2918
Other Schools – See Roseville

United CUSD 304 900/PK-12
1905 100th St 61462 309-734-9413
Jeffrey Whitsitt, supt. Fax 734-0223
united.k12.il.us/
United HS 300/9-12
1905 100th St 61462 309-734-9411
Amy Schmitz, prin. Fax 734-6090
United JHS 200/6-8
2140 State Highway 135 61462 309-734-8511
Kristen Nelson, prin. Fax 734-6094

Monmouth College Post-Sec.
700 E Broadway 61462 800-747-2687

Monticello, Piatt, Pop. 5,493
Monticello CUSD 25 1,700/PK-12
2 Sage Dr 61856 217-762-8511
Dr. Victor Zimmerman, supt. Fax 762-8534
www.sages.us
Monticello HS 600/9-12
1 Sage Dr 61856 217-762-8511
Tip Reedy, prin. Fax 762-7421
Monticello MS 400/6-8
2015 E Washington St 61856 217-762-8511
Jeanne Handley, prin. Fax 762-7765

Mooseheart, Kane

Mooseheart S 200/PK-12
255 W James J Davis Dr 60539 630-906-3646
Gary Urwiler, dir. Fax 906-3617

Morris, Grundy, Pop. 13,509
Grundy Area Vocational Center
1002 Union St 60450 815-942-4390
Lance Copes, dir. Fax 942-6650
www.gavc-il.org
Grundy AVC Vo/Tech
1002 Union St 60450 815-942-4390
Lance Copes, dir. Fax 942-6650

Morris Community HSD 101 1,000/9-12
1000 Union St 60450 815-941-5327
Patrick Halloran Ed.D., supt. Fax 941-5407
www.morrishs.org
Morris HS 1,000/9-12
1000 Union St Ste 1 60450 815-941-5341
Kelly Hussey, prin. Fax 941-5405

Morris SD 54 1,200/PK-8
54 White Oak Dr 60450 815-942-0056
Teri Shaw, supt. Fax 942-0240
dist54.mornet.org
Shabbona MS 400/6-8
725 School St 60450 815-942-3605
Anthony Wilkinson, prin. Fax 941-4531

Morrison, Whiteside, Pop. 4,151
Morrison CUSD 6 1,100/PK-12
643 Genesee Ave 61270 815-772-2064
Dr. Suellen Girard, supt. Fax 772-4644
www.morrisonschools.org
Morrison HS 300/9-12
643 Genesee Ave 61270 815-772-4071
Scott Vance, prin. Fax 772-4644
Morrison JHS 300/6-8
300 Academic Dr 61270 815-772-7264
Darryl Hogue, prin. Fax 772-2531

Morrison Institute of Technology Post-Sec.
701 Portland Ave 61270 815-772-7218

Morrisonville, Christian, Pop. 1,053
Morrisonville CUSD 1 300/PK-12
PO Box 13 62546 217-526-4431
Jerry Wesley, supt. Fax 526-4433
www.mohawks.net
Morrisonville HS 100/9-12
PO Box 13 62546 217-526-4432
Ann Little, prin. Fax 526-4452
Morrisonville JHS 50/7-8
PO Box 13 62546 217-526-4432
Ann Little, prin. Fax 526-4452

Morton, Tazewell, Pop. 16,106
Morton CUSD 709 2,800/PK-12
1050 S 4th Ave Ste 200 61550 309-263-2581
Dr. Lindsey Hall, supt. Fax 266-6320
www.morton709.org
Morton HS 1,000/9-12
350 N Illinois Ave 61550 309-266-7182
Marjorie Johnson, prin. Fax 263-2168
Morton JHS 400/7-8
225 E Jackson St 61550 309-266-6522
Lee Hoffman, prin. Fax 284-5031

Morton Grove, Cook, Pop. 22,739
Golf ESD 67 600/PK-8
9401 Waukegan Rd 60053 847-966-8200
Dr. Jamie Reilly, supt. Fax 966-8290
www.golf67.net
Golf MS 300/5-8
9401 Waukegan Rd 60053 847-965-3740
Erin Stein, prin. Fax 966-9493

Mounds, Pulaski, Pop. 797
Meridian CUSD 101 600/PK-12
208 Valley Rd 62964 618-342-6776
Terry Moreland, supt. Fax 342-6401
www.meridian101.com
Meridian HS 200/9-12
1401 Mounds Rd 62964 618-342-6778
Terrance Gaddy, prin. Fax 342-6856

Mount Carmel, Wabash, Pop. 7,195
Wabash CUSD 348 1,700/K-12
218 W 13th St 62863 618-262-4181
Tim Buss, supt. Fax 262-7912
www.wabash348.com
Mount Carmel HS 600/9-12
201 N Pear St 62863 618-262-5104
Pat Cheesman, prin. Fax 262-8781
Mount Carmel MS 400/6-8
1520 Poplar St 62863 618-262-5699
Steven Holt, prin. Fax 263-9096

Wabash Valley College Post-Sec.
2200 College Dr 62863 618-262-8641

Mount Carroll, Carroll, Pop. 1,702
West Carroll CUSD 314
Supt. — See Thomson
West Carroll MS 300/6-8
633 S East St 61053 815-244-2002
Julie Katzenberger, prin. Fax 244-1051

Mount Morris, Ogle, Pop. 2,953
Oregon CUSD 220
Supt. — See Oregon
Rahn JHS 200/7-8
105 W Brayton Rd 61054 815-734-6134
Kip Crandall, prin. Fax 734-7129

Mount Olive, Macoupin, Pop. 2,093
Mount Olive CUSD 5 600/PK-12
804 W Main St 62069 217-999-7831
Patrick Murphy, supt. Fax 999-2150
www.mtoliveschools.org
Mount Olive HS 200/9-12
804 W Main St 62069 217-999-4231
Shane Schuricht, prin. Fax 999-4302

Mount Prospect, Cook, Pop. 53,352
CCSD 59
Supt. — See Arlington Heights
Holmes JHS 500/6-8
1900 W Lonnquist Blvd 60056 847-593-4390
Dr. Robert Bohanek, prin. Fax 593-7386

Mount Prospect SD 57 2,100/PK-8
701 W Gregory St 60056 847-394-7300
Dr. Elaine Aumiller, supt. Fax 394-7311
www.d57.org
Lincoln MS 700/6-8
700 W Lincoln St 60056 847-394-7350
Jason Kaiz, prin. Fax 394-7358

River Trails SD 26 1,400/PK-8
1900 E Kensington Rd 60056 847-297-4120
Dane Delli Ph.D., supt. Fax 297-4124
www.rtsd26.org
River Trails MS 500/6-8
1000 N Wolf Rd 60056 847-298-1750
Keir Rogers, prin. Fax 298-2639

Township HSD 214
Supt. — See Arlington Heights
Prospect HS 2,100/9-12
801 W Kensington Rd 60056 847-718-5200
Kurt Laakso, prin. Fax 718-5216

Christian Life College Post-Sec.
400 E Gregory St 60056 847-259-1840
ITT Technical Institute Post-Sec.
1401 Feehanville Dr 60056 847-375-8800

Mount Pulaski, Logan, Pop. 1,560
Mount Pulaski CUSD 23 500/PK-12
119 N Garden St Ste 2 62548 217-792-7222
Todd Hamm, supt. Fax 792-5551
www.mtpulaski.k12.il.us
Mount Pulaski HS 200/9-12
206 S Spring St 62548 217-792-3209
Terry Morgan, prin. Fax 792-3248

Mount Sterling, Brown, Pop. 2,006
Brown County CUSD 1 800/PK-12
503 NW Cross St 62353 217-773-3359
Stan Adcock, supt. Fax 773-2121
www.bchornets.com/
Brown County HS 200/9-12
500 E Main St 62353 217-773-3345
Van Wilson, prin. Fax 773-2128
Brown County MS 200/5-8
504 E Main St 62353 217-773-9152
Ray Driskell, prin. Fax 773-9121

Mount Vernon, Jefferson, Pop. 14,904
Mount Vernon Area Vocational Center
320 S 7th St 62864 618-246-5602
Robert Knutson, dir. Fax 244-8049
Mount Vernon Area Vocational Center Vo/Tech
320 S 7th St 62864 618-246-5602
Robert Knutson, dir. Fax 244-8049

Mount Vernon CSD 80 1,700/PK-8
2710 North St 62864 618-244-8080
Mike Green, supt. Fax 244-8082
district.mtv80.org
Casey MS 400/6-8
1829 Broadway St 62864 618-244-8060
Mary McGreer, prin. Fax 244-8014

Mount Vernon Township HSD 201 1,300/9-12
320 S 7th St 62864 618-244-3700
Dr. Michael Smith, supt. Fax 244-3047
www.mvths.org
Mount Vernon HS 1,300/9-12
320 S 7th St 62864 618-244-3700
Wes Olson, prin. Fax 244-8047

DuQuoin Beauty College Post-Sec.
212 S 20th St 62864 618-542-9777

Mount Zion, Macon, Pop. 5,766
Mount Zion CUSD 3 2,500/PK-12
455 Elm St 62549 217-864-2366
Dr. Travis Roundcount, supt. Fax 864-2200
www.mtzion.k12.il.us
Mount Zion HS 800/9-12
305 S Henderson St 62549 217-864-2363
Kraig Garber, prin. Fax 864-5815
Mount Zion JHS 400/7-8
315 S Henderson St 62549 217-864-2369
Jerry Birkey, prin. Fax 864-6829

Moweaqua, Shelby, Pop. 1,822
Central A & M CUSD 21
Supt. — See Assumption
Central A & M HS 300/9-12
229 E Pine St 62550 217-768-3866
Judy Fitzgerald, prin. Fax 768-3797

Mulberry Grove, Bond, Pop. 626
Mulberry Grove CUSD 1 400/PK-12
801 W Wall St 62262 618-326-8812
Michael Gauch, supt. Fax 326-8482
www.mgschools.com
Mulberry Grove HS 100/9-12
801 W Wall St 62262 618-326-8221
Ryan Bauer, prin. Fax 326-8482
Mulberry Grove JHS 100/7-8
801 W Wall St 62262 618-326-8221
Ryan Bauer, prin. Fax 326-8482

Mundelein, Lake, Pop. 30,630
Diamond Lake SD 76 1,200/PK-8
500 Acorn Ln 60060 847-566-9221
Dr. Joseph Petrella, supt. Fax 566-5689
www.d76.lake.k12.il.us/
West Oak MS 500/5-8
500 Acorn Ln 60060 847-566-9220
Christopher Willeford, prin. Fax 970-3534

Fremont SD 79 2,300/PK-8
28855 N Fremont Center Rd 60060 847-566-0169
Dr. Jill Gildea, supt. Fax 566-7280
www.fsd79.org
Fremont MS 800/6-8
28871 N Fremont Center Rd 60060 847-566-9384
Pam Motsenbocker, prin. Fax 566-7805

Mundelein Consolidated HSD 120 2,200/9-12
1350 W Hawley St 60060 847-949-2200
Dr. Jody Ware, supt. Fax 949-4756
www.d120.org/
Mundelein Consolidated HS 2,200/9-12
1350 W Hawley St 60060 847-949-2200
Dr. Anthony Kroll, prin. Fax 949-0599

Mundelein ESD 75 1,300/PK-8
470 N Lake St 60060 847-949-2700
Cynthia Heidorn Ph.D., supt. Fax 949-2727
www.district75.org
Sandburg MS 600/PK-PK, 6-
855 W Hawley St 60060 847-949-2707
Mark Pilut, prin. Fax 949-2716

Carmel HS 1,400/9-12
1 Carmel Pkwy 60060 847-566-3000
Lynne Strutzel, prin. Fax 566-8465
University of St. Mary of the Lake Post-Sec.
1000 E Maple Ave 60060 847-566-6401

Murphysboro, Jackson, Pop. 7,754
Murphysboro CUSD 186 2,100/PK-12
593 Ava Rd 62966 618-684-3781
Christopher Grode, supt. Fax 684-2465
www.cusd186.org
Murphysboro HS 600/9-12
50 Blackwood Dr 62966 618-687-2336
Tony Wilson, prin. Fax 687-3532
Murphysboro MS 400/6-8
2125 Spruce St 62966 618-684-3041
Jeff Keener, prin. Fax 687-1042

Naperville, DuPage, Pop. 138,897
Indian Prairie CUSD 204
Supt. — See Aurora
Crone MS 1,200/6-8
4020 111th St 60564 630-428-5600
Allan Davenport, prin. Fax 428-5601
Gregory MS 1,000/6-8
2621 Springdale Cir 60564 630-428-6300
Stephen Severson, prin. Fax 428-6301
Hill MS 900/6-8
1836 Brookdale Rd 60563 630-428-6200
Darrell Echols, prin. Fax 428-6201
Neuqua Valley Gold Campus 1,000/9-9
3220 Cedar Glade Dr 60564 630-428-6400
Maree Russavage, prin. Fax 428-6401
Neuqua Valley HS 3,200/10-12
2360 95th St 60564 630-428-6000
Robert McBride, prin. Fax 428-6001
Scullen MS 1,000/6-8
2815 Mistflower Ln 60564 630-428-7000
Mark Trucenbrod, prin. Fax 428-7001

Naperville CUSD 203 17,800/PK-12
203 W Hillside Rd 60540 630-420-6300
Dan Bridges, supt. Fax 420-1066
www.naperville203.org
Jefferson JHS 900/6-8
1525 N Loomis St 60563 630-420-6307
Nancy Voise, prin. Fax 420-6930
Lincoln JHS 900/6-8
1320 Olympus Dr 60565 630-420-6370
Patrick Gaskin, prin. Fax 637-4582
Madison JHS 800/6-8
1000 River Oak Dr 60565 630-420-4257
Erin Anderson, prin. Fax 420-6402
Naperville Central HS 2,900/9-12
440 Aurora Ave 60540 630-420-6420
William Wiesbrook, prin. Fax 369-6247
Naperville North HS 3,200/9-12
899 N Mill St 60563 630-420-6484
Kevin Pobst, prin. Fax 420-4255
Washington JHS 600/6-8
201 N Washington St 60540 630-420-6390
David Kanne, prin. Fax 420-6474
Other Schools – See Lisle

DeVry University Post-Sec.
2056 Westings Ave Ste 40 60563 630-428-9086
Naperville Christian Academy 100/PK-12
1451 Raymond Dr Ste 200 60563 630-637-9622
Jon McCord, hdmstr. Fax 983-6929
North Central College Post-Sec.
30 N Brainard St 60540 630-637-5100
Northwestern College Post-Sec.
1809 N Mill St 60563 888-205-2283

Nashville, Washington, Pop. 3,221
Nashville Community HSD 99 500/9-12
1300 S Mill St 62263 618-327-8286
Wendy Davis, supt. Fax 327-4512
www.county.washington.k12.il.us
Nashville Community HS 500/9-12
1300 S Mill St 62263 618-327-8286
Justin Elms, prin. Fax 327-4512

Nauvoo, Hancock, Pop. 1,136
Nauvoo-Colusa CUSD 325 300/PK-8
PO Box 308 62354 217-453-6639
Kent Young, supt. Fax 453-6395
www.nauvoo-colusa.com
Nauvoo-Colusa JHS 100/7-8
PO Box 308 62354 217-453-2231
Kent Young, prin. Fax 453-6395

Neoga, Cumberland, Pop. 1,622
Neoga CUSD 3 800/PK-12
PO Box 280 62447 217-895-2201
Charles Castle, supt. Fax 895-3476
www.neoga.k12.il.us
Neoga HS 200/9-12
PO Box 280 62447 217-895-2205
Benjamin Johnson, prin. Fax 895-3957
Neoga MS 200/4-8
PO Box 310 62447 217-895-2200
Seth James, prin. Fax 895-2974

Newark, Kendall, Pop. 984
Newark CCSD 66 200/PK-8
503 Chicago Rd 60541 815-695-5143
Dr. Genevieve Cepela, supt. Fax 695-5776
Other Schools – See Millbrook

Newark Community HSD 18 200/9-12
413 Chicago Rd 60541 815-695-5164
Amy Smith, supt. Fax 695-5752
www.newarkhs.k12.il.us
Newark Community HS 200/9-12
413 Chicago Rd 60541 815-695-5164
Douglas Hoster, prin. Fax 695-5752

New Athens, Saint Clair, Pop. 2,032
New Athens CUSD 60 600/PK-12
501 Hanft St 62264 618-475-2174
Brian Karraker, supt. Fax 475-2176
www.na60.org
New Athens HS 200/9-12
501 Hanft St 62264 618-475-2173
Dennis Works, prin. Fax 475-2176
New Athens JHS 100/6-8
501 Hanft St 62264 618-475-2172
Jim Marlow, prin. Fax 475-2176

New Berlin, Sangamon, Pop. 1,336
New Berlin CUSD 16 800/PK-12
600 N Cedar St 62670 217-488-2040
Adam Ehrman, supt.
cusd16.k12.il.us
New Berlin HS 200/9-12
PO Box 230 62670 217-488-6012
Hattie Doyle, prin. Fax 488-3207
New Berlin JHS 200/6-8
PO Box 230 62670 217-488-6012
Megan Doerfler, prin. Fax 488-3207

New Lenox, Will, Pop. 24,189
Lincoln-Way Community HSD 210 7,300/9-12
1801 E Lincoln Hwy 60451 815-462-2100
Dr. Lawrence Wyllie, supt. Fax 462-2519
www.lw210.org
Lincoln-Way Central HS 2,000/9-12
1801 E Lincoln Hwy 60451 815-462-2100
Dr. Steven Provis, prin. Fax 485-7648
Lincoln Way West HS 1,300/9-12
21701 Gougar Rd 60451 815-717-3500
Dr. Monica Schmitt, prin. Fax 717-3509
Other Schools – See Frankfort

New Lenox SD 122 5,500/PK-8
102 S Cedar Rd 60451 815-485-2169
Dr. Michael Sass, supt. Fax 485-2236
www.nlsd122.org
Liberty JHS 600/7-8
151 Lenox St 60451 815-462-7951
Shane Street, prin. Fax 462-0672
Martino JHS 600/7-8
731 E Joliet Hwy 60451 815-485-7593
Bonnie Groen, prin. Fax 485-9578

Providence Catholic HS 1,200/9-12
1800 W Lincoln Hwy 60451 815-485-2136
Don Sebestyen, prin. Fax 485-2709

Newton, Jasper, Pop. 2,823
Jasper County CUSD 1 1,100/PK-12
609 S Lafayette St 62448 618-783-8459
Dan Cox, supt. Fax 783-3679
www.cusd1.jasper.k12.il.us
Jasper County JHS 200/7-8
1104 W Jourdan St 62448 618-783-4202
Travis Wyatt, prin. Fax 783-4257
Newton Community HS 500/9-12
201 Westend Ave 62448 618-783-2303
Rick Athey, prin. Fax 783-3783

Niantic, Macon, Pop. 703
Sangamon Valley CUSD 9 800/PK-12
PO Box 200 62551 217-668-2338
Ernie Fowler, supt. Fax 668-2406
www.sv.k12.il.us
Sangamon Valley HS 200/9-12
PO Box 200 62551 217-668-2392
Bob Meadows, prin. Fax 668-2406
Other Schools – See Illiopolis

Niles, Cook, Pop. 29,272
East Maine SD 63
Supt. — See Des Plaines
Gemini JHS 700/7-8
8955 N Greenwood Ave 60714 847-827-1181
Richard Groeling, prin. Fax 827-3499

Park Ridge-Niles CCSD 64
Supt. — See Park Ridge
Emerson MS 800/6-8
8101 N Cumberland Ave 60714 847-318-8110
Jim Morrison, prin. Fax 318-8122

Logos Christian Academy 200/PK-12
7280 N Caldwell Ave 60714 847-647-9456
Larry Murg, prin. Fax 647-7916
Niles School of Cosmetology Post-Sec.
8057 N Milwaukee Ave 60714 847-965-8061
Notre Dame HS 800/9-12
7655 W Dempster St 60714 847-965-2900
Daniel Tully, pres. Fax 965-2975

Noble, Richland, Pop. 667
West Richland CUSD 2 400/PK-12
PO Box 157 62868 618-723-2334
Don Haile, supt. Fax 723-2113
www.wrsd2.net
West Richland HS 100/9-12
PO Box 157 62868 618-723-2335
Kevin Westall, prin. Fax 723-2966
West Richland JHS 100/7-8
PO Box 157 62868 618-723-2335
Kevin Westall, prin. Fax 723-2966

Nokomis, Montgomery, Pop. 2,240
Nokomis CUSD 22 600/PK-12
511 Oberle St 62075 217-563-7311
Scott Doerr, supt. Fax 563-2549
www.nokomis.k12.il.us
Nokomis HS 200/9-12
511 Oberle St 62075 217-563-2014
Tim Page, prin. Fax 563-2671
Nokomis JHS 100/6-8
511 Oberle St 62075 217-563-4323
Don Markey, prin. Fax 563-4322

Normal, McLean, Pop. 51,379
ISU Lab SD 1,000/PK-12
ISU Campus Box 5300 61790 309-438-8542
Dr. Jeffrey Hill, supt. Fax 438-3813
www.uhigh.ilstu.edu/labschool/unitwide.html
University HS 600/9-12
ISU Campus Box 7100 61790 309-438-8542
Dr. Jeffrey Hill, prin. Fax 438-5198

McLean County Unit SD 5 12,900/PK-12
1809 Hovey Ave 61761 309-557-4400
Dr. Gary Niehaus, supt. Fax 557-4501
www.unit5.org
Chiddix JHS 900/6-8
300 S Walnut St 61761 309-557-4405
Timothy Green, prin. Fax 557-4506
Field Vocational Training Center Vo/Tech
412 E Cypress St 61761 309-557-4440
Jane Collins, coord. Fax 557-4534
Kingsley JHS 1,100/6-8
303 Kingsley St 61761 309-557-4407
Dr. Lynette Mehall, prin. Fax 557-4508
Normal Community HS 1,900/9-12
3900 E Raab Rd 61761 309-557-4401
David Bollmann, prin. Fax 557-4502
Normal Community West HS 1,600/9-12
501 N Parkside Rd 61761 309-557-4402
David Johnson, prin. Fax 557-4503
Parkside JHS 900/6-8
101 N Parkside Rd 61761 309-557-4408
Dan Lamboley, prin. Fax 557-4509
Other Schools – See Bloomington

Calvary Christian Academy 300/PK-12
1017 N School St 61761 309-452-7912
Christel Denault, prin. Fax 451-0033
Heartland Community College Post-Sec.
1500 W Raab Rd 61761 309-268-8000
Illinois State University Post-Sec.
Campus Box 4000 61790 309-438-2111

Norridge, Cook, Pop. 14,463
Ridgewood Community HSD 234 900/9-12
7500 W Montrose Ave 60706 708-456-4242
Dr. Robert Lupo, supt. Fax 456-8238
www.ridgenet.org
Ridgewood Community HS 900/9-12
7500 W Montrose Ave 60706 708-456-4242
Jennifer Kelsall, prin. Fax 456-8238

Norris City, White, Pop. 1,272
Norris City-Omaha-Enfield CUSD 3 700/PK-12
PO Box 399 62869 618-378-3222
Cliff Karnes, supt. Fax 378-3286
Norris City-Omaha-Enfield HS 200/9-12
PO Box 399 62869 618-378-3312
Matt Vollman, prin. Fax 378-3364

North Aurora, Kane, Pop. 16,455
Aurora West Unit SD 129
Supt. — See Aurora
Jewel MS 700/6-8
1501 Waterford Rd 60542 630-301-5010
Dr. Greg Scalia, prin. Fax 907-3161

Everest College Post-Sec.
150 S Lincolnway Ste 100 60542 630-896-2140

Northbrook, Cook, Pop. 32,798
Northbrook ESD 27 1,100/PK-8
1250 Sanders Rd 60062 847-498-2610
Dr. David Kroeze, supt. Fax 498-5916
www.nb27.org
Wood Oaks JHS 400/6-8
1250 Sanders Rd 60062 847-272-1900
Robert McElligott, prin. Fax 480-4834

Northbrook SD 28 1,700/PK-8
1475 Maple Ave 60062 847-498-7900
Dr. Larry Hewitt, supt. Fax 498-7970
www.northbrook28.net
Northbrook JHS 600/6-8
1475 Maple Ave 60062 847-498-7920
Scott Meek, prin. Fax 656-1712

Northbrook/Glenview SD 30 1,100/K-8
2374 Shermer Rd 60062 847-498-4190
Dr. Edward Tivador, supt. Fax 498-8981
www.district30.org
Maple S 400/6-8
2370 Shermer Rd 60062 847-400-8900
Dr. Nathan Carter, prin. Fax 272-0979

Northfield Township HSD 225
Supt. — See Glenview
Glenbrook North HS 2,100/9-12
2300 Shermer Rd 60062 847-509-2400
Paul Pryma, prin. Fax 509-2411

West Northfield SD 31 900/K-8
3131 Techny Rd 60062 847-272-6880
Dr. Alexandra Nicholson, supt. Fax 272-4818
www.district31.net/
Field MS 300/6-8
2055 Landwehr Rd 60062 847-272-6884
Erin Murphy, prin. Fax 272-1050

Sager Soloman Schechter MS 300/6-8
3210 Dundee Rd 60062 847-412-5700
Linda Foster, head sch Fax 412-5837

North Chicago, Lake, Pop. 31,474
North Chicago SD 187 3,900/PK-12
2000 Lewis Ave 60064 847-689-8150
Dr. Ben Martindale, supt. Fax 689-6328
d187.org
Neal Math Science Academy 600/7-8
1905 Argonne Dr 60064 847-689-6313
Michael Grenda, prin. Fax 689-6332
North Chicago Community HS 900/9-12
1717 17th St 60064 847-578-7400
Dr. Eric Gallagher, prin. Fax 689-7473

R. Franklin University of Medicine Post-Sec.
3333 Green Bay Rd 60064 847-578-3000

Northfield, Cook, Pop. 5,375
New Trier Township HSD 203 4,100/9-12
7 Happ Rd 60093 847-446-7000
Dr. Linda Yonke, supt. Fax 446-0874
www.newtrier.k12.il.us
New Trier Township HS -Northfield Campus 1,100/9-9
7 Happ Rd 60093 847-446-7000
Paul Waechtler, prin. Fax 784-7500
Other Schools – See Winnetka

Sunset Ridge SD 29 500/K-8
525 Sunset Ridge Rd 60093 847-881-9456
Dr. Linda Vieth, supt.
www.sunsetridge29.net
Sunset Ridge MS 300/4-8
525 Sunset Ridge Rd 60093 847-881-9400
Dr. Shelley Carey, prin.

Christian Heritage Academy 400/PK-12
315 Waukegan Rd 60093 847-446-5252
David Roth Ed.D., admin. Fax 446-5267

Northlake, Cook, Pop. 12,227
Berkeley SD 87
Supt. — See Berkeley
Northlake MS 400/6-8
202 S Lakewood Ave 60164 708-449-3195
Sunil Mody, prin. Fax 547-2548

Leyden Community HSD 212
Supt. — See Franklin Park
West Leyden HS 1,700/9-12
1000 N Wolf Rd 60164 847-451-3154
Wilford Wagner, prin. Fax 451-3180

Oak Brook, DuPage, Pop. 7,720
Butler SD 53 400/PK-8
2801 York Rd 60523 630-573-2887
Dr. Sandra Martin, supt. Fax 573-5374
www.butler53.com
Butler JHS 100/6-8
2801 York Rd 60523 630-573-2760
Stephanie Palmer, prin. Fax 573-1725

Hair Professionals Acad of Cosmetology Post-Sec.
1200 Harger Rd Ste 100 60523 630-653-6630
ITT Technical Institute Post-Sec.
800 Jorie Blvd Ste 100 60523 630-472-7000

Oak Forest, Cook, Pop. 27,551
Arbor Park SD 145 1,400/PK-8
17301 Central Ave 60452 708-687-8040
Allen Jebens, supt. Fax 687-9498
www.arbor145.org
Arbor Park MS 600/5-8
17303 Central Ave 60452 708-687-5330
Mary Beth Sexton, prin. Fax 535-4527

Bremen Community HSD 228
Supt. — See Midlothian
Oak Forest HS 1,500/9-12
15201 Central Ave 60452 708-687-0500
Brad Sikora, prin. Fax 687-0594

Forest Ridge SD 142 1,700/PK-8
15000 Laramie Ave 60452 708-687-3334
Dr. Margaret Longo, supt. Fax 687-2970
www.d142.org
Hille MS 600/6-8
5800 151st St 60452 708-687-2860
Courtney Orzel, prin. Fax 687-8569

Capri Beauty College Post-Sec.
15815 Rob Roy Dr 60452 708-687-3020
John Amico's School of Hair Design Post-Sec.
15301 Cicero Ave 60452 708-687-7800

Oakland, Coles, Pop. 873
Oakland CUSD 5 300/PK-12
PO Box 200 61943 217-346-2555
Lance Landeck, supt. Fax 346-2267
www.oak.k12.il.us
Oakland HS 100/9-12
PO Box 200 61943 217-346-2118
Patty Stark, prin. Fax 346-2267

Oak Lawn, Cook, Pop. 55,942
Community HSD 218 5,900/9-12
10701 Kilpatrick Ave 60453 708-424-2000
Dr. John Byrne, supt. Fax 424-6389
www.chsd218.org
Richards HS 1,800/9-12
10601 Central Ave 60453 708-499-2550
John Hallberg, prin. Fax 499-6941
Other Schools – See Blue Island, Palos Heights, Robbins

Oak Lawn Community HSD 229 1,800/9-12
9400 Southwest Hwy 60453 708-424-5200
Dr. Michael Riordan, supt. Fax 424-5297
www.olchs.org
Oak Lawn Community HS 1,800/9-12
9400 Southwest Hwy 60453 708-424-5200
Dr. Michael Riordan, prin. Fax 424-5263

Oak Lawn-Hometown SD 123 3,000/PK-8
4201 W 93rd St 60453 708-423-0150
Dr. Art Fessler, supt. Fax 423-0160
www.d123.org/
Oak Lawn-Hometown MS 1,000/6-8
5345 W 99th St 60453 708-499-6400
Paul Enderle, prin. Fax 499-7684

Ridgeland SD 122 2,300/PK-8
6500 W 95th St 60453 708-599-5550
Julie Shellberg, supt. Fax 599-5626
www.ridgeland122.com
Simmons MS 800/6-8
6450 W 95th St 60453 708-599-8540
Tracy Flood, prin. Fax 599-8015

Cameo Beauty Academy Post-Sec.
9714 S Cicero Ave 60453 708-636-4660
Southside Baptist S 100/PK-12
5220 W 105th St 60453 708-425-3435
Robert Burckart, prin. Fax 425-9016

Oak Park, Cook, Pop. 50,159
Oak Park ESD 97 5,400/PK-8
970 Madison St 60302 708-524-3000
Dr. Albert Roberts, supt. Fax 524-3019
www.op97.org
Brooks MS 800/6-8
325 S Kenilworth Ave 60302 708-524-3050
Michael Michowski, prin. Fax 524-3036
Julian MS 900/6-8
416 S Ridgeland Ave 60302 708-524-3040
Todd Fitzgerald, prin. Fax 524-3035

Oak Park-River Forest SD 200 3,200/9-12
201 N Scoville Ave 60302 708-383-0700
Steven Isoye, supt. Fax 434-3917
www.oprfhs.org
Oak Park-River Forest HS 3,200/9-12
201 N Scoville Ave 60302 708-383-0700
Nathaniel Rouse, prin. Fax 434-3917

Fenwick HS 1,200/9-12
505 Washington Blvd 60302 708-386-0127
Peter Groom, prin. Fax 386-3052
Resurrection University Post-Sec.
3 Erie Ct 60302 708-763-6530

Oakwood, Vermilion, Pop. 1,576
Oakwood CUSD 76 1,100/PK-12
12190 US Route 150 61858 217-446-6081
Karen Perry, supt. Fax 446-6218
www.oakwood.k12.il.us
Other Schools – See Danville, Fithian

Oblong, Crawford, Pop. 1,457
Oblong CUSD 4 600/PK-12
PO Box 40 62449 618-592-3933
Jeffery Patchett, supt. Fax 592-3427
www.oblongschools.net
Oblong HS 200/9-12
700 S Range St 62449 618-592-4235
Fritz Wheeler, prin. Fax 592-3540

Odin, Marion, Pop. 1,064
Odin SD 722 300/PK-12
102 S Merritt St 62870 618-775-8266
Stephen Westrick, supt. Fax 775-8268
www.odinpublicschools.org
Odin HS 100/9-12
102 S Merritt St 62870 618-775-8266
Sheri Uchitjil, prin. Fax 775-8268

O Fallon, Saint Clair, Pop. 27,465
Central SD 104 500/PK-8
309 Hartman Ln 62269 618-632-6336
John Bute, supt. Fax 632-0870
www.central104.org
Arthur MS 200/5-8
160 Saint Ellen Mine Rd 62269 618-622-9685
Jered Weh, prin. Fax 622-8691

O'Fallon CCSD 90 2,700/PK-8
118 E Washington St 62269 618-632-3666
Dr. Todd Koehl, supt. Fax 632-7864
www.of90web.net
Carriel JHS 6-8
450 N 7 Hills Rd 62269 618-632-3666
Dr. Douglas Wood, prin. Fax 622-2940
Fulton JHS 500/6-8
307 Kyle Rd 62269 618-628-0090
Joi Wills, prin. Fax 624-9390

O'Fallon Township HSD 203 2,500/9-12
600 S Smiley St 62269 618-632-3507
Dr. Darcy Benway, supt. Fax 632-9730
www.oths.k12.il.us/
O'Fallon HS - Milburn 600/9-9
650 Milburn School Rd 62269 618-622-9647
Richard Bickel, prin. Fax 622-9630
O'Fallon HS - Smiley 1,900/10-12
600 S Smiley St 62269 618-632-3507
Richard Bickel, prin. Fax 206-2468

First Baptist Academy 200/K-12
1111 E US Highway 50 62269 618-726-6040
Jackye Biehl, admin. Fax 632-8029

Oglesby, LaSalle, Pop. 3,742
Oglesby ESD 125 600/PK-8
755 Bennett Ave 61348 815-883-9297
Michael Pillion, supt. Fax 883-3568
www.ops125.net

Washington MS 200/6-8
212 W Walnut St 61348 815-883-3517
Cindy Pozzi, prin. Fax 883-9282

Illinois Valley Community College Post-Sec.
815 N Orlando Smith St 61348 815-224-2720

Ohio, Bureau, Pop. 504
Ohio Community HSD 505 50/9-12
PO Box 478 61349 815-376-2934
Sharon Sweger, supt. Fax 376-2102
Ohio Community HS 50/9-12
PO Box 478 61349 815-376-4414
Jason Wilt, prin. Fax 376-2102

Okawville, Washington, Pop. 1,424
West Washington County CUSD 10 500/K-12
PO Box 27 62271 618-243-6454
Scott Fuhrhop, supt. Fax 243-6454
www.okawville-k12.org
Okawville JSHS 300/6-12
400 S Hanover St 62271 618-243-5201
Mike Rumsey, prin. Fax 243-6110

Olney, Richland, Pop. 9,020
East Richland CUSD 1 2,100/PK-12
1100 E Laurel St 62450 618-395-2324
Marilyn Holt, supt. Fax 392-4147
www.east.rchlnd.k12.il.us
East Richland HS 600/9-12
1200 E Laurel St 62450 618-393-2191
Chris Simpson, prin. Fax 395-1256
East Richland MS 400/6-8
1099 N Van St 62450 618-395-4372
Andy Thomann, prin. Fax 392-3399

Olney Central College Post-Sec.
305 N West St 62450 618-395-7777

Olympia Fields, Cook, Pop. 4,901
Rich Township HSD 227 4,000/9-12
20550 S Cicero Ave 60461 708-679-5800
Donna Leak Ph.D., supt. Fax 679-5740
www.rich227.org
Rich Central HS 1,500/9-12
3600 W 203rd St 60461 708-679-5600
Jammie Poole, prin. Fax 679-5632
Other Schools – See Park Forest, Richton Park

Onarga, Iroquois, Pop. 1,354
Iroquois West CUSD 10
Supt. — See Gilman
Iroquois West MS 200/6-8
303 N Evergreen St 60955 815-268-4355
Vicki Killus, prin. Fax 268-7608

Oneida, Knox, Pop. 697
ROWVA CUSD 208 700/PK-12
PO Box 69 61467 309-483-3711
Lloyd Little, supt. Fax 483-6123
www.rowva.k12.il.us
ROWVA HS 200/9-12
PO Box 69 61467 309-483-6371
Joe Peters, prin. Fax 483-8223
ROWVA JHS 100/7-8
PO Box 69 61467 309-483-2803
Nancy Hroziencik, prin. Fax 483-6378

Opdyke, Jefferson, Pop. 247
Opdyke-Belle-Rive CCSD 5
Supt. — See Belle Rive
Opdyke MS 100/5-8
19380 E 4th St 62872 618-756-2492
John Ashby, prin. Fax 756-2355

Orangeville, Stephenson, Pop. 784
Orangeville CUSD 203 400/PK-12
201 S Orange St 61060 815-789-4289
Dr. Doug DeSchepper, supt. Fax 789-4709
www.orangevillecusd.com/
Orangeville HS 100/9-12
201 S Orange St 61060 815-789-4289
Mark Schudel, prin. Fax 789-4709
Orangeville JHS 100/7-8
201 S Orange St 61060 815-789-4289
Mark Schudel, prin. Fax 789-4709

Oregon, Ogle, Pop. 3,686
Oregon CUSD 220 1,200/PK-12
206 S 10th St 61061 815-732-2186
Thomas Mahoney, supt. Fax 732-2187
www.ocusd.net
Oregon HS 500/9-12
210 S 10th St 61061 815-732-6241
Phillip Caposey, prin. Fax 732-3361
Other Schools – See Mount Morris

Orion, Henry, Pop. 1,846
Orion CUSD 223 1,000/PK-12
PO Box 189 61273 309-526-3388
David Deets, supt. Fax 526-3711
orionschools.us/
Orion HS 300/9-12
PO Box 39 61273 309-526-3361
Nathan DeBaillie, prin. Fax 526-3854
Orion MS 200/6-8
PO Box 129 61273 309-526-3392
Tiffany Springer, prin. Fax 526-3872

Orland Hills, Cook, Pop. 7,042
Consolidated HSD 230
Supt. — See Orland Park
Andrew HS 2,300/9-12
9001 171st St, 708-342-5800
Robert Nolting, prin. Fax 532-7383

Orland Park, Cook, Pop. 56,112
Consolidated HSD 230 8,300/9-12
15100 S 94th Ave 60462 708-745-5203
Dr. James Gay, supt. Fax 349-2105
www.d230.org

Sandburg HS 3,600/9-12
13300 S La Grange Rd 60462 708-671-3100
Dr. Julia Wheaton, prin. Fax 361-9714
Other Schools – See Orland Hills, Palos Hills

Orland SD 135 5,200/K-8
15100 S 94th Ave 60462 708-364-3306
Dr. Carol Kunst, supt. Fax 873-6479
www.orland135.org
Century JHS 800/6-8
10801 W 159th St 60467 708-364-3500
Cindy Finley, prin. Fax 349-5840
Jerling JHS 700/6-8
8851 W 151st St 60462 708-364-3700
Dave Kennedy, prin. Fax 873-6457
Orland JHS 500/6-8
14855 West Ave 60462 708-364-4200
Linda Kane, prin. Fax 349-5843

ITT Technical Institute Post-Sec.
11551 184th Pl 60467 708-326-3200
Robert Morris University Post-Sec.
43 Orland Square Dr 60462 800-762-5960

Oswego, Kendall, Pop. 29,822
Oswego CUSD 308 16,600/PK-12
4175 State Route 71 60543 630-636-3080
Dr. Matthew Wendt, supt. Fax 636-3688
www.oswego308.org
Oswego East HS 2,100/9-12
1525 Harvey Rd 60543 630-636-2200
Jeff Craig, prin. Fax 636-2454
Oswego HS 2,100/9-12
4250 State Route 71 60543 630-636-2000
Mike Wayne, prin. Fax 636-2199
Plank JHS 800/6-8
510 Secretariat Ln 60543 630-551-9400
Jamie Max, prin. Fax 551-9691
Thompson JHS 900/6-8
440 Boulder Hill Pass 60543 630-636-2600
Shannon Leuders, prin. Fax 636-2691
Traughber JHS 1,000/6-8
570 Colchester Dr 60543 630-636-2700
Ralph Kober, prin. Fax 636-2791
Other Schools – See Aurora

Hair Professionals School of Cosmetology Post-Sec.
PO Box 40 60543 630-554-2266

Ottawa, LaSalle, Pop. 18,544
Ottawa ESD 141 2,000/PK-8
320 W Main St 61350 815-433-1133
Cleve Threadgill, supt. Fax 433-1888
ottawaelementaryschools.com
Shepherd MS 400/7-8
701 E McKinley Rd 61350 815-434-7925
Lori Kimes, prin. Fax 433-9447

Ottawa Township HSD 140 1,400/9-12
211 E Main St 61350 815-433-1323
Matt Winchester, supt. Fax 433-1338
www.ottawahigh.com
Ottawa Township HS 1,400/9-12
211 E Main St 61350 815-433-1323
Mike Cushing, prin. Fax 433-1338

Marquette Academy 200/K-12
1000 Paul St 61350 815-433-0125
Brooke Rick, prin. Fax 433-2632

Palatine, Cook, Pop. 67,495
Palatine CCSD 15 11,800/PK-8
580 N 1st Bank Dr 60067 847-963-3000
Scott Thompson, supt. Fax 963-3200
www.ccsd15.net
Sundling JHS 700/7-8
1100 N Smith St 60067 847-963-3700
Jason Dietz, prin. Fax 963-3706
Winston Campus JHS 700/7-8
900 E Palatine Rd 60074 847-963-7400
Rene Carranza, prin. Fax 963-7406
Other Schools – See Rolling Meadows

Township HSD 211 10,700/9-12
1750 S Roselle Rd 60067 847-755-6600
Dr. Nancy Robb, supt. Fax 755-6810
www.d211.org
District 211 Academy - North 50/Alt
335 E Illinois Ave 60067 847-755-6700
Francesca Anderson, admin. Fax 755-6858
Fremd HS 2,500/9-12
1000 S Quentin Rd 60067 847-755-2600
Dr. Lisa Small, prin. Fax 755-2623
Palatine HS 2,300/9-12
1111 N Rohlwing Rd 60074 847-755-1600
Gary Steiger, prin. Fax 755-1623
Other Schools – See Hoffman Estates, Schaumburg, Streamwood

William Rainey Harper College Post-Sec.
1200 W Algonquin Rd 60067 847-925-6000

Palestine, Crawford, Pop. 1,359
Palestine CUSD 3 400/PK-12
PO Box 217 62451 618-586-2713
Joe Sornberger, supt. Fax 586-2905
palestine.k12.il.us/
Palestine HS 100/9-12
102 N Main St 62451 618-586-2712
Tangi Waldrop, prin. Fax 586-5328

Palmyra, Macoupin, Pop. 692
Northwestern CUSD 2 300/PK-12
30953 Route 111 62674 217-436-2210
Patrick Bowman, supt. Fax 436-2701
northwestern.k12.il.us
Northwestern HS 100/9-12
30889 Route 111 62674 217-436-2011
Brenda Mitchell, prin. Fax 436-9112
Northwestern JHS 50/7-8
30889 Route 111 62674 217-436-2011
Brenda Mitchell, prin. Fax 436-9112

Palos Heights, Cook, Pop. 12,393
Community HSD 218
Supt. — See Oak Lawn
Shepard HS 2,000/9-12
13049 S Ridgeland Ave 60463 708-371-1111
Josh Barron, prin. Fax 371-7688

Palos Heights SD 128 800/PK-8
12809 S McVickers Ave 60463 708-597-9040
Dr. Kathleen Casey, supt. Fax 597-9089
www.d128.k12.il.us
Independence JHS 300/6-8
6610 W Highland Dr 60463 708-448-0737
Dr. Paul McDermott, prin. Fax 448-0179

Chicago Christian HS 400/9-12
12001 S Oak Park Ave 60463 708-388-7650
Bob Payne, prin. Fax 388-0154
Trinity Christian College Post-Sec.
6601 W College Dr 60463 708-597-3000

Palos Hills, Cook, Pop. 17,273
Consolidated HSD 230
Supt. — See Orland Park
Stagg HS 2,500/9-12
8015 W 111th St 60465 708-974-7400
Eric Olsen, prin. Fax 974-0803

North Palos SD 117 2,900/PK-8
7825 W 103rd St 60465 708-598-5500
Dr. Jeannie Stachowiak, supt. Fax 598-5539
www.npd117.net/
Other Schools – See Hickory Hills

Hair Professionals Career College Post-Sec.
10321 S Roberts Rd 60465 708-430-1755
Moraine Valley Community College Post-Sec.
9000 W College Pkwy 60465 708-974-4300

Palos Park, Cook, Pop. 4,788
Palos CCSD 118 1,900/PK-8
8800 W 119th St 60464 708-448-4800
Dr. Joseph Dubec, supt. Fax 448-4880
www.palos118.org
Palos South MS 700/6-8
13100 S 82nd Ave 60464 708-448-5971
Christopher Bingen, prin. Fax 448-0754

Pana, Christian, Pop. 5,807
Pana CUSD 8 1,400/PK-12
PO Box 377 62557 217-562-1500
Dr. David Lett, supt. Fax 562-1501
www.panaschools.com
Pana HS 500/9-12
PO Box 377 62557 217-562-6600
Gayle McRoberts, prin. Fax 562-6714
Pana JHS 200/7-8
PO Box 377 62557 217-562-6500
Paul Lauff, prin. Fax 562-6712
Pana Adult Center Adult
PO Box 377 62557 217-562-6695
Don Kroski, prin. Fax 562-4534

Paris, Edgar, Pop. 8,761
Paris CUSD 4 500/PK-8
15601 US Highway 150 61944 217-465-5391
Lorraine Bailey, supt. Fax 466-1225
www.crestwood.k12.il.us
Crestwood JHS 200/6-8
15601 US Highway 150 61944 217-465-5391
Danette Young, prin. Fax 466-1225

Paris-Union SD 95 1,600/PK-12
300 S Eads Ave 61944 217-465-8448
Connie Sutton, supt. Fax 463-2243
www.paris95.k12.il.us
Mayo MS 300/6-8
310 E Wood St 61944 217-466-3050
Jeremy Larson, prin. Fax 466-3905
Paris Cooperative HS 600/9-12
309 S Main St 61944 217-466-1175
Dave Meister, dir. Fax 466-1903

Park Forest, Cook, Pop. 21,337
Park Forest SD 163 1,900/PK-8
242 S Orchard Dr 60466 708-668-9400
Dr. Joyce Carmine, supt. Fax 748-9359
www.sd163.com
Forest Trail MS 600/6-8
215 Wilson St 60466 708-668-9600
Dr. Carolyn Stroud, prin. Fax 503-2297

Rich Township HSD 227
Supt. — See Olympia Fields
Rich East Campus HS 1,200/9-12
300 Sauk Trl 60466 708-679-6100
Mark Kramer, prin. Fax 679-7330

Park Ridge, Cook, Pop. 37,078
Maine Township HSD 207 6,900/9-12
1131 S Dee Rd 60068 847-696-3600
Dr. Kenneth Wallace, supt. Fax 696-3254
www.maine207.org
Alternative Resource Center 50/Alt
1111 S Dee Rd 60068 847-692-8037
Norman Kane, dir. Fax 696-3254
Maine East HS 1,900/9-12
2601 Dempster St 60068 847-825-4484
Michael Pressler, prin. Fax 825-1636
Maine South HS 2,600/9-12
1111 S Dee Rd 60068 847-825-7711
Shawn Messmer, prin. Fax 825-0677
Other Schools – See Des Plaines

Park Ridge-Niles CCSD 64 4,300/PK-8
164 S Prospect Ave 60068 847-318-4300
Dr. Philip Bender, supt. Fax 318-4351
www.d64.org
Lincoln MS 700/6-8
200 S Lincoln Ave 60068 847-318-4215
Dr. Anthony Murray, prin. Fax 318-4210
Other Schools – See Niles

Patoka, Marion, Pop. 584
Patoka CUSD 100 300/PK-12
1220 Kinoka Rd 62875 618-432-5440
Mike Conlon, supt. Fax 432-5306
www.schools.lth5.k12.il.us/patoka
Patoka HS 100/9-12
1220 Kinoka Rd 62875 618-432-5440
Leslie Venezia, prin. Fax 432-5306
Patoka JHS 50/7-8
1220 Kinoka Rd 62875 618-432-5200
Leslie Venezia, prin. Fax 432-5306

Pawnee, Sangamon, Pop. 2,672
Pawnee CUSD 11 500/PK-12
810 4th St 62558 217-625-2471
Gary Alexander, supt. Fax 625-2251
www.pawneeschools.com/
Pawnee JSHS 200/7-12
810 4th St 62558 217-625-2471
Tim Kratochvil, prin. Fax 625-2251

Paw Paw, Lee, Pop. 862
Paw Paw CUSD 271 300/PK-12
PO Box 508 61353 815-627-2841
Robert Priest, supt. Fax 627-2971
www.2paws.net/
Paw Paw JSHS 200/7-12
PO Box 37 61353 815-627-2671
Chuck Schneider, prin. Fax 627-8481

Paxton, Ford, Pop. 4,437
Paxton-Buckley-Loda CUSD 10 1,500/PK-12
PO Box 50 60957 217-379-3314
Clifford McClure, supt. Fax 379-2862
www.pbl.k12.il.us
Paxton-Buckley-Loda HS 500/9-12
PO Box 50 60957 217-379-4331
Trent Eshleman, prin. Fax 379-2491
Paxton-Buckley-Loda JHS 400/6-8
PO Box 50 60957 217-379-9202
David Snider, prin. Fax 379-9169

Payson, Adams, Pop. 1,023
Payson CUSD 1 500/PK-12
406 W State St 62360 217-656-3323
Donna Veile, supt. Fax 656-4042
www.cusd1.org
Seymour JSHS 200/7-12
420 W Brainard St 62360 217-656-3355
Brian Maloy, prin. Fax 656-3584

Pearl City, Stephenson, Pop. 832
Pearl City CUSD 200 500/PK-12
PO Box 9 61062 815-443-2715
Timothy Thill, supt. Fax 443-2237
www.pcwolves.net/
Pearl City HS 100/9-12
PO Box 9 61062 815-443-2715
Jay Mullens, prin. Fax 443-2237
Pearl City JHS 100/7-8
PO Box 9 61062 815-443-2715
Jay Mullens, prin. Fax 443-2237

Pecatonica, Winnebago, Pop. 2,172
Pecatonica CUSD 321 1,000/PK-12
PO Box 419 61063 815-239-1639
William Faller, supt. Fax 239-2125
www.pecschools.com/
Pecatonica Community MS 300/5-8
PO Box 419 61063 815-239-2612
Timothy King, prin. Fax 239-1274
Pecatonica HS 300/9-12
PO Box 419 61063 815-239-2611
Todd France, prin. Fax 239-9128

Pekin, Tazewell, Pop. 33,678
Pekin Community HSD 303 2,000/9-12
320 Stadium Dr 61554 309-477-4222
Paula Davis, supt. Fax 477-4376
www.pekinhigh.net
Pekin Community HS 2,000/9-12
1903 Court St 61554 309-347-4331
Melissa Bloom, prin. Fax 477-4377

Pekin SD 108 3,700/PK-8
501 Washington St 61554 309-477-4700
Dr. Bill Link, supt. Fax 477-4701
www.pekin.net/pekin108
Broadmoor JHS 400/7-8
501 Maywood Ave 61554 309-477-4731
Marc Fogal, prin. Fax 477-4739
Edison JHS 400/7-8
1400 Earl St 61554 309-477-4732
Bill Heisel, prin. Fax 477-4738

Peoria, Peoria, Pop. 111,234
Dunlap CUSD 323 3,600/PK-12
3020 W Willow Knolls Dr 61614 309-691-3955
Dr. Jay Marino, supt. Fax 691-6764
www.dunlapcusd.net
Other Schools – See Dunlap

Norwood ESD 63 500/PK-8
6521 W Farmington Rd 61604 309-676-3523
Dr. Abby Humbles, supt. Fax 676-6099
www.norwood63.org
Norwood MS 200/5-8
6521 W Farmington Rd 61604 309-676-3683
Erik Estill, prin. Fax 676-6099

Peoria SD 150 13,100/PK-12
3202 N Wisconsin Ave 61603 309-672-6768
Dr. Grenita Lathan, supt. Fax 672-6708
www.psd150.org
Bills MS 200/5-8
6001 N Frostwood Pkwy 61615 309-693-4437
Laura Rodgers, prin. Fax 693-4438
Knoxville Center for Student Success 100/Alt
2628 N Knoxville Ave 61604 309-439-0000
Eric Thomas, prin. Fax 282-0007
Lincoln MS 300/6-8
700 Mary St 61603 309-672-6542
Ursula Brown, prin. Fax 676-6615
Lindbergh MS 400/5-8
6327 N Sheridan Rd 61614 309-693-4427
Mike Plunkett, prin. Fax 693-0499
Manual Academy 1,100/7-12
811 S Griswold St 61605 309-672-6600
Taunya Jenkins, prin. Fax 672-6605
Peoria HS 1,400/9-12
1615 N North St 61604 309-672-6630
Brett Elliott, prin. Fax 685-5803
Richwoods HS 1,500/9-12
6301 N University St 61614 309-693-4400
Cindy Clark, prin. Fax 693-4414
Rolling Acres-Edison MS 300/5-8
5617 N Merrimac Ave 61614 309-689-1100
Michael Barber, prin. Fax 693-4423
Sterling MS 200/5-8
2315 N Sterling Ave 61604 309-672-6557
Donna O'Day, prin. Fax 681-8286
Trewyn MS 300/5-8
1419 S Folkers Ave 61605 309-672-6500
Renee Andrews, prin. Fax 673-8537
Von Steuben MS 400/5-8
801 E Forrest Hill Ave 61603 309-672-6561
Randy Simmons, prin. Fax 685-7631
Washington Gifted MS 200/5-8
3706 N Grand Blvd 61614 309-672-6563
David Poehls, prin. Fax 672-6564
Woodruff Technical Center Alt
1800 NE Perry Ave 61603 309-672-6665
Ryan Olson, prin. Fax 282-5260
Other Schools – See West Peoria

Pleasant Valley SD 62 400/PK-8
4623 W Red Bud Dr 61604 309-673-6750
Dr. Allen Johnson, supt. Fax 674-0165
peoria.k12.il.us
Pleasant Valley MS 300/PK-K, 5-8
3314 W Richwoods Blvd 61604 309-679-0634
Nicholas Sutton, prin. Fax 679-0652

Bradley University Post-Sec.
1501 W Bradley Ave 61625 309-676-7611
Methodist College Post-Sec.
415 NE Saint Mark Ct 61603 309-672-5513
Midstate College Post-Sec.
411 W Northmoor Rd 61614 309-692-4092
Peoria Christian S 1,000/PK-12
3506 N California Ave 61603 309-686-4500
Becky Gardner, admin. Fax 686-2569
Peoria Notre Dame HS 800/9-12
5105 N Sheridan Rd 61614 309-691-8741
Charlie Roy, prin. Fax 691-0875
Robert Morris University Post-Sec.
211 Fulton St 61602 800-762-5960
St. Francis Medical Center Post-Sec.
530 NE Glen Oak Ave 61603 309-655-2000
St. Francis Medical Ctr. Coll./Nursing Post-Sec.
511 NE Greenleaf St 61603 309-655-2201

Peoria Heights, Peoria, Pop. 5,986
Peoria Heights CUSD 325 800/PK-12
500 E Glen Ave 61616 309-686-8800
Eric Heath, supt. Fax 686-8801
www.phcusd325.net
Peoria Heights HS 200/9-12
508 E Glen Ave 61616 309-686-8803
Joseph Stoner, prin. Fax 686-8808

Peoria Christian S - Monroe 300/5-8
3725 N Monroe Ave 61616 309-681-0500
Mark Zotz, prin. Fax 681-9371

Peotone, Will, Pop. 4,103
Peotone CUSD 207U 1,900/K-12
212 W Wilson St 60468 708-258-0991
Steve Stein, supt. Fax 258-0994
www.peotoneschools.org
Peotone HS 700/9-12
605 W North St 60468 708-258-3236
Deanna Oliver, prin. Fax 258-6991
Peotone JHS 500/6-8
1 Blue Devil Dr 60468 708-258-3246
Scott Wenzel, prin. Fax 258-6669

Perry, Pike, Pop. 397
Griggsville-Perry CUSD 4
Supt. — See Griggsville
Griggsville-Perry MS 100/5-8
PO Box 98 62362 217-236-9161
Pollee Craven, prin. Fax 236-7221

Peru, LaSalle, Pop. 10,189
Peru ESD 124 1,100/PK-8
1800 Church St 61354 815-223-0486
Mark Cross, supt. Fax 223-0490
www.perued.net
Parkside MS 500/5-8
1800 Church St 61354 815-223-7723
Lori Madden, prin. Fax 223-0285

St. Bede Academy 300/9-12
24 W US Highway 6 61354 815-223-3140
Michelle Mershon, prin. Fax 223-8580

Petersburg, Menard, Pop. 2,232
PORTA CUSD 202 1,200/PK-12
PO Box 202 62675 217-632-3803
Matthew Brue, supt. Fax 632-3221
www.porta202.org
PORTA HS 400/9-12
PO Box 202 62675 217-632-3216
Darren Hartry, prin. Fax 632-5446
PORTA JHS 200/7-8
PO Box 202 62675 217-632-3219
Jeff Hill, prin. Fax 632-5448

Phoenix, Cook, Pop. 1,934
South Holland SD 151
Supt. — See South Holland
Coolidge MS 500/6-8
15500 7th Ave 60426 708-339-5300
Patricia Payne, prin. Fax 339-5327

Piasa, Macoupin
Southwestern CUSD 9
Supt. — See Brighton
Southwestern HS 500/9-12
PO Box 100 62079 618-729-3211
Mark Bearley, prin. Fax 729-4276
Southwestern MS 300/7-8
PO Box 70 62079 618-729-3217
Scott Hopkins, prin. Fax 729-9231

Pinckneyville, Perry, Pop. 5,604
Pinckneyville Community HSD 101 400/9-12
600 E Water St 62274 618-357-5013
Keith Hagene, supt. Fax 357-6045
www.pchspanthers.com
Pinckneyville Community HS 400/9-12
600 E Water St 62274 618-357-5013
Dustin Foutch, prin. Fax 357-6045

Pinckneyville SD 50 600/PK-8
301 W Mulberry St 62274 618-357-9096
Tim O'Leary, supt. Fax 357-8731
www.p50.perry.k12.il.us
Pinckneyville MS 300/5-8
700 E Water St 62274 618-357-2724
Mark Rohlfing, prin.

Piper City, Ford, Pop. 823
Tri-Point CUSD 6-J
Supt. — See Kempton
Tri-Point MS 200/K-K, 4-8
PO Box 158 60959 815-686-2247
Duane Hitchens, prin. Fax 686-2663

Pittsfield, Pike, Pop. 4,559
Pikeland CUSD 10 1,300/PK-12
512 S Madison St 62363 217-285-2147
Paula Hawley, supt. Fax 285-5059
www.pikeland.net
Pikeland Community S 600/3-8
601 Piper Ln 62363 217-285-9462
Lisa Jockisch, prin. Fax 285-9551
Pittsfield HS 400/9-12
201 E Higbee St 62363 217-285-6888
Angie Greger, prin. Fax 285-9583

Plainfield, Will, Pop. 38,856
Plainfield CCSD 202 28,800/PK-12
15732 S Howard St 60544 815-577-4000
Dr. John Harper, supt. Fax 439-9705
www.psd202.org
Drauden Point MS 800/6-8
1911 Drauden Rd, 815-577-4900
Patrick Flynn, prin. Fax 439-9385
Heritage Grove MS 700/6-8
12425 S Van Dyke Rd, 815-439-4810
Stephen Diveley, prin. Fax 436-4661
Indian Trail MS 800/6-8
14723 S Eastern Ave 60544 815-436-6128
Christian Rivara, prin. Fax 436-7536
Jones MS 900/6-8
15320 W Wallin Dr 60544 815-267-3600
Dr. Edward Boswell, prin. Fax 439-7201
Kennedy MS 1,100/6-8
12350 Essington Rd, 815-439-8024
Jennifer Orlos, prin. Fax 254-7375
Plainfield Academy 200/Alt
23930 W Lockport St 60544 815-439-5521
Tod Schnowske, prin. Fax 439-7014
Plainfield Central HS 2,200/9-12
24120 W Fort Beggs Dr 60544 815-436-3200
Robert Smith, prin. Fax 439-2882
Plainfield East HS 1,800/9-12
12001 Naperville Rd, 815-577-0324
Anthony Manville, prin. Fax 577-0979
Plainfield North HS 1,800/9-12
12005 S 248th Ave, 815-609-8506
Raymond Epperson, prin. Fax 254-6138
Plainfield South HS 2,400/9-12
7800 Caton Farm Rd, 815-439-5555
David Travis, prin. Fax 436-5108
Timber Ridge MS 1,100/6-8
2101 S Bronk Rd, 815-439-3410
Dean Kariotakis, prin. Fax 439-3412
Other Schools – See Joliet

Troy CCSD 30C 4,500/PK-8
5800 Theodore Dr, 815-577-6760
Don White Ph.D., supt. Fax 577-3795
www.troy30c.org
Troy MS 1,000/7-8
5800 Theodore Dr, 815-230-9920
Matthew Jeffrey, prin. Fax 577-2867

Plano, Kendall, Pop. 10,709
Plano CUSD 88 2,300/PK-12
800 S Hale St 60545 630-552-8978
Dr. Hector Garcia, supt. Fax 552-8548
www.plano88.org/
Plano HS 600/9-12
704 W Abe St 60545 630-552-3178
Eric Benson, prin. Fax 552-8824
Plano MS 300/7-8
804 S Hale St 60545 630-552-3608
Mark Heller, prin. Fax 552-3802

Pleasant Hill, Pike, Pop. 964
Pleasant Hill CUSD 3 300/PK-12
PO Box 277 62366 217-734-2311
Ron Edwards, supt. Fax 734-2629
www.phwolves.com
Pleasant Hill HS 100/9-12
PO Box 277 62366 217-734-2311
Ryan Lowe, prin. Fax 734-2725

Pleasant Plains, Sangamon, Pop. 790
Pleasant Plains CUSD 8 1,300/PK-12
PO Box 20 62677 217-626-1041
Jerry Schutz, supt. Fax 626-1082
www.ppcusd8.org
Pleasant Plains HS 500/9-12
PO Box 320 62677 217-626-1044
Mike Ward, prin. Fax 626-1667
Pleasant Plains MS 400/5-8
2455 N Farmingdale Rd 62677 217-626-1061
Jill Lanier, prin. Fax 626-2272

Polo, Ogle, Pop. 2,326
Polo CUSD 222 700/PK-12
100 S Union Ave 61064 815-946-3815
Christopher Rademacher, supt. Fax 946-2493
www.polo222.org/
Aplington MS 200/6-8
610 E Mason St 61064 815-946-2519
Mark Downey, prin. Fax 946-2537
Polo Community HS 200/9-12
100 S Union Ave 61064 815-946-3314
Andy Faivre, prin. Fax 946-2493

Pontiac, Livingston, Pop. 11,777
Livingston Area Career Center
1100 E Indiana Ave 61764 815-842-2557
Tera Graves, dir. Fax 842-1005
Livingston Area Career Center Vo/Tech
1100 E Indiana Ave 61764 815-842-2557
Tera Graves, dir. Fax 842-1005

Pontiac CCSD 429 1,300/PK-8
117 W Livingston St 61764 815-844-5632
Kevin Lipke, supt. Fax 844-5773
www.pontiac429.org/
Pontiac JHS 400/6-8
600 N Morrow St 61764 815-842-4343
Judy Donze, prin. Fax 844-6230

Pontiac Township HSD 90 700/9-12
1100 E Indiana Ave 61764 815-844-6113
Jon Kilgore, supt. Fax 844-6116
www.pontiac.k12.il.us
Pontiac HS 700/9-12
1100 E Indiana Ave 61764 815-844-6113
Eric Bohm, prin. Fax 844-6116

Poplar Grove, Boone, Pop. 4,959
North Boone CUSD 200 1,700/PK-12
6248 N Boone School Rd 61065 815-765-3322
Dr. Steven Baule, supt. Fax 765-2053
www.nbcusd.org
North Boone HS 500/9-12
17823 Poplar Grove Rd 61065 815-765-3311
Jacob Hubert, prin. Fax 765-3316
North Boone MS 300/7-8
17641 Poplar Grove Rd 61065 815-765-9274
Lindsay Abbeduto, prin. Fax 765-9275

Port Byron, Rock Island, Pop. 1,628
Riverdale CUSD 100 1,200/PK-12
9624 256th St N 61275 309-523-3184
Ronald Jacobs, supt. Fax 523-3550
riverdaleschools.org
Riverdale HS 300/9-12
9622 256th St N 61275 309-523-3181
Rick Dwyer, prin. Fax 523-2885
Riverdale MS 200/6-8
9822 256th St N 61275 309-523-3131
James Jennings, prin. Fax 523-3934

Posen, Cook, Pop. 5,912
Posen-Robbins ESD 143-5 1,800/PK-8
14025 S Harrison Ave 60469 708-388-7200
Gregory Wright M.Ed., supt. Fax 388-3868
www.prsd1435.org
Other Schools – See Robbins

Princeton, Bureau, Pop. 7,583
Princeton ESD 115 1,300/PK-8
506 E Dover Rd 61356 815-875-3162
Tim Smith, supt. Fax 875-3101
www.princeton115schools.org
Logan JHS 400/6-8
302 W Central Ave 61356 815-875-6415
J.D. Orwig, prin. Fax 872-0034

Princeton HSD 500 600/9-12
103 S Euclid Ave 61356 815-875-3308
Kirk Haring, supt. Fax 875-8525
www.phs-il.org
Princeton HS 600/9-12
103 S Euclid Ave 61356 815-875-3308
Andy Berlinski, prin. Fax 875-8525

Princeville, Peoria, Pop. 1,723
Princeville CUSD 326 800/PK-12
302 Cordis Ave 61559 309-385-2213
Shannon Duling, supt. Fax 385-1823
www.princeville326.org/
Princeville HS 200/9-12
302 Cordis Ave 61559 309-385-4660
Richard Thole, prin. Fax 385-1110

Prophetstown, Whiteside, Pop. 2,069
Prophetstown-Lyndon-Tampico CUSD 3 1,000/PK-12
79 Grove St 61277 815-537-5101
Dave Rogers, supt. Fax 537-5102
plt3.org

Prophetstown HS 300/9-12
310 W Riverside Dr 61277 815-537-5161
Kevin Parker, prin. Fax 537-5102
Other Schools – See Tampico

Prospect Heights, Cook, Pop. 16,131
Prospect Heights SD 23 900/PK-8
700 N Schoenbeck Rd 60070 847-870-3850
Dr. Deb Wilson, supt. Fax 870-3896
www.d23.org/
MacArthur MS 500/6-8
700 N Schoenbeck Rd 60070 847-870-3879
Steven Lee, prin. Fax 870-3881

Quincy, Adams, Pop. 39,738
Quincy Area Vocational Technical Center
219 Baldwin Dr 62301 217-224-3775
Mark Pfleiger, dir. Fax 221-4800
www.qps.org/qavtc/
Quincy Area Vocational Technical Center Vo/Tech
219 Baldwin Dr 62301 217-224-3775
Mark Pfleiger, dir. Fax 221-4800

Quincy SD 172 6,600/PK-12
1416 Maine St 62301 217-223-8700
Christie Dickens, supt. Fax 228-7162
www.qps.org
Quincy JHS 1,400/7-9
100 S 14th St 62301 217-222-3073
Dan Sparrow, prin. Fax 228-7185
Quincy SHS 1,300/10-12
3322 Maine St 62301 217-224-3770
Danielle Edgar, prin. Fax 228-7149

Blessing Hospital Post-Sec.
PO Box 7005 62305 217-223-8400
Blessing-Rieman College of Nursing Post-Sec.
PO Box 7005 62305 217-228-5520
Gem City College Post-Sec.
700 State St 62301 217-222-0391
John Wood Community College Post-Sec.
1301 S 48th St 62305 217-224-6500
Quincy Christian S 100/PK-12
PO Box 3643 62305 217-223-5698
Bob Murray, admin. Fax 223-5724
Quincy Notre Dame HS 400/9-12
1400 S 11th St 62301 217-223-2479
Mark McDowell, prin. Fax 223-0023
Quincy University Post-Sec.
1800 College Ave 62301 217-222-8020
Vatterott College Post-Sec.
3609 N Marx Dr 62305 217-224-0600

Ramsey, Fayette, Pop. 1,024
Ramsey CUSD 204 500/PK-12
702 W 6th St 62080 618-423-2335
Melissa Rittor, supt. Fax 423-2314
www.ramsey.fayette.k12.il.us
Ramsey HS 100/9-12
702 W 6th St 62080 618-423-2333
Ginger Edwards, prin. Fax 423-2314

Rantoul, Champaign, Pop. 12,421
Rantoul CSD 137 1,500/PK-8
400 E Wabash Ave 61866 217-893-4171
Michelle Ramage, supt. Fax 892-4313
www.rcs.k12.il.us
Eater JHS, 400 E Wabash Ave 61866 400/6-8
Mike Penicook, prin. 217-892-2115

Rantoul Township HSD 193 800/9-12
200 S Sheldon St 61866 217-892-2151
Scott Amerio, supt. Fax 892-4442
www.rths.k12.il.us
Rantoul Township HS 800/9-12
200 S Sheldon St 61866 217-892-2151
Todd Wilson, prin. Fax 892-4442

Raymond, Montgomery, Pop. 996
Panhandle CUSD 2 600/PK-12
PO Box 49 62560 217-229-4215
Aaron Hopper, supt. Fax 229-4216
www.panhandle.k12.il.us/
Lincolnwood HS 200/9-12
507 N Prairie St 62560 217-229-4237
Chad Langheim, prin. Fax 229-3005
Lincolnwood JHS 100/6-8
507 N Prairie St 62560 217-229-4237
Chad Langheim, prin. Fax 229-3005

Red Bud, Randolph, Pop. 3,675
Red Bud CUSD 132 1,100/PK-12
815 Locust St 62278 618-282-3507
Jonathan Tallman, supt. Fax 282-6151
www.redbud132.org
Red Bud HS 400/9-12
815 Locust St 62278 618-282-3826
Dustin Nail, prin. Fax 282-6828

Richmond, McHenry, Pop. 1,854
Nippersink SD 2 1,500/PK-8
10006 N Main St 60071 815-678-4242
Dr. Dan Oest, supt. Fax 678-2810
www.nippersinkdistrict2.org
Nippersink MS 600/6-8
10006 N Main St 60071 815-678-7129
Tim Molitor, prin. Fax 678-7210

Richmond-Burton Community HSD 157 800/9-12
8311 IL Route 31 60071 815-678-4525
Dr. Dan Oest, supt. Fax 678-4324
www.rbchs.com
Richmond-Burton HS 800/9-12
8311 IL Route 31 60071 815-678-4525
Tom Lind, prin. Fax 678-4324

Richton Park, Cook, Pop. 13,324
Matteson ESD 162 3,200/PK-8
14601 Sauk Trl Ste 2 60471 708-748-0100
Dr. Blondean Davis, supt. Fax 748-7302
www.sd162.org
Other Schools – See Matteson

Rich Township HSD 227
Supt. — See Olympia Fields
Rich South Campus HS 1,400/9-12
5000 Sauk Trl 60471 708-679-3000
Cynthia Hudson, prin. Fax 679-3168

Riverdale, Cook, Pop. 13,395
Dolton SD 148 2,000/PK-8
114 W 144th St 60827 708-841-2290
Dr. Jayne Purcell, supt. Fax 841-5048
www.district148.net
Washington JHS 200/7-8
13900 S School St 60827 708-201-2078
Dorothy Jeter, prin. Fax 201-4971
Other Schools – See Dolton

River Forest, Cook, Pop. 10,962
River Forest SD 90 1,400/PK-8
7776 Lake St 60305 708-771-8282
Edward Condon Ph.D., supt. Fax 771-8291
www.district90.org/
Roosevelt JHS 600/5-8
7560 Oak Ave 60305 708-366-9230
Larry Garstki, prin. Fax 771-3962

Concordia University Chicago Post-Sec.
7400 Augusta St 60305 708-771-8300
Dominican University Post-Sec.
7900 Division St 60305 708-366-2490
Trinity HS 500/9-12
7574 Division St 60305 708-771-8383
Dr. Antonia Bouillette, prin. Fax 488-2014

River Grove, Cook, Pop. 10,116

Guerin College Preparatory HS 600/9-12
8001 Belmont Ave 60171 708-453-6233
Karen Booth, pres. Fax 453-6296
Triton College Post-Sec.
2000 5th Ave 60171 708-456-0300

Riverside, Cook, Pop. 8,771
Riverside Brookfield Township HSD 208 1,400/9-12
160 Ridgewood Rd 60546 708-442-7500
Dr. Kevin Skinkis, supt. Fax 447-5570
www.rbhs208.net
Riverside Brookfield Township HS 1,400/9-12
160 Ridgewood Rd 60546 708-442-7500
Pamela Bylsma, prin. Fax 442-7840

Riverside SD 96 1,500/PK-8
63 Woodside Rd 60546 708-447-5007
Dr. Bhavna Sharma-Lewis, supt. Fax 447-3252
www.district96.org
Hauser JHS 500/6-8
65 Woodside Rd 60546 708-447-3896
Leslie Berman, prin. Fax 447-5180

Riverton, Sangamon, Pop. 3,413
Riverton CUSD 14 1,500/PK-12
PO Box 1010 62561 217-629-6009
Dr. Tom Mulligan, supt. Fax 629-6008
www.rivertonschools.org
Riverton HS 400/9-12
PO Box 560 62561 217-629-6003
Bill Lamkey, prin. Fax 629-6020
Riverton MS 500/5-8
PO Box 530 62561 217-629-6002
Fred Lamkey, prin. Fax 629-6017

Roanoke, Woodford, Pop. 2,057
Roanoke-Benson CUSD 60 600/PK-12
PO Box 320 61561 309-923-8921
Rohn Peterson, supt. Fax 923-7508
www.rb60.com/
Roanoke-Benson HS 200/9-12
PO Box 320 61561 309-923-8401
Michael Tresnak, prin. Fax 923-7508
Other Schools – See Benson

Linn Mennonite Christian S 50/K-12
1594 County Road 1700 N 61561 309-923-5641
Jon Yoder, pres.

Robbins, Cook, Pop. 5,299
Community HSD 218
Supt. — See Oak Lawn
Delta Learning Center 100/Alt
3940 W Midlothian 60472 708-371-1880
Joe Fowler, prin. Fax 371-4782

Posen-Robbins ESD 143-5
Supt. — See Posen
Kellar JHS 500/6-8
14123 S Lydia Ave 60472 708-388-7201
Rochelle James M.A., prin. Fax 388-6177

Robinson, Crawford, Pop. 7,621
Robinson CUSD 2 1,600/PK-12
PO Box 190 62454 618-544-7511
Josh Quick, supt. Fax 544-7511
www.robinsonschools.com/
Nuttall MS 300/6-8
PO Box 190 62454 618-544-8618
Sue Catt, prin. Fax 544-8618
Robinson HS 500/9-12
PO Box 190 62454 618-544-9510
Troy Hickey, prin. Fax 544-9510

Lincoln Trail College Post-Sec.
11220 State Highway 1 62454 618-544-8657

Rochelle, Ogle, Pop. 9,466
Rochelle CCSD 231 1,700/PK-8
444 N 8th St 61068 815-562-6363
Todd Prusator, supt. Fax 562-5500
www.d231.rochelle.net
Rochelle MS 600/6-8
111 School Ave 61068 815-562-7997
Mike Valentine, prin. Fax 562-8527

Rochelle Township HSD 212 900/9-12
1401 Flagg Rd 61068 815-562-4161
Richard Craven, supt. Fax 562-6693
www.rths.rochelle.net/
Rochelle Township HS 900/9-12
1401 Flagg Rd 61068 815-562-4161
Travis McGuire, prin. Fax 562-6693

Rochester, Sangamon, Pop. 3,622
Rochester CUSD 3A 2,300/PK-12
4 Rocket Dr 62563 217-498-6210
Dr. Thomas Bertrand, supt. Fax 498-8045
www.rochester3a.sangamon.k12.il.us
Rochester HS 700/9-12
1 Rocket Dr 62563 217-498-9761
Dennis Canny, prin. Fax 498-9825
Rochester JHS 300/7-8
3 Rocket Dr 62563 217-498-9761
Brent Ashbaugh, prin. Fax 498-6204

Rock Falls, Whiteside, Pop. 9,103
Rock Falls ESD 13 1,000/PK-8
602 4th Ave 61071 815-626-2604
Dan Arickx, supt. Fax 626-2627
www.rfsd13.org
Rock Falls MS 300/6-8
1701 12th Ave 61071 815-626-2626
Jeffrey Brown, prin. Fax 626-3198

Rock Falls Township HSD 301 700/9-12
101 12th Ave 61071 815-625-3886
Dr. Jane Eichman, supt. Fax 625-3889
www.wside.k12.il.us/rfhs
Rock Falls Township HS 700/9-12
101 12th Ave 61071 815-625-3886
Ron McCord, prin. Fax 625-3889

Rockford, Winnebago, Pop. 148,827
Rockford SD 205 27,300/PK-12
501 7th St 61104 815-966-3000
Dr. Robert Willis, supt. Fax 966-3193
www.rps205.com/
Auburn HS 1,800/9-12
5110 Auburn St 61101 815-966-3300
Ryan Reinecke, prin. Fax 966-3911
Eisenhower MS 1,000/6-8
3525 Spring Creek Rd 61107 815-229-2450
Jeff Carlson, prin. Fax 229-2456
Flinn MS 900/6-8
2525 Ohio Pkwy 61108 815-229-2800
Randy Bay, prin. Fax 229-2894
Guilford HS 2,000/9-12
5620 Spring Creek Rd 61114 815-654-4870
Janice Hawkins, prin. Fax 654-4901
Jefferson HS 1,800/9-12
4145 Samuelson Rd 61109 815-874-9536
Don Rundall, prin. Fax 874-2800
Kennedy MS 700/6-8
520 Pierpont Ave 61103 815-654-4880
Marcus Lewis, prin. Fax 654-4874
Lincoln MS 700/6-8
1500 Charles St 61104 815-229-2400
Jason Grey, prin. Fax 229-2420
Marshall S 4-8
4664 N Rockton Ave 61103 815-490-5400
Jill Faber, prin.
Rockford East HS 1,400/9-12
2929 Charles St 61108 815-229-2100
Patrick Enright, prin. Fax 229-2113
Rockford Environmental Science Academy 1,200/6-8
1800 Ogilby Rd 61102 815-489-5509
William Ady, prin. Fax 966-5360
Roosevelt Community Education Center 400/Alt
978 Haskell Ave 61103 815-966-3265
Dr. Heidi Houy, prin. Fax 966-3178
West MS 600/6-8
1900 N Rockton Ave 61103 815-966-3200
Maceo Rainey, prin. Fax 966-3216

Berean Baptist Christian S 300/PK-12
5626 Safford Rd 61101 815-962-4841
Douglas Swanson, admin. Fax 962-4851
Boylan Central Catholic HS 1,200/9-12
4000 Saint Francis Dr 61103 815-877-0531
Jerry Kerrigan, admin. Fax 877-2544
Christian Life Schools 700/PK-12
5950 Spring Creek Rd 61114 815-877-5749
Larry Goodrich, prin. Fax 877-4358
Educators of Beauty Post-Sec.
2601B N Mulford Rd 61114 815-639-9200
Keith S 300/PK-12
1 Jacoby Pl 61107 815-399-8823
Alan Gibby, hdmstr. Fax 399-2470
North Love Christian S 100/PK-12
5301 E Riverside Blvd 61114 815-877-6021
Tom Seeley, admin. Fax 877-6076
Rasmussen College Post-Sec.
6000 E State St Fl 4 61108 815-316-4800
Rockford Career College Post-Sec.
1130 S Alpine Rd Ste 100 61108 815-965-8616
Rockford Christian S 1,100/PK-12
1401 N Bell School Rd 61107 815-391-8000
Randy Taylor, supt. Fax 391-8004
Rockford College Post-Sec.
5050 E State St 61108 815-226-4000
Rockford Lutheran JSHS 600/6-12
3411 N Alpine Rd 61114 815-877-9551
Don Kortze, prin. Fax 877-4024
Rockford Memorial Hospital Post-Sec.
2400 N Rockton Ave 61103 815-971-5000
Rock Valley College Post-Sec.
3301 N Mulford Rd 61114 815-921-7821
St. Anthony College of Nursing Post-Sec.
5658 E State St 61108 815-395-5091
St. Anthony Medical Center Post-Sec.
5666 E State St 61108 815-226-2000
Spectrum S 200/PK-12
2909 N Main St 61103 815-877-1600
Christine Klekamp, dir. Fax 877-1685

Swedish-American Hospital — Post-Sec.
1401 E State St 61104 — 815-968-4400

Rock Island, Rock Island, Pop. 37,879
Rock Island-Milan SD 41 — 5,700/PK-12
2101 6th Ave 61201 — 309-793-5900
Dr. Michael Oberhaus, supt. — Fax 793-5905
rockislandschools.org
Edison JHS — 400/7-8
4141 9th St 61201 — 309-793-5920
Gary Flecker, prin. — Fax 793-5919
Marshall Center — 100/Alt
600 11th Ave 61201 — 309-793-5924
Phillip Ambrose, prin. — Fax 793-5937
Rock Island HS — 1,600/9-12
1400 25th Ave 61201 — 309-793-5950
Tim Wernentin, prin. — Fax 793-9866
Washington JHS — 500/7-8
3300 18th Ave 61201 — 309-793-5915
Egan Colbrese, prin. — Fax 793-5917

Alleman HS — 500/9-12
1103 40th St 61201 — 309-786-7793
Colin Letendre, prin. — Fax 786-7834
Augustana College — Post-Sec.
639 38th St 61201 — 309-794-7000
Trinity College of Nursing — Post-Sec.
2122 25th Ave 61201 — 309-779-7700

Rockton, Winnebago, Pop. 7,573
Hononegah Community HSD 207 — 2,200/9-12
307 Salem St 61072 — 815-624-5010
Lynn Gibson, supt. — Fax 624-5029
www.hononegah.org
Hononegah Community HS — 2,200/9-12
307 Salem St 61072 — 815-624-5005
Todd Hencsik, prin. — Fax 624-5025

Rockton SD 140 — 1,500/PK-8
1050 E Union St 61072 — 815-624-7143
Dr. Michael Greenlee, supt. — Fax 624-4640
rockton140.org
Mack MS — 500/6-8
11810 Old River Rd 61072 — 815-624-2611
Kindyl Etnyre, prin. — Fax 624-5900

Rolling Meadows, Cook, Pop. 23,765
Palatine CCSD 15
Supt. — See Palatine
Plum Grove JHS — 800/7-8
2600 Plum Grove Rd 60008 — 847-963-7600
Dr. Kerry Swalwell, prin. — Fax 963-7606
Sandburg JHS — 500/7-8
2600 Martin Ln 60008 — 847-963-7800
Greta Rakow, prin. — Fax 963-7806

Township HSD 214
Supt. — See Arlington Heights
Rolling Meadows HS — 1,800/9-12
2901 Central Rd 60008 — 847-718-5600
Eileen Hart, prin. — Fax 718-5617
Young Adult Program — 50/Alt
2901 Central Rd 60008 — 847-718-5787
Sharyn Marsh, dir. — Fax 718-5617

Romeoville, Will, Pop. 38,967
Valley View CUSD 365U — 17,600/PK-12
755 Dalhart Ave 60446 — 815-886-2700
Dr. James Mitchem, supt. — Fax 886-7294
www.vvsd.org/
Lukancic MS — 600/6-8
725 W Normantown Rd 60446 — 815-886-2216
Tricia Rollerson, prin. — Fax 886-2264
Martinez MS — 800/6-8
590 Belmont Dr 60446 — 815-886-6100
Sarah DeDonato, prin. — Fax 886-7264
Romeoville HS — 1,800/9-12
100 N Independence Blvd 60446 — 815-886-1800
Derek Kinder, prin. — Fax 886-7272
Other Schools – See Bolingbrook

Wilco Area Career Center
500 Wilco Blvd 60446 — 815-838-6941
Katrina Plese, dir. — Fax 838-1163
www.wilco.k12.il.us
Wilco Area Career Center — Vo/Tech
500 Wilco Blvd 60446 — 815-838-6941
Katrina Plese, dir. — Fax 838-1163

Illinois Welding School — Post-Sec.
1315 Enterprise Dr Ste E 60446 — 630-679-0566
Lewis University — Post-Sec.
1 University Pkwy 60446 — 815-838-0500
Rasmussen College — Post-Sec.
1400 W Normantown Rd 60446 — 815-306-2600

Roodhouse, Greene, Pop. 1,796
North Greene Unit SD 3
Supt. — See White Hall
North Greene JHS — 100/7-8
403 W North St 62082 — 217-589-4623
Cynthia Rice, prin. — Fax 589-4028

Roscoe, Winnebago, Pop. 10,602
Kinnikinnick CCSD 131 — 1,700/PK-8
5410 Pine Ln 61073 — 815-623-2837
Keli Freedlund, supt. — Fax 623-9285
www.kinn131.org
Roscoe MS — 700/6-8
6121 Elevator Rd 61073 — 815-623-2837
Julie Cropp, prin. — Fax 623-7604

Roselle, DuPage, Pop. 22,408
Lake Park Community HSD 108 — 2,800/9-12
590 Medinah Rd 60172 — 630-529-4500
Lynne Panega, supt. — Fax 295-5414
www.lphs.org
Lake Park HS East — 1,400/9-10
600 Medinah Rd 60172 — 630-529-4500
Jim Roberts, prin. — Fax 295-5212
Lake Park HS West — 1,400/11-12
500 W Bryn Mawr Ave 60172 — 630-529-4500
Janet Constien, prin. — Fax 295-2932

Medinah SD 11 — 700/K-8
700 E Granville Ave 60172 — 630-893-3737
Dr. Joseph Bailey, supt. — Fax 893-4947
www.medinah11.org
Medinah MS — 300/6-8
700 E Granville Ave 60172 — 630-893-3838
Andrew Grimm, prin. — Fax 893-5198

Roselle SD 12 — 700/K-8
100 E Walnut St 60172 — 630-529-2091
Dr. Lori Bein, supt. — Fax 529-2467
www.sd12.k12.il.us/
Roselle MS — 200/6-8
500 S Park St 60172 — 630-529-1600
Kathleen Schneiter, prin. — Fax 529-1882

Roseville, Warren, Pop. 986
Monmouth-Roseville CUSD 238
Supt. — See Monmouth
Monmouth-Roseville JHS — 200/7-8
200 E Gossett St 61473 — 309-426-2682
Donald Farr, prin. — Fax 426-2303

Round Lake, Lake, Pop. 17,862
Round Lake Area SD 116 — 7,000/PK-12
316 S Rosedale Ct 60073 — 847-270-9000
Dr. Constance Collins, supt. — Fax 546-3538
www.rlas-116.org/
Magee MS — 700/6-8
500 N Cedar Lake Rd 60073 — 847-546-8800
Jodi Megerle, prin. — Fax 740-3836
Round Lake HS — 1,900/9-12
800 High School Dr 60073 — 847-270-9300
Dr. Kurt Sinclair, prin. — Fax 546-5872
Other Schools – See Round Lake Heights

Round Lake Heights, Lake, Pop. 2,629
Round Lake Area SD 116
Supt. — See Round Lake
Round Lake MS — 900/6-8
2000 Lotus Dr 60073 — 847-270-9400
Jeffry Prickett, prin. — Fax 270-9419

Roxana, Madison, Pop. 1,531
Roxana CUSD 1 — 1,900/PK-12
401 Chaffer Ave 62084 — 618-254-7544
Debra Kreutztrager, supt. — Fax 254-7547
www.roxanaschools.org
Roxana HS — 600/9-12
401 Chaffer Ave 62084 — 618-254-7553
Tom Roth, prin. — Fax 254-7580
Roxana JHS — 400/6-8
401 Chaffer Ave 62084 — 618-254-7560
Steve Mayerhofer, prin. — Fax 254-8107

Royal, Champaign, Pop. 293
Prairieview-Ogden CCSD 197 — 200/K-8
PO Box 27 61871 — 217-583-3300
Victor White, supt. — Fax 583-3391
www.pvo.k12.il.us/
Other Schools – See Thomasboro

Rushville, Schuyler, Pop. 3,179
Schuyler-Industry CUSD 5 — 1,100/PK-12
740 Maple Ave 62681 — 217-322-4311
Dr. William Mattingly, supt. — Fax 322-4398
www.sid5.com/
Rushville-Industry HS — 300/9-12
730 N Congress St 62681 — 217-322-4311
Ryan Plattenberger, prin. — Fax 322-2844
Schuyler-Industry MS — 300/5-8
750 N Congress St 62681 — 217-322-4311
Jim Shepherd, prin. — Fax 322-3938

Saint Anne, Kankakee, Pop. 1,243
Saint Anne Community HSD 302 — 200/9-12
PO Box 630 60964 — 815-422-5022
Richard Levek, supt. — Fax 422-5023
www.sachs.k12.il.us/
Saint Anne Community HS — 200/9-12
PO Box 630 60964 — 815-427-8141
Ramie Kolitwenzew, prin. — Fax 427-8609

Saint Charles, Kane, Pop. 32,580
Saint Charles CUSD 303 — 13,100/PK-12
201 S 7th St 60174 — 331-228-2000
Dr. Donald Schlomann, supt. — Fax 228-2001
www.d303.org
Haines MS — 1,100/6-8
305 S 9th St 60174 — 331-228-3100
Pamela Jensen, prin. — Fax 228-3101
Saint Charles East HS — 2,200/9-12
1020 Dunham Rd 60174 — 331-228-4000
Charlie Kyle, prin. — Fax 228-4001
Saint Charles North HS — 2,100/9-12
255 Red Gate Rd 60175 — 331-228-4400
Audra Christenson, prin. — Fax 228-4401
Thompson MS — 900/6-8
705 W Main St 60174 — 331-228-3400
Timothy Loversky, prin. — Fax 228-3401
Wredling MS — 1,300/6-8
1200 Dunham Rd 60174 — 331-228-3400
Stephen Morrill, prin. — Fax 228-3401

Saint Elmo, Fayette, Pop. 1,414
Saint Elmo CUSD 202 — 500/PK-12
1200 N Walnut St 62458 — 618-829-3264
Deborah Philpot, supt. — Fax 829-5161
www.stelmo.org
Saint Elmo HS — 100/9-12
300 W 12th St 62458 — 618-829-3227
Brian Garrard, prin. — Fax 829-5161
Saint Elmo JHS — 100/7-8
300 W 12th St 62458 — 618-829-3227
Brian Garrard, prin. — Fax 829-5161

Saint Jacob, Madison, Pop. 1,092
Triad CUSD 2
Supt. — See Troy
Triad MS — 800/6-8
9539 US Highway 40 62281 — 618-644-5511
Cathie Buller, prin. — Fax 644-9435

Saint Joseph, Champaign, Pop. 3,931
Saint Joseph CCSD 169 — 900/PK-8
PO Box 409 61873 — 217-469-2291
Todd Pence, supt. — Fax 469-8906
www.stjoe.k12.il.us
Saint Joseph MS — 400/5-8
PO Box 409 61873 — 217-469-2334
Chris Graham, prin. — Fax 469-2537

Saint Joseph-Ogden Community HSD 305 — 500/9-12
PO Box 890 61873 — 217-469-2586
James Acklin, supt.
www.sjo.k12.il.us
Saint Joseph-Ogden HS — 500/9-12
PO Box 890 61873 — 217-469-2332
Brian Brooks, prin. — Fax 469-8290

Salem, Marion, Pop. 7,393
Salem Community HSD 600 — 800/9-12
1200 N Broadway Ave 62881 — 618-548-0727
Brad Detering, supt. — Fax 548-8021
www.salemhigh.com
Salem Community HS — 800/9-12
1200 N Broadway Ave 62881 — 618-548-0727
Brad Detering, prin. — Fax 548-8021

Salem SD 111 — 1,000/PK-8
1300 Hawthorn Rd 62881 — 618-548-7702
Mark Cartwright, supt. — Fax 548-7714
www.salem111.com
Franklin Park MS — 600/PK-PK, 4-
1325 N Franklin St 62881 — 618-548-7704
David Conklin, prin. — Fax 548-7712

Sandoval, Marion, Pop. 1,257
Sandoval CUSD 501 — 500/PK-12
859 W Missouri Ave 62882 — 618-247-3233
Jennifer Garrison, supt. — Fax 247-3243
www.sandoval501.org
Sandoval HS — 100/9-12
859 W Missouri Ave 62882 — 618-247-3361
Annie Gray, prin. — Fax 247-3235
Sandoval JHS — 100/7-8
859 W Missouri Ave 62882 — 618-247-3361
Annie Gray, prin. — Fax 247-3235

Sandwich, DeKalb, Pop. 7,330
Indian Valley Vocational Center
600 Lions Rd 60548 — 815-786-9873
Ron Pieper, dir. — Fax 786-6928
www.ivvc.net
Indian Valley Vocational Center — Vo/Tech
600 Lions Rd 60548 — 815-786-9873
Ron Pieper, dir. — Fax 786-6928

Sandwich CUSD 430 — 2,400/PK-12
720 S Wells St 60548 — 815-786-2187
Rick Schmitt, supt. — Fax 786-6229
www.sandwich430.org
Sandwich Community HS — 700/9-12
515 Lions Rd 60548 — 815-786-2157
Mitchell Nystedt, prin. — Fax 786-2632
Sandwich MS — 500/6-8
600 S Wells St 60548 — 815-786-2138
B.J. Richardson, prin. — Fax 786-6606

Sauk Village, Cook, Pop. 10,221
CCSD 168 — 1,600/PK-8
21899 Torrence Ave 60411 — 708-758-1610
Al Travaglini, supt. — Fax 758-5929
www.d168.org
Rickover JHS — 500/6-8
22151 Torrence Ave 60411 — 708-758-1900
Julie Iverson, prin. — Fax 758-1601

Savanna, Carroll, Pop. 3,017
West Carroll CUSD 314
Supt. — See Thomson
West Carroll HS — 400/9-12
500 Cragmoor St 61074 — 815-273-7715
Robert Lamb, prin. — Fax 273-7819

Scales Mound, Jo Daviess, Pop. 373
Scales Mound CUSD 211 — 200/PK-12
210 Main St 61075 — 815-845-2215
Steve Bianchetta, supt. — Fax 845-2238
www.scalesmound.net
Scales Mound HS — 100/9-12
210 Main St 61075 — 815-845-2215
Dr. Matthew Wiederholt, prin. — Fax 845-2238
Scales Mound JHS — 50/6-8
210 Main St 61075 — 815-845-2215
Dr. Matthew Wiederholt, prin. — Fax 845-2238

Schaumburg, Cook, Pop. 72,713
Schaumburg CCSD 54 — 14,200/PK-8
524 E Schaumburg Rd 60194 — 847-357-5000
Ed Rafferty, supt. — Fax 357-5006
www.sd54.org
Addams JHS — 700/7-8
700 S Springinsguth Rd 60193 — 847-357-5900
Steve Pearce, prin. — Fax 357-5901
Frost JHS — 600/7-8
320 W Wise Rd 60193 — 847-357-6800
Scott Ross, prin. — Fax 357-6801
Keller JHS — 600/7-8
820 Bode Rd 60194 — 847-357-6500
Sue Mayernick, prin. — Fax 357-6501
Other Schools – See Elk Grove Village, Hoffman Estates

Township HSD 211
Supt. — See Palatine
Schaumburg HS — 2,200/9-12
1100 W Schaumburg Rd 60194 — 847-755-4600
Timothy Little, prin. — Fax 755-4623

American Intercontinental Univ Online — Post-Sec.
231 N Martingale Rd Fl 6 60173 — 877-701-3800

Argosy University/Schaumburg Post-Sec.
999 N Plaza Dr Ste 111 60173 847-969-4900
DeVry University Post-Sec.
1051 Perimeter Dr Fl 9 60173 847-330-0040
International Academy of Design & Tech Post-Sec.
935 National Pkwy 60173 847-969-2800
Lake Forest Graduate Sch. of Management Post-Sec.
1300 E Woodfield Rd Ste 600 60173 847-234-5005
Prince Institute Post-Sec.
1300 E Woodfield Rd Ste 110 60173 847-592-6600
Robert Morris University Post-Sec.
1000 E Woodfield Rd 60173 800-225-1520
Roosevelt University Post-Sec.
1400 N Roosevelt Blvd 60173 847-619-7300
Schaumburg Christian S 1,200/PK-12
200 N Roselle Rd 60194 847-885-3230
Jim Toth, admin. Fax 885-3354
The Illinois Institute of Art Post-Sec.
1000 N Plaza Dr Ste 100 60173 847-619-3450

Schiller Park, Cook, Pop. 11,679
Schiller Park SD 81 1,200/PK-8
9760 Soreng Ave 60176 847-671-1816
Kimberly Boryszewski, supt. Fax 671-1872
www.sd81.org
Lincoln MS 400/6-8
9750 Soreng Ave 60176 847-678-2916
Constance Stavrou, prin. Fax 678-4059

Sciota, McDonough, Pop. 61
West Prairie CUSD 103
Supt. — See Colchester
West Prairie HS 200/9-12
18575 E 800th St 61475 309-456-3750
John Bushmire, prin. Fax 456-3997

Seneca, LaSalle, Pop. 2,330
Seneca CCSD 170 500/PK-8
174 Oak St 61360 815-357-8744
Eric Misener, supt. Fax 357-1516
www.sgs170.org
Seneca MS South Campus 200/5-8
174 Oak St 61360 815-357-8744
Shane Severson, prin. Fax 357-1078

Seneca Township HSD 160 400/9-12
PO Box 20 61360 815-357-5000
Dr. Jim Carlson, supt. Fax 357-5050
www.senecahs.org
Seneca HS 400/9-12
PO Box 20 61360 815-357-5000
Marty Voiles, prin. Fax 357-1216

Serena, LaSalle
Serena CUSD 2 800/K-12
PO Box 107 60549 815-496-2850
Daniel Joyce, supt. Fax 496-2987
www.unit2.net
Serena Community HS 300/9-12
PO Box 107 60549 815-496-2361
Patrick Leonard, prin. Fax 496-2987

Sesser, Franklin, Pop. 1,900
Sesser-Valier CUSD 196 700/PK-12
4626 State Highway 154 62884 618-625-5105
Dr. Jason D. Henry, supt. Fax 625-6696
www.s-v.frnkln.k12.il.us/
Sesser-Valier HS 200/9-12
4626 State Highway 154 62884 618-625-5105
Wesley R. Choate, prin. Fax 625-6696
Sesser-Valier JHS 200/6-8
4626 State Highway 154 62884 618-625-5105
Judy L. Logsdon, prin. Fax 625-3040

Shabbona, DeKalb, Pop. 921
Indian Creek CUSD 425 800/K-12
506 S Shabbona Rd 60550 815-824-2197
Pamela Rockwood, supt. Fax 824-2199
www.indiancreekschools.org
Indian Creek HS 300/9-12
506 S Shabbona Rd 60550 815-824-2197
Sarah Montgomery, prin. Fax 824-2199
Other Schools – See Waterman

Shannon, Carroll, Pop. 753
Eastland CUSD 308
Supt. — See Lanark
Eastland MS 300/3-8
601 S Chestnut St 61078 815-864-2300
Darcie Feltmeyer, prin. Fax 864-2281

Shelbyville, Shelby, Pop. 4,676
Shelbyville CUSD 4 1,100/PK-12
720 W Main St 62565 217-774-4626
Denise Bence, supt. Fax 774-2521
www.shelbyville.k12.il.us/
Moulton MS 500/4-8
1101 W North 6th St 62565 217-774-2169
Russell Tomblin, prin. Fax 774-3042
Shelbyville HS 300/9-12
1001 W North 6th St 62565 217-774-3926
Richard Stuart, prin. Fax 774-5836

Sherrard, Mercer, Pop. 637
Sherrard CUSD 200 1,500/PK-12
PO Box 369 61281 309-593-4075
Rebecca Rodocker, supt. Fax 593-4078
www.sherrard.us
Sherrard HS 500/9-12
4701 176th Ave 61281 309-593-2175
Garet Egel, prin. Fax 593-2775
Sherrard JHS 200/7-8
4701 176th Ave 61281 309-593-2135
Linda Goff, prin. Fax 593-2143

Shiloh, Saint Clair, Pop. 12,229
Shiloh Village SD 85 600/PK-8
125 Diamond Ct 62269 618-632-7434
Dale Sauer, supt. Fax 632-8343
www.shiloh.stclair.k12.il.us
Shiloh MS 300/5-8
1 Wildcat Xing 62269 618-632-7434
Jeff Alt, prin. Fax 632-8343

Sidell, Vermilion, Pop. 607
Jamaica CUSD 12 400/PK-12
7087 N 600 East Rd 61876 217-288-9306
Dr. Phil Harrison, supt. Fax 288-9306
209.174.164.101/default.html
Jamaica HS 100/9-12
7087 N 600 East Rd 61876 217-288-9392
Dr. Phil Harrison, prin. Fax 288-9306
Jamaica JHS 100/6-8
7087 N 600 East Rd 61876 217-288-9394
Mollie Pletch, prin.

Silvis, Rock Island, Pop. 7,322
Silvis SD 34 600/PK-8
1305 5th Ave 61282 309-792-9325
Ray Bergles, supt. Fax 792-8092
www.silvis34.com
Other Schools – See East Moline

Skokie, Cook, Pop. 62,756
Niles Township HSD 219 4,600/9-12
7700 Gross Point Rd 60077 847-626-3000
Dr. Nanciann Gatta, supt. Fax 626-3090
www.niles219.org
Niles Central S 50/Alt
7700 Gross Point Rd 60077 847-626-3120
John Frampton, dir. Fax 626-3080
Niles North HS 2,100/9-12
9800 Lawler Ave 60077 847-626-2000
Dr. Ryan McTague, prin. Fax 626-3424
Niles West HS 2,500/9-12
5701 Oakton St 60077 847-626-2500
Kaine Osburn, prin. Fax 626-3693

Skokie SD 68 1,700/PK-8
9440 Kenton Ave 60076 847-676-9000
Dr. Frances McTague, supt. Fax 676-9232
www.skokie68.org
Old Orchard JHS 700/PK-PK, 6-
9310 Kenton Ave 60076 847-676-9010
Robyn Hawley, prin. Fax 676-3827

Skokie SD 69 1,700/PK-8
5050 Madison St 60077 847-675-7666
Dr. Quintin Shepherd, supt. Fax 675-7675
www.skokie69.net
Lincoln JHS 500/6-8
7839 Lincoln Ave 60077 847-676-3545
Paul Bleuher, prin. Fax 676-3595

Skokie SD 73-5 1,100/PK-8
8000 E Prairie Rd 60076 847-324-0509
Kate Donegan, supt. Fax 673-1282
www.sd735.org
McCracken MS 400/6-8
8000 E Prairie Rd 60076 847-673-1220
Allison Stein, prin. Fax 673-1282

Computer Systems Institute Post-Sec.
8930 Gross Point Rd 60077 847-967-5030
Everest College Post-Sec.
9811 Woods Dr Ste 200 60077 847-470-0277
Fasman Yeshiva HS 100/9-12
7135 Carpenter Rd 60077 847-982-2500
Rabbi Moshe Wender, prin. Fax 674-6381
Hebrew Theological College Post-Sec.
7135 Carpenter Rd 60077 847-982-2500
Knowledge Systems Institute Post-Sec.
3420 Main St 60076 847-679-3135
Zarem/Golde ORT Technical Institute Post-Sec.
5440 Fargo Ave 60077 847-324-5588

Somonauk, DeKalb, Pop. 1,867
Somonauk CUSD 432 900/PK-12
501 W Market St 60552 815-498-2314
Dawn Green, supt. Fax 498-9523
www.somonauk.net
Somonauk HS 300/9-12
501 W Market St 60552 815-498-2314
Justin Snider M.Ed., prin. Fax 498-9841
Somonauk MS 300/5-8
501 W Market St 60552 815-498-1866
Jay Streicher, prin. Fax 498-1647

South Beloit, Winnebago, Pop. 7,705
Prairie Hill CCSD 133 800/K-8
6605 Prairie Hill Rd 61080 815-389-3964
Ted Rehl, supt. Fax 389-6107
www.prairiehill.org
Willowbrook MS 300/5-8
6605 Prairie Hill Rd 61080 815-389-3957
Wes Heiar, prin. Fax 389-6107

South Beloit CUSD 320 1,000/PK-12
850 Hayes Ave 61080 815-389-3478
Scott Fisher, supt. Fax 389-3477
www.sbsobos.org/
South Beloit HS 300/9-12
245 Prairie Hill Rd 61080 815-389-9004
Donna Kiel, prin. Fax 389-9268
South Beloit JHS 100/7-8
840 Blackhawk Blvd 61080 815-389-1421
Michael McCoy, prin. Fax 389-8811

South Elgin, Kane, Pop. 21,549
SD U-46
Supt. — See Elgin
Kenyon Woods MS 1,000/7-8
1515 Raymond St 60177 847-289-6685
Mike Demovsky, prin. Fax 628-6166
South Elgin HS 2,700/9-12
760 E Main St 60177 847-289-3760
James Edwards, prin. Fax 888-7014

South Holland, Cook, Pop. 21,729
South Holland SD 150 1,000/PK-8
848 E 170th St 60473 708-339-4240
Dr. Jerry Jordan, supt. Fax 339-4244
www.sd150.org
McKinley JHS 400/6-8
16949 Cottage Grove Ave 60473 708-339-8500
Todd Whitaker, prin. Fax 331-5805

South Holland SD 151 1,400/PK-8
525 E 162nd St 60473 708-339-1516
Dr. Teresa D. Hill, supt. Fax 331-7600
www.shsd151.org
Other Schools – See Phoenix

Thornton Township HSD 205 5,700/9-12
465 E 170th St 60473 708-225-4000
John Thomas, supt. Fax 225-4004
www.district205.net
Thornwood HS 2,000/9-12
17101 S Park Ave 60473 708-225-4701
Darcelle Williams, prin. Fax 225-5033
Other Schools – See Dolton, Harvey

Seton Academy 300/9-12
16100 Seton Dr 60473 708-333-6300
Marianne Lynch, prin. Fax 333-1534
South Suburban College of Cook County Post-Sec.
15800 State St 60473 708-596-2000

South Roxana, Madison, Pop. 2,033

Bethel Christian Academy 100/PK-12
PO Box 87207 62087 618-254-0188
RaNell Consiglio, prin. Fax 254-2067

Sparland, Marshall, Pop. 403
Midland CUSD 7
Supt. — See Varna
Midland MS 200/5-8
901 Hilltop Dr 61565 309-469-3131
Peg Frey, prin. Fax 469-5701

Sparta, Randolph, Pop. 4,242
Sparta CUSD 140 1,300/PK-12
203B Dean Ave 62286 618-443-5331
Dr. Larry Beattie, supt. Fax 443-2023
www.sparta.k12.il.us
Sparta HS 400/9-12
205 W Hood St 62286 618-443-4341
R. Scott Beckley, prin. Fax 443-5059
Sparta-Lincoln MS 400/4-8
203A Dean Ave 62286 618-443-5331
Dennis Hall, prin. Fax 443-2892

Springfield, Sangamon, Pop. 113,193
Capital Area Career Center
2201 Toronto Rd Ste B, 217-529-5431
Bob Klingborg, dir. Fax 529-7861
capital.tec.il.us
Capital Area Career Center Vo/Tech
2201 Toronto Rd Ste B, 217-529-5431
Bob Klingborg, dir. Fax 529-7861

Springfield SD 186 14,200/PK-12
1900 W Monroe St 62704 217-525-3000
Dr. Walter Milton, supt. Fax 525-3005
www.sps186.org/
Capital College Preparatory Academy 6-8
1101 S 15th St 62703 217-535-2752
Chris Colgren, prin. Fax 525-3333
Douglas S 50/Alt
444 W Reynolds St 62702 217-525-4400
Kari Borders, prin. Fax 525-4401
Franklin MS 700/6-8
1200 Outer Park Dr 62704 217-525-3164
Kristine Huddleston, prin. Fax 525-7937
Grant MS 600/6-8
1800 W Monroe St 62704 217-525-3170
Tammie Bolden, prin. Fax 525-3390
Jefferson MS 600/6-8
3001 S Allis St 62703 217-525-3176
Cheree Morrison, prin. Fax 525-3293
Lanphier HS 1,200/9-12
1300 N 11th St 62702 217-525-3080
Artie Doss, prin. Fax 525-3084
Lincoln Magnet MS 300/6-8
300 S 11th St 62703 217-525-3236
Nichole Heyen, prin. Fax 525-3294
Springfield HS 1,600/9-12
101 S Lewis St 62704 217-525-3100
Michael Grossen, prin. Fax 525-3122
Springfield Learning Academy Alt
101 E Laurel St 62704 217-525-3358
Frankie Baker-Brown, prin. Fax 525-3090
Springfield Southeast HS 1,300/9-12
2350 E Ash St 62703 217-525-3130
Jason Wind, prin. Fax 525-3139
Washington MS 500/6-8
2300 E Jackson St 62703 217-525-3182
Susan Palmer, prin. Fax 525-3319
Lawrence Education Center Adult
101 E Laurel St 62704 217-525-3144
Kathi Lee-Deassuncao, prin. Fax 525-3090

Calvary Academy 300/PK-12
1730 W Jefferson St 62702 217-546-5987
Dr. Jay Hinckley, prin. Fax 321-1063
Lincoln Land Community College Post-Sec.
PO Box 19256 62794 217-786-2200
Lutheran HS 200/9-12
3500 W Washington St, 217-546-6363
Steve Zielke, prin. Fax 546-6489
Midwest Technical Institute Post-Sec.
2731 N Farmers Market Rd 62707 800-814-5124
Robert Morris University Post-Sec.
3101 Montvale Dr 62704 800-762-5960
Sacred Heart-Griffin HS 800/9-12
1200 W Washington St 62702 217-787-1595
Sr. Margaret Joanne Grueter, prin. Fax 787-9856
St. John's College Post-Sec.
729 E Carpenter St 62702 217-525-5628
St. John's Hospital Post-Sec.
800 E Carpenter St 62769 217-544-6464
University of Illinois at Springfield Post-Sec.
1 University Plz 62703 217-206-6600

Spring Grove, McHenry, Pop. 5,732
Fox Lake Grade SD 114 800/PK-8
29067 W Grass Lake Rd 60081 847-973-4114
John Donnellan, supt. Fax 973-4010
www.foxlake114.org
Other Schools – See Fox Lake

Spring Valley, Bureau, Pop. 5,488
Hall HSD 502 400/9-12
800 W Erie St 61362 815-664-4500
Michael Struna, supt. Fax 664-2300
www.hallhighschool.org
Hall HS 400/9-12
800 W Erie St 61362 815-664-2100
Michael Struna, prin. Fax 664-2300

Stanford, McLean, Pop. 590
Olympia CUSD 16 1,900/PK-12
903 E 800 North Rd 61774 309-379-6011
Brad Hutchison, supt. Fax 379-2328
www.olympia.org
Olympia HS 600/9-12
7832 N 100 East Rd 61774 309-379-5911
Dr. Lance Thurman, prin. Fax 379-2583
Olympia MS 400/6-8
911 E 800 North Rd 61774 309-379-5941
Andrew Walsh, prin. Fax 379-5411

Staunton, Macoupin, Pop. 5,081
Staunton CUSD 6 1,300/PK-12
801 N Deneen St 62088 618-635-2962
Kyle Hlafka, supt. Fax 635-2994
www.stauntonschools.org/
Staunton HS 400/9-12
801 N Deneen St 62088 618-635-3838
David Snider, prin. Fax 635-2834
Staunton JHS 300/6-8
801 N Deneen St 62088 618-635-3831
Brooke Wiemers, prin. Fax 635-4637

Steeleville, Randolph, Pop. 2,076
Steeleville CUSD 138 400/PK-12
609 S Sparta St 62288 618-965-3469
Stephanie Mulholland, supt. Fax 965-3433
www.steeleville138.org
Steeleville HS 100/9-12
701 S Sparta St 62288 618-965-3432
Jennifer Hagel, prin. Fax 965-3433

Steger, Will, Pop. 9,382
Steger SD 194 1,600/PK-8
3753 Park Ave 60475 708-755-0022
Dave Thieman, supt. Fax 755-9512
www.sd194.org/
Columbia Central MS 500/6-8
94 Richton Rd 60475 708-755-0021
Mike Smith, prin. Fax 755-1877

Sterling, Whiteside, Pop. 15,098
Sterling CUSD 5 3,400/PK-12
410 E Le Fevre Rd 61081 815-626-5050
Tad Everett, supt. Fax 622-4113
www.sterlingpublicschools.org
Challand MS 800/6-8
1700 6th Ave 61081 815-626-3300
Kathy Howard, prin. Fax 622-4173
Sterling HS 1,000/9-12
1608 4th Ave 61081 815-625-6800
Jason Austin, prin. Fax 622-4157

Whiteside Area Career Center
1608 5th Ave 61081 815-626-5810
Kim Purvis, supt.
Whiteside Area Career Center Vo/Tech
1608 5th Ave 61081 815-626-5810
Kim Purvis, prin.

Educators of Beauty Post-Sec.
211 E 3rd St 61081 815-625-0247
Newman Central Catholic HS 200/9-12
1101 W 23rd St 61081 815-625-0500
Andreas Edmondson, admin. Fax 625-8444

Stillman Valley, Ogle, Pop. 1,114
Meridian CUSD 223 1,900/PK-12
207 W Main St 61084 815-645-2606
Dr. Robert Willis, supt. Fax 645-4325
www.meridian223.org
Meridian JHS 400/6-8
207 W Main St 61084 815-645-2277
Jill Davis, prin. Fax 645-8181
Stillman Valley HS 600/9-12
425 S Pine St 61084 815-645-2291
Phillip Caposey, prin. Fax 645-8145

Stockton, Jo Daviess, Pop. 1,848
Stockton CUSD 206 600/PK-12
540 N Rush St 61085 815-947-3391
Dr. David Gilliland, supt. Fax 947-2673
www.stocktonschools.com
Stockton HS 200/9-12
540 N Rush St 61085 815-947-3323
Dr. David Gilliland, prin. Fax 947-2673
Stockton MS 200/5-8
500 N Rush St 61085 815-947-3702
Brad Fox, prin. Fax 947-2114

Strasburg, Shelby, Pop. 465
Stewardson-Strasburg CUSD 5A 400/PK-12
RR 1 Box 67 62465 217-682-3355
Michele Lindenmeyer, supt. Fax 682-3305
www.sscusd.k12.il.us
Stewardson-Strasburg JSHS 200/7-12
RR 1 Box 67 62465 217-682-3355
Mark Giertz, prin. Fax 682-3305

Streamwood, Cook, Pop. 39,124
SD U-46
Supt. — See Elgin
Canton MS 700/7-8
1100 Sunset Cir 60107 630-213-5525
Jeff Smith, prin. Fax 213-5709
Streamwood HS 2,100/9-12
701 W Schaumburg Rd 60107 630-213-5500
Terri Lozier, prin. Fax 483-5909
Tefft MS 800/7-8
1100 Shirley Ave 60107 630-213-5535
Lavonne Smiley, prin. Fax 213-5646

Township HSD 211
Supt. — See Palatine
District 211 Academy - South 50/Alt
1544 Brandy Pkwy 60107 847-755-6840
Amy Friel, admin. Fax 755-6842

Streator, LaSalle, Pop. 13,509
Streator ESD 44 2,000/PK-8
1520 N Bloomington St 61364 815-672-2926
Matt Wilkinson, supt. Fax 673-2032
www.ses44.net/
Northlawn JHS 600/6-8
202 E 1st St 61364 815-672-4558
Keri Nuckles, prin. Fax 672-8109

Streator Twp. HSD 40 900/9-12
202 W Lincoln Ave 61364 815-672-0545
Dr. Kevin Myers, supt. Fax 673-3637
www.streatorhs.org
Streator Twp. HS 900/9-12
202 W Lincoln Ave 61364 815-672-0545
Amy Mascal, prin. Fax 673-3637

Woodland CUSD 5 500/PK-12
5800 E 3000 North Rd 61364 815-672-5974
Dr. Steve Endress, supt. Fax 673-1630
www.woodland5.org/
Woodland HS 100/9-12
5800 E 3000 North Rd 61364 815-672-2900
Debra Derby, prin.

Stronghurst, Henderson, Pop. 875
West Central CUSD 235
Supt. — See Biggsville
West Central MS 200/6-8
PO Box 179 61480 309-924-1681
Jeff Nichols, prin. Fax 924-1122

Sugar Grove, Kane, Pop. 8,881
Kaneland CUSD 302
Supt. — See Maple Park
Harter MS 1,100/6-8
1601 N Esker Dr 60554 630-466-8400
Bryan Zwemke, prin. Fax 466-1999

Waubonsee Community College Post-Sec.
Route 47 at Waubonsee Dr 60554 630-466-7900

Sullivan, Moultrie, Pop. 4,417
Sullivan CUSD 300 1,200/PK-12
725 N Main St 61951 217-728-8341
Terry Pearcy, supt. Fax 728-4139
home.sullivan.k12.il.us
Sullivan HS 400/9-12
725 N Main St 61951 217-728-8311
Brad Tuttle, prin. Fax 728-4139
Sullivan MS 300/6-8
713 N Main St 61951 217-728-8381
Jerry Calandrilla, prin. Fax 728-4139

Summit, Cook
Summit SD 104 1,700/PK-8
6021 S 74th Ave 60501 708-458-0505
Dr. Troy J. Whalen, supt. Fax 458-0532
www.sd104.us
Heritage MS 500/6-8
6021 S 74th Ave 60501 708-458-7590
Dennis Lewis, prin. Fax 728-3111

Summit Argo, Cook, Pop. 10,942
Argo Community HSD 217 1,700/9-12
7329 W 63rd St 60501 708-728-3200
Dr. Kevin O'Mara, supt. Fax 728-3155
www.argohs.net
Argo Community HS 1,700/9-12
7329 W 63rd St 60501 708-728-3200
David Frusher, prin. Fax 728-3155

Swansea, Saint Clair, Pop. 13,123
Wolf Branch SD 113 900/K-8
410 Huntwood Rd 62226 618-277-2100
Scott Harres, supt. Fax 235-2376
www.wolfbranchschooldistrict.org/
Wolf Branch MS 300/6-8
410 Huntwood Rd 62226 618-277-2100
Jeffrey Burkett, prin. Fax 277-5461

Sycamore, DeKalb, Pop. 17,257
Sycamore CUSD 427 3,700/K-12
245 W Exchange St Ste 1 60178 815-899-8100
Kathy Countryman, supt. Fax 899-8110
www.syc427.org
Sycamore HS 1,200/9-12
555 Spartan Trl 60178 815-899-8131
Tim Carlson, prin. Fax 899-8166
Sycamore MS 900/6-8
150 Maplewood Dr 60178 815-899-8170
Jim Cleven, prin. Fax 899-8177

Cornerstone Christian Academy 400/PK-12
355 N Cross St 60178 815-895-8522
Tom Olmstead, admin. Fax 895-8717
Hair Professionals Career College Post-Sec.
2245 Gateway Dr 60178 815-756-3596

Table Grove, Fulton, Pop. 410
V I T CUSD 2 400/PK-12
1502 E US Highway 136 61482 309-758-5138
Michael Curry, supt. Fax 758-5298
vit.k12.il.us
V I T HS 100/9-12
1500 E US Highway 136 61482 309-758-5136
Phil Snowden, prin. Fax 758-5126
V I T JHS 100/7-8
1500 E US Highway 136 61482 309-758-5136
Phil Snowden, prin. Fax 758-5126

Tamms, Alexander, Pop. 620
Egyptian CUSD 5 500/PK-12
20023 Diswood Rd 62988 618-776-5306
Brad Misner, supt. Fax 776-5122
www.egyptianschool.com
Egyptian HS 100/9-12
20023 Diswood Rd 62988 618-776-5251
Chuck Doty, prin. Fax 776-5122
Egyptian JHS 100/6-8
20023 Diswood Rd 62988 618-776-5251
Chuck Doty, prin. Fax 776-5122

Five County Regional Vocational System
PO Box 70 62988 618-747-2703
Jerry Ohlau, dir. Fax 747-2872
Five County Regional Vocational Center Vo/Tech
PO Box 70 62988 618-747-2703
Jerry Ohlau, dir. Fax 747-2872

Tampico, Whiteside, Pop. 788
Prophetstown-Lyndon-Tampico CUSD 3
Supt. — See Prophetstown
Tampico MS 200/6-8
PO Box 189 61283 815-438-3085
Chad Colmone, prin. Fax 438-3095

Taylor Ridge, Rock Island
Rockridge CUSD 300 1,300/PK-12
14110 134th Ave W 61284 309-793-8001
Chester Lien, supt. Fax 795-1719
rockridgeschools.org
Rockridge HS 400/9-12
14110 134th Ave W 61284 309-793-8020
Katy Hasson, prin. Fax 795-1763
Rockridge JHS 200/7-8
14110 134th Ave W 61284 309-793-8040
Mike Ruff, prin. Fax 795-9823

Taylorville, Christian, Pop. 11,116
Taylorville CUSD 3 2,000/PK-12
512 W Spresser St 62568 217-824-4951
Dr. Greggory Fuerstenau, supt. Fax 824-5157
www.taylorvilleschools.com
Taylorville HS 900/9-12
815 W Springfield Rd 62568 217-824-2268
Robert Richardson, prin. Fax 824-3352
Taylorville JHS 600/5-8
120 E Bidwell St 62568 217-824-4924
Kirk Kettelkamp, prin. Fax 824-7180

VisionWay Christian S 200/PK-12
1124 N Webster St 62568 217-824-6722
Glenna Tolliver, prin. Fax 824-6622

Teutopolis, Effingham, Pop. 1,530
Teutopolis CUSD 50 1,200/PK-12
PO Box 607 62467 217-857-3535
William Fritcher, supt. Fax 857-6265
www.teutopolisschools.org/
Teutopolis HS 400/9-12
801 W Main St 62467 217-857-3139
Greg Beck, prin. Fax 857-3473
Teutopolis JHS 200/7-8
904 W Water St 62467 217-857-6678
Patrick Drees, prin. Fax 857-6051

Thomasboro, Champaign, Pop. 1,098
Prairieview-Ogden CCSD 197
Supt. — See Royal
Prairieview-Ogden JHS 100/7-8
2499 County Road 2100 E 61878 217-694-4122
Steve Fiscus, admin. Fax 694-4123

Thompsonville, Franklin, Pop. 542
Thompsonville CUSD 174 300/K-12
21191 Shawneetown Rd 62890 618-627-2446
Chris Grant, supt. Fax 627-2446
thompsonville.il.schoolwebpages.com/
Thompsonville HS 100/9-12
21135 Shawneetown Rd 62890 618-627-2301
Kim Kaytor, prin. Fax 627-2446

Thompsonville Christian S 50/K-10
PO Box 53 62890 618-627-2065
Nancy O'Brien, prin. Fax 627-2726

Thomson, Carroll, Pop. 585
West Carroll CUSD 314 1,200/PK-12
801 South St 61285 815-259-2735
Craig Mathers, supt. Fax 259-3561
www.wc314.org/
Other Schools – See Mount Carroll, Savanna

Tinley Park, Cook, Pop. 56,069
Bremen Community HSD 228
Supt. — See Midlothian
Tinley Park HS 1,300/9-12
6111 175th St 60477 708-532-1900
Theresa Nolan, prin. Fax 532-4332

CCSD 146 2,300/PK-8
6611 171st St 60477 708-614-4500
Jeff Stawick, supt. Fax 614-8992
www.district146.org
Central MS 800/6-8
18146 Oak Park Ave 60477 708-614-4510
Randy Fortin, prin. Fax 614-7271

Kirby SD 140 3,800/PK-8
16931 Grissom Dr 60477 708-532-6462
Dr. Michael Byrne, supt. Fax 532-1512
www.ksd140.org
Grissom MS 700/6-8
17000 80th Ave 60477 708-429-3030
Shawn Olson, prin. Fax 532-8529
Prairie View MS 700/6-8
8500 175th St, 708-532-8540
Kristine Roth, prin. Fax 532-8544

DeVry University — Post-Sec.
18624 W Creek Dr 60477 — 708-342-3300
Fox College — Post-Sec.
18020 Oak Park Ave 60477 — 708-444-4500
Paul Mitchell The School — Post-Sec.
18454 W Creek Dr 60477 — 708-478-6907

Toledo, Cumberland, Pop. 1,235
Cumberland CUSD 77 — 900/PK-12
1496 Illinois Route 121 62468 — 217-923-3132
Russell Ragon, supt. — Fax 923-3132
www.cumberland.k12.il.us
Cumberland HS — 300/9-12
1496 Illinois Route 121 62468 — 217-923-3133
Todd Hall, prin. — Fax 923-5514
Cumberland MS — 200/6-8
1496 Illinois Route 121 62468 — 217-923-3135
Kevin Maynard, prin. — Fax 923-5449

Tolono, Champaign, Pop. 3,389
Tolono CUSD 7 — 1,600/PK-12
PO Box 720 61880 — 217-485-6510
Andrew Larson, supt. — Fax 485-3091
www.unitsevenschools.com
Unity HS — 500/9-12
1127 County Road 800 N 61880 — 217-485-6230
Phil Morrison, prin. — Fax 485-6220
Unity JHS — 400/6-8
1121 County Road 800 N 61880 — 217-485-6735
Mary Hettinger, prin. — Fax 485-3218

Toulon, Stark, Pop. 1,289
Stark County CUSD 100
Supt. — See Wyoming
Stark County HS — 300/9-12
PO Box 419 61483 — 309-286-4451
Michael Domico, prin. — Fax 286-3321
Stark County JHS, PO Box 659 61483 — 200/6-8
Michael Domico, prin. — 309-286-3451

Tremont, Tazewell, Pop. 2,212
Tremont CUSD 702 — 1,000/PK-12
400 W Pearl St 61568 — 309-925-3461
Jeff Hinman, supt. — Fax 925-5817
www.tremont702.net
Tremont HS — 300/9-12
400 W Pearl St 61568 — 309-925-3823
Sean Berry, prin. — Fax 925-5817
Tremont JHS — 300/5-8
400 W Pearl St 61568 — 309-925-3823
Jeremy Garrett, prin. — Fax 925-5817

Trenton, Clinton, Pop. 2,693
Wesclin CUSD 3 — 1,400/PK-12
10003 State Route 160 62293 — 618-224-7583
David Daum, supt. — Fax 224-9106
wesclin.k12.il.us
Wesclin HS — 400/9-12
10003 State Route 160 62293 — 618-224-7341
John Isenhower, prin. — Fax 224-9106
Wesclin JHS — 200/7-8
10003 State Route 160 62293 — 618-224-7355
Roger Freeze, prin. — Fax 224-7085

Troy, Madison, Pop. 9,707
Triad CUSD 2 — 3,600/PK-12
203 E Throp St 62294 — 618-667-5400
Leigh Lewis, supt. — Fax 667-8854
www.triadunit2.org
Triad HS — 1,200/9-12
703 E US Highway 40 62294 — 618-667-5409
Rodney Winslow, prin. — Fax 667-8853
Other Schools – See Saint Jacob

Tuscola, Douglas, Pop. 4,425
Tuscola CUSD 301 — 1,000/PK-12
409 S Prairie St 61953 — 217-253-4241
Michael Smith, supt. — Fax 253-4522
www.tuscola.k12.il.us/
East Prairie JHS — 300/5-8
409 S Prairie St 61953 — 217-253-2828
Carol Munson, prin. — Fax 253-3236
Tuscola HS — 300/9-12
500 S Prairie St 61953 — 217-253-2377
Brad Allen, prin. — Fax 253-4861

Ullin, Pulaski, Pop. 448
Century CUSD 100 — 400/PK-12
4721 Shawnee College Rd 62992 — 618-845-3447
Leslie Varble, supt. — Fax 845-3476
www.centuryschooldistrict100.com/
Century JSHS — 200/7-12
4721 Shawnee College Rd 62992 — 618-845-3518
Leslie Varble, prin. — Fax 845-3476

Shawnee Community College — Post-Sec.
8364 Shawnee College Rd 62992 — 618-634-3200

University Park, Will, Pop. 6,997
Crete-Monee CUSD 201U
Supt. — See Crete
Crete-Monee MS — 700/7-8
635 Olmstead Ln, — 708-367-2400
Kokona Chrisos, prin. — Fax 672-2777

Governors State University — Post-Sec.
1 University Pkwy, — 708-534-5000

Urbana, Champaign, Pop. 39,989
University of IL Lab S — 300/8-12
1212 W Springfield Ave 61801 — 217-333-2870
Dr. Jeffrey Wakington, supt.
University of Illinois HS — 300/8-12
1212 W Springfield Ave 61801 — 217-333-2870
Susan Kovacs, dir.
Urbana SD 116 — 4,200/PK-12
PO Box 3039 61803 — 217-384-3636
Don Owen Ed.D., supt. — Fax 337-4973
www.usd116.org
Urbana HS — 1,100/9-12
1002 S Race St 61801 — 217-384-3505
Joseph Wiemelt, prin. — Fax 384-3532
Urbana MS — 800/6-8
1201 S Vine St 61801 — 217-384-3685
Scott Woods, prin. — Fax 367-3156

Concept College of Cosmetology — Post-Sec.
129 N Race St 61801 — 217-344-7550
Kingswood S — 50/K-12
PO Box 834 61803 — 217-344-5540
Marsh Jones, hdmstr. — Fax 344-5535
University of Illinois — Post-Sec.
901 W Illinois St 61801 — 217-333-1000

Utica, LaSalle, Pop. 1,346
Waltham Community CESD 185 — 200/K-8
946 N 33rd Rd 61373 — 815-667-4790
Dr. Larry Carlton, supt. — Fax 667-4462
wesd185.org
Waltham North S — 200/3-8
946 N 33rd Rd 61373 — 815-667-4417
Kristine Eager, prin. — Fax 667-4462

Valmeyer, Monroe, Pop. 1,250
Valmeyer CUSD 3 — 500/PK-12
300 S Cedar Bluff Dr 62295 — 618-935-2100
Eric Frankford, supt. — Fax 935-2108
www.valmeyerk12.org
Valmeyer HS — 100/9-12
300 S Cedar Bluff Dr 62295 — 618-935-2100
Eric Frankford, prin. — Fax 935-2108
Valmeyer JHS — 100/6-8
300 S Cedar Bluff Dr 62295 — 618-939-2100
Teena Riechmann, prin. — Fax 939-2108

Vandalia, Fayette, Pop. 6,969
Okaw Area Vocational Center
1109 N 8th St 62471 — 618-283-5150
Nick Casey, supt.
Okaw Area Vocational Center — Vo/Tech
1109 N 8th St 62471 — 618-283-5150
Nick Casey, prin.

Vandalia CUSD 203 — 1,500/PK-12
1109 N 8th St 62471 — 618-283-4525
Rich Well, supt. — Fax 283-4107
www.vcs.fayette.k12.il.us/
Vandalia Community HS — 400/9-12
1109 N 8th St 62471 — 618-283-5155
Randy Protz, prin. — Fax 283-9855
Vandalia JHS — 500/5-8
1011 W Fletcher St 62471 — 618-283-5151
Brian Kern, prin. — Fax 283-8165

Varna, Marshall, Pop. 382
Midland CUSD 7 — 800/PK-12
1830 State Route 17 61375 — 309-463-2364
Rolf Sivertsen, supt. — Fax 463-2467
www.midland-7.org
Midland HS — 300/9-12
1830 State Route 17 61375 — 309-463-2095
Dan Mair, prin. — Fax 463-2630
Other Schools – See Sparland

Vergennes, Jackson, Pop. 291
Elverado CUSD 196
Supt. — See Elkville
Elverado JHS — 100/6-8
PO Box 35 62994 — 618-684-3527
Belinda Conner, prin. — Fax 687-3363

Vernon Hills, Lake, Pop. 24,688
Community HSD 128 — 3,300/9-12
50 Lakeview Pkwy Ste 101 60061 — 847-247-4500
Dr. Prentiss Lea, supt. — Fax 247-4543
www.d128.org/
Vernon Hills HS — 1,300/9-12
145 Lakeview Pkwy 60061 — 847-932-2000
Dr. Ellen Cwick, prin. — Fax 932-2049
Other Schools – See Libertyville

Hawthorn CCSD 73 — 3,300/PK-8
841 W End Ct 60061 — 847-990-4200
Nick Brown, supt. — Fax 367-3290
www.hawthorn73.org
Hawthorn MS North — 600/6-8
201 W Hawthorn Pkwy 60061 — 847-990-4400
Robert Collins, prin. — Fax 367-8124
Hawthorn MS South — 600/6-8
600 N Aspen Dr 60061 — 847-990-4100
Rob Natale, prin. — Fax 816-9259

Vienna, Johnson, Pop. 1,414
Vienna HSD 133 — 400/9-12
601 N 1st St 62995 — 618-658-4461
Edwin Shoemate, supt. — Fax 658-9727
www.viennahighschool.com
Vienna HS — 400/9-12
601 N 1st St 62995 — 618-658-3011
Patrick Harner, prin. — Fax 658-9727

Villa Grove, Douglas, Pop. 2,492
Villa Grove CUSD 302 — 600/PK-12
400 N Sycamore St 61956 — 217-832-2261
Dr. Mary Ann Manos, supt. — Fax 832-8615
www.vg302.org
Villa Grove HS — 200/9-12
400 N Sycamore St 61956 — 217-832-2321
Dr. Mary Ann Manos, prin. — Fax 832-8689
Villa Grove JHS — 100/7-8
400 N Sycamore St 61956 — 217-832-2261
Marke Hatfield, prin. — Fax 832-8615

Villa Park, DuPage, Pop. 21,596
DuPage County SD 45 — 3,300/PK-8
255 W Vermont St 60181 — 630-516-7700
Dr. Janice Rosales, supt. — Fax 530-1624
www.d45.org/
Jackson MS — 700/6-8
301 W Jackson St 60181 — 630-516-7600
Tony Palmisano, prin. — Fax 530-6271
Jefferson MS — 400/6-8
255 W Vermont St 60181 — 630-516-7800
Raul Gaston, prin. — Fax 993-6348

DuPage HSD 88
Supt. — See Addison
Willowbrook HS — 2,100/9-12
1250 S Ardmore Ave 60181 — 630-530-3439
Daniel Krause, prin. — Fax 530-3401

Salt Creek SD 48 — 500/PK-8
1110 S Villa Ave 60181 — 630-279-8400
Dr. John Correll, supt. — Fax 279-6167
www.saltcreek48.org
Albright MS — 200/5-8
1110 S Villa Ave 60181 — 630-279-6160
Scott Jackson, prin. — Fax 279-1614

Cannella School of Hair Design — Post-Sec.
617 W North Ave 60181 — 630-833-6118
Islamic Foundation S — 700/PK-12
300 W Highridge Rd 60181 — 630-941-8800
Mushtag Ikramullah, dir. — Fax 941-8804
Ms. Robert's Academy of Beauty Culture — Post-Sec.
17 E Park Blvd 60181 — 630-941-3880

Virden, Macoupin, Pop. 3,404
North Mac CUSD 34
Supt. — See Girard
North Mac HS — 200/9-12
231 W Fortune St 62690 — 217-965-4127
Rob Horn, prin. — Fax 965-4006

Virginia, Cass, Pop. 1,600
Virginia CUSD 64 — 400/PK-12
651 S Morgan St 62691 — 217-452-3085
Brent ODaniell, supt. — Fax 452-3088
www.go-redbirds.com
Virginia HS — 100/9-12
651 S Morgan St 62691 — 217-452-3087
Travis Davis, prin. — Fax 452-3088
Virginia JHS — 50/6-8
651 S Morgan St 62691 — 217-452-3363
Travis Davis, prin. — Fax 452-3088

Wadsworth, Lake, Pop. 3,763
Millburn CCSD 24 — 1,000/PK-8
18550 W Millburn Rd 60083 — 847-356-8331
Jason Lind, supt. — Fax 356-9722
www.millburn24.net/
Other Schools – See Lindenhurst

Waltonville, Jefferson, Pop. 432
Waltonville CUSD 1 — 400/PK-12
804 W Knob St 62894 — 618-279-7211
Shlonda Horton, supt. — Fax 279-3291
www.wcusd1.org
Waltonville HS — 100/9-12
804 W Knob St 62894 — 618-279-7211
Shlonda Horton, prin. — Fax 279-7212

Warren, Jo Daviess, Pop. 1,421
Warren CUSD 205 — 400/PK-12
311 S Water St 61087 — 815-745-2653
Francis Fennell, supt. — Fax 745-2037
www.205warren.net
Warren JSHS — 200/6-12
311 S Water St 61087 — 815-745-2641
Shawn Teske, prin. — Fax 745-2654

Warrensburg, Macon, Pop. 1,195
Warrensburg-Latham CUSD 11 — 1,000/PK-12
430 W North St 62573 — 217-672-3514
Kristen Kendrick, supt. — Fax 672-8468
www.wl.k12.il.us
Warrensburg-Latham HS — 300/9-12
427 W North St 62573 — 217-672-3531
Ken Hatcher, prin. — Fax 672-3770
Warrensburg-Latham MS — 200/6-8
425 W North St 62573 — 217-672-3321
Michael Gardner, prin.

Warrenville, DuPage, Pop. 12,933
CUSD 200
Supt. — See Wheaton
Hubble MS — 800/6-8
3S600 Herrick Rd 60555 — 630-821-7900
Dr. Beth Sullivan, prin. — Fax 821-7901

Carmel Montessori Academy — 100/PK-12
3S238 State Route 59 60555 — 630-393-2995

Warsaw, Hancock, Pop. 1,585
Warsaw CUSD 316 — 500/PK-12
340 S 11th St 62379 — 217-256-4282
Matt Runge, supt. — Fax 256-4282
warsawschool.com
Warsaw HS, 340 S 11th St 62379 — 200/9-12
Bob Gound, prin. — 217-256-4281

Washburn, Marshall, Pop. 1,146
Lowpoint-Washburn CUSD 21 — 400/PK-12
PO Box 580 61570 — 309-248-7522
Parker Deitrich, supt. — Fax 248-7518
www.washburn.k12.il.us
Lowpoint-Washburn JSHS — 200/7-12
PO Box 580 61570 — 309-248-7521
Mark Zulz, prin. — Fax 248-7410

Washington, Tazewell, Pop. 14,931
Central SD 51 — 900/PK-8
1301 Eagle Ave 61571 — 309-444-3943
Dr. Chad Allaman, supt. — Fax 444-9898
www.central51.net

Central IS 500/4-8
1301 Eagle Ave 61571 309-444-3943
Brian Hoelscher, prin. Fax 444-3414

District 50 Schools 800/PK-8
304 E Almond Dr 61571 309-745-8914
Patrick Martin, supt. Fax 745-5417
www.d50schools.com
Manor MS, 1014 School St 61571 400/4-8
Angela Ludlum, prin. 309-745-3921

Washington Community HSD 308 1,200/9-12
115 Bondurant St 61571 309-444-7704
Dr. James Dunnan, supt. Fax 444-7451
www.wacohi.net/
Washington Comm HS 1,200/9-12
115 Bondurant St 61571 309-444-7704
Dr. James Dunnan, admin. Fax 444-7451

Washington SD 52 800/PK-8
303 Jackson St 61571 309-444-4182
Dr. John Tignor, supt. Fax 444-8538
www.d52schools.com
Washington MS 400/5-8
1100 N Main St 61571 309-444-3361
Jon Smith, prin. Fax 444-3941

Waterloo, Monroe, Pop. 9,722
Waterloo CUSD 5 2,400/PK-12
219 Park St 62298 618-939-3453
James Helton, supt. Fax 939-4578
www.wcusd5.net
Waterloo HS 900/9-12
505 E Bulldog 62298 618-939-3455
Brian Charron, prin. Fax 939-5180
Waterloo JHS 600/6-8
200 Bellefontaine Dr 62298 618-939-3457
Nick Schwartz, prin. Fax 939-1383

Gibault Catholic HS 200/9-12
501 Columbia Ave 62298 618-939-3883
Russell Hart, prin. Fax 939-7215

Waterman, DeKalb, Pop. 1,482
Indian Creek CUSD 425
Supt. — See Shabbona
Indian Creek MS 200/6-8
425 S Elm St 60556 815-264-7712
Paula Kennedy, prin. Fax 264-7826

Watseka, Iroquois, Pop. 5,192
Iroquois County CUSD 9 1,200/K-12
1411 W Lafayette St 60970 815-432-4931
Kenneth Lee, supt. Fax 432-6889
www.watseka-u9.k12.il.us
Raymond MS 300/6-8
101 W Mulberry St 60970 815-432-2115
Ryan McGuckin, prin. Fax 432-6896
Watseka Community HS 400/9-12
138 S Belmont Ave 60970 815-432-2486
James Bunting, prin. Fax 432-5578

Wauconda, Lake, Pop. 13,421
Wauconda CUSD 118 4,400/PK-12
555 N Main St 60084 847-526-7690
Dr. Daniel J. Coles, supt. Fax 526-1019
www.d118.org
Wauconda HS 1,300/9-12
555 N Main St 60084 847-526-6611
Daniel Klett, prin. Fax 487-3595
Wauconda MS 500/6-8
215 Slocum Lake Rd 60084 847-526-2122
Cameron Willis, prin. Fax 487-3597
Other Schools – See Island Lake

Frassati Academy 6-8
316 W Mill St 60084 847-487-5600
Dr. Diane Vida, prin. Fax 487-5611

Waukegan, Lake, Pop. 87,117
Waukegan CUSD 60 16,400/PK-12
1201 N Sheridan Rd 60085 847-336-3100
Dr. Donaldo Batiste, supt. Fax 360-5634
www.wps60.org
Abbott MS 700/6-8
1319 Washington St 60085 847-360-5487
Timothy Bryner, prin. Fax 360-5394
Benny MS 600/6-8
1401 Montesano Ave 60087 847-360-5460
Minerva Cruz-Familar, prin. Fax 360-5395
Jefferson MS 900/6-8
600 S Lewis Ave 60085 847-360-5473
Nicole Fishman, prin. Fax 360-5396
Juarez MS 700/6-8
201 N Butrick St 60085 847-599-4200
Dr. Cathy Watkins, prin. Fax 263-4797
Waukegan Alternative S 100/Alt
1020 Glen Rock Ave 60085 847-360-5540
Grant Flink, dir. Fax 360-5373
Waukegan HS - Brookside Campus 3,000/10-12
2325 Brookside Ave 60085 847-360-5600
Brian Riegler, prin. Fax 360-5399
Waukegan HS - Washington Campus 1,200/9-9
1011 Washington St 60085 847-360-5600
Brian Riegler, prin. Fax 599-4205
Webster MS 600/6-8
930 New York St 60085 847-360-5484
Tierney Eppinger, prin. Fax 360-5397

Cristo Rey St. Martin College Prep HS 200/9-12
515 S Martin Luther King Jr 60085 847-623-5500
Michael Odiotti, prin. Fax 623-5604
Lake County Baptist S 100/PK-12
1550 W Yorkhouse Rd 60087 847-623-7600
Timothy Kowach, prin. Fax 623-2085
Robert Morris University Post-Sec.
1507 S Waukegan Rd 60085 800-762-5960

Waverly, Morgan, Pop. 1,296
Waverly CUSD 6 300/PK-12
201 N Miller St 62692 217-435-8121
Dr. Debra Rust, supt. Fax 435-3431
www.waverlyscotties.com
Waverly HS 100/6-12
201 N Miller St 62692 217-435-2211
Steve Cline, prin. Fax 435-3431

Wayne City, Wayne, Pop. 1,023
Wayne City CUSD 100 500/K-12
PO Box 457 62895 618-895-3103
Jeff Mitchell, supt. Fax 895-2331
Wayne City JSHS 200/7-12
PO Box 427 62895 618-895-3103
Myron Caudle, prin. Fax 895-2331

Weldon, DeWitt, Pop. 425
Deland-Weldon CUSD 57
Supt. — See De Land
Deland-Weldon MS 50/7-8
2311 N 300 East Rd 61882 217-736-2401
Russell Corey, prin. Fax 736-2654

Westchester, Cook, Pop. 16,532
Westchester SD 92-5 1,200/K-8
9981 Canterbury St 60154 708-450-2700
Michael Dziallo, supt. Fax 450-2718
www.sd925.org
Westchester MS 400/6-8
1620 Norfolk Ave 60154 708-450-2735
Gregory Leban, prin. Fax 450-2752

St. Joseph HS 800/9-12
10900 W Cermak Rd 60154 708-562-4433
Ronald Hoover, prin. Fax 562-4459

West Chicago, DuPage, Pop. 26,802
Benjamin SD 25 800/PK-8
28W250 Saint Charles Rd 60185 630-876-7800
Dr. Philip Ehrhardt, supt. Fax 876-3325
www.bendist25.org
Benjamin MS 400/5-8
28W300 Saint Charles Rd 60185 630-876-7820
Joseph Salmieri, prin. Fax 231-3886

Community HSD 94 2,100/9-12
326 Joliet St 60185 630-876-6200
Dr. Douglas Domeracki, supt. Fax 876-6241
www.d94.org
Community HS 2,100/9-12
326 Joliet St 60185 630-876-6200
Dr. Moses Cheng, prin. Fax 876-6241

West Chicago ESD 33 4,100/PK-8
312 E Forest Ave 60185 630-293-6000
Dr. Kathy Wolfe, supt. Fax 293-6088
wcesd33-il.schoolloop.com
West Chicago MS 800/7-8
238 E Hazel St 60185 630-293-6060
Pat Roszkowski, prin. Fax 562-2586

Central Medical Education Post-Sec.
550 E Washington St 60185 630-682-1600
Wheaton Academy 700/9-12
900 Prince Crossing Rd 60185 630-562-7500
Dr. Gene Frost, head sch Fax 231-1469

West Dundee, Kane
CUSD 300
Supt. — See Carpentersville
Dundee MS 1,000/6-8
4200 W Main St 60118 847-426-1485
Dr. Joseph Schumacher, prin. Fax 426-4008

Hair Professionals Academy Post-Sec.
825 Village Quarter Rd # B 60118 847-836-5900

Western Springs, Cook, Pop. 12,882
Lyons Township HSD 204
Supt. — See La Grange
Lyons Township HS South Campus 2,000/9-10
4900 Willow Springs Rd 60558 708-579-6500
Dave Franson, prin. Fax 588-7473

Western Springs SD 101 1,600/PK-8
4335 Howard Ave 60558 708-246-3700
Dr. Brian Barnhart, supt. Fax 482-2581
www.d101.org
McClure JHS 500/6-8
4225 Wolf Rd 60558 708-246-7590
F. Daniel Chick, prin. Fax 246-4370

West Frankfort, Franklin, Pop. 8,100
Frankfort CUSD 168 1,900/PK-12
900 N Cherry St 62896 618-937-2421
Gregory Goins, supt. Fax 932-2025
www.wfschools.org
Central JHS 300/7-8
1500 E 9th St 62896 618-937-2444
Charley Cass, prin. Fax 937-2445
Frankfort Community HS 500/9-12
601 E Main St 62896 618-932-3126
Danny Stevens, prin. Fax 932-6515

Westmont, DuPage, Pop. 24,243
CUSD 201 1,600/PK-12
200 N Linden Ave 60559 630-468-8000
Kevin Carey, supt. Fax 969-9022
www.cusd201.org
Westmont HS 500/9-12
909 Oakwood Dr 60559 630-468-8100
Jack Baldermann, prin. Fax 654-2758
Westmont JHS 300/6-8
944 Oakwood Dr 60559 630-468-8200
John Jonak, prin. Fax 654-2203

Maercker SD 60 1,300/PK-8
1 S Cass Ave Ste 202 60559 630-515-4840
Jamie Reilly, supt. Fax 515-4845
www.maercker.org
Other Schools – See Willowbrook

West Peoria, Peoria, Pop. 4,328
Peoria SD 150
Supt. — See Peoria
Coolidge MS 200/5-8
2708 W Rohmann Ave 61604 309-672-6506
Thomas Blumer, prin. Fax 673-7605

Westville, Vermilion, Pop. 3,171
Westville CUSD 2 1,300/K-12
125 W Ellsworth St 61883 217-267-3141
James Owens, supt. Fax 267-3144
www.westville.k12.il.us
Westville HS 400/9-12
918 N State St 61883 217-267-2183
Guy Goodlove, prin. Fax 267-7593
Westville JHS 200/7-8
412 Moses Ave 61883 217-267-2185
Jared Ellison, prin. Fax 267-3621

Wheaton, DuPage, Pop. 51,936
CUSD 200 13,400/PK-12
130 W Park Ave 60189 630-682-2002
Dr. Brian Harris, supt. Fax 682-2068
www.cusd200.org
Edison MS 700/6-8
1125 S Wheaton Ave 60189 630-682-2050
Rachel Bednar, prin. Fax 682-2337
Franklin MS 800/6-8
211 E Franklin St 60187 630-682-2060
David Bendis, prin. Fax 682-2340
Monroe MS 700/6-8
1855 Manchester Rd 60187 630-682-2285
Bryan Buck, prin. Fax 682-2331
Wheaton North HS 2,200/9-12
701 W Thomas Rd 60187 630-784-7300
Jill Bullo, prin. Fax 682-2158
Wheaton/Warrenville South HS 2,300/9-12
1920 S Wiesbrook Rd 60189 630-784-7200
Dave Claypool, prin. Fax 682-2042
Other Schools – See Warrenville

Clapham S 100/PK-10
PO Box 209 60187 630-547-5125
Doug Reynolds, head sch Fax 597-2449
St. Francis HS 800/9-12
2130 W Roosevelt Rd 60187 630-668-5800
Raeann Huhn, prin. Fax 668-5893
Wheaton College Post-Sec.
501 College Ave 60187 630-752-5000

Wheeling, Cook, Pop. 37,130
Township HSD 214
Supt. — See Arlington Heights
Wheeling HS 1,800/9-12
900 S Elmhurst Rd 60090 847-718-7000
Dr. Lazaro Lopez, prin. Fax 718-7007

Wheeling CCSD 21 6,600/PK-8
999 W Dundee Rd 60090 847-537-8270
Dr. Kate Hyland, supt. Fax 520-2848
www.ccsd21.org
Holmes MS 700/6-8
221 S Wolf Rd 60090 847-520-2790
Martin Hopkins, prin. Fax 419-3073
London MS 700/6-8
1001 W Dundee Rd 60090 847-520-2745
Bob Gurney, prin. Fax 520-2842
Other Schools – See Buffalo Grove

SOLEX College Post-Sec.
350 E Dundee Rd 60090 847-229-9595
Worsham College of Mortuary Science Post-Sec.
495 Northgate Pkwy 60090 847-808-8444

White Hall, Greene, Pop. 2,509
North Greene Unit SD 3 900/PK-12
407 N Main St 62092 217-374-2842
Les Stevens, supt. Fax 374-2849
www.northgreene.com
North Greene HS 300/9-12
546 N Main St 62092 217-374-2131
Keppen Clanton, prin. Fax 374-2132
Other Schools – See Roodhouse

Williamsfield, Knox, Pop. 574
Williamsfield CUSD 210 300/PK-12
PO Box 179 61489 309-639-2219
Mary Bush, supt. Fax 639-2618
www.billtown.org
Williamsfield HS, PO Box 179 61489 100/9-12
Mary Bush, prin. 309-639-2216
Williamsfield MS, PO Box 179 61489 100/6-8
Mary Bush, prin. 309-639-2216

Williamsville, Sangamon, Pop. 1,465
Williamsville CUSD 15 1,400/PK-12
800 S Walnut St 62693 217-566-2014
David Root, supt. Fax 566-2183
www.wcusd15.org
Williamsville HS 400/9-12
900 S Walnut St 62693 217-566-3361
Russel Galusha, prin. Fax 566-3792
Williamsville JHS 300/6-8
500 S Walnut St 62693 217-566-3600
Clay Shoufler, prin. Fax 566-2475

Willowbrook, DuPage, Pop. 8,420
Gower SD 62 900/PK-8
7700 Clarendon Hills Rd 60527 630-986-5383
Steve Griesbach, supt. Fax 323-3074
www.gower62.com
Other Schools – See Burr Ridge

Maercker SD 60
Supt. — See Westmont
Westview Hills MS 500/6-8
630 65th St 60527 630-515-4830
Sean Nugent, prin. Fax 515-4835

Wilmette, Cook, Pop. 26,500
Avoca SD 37 600/PK-8
2921 Illinois Rd 60091 847-251-3587
Kevin Jauch, supt. Fax 251-7742
avoca37.org
Murphy MS 300/PK-PK, 6-
2921 Illinois Rd 60091 847-251-3617
Dr. Deanna Reed, prin. Fax 251-4179

Wilmette SD 39 3,600/PK-8
615 Locust Rd 60091 847-256-2450
Ray Lechner, supt. Fax 256-1920
www.wilmette39.org
Wilmette JHS 800/7-8
620 Locust Rd 60091 847-256-7280
David Palzet, prin. Fax 256-0204

Loyola Academy 2,100/9-12
1100 Laramie Ave 60091 847-256-1100
Kathryn Baal Ph.D., prin. Fax 853-4512
Regina Dominican HS 400/9-12
701 Locust Rd 60091 847-256-7660
Meg Bigane, prin. Fax 256-3726

Wilmington, Will, Pop. 5,660
Wilmington CUSD 209U 1,500/PK-12
209U Wildcat Ct 60481 815-926-1751
Jay Plese, supt. Fax 926-1692
www.wilmington.will.k12.il.us
Wilmington HS 500/9-12
209 Wildcat Ct 60481 815-926-1752
Kevin Feeney, prin. Fax 926-1691
Wilmington MS 300/6-8
715 S Joliet St 60481 815-476-2189
Beth Norman, prin. Fax 476-1941

Winchester, Scott, Pop. 1,579
Winchester CUSD 1 700/PK-12
149 S Elm St 62694 217-742-3175
David Roberts, supt. Fax 742-3312
www.winchesterschools.net
Winchester HS, 200 W Cross St 62694 200/9-12
Shane Gordon, prin. 217-742-3151

Windsor, Shelby, Pop. 1,177
Windsor CUSD 1 400/PK-12
1424 Minnesota Ave 61957 217-459-2636
Sharon Keck, supt. Fax 459-2661
www.windsor.k12.il.us
Windsor JSHS 200/7-12
1424 Minnesota Ave 61957 217-459-2636
Erik Van Hoveln, prin. Fax 459-2794

Winfield, DuPage, Pop. 8,924
Winfield SD 34 400/PK-8
0S150 Winfield Rd 60190 630-909-4900
Dr. Gwynne Kell, supt. Fax 260-2382
www.winfield34.org/
Winfield Central S 200/3-8
0S150 Park St 60190 630-909-4960
Dawn Reinke, prin. Fax 933-9236

Winnebago, Winnebago, Pop. 3,067
Winnebago CUSD 323 1,400/PK-12
304 E McNair Rd 61088 815-335-2456
Dr. Dennis Harezlak, supt. Fax 335-7574
www.winnebagoschools.org/
Winnebago HS 600/9-12
200 E McNair Rd 61088 815-335-2336
Beth Summers, prin. Fax 335-7548
Winnebago MS 400/6-8
407 N Elida St 61088 815-335-2364
Catherine Finley, prin. Fax 335-1437

Winnetka, Cook, Pop. 12,045
New Trier Township HSD 203
Supt. — See Northfield
New Trier Township HS - Winnetka Campus 3,100/10-12
385 Winnetka Ave 60093 847-446-7000
Denise Hibbard, prin. Fax 835-9851

Winnetka SD 36 1,900/PK-8
1235 Oak St 60093 847-446-9400
Thomas Hagerman, supt. Fax 446-9408
www.winnetka36.org
Washburne MS 500/7-8
515 Hibbard Rd 60093 847-446-5892
Dr. Cathy Rosen, prin. Fax 446-1380

Hadley School for the Blind Post-Sec.
700 Elm St 60093 847-446-8111
Music Center of the North Shore Post-Sec.
300 Green Bay Rd 60093 847-446-3822
North Shore Country Day S 500/PK-12
310 Green Bay Rd 60093 847-446-0674
Thomas Doar, hdmstr. Fax 446-0675

Winthrop Harbor, Lake, Pop. 6,595
Winthrop Harbor SD 1 600/K-8
500 North Ave 60096 847-731-3085
Dr. Dennis Guiser, supt. Fax 731-3156
www.whsd1.org
North Prairie JHS 300/5-8
500 North Ave 60096 847-731-3089
Carrie Nottingham, prin. Fax 731-3152

Wolf Lake, Union
Shawnee CUSD 84 400/K-12
3365 N State Route 3 62998 618-833-5709
Shelly Clover-Hill, supt. Fax 833-4171
www.shawneedistrict84.com/
Shawnee HS 100/9-12
3365 N State Route 3 62998 618-833-5307
Mike Hanson, prin. Fax 833-5468
Shawnee JHS 100/5-8
3365 N State Route 3 62998 618-833-5307
Mike Hanson, prin. Fax 833-5468

Wood Dale, DuPage, Pop. 13,602
Wood Dale SD 7 1,200/PK-8
543 N Wood Dale Rd 60191 630-595-9510
Dr. John Corbett, supt. Fax 595-5625
www.wd7.org
Wood Dale JHS 400/6-8
655 N Wood Dale Rd 60191 630-766-6210
Dr. Anthony Murray, prin. Fax 766-1839

Woodhull, Henry, Pop. 803
Alwood CUSD 225 400/PK-12
301 E 5th Ave 61490 309-334-2719
Shannon Bumann, supt. Fax 334-2925
www.alwood.net
Alwood MSHS 200/6-12
301 E 5th Ave 61490 309-334-2102
Andrew Mitchell, prin. Fax 334-2632

Woodlawn, Jefferson, Pop. 691
Woodlawn Community HSD 205 200/9-12
300 N Central St 62898 618-735-2631
David Larkin, supt. Fax 735-2032
Woodlawn Community HS 200/9-12
300 N Central St 62898 618-735-2631
Dave Larkin, supt. Fax 735-2032

Woodridge, DuPage, Pop. 34,058
Woodridge SD 68 2,900/PK-8
7925 Janes Ave 60517 630-985-7925
Dr. Cathy Skinner, supt. Fax 910-2060
www.woodridge68.org
Jefferson JHS 600/7-8
7200 Janes Ave 60517 630-852-8010
Dr. William Schmidt, prin. Fax 969-7168

Westwood College Post-Sec.
7155 Janes Ave 60517 630-434-7655

Wood River, Madison, Pop. 10,543
East Alton-Wood River Community HSD 14 600/9-12
777 N Wood River Ave 62095 618-254-3151
John Pearson, supt. Fax 254-9113
www.eawr.madison.k12.il.us/
East Alton-Wood River HS 600/9-12
777 N Wood River Ave 62095 618-254-3151
Leigh Robinson, prin. Fax 254-9113

Wood River-Hartford ESD 15 800/PK-8
501 E Lorena Ave 62095 618-254-0607
Dr. Patrick Anderson, supt. Fax 254-9048
www.wrh15.org/
Lewis-Clark JHS 200/6-8
501 E Lorena Ave 62095 618-254-4355
Mark Begando, prin. Fax 254-7600

Woodstock, McHenry, Pop. 24,445
Woodstock CUSD 200 6,200/PK-12
227 W Judd St 60098 815-338-8200
Ellyn Wrzeski, supt. Fax 338-2005
www.woodstockschools.org/
Creekside MS 700/6-8
3201 Hercules Rd 60098 815-337-5200
Robert Hackbart, prin. Fax 206-0476
Northwood MS 600/6-8
2121 N Seminary Ave 60098 815-338-4900
Jake Wakitsch, prin. Fax 337-2150
Woodstock HS 1,000/9-12
501 W South St 60098 815-338-4370
Corey Tafoya, prin. Fax 334-0811
Woodstock North HS 900/9-12
3000 Raffel Rd 60098 815-334-2100
Brian McAdow, prin. Fax 334-2101

Marian Central Catholic HS 700/9-12
1001 McHenry Ave 60098 815-338-4220
Thomas Landers, prin. Fax 338-4253

Worth, Cook, Pop. 10,649
Worth SD 127 1,000/PK-8
11218 S Ridgeland Ave 60482 708-448-2800
Dr. Rita Wojtylewski, supt. Fax 448-6215
www.worthschools.org
Worth JHS 300/6-8
11151 S New England Ave 60482 708-448-2803
Joseph Zampillo, prin. Fax 448-6155

Wyoming, Stark, Pop. 1,418
Stark County CUSD 100 800/PK-12
300 W Van Buren St 61491 309-695-6123
Jerry Klooster, supt.
www.stark100.com
Other Schools – See Toulon

Yorkville, Kendall, Pop. 16,715
Yorkville CUSD 115 4,900/PK-12
PO Box 579 60560 630-553-4382
Dr. Tim Shimp, supt. Fax 553-4398
www.y115.org
Yorkville HS 1,100/10-12
797 Game Farm Rd 60560 630-553-4380
Ron Kiesewetter, prin. Fax 553-4397
Yorkville HS Academy 9-9
702 Game Farm Rd 60560 630-553-4385
Ron Kiesewetter, prin. Fax 553-4592
Yorkville MS 800/7-8
920 Prairie Crossing Dr 60560 630-553-4544
Adam Zbrozek, prin. Fax 553-5181

Parkview Christian Academy 50/PK-12
201 W Center St 60560 630-553-5158
Deborah Benson, supt. Fax 553-3370

Zeigler, Franklin, Pop. 1,781
Zeigler-Royalton CUSD 188 700/PK-12
PO Box 38 62999 618-596-5841
George Wilkerson, supt. Fax 596-6789
www.z-r.frnkln.k12.il.us
Zeigler-Royalton HS 200/9-12
PO Box 38 62999 618-596-5841
Quent Hamilton, prin. Fax 596-6789
Zeigler-Royalton JHS 100/7-8
PO Box 87 62999 618-596-2121
Charles Bleyer, prin. Fax 596-2075

Zion, Lake, Pop. 23,535
Zion ESD 6 2,600/PK-8
2200 Bethesda Blvd 60099 847-872-5455
Dr. John Ahlgrim, supt. Fax 746-1280
www.zion6.com
Zion Central JHS 500/7-8
1716 27th St 60099 847-746-1431
Joseph Kent, prin. Fax 746-9750

Zion-Benton Township HSD 126 2,800/9-12
1 ZB Way 60099 847-731-9300
Dr. Chris Clark, supt. Fax 731-4441
www.zbths.org
New Tech High @ Zion-Benton East 300/9-12
1634 23rd St 60099 847-731-9800
Anne Buck, prin. Fax 746-5428
Zion-Benton Township HS 2,500/9-12
1 ZB Way 60099 847-731-9300
Chris Pawelczyk, prin. Fax 731-4408

INDIANA

INDIANA DEPARTMENT OF EDUCATION
151 W Ohio St Ste X, Indianapolis 46204
Telephone 317-232-6610
Fax 317-232-8004
Website http://www.doe.in.gov

Superintendent of Public Instruction Glenda Ritz

INDIANA BOARD OF EDUCATION
200 W Washington St Ste 229, Indianapolis 46204-2798

Chairperson Tony Bennett

EDUCATIONAL SERVICE CENTERS (ESC)

Central Indiana ESC
Dr. MaryAnn Dewan, dir. 317-387-7100
6321 La Pas Trl Fax 328-7298
Indianapolis 46268
www.ciesc.k12.in.us/

East Central ESC
Larry John, dir., 1601 Indiana Ave 765-825-1247
Connersville 47331 Fax 825-2532
www.ecesc.k12.in.us/

Northern Indiana ESC
Ted Chittum, dir. 574-254-0111
56535 Magnetic Dr Fax 254-0148
Mishawaka 46545
www.niesc.k12.in.us/

Northwest Indiana ESC
Edward Schoenfelt, dir. 219-926-5555
48 W 900 N, Chesterton 46304 Fax 926-5553
www.nwiesc.k12.in.us/

Region 8 ESC
Joshua Wenning, dir. 260-724-6200
251 W 850 N, Decatur 46733 Fax 244-6201
www.r8esc.k12.in.us/

Southern Indiana ESC
J. Scott Turney, dir. 812-482-6641
1102 Tree Lane Dr, Jasper 47546 Fax 482-6652
www.siec.k12.in.us/

Wabash Valley ESC
Dr. Dennis Cahill, dir. 765-463-1589
3061 Benton St Fax 463-1580
West Lafayette 47906
www.esc5.k12.in.us/

West Central ESC
Valerie Buchanan, dir. 765-653-2727
PO Box 21, Greencastle 46135 Fax 653-7897
www.wciesc.k12.in.us/

William E. Wilson ESC
Dr. Phil Partenheimer, dir. 812-256-8000
2101 Grace Ave Fax 256-8012
Charlestown 47111
www.wesc.k12.in.us/

PUBLIC, PRIVATE AND CATHOLIC SECONDARY SCHOOLS

Akron, Kosciusko, Pop. 1,159
Tippecanoe Valley SC 2,100/K-12
8343 S State Road 19 46910 574-353-7741
Brett Boggs, supt. Fax 353-7743
www.tvsc.k12.in.us
Tippecanoe Valley HS 600/9-12
8345 S State Road 19 46910 574-353-7031
Kirk Doehrmann, prin. Fax 353-1016
Tippecanoe Valley MS 500/6-8
11303 W 800 S 46910 574-353-7353
Blaine Conley, prin. Fax 353-7189

Albion, Noble, Pop. 2,325
Central Noble Community SC 1,300/K-12
200 E Main St 46701 260-636-2175
Chris Daughtry, supt. Fax 636-7918
www.centralnoble.k12.in.us/
Central Noble HS 400/9-12
302 Cougar Ct 46701 260-636-2117
Geoff Brose, prin. Fax 636-2791
Central Noble MS 300/6-8
401 E Highland St 46701 260-636-2279
Geoff Brose, prin. Fax 636-2461

Alexandria, Madison, Pop. 5,088
Alexandria Community SC 1,600/PK-12
202 E Washington St 46001 765-724-4496
Dr. Alice Johnson, supt. Fax 724-5049
www.alex.k12.in.us
Alexandria-Monroe JSHS 800/7-12
1 Burden Ct 46001 765-724-4413
Jim Regenold, prin. Fax 724-5041

Anderson, Madison, Pop. 54,768
Anderson Community SC 5,100/PK-12
1600 Hillcrest Ave 46011 765-641-2000
Felix Chow Ed.D., supt. Fax 641-2080
www.acsc.net
Anderson HS 1,400/9-12
4610 Madison Ave 46013 765-641-2037
Terry Thompson, prin. Fax 641-2041
Highland MS 400/6-8
2108 E 200 N 46012 765-641-2059
Kelly Durr, prin. Fax 641-2064

Frankton-Lapel Community SD 2,900/PK-12
7916 W 300 N 46011 765-734-1261
Bobby Fields, supt. Fax 734-1129
www.flcs.k12.in.us/
Other Schools – See Frankton, Lapel

Anderson Christian S 200/PK-12
2625 Lindberg Rd 46012 765-649-0123
Thomas Snell, admin. Fax 649-3844
Anderson University Post-Sec.
1100 E 5th St 46012 765-649-9071
Apex School of Beauty Culture Post-Sec.
333 Jackson St 46016 765-642-7560
Harrison College Post-Sec.
140 E 53rd St 46013 765-644-7514
Indiana Christian Academy 100/PK-12
432 W 300 N 46012 765-643-7884
Kevin Plew, prin. Fax 683-4200
Liberty Christian HS 300/7-12
2323 Columbus Ave 46016 765-644-7774
Amy Conrad, prin. Fax 644-7779

Angola, Steuben, Pop. 8,487
Metropolitan SD of Steuben County 3,100/K-12
400 S Martha St 46703 260-665-2854
Dr. Brent Wilson, supt. Fax 665-9155
www.msdsteuben.k12.in.us
Angola HS 1,000/9-12
350 S John McBride Ave 46703 260-665-2186
Travis Heavin, prin. Fax 665-7012
Angola MS 700/6-8
1350 E Maumee St 46703 260-665-9581
Ann Rice, prin. Fax 665-9583

Trine University Post-Sec.
1 University Ave 46703 260-665-4100

Arcadia, Hamilton, Pop. 1,652
Hamilton Heights SC 2,300/PK-12
PO Box 469 46030 317-984-3538
Anthony Cook, supt. Fax 984-3042
www.hhsc.k12.in.us
Hamilton Heights HS 700/9-12
PO Box 379 46030 317-984-3551
Jarrod Mason, prin. Fax 984-3554
Hamilton Heights MS 500/6-8
PO Box 609 46030 317-984-3588
Elizabeth Wright, prin. Fax 984-3231

Argos, Marshall, Pop. 1,665
Argos Community SD 700/K-12
410 N First St 46501 574-892-5139
Dr. Jennifer Lucht, supt. Fax 892-6527
www.argos.k12.in.us/
Argos Community JSHS 300/7-12
500 Yearick St 46501 574-892-5137
Nick Medich, prin. Fax 892-4712

Attica, Fountain, Pop. 3,214
Attica Consolidated SC 900/PK-12
205 E Sycamore St 47918 765-762-7000
Derek Marshall, supt. Fax 762-7007
www.attica.k12.in.us
Attica JSHS 400/7-12
211 E Sycamore St 47918 765-762-7000
Johnathan Hoke, prin. Fax 762-7017

Auburn, DeKalb, Pop. 12,632

Lakewood Park Christian S 500/PK-12
5555 County Road 29 46706 260-925-1393
Dr. Ed Yoder, supt. Fax 925-5010

Aurora, Dearborn, Pop. 3,721
South Dearborn Community SC 3,000/PK-12
6109 Squire Pl 47001 812-926-2090
Dr. John Mehrle, supt. Fax 926-4216
www.sdcsc.k12.in.us
South Dearborn HS 900/9-12
5770 Highlander Pl 47001 812-926-3772
Jason Cheek, prin. Fax 926-4162
South Dearborn MS 500/7-8
5850 Squire Pl 47001 812-926-6298
Todd Bowers, prin. Fax 926-2149

Austin, Scott, Pop. 4,251
Scott County SD 1 1,300/PK-12
PO Box 9 47102 812-794-8750
Berley Goodin, supt. Fax 794-8765
www.scsd1.com/
Austin HS 400/9-12
401 S Highway 31 47102 812-794-8730
Sherman Smith, prin. Fax 794-8739
Austin MS 400/6-8
401 S Highway 31 47102 812-794-8740
David Deaton, prin. Fax 794-8739

Avon, Hendricks, Pop. 12,177
Avon Community SC 7,900/K-12
7203 E US Highway 36 46123 317-544-6000
Dr. Margaret Hoernemann, supt. Fax 544-6001
www.avon-schools.org
Avon HS 2,500/9-12
7575 E County Road 150 S 46123 317-544-5000
Matt Shockley, prin. Fax 544-5001
Avon MS North 700/7-8
1251 N Dan Jones Rd 46123 317-544-5500
Susan Green, prin. Fax 544-5501
Avon MS South 700/7-8
7199 E US Highway 36 46123 317-544-5700
Dan Chapin, prin. Fax 544-5701

Bainbridge, Putnam, Pop. 737
North Putnam Community SD 1,700/PK-12
300 N Washington St 46105 765-522-6218
Daniel Noel, supt. Fax 522-3562
www.nputnam.k12.in.us
Other Schools – See Roachdale

Batesville, Franklin, Pop. 6,459
Batesville Community SC 1,900/PK-12
PO Box 121 47006 812-934-2194
Dr. James Roberts, supt. Fax 933-0833
www.batesville.k12.in.us
Batesville HS 700/9-12
1 Bulldog Blvd 47006 812-934-4384
Andy Allen, prin. Fax 934-5964
Batesville MS 500/6-8
201 N Mulberry St 47006 812-934-5175
Dave Strouse, prin. Fax 933-0834

Bedford, Lawrence, Pop. 13,252
North Lawrence Community SD 5,400/PK-12
PO Box 729 47421 812-279-3521
Dr. Dennis Turner, supt. Fax 275-1577
www.nlcs.k12.in.us
Bedford MS 600/6-8
1501 N St 47421 812-279-9781
David Schlegel, prin. Fax 277-3218
Bedford-North Lawrence HS 1,700/9-12
595 Stars Blvd 47421 812-279-9756
Roger Dean, prin. Fax 279-9304
North Lawrence Career Ctr Vo/Tech
258 BNL Dr 47421 812-279-3561
Duane Martin, prin. Fax 275-1578
Shawswick MS 200/6-8
71 Shawswick School Rd 47421 812-275-6121
James Pentzer, prin. Fax 275-0543
Other Schools – See Oolitic

Beech Grove, Marion, Pop. 13,930
Beech Grove CSD 2,600/PK-12
5334 Hornet Ave 46107 317-788-4481
Dr. Paul Kaiser, supt. Fax 782-4065
www.bgcs.k12.in.us
Beech Grove HS 800/9-12
5330 Hornet Ave 46107 317-786-1447
Steve Cox, prin. Fax 781-2920
Beech Grove MS 400/7-8
1248 Buffalo St 46107 317-784-6649
Thomas Gearhart, prin. Fax 781-2926

St. Francis Hospital Center Post-Sec.
1600 Albany St 46107 317-783-8220

Berne, Adams, Pop. 3,972
South Adams SD 1,400/PK-12
1075 Starfire Way 46711 260-589-3133
Scott Litwiller, supt. Fax 589-2065
www.southadams.k12.in.us
South Adams HS 400/9-12
1000 Parkway St 46711 260-589-3131
Trent Lehman, prin. Fax 589-3042
South Adams MS 300/6-8
1212 Starfire Way 46711 260-589-1102
Jeff Rich, prin. Fax 589-2112

Bicknell, Knox, Pop. 2,893
North Knox SC 700/K-12
11110 N State Road 159 47512 812-735-4434
Darrel Bobe, supt. Fax 328-6262
www.nknox.k12.in.us
North Knox Alternative Education Alt
524 W 11th St 47512 812-882-7538
Don Osburn, prin. Fax 328-6262
North Knox JSHS 400/7-12
10890 N State Road 159 47512 812-735-2990
Matt Sandefer, prin. Fax 328-2155

Bloomfield, Greene, Pop. 2,386
Bloomfield SD 1,100/K-12
PO Box 266 47424 812-384-4507
Daniel Sichting, supt. Fax 384-0172
www.bsd.k12.in.us
Bloomfield JSHS 500/7-12
PO Box 266 47424 812-384-4550
David Dean, prin. Fax 384-1422

Eastern Greene SD 1,300/PK-12
1471 N State Road 43 47424 812-825-5722
Dr. Ty Mungle, supt. Fax 825-9413
www.egreene.k12.in.us/
Eastern Greene HS 400/9-12
11064 E State Road 54 47424 812-825-5621
Kevin Frank, prin. Fax 825-6661
Eastern Greene MS 400/5-8
10503 E State Road 54 47424 812-825-5010
Doug Lewis, prin. Fax 825-7386

Bloomington, Monroe, Pop. 78,128
Monroe County Community SC 10,500/PK-12
315 E North Dr 47401 812-330-7700
Judith DeMuth Ed.D., supt. Fax 330-7813
www.mccsc.edu
Academy of Science & Entrepreneurship 9-12
444 S Patterson Dr 47403 812-330-2480
Dr. Bruce Colston, prin. Fax 330-2481
Batchelor MS 600/7-8
900 W Gordon Pike 47403 812-330-7763
Eric Gilpin, prin. Fax 330-7766
Bloomington Graduation S Alt
705 W Coolidge Dr 47403 812-330-7837
Rob Moore, dir. Fax 330-7789
Bloomington HS North 1,600/9-12
3901 N Kinser Pike 47404 812-330-7724
Jeffry Henderson, prin. Fax 330-7805
Bloomington HS South 1,700/9-12
1965 S Walnut St 47401 812-330-7714
Mark Fletcher, prin. Fax 330-7810
Hoosier Hills Career Center Vo/Tech
3070 N Prow Rd 47404 812-330-7730
Alan Dafoe, dir. Fax 330-7807
Jackson Creek MS 500/7-8
3980 S Sare Rd 47401 812-330-2451
David Pillar, prin. Fax 330-2457
Tri-North MS 500/7-8
1000 W 15th St 47404 812-330-7745
Dr. Gale Hill, prin. Fax 330-7799
Broadview Learning Center Adult
705 W Coolidge Dr 47403 812-330-7731
Robert Moore, prin. Fax 330-7789

Bloomington Hospital Post-Sec.
PO Box 1149 47402 812-336-6821
Hair Arts Academy Post-Sec.
1681 N College Ave 47404 812-339-1117
Harmony S 200/PK-12
PO Box 1787 47402 812-334-8349
Steve Bonchek, dir. Fax 333-3435
Indiana University Post-Sec.
107 S Indiana Ave 47405 812-855-4848
Ivy Tech Community College - Bloomington Post-Sec.
200 N Daniels Way 47404 812-332-1559
Lighthouse Christian Academy 200/K-12
1201 W That Rd 47403 812-824-2000
Don Wilson M.Ed., prin. Fax 824-2017

Bluffton, Wells, Pop. 9,806
Metro SD of Bluffton-Harrison 1,500/K-12
805 E Harrison Rd 46714 260-824-2620
Wayne Barker, supt. Fax 824-6011
www.bhmsd.k12.in.us
Bluffton-Harrison MS 400/5-8
1500 Stogdill Rd 46714 260-824-3536
Tom Gibson, prin. Fax 824-6011
Bluffton HS 500/9-12
1 Tiger Trl 46714 260-824-3724
Steve Baker, prin. Fax 824-6011

Boone Grove, Porter
Porter Township SC
Supt. — See Valparaiso
Boone Grove MS 400/6-8
325 W 550 S 46302 219-464-4828
Paul Schlottman, prin. Fax 465-0999

Boonville, Warrick, Pop. 6,171
Warrick County SC 9,900/K-12
300 E Gum St 47601 812-897-0400
Brad Schneider, supt. Fax 897-6033
www.warrick.k12.in.us/
Boonville HS 900/9-12
300 N 1st St 47601 812-897-4701
Mike Whitten, prin. Fax 897-6061
Boonville MS 700/6-8
555 N Yankeetown Rd 47601 812-897-1420
William Wilder, prin. Fax 897-6584
Other Schools – See Lynnville, Newburgh

Borden, Clark, Pop. 799
West Clark Community SC
Supt. — See Sellersburg
Borden JSHS 400/7-12
PO Box 260 47106 812-967-2087
Lisa Nale, prin. Fax 967-2086

Bourbon, Marshall, Pop. 1,801
Triton SC 1,000/K-12
100 Triton Dr 46504 574-342-2255
Donna Burroughs, supt. Fax 342-8165
www.triton.k12.in.us/
Triton JSHS 500/7-12
300 Triton Dr 46504 574-342-6505
Michael Chobanov, prin. Fax 342-8175

Brazil, Clay, Pop. 7,835
Clay Community SD 4,500/PK-12
1013 S Forest Ave 47834 812-443-4461
Kimberly Tucker, supt. Fax 442-0849
www.clay.k12.in.us
North Clay MS 800/6-8
3450 W State Road 340 47834 812-448-1530
Jeffery Fritz, prin. Fax 442-0608
Northview HS 1,100/9-12
3150 W State Road 340 47834 812-448-2661
Ernie Simpson, prin. Fax 446-2647
Other Schools – See Clay City

Bremen, Marshall, Pop. 4,550
Bremen Public SD 1,500/K-12
512 W Grant St 46506 574-546-3929
Russ Mikel, supt. Fax 546-6303
www.bps.k12.in.us
Bremen HS 500/9-12
511 W Grant St 46506 574-546-3511
Bruce Jennings, prin. Fax 546-5477

Bristol, Elkhart, Pop. 1,559

Kessington Christian S 50/PK-12
19153 County Road 104 46507 574-848-4987
Nancy Stump, admin. Fax 641-2118

Brookville, Franklin, Pop. 2,579
Franklin County Community SC 3,000/PK-12
225 E 10th St 47012 765-647-4128
Dr. Debbie Howell, supt. Fax 647-2417
www.fccsc.k12.in.us
Brookville MS 500/5-8
9092 Wildcat Ln 47012 765-647-6040
Dr. Gary Frost, prin. Fax 647-4960
Franklin County HS 1,000/9-12
1 Wildcat Ln 47012 765-647-4101
Dr. Kent Grider, prin. Fax 647-2732

Brownsburg, Hendricks, Pop. 20,984
Brownsburg Community SC 7,500/PK-12
444 E Tilden Dr 46112 317-852-5726
Jim Snapp, supt. Fax 852-1015
www.brownsburg.k12.in.us
Brownsburg East MS 1,000/6-8
1250 Airport Rd 46112 317-852-2386
Marsha Webster, prin. Fax 852-1023
Brownsburg HS 2,200/9-12
1000 S Odell St 46112 317-852-2258
Bret Daghe, prin. Fax 852-1490
Brownsburg West MS 700/6-8
1555 S Odell St 46112 317-852-3143
Jeffrey Hubble, prin. Fax 858-4100
Harris Academy Alt
725 S Green St Ste A 46112 317-852-1010
Bill Titus, dir. Fax 852-1012

Bethesda Christian S 400/PK-12
7950 N County Road 650 E 46112 317-858-2820
Don Criss, supt. Fax 858-2819

Brownstown, Jackson, Pop. 2,921
Brownstown Central Community SC 1,700/PK-12
608 W Commerce St 47220 812-358-4271
Jim Terrell, supt. Fax 358-5303
www.btownccs.k12.in.us
Brownstown Central HS 600/9-12
500 N Elm St 47220 812-358-3453
Joseph Sheffer, prin. Fax 358-5318
Brownstown Central MS 400/6-8
520 W Walnut St 47220 812-358-4947
Greg Walker, prin. Fax 358-3940

Bunker Hill, Miami, Pop. 866
Maconaquah SC 2,300/PK-12
7932 S Strawtown Pike 46914 765-689-9131
Dr. Douglas Arnold, supt. Fax 689-0995
www.maconaquah.k12.in.us
Maconaquah HS 700/9-12
256 E 800 S 46914 765-689-9131
David Noonan, prin. Fax 689-9528
Maconaquah MS 500/6-8
594 E 800 S 46914 765-689-9131
Craig Jernagan, prin. Fax 689-9360

Butler, DeKalb, Pop. 2,658
DeKalb County Eastern Community SD 1,400/K-12
300 E Washington St 46721 260-868-2125
Dr. Jeffrey Stephens, supt. Fax 868-2562
www.dekalbeastern.com
Eastside JSHS 700/7-12
603 E Green St 46721 260-868-2186
Larry Yoder, prin. Fax 868-5773

Cambridge City, Wayne, Pop. 1,861
Western Wayne SD
Supt. — See Pershing
Lincoln HS 400/9-12
205 E Parkway Dr 47327 765-478-5916
Michael Cerqua, prin. Fax 478-3262
Lincoln MS 200/6-8
205 E Parkway Dr 47327 765-478-5840
Michael Cerqua, prin. Fax 478-3265

Campbellsburg, Washington, Pop. 579
West Washington SC 900/K-12
9699 W Mount Tabor Rd 47108 812-755-4996
Gerald Jackson, supt. Fax 755-4843
www.wwcs.k12.in.us
West Washington JSHS 400/7-12
8028 W Batts Rd 47108 812-755-4996
Karen York, prin. Fax 755-4460

Cannelton, Perry, Pop. 1,540
Cannelton CSD 300/PK-12
109 S 3rd St Ste A 47520 812-547-2637
Marion Chapman, supt. Fax 547-4142
www.cannelton.k12.in.us
Cannelton HS 100/6-12
109 S 3rd St 47520 812-547-3296
Marion Chapman, prin. Fax 548-2288

Carmel, Hamilton, Pop. 77,695
Carmel Clay SD 15,500/PK-12
5201 E Main St 46033 317-844-9961
Dr. R. Stephen Tegarden, supt. Fax 844-9965
www.ccs.k12.in.us
Carmel HS 4,400/9-12
520 E Main St 46032 317-846-7721
John Williams, prin. Fax 571-4066
Carmel MS 1,200/6-8
300 S Guilford Rd 46032 317-846-7331
Lila Jay, prin. Fax 571-4067
Clay MS 1,200/6-8
5150 E 126th St 46033 317-844-7251
Todd Crosby, prin. Fax 571-4020
Creekside MS 1,400/6-8
3525 W 126th St 46032 317-733-6420
Tom Harmas, prin. Fax 733-6422

University HS of Indiana 200/9-12
2825 W 116th St 46032 317-733-4475
Charles Webster, head sch Fax 733-4484

Castleton, Marion, Pop. 36

Kaye Beauty College Post-Sec.
6346 E 82nd St 46250 317-576-0224

Cayuga, Vermillion, Pop. 1,146
North Vermillion Community SC 700/K-12
5551 N Falcon Dr 47928 765-492-4033
Michael Turner, supt. Fax 492-7001
www.nvc.k12.in.us
North Vermillion JSHS 400/7-12
5555 N Falcon Dr 47928 765-492-3364
Jayne Ann Virostko, prin. Fax 492-7006

Cedar Lake, Lake, Pop. 11,431
Hanover Community SC 2,000/K-12
PO Box 645 46303 219-374-3500
Thomas Taylor, supt. Fax 374-4411
www.hanover.k12.in.us
Hanover Central HS 600/9-12
10120 W 133rd Ave 46303 219-374-3800
Justin Biggs, prin. Fax 374-4408
Hanover Central MS 500/6-8
10631 W 141st Ave 46303 219-374-3900
Tony Hiatt, prin. Fax 374-8926

Centerville, Wayne, Pop. 2,522
Centerville-Abington Community SD 1,700/PK-12
115 W South St 47330 765-855-3475
Philip Stevenson, supt. Fax 855-2524
www.centerville.k12.in.us
Centerville-Abington JHS 300/7-8
509 Willow Grove Rd 47330 765-855-5113
Rick Schauss, prin. Fax 855-5207
Centerville HS 600/9-12
507 Willow Grove Rd 47330 765-855-3481
Mikel McCoy, prin. Fax 855-3484

Chalmers, White, Pop. 504
Frontier SC 800/K-12
PO Box 809 47929 219-984-5009
Cathy Rowe, supt. Fax 984-5022
www.frontier.k12.in.us
Frontier JSHS 400/7-12
1 Falcon Dr 47929 219-984-5437
Cathy Rowe, prin. Fax 984-5360

Charlestown, Clark, Pop. 7,449
Greater Clark County SD
Supt. — See Jeffersonville
Charlestown HS 700/9-12
1 Pirate Pl 47111 812-256-3328
Keith Hedges, prin. Fax 256-7274
Charlestown MS 600/6-8
8804 High Jackson Rd 47111 812-256-6363
Joyce Traub, prin. Fax 256-7282

Charlottesville, Hancock
Eastern Hancock County Community SC 1,100/PK-12
10370 E County Road 250 N 46117 317-467-0064
James Harris, supt. Fax 936-5516
www.easternhancock.org
Eastern Hancock HS 400/9-12
10320 E County Road 250 N 46117 317-936-5595
David Pfaff, prin. Fax 936-5050
Eastern Hancock MS 300/6-8
10380 E County Road 250 N 46117 317-936-5324
David Pfaff, prin. Fax 936-5050

Chesterton, Porter, Pop. 12,902
Duneland SC 5,900/K-12
601 W Morgan Ave 46304 219-983-3600
Dr. Dirk Baer, supt. Fax 983-3614
www.duneland.k12.in.us
Chesterton HS 2,000/9-12
2125 S 11th St 46304 219-983-3730
Jim Goetz, prin. Fax 983-3775
Chesterton MS 900/7-8
651 W Morgan Ave 46304 219-983-3776
Craig Stafford, prin. Fax 983-3798

Fairhaven Baptist Academy 200/PK-12
86 E Oak Hill Rd 46304 219-926-6636
Brian Rinehart, prin. Fax 926-1111

Churubusco, Whitley, Pop. 1,774
Smith-Green Community SD 1,300/PK-12
222 W Tulley St 46723 260-693-2007
Galen Mast, supt. Fax 693-6434
www.sgcs.k12.in.us/
Churubusco JSHS 700/6-12
1 Eagle Dr 46723 260-693-2131
Jim Folland, prin. Fax 693-3673

Cicero, Hamilton, Pop. 4,762

Indiana Academy 100/9-12
24815 State Road 19 46034 317-984-3575
Jeremy Hall, prin. Fax 984-5081

Clarksville, Clark, Pop. 21,221
Clarksville Community SC 1,400/PK-12
200 Ettels Ln 47129 812-282-7753
Kim Knott, supt. Fax 282-7754
www.ccsc.k12.in.us/
Clarksville HS 500/9-12
800 Dr Dot Lewis Dr 47129 812-282-8231
Brian Allred, prin. Fax 282-8234
Clarksville MS 400/5-8
101 Ettels Ln 47129 812-282-8235
Scott Gardner, prin. Fax 280-5004

Our Lady of Providence JSHS 500/7-12
707 Providence Way 47129 812-945-2538
Melinda Ernstberger, prin. Fax 981-2538
PJ's College of Cosmetology Post-Sec.
1414 Blackiston Mill Rd 47129 812-282-0459

Clay City, Clay, Pop. 856
Clay Community SD
Supt. — See Brazil
Clay City JSHS 400/7-12
601 Lankford St 47841 812-939-2154
Jeff Bell, prin. Fax 939-3170

Clayton, Hendricks, Pop. 965
Mill Creek Community SC 1,600/PK-12
6631 S County Road 200 W 46118 317-539-9200
Dr. Patrick Spray, supt. Fax 539-9215
www.mccsc.k12.in.us/
Cascade HS 500/9-12
6565 S County Road 200 W 46118 317-539-9315
Catherine Tooley, prin. Fax 539-9350
Cascade MS 400/6-8
6423 S County Road 200 W 46118 317-539-9285
Eric Sieferman, prin. Fax 539-9310

Clinton, Vermillion, Pop. 4,826
South Vermillion Community SC 2,000/PK-12
PO Box 387 47842 765-832-2426
David Chapman, supt. Fax 832-7391
www.svcs.k12.in.us
South Vermillion HS 600/9-12
770 Wildcat Dr 47842 765-832-3551
Don Harman, prin. Fax 832-5310
South Vermillion MS 500/6-8
900 Wildcat Dr 47842 765-832-7727
Angela Harris, prin. Fax 832-5316

Cloverdale, Putnam, Pop. 2,143
Cloverdale Community SC 1,300/PK-12
310 E Logan St 46120 765-795-4664
Carrie Milner, supt. Fax 795-5166
www.cloverdale.k12.in.us
Cloverdale HS 400/9-12
205 E Market St 46120 765-795-4203
Sonny Stoltz, prin. Fax 795-4381
Cloverdale MS 400/5-8
312 E Logan St 46120 765-795-2900
Stacey Baugh, prin. Fax 795-2901

Columbia City, Whitley, Pop. 8,635
Whitley County Consolidated SD 3,600/PK-12
107 N Walnut St 46725 260-244-5772
Patricia O'Connor, supt. Fax 244-4099
www.wccs.k12.in.us
Columbia City HS 1,100/9-12
600 N Whitley St 46725 260-244-6136
Jennifer Reiff, prin. Fax 244-5610
Indian Springs MS 800/6-8
1692 S State Road 9 46725 260-244-5148
Jan Boylen, prin. Fax 244-4710

Columbus, Bartholomew, Pop. 43,281
Bartholomew Consolidated SC 11,300/PK-12
1200 Central Ave 47201 812-376-4220
Dr. John Quick, supt. Fax 376-4486
www.bcsc.k12.in.us
Central MS 900/7-8
725 7th St 47201 812-376-4287
Randy Gratz, prin. Fax 376-4511
Columbus Area Career Connection Vo/Tech
1400 25th St 47201 812-376-4240
Gene Hack, dir. Fax 376-4699
Columbus East HS 1,600/9-12
230 S Marr Rd 47201 812-376-4369
Mark Newell, prin. Fax 376-4358
Columbus North HS 2,000/9-12
1400 25th St 47201 812-376-4432
David Clark, prin. Fax 376-4291
Columbus Signature Acad - Central 7-8
725 7th St 47201 812-376-4287
Randy Gratz, admin. Fax 376-4511
Columbus Signature Acad - NewTech 9-12
2205 25th St 47201 812-376-4595
Mike Reed, prin. Fax 376-4511
McDowell Educational Center Alt
2700 McKinley Ave 47201 812-376-4451
Andrea Quick, dir. Fax 376-4512
Northside MS 800/7-8
1400 27th St 47201 812-376-4405
Amy Dixon, prin. Fax 376-4479

Columbus Christian S 200/PK-12
3170 Indiana Ave 47201 812-372-3780
Kendall Wildey, admin. Fax 372-3878
Columbus Regional Hospital Post-Sec.
2400 17th St 47201 812-376-5439
Harrison College Post-Sec.
2222 Poshard Dr 47203 812-379-9000
Ivy Tech Community College - Columbus Post-Sec.
4475 Central Ave 47203 812-372-9925

Connersville, Fayette, Pop. 13,304
Fayette County SC 3,800/PK-12
1401 Spartan Dr 47331 765-825-2178
Dr. Russell Hodges, supt. Fax 825-8060
www.fayette.k12.in.us
Connersville HS 1,200/9-12
1100 Spartan Dr 47331 765-825-1151
Patricia Flowers, prin. Fax 825-0777
Connersville MS 600/7-8
1900 N Grand Ave 47331 765-825-1139
Beth Denham, prin. Fax 827-4346
Whitewater Technical Career Center Vo/Tech
1300 Spartan Dr 47331 765-825-0521
Milton Eley, dir. Fax 827-0836

Converse, Miami, Pop. 1,252
Oak Hill United SC 1,600/K-12
PO Box 550 46919 765-395-3341
Joel Martin, supt. Fax 395-3343
www.ohusc.k12.in.us
Oak Hill HS 500/9-12
7756 W Delphi Pike Ste 27 46919 765-384-4381
Michael McDivitt, prin. Fax 384-5414
Oak Hill JHS 200/7-8
7760 W Delphi Pike Ste 27 46919 765-384-4385
Greg Perkins, prin. Fax 384-4386

Corydon, Harrison, Pop. 3,080
South Harrison Community SD 3,100/K-12
315 S Harrison Dr 47112 812-738-2168
Dr. Neyland Clark, supt. Fax 738-2158
www.shcsc.k12.in.us/
Corydon Central HS 800/9-12
375 Country Club Rd 47112 812-738-4181
Jennie Capelle, prin. Fax 738-1145
Corydon Central JHS 400/7-8
377 Country Club Rd 47112 812-738-4184
Mark Black, prin. Fax 738-5752
Other Schools – See Elizabeth

Covington, Fountain, Pop. 2,619
Covington Community SC 1,000/PK-12
601 Market St 47932 765-793-4877
Kirk Booe Ph.D., supt. Fax 793-5209
www.covington.k12.in.us/
Covington Community HS 300/9-12
1017 6th St 47932 765-793-2286
Adam Welchans, prin. Fax 793-5200
Covington MS 200/6-8
514 Railroad St 47932 765-793-4451
Steve Reynolds, prin. Fax 793-5200

Crawfordsville, Montgomery, Pop. 15,708
Crawfordsville Community SD 2,500/PK-12
1000 Fairview Ave 47933 765-362-2342
Kathleen Steele, supt. Fax 364-3237
www.cville.k12.in.us
Crawfordsville HS 700/9-12
1 W Athenian Dr 47933 765-362-2340
Greg Hunt, prin. Fax 364-3200
Tuttle MS 500/6-8
612 S Elm St 47933 765-362-2992
John Strickland, prin. Fax 364-3219

North Montgomery Community SC 2,100/PK-12
480 W 580 N 47933 765-359-2112
Dr. Colleen Moran, supt. Fax 359-2111
www.nm.k12.in.us/
North Montgomery HS 600/9-12
5945 N US Highway 231 47933 765-362-5140
Doug Miller, prin. Fax 362-6710
Northridge MS 500/6-8
482 W 580 N 47933 765-364-1071
Angela Blessing, prin. Fax 362-7985

South Montgomery Community SC
Supt. — See New Market
Southmont HS 600/9-12
6425 S US Highway 231 47933 765-866-0350
Kevin Stewart, prin. Fax 866-2044
Southmont JHS 300/7-8
6460 S US Highway 231 47933 765-866-2023
Mike Sowers, prin. Fax 866-2045

Maranatha Christian S 50/K-12
PO Box 29 47933 765-364-0628
Gloria Stevens, prin. Fax 362-0151
Wabash College Post-Sec.
301 W Wabash Ave 47933 765-361-6100

Crothersville, Jackson, Pop. 1,577
Crothersville Community SD 500/K-12
201 S Preston St 47229 812-793-2601
Dr. Terry Goodin, supt. Fax 793-3004
www.crothersville.k12.in.us/
Crothersville JSHS 300/6-12
109 N Preston St 47229 812-793-2051
David Schill, prin. Fax 793-3004

Crown Point, Lake, Pop. 27,010
Crown Point Community SC 7,600/PK-12
200 E North St 46307 219-663-3371
Dr. Teresa Eineman, supt. Fax 662-3414
www.cps.k12.in.us
Colonel John Wheeler MS 900/6-8
401 W Joliet St 46307 219-663-2173
Timothy Vassar, prin. Fax 662-4378
Crown Point HS 2,500/9-12
1500 S Main St 46307 219-663-4885
Chip Pettit, prin. Fax 662-5661
Taft MS 900/6-8
1000 S Main St 46307 219-663-1507
Michael Hazen, prin. Fax 662-4349

St. Anthony School of Echocardiography Post-Sec.
1201 S Main St 46307 219-757-6132

Culver, Marshall, Pop. 1,330
Culver Community SC 900/K-12
PO Box 231 46511 574-842-3364
Brad Schuldt, supt. Fax 842-4615
www.culver.k12.in.us
Culver Community HS 300/9-12
701 School St 46511 574-842-3391
Albert Hanselman, prin. Fax 842-3392
Culver Community MS 200/7-8
1 Cavalier Dr 46511 574-842-5690
Julie Berndt, prin. Fax 842-5691

Culver Academies 800/9-12
1300 Academy Rd 46511 574-842-7000
John Buxton, hdmstr. Fax 842-8161

Daleville, Delaware, Pop. 1,631
Daleville Community SD 800/K-12
14300 W 2nd St 47334 765-378-3329
Paul Garrison, supt. Fax 378-3649
www.daleville.k12.in.us
Daleville JSHS 400/7-12
8400 S Bronco Dr 47334 765-378-3371
A. Rae Floyd M.A., prin. Fax 378-4076

Danville, Hendricks, Pop. 8,895
Danville Community SC 2,600/PK-12
200 Warrior Way 46122 317-745-2212
Dr. Denis Ward, supt. Fax 745-3924
www.danville.k12.in.us
Central Normal Campus Alt
49 N Wayne St 46122 317-745-7942
James Bryant, dir. Fax 745-3886
Danville Community HS 800/9-12
100 Warrior Way 46122 317-745-6431
Paul Hamann, prin. Fax 745-3908
Danville Community MS 800/5-8
1425 W Lincoln St 46122 317-745-5491
Matthew Vandermark, prin. Fax 745-3949

Decatur, Adams, Pop. 9,334
North Adams Community SD 2,000/PK-12
625 Stadium Dr 46733 260-724-7146
Wylie Sirk Ph.D., supt. Fax 724-4777
www.nadams.k12.in.us
Bellmont HS 800/9-12
1000 E North Adams Dr 46733 260-724-7121
Kim Harsh, prin. Fax 724-7826
Bellmont MS 500/5-8
1200 E North Adams Dr 46733 260-724-3137
Scott Miller, prin. Fax 724-4495

Delphi, Carroll, Pop. 2,860
Delphi Community SC 1,700/PK-12
501 Armory Rd 46923 765-564-2100
Ralph Walker, supt. Fax 564-6919
www.delphi.k12.in.us/
Delphi Community HS 500/9-12
301 Armory Rd 46923 765-564-3481
Kyle Trebley, prin. Fax 564-3260
Delphi Community MS 400/6-8
401 Armory Rd 46923 765-564-3411
Kyle Trebley, prin. Fax 564-2135

Demotte, Jasper, Pop. 3,774

Covenant Christian HS 100/9-12
PO Box 369 46310 219-987-7651
Clarence Oudman, admin. Fax 987-7652

Denver, Miami, Pop. 480
North Miami Community SD 1,000/K-12
PO Box 218 46926 765-985-3891
Cathy Egolf, supt. Fax 985-3904
www.nmcs.k12.in.us/
North Miami MSHS 500/7-12
570 E 900 N 46926 765-985-2931
Nathan Stauffer, prin. Fax 985-2056

Donaldson, Marshall

Ancilla College Post-Sec.
PO Box 1 46513 574-936-8898

Dubois, Dubois, Pop. 488
Northeast Dubois County SC 1,000/PK-12
5379 E Main St 47527 812-678-2781
William Hochgesang, supt. Fax 678-4418
www.nedubois.k12.in.us
Dubois MS 300/5-8
4550 N 4th St 47527 812-678-2181
Ryan Case, prin. Fax 678-2282
Northeast Dubois HS 300/9-12
4711 N Dubois Rd NE 47527 812-678-2251
Rick Gladish, prin. Fax 678-3991

Dugger, Sullivan, Pop. 917
Northeast SC
Supt. — See Hymera
Union JSHS 200/7-12
7356 E County Road 50 S 47848 812-648-2729
Shane Reese, prin. Fax 648-2594

Dunkirk, Jay, Pop. 2,346
Jay SC
Supt. — See Portland
West Jay MS 300/6-8
140 E Highland Ave 47336 765-768-7648
Mike Crull, prin. Fax 768-6152

Dyer, Lake, Pop. 16,198
Lake Central SC
Supt. — See Saint John
Kahler MS 1,100/5-8
600 Joliet St 46311 219-865-3535
Karen Brownell, prin. Fax 865-4428

Heritage Christian HS 50/9-12
10790 Calumet Ave 46311 219-558-2660
Fax 558-2664
Mid-America Reformed Seminary Post-Sec.
229 Seminary Dr 46311 219-864-2400

East Chicago, Lake, Pop. 29,444
City of East Chicago SD 5,600/PK-12
210 E Columbus Dr 46312 219-391-4100
Michael Harding, supt. Fax 391-4126
www.ecps.org
Block MS 600/7-8
2700 Cardinal Dr 46312 219-391-4084
James Kendall, prin. Fax 391-4282
East Chicago Central HS 1,600/9-12
1100 W Columbus Dr 46312 219-391-4000
Wendel McCollum, prin. Fax 391-4049

Edinburgh, Johnson, Pop. 4,440
Edinburgh Community SC 900/K-12
202 Keeley St 46124 812-526-2681
Dr. William A. Glentzer, supt. Fax 526-0271
www.ecsc.k12.in.us
Edinburgh Community HS 300/9-12
300 Keeley St 46124 812-526-5501
Kevin Rockey, prin. Fax 526-3439
Edinburgh Community MS 200/6-8
300 Keeley St 46124 812-526-3418
Josh Edwards, prin. Fax 526-3439

Elizabeth, Harrison, Pop. 161
South Harrison Community SD
Supt. — See Corydon
South Central JSHS 400/6-12
6675 E Highway 11 SE 47117 812-969-2941
David Beaver, prin. Fax 969-3019

Elkhart, Elkhart, Pop. 49,305
Baugo Community SD 2,000/K-12
29125 County Road 22 46517 574-293-8583
James DuBois, supt. Fax 294-2171
www.baugo.org/
Jimtown HS 600/9-12
59021 County Road 3 46517 574-295-2343
Jeffery Ziegler, prin. Fax 294-2171
Jimtown JHS 300/7-8
58903 County Road 3 46517 574-294-6586
Michael Stout, prin. Fax 294-8557

Concord Community SD 4,900/K-12
59040 Minuteman Way 46517 574-875-5161
Wayne Stubbs, supt. Fax 875-8762
www.concord.k12.in.us
Concord Community HS 1,500/9-12
59117 Minuteman Way 46517 574-875-6524
Dan Cunningham, prin. Fax 875-8580
Concord JHS 800/7-8
59397 County Road 11 46517 574-875-5122
Rob Zook, prin. Fax 875-1089

Elkhart Community SD 13,100/PK-12
2720 California Rd 46514 574-262-5500
Dr. Robert Haworth, supt. Fax 262-5733
www.elkhart.k12.in.us
Elkhart Area Career Ctr Vo/Tech
2424 California Rd 46514 574-262-5650
William Kovach, dir. Fax 262-5801
Elkhart Central HS 1,800/9-12
1 Blazer Blvd 46516 574-295-4700
Frank Serge, prin. Fax 295-4712
Elkhart Memorial HS 1,800/9-12
2608 California Rd 46514 574-262-5600
Mark Tobolski, prin. Fax 262-5625
Moran MS 600/7-8
200 W Lusher Ave 46517 574-295-4805
Matthew Werbiansky, prin. Fax 295-4807
North Side MS 600/7-8
300 Lawrence St 46514 574-262-5570
Sara Jackowiak, prin. Fax 262-5573
West Side MS 700/7-8
101 S Nappanee St 46514 574-295-4815
Kristie Stutsman, prin. Fax 295-4812

Anabaptist Mennonite Biblical Seminary Post-Sec.
3003 Benham Ave 46517 574-295-3726
Elkhart Christian Academy 500/PK-12
25943 County Road 22 46517 574-293-1609
Sue Alberts, admin. Fax 293-3238
Harrison College Post-Sec.
56075 Parkway Ave 46516 574-522-0397

Ellettsville, Monroe, Pop. 6,255
Richland-Bean Blossom Community SC 2,900/PK-12
600 Edgewood Dr 47429 812-876-7100
Steven Kain, supt. Fax 876-7020
www.rbbcsc.k12.in.us/
Edgewood HS 800/9-12
601 S Edgewood Dr 47429 812-876-2277
Dirk Ackerman, prin. Fax 876-9163
Edgewood JHS 600/6-8
851 W Edgewood Dr 47429 812-876-2005
Melissa Pogue, prin. Fax 876-8985

Elnora, Daviess, Pop. 631
North Daviess Community SD 1,100/K-12
5494 E State Road 58 47529 812-636-8000
Robert Bell, supt. Fax 636-7546
www.ndaviess.k12.in.us
North Daviess JSHS 500/7-12
5494 E State Road 58 47529 812-636-8000
Jed Jerrels, prin. Fax 636-7255

Elwood, Madison, Pop. 8,510
Elwood Community SC 1,600/K-12
1306 N Anderson St 46036 765-552-9861
Glen Nelson, supt. Fax 552-8088
www.elwood.k12.in.us
Elwood Community HS 500/9-12
1137 N 19th St 46036 765-552-9854
David Retherford, prin. Fax 552-1044
Elwood Community MS 600/4-8
1207 N 19th St 46036 765-552-7378
Teresa Boucher, prin. Fax 552-2017
Hinds Career Center Vo/Tech
1105 N 19th St 46036 765-552-9881
James Pearson, dir. Fax 552-2021

Eminence, Morgan
Eminence Community SC 500/K-12
PO Box 135 46125 765-528-2101
Murray Pride, supt. Fax 528-2262
www.eminence.k12.in.us
Eminence JSHS 300/6-12
PO Box 105 46125 765-528-2221
Jeff Gibboney, prin. Fax 528-2276

Evansville, Vanderburgh, Pop. 114,065
Evansville-Vanderburgh SC 22,000/PK-12
951 Walnut St 47713 812-435-8453
Dr. David Smith, supt. Fax 435-8421
www.evscschools.com/
Academy for Innovative Studies 200/Alt
3013 N 1st Ave 47710 812-435-8316
Kenneth Walker, prin. Fax 435-8517
Bosse HS 800/9-12
1300 Washington Ave 47714 812-477-1661
Sheila Huff, prin. Fax 474-6976
Central HS 1,500/9-12
5400 N 1st Ave 47710 812-435-8292
Darla Hoover, prin. Fax 435-8515
Harrison HS 1,500/9-12
211 Fielding Rd 47715 812-477-1046
Elizabeth Wells, prin. Fax 474-4125
Helfrich Park MS 600/6-8
2603 W Maryland St 47712 812-435-8246
Timothy McIntosh, prin. Fax 435-8249
McGary MS 300/6-8
1535 Joyce Ave 47714 812-476-3035
Tammy Dexter, prin. Fax 474-6919
New Tech Institute 9-12
1901 Lynch Rd 47711 812-435-0967
Mike Allen, prin. Fax 435-8568
North HS 1,600/9-12
15331 Highway 41 N 47725 812-435-8283
John Skinner, prin. Fax 435-8349
North JHS 7-8
15325 Highway 41 N 47725 812-435-0975
Aaron Huff, prin.
Perry Heights MS 500/6-8
5800 Hogue Rd 47712 812-435-8326
Charles Goodman, prin. Fax 435-8363
Plaza Park MS 700/6-8
7301 Lincoln Ave 47715 812-476-4971
Shane Browder, prin. Fax 474-6922
Reitz HS 1,400/9-12
350 Dreier Blvd 47712 812-435-8206
Beth Carnahan, prin. Fax 435-8217
Southern IN Career and Technical Center Vo/Tech
1901 Lynch Rd 47711 812-435-8438
Cory Herrin, prin. Fax 435-8366
Thomkins MS 800/6-8
1300 W Mill Rd 47710 812-435-8323
Bryan Perry, prin. Fax 435-8588
Washington MS 500/6-8
1801 Washington Ave 47714 812-477-8983
Jay Hille, prin. Fax 474-6930

Evansville Day S 300/PK-12
3400 N Green River Rd 47715 812-476-3039
Kendall Berry, head sch Fax 476-4061
Harrison College Post-Sec.
4601 Theatre Dr 47715 812-476-6000
Ivy Tech Community College - Southwest Post-Sec.
3501 N 1st Ave 47710 812-426-2865
Mater Dei HS 500/9-12
1300 Harmony Way 47720 812-426-2258
Chris Tanner, prin. Fax 421-5717
Reitz Memorial HS 800/9-12
1500 Lincoln Ave 47714 812-476-4973
Cyndi Schneider, prin. Fax 474-2942
Roger's Academy of Hair Design Post-Sec.
2903 Mount Vernon Ave 47712 812-429-0110
University of Evansville Post-Sec.
1800 Lincoln Ave 47714 812-488-2000
University of Southern Indiana Post-Sec.
8600 University Blvd 47712 812-464-8600
Westside Catholic S St. Boniface Campus 100/4-8
2031 W Michigan St 47712 812-422-1014
Tracey Unfried, prin. Fax 422-1057

Fairland, Shelby, Pop. 314
Northwestern Cons SC of Shelby County 1,500/PK-12
4920 W 600 N 46126 317-835-7461
W. Shane Robbins Ed.D., supt. Fax 835-4441
www.nwshelby.k12.in.us/
Triton Central HS 500/9-12
4774 W 600 N 46126 317-835-3000
Todd Gowen, prin. Fax 480-1887
Triton Central MS 500/5-8
4740 W 600 N 46126 317-835-3006
Mark Watkins, prin. Fax 835-3008

Fairmount, Grant, Pop. 2,932
Madison-Grant United SC 1,300/PK-12
11580 S E 00 W 46928 765-948-4143
John Trout, supt. Fax 948-4150
www.mgargylls.com
Madison-Grant HS 500/9-12
11700 S E 00 W 46928 765-948-4141
Phil Nikirk, prin. Fax 948-4874
Madison-Grant JHS 200/7-8
11640 S E 00 W 46928 765-948-5132
Chris Smedley, prin. Fax 948-3671

Farmersburg, Sullivan, Pop. 1,110
Northeast SC
Supt. — See Hymera
North Central JSHS 500/7-12
910 E County Road 975 N 47850 812-397-2132
Candace Fritz, prin. Fax 397-2133

Ferdinand, Dubois, Pop. 2,150
Southeast Dubois County SC 1,400/PK-12
432 E 15th St 47532 812-367-1653
Richard Allen, supt. Fax 367-1075
www.sedubois.k12.in.us
Forest Park JSHS 700/7-12
1440 Michigan St 47532 812-367-1831
Jeffrey Jessee, prin. Fax 367-1172

Fishers, Hamilton, Pop. 75,207
Hamilton Southeastern SD 17,600/K-12
13485 Cumberland Rd 46038 317-594-4100
Dr. Brian Smith, supt. Fax 594-4109
www.hse.k12.in.us/
Fishers HS 2,200/9-12
13000 Promise Rd 46038 317-915-4290
Jason Urban, prin. Fax 915-4299
Fishers JHS 900/7-8
13257 Cumberland Rd 46038 317-594-4150
Crystal Thorpe, prin. Fax 594-4159
Hamilton Southeastern Freshman Center 9-9
12001 Olio Rd, 317-594-4390
Kim Lippe, prin. Fax 594-4399
Hamilton Southeastern HS 2,000/10-12
13910 E 126th St, 317-594-4190
Matt Kegley, prin. Fax 594-4199
Hamilton Southeastern JHS 900/7-8
12278 Cyntheanne Rd, 317-594-4120
Tim Mankin, prin. Fax 594-4129
Riverside JHS 1,000/7-8
10910 Eller Rd 46038 317-915-4280
Rob Huesing, prin. Fax 915-4289

Flora, Carroll, Pop. 2,010
Carroll Consolidated SC 1,100/K-12
2 S 3rd St 46929 574-967-4113
Christopher Lagoni, supt. Fax 967-3831
www.carroll.k12.in.us/
Carroll JSHS 500/7-12
2362 E State Road 18 46929 574-967-4157
Angela Moreman, prin. Fax 967-4027

Floyds Knobs, Floyd
New Albany Floyd County Consolidated SD
Supt. — See New Albany
Floyd Central HS 1,700/9-12
6575 Old Vincennes Rd 47119 812-542-8504
Janie Whaley, prin. Fax 542-4795

Fort Branch, Gibson, Pop. 2,743
South Gibson SC 2,000/K-12
1029 W 650 S 47648 812-753-4230
Stacey Humbaugh, supt. Fax 753-4081
www.sgibson.k12.in.us
Gibson Southern HS 700/9-12
3499 W 800 S 47648 812-753-3011
Scott Reid, prin. Fax 753-4862

Fortville, Hancock, Pop. 3,887
Mt. Vernon Community SC 3,000/PK-12
1776 W State Road 234 46040 317-485-3100
Dr. William Riggs, admin. Fax 485-3113
www.mvcsc.k12.in.us
8th Grade Academy 300/8-8
8112 N 200 W 46040 317-485-3131
Scott Shipley, prin. Fax 482-0027
Mt. Vernon HS 1,100/9-12
8112 N 200 W 46040 317-485-3131
Bernie Campbell, prin. Fax 485-3154

Fort Wayne, Allen, Pop. 246,159
East Allen County SD
Supt. — See New Haven
East Allen University 9-10
6501 Wayne Trce 46816 260-446-0240
Doug Hicks, prin. Fax 446-0249
Harding JHS 700/7-8
6501 Wayne Trce 46816 260-446-0240
Teresa Gremaux, prin. Fax 446-0249

Fort Wayne Community SD 31,100/PK-12
1200 S Clinton St 46802 260-467-1000
Dr. Wendy Robinson, supt. Fax 467-1980
www.fwcs.k12.in.us
Anthis Career Center Vo/Tech
1200 Barr St 46802 260-467-1010
Larry Gerardot, prin. Fax 425-7609
Blackhawk MS 900/6-8
7200 E State Blvd 46815 260-467-4885
Kara Froning, prin. Fax 467-4943
Jefferson MS 700/6-8
5303 Wheelock Rd 46835 260-467-4825
Jeff King, prin. Fax 467-4883
Kekionga MS 500/6-8
2929 Engle Rd 46809 260-467-6600
Jennifer Mable, prin. Fax 467-6658
Lakeside MS 500/6-8
2100 Lake Ave 46805 260-467-8625
Alan Jones, prin. Fax 467-8672
Lane MS 600/6-8
4901 Vance Ave 46815 260-467-4400
Mark Bailey, prin. Fax 467-4437
Memorial Park MS 600/6-8
2200 Maumee Ave 46803 260-467-5300
Tim Rayl, prin. Fax 467-5298
Miami MS 800/6-8
8100 Amherst Dr 46819 260-467-8560
Adam Swinford, prin. Fax 467-8606
Northrop HS 2,300/9-12
7001 Coldwater Rd 46825 260-467-2300
Barbara Ahlersmeyer, prin. Fax 467-2301
North Side HS 1,800/9-12
475 E State Blvd 46805 260-467-2800
Chad Hissong, prin. Fax 467-2690
Northwood MS 700/6-8
1201 E Washington Center Rd 46825 260-467-2930
Austin Couch, prin. Fax 467-2987
Portage MS 500/6-8
3521 Taylor St 46802 260-467-4500
Michael Christner, prin. Fax 467-4497
Shawnee MS 800/6-8
1000 E Cook Rd 46825 260-467-6525
Matt Schiebel, prin. Fax 467-6527
Snider HS 2,000/9-12
4600 Fairlawn Pass 46815 260-467-4600
Deb Watson, prin. Fax 467-4729
South Side HS 1,600/9-12
3601 S Calhoun St 46807 260-467-2600
Carlton Mable, prin. Fax 467-2663
Ward Education Center Alt
3501 Warsaw St 46806 260-467-4570
Gradlin Pruitt, prin. Fax 467-5497
Wayne HS 1,600/9-12
9100 Winchester Rd 46819 260-467-6400
John Houser, prin. Fax 467-6490

Metro SD of Southwest Allen County 7,000/K-12
4824 Homestead Rd 46814 260-431-2051
Dr. Steve Yager, supt. Fax 431-2063
www.sacs.k12.in.us
Homestead HS 2,200/9-12
4310 Homestead Rd 46814 260-431-2200
Park Ginder, prin. Fax 431-2299
Summit MS 700/6-8
4509 Homestead Rd 46814 260-431-2502
Josh St. John, prin. Fax 431-2599
Woodside MS 1,000/6-8
2310 W Hamilton Rd S 46814 260-431-2701
Jerry Schillinger, prin. Fax 431-2799

Northwest Allen County SD 5,800/PK-12
13119 Coldwater Rd 46845 260-637-3155
Chris Himsel, supt. Fax 637-8355
www.nacs.k12.in.us/
Allen County Youth Services Center 50/Alt
11805 Lima Rd 46818 260-449-3561
Sue Dowling, dir. Fax 449-7943
Carroll Freshman Center 9-9
3905 Carroll Rd 46818 260-338-5360
Tanya Pickett, prin. Fax 637-5868
Carroll HS 1,400/10-12
3701 Carroll Rd 46818 260-637-3161
Deborah Neumeyer, prin. Fax 637-8356
Carroll MS 800/6-8
4027 Hathaway Rd 46818 260-637-5159
John Miller, prin. Fax 637-5478
Maple Creek MS 700/6-8
425 Union Chapel Rd 46845 260-338-0802
Mark Seele, prin. Fax 338-0369

Bishop Dwenger HS 1,100/9-12
1300 E Washington Center Rd 46825 260-496-4700
Jason Schiffli, prin. Fax 496-4702
Bishop Luers HS 500/9-12
333 E Paulding Rd 46816 260-456-1261
Mary Keefer, prin. Fax 456-1262
Blackhawk Christian S 800/PK-12
7400 E State Blvd 46815 260-493-7400
Bill Hartman, supt. Fax 749-8527
Brown Mackie College Post-Sec.
3000 E Coliseum Blvd 46805 260-484-4400
Canterbury S 300/9-12
3210 Smith Rd 46804 260-436-0746
Jonathan Hancock, hdmstr. Fax 436-5137
Concordia Lutheran HS 700/9-12
1601 Saint Joe River Dr 46805 260-483-1102
Terry Breininger, dir. Fax 471-0180
Concordia Theological Seminary Post-Sec.
6600 N Clinton St 46825 260-452-2100
Fort Wayne School of Radiography Post-Sec.
700 Broadway 46802 260-425-3990
Harrison College Post-Sec.
6413 N Clinton St 46825 260-471-7667
Indiana Tech Post-Sec.
1600 E Washington Blvd 46803 260-422-5561
Indiana Univ-Purdue Univ at Fort Wayne Post-Sec.
2101 E Coliseum Blvd 46805 260-481-6100
International Business College Post-Sec.
5699 Coventry Ln 46804 260-459-4500
ITT Technical Institute Post-Sec.
2810 Dupont Commerce Ct 46825 260-497-6200
Ivy Tech Community College - Northeast Post-Sec.
3800 N Anthony Blvd 46805 260-482-9171
MedTech College Post-Sec.
7230 Engle Rd Ste 200 46804 260-436-3272
National College Post-Sec.
6131 N Clinton St 46825 260-483-1605
Ravenscroft Beauty College Post-Sec.
6110 Stellhorn Rd 46815 260-486-8868
Rudae's School of Beauty Culture Post-Sec.
5317 Coldwater Rd 46825 260-483-2466
The Masters of Cosmetology College Post-Sec.
1732 Bluffton Rd 46809 260-747-6667
University of St. Francis Post-Sec.
2701 Spring St 46808 260-399-7999

Fountain City, Wayne, Pop. 783
Northeastern Wayne SD 1,100/PK-12
PO Box 406 47341 765-847-2821
Dr. Tim Edsell, supt. Fax 847-5355
www.nws.k12.in.us
Northeastern JSHS 500/7-12
7295 N US Highway 27 47341 765-847-2591
Dennis Metzger, prin. Fax 847-2875

Fowler, Benton, Pop. 2,292
Benton Community SC 1,900/PK-12
PO Box 512 47944 765-884-0850
Destin Haas, supt. Fax 884-1614
www.benton.k12.in.us
Other Schools – See Oxford

Francesville, Pulaski, Pop. 873
West Central SC 900/K-12
117 E Montgomery St 47946 219-567-9161
Charles Mellon, supt. Fax 567-9761
www.west-central.k12.in.us
West Central HS 300/9-12
1852 S US Highway 421 47946 219-567-9119
Don Street, prin. Fax 567-2597
West Central MS 200/6-8
1850 S US Highway 421 47946 219-567-2534
Don Street, prin. Fax 567-9535

Frankfort, Clinton, Pop. 16,300
Clinton Prairie SC 1,000/K-12
4431 W Old State Road 28 46041 765-659-1339
John Sampson, supt. Fax 659-5305
www.clintonprairie.com
Clinton Prairie JSHS 400/7-12
2400 S County Road 450 W 46041 765-659-3305
Brent Miler, prin. Fax 659-3205

Frankfort Community SC 3,200/PK-12
2400 E Wabash St 46041 765-654-5585
Donald DeWeese, supt. Fax 659-6220
www.frankfortschools.org
Frankfort HS 900/9-12
1 S Maish Rd 46041 765-654-8545
Steve Edwards, prin. Fax 654-9224
Frankfort MS 700/6-8
329 N Maish Rd 46041 765-659-3321
Dennis Howland, prin. Fax 659-6260

Franklin, Johnson, Pop. 23,366
Franklin Community SC 4,700/K-12
998 Grizzly Cub Dr 46131 317-738-5800
David Clendening, supt. Fax 738-5812
www.franklinschools.org
Franklin Community HS 1,600/9-12
2600 Cumberland Dr 46131 317-738-5700
Doug Harter, prin. Fax 738-5703
Franklin Community MS 800/7-8
625 Grizzly Cub Dr 46131 317-346-8400
Pam Millikan, prin. Fax 346-8411

Franklin College Post-Sec.
101 Branigin Blvd 46131 317-738-8000

Frankton, Madison, Pop. 1,842
Frankton-Lapel Community SD
Supt. — See Anderson
Frankton JSHS 700/7-12
610 E Clyde St 46044 765-754-7879
Jerry Hoss, prin. Fax 754-8594

Fremont, Steuben, Pop. 2,131
Fremont Community SD 1,100/K-12
PO Box 665 46737 260-495-5005
Loraine Vaughn, supt. Fax 495-9798
fremontcommunityschoolsindiana.org
Fremont HS 400/9-12
PO Box 655 46737 260-495-9876
Mark Sherbondy, prin. Fax 495-1838
Fremont MS 300/5-8
PO Box 770 46737 260-495-6100
Mark Fowerbaugh, prin. Fax 495-7301

French Lick, Orange, Pop. 1,754
Springs Valley Community SC 1,000/K-12
498 S Larry Bird Blvd 47432 812-936-4474
Todd Pritchett, supt. Fax 936-9392
www.svalley.k12.in.us
Springs Valley Community JSHS 500/6-12
326 S Larry Bird Blvd 47432 812-936-9984
Troy Pritchett, prin. Fax 936-9266

Fulton, Fulton, Pop. 332
Caston SC 800/K-12
PO Box 128 46931 574-857-2035
Dan Foster, supt. Fax 857-6795
www.caston.k12.in.us/
Caston JSHS 400/7-12
PO Box 128 46931 574-857-3505
Adam Strasser, prin. Fax 857-6795

Garrett, DeKalb, Pop. 6,210
Garrett-Keyser-Butler Community SD 1,800/K-12
801 E Houston St 46738 260-357-3185
Dennis Stockdale, supt. Fax 357-4565
www.gkb.k12.in.us
Garrett HS 600/9-12
801 E Houston St 46738 260-357-4114
Matthew Smith, prin. Fax 357-5000
Garrett MS 500/5-8
801 E Houston St 46738 260-357-5745
Linda DePew, prin. Fax 357-3575
Other Schools – See Kendallville

Gary, Lake, Pop. 78,995
Gary Community SC 9,700/PK-12
620 E 10th Pl 46402 219-881-5401
Dr. Cheryl Pruitt, supt. Fax 881-4102
www.garycsc.k12.in.us/
Dunbar-Pulaski MS 7-8
920 E 19th Ave 46407 219-886-6516
Michael Collins, prin. Fax 886-6512
Gary Career Center Vo/Tech
1800 E 35th Ave 46409 219-962-7571
Robert Doctor, prin. Fax 962-6269
New Tech S Vo/Tech
1800 E 35th Ave 46409 219-963-2901
Esther Goodes, prin. Fax 886-6455
Wallace STEM Academt 1,200/7-12
415 W 45th Ave 46408 219-980-6305
LaTanza Borden, prin. Fax 981-4462
West Side Leadership Academy 1,700/7-12
900 Gerry St 46406 219-977-2100
Vera Blount, prin. Fax 977-2168
Wirt/Emerson Visual Performing Arts JSHS 500/6-12
210 N Grand Blvd 46403 219-938-1161
Dr. Adrian Richie, prin. Fax 938-7544

Lake Ridge SC 2,000/K-12
6111 W Ridge Rd 46408 219-838-1819
Dr. Sharon Johnson-Shirley, supt. Fax 989-7802
www.lakeridge.k12.in.us
Calumet HS 600/9-12
3900 Calhoun St 46408 219-838-6990
Angela Piazza, prin. Fax 989-7849
Lake Ridge MS 500/6-8
3601 W 41st Ave 46408 219-980-0730
Renee Pluchinsky, prin. Fax 980-0731

Indiana University Northwest Post-Sec.
3400 Broadway 46408 219-980-6500
Ivy Tech Community College - Northwest Post-Sec.
1440 E 35th Ave 46409 219-981-1111

Gas City, Grant, Pop. 5,872
Mississinewa Community SC 2,500/PK-12
424 E South A St 46933 765-674-8528
Michael Powell, supt. Fax 674-8529
www.olemiss.k12.in.us/
Baskett MS 600/6-8
125 N Broadway St 46933 765-674-8536
J. Eckstein, prin. Fax 677-4452
Mississinewa HS 700/9-12
1 Indian Trail Dr 46933 765-674-2248
Lezlie Winter, prin. Fax 677-4424

Gaston, Delaware, Pop. 858
Wes-Del Community SD 800/K-12
10290 N County Road 600 W 47342 765-358-4006
Michael Bush, supt. Fax 358-4065
www.wes-del.k12.in.us/
Wes-Del MSHS 500/6-12
10000 N County Road 600 W 47342 765-358-4091
Derick Bright, prin. Fax 358-3514

Georgetown, Floyd, Pop. 2,851
New Albany Floyd County Consolidated SD
Supt. — See New Albany
Highland Hills MS 1,500/5-8
3492 Edwardsville Galena Rd 47122 812-542-8501
Steve Griffin, prin. Fax 542-4792

Goshen, Elkhart, Pop. 31,231
Fairfield Community SD 2,100/K-12
67240 County Road 31 46528 574-831-2188
Steve Thalheimer, supt. Fax 831-5698
www.fairfield.k12.in.us
Fairfield JSHS 900/7-12
67530 US Highway 33 46526 574-831-2184
Amy Bertram, prin. Fax 831-2187

Goshen Community SD 6,400/K-12
613 E Purl St 46526 574-533-8631
Dr. Diane Woodworth, supt. Fax 533-2505
www.goshenschools.org/
Goshen HS 1,800/9-12
401 Lincolnway E 46526 574-533-8651
Dr. Barry Younghans, prin. Fax 534-1567
Goshen MS 1,400/6-8
1216 S Indiana Ave 46526 574-533-0391
Lori Schreiner, prin. Fax 534-3042

Bethany Christian S 300/4-12
2904 S Main St 46526 574-534-2567
Allan Dueck, prin. Fax 533-0150
Clinton Christian S 100/K-12
61763 County Road 35 46528 574-642-3940
Gail Schrock, admin. Fax 642-3674
Goshen College Post-Sec.
1700 S Main St 46526 574-535-7000

Granger, Saint Joseph, Pop. 29,968
Penn-Harris-Madison SC
Supt. — See Mishawaka
Discovery MS 900/6-8
10050 Brummitt Rd 46530 574-674-6010
Sheryll Harper, prin. Fax 679-4214

Granger Christian S 200/K-12
52025 Gumwood Rd 46530 574-272-5815
R. Carpenter, prin. Fax 968-2664

Greencastle, Putnam, Pop. 10,164
Area 30 Career Center
1 N Calbert Way Ste A 46135 765-653-3515
Lora Busch, dir. Fax 653-3618
www.area30.k12.in.us/
Area 30 Career Center Vo/Tech
1 N Calbert Way Ste A 46135 765-653-3515
Lora Busch, dir. Fax 653-3618

Greencastle Community SC 2,000/PK-12
PO Box 480 46135 765-653-9771
Dr. Lori Richmond, supt. Fax 653-1282
www.greencastle.k12.in.us
Greencastle HS 600/9-12
910 E Washington St 46135 765-653-9711
Jennifer Shepherd, prin. Fax 653-4773
Greencastle MS 500/6-8
400 Percy L Julian Dr 46135 765-653-9774
Tamra Walker, prin. Fax 653-5381

South Putnam Community SD 1,000/K-12
3999 S US Highway 231 46135 765-653-3119
Bruce Bernhardt, supt. Fax 653-7476
www.sputnam.k12.in.us
South Putnam MSHS 600/6-12
1780 E US Highway 40 46135 765-653-3148
Kieth Puckett, prin. Fax 653-3149

DePauw University Post-Sec.
PO Box 37 46135 765-658-4800

Greenfield, Hancock, Pop. 20,372
Greenfield-Central Community SD 4,000/PK-12
110 W North St 46140 317-462-4434
Dr. Linda Gellert, supt. Fax 467-4227
www.gcsc.k12.in.us/
Greenfield-Central HS 1,400/9-12
810 N Broadway St 46140 317-462-9211
Steven Bryant, prin. Fax 467-6723
Greenfield Central JHS 7-8
1440 N Franklin St 46140 317-477-4616
Harold Olin, prin. Fax 477-4617

Hancock Memorial Hospital Post-Sec.
801 N State St 46140 317-462-0457
PJ's College of Cosmetology Post-Sec.
1400 W Main St 46140 317-462-9239

Greensburg, Decatur, Pop. 11,380
Decatur County Community SD 2,200/PK-12
2020 N Montgomery Rd 47240 812-663-4595
Johnny Budd, supt. Fax 663-4168
www.decaturco.k12.in.us
North Decatur JSHS 600/7-12
3172 N State Road 3 47240 812-663-4204
Gary Cook, prin. Fax 663-9606
South Decatur JSHS 500/7-12
8885 S State Road 3 47240 812-591-3330
Jim Jameson, prin. Fax 591-3331

Greensburg Community SC 2,300/K-12
1312 W Westridge Pkwy 47240 812-663-4774
Tom Hunter, supt. Fax 663-5713
www.greensburg.k12.in.us
Greensburg Community HS 600/9-12
1000 E Central Ave 47240 812-663-7176
Philip Chapple, prin. Fax 663-8911
Greensburg Community JHS 500/6-8
505 E Central Ave 47240 812-663-7523
Dave Strouse, prin. Fax 663-9425

Greentown, Howard, Pop. 2,402
Eastern Howard SC 1,300/K-12
221 W Main St Ste 1 46936 765-628-3391
Tracy Caddell Ed.D., supt. Fax 628-5017
www.eastern.k12.in.us
Eastern JSHS 700/7-12
421 S Harrison St 46936 765-628-3333
Keith Richie Ed.D., prin. Fax 628-5021

Greenwood, Johnson, Pop. 48,867
Center Grove Community SC 7,700/K-12
4800 W Stones Crossing Rd 46143 317-881-9326
Richard Arkanoff, supt. Fax 881-0241
www.centergrove.k12.in.us
Center Grove HS 2,400/9-12
2717 S Morgantown Rd 46143 317-881-0581
Doug Bird, prin. Fax 885-4509
Center Grove MS Central 900/6-8
4900 W Stones Crossing Rd 46143 317-882-9391
Nora Hoover, prin. Fax 885-4534
Center Grove MS North 900/6-8
202 N Morgantown Rd 46142 317-885-8800
Scott Johnson, prin. Fax 885-3388

Central Nine Career Center SD
1999 US Highway 31 S 46143 317-888-4401
Stephen Hagen, dir. Fax 865-8670
www.central9.k12.in.us
Central Nine Career Center Vo/Tech
1999 US Highway 31 S 46143 317-888-4401
Stan Wilkison, prin. Fax 885-8670

Clark-Pleasant Community SC
Supt. — See Whiteland
Clark Pleasant MS 900/7-8
1354 E Worthsville Rd 46143 317-535-7121
Tim Rinehold, prin. Fax 535-2064

Greenwood Community SC 3,800/K-12
605 W Smith Valley Rd 46142 317-889-4060
Dr. David Edds, supt. Fax 889-4068
gws.k12.in.us
Greenwood Community HS 1,200/9-12
615 W Smith Valley Rd 46142 317-889-4000
James Kaylor, prin. Fax 889-4039
Greenwood MS 900/6-8
523 S Madison Ave 46142 317-889-4040
Vicki Noblitt, prin. Fax 889-4044

Greenwood Christian Academy 500/PK-12
835 W Worthsville Rd 46143 317-215-5300
Bruce Peters, hdmstr. Fax 535-1070
MedTech College Post-Sec.
1500 American Way 46143 317-534-0322

Griffith, Lake, Pop. 16,641
Griffith Public SD 2,500/K-12
PO Box 749 46319 219-924-4250
Dr. Peter Morikis, supt. Fax 922-5933
www.griffith.k12.in.us
Griffith HS 900/9-12
600 N Wiggs St 46319 219-924-4281
William Cope, prin. Fax 922-5920
Griffith MS 400/7-8
600 N Raymond St 46319 219-924-4280
Edward Skaggs, prin. Fax 922-5927

Hagerstown, Wayne, Pop. 1,765
Nettle Creek SC 1,200/PK-12
297 E Northmarket St 47346 765-489-4543
Dr. William Doering, supt. Fax 489-4914
www.nettlecreek.k12.in.us
Hagerstown JSHS 600/7-12
701 Baker Rd 47346 765-489-4511
Mark Childs, prin. Fax 489-4333

Hamilton, DeKalb, Pop. 1,521
Hamilton Community SD 500/K-12
903 S Wayne St 46742 260-488-2513
Jon Willman, supt. Fax 488-2348
www.hamiltoncomm.com/
Hamilton Community HS 200/7-12
903 S Wayne St 46742 260-488-2161
Christy Haupert, prin. Fax 488-3149

Hamlet, Starke, Pop. 787
Oregon-Davis SC 600/K-12
5998 N 750 E 46532 574-867-2111
Dr. Steven Disney, supt. Fax 867-8191
www.od.k12.in.us
Oregon-Davis JSHS 300/7-12
5990 N 750 E 46532 574-867-4561
Greg Briles, prin. Fax 867-2481

Hammond, Lake, Pop. 79,563
Hammond CSD 14,200/PK-12
41 Williams St 46320 219-933-2400
Dr. Walter Watkins, supt. Fax 933-2495
www.hammond.k12.in.us
Area Career Center Vo/Tech
5727 Sohl Ave 46320 219-933-2428
Michael Zimmerman, prin. Fax 933-1680
Eggers MS 700/6-8
5825 Blaine Ave 46320 219-933-2449
Rhoderick Poats, prin. Fax 933-1675
Gavit MSHS 1,500/6-12
1670 175th St 46324 219-989-7328
Michelle Ondas, prin. Fax 989-7333
Hammond HS 900/9-12
5926 Calumet Ave 46320 219-933-2442
Leslie Yanders, prin. Fax 933-1688
Morton HS 1,200/9-12
6915 Grand Ave 46323 219-989-7316
Douglas Friend, prin. Fax 989-7321
Scott MS 900/6-8
3635 173rd St 46323 219-989-7340
Kristopher Rivera, prin. Fax 989-7342
Other Schools – See Whiting

Bishop Noll Institute 400/9-12
1519 Hoffman St 46327 219-932-9058
Fax 853-1736
Kaplan College Post-Sec.
7833 Indianapolis Blvd 46324 219-844-0100
Purdue University Calumet Post-Sec.
2200 169th St 46323 219-989-2400
St. Margaret Hospital Post-Sec.
5454 Hohman Ave 46320 219-932-2300

Hanover, Jefferson, Pop. 3,496
Southwestern-Jefferson County Cons SC 1,300/K-12
239 S Main Cross St 47243 812-866-6250
Stephen Telfer, supt. Fax 866-6256
www.swjcs.k12.in.us/
Southwestern HS 400/9-12
167 S Main Cross St 47243 812-866-6230
Jeff Bates, prin. Fax 866-6233
Southwestern MS 300/6-8
167 S Main Cross St 47243 812-866-6220
Trevor Jones, prin. Fax 866-4680

Hanover College Post-Sec.
PO Box 108 47243 812-866-7000

Harlan, Allen, Pop. 1,616

Harlan Christian S 200/PK-12
17108 State Road 37 46743 260-657-5147
Terry Carter, prin. Fax 657-1677

Hartford City, Blackford, Pop. 6,115
Blackford County SD 1,900/PK-12
668 W 200 S 47348 765-348-7550
Ken Kline, supt. Fax 348-7552
www.bcs.k12.in.us
Blackford HS 600/9-12
2392 N State Road 3 47348 765-348-7560
Lisa Smith, prin. Fax 348-7568
Blackford JHS 300/7-8
800 W Van Cleve St 47348 765-348-7590
Scott Shimer, prin. Fax 348-7593

Hebron, Porter, Pop. 3,695
Metro SD of Boone Township 1,100/K-12
307 S Main St 46341 219-996-4771
George Letz, supt. Fax 996-5777
www.hebronschools.k12.in.us/
Hebron HS 300/9-12
509 S Main St 46341 219-996-4771
Mark Lutze, prin. Fax 996-5777
Hebron MS 200/6-8
307 S Main St 46341 219-996-4771
Lori Pavelll, prin. Fax 996-5777

Henryville, Clark, Pop. 1,892
West Clark Community SC
Supt. — See Sellersburg
Henryville JSHS 600/7-12
213 N Ferguson St 47126 812-294-1455
Troy Albert, prin. Fax 294-4276

Highland, Lake, Pop. 23,446
Town of Highland SD 3,100/K-12
9145 Kennedy Ave 46322 219-924-7400
Michael Boskovich, supt. Fax 922-5637
www.highland.k12.in.us
Highland HS 1,200/9-12
9135 Erie St 46322 219-922-5610
Patrick Weil, prin. Fax 922-5636
Highland MS 600/6-8
2941 41st St 46322 219-922-5620
Terry Mucha, prin. Fax 922-2270

Creative Hair Styling Academy Post-Sec.
2549 Highway Ave 46322 219-838-2004

Hobart, Lake, Pop. 28,672
Hobart CSD 3,700/PK-12
32 E 7th St 46342 219-942-8885
Dr. Peggy Buffington, supt. Fax 942-0081
www.hobart.k12.in.us
Hobart HS 1,300/9-12
2211 E 10th St 46342 219-942-8521
Brent Martinson, prin. Fax 942-3326
Hobart MS 1,000/6-8
36 E 8th St 46342 219-942-8541
Carolie Warren, prin. Fax 947-7194

River Forest Community SC 1,600/K-12
3250 Michigan St 46342 219-962-2909
Dr. James Rice, supt. Fax 962-4951
www.rfcsc.k12.in.us
River Forest JSHS 700/7-12
3300 Indiana St 46342 219-962-7551
Shayne Snider, prin. Fax 962-8338

College of Court Reporting Post-Sec.
111 W 10th St Ste 111 46342 866-294-3974

Hope, Bartholomew, Pop. 2,080
Flat Rock-Hawcreek SC 1,000/PK-12
9423 N State Road 9 47246 812-546-2000
Kathy Griffey, supt. Fax 546-5617
www.flatrock.k12.in.us
Hauser JSHS 400/7-12
9273 N State Road 9 47246 812-546-4421
Shawn Price, prin. Fax 546-2005

Howe, Lagrange, Pop. 791

Howe S 100/7-12
PO Box 240 46746 260-562-2131
George Douglass, supt. Fax 562-3678

Huntingburg, Dubois, Pop. 6,020
Southwest Dubois County SC 1,700/PK-12
113 N Jackson St 47542 812-683-3971
Mike Eineman, supt. Fax 683-2752
www.swdubois.k12.in.us
Southridge HS 500/9-12
1110 S Main St 47542 812-683-2272
Mike Eineman, prin. Fax 683-2010
Southridge MS 400/6-8
1112 S Main St 47542 812-683-3372
Al Mihajlovits, prin. Fax 683-2817

Huntington, Huntington, Pop. 17,196
Huntington County Community SC 5,800/K-12
2485 Waterworks Rd 46750 260-356-8312
Tracey Shafer, supt. Fax 358-2222
www.hccsc.k12.in.us
Crestview MS 700/6-8
1151 W 500 N 46750 260-356-6210
Chuck Werth, prin. Fax 358-2232
Huntington North HS 1,900/9-12
450 MacGahan St 46750 260-356-6104
Chad Daugherty, prin. Fax 358-2210
Riverview MS 600/6-8
2465 Waterworks Rd 46750 260-356-0910
Curt Crago, prin. Fax 358-2243

Huntington University Post-Sec.
2303 College Ave 46750 260-356-6000

Hymera, Sullivan, Pop. 795
Northeast SC 1,400/PK-12
PO Box 493 47855 812-383-5761
Dr. Mark Baker, supt. Fax 383-4591
www.nesc.k12.in.us/
Other Schools – See Dugger, Farmersburg

Indianapolis, Marion, Pop. 800,178
Franklin Township Community SC 7,100/PK-12
6141 S Franklin Rd 46259 317-862-2411
Dr. Flora Reichanadter, supt. Fax 862-7238
www.ftcsc.k12.in.us
Franklin Central HS 2,600/9-12
6215 S Franklin Rd 46259 317-862-6646
Kevin Koers, prin. Fax 862-7262

Franklin Township MS East 800/6-8
10440 Indian Creek Rd S 46259 317-803-8100
Chase Huotari, prin. Fax 803-8199
Franklin Township MS West 700/6-8
7620 E Edgewood Ave 46239 317-862-2446
Nathan Day, prin. Fax 862-7271

Indianapolis SD 28,100/PK-12
120 E Walnut St 46204 317-226-4000
Eugene White Ed.D., supt. Fax 226-4936
www.ips.k12.in.us
Alternative Education Center @ Coleman 100/Alt
1740 E 30th St 46218 317-226-4110
Cassandra Shipp, prin. Fax 226-3539
Arsenal Technical HS 2,200/9-12
1500 E Michigan St 46201 317-693-5300
Lawrence Yarrell, admin. Fax 226-3932
Attucks Medical Magnet HS 800/6-12
1140 Dr Mrtn Lthr Kng Jr St 46202 317-226-2800
Stephanie Nixon, prin. Fax 226-3495
Broad Ripple HS for Arts & Humanities 1,000/7-12
1115 Broad Ripple Ave 46220 317-693-5700
Mike Akers, admin. Fax 226-3783
Career & Technology Center Vo/Tech
725 N Oriental St 46202 317-693-5430
Sarah Bogard, admin. Fax 226-3709
Harshman Magnet MS 400/7-8
1501 E 10th St 46201 317-226-4101
Robert Guffin, prin. Fax 226-3444
Key Learning Community S - River 500/K-12
777 S White River Pky West 46203 317-226-4992
Sheila Seedhouse, prin. Fax 226-3049
Longfellow MS 300/7-8
510 Laurel St 46203 317-226-4228
Brian Burke, prin. Fax 226-3756
Marshall Community HS 600/7-12
10101 E 38th St 46235 317-693-5460
Brian Dinkins, prin. Fax 226-3718
New Horizon Alternative S 700/Alt
510 Laurel St 46203 317-226-4112
Jethroe Knazze, prin. Fax 226-4018
Northwest HS 800/9-12
5525 W 34th St 46224 317-693-5600
Phyllis Barnes, prin. Fax 226-3409
Shortridge Magnet HS for Law/Pub Policy 600/6-12
3401 N Meridian St 46208 317-226-2810
Stan Law, prin. Fax 226-3725
Washington Community HS 700/7-12
2215 W Washington St 46222 317-693-5555
Teresa Ezell, prin. Fax 226-3273
Day Adult HS @ Hope Ed Ctr Adult
1301 E 16th St 46202 317-226-4116
Vickie Nowlin, prin. Fax 226-4524

Metro SD of Decatur Township 6,500/PK-12
5275 Kentucky Ave 46221 317-856-5265
Nathan Davis Ed.D., admin. Fax 856-2156
www.msddecatur.k12.in.us
Decatur Central HS 1,800/9-12
5251 Kentucky Ave 46221 317-856-5288
Joe Preda, prin. Fax 856-2157
Decatur MS 1,000/7-8
5108 S High School Rd 46221 317-856-5274
Mark Anderson, prin. Fax 856-2163

Metro SD of Perry Township 14,300/PK-12
6548 Orinoco Ave 46227 317-789-3700
Dr. Thomas Little, supt. Fax 789-3709
www.msdpt.k12.in.us
Perry Meridian HS 2,300/9-12
401 W Meridian School Rd 46217 317-789-4400
Rolland Abraham, prin. Fax 789-4479
Perry Meridian MS 1,100/7-8
202 W Meridian School Rd 46217 317-789-4100
David Rohl, prin. Fax 865-2710
Southport HS 2,200/9-12
971 E Banta Rd 46227 317-789-4800
Barbara Brouwer, prin. Fax 780-4325
Southport MS 1,100/7-8
5715 S Keystone Ave 46227 317-789-4600
Brian Knight, prin. Fax 780-4302

Metro SD of Pike Township 11,100/PK-12
6901 Zionsville Rd 46268 317-293-0393
Nathaniel Jones, supt. Fax 297-7896
www.pike.k12.in.us
Guion Creek MS 900/6-8
4401 W 52nd St 46254 317-293-4549
Kurt Benjamin, prin. Fax 298-2794
Lincoln MS 900/6-8
5353 W 71st St 46268 317-291-9499
Dan Kuznik, prin. Fax 297-1673
New Augusta Public Academy North 800/6-8
6450 Rodebaugh Rd 46268 317-387-4328
Kenneth Coudret, prin. Fax 388-7786
Pike Freshman Center 800/9-9
6801 Zionsville Rd 46268 317-347-8600
Troy Inman, prin. Fax 347-8555
Pike HS 2,300/10-12
5401 W 71st St 46268 317-291-5250
Troy Inman, prin. Fax 328-7239
Pike Prep Academy Alt
7140 Waldemar Dr 46268 317-347-8351
Roy Dobbs, prin. Fax 298-0681

Metro SD of Warren Township 10,800/PK-12
975 N Post Rd 46219 317-869-4300
Dr. Dena Cushenberry, supt. Fax 869-4348
www.warren.k12.in.us
Creston MS 600/7-8
10925 Prospect St 46239 317-532-6800
Chad Reedy, prin. Fax 532-6899
Raymond Park MS 600/7-8
8575 E Raymond St 46239 317-532-8900
John Kleine, prin. Fax 532-8999
Renaissance S 300/Alt
8931 E 30th St 46219 317-532-2975
Matt Dingman, dir. Fax 532-2951
Stonybrook MS 600/7-8
11300 Stony Brook Dr 46229 317-532-8800
Pam Griffin, prin. Fax 532-8899
Walker Career Center Vo/Tech
9651 E 21st St 46229 317-532-6150
Cindy Frey, dir. Fax 532-6199
Warren Central HS 3,700/9-12
9500 E 16th St 46229 317-532-6200
Rich Shepler, prin. Fax 532-6459

Metro SD of Wayne Township 16,100/PK-12
1220 S High School Rd 46241 317-988-8600
Jeffrey Butts Ph.D., supt. Fax 243-5744
www.wayne.k12.in.us
Chapel Hill 7th & 8th Grade Center 1,100/7-8
7320 W 10th St 46214 317-988-8800
Sheri Patterson, prin. Fax 988-8949
Davis 9th Grade Center 1,200/9-9
1150 N Girls School Rd 46214 317-988-7500
Rebecca Daugherty, prin. Fax 484-3124
Davis HS 3,400/10-12
1200 N Girls School Rd 46214 317-988-7000
Sandi Squire, prin. Fax 988-7311
Davis University HS 300/10-12
1155 S High School Rd 46241 317-988-7800
Wendy Skibinski, prin. Fax 243-5683
Lynhurst 7th & 8th Grade Center 1,200/7-8
2805 S Lynhurst Dr 46241 317-988-8100
Dan Wilson, prin. Fax 243-5532

Metropolitan SD of Lawrence Township 15,400/PK-12
6501 Sunnyside Rd 46236 317-423-8200
Dr. Concetta Raimondi, supt. Fax 543-3534
www.ltschools.org/
Belzer MS 1,200/7-8
7555 E 56th St 46226 317-964-6200
Troy Knoderer, prin. Fax 543-3355
Fall Creek Valley MS 1,200/7-8
9701 E 63rd St 46236 317-964-6600
Kathy Luessow, prin. Fax 823-5497
Lawrence Central HS 2,600/9-12
7300 E 56th St 46226 317-964-7400
Rocco Valadez, prin. Fax 543-3348
Lawrence North HS 2,500/9-12
7802 Hague Rd 46256 317-964-7700
Brett Crousore, prin. Fax 576-6406
McKenzie Career Center Vo/Tech
7250 E 75th St 46256 317-964-8000
Barry Norman, prin. Fax 849-2546

Metropolitan SD of Washington Township 10,900/PK-12
8550 Woodfield Crossing 46240 317-845-9400
Dr. Nikki Woodson, supt. Fax 205-3384
www.msdwt.k12.in.us
Eastwood MS 700/6-8
4401 E 62nd St 46220 317-259-5401
Matt Kaiser, prin. Fax 259-5407
Light Career Center Vo/Tech
1901 E 86th St 46240 317-259-5265
Shawn Wright-Browner, dir. Fax 259-5298
North Central HS 3,500/9-12
1801 E 86th St 46240 317-259-5301
Bryant Branigan, prin. Fax 259-5369
Northview MS 800/6-8
8401 Westfield Blvd 46240 317-259-5421
Tina Merriweather, prin. Fax 259-5431
Westlane MS 900/6-8
1301 W 73rd St 46260 317-259-5412
Linda Lawrence, prin. Fax 259-5409

American College of Education Post-Sec.
101 W Ohio St Ste 1200 46204 800-280-0307
Art Institute of Indianapolis Post-Sec.
3500 Depauw Blvd 46268 317-613-4800
Aviation Institute of Maintenance Post-Sec.
7251 W McCarty St 46241 317-243-4519
Baptist Academy 200/PK-12
2565 Villa Ave 46203 317-788-1587
Tracy Brown, admin. Fax 781-4759
Bishop Silas Chatard HS 700/9-12
5885 Crittenden Ave 46220 317-251-1451
John Atha, prin. Fax 251-3648
Brebeuf Jesuit Prep S 800/9-12
2801 W 86th St 46268 317-524-7050
LaTonya Turner, admin. Fax 524-7148
Brown Mackie College Post-Sec.
1200 N Meridian St Ste 100 46204 317-554-8300
Butler University Post-Sec.
4600 Sunset Ave 46208 317-940-8000
Calvary Christian S 200/PK-12
3939 S Keystone Ave 46227 317-789-8710
Fax 789-8718
Cardinal Ritter JSHS 600/7-12
3360 W 30th St 46222 317-924-4333
Jo Hoy, prin. Fax 927-7822
Cathedral HS 1,300/9-12
5225 E 56th St 46226 317-542-1481
David Worland, prin. Fax 543-5050
Chamberlain College of Nursing Post-Sec.
9100 Keystone Xing 46240 317-816-7335
Christian Theological Seminary Post-Sec.
1000 W 42nd St 46208 317-924-1331
Colonial Christian S 200/PK-12
8140 Union Chapel Rd 46240 317-253-0649
Dr. Kevin Suiter, admin. Fax 254-2840
Community Hospital of Indianapolis Post-Sec.
1500 N Ritter Ave 46219 317-355-5529
Covenant Christian HS 300/9-12
7525 W 21st St 46214 317-390-0202
Andy Goodwin, prin. Fax 390-6823
Crosspointe Christian Academy 200/PK-12
220 Country Club Rd 46234 317-271-1600
Brent Floyd, admin. Fax 209-8227
Crossroads Bible College Post-Sec.
601 N Shortridge Rd 46219 317-789-8255
DeVry University Post-Sec.
9100 Keystone Xing Ste 100 46240 317-581-8854
Empire Beauty School Post-Sec.
3810 E Southport Rd 46237 317-781-0959
Fortis College Post-Sec.
9001 Wesleyan Rd Ste 101 46268 317-808-4800
Franklin University Post-Sec.
8415 Allison Pointe Ste 400 46250 319-429-3100
Harrison College Post-Sec.
550 E Washington St 46204 317-264-5656
Harrison College Post-Sec.
6300 Technology Center Dr 46278 317-873-6500
Harrison College Post-Sec.
8150 Brookville Rd 46239 317-375-8000
Harrison College - Online Post-Sec.
500 N Meridian St Ste 500 46204 317-217-6815
Heritage Christian S 1,500/PK-12
6401 E 75th St 46250 317-849-3441
Jeff Freeman, admin. Fax 594-5863
Horizon Christian S 300/PK-12
7702 Indian Lake Rd 46236 317-823-4538
Jim Downey, prin. Fax 826-2438
Indianapolis Christian S 50/K-12
620 E 10th St 46202 317-636-4560
Fax 636-1160
Indiana School for the Deaf Post-Sec.
1200 E 42nd St 46205 317-924-4374
Indiana State School for the Blind Post-Sec.
7725 N College Ave 46240 317-253-1481
Indiana University School of Allied Hlth Post-Sec.
1140 W Michigan St 46202 317-274-4702
Indiana Univ-Purdue Univ at Indianapolis Post-Sec.
355 Lansing St 46202 317-274-5555
International Business College Post-Sec.
7205 Shadeland Sta 46256 317-813-2300
International S of Indiana 600/PK-12
4330 Michigan Rd 46208 317-923-1951
David Garner, hdmstr. Fax 923-1910
ITT Technical Institute Post-Sec.
9511 Angola Ct 46268 317-875-8640
ITT Technical Institute Post-Sec.
2525 N Shadeland Ave Ste 10 46219 317-351-3800
Ivy Tech Community College - Central IN Post-Sec.
50 W Fall Creek Pkwy N Dr 46208 317-921-4800
Kaplan College Post-Sec.
4200 S East St 46227 317-782-0315
Lincoln College of Technology Post-Sec.
7225 Winton Dr # 128 46268 317-632-5553
Lutheran HS 300/9-12
5555 S Arlington Ave 46237 317-787-5474
Mike Brandt, head sch Fax 787-2794
Marian University Post-Sec.
3200 Cold Spring Rd 46222 317-955-6000
Martin University Post-Sec.
PO Box 18567 46218 317-543-3235
MedTech College Post-Sec.
6612 E 75th St Ste 300 46250 317-845-0100
Methodist Hosp/Clarian Health Partners Post-Sec.
PO Box 1367 46206 317-929-5900
National College Post-Sec.
6060 Castleway West Dr 46250 317-578-7353
Park Tudor S 1,000/PK-12
7200 N College Ave 46240 317-415-2700
Dr. Matthew Miller, head sch Fax 254-2714
Providence Cristo Rey HS 100/9-12
75 N Belleview Pl 46222 317-860-1000
Sr. Jeanne Hagelskamp, prin.
Reppert School of Auctioneering Post-Sec.
6851 Madison Ave 46227 317-300-1075
Roncalli HS 1,100/9-12
3300 Prague Rd 46227 317-787-8277
Charles Weisenbach, prin. Fax 788-4095
Scecina Memorial HS 300/9-12
5000 Nowland Ave 46201 317-356-6377
John Hegarty, prin. Fax 322-4287
Suburban Christian S 100/PK-12
722 E County Line Rd 46227 317-888-3366
Jeremy Wilhelm, prin. Fax 884-4025
TCM International Institute Post-Sec.
PO Box 24560 46224 317-299-0333
The Chef's Academy Post-Sec.
644 E Washington St 46204 800-919-2500
University of Indianapolis Post-Sec.
1400 E Hanna Ave 46227 317-788-3368

Jasonville, Greene, Pop. 2,204
Metro SD Shakamak 800/K-12
9233 Shakamak School Rd 47438 812-665-3550
Mike Mogan, supt. Fax 665-5001
www.shakamak.k12.in.us/
Shakamak JSHS 400/7-12
9233 Shakamak School Rd 47438 812-665-3550
Chris Ross, prin. Fax 665-5001

Jasper, Dubois, Pop. 14,939
Greater Jasper Consolidated SD 3,200/PK-12
1520 Saint Charles St 47546 812-482-1801
Dr. Tracy Lorey, supt. Fax 482-3388
www.gjcs.k12.in.us
Jasper HS 1,100/9-12
1600 Saint Charles St 47546 812-482-6050
Brian Wilson, prin. Fax 634-3971
Jasper MS 800/6-8
3600 N Portersville Rd 47546 812-482-6454
David Hubster, prin. Fax 482-6457

Jeffersonville, Clark, Pop. 43,626
Greater Clark County SD 10,700/PK-12
2112 Utica Sellersburg Rd 47130 812-283-0701
Dr. Andrew Melin, supt. Fax 288-4804
www.gcs.k12.in.us
Clark County MSHS 6-12
2710 E 10th St 47130 812-288-4837
James Sexton, prin. Fax 288-4829
Corden Porter S 100/Alt
630 Meigs Ave 47130 812-288-4891
Bunny Nash-Gardner, prin. Fax 288-4843
Jeffersonville HS 2,100/9-12
2315 Allison Ln 47130 812-282-6601
James Sexton, prin. Fax 288-4812

Parkview MS 800/6-8
1600 Brigman Ave 47130 812-288-4844
Mark Laughner, prin. Fax 288-2849
River Valley MS 900/6-8
2220 Veterans Pkwy 47130 812-288-4848
Michael Denny, prin. Fax 288-4851
Other Schools – See Charlestown, New Washington

Mid-America College of Funeral Service Post-Sec.
3111 Hamburg Pike 47130 812-288-8878
Ottawa University Post-Sec.
287 Quartermaster Ct 47130 812-280-7271

Jonesboro, Grant, Pop. 1,733

King's Academy 100/K-12
1201 S Water St 46938 765-674-1722
Tony Miner, hdmstr. Fax 674-7322

Kendallville, Noble, Pop. 9,716
East Noble SC 3,800/K-12
126 W Rush St 46755 260-347-2502
Ann Linson, supt. Fax 347-0111
www.eastnoble.net
Alternative Learning Center Alt
702 Dowling St 46755 260-349-0814
Craig Sloan, prin. Fax 347-1242
East Noble HS 1,300/9-12
901 Garden St 46755 260-347-2032
Steve Peterson, prin. Fax 347-2362
East Noble MS 600/7-8
401 E Diamond St 46755 260-347-0100
Andrew Deming, prin. Fax 347-7168

Garrett-Keyser-Butler Community SD
Supt. — See Garrett
Four County Area Voc Coop Vo/Tech
1607 Dowling St 46755 260-349-0250
Tim Holcomb, prin. Fax 349-0240

Kentland, Newton, Pop. 1,729
South Newton SC 900/PK-12
13232 S 50 E 47951 219-474-5184
Todd Rudnick, supt. Fax 474-6966
www.newton.k12.in.us/
South Newton HS 300/9-12
13102 S 50 E 47951 219-474-5167
Charles Huckstep, prin. Fax 474-6592
South Newton MS 200/6-8
13100 S 50 E 47951 219-474-5167
Tansey Mulligan, prin. Fax 474-3624

Knightstown, Henry, Pop. 2,153
C.A. Beard Memorial SC 1,300/K-12
8139 W US Highway 40 46148 765-345-5101
Amy Rauch, supt. Fax 345-5103
www.cabeard.k12.in.us
Knightstown HS 400/9-12
8149 W US Highway 40 46148 765-345-5153
Scott Ritchie, prin. Fax 345-7977
Knightstown IS 400/5-8
1 Panther Trl 46148 765-345-5455
Christopher Bundy, prin. Fax 345-5523

Knox, Starke, Pop. 3,653
Knox Community SC 2,000/K-12
2 Redskin Trl 46534 574-772-1600
A.J. Gappa, supt. Fax 772-1608
www.knox.k12.in.us
Knox Community HS 600/9-12
1 Redskin Trl 46534 574-772-1670
Dr. Elizabeth Hatlitt, prin. Fax 772-1681
Knox Community MS 500/6-8
901 S Main St 46534 574-772-1654
David Miller, prin. Fax 772-1664

Kokomo, Howard, Pop. 44,079
Kokomo-Center Twp Consolidated SC 6,800/PK-12
PO Box 2188 46904 765-455-8000
Jeff Hauswald, supt. Fax 455-8018
www.kokomo.k12.in.us
Central International (KEY) MS 600/6-8
303 E Superior St 46901 765-454-7000
Michael Sargent, prin. Fax 454-7007
Kokomo Area Career Ctr Vo/Tech
2415 S Berkley Rd 46902 765-455-8021
James Stradling, dir. Fax 454-7014
Kokomo HS 2,000/9-12
2501 S Berkley Rd 46902 765-455-8040
Rick Hagenow, prin. Fax 455-8060
Lincoln Alternative MS Alt
721 W Jackson St 46901 765-454-7120
Heidi Gutwein, prin. Fax 454-7055
Maple Crest MS 600/6-8
2727 S Washington St 46902 765-455-8085
Kathryn Reckard, prin. Fax 455-8062
McKinley Alternative S Alt
1217 W Carter St 46901 765-454-7080
Heidi Gutwein, prin. Fax 454-7081

Northwestern SC 1,600/K-12
3075 N Washington St 46901 765-452-3060
Ryan Snoddy, supt. Fax 452-3065
nwsc.k12.in.us
Northwestern HS 600/9-12
3431 N 400 W 46901 765-454-2332
Al Remaly, prin. Fax 454-2333
Northwestern MS 300/7-8
3431 N 400 W 46901 765-454-2323
Brett Davis, prin. Fax 457-2324

Taylor Community SC 1,400/PK-12
3750 E 300 S 46902 765-453-3035
Dr. Robert L. Foreman, supt. Fax 455-8531
www.taylor.k12.in.us
Taylor HS 500/9-12
3794 E 300 S 46902 765-453-1101
Eric Hartman, prin. Fax 455-5163
Taylor MS 300/6-8
3794 E 300 S 46902 765-455-5186
Heather Hord, prin. Fax 455-5157

Indiana University at Kokomo Post-Sec.
2300 S Washington St 46902 765-453-2000
Ivy Tech Community College - Kokomo Post-Sec.
PO Box 1373 46903 765-459-0561
Rudae's School of Beauty Culture Post-Sec.
208 W Jefferson St 46901 765-459-4197
St. Joseph Hospital & Health Center Post-Sec.
1907 W Sycamore St 46901 765-452-5611

Kouts, Porter, Pop. 1,870
East Porter County SC 2,400/K-12
PO Box 370 46347 219-766-2214
Dr. Rod Gardin, supt. Fax 766-2885
epcsc.schoolwires.net/
Kouts MSHS 400/6-12
PO Box 699 46347 219-766-2231
Terry Brownell, prin. Fax 766-3763
Other Schools – See Valparaiso

La Crosse, LaPorte, Pop. 550
Tri Township School Corp 300/K-12
11 N Michigan St 46348 219-754-2461
Timothy Somers, supt. Fax 754-2511
La Crosse HS 100/9-12
PO Box 360 46348 219-754-2461
Timothy Somers, prin. Fax 754-2511

Lafayette, Tippecanoe, Pop. 65,793
Lafayette SC 7,100/K-12
2300 Cason St 47904 765-771-6000
Les Huddle, supt. Fax 771-6049
www.lsc.k12.in.us
Jefferson HS 2,200/9-12
1801 S 18th St 47905 765-772-4700
Jeff Studebaker, prin. Fax 772-4713
Oakland HS 100/9-12
611 S 21st St 47905 765-771-6130
Clare Lutgen, prin. Fax 771-6134
Tecumseh JHS 1,000/7-8
2101 S 18th St 47905 765-772-4750
Brett Gruetzmacher, prin. Fax 772-4763

Tippecanoe SC 11,800/K-12
21 Elston Rd 47909 765-474-2481
Dr. Scott Hanback, supt. Fax 474-0533
www.tsc.k12.in.us
East Tipp MS 400/6-8
7501 E 300 N 47905 765-589-3566
Shaad Buss, prin. Fax 589-3129
McCutcheon HS 1,800/9-12
4951 US Highway 231 S 47909 765-474-1488
John Beeker, prin. Fax 477-9710
Southwestern MS 400/6-8
2100 W 800 S 47909 765-538-3025
Karen Smith, prin. Fax 538-2877
Wainwright MS 400/6-8
7501 E 700 S 47905 765-269-8350
Dr. Neal McCutcheon, prin. Fax 269-8359
Wea Ridge MS 600/6-8
4410 S 150 E 47909 765-471-2164
Cory Marshall, prin. Fax 474-5347
Other Schools – See West Lafayette

Central Catholic JSHS 300/7-12
2410 S 9th St 47909 765-474-2496
Joe Brettenacher, prin. Fax 474-8752
Faith Christian S 600/PK-12
5526 State Road 26 E 47905 765-447-2727
Scott Grass, supt. Fax 449-3737
Harrison College Post-Sec.
4705 Meijer Ct 47905 765-447-9550
Ivy Tech Community College - Lafayette Post-Sec.
PO Box 6299 47903 765-269-5000
Lafayette Beauty Academy Post-Sec.
833 Ferry St 47901 765-742-0068
St. Elizabeth School of Nursing Post-Sec.
1508 Tippecanoe St 47904 765-423-6400

Lagrange, Lagrange, Pop. 2,609
Lakeland SC 2,200/K-12
200 S Cherry St 46761 260-499-2400
Risa Herber, supt. Fax 463-4800
www.lakeland.k12.in.us
Lakeland HS 700/9-12
805 E 075 N 46761 260-499-2470
Eva Merkel, prin. Fax 463-4058
Lakeland MS 500/6-8
1055 E 075 N 46761 260-499-2480
Karen Lake, prin. Fax 463-2648

Prairie Heights Community SC 1,400/K-12
305 S 1150 E 46761 260-351-3214
Alan Middleton, supt. Fax 351-3614
www.ph.k12.in.us/
Prairie Heights HS 500/9-12
245 S 1150 E 46761 260-351-3214
Donell Housel, prin. Fax 351-3848
Prairie Heights MS 400/5-8
395 S 1150 E 46761 260-351-3214
Jeff Reed, prin. Fax 351-2182

Lake Station, Lake, Pop. 12,350
Lake Station Community SD 1,400/K-12
2500 Pike St 46405 219-962-1159
Dan DeHaven, supt. Fax 962-4011
www.lakes.k12.in.us
Edison JSHS 700/7-12
3304 Parkside Ave 46405 219-962-8531
Bruce Bush, prin. Fax 962-2064

Lakeville, Saint Joseph, Pop. 778
Union-North United SC 1,200/K-12
22601 Tyler Rd 46536 574-784-8141
Mitchell Mawhorter, supt. Fax 784-2181
www.unorth.k12.in.us
Laville JSHS 600/7-12
69969 US Highway 31 46536 574-784-3151
Nathan McKeand, prin. Fax 784-8695

Lanesville, Harrison, Pop. 557
Lanesville Community SC 700/K-12
2725 Crestview Ave NE 47136 812-952-2555
Steve Morris, supt. Fax 952-3762
www.lanesville.k12.in.us/
Lanesville JSHS 300/7-12
2725 Crestview Ave NE 47136 812-952-2555
Steve Morris, prin. Fax 952-3762

Lapel, Madison, Pop. 2,035
Frankton-Lapel Community SD
Supt. — See Anderson
Lapel HS 400/9-12
1850 S 900 W 46051 765-534-3036
Greg Granger, prin. Fax 534-4498
Lapel MS 300/6-8
2883 S State Road 13 46051 765-534-3137
Bill Chase, prin. Fax 534-3883

La Porte, LaPorte, Pop. 21,655
La Porte Community SC 6,300/K-12
1921 A St 46350 219-362-7056
Rande Thorpe, supt. Fax 324-9347
www.lpcsc.k12.in.us
Boston MS 800/6-8
1000 Harrison St 46350 219-326-6930
Deborah Carter, prin. Fax 324-7108
Kesling MS 800/6-8
306 E 18th St 46350 219-362-7507
Bill Wilmsen, prin. Fax 324-5712
La Porte HS 1,800/9-12
602 F St 46350 219-362-3102
Ben Tonagel, prin. Fax 324-2142

La Lumiere S 200/9-12
PO Box 5005 46352 219-326-7450
Michael Kennedy, hdmstr. Fax 325-3185

Larwill, Whitley, Pop. 280
Whitko Community SC
Supt. — See Pierceton
Whitko MS 500/6-8
710 N State Road 5 46764 260-327-3603
Parrish Kruger, prin. Fax 327-3805

Lawrenceburg, Dearborn, Pop. 4,938
Lawrenceburg Community SC 1,900/K-12
300 Tiger Blvd 47025 812-537-7200
Karl Galey, supt. Fax 537-0759
www.lburg.k12.in.us
Greendale MS 400/6-8
200 Tiger Blvd 47025 812-537-7259
Kevin Self, prin. Fax 537-6385
Lawrenceburg HS 600/9-12
100 Tiger Blvd 47025 812-537-7219
Bill Snyder, prin. Fax 537-7221

Lebanon, Boone, Pop. 15,595
Lebanon Community SC 3,000/K-12
1810 N Grant St 46052 765-482-0380
Dr. Robert Taylor, supt. Fax 483-3053
www.leb.k12.in.us/
Lebanon HS 1,000/9-12
510 Essex Dr 46052 765-482-0400
Kevin O'Rourke, prin. Fax 483-3040
Lebanon MS 800/6-8
1800 N Grant St 46052 765-482-3400
Doyle Dunshee, prin. Fax 483-3049

Leo, Allen
East Allen County SD
Supt. — See New Haven
Leo JSHS 1,300/7-12
14600 Amstutz Rd 46765 260-446-0180
Dr. Neal Brown, prin. Fax 446-0189

Leopold, Perry
Perry Central Community SC 1,100/PK-12
18677 Old State Road 37 47551 812-843-5576
Mary Roberson, supt. Fax 843-4746
www.pccs.k12.in.us/
Perry Central JSHS 500/7-12
18677 Old State Road 37 47551 812-843-5121
Seth Clark, prin. Fax 843-4198

Liberty, Union, Pop. 2,110
Union County/College Corner JSD 1,400/K-12
107 S Layman St 47353 765-458-7471
Dr. Zach Rozelle, supt. Fax 458-5647
www.uc.k12.in.us/
Union County HS 500/9-12
410 Patriot Blvd 47353 765-458-5136
Connie Rosenberger, prin. Fax 458-6315
Union County MS 400/6-8
488 E State Road 44 47353 765-458-7438
Vicky Snyder, prin. Fax 458-6041

Ligonier, Noble, Pop. 4,376
West Noble SC 2,100/K-12
5050 N US Highway 33 46767 260-894-3191
Dr. Dennis VanDuyne, supt. Fax 894-3260
westnoble.k12.in.us/
West Noble HS 700/9-12
5094 N US Highway 33 46767 260-894-3191
Greg Baker, prin. Fax 894-4708
West Noble MS 800/5-8
5194 N US Highway 33 46767 260-894-3191
Melanie Tijerina, prin. Fax 894-4703

Lincoln City, Spencer
North Spencer County SC 2,000/PK-12
PO Box 316 47552 812-937-2400
Dan Scherry, supt. Fax 937-7187
www.nspencer.k12.in.us
Heritage Hills HS 700/9-12
3644 E County Road 1600 N 47552 812-937-4472
Nick Alcorn, prin. Fax 937-4878

Heritage Hills MS 300/7-8
PO Box 1777 47552 812-937-4472
Chad Schneiders, prin. Fax 937-4327

Linton, Greene, Pop. 5,354
Linton-Stockton SC 1,400/K-12
801 1st St NE 47441 812-847-6020
Nick Karazsia, supt. Fax 847-8659
www.lssc.k12.in.us/
Linton-Stockton HS 300/9-12
10 H St NE 47441 812-847-6024
Nathan Moore, prin. Fax 847-6037
Linton-Stockton MS 300/6-8
109 I St NE 47441 812-847-6022
Jeff Sparks, prin. Fax 847-6032

Lizton, Hendricks, Pop. 481
North West Hendricks SD 1,900/K-12
PO Box 70 46149 317-994-4100
Richard King, supt. Fax 994-5963
www.hendricks.k12.in.us/
Tri-West HS 600/9-12
7883 N State Road 39 46149 317-994-4000
Adam Benner, prin. Fax 994-5106
Tri-West MS 400/6-8
555 W US Highway 136 46149 317-994-4200
Ryan Nickoli, prin. Fax 994-4230

Logansport, Cass, Pop. 18,151
Logansport Community SC 4,200/PK-12
2829 George St 46947 574-722-2911
Michele Starkey, supt. Fax 753-0143
www.lcsc.k12.in.us
Century Career Center Vo/Tech
2500 Hopper St 46947 574-722-3811
Clark Miller, dir. Fax 753-7649
Columbia MS 500/6-8
1300 N 3rd St 46947 574-753-3797
Greg Grostefon, prin. Fax 753-6159
Lincoln MS 500/6-8
2901 Usher St 46947 574-753-7115
Jeff Canady, prin. Fax 753-5826
Logansport Community HS 1,300/9-12
1 Berry Ln 46947 574-753-0441
Matt Jones, prin. Fax 753-3688

Loogootee, Martin, Pop. 2,735
Loogootee Community SC 1,000/K-12
PO Box 282 47553 812-295-2595
Larry Weitkamp, supt. Fax 295-5595
www.loogootee.k12.in.us/
Loogootee JSHS 500/7-12
201 Brooks Ave 47553 812-295-3254
John Mullen, prin. Fax 295-3694

Lowell, Lake, Pop. 9,196
Tri-Creek SC 3,700/K-12
195 W Oakley Ave 46356 219-696-6661
Dr. Debra Howe, supt. Fax 696-2150
www.tricreek.k12.in.us/
Lowell HS 1,300/9-12
2051 E Commercial Ave 46356 219-696-7733
Fax 696-0042
Lowell MS 900/6-8
19250 Cline St 46356 219-696-7701
Rebecca Pavich, prin. Fax 690-2620

Lynn, Randolph, Pop. 1,088
Randolph Southern SC 600/K-12
1 Rebel Dr 47355 765-874-1181
Donnie Bowsman, supt. Fax 874-1298
www.rssc.k12.in.us
Randolph Southern JSHS 300/7-12
2 Rebel Dr 47355 765-874-2541
Michael Manning, prin. Fax 874-1298

Lynnville, Warrick, Pop. 881
Warrick County SC
Supt. — See Boonville
Tecumseh JSHS 400/7-12
5244 W State Route 68 47619 812-922-3237
Richard Lance, prin. Fax 922-3608

Madison, Jefferson, Pop. 11,775
Madison Consolidated SD 2,900/K-12
2421 Wilson Ave 47250 812-274-8001
Dr. Ginger Bolinger, supt. Fax 274-8507
www.madison.k12.in.us
Madison Consolidated HS 1,100/9-12
743 Clifty Dr 47250 812-274-8002
Kevin Yancey, prin. Fax 274-8788
Madison Consolidated JHS 800/6-8
701 8th St 47250 812-274-8003
Jill Mires, prin. Fax 274-8558

Christian Academy at Madison 100/PK-12
477 W Hutchinson Ln 47250 812-273-5000
Anna Gosman, admin. Fax 265-0700
Ivy Tech Community College - Southeast Post-Sec.
590 Ivy Tech Dr 47250 812-265-2580
Kent Christian Academy 50/PK-12
8082 W Kent SR 256 47250 812-866-3313
Brian Schulz, admin.
King's Daughter's Hospital Post-Sec.
PO Box 447 47250 812-265-5211
Shawe Memorial JSHS 200/7-12
201 W State St 47250 812-273-2150
Steve Hesse, prin. Fax 273-6694

Marengo, Crawford, Pop. 809
Crawford County Community SC 1,600/PK-12
5805 E Administration Rd 47140 812-365-2135
Dr. Mark Eastridge, supt. Fax 365-2783
www.cccs.k12.in.us/
Crawford County JSHS 700/7-12
1130 S State Road 66 47140 812-365-2125
Karen Sheller, prin. Fax 365-2127

Marion, Grant, Pop. 29,023
Eastbrook Community SC 1,700/K-12
560 S 900 E 46953 765-664-0624
Brett Garrett, supt. Fax 664-0626
www.eastbrookschools.net
Eastbrook HS 700/9-12
560 S 900 E 46953 765-664-1214
Patrick McLaughlin, prin. Fax 664-1216
Eastbrook JHS 300/7-8
560 S 900 E 46953 765-668-7136
Elizabeth Duckwall, prin. Fax 668-7137

Marion Community SD 4,100/PK-12
1240 S Adams St 46953 765-662-2546
Stephen Edwards, supt. Fax 651-2043
www.marion.k12.in.us/
Marion HS 1,300/9-12
750 W 26th St 46953 765-664-9051
Lennon Brown, prin. Fax 662-0383
McCulloch JHS 600/7-8
3528 S Washington St 46953 765-674-6917
Jim Fox, prin. Fax 674-8943
Tucker Career & Technology Center Vo/Tech
107 S Pennsylvania St 46952 765-664-9091
Amanda McCammon, dir. Fax 651-2048

Indiana Wesleyan University Post-Sec.
4201 S Washington St 46953 765-674-6901
Lakeview Christian S 100/K-12
5318 S Western Ave 46953 765-677-4266
Douglas Ballinger, admin. Fax 677-4269

Marshall, Parke, Pop. 323
Turkey Run Community SC 600/PK-12
1497 E State Road 47 47859 765-597-2750
Dr. Thomas Rohr, supt. Fax 597-2755
www.tr.k12.in.us
Turkey Run JSHS 300/6-12
1551 E State Road 47 47859 765-597-2700
Dwight Ashley, prin. Fax 597-4202

Martinsville, Morgan, Pop. 11,701
Metro SD of Martinsville 5,400/PK-12
460 S Main St 46151 765-342-6641
Ron Furniss, supt. Fax 342-6877
msdadmin.scican.net
Hammons S 50/Alt
159 N 2nd St 46151 765-342-0120
Don Alkire, prin. Fax 349-5256
Martinsville East MS 700/6-8
1459 E Columbus St 46151 765-342-6675
Eric Bowlen, prin. Fax 349-5236
Martinsville HS 1,700/9-12
1360 E Gray St 46151 765-342-5571
Don Alkire, prin. Fax 349-5256
Martinsville West MS 600/6-8
109 E Garfield Ave 46151 765-342-6628
Suzie Lipps, prin. Fax 349-5232

Tabernacle Christian S 100/K-12
2189 Burton Ln 46151 765-342-0501
Fax 342-0502

Medora, Jackson, Pop. 677
Medora Community SC 300/K-12
PO Box 369 47260 812-966-2210
Tom Judd, supt. Fax 966-2217
www.medorahornets.org/
Medora JSHS 100/7-12
PO Box 248 47260 812-966-2201
Brad McCammon, prin. Fax 966-2209

Merrillville, Lake, Pop. 34,497
Merrillville Community SC 7,100/K-12
6701 Delaware St 46410 219-650-5300
Dr. Anthony Lux, supt. Fax 650-5320
www.mvsc.k12.in.us
Merrillville HS 2,400/9-12
276 E 68th Pl 46410 219-650-5307
Mike Krutz, prin. Fax 650-5391
Pierce MS 1,100/7-8
199 E 70th Ave 46410 219-650-5308
Paul McKinney, prin. Fax 650-5483

Andrean HS 600/9-12
5959 Broadway 46410 219-887-5281
Mary Beth Ginalski, prin. Fax 981-5072
Brown Mackie College Post-Sec.
1000 E 80th Pl Ste 205M 46410 219-769-3321
DeVry University Post-Sec.
1000 E 80th Pl Ste 222N 46410 219-736-7440
Everest College Post-Sec.
8585 Broadway Ste 200 46410 219-756-6811
ITT Technical Institute Post-Sec.
8488 Georgia St 46410 219-738-6100
Merrillville Beauty College Post-Sec.
48 W 67th Pl 46410 219-769-2232
Success School Post-Sec.
8101 Polo Club Dr 46410 219-736-9999

Michigan City, LaPorte, Pop. 30,502
Michigan City Area SD 6,200/PK-12
408 S Carroll Ave 46360 219-873-2000
Dr. Barbara Eason-Watkins, supt. Fax 873-2072
www.mcas.k12.in.us
Barker MS 400/6-8
319 Barker Rd 46360 219-873-2057
Dr. Mohamed Mroueh, prin. Fax 873-3099
Elston MS 600/6-8
317 Detroit St 46360 219-873-2035
Kelly Fargo, prin. Fax 873-2157
Krueger MS 400/6-8
2001 Springland Ave 46360 219-873-2061
Vera Jones, prin. Fax 873-2063
Michigan City HS 1,900/9-12
8466 W Pahs Rd 46360 219-873-2044
Wendell McCollum, prin. Fax 873-2055

Smith Area Career Center Vo/Tech
817 Lafayette St 46360 219-873-2120
Audra Peterson, dir. Fax 873-2068

Brown Mackie College Post-Sec.
1001 E US Highway 20 46360 219-877-3100
Lakeshore Medical Lab Training Programs Post-Sec.
402 Franklin St 46360 219-872-7032
Marquette Catholic HS 200/9-12
306 W 10th St 46360 219-873-1325
James White, prin. Fax 873-1327

Michigantown, Clinton, Pop. 463
Clinton Central SC 1,100/K-12
PO Box 118 46057 765-249-2515
Dr. Celia Shand, supt. Fax 249-2504
www.clinton.k12.in.us/
Clinton Central JSHS 500/7-12
PO Box 178 46057 765-249-2255
Mike Poiry, prin. Fax 249-0214

Middlebury, Elkhart, Pop. 3,377
Middlebury Community SD 4,300/K-12
56853 Northridge Dr 46540 574-825-9425
Jane Allen, supt. Fax 825-9426
www.mcsin-k12.org/
Northridge HS 1,300/9-12
56779 Northridge Dr 46540 574-825-2142
Gerald Rasler, prin. Fax 825-1473
Northridge MS 1,000/6-8
56691 Northridge Dr 46540 574-825-9531
Robby Goodman, prin. Fax 825-9154

Middletown, Henry, Pop. 2,295
Shenandoah SC 1,400/K-12
5100 N Raider Rd 47356 765-354-2266
Ronald Green, supt. Fax 354-2274
www.shenandoah.k12.in.us/
Shenandoah HS 400/9-12
7354 W US Highway 36 47356 765-354-6640
Charles Willis, prin. Fax 354-3110
Shenandoah MS 300/6-8
5156 N Raider Rd 47356 765-354-6638
Greg Allen, prin. Fax 354-3120

Milan, Ripley, Pop. 1,874
Milan Community SC 1,200/K-12
412 E Carr St 47031 812-654-2365
Paul Ketcham M.S., supt. Fax 654-2441
www.milan.k12.in.us
Milan HS 400/9-12
609 N Warpath Dr 47031 812-654-3096
Ryan Langferman, prin. Fax 654-2368
Milan MS 300/6-8
609 N Warpath Dr 47031 812-654-1616
Patrick Murphy, prin. Fax 654-2368

Mishawaka, Saint Joseph, Pop. 46,961
Penn-Harris-Madison SC 10,300/K-12
55900 Bittersweet Rd 46545 574-259-7941
Dr. Jerry Thacker, supt. Fax 258-9547
www.phm.k12.in.us
Grissom MS 600/6-8
13881 Kern Rd 46544 574-633-4061
Tammy Matz, prin. Fax 633-2134
Penn HS 3,400/9-12
56100 Bittersweet Rd 46545 574-259-7961
Steve Hope, prin. Fax 258-9543
Schmucker MS 1,000/6-8
56045 Bittersweet Rd 46545 574-259-5661
Janet Scott, prin. Fax 259-0807
Other Schools – See Granger

School City of Mishawaka 5,200/K-12
1402 S Main St 46544 574-254-4500
Dr. Terry Barker, supt. Fax 254-4585
www.mishawaka.k12.in.us
Mishawaka HS 1,600/9-12
1202 Lincolnway E 46544 574-254-7300
Jerome Calderone, prin. Fax 254-7481
Young MS 800/7-8
1801 N Main St 46545 574-254-3600
Mickey Roelandts, prin. Fax 258-3021

Bais Yaakov of Indiana 50/9-12
302 W 8th St 46544 574-257-0689
Bethel College Post-Sec.
1001 Bethel Cir 46545 574-807-7000
Marian HS 700/9-12
1311 S Logan St 46544 574-259-5257
Carl Loesch, prin. Fax 258-7668

Mitchell, Lawrence, Pop. 4,315
Mitchell Community SD 2,000/PK-12
441 N 8th St 47446 812-849-4481
Dr. Steve Phillips, supt. Fax 849-2133
www.mitchell.k12.in.us
Mitchell HS 600/9-12
1000 W Bishop Blvd 47446 812-849-3663
Sean Vandeventer, prin. Fax 849-5368
Mitchell JHS 500/6-8
1010 W Bishop Blvd 47446 812-849-3747
Jennifer Caruso, prin. Fax 849-5841

Modoc, Randolph, Pop. 190
Union SC 400/K-12
8707 W US Highway 36 47358 765-853-5464
Fred Herron, supt. Fax 853-5070
www.usc.k12.in.us
Union JSHS 200/7-12
8707 W US Highway 36 47358 765-853-5421
Allen Hayne, prin. Fax 853-6057

Monon, White, Pop. 1,750
North White SC 700/PK-12
121 W State Road 16 47959 219-253-6618
Nicholas Eccles, supt. Fax 253-6488
www.nwhite.k12.in.us/

North White JSHS 400/7-12
310 E Broadway St 47959 219-253-6638
Curtis D. Craig, prin. Fax 253-7004
Other Schools – See Monticello

Monroe, Adams, Pop. 839
Adams Central Community SD 1,200/K-12
222 W Washington St 46772 260-692-6193
Michael Pettibone, supt. Fax 692-6198
www.accs.k12.in.us/
Adams Central HS 400/9-12
222 W Washington St 46772 260-692-6151
Jason Witzigreuter, prin. Fax 692-6192
Adams Central MS 300/6-8
222 W Washington St 46772 260-692-6151
Aaron McClure, prin. Fax 692-6192

Monroeville, Allen, Pop. 1,229
East Allen County SD
Supt. — See New Haven
Heritage JSHS 800/7-12
13608 Monroeville Rd 46773 260-446-0140
Matt Widenhoefer, prin. Fax 446-0146

Monrovia, Morgan, Pop. 1,058
Monroe-Gregg SD 1,600/PK-12
135 S Chestnut St 46157 317-996-3720
Dr. Julie Wood, supt. Fax 996-2977
www.m-gsd.org/
Monrovia HS 500/9-12
135 S Chestnut St 46157 317-996-2259
Mike Springer, prin. Fax 996-3519
Monrovia MS 300/6-8
135 S Chestnut St 46157 317-996-2352
Yolanda Goodpaster, prin. Fax 996-3429

Montezuma, Parke, Pop. 1,013
Southwest Parke Community SC 900/K-12
4851 S Coxville Rd 47862 765-569-2073
Leonard Orr, supt. Fax 569-0309
www.swparke.k12.in.us
Riverton Parke JSHS 500/7-12
4907 S Coxville Rd 47862 765-569-2045
Dennis Moody, prin. Fax 569-2047

Montgomery, Daviess, Pop. 341
Barr-Reeve Community SD 700/K-12
PO Box 97 47558 812-486-3220
Travis Madison, supt. Fax 486-3509
www.barr.k12.in.us
Barr-Reeve MSHS 300/6-12
PO Box 129 47558 812-486-3265
Jeff Doyle, prin. Fax 486-2829

Monticello, White, Pop. 5,324
North White SC
Supt. — See Monon
White County Academic Skills Center Adult
315 N Illinois St 47960 574-583-5158
Suzy Karberg, dir. Fax 583-4231

Twin Lakes SC 2,500/PK-12
565 S Main St 47960 574-583-7211
Dr. Thomas Fletcher, supt. Fax 583-2679
www.twinlakes.k12.in.us/
Roosevelt MS 600/6-8
721 W Broadway St 47960 574-583-5552
Scott Clifford, prin. Fax 583-3675
Twin Lakes HS 800/9-12
300 S 3rd St 47960 574-583-7108
Scott Leverenz, prin. Fax 583-2679

Mooresville, Morgan, Pop. 9,219
Mooresville Consolidated SC 4,500/PK-12
11 W Carlisle St 46158 317-831-0950
Dr. Larry Moore, supt. Fax 831-9202
www.mooresvilleschools.org
Hadley MS 700/7-8
200 W Carlisle St 46158 317-831-9208
Jacob Allen, prin. Fax 831-9249
Mooresville HS 1,300/9-12
550 N Indiana St 46158 317-831-9203
Chuck Muston, prin. Fax 831-9206

Morocco, Newton, Pop. 1,125
North Newton SC 1,500/K-12
PO Box 8 47963 219-285-2228
Brian Smith, supt. Fax 285-2708
www.nn.k12.in.us/
North Newton JSHS 700/7-12
1641 W 250 N 47963 219-285-2252
Jeff Hettinger, prin. Fax 285-2881

Morristown, Shelby, Pop. 1,211
Shelby Eastern SD
Supt. — See Shelbyville
Morristown JSHS 400/6-12
PO Box 960 46161 765-763-1221
Mike Brown, prin. Fax 763-7170

Mount Summit, Henry, Pop. 346
Blue River Valley SD 700/PK-12
PO Box 217 47361 765-836-4816
Stephen Welsh, supt. Fax 836-4817
www.brv.k12.in.us
Other Schools – See New Castle

Mount Vernon, Posey, Pop. 6,543
Metro SD of Mt. Vernon 2,300/PK-12
1000 W 4th St 47620 812-838-4471
Dr. Tom Kopatich, supt. Fax 833-2078
www.msdmv.k12.in.us
Mount Vernon HS 800/9-12
700 Harriett St 47620 812-838-4356
Tom Russell, prin. Fax 833-2099
Mount Vernon JHS 600/6-8
701 Tile Factory Rd 47620 812-833-2077
Kyle Jones, prin. Fax 833-2083

Muncie, Delaware, Pop. 68,179
Cowan Community SC 800/K-12
9401 S Nottingham St 47302 765-289-4866
Dennis Chambers, supt. Fax 284-0315
www.cowan.k12.in.us
Cowan JSHS 300/7-12
9401 S Nottingham St 47302 765-289-7128
James Suding, prin. Fax 741-5954

Delaware Community SC 2,700/K-12
7821 N State Road 3 47303 765-284-5074
Steven Hall, supt. Fax 284-5259
www.delcomschools.org
Delta HS 900/9-12
3400 E State Road 28 47303 765-288-5597
Christopher Conley, prin. Fax 288-8498
Delta MS 600/6-8
9800 N County Road 200 E 47303 765-747-0869
Tom Johns, prin. Fax 213-2131

Muncie Community SD 6,900/K-12
2501 N Oakwood Ave 47304 765-747-5211
Tim Heller, supt. Fax 747-5341
www.muncie.k12.in.us
Muncie Area Career Center Vo/Tech
2500 N Elgin St 47303 765-747-5250
JoAnn McCowan, dir. Fax 747-5455
Muncie Central HS 900/9-12
801 N Walnut St 47305 765-747-5260
Tom Jarvis, prin. Fax 747-5314
Muncie Southside HS 1,000/9-12
1601 E 26th St 47302 765-747-5320
Rebecca Thompson, prin. Fax 747-5325
Northside MS 800/6-8
2400 W Bethel Ave 47304 765-747-5290
Jackie Samuels, prin. Fax 751-0616
Wilson MS 800/6-8
3100 S Tillotson Ave 47302 765-747-5370
Chuck Reynolds, prin. Fax 751-0666

University Schools 900/K-12
2000 W University Ave 47306 765-285-8488
Dr. William Sharp, supt. Fax 285-2166
www.bsu.edu
Burris Laboratory S 600/K-12
2201 W University Ave 47306 765-285-8600
Cathlene Darragh, prin. Fax 285-8620
IN Academy for Science Math & Humanities 300/11-12
301 N Talley Ave 47303 765-285-7457
Dr. David Williams, prin. Fax 285-2777

Ball Memorial Hospital Post-Sec.
2401 W University Ave 47303 765-747-3393
Ball State University Post-Sec.
2000 W University Ave 47306 765-289-1241
Harrison College Post-Sec.
411 W Riggin Rd 47303 765-288-8681
Heritage Hall Christian S 200/PK-12
6401 W River Rd 47304 765-289-6371
Dr. Dennis Ice, hdmstr. Fax 213-2245
Ivy Tech Community College - East Centrl Post-Sec.
4301 S Cowan Rd 47302 765-289-2291
PJ's College of Cosmetology Post-Sec.
3100 W Kilgore Ave 47304 765-289-6144

Munster, Lake, Pop. 23,303
Town of Munster SD 4,100/K-12
8616 Columbia Ave 46321 219-836-9111
Richard Sopko, supt. Fax 836-3215
www.munster.k12.in.us
Munster HS 1,600/9-12
8808 Columbia Ave 46321 219-836-3200
Steven Tripenfeldas, prin. Fax 836-3203
Wright MS 900/6-8
8650 Columbia Ave 46321 219-836-6260
David Knish, prin. Fax 836-0501

Nappanee, Elkhart, Pop. 6,570
Wa-Nee Community SD 3,100/K-12
1300 N Main St 46550 574-773-3131
Joe Sabo, supt. Fax 773-5593
www.wanee.org
Northwood HS 900/9-12
2101 N Main St 46550 574-773-4127
David Maugel, prin. Fax 773-4099
Other Schools – See Wakarusa

United Christian S 100/1-12
29522 County Road 52 46550 574-773-7505
Terrill Yoder, admin. Fax 773-7513

Nashville, Brown, Pop. 795
Brown County SC 1,900/PK-12
PO Box 38 47448 812-988-6601
David Shaffer, supt. Fax 988-5403
www.brownco.k12.in.us
Brown County HS 800/9-12
PO Box 68 47448 812-988-6606
Shane Killinger, prin. Fax 988-5422
Brown County JHS 300/7-8
PO Box 578 47448 812-988-6605
Brian Garman, prin. Fax 988-5415

New Albany, Floyd, Pop. 35,385
New Albany Floyd County Consolidated SD 11,700/PK-12
PO Box 1087 47151 812-949-4200
Dr. Bruce Hibbard, supt. Fax 949-6900
www.nafcs.k12.in.us
Hazelwood MS 1,000/5-8
1021 Hazelwood Ave 47150 812-542-8502
Jessica Waters, prin. Fax 542-4793
New Albany HS 2,000/9-12
1020 Vincennes St 47150 812-542-8506
Janet Page, prin. Fax 542-4797
Prosser Career Education Center Vo/Tech
4202 Charlestown Rd 47150 812-542-8508
Cathy Wheeler, prin. Fax 542-4799

Scribner MS 1,000/5-8
910 Old Vincennes Rd 47150 812-542-8503
Keith Bush, prin. Fax 542-4794
Other Schools – See Floyds Knobs, Georgetown

Christian Academy of Indiana 800/PK-12
1000 Academy Dr 47150 812-944-6200
Timothy Greener, supt. Fax 944-6903
Indiana University Southeast Post-Sec.
4201 Grant Line Rd 47150 812-941-2333

Newburgh, Warrick, Pop. 3,276
Warrick County SC
Supt. — See Boonville
Castle HS 1,900/9-12
3344 State Route 261 47630 812-853-3331
Andy Byers, prin. Fax 853-9886
Castle North MS 700/6-8
2800 State Route 261 47630 812-853-7347
John Bertram, prin. Fax 858-1089
Castle South MS 700/6-8
3711 Casey Rd 47630 812-490-7930
Jim Hood, prin. Fax 490-7925
Warrick Education Center Alt
3199 State Route 261 47630 812-858-4309
Drew Gerth, prin. Fax 858-3420

ITT Technical Institute Post-Sec.
10999 Stahl Rd 47630 812-858-1600
Newburgh Christian S 50/PK-12
PO Box 644 47629 812-842-0455
Pamela Glover, admin. Fax 842-0455

New Carlisle, Saint Joseph, Pop. 1,830
New Prairie United SC 2,800/K-12
5327 N Cougar Rd 46552 574-654-7273
Jim Dermody, supt. Fax 654-7274
www.npusc.k12.in.us
New Prairie HS 900/9-12
5333 N Cougar Rd 46552 574-654-7271
Greg Dettinger, prin. Fax 654-3390
New Prairie MS 700/6-8
5325 N Cougar Rd 46552 574-654-3070
Jim Holifield, prin. Fax 654-7009

New Castle, Henry, Pop. 17,809
Blue River Valley SD
Supt. — See Mount Summit
Blue River Valley JSHS 300/7-12
4741 N Hillsboro Rd 47362 765-836-4811
Jason Slopsema, prin. Fax 836-3255

New Castle Community SC 3,700/K-12
322 Elliott Ave 47362 765-521-7201
Stephen Fisher, supt. Fax 521-7268
www.nccsc.k12.in.us
New Castle Chrysler HS 1,200/9-12
801 Parkview Dr 47362 765-593-6670
Christopher Walker, prin. Fax 593-6585
New Castle MS 600/7-8
601 Parkview Dr 47362 765-521-7230
Jaci Hadsell, prin. Fax 521-7269
North Campus Alternative S Alt
329 S 5th St 47362 765-521-7237
Amy Blake, prin. Fax 593-6652

New Haven, Allen, Pop. 14,574
East Allen County SD 7,400/PK-12
1240 State Road 930 E 46774 260-446-0100
Kenneth Folks, supt. Fax 446-0107
www.eacs.k12.in.us
New Haven HS 900/9-12
1300 Green Rd 46774 260-446-0220
Greg Mohler, prin. Fax 446-0228
New Haven MS 600/6-8
900 Prospect Ave 46774 260-446-0230
Doug Pickett, prin. Fax 446-0236
Other Schools – See Fort Wayne, Leo, Monroeville, Woodburn

New Market, Montgomery, Pop. 636
South Montgomery Community SC 1,900/K-12
PO Box 8 47965 765-866-0203
Dr. Robert Foreman, supt. Fax 866-0736
www.southmont.k12.in.us
Other Schools – See Crawfordsville

New Palestine, Hancock, Pop. 2,034
Southern Hancock County Community SC 3,000/PK-12
PO Box 508 46163 317-861-4463
James Halik, supt. Fax 861-2142
corp.newpal.k12.in.us/
Doe Creek MS 600/7-8
PO Box 478 46163 317-861-4487
James Voelz, prin. Fax 861-2136
New Palestine HS 1,100/9-12
PO Box 448 46163 317-861-4417
Keith Fessler, prin. Fax 861-2125

New Washington, Clark, Pop. 563
Greater Clark County SD
Supt. — See Jeffersonville
New Washington MSHS 500/6-12
226 N Highway 62 47162 812-293-3368
Ben Ledbetter, prin. Fax 293-5803

Noblesville, Hamilton, Pop. 51,089
Noblesville SD 7,900/PK-12
1775 Field Dr 46060 317-773-3171
Libbie Conner Ed.D., supt. Fax 773-7845
www.noblesvilleschools.org
Noblesville East MS 1,400/6-8
300 N 17th St 46060 317-773-0782
Ryan Rich, prin. Fax 776-6261
Noblesville HS 2,500/9-12
18111 Cumberland Rd 46060 317-773-4680
Jeff Bryant, prin. Fax 776-6289
Noblesville West MS 700/6-8
19900 Hague Rd, 317-776-7792
Stacey Swan, prin. Fax 776-7797

Kaye Beauty College — Post-Sec.
1111 S 10th St 46060 — 317-773-6189
St. Theodore Guerin HS — 500/9-12
15300 N Gray Rd, — 317-582-0120
James McNeany, prin. — Fax 582-0140

North Judson, Starke, Pop. 1,752
North Judson-San Pierre SC — 1,300/K-12
801 Campbell Dr 46366 — 574-896-2155
Lynn Johnson, supt. — Fax 896-2156
www.njsp.k12.in.us
North Judson MS — 300/6-8
950 Campbell Dr 46366 — 574-896-2167
Kelly Shepherd, prin. — Fax 896-3036
North Judson-San Pierre HS — 500/9-12
1 Bluejay Dr 46366 — 574-896-2158
Annette Zupin, prin. — Fax 896-3945

North Manchester, Wabash, Pop. 6,040
Manchester Community SD — 1,500/K-12
404 W 9th St 46962 — 260-982-7518
Dr. Bill Reichhart, supt. — Fax 982-4583
www.mcs.k12.in.us
Manchester JSHS — 600/7-12
1 Squire Dr 46962 — 260-982-2196
Nancy Alspaugh, prin. — Fax 982-1034

Manchester University — Post-Sec.
604 E College Ave 46962 — 260-982-5000

North Vernon, Jennings, Pop. 6,629
Jennings County SC — 5,000/K-12
34 W Main St 47265 — 812-346-4483
Dr. Terry Sargent, supt. — Fax 346-4490
www.jcsc.org
Jennings County Academy of Learning — 100/Alt
100 S Webster St 47265 — 812-346-7830
Mike Green, prin. — Fax 346-4193
Jennings County HS — 1,600/9-12
800 W Walnut St 47265 — 812-346-5588
Tim Taylor, prin. — Fax 346-4232
Jennings County MS — 800/7-8
820 W Walnut St 47265 — 812-346-4940
George Grubbs, prin. — Fax 346-4497

Notre Dame, Saint Joseph, Pop. 5,766

Holy Cross College — Post-Sec.
PO Box 308 46556 — 574-239-8377
St. Mary's College 46556 — Post-Sec.
574-284-4000
University of Notre Dame — Post-Sec.
220 Main Building 46556 — 574-631-5000

Oakland City, Gibson, Pop. 2,406
East Gibson SC — 1,000/PK-12
941 S Franklin St 47660 — 812-749-4755
Dr. Henry Brewster, supt. — Fax 749-3343
www.egsc.k12.in.us
Wood Memorial HS — 300/9-12
943 S Franklin St 47660 — 812-749-4757
Roger Benson, prin. — Fax 749-3512
Wood Memorial JHS — 100/7-8
945A S Franklin St 47660 — 812-749-4715
Roger Benson, prin. — Fax 749-4988

Oakland City University — Post-Sec.
138 N Lucretia St 47660 — 812-749-4781

Oldenburg, Franklin, Pop. 669

Oldenburg Academy — 200/9-12
PO Box 200 47036 — 812-934-4440
Bettina Rose, prin. — Fax 934-4838

Oolitic, Lawrence, Pop. 1,177
North Lawrence Community SD
Supt. — See Bedford
Oolitic MS — 400/6-8
903 Hoosier Ave 47451 — 812-275-7551
Steve Underwood, prin. — Fax 277-3219

Orleans, Orange, Pop. 2,135
Orleans Community SD — 800/K-12
173 Marley St 47452 — 812-865-2688
Gary McClintic, supt. — Fax 865-3428
www.orleans.k12.in.us/
Orleans JSHS — 400/7-12
200 W Wilson St 47452 — 812-865-2688
Roy Kline, prin. — Fax 865-3532

Osgood, Ripley, Pop. 1,609
Jac-Cen-Del Community SC — 800/PK-12
723 N Buckeye St 47037 — 812-689-4114
Dr. Leanna Phillippe, supt. — Fax 689-7423
www.jaccendel.k12.in.us/
Jac-Cen-Del MSHS — 400/6-12
4586 N US Highway 421 47037 — 812-689-4643
Norbert Martini, prin. — Fax 689-0152

Ossian, Wells, Pop. 3,255
Northern Wells Community SD — 2,600/PK-12
312 N Jefferson St 46777 — 260-622-4125
Dr. Scott Mills, supt. — Fax 622-7893
www.nwcs.k12.in.us
Norwell HS — 900/9-12
1100 E US Highway 224 46777 — 260-543-2213
Mark Misch, prin. — Fax 543-2591
Norwell MS — 600/6-8
1100 E US Highway 224 46777 — 260-543-2218
Tim Wilson, prin. — Fax 543-2510

Oxford, Benton, Pop. 1,155
Benton Community SC
Supt. — See Fowler
Benton Central JSHS — 900/7-12
4241 E 300 S 47971 — 765-884-1600
Corey Robb, prin. — Fax 884-8445

Paoli, Orange, Pop. 3,640
Paoli Community SC — 1,600/K-12
501 Elm St 47454 — 812-723-4717
Casey Brewster, supt. — Fax 723-5100
www.paoli.k12.in.us
Paoli JSHS — 700/7-12
501 Elm St 47454 — 812-723-3905
Todd Hitchcock, prin. — Fax 723-4459

Parker City, Randolph, Pop. 1,400
Monroe Central SC — 1,000/K-12
1918 N 1000 W 47368 — 765-468-6868
Reece Mann, supt. — Fax 468-6578
www.monroecentral.org
Monroe Central JSHS — 500/7-12
1878 N 1000 W 47368 — 765-468-7545
Adrian Moulton, prin. — Fax 468-8878

Pekin, Washington, Pop. 1,385
East Washington SC — 1,700/K-12
1050 N Eastern School Rd 47165 — 812-967-3926
Steve Darnell, supt. — Fax 967-5797
www.ewsc.k12.in.us
Eastern HS — 500/9-12
1100 N Eastern School Rd 47165 — 812-967-3931
Darin Farris, prin. — Fax 967-5767
East Washington MS — 500/5-8
1100 N Eastern School Rd 47165 — 812-967-5000
Amber Sater, prin. — Fax 967-5737

Pendleton, Madison, Pop. 4,212
South Madison Community SC — 4,300/PK-12
203 S Heritage Way 46064 — 765-778-2152
Joseph Buck, supt. — Fax 778-8207
www.smadison.k12.in.us
Pendleton Heights HS — 1,200/9-12
1 Arabian Dr 46064 — 765-778-2161
Mark Hall, prin. — Fax 778-0605
Pendleton Heights MS — 700/7-8
7450 S 300 W 46064 — 765-778-2139
Daniel Joyce, prin. — Fax 778-0557

Pershing, Wayne, Pop. 406
Western Wayne SD — 1,100/K-12
PO Box 217 47370 — 765-478-5375
Dr. Robert Mahon, supt. — Fax 478-4577
www.wwayne.k12.in.us
Other Schools – See Cambridge City

Peru, Miami, Pop. 11,168
Peru Community SC — 2,100/PK-12
35 W 3rd St 46970 — 765-473-3081
Charles Brimbury, supt. — Fax 472-5129
www.peru.k12.in.us
KEYS Academy — Alt
19 Park Dr 46970 — 765-472-5150
Sheri Spiker, dir. — Fax 472-5157
Peru HS — 700/9-12
401 N Broadway 46970 — 765-472-3301
Kenneth Hanson, prin. — Fax 472-5148
Peru JHS — 300/7-8
30 Daniel St 46970 — 765-473-3084
Sam Watkins, prin. — Fax 473-4007

Petersburg, Pike, Pop. 2,365
Pike County SC — 2,000/PK-12
907 E Walnut St 47567 — 812-354-8731
Suzanne Blake, supt. — Fax 354-8733
www.pcsc.k12.in.us
Pike Central HS — 600/9-12
1810 E State Road 56 47567 — 812-354-8478
Winter Fiscus, prin. — Fax 789-2992
Pike Central MS — 400/6-8
1814 E State Road 56 47567 — 812-354-8478
Chad Whitehead, prin. — Fax 354-9559

Pierceton, Kosciusko, Pop. 1,004
Whitko Community SC — 1,900/K-12
PO Box 114 46562 — 574-594-2658
Steven Clason, supt. — Fax 594-2326
www.whitko.org
Other Schools – See Larwill, South Whitley

Plainfield, Hendricks, Pop. 27,200
Plainfield Community SC — 4,700/K-12
985 Longfellow Ln 46168 — 317-839-2578
Scott Olinger, supt. — Fax 838-3664
www.plainfield.k12.in.us
Plainfield Community MS — 1,100/6-8
709 Stafford Rd 46168 — 317-838-3966
Jerry Goldsberry, prin. — Fax 838-3965
Plainfield HS — 1,400/9-12
1 Red Pride Dr 46168 — 317-839-7711
Kellie Jacobs, prin. — Fax 838-3671

PJ's College of Cosmetology — Post-Sec.
2026 Stafford Rd 46168 — 317-839-2761

Plymouth, Marshall, Pop. 9,894
Plymouth Community SC — 3,500/PK-12
611 Berkley St 46563 — 574-936-3115
Daniel Tyree, supt. — Fax 936-3160
www.plymouth.k12.in.us/
Lincoln JHS — 600/7-8
220 N Liberty St 46563 — 574-936-3113
Reid Gault, prin. — Fax 936-3574
Plymouth HS — 1,100/9-12
1 Big Red Dr 46563 — 574-936-2178
Jim Condon, prin. — Fax 936-4842

Poneto, Wells, Pop. 166
Southern Wells Community SD — 800/K-12
9120 S 300 W 46781 — 765-728-5537
James Craig, supt. — Fax 728-8124
www.swraiders.com
Southern Wells JSHS — 400/7-12
9120 S 300 W 46781 — 765-728-5534
Chad Yencer, prin. — Fax 728-8124

Portage, Porter, Pop. 36,264
Portage Township SD — 8,300/PK-12
6240 US Highway 6 46368 — 219-762-6511
Dr. E. Ric Frataccia, supt. — Fax 762-3263
www.portage.k12.in.us
Fegely MS — 800/6-8
5384 Stone Ave 46368 — 219-763-8150
Philip Misecko, prin. — Fax 763-8157
Portage HS — 2,700/9-12
6450 US Highway 6 46368 — 219-763-8100
Caren Swickard, prin. — Fax 764-6062
Willowcreek MS — 1,200/6-8
5962 Central Ave 46368 — 219-763-8090
Michelle Stewart, prin. — Fax 763-8069

Portage Christian S — 200/PK-12
PO Box 28 46368 — 219-762-8962
Larry Pender, supt. — Fax 763-9931

Portland, Jay, Pop. 6,162
Jay SC — 3,600/PK-12
PO Box 1239 47371 — 260-726-9341
Dr. Timothy Long, supt. — Fax 726-4959
www.jayschools.k12.in.us
East Jay MS — 600/6-8
225 E Water St 47371 — 260-726-9371
Lee Newman, prin. — Fax 726-2383
Jay County HS — 1,100/9-12
2072 W State Road 67 47371 — 260-726-9306
Phil Ford, prin. — Fax 726-9760
Other Schools – See Dunkirk

Poseyville, Posey, Pop. 1,039
Metro SD of North Posey County — 1,300/PK-12
101 N Church St 47633 — 812-874-2243
Todd Camp, supt. — Fax 874-8806
www.northposey.k12.in.us/
North Posey HS — 500/9-12
5900 High School Rd 47633 — 812-673-4242
Scott Strieter, prin. — Fax 673-6616
North Posey JHS — 200/7-8
5800 High School Rd 47633 — 812-673-4244
Steven Kavanaugh, prin. — Fax 673-6622

Princeton, Gibson, Pop. 8,390
North Gibson SC — 2,100/K-12
1108 N Embree St 47670 — 812-385-4851
Dr. Brian Harmon, supt. — Fax 386-1531
www.ngsc.k12.in.us
Princeton Community HS — 700/9-12
1101 N Main St 47670 — 812-385-2591
Jon Abbey, prin. — Fax 386-1535
Princeton Community MS — 500/6-8
410 E State St 47670 — 812-385-2020
Kevin Spitler, prin. — Fax 386-6746

Ramsey, Harrison
North Harrison Community SC — 2,300/K-12
1260 Highway 64 NW 47166 — 812-347-2407
D. John Thomas, supt. — Fax 347-2870
www.nhcs.k12.in.us
North Harrison HS — 700/9-12
1070 Highway 64 NW 47166 — 812-347-2741
Stephen Hatton, prin. — Fax 347-2875
North Harrison MS — 500/6-8
1180 Highway 64 NW 47166 — 812-347-2421
Nathan Freed, prin. — Fax 347-2835

Rensselaer, Jasper, Pop. 5,800
Rensselaer Central SC — 1,700/PK-12
605 W Grove St 47978 — 219-866-7822
Ned Speicher, supt. — Fax 866-8360
www.rensselaerschools.org
Rensselaer Central HS — 600/9-12
1106 E Grace St 47978 — 219-866-5175
William Zimmer, prin. — Fax 866-5135
Rensselaer Central MS — 400/6-8
1106 E Bomber Dr 47978 — 219-866-4661
Kelly Berenda, prin. — Fax 866-2103

St. Joseph's College — Post-Sec.
PO Box 870 47978 — 219-866-6000

Richmond, Wayne, Pop. 35,381
Richmond Community SC — 3,800/K-12
300 Hub Etchison Pkwy 47374 — 765-973-3300
Allen Bourff, supt. — Fax 973-3417
www.rcs.k12.in.us
Community Youth Services — 100/Alt
315 NW 3rd St 47374 — 765-973-3496
Pam Hilligoss, prin. — Fax 935-6303
Logos Lab S — Alt
900 S L St 47374 — 765-973-3412
Gwinn Gibbs, prin. — Fax 973-3712
Richmond HS — 1,500/9-12
380 Hub Etchison Pkwy 47374 — 765-973-3424
Rae Woolpy, prin. — Fax 973-3716
Test IS — 400/5-8
33 S 22nd St 47374 — 765-973-3412
Stacy Mopps, prin. — Fax 973-3712
Worth IS — 400/5-8
222 NW 7th St 47374 — 765-973-3495
Richard Bryant, prin. — Fax 973-3703
Warner Adult Education Center — Adult
302 N 7th St 47374 — 765-973-3486
Rusty Hensley, prin. — Fax 935-1825

Bethany Theological Seminary — Post-Sec.
615 National Rd W 47374 — 800-287-8822
David Demuth Institute of Cosmetology — Post-Sec.
1301 S 8th Pl 47374 — 765-935-7964
Earlham Coll. & Earlham Sch. of Religion — Post-Sec.
801 National Rd W 47374 — 765-983-1200
Indiana University East — Post-Sec.
2325 Chester Blvd 47374 — 765-973-8200
Ivy Tech Community College - Richmond — Post-Sec.
2357 Chester Blvd 47374 — 765-966-2656

New Creations Christian S — 50/K-12
6400 National Rd E 47374 — 765-935-2790
Rev. Bev Hodgin, prin. — Fax 935-3961
PJ's College of Cosmetology — Post-Sec.
115 N 9th St 47374 — 765-962-3005
Reid Hospital & Health Care Services — Post-Sec.
1401 Chester Blvd 47374 — 765-983-3167
Seton Catholic JSHS — 100/7-12
233 S 5th St 47374 — 765-965-6956
Rick Ruhl, prin. — Fax 935-9930

Rising Sun, Ohio, Pop. 2,292
Rising Sun-Ohio County Community SD — 900/K-12
110 S Henrietta St 47040 — 812-438-2655
Stephen Patz, supt. — Fax 438-4636
www.risingsunschools.com/
Rising Sun HS — 200/9-12
210 S Henrietta St 47040 — 812-438-2652
Keith Majewski, prin. — Fax 438-2431

Roachdale, Putnam, Pop. 922
North Putnam Community SD
Supt. — See Bainbridge
North Putnam HS — 600/9-12
8869 N County Road 250 E 46172 — 765-522-6282
Alan Zerkel, prin. — Fax 522-2862
North Putnam MS — 400/6-8
8905 N County Road 250 E 46172 — 765-522-2900
Dr. Terry Tippin, prin. — Fax 522-2863

Rochester, Fulton, Pop. 6,144
Rochester Community SC — 1,900/PK-12
PO Box 108 46975 — 574-223-2159
Daniel Ronk, supt. — Fax 223-4909
www.rochester.k12.in.us
Rochester Community HS — 600/9-12
PO Box 108 46975 — 574-223-2176
Bradley Snyder, prin. — Fax 223-3401
Rochester Community MS — 400/6-8
PO Box 108 46975 — 574-223-2280
Jana Vance, prin. — Fax 223-1531

Rockport, Spencer, Pop. 2,241
South Spencer County SC — 1,500/PK-12
PO Box 26 47635 — 812-649-2591
Candis Haskell, supt. — Fax 649-4249
www.sspencer.k12.in.us
South Spencer HS — 500/9-12
1142 N Orchard Rd 47635 — 812-649-9157
Angela Gladish, prin. — Fax 649-2214
South Spencer MS — 400/6-8
1298 N Orchard Rd 47635 — 812-649-2203
J. Wilson, prin. — Fax 649-9630

Rockville, Parke, Pop. 2,594
Rockville Community SC — 800/K-12
602 Howard Ave 47872 — 765-569-5582
Dr. Thomas Rohr, supt. — Fax 569-6650
www.rockville.k12.in.us
Rockville JSHS — 400/7-12
506 N Beadle St 47872 — 765-569-5686
Dave Mahurin, prin. — Fax 569-1047

Rossville, Clinton, Pop. 1,638
Rossville Consolidated SD — 1,000/K-12
PO Box 11 46065 — 765-379-2990
Dr. James Hanna, supt. — Fax 379-3014
www.rcsd.k12.in.us
Rossville HS — 300/9-12
PO Box 530 46065 — 765-379-2551
Jeffery Hoover, prin. — Fax 379-2556
Rossville MS — 200/6-8
PO Box 530 46065 — 765-379-2551
Shawn McCracken, prin. — Fax 379-2556

Royal Center, Cass, Pop. 854
Pioneer Regional SC — 1,000/K-12
PO Box 577 46978 — 574-643-2605
Dr. David Bess, supt. — Fax 643-9977
www.pioneer.k12.in.us/
Pioneer JSHS — 500/7-12
PO Box 547 46978 — 574-643-3145
Robert Brock, prin. — Fax 643-2020

Rushville, Rush, Pop. 6,250
Rush County SD — 2,900/PK-12
330 W 8th St 46173 — 765-932-4186
Dr. John Williams, supt. — Fax 938-1608
rcs.rushville.k12.in.us/
Rush MS — 400/7-8
1601 N Sexton St 46173 — 765-932-2968
Marla Stevens, prin. — Fax 938-2011
Rushville Consolidated HS — 800/9-12
1201 Lions Path 46173 — 765-932-3901
Matt Vance, prin. — Fax 932-4051

Russiaville, Howard, Pop. 1,087
Western SC — 2,600/K-12
2600 S 600 W 46979 — 765-883-5576
Randy McCracken, supt. — Fax 883-7946
www.western.k12.in.us
Western HS — 800/9-12
2600 S 600 W 46979 — 765-883-5541
Rick Davis, prin. — Fax 883-4522
Western MS — 600/6-8
2600 S 600 W 46979 — 765-883-5566
Julie Pownall, prin. — Fax 883-4531

Saint John, Lake, Pop. 14,717
Lake Central SC — 10,200/PK-12
8260 Wicker Ave 46373 — 219-365-8507
Dr. Lawrence Veracco, supt. — Fax 365-6406
www.lcsc.us
Clark MS — 1,100/5-8
8915 W 93rd Ave 46373 — 219-365-9203
Scott Graber, prin. — Fax 365-9348
Lake Central Freshmen Center — 800/9-9
8410 Wicker Ave 46373 — 219-365-2760
Ken Miller, prin. — Fax 365-6640
Lake Central HS — 2,400/10-12
8400 Wicker Ave 46373 — 219-365-8551
Robert McDermott, prin. — Fax 365-7156
Other Schools – See Dyer, Schererville

Saint Leon, Franklin, Pop. 670
Sunman-Dearborn Community SC — 4,200/K-12
1 Trojan Ln Ste B, Brookville IN 47012 — 812-623-2291
Dr. Jeffrey Hendrix, supt. — Fax 623-3341
sunmandearborn.k12.in.us
East Central HS — 1,400/9-12
1 Trojan Ln Ste A, Brookville IN 47012 — 812-576-4811
Robert Shipley, prin. — Fax 576-2047
Sunman-Dearborn MS — 700/7-8
8356 Schuman Rd, Brookville IN 47012 — 812-576-3500
Lisa Baudendistel, prin. — Fax 576-3506

Saint Mary of the Woods, Vigo, Pop. 793

St. Mary-of-the-Woods College — Post-Sec.
1 St Mary of Woods Coll 47876 — 812-535-5151

Saint Meinrad, Spencer, Pop. 700

St. Meinrad School of Theology — Post-Sec.
200 Hill Dr 47577 — 812-357-6611

Salem, Washington, Pop. 6,263
Salem Community SD — 2,000/K-12
500 N Harrison St 47167 — 812-883-4437
Dr. D. Lynn Reed, supt. — Fax 883-1031
www.salemschools.com/
Salem HS — 600/9-12
700 N Harrison St 47167 — 812-883-3904
Derek Smith, prin. — Fax 883-3905
Salem MS — 500/6-8
1001 N Harrison St 47167 — 812-883-3808
Ray Oppel, prin. — Fax 883-8049

Schererville, Lake, Pop. 28,917
Lake Central SC
Supt. — See Saint John
Grimmer MS — 1,000/5-8
225 W 77th Ave 46375 — 219-865-6985
John Alessia, prin. — Fax 865-4423

Don Roberts Beauty Academy — Post-Sec.
152 E US Highway 30 46375 — 219-864-1600

Scottsburg, Scott, Pop. 6,707
Scott County SD 2 — 2,800/PK-12
375 E Mcclain Ave 47170 — 812-752-8946
Dr. Philip Deardorff, supt. — Fax 752-8951
www.scsd2.k12.in.us/
Scottsburg HS — 900/9-12
500 S Gardner St 47170 — 812-752-8927
Ric Manns, prin. — Fax 752-6207
Scottsburg MS — 600/6-8
425 S 3rd St 47170 — 812-752-8926
Kristin Nass, prin. — Fax 752-8864

Sellersburg, Clark, Pop. 6,055
West Clark Community SC — 4,600/PK-12
601 Renz Ave 47172 — 812-246-3375
Monty Schneider, supt. — Fax 246-9731
www.wclark.k12.in.us
Silver Creek HS — 700/9-12
557 Renz Ave 47172 — 812-246-3391
Michael Crabtree, prin. — Fax 246-8184
Silver Creek MS — 500/6-8
495 N Indiana Ave 47172 — 812-246-4421
Al Eckert, prin. — Fax 246-7430
West Clark Education Center — Alt
206 N New Albany St 47172 — 812-248-7130
Ryan Apple, dir.
Other Schools – See Borden, Henryville

Ivy Tech Community College - Southern — Post-Sec.
8204 Highway 311 47172 — 812-246-3301

Selma, Delaware, Pop. 856
Liberty-Perry Community SC — 1,100/K-12
PO Box 337 47383 — 765-282-5615
Bryan Rausch, supt. — Fax 281-3733
www.selma.k12.in.us
Selma MS — 300/6-8
10501 E County Road 167 S 47383 — 765-288-7242
Dennis Thompson, prin. — Fax 281-3727
Wapahani HS — 400/9-12
10401 E County Road 167 S 47383 — 765-289-7323
Dr. Chad Briggs, prin. — Fax 281-3724

Seymour, Jackson, Pop. 17,275
Seymour Community SD — 4,300/PK-12
1638 S Walnut St 47274 — 812-522-3340
Teran Armstrong Ph.D., supt. — Fax 522-8031
www.scsc.k12.in.us
Seymour HS — 1,300/9-12
1350 W 2nd St 47274 — 812-522-4384
Greg Prange, prin. — Fax 523-2347
Seymour MS — 900/6-8
920 N Obrien St 47274 — 812-522-5453
Doug McClure, prin. — Fax 523-8134

Trinity Lutheran HS — 100/9-12
7120 N County Road 875 E 47274 — 812-524-8547
Daniel Sievert, prin. — Fax 524-8523

Sharpsville, Tipton, Pop. 600
Tri-Central Community SD — 900/K-12
4774 N 200 W 46068 — 765-963-2585
Tim Garland, supt. — Fax 963-3042
www.tccs.k12.in.us/
Tri Central MSHS — 500/6-12
2115 W 500 N 46068 — 765-963-2560
Dave Driggs, prin. — Fax 963-6844

Shelbyville, Shelby, Pop. 18,951
Blue River Career Programs
801 Saint Joseph St 46176 — 317-392-4191
Steve Shaw, dir. — Fax 392-5741
www.brcp.k12.in.us
Blue River Career Center — Vo/Tech
801 Saint Joseph St 46176 — 317-392-4191
Steve Shaw, dir. — Fax 392-5741
Shelby Eastern SD — 1,400/K-12
2451 N 600 E 46176 — 765-544-2246
Don Swisher, supt. — Fax 544-2247
www.ses.k12.in.us/
Other Schools – See Morristown, Waldron
Shelbyville Central SD — 4,000/K-12
803 Saint Joseph St 46176 — 317-392-2505
Dr. David Adams, supt. — Fax 392-5737
www.shelbycs.k12.in.us
Shelbyville HS — 1,200/9-12
2003 S Miller St 46176 — 317-398-9731
Kathleen Miltz, prin. — Fax 392-5709
Shelbyville MS — 900/6-8
1200 W McKay Rd 46176 — 317-392-2551
Ryan Mikus, prin. — Fax 392-5713
Southwestern Cons Shelby County SC — 700/K-12
3406 W 600 S 46176 — 317-729-5746
Paula Maurer, supt. — Fax 729-5330
www.swshelby.k12.in.us
Southwestern JSHS — 300/7-12
3406 W 600 S 46176 — 317-729-5122
Curtis Chase, prin. — Fax 729-2424

Sheridan, Hamilton, Pop. 2,630
Sheridan Community SD — 1,100/PK-12
24795 Hinesley Rd 46069 — 317-758-4172
Dr. Derek Arrowood, supt. — Fax 758-6248
www.scs.k12.in.us/
Sheridan HS — 400/9-12
24185 Hinesley Rd 46069 — 317-758-4431
Jane Newblom, prin. — Fax 758-2406
Sheridan MS — 200/6-8
3030 W 246th St 46069 — 317-758-6780
Jane Newblom, prin. — Fax 758-2435

Shoals, Martin, Pop. 746
Shoals Community SC — 600/PK-12
11741 Ironton Rd 47581 — 812-247-2060
Dr. Joan Keller, supt. — Fax 247-2278
shoals.k12.in.us/
Shoals Community JSHS — 300/7-12
7900 US Highway 50 47581 — 812-247-2090
Candace Roush, prin. — Fax 247-2056

South Bend, Saint Joseph, Pop. 97,691
South Bend Community SC — 19,700/PK-12
215 S Saint Joseph St 46601 — 574-283-8000
Dr. Carole Schmidt, supt. — Fax 283-8143
www.sbcsc.k12.in.us
Adams HS — 1,700/9-12
808 S Twyckenham Dr 46615 — 574-283-7700
Otha Reese, prin. — Fax 283-7704
Brown Intermediate Center — 500/5-8
737 Beale St 46616 — 574-287-9680
Joseph Somers, prin. — Fax 283-5581
Clay HS — 1,400/9-12
19131 Darden Rd 46637 — 574-243-7000
Mansour Eid, prin. — Fax 243-7005
Clay Intermediate Center — 600/5-8
52900 Lily Rd 46637 — 574-243-7145
Frances Beard, prin. — Fax 243-7151
Dickinson Intermediate Fine Arts Academy — 600/5-8
4404 Elwood Ave 46628 — 574-283-7625
Thomas Sims, prin. — Fax 283-7633
Edison Intermediate Center — 600/5-8
2701 Eisenhower Ave 46615 — 574-283-8900
Carmen Williams, prin. — Fax 283-8903
Greene Intermediate Center — 400/5-8
24702 Roosevelt Rd 46614 — 574-283-7900
Sherry Bolden-Simpson, prin. — Fax 283-7903
Jackson Intermediate Center — 700/5-8
5001 Miami St 46614 — 574-231-5600
Margaret Schaller, prin. — Fax 231-5605
Jefferson IS — 500/5-8
528 S Eddy St 46617 — 574-283-8700
Byron Sanders, prin. — Fax 283-8703
LaSalle Intermediate Academy — 800/5-8
2701 Elwood Ave 46628 — 574-283-7500
Nathan Boyd, prin. — Fax 283-7513
Marshall Intermediate Center — 500/5-8
1433 Byron Dr 46614 — 574-231-5801
James Bowen, prin. — Fax 231-5804
Navarre Intermediate Center — 600/5-8
4702 Ford St 46619 — 574-283-7345
Derrick White, prin. — Fax 283-7351
New Tech HS — 9-12
1902 Fellows St 46613 — 574-283-8500
John Kennedy, prin. — Fax 283-8077
Riley HS — 1,500/9-12
1902 Fellows St 46613 — 574-283-8400
Francois Bayingana, prin. — Fax 283-8405
Rise Up Academy — 100/Alt
19010 Adams Rd 46637 — 574-243-7300
George Azar, prin. — Fax 243-7303
Washington HS — 1,300/9-12
4747 W Washington St 46619 — 574-283-7200
George McCullough, prin. — Fax 283-7205
Adult Education — Adult
3206 Sugar Maple Ct 46628 — 574-283-7505
Laura Marzotto, dir. — Fax 283-7549

Brown Mackie College — Post-Sec.
3454 Douglas Rd 46635 — 574-237-0774
Community Baptist Christian S — 200/PK-12
5715 Miami St 46614 — 574-291-3620
Jay Bradford, prin. — Fax 291-3648
Indiana University South Bend — Post-Sec.
PO Box 7111 46634 — 574-520-4872

ITT Technical Institute — Post-Sec.
17390 Dugdale Dr 46635 — 574-247-8300
Ivy Tech Community College North Central — Post-Sec.
220 Dean Johnson Blvd 46601 — 574-289-7001
National College — Post-Sec.
1030 E Jefferson Blvd 46617 — 574-307-7100
Purdue University-College of Technology — Post-Sec.
PO Box 7111 46634 — 574-520-4180
St. Joseph HS — 800/9-12
435 N Notre Dame Ave 46617 — 574-233-6137
Susan Richter, prin. — Fax 232-3482
Trinity S at Greenlawn — 200/7-12
107 S Greenlawn Ave 46617 — 574-287-5590
John A. Lee, head sch — Fax 236-6628
Yeshiva of South Bend — 50/9-12
3207 High St 46614 — 574-291-4239
Dovid Abraham, admin. — Fax 291-0043

South Whitley, Whitley, Pop. 1,743
Whitko Community SC
Supt. — See Pierceton
Whitko HS — 600/9-12
1 Big Blue Ave 46787 — 260-723-5146
David Parker, prin. — Fax 723-4724

Speedway, Marion, Pop. 11,556
Town of Speedway SD — 1,500/PK-12
5335 W 25th St 46224 — 317-244-0236
Kenneth Hull, supt. — Fax 486-4843
www.speedwayschools.org
Speedway HS — 500/9-12
5357 W 25th St 46224 — 317-244-7238
Timothy McRoberts, prin. — Fax 486-4838
Speedway JHS — 200/7-8
5151 W 14th St 46224 — 317-244-3359
John Dizney, prin. — Fax 486-4845

Spencer, Owen, Pop. 2,205
Spencer-Owen Community SD — 2,800/PK-12
205 E Hillside Ave 47460 — 812-829-2233
Greg Linton, supt. — Fax 829-6614
www.socs.k12.in.us
Owen Valley HS — 900/9-12
622 W State Highway 46 47460 — 812-829-2266
Rhonda Schafer, prin. — Fax 829-6605
Owen Valley MS — 500/7-8
626 W State Highway 46 47460 — 812-829-2249
Aaron LaGrange, prin. — Fax 829-6635

Straughn, Henry, Pop. 222
South Henry SC — 800/K-12
6972 S State Road 103 47387 — 765-987-7882
Wesley Hammond, supt. — Fax 987-7589
www.shenry.k12.in.us/
Tri JSHS — 400/7-12
6972 S State Road 103 47387 — 765-987-7988
Keith Isaacs, prin. — Fax 987-8446

Sullivan, Sullivan, Pop. 4,203
Southwest SC — 1,700/PK-12
110 N Main St 47882 — 812-268-6311
Chris Stitzle, supt. — Fax 268-6312
www.swest.k12.in.us/
Sullivan HS — 500/9-12
902 N Section St 47882 — 812-268-6301
David Springer, prin. — Fax 268-6303
Sullivan MS — 300/6-8
415 W Frakes St 47882 — 812-268-4000
Dustin Hitt, prin. — Fax 268-5368

Switz City, Greene, Pop. 291
White River Valley SD — 800/K-12
PO Box 1470 47465 — 812-659-1424
Robert Hacker, supt. — Fax 659-2278
www.wrv.k12.in.us
White River Valley JSHS — 400/7-12
PO Box 1470 47465 — 812-659-2274
Lee Ann Engelhardt, prin. — Fax 659-2283

Syracuse, Kosciusko, Pop. 2,781
Wawasee Community SC — 3,300/PK-12
1 Warrior Path Bldg 2 46567 — 574-457-3188
Dr. Thomas Edington, supt. — Fax 457-4962
www.wawasee.k12.in.us/
Wawasee HS — 1,000/9-12
1 Warrior Path Bldg 1 46567 — 574-457-3147
Donald Harman, prin. — Fax 457-4364
Wawasee MS — 500/6-8
9850 N State Road 13 46567 — 574-457-8839
Dennis Howland, prin. — Fax 457-3575

Tell City, Perry, Pop. 7,212
Tell City-Troy Township SC — 1,500/PK-12
837 17th St 47586 — 812-547-3300
Lynn Blinzinger, supt. — Fax 547-9704
www.tellcity.k12.in.us
Tell City JSHS — 700/7-12
900 12th St 47586 — 812-547-3131
Dale Stewart, prin. — Fax 547-9705

Terre Haute, Vigo, Pop. 59,043
Vigo County SC — 15,600/PK-12
PO Box 3703 47803 — 812-462-4011
Daniel Tanoos, supt. — Fax 462-4115
www.vigoschools.org/
Honey Creek MS — 800/6-8
6601 S Carlisle St 47802 — 812-462-4372
Nolan Cox, prin. — Fax 462-4367
McLean Alternative HS — 200/Alt
961 Lafayette Ave 47804 — 812-462-4330
Scotia Brown, prin. — Fax 462-4017
Otter Creek MS — 700/6-8
4801 N Lafayette St 47805 — 812-462-4391
Dr. Tammy Rowshandel, prin. — Fax 462-4388
Scott MS — 500/6-8
1000 Grant St 47802 — 812-462-4381
Greg Gauer, prin. — Fax 462-4370
Terre Haute North Vigo HS — 2,100/9-12
3434 Maple Ave 47804 — 812-462-4312
Robin Smith, prin. — Fax 462-4204
Terre Haute South Vigo HS — 1,800/9-12
3737 S 7th St 47802 — 812-462-4252
Chris Mauk, prin. — Fax 462-4408
Washington Alternative HS — 100/Alt
3707 S 7th St 47802 — 812-462-4427
Dr. Karen Andrews, prin. — Fax 462-4066
Wilson MS — 800/6-8
301 S 25th St 47803 — 812-462-4396
Dr. Sharon Pitts, prin. — Fax 232-2217
Other Schools – See West Terre Haute

Harrison College — Post-Sec.
1378 S State Road 46 47803 — 812-877-2100
Indiana State University — Post-Sec.
200 N 7th St 47809 — 812-237-6311
Ivy Tech Community College Wabash Valley — Post-Sec.
8000 S Education Dr 47802 — 812-299-1121
Rose-Hulman Institute of Technology — Post-Sec.
5500 Wabash Ave 47803 — 812-877-1511
Terre Haute Adventist S — 50/K-10
900 S 29th St 47803 — 812-232-1339
Karen Shinn, prin.

Thorntown, Boone, Pop. 1,514
Western Boone County Community SD — 1,800/PK-12
1201 N State Road 75 46071 — 765-482-6333
Dr. Judi Hendrix, supt. — Fax 482-0890
www.weboschools.org/
Western Boone JSHS — 900/7-12
1205 N State Road 75 46071 — 765-482-6143
Rob Ramey, prin. — Fax 482-6146

Tipton, Tipton, Pop. 5,058
Tipton Community SC — 1,800/K-12
221 N Main St 46072 — 765-675-2147
Kevin Emsweller, supt. — Fax 675-3857
www.tcsc.k12.in.us
Tipton HS — 600/9-12
619 S Main St 46072 — 765-675-7431
Joe Rushton, prin. — Fax 675-9519
Tipton MS — 500/6-8
817 S Main St 46072 — 765-675-7521
Shayne Clark, prin. — Fax 675-9027

Topeka, Lagrange, Pop. 1,128
Westview SC — 2,300/K-12
1545 S 600 W 46571 — 260-768-4404
Dr. Randall Zimmerly, supt. — Fax 768-7368
www.westview.k12.in.us
Westview JSHS — 700/7-12
1635 S 600 W 46571 — 260-768-4146
Rich Cory, prin. — Fax 768-7611

Trafalgar, Johnson, Pop. 1,089
Nineveh-Hensley-Jackson United SC — 1,900/K-12
802 S Indian Creek Dr 46181 — 317-878-2100
Dr. Matthew Prusiecki, supt. — Fax 878-5765
www.nhj.k12.in.us
Indian Creek HS — 600/9-12
803 W Indian Creek Dr 46181 — 317-878-2110
Maria Woodke, prin. — Fax 878-2112
Indian Creek MS — 500/6-8
801 W Indian Creek Dr 46181 — 317-878-2130
Connie Richhart, prin. — Fax 878-2149

Union City, Randolph, Pop. 3,547
Randolph Eastern SC — 900/K-12
907 N Plum St 47390 — 765-964-4994
Brent Lehman, supt. — Fax 964-6590
www.resc.k12.in.us/
Union City Community HS — 300/9-12
603 N Walnut St 47390 — 765-964-4840
Jim Bush, prin. — Fax 964-3775
West Side MS — 200/6-8
731 N Plum St 47390 — 765-964-4830
Mark Winkle, prin. — Fax 964-7344

Union Mills, LaPorte
South Central Community SC — 900/K-12
9808 S 600 W 46382 — 219-767-2263
Christopher Smith, supt. — Fax 767-2260
www.scentral.k12.in.us/
South Central JSHS — 500/7-12
9808 S 600 W 46382 — 219-767-2266
Sandra Graves, prin. — Fax 767-2260

Upland, Grant, Pop. 3,790

Taylor University — Post-Sec.
236 W Reade Ave 46989 — 800-882-3456

Valparaiso, Porter, Pop. 31,160
East Porter County SC
Supt. — See Kouts
Morgan Township MSHS — 400/6-12
299 S State Road 49 46383 — 219-462-5883
Dolores Mueller, prin. — Fax 462-4014
Washington Township MSHS — 400/6-12
381 E State Road 2 46383 — 219-464-3598
Jerry Hale, prin. — Fax 462-3372

Porter Township SC — 1,300/K-12
248 S 500 W 46385 — 219-477-4933
Dr. Stacey Schmidt, supt. — Fax 477-4834
www.ptsc.k12.in.us
Boone Grove HS — 500/9-12
260 S 500 W 46385 — 219-988-4481
Garry DeRossett, prin. — Fax 988-4431
Other Schools – See Boone Grove

Union Township SC — 1,700/K-12
599 W 300 N Ste A 46385 — 219-759-2531
John Hunter, supt. — Fax 759-3250
www.union.k12.in.us
Union Township MS — 400/6-8
599 W 300 N 46385 — 219-759-2562
Jerry Lasky, prin. — Fax 759-4359
Wheeler HS — 500/9-12
587 W 300 N 46385 — 219-759-2561
Donald Gandy, prin. — Fax 759-5602

Valparaiso Community SD — 6,400/K-12
3801 Campbell St 46385 — 219-531-3000
Dr. Jim McCall, supt. — Fax 531-3009
www.valpo.k12.in.us
Franklin MS — 800/6-8
605 Campbell St 46385 — 219-531-3020
Christopher Fields, prin. — Fax 531-3026
Jefferson MS — 700/6-8
1600 Roosevelt Rd 46383 — 219-531-3140
Jim Polite, prin. — Fax 531-3146
Porter County Career Ctr — Vo/Tech
1005 Franklin St 46383 — 219-531-3170
Jon Groth, prin. — Fax 531-3173
Valparaiso HS — 2,100/9-12
2727 Campbell St 46385 — 219-531-3070
Reid Amones, prin. — Fax 531-3076

Don Roberts Beauty School — Post-Sec.
1354 Lincolnway 46385 — 219-462-5189
Porter Memorial Hospital — Post-Sec.
814 Laporte Ave 46383 — 219-465-4883
South Haven Christian S — 100/PK-12
786 Juniper Rd 46385 — 219-759-5313
Michael Owney, admin. — Fax 759-1577
Valparaiso University 46383 — Post-Sec.
219-464-5000
Victory Christian Academy — 200/PK-12
3805 LaPorte Ave 46383 — 219-548-8803
Joyce Folk, admin. — Fax 548-7413

Veedersburg, Fountain, Pop. 2,156
Southeast Fountain SC — 1,300/K-12
744 E US Highway 136 47987 — 765-294-2254
Doug Allison, supt. — Fax 294-3200
www.sefschools.org/
Fountain Central JSHS — 600/7-12
750 E US Highway 136 47987 — 765-294-2206
Tony Coleman, prin. — Fax 294-3204

Versailles, Ripley, Pop. 2,089
South Ripley Community SC — 1,200/K-12
PO Box 690 47042 — 812-689-6282
Robert D. Moorhead, supt. — Fax 689-6760
www.sripley.k12.in.us
South Ripley HS — 400/9-12
1589 S Benham Rd 47042 — 812-689-5303
Dr. David Wintin, prin. — Fax 689-6715
South Ripley JHS — 200/7-8
1589 S Benham Rd 47042 — 812-689-0909
Rodney Hite, prin. — Fax 689-6970

Southeastern Career SC
901 W US Highway 50 47042 — 812-689-5253
Brad Street, supt. — Fax 689-6977
www.sccusa.org
Southeastern Career Center — Vo/Tech
901 W US Highway 50 47042 — 812-689-5253
James Rogers, prin. — Fax 689-6977

Vevay, Switzerland, Pop. 1,662
Switzerland County SC — 1,400/PK-12
1040 W Main St 47043 — 812-427-2611
Mike Jones, supt. — Fax 427-2044
www.switzerland.k12.in.us
Switzerland County HS — 400/9-12
1020 W Main St 47043 — 812-427-2626
Gregg Goewert, prin. — Fax 427-3445
Switzerland County MS — 200/7-8
1004 W Main St 47043 — 812-427-3809
John Druba, prin. — Fax 427-3807

Vincennes, Knox, Pop. 18,142
South Knox SC — 1,200/K-12
6116 E State Road 61 47591 — 812-726-4440
Tim Grove, supt. — Fax 743-2110
www.sknox.k12.in.us
South Knox MSHS — 600/7-12
6136 E State Road 61 47591 — 812-726-4450
Jeff Dhonau, prin. — Fax 726-4545

Twin Rivers Career & Technical Education
PO Box 1266 47591 — 812-882-0801
James Roberts, dir. — Fax 882-0802
www.twinriversarea.org
Twin Rivers Career & Technical Education — Vo/Tech
PO Box 1266 47591 — 812-882-0801
James Roberts, dir. — Fax 882-0802

Vincennes Community SC — 2,700/K-12
1712 S Quail Run Rd 47591 — 812-882-4844
Gregory T. Parsley, supt. — Fax 885-1427
www.vcsc.k12.in.us
Clark MS — 600/6-8
1926 S Richard Bauer Dr 47591 — 812-882-5172
Ryan Clark, prin. — Fax 885-1419
Lincoln HS — 800/9-12
1545 S Hart Street Rd 47591 — 812-882-8480
Stephen Combs, prin. — Fax 885-1431

Good Samaritan Hospital — Post-Sec.
520 S 7th St 47591 — 812-885-3195
Rivet MSHS — 200/6-12
210 Barnett St 47591 — 812-882-6215
Janice Jones, prin. — Fax 886-1939
Vincennes Beauty College — Post-Sec.
12 S 2nd St 47591 — 812-882-1086
Vincennes University — Post-Sec.
1002 N 1st St 47591 — 812-888-8888

Wabash, Wabash, Pop. 10,549
Heartland Career Center SD
79 S 200 W 46992 — 260-563-7481
Gary Sweet, supt. — Fax 563-5544
www.hcc.k12.in.us
Heartland Career Ctr — Vo/Tech
79 S 200 W 46992 — 260-563-7481
Mark Hobbs, prin. — Fax 563-5544

Metro SD of Wabash County 1,900/K-12
204 N 300 W 46992 260-563-8050
Dr. Sandra Weaver, supt. Fax 569-6836
www.msdwc.k12.in.us
Northfield JSHS 600/7-12
154 W 200 N 46992 260-563-8050
Mike Keaffaber, prin. Fax 569-6839
Southwood JSHS 600/7-12
564 E State Road 124 46992 260-563-8050
Tim Drake, prin. Fax 569-6843
Whites JSHS 100/Alt
5233 S 50 E 46992 260-563-1158
Troy Friedersdorf, prin. Fax 563-5272

Wabash CSD 1,500/K-12
PO Box 744 46992 260-563-2151
Jason Callahan, supt. Fax 563-2066
www.apaches.k12.in.us
Wabash HS 400/9-12
580 N Miami St 46992 260-563-4131
Josh Blossom, prin. Fax 563-6806
Wabash MS 300/6-8
150 Colerain St 46992 260-563-4137
Scott Bumgardener, prin. Fax 569-9805

Wakarusa, Elkhart, Pop. 1,739
Wa-Nee Community SD
Supt. — See Nappanee
Northwood MS 700/6-8
301 N Elkhart St 46573 574-862-2710
George Roelandts, prin. Fax 862-2327

Waldron, Shelby, Pop. 796
Shelby Eastern SD
Supt. — See Shelbyville
Waldron JSHS 400/6-12
PO Box 369 46182 765-525-6822
Mark Lane, prin. Fax 525-9727

Walkerton, Saint Joseph, Pop. 2,125
John Glenn SC 1,900/K-12
101 John Glenn Dr 46574 574-586-3129
Richard Reese, supt. Fax 586-2660
www.jgsc.k12.in.us
Glenn HS 600/9-12
201 John Glenn Dr 46574 574-586-3195
William Morton, prin. Fax 586-3905
Urey MS 300/7-8
407 Washington St 46574 574-586-3184
Mark Maudlin, prin. Fax 586-3714

Walton, Cass, Pop. 1,033
Southeastern SC 1,500/K-12
6422 E State Road 218 46994 574-626-2525
Trudie Hedrick, supt. Fax 626-2751
www.sesc.k12.in.us
Cass JSHS 800/7-12
6422 E State Road 218 46994 574-626-2511
William Isaacs, prin. Fax 626-2172

Warsaw, Kosciusko, Pop. 13,362
Warsaw Community SC 6,900/K-12
PO Box 288 46581 574-371-5098
Craig Hintz Ed.D., supt. Fax 371-5046
www.warsaw.k12.in.us
Edgewood MS 600/7-8
900 S Union St 46580 574-371-5096
JoElla Smyth, prin. Fax 371-5010
Gateway Educational Center Alt
201 N Union St 46580 574-371-5019
Steve Ferber, prin. Fax 371-5033
Lakeview MS 500/7-8
848 E Smith St 46580 574-269-7211
Jon Lippe, prin. Fax 371-5013
Warsaw Community HS 2,100/9-12
1 Tiger Ln 46580 574-371-5099
Troy Akers, prin. Fax 371-5012

Washington, Daviess, Pop. 11,354
Washington Community SD 2,500/K-12
301 E South St 47501 812-254-5536
Dr. Dan Roach, supt. Fax 254-8346
www.wcs.k12.in.us
Washington HS 800/9-12
608 E Walnut St 47501 812-254-3860
LeAnne Kelley, prin. Fax 254-8374
Washington JHS 400/7-8
210 NE 6th St 47501 812-254-2682
Mark Arnold, prin. Fax 254-8381

Washington Catholic MSHS 100/6-12
201 NE 2nd St 47501 812-254-2050
Karie Craney, prin. Fax 254-8746

Waterloo, DeKalb, Pop. 2,205
DeKalb County Central United SC 4,000/PK-12
3326 County Road 427 46793 260-920-1011
Sherry Grate Ed.D., supt. Fax 837-7767
www.dekalbcentral.net
DeKalb HS 1,300/9-12
3424 County Road 427 46793 260-920-1012
Park Ginder, prin. Fax 837-7841
DeKalb MS 1,000/6-8
3338 County Road 427 46793 260-920-1013
Thomas Sanborn, prin. Fax 837-7812

Westfield, Hamilton, Pop. 29,609
Westfield Washington SD 6,300/PK-12
322 W Main St 46074 317-867-8000
Dr. Mark Keen, supt. Fax 867-0929
www.wws.k12.in.us
Westfield HS 1,800/9-12
18250 N Union St 46074 317-867-6800
Dr. Stacy McGuire, prin. Fax 867-2909
Westfield MS 900/7-8
345 W Hoover St 46074 317-867-6600
Linda Konkle, prin. Fax 867-1407

West Lafayette, Tippecanoe, Pop. 29,004
Tippecanoe SC
Supt. — See Lafayette
Battle Ground MS 400/6-8
6100 N 50 W 47906 765-269-8140
Dr. BeAnn Younker, prin. Fax 269-8215
Harrison HS 1,700/9-12
5701 N 50 W 47906 765-463-3511
Allen Remaly, prin. Fax 463-1477
Klondike MS 400/6-8
3307 Klondike Rd 47906 765-463-2544
Christine Cannon, prin. Fax 497-9413

West Lafayette Community SC 2,200/K-12
1130 N Salisbury St 47906 765-746-1602
Dr. Rocky Killion, supt. Fax 746-1644
www.wl.k12.in.us/
West Lafayette HS 700/9-12
1105 N Grant St 47906 765-746-0400
Ronald Shriner, prin. Fax 746-0422
West Lafayette JHS 300/7-8
1105 N Grant St 47906 765-746-0404
Daniel Walbaum, prin. Fax 746-0420

Purdue University Post-Sec.
610 Purdue Mall 47907 765-494-4600

West Lebanon, Warren, Pop. 721
Metro SD of Warren County
Supt. — See Williamsport
Seeger Memorial JSHS 600/7-12
1222 S State Road 263 47991 765-893-4445
Dan Nelson, prin. Fax 893-8354

West Terre Haute, Vigo, Pop. 2,213
Vigo County SC
Supt. — See Terre Haute
West Vigo HS 600/9-12
4590 W Sarah Myers Dr 47885 812-462-4282
Tom Balitewicz, prin. Fax 462-4090
West Vigo MS 400/6-8
4750 W Sarah Myers Dr 47885 812-462-4361
Julie Lautenschlager, prin. Fax 462-4358

Westville, LaPorte, Pop. 5,829
Metro SD of New Durham Township 900/K-12
207 E Valparaiso St 46391 219-785-2239
Dr. Curtiss Strietelmeier, supt. Fax 785-4584
www.westville.k12.in.us/
Westville JSHS 400/7-12
207 E Valparaiso St 46391 219-785-2531
Chris George, prin. Fax 785-2990

Purdue University North Central Post-Sec.
1401 S US Highway 421 46391 219-785-5200

Wheatfield, Jasper, Pop. 846
Kankakee Valley SC 3,200/K-12
PO Box 278 46392 219-987-4711
Sharon Sanelli, supt. Fax 987-4710
www.kv.k12.in.us
Kankakee Valley HS 1,100/9-12
3923 W State Road 10 46392 219-956-3143
Keeman Lobsiger, prin. Fax 956-4639
Kankakee Valley MS 600/6-8
5258 W State Road 10 46392 219-987-8810
William Auker, prin. Fax 987-2540

Whiteland, Johnson, Pop. 4,117
Clark-Pleasant Community SC 5,900/K-12
50 Center St 46184 317-535-7579
Dr. Becky Courtney-Knight, supt. Fax 535-4931
www.cpcsc.k12.in.us
Clark Pleasant Academy Alt
129 N US Highway 31 46184 317-535-3240
Kara Larkin, dir. Fax 535-0189
Whiteland Community HS 1,700/9-12
300 Main St 46184 317-535-7562
John Schilawski, admin. Fax 535-7509
Other Schools – See Greenwood

Whitestown, Boone, Pop. 2,806
Zionsville Community SC
Supt. — See Zionsville
Zionsville West MS 800/5-8
5565 S 700 E 46075 317-873-1240
Kris Devereaux, prin. Fax 769-6909

Traders Point Christian Academy 600/PK-12
6600 S Indianapolis Rd 46075 317-769-2450
Toni Kanzler, admin. Fax 769-2456

Whiting, Lake, Pop. 4,948
Hammond CSD
Supt. — See Hammond
Clark MSHS 1,600/6-12
1921 Davis Ave 46394 219-659-3522
Robert Wilson, prin. Fax 659-1599

Whiting CSD 1,100/PK-12
1500 Center St 46394 219-659-0656
Dr. Sandra Martinez, supt. Fax 473-4008
www.whiting.k12.in.us
Whiting HS 400/9-12
1751 Oliver St 46394 219-659-0255
Jay Harker, prin. Fax 473-1341
Whiting MS 200/6-8
1800 New York Ave 46394 219-473-1344
Cindy Scroggins, prin. Fax 473-4017

Calumet College of St. Joseph Post-Sec.
2400 New York Ave 46394 219-473-7770

Williamsport, Warren, Pop. 1,888
Metro SD of Warren County 1,200/K-12
101 N Monroe St 47993 765-762-3364
Ralph Shrader, supt. Fax 762-6623
www.msdwarco.k12.in.us/
Other Schools – See West Lebanon

Winamac, Pulaski, Pop. 2,467
Eastern Pulaski Community SC 1,200/K-12
711 School Dr 46996 574-946-4010
Dr. Robert Klitzman, supt. Fax 946-4510
www.epulaski.k12.in.us/
Winamac Community HS 400/9-12
715 School Dr 46996 574-946-6151
Rick Defries, prin. Fax 946-4219
Winamac Community MS 300/6-8
715 School Dr 46996 574-946-6525
Ryan Dickinson, prin. Fax 946-4219

Winchester, Randolph, Pop. 4,890
Randolph Central SC 1,700/K-12
103 N East St 47394 765-584-1401
Dr. Gregory Hinshaw, supt. Fax 584-1403
www.rc.k12.in.us
Driver MS 400/6-8
126 S Middle School Rd 47394 765-584-4671
Greg Kile, prin. Fax 584-6271
Winchester Community HS 500/9-12
700 N Union St 47394 765-584-8201
Thomas Osborn, prin. Fax 584-8204

Winona Lake, Kosciusko, Pop. 4,854

Grace College & Seminary Post-Sec.
200 Seminary Dr 46590 574-372-5100
Lakeland Christian Academy 100/7-12
1093 S 250 E 46590 574-267-7265
Joy Lavender, admin. Fax 267-5687

Wolcott, White, Pop. 982
Tri-County SC 800/K-12
105 N 2nd St 47995 219-279-2418
Dr. Gib Crimmins, supt. Fax 279-2242
www.trico.k12.in.us
Tri-County MSHS 300/7-12
11298 W 100 S 47995 219-279-2105
Kathy Goad, prin. Fax 279-2108

Woodburn, Allen, Pop. 1,511
East Allen County SD
Supt. — See New Haven
Woodlan JSHS 700/7-12
17215 Woodburn Rd 46797 260-446-0290
Ron Kammeyer, prin. Fax 446-0298

Yorktown, Delaware, Pop. 9,307
Yorktown Community SC 2,300/K-12
2311 S Broadway St 47396 765-759-2720
Jennifer McCormick, supt. Fax 759-7894
www.yorktown.k12.in.us
Yorktown HS 800/9-12
1100 S Tiger Dr 47396 765-759-2550
Kelly Wittman, prin. Fax 759-4040
Yorktown MS 600/6-8
8820 W Smith St 47396 765-759-2660
Heath Dudley, prin. Fax 759-3243

Zionsville, Boone, Pop. 13,972
Zionsville Community SC 5,300/PK-12
900 Mulberry St 46077 317-873-2858
Scott Robison, supt. Fax 873-8003
www.zcs.k12.in.us
Zionsville Community HS 1,700/9-12
1000 Mulberry St 46077 317-873-3355
Tim East, prin. Fax 873-8002
Zionsville MS 900/5-8
900 N Ford Rd 46077 317-873-2426
Sean Conner, prin. Fax 733-4001
Other Schools – See Whitestown

IOWA

IOWA DEPARTMENT OF EDUCATION
400 E 14th St, Des Moines 50319-0146
Telephone 515-281-5294
Fax 515-242-5988
Website educateiowa.gov/

Director of Education Dr. Brad Buck

IOWA BOARD OF EDUCATION
400 E 14th St, Des Moines 50319-9000

President Rosie Hussey

AREA EDUCATION AGENCIES (AEA)

AEA 267
Roark Horn, admin. 319-273-8200
3712 Cedar Heights Dr Fax 273-8229
Cedar Falls 50613
www.aea267.k12.ia.us

Grant Wood AEA 10
Joe Crozier, admin., 4401 6th St SW 319-399-6700
Cedar Rapids 52404 Fax 399-6457
www.aea10.k12.ia.us/

Great Prairie AEA
Dr. Jon Sheldahl, admin. 641-682-8591
2814 N Court St, Ottumwa 52501 Fax 682-9083
www.gpaea.k12.ia.us

Green Hills AEA
Lane Plugge, admin. 712-366-0503
PO Box 1109, Council Bluffs 51502 Fax 366-7772
www.ghaea.org

Heartland AEA 11
Paula Vincent, admin. 515-270-9030
6500 Corporate Dr Fax 270-5383
Johnston 50131
www.aea11.k12.ia.us/

Keystone AEA 1
Gary Stumberg, admin. 563-245-1480
1400 2nd St NW, Elkader 52043 Fax 245-1484
www.aea1.k12.ia.us

Mississippi Bend AEA 9
Glen Pelecky, admin. 563-359-1371
729 21st St, Bettendorf 52722 Fax 359-5967
www.aea9.k12.ia.us/

Northwest AEA
Tim Grieves, admin. 712-222-6000
1520 Morningside Ave Fax 222-6123
Sioux City 51106
www.nwaea.k12.ia.us/

Prairie Lakes AEA 8
Jeff Herzberg, admin. 712-335-3588
500 NE 6th St, Pocahontas 50574 Fax 335-4600
www.aea8.k12.ia.us/

PUBLIC, PRIVATE AND CATHOLIC SECONDARY SCHOOLS

Ackley, Hardin, Pop. 1,584
AGWSR Community SD 600/PK-12
511 State St 50601 641-847-2611
Steve Lane, supt. Fax 847-2612
www.agwsr.org
AGWSR HS 200/9-12
918 4th Ave 50601 641-847-2633
Joel Bagley, prin. Fax 847-3345
Other Schools – See Wellsburg

Adair, Guthrie, Pop. 778
Adair-Casey Community SD 300/PK-12
3384 Indigo Ave 50002 641-746-2241
Steve Smith, supt. Fax 746-2243
accs.k12.ia.us
Adair-Casey JSHS 200/7-12
3384 Indigo Ave 50002 641-746-2241
Cynthia Jensen, prin. Fax 746-2243

Adel, Dallas, Pop. 3,654
Adel DeSoto Minburn Community SD 1,300/PK-12
801 Nile Kinnick Dr S 50003 515-993-4283
Greg Dufoe, supt. Fax 993-4866
www.adel.k12.ia.us
ADM HS 400/9-12
801 Nile Kinnick Dr S 50003 515-993-4584
Lee Greibel, prin. Fax 993-3025
ADM MS 100/6-8
801 Nile Kinnick Dr S 50003 515-993-3490
Kim Timmerman, prin. Fax 993-1956

Afton, Union, Pop. 842
East Union Community SD 400/PK-12
1916 High School Dr 50830 641-347-5215
Pam Vogel Ph.D., supt. Fax 347-5514
www.east-union.k12.ia.us
East Union MSHS 200/6-12
1916 High School Dr 50830 641-347-8421
Mark Weis, prin. Fax 347-5514

Akron, Plymouth, Pop. 1,468
Akron Westfield Community SD 600/PK-12
PO Box 950 51001 712-568-2616
Randy Collins, supt. Fax 568-2997
www.akron-westfield.k12.ia.us
Akron Westfield HS 200/9-12
PO Box 950 51001 712-568-2020
Derek Briggs, prin. Fax 568-2997
Akron Westfield MS 100/6-8
PO Box 950 51001 712-568-2020
Derek Briggs, prin. Fax 568-2997

Albia, Monroe, Pop. 3,726
Albia Community SD 1,100/PK-12
701 Washington Ave E 52531 641-932-2161
Kevin Crall, supt. Fax 932-5192
www.albia.k12.ia.us
Albia HS 400/9-12
503 B Ave E 52531 641-932-2161
Linda Hoskins, prin. Fax 932-7069
Albia JHS 200/7-8
505 C Ave E 52531 641-932-2161
Linda Hoskins, prin. Fax 932-7069

Alburnett, Linn, Pop. 663
Alburnett Community SD 600/K-12
PO Box 400 52202 319-842-2261
Dani Trimble, supt. Fax 842-2398
www.alburnett.k12.ia.us
Alburnett JSHS 300/7-12
PO Box 400 52202 319-842-2263
Joshua Henriksen, prin. Fax 842-2398

Algona, Kossuth, Pop. 5,513
Algona Community SD 1,100/PK-12
600 S Hale St 50511 515-295-3528
Marty Fonley, supt. Fax 295-5166
www.algona.k12.ia.us
Algona HS 400/9-12
601 S Hale St 50511 515-295-7207
Jared Cecil, prin. Fax 295-9273
Algona MS 300/5-8
601 S Hale St 50511 515-295-7207
Gregory Stewart, prin. Fax 295-9273

Bishop Garrigan HS 200/9-12
1224 N Mccoy St 50511 515-295-3521
Lynn Miller, prin. Fax 295-7739

Alleman, Polk, Pop. 426
North Polk Community SD 1,200/PK-12
13960 NE 6th Ave 50007 515-984-3400
Dr. Dan Mart, supt. Fax 685-2002
www.northpolk.org
North Polk HS 400/9-12
13960 NE 6th Ave 50007 515-984-3400
Jack Christensen, prin. Fax 685-2004
North Polk MS 200/6-8
315 NE 141st Ave 50007 515-984-3400
Jon Richards, prin. Fax 685-3520

Allison, Butler, Pop. 1,024
North Butler Community SD 700/PK-12
PO Box 428 50602 319-267-2205
Terry Kenealy, supt. Fax 267-2926
www.northbutler.k12.ia.us/
North Butler MS 200/5-8
PO Box 428 50602 319-267-2552
Terry Kenealy, prin. Fax 267-2926
Other Schools – See Greene

Alta, Buena Vista, Pop. 1,871
Alta Community SD 400/PK-12
101 W 5th St 51002 712-200-1010
Lynn Evans, supt. Fax 200-1602
www.alta.k12.ia.us
Alta-Aurelia HS 200/9-12
1009 S Main St 51002 712-200-1331
Tom Ryherd, prin. Fax 200-1602

Alton, Sioux, Pop. 1,209
MOC-Floyd Valley Community SD
Supt. — See Orange City
MOC-Floyd Valley MS 300/6-8
1104 5th Ave 51003 712-756-4128
Cam Smith, prin. Fax 756-4100

Ames, Story, Pop. 57,846
Ames Community SD 4,400/PK-12
415 Stanton Ave 50014 515-268-6600
Dr. Tim Taylor, supt. Fax 268-6633
www.ames.k12.ia.us
Ames HS 1,400/9-12
1921 Ames High Dr 50010 515-817-0600
Spence Evans, prin. Fax 817-0601
Ames MS 900/6-8
3915 Mortensen Rd 50014 515-268-2400
Pam Stangeland, prin. Fax 268-2419

Antioch School of Church Planting Post-Sec.
2400 Oakwood Rd 50014 515-292-9694
Iowa State University 50011 Post-Sec.
515-294-4111
Professional Cosmetology Institute Post-Sec.
309 Kitty Hawk Dr 50010 515-232-7250

Anamosa, Jones, Pop. 5,484
Anamosa Community SD 1,300/PK-12
200 S Garnavillo St 52205 319-462-4321
Lisa Beames, supt. Fax 462-4322
www.anamosa.k12.ia.us
Anamosa HS 500/9-12
209 Sadie St 52205 319-462-3594
Chris Basinger, prin. Fax 462-2332
Anamosa MS 300/5-8
200 S Garnavillo St 52205 319-462-3553
Linda Vaughn, prin. Fax 462-3309

Andrew, Jackson, Pop. 431
Andrew Community SD 200/PK-8
PO Box 230 52030 563-672-3221
Andy Crozier, supt. Fax 672-9750
www.andrew.k12.ia.us
Andrew MS 50/6-8
PO Box 230 52030 563-672-3221
Andy Crozier, prin. Fax 672-9750

Anita, Cass, Pop. 970
CAM Community SD 500/PK-12
1000 Victory Park Rd 50020 712-762-3231
Steve Pelzer, supt. Fax 762-3713
www.camcougars.org
CAM HS 100/9-12
1000 Victory Park Rd 50020 712-762-3231
Dominic Giegerich, prin. Fax 762-3713
Other Schools – See Massena

Ankeny, Polk, Pop. 45,034
Ankeny Community SD 10,800/PK-12
PO Box 189 50021 515-965-9600
Dr. Bruce Kimpston, supt. Fax 965-4234
www.ankenyschools.org/
Ankeny Centennial HS 1,000/10-12
2220 NW State St, 515-965-9610
Dr. Jen Lindaman, prin. Fax 964-5070
Ankeny HS 1,600/10-12
1155 SW Cherry St, 515-965-9630
Dr. Jeff Hawkins, prin. Fax 965-2974
Northview MS 1,200/8-9
1302 N Ankeny Blvd, 515-965-9700
Bev Kuehn, prin. Fax 965-9639

Southview MS 600/8-9
1020 SW Cherry St, 515-965-9635
Dan Meyer, admin. Fax 965-9223

Ankeny Christian Academy 300/PK-12
1604 W 1st St, 515-965-8114
Joyce Hansen, admin. Fax 965-8210
Des Moines Area Community College Post-Sec.
2006 S Ankeny Blvd, 515-964-6200
Faith Baptist Bible College Post-Sec.
1900 NW 4th St, 515-964-0601
INSTE Bible College Post-Sec.
2302 SW 3rd St, 515-289-9200

Anthon, Woodbury, Pop. 561
Maple Valley-Anthon Oto Community SD
Supt. — See Mapleton
Maple Valley-Anthon Oto MS 100/6-8
PO Box E 51004 712-373-5244
Jane Ellis, prin. Fax 373-5326

Aplington, Butler, Pop. 1,123
Aplington-Parkersburg Community SD
Supt. — See Parkersburg
Aplington-Parkersburg MS 200/6-8
215 10th St 50604 319-347-6621
Brian Buseman, prin. Fax 347-2395

Arlington, Fayette, Pop. 428
Starmont Community SD 600/PK-12
3202 40th St 50606 563-933-4598
Matt O'Loughlin, supt. Fax 933-2134
www.starmont.k12.ia.us
Starmont HS 200/9-12
3202 40th St 50606 563-933-2218
Marc Snavely, prin. Fax 933-2134
Starmont MS 100/6-8
3202 40th St 50606 563-933-2218
Marc Snavely, prin. Fax 933-2134

Armstrong, Emmet, Pop. 919
Armstrong-Ringsted Community SD 100/9-12
PO Box 75 50514 712-868-3550
Matt Berninghaus, supt. Fax 868-3550
www.armstrong.k12.ia.us
Armstrong-Ringsted HS 100/9-12
PO Box 75 50514 712-868-3542
Matt Berninghaus, prin. Fax 868-3550

Arnolds Park, Dickinson, Pop. 1,120
Okoboji Community SD
Supt. — See Milford
Okoboji MS 200/5-8
10 W Broadway St 51331 712-332-5641
Ryan Cunningham, prin. Fax 332-7180

Atlantic, Cass, Pop. 7,038
Atlantic Community SD 1,500/PK-12
1100 Linn St 50022 712-243-4252
Mike Amstein Ed.D., supt. Fax 243-8023
www.atlanticiaschools.org/
Atlantic HS 500/9-12
1201 E 14th St 50022 712-243-5358
Heather McKay, prin. Fax 243-8007
Atlantic MS 300/6-8
1100 Linn St 50022 712-243-1330
Josh Rasmussen, prin. Fax 243-7732
Cass County Educational Opportunity Ctr 50/Alt
1209 Sunnyside Ln 50022 712-243-3535
Heather McKay, prin. Fax 243-8069

Audubon, Audubon, Pop. 2,169
Audubon Community SD 600/PK-12
800 3rd Ave 50025 712-563-2607
Brett Gibbs, supt. Fax 563-3607
www.audubon.k12.ia.us/
Audubon MSHS 400/5-12
800 3rd Ave 50025 712-563-2607
Eric Trager, prin. Fax 563-3607

Aurelia, Cherokee, Pop. 1,026
Aurelia Community SD 100/PK-8
PO Box 367 51005 712-434-2284
Lynn Evans, supt. Fax 434-2053
www.aurelia.k12.ia.us
Aurelia MS 100/6-8
PO Box 367 51005 712-434-5595
Ann Sandine, prin. Fax 434-2053

Avoca, Pottawattamie, Pop. 1,501
A-H-S-T Community SD 600/PK-12
PO Box 158 51521 712-343-6364
Jesse Ulrich, supt. Fax 343-2170
www.ahst.k12.ia.us
A-H-S-T HS 200/7-12
PO Box 158 51521 712-343-6364
Cynthia Phillips, prin. Fax 343-6915

Baxter, Jasper, Pop. 1,091
Baxter Community SD 500/K-12
PO Box 189 50028 641-227-3102
Matt Patton, supt. Fax 227-3217
www.baxter.k12.ia.us
Baxter JSHS 200/7-12
PO Box 189 50028 641-227-3103
Robert Luther, prin. Fax 227-3217

Bedford, Taylor, Pop. 1,430
Bedford Community SD 600/PK-12
PO Box 234 50833 712-523-2656
Joe Drake, supt. Fax 523-3166
www.bedford.k12.ia.us
Bedford MSHS 300/6-12
PO Box 234 50833 712-523-2656
Dana Nally, prin. Fax 523-2308

Belle Plaine, Benton, Pop. 2,512
Belle Plaine Community SD 600/PK-12
707 7th St 52208 319-444-3611
William Lynch, supt. Fax 444-3617
www.belle-plaine.k12.ia.us
Belle Plaine JSHS 200/7-12
610 13th Ave 52208 319-444-3720
Cherie Brown, prin. Fax 444-4507

Bellevue, Jackson, Pop. 2,180
Bellevue Community SD 700/PK-12
1601 State St 52031 563-872-4913
Dr. Mike Healy, supt. Fax 872-3216
www.bellevue.k12.ia.us
Bellevue MSHS 400/6-12
1601 State St 52031 563-872-4001
Tom Meyer, prin. Fax 872-3298

Marquette HS 100/9-12
502 Franklin St 52031 563-872-3356
James Squiers, prin. Fax 872-3285

Belmond, Wright, Pop. 2,355
Belmond-Klemme Community SD 700/PK-12
411 10th Ave NE 50421 641-444-4300
Marshall Lewis, supt. Fax 444-4524
www.bkcsd.org
Belmond-Klemme Alternative S 50/Alt
411 10th Ave NE 50421 641-444-4300
Eric Dockstader, prin. Fax 444-4097
Belmond-Klemme Community JSHS 300/7-12
411 10th Ave NE 50421 641-444-4300
Eric Dockstader, prin. Fax 444-4097

Bettendorf, Scott, Pop. 32,699
Bettendorf Community SD 4,400/PK-12
PO Box 1150 52722 563-359-3681
Dr. Theron Schutte, supt. Fax 359-3685
www.bettendorf.k12.ia.us
Bettendorf HS 1,400/9-12
3333 18th St 52722 563-332-7001
Jimmy Casas, prin. Fax 332-2326
Bettendorf MS 1,000/6-8
2030 Middle Rd 52722 563-359-3686
Lisa Reid, prin. Fax 359-3855
Edison Education Center Alt
438 16th St 52722 563-359-9375
Fax 359-5565

Pleasant Valley Community SD 3,800/PK-12
525 Belmont Rd 52722 563-332-5550
Jim Spelhaug, supt. Fax 332-4372
www.pleasval.k12.ia.us
Other Schools – See Le Claire, Riverdale

Brown Mackie College Post-Sec.
2119 Kimberly Rd 52722 563-344-1500
Morning Star Academy 200/PK-12
1426 Tanglefoot Ln 52722 563-359-5700
Casey Shutt, hdmstr. Fax 359-5737
Rivermont Collegiate 200/PK-12
1821 Sunset Dr 52722 563-359-1366
Fax 359-7576

Blairsburg, Hamilton, Pop. 214
Northeast Hamilton Community SD 300/PK-12
606 Illinois St 50034 515-325-6234
Patrick Hocking, supt. Fax 325-6235
www.ne-hamilton.k12.ia.us
Northeast Hamilton HS 100/9-12
606 Illinois St 50034 515-325-6234
Dennis Bahr, prin. Fax 325-6235
Northeast Hamilton MS 100/6-8
606 Illinois St 50034 515-325-6234
Patrick Hocking, prin. Fax 325-6235

Bloomfield, Davis, Pop. 2,620
Davis County Community SD 1,200/PK-12
608 S Washington St 52537 641-664-2200
Dan Maeder, supt. Fax 664-2221
www.dcmustangs.com/
Davis County HS 300/9-12
503 E Locust St 52537 641-664-2200
Jeff Graves, prin. Fax 664-1763
Davis County MS 400/5-8
500 E North St 52537 641-664-2200
Ryan Woods, prin. Fax 664-1767

Bonaparte, Van Buren, Pop. 432
Harmony Community SD 400/PK-12
602 8th St 52620 319-592-3600
Kerry Phillips, supt. Fax 592-3690
www.harmonycsd.org
Other Schools – See Farmington

Bondurant, Polk, Pop. 3,802
Bondurant-Farrar Community SD 1,400/PK-12
300 Garfield St SW 50035 515-967-7819
Peggy Vint, supt. Fax 967-7847
www.bondurant.k12.ia.us/
Bondurant-Farrar HS 400/9-12
1000 Grant St N 50035 515-957-8191
Michael Kramer, prin. Fax 957-8224
Bondurant-Farrar MS 400/5-8
300 Garfield St SW 50035 515-967-3711
Chad Carlson, prin. Fax 957-9924

Boone, Boone, Pop. 12,525
Boone Community SD 2,200/PK-12
500 7th St 50036 515-433-0750
Dr. Bradley Manard, supt. Fax 433-0753
boone.k12.ia.us/
Boone HS 700/9-12
500 7th St 50036 515-433-0890
Benjamin Johnson, prin. Fax 433-0989
Boone MS 700/5-8
1640 1st St 50036 515-433-0020
Carolyn Manard, prin. Fax 433-0026
Futures HS 50/Alt
727 W Mamie Eisenhower Ave 50036 515-433-0885
Benjamin Johnson, prin. Fax 433-8941

Des Moines Area Community College Post-Sec.
1125 Hancock Dr 50036 515-432-7203

Britt, Hancock, Pop. 2,051
West Hancock Community SD 700/PK-12
PO Box 278 50423 641-843-3833
Wayne Kronemann, supt. Fax 843-4717
www.whancock.org/
West Hancock HS 200/9-12
PO Box 278 50423 641-843-3863
Jeff Recker, prin. Fax 843-4633
Other Schools – See Kanawha

Brooklyn, Poweshiek, Pop. 1,455
Brooklyn-Guernsey-Malcom Community SD 600/PK-12
1090 Jackson St 52211 641-522-7058
Brad Hohensee, supt. Fax 522-7211
www.brooklyn.k12.ia.us
Brooklyn-Guernsey-Malcom JSHS 300/7-12
1090 Jackson St 52211 641-522-7058
Rick Radcliffe, prin. Fax 522-7211

Buffalo Center, Winnebago, Pop. 902
North Iowa Community SD 500/PK-12
111 3rd Ave NW 50424 641-562-2525
Cory Myer, supt. Fax 562-2921
www.northiowa.org
North Iowa HS 200/9-12
111 3rd Ave NW 50424 641-562-2525
Mike Embrock, prin. Fax 562-2921
North Iowa MS 100/6-8
111 3rd Ave NW 50424 641-562-2525
Mike Embrock, prin. Fax 562-2921

Burlington, Des Moines, Pop. 24,989
Burlington Community SD 3,800/PK-12
1429 West Ave 52601 319-753-6791
Jane Evans, supt. Fax 753-6796
www.bcsds.org
Burlington Alternative HS 100/Alt
2132 Madison Ave 52601 319-753-5092
Tom Messinger, prin. Fax 753-6962
Burlington Community HS 1,200/9-12
421 Terrace Dr 52601 319-753-2211
Tom Messinger, prin. Fax 753-6634
Leopold MS 400/6-8
3075 Sunnyside Ave 52601 319-752-8390
Brian Gravel, prin. Fax 752-8447
Stone MS 6-8
3000 Mason Rd 52601 319-752-4393
Brian Johnson, prin. Fax 752-7437

Great River Christian S 100/PK-12
426 Harrison Ave 52601 319-753-2255
Jon Frischkorn, admin. Fax 753-2030
Notre Dame HS 100/6-12
702 S Roosevelt Ave 52601 319-754-8431
Ron Glasgow, prin. Fax 752-8690

Burnside, Webster
Southeast Webster-Grand Community SD 600/PK-12
PO Box 49 50521 515-359-2235
Launi Dane, supt. Fax 359-2236
www.se-webster.k12.ia.us
Southeast Webster-Grand HS 200/9-12
PO Box 49 50521 515-359-2235
Rich Wagner, prin. Fax 359-2236
Other Schools – See Dayton

Bussey, Marion, Pop. 420
Twin Cedars Community SD 500/PK-12
2204 Highway G71 50044 641-944-5241
Brian VanderSluis, supt. Fax 944-5824
www.twincedars.k12.ia.us
Twin Cedars JSHS 200/7-12
2204 Highway G71 50044 641-944-5243
Dave Roby, prin. Fax 944-5225

Calmar, Winneshiek, Pop. 970
South Winneshiek Community SD 600/PK-12
PO Box 430 52132 563-562-3269
Chris Hoover, supt. Fax 562-3260
www.s-winneshiek.k12.ia.us
South Winneshiek HS 300/9-12
PO Box 430 52132 563-562-3226
Mary Recker, prin. Fax 562-3228
Other Schools – See Ossian

C F S Consolidated S 50/6-8
PO Box 815 52132 563-562-3291
Kathryn Schmitt, prin. Fax 562-3292
Northeast Iowa Community College Post-Sec.
PO Box 400 52132 563-562-3263

Camanche, Clinton, Pop. 4,417
Camanche Community SD 1,100/PK-12
702 13th Ave 52730 563-259-3000
Thomas Parker, supt. Fax 259-3005
www.camanche.k12.ia.us
Camanche HS 300/9-12
937 9th Ave 52730 563-259-3008
Chuck Wiebenga, prin. Fax 259-3048
Camanche MS 300/5-8
1400 9th St 52730 563-259-3014
Justin Shaffer, prin. Fax 259-3031

Carlisle, Warren, Pop. 3,818
Carlisle Community SD 2,000/PK-12
430 School St 50047 515-989-3589
Bryce Amos, supt. Fax 989-3075
www.carlisle.k12.ia.us
Carlisle HS 500/9-12
430 School St 50047 515-989-0831
Michael Anthony, prin. Fax 989-3075

Carlisle MS 500/6-8
325 Scotch Ridge Rd 50047 515-989-0833
Keri Schlueter, prin. Fax 989-4521

Carroll, Carroll, Pop. 9,988
Carroll Community SD 1,800/PK-12
1026 N Adams St 51401 712-792-8001
Robert Cordes, supt. Fax 792-8008
www.carroll.k12.ia.us
Carroll Alternative S 50/Alt
1026 N Adams St 51401 712-792-8020
Steve Haluska, prin. Fax 792-8008
Carroll HS 600/9-12
2809 N Grant Rd 51401 712-792-8010
Steve Haluska, prin. Fax 792-8118
Carroll MS 300/6-8
3203 N Grant Rd 51401 712-792-8020
Jerry Raymond, prin. Fax 792-8024

Des Moines Area Community College Post-Sec.
906 N Grant Rd 51401 712-792-1755
Kuemper Catholic HS 300/9-12
109 S Clark St 51401 712-792-3596
Penny Miller, prin. Fax 792-8070
Kuemper Catholic MS 200/6-8
1519 N West St 51401 712-792-2123
Earl Schiltz, prin. Fax 792-3365

Carson, Pottawattamie, Pop. 809
Riverside Community SD 500/PK-12
PO Box 218 51525 712-484-2212
James Sutton Ed.D., supt. Fax 484-3957
www.riversideschools.org/
Other Schools – See Oakland

Cascade, Dubuque, Pop. 2,146
Western Dubuque Community SD
Supt. — See Farley
Cascade JSHS 400/7-12
505 Johnson St NW 52033 563-852-3201
Greg VanderLugt, prin. Fax 852-7186

Cedar Falls, Black Hawk, Pop. 38,680
Cedar Falls Community SD 4,800/PK-12
1002 W 1st St 50613 319-553-3000
Dr. Andy Pattee, supt. Fax 277-0614
www.cfschools.org/
Cedar Falls SHS 1,100/10-12
1015 Division St 50613 319-553-2500
Rich Powers, prin. Fax 277-4604
Holmes JHS 500/7-9
505 Holmes Dr 50613 319-553-2650
David Welter, prin. Fax 277-0571
Peet JHS 600/7-9
525 E Seerley Blvd 50613 319-553-2710
Jason Wedgbury, prin. Fax 266-8839

Kaplan University Post-Sec.
7009 Nordic Dr 50613 319-277-0220
La' James International College Post-Sec.
6322 University Ave 50613 319-277-2150
University of Northern Iowa Post-Sec.
1227 W 27th St 50614 319-273-2311
Valley Lutheran HS 50/6-12
4520 Rownd St 50613 319-266-4565
Glenn Rollins, dir. Fax 266-4054

Cedar Rapids, Linn, Pop. 122,869
Cedar Rapids Community SD 15,900/PK-12
2500 Edgewood Rd NW 52405 319-558-2000
Dr. David Benson, supt. Fax 558-2224
www.cr.k12.ia.us
Franklin MS 600/6-8
300 20th St NE 52402 319-558-2452
Shannon Bucknell, prin. Fax 398-2454
Harding MS 900/6-8
4801 Golf St NE 52402 319-558-2254
Linda Reysack, prin. Fax 378-0671
Jefferson HS 1,500/9-12
1243 20th St SW 52404 319-558-2435
Charles McDonnell, prin. Fax 398-2442
Kennedy HS 1,800/9-12
4545 Wenig Rd NE 52402 319-558-2251
Mary Wilcynski, prin. Fax 294-1118
McKinley MS 600/6-8
620 10th St SE 52403 319-558-2348
Steve Goodall, prin. Fax 398-2347
Metro HS 500/Alt
1212 7th St SE 52401 319-558-2193
Dr. David Brown, prin. Fax 398-2117
Roosevelt MS 600/6-8
300 13th St NW 52405 319-558-2153
Autumn Pino, prin. Fax 398-2424
Taft MS 700/6-8
5200 E Ave NW 52405 319-558-2243
Gary Hatfield, prin. Fax 654-8619
Washington HS 1,400/9-12
2205 Forest Dr SE 52403 319-558-2161
Ralph Plagman, prin. Fax 398-2016
Wilson MS 300/6-8
2301 J St SW 52404 319-558-2156
Andrew Eley, prin. Fax 398-2368

College Community SD 4,900/PK-12
401 76th Ave SW 52404 319-848-5200
John Speer, supt. Fax 848-4019
www.prairiepride.org
Prairie HS 1,000/10-12
401 76th Ave SW 52404 319-848-5340
Mark Gronemeyer, prin. Fax 848-5201
Prairie Point MS/9th Grade Academy 1,000/7-9
401 76th Ave SW 52404 319-848-5500
Greg Leytem, prin. Fax 848-5520

American College of Hairstyling Post-Sec.
1531 1st Ave SE 52402 319-362-1488
Capri College Post-Sec.
2945 Williams Pkwy SW 52404 319-364-1541
Cedar Valley Christian S 200/PK-12
3636 Cottage Grove Ave SE 52403 319-366-7462
Jeffrey Pospisil, prin. Fax 247-0037
Coe College Post-Sec.
1220 1st Ave NE 52402 319-399-8000
Holy Family - LaSalle MS 200/6-8
3700 1st Ave NW 52405 319-396-7792
Rick Louk, prin. Fax 390-6527
ITT Technical Institute Post-Sec.
3735 Queen Ct SW 52404 319-297-3400
Kaplan University Post-Sec.
3165 Edgewood Pkwy SW 52404 319-363-0481
Kirkwood Community College Post-Sec.
PO Box 2068 52406 319-398-5411
Mercy-St. Luke's Hospital Post-Sec.
1026 A Ave NE 52402 319-369-7204
Mt. Mercy University Post-Sec.
1330 Elmhurst Dr NE 52402 319-363-8213
Regis MS 400/6-8
735 Prairie Dr NE 52402 319-378-0547
Beth Globokar, prin. Fax 247-6099
Xavier HS 800/9-12
6300 42nd St NE 52411 319-294-6635
Tom Keating, prin. Fax 294-6712

Center Point, Linn, Pop. 2,394
Center Point-Urbana Community SD 1,400/PK-12
PO Box 296 52213 319-849-1102
Alan Marshall, supt. Fax 849-2312
www.cpuschools.org/
Center Point-Urbana HS 400/9-12
PO Box 296 52213 319-849-1102
Rob Libolt, prin. Fax 849-2068
Center Point-Urbana MS 300/6-8
PO Box 296 52213 319-849-1102
Brent Winterhof, prin. Fax 443-2764

Centerville, Appanoose, Pop. 5,460
Centerville Community SD 1,200/PK-12
PO Box 370 52544 641-856-0601
Anthony Ryan, supt. Fax 856-0656
www.centerville.k12.ia.us
Appanoose County Campus 50/Alt
PO Box 370 52544 641-856-0890
Roger Raum, prin.
Centerville HS 400/9-12
600 CHS Dr 52544 641-856-0813
Roger Raum, prin. Fax 856-0809
Howar JHS 200/7-8
850 S Park Ave 52544 641-856-0760
Bruce Karpen, prin. Fax 856-0761

Indian Hills Community College Post-Sec.
721 N 1st St 52544 641-856-2143

Central City, Linn, Pop. 1,249
Central City Community SD 400/PK-12
400 Barber St 52214 319-438-6181
Karl Kurt, supt. Fax 438-6110
www.central-city.k12.ia.us
Central City HS 100/9-12
400 Barber St 52214 319-438-6182
Jason McLaughlin, prin. Fax 438-6110
Central City MS 100/7-8
400 Barber St 52214 319-438-6181
Jason McLaughlin, prin. Fax 438-6110

Chariton, Lucas, Pop. 4,293
Chariton Community SD 1,400/PK-12
PO Box 738 50049 641-774-5967
Paula Wright, supt. Fax 774-8511
www.chariton.k12.ia.us/
Chariton HS 500/9-12
501 N Grand St 50049 641-774-5066
Tracy Hall, prin. Fax 774-8511
Chariton MS 300/6-8
1300 N 16th St 50049 641-774-5114
Brian Zimmerli, prin. Fax 774-4109

Charles City, Floyd, Pop. 7,583
Charles City Community SD 1,500/PK-12
500 N Grand Ave 50616 641-257-6500
Andy Pattee, supt. Fax 257-6509
www.charlescityschools.org
Charles City HS 500/9-12
1 Comet Dr 50616 641-257-6510
Nancy Heiter, prin. Fax 257-1175
Charles City MS 300/6-8
500 N Grand Ave 50616 641-257-6530
Rick Gabel, prin. Fax 228-9842
Lane HS, 502 N Jackson St 50616 Alt
Nancy Heiter, prin. 641-426-5975

Charter Oak, Crawford, Pop. 501
Charter Oak-Ute Community SD 300/PK-12
PO Box 77 51439 712-678-3325
Rollie Wiebers, supt. Fax 678-3626
www.charter-oak-ute.k12.ia.us/
Charter Oak-Ute HS 100/9-12
PO Box 77 51439 712-678-3325
Rollie Wiebers, prin. Fax 678-3626
Charter Oak-Ute JHS 50/7-8
PO Box 77 51439 712-678-3325
Rollie Wiebers, prin. Fax 678-3626

Cherokee, Cherokee, Pop. 5,205
Cherokee Community SD 1,000/PK-12
600 W Bluff St 51012 712-225-6767
John Chalstrom, supt. Fax 225-6769
www.ccsd.k12.ia.us/
Cherokee MS 300/5-8
600 W Bluff St 51012 712-225-6750
Larry Weede, prin. Fax 225-4841
Little Sioux Success Center 50/Alt
600 W Bluff St 51012 712-225-6755
Patty Beyer, prin. Fax 225-6765
Washington HS 300/9-12
600 W Bluff St 51012 712-225-6755
Neil Phipps, prin. Fax 225-6765

Churdan, Greene, Pop. 379
Paton-Churdan Community SD 200/PK-12
PO Box 157 50050 515-389-3111
Leonard Griffith, supt. Fax 389-3113
www.paton-churdan.k12.ia.us
Paton-Churdan JSHS 100/6-12
PO Box 157 50050 515-389-3111
Annie Smith, prin. Fax 389-3113

Clarence, Cedar, Pop. 966
North Cedar Community SD
Supt. — See Stanwood
North Cedar MS 300/5-8
PO Box 310 52216 563-452-3179
Mark Glover, prin. Fax 452-3890

Clarinda, Page, Pop. 5,483
Clarinda Community SD 1,200/PK-12
PO Box 59 51632 712-542-5165
Paul Honnold, supt. Fax 542-3802
www.clarinda.k12.ia.us
Clarinda Alternative HS 50/Alt
PO Box 59 51632 712-542-5165
Teresa Nook, prin. Fax 542-3802
Clarinda HS 300/9-12
PO Box 59 51632 712-542-5167
Teresa Nook, prin. Fax 542-4305
Clarinda MS 300/5-8
PO Box 59 51632 712-542-2132
Gary McNeal, prin. Fax 542-5949

Iowa Western Community College Post-Sec.
923 E Washington St 51632 712-542-5117

Clarion, Wright, Pop. 2,837
Clarion-Goldfield Community SD 900/PK-12
319 3rd Ave NE 50525 515-532-3423
Robert Olson, supt. Fax 532-2628
www.clargold.org
Clarion-Goldfield HS 300/9-12
1111 Willow Dr 50525 515-532-2895
Dennis March, prin. Fax 532-2897
Clarion-Goldfield MS 200/6-8
300 3rd Ave NE 50525 515-532-2412
Steve Haberman, prin. Fax 532-2741

Clarksville, Butler, Pop. 1,422
Clarksville Community SD 300/PK-12
318 N Mather St 50619 319-278-4008
Eric Wood, supt. Fax 278-4618
www.clarksville.k12.ia.us/
Clarksville JSHS 200/6-12
318 N Mather St 50619 319-278-4273
Robert Saathoff, prin. Fax 278-4981

Clear Lake, Cerro Gordo, Pop. 7,667
Clear Lake Community SD 1,400/PK-12
1529 3rd Ave N 50428 641-357-2181
Anita Micich, supt. Fax 357-2182
www.clearlakeschools.org
Clear Lake HS 500/9-12
125 N 20th St 50428 641-357-5235
Chris Murphy, prin. Fax 357-6218
Clear Lake MS 300/6-8
1601 3rd Ave N 50428 641-357-6114
Daniel Long, prin. Fax 357-8353

Clinton, Clinton, Pop. 26,311
Clinton Community SD 3,800/PK-12
1401 12th Ave N 52732 563-243-9600
Deborah Olson, supt. Fax 243-2415
www.clinton.k12.ia.us
Clinton HS 1,100/9-12
817 8th Ave S 52732 563-243-7540
Karinne Tharaldson-Jones, prin. Fax 243-9612
Lincoln HS 200/Alt
1850 S Bluff Blvd 52732 563-242-8137
Brian Galusha, prin. Fax 243-1964
Lyons MS 400/6-8
2810 N 4th St 52732 563-242-7858
Dan Boyd, prin. Fax 242-6168
Washington MS 500/6-8
751 2nd Ave S 52732 563-243-0466
Brian Kenney, prin. Fax 242-3735

Ashford University Post-Sec.
400 N Bluff Blvd 52732 866-711-1700
Clinton Community College Post-Sec.
1000 Lincoln Blvd 52732 563-244-7000
Prince of Peace Catholic S 300/PK-12
312 S 4th St 52732 563-242-1663
Nancy Peart, prin. Fax 243-8272

Clive, Polk, Pop. 15,239
West Des Moines Community SD
Supt. — See West Des Moines
Indian Hills JHS 600/7-8
9401 Indian Hills Dr 50325 515-633-4700
Shane Christensen, prin. Fax 633-4799

ITT Technical Institute Post-Sec.
1860 NW 118th St Ste 110 50325 515-327-5500

Colfax, Jasper, Pop. 2,079
Colfax-Mingo Community SD 600/PK-12
204 N League Rd 50054 515-674-3646
Marty Lucas, supt. Fax 674-3921
www.colfax-mingo.k12.ia.us
Colfax-Mingo JSHS 300/7-12
204 N League Rd 50054 515-674-4111
Todd Jones, prin. Fax 674-4940

College Springs, Page, Pop. 207
South Page Community SD 200/PK-12
PO Box 98 51637 712-582-3212
Gregg Cruickshank, supt. Fax 582-3217
www.southpageschools.com
South Page JSHS 100/7-12
PO Box 98 51637 712-582-3211
Denise Green, prin. Fax 582-3217

Colo, Story, Pop. 872
Colo-Nesco Comm SD 300/PK-12
PO Box 136 50056 641-377-2284
Jim Verlengia, supt. Fax 377-2283
www.colo-nesco.k12.ia.us
Colo-Nesco JSHS 100/7-12
PO Box 136 50056 641-377-2282
Brandon Kelley, prin. Fax 377-2283

Columbus Junction, Louisa, Pop. 1,878
Columbus Community SD 900/PK-12
1210 Colton St 52738 319-728-2911
Marlene Johnson, supt. Fax 728-8750
www.columbuscsd.org
Columbus Community HS 300/9-12
1004 Colton St 52738 319-728-2231
Jeff Maeder, prin. Fax 728-2205
Columbus Community JHS 100/7-8
1004 Colton St 52738 319-728-2233
Jeff Maeder, prin. Fax 728-2205

Conrad, Grundy, Pop. 1,100
BCLUW Community SD 600/K-12
PO Box 670 50621 641-366-2819
Ben Petty, supt. Fax 366-2175
www.bcluw.k12.ia.us
BCLUW HS 200/9-12
PO Box 670 50621 641-366-2810
Cari Teske, prin. Fax 366-2951
Other Schools – See Union

Coon Rapids, Carroll, Pop. 1,296
Coon Rapids-Bayard Community SD 400/PK-12
PO Box 297 50058 712-999-2207
Rich Stoffers, supt. Fax 999-7740
www.crbcrusaders.org
Coon Rapids-Bayard Intermediate JSHS 300/4-12
PO Box 297 50058 712-999-2208
Brent Jorth, prin. Fax 999-7740

Coralville, Johnson, Pop. 18,406
Iowa City Community SD
Supt. — See Iowa City
Northwest JHS 600/7-8
1507 8th St 52241 319-688-1060
Gregg Shoultz, prin. Fax 688-1069

Corning, Adams, Pop. 1,626
Corning Community SD 400/PK-12
904 8th St 50841 641-322-4242
William Stone, supt. Fax 322-4243
www.corningcsd.org
Corning JSHS 200/7-12
904 8th St 50841 641-322-4245
Kent Jorgensen, prin. Fax 322-5149

Correctionville, Woodbury, Pop. 815
River Valley Community SD 500/PK-12
PO Box 8 51016 712-372-4420
Donita Joens, supt. Fax 372-4677
www.river-valley.k12.ia.us/
River Valley JSHS 200/7-12
PO Box 8 51016 712-372-4656
Tim Scott, prin. Fax 372-4784

Corwith, Hancock, Pop. 307
Corwith-Wesley Community SD 100/7-12
PO Box 220 50430 515-583-2304
Jon Hueser, supt. Fax 583-2030
www.corwith-wesley.k12.ia.us
Corwith-Wesley MSHS 100/7-12
PO Box 220 50430 515-583-2304
Jon Hueser, supt. Fax 583-2030

Corydon, Wayne, Pop. 1,578
Wayne Community SD 600/PK-12
102 N Dekalb St 50060 641-872-2184
Dave Daughton, supt. Fax 872-2091
www.wayne.k12.ia.us
Wayne Community JSHS 300/7-12
102 N Dekalb St 50060 641-872-2184
Stacy Snyder, prin. Fax 872-2091

Council Bluffs, Pottawattamie, Pop. 61,150
Council Bluffs Community SD 9,000/PK-12
12 Scott St 51503 712-328-6446
Martha Bruckner, supt. Fax 328-6548
www.cbcsd.org/
Jefferson HS 1,300/9-12
2501 W Broadway 51501 712-328-6493
Jason Plourde, prin. Fax 328-6497
Kanesville Alternative Learning Ctr 300/Alt
807 Avenue G 51503 712-328-6510
Jesse Tvrdy, prin. Fax 328-6511
Kirn MS 900/6-8
100 North Ave 51503 712-328-6454
Melissa Byington, prin. Fax 328-6554
Lincoln HS 1,400/9-12
1205 Bonham St 51503 712-328-6481
Todd Barnett, prin. Fax 328-6485
Tucker Career & College Center Vo/Tech
815 N 18th St 51501 712-328-6408
Cyle Forney, prin. Fax 328-6425
Wilson MS 900/6-8
715 N 21st St 51501 712-328-6476
Kim Kazmierczak, prin. Fax 328-6479

Lewis Central Community SD 3,200/PK-12
1600 E South Omaha Brdge Rd 51503 712-366-8202
Mark Schweer, supt. Fax 366-8315
www.lewiscentral.org/
Lewis Central HS 900/9-12
3504 Harry Langdon Blvd 51503 712-366-8322
Joel Beyenhof, prin. Fax 366-8340
Lewis Central MS 700/6-8
3820 Harry Langdon Blvd 51503 712-366-8251
Jim Dermody, prin. Fax 366-8324

EQ School of Hair Design Post-Sec.
536 W Broadway 51503 712-328-2613
Heartland Christian S 100/PK-12
400 Wright Rd 51501 712-322-5817
William Ross, prin. Fax 322-4287
Iowa School for the Deaf Post-Sec.
3501 Harry Langdon Blvd 51503 712-366-0571
Iowa Western Community College Post-Sec.
2700 College Rd 51503 712-325-3200
Jennie Edmundson Memorial Hospital Post-Sec.
933 E Pierce St 51503 712-328-6239
St. Albert HS 400/7-12
400 Gleason Ave 51503 712-328-2316
David Schweitzer, prin. Fax 328-8316

Cresco, Howard, Pop. 3,829
Howard-Winneshiek Community SD 1,200/PK-12
1000 Schroder Dr 52136 563-547-2762
John Carver, supt. Fax 547-5973
www.howard-winn.k12.ia.us
Cresco JHS 200/6-8
1000 4th Ave E 52136 563-547-2300
Todd Knobloch, prin. Fax 547-2679
Crestwood Alternative S 50/Alt
205 3rd Ave W 52136 563-547-2310
Tim Felderman, prin.
Crestwood HS 400/9-12
1000 Schroder Dr 52136 563-547-2764
Tim Felderman, prin. Fax 547-4650

Total Look Sch of Cosmetology & Massage Post-Sec.
806 3rd St W 52136 563-547-3624

Creston, Union, Pop. 7,756
Creston Community SD 1,400/PK-12
801 N Elm St 50801 641-782-7028
Chuck Scott, supt. Fax 782-7020
www.crestonschools.org
Creston HS 500/9-12
601 W Townline St 50801 641-782-2116
Bill Messerole, prin. Fax 782-9502
Creston MS 300/6-8
805 Academic Ave 50801 641-782-2129
Larry Otten, prin.
High Lakes Country Academy 50/Alt
801 N Elm St 50801 641-782-4375
Bill Messerole, prin.

Southwestern Community College Post-Sec.
1501 W Townline St 50801 641-782-7081

Dakota City, Humboldt, Pop. 834
Humboldt Community SD 1,100/PK-12
PO Box 130 50529 515-332-1330
Greg Darling, supt. Fax 332-4478
www.humboldt.k12.ia.us
Other Schools – See Humboldt

Dallas Center, Dallas, Pop. 1,610
Dallas Center-Grimes Community SD 1,900/PK-12
PO Box 512 50063 515-992-3866
Scott Grimes, supt. Fax 992-3079
www.dc-grimes.k12.ia.us
Other Schools – See Grimes

Danville, Des Moines, Pop. 929
Danville Community SD 600/PK-12
419 S Main St 52623 319-392-4221
Gary DeLacy, supt. Fax 392-8390
www.danvillecsd.org
Danville JSHS 300/7-12
419 S Main St 52623 319-392-4221
Theresa Ritters, prin. Fax 392-8704

Davenport, Scott, Pop. 96,534
Davenport Community SD 15,200/PK-12
1606 Brady St 52803 563-336-5000
Arthur Tate, supt. Fax 336-5080
www.davenportschools.org
Central HS 1,400/9-12
1120 N Main St 52803 563-323-9900
Robert Scott, prin. Fax 323-3110
Kimberly Center 200/Alt
1002 W Kimberly Rd 52806 563-386-5840
Sheri Womack, prin. Fax 386-9764
North HS 1,000/9-12
626 W 53rd St 52806 563-388-9880
Jay Chelf, prin. Fax 388-9456
Smart IS 500/6-8
1934 W 5th St 52802 563-323-1837
Linda Heiden, prin. Fax 323-3093
Sudlow IS 700/6-8
1414 E Locust St 52803 563-326-3502
Bruce Potts, prin. Fax 326-2248
West HS 1,900/9-12
3505 W Locust St 52804 563-386-5500
Mike Lawler, prin. Fax 386-5508
Williams IS 700/6-8
3040 N Division St 52804 563-391-6550
Scott McKissick, prin. Fax 391-0149
Wood IS 700/6-8
5701 N Division St 52806 563-391-6350
Sheri Simpson-Schultz, prin. Fax 391-4416

Young IS 300/6-8
1702 N Main St 52803 563-326-4432
Marianne Corbin, prin. Fax 326-1165
Other Schools – See Walcott

Assumption HS 400/9-12
1020 W Central Park Ave 52804 563-326-5313
Bridget Murphy, prin. Fax 326-3510
Capri College Post-Sec.
2540 E 53rd St 52807 563-388-6642
Hamilton Technical College Post-Sec.
1011 E 53rd St 52807 563-386-3570
Kaplan University Post-Sec.
1801 E Kimberly Rd Ste 1 52807 563-355-3500
La' James College of Hairstyling Post-Sec.
5205 N Brady St 52806 563-441-7900
Palmer College of Chiropractic Post-Sec.
1000 Brady St 52803 563-884-5000
St. Ambrose University Post-Sec.
518 W Locust St 52803 563-333-6000

Dayton, Webster, Pop. 832
Southeast Webster-Grand Community SD
Supt. — See Burnside
Southeast Webster-Grand JHS 100/7-8
30850 Paragon Ave 50530 515-359-2235
Rich Wagner, prin. Fax 359-2236

Decorah, Winneshiek, Pop. 8,056
Decorah Community SD 1,700/PK-12
510 Winnebago St 52101 563-382-4208
Michael Haluska, supt. Fax 387-0753
decorah.k12.ia.us/
Decorah HS 600/9-12
100 E Claiborne Dr 52101 563-382-3643
Kim Sheppard, prin. Fax 382-3107
Decorah MS 500/5-8
405 Winnebago St 52101 563-382-8427
Leona Hoth, prin. Fax 387-4052

North Winneshiek Community SD 200/PK-8
3495 N Winn Rd 52101 563-735-5411
Tim Dugger, supt. Fax 735-5430
www.n-winn.k12.ia.us/
North Winneshiek MS 50/6-8
3495 N Winn Rd 52101 563-735-5411
Tim Dugger, prin. Fax 735-5430

Luther College Post-Sec.
700 College Dr 52101 563-387-2000

Delhi, Delaware, Pop. 456
Maquoketa Valley Community SD 700/PK-12
PO Box 186 52223 563-922-9422
Doug Tuetken, supt. Fax 922-2160
www.maquoketa-v.k12.ia.us
Maquoketa Valley HS 200/9-12
PO Box 186 52223 563-922-2091
Doug Tuetken, prin. Fax 922-3026
Maquoketa Valley MS 200/6-8
PO Box 186 52223 563-922-9411
Tracy Morrison, prin. Fax 922-9502

Denison, Crawford, Pop. 8,238
Denison Community SD 2,100/K-12
819 N 16th St 51442 712-263-2176
Michael Pardun, supt. Fax 263-5233
www.denison.k12.ia.us
Denison Alternative HS 100/Alt
10 Opportunity Dr 51442 712-265-2349
Lynn Torr, prin. Fax 265-2397
Denison HS 700/9-12
819 N 16th St 51442 712-263-3101
Lynn Torr, prin. Fax 263-6009
Denison MS 400/6-8
1201 N 16th St 51442 712-263-9393
Patricia Roush, prin. Fax 263-5418

Denver, Bremer, Pop. 1,773
Denver Community SD 600/PK-12
PO Box 384 50622 319-984-6323
Kathryn Enslin, supt. Fax 984-5345
www.denver.k12.ia.us
Denver HS 200/9-12
PO Box 384 50622 319-984-5639
Paul Gebel, prin. Fax 984-5630
Denver MS 200/6-8
PO Box 384 50622 319-984-6041
Paul Gebel, prin. Fax 984-5630

Des Moines, Polk, Pop. 197,701
Des Moines Independent Community SD 30,100/PK-12
901 Walnut St 50309 515-242-7911
Thomas Ahart, supt. Fax 242-7579
www.dmschools.org/
Brody MS 700/6-8
2501 Park Ave 50321 515-242-8443
Thomas Hoffman, prin. Fax 244-0927
Callanan MS 600/6-8
3010 Center St 50312 515-242-8101
Doug Calaway, prin. Fax 242-8103
Casady Alternative Center Alt
1801 16th St 50314 515-323-8641
Randi Oleson, prin. Fax 323-8617
Des Moines Central Campus 50/Alt
1800 Grand Ave 50309 515-242-7846
Gary McClanahan, prin. Fax 242-7598
East HS 2,300/9-12
815 E 13th St 50316 515-242-7788
Steven Johns, prin. Fax 242-7958
Goodrell MS 600/6-8
3300 E 29th St 50317 515-242-8444
Dawn Stahly, prin. Fax 264-9057
Harding MS 600/6-8
203 E Euclid Ave 50313 515-242-8445
Maureen Taylor, prin. Fax 244-3566

Hiatt MS 600/6-8
1214 E 15th St 50316 515-242-8450
Debra Chapman, prin. Fax 266-6390
Hoover HS 1,100/9-12
4800 Aurora Ave 50310 515-242-7300
Doug Wheeler, prin. Fax 242-7308
Hoyt MS 600/6-8
2700 E 42nd St 50317 515-242-8446
Laura Kacer, prin. Fax 265-5059
Lincoln HS 2,300/9-12
2600 SW 9th St 50315 515-242-7500
Paul Williamson, prin. Fax 242-7517
McCombs MS 600/6-8
201 County Line Rd 50320 515-242-8447
Nancy Croy, prin. Fax 287-2644
Meredith MS 600/6-8
4827 Madison Ave 50310 515-242-7250
Cindy Flesch, prin. Fax 242-8291
Merrill MS 600/6-8
5301 Grand Ave 50312 515-242-8448
Alex Hanna, prin. Fax 274-9691
North HS 1,100/9-12
501 Holcomb Ave 50313 515-242-7200
Matt Smith, prin. Fax 242-7319
Roosevelt HS 1,600/9-12
4419 Center St 50312 515-242-7272
Kathie Danielson, prin. Fax 242-7350
Scavo HS 300/Alt
3725 52nd St 50310 515-242-7589
Rich Blonigan, prin. Fax 242-7591
Weeks MS 700/6-8
901 E Park Ave 50315 515-242-8449
Audrey Rieken, prin. Fax 288-6755

Saydel Community SD 1,100/PK-12
5740 NE 14th St 50313 515-264-0866
Brad Buck, supt. Fax 264-0869
www.saydel.k12.ia.us
Saydel HS 400/9-12
5601 NE 7th St 50313 515-262-9325
Tracy Hook, prin. Fax 266-8497
Woodside MS 300/5-8
5810 NE 14th St 50313 515-265-3451
Christopher Feldhans, prin. Fax 265-0950

AIB College of Business Post-Sec.
2500 Fleur Dr 50321 515-244-4221
American College of Hairstyling Post-Sec.
603 E 6th St 50309 515-244-0971
Des Moines University Post-Sec.
3200 Grand Ave 50312 515-271-1400
Drake University Post-Sec.
2507 University Ave 50311 515-271-2011
Grandview Park Baptist S 300/PK-12
1701 E 33rd St 50317 515-265-7579
Dick McWilliams, admin. Fax 266-9834
Grand View University Post-Sec.
1200 Grandview Ave 50316 515-263-2800
Iowa Methodist Medical Center Post-Sec.
1200 Pleasant St 50309 515-241-6201
Iowa School of Beauty Post-Sec.
3305 70th St 50322 515-278-9939
Mercy College of Health Sciences Post-Sec.
928 6th Ave 50309 515-643-3180
Vatterott College - Des Moines Post-Sec.
7000 Fleur Dr 50321 515-309-9000

De Witt, Clinton, Pop. 5,259
Central Clinton Community SD 1,600/PK-12
PO Box 110 52742 563-659-0700
Dan Peterson, supt. Fax 659-0707
www.central-clinton.k12.ia.us
Central Alternative Program 50/Alt
PO Box 110 52742 563-659-4713
George Pickup, prin. Fax 659-0714
Central HS 500/9-12
PO Box 110 52742 563-659-0715
George Pickup, prin. Fax 659-0714
Central MS 200/7-8
PO Box 110 52742 563-659-0735
Jim Wichman, prin. Fax 659-0766

Diagonal, Ringgold, Pop. 330
Diagonal Community SD 100/PK-12
403 W 2nd St 50845 641-734-5331
Karleen Stephens, supt. Fax 734-5729
www.diagonal.k12.ia.us
Diagonal JSHS 100/6-12
403 W 2nd St 50845 641-734-5331
Larry Tepley, prin. Fax 734-5729

Dike, Grundy, Pop. 1,205
Dike-New Hartford Community SD 600/PK-12
PO Box D 50624 319-989-2552
Larry Hunt, supt. Fax 989-2735
www.dnhcsd.org
Dike-New Hartford HS 200/9-12
PO Box D 50624 319-989-2485
Irvine Laube, prin. Fax 989-2735
Other Schools – See New Hartford

Donnellson, Lee, Pop. 907
Central Lee Community SD 1,000/PK-12
2642 Highway 218 52625 319-835-9510
John Henriksen, supt. Fax 835-3910
www.central-lee.k12.ia.us
Central Lee HS 300/9-12
2642 Highway 218 52625 319-835-9510
Rusty Shockley, prin. Fax 835-5709
Central Lee MS 200/6-8
2642 Highway 218 52625 319-835-9510
Kim Ensminger, prin. Fax 835-5020

Dubuque, Dubuque, Pop. 56,421
Dubuque Community SD 10,500/PK-12
2300 Chaney Rd 52001 563-552-3000
Stan Rheingans, supt. Fax 552-3026
www.dbqschools.org
Dubuque SHS 1,600/9-12
1800 Clarke Dr 52001 563-552-5500
Rick Colpitts, prin. Fax 552-5502
Hempstead HS 1,800/9-12
3715 Pennsylvania Ave 52002 563-552-5200
Lee Kolker, prin. Fax 552-5231
Jefferson MS 600/6-8
1105 Althauser Ave 52001 563-552-4700
Phillip Kramer, prin. Fax 552-4701
Roosevelt MS 1,200/6-8
2001 Radford Rd 52002 563-552-5000
Dale Lass, prin. Fax 552-5001
Washington MS 600/6-8
51 N Grandview Ave 52001 563-552-4800
Mark Burns, prin. Fax 552-4801

Capri College Post-Sec.
395 Main St 52001 563-588-2379
Clarke University Post-Sec.
1550 Clarke Dr 52001 563-588-6300
Emmaus Bible College Post-Sec.
2570 Asbury Rd 52001 563-588-8000
Loras College Post-Sec.
1450 Alta Vista St 52001 563-588-7100
Mazzuchelli MS 500/6-8
2005 Kane St 52001 563-582-7236
Kim Hermsen, prin. Fax 582-7857
University of Dubuque Post-Sec.
2000 University Ave 52001 563-589-3000
Wahlert HS 600/9-12
2005 Kane St 52001 563-583-9771
Ron Meyers, prin. Fax 583-9775
Wartburg Theological Seminary Post-Sec.
PO Box 5004 52004 563-589-0200

Dunkerton, Black Hawk, Pop. 848
Dunkerton Community SD 500/PK-12
509 S Canfield St 50626 319-822-4295
Jim Stanton, supt. Fax 822-9456
www.dunkerton.k12.ia.us
Dunkerton JSHS 200/7-12
509 S Canfield St 50626 319-822-4295
Justin Urbanek, prin. Fax 822-9456

Dunlap, Harrison, Pop. 1,032
Boyer Valley Community SD 500/PK-12
1102 Iowa Ave 51529 712-643-2251
Thomas Vint, supt. Fax 643-2279
www.boyer-valley.k12.ia.us
Boyer Valley MSHS 200/PK-PK, 6-
1102 Iowa Ave 51529 712-643-2258
Chad Straight, prin. Fax 643-2279

Durant, Cedar, Pop. 1,820
Durant Community SD 700/K-12
408 7th St 52747 563-785-4432
Duane Bennett, supt. Fax 785-4611
www.durant.k12.ia.us
Durant HS 300/9-12
408 7th St 52747 563-785-4431
Anthony Neumann, prin. Fax 785-6558
Durant MS 200/5-8
408 7th St 52747 563-785-4433
Rebecca Stineman, prin. Fax 785-6558

Dyersville, Dubuque, Pop. 4,031

Beckman HS 500/7-12
1325 9th St SE 52040 563-875-7188
Patrick Meade, prin. Fax 875-7242

Dysart, Tama, Pop. 1,367
Union Community SD
Supt. — See La Porte City
Union MS 300/6-8
PO Box 159 52224 319-476-5100
Mark Albertsen, prin. Fax 476-2385

Eagle Grove, Wright, Pop. 3,540
Eagle Grove Community SD 800/PK-12
325 N Commercial Ave 50533 515-448-4749
Jess Toliver, supt. Fax 448-3156
www.eagle-grove.k12.ia.us
Blue MS 200/5-8
1015 NW 2nd St 50533 515-448-4767
Scott Jeske, prin. Fax 448-5527
Eagle Grove HS 200/9-12
415 NW 2nd St 50533 515-448-5143
Jeff Siebersma, prin. Fax 448-3583

Earlham, Madison, Pop. 1,435
Earlham Community SD 600/PK-12
PO Box 430 50072 515-758-2235
Michael Wright, supt. Fax 758-2215
home.ecsdcards.com/
Earlham HS 200/9-12
PO Box 430 50072 515-758-2235
Dave Wempen, prin. Fax 758-2215
Earlham MS 100/7-8
PO Box 430 50072 515-758-2214
Dave Wempen, prin. Fax 758-2215

Early, Sac, Pop. 548
Schaller-Crestland Community SD
Supt. — See Schaller
Ridge View MS 200/6-8
PO Box 377 50535 712-273-5192
Ellen Pickhinke, prin. Fax 273-5120

Eddyville, Wapello, Pop. 1,011
Eddyville-Blakesburg-Fremont Cmmunity SD 900/PK-12
PO Box 429 52553 641-969-4226
Dean Cook, supt. Fax 969-4547
www.ebcsd.com/
Eddyville-Blakesburg-Fremont HS 300/9-12
1301 Berdan Ext 52553 641-969-4288
Matt Johnston, prin. Fax 969-4574
Eddyville-Blakesburg-Fremont JHS 100/7-8
1301 Berdan Ext 52553 641-938-2202
Matt Johnston, prin. Fax 938-2613

Edgewood, Clayton, Pop. 857
Edgewood-Colesburg Community SD 600/PK-12
PO Box 315 52042 563-928-6411
Ed Klamfoth, supt. Fax 928-6414
www.edge-cole.k12.ia.us
Edgewood-Colesburg JSHS 300/7-12
PO Box 316 52042 563-928-6412
Dawn Voss, prin. Fax 928-6414

Eldon, Wapello, Pop. 923
Cardinal Community SD 600/PK-12
4045 Ashland Rd 52554 641-652-7531
Joel Pedersen, supt. Fax 652-3143
www.cardinalcomet.com
Cardinal MSHS 400/6-12
4045 Ashland Rd 52554 641-652-7531
Joel Pedersen, supt. Fax 652-3143

Eldora, Hardin, Pop. 2,695
Eldora-New Providence Community SD 600/PK-12
1010 Edgington Ave 50627 641-939-5631
Jay Mathis, supt. Fax 939-3667
www.eldora-np.k12.ia.us
Eldora-New Providence HS 300/9-12
1800 24th St 50627 641-939-3421
Randall Fahr, prin. Fax 939-3423

Eldridge, Scott, Pop. 5,557
North Scott Community SD 2,900/K-12
251 E Iowa St 52748 563-285-4819
Jeff Schwiebert, supt. Fax 285-6075
www.north-scott.k12.ia.us
North Scott HS 900/9-12
200 S 1st St 52748 563-285-9631
Shane Knoche, prin. Fax 285-9308
North Scott JHS 500/7-8
502 S 5th St 52748 563-285-8272
David Griffin, prin. Fax 285-6045

Elgin, Fayette, Pop. 680
Valley Community SD 300/K-8
23493 Canoe Rd 52141 563-426-5501
Duane Willhite, supt. Fax 426-5502
www.valley.k12.ia.us
North Fayette Valley MS 100/7-8
23493 Canoe Rd 52141 563-426-5551
Sharon Rich, prin. Fax 426-5502

Elkader, Clayton, Pop. 1,265
Central Community SD 500/PK-12
400 1st St NW 52043 563-245-1751
Allan Nelson, supt. Fax 245-1763
www.central.k12.ia.us/
Central Community JSHS 200/6-12
400 1st St NW 52043 563-245-1750
Dan Yanda, prin. Fax 245-1763

Elk Horn, Shelby, Pop. 661
Elk Horn-Kimballton Community SD 200/PK-12
PO Box 388a 51531 712-764-4616
Dean Schnoes, supt. Fax 764-4626
www.exira-ehk.k12.ia.us/
Exira-Elk Horn-Kimballton HS 100/9-12
PO Box 388a 51531 712-764-4606
David Johnson, prin. Fax 764-4626

Emmetsburg, Palo Alto, Pop. 3,872
Emmetsburg Community SD 800/PK-12
205 King St 50536 712-852-3201
John Joynt, supt. Fax 852-3338
www.emmetsburg.k12.ia.us
Emmetsburg HS 200/9-12
205 King St 50536 712-852-2966
Fred Matlage, prin. Fax 852-3317
Emmetsburg MS 200/5-8
205 King St 50536 712-852-2892
Fred Matlage, prin. Fax 852-3811

Iowa Lakes Community College Post-Sec.
3200 College Dr 50536 712-852-3554

Epworth, Dubuque, Pop. 1,855
Western Dubuque Community SD
Supt. — See Farley
Western Dubuque HS 800/9-12
PO Box 379 52045 563-876-3442
Dave Hoeger, prin. Fax 876-5512

Divine Word College Post-Sec.
PO Box 380 52045 563-876-3353

Essex, Page, Pop. 789
Essex Community SD 200/K-12
111 Forbes St 51638 712-379-3117
Jim Dick, supt. Fax 379-3200
www.ehs-ees.com/
Essex JSHS 100/7-12
111 Forbes St 51638 712-379-3115
Robert Brecht, prin. Fax 379-3200

Estherville, Emmet, Pop. 6,305
Estherville Lincoln Central Comm SD 1,400/PK-12
1814 7th Ave S 51334 712-362-8460
Tara Paul, supt. Fax 362-2410
www.estherville.k12.ia.us

Estherville Lincoln Central HS | 400/9-12
1520 Central Ave 51334 | 712-362-2659
Frank Christenson, prin. | Fax 362-2406
Estherville Lincoln Central MS | 400/5-8
1430 1st Ave S 51334 | 712-362-2335
Nathan Essary, prin. | Fax 362-7822

Iowa Lakes Community College | Post-Sec.
300 S 18th St 51334 | 712-362-7945

Evansdale, Black Hawk, Pop. 4,640
Waterloo Community SD
Supt. — See Waterloo
Bunger MS | 400/6-8
157 S Roosevelt Rd 50707 | 319-433-2550
Andrew Miehe, prin. | Fax 433-2564

Everly, Clay, Pop. 602
Clay Central/Everly Community SD
Supt. — See Royal
Clay Central/Everly JSHS | 100/7-12
PO Box 110 51338 | 712-834-2227
Curt Busch, prin. | Fax 834-2193

Exira, Audubon, Pop. 839
Exira - EHK Community SD | 50/PK-K, 4-8
PO Box 335 50076 | 712-268-5555
Dean Schnoes, supt. | Fax 268-5319
exira-ehk.k12.ia.us/
Exira/EHK MS | 50/PK-K, 4-8
PO Box 335 50076 | 712-268-5318
Steven Humphrey, prin. | Fax 268-5319

Fairbank, Buchanan, Pop. 1,107
Wapsie Valley Community SD | 800/PK-12
2535 Viking Ave 50629 | 319-638-6711
Chad Garber, supt. | Fax 638-7061
www.wapsievalleyschools.com/
Wapsie Valley JSHS | 300/7-12
2535 Viking Ave 50629 | 319-638-6711
Josh Johnson, prin. | Fax 638-7061

Fairfield, Jefferson, Pop. 9,274
Fairfield Community SD | 1,700/PK-12
403 S 20th St 52556 | 641-472-2655
Arthur Sathoff, supt. | Fax 472-0269
www.fairfieldsfuture.org/
Fairfield HS | 600/9-12
605 E Broadway Ave 52556 | 641-472-2059
Aaron Becker, prin. | Fax 472-4703
Fairfield MS | 500/5-8
404 W Fillmore Ave 52556 | 641-472-5019
Laura Atwood, prin. | Fax 472-5301

Maharishi S of the Age of Enlightenment | 200/PK-12
804 Dr Robert Keith Wallace 52556 | 641-472-9400
Richard Beall Ph.D., head sch | Fax 472-1211
Maharishi University of Management | Post-Sec.
1000 N 4th St 52557 | 641-472-7000

Farley, Dubuque, Pop. 1,531
Western Dubuque Community SD | 2,900/PK-12
PO Box 68 52046 | 563-744-3885
Jeffory Corkery, supt. | Fax 744-3093
www.wdbqschools.org
Drexler Middle IS | 500/5-8
PO Box 279 52046 | 563-744-3371
Mary Jane Maher, prin. | Fax 744-3711
Other Schools – See Cascade, Epworth

Farmington, Van Buren, Pop. 661
Harmony Community SD
Supt. — See Bonaparte
Harmony JSHS | 200/7-12
33727 Route J40 52626 | 319-592-3192
Heather Lightfoot, prin. | Fax 592-3135

Farragut, Fremont, Pop. 484
Farragut Community SD | 200/PK-12
PO Box 36 51639 | 712-385-8131
Jay Lutt, supt. | Fax 385-8135
www.farragutschools.org
Nishnabotna HS | 100/9-12
PO Box 36 51639 | 712-385-8131
Roger Pearson, prin. | Fax 385-8135

Fayette, Fayette, Pop. 1,319
North Fayette Community SD
Supt. — See West Union
North Fayette MS | 100/7-8
200 Volga St 52142 | 563-425-3303
Mark Nuss, dean | Fax 425-3304

Upper Iowa University | Post-Sec.
PO Box 1857 52142 | 563-425-5200

Fontanelle, Adair, Pop. 671
Nodaway Valley Community SD
Supt. — See Greenfield
Nodaway Valley MS | 200/5-8
112 S 1st St 50846 | 641-745-2291
Craig Juffer, prin. | Fax 745-3501

Forest City, Winnebago, Pop. 4,101
Forest City Community SD | 1,200/PK-12
PO Box 270 50436 | 641-585-2323
Darwin Lehmann, supt. | Fax 585-5218
www.forestcity.k12.ia.us
Forest City Alternative S | 50/Alt
PO Box 270 50436 | 641-585-2324
Ken Baker, prin. | Fax 585-3034
Forest City HS | 400/9-12
206 W School St 50436 | 641-585-2324
Ken Baker, prin. | Fax 585-3034
Forest City MS | 300/6-8
216 W School St 50436 | 641-585-4772
Zach Dillavou, prin. | Fax 585-3432

Forest City Christian S | 50/PK-12
305 Walnut St 50436 | 641-585-3233
Ivon Tokheim, admin. | Fax 585-1390
Waldorf College | Post-Sec.
106 S 6th St 50436 | 800-292-1903

Fort Dodge, Webster, Pop. 24,736
Fort Dodge Community SD | 3,400/PK-12
104 S 17th St 50501 | 515-576-1161
Dr. Douglas VanZyl, supt. | Fax 576-1988
www.fort-dodge.k12.ia.us
Fort Dodge HS | 1,200/9-12
819 N 25th St 50501 | 515-955-1770
David Keane, prin. | Fax 955-3374
Phillips MS | 500/7-8
1015 5th Ave N 50501 | 515-574-5711
Dr. Joseph Libby, prin. | Fax 576-3160
Willard Alternative Education HS | 100/Alt
104 S 17th St 50501 | 515-576-7305
David Keane, prin. | Fax 576-1988

Iowa Central Community College | Post-Sec.
1 Triton Cir 50501 | 515-576-7201
La' James International College | Post-Sec.
2419 5th Ave S 50501 | 515-576-3119
St. Edmond HS | 400/6-12
501 N 22nd St 50501 | 515-955-5850
John Howard, prin. | Fax 955-3569

Fort Madison, Lee, Pop. 10,836
Fort Madison Community SD | 1,700/PK-12
PO Box 1423 52627 | 319-372-7252
Kenneth Marang, supt. | Fax 372-7255
www.ft-madison.k12.ia.us
Fort Madison Alternative S | 100/Alt
1602 Avenue F Ste 1 52627 | 319-372-8093
Greg Smith, prin. | Fax 372-8148
Fort Madison HS | 600/9-12
2001 Avenue B 52627 | 319-372-1862
Greg Smith, prin. | Fax 372-1325
Fort Madison MS | 500/4-8
502 48th St 52627 | 319-372-4687
Todd Dirth, prin. | Fax 372-0378

Holy Trinity HS | 200/7-12
2600 Avenue A 52627 | 319-372-2486
Chuck Elbert, prin. | Fax 372-6310

Fredericksburg, Chickasaw, Pop. 923
Fredericksburg Community SD | 300/K-8
401 E High St 50630 | 563-237-5364
Rick Pederson, supt. | Fax 237-5888
www.fburg.k12.ia.us
Sumner-Fredericksburg MS | 200/6-8
PO Box 337 50630 | 563-237-5334
Jill Glenn, prin. | Fax 237-6329

Garden Grove, Decatur, Pop. 208
Mormon Trail Community SD
Supt. — See Humeston
Mormon Trail JSHS | 100/7-12
PO Box 177 50103 | 641-443-3425
Steve Hunt, prin. | Fax 443-2644

Garnavillo, Clayton, Pop. 742
Clayton Ridge Community SD
Supt. — See Guttenberg
Clayton Ridge MS | 200/5-8
PO Box 9 52049 | 563-964-2321
Shane Wahls, prin. | Fax 964-2756

Garner, Hancock, Pop. 3,097
Garner-Hayfield Community SD | 700/PK-12
PO Box 449 50438 | 641-923-2718
Tyler Williams, supt. | Fax 923-3825
www.garner.k12.ia.us
Garner-Hayfield/Ventura HS | 300/9-12
PO Box 449 50438 | 641-923-2632
Jim Haag, prin. | Fax 923-4005

Garwin, Tama, Pop. 518
GMG Community SD | 500/PK-12
306 Park St 50632 | 641-499-2239
Ben Petty, supt. | Fax 499-2159
www.garwin.k12.ia.us
GMG JSHS | 200/7-12
306 Park St 50632 | 641-499-2005
Mark Polich, prin. | Fax 499-2552

George, Lyon, Pop. 1,076
George-Little Rock Community SD | 500/PK-12
PO Box 6 51237 | 712-475-3311
Janel Guse, supt. | Fax 475-3574
george-littlerock.org/
George-Little Rock HS | 100/9-12
PO Box 6 51237 | 712-475-3311
Mike Munson, prin. | Fax 475-6573
Other Schools – See Little Rock

Gilbert, Story, Pop. 1,068
Gilbert Community SD | 1,300/PK-12
103 Mathews Dr 50105 | 515-232-3740
Lindsey Beecher, supt. | Fax 232-0099
www.gilbert.k12.ia.us
Gilbert HS | 400/9-12
103 Mathews Dr 50105 | 515-232-3738
Greg Fisher, prin. | Fax 232-0099
Gilbert MS | 400/5-8
201 E Mathews Dr 50105 | 515-232-0540
Chris Billings, prin. | Fax 232-0541

Gilbertville, Black Hawk, Pop. 708

Don Bosco HS | 200/9-12
405 16th Ave 50634 | 319-296-1692
Eric Eckerman, prin. | Fax 296-1693

Gilman, Marshall, Pop. 508
East Marshall Community SD | 900/PK-12
PO Box 159 50106 | 641-498-7481
Dianne Anderson, supt. | Fax 498-2035
www.e-marshall.k12.ia.us
East Marshall MS | 300/5-8
PO Box 159 50106 | 641-498-7483
Robert Schelp, prin. | Fax 498-2180
Other Schools – See Le Grand

Gladbrook, Tama, Pop. 941
Gladbrook-Reinbeck Community SD
Supt. — See Reinbeck
Gladbrook-Reinbeck MS | 200/5-8
PO Box 370 50635 | 641-473-2842
Brian Williams, prin. | Fax 473-2913

Glenwood, Mills, Pop. 5,209
Glenwood Community SD | 2,200/PK-12
103 Central St Ste 300 51534 | 712-527-9034
Devin Embray, supt. | Fax 527-4287
www.glenwoodschools.org
Glenwood HS | 700/9-12
504 Sharp St 51534 | 712-527-4897
Kerry Newman, prin. | Fax 527-9554
Glenwood MS | 500/6-8
400 Sivers Rd 51534 | 712-527-4887
Heidi Stanley, prin. | Fax 527-3411

Glidden, Carroll, Pop. 1,142
Glidden-Ralston Community SD | 400/PK-12
PO Box 488 51443 | 712-659-3411
David Haggard, supt. | Fax 659-2248
www.glidden-ralston.k12.ia.us
Glidden-Ralston JSHS | 200/7-12
PO Box 488 51443 | 712-659-2205
Kreg Lensch, prin. | Fax 659-2248

Goose Lake, Clinton, Pop. 238
Northeast Community SD | 700/PK-12
PO Box 66 52750 | 563-577-2249
James Cox, supt. | Fax 577-2450
www.northeast.k12.ia.us
Northeast Alternative HS | 50/Alt
PO Box 116 52750 | 563-577-2249
Bryce Bielenberg, prin. | Fax 577-2248
Northeast MSHS | 400/7-12
PO Box 70 52750 | 563-577-2249
Alicia Christiansen, prin. | Fax 577-2248

Gowrie, Webster, Pop. 1,027
Prairie Valley Community SD | 700/PK-12
PO Box 49 50543 | 515-352-5575
Launi Dane, supt. | Fax 352-5573
www.prairievalley.k12.ia.us
Prairie Valley JSHS | 300/7-12
PO Box 49 50543 | 515-352-3142
Dennis Hammen, prin. | Fax 352-3143

Graettinger, Palo Alto, Pop. 839
Graettinger-Terril Community SD | 200/PK-12
PO Box 58 51342 | 712-859-3286
Fax 859-3509
www.gtschools.k12.ia.us/
Graettinger-Terril MSHS | 100/6-12
PO Box 58 51342 | 712-859-3286
Teresa Alesch, prin. | Fax 859-3509

Granville, Sioux, Pop. 307

Spalding HS | 100/7-12
PO Box 168 51022 | 712-727-3451
Lisa Hamerlinck, prin. | Fax 727-3455

Greene, Butler, Pop. 1,121
North Butler Community SD
Supt. — See Allison
North Butler HS | 200/9-12
PO Box 190 50636 | 641-816-5631
Dan Huff, prin. | Fax 816-5921

Greenfield, Adair, Pop. 1,975
Nodaway Valley Community SD | 700/PK-12
410 NW 2nd St 50849 | 641-743-6127
Casey Berlau, supt. | Fax 343-7173
www.nodawayvalley.org/
Nodaway Valley HS | 200/9-12
410 NW 2nd St 50849 | 641-743-6141
Lanny Kliefoth, prin. | Fax 343-7040
Other Schools – See Fontanelle

Grimes, Polk, Pop. 8,166
Dallas Center-Grimes Community SD
Supt. — See Dallas Center
Dallas Center-Grimes Community HS | 400/10-12
2555 W 1st St 50111 | 515-986-9747
Cary Justmann, prin. | Fax 986-9734
Dallas Center-Grimes Meadows | 8-9
2555 W 1st St Ste 200 50111
Lori Phillips, prin.

Grinnell, Poweshiek, Pop. 9,024
Grinnell-Newburg Community SD | 1,800/PK-12
927 4th Ave 50112 | 641-236-2700
Todd Abrahamson, supt. | Fax 236-2699
www.grinnell-k12.org
Grinnell Community HS | 600/9-12
1333 Sunset St 50112 | 641-236-2720
Kevin Seney, prin. | Fax 236-2692
Grinnell Community MS | 500/5-8
132 East St S 50112 | 641-236-2750
Sara Hegg-Dunne, prin. | Fax 236-2732
Grinnell New Horizons Alternative HS | Alt
927 4th Ave 50112 | 641-236-2720
Kevin Seney, prin. | Fax 236-2692

Grinnell College | Post-Sec.
PO Box 805 50112 | 641-269-4000

Griswold, Cass, Pop. 1,029
Griswold Community SD 600/PK-12
PO Box 280 51535 712-778-2152
Dana Kunze, supt. Fax 778-4145
www.griswoldschools.org/
Griswold MSHS 300/6-12
PO Box 280 51535 712-778-2154
T. J. Dunphy, prin. Fax 778-2161

Grundy Center, Grundy, Pop. 2,679
Grundy Center Community SD 500/PK-12
1301 12th St 50638 319-825-5418
Cassandra Murra, supt. Fax 825-5419
www.spartanpride.net
Grundy Center MSHS 200/5-12
1006 M Ave 50638 319-825-5449
Steve VanderPol, prin. Fax 825-6415

Guthrie Center, Guthrie, Pop. 1,559
Guthrie Center Community SD 500/PK-12
906 School St 50115 641-332-2972
Steve Smith, supt. Fax 332-2973
www.guthrie.k12.ia.us
Guthrie Center JSHS 200/7-12
906 School St 50115 641-332-2236
Garold Thomas, prin. Fax 332-2973

Guttenberg, Clayton, Pop. 1,910
Clayton Ridge Community SD 600/PK-12
PO Box 520 52052 563-252-2341
Allen Nelson, supt. Fax 252-2656
www.claytonridge.k12.ia.us
Clayton Ridge HS 200/9-12
PO Box 520 52052 563-252-2342
Kris Einck, prin. Fax 252-2656
Other Schools – See Garnavillo

Hamburg, Fremont, Pop. 1,176
Hamburg Community SD 200/PK-8
105 E St 51640 712-382-2703
Jay Lutt, supt. Fax 385-3181
www.hamburg.k12.ia.us
Nishnabotna MS 50/6-8
105 E St 51640 712-382-2703
Jan Harris, prin. Fax 382-1211

Hampton, Franklin, Pop. 4,420
Hampton-Dumont Community SD 1,200/PK-12
601 12th Ave NE 50441 641-456-2175
Todd Lettow, supt. Fax 456-5750
www.hampton-dumont.k12.ia.us/
Hampton-Dumont HS 400/9-12
101 12th Ave NW 50441 641-456-4893
Steve Madson, prin. Fax 456-4569
Hampton-Dumont MS 400/4-8
601 12th Ave NE 50441 641-456-4735
Anthony Spradlin, prin. Fax 456-2023

Harlan, Shelby, Pop. 5,057
Harlan Community SD 1,600/PK-12
2102 Durant St 51537 712-755-2152
Justin Wagner, supt. Fax 755-7312
www.harlan.k12.ia.us
Harlan Community HS 500/9-12
2102 Durant St 51537 712-755-3101
John Connell, prin. Fax 755-7705
Harlan Community MS 400/6-8
2108 Durant St 51537 712-755-3196
Bill Mueller, prin. Fax 755-3699

Hartley, O'Brien, Pop. 1,644
Hartley-Melvin-Sanborn Community SD 600/PK-12
240 1st St SE 51346 712-928-2022
Bill Thompson, supt. Fax 928-3536
www.hartley-ms.k12.ia.us
Hartley-Melvin-Sanborn HS 200/9-12
PO Box 206 51346 712-928-3406
Mark Petersen, prin. Fax 928-2152
Other Schools – See Sanborn

Hastings, Mills, Pop. 151
East Mills Community SD 300/PK-12
58962 380th St 51540 712-624-8700
Paul Croghan, supt. Fax 624-8279
www.emschools.org
Other Schools – See Malvern

Hawarden, Sioux, Pop. 2,534
West Sioux Community SD 600/PK-12
1300 Falcon Dr 51023 712-551-1461
Randy Collins, supt. Fax 551-1367
www.westsiouxschools.org/
West Sioux HS 200/9-12
1300 Falcon Dr 51023 712-551-1181
Ryan Kramer, prin. Fax 551-1514
West Sioux MS 100/6-8
1300 Falcon Dr 51023 712-551-1022
Ryan Kramer, prin. Fax 551-1367

Hinton, Plymouth, Pop. 925
Hinton Community SD 600/PK-12
PO Box 128 51024 712-947-4329
Pete Stuerman, supt. Fax 947-4427
www.hintonschool.com/
Hinton HS 200/9-12
PO Box 128 51024 712-947-4328
Susan Martens, prin. Fax 947-4427
Hinton MS 200/4-8
PO Box 128 51024 712-947-4328
Peter Stuerman, prin. Fax 947-4947

Holstein, Ida, Pop. 1,384
Galva-Holstein Community SD 500/PK-12
PO Box 320 51025 712-368-4353
Dave Kwikkel, supt. Fax 368-4843
www.rvraptors.org/
Ridge View HS 200/9-12
PO Box 320 51025 712-368-4353
Ken Slater, prin. Fax 368-4843

Holy Cross, Dubuque, Pop. 372

LaSalle S - Holy Cross Center 100/4-8
PO Box 368 52053 563-870-2405
Steven Cornelius, prin. Fax 870-4101

Hubbard, Hardin, Pop. 843
Hubbard-Radcliffe Community SD 400/PK-8
PO Box 129 50122 641-864-2211
Joel Semprini, supt. Fax 864-2422
www.hubbard.k12.ia.us
South Hardin MS 200/6-8
PO Box 129 50122 641-864-2211
Patricia Heinz, prin. Fax 864-2422

Hudson, Black Hawk, Pop. 2,275
Hudson Community SD 600/K-12
PO Box 240 50643 319-988-3233
Anthony Voss, supt. Fax 988-3235
www.hudson.k12.ia.us
Hudson HS 300/9-12
PO Box 240 50643 319-988-4226
Jeff Dieken, prin. Fax 988-4174
Hudson MS 100/7-8
PO Box 240 50643 319-988-4137
Jeff Dieken, prin. Fax 988-4137

Hull, Sioux, Pop. 2,161
Boyden-Hull Community SD 600/K-12
PO Box 678 51239 712-439-2711
Steve Grond, supt. Fax 439-1419
www.boyden-hull.k12.ia.us
Boyden-Hull JSHS 300/7-12
PO Box 678 51239 712-439-2440
Dan Pottebaum, prin. Fax 439-1419

Western Christian HS 300/9-12
PO Box 658 51239 712-439-1013
Dan Barkel, prin. Fax 439-1407

Humboldt, Humboldt, Pop. 4,652
Humboldt Community SD
Supt. — See Dakota City
Humboldt HS 400/9-12
1500 Wildcat Rd 50548 515-332-1430
Lori Westhoff, prin. Fax 332-7150
Humboldt MS 300/5-8
1400 Wildcat Rd 50548 515-332-2812
Brenda Geitzenauer, prin. Fax 332-2023

Humeston, Wayne, Pop. 485
Mormon Trail Community SD 200/PK-12
PO Box 156 50123 641-877-2521
Alan Miller, supt. Fax 877-3400
www.mormontrailcsd.org/
Other Schools – See Garden Grove

Huxley, Story, Pop. 3,264
Ballard Community SD 1,400/PK-12
PO Box 307 50124 515-597-2811
Herman Maxey, supt. Fax 597-2965
www.ballard.k12.ia.us/
Ballard Community HS 400/9-12
PO Box 307 50124 515-597-2971
John Ronca, prin. Fax 597-2964
Ballard Community MS 200/6-8
PO Box 307 50124 515-597-2815
Thomas Maher, prin. Fax 597-2818

Ida Grove, Ida, Pop. 2,129
Odebolt-Arthur/Battle Creek-Ida Grove SD 900/PK-12
900 John Montgomery Dr 51445 712-364-3687
Dr. Nick Ouellette, supt. Fax 364-3609
www.oabcig.org
Odebolt-Arthur/Battle Creek-Ida Grove HS 300/9-12
900 John Montgomery Dr 51445 712-364-3371
Patrick Miller, prin. Fax 364-4463
Other Schools – See Odebolt

Independence, Buchanan, Pop. 5,911
Independence Community SD 1,100/PK-12
1207 1st St W 50644 319-334-7400
Jean Peterson, supt. Fax 334-7404
www.independence.k12.ia.us/
Buchanan County Success Center 50/Alt
2349 Jamestown Ave Ste 2C 50644 319-334-7440
Jennifer Sornson, prin.
Independence JSHS 400/7-12
514 5th Ave SE 50644 319-334-7405
Jennifer Sornson, prin. Fax 334-6096

Indianola, Warren, Pop. 14,597
Indianola Community SD 3,500/PK-12
1304 E 2nd Ave 50125 515-961-9500
Dr. Michael Teigland, supt. Fax 961-9505
www.indianola.k12.ia.us
Indianola HS 1,000/9-12
1304 E 1st Ave 50125 515-961-9510
Brian Carico, prin. Fax 961-9519
Indianola MS 800/6-8
403 S 15th St 50125 515-961-9530
Annette Jauron, prin. Fax 961-9535

Simpson College Post-Sec.
701 N C St 50125 515-961-6251

Inwood, Lyon, Pop. 809
West Lyon Community SD 800/PK-12
1787 Iowa 182 Ave 51240 712-753-4917
Jim Hargens, supt. Fax 753-4928
www.west-lyon.k12.ia.us/
West Lyon HS 200/9-12
1787 Iowa 182 Ave 51240 712-753-4917
Doug Jiskoot, prin. Fax 753-4928
West Lyon JHS 100/7-8
1787 Iowa 182 Ave 51240 712-753-4917
Doug Jiskoot, prin. Fax 753-4928

Iowa City, Johnson, Pop. 66,297
Iowa City Community SD 11,500/PK-12
1725 N Dodge St 52245 319-688-1000
Stephen Murley, supt. Fax 688-1009
www.edline.net/pages/ICCSD/
Iowa City HS 1,400/9-12
1900 Morningside Dr 52245 319-688-1040
John Bacon, prin. Fax 688-1049
Southeast JHS 700/7-8
2501 Bradford Dr 52240 319-688-1070
Deb Wretman, prin. Fax 688-1079
Tate HS 100/Alt
1528 Mall Dr 52240 319-688-1080
Ann Browning, prin. Fax 688-1089
West HS 1,900/9-12
2901 Melrose Ave 52246 319-688-1050
Jerry Arganbright, prin. Fax 688-1059
Other Schools – See Coralville, North Liberty

La' James International College Post-Sec.
227 E Market St 52245 319-337-2109
Regina HS 400/7-12
2150 Rochester Ave 52245 319-338-5436
Glenn Plummer, prin. Fax 887-3817
University of Iowa Post-Sec.
107 Calvin Hall 52242 319-335-3500

Iowa Falls, Hardin, Pop. 5,192
Iowa Falls Community SD 1,100/PK-12
710 North St 50126 641-648-6400
Dr. John Robbins, supt. Fax 648-6401
www.ifacadets.net
Iowa Falls - Alden HS 400/9-12
1903 Taylor Ave 50126 641-648-6440
Clyde Tarrence, prin. Fax 648-3222
Riverbend MS 200/7-8
1124 Union St 50126 641-648-6430
Jeff Burchfield, prin. Fax 648-6432

Ellsworth Community College Post-Sec.
1100 College Ave 50126 800-322-9235

Janesville, Bremer, Pop. 923
Janesville Consolidated SD 300/PK-12
PO Box 478 50647 319-987-2581
B.J. Meaney, supt. Fax 987-2824
www.janesville.k12.ia.us
Janesville JSHS 200/6-12
PO Box 478 50647 319-987-2581
Jen Poock, prin. Fax 987-2824

Jefferson, Greene, Pop. 4,314
Jefferson-Scranton Community SD 1,000/PK-12
204 W Madison St 50129 515-386-4168
Tim Christensen, supt. Fax 386-3591
www.jefferson-scranton.k12.ia.us
Greene County HS 300/9-12
101 Ram Dr 50129 515-386-2188
Brain Phillips, prin. Fax 386-2159
Greene County MS 200/7-8
203 W Harrison St 50129 515-386-8126
Karen Younie, prin. Fax 386-4412

Jesup, Buchanan, Pop. 2,492
Jesup Community SD 900/PK-12
PO Box 287 50648 319-827-1700
Nathan Marting, supt. Fax 827-3905
www.jesup.k12.ia.us
Jesup HS 200/9-12
PO Box 287 50648 319-827-1700
Rodney Chamberlin, prin. Fax 827-3905
Jesup MS 200/5-8
PO Box 287 50648 319-827-1700
Lisa Loecher, prin. Fax 827-3905

Jewell, Hamilton, Pop. 1,204
South Hamilton Community SD 700/PK-12
315 Division St 50130 515-827-5479
Tim Johnson, supt. Fax 827-5368
www.s-hamilton.k12.ia.us
South Hamilton MSHS 300/7-12
315 Division St 50130 515-827-5418
W. Scott Dryer, prin. Fax 827-5368

Johnston, Polk, Pop. 17,014
Johnston Community SD 6,300/PK-12
PO Box 10 50131 515-278-0470
Clay Guthmiller, supt. Fax 278-5884
www.johnston.k12.ia.us
Johnston MS 900/8-9
PO Box 10 50131 515-278-0476
Brian Carico, prin. Fax 278-0130
Johnston SHS 1,300/10-12
PO Box 10 50131 515-278-0449
Brent Riessen, prin. Fax 276-5795

La' James International College Post-Sec.
8805 Chambery Blvd 50131 515-278-2208

Kalona, Washington, Pop. 2,347
Mid-Prairie Community SD
Supt. — See Wellman
Mid-Prairie MS 300/6-8
713 F Ave 52247 319-656-2241
Nancy Hurd, prin. Fax 656-2207

Iowa Mennonite HS 100/9-12
1421 540th St SW 52247 319-656-2073
Tony Miller, prin. Fax 656-2073
Shiloh University Post-Sec.
100 Shiloh Dr 52247 319-656-2447

Kanawha, Hancock, Pop. 646
West Hancock Community SD
Supt. — See Britt

West Hancock MS 200/5-8
PO Box 130 50447 641-762-3261
Ruth Verbrugge, prin. Fax 762-3263

Keokuk, Lee, Pop. 10,499
Keokuk Community SD 1,500/PK-12
1721 Franklin St 52632 319-524-1402
Tim Hood, supt. Fax 524-1114
www.keokukschools.org
Keokuk HS 700/9-12
2285 Middle Rd 52632 319-524-2542
Zach Wigle, prin. Fax 524-1784
Keokuk MS 500/6-8
2002 Orleans Ave 52632 319-524-3737
Gary Benda, prin. Fax 524-1511

Southeastern Community College Post-Sec.
PO Box 6007 52632 319-524-3221

Keosauqua, Van Buren, Pop. 1,003
Van Buren Community SD 600/PK-12
405 4th St 52565 319-293-3334
Dr. Pam Ewell, supt. Fax 293-3301
www.van-buren.k12.ia.us
Van Buren Community HS 200/9-12
405 4th St 52565 319-293-3183
Chuck Banks, prin. Fax 293-3345
Van Buren MS 100/7-8
405 4th St 52565 319-293-3803
Chuck Banks, prin. Fax 293-3301

Keota, Keokuk, Pop. 998
Keota Community SD 300/PK-12
PO Box 88 52248 641-636-2189
Mark Schneider, supt. Fax 636-3009
www.keota.k12.ia.us/
Keota JSHS 100/7-12
PO Box 88 52248 641-636-3491
Lisa Brenneman, prin. Fax 636-2210

Kingsley, Plymouth, Pop. 1,392
Kingsley-Pierson Community SD 500/K-12
PO Box 520 51028 712-378-2861
Scott Bailey, supt. Fax 378-3729
www.kingsley-pierson.k12.ia.us
Kingsley-Pierson HS 100/9-12
PO Box 520 51028 712-378-2861
Scott Bailey, prin. Fax 378-3729
Other Schools – See Pierson

Knoxville, Marion, Pop. 7,242
Knoxville Community SD 1,300/PK-12
309 W Main St 50138 641-842-6552
Randy Flack, supt. Fax 842-2109
www.kcsd.k12.ia.us
GOAL Alternative S 50/Alt
614 E Washington St 50138 641-842-4533
Jill Van Woerkom, prin. Fax 828-8695
Knoxville HS 600/9-12
1811 W Madison St 50138 641-842-2173
Kevin Crawford, prin. Fax 842-2066
Knoxville MS 400/6-8
102 N Lincoln St 50138 641-842-3315
Brian McNeill, prin. Fax 842-5754

Lake City, Calhoun, Pop. 1,715
Southern Cal Community SD 700/PK-12
PO Box 45 51449 712-464-7210
Jeff Kruse, supt. Fax 464-3724
www.scc.k12.ia.us
South Central Calhoun HS 100/9-12
PO Box 45 51449 712-464-7211
Randy Martin, prin. Fax 464-1012
Other Schools – See Rockwell City

Lake Mills, Winnebago, Pop. 2,090
Lake Mills Community SD 700/K-12
102 S 4th Ave E 50450 641-592-0881
Daryl Sherman, supt. Fax 592-0883
www.lake-mills.k12.ia.us
Lake Mills HS 200/9-12
102 S 4th Ave E 50450 641-592-0893
James Scholbrock, prin. Fax 592-0883
Lake Mills MS 200/6-8
102 S 4th Ave E 50450 641-592-0894
James Scholbrock, prin. Fax 592-0883

Lake Park, Dickinson, Pop. 1,094
Harris-Lake Park Community SD 400/PK-12
PO Box 8 51347 712-832-3809
Dennis Peters, supt. Fax 832-3812
www.harris-lp.k12.ia.us
Harris-Lake Park MSHS 200/6-12
PO Box 8 51347 712-832-3809
Dennis Peters, prin. Fax 832-3812

Lake View, Sac, Pop. 1,137
East Sac County SD 1,000/PK-12
PO Box 110 51450 712-665-5000
Dr. Kevin Fiene, supt. Fax 665-5021
www.eastsac.k12.ia.us/
East Sac County HS 300/9-12
PO Box 110 51450 712-665-5001
Kevin Litterer, prin. Fax 665-5022
Other Schools – See Sac City

Lamoni, Decatur, Pop. 2,266
Lamoni Community SD 400/PK-12
202 N Walnut St 50140 641-784-3342
Chris Coffelt, supt. Fax 784-6548
lamoni.k12.ia.us
Lamoni HS 100/9-12
202 N Walnut St 50140 641-784-3351
Ed Huenemann, prin. Fax 784-6548
Lamoni MS 100/6-8
202 N Walnut St 50140 641-784-7299
Ed Huenemann, prin. Fax 784-6548

Graceland University Post-Sec.
1 University Pl 50140 641-784-5000

Lansing, Allamakee, Pop. 998
Eastern Allamakee Community SD 400/PK-12
569 Center St 52151 563-538-4201
Dale Crozier, supt. Fax 538-4969
www.e-allamakee.k12.ia.us/
Kee HS 100/9-12
569 Center St 52151 563-538-4201
Mary Hogan, prin. Fax 538-4969
Lansing MS 100/5-8
569 Center St 52151 563-538-4201
Mary Hogan, prin. Fax 538-4969

La Porte City, Black Hawk, Pop. 2,264
Union Community SD 1,200/K-12
200 Adams St 50651 319-342-2674
Neil Mullen, supt. Fax 342-2393
www.union.k12.ia.us/
Union HS 400/9-12
200 Adams St 50651 319-342-2697
Travis Fleshner, prin. Fax 342-2393
Other Schools – See Dysart

Latimer, Franklin, Pop. 507
CAL Community SD 300/PK-12
1441 Gull St 50452 641-579-6087
Dwight Widen, supt. Fax 579-6408
www.cal.k12.ia.us
CAL HS 100/7-12
1441 Gull St 50452 641-579-6086
Robert Meier, prin. Fax 579-6408

Laurens, Pocahontas, Pop. 1,251
Laurens-Marathon Community SD 300/PK-12
300 W Garfield St 50554 712-841-5000
Iner Joelson, supt. Fax 841-5010
www.laurens-marathon.k12.ia.us
Laurens-Marathon HS 100/9-12
300 W Garfield St 50554 712-841-5000
JoAnne Morenz, prin. Fax 841-5010
Laurens-Marathon MS 100/6-8
300 W Garfield St 50554 712-841-5000
JoAnne Morenz, prin. Fax 841-5010

Lawton, Woodbury, Pop. 902
Lawton-Bronson Community SD 600/PK-12
100 Tara Way 51030 712-944-5183
Jeff Thelander, supt. Fax 944-5568
www.lawton-bronson.k12.ia.us
Lawton JSHS 300/7-12
100 Tara Way 51030 712-944-5181
Rachel Binneboese, prin. Fax 944-5568

Le Claire, Scott, Pop. 3,701
Pleasant Valley Community SD
Supt. — See Bettendorf
Pleasant Valley JHS 600/7-8
3501 Wisconsin St 52753 563-332-0200
Trampus Budde, prin. Fax 332-0205

Le Grand, Marshall, Pop. 933
East Marshall Community SD
Supt. — See Gilman
East Marshall HS 300/9-12
PO Box A 50142 641-479-2785
Rex Kozak, prin. Fax 479-2601

Le Mars, Plymouth, Pop. 9,729
Le Mars Community SD 2,100/PK-12
940 Lincoln St SW 51031 712-546-4155
Dr. Todd Wendt, supt. Fax 546-5934
www.lemars.k12.ia.us
Individualized Learning Center 50/Alt
940 Lincoln St SW 51031 712-546-5858
Mark Iverson, prin. Fax 546-5934
Le Mars HS 600/9-12
940 Lincoln St SW 51031 712-546-4153
Mark Iverson, prin. Fax 546-9581
Le Mars MS 500/6-8
940 Lincoln St SW 51031 712-546-7022
Steve Shanks, prin. Fax 546-7024

Gehlen Catholic HS 200/7-12
709 Plymouth St NE 51031 712-546-5126
Jeff Alesch, prin. Fax 546-9384

Lenox, Taylor, Pop. 1,401
Lenox Community SD 400/PK-12
600 S Locust St 50851 641-333-2244
David Henrichs, supt. Fax 333-2247
www.lenox.k12.ia.us
Lenox JSHS 200/7-12
600 S Locust St 50851 641-333-2244
Mike Still, prin. Fax 333-2247

Leon, Decatur, Pop. 1,972
Central Decatur Community SD 700/PK-12
1201 NE Poplar St 50144 641-446-4819
Chris Coffelt, supt. Fax 446-7990
www.central-decatur.k12.ia.us/
Central Decatur JSHS 300/7-12
1201 NE Poplar St 50144 641-446-4816
Rudy Evertsen, prin. Fax 446-7990

Letts, Louisa, Pop. 371
Louisa-Muscatine Community SD 900/PK-12
14478 170th St 52754 319-726-3541
Mike Van Sickle, supt. Fax 726-3334
www.lmcsd.org
Louisa-Muscatine HS 300/9-12
14354 170th St 52754 319-726-3421
Chris Parkhurst, prin. Fax 726-3649
Louisa-Muscatine JHS 100/7-8
14354 170th St 52754 319-726-3421
Stacy Beatty, prin. Fax 726-3649

Liberty Center, Warren
Southeast Warren Community SD 500/PK-12
PO Box 19 50145 641-466-3510
Delane Galvin, supt. Fax 466-3525
www.se-warren.k12.ia.us
Southeast Warren JSHS 200/7-12
PO Box 19 50145 641-466-3331
Delane Galvin, prin. Fax 466-3525

Lisbon, Linn, Pop. 2,132
Lisbon Community SD 700/PK-12
PO Box 839 52253 319-455-2075
Brad Laures, supt. Fax 455-2733
www.lisbon.k12.ia.us
Lisbon HS 200/9-12
PO Box 839 52253 319-455-2106
Ian Dye, prin. Fax 455-3208
Lisbon MS 100/6-8
PO Box 839 52253 319-455-2659
Ian Dye, prin. Fax 455-2733

Little Rock, Lyon, Pop. 458
George-Little Rock Community SD
Supt. — See George
George-Little Rock MS 100/6-8
PO Box 247 51243 712-479-2771
Janel Guse, prin. Fax 479-2770

Logan, Harrison, Pop. 1,523
Logan-Magnolia Community SD 700/PK-12
1200 N 2nd Ave 51546 712-644-2250
James Hammrich, supt. Fax 644-2934
www.lomaschools.org
Logan-Magnolia JSHS 300/7-12
1200 N 2nd Ave 51546 712-644-2250
Christi Gochenour, prin. Fax 644-2934

Lone Tree, Johnson, Pop. 1,281
Lone Tree Community SD 500/PK-12
PO Box 520 52755 319-629-4212
Michael Reeves, supt. Fax 629-4324
www.lone-tree.k12.ia.us
Lone Tree JSHS 200/6-12
PO Box 520 52755 319-629-4610
Mark Hopkins, prin. Fax 629-4324

Mc Gregor, Clayton, Pop. 856
MFL MarMac Community SD
Supt. — See Monona
MFL MarMac MS 200/4-8
PO Box D 52157 563-873-3463
Josh Mallicoat, prin. Fax 873-2371

Madrid, Boone, Pop. 2,521
Madrid Community SD 600/K-12
201 N Main St 50156 515-795-3241
Brian Horn, supt. Fax 795-2121
madrid.k12.ia.us
Madrid HS 200/9-12
599 N Kennedy Ave 50156 515-795-3240
Ryan Ridout, prin. Fax 795-4408
Madrid JHS 100/7-8
599 N Kennedy Ave 50156 515-795-3240
Ryan Ridout, prin. Fax 795-4408

Malvern, Mills, Pop. 1,127
East Mills Community SD
Supt. — See Hastings
East Mills JSHS 200/7-12
1505 E 15th St 51551 712-624-8645
Andy Irwin, prin. Fax 624-8124
East Mills Learning Center 50/Alt
409 E 9th St 51551 712-624-8681
Paul Croghan, admin. Fax 624-8440

Manchester, Delaware, Pop. 5,134
West Delaware County Community SD 1,600/PK-12
701 New St 52057 563-927-3515
Dr. Kristen Rickey, supt. Fax 927-2785
www.w-delaware.k12.ia.us
West Delaware HS 500/9-12
605 New St 52057 563-927-3515
Jon Nordaas, prin. Fax 927-6222
West Delaware MS 500/5-8
1101 Doctor St 52057 563-927-3515
Lisa Wunn, prin. Fax 927-9115

Manilla, Crawford, Pop. 772
IKM-Manning Community SD 800/PK-12
PO Box 580 51454 712-654-2852
Thomas Ward, supt. Fax 654-9280
www.ikm-manning.k12.ia.us/
IKM-Manning MS 200/5-8
PO Box 580 51454 712-654-9385
Sharon Whitson, prin. Fax 654-9282
Other Schools – See Manning

Manly, Worth, Pop. 1,311
Central Springs Community SD 800/PK-12
PO Box 190 50456 641-454-2211
Steve Ward, supt. Fax 454-2212
www.centralsprings.net/
Central Springs HS 300/9-12
PO Box 190 50456 641-454-2208
Ken Estes, prin. Fax 454-2212
Other Schools – See Nora Springs

Manning, Carroll, Pop. 1,493
IKM-Manning Community SD
Supt. — See Manilla
IKM-Manning HS 200/9-12
209 10th St 51455 712-655-3781
Brian Wall, prin. Fax 655-3311

Manson, Calhoun, Pop. 1,685
Manson Northwest Webster Community SD 700/PK-12
PO Box 387 50563 712-469-2202
Mark Egli, supt. Fax 469-2298
www.mnwcougars.com

Manson Northwest Webster MSHS 400/7-12
1601 15th St 50563 712-469-2245
Shawn Holloway, prin. Fax 469-3131

Mapleton, Monona, Pop. 1,204
Maple Valley-Anthon Oto Community SD 700/PK-12
501 S 7th St 51034 712-881-1315
Steve Oberg, supt. Fax 881-1316
www.maple-valley.k12.ia.us
Maple Valley-Anthon Oto HS 300/9-12
501 S 7th St 51034 712-881-1317
Dan Dougherty, prin. Fax 881-1321
Other Schools – See Anthon

Maquoketa, Jackson, Pop. 5,978
Maquoketa Community SD 1,500/PK-12
612 S Vermont St 52060 563-652-4984
Dr. Kim Huckstadt, supt. Fax 652-6958
www.maquoketa.k12.ia.us
Maquoketa HS 600/9-12
600 Washington St 52060 563-652-2451
Mark Vervaecke, prin. Fax 652-5324
Maquoketa MS 300/6-8
200 E Locust St 52060 563-652-4956
Christine Snell, prin. Fax 652-6885

Marcus, Cherokee, Pop. 1,110
Marcus-Meriden-Cleghorn Community SD 400/PK-12
PO Box 667 51035 712-376-4171
Jan Brandhorst, supt. Fax 376-4302
www.marcus-mer-cleg.k12.ia.us
Marcus-Meriden-Cleghorn Community HS 200/7-12
PO Box 667 51035 712-376-4172
Mike Rundall, prin. Fax 376-4302

Marengo, Iowa, Pop. 2,516
Iowa Valley Community SD 600/PK-12
359 E Hilton St 52301 319-642-7714
Alan Jensen, supt. Fax 642-3023
www.iowa-valley.k12.ia.us
Iowa Valley JSHS 300/7-12
359 E Hilton St 52301 319-642-3332
Shawn Kreman, prin. Fax 642-3023

Marion, Linn, Pop. 34,170
Linn-Mar Community SD 6,400/PK-12
2999 10th St 52302 319-447-3000
Dr. Kathleen Mulholland, supt. Fax 377-9252
www.linnmar.k12.ia.us/
Excelsior MS 800/6-8
3555 10th St 52302 319-447-3130
John Christian, prin. Fax 373-4930
Linn-Mar HS 1,700/9-12
3111 10th St 52302 319-447-3040
Jeffrey Gustason, prin. Fax 377-0486
Oak Ridge MS 700/6-8
4901 Alburnett Rd 52302 319-447-3410
Erica Rausch, prin. Fax 373-3222

Marion ISD 1,700/PK-12
PO Box 606 52302 319-377-4691
Sarah Pinion, supt. Fax 377-4692
www.marion.k12.ia.us/
Marion HS 600/9-12
675 S 15th St 52302 319-377-9891
Greg Semler, prin. Fax 377-7621
Vernon MS 500/5-8
1350 4th Ave 52302 319-377-9401
Phillip Cochran, prin. Fax 377-7670

Marshalltown, Marshall, Pop. 27,096
Marshalltown Community SD 5,000/PK-12
317 Columbus Dr 50158 641-754-1000
Dr. Marvin Wade, supt. Fax 754-1003
www.marshalltown.k12.ia.us
Marshalltown HS 1,600/9-12
1602 S 2nd Ave 50158 641-754-1130
Aiddy Phomvisay, prin. Fax 754-1136
Miller MS 700/7-8
125 S 11th St 50158 641-754-1110
Jacy Large, prin. Fax 754-1115

Iowa School of Beauty Post-Sec.
112 Nicholas Dr 50158 641-752-4223
Marshalltown Community College Post-Sec.
3700 S Center St 50158 641-752-7106

Martensdale, Warren, Pop. 462
Martensdale-St. Marys Community SD 500/PK-12
PO Box 350 50160 641-764-2466
Dr. Bob Newsum, supt. Fax 764-2100
www.mstm.us/
Martensdale-St. Marys JSHS 200/7-12
PO Box 350 50160 641-764-2486
Mike Crozier, prin. Fax 764-2100

Mason City, Cerro Gordo, Pop. 27,653
Mason City Community SD 3,700/PK-12
1515 S Pennsylvania Ave 50401 641-421-4400
Anita Micich, supt. Fax 421-4448
www.masoncityschools.org
Adams MS 600/7-8
29 S Illinois Ave 50401 641-421-4420
Gary Van Hemert, prin. Fax 421-4476
Alternative HS 100/Alt
19 N Illinois Ave 50401 641-421-4426
David Ciccetti, prin. Fax 421-3362
Mason City HS 1,100/9-12
1700 4th St SE 50401 641-421-4431
T.J. Jumper, prin. Fax 421-4523

Kaplan University Post-Sec.
2570 4th St SW 50401 641-423-2530
La' James College Post-Sec.
24 2nd St NE 50401 641-424-2161
Newman HS 200/9-12
2445 19th St SW 50401 641-423-6939
Tony Adams, prin. Fax 423-6653

North Iowa Area Community College Post-Sec.
500 College Dr 50401 641-423-1264
North Iowa Christian S 50/K-12
811 N Kentucky Ave 50401 641-423-6440
Janna Voss, admin. Fax 423-6440
North Iowa Mercy Health Center Post-Sec.
1000 4th St SW 50401 641-422-7722
World Wide College of Auctioneering Post-Sec.
PO Box 949 50402 800-423-5242

Massena, Cass, Pop. 355
CAM Community SD
Supt. — See Anita
CAM MS 100/6-8
207 E 6th St 50853 712-779-2212
Larry Hunt, prin. Fax 779-3365

Maxwell, Story, Pop. 916
Collins-Maxwell Community SD 500/PK-12
400 Metcalf St 50161 515-387-1115
Jason Ellingson, supt. Fax 387-8842
www.collins-maxwell.k12.ia.us
Collins-Maxwell MSHS 300/6-12
400 Metcalf St 50161 515-387-1115
Josh Griffith, prin. Fax 387-8842

Maynard, Fayette, Pop. 516
West Central Community SD 300/K-12
PO Box 54 50655 563-637-2283
Stuart Fuhs, supt. Fax 637-2294
www.w-central.k12.ia.us/
West Central HS 100/9-12
PO Box 54 50655 563-637-2283
Stuart Fuhs, prin. Fax 637-2294

Mediapolis, Des Moines, Pop. 1,547
Mediapolis Community SD 800/PK-12
PO Box 358 52637 319-394-3101
Greg Ray, supt. Fax 394-3021
www.meposchools.org/
Mediapolis HS 300/9-12
725 N Northfield St 52637 319-394-3101
Roger Thornburg, prin. Fax 394-9198
Mediapolis MS 200/6-8
725 N Northfield St 52637 319-394-3101
Roger Thornburg, prin. Fax 394-9198

Melcher, Marion, Pop. 1,280
Melcher-Dallas Community SD 300/PK-12
PO Box 489 50163 641-947-2321
Delane Galvin, supt. Fax 947-2203
www.melcher-dallas.k12.ia.us
Melcher-Dallas HS 100/9-12
PO Box 158 50163 641-947-3731
Jon Suntken, prin. Fax 947-2203
Melcher-Dallas JHS 50/7-8
PO Box 158 50163 641-947-3731
Greg Horstmann, prin. Fax 947-2203

Milford, Dickinson, Pop. 2,878
Okoboji Community SD 1,000/PK-12
PO Box 147 51351 712-338-4757
Gary Janssen, supt. Fax 338-4758
www.okoboji.k12.ia.us
Okoboji HS 300/9-12
PO Box 147 51351 712-338-2446
Brian Downing, prin. Fax 338-2550
Other Schools – See Arnolds Park

Missouri Valley, Harrison, Pop. 2,810
Missouri Valley Community SD 800/PK-12
109 E Michigan St 51555 712-642-2706
Deidre Drees, supt. Fax 642-2456
www.movalleyschools.org
Missouri Valley HS 300/9-12
605 Lincoln Hwy 51555 712-642-4149
Kristie Kruckman, prin. Fax 642-4624
Missouri Valley MS 200/6-8
607 Lincoln Hwy 51555 712-642-2707
Brent Hoesing, prin. Fax 642-3738

Mondamin, Harrison, Pop. 398
West Harrison Community SD 400/PK-12
410 Pine St 51557 712-646-2231
Joel Foster, supt. Fax 646-2891
www.w-harrison.k12.ia.us/
West Harrison MSHS 200/7-12
410 Pine St 51557 712-646-2231
Dan Peterson, prin. Fax 646-2891

Monona, Clayton, Pop. 1,540
MFL MarMac Community SD 700/PK-12
PO Box D 52159 563-539-4795
Dr. Dale Crozier, supt. Fax 539-4913
www.mflmarmac.k12.ia.us
MFL MarMac HS 300/9-12
PO Box D 52159 563-539-2031
Josh Mallicoat, prin. Fax 539-4694
Other Schools – See Mc Gregor

Monroe, Jasper, Pop. 1,825
PCM Community SD 1,100/PK-12
PO Box 610 50170 641-259-2751
Jane Babcock, supt. Fax 259-2753
www.pcmonroe.k12.ia.us
PCM HS 300/9-12
PO Box 610 50170 641-259-2315
Scott Bridges, prin. Fax 259-2317
Other Schools – See Prairie City

Montezuma, Poweshiek, Pop. 1,455
Montezuma Community SD 500/K-12
PO Box 580 50171 641-623-5185
Dave Versteeg, supt. Fax 623-5733
www.montezuma.k12.ia.us
Montezuma HS 200/9-12
PO Box 580 50171 641-623-5121
Brian Moretz, prin. Fax 623-5733
Montezuma JHS 100/7-8
PO Box 580 50171 641-623-5121
Brian Moretz, prin. Fax 623-5733

Monticello, Jones, Pop. 3,779
Monticello Community SD 1,100/PK-12
711 S Maple St 52310 319-465-5963
Chris Anderson, supt. Fax 465-4092
www.monticello.k12.ia.us/
Monticello HS 400/9-12
850 E Oak St 52310 319-465-6597
Joan Young, prin. Fax 465-4253
Monticello MS 300/5-8
217 S Maple St 52310 319-465-3575
William Gilkerson, prin. Fax 465-6959

Moravia, Appanoose, Pop. 658
Moravia Community SD 400/PK-12
505 N Trussell Ave 52571 641-724-3240
Brad Breon, supt. Fax 724-0629
www.moravia.k12.ia.us
Moravia JSHS 200/7-12
505 N Trussell Ave 52571 641-724-3241
Kathy Carr, prin. Fax 724-0629

Moulton, Appanoose, Pop. 600
Moulton-Udell Community SD 200/PK-12
305 E 8th St 52572 641-642-3665
Anthony Ryan, supt. Fax 642-3461
www.moulton-udell.k12.ia.us
Moulton-Udell JSHS 100/7-12
305 E 8th St 52572 641-642-8131
Randy Alger, prin. Fax 642-3461

Mount Ayr, Ringgold, Pop. 1,687
Mount Ayr Community SD 600/PK-12
1001 E Columbus St 50854 641-464-0500
Joe Drake, supt. Fax 464-2325
www.mtayrschools.org
Mount Ayr JSHS 300/7-12
1001 E Columbus St 50854 641-464-0510
Lynne Wallace, prin. Fax 464-2325

Mount Pleasant, Henry, Pop. 8,462
Mount Pleasant Community SD 2,100/PK-12
400 E Madison St 52641 319-385-7750
John Roederer, supt. Fax 385-7788
www.mt-pleasant.k12.ia.us
Mount Pleasant HS 600/9-12
2104 S Grand Ave 52641 319-385-7700
Todd Liechty, prin. Fax 385-7789
Mount Pleasant MS 500/6-8
400 E Madison St 52641 319-385-7730
Darren Hanna, prin. Fax 385-7735
WisdomQuest Education Center 50/Alt
400 E Madison St 52641 319-385-7709
Scot Lamm, prin. Fax 385-7715

Iowa Wesleyan College Post-Sec.
601 N Main St 52641 319-385-8021
Mount Pleasant Christian S 100/PK-12
1505 E Washington St 52641 319-385-8613
Tina Hill, admin. Fax 385-8415

Mount Vernon, Linn, Pop. 4,439
Mount Vernon Community SD 1,300/PK-12
525 Palisades Rd SW 52314 319-895-8845
Dr. Gary O'Malley, supt. Fax 895-8875
www.mountvernon.k12.ia.us
Mount Vernon HS 400/9-12
731 Palisades Rd SW 52314 319-895-8843
Steve Brand, prin. Fax 895-6185
Mount Vernon MS 400/5-8
525 Palisades Rd SW 52314 319-895-6254
Noreen Bush, prin. Fax 895-8134

Cornell College Post-Sec.
600 1st St SW 52314 319-895-4000

Moville, Woodbury, Pop. 1,596
Woodbury Central Community SD 700/PK-12
408 S 4th St 51039 712-873-3128
Doug Glackin, supt. Fax 873-3162
www.woodbury-central.k12.ia.us
Woodbury Central HS 200/9-12
408 S 4th St 51039 712-873-3128
Dan Bormann, prin. Fax 873-3162
Woodbury Central MS 100/6-8
408 S 4th St 51039 712-873-3128
Don Bormann, prin. Fax 873-3162

Murray, Clarke, Pop. 756
Murray Community SD 300/PK-12
PO Box 187 50174 641-447-2517
Alan Miller, supt. Fax 447-2313
www.murraycsd.org
Murray JSHS 100/7-12
PO Box 187 50174 641-447-2517
Beverly Brown, prin. Fax 447-2313

Muscatine, Muscatine, Pop. 22,599
Muscatine Community SD 5,200/PK-12
2900 Mulberry Ave 52761 563-263-7223
William Decker, supt. Fax 263-7729
www.muscatine.k12.ia.us
Central MS 600/6-8
901 Cedar St 52761 563-263-7784
Terry Hogenson, prin. Fax 263-0145
Muscatine HS 1,600/9-12
2705 Cedar St 52761 563-263-6141
Robert Weaton, prin. Fax 264-1794
West MS 600/6-8
600 Kindler Ave 52761 563-263-0411
John Lawrence, prin. Fax 263-6645

Muscatine Community College Post-Sec.
152 Colorado St 52761 563-288-6001

Nashua, Chickasaw, Pop. 1,656
Nashua-Plainfield Community SD 700/PK-12
PO Box 569 50658 641-435-4835
Randall Strabala, supt. Fax 435-4835
www.nashua-plainfield.k12.ia.us
Nashua-Plainfield HS 200/9-12
PO Box 569 50658 641-435-4166
Erik Smith, prin. Fax 435-4167
Other Schools – See Plainfield

Neola, Pottawattamie, Pop. 840
Tri-Center Community SD 800/PK-12
33980 310th St 51559 712-485-2257
Brett Nanninga, supt. Fax 485-2411
www.tri-center.k12.ia.us
Tri-Center HS 200/9-12
33980 310th St 51559 712-485-2257
Angela Huseman, prin. Fax 485-2411
Tri-Center MS 200/6-8
33980 310th St 51559 712-485-2211
Brian Wedemeyer, prin. Fax 485-2402

Nevada, Story, Pop. 6,711
Nevada Community SD 1,600/PK-12
1035 15th St 50201 515-382-2783
Jim Walker, supt. Fax 382-2836
www.nevada.k12.ia.us
Nevada HS 400/9-12
1001 15th St 50201 515-382-3521
Justin Gross, prin. Fax 382-2935
Nevada MS 400/5-8
1035 15th St 50201 515-382-2751
Chris Schmidt, prin. Fax 382-2836

Newell, Buena Vista, Pop. 875
Newell-Fonda Community SD 300/PK-12
PO Box 297 50568 712-272-3324
Jeff Dicks, supt. Fax 272-4276
www.newell-fonda.k12.ia.us
Newell-Fonda HS 100/9-12
PO Box 297 50568 712-272-3325
Alynn Coppock, prin. Fax 272-4276

New Hampton, Chickasaw, Pop. 3,557
New Hampton Community SD 1,100/PK-12
710 W Main St 50659 641-394-2134
Jay Jurrens, supt. Fax 394-2921
www.new-hampton.k12.ia.us
Education Options 50/Alt
710 W Main St 50659 641-394-2144
Sarah Updegraff, prin.
New Hampton HS 400/9-12
710 W Main St 50659 641-394-2144
Sarah Updegraff, prin. Fax 394-6046
New Hampton MS 300/5-8
206 W Main St 50659 641-394-2259
Susan Anderson, prin. Fax 394-2662

New Hartford, Butler, Pop. 512
Dike-New Hartford Community SD
Supt. — See Dike
Dike-New Hartford JHS 100/5-8
PO Box 214 50660 319-983-2206
Jerold Martinek, prin. Fax 983-2207

New London, Henry, Pop. 1,877
New London Community SD 500/PK-12
PO Box 97 52645 319-367-0512
Steve McAllister, supt. Fax 367-0513
www.new-london.k12.ia.us
New London JSHS 300/6-12
PO Box 97 52645 319-367-0500
Scott Kracht, prin. Fax 367-0501

New Sharon, Mahaska, Pop. 1,287
North Mahaska Community SD 600/PK-12
PO Box 89 50207 641-637-4187
Randy Moffit, supt. Fax 637-4559
www.n-mahaska.k12.ia.us
North Mahaska JSHS 200/7-12
PO Box 89 50207 641-637-4187
Douglas Ray, prin. Fax 637-4559

Newton, Jasper, Pop. 15,101
Newton Community SD 2,900/PK-12
700 N 4th Ave E 50208 641-792-5809
Steven McDermott, supt. Fax 792-9159
www.newton.k12.ia.us
Basics & Beyond Alternative S 100/Alt
700 N 4th Ave E 50208 641-792-0335
Laura Selover, prin. Fax 792-0332
Berg MS 500/7-8
1900 N 5th Ave E 50208 641-792-7741
Scott Bauer, prin. Fax 792-7779
Newton HS 900/9-12
800 E 4th St S 50208 641-792-5797
Bill Peters, prin. Fax 792-0005

Des Moines Area Community College Post-Sec.
600 N 2nd Ave W 50208 641-791-3622

Nora Springs, Floyd, Pop. 1,424
Central Springs Community SD
Supt. — See Manly
Central Springs MS 200/5-8
PO Box 367 50458 641-749-5301
Lynn Baldus, prin. Fax 749-5898

North English, Iowa, Pop. 1,037
English Valleys Community SD 600/PK-12
PO Box 490 52316 319-664-3634
Alan Jensen, supt. Fax 664-3636
www.english-valleys.k12.ia.us
English Valleys JSHS 300/7-12
PO Box 490 52316 319-664-3631
Martin Van Roekel, prin. Fax 664-3670

North Liberty, Johnson, Pop. 13,098
Iowa City Community SD
Supt. — See Iowa City
North Central JHS 400/7-8
180 Forevergreen Rd E 52317 319-688-1210
Jane Fry, prin. Fax 688-1219

Northwood, Worth, Pop. 1,968
Northwood-Kensett Community SD 500/K-12
PO Box 289 50459 641-324-2021
Thomas Nugent, supt. Fax 324-2092
www.nwood-kensett.k12.ia.us
Northwood-Kensett JSHS 300/7-12
PO Box 289 50459 641-324-2142
Keith Fritz, prin. Fax 324-2174

Norwalk, Warren, Pop. 8,841
Norwalk Community SD 2,500/PK-12
906 School Ave 50211 515-981-0676
Dennis Wulf, supt. Fax 981-0559
www.norwalk.k12.ia.us/
Eastview 8/9 S 8-9
1600 North Ave 50211 515-981-9655
Dr. Jody Ratigan, prin. Fax 981-9706
Norwalk HS 800/9-12
1201 North Ave 50211 515-981-4201
Dale Barnhill, prin. Fax 981-9875
Norwalk MS 600/6-8
200 Cherry St 50211 515-981-0435
Ken Foster, prin. Fax 981-0771

Oakland, Pottawattamie, Pop. 1,517
Riverside Community SD
Supt. — See Carson
Riverside Community HS 200/7-12
PO Box 428 51560 712-482-6464
David Gute, prin. Fax 482-3074

Odebolt, Sac, Pop. 1,011
Odebolt-Arthur/Battle Creek-Ida Grove SD
Supt. — See Ida Grove
Odebolt-Arthur/Battle Creek-Ida Grove MS 100/6-8
600 S Maple St 51458 712-668-2827
Doug Mogensen, prin. Fax 668-2631

Oelwein, Fayette, Pop. 6,310
Oelwein Community SD 1,300/PK-12
307 8th Ave SE 50662 319-283-3536
Steve Westerberg, supt. Fax 283-4497
www.oelwein.k12.ia.us
Oelwein HS 400/9-12
315 8th Ave SE 50662 319-283-2731
Chad Kohagen, prin. Fax 283-1689
Oelwein MS 300/6-8
300 12th Ave SE 50662 319-283-3015
Mary Beth Steggall, prin. Fax 283-9813

Ogden, Boone, Pop. 2,032
Ogden Community SD 700/PK-12
PO Box 250 50212 515-275-2894
Brad Jermeland, supt. Fax 275-4537
www.ogdenschools.org/
Ogden HS 200/9-12
PO Box 250 50212 515-275-4034
Shawn Zanders, prin. Fax 275-4972
Ogden MS 200/5-8
PO Box 250 50212 515-275-2912
Dave Neubauer, prin. Fax 275-2908

Onawa, Monona, Pop. 2,968
West Monona Community SD 500/PK-12
1314 15th St 51040 712-433-2043
Lyle Schwartz, supt. Fax 433-3803
www.westmonona.org
West Monona HS 200/9-12
1314 15th St 51040 712-433-2453
Scot Aden, prin. Fax 433-3803
West Monona MS 100/6-8
1314 15th St 51040 712-433-9098
Jeremy Braden, prin. Fax 433-1142

Orange City, Sioux, Pop. 5,966
MOC-Floyd Valley Community SD 1,400/PK-12
PO Box 257 51041 712-737-4873
Russ Adams, supt. Fax 737-8789
www.moc-fv.k12.ia.us/
MOC-Floyd Valley HS 400/9-12
615 8th St SE 51041 712-737-4871
Mike Mulder, prin. Fax 737-3933
Other Schools – See Alton

Northwestern College Post-Sec.
101 7th St SW 51041 712-707-7000
Unity Christian HS 300/9-12
216 Michigan Ave SW 51041 712-737-4114
Wayne Dykstra, prin. Fax 737-2686

Orient, Adair, Pop. 408
Orient-Macksburg Community SD 100/PK-12
PO Box 129 50858 641-337-5061
Clark Wicks, supt. Fax 337-5013
www.o-mschools.org
Orient-Macksburg Community S 100/PK-12
PO Box 129 50858 641-337-5061
Teresa Thompson, prin. Fax 337-5013

Osage, Mitchell, Pop. 3,601
Osage Community SD 900/PK-12
820 Sawyer Dr 50461 641-732-5381
Steve Bass, supt. Fax 732-5381
www.osage.k12.ia.us
Osage HS 300/9-12
820 Sawyer Dr 50461 641-732-3102
Tim Hejhal, prin. Fax 732-3456
Osage MS 300/5-8
820 Sawyer Dr 50461 641-732-3127
Jay Marley, prin. Fax 732-5450

Osceola, Clarke, Pop. 4,887
Clarke Community SD 1,500/PK-12
802 N Jackson St 50213 641-342-4969
Ned Cox, supt. Fax 342-6101
www.clarke.k12.ia.us
Clarke Community HS 400/9-12
800 N Jackson St 50213 641-342-6505
Kim Antisdel, prin. Fax 342-2213
Clarke Learning Center 50/Alt
802 N Jackson St 50213 641-342-2804
Kim Antisdel, prin. Fax 342-2804
Clarke MS 200/7-8
800 N Jackson St 50213 641-342-4221
Jeff Sogard, prin. Fax 342-2213

Oskaloosa, Mahaska, Pop. 11,273
Oskaloosa Community SD 2,400/PK-12
PO Box 710 52577 641-673-8345
Russell Reiter, supt. Fax 673-8370
www.oskaloosa.k12.ia.us
Oskaloosa HS 700/9-12
1816 N 3rd St 52577 641-673-3407
Stacy Bandy, prin. Fax 672-2440
Oskaloosa MS 500/6-8
1704 N 3rd St 52577 641-673-8308
Andy Hotek, prin. Fax 673-8308

William Penn University Post-Sec.
201 Trueblood Ave 52577 800-677-9076

Ossian, Winneshiek, Pop. 842
South Winneshiek Community SD
Supt. — See Calmar
South Winneshiek MS 100/6-8
PO Box 298 52161 563-532-9365
Barb Schwamman, prin. Fax 532-9855

Ottumwa, Wapello, Pop. 24,651
Ottumwa Community SD 4,600/PK-12
422 McCarroll Dr 52501 641-684-6596
Davis Eidahl, supt. Fax 684-6522
www.ottumwaschools.com
Accelerated College Career Academy Alt
15260 Truman St 52501 641-683-1342
John Ohlinger, admin. Fax 684-6854
Evans MS 1,000/6-8
812 Chester Ave 52501 641-684-6511
Dave Harper, prin. Fax 684-7386
Ottumwa HS 1,400/9-12
501 E 2nd St 52501 641-683-4444
Mark Hanson, prin. Fax 682-7528

Indian Hills Community College Post-Sec.
525 Grandview Ave 52501 641-683-5111
Iowa School of Beauty Post-Sec.
609 W 2nd St 52501 641-684-6504

Oxford, Johnson, Pop. 790
Clear Creek Amana Community SD 1,700/PK-12
PO Box 487 52322 319-828-4510
Tim Kuehl, supt. Fax 828-4743
www.ccaschools.org
Other Schools – See Tiffin

Packwood, Jefferson, Pop. 200
Pekin Community SD 600/PK-12
1062 Birch Ave 52580 319-695-3707
Frederick Whipple, supt. Fax 695-5130
www.pekincsd.org
Pekin HS 200/9-12
1062 Birch Ave 52580 319-695-3705
Nathan Wood, prin. Fax 661-2353
Pekin Learning Center 50/Alt
1062 Birch Ave 52580 641-695-3705
Nathan Wood, prin. Fax 695-5130

Panora, Guthrie, Pop. 1,114
Panorama Community SD 600/PK-12
PO Box 39 50216 641-755-4144
Kathryn Elliott, supt. Fax 755-3008
www.panorama.k12.ia.us/
Panorama MSHS 200/6-12
PO Box 39 50216 641-755-2317
Mark Johnston, prin. Fax 755-3008

Parkersburg, Butler, Pop. 1,860
Aplington-Parkersburg Community SD 900/PK-12
610 N Johnson St 50665 319-346-1571
Jon Thompson, supt. Fax 346-1012
www.a-pcsd.net
Aplington-Parkersburg HS 300/9-12
610 N Johnson St 50665 319-346-1571
David Meyer, prin. Fax 346-1012
Other Schools – See Aplington

Paullina, O'Brien, Pop. 1,052
South O'Brien Community SD 600/PK-12
PO Box 638 51046 712-949-2115
Dan Moore, supt. Fax 949-2149
www.s-obrien.k12.ia.us
South O'Brien Secondary S 300/7-12
PO Box 638 51046 712-949-3454
Bill Boer, prin. Fax 949-3453

Pella, Marion, Pop. 10,224
Pella Community SD 2,300/PK-12
PO Box 468 50219 641-628-1111
Greg Ebeling, supt. Fax 628-1116
www.pella.k12.ia.us
Pella Community HS 700/9-12
212 E University St 50219 641-628-3870
Eric Nelson, prin. Fax 628-7402
Pella Community MS 300/7-8
613 E 13th St 50219 641-628-4784
Josh Manning, prin. Fax 628-6804

Central College Post-Sec.
812 University St 50219 641-628-9000

Pella Christian HS 300/9-12
300 Eagle Ln 50219 641-628-4440
Darryl De Ruiter, prin. Fax 628-3530

Peosta, Dubuque, Pop. 1,367

Northeast Iowa Community College Post-Sec.
8342 NICC Dr 52068 563-556-5110

Perry, Dallas, Pop. 7,599
Perry Community SD 1,900/PK-12
1102 Willis Ave Ste 200 50220 515-465-4656
Lynn Ubben, supt. Fax 465-4025
www.perry.k12.ia.us/
Perry HS 600/9-12
1200 18th St 50220 515-465-3503
Dan Marburger, prin. Fax 465-5977
Perry MS 400/6-8
1200 18th St 50220 515-465-3531
Shaun Kruger, prin. Fax 465-8555

Pierson, Woodbury, Pop. 361
Kingsley-Pierson Community SD
Supt. — See Kingsley
Pierson MS 100/6-8
321 4th St 51048 712-375-5939
Robert Wiese, prin. Fax 375-5771

Plainfield, Bremer, Pop. 430
Nashua-Plainfield Community SD
Supt. — See Nashua
Nashua-Plainfield MS 200/5-8
PO Box 38 50666 319-276-4451
Edwin Anderson, prin. Fax 276-3541

Pleasant Hill, Polk, Pop. 8,612
Southeast Polk Community SD 5,800/PK-12
8379 NE University Ave 50327 515-967-4294
Craig Menozzi, supt. Fax 967-4257
www.southeastpolk.org/
Southeast Polk HS 1,800/9-12
7945 NE University Ave 50327 515-967-6631
Stephen Pettit, prin. Fax 967-5117
Southeast Polk JHS 1,000/7-8
8325 NE University Ave 50327 515-967-5509
Mike Dailey, prin. Fax 967-1676

Pleasantville, Marion, Pop. 1,681
Pleasantville Community SD 700/PK-12
415 Jones St 50225 515-848-0555
Bob Miller, supt. Fax 848-0561
www.pleasantville.k12.ia.us
Pleasantville HS 200/9-12
415 Jones St 50225 515-848-0541
Gary Friday, prin. Fax 848-0561
Pleasantville MS 100/6-8
415 Jones St 50225 515-848-0528
Gary Friday, prin. Fax 848-0561

Pocahontas, Pocahontas, Pop. 1,776
Pocahontas Area Community SD 600/PK-12
202 1st Ave SW 50574 712-335-4311
Joseph Kramer, supt. Fax 335-4206
www.pocahontas.k12.ia.us/
Pocahontas Area JSHS 200/7-12
205 2nd Ave NW 50574 712-335-4848
Roger Francis, prin. Fax 335-3420
Pocahontas Area Reg Learning Center 50/Alt
202 1st Ave SW 50574 712-335-5971
Roger Francis, prin.

Postville, Allamakee, Pop. 2,192
Postville Community SD 500/PK-12
PO Box 717 52162 563-864-7651
Abe Maske, supt. Fax 864-7659
www.postville.k12.ia.us
Mott HS 100/9-12
PO Box 717 52162 563-864-7651
Brendan Knudtson, prin. Fax 864-7659

Prairie City, Jasper, Pop. 1,659
PCM Community SD
Supt. — See Monroe
PCM MS 200/6-8
PO Box 490 50228 515-994-2686
Stephanie Langstraat, prin. Fax 994-2686

Preston, Jackson, Pop. 1,004
Preston Community SD 300/K-12
121 S Mitchell St 52069 563-689-3431
Robert Lagerblade, supt. Fax 689-5823
www.prestonschools.com
Preston JSHS 200/7-12
321 W School St 52069 563-689-4221
David Miller, prin. Fax 689-4222

Redfield, Dallas, Pop. 817
West Central Valley Community SD
Supt. — See Stuart
West Central Valley MS 200/6-8
PO Box B 50233 515-833-2331
Anthony Lohse, prin. Fax 833-2629

Red Oak, Montgomery, Pop. 5,681
Red Oak Community SD 1,300/PK-12
2011 N 8th St 51566 712-623-6600
Terry Schmidt, supt. Fax 623-6603
www.redoakschooldistrict.com
Alternative HS 50/Alt
2011 N 8th St 51566 712-623-6610
Jedd Sherman, prin. Fax 623-6613
Red Oak HS 400/9-12
2011 N 8th St 51566 712-623-6610
Jedd Sherman, prin. Fax 623-6613
Red Oak MS 300/6-8
308 E Corning St 51566 712-623-6620
Nate Perrien, prin. Fax 623-6626

Reinbeck, Grundy, Pop. 1,657
Gladbrook-Reinbeck Community SD 600/PK-12
300 Cedar St 50669 319-345-2712
Shawn Holloway, supt. Fax 345-2242
www.gr-rebels.net
Gladbrook-Reinbeck HS 200/9-12
600 Blackhawk St 50669 319-345-2921
Matt Leeman, prin. Fax 345-6432
Other Schools – See Gladbrook

Remsen, Plymouth, Pop. 1,653
Remsen-Union Community SD 400/PK-12
511 Roosevelt Ave 51050 712-786-1101
Kenneth Howard, supt. Fax 786-1104
www.remsen-union.k12.ia.us/
Remsen-Union HS 100/9-12
511 Roosevelt Ave 51050 712-786-1101
Steve Harman, prin. Fax 786-1104
Remsen-Union MS 100/6-8
511 Roosevelt Ave 51050 712-786-1192
Steve Harmon, prin. Fax 786-1104

St. Marys HS 100/9-12
523 Madison St 51050 712-786-1433
John Hughes, prin Fax 786-2499

Riceville, Howard, Pop. 779
Riceville Community SD 100/K-12
912 Woodland Ave 50466 641-985-2288
Dr. Steve Nicholson, supt. Fax 985-4171
www.riceville.k12.ia.us
Riceville Community S 100/K-12
912 Woodland Ave 50466 641-985-2288
Cory Schumann, prin. Fax 985-4171

Riverdale, Scott, Pop. 403
Pleasant Valley Community SD
Supt. — See Bettendorf
Pleasant Valley HS 1,200/9-12
604 Belmont Rd 52722 563-332-5151
David Zimmer, prin. Fax 332-8525

Scott Community College Post-Sec.
500 Belmont Rd 52722 563-441-4001

Riverside, Washington, Pop. 985
Highland Community SD 800/PK-12
1715 Vine Ave 52327 319-648-3822
Chris Armstrong, supt. Fax 648-4055
www.highland.k12.ia.us
Highland HS 200/9-12
1715 Vine Ave 52327 319-648-2891
Angela Hazelett, prin. Fax 648-3310
Highland MS 200/6-8
1715 Vine Ave 52327 319-648-5018
Joel Diederichs, prin. Fax 648-4055

Rockford, Floyd, Pop. 856
Rudd-Rockford-Marble Rock Community SD 500/PK-12
PO Box 218 50468 641-756-3610
Paul Bisgard, supt. Fax 756-2369
www.rockford.k12.ia.us
Rockford JSHS 200/7-12
PO Box 218 50468 641-756-3813
Keith Turner, prin. Fax 756-2369

Rock Rapids, Lyon, Pop. 2,533
Central Lyon Community SD 700/PK-12
PO Box 471 51246 712-472-2664
Dave Ackerman, supt. Fax 472-3543
www.central-lyon.k12.ia.us/
Central Lyon HS 200/9-12
PO Box 471 51246 712-472-4051
David Ackerman, admin. Fax 472-2115
Central Lyon MS 100/6-8
PO Box 471 51246 712-472-4041
Dan Kruse, prin. Fax 472-2346

Rock Valley, Sioux, Pop. 3,334
Rock Valley Community SD 800/PK-12
1712 20th Ave 51247 712-476-2701
Chad Janzen, supt. Fax 476-2125
www.rvcsd.org
Rock Valley JSHS 400/6-12
1712 20th Ave 51247 712-476-2701
Nicole Roder, prin. Fax 476-2125

Netherlands Reformed Christian S 400/K-12
712 20th Ave SE 51247 712-476-2821
Daniel Breuer, prin. Fax 476-5438

Rockwell, Cerro Gordo, Pop. 1,034
West Fork SD 700/PK-12
PO Box 60 50469 641-882-3236
Darrin Strike, supt. Fax 822-4882
www.westforkschool.org/
West Fork MS 200/5-8
PO Box 60 50469 641-822-3264
Abe Maske, prin. Fax 822-3273
Other Schools – See Sheffield

Rockwell City, Calhoun, Pop. 1,695
Southern Cal Community SD
Supt. — See Lake City
South Central Calhoun MS 400/4-8
1000 Tonawanda St 50579 712-297-8111
Marc DeMoss, prin. Fax 297-7320

Roland, Story, Pop. 1,275
Roland-Story Community SD
Supt. — See Story City
Roland-Story MS 300/5-8
206 S Main St 50236 515-388-4348
John Sheahan, prin. Fax 388-4435

Royal, Clay, Pop. 436
Clay Central/Everly Community SD 300/PK-12
PO Box 110 51357 712-933-2241
Dennis McClain, supt. Fax 933-2243
www.claycentraleverly.new.rschooltoday.com
Other Schools – See Everly

Ruthven, Palo Alto, Pop. 734
Ruthven-Ayrshire Community SD 300/PK-12
PO Box 159 51358 712-837-5211
Andrew Woiwood, supt. Fax 837-5210
www.ruthven.k12.ia.us
Ruthven-Ayrshire JSHS 100/7-12
PO Box 159 51358 712-837-5212
Jon Josephson, prin. Fax 837-5210

Sac City, Sac, Pop. 2,191
East Sac County SD
Supt. — See Lake View
East Sac County MS 300/5-8
300 S 11th St 50583 712-662-3259
Denny Olhausen, prin. Fax 662-4323
Sac County Flex Ed Center Alt
400 S 16th St 50583 712-662-4907
Gene Coon, lead tchr. Fax 662-7602

Saint Ansgar, Mitchell, Pop. 1,101
St. Ansgar Community SD 600/PK-12
PO Box 398 50472 641-713-4681
Jody Gray, supt. Fax 713-4042
www.st-ansgar.k12.ia.us
Saint Ansgar HS 200/9-12
PO Box 398 50472 641-713-4720
Lynn Baldus, prin. Fax 713-2449
Saint Ansgar MS 200/5-8
PO Box 398 50472 641-713-4720
Lynn Baldus, prin. Fax 713-4042

Sanborn, O'Brien, Pop. 1,402
Hartley-Melvin-Sanborn Community SD
Supt. — See Hartley
Hartley-Melvin-Sanborn MS 200/5-8
PO Box 557 51248 712-930-3281
Mark Dorhout, prin. Fax 930-5414

Schaller, Sac, Pop. 764
Schaller-Crestland Community SD 400/PK-8
PO Box 249 51053 712-275-4267
Dave Kwikkel, supt. Fax 275-4269
www.rvraptors.org
Other Schools – See Early

Schleswig, Crawford, Pop. 871
Schleswig Community SD 200/PK-8
PO Box 250 51461 712-676-3313
Brian Johnson, supt. Fax 676-3539
www.schleswig.k12.ia.us
Schleswig MS 100/5-8
PO Box 250 51461 712-676-3313
David Galvin, prin. Fax 676-3539

Sergeant Bluff, Woodbury, Pop. 4,152
Sergeant Bluff-Luton Community SD 1,500/PK-12
201 Port Neal Rd 51054 712-943-4338
Rod Earleywine, supt. Fax 943-1131
www.sblschools.com
Sergeant Bluff-Luton HS 500/9-12
708 Warrior Rd 51054 712-943-5561
Jason Klingingsmith, prin. Fax 943-5887
Sergeant Bluff-Luton MS 300/6-8
208 Port Neal Rd 51054 712-943-4235
Bill McKelvey, prin. Fax 943-8780

Seymour, Wayne, Pop. 696
Seymour Community SD 200/PK-12
100 S Park Ave 52590 641-898-2291
Dave Lockridge, supt. Fax 898-7500
www.seymour.k12.ia.us/
Seymour JSHS 100/7-12
100 S Park Ave 52590 641-898-2291
Dave Lockridge, prin. Fax 898-7500

Sheffield, Franklin, Pop. 1,165
West Fork SD
Supt. — See Rockwell
West Fork HS 200/9-12
PO Box 617 50475 641-892-4461
Randy Bushbaum, prin. Fax 892-4335

Sheldon, O'Brien, Pop. 5,156
Sheldon Community SD 1,000/PK-12
1700 E 4th St 51201 712-324-2504
Robin Spears, supt. Fax 324-5607
www.sheldon.k12.ia.us
Sheldon HS 300/9-12
1700 E 4th St 51201 712-324-2501
Matt Meendering, prin. Fax 324-5607
Sheldon MS 300/5-8
310 23rd Ave 51201 712-324-4346
Cindy Barwick, prin. Fax 324-4347

Northwest Iowa Community College Post-Sec.
603 W Park St 51201 712-324-5061

Shenandoah, Page, Pop. 5,088
Shenandoah Community SD 1,100/PK-12
304 W Nishna Rd 51601 712-246-1581
Jeffrey Hiser, supt. Fax 246-3722
www.shenandoah.k12.ia.us
Shenandoah HS 300/9-12
1000 Mustang Dr 51601 712-246-4727
Sandy Hilding, prin. Fax 246-2842
Shenandoah MS 300/5-8
601 Dr Creighton Cir 51601 712-246-2520
Jason Shaffer, prin. Fax 246-6390

Sibley, Osceola, Pop. 2,785
Sibley-Ocheyedan Community SD 800/PK-12
120 11th Ave NE 51249 712-754-2533
Tom Becker, supt. Fax 754-2534
www.thegenerals.org
Sibley-Ocheyedan HS 200/9-12
120 11th Ave NE 51249 712-754-3601
Steven Bruder, prin. Fax 754-2534
Sibley-Ocheyedan MS 200/5-8
120 11th Ave NE 51249 712-754-2542
Mike Morran, prin. Fax 754-3651

Sidney, Fremont, Pop. 1,125
Sidney Community SD 400/PK-12
PO Box 609 51652 712-374-2141
Gregg Cruickshank, supt. Fax 374-2013
sidneyschools.org
Sidney JSHS 200/6-12
PO Box 609 51652 712-374-2731
Michael Eldridge, prin. Fax 374-2013

Sigourney, Keokuk, Pop. 2,051
Sigourney Community SD 600/PK-12
300 W Kelley St 52591 641-622-2025
Benita Gonzales, supt. Fax 622-2319
www.sigourneyschools.com
New Directions Learning Center 50/Alt
907 E Pleasant Valley St 52591 641-622-3108
Kim Harmon, prin.
Sigourney JSHS 300/7-12
907 E Pleasant Valley St 52591 641-622-2010
Kim Harmon, prin. Fax 622-2047

Sioux Center, Sioux, Pop. 7,004
Sioux Center Community SD 1,000/PK-12
550 9th St NE 51250 712-722-2985
Patrick O'Donnell, supt. Fax 722-2986
www.sioux-center.k12.ia.us
Sioux Center HS 300/9-12
550 9th St NE 51250 712-722-2981
Gary McEldowney, prin. Fax 722-2930
Sioux Center MS 300/5-8
550 9th St NE 51250 712-722-3783
Julie Schley, prin. Fax 722-3782

Dordt College Post-Sec.
498 4th Ave NE 51250 712-722-6000

Sioux City, Woodbury, Pop. 80,564
Sioux City Community SD 12,300/PK-12
627 4th St 51101 712-279-6667
Dr. Paul Gausman, supt. Fax 279-6690
www.siouxcityschools.org/
East HS 1,300/9-12
5011 Mayhew Ave 51106 712-274-4000
Richard Todd, prin. Fax 274-4670
East MS 1,000/6-8
5401 Lorraine Ave 51106 712-274-4030
Dr. Michael Rogers, prin. Fax 274-4668
North HS 1,400/9-12
4200 Cheyenne Blvd 51104 712-279-7000
Ryan Dumkreiger, prin. Fax 239-8270
North MS 1,000/6-8
2101 Outer Dr N 51108 712-279-6804
Jeanene Sampson, prin. Fax 277-5941
West HS 1,200/9-12
2001 Casselman St 51103 712-279-6772
Jacqueline Wyant, prin. Fax 279-6790
West MS 900/6-8
3301 W 19th St 51103 712-279-6813
Cynthia Washinowski, prin. Fax 277-6138

Bio-Chi Institute Post-Sec.
1925 Geneva St 51103 712-252-1157
Bishop Heelan HS 600/9-12
1021 Douglas St 51105 712-252-0573
Chris Bork, prin. Fax 252-4897
Briar Cliff University Post-Sec.
3303 Rebecca St 51104 712-279-5321
Holy Cross S / Blessed Sacrament Ctr 300/3-8
3030 Jackson St 51104 712-277-4739
Michael Sweeney, prin. Fax 258-3698
Iowa School of Beauty Post-Sec.
3320 Line Dr 51106 712-274-9733
Mater Dei S - Nativity Center 100/6-8
4243 Natalia Way 51106 712-274-0268
Mary Fischer, prin. Fax 274-0377
Mercy Medical Center - Sioux City Post-Sec.
801 5th St 51101 712-279-2018
Morningside College Post-Sec.
1501 Morningside Ave 51106 712-274-5000
St. Luke's College Post-Sec.
2720 Stone Park Blvd 51104 712-279-3149
Siouxland Community Christian S 200/PK-12
6100 Morningside Ave 51106 712-276-4732
Steven Peters, supt. Fax 276-4752
Western Iowa Tech Community College Post-Sec.
4647 Stone Ave 51106 712-274-6400

Sioux Rapids, Buena Vista, Pop. 775
Sioux Central Community SD 700/PK-12
4440 US Highway 71 50585 712-283-2571
Scott Williamson, supt. Fax 283-2989
www.sioux-central.k12.ia.us
Sioux Central HS 300/9-12
4440 US Highway 71 50585 712-283-2571
Jeff Scharn, prin. Fax 283-2285
Sioux Central MS 100/6-8
4440 US Highway 71 50585 712-283-2571
Jeff Scharn, prin. Fax 283-2285

Sloan, Woodbury, Pop. 970
Westwood Community SD 600/PK-12
1000 Rebel Way 51055 712-428-3355
Lance Ridgely, supt. Fax 428-3246
www.westwood.k12.ia.us/
Westwood JSHS 300/7-12
1000 Rebel Way 51055 712-428-3303
Matt Drees, prin. Fax 428-3246

Solon, Johnson, Pop. 2,019
Solon Community SD 1,300/PK-12
301 S Iowa St 52333 319-624-3401
Sam Miller, supt. Fax 624-2518
www.solon.k12.ia.us
Solon HS 400/9-12
600 W 5th St 52333 319-624-3401
Nathan Wear, prin. Fax 624-4091
Solon MS 400/5-8
313 S Iowa St 52333 319-624-3401
Mike Herdliska, prin. Fax 624-2518

Spencer, Clay, Pop. 11,130
Spencer Community SD 1,900/PK-12
PO Box 200 51301 712-262-8950
Terry Hemann, supt. Fax 262-1116
www.spenceriowaschools.com/
Spencer HS 700/9-12
PO Box 200 51301 712-262-1700
Joe Mueting, prin. Fax 262-5704
Spencer MS 300/6-8
PO Box 200 51301 712-262-3345
Steve Barber, prin. Fax 264-3444

Iowa Lakes Community College Post-Sec.
1900 Grand Ave Ste B1 51301 712-262-7141

Spirit Lake, Dickinson, Pop. 4,786
Spirit Lake Community SD 1,200/PK-12
2701 Hill Ave 51360 712-336-2820
David Smith Ed.D., supt. Fax 336-4641
www.spirit-lake.k12.ia.us/
Spirit Lake HS 400/9-12
2701 Hill Ave 51360 712-336-3707
Kevin Range, prin. Fax 336-3714
Spirit Lake MS 400/5-8
2701 Hill Ave 51360 712-336-1370
Terry Bruinsma, prin. Fax 336-4758

The Faust Institute of Cosmetology Post-Sec.
1543 18th St Ste 15 51360 712-336-0512

Springville, Linn, Pop. 1,066
Springville Community SD 400/K-12
400 Academy St 52336 319-854-6197
Brian Ney, supt. Fax 854-6199
www.springville.k12.ia.us
Springville JSHS 200/6-12
400 Academy St 52336 319-854-6196
Nick Merritt, prin. Fax 854-7891

Stanton, Montgomery, Pop. 688
Stanton Community SD 300/K-12
605 Elliott St 51573 712-829-2162
Terry Christie, supt. Fax 829-2164
www.stantonschools.com
Stanton JSHS 100/6-12
605 Elliott St 51573 712-829-2162
Kevin Blunt, prin. Fax 829-2164

Stanwood, Cedar, Pop. 676
North Cedar Community SD 800/PK-12
PO Box 247 52337 563-942-3358
Mike Cooper, supt. Fax 942-3596
www.north-cedar.k12.ia.us
North Cedar HS 300/9-12
PO Box 247 52337 563-942-3341
Dain Jeppson, prin. Fax 942-3596
Other Schools – See Clarence

State Center, Marshall, Pop. 1,450
West Marshall Community SD 800/PK-12
PO Box 670 50247 641-483-2660
Ned Sellers, supt. Fax 483-2665
www.w-marshall.k12.ia.us
West Marshall HS 300/9-12
PO Box 670 50247 641-483-2136
James Henrich, prin. Fax 483-2172
West Marshall MS 200/6-8
PO Box 340 50247 641-483-2165
Jeff Barry, prin. Fax 483-3095

Storm Lake, Buena Vista, Pop. 10,411
Storm Lake Community SD 2,200/PK-12
PO Box 638 50588 712-732-8060
Dr. Carl Turner, supt. Fax 732-8063
www.slcsd.org
Storm Lake HS 700/9-12
PO Box 638 50588 712-732-8065
Beau Ruleaux, prin. Fax 732-8068
Storm Lake MS 600/5-8
PO Box 638 50588 712-732-8080
Jay Slight, prin. Fax 732-8084

Buena Vista University Post-Sec.
610 W 4th St 50588 712-749-2351
St. Mary MSHS 200/5-12
304 Seneca St 50588 712-732-4166
Erv Rowlands, prin. Fax 732-4590
The Faust Institute of Cosmetology Post-Sec.
1290 Lake Ave 50588 712-732-6571

Story City, Story, Pop. 3,411
Roland-Story Community SD 1,000/PK-12
1009 Story St 50248 515-733-4301
Mike Billings, supt. Fax 733-2131
www.roland-story.k12.ia.us
Roland-Story HS 300/9-12
1009 Story St 50248 515-733-4329
Steve Schlatter, prin. Fax 733-2131
Other Schools – See Roland

Stuart, Guthrie, Pop. 1,630
West Central Valley Community SD 900/PK-12
PO Box 550 50250 515-523-1165
Dr. David Arnold, supt. Fax 523-1166
www.wcv.k12.ia.us
West Central Valley HS 300/9-12
PO Box 550 50250 515-523-1313
Deborah Wilson, prin. Fax 523-2765
Other Schools – See Redfield

Sully, Jasper, Pop. 821
Lynnville-Sully Community SD 500/K-12
PO Box 210 50251 641-594-4445
Shane Ehresman, supt. Fax 594-2770
www.lshawks.org
Lynnville-Sully HS 200/9-12
PO Box 210 50251 641-594-4445
Matt Rasmusson, prin. Fax 594-2770
Lynnville-Sully MS 100/6-8
PO Box 210 50251 641-594-4445
Teri Bowlin, prin. Fax 594-2770

Sumner, Bremer, Pop. 2,021
Sumner Community SD 500/PK-12
802 W 6th St 50674 563-578-3341
Rick Pederson, supt. Fax 578-3424
www.sumner.k12.ia.us/
Sumner-Fredericksburg HS 300/9-12
802 W 6th St 50674 563-578-3341
Allan Eckelman, prin. Fax 578-3424

Swea City, Kossuth, Pop. 535
North Kossuth Community SD 300/PK-8
PO Box 567 50590 515-272-4361
Mike Landstrum, supt. Fax 272-0091
www.nsk.k12.ia.us
North Union MS 100/6-8
PO Box 567 50590 515-272-4361
Mike Landstrum, prin. Fax 272-4391

Tabor, Fremont, Pop. 1,036
Fremont-Mills Community SD 400/PK-12
PO Box 310 51653 712-629-2325
Christopher Herrick, supt. Fax 629-5155
www.fmtabor.org
Fremont-Mills MSHS 200/7-12
PO Box 310 51653 712-629-2325
Jeremy Christiansen, prin. Fax 629-5155

Tama, Tama, Pop. 2,803
South Tama County Community SD 1,600/PK-12
1702 Harding St 52339 641-484-4811
Kerri Nelson, supt. Fax 484-4861
www.s-tama.k12.ia.us/
Partnership HS 50/Alt
215 W 9th St 52339 641-484-3085
Roy Frakes, prin. Fax 484-3924
South Tama County HS 400/9-12
1715 Harding St 52339 641-484-4345
Roy Frakes, prin. Fax 484-5152
Other Schools – See Toledo

Thornburg, Keokuk, Pop. 67
Tri-County Community SD 300/PK-12
PO Box 17 50255 641-634-2408
Benita Gonzales, supt. Fax 634-2145
www.tri-county.k12.ia.us/
Tri-County HS 100/9-12
PO Box 17 50255 641-634-2636
Alessandra Steinke, prin. Fax 634-2145

Tiffin, Johnson, Pop. 1,895
Clear Creek Amana Community SD
Supt. — See Oxford
Clear Creek Amana HS 500/9-12
PO Box 199 52340 319-545-2361
Mark Moody, prin. Fax 545-2863
Clear Creek Amana MS 400/6-8
PO Box 530 52340 319-545-4490
Brad Fox, prin. Fax 545-4094

Tipton, Cedar, Pop. 3,193
Tipton Community SD 900/PK-12
400 E 6th St 52772 563-886-6121
Richard Grimoskas, supt. Fax 886-2341
www.tipton.k12.ia.us
Tipton HS 300/9-12
400 E 6th St 52772 563-886-6027
Chris Habben, prin. Fax 886-2341
Tipton MS 200/5-8
400 E 6th St 52772 563-886-6025
Sue O'Donnell, prin. Fax 886-2555

Toledo, Tama, Pop. 2,265
South Tama County Community SD
Supt. — See Tama
South Tama County MS 300/6-8
201 S Green St 52342 641-484-4121
Eric Townsley, prin. Fax 484-2699

Traer, Tama, Pop. 1,686
North Tama County Community SD 500/K-12
605 Walnut St 50675 319-478-2265
Robert Cue, supt. Fax 478-2917
www.n-tama.k12.ia.us
North Tama JSHS 300/7-12
605 Walnut St 50675 319-478-2265
Paul Rea, prin. Fax 478-2917

Treynor, Pottawattamie, Pop. 919
Treynor Community SD 700/K-12
PO Box 369 51575 712-487-3414
Kevin Elwood, supt. Fax 487-3332
www.treynorschools.org
Treynor HS 200/9-12
PO Box 369 51575 712-487-3804
Tim Navara, prin. Fax 487-3332
Treynor MS 200/6-8
PO Box 369 51575 712-487-3181
Jenny Berens, prin. Fax 487-3567

Tripoli, Bremer, Pop. 1,304
Tripoli Community SD 500/PK-12
209 8th Ave SW 50676 319-882-4201
Troy Heller, supt. Fax 882-3103
www.tripoli.k12.ia.us
Tripoli JSHS 200/6-12
209 8th Ave SW 50676 319-882-4202
Troy Heller, supt. Fax 882-3103

Troy Mills, Linn
North Linn Community SD 700/PK-12
PO Box 200 52344 319-224-3291
Larry Boer, supt. Fax 224-3727
www.northlinn.k12.ia.us
North Linn HS 200/9-12
PO Box 200 52344 319-224-3291
Scott Beaty, prin. Fax 224-3232
North Linn MS 200/6-8
PO Box 200 52344 319-224-3291
Scott Beaty, prin. Fax 224-3232

Truro, Madison, Pop. 481
Interstate 35 Community SD 800/PK-12
PO Box 79 50257 641-765-4291
Jeff Craig, supt. Fax 765-4593
www.i-35.k12.ia.us
Interstate 35 HS 300/9-12
PO Box 79 50257 641-765-4818
Jeff Snider, prin. Fax 765-4820
Interstate 35 MS 200/6-8
PO Box 200 50257 641-765-4908
Jeff Snider, prin. Fax 765-4905

Underwood, Pottawattamie, Pop. 909
Underwood Community SD 800/PK-12
PO Box 130 51576 712-566-2332
Ed Hawks, supt. Fax 566-2070
www.underwoodeagles.org/
Underwood HS 200/9-12
PO Box 130 51576 712-566-2703
Matt McDonough, prin. Fax 566-2712
Underwood MS 200/6-8
PO Box 130 51576 712-566-2332
J. Lewis Curtis, prin. Fax 566-2070

Union, Hardin, Pop. 394
BCLUW Community SD
Supt. — See Conrad
BCLUW MS 200/5-8
704 Commercial St 50258 641-486-5371
Dirk Borgman, prin. Fax 486-5372

Urbandale, Polk, Pop. 38,851
Urbandale Community SD 3,900/PK-12
11152 Aurora Ave 50322 515-457-5000
Dr. Doug Stilwell, supt. Fax 457-5018
www.urbandaleschools.com/
Metro West Learning Academy Alt
4420 NW Urbandale Dr 50322 515-986-3171
Carla Krogman, prin. Fax 986-4676
Urbandale HS 1,200/9-12
7111 Aurora Ave 50322 515-457-6800
Richard Hutchinson, prin. Fax 457-6810
Urbandale MS 900/6-8
7701 Aurora Ave 50322 515-457-6600
Daniel Meyer, prin. Fax 457-6610

Des Moines Christian S 800/PK-12
13007 Douglas Pkwy Ste 100 50323 515-252-2480
Dr. Bob Stouffer, supt. Fax 251-6911
Kaplan University Post-Sec.
4655 121st St 50323 515-727-2100

Van Horne, Benton, Pop. 678
Benton Community SD 1,600/PK-12
PO Box 70 52346 319-228-8701
Gary Zittergruen, supt. Fax 228-8254
www.benton.k12.ia.us
Benton Community HS 500/9-12
PO Box 70 52346 319-228-8701
James Bieschke, prin. Fax 228-8747
Benton Community MS 200/7-8
PO Box 70 52346 319-228-8701
Jo Prusha, prin. Fax 228-8747

Van Meter, Dallas, Pop. 1,006
Van Meter Community SD 600/K-12
PO Box 257 50261 515-996-9960
Deron Durflinger, supt. Fax 996-9954
www.vmbulldogs.com/
Van Meter JSHS 300/6-12
PO Box 257 50261 515-996-2221
Deron Durflinger, prin. Fax 996-2488

Ventura, Cerro Gordo, Pop. 712
Ventura Community SD 200/K-8
PO Box 18 50482 641-829-4482
Tyler Williams, supt. Fax 829-3906
www.venturaschools.org
Ventura-Garner-Hayfield JHS 100/7-8
PO Box 18 50482 641-829-4484
Debra Stenhard, prin. Fax 829-3995

Victor, Iowa, Pop. 887
H-L-V Community SD 400/PK-12
PO Box B 52347 319-647-2161
William Lynch, supt. Fax 647-2164
www.hlv.k12.ia.us
H-L-V JSHS 200/7-12
PO Box B 52347 319-647-2161
Cory Lahndorf, prin. Fax 647-2164

Villisca, Montgomery, Pop. 1,244
Villisca Community SD 400/PK-12
406 E 3rd St 50864 712-826-2552
William Stone, supt. Fax 826-4072
www.villiscaschools.org/
Villisca Community JSHS 200/6-12
406 E 3rd St 50864 712-826-2552
Lora Top, prin. Fax 826-4072

Vinton, Benton, Pop. 5,202
Vinton-Shellsburg Community SD 1,700/PK-12
1502 C Ave 52349 319-436-4728
Mary Jo Hainstock, supt. Fax 472-3889
www.vscsd.org
Vinton-Shellsburg HS 500/9-12
210 W 21st St 52349 319-436-4728
Matt Kingsbury, prin. Fax 472-5704
Vinton-Shellsburg MS 400/6-8
212 W 15th St 52349 319-436-4728
Shelly Petersen, prin. Fax 472-4014

Iowa Braille and Sight Saving School Post-Sec.
1002 G Ave 52349 319-472-5221

Walcott, Scott, Pop. 1,613
Davenport Community SD
Supt. — See Davenport
Walcott IS 400/6-8
545 E James St 52773 563-284-6253
Virginia Weipert, prin. Fax 284-5081

Walker, Linn, Pop. 783

Cono Christian S 100/K-12
3269 Quasqueton Ave 52352 319-448-4395
Thomas Jahl, hdmstr. Fax 448-4397

Walnut, Pottawattamie, Pop. 778
Walnut Community SD 200/PK-12
PO Box 528 51577 712-784-2251
Jim Hammrich, supt. Fax 784-2177
walnutcsd.sharpschool.net/
Walnut HS 100/9-12
PO Box 528 51577 712-784-3615
Kent Klinkefus, prin. Fax 784-2177
Walnut MS 50/6-8
PO Box 528 51577 712-784-3615
Kent Klinkefus, prin. Fax 784-2177

Wapello, Louisa, Pop. 2,049
Wapello Community SD 800/PK-12
406 Mechanic St 52653 319-523-3641
Mike Peterson, supt. Fax 523-8151
www.wapello.k12.ia.us
Wapello HS 200/9-12
501 Buchanan Ave 52653 319-523-3241
Steve Bohlen, prin. Fax 523-4408
Wapello JHS 100/7-8
501 Buchanan Ave 52653 319-523-8131
Steve Bohlen, prin. Fax 523-4408

Washington, Washington, Pop. 7,169
Washington Community SD 1,300/K-12
PO Box 926 52353 319-653-6543
Mike Jorgensen, supt. Fax 653-5685
www.washington.k12.ia.us/
Assure Center Alternative S 50/Alt
105 Westview Dr 52353 319-653-7378
Teresa Beenblossom, prin. Fax 398-1043
Washington HS 400/9-12
PO Box 271 52353 319-653-2143
Erik Buchholz, prin. Fax 653-6751
Washington MS 300/6-8
PO Box 490 52353 319-653-5414
Curt Mayer, prin. Fax 653-7350

Waterloo, Black Hawk, Pop. 66,424
Waterloo Community SD 10,100/PK-12
1516 Washington St 50702 319-433-1800
Dr. Gary Norris, supt. Fax 433-1886
www.waterloo.k12.ia.us
Carver Academy 500/6-8
1505 Logan Ave 50703 319-433-2500
Brad Schweppe, prin. Fax 433-2548
Central MS 500/6-8
1350 Katoski Dr 50701 319-433-2100
John Netty, prin. Fax 433-2149
East HS 1,100/9-12
214 High St 50703 319-433-2400
Marla Padget, prin. Fax 433-2498
Expo HS 300/Alt
1410 Independence Ave 50703 319-433-1930
Brendan Shavers, prin. Fax 433-1933
Hoover MS 800/6-8
630 Hillcrest Rd 50701 319-433-2830
Dan Cox, prin. Fax 433-2843
West HS 1,600/9-12
425 E Ridgeway Ave 50702 319-433-2700
Leslie Morris, prin. Fax 433-2749
Other Schools – See Evansdale

Allen College Post-Sec.
1825 Logan Ave 50703 319-226-2000
College of Hair Design Post-Sec.
722 Water St Apt 201 50703 319-232-9995
Columbus HS 300/9-12
3231 W 9th St 50702 319-233-3358
Tom Ulses, prin. Fax 235-0733
Covenant Medical Center Post-Sec.
3421 W 9th St 50702 319-272-7296
Hawkeye Community College Post-Sec.
PO Box 8015 50704 319-296-2320
Waterloo Christian S 200/PK-12
1307 W Ridgeway Ave 50701 319-235-9309
Lisa Goedken, prin. Fax 833-4780

Waucoma, Fayette, Pop. 253
Turkey Valley Community SD 500/PK-12
3219 Highway 24 52171 563-776-6011
Chris Hoover, supt. Fax 776-4271
www.turkey-v.k12.ia.us
Turkey Valley JSHS 300/7-12
3219 Highway 24 52171 563-776-6011
Carol Knoll, prin. Fax 776-4271

Waukee, Dallas, Pop. 13,637
Waukee Community SD 6,000/PK-12
560 SE University Ave 50263 515-987-5161
Dr. David Wilkerson, supt. Fax 987-2701
www.waukee.k12.ia.us
Prairieview S 500/9-9
655 SE University Ave 50263 515-987-2770
Juley Murphy-Tiernan, prin. Fax 987-2789
Waukee MS 700/6-8
905 Warrior Ln 50263 515-987-5177
Amy Johnson, prin. Fax 987-2741
Waukee SHS 1,000/10-12
555 SE University Ave 50263 515-987-5163
Kirk Johnson, prin. Fax 987-2784
Waukee South MS 700/6-8
2350 SE La Grant Pkwy 50263 515-987-3222
Michelle Lettington, prin. Fax 987-3233

Waukon, Allamakee, Pop. 3,873
Allamakee Community SD 1,200/PK-12
1059 3rd Ave NW 52172 563-568-3409
Dave Herold, supt. Fax 568-2677
www.allamakee.k12.ia.us/
Allamakee JHS 200/7-8
1059 3rd Ave NW 52172 563-568-6321
Joe Griffith, prin. Fax 568-2677
Waukon HS 400/9-12
1061 3rd Ave NW 52172 563-568-3466
Daniel Diercks, prin. Fax 568-3165

Waverly, Bremer, Pop. 9,752
Waverly-Shell Rock Community SD 1,700/PK-12
1415 4th Ave SW 50677 319-352-3630
Ed Klamfoth, supt. Fax 352-5676
www.wsr.k12.ia.us
Greenview Alternative S 50/Alt
1405 4th Ave SW 50677 319-352-9273
Jere Vyverberg, prin.
Waverly-Shell Rock HS 700/9-12
1405 4th Ave SW 50677 319-352-2087
David Fox, prin. Fax 352-2098
Waverly-Shell Rock MS 300/7-8
501 Heritage Way 50677 319-352-3632
Roger Wilcox, prin. Fax 352-5199

Wartburg College Post-Sec.
PO Box 1003 50677 319-352-8200

Wayland, Henry, Pop. 957
Waco Community SD 500/PK-12
PO Box 158 52654 319-256-6200
Pat Coen, supt. Fax 256-6213
www.wacohs.com
Waco JSHS 200/7-12
PO Box 158 52654 319-256-6200
Todd Werner, prin. Fax 256-6211

Webster City, Hamilton, Pop. 7,961
Webster City Community SD 1,700/PK-12
825 Beach St 50595 515-832-9200
Mike Sherwood, supt. Fax 832-9204
www.webster-city.k12.ia.us
Webster City HS 500/9-12
1001 Lynx Ave 50595 515-832-9210
John Ekin, prin. Fax 832-9215
Webster City MS 500/5-8
1101 Des Moines St 50595 515-832-9220
Becky Hacker-Kluver, prin. Fax 832-9225

Wellman, Washington, Pop. 1,387
Mid-Prairie Community SD 1,200/PK-12
PO Box 150 52356 319-646-6093
Mark Schneider, supt. Fax 646-2093
www.mid-prairie.k12.ia.us
Alternative Learning Center Alt
PO Box 150 52356 319-646-6096
Amy Shalla, prin. Fax 646-2093
Mid-Prairie HS 300/9-12
PO Box 150 52356 319-646-6091
Gerry Beeler, prin. Fax 646-6097
Other Schools – See Kalona

Wellsburg, Grundy, Pop. 703
AGWSR Community SD
Supt. — See Ackley
AGWSR MS 200/4-8
PO Box 188 50680 641-869-5121
Sheryl Arends, prin. Fax 869-3426

West Bend, Palo Alto, Pop. 779
West Bend - Mallard Community SD 300/K-12
PO Box 247 50597 515-887-7821
Nancy Schmitz, supt. Fax 887-7853
www.west-bend.k12.ia.us
West Bend - Mallard HS 100/9-12
PO Box 247 50597 515-887-7831
Amanda Schmidt, prin. Fax 887-7853
West Bend - Mallard MS 100/6-8
PO Box 247 50597 515-887-7831
Amanda Schmidt, prin. Fax 887-7853

West Branch, Cedar, Pop. 2,295
West Branch Community SD 800/PK-12
PO Box 637 52358 319-643-7213
Kevin Hatfield, supt. Fax 643-7122
www.west-branch.k12.ia.us
West Branch HS 300/9-12
PO Box 637 52358 319-643-7216
Michelle Lukavsky, prin. Fax 643-2415
West Branch MS 200/6-8
PO Box 637 52358 319-643-5324
Sara Oswald, prin. Fax 643-5447

Scattergood Friends S 50/9-12
1951 Delta Ave 52358 319-643-7600
Christine Ashley, hdmstr. Fax 643-7485

West Burlington, Des Moines, Pop. 2,909
West Burlington ISD 700/PK-12
607 Ramsey St 52655 319-752-8747
David Schmitt, supt. Fax 754-9382
www.wbschools.us
West Burlington HS 200/9-12
408 W Van Weiss Blvd 52655 319-752-7138
Bruce Snodgrass, prin. Fax 754-0075
West Burlington JHS 100/6-8
408 W Van Weiss Blvd 52655 319-752-7138
Bruce Snodgrass, prin. Fax 754-0075

Southeastern Community College Post-Sec.
PO Box 180 52655 319-752-2731

West Des Moines, Polk, Pop. 55,623
West Des Moines Community SD 8,700/PK-12
3550 Mills Civic Pkwy 50265 515-633-5000
Dr. Peter Ansingh, supt. Fax 633-5099
www.wdmcs.org
Stilwell JHS 700/7-8
1601 Vine St 50265 515-633-6000
Tim Miller, prin. Fax 633-6099
Valley HS 2,000/10-12
3650 Woodland Ave 50266 515-633-4000
Jim Mollison, prin. Fax 633-4099
Valley Southwoods Freshman HS 700/9-9
625 S 35th St 50265 515-633-4500
Kent Abrahamson, prin. Fax 633-4599
Walnut Creek Alternative HS 200/Alt
1020 8th St 50265 515-633-6480
Dr. Kim Davis, prin. Fax 633-6499
Other Schools – See Clive

Dowling Catholic HS 1,300/9-12
1400 Buffalo Rd 50265 515-225-3000
Dr. James Dowdle, prin. Fax 222-1056
Iowa Christian Academy 300/PK-12
2501 Vine St 50265 515-221-3999
Dr. Brenda Hillman, admin. Fax 225-2387

West Liberty, Muscatine, Pop. 3,704
West Liberty Community SD 1,200/PK-12
111 W 7th St 52776 319-627-2116
Steve Hanson, supt. Fax 627-2963
www.wl.k12.ia.us
West Liberty HS 300/9-12
310 W Maxson Ave 52776 319-627-2115
James Hamilton, prin. Fax 627-2046
West Liberty MS 200/6-8
203 E 7th St 52776 319-627-2118
Vicki Vernon, prin. Fax 627-2092

Westside, Crawford, Pop. 299
Ar-We-Va Community SD 100/PK-12
PO Box 108 51467 712-663-4311
Kurt Brosamle, supt. Fax 663-4313
www.ar-we-va.k12.ia.us
Westside JSHS 100/6-12
PO Box 108 51467 712-663-4312
Kurt Brosamle, prin. Fax 663-4313

West Union, Fayette, Pop. 2,464
North Fayette Community SD 700/PK-12
PO Box 73 52175 563-422-3851
Duane Willhite, supt. Fax 422-3854
www.n-fayette.k12.ia.us
North Fayette HS 300/9-12
PO Box 73 52175 563-422-3852
Todd Wolverton, prin. Fax 422-5798
Other Schools – See Fayette

Wheatland, Clinton, Pop. 762
Calamus-Wheatland Community SD 600/PK-12
PO Box 279 52777 563-374-1292
Lonnie Luepker, supt. Fax 374-1080
www.cal-wheat.k12.ia.us
Calamus-Wheatland JSHS 300/7-12
PO Box 279 52777 563-374-1292
Christine Meyer, prin. Fax 374-1080

Whiting, Monona, Pop. 758
Whiting Community SD 200/PK-12
PO Box 295 51063 712-455-2468
Carolyn Eide, supt. Fax 455-2601
www.whitingcsd.org
Whiting JSHS 100/6-12
PO Box 295 51063 712-455-2468
Gary Schrage, prin. Fax 455-2601

Williamsburg, Iowa, Pop. 3,044
Williamsburg Community SD 1,000/PK-12
PO Box 120 52361 319-668-1059
Dr. Carol Montz, supt. Fax 668-9311
www.williamsburg.k12.ia.us
Williamsburg JSHS 600/7-12
PO Box 120 52361 319-668-1050
Lynell O'Connor, prin. Fax 668-9311

Wilton, Muscatine, Pop. 2,767
Wilton Community SD 800/PK-12
1002 Cypress St 52778 563-732-2035
Joe Burnett, supt. Fax 732-4121
www.wiltoncsd.org/
Wilton JSHS 400/7-12
1002 Cypress St 52778 563-732-2629
Ken Crawford, prin. Fax 732-4121

Winfield, Henry, Pop. 1,123
Winfield-Mt. Union Community SD 500/PK-12
PO Box E 52659 319-257-7700
Patrick Coen, supt. Fax 257-7714
www.wmu.k12.ia.us/
Winfield-Mt. Union JSHS 300/6-12
PO Box E 52659 319-257-7701
David Edwards, prin. Fax 257-7703

Winterset, Madison, Pop. 5,159
Winterset Community SD 1,800/PK-12
PO Box 30 50273 515-462-2718
Dr. Susan Meade, supt. Fax 462-2732
www.winterset.k12.ia.us
Winterset HS 500/9-12
624 Husky Dr 50273 515-462-3320
Lee Schipull, prin. Fax 462-2178
Winterset JHS 300/7-8
720 Husky Dr 50273 515-462-3336
Kate Wharton, prin. Fax 462-2178

Winthrop, Buchanan, Pop. 845
East Buchanan Community SD 600/PK-12
414 5th St N 50682 319-935-3767
Daniel Fox, supt. Fax 935-3749
www.east-buc.k12.ia.us
East Buchanan HS 200/9-12
414 5th St N 50682 319-935-3367
Tom Mossman, prin. Fax 935-3615
East Buchanan MS 100/6-8
414 5th St N 50682 319-935-3367
Tom Mossman, prin. Fax 935-3615

Woodbine, Harrison, Pop. 1,455
Woodbine Community SD 500/PK-12
501 Weare St 51579 712-647-2411
Thomas Vint, supt. Fax 647-2526
www.woodbineschools.com
Woodbine HS 200/7-12
501 Weare St 51579 712-647-2227
Sam Swenson, prin. Fax 647-2279

Woodward, Dallas, Pop. 1,006
Woodward-Granger Community SD 1,100/PK-12
306 W 3rd St 50276 515-438-4333
Brad Anderson, supt. Fax 438-2497
www.woodward-granger.k12.ia.us
Woodward Academy 300/Alt
1251 334th St 50276 515-438-3481
Abby Kray, prin. Fax 438-3489
Woodward-Granger HS 200/9-12
306 W 3rd St 50276 515-438-2115
Karen Broderick, prin. Fax 438-2497
Woodward-Granger MS 200/6-8
306 W 3rd St 50276 515-438-4653
Karen Broderick, prin. Fax 438-4329

Wyoming, Jones, Pop. 513
Midland Community SD 300/PK-12
PO Box 109 52362 563-488-2292
Brian Rodenberg, supt. Fax 488-2253
www.midland.k12.ia.us
Midland MSHS 200/6-12
PO Box 109 52362 563-488-2292
Chad Blanchard, prin. Fax 488-2253

KANSAS

KANSAS DEPARTMENT OF EDUCATION
120 SE 10th Ave, Topeka 66612-1182
Telephone 785-296-3202
Fax 785-296-7933
Website http://www.ksde.org

Commissioner of Education Dr. Diane DeBacker

KANSAS BOARD OF EDUCATION
120 SE 10th Ave, Topeka 66612-1103

Chairperson David Dennis

PUBLIC, PRIVATE AND CATHOLIC SECONDARY SCHOOLS

Abilene, Dickinson, Pop. 6,690
Abilene USD 435 — 1,600/PK-12
PO Box 639 67410 — 785-263-2630
Dr. Tim Shafer, supt. — Fax 263-7610
www.abileneschools.org/
Abilene HS — 500/9-12
1300 N Cedar St 67410 — 785-263-1260
Ben Smith, prin. — Fax 263-3327
Abilene MS — 400/6-8
500 NW 14th St 67410 — 785-263-1471
Ron Wilson, prin. — Fax 263-4443

Agra, Phillips, Pop. 263
Thunder Ridge SD
Supt. — See Kensington
Thunder Ridge MS — 100/PK-PK, 4-
941 Kansas Ave 67621 — 785-638-2244
Beth Norris, prin. — Fax 638-2254

Allen, Lyon, Pop. 176
North Lyon County USD 251
Supt. — See Americus
Northern Heights HS — 200/9-12
1208 Road 345 66833 — 620-528-3521
David Kehres, prin. — Fax 528-3392

Alma, Wabaunsee, Pop. 821
Mill Creek Valley USD 329 — 500/PK-12
PO Box 157 66401 — 785-765-3394
Dr. James R. Kenworthy, supt. — Fax 765-3624
www.usd329.com/
Wabaunsee HS — 100/9-12
912 Missouri Ave 66401 — 785-765-3315
Jeff Stuewe, prin. — Fax 765-3523
Other Schools – See Paxico

Almena, Norton, Pop. 407
Northern Valley USD 212 — 200/PK-12
PO Box 217 67622 — 785-669-2445
Steve Taylor, supt. — Fax 669-2263
www.nvhuskies.org
Northern Valley HS — 100/9-12
PO Box 217 67622 — 785-669-2445
Steve Taylor, prin. — Fax 669-2263
Other Schools – See Long Island

Altamont, Labette, Pop. 1,042
Labette County USD 506 — 1,700/PK-12
PO Box 189 67330 — 620-784-5326
Dr. John Wyrick, supt. — Fax 784-5879
www.usd506.org
Labette County HS — 500/9-12
PO Box 407 67330 — 620-784-5321
Marty Anderson, prin. — Fax 784-2682

Alta Vista, Wabaunsee, Pop. 442
Morris County USD 417
Supt. — See Council Grove
Prairie Heights MS — 100/5-8
801 Center St 66834 — 785-499-6313
Cynthia Schrader, prin. — Fax 499-5342

Altoona, Wilson, Pop. 399
Altoona-Midway USD 387 — 200/K-12
PO Box 128 66710 — 620-568-5725
Dr. Don Grover, supt. — Fax 568-5755
www.altoonamidway.org/
Other Schools – See Buffalo

Americus, Lyon, Pop. 875
North Lyon County USD 251 — 400/PK-12
PO Box 527 66835 — 620-443-5116
Mike Nulton, supt. — Fax 443-5659
www.usd251.org/
Other Schools – See Allen

Andale, Sedgwick, Pop. 920
Renwick USD 267 — 2,000/PK-12
PO Box 68 67001 — 316-444-2165
Tracy Bourne, supt. — Fax 445-2241
www.usd267.com
Andale HS — 400/9-12
PO Box 28 67001 — 316-444-2607
Stan May, prin. — Fax 445-2501
Other Schools – See Garden Plain

Andover, Butler, Pop. 11,537
Andover USD 385 — 5,400/PK-12
1432 N Andover Rd 67002 — 316-218-4660
Greg Rasmussen, supt. — Fax 733-3604
www.usd385.org
Andover Central HS — 800/9-12
603 E Central Ave 67002 — 316-218-4700
Cheryl Hochhalter, prin. — Fax 733-7798
Andover Central MS — 600/6-8
903 E Central Ave 67002 — 316-218-4710
Tim Hayden, prin. — Fax 733-8563
Andover HS — 800/9-12
1744 N Andover Rd 67002 — 316-218-4600
Bob Baier, prin. — Fax 733-3681
Andover MS — 600/6-8
1628 N Andover Rd 67002 — 316-218-4610
Deb Regier, prin. — Fax 733-4165

Anthony, Harper, Pop. 2,226
Anthony-Harper USD 361 — 800/PK-12
PO Box 486 67003 — 620-842-5183
Josh Swartz, supt. — Fax 842-5307
www.usd361.org/
Chaparral HS — 200/9-12
467 N State Road 14 67003 — 620-842-5155
Sandy Nichols, prin. — Fax 896-2927

Argonia, Sumner, Pop. 493
Argonia USD 359 — 200/PK-12
202 E Allen St 67004 — 620-435-6311
Dr. Julie Dolley, supt. — Fax 435-6623
www.argonia359.org
Argonia JSHS — 100/6-12
202 E Allen St 67004 — 620-435-6611
Travis Riebel, prin. — Fax 435-6358

Arkansas City, Cowley, Pop. 11,966
Arkansas City USD 470 — 2,700/PK-12
PO Box 1028 67005 — 620-441-2000
Ron Ballard, supt. — Fax 441-2009
usd470.schoolfusion.us/
Arkansas City HS — 800/9-12
1200 W Radio Ln 67005 — 620-441-2010
Dr. David Zumwalt, prin. — Fax 441-2021
Arkansas City MS — 600/6-8
400 E Kansas Ave 67005 — 620-441-2030
William Pfannenstiel, prin. — Fax 441-2036

Ark City Christian Academy — 100/PK-12
PO Box 1181 67005 — 620-442-0022
Tamen Eis, prin. — Fax 442-0022
Cowley County Community College — Post-Sec.
PO Box 1147 67005 — 620-442-0430

Arma, Crawford, Pop. 1,474
Northeast USD 246 — 500/K-12
PO Box 669 66712 — 620-347-4116
Greg Gorman, supt. — Fax 347-4087
www.usd246.org
Northeast HS — 200/9-12
PO Box 669 66712 — 620-347-4115
Jason Clemensen, prin. — Fax 347-4149

Ashland, Clark, Pop. 841
Ashland USD 220 — 200/PK-12
PO Box 187 67831 — 620-635-2220
Bill Day, supt. — Fax 635-2637
www.ashland.k12.ks.us
Ashland HS — 100/9-12
PO Box 187 67831 — 620-635-2814
Bill Day, prin. — Fax 635-2637
Ashland JHS — 50/7-8
PO Box 187 67831 — 620-635-2814
Bill Day, prin. — Fax 635-2637

Atchison, Atchison, Pop. 10,700
Atchison USD 409 — 1,700/PK-12
626 Commercial St 66002 — 913-367-4384
Dr. Susan Myers, supt. — Fax 367-2246
www.usd409.net/
Atchison Alternative S — 50/Alt
215 N 8th St 66002 — 913-360-6540
Gerre Martin, prin. — Fax 360-6544
Atchison HS — 500/9-12
1500 Riley St 66002 — 913-367-4162
Forrest Covey, prin. — Fax 367-0415
Atchison MS — 300/6-8
301 N 5th St 66002 — 913-367-5363
James Bryon Hanson, prin. — Fax 367-1302

Benedictine College — Post-Sec.
1020 N 2nd St 66002 — 913-367-5340
Highland Community College-Technical Ctr — Post-Sec.
1501 Riley St 66002 — 913-367-6204
Maur Hill - Mount Academy — 200/9-12
1000 Green St 66002 — 913-367-5482
Monika King, prin. — Fax 367-5096

Attica, Harper, Pop. 621
Attica USD 511 — 200/PK-12
PO Box 415 67009 — 620-254-7661
Troy Piper, supt. — Fax 254-7872
www.usd511.net
Attica JSHS — 50/7-12
PO Box 415 67009 — 620-254-7915
Troy Piper, prin. — Fax 254-7872

Atwood, Rawlins, Pop. 1,181
Rawlins County USD 105 — 300/PK-12
205 N 4th St Ste 1 67730 — 785-626-3236
Adam McDaniel, supt. — Fax 626-3083
www.usd105.org
Rawlins County JSHS — 100/7-12
100 N 8th St 67730 — 785-626-3289
Delbert Schmidt, prin. — Fax 626-1022

Augusta, Butler, Pop. 9,098
Augusta USD 402 — 2,200/PK-12
2345 Greyhound Dr 67010 — 316-775-5484
Dr. John Black, supt. — Fax 775-5035
www.usd402.com
Augusta HS — 600/9-12
2020 Ohio St 67010 — 316-775-5461
Donna Zerr, prin. — Fax 775-3484
Augusta MS — 500/6-8
1001 State St 67010 — 316-775-6383
Eileen Dreiling, prin. — Fax 775-3853

Axtell, Marshall, Pop. 393
Prairie Hills USD 113
Supt. — See Sabetha
Axtell JSHS — 100/5-12
504 Pine St 66403 — 785-736-2237
Bob Bartkoski, prin. — Fax 736-2295

Baileyville, Nemaha, Pop. 178
Nemaha Central USD 115
Supt. — See Seneca
B & B JSHS — 100/7-12
PO Box 69 66404 — 785-336-6631
Justin Coup, prin. — Fax 336-2835

Baldwin City, Douglas, Pop. 4,416
Baldwin City USD 348 — 1,300/PK-12
PO Box 67 66006 — 785-594-2721
Paul Dorathy, supt. — Fax 594-3408
www.usd348.com/
Baldwin HS — 400/9-12
PO Box 67 66006 — 785-594-2725
Rob McKim, prin. — Fax 594-2858
Baldwin JHS — 300/6-8
PO Box 67 66006 — 785-594-2448
Tammy Thomasson, prin. — Fax 594-2449

Baker University — Post-Sec.
PO Box 65 66006 — 785-594-6451

Barnes, Washington, Pop. 159
Barnes USD 223 — 400/PK-12
PO Box 188 66933 — 785-763-4231
Rick Simoncic, supt. — Fax 763-4461
www.usd223.org
Other Schools – See Hanover, Linn

Basehor, Leavenworth, Pop. 4,548
Basehor-Linwood USD 458 — 2,200/K-12
PO Box 282 66007 — 913-724-1396
David Howard, supt. — Fax 724-2709
www.usd458.org

Basehor-Linwood HS 800/9-12
2108 N 155th St 66007 913-724-2266
Sherry Reeves, prin. Fax 724-2040
Other Schools – See Bonner Springs

Baxter Springs, Cherokee, Pop. 3,956
Baxter Springs USD 508 1,000/PK-12
1108 Military Ave 66713 620-856-2375
Dennis Burke, supt. Fax 856-3943
www.usd508.org
Baxter Springs HS 300/9-12
100 N Military Ave 66713 620-856-3366
David Pendergraft, prin. Fax 856-2918
Baxter Springs MS 200/6-8
1520 Cleveland Ave 66713 620-856-3355
Jason Walker, prin. Fax 856-3943

Bel Aire, Sedgwick, Pop. 6,561
Wichita USD 259
Supt. — See Wichita
Northeast Magnet HS 600/9-12
5550 N Lycee St 67226 316-973-2300
Gil Alvarez, prin. Fax 973-2307

Sunrise Christian Academy 600/PK-12
5500 E 45th St N 67220 316-744-9262
Dr. Robert Lindsted, supt. Fax 744-7449

Belle Plaine, Sumner, Pop. 1,652
Belle Plaine USD 357 700/PK-12
PO Box 760 67013 620-488-2288
Dr. Rose Kane, supt. Fax 488-3517
www.usd357.org
Belle Plaine HS 200/9-12
PO Box 8 67013 620-488-2421
Monte Stewart, prin. Fax 488-3536
Belle Plaine MS 200/5-8
PO Box 457 67013 620-488-2222
Morey Balzer, prin. Fax 488-3391

Belleville, Republic, Pop. 1,978
Republic County USD 109 500/K-12
PO Box 469 66935 785-527-5621
Brian Harris, supt. Fax 527-5375
www.usd109.org/
Republic County JSHS 200/7-12
PO Box 469 66935 785-527-2281
Alan Sheets, prin. Fax 527-5505

Beloit, Mitchell, Pop. 3,807
Beloit USD 273 800/PK-12
PO Box 547 67420 785-738-3261
Dr. Joe Harrison, supt. Fax 738-4103
usd273.org
Alternative Learning Center Alt
PO Box 506 67420 785-738-5275
Karen Niemczyk, prin. Fax 738-9967
Beloit JSHS 300/7-12
PO Box 606 67420 785-738-3593
Daryl Moore, prin. Fax 738-5500

North Central Kansas Technical College Post-Sec.
PO Box 507 67420 785-738-2276
St. John Catholic HS 100/7-12
209 S Cherry St 67420 785-738-2942
Marcy Kee, prin. Fax 738-4462

Bennington, Ottawa, Pop. 670
Twin Valley USD 240 600/PK-12
PO Box 38 67422 785-488-3325
Richard Harlan, supt. Fax 488-3326
www.usd240.org
Bennington HS 100/9-12
PO Box 8 67422 785-488-3321
Steve Rivers, prin. Fax 488-2939
Other Schools – See Tescott

Benton, Butler, Pop. 874
Circle USD 375
Supt. — See Towanda
Circle MS 300/7-8
14697 SW 20th St 67017 316-778-1470
Doug Bacon, prin. Fax 778-1749

Bird City, Cheyenne, Pop. 441
Cheylin USD 103 100/K-12
PO Box 28 67731 785-734-2341
Bruce Bolen, supt. Fax 734-2489
www.cheylin.com/
Cheylin JSHS 100/7-12
PO Box 28 67731 785-734-2341
Bruce Bolen, prin. Fax 734-2489

Blue Rapids, Marshall, Pop. 1,010
Valley Heights USD 498
Supt. — See Waterville
Valley Heights JSHS 200/7-12
2274 6th Rd 66411 785-363-2508
Don Potter, prin. Fax 363-2072

Bonner Springs, Wyandotte, Pop. 7,122
Basehor-Linwood USD 458
Supt. — See Basehor
Basehor-Linwood MS 500/6-8
15900 Conley Rd 66012 913-724-2976
Mike Wiley, prin. Fax 955-7074

Bonner Springs USD 204 2,500/PK-12
PO Box 435 66012 913-422-5600
Dr. Robert Van Maren, supt. Fax 422-4193
www.usd204.net
Bonner Springs HS 700/9-12
PO Box 216 66012 913-422-5121
Joe Hornback, prin. Fax 422-7284
Clark MS 600/6-8
PO Box 336 66012 913-422-5115
Dr. Steve Cook, prin. Fax 422-1644

Brewster, Thomas, Pop. 303
Brewster USD 314 100/PK-12
PO Box 220 67732 785-694-2236
Janci Mills, supt. Fax 694-2746
www.usd314.k12.ks.us
Brewster HS 50/7-12
PO Box 220 67732 785-694-2236
Janci Mills, prin. Fax 694-2746

Brookville, Saline, Pop. 257
Ell-Saline USD 307 500/K-12
PO Box 157 67425 785-225-6813
Jerry Minneman, supt. Fax 225-6815
www.ellsaline.org
Ell-Saline MSHS 200/7-12
414 E Anderson St 67425 785-225-6633
Susan Wildeman, prin. Fax 225-6694

Bucklin, Ford, Pop. 775
Bucklin USD 459 300/PK-12
PO Box 8 67834 620-826-3828
Dr. Kelly Arnberger, supt. Fax 826-3377
www.bucklinschools.com
Bucklin HS 100/9-12
PO Box 8 67834 620-826-3241
Jason Crawford, prin. Fax 826-9966

Buffalo, Wilson, Pop. 229
Altoona-Midway USD 387
Supt. — See Altoona
Altoona-Midway MSHS 100/6-12
20704 US 75 Hwy 66717 620-537-7711
Brent Mumford, prin. Fax 537-2641

Buhler, Reno, Pop. 1,319
Buhler USD 313 2,300/PK-12
PO Box 320 67522 620-543-2258
Dr. Dan Stiffler, supt. Fax 543-2510
www.buhlerschools.org
Buhler HS 700/9-12
PO Box 350 67522 620-543-2255
Mike Berblinger, prin. Fax 543-2853
Other Schools – See Hutchinson

Burden, Cowley, Pop. 531
Central USD 462 400/PK-12
PO Box 128 67019 620-438-2218
Marian Hedges, supt. Fax 438-2217
www.usd462.org
Central JSHS 200/7-12
PO Box 128 67019 620-438-2215
Shane Walter, prin. Fax 438-2217

Burlingame, Osage, Pop. 917
Burlingame USD 454 400/PK-12
100 Bloomquist Dr Ste A 66413 785-654-3328
Allen Konicek, supt. Fax 654-3570
www.usd454.net
Burlingame JSHS 200/7-12
100 Bloomquist Dr Ste A 66413 785-654-3315
Tammy Baird, prin. Fax 654-3191

Burlington, Coffey, Pop. 2,635
Burlington USD 244 800/PK-12
200 S 6th St 66839 620-364-8478
Cliff Williams, supt. Fax 364-8548
www.usd244ks.org
Burlington HS 200/9-12
830 Cross St 66839 620-364-8672
Shawn Thomas, prin. Fax 364-8680
Burlington MS 300/5-8
720 Cross St 66839 620-364-2156
Dallas Scothorn, prin. Fax 364-8560

Burrton, Harvey, Pop. 886
Burrton USD 369 200/K-12
PO Box 369 67020 620-463-3840
Jeff Shearon, supt. Fax 463-2636
www.burrton.schoolfusion.us
Burrton HS 100/6-12
PO Box 369 67020 620-463-3820
Joan Simoneau, prin. Fax 463-2096

Victory Village Christian Academy 50/7-12
201 S Victory Rd 67020 620-463-6112
Rev. Bill Cowell, prin. Fax 463-2631

Bushton, Rice, Pop. 274
Central Plains USD 112
Supt. — See Holyrood
Central Plains MS 100/5-8
500 S Main St 67427 620-562-3596
Jane Oeser, prin. Fax 562-3248

Caldwell, Sumner, Pop. 1,059
Caldwell USD 360 200/PK-12
22 N Webb St 67022 620-845-2585
Alan Jamison, supt. Fax 845-2610
www.usd360.com
Caldwell Secondary S 100/6-12
31 N Osage St 67022 620-845-2585
Kevin Schmidt, prin. Fax 845-2534

Caney, Montgomery, Pop. 2,080
Caney Valley USD 436 900/PK-12
700 E Bullpup Blvd 67333 620-879-9200
Danny Fulton, supt. Fax 879-9209
caney.com/usd_436/
Caney Valley JSHS 400/7-12
601 E Bullpup Blvd 67333 620-879-9220
William Ellis, prin. Fax 879-9227

Canton, McPherson, Pop. 732
Canton-Galva USD 419 400/PK-12
PO Box 317 67428 620-628-4901
Bill Seidl, supt. Fax 628-4380
cantongalva.ks.schoolwebpages.com
Canton-Galva HS 100/9-12
PO Box 275 67428 620-628-4401
Brent Kaemfe, prin. Fax 628-4951
Other Schools – See Galva

Carbondale, Osage, Pop. 1,411
Santa Fe Trail USD 434 1,100/PK-12
1663 E US Highway 56 66414 785-665-7168
Steve Pegram, supt. Fax 665-7164
www.usd434.org
Carbondale Attendance Center 300/5-8
315 N 4th St 66414 785-836-7188
Michael Flax, prin. Fax 836-7696
Santa Fe Trail HS 300/9-12
15701 S California Rd 66414 785-665-7161
David Swaim, prin. Fax 665-7193

Cawker City, Mitchell, Pop. 462
Waconda USD 272 300/K-12
PO Box 326 67430 785-781-4328
Jeff Travis, supt. Fax 781-4318
www.usd272.org
Lakeside JHS 100/7-8
PO Box 46 67430 785-781-4911
James Giesbrecht, prin. Fax 781-4861
Other Schools – See Downs

Cedar Vale, Chautauqua, Pop. 554
Cedar Vale USD 285 100/PK-12
PO Box 458 67024 620-758-2265
Lance Rhodd, supt. Fax 758-2647
www.cvs285.net
Cedar Vale JSHS 100/6-12
PO Box 458 67024 620-758-2791
Jackie Burdette, prin. Fax 758-2704

Centralia, Nemaha, Pop. 501
Vermillion USD 380
Supt. — See Vermillion
Centralia JSHS 100/7-12
PO Box 367 66415 785-857-3324
John Whetzal, prin. Fax 857-3847

Chanute, Neosho, Pop. 8,951
Chanute USD 413 2,000/PK-12
315 Chanute 35 Pkwy 66720 620-432-2500
Dr. James Hardy, supt. Fax 431-6810
www.usd413.org/
Chanute HS 600/9-12
1501 W 36th St 66720 620-432-2510
Kent Wire, prin. Fax 431-3020
Royster MS 400/6-8
400 W Main St 66720 620-432-2520
Brad Miner, prin. Fax 431-7841

Neosho County Community College Post-Sec.
800 W 14th St 66720 620-431-2820

Chapman, Dickinson, Pop. 1,368
Chapman USD 473 900/K-12
PO Box 249 67431 785-922-6521
Lacee Sell, supt. Fax 922-6446
usd473.net
Chapman HS 300/9-12
PO Box 249 67431 785-922-6561
Kevin Suther, prin. Fax 922-7162
Chapman MS 200/6-8
PO Box 249 67431 785-922-6555
Bruce Hurford, prin. Fax 922-6601

Chase, Rice, Pop. 461
Chase-Raymond USD 401 100/K-12
313 E Avenue C 67524 620-938-2913
Carl Helm, supt. Fax 938-2622
www.usd401.com/
Chase HS 50/9-12
313 E Avenue C 67524 620-938-2923
Glenna Grinstead, prin. Fax 938-2456
Raymond JHS 50/7-8
313 E Avenue C 67524 620-938-2923
Glenna Grinstead, prin. Fax 938-2456

Cheney, Sedgwick, Pop. 2,072
Cheney USD 268 800/PK-12
100 W 6th Ave 67025 316-542-3512
David Grover, supt. Fax 542-0326
www.cheney268.com
Cheney HS 300/9-12
100 W 6th Ave 67025 316-542-3113
Greg Rosenhagen, prin. Fax 542-3789
Cheney MS 200/6-8
100 W 6th Ave 67025 316-542-0060
Amy Wallace, prin. Fax 542-3789

Cherokee, Crawford, Pop. 696
Cherokee USD 247 700/K-12
506 S Smelter St 66724 620-457-8350
Dr. Glenn Fortmayer, supt. Fax 457-8428
www.usd247.com
Southeast HS 200/9-12
126 W 400 Hwy 66724 620-457-8365
Larry Malle, prin. Fax 457-8389

Cherryvale, Montgomery, Pop. 2,326
Cherryvale USD 447 900/PK-12
618 E 4th St 67335 620-336-8130
Randy Wagoner, supt. Fax 336-8133
www.usd447schools.org/
Cherryvale JSHS 400/7-12
700 S Carson St 67335 620-336-8100
George Owens, prin. Fax 336-8110

Chetopa, Labette, Pop. 1,068
Chetopa - St. Paul USD 505 400/PK-12
430 Elm St 67336 620-236-7244
Susan Beeson, supt. Fax 236-4271
www.usd505.org
Chetopa HS 100/7-12
430 Elm St 67336 620-236-7244
Kelly Nading, prin. Fax 236-4271
Other Schools – See Saint Paul

Cimarron, Gray, Pop. 2,164
Cimarron-Ensign USD 102 — 700/K-12
PO Box 489 67835 — 620-855-7743
Mike Waters, supt. — Fax 855-7745
www.cimarronschools.net
Cimarron JSHS — 300/7-12
PO Box 489 67835 — 620-855-3323
Bill Brown, prin. — Fax 855-3219

Claflin, Barton, Pop. 637
Central Plains USD 112
Supt. — See Holyrood
Central Plains HS — 100/9-12
PO Box 348 67525 — 620-587-3801
Toby Holmes, prin. — Fax 587-3677

Clay Center, Clay, Pop. 4,283
Clay Center USD 379 — 1,400/K-12
PO Box 97 67432 — 785-632-3176
Michael Folks, supt. — Fax 632-5020
www.usd379.org/
Clay Center Community HS — 300/9-12
1630 9th St 67432 — 785-632-2131
Bud Young, prin. — Fax 632-2076
Clay Center Community MS — 200/6-8
935 Prospect St 67432 — 785-632-3232
Keith Hoffman, prin. — Fax 632-6013
Other Schools – See Wakefield

Clearwater, Sedgwick, Pop. 2,443
Clearwater USD 264 — 1,200/PK-12
PO Box 248 67026 — 620-584-2091
Mike Roth, supt. — Fax 584-6705
www.usd264.org
Clearwater HS — 400/9-12
PO Box 248 67026 — 620-584-2361
Bob Mellen, prin. — Fax 584-2083
Clearwater MS — 200/7-8
PO Box 248 67026 — 620-584-2036
Keith Pauly, prin. — Fax 584-2199

Clifton, Washington, Pop. 552
Clifton-Clyde USD 224
Supt. — See Clyde
Clifton-Clyde MS — 100/4-8
PO Box B 66937 — 785-455-3323
Eric Sacco, prin. — Fax 455-3524

Clyde, Cloud, Pop. 706
Clifton-Clyde USD 224 — 300/PK-12
616 N High St Ste 2 66938 — 785-446-2098
Corey Reese, supt. — Fax 446-3000
www.usd224.com/
Clifton-Clyde HS — 100/9-12
616 N High St Ste 1 66938 — 785-446-3444
Corey Reese, prin. — Fax 446-3458
Other Schools – See Clifton

Coffeyville, Montgomery, Pop. 9,654
Coffeyville USD 445 — 1,800/PK-12
615 Ellis St 67337 — 620-252-6400
Robert J. Morton Ed.D., supt. — Fax 252-6807
cvilleschools.com
Field Kindley Memorial HS — 500/9-12
1110 W 8th St 67337 — 620-252-6410
Blake Vargas, prin. — Fax 252-6818
NADO, 200 Walnut St 67337 — Alt
Virgil Horn, dir. — 620-252-6440
Roosevelt MS — 200/7-8
1000 W 8th St 67337 — 620-252-6420
Jeffrey Pegues, prin. — Fax 252-6844

Coffeyville Community College — Post-Sec.
400 W 11th St 67337 — 620-251-7700

Colby, Thomas, Pop. 5,323
Colby USD 315 — 900/K-12
600 W 3rd St 67701 — 785-460-5000
Terrel Harrison, supt. — Fax 460-5050
www.colbyeagles.org/
Colby HS — 300/9-12
1890 S Franklin Ave 67701 — 785-460-5300
Jeff Wallingford, prin. — Fax 460-5350
Colby MS — 200/6-8
750 W 3rd St 67701 — 785-460-5200
Robb Ross, prin. — Fax 460-5250

Colby Community College — Post-Sec.
1255 S Range Ave 67701 — 785-462-3984
Heartland Christian S — 100/PK-12
1995 W 4th St 67701 — 785-460-6419
Renee Schmeiser, admin. — Fax 460-8337

Coldwater, Comanche, Pop. 813
South Central USD 300 — 300/K-12
PO Box 721 67029 — 620-582-2181
Michael Baldwin, supt. — Fax 582-2540
www.southcentralusd300.org
South Central HS — 100/9-12
PO Box 578 67029 — 620-582-2158
Ty Theurer, prin. — Fax 582-2535
Other Schools – See Protection

Colony, Anderson, Pop. 394
Crest USD 479 — 200/K-12
PO Box 305 66015 — 620-852-3540
Jerry Turner, supt. — Fax 852-3542
www.usd479.org
Crest HS — 100/9-12
PO Box 325 66015 — 620-852-3521
Jerry Turner, prin. — Fax 852-3357

Columbus, Cherokee, Pop. 3,208
Columbus USD 493 — 1,100/PK-12
802 S Highschool Ave 66725 — 620-429-3661
David Carriger, supt. — Fax 429-2673
www.usd493.com
Central S — 400/4-8
810 S Highschool Ave 66725 — 620-429-3943
James Bolden, prin. — Fax 429-2882
Columbus HS — 300/9-12
124 S Highschool Ave 66725 — 620-429-3821
Tony Shearburn, prin. — Fax 429-3657

Concordia, Cloud, Pop. 5,314
Concordia USD 333 — 1,100/K-12
217 W 7th St 66901 — 785-243-3518
Beverly Mortimer, supt. — Fax 243-8883
www.usd333.com
Concordia JSHS — 500/7-12
436 W 10th St 66901 — 785-243-2452
Quentin Breese, prin. — Fax 243-8805

Cloud County Community College — Post-Sec.
2221 Campus Dr 66901 — 785-243-1435

Conway Springs, Sumner, Pop. 1,251
Conway Springs USD 356 — 600/K-12
110 N Monnett St 67031 — 620-456-2961
Clay Murphy, supt. — Fax 456-3173
www.usd356.org
Conway Springs HS — 200/9-12
607 W Saint Louis St 67031 — 620-456-2963
Lelin George, prin. — Fax 456-3314
Conway Springs MS — 100/6-8
112 N Cranmer St 67031 — 620-456-2965
James O'Brien, prin. — Fax 456-3313

Copeland, Gray, Pop. 310
Copeland USD 476 — 100/PK-8
PO Box 156 67837 — 620-668-5565
Jay Zehr, supt. — Fax 668-5568
www1.usd476.org:81/
South Gray JHS — 50/6-8
PO Box 156 67837 — 620-668-5565
Jay Zehr, prin. — Fax 668-5568

Cottonwood Falls, Chase, Pop. 897
Chase County USD 284 — 300/K-12
PO Box 569 66845 — 620-273-6303
Jeffrey Kohlman, supt. — Fax 273-6717
www.usd284.org/
Chase County JSHS — 100/7-12
PO Box 400 66845 — 620-273-6354
Jay Talkington, prin. — Fax 273-8337

Council Grove, Morris, Pop. 2,159
Morris County USD 417 — 800/PK-12
17 Wood St 66846 — 620-767-5192
Dr. Mike Ford, supt. — Fax 767-5444
www.usd417.net
Council Grove HS — 200/9-12
129 Hockaday St 66846 — 620-767-5149
Kelly McDiffett, prin. — Fax 767-7280
Council Grove MS — 100/6-8
706 E Main St 66846 — 620-767-6852
Mike Estes, prin. — Fax 767-5260
Other Schools – See Alta Vista

Courtland, Republic, Pop. 285
Pike Valley USD 426
Supt. — See Scandia
Pike Valley JHS — 100/6-8
PO Box 320 66939 — 785-374-4221
Mike Gritten, prin. — Fax 374-4268

Cunningham, Kingman, Pop. 450
Cunningham USD 332 — 200/K-12
PO Box 67 67035 — 620-298-3271
Glen Davis, supt. — Fax 298-2562
www.usd332.org/
Cunningham HS — 100/9-12
PO Box 98 67035 — 620-298-2473
Bob Stackhouse, prin. — Fax 298-5005

Damar, Rooks, Pop. 131
Palco USD 269
Supt. — See Palco
Damar JHS — 50/6-8
PO Box 38 67632 — 785-839-4265
Ian Margreiter, prin. — Fax 839-4278

Deerfield, Kearny, Pop. 694
Deerfield USD 216 — 300/PK-12
803 Beech 67838 — 620-426-8516
Amy DeLaRosa, supt. — Fax 426-7890
www.usd216.org/
Deerfield HS — 100/9-12
803 Beech 67838 — 620-426-8401
Nathan Reed, prin. — Fax 426-6903
Deerfield MS — 100/6-8
803 Beech 67838 — 620-426-8401
Janelle Robins-Gaede, prin. — Fax 426-6903

Denton, Doniphan, Pop. 142
Doniphan West USD 111
Supt. — See Highland
Doniphan West MS — 100/6-8
642 Highway 20 E 66017 — 785-359-6526
Kristin Ellis, prin. — Fax 359-6522

Derby, Sedgwick, Pop. 21,570
Derby USD 260 — 6,700/PK-12
120 E Washington St 67037 — 316-788-8400
Craig Wilford, supt. — Fax 788-8526
www.derbyschools.com
Derby HS — 1,800/9-12
920 N Rock Rd 67037 — 316-788-8500
Tim Hamblin, prin. — Fax 788-8593
Derby MS — 1,000/7-8
801 E Madison Ave 67037 — 316-788-8580
Clinton Shipley, prin. — Fax 788-8062

De Soto, Johnson, Pop. 5,615
De Soto USD 232 — 6,600/PK-12
35200 W 91st St 66018 — 913-667-6200
Doug Sumner Ed.D., supt. — Fax 667-6201
www.usd232.org
De Soto HS — 600/9-12
35000 W 91st St 66018 — 913-667-6250
Mark Meyer, prin. — Fax 667-6251
Lexington Trails MS — 300/6-8
8800 Penner Ave 66018 — 913-667-6260
Steve Ludwig, prin. — Fax 667-6261
Other Schools – See Lenexa, Shawnee

Dexter, Cowley, Pop. 275
Dexter USD 471 — 100/PK-12
PO Box 97 67038 — 620-876-5415
Dr. Ron Ledford, supt. — Fax 876-5548
www.usd471.org
Dexter JSHS — 100/7-12
PO Box 97 67038 — 620-876-5415
Robert Holmes, prin. — Fax 876-5548

Dighton, Lane, Pop. 1,017
Dighton USD 482 — 300/PK-12
PO Box 878 67839 — 620-397-2835
Joel Applegate, supt. — Fax 397-5932
www.usd482.org
Dighton JSHS — 100/7-12
PO Box 939 67839 — 620-397-5333
James Keenan, prin. — Fax 397-5338

Dodge City, Ford, Pop. 26,977
Dodge City USD 443 — 5,600/K-12
PO Box 460 67801 — 620-371-1070
Alan Cunningham, supt. — Fax 227-1687
www.usd443.org
Comanche MS — 300/6-8
1601 1st Ave 67801 — 620-371-1100
Marc Woofter, prin. — Fax 339-4802
Dodge City HS — 1,800/9-12
2201 W Ross Blvd 67801 — 620-227-1611
Jacque Feist, prin. — Fax 227-1680
Dodge City MS — 800/6-8
2000 6th Ave 67801 — 620-227-1610
Mike King, prin. — Fax 227-1731

Dodge City Community College — Post-Sec.
2501 N 14th Ave 67801 — 620-225-1321

Douglass, Butler, Pop. 1,675
Douglass USD 396 — 700/PK-12
921 E 1st St 67039 — 316-747-3300
Robert Reynolds, supt. — Fax 747-3305
www.usd396.net/
Douglass HS — 200/9-12
910 E 1st St 67039 — 316-747-3310
Brian Gee, prin. — Fax 747-3315
Sisk MS — 200/6-8
950 E 1st St 67039 — 316-747-3340
Robert Swigart, prin. — Fax 747-3346

Downs, Osborne, Pop. 896
Waconda USD 272
Supt. — See Cawker City
Lakeside HS — 100/9-12
PO Box 247 67437 — 785-454-3332
Jeff Travis, prin. — Fax 454-3747

Easton, Leavenworth, Pop. 251
Easton USD 449 — 700/PK-12
32502 Easton Rd 66020 — 913-651-9740
Charles Coblentz, supt. — Fax 324-5237
www.easton449.org
Pleasant Ridge HS — 200/9-12
32500 Easton Rd 66020 — 913-651-5556
Andy Metsker, prin. — Fax 254-3089
Pleasant Ridge MS — 200/6-8
32504 Easton Rd 66020 — 913-651-5522
Lisa Powers, prin. — Fax 324-5237

Effingham, Atchison, Pop. 540
Atchison County Community USD 377 — 700/PK-12
PO Box 289 66023 — 913-833-5050
Stephen Wiseman, supt. — Fax 833-5210
www.usd377.org/
Atchison County Community JSHS — 300/7-12
PO Box 289 66023 — 913-833-2240
Deanna Scherer, prin. — Fax 833-5210

Elbing, Butler, Pop. 228

Berean Academy — 300/PK-12
201 S Elbing Rd 67041 — 316-799-2211
Terry Tilson, supt. — Fax 799-2601

El Dorado, Butler, Pop. 12,711
El Dorado USD 490 — 1,900/PK-12
124 W Central Ave 67042 — 316-322-4800
Sue Givens, supt. — Fax 322-4801
www.eldoradoschools.org
ACE Alternative S — Alt
1266 SE Bluestem Rd 67042 — 316-322-4880
Angie Adelsperger, prin. — Fax 322-4881
El Dorado HS — 600/9-12
401 McCollum Rd 67042 — 316-322-4810
Kevin House, prin. — Fax 322-4811
El Dorado MS — 400/6-8
500 W Central Ave 67042 — 316-322-4820
Karla King, prin. — Fax 322-4821

Butler Community College — Post-Sec.
901 S Haverhill Rd 67042 — 316-321-2222

Elkhart, Morton, Pop. 2,178
Elkhart USD 218 — 600/PK-12
PO Box 999 67950 — 620-697-2195
Nancy Crowell, supt. — Fax 697-2607
www.usd218.org
Elkhart HS — 100/9-12
PO Box 999 67950 — 620-697-2193
Rex Richardson, prin. — Fax 697-4415
Elkhart MS — 200/5-8
PO Box 999 67950 — 620-697-2197
Diane Finn, prin. — Fax 697-4828

Ellinwood, Barton, Pop. 2,100
Ellinwood USD 355 — 400/K-12
300 N Schiller Ave 67526 — 620-564-3226
Ben Jacobs, supt. — Fax 564-2206
www.usd355.org/
Ellinwood HS — 100/9-12
210 E 2nd St 67526 — 620-564-3136
Shawn Henderson, prin. — Fax 564-2816
Ellinwood MS — 100/7-8
210 E 2nd St 67526 — 620-564-3136
Shawn Henderson, prin. — Fax 564-2816

Ellis, Ellis, Pop. 2,048
Ellis USD 388 — 400/PK-12
PO Box 256 67637 — 785-726-4281
Robert Young, supt. — Fax 726-4677
www.usd388.k12.ks.us
Ellis HS — 100/9-12
PO Box 300 67637 — 785-726-3151
Corey Burton, prin. — Fax 726-3169

Ellsworth, Ellsworth, Pop. 3,090
Ellsworth USD 327 — 600/K-12
PO Box 306 67439 — 785-472-5561
Eric Reid, supt. — Fax 472-5563
www.usd327.org
Ellsworth JSHS — 300/7-12
211 W 11th St 67439 — 785-472-4471
Dale Brungardt, prin. — Fax 472-8109

Elwood, Doniphan, Pop. 1,173
Riverside USD 114 — 700/PK-12
PO Box 49 66024 — 913-365-5632
Michael Newman, supt. — Fax 365-5967
www.usd114.org
AIM HS — 50/Alt
PO Box 49 66024 — 913-365-1100
Bob Blair, prin. — Fax 365-5946
Riverside MS — 100/6-8
PO Box 368 66024 — 913-365-6735
Robert Hampton, prin. — Fax 365-3503
Other Schools – See Wathena

Emporia, Lyon, Pop. 24,437
Emporia USD 253 — 3,600/PK-12
PO Box 1008 66801 — 620-341-2200
Theresa Davidson, supt. — Fax 341-2205
www.usd253.org
Emporia HS — 1,300/9-12
3302 W 18th Ave 66801 — 620-341-2365
Scott Sheldon, prin. — Fax 341-2376
Emporia MS — 600/6-8
2300 Graphic Arts Rd 66801 — 620-341-2335
Wendy Moore, prin. — Fax 341-2341
Flint Hills Learning Center — Alt
1624 Industrial Rd 66801 — 620 341-2251
Tell Kirk, prin. — Fax 343-6789

Emporia State University — Post-Sec.
1200 Commercial St 66801 — 620-341-1200
Flint Hills Technical College — Post-Sec.
3301 W 18th Ave 66801 — 620-343-4600

Erie, Neosho, Pop. 1,145
Erie-Galesburg USD 101 — 600/PK-12
PO Box 137 66733 — 620-244-3264
John Wyrick, supt. — Fax 244-3664
www.usd101.com
Other Schools – See Galesburg

Eskridge, Wabaunsee, Pop. 526
Mission Valley USD 330 — 400/PK-12
PO Box 158 66423 — 866-557-6686
Braden Anshutz, supt. — Fax 409-6216
www.mv330.org
Mission Valley HS — 200/7-12
12913 Mission Valley Rd 66423 — 866-557-6686
Charles Chesmore, prin. — Fax 409-6218

Eudora, Douglas, Pop. 5,992
Eudora USD 491 — 1,500/PK-12
PO Box 500 66025 — 785-542-4910
Don Grosdidier, supt. — Fax 542-4909
www.eudoraschools.org/
Eudora - De Soto Technical Education Ctr — Vo/Tech
PO Box 712 66025 — 785-542-4986
Ron Abel, prin. — Fax 542-4970
Eudora HS — 400/9-12
PO Box 712 66025 — 785-542-4980
G.A. Buie, prin. — Fax 542-4990
Eudora MS — 300/6-8
PO Box 701 66025 — 785-542-4960
Denise Kendall, prin. — Fax 542-4970

Eureka, Greenwood, Pop. 2,592
Eureka USD 389 — 700/PK-12
216 N Main St 67045 — 620-583-5588
Randy Corns, supt. — Fax 583-8200
www.389ks.org
Eureka JSHS — 300/7-12
815 N Jefferson St 67045 — 620-583-7428
Bret Howard, prin. — Fax 583-8222

Everest, Brown, Pop. 283
South Brown County USD 430
Supt. — See Horton
Everest MS — 200/5-8
221 S 7th St 66424 — 785-548-7536
Jackie Wenger, prin. — Fax 548-7538

Fort Leavenworth, Leavenworth, Pop. 1,300
Ft. Leavenworth USD 207 — 2,000/K-9
207 Education Way 66027 — 913-651-7373
Keith Mispagel, supt. — Fax 758-6010
www.usd207.org
Patton JHS — 400/7-9
1 Patton Cir 66027 — 913-651-7371
Christopher Kase, prin. — Fax 758-6097

Fort Riley, Geary, Pop. 7,475
Geary County USD 475
Supt. — See Junction City
Fort Riley MS — 700/6-8
4020 1st Division Rd 66442 — 785-717-4500
Joseph Handlos, prin. — Fax 717-4501

Fort Scott, Bourbon, Pop. 7,870
Ft. Scott USD 234 — 1,900/PK-12
424 S Main St 66701 — 620-223-0800
Dr. Diane Gross, supt. — Fax 223-2760
www.usd234.org
Fort Scott HS — 600/9-12
1005 S Main St 66701 — 620-223-0600
Bob Beckham, prin. — Fax 223-5368
Fort Scott MS — 400/6-8
1105 E 12th St 66701 — 620-223-3262
D.J. Brown, prin. — Fax 223-8946

Fort Scott Community College — Post-Sec.
2108 Horton St 66701 — 620-223-2700

Fowler, Meade, Pop. 579
Fowler USD 225 — 200/PK-12
PO Box 170 67844 — 620-646-5661
Dr. Bobbi Williams, supt. — Fax 646-5713
www.usd225.org/
Fowler HS — 100/7-12
PO Box 140 67844 — 620-646-5221
Pam Leiker, prin. — Fax 646-5295

Frankfort, Marshall, Pop. 726
Vermillion USD 380
Supt. — See Vermillion
Frankfort JSHS — 100/7-12
PO Box 203 66427 — 785-292-4486
Dean Dalinghaus, prin. — Fax 292-4636

Fredonia, Wilson, Pop. 2,433
Fredonia USD 484 — 800/PK-12
PO Box 539 66736 — 620-378-4177
Jim Porter, supt. — Fax 378-4345
www.fredoniaks.com
Fredonia HS — 200/9-12
916 Robinson St 66736 — 620-378-4172
Jim Lambert, prin. — Fax 378-4398
Fredonia MS — 200/6-8
203 N 8th St 66736 — 620-378-4167
Laura Fitzmorris, prin. — Fax 378-3635

Frontenac, Crawford, Pop. 3,381
Frontenac USD 249 — 900/PK-12
208 S Cayuga St 66763 — 620-231-7551
Dr. Dale Slagle, supt. — Fax 231-1312
www.frontenac249.org
Frontenac HS — 200/9-12
201 S Crawford St 66763 — 620-231-7550
Ted Hessong, prin. — Fax 231-2043
Frontenac JHS — 200/6-8
208 S Cayuga St 66763 — 620-232-6370
Mike Martin, prin. — Fax 231-1312

Galena, Cherokee, Pop. 2,973
Galena USD 499 — 800/PK-12
702 E 7th St 66739 — 620-783-4499
Brian Smith, supt. — Fax 783-5547
www.galena499.org/
Galena HS — 200/9-12
702 E 7th St 66739 — 620-783-4499
Toby VanCleave, prin. — Fax 783-1780
Galena MS — 200/6-8
702 E 7th St 66739 — 620-783-4499
Toby VanCleave, prin. — Fax 783-5214

Galesburg, Neosho, Pop. 125
Erie-Galesburg USD 101
Supt. — See Erie
Galesburg MS — 100/6-8
PO Box 147 66740 — 620-763-2470
Steve Oliver, prin. — Fax 763-2224

Galva, McPherson, Pop. 861
Canton-Galva USD 419
Supt. — See Canton
Canton-Galva MS — 100/4-8
PO Box 96 67443 — 620-654-3321
Jim Struber, prin. — Fax 654-3335

Garden City, Finney, Pop. 26,301
Garden City USD 457 — 7,200/PK-12
1205 Fleming St 67846 — 620-805-7000
Richard Atha Ph.D., supt. — Fax 805-7190
www.gckschools.com
Garden City Alternate Education Center — 100/Alt
1312 N 7th St 67846 — 620-805-8600
Mark Ronn, prin. — Fax 805-8193
Garden City HS — 2,000/9-12
2720 Buffalo Way Blvd 67846 — 620-805-5400
James Mireles, prin. — Fax 805-5615
Good MS — 500/7-8
1412 N Main St 67846 — 620-805-8100
Brad Springston, prin. — Fax 805-8150
Henderson MS — 600/7-8
2406 Fleming St 67846 — 620-805-8500
Glenda LaBarbera, prin. — Fax 805-8598

Garden City Community College — Post-Sec.
801 N Campus Dr 67846 — 620-276-7611

Garden Plain, Sedgwick, Pop. 838
Renwick USD 267
Supt. — See Andale
Garden Plain HS — 200/9-12
PO Box 128 67050 — 316-531-2272
Troy McChristian, prin. — Fax 535-2727

Gardner, Johnson, Pop. 18,628
Gardner Edgerton USD 231 — 4,900/PK-12
PO Box 97 66030 — 913-856-2000
Dr. Bill Gilhaus, supt. — Fax 856-7330
www.usd231.com
Gardner Edgerton HS — 1,300/9-12
425 N Waverly Rd 66030 — 913-856-2600
Tim Brady, prin. — Fax 856-8218
Pioneer Ridge MS — 700/5-8
16200 S Kill Creek Rd 66030 — 913-856-3850
Tim Drake, prin. — Fax 856-3694
Wheatridge MS — 800/5-8
318 E Washington St 66030 — 913-856-2900
Heath Sigg, prin. — Fax 856-2980

Garnett, Anderson, Pop. 3,385
Garnett USD 365 — 1,000/PK-12
PO Box 328 66032 — 785-448-6155
Donald Blome, supt. — Fax 448-6157
www.usd365.org
Anderson County JSHS — 500/7-12
1100 W Highway 31 66032 — 785-448-3115
Kenny Kellstadt, prin. — Fax 448-6670

Gas, Allen, Pop. 559
Iola USD 257
Supt. — See Iola
Crossroads Learning Center — Alt
PO Box 300 66742 — 620-365-4881
Timothy Seibel, prin. — Fax 365-4730

Girard, Crawford, Pop. 2,739
Girard USD 248 — 1,100/PK-12
415 N Summit St 66743 — 620-724-4325
Blaise Bauer, supt. — Fax 724-8446
www.girard248.org/
Girard HS — 300/9-12
415 N Summit St 66743 — 620-724-4326
Todd Ferguson, prin. — Fax 724-6136
Girard MS — 200/6-8
415 N Summit St 66743 — 620-724-4114
Randy Heatherly, prin. — Fax 724-4610

Glasco, Cloud, Pop. 493
Southern Cloud USD 334
Supt. — See Miltonvale
Glasco HS — 50/9-12
PO Box 158 67445 — 785-568-2291
Eric Winters, prin. — Fax 568-2298

Goddard, Sedgwick, Pop. 4,232
Goddard USD 265 — 5,400/K-12
PO Box 249 67052 — 316-794-4000
Dr. Justin Henry, supt. — Fax 794-2222
www.goddardusd.com
Eisenhower HS — 800/9-12
PO Box 789 67052 — 316-794-4190
Bill Kelley, prin. — Fax 794-4191
Eisenhower MS — 400/7-8
PO Box 349 67052 — 316-794-4150
Jerold Longabaugh, prin. — Fax 794-4063
Goddard Academy — 9-12
PO Box 318 67052 — 316-794-4142
James Burkhart, prin. — Fax 794-4143
Goddard HS — 1,500/9-12
PO Box 189 67052 — 316-794-4100
Doug Bridwell, prin. — Fax 794-4130
Goddard MS — 400/7-8
PO Box 279 67052 — 316-794-4230
Lisa Hogarth, prin. — Fax 794-4254

Goessel, Marion, Pop. 530
Goessel USD 411 — 300/K-12
PO Box 68 67053 — 620-367-4601
Dr. John Fast, supt. — Fax 367-4603
www.usd411.org
Goessel JSHS — 100/6-12
PO Box 6 67053 — 620-367-2242
Scott Boden, prin. — Fax 367-2571

Goodland, Sherman, Pop. 4,416
Goodland USD 352 — 800/PK-12
PO Box 509 67735 — 785-890-2397
Bill Biermann, supt. — Fax 890-8504
www.usd352.org
Goodland HS — 200/9-12
PO Box 509 67735 — 785-890-5656
Greg Ferguson, prin. — Fax 890-8517
Grant JHS — 200/6-8
PO Box 509 67735 — 785-890-7561
Steve Raymer, prin. — Fax 890-8525

Northwest Kansas Technical College — Post-Sec.
1209 Harrison St 67735 — 785-890-3641

Grainfield, Gove, Pop. 277
Wheatland USD 292 — 100/PK-12
PO Box 165 67737 — 785-673-4213
Gary Kraus, supt. — Fax 673-4234
www.usd292.org
Wheatland HS — 50/9-12
PO Box 149 67737 — 785-673-4223
Gary Kraus, prin. — Fax 673-4234

Great Bend, Barton, Pop. 15,763
Great Bend USD 428 — 2,900/PK-12
201 S Patton Rd 67530 — 620-793-1500
Dr. Thomas Vernon, supt. — Fax 793-1585
www.usd428.net
Great Bend HS — 1,000/9-12
2027 Morton St 67530 — 620-793-1521
Tim Friess, prin. — Fax 793-1537
Great Bend MS — 500/7-8
1919 Harrison St 67530 — 620-793-1510
David Reiser, prin. — Fax 793-1549

Barton County Community College — Post-Sec.
245 NE 30 Rd 67530 — 620-792-2701

Greensburg, Kiowa, Pop. 767
Kiowa County USD 422 300/PK-12
710 S Main St 67054 620-723-2145
Darin Headrick, supt. Fax 723-2705
www.usd422.org
Kiowa County HS 100/9-12
720 S Main St 67054 620-723-2164
Randy Fulton, prin. Fax 723-2019

Gridley, Coffey, Pop. 338
Le Roy-Gridley USD 245
Supt. — See Le Roy
Southern Coffey County JHS 100/6-8
PO Box 426 66852 620-836-2151
J.J. Edwards, prin. Fax 836-4041

Grinnell, Gove, Pop. 259
Grinnell USD 291 50/K-8
PO Box 68 67738 785-824-3277
Mike McDermeit, supt. Fax 824-3215
www.usd291.com/
Grinnell MS 50/5-8
PO Box 68 67738 785-824-3277
Mike McDermeit, prin. Fax 824-3215

Gypsum, Saline, Pop. 398
Southeast of Saline USD 306 700/K-12
5056 E Highway K4 67448 785-536-4291
Richard Proffitt, supt. Fax 536-4247
www.usd306.k12.ks.us
Southeast Saline JSHS 400/7-12
5056 E Highway K4 67448 785-536-4286
Monte Couchman, prin. Fax 536-4292

Halstead, Harvey, Pop. 2,058
Halstead-Bentley USD 440 800/K-12
521 W 6th St 67056 316-835-2641
Tom Alstrom, supt. Fax 835-2305
www.usd440.com
Halstead HS 200/9-12
521 W 6th St 67056 316-835-2682
Joe Gerber, prin. Fax 835-3673
Halstead MS 300/4-8
221 W 6th St 67056 316-835-2694
Matt McKee, prin. Fax 835-2469

Hamilton, Greenwood, Pop. 262
Hamilton USD 390 100/K-12
2596 W Rd N 66853 620-678-3244
Greg Markowitz, supt. Fax 678-3321
www.hamilton390.net
Hamilton HS 50/7-12
2596 W Rd N 66853 620-678-3651
Diana Riley, prin. Fax 678-3321

Hanover, Washington, Pop. 680
Barnes USD 223
Supt. — See Barnes
Hanover HS 100/9-12
209 E North St 66945 785-337-2281
Larry Geist, prin. Fax 337-2307

Hartford, Lyon, Pop. 364
Southern Lyon County USD 252 600/PK-12
PO Box 278 66854 620-392-5519
Michael Argabright, supt. Fax 392-5841
www.usd252.org/
Hartford JSHS 100/7-12
PO Box 218 66854 620-392-5515
Aaric Davis, prin. Fax 392-5960
Other Schools – See Olpe

Haven, Reno, Pop. 1,205
Haven USD 312 900/PK-12
PO Box 130 67543 620-465-7727
Dr. Patrick Call, supt. Fax 465-3595
www.havenschools.com
Haven HS 300/9-12
PO Box C 67543 620-465-2585
Marty Nienstedt, prin. Fax 465-7729
Haven MS 100/7-8
PO Box B 67543 620-465-2587
Marty Nienstedt, prin. Fax 465-2588

Haviland, Kiowa, Pop. 699

Barclay College Post-Sec.
607 N Kingman St 67059 620-862-5252

Hays, Ellis, Pop. 20,202
Hays USD 489 2,600/PK-12
323 W 12th St 67601 785-623-2400
Dr. Will Roth, supt. Fax 623-2409
www.usd489.com/
Hays HS 800/9-12
2300 E 13th St 67601 785-623-2600
Mike Hester, prin. Fax 623-2609
Hays MS 400/6-8
201 E 29th St 67601 785-623-2450
Craig Pallister, prin. Fax 623-2456

Fort Hays State University Post-Sec.
600 Park St 67601 785-628-4000
Hays Academy of Hair Design Post-Sec.
1214 E 27th St 67601 785-628-6624
Thomas More Prep-Marian JSHS 200/7-12
1701 Hall St 67601 785-625-6577
Kathy Taylor, prin. Fax 625-3912

Haysville, Sedgwick, Pop. 10,516
Haysville USD 261 5,100/PK-12
1745 W Grand Ave 67060 316-554-2200
Dr. John Burke, supt. Fax 554-2230
www.usd261.com
Haysville HS Alt
106 Stewart Ave 67060 316-554-2231
Mark Foster, admin. Fax 554-2328
Haysville MS 600/6-8
900 W Grand Ave 67060 316-554-2251
Dr. Mike Maurer, prin. Fax 554-2258
Haysville West MS 700/6-8
1956 W Grand Ave 67060 316-554-2370
Ildo Martins, prin. Fax 554-2377
Other Schools – See Wichita

Healy, Lane, Pop. 233
Healy USD 468 100/PK-12
5006 N Dodge Rd 67850 620-398-2248
Dr. John LaFave, supt. Fax 398-2435
www.usd468.org
Healy JSHS 50/7-12
5006 N Dodge Rd 67850 620-398-2248
John LaFave, prin. Fax 398-2435

Herington, Dickinson, Pop. 2,456
Herington USD 487 500/PK-12
19 N Broadway 67449 785-258-2263
John Thissen, supt. Fax 258-2982
www.usd487.org/
Herington HS 200/9-12
1401 N D St 67449 785-258-2261
Ken Arnhold, prin. Fax 258-3013
Herington MS 100/6-8
1317 N D St 67449 785-258-2448
Ken Arnhold, prin. Fax 258-3976

Hesston, Harvey, Pop. 3,645
Hesston USD 460 800/K-12
PO Box 2000 67062 620-327-4931
Paul Becker, supt. Fax 327-7157
www.hesstonschools.org
Hesston HS 300/9-12
PO Box 2000 67062 620-327-7122
Ty Rhodes, prin. Fax 327-7138
Hesston MS 300/5-8
PO Box 2000 67062 620-327-7111
Ben Proctor, prin. Fax 327-7115

Hesston College Post-Sec.
PO Box 3000 67062 620-327-4221

Hiawatha, Brown, Pop. 3,067
Hiawatha USD 415 900/K-12
PO Box 398 66434 785-742-2266
Penny Hargrove, supt. Fax 742-3312
www.hiawathaschools.org/
Hiawatha HS 300/9-12
600 Red Hawk Dr 66434 785-742-3312
Alan Jeffery, prin. Fax 742-7156
Hiawatha MS 200/5-8
307 S Morrill Ave 66434 785-742-4172
David Coufal, prin. Fax 742-1744

Highland, Doniphan, Pop. 980
Doniphan West USD 111 400/PK-12
202 W Illinois St 66035 785-442-3671
Rex Bollinger, supt. Fax 442-3663
www.usd111.org/
Doniphan West HS 200/9-12
402 E Main St 66035 785-442-3286
Chris Lackey, prin. Fax 442-3289
Other Schools – See Denton

Highland Community College Post-Sec.
606 W Main St 66035 785-442-6000

Hill City, Graham, Pop. 1,438
Graham County USD 281 400/PK-12
PO Box 309 67642 785-421-2135
Jim Hickel, supt. Fax 421-5657
www.usd281.com
Hill City JSHS 200/7-12
PO Box 160 67642 785-421-2117
Alan Stein, prin. Fax 421-3029

Hillsboro, Marion, Pop. 2,935
Durham-Hillsboro-Lehigh USD 410 600/PK-12
416 S Date St 67063 620-947-3184
Steve Noble, supt. Fax 947-3475
www.usd410.net
Hillsboro HS 200/9-12
500 E Grand Ave 67063 620-947-3991
Max Heinrichs, prin. Fax 947-3251
Hillsboro MS 100/6-8
400 E Grand Ave 67063 620-947-3297
Greg Brown, prin. Fax 947-5565

Tabor College Post-Sec.
400 S Jefferson St 67063 620-947-3121

Hoisington, Barton, Pop. 2,656
Hoisington USD 431 700/PK-12
165 W 3rd St 67544 620-653-4134
Bill Lowry, supt. Fax 653-4073
www.usd431.net/
Hoisington HS 200/9-12
218 E 7th St 67544 620-653-2141
Meg Wilson, prin. Fax 653-4164
Hoisington MS 200/5-8
360 W 11th St 67544 620-653-4951
Patricia Reinhardt, prin. Fax 653-4483

Holcomb, Finney, Pop. 2,058
Holcomb USD 363 1,000/PK-12
PO Box 8 67851 620-277-2629
Jean Rush, supt. Fax 277-2010
www.usd363.com/
Holcomb HS 300/9-12
PO Box 38 67851 620-277-2063
Rob Schneeberger, prin. Fax 277-0240
Holcomb MS 200/6-8
PO Box 89 67851 620-277-2699
Chad Krug, prin. Fax 277-0239

Holton, Jackson, Pop. 3,248
Holton USD 336 1,000/PK-12
PO Box 352 66436 785-364-3650
Nancy Meyer, supt. Fax 364-3975
www.holton.k12.ks.us
Holton HS 300/9-12
901 New York Ave 66436 785-364-2181
Rod Wittmer, prin. Fax 364-5360
Holton MS 200/6-8
900 Iowa Ave 66436 785-364-2441
Michael Kimberlin, prin. Fax 364-5460

North Jackson USD 335 400/PK-12
12692 266th Rd 66436 785-364-2194
Adrianne Walsh, supt. Fax 364-4346
www.jhcobras.net
Jackson Heights HS 200/7-12
12719 266th Rd 66436 785-364-2195
Darren Shupe, prin. Fax 364-2487

Holyrood, Ellsworth, Pop. 439
Central Plains USD 112 400/PK-12
PO Box 168 67450 785-252-3695
Steve Woolf, supt. Fax 252-3697
www.usd112.org
Other Schools – See Bushton, Claflin, Wilson

Hope, Dickinson, Pop. 357
Rural Vista USD 481
Supt. — See White City
Hope HS 100/9-12
PO Box 218 67451 785-366-7221
Mike Teeter, prin. Fax 366-7115

Horton, Brown, Pop. 1,718
South Brown County USD 430 600/PK-12
522 Central Ave 66439 785-486-2611
Dr. Steven Davies, supt. Fax 486-2496
usd430.k12.ks.us
Horton HS 200/9-12
1120 1st Ave E 66439 785-486-2151
David Norman, prin. Fax 486-2909
Other Schools – See Everest

Howard, Elk, Pop. 671
West Elk USD 282 300/PK-12
PO Box 607 67349 620-374-2113
Corey Reese, supt. Fax 374-2414
Howard West Elk S 300/PK-12
PO Box 278 67349 620-374-2147
Juli Young, prin. Fax 374-2116

Hoxie, Sheridan, Pop. 1,186
Hoxie USD 412 400/PK-12
PO Box 348 67740 785-675-3258
Scott Hoyt, supt. Fax 675-2126
www.hoxie.org/
Hoxie JSHS 100/7-12
PO Box 989 67740 785-675-3286
Gary Johnson, prin. Fax 675-2270

Hoyt, Jackson, Pop. 649
Royal Valley USD 337
Supt. — See Mayetta
Royal Valley HS 300/9-12
PO Box 128 66440 785-986-6251
James Holloman, prin. Fax 986-6479

Hugoton, Stevens, Pop. 3,876
Hugoton USD 210 1,100/PK-12
205 E 6th St 67951 620-544-4397
Mark Crawford, supt. Fax 544-7138
www.usd210.org
Hugoton HS 300/9-12
215 W 11th St 67951 620-544-4311
Gregg Errebo, prin. Fax 544-7392
Hugoton MS 200/7-8
115 W 11th St 67951 620-544-4341
Lance Custer, prin. Fax 544-4856

Humboldt, Allen, Pop. 1,917
Humboldt USD 258 500/K-12
801 New York St 66748 620-473-3121
K.B. Criss, supt. Fax 473-2023
www.usd258.net
Humboldt HS 200/9-12
1020 New York St 66748 620-473-2251
John Johnson, prin. Fax 473-2086
Humboldt MS 100/6-8
1105 Bridge St 66748 620-473-3348
Kay Bolt, prin. Fax 473-3141
Humboldt Tech Building Vo/Tech
1116 New York St 66748 620-473-2251
John Johnson, prin. Fax 473-2086

Hutchinson, Reno, Pop. 41,132
Buhler USD 313
Supt. — See Buhler
Prairie Hills MS 300/7-8
3200 Lucille Dr 67502 620-662-6027
Todd Fredrickson, prin Fax 694-1002

Hutchinson USD 308 4,400/PK-12
PO Box 1908 67504 620-615-4000
Dr. Shelly Kiblinger, supt. Fax 615-4010
www.usd308.com
Hutchinson HS 1,300/9-12
810 E 13th Ave 67501 620-615-4100
Ronn Roehm, prin. Fax 615-4200
Hutchinson MS 8 400/8-8
200 W 14th Ave 67501 620-615-4801
Jim Menze, prin. Fax 615-4802

Nickerson USD 309 1,200/K-12
4501 W 4th Ave 67501 620-663-7141
Dr. William Hagerman, supt. Fax 663-7148
www.usd309ks.org
Reno Valley MS 200/7-8
1616 Wilshire Dr 67501 620-662-4573
Vince Naccarato, prin. Fax 662-6708
Other Schools – See Nickerson

Central Christian S 200/PK-12
1910 E 30th Ave 67502 620-663-2174
Tim Kuhns, admin. Fax 663-2176

Hutchinson Community College — Post-Sec.
1300 N Plum St 67501 — 620-665-3500
Pilgrim Christian S — 100/1-12
7213 W Mills Ave 67501 — 620-567-3242
Wesley Schrock, prin.
Sidney's Hairdressing College — Post-Sec.
200 E 3rd Ave 67501 — 620-662-5481
Trinity Catholic HS — 300/7-12
1400 E 17th Ave 67501 — 620-662-5800
Joe Hammersmith, prin. — Fax 662-1233

Independence, Montgomery, Pop. 9,137
Independence USD 446 — 1,600/K-12
PO Box 487 67301 — 620-332-1800
Chuck Schmidt, supt. — Fax 332-1811
www.indyschools.com
Independence HS — 600/9-12
1301 N 10th St 67301 — 620-332-1815
Mitch Shaw, prin. — Fax 332-1831
Independence MS — 400/6-8
300 W Locust St 67301 — 620-332-1836
Mark Hayward, prin. — Fax 332-1841

Independence Community College — Post-Sec.
1057 W College Ave 67301 — 620-331-4100

Ingalls, Gray, Pop. 304
Ingalls USD 477 — 300/PK-12
PO Box 99 67853 — 620-335-5136
Dave Novack, supt. — Fax 335-5678
www.ingallsusd477.com/
Ingalls JSHS — 100/6-12
PO Box 99 67853 — 620-335-5198
Steve Johnson, prin. — Fax 335-5801

Inman, McPherson, Pop. 1,343
Inman USD 448 — 400/PK-12
PO Box 129 67546 — 620-585-6424
Kevin Case, supt. — Fax 585-2689
www.usd448.com/
Inman JSHS — 200/7-12
PO Box 279 67546 — 620-585-6441
Scott Friesen, prin. — Fax 585-2797

Iola, Allen, Pop. 5,562
Iola USD 257 — 1,300/K-12
408 N Cottonwood St 66749 — 620-365-4700
Brian Pekarek, supt. — Fax 365-4708
www.usd257.org
Iola HS — 400/9-12
300 E Jackson Ave 66749 — 620-365-4715
Stacey Fager, prin. — Fax 365-4730
Iola MS — 300/6-8
600 East St 66749 — 620-365-4785
Jack Stanley, prin. — Fax 365-4770
Other Schools – See Gas

Allen Community College — Post-Sec.
1801 N Cottonwood St 66749 — 620-365-5116

Jetmore, Hodgeman, Pop. 861
Hodgeman County USD 227 — 300/PK-12
PO Box 398 67854 — 620-357-8301
Doug Chaney, supt. — Fax 357-8437
www.usd227.org/
Hodgeman County HS — 100/7-12
PO Box 100 67854 — 620-357-8378
Curtis Klein, prin. — Fax 357-6563

Johnson, Stanton, Pop. 1,483
Stanton County USD 452 — 400/PK-12
PO Box C 67855 — 620-492-6226
Angela Lawrence, supt. — Fax 492-1326
www.usd452.org
Stanton County JSHS — 100/7-12
PO Box C 67855 — 620-492-6284
Bob Homer, prin. — Fax 492-1326

Junction City, Geary, Pop. 21,775
Geary County USD 475 — 7,900/PK-12
PO Box 370 66441 — 785-717-4000
Ronald Walker, supt. — Fax 717-4003
web.usd475.org/
Dixon Center for Innovative Studies — Alt
920 W 6th St 66441 — 785-717-4710
Thomas Wesoloski, prin. — Fax 717-4711
Junction City HS — 1,700/9-12
900 N Eisenhower Dr 66441 — 785-717-4200
Melissa Sharp, prin. — Fax 717-4201
Junction City MS — 1,000/6-8
700 Wildcat Ln 66441 — 785-717-4400
Mary Wright, prin. — Fax 717-4401
Other Schools – See Fort Riley

St. Xaviers S — 100/K-12
200 N Washington St 66441 — 785-238-2841
Russell Swisher, prin. — Fax 238-5021

Kansas City, Wyandotte, Pop. 142,097
Kansas City USD 500 — 19,000/PK-12
2010 N 59th St 66104 — 913-551-3200
Dr. Cynthia Lane, supt. — Fax 551-3217
kckps.cloudaccess.net
Argentine MS — 600/6-8
2123 Ruby Ave 66106 — 913-627-6750
Jereme Brueggeman, prin. — Fax 627-6783
Arrowhead MS — 600/6-8
1715 N 82nd St 66112 — 913-627-6600
Laurie Boyd, prin. — Fax 627-6654
Central MS — 600/6-8
925 Ivandale St 66101 — 913-627-6150
Kris Scott, prin. — Fax 627-6152
Coronado MS — 400/6-8
1735 N 64th Ter 66102 — 913-627-6300
Jewell Ragsdale, prin. — Fax 627-6358
Eisenhower MS — 500/6-8
2901 N 72nd St 66109 — 913-627-6450
Freda Ogburn, prin. — Fax 627-6455
Harmon HS — 1,200/9-12
2400 Steele Rd 66106 — 913-627-7050
Slyvia Parra, prin. — Fax 627-7185
Northwest Magnet MS — 400/6-8
2400 N 18th St 66104 — 913-627-4000
Carnest Mitchell, prin. — Fax 627-4052
Rosedale MS — 600/6-8
3600 Springfield St 66103 — 913-627-6900
Nanette Coleman, prin. — Fax 627-6957
Schlagle HS — 800/9-12
2214 N 59th St 66104 — 913-627-7500
Dr. Maritza Paul-Newby, prin. — Fax 627-7555
Sumner Academy/Arts & Sciences — 900/8-12
1610 N 8th St 66101 — 913-627-7200
Dr. Eugene Fite, prin. — Fax 627-7205
Washington HS — 1,000/9-12
7340 Leavenworth Rd 66109 — 913-627-7800
Kelli Lorton, prin. — Fax 627-7850
West MS — 400/6-8
2600 N 44th St 66104 — 913-627-6000
Shelly Beech, prin. — Fax 627-6053
Wyandotte HS — 1,200/9-12
2501 Minnesota Ave 66102 — 913-627-7650
Mary Stewart, prin. — Fax 627-7700

Piper-Kansas City USD 203 — 1,600/PK-12
12036 Leavenworth Rd 66109 — 913-721-2088
Steve Adams, supt. — Fax 721-3573
www.piperschools.com/
Piper HS — 500/9-12
4400 N 107th St 66109 — 913-721-2100
Tim Conrad, prin. — Fax 721-3867
Piper MS — 400/6-8
4410 N 107th St 66109 — 913-721-1144
Stephen Mercer, prin. — Fax 721-1526

Turner USD 202 — 3,400/PK-12
800 S 55th St 66106 — 913-288-4100
Dr. Michelle Sedler, supt. — Fax 288-3401
www.turnerusd202.org/
Endeavor Alternative S — Alt
2540 Junction Rd 66106 — 913-288-3690
Rena Duewel, prin. — Fax 288-3691
Turner HS — 1,200/9-12
2211 S 55th St 66106 — 913-288-3300
Paul Colwell, prin. — Fax 288-3301
Turner MS — 600/7-8
1312 S 55th St 66106 — 913-288-4000
Ben Pretz, prin. — Fax 288-4001

Bishop Ward HS — 300/9-12
708 N 18th St 66102 — 913-371-1201
Ann Connor, prin. — Fax 371-2145
Donnelly College — Post-Sec.
608 N 18th St 66102 — 913-621-8700
Kansas City Kansas Community College — Post-Sec.
7250 State Ave 66112 — 913-334-1100
Kansas State School for the Blind — Post-Sec.
1100 State Ave 66102 — 913-281-3308
University of Kansas Medical Center — Post-Sec.
3901 Rainbow Blvd 66160 — 913-588-5000
Valor Christian S — 100/PK-12
3650 N 67th St 66104 — 913-608-7705

Kensington, Smith, Pop. 463
Thunder Ridge SD — 300/PK-12
128 S Kansas St 66951 — 785-476-2218
Jeff Yoxall, supt. — Fax 476-2258
usd110.net
Thunder Ridge HS — 100/9-12
209 E Ash St 66951 — 785-476-2217
Jeff Yoxall, prin. — Fax 476-2210
Other Schools – See Agra

Kingman, Kingman, Pop. 3,142
Kingman-Norwich USD 331 — 1,100/PK-12
115 N Main St 67068 — 620-532-3134
Dr. Robert Diepenbrock, supt. — Fax 532-3251
www.knusd331.com/
Kingman HS — 300/9-12
260 W Kansas Ave 67068 — 620-532-3136
Andy Albright, prin. — Fax 532-3027
Kingman MS — 200/6-8
607 N Spruce St 67068 — 620-532-3186
Brent Garrison, prin. — Fax 532-5137
Other Schools – See Norwich

Kiowa, Barber, Pop. 1,012
South Barber County USD 255 — 200/PK-12
512 Main St 67070 — 620-825-4115
Brad Morris, supt. — Fax 825-4145
www.southbarber.com/
South Barber JSHS — 100/7-12
1220 N 8th St 67070 — 620-825-4214
Brent Shaffer, prin. — Fax 825-4250

Kismet, Seward, Pop. 456
Kismet-Plains USD 483 — 700/PK-12
17222 Mustang Rd 67859 — 620-563-7103
Elton Argo, supt. — Fax 563-7348
www.usd483.net
Southwestern Heights HS — 200/9-12
17222 Mustang Rd 67859 — 620-563-7292
Dan Frisby, prin. — Fax 563-7383
Southwestern Heights JHS — 200/6-8
17222 Mustang Rd 67859 — 620-563-7100
Mark Webb, prin. — Fax 563-7342

La Crosse, Rush, Pop. 1,335
La Crosse USD 395 — 300/K-12
PO Box 778 67548 — 785-222-2505
Bill Keeley, supt. — Fax 222-3240
www.usd395.org
La Crosse HS — 100/9-12
PO Box 810 67548 — 785-222-2528
Kathy Keeley, prin. — Fax 222-3480
La Crosse MS — 50/7-8
PO Box 810 67548 — 785-222-3030
Kathy Keeley, prin. — Fax 222-3480

LaCygne, Linn, Pop. 1,138
Prairie View USD 362 — 1,000/PK-12
13799 KS Highway 152, — 913-757-2677
Chris Kleidosty, supt. — Fax 757-4442
www.pv362.org
Prairie View HS — 300/9-12
13731 KS Highway 152, — 913-757-4447
Timothy Weis, prin. — Fax 757-4443
Prairie View MS — 200/6-8
13667 KS Highway 152, — 913-757-4497
Ken Bolt, prin. — Fax 757-2728

Lakin, Kearny, Pop. 2,182
Lakin USD 215 — 600/PK-12
1003 W Kingman Ave 67860 — 620-355-6761
Kerry Lacock, supt. — Fax 355-7317
www.usd215.org/
Lakin HS — 200/9-12
407 N Campbell St 67860 — 620-355-6411
Ron Overeem, prin. — Fax 355-6460
Lakin MS — 200/5-8
1201 W Kingman Ave 67860 — 620-355-6973
Mike Ward, prin. — Fax 355-8313

Langdon, Reno, Pop. 42
Fairfield USD 310 — 200/K-12
16115 S Langdon Rd 67583 — 620-596-2152
Mary Treaster, supt. — Fax 596-2835
www.usd310.org
Fairfield HS — 100/9-12
16115 S Langdon Rd 67583 — 620-596-2481
Jesse Janssen, prin. — Fax 596-2384
Fairfield MS — 100/5-8
16115 S Langdon Rd 67583 — 620-596-2615
Shawn Koehn, prin. — Fax 596-2112

Lansing, Leavenworth, Pop. 10,978
Lansing USD 469 — 2,600/PK-12
401 S 2nd St 66043 — 913-727-1100
Dr. Randal Bagby, supt. — Fax 727-1619
www.usd469.net/
Lansing HS — 800/9-12
220 Lion Ln 66043 — 913-727-3357
Steve Dike, prin. — Fax 727-2001
Lansing MS — 600/6-8
509 Ida St 66043 — 913-727-1197
Kerry Brungardt, prin. — Fax 727-1349

Larned, Pawnee, Pop. 3,979
Ft. Larned USD 495 — 1,100/PK-12
120 E 6th St 67550 — 620-285-3185
Jon Flint, supt. — Fax 285-2973
www.usd495.net
Larned HS — 300/9-12
815 Corse Ave 67550 — 620-285-2151
Troy Langdon, prin. — Fax 285-7148
Larned MS — 300/5-8
904 Corse Ave 67550 — 620-285-8430
Derek Reinhardt, prin. — Fax 285-8433

Lawrence, Douglas, Pop. 84,434
Lawrence USD 497 — 9,400/PK-12
110 McDonald Dr 66044 — 785-832-5000
Dr. Rick Doll, supt. — Fax 832-5016
www.usd497.org
Lawrence Free State HS — 1,100/9-12
4700 Overland Dr 66049 — 785-832-6050
Ed West, prin. — Fax 832-6099
Lawrence HS — 1,200/9-12
1901 Louisiana St 66046 — 785-832-5050
Matt Brungardt, prin. — Fax 832-5066
Lawrence Liberty Memorial Central MS — 300/6-8
1400 Massachusetts St 66044 — 785-832-5400
Jeff Harkin, prin. — Fax 832-5403
Lawrence South MS — 400/6-8
2734 Louisiana St 66046 — 785-832-5450
Will Fernandez, prin. — Fax 832-5453
Lawrence Southwest MS — 400/6-8
2511 Inverness Dr 66047 — 785-832-5550
Kristen Ryan, prin. — Fax 832-5554
Lawrence West MS — 400/6-8
2700 Harvard Rd 66049 — 785-832-5500
Myron Melton, prin. — Fax 832-5504

Bishop Seabury Academy — 100/6-12
4120 Clinton Pkwy 66047 — 785-832-1717
Dr. Don Schawang, hdmstr. — Fax 832-1919
Haskell Indian Nations University — Post-Sec.
155 Indian Ave 66046 — 785-749-8404
Pinnacle Career Institute — Post-Sec.
1601 W 23rd St Ste 200 66046 — 785-841-9640
University of Kansas — Post-Sec.
1450 Jayhawk Blvd 66045 — 785-864-2700
Veritas Christian S — 100/K-12
256 N Michigan St 66044 — 785-749-0083
Kelli Huslig M.Ed., admin. — Fax 749-0580

Leavenworth, Leavenworth, Pop. 33,833
Leavenworth USD 453 — 3,700/PK-12
PO Box 969 66048 — 913-684-1400
Dr. Kelly Crane, supt. — Fax 684-1407
www.usd453.org
Leavenworth HS — 1,200/9-12
2012 10th Ave 66048 — 913-684-1550
Dr. Thomas Barry, prin. — Fax 684-1555
Warren MS — 500/7-8
PO Box 7 66048 — 913-684-1530
Dr. Leeann Fitzgerald, prin. — Fax 684-1539

Immaculata HS — 100/9-12
600 Shawnee St 66048 — 913-682-3900
Helen Schwinn, prin. — Fax 682-9036
University of Saint Mary — Post-Sec.
4100 S 4th St 66048 — 913-682-5151

Leawood, Johnson, Pop. 31,391
Blue Valley USD 229
Supt. — See Overland Park

Leawood MS 500/6-8
2410 W 123rd St 66209 913-239-5300
Marcia Wiseman Ed.D., prin. Fax 239-5348
Prairie Star MS 700/6-8
14201 Mission Rd 66224 913-239-5600
Lyn Rantz Ed.D., prin. Fax 239-5648

Lebo, Coffey, Pop. 937
Lebo-Waverly USD 243
Supt. — See Waverly
Lebo HS 100/7-12
PO Box 45 66856 620-256-6341
Darla Long, prin. Fax 256-6342

Lenexa, Johnson, Pop. 47,046
De Soto USD 232
Supt. — See De Soto
Mill Creek MS 600/6-8
8001 Mize Blvd 66227 913-667-3512
Larry Breedlove, prin. Fax 422-9229

Brown Mackie College Post-Sec.
9705 Lenexa Dr 66215 913-768-1900
Christ Preparatory Academy K-12
15700 W 87th Street Pkwy 66219 913-831-1345
Ron Lawlor, admin. Fax 438-1402
St. James Academy 600/9-12
24505 Prairie Star Pkwy 66227 913-254-4200
Karla Leibham, prin. Fax 254-4221
The Art Institutes International Post-Sec.
8208 Melrose Dr 66214 913-217-4600

Leon, Butler, Pop. 678
Bluestem USD 205 400/PK-12
625 S Mill Rd 67074 316-742-3261
Randy Rivers, supt. Fax 742-9265
www.usd205.com
Bluestem JSHS 200/7-12
500 S Bluestem Dr 67074 316-742-3281
Joel Lovesee, prin. Fax 742-3813

Leoti, Wichita, Pop. 1,520
Leoti USD 467 500/PK-12
PO Box 967 67861 620-375-4677
Keith Higgins, supt. Fax 375-2304
www.leoti.org/
Wichita County JSHS 200/7-12
PO Box K 67861 620-375-2213
Boyd Hutchinson, prin. Fax 375-4958

Le Roy, Coffey, Pop. 552
Le Roy-Gridley USD 245 300/PK-12
PO Box 278 66857 620-964-2212
Mike Kastle, supt. Fax 964-2413
usd245ks.org/
Southern Coffey County HS 100/9-12
PO Box 188 66857 620-964-2217
J.J. Edwards, prin. Fax 964-2410
Other Schools – See Gridley

Liberal, Seward, Pop. 20,195
Liberal USD 480 4,800/PK-12
PO Box 949 67905 620-604-1010
Paul Larkin, supt. Fax 604-1011
www.usd480.net/
Liberal HS 1,200/9-12
1611 W 2nd St 67901 620-604-1200
Keith Adams, prin. Fax 604-1201
Liberal South MS 300/7-8
950 S Grant Ave 67901 620-604-1300
Gilberto Rito, prin. Fax 604-1301
Liberal West MS 300/7-8
500 N Western Ave 67901 620-604-1400
Troy McCarter, prin. Fax 604-1501

Seward County Community College Post-Sec.
PO Box 1137 67905 620-624-1951

Lincoln, Lincoln, Pop. 1,283
Lincoln USD 298 400/PK-12
PO Box 289 67455 785-524-4436
Gary Nelson, supt. Fax 524-3080
www.usd298.com
Lincoln JSHS 200/7-12
PO Box 269 67455 785-524-4193
David Kirkendall, prin. Fax 524-5114

Lindsborg, McPherson, Pop. 3,384
Smoky Valley USD 400 1,000/PK-12
126 S Main St 67456 785-227-2981
Glen Suppes, supt. Fax 227-2982
www.smokyvalley.org/
Smoky Valley HS 300/9-12
1 Viking Blvd 67456 785-227-2909
Marc Williams, prin. Fax 227-2900
Smoky Valley MS 200/5-8
401 N Cedar St 67456 785-227-4249
John Denk, prin. Fax 227-3650

Bethany College Post-Sec.
335 E Swensson Ave 67456 785-227-3311

Linn, Washington, Pop. 406
Barnes USD 223
Supt. — See Barnes
Linn HS 100/9-12
300 Parkview St 66953 785-348-5531
Mike Savage, prin. Fax 348-5534

Little River, Rice, Pop. 556
Little River USD 444 400/PK-12
PO Box 218 67457 620-897-6325
Dr. Milt Dougherty, supt. Fax 897-6788
www.usd444.com/
Little River HS 100/9-12
PO Box 8 67457 620-897-6201
Dawn Johnson, prin. Fax 897-6203
Little River JHS 100/6-8
PO Box 8 67457 620-897-6201
Dawn Johnson, prin. Fax 897-6203

Logan, Phillips, Pop. 588
Logan USD 326 200/K-12
PO Box 98 67646 785-689-7595
Larry M. Lysell M.S., supt. Fax 689-7517
www.usd326.k12.ks.us/
Logan HS 100/7-12
PO Box 98 67646 785-689-7574
Larry M. Lysell M.S., prin. Fax 689-7543

Long Island, Phillips, Pop. 134
Northern Valley USD 212
Supt. — See Almena
Long Island MS 100/5-8
PO Box 98 67647 785-854-7681
Marvin Gebhard, prin. Fax 854-7684

Longton, Elk, Pop. 339
Elk Valley USD 283 200/PK-12
PO Box 87 67352 620-642-2811
Scott Hills, supt. Fax 642-6551
www.usd283.org
Elk Valley HS 100/6-12
PO Box 87 67352 620-642-2215
Scott Hills, prin. Fax 642-3361

Lost Springs, Marion, Pop. 64
Centre USD 397 300/PK-12
PO Box 38 66859 785-983-4304
Jerri Kemble, supt. Fax 983-4352
www.usd397.com/
Centre S 300/PK-12
2374 310th St 66859 785-983-4321
Jerri Kemble, prin. Fax 983-4352

Louisburg, Miami, Pop. 4,257
Louisburg USD 416 1,700/PK-12
PO Box 550 66053 913-837-1700
Sharon Zoellner Ph.D., supt. Fax 837-1701
www.usd416.org
Louisburg HS 500/9-12
PO Box 399 66053 913-837-1720
Dave Tappan, prin. Fax 837-1799
Louisburg MS 400/6-8
PO Box 308 66053 913-837-1800
Cindy Fouraker, prin. Fax 837-1801
Peoria Street Learning Center 50/Alt
146 Harvest Dr 66053 913-837-3458
Ralph Beachum, prin. Fax 837-5954

Lyndon, Osage, Pop. 1,040
Lyndon USD 421 500/PK-12
PO Box 488 66451 785-828-4413
Brian Spencer, supt. Fax 828-3686
www.usd421.org
Lyndon HS 200/9-12
PO Box 488 66451 785-828-4911
Brad Marcotte, prin. Fax 828-4221

Lyons, Rice, Pop. 3,662
Lyons USD 405 800/PK-12
800 S Workman St 67554 620-257-5196
Bill Day, supt. Fax 257-5197
www.usd405.com
Lyons HS 200/9-12
601 E American Rd 67554 620-257-5114
Kelly Nusser, prin. Fax 257-3194
Lyons MS 200/6-8
401 S Douglas Ave 67554 620-257-3961
Kevin Logan, prin. Fax 257-3518
Rice County Learning Ctr Alt
110 E 1st St 67554 620-257-7060
Larry Walker, dir. Fax 257-7060

Macksville, Stafford, Pop. 542
Macksville USD 351 300/PK-12
PO Box 487 67557 620-348-3415
Mike Harvey, supt. Fax 348-3217
www.usd351.com
Macksville HS 100/9-12
PO Box 307 67557 620-348-2475
Toby Conrad, prin. Fax 348-2631

Mc Louth, Jefferson, Pop. 860
Mc Louth USD 342 500/PK-12
PO Box 40 66054 913-796-2201
Steve Splichal, supt. Fax 796-6440
www.mclouth.org
Mc Louth HS 200/9-12
PO Box 40 66054 913-796-6122
Troy Keiswetter, prin. Fax 796-6124
Mc Louth MS 100/6-8
PO Box 40 66054 913-796-6122
Troy Keiswetter, prin. Fax 796-6124

Mc Pherson, McPherson, Pop. 12,895
Mc Pherson USD 418 2,300/PK-12
514 N Main St 67460 620-241-9400
Dr. Randy Watson, supt. Fax 241-9410
www.mcpherson.com/418
Mc Pherson HS 700/9-12
801 E 1st St 67460 620-241-9500
Bret McClendon, prin. Fax 241-9506
Mc Pherson MS 500/6-8
700 E Elizabeth St 67460 620-241-9450
Brad Plackemeier, prin. Fax 241-9456

Central Christian College of Kansas Post-Sec.
PO Box 1403 67460 620-241-0723
Elyria Christian S 200/K-12
1644 Comanche Rd 67460 620-241-2994
Phillip Gray, admin. Fax 241-1238
McPherson College Post-Sec.
1600 E Euclid St 67460 620-242-0400

Madison, Greenwood, Pop. 687
Madison-Virgil USD 386 300/PK-12
PO Box 398 66860 620-437-2910
Ryan Bradbury, supt. Fax 437-2916
www.usd386.net
Madison HS 100/7-12
PO Box 398 66860 620-437-2912
Ryan Bradbury, prin. Fax 437-2911

Maize, Sedgwick, Pop. 3,313
Maize USD 266 6,500/K-12
905 W Central St 67101 316-722-0614
Doug Powers, supt. Fax 722-8538
www.usd266.com
Complete HS Maize Alt
745 W Central St 67101 316-722-4790
Kristy Custer, prin. Fax 729-0621
Maize HS 1,500/9-12
11600 W 45th St N 67101 316-722-0441
Chris Botts, prin. Fax 722-6214
Maize MS 800/6-8
4600 N Maize Rd 67101 316-729-2464
Brian Thompson, prin. Fax 729-2479
Other Schools – See Wichita

Manhattan, Riley, Pop. 50,618
Manhattan-Ogden USD 383 6,300/PK-12
2031 Poyntz Ave 66502 785-587-2000
Dr. Robert Shannon, supt. Fax 587-2006
www.usd383.org
Anthony MS 500/7-8
2501 Browning Ave 66502 785-587-2890
Vickie Kline, prin. Fax 587-2899
Eisenhower MS 400/7-8
800 Walters Dr 66502 785-587-2880
Tracy Newell, prin. Fax 587-2888
Manhattan HS West/East Campus 1,900/9-12
2100 Poyntz Ave 66502 785-587-2100
Greg Hoyt, prin. Fax 587-2132

American Institute of Baking Post-Sec.
PO Box 3999 66505 785-537-4750
Crum's Beauty College Post-Sec.
512 Poyntz Ave 66502 785-776-4794
Flint Hills Christian S 200/PK-12
3905 Green Valley Rd 66502 785-776-2223
Tim McDonald, admin. Fax 776-3016
Kansas State University 66506 Post-Sec.
785-532-6250
Manhattan Area Technical College Post-Sec.
3136 Dickens Ave 66503 785-587-2800
Manhattan Christian College Post-Sec.
1415 Anderson Ave 66502 785-539-3571

Mankato, Jewell, Pop. 856
Rock Hills USD 107 200/PK-12
109 E Main St 66956 785-378-3102
Nadine Smith, supt. Fax 378-3438
www.usd107.org/
Rock Hills JSHS 100/7-12
109 E Main St 66956 785-378-3126
Allen Walter, prin. Fax 378-3530

Marion, Marion, Pop. 1,911
Marion-Florence USD 408 600/K-12
101 N Thorp St 66861 620-382-2117
Lee Leiker, supt. Fax 382-2118
www.usd408.com
Marion HS 200/9-12
701 E Main St 66861 620-382-2168
Tod Gordon, prin. Fax 382-6021
Marion MS 100/7-8
125 S Lincoln St 66861 620-382-6070
Missy Stubenhofer, prin. Fax 382-6073

Marysville, Marshall, Pop. 3,251
Marysville USD 364 700/PK-12
211 S 10th St 66508 785-562-5308
Dr. Randy Freeman, supt. Fax 562-5309
www.marysvilleschools.org
Marysville HS 200/9-12
1111 Walnut St 66508 785-562-5386
Sheri Harmer, prin. Fax 562-5390
Marysville JHS 100/7-8
1005 Walnut St 66508 785-562-5356
Cindy Scarbrough, prin. Fax 562-5390

Mayetta, Jackson, Pop. 325
Royal Valley USD 337 900/PK-12
PO Box 219 66509 785-966-2246
John Rundle, supt. Fax 966-2490
www.rv337.com/
Royal Valley MS 300/5-8
PO Box 189 66509 785-966-2251
Aaric Davis, prin. Fax 966-2833
Other Schools – See Hoyt

Meade, Meade, Pop. 1,700
Meade USD 226 500/PK-12
PO Box 400 67864 620-873-2081
Kenneth Harshberger, supt. Fax 873-2201
www.usd226.org/
Meade HS 200/9-12
PO Box 400 67864 620-873-2981
Scott Moshier, prin. Fax 873-2201

Medicine Lodge, Barber, Pop. 1,980
Barber County North USD 254 500/PK-12
PO Box 288 67104 620-886-3370
Mark Buck, supt. Fax 886-3640
www.usd254.org/
Medicine Lodge JSHS 200/7-12
400 W Eldorado Ave 67104 620-886-5667
Darryl Honas, prin. Fax 886-3053

Melvern, Osage, Pop. 380
Marais Des Cygnes Valley USD 456 200/K-12
PO Box 158 66510 785-549-3521
Darrel Finch, supt. Fax 549-3659
www.usd456.org
Marais Des Cygnes Valley MSHS 100/6-12
PO Box 158 66510 785-549-3313
Steve Burkdoll, prin. Fax 549-3576

Meriden, Jefferson, Pop. 803
Jefferson West USD 340 800/PK-12
PO Box 267 66512 785-484-3444
A. Patton Happer, supt. Fax 484-3148
www.usd340.org
Jefferson West HS 300/9-12
PO Box 268 66512 785-484-3331
Rhonda Frakes, prin. Fax 484-2021
Jefferson West MS 300/5-8
PO Box 410 66512 785-484-2900
John Hamon, prin. Fax 484-2904

Miltonvale, Cloud, Pop. 532
Southern Cloud USD 334 200/K-12
PO Box 334 67466 785-427-3334
Roger Perkins, supt. Fax 427-2422
sc334.org
Miltonvale HS 50/7-12
PO Box 394 67466 785-427-3250
Regina Wallace, prin. Fax 427-3181
Other Schools – See Glasco

Minneapolis, Ottawa, Pop. 2,009
North Ottawa County USD 239 600/K-12
PO Box 257 67467 785-392-2167
Larry Combs Ph.D., supt. Fax 392-3038
www.usd239.org/
Minneapolis JSHS 300/7-12
PO Box 317 67467 785-392-2113
Jay Macy, prin. Fax 392-2275

Minneola, Clark, Pop. 728
Minneola USD 219 300/K-12
PO Box 157 67865 620-885-4372
Mark Walker, supt. Fax 885-4509
www.usd219.org/
Minneola HS 100/9-12
PO Box 157 67865 620-885-4611
Brandon Haynes, prin. Fax 885-4509

Montezuma, Gray, Pop. 959
Montezuma USD 371 200/PK-12
PO Box 355 67867 620-846-2283
Jay Zehr, supt. Fax 846-2294
sghs.musd371.k12.ks.us
South Gray HS 100/9-12
PO Box 355 67867 620-846-2281
Tim Skinner, prin. Fax 846-2181

Moran, Allen, Pop. 543
Marmaton Valley USD 256 300/K-12
128 W Oak St 66755 620-237-4250
David Hardage, supt. Fax 237-8872
www.usd256.org
Marmaton Valley HS 200/7-12
128 W Oak St 66755 620-237-4251
Jeremy Boldra, prin. Fax 237-4576

Moscow, Stevens, Pop. 304
Moscow USD 209 200/K-12
PO Box 158 67952 620-598-2205
Stuart Moore, supt. Fax 598-2233
usd209.weebly.com
Moscow HS 100/6-12
PO Box 160 67952 620-598-2250
Stuart Moore, prin. Fax 598-2233

Mound City, Linn, Pop. 679
Jayhawk USD 346 500/PK-12
PO Box 278 66056 913-795-2247
Royce Powelson, supt. Fax 795-2185
www.usd346.org/
Jayhawk-Linn JSHS 200/7-12
PO Box D 66056 913-795-2224
Danny Brown, prin. Fax 795-9906

Moundridge, McPherson, Pop. 1,722
Moundridge USD 423 400/K-12
PO Box K 67107 620-345-5500
Chad Higgins, supt. Fax 345-8617
www.usd423.org
Moundridge HS 100/9-12
PO Box 610 67107 620-345-5500
Clark Wedel, prin. Fax 345-5218
Moundridge MS 100/6-8
PO Box 607 67107 620-345-5500
Clark Wedel, prin. Fax 345-5307

Mulvane, Sedgwick, Pop. 5,964
Mulvane USD 263 1,900/PK-12
PO Box 130 67110 316-777-1102
Brad Rahe, supt. Fax 777-1103
www.usd263.k12.ks.us
Mulvane HS 600/9-12
1900 N Rock Rd 67110 316-777-1183
Jay Ensley, prin. Fax 777-2228
Mulvane MS 400/6-8
915 Westview Dr 67110 316-777-2022
Traci Becker, prin. Fax 777-4967

Natoma, Osborne, Pop. 333
Paradise USD 399 200/PK-12
PO Box 100 67651 785-885-4843
Aaron Homburg, supt. Fax 885-4523
www.usd399.com/
Natoma HS 100/7-12
PO Box 100 67651 785-885-4849
Aaron Homburg, prin. Fax 885-4523

Neodesha, Wilson, Pop. 2,454
Neodesha USD 461 700/PK-12
PO Box 88 66757 620-325-2610
Daryl Pruter, supt. Fax 325-2368
www.neodesha.k12.ks.us
Neodesha JSHS 300/7-12
1000 N 8th St 66757 620-325-3015
Terence Wilson, prin. Fax 325-2382

Ness City, Ness, Pop. 1,441
Ness City USD 303 300/PK-12
414 E Chestnut St 67560 785-798-2210
Randall Jansonius, supt. Fax 798-3581
www.nesscityschools.org
Ness City JSHS 200/7-12
200 N 5th St 67560 785-798-3991
Tom Flax, prin. Fax 798-3064

Newton, Harvey, Pop. 18,716
Newton USD 373 2,800/K-12
308 E 1st St 67114 316-284-6200
Dr. Deborah Hamm, supt. Fax 284-6207
www.newton.k12.ks.us
Chisholm MS 300/7-8
900 E 1st St 67114 316-284-6260
Vicki Rivero, prin. Fax 284-6267
Newton HS 1,000/9-12
900 W 12th St 67114 316-284-6280
Roger Erickson, prin. Fax 284-6288

Nickerson, Reno, Pop. 1,065
Nickerson USD 309
Supt. — See Hutchinson
Nickerson HS 300/9-12
305 S Nickerson St 67561 620-422-3226
Kevin Abbott, prin. Fax 422-3229

North Newton, McPherson, Pop. 1,738

Bethel College Post-Sec.
300 E 27th St 67117 316-283-2500

Norton, Norton, Pop. 2,877
Norton USD 211 700/PK-12
105 E Waverly St 67654 785-877-3386
Greg Mann, supt. Fax 877-2030
www.usd211.org/
Norton Community HS 200/9-12
513 W Wilberforce St 67654 785-877-3338
Rudy Perez, prin. Fax 877-6940
Norton JHS 100/7-8
706 Jones Ave 67654 785-877-5851
Dustin McEwen, prin. Fax 877-3771

Norwich, Kingman, Pop. 478
Kingman-Norwich USD 331
Supt. — See Kingman
Norwich HS 100/9-12
PO Box 10 67118 620-478-2235
Wayne Morrow, prin. Fax 478-2879
Norwich MS 50/6-8
PO Box 10 67118 620-478-2235
Wayne Morrow, prin. Fax 478-2879

Oakley, Logan, Pop. 2,023
Oakley USD 274 400/PK-12
621 Center Ave Ste 103 67748 785-671-4588
Bill Steiner, supt. Fax 671-3044
www.oakleyschoolsks.com/
Oakley HS 100/9-12
118 W 7th St 67748 785-671-3241
Marlo Klassen, prin. Fax 671-3743
Oakley MS 100/6-8
611 Center Ave 67748 785-671-3820
Fred Teeter, prin. Fax 671-3010

Oberlin, Decatur, Pop. 1,774
Oberlin USD 294 400/PK-12
131 E Commercial St 67749 785-475-3805
Duane Dorshorst, supt. Fax 475-3076
www.usd294.org
Decatur Community JSHS 200/7-12
605 E Commercial St 67749 785-475-2231
Benjamin Jimenez, prin. Fax 475-2802

Olathe, Johnson, Pop. 122,644
Olathe USD 233 26,600/PK-12
PO Box 2000 66063 913-780-7000
Dr. Marlin Berry, supt. Fax 780-8007
www.olatheschools.com/
California Trail MS 900/6-8
13775 W 133rd St 66062 913-780-7220
Connie Viebrock, prin. Fax 780-7229
Chisholm Trail MS 800/6-8
16700 W 159th St 66062 913-780-7240
Steve Skoczek, prin. Fax 780-7249
Frontier Trail MS 800/6-8
15300 W 143rd St 66062 913-780-7210
Rod Smith, prin. Fax 780-7216
Indian Trail MS 600/6-8
1440 E 151st St 66062 913-780-7230
Becky Vrbas, prin. Fax 780-7234
Mission Trail MS 6-8
1001 N Persimmon Dr 66061 913-780-7260
Dr. Jim McMullen, prin. Fax 780-7269
Olathe East HS 2,100/9-12
14545 W 127th St 66062 913-780-7120
Bill Weber, prin. Fax 780-7137
Olathe North HS 1,900/9-12
600 E Prairie St 66061 913-780-7140
David Morford, prin. Fax 780-7837
Olathe Northwest HS 1,700/9-12
21300 College Blvd 66061 913-780-7150
Dr. Gwen Poss, prin. Fax 780-7159
Olathe South HS 2,000/9-12
1640 E 151st St 66062 913-780-7160
Phil Clark, prin. Fax 780-7170
Oregon Trail MS 400/6-8
1800 W Dennis Ave 66061 913-780-7250
Steve Massey, prin. Fax 780-7256
Pioneer Trail MS 700/6-8
15100 W 127th St 66062 913-780-7270
Dr. Michael Wolgast, prin. Fax 780-7278
Prairie Learning Center Alt
10975 S Lone Elm Rd 66061 913-780-7014
David Sasser, admin. Fax 780-8219
Prairie Trail MS 700/6-8
21600 W 107th St 66061 913-780-7280
Stacey Yurkovich, prin. Fax 780-7289

Santa Fe Trail MS 600/6-8
1100 N Ridgeview Rd 66061 913-780-7290
Kerry Lane, prin. Fax 780-7296

Kansas School for the Deaf Post-Sec.
450 E Park St 66061 913-791-0573
Mid-America Nazarene University Post-Sec.
2030 E College Way 66062 913-782-3750
Superior School of Hairdressing Post-Sec.
1215 E Santa Fe St 66061 913-782-4004

Olpe, Lyon, Pop. 541
Southern Lyon County USD 252
Supt. — See Hartford
Olpe HS 200/7-12
PO Box 206 66865 620-475-3223
Shane Clark, prin. Fax 475-3951

Onaga, Pottawatomie, Pop. 694
Onaga-Havensville-Wheaton USD 322 300/PK-12
PO Box 60 66521 785-889-4614
Fred Marten, supt. Fax 889-4662
www.usd322.org
Onaga HS 100/9-12
PO Box 458 66521 785-889-4251
Fred Marten, prin. Fax 889-4944

Osage City, Osage, Pop. 2,899
Osage City USD 420 700/K-12
520 Main St 66523 785-528-3176
Troy Hutton, supt. Fax 528-3932
www.usd420.org
Osage City HS 200/9-12
515 Ellinwood St 66523 785-528-3172
Tony Heward, prin. Fax 528-2980
Osage City MS 200/6-8
420 S 5th St 66523 785-528-3175
Tim Riemann, prin. Fax 528-2980

Osawatomie, Miami, Pop. 4,349
Osawatomie USD 367 1,200/PK-12
1200 Trojan Dr 66064 913-755-4172
Gary French, supt. Fax 755-2031
www.usd367.org/
Osawatomie HS 400/9-12
1200 Trojan Dr 66064 913-755-2191
Doug Chisam, prin. Fax 755-2645
Osawatomie MS 300/6-8
428 Pacific Ave 66064 913-755-4155
Dan Welch, prin. Fax 755-2197

Osborne, Osborne, Pop. 1,422
Osborne County USD 392 300/PK-12
234 W Washington St 67473 785-346-2145
Keith Hall, supt. Fax 346-2448
www.usd392.k12.ks.us
Osborne JSHS 100/7-12
219 N 2nd St 67473 785-346-2143
Tom Conway, prin. Fax 346-2331

Oskaloosa, Jefferson, Pop. 1,096
Oskaloosa USD 341 500/PK-12
404 Park St 66066 785-863-2539
Jon Pfau, supt. Fax 863-3080
www.usd341.org
Oskaloosa JSHS 200/7-12
404 Park St 66066 785-863-2281
Douglas Beisel, prin. Fax 863-3106

Oswego, Labette, Pop. 1,768
Oswego USD 504 500/PK-12
PO Box 129 67356 620-795-2126
Mark LaTurner, supt. Fax 795-4871
www.usd504.org
Oswego HS 100/9-12
PO Box 129 67356 620-795-2125
Cynthia Sanders, prin. Fax 795-2130
Oswego MS 100/6-8
PO Box 129 67356 620-795-4724
Janie Allison, prin. Fax 795-4799

Otis, Rush, Pop. 278
Otis-Bison USD 403 200/PK-12
PO Box 227 67565 785-387-2201
Dr. Milt Dougherty, supt. Fax 387-2203
www.usd403.org/
Otis-Bison JSHS 100/7-12
PO Box 257 67565 785-387-2337
Mark Goodheart, prin. Fax 387-2557

Ottawa, Franklin, Pop. 12,279
Ottawa USD 290 2,300/PK-12
1404 S Ash St 66067 785-229-8010
Dean Katt, supt. Fax 229-8019
www.usd290.org
Career Technology Educational Coop Vo/Tech
908 W 11th St 66067 785-229-8020
Rick Johnson, prin. Fax 229-8029
Ottawa HS 700/9-12
1120 S Ash St 66067 785-229-8020
Ryan Cobbs, prin. Fax 229-8029
Ottawa MS 600/6-8
1230 S Ash St 66067 785-229-8030
Carmen Schaefer, prin. Fax 229-8039

Bethel Christian Academy 50/K-12
3755 Nevada Rd 66067 785-242-1226
Donita Callahan, admin. Fax 242-1226
Ottawa University Post-Sec.
1001 S Cedar St 66067 785-242-5200

Overland Park, Johnson, Pop. 169,666
Blue Valley USD 229 20,300/PK-12
PO Box 23901 66283 913-239-4000
Tom Trigg Ed.D., supt. Fax 239-4150
www.bluevalleyk12.org
Aubry Bend MS 6-8
12501 W 175th St, 913-624-2300
Diana Tate, prin. Fax 624-2348

Blue Valley Academy | Alt
7500 W 149th Ter 66223 | 913-239-4629
Valerie Jennings, prin. | Fax 239-4534
Blue Valley MS | 500/6-8
5001 W 163rd Ter, | 913-239-5100
Roxana Rogers, prin. | Fax 239-5148
Blue Valley North HS | 1,500/9-12
12200 Lamar Ave 66209 | 913-239-3000
David Stubblefield, prin. | Fax 239-3038
Blue Valley Northwest HS | 1,700/9-12
13260 Switzer Rd 66213 | 913-239-3400
Amy Murphy Ed.D., prin. | Fax 239-3555
Blue Valley Southwest HS | 9-12
17600 S Quivira Rd, | 913-624-2000
Scott Roberts, prin. | Fax 624-2048
Blue Valley West HS | 1,300/9-12
16200 Antioch Rd, | 913-239-3700
Tony Lake Ed.D., prin. | Fax 239-3880
Center for Advanced Professional Studies | 11-12
7501 W 149th Ter 66223 | 913-239-5900
Chad Ralston, dir. | Fax 239-5948
Harmony MS | 600/6-8
10101 W 141st St 66221 | 913-239-5200
Sheila Albers, prin. | Fax 239-5248
Lakewood MS | 700/6-8
6601 Edgewater Dr 66223 | 913-239-5800
Scott Currier, prin. | Fax 239-5848
Overland Trail MS | 600/6-8
6201 W 133rd St 66209 | 913-239-5400
Phoebe Lewis, prin. | Fax 239-5448
Oxford MS | 600/6-8
12500 Switzer Rd 66213 | 913-239-5500
Linda Crosthwait, prin. | Fax 239-5548
Other Schools – See Leawood, Stilwell

American Academy of Hair Design | Post-Sec.
11401 W 112th Ter 66210 | - -
B-Street Design School of Intl Hair Stlg | Post-Sec.
10324 Mastin St 66212 | 913-492-4114
Cleveland Chiropractic College | Post-Sec.
10850 Lowell Ave 66210 | 913-234-0600
Heritage Christian Academy | 400/PK-12
9333 W 159th St 66221 | 913-681-7622
Rick Lukianuk, pres. | Fax 851-8056
Johnson County Community College | Post-Sec.
12345 College Blvd 66210 | 913-469-8500
LaBaron Hairdressing Academy | Post-Sec.
8119 Robinson St 66204 | 913-642-0077
Ottawa University | Post-Sec.
4370 W 109th St Ste 200 66211 | 913-266-8600
Overland Christian S | 50/PK-12
7401 Metcalf Ave 66204 | 913-722-0272
Chad Pollard, admin. | Fax 403-0595
St. Thomas Aquinas HS | 1,100/9-12
11411 Pflumm Rd 66215 | 913-345-1411
Dr. Rebecca Heidlage, pres. | Fax 345-2319
Wright Career College | Post-Sec.
10700 Metcalf Ave 66210 | 913-385-7700

Oxford, Sumner, Pop. 1,034
Oxford USD 358 | 400/PK-12
PO Box 937 67119 | 620-455-2227
Mark Whitener, supt. | Fax 455-3680
www.usd358.com
Oxford JSHS | 200/6-12
PO Box 970 67119 | 620-455-2410
Mark Whitener, prin. | Fax 455-3741

Palco, Rooks, Pop. 275
Palco USD 269 | 200/PK-12
PO Box B 67657 | 785-737-4635
Lisa Gehring, supt. | Fax 737-4636
www.usd269.k12.ks.us/
Palco HS | 100/9-12
PO Box 29 67657 | 785-737-4645
Ian Margreiter, prin. | Fax 737-4646
Other Schools – See Damar

Paola, Miami, Pop. 5,476
Paola USD 368 | 1,900/K-12
1115 E 303rd St 66071 | 913-294-8000
Judy Welter, supt. | Fax 294-8001
www.usd368.org/
Paola HS | 600/9-12
401 Angela St 66071 | 913-294-8010
Phil Bressler, prin. | Fax 294-8011
Paola MS | 400/6-8
405 N Hospital Dr 66071 | 913-294-8030
Mark Bloustine, prin. | Fax 294-8031

Parsons, Labette, Pop. 10,094
Parsons USD 503 | 800/PK-12
PO Box 1056 67357 | 620-421-5950
Dr. Shelly Martin, supt. | Fax 421-5954
www.vikingnet.net
Parsons HS | 400/9-12
3030 Morton Ave 67357 | 620-421-3660
Matt Rogers, prin. | Fax 423-8816
Parsons MS | 300/6-8
2719 Main St 67357 | 620-421-4190
Terry Smith, prin. | Fax 423-8822

Labette Community College | Post-Sec.
200 S 14th St 67357 | 620-421-6700

Paxico, Wabaunsee, Pop. 208
Mill Creek Valley USD 329
Supt. — See Alma
Mill Creek Valley JHS | 100/7-8
PO Box 128 66526 | 785-636-5353
Cleion Morton, prin. | Fax 636-5116

Peabody, Marion, Pop. 1,179
Peabody-Burns USD 398 | 300/PK-12
506 N Elm St 66866 | 620-983-2198
Ron Traxson, supt. | Fax 983-2247
www.usd398.net
Peabody-Burns JSHS | 200/6-12
810 N Sycamore St 66866 | 620-983-2196
Tim Robertson, prin. | Fax 983-2773

Perry, Jefferson, Pop. 910
Perry USD 343 | 900/PK-12
PO Box 729 66073 | 785-597-5138
Dr. Denis Yoder, supt. | Fax 597-2254
www.usd343.org/
Perry-Lecompton HS | 300/9-12
PO Box 18 66073 | 785-597-5124
J.B. Elliott, prin. | Fax 597-5177
Perry-Lecompton MS | 300/5-8
PO Box 31 66073 | 785-597-5159
Josh Woodward, prin. | Fax 597-5014

Phillipsburg, Phillips, Pop. 2,555
Phillipsburg USD 325 | 600/PK-12
240 S 7th St 67661 | 785-543-5281
Mike Gower, supt. | Fax 543-2271
www.usd325.com
Phillipsburg HS | 200/9-12
410 S 7th St 67661 | 785-543-5251
Todd Bowman, prin. | Fax 543-6305
Phillipsburg MS | 200/5-8
647 7th St 67661 | 785-543-5114
Kent Otte, prin. | Fax 543-2934

Pittsburg, Crawford, Pop. 19,561
Pittsburg USD 250 | 2,600/K-12
PO Box 75 66762 | 620-235-3100
Destry Brown, supt. | Fax 235-3106
www.usd250.org
Pittsburg HS | 700/9-12
1978 E 4th St 66762 | 620-235-3200
Jon Bishop, prin. | Fax 235-3210
Pittsburg MS | 600/6-8
1310 N Broadway St 66762 | 620-235-3240
Lonnie Moser, prin. | Fax 235-3248

Pittsburg State University | Post-Sec.
1701 S Broadway St 66762 | 620-231-7000
St. Mary's Colgan HS | 200/7-12
212 E 9th St 66762 | 620-231-4690
Tom Compton, prin. | Fax 231-0690

Plainville, Rooks, Pop. 1,886
Plainville USD 270 | 400/PK-12
111 W Mill St 67663 | 785-434-4678
Gail Dunbar, supt. | Fax 434-7404
www.usd270.net/
Plainville HS | 100/9-12
202 SE Cardinal Ave 67663 | 785-434-4547
Dr. Susan Brenner-Camp, prin. | Fax 434-4689

Pleasanton, Linn, Pop. 1,187
Pleasanton USD 344 | 300/K-12
PO Box 480 66075 | 913-352-8534
Travis Laver, supt. | Fax 352-6588
www.usd344.org/
Pleasanton HS | 200/7-12
PO Box 480 66075 | 913-352-8701
Paul Walrod, prin. | Fax 352-6588

Pomona, Franklin, Pop. 819
West Franklin USD 287 | 700/PK-12
510 E Franklin St 66076 | 785-566-3396
Dotson Bradbury, supt. | Fax 566-8325
www.usd287.org
West Franklin HS | 200/9-12
511 E Franklin St 66076 | 785-566-3392
Rick Smith, prin. | Fax 566-8454
West Franklin MS | 200/6-8
331 Tyler St 66076 | 785-566-3541
Rick Smith, prin. | Fax 566-3634

Prairie Village, Johnson, Pop. 21,158

Kansas City Christian S | 400/PK-12
4801 W 79th St 66208 | 913-648-5227
Bill Glotzbach, admin. | Fax 648-5269

Pratt, Pratt, Pop. 6,720
Pratt USD 382 | 800/PK-12
401 S Hamilton St 67124 | 620-672-4500
Dr. Suzan Patton, supt. | Fax 672-4509
www.usd382.com
Liberty MS | 200/6-8
300 S Iuka St 67124 | 620-672-4530
Tony Helfrich, prin. | Fax 672-4539
Pratt HS | 300/9-12
400 S Hamilton St 67124 | 620-672-4540
Steve Blankenship, prin. | Fax 672-4549

Skyline USD 438 | 400/K-12
20269 W US Highway 54 67124 | 620-672-5651
Mike Sanders, supt. | Fax 672-9377
www.usd438.k12.ks.us
Skyline HS | 100/9-12
20269 W US Highway 54 67124 | 620-672-5651
Herb McPherson, prin. | Fax 672-9377

Pratt Community College | Post-Sec.
348 NE State Road 61 67124 | 620-672-5641

Pretty Prairie, Reno, Pop. 669
Pretty Prairie USD 311 | 300/PK-12
PO Box 218 67570 | 620-459-6241
Brad Wade, supt. | Fax 459-6810
www.usd311.com
Pretty Prairie HS | 100/9-12
PO Box 326 67570 | 620-459-6313
Randy Hendrickson, prin. | Fax 459-6935
Pretty Prairie MS | 100/5-8
PO Box 307 67570 | 620-459-6911
Randy Hendrickson, prin. | Fax 459-6729

Protection, Comanche, Pop. 508
South Central USD 300
Supt. — See Coldwater
South Central MS | 100/6-8
PO Box 38 67127 | 620-622-4545
Matt Jellison, prin. | Fax 622-4844

Quinter, Gove, Pop. 912
Quinter USD 293 | 300/PK-12
PO Box 540 67752 | 785-754-2470
Linda Zeigler, supt. | Fax 754-3365
www.quinterhs.org
Quinter JSHS | 100/7-12
PO Box 459 67752 | 785-754-3660
Toby Countryman, prin. | Fax 754-3905

Randolph, Riley, Pop. 158
Blue Valley USD 384 | 200/K-12
PO Box 98 66554 | 785-293-5256
Brady Burton, supt. | Fax 293-5607
www.usd384.org/
Blue Valley HS | 100/9-12
PO Box 68 66554 | 785-293-5255
Marion Mazouch, prin. | Fax 293-5372
Randolph MS | 100/5-8
PO Box 38 66554 | 785-293-5253
Marion Mazouch, prin. | Fax 293-5607

Ransom, Ness, Pop. 292
Western Plains USD 106 | 200/PK-12
100 School St 67572 | 785-731-2352
Roger Stumpf, supt. | Fax 731-2235
www.usd106.org/
Western Plains HS | 50/9-12
100 School St 67572 | 785-731-2352
Roger Stumpf, prin. | Fax 731-2235

Rexford, Thomas, Pop. 229
Golden Plains USD 316
Supt. — See Selden
Golden Plains HS | 100/9-12
PO Box 100 67753 | 785-687-3265
Darrin Herl, prin. | Fax 687-2285
Golden Plains MS | 50/6-8
PO Box 100 67753 | 785-687-3265
Darrin Herl, prin. | Fax 687-2285

Richmond, Franklin, Pop. 461
Central Heights USD 288 | 600/PK-12
3521 Ellis Rd 66080 | 785-869-3455
James White, supt. | Fax 869-2675
www.usd288.org/
Central Heights HS | 200/9-12
3521 Ellis Rd 66080 | 785-869-3455
Tom Horstick, prin. | Fax 869-2675
Central Heights MS | 200/6-8
3521 Ellis Rd 66080 | 785-869-3455
Buddy Welch, prin. | Fax 869-2675

Riley, Riley, Pop. 930
Riley County USD 378 | 700/PK-12
PO Box 326 66531 | 785-485-4000
Brad Starnes, supt. | Fax 485-2860
www.usd378.org/
Riley County HS | 200/9-12
PO Box 38 66531 | 785-485-4020
Eric Swanson, prin. | Fax 485-2426

Riverton, Cherokee, Pop. 874
Riverton USD 404 | 800/PK-12
PO Box 290 66770 | 620-848-3386
Todd Berry, supt. | Fax 848-9853
www.usd404.org/
Riverton HS | 200/9-12
PO Box 290 66770 | 620-848-3388
Cory White, prin. | Fax 848-3609
Riverton MS | 200/6-8
PO Box 260 66770 | 620-848-3355
Becky Murray, prin. | Fax 848-3288

Roeland Park, Johnson, Pop. 6,575

Bishop Miege HS | 900/9-12
5041 Reinhardt Dr 66205 | 913-262-2700
Randy Salisbury, prin. | Fax 262-2752

Rolla, Morton, Pop. 432
Rolla USD 217 | 200/PK-12
PO Box 167 67954 | 620-593-4344
Stuart Sutton, supt. | Fax 593-4250
www.usd217.org
Rolla HS | 100/6-12
PO Box 167 67954 | 620-593-4345
Gardell Schnable, prin. | Fax 593-4204

Rosalia, Butler, Pop. 169
Flinthills USD 492 | 200/K-12
PO Box 188 67132 | 620-476-2237
Justin Lockwood, supt. | Fax 476 2253
www.usd492.org/
Flinthills HS | 100/9-12
PO Box 188 67132 | 620-476-2215
Justin Lockwood, prin. | Fax 476-2244
Flinthills MS | 7-8
PO Box 188 67132 | 620-476-2218
Larry Gawith, prin. | Fax 476-2391

Rose Hill, Butler, Pop. 3,842
Rose Hill USD 394 | 1,800/PK-12
104 N Rose Hill Rd 67133 | 316-776-3300
Randal Chickadonz, supt. | Fax 776-3309
www.usd394.com
Rose Hill HS | 600/9-12
104 N Rose Hill Rd 67133 | 316-776-3360
Shannon Haydock, prin. | Fax 776-3378
Rose Hill MS | 400/6-8
104 N Rose Hill Rd 67133 | 316-776-3320
Kay Walker, prin. | Fax 776-3319

Rossville, Shawnee, Pop. 1,132
Kaw Valley USD 321
Supt. — See Saint Marys

Rossville HS 300/7-12
PO Box 68 66533 785-584-6193
Toby McCullough, prin. Fax 584-6379

Rozel, Pawnee, Pop. 156
Pawnee Heights USD 496 100/K-12
PO Box 98 67574 620-527-4212
Daniel Binder, supt. Fax 527-4215
www.phtigers.net
Pawnee Heights S 100/K-12
PO Box 97 67574 620-527-4211
Daniel Binder, prin. Fax 527-4215

Russell, Russell, Pop. 4,436
Russell County USD 407 800/K-12
802 N Main St 67665 785-483-2173
David Couch, supt. Fax 483-2175
www.usd407.org/
Ruppenthal MS 200/6-8
400 N Elm St 67665 785-483-3174
Gaylon Walter, prin. Fax 483-5386
Russell HS 300/9-12
565 E State St 67665 785-483-5631
Larry Bernard, prin. Fax 483-5636

Sabetha, Nemaha, Pop. 2,538
Prairie Hills USD 113 1,100/PK-12
1619 S Old Hwy 75 66534 785-284-2175
Bill Orth, supt. Fax 284-3739
www.usd113.org
Sabetha HS 200/9-12
1011 Blue Jay Blvd 66534 785-284-2155
Todd Evans, prin. Fax 284-2600
Sabetha MS 200/6-8
751 Blue Jay Blvd 66534 785-284-2151
Thomas Palmer, prin. Fax 284-0061
Other Schools – See Axtell, Wetmore

Saint Francis, Cheyenne, Pop. 1,327
St. Francis Community USD 297 300/K-12
PO Box 1110 67756 785-332-8182
Robert Schiltz, supt. Fax 332-8181
www.usd297.org/
Saint Francis JSHS 100/7-12
PO Box 1110 67756 785-332-8153
Scott Carmichael, prin. Fax 332-8181

Saint George, Pottawatomie, Pop. 611
Rock Creek USD 323
Supt. — See Westmoreland
Rock Creek JSHS 400/7-12
9355 Flush Rd 66535 785-494-8591
Eric Koppes, prin. Fax 494-8595

Saint John, Stafford, Pop. 1,281
St. John-Hudson USD 350 300/K-12
505 N Broadway St 67576 620-549-3564
Joshua P. Meyer, supt. Fax 549-3964
www.usd350.com/
Saint John JSHS 100/7-12
505 N Broadway St 67576 620-549-3277
Mike Burgan, prin. Fax 549-6289

Saint Marys, Pottawatomie, Pop. 2,562
Kaw Valley USD 321 1,100/K-12
411 W Lasley St 66536 785-437-2254
James McDaniel, supt. Fax 437-3155
www.kawvalley.k12.ks.us/
Saint Marys HS 300/7-12
601 E Lasley St 66536 785-437-6257
Mark McBeth, prin. Fax 437-3460
Other Schools – See Rossville

Saint Paul, Neosho, Pop. 622
Chetopa - St. Paul USD 505
Supt. — See Chetopa
Saint Paul HS 100/7-12
PO Box 68 66771 620-449-2245
Warren McGown, prin. Fax 449-8960

Salina, Saline, Pop. 46,386
Salina USD 305 7,000/PK-12
PO Box 797 67402 785-309-4700
William Hall, supt. Fax 309-4737
www.usd305.com
Alternative S Alt
1835 S Broadway Blvd 67401 785-309-4900
Jim Burkhart, prin.
Lakewood MS 800/6-8
1135 E Lakewood Cir 67401 785-309-4000
Sherri Louthan, prin. Fax 309-4001
Opportunity Now Alt
219 S 3rd St 67401 785-309-5200
Jeff Hayes, coord. Fax 826-4746
Salina Central HS 1,000/9-12
650 E Crawford St 67401 785-309-3500
Shanna Rector, prin. Fax 309-3501
Salina South HS 1,100/9-12
730 E Magnolia Rd 67401 785-309-3700
Linn Exline, prin. Fax 309-3701
Salina South MS 800/6-8
2040 S 4th St 67401 785-309-3900
Beth Morrison, prin. Fax 309-3901
Salina Adult Education Center Adult
2620 Centennial Rd 67401 785-309-4660
Kelly Mobray, dir. Fax 309-4669

Academy of Hair Design Post-Sec.
115 S 5th St 67401 785-825-8155
Brown Mackie College Post-Sec.
2106 S 9th St 67401 800-365-0433
Kansas State University Post-Sec.
2310 Centennial Rd 67401 785-826-2640
Kansas Wesleyan University Post-Sec.
100 E Claflin Ave 67401 785-827-5541
Sacred Heart HS 300/7-12
234 E Cloud St 67401 785-827-4422
John Krajicek, prin. Fax 827-8648

St. Johns Military S 100/6-12
PO Box 5020 67402 785-823-7231
Andrew England, pres. Fax 309-5489
Salina Area Technical College Post-Sec.
2562 Centennial Rd 67401 785-309-3100
Salina Christian Academy 200/PK-12
1009 Highland Ave 67401 785-452-9929
Duane Custer, prin. Fax 825-2506

Satanta, Haskell, Pop. 1,111
Satanta USD 507 400/PK-12
PO Box 279 67870 620-649-2234
Ardith Dunn, supt. Fax 649-2668
www.usd507.org
Satanta JSHS 200/7-12
PO Box 69 67870 620-649-2611
Ron Levan, prin. Fax 649-2658

Scandia, Republic, Pop. 370
Pike Valley USD 426 200/K-12
PO Box 291 66966 785-335-2206
Chris Vignery, supt. Fax 335-2219
www.pikevalley.com
Pike Valley HS 100/9-12
PO Box 139 66966 785-335-2294
Chris Vignery, prin. Fax 335-2386
Other Schools – See Courtland

Scott City, Scott, Pop. 3,797
Scott County USD 466 900/PK-12
PO Box 288 67871 620-872-7600
Bill Wilson, supt. Fax 872-7609
www.usd466.com/
Scott City HS 300/9-12
712 S Main St 67871 620-872-7620
Shelly Turner, prin. Fax 872-7629
Scott City MS 300/5-8
809 W 9th St 67871 620-872-7640
Jim Howard, prin. Fax 872-7649

Sedan, Chautauqua, Pop. 1,096
Chautauqua County Community USD 286 400/PK-12
302 Sherman St 67361 620-725-3187
David Jackson, supt. Fax 725-5642
www.usd286.org
Sedan HS 200/7-12
416 E Elm St 67361 620-725-3186
Mike Stice, prin. Fax 725-3188

Sedgwick, Harvey, Pop. 1,672
Sedgwick USD 439 600/K-12
PO Box K 67135 316-772-5783
Michael Hull, supt. Fax 772-0274
www.usd439.com
Sedgwick HS 200/9-12
PO Box K 67135 316-772-5155
Mike Hilliard, prin. Fax 772-0334

Selden, Sheridan, Pop. 219
Golden Plains USD 316 200/PK-12
PO Box 199 67757 785-386-4559
Darrn Heil, supt. Fax 386-4562
usd316.k12.ks.us/
Other Schools – See Rexford

Seneca, Nemaha, Pop. 1,982
Nemaha Central USD 115 600/PK-12
318 Main St 66538 785-336-6101
Darrel Kohlman, supt. Fax 336-2268
www.usd115.org/
Nemaha Valley HS 200/9-12
214 N 11th St 66538 785-336-3557
Patrick McKernan, prin. Fax 336-3672
Other Schools – See Baileyville

Sharon Springs, Wallace, Pop. 741
Wallace County USD 241 200/PK-12
521 N Main St 67758 785-852-4252
David Porter, supt. Fax 852-4603
www.usd241.org/
Wallace County HS 100/9-12
521 N Main St 67758 785-852-4240
David Porter, prin. Fax 852-4603

Shawnee, Johnson, Pop. 60,803
De Soto USD 232
Supt. — See De Soto
Mill Valley HS 1,100/9-12
5900 Monticello Rd 66226 913-422-4351
Tobie Waldeck, prin. Fax 422-4039
Monticello Trails MS 700/6-8
6100 Monticello Rd 66226 913-422-1100
Brian Schwanz, prin. Fax 422-4990

Academy of Aesthetics Arts Post-Sec.
10316 Shawnee Mission Pkwy 66203 913-962-9772
Central Baptist Theological Seminary Post-Sec.
6601 Monticello Rd 66226 800-677-2287
Maranatha Christian Academy 300/7-12
6826 Lackman Rd 66217 913-631-0637
Mark Schultze, supt. Fax 631-0899
Midland Adventist Academy 100/K-12
6915 Maurer Rd 66217 913-268-7400
Randy Bovee, prin. Fax 268-4968

Shawnee Mission, See Merriam
Shawnee Mission USD 512 26,000/PK-12
7235 Antioch Rd 66204 913-993-6200
Dr. Jim Hinson, supt. Fax 993-6247
www.smsd.org
Broadmoor Technical Center Vo/Tech
6701 W 83rd St 66204 913-993-9700
Maureen Markland, coord. Fax 993-9799
Hocker Grove MS 500/7-8
10400 Johnson Dr 66203 913-993-0200
Dr. Scott Sherman, prin. Fax 993-0399
Horizons HS Alt
5900 Lamar Ave 66202 913-993-9500
Molli Anderson, prin. Fax 993-9599
Indian Hills MS 500/7-8
6400 Mission Rd 66208 913-993-0400
Carla Allen, prin. Fax 993-0599
Indian Woods MS 600/7-8
9700 Woodson Dr 66207 913-993-0600
Jim Wink, prin. Fax 993-0799
Shawnee Mission East HS 1,900/9-12
7500 Mission Rd 66208 913-993-6600
John McKinney, prin. Fax 993-6899
Shawnee Mission North HS 1,700/9-12
7401 Johnson Dr 66202 913-993-6900
Richard Kramer, prin. Fax 993-7099
Shawnee Mission Northwest HS 1,900/9-12
12701 W 67th St 66216 913-993-7200
Dr. William Harrington, prin. Fax 993-7499
Shawnee Mission South HS 1,400/9-12
5800 W 107th St 66207 913-993-7500
Dr. Joe Gilhaus, prin. Fax 993-7799
Shawnee Mission West HS 1,800/9-12
8800 W 85th St 66212 913-993-7800
Dr. Julie Crain, prin. Fax 993-8099
Trailridge MS 500/7-8
7500 Quivira Rd 66216 913-993-1000
Bonnie Welty, prin. Fax 993-1199
Westridge MS 900/7-8
9300 Nieman Rd 66214 913-993-1200
Eric Rembold, prin. Fax 993-1399

Silver Lake, Shawnee, Pop. 1,409
Silver Lake USD 372 800/PK-12
PO Box 39 66539 785-582-4026
Tim Hallacy, supt. Fax 582-5259
www.silverlakeschools.org/
Silver Lake JSHS 400/7-12
PO Box 39 66539 785-582-4639
Brad Womack, prin. Fax 582-4265

Smith Center, Smith, Pop. 1,647
Smith Center USD 237 400/PK-12
216 S Jefferson St 66967 785-282-6665
Ron Meitler, supt. Fax 282-6518
www.usd237.com
Smith Center JSHS 200/7-12
300 Roger Barta Way 66967 785-282-6609
Greg Koelsch, prin. Fax 282-5206

Solomon, Dickinson, Pop. 1,069
Solomon USD 393 400/K-12
113 E 7th St 67480 785-655-2541
Jeremy Boldra, supt. Fax 655-2505
www.usd393.net
Solomon HS 200/6-12
409 N Pine St 67480 785-655-2551
Dustin Dooley, prin. Fax 655-3011

South Haven, Sumner, Pop. 360
South Haven USD 509 200/PK-12
PO Box 229 67140 620-892-5216
John Showman, supt. Fax 892-5814
www.usd509.org/
South Haven JSHS 100/6-12
PO Box 229 67140 620-892-5215
Lynn Archer, prin. Fax 892-5814

Spearville, Ford, Pop. 771
Spearville USD 381 400/K-12
PO Box 338 67876 620-385-2676
Daryl Stegman, supt. Fax 385-2614
www.usd381.org/
Spearville JSHS 200/6-12
PO Box 158 67876 620-385-2631
Patrick Crowdis, prin. Fax 385-2641

Spring Hill, Johnson, Pop. 5,340
Spring Hill USD 230 3,200/PK-12
101 E South St 66083 913-592-7200
Dr. Barton Goering, supt. Fax 592-7270
www.usd230.org
Spring Hill HS 600/9-12
19701 S Ridgeview Rd 66083 913-592-7299
Steve Fleer, prin. Fax 592-2847
Spring Hill MS South 300/7-8
301 E South St 66083 913-592-7288
Rodney Sprague, prin. Fax 592-5424

Stafford, Stafford, Pop. 1,029
Stafford USD 349 200/PK-12
PO Box 400 67578 620-234-5243
Dr. Mary Jo Taylor, supt. Fax 234-6986
stafford.ks.schoolwebpages.com
Stafford HS 100/9-12
PO Box 370 67578 620-234-5248
Russell Orton, prin. Fax 234-6041

Sterling, Rice, Pop. 2,287
Sterling USD 376 500/PK-12
PO Box 188 67579 620-278-3621
Dr. Fred Dierksen, supt. Fax 278-3882
www.usd376.com
Sterling HS 200/9-12
308 E Washington Ave 67579 620-278-2171
Bill Anderson, prin. Fax 278-3237
Sterling JHS 100/7-8
412 N 5th St 67579 620-278-3646
Bill Anderson, prin. Fax 278-3673

Sterling College Post-Sec.
125 W Cooper St 67579 620-278-2173

Stilwell, Johnson
Blue Valley USD 229
Supt. — See Overland Park
Blue Valley HS 1,200/9-12
6001 W 159th St 66085 913-239-4800
Scott Bacon, prin. Fax 239-4835
Pleasant Ridge MS 800/6-8
9000 W 165th St 66085 913-239-5700
Brett Potts Ed.D., prin. Fax 239-5748

Stockton, Rooks, Pop. 1,312
Stockton USD 271 300/PK-12
201 N Cypress St 67669 785-425-6367
Allaire Homburg, supt. Fax 425-6923
www.usd271.k12.ks.us/
Stockton HS 100/9-12
105 N Cypress St 67669 785-425-6784
Bob Becker, prin. Fax 425-6200

Sublette, Haskell, Pop. 1,442
Sublette USD 374 400/PK-12
PO Box 670 67877 620-675-2277
Rex Bruce, supt. Fax 675-2652
www.usd374.org/
Sublette MSHS 100/7-12
PO Box 460 67877 620-675-2232
Cesar Pena, prin. Fax 675-8347

Sylvan Grove, Lincoln, Pop. 277
Sylvan USD 299 200/PK-12
504 W 4th St 67481 785-526-7175
Jude Stecklein, supt. Fax 526-7182
www.usd299.org/
Sylvan-Lucas Unified JSHS 100/7-12
504 W 4th St 67481 785-526-7175
Devon Walter, prin. Fax 526-7182

Syracuse, Hamilton, Pop. 1,789
Syracuse USD 494 500/PK-12
PO Box 1187 67878 620-384-7872
Kenneth Bridges, supt. Fax 384-7692
www.usd494.org
Syracuse JSHS 200/7-12
PO Box 1187 67878 620-384-7446
Paul Zuzelski, prin. Fax 384-6686

Tecumseh, Shawnee
Shawnee Heights USD 450 3,600/PK-12
4401 SE Shawnee Heights Rd 66542 785-379-5800
Dr. Martin Stessman, supt. Fax 379-5810
www.usd450.net
Shawnee Heights HS 1,100/9-12
4201 SE Shawnee Heights Rd 66542 785-379-5880
Alan Beam, prin. Fax 379-5889
Shawnee Heights MS 600/7-8
4335 SE Shawnee Heights Rd 66542 785-379-5830
Jennifer Bessolo, prin. Fax 379-5848

Tescott, Ottawa, Pop. 315
Twin Valley USD 240
Supt. — See Bennington
Tescott HS 100/9-12
PO Box 196 67484 785-283-4774
Dr. Becky Cheney, prin. Fax 283-4347

Tipton, Mitchell, Pop. 210

Tipton Catholic JSHS 50/7-12
PO Box 146 67485 785-373-5835
Gery Hake, prin. Fax 373-5637

Tonganoxie, Leavenworth, Pop. 4,915
Tonganoxie USD 464 1,900/K-12
PO Box 199 66086 913-845-2153
Randall Weseman, supt. Fax 845-3629
www.tong464.org/
Tonganoxie HS 600/9-12
PO Box 179 66086 913-845-2654
Jamie Carlisle, prin. Fax 845-3716
Tonganoxie JHS 600/5-8
PO Box 980 66086 913-845-2627
Dr. Jill Dickerson, prin. Fax 845-2734

Topeka, Shawnee, Pop. 122,701
Auburn Washburn USD 437 7,000/PK-12
5928 SW 53rd St 66610 785-339-4000
Dr. Brenda Dietrich, supt. Fax 339-4025
www.usd437.net
Pathway Learning Center Alt
4101 SW Martin Dr 66609 785-339-4270
David Cromer, prin. Fax 339-4275
Washburn Rural Alternative HS 1,200/Alt
5900 SW 61st St 66619 785-339-4900
Linda Thornburgh, prin. Fax 339-4925
Washburn Rural HS 1,700/9-12
5900 SW 61st St 66619 785-339-4100
Ed Raines, prin. Fax 339-4125
Washburn Rural MS 900/7-8
5620 SW 61st St 66619 785-339-4300
Gerald Meier, prin. Fax 339-4325

Seaman USD 345 3,800/PK-12
901 NW Lyman Rd 66608 785-575-8600
Mike Mathes, supt. Fax 575-8620
www.usd345.com/
Seaman HS 1,100/9-12
4850 NW Rochester Rd 66617 785-286-8300
Ron Vinduska, prin. Fax 286-8320
Seaman MS 600/7-8
5620 NW Topeka Blvd 66617 785-286-8400
Robert Horton, prin. Fax 286-8403

Topeka USD 501 12,800/PK-12
624 SW 24th St 66611 785-295-3000
Dr. Julie Ford, supt. Fax 575-6161
www.topekapublicschools.net/
Chase MS 400/6-8
2250 NE State St 66616 785-295-3840
Teresa Songs, prin. Fax 575-6632
Eisenhower MS 500/6-8
3305 SE Minnesota Ave 66605 785-274-6160
Rebecca Morrisey, prin. Fax 274-4603
French MS 600/6-8
5257 SW 33rd St 66614 785-438-4150
Kelli Hoffman, prin. Fax 271-3609
Highland Park HS 700/9-12
2424 SE California Ave 66605 785-274-6000
Dr. Beryl New, prin. Fax 274-4896
Jardine MS 500/6-8
2600 SW 33rd St 66611 785-274-6330
Mike Haire, prin. Fax 274-4768
Landon MS 500/6-8
731 SW Fairlawn Rd 66606 785-438-4220
David Boggs, prin. Fax 271-3737
Robinson MS 400/6-8
1125 SW 14th St 66604 785-295-3770
Tammy Hazelton, prin. Fax 575-6720
Topeka HS 1,700/9-12
800 SW 10th Ave 66612 785-295-3150
Dr. Linda Wiley, prin. Fax 575-6255
Topeka West HS 1,000/9-12
2001 SW Fairlawn Rd 66604 785-438-4000
Jeanne Carton, prin. Fax 271-3497
Washburn Institute of Technology Vo/Tech
5724 SW Huntoon St 66604 785-273-7140
Dr. Joseph Emmons, dean Fax 273-7080
Adult Education Center Adult
5724 SW Huntoon St 66604 785-228-6406
Patricia Williamson, coord. Fax 273-7080

Baker University School of Nursing Post-Sec.
1500 SW 10th Ave 66604 888-866-4242
Bryan University Post-Sec.
1527 SW Fairlawn Rd 66604 785-272-0889
Cair Paravel Latin S 300/K-12
635 SW Clay St 66606 785-232-3878
Community College of Cosmetology Post-Sec.
3602 SW Topeka Blvd 66611 785-267-7701
Hayden HS 500/9-12
401 SW Gage Blvd 66606 785-272-5210
Mark Madsen, prin. Fax 272-2975
Heritage Christian S 200/PK-12
2000 NW Clay St 66608 785-286-0427
Janeal Lischke, admin. Fax 286-9898
Washburn Institute of Technology Post-Sec.
5724 SW Huntoon St 66604 785-273-7140
Washburn University Post-Sec.
1700 SW College Ave 66621 785-670-1010
Wichita Technical Institute - Topeka Post-Sec.
3712 SW Burlingame Rd 66609 785-354-4568

Towanda, Butler, Pop. 1,426
Circle USD 375 1,600/K-12
PO Box 9 67144 316-541-2577
Jim Keller, supt. Fax 536-2249
www.usd375.org
Circle HS 500/9-12
PO Box 158 67144 316-541-2277
Todd Dreifort, prin. Fax 541-2115
Other Schools – See Benton

Troy, Doniphan, Pop. 1,001
Troy USD 429 400/PK-12
PO Box 190 66087 785-985-3950
Sue King, supt. Fax 985-3688
www.troyusd.org/
Troy MSHS 200/7-12
PO Box 160 66087 785-985-3533
Jared Wigger, prin. Fax 985-3885

Tyro, Montgomery, Pop. 209

Tyro Community Christian S 100/K-12
PO Box 308 67364 620-289-4450
Terry Byrd, admin. Fax 289-4283

Udall, Cowley, Pop. 727
Udall USD 463 400/PK-12
303 S Seymour St 67146 620-782-3355
Kim Stephens, supt. Fax 782-9690
www.usd463.org/
Udall HS 100/9-12
301 W 4th St 67146 620-782-3623
Brian Rowley, prin. Fax 782-9689
Udall MS 100/6-8
301 W 4th St 67146 620-782-3623
Brian Rowley, prin. Fax 782-9689

Ulysses, Grant, Pop. 6,107
Ulysses USD 214 1,600/PK-12
111 S Baughman St 67880 620-356-3655
David Younger, supt. Fax 356-5181
www.ulysses.org
Kepley MS 400/6-8
113 N Colorado St 67880 620-356-3025
Juan Perez, prin. Fax 356-3024
Ulysses HS 400/9-12
501 N Mccall St 67880 620-356-1380
Rodger Hilton, prin. Fax 356-5566

Uniontown, Bourbon, Pop. 268
Uniontown USD 235 500/PK-12
601 5th St 66779 620-756-4302
Randy Rockhold, supt. Fax 756-4492
www.uniontown235.org
Uniontown HS 200/7-12
601 5th St 66779 620-756-4301
Randy Rockhold, prin. Fax 756-4492

Valley Center, Sedgwick, Pop. 6,673
Valley Center USD 262 2,600/PK-12
143 S Meridian Ave 67147 316-755-7000
Cory Gibson, supt. Fax 755-7001
www.usd262.net
Valley Center HS 800/9-12
9600 N Meridian Ave 67147 316-755-7070
Jamie Lewis, prin. Fax 755-7071
Valley Center MS 400/7-8
800 N Meridian Ave 67147 316-755-7060
Kent Hipp, prin. Fax 755-7061

Valley Falls, Jefferson, Pop. 1,187
Valley Falls USD 338 400/PK-12
700 Oak St 66088 785-945-3214
Loren Feldkamp, supt. Fax 945-6780
www.usd338.com
Valley Falls HS 200/9-12
601 Elm St 66088 785-945-3229
Susan Grey, prin. Fax 945-3220

Vermillion, Marshall, Pop. 108
Vermillion USD 380 600/PK-12
209 School St 66544 785-382-6216
Richard Flores, supt. Fax 382-6213
www.usd380.org
Other Schools – See Centralia, Frankfort

Victoria, Ellis, Pop. 1,204
Victoria USD 432 200/K-12
PO Box 139 67671 785-735-9212
Linda Kenne, supt. Fax 735-9229
www.usd432.org/
Victoria HS 100/7-12
PO Box 20 67671 785-735-9211
John Linn, prin. Fax 735-9208

Wakeeney, Trego, Pop. 1,842
WaKeeney USD 208 400/PK-12
527 Russell Ave 67672 785-743-2145
Dr. George Griffith, supt. Fax 743-2071
www.tregoeagles.com/
Trego Community HS 100/9-12
1200 Russell Ave 67672 785-743-2061
John Luhrs, prin. Fax 743-2449

Wakefield, Clay, Pop. 948
Clay Center USD 379
Supt. — See Clay Center
Wakefield HS 100/9-12
PO Box 40 67487 785-461-5437
Dan Wagner, prin. Fax 461-5892

Wamego, Pottawatomie, Pop. 4,265
Wamego USD 320 1,400/PK-12
510 E US Highway 24 66547 785-456-7643
Denise O'Dea, supt. Fax 456-8125
www.usd320.com
Wamego HS 400/9-12
801 Lincoln St 66547 785-456-2214
Tim Winter, prin. Fax 456-7382
Wamego MS 300/6-8
1701 Kaw Valley Rd 66547 785-456-7682
Vici Jennings, prin. Fax 456-2944

Washington, Washington, Pop. 1,122
Washington County USD 108 400/PK-12
PO Box 275 66968 785-325-2261
Michael Stegman, supt. Fax 325-2771
www.usd108.org/
Washington County HS 200/7-12
PO Box 275 66968 785-325-2261
Phil Wilson, prin. Fax 325-2138

Waterville, Marshall, Pop. 672
Valley Heights USD 498 400/K-12
PO Box 89 66548 785-363-2398
John Bergkamp, supt. Fax 363-2269
www.valleyheights.org/
Other Schools – See Blue Rapids

Wathena, Doniphan, Pop. 1,344
Riverside USD 114
Supt. — See Elwood
Riverside HS 200/9-12
PO Box 38 66090 785-989-4426
Robert Blair, prin. Fax 989-3317

Waverly, Coffey, Pop. 580
Lebo-Waverly USD 243 500/PK-12
PO Box 457 66871 785-733-2651
Dr. Patti Bishop, supt. Fax 733-2707
www.usd243ks.org/
Waverly HS 100/7-12
PO Box 457 66871 785-733-2561
Mark Farrar, prin. Fax 733-2756
Other Schools – See Lebo

Wellington, Sumner, Pop. 7,956
Wellington USD 353 1,600/K-12
PO Box 648 67152 620-326-4300
Dr. Rick Weiss, supt. Fax 326-4304
www.usd353.com/
Roosevelt Education Center Alt
201 N B St 67152 620-326-4330
Zachary Lawrence, dir. Fax 326-4332
Wellington HS 500/9-12
1700 E 16th St 67152 620-326-4310
Dale Adams, prin. Fax 326-4383
Wellington MS 400/6-8
605 N A St 67152 620-326-4320
Jamie Ybarra, prin. Fax 326-4390

Wellsville, Franklin, Pop. 1,818
Wellsville USD 289 900/PK-12
602 Walnut St 66092 785-883-2388
Jerald Henn, supt. Fax 883-4453
www.wellsville-usd289.org
Wellsville HS 200/9-12
602 Walnut St 66092 785-883-2057
Sheldon Pokorney, prin. Fax 883-2294
Wellsville MS 200/6-8
602 Walnut St 66092 785-883-4350
Mitchell Lubin, prin. Fax 883-2260

Weskan, Wallace, Pop. 159
Weskan USD 242 100/PK-12
219 Coyote Blvd 67762 785-943-5222
Dave Hale, supt. Fax 943-5303
www.weskanschools.org/
Weskan JSHS 100/7-12
219 Coyote Blvd 67762 785-943-5222
Dave Hale, supt. Fax 943-5303

Westmoreland, Pottawatomie, Pop. 771
Rock Creek USD 323 900/PK-12
PO Box 70 66549 785-457-3732
Dr. Darrel Stufflebeam, supt. Fax 457-3701
www.rockcreekschools.org
Other Schools – See Saint George

Wetmore, Nemaha, Pop. 364
Prairie Hills USD 113
Supt. — See Sabetha
Wetmore HS 100/9-12
PO Box AB 66550 785-866-2860
Janelle Boden, prin. Fax 866-5450

White City, Morris, Pop. 611
Rural Vista USD 481 400/PK-12
PO Box 98 66872 785-349-2964
Ralph Blevins, supt. Fax 349-2965
www.usd481.org
White City HS, PO Box 98 66872 100/9-12
Kate Robinson, prin. 785-349-2211
Other Schools – See Hope

Whitewater, Butler, Pop. 694
Remington-Whitewater USD 206 500/K-12
PO Box 243 67154 316-799-2115
James Regier, supt. Fax 799-2307
www.usd206.org
Remington HS 200/9-12
8850 NW Meadowlark Rd 67154 316-799-2123
Tim Bumgarner, prin. Fax 799-2943
Remington MS 200/5-8
PO Box 99 67154 316-799-2131
Bruce Krase, prin. Fax 799-2581

Wichita, Sedgwick, Pop. 369,464
Haysville USD 261
Supt. — See Haysville
Haysville Campus HS 1,500/9-12
2100 W 55th St S 67217 316-554-2236
Myron Regier, prin. Fax 554-2241

Maize USD 266
Supt. — See Maize
Maize South HS 600/9-12
3701 N Tyler Rd 67205 316-462-8000
Dave Hickerson, prin. Fax 462-8001
Maize South MS 800/6-8
3403 N Tyler Rd 67205 316-722-0421
Jess Herbig, prin. Fax 722-4077

Wichita USD 259 46,400/PK-12
201 N Water St 67202 316-973-4000
John Allison, supt. Fax 973-4595
www.usd259.com
Allison Traditional Magnet MS 500/6-8
221 S Seneca St 67213 316-973-4800
Justin Kasel, prin. Fax 973-4810
Arkansas Avenue Gateway S Alt
640 N Emporia St 67214 316-973-3215
Steve Holbrook, prin. Fax 973-3210
Brooks Technology & Arts Magnet MS 600/6-8
3802 E 27th St N 67220 316-973-6450
Robert Garner, prin. Fax 973-6581
Coleman MS 600/6-8
1544 N Governeour Rd 67206 316-973-6600
Jeff Freund, prin. Fax 973-6699
Curtis MS 700/6-8
1031 S Edgemoor St 67218 316-973-7350
Stephanie Wasko, prin Fax 973-7410
Hadley MS 900/6-8
1101 N Dougherty Ave 67212 316-973-7800
Charles Wakefield, prin. Fax 973-7816
Hamilton MS 500/6-8
1407 S Broadway St 67211 316-973-5350
Amy Hungria, prin. Fax 973-5360
Jardine Technology Magnet MS 300/6-8
3550 E Ross Pkwy 67210 316-973-4300
Lura Atherly, prin. Fax 973-4310
Marshall MS 500/6-8
1510 N Payne Ave 67203 316-973-9000
Ron Stubbs, prin. Fax 973-9010
Mayberry Cultural & Fine Arts Magnet MS 600/6-8
207 S Sheridan St 67213 316-973-5800
Tim Seguine, prin. Fax 973-5808
Mead MS 500/6-8
2601 E Skinner St 67211 316-973-8500
Toby Martin, prin. Fax 973-8503
Metro Boulevard Alternative HS 100/Alt
1847 N Chautauqua Ave 67214 316-973-0500
Lisa Wyatt, prin. Fax 973-0510
Metro-Meridian Alternative S 100/Alt
301 S Meridian Ave 67213 316-973-0550
Ron Riley, prin. Fax 973-0560
Pleasant Valley MS 600/6-8
2220 W 29th St N 67204 316-973-8000
Victoria Manning, prin. Fax 973-8008
Robinson MS 800/6-8
328 N Oliver Ave 67208 316-973-8600
Amy Champlin, prin. Fax 973-8625
Sowers Alternative HS 200/Alt
2400 Wassall St 67216 316-973-1600
Jackie Hultman, prin. Fax 973-1610
Stucky MS 700/6-8
4545 N Broadview Cir 67220 316-973-8400
Jennifer Sinclair, prin. Fax 973-8410
Truesdell MS 800/6-8
2464 S Glenn Ave 67217 316-973-3900
Terrell Davis, prin. Fax 973-3904
Wells Alternative MS 100/Alt
1221 E Galena St Ste 373 67216 316-973-7650
Tim Finkbeiner, prin. Fax 973-7673
Wichita East HS 2,300/9-12
2301 E Douglas Ave 67211 316-973-7200
Ken Thiessen, prin. Fax 973-7224
Wichita Heights HS 1,600/9-12
5301 N Hillside St 67219 316-973-1400
Bruce Deterding, prin. Fax 973-1410
Wichita North HS 2,000/9-12
1437 N Rochester St 67203 316-973-6300
Sherman Padgett, prin. Fax 973-6190
Wichita Northwest HS 1,500/9-12
1220 N Tyler Rd 67212 316-973-6000
Karen Pickert, prin. Fax 973-6070
Wichita Southeast HS 1,600/9-12
903 S Edgemoor St 67218 316-973-2700
Leroy Parks, prin. Fax 973-2755
Wichita South HS 1,500/9-12
701 W 33rd St S 67217 316-973-5450
Cara Ledy, prin. Fax 973-5519
Wichita West HS 1,200/9-12
820 S Osage St 67213 316-973-3600
Joel Hudson, prin. Fax 973-3657
Wilbur MS 900/6-8
340 N Tyler Rd 67212 316-973-1100
Mark Jolliffe, prin. Fax 973-1090
Dunbar Learning Center Adult
923 N Cleveland Ave 67214 316-866-8153
Renee Erickson, prin. Fax 866-8157
Towne East Education Center Adult
7700 E Kellogg Dr 67207 316-973-4105
Renee Erickson, prin.
Towne West Education Center Adult
4600 W Kellogg Dr Ste 1 67209 316-973-4100
Renee Erickson, prin.
Other Schools – See Bel Aire

Bishop Carroll Catholic HS 1,100/9-12
8101 W Central Ave 67212 316-722-2390
Vanessa Harshbarger, prin. Fax 722-6670
Classical S of Wichita 100/K-12
6355 Willowbrook St 67218 316-773-9279
Ken Anderson, hdmstr. Fax 866-2479
Classic College of Hair Design Post-Sec.
1675 S Rock Rd Ste 101 67207 316-681-2288
Friends University Post-Sec.
2100 W University Ave 67213 316-295-5000
Heritage College Post-Sec.
2800 S Rock Rd 67210 316-681-1615
Independent S 600/K-12
8317 E Douglas Ave 67207 316-686-0152
ITT Technical Institute Post-Sec.
8111 E 32nd St N Ste 103 67226 316-609-4100
Kansas College of Chinese Medicine Post-Sec.
9235 E Harry St Bldg 200 67207 316-691-8822
Kapaun Mt. Carmel Catholic HS 900/9-12
8506 E Central Ave 67206 316-634-0315
Chris Bloomer, prin. Fax 636-2437
Newman University Post-Sec.
3100 W McCormick St 67213 316-942-4291
Old Town Barber College Post-Sec.
1207 E Douglas Ave 67211 316-264-4891
Paul Mitchell the School Post-Sec.
3242 N Rock Rd Ste 106 67226 316-630-0600
Trinity Academy 300/9-12
12345 E 21st St N 67206 316-634-0909
Matt Brewer, hdmstr. Fax 634-0928
Vatterott College Post-Sec.
8853 E 37th St N 67226 316-634-0066
Wichita Adventist Christian Academy 50/K-10
2725 S Osage Ave 67217 316-267-9472
Sharon Burton, prin. Fax 267-1065
Wichita Area Technical College Post-Sec.
4501 E 47th St S 67210 316-677-1500
Wichita Area Technical College Post-Sec.
4004 N Webb Rd 67226 316-677-9400
Wichita Area Technical College - Grove Post-Sec.
301 S Grove St 67211 316-677-9400
Wichita Collegiate S 1,000/PK-12
9115 E 13th St N 67206 316-634-0433
Tom Davis, hdmstr. Fax 634-0598
Wichita State University Post-Sec.
1845 Fairmount St 67260 316-978-3456
Wichita Technical Institute Post-Sec.
2051 S Meridian Ave 67213 316-943-2241
Wichita Technical Institute - East Post-Sec.
6130 E Central Ave 67208 316-943-2241
Wright Career College Post-Sec.
7700 E Kellogg Dr 67207 316-927-7700
Xenon International Academy Post-Sec.
3804 W Douglas Ave 67203 316-943-5516

Wilson, Ellsworth, Pop. 759
Central Plains USD 112
Supt. — See Holyrood
Wilson JSHS 100/7-12
PO Box 220 67490 785-658-2202
Brian Smith, prin. Fax 658-2205

Winchester, Jefferson, Pop. 551
Jefferson County North USD 339 500/PK-12
310 5th St 66097 913-774-2000
Denise Jennings, supt. Fax 774-2027
www.usd339.net
Jefferson County North HS 200/9-12
302 5th St 66097 913-774-8515
Gary Bedigrew, prin. Fax 774-8535

Winfield, Cowley, Pop. 11,966
Winfield USD 465 2,400/PK-12
1407 Wheat Rd 67156 620-221-5100
Dr. J.K. Campbell, supt. Fax 221-0508
www.usd465.com
Winfield HS 700/9-12
300 Viking Blvd 67156 620-221-5160
Trenton Creeden, prin. Fax 221-5165
Winfield MS 300/7-8
130 Viking Blvd 67156 620-221-5130
Suzie Cochran, prin. Fax 221-5147

Southwestern College Post-Sec.
100 College St 67156 620-229-6000

Winona, Logan, Pop. 161
Triplains USD 275 100/PK-12
PO Box 97 67764 785-846-7869
Lamar Bergsten, supt. Fax 846-7767
Winona HS 50/9-12
PO Box 97 67764 785-846-7496
Lamar Bergsten, prin. Fax 846-7767

Yates Center, Woodson, Pop. 1,379
Woodson USD 366 500/PK-12
PO Box 160 66783 620-625-8804
Rusty Arnold, supt. Fax 625-8806
www.usd366.net
Yates Center HS 100/9-12
PO Box 160 66783 620-625-8820
Jeremy Luedke, prin. Fax 625-8850

KENTUCKY

KENTUCKY DEPARTMENT OF EDUCATION
500 Mero St, Frankfort 40601-1987
Telephone 502-564-4770
Fax 502-564-5680
Website http://www.education.ky.gov

Commissioner of Education Terry Holliday Ph.D

KENTUCKY BOARD OF EDUCATION
500 Mero St Ste 1, Frankfort 40601-1957

Chairperson David Karem

PUBLIC, PRIVATE AND CATHOLIC SECONDARY SCHOOLS

Albany, Clinton, Pop. 1,999
Clinton County SD 1,800/PK-12
2353 N Highway 127 42602 606-387-6480
Charlotte Bernard, supt. Fax 387-5437
www.clinton.kyschools.us
Clinton County HS 500/9-12
65 High School Dr 42602 606-387-5569
Sheldon Harlan, prin. Fax 387-8659
Clinton County MS 500/5-8
169 Middle School Rd 42602 606-387-6466
Pam Bale, prin. Fax 387-6469

Kentucky Tech System
Supt. — See Frankfort
Clinton County Area Technology Center Vo/Tech
151 Armstrong Honeycutt Dr 42602 606-387-6448
Stesha Flowers, prin. Fax 387-4035

Alexandria, Campbell, Pop. 8,396
Campbell County SD 4,700/PK-12
101 Orchard Ln 41001 859-635-2173
Glen Miller, supt. Fax 448-2439
www.campbell.kyschools.us/
Campbell County Day Treatment 50/Alt
51 Orchard Ln 41001 859-635-9113
Alvin Elsbernd, prin. Fax 448-2781
Campbell County HS 1,400/9-12
909 Camel Xing 41001 859-635-4161
Renee Boots, prin. Fax 448-4886
Campbell County MS 1,100/6-8
8000 Alexandria Pike 41001 859-635-6077
Jason Smith, prin. Fax 448-4863

Kentucky Tech System
Supt. — See Frankfort
McCormick Area Technology Center Vo/Tech
50 Orchard Ln 41001 859-635-4101
Joseph Amann, prin. Fax 635-2766

Bishop Brossart HS 400/9-12
4 Grove St 41001 859-635-2108
Richard Stewart, prin. Fax 635-2135

Ashland, Boyd, Pop. 21,270
Ashland ISD 3,100/K-12
PO Box 3000 41105 606-327-2706
Stephen Gilmore, supt. Fax 327-2705
www.ashland.k12.ky.us/
Ashland Central Alternative S 50/Alt
2800 Kansas St 41102 606-327-1758
David Greene, prin. Fax 327-2718
Blazer HS 900/9-12
1500 Blazer Blvd 41102 606-327-6040
Derek Runyon, prin. Fax 324-0517
Verity MS 500/7-8
2800 Kansas St 41102 606-327-2727
David Greene, prin. Fax 327-2765

Boyd County SD 3,300/PK-12
1104 Bob McCullough Dr 41102 606-928-4141
R. Brock Walter, supt. Fax 928-4771
www.boyd.kyschools.us
Boyd County Career & Technical Center Vo/Tech
12300 Midland Trail Rd 41102 606-928-7120
Loretta Dixon, dir. Fax 928-6432
Boyd County HS 900/9-12
14375 Lions Ln 41102 606-928-7100
Dan Imes, prin. Fax 928-1312
Boyd County MS 700/6-8
1226 Summitt Rd 41102 606-928-9547
Bill Boblett, prin. Fax 928-2067
Other Schools – See Rush

Fairview ISD 800/PK-12
2201 Main St W 41102 606-324-3877
Bill Musick, supt. Fax 324-2288
www.fairview.kyschools.us
Fairview JSHS 400/7-12
2123 Main St W 41102 606-324-9226
Garry McPeek, prin. Fax 325-1486

Ashland Community and Technical College Post-Sec.
1400 College Dr 41101 606-326-2000
Rose Hill Christian S 300/PK-12
1001 Winslow Rd 41102 606-324-6105
Dr. Jerry Foster, prin. Fax 324-6420

Augusta, Bracken, Pop. 1,171
Augusta ISD 300/PK-12
307 Bracken St 41002 606-756-2545
Lisa McCane, supt. Fax 756-2149
www.augusta.kyschools.us
Augusta JSHS 100/7-12
207 Bracken St 41002 606-756-2105
Robin Kelsch, prin. Fax 756-3000

Barbourville, Knox, Pop. 3,119
Barbourville ISD 700/PK-12
PO Box 520 40906 606-546-3120
Larry Warren, supt. Fax 546-3452
www.barbourvilleind.com
Barbourville City S 700/PK-12
PO Box 520 40906 606-546-3129
Paul Middleton, prin. Fax 546-3337

Kentucky Tech System
Supt. — See Frankfort
Knox County Area Technology Center Vo/Tech
210 Wall St 40906 606-546-5320
Ralph Halcomb, prin. Fax 546-3818

Knox County SD 4,700/PK-12
200 Daniel Boone Dr 40906 606-546-3157
Walter Hulett, supt. Fax 546-2819
www.knox.kyschools.us
Knox Appalachian S 50/Alt
PO Box 970 40906 606-546-2568
Roger Vanover, prin. Fax 545-7068
Knox Central HS 900/9-12
100 Panther Way 40906 606-546-9253
Tim Melton, prin. Fax 546-5684
Knox County Learning Academy 50/Alt
135 Wall St 40906 606-545-5410
Roger Vanover, prin. Fax 546-5267
Knox County MS 500/7-8
311 N Main St 40906 606-545-5267
Kelly Sprinkles, prin. Fax 546-2161
Other Schools – See Corbin

Union College Post-Sec.
310 College St 40906 606-546-4151

Bardstown, Nelson, Pop. 11,437
Bardstown ISD 2,700/PK-12
308 N 5th St 40004 502-331-8800
Brent Holsclaw, supt. Fax 331-8830
www.bardstown.kyschools.us
Bardstown HS 600/9-12
400 N 5th St 40004 502-331-8802
Chris Pickett, prin. Fax 331-8832
Bardstown MS 500/6-8
410 N 5th St 40004 502-331-8803
Bob Blackmon, prin. Fax 331-8833

Kentucky Tech System
Supt. — See Frankfort
Nelson County Area Technology Center Vo/Tech
1060 Bloomfield Rd 40004 502-348-9096
Rodney Nokes, prin. Fax 348-9097

Nelson County SD 5,000/PK-12
288 Wildcat Ln 40004 502-349-7000
Anthony Orr, supt. Fax 349-7004
www.nelson.kyschools.us
Horizons Academy 100/Alt
304 Wildcat Ln 40004 502-349-7045
Penny Bradley, prin. Fax 349-7044
Nelson County HS 1,500/9-12
1070 Bloomfield Rd 40004 502-349-7010
Eric Gilpin, prin. Fax 349-7017
Nelson HS 9-12
2885 New Shepherdsville Rd 40004 502-349-4650
Wes Bradley, prin. Fax 349-4651
Old Kentucky Home MS 400/6-8
301 Wildcat Ln 40004 502-349-7040
Dr. Jennifer Miller, prin. Fax 349-7042
Other Schools – See Bloomfield

Bethlehem HS 300/9-12
309 W Stephen Foster Ave 40004 502-348-8594
Tom Hamilton, prin. Fax 349-1247

Bardwell, Carlisle, Pop. 716
Carlisle County SD 800/PK-12
4557 State Route 1377 42023 270-628-3800
Jay Simmons, supt. Fax 628-5477
www.carlisle.kyschools.us
Carlisle County HS 300/9-12
4557 State Route 1377 42023 270-628-3800
Kelli Edging, prin. Fax 628-3837
Carlisle County MS 200/6-8
4557 State Route 1377 42023 270-628-3800
DeeAnne Arant, prin. Fax 628-3974

Barlow, Ballard, Pop. 654
Ballard County SD 1,500/PK-12
3465 Paducah Rd 42024 270-665-8400
Casey Allen, supt. Fax 665-9844
www.ballard.kyschools.us
Ballard County MS 300/6-8
3565 Paducah Rd 42024 270-665-8400
Kevin Estes, prin. Fax 665-5153
Ballard County Technical & Career Center Vo/Tech
11 Vocational School Rd 42024 270-665-8400
David Meinschein, prin. Fax 665-5006
Ballard Memorial HS 400/9-12
3561 Paducah Rd 42024 270-665-8400
David Meinschein, prin. Fax 665-5312

Baxter, Harlan
Harlan County SD
Supt. — See Harlan
Harlan County HS 1,200/9-12
4000 N US Highway 119 40806 606-574-2020
Edna Burkhart, prin. Fax 574-0493

Beattyville, Lee, Pop. 1,296
Kentucky Tech System
Supt. — See Frankfort
Lee County Area Technology Center Vo/Tech
PO Box B 41311 606-464-5018
Craig Herald, prin. Fax 464-0663

Lee County SD 1,100/K-12
PO Box 668 41311 606-464-5000
Jim Evans, supt. Fax 464-5009
www.lee.kyschools.us
Lee County HS 300/9-12
PO Box J 41311 606-464-5005
Mark Murray, prin. Fax 464-5014
Lee County MS 300/6-8
PO Box N 41311 606-464-5010
Karen Angel, prin. Fax 464-5011

Bedford, Trimble, Pop. 584
Trimble County SD 1,400/K-12
PO Box 275 40006 502-255-3201
Marcia Haney-Dunaway, supt. Fax 255-5105
www.trimble.kyschools.us/
Trimble County HS 400/9-12
1029 Highway 421 N 40006 502-255-7781
Rachael Adams, prin. Fax 255-5126
Trimble County MS 400/6-8
116 Wentworth Ave 40006 502-255-7361
Mike Genton, prin. Fax 255-5102

Belfry, Pike
Kentucky Tech System
Supt. — See Frankfort
Belfry Area Technology Center Vo/Tech
PO Box 280 41514 606-353-4951
Annette Harris, prin. Fax 353-0868

Pike County SD
Supt. — See Pikeville
Belfry HS 800/9-12
PO Box 160 41514 606-237-3900
Mark Gannon, prin. Fax 237-5119
Belfry MS 600/6-8
PO Box 850 41514 606-353-7230
Matthew Mercer, prin. Fax 353-0530

Bellevue, Campbell, Pop. 5,875
Bellevue ISD 800/PK-12
219 Center St 41073 859-261-2108
Wayne Starnes, supt. Fax 261-1708
www.bellevue.kyschools.us
Bellevue HS 400/7-12
201 Center St 41073 859-261-2980
Dave Eckstein, prin. Fax 261-1825

Daymar College Post-Sec.
119 Fairfield Ave 41073 859-291-0800

Benton, Marshall, Pop. 4,312
Marshall County SD 4,900/PK-12
86 High School Rd 42025 270-527-8628
Trent Lovett, supt. Fax 527-0804
www.marshall.kyschools.us
Benton MS 300/6-8
906 Joe Creason Dr 42025 270-527-9091
Jill Darnall, prin. Fax 527-9992
Marshall County HS 1,400/9-12
416 High School Rd 42025 270-527-1453
Amy Waggoner, prin. Fax 527-0578
Marshall County Technical Center Vo/Tech
341 High School Rd 42025 270-527-8648
Stacey Bradley, dir. Fax 527-1920
South Marshall MS 300/6-8
85 Sid Darnall Rd 42025 270-527-3828
Brian Harper, prin. Fax 527-7616
STAR Academy 50/Alt
86 High School Rd 42025 270-252-1394
David Morris, dir. Fax 252-1394
Other Schools – See Calvert City

Christian Fellowship S 100/PK-12
1343 US Highway 68 E 42025 270-527-8377
Bill Rowley, admin. Fax 527-2872

Berea, Madison, Pop. 13,252
Berea ISD 1,100/PK-12
3 Pirate Pkwy 40403 859-986-8446
Mike Hogg, supt. Fax 986-1839
www.berea.kyschools.us/
Berea Community HS 300/9-12
1 Pirate Pkwy 40403 859-986-4911
Donna Lovell, prin. Fax 986-4640
Berea Community MS 300/6-8
1 Pirate Pkwy 40403 859-986-4911
Donna Lovell, prin. Fax 986-4640

Madison County SD
Supt. — See Richmond
Farristown MS 6-8
751 Farristown Industrial 40403 859-387-8600
Alicia Hunter, prin. Fax 986-3092
Foley MS 900/6-8
275 Glades Rd 40403 859-625-6140
Arno Norwell, prin. Fax 986-3362
Madison Southern HS 1,000/9-12
279 Glades Rd 40403 859-625-6148
David Gilliam, prin. Fax 986-3092

Berea College Post-Sec.
101 Chestnut St 40403 859-985-3000

Beverly, Bell

Red Bird Mission S 200/K-12
15420 Highway 66 40913 606-598-2416
Dr. Taylor Collins, dir. Fax 598-7314

Blackey, Letcher, Pop. 120
Letcher County SD
Supt. — See Whitesburg
Letcher MS 100/6-8
160 LHS Dr 41804 606-633-7812
Ricky Warf, prin. Fax 633-5731

Bloomfield, Nelson, Pop. 831
Nelson County SD
Supt. — See Bardstown
Bloomfield MS 400/6-8
96 Arnold Ln 40008 502-349-7201
Jim Beavers, prin. Fax 349-7203

Booneville, Owsley, Pop. 81
Owsley County SD 900/PK-12
14 Old KY 11 41314 606-593-6363
Timothy Bobrowski, supt. Fax 593-6368
www.owsley.kyschools.us
Owsley County JSHS 400/7-12
177 Shepherd Rd 41314 606-593-5185
Gary Cornett, prin. Fax 593-6312

Bowling Green, Warren, Pop. 56,664
Bowling Green ISD 3,800/PK-12
1211 Center St 42101 270-746-2200
Joe Tinius, supt. Fax 746-2205
www.bgreen.kyschools.us/
Academy at 11th Street 50/Alt
877 E 11th Ave 42101 270-746-2321
Marisa Duarte, dir. Fax 746-2325
Bowling Green HS 1,100/9-12
1801 Rockingham Ave 42104 270-746-2300
Gary Fields, prin. Fax 746-2305
Bowling Green JHS 900/6-8
900 Campbell Ln 42104 270-746-2290
Cynthia West, prin. Fax 746-2295
Children's Stabilization Unit 50/Alt
501 Chestnut St 42101 270-781-3997
Josh Long, lead tchr. Fax 781-8987

Kentucky Tech System
Supt. — See Frankfort
Warren County Area Technology Center Vo/Tech
365 Technology Way 42101 270-746-7205
Don Evans, prin. Fax 746-7207

Warren County SD 13,800/PK-12
PO Box 51810 42102 270-781-5150
Tim Murley, supt. Fax 781-2392
www.warrencountyschools.org/
Bellewood Alternative S 50/Alt
331 Brookwood Dr 42101 270-782-2756
Vivian Hudson, dir. Fax 793-0704
Drakes Creek MS 500/7-8
704 Cypress Wood Ln 42104 270-843-0165
Daryl Woods, prin. Fax 782-6138
Greenwood HS 1,200/9-12
5065 Scottsville Rd 42104 270-842-3627
Greg Dunn, prin. Fax 842-2037
Jackson Academy Alt
877 Jackson St 42101 270-467-0293
Matthew Bastin, prin.
Lighthouse Academy 100/Alt
877 Jackson St 42101 270-782-5410
Matt Bastin, lead tchr. Fax 782-3240
Moss MS 500/7-8
2565 Russellville Rd 42101 270-843-0166
Jerry Nole, prin. Fax 843-8512
South Warren HS 800/9-12
8140 Nashville Rd 42101 270-467-7500
Terry Cook, prin. Fax 467-7506
South Warren MS 500/7-8
295 Richpond Rd 42104 270-467-7510
Eddy Bushelman, prin. Fax 467-7516
Warren Central HS 1,000/9-12
559 Morgantown Rd 42101 270-842-7302
Tina Prunty, prin. Fax 781-5115
Warren East HS 900/9-12
6867 Louisville Rd 42101 270-781-1277
Damon Tabor, prin. Fax 843-2610
Warren East MS 500/7-8
7031 Louisville Rd 42101 270-843-0181
David Cloyd, prin. Fax 781-8565

Anchored Christian S 100/K-12
1807 Cave Mill Rd 42104 270-781-9077
Betty Jo Hicks, prin. Fax 781-8122
Bowling Green Christian Academy 200/PK-12
1730 Destiny Ln 42104 270-782-9552
Tim Pettit, admin. Fax 782-9585
Bowling Green Technical College Post-Sec.
1845 Loop St 42101 270-901-1000
Bowling Green Technical College Post-Sec.
1127 Morgantown Rd 42101 270-746-7807
Daymar College Post-Sec.
2421 Industrial Dr 42101 270-843-6750
PJs College of Cosmetology Post-Sec.
1901 Russellville Rd 42101 270-842-8149
Western Kentucky University Post-Sec.
1906 College Heights Blvd 42101 270-745-0111

Brandenburg, Meade, Pop. 2,585
Kentucky Tech System
Supt. — See Frankfort
Meade County Area Technology Center Vo/Tech
110 Greer St 40108 270-422-3955
Faye Campbell, prin. Fax 422-3307

Meade County SD 5,000/PK-12
1155 Old Ekron Rd 40108 270-422-7500
Mitch Crump, supt. Fax 422-5494
www.meade.kyschools.us
Meade County HS 1,500/9-12
938 Old State Rd 40108 270-422-7515
William Adams, prin. Fax 422-3928
Pepper MS 800/7-8
1085 Old Ekron Rd 40108 270-422-7530
Chad Butler, prin. Fax 422-5515

Brooksville, Bracken, Pop. 638
Bracken County SD 1,100/PK-12
348 W Miami St 41004 606-735-2523
Jeff Aulick, supt. Fax 735-3640
www.bracken.k12.ky.us
Bracken County HS 400/9-12
PO Box 128 41004 606-735-3153
Mike Hunter, prin. Fax 735-2549
Bracken County MS 300/6-8
167 Parsley Dr 41004 606-735-3425
Leah Jefferson, prin. Fax 735-2057

Brownsville, Edmonson, Pop. 829
Edmonson County SD 2,000/PK-12
PO Box 129 42210 270-597-2101
Patrick Waddell, supt. Fax 597-2103
www.edmonson.k12.ky.us
Edmonson County HS 600/9-12
220 Wild Cat Way 42210 270-597-2151
Brian Alexander, prin. Fax 597-2962
Edmonson County MS 300/7-8
210 Wild Cat Way 42210 270-597-2932
Kyle Cassady, prin. Fax 597-2182

Buckhorn, Perry, Pop. 162
Perry County SD
Supt. — See Hazard
Buckhorn HS 200/9-12
18392 KY Highway 28 41721 606-398-7176
Lisa Weist, prin. Fax 398-7930

Burgin, Mercer, Pop. 946
Burgin ISD 500/PK-12
PO Box B 40310 859-748-4000
Richard Webb, supt. Fax 748-4010
www.burgin.k12.ky.us
Burgin HS 200/6-12
PO Box B 40310 859-748-5282
Martha Collier, prin. Fax 748-4002

Burkesville, Cumberland, Pop. 1,484
Cumberland County SD 1,000/K-12
PO Box 420 42717 270-864-3377
Glen Murphy, supt. Fax 864-5803
www.cland.k12.ky.us
Cumberland County HS 300/9-12
PO Box 380 42717 270-864-3451
Daryl Murphy, prin. Fax 864-1284
Cumberland County MS 200/6-8
PO Box 70 42717 270-864-5818
Tim Parson, prin. Fax 864-2590

Burlington, Boone, Pop. 15,646
Boone County SD
Supt. — See Florence
Camp Ernst MS 900/6-8
6515 Camp Ernst Rd 41005 859-534-4000
Eric McArtor, prin. Fax 534-4001

Burna, Livingston, Pop. 254
Livingston County SD
Supt. — See Smithland
Livingston County MS 200/7-8
1370 US Highway 60 E 42028 270-988-3263
Lisa Huddleston, prin. Fax 988-2518

Butler, Pendleton, Pop. 586
Pendleton County SD
Supt. — See Falmouth
Sharp MS 600/6-8
35 Wright Rd 41006 859-472-7000
Adam Cross, prin. Fax 472-7011

Cadiz, Trigg, Pop. 2,498
Trigg County SD 2,000/K-12
202 Main St 42211 270-522-6075
Travis Hamby, supt. Fax 522-7782
www.trigg.kyschools.us
Trigg County HS 600/9-12
203 Main St 42211 270-522-2200
Shannon Burcham, prin. Fax 522-2224
Trigg County MS 500/6-8
206 Lafayette St 42211 270-522-2210
Kristie Miller, prin. Fax 522-2203

Calhoun, McLean, Pop. 758
McLean County SD 1,600/K-12
PO Box 245 42327 270-273-5257
Tres Settle, supt. Fax 273-5259
www.mclean.kyschools.us/
McLean County HS 500/9-12
1859 State Route 136 E 42327 270-273-5278
Ashley Troutman, prin. Fax 273-5208
McLean County MS 400/6-8
1901 State Route 136 E 42327 270-273-5191
Shannon Lindsey, prin. Fax 273-9876

Calvert City, Marshall, Pop. 2,542
Marshall County SD
Supt. — See Benton
North Marshall MS 500/6-8
3110 US Highway 95 42029 270-395-7108
Aimee Lepisto, prin. Fax 395-5449

Campbellsville, Taylor, Pop. 8,884
Campbellsville ISD 1,100/PK-12
136 S Columbia Ave 42718 270-465-4162
Mike Deaton, supt. Fax 465-3918
www.cville.kyschools.us/
Campbellsville HS 200/9-12
230 W Main St 42718 270-465-8774
Kirby Smith, prin. Fax 789-4007
Campbellsville MS 300/5-8
315 Roberts Rd 42718 270-465-5121
David Petett, prin. Fax 789-3718
Eagle Academy 100/Alt
230 W Main St 42718 270-465-6337
Tim Bailey, dir. Fax 465-9777

Taylor County SD 2,700/PK-12
1209 E Broadway St 42718 270-465-5371
Roger Cook, supt. Fax 789-3954
www.taylor.kyschools.us
Taylor County HS 800/9-12
300 Ingram Ave 42718 270-465-4431
Charles Higdon, prin. Fax 465-5731
Taylor County MS 600/6-8
1207 E Broadway St 42718 270-465-2877
Tony Jewell, prin. Fax 789-1753

Campbellsville University Post-Sec.
1 University Dr 42718 270-789-5000

Campton, Wolfe, Pop. 434
Wolfe County SD 1,300/K-12
PO Box 160 41301 606-668-8002
Kenny Bell, supt. Fax 668-8050
www.wolfe.kyschools.us
Wolfe County HS 400/9-12
PO Box 790 41301 606-668-8202
Greg Creech, prin. Fax 668-8250
Wolfe County MS 200/7-8
PO Box 460 41301 606-668-8152
Wilma Terrill, prin. Fax 668-8100

Bethany Christian S 50/PK-12
17 Bethany Cir 41301 606-668-6353
Geneva Pence, prin. Fax 668-7315

Carlisle, Nicholas, Pop. 1,984
Nicholas County SD 1,200/PK-12
395 W Main St 40311 859-289-3770
Gregory Reid, supt. Fax 289-3777
www.nicholas.kyschools.us
Nicholas County JSHS 500/7-12
103 School Dr 40311 859-289-3780
Marty Feltner, prin. Fax 289-6429

Motif Beauty Academy Post-Sec.
225 Elderberry Dr 40311 859-745-5886

Carrollton, Carroll, Pop. 3,854
Carroll County SD 1,800/K-12
813 Hawkins St 41008 502-732-7070
Lisa James, supt. Fax 732-7073
www.carroll.kyschools.us
Carroll County Alternative S 50/Alt
519 Park Ave 41008 502-732-7112
Ed Nelson, lead tchr. Fax 732-7113
Carroll County HS 600/9-12
1706 Highland Ave 41008 502-732-7075
Tom Stephens, prin. Fax 732-7012
Carroll County MS 400/6-8
408 5th St 41008 502-732-7080
Dana Oak, prin. Fax 732-7107

Kentucky Tech System
Supt. — See Frankfort
Carroll County Area Technology Center Vo/Tech
1704 Highland Ave 41008 502-732-4479
Mary Stratton, prin. Fax 732-4837

Christian Academy of Carrollton 100/PK-12
1703 Easter Day Rd 41008 502-732-4734
Katie Matson, admin. Fax 732-4732

Cave City, Barren, Pop. 2,196
Caverna ISD 800/PK-12
1102 N Dixie Hwy 42127 270-773-2530
Samuel Dick, supt. Fax 773-2524
www.caverna.k12.ky.us
Other Schools – See Horse Cave

Cecilia, Hardin, Pop. 563
Hardin County SD
Supt. — See Elizabethtown
Central Hardin HS 1,800/9-12
3040 Leitchfield Rd 42724 270-737-6800
Tim Isaacs, prin. Fax 765-3889
West Hardin MS 600/6-8
10471 Leitchfield Rd 42724 270-862-3924
Jon Thomas, prin. Fax 862-3647

Clinton, Hickman, Pop. 1,362
Hickman County SD 800/PK-12
416 N Waterfield Dr 42031 270-653-2341
Kenny Wilson, supt. Fax 653-6007
www.hickman.kyschools.us
Hickman County HS 300/7-12
301 James H Phillips Dr 42031 270-653-4044
Larry Farlee, prin. Fax 653-3200

Daymar College Post-Sec.
1171 US Highway 51 S 42031 270-653-9800

Cloverport, Breckinridge, Pop. 1,138
Cloverport ISD 300/PK-12
PO Box 37 40111 270-788-3910
Dr. John Millay, supt. Fax 788-6290
www.cloverport.kyschools.us
Fraize HS 100/9-12
101 4th St 40111 270-788-3388
Dwayne Bishop, prin. Fax 788-6640
Fraize MS 100/6-8
101 4th St 40111 270-788-3388
Dwayne Bishop, prin. Fax 788-6640

Columbia, Adair, Pop. 4,378
Adair County SD 2,600/PK-12
1204 Greensburg St 42728 270-384-2476
Alan Reed, supt. Fax 384-5841
www.adair.kyschools.us
Adair County HS 800/9-12
526 Indian Dr 42728 270-384-2751
Troy Young, prin. Fax 384-6900
Adair County MS 400/7-8
322 General John Adair Dr 42728 270-384-5308
Alma Rich, prin. Fax 384-2168
Adair County Youth Development Center 50/Alt
PO Box 39 42728 270-384-0811
Alan Reed, prin. Fax 384-2122

Lindsey Wilson College Post-Sec.
210 Lindsey Wilson St 42728 270-384-2126

Corbin, Whitley, Pop. 7,232
Corbin ISD 2,800/PK-12
108 Roy Kidd Ave 40701 606-528-1303
Ed McNeel, supt. Fax 523-1747
www.corbinschools.org
Corbin Educational Center 50/Alt
901 S Main St 40701 606-523-4080
Tom Greer, admin. Fax 523-3614
Corbin HS 700/9-12
1901 Snyder St 40701 606-528-3902
John Faulconer, prin. Fax 523-3627
Corbin MS 400/7-8
706 S Kentucky Ave 40701 606-523-3619
Ramona Davis, prin. Fax 523-3621

Kentucky Tech System
Supt. — See Frankfort
Corbin Area Technology Center Vo/Tech
1909 Snyder St 40701 606-528-5338
Patty Crawford, prin. Fax 528-0532

Knox County SD
Supt. — See Barbourville
Lynn Camp JSHS 500/7-12
100 N KY 830 40701 606-528-5429
Amy Bays, prin. Fax 528-4750

Covington, Kenton, Pop. 39,321
Covington ISD 3,900/PK-12
25 E 7th St 41011 859-392-1000
Lynda Jackson, supt. Fax 292-5808
covschools.us/
Holmes HS 800/9-12
2500 Madison Ave 41014 859-655-9545
Dennis Maines, prin. Fax 581-7259
Holmes MS 700/6-8
2500 Madison Ave 41014 859-392-1100
Sean Bohannon, prin. Fax 292-5810
Covington Adult HS Adult
1030 Old State Rd 41011 859-292-2864
Stephanie Trenkamp, coord. Fax 292-5866
Other Schools – See Park Hills

Calvary Christian S 400/PK-12
5955 Taylor Mill Rd 41015 859-356-9201
Dr. Bill Dickens, admin. Fax 356-8962
Covington Catholic HS 500/9-12
1600 Dixie Hwy 41011 859-491-2247
Bob Rowe, prin. Fax 448-2242
Covington Latin HS 200/8-12
21 E 11th St 41011 859-291-7044
Mo Woltering, hdmstr. Fax 291-1939
Holy Cross HS 500/9-12
3617 Church St 41015 859-431-1335
Michael Holtz, prin. Fax 655-2184

Crestview Hills, Kenton, Pop. 3,111

Thomas More College Post-Sec.
333 Thomas More Pkwy 41017 859-344-3332

Crestwood, Oldham, Pop. 4,447
Oldham County SD 11,900/PK-12
6165 W Highway 146 40014 502-241-3500
Dr. Will Wells, supt. Fax 241-3209
www.oldham.kyschools.us/
East Oldham MS 600/6-8
1201 E Highway 22 40014 502-222-8480
Jim Ross, prin. Fax 222-8489
South Oldham HS 1,100/9-12
5901 Veterens Memorial Pkwy 40014 502-241-6681
Jeff Griffin, prin. Fax 241-0955
South Oldham MS 700/6-8
6403 W Highway 146 40014 502-241-0320
Eric Gilpin, prin. Fax 241-1438
Other Schools – See Goshen, La Grange

Trend Setter's Academy of Beauty Culture Post-Sec.
6539 W Highway 22 40014 502-241-0565

Crittenden, Grant, Pop. 3,774
Kenton County SD
Supt. — See Fort Wright
Northern Kentucky Youth Development Ctr. 50/Alt
15600 Turner Dr 41030 859-356-3091
Doug Doan, prin. Fax 356-0022

Cromwell, Ohio
Butler County SD
Supt. — See Morgantown
Green River S 50/Alt
363 Boys Camp Rd 42333 270-526-5276
Jim Green, prin. Fax 526-5276

Cumberland, Harlan, Pop. 2,210

Southeast Kentucky Community/Tech Coll Post-Sec.
700 College Rd 40823 606-589-2145

Cynthiana, Harrison, Pop. 6,302
Harrison County SD 3,000/K-12
308 Webster Ave 41031 859-234-7110
Andy Dotson, supt. Fax 234-8164
www.harrison.kyschools.us
Harrison County HS 900/9-12
320 Webster Ave 41031 859-234-7117
Amy Coleman, prin. Fax 234-0115
Harrison County MS 700/6-8
269 Education Dr 41031 859-234-7123
Michael McIntire, prin. Fax 234-8385

Kentucky Tech System
Supt. — See Frankfort
Harrison County Area Technology Center Vo/Tech
327 Webster Ave 41031 859-234-5286
Diana Gordon, prin. Fax 234-0658

Danville, Boyle, Pop. 15,790
Boyle County SD 2,800/PK-12
352 N Danville Byp 40422 859-236-6634
Mike LaFavers, supt. Fax 236-8624
www.boyle.kyschools.us
Boyle County Day Treatment Center 50/Alt
1637 Perryville Rd 40422 859-236-5047
LuAnn Littlefield, dir.
Boyle County HS 900/9-12
1637 Perryville Rd 40422 859-236-5047
Will Begley, prin. Fax 236-7820
Boyle County MS 600/6-8
1651 Perryville Rd 40422 859-236-4212
Steve Karsner, prin. Fax 236-9596

Danville ISD 1,700/PK-12
152 E Martin L King Blvd 40422 859-238-1300
Dr. Carmen Coleman, supt. Fax 238-1330
www.danvilleschools.net
Bate MS 400/6-8
460 Stanford Ave 40422 859-238-1305
Dr. Amy Galloway, prin. Fax 238-1343
Danville HS 500/9-12
203 E Lexington Ave 40422 859-238-1308
Aaron Etherington, prin. Fax 936-8401

Centre College Post-Sec.
600 W Walnut St 40422 859-238-5200
Danville Christian Academy 200/PK-12
2170 Shakertown Rd 40422 859-236-2177
Debra Lucas, hdmstr. Fax 236-6759
Kentucky School for the Deaf Post-Sec.
S 2nd St 40422 859-239-7017
National College Post-Sec.
115 E Lexington Ave 40422 859-236-6991

Dawson Springs, Hopkins, Pop. 2,724
Dawson Springs ISD 700/PK-12
118 E Arcadia Ave 42408 270-797-3811
Alexis Seymore, supt. Fax 797-5201
www.dsprings.k12.ky.us/
Dawson Springs HS 300/7-12
317 Eli St 42408 270-797-2957
Kevin Stockman, prin. Fax 797-5204

Dayton, Campbell, Pop. 5,244
Dayton ISD 900/PK-12
200 Clay St 41074 859-491-6565
Jay Brewer, supt. Fax 292-3995
www.dayton.kyschools.us
Dayton HS 400/7-12
200 Greendevil Ln 41074 859-292-7486
Rick Wolf, prin. Fax 261-1606

Dixon, Webster, Pop. 785
Kentucky Tech System
Supt. — See Frankfort
Webster County Area Technology Center Vo/Tech
PO Box 230 42409 270-639-5035
Lawrence Garrity, prin. Fax 639-5545

Webster County SD 2,000/PK-12
28 State Route 1340 42409 270-639-5083
James Kemp, supt. Fax 639-0117
www.webster.kyschools.us/
Webster County HS 600/9-12
1922 US Highway 41A S 42409 270-639-5092
Tim Roy, prin. Fax 639-0128

Dry Ridge, Grant, Pop. 2,166
Grant County SD
Supt. — See Williamstown
Grant County HS 1,100/9-12
715 Warsaw Rd 41035 859-824-9739
Claudette Herald, prin. Fax 824-9756
Grant County MS 900/6-8
305 School Rd 41035 859-824-7161
Tim Grayson, prin. Fax 824-7163

Eastern, Floyd
Floyd County SD
Supt. — See Prestonsburg
Allen Central HS 400/9-12
PO Box 139 41622 606-358-9543
Larry Begley, prin. Fax 358-9247
Allen Central MS 300/6-8
PO Box 193 41622 606-358-0110
Wes Halbert, prin. Fax 358-0112

Eddyville, Lyon, Pop. 2,514
Lyon County SD 700/K-12
217 Jenkins Rd 42038 270-388-9715
Quin Sutton, supt. Fax 388-4962
www.lyon.kyschools.us
Lyon County HS 300/9-12
209 W Fairview Ave 42038 270-388-9715
Robin Hurst, prin. Fax 388-2296
Lyon County MS 200/6-8
201A W Fairview Ave 42038 270-388-9715
Robert Richey, prin. Fax 388-0517

Edgewood, Kenton, Pop. 8,503
Kenton County SD
Supt. — See Fort Wright
Dixie Heights HS 1,400/9-12
3010 Dixie Hwy 41017 859-341-7650
Karen Hendrix, prin. Fax 341-2531
Turkey Foot MS 1,000/6-8
3230 Turkeyfoot Rd 41017 859-341-0216
Tom Arnzen, prin. Fax 341-7217

St. Elizabeth Medical Center Post-Sec.
1 Medical Village Dr 41017 859-301-2170

Edmonton, Metcalfe, Pop. 1,584
Metcalfe County SD 1,000/PK-12
109 Sartin Dr 42129 270-432-3171
Dr. Benny Lile, supt. Fax 432-3170
www.metcalfe.kyschools.us
Metcalfe County HS 500/9-12
208 Randolph St 42129 270-432-2481
Kelly Bell, prin. Fax 432-2714
Metcalfe County MS 200/6-8
208 Randolph St Lot 1 42129 270-432-3359
Allen Trotter, prin. Fax 432-5828

Elizabethtown, Hardin, Pop. 27,593
Elizabethtown ISD 2,400/PK-12
219 Helm St 42701 270-765-6146
Gary French, supt. Fax 765-2158
www.etown.k12.ky.us
Elizabethtown HS 700/9-12
620 N Mulberry St 42701 270-769-3381
Steve Smallwood, prin. Fax 769-2539
Stone MS 600/6-8
323 Morningside Dr 42701 270-769-6343
Beth Mather, prin. Fax 769-6749
Valley View Education Center Alt
701 Hawkins Dr 42701 270-769-2359
Fax 769-3860

Hardin County SD 13,800/PK-12
65 W A Jenkins Rd 42701 270-769-8800
Nannette Johnston, supt. Fax 769-8888
www.hardin.kyschools.us/
Bluegrass MS 600/6-8
170 W A Jenkins Rd 42701 270-765-2658
Michael Elmore, prin. Fax 737-0450
Hardin HS 1,100/9-12
384 W A Jenkins Rd 42701 270-769-8906
Lynne Gibson, prin. Fax 769-8996
Mulberry Helm Education Center 100/Alt
114 S Mulberry St 42701 270-769-8866
Eric Vowels, dir. Fax 769-8869
Other Schools – See Cecilia, Glendale, Radcliff, Vine Grove

Elizabethtown Beauty School Post-Sec.
308 N Miles St 42701 270-765-2118
Elizabethtown Community & Technical Coll Post-Sec.
600 College Street Rd 42701 270-769-2371
Trend Setter's Academy of Beauty Culture Post-Sec.
622B Westport Rd 42701 270-765-5243

Elkton, Todd, Pop. 2,020
Todd County SD 2,100/PK-12
205 Airport Rd 42220 270-265-2436
Wayne Benningfield, supt. Fax 265-5414
www.todd.kyschools.us
Todd County Central HS 600/9-12
806 S Main St 42220 270-265-2506
Todd Marshall, prin. Fax 265-9408
Todd County MS 400/6-8
515 W Main St 42220 270-265-2511
Connie Wofford, prin. Fax 265-9414

Eminence, Henry, Pop. 2,433
Eminence ISD 600/PK-12
291 W Broadway St 40019 502-845-4788
Buddy Berry, supt. Fax 845-2339
www.eminence.kyschools.us/
Eminence JSHS 300/5-12
254 W Broadway St 40019 502-845-5427
Shannon Treece, prin. Fax 845-1310

Erlanger, Kenton, Pop. 17,704
Erlanger-Elsmere ISD 2,300/PK-12
500 Graves Ave 41018 859-727-2009
Dr. Kathlyn Burkhardt, supt. Fax 727-5653
www.erlanger.kyschools.us
Bartlett Educational Center 50/Alt
305 Bartlett Ave 41018 859-342-2460
Chris Klosinski, prin. Fax 342-2423
Lloyd HS 600/9-12
450 Bartlett Ave 41018 859-727-1555
John Riehemann, prin. Fax 727-5912
Tichenor MS 500/6-8
305 Bartlett Ave 41018 859-727-2255
Bryant Gillis, prin. Fax 342-2425

St. Henry HS 500/9-12
3755 Scheben Dr 41018 859-525-0255
David Otte, prin. Fax 525-5855

Fairdale, Jefferson, Pop. 6,563
Jefferson County SD
Supt. — See Louisville
Fairdale HS Magnet Career Academy 1,000/9-12
1001 Fairdale Rd 40118 502-485-8248
Brad Weston, prin. Fax 485-8761

Falmouth, Pendleton, Pop. 2,146
Pendleton County SD 2,600/PK-12
2525 US Highway 27 N 41040 859-654-6911
R. Anthony Strong, supt. Fax 654-6143
pendleton.kyschools.us
Pendleton County HS 800/9-12
2359 US Highway 27 N 41040 859-654-3355
Tony Dietrich, prin. Fax 654-4235
Other Schools – See Butler

Fern Creek, Jefferson, Pop. 16,406
Jefferson County SD
Supt. — See Louisville
Fern Creek Traditional HS 1,400/9-12
9115 Fern Creek Rd 40291 502-485-8251
Houston Barber, prin. Fax 485-8032

Flemingsburg, Fleming, Pop. 2,619
Fleming County SD 2,300/K-12
211 W Water St 41041 606-845-5851
Thomas Price, supt. Fax 849-3158
www.fleming.kyschools.us
Fleming County HS 700/9-12
1658 Elizaville Rd 41041 606-845-6601
Mark Leet, prin. Fax 845-3102
Simons MS 300/7-8
242 W Water St 41041 606-845-9331
Lesia Eldridge, prin. Fax 849-2309

Florence, Boone, Pop. 29,280
Boone County SD 19,000/K-12
8330 US Highway 42 41042 859-283-1003
Randy Poe, supt. Fax 282-2376
www.boone.kyschools.us
Alternative Center for Education Alt
99 Center St 41042 859-282-2163
Tony Pastura, prin. Fax 282-2165
Boone County HS 1,400/9-12
7056 Burlington Pike 41042 859-282-5655
Mark Raleigh, prin. Fax 282-5653
Jones MS 600/6-8
8000 Spruce Dr 41042 859-282-4610
David Rust, prin. Fax 282-2364
Ockerman MS 900/6-8
8300 US Highway 42 41042 859-282-3240
David Claggett, prin. Fax 282-3242
Other Schools – See Burlington, Hebron, Union

Beckfield College Post-Sec.
16 Spiral Dr 41042 859-371-9393
Gateway Community & Technical College Post-Sec.
500 Technology Way 41042 859-441-4500
Hair Design School Post-Sec.
7285 Turfway Rd 41042 859-283-2690
Heritage Academy 100/PK-12
7216 US Highway 42 41042 859-525-0213
Howard Davis, admin. Fax 525-0650
Lincoln College of Technology Post-Sec.
8095 Connector Dr 41042 859-282-9999
National College Post-Sec.
7627 Ewing Blvd 41042 859-525-6510

Fort Knox, Hardin, Pop. 9,669

Sullivan University Post-Sec.
63 Quartermaster St 40121 502-942-8500

Fort Mitchell, Kenton, Pop. 8,095
Beechwood ISD 1,100/PK-12
50 Beechwood Rd 41017 859-331-3250
Dr. Steve Hutton, supt. Fax 331-7528
www.beechwood.kyschools.us/
Beechwood JSHS 500/7-12
54 Beechwood Rd 41017 859-331-1220
Ben Zimmerman, prin. Fax 426-3744

Brown Mackie College Post-Sec.
309 Buttermilk Pike 41017 859-341-5627

Fort Thomas, Campbell, Pop. 16,124
Fort Thomas ISD 2,700/PK-12
28 N Fort Thomas Ave 41075 859-781-3333
Gene Kirchner, supt. Fax 442-4016
www.fortthomas.kyschools.us/
Highlands HS 800/9-12
2400 Memorial Pkwy 41075 859-781-5900
Brian Robinson, prin. Fax 441-9271
Highlands MS 600/6-8
2350 Memorial Pkwy 41075 859-441-5222
Mark Goetz, prin. Fax 441-9371

Fort Wright, Kenton, Pop. 5,642
Kenton County SD 14,400/PK-12
1055 Eaton Dr 41017 859-344-8888
Dr. Terri Cox-Cruey, supt. Fax 344-1531
www.kenton.kyschools.us/

Other Schools – See Crittenden, Edgewood, Independence, Taylor Mill

Frankfort, Franklin, Pop. 24,820
Frankfort ISD 600/PK-12
959 Leestown Ln 40601 502-875-8661
Rich Crowe, supt. Fax 875-8663
www.frankfort.kyschools.us
Capitol City Preparatory 50/Alt
328 Shelby St 40601 502-875-8650
Alan Spade, dir. Fax 875-8652
Frankfort HS 200/9-12
328 Shelby St 40601 502-875-8655
Michael Godbey, prin. Fax 875-8657

Franklin County SD 5,800/PK-12
916 E Main St 40601 502-695-6700
Chrissy Jones, supt. Fax 695-6708
www.franklin.kyschools.us
Academy 50/Alt
400 Democrat Dr 40601 502-695-6720
Melissa Rogers, prin. Fax 695-9618
Bondurant MS 600/6-8
300 Bondurant Dr 40601 502-875-8440
Casey Sparrow, prin. Fax 875-8442
Elkhorn MS 700/6-8
1060 E Main St 40601 502-695-6740
Willie Bartley, prin. Fax 695-6745
Franklin Co. Career & Technical Center Vo/Tech
1106 E Main St 40601 502-695-6790
Karen Schneider, dir. Fax 695-6791
Franklin County HS 900/9-12
1100 E Main St 40601 502-695-6750
Stirling Sampson, prin. Fax 695-6755
Western Hills HS 800/9-12
100 Doctors Dr 40601 502-875-8400
Rita Rector, prin. Fax 227-4568

Kentucky Tech System
500 Mero St 40601 502-564-4286
Dr. Dale Winkler, dir. Fax 564-4800
www.kytech.ky.gov
Other Schools – See Albany, Alexandria, Barbourville, Bardstown, Beattyville, Belfry, Bowling Green, Brandenburg, Carrollton, Corbin, Cynthiana, Dixon, Glasgow, Greensburg, Greenup, Harned, Harrodsburg, Hartford, Hebron, Hickman, Hindman, Hyden, Inez, Jackson, Lancaster, Lebanon, Liberty, Mc Kee, Manchester, Martin, Mayfield, Maysville, Monticello, Morgantown, Mount Sterling, Mount Vernon, Murray, Paducah, Pikeville, Pineville, Princeton, Richmond, Russell, Russell Springs, Russellville, Shelbyville, Shepherdsville, Somerset, Stanford, Tompkinsville, West Liberty, Whitesburg, Winchester

---

Frankfort Christian Academy 400/PK-12
1349 US Highway 421 S 40601 502-695-0744
Paul Sims, admin. Fax 695-8725
Kentucky State University Post-Sec.
400 E Main St 40601 502-597-6000

Franklin, Simpson, Pop. 8,221
Simpson County SD 3,100/PK-12
430 S College St 42134 270-586-8877
James Flynn, supt. Fax 586-2011
www.simpson.kyschools.us
Franklin Simpson HS 900/9-12
400 S College St 42134 270-586-3273
Tim Schlosser, prin. Fax 586-2021
Franklin Simpson MS 700/6-8
322 S College St 42134 270-586-4401
Craig Delk, prin. Fax 586-2048
Learning Opportunities Center 50/Alt
229 Joker Phillips St 42134 270-586-2039
Crystal Bayles, prin. Fax 586-2047

Frenchburg, Menifee, Pop. 482
Menifee County SD 1,100/PK-12
PO Box 110 40322 606-768-8002
Charles Mitchell, supt. Fax 768-8050
www.menifee.kyschools.us/
Menifee County HS 300/9-12
119 Indian Creek Rd 40322 606-768-8102
Brenda Warren, prin. Fax 768-8200

Fulton, Fulton, Pop. 2,370
Fulton ISD 400/PK-12
304 W State Line St 42041 270-472-1553
Tamara Smith, supt. Fax 472-6921
www.fultonind.kyschools.us
Fulton Independent HS 200/7-12
700 Stephen Beale Dr 42041 270-472-1741
Donna Garland, prin. Fax 472-6135

Georgetown, Scott, Pop. 28,525
Scott County SD 8,100/PK-12
PO Box 578 40324 502-863-3663
Patricia Putty, supt. Fax 863-5367
www.scott.kyschools.us
Elkhorn Crossing HS 9-12
2001 Frankfort Rd 40324 502-570-4920
Michelle Nichols, prin. Fax 873-2610
Georgetown MS 500/6-8
730 S Hamilton St 40324 502-863-3805
Rhonda Schornick, prin. Fax 867-1372
Ninth Grade Center 700/9-9
1072 Cardinal Dr 40324 502-863-4635
Dwayne Ellison, prin. Fax 868-0515
Royal Spring MS 700/6-8
332 Champion Way 40324 502-570-2390
Shannon Gullett, prin. Fax 863-3621
Scott County Cardinal Academy Alt
1076 Cardinal Dr 40324 502-863-4057
Joretta Crowe, dir. Fax 863-4432
Scott County MS 700/6-8
1036 Cardinal Dr 40324 502-863-7202
Jennifer Sutton, prin. Fax 863-7452
Scott County SHS 1,600/10-12
1080 Cardinal Dr 40324 502-863-4131
Frank Howatt, prin. Fax 867-0544

Georgetown College Post-Sec.
400 E College St 40324 502-863-8000

Glasgow, Barren, Pop. 13,692
Barren County SD 4,500/PK-12
202 W Washington St 42141 270-651-3787
Bo Matthews, supt. Fax 651-8836
www.barren.kyschools.us
Barren County HS 1,000/10-12
507 Trojan Trl 42141 270-651-6315
Steve Riley, prin. Fax 651-9211
Barren County MS 700/7-8
555 Trojan Trl 42141 270-651-4909
Lori Downs, prin. Fax 651-5137
College Street Campus Alt
304 E College St 42141 270-629-6554
Dan Belding, dir. Fax 629-2267
Trojan Academy 9-9
505 Trojan Trl 42141 270-629-5505
Amy Allen, prin. Fax 629-5504

Glasgow ISD 1,900/PK-12
PO Box 1239 42142 270-651-6757
D. Sean Howard, supt. Fax 651-9791
www.glasgow.kyschools.us/
Glasgow HS 600/9-12
1601 Columbia Ave 42141 270-651-8801
Keith Hale, prin. Fax 651-5189
Glasgow MS 400/6-8
105 Scottie Dr 42141 270-651-2256
Scott Jones, prin. Fax 651-3090
Happy Valley Learning Center 50/Alt
629 W Cherry St 42141 270-651-3804
Tommy Elliott, dir. Fax 651-7901
Success Academy 50/Alt
1601 Columbia Ave 42141 270-651-8801
Mike Vaught, dir. Fax 651-5189

Kentucky Tech System
Supt. — See Frankfort
Barren County Area Technology Center Vo/Tech
491 Trojan Trl 42141 270-651-2196
Ashley Bell, prin. Fax 651-2197

Bowling Green Technical College Post-Sec.
129 State Ave 42141 270-651-5373
Glasgow Christian Academy 100/PK-12
600 Old Cavalry Dr 42141 270-651-7729
Tracy Shaw, admin. Fax 651-6811
PJs College of Cosmetology Post-Sec.
920 Happy Valley Rd 42141 270-651-6553

Glendale, Hardin
Hardin County SD
Supt. — See Elizabethtown
East Hardin MS 700/6-8
129 College St 42740 270-369-7370
Daniel Lockwood, prin. Fax 369-6380

Goshen, Oldham, Pop. 900
Oldham County SD
Supt. — See Crestwood
North Oldham HS 900/9-12
1815 S Highway 1793 40026 502-228-0158
Lisa Jarrett, prin. Fax 228-7735
North Oldham MS 900/6-8
1801 S Highway 1793 40026 502-228-9998
Carrie Pitsenberger, prin. Fax 228-0985

Grayson, Carter, Pop. 4,170
Carter County SD 4,900/PK-12
228 S Carol Malone Blvd 41143 606-474-6696
Ronnie Dotson, supt. Fax 474-6125
www.carter.kyschools.us
East Carter County HS 800/9-12
405 Hitchins Rd 41143 606-474-5714
Larry Kiser, prin. Fax 475-9200
East Carter MS 600/6-8
1 Spirit Ln 41143 606-474-5156
Shannon Wilburn, prin. Fax 474-2034
Other Schools – See Olive Hill

Kentucky Christian University Post-Sec.
100 Academic Pkwy 41143 606-474-3000

Greensburg, Green, Pop. 2,133
Green County SD 1,700/K-12
PO Box 369 42743 270-932-5231
James Frank, supt. Fax 932-3624
www.green.kyschools.us/
Green County HS 500/9-12
PO Box 227 42743 270-932-6610
Karen Marcum, prin. Fax 932-3214
Green County MS 400/6-8
PO Box 176 42743 270-932-6615
Timothy Deaton, prin. Fax 932-7617

Kentucky Tech System
Supt. — See Frankfort
Green County Area Technology Center Vo/Tech
102 Carlisle Ave 42743 270-932-6605
Linda Floyd, prin. Fax 932-3072

Greenup, Greenup, Pop. 1,174
Greenup County SD 2,900/K-12
45 Musketeer Dr 41144 606-473-9819
Steve Hall, supt. Fax 473-5710
www.greenup.kyschools.us/
Greenup County HS 900/9-12
196 Musketeer Dr 41144 606-473-9812
Sue Davis, prin. Fax 473-7854
Other Schools – See South Shore, Wurtland

Kentucky Tech System
Supt. — See Frankfort
Greenup County Area Technology Center Vo/Tech
146 Musketeer Dr 41144 606-473-9344
Sarah Johnson, prin. Fax 473-9177

Greenville, Muhlenberg, Pop. 4,256
Muhlenberg County SD
Supt. — See Powderly

Muhlenberg County Career Alternative HS 100/Alt
3875 State Route 181 N 42345 270-338-5460
Jim Price, lead tchr. Fax 338-4918
Muhlenberg County Career & Tech Center Vo/Tech
201 Airport Rd 42345 270-338-1271
Donna Bumps, prin. Fax 338-6802
Muhlenberg County HS East Campus 700/9-10
2900 State Route 176 42345 270-338-9409
Donna Bumps, prin. Fax 338-9710
Muhlenberg County HS West Campus 700/11-12
501 Robert L Draper Way 42345 270-338-0040
Donna Bumps, prin. Fax 338-2442
Muhlenberg North MS 600/6-8
1000 N Main St 42345 270-338-3550
Steve Sparks, prin. Fax 338-2911
Muhlenberg South MS 600/6-8
200 Pritchett Dr 42345 270-338-4650
Brian Lile, prin. Fax 338-0151
Renaissance Center 50/Alt
203 Airport Rd 42345 270-338-0662
Randy McCarty, prin. Fax 338-2194

Hagerhill, Johnson
Johnson County SD
Supt. — See Paintsville
Johnson County Alternative S 50/Alt
7279 US Highway 321 S 41222 606-789-2077
Ben Hamilton, prin. Fax 789-2525

Hardinsburg, Breckinridge, Pop. 2,302
Breckinridge County SD 2,700/PK-12
86 Airport Rd 40143 270-756-3000
Janet L. Meeks, supt. Fax 756-6888
www.breck.kyschools.us
Other Schools – See Harned

Harlan, Harlan, Pop. 1,720
Harlan County SD 4,100/PK-12
251 Ball Park Rd 40831 606-573-4330
T. Michael Howard, supt. Fax 573-5767
www.harlan.kyschools.us
Other Schools – See Baxter

Harlan ISD 800/K-12
420 E Central St 40831 606-573-8700
David Johnson, supt. Fax 573-8711
www.harlan-ind.k12.ky.us
Harlan MSHS 500/5-12
420 E Central St 40831 606-573-8750
Stacy Noah, prin. Fax 573-8753

Jenny Lea Academy of Cosmetology Post-Sec.
114 N Cumberland Ave 40831 606-573-9817

Harned, Breckinridge
Breckinridge County SD
Supt. — See Hardinsburg
Breckinridge County HS 900/9-12
PO Box 10 40144 270-756-3080
Nick Carter, prin. Fax 756-3090
Breckinridge County MS 600/6-8
PO Box 39 40144 270-756-3060
Jayme Knochel, prin. Fax 756-3061

Kentucky Tech System
Supt. — See Frankfort
Breckinridge County Area Technology Ctr. Vo/Tech
PO Box 68 40144 270-756-2138
Thomas Thompson, prin. Fax 756-2878

Harrodsburg, Mercer, Pop. 8,110
Kentucky Tech System
Supt. — See Frankfort
Harrodsburg Area Technology Center Vo/Tech
PO Box 628 40330 859-734-9329
Tony Webb, prin. Fax 734-3613

Mercer County SD 3,100/PK-12
371 E Lexington St 40330 859-733-7000
Dennis Davis, supt. Fax 733-7004
www.mercer.kyschools.us/
Hughes Jones Harrodsburg Area Tech Ctr Vo/Tech
661 Tapp Rd 40330 859-734-9329
Fax 734-3613
King MS 700/6-8
1101 Moberly Rd 40330 859-733-7060
Terry Gordon, prin. Fax 733-7064
Mercer Central Alternative S 50/Alt
937 Moberly Rd 40330 859-733-7120
Gayla Jenkins, prin. Fax 733-7104
Mercer County 9th Grade Academy 200/9-9
937 Moberly Rd 40330 859-733-7100
Gayla Jenkins, prin. Fax 733-7104
Mercer County SHS 700/10-12
1124 Moberly Rd 40330 859-733-7160
Malissa Hutchins, prin. Fax 733-7164

Hartford, Ohio, Pop. 2,636
Kentucky Tech System
Supt. — See Frankfort
Ohio County Area Technology Center Vo/Tech
1406 S Main St 42347 270-274-9612
Brad Sisk, prin. Fax 274-9633

Ohio County SD 4,000/PK-12
PO Box 70 42347 270-298-3249
Scott Lewis, supt. Fax 298-3886
www.ohio.kyschools.us/
Ohio County HS 1,100/9-12
1400 S Main St 42347 270-274-3366
Greg Decker, prin. Fax 274-9482
Ohio County MS 600/7-8
1404 S Main St 42347 270-274-7893
Cheston Hoover, prin. Fax 274-7320

Hawesville, Hancock, Pop. 930
Hancock County SD 1,700/PK-12
83 State Route 3543 42348 270-927-6914
Kyle Estes, supt. Fax 927-6916
www.hancock.kyschools.us
Other Schools – See Lewisport

Hazard, Perry, Pop. 4,362
Hazard ISD 900/K-12
705 Main St 41701 606-436-3911
Sandra Johnson, supt. Fax 436-2742
www.hazard.kyschools.us
Hazard HS 300/9-12
157 Bulldog Ln 41701 606-439-1318
Donald Mobelini, prin. Fax 439-2285
Hazard MS 300/5-8
325 School St 41701 606-436-4421
Vivian Carter, prin. Fax 435-0407

Knott County SD
Supt. — See Hindman
Cordia HS 100/7-12
6050 Lotts Creek Rd 41701 606-785-4457
Jonathan Mullins, prin. Fax 785-4669

Perry County SD 4,300/PK-12
315 Park Ave 41701 606-439-5814
John Paul Amis, supt. Fax 439-2512
www.perry.kyschools.us/
Perry County Central HS 1,000/9-12
305 Park Ave 41701 606-439-5888
Neal Feltner, prin. Fax 439-2825
Other Schools – See Buckhorn

Hazard Community & Technical College Post-Sec.
1 Community College Dr 41701 606-436-4282

Hebron, Boone, Pop. 5,808
Boone County SD
Supt. — See Florence
Conner HS 1,200/9-12
3310 Cougar Path 41048 859-334-4400
Tim Hitzfield, prin. Fax 334-4406
Conner MS 1,000/6-8
3300 Cougar Path 41048 859-334-4410
James Brewer, prin. Fax 334-4435

Kentucky Tech System
Supt. — See Frankfort
Boone County Area Technology Center Vo/Tech
3320 Cougar Path 41048 859-689-7855
Garry Harper, prin. Fax 689-7828

Cornerstone Classical Christian Academy K-12
1746 Coachtrail Dr 41048 859-640-5147
John Davis, hdmstr.

Henderson, Henderson, Pop. 28,141
Henderson County SD 6,900/PK-12
1805 2nd St 42420 270-831-5000
Dr. Thomas Richey, supt. Fax 831-5009
www.henderson.kyschools.us/
Central Academy 100/Alt
851 Center St 42420 270-831-5100
Lisa Horn, prin. Fax 831-5103
Henderson County Area Technology Center Vo/Tech
2424 Zion Rd 42420 270-831-8850
Victor Doty, prin. Fax 831-8853
Henderson County HS 2,000/9-12
2424 Zion Rd 42420 270-831-8800
Sally Sugg, prin. Fax 831-8870
Henderson County North MS 800/6-8
1707 2nd St 42420 270-831-5060
Chad Thompson, prin. Fax 831-5064
Henderson County South MS 600/6-8
800 S Alves St 42420 270-831-5050
Ryan Reusch, prin. Fax 831-5058

Henderson Community College Post-Sec.
2660 S Green St 42420 270-827-1867
Pat Wilson Beauty College Post-Sec.
326 N Main St 42420 270-826-5195

Hickman, Fulton, Pop. 2,360
Fulton County SD 500/PK-12
2780 Moscow Ave 42050 270-236-3923
Dennis Bledsoe, supt. Fax 236-2184
www.fulton.kyschools.us
Fulton County HS 200/9-12
2740 Moscow Ave 42050 270-236-3904
Tracey Lamb, prin. Fax 236-9004

Kentucky Tech System
Supt. — See Frankfort
Fulton County Area Technology Center Vo/Tech
2720 Moscow Ave 42050 270-236-2517
Tom Pyron, prin. Fax 236-9395

Highland Heights, Campbell, Pop. 6,806

Northern Kentucky University Post-Sec.
400 Nunn Dr 41099 859-572-5100

Hi Hat, Floyd
Floyd County SD
Supt. — See Prestonsburg
South Floyd MSHS 300/6-12
299 Mt Raider Dr 41636 606-452-9600
Joe Marson, prin. Fax 452-2155

Hindman, Knott, Pop. 768
Kentucky Tech System
Supt. — See Frankfort
Knott County Area Technology Center Vo/Tech
1996 Highway 160 S 41822 606-785-5350
Patrick Goodin, prin. Fax 785-5445

Knott County SD 2,500/PK-12
PO Box 869 41822 606-785-3153
Kimberly King, supt. Fax 785-0800
www.knott.kyschools.us/
Knott County Central HS 700/9-12
76 Patriot Ln 41822 606-785-3166
Bobby Pollard, prin. Fax 785-3169
Other Schools – See Hazard

Hodgenville, Larue, Pop. 3,149
LaRue County SD 2,300/K-12
208 College St 42748 270-358-4111
Sam Sanders, supt. Fax 358-3053
www.larue.kyschools.us/
LaRue County HS 700/9-12
925 S Lincoln Blvd 42748 270-358-2210
Paul Mullins, prin. Fax 358-9469
LaRue County MS 500/6-8
911 S Lincoln Blvd 42748 270-358-3196
Jason Detre, prin. Fax 358-3946

Hopkinsville, Christian, Pop. 30,860
Christian County SD 8,800/K-12
PO Box 609 42241 270-887-7000
Mary Ann Gemmill, supt. Fax 887-1267
www.christian.kyschools.us/
Career & Technical Center Vo/Tech
705 N Elm St 42240 270-887-7030
Brad Hawkins, prin. Fax 887-1242
Christian County HS 1,300/9-12
220 Glass Ave 42240 270-887-7050
Michael Stevenson, prin. Fax 887-1294
Christian County MS 800/6-8
210 Glass Ave 42240 270-887-7070
Debbie Upton, prin. Fax 887-1189
Hopkinsville HS 1,100/9-12
430 Koffman Dr 42240 270-887-7110
Demetria Choice, prin. Fax 887-1118
Hopkinsville MS 700/6-8
434 Koffman Dr 42240 270-887-7130
Wendy Duvall, prin. Fax 887-1234
North Drive MS 400/6-8
831 North Dr 42240 270-887-7150
Kim Stevenson, prin. Fax 887-1287

Brown Mackie College Post-Sec.
4001 Fort Campbell Blvd 42240 270-886-1302
Heritage Christian Academy 400/PK-12
8349 Eagle Way 42240 270-885-2417
Linda Garris, hdmstr. Fax 885-0094
Hopkinsville Community College Post-Sec.
PO Box 2100 42241 270-707-3700
University Heights Academy 400/PK-12
1300 Academy Dr 42240 270-886-0254
Pam Nunn, prin. Fax 886-2716

Horse Cave, Hart, Pop. 2,268
Caverna ISD
Supt. — See Cave City
Caverna HS 200/9-12
2276 S Dixie St 42749 270-773-2828
Brad Phipps, prin. Fax 773-2825
Caverna MS 200/6-8
2278 S Dixie St 42749 270-773-4665
Barry Nesbitt, prin. Fax 773-4668

Hyden, Leslie, Pop. 362
Kentucky Tech System
Supt. — See Frankfort
Leslie County Area Technology Center Vo/Tech
PO Box 902 41749 606-672-2859
Dwight Lewis, prin. Fax 672-4943

Leslie County SD 1,700/PK-12
PO Box 949 41749 606-672-2397
Larry Sparks, supt. Fax 672-4224
www.leslie.kyschools.us
Leslie County HS 500/9-12
PO Box 970 41749 606-672-2337
Kevin Gay, prin. Fax 672-2858

Frontier Nursing University Post-Sec.
PO Box 528 41749 606-672-2312

Independence, Kenton, Pop. 24,387
Kenton County SD
Supt. — See Fort Wright
Kenton HS 1,600/9-12
11132 Madison Pike 41051 859-960-0100
Martha Setters, prin. Fax 960-0360
Success Academy Alt
11800 Taylor Mill Rd 41051 859-356-1502
Clay Dawson, prin. Fax 356-4594
Summit View MS 700/6-8
5002 Madison Pike 41051 859-363-4800
K.C. Ratliff, prin. Fax 363-4804
Twenhofel MS 800/6-8
11846 Taylor Mill Rd 41051 859-356-5559
Shannon Gross, prin. Fax 356-1137

Community Christian Academy 300/PK-12
11875 Taylor Mill Rd 41051 859-356-7990
Tara Bates, prin. Fax 356-7991

Inez, Martin, Pop. 715
Kentucky Tech System
Supt. — See Frankfort
Martin County Area Technology Center Vo/Tech
7900 Highway 645 41224 606-298-3879
Martha Williams, prin. Fax 298-7240

Martin County SD 2,300/PK-12
PO Box 366 41224 606-298-3572
Mark Blackburn, supt. Fax 298-4427
www.martin.kyschools.us/
Clark HS 600/9-12
1825 Blacklog Rd 41224 606-298-3591
Robbie Fletcher, prin. Fax 298-5148
Inez MS 300/6-8
5001 Middle School Dr 41224 606-298-3264
Brent Haney, prin. Fax 298-7314
Other Schools – See Warfield

Irvine, Estill, Pop. 2,691
Estill County SD 2,500/PK-12
PO Box 930 40336 606-723-2181
Bert Hensley, supt. Fax 723-6029
www.estill.kyschools.us/
Estill County HS 700/9-12
2675 Winchester Rd 40336 606-723-3537
Blain Click, prin. Fax 723-4894

Estill County MS 500/6-8
2805 Winchester Rd 40336 606-723-5136
Tim Burkhart, prin. Fax 723-2041

Jackson, Breathitt, Pop. 2,211
Breathitt County SD 1,900/PK-12
PO Box 750 41339 606-666-2491
Melanie Stevens, supt. Fax 666-2493
www.breathitt.kyschools.us
Breathitt County Day Treatment Center 50/Alt
3826 Highway 15 S 41339 606-666-8820
Sabrina Turner, lead tchr. Fax 666-8597
Breathitt County HS 500/9-12
2307 Bobcat Ln 41339 606-666-7511
Derek McKnight, prin. Fax 666-7765
Cadet Leadership and Educ Alternative 50/Alt
2665 Highway 30 W 41339 606-295-2267
Dean Smith, lead tchr. Fax 295-2274
Sebastian MS 200/7-8
244 L B J Rd 41339 606-666-8894
Reggie Hamilton, prin. Fax 666-5336

Jackson ISD 400/PK-12
940 Highland Ave 41339 606-666-4979
Timothy Spencer, supt. Fax 666-4350
www.jacksonind.kyschools.us/
Jackson City S 400/PK-12
940 Highland Ave 41339 606-666-5164
James Yount, prin. Fax 666-2555

Kentucky Tech System
Supt. — See Frankfort
Breathitt County Area Technology Center Vo/Tech
PO Box 786 41339 606-666-5153
Margaret Gross, prin. Fax 666-5394

Oakdale Christian Academy 50/7-12
5801 Beattyville Rd 41339 606-666-5422
Daniel Fisher, pres. Fax 666-5422

Jamestown, Russell, Pop. 1,780
Russell County SD 3,000/PK-12
404 S Main St 42629 270-343-3191
Kenny Pickett, supt. Fax 343-3072
www.russell.kyschools.us
Other Schools – See Russell Springs

Jeffersontown, Jefferson, Pop. 25,990
Jefferson County SD
Supt. — See Louisville
Jeffersontown HS Magnet Career Academy 1,200/9-12
9600 Old Six Mile Ln 40299 502-485-8275
Martin Pollio, prin. Fax 485-8832

Jenkins, Letcher, Pop. 2,198
Jenkins ISD 600/PK-12
PO Box 74 41537 606-832-2183
Deborah Watts, supt. Fax 832-2181
www.jenkins.kyschools.us
Jenkins MSHS 300/7-12
PO Box 552 41537 606-832-2184
David Loo, prin. Fax 832-4283

La Grange, Oldham, Pop. 7,910
Oldham County SD
Supt. — See Crestwood
Buckner Alternative HS 100/Alt
1350 N Highway 393 40031 502-222-3767
Jonathan Wosoba, prin. Fax 222-3769
Oldham County HS 1,400/9-12
1150 N Highway 393 40031 502-222-9461
Brent Deaves, prin. Fax 222-0558
Oldham County MS 800/6-8
4305 Brown Blvd 40031 502-222-1451
Chris Kraft, prin. Fax 222-5178

Lancaster, Garrard, Pop. 3,397
Garrard County SD 2,700/PK-12
322 W Maple Ave 40444 859-792-3018
Paul Mullins, supt. Fax 792-4733
www.garrard.kyschools.us
Garrard County HS 700/9-12
599 Industry Rd 40444 859-792-2146
Kalem Gresham, prin. Fax 792-4352
Garrard MS 600/6-8
304 W Maple Ave 40444 859-792-2108
Andrew Pickerill, prin. Fax 792-9618

Kentucky Tech System
Supt. — See Frankfort
Garrard County Area Technology Center Vo/Tech
306 W Maple Ave 40444 859-792-2144
David Horseman, prin. Fax 792-4058

Lawrenceburg, Anderson, Pop. 10,349
Anderson County SD 4,000/PK-12
1160 Bypass N 40342 502-839-3406
Sheila Mitchell, supt. Fax 839-1298
www.anderson.kyschools.us
Anderson County HS 1,200/9-12
1 Bearcat Dr 40342 502-839-5118
Ronnie Fields, prin. Fax 839-3486
Anderson County MS 900/6-8
1 Mustang Trl 40342 502-839-9261
Gina Fultz, prin. Fax 839-2534

Christian Academy of Lawrenceburg 100/PK-12
126 N Main St 40342 502-839-9992
Steve Carmichael, admin. Fax 839-3728

Lebanon, Marion, Pop. 5,374
Kentucky Tech System
Supt. — See Frankfort
Marion County Area Technology Center Vo/Tech
721 E Main St 40033 270-692-3155
Brandon Bardin, prin. Fax 692-1357

Marion County SD 3,200/PK-12
755 E Main St 40033 270-692-3721
Taylora Schlosser, supt. Fax 692-1899
www.marion.kyschools.us/
Lebanon MS 400/6-8
200 Corporate Dr 40033 270-692-3441
Todd Farmer, prin. Fax 692-0266
Marion County HS 1,000/9-12
735 E Main St 40033 270-692-6066
Mike Abell, prin. Fax 692-6248
St. Charles MS 300/6-8
1155 Highway 327 40033 270-692-4578
Buffy Mann, prin. Fax 692-1176
Spalding Academy 50/Alt
721 E Main St 40033 270-692-0690
Eric King, prin.

Leitchfield, Grayson, Pop. 6,624
Grayson County SD 4,300/PK-12
PO Box 4009 42755 270-259-4011
Barry Anderson, supt. Fax 259-4756
www.grayson.kyschools.us
Grayson County Alternative S 50/Alt
340 School House Rd 42754 270-259-2800
Kelly Shawn Majors, dir. Fax 259-2802
Grayson County HS 1,300/9-12
340 School House Rd 42754 270-259-4078
Todd Johnston, prin. Fax 259-6131
Grayson County MS 900/6-8
726 John Hill Taylor Dr 42754 270-259-4175
Jim Blain, prin. Fax 259-5875
Grayson County Technology Center Vo/Tech
252 School House Rd 42754 270-259-3195
Cynthia Smith, dir. Fax 259-8082

Leitchfield Christian Academy 100/PK-12
106 E Walnut St 42754 270-259-4076
Linda Gentry, prin. Fax 259-3240

Lewisport, Hancock, Pop. 1,650
Hancock County SD
Supt. — See Hawesville
Hancock County HS 500/9-12
80 State Route 271 S 42351 270-927-6953
Rick Lasley, prin. Fax 927-8677
Hancock County MS 400/6-8
100 State Route 271 S 42351 270-927-6255
Diane Hatchett, prin. Fax 927-9895

Lexington, Fayette, Pop. 288,987
Fayette County SD 38,300/PK-12
701 E Main St 40502 859-381-4100
Tom Shelton, supt. Fax 381-4303
www.fcps.net
Beaumont MS 1,000/6-8
2080 Georgian Way 40504 859-381-3094
Kate McAnelly, prin. Fax 381-3109
Bryan Station HS 1,900/9-12
201 Eastin Rd 40505 859-381-3308
Mike Henderson, prin. Fax 381-3330
Bryan Station MS 600/6-8
1865 Wickland Dr 40505 859-381-3288
Lester Diaz, prin. Fax 381-3292
Clark MS 900/6-8
3341 Clays Mill Rd 40503 859-381-3036
Lisa Goodin, prin. Fax 381-3037
Clay HS 2,200/9-12
2100 Fontaine Rd 40502 859-381-3423
Greg Quenon, prin. Fax 381-3430
Crawford MS 500/6-8
1813 Charleston Dr 40505 859-381-3370
Mike Jones, prin. Fax 381-3378
Dunbar HS 2,100/9-12
1600 Man O War Blvd 40513 859-381-3546
Betsy Rains, prin. Fax 381-3560
Eastside Technical Center Vo/Tech
2208 Liberty Rd 40509 859-381-3740
Joe Norman, prin. Fax 381-3747
Hayes MS 900/6-8
260 Richardson Pl 40509 859-381-4920
Sherri Heise, prin. Fax 381-4937
King Academy of Excellence 100/Alt
2200 Liberty Rd 40509 859-381-4040
Mark Sellers, dir. Fax 381-4031
Lafayette HS 1,900/9-12
401 Reed Ln 40503 859-381-3474
Bryne Jacobs, prin. Fax 381-3487
Learning Center at Linlee Alt
2420 Spurr Rd 40511 859-381-0597
Ron Chi, prin. Fax 246-1135
Leestown MS 500/6-8
2010 Leestown Rd 40511 859-381-3181
Cynthia Lawson, prin. Fax 381-3180
Lexington Traditional Magnet MS 800/6-8
350 N Limestone 40508 859-381-3192
Sharma Nachlinger, prin. Fax 381-3199
Locust Trace AgriScience Farm Vo/Tech
242 LocustFarm Rd 40511 859-381-3990
Joe Norman, prin. Fax 381-3989
Morton MS 800/6-8
1225 Tates Creek Rd 40502 859-381-3533
Rhonda Runyon, prin. Fax 381-3536
Opportunity Middle College S 100/Alt
164 Opportunity Way 40511 859-246-6379
Frank LaBoone, prin. Fax 246-6889
School for Creative and Performing Arts 300/4-8
400 Lafayette Pkwy 40503 859-381-3332
Beth Randolph, prin. Fax 381-3334
Southern MS 700/6-8
400 Wilson Downing Rd 40517 859-381-3582
Jane Dreidame, prin. Fax 381-3588
Southside Technical Center Vo/Tech
1800 Harrodsburg Rd 40504 859-381-3603
Daryn Morris, prin. Fax 381-3807
Stables Alt
4089 Iron Works Pkwy 40511 859-333-5827
Racher Baker, dir. Fax 381-4312
Tates Creek HS 1,700/9-12
1111 Centre Pkwy 40517 859-381-3620
Sam Meaux, prin. Fax 381-3635
Tates Creek MS 700/6-8
1105 Centre Pkwy 40517 859-381-3052
Eric Thornsbury, prin. Fax 381-3053
Winburn MS 600/6-8
1060 Winburn Dr 40511 859-381-3967
Tina Stevenson, prin. Fax 381-3971
Woodson Academy Alt
1813 Charleston Dr 40505 859-381-3933
Jaynae Laine, prin. Fax 381-4792

Blue Grass Baptist S 200/K-12
3743 Red River Dr 40517 859-272-1217
Dr. Kevin Davidson, prin. Fax 273-8658
Bluegrass Community & Technical College Post-Sec.
470 Cooper Dr 40506 859-246-6200
Employment Solutions Coll for Tech Educ Post-Sec.
1165 Centre Pkwy Ste 120 40517 859-272-5225
ITT Technical Institute Post-Sec.
2473 Fortune Dr Ste 180 40509 859-246-3300
Kaufman Beauty School Post-Sec.
701 E High St 40502 859-266-0693
Lexington Catholic HS 800/9-12
2250 Clays Mill Rd 40503 859-277-7183
Sally Stevens, prin. Fax 276-5086
Lexington Christian Academy 1,200/PK-12
450 W Reynolds Rd 40503 859-422-5700
Ollie Gibbs, hdmstr. Fax 223-3769
Lexington Theological Seminary Post-Sec.
631 S Limestone 40508 859-252-0361
MedTech College Post-Sec.
1648 McGrathiana Pkwy # 200 40511 859-410-2110
National College Post-Sec.
2376 Sir Barton Way 40509 859-253-0621
St. Joseph's Hospital Post-Sec.
1 Saint Joseph Dr 40504 859-278-3436
Sayre S 500/PK-12
194 N Limestone 40507 859-254-1361
Stephen Manella, head sch Fax 231-0508
Spencerian College Post-Sec.
1575 Winchester Rd 40505 859-223-9608
Strayer University Post-Sec.
220 Lexington Green Cir 550 40503 859-971-4400
Sullivan University Post-Sec.
2355 Harrodsburg Rd 40504 859-276-4357
Transylvania University Post-Sec.
300 N Broadway 40508 859-233-8300
University of Kentucky 40506 Post-Sec.
859-257-9000
Univ. of Kentucky Chandler Medical Ctr. Post-Sec.
103 Administration Plz A311 40536 859-323-5126

Liberty, Casey, Pop. 2,153
Casey County SD 2,300/PK-12
1922 N US 127 42539 606-787-6941
Linda Hatter, supt. Fax 787-5231
www.casey.kyschools.us/
Casey County HS 700/9-12
1841 E KY 70 42539 606-787-6151
Barry Lee, prin. Fax 787-8654
Casey County MS 300/7-8
1673 E KY 70 42539 606-787-6769
Kathy Fogle, prin. Fax 787-5337

Kentucky Tech System
Supt. — See Frankfort
Casey County Area Technology Center Vo/Tech
1723 E KY 70 42539 606-787-6241
Carmela Clark, prin. Fax 787-6243

Lick Creek, Pike, Pop. 221
Pike County SD
Supt. — See Pikeville
East Ridge HS 700/9-12
19471 Lick Mountain Rd 41540 606-835-2811
Kevin Justice, prin. Fax 835-2899

London, Laurel, Pop. 7,883
Laurel County SD 9,200/PK-12
718 N Main St 40741 606-862-4600
Doug Bennett, supt. Fax 862-4601
www.laurel.k12.ky.us
McDaniel Learning Center 50/Alt
275 S Laurel Rd 40744 606-862-4781
Roger Wright, prin. Fax 862-4782
North Laurel HS 1,400/9-12
1300 E Hal Rogers Pkwy 40741 606-862-4699
Michael Black, prin. Fax 862-4701
North Laurel MS 1,100/6-8
101 Johnson Rd 40741 606-862-4715
Steve Morris, prin. Fax 862-4717
South Laurel HS 1,300/9-12
201 S Laurel Rd 40744 606-862-4727
David Cummins, prin. Fax 862-4728
South Laurel MS 1,100/6-8
223 S Laurel Rd 40744 606-862-4745
Jeff Reed, prin. Fax 862-4746

Lost Creek, Breathitt

Riverside Christian S 100/K-12
114 Riverside School Rd 41348 606-666-2359
Lorie Keck, prin. Fax 666-5211

Louisa, Lawrence, Pop. 2,448
Lawrence County SD 2,500/PK-12
50 Bulldog Ln 41230 606-638-9671
Mike Armstrong, supt. Fax 638-0128
www.lawrence.kyschools.us
Lawrence County HS 700/9-12
100 Bulldog Ln 41230 606-638-9676
Lonnie Cook, prin. Fax 638-3227
Louisa MS 300/6-8
9 Bulldog Ln 41230 606-638-4090
Thomas Castle, prin. Fax 638-4865

Louisville, Jefferson, Pop. 248,762
Jefferson County SD 94,400/PK-12
PO Box 34020 40232 502-485-3011
Dr. Donna Hargens, supt. Fax 485-3991
www.jefferson.k12.ky.us
Academy @ Shawnee 500/K-12
4001 Herman St 40212 502-485-8326
Keith Look, prin. Fax 485-8738
Atherton HS 1,200/9-12
3000 Dundee Rd 40205 502-485-8202
Tom Aberli, prin. Fax 485-8985
Ballard HS 1,800/9-12
6000 Brownsboro Rd 40222 502-485-8206
James Jury, prin. Fax 485-8856
Barret MS 600/6-8
2561 Grinstead Dr 40206 502-485-8207
Tom Wortham, prin. Fax 485-8579

Breckinridge Metropolitan HS 100/Alt
1128 E Broadway 40204 502-485-6678
Stuart Cripe, prin. Fax 485-6680
Brown S 700/K-12
546 S 1st St 40202 502-485-8216
Timothy Healy, prin. Fax 485-8741
Buechel Metropolitan HS 200/Alt
1960 Bashford Manor Ln 40218 502-485-8316
Joey Riddle, prin. Fax 485-8791
Butler HS 1,700/9-12
2222 Crums Ln 40216 502-485-8220
William Allen, prin. Fax 485-8517
Carrithers MS 500/6-8
4320 Billtown Rd 40299 502-485-8224
Pat Gausepohl, prin. Fax 485-8394
Central HS Magnet Career Academy 1,100/9-12
1130 W Chestnut St 40203 502-485-8226
Dan Withers, prin. Fax 485-7034
Conway MS 900/6-8
6300 Terry Rd 40258 502-485-8233
Gregory Fehr, prin. Fax 485-8076
Doss HS Magnet Career Academy 900/9-12
7601 Saint Andrews Church 40214 502-485-8239
Ken Moeller, prin. Fax 485-8080
DuPont Manual HS 1,900/9-12
120 W Lee St 40208 502-485-8241
Larry Wooldridge, prin. Fax 485-8035
DuValle Education Center 100/Alt
3610 Bohne Ave 40211 502-485-3558
Connie Hayes, prin. Fax 485-6790
Farnsley MS 1,100/6-8
3400 Lees Ln 40216 502-485-8242
Rob Stephenson, prin. Fax 485-8663
Highland MS 1,000/6-8
1700 Norris Pl 40205 502-485-8266
Steven Heckman, prin. Fax 485-8831
Iroquois HS Magnet Career Academy 1,100/9-12
4615 Taylor Blvd 40215 502-485-8269
Chris Perkins, prin. Fax 485-8033
Jefferson County HS 600/9-12
900 S Floyd St 40203 502-485-3173
Jerry Keepers, prin. Fax 485-3671
Jefferson County Traditional MS 900/6-8
1418 Morton Ave 40204 502-485-8272
Teri Reed, prin. Fax 485-8635
Jefferson MS 1,000/6-8
1501 Rangeland Rd 40219 502-485-8273
Kimberly Gregory, prin. Fax 485-8045
Johnson Traditional MS 900/6-8
2509 Wilson Ave 40210 502-485-8277
Beverly Johnson, prin. Fax 485-8679
Kammerer MS 900/6-8
7315 Wesboro Rd 40222 502-485-8279
Stacie Gamble, prin. Fax 485-8618
Kennedy Metro MS 100/5-8
4515 Taylorsville Rd 40220 502-485-6950
Donald Reid, prin. Fax 491-7290
Knight MS 500/6-8
9803 Blue Lick Rd 40229 502-485-8287
Faith Stroud, prin. Fax 485-8073
Lassiter MS 800/6-8
8200 Candleworth Dr 40214 502-485-8288
Jonathan Cesler, prin. Fax 485-8373
Liberty HS 300/Alt
3307 E Indian Trl 40213 502-485-7100
David Armour, prin. Fax 485-7102
Louisville Male HS 1,700/9-12
4409 Preston Hwy 40213 502-485-8292
Ted Boehm, prin. Fax 485-8770
Maryhurst S 100/Alt
1015 Dorsey Ln 40223 502-245-1576
Michele Eckels, prin. Fax 245-7470
Meyzeek MS 1,000/6-8
828 S Jackson St 40203 502-485-8299
Chris Burba, prin. Fax 485-8641
Moore Traditional HS 700/9-12
6415 Outer Loop 40228 502-485-8304
Vicki Lete, prin. Fax 485-8168
Myers MS 700/6-8
3741 Pulliam Dr 40218 502-485-8305
Jack Baldwin, prin. Fax 485-8157
Newburg MS 900/6-8
4901 Exeter Ave 40218 502-485-8306
Dianna Drake-Hicks, prin. Fax 485-8883
Noe MS 1,300/6-8
121 W Lee St 40208 502-485-8307
Janice McDowell, prin. Fax 485-8056
Olmsted Academy North 800/6-8
4530 Bellevue Ave 40215 502-485-8331
Bill Perkins, prin. Fax 485-8381
Olmsted Academy South 700/6-8
5650 Southern Pkwy 40214 502-485-8270
Angela Allen, prin. Fax 485-8380
Phoenix S of Discovery 300/6-12
10200 Dixie Hwy 40272 502-485-7700
David Bennett, prin. Fax 485-7701
Pleasure Ridge Park HS Magnet Academy 1,900/9-12
5901 Greenwood Rd 40258 502-485-8311
David Johnson, prin. Fax 485-8093
Ramsey MS 700/6-8
6409 Gellhaus Ln 40299 502-485-8391
Jennifer Colley, prin. Fax 485-8973
Seneca HS Magnet Career Academy 1,500/9-12
3510 Goldsmith Ln 40220 502-485-8323
Michelle Dillard, prin. Fax 485-8174
Southern HS Magnet Career Academy 1,200/9-12
8620 Preston Hwy 40219 502-485-8330
Bryce Hibbard, prin. Fax 485-8029
Waggener Traditional HS 800/9-12
330 S Hubbards Ln 40207 502-485-8340
Katy Zeitz, prin. Fax 485-8140
Western Math Science Tech Magnet HS 800/9-12
2501 Rockford Ln 40216 502-485-8344
David Mike, prin. Fax 485-8969
Western MS 300/6-8
2201 W Main St 40212 502-485-8345
Bill Anderson, prin. Fax 485-8047
Westport MS and Fine Arts Academy 800/6-8
8100 Westport Rd 40222 502-485-8346
Staci Eddleman, prin. Fax 485-8590

Youth Performing Arts JSHS 7-12
1517 S 2nd St 40208 502-485-8355
Larry Wooldridge, prin. Fax 485-8808
Other Schools – See Fairdale, Fern Creek, Jeffersontown, Middletown, Valley Station

---

Assumption HS 900/9-12
2170 Tyler Ln 40205 502-458-9551
Rebecca Henle, prin. Fax 454-8411
ATA College Post-Sec.
10180 Linn Station Rd #A200 40223 502-371-8383
Bellarmine University Post-Sec.
2001 Newburg Rd 40205 502-272-8131
Beth Haven Christian S 200/PK-12
5515 Johnsontown Rd 40272 502-937-3516
Fax 937-3364
Brown Mackie College Post-Sec.
3605 Fern Valley Rd 40219 502-968-7191
Christian Academy of Louisville 2,400/PK-12
700 S English Station Rd 40245 502-244-3225
Timothy Greener, supt. Fax 244-1824
Covenant Classical Academy 50/K-10
13902 Factory Ln 40245 502-243-0404
R. Lance Harris, hdmstr. Fax 243-0404
Daymar College Post-Sec.
4112 Fern Valley Rd 40219 502-495-1040
Daymar College - Online Post-Sec.
3309 Collins Ln 40245 888-338-3538
DeSales HS 300/9-12
425 W Kenwood Dr 40214 502-368-6519
Suzanne Barnett, prin. Fax 366-6172
DeVry University Post-Sec.
10172 Linn Station Rd # 300 40223 502-326-2860
Evangel Christian S 200/K-12
5400 Minor Ln 40219 502-968-7744
Dr. Roger Hoagland, supt. Fax 400-1906
Galen College of Nursing Post-Sec.
1031 Zorn Ave Ste 400 40207 502-410-6200
Hair Design School Post-Sec.
1049 Bardstown Rd 40204 502-459-8150
Hair Design School Post-Sec.
5120 Dixie Hwy 40216 502-447-0111
Hair Design School Post-Sec.
5314 Bardstown Rd 40291 502-499-0070
Holy Cross HS 200/9-12
5144 Dixie Hwy 40216 502-447-4363
Danielle Wiegandt, prin. Fax 448-1062
ITT Technical Institute Post-Sec.
9500 Ormsby Station Rd #100 40223 502-327-7424
Jefferson Community & Technical College Post-Sec.
109 E Broadway 40202 502-213-5333
Kentucky Country Day S 900/PK-12
4100 Springdale Rd 40241 502-423-0440
Brad Lyman, hdmstr. Fax 423-0445
Kentucky School for the Blind Post-Sec.
1867 Frankfort Ave 40206 502-897-1583
Louisville Bible College Post-Sec.
8211 Restoration Dr 40228 502-231-5221
Louisville Collegiate S 700/PK-12
2427 Glenmary Ave 40204 502-479-0340
Scott Prince, head sch Fax 454-8549
Louisville Jr. Academy 100/K-12
2988 Newburg Rd 40205 502-452-2965
David Matthews, prin. Fax 452-2965
Louisville Presbyterian Seminary Post-Sec.
1044 Alta Vista Rd 40205 502-895-3411
Mercy Academy HS 600/9-12
5801 Fegenbush Ln 40228 502-671-2010
Amy Elstone, prin. Fax 491-0661
National College Post-Sec.
4205 Dixie Hwy 40216 502-447-7634
Nativity Academy at St. Boniface 100/6-8
531 E Liberty St 40202 502-855-3300
Meghan Weyland M.Ed., prin. Fax 562-2192
Paul Mitchell The School Post-Sec.
156 N Hurstbourne Pkwy 40222 502-583-1018
Pitt Academy 50/PK-12
6010 Preston Hwy 40219 502-966-6979
Renee Doty, prin. Fax 962-8878
Portland Christian S East 100/K-12
8509 Westport Rd 40242 502-429-3727
Mary Jodell Seay, dir. Fax 326-2682
Presentation Academy 300/9-12
861 S 4th St 40203 502-583-5935
Barbara Wine, prin. Fax 583-1342
Sacred Heart Academy 800/9-12
3175 Lexington Rd 40206 502-897-6097
Mary McCoy, prin. Fax 893-0120
Sacred Heart S for the Arts 200/K-12
3105 Lexington Rd 40206 502-897-1816
Lynn Slaughter, dir. Fax 896-3927
St. Francis HS 100/9-12
233 W Broadway 40202 502-736-1000
Alexandra Thurstone, head sch Fax 736-1049
St. Xavier HS 1,500/9-12
1609 Poplar Level Rd 40217 502-637-4712
Francisco Espinosa, prin. Fax 634-2171
Simmons College of Kentucky Post-Sec.
1018 S 7th St 40203 502-776-1443
Southern Baptist Theological Seminary Post-Sec.
2825 Lexington Rd 40280 502-897-4011
Spalding University Post-Sec.
845 S 3rd St 40203 502-585-9911
Spencerian College Post-Sec.
4627 Dixie Hwy 40216 502-447-1000
Sullivan College of Technology & Design Post-Sec.
3901 Atkinson Square Dr 40218 800-844-6528
Sullivan University Post-Sec.
3101 Bardstown Rd 40205 502-456-6505
Trend Setter's Academy of Beauty Culture Post-Sec.
7283 Dixie Hwy 40258 502-937-6816
Trend Setter's Academy of Beauty Culture Post-Sec.
8111 Preston Hwy 40219 502-962-7710
Trinity HS 1,400/9-12
4011 Shelbyville Rd 40207 502-895-9427
Daniel Zoeller, prin. Fax 895-6837
University of Louisville Post-Sec.
2301 S 3rd St 40208 502-852-5555
Valiant Christian Academy 100/PK-12
5627 New Cut Rd 40214 502-368-0080
Kristine Salvo, admin. Fax 361-5179

Valor Traditional Academy 100/K-12
11501 Schlatter Rd 40291 502-239-3345
JP Fugate, hdmstr. Fax 239-3344
Walden S 300/K-12
4238 Westport Rd 40207 502-893-0433
Ned Southworth, hdmstr. Fax 895-8668
Whitefield Academy 800/PK-12
7711 Fegenbush Ln 40228 502-239-2509
Jacob Saltsman, prin. Fax 239-3144

Ludlow, Kenton, Pop. 4,360
Ludlow ISD 900/PK-12
525 Elm St 41016 859-261-8210
Mike Borchers, supt. Fax 291-6811
www.ludlow.kyschools.us/
Ludlow HS 500/7-12
515 Elm St 41016 859-261-8211
Joe Beard, prin. Fax 655-7536

Mc Kee, Jackson, Pop. 793
Jackson County SD 2,300/PK-12
PO Box 217 40447 606-287-7181
Mike Smith, supt. Fax 287-8469
www.jackson.kyschools.us
Jackson County HS 600/9-12
PO Box 427 40447 606-287-7155
Keith Hays, prin. Fax 287-2123
Jackson County MS 500/6-8
PO Box 1329 40447 606-287-8351
Stephen Gabbard, prin. Fax 287-8360

Kentucky Tech System
Supt. — See Frankfort
Jackson County Area Technology Center Vo/Tech
PO Box 1509 40447 606-287-2163
Alonzo Moore, prin. Fax 287-7538

Madisonville, Hopkins, Pop. 19,131
Hopkins County SD 6,900/PK-12
320 S Seminary St 42431 270-825-6000
James Stevens, supt. Fax 825-6072
www.hopkins.kyschools.us
Browning Springs MS 500/6-8
357 W Arch St 42431 270-825-6006
Paula Wampler, prin. Fax 825-6009
Hopkins County Academy 50/Alt
150 School St 42431 270-825-6122
Pam Todd, prin. Fax 825-6140
Hopkins County Central HS 1,000/9-12
6625 Hopkinsville Rd 42431 270-825-6133
Tommy Burrough, prin. Fax 825-6135
Madison MS 500/6-8
510 Brown Rd 42431 270-825-6160
Tamara Winters, prin. Fax 825-6016
Madisonville North Hopkins HS 1,000/9-12
4515 Hanson Rd 42431 270-825-6017
Deanna Ashby, prin. Fax 825-6045
Other Schools – See Nortonville

Daymar College Post-Sec.
1105 National Mine Rd 42431 270-643-0312
Madisonville Community College Post-Sec.
2000 College Dr 42431 270-821-2250

Manchester, Clay, Pop. 1,245
Clay County SD 3,500/PK-12
128 Richmond Rd 40962 606-598-2168
Reecia Samples, supt. Fax 598-7829
www.clay.kyschools.us
Clay County HS 1,000/9-12
415 Clay County High Rd 40962 606-598-3737
Michael Gregory, prin. Fax 598-8976
Clay County MS 500/7-8
239 Richmond Rd 40962 606-598-1810
Steve Burchfield, prin. Fax 598-1230
Horse Creek Learning Center Alt S 50/Alt
239 Richmond Rd 40962 606-598-1601
James Hollin, dir. Fax 599-0991

Kentucky Tech System
Supt. — See Frankfort
Clay County Area Technology Center Vo/Tech
1097 N Highway 11 40962 606-598-2194
Anthony Young, prin. Fax 598-4201

Southeast School of Cosmetology Post-Sec.
PO Box 493 40962 606-598-7901

Marion, Crittenden, Pop. 3,006
Crittenden County SD 1,300/K-12
601 W Elm St 42064 270-965-3525
Dr. Rachel Yarbrough, supt. Fax 965-9064
www.crittenden.kyschools.us/
Crittenden County HS 400/9-12
519 1/2 W Gum St 42064 270-965-2248
Rhonda Callaway, prin. Fax 965-2797
Crittenden County MS 300/6-8
519 W Gum St 42064 270-965-5221
Teresa Marshall, prin. Fax 965-5082

Martin, Floyd, Pop. 630
Floyd County SD
Supt. — See Prestonsburg
Renaissance Learning Center 50/Alt
PO Box 1390 41649 606-285-3634
Roy Johnson, dir. Fax 285-3031

Kentucky Tech System
Supt. — See Frankfort
Floyd County Area Technology Center Vo/Tech
1024 KY Route 122 41649 606-285-3088
Lenville Martin, prin. Fax 285-0274

Piarist S 100/6-12
PO Box 870 41649 606-285-3950
Rev. Thomas Carroll, prin. Fax 285-3950

Mayfield, Graves, Pop. 9,719
Graves County SD 4,700/PK-12
2290 State Route 121 N 42066 270-328-2656
Pete Galloway, supt. Fax 328-1561
www.graves.kyschools.us

Gateway Academy HS 50/Alt
100 E Lockridge St 42066 270-328-4979
Donna Crouch, prin. Fax 247-0051
Genesis Alternative S 50/Alt
4747 Old Dublin Rd 42066 270-623-6144
Earl McManus, prin. Fax 623-6146
Graves County HS 1,400/9-12
1107 W Housman St 42066 270-674-6242
Matt Madding, prin. Fax 247-8540
Graves County MS 700/7-8
625 Jimtown Rd 42066 270-674-4890
Andy Williams, prin. Fax 251-3693
Mayfield Youth Development Center 50/Alt
3179 State Route 45 S 42066 270-247-3237
Earl McManus, prin. Fax 247-2605

Kentucky Tech System
Supt. — See Frankfort
Mayfield/Graves County Area Tech Center Vo/Tech
710 Douthitt St 42066 270-247-4710
Steve Arant, prin. Fax 247-4721

Mayfield ISD 1,400/PK-12
914 E College St 42066 270-247-3868
Lonnie Burgett, supt. Fax 247-3854
www.mayfield.kyschools.us/
Mayfield HS 400/9-12
700 Douthitt St 42066 270-247-4461
Don Hubbard, prin. Fax 247-9624
Mayfield MS 300/6-8
112 W College St 42066 270-247-7521
Kim Reed, prin. Fax 247-8297

Mid-Continent University Post-Sec.
99 E Powell Rd 42066 270-247-8521
Northside Baptist Christian S 100/PK-12
711 N 12th St 42066 270-247-0516
Emily Burge, prin. Fax 247-7125

Maysville, Mason, Pop. 8,803
Kentucky Tech System
Supt. — See Frankfort
Mason County Area Technology Center Vo/Tech
646 Kenton Station Rd 41056 606-759-7101
Jeremy McCloud, prin. Fax 759-7568

Mason County SD 2,900/PK-12
PO Box 130 41056 606-564-5563
Tim Moore, supt. Fax 564-5392
www.masoncoschools.com
Mason County HS 800/9-12
1320 US Highway 68 41056 606-564-3393
Steven Appelman, prin. Fax 564-5360
Mason County MS 600/6-8
420 Chenault Dr 41056 606-564-6748
Justin Moore, prin. Fax 564-5958

Maysville Community & Technical College Post-Sec.
1755 US Highway 68 41056 606-759-7141
St. Patrick S 300/PK-12
318 Limestone St 41056 606-564-5949
Anne Poe, prin. Fax 564-8795

Middlesboro, Bell, Pop. 10,068
Middlesboro ISD 1,400/K-12
PO Box 959 40965 606-242-8800
Dr. Rita Cook, supt. Fax 242-8805
www.mboro.kyschools.us/
Middlesboro Central Alternative HS 50/Alt
PO Box 959 40965 606-242-8818
Steve Spangler, prin. Fax 242-8815
Middlesboro HS 500/9-12
4404 W Cumberland Ave 40965 606-242-8820
Sheila Smith, prin. Fax 242-8825
Middlesboro MS 300/6-8
4400 W Cumberland Ave 40965 606-242-8880
Terry Bradley, prin. Fax 242-8885

Collins School of Cosmetology Post-Sec.
111 W Chester Ave 40965 606-248-3602
Gateway Christian S, PO Box Z 40965 PK-10
William Bingham, prin. 606-248-0557

Middletown, Jefferson, Pop. 7,092
Jefferson County SD
Supt. — See Louisville
Crosby MS 1,300/6-8
303 Gatehouse Ln 40243 502-485-8235
Michael Kelly, prin. Fax 485-8424
Eastern HS 2,100/9-12
12400 Old Shelbyville Rd 40243 502-485-8243
Lana Kaelin, prin. Fax 485-3883

Midway, Woodford, Pop. 1,609

Midway College Post-Sec.
512 E Stephens St 40347 800-755-0031

Monticello, Wayne, Pop. 6,123
Kentucky Tech System
Supt. — See Frankfort
Wayne County Area Technology Center Vo/Tech
150 Cardinal Way 42633 606-348-8424
John Kinnett, prin. Fax 348-5090

Monticello ISD 900/PK-12
161 College St 42633 606-348-5311
Gary Abbott, supt. Fax 348-3664
www.monticello.kyschools.us/
Monticello HS 300/9-12
160 Cave St 42633 606-348-5312
Roger Keith, prin. Fax 348-3039
Monticello MS 200/6-8
160 Cave St 42633 606-348-5312
Roger Keith, prin. Fax 348-3039

Wayne County SD 2,300/PK-12
1025 S Main St 42633 606-348-8484
John Dalton, supt. Fax 348-0734
www.wayne.kyschools.us
Lake Cumberland Youth Development Center 50/Alt
9000 Highway 1546 42633 606-348-4201
Tillie Slagle, lead tchr. Fax 348-7501
Otter Creek Academy 50/Alt
1441 Old Bethel Church Rd 42633 606-343-0203
Peggy Shearer, prin. Fax 343-0301
Wayne County HS 700/9-12
2 Kenny Davis Blvd 42633 606-348-5575
Brian Dishman, prin. Fax 348-3458
Wayne County MS 400/6-8
95 Champion Dr 42633 606-348-6691
Melissa Gossage, prin. Fax 348-5495

Morehead, Rowan, Pop. 6,756
Rowan County SD 3,400/PK-12
121 E 2nd St 40351 606-784-8928
Marvin Moore, supt. Fax 783-1011
www.rowan.kyschools.us/
Rowan County MS 700/6-8
555 Viking Dr 40351 606-784-8911
Jay Padula, prin. Fax 784-5579
Rowan County SHS 900/9-12
499 Viking Dr 40351 606-784-8956
Debbie Howes, prin. Fax 784-1067

Lakeside Christian Academy 200/PK-12
2535 US Highway 60 W 40351 606-784-2751
Adam Eldridge, admin. Fax 784-0056
Morehead State University Post-Sec.
150 University Blvd 40351 800-585-6781

Morganfield, Union, Pop. 3,234
Union County SD 2,200/PK-12
510 S Mart St 42437 270-389-1694
Patricia Sheffer, supt. Fax 389-9806
www.union.kyschools.us
Clements Victory Technical HS Vo/Tech
2302 US Highway 60 E 42437 270-389-2419
Claudia Stocking, prin. Fax 389-9383
Union County HS 700/9-12
4464 US Highway 60 W 42437 270-389-1454
Evan Jackson, prin. Fax 389-2715
Union County Learning Academy 50/Alt
4464 US Highway 60 W 42437 270-389-3553
Kent Green, prin. Fax 389-3554
Union County MS 500/6-8
4465 US Highway 60 W 42437 270-389-0224
Tommy Ransom, prin. Fax 389-0245

Morgantown, Butler, Pop. 2,380
Butler County SD 2,100/PK-12
203 N Tyler St 42261 270-526-5624
Scott Howard, supt. Fax 526-5625
www.butlerschools.net
Butler County HS 600/9-12
1852 S Main St 42261 270-526-2204
Patrick O'Driscoll, prin. Fax 526-2208
Butler County Learning Center 50/Alt
178 Academic Way Dept 300 42261 270-526-2264
Tim Freeman, lead tchr. Fax 526-2305
Butler County MS 500/6-8
PO Box 10 42261 270-526-5647
Robert Tuck, prin. Fax 526-3238
Other Schools – See Cromwell

Kentucky Tech System
Supt. — See Frankfort
Butler County Area Technology Center Vo/Tech
178 Academic Way Dept 400 42261 270-526-2223
Ray Hammer, prin. Fax 526-2273

Mount Olivet, Robertson, Pop. 297
Robertson County SD 200/K-12
1762 Sardis Rd 41064 606-724-5431
Charles Brown, supt. Fax 724-5921
school.robertson.k12.ky.us
Deming S 200/K-12
PO Box 168 41064 606-724-5421
Jamey Johnson, prin. Fax 724-5225

Mount Sterling, Montgomery, Pop. 6,810
Kentucky Tech System
Supt. — See Frankfort
Montgomery County Area Technology Ctr Vo/Tech
682 Woodford Dr 40353 859-498-1103
Melanie Jamison, prin. Fax 498-5960

Montgomery County SD 3,900/PK-12
700 Woodford Dr 40353 859-497-8760
Joshua Powelll, supt. Fax 497-8780
www.montgomery.kyschools.us
McNabb MS 700/7-8
3570 Indian Mound Dr 40353 859-497-8770
Russell Halsey, prin. Fax 497-9683
Montgomery County HS 1,200/9-12
724 Woodford Dr 40353 859-497-8765
James Dusso, prin. Fax 497-8705
Sterling S Alt
212 N Maysville St 40353 859-497-8761
Hopey Newkirk, dir. Fax 497-8780

Nu-Tek Academy of Beauty Post-Sec.
153 Evans Ave 40353 859-498-4460

Mount Vernon, Rockcastle, Pop. 2,459
Kentucky Tech System
Supt. — See Frankfort
Rockcastle County Area Technology Center Vo/Tech
1555 Lake Cumberland Rd 40456 606-256-4346
Ralph Baker, prin. Fax 256-4337

Rockcastle County SD 3,000/PK-12
245 Richmond St 40456 606-256-2125
David Pensol, supt. Fax 256-2126
www.rockcastle.kyschools.us/
Rockcastle Acad for Academic Achievement 50/Alt
PO Box 1730 40456 606-256-3846
Fax 256-1027
Rockcastle County HS 800/9-12
PO Box 1410 40456 606-256-4816
Jennifer Mattingly, prin. Fax 256-3755
Rockcastle County MS 600/6-8
PO Box 1730 40456 606-256-5118
Chris Hendrickson, prin. Fax 256-2622

Mount Washington, Bullitt, Pop. 9,010
Bullitt County SD
Supt. — See Shepherdsville
Bullitt East HS 1,300/9-12
11450 Highway 44 E 40047 502-869-6400
Willie Foster, prin. Fax 538-0308
Eastside MS 600/6-8
6925 Highway 44 E 40047 502-869-5000
Bonita Franklin, prin. Fax 538-0659
Mt. Washington MS 500/6-8
269 Water St 40047 502-869-5200
Dr. Denise Allen, prin. Fax 538-0703

Munfordville, Hart, Pop. 1,588
Hart County SD 2,400/PK-12
25 Quality St 42765 270-524-2631
Ricky Line, supt. Fax 524-2634
www.hart.kyschools.us
Hart County HS 700/9-12
1014 S Dixie Hwy 42765 270-524-9341
Greg Cecil, prin. Fax 524-3251

Murray, Calloway, Pop. 17,409
Calloway County SD 3,200/PK-12
PO Box 800 42071 270-762-7300
Kennith Bargo, supt. Fax 762-7310
www.calloway.kyschools.us
Calloway County HS 900/9-12
2108 College Farm Rd 42071 270-762-7374
Heath Walls, prin. Fax 762-7380
Calloway County MS 700/6-8
2112 College Farm Rd 42071 270-762-7355
Amy Turner, prin. Fax 762-7360

Kentucky Tech System
Supt. — See Frankfort
Murray/Calloway County Area Tech Center Vo/Tech
1800 Sycamore St 42071 270-753-1870
Dennis Harper, prin. Fax 759-9656

Murray ISD 1,400/PK-12
208 S 13th St 42071 270-753-4363
Bob Rogers, supt. Fax 759-4906
www.murray.kyschools.us
Murray HS 500/9-12
501 Doran Rd 42071 270-753-5202
Teresa Speed, prin. Fax 753-8391
Murray MS 500/4-8
801 Main St 42071 270-753-5125
Lou Carter, prin. Fax 753-9039

Ezell's Cosmetology School Post-Sec.
PO Box 1431 42071 270-753-4723
Murray State University Post-Sec.
102 Curris Ctr 42071 800-272-4678

Neon, Letcher, Pop. 749
Letcher County SD
Supt. — See Whitesburg
Fleming Neon MS 100/6-8
PO Box 425 41840 606-855-7864
Gracie Maggard, prin. Fax 855-4485

New Castle, Henry, Pop. 887
Henry County SD 2,300/PK-12
326 S Main St 40050 502-845-8600
Tim Abrams, supt. Fax 845-8601
www.henry.kyschools.us
Henry County HS 700/9-12
1120 Eminence Rd 40050 502-845-8670
Shannon Sageser, prin. Fax 845-8671
Henry County MS 500/6-8
1124 Eminence Rd 40050 502-845-8660
Zach Woods, prin. Fax 845-8661

Newport, Campbell, Pop. 14,797
Newport ISD 1,400/PK-12
301 E 8th St 41071 859-292-3004
Kelly Middleton, supt. Fax 292-3073
www.newportwildcats.org/
Newport HS 400/9-12
900 E 6th St 41071 859-292-3023
Antonio Watts, prin. Fax 292-8340
Newport MS 200/6-8
30 W 8th St 41071 859-292-3017
Mark Krebs, prin. Fax 292-3049
Newport Alternate HS Adult
30 W 8th St 41071 859-292-3056
Nichole Cottongim, coord. Fax 292-3099

Brighton Center for Employment Training Post-Sec.
601 Washington Ave Ste 140 41071 859-491-8303
Holy Trinity JHS 50/6-8
840 Washington Ave 41071 859-292-0487
Jeff Finke, prin. Fax 431-8745
Newport Central Catholic HS 400/9-12
13 Carothers Rd 41071 859-292-0001
Carl Foster, prin. Fax 292-0656

Nicholasville, Jessamine, Pop. 27,423
Jessamine County SD 7,700/PK-12
871 Wilmore Rd 40356 859-885-4179
Lu Young, supt. Fax 887-4811
www.jessamine.k12.ky.us
East Jessamine HS 1,100/9-12
815 Sulphur Well Pike 40356 859-885-7240
Janet Granada, prin. Fax 881-0161
East Jessamine MS 900/6-8
901 Union Mill Rd 40356 859-885-5561
Donna Givens, prin. Fax 887-1797
West Jessamine HS 1,000/9-12
2101 Wilmore Rd 40356 859-887-2421
Ed Jones, prin. Fax 887-8854
West Jessamine MS 800/6-8
1400 Wilmore Rd 40356 859-885-2244
James Freeman, prin. Fax 885-8078

Other Schools – See Wilmore

Barrett & Company School of Hair Design Post-Sec.
973 Kimberly Sq 40356 859-885-9136

Nortonville, Hopkins, Pop. 1,195
Hopkins County SD
Supt. — See Madisonville
South Hopkins MS 500/6-8
9140 Hopkinsville Rd 42442 270-825-6125
Stuart Fitch, prin. Fax 825-6085

Olive Hill, Carter, Pop. 1,580
Carter County SD
Supt. — See Grayson
Carter County Career & Technical Center Vo/Tech
15 Grahn Rd 41164 606-286-4022
Steve Stubbs, prin. Fax 286-6333
West Carter County HS 600/9-12
PO Box 1479 41164 606-286-2481
John Baumgardner, prin. Fax 286-8026
West Carter County MS 500/6-8
PO Box 1510 41164 606-286-5354
Ryan Tomolonis, prin. Fax 286-8556

Oneida, Clay, Pop. 406

Oneida Baptist Institute 300/K-12
PO Box 67 40972 606-847-4111
Dan Stockton, prin. Fax 847-4496

Owensboro, Daviess, Pop. 55,842
Daviess County SD 11,300/PK-12
PO Box 21510 42304 270-852-7000
Owens Saylor, supt. Fax 852-7010
www.daviess.kyschools.us/
Apollo HS 1,300/9-12
2280 Tamarack Rd 42301 270-852-7100
Charles Broughton, prin. Fax 852-7110
Burns MS 800/6-8
4610 Goetz Dr 42301 270-852-7400
Dane Ferguson, prin. Fax 852-7410
College View MS 800/6-8
5061 New Hartford Rd 42303 270-852-7500
Jennifer Crume, prin. Fax 852-7510
Daviess County HS 1,600/9-12
4255 New Hartford Rd 42303 270-852-7300
Matt Mason, prin. Fax 852-7310
Daviess County MS 800/6-8
1415 E 4th St 42303 270-852-7600
Kelly Skeens, prin. Fax 852-7610
Other Schools – See Utica

Owensboro ISD 4,200/PK-12
450 Griffith Ave 42301 270-686-1000
Dr. Nicholas Brake, supt. Fax 684-5756
www.owensboro.kyschools.us
Owensboro HS 1,000/9-12
1800 Frederica St 42301 270-686-1110
Anita Burnette, prin. Fax 686-1019
Owensboro MS - North Campus 600/7-8
1300 Booth Ave 42301 270-686-1130
George Powell, prin. Fax 686-1173
Seven Hills Alternative S 50/Alt
2401 McConnell Ave 42303 270-686-1120
Mike West, prin. Fax 686-1036

Brescia University Post-Sec.
717 Frederica St 42301 270-685-3131
Daymar College Post-Sec.
3361 Buckland Sq 42301 270-926-4040
Kentucky Wesleyan College Post-Sec.
3000 Frederica St 42301 270-926-3111
Mr. Jim's College of Cosmetology Post-Sec.
1240 Carter Rd 42301 270-684-3505
Owensboro Catholic HS 400/9-12
1524 W Parrish Ave 42301 270-684-3215
Gates Settle, prin. Fax 684-7050
Owensboro Catholic MS 200/7-8
2540 Christie Pl 42301 270-683-0480
David Kessler, prin. Fax 683-0495
Owensboro Community & Technical College Post-Sec.
4800 New Hartford Rd 42303 270-686-4400
Owensboro Mercy Health System Post-Sec.
811 E Parrish Ave 42303 270-688-2100

Owenton, Owen, Pop. 1,301
Owen County SD 1,800/PK-12
1600 Highway 22 E 40359 502-484-3934
David Raleigh, supt. Fax 484-9095
www.owen.kyschools.us
Bowling MS 400/5-8
2380 Highway 22 E 40359 502-484-5701
Jo Ella Wallace, prin. Fax 484-3044
Owen County HS 600/9-12
2340 Highway 22 E 40359 502-484-5509
Duane Kline, prin. Fax 484-0444

Owingsville, Bath, Pop. 1,507
Bath County SD 2,000/PK-12
405 W Main St 40360 606-674-6314
Fax 674-2647
www.bath.kyschools.us
Bath County HS 600/9-12
645 Chenault Dr 40360 606-674-6325
Paul Prater, prin. Fax 674-9188
Bath County MS 500/6-8
335 W Main St 40360 606-674-8165
John Slone, prin. Fax 674-2676

Paducah, McCracken, Pop. 24,294
Kentucky Tech System
Supt. — See Frankfort
Paducah Area Technology Center Vo/Tech
2400 Adams St 42003 270-443-6592
Donald Wann, prin. Fax 442-6233

McCracken County SD 7,200/PK-12
435 Berger Rd 42003 270-538-4000
Dr. Nancy Waldrop, supt. Fax 538-4001
www.mccracken.kyschools.us/
Commonwealth Community College HS 11-12
4810 Alben Barkley Dr 42001 270-534-3350
Donna Wear, prin.
Lone Oak HS 900/9-12
225 John E Robinson Dr 42001 270-538-4150
Matthew Houser, prin. Fax 538-4151
Lone Oak MS 700/6-8
300 Cumberland Ave 42001 270-538-4130
Brent Buchanan, prin. Fax 538-4131
McCracken County HS 9-12
6530 US Highway 60 W 42001 270-538-4000
Michael Ceglinski, prin.
Reidland HS 500/9-12
5349 Old Benton Rd 42003 270-538-4210
Victor Zimmerman, prin. Fax 538-4211
Reidland MS 400/6-8
5347 Benton Rd 42003 270-538-4190
Susan Nelson, prin. Fax 538-4191
Other Schools – See West Paducah

Paducah ISD 2,900/PK-12
PO Box 2550 42002 270-444-5600
Randy Greene, supt. Fax 444-5607
www.paducah.kyschools.us/
Paducah MS 600/6-8
342 Lone Oak Rd 42001 270-444-5710
Tim Huddleston, prin. Fax 444-5709
Paducah Tilghman HS 800/9-12
2400 Washington St 42003 270-444-5650
Arthur Davis, prin. Fax 444-5659

Community Christian Academy 200/K-12
110 Lebanon Church Rd 42003 270-554-1651
Chad Pruitt, hdmstr. Fax 554-6968
Daymar College Post-Sec.
509 S 30th St 42001 270-444-9950
St. Mary HS 200/9-12
1243 Elmdale Rd 42003 270-442-1681
Lisa Aly, prin. Fax 442-7920
St. Mary MS 100/6-8
1243 Elmdale Rd 42003 270-442-1681
Lisa Aly, prin. Fax 442-7920
West Kentucky Comm. & Technical College Post-Sec.
4810 Alben Barkley Dr 42001 270-554-9200

Paintsville, Johnson, Pop. 3,422
Johnson County SD 3,800/PK-12
253 N Mayo Trl 41240 606-789-2530
Steve Trimble, supt. Fax 789-2506
www.johnson.kyschools.us/
Johnson Central HS 1,000/9-12
257 N Mayo Trl 41240 606-789-2500
Noel Crum, prin. Fax 789-2547
Johnson County MS 600/7-8
251 N Mayo Trl 41240 606-789-4133
Tim Adams, prin. Fax 789-4135
Other Schools – See Hagerhill

Paintsville ISD 800/PK-12
305 2nd St 41240 606-789-2654
Coy Samons, supt. Fax 789-7412
www.paintsville.kyschools.us/
Paintsville MSHS 300/7-12
225 2nd St 41240 606-789-2656
Chuck McClure, prin. Fax 789-2582
Other Schools – See Prestonsburg

Paris, Bourbon, Pop. 8,356
Bourbon County SD 2,900/PK-12
3343 Lexington Rd 40361 859-987-2180
Lana Fryman, supt. Fax 987-2182
www.bourbon.kyschools.us/
Bourbon County HS 800/9-12
3341 Lexington Rd 40361 859-987-2185
David Horseman, prin. Fax 987-5850
Bourbon County MS 600/6-8
3339 Lexington Rd 40361 859-987-2189
Travis Earlywine, prin. Fax 987-5854

Paris ISD 800/PK-12
310 W 7th St 40361 859-987-2160
Gary Wiseman, supt. Fax 987-6749
www.paris.kyschools.us
Paris HS 200/9-12
308 W 7th St 40361 859-987-2168
Jamie Dailey, prin. Fax 987-2132
Paris MS 200/6-8
304 W 7th St 40361 859-987-2163
Jamie Dailey, prin. Fax 987-2164

Park Hills, Kenton, Pop. 2,906
Covington ISD
Supt. — See Covington
Holmes Alternative Center 50/Alt
1030 Old State Rd 41011 859-581-7513
Tony Perkins, dir. Fax 581-7515

Notre Dame Academy 600/9-12
1699 Hilton Dr 41011 859-261-4300
Dr. Laura Koehl, prin. Fax 292-7722

Phelps, Pike, Pop. 888
Pike County SD
Supt. — See Pikeville
Phelps HS 400/7-12
PO Box 925 41553 606-456-3482
Mike Hamilton, prin. Fax 456-8988

Pikeville, Pike, Pop. 6,797
Kentucky Tech System
Supt. — See Frankfort
Millard Area Technology Center Vo/Tech
7925 Millard Hwy 41501 606-437-6059
Jim Hamilton, prin. Fax 437-0502

Pike County SD 8,900/K-12
316 S Mayo Trl 41501 606-433-9200
Roger Wagner, supt. Fax 432-3321
www.pike.kyschools.us
Northpoint Academy Alt
5279 N Mayo Trl 41501 606-433-0181
Harold Wallace, prin. Fax 433-0626
Pike County Central HS 700/9-12
100 Winners Circle Dr 41501 606-432-4352
David Rowe, prin. Fax 432-7733
Shelby Valley HS 600/9-12
125 Douglas Park 41501 606-639-0033
Greg Napier, prin. Fax 639-2074
Other Schools – See Belfry, Lick Creek, Phelps

Pikeville ISD 1,200/PK-12
148 2nd St 41501 606-432-8161
Jerry Green, supt. Fax 432-2119
www.pikeville.kyschools.us
Pikeville JSHS 500/7-12
120 Championship Dr 41501 606-432-0185
Michael Rowe, prin. Fax 432-2022

East Kentucky Beauty College Post-Sec.
5333 N Mayo Trl 41501 606-432-3627
National College Post-Sec.
50 National College Blvd 41501 606-478-7200
Pikeville Medical Center Post-Sec.
911 Bypass Rd 41501 606-437-3500
University of Pikeville Post-Sec.
147 Sycamore St 41501 606-218-5250

Pine Knot, McCreary, Pop. 1,596
McCreary County SD
Supt. — See Stearns
Pine Knot Career Institute Vo/Tech
PO Box 1990 42635 606-354-2176
Michael Cash, prin. Fax 354-2170

Pineville, Bell, Pop. 1,711
Bell County SD 2,900/PK-12
PO Box 340 40977 606-337-7051
Yvonne Gilliam, supt. Fax 337-1412
www.bell.kyschools.us
Bell County Alternative S 50/Alt
9828 US Highway 25 E 40977 606-337-0957
Dale Hoskins, prin. Fax 337-7103
Bell County HS 800/9-12
9824 US Highway 25 E 40977 606-337-7061
Richard Gambrel, prin. Fax 337-0867

Kentucky Tech System
Supt. — See Frankfort
Bell County Area Technology Center Vo/Tech
9828 US Highway 25 E 40977 606-337-3094
David Sowders, prin. Fax 337-9053

Pineville ISD 600/PK-12
401 W Virginia Ave 40977 606-337-5701
Terry Hayes, supt. Fax 337-9983
www.pineville.kyschools.us
Pineville JSHS 300/7-12
401 W Virginia Ave 40977 606-337-2361
William Keyes, prin. Fax 337-3720

Clear Creek Baptist Bible College Post-Sec.
300 Clear Creek Rd 40977 606-337-3196

Pippa Passes, Knott, Pop. 530

Alice Lloyd College Post-Sec.
100 Purpose Rd 41844 606-368-6000
Buchanan S 100/K-12
100 Purpose Rd 41844 606-368-6108
Amanda Clark, admin. Fax 368-6216

Pleasureville, Henry, Pop. 817
Shelby County SD
Supt. — See Shelbyville
Shelby County Education Center 50/Alt
8472 Cropper Rd 40057 502-461-7540
Steve Coleman, prin. Fax 461-9021

Powderly, Muhlenberg, Pop. 738
Muhlenberg County SD 5,400/PK-12
510 W Main St 42367 270-338-2871
Dale Todd, supt. Fax 338-0529
www.mberg.k12.ky.us/
Other Schools – See Greenville

Prestonsburg, Floyd, Pop. 3,226
Floyd County SD 5,700/K-12
106 N Front Ave 41653 606-886-2354
Henry Webb, supt. Fax 886-8862
www.floyd.kyschools.us
Adams MS 300/6-8
2520 S Lake Dr 41653 606-886-2671
Thomas Poe, prin. Fax 886-7026
Prestonsburg HS 600/9-12
825 Blackcat Blvd 41653 606-886-2252
Jerry Butcher, prin. Fax 886-1745
Other Schools – See Eastern, Hi Hat, Martin, Stanville

Paintsville ISD
Supt. — See Paintsville
Perkins Job Corp Academy 100/Alt
478 Meadows Br 41653 606-886-1037
John Brown, prin. Fax 886-6048

Big Sandy Community & Technical College Post-Sec.
1 Bert Combs Dr 41653 606-886-3863

Princeton, Caldwell, Pop. 6,185
Caldwell County SD 2,000/PK-12
PO Box 229 42445 270-365-8000
Carrell Boyd, supt. Fax 365-5742
www.caldwell.kyschools.us/
Caldwell County HS 600/9-12
350 Beckner Ln 42445 270-365-8010
Christy Phelps, prin. Fax 365-9742
Caldwell County MS 500/6-8
440 Beckner Ln 42445 270-365-8020
Chad Burgett, prin. Fax 365-9573

Kentucky Tech System
Supt. — See Frankfort
Caldwell County Area Technology Center Vo/Tech
130 Vocational School Rd 42445 270-365-5563
Donna Gray, prin. Fax 365-5609

Raceland, Greenup, Pop. 2,412
Raceland-Worthington ISD 1,100/PK-12
600 Rams Blvd 41169 606-836-2144
Larry Coldiron, supt. Fax 833-5807
www.raceland.kyschools.us
Raceland-Worthington HS 500/7-12
500 Rams Blvd 41169 606-836-8221
Mickey Dixon, prin. Fax 494-2341

Radcliff, Hardin, Pop. 20,329
Hardin County SD
Supt. — See Elizabethtown
North Hardin HS 1,400/9-12
801 S Logsdon Pkwy 40160 270-351-3167
Lonnie Dennis, prin. Fax 352-4512
North MS 600/6-8
100 Trojan Way 40160 270-352-3340
Laura McGray, prin. Fax 352-3341

North Hardin Christian S 400/PK-12
1298 Rogersville Rd 40160 270-351-7700

Richmond, Madison, Pop. 30,594
Kentucky Tech System
Supt. — See Frankfort
Madison County Area Technology Center Vo/Tech
PO Box 809 40476 859-624-4520
Douglas West, prin. Fax 624-9659

Madison County SD 11,000/PK-12
PO Box 768 40476 859-624-4500
Thomas Floyd, supt. Fax 624-4508
www.madison.kyschools.us
Caudill MS 500/6-8
1428 Robert R Martin Bypass 40475 859-625-6172
Ken Bicknell, prin. Fax 623-2652
Clark-Moores MS 500/6-8
1143 Berea Rd 40475 859-624-4545
Larry Barton, prin. Fax 624-4534
Madison Central HS 1,700/9-12
705 N 2nd St 40475 859-625-6109
Elmer Thomas, prin. Fax 623-3925
Madison MS 500/6-8
101 Summit St 40475 859-624-4550
Steve Evans, prin. Fax 624-4543
Middle College at EKU Alt
521 Lancaster Ave 40475 859-622-7555
John Fields, prin. Fax 622-7558
Model Laboratory S at EKU 700/PK-12
521 Lancaster Ave 40475 859-622-3766
James Dantic, dir. Fax 622-6658
Other Schools – See Berea

Bluegrass Christian S 100/PK-12
211 Pin Oak Dr 40475 859-624-3083
Bonita Cobb, head sch Fax 624-3099
Eastern Kentucky University Post-Sec.
521 Lancaster Ave 40475 859-622-1000
National College Post-Sec.
125 S Killarney Ln 40475 859-623-8956

Rockholds, Whitley, Pop. 388
Whitley County SD
Supt. — See Williamsburg
Whitley County Alternative S 50/Alt
PO Box 254 40759 606-539-9280
Terry Huddleston, prin. Fax 549-0609

Rush, Boyd
Boyd County SD
Supt. — See Ashland
Ramey-Estep HS 100/7-12
2901 Pigeon Roost Rd 41168 606-928-5801
Elizabeth Brewster, prin. Fax 928-2145

Russell, Greenup, Pop. 3,354
Kentucky Tech System
Supt. — See Frankfort
Russell Area Technology Center Vo/Tech
705 Red Devil Ln 41169 606-836-1256
Keith Parsons, prin. Fax 836-3784

Russell ISD 2,200/PK-12
409 Belfonte St 41169 606-836-9679
Dr. Susan Compton, supt. Fax 836-2865
www.russellind.kyschools.us
Russell HS 600/9-12
709 Red Devil Ln 41169 606-836-9658
Allan Thompson, prin. Fax 836-9650
Russell MS 500/6-8
707 Red Devil Ln 41169 606-836-8135
Sean Horne, prin. Fax 836-0614

Russell Springs, Russell, Pop. 2,403
Kentucky Tech System
Supt. — See Frankfort
Lake Cumberland Area Technology Center Vo/Tech
2330 S Highway 127 42642 270-866-6175
Jeff Adams, prin. Fax 866-2424

Russell County SD
Supt. — See Jamestown
Russell County HS 800/9-12
2166 S Highway 127 42642 270-866-3341
Keith Ellis, prin. Fax 866-8830
Russell County MS 400/7-8
2258 S Highway 127 42642 270-866-2224
Doug Holmes, prin. Fax 866-8679

Russellville, Logan, Pop. 6,795
Kentucky Tech System
Supt. — See Frankfort
Russellville Area Technology Center Vo/Tech
1103 W 9th St 42276 270-726-8432
Eric Keeling, prin. Fax 726-6303

Logan County SD 3,600/PK-12
PO Box 417 42276 270-726-2436
Marshall Kemp, supt. Fax 726-8892
www.logan.k12.ky.us/
Logan County HS 1,100/9-12
2200 Bowling Green Rd 42276 270-726-8454
Wilson C. Jaynes, prin. Fax 726-1108

Russellville ISD 1,000/PK-12
355 S Summer St 42276 270-726-8405
Leon Smith, supt. Fax 726-4036
www.russellville.kyschools.us/
Russellville JSHS 400/6-12
1101 W 9th St 42276 270-726-8421
Kim McDaniel, prin. Fax 726-3685

Daymar College Post-Sec.
160 Shelton Ln 42276 270-726-8311

Saint Catharine, Washington

Saint Catharine College Post-Sec.
2735 Bardstown Rd 40061 859-336-5082

Salyersville, Magoffin, Pop. 1,875
Magoffin County SD 2,200/PK-12
PO Box 109 41465 606-349-6117
Joe Hunley, supt. Fax 349-3417
www.magoffinschools.us/
Magoffin County Career & Technical Ctr Vo/Tech
209 Hornet Dr 41465 606-349-5188
Fax 349-5345
Magoffin County HS 600/9-12
201 Hornet Dr 41465 606-349-2011
Tony Skaggs, prin. Fax 349-5345
Whitaker MS 300/7-8
221 Hornet Dr 41465 606-349-5190
Johnnie Johnson, prin. Fax 349-5139

Sandy Hook, Elliott, Pop. 666
Elliott County SD 1,100/K-12
PO Box 767 41171 606-738-8002
C. Thomas Potter Ed.D., supt. Fax 738-8050
www.elliott.kyschools.us
Elliott County JSHS 500/7-12
PO Box 687 41171 606-738-8052
Zachary Mayse, prin. Fax 738-8000

Scottsville, Allen, Pop. 4,154
Allen County SD 3,400/PK-12
570 Oliver St 42164 270-618-3181
Randall Jackson, supt. Fax 618-3185
www.allen.kyschools.us
Allen County Scottsville HS 900/9-12
1545 Bowling Green Rd 42164 270-622-4119
Brian Carter, prin. Fax 622-5882
Allen County Technical Center Vo/Tech
1501 Bowling Green Rd 42164 270-622-4711
Adonica Spears, dir. Fax 622-7006
Bazzell MS 400/7-8
201 New Gallatin Rd 42164 270-622-7140
Melissa Towery, prin. Fax 622-4649

Daymar College Post-Sec.
1138 Old Gallatin Rd 42164 270-237-3577

Shelbyville, Shelby, Pop. 13,656
Kentucky Tech System
Supt. — See Frankfort
Shelby County Area Technology Center Vo/Tech
230 Rocket Ln 40065 502-633-6554
Susan Wiley, prin. Fax 633-4212

Shelby County SD 6,700/PK-12
PO Box 159 40066 502-633-2375
Kimi Willhoite, supt. Fax 633-1988
www.shelby.kyschools.us
Collins HS 1,100/8-12
801 Discovery Blvd 40065 502-647-1160
John Leeper, prin. Fax 647-1161
Shelby County HS 1,200/8-12
1701 Frankfort Rd 40065 502-633-2344
Eddie Oakley, prin. Fax 647-0238
Other Schools – See Pleasureville

Cornerstone Christian Academy 200/PK-12
3850 Frankfort Rd 40065 502-633-4070
David Ladner, hdmstr. Fax 633-4605

Shepherdsville, Bullitt, Pop. 11,048
Bullitt County SD 12,800/PK-12
1040 Highway 44 E 40165 502-869-8000
Keith Davis, supt. Fax 543-3608
www.bullittschools.org
Bernheim MS 500/6-8
700 Audubon Dr 40165 502-869-4000
Jennifer Harrison, prin. Fax 543-5299
Bullitt Central HS 1,200/9-12
1330 Highway 44 E 40165 502-869-6000
Christy Coulter, prin. Fax 543-1797
Bullitt Lick MS 500/6-8
555 W Blue Lick Rd 40165 502-869-5400
Rob Fulk, prin. Fax 543-1685
Hebron MS 400/6-8
3300 E Hebron Ln 40165 502-869-4200
Steve Miracle, prin. Fax 957-6014
North Bullitt HS 1,200/9-12
3200 E Hebron Ln 40165 502-869-6200
Jeff Marshall, prin. Fax 957-6762
Riverview Opportunity Center 100/Alt
383 High School Dr 40165 502-869-6600
Brenda Pirtle, prin. Fax 543-1792
Zoneton MS 500/6-8
797 Old Preston Hwy N 40165 502-869-4400
Rita Muratalla, prin. Fax 955-7027
Other Schools – See Mount Washington

Kentucky Tech System
Supt. — See Frankfort
Bullitt County Area Technology Center Vo/Tech
395 High School Dr 40165 502-543-7018
Brady Southwood, prin. Fax 543-1691

Silver Grove, Campbell, Pop. 1,083
Silver Grove ISD 300/PK-12
PO Box 400 41085 859-441-3894
Ken Ellis, supt. Fax 441-4299
www.silvergrove.kyschools.us
Silver Grove S 300/PK-12
PO Box 400 41085 859-441-3873
Wes Murray, prin. Fax 441-4299

Smithland, Livingston, Pop. 299
Livingston County SD 1,300/PK-12
127 E Adair St 42081 270-928-2111
Darryl Chittenden, supt. Fax 928-2112
www.livingston.kyschools.us/
Livingston Central HS 400/9-12
750 US Highway 60 W 42081 270-928-2065
Scott Gray, prin. Fax 928-2066
Other Schools – See Burna

Somerset, Pulaski, Pop. 11,017
Kentucky Tech System
Supt. — See Frankfort
Pulaski County Area Technology Center Vo/Tech
3865 S Highway 27 Ste 101 42501 606-678-2998
Beth Hargis, prin. Fax 678-3032

Pulaski County SD 7,800/K-12
PO Box 1055 42502 606-679-1123
Steve Butcher, supt. Fax 679-1438
www.pulaski.net
Northern MS 800/6-8
650 Oak Leaf Ln 42503 606-678-5230
Shelly Hargis, prin. Fax 678-2729
Pulaski Central S 100/Alt
500 Chandler St 42501 606-677-9986
Tammy Roberts, admin. Fax 677-9885
Pulaski County HS 1,100/9-12
511 E University Dr 42503 606-679-1574
Mike Murphy, prin. Fax 677-2771
Southern MS 900/6-8
200 Enterprise Dr 42501 606-679-6855
Troy Dotson, prin. Fax 679-2270
Southwestern HS 1,100/9-12
1765 WTLO Rd 42503 606-678-9000
Danita Ellis, prin. Fax 678-9277

Somerset ISD 1,500/PK-12
305 College St 42501 606-679-4451
Boyd Randolph, supt. Fax 678-0864
www.somerset.kyschools.us
Meece MS 400/5-8
210 Barnett St 42501 606-678-5821
Calvin Rollyson, prin. Fax 678-2934
Somerset HS 500/9-12
301 College St 42501 606-678-4721
Wesley Cornett, prin. Fax 677-0087

Somerset Christian S 300/PK-12
815 Grande Central Blvd 42503 606-451-1600
John Hale, prin. Fax 677-9850
Somerset Community College Post-Sec.
808 Monticello St 42501 877-629-9722

S Portsmouth, Greenup

Harvest Christian Academy 100/K-12
PO Box 398 41174 606-932-3007
Don Gibson, prin.

South Shore, Greenup, Pop. 1,096
Greenup County SD
Supt. — See Greenup
McKell MS 300/6-8
129 Bulldog Ln 41175 606-932-3221
Nathan Sutton, prin. Fax 932-9844

Springfield, Washington, Pop. 2,454
Washington County SD 1,700/PK-12
PO Box 72 40069 859-336-5470
Robin Cochran, supt. Fax 336-5480
www.washington.kyschools.us
Washington County HS 500/9-12
601 Lincoln Park Rd 40069 859-336-5475
Paul Terrell, prin. Fax 336-5983
Washington County MS 200/6-8
603 Lincoln Park Rd 40069 859-336-5475
Tyler Howard, prin. Fax 336-5477

Stanford, Lincoln, Pop. 3,439
Kentucky Tech System
Supt. — See Frankfort
Lincoln County Area Technology Center Vo/Tech
422 Education Way 40484 606-365-8500
Amy Tracy, prin. Fax 365-8504

Lincoln County SD 4,000/PK-12
PO Box 265 40484 606-365-2124
Karen Hatter, supt. Fax 365-1660
www.lincoln.kyschools.us
Fort Logan JSHS 100/Alt
PO Box 265 40484 606-365-1333
Scott Montgomery, prin. Fax 365-4020
Lincoln County HS 1,100/9-12
60 Education Way 40484 606-365-9111
Tim Godbey, prin. Fax 365-1750
Lincoln County MS 600/7-8
285 Education Way 40484 606-365-8400
Debbie Sims, prin. Fax 365-8600

Stanton, Powell, Pop. 2,713
Powell County SD 2,400/PK-12
PO Box 430 40380 606-663-3300
Michael Tate, supt. Fax 663-3303
www.powell.kyschools.us
Powell County Alternative S 50/Alt
691 Breckenridge St 40380 606-663-3505
Kenny Rice, dir. Fax 663-3303
Powell County HS 700/9-12
700 W College Ave 40380 606-663-3320
Kyle Lively, prin. Fax 663-3406
Powell County MS 500/6-8
770 W College Ave 40380 606-663-3308
Virginia Todd, prin. Fax 663-3307

Stanville, Floyd
Floyd County SD
Supt. — See Prestonsburg
Betsy Layne HS 400/9-12
554 Bobcat Blvd 41659 606-478-9138
Cassandra Akers, prin. Fax 478-3805

Stearns, McCreary, Pop. 1,397
McCreary County SD 3,100/PK-12
120 Raider Way 42647 606-376-2591
Arthur Wright, supt. Fax 376-5584
www.mccreary.kyschools.us
McCreary Central Academy 100/Alt
400 Raider Way 42647 606-376-1477
Sharon Privett, prin. Fax 376-1478
McCreary Central HS 800/9-12
400 Raider Way 42647 606-376-5051
Sharon Privett, prin. Fax 376-3005
McCreary County MS 400/7-8
180 Raider Way 42647 606-376-5081
Clint Taylor, prin. Fax 376-9580
Other Schools – See Pine Knot

Taylor Mill, Kenton, Pop. 6,506
Kenton County SD
Supt. — See Fort Wright
Scott HS 1,000/9-12
5400 Old Taylor Mill Rd 41015 859-356-3146
Dr. Brennon Sapp, prin. Fax 356-5516
Woodland MS 800/6-8
5399 Old Taylor Mill Rd 41015 859-356-7300
Tara Sides, prin. Fax 356-7595

Taylorsville, Spencer, Pop. 749
Spencer County SD 2,800/PK-12
207 W Main St 40071 502-477-3250
Charles Adams, supt. Fax 477-3259
publicschools.spencercounty.ky.gov
Hillview Academy 50/Alt
PO Box 249 40071 502-477-1530
Bob Hafendorfer, prin. Fax 477-1760
Spencer County HS 800/9-12
520 Taylorsville Rd 40071 502-477-3255
Curt Haun, prin. Fax 477-3212
Spencer County MS 700/6-8
1263 Mount Washington Rd 40071 502-477-3260
Ed Downs, prin. Fax 477-6796

Tompkinsville, Monroe, Pop. 2,360
Kentucky Tech System
Supt. — See Frankfort
Monroe County Area Technology Center Vo/Tech
757 Old Mulkey Rd 42167 270-487-8261
Lee Ann Wall, prin. Fax 487-0094

Monroe County SD 2,000/PK-12
309 Emberton St 42167 270-487-5456
Lewis Carter, supt. Fax 487-5571
www.monroe.kyschools.us
Monroe County HS 600/9-12
755 Old Mulkey Rd 42167 270-487-6217
Phillip Bartley, prin. Fax 487-8274
Monroe County MS 400/6-8
600 S Main St 42167 270-487-9624
Tony Harlan, prin. Fax 487-9534

Union, Boone, Pop. 5,294
Boone County SD
Supt. — See Florence
Cooper HS 1,000/9-12
2855 Longbranch Rd 41091 859-384-5040
Michael Wilson, prin. Fax 384-5049
Gray MS 1,000/6-8
10400 US Highway 42 41091 859-384-5333
Todd Novak, prin. Fax 384-5318
Ryle HS 1,600/9-12
10379 US Highway 42 41091 859-384-5300
Matthew Turner, prin. Fax 384-5312

Utica, Daviess
Daviess County SD
Supt. — See Owensboro
Beacon Central Alternative S 100/Alt
6500 US Highway 231 42376 270-852-7200
Tony Bryant, prin. Fax 852-7210

Valley Station, Jefferson, Pop. 22,840
Jefferson County SD
Supt. — See Louisville
Frost MS 400/6-8
13700 Sandray Blvd 40272 502-485-8256
Jennifer Wilt, prin. Fax 485-8453
Stuart MS 1,100/6-8
4601 Valley Station Rd 40272 502-485-8334
DeLena Alexander, prin. Fax 485-8713
Valley Traditional HS 900/9-12
10200 Dixie Hwy 40272 502-485-8339
Gary Hurt, prin. Fax 485-8666

Vanceburg, Lewis, Pop. 1,503
Lewis County SD 2,400/PK-12
PO Box 159 41179 606-796-2811
Maurice Reeder, supt. Fax 796-3081
www.lewis.kyschools.us/
Lewis County HS 700/9-12
PO Box 99 41179 606-796-2823
Fax 796-3066
Lewis County MS 500/6-8
PO Box 69 41179 606-796-6228
Brenda Box, prin. Fax 796-6255
Meade Vocational Education Center Vo/Tech
PO Box 130 41179 606-796-6106
Tiffany Felty, prin. Fax 796-9739

Vancleve, Breathitt

Kentucky Mountain Bible College Post-Sec.
PO Box 10 41385 606-693-5000
Mt. Carmel S 100/K-12
PO Box 2 41385 606-666-5008
John Mills, prin. Fax 666-4612

Versailles, Woodford, Pop. 8,423
Woodford County SD 4,000/PK-12
330 Pisgah Rd 40383 859-879-4600
D. Scott Hawkins, supt. Fax 873-1614
ilearn.woodfordschools.org/
Safe Harbor Academy 50/Alt
299 S Main St 40383 859-879-4694
Brian Tackett, prin. Fax 873-1328
Woodford County HS 1,200/9-12
180 Frankfort St 40383 859-879-4630
Rob Akers, prin. Fax 873-7731
Woodford County MS 900/6-8
100 School House Rd 40383 859-879-4650
Blake Konny, prin. Fax 873-4436

Villa Hills, Kenton, Pop. 7,410

Villa Madonna Academy 300/9-12
2500 Amsterdam Rd 41017 859-331-6333
Pamela McQueen, prin. Fax 331-8615

Vine Grove, Hardin, Pop. 4,350
Hardin County SD
Supt. — See Elizabethtown
Alton MS 700/6-8
100 Country Club Rd 40175 270-877-2135
Jama Bennett, prin. Fax 877-6297
Brown Street Center 100/Alt
400 Brown St 40175 270-877-2100
Robert King, prin. Fax 877-2820

Walton, Boone, Pop. 3,572
Walton-Verona ISD 1,600/PK-12
16 School Rd 41094 859-485-4181
Dr. Robert Storer, supt. Fax 485-1810
wv.kyschools.us
Walton-Verona HS 500/9-12
30 School Rd 41094 859-485-7721
Mark Krummen, prin. Fax 485-7739
Walton-Verona MS 500/5-8
32 School Rd 41094 859-485-7721
Kim Lake, prin. Fax 485-7739

Warfield, Martin, Pop. 269
Martin County SD
Supt. — See Inez
Warfield MS 200/6-8
130 Middle School Rd 41267 606-395-5900
David Nichols, prin. Fax 395-5902

Warsaw, Gallatin, Pop. 1,574
Gallatin County SD 1,700/PK-12
75 Boardwalk 41095 859-567-2828
Dorothy Perkins, supt. Fax 567-4528
www.gallatin.kyschools.us
Gallatin County Alternative S 50/Alt
25 Boardwalk 41095 859-567-7100
Greg Ulasiewicz, dir.
Gallatin County HS 500/9-12
70 Wildcat Cir 41095 859-567-7640
Roxann Booth, prin. Fax 567-8222
Gallatin County MS 300/6-8
88 Pawprint Path 41095 859-567-5860
Curt Bieger, prin. Fax 567-6107

West Liberty, Morgan, Pop. 3,396
Kentucky Tech System
Supt. — See Frankfort
Morgan County Area Technology Center Vo/Tech
PO Box 249 41472 606-743-8452
Ronnie Woods, prin. Fax 743-8500

Morgan County SD 2,100/K-12
212 University Dr 41472 606-743-8002
Deatrah Barnett, supt. Fax 743-8050
www.morgan.kyschools.us/
Morgan County HS 600/9-12
150 Road To Success 41472 606-743-8052
Joseph Gamble, prin. Fax 743-8100
Morgan County MS 500/6-8
380 Road To Success 41472 606-743-8102
Terry Whitt, prin. Fax 743-8150

West Paducah, McCracken
McCracken County SD
Supt. — See Paducah
Heath HS 600/9-12
4330 Metropolis Lake Rd 42086 270-538-4090
Jon Reid, prin. Fax 538-4091
Heath MS 400/6-8
4336 Metropolis Lake Rd 42086 270-538-4070
Matthew Blackwell, prin. Fax 538-4071

Whitesburg, Letcher, Pop. 2,131
Kentucky Tech System
Supt. — See Frankfort
Letcher County Area Technology Center Vo/Tech
515 Cougar Dr 41858 606-633-5053
Danny Vance, prin. Fax 633-8084

Letcher County SD 2,900/PK-12
224 Parks St 41858 606-633-4455
Tony Sergent, supt. Fax 633-4724
www.letcher.kyschools.us
Letcher County Alternative S 50/Alt
185 Circle Dr Ste A 41858 606-633-5559
David Chaltas, lead tchr. Fax 633-2459
Letcher County Central HS 900/9-12
435 Cougar Dr 41858 606-633-2339
Stephen Boggs, prin. Fax 633-2447
Whitesburg MS 200/6-8
366 Parks St 41858 606-633-2761
Henry Frazier, prin. Fax 633-4137
Other Schools – See Blackey, Neon

Jenny Lea Academy of Cosmetology Post-Sec.
74 Parkway Plaza Loop 41858 606-633-8784

Whitesville, Daviess, Pop. 544

Trinity HS 100/9-12
10510 Main Cross St 42378 270-233-5184
Ron Williams, prin. Fax 233-9293

Williamsburg, Whitley, Pop. 5,159
Whitley County SD 4,600/PK-12
300 Main St 40769 606-549-7000
Scott Paul, supt. Fax 549-7006
www.whitley.kyschools.us
Whitley County HS 1,200/9-12
350 Boulevard Of Champions 40769 606-549-7025
Alan Sweet, prin. Fax 549-7035
Whitley County MS 600/7-8
351 Boulevard Of Champions 40769 606-549-7050
Stuart Conlin, prin. Fax 549-7055
Other Schools – See Rockholds

Williamsburg ISD 800/PK-12
1000 Main St 40769 606-549-6044
Dennis Byrd, supt. Fax 549-6076
www.wburg.kyschools.us
Williamsburg Alternative Center 50/Alt
1000 Main St 40769 606-539-0414
Mike Maxey, lead tchr. Fax 539-9230
Williamsburg S 700/PK-12
1000 Main St 40769 606-549-6044
Gary Peters, prin. Fax 549-6076

University of the Cumberlands Post-Sec.
6178 College Station Dr 40769 606-549-2200

Williamstown, Grant, Pop. 3,887
Grant County SD 3,800/K-12
820 Arnie Risen Blvd 41097 859-824-3323
Ron Livingood, supt. Fax 824-3508
www.grant.kyschools.us
Eagle Creek Academy 50/Alt
1505 N Main St 41097 859-824-7706
Paul Bodenhamer, prin. Fax 824-7067
Other Schools – See Dry Ridge

Williamstown ISD 900/PK-12
300 Helton St 41097 859-824-7144
Sally Skinner, supt. Fax 824-3237
www.williamstown.kyschools.us/
Williamstown JSHS 400/6-12
300 Helton St 41097 859-824-4421
Brandy Feagan, prin. Fax 824-3745

Wilmore, Jessamine, Pop. 3,637
Jessamine County SD
Supt. — See Nicholasville
Jessamine Career & Technology Center Vo/Tech
881 Wilmore Rd, 859-881-8324
C. Dexter Knight, prin. Fax 887-9051
Providence S 100/Alt
210 S Lexington Ave 40390 859-887-4600
Denise Adams, prin. Fax 887-9973

Asbury Theological Seminary Post-Sec.
204 N Lexington Ave 40390 800-227-2879
Asbury University Post-Sec.
1 Macklem Dr 40390 859-858-3511

Winchester, Clark, Pop. 18,061
Clark County SD 5,400/K-12
1600 W Lexington Ave 40391 859-744-4545
Elaine Farris, supt. Fax 745-3935
www2.clarkschools.net
Clark HS 1,700/9-12
620 Boone Ave 40391 859-744-6111
David Bolen, prin. Fax 745-2418
Clark MS 700/6-8
1645 Martin Luther King Jr 40391 859-744-0427
Pamela Whitesides, prin. Fax 745-3907
Conkwright MS 600/6-8
360 Mount Sterling Rd 40391 859-744-8433
Patrice Thompson, prin. Fax 745-2027

Kentucky Tech System
Supt. — See Frankfort
Clark County Area Technology Center Vo/Tech
650 Boone Ave 40391 859-744-1250
Michael Kindred, prin. Fax 744-9979

Winchester Christian Academy 100/6-12
PO Box 617 40392 859-745-6026
Charlotte Jernigan, prin. Fax 744-5830

Wurtland, Greenup, Pop. 983
Greenup County SD
Supt. — See Greenup
Wurtland MS 400/6-8
700 Center St 41144 606-836-1023
Dan Imes, prin. Fax 836-3939

LOUISIANA

LOUISIANA DEPARTMENT OF EDUCATION
PO Box 94064, Baton Rouge 70804-9064
Telephone 225-342-3602
Fax 225-342-7316
Website http://www.louisianaschools.net/default.html

Superintendent of Education John White

LOUISIANA BOARD OF EDUCATION
PO Box 94064, Baton Rouge 70804-9064

President Penny Dastugue

PUBLIC, PRIVATE AND CATHOLIC SECONDARY SCHOOLS

Abbeville, Vermilion, Pop. 12,038
Vermilion Parish SD 9,200/PK-12
PO Box 520 70511 337-898-5770
Jerome Puyau, supt. Fax 898-0939
www.vrml.k12.la.us
Abbeville HS 600/9-12
1305 Wildcat Dr 70510 337-893-1874
Ivy Landry, prin. Fax 893-0935
Williams MS 600/6-8
1105 Prairie Ave 70510 337-893-3943
Mikal Stall, prin. Fax 893-5190
Other Schools – See Erath, Gueydan, Kaplan, Maurice

South Louisiana Community College Post-Sec.
1301 Clover St 70510 337-893-4984
Vermilion Catholic HS 200/9-12
425 Park Ave 70510 337-893-6636
Michael Guilbeaux, prin. Fax 898-0394

Albany, Livingston, Pop. 1,080
Livingston Parish SD
Supt. — See Livingston
Albany HS 600/9-12
PO Box 1090 70711 225-567-9319
Jill Prokop, prin. Fax 567-9162
Albany MS 500/6-8
PO Box 1210 70711 225-567-5231
Rachel Jenkins, prin. Fax 567-9177

Alexandria, Rapides, Pop. 46,974
Rapides Parish SD 23,400/PK-12
PO Box 1230 71309 318-487-0888
Gary Jones, supt. Fax 449-3190
www.rpsb.us/
Alexandria HS 1,100/9-12
800 Ola St 71303 318-448-8234
Duane Urbina, prin. Fax 487-9994
Alexandria Magnet MS 500/6-8
122 Maryland Ave 71301 318-445-5343
Tim Tharp, prin. Fax 442-8650
Bolton HS 700/9-12
2101 Vance Ave 71301 318-448-3628
Misty Slayter, prin. Fax 448-4329
Brame MS 800/6-8
4800 Dawn St 71301 318-443-3688
Walter Fall, prin. Fax 442-3966
Peabody Magnet HS 700/9-12
2727 Jones Ave 71302 318-448-3457
Lee Dotson, prin. Fax 487-0771
Smith Magnet MS 400/6-8
3100 Jones Ave 71302 318-445-6241
Norvella Williams, prin. Fax 445-9255
Other Schools – See Ball, Deville, Glenmora, Hineston, Lecompte, Lena, Pineville, Tioga, Woodworth

---

Blue Cliff College-Alexandria Post-Sec.
1505 Metro Dr Ste 1 71301 318-445-2778
Central Louisiana Technical College Post-Sec.
PO Box 5698 71307 318-487-5443
Grace Christian S 400/PK-12
4900 Jackson Street Ext 71303 318-445-8735
Kay Blackburn, prin. Fax 443-1034
Holy Savior Menard HS 500/7-12
4603 Coliseum Blvd 71303 318-445-8233
Joel Desselle, prin. Fax 448-8170
Louisiana State University at Alexandria Post-Sec.
8100 Highway 71 S 71302 318-445-3672
Rapides Regional Medical Center Post-Sec.
PO Box 30101 71301 318-473-3150

Amite, Tangipahoa, Pop. 4,112
Tangipahoa Parish SD 18,300/PK-12
59656 Puleston Rd 70422 985-748-7153
Mark Kolwe, supt. Fax 748-8587
www.tangischools.org
Amite HS 500/9-12
403 S Laurel St 70422 985-748-9301
Mildred Johnson, prin. Fax 748-2814
West Side MS 500/5-8
401 W Oak St 70422 985-748-9073
Ashley Walker, prin. Fax 748-9225
Other Schools – See Hammond, Independence, Kentwood, Loranger, Ponchatoula, Tickfaw

---

Oak Forest Academy 700/PK-12
600 Walnut St 70422 985-748-4321
Jason Brabham, prin. Fax 748-4320

Anacoco, Vernon, Pop. 864
Vernon Parish SD
Supt. — See Leesville
Anacoco JSHS 400/7-12
4740 Port Arthur Ave 71403 337-239-3039
Norman Beason, prin. Fax 238-4228

Arcadia, Bienville, Pop. 2,890
Bienville Parish SD 2,300/PK-12
PO Box 418 71001 318-263-9416
William Britt, supt. Fax 263-3100
www.bpsb.us/
Arcadia JSHS 300/6-12
967 Daniel St 71001 318-263-2264
Jeffery Sampson, prin. Fax 263-9703
Other Schools – See Castor, Gibsland, Ringgold, Saline

Archibald, Richland
Richland Parish SD
Supt. — See Rayville
Richland Career Center Vo/Tech
3768 Highway 15 71218 318-248-2461
Perry Smith, prin. Fax 248-2465

Arnaudville, Saint Landry, Pop. 1,048
St. Landry Parish SD
Supt. — See Opelousas
Arnaudville MS 300/5-8
PO Box 770 70512 337-754-5320
Elsie Semien, prin. Fax 754-5326
Beau Chene HS 800/9-12
7076 Highway 93 70512 337-662-5815
Keith James, prin. Fax 662-3688

Athens, Claiborne, Pop. 242

Mount Olive Christian S 100/PK-12
15349 Highway 9 71003 318-258-5661
Fax 258-5662

Atlanta, Winn, Pop. 159
Winn Parish SD
Supt. — See Winnfield
Atlanta S 200/PK-12
118 School Rd 71404 318-628-4613
Bridgette Bartlett, prin. Fax 628-4247

Avondale, Jefferson, Pop. 4,884
Jefferson Parish SD
Supt. — See Harvey
Ford MS 500/6-8
435 S Jamie Blvd 70094 504-436-2474
Faith Joseph, prin. Fax 436-0604

Baker, East Baton Rouge, Pop. 13,732
City of Baker SD 1,900/PK-12
PO Box 680 70704 225-774-5795
Ulysses Joseph, supt. Fax 774-5797
www.bakerschools.org
Baker Alternative Learning Center 50/Alt
3200 Groom Rd 70714 225-775-7159
Hamilton Brock, prin. Fax 775-3286
Baker HS 500/9-12
3200 Groom Rd 70714 225-775-1259
Traci Morgan, prin. Fax 775-4011
Baker MS 400/6-8
5903 Groom Rd 70714 225-775-9750
Josie Williams, prin. Fax 775-9753

Bethany Christian S 400/PK-12
13855 Plank Rd 70714 225-774-0133
Carolyn DeSalvo, prin. Fax 774-0163

Baldwin, Saint Mary, Pop. 2,394
St. Mary Parish SD
Supt. — See Centerville
Boudreaux MS 300/6-8
18333 Highway 182 70514 337-924-7990
Magdalene Drexler, prin. Fax 924-7999
West St. Mary HS 400/9-12
PO Box 120 70514 337-924-7990
Dr. Derrick White, prin. Fax 924-7999

Ball, Rapides, Pop. 3,932
Rapides Parish SD
Supt. — See Alexandria
Tioga JHS 500/7-8
1150 Tioga Rd 71405 318-640-9412
Jeff Powell, prin. Fax 640-0126

Basile, Evangeline, Pop. 1,791
Evangeline Parish SD
Supt. — See Ville Platte
Basile JSHS 400/5-12
2835 2nd St 70515 337-432-5012
Georgeanna Courville, prin. Fax 432-6414

Bastrop, Morehouse, Pop. 11,255
Morehouse Parish SD 4,500/PK-12
PO Box 872 71221 318-281-5784
George Noflin Ph.D., supt. Fax 283-3456
www.mpsb.us
Bastrop HS 1,100/8-12
402 Highland Ave 71220 318-281-0194
Dr. David Nordman, prin. Fax 281-0457
Morehouse Alternative S 50/Alt
1607 Martin L King S 71220 318-281-1407
Howard Loche, prin. Fax 283-3460
Morehouse JHS 500/6-8
1001 W Madison Ave 71220 318-281-0776
Shelia Minor, prin. Fax 283-1846

Bastrop Beauty School #1 Post-Sec.
117 S Vine St 71220 318-281-8652
Prairie View Academy 300/K-12
9942 Edwin St 71220 318-281-7044

Baton Rouge, East Baton Rouge, Pop. 226,740
Central Community SD 3,400/PK-12
PO Box 78094 70837 225-262-1919
Michael Faulk, supt. Fax 262-1989
www.centralcss.org
Central HS 1,200/9-12
10200 E Brookside Dr 70818 225-261-3438
Bob Wales, prin. Fax 261-3501
Central MS 900/6-8
12656 Sullivan Rd 70818 225-261-2237
Sandy Davis, prin. Fax 261-9973

East Baton Rouge Parish SD 41,400/PK-12
PO Box 2950 70821 225-922-5400
John Dilworth, supt. Fax 922-5499
www.ebrschools.org/
Arlington Prepatory Academy 100/Alt
931 Dean Lee Dr 70820 225-766-8188
Margot Morgan-Forbes, prin. Fax 757-1276
Baton Rouge Magnet HS 1,300/9-12
2825 Government St 70806 225-383-0520
Nanette Greer, prin. Fax 344-3066
Belaire HS 900/9-12
12121 Tams Dr 70815 225-272-1860
Angela Domingue, prin. Fax 272-3782
Broadmoor HS 1,000/9-12
10100 Goodwood Blvd 70815 225-926-1420
Daryl Glueck, prin. Fax 928-5472
Broadmoor MS 700/6-8
1225 Sharp Rd 70815 225-272-0540
Denise Charbonnet, prin. Fax 272-0195
Capitol MS 500/6-8
5100 Greenwell Springs Rd 70806 225-231-9292
Viola Jackson, prin. Fax 231-9291
East Baton Rouge Accelerated Academy 200/Alt
5959 Cadillac St 70811 225-356-0256
Vincent Perry, prin. Fax 356-4960
Glasgow MS 600/6-8
1676 Glasgow Ave 70808 225-925-2942
Dianne Talbot, prin. Fax 928-3565
Glen Oaks HS 600/9-12
6650 Cedar Grove Dr 70812 225-356-4306
Onetha Wheeler, prin. Fax 359-6782
Lee HS 600/9-12
1105 Lee Dr 70808 225-383-7744
Averill Sanders, prin. Fax 346-8196

Mayfair MS 300/6-8
9880 Hyacinth Ave 70810 225-761-7849
Louis Moore, prin. Fax 766-4507
McKinley HS 1,200/9-12
800 E Mckinley St 70802 225-344-7696
Armond Brown, prin. Fax 387-5435
McKinley Magnet MS 700/6-8
1050 Eddie Robinson Sr Dr 70802 225-388-0089
Herman Brister, prin. Fax 387-1434
Northdale Academy 200/Alt
10755 Cletus Dr 70815 225-272-2036
Leroy Helire, prin. Fax 273-2125
Park Forest MS 1,000/6-8
3760 Aletha Dr 70814 225-275-6650
Curtis Walker, prin. Fax 275-3058
Scotlandville Magnet HS 1,300/9-12
9870 Scotland Ave 70807 225-775-3715
Howard Davis, prin. Fax 774-3767
Scotlandville Pre-Engineering Academy 200/6-8
2555 DeSoto Dr 70807 225-775-0776
Edwin Chastang, prin. Fax 775-2104
Sherwood MS 800/6-8
1020 Marlbrook Dr 70815 225-272-3090
Phyllis Crawford, prin. Fax 273-9459
Southeast MS 900/6-8
15000 S Harrells Ferry Rd 70816 225-753-5930
Amber Boyd, prin. Fax 756-8601
Staring Education Center 100/Alt
1645 N Foster Dr 70806 225-357-0139
Clara Joseph, prin. Fax 356-6358
Tara HS 1,100/9-12
9002 Whitehall Ave 70806 225-927-6100
Johnny Jackson, prin. Fax 928-0122
Valley Park S 300/Alt
4510 Bawell St 70808 225-926-9765
Ernest Morris, prin. Fax 926-8758
Westdale MS 900/6-8
5650 Claycut Rd 70806 225-924-1308
Sherry Brock, prin. Fax 926-9929
Woodlawn HS 1,300/9-12
15755 Jefferson Hwy 70817 225-753-1200
James Newman, prin. Fax 751-9269
Woodlawn MS 1,000/6-8
14939 Tiger Bend Rd 70817 225-751-0436
Shelly Colvin, prin. Fax 753-0159
Other Schools – See Pride

Recovery SD
Supt. — See New Orleans
Capitol HS 200/9-12
1000 N 23rd St 70802 225-239-7506
Roy Walker, prin. Fax 359-6782
Istrouma Magnet HS 700/9-12
3730 Winbourne Ave 70805 225-239-7515
Robert Webb, prin. Fax 663-2950

Baton Rouge College Post-Sec.
1900 Lobdell Blvd 70806 225-292-5464
Baton Rouge Community College Post-Sec.
201 Community College Dr 70806 225-216-8000
Baton Rouge General Medical Center Post-Sec.
PO Box 2511 70821 225-387-7767
Baton Rouge International S 300/PK-12
5015 Auto Plex Dr 70809 225-293-4338
Fax 293-4307
Baton Rouge School of Computers Post-Sec.
9352 Interline Ave 70809 225-923-2525
Brighton S 200/K-12
12108 Parkmeadow Ave 70816 225-291-2524
Kenneth Payne, prin. Fax 291-8587
Camelot College Post-Sec.
2618 Wooddale Blvd # A 70805 225-928-3005
Capital Area Technical College Post-Sec.
3250 N Acadian Thruway E 70805 225-359-9201
Catholic HS 1,000/8-12
855 Hearthstone Dr 70806 225-383-0397
Lisa Harvey, prin. Fax 383-0381
Christian Life Academy 600/PK-12
2037 Quail Dr 70808 225-769-6760
Delta College of Arts & Technology Post-Sec.
7380 Exchange Pl 70806 225-928-7770
Diesel Driving Academy Post-Sec.
8067 Airline Hwy 70815 225-929-9990
Domestic Health Care Institute Post-Sec.
4826 Jamestown Ave 70808 225-925-5312
Dunham S 800/PK-12
11111 Roy Emerson Dr 70810 225-767-7097
Bobby Welch, hdmstr. Fax 767-7056
Episcopal S of Baton Rouge 900/PK-12
3200 Woodland Ridge Blvd 70816 225-753-3180
Hugh McIntosh, head sch Fax 756-0507
Family Christian Academy 200/K-12
PO Box 262550 70826 225-768-3026
Fax 768-3213
Hosanna Christian Academy 600/PK-12
8850 Goodwood Blvd 70806 225-926-4885
Josh LeSage, admin. Fax 926-8458
ITI Technical College Post-Sec.
13944 Airline Hwy 70817 225-752-4230
ITT Technical Institute Post-Sec.
14111 Airline Hwy Ste 101 70817 225-754-5800
Jehovah-Jireh Christian Academy 100/PK-12
1771 Lobdell Blvd 70806 225-932-2357
Glenda Colbert, prin. Fax 932-2360
Lockworks Academie of Hairdressing Post-Sec.
2834 S Sherwood Forest Blvd 70816 225-295-1435
Louisiana Culinary Institute Post-Sec.
10550 Airline Hwy 70816 225-769-8820
Louisiana School for the Deaf Post-Sec.
PO Box 3074 70821 225-769-8160
Louisiana School/Visually Impaired Post-Sec.
PO Box 4328 70821 225-757-3482
Louisiana State University & A & M Coll. Post-Sec.
Louisiana State Univ 70803 225-578-3202
Louisiana State University Law Center Post-Sec.
1 E Campus Dr 70803 225-578-5292

Medical Training College Post-Sec.
10525 Plaza Americana Dr 70816 225-926-5820
MedVance Institute Post-Sec.
9255 Interline Ave 70809 225-248-1015
Our Lady of the Lake College Post-Sec.
5414 Brittany Dr Ste A 70808 225-768-1700
Our Lady of the Lake Medical Center Post-Sec.
5000 Hennessy Blvd 70808 225-769-7799
Parkview Baptist S 1,400/K-12
5750 Parkview Church Rd 70816 225-291-2500
Dr. Don Mayes, hdmstr. Fax 293-4135
Redemptorist HS 800/7-12
4000 Saint Gerard Ave 70805 225-357-0936
Dr. Maribeth Andereck, prin. Fax 357-4555
Remington College Post-Sec.
10551 Coursey Blvd 70816 225-236-3200
Riverdale Christian Academy 200/PK-12
2791 Oneal Ln 70816 225-753-6722
Fax 751-4341
Runnels S 800/PK-12
17255 S Harrells Ferry Rd 70816 225-751-5712
St. Joseph's Academy 900/9-12
3015 Broussard St 70808 225-383-7207
Linda Harvison, prin. Fax 344-5714
St. Michael the Archangel HS 700/9-12
PO Box 86110 70879 225-753-9782
Ellen Lee, prin. Fax 753-0605
Southern University and A&M College Post-Sec.
Southern University 70813 225-771-4500
Virginia College Post-Sec.
9501 Cortana Pl 70815 225-236-3900

Bell City, Calcasieu
Calcasieu Parish SD
Supt. — See Lake Charles
Bell City S 600/K-12
PO Box 100 70630 337-217-4500
Reinette Guillory, prin. Fax 217-4501

Belle Chasse, Plaquemines, Pop. 12,371
Plaquemines Parish SD 3,800/PK-12
1484 Woodland Hwy 70037 504-595-6400
Denis Rousselle, supt. Fax 398-9990
www.ppsb.org
Belle Chasse HS 900/9-12
8346 Highway 23 70037 504-595-6600
Jemi Carlone, prin. Fax 393-1182
Belle Chasse MS 700/5-8
13476 Highway 23 70037 504-595-6640
Joe Williamson, prin. Fax 656-2399
Other Schools – See Braithwaite, Port Sulphur

Belle Rose, Assumption, Pop. 1,892
Assumption Parish SD
Supt. — See Napoleonville
Belle Rose MS 200/5-8
PO Box 229 70341 225-473-8917
Stacy Garrison, prin. Fax 473-8429

Benton, Bossier, Pop. 1,921
Bossier Parish SD 20,300/PK-12
PO Box 2000 71006 318-549-5000
D.C. Machen, supt. Fax 549-5004
www.bossierschools.org
Benton HS 800/9-12
6136 Highway 3 71006 318-549-5240
Mitch Downey, prin. Fax 549-5252
Benton MS 700/6-8
6140 Highway 3 71006 318-549-5310
Dwayne Slack, prin. Fax 549-5323
Other Schools – See Bossier City, Haughton, Plain Dealing, Shreveport

Berwick, Saint Mary, Pop. 4,860
St. Mary Parish SD
Supt. — See Centerville
Berwick HS 500/9-12
700 Pattie Dr 70342 985-384-8450
Buffy Fegenbush, prin. Fax 384-8505
Berwick JHS 400/6-8
3955 Highway 182 70342 985-384-5664
Thomas Bourgeois, prin. Fax 384-5663

Bogalusa, Washington, Pop. 12,052
Bogalusa City SD 2,100/PK-12
1705 Sullivan Dr 70427 985-281-2100
Toni Breaux, supt. Fax 735-8828
www.bogalusaschools.org/
Bogalusa HS 400/9-12
PO Box 580 70429 985-281-2163
Lesley McKinley, prin. Fax 735-9768
Bogalusa MS 400/5-8
1403 North Ave 70427 985-281-2230
Marie Goff, prin. Fax 735-6430
Northside Tech MS 200/5-8
517 Mississippi Ave 70427 985-281-2202
Leslie Raborn, prin. Fax 732-3502

Ben's Ford Christian School 500/PK-12
59253 Mount Pleasant Rd 70427 985-735-0387
Sharon McGehee, admin. Fax 735-0382
Northshore Technical Community College Post-Sec.
1710 Sullivan Dr 70427 985-732-6640

Bossier City, Bossier, Pop. 59,796
Bossier Parish SD
Supt. — See Benton
Airline HS 1,600/9-12
2801 Airline Dr 71111 318-549-5080
Jason Rowland, prin. Fax 549-5093
Bossier HS 600/9-12
777 Bearkat Dr 71111 318-549-6680
David Thrash, prin. Fax 549-6693
Cope MS 700/6-8
4814 Shed Rd 71111 318-549-5380
Judy Grooms, prin. Fax 549-5393
Elm Grove MS 900/6-8
4301 Panther Dr 71112 318-759-2400
Terrie Johnson, prin. Fax 759-2409

Greenacres MS 800/6-8
2220 Airline Dr 71111 318-549-6210
Kathy Bouck, prin. Fax 549-6223
Mitchell Education Center 100/Alt
1518 Cox St 71111 318-549-6810
Warren Saucier, admin. Fax 549-6823
Parkway HS 1,100/9-12
2010 Colleen St 71112 318-759-2200
Dr. Nichole Bourgeois, prin. Fax 759-2213
Rusheon MS 500/6-8
2401 Old Minden Rd 71112 318-549-6610
Judy Madden, prin. Fax 549-6623
Adult Learning Center Adult
415 Monroe St 71111 318-549-6839
Jeanie Armstrong, coord. Fax 549-6842

Bossier Parish Community College Post-Sec.
6220 E Texas St 71111 318-678-6000
Pat Goins Benton Road Beauty School Post-Sec.
1701 Old Minden Rd Ste 36 71111 318-746-7674

Bourg, Terrebonne, Pop. 2,533
Terrebonne Parish SD
Supt. — See Houma
South Terrebonne HS 1,000/9-12
3879 Highway 24 70343 985-868-7850
Dane Voisin, prin. Fax 868-1691

Boutte, Saint Charles, Pop. 3,028
St. Charles Parish SD
Supt. — See Luling
Hahnville HS 1,500/9-12
200 Tiger Dr 70039 985-758-7537
Ken Oertling, prin. Fax 758-9876

Braithwaite, Plaquemines
Plaquemines Parish SD
Supt. — See Belle Chasse
Phoenix S 200/PK-12
13073 Highway 15 70040 504-595-6480
Kristie Williams, prin. Fax 333-7073

Breaux Bridge, Saint Martin, Pop. 8,038
St. Martin Parish SD
Supt. — See Saint Martinville
Breaux Bridge HS 900/9-12
1015 Breaux Bridge Sr High 70517 337-332-3131
Rene Angelle, prin. Fax 332-4058
Breaux Bridge JHS 300/7-8
100 Martin St 70517 337-332-2844
Denise Frederick, prin. Fax 332-4831

Broussard, Lafayette, Pop. 8,078
Lafayette Parish SD
Supt. — See Lafayette
Broussard MS 600/5-8
1325 S Morgan Ave 70518 337-521-7870
John Mouton, prin. Fax 521-7871

Episcopal S of Acadiana 500/PK-12
1557 Smede Hwy 70518 337-365-1416
Dr. Charles Skipper, hdmstr. Fax 367-9841

Brusly, West Baton Rouge, Pop. 2,561
West Baton Rouge Parish SD
Supt. — See Port Allen
Brusly HS 500/9-12
630 Frontage Rd 70719 225-749-2815
Walt Lemoine, prin. Fax 749-8563
Brusly MS 500/6-8
601 N Kirkland St 70719 225-749-3123
Callie Kershaw, prin. Fax 749-8570

Bunkie, Avoyelles, Pop. 4,132
Avoyelles Parish SD
Supt. — See Marksville
Bunkie HS 500/7-12
435 Evergreen St 71322 318-346-6216
Dewayne Vines, prin. Fax 346-9611

Calhoun, Ouachita, Pop. 674
Ouachita Parish SD
Supt. — See Monroe
Calhoun MS 500/6-8
191 Highway 80 E 71225 318-644-5840
Werner Aswell, prin. Fax 644-5418

Calvin, Winn, Pop. 236
Winn Parish SD
Supt. — See Winnfield
Calvin S 300/PK-12
PO Box 80 71410 318-727-8784
Rodney Shelton, prin. Fax 727-9224

Cameron, Cameron, Pop. 399
Cameron Parish SD 1,300/PK-12
PO Box 1548 70631 337-775-5784
Stephanie Rodrigue, supt. Fax 775-5097
www.camsch.org
Johnson Bayou S 100/PK-12
6304 Gulf Beach Hwy 70631 337-569-2138
Brenda Sanders, prin. Fax 569-2673
Other Schools – See Grand Chenier, Hackberry, Lake Charles

Campti, Natchitoches, Pop. 1,035
Natchitoches Parish SD
Supt. — See Natchitoches
Lakeview HS 300/9-12
7305 Highway 9 71411 318-476-3360
William Hymes, prin. Fax 476-2851

Carencro, Lafayette, Pop. 7,438
Lafayette Parish SD
Supt. — See Lafayette
Carencro MS 600/6-8
4301 N University Ave 70520 337-521-7880
Dr. Spurgeon Banyard, prin. Fax 521-7881

Castor, Bienville, Pop. 258
Bienville Parish SD
Supt. — See Arcadia
Castor S 500/PK-12
PO Box 69 71016 318-544-7271
Dr. James Guin, prin. Fax 544-9077

Cecilia, Saint Martin, Pop. 1,957
St. Martin Parish SD
Supt. — See Saint Martinville
Cecilia HS 700/9-12
PO Box 360 70521 337-667-6221
Anthony Polotzola, prin. Fax 667-6795
Cecilia JHS 400/7-8
PO Box 129 70521 337-667-6226
Charee Theriot, prin. Fax 667-7352

Centerville, Saint Mary
St. Mary Parish SD 9,500/PK-12
PO Box 170 70522 337-836-9661
Dr. Donald Aguillard, supt. Fax 836-5461
www.stmary.k12.la.us
Centerville S 600/PK-12
PO Box 59 70522 337-836-5103
Mike Galler, prin. Fax 836-9594
Other Schools – See Baldwin, Berwick, Franklin, Morgan City, Patterson

Central, East Baton Rouge, Pop. 26,615

Central Private S 400/PK-12
12801 Centerra Ct, 225-261-3341
Ellen Frazier, hdmstr. Fax 261-3490

Chalmette, Saint Bernard, Pop. 16,314
St. Bernard Parish SD 6,700/PK-12
200 E Saint Bernard Hwy 70043 504-301-2000
Doris Voitier, supt. Fax 301-2010
www.stbernard.k12.la.us
Chalmette HS 1,400/9-12
1100 E Judge Perez Dr 70043 504-301-2600
Wayne Warner, prin. Fax 301-2610
Jackson MS 400/6-8
201 8th St 70043 504-301-1500
Montrelle Sinegar, prin. Fax 301-1510
Rowley Alternative S 200/Alt
49 Madison Ave 70043 504-301-4001
Pat Pourciau, prin. Fax 301-4010
Other Schools – See Meraux, Saint Bernard

Nunez Community College Post-Sec.
3710 Paris Rd 70043 504-278-6200

Chauvin, Terrebonne, Pop. 2,885
Terrebonne Parish SD
Supt. — See Houma
Lacache MS 400/4-8
5266 Highway 56 70344 985-594-3945
Melissa Badeaux, prin. Fax 594-4128

Choudrant, Lincoln, Pop. 836
Lincoln Parish SD
Supt. — See Ruston
Choudrant HS 300/7-12
PO Box 220 71227 318-768-2542
Lisa Bastion, prin. Fax 768-4182

Church Point, Acadia, Pop. 4,487
Acadia Parish SD
Supt. — See Crowley
Church Point HS 500/9-12
305 E Lougarre St 70525 337-684-5472
Lee Ward Bellard, prin. Fax 684-5137
Church Point MS 300/6-8
340 W Martin Luther King Dr 70525 337-684-6381
Katie Jolivette, prin. Fax 684-0123

Clarks, Caldwell, Pop. 1,011

Old Bethel Christian Academy 100/PK-12
PO Box 95 71415 318-649-0281
Sandra Richmond, prin. Fax 649-0281

Clinton, East Feliciana, Pop. 1,628
East Feliciana Parish SD 2,100/PK-12
PO Box 397 70722 225-683-8277
Henderson Lewis Ph.D., supt. Fax 683-3320
www.efpsb.k12.la.us
East Feliciana Freshman Academy 100/9-9
12732 Silliman St 70722 225-683-8277
East Feliciana MS 400/6-8
PO Box 166 70722 225-683-3321
Keisha Netterville, prin. Fax 683-5115
East Feliciana Parish Enrichment Academy 50/Alt
PO Box 397 70722 225-683-5542
Ella Philson, prin. Fax 683-3320
Other Schools – See Jackson

Silliman Institute 400/PK-12
PO Box 946 70722 225-683-5383
Ann Kent, admin. Fax 683-6728

Colfax, Grant, Pop. 1,531
Grant Parish SD 3,300/PK-12
PO Box 208 71417 318-627-3274
Sheila Jackson, supt. Fax 627-5931
www.gpsb.org
Other Schools – See Dry Prong, Georgetown, Montgomery

Columbia, Caldwell, Pop. 387
Caldwell Parish SD 1,500/PK-12
PO Box 1019 71418 318-649-2689
Karla Tollett, supt. Fax 649-0636
www.caldwelledu.org/
Caldwell Parish HS 400/9-12
163 Spartan Dr 71418 318-649-2750
Sherry Jones, prin. Fax 649-0021

Caldwell Parish JHS 200/7-8
114 Trojan Dr 71418 318-649-2340
Blaine Dauzat, prin. Fax 649-2341

Converse, Sabine, Pop. 416
Sabine Parish SD
Supt. — See Many
Converse S 500/K-12
PO Box 10 71419 318-567-2673
Terri Webb, prin. Fax 567-3400

Cottonport, Avoyelles, Pop. 1,987

Central Louisiana Technical College Post-Sec.
508 Choupique Ln 71327 318-876-2801

Coushatta, Red River, Pop. 1,958
Red River Parish SD 1,500/PK-12
PO Box 1369 71019 318-932-4081
Kay Easley, supt. Fax 932-3081
www.rrbulldogs.com/
Red River HS 400/9-12
PO Box 409 71019 318-932-4913
Carroll Daniels, prin. Fax 932-5344
Red River JHS 300/6-8
915 E Carrol St 71019 318-932-5265
Jacqueline Daniels, prin. Fax 932-9052

Riverdale Academy 300/PK-12
100 Riverdale Rd 71019 318-932-5876
Jamie Lawrence, prin. Fax 932-4355

Covington, Saint Tammany, Pop. 8,662
St. Tammany Parish SD 36,000/PK-12
PO Box 940 70434 985-892-2276
Trey Folse, supt. Fax 898-3267
www.stpsb.org
Covington HS 1,500/9-12
73030 Lions Dr 70433 985-892-3422
Deborah McCollum, prin. Fax 875-9699
Pitcher JHS 300/7-8
415 S Jefferson Ave 70433 985-892-3021
Roslyn Hanson, prin. Fax 892-1188
Other Schools – See Folsom, Madisonville, Mandeville, Pearl River, Slidell

Archbishop Hannan HS 500/8-12
71324 Highway 1077 70433 985-249-6363
Fr. Charles Latour, prin. Fax 249-6370
Aveda Institute Post-Sec.
1355 Polders Ln 70433 985-892-9953
Christ Episcopal S 500/1-12
80 Christwood Blvd 70433 985-871-9902
John Morvant, hdmstr. Fax 871-9912
Delta College Post-Sec.
19231 N 6th St 70433 985-892-6651
Northlake Christian S 900/PK-12
70104 Wolverine Dr 70433 985-635-0400
Rev. L. Joe Shorter Ph.D., hdmstr. Fax 893-4363
St. Paul's HS 900/8-12
PO Box 928 70434 985-892-3200
Br. Raymond Bulliard, prin. Fax 892-4048
St. Scholastica Academy 700/8-12
PO Box 1210 70434 985-892-2540
Mary Kathryn Villere, prin. Fax 893-5256

Crowley, Acadia, Pop. 13,095
Acadia Parish SD 9,500/PK-12
PO Box 309 70527 337-783-3664
John Bourque, supt. Fax 783-3761
www.acadia.k12.la.us/
Acadia Parish Alternative S 50/Alt
404 W 12th St 70526 337-783-7188
Eric Stutes, prin. Fax 785-0794
Crowley HS 600/9-12
263 Hensgens Rd 70526 337-783-5313
Jim McKeiver, prin. Fax 783-7796
Crowley MS 500/6-8
401 W Northern Ave 70526 337-783-5305
Chad Lemelle, prin. Fax 783-5338
Other Schools – See Church Point, Iota, Midland, Rayne

Acadiana Technical College Post-Sec.
1933 W Hutchinson Ave 70526 337-788-7521
Northside Christian S 300/K-12
809 E Northern Ave 70526 337-783-3620
Rev. Randy Trahan, prin. Fax 788-3461
Notre Dame HS 400/9-12
910 N Eastern Ave 70526 337-783-3519
Cindy Istre, prin. Fax 788-2115

Cut Off, Lafourche, Pop. 5,828
Lafourche Parish SD
Supt. — See Thibodaux
Opportunity Place South Campus Adult
14669 E Main St 70345 985-632-3169
Fax 632-4384

Darrow, Ascension
Ascension Parish SD
Supt. — See Donaldsonville
Ascension Parish Alternative S 200/Alt
38606 Highway 22 70725 225-391-6850
Jerry Elie, prin. Fax 474-2774

Delcambre, Vermilion, Pop. 1,846
Iberia Parish SD
Supt. — See New Iberia
Delcambre JSHS 500/6-12
601 W Main St 70528 337-685-2595
Todd Saunier, prin. Fax 685-6099

Delhi, Richland, Pop. 2,885
Richland Parish SD
Supt. — See Rayville
Delhi HS 200/9-12
413 Main St 71232 318-878-2235
Kenneth Jenkins, prin. Fax 878-8967

Delhi MS 200/5-8
106 Toombs St 71232 318-878-3748
Shirley McDade, prin. Fax 878-3749

Denham Springs, Livingston, Pop. 10,120
Livingston Parish SD
Supt. — See Livingston
Denham Springs Freshman HS 700/9-9
940 N Range Ave 70726 225-665-7890
Ken Magee, prin. Fax 665-1865
Denham Springs JHS 900/6-8
401 Hatchell Ln 70726 225-665-8898
Bryan Wax, prin. Fax 665-8601
Denham Springs SHS 1,300/10-12
1000 N Range Ave 70726 225-665-8851
Kelly Jones, prin. Fax 665-4082
Juban Parc JHS 6-8
12470 Brown Rd 70726 225-664-1001
Jeff Frizell, prin. Fax 664-5000
Live Oak HS 1,200/9-12
35086 Hwy 16 70706 225-665-8858
Tracy McRae, prin. Fax 665-8850
Southside JHS 500/6-8
26535 LA Highway 16 70726 225-664-4221
Carlos Williams, prin. Fax 664-3307

Community Christian Academy 100/PK-12
400 N River Rd 70726 225-665-5696
Joyce Wilson, prin. Fax 665-3098
Denham Springs Beauty College Post-Sec.
923 Florida Ave SE 70726 225-665-6188

Dequincy, Calcasieu, Pop. 3,178
Calcasieu Parish SD
Supt. — See Lake Charles
DeQuincy HS 400/9-12
207 N Overton St 70633 337-217-4530
Craig Neal, prin. Fax 217-4531
DeQuincy MS 300/6-8
1603 W 4th St 70633 337-217-4770
Billy Kellogg, prin. Fax 217-4771

Deridder, Beauregard, Pop. 10,238
Beauregard Parish SD 6,000/PK-12
PO Box 938 70634 337-463-5551
Timothy Cooley M.Ed., supt. Fax 463-6735
www.beau.k12.la.us/
Beauregard Alternative Program 50/Alt
506 Martin Luther King Dr 70634 337-462-2709
Cord Ensminger, prin. Fax 462-2710
DeRidder HS 800/9-12
723 ONeal St 70634 337-463-3266
Debbie Dixon, prin. Fax 463-9358
DeRidder JHS 600/6-8
415 N Frusha Dr 70634 337-463-9083
Eddie Joslin, prin. Fax 463-7696
East Beauregard HS 400/6-12
5364 Highway 113 70634 337-328-7511
Larry Hollie, prin. Fax 328-8132
Other Schools – See Longville, Merryville, Singer

Beckwith Christian S 100/PK-12
5525 Highway 27 70634 337-463-3437
James Alexander, admin. Fax 563-8265

Destrehan, Saint Charles, Pop. 11,371
St. Charles Parish SD
Supt. — See Luling
Destrehan HS 1,500/9-12
1 Wildcat Ln 70047 985-764-9946
Stephen Weber, prin. Fax 764-9948
Hurst MS 500/7-8
170 Road Runner Ln 70047 985-764-6367
Steven Guitterrez, prin. Fax 764-2678

Deville, Rapides, Pop. 1,751
Rapides Parish SD
Supt. — See Alexandria
Buckeye JSHS 1,000/6-12
PO Box 439 71328 318-466-5678
Jonathan Garrett, prin. Fax 466-9269

Dodson, Winn, Pop. 331
Winn Parish SD
Supt. — See Winnfield
Dodson S 300/PK-12
PO Box 97 71422 318-628-2172
Mike Hearne, prin. Fax 628-7515

Donaldsonville, Ascension, Pop. 7,399
Ascension Parish SD 18,900/PK-12
PO Box 189 70346 225-391-7000
Patrice Pujol, supt. Fax 473-7820
www.apsb.org
Donaldsonville HS 400/9-12
100 Tiger Dr 70346 225-391-7900
Esrom Pitre, prin. Fax 473-4496
Lowery MS 100/6-8
2389 Highway 1 S Ste A 70346 225-391-7550
Fax 473-2514
Other Schools – See Darrow, Geismar, Gonzales, Prairieville, Saint Amant

Ascension Catholic HS 200/9-12
311 Saint Vincent St 70346 225-473-9227
Sandy Pizzolato, prin. Fax 473-9235

Doyline, Webster, Pop. 803
Webster Parish SD
Supt. — See Minden
Doyline S 300/PK-12
PO Box 657 71023 318-745-2118
Grady Smith Ph.D., prin. Fax 745-3695

Dry Prong, Grant, Pop. 434
Grant Parish SD
Supt. — See Colfax

Grant Academy 50/Alt
17771 Highway 167 71423 318-899-3999
Randy Crawford, prin. Fax 899-5555
Grant HS 700/9-12
17779 Highway 167 71423 318-899-3331
Randy Crawford, prin. Fax 899-5724
Grant JHS 400/7-8
17773 Highway 167 71423 318-899-5697
Robert Smith, prin. Fax 899-7346

Dubach, Lincoln, Pop. 952
Lincoln Parish SD
Supt. — See Ruston
Dubach HS 200/6-12
7710 Fellowship Rd 71235 318-777-3470
Judy Mabry, prin. Fax 777-8409

Dulac, Terrebonne, Pop. 1,389
Terrebonne Parish SD
Supt. — See Houma
Grand Caillou MS 200/7-8
6741 Grand Caillou Rd 70353 985-563-4488
Cindy Gray, prin. Fax 563-7838

Duson, Lafayette, Pop. 1,682
Lafayette Parish SD
Supt. — See Lafayette
Judice MS 500/6-8
2645 S Fieldspan Rd 70529 337-521-7890
Samuel Clay, prin. Fax 521-7891

Edgard, Saint John the Baptist, Pop. 2,428
St. John The Baptist Parish SD
Supt. — See Reserve
West St. John HS 200/8-12
PO Box 160 70049 985-497-3271
Erica Merrick, prin. Fax 497-5009

Elizabeth, Allen, Pop. 531
Allen Parish SD
Supt. — See Oberlin
Elizabeth S 300/PK-12
PO Box 580 70638 318-634-5341
Keith Morgan, prin. Fax 634-5218

Elton, Jefferson Davis, Pop. 1,103
Jefferson Davis Parish SD
Supt. — See Jennings
Elton JSHS 300/6-12
903 2nd St 70532 337-584-2991
Danielle Simien, prin. Fax 584-2244

Indian Bible Academy 50/1-12
152 Indian Church Rd 70532 337-584-5151
John Cernek, admin. Fax 584-5151

Epps, West Carroll, Pop. 844
West Carroll Parish SD
Supt. — See Oak Grove
Epps S 400/PK-12
PO Box 277 71237 318-926-3624
Edwin Guchereau, prin. Fax 926-5655

Erath, Vermilion, Pop. 2,099
Vermilion Parish SD
Supt. — See Abbeville
Erath HS 500/9-12
808 S Broadway St 70533 337-937-8451
Jed Hebert, prin. Fax 937-5109
Erath MS 400/6-8
800 S Broadway St 70533 337-937-4441
Lynn Moss, prin. Fax 937-5125

Eunice, Saint Landry, Pop. 10,256
St. Landry Parish SD
Supt. — See Opelousas
Eunice Career & Technical Education Ctr. Vo/Tech
421 S 10th St 70535 337-457-8686
Kristine Joubert, prin. Fax 457-0307
Eunice HS 600/9-12
301 S Bobcat Dr 70535 337-457-3011
Mitchell Fontenot, prin. Fax 457-3720
Eunice JHS 400/7-8
751 W Oak Ave 70535 337-457-7386
Lakesha Miller, prin. Fax 457-1764

Louisiana Academy of Beauty Post-Sec.
550 E Laurel Ave 70535 337-457-7627
Louisiana State University Eunice Post-Sec.
2048 Johnson Hwy 70535 337-457-7311
St. Edmund HS 300/7-12
351 W Magnolia Ave 70535 337-457-3777
Beth Christ, prin. Fax 457-2510

Evans, Vernon
Vernon Parish SD
Supt. — See Leesville
Evans S 400/PK-12
PO Box 69 70639 337-286-5289
Mike Kay, prin. Fax 286-9298

Farmerville, Union, Pop. 3,818
Union Parish SD 2,300/PK-12
PO Box 308 71241 318-368-9715
Dr. George Cannon, supt. Fax 368-1012
www.unionpsd.org
Farmerville JHS 200/7-8
606 Bernice St 71241 318-368-9235
Kristi Auger, prin. Fax 368-1989
Union Parish HS 600/9-12
300 Anthony St 71241 318-368-2661
David Gray, prin. Fax 368-2229

Union Christian Academy 400/PK-12
110 W Hill St 71241 318-368-8890
Bill Ritz, pres. Fax 368-2920

Ferriday, Concordia, Pop. 3,491
Concordia Parish SD
Supt. — See Vidalia
Concordia Education Center 50/Alt
160 Kindergarten Rd 71334 318-757-3941
Lillian Franklin, prin. Fax 757-3330
Ferriday HS 300/9-12
801 EE Wallace Blvd N 71334 318-757-8626
James Davis, prin. Fax 757-0763
Ferriday JHS 300/6-8
201 Martin Luther King Blvd 71334 318-757-8695
Arlana Davis, prin. Fax 757-8696

Central Louisiana Technical College Post-Sec.
PO Box 1465 71334 318-757-6501

Florien, Sabine, Pop. 616
Sabine Parish SD
Supt. — See Many
Florien S 600/PK-12
500 High School Rd 71429 318-586-3681
Eddie Jones, prin. Fax 586-3822

Folsom, Saint Tammany, Pop. 708
St. Tammany Parish SD
Supt. — See Covington
Folsom JHS 200/6-8
83055 Hay Hollow Rd 70437 985-796-3724
Sharon Garrett, prin. Fax 796-3701

Forest, West Carroll, Pop. 348
West Carroll Parish SD
Supt. — See Oak Grove
Forest S 500/PK-12
PO Box 368 71242 318-428-3672
James Harris, prin. Fax 428-8875

Franklin, Saint Mary, Pop. 7,561
St. Mary Parish SD
Supt. — See Centerville
Franklin HS 400/9-12
1401 Cynthia St 70538 337-828-0143
Tybus Burdett, prin. Fax 828-0184
Franklin JHS 300/6-8
525 Morris St 70538 337-828-0855
Molly Stadalis, prin. Fax 828-5095
St. Mary Parish Alternative S 100/Alt
131 Clausen Rd S 70538 337-836-9388
Harry Williams, admin. Fax 836-9397
Franklin Adult Education Learning Center Adult
1706 Main St 70538 337-828-0121
Jody Charpentier, coord. Fax 828-0196

Hanson Memorial HS 300/6-12
903 Anderson St 70538 337-828-3487
Kim Adams, prin. Fax 828-0787

Franklinton, Washington, Pop. 3,833
Washington Parish SD 5,200/PK-12
PO Box 587 70438 985-839-3436
Darrell Fairburn, supt. Fax 839-5464
www.wpsb.org
Franklinton HS 800/9-12
1 Demon Cir 70438 985-839-6781
Lisa Tanner, prin. Fax 839-9830
Franklinton JHS 700/6-8
617 Main St 70438 985-839-3501
Pauline Bankston, prin. Fax 839-6912
Pine JSHS 600/6-12
1 Raider Dr 70438 985-848-5243
Jennifer Thomas, prin. Fax 848-9433
Other Schools – See Mount Hermon, Varnado

Bowling Green S 400/PK-12
700 Varnado St 70438 985-839-5317

French Settlement, Livingston, Pop. 1,104
Livingston Parish SD
Supt. — See Livingston
French Settlement JSHS 400/7-12
15875 LA Highway 16 70733 225-698-3561
Lance Hutson, prin. Fax 698-6458

Galliano, Lafourche, Pop. 7,495
Lafourche Parish SD
Supt. — See Thibodaux
South Lafourche HS 1,200/9-12
PO Box 160 70354 985-632-5721
Gaye Cheramie, prin. Fax 632-6723

Geismar, Ascension
Ascension Parish SD
Supt. — See Donaldsonville
Dutchtown HS 1,800/9-12
13165 Highway 73 70734 225-391-6200
Edith Walker, prin. Fax 677-8191
Dutchtown MS 700/6-8
13078 Highway 73 70734 225-391-7800
Doug Walker, prin. Fax 621-2351

Georgetown, Grant, Pop. 323
Grant Parish SD
Supt. — See Colfax
Georgetown S 300/PK-12
PO Box 99 71432 318-827-5306
Carla Lasyone Ph.D., prin. Fax 827-9481

Gibsland, Bienville, Pop. 966
Bienville Parish SD
Supt. — See Arcadia
Gibsland-Coleman S 200/K-12
PO Box 70 71028 318-843-6247
Christopher Jackson, prin. Fax 843-9804

Glenmora, Rapides, Pop. 1,328
Rapides Parish SD
Supt. — See Alexandria
Glenmora JSHS 200/7-12
PO Box 697 71433 318-748-8145
Brian Parmley, prin. Fax 748-8146
Plainview S 300/PK-12
PO Box 698 71433 318-634-5944
Sonia Rasmussen, prin. Fax 634-5389

Golden Meadow, Lafourche, Pop. 2,060
Lafourche Parish SD
Supt. — See Thibodaux
Golden Meadow MS 400/6-8
630 S Bayou Dr 70357 985-475-7314
Timothy Long, prin. Fax 475-6623

Gonzales, Ascension, Pop. 9,648
Ascension Parish SD
Supt. — See Donaldsonville
Central MS 600/6-8
14101 Roddy Rd 70737 225-391-6400
Monica Hills, prin. Fax 621-2682
East Ascension HS 1,500/9-12
612 E Worthy St 70737 225-391-6100
Traci McCorkle, prin. Fax 621-2397
Gonzales MS 600/6-8
1502 W Orice Roth Rd 70737 225-391-6450
Lori Charlet, prin. Fax 621-2509

Ascension Christian HS 100/8-12
14408 E A Academy Rd 70737 225-622-2800
Mark Pellegrin M.S., supt. Fax 622-2875
St. Theresa S 500/3-8
212 E New River St 70737 225-647-2803
Christine Musso, prin. Fax 647-7814

Grambling, Lincoln, Pop. 4,930
Lincoln Parish SD
Supt. — See Ruston
Grambling State University Lab. HS 100/9-12
407 Central Ave 71245 318-274-6153
Sandra Boston, prin. Fax 274-3215
Grambling State University Lab. MS 100/6-8
407 Central Ave 71245 318-274-6531
Sandra Boston, prin. Fax 274-3360

Grambling State University Post-Sec.
403 Main St 71245 318-274-3811

Grand Cane, DeSoto, Pop. 242

Central S 200/K-12
PO Box 187 71032 318-858-3319
Dr. Robert Peters, hdmstr. Fax 858-6394

Grand Chenier, Cameron
Cameron Parish SD
Supt. — See Cameron
South Cameron S 300/PK-12
753 Oak Grove Hwy 70643 337-542-4628
Robert Kimball, prin. Fax 542-4419

Grand Coteau, Saint Landry, Pop. 940

School of the Sacred Heart 500/PK-12
PO Box 310 70541 337-662-5275
Lynne Lieux, hdmstr. Fax 662-3011

Grand Isle, Jefferson, Pop. 1,269
Jefferson Parish SD
Supt. — See Harvey
Grand Isle S 100/PK-12
PO Box 995 70358 985-787-2577
Richard Augustin, prin. Fax 787-3878

Grant, Allen
Allen Parish SD
Supt. — See Oberlin
Fairview S 400/PK-12
PO Box 216 70644 318-634-5354
Pylla Turner, prin. Fax 634-5357

Gray, Terrebonne, Pop. 5,450
Terrebonne Parish SD
Supt. — See Houma
Bourgeois HS 1,000/9-12
1 Reservation Ct 70359 985-872-3277
Mary Olivier, prin. Fax 872-3270

Greensburg, Saint Helena, Pop. 714
Recovery SD
Supt. — See New Orleans
St. Helena Central MS 400/5-8
1590 Highway 1042 70441 225-222-6291
Monique Montgomery, prin. Fax 222-6780

St. Helena Parish SD 800/PK-12
PO Box 540 70441 225-222-4349
Dr. Kelli Joseph, supt. Fax 222-4937
www.sthpk-12.net
St. Helena Central HS 300/9-12
14340 Highway 37 70441 225-222-4402
Reginald Douglas, prin. Fax 222-6986

Northshore Technical Community College Post-Sec.
PO Box 1300 70441 225-222-4251

Gretna, Jefferson, Pop. 17,467
Jefferson Parish SD
Supt. — See Harvey
Gretna MS 700/6-8
910 Gretna Blvd 70053 504-366-0120
Edith Dozier, prin. Fax 366-8807
Jefferson HS 400/9-12
17 Gretna Blvd 70053 504-363-4300
Dr. Gerard LeBlanc, prin. Fax 361-1114
Livaudais MS 600/6-8
925 Lamar Ave 70056 504-393-7544
Carl Nini, prin. Fax 393-9610
Ruppel Academy for Advanced Studies 200/7-8
815 Huey P Long Ave 70053 504-361-8905
Debra Cooper, prin. Fax 361-0792

Gretna Career College Post-Sec.
1415 Whitney Ave 70053 504-366-5409

Gueydan, Vermilion, Pop. 1,385
Vermilion Parish SD
Supt. — See Abbeville
Gueydan HS 200/6-12
901 Main St 70542 337-536-6938
Luddy Herpin, prin. Fax 536-7000

Hackberry, Cameron, Pop. 1,258
Cameron Parish SD
Supt. — See Cameron
Hackberry S 200/PK-12
1390 School St 70645 337-762-3305
Carl Langley, prin. Fax 762-3304

Hammond, Tangipahoa, Pop. 19,799
Tangipahoa Parish SD
Supt. — See Amite
Hammond High Magnet S 1,100/9-12
45168 River Rd 70401 985-345-7235
Chad Troxclair, prin. Fax 345-5252
Hammond Jr High Magnet S 500/7-8
111 J W Davis Dr 70403 985-345-2654
Terran Perry, prin. Fax 542-4215
Tangipahoa Parish PM HS Adult
411 E Crystal St 70401 985-474-8762
Marilyn Dunn, prin. Fax 474-8769

Compass Career College Post-Sec.
42353 Deluxe Plz Ste 20 70403 985-419-2050
North Oaks Medical Center Post-Sec.
15790 Medical Arts Dr 70403 985-543-6600
Northshore Technical Community College Post-Sec.
PO Box 489 70404 985-543-4120
St. Thomas Aquinas HS 400/9-12
14520 Voss Dr 70401 985-542-7662
Jose Becerra, prin. Fax 542-4010
Southeastern Louisiana University Post-Sec.
PO Box 784 70404 985-549-2000

Harrisonburg, Catahoula, Pop. 340
Catahoula Parish SD 1,100/PK-12
PO Box 690 71340 318-744-5727
Dr. Gwile Freeman, supt. Fax 744-9221
cpsbla.org/
Harrisonburg HS 100/K-12
PO Box 710 71340 318-744-5273
S. Floyd, prin. Fax 744-5273
Other Schools – See Jonesville, Sicily Island

Harvey, Jefferson, Pop. 20,018
Jefferson Parish SD 43,400/PK-12
501 Manhattan Blvd 70058 504-349-7600
Dr. James Meza, supt. Fax 349-7960
www.jppss.k12.la.us
Cox HS 1,000/9-12
2200 Lapalco Blvd 70058 504-367-6388
Darvell Edwards, prin. Fax 367-3176
West Jefferson HS 1,300/9-12
2200 8th St 70058 504-368-6055
Vanessa Brown-Lewis, prin. Fax 368-0535
Other Schools – See Avondale, Grand Isle, Gretna, Jefferson, Kenner, Lafitte, Marrero, Metairie, Westwego

Haughton, Bossier, Pop. 3,398
Bossier Parish SD
Supt. — See Benton
Haughton HS 1,100/9-12
210 E McKinley Ave 71037 318-549-5450
Gene Couvillion, prin. Fax 549-5470
Haughton MS 900/6-8
395 S Elm St 71037 318-549-5560
Waylon Bates, prin. Fax 549-5573

Haynesville, Claiborne, Pop. 2,308
Claiborne Parish SD
Supt. — See Homer
Haynesville JSHS 400/4-12
9930 Highway 79 71038 318-624-0905
Scott Johnston, prin. Fax 624-2488

Claiborne Academy 200/PK-12
6741 Highway 79 71038 318-927-2747
Jane Stevens Brown, hdmstr. Fax 927-4519

Hineston, Rapides
Rapides Parish SD
Supt. — See Alexandria
Oak Hill HS 400/7-12
PO Box 269 71438 318-793-2014
Kerry Rogers, prin. Fax 793-8589

Holden, Livingston
Livingston Parish SD
Supt. — See Livingston
Holden S 700/K-12
30120 LA 441 Hwy 70744 225-567-9367
Paula Green, prin. Fax 567-5248

Homer, Claiborne, Pop. 3,200
Claiborne Parish SD 1,800/PK-12
PO Box 600 71040 318-927-3502
Janice Williams, supt. Fax 927-9184
www.claibornepsb.org/
Homer HS 300/9-12
1008 N Main St 71040 318-927-2985
Carrie Hathorn, prin. Fax 927-4733
Homer JHS 200/6-8
612 Pelican Dr 71040 318-927-2826
Craig Roberson, prin. Fax 927-4376
Other Schools – See Haynesville, Summerfield

Hornbeck, Vernon, Pop. 464
Vernon Parish SD
Supt. — See Leesville
Hornbeck S 500/PK-12
PO Box 9 71439 318-565-4440
Cecil Richmond, prin. Fax 565-4136

Houma, Terrebonne, Pop. 33,132
Lafourche Parish SD
Supt. — See Thibodaux
Bayou Blue MS 500/5-8
196 Mazerac St 70364 985-851-1952
Edmond Adams, prin. Fax 851-1849

Terrebonne Parish SD 18,600/PK-12
PO Box 5097 70361 985-876-7400
Philip Martin, supt. Fax 872-0054
www.tpsd.org
East Street Alternative S 50/Alt
609 East St 70363 985-876-1093
Tommy Salter, prin. Fax 851-7931
Ellender Memorial HS 1,000/9-12
3012 Patriot Dr 70363 985-868-7903
Cory Butler, prin. Fax 868-3503
Evergreen JHS 1,100/7-9
5000 W Main St 70360 985-876-2606
Mark Torbert, prin. Fax 868-4395
Houma JHS 1,100/7-9
315 Saint Charles St 70360 985-872-1511
Tom Soudelier, prin. Fax 872-5121
Oaklawn JHS 400/7-8
2215 Acadian Dr 70363 985-872-3904
Clyde Washington, prin. Fax 917-1917
Terrebonne Career & Tech HS Vo/Tech
3051 Patriot Dr 70363 985-851-1163
William Simmons, prin. Fax 851-4480
Terrebonne HS 1,000/9-12
7318 Main St 70360 985-879-3377
Graham Douglas, prin. Fax 223-2270
Bayou Cane Adult Education Adult
6484 W Main St 70360 985-876-3180
Marilyn Schwartz, coord. Fax 876-0411
Other Schools – See Bourg, Chauvin, Dulac, Gray, Montegut, Schriever

---

Blue Cliff College-Houma Post-Sec.
803 Barrow St 70360 985-601-4000
Covenant Christian Academy 200/K-12
4863 W Park Ave 70364 985-851-7567
Dr. Steve Folmar, hdmstr. Fax 851-1087
Houma Christian S 300/PK-12
109 Valhi Blvd 70360 985-851-7423
James Champagne, prin. Fax 872-4958
Omega Institute of Cosmetology Post-Sec.
229 S Hollywood Rd 70360 985-876-9334
South Louisiana Beauty College Post-Sec.
300 Howard Ave 70363 985-873-8978
Vandebilt Catholic HS 900/8-12
209 S Hollywood Rd 70360 985-876-2551
Jim Reiss, prin. Fax 868-9774

Independence, Saint Helena, Pop. 1,638
Tangipahoa Parish SD
Supt. — See Amite
Independence HS 500/9-12
270 Tiger Ave 70443 985-878-9436
Hugh Wallace, prin. Fax 878-4831
Independence Middle Magnet S 300/5-8
300 W 2nd St 70443 985-878-4376
Alexa Hookfin, prin. Fax 878-4848

Iota, Acadia, Pop. 1,481
Acadia Parish SD
Supt. — See Crowley
Iota HS 400/9-12
456 S 5th St 70543 337-779-2534
Dr. Gibson Miller, prin. Fax 779-2872
Iota MS 200/6-8
426 S 5th St 70543 337-779-2536
Debra Seibert, prin. Fax 779-2594

Iowa, Calcasieu, Pop. 2,909
Calcasieu Parish SD
Supt. — See Lake Charles
Iowa HS 600/9-12
401 W Miller Ave 70647 337-217-4380
Michael Oakley, prin. Fax 217-4381

Jackson, East Feliciana, Pop. 3,776
East Feliciana Parish SD
Supt. — See Clinton
East Feliciana HS 300/10-12
3501 Highway 10 70748 225-634-5931
M. Harris, prin. Fax 634-3207

Capital Area Technical College Post-Sec.
3337 Highway 10 70748 225-634-2636

Jeanerette, Iberia, Pop. 5,487
Iberia Parish SD
Supt. — See New Iberia
Jeanerette HS 300/9-12
8217 E Old Spanish Trl 70544 337-276-6038
Heath Hulin, prin. Fax 276-5016

Jefferson, Jefferson, Pop. 11,058
Jefferson Parish SD
Supt. — See Harvey
Martyn Alternative S 50/Alt
1108 Shrewsbury Rd 70121 504-838-6933
Theresa Henderson, prin. Fax 838-6921
Riverdale HS 700/9-12
240 Riverdale Dr 70121 504-833-7288
Denise Carpenter, prin. Fax 837-5401
Riverdale MS 700/6-8
3900 Jefferson Hwy 70121 504-828-2706
Randy Bennett, prin. Fax 833-5125
Taylor Science & Tech Academy 300/6-12
2012 Jefferson Hwy 70121 504-838-2249
Jaime Zapico, prin. Fax 838-7029

Jena, LaSalle, Pop. 3,373
LaSalle Parish SD 2,600/PK-12
PO Box 90 71342 318-992-2161
Roy Breithaupt, supt. Fax 992-8457
www.lasallepsb.com
Jena HS 400/9-12
PO Box 89 71342 318-992-5195
Glen Joiner, prin. Fax 992-4797
Jena JHS 300/6-8
PO Box 920 71342 318-992-5815
Rhonda Russell, prin. Fax 992-6392
LaSalle Parish Alternative S Alt
PO Box 90 71342 318-992-8905
Fax 992-8913
Other Schools – See Olla, Urania

Jennings, Jefferson Davis, Pop. 10,205
Jefferson Davis Parish SD 5,800/PK-12
PO Box 640 70546 337-824-1834
David Clayton, supt. Fax 824-9737
www.jeffersondavis.org
Hathaway S 500/PK-12
4040 Pine Island Hwy 70546 337-824-4452
Mona Miller, prin. Fax 824-2769
Jennings HS 900/7-12
2310 N Sherman St 70546 337-824-0642
Benjamin Oustalet, prin. Fax 824-5585
Other Schools – See Elton, Lacassine, Lake Arthur, Roanoke, Welsh

---

Bethel Christian S 200/PK-12
15147 Highway 102 70546 337-824-0020
Patti Landers, prin. Fax 824-0579

Jonesboro, Jackson, Pop. 4,648
Jackson Parish SD 2,200/PK-12
PO Box 705 71251 318-259-4456
Wayne Alford, supt. Fax 259-2527
www.jpsb.us/
Jonesboro-Hodge HS 300/9-12
225 Pershing Hwy 71251 318-259-4138
Ted Reeves, prin. Fax 259-2701
Jonesboro-Hodge MS 300/5-8
440 Old Winnfield Rd 71251 318-259-6611
Norman Amos, prin. Fax 259-9699
Weston S 600/PK-12
213 Highway 505 71251 318-259-7313
Dr. Robin Potts, prin. Fax 259-1056
Other Schools – See Quitman

Jonesville, Catahoula, Pop. 2,258
Catahoula Parish SD
Supt. — See Harrisonburg
Block HS 200/8-12
300 Division St 71343 318-339-7996
Jeffrey Odom, prin. Fax 339-7901
Catahoula Parish Alternative S Alt
300 Division St 71343 318-339-7996
Andrea Cruse, prin. Fax 339-7901
Central S 100/K-12
244 Larto Bayou Rd 71343 318-339-7574
Johnnie Adams, prin. Fax 339-7925

Kaplan, Vermilion, Pop. 4,526
Vermilion Parish SD
Supt. — See Abbeville
Kaplan HS 500/9-12
200 E Pirates Ln 70548 337-643-6385
Laura LeBeouf, prin. Fax 643-3543
Rost MS 400/5-8
112 W 6th St 70548 337-643-8545
David Dupuis, prin. Fax 643-7013

Kenner, Jefferson, Pop. 65,713
Jefferson Parish SD
Supt. — See Harvey
Bonnabel Magnet Academy HS 1,600/9-12
2801 Bruin Dr 70065 504-443-4564
Dawn Kalb, prin. Fax 443-3401
Martyn Academy for Career Preparation 100/Alt
2801 Bruin Dr 70065 504-303-6800
Dr. David Charles, prin. Fax 303-6825
Roosevelt MS 600/6-8
3315 Maine Ave 70065 504-443-1361
Mera Bercy, prin. Fax 443-3425

Herzing University Post-Sec.
2500 Williams Blvd 70062 504-733-0074
John Jay Kenner Academy Post-Sec.
2844 Tennessee Ave 70062 504-467-2951
Southwest University Post-Sec.
2200 Veterans Memorial Blvd 70062 504-468-2900

Kentwood, Tangipahoa, Pop. 2,191
Tangipahoa Parish SD
Supt. — See Amite
Kentwood High Magnet S 300/7-12
PO Box 88 70444 985-229-2881
Rochelle Bates, prin. Fax 229-6031
Sumner HS 500/9-12
15841 Highway 440 70444 985-229-8805
Lisa Fussell, prin. Fax 229-2043
Sumner MS 400/6-8
15649 Highway 440 70444 985-310-2152
Brenda Johnson, prin. Fax 229-4257

Kilbourne, West Carroll, Pop. 412
West Carroll Parish SD
Supt. — See Oak Grove
Kilbourne S 300/PK-12
PO Box 339 71253 318-428-3721
Truman Smith, prin. Fax 428-3860

Kinder, Allen, Pop. 2,412
Allen Parish SD
Supt. — See Oberlin
Kinder HS 300/9-12
145 Highway 383 70648 337-738-2886
Loma Bertrand, prin. Fax 738-5665
Kinder MS 300/5-8
414 N 12th St 70648 337-738-3223
Tracey Odom, prin. Fax 738-3425

Labadieville, Assumption, Pop. 1,837
Assumption Parish SD
Supt. — See Napoleonville
Labadieville MS 300/5-8
2747 Highway 1 70372 985-526-4227
Corey Crochet, prin. Fax 526-4163

Lacassine, Jefferson Davis, Pop. 475
Jefferson Davis Parish SD
Supt. — See Jennings
Lacassine S 600/PK-12
PO Box 50 70650 337-588-4205
David Troutman, prin. Fax 588-4283

Lafayette, Lafayette, Pop. 118,722
Lafayette Parish SD 29,700/PK-12
PO Box 2158 70502 337-521-7000
Dr. Pat Cooper, supt. Fax 233-0977
www.lpssonline.com
Acadiana HS 1,700/9-12
315 Rue Du Belier 70506 337-521-7950
David LeJeune, prin. Fax 521-7951
Acadian MS 600/5-8
4201 Moss St 70507 337-521-7840
Linda Nance, prin. Fax 521-7841
Alleman MS 1,000/5-8
600 Roselawn Blvd 70503 337-521-7850
Kathy Aloisio, prin. Fax 521-7851
Breaux MS 700/6-8
1400 S Orange St 70501 337-521-7860
Loretta Caldwell, prin. Fax 521-7861
Carencro HS 1,400/9-12
721 W Butcher Switch Rd 70507 337-521-7960
Ken Roebuck, prin. Fax 521-7961
Comeaux HS 1,900/9-12
100 W Bluebird St 70508 337-521-7970
Joseph Craig, prin. Fax 521-7971
Early College Academy 200/9-12
1101 Bertrand Dr 70506 337-521-8956
Anne Castille, prin. Fax 262-1940
Lafayette HS 2,300/9-12
3000 W Congress St 70506 337-984-5284
Dr. Patrick Leonard, prin. Fax 984-0153
Lafayette MS 500/6-8
1301 W University Ave 70506 337-521-7900
Monique Magee, prin. Fax 521-7901
Martin MS 700/5-8
401 Broadmoor Blvd 70503 337-521-7910
Fax 521-7911
Moss Preparatory Program Alt
801 Mudd Ave 70501 337-521-7580
Jody Duhon, admin. Fax 521-7581
Northside HS 900/9-12
301 Dunand St 70501 337-521-7990
Melinda Voorhies, prin. Fax 521-7991
Smith Career Center Vo/Tech
200 18th St 70501 337-521-7570
Alicia Caesar, prin. Fax 521-7571
Thibodaux STEM Magnet Academy 50/6-10
805 Teurlings Dr 70501 337-521-7920
Jeff Debetaz, prin. Fax 521-7921
Other Schools – See Broussard, Carencro, Duson, Scott, Youngsville

Ascension Episcopal S 700/PK-12
1030 Johnston St 70501 337-233-9748
Dr. David Rath, hdmstr. Fax 269-9768
Blue Cliff College Post-Sec.
120 James Comeaux Rd 70508 337-269-0620
Cosmetology Training Center Post-Sec.
2516 Johnston St 70503 337-237-6868
Delta College of Arts & Technology Post-Sec.
200 Republic Ave Ste F 70508 337-988-5455
Lafayette Christian Academy 700/PK-12
220 Portland Ave 70507 337-234-9860
Lafayette General Medical Center Post-Sec.
PO Box 52009 70505 337-261-7381
Lockworks Academie of Hairdressing Post-Sec.
2922 Johnston St 70503 337-233-0511
Remington College Post-Sec.
303 Rue Louis XIV 70508 337-981-4010
Ronnie & Dorman's School of Hair Design Post-Sec.
201 Saint Joseph St 70506 337-232-1806
St. Genevieve MS 200/6-8
1500 E Willow St 70501 337-266-5553
Julie Champagne, prin. Fax 266-5775
St. Thomas More HS 1,000/9-12
450 E Farrel Rd 70508 337-988-3700
Audrey Menard, prin. Fax 988-2911
South Louisiana Community College Post-Sec.
1101 Bertrand Dr 70506 337-521-8896
South Louisiana Community College Post-Sec.
320 Devalcourt St 70506 337-521-8896
Teurlings Catholic HS 700/9-12
139 Teurlings Dr 70501 337-235-5711
Michael Boyer, prin. Fax 234-8057
Unitech Training Academy Post-Sec.
3605 Ambassador Caffery Pky 70503 337-988-6764
University Medical Center Post-Sec.
2390 W Congress St 70506 337-261-6004
University of Louisiana at Lafayette Post-Sec.
104 E University Ave 70503 337-482-1000

Lafitte, Jefferson, Pop. 956
Jefferson Parish SD
Supt. — See Harvey
Fisher MSHS 400/7-12
2529 Jean Lafitte Blvd 70067 504-689-3665
George Hebert, prin. Fax 689-7556

Lake Arthur, Jefferson Davis, Pop. 2,693
Jefferson Davis Parish SD
Supt. — See Jennings
Lake Arthur JSHS 400/7-12
4374 Tiger Ln 70549 337-774-5152
Brant Smith, prin. Fax 774-2522

Lake Charles, Calcasieu, Pop. 70,438
Calcasieu Parish SD 33,000/PK-12
PO Box 800 70602 337-217-4000
Wayne Savoy, supt. Fax 217-4001
www.cpsb.org
Barbe HS 1,900/9-12
2200 W McNeese St 70605 337-217-4460
Beth Fraser, prin. Fax 217-4461
Calcasieu Parish Alternative HS 100/Alt
2903 Opelousas St 70615 337-217-4290
Kenny Brown, prin. Fax 217-4291
College St Vocational Ctr/Westlake T & I Vo/Tech
736 E College St 70607 337-217-4370
George Albers, prin. Fax 217-4371
Houston HS 1,200/9-12
880 Sam Houston Jones Pkwy 70611 337-217-4480
Mike Reed, prin. Fax 217-4481
LaGrange HS 1,000/9-12
3420 Louisiana Ave 70607 337-217-4960
Rico Guillory, prin. Fax 217-4961
Lake Charles/Boston Academy 400/9-12
1509 Enterprise Blvd 70601 337-217-4390
Charles Adkins, prin. Fax 217-4391
Molo Magnet MS 400/6-8
2300 Medora St 70601 337-217-4710
Shonna Anderson, prin. Fax 217-4711
Moss Bluff MS 900/6-8
297 Park Rd 70611 337-217-4570
John Duhon, prin. Fax 217-4571
Oak Park MS 500/6-8
2200 Oak Park Blvd 70601 337-217-4830
Martin Guillory, prin. Fax 217-4831
Reynaud MS 200/6-8
745 S Shattuck St 70601 337-217-4800
Carolyn Thomas-Clark, prin. Fax 217-4801
STEPS HS 9-12
3820 Bennett Johnston Ave 70615 337-491-2607
Doug McCullor, prin. Fax 491-2649
Washington-Marion Magnet HS 700/9-12
2802 Pineview St 70615 337-217-4540
Robert Pete, prin. Fax 217-4541
Welsh MS 1,300/6-8
1500 W Mcneese St 70605 337-217-4410
Bobby Jack Thompson, prin. Fax 217-4412
White MS 600/6-8
1000 E McNeese St 70607 337-217-4810
Christopher Fontenot, prin. Fax 217-4811
Adult & Continuing Education Adult
1015 6th Ave 70601 337-217-4220
James Powers, prin. Fax 217-4221
Other Schools – See Bell City, Dequincy, Iowa, Starks, Sulphur, Vinton, Westlake

Cameron Parish SD
Supt. — See Cameron
Grand Lake S 700/PK-12
1039 Highway 384 70607 337-905-2231
David Duhon, prin. Fax 905-2961

Covenant Grace Academy 50/K-12
2110 E McNeese St 70607 337-474-2424
Marla Pennick, admin.
Delta School of Business and Technology Post-Sec.
517 Broad St 70601 337-439-5765
Hamilton Christian Academy 500/PK-12
1415 8th St 70601 337-439-1178
Lake Charles Memorial Hospital Post-Sec.
1701 Oak Park Blvd 70601 337-494-3200
McNeese State University Post-Sec.
4205 Ryan St 70605 337-475-5000
St. Louis HS 500/9-12
1620 Bank St 70601 337-436-7275
Deborah Frank, pres. Fax 436-6792
St. Patrick's Hospital Post-Sec.
524 S Ryan St 70601 337-491-7730
Sowela Technical Community College Post-Sec.
3820 Senator Johnston Ave 70615 337-491-2698
Stage One - The Hair School Post-Sec.
209 W College St 70605 337-474-0533

Lake Providence, East Carroll, Pop. 3,969
East Carroll Parish SD 900/PK-12
PO Box 792 71254 318-559-2222
Dr. Voleria Millikin, supt. Fax 559-3864
www.e-carrollschools.org
Griffin Middle Academy 300/6-8
1205 Charles D Jones Blvd 71254 318-559-1395
Janice Harris, prin. Fax 559-0679
Lake Providence HS 300/9-12
700 Martin Luther King Jr 71254 318-559-1984
Andre Williams, prin. Fax 559-5380

Briarfield Academy 200/PK-12
301 Riddle Ln 71254 318-559-2360
Lance Prine, hdmstr. Fax 559-2360

Laplace, Saint John the Baptist, Pop. 29,464

St. Charles Catholic HS 500/8-12
100 Dominican Rd 70068 985-652-3809
Andrew Cupit, prin. Fax 652-2609

Larose, Lafourche, Pop. 7,283
Lafourche Parish SD
Supt. — See Thibodaux
Larose-Cut Off MS 500/6-8
13356 W Main St 70373 985-693-3273
Carla Robbins, prin. Fax 693-3270

Lecompte, Rapides, Pop. 1,209
Rapides Parish SD
Supt. — See Alexandria
Rapides HS 200/9-12
PO Box 770 71346 318-776-9371
Bryan Runyan, prin. Fax 776-5844

Red River Academy 100/7-12
PO Box 1255 71346 318-776-5655
Brent Hall, prin. Fax 776-5654

Leesville, Vernon, Pop. 6,343
Vernon Parish SD 10,000/PK-12
201 Belview Rd 71446 337-239-3401
Jackie Self, supt. Fax 238-5777
www.vpsb.k12.la.us
Hicks S 300/PK-12
1296 Hicks School Rd 71446 337-239-9645
Randy Lansdale, prin. Fax 239-6149
Leesville HS 900/9-12
502 Berry Ave 71446 337-239-3464
Mark Freshley, prin. Fax 239-2485
Leesville JHS 500/7-8
480 Berry Ave 71446 337-239-3874
Angel Williams, prin. Fax 238-4113
Pickering JSHS 500/7-12
180 Lebleu Rd 71446 337-537-1555
Hubert Jordan, prin. Fax 537-3019
Vernon Parish Optional S 50/Alt
1100 Abe Allen Memorial Dr 71446 337-392-0008
Roger Rolon, prin. Fax 392-0009
Other Schools – See Anacoco, Evans, Hornbeck, Pitkin, Rosepine, Simpson

Central Louisiana Technical College Post-Sec.
15014 Lake Charles Hwy 71446 337-537-3135
Faith Training Christian Academy 400/PK-12
603 E Mechanic St 71446 337-329-1569

Lena, Rapides
Rapides Parish SD
Supt. — See Alexandria
Northwood S 800/PK-12
8830 Highway 1 N 71447 318-793-8021
Dana Nolan, prin. Fax 793-8503

Livingston, Livingston, Pop. 1,758
Livingston Parish SD 23,100/PK-12
PO Box 1130 70754 225-686-7044
John Watson, supt. Fax 686-3052
www.lpsb.org
Doyle JSHS 500/7-12
PO Box 160 70754 225-686-2318
Thomas Hodges, prin. Fax 686-2701
Other Schools – See Albany, Denham Springs, French Settlement, Holden, Maurepas, Springfield, Walker, Watson

Livonia, Pointe Coupee, Pop. 1,418
Pointe Coupee Parish SD
Supt. — See New Roads
Livonia HS 700/7-12
PO Box 549 70755 225-637-2532
Stacey Gueho, prin. Fax 637-3024

Lockport, Lafourche, Pop. 2,549
Lafourche Parish SD
Supt. — See Thibodaux
Lockport MS 300/6-8
720 Main St 70374 985-532-2597
Jarod Martin, prin. Fax 532-5811

Logansport, DeSoto, Pop. 1,527
DeSoto Parish SD
Supt. — See Mansfield
Logansport S 300/PK-12
PO Box 549 71049 318-697-4873
Bridgette Brown, prin. Fax 697-1120
Stanley S 400/PK-12
14323 Highway 84 71049 318-697-2664
Carolyn Phillips, prin. Fax 697-5984

Longville, Beauregard, Pop. 621
Beauregard Parish SD
Supt. — See Deridder
South Beauregard JSHS 700/7-12
151 Longville Church Rd 70652 337-725-3536
Tammy Crain, prin. Fax 725-6222

Loranger, Tangipahoa
Tangipahoa Parish SD
Supt. — See Amite
Loranger HS 600/9-12
PO Box 560 70446 985-878-6271
Rhea Marrs, prin. Fax 878-4875
Loranger MS 600/5-8
PO Box 469 70446 985-878-9455
Catherine Perry, prin. Fax 878-4907

Loreauville, Iberia, Pop. 881
Iberia Parish SD
Supt. — See New Iberia
Loreauville JSHS 400/7-12
PO Box 446 70552 337-229-4701
Karen Bashay, prin. Fax 229-4275

Luling, Saint Charles, Pop. 11,952
St. Charles Parish SD 9,700/PK-12
13855 River Rd 70070 985-785-6289
Felecia Gomez-Walker, supt. Fax 785-1025
www.stcharles.k12.la.us
Smith MS 300/6-8
281 Sugarland Pkwy 70070 985-331-1018
Harold Blood, prin. Fax 331-9385
Other Schools – See Boutte, Destrehan, Paradis, Saint Rose

Lutcher, Saint James, Pop. 3,521
St. James Parish SD 3,600/PK-12
PO Box 338 70071 225-258-4500
Alonzo Luce Ph.D., supt. Fax 869-8845
www.stjames.k12.la.us
Career & Technology Center Vo/Tech
PO Box 338 70071 225-258-4571
Mike Avant, dir. Fax 869-7935

Lutcher HS 1,100/7-12
PO Box 489 70071 225-869-5741
Dr. Daryl Scoggin, prin. Fax 869-8872
Other Schools – See Saint James, Vacherie

Madisonville, Saint Tammany, Pop. 704
St. Tammany Parish SD
Supt. — See Covington
Madisonville JHS 600/5-8
PO Box 850 70447 985-845-3355
Dwayne Kern, prin. Fax 845-9018

Mamou, Evangeline, Pop. 3,194
Evangeline Parish SD
Supt. — See Ville Platte
Mamou JSHS 800/5-12
1008 7th St 70554 337-468-5793
Liz Chatelain, prin. Fax 468-2220

Mandeville, Saint Tammany, Pop. 11,401
St. Tammany Parish SD
Supt. — See Covington
Fontainebleau HS 1,800/9-12
100 Bulldog Dr 70471 985-892-7112
Johnny Vitrano, prin. Fax 892-9894
Fountainebleau JHS 900/7-8
100 Hurricane Aly 70471 985-875-7501
Dr. Timothy Schneider, prin. Fax 875-7650
Lakeshore HS 700/9-12
26301 Highway 1088 70448 985-624-5046
Brennan McCurley, prin. Fax 624-5202
Mandeville HS 1,600/9-12
1 Skipper Dr 70471 985-626-5225
Bruce Bundy, prin. Fax 626-5298
Mandeville JHS 700/7-8
639 Carondelet St 70448 985-626-4428
Mary Ann Cucchiara, prin. Fax 674-0401
Monteleone JHS 500/7-8
63000 Blue Marlin Dr 70448 985-951-8088
Donna Addison, prin. Fax 951-8083

Mangham, Richland, Pop. 672
Richland Parish SD
Supt. — See Rayville
Mangham HS 200/9-12
PO Box 348 71259 318-248-2485
Connie Williams, prin. Fax 248-2406
Mangham JHS 200/6-8
810 McConnel St 71259 318-248-2729
Connie Williams, prin. Fax 248-2931

Mansfield, DeSoto, Pop. 4,973
DeSoto Parish SD 4,800/PK-12
201 Crosby St 71052 318-872-2836
Dr. Cade Brumley, supt. Fax 872-1324
www.desotopsb.com
DeSoto Parish Alternative S 50/Alt
2269 Whaley St 71052 318-871-0493
Toras Hill, prin. Fax 871-0496
Mansfield HS 400/9-12
401 Kings Hwy 71052 318-872-0793
Sedric Clark, prin. Fax 872-2223
Mansfield MS 300/5-8
1915 McArthur Dr 71052 318-872-1309
Grayson Collins, prin. Fax 872-1319
Other Schools – See Logansport, Stonewall

Northwest Louisiana Technical College Post-Sec.
943 Oxford Rd 71052 318-872-2243

Many, Sabine, Pop. 2,778
Sabine Parish SD 4,100/PK-12
PO Box 1079 71449 318-256-9228
Dr. Sara Ebarb, supt. Fax 256-0105
www.sabine.k12.la.us
Many HS 300/9-12
100 Tiger Dr 71449 318-256-2114
Norman Booker, prin. Fax 256-0492
Many JHS 400/4-8
1801 Natchitoches Hwy 71449 318-256-3573
Madeline Owens, prin. Fax 256-2846
Other Schools – See Converse, Florien, Negreet, Noble, Pleasant Hill, Zwolle

---

Northwest Louisiana Technical College Post-Sec.
PO Box 790 71449 318-256-4101

Marksville, Avoyelles, Pop. 5,505
Avoyelles Parish SD 6,000/PK-12
221 Tunica Dr W 71351 318-253-5982
Dwayne Lemoine, supt. Fax 253-5178
www.avoyellespsb.com
Marksville HS 900/7-12
407 W Bontemps St 71351 318-253-9356
Marvin Hall, prin. Fax 253-4256
Other Schools – See Bunkie, Moreauville

Marrero, Jefferson, Pop. 32,762
Jefferson Parish SD
Supt. — See Harvey
Cullier Career Center Vo/Tech
1429 Ames Blvd Ste B 70072 504-340-6963
Mark Perry, prin. Fax 341-1022
Douglass Academy for Career Preparation 100/9-12
4300 Patriot St 70072 504-368-5962
Vanessa Brown-Lewis, prin. Fax 362-1904
Ehret HS 1,700/9-12
4300 Patriot St 70072 504-340-7651
Maria Landry, prin. Fax 340-7295
Ellender MS 800/6-8
4501 E Ames Blvd 70072 504-341-9469
Dawn Matherne, prin. Fax 348-0054
Higgins HS 1,500/9-12
7201 Lapalco Blvd 70072 504-341-2273
David Lewis, prin. Fax 341-8110
Marrero MS 600/6-8
4100 7th St 70072 504-341-5842
Christina Conforto, prin. Fax 341-0004
Truman MS 500/6-8
5417 Ehret Rd 70072 504-341-0961
Gary Barras, prin. Fax 347-4497
Westbank Community S 100/Alt
2590 Barataria Blvd 70072 504-371-4651
Preston Gassery, prin. Fax 371-8378

Academy of Our Lady HS 700/8-12
537 Avenue D 70072 504-341-6217
Sr. Michelle Geiger, prin. Fax 341-6229
Archbishop Shaw HS 600/8-12
1000 Barataria Blvd 70072 504-340-6727
Rev. Lou Konopelski, prin. Fax 340-7899
Conquering Word Christian Academy 200/PK-12
812 Avenue F 70072 504-328-2273
Carolyn Treaudo Ph.D., prin. Fax 328-2204

Maurepas, Livingston
Livingston Parish SD
Supt. — See Livingston
Maurepas S 400/K-12
PO Box 39 70449 225-695-6111
Peggy Fontenot, prin. Fax 695-3265

Maurice, Vermilion, Pop. 953
Vermilion Parish SD
Supt. — See Abbeville
North Vermilion HS 800/7-12
11609 LA Highway 699 70555 337-898-1491
Gregory Theriot, prin. Fax 893-8684

Meraux, Saint Bernard, Pop. 5,703
St. Bernard Parish SD
Supt. — See Chalmette
Trist MS 500/6-8
1 Pirates Cv 70075 504-872-9402
Denise Pritchard, prin. Fax 872-9426

Merryville, Beauregard, Pop. 1,088
Beauregard Parish SD
Supt. — See Deridder
Merryville S 500/K-12
7061 Highway 110 W 70653 337-825-8046
Scott Pousson, prin. Fax 825-6443

Metairie, Jefferson, Pop. 136,499
Jefferson Parish SD
Supt. — See Harvey
Adams MS 800/6-8
5525 Henican Pl 70003 504-887-5240
Ginger Bruce, prin. Fax 887-0173
East Jefferson HS 1,100/9-12
400 Phlox Ave 70001 504-888-7171
James Kytle, prin. Fax 888-2072
Harris MS 800/6-8
911 Elise Ave 70003 504-733-0867
Otis Guichet, prin. Fax 733-0953
Haynes Academy for Advanced Studies 700/6-12
1416 Metairie Rd 70005 504-837-8300
Jerome Helmstetter, prin. Fax 837-2110
King HS 1,200/9-12
4301 Grace King Pl 70002 504-888-7334
Meg Griffon, prin. Fax 888-2082
Meisler MS 800/6-8
3700 Cleary Ave 70002 504-888-5832
Semaj Allen-Raymond M.Ed., prin. Fax 888-5855

Archbishop Chapelle HS 900/8-12
8800 Veterans Memorial Blvd 70003 504-467-3105
Cathy Yaeger, prin. Fax 466-3191
Archbishop Rummel HS 1,000/8-12
PO Box 663 70004 504-834-5592
Michael Scalco, prin. Fax 832-4016
Blue Cliff College Post-Sec.
3200 Cleary Ave 70002 504-456-3141
Crescent City Christian S 400/PK-12
4828 Utica St 70006 504-885-4700
David Jochum, admin. Fax 885-4703
Ecole Classique S 300/PK-12
5236 Glendale St 70006 504-887-3507
Sal Frederico, hdmstr. Fax 887-8140
Lutheran HS 100/9-12
3864 17th St 70002 504-455-4062
Lois Rost, prin. Fax 455-4453
Metairie Park Country Day S 800/PK-12
300 Park Rd 70005 504-837-5204
Carolyn Chandler, hdmstr. Fax 837-0015
Ridgewood Preparatory S 200/PK-12
201 Pasadena Ave 70001 504-835-2545
M. J. Montgomery, hdmstr. Fax 837-1864
St. Martin's Episcopal S 700/PK-12
225 Green Acres Rd 70003 504-733-0353
Walter Baer, hdmstr. Fax 736-8800

Midland, Acadia
Acadia Parish SD
Supt. — See Crowley
Midland JSHS 300/8-12
735 S Crocker St 70559 337-783-3310
Clyde Briley, prin. Fax 783-3332

Minden, Webster, Pop. 12,925
Webster Parish SD 5,100/PK-12
PO Box 520 71058 318-377-7052
Steve Dozier, supt. Fax 377-4114
www.websterpsb.org
Minden HS 800/9-12
PO Box 838 71058 318-377-2766
Robin Tucker, prin. Fax 377-3236
Webster JHS 500/7-8
700 E Union St 71055 318-377-3847
Elena Black, prin. Fax 377-1943
Webster Parish Alternative S 100/Alt
109 Clerk St 71055 318-377-5418
Fax 371-6748
Other Schools – See Doyline, Sarepta, Sibley, Springhill

Glenbrook S 400/K-12
1674 Country Club Cir 71055 318-377-2135
Darden Gladney, hdmstr. Fax 377-0578
Northwest Louisiana Technical College Post-Sec.
PO Box 835 71058 318-371-3035

Monroe, Ouachita, Pop. 48,278
Monroe City SD 8,000/PK-12
PO Box 4180 71211 318-325-0601
Brent Vidrine, supt. Fax 812-3604
www.mcschools.net
Carroll Magnet HS 600/9-12
2939 Renwick St 71201 318-387-8441
Tammye Turpin Ed.D., prin. Fax 325-6305
Carroll Magnet JHS 300/7-8
2913 Renwick St 71201 318-322-1683
Fax 322-0833
King MS 300/7-8
3716 Nutland Rd 71202 318-387-1825
Alvin Williams, prin. Fax 325-4285
Lee JHS 500/7-8
1600 N 19th St 71201 318-323-1143
Dana Mullins, prin. Fax 325-5236
Monroe City Alternative S 50/Alt
300 Sherrouse Ave 71203 318-343-3258
Robert Rash, prin. Fax 343-6141
Neville HS 900/9-12
600 Forsythe Ave 71201 318-323-2237
Whitney Martin, prin. Fax 387-8774
Wossman HS 700/9-12
1600 Arizona Ave 71202 318-387-2932
Sam Moore, prin. Fax 322-1378

Ouachita Parish SD 18,800/PK-12
PO Box 1642 71210 318-432-5000
Dr. Robert Webber, supt. Fax 432-5221
www.opsb.net
Ouachita JHS 700/7-8
5500 Blanks St 71203 318-345-5100
Marsha Baker, prin. Fax 345-3308
Ouachita Parish HS 1,200/9-12
681 Highway 594 71203 318-343-2769
Todd Guice, prin. Fax 343-9594
Richwood HS 500/9-12
5901 Highway 165 Byp 71202 318-361-0467
Dr. Sharilynn Loche, prin. Fax 361-9810
Richwood MS 300/7-8
5855 Highway 165 Byp 71202 318-432-2000
Orlando Freemont, prin. Fax 432-2049
Sterlington HS 300/9-12
233 Keystone Rd 71203 318-665-2725
Dell Ashley, prin. Fax 665-2727
Other Schools – See Calhoun, Sterlington, West Monroe

Career Technical College Post-Sec.
2319 Louisville Ave 71201 318-323-2889
Cloyd's Beauty School #2 Inc. Post-Sec.
1311 Winnsboro Rd 71202 318-322-5314
Cloyd's Beauty School #3 Inc. Post-Sec.
2514 Ferrand St 71201 318-322-5314
Louisiana Delta Community College Post-Sec.
7500 Millhaven Rd 71203 318-345-9000
Ouachita Christian S 700/PK-12
7065 Highway 165 N 71203 318-325-6000
River Oaks S 400/PK-12
600 Finks Hideaway Rd 71203 318-343-4185
Dr. William Middleton, hdmstr. Fax 343-1107
St. Francis Medical Center Post-Sec.
PO Box 1901 71210 318-327-4141
St. Frederick HS 200/7-12
3300 Westminister Ave 71201 318-323-9636
Guy Farber, prin. Fax 323-7456
University of Louisiana at Monroe Post-Sec.
700 University Ave 71209 318-342-1000

Montegut, Terrebonne, Pop. 1,507
Terrebonne Parish SD
Supt. — See Houma
Montegut MS 600/5-8
138 Dolphin St 70377 985-594-5886
Kim Vauclin, prin. Fax 594-9666

Monterey, Concordia, Pop. 437
Concordia Parish SD
Supt. — See Vidalia
Monterey S 500/PK-12
PO Box 127 71354 318-386-2214
John Bostic, prin. Fax 386-7356

Montgomery, Grant, Pop. 714
Grant Parish SD
Supt. — See Colfax
Montgomery HS 200/7-12
PO Box 428 71454 318-646-2879
Patti Williams, prin. Fax 646-3926

Moreauville, Avoyelles, Pop. 900
Avoyelles Parish SD
Supt. — See Marksville
Avoyelles HS 800/7-12
287 Main St 71355 318-985-2361
Brent Whiddon, prin. Fax 985-2786

Morgan City, Saint Mary, Pop. 12,212
St. Mary Parish SD
Supt. — See Centerville
Morgan City HS 700/9-12
2400 Tiger Dr 70380 985-384-1754
Milton Fabre, prin. Fax 384-7054
Morgan City JHS 600/6-8
911 Marguerite St 70380 985-384-5922
Kenneth Holmes, prin. Fax 385-4170
Morgan City Adult Learning Center Adult
PO Box 830 70381 985-385-0502

Central Catholic HS 200/7-12
2100 Cedar St Unit 1 70380 985-385-5372
Vic Bonnaffee, prin. Fax 385-3444

South Central Louisiana Technical Coll Post-Sec.
900 Youngs Rd 70380 985-380-2957

Mount Hermon, Washington
Washington Parish SD
Supt. — See Franklinton
Mount Hermon S 500/PK-12
36119 Highway 38 70450 985-877-4642
Debra Byrd, prin. Fax 877-4710

Napoleonville, Assumption, Pop. 653
Assumption Parish SD 3,800/PK-12
4901 Highway 308 70390 985-369-7251
Earl Martinez, supt. Fax 369-2530
www.assumptionschools.com
Assumption HS 1,100/9-12
4880 Highway 308 70390 985-369-2956
Niles Riche, prin. Fax 369-6252
Napoleonville MS 300/5-8
4847 Highway 1 70390 985-369-6587
Shawn Preston, prin. Fax 369-6595
Other Schools – See Belle Rose, Labadieville, Pierre Part

Natchitoches, Natchitoches, Pop. 17,968
Natchitoches Parish SD 6,800/PK-12
PO Box 16 71458 318-352-2358
Dr. Derwood Duke, supt. Fax 352-8138
www.nat.k12.la.us/
Jackson Technical Center 100/Alt
1621 Welch St 71457 318-357-9410
Alvin Brossette, prin. Fax 357-8677
Natchitoches Central HS 1,200/9-12
6513 Highway 1 Byp 71457 318-352-2211
Jessie Skinner, prin. Fax 357-8837
NSU Middle Lab S 200/6-8
Tec Pod Bldg NSU 71497 318-357-4509
Ben LaGrone, prin. Fax 357-4260
Other Schools – See Campti

Northwestern State University Post-Sec.
175 Sam Sibley Dr 71497 318-357-6011
Northwest Louisiana Technical College Post-Sec.
PO Box 657 71458 318-357-3162
St. Mary's S 400/PK-12
PO Box 2070 71457 318-352-8394
Phyllis Scott, prin. Fax 352-5798

Negreet, Sabine
Sabine Parish SD
Supt. — See Many
Negreet S 500/PK-12
PO Box 14 71460 318-256-2349
Gene Wright, prin. Fax 256-5868

New Iberia, Iberia, Pop. 30,160
Iberia Parish SD 13,100/PK-12
PO Box 200 70562 337-365-2341
Dale Henderson, supt. Fax 365-6996
www.iberia.k12.la.us
Alternative Center for Education 100/Alt
500 Bank Ave 70560 337-369-3696
Maxine Jones, prin. Fax 365-5111
Anderson Street MS 400/7-8
1059 Anderson St 70560 337-365-3932
James Russell, prin. Fax 367-8285
Belle Place MS 500/7-8
4110 Loreauville Rd 70563 337-364-2141
Curtis Coquat, prin. Fax 365-9463
Iberia MS 600/7-8
613 Weeks Island Rd 70560 337-364-3927
Michael Bonin, prin. Fax 365-9681
Iberia Parish Career Center Vo/Tech
618 Recreation Dr 70560 337-365-7231
Chris Broussard, prin. Fax 367-0875
New Iberia HS 1,600/9-12
1301 E Admiral Doyle Dr 70560 337-369-6714
Curt Landry, prin. Fax 364-6920
Westgate HS 1,100/9-12
2305 Jefferson Island Rd 70560 337-365-2431
Neely Moore, prin. Fax 364-3487
Other Schools – See Delcambre, Jeanerette, Loreauville

Assembly Christian S 300/PK-12
4219 E Admiral Doyle Dr 70560 337-364-4340
Bristow Academy Post-Sec.
1113 Vortex Dr 70560 337-364-8909
Catholic HS 900/4-12
1301 Delasalle Dr 70560 337-364-5116
Ray Simon, prin. Fax 364-5041
Highland Baptist Christian S 500/PK-12
708 Angers St 70563 337-364-2273
Janie C. Lamothe, admin. Fax 369-6303
Neill Institute Post-Sec.
1301A W Saint Peter St 70560 337-365-6570
South Louisiana Community College Post-Sec.
609 Ember Dr 70560 337-373-0011

New Orleans, Orleans, Pop. 338,397
Orleans Parish SD 7,900/PK-12
3520 General Degaulle Dr 70114 504-304-3520
Fax 309-2865
www.opsb.us
McDonogh 35 HS 900/7-12
1331 Kerlerec St 70116 504-324-7600
Delores Winfield, prin. Fax 942-0276

Recovery SD 27,400/PK-12
1615 Poydras St Ste 1400 70112 504-373-6200
Patrick Dobard, supt. Fax 309-3647
www.rsdla.net/
Abramson Science and Tech Charter S 600/K-12
5552 Read Blvd 70127 504-373-6275
Edward Brown, prin. Fax 244-4417
Carver HS 300/10-12
3059 Higgins Blvd 70126 504-373-6226
Isaac Pollack, prin. Fax 941-5482
Cohen HS 200/11-12
3520 Dryades St 70115 504-373-6204
Jennifer Grace, prin. Fax 324-9823
Landry HS 8-12
1201 L B Landry Ave 70114 504-373-6257
Vera Triplett, prin. Fax 308-3625
Reed HS 600/9-12
5316 Michoud Blvd 70129 504-373-6217
Michael McKenzie, prin. Fax 255-9802
Schwartz Academy 100/Alt
709 Park Blvd 70114 504-312-0739
Katrinia Horton, prin.
Other Schools – See Baton Rouge, Greensburg, Shreveport

Academy of the Sacred Heart HS 300/9-12
4521 Saint Charles Ave 70115 504-891-1943
Dr. Yvonne Adler, prin. Fax 891-9939
Academy of the Sacred Heart MS 200/5-8
4521 Saint Charles Ave 70115 504-891-1943
Kim Duckworth, prin. Fax 891-9939
Bishop McManus Academy 200/PK-12
13123 I 10 Service Rd 70128 504-246-5121
Dr. Tonilynn Tyson, prin. Fax 246-5564
Brother Martin HS 1,200/7-12
4401 Elysian Fields Ave 70122 504-283-1561
Gregory Rando, prin. Fax 286-8462
Cabrini HS 500/8-12
1400 Moss St 70119 504-482-1193
Yvonne Hrapmann, prin. Fax 483-8671
Cameron College Post-Sec.
2740 Canal St 70119 504-821-5881
De La Salle HS 400/8-12
5300 Saint Charles Ave 70115 504-895-5717
Peggy St. John, prin. Fax 895-1300
Delgado Community College Post-Sec.
615 City Park Ave 70119 504-671-5000
Dillard University Post-Sec.
2601 Gentilly Blvd 70122 504-283-8822
Eastern College of Health Vocations Post-Sec.
201 Evans Rd 70123 504-885-3353
Holy Cross S 1,000/5-12
5500 Paris Ave 70122 504-942-3100
Charles DiGange, prin. Fax 286-5665
Holy Rosary HS 100/8-12
2437 Jena St 70115 504-482-7173
Len Enger, prin. Fax 482-7229
Jesuit HS 1,300/8-12
4133 Banks St 70119 504-486-6631
Michael Giambelluca, prin. Fax 483-3942
Louisiana State Univ. Health Sci. Center Post-Sec.
433 Bolivar St 70112 504-568-4808
Loyola University New Orleans Post-Sec.
6363 Saint Charles Ave 70118 504-865-2011
McGehee S 500/PK-12
2343 Prytania St 70130 504-561-1224
Eileen Powers, head sch Fax 525-7910
Medical Center of Louisiana/Charity Cmps Post-Sec.
1541 Tulane Ave 70112 504-568-2311
Moler Beauty College Post-Sec.
3968 Old Gentilly Rd 70126 504-282-2539
Mt. Carmel Academy 1,200/8-12
7027 Milne Blvd 70124 504-288-7626
Sr. Camille Anne Campbell, prin. Fax 288-7629
Newman S 900/PK-12
1903 Jefferson Ave 70115 504-899-5641
Dr. T.J. Locke, head sch Fax 896-8597
New Orleans Baptist Theological Seminary Post-Sec.
3939 Gentilly Blvd 70126 504-282-4455
Notre Dame Seminary Post-Sec.
2901 S Carrollton Ave 70118 504-866-7426
Ochsner School of Allied Health Sciences Post-Sec.
1514 Jefferson Hwy 70121 504-842-3267
Our Lady of Holy Cross College Post-Sec.
4123 Woodland Dr 70131 504-394-7744
St. Augustine HS 900/6-12
2600 A P Tureaud Ave 70119 504-944-2424
Eric Smith, prin. Fax 947-7712
St. Marys Academy 600/K-12
6905 Chef Menteur Hwy 70126 504-245-0200
Sr. Jennie Jones, prin. Fax 245-0422
St. Marys Dominican HS 900/8-12
7701 Walmsley Ave 70125 504-865-9401
Carolyn Favre M.Ed., prin. Fax 866-5958
Southern University at New Orleans Post-Sec.
6400 Press Dr 70126 504-286-5000
Touro Infirmary Post-Sec.
1401 Foucher St 70115 504-897-8244
Tulane University Post-Sec.
6823 Saint Charles Ave 70118 504-865-5000
University of New Orleans Post-Sec.
2000 Lakeshore Dr 70148 504-280-6000
Ursuline Academy HS 400/8-12
2635 State St 70118 504-861-9150
John Gabriel, prin. Fax 861-7392
William Carey University Post-Sec.
4103 Chef Mentuer Hwy 70126 504-286-3275
Xavier University Post-Sec.
1 Drexel Dr 70125 504-486-7411
Xavier University Prep HS 300/7-12
5116 Magazine St 70115 504-899-6061
Cheryllyn Branche, prin. Fax 899-3177

New Roads, Pointe Coupee, Pop. 4,804
Pointe Coupee Parish SD 2,800/PK-12
PO Box 579 70760 225-638-8674
Linda D'Amico, supt. Fax 638-3904
www.pcpsb.net
Other Schools – See Livonia

Capital Area Technical College Post-Sec.
605 Hospital Rd 70760 225-638-8613
Catholic HS of Pte. Coupee 300/7-12
504 4th St W 70760 225-638-3469
Colleen Caillet, prin. Fax 638-6471
False River Academy 500/PK-12
201 Major Pkwy 70760 225-638-3783
Kenneth LeBeau, prin. Fax 638-8555

Noble, Sabine, Pop. 244
Sabine Parish SD
Supt. — See Many
Ebarb S 300/PK-12
5340 Highway 482 71462 318-645-9402
Darrin Dyess, prin. Fax 645-4689

Oakdale, Allen, Pop. 7,688
Allen Parish SD
Supt. — See Oberlin
Oakdale HS 300/9-12
101 N 13th St 71463 318-335-2338
Nancy Willis, prin. Fax 335-3257
Oakdale MS 400/5-8
124 S 13th St 71463 318-335-1558
Robbyn Tarver, prin. Fax 335-4690

Central Louisiana Technical College Post-Sec.
117 Highway 1152 71463 318-335-3944

Oak Grove, West Carroll, Pop. 1,714
West Carroll Parish SD 2,100/PK-12
314 E Main St 71263 318-428-2378
Kent Davis, supt. Fax 428-3775
www.wcpsb.com
Oak Grove JSHS 500/6-12
501 W Main St 71263 318-428-2308
Emily Bradley, prin. Fax 428-2311
Other Schools – See Epps, Forest, Kilbourne

Oberlin, Allen, Pop. 1,727
Allen Parish SD 4,300/PK-12
PO Box C 70655 337-639-4311
Michael Doucet, supt. Fax 639-2346
www.allen.k12.la.us
Oberlin HS 300/7-12
PO Box D 70655 337-639-4341
Tonya Rider, prin. Fax 639-2508
Other Schools – See Elizabeth, Grant, Kinder, Oakdale, Reeves

Olla, LaSalle, Pop. 1,375
LaSalle Parish SD
Supt. — See Jena
LaSalle HS 200/9-12
PO Box 458 71465 318-495-5165
Ronda Richardson, prin. Fax 495-5503

Opelousas, Saint Landry, Pop. 16,425
St. Landry Parish SD 14,500/PK-12
PO Box 310 70571 337-948-3657
Joseph Cassimere, supt. Fax 942-0204
www.slp.k12.la.us
Magnet Academy for Cultural Arts 300/7-12
1100 Leo St 70570 337-948-6310
Stella Thomas, prin. Fax 942-6195
Northwest HS 500/9-12
3746 Highway 104 70570 337-543-2255
Gregory Campbell, prin. Fax 543-8796
Opelousas HS 700/9-12
PO Box 1269 70571 337-942-5634
Rodney Johnson, prin. Fax 942-6219
Opelousas JHS 400/7-8
730 S Market St 70570 337-942-4957
Jude Victorian, prin. Fax 942-2659
Plaisance MS 300/5-8
3264 Highway 167 70570 337-826-3335
Larry Watson, prin. Fax 826-7062
St. Landry Accelerated Transition S 100/7-8
152 Violet Dr 70570 337-948-4763
Charles Vidrine, prin. Fax 948-9792
Other Schools – See Arnaudville, Eunice, Port Barre, Sunset, Washington

---

Family Worship Christian Acadmey 100/PK-12
368 Compress Rd 70570 337-942-1563
Alysia Richard, prin. Fax 942-1521
Opelousas Catholic S 700/K-12
428 E Prudhomme St 70570 337-942-5404
Perry Fontenot, prin. Fax 942-5922
Opelousas School of Cosmetology Post-Sec.
529 E Vine St 70570 337-942-6147
South Louisiana Community College Post-Sec.
332 E South St 70570 337-948-0239
Westminster Christian Academy 1,000/PK-12
186 Westminster Dr 70570 337-948-8607
Merida Brooks, supt. Fax 948-8983

Paradis, Saint Charles, Pop. 1,269
St. Charles Parish SD
Supt. — See Luling
Martin MS 600/7-8
434 South St 70080 985-758-7579
Erin Raiford, prin. Fax 758-7570

Parks, Saint Martin, Pop. 645
St. Martin Parish SD
Supt. — See Saint Martinville
Parks MS 400/5-8
1010 Saint Louis Dr Ste A 70582 337-845-4753
Wanda Phillips, prin. Fax 845-5532

Patterson, Saint Mary, Pop. 6,020
St. Mary Parish SD
Supt. — See Centerville
Patterson HS 500/9-12
2525 Main St 70392 985-395-2675
Rachael Wilson, prin. Fax 395-5453
Patterson JHS 600/4-8
1101 1st St 70392 985-395-6772
Suzanne Bergeron, prin. Fax 395-6773

Pearl River, Saint Tammany, Pop. 2,460
St. Tammany Parish SD
Supt. — See Covington
Creekside JHS 500/6-8
65434 Highway 41 70452 985-863-5882
Lisa Virga, prin. Fax 863-7658

Pearl River HS 800/9-12
39110 Rebel Ln 70452 985-863-2591
Michael Winkler, prin. Fax 863-5934

Pierre Part, Assumption, Pop. 3,145
Assumption Parish SD
Supt. — See Napoleonville
Pierre Part MS 300/5-8
3321 Highway 70 S 70339 985-252-6359
Wanda Templet, prin. Fax 252-3918

Pine Prairie, Evangeline, Pop. 1,598
Evangeline Parish SD
Supt. — See Ville Platte
Pine Prairie S 800/PK-12
PO Box 200 70576 337-599-2300
Barbara Lee, prin. Fax 599-2003

Pineville, Rapides, Pop. 14,277
Rapides Parish SD
Supt. — See Alexandria
Pineville HS 1,200/9-12
1511 Line St 71360 318-442-8990
Karl Carpenter, prin. Fax 487-1984
Pineville JHS 600/7-8
501 Edgewood Dr 71360 318-640-0512
Columbus Goodman, prin. Fax 640-9692
Slocum Learning Center 50/9-12
901 Crepe Myrtle St 71360 318-445-7017
Marguerite McNeely, prin. Fax 445-5690

Louisiana College Post-Sec.
1140 College Dr 71360 318-487-7011
Pineville Beauty School Post-Sec.
1008 Main St 71360 318-445-1040

Pitkin, Vernon, Pop. 566
Vernon Parish SD
Supt. — See Leesville
Pitkin S 500/PK-12
PO Box 307 70656 318-358-3121
Kevin Lambright, prin. Fax 358-3580

Plain Dealing, Bossier, Pop. 996
Bossier Parish SD
Supt. — See Benton
LA New Tech @ Plain Dealing 200/6-12
300 E Vance St 71064 318-759-2700
Yolanda Jefferson, prin. Fax 759-2713

Plaquemine, Iberville, Pop. 7,074
Iberville Parish SD 4,500/PK-12
PO Box 151 70765 225-687-4341
Dr. P. Edward Cancienne, supt. Fax 687-5408
www.ipsb.net
Iberville Parish Optional Education Ctr 50/Alt
58060 Plaquemine St 70764 225-687-7066
Dianna Outlaw, prin. Fax 687-7390
Math Science & Arts Academy West K-12
PO Box 151 70765 225-687-6845
Fax 687-6826
Plaquemine HS 1,100/7-12
59595 Belleview Dr 70764 225-687-6367
Chandler Smith, prin. Fax 687-4422
Other Schools – See Saint Gabriel, White Castle

Capital Area Technical College Post-Sec.
59125 Bayou Rd 70764 225-687-6392
St. John HS 300/7-12
24250 Regina St 70764 225-687-3056
Cherie Schlatre, prin. Fax 687-3530

Plaucheville, Avoyelles, Pop. 243

St. Joseph S 400/PK-12
PO Box 59 71362 318-922-3401
Br. Anthony Dugas, prin. Fax 922-3776

Pleasant Hill, Sabine, Pop. 710
Sabine Parish SD
Supt. — See Many
Pleasant Hill S 300/PK-12
PO Box 8 71065 318-796-3670
Joseph Self, prin. Fax 796-2034

Ponchatoula, Tangipahoa, Pop. 6,436
Tangipahoa Parish SD
Supt. — See Amite
Ponchatoula HS 1,700/9-12
19452 Highway 22 70454 985-386-3514
Daniel Strickland, prin. Fax 386-0011
Ponchatoula JHS 800/7-8
315 E Oak St 70454 985-370-5322
Bobby Matthews, prin. Fax 370-5327

Port Allen, West Baton Rouge, Pop. 5,131
West Baton Rouge Parish SD 3,600/PK-12
3761 Rosedale Rd 70767 225-343-8309
David Corona, supt. Fax 387-2101
www.wbrschools.net
Devall MS 200/5-8
11851 N River Rd 70767 225-627-4268
James Jackson, prin. Fax 627-4278
Port Allen HS 400/9-12
3553 Rosedale Rd 70767 225-383-1107
Warren LeJeune, prin. Fax 344-6312
Port Allen MS 200/6-8
610 Rosedale Rd 70767 225-383-5777
Dr. Jonathon Szymanski, prin. Fax 346-5030
Other Schools – See Brusly

Port Barre, Saint Landry, Pop. 2,017
St. Landry Parish SD
Supt. — See Opelousas
Port Barre MS 400/5-8
PO Box 69 70577 337-585-7256
William Edgar Duplechain, prin. Fax 585-2290
Port Barre MSHS 400/5-12
PO Box 69 70577 337-585-7256
William Duplechain, prin. Fax 585-2290

Port Sulphur, Plaquemines, Pop. 1,706
Plaquemines Parish SD
Supt. — See Belle Chasse
Plaquemines Parish Learning Center Alt
26892 Highway 23 70083 504-595-6410
John Vanison, prin. Fax 398-4366
South Plaquemines HS 400/7-12
311 Civic Dr 70083 504-595-6435
John Barthelemy, prin. Fax 564-1337

Prairieville, Ascension, Pop. 26,585
Ascension Parish SD
Supt. — See Donaldsonville
Galvez MS 600/6-8
42018 Highway 933 70769 225-391-6350
Sandy Waguespack, prin. Fax 621-2434
Prairieville MS 700/6-8
16200 Highway 930 70769 225-391-6300
Diane Gautreau, prin. Fax 673-4883

Pride, East Baton Rouge
East Baton Rouge Parish SD
Supt. — See Baton Rouge
Northeast JSHS 600/7-12
13700 Pride Port Hudson Rd 70770 225-654-5808
Jessie LeBlanc, prin. Fax 654-5591

Quitman, Jackson, Pop. 180
Jackson Parish SD
Supt. — See Jonesboro
Quitman S 600/PK-12
PO Box 38 71268 318-259-2698
Steve Shovan, prin. Fax 259-1139

Raceland, Lafourche, Pop. 10,053
Lafourche Parish SD
Supt. — See Thibodaux
Central Lafourche HS 1,300/9-12
4820 Highway 1 70394 985-532-3319
Chris Kimball, prin. Fax 532-3822
Raceland MS 300/6-8
PO Box C 70394 985-537-5140
Nancy Curole, prin. Fax 537-5182
Opportunity Place Central Campus Adult
190 Johnny Dufrene Dr 70394 985-532-3114
Fax 532-3110

Rayne, Acadia, Pop. 7,834
Acadia Parish SD
Supt. — See Crowley
Armstrong MS 400/6-8
700 Martin Luther King Blvd 70578 337-334-3377
Marshall Thibodeaux, prin. Fax 334-2681
Rayne HS 600/9-12
1016 N Polk St 70578 337-334-3691
John Prudhomme, prin. Fax 334-5568

Rayville, Richland, Pop. 3,658
Richland Parish SD 4,000/PK-12
PO Box 599 71269 318-728-5064
Sheldon Jones, supt. Fax 728-6366
www.richland.k12.la.us
Rayville HS 500/9-12
193 Highway 3048 71269 318-728-3296
Tommy Watson, prin. Fax 728-5652
Rayville JHS 200/6-8
225 Highway 3048 71269 318-728-3618
Tony Guirlando, prin. Fax 728-9374
Other Schools – See Archibald, Delhi, Mangham

Riverfield Academy 300/PK-12
115 Riverfield Dr 71269 318-728-3281
Sherri Slade, admin. Fax 728-3285

Reeves, Allen, Pop. 230
Allen Parish SD
Supt. — See Oberlin
Reeves S 300/PK-12
13770 Highway 113 70658 337-666-2414
Brenda Green, prin. Fax 666-2812

Reserve, Saint John the Baptist, Pop. 9,667
St. John The Baptist Parish SD 6,200/PK-12
PO Box AL 70084 985-536-1106
Kevin George, supt. Fax 536-1109
www.stjohn.k12.la.us
East St. John HS 1,400/9-12
1 Wildcat Dr 70084 985-536-4226
Patricia Triche, prin. Fax 536-4286
St. John Alternative S 100/Alt
1880 Highway 44 70084 985-536-4283
Phyllis Clark, prin. Fax 536-4527
Other Schools – See Edgard

Riverside Academy 800/PK-12
332 Railroad Ave 70084 985-536-4246
South Central Louisiana Technical Coll Post-Sec.
181 Regala Park Rd 70084 985-536-4418

Ringgold, Bienville, Pop. 1,471
Bienville Parish SD
Supt. — See Arcadia
Ringgold JSHS 300/6-12
4044 Bienville Rd Ste B 71068 318-894-2271
Eric Carter, prin. Fax 894-4444

River Ridge, Jefferson, Pop. 13,340

Curtis Christian S 800/K-12
10125 Jefferson Hwy 70123 504-737-4621

Roanoke, Jefferson Davis, Pop. 537
Jefferson Davis Parish SD
Supt. — See Jennings
Welsh-Roanoke JHS 200/6-8
8150 Highway 90 70581 337-753-2317
Linda Bard, prin. Fax 753-2245

Rosepine, Vernon, Pop. 1,651
Vernon Parish SD
Supt. — See Leesville
Rosepine JSHS 500/7-12
PO Box 369 70659 337-463-6079
Steve Thomas, prin. Fax 462-6132

Ruston, Lincoln, Pop. 21,600
Lincoln Parish SD 5,100/PK-12
410 S Farmerville St 71270 318-255-1430
Danny Bell, supt. Fax 255-3203
www.lincolnschools.org/
Ruston HS 1,100/9-12
900 Bearcat Dr 71270 318-255-0807
Mike Milstead, prin. Fax 251-2202
Ruston JHS 500/7-8
481 Tarbutton Rd 71270 318-251-1601
Tim Nutt, prin. Fax 254-5235
Other Schools – See Choudrant, Dubach, Grambling, Simsboro

Bethel Christian S 100/PK-12
2901 Winona Dr 71270 318-255-1112
Nancy Stevenson, admin. Fax 513-1113
Cedar Creek S 600/PK-12
2400 Cedar Creek Dr 71270 318-255-7707
Andrew Yepson, head sch Fax 251-2846
Louisiana Tech University Post-Sec.
PO Box 3168 71272 318-257-0211
Pat Goins Ruston Beauty School Post-Sec.
213 W Alabama Ave 71270 318-255-2717

Saint Amant, Ascension
Ascension Parish SD
Supt. — See Donaldsonville
Saint Amant HS 1,700/9-12
12035 Highway 431 70774 225-391-6000
Mia Edwards, prin. Fax 621-2575
Saint Amant MS 500/6-8
44317 Highway 429 70774 225-391-6500
Christy Bourgeois, prin. Fax 621-2593

Saint Benedict, Saint Tammany

St. Joseph Seminary College 70457 Post-Sec.
985-892-1800

Saint Bernard, Saint Bernard
St. Bernard Parish SD
Supt. — See Chalmette
Saint Bernard MS 300/6-8
2601 Torres Dr 70085 504-267-7878
Susan Deffes, prin.

Saint Francisville, West Feliciana, Pop. 1,749
West Feliciana Parish SD 2,100/PK-12
PO Box 1910 70775 225-635-3891
Hollis Milton, supt. Fax 635-0108
www.wfpsb.org
West Feliciana HS 600/9-12
PO Box 580 70775 225-635-4561
James Carroll, prin. Fax 635-5588
West Feliciana MS 500/6-8
PO Box 690 70775 225-635-3898
Benjamin Necaise, prin. Fax 635-6925

Saint Gabriel, Iberville, Pop. 6,621
Iberville Parish SD
Supt. — See Plaquemine
East Iberville S 500/PK-12
3285 Highway 75 70776 225-642-0032
Michael Eskridge, prin. Fax 642-9607
Math Science & Arts Academy East K-12
1825 Highway 30 70776 225-238-0150
Charles Johnson, admin. Fax 642-9748

Saint James, Saint James, Pop. 827
St. James Parish SD
Supt. — See Lutcher
Saint James HS 600/7-12
PO Box 101 70086 225-265-3911
Michael Kennedy, prin. Fax 265-2455

Saint Joseph, Tensas, Pop. 1,163
Tensas Parish SD 700/PK-12
PO Box 318 71366 318-766-3269
Carol Johnson, supt. Fax 766-3634
www.tensaspsb.org/
Tensas HS 200/7-12
720 Plank Rd 71366 318-766-3585
Lakeyshure Marzell, prin. Fax 766-7988

Tensas Academy 200/PK-12
PO Box 555 71366 318-766-4384
Jimmy Comeaux, hdmstr. Fax 766-3559

Saint Martinville, Saint Martin, Pop. 6,047
St. Martin Parish SD 8,100/PK-12
PO Box 859 70582 337-394-6261
Dr. Lottie Beebe, supt. Fax 394-6387
saintmartinschools.org
JCEP Alt
1120 S M L King Jr Dr 70582 337-394-7634
St. Martinville HS 800/9-12
762 N Main St 70582 337-394-3135
Michael Kreamer, prin. Fax 394-8045
St. Martinville JHS 400/6-8
7190 Main Hwy 70582 337-394-4764
Elizabeth Thibeaux, prin. Fax 394-9619
Other Schools – See Breaux Bridge, Cecilia, Parks

Saint Rose, Saint Charles, Pop. 8,003
St. Charles Parish SD
Supt. — See Luling
Cammon MS 300/6-8
234 Pirate Dr 70087 504-467-4536
Tamika Green, prin. Fax 468-3873

ITT Technical Institute Post-Sec.
140 James Dr E 70087 504-463-0338

Saline, Bienville, Pop. 271
Bienville Parish SD
Supt. — See Arcadia
Saline S 300/PK-12
PO Box 129 71070 318-576-3215
Daryl Savage, prin. Fax 576-9068

Sarepta, Webster, Pop. 889
Webster Parish SD
Supt. — See Minden
North Webster JHS 100/6-8
6041 Highway 2 71071 318-847-4301
Cyndi Hair, prin. Fax 847-4891

Schriever, Terrebonne, Pop. 6,745
Terrebonne Parish SD
Supt. — See Houma
Price S 50/Alt
1849 W Park Ave 70395 985-868-3105
Clyde Washington, prin. Fax 447-7498

L.E. Fletcher Technical Community Coll Post-Sec.
1407 Highway 311 70395 985-857-3655

Scott, Lafayette, Pop. 8,472
Lafayette Parish SD
Supt. — See Lafayette
Scott MS 800/5-8
116 Marie St 70583 337-521-7930
Fax 521-7931

Shreveport, Caddo, Pop. 196,498
Bossier Parish SD
Supt. — See Benton
Bossier Parish Technical S Vo/Tech
2010 N Market St 71107 318-676-7811
Carol Johnston, prin. Fax 221-6729

Caddo Parish SD 38,600/PK-12
PO Box 32000 71130 318-603-6300
Gerald Dawkins Ed.D., supt. Fax 631-5241
www.caddo.k12.la.us/
Academic Recovery & Career Discovery Ctr 200/Alt
401 N Holzman St 71101 318-222-5606
Guy Cooper, prin. Fax 227-8097
Bickham MS 600/6-8
7240 Old Mooringsport Rd 71107 318-929-4106
Shannon Wall, prin. Fax 929-2416
Broadmoor MS Laboratory 600/6-8
441 Atlantic Ave 71105 318-861-2403
Billy Williams, prin. Fax 865-4142
Byrd HS 2,200/9-12
3201 Line Ave 71104 318-869-2567
Gerald Badgley, prin. Fax 869-2253
Caddo Career/Tech Center Vo/Tech
5950 Union Ave 71108 318-636-5150
Richard Dezendorf, prin. Fax 621-9138
Caddo East Alternative S Alt
1020 Shreveport Barksdale 71105 318-230-0615
Dr. Minty James, dir.
Caddo Middle Career & Technology S 400/6-8
6310 Clift Ave 71106 318-868-2753
Tellauance Graham, prin. Fax 868-2755
Caddo North Alternative S Alt
3000 N Market St 71107 318-272-9223
Joyce Scott, dir.
Caddo Parish Magnet HS 1,100/9-12
1601 Viking Dr 71101 318-221-2501
Mary Rounds, prin. Fax 227-1393
Caddo Parish Magnet MS 1,300/6-8
7635 Cornelious Ln 71106 318-868-6588
Keith Burton, prin. Fax 865-6125
Caddo South Alternative S Alt
8805 Jewella Ave 71108 318-272-1253
Jerlonda Snowden, dir.
Caddo West Alternative S Alt
3714 Greenwood Rd 71109 318-272-5510
James Clark, dir.
Fair Park JSHS 800/7-12
3222 Greenwood Rd 71109 318-635-8181
Jerry Davis, prin. Fax 631-1982
Green Oaks Performing Arts Academy 400/7-12
2550 Thomas E Howard Dr 71107 318-425-3411
Marvin Alexander, prin. Fax 425-3414
Huntington JSHS 900/7-12
6801 Rasberry Ln 71129 318-687-6655
Travis Smith, prin. Fax 687-0943
Northwood HS 1,000/9-12
5939 Old Mooringsport Rd 71107 318-929-3513
Darlene Simons, prin. Fax 929-7498
Ridgewood MS 500/6-8
2001 Ridgewood Dr 71118 318-686-0383
Scott Aymond, prin. Fax 686-0390
Shreve HS 1,600/9-12
6115 E Kings Hwy 71105 318-865-7137
Dr. Sandra McCalla, prin. Fax 865-5041
Shreveport Job Corps Opportunity Center 300/Alt
2815 Lillian St 71109 318-227-9331
Lionel Fraser, dir. Fax 212-0203
Southwood HS 1,300/9-12
9000 Walker Rd 71118 318-686-9512
Jeff Roberts, prin. Fax 687-7588
Washington New Tech JSHS 300/7-12
2104 Milam St 71103 318-222-2186
Patrick Greer, prin. Fax 226-0628
Woodlawn Leadership Academy 700/7-12
7340 Wyngate Blvd 71106 318-686-3161
Anthony Tisdale, prin. Fax 687-6787
Youree Drive MS 1,100/6-8
6008 Youree Dr 71105 318-868-5324
Rick Carson, prin. Fax 861-5086
Other Schools – See Vivian

Recovery SD
Supt. — See New Orleans
Linear Leadership Academy 200/6-8
1845 Linear St 71107 318-221-1589
Nancy Putman, prin. Fax 221-0130

American Commercial College Post-Sec.
3014 Knight St 71105 866-648-2112
American School of Business Post-Sec.
702 Professional Dr N 71105 318-798-3333
Ayers Institute Post-Sec.
8820 Jewella Ave 71108 318-635-0280
Blue Cliff College Post-Sec.
8731 Park Plaza Dr 71105 318-798-6868
Calvary Baptist Academy 1,100/PK-12
9333 Linwood Ave 71106 318-687-4923
Rhonda Honea, prin. Fax 687-4925
Centenary College of Louisiana Post-Sec.
2911 Centenary Blvd 71104 318-869-5011
Diesel Driving Academy Post-Sec.
3523 Greenwood Rd 71109 318-636-6300
Evangel Christian Academy 800/PK-12
7425 Broadacres Rd 71129 318-688-7061
Guy's Academy Hair Skin and Nails Post-Sec.
1141 Shreveport Barksdale 71105 318-865-5591
Louisiana State University Post-Sec.
1 University Pl 71115 318-797-5000
Louisiana State Univ Health Sciences Ctr Post-Sec.
1501 Kings Hwy 71103 318-675-5000
Loyola College Prep S 400/9-12
921 Jordan St 71101 318-221-2675
John LeBlanc, prin. Fax 221-2678
Northwest Louisiana Technical College Post-Sec.
2010 N Market St 71107 318-676-7811
Overton Brooks VA Medical Center Post-Sec.
510 E Stoner Ave 71101 318-424-6037
Remington College Post-Sec.
2106 Bert Kouns Industrial 71118 800-560-6192
Southern University at Shreveport Post-Sec.
3050 M L King Dr 71107 318-670-6000

Sibley, Webster, Pop. 1,205
Webster Parish SD
Supt. — See Minden
Lakeside JSHS 400/7-12
9090 Highway 371 71073 318-377-2133
Johnny Rowland, prin. Fax 382-0733

Sicily Island, Catahoula, Pop. 519
Catahoula Parish SD
Supt. — See Harrisonburg
Sicily Island HS 100/PK-12
PO Box 128 71368 318-389-5337
Marguerita Krause, prin. Fax 389-5309

Simpson, Vernon, Pop. 631
Vernon Parish SD
Supt. — See Leesville
Simpson S 400/PK-12
PO Box 8 71474 337-383-7810
Lee Coriell, prin. Fax 383-7655

Simsboro, Lincoln, Pop. 828
Lincoln Parish SD
Supt. — See Ruston
Simsboro S 500/K-12
1 Tiger Dr 71275 318-247-6265
Ricky Durrett, prin. Fax 247-6276

Singer, Beauregard, Pop. 282
Beauregard Parish SD
Supt. — See Deridder
Singer S 300/K-12
153 Highway 110 E 70660 337-463-5908
Theresa Harlow, prin. Fax 463-0199

Slidell, Saint Tammany, Pop. 26,521
St. Tammany Parish SD
Supt. — See Covington
Boyet JHS 700/7-8
59295 Rebel Dr 70461 985-643-3775
Mitchell Stubbs, prin. Fax 643-9470
Clearwood JHS 600/4-8
130 Clearwood Dr 70458 985-641-8200
Alan Bennett, prin. Fax 641-7122
Northshore HS 1,500/9-12
100 Panther Dr 70461 985-649-6400
Dr. Michael Peterson, prin. Fax 649-3613
St. Tammany JHS 600/6-8
701 Cleveland Ave 70458 985-643-1592
Vincent DiCarlo, prin. Fax 643-5873
Salmen HS 900/9-12
300 Spartan Dr 70458 985-643-7359
Terri Wortmann, prin. Fax 645-8776
Slidell HS 1,700/9-12
1 Tiger Dr 70458 985-643-2992
William Percy, prin. Fax 649-6853
Slidell JHS 700/7-8
333 Pennsylvania Ave 70458 985-641-5914
Patrick Mackin, prin. Fax 641-6397

Academy of Creative Hair Design Post-Sec.
740 Oak Harbor Blvd 70458 985-643-2614
First Baptist Christian S 300/1-12
4141 Pontchartrain Dr 70458 985-643-3725
Mona Nelson, admin. Fax 641-9205
Pope John Paul II HS 400/9-12
1901 Jaguar Dr 70461 985-649-0914
Martha Mundine, prin. Fax 649-5494

Sorrento, Ascension, Pop. 1,385

River Parishes Community College Post-Sec.
PO Box 310 70778 225-675-8270

Springfield, Livingston, Pop. 483
Livingston Parish SD
Supt. — See Livingston
Springfield HS 300/9-12
PO Box 39 70462 225-294-3256
Norman Picou, prin. Fax 294-4800
Springfield MS 300/5-8
PO Box 40 70462 225-294-3306
Dwayne Pykes, prin. Fax 294-3307

Springhill, Webster, Pop. 5,214
Webster Parish SD
Supt. — See Minden
North Webster HS 500/9-12
101 S Arkansas St 71075 318-539-2563
Jeff Franklin, prin. Fax 539-2569

Starks, Calcasieu, Pop. 662
Calcasieu Parish SD
Supt. — See Lake Charles
Starks S 400/PK-12
PO Box 69 70661 337-217-4820
Vickie Poole, prin. Fax 217-4821

Sterlington, Ouachita, Pop. 1,568
Ouachita Parish SD
Supt. — See Monroe
Sterlington MS 6-8
206 High Ave 71280 318-432-2100
Chris Cox, prin. Fax 432-2149

Stonewall, DeSoto, Pop. 1,797
DeSoto Parish SD
Supt. — See Mansfield
North DeSoto HS 500/9-12
PO Box 430 71078 318-925-6917
Bart Weaver, prin. Fax 925-1940
North DeSoto MS 500/6-8
PO Box 310 71078 318-925-4520
Keith Simmons, prin. Fax 925-4719

Sulphur, Calcasieu, Pop. 20,056
Calcasieu Parish SD
Supt. — See Lake Charles
LeBlanc MS/Drost Special 400/6-8
1100 N Crocker St 70663 337-217-4510
Joe David, prin. Fax 217-4511
Lewis MS 900/6-8
1752 Cypress St 70663 337-217-4700
Robert Barrentine, prin. Fax 217-4701
Sulphur 9th Grade Campus 600/9-9
600 Willow Ave 70663 337-217-4440
Charles Hansen, prin. Fax 217-4441
Sulphur SHS 1,400/10-12
100 Sycamore St 70663 337-217-4430
Keith Bonin, prin. Fax 217-4434

Parkview Baptist S 100/K-12
1623 Picard Rd 70663 337-527-7089
Sue Chesson, admin. Fax 528-2291

Summerfield, Claiborne
Claiborne Parish SD
Supt. — See Homer
Summerfield S 300/PK-12
PO Box 158 71079 318-927-3621
James Scriber, prin. Fax 927-9160

Sunset, Saint Landry, Pop. 2,868
St. Landry Parish SD
Supt. — See Opelousas
Sunset MS 300/5-8
236 Church Hill St 70584 337-662-3194
Marquet Rideau, prin. Fax 662-3478

Tallulah, Madison, Pop. 7,266
Madison Parish SD 1,900/PK-12
301 S Chestnut St 71282 318-574-3616
Lisa Wilmore, supt. Fax 574-3667
www.madisonpsb.org/
Christian Acres Alternative S 100/Alt
200 Bailey St 71282 318-574-1563
Glenda Douglas, prin. Fax 574-1563
Madison HS 400/9-12
1234 Madison High Dr S 71282 318-574-3529
Warren Trimble, prin. Fax 574-2399
Madison MS 400/6-8
1233 Madison High Dr S 71282 318-574-0933
Fax 574-9199

Tallulah Academy-Delta Christian S 300/PK-12
700 Wood St 71282 318-574-2606
Fax 574-3390

Thibodaux, Lafourche, Pop. 14,384
Lafourche Parish SD 14,400/PK-12
PO Box 879 70302 985-446-5631
Jo Ann Matthews, supt. Fax 446-0801
www.lafourche.k12.la.us
East Thibodaux MS 300/6-8
802 E 7th St 70301 985-446-5616
Tanya Richard, prin. Fax 446-5610
Sixth Ward MS 300/6-8
PO Box 1236 70302 985-633-2449
Kenny Delcambre, prin. Fax 633-7373
Thibodaux HS 1,500/8-12
1355 Tiger Dr 70301 985-447-4071
Glenn Haydel, prin. Fax 447-4077
West Thiboudaux MS 400/6-8
1111 E 12th St 70301 985-446-6889
Ann Danos, prin. Fax 447-1777
Opportunity Place North Campus Adult
2134 Highway 308 70301 985-447-5656
Fax 447-5654
Other Schools – See Cut Off, Galliano, Golden Meadow, Houma, Larose, Lockport, Raceland

---

Nicholls State University Post-Sec.
906 E 1st St 70310 985-446-8111
South Central Louisiana Technical Coll Post-Sec.
1425 Tiger Dr 70301 985-447-0924

White HS 700/8-12
555 Cardinal Dr 70301 985-446-8486
Michelle Chiasson, prin. Fax 448-1275

Tickfaw, Tangipahoa, Pop. 685
Tangipahoa Parish SD
Supt. — See Amite
Nesom MS 500/6-8
PO Box 280 70466 985-345-2166
James Keith, prin. Fax 345-3731

Tioga, Rapides
Rapides Parish SD
Supt. — See Alexandria
Tioga HS 900/9-12
PO Box 1030 71477 318-640-9661
Kim Bennett, prin. Fax 640-9757

Urania, LaSalle, Pop. 1,308
LaSalle Parish SD
Supt. — See Jena
LaSalle JHS 200/6-8
PO Box 520 71480 318-495-3474
Steve Long, prin. Fax 495-3478

Vacherie, Saint James, Pop. 2,354
St. James Parish SD
Supt. — See Lutcher
Science & Math Academy 7-12
3125 Valcour Aime St 70090 225-258-4600
Pam Bourgeois, dir. Fax 265-7093

Varnado, Washington, Pop. 1,459
Washington Parish SD
Supt. — See Franklinton
Varnado HS 200/6-12
25543 Washington St, Angie LA 70426 985-732-2025
Randy Branch, prin. Fax 732-5198

Vidalia, Concordia, Pop. 4,268
Concordia Parish SD 3,900/PK-12
PO Box 950 71373 318-336-4226
Paul Nelson Ph.D., supt. Fax 336-5875
www.cpsbla.us/
Vidalia HS 400/9-12
2201 Murray Dr 71373 318-336-6231
Rick Brown, prin. Fax 336-6233
Vidalia JHS 500/6-8
210 Gillespie St 71373 318-336-6227
Whest Shirley, prin. Fax 336-6229
Other Schools – See Ferriday, Monterey

Vidalia Beauty School Post-Sec.
208 Westside Dr 71373 318-336-2377

Ville Platte, Evangeline, Pop. 7,370
Evangeline Parish SD 6,000/PK-12
1123 Te Mamou Rd 70586 337-363-6651
Toni Hamlin, supt. Fax 363-8086
www.epsb.com
Evangeline Central Alternative S 100/Alt
4587 Vidrine Rd 70586 337-363-1089
Dexter Brown, prin. Fax 363-3051
Ville Platte HS 800/5-12
210 W Cotton St 70586 337-363-3387
Kelli Lafleur, prin. Fax 363-7274
Other Schools – See Basile, Mamou, Pine Prairie

Christian Heritage Academy 100/PK-12
607 Prosper St 70586 337-363-7690
Sue Pomier, prin. Fax 363-7699
Sacred Heart HS 200/9-12
114 Trojan Ln 70586 337-363-1475
Diane Fontenot, prin. Fax 363-0348
South Louisiana Community College Post-Sec.
1124 Vocational Dr Ward 1 70586 337-363-2197

Vinton, Calcasieu, Pop. 3,128
Calcasieu Parish SD
Supt. — See Lake Charles
Vinton HS 300/9-12
1603 Grace Ave 70668 337-217-4400
Mitch Manuel, prin. Fax 217-4401
Vinton MS 200/6-8
900 Horridge St 70668 337-217-4720
Gena Granger, prin. Fax 217-4721

Vivian, Caddo, Pop. 3,629
Caddo Parish SD
Supt. — See Shreveport
North Caddo HS 300/9-12
201 Airport Dr 71082 318-375-3258
H. Kenneth Berg, prin. Fax 222-8430

Walker, Livingston, Pop. 6,061
Livingston Parish SD
Supt. — See Livingston
North Corbin JHS 600/6-8
32725 N Corbin Rd 70785 225-686-2038
Dennis DeLee, prin. Fax 686-2690
Pine Ridge S 100/Alt
PO Box 72 70785 225-664-4823
Tony Terry, prin. Fax 664-2984
Walker Freshman HS 400/9-9
PO Box 659 70785 225-664-0243
David Clark, prin. Fax 665-0512
Walker SHS 1,000/10-12
12646 Burgess Ave 70785 225-664-4825
Jason St. Pierre, prin. Fax 664-4321
Westside JHS 600/6-8
12615 Burgess Ave 70785 225-665-8259
Steve Link, prin. Fax 665-8283

Washington, Saint Landry, Pop. 948
St. Landry Parish SD
Supt. — See Opelousas
North Central HS 300/5-12
6579 Highway 10 70589 337-623-4239
Jerome Robinson, prin. Fax 623-5360
Washington Career & Technical Education Vo/Tech
PO Box 430 70589 337-826-7360
Tracy Beard, prin. Fax 826-5264

Watson, Livingston, Pop. 1,038
Livingston Parish SD
Supt. — See Livingston
Live Oak MS 1,000/6-8
PO Box 470 70786 225-664-3211
Ryan Hodges, prin. Fax 664-1551

Welsh, Jefferson Davis, Pop. 3,178
Jefferson Davis Parish SD
Supt. — See Jennings
Welsh HS 300/9-12
306 Bourgeois St 70591 337-734-2361
Robin Primeaux, prin. Fax 734-4149

Westlake, Calcasieu, Pop. 4,510
Calcasieu Parish SD
Supt. — See Lake Charles
Arnett MS 400/6-8
400 Sulphur Ave 70669 337-217-4630
Marc Jardel, prin. Fax 217-4631
Westlake HS 500/9-12
1000 Garden Dr 70669 337-217-4950
Lee Crick, prin. Fax 217-4951
Westlake HS T & I Vo/Tech
2307 Jones St 70669 337-217-4375
Gary Singer, prin. Fax 217-4376

West Monroe, Ouachita, Pop. 12,872
Ouachita Parish SD
Supt. — See Monroe
Good Hope MS 600/6-8
400 Good Hope Rd 71291 318-396-9693
Twainna Calhoun, prin. Fax 397-5110
Ouachita Parish Alternative Center 200/Alt
1600 N 7th St 71291 318-323-5991
Scott Stone, prin. Fax 323-5946
Riser MS 500/6-8
100 Price Dr 71292 318-387-0567
Rodney Lloyd, prin. Fax 387-9072
West Monroe HS 1,900/9-12
201 Riggs St 71291 318-323-3771
Shere Lynne May, prin. Fax 388-4594
West Ouachita HS 1,000/9-12
4061 Caples Rd 71292 318-249-2117
Mickey Merritt, prin. Fax 249-4774
West Ridge MS 700/6-8
6977 Cypress St 71291 318-397-8444
Jim McKay, prin. Fax 397-9376
Woodlawn MS 300/6-8
175 Woodlawn School Rd 71292 318-325-1574
Charles Dykes, prin. Fax 325-9858

Claiborne Christian S 200/PK-12
334 Laird St 71291 318-396-7968
Lee Taylor, head sch Fax 397-0567
Cloyd's Beauty School #1 Inc. Post-Sec.
603 Natchitoches St 71291 318-322-5314
Northeast Baptist S 200/PK-12
5225 I 20 Service Rd 71292 318-325-2077
Anita Watson, prin. Fax 998-0193

Westwego, Jefferson, Pop. 8,397
Jefferson Parish SD
Supt. — See Harvey

Worley MS 600/6-8
801 Spartan Ln 70094 504-348-4964
Ira Wilson, prin. Fax 348-7057

White Castle, Iberville, Pop. 1,872
Iberville Parish SD
Supt. — See Plaquemine
White Castle HS 300/7-12
32695 Graham St 70788 225-545-3621
Fax 545-2964

Winnfield, Winn, Pop. 4,766
Winn Parish SD 2,600/PK-12
PO Box 430 71483 318-628-6936
Steve Bartlett, supt. Fax 628-2582
www.winnpsb.org
Winnfield HS 400/9-12
631 Thomas Mill Rd 71483 318-628-3506
Dr. Jane Griffin, prin. Fax 628-3417
Winnfield MS 400/6-8
685 Thomas Mill Rd 71483 318-628-2765
Kaye Pyles, prin. Fax 628-1838
Winn Parish Adult Learning Center Adult
403 W South Ave 71483 318-628-3492
Mike Austin, dir. Fax 628-7280
Other Schools – See Atlanta, Calvin, Dodson

Central Louisiana Technical College Post-Sec.
304 S Jones St 71483 318-628-4342

Winnsboro, Franklin, Pop. 4,862
Franklin Parish SD 3,000/PK-12
7293 Prairie Rd 71295 318-435-9046
Dr. Lanny Johnson, supt. Fax 435-3392
www.fpsb.us
Franklin Parish HS 700/9-12
1600 Glover Dr 71295 318-435-5676
Fax 435-6493
White Learning Center 100/Alt
5915 Highway 4 71295 318-435-5505
Ken Blackson, prin. Fax 435-0457

Family Community Christian S 500/PK-12
2023 Highway 15 71295 318-435-4791
Elizabeth Rigdon, prin. Fax 435-4792
Franklin Academy 200/K-12
2110 Loop Rd 71295 318-435-9520
Phil Jackson, prin. Fax 435-9508

Woodworth, Rapides, Pop. 1,087
Rapides Parish SD
Supt. — See Alexandria
Dormon JHS 7-8
8906 Highway 165 S 71485 318-473-4066
Shannon Alford, prin. Fax 473-1890

Youngsville, Lafayette, Pop. 8,025
Lafayette Parish SD
Supt. — See Lafayette
Youngsville MS 800/5-8
600 Church St 70592 337-521-7940
Darrel Combs, prin. Fax 521-7941

Youngsville Christian S 100/PK-12
214 Church St 70592 337-856-8693
Daina Jackson, admin. Fax 856-8675

Zachary, East Baton Rouge, Pop. 14,763
Zachary Community SD 5,000/PK-12
3755 Church St 70791 225-658-4969
Scott Devillier, supt. Fax 658-5261
www.zacharyschools.org
Northwestern MS 1,200/6-8
5200 E Central Ave 70791 225-654-9201
Debby Brian, prin. Fax 658-2025
Port Hudson Career Academy 50/Alt
205 W Flonacher Rd 70791 225-658-7381
Patrick Jenkins, prin. Fax 658-7385
Zachary HS 1,300/9-12
4100 Bronco Ln 70791 225-654-2776
Wes Watts, prin. Fax 658-0010

Zachary Christian Academy 100/PK-12
20810 Plank Rd 70791 225-654-8925
Dr. Charles Watts, admin. Fax 654-7995

Zwolle, Sabine, Pop. 1,697
Sabine Parish SD
Supt. — See Many
Zwolle JSHS 300/7-12
PO Box 188 71486 318-645-6104
Chad Crow, prin. Fax 645-4830

MAINE

MAINE DEPARTMENT OF EDUCATION
23 State House Sta, Augusta 04333-0023
Telephone 207-624-6600
Fax 207-624-6700
Website http://www.maine.gov/education/index.shtml

Commissioner of Education Stephen Bowen

MAINE BOARD OF EDUCATION
23 State House Station, Augusta 04333-0023

Chairperson Steven Pound

PUBLIC, PRIVATE AND CATHOLIC SECONDARY SCHOOLS

Ashland, Aroostook, Pop. 707
RSU 32 / MSAD 32 200/PK-12
PO Box 289 04732 207-435-3661
Gehrig Johnson Ph.D., supt. Fax 435-8421
www.sad32.org/
Ashland District S 200/PK-12
PO Box 369 04732 207-435-3481
Christopher Hallett, prin. Fax 435-6417

Auburn, Androscoggin, Pop. 22,603
Auburn SD 3,700/PK-12
PO Box 800 04212 207-784-6431
Katherine Grondin, supt. Fax 333-6628
www.auburnschl.edu
Auburn MS 500/7-8
38 Falcon Dr 04210 207-333-6654
James Hand, prin. Fax 784-1359
Franklin Alternative S 100/Alt
23 High St 04210 207-782-3242
Russell Barlow, prin. Fax 783-4189
Little HS 1,000/9-12
77 Harris St 04210 207-333-6652
James Miller, prin. Fax 784-9243
Merrill Hill Alternative S 50/Alt
23 High St 04210 207-783-3242
Russell Barlow, prin.

Central Maine Community College Post-Sec.
1250 Turner St 04210 207-755-5100
St. Dominic Academy 300/7-12
121 Gracelawn Rd 04210 207-782-6911
Donald Fournier, prin. Fax 795-6439

Augusta, Kennebec, Pop. 18,710
Augusta SD 2,300/PK-12
12 Gedney St 04330 207-626-2468
James Anastasio, supt. Fax 626-2444
www.augustaschools.org/
Capitol Area Technical Center Vo/Tech
40 Pierce Dr 04330 207-626-2475
Peter Gagnon, dir. Fax 626-2498
Cony JSHS 1,100/7-12
60 Pierce Dr 04330 207-626-2460
Kim Silsby, prin. Fax 626-2541

University of Maine at Augusta Post-Sec.
46 University Dr 04330 207-621-3000

Baileyville, Washington
AOS 90 - EMASS 800/PK-12
PO Box 580 04694 207-427-6913
Fax 427-3166
Woodland JSHS 200/7-12
14 First Ave 04694 207-427-3325
Patricia Metta, prin. Fax 427-3950
Other Schools – See Lee

Bangor, Penobscot, Pop. 32,402
Applied Technology Region
Supt. — None
United Technologies Center-Region 4 Vo/Tech
200 Hogan Rd 04401 207-942-5296
Fred Woodman, dir. Fax 942-0776

Bangor SD 3,900/PK-12
73 Harlow St 04401 207-992-4150
Dr. Betsy Webb, supt. Fax 992-4163
www.bangorschools.net
Bangor HS 1,300/9-12
885 Broadway 04401 207-992-5500
Paul Butler, prin. Fax 941-6212
Cohen MS 400/6-8
304 Garland St 04401 207-941-6230
Gary Gonyar, prin. Fax 941-6235
Doughty MS 400/6-8
143 5th St 04401 207-941-6220
Robert MacDonald, prin. Fax 947-7606

All Saints S - St. John Campus 100/4-8
PO Box 1749 04402 207-942-0955
Joseph Gallant, prin. Fax 942-2398
Bangor Christian S 300/PK-12
1476 Broadway 04401 207-947-7356
Jim Frost, hdmstr. Fax 262-9528
Bangor Theological Seminary Post-Sec.
PO Box 411 04402 800-287-6781
Bapst Memorial HS 400/9-12
100 Broadway 04401 207-947-0313
Melville MacKay, head sch Fax 941-2474
Beal College Post-Sec.
99 Farm Rd 04401 207-947-4591
Eastern Maine Community College Post-Sec.
354 Hogan Rd 04401 207-974-4600
Eastern Maine Medical Center Post-Sec.
489 State St 04401 207-973-7051
Empire Beauty School Post-Sec.
639 Broadway 04401 207-942-0039
Husson University Post-Sec.
1 College Cir 04401 207-941-7000
New England School of Communications Post-Sec.
1 College Cir 04401 207-941-7176

Bar Harbor, Hancock, Pop. 2,528

College of the Atlantic Post-Sec.
105 Eden St 04609 207-288-5015

Bath, Sagadahoc, Pop. 8,327
RSU 1 2,100/PK-12
34 Wing Farm Pkwy 04530 207-443-6601
Dr. Patrick Manuel, supt. Fax 443-8295
www.rsu1.org/
Bath MS 400/6-8
6 Old Brunswick Rd 04530 207-443-8270
Louis Solebello, prin. Fax 443-8273
Bath Regional Vocational Center Vo/Tech
800 High St 04530 207-443-8257
Joel Austin, prin. Fax 443-8256
Morse HS 700/9-12
826 High St 04530 207-443-8250
Jay Pinkerton, prin. Fax 443-8268

Hyde S 100/9-12
616 High St 04530 207-443-5584
Ross Sanner, admin. Fax 443-1450

Belfast, Waldo, Pop. 6,555
RSU 20 2,600/PK-12
PO Box 363 04915 207-338-1960
Brian Carpenter, supt. Fax 338-4597
www.rsu20.org/
Belfast Area HS 600/9-12
98 Waldo Ave 04915 207-338-1790
Stephen Fitzpatrick, prin. Fax 338-6713
Howard MS 400/6-8
173 Lincolnville Ave 04915 207-338-3320
Kimberly Buckheit, prin. Fax 338-5588
Adult Education Adult
6B Lions Way 04915 207-338-3197
Darrell Gilman Ed.D., prin. Fax 338-2960
Other Schools – See Searsport

Bethel, Oxford
RSU 44 / MSAD 44 900/K-12
1 Parkway Ste 204 04217 207-824-2185
David Murphy Ed.D., supt. Fax 824-2725
www.sad44.org
Telstar HS 300/9-12
284 Walkers Mills Rd 04217 207-824-2136
Daniel Hart, prin. Fax 824-7130
Telstar MS 200/6-8
284 Walkers Mills Rd 04217 207-824-2136
Clark Rafford, prin. Fax 824-0496

Gould Academy 200/9-12
PO Box 860 04217 207-824-7700
Matt Ruby, head sch Fax 824-7711

Biddeford, York, Pop. 20,950
Biddeford SD 2,600/K-12
PO Box 1865 04005 207-282-8280
Jeremy Ray, supt. Fax 284-7956
www.biddschools.org
Biddeford HS 900/9-12
20 Maplewood Ave 04005 207-282-1596
Britton Wolfe, prin. Fax 282-8275
Biddeford MS 600/6-8
25 Tiger Way 04005 207-282-6400
Charles Lomonte, prin. Fax 282-6040
Biddeford Regional Center of Tech Vo/Tech
10 Maplewood Ave 04005 207-282-1501
Peg Levasseur, prin. Fax 282-7986

University of New England Post-Sec.
11 Hills Beach Rd 04005 207-283-0171

Bingham, Somerset, Pop. 749
RSU 83 / MSAD 13 300/PK-12
PO Box 649 04920 207-672-5502
Virginia Rebar, supt. Fax 672-5502
www.sad13.org
Quimby MS 100/5-8
PO Box 649 04920 207-672-5500
Juliana Richard, prin. Fax 672-5502
Upper Kennebec Valley HS 100/9-12
PO Box 669 04920 207-672-3300
Juliana Richard, prin. Fax 672-4485

Blue Hill, Hancock, Pop. 936

Stevens Academy 300/9-12
23 Union St 04614 207-374-2808

Boothbay Harbor, Lincoln, Pop. 1,073
AOS 98 - RCSS 800/PK-12
51 Emery Ln 04538 207-633-2874
Eileen King, supt. Fax 633-5458
sites.google.com/site/boothbayschools/schools-of-union-49
Boothbay Region HS 200/9-12
236 Townsend Ave 04538 207-633-2421
Daniel Welch, prin. Fax 633-7129

Brewer, Penobscot, Pop. 9,320
Brewer SD 1,700/PK-12
261 Center St 04412 207-989-3160
Dr. Daniel Lee, supt. Fax 989-8622
www.breweredu.org/
Brewer HS 700/9-12
79 Parkway S 04412 207-989-4140
David Wall, prin. Fax 989-8659

Bridgton, Cumberland, Pop. 2,035
RSU 61 / MSAD 61 1,900/K-12
900 Portland Rd 04009 207-647-3048
Kathleen Beecher, supt. Fax 647-5682
www.lakeregionschools.org
Other Schools – See Naples

Brunswick, Cumberland, Pop. 14,835
Applied Technology Region
Supt. — None
Maine Vocational Region 10 Vo/Tech
68 Church Rd 04011 207-729-6622
Barry Lohnes, dir. Fax 721-0907

Brunswick SD 1,800/K-12
46 Federal St 04011 207-319-1900
Paul Perzanoski, supt. Fax 725-1700
www.brunswick.k12.me.us/
Brunswick HS 1,000/9-12
116 Maquoit Rd 04011 207-319-1910
Arthur Abelmann, prin. Fax 798-5515
Brunswick JHS 600/6-8
65 Columbia Ave 04011 207-319-1930
Walter Wallace, prin. Fax 721-0602

Bowdoin College Post-Sec.
5000 College Sta 04011 207-725-3000

Buckfield, Oxford
RSU 10
Supt. — See Dixfield
Buckfield JSHS 300/7-12
160 Morrill St 04220 207-336-2151
George Reuter, prin. Fax 336-2460

Bucksport, Hancock, Pop. 2,843
RSU 25 1,000/PK-12
62 Mechanic St 04416 207-469-7311
James Boothby, supt. Fax 469-6640
www.rsu25.org/
Bucksport HS 400/9-12
102 Broadway 04416 207-469-6650
Daniel Clifford, prin. Fax 469-2081

Bucksport MS 300/5-8
100 Miles Ln 04416 207-469-6647
Ivan Braun, prin. Fax 469-2068

Buxton, York
RSU 6 / MSAD 6 3,400/PK-12
94 Main St 04093 207-929-3831
Frank Sherburne, supt. Fax 929-5955
www.bonnyeagle.org
Bonny Eagle MS 900/6-8
92 Sokokis Trl 04093 207-929-3833
Michael Roy, prin. Fax 929-9181
Other Schools – See Standish

Calais, Washington, Pop. 3,074
AOS 77 - SCSS 600/PK-12
32 Blue Devil Hl 04619 207-454-7561
James Underwood, supt. Fax 454-2516
Other Schools – See Eastport

Calais SD 700/PK-12
32 Blue Devil Hl 04619 207-454-7561
Raymond Freve, supt. Fax 454-2296
Calais MSHS 400/7-12
34 Blue Devil Hl Ste 2 04619 207-454-2591
Daniel Cohnstaedt, prin. Fax 454-0306
Saint Croix Regional Tech Center Vo/Tech
34 Blue Devil Hl Ste 1 04619 207-454-2581
Fax 454-2597

Washington County Community College Post-Sec.
1 College Dr 04619 207-454-1000

Camden, Knox, Pop. 3,526
MSAD 28 / Five Town CSD 1,400/K-12
7 Lions Ln 04843 207-236-3358
Elaine Nutter, supt. Fax 236-7810
www.fivetowns.net
Camden-Rockport MS 300/5-8
34 Knowlton St 04843 207-236-7805
Maria Libby, prin. Fax 236-7815
Other Schools – See Rockport

Cape Elizabeth, Cumberland, Pop. 8,854
Cape Elizabeth SD 1,700/K-12
PO Box 6267 04107 207-799-2217
Meredith Nadeau, supt. Fax 799-2914
www.cape.k12.me.us
Cape Elizabeth HS 600/9-12
345 Ocean House Rd 04107 207-799-3309
Jeffrey Shedd, prin. Fax 767-8050
Cape Elizabeth MS 600/5-8
14 Scott Dyer Rd 04107 207-799-8176
Douglas Perley, prin. Fax 767-0832

Caribou, Aroostook, Pop. 8,094
Eastern Aroostook Regional Sch Unit 39 1,800/PK-12
628 Main St 04736 207-496-6311
Franklin McElwain, supt. Fax 498-3261
www.rsu39.org
Caribou HS 600/9-12
308 Sweden St 04736 207-493-4260
Mark Jones, prin. Fax 493-4244
Caribou MS 300/6-8
21 Glenn St 04736 207-493-4240
Leland Caron, prin. Fax 493-4243
Caribou Regional Technology Center Vo/Tech
308 Sweden St Ste 1 04736 207-493-4270
Ralph Conroy, prin. Fax 493-4242
Adult Education Adult
75 Bennett Dr Ste 2 04736 207-493-4272
Dan MacDonald, dir.
Other Schools – See Limestone

Empire Beauty School Post-Sec.
30 Skyway Dr 04736 207-498-6067

Carmel, Penobscot
RSU 87 / MSAD 23 700/PK-8
44 Plymouth Rd 04419 207-848-5173
John Backus, supt. Fax 848-5196
www.msad23.org
Caravel MS 200/5-8
520 Irish Rd 04419 207-848-3615
Rhonda Sperrey, prin. Fax 848-0884

Castine, Hancock, Pop. 1,015

Maine Maritime Academy Post-Sec.
66 Pleasant St 04420 207-326-4311

Charleston, Penobscot

Highview Christian Academy 100/PK-12
739 Main Rd 04422 207-285-7978
Jay H. Philbrick, hdmstr. Fax 285-7978

Corinth, Penobscot
RSU 64 / MSAD 64 1,200/K-12
PO Box 279 04427 207-285-3334
Daniel Higgins, supt. Fax 285-4343
www.rsu64schools.org
Central HS 400/9-12
PO Box 370 04427 207-285-3326
Garry Spencer, prin. Fax 285-4342
Central MS 300/6-8
PO Box 19 04427 207-285-3177
Jonathan Perry, prin. Fax 285-4350

Cumberland Center, Cumberland, Pop. 2,477
RSU 51 / MSAD 51 2,100/K-12
PO Box 6A 04021 207-829-4800
Robert Hasson, supt. Fax 829-4802
www.msad51.org
Greely HS 700/9-12
303 Main St 04021 207-829-4805
Dan McKeone, prin. Fax 829-2256
Greely MS 500/6-8
351 Tuttle Rd 04021 207-829-4815
Kim Brandt, prin. Fax 829-4819

Danforth, Washington
RSU 84 / MSAD 14
Supt. — See Hodgdon
East Grand S 100/PK-12
31 Houlton Rd 04424 207-448-2260
Dale Fiske, prin. Fax 448-7880

Deer Isle, Hancock
Deer Isle - Stonington Community SD
Supt. — See Sargentville
Deer Isle - Stonington HS 200/9-12
251 N Deer Isle Rd 04627 207-348-2303
Todd West, prin. Fax 348-2304

Dexter, Penobscot, Pop. 2,129
AOS 94 - S46HRSD 700/PK-12
175 Fern Rd Ste 1 04930 207-924-6000
Kevin Jordan, supt. Fax 924-7660
www.aos94.org
Dexter HS 300/9-12
12 Abbott Hill Rd 04930 207-924-5536
Stephen Bell, prin. Fax 924-7673
Tri-County Regional Technology Center Vo/Tech
14 Abbott Hill Rd 04930 207-924-7670
Nick Vafiades, prin. Fax 924-5539

Dixfield, Oxford, Pop. 1,056
RSU 10 2,800/PK-12
33 Nash St 04224 207-562-7254
Craig King Ed.D., supt. Fax 562-7059
rsu10schools.com/
Dirigo HS 300/9-12
145 Weld St 04224 207-562-4251
Mike Poulin, prin. Fax 562-6074
Dirigo HS-East Campus 9-12
33 Nash St 04224 207-562-7254
Mike Poulin, prin. Fax 562-7059
Dirigo MS 200/6-8
45 Middle School Dr 04224 207-562-7552
Celena Ranger, prin. Fax 562-8329
Other Schools – See Buckfield, Mexico, Rumford

Dover Foxcroft, Piscataquis, Pop. 3,077
RSU 68 / MSAD 68 700/PK-8
63 Harrison Ave Ste C 04426 207-564-6535
Alan Smith, supt. Fax 564-3487
www.sad68.org
Se Do Mo Cha MS 300/5-8
63 Harrison Ave 04426 207-564-6535
Julie Kimball, prin. Fax 564-6531

Foxcroft Academy 500/9-12
975 W Main St 04426 207-564-8351
Arnold Shorey, head sch Fax 564-8394

Dyer Brook, Aroostook
RSU 50 800/PK-12
922 Dyer Brook Rd, 207-757-8223
Larry Malone, supt. Fax 757-8257
www.rsu50.org
Southern Aroostook Community S 400/K-12
922 Dyer Brook Rd, 207-757-8206
Jon Porter, prin. Fax 757-8257
Other Schools – See Stacyville

East Machias, Washington

Washington Academy 400/9-12
PO Box 190 04630 207-255-8301
Judson McBrine, hdmstr. Fax 255-8303

East Millinocket, Penobscot, Pop. 1,552
Great Northern School System AOS 66 500/K-12
45 North St Ste 2 04430 207-746-3500
Quentin Clark, supt. Fax 746-3516
Schenck HS 200/9-12
45 North St 04430 207-746-3511
John Farrington, prin. Fax 746-3516
Other Schools – See Medway

Millinocket SD 400/K-12
45 North St Ste 2 04430 207-723-6400
Kenneth Smith Ed.D., supt. Fax 447-6599
www.millinocketschools.org/
Other Schools – See Millinocket

Easton, Aroostook
Easton SD 200/PK-12
PO Box 126 04740 207-488-7700
Roger Shaw, supt. Fax 488-2840
eastonschools.org
Easton JSHS 100/7-12
PO Box 66 04740 207-488-7702
Jane Sincerbeaux, prin. Fax 488-7707

Eastport, Washington, Pop. 1,291
AOS 77 - SCSS
Supt. — See Calais
Shead HS 100/9-12
89 High St 04631 207-853-6254
Paul Theriault, prin. Fax 853-2919

Westlawn Institute of Marine Technology Post-Sec.
16 Deep Cove Rd 04631 207-853-6600

East Waterboro, York
RSU 57 / MSAD 57
Supt. — See Waterboro
Massabesic MS 800/6-8
134 Old Alfred Rd 04030 207-247-6121
Mark Fisher, prin. Fax 247-8621

Eliot, York
RSU 35 / MSAD 35 2,400/PK-12
180 Depot Rd 03903 207-439-2438
Mary Nash, supt. Fax 439-2531
www.msad35.net/
Marshwood MS 600/6-8
626 Harold L Dow Hwy 03903 207-439-1399
John Caverly, prin. Fax 439-3504

Other Schools – See South Berwick

Ellsworth, Hancock, Pop. 7,675
RSU 24 2,600/PK-12
248 State St Ste 3A 04605 207-667-8136
Suzanne Lukas, supt. Fax 667-6493
www.rsu24.org
Ellsworth HS 600/9-12
299 State St 04605 207-667-4722
Renee Thompson, prin. Fax 667-5027
Hancock County Tech Center Vo/Tech
112 Boggy Brook Rd 04605 207-667-9729
Amy Boles, dir. Fax 667-7138
Other Schools – See Sullivan

Acadia Christian S 100/PK-12
PO Box 1082 04605 207-664-0182
Troy Alley, prin. Fax 664-0197

Fairfield, Kennebec, Pop. 2,598
RSU 49 / MSAD 49 2,400/PK-12
8 School St 04937 207-453-4200
Dean Baker, supt. Fax 453-4208
www.msad49.org
Lawrence HS 800/9-12
9 School St 04937 207-453-4200
Pamela Swett, prin. Fax 453-4219
Lawrence JHS 400/7-8
7 School St 04937 207-453-4200
Roberta Hersom, prin. Fax 453-4214

Kennebec Valley Community College Post-Sec.
92 Western Ave 04937 207-453-5000

Falmouth, Cumberland, Pop. 1,834
Falmouth SD 1,900/K-12
51 Woodville Rd 04105 207-781-3200
Barbara Powers, supt. Fax 781-5711
www.falmouthschools.org
Falmouth HS 700/9-12
74 Woodville Rd 04105 207-781-7429
Gregg Palmer, prin. Fax 781-3985
Falmouth MS 500/6-8
52 Woodville Rd 04105 207-781-3740
Sue Palfrey, prin. Fax 321-0108

Maine Educational Center for the Deaf Post-Sec.
Mackworth Island 04105 207-781-3165

Farmingdale, Kennebec, Pop. 1,939
RSU 2
Supt. — See Hallowell
Hall-Dale HS 300/9-12
97 Maple St 04344 207-622-6211
Mark Tinkham, prin. Fax 626-0355
Hall-Dale MS 200/6-8
111 Maple St 04344 207-622-4162
Mark Tinkham, prin. Fax 622-7515

Farmington, Franklin, Pop. 4,199
RSU 9 - Mt. Blue Regional SD 2,200/K-12
115 Learning Ln 04938 207-778-6571
Michael Cormier, supt. Fax 778-4160
www.mtbluersd.org/
Foster Reg Applied Tech Center Vo/Tech
374 High St 04938 207-778-3562
Glenn Kapiloff, prin. Fax 778-3562
Mt. Blue HS 700/9-12
129 Seamon Rd 04938 207-778-3561
Monique Poulin, prin. Fax 778-3564
Mt. Blue MS 400/7-8
269 Middle St 04938 207-778-3511
Gary Oswald, prin. Fax 778-5810

University of Maine Farmington Post-Sec.
111 South St 04938 207-778-7050

Fort Fairfield, Aroostook, Pop. 1,799
AOS 99 - MCSS 1,000/PK-12
28 High School Dr Ste B 04742 207-473-4455
Marc Gendron, supt. Fax 473-4095
www.msad20.org/
Fort Fairfield MSHS 300/6-12
28 High School Dr Ste A 04742 207-472-3271
Tanya Belanger, prin. Fax 472-3281
Other Schools – See Mars Hill

Fort Kent, Aroostook, Pop. 2,423
AOS 95 - SJVAOS 1,000/PK-12
84 Pleasant St Ste 1 04743 207-834-3189
Timothy Doak, supt. Fax 834-3395
www.sad27.org/
Fort Kent Community HS 300/9-12
84 Pleasant St 04743 207-834-5540
Dawn Dougan, prin. Fax 834-2723

University of Maine Fort Kent Post-Sec.
23 University Dr 04743 207-834-7500

Freeport, Cumberland, Pop. 1,447
RSU 5 1,800/PK-12
17 West St 04032 207-865-0928
Shannon Welsh Ed.D., supt. Fax 865-2855
rsu5.org/
Freeport HS 500/9-12
30 Holbrook St 04032 207-865-4706
Robert Strong, prin. Fax 865-2900
Freeport MS 300/6-8
19 Kendall Ln 04032 207-865-6051
Raymond Grogan, prin. Fax 865-2902

Merriconeag Waldorf S 200/K-12
57 Desert Rd 04032 207-865-3900
Fax 865-6822
Pine Tree Academy 100/PK-12
67 Pownal Rd 04032 207-865-4747
Fax 865-1768

Frenchville, Aroostook
RSU 33 / MSAD 33 — 300/PK-12
PO Box 9 04745 — 207-543-7334
Dr. Fern Desjardins, supt. — Fax 543-6242
www.msad33.org
St. John Valley Tech Center — Vo/Tech
PO Box 509 04745 — 207-543-6606
David Morse, dir. — Fax 543-6115
Other Schools – See Saint Agatha

Fryeburg, Oxford, Pop. 1,595
RSU 72 / MSAD 72 — 800/PK-8
124 Portland St 04037 — 207-935-2600
Gary MacDonald, supt. — Fax 935-3787
www.msad72.k12.me.us/
Ockett MS — 300/6-8
25 Molly Ockett Dr 04037 — 207-935-2401
Jay Robinson, prin. — Fax 935-4470

Fryeburg Academy — 700/9-12
745 Main St 04037 — 207-935-2001
Daniel Lee, hdmstr. — Fax 935-4292

Gardiner, Kennebec, Pop. 5,663
MSAD 11 — 2,200/PK-12
150 Highland Ave 04345 — 207-582-5346
Patricia Hopkins, supt. — Fax 582-8305
www.msad11.org
Gardiner Area HS — 700/9-12
40 W Hill Rd 04345 — 207-582-3150
Chad Kempton, prin. — Fax 582-0434
Gardiner Regional MS — 500/6-8
161 Cobbossee Ave 04345 — 207-582-1326
Todd Sanders, prin. — Fax 582-6823

Glenburn, See Bangor
RSU 26 — 1,300/K-12
983 Hudson Rd 04401 — 207-942-4405
Douglas Smith, supt. — Fax 942-4250
www.riversidersu.org
Other Schools – See Orono

Gorham, Cumberland, Pop. 6,775
Gorham SD — 3,000/K-12
75 South St Ste 2 04038 — 207-222-1012
Theodore Sharpe, supt. — Fax 839-8885
www.gorhamschools.org/
Gorham HS — 900/9-12
41 Morrill Ave 04038 — 207-222-1100
Christopher Record, prin. — Fax 839-7742
Gorham MS — 600/6-8
106 Weeks Rd 04038 — 207-222-1220
Robert Riley, prin. — Fax 839-4092

Gray, Cumberland, Pop. 877
RSU 15 / MSAD 15 — 2,000/K-12
14 Shaker Rd 04039 — 207-657-3335
Bruce Beasley, supt. — Fax 657-2040
www.msad15.org/
Gray-New Gloucester HS — 500/9-12
10 Libby Hill Rd 04039 — 207-657-3323
Paul Penna, prin. — Fax 657-3329
Gray-New Gloucester MS — 600/5-8
31 Libby Hill Rd 04039 — 207-657-4994
Sherry Levesque, prin. — Fax 657-5219

Greenville, Piscataquis, Pop. 1,245
Union SD 60 — 100/PK-12
PO Box 100 04441 — 207-695-3708
Beth Lorigan, supt. — Fax 695-3709
www.ghslakers.org
Greenville Consolidated S — 100/PK-12
PO Box 100 04441 — 207-695-2666
Kelly MacFadyen, prin. — Fax 695-4614

Guilford, Piscataquis, Pop. 885
RSU 80 / MSAD 4 — 400/PK-12
25 Campus Dr 04443 — 207-876-3444
Paul Stearns, supt. — Fax 876-3446
www.sad4.com/
Piscataquis Community JSHS — 200/7-12
9 Campus Dr 04443 — 207-876-4625
Kevin Harrington, prin. — Fax 876-4628

Hallowell, Kennebec, Pop. 2,343
RSU 2 — 2,100/PK-12
7 Reed St 04347 — 207-622-6351
Virgel Hammonds, supt. — Fax 622-7866
www.kidsrsu.org
Other Schools – See Farmingdale, Monmouth, Richmond

Hampden, Penobscot, Pop. 4,292
RSU 22 / MSAD 22 — 2,100/PK-12
24 Main Rd N 04444 — 207-862-3255
Richard Lyons, supt. — Fax 862-2789
www.sad22.us/
Hampden Academy — 700/9-12
89 Western Ave 04444 — 207-862-3791
Ruey Yehle, prin. — Fax 862-4577
Reeds Brook MS — 300/6-8
28A Main Rd S 04444 — 207-862-3540
Anita McCafferty, prin. — Fax 862-3551
Other Schools – See Winterport

Harrington, Washington
RSU 37 / MSAD 37 — 700/K-12
1020 Sacarap Rd 04643 — 207-483-2734
Ronald Ramsay, supt. — Fax 483-6051
www.msad37.org/
Narraguagus HS — 200/9-12
1611 Main St 04643 — 207-483-2746
John Sawyer, prin. — Fax 483-2771

Hartland, Somerset, Pop. 799
RSU 19
Supt. — See Newport
Somerset Valley MS — 300/5-8
45 Blake St 04943 — 207-938-4770
Don Roux, prin. — Fax 938-2114

Hebron, Oxford

Hebron Academy — 300/6-12
PO Box 309 04238 — 207-966-2100
John King, hdmstr. — Fax 966-1111

Hermon, See Bangor
Hermon SD — 1,200/PK-12
31 Billings Rd 04401 — 207-848-4000
Patricia Duran, supt. — Fax 848-5226
www.hermon.net
Hermon HS — 500/9-12
2415 Route 2 04401 — 207-848-4000
Brian Walsh, prin. — Fax 848-5591
Hermon MS — 300/5-8
29 Billings Rd 04401 — 207-848-4000
Gerald Kiesman, prin. — Fax 848-2163

Hiram, Oxford
RSU 55 / MSAD 55 — 1,100/K-12
137 S Hiram Rd 04041 — 207-625-2490
Sylvia Pease, supt. — Fax 625-7065
www.sad55.org
Sacopee Valley HS — 400/9-12
115 S Hiram Rd 04041 — 207-625-3208
Ryan Caron, prin. — Fax 625-7869
Sacopee Valley MS — 400/5-8
137 S Hiram Rd 04041 — 207-625-2450
Michael Lynch, prin. — Fax 625-2465

Hodgdon, Aroostook
RSU 70 / MSAD 70 — 500/PK-12
175 Hodgdon Mills Rd 04730 — 207-532-3015
Robert McDaniel, supt. — Fax 532-2679
www.msad70.org
Hodgdon HS — 200/9-12
174 Hodgdon Mills Rd 04730 — 207-532-2413
Mary Harbison, prin. — Fax 532-4043

RSU 84 / MSAD 14 — 100/PK-12
175 Hodgdon Mills Rd 04730 — 207-532-3015
Robert McDaniel, supt. — Fax 532-2679
www.eastgrandschool.org
Other Schools – See Danforth

Holden, Penobscot
RSU 63 / MSAD 63 — 600/K-8
202 Kidder Hill Rd 04429 — 207-843-7851
David Anderson, supt. — Fax 843-7295
www.sad63.net/
Holbrook MS — 300/5-8
202 Kidder Hill Rd 04429 — 207-843-7769
Richard Modery, prin. — Fax 843-4328

Houlton, Aroostook, Pop. 4,790
Applied Technology Region
Supt. — None
Region 2 School of Applied Tech — Vo/Tech
PO Box 307 04730 — 207-532-9541
Dave Keaton, dir. — Fax 532-6975

RSU 29 / MSAD 29 — 1,300/PK-12
PO Box 190 04730 — 207-532-6555
Mike Hammer, supt. — Fax 532-6481
www.sad29.k12.me.us/
Houlton HS — 400/9-12
7 Bird St 04730 — 207-532-6551
Martin Bouchard, prin. — Fax 532-6282
Houlton JHS — 200/7-8
7 Bird St 04730 — 207-532-6551
Martin Bouchard, prin. — Fax 532-6282

Greater Houlton Christian Academy — 200/PK-12
27 School St 04730 — 207-532-0736
John Bishop, head sch — Fax 532-9553

Howland, Penobscot, Pop. 1,083
AOS 43
Supt. — See Lagrange
Hichborn MS — 100/6-8
23 Cross St 04448 — 207-732-3113
Carol Marcinkus, prin. — Fax 732-8331
Penobscot Valley HS — 200/9-12
23 Cross St 04448 — 207-732-3111
Carol Marcinkus, prin. — Fax 732-8328

Islesboro, Waldo
Islesboro SD — 100/K-12
PO Box 118 04848 — 207-734-6723
Joseph Mattos, supt. — Fax 734-8159
ics.islesboro.k12.me.us
Islesboro Central S — 100/K-12
PO Box 118 04848 — 207-734-2251
Heather Knight, prin. — Fax 734-8159

Jackman, Somerset
RSU 82 / MSAD 12 — 200/K-12
606 Main St 04945 — 207-668-5291
John Davis, supt. — Fax 668-4482
www.sad12.com
Forest Hills Consolidated S — 200/K-12
606 Main St 04945 — 207-668-5291
Denise Plante, prin. — Fax 668-4482

Jay, Franklin
RSU 73
Supt. — See Livermore Falls
Spruce Mountain HS North — 200/9-12
33 Community Dr 04239 — 207-897-4336
Thomas Plourde, prin. — Fax 897-9313
Spruce Mountain MS — 200/6-8
23 Community Dr 04239 — 207-897-4319
Scott Albert, prin. — Fax 897-3513

Jonesport, Washington
Moosabec Community SD — 100/9-12
127 Snare Creek Ln 04649 — 207-497-2154
Denis Howard, supt. — Fax 497-2703
www.union103.org
Jonesport-Beals HS — 100/9-12
180 Snare Creek Ln 04649 — 207-497-5454
Michael Kelley, prin. — Fax 497-3004

Kennebunk, York, Pop. 5,151
RSU 21 — 2,400/PK-12
177 Alewive Rd 04043 — 207-985-1100
Andrew Dolloff, supt. — Fax 985-1104
www.rsu21.net/
Kennebunk HS — 700/9-12
89 Fletcher St 04043 — 207-985-1110
Susan Cressey, prin. — Fax 985-1350
Kennebunk MS — 500/6-8
60 Thompson Rd 04043 — 207-467-8004
Jeff Rodman, prin. — Fax 467-9059

Heartwood College of Art — Post-Sec.
123 York St 04043 — 207-985-0985

Kennebunkport, York, Pop. 1,232

The Landing School — Post-Sec.
PO Box 1490 04046 — 207-985-7976

Kents Hill, Kennebec

Kents Hill S — 300/9-12
PO Box 257 04349 — 207-685-4914
Jeremy LaCasse, hdmstr. — Fax 685-9529

Kittery, York, Pop. 4,483
Kittery SD — 1,000/K-12
200 Rogers Rd 03904 — 207-475-1334
Allyn Hutton, supt. — Fax 439-5407
www.kitteryschools.com
Shapleigh MS — 400/4-8
43 Stevenson Rd 03904 — 207-439-2572
Wanda Avery, admin. — Fax 439-9958
Traip Academy — 300/9-12
12 Williams Ave 03904 — 207-439-1121
Eric Waddell, prin. — Fax 439-3789

Lagrange, Penobscot
AOS 43 — 1,300/PK-12
20 Howland Rd 04453 — 207-943-7317
Michael Wright, supt. — Fax 943-5314
www.msad31.com/
Other Schools – See Howland, Milo

Lee, Penobscot
AOS 90 - EMASS
Supt. — See Baileyville
Mt. Jefferson JHS — 100/5-8
61 Winn Rd 04455 — 207-738-2866
Pamela Hamilton, prin. — Fax 738-3817

Lee Academy — 300/9-12
26 Winn Rd 04455 — 207-738-2252

Lewiston, Androscoggin, Pop. 35,657
Lewiston SD — 4,900/PK-12
36 Oak St 04240 — 207-795-4100
Bill Webster, supt. — Fax 795-4177
www.lewistonpublicschools.org/
Lewiston HS — 1,400/9-12
156 East Ave 04240 — 207-795-4190
Fax 795-4119
Lewiston MS — 600/7-8
75 Central Ave 04240 — 207-795-4180
Shawn Chabot, prin. — Fax 753-1789
Lewiston Regional Technical Center — Vo/Tech
156 East Ave 04240 — 207-795-4144
Robert Callahan, dir. — Fax 795-4147

Bates College — Post-Sec.
2 Andrews Rd 04240 — 207-786-6255
Central Maine Christian Academy — 100/PK-12
390 Main St 04240 — 207-777-0007
Patricia St. Hilaire, admin. — Fax 777-0007
College of Nursing & Health Professions — Post-Sec.
70 Middle St 04240 — 207-795-2840
Mr. Bernard's School of Hair Fashion — Post-Sec.
711 Lisbon St 04240 — 207-783-7765
Vineyard Christian S — 100/PK-12
PO Box 1610 04241 — 207-784-9500

Limestone, Aroostook, Pop. 1,068
Eastern Aroostook Regional Sch Unit 39
Supt. — See Caribou
Limestone Community S — 300/PK-12
93 High St 04750 — 207-325-4742
Susan Whtie, prin. — Fax 325-4969

Maine School of Science & Mathematics — 100/10-12
95 High St 04750 — 207-325-3303
Luke C. Shorty, dir. — Fax 325-3340
www.mssm.org/
Maine S of Science & Mathematics — 100/10-12
95 High St 04750 — 207-325-3303
Luke C. Shorty, dir. — Fax 325-3340

Lincoln, Penobscot, Pop. 2,837
Applied Technology Region
Supt. — None
North Penobscot Tech-Region 3 — Vo/Tech
35 W Broadway 04457 — 207-794-3004
Fax 794-8049

RSU 67 — 1,200/PK-12
57 Main St 04457 — 207-794-6500
Raymond Freve, supt. — Fax 794-2600
www.rsu67.org
Mattanawcook Academy — 400/9-12
33 Reed Dr 04457 — 207-794-6711
Henry Pietras, prin. — Fax 794-3205
Mattanawcook JHS — 400/5-8
41 School St 04457 — 207-794-8935
Christopher Cowing, prin. — Fax 794-2601

Lisbon, See Lisbon Falls
Lisbon SD 1,400/PK-12
19 Gartley St 04250 207-353-6711
Richard Green, supt. Fax 353-3032
www.lisbonschoolsme.org/
Gartley Street S 50/Alt
19 Gartley St 04250 207-353-6711
Kenneth Healey, prin. Fax 353-3032
Other Schools – See Lisbon Falls

Lisbon Falls, Androscoggin, Pop. 4,031
Lisbon SD
Supt. — See Lisbon
Lisbon HS 400/9-12
2 Sugg Dr 04252 207-353-3030
Kenneth Healey, prin. Fax 353-7908
Sugg MS 300/6-8
4 Sugg Dr 04252 207-353-3055
Darren Akerman, prin. Fax 353-3053

Livermore Falls, Androscoggin, Pop. 1,558
RSU 73 1,300/PK-12
9 Cedar St 04254 207-897-6722
Robert Wall, supt. Fax 897-2362
rsu73.org
Spruce Mountain HS South 300/10-12
25 Cedar St 04254 207-897-3428
Steven Leunig, prin. Fax 897-2254
Other Schools – See Jay

Machias, Washington, Pop. 1,257
AOS 96 - MBASS 900/PK-12
291 Court St 04654 207-255-6585
Scott Porter, supt. Fax 255-8054
Coastal Washington City Inst of Tech Vo/Tech
192 Court St 04654 207-255-3812
Kenneth Johnson, dir. Fax 255-8054
Machias Memorial HS 100/9-12
1 Bulldog Ln 04654 207-255-3812
Brian Leavitt, prin. Fax 255-3093

University of Maine at Machias Post-Sec.
116 OBrien Ave 04654 207-255-1200

Madawaska, Aroostook, Pop. 2,953
Madawaska SD 600/PK-12
328 Saint Thomas St Ste 201 04756 207-728-3346
Terry Wood, supt. Fax 728-7823
www.madawaskaschools.org/
Madawaska MSHS 300/7-12
135 7th Ave 04756 207-728-3371
Wayne Anderson, prin. Fax 728-3636

Madison, Somerset, Pop. 2,594
RSU 59 / MSAD 59 1,000/PK-12
205 Main St 04950 207-696-3323
Todd LeRoy, supt. Fax 696-5631
www.sad59.k12.me.us/
Madison Area Memorial HS 300/9-12
486 Main St 04950 207-696-3395
Stephen Ouellette, prin. Fax 696-5644
Madison JHS 200/5-8
205 Main St 04950 207-696-3381
Bonnie Levesque, prin. Fax 696-5640

Mars Hill, Aroostook, Pop. 965
AOS 99 - MCSS
Supt. — See Fort Fairfield
Central Aroostook JSHS 200/7-12
PO Box 310 04758 207-425-2811
Kevin Grass, prin. Fax 429-8460

Medway, Penobscot
Great Northern School System AOS 66
Supt. — See East Millinocket
Medway MS 100/5-8
25 Middle School Dr 04460 207-746-3470
Dawn Pray, prin. Fax 746-9435

Mexico, Oxford, Pop. 1,718
Applied Technology Region
Supt. — None
School of Applied Tech-Region 9 Vo/Tech
377 River Rd 04257 207-364-3764
Brenda Gammon, dir. Fax 364-2074

RSU 10
Supt. — See Dixfield
Mountain Valley MS 300/6-8
58 Highland Ter 04257 207-364-7926
Ryan Casey, prin. Fax 364-5608

Millinocket, Penobscot, Pop. 4,427
Millinocket SD
Supt. — See East Millinocket
Stearns JSHS 200/7-12
199 State St 04462 207-723-6430
Linda MacKenzie, prin. Fax 723-6437

Milo, Piscataquis, Pop. 1,832
AOS 43
Supt. — See Lagrange
Penquis Valley HS 300/7-12
48 Penquis Dr 04463 207-943-7346
Matthew Hackett, prin. Fax 943-5333

Monmouth, Kennebec
RSU 2
Supt. — See Hallowell
Monmouth Academy 200/9-12
96 Academy Rd 04259 207-933-4416
Richard Amero, prin. Fax 933-7222
Monmouth MS 300/4-8
PO Box 240 04259 207-933-9002
Stephen Philbrook, prin. Fax 933-7252

Mount Desert, Hancock
AOS 91 - MDIRSS 1,600/K-12
PO Box 60 04660 207-288-5049
Howard Colter, supt. Fax 288-5071
www.mdirss.org
Mt. Desert Island HS 500/9-12
PO Box 180 04660 207-288-5011
Matthew Garrity-Janger, prin. Fax 288-0692

Naples, Cumberland, Pop. 423
RSU 61 / MSAD 61
Supt. — See Bridgton
Lake Region HS 600/9-12
1877 Roosevelt Trl 04055 207-693-6221
Theodore Finn, prin. Fax 693-4591
Lake Region MS 400/6-8
204 Kansas Rd 04055 207-647-8403
Tonya Arnold, prin. Fax 647-0991
Lake Region Vocational Center Vo/Tech
1879 Roosevelt Trl 04055 207-693-3864
Rosie Schacht, dir. Fax 693-3864

Newcastle, Lincoln, Pop. 659

Lincoln Academy 600/9-12
81 Academy Hl 04553 207-563-3596
Jay Pinkerton, prin. Fax 563-1067

Newport, Penobscot, Pop. 1,726
RSU 19 2,400/PK-12
PO Box 40 04953 207-368-5091
Gregory Potter, supt. Fax 368-2192
www.rsu19.org/
Nokomis Regional HS 700/9-12
266 Williams Rd 04953 207-368-4354
Mary Nadeau, prin. Fax 368-3276
Sebasticook Valley MS 300/5-8
337 Williams Rd 04953 207-368-4592
Jason Tardy, prin. Fax 368-4598
Other Schools – See Hartland

New Vineyard, Franklin

New Life Christian S 50/K-12
PO Box 242 04956 207-778-9065
Herman Ellis, admin. Fax 778-9065

Norridgewock, Somerset, Pop. 1,411

Riverview Memorial S 50/K-10
201 Mercer Rd 04957 207-634-2641
Fax 634-2641

North Anson, Somerset
RSU 74 / MSAD 74 800/PK-12
PO Box 219 04958 207-635-2727
Kenneth Coville, supt. Fax 635-3599
www.sad74.k12.me.us
Carrabec HS 300/9-12
PO Box 220 04958 207-635-2296
Dr. Regina Campbell, prin. Fax 635-2276

North Berwick, York, Pop. 1,596
RSU 60 / MSAD 60 2,500/K-12
PO Box 819 03906 207-676-2234
Steven Connolly, supt. Fax 676-3229
www.sad60.k12.me.us
Noble HS 1,000/8-12
388 Somersworth Rd 03906 207-676-2843
Joseph Findlay, prin. Fax 676-2842

North Haven, Knox
RSU 7 / MSAD 7 100/PK-12
93 Pulpit Harbor Rd 04853 207-867-4707
Alton Hadley, supt. Fax 867-4438
North Haven Community S 100/PK-12
93 Pulpit Harbor Rd 04853 207-867-4707
Amy Marx, prin. Fax 867-4438

Norway, Oxford, Pop. 2,676
Applied Technology Region
Supt. — None
Oxford Hills Tech-Region 11 Vo/Tech
PO Box 313 04268 207-743-7756
Shawn Lambert, prin. Fax 743-0667

Oakland, Kennebec, Pop. 2,571
RSU 18 3,000/PK-12
41 Heath St 04963 207-465-7384
Gary N. Smith, supt. Fax 465-9130
www.rsu18.org/
Messalonskee HS 800/9-12
131 Messalonskee High Dr 04963 207-465-7381
Jonathan Moody, prin. Fax 465-9151
Messalonskee MS 600/6-8
33 School Bus Dr 04963 207-465-2167
Mark Hatch, prin. Fax 465-9683
Other Schools – See South China

Old Orchard Beach, York, Pop. 8,527
RSU 23
Supt. — See Saco
Loranger MS 300/4-8
148 Saco Ave 04064 207-934-4848
Lloyd Crocker, prin. Fax 934-3712
Old Orchard Beach HS 300/9-12
40 E Emerson Cummings Blvd 04064 207-934-4461
Richard DiFusco, prin. Fax 934-3705

Old Town, Penobscot, Pop. 7,682
RSU 34 1,500/PK-12
156 Oak St Ste 2 04468 207-827-7171
David Walker, supt. Fax 827-3922
www.rsu34.org/
Leonard MS 300/6-8
156 Oak St 04468 207-827-3900
John Keane, prin. Fax 827-3922
Old Town HS 600/9-12
203 Stillwater Ave 04468 207-827-3910
Scott Gordon, prin. Fax 827-3918

Orono, Penobscot, Pop. 9,316
RSU 26
Supt. — See Glenburn
Orono HS 300/9-12
14 Goodridge Dr 04473 207-866-4916
Jim Chasse, prin. Fax 866-7116
Orono MS 100/6-8
14 Goodridge Dr 04473 207-866-2350
Jeffrey Paul, prin. Fax 866-7111

University of Maine 04469 Post-Sec.
207-581-1110

Orrington, Penobscot

Calvary Chapel Christian S 100/PK-12
154 River Rd 04474 207-991-9684
Eric Meyerson, prin. Fax 989-0687

Oxford, Oxford, Pop. 1,240
RSU 17 / MSAD 17 3,400/PK-12
1570 Main St Ste 11 04270 207-743-8972
Rick Colpitts, supt. Fax 743-2878
www.sad17.k12.me.us/
Other Schools – See South Paris

Phillips, Franklin
RSU 58 / MSAD 58 800/K-12
1401 Rangeley Rd 04966 207-639-2086
Brenda Joy Stevens, supt. Fax 639-5120
www.sad58.k12.me.us/
Other Schools – See Salem

Pittsfield, Somerset, Pop. 3,092
RSU 53 / MSAD 53 800/PK-8
167 School St Ste A 04967 207-487-5107
Fax 487-6310
www.msad53.org/
Warsaw MS 300/5-8
167 School St 04967 207-487-5145
Kristen Gilbert, prin. Fax 487-4511

Maine Central Institute 400/9-12
295 Main St 04967 207-487-3355
Christopher Hopkins, head sch Fax 487-3512

Poland, Androscoggin
RSU 16 1,700/PK-12
3 Aggregate Rd 04274 207-998-2727
Tina Meserve, supt. Fax 998-2753
www.rsu16.org
Poland Regional HS 500/9-12
1457 Maine St 04274 207-998-5400
Catherine Medd, prin. Fax 998-5060
Whittier MS 300/7-8
1457 Maine St 04274 207-998-5400
Shawn Vincent, prin. Fax 998-5060

Portland, Cumberland, Pop. 64,466
Portland SD 7,100/K-12
196 Allen Ave 04103 207-874-8100
Emmanuel Caulk, supt. Fax 874-8199
www2.portlandschools.org
Casco Bay HS 300/9-12
196 Allen Ave 04103 207-874-8160
Derek Pierce, prin. Fax 797-5437
Deering HS 1,000/9-12
370 Stevens Ave 04103 207-874-8260
Ira Waltz, prin. Fax 874-8153
King MS 500/6-8
92 Deering Ave 04102 207-874-8140
Michael McCarthy, prin. Fax 874-8290
Lincoln MS 400/6-8
522 Stevens Ave 04103 207-874-8145
Steven Nolan, prin. Fax 874-8288
Moore MS 500/6-8
171 Auburn St 04103 207-874-8150
Stephen Rogers, prin. Fax 874-8272
Portland Arts & Technology HS Vo/Tech
196 Allen Ave 04103 207-874-8165
Michael Johnson, dir. Fax 874-8170
Portland HS 1,000/9-12
284 Cumberland Ave 04101 207-874-8250
Deborah Migneault, prin. Fax 874-8248
West S 50/Alt
57 Douglass St 04102 207-874-8225
Erin Frazier, dir. Fax 874-8292

Cheverus HS 500/9-12
267 Ocean Ave 04103 207-774-6238
John Mullen, prin. Fax 828-0207
Empire Beauty School Post-Sec.
319 Marginal Way 04101 207-774-9413
Inst for Doctoral Studies in Visual Arts Post-Sec.
130 Neal St 04102 207-771-8887
Maine College of Art Post-Sec.
522 Congress St Ste 4 04101 207-775-3052
McAuley HS 200/9-12
631 Stevens Ave 04103 207-797-3802
Margaret Downing, prin. Fax 797-3804
Mercy Hospital Post-Sec.
144 State St 04101 207-879-3000
University of New England Post-Sec.
716 Stevens Ave 04103 207-797-7261
University of Southern Maine Post-Sec.
PO Box 9300 04104 207-780-4141
Waynflete S 500/PK-12
360 Spring St 04102 207-774-5721
Mark Segar, hdmstr. Fax 772-4782

Presque Isle, Aroostook, Pop. 9,565
RSU 79 / MSAD 1 1,900/PK-12
PO Box 1118 04769 207-764-4101
Gehrig Johnson, supt. Fax 764-4103
www.sad1.org/
Presque Isle HS 500/9-12
16 Griffin St 04769 207-764-0121
Donna Lisnik, prin. Fax 764-7720
Presque Isle MS 400/6-8
569 Skyway St 04769 207-764-4474
Anne Blanchard, prin. Fax 768-3447

Presque Isle Regional Tech Center — Vo/Tech
79 Blake St 04769 — 207-764-1356
Fax 764-8107

Northern Maine Community College — Post-Sec.
33 Edgemont Dr 04769 — 207-768-2700
University of Maine at Presque Isle — Post-Sec.
181 Main St 04769 — 207-768-9400

Rangeley, Franklin
RSU 78 — 200/K-12
PO Box 97 04970 — 207-864-3311
Brian Foster, supt. — Fax 864-2451
Rangeley Lakes Regional S — 200/K-12
PO Box 97 04970 — 207-864-3311
Sharon Connally, prin. — Fax 864-2451

Raymond, Cumberland
RSU 14 - Windham Raymond
Supt. — See Windham
Jordan-Small MS — 200/5-8
423 Webbs Mills Rd 04071 — 207-655-4743
Randolph Crockett, prin. — Fax 655-6952

Readfield, Kennebec
RSU 38 — 1,300/PK-12
45 Millard Harrison Dr 04355 — 207-685-3336
Dr. Donna H. Wolfrom, supt. — Fax 685-4703
www.maranacook.org/
Maranacook Community HS — 400/9-12
2250 Millard Harrison Dr 04355 — 207-685-4923
Dwayne Conway, prin. — Fax 685-9597
Maranacook Community MS — 300/6-8
2100 Millard Harrison Dr 04355 — 207-685-3128
Cathy Jacobs, prin. — Fax 685-9876

Richmond, Sagadahoc, Pop. 1,737
RSU 2
Supt. — See Hallowell
Richmond MSHS — 200/6-12
132 Main St 04357 — 207-737-4348
Steve Lavoie, prin. — Fax 737-8707

Rockland, Knox, Pop. 7,144
Applied Technology Region
Supt. — None
Mid-Coast School of Tech-Region 8 — Vo/Tech
1 Main St 04841 — 207-594-2161
Fax 594-7506

RSU 13 — 1,600/K-12
28 Lincoln St 04841 — 207-596-6620
Lew Collins, supt. — Fax 596-2004
www.rsu13.org
Oceanside HS East — 300/10-12
400 Broadway 04841 — 207-596-2010
Thomas Forti, prin. — Fax 596-2028
Other Schools – See Thomaston

Rockport, Knox
MSAD 28 / Five Town CSD
Supt. — See Camden
Camden Hills Regional HS — 700/9-12
25 Keelson Dr 04856 — 207-236-7800
Nick Ithomitis, prin. — Fax 236-7813

Rumford, Oxford, Pop. 4,160
RSU 10
Supt. — See Dixfield
Mountain Valley HS — 400/9-12
799 Hancock St 04276 — 207-364-4547
Matthew Gilbert, prin. — Fax 364-3436

Sabattus, Androscoggin
RSU 4
Supt. — See Wales
Oak Hill MS — 200/6-8
40 Ball Park Rd 04280 — 207-375-6961
Jeff Ireland, prin. — Fax 375-8871

Saco, York, Pop. 18,250
RSU 23 — 3,000/PK-12
90 Beach St 04072 — 207-284-4505
Patrick Phillips, supt. — Fax 284-5951
www.rsu23.org
Saco MS — 800/6-8
40 Buxton Rd 04072 — 207-282-4181
Laurie Wood, prin. — Fax 286-1807
Saco Transition Program — 50/Alt
80 Common St 04072 — 207-286-2091
Stephanie Jackson, lead tchr. — Fax 284-5951
Other Schools – See Old Orchard Beach

Thornton Academy — 1,500/6-12
438 Main St 04072 — 207-282-3361
Carl Stasio, hdmstr. — Fax 282-3508

Saint Agatha, Aroostook
RSU 33 / MSAD 33
Supt. — See Frenchville
Wisdom MSHS — 200/7-12
PO Box 69 04772 — 207-543-7717
Tammy LeBlanc, prin. — Fax 543-6316

Salem, Franklin
RSU 58 / MSAD 58
Supt. — See Phillips
Mt. Abram Regional HS — 300/9-12
1513 Salem Rd, — 207-678-2701
Fax 678-2668

Sanford, York, Pop. 9,565
Sanford SD — 3,000/K-12
917 Main St Ste 200 04073 — 207-324-2810
David Theoharides, supt. — Fax 324-5742
www.sanford.org
Sanford HS — 1,200/9-12
52 Sanford High Blvd 04073 — 207-324-4050
Jedediah Petsinger, prin. — Fax 324-3022
Sanford JHS — 400/6-8
708 Main St 04073 — 207-324-3114
Andrew Patin, prin. — Fax 490-5139
Sanford Regional Vocational Center — Vo/Tech
52 Sanford High Blvd 04073 — 207-324-2942
Jim Stopa, dir. — Fax 324-2957

Sargentville, Hancock
Deer Isle - Stonington Community SD — 400/K-12
9 Caterpillar Hill Rd 04673 — 207-359-8400
Mark Jenkins, supt. — Fax 359-8451
Other Schools – See Deer Isle

Scarborough, Cumberland, Pop. 4,340
Scarborough SD — 3,300/K-12
PO Box 370 04070 — 207-730-4100
George Entwistle, supt. — Fax 730-4104
www.scarborough.k12.me.us
Scarborough HS — 1,100/9-12
11 Municipal Dr 04074 — 207-730-5000
Dean Auriemma, prin. — Fax 730-5007
Scarborough MS — 800/6-8
21 Quentin Dr 04074 — 207-730-4800
Barbara Hathorn, prin. — Fax 730-4804

Searsport, Waldo, Pop. 985
RSU 20
Supt. — See Belfast
Searsport District HS — 200/9-12
24 Mortland Rd 04974 — 207-548-2313
Brian Campbell, prin. — Fax 548-2354
Searsport District MS — 200/6-8
26 Mortland Rd 04974 — 207-548-2313
Brian Campbell, prin. — Fax 548-2354

Skowhegan, Somerset, Pop. 6,196
RSU 54 / MSAD 54 — 2,600/PK-12
196 W Front St 04976 — 207-474-9508
Brent Colbry, supt. — Fax 474-7422
www.msad54.org/
Skowhegan Area HS — 800/9-12
61 Academy Cir 04976 — 207-474-5511
Richard Wilson, prin. — Fax 474-0992
Skowhegan Area MS — 400/6-8
155 Academy Cir 04976 — 207-474-3339
Zachary Longyear, prin. — Fax 474-9588
Somerset Career & Technical Center — Vo/Tech
61 Academy Cir 04976 — 207-474-2151
David Dorr, prin. — Fax 858-4879

Somerville, Lincoln
Sheepscot Valley RSU 12 — 1,500/PK-12
665 Patricktown Rd Ste 2 04348 — 207-549-3261
Howard Tuttle, supt. — Fax 549-3082
www.svrsu.org/
Other Schools – See Wiscasset

South Berwick, York
RSU 35 / MSAD 35
Supt. — See Eliot
Marshwood HS — 700/9-12
260 Dow Hwy 03908 — 207-384-4500
Paul Mehlhorn, prin. — Fax 384-4508

Berwick Academy — 500/K-12
31 Academy St 03908 — 207-384-2164
Gregory Schneider, hdmstr. — Fax 384-3332
Seacoast Christian S — 200/PK-12
PO Box 325 03908 — 207-384-5759
Roy Reynolds, admin. — Fax 384-2303

South China, Kennebec
RSU 18
Supt. — See Oakland
China MS — 200/5-8
773 Lakeview Dr 04358 — 207-445-1500
Carl Gartley, prin. — Fax 445-3278

Erskine Academy — 700/9-12
309 Windsor Rd 04358 — 207-445-2962

South Paris, Oxford, Pop. 2,214
RSU 17 / MSAD 17
Supt. — See Oxford
Oxford Hills Comprehensive HS — 1,100/9-12
256 Main St 04281 — 207-743-8914
Theodore Moccia, prin. — Fax 743-5326
Oxford Hills MS — 600/7-8
100 Pine St 04281 — 207-743-5946
Troy Eastman, prin. — Fax 743-8048

South Portland, Cumberland, Pop. 24,549
South Portland SD — 3,100/PK-12
130 Wescott Rd 04106 — 207-871-0555
Suzanne Godin, supt. — Fax 871-0559
www.spsd.org
Mahoney MS — 300/6-8
240 Ocean St 04106 — 207-799-7386
Carrie Stilphen, prin. — Fax 767-7731
Memorial MS — 400/6-8
120 Wescott Rd 04106 — 207-773-5629
Megan Welter, prin. — Fax 772-4597
South Portland HS — 900/9-12
637 Highland Ave 04106 — 207-767-3266
Ryan Caron, prin. — Fax 767-7713

Greater Portland Christian S — 100/PK-12
1338 Broadway 04106 — 207-767-5123
Keith Dawson, head sch — Fax 767-5124
Kaplan University-Maine — Post-Sec.
265 Western Ave 04106 — 207-774-6126
Maine Medical Center — Post-Sec.
SMTC Fort Rd 04106 — 207-767-9589
Southern Maine Community College — Post-Sec.
2 Fort Rd 04106 — 207-741-5500

Stacyville, Penobscot
RSU 50
Supt. — See Dyer Brook
Katahdin MSHS — 200/7-12
PO Box 50, — 207-365-4218
Eryn Schmidt, prin. — Fax 365-6011

Standish, Cumberland, Pop. 464
RSU 6 / MSAD 6
Supt. — See Buxton
Bonny Eagle HS — 1,200/9-12
700 Saco Rd 04084 — 207-929-3840
Beth Schultz, prin. — Fax 929-9147

St. Joseph's College of Maine — Post-Sec.
278 Whites Bridge Rd 04084 — 207-892-6766

Sullivan, Hancock
RSU 24
Supt. — See Ellsworth
Sumner Memorial HS — 300/9-12
2456 US Hwy 1 04664 — 207-422-3510
Marianne Deraps, prin. — Fax 422-6463

Thomaston, Knox, Pop. 1,856
RSU 13
Supt. — See Rockland
Oceanside HS West — 100/8-9
47 Valley St 04861 — 207-354-2502
Lawrence Schooley, prin. — Fax 354-2369

Thorndike, Waldo
RSU 3 / MSAD 3
Supt. — See Unity
Mt. View HS — 500/9-12
577 Mount View Rd 04986 — 207-568-3255
Cheri Towle, prin. — Fax 568-4315
Mt. View MS — 300/6-8
575 Mount View Rd 04986 — 207-568-7561
Martha Witham, prin. — Fax 568-7590

Topsham, Sagadahoc, Pop. 5,854
RSU 75 / MSAD 75 — 2,600/K-12
50 Republic Ave 04086 — 207-729-9961
Bradley Smith, supt. — Fax 725-9354
www.link75.org/
Mt. Ararat HS — 900/9-12
73 Eagles Way 04086 — 207-729-2951
Craig King Ph.D., prin. — Fax 729-2953
Mt. Ararat MS — 600/6-8
66 Republic Ave 04086 — 207-729-2950
Bill Zima, prin. — Fax 729-2964

Turner, Androscoggin
RSU 52 / MSAD 52 — 2,100/PK-12
486 Turner Ctr Rd 04282 — 207-225-1000
Dr. Henry Aliberti, supt. — Fax 225-5608
www.msad52.org
Leavitt Area HS — 600/9-12
21 Matthews Way 04282 — 207-225-1100
Eben Shaw, prin. — Fax 225-3978
Tripp MS — 300/7-8
65 Matthews Way 04282 — 207-225-1070
Gail Marine, prin. — Fax 225-2102

Union, Knox
RSU 40 / MSAD 40 — 1,900/K-12
1070 Heald Hwy 04862 — 207-785-2277
Susan Pratt, supt. — Fax 785-3119
www.msad40.org
Other Schools – See Waldoboro

Unity, Waldo, Pop. 459
RSU 3 / MSAD 3 — 1,400/PK-12
84 School St 04988 — 207-948-6136
Heather Perry, supt. — Fax 948-6173
www.msad3.org
Other Schools – See Thorndike

Unity College — Post-Sec.
90 Quaker Hill Rd 04988 — 207-948-9100

Van Buren, Aroostook, Pop. 1,897
RSU 88 / MSAD 24 — 300/PK-12
169 Main St Ste 101 04785 — 207-868-2746
Lawrence Worcester, supt. — Fax 868-5420
www.msad24.org/
Van Buren District HS — 100/9-12
169 Main St Ste 102 04785 — 207-868-5274
Chad Bell, prin. — Fax 868-3537
Van Buren Regional Technology Center — Vo/Tech
169 Main St Ste 102 04785 — 207-868-2746
Chad Bell, dir. — Fax 868-5420

Vinalhaven, Knox
RSU 8 / MSAD 8 — 200/PK-12
22 Arcola Ln 04863 — 207-863-4800
Bruce Mailloux, supt. — Fax 863-4572
www.vinalhavenschool.org/
Vinalhaven S — 200/PK-12
22 Arcola Ln 04863 — 207-863-4800
Robb Warren, prin. — Fax 863-4572

Waldo, See Belfast
Applied Technology Region
Supt. — None
Waldo County Tech Center-Region 7 — Vo/Tech
1022 Waterville Rd 04915 — 207-342-5231
Chris Downing, dir. — Fax 342-4070

Waldoboro, Lincoln, Pop. 1,207
RSU 40 / MSAD 40
Supt. — See Union
Medomak MS — 300/7-8
318 Manktown Rd 04572 — 207-832-5028
Ben Vail, prin. — Fax 832-5710
Medomak Valley HS — 600/9-12
320 Manktown Rd 04572 — 207-832-5389
Harold Wilson, prin. — Fax 832-2280

Wales, Androscoggin
RSU 4 1,300/PK-12
971 Gardiner Rd 04280 207-375-4273
James Hodgkin, supt. Fax 375-2522
www.rsu4.org
Oak Hill HS 500/9-12
PO Box 400 04280 207-375-4950
Patricia Doyle, prin. Fax 375-4048
Other Schools – See Sabattus

Washburn, Aroostook, Pop. 987
RSU 45 / MSAD 45 400/PK-12
33 School St 04786 207-455-8301
Ed Buckley, supt. Fax 455-8217
www.msad45.net/
Washburn District HS 100/9-12
1359 Main St 04786 207-455-4501
Ricky Bragg, prin. Fax 455-4509

Waterboro, York
RSU 57 / MSAD 57 3,400/K-12
86 West Rd 04087 207-247-3221
Dr. John Davis, supt. Fax 247-3477
www.rsu57.org
Massabesic HS 1,100/9-12
88 West Rd 04087 207-247-3141
Christian Elkington, prin. Fax 247-3146
Other Schools – See East Waterboro

Waterville, Kennebec, Pop. 15,358
AOS 92 - KVCS 3,700/PK-12
25 Messalonskee Ave 04901 207-873-4281
Eric Haley, supt. Fax 872-5531
www.aos92.org/
Mid Maine Technical Center Vo/Tech
3 Brooklyn Ave 04901 207-873-0102
Peter Hallen, dir. Fax 873-7057
Waterville HS 600/9-12
1 Brooklyn Ave 04901 207-873-2751
Don Reiter, prin. Fax 873-7058
Waterville JHS 400/6-8
100 W River Rd 04901 207-873-2144
Carol Dodge, prin. Fax 873-5752
Other Schools – See Winslow

Colby College Post-Sec.
4000 Mayflower Hill Dr 04901 207-859-4000
Empire Beauty School Post-Sec.
251 Kennedy Memorial Dr 04901 207-873-0682
Temple Academy 100/PK-12
60 W River Rd 04901 207-873-5325
Denise Lafountain, prin. Fax 692-2659
Thomas College Post-Sec.
180 W River Rd 04901 207-859-1111

Wells, York
Wells-Ogunquit Community SD 1,400/K-12
1460 Post Rd 04090 207-646-8331
Elaine Tomaszewski, supt. Fax 646-0314
www.k12wocsd.net/
Wells HS 400/9-12
200 Sanford Rd 04090 207-646-7011
James Daly, prin. Fax 646-4842
Wells JHS 500/5-8
1470 Post Rd 04090 207-646-5142
Christopher Chessie, prin. Fax 646-2899

Fidelitas Academy 50/9-12
952 Post Rd Unit 7 04090 207-965-6171
Nancy Parsons M.Ed., admin.
York County Community College Post-Sec.
112 College Dr 04090 207-646-9282

Westbrook, Cumberland, Pop. 17,059
Westbrook SD 1,900/PK-12
117 Stroudwater St 04092 207-854-0800
Marc Gousse, supt. Fax 854-0809
www.westbrookschools.org
Westbrook HS 700/9-12
125 Stroudwater St 04092 207-854-0810
Jonathan Ross, prin. Fax 854-0812
Westbrook MS 500/5-8
471 Stroudwater St 04092 207-854-0830
Matthew Nelson, dean Fax 854-0858
Westbrook Regional Technology Center Vo/Tech
125 Stroudwater St 04092 207-854-0820
Todd Fields, dir. Fax 854-0822

Windham, Cumberland, Pop. 13,020
RSU 14 - Windham Raymond 3,300/K-12
228 Windham Center Rd 04062 207-892-1800
Sanford Prince, supt. Fax 892-1805
www.windham.k12.me.us
Windham HS 1,000/9-12
406 Gray Rd 04062 207-892-1810
Chris Howell, prin. Fax 892-1813
Windham MS 600/6-8
408 Gray Rd 04062 207-892-1820
Charles Haddock, prin. Fax 892-1826
Other Schools – See Raymond

Windham Christian Academy 100/PK-12
1051 Roosevelt Trl 04062 207-892-2244
Roy Mickelson, prin. Fax 893-1289

Winslow, Kennebec, Pop. 7,626
AOS 92 - KVCS
Supt. — See Waterville
Winslow HS 500/9-12
20 Danielson St 04901 207-872-1990
Chad Bell, prin. Fax 872-1993
Winslow JHS 300/6-8
6 Danielson St 04901 207-872-1973
Kevin Michaud, prin. Fax 872-1977

Winterport, Waldo, Pop. 1,327
RSU 22 / MSAD 22
Supt. — See Hampden
Wagner MS 100/5-8
19 Williams Way 04496 207-223-4309
Richard Glencross, prin. Fax 223-4325

Winthrop, Kennebec, Pop. 2,622
AOS 97 - WKCS 900/PK-12
17A Highland Ave 04364 207-377-2296
Gary Rosenthal, supt. Fax 377-2708
www.aos97.org
Winthrop HS 200/9-12
211 Rambler Rd 04364 207-377-2228
Keith Morin, prin. Fax 377-7486
Winthrop MS 200/6-8
400 Rambler Rd 04364 207-377-2249
Karen Criss, prin. Fax 377-3667

Wiscasset, Lincoln, Pop. 1,086
Sheepscot Valley RSU 12
Supt. — See Somerville
Wiscasset HS 200/9-12
272 Gardiner Rd 04578 207-882-7722
Deborah Taylor, prin. Fax 882-8251
Wiscasset MS 200/5-8
83 Federal St 04578 207-882-7767
Linda Bleile, prin. Fax 882-8279

Yarmouth, Cumberland, Pop. 5,801
Yarmouth SD 1,400/K-12
101 McCartney St 04096 207-846-5586
Ron Barker, supt. Fax 846-2339
www.yarmouthschools.org
Harrison MS 400/5-8
220 McCartney St 04096 207-846-2499
Bruce Brann, prin. Fax 846-2489
Yarmouth HS 500/9-12
286 W Elm St 04096 207-846-5535
Edward Hall, prin. Fax 846-2326

North Yarmouth Academy 300/5-12
148 Main St 04096 207-846-9051
Brad Choyt, hdmstr. Fax 846-8829

York, York, Pop. 9,818
York SD 1,900/K-12
469 US Route 1 03909 207-363-3403
Debra Dunn, supt. Fax 363-5602
www.yorkschools.org/
York HS 600/9-12
1 Robert Stevens Dr 03909 207-363-3621
Robert Stevens, prin. Fax 363-1809
York MS 600/5-8
30 Organug Rd 03909 207-363-4214
David Williams, prin. Fax 363-1815

MARYLAND

MARYLAND DEPARTMENT OF EDUCATION

200 W Baltimore St, Baltimore 21201-2549
Telephone 410-767-0600
Fax 410-333-6033
Website http://www.marylandpublicschools.org

Superintendent of Schools Lillian Lowery Ed.D

MARYLAND BOARD OF EDUCATION

200 W Baltimore St, Baltimore 21201-2549

President Dr. Charlene Dukes

PUBLIC, PRIVATE AND CATHOLIC SECONDARY SCHOOLS

Aberdeen, Harford, Pop. 14,190
Harford County SD
Supt. — See Bel Air
Aberdeen HS 1,500/9-12
251 Paradise Rd 21001 410-273-5500
Michael O'Brien, prin. Fax 273-5587
Aberdeen MS 1,100/6-8
111 Mount Royal Ave 21001 410-273-5510
Chandra Krantz, prin. Fax 273-5542
Alternative Education Program 100/Alt
253 Paradise Rd 21001 410-273-5594
Michael Thatcher, coord. Fax 273-5592

Abingdon, Harford

New Covenant Christian S 200/PK-12
128 Saint Marys Church Rd 21009 443-512-0771
Mark Cox, head sch Fax 569-3846

Accident, Garrett, Pop. 323
Garrett County SD
Supt. — See Oakland
Northern Garrett County HS 500/9-12
86 Pride Pkwy 21520 301-746-8668
Gary Reichenbecher, prin. Fax 746-8942
Northern MS 400/6-8
371 Pride Pkwy 21520 301-746-8165
Karen DeVore, prin. Fax 746-8865
Northern Evening HS Adult
86 Pride Pkwy 21520 301-746-8668
Russell Settle, prin. Fax 746-8942

Accokeek, Prince George's, Pop. 10,314
Prince George's County SD
Supt. — See Upper Marlboro
Accokeek Academy 800/5-8
14400 Berry Rd 20607 301-203-3200
Judy Adams, prin. Fax 203-3207

Adelphi, Prince George's, Pop. 14,821
Prince George's County SD
Supt. — See Upper Marlboro
Buck Lodge MS 700/7-8
2611 Buck Lodge Rd 20783 301-431-6290
James Richardson, prin. Fax 445-8404

University of Maryland University Coll Post-Sec.
3501 University Blvd E 20783 301-985-7000

Annapolis, Anne Arundel, Pop. 37,674
Anne Arundel County SD 75,200/PK-12
2644 Riva Rd 21401 410-222-5000
Kevin Maxwell Ph.D., supt. Fax 222-5602
www.aacps.org/
Annapolis HS 1,500/9-12
2700 Riva Rd 21401 410-266-5240
Donald Lilley, prin. Fax 266-0687
Annapolis MS 600/6-8
1399 Forest Dr 21403 410-267-8658
Dennis Kelly, prin. Fax 267-8924
Bates MS 600/6-8
701 Chase St 21401 410-263-0270
Paul DeRoo, prin. Fax 263-0295
Broadneck HS 2,200/9-12
1265 Green Holly Dr, 410-757-1300
David Smith, prin. Fax 757-5621
Annapolis Evening HS Adult
2700 Riva Rd 21401 410-224-2924
Patricia Suriano, admin.
Other Schools – See Arnold, Baltimore, Crownsville, Edgewater, Fort Meade, Gambrills, Glen Burnie, Harwood, Linthicum Heights, Lothian, Millersville, Odenton, Pasadena, Severn, Severna Park

---

Annapolis Area Christian S 800/PK-12
716 Bestgate Rd 21401 410-519-5300
Rick Kempton, supt. Fax 573-6866
Key S 700/PK-12
534 Hillsmere Dr 21403 410-263-9231
Marcella Yedid, hdmstr. Fax 280-5516
St. John's College Post-Sec.
PO Box 2800 21404 410-626-2522
St. Mary's HS 500/9-12
113 Duke of Gloucester St 21401 410-263-3294
Richard Bayhan, prin. Fax 269-7843
United States Naval Academy Post-Sec.
121 Blake Rd 21402 410-293-4361

Arnold, Anne Arundel, Pop. 22,629
Anne Arundel County SD
Supt. — See Annapolis
Magothy River MS 800/6-8
241 Peninsula Farm Rd 21012 410-544-0926
Christopher Mirenzi, prin. Fax 544-1867
Severn River MS 800/6-8
241 Peninsula Farm Rd 21012 410-544-0922
June Eyet, prin. Fax 315-8006

Anne Arundel Community College Post-Sec.
101 College Pkwy 21012 410-777-2222

Baltimore, Baltimore, Pop. 609,299
Anne Arundel County SD
Supt. — See Annapolis
Brooklyn Park MS 400/6-8
200 Hammonds Ln 21225 410-636-2967
Maisha Gillins, prin. Fax 636-1774

Baltimore CSD 81,500/PK-12
200 E North Ave 21202 443-984-2000
Dr. Andres Alonso, admin. Fax 396-8898
www.bcps.k12.md.us
Accelerator, 6301 Pioneer Dr 21214 Alt
Marvin Darden, prin. 410-396-6435
Achievement Academy at Harbor City 400/9-12
2555 Harford Rd 21218 410-396-6241
Tajah Gross, prin.
Baltimore Antioch Diploma Plus HS 300/8-12
2555 Harford Rd 21218 443-642-2021
Daric Jackson, prin.
Baltimore City College HS 1,300/9-12
3220 The Alameda 21218 410-396-6557
Cindy Harcum, prin. Fax 243-0669
Baltimore Civitas MSHS 400/6-12
2000 Edgewood St 21216 443-642-2938
Tammy Mays, prin.
Baltimore Community HS 300/Alt
6820 Fait Ave 21224 443-642-2035
Leslie Lewis, prin.
Baltimore Design MSHS 6-8
1101 Winston Ave 21212 443-642-2311
Nathan Burns, prin.
Baltimore Leadership S for Young Women 200/6-9
128 W Franklin St 21201 443-642-2048
Lorna Hanley, prin. Fax 338-2684
Baltimore Liberation Diploma Plus HS 300/8-12
2801 N Dukeland St 21216 443-642-2055
Michael Manning, prin.
Baltimore Polytechnic Institute Vo/Tech
1400 W Cold Spring Ln 21209 410-396-7026
Jacqueline Williams, prin. Fax 235-5027
Baltimore Rising Star Academy 100/Alt
2200 Sinclair Ln 21213 443-642-2126
Laura D'Anna, prin.
Baltimore S for the Arts 400/9-12
712 Cathedral St 21201 443-642-5165
Christopher Ford, prin.
Career Academy Vo/Tech
101 W 24th St 21218 410-396-7454
Gus Herrington, prin.
Carver Voc-Tech HS Vo/Tech
2201 Presstman St 21216 410-396-0553
Kirk Sykes, prin. Fax 396-0059
Chesapeake Center for Youth Development Alt
301 E Patapsco Ave 21225 410-355-4698
Bonnie Brobst, dir. Fax 354-8160
Digital Harbor HS 1,200/9-12
1100 Covington St 21230 443-984-1256
Brian Eyer, prin. Fax 539-7270
Douglass HS 900/9-12
2301 Gwynns Falls Pkwy 21217 410-396-7821
Antonio Hurt, prin. Fax 523-7557
Dunbar HS 700/9-12
1400 Orleans St 21231 443-642-4478
Kristina Kyles, prin. Fax 545-7526
Eager Street Academy 100/Alt
401 E Eager St 21202 410-209-4091
Dr. James Scofield, prin. Fax 209-4268
Edmondson-Westside HS 1,000/9-12
501 N Athol Ave Ste 1 21229 410-396-0685
Karl Perry, prin. Fax 545-7715
Excel Academy 400/9-12
1001 W Saratoga St 21223 410-396-1290
Tammatha Woodhouse, prin. Fax 947-7941
Forest Park HS 600/9-12
3701 Eldorado Ave 21207 410-396-0753
Monica Dailey, prin. Fax 396-0143
Franklin HS, 1201 Cambria St 21225 200/9-12
Christopher Battaglia, prin. 410-396-1373
Friendship Academy of Engring & Tech 600/6-12
2500 E Northern Pkwy 21214 443-642-5616
Katrice Wiley, prin.
Friendship Acad of Science & Technology 500/6-12
801 S Highland Ave 21224 443-642-3182
Frank Little, prin.
Garrison MS 300/6-8
3910 Barrington Rd 21207 410-396-0735
James Sargent, prin. Fax 545-7861
Green Street Academy 6-8
201 N Bend Rd 21229 443-642-2068
Crystal Harden, prin.
Heritage HS 700/9-12
2801 Saint Lo Dr 21213 410-396-6637
Stephanie Farmer, prin. Fax 467-5560
Knowledge and Success Academy 400/6-11
201 N Bend Rd 21229 443-642-2670
Tony Edwards, prin.
Lewis HS, 6401 Pioneer Dr 21214 400/9-12
Barney Wilson, prin. 410-545-1746
March MS, 2050 N Wolfe St 21213 400/6-8
Iona Spikes, prin. 443-984-3699
Maritime Industries Academy HS 500/9-12
5001 Sinclair Ln 21206 410-396-0242
Dorian Barnes, prin.
MD Academy of Tech & Health Sci MSHS 6-12
2801 N Dukeland St 21216 410-545-0955
Rebekah Ghosh, prin.
Mergenthaler Vo-Tech HS Vo/Tech
3500 Hillen Rd 21218 410-396-6496
Craig Rivers, prin. Fax 243-5354
Middle Alternative Program Alt
1601 E Pratt St 21231 443-396-1720
Duane Dowell, prin.
NACA Freedom and Democracy II 100/6-9
2500 E Northern Pkwy 21214 443-642-2031
Linda Johnson-Brown, prin.
Northeast MS 500/6-8
5001 Moravia Rd 21206 410-396-9220
Susan Baldwin, prin. Fax 396-1680
Northwestern HS 900/9-12
6900 Park Heights Ave 21215 410-396-0646
Kevin Simmons, prin. Fax 396-0866
Patterson HS 1,400/9-12
100 Kane St 21224 410-396-9276
Vance Benton, prin. Fax 633-0179
Savage Institute of Visual Arts 600/9-12
1500 Harlem Ave 21217 443-396-7701
Tracey Hicks, prin.
Southside Academy 200/10-12
2700 Seamon Ave 21225 410-545-3528
Denise Gordon, prin.
Stadium S, 1300 Gorsuch Ave 21218 300/6-8
Ronald Shelly, dir. 443-984-2682
Success Academy Alt
200 E North Ave 21202 443-642-2101
Eugene Chong Qui, prin.
Thomas Medical Arts Academy 500/9-12
100 N Calhoun St 21223 410-984-2831
Starletta Jackson, prin.
Vanguard Collegiate MS 6-9
5000 Truesdale Rd 21206 443-642-2069
Esther Wallace, prin.
Washington MS 300/6-8
1301 McCulloh St 21217 410-396-7734
Debbie Thomas, prin. Fax 396-0552
W.E.B. Dubois HS 500/9-12
2201 Pinewood Ave 21214 410-396-6435
Delores Berry, prin. Fax 254-5936

Western HS 900/9-12
4600 Falls Rd 21209 410-396-7040
Alisha Trusty, prin. Fax 396-7492
Youth Opportunity S Alt
1510 W Lafayette Ave 21217 410-962-1905
Rhonda Alexander, prin.

Baltimore County SD
Supt. — See Towson
Arbutus MS 700/6-8
5525 Shelbourne Rd 21227 410-887-1402
Michelle Feeney, prin. Fax 536-1164
Bridge Center 50/Alt
1740 Twin Springs Rd Ste C 21227 410-887-6832
Lance Williams, prin. Fax 887-4417
Carver Center for Arts & Technology 800/9-12
938 York Rd 21204 410-887-2775
Karen Steele, prin. Fax 769-9114
Catonsville Center/Alternative Studies 100/Alt
901 S Rolling Rd 21228 410-887-0934
David Lloyd, prin. Fax 747-1789
Catonsville HS 1,800/9-12
421 Bloomsbury Ave 21228 410-887-0808
Deborah Bittner, prin. Fax 747-9473
Chesapeake HS 1,100/9-12
1801 Turkey Point Rd 21221 410-887-0100
Maria Lowry, prin. Fax 682-3426
Crossroads Center 200/Alt
11640 Crossroads Cir 21220 410-887-2275
Donna Vlachos, prin.
Deep Creek MS 800/6-8
1000 S Marlyn Ave 21221 410-887-0112
Dwan Pinamonti, prin. Fax 391-6534
Dumbarton MS 900/6-8
300 Dumbarton Rd Ste 1 21212 410-887-3176
Kelly Erdman, prin. Fax 887-3176
Dundalk HS 1,200/9-12
1901 Delvale Ave 21222 410-887-7023
Paul Shouldice, prin. Fax 887-7025
Dundalk MS 500/6-8
7400 Dunmanway 21222 410-887-7018
Seth Barish, prin. Fax 887-7284
Eastern Technical HS 1,300/9-12
1100 Mace Ave 21221 410-887-0190
Thomas Evans, prin. Fax 887-0424
Golden Ring MS 600/6-8
6700 Kenwood Ave 21237 410-887-0130
Kandice Taylor, prin. Fax 682-6750
Holabird MS 600/6-8
1701 Delvale Ave 21222 410-887-7049
Julie Dellone, prin. Fax 887-7275
Kenwood HS 1,700/9-12
501 Stemmers Run Rd 21221 410-887-0153
Paul Martin, prin. Fax 887-6382
Lansdowne HS 1,200/9-12
3800 Hollins Ferry Rd 21227 410-887-1415
Kenneth Miller, prin. Fax 887-1461
Lansdowne MS 600/6-8
2400 Lansdowne Rd 21227 410-887-1411
Nicole Norris, prin. Fax 887-1412
Loch Raven HS 1,000/9-12
1212 Cowpens Ave 21286 410-887-3525
Bonnie Lambert, prin. Fax 887-5898
Loch Raven Technical Academy 700/6-8
8101 La Salle Rd 21286 410-887-3518
Stacey Johnson, prin. Fax 821-6398
Meadowood Education Center 50/Alt
1849 Gwynn Oak Ave 21207 410-887-6888
Damien Ingram, prin. Fax 887-6889
Middle River MS 900/6-8
800 Middle River Rd 21220 410-887-0165
Walter Mills, prin. Fax 887-0167
Milford Mill Academy 1,300/9-12
3800 Washington Ave 21244 410-887-0660
Nathaniel Gibson, prin. Fax 887-0681
Old Court MS 600/6-8
4627 Old Court Rd 21208 410-887-0742
Kyria Joseph, prin. Fax 887-0670
Overlea HS 1,000/9-12
5401 Kenwood Ave 21206 410-887-5241
Elizabeth Parker, prin. Fax 661-0174
Parkville MS 1,000/6-8
8711 Avondale Rd 21234 410-887-5250
Erin O'Toole-Trivas, prin. Fax 887-5315
Patapsco HS & Center for the Arts 1,500/9-12
8100 Wise Ave 21222 410-887-7060
Ryan Imbriale, prin. Fax 887-7062
Perry Hall HS 2,200/9-12
4601 Ebenezer Rd 21236 410-887-5108
George Roberts, prin. Fax 887-5116
Perry Hall MS 1,600/6-8
4300 Ebenezer Rd 21236 410-887-5100
Allen Zink, prin. Fax 887-5152
Pikesville HS 900/9-12
7621 Labyrinth Rd 21208 410-887-1217
Edmund Mitzel, prin. Fax 486-8436
Pikesville MS 1,000/6-8
7701 7 Mile Ln 21208 410-887-1207
Maria Talarigo, prin. Fax 887-1259
Pine Grove MS 900/6-8
9200 Old Harford Rd 21234 410-887-5270
Sandra Reid, prin. Fax 668-5237
Rosedale Center 200/Alt
8200 Old Philadelphia Rd 21237 410-887-0133
Sherrilyn Backof, prin. Fax 887-0473
Sollers Point Technical HS Vo/Tech
325 Sollers Point Rd 21222 410-887-7075
Michael Weglein, prin. Fax 887-7238
Southwest Academy 700/6-8
6200 Johnnycake Rd 21207 410-887-0825
Karen Barnes, prin. Fax 887-0829
Sparrows Point HS 800/9-12
7400 N Point Rd 21219 410-887-7517
Samuel Wynkoop, prin. Fax 477-4311
Sparrows Point MS 500/6-8
7400 N Point Rd 21219 410-887-7524
Lisa Perry, prin. Fax 477-6953
Stemmers Run MS 700/6-8
201 Stemmers Run Rd 21221 410-887-0177
Gordon Webb, prin. Fax 918-1787
Stricker MS 800/6-8
7855 Trappe Rd 21222 410-887-7038
Kathleen Owens, prin. Fax 285-1864
Sudbrook Magnet MS 1,000/6-8
4300 Bedford Rd 21208 410-887-6720
Sharon Robbins, prin. Fax 887-6737
Towson HS 1,400/9-12
69 Cedar Ave 21286 410-887-3608
Dr. Jane Barranger, prin. Fax 583-1375
Western S of Technology 900/9-12
100 Kenwood Ave 21228 410-887-0840
Murray Parker, prin. Fax 887-1024
Windsor Mill MS 600/6-8
8300 Windsor Mill Rd 21244 410-887-0618
Mark Brown, prin. Fax 496-1308
Woodlawn HS 1,600/9-12
1801 Woodlawn Dr 21207 410-887-1309
Brian Scriven, prin. Fax 887-1324
Woodlawn MS 600/6-8
3033 Saint Lukes Ln 21207 410-887-1304
April Jones, prin. Fax 298-4352

All-State Career School Post-Sec.
2200 Broening Hwy Ste 160 21224 410-631-1818
Archbishop Curley HS 600/9-12
3701 Sinclair Ln 21213 410-485-5000
Philip Piercy, dean Fax 483-2545
Arlington Baptist S 200/PK-12
3030 N Rolling Rd 21244 410-655-9300
Kim Parsons, admin. Fax 496-3901
Bais HaMedrash & Mesivta of Baltimore Post-Sec.
6823 Old Pimlico Rd 21209 410-486-0006
Bais Hamedrash & Mesivta S of Baltimore 100/9-12
6823 Old Pimlico Rd 21209 410-486-0006
Bais Yaakov Eva Winer HS 400/9-12
6302 Smith Ave 21209 443-548-7700
Baltimore Actors Theatre Conservatory 50/K-12
300 Dumbarton Rd Ste 2 21212 410-337-8519
Fax 337-8582
Baltimore City Community College Post-Sec.
2901 Liberty Heights Ave 21215 410-462-8300
Baltimore School of Massage Post-Sec.
517 Progress Dr Ste A-L 21207 410-944-8855
Baltimore Studio of Hair Design Post-Sec.
318 N Howard St 21201 410-539-1935
Beren HS 200/9-12
400 Mount Wilson Ln 21208 410-484-7200
Beth Tfiloh Dahan Community S PK-12
3300 Old Court Rd 21208 410-486-1905
Zipora Schorr, dir. Fax 415-6348
Bnos Yisroel S of Baltimore 400/PK-12
6300 Park Heights Ave 21215 443-524-3200
Ahuvah Heyman, dir. Fax 367-8510
Boys Latin S of Maryland 600/K-12
822 W Lake Ave 21210 410-377-5192
Christopher Post, hdmstr. Fax 377-4312
Broadcasting Institute of Maryland Post-Sec.
7200 Harford Rd 21234 410-254-2770
Bryn Mawr S 800/PK-12
109 W Melrose Ave 21210 410-323-8800
Maureen Walsh, hdmstr. Fax 377-8963
Calvert Hall College HS 1,200/9-12
8102 La Salle Rd 21286 410-825-4266
Louis Heidrick, prin. Fax 825-6826
Catholic HS of Baltimore 300/9-12
2800 Edison Hwy 21213 410-732-6200
Marty Meyd, prin. Fax 732-7639
Community College of Baltimore County Post-Sec.
7200 Sollers Point Rd 21222 443-840-2222
Coppin State University Post-Sec.
2500 W North Ave 21216 410-951-3000
Cristo Rey Jesuit HS 9-12
420 S Chester St 21231 410-727-3255
Thomas Malone, prin. Fax 573-9898
Faith Theological Seminary Post-Sec.
529 Walker Ave 21212 410-323-6211
Fortis Institute Post-Sec.
6901 Security Blvd Ste 21 21244 410-907-8110
Friends S of Baltimore 1,000/PK-12
5114 N Charles St 21210 410-649-3200
Matthew Micciche, hdmstr. Fax 649-3213
Gilman S 1,000/K-12
5407 Roland Ave 21210 410-323-3800
John Schmick, hdmstr. Fax 864-2812
Goucher College Post-Sec.
1021 Dulaney Valley Rd 21204 410-337-6000
Greater Baltimore Medical Center Post-Sec.
6701 N Charles St 21204 410-828-2121
Institute of Notre Dame 300/9-12
901 N Aisquith St 21202 410-522-7800
Dr. Gail Donahue, prin. Fax 522-7810
Johns Hopkins University Post-Sec.
3400 N Charles St 21218 410-516-8000
Loyola University Maryland Post-Sec.
4501 N Charles St 21210 800-221-9107
Maryland Beauty Academy of Essex Post-Sec.
505 Eastern Blvd 21221 410-686-4477
Maryland General Hospital Post-Sec.
827 Linden Ave 21201 410-995-8600
Maryland Institute College of Art Post-Sec.
1300 W Mount Royal Ave 21217 410-669-9200
Maryland School for the Blind Post-Sec.
3501 Taylor Ave 21236
Mercy HS 400/9-12
1300 E Northern Pkwy 21239 410-433-8880
Pegeen D'Agostino, prin. Fax 323-8816
Mercy Hospital Post-Sec.
301 Saint Paul St 21202 410-332-9202
Morgan State University Post-Sec.
1700 E Cold Spring Ln 21251 443-885-3333
Mother Seton Academy 100/6-8
2215 Greenmount Ave 21218 410-563-2833
Laura Peterson, prin. Fax 563-7354
Mt. St. Joseph HS 1,000/9-12
4403 Frederick Ave 21229 410-644-3300
Barry Fitzpatrick, prin. Fax 646-6221
Mt. Zion Baptist Christian S 200/PK-12
2000 E Belvedere Ave 21239 410-426-2309
Fax 426-5412
Ner Israel Rabbinical College Post-Sec.
400 Mount Wilson Ln 21208 410-484-7200
North American Trade Schools Post-Sec.
6901 Security Blvd Ste 16 21244 410-298-4844
Notre Dame of Maryland University Post-Sec.
4701 N Charles St 21210 410-435-0100
Our Lady of Mt. Carmel HS 200/9-12
1706 Old Eastern Ave 21221 410-686-1023
Kathleen Sipes, prin. Fax 686-2361
Park S of Baltimore 900/PK-12
2425 Old Court Rd 21208 410-339-7070
Dan Paradis, hdmstr. Fax 339-4125
Peabody Institute Johns Hopkins Univ. Post-Sec.
1 E Mount Vernon Pl 21202 410-234-4500
Rabbi Benjamin Steinberg MS 300/6-8
6300 Smith Ave 21209 443-548-7700
Roland Park Country S 700/PK-12
5204 Roland Ave 21210 410-323-5500
Jean Waller Brune, head sch Fax 323-2164
St. Frances Academy 300/9-12
501 E Chase St 21202 410-539-5794
Dr. Curtis Turner, prin. Fax 685-2650
St. Ignatius Loyola Academy 100/6-8
740 N Calvert St 21202 410-539-8268
Teresa Scott, prin. Fax 539-4821
St. Mary's Seminary & University Post-Sec.
5400 Roland Ave 21210 410-864-4000
Seton Keough HS 500/9-12
1201 S Caton Ave Ste 1 21227 410-646-4444
Angela Calamari, prin. Fax 368-1591
Sisters Academy of Baltimore 100/5-8
139 1st Ave 21227 410-242-1212
Sr. Debra Liesen, prin. Fax 242-5104
Sojourner-Douglass College Post-Sec.
200 N Central Ave 21202 410-276-0306
Stratford University Post-Sec.
210 S Central Ave 21202 410-752-4710
Talmudical Academy 700/K-12
4445 Old Court Rd 21208 410-484-6600
TESST College of Technology Post-Sec.
1520 S Caton Ave 21227 410-644-6400
Union Memorial Hospital Post-Sec.
201 E University Pkwy 21218 410-554-2739
University of Baltimore Post-Sec.
1420 N Charles St 21201 410-837-4200
University of Maryland Baltimore Post-Sec.
620 W Lexington St 21201 410-706-3100
University of Maryland Baltimore County Post-Sec.
1000 Hilltop Cir 21250 410-455-1000
Waldorf S of Baltimore 200/PK-12
4801 Tamarind Rd 21209 410-367-6808
Fax 664-4221

Bel Air, Harford, Pop. 9,934
Harford County SD 38,300/PK-12
102 S Hickory Ave 21014 410-838-7300
Dr. Robert Tomback, supt. Fax 893-2478
www.hcps.org/
Bel Air HS 1,600/9-12
100 Heighe St 21014 410-638-4600
Gregory Komondor, prin. Fax 638 4604
Bel Air MS 1,300/6-8
99 Idlewild St 21014 410-638-4140
Sean Abel, prin. Fax 638-4144
Harford Technical HS Vo/Tech
200 Thomas Run Rd 21015 410-638-3804
Charles Hagan, prin. Fax 638-3820
Patterson Mill HS 1,000/9-12
85 Patterson Mill Rd 21015 410-638-4640
Wayne Thibeault, prin. Fax 638-4646
Patterson Mill MS 800/6-12
85 Patterson Mill Rd 21015 410-638-4640
Wayne Thibeault, prin. Fax 638-4646
Southampton MS 1,300/6-8
1200 Moores Mill Rd 21014 410-638-4150
Glenn Jensen, prin. Fax 638-4305
Wright HS 1,600/9-12
1301 N Fountain Green Rd 21015 410-638-4110
Marlene Molter, prin. Fax 638-4114
Other Schools – See Aberdeen, Edgewood, Fallston, Havre de Grace, Joppa, Pylesville

---

Carroll S 700/9-12
703 E Churchville Rd 21014 410-879-2480
Madelyn Ball, prin. Fax 836-8514
Harford Community College Post-Sec.
401 Thomas Run Rd 21015 443-412-2000
International Beauty School Post-Sec.
227 Archer St 21014 410-838-0845
John Carroll HS 900/9-12
703 E Churchville Rd 21014 410-879-2480
Richard O'Hara, pres. Fax 836-8514
St. Margaret MS 300/6-8
1716 E Churchville Rd Ste A 21015 410-877-9660
Madeleine Hobik, prin. Fax 420-9322

Beltsville, Prince George's, Pop. 16,294
Prince George's County SD
Supt. — See Upper Marlboro
High Point HS 2,200/9-12
3601 Powder Mill Rd 20705 301-572-6400
Sandra Jimenez, prin. Fax 572-6481
King MS 700/6-8
4545 Ammendale Rd 20705 301-572-0650
Robin Wiltison, prin. Fax 572-0668

TESST Technology Institute Post-Sec.
4600 Powder Mill Rd Ste 500 20705 301-937-8448

Berlin, Worcester, Pop. 4,357
Worcester County SD
Supt. — See Newark

Decatur HS 1,400/9-12
9913 Seahawk Rd 21811 410-641-2171
Tom Zimmer, prin. Fax 641-1135
Decatur MS 600/7-8
9815 Seahawk Rd 21811 410-641-2846
Lynne Barton, prin. Fax 641-3274

Worcester Preparatory S 500/PK-12
508 S Main St 21811 410-641-3575
Dr. Barry Tull, hdmstr. Fax 641-3586

Bethesda, Montgomery, Pop. 59,121
Montgomery County SD
Supt. — See Rockville
Bethesda-Chevy Chase HS 1,800/9-12
4301 E West Hwy 20814 240-497-6300
Karen Lockard, prin. Fax 497-6306
Glenmont MS Alt
8001 Lynbrook Dr 20814 301-657-4977
Laura Shabazz, contact Fax 657-4970
Johnson HS 2,200/9-12
6400 Rock Spring Dr 20814 301-803-7100
Jennifer Baker, prin. Fax 571-6916
North Bethesda MS 800/6-8
8935 Bradmoor Dr 20817 301-571-3883
Alton Sumner, prin. Fax 571-3881
Pyle MS 1,300/6-8
6311 Wilson Ln 20817 301-320-6540
Jennifer Webster, prin. Fax 320-6647
Westland MS 1,000/6-8
5511 Massachusetts Ave 20816 301-320-6515
Alison Serino, prin. Fax 320-7054
Whitman HS 2,000/9-12
7100 Whittier Blvd 20817 301-320-6600
Dr. Alan Goodwin, prin. Fax 320-6594

DeVry University Post-Sec.
4550 Montgomery Ave Ste 100 20814 301-652-8477
Holton-Arms S 600/3-12
7303 River Rd 20817 301-365-5300
Susanna Jones, hdmstr. Fax 365-6085
Landon S 700/3-12
6101 Wilson Ln 20817 301-320-3200
David Armstrong, hdmstr. Fax 320-2787
Lycee Rochambeau 1,100/PK-12
9600 Forest Rd 20814 301-530-8260
Stone Ridge S of the Sacred Heart 600/PK-12
9101 Rockville Pike 20814 301-657-4322
Catherine Karrels, hdmstr. Fax 644-1599
The SANS Technology Institute Post-Sec.
8120 Woodmont Ave Ste 205 20814 301-654-7267
Washington Conservatory of Music Post-Sec.
1 Westmoreland Cir 20816 301-320-2770
Washington Waldorf S 300/PK-12
4800 Sangamore Rd 20816 301-229-6107
Jennifer Page, chrpsn. Fax 229-9379

Bladensburg, Prince George's, Pop. 9,010
Prince George's County SD
Supt. — See Upper Marlboro
Annapolis Road Academy 100/Alt
5150 Annapolis Rd 20710 301-209-3580
Agnes Brown-Jones, prin. Fax 209-3569
Bladensburg HS 1,900/9-12
4200 57th Ave 20710 301-887-6700
BernNadette Mahoney, prin. Fax 887-6710
Community Based Classroom 100/Alt
5150 Annapolis Rd 20710 301-985-5149
Dr. Tammy Williams, prin. Fax 985-1794

Elizabeth Seton HS 600/9-12
5715 Emerson St 20710 301-864-4532
Sharon Pasterick, prin. Fax 864-8946

Boonsboro, Washington, Pop. 3,310
Washington County SD
Supt. — See Hagerstown
Boonsboro HS 900/9-12
10 Campus Ave 21713 301-766-8022
Peggy Pugh, prin. Fax 791-4138
Boonsboro MS 800/6-8
1 J H Wade Dr 21713 301-766-8038
Paul Engle, prin. Fax 432-2644

Bowie, Prince George's, Pop. 52,916
Prince George's County SD
Supt. — See Upper Marlboro
Bowie HS 2,900/9-12
15200 Annapolis Rd 20715 301-805-2600
Derwanna Bey, prin. Fax 805-2619
Ogle MS 900/6-8
4111 Chelmont Ln 20715 301-805-2641
Mark Covington, prin. Fax 805-6674
Tall Oaks Vocational HS Vo/Tech
2112 Church Rd 20721 301-390-0230
Dr. Larry McCray, prin. Fax 390-0228
Tasker MS 1,000/6-8
4901 Collington Rd 20715 301-805-2660
Ingrid Johnson, prin. Fax 805-2663

Belair Baptist Christian Academy 50/PK-12
2801 Belair Dr 20715 301-262-0578
Dr. Gary Kohl, admin. Fax 262-0578
Bowie State University Post-Sec.
14000 Jericho Park Rd 20715 301-860-4000

Brandywine, Prince George's, Pop. 6,567
Prince George's County SD
Supt. — See Upper Marlboro
Gwynn Park HS 1,200/9-12
13800 Brandywine Rd 20613 301-372-0140
Tracie Miller, prin. Fax 372-0149
Gwynn Park MS 600/6-8
8000 Dyson Rd 20613 301-372-0120
Danielle Moore, prin. Fax 372-0119

Brooklandville, Baltimore

Maryvale Prep HS 400/6-12
11300 Falls Rd 21022 410-252-3366
Donna Bridickas, prin. Fax 561-1826
St. Paul's S 800/PK-12
PO Box 8100 21022 410-825-4400
David Faus, head sch Fax 427-0390
St. Paul's S for Girls 400/5-12
PO Box 8000 21022 410-823-6323
Penny Evins, hdmstr. Fax 828-7238

Brunswick, Frederick, Pop. 5,703
Frederick County SD
Supt. — See Frederick
Brunswick HS 800/9-12
101 Cummings Dr 21716 240-236-8600
Nancy Doll, prin. Fax 236-8601
Brunswick MS 500/6-8
301 Cummings Dr 21716 240-236-5400
Barbara Keiling, prin. Fax 236-5401

Buckeystown, Frederick, Pop. 1,012

St. John's Catholic Prep S 300/9-12
PO Box 909 21717 301-662-4210
Chris Cosentino, prin. Fax 892-6877

Burtonsville, Montgomery, Pop. 8,050
Montgomery County SD
Supt. — See Rockville
Banneker MS 800/6-8
14800 Perrywood Dr 20866 301-989-5747
Dr. Tamitha Campbell, prin. Fax 879-1032
Paint Branch HS 1,800/9-12
14121 Old Columbia Pike 20866 301-989-5600
Jeanette Dixon, prin. Fax 989-5609

California, Saint Mary's, Pop. 11,416

Blades School of Hair Design Post-Sec.
PO Box 226 20619 301-862-9797

Callaway, Saint Mary's

King's Christian Academy 200/PK-12
20738 Point Lookout Rd 20620 301-994-3080
Kevin Fry, admin. Fax 994-3087

Cambridge, Dorchester, Pop. 12,038
Dorchester County SD 4,600/PK-12
PO Box 619 21613 410-228-4747
Dr. Henry Wagner, supt. Fax 228-1847
www.dcps.k12.md.us
Cambridge-South Dorchester HS 800/9-12
2475 Cambridge Beltway 21613 410-228-9224
Dave Bromwell, prin. Fax 228-0724
Dorchester Career and Technology Center Vo/Tech
2465 Cambridge Beltway 21613 410-901-6950
Kermit Hines, prin. Fax 221-8589
Maces Lane MS 500/6-8
1101 Maces Ln 21613 410-228-2111
Susie Price, prin. Fax 221-5278
Other Schools – See Hurlock

Capitol Heights, Prince George's, Pop. 4,271
Prince George's County SD
Supt. — See Upper Marlboro
Central HS 1,100/9-12
200 Cabin Branch Rd 20743 301-499-7080
Charoscar Coleman, prin. Fax 499-7087
Fairmont Heights HS 800/9-12
1401 Nye St 20743 301-925-1360
Nakia Nicholson, prin. Fax 925-2371
Walker Mill MS 800/7-8
800 Karen Blvd 20743 301-808-4055
Nicole Clifton, prin. Fax 808-4039

Maple Springs Baptist Bible Coll. & Sem. Post-Sec.
4130 Belt Rd 20743 301-736-3631

Catonsville, Baltimore, Pop. 40,573
Baltimore County SD
Supt. — See Towson
Catonsville MS 700/6-8
2301 Edmondson Ave 21228 410-887-0803
Michael Thorne, prin. Fax 887-1036

Community College of Baltimore County Post-Sec.
800 S Rolling Rd 21228 443-840-2222
Mt. de Sales Academy 500/9-12
700 Academy Rd 21228 410-744-8498
Sr. Anne Catherine, prin. Fax 747-5105

Centreville, Queen Anne's, Pop. 4,193
Queen Anne's County SD 7,800/PK-12
202 Chesterfield Ave 21617 410-758-2403
Dr. Carol Williamson, supt. Fax 758-8207
www.qacps.k12.md.us
Centreville MS 500/6-8
231 Ruthsburg Rd 21617 410-758-0883
Jacquelyn Wilhelm, prin. Fax 758-4447
Queen Anne's County HS 1,200/9-12
125 Ruthsburg Rd 21617 410-758-0500
Jacquelyn Wilhelm, prin. Fax 758-4454
Other Schools – See Stevensville, Sudlersville

Gunston S 100/9-12
PO Box 200 21617 410-758-0620
John Lewis, hdmstr. Fax 758-0628

Cheltenham, Prince George's
Prince George's County SD
Supt. — See Upper Marlboro
Croom Vocational HS Vo/Tech
9400 Surratts Rd 20623 301-372-8846
William Henderson, prin. Fax 372-3422

Chesapeake City, Cecil, Pop. 671
Cecil County SD
Supt. — See Elkton
Bohemia Manor HS 700/9-12
2755 Augustine Herman Hwy 21915 410-885-2075
John Roush, prin. Fax 885-2485
Bohemia Manor MS 500/6-8
2757 Augustine Herman Hwy 21915 410-885-2095
Dr. Ann Little, prin. Fax 885-2485

Chestertown, Kent, Pop. 5,140
Kent County SD
Supt. — See Rock Hall
Kent County MS 500/6-8
402 E Campus Ave 21620 410-778-1771
Gary McCulloch, prin. Fax 778-6541

Washington College Post-Sec.
300 Washington Ave 21620 410-778-2800

Clarksburg, Montgomery, Pop. 13,276
Montgomery County SD
Supt. — See Rockville
Clarksburg HS 1,800/9-12
22500 Wims Rd 20871 301-444-3000
James Koutsos, prin. Fax 444-3595
Rocky Hill MS 1,000/6-8
22401 Brick Haven Way 20871 301-353-8282
Gregory Edmundson, prin. Fax 601-3197

Clarksville, Howard
Howard County SD
Supt. — See Ellicott City
Clarksville MS 700/6-8
6535 S Trotter Rd 21029 410-313-7057
Melissa Shindel, prin. Fax 313-7061
River Hill HS 1,400/9-12
12101 Clarksville Pike 21029 410-313-7120
Nicholas Novack, prin. Fax 313-7406

Clear Spring, Washington, Pop. 356
Washington County SD
Supt. — See Hagerstown
Clear Spring HS 500/9-12
12630 Broadfording Rd 21722 301-766-8082
James Aleshire, prin. Fax 842-0082
Clear Spring MS 400/6-8
12628 Broadfording Rd 21722 301-766-8094
Scott Noll, prin. Fax 842-3826

Clinton, Prince George's, Pop. 35,163
Prince George's County SD
Supt. — See Upper Marlboro
Decatur MS 600/6-8
8200 Pinewood Dr 20735 301-449-4950
Barry Cyrus, prin. Fax 449-2105
Surrattsville HS 900/9-12
6101 Garden Dr 20735 301-599-2453
Kristi Holden, prin. Fax 599-2565

Grace Brethren Christian S 600/PK-12
6501 Surratts Rd 20735 301-868-1600
George Hornickel, dir. Fax 868-9475

Cockeysville, Baltimore, Pop. 20,195
Baltimore County SD
Supt. — See Towson
Cockeysville MS 800/6-8
10401 Greenside Dr 21030 410-887-7626
Deborah Magness, prin. Fax 887-7628

College Park, Prince George's, Pop. 29,403

University of Maryland College Park Post-Sec.
20742 301-405-1000

Colora, Cecil

West Nottingham Academy 100/9-12
1079 Firetower Rd 21917 410-658-5556
Stephen Brotschul, head sch Fax 658-6790

Columbia, Howard, Pop. 95,623
Howard County SD
Supt. — See Ellicott City
Atholton HS 1,500/9-12
6520 Freetown Rd 21044 410-313-7065
Jennifer Clements, prin. Fax 313-7078
Hammond HS 1,300/9-12
8800 Guilford Rd 21046 410-313-7615
Marcy Leonard, prin. Fax 313-7632
Harper's Choice MS 500/6-8
5450 Beaverkill Rd 21044 410-313-6929
Restia Whitaker, prin. Fax 313-5612
Lake Elkhorn MS 6-8
6700 Cradlerock Way 21045 410-313-7600
Jennifer Peduzzi, prin. Fax 313-7633
Long Reach HS 1,200/9-12
6101 Old Dobbin Ln 21045 410-313-7117
David Burton, prin. Fax 313-7422
Oakland Mills HS 1,200/9-12
9410 Kilimanjaro Rd 21045 410-313-6945
Frank Eastham, prin. Fax 313-6948
Oakland Mills MS 400/6-8
9540 Kilimanjaro Rd 21045 410-313-6937
Shiney John, prin. Fax 313-7447
Wilde Lake HS 1,300/9-12
5460 Trumpeter Rd 21044 410-313-6965
James LeMon, prin. Fax 313-6972
Wilde Lake MS 500/6-8
10481 Cross Fox Ln 21044 410-313-6957
Thomas Saunders, prin. Fax 313-6963

Atholton Adventist Academy 200/PK-10
6520 Martin Rd 21044 410-740-2425
Marilynn Peeke, prin. Fax 740-2545
Howard Community College Post-Sec.
10901 Little Patuxent Pkwy 21044 443-518-1200

Lincoln College of Technology — Post-Sec.
9325 Snowden River Pkwy 21046 — 410-290-7100

Cresaptown, Allegany, Pop. 4,546
Allegany County SD
Supt. — See Cumberland
Center for Career & Technical Education — Vo/Tech
14211 McMullen Hwy SW 21502 — 301-729-6486
Harry Smith, prin. — Fax 729-0661

Calvary Christian Academy — 300/PK-12
PO Box 5154 21505 — 301-729-0791
Daniel Thompson, admin. — Fax 729-1648

Crisfield, Somerset, Pop. 2,671
Somerset County SD
Supt. — See Westover
Crisfield Academy/HS — 400/8-12
210 N Somerset Ave 21817 — 410-968-0150
James Conrow, prin. — Fax 968-1178

Crownsville, Anne Arundel, Pop. 1,733
Anne Arundel County SD
Supt. — See Annapolis
Moss Academy — 100/Alt
45 Community Pl 21032 — 410-222-3836
Wendy Slaughter, prin. — Fax 932-3149

Indian Creek Upper S — 200/9-12
1130 Anne Chambers Way 21032 — 410-849-5151
Dr. Richard Branson, head sch — Fax 841-2623

Cumberland, Allegany, Pop. 20,280
Allegany County SD — 8,700/PK-12
PO Box 1724 21501 — 301-759-2000
Dr. David Cox, supt. — Fax 759-2029
www.acps.allconet.org
Allegany HS — 900/9-12
616 Sedgwick St 21502 — 301-777-8110
Michael Calhoun, prin. — Fax 759-2534
Braddock MS — 600/6-8
909 Holland St 21502 — 301-777-7990
Danny Carter, prin. — Fax 777-9741
Ft. Hill HS — 900/9-12
500 Greenway Ave 21502 — 301-777-2570
Stephen Lewis, prin. — Fax 777-2572
Washington MS — 600/6-8
200 N Massachusetts Ave 21502 — 301-777-5360
Kim Green, prin. — Fax 777-8452
Other Schools – See Cresaptown, Frostburg, Lonaconing

Allegany College of Maryland — Post-Sec.
12401 Willowbrook Rd 21502 — 301-784-5000
Bishop Walsh S — 600/PK-12
700 Bishop Walsh Rd 21502 — 301-724-5360
Shelby Webb, prin. — Fax 722-0555
International Beauty School — Post-Sec.
119 N Centre St 21502 — 301-777-3020
Lighthouse Christian Academy — 100/PK-12
2020 Bedford St 21502 — 301-777-7375
Fax 777-3497

Damascus, Montgomery, Pop. 14,848
Montgomery County SD
Supt. — See Rockville
Baker MS — 500/7-8
25400 Oak Dr 20872 — 301-253-7010
Louise Worthington, prin. — Fax 253-7020
Damascus HS — 1,300/9-12
25921 Ridge Rd 20872 — 301-253-7030
Robert Domergue, prin. — Fax 253-7046

Denton, Caroline, Pop. 4,304
Caroline County SD — 5,500/PK-12
204 Franklin St 21629 — 410-479-1460
Dr. Khalid N. Mumin, supt. — Fax 479-0108
cl.k12.md.us
Lockerman MS — 800/6-8
410 Lockerman St 21629 — 410-479-2760
LeTrecia Gloster, prin. — Fax 479-3594
Other Schools – See Federalsburg, Ridgely

Easton, Talbot, Pop. 15,604
Talbot County SD — 4,100/PK-12
PO Box 1029 21601 — 410-822-0330
Dr. Karen Salmon, supt. — Fax 820-4260
www.tcps.k12.md.us/
Easton HS — 1,200/9-12
723 Mecklenburg Ave 21601 — 410-822-4180
David Stofa, prin. — Fax 819-5814
Easton MS — 700/6-8
201 Peach Blossom Ln 21601 — 410-822-2910
Norby Lee, prin. — Fax 822-7210
Other Schools – See Saint Michaels

Chesapeake Christian S — 200/PK-12
1009 N Washington St 21601 — 410-822-7600
Deborah Whitter, prin. — Fax 822-1947
SS. Peter & Paul HS — 200/9-12
900 High St 21601 — 410-822-2275
James Nemeth, prin. — Fax 822-1767

Edgewater, Anne Arundel, Pop. 8,834
Anne Arundel County SD
Supt. — See Annapolis
Center of Applied Technology-South — Vo/Tech
211 Central Ave E 21037 — 410-956-5900
Thomas Milans, prin. — Fax 956-5905
Central MS — 1,100/6-8
221 Central Ave E 21037 — 410-956-5800
Mildred Beall, prin. — Fax 956-1266
South River HS — 2,100/9-12
201 Central Ave E 21037 — 410-956-5600
William Myers, prin. — Fax 956-5137
South River Evening HS — Adult
201 Central Ave E 21037 — 410-956-0462
Rosaria Jablonski, admin. — Fax 956-5919

Edgewood, Harford, Pop. 24,585
Harford County SD
Supt. — See Bel Air
Edgewood HS — 1,200/9-12
2415 Willoughby Beach Rd 21040 — 410-612-1500
Larissa Santos, prin. — Fax 612-1585
Edgewood MS — 1,000/6-8
2311 Willoughby Beach Rd 21040 — 410-612-1518
Patrice Brown, prin. — Fax 612-1523

Eldersburg, Carroll, Pop. 30,093
Carroll County SD
Supt. — See Westminster
Liberty HS — 1,200/9-12
5855 Bartholow Rd 21784 — 410-751-3560
Thomas Clowes, prin. — Fax 751-3564

Elkridge, Howard, Pop. 15,025
Howard County SD
Supt. — See Ellicott City
Elkridge Landing MS — 700/6-8
7085 Montgomery Rd 21075 — 410-313-5040
Gina Cash, prin. — Fax 313-5045
Mayfield Woods MS — 700/6-8
7950 Red Barn Way 21075 — 410-313-5022
JoAnn Hutchens, prin. — Fax 313-5029

Elkton, Cecil, Pop. 14,914
Cecil County SD — 15,900/PK-12
201 Booth St 21921 — 410-996-5400
D'Ette Devine Ed.D., supt. — Fax 996-5454
www.ccps.org
Cherry Hill MS — 500/6-8
2535 Singerly Rd 21921 — 410-996-5020
Berkeley Orr, prin. — Fax 996-5435
Elkton HS — 1,100/9-12
110 James St 21921 — 410-996-5000
Wes Zimmerman, prin. — Fax 996-5646
Elkton MS — 600/6-8
615 North St 21921 — 410-996-5010
Dr. Stuart Hutchinson, prin. — Fax 996-5639
Other Schools – See Chesapeake City, North East, Perryville, Rising Sun

---

Tri-State Christian Academy — 300/PK-12
146 Appleton Rd 21921 — 410-398-6444
Keith Wilson, hdmstr. — Fax 688-4847

Ellicott City, Howard, Pop. 64,049
Howard County SD — 50,000/PK-12
10910 State Route 108 21042 — 410-313-6600
Dr. Renee Foose, supt. — Fax 313-6674
www.hcpss.org
Bonnie Branch MS — 700/6-8
4979 Ilchester Rd 21043 — 410-313-2580
Carolyn Jameson, prin. — Fax 313-2586
Burleigh Manor MS — 600/6-8
4200 Centennial Ln 21042 — 410-313-2507
Claire Hafets, prin. — Fax 313-2513
Centennial HS — 1,500/9-12
4300 Centennial Ln 21042 — 410-313-2856
Carl Perkins, prin. — Fax 313-2891
Dunloggin MS — 500/6-8
9129 Northfield Rd 21042 — 410-313-2831
Cher Jones, prin. — Fax 313-2530
Ellicott Mills MS — 700/6-8
4445 Montgomery Rd 21043 — 410-313-2839
Michael Goins, prin. — Fax 313-2845
Folly Quarter MS — 600/6-8
13500 Triadelphia Rd 21042 — 410-313-1506
Rick Wilson, prin. — Fax 313-1509
Homewood S — 100/Alt
10914 State Route 108 21042 — 410-313-7081
Tina Maddox, prin. — Fax 313-7130
Howard HS — 1,600/9-12
8700 Old Annapolis Rd 21043 — 410-313-2867
Gina Massella, prin. — Fax 313-2870
Mt. Hebron HS — 1,500/9-12
9440 Old Frederick Rd 21042 — 410-313-2880
Scott Ruehl, prin. — Fax 313-2543
Patapsco MS — 600/6-8
8885 Old Frederick Rd 21043 — 410-313-2848
Cynthia Dillon, prin. — Fax 313-2852
Other Schools – See Clarksville, Columbia, Elkridge, Fulton, Glenelg, Glenwood, Jessup, Laurel, Marriottsville

---

Glenelg Country S — 800/PK-12
12793 Folly Quarter Rd 21042 — 410-531-8600
Greg Ventre, hdmstr. — Fax 531-7363

Emmitsburg, Frederick, Pop. 2,774

Mt. St. Mary's University — Post-Sec.
16300 Old Emmitsburg Rd 21727 — 301-447-6122

Fallston, Harford, Pop. 8,862
Harford County SD
Supt. — See Bel Air
Fallston HS — 1,100/9-12
2301 Carrs Mill Rd 21047 — 410-638-4120
Richard Jester, prin. — Fax 638-4125
Fallston MS — 900/6-8
2303 Carrs Mill Rd 21047 — 410-638-4129
Joseph Mascari, prin. — Fax 638-4237

Federalsburg, Caroline, Pop. 2,672
Caroline County SD
Supt. — See Denton
Richardson HS — 500/9-12
25320 Richardson Rd 21632 — 410-754-5575
Susan McCandless, prin. — Fax 754-3497
Richardson MS — 400/6-8
25390 Richardson Rd 21632 — 410-754-5263
Lynn Willey, prin. — Fax 754-5695

Finksburg, Carroll

Gerstell Academy — 300/PK-12
2500 Old Westminster Pike 21048 — 410-861-3000
Frederick Smith, pres. — Fax 861-3006

Forestville, Prince George's, Pop. 12,138
Prince George's County SD
Supt. — See Upper Marlboro
Forestville Military Academy — 800/9-12
7001 Beltz Dr 20747 — 301-817-0400
Nathaniel Laney, prin. — Fax 817-0416
Suitland HS — 2,400/9-12
5200 Silver Hill Rd 20747 — 301-817-0500
Nate Newman, prin. — Fax 817-0515

Bishop McNamara HS — 900/9-12
6800 Marlboro Pike 20747 — 301-735-8401
Michael Hunt, prin. — Fax 735-0934

Fort Meade, Anne Arundel, Pop. 8,776
Anne Arundel County SD
Supt. — See Annapolis
MacArthur MS — 1,200/6-8
3500 Rockenbach Rd 20755 — 410-674-0032
Stacy Gray, prin. — Fax 674-8021
Meade HS — 2,300/9-12
1100 Clark Rd 20755 — 410-674-7710
John Yore, prin. — Fax 551-8210
Meade MS — 700/6-8
1103 26th St 20755 — 410-674-2355
William Goodman, prin. — Fax 674-6590
Meade Evening HS — Adult
1100 Clark Rd 20755 — 410-674-7415
John France, admin.

Fort Washington, Prince George's, Pop. 23,036
Prince George's County SD
Supt. — See Upper Marlboro
Friendly HS — 1,500/9-12
10000 Allentown Rd 20744 — 301-449-4900
Raynah Adams, prin. — Fax 449-4911
Gourdine MS — 600/6-8
8700 Allentown Rd 20744 — 301-449-4940
Leatriz Covington, prin. — Fax 449-4948
Oxon Hill MS — 600/7-8
9570 Fort Foote Rd 20744 — 301-749-4270
Wendell Coleman, prin. — Fax 749-4286

National Christian Academy — 300/PK-12
6700 Bock Rd 20744 — 301-567-9507
Andrew Stewart M.Ed., prin. — Fax 567-7438

Frederick, Frederick, Pop. 63,120
Frederick County SD — 39,600/PK-12
191 S East St 21701 — 301-644-5000
Theresa Alban, supt. — Fax 696-6823
www.fcps.org
Ballenger Creek MS — 700/6-8
5525 Ballenger Creek Pike 21703 — 240-236-5700
Mita Badshah, prin. — Fax 236-5701
Career and Technology Center — Vo/Tech
7922 Opossumtown Pike 21702 — 240-236-8500
Gregory Solberg, prin. — Fax 236-8501
Crestwood MS — 600/6-8
7100 Foxcroft Dr 21703 — 240-566-9000
Dr. Dan Lippy, prin. — Fax 566-9001
Frederick HS — 1,300/9-12
650 Carroll Pkwy 21701 — 240-236-7000
Kathy Campagnoli, prin. — Fax 236-7015
Heather Ridge S — Alt
1445 Taney Ave 21702 — 240-236-8000
Denise Flora, prin. — Fax 236-8001
Johnson HS — 1,700/9-12
1501 N Market St 21701 — 240-236-8200
Marlene Tarr, prin. — Fax 236-8201
Johnson MS — 500/6-8
1799 Schifferstadt Blvd 21701 — 240-236-4900
Neal Case, prin. — Fax 236-4901
Linganore HS — 1,700/9-12
12013 Old Annapolis Rd 21701 — 240-566-9700
Dave Kehne, prin. — Fax 566-9701
Monocacy MS — 800/6-8
8009 Opossumtown Pike 21702 — 240-236-4700
Brian Vasquenza, prin. — Fax 236-4701
Tuscarora HS — 1,500/9-12
5312 Ballenger Creek Pike 21703 — 240-236-6400
Kathleen Schlappal, prin. — Fax 236-6401
West Frederick MS — 800/6-8
515 W Patrick St 21701 — 240-236-4000
Frank Vetter, prin. — Fax 236-4050
Flexible Evening HS — Adult
1799 Schifferstadt Blvd 21701 — 240-236-8450
Dr. Stacy Adamiak, prin. — Fax 236-8451
Other Schools – See Brunswick, Ijamsville, Middletown, New Market, Thurmont, Walkersville

---

Frederick Adventist S — 100/PK-10
6437 Jefferson Pike 21703 — 301-663-0363
Robin Correia, prin. — Fax 698-8226
Frederick Community College — Post-Sec.
7932 Opossumtown Pike 21702 — 301-846-2400
Hood College — Post-Sec.
401 Rosemont Ave 21701 — 301-663-3131
Maryland School for the Deaf — Post-Sec.
PO Box 250 21705
New Life Christian S — 200/K-12
5909 Jefferson Pike 21703 — 301-663-8418
Jason Burrell, hdmstr. — Fax 698-1583

Frostburg, Allegany, Pop. 8,847
Allegany County SD
Supt. — See Cumberland
Eckhart Alternative S — Alt
17000 National Hwy SW 21532 — 301-689-3483
James Koon, admin. — Fax 689-2567

Mountain Ridge HS 1,000/9-12
100 Dr Nancy S Grasmick Ln 21532 301-689-3377
Gene Morgan, prin. Fax 689-8709

Frostburg State University Post-Sec.
101 Braddock Rd 21532 301-687-4000

Fulton, Howard, Pop. 1,957
Howard County SD
Supt. — See Ellicott City
Lime Kiln MS 600/6-8
11650 Scaggsville Rd 20759 410-880-5988
Scott Conroy, prin. Fax 880-5996
Reservoir HS 1,500/9-12
11550 Scaggsville Rd 20759 410-888-8850
Patrick Saunderson, prin. Fax 888-8849

Gaithersburg, Montgomery, Pop. 57,995
Montgomery County SD
Supt. — See Rockville
Forest Oak MS 900/6-8
651 Saybrooke Oaks Blvd 20877 301-670-8242
Art Williams, prin. Fax 840-5322
Gaithersburg HS 2,000/9-12
314 S Frederick Ave 20877 301-840-4700
Dr. Christine Collins, prin. Fax 840-4707
Gaithersburg MS 400/7-8
2 Teachers Way 20877 301-840-4554
Carol Goddard, prin. Fax 840-4570
Hadley Farms MS Alt
7401 Hadley Farms Dr 20879 301-548-4960
Debbie Buchanan, prin. Fax 548-4964
Lakelands Park MS 900/6-8
1200 Main St 20878 301-670-1400
Deborah Higdon, prin. Fax 670-1418
Montgomery Village MS 600/6-8
19300 Watkins Mill Rd 20886 301-840-4660
Dr. Edgar Malker, prin. Fax 840-6388
Quince Orchard HS 1,800/9-12
15800 Quince Orchard Rd 20878 301-840-4686
Carole Working, prin. Fax 840-4699
Ridgeview MS 500/7-8
16600 Raven Rock Dr 20878 301-840-4770
Monifa McKnight, prin. Fax 840-4679
Shady Grove MS 600/6-8
8100 Midcounty Hwy 20877 301-548-7540
Edward Owusu, prin. Fax 548-7535
Watkins Mill HS 1,600/9-12
10301 Apple Ridge Rd 20886 301-840-3959
Scott Murphy, prin. Fax 840-3980

Aesthetics Institutes of Cosmetology Post-Sec.
15958 Shady Grove Rd Unit C 20877 301-330-9252
Avalon S 100/2-12
200 W Diamond Ave 20877 301-963-8022
Kevin Davern, hdmstr. Fax 963-8027
Covenant Life S 300/K-12
7503 Muncaster Mill Rd 20877 301-869-4500
Jamie Leach, hdmstr. Fax 948-4920
Sodexho Marriott Healthcare Mid-Atlantic Post-Sec.
9801 Washingtonian Blvd 20878 301-987-4127

Gambrills, Anne Arundel, Pop. 2,747
Anne Arundel County SD
Supt. — See Annapolis
Arundel HS 1,900/9-12
1001 Annapolis Rd 21054 410-674-6500
Sharon Stratton, prin. Fax 672-3711
Crofton MS 1,200/6-8
2301 Davidsonville Rd 21054 410-793-0280
Nuria Williams, prin. Fax 793-0295

Germantown, Montgomery, Pop. 83,263
Montgomery County SD
Supt. — See Rockville
Clemente MS 1,100/6-8
18808 Waring Station Rd 20874 301-601-0344
Khadija Barkley, prin. Fax 601-0370
King MS 600/6-8
13737 Wisteria Dr 20874 301-353-8080
Dana Davison, prin. Fax 601-0399
Kingsview MS 900/6-8
18909 Kingsview Rd 20874 301-601-4611
James D'Andrea, prin. Fax 601-4610
Neelsville MS 900/6-8
11700 Neelsville Church Rd 20876 301-353-8064
Vicky Lake-Parcan, prin. Fax 353-8094
Northwest HS 2,100/9-12
13501 Richter Farm Rd 20874 301-601-4660
Lance Dempsey, prin. Fax 601-4662
Seneca Valley HS 1,300/9-12
19401 Crystal Rock Dr 20874 301-353-8000
Marc Cohen, prin. Fax 353-8004

Montgomery College Post-Sec.
20200 Observation Dr 20876 240-567-7700

Glen Burnie, Anne Arundel, Pop. 65,521
Anne Arundel County SD
Supt. — See Annapolis
Corkran MS 600/6-8
7600 Quarterfield Rd 21061 410-222-6493
Jolyn Davis, prin. Fax 761-3853
Glen Burnie HS 1,900/9-12
7550 Baltimore Annapolis Bl 21060 410-761-8950
Vickie Plitt, prin. Fax 761-3711
Marley MS 800/6-8
10 Davis Ct 21060 410-761-0934
Kevin Buckley, prin. Fax 761-0736
North County HS 1,900/9-12
10 1st Ave E 21061 410-222-6970
William Heiser, prin. Fax 222-6976
Glen Burnie Evening HS Adult
7550 Baltimore Annapolis Bl 21060 410-761-3664
Kathleen Dugan, admin. Fax 863-4531

Glencoe, Baltimore

Oldfields S 100/7-12
1500 Glencoe Rd 21152 410-472-4800
Taylor Smith, hdmstr. Fax 472-3141

Glenelg, Howard
Howard County SD
Supt. — See Ellicott City
Glenelg HS 1,200/9-12
14025 Burntwoods Rd 21737 410-313-5528
Karl Schindler, prin. Fax 313-5540

Glenwood, Howard
Howard County SD
Supt. — See Ellicott City
Glenwood MS 600/6-8
2680 Route 97 21738 410-313-5520
Dave Brown, prin. Fax 313-5534

Great Mills, Saint Mary's
St. Mary's County SD
Supt. — See Leonardtown
Great Mills HS 1,700/9-12
21130 Great Mills Rd 20634 301-863-4001
Jake Heibel, prin. Fax 863-4006

Greenbelt, Prince George's, Pop. 22,408
Prince George's County SD
Supt. — See Upper Marlboro
Greenbelt MS 700/6-8
6301 Breezewood Dr 20770 301-513-5040
Warren Tweedy, prin. Fax 513-5097
Roosevelt HS 2,700/9-12
7601 Hanover Pkwy 20770 301-513-5400
Reginald McNeill, prin. Fax 513-5047

Lancaster Bible College Post-Sec.
7852 Walker Dr Ste 100 20770 301-552-1400

Hagerstown, Washington, Pop. 37,853
Washington County SD 22,800/PK-12
PO Box 730 21741 301-766-2800
Dr. Clayton Wilcox, supt. Fax 766-2829
www.wcps.k12.md.us/
Antietam Academy Alt
40 W Oak Ridge Dr 21740 301-766-8447
Ike Williams, prin. Fax 766-8479
Hicks MS 800/6-8
1321 S Potomac St 21740 301-766-8110
Deron Crawford, prin. Fax 766-8116
Ingram S for the Arts 200/9-12
7 S Potomac St 21740 301-766-8840
Michael Thorsen, prin. Fax 766-8849
Northern MS 700/6-8
701 Northern Ave 21742 301-766-8258
Michael Chilcutt, prin. Fax 797-5887
North Hagerstown HS 1,300/9-12
1200 Pennsylvania Ave 21742 301-766-8238
Duane McNairn, prin. Fax 733-3158
South Hagerstown HS 1,300/9-12
1101 S Potomac St 21740 301-766-8369
Dr. Timothy Dawson, prin. Fax 766-8474
Washington County Technical HS Vo/Tech
50 W Oak Ridge Dr 21740 301-766-8050
Jeff Stouffer, prin. Fax 797-9743
Western Heights MS 700/6-8
1300 Marshall St 21740 301-766-8403
Michael Kuhaneck, prin. Fax 491-4136
Evening HS Adult
40 W Oak Ridge Dr 21740 301-766-8059
James Moore, admin.
Other Schools – See Boonsboro, Clear Spring, Hancock, Smithsburg, Williamsport

Award Beauty School Post-Sec.
26 E Antietam St 21740 301-733-4520
Broadfording Christian Academy 300/PK-12
13535 Broadfording Church 21740 301-797-8886
William Wyand, supt. Fax 797-3155
Grace Academy 300/PK-12
13321 Cearfoss Pike 21740 301-733-2033
Jack Appleby, hdmstr. Fax 733-4706
Hagerstown Community College Post-Sec.
11400 Robinwood Dr 21742 240-500-2530
Heritage Academy 200/PK-12
12215 Walnut Pt W 21740 301-582-2600
Dr. Dewitt Powell, prin. Fax 582-2603
Highland View Academy 100/9-12
10100 Academy Dr 21740 301-739-8480
Kaplan University Post-Sec.
18618 Crestwood Dr 21742 301-766-3600
Paradise Mennonite S 200/1-10
19308 Air View Rd 21742 301-733-1368
Pittsburgh Institute of Aeronautics Post-Sec.
18450 Showalter Rd 21742 800-444-1440
St. James S 200/8-12
17641 College Rd 21740 301-733-9330
Rev. D. Stuart Dunnan, hdmstr. Fax 739-1310
St. Maria Goretti HS 200/9-12
1535 Oak Hill Ave 21742 301-739-4266
Richard Fairley, prin. Fax 739-4261

Hampstead, Carroll, Pop. 6,228
Carroll County SD
Supt. — See Westminster
North Carroll HS 800/9-12
1400 Panther Dr 21074 410-751-3450
Kimberly Dolch, prin. Fax 751-3457
North Carroll MS 600/6-8
2401 Hanover Pike 21074 410-751-3440
James Carver, prin. Fax 751-3464
Shiloh MS 700/6-8
3675 Willow St 21074 410-386-4570
Jeffrey Alisauckas, prin. Fax 386-4579

Hancock, Washington, Pop. 1,530
Washington County SD
Supt. — See Hagerstown
Hancock MSHS 300/6-12
289 W Main St 21750 301-766-8186
Rodney Gayman, prin. Fax 678-7218

Hanover, Anne Arundel

ITT Technical Institute Post-Sec.
7030 Dorsey Rd Ste 100 21076 410-694-4700

Harwood, Anne Arundel
Anne Arundel County SD
Supt. — See Annapolis
Southern HS 1,100/9-12
4400 Solomons Island Rd 20776 410-867-7100
Marc Procaccini, prin. Fax 867-7100

Havre de Grace, Harford, Pop. 12,505
Harford County SD
Supt. — See Bel Air
Havre De Grace HS 700/9-12
700 Congress Ave 21078 410-939-6600
James Reynolds, prin. Fax 939-6667
Havre De Grace MS 500/6-8
401 Lewis Ln 21078 410-939-6608
Anthony Bess, prin. Fax 939-6613

Helen, Saint Mary's
St. Mary's County SD
Supt. — See Leonardtown
Brent MS 1,000/6-8
29675 Point Lookout Rd 20635 301-884-4635
Mike Egan, prin. Fax 884-8937

Huntingtown, Calvert
Calvert County SD
Supt. — See Prince Frederick
Huntingtown HS 1,700/9-12
4125 Solomons Island Rd 20639 410-414-7036
Rick Weber, prin. Fax 535-2865
Plum Point MS 700/6-8
1475 Plum Point Rd 20639 410-535-7400
Zachary Seawell, prin. Fax 535-7413
Adult Education Adult
4105 Old Town Rd 20639 410-535-7382
Fax 535-7383

Calverton S 400/PK-12
300 Calverton School Rd 20639 410-535-0216
Daniel Hildebrand, hdmstr. Fax 535-6934

Hurlock, Dorchester, Pop. 2,049
Dorchester County SD
Supt. — See Cambridge
North Dorchester HS 500/9-12
5875 Cloverdale Rd 21643 410-943-4511
Lynn Sorrells, prin. Fax 943-3499
North Dorchester MS 400/6-8
5745 Cloverdale Rd 21643 410-943-3322
Vaughn Evans, prin. Fax 943-3797

Hyattsville, Prince George's, Pop. 17,068
Prince George's County SD
Supt. — See Upper Marlboro
Hyattsville MS 700/7-8
6001 42nd Ave 20781 301-209-5830
Kimberly Washington, prin. Fax 209-5849
Northwestern HS 2,500/9-12
7000 Adelphi Rd 20782 301-985-1820
Edgar Batenga, prin. Fax 985-1833
Orem MS 700/6-8
6100 Editors Park Dr 20782 301-853-0840
Theresa Merrifield, prin. Fax 853-0839
Northwestern Evening HS Adult
7000 Adelphi Rd 20782 301-985-1460
William Kitchings, prin. Fax 985-5749

Chelsea S 100/5-12
2970 Belcrest Center Dr 20782 301-585-1430
Katherine Fedalen M.Ed., hdmstr. Fax 585-9621
De Matha Catholic HS 1,000/9-12
4313 Madison St 20781 240-764-2200
Dr. Daniel McMahon, prin. Fax 764-2275

Ijamsville, Frederick, Pop. 350
Frederick County SD
Supt. — See Frederick
Oakdale HS 9-12
5850 Eaglehead Dr 21754 240-566-9400
Dr. George Seaton, prin. Fax 566-9401
Oakdale MS 100/6-8
9840 Old National Pike 21754 240-236-5500
Michelle Concepcion, prin. Fax 236-5501
Urbana HS 1,700/9-12
3471 Campus Dr 21754 240-236-7600
Jay Berno, prin. Fax 236-7601
Urbana MS 700/6-8
3511 Pontius Ct 21754 240-566-9200
Gwendolyn Dorsey, prin. Fax 566-9201
Windsor Knolls MS 900/6-8
11150 Windsor Rd 21754 240-236-5000
T.C. Suter, prin. Fax 236-5001

Friends Meeting S 100/PK-12
3232 Green Valley Rd 21754 301-798-0288
Wilford Graham, hdmstr. Fax 798-0299

Indian Head, Charles, Pop. 3,706
Charles County SD
Supt. — See La Plata
Henson MS 600/6-8
3535 Livingston Rd 20640 301-375-8550
Sonia Jones, prin. Fax 375-9216
Lackey HS 1,300/9-12
3000 Chicamuxen Rd 20640 301-743-5431
James Short, prin. Fax 743-9076
Smallwood MS 500/6-8
4990 Indian Head Hwy 20640 301-743-5422
Kathy Perriello, prin. Fax 753-8421

Jessup, Howard, Pop. 7,088
Howard County SD
Supt. — See Ellicott City
Patuxent Valley MS 700/6-8
9151 Vollmerhausen Rd 20794 410-880-5840
Robert Motley, prin. Fax 880-5846

Joppa, Harford, Pop. 12,356
Harford County SD
Supt. — See Bel Air
Joppatowne HS 900/9-12
555 Joppa Farm Rd 21085 410-612-1510
Pamela Zeigler, prin. Fax 612-1528
Magnolia MS 700/6-8
299 Fort Hoyle Rd 21085 410-612-1525
Melissa Mickey, prin. Fax 612-1598

Kensington, Montgomery, Pop. 2,142
Montgomery County SD
Supt. — See Rockville
Einstein HS 1,600/9-12
11135 Newport Mill Rd 20895 301-929-2200
James Fernandez, prin. Fax 962-1016
Newport Mill MS 600/6-8
11311 Newport Mill Rd 20895 301-929-2244
Panagiota Tsonis, prin. Fax 929-2274

Academy of the Holy Cross 600/9-12
4920 Strathmore Ave 20895 301-942-2100
Ann Nichols, prin. Fax 929-6440
Brookewood S 50/1-12
10401 Armory Ave 20895 301-949-7997
Joseph McPherson, hdmstr. Fax 949-0069

Kingsville, Baltimore, Pop. 4,276

Open Bible Christian Academy 300/PK-12
13 Open Bible Way 21087 410-593-9940
William Trautman, hdmstr. Fax 593-9942
Redeemer Classical Christian S 200/PK-12
6415 Mount Vista Rd 21087 410-592-9625
Terry Cellini, admin. Fax 817-6904

Landover, Prince George's, Pop. 22,690
Prince George's County SD
Supt. — See Upper Marlboro
Gholson MS 700/7-8
900 Nalley Rd 20785 301-883-8390
Ebony Cross, prin. Fax 883-8394
Kenmoor MS 700/7-8
2500 Kenmoor Dr 20785 301-925-2300
Maha Fadli, prin. Fax 925-2317

Fortis College Post-Sec.
4351 Garden City Dr 20785 301-459-3650
Sanford-Brown Institute Post-Sec.
8401 Corporate Dr Ste 500 20785 301-918-8221

Lanham, Prince George's, Pop. 9,991

Washington Bible College Post-Sec.
6511 Princess Garden Pkwy 20706 301-552-1400

Lanham Seabrook, Prince George's, Pop. 16,792
Prince George's County SD
Supt. — See Upper Marlboro
DuVal HS 1,600/9-12
9880 Good Luck Rd 20706 301-918-8600
Alice Swift-Howard, prin. Fax 918-8606
Johnson MS 700/7-8
5401 Barker Pl 20706 301-918-8680
Dr. Michael Robinson, prin. Fax 918-8688

Lanham Christian S 200/PK-12
8400 Good Luck Rd 20706 301-552-9102
Rev. Randy Burr, dir. Fax 552-2021

La Plata, Charles, Pop. 8,508
Charles County SD 26,800/PK-12
PO Box 2770 20646 301-932-6610
James Richmond, supt. Fax 932-6651
www.ccboe.com
La Plata HS 1,400/9-12
6035 Radio Station Rd 20646 301-934-1100
Evelyn Arnold, prin. Fax 934-5657
Somers MS 900/6-8
300 Willow Ln 20646 301-934-4663
Stephanie Wesolowski, prin. Fax 934-2982
Other Schools – See Indian Head, Newburg, Pomfret, Waldorf

College of Southern Maryland Post-Sec.
PO Box 910 20646 301-934-2251

Largo, Prince George's, Pop. 10,502
Prince George's County SD
Supt. — See Upper Marlboro
Academy of Health Sciences at PGCC 100/9-9
301 Largo Rd Rm 119 20774 301-583-1593
Dr. Kathy Richard-Andrews, prin.

Prince George's Community College Post-Sec.
301 Largo Rd 20774 301-336-6000
Progressive Christian Academy 100/PK-12
610 Largo Rd 20774 301-812-7777
Rev. Don Massey, hdmstr. Fax 449-0382

Laurel, Prince George's, Pop. 24,374
Howard County SD
Supt. — See Ellicott City
Hammond MS 500/6-8
8110 Aladdin Dr 20723 410-880-5830
Kerry Dufresne, prin. Fax 880-5837
Murray Hill MS 700/6-8
9989 Winter Sun Rd 20723 410-880-5897
Donyall Dickey, prin. Fax 317-5048

Prince George's County SD
Supt. — See Upper Marlboro
Eisenhower MS 800/7-8
13725 Briarwood Dr 20708 301-497-3620
Brenda Chapman, prin. Fax 497-3637
Laurel HS 1,900/9-12
8000 Cherry Ln 20707 301-497-2050
Dwayne Jones, prin. Fax 497-2068

Capitol College Post-Sec.
11301 Springfield Rd 20708 800-950-1992
St. Vincent Pallotti HS 500/9-12
113 Saint Marys Pl 20707 301-725-3228
David McKenzie, prin. Fax 776-4343
Tai Sophia Institute Post-Sec.
7750 Montpelier Rd 20723 410-888-9048

Leonardtown, Saint Mary's, Pop. 2,832
St. Mary's County SD 17,200/PK-12
PO Box 641 20650 301-475-5511
Dr. Michael Martirano, supt. Fax 475-4262
www.smcps.org/
Forrest Career & Technology Center Vo/Tech
24005 Point Lookout Rd 20650 301-475-0242
Theo Cramer, dir. Fax 475-0245
Leonardtown HS 2,000/9-12
23995 Point Lookout Rd 20650 301-475-0200
Maureen Montgomery, prin. Fax 475-0204
Leonardtown MS 900/6-8
24015 Point Lookout Rd 20650 301-475-0230
Lisa Bachner, prin. Fax 475-0237
St. Mary's County Evening HS Adult
23995 Point Lookout Rd 20650 301-475-0200
Elizabeth Beasley, prin.
Other Schools – See Great Mills, Helen, Lexington Park, Morganza

---

St. Mary's Ryken HS 700/9-12
22600 Camp Calvert Rd 20650 301-475-2814
Rick Wood, prin. Fax 373-4195

Lexington Park, Saint Mary's, Pop. 11,085
St. Mary's County SD
Supt. — See Leonardtown
Esperanza MS 800/6-8
22790 Maple Rd 20653 301-863-4016
Jill Snyder-Mills, prin. Fax 863-4020
Fairlead Academy Alt
20833 Great Mills Rd 20653 301-863-4090
Wendy Zimmerman, dean Fax 863-4013
Spring Ridge MS 1,000/6-8
19856 Three Notch Rd 20653 301-863-4031
Angela Fulp, prin. Fax 863-4035

Linthicum Heights, Anne Arundel, Pop. 2,980
Anne Arundel County SD
Supt. — See Annapolis
Lindale MS 800/6-8
415 Andover Rd 21090 410-691-4344
George Lindley, prin. Fax 691-4359

Lonaconing, Allegany, Pop. 1,197
Allegany County SD
Supt. — See Cumberland
Westmar MS 300/6-8
16915 Lower Georges Creek 21539 301-463-5751
Toby Eirich, prin. Fax 359-8049

Lothian, Anne Arundel
Anne Arundel County SD
Supt. — See Annapolis
Southern MS 800/6-8
5235 Solomons Island Rd 20711 410-222-1659
Jason Dykstra, prin. Fax 867-0231

Lusby, Calvert, Pop. 1,786
Calvert County SD
Supt. — See Prince Frederick
Mill Creek MS 600/6-8
12200 Southern Connector 20657 410-535-7824
Rebecca Bowen, prin. Fax 535-7829
Patuxent HS 1,200/9-12
12485 Southern Connector Bl 20657 410-535-7865
Nancy Highsmith, prin. Fax 535-7875
Southern MS 600/6-8
9615 H G Trueman Rd 20657 410-535-7877
Jaime Webster, prin. Fax 535-7879

Lutherville, Baltimore, Pop. 6,362
Baltimore County SD
Supt. — See Towson
Ridgely MS 1,000/6-8
121 E Ridgely Rd 21093 410-887-7650
Susan Evans, prin. Fax 887-7834

Mc Henry, Garrett

Garrett College Post-Sec.
687 Mosser Rd 21541 301-387-3000

Manchester, Carroll, Pop. 4,742
Carroll County SD
Supt. — See Westminster
Manchester Valley HS 800/9-12
3300 Maple Grove Rd 21102 410-386-1673
Randy Clark, prin. Fax 386-1561

Mardela Springs, Wicomico, Pop. 336
Wicomico County SD
Supt. — See Salisbury
Mardela MSHS 700/6-12
24940 Delmar Rd 21837 410-677-5142
Rick Briggs, prin. Fax 677-5166

Marion Station, Somerset
Somerset County SD
Supt. — See Westover
Somerset Promise Academy/Marion Adult Ed 200/Alt
28573 Hudson Corner Rd 21838 410-623-2385
Sidney Hankerson, prin. Fax 623-2114

Marriottsville, Howard
Howard County SD
Supt. — See Ellicott City
Marriotts Ridge HS 1,300/9-12
12100 Woodford Dr 21104 410-313-5568
Adrianne Kaufman, prin. Fax 313-5574
Mount View MS 700/6-8
12101 Woodford Dr 21104 410-313-5545
Kathy McKinley, prin. Fax 313-5551

Chapelgate Christian Academy 400/6-12
2600 Marriottsville Rd 21104 410-442-5888
Robin Van Ness, hdmstr. Fax 442-5820

Middletown, Frederick, Pop. 4,076
Frederick County SD
Supt. — See Frederick
Middletown HS 1,300/9-12
200 Schoolhouse Dr 21769 240-236-7400
Denise Fargo-Devine, prin. Fax 236-7450
Middletown MS 800/6-8
100 Martha Mason St 21769 240-236-4200
Everett Warren, prin. Fax 236-4250

Millersville, Anne Arundel
Anne Arundel County SD
Supt. — See Annapolis
Old Mill HS 2,300/9-12
600 Patriot Ln 21108 410-969-9010
James Todd, prin. Fax 969-1620
Old Mill MS North 900/6-8
610 Patriot Ln 21108 410-969-5950
Sean McElhaney, prin. Fax 969-2612
Old Mill MS South 700/6-8
620 Patriot Ln 21108 410-969-7000
Carolyn Burton-Page, prin. Fax 969-5157

Rockbridge Academy 300/K-12
911 Generals Hwy 21108 410-923-1171
Michael McKenna, hdmstr. Fax 923-6588
Strayer University Post-Sec.
1520 Jabez Run 21108 410-923-4500

Mitchellville, Prince George's, Pop. 10,692
Prince George's County SD
Supt. — See Upper Marlboro
Just MS 800/7-8
1300 Campus Way N 20721 301-808-4040
Kelvin Moore, prin. Fax 808-4050

Woodstream Christian Academy 500/K-12
9800 Lottsford Rd 20721 301-955-1160
Dr. Robert Wingfield, chncllr. Fax 955-1169

Monkton, Baltimore
Baltimore County SD
Supt. — See Towson
Hereford MS 900/6-8
712 Corbett Rd 21111 410-887-7902
Cathryn Walrod, prin. Fax 887-7904

Montgomery Village, Montgomery, Pop. 30,917

Living Grace Christian S 100/K-10
20300 Pleasant Ridge Dr 20886 301-840-9830
Dr. Daniel Switzer, prin. Fax 840-8005

Morganza, Saint Mary's
St. Mary's County SD
Supt. — See Leonardtown
Chopticon HS 1,500/9-12
25390 Colton Point Rd 20660 301-475-0215
Garth Bowling, prin. Fax 475-0222

Mount Airy, Carroll, Pop. 9,125
Carroll County SD
Supt. — See Westminster
Mount Airy MS 600/6-8
102 Watersville Rd 21771 410-751-3554
Karl Streaker, prin. Fax 751-3556

Mount Airy Christian Academy 400/K-12
16700 Old Frederick Rd 21771 410-489-4321
Vicky Webster, admin. Fax 489-4492

Mount Rainier, Prince George's, Pop. 7,916

Washington United Christian Academy 100/PK-12
3501 Bunker Hill Rd 20712 301-807-9397
Abraham Moses, prin. Fax 277-0308

Newark, Worcester, Pop. 331
Worcester County SD 6,700/PK-12
6270 Worcester Hwy 21841 410-632-5000
Jerry Wilson, supt. Fax 632-0364
www.worcesterk12.com/
Worcester Technical HS Vo/Tech
6290 Worcester Hwy 21841 410-632-5050
Caroline Bloxum, prin. Fax 632-5059
Other Schools – See Berlin, Pocomoke City, Snow Hill

Newburg, Charles
Charles County SD
Supt. — See La Plata
Piccowaxen MS 500/6-8
12834 Rock Point Rd 20664 301-934-1977
Kenneth Schroeck, prin. Fax 934-1628

New Carrollton, Prince George's, Pop. 11,918
Prince George's County SD
Supt. — See Upper Marlboro
Carroll MS 800/6-8
6130 Lamont Dr 20784 301-918-8640
David Curry, prin. Fax 918-8646

Hair Academy Post-Sec.
8435 Annapolis Rd 20784 301-459-2509

New Market, Frederick, Pop. 644
Frederick County SD
Supt. — See Frederick
New Market MS 500/6-8
125 W Main St 21774 240-236-4600
Jennifer Bingman, prin. Fax 236-4650

New Windsor, Carroll, Pop. 1,365
Carroll County SD
Supt. — See Westminster
New Windsor MS 400/6-8
1000 Green Valley Rd 21776 410-751-3355
Erin Brilhart, prin. Fax 751-3358

North Bethesda, Montgomery, Pop. 42,508

Georgetown Preparatory S 500/9-12
10900 Rockville Pike 20852 301-493-5000
Jeffrey Jones, hdmstr. Fax 493-6128

North East, Cecil, Pop. 3,496
Cecil County SD
Supt. — See Elkton
Cecil County S of Technology Vo/Tech
900 N East Rd 21901 410-996-6250
Lewis Frbe, prin. Fax 996-6256
North East HS 1,100/9-12
300 Irishtown Rd 21901 410-996-6200
Kathleen Kist, prin. Fax 996-6264
North East MS 700/6-8
200 E Cecil Ave 21901 410-996-6210
Al Volpe, prin. Fax 996-6236
Rising Sun HS 1,200/9-12
100 Tiger Dr 21901 410-658-9115
Anne Gellrich, prin. Fax 658-9121

Cecil College Post-Sec.
1 Seahawk Dr 21901 410-287-1000
Tome S 500/K-12
581 S Maryland Ave 21901 410-287-2050

Oakland, Garrett, Pop. 1,908
Garrett County SD 3,800/PK-12
40 S 2nd St 21550 301-334-8900
Dr. Janet Wilson, supt. Fax 334-7621
www.ga.k12.md.us/
Southern Garrett County HS 800/9-12
345 Oakland Dr 21550 301-334-9447
James Maddy, prin. Fax 334-0962
Southern MS 500/6-8
605 Harvey Winters Dr 21550 301-334-8881
Jason Shank, prin. Fax 334-2315
Southern Evening HS Adult
345 Oakland Dr 21550 301-334-9447
James Maddy, prin. Fax 334-0962
Other Schools – See Accident

Odenton, Anne Arundel, Pop. 35,750
Anne Arundel County SD
Supt. — See Annapolis
Arundel MS 900/6-8
1179 Hammond Ln 21113 410-674-6900
Yolanda Clark, prin. Fax 674-6593

Lighthouse Christian Academy 50/6-12
1460 Berger St 21113 410-305-0701
Rev. Sherise Webb M.Ed., prin. Fax 305-0702

Olney, Montgomery, Pop. 33,044
Montgomery County SD
Supt. — See Rockville
Farquhar MS 600/6-8
16915 Batchellors Forest Rd 20832 301-924-3100
Diane Morris, prin. Fax 924-3152
Parks MS 900/6-8
19200 Olney Mill Rd 20832 301-924-3180
Dr. Donna Jones, prin. Fax 924-3288

Our Lady of Good Counsel HS 1,300/9-12
17301 Old Vic Blvd 20832 240-283-3200
Dr. Paul Barker, pres. Fax 283-3250
Washington Christian Academy 300/K-12
16227 Batchellors Forest Rd 20832 240-390-0429
Dave Hawes, head sch Fax 559-0115

Owings, Calvert, Pop. 2,102
Calvert County SD
Supt. — See Prince Frederick
Northern HS 1,600/9-12
2950 Chaneyville Rd 20736 410-257-1519
Sylvia Lawson, prin. Fax 257-1530
Northern MS 700/6-8
2954 Chaneyville Rd 20736 410-257-1622
Darrel Prioleau, prin. Fax 257-1623
Windy Hill MS 700/6-8
9560 Boyds Turn Rd 20736 410-257-1560
Karen Burnett, prin. Fax 257-4586

Owings Mills, Baltimore, Pop. 29,714
Baltimore County SD
Supt. — See Towson
New Town HS 900/9-12
4931 New Town Blvd 21117 410-887-1614
Sam Mustipher, prin. Fax 654-8897
Owings Mills HS 1,000/9-12
124 Tollgate Rd 21117 410-887-1700
Diane Garbarino, prin. Fax 581-1713

Empire Beauty School Post-Sec.
9616 Reistertown Rd Ste 105 21117 866-232-2771
Garrison Forest S 700/PK-12
300 Garrison Forest Rd 21117 410-363-1500
G. Peter O'Neill, hdmstr. Fax 363-8441
ITT Technical Institute Post-Sec.
11301 Red Run Blvd 21117 443-394-7115
Jemicy S 100/9-12
11202 Garrison Forest Rd 21117 410-653-2700
Ben Shifrin, hdmstr. Fax 753-8085
McDonogh S 1,300/K-12
PO Box 380 21117 410-363-0600
Charles Britton, hdmstr. Fax 581-4777

Oxon Hill, Prince George's, Pop. 17,298
Prince George's County SD
Supt. — See Upper Marlboro
Oxon Hill HS 1,700/9-12
6701 Leyte Dr 20745 301-749-4300
Dr. Jean-Paul Cadet, prin. Fax 749-4320
Potomac HS 1,200/9-12
5211 Boydell Ave 20745 301-702-3900
Robynne Prince, prin. Fax 702-3886

Parkton, Baltimore
Baltimore County SD
Supt. — See Towson
Hereford HS 1,400/9-12
17301 York Rd 21120 410-887-1905
Andrew Last, prin. Fax 887-1944

Parkville, Baltimore, Pop. 30,034
Baltimore County SD
Supt. — See Towson
Parkville HS 1,600/9-12
2600 Putty Hill Ave 21234 410-887-5257
Charlene Dimino, prin. Fax 668-7503

Pasadena, Anne Arundel, Pop. 23,755
Anne Arundel County SD
Supt. — See Annapolis
Chesapeake Bay MS 1,200/6-8
4804 Mountain Rd 21122 410-437-2400
Reginald Farrare, prin. Fax 437-9920
Chesapeake HS 1,800/9-12
4798 Mountain Rd 21122 410-255-9600
Frank Drazan, prin. Fax 360-4364
Fox MS 900/6-8
7922 Outing Ave 21122 410-437-5512
Russell Austin, prin. Fax 360-1511
Northeast HS 1,400/9-12
1121 Duvall Hwy 21122 410-437-6400
Jason Williams, prin. Fax 437-7012

Perry Hall, Baltimore, Pop. 27,923

Perry Hall Christian S 300/PK-12
3919 Schroeder Ave 21128 410-256-4886
Steve Taylor, head sch Fax 256-5451

Perryville, Cecil, Pop. 4,257
Cecil County SD
Supt. — See Elkton
Perryville HS 800/9-12
1696 Perryville Rd 21903 410-996-6000
Charles Helm, prin. Fax 996-6027
Perryville MS 600/6-8
850 Aiken Ave 21903 410-996-6010
Justin Zimmerman, prin. Fax 996-6048

Pocomoke City, Worcester, Pop. 4,103
Worcester County SD
Supt. — See Newark
Pocomoke HS 300/9-12
1817 Old Virginia Rd 21851 410-632-5180
Annette Wallace, prin. Fax 632-5189
Pocomoke MS 500/4-8
800 8th St 21851 410-632-5150
Todd Hall, prin. Fax 632-5159

Pomfret, Charles, Pop. 498
Charles County SD
Supt. — See La Plata
McDonough HS 1,300/9-12
7165 Marshall Corner Rd 20675 301-934-2944
Bradley Snow, prin. Fax 753-8408
Stethem Educational Center 100/Alt
7775 Marshall Corner Rd 20675 301-753-1757
Thomas Weirich, prin. Fax 934-0165

Poolesville, Montgomery, Pop. 4,780
Montgomery County SD
Supt. — See Rockville
Poole MS 400/6-8
17014 Tom Fox Ave 20837 301-972-7979
Charlotte Boucher, prin. Fax 972-7982
Poolesville JSHS 1,200/7-12
17501 W Willard Rd 20837 301-972-7900
Deena Levine, prin. Fax 972-7943

Potomac, Montgomery, Pop. 43,827
Montgomery County SD
Supt. — See Rockville
Churchill HS 2,100/9-12
11300 Gainsborough Rd 20854 301-469-1200
Dr. Joan Benz, prin. Fax 469-1208

Alim Academy 100/PK-12
7917 Montrose Rd 20854 301-340-6713
Fax 340-7339
Bullis S 600/3-12
10601 Falls Rd 20854 301-299-8500
Gerald Boarman Ph.D., hdmstr. Fax 299-9050
Connelly Holy Child S 300/6-12
9029 Bradley Blvd 20854 301-365-0955
Maureen Appel, hdmstr. Fax 365-0981
German S Washington DC 500/PK-12
8617 Chateau Dr 20854 301-365-4400
Waldemar Gries, head sch Fax 365-3905
Heights S 500/3-12
10400 Seven Locks Rd 20854 301-365-4300
Alvaro de Vicente, hdmstr. Fax 365-4303
McLean S of Maryland 400/K-12
8224 Lochinver Ln 20854 301-299-8277
Darlene Pierro, head sch Fax 299-1639
St. Andrew's Episcopal S 400/4-12
8804 Postoak Rd 20854 301-983-5200
Robert Kosasky, hdmstr. Fax 983-4710

Prince Frederick, Calvert, Pop. 2,434
Calvert County SD 16,800/PK-12
1305 Dares Beach Rd 20678 410-535-1700
Dr. Jack Smith, supt. Fax 535-7476
www.calvertnet.k12.md.us
Calvert Career Ctr Vo/Tech
330 Dorsey Rd 20678 410-535-7450
Mark Wilding, prin. Fax 535-7418
Calvert Country S 100/Alt
1350 Dares Beach Rd 20678 410-535-7300
Diane Black, prin. Fax 535-7303
Calvert HS 1,200/9-12
520 Fox Run Blvd 20678 410-535-7330
Susan Johnson, prin. Fax 535-7200
Calvert MS 500/6-8
655 Chesapeake Blvd 20678 410-535-7355
Bruce Hutchinson, prin. Fax 535-7430
Other Schools – See Huntingtown, Lusby, Owings

Princess Anne, Somerset, Pop. 3,212
Somerset County SD
Supt. — See Westover
Washington Academy/HS 600/8-12
10902 Old Princess Anne Rd 21853 410-651-0480
William Johnson, prin. Fax 651-0235

University of Maryland Eastern Shore Post-Sec.
11868 Academic Oval 21853 410-651-2200

Pylesville, Harford, Pop. 684
Harford County SD
Supt. — See Bel Air
North Harford HS 1,400/9-12
211 Pylesville Rd 21132 410-638-3650
W. Edward Herbold, prin. Fax 638-3666
North Harford MS 1,100/6-8
112 Pylesville Rd 21132 410-638-3658
Karl Wickman, prin. Fax 638-3669

Randallstown, Baltimore, Pop. 31,696
Baltimore County SD
Supt. — See Towson
Deer Park Magnet MS 1,200/6-8
9830 Winands Rd 21133 410-887-0726
Delores Tedeschi-Butler, prin. Fax 887-0704
Randallstown HS 1,100/9-12
4000 Offutt Rd 21133 410-887-0748
John Ward, prin. Fax 887-0759

Reisterstown, Baltimore, Pop. 25,217
Baltimore County SD
Supt. — See Towson
Franklin HS 1,600/9-12
12000 Reisterstown Rd 21136 410-887-1119
Patrick McCusker, prin. Fax 833-4434
Franklin MS 1,300/6-8
10 Cockeys Mill Rd 21136 410-887-1114
Charlyn Maul, prin. Fax 517-2548

Forbush S at Glyndon 100/PK-12
407 Central Ave 21136 410-517-5400
James Truscello, dir. Fax 517-5600
Maryland Beauty Academy Post-Sec.
152 Chartley Dr 21136 410-517-0442

Ridgely, Caroline, Pop. 1,595
Caroline County SD
Supt. — See Denton
Caroline Career & Technology Ctr Vo/Tech
10855 Central Ave 21660 410-479-0100
Eugene Smith, prin. Fax 479-1308
North Caroline HS 1,100/9-12
10990 River Rd 21660 410-479-2332
Conrad Judy, prin. Fax 479-2743

Rising Sun, Cecil, Pop. 2,742
Cecil County SD
Supt. — See Elkton
Rising Sun MS 700/6-8
289 Pearl St 21911 410-658-5535
Richard Edwards, prin. Fax 658-9173

Riverdale, Prince George's, Pop. 5,120
Prince George's County SD
Supt. — See Upper Marlboro
Parkdale HS 2,200/9-12
6001 Good Luck Rd 20737 301-513-5700
Cheryl Logan, prin. Fax 513-5209
Wirt MS 800/6-8
62nd Pl and Tuckerman St 20737 301-985-1720
Prentice Christian, prin. Fax 985-1440

Rock Hall, Kent, Pop. 1,286
Kent County SD 2,100/PK-12
5608 Boundary Ave 21661 410-778-1595
Dr. Karen Couch, supt. Fax 778-6193
www.kent.k12.md.us
Other Schools – See Chestertown, Worton

Rockville, Montgomery, Pop. 59,311
Montgomery County SD 142,100/PK-12
850 Hungerford Dr 20850 301-279-3381
Dr. Joshua Starr, supt. Fax 279-3205
www.montgomeryschoolsmd.org
Cabin John MS 900/6-8
10701 Gainsborough Rd 20854 301-469-1150
Dr. Paulette Smith, prin. Fax 469-1003
Fleet Street MS Alt
14501 Avery Rd 20853 301-517-5860
Carthel Russell, coord. Fax 517-5922
Frost MS 1,100/6-8
9201 Scott Dr 20850 301-279-3949
Dr. Joey Jones, prin. Fax 279-3956
Hoover MS 1,000/6-8
6300 Tilden Ln 20852 301-469-1010
Billie-Jean Bensen, prin. Fax 469-1013
Magruder HS 1,800/9-12
5939 Muncaster Mill Rd 20855 301-840-4600
Leroy Evans, prin. Fax 840-4617

Montgomery HS 2,000/9-12
250 Richard Montgomery Dr 20852 301-610-8000
Dr. Nelson McLeod, prin. Fax 279-8428
Needwood Academy Alt
14501 Avery Rd 20853 301-279-4912
Melanie Humphries, coord. Fax 279-4908
Parkland MS 800/6-8
4610 W Frankfort Dr 20853 301-438-5700
Dr. Benjamin OuYang, prin. Fax 460-2699
Phoenix at Needwood Academy Alt
14501 Avery Rd 20853 301-279-4925
Patti Jenkins, lead tchr. Fax 840-4539
Randolph Academy Alt
14501 Avery Rd 20853 301-517-8616
Andrea Carter, coord. Fax 517-5068
Redland MS 600/6-8
6505 Muncaster Mill Rd 20855 301-840-4680
Robert Sinclair, prin. Fax 670-2231
Rockville HS 1,300/9-12
2100 Baltimore Rd 20851 301-517-8105
Dr. Debra Munk, prin. Fax 517-8288
Tilden MS 500/7-8
11211 Old Georgetown Rd 20852 301-230-5930
Irina LaGrange, prin. Fax 230-5991
West MS 1,000/6-8
651 Great Falls Rd 20850 301-279-3979
Nanette Poirier, prin. Fax 517-8216
Wood MS 800/6-8
14615 Bauer Dr 20853 301-460-2150
Eugenia Dawson, prin. Fax 460-2104
Wootton HS 2,400/9-12
2100 Wootton Pkwy 20850 301-279-8550
Dr. Michael Doran, prin. Fax 279-8569
Other Schools – See Bethesda, Burtonsville, Clarksburg, Damascus, Gaithersburg, Germantown, Kensington, Olney, Poolesville, Potomac, Sandy Spring, Silver Spring

---

Berman Hebrew Academy 700/PK-12
13300 Arctic Ave 20853 301-962-9400
Dr. Joshua Levisohn, hdmstr. Fax 962-3991
Montgomery College Post-Sec.
51 Mannakee St 20850 240-567-5000
Montrose Christian S 300/PK-12
5100 Randolph Rd 20852 301-770-5335
Ken Fentress, chncllr. Fax 871-7345
Omega Studios School of Applied Arts Post-Sec.
5609 Fishers Ln 20852 301-230-9100
Smith Jewish Day S 700/7-12
11710 Hunters Ln 20852 301-881-1400
Rabbi Mitchel Malkus, head sch Fax 230-1986
Strayer University Post-Sec.
4 Research Pl Ste 100 20850 301-548-5500

Saint Marys City, Saint Mary's, Pop. 3,200

St. Mary's College of Maryland Post-Sec.
18952 E Fisher Rd 20686 240-895-2000

Saint Michaels, Talbot, Pop. 1,017
Talbot County SD
Supt. — See Easton
Saint Michaels MSHS 400/7-12
200 Seymour Ave 21663 410-745-2852
Helga Einhorn, prin. Fax 745-9939

Salisbury, Wicomico, Pop. 29,461
Wicomico County SD 14,400/PK-12
PO Box 1538 21802 410-677-4400
Dr. John Fredericksen, supt. Fax 677-4444
www.wcboe.org
Bennett HS 1,300/9-12
300 E College Ave 21804 410-677-5141
Steve Grudis, prin. Fax 677-5126
Bennett MS 900/6-8
200 E College Ave 21804 410-677-5140
Liza Hastings, prin. Fax 677-5133
Choices Alt
28929 Adventist Dr 21801 410-677-5220
Kelly Morris-Springston, prin. Fax 677-5220
Parkside HS 1,100/9-12
1015 Beaglin Park Dr 21804 410-677-5143
Micah Stauffer, prin. Fax 677-5104
Salisbury MS 800/6-8
607 Morris St 21801 410-677-5149
Amy Eskridge, prin. Fax 677-5122
Wicomico HS 1,100/9-12
201 Long Ave 21804 410-677-5146
Don Brady, prin. Fax 677-5151
Wicomico MS 700/6-8
635 E Main St 21804 410-677-5145
Lillie Giddens, prin. Fax 677-5197
Evening HS Adult
201 Long Ave 21804 410-677-4537
David Harner, admin. Fax 677-4418
Other Schools – See Mardela Springs

Del-Mar-Va Beauty Academy Post-Sec.
111 Milford St 21804 410-742-7929
Salisbury Christian S 600/PK-12
807 Parker Rd 21804 410-546-0661
Dr. James Fox, hdmstr. Fax 546-4674
Salisbury School of Maryland 400/PK-12
6279 Hobbs Rd 21804 410-742-4464
James Landi, hdmstr. Fax 546-2310
Salisbury University Post-Sec.
1101 Camden Ave 21801 410-543-6000
Wor-Wic Community College Post-Sec.
32000 Campus Dr 21804 410-334-2800

Sandy Spring, Montgomery, Pop. 3,092
Montgomery County SD
Supt. — See Rockville
Sherwood HS 2,100/9-12
300 Olney Sandy Spring Rd 20860 301-924-3200
William Gregory, prin. Fax 924-3220

Sandy Spring Friends S 600/PK-12
16923 Norwood Rd 20860 301-774-7455
Thomas Gibian, hdmstr. Fax 924-1115

Severn, Anne Arundel, Pop. 42,378
Anne Arundel County SD
Supt. — See Annapolis
Center of Applied Technology-North Vo/Tech
800 Stevenson Rd 21144 410-969-3100
Dan Schaffhauser, prin. Fax 696-3684

Archbishop Spalding HS 1,200/9-12
8080 New Cut Rd 21144 410-969-9105
Lewis VanWambeke, prin. Fax 969-1026

Severna Park, Anne Arundel, Pop. 37,032
Anne Arundel County SD
Supt. — See Annapolis
Severna Park HS 1,900/9-12
60 Robinson Rd 21146 410-544-0900
Patrick Bathras, prin. Fax 647-2978
Severna Park MS 1,400/6-8
450 Jumpers Hole Rd 21146 410-647-7900
Sharon Hansen, prin. Fax 431-5376
Severna Park Evening HS Adult
60 Robinson Rd 21146 410-544-0182
Sonja Davenport, admin.

Severn S 600/6-12
201 Water St 21146 410-647-7700
Douglas Lagarde, hdmstr. Fax 544-9455

Silver Spring, Montgomery, Pop. 69,258
Montgomery County SD
Supt. — See Rockville
Argyle MS 800/6-8
2400 Bel Pre Rd 20906 301-460-2400
Robert Dodd, prin. Fax 460-2423
Blair HS 2,800/9-12
51 University Blvd E 20901 301-649-2800
Renay Johnson, prin. Fax 649-2830
Blake HS 1,900/9-12
300 Norwood Rd 20905 301-879-1300
Christopher Berry, prin. Fax 879-1306
Briggs-Chaney MS 900/6-8
1901 Rainbow Dr 20905 301-989-6000
Dr. Tamitha Campbell, prin. Fax 989-6020
Eastern MS 800/6-8
300 University Blvd E 20901 301-650-6650
Casey Crouse, prin. Fax 650-6657
Edison HS of Technology Vo/Tech
12501 Dalewood Dr 20906 301-929-2175
Carlos Hamlin, prin. Fax 929-2177
Kennedy HS 1,600/9-12
1901 Randolph Rd 20902 301-929-2100
Dr. Eric Minus, prin. Fax 929-2240
Key MS 900/6-8
910 Schindler Dr 20903 301-422-5600
Myriam Rogers, prin. Fax 434-1375
Lee MS 600/6-8
11800 Monticello Ave 20902 301-649-8100
Joseph Rubens, prin. Fax 649-8110
Loiederman MS 800/6-8
12701 Goodhill Rd 20906 301-929-2282
Nicole Sosik, prin. Fax 962-5993
Northwood HS 1,400/9-12
919 University Blvd W 20901 301-649-8088
Henry Johnson, prin. Fax 649-8285
Silver Spring International MS 800/6-8
313 Wayne Ave 20910 301-650-6544
John Haas, prin. Fax 562-5244
Sligo MS 500/6-8
1401 Dennis Ave 20902 301-649-8121
Richard Rhodes, prin. Fax 649-8145
Springbrook HS 1,700/9-12
201 Valley Brook Dr 20904 301-989-5700
Samuel Rivera, prin. Fax 622-1875
Takoma Park MS 800/6-8
7611 Piney Branch Rd 20910 301-650-6444
Mildred Charley-Greene, prin. Fax 650-6430
Wheaton HS 1,200/9-12
12601 Dalewood Dr 20906 301-929-2050
Kevin Lowndes, prin. Fax 929-2081
White Oak MS 600/6-8
12201 New Hampshire Ave 20904 301-989-5780
Virginia de los Santos, prin. Fax 989-5696

Barrie S 300/PK-12
13500 Layhill Rd 20906 301-576-2800
Charles Abelmann, hdmstr. Fax 576-2803
Columbia College Post-Sec.
12125 Veirs Mill Rd 20906 301-929-0565
Everest Institute Post-Sec.
8757 Georgia Ave Ste 650 20910 301-495-4400
Griggs International Academy Post-Sec.
PO Box 4437 20914 301-680-6570
Griggs University Post-Sec.
PO Box 4437 20914 301-680-6570
Holy Cross Hospital Post-Sec.
1500 Forest Glen Rd 20910 301-905-1216
Medtech College Post-Sec.
1100 Wayne Ave Ste 100 20910 301-608-2300
Montgomery Beauty School Post-Sec.
8736 Arliss St 20901 301-459-2509
National Labor College Post-Sec.
1000 New Hampshire Ave 20903 301-431-6400
Nora S 100/9-12
955 Sligo Ave 20910 301-495-6672
Dave Mullen, hdmstr. Fax 495-7829
Yeshiva College of the Nations Capital Post-Sec.
1216 Arcola Ave 20902 301-593-2534
Yeshiva of Greater Washington - Boys Div 100/7-12
1216 Arcola Ave 20902 301-649-7077
Yeshiva of Greater Washington-Girls Div 200/7-12
2010 Linden Ln 20910 301-962-5111

Smithsburg, Washington, Pop. 2,924
Washington County SD
Supt. — See Hagerstown
Smithsburg HS 800/9-12
66 N Main St 21783 301-766-8337
Karim Shortridge, prin. Fax 824-2617
Smithsburg MS 700/6-8
68 N Main St 21783 301-766-8353
Dr. Stephen Tarason, prin. Fax 824-5147

Snow Hill, Worcester, Pop. 2,063
Worcester County SD
Supt. — See Newark
Snow Hill HS 300/9-12
305 S Church St 21863 410-632-5270
Tom Davis, prin. Fax 632-5279
Snow Hill MS 400/4-8
522 Coulbourne Ln 21863 410-632-5240
Aaron Dale, prin. Fax 632-5249

Spencerville, Montgomery, Pop. 1,516

Spencerville Adventist Academy 400/PK-12
2502 Spencerville Rd 20868 301-421-9101
Brian Kittleson, prin. Fax 421-0007

Springdale, Prince George's, Pop. 2,957
Prince George's County SD
Supt. — See Upper Marlboro
Flowers HS 2,400/9-12
10001 Ardwick Ardmore Rd 20774 301-636-8000
Gorman Brown, prin. Fax 636-8008

Stevenson, Baltimore

St. Timothy's S 200/9-12
8400 Greenspring Ave 21153 410-486-7400
Randy Stevens, hdmstr. Fax 486-1167
Stevenson University Post-Sec.
1525 Greenspring Valley Rd 21153 410-486-7000

Stevensville, Queen Anne's, Pop. 6,708
Queen Anne's County SD
Supt. — See Centreville
Kent Island HS 1,200/9-12
900 Love Point Rd 21666 410-604-2070
John Schrecongost, prin. Fax 604-2089
Matapeake MS 400/6-8
671 Romancoke Rd 21666 410-643-7330
Angela Holocker, prin. Fax 643-7445
Stevensville MS 500/6-8
610 Main St 21666 410-643-3194
Kevin Kintop, prin. Fax 643-3046

Sudlersville, Queen Anne's, Pop. 476
Queen Anne's County SD
Supt. — See Centreville
Sudlersville MS 300/6-8
600 Charles St 21668 410-438-3151
Leigh Veditz, prin. Fax 438-3489

Eastern Shore Junior Academy 50/PK-12
407 Dudley Corners Rd 21668 410-505-4074
Fax 438-3778

Suitland, Prince George's, Pop. 25,409
Prince George's County SD
Supt. — See Upper Marlboro
Drew-Freeman MS 800/7-8
2600 Brooks Dr 20746 301-817-0900
Dr. Marla Philpot-Dean, prin. Fax 817-0915
Green Valley Academy 100/Alt
2001 Shadyside Ave 20746 301-817-3100
Gordon Libby, prin.

Sykesville, Carroll, Pop. 4,375
Carroll County SD
Supt. — See Westminster
Century HS 1,200/9-12
355 Ronsdale Rd 21784 410-386-4400
Andrew Cockley, prin. Fax 386-4413
Oklahoma Road MS 700/6-8
6300 Oklahoma Rd 21784 410-751-3600
David Watkins, prin. Fax 751-3604
South Carroll HS 1,100/9-12
1300 W Old Liberty Rd 21784 410-751-3575
Jeff Hopkins, prin. Fax 751-3587
Sykesville MS 800/6-8
7301 Springfield Ave 21784 410-751-3545
Ralph Billings, prin. Fax 751-3573

Takoma Park, Montgomery, Pop. 16,094

Don Bosco Cristo Rey HS 300/9-12
1010 Larch Ave 20912 301-891-4750
Larry Savoy, prin. Fax 270-1459
Montgomery College Post-Sec.
7600 Takoma Ave 20912 240-567-5000
Takoma Academy 200/9-12
8120 Carroll Ave 20912 301-434-4700
Carla Thrower, prin. Fax 434-4814
Washington Adventist Hospital Post-Sec.
7600 Carroll Ave 20912 301-891-7600
Washington Adventist University Post-Sec.
7600 Flower Ave 20912 301-891-4000

Taneytown, Carroll, Pop. 6,558
Carroll County SD
Supt. — See Westminster
Northwest MS 500/6-8
99 Kings Dr 21787 410-751-3270
Angie McCauslin, prin. Fax 751-3275

Temple Hills, Prince George's, Pop. 7,677
Prince George's County SD
Supt. — See Upper Marlboro
Crossland HS 1,400/9-12
6901 Temple Hill Rd 20748 301-449-4800
Charles Thomas, prin. Fax 449-4801

Marshall MS 800/6-8
4909 Brinkley Rd 20748 301-702-7540
Fletcher James, prin. Fax 702-7555
Stoddert MS 700/6-8
2501 Olson St 20748 301-702-7500
Hillary Garner, prin. Fax 702-7515
Crossland Evening HS Adult
6901 Temple Hill Rd 20748 301-449-4994
William Kitchings, prin. Fax 449-2126

Thurmont, Frederick, Pop. 6,091
Frederick County SD
Supt. — See Frederick
Catoctin HS 1,000/9-12
14745 Sabillasville Rd 21788 240-236-8100
Bernard Quesada, prin. Fax 236-8101
Thurmont MS 700/6-8
408 E Main St 21788 240-236-5100
Jennifer Powell, prin. Fax 236-5101

Timonium, Baltimore, Pop. 9,759
Baltimore County SD
Supt. — See Towson
Dulaney HS 1,900/9-12
255 E Padonia Rd 21093 410-887-7633
Lynda Whitlock, prin. Fax 666-8915

R. Paul Academy of Cosmetology Arts/Sci Post-Sec.
1811 York Rd Ste B 21093 410-252-4481

Towson, Baltimore, Pop. 54,024
Baltimore County SD 104,100/PK-12
6901 N Charles St 21204 410-887-4554
S. Dallas Dance Ph.D., supt. Fax 887-4309
www.bcps.org
Other Schools – See Baltimore, Catonsville, Cockeysville, Lutherville, Monkton, Owings Mills, Parkton, Parkville, Randallstown, Reisterstown, Timonium

---

Baltimore Lutheran HS 200/6-12
1145 Concordia Dr 21286 410-825-2323
Alan Freeman, admin. Fax 825-2506
Loyola Blakefield HS 1,000/6-12
500 Chestnut Ave 21204 410-823-0601
Anthony Day, prin. Fax 823-5277
Medix School Post-Sec.
700 York Rd 21204 410-337-5155
Notre Dame Preparatory S 800/6-12
815 Hampton Ln 21286 410-825-0590
Laurie Jones, prin. Fax 321-4809
TESST College of Technology Post-Sec.
803 Glen Eagles Ct 21286 410-296-5350
Towson State University Post-Sec.
8000 York Rd 21252 410-704-2000

Union Bridge, Carroll, Pop. 956
Carroll County SD
Supt. — See Westminster
Key HS 1,100/9-12
3825 Bark Hill Rd 21791 410-751-3320
John Baugher, prin. Fax 751-3325

Upper Marlboro, Prince George's, Pop. 606
Prince George's County SD 123,800/PK-12
14201 School Ln 20772 301-952-6000
Dr. Alvin Crawley, supt. Fax 627-6576
www.pgcps.org
Douglass HS 1,100/9-12
8000 Croom Rd 20772 301-952-2400
Rudolph Saunders, prin. Fax 627-3377
Kettering MS 600/6-8
65 Herrington Dr 20774 301-808-4060
Amin Salaam, prin. Fax 808-5920
Largo HS 1,300/9-12
505 Largo Rd 20774 301-808-8880
Angelique Marcus, prin. Fax 808-4066
Madison MS 900/7-8
7300 Woodyard Rd 20772 301-599-2422
Courtney King, prin. Fax 599-2562
Wise HS 2,700/9-12
12650 Brooke Ln 20772 301-780-2100
Carletta Marrow, prin. Fax 780-2112
Other Schools – See Accokeek, Adelphi, Beltsville, Bladensburg, Bowie, Brandywine, Capitol Heights, Cheltenham, Clinton, Forestville, Fort Washington, Greenbelt, Hyattsville, Landover, Lanham Seabrook, Largo, Laurel, Mitchellville, New Carrollton, Oxon Hill, Riverdale, Springdale, Suitland, Temple Hills

---

Clinton Christian S 600/PK-12
6707 Woodyard Rd 20772 301-599-9600
Carlos Williams, prin. Fax 599-9603
Excellence Christian S 200/PK-12
9010 Frank Tippett Rd 20772 301-868-1873
Erika Lee Ed.D., prin. Fax 868-1877
Riverdale Baptist S 800/PK-12
1133 Largo Rd 20774 301-249-7000
Eric Harrison, head sch Fax 249-3425

Waldorf, Charles, Pop. 64,982
Charles County SD
Supt. — See La Plata
Davis MS 1,100/6-8
2495 Davis Rd 20603 301-638-0858
Wendell Martin, prin. Fax 638-3562
Hanson MS 800/6-8
12350 Vivian Adams Dr 20601 301-645-4520
Kathy-Lynn Kiessling, prin. Fax 870-1182
Mattawoman MS 1,000/6-8
10145 Berry Rd 20603 301-645-7708
Douglass Dolan, prin. Fax 638-0043
North Point HS 2,200/9-12
2500 Davis Rd 20603 301-753-1759
Kimberly Hill, prin. Fax 885-2347
Stoddert MS 700/6-8
2040 Saint Thomas Dr 20602 301-645-1334
Robert Babiak, prin. Fax 870-1183
Stone HS 1,500/9-12
3785 Leonardtown Rd 20601 301-645-2601
Michael Meiser, prin. Fax 932-4278
Westlake HS 1,500/9-12
3300 Middletown Rd 20603 301-645-8857
Chrystal Benson, prin. Fax 932-8583

Aaron's Academy of Beauty Post-Sec.
11690 Doolittle Dr 20602 301-645-3681
Grace Christian Academy of Maryland 400/PK-12
13000 Zekiah Dr 20601 301-645-0406
Wayne Knode, dir. Fax 645-7463

Walkersville, Frederick, Pop. 5,663
Frederick County SD
Supt. — See Frederick
Walkersville HS 1,200/9-12
81 W Frederick St 21793 240-236-7200
Michael Concepcion, prin. Fax 236-7250
Walkersville MS 800/6-8
55 W Frederick St 21793 240-236-4400
Jamie Aliveto, prin. Fax 236-4401

Westminster, Carroll, Pop. 18,162
Carroll County SD 27,200/PK-12
125 N Court St 21157 410-751-3000
Stephen Guthrie, supt. Fax 751-3030
www.carrollk12.org/
Carroll County Career & Tech Center Vo/Tech
1229 Washington Rd 21157 410-751-3669
William Eckles, prin. Fax 751-3677
Gateway S 100/Alt
45 Kate Wagner Rd 21157 410-751-3691
Ruthanne Kenney, admin. Fax 751-3687
Westminster East MS 700/6-8
121 Longwell Ave 21157 410-751-3656
Christian Roemer, prin. Fax 751-3660
Westminster HS 1,700/9-12
1225 Washington Rd 21157 410-751-3630
Kenneth Goncz, prin. Fax 751-3640
Westminster West MS 1,000/6-8
60 Monroe St 21157 410-751-3661
Amy Gromada, prin. Fax 751-3667
Winters Mill HS 1,200/9-12
560 Gorsuch Rd 21157 410-386-1500
Eric King, prin. Fax 386-1513
Other Schools – See Eldersburg, Hampstead, Manchester, Mount Airy, New Windsor, Sykesville, Taneytown, Union Bridge

---

Carroll Christian S 200/PK-12
550 Baltimore Blvd 21157 410-876-3838
Fax 876-7766
Carroll Community College Post-Sec.
1601 Washington Rd 21157 410-386-8000
Faith Christian S 100/PK-12
30 N Cranberry Rd 21157 410-848-8875
Dr. Susanna Oliver, prin. Fax 848-9051
McDaniel College Post-Sec.
2 College Hl 21157 410-848-7000

Westover, Somerset
Somerset County SD 3,100/PK-12
7982A Tawes Campus Dr 21871 410-651-1616
Dr. Marjorie E. Miles, supt. Fax 651-2931
www.somerset.k12.md.us
Tawes Technology & Career Center Vo/Tech
7982 Tawes Campus Dr 21871 410-651-2285
Glen Ennis, prin. Fax 651-3154
Other Schools – See Crisfield, Marion Station, Princess Anne

Holly Grove Christian S 500/PK-12
7317 Mennonite Church Rd 21871 410-957-0222
Michael Rohrer, prin. Fax 957-4250

White Plains, Charles, Pop. 3,560

Southern Maryland Christian Academy 300/PK-12
PO Box 1668 20695 301-870-2550
Matthew Gaines, admin. Fax 934-2855

Williamsport, Washington, Pop. 2,115
Washington County SD
Supt. — See Hagerstown
Springfield MS 800/6-8
334 Sunset Ave 21795 301-766-8389
Jennifer Ruppenthal, prin. Fax 766-8401
Williamsport HS 900/9-12
5 S Clifton Dr 21795 301-766-8423
April Bishop, prin. Fax 223-9610

Gateway Christian Academy 100/PK-12
PO Box 590 21795 301-582-4595
Renee Wyand, prin. Fax 223-5972

Worton, Kent, Pop. 248
Kent County SD
Supt. — See Rock Hall
Kent County HS 600/9-12
25301 Lambs Meadow Rd 21678 410-778-4540
Tracey Williams, prin. Fax 778-4266

Wye Mills, Talbot

Chesapeake College Post-Sec.
PO Box 8 21679 410-822-5400

MASSACHUSETTS

MASSACHUSETTS DEPARTMENT OF EDUCATION
75 Pleasant St, Malden 02148-4906
Telephone 781-388-3000
Fax 781-388-3770
Website http://www.doe.mass.edu

Commissioner of Education Mitchell Chester

MASSACHUSETTS BOARD OF EDUCATION
75 Pleasant St, Malden 02148-4906

Chairperson Maura Banta

PUBLIC, PRIVATE AND CATHOLIC SECONDARY SCHOOLS

Abington, Plymouth, Pop. 15,563
Abington SD 1,400/PK-12
171 Adams St 02351 781-982-2150
Peter Schafer, supt. Fax 982-2157
www.abingtonps.info
Abington HS 500/9-12
201 Gliniewicz Way 02351 781-982-2160
Teresa Sullivan-Cruz, prin. Fax 982-0061
Frolio MS 400/7-8
1071 Washington St 02351 781-982-2170
Roseanne Kurposka, prin. Fax 982-2173

Acton, Middlesex
Acton-Boxborough Regional SD 2,900/7-12
16 Charter Rd 01720 978-264-4700
Stephen Mills, supt. Fax 264-3340
ab.mec.edu
Acton-Boxborough Regional HS 2,000/9-12
36 Charter Rd 01720 978-264-4700
Alexandra Callen, prin. Fax 264-3345
Grey JHS 1,000/7-8
16 Charter Rd 01720 978-264-4700
Andrew Shen, prin. Fax 264-3343

Acushnet, Bristol, Pop. 3,170
Acushnet SD 1,000/PK-8
708 Middle Rd Ste 1 02743 508-998-0260
Stephen Donovan, supt. Fax 998-0262
www.acushnet.k12.ma.us
Ford MS 500/5-8
708 Middle Rd 02743 508-998-0265
Christopher Green, prin. Fax 998-7316

Agawam, Hampden, Pop. 28,599
Agawam SD
Supt. — See Feeding Hills
Agawam HS 1,300/9-12
760 Cooper St 01001 413-821-0521
Steven Lemanski, prin. Fax 821-0536

Amesbury, Essex, Pop. 12,109
Amesbury SD 2,400/PK-12
5 Highland St 01913 978-388-0507
Michele Robinson, supt. Fax 388-8315
www.amesburyma.gov
Amesbury HS 600/9-12
5 Highland St 01913 978-388-4800
Norman Hammond, prin. Fax 388-3393
Amesbury MS 800/5-8
220 Main St 01913 978-388-0515
Michael Curry, prin. Fax 388-1626

Amherst, Hampshire, Pop. 17,824
Amherst-Pelham SD 1,600/7-12
170 Chestnut St 01002 413-362-1810
Maria Geryk, supt. Fax 549-6108
www.arps.org/
Amherst Regional HS 1,100/9-12
21 Mattoon St 01002 413-362-1700
Mark Jackson, prin. Fax 549-9704
Amherst Regional MS 500/7-8
170 Chestnut St 01002 413-362-1850
Betsy Dinger, prin. Fax 549-9812

Amherst College Post-Sec.
PO Box 5000 01002 413-542-2000
Hampshire College Post-Sec.
893 West St 01002 413-549-4600
University of Massachusetts 01003 Post-Sec.
413-545-0111

Andover, Essex, Pop. 8,592
Andover SD 6,200/PK-12
36 Bartlet St 01810 978-623-8501
Dr. Marinel McGrath, supt. Fax 623-8505
www.aps1.net
Andover HS 1,800/9-12
80 Shawsheen Rd 01810 978-623-8632
Christopher Lord, prin. Fax 623-8636
Andover West MS 500/6-8
98 Shawsheen Rd 01810 978-623-8700
Steve Murray, prin. Fax 623-8720
Doherty MS 600/6-8
50 Bartlet St 01810 978-623-8750
Robin Wilson, prin. Fax 623-8770
Wood Hill MS 400/6-8
11 Cross St 01810 978-623-8925
Patrick Bucco, prin. Fax 623-8929

Greater Lawrence Technical SD
57 River Rd 01810 978-686-0194
John Lavoie, supt. Fax 687-6209
www.glts.net
Greater Lawrence Technical S Vo/Tech
57 River Rd 01810 978-686-0194
Elizabeth Freedman, prin. Fax 687-6209

Massachusetts School of Law at Andover Post-Sec.
500 Federal St 01810 978-681-0800
Phillips Academy 9-12
180 Main St 01810 978-749-4000
John Palfrey, head sch Fax 749-4068

Arlington, Middlesex, Pop. 41,750
Arlington SD 4,800/PK-12
869 Massachusetts Ave 02476 781-316-3523
Kathleen Bodie, supt. Fax 316-3509
www.arlington.k12.ma.us
Arlington HS 1,200/9-12
869 Massachusetts Ave 02476 781-316-3591
Mary Villano, prin. Fax 316-3504
Ottoson MS 1,100/6-8
63 Acton St 02476 781-316-3744
Timothy Ruggere, prin. Fax 641-5436

Arlington Catholic HS 800/9-12
16 Medford St 02474 781-646-7770
Stephen Biagioni, prin. Fax 648-8345

Ashburnham, Worcester
Ashburnham-Westminster Regional SD 2,300/PK-12
11 Oakmont Dr 01430 978-827-1434
Ralph Hicks, supt. Fax 827-5969
www.awrsd.org
Oakmont Regional HS 700/9-12
9 Oakmont Dr 01430 978-827-5907
David Uminski, prin. Fax 827-1413
Overlook MS 600/6-8
10 Oakmont Dr 01430 978-827-1425
Philip Saisa, prin. Fax 827-1423

Cushing Academy 400/9-12
PO Box 8000 01430 978-827-7000
Dr. James Tracy, hdmstr. Fax 827-7500

Ashland, Middlesex, Pop. 12,066
Ashland SD 2,500/PK-12
87 W Union St 01721 508-881-0150
Brooke Clenchy, supt. Fax 881-0161
www.ashland.k12.ma.us
Ashland HS 700/9-12
65 E Union St 01721 508-881-0177
James Adams, prin. Fax 881-0186
Ashland MS 600/6-8
87 W Union St 01721 508-881-0167
David DiGirolamo, prin. Fax 881-0169

Athol, Worcester, Pop. 8,127
Athol-Royalston SD 1,500/PK-12
PO Box 968 01331 978-249-2400
Anthony Polito, supt. Fax 249-2402
www.arrsd.org/
Athol HS 400/9-12
2363 Main St 01331 978-249-2435
Brian Beck, prin. Fax 249-7217
Athol-Royalston MS 500/5-8
1062 Pleasant St 01331 978-249-2430
William Chiasson, prin. Fax 249-0055

Attleboro, Bristol, Pop. 42,657
Attleboro SD 5,900/PK-12
100 Rathbun Willard Dr 02703 508-222-0012
Pia Durkin Ph.D., supt. Fax 223-1577
www.attleboroschools.com
Attleboro HS 1,700/9-12
100 Rathbun Willard Dr 02703 508-222-5150
William Runey, prin. Fax 223-1579
Brennan MS 600/5-8
320 Rathbun Willard Dr 02703 508-222-6260
Karen Saltzman, prin. Fax 223-1555
Coelho MS 600/5-8
99 Brown St 02703 508-761-7551
Andrew Boles, prin. Fax 399-6506
Wamsutta MS 600/5-8
300 Locust St 02703 508-223-1540
Karol Coffin, prin. Fax 226-2087

Bishop Feehan HS 1,000/9-12
70 Holcott Dr 02703 508-226-6223
Dr. George Milot, prin. Fax 226-7696

Auburn, Worcester, Pop. 15,005
Auburn SD 2,300/PK-12
5 West St 01501 508-832-7755
Dr. Maryellen Brunelle, supt. Fax 832-7757
www.auburn.k12.ma.us
Auburn HS 700/9-12
99 Auburn St 01501 508-832-7711
Casey Handfield, prin. Fax 832-7710
Auburn MS 500/6-8
10 Swanson Rd 01501 508-832-7722
Joseph Gagnon, prin. Fax 832-8655

Avon, Norfolk, Pop. 4,558
Avon SD 800/PK-12
1 Patrick Clark Dr 02322 508-588-0230
Dr. Margaret Frieswyk, supt. Fax 559-1081
www.avon.k12.ma.us/
Avon MSHS 400/7-12
285 W Main St 02322 508-583-4822
Sharon Hansen, prin. Fax 588-5501

Ayer, Middlesex, Pop. 2,780
Ayer Shirley SD 1,700/PK-12
141 Washington St 01432 978-772-8600
Carl Mock, supt. Fax 772-7444
www.asrsd.org
Ayer Shirley HS 300/9-12
141 Washington St 01432 978-772-8600
Brian Haas, prin. Fax 772-8615
Other Schools – See Shirley

Babson Park, Norfolk

Babson College Post-Sec.
231 Forest St 02457 781-235-1200

Baldwinville, Worcester, Pop. 2,008
Narragansett Regional SD 1,300/PK-12
462 Baldwinville Rd 01436 978-939-5661
Ruth S. Miler, supt. Fax 939-5179
www.nrsd.org/
Narragansett MS 500/5-8
460 Baldwinville Rd 01436 978-393-5928
Peter Cushing, prin. Fax 939-8422
Narragansett Regional HS 500/9-12
464 Baldwinville Rd 01436 978-939-5388
Shawn Rickan, prin. Fax 939-5723

Barnstable, Barnstable, Pop. 48,854

Trinity Christian Academy 100/PK-12
979 Mary Dunn Rd 02630 508-790-0114
Ben Haskell, hdmstr. Fax 790-1293

Barre, Worcester, Pop. 998
Quabbin SD 2,900/PK-12
872 South St 01005 978-355-4668
Dr. Maureen Marshall, supt. Fax 355-6756
www.qrsd.org/
Quabbin Regional HS 900/9-12
800 South St 01005 978-355-4651
Raymond Dewar, prin. Fax 355-0163
Quabbin Regional MS 500/7-8
800 South St 01005 978-355-5042
Susanne Musnicki, prin. Fax 355-6104

Bedford, Middlesex, Pop. 12,996
Bedford SD 2,400/K-12
97 McMahon Rd 01730 781-275-7588
Jonathan Sills, supt. Fax 275-0885
www.bedford.k12.ma.us
Bedford HS 800/9-12
9 Mudge Way 01730 781-275-1700
Henry Turner, prin. Fax 275-6664

Glenn MS 600/6-8
99 McMahon Rd 01730 781-275-3201
Kevin Tracey, prin. Fax 275-7632

Middlesex Community College Post-Sec.
591 Springs Rd 01730 781-280-3200
National Aviation Academy of New England Post-Sec.
150 Hanscom Dr 01730 781-274-8448

Belchertown, Hampshire, Pop. 2,339
Belchertown SD 2,600/PK-12
PO Box 841 01007 413-323-0423
Dr. Judith Houle, supt. Fax 323-0448
www.belchertownps.org
Belchertown HS 800/9-12
142 Springfield Rd 01007 413-323-9419
Christine Vigneux, prin. Fax 323-9406
Jabish Brook MS 400/7-8
62 N Washington St 01007 413-323-0433
Thomas Ruscio, prin. Fax 323-0450

Bellingham, Norfolk, Pop. 4,778
Bellingham SD 2,600/PK-12
60 Harpin St 02019 508-883-1706
Edward Fleury, supt. Fax 883-0180
www.bellinghamk12.org
Bellingham HS 700/9-12
60 Blackstone St 02019 508-966-3761
Peter Marano, prin. Fax 966-4183
Memorial MS 800/5-8
130 Blackstone St 02019 508-883-2330
William Tranter, prin. Fax 883-2037
Primavera Alternative HS 50/Alt
80 Harpin St 02019 508-883-5403
Jeffrey Croteau, dir. Fax 883-5408

Belmont, Middlesex, Pop. 24,057
Belmont SD 3,900/K-12
644 Pleasant St 02478 617-993-5401
Thomas Kingston, supt. Fax 993-5409
www.belmont.k12.ma.us
Belmont HS 1,100/9-12
221 Concord Ave 02478 617-484-5900
Dan Richards, prin. Fax 484-5909
Chenery MS 1,200/5-8
95 Washington St 02478 617-993-5800
Kristen St. George, prin. Fax 993-5809

Belmont Hill S 500/7-12
350 Prospect St 02478 617-484-4410
Dr. Richard Melvoin, hdmstr. Fax 484-4688
Waldorf HS of Massachusetts Bay 100/9-12
160 Lexington St 02478 617-489-6600
Mara White, admin. Fax 489-6619

Berkley, Bristol
Berkley SD 900/PK-8
21 N Main St 02779 508-822-5220
Thomas Lynch, supt. Fax 823-1772
www.berkleypublicschools.org
Berkley MS 400/5-8
21 N Main St 02779 508-884-9434
Kimberly Hebert, prin. Fax 386-1044

Beverly, Essex, Pop. 38,805
Beverly SD 4,200/PK-12
502 Cabot St 01915 978-921-6100
Marie Galinski Ed.D., supt. Fax 922-6597
www.beverlyschools.org/index2.shtm
Beverly HS 1,200/9-12
100 Sohier Rd 01915 978-921-6132
Sean Gallagher, prin. Fax 927-9460
Briscoe MS 900/6-8
7 Sohier Rd 01915 978-921-6103
Matthew Poska, prin. Fax 927-7781

Endicott College Post-Sec.
376 Hale St 01915 978-927-0585
Montserrat College of Art Post-Sec.
23 Essex St 01915 978-921-4242
Waring S 200/6-12
35 Standley St 01915 978-927-8793
Melville Brown, hdmstr. Fax 921-2107

Billerica, Middlesex, Pop. 37,609
Billerica SD 5,700/K-12
365 Boston Rd 01821 978-528-8500
Tim Piwowar, supt. Fax 436-9595
www.billerica.k12.ma.us
Billerica Memorial HS 1,500/9-12
35 River St 01821 978-528-8700
Kevin Soraghan, prin. Fax 528-8719
Locke MS 700/6-8
110 Allen Rd 01821 978-528-8650
Anthony Garas, prin. Fax 528-8659
Marshall MS 800/6-8
15 Floyd St 01821 978-528-8671
Roland Boucher, prin. Fax 528-8679

Shawsheen Valley Vocational Technical SD
100 Cook St 01821 978-667-2111
Charles Lyons, supt. Fax 663-6272
www.shawsheen.tech.org
Shawsheen Valley Technical HS Vo/Tech
100 Cook St 01821 978-667-2111
Robert Kanelas, prin. Fax 663-6272

Blackstone, Worcester, Pop. 8,023
Blackstone-Millville Regional SD 2,000/PK-12
175 Lincoln St 01504 508-883-4400
Kimberly B. Shaver-Hood, supt. Fax 883-9892
www.bmrsd.net
Blackstone-Millville Regional HS 600/9-12
175 Lincoln St 01504 508-876-0117
Michael Dudek, prin. Fax 883-9892
Hartnett MS 500/6-8
35 Federal St 01504 508-876-0190
Justin Cameron, prin. Fax 876-0198

Bolton, Worcester
Nashoba Regional SD 3,100/PK-12
50 Mechanic St 01740 978-779-0539
Michael Wood Ed.D., supt. Fax 779-5537
www.nrsd.net
Nashoba Regional HS 1,000/9-12
12 Green Rd 01740 978-779-2257
Perry Graham, prin. Fax 779-2720
Other Schools – See Lancaster, Stow

Boston, Suffolk, Pop. 592,375
Boston SD 51,400/PK-12
26 Court St Ste 10 02108 617-635-9000
Dr. Carol Johnson, supt. Fax 635-9059
www.bostonpublicschools.org/
Boston Arts Academy 400/Alt
174 Ipswich St 02215 617-635-6470
Anne Clark, hdmstr. Fax 635-8854
Boston Latin S 2,400/7-12
78 Avenue Louis Pasteur 02115 617-635-8895
Lynne Teta, hdmstr. Fax 635-7883
Boston Middle School Academy 50/Alt
215 Dorchester St 02127 617-635-1534
Yvonne Vest, dir. Fax 635-1539
Fenway HS 300/9-12
174 Ipswich St 02215 617-635-9911
Dr. Peggy Kemp, hdmstr. Fax 635-9204
Quincy Upper S 500/6-12
152 Arlington St 02116 617-635-8940
Stephen Cirasuolo, prin. Fax 635-1524
Snowden International HS 400/9-12
150 Newbury St 02116 617-635-9989
Cara Livermore, hdmstr. Fax 635-9996
Other Schools – See Brighton, Charlestown, Dorchester, East Boston, Hyde Park, Jamaica Plain, Mattapan, Roslindale, Roxbury, South Boston, West Roxbury

---

Bay State College Post-Sec.
122 Commonwealth Ave 02116 617-217-9000
Benjamin Franklin Inst. of Technology Post-Sec.
41 Berkeley St 02116 617-423-4630
Berklee College of Music Post-Sec.
1140 Boylston St 02215 617-266-1400
Beth Israel Healthcare Post-Sec.
330 Brookline Ave 02215 617-667-2539
Blaine The Beauty Career School Post-Sec.
30 West St 02111 617-266-2661
Boston Architectural College Post-Sec.
320 Newbury St 02115 617-262-5000
Boston Baptist College Post-Sec.
950 Metropolitan Ave 02136 617-364-3510
Boston Conservatory Post-Sec.
8 Fenway 02215 617-536-6340
Boston Trinity Academy 200/6-12
17 Hale St 02136 617-364-3700
Frank Guerra, hdmstr. Fax 364-3800
Boston University Post-Sec.
121 Bay State Rd 02215 617-353-2000
Boston University Academy 200/9-12
1 University Rd 02215 617-353-9000
James Berkman, hdmstr. Fax 353-8999
Brigham and Women's Hospital Post-Sec.
75 Francis St 02115 617-732-7493
Bunker Hill Community College Post-Sec.
250 Rutherford Ave 02129 617-228-2000
Cathedral HS 300/7-12
74 Union Park St 02118 617-542-2325
Bob McGurrin, prin. Fax 542-1745
Children's Hospital Post-Sec.
300 Longwood Ave 02115 617-355-6433
Commonwealth S 200/9-12
151 Commonwealth Ave 02116 617-266-7525
William Wharton, head sch Fax 266-5769
Cristo Rey HS 300/9-12
100 Savin Hill Ave 02125 617-825-2580
Rev. Jose Medina, prin. Fax 825-2613
Emerson College Post-Sec.
120 Boylston St 02116 617-824-8500
Emmanuel College Post-Sec.
400 Fenway 02115 617-735-9715
Fisher College Post-Sec.
118 Beacon St 02116 617-236-8800
Kaplan Career Institute Post-Sec.
540 Commonwealth Ave 02215 800-935-1857
Massachusetts College of Art and Design Post-Sec.
621 Huntington Ave 02115 617-879-7000
MA College of Pharmacy & Health Sciences Post-Sec.
179 Longwood Ave 02115 617-732-2800
Massachusetts School Professional Psych. Post-Sec.
221 Rivermoor St 02132 617-327-6777
MGH Institute of Health Professions Post-Sec.
36 1st Ave 02129 617-726-2947
New England College of Business/Finance Post-Sec.
10 High St Ste 204 02110 617-951-2350
New England College of Optometry Post-Sec.
424 Beacon St 02115 800-824-5526
New England Conservatory of Music Post-Sec.
290 Huntington Ave 02115 617-585-1100
New England Law \ Boston Post-Sec.
154 Stuart St 02116 617-451-0010
New England School of Art & Design Post-Sec.
75 Arlington St 02116 617-573-8785
New England School of Photography Post-Sec.
537 Commonwealth Ave 02215 617-437-1868
Newman Preparatory S 300/9-12
247 Marlborough St 02116 617-267-4530
Harry Lynch, hdmstr. Fax 267-7070
North Bennet Street School Post-Sec.
39 N Bennet St 02113 617-227-0155
Northeastern University Post-Sec.
360 Huntington Ave 02115 617-373-2000
St. Joseph Preparatory HS 200/9-12
617 Cambridge St 02134 617-254-8383
Thomas Nunan, prin. Fax 254-0240
School of the Museum of Fine Arts Post-Sec.
230 Fenway 02115 617-267-6100
Simmons College Post-Sec.
300 Fenway 02115 617-521-2000
Suffolk University Post-Sec.
8 Ashburton Pl 02108 617-573-8000
University of Massachusetts Boston Post-Sec.
100 William T Mrrissey Blvd 02125 617-287-5000
Urban College of Boston Post-Sec.
178 Tremont St 02111 617-348-6359
Veterans Administration Medical Center Post-Sec.
150 S Huntington Ave 02130 617-232-9500
Wentworth Institute of Technology Post-Sec.
550 Huntington Ave 02115 617-989-4590
Wheelock College Post-Sec.
200 Riverway 02215 617-879-2000
Winsor S 400/5-12
103 Pilgrim Rd 02215 617-735-9500
Rachel Friis Stettler, dir. Fax 739-5519

Bourne, Barnstable, Pop. 1,380
Bourne SD 2,300/PK-12
36 Sandwich Rd 02532 508-759-0660
Steven Lamarche, supt. Fax 759-1107
www.bourne.k12.ma.us
Bourne HS 600/9-12
75 Waterhouse Rd 02532 508-759-0670
Amy Cetner, prin. Fax 759-0677
Bourne MS 800/5-8
77 Waterhouse Rd 02532 508-759-0690
Melissa Stafford, prin. Fax 759-0695

Upper Cape Cod Vo-Tech SD
220 Sandwich Rd 02532 508-759-7711
Richard Dutch, supt. Fax 759-7208
www.uppercapetech.com
Upper Cape Cod Regional Technical S Vo/Tech
220 Sandwich Rd 02532 508-759-7711
Roger Forget, prin. Fax 759-7208

Boylston, Worcester
Berlin-Boylston SD 400/6-12
215 Main St 01505 508-869-2837
Nadine Ekstrom, supt. Fax 869-0023
bbrsd.org
Tahanto Regional MSHS 400/6-12
1001 Main St 01505 508-869-2333
Diane Tucceri, prin. Fax 869-0175

Bradford, See Haverhill

Bradford Christian Academy 100/5-12
97 Oxford Ave 01835 978-373-7900
Victoria Kennedy, hdmstr. Fax 373-7977

Braintree, Norfolk, Pop. 33,800
Braintree SD 5,400/K-12
348 Pond St 02184 781-380-0130
Maureen Murray Ed.D., supt. Fax 380-0146
www.braintreeschools.org
Braintree HS 1,500/9-12
128 Town St 02184 781-848-4000
James Lee, hdmstr. Fax 380-0116
East MS 700/6-8
305 River St 02184 781-380-0170
John Sheehan, prin. Fax 848-4522
South MS 600/6-8
232 Peach St 02184 781-380-0160
Edward McDonough, prin. Fax 380-0164

Archbishop Williams HS 500/9-12
80 Independence Ave 02184 781-843-3636
Dr. Carmen Mariano, prin. Fax 843-3782
Thayer Academy 700/6-12
745 Washington St 02184 781-843-3580
Ted Koskores, hdmstr. Fax 843-2916

Bridgewater, Plymouth, Pop. 7,639
Bridgewater-Raynham Regional SD 5,700/PK-12
166 Mount Prospect St 02324 508-279-2140
Dr. Jacqueline Forbes, supt. Fax 697-7012
www.bridge-rayn.org
Bridgewater MS 600/7-8
166 Mount Prospect St 02324 508-279-2100
Lynn Bastoni, prin. Fax 279-2104
Bridgewater-Raynham Regional HS 1,600/9-12
415 Center St 02324 508-697-6902
Angela Watson, prin. Fax 279-2110
Other Schools – See Raynham

Bridgewater State University Post-Sec.
131 Summer St 02325 508-531-1000

Brighton, See Boston
Boston SD
Supt. — See Boston
Another Course to College S 200/9-12
20 Warren St 02135 617-635-8865
Lisa Gilbert-Smith, hdmstr. Fax 635-8866
Brighton HS 1,200/9-12
25 Warren St 02135 617-635-9873
Frederick McDowell, hdmstr. Fax 635-9892
Lyon HS 9-12
95 Beechcroft St 02135 617-635-8351
Jean-Dominique Anoh, prin. Fax 635-8353

Bais Yaakov of Boston HS 50/9-12
198 Strathmore Rd 02135 617-254-7547
Everest Institute Post-Sec.
1505 Commonwealth Ave 02135 888-741-4270
Margolis Mesivta of Greater Boston 50/9-12
34 Sparhawk St 02135 617-779-0166
Saint John's Seminary Post-Sec.
127 Lake St 02135 617-254-2610

Brockton, Plymouth, Pop. 79,948
Brockton SD 15,900/PK-12
43 Crescent St 02301 508-580-7000
John Jerome, supt. Fax 580-7513
www.bpsma.org/

Ashfield MS 500/6-8
225 Coe Rd 02302 508-580-7268
Barbara Lovell, prin. Fax 580-7072
Brockton Champion HS 200/Alt
175 Warren Ave 02301 508-894-4377
Mark St. Louis, admin. Fax 894-4380
Brockton HS 4,100/9-12
470 Forest Ave 02301 508-580-7633
Michael Thomas, prin. Fax 580-7600
East MS 500/6-8
464 Centre St 02302 508-580-7351
Kelly Silva, prin. Fax 580-7090
Edison Academy 9-12
700 Belmont St 02301 508-580-7638
Scott Pearsons, prin. Fax 580-7987
Goddard Alternative S 300/Alt
20 Union St 02301 508-580-7203
John Lander, prin. Fax 580-7083
North MS 400/6-8
108 Oak St 02301 508-580-7371
Sean Ahern, prin. Fax 580-7088
Plouffe Academy 600/6-8
250 Crescent St 02302 508-894-4301
Michelle Nessralla, prin. Fax 894-4300
Russell Alternative S 100/Alt
175 Warren Ave 02301 508-580-7033
Mark St. Louis, prin. Fax 580-7943
South MS 500/6-8
105 Keith Avenue Ext 02301 508-580-7311
Kevin Karo, prin. Fax 580-7089
West MS 600/6-8
271 West St 02301 508-580-7381
Clifford Murray, prin. Fax 580-7307

Ailano School of Cosmetology Post-Sec.
541 West St 02301 508-583-5433
Brockton Hospital Post-Sec.
680 Centre St 02302 508-941-7044
Cardinal Spellman HS 700/9-12
738 Court St 02302 508-583-6875
Paul Kelly, prin. Fax 580-1977
LaBaron Hairdressing Academy Post-Sec.
240 Liberty St 02301 508-583-1700
Lincoln Technical Institute Post-Sec.
365 Westgate Dr 02301 508-941-0730
Massasoit Community College Post-Sec.
1 Massasoit Blvd 02302 508-588-9100
Sullivan and Cogliano Training Center Post-Sec.
460 Belmont St 02301 508-584-9909
Trinity Catholic Academy - Upper Campus 200/4-8
37 Erie Ave 02302 508-583-6225
Annette Bailey, prin. Fax 583-6229

Brookline, Norfolk, Pop. 57,031
Brookline SD 6,600/PK-12
333 Washington St 02445 617-730-2403
Dr. William Lupini, supt. Fax 730-2601
www.brookline.k12.ma.us/
Brookline HS 1,700/9-12
115 Greenough St 02445 617-713-5000
Deborah Holman, prin. Fax 713-5005

Boston Graduate Sch for Psychoanalysis Post-Sec.
1581 Beacon St 02446 617-277-3915
Dexter S 400/PK-12
20 Newton St 02445 617-522-5544
Todd Vincent, hdmstr. Fax 522-8166
Hellenic College/Holy Cross Sch Theology Post-Sec.
50 Goddard Ave 02445 617-731-3500
Maimonides S 600/K-12
34 Philbrick Rd 02445 617-232-4452
Rabbi David Saltzman, prin. Fax 566-2061
Newbury College Post-Sec.
129 Fisher Ave 02445 617-730-7000
New England Institute of Art Post-Sec.
10 Brookline Pl 02445 617-739-1700
Southfield S 400/PK-12
10 Newton St 02445 617-522-6980
Jacalyn Wright, admin. Fax 522-8166

Burlington, Middlesex, Pop. 24,055
Burlington SD 3,600/K-12
123 Cambridge St 01803 781-270-1800
Dr. Eric Conti, supt. Fax 270-1773
www.bpsk12.org
Burlington HS 1,000/9-12
123 Cambridge St 01803 781-270-1836
Mark Sullivan, prin. Fax 229-4893
Simonds MS 800/6-8
114 Winn St 01803 781-270-1781
Richard Connors, prin. Fax 229-4980

Buzzards Bay, Barnstable, Pop. 3,756

Massachusetts Maritime Academy Post-Sec.
101 Academy Dr 02532 508-830-5000

Byfield, Essex
Triton Regional SD 3,100/PK-12
112 Elm St 01922 978-465-2397
Christopher Farmer, supt. Fax 465-8599
www.trsd.net
Triton Regional HS 800/9-12
112 Elm St 01922 978-462-8171
Kathryn Dawe, prin. Fax 465-6868
Triton Regional MS 500/7-8
112 Elm St 01922 978-463-5845
Jared Fulgoni, prin. Fax 465-6868

Governor's Academy 400/9-12
1 Elm St 01922 978-465-1763
Fax 463-9896

Cambridge, Middlesex, Pop. 100,799
Cambridge SD 4,900/PK-12
159 Thorndike St 02141 617-349-6400
Dr. Jeffrey Young, supt. Fax 349-6496
www.cpsd.us

Cambridge Rindge & Latin HS 1,600/9-12
459 Broadway 02138 617-349-6630
Damon Smith, prin. Fax 349-6749
Cambridge Street Upper S 6-8
850 Cambridge St 02141 617-349-6400
Manuel Fernandez, prin.
Putnam Avenue Upper S 6-8
158 Spring St 02141 617-349-7780
Mirko Chardin, prin.
Rindge Avenue Upper S 6-8
70 Rindge Ave 02140 617-349-4060
Ralph Watson, prin.
Vassal Lane Upper S 6-8
197 Vassal Ln 02138 617-349-6550
Jamel Adkins-Sharif, prin.

Boston Archdiocesan Choir S 100/5-8
29 Mount Auburn St 02138 617-868-8658
William McIvor, hdmstr. Fax 354-7092
Buckingham Browne & Nichols S 1,000/PK-12
80 Gerrys Landing Rd 02138 617-800-2135
Geordie Mitchell, admin.
Cambridge College Post-Sec.
1000 Massachusetts Ave 02138 617-868-1000
Cambridge School of Culinary Arts Post-Sec.
2020 Massachusetts Ave 02140 617-354-2020
Episcopal Divinity School Post-Sec.
99 Brattle St 02138 617-868-3450
Harvard University Post-Sec.
Massachusetts Hall 02138 617-495-1000
Hult International Business School Post-Sec.
1 Education St 02141 617-746-1990
International School of Boston 600/PK-12
45 Matignon Rd 02140 617-499-1451
Dr. Richard Blumenthal, head sch Fax 499-1454
Le Cordon Bleu College of Culinary Arts Post-Sec.
215 1st St 02142 888-394-6222
Lesley University Post-Sec.
29 Everett St 02138 617-868-9600
Massachusetts Institute of Technology Post-Sec.
77 Massachusetts Ave 02139 617-253-1000
Matignon HS 400/9-12
1 Matignon Rd 02140 617-876-1212
Joseph DiSarcina, prin. Fax 661-3905

Canton, Norfolk, Pop. 18,530
Blue Hills Regional Vocational SD
800 Randolph St 02021 781-828-5800
James Quaglia, supt. Fax 828-3872
www.bluehills.org
Blue Hills Regional Technical S Vo/Tech
800 Randolph St 02021 781-828-5800
Michael Barrett, prin. Fax 828-3872

Canton SD 3,200/PK-12
960 Washington St 02021 781-821-5060
Jeff Granatino Ed.D., supt. Fax 575-6500
www.cantonma.org
Canton HS 900/9-12
900 Washington St 02021 781-821-5050
Derek Folan, prin. Fax 821-5052
Galvin MS 800/6-8
55 Pecunit St 02021 781-821-5070
William Conard, prin. Fax 575-6509

Bay State School of Technology Post-Sec.
225 Turnpike St 02021 781-828-3434
Porter and Chester Institute Post-Sec.
5 Campanelli Cir 02021 781-830-0350

Carver, Plymouth
Carver SD 1,800/PK-12
3 Carver Square Blvd 02330 508-866-6160
Elizabeth Sorrell, supt. Fax 866-2920
www.carver.org
Carver MSHS 900/6-12
60 S Meadow Rd 02330 508-866-6140
Scott Knief, prin. Fax 866-5639

Charlemont, Franklin

Academy at Charlemont 100/7-12
1359 Route 2 E 01339 413-339-4912
David Perry, hdmstr. Fax 339-4324

Charlestown, See Boston
Boston SD
Supt. — See Boston
Charlestown HS 900/9-12
240 Medford St 02129 617-635-9914
William Thomas, hdmstr. Fax 635-9928
Edwards MS 500/6-8
28 Walker St 02129 617-635-8516
Leo Flanagan, prin. Fax 635-8522

Kaplan Career Institute Post-Sec.
570 Rutherford Ave 02129 617-580-4010

Charlton, Worcester
Dudley-Charlton Regional SD
Supt. — See Dudley
Charlton MS 800/5-8
2 Oxford Rd 01507 508-248-1423
Dean Packard, prin. Fax 248-1418

Southern Worcester Co. Reg Vocational SD
57 Old Muggett Hill Rd 01507 508-248-5971
John Lafleche, supt. Fax 248-4747
www.baypath.tec.ma.us
Bay Path Regional Vocational Tech HS Vo/Tech
57 Old Muggett Hill Rd 01507 508-248-5971
Clifford Cloutier, prin. Fax 248-4747

Chatham, Barnstable, Pop. 1,395
Monomoy SD 2,000/PK-12
425 Crowell Rd 02633 508-430-7200
Dr. Carolyn Cragin, supt. Fax 430-7205
www.monomoy.edu/

Chatham HS 200/9-12
425 Crowell Rd 02633 508-945-5140
Paul Mangelinkx, prin. Fax 945-5110
Chatham MS 200/5-8
425 Crowell Rd 02633 508-945-5148
Lisa Sjostrom, prin. Fax 945-5143
Other Schools – See Harwich

Chelmsford, Middlesex, Pop. 33,858
Chelmsford SD 5,200/K-12
230 North Rd 01824 978-251-5100
Donald Yeoman Ed.D., supt. Fax 251-5110
www.chelmsford.k12.ma.us/
McCarthy MS 900/5-8
250 North Rd 01824 978-251-5122
Kurt McPhee, prin. Fax 251-5130
Parker MS 800/5-8
75 Graniteville Rd 01824 978-251-5133
Jeffrey Parks, prin. Fax 251-5140
Other Schools – See North Chelmsford

Chelsea, Suffolk, Pop. 34,185
Chelsea SD 5,600/PK-12
500 Broadway 02150 617-466-4477
Mary Bourque, supt. Fax 889-8361
chelseaschools.com
Browne S 500/5-8
180 Walnut St 02150 617-466-5253
David Liebowitz, prin. Fax 889-8459
Chelsea HS 1,300/9-12
299 Everett Ave 02150 617-466-5000
Joseph Mullaney, prin. Fax 889-8468
Clark Avenue S 600/5-8
8 Clark Ave 02150 617-466-5100
Mary Leverone, prin. Fax 889-7539
Wright Science & Technology Acad 500/5-8
180 Walnut St 02150 617-466-5240
Andrew O'Brien, prin. Fax 889-8463

Everest Institute Post-Sec.
70 Everett Ave 02150 617-889-5999

Cheshire, Berkshire, Pop. 507
Adams-Cheshire Regional SD 1,400/PK-12
191 Church St 01225 413-743-2939
Kristen Gordon, supt. Fax 743-4135
www.acrsd.net
Hoosac Valley HS 700/6-12
125 Savoy Rd 01225 413-743-5200
Vinnie Regan, prin. Fax 743-8420

Chestnut Hill, See Newton

Beaver Country Day S 500/6-12
791 Hammond St 02467 617-738-2700
Peter Hutton, head sch Fax 738-2701
Boston College Post-Sec.
140 Commonwealth Ave 02467 617-552-8000
Brimmer and May S 400/PK-12
69 Middlesex Rd 02467 617-566-7462
Judy Guild, head sch Fax 734-5147
Pine Manor College Post-Sec.
400 Heath St 02467 617-731-7000

Chicopee, Hampden, Pop. 54,468
Chicopee SD 7,800/PK-12
180 Broadway St 01020 413-594-3410
Richard Rege, supt. Fax 594-3552
www.chicopee.mec.edu/
Bellamy MS 1,000/6-8
314 Pendleton Ave 01020 413-594-3527
Matthew Francis, prin. Fax 594-1837
Chicopee Academy 100/Alt
650 Front St 01013 413-594-3433
John Leonard, prin. Fax 594-1852
Chicopee Comprehensive HS 1,400/9-12
617 Montgomery St 01020 413-594-3534
Derek Morrison, prin. Fax 594-3492
Chicopee HS 1,200/9-12
820 Front St 01020 413-594-3437
Roland Joyal, prin. Fax 594-3500
Fairview Veterans MS 700/6-8
26 Memorial Ave 01020 413-594-3501
Kristopher Theriault, prin. Fax 594-3509

College of Our Lady of Elms Post-Sec.
291 Springfield St 01013 413-594-2761
Holyoke Catholic HS 300/9-12
134 Springfield St 01013 413-331-2480
Theresa Kitchell, prin. Fax 331-2708
Porter and Chester Institute Post-Sec.
134 Dulong Cir 01022 413-593-3339
Salter College Post-Sec.
645 Shawinigan Dr 01020 413-206-0300

Clinton, Worcester, Pop. 7,209
Clinton SD 1,900/PK-12
150 School St 01510 978-365-4200
Terrance Ingano, supt. Fax 365-5037
clinton.k12.ma.us
Clinton HS 500/9-12
200 W Boylston St 01510 978-365-4208
James Hastings, prin. Fax 365-4237
Clinton MS 700/4-8
100 W Boylston St 01510 978-365-4220
Annmarie Sargent, prin. Fax 368-7256

Cohasset, Norfolk, Pop. 7,075
Cohasset SD 1,500/PK-12
143 Pond St 02025 781-383-6111
Barbara Cataldo, supt. Fax 383-6507
www.cohassetk12.org
Cohasset MSHS 700/6-12
143 Pond St 02025 781-383-6100
Carolyn Connolly, prin. Fax 383-6556

Concord, Middlesex, Pop. 4,700
Concord SD 1,900/PK-8
120 Meriam Rd 01742 978-318-1500
Diana Rigby, supt. Fax 318-1537
www.concordpublicschools.net
Concord MS 600/6-8
835 Old Marlboro Rd 01742 978-318-1380
Lynne Beattie, prin. Fax 318-1392

Concord-Carlisle SD 1,200/9-12
120 Meriam Rd 01742 978-318-1500
Diana Rigby, supt. Fax 318-1537
www.concordpublicschools.net
Concord-Carlisle HS 1,200/9-12
500 Walden St 01742 978-318-1400
Peter Badalament, prin. Fax 318-1435

Concord Academy 400/9-12
166 Main St 01742 978-402-2200
Richard G. Hardy, head sch Fax 402-2210
Fenn S 300/4-9
516 Monument St 01742 978-369-5800
Gerard J.G. Ward, admin. Fax 371-7520
Middlesex S 400/9-12
PO Box 9122 01742 978-369-2550
Kathleen Carroll Giles, head sch Fax 369-3846

Conway, Franklin

Conway School of Landscape Design Post-Sec.
PO Box 179 01341 413-369-4044

Dalton, Berkshire, Pop. 7,155
Central Berkshire Regional SD 1,900/PK-12
PO Box 299 01227 413-684-0320
Dr. William Cameron, supt. Fax 684-4088
www.cbrsd.org
Nessacus Regional MS 500/6-8
35 Fox Rd 01226 413-684-0780
John Martin, prin. Fax 684-4214
Wahconah Regional HS 600/9-12
150 Old Windsor Rd 01226 413-684-1330
James Conro, prin. Fax 684-5032

Danvers, Essex, Pop. 26,232
Danvers SD 3,600/PK-12
64 Cabot Rd 01923 978-777-4539
Lisa Dana, supt. Fax 777-8931
www.danvers.mec.edu
Danvers HS 1,000/9-12
60 Cabot Rd 01923 978-777-8925
Susan Ambrozavitch, prin. Fax 777-8931
Holten-Richmond MS 900/6-8
55 Conant St 01923 978-774-8590
Adam Federico, prin. Fax 762-8686

North Shore Community College Post-Sec.
1 Ferncroft Rd 01923 978-762-4000
St. Johns Preparatory S 1,300/9-12
72 Spring St 01923 978-774-1050
Keith Crowley Ph.D., prin. Fax 624-1315

Dedham, Norfolk, Pop. 24,346
Dedham SD 2,900/PK-12
100 Whiting Ave 02026 781-326-5622
June Doe, supt. Fax 320-0193
www.dedham.k12.ma.us
Dedham HS 800/9-12
140 Whiting Ave 02026 781-326-4773
Ron McCarthy, prin. Fax 320-8126
Dedham MS 600/6-8
70 Whiting Ave 02026 781-326-6900
Debra Gately, prin. Fax 461-0354

Noble And Greenough S 600/7-12
10 Campus Dr 02026 781-326-3700
Robert Henderson, hdmstr. Fax 320-1329
Ursuline Academy 400/7-12
85 Lowder St 02026 781-326-6161
Mary Jo Keaney, prin. Fax 326-4898

Deerfield, Franklin, Pop. 620

Deerfield Academy 700/9-12
PO Box 65 01342 413-774-1400
Dr. Margarita Curtis, hdmstr. Fax 772-1129
Eaglebrook S 300/6-9
PO Box 7 01342 413-774-7411
Andrew Chase, hdmstr. Fax 774-9136

Dighton, Bristol
Bristol County Agricultural SD
135 Center St 02715 508-669-6744
Krista Paynton, supt. Fax 669-6747
www.bcahs.com
Bristol County Agricultural HS Vo/Tech
135 Center St 02715 508-669-6744
Stephen Dempsey, prin. Fax 669-6747

Dighton-Rehoboth Regional SD
Supt. — See North Dighton
Dighton MS 400/5-8
1250R Somerset Ave 02715 508-669-4200
Richard Wheeler, prin. Fax 669-4210

Dorchester, See Boston
Boston SD
Supt. — See Boston
Boston International HS 200/9-12
100 Maxwell St 02124 617-635-9373
Nicole Bahnam, hdmstr. Fax 635-8224
Boston Latin Academy 1,700/7-12
205 Townsend St 02121 617-635-9957
Emilia Pastor, hdmstr. Fax 635-6696
Burke HS 700/9-12
60 Washington St 02121 617-635-9837
Lindsa McIntyre, hdmstr. Fax 635-9852
Community Academy of Science & Health 400/9-12
11 Charles St 02122 617-635-8950
Tonya Freeman-Wisdom, prin. Fax 635-8948
Dorchester Academy 400/9-12
18 Croftland Ave 02124 617-635-9730
Kwesi Moody, hdmstr. Fax 635-8847
Frederick Pilot MS 600/6-8
270 Columbia Rd 02121 617-635-1650
Donna Mack, prin. Fax 635-1637
Harbor S 300/6-8
11 Charles St 02122 617-635-6365
Leah Blake, prin. Fax 635-6367
McCormack MS 600/6-8
315 Mount Vernon St 02125 617-635-8657
Michael Sabin, prin. Fax 635-9788
Newcomers Academy 200/9-12
100 Maxwell St 02124 617-635-7993
Nicole Bahnam, dir. Fax 635-7990
TechBoston Academy 300/6-12
9 Peacevale Rd 02124 617-635-1615
Mary Skipper, hdmstr. Fax 635-1622
Boston Adult Technical Academy Adult
429 Norfolk St 02124 617-635-1542
Sheila Azores, hdmstr. Fax 635-6362

Boston College HS 1,600/7-12
150 William T Morrissey 02125 617-436-3900
Stephen Hughes, prin. Fax 474-5105
City Vision College Post-Sec.
31 Torrey St 02124 816-960-2008
Epiphany S 100/5-8
154 Centre St 02124 617-326-0425
Rev. John Finley, admin. Fax 326-0424
Laboure College Post-Sec.
2120 Dorchester Ave 02124 617-296-8300
Seton Academy 100/9-12
2220 Dorchester Ave 02124 617-296-1087
Maureen White Ph.D., prin. Fax 296-1089

Douglas, Worcester
Douglas SD 1,600/PK-12
21 Davis St 01516 508-476-7901
Nancy Lane, supt. Fax 476-3719
www.douglas.k12.ma.us/
Douglas MSHS 600/8-12
33 Davis St 01516 508-476-4100
Kevin Maines, prin. Fax 476-7310

Dover, Norfolk, Pop. 2,253
Dover-Sherborn SD 1,200/6-12
157 Farm St 02030 508-785-0036
Valerie Spriggs, supt. Fax 785-2239
www.doversherborn.org
Dover-Sherborn Regional HS 600/9-12
9 Junction St 02030 508-785-1730
Denise Lonergan, prin. Fax 785-8141
Dover-Sherborn Regional MS 600/6-8
155 Farm St 02030 508-785-0635
Scott Kellett, prin. Fax 785-0796

Dracut, Middlesex, Pop. 25,594
Dracut SD 4,000/PK-12
2063 Lakeview Ave 01826 978-957-2660
Steven Stone, supt. Fax 957-2682
www.dracutps.org
Dracut HS 1,100/9-12
1540 Lakeview Ave 01826 978-957-1500
Richard Manley, prin. Fax 957-9717
Lakeview JHS 700/7-8
1570 Lakeview Ave 01826 978-957-3330
Robert Fitzgerald, prin. Fax 957-4075

Dudley, Worcester, Pop. 3,700
Dudley-Charlton Regional SD 4,200/PK-12
68 Dudley Oxford Rd 01571 508-943-6888
Sean Gilrein, supt. Fax 943-1077
www.dcrsd.org/
Dudley MS 600/5-8
70 Dudley Oxford Rd 01571 508-943-2224
Gregg Desto, prin. Fax 949-0720
Shepherd Hill Regional HS 1,200/9-12
68 Dudley Oxford Rd 01571 508-943-6700
Mary Pierangeli, prin. Fax 943-5956
Other Schools – See Charlton

Nichols College Post-Sec.
124 Center Rd 01571 508-213-1560

Duxbury, Plymouth, Pop. 1,793
Duxbury SD 3,200/PK-12
130 Saint George St 02332 781-934-7600
Dr. Benedict Tantillo, supt. Fax 934-7644
www.duxbury.k12.ma.us
Duxbury HS 1,000/9-12
130 Saint George St 02332 781-934-7650
Andrew Stephens, prin. Fax 934-7617
Duxbury MS 800/6-8
71 Alden St 02332 781-934-7640
Blake Dalton, prin. Fax 934-7608

East Boston, See Boston
Boston SD
Supt. — See Boston
East Boston HS 1,400/9-12
86 White St 02128 617-635-9896
Michael Rubin, hdmstr. Fax 635-9726

East Bridgewater, Plymouth, Pop. 11,104
East Bridgewater SD 2,300/PK-12
11 Plymouth St 02333 508-378-8200
Fax 378-8225
www.ebps.net
East Bridgewater HS 600/9-12
11 Plymouth St 02333 508-378-8214
Paul Vieira, prin. Fax 378-8226
Mitchell MS 1,000/4-8
435 Central St 02333 508-378-8209
Andrew Gentile, prin. Fax 378-8228

East Falmouth, Barnstable, Pop. 5,768
Falmouth SD 3,700/PK-12
340 Teaticket Hwy 02536 508-548-0151
Dr. Bonny Gifford, supt. Fax 457-9032
www.falmouth.k12.ma.us
Other Schools – See Falmouth

Easthampton, Hampshire, Pop. 16,004
Easthampton SD 1,600/PK-12
50 Payson Ave Ste 200 01027 413-529-1500
Nancy Follansbee, supt. Fax 529-1567
www.easthampton.k12.ma.us
Easthampton HS 400/9-12
70 Williston Ave 01027 413-529-1585
Vito Perrone, prin. Fax 529-1591
White Brook MS 500/5-8
200 Park St 01027 413-529-1530
Allison Rebello, prin. Fax 529-1534

Williston Northampton S 500/7-12
19 Payson Ave 01027 413-529-3000
Robert Hill, hdmstr. Fax 527-9494

East Longmeadow, Hampden, Pop. 13,367
East Longmeadow SD 2,800/K-12
180 Maple St 01028 413-525-5450
Gordon Smith, supt. Fax 525-5456
www.eastlongmeadowma.gov/schools.htm
Birchland Park MS 700/6-8
50 Hanward Hl 01028 413-525-5480
Kathleen Hill, prin. Fax 525-5320
East Longmeadow HS 900/9-12
180 Maple St 01028 413-525-5460
Gina Flanagan, prin. Fax 525-5496

East Sandwich, Barnstable, Pop. 3,915
Sandwich SD 3,400/PK-12
365 Quaker Meeting House Rd 02537 508-888-1054
Dr. C. Richard Canfield, supt. Fax 888-9505
www.sandwichk12.org
Sandwich HS 1,000/9-12
365 Quaker Meeting House Rd 02537 508-888-4900
Ellin Booras, prin. Fax 833-8392

Riverview S 200/6-12
551 Route 6A 02537 508-888-0489
Maureen Brenner, head sch Fax 833-7001

East Walpole, Norfolk, Pop. 3,800
Walpole SD
Supt. — See Walpole
Bird MS 500/6-8
625 Washington St 02032 508-660-7226
Bridget Gough, prin. Fax 660-7229

East Weymouth, Norfolk
Weymouth SD
Supt. — See Weymouth
Adams MS 1,000/5-8
89 Middle St 02189 781-335-1100
Daniel Birolini, prin. Fax 340-2544
Chapman MS 1,000/5-8
1051 Commercial St 02189 781-337-4500
Kathleen Sheridan, prin. Fax 340-2594

Everett, Middlesex, Pop. 38,826
Everett SD 6,100/PK-12
121 Vine St 02149 617-389-7950
Frederick Foresteire, supt. Fax 394-2408
www.everett.k12.ma.us/
Everett HS 1,700/9-12
100 Elm St 02149 617-394-2490
Erick Naumann, prin. Fax 389-5841

Pope John XXIII Central HS 200/9-12
888 Broadway 02149 617-389-0240
Dr. Thomas Ryan, prin. Fax 389-2201

Fairhaven, Bristol, Pop. 16,132
Fairhaven SD 2,000/PK-12
128 Washington St 02719 508-979-4000
Dr. Robert Baldwin, supt. Fax 979-4149
www.fairhavenps.org/
Fairhaven HS 600/9-12
12 Huttleston Ave 02719 508-979-4052
Tara Quirk, prin. Fax 979-4140
Hastings MS 500/6-8
30 School St 02719 508-979-4063
Wayne Miller, prin. Fax 979-4068

Fall River, Bristol, Pop. 86,097
Fall River SD 9,100/PK-12
417 Rock St 02720 508-675-8420
Meg Mayo-Brown, supt. Fax 675-8462
www.fallriverschools.org/
Durfee HS 2,300/9-12
360 Elsbree St 02720 508-675-8100
Paul Marshall, prin. Fax 675-8186
Kuss MS 600/6-8
52 Globe Mills Ave 02724 508-675-8335
Michael Procaccini, prin. Fax 675-1984
Lord MS 500/6-8
151 Amity St 02721 508-675-8208
Thomas Johnson, prin. Fax 675-8253
Morton MS 600/6-8
290 Rock St 02720 508-675-8340
Sheryl Rabbitt, prin. Fax 675-8414
Resiliency Preparatory S 200/Alt
276 Maple St 02720 508-675-8230
Jessica Insana, prin. Fax 235-2661
Talbot MS 600/6-8
124 Melrose St 02723 508-675-8350
Elizabeth Coogan, prin. Fax 675-8356

Greater Fall River Vocational SD
251 Stonehaven Rd 02723 508-678-2891
Marta Montleon, supt. Fax 679-6423
www.dimanregional.org/
Diman Regional Vocational Technical HS Vo/Tech
251 Stonehaven Rd 02723 508-678-2891
Brian Bentley, prin. Fax 679-6423

Bishop Connolly HS 300/9-12
373 Elsbree St 02720 508-676-1071
Christopher Myron, prin. Fax 676-8594
Bristol Community College Post-Sec.
777 Elsbree St 02720 508-678-2811
Rob Roy Academy Post-Sec.
260 S Main St 02721 508-672-4751
Salter School Post-Sec.
82 Hartwell St 02721 508-730-2740

Falmouth, Barnstable, Pop. 3,663
Falmouth SD
Supt. — See East Falmouth
Falmouth HS 900/9-12
874 Gifford Street Ext 02540 508-540-2200
Joe Driscoll, prin. Fax 548-7515
Lawrence MS 600/7-8
113 Lakeview Ave 02540 508-548-0606
Nancy Taylor, prin. Fax 457-9778

Falmouth Academy 200/7-12
7 Highfield Dr 02540 508-457-9696
David Faus, hdmstr. Fax 457-4112
National Grad. Sch. Quality Systems Mgmt Post-Sec.
186 Jones Rd 02540 508-457-1313

Feeding Hills, Hampden, Pop. 5,450
Agawam SD 4,100/K-12
1305 Springfield St Ste 1 01030 413-821-0548
William Sapelli, supt. Fax 789-1835
www.agawampublicschools.org
Agawam JHS 700/7-8
1305 Springfield St Ste 2 01030 413-821-0561
Norman Robbins, prin. Fax 786-4240
Other Schools – See Agawam

Fiskdale, Worcester, Pop. 2,545
Tantasqua SD 1,800/7-12
320 Brookfield Rd 01518 508-347-3077
Erin Nosek, supt. Fax 347-2697
www.tantasqua.org
Tantasqua Regional HS 900/9-12
319 Brookfield Rd 01518 508-347-9301
Michael Lucas, prin. Fax 347-1061
Tantasqua Regional JHS 600/7-8
320 Brookfield Rd 01518 508-347-7381
Christopher Starczewski, prin. Fax 347-3994
Tantasqua Regional Tech HS Vo/Tech
319 Brookfield Rd 01518 508-347-3045
Mark Wood, prin. Fax 347-1061

Fitchburg, Worcester, Pop. 39,363
Fitchburg SD 4,600/PK-12
376 South St 01420 978-345-3200
Andre Ravenelle, supt. Fax 348-2305
www.fitchburgschools.org
Fitchburg Alternative S 200/Alt
111 Goodrich St 01420 978-345-3244
Mike Pelland, prin. Fax 345-3204
Fitchburg HS 1,100/9-12
140 Arnhow Farm Rd 01420 978-345-3240
Jeremy Roche, prin. Fax 348-2303
Longsjo MS 600/5-8
98 Academy St 01420 978-343-2146
Craig Chalifoux, prin. Fax 348-2323
Memorial MS 700/5-8
615 Rollstone St 01420 978-345-3295
Francis Thomas, prin. Fax 343-2121

Montachusett Regional Vo/Tech HSD
1050 Westminster St 01420 978-345-9200
Steven Sharek, supt. Fax 345-9165
www.montytech.net
Montachusett Reg Vocational Technical HS Vo/Tech
1050 Westminster St 01420 978-345-9200
Nicholas DeSimone, prin. Fax 348-1176

Fitchburg State University Post-Sec.
160 Pearl St 01420 978-345-2151
Henri's School of Hair Design Post-Sec.
PO Box 2244 01420 978-342-6061
Notre Dame HS 50/7-12
151 South St 01420 978-343-7635
Jeffrey Hammond, prin. Fax 343-6579
St. Bernards HS 400/9-12
45 Harvard St 01420 978-342-3212
James Conry, admin. Fax 345-8067

Florence, See Northampton
Northampton SD
Supt. — See Northampton
Kennedy MS 600/6-8
100 Bridge Rd 01062 413-587-1489
Lesley Wilson, prin. Fax 587-1495

Foxboro, Norfolk, Pop. 5,706
Foxborough SD 2,800/PK-12
60 South St 02035 508-543-1660
Dr. Debra Spinelli, supt. Fax 543-4793
www.foxborough.k12.ma.us
Ahern MS 900/5-8
111 Mechanic St 02035 508-543-1610
Susan Abrams, prin. Fax 543-1613
Foxborough HS 800/9-12
120 South St 02035 508-543-1616
Diana Myers-Pachla, prin. Fax 698-6517

Framingham, Middlesex, Pop. 61,638
Framingham SD 8,200/PK-12
454 Water St 01701 508-626-9117
Stacy Scott, supt. Fax 626-9119
www.framingham.k12.ma.us
Cameron MS 500/6-8
215 Elm St 01701 508-879-2290
Judith Kelly, prin. Fax 788-3560
Framingham HS 2,200/9-12
115 A St 01701 508-620-4963
Michael Welch, prin. Fax 877-6603
Fuller MS 500/6-8
31 Flagg Dr 01702 508-620-4956
Juan Rodriguez, prin. Fax 628-1308
Walsh MS 700/6-8
301 Brook St 01701 508-626-9180
Teresa Carney, prin. Fax 626-9167

South Middlesex Regional Technical SD
750 Winter St 01702 508-416-2100
James Lynch, supt. Fax 416-2342
www.keefetech.org
Keefe Technical HS Vo/Tech
750 Winter St 01702 508-416-2100
Jonathan Evans, prin. Fax 416-2342

Blaine The Beauty Career School Post-Sec.
624 Worcester Rd 01702 508-370-3700
Blaine The Beauty Career School Post-Sec.
624 Worcester Rd 01702 508-370-7447
Framingham State College Post-Sec.
PO Box 9101 01701 508-620-1220
Marian HS 300/9-12
273 Union Ave 01702 508-875-7646
Sr. Catherine Clifford, prin. Fax 875-0838

Franklin, Norfolk, Pop. 30,893
Franklin SD 6,000/PK-12
355 E Central St 02038 508-541-5243
Maureen Sabolinski, supt. Fax 533-0321
www.franklin.k12.ma.us
Franklin HS 1,600/9-12
218 Oak St 02038 508-528-5600
Peter Light, prin. Fax 541-2107
Mann MS 500/6-8
224 Oak St 02038 508-553-0322
Shawn Fortin, prin. Fax 541-7071
Remington MS 500/6-8
628 Washington St 02038 508-541-2130
Paul Peri, prin. Fax 541-2124
Sullivan MS 400/6-8
500 Lincoln St 02038 508-553-0322
Beth Wittcoff, prin. Fax 542-2109

Tri-County Regional Vocational Tech SD
147 Pond St 02038 508-528-5400
Stephen Dockray, supt. Fax 528-6074
www.tri-county.tc
Tri-County Regional Vo Tech HS Vo/Tech
147 Pond St 02038 508-528-5400
Jean Mallon, prin. Fax 528-6074

Dean College Post-Sec.
99 Main St 02038 508-541-1508

Gardner, Worcester, Pop. 19,860
Gardner SD 2,500/PK-12
70 Waterford St 01440 978-632-1000
Carol Daring Ph.D., supt. Fax 632-1164
www.gardnerk12.org
Gardner Academy for Learning/Technology 9-12
75 E Broadway 01440 978-632-1606
Mark Pellegrino, prin. Fax 632-1164
Gardner HS 700/9-12
200 Catherine St 01440 978-632-1600
Donna Pierce, prin. Fax 630-4040
Gardner MS 600/6-8
297 Catherine St 01440 978-632-1603
Kimberly Davis, prin. Fax 632-4234

Mt. Wachusett Community College Post-Sec.
444 Green St 01440 978-632-6600

Georgetown, Essex
Georgetown SD 1,700/PK-12
51 North St 01833 978-352-5777
Carol Jacobs, supt. Fax 352-5778
www.georgetown.k12.ma.us
Georgetown MSHS 800/6-12
11 Winter St 01833 978-352-5790
Peter Lucia, prin. Fax 352-5798

Gloucester, Essex, Pop. 28,371
Gloucester SD 3,200/PK-12
6 School House Rd 01930 978-281-9800
Richard Safier, supt. Fax 281-9899
www.gloucesterschools.com
Gloucester HS 1,100/9-12
32 Leslie O Johnson Rd 01930 978-281-9870
Erik Anderson, prin. Fax 281-9733
O'Maley MS 700/6-8
32 Cherry St 01930 978-281-9850
Debra Lucey, prin. Fax 281-9890

Grafton, Worcester
Grafton SD 2,400/PK-12
30 Providence Rd 01519 508-839-5421
James Cummings Ed.D., supt. Fax 839-7618
www.grafton.k12.ma.us
Grafton Memorial HS 700/9-12
24 Providence Rd 01519 508-839-5425
James Pignataro, prin. Fax 839-8544
Grafton MS 400/7-8
22 Providence Rd 01519 508-839-5420
Kristen Gasper, prin. Fax 839-8528

Granby, Hampshire, Pop. 1,346
Granby SD 1,100/PK-12
387 E State St 01033 413-467-7193
Dr. Isabelina Rodriguez, supt. Fax 467-3909
www.granbyschoolsma.org/
Granby JSHS 600/7-12
385 E State St 01033 413-467-7105
Peter Dufresne, prin. Fax 467-3909

MacDuffie S 200/6-12
66 School St, 413-255-0000
Steve Griffin, head sch Fax 467-1607

Great Barrington, Berkshire, Pop. 2,177
Berkshire Hills SD
Supt. — See Stockbridge
Monument Mountain Regional HS 500/9-12
600 Stockbridge Rd 01230 413-528-3346
Marianne Young, prin. Fax 528-9267
Monument Valley Regional MS 400/5-8
313 Monument Valley Rd 01230 413-644-2300
Ben Doren, prin. Fax 644-2394

Bard College at Simon's Rock Post-Sec.
84 Alford Rd 01230 413-644-4400
Great Barrington Waldorf HS 50/9-12
PO Box 905 01230 413-528-8833
Stephen Sagarin Ph.D., admin. Fax 528-5132

Greenfield, Franklin, Pop. 14,016
Greenfield SD 1,500/PK-12
141 Davis St 01301 413-772-1311
Susan Hollins Ph.D., supt. Fax 774-7940
www.gpsk12.org/
Greenfield HS 500/8-12
1 Lenox Ave 01301 413-772-1350
Donna Woodcock, prin. Fax 774-6204

Greenfield Community College Post-Sec.
1 College Dr 01301 413-775-1000
Stoneleigh-Burnham S 200/7-12
574 Bernardston Rd 01301 413-774-2711
Sally Mixsell, head sch Fax 772-2602

Groton, Middlesex, Pop. 1,106
Groton-Dunstable Regional SD 2,800/PK-12
PO Box 729 01450 978-448-5505
Joseph Mastrocola, supt. Fax 448-9402
www.gdrsd.org
Groton-Dunstable Regional HS 900/9-12
PO Box 730 01450 978-448-6362
Michael Mastrullo, prin. Fax 448-0390
Groton-Dunstable Regional MS 900/5-8
PO Box 727 01450 978-448-6155
Steven Silverman, prin. Fax 448-1201

Groton S 400/8-12
PO Box 991 01450 978-448-3363
Temba Maqubela, hdmstr. Fax 448-3100
Lawrence Academy 400/9-12
PO Box 992 01450 978-448-6535
Dan Scheibe, hdmstr. Fax 448-9208

Hadley, Hampshire
Hadley SD 700/PK-12
125 Russell St 01035 413-586-0822
Donna Moyer, supt. Fax 582-6453
www.hadleyschools.org
Hopkins Academy 300/7-12
131 Russell St 01035 413-584-1106
Michael Rooney, prin. Fax 582-6455

Hartsbrook S 300/PK-12
193 Bay Rd 01035 413-584-3198
Fax 586-9438

Hamilton, Essex
Hamilton-Wenham SD
Supt. — See Wenham
Hamilton-Wenham Regional HS 700/9-12
775 Bay Rd 01982 978-468-0400
Eric Tracy, prin. Fax 468-0241
Miles River MS 400/6-8
787 Bay Rd 01982 978-468-0362
John Driscoll, prin. Fax 468-8454

Hampden, Hampden
Hampden-Wilbraham SD
Supt. — See Wilbraham
Burgess MS 300/5-8
85 Wilbraham Rd 01036 413-566-8950
Peter Dufresne, prin. Fax 566-2163

Hanover, Plymouth, Pop. 11,912
Hanover SD 2,700/PK-12
188 Broadway 02339 781-878-0786
Kristine E. Nash Ed.D., supt. Fax 871-3374
www.hanoverschools.org
Hanover HS 700/9-12
287 Cedar St 02339 781-878-5450
Dr. Thomas Raab, prin. Fax 871-0590
Hanover MS 900/5-8
45 Whiting St 02339 781-871-1122
Charles Egan, prin. Fax 871-8792

South Shore Regional Vo Tech SD
476 Webster St 02339 781-878-8822
Thomas Hickey Ed.D., supt. Fax 982-0281
www.ssvotech.org
South Shore Vocational Technical HS Vo/Tech
476 Webster St 02339 781-878-8822
Margaret Dutch, prin. Fax 982-0281

Hanscom AFB, See Bedford
Lincoln SD
Supt. — See Lincoln
Hanscom MS 200/4-8
6 Ent Rd 01731 781-274-0050
Erich Ledebuhr, prin. Fax 274-7329

Hanson, Plymouth, Pop. 2,089
Whitman-Hanson SD
Supt. — See Whitman
Hanson MS 500/6-8
111 Liberty St 02341 781-618-7575
M. Catherine Wollak, prin. Fax 618-8815

Hardwick, Worcester

Eagle Hill S 200/8-12
PO Box 116 01037 413-477-6000
Dr. P.J. McDonald, hdmstr. Fax 477-6837

Harvard, Worcester
Harvard SD 1,300/PK-12
39 Mass Ave 01451 978-456-4140
Joseph Connelly, supt. Fax 456-8592
www.psharvard.org
Bromfield S 700/6-12
14 Mass Ave 01451 978-456-4152
James O'Shea, prin. Fax 456-3013

Harwich, Barnstable
Cape Cod Regional Technical HSD
351 Pleasant Lake Ave 02645 508-432-4500
Robert Sanborn, supt. Fax 432-7916
capetech.us
Cape Cod Regional Technical HS Vo/Tech
351 Pleasant Lake Ave 02645 508-432-4500
Billy Terranova, prin. Fax 430-2430

Monomoy SD
Supt. — See Chatham
Harwich HS 300/9-12
75 Oak St 02645 508-430-7207
Kevin Turner, prin. Fax 430-7223
Harwich MS 400/5-8
204 Sisson Rd 02645 508-430-7212
Leonard Phelan, prin. Fax 430-7230

Hatfield, Hampshire, Pop. 1,311
Hatfield SD 500/PK-12
34 School St 01038 413-247-5641
John Robert, supt. Fax 247-0201
hatfieldps.net
Smith Academy 200/7-12
34 School St 01038 413-247-5641
Andrew Berrios, prin. Fax 247-0201

Hathorne, Essex
Essex Agricultural & Technical HSD
PO Box 362 01937 978-774-0050
Roger Bourgeois, supt. Fax 774-6530
www.agtech.org
Essex Agricultural & Technical HS Vo/Tech
PO Box 362 01937 978-774-0050
Joy White, prin. Fax 774-6530

Haverhill, Essex, Pop. 59,811
Haverhill SD 7,500/PK-12
4 Summer St Ste 104 01830 978-374-3400
James Scully, supt. Fax 374-3422
www.haverhill-ps.org/
Haverhill Alternative S 50/Alt
415 Primrose St 01830 978-374-3482
John DePolo, prin. Fax 372-6070
Haverhill HS 1,700/9-12
137 Monument St 01832 978-374-5700
Bernard Nangle, prin. Fax 374-5705
Hunking MS 500/6-8
100 Winchester St 01835 978-374-5787
Jared Fulgoni, prin. Fax 372-5890
Nettle MS 500/5-8
150 Boardman St 01830 978-374-5792
Michael Rossi, prin. Fax 374-3441
TEACH - Therapeutic Educ Assessment Ctr 50/Alt
415 Primrose St 01830 978-374-7486
John DePolo, prin. Fax 372-6070
Whittier MS 500/5-8
256 Concord St 01830 978-374-5782
Toni Donais, prin. Fax 372-5999

Whittier Regional Vocational SD
115 Amesbury Line Rd 01830 978-373-4101
William DeRosa, supt. Fax 521-0260
www.whittier.tec.ma.us
Whittier Regional Vocational HS Vo/Tech
115 Amesbury Line Rd 01830 978-373-4101
Maureen Lynch, prin. Fax 521-0260

Northern Essex Community College Post-Sec.
100 Elliott St 01830 978-556-3000
Zion Bible College Post-Sec.
320 S Main St 01835 978-478-3400

Hingham, Plymouth, Pop. 5,570
Hingham SD 4,100/PK-12
220 Central St 02043 781-741-1500
Dorothy Galo, supt. Fax 749-7457
www.hinghamschools.com/
Hingham HS 1,100/9-12
17 Union St 02043 781-741-1560
Paula Girouard McCann, prin. Fax 741-1515
Hingham MS 900/6-8
1103 Main St 02043 781-741-1550
Roger Boddie, prin. Fax 749-6297

Notre Dame Academy 600/9-12
1073 Main St 02043 781-749-5930
Kathleen Colin, prin. Fax 749-8366

Holbrook, Norfolk, Pop. 10,445
Holbrook SD 1,200/PK-12
245 S Franklin St 02343 781-767-1226
Dr. Patricia Lally, supt. Fax 767-1312
www.holbrook.k12.ma.us/
Holbrook JSHS 500/7-12
245 S Franklin St 02343 781-767-4616
Vincent Hayward, prin. Fax 767-2697

Holden, Worcester, Pop. 14,628
Wachusett Regional SD
Supt. — See Jefferson
Mountview MS 800/6-8
270 Shrewsbury St 01520 508-829-5577
Erik Githmark, prin. Fax 829-3711
Wachusett Regional HS 2,000/9-12
1401 Main St 01520 508-829-6771
William Beando, prin. Fax 829-4895

Holliston, Middlesex, Pop. 12,926
Holliston SD 2,900/PK-12
370 Hollis St 01746 508-429-0654
Bradford Jackson, supt. Fax 429-0653
www.holliston.k12.ma.us/
Adams MS 600/6-8
323 Woodland St 01746 508-429-0657
Peter Botelho, prin. Fax 429-0690
Holliston HS 900/9-12
370 Hollis St 01746 508-429-0677
Michael Cournoyer, prin. Fax 429-8225

Holyoke, Hampden, Pop. 39,370
Holyoke SD 5,700/PK-12
57 Suffolk St Ste 101 01040 413-534-2005
David Dupont, supt. Fax 534-2297
www.hps.holyoke.ma.us
Dean Vocational Technical HS Vo/Tech
1045 Main St 01040 413-534-2071
Jonathan Carter, prin. Fax 536-9694
Holyoke HS 1,300/9-12
500 Beech St 01040 413-534-2020
Diane Bauer, prin. Fax 534-2098

Springfield SD
Supt. — See Springfield
Early College HS @ HCC 9-12
303 Homestead Ave 01040 413-552-2176
Dwight Hall, dir.

Holyoke Community College Post-Sec.
303 Homestead Ave 01040 413-538-7000

Hopedale, Worcester, Pop. 3,687
Hopedale SD 1,300/PK-12
25 Adin St 01747 508-634-2220
Dennis Breen, supt. Fax 478-1471
www.hopedale.k12.ma.us
Hopedale JSHS 500/7-12
25 Adin St 01747 508-634-2217
Derek Atherton, prin. Fax 634-4319

Hopkinton, Middlesex, Pop. 2,531
Hopkinton SD 3,500/PK-12
89 Hayden Rowe St 01748 508-417-9360
Dr. Steven Hiersche, supt. Fax 497-9833
www.hopkinton.k12.ma.us
Hopkinton HS 1,000/9-12
90 Hayden Rowe St 01748 508-497-9820
Evan Bishop, prin. Fax 497-9829
Hopkinton MS 800/6-8
88 Hayden Rowe St 01748 508-497-9830
Alan Keller Ed.D., prin. Fax 497-9803

Hudson, Middlesex, Pop. 14,374
Hudson SD 2,900/PK-12
155 Apsley St 01749 978-567-6100
Kevin Lyons, supt. Fax 567-6123
www.hudson.k12.ma.us
Hudson JSHS 1,100/8-12
69 Brigham St 01749 978-567-6250
Brian Reagan, prin. Fax 567-6285

Hull, Plymouth, Pop. 10,097
Hull SD 1,200/PK-12
180 Harborview Rd 02045 781-925-4400
Kathleen Tyrell, supt. Fax 925-8042
www.town.hull.ma.us
Hull HS 400/9-12
180 Main St 02045 781-925-3000
Michael Devine, prin. Fax 925-3071
Memorial MS 300/6-8
81 Central Ave 02045 781-925-2040
Anthony Hrivnak, prin. Fax 925-8002

Huntington, Hampshire, Pop. 920
Gateway SD 900/PK-12
12 Littleville Rd 01050 413-685-1000
Dr. David Hopson, supt. Fax 667-8739
www.grsd.org
Gateway Regional JSHS 300/7-12
12 Littleville Rd 01050 413-685-1100
Jason Finnie, prin. Fax 667-5593

Hyannis, Barnstable, Pop. 14,120
Barnstable SD 4,000/PK-12
PO Box 955 02601 508-862-4953
Mary Czajkowski, supt. Fax 790-6454
www.barnstable.k12.ma.us/
Barnstable HS 2,000/8-12
744 W Main St 02601 508-790-6445
Patrick Clark, prin. Fax 790-6430

Blaine The Beauty Career School Post-Sec.
259 North St Ste 3 02601 508-771-1680
Pope John Paul II HS 100/9-12
120 High School Rd 02601 508-862-6336
Christopher Keavy, prin. Fax 862-6339
St. Francis Xavier Prep S 300/5-8
33 Cross St 02601 508-771-7200
Robert Deburro, hdmstr. Fax 771-7233

Hyde Park, See Boston
Boston SD
Supt. — See Boston
Boston Community Leadership Academy 500/9-12
655 Metropolitan Ave 02136 617-635-8937
Brett Dickens, hdmstr. Fax 635-8942
New Mission HS 300/9-12
655 Metropolitan Ave 02136 617-635-6425
Naia Wilson, hdmstr. Fax 635-7698
Rogers MS 600/6-8
15 Everett St 02136 617-635-8700
Corbett Coutts, prin. Fax 635-8708

Parkside Christian Academy 200/PK-12
20 Como Rd 02136 617-522-1841
Michael Dixon Ph.D., head sch Fax 524-9583

Indian Orchard, See Springfield
Springfield SD
Supt. — See Springfield
Springfield Public Day HS 300/Alt
90 Berkshire St 01151 413-787-7036
Rhonda Jacobs, prin. Fax 787-6828

Ipswich, Essex, Pop. 4,128
Ipswich SD 2,100/PK-12
1 Lord Sq 01938 978-356-2935
Richard Korb, supt. Fax 356-0445
www.ipswichschools.org
Ipswich HS 700/9-12
134 High St 01938 978-356-3137
David Dalton, prin. Fax 356-3720
Ipswich MS 500/6-8
130 High St 01938 978-356-3535
David Fabrizio, prin. Fax 412-8169

Jamaica Plain, See Boston
Boston SD
Supt. — See Boston
Community Academy 50/Alt
25 Glen Rd 02130 617-635-7734
Carol Moore, prin. Fax 635-7731
English HS 800/9-12
144 McBride St 02130 617-635-8979
Ligia Noriega-Murphy, prin. Fax 635-8988
Muniz Academy, 20 Child St 02130 9-12
Dr. Dania Vazquez, prin. 617-470-6907

Jefferson, Worcester
Wachusett Regional SD 7,200/PK-12
1745 Main St 01522 508-829-1670
Thomas Pandiscio Ed.D., supt. Fax 829-1680
www.wrsd.net
Other Schools – See Holden, Rutland, Sterling

Kingston, Plymouth, Pop. 5,491
Silver Lake Regional SD 1,800/7-12
250 Pembroke St 02364 781-585-4313
John Tuffy, supt. Fax 585-2994
www.slrsd.org
Silver Lake Regional HS 1,200/9-12
260 Pembroke St 02364 781-585-3844
James Mulcahy, prin. Fax 585-6544
Silver Lake Regional MS 600/7-8
256 Pembroke St 02364 781-582-3555
James Dupille, prin. Fax 582-3599

Sacred Heart HS 600/7-12
399 Bishops Hwy 02364 781-585-7511
Michael Gill, prin. Fax 396-3230

Lakeville, Plymouth
Freetown-Lakeville SD 2,900/PK-12
98 Howland Rd 02347 508-923-2000
Jessica Aran, supt. Fax 923-0934
www.freelake.org/
Apponequet Regional HS 800/9-12
100 Howland Rd 02347 508-947-2660
David Patota, prin. Fax 946-2350
Freetown-Lakeville MS 800/6-8
96 Howland Rd 02347 508-923-3518
Ralph Olsen, prin. Fax 946-2050

Lancaster, Worcester
Nashoba Regional SD
Supt. — See Bolton
Burbank MS 300/6-8
1 Hollywood Dr 01523 978-365-4558
Patrick Perkins, prin. Fax 365-6882

Lawrence, Essex, Pop. 75,608
Lawrence SD 12,300/PK-12
255 Essex St 01840 978-975-5900
Jeffrey Riley, supt. Fax 722-8550
www.lawrence.k12.ma.us
Arlington MS 500/5-8
150 Arlington St 01841 978-975-5930
Robin Finn, prin. Fax 722-8519
Business Management & Finance HS 500/9-12
70-71 N Parish Rd 01843 978-946-0713
Carline Pignato, prin. Fax 722-8501
Frost MS 500/5-8
33 Hamlet St 01843 978-975-5941
Ellen Baranowski, prin. Fax 722-8513
Guilmette MS 500/5-8
80 Bodwell St 01841 978-722-8270
Mary Giordano, prin. Fax 722-8524
Health & Human Services HS 500/9-12
70-71 N Parish Rd 01843 978-946-0735
Paul Neal, prin. Fax 722-8502
Humanities & Leadership Development HS 500/9-12
70-71 N Parish Rd 01843 978-946-0724
Michael Fiato, prin. Fax 722-8503
International HS 500/9-12
70-71 N Parish Rd 01843 978-946-0712
Geraldo Acosta, prin. Fax 722-8504
HS Learning Center 300/9-12
183 Haverhill St 01840 978-975-5917
Christina DiBenedetto, prin. Fax 722-8531
Leonard MS 200/7-8
60 Allen St 01840 978-975-5962
Dr. Edward Reynoso, prin. Fax 722-8533
Mathematics Science & Technology HS 500/9-12
70-71 N Parish Rd 01843 978-946-0719
Timothy McCarron, prin. Fax 722-8505

Parthum MS 600/5-8
255 E Haverhill St 01841 978-691-7224
Peter Lefebre, prin. Fax 722-8536
Performing & Fine Arts HS 500/9-12
70-71 N Parish Rd 01843 978-946-0766
Paul Beninato, prin. Fax 722-8506
South Lawrence East MS 400/6-8
165 Crawford St 01843 978-975-5993
Alyce Merlino, prin. Fax 722-8538

Bellesini Academy 100/5-8
94 Bradford St 01840 978-989-0004
Julie DeFillippo, dir. Fax 989-9404
Central Catholic HS 1,300/9-12
300 Hampshire St 01841 978-682-0260
Doreen Keller, prin. Fax 685-2707
Esperanza Academy S of Hope 100/5-8
198 Garden St 01840 978-686-4673
Christopher Wilson, head sch Fax 681-1591
Notre Dame Cristo Rey HS 300/9-12
303 Haverhill St 01840 978-689-8222
Thomas Arria, prin. Fax 689-8728

Lee, Berkshire, Pop. 2,028
Lee SD 800/PK-12
480 Pleasant St Ste B200 01238 413-243-0276
Alfred Skrocki, supt. Fax 243-4995
www.leepublicschools.net
Lee MSHS 500/7-12
300 Greylock St 01238 413-243-2781
Joseph Turmel, prin. Fax 243-4105

Leicester, Worcester, Pop. 10,191
Leicester SD 1,900/PK-12
1078 Main St 01524 508-892-7040
Dr. Judith J. Paolucci, supt. Fax 892-7043
www.leicester.k12.ma.us/
Leicester HS 500/9-12
174 Paxton St 01524 508-892-7030
Thomas Lauder, prin. Fax 892-7034
Leicester MS 400/6-8
70 Winslow Ave 01524 508-892-7055
Jennifer Sauter, prin. Fax 892-7047

Lenox, Berkshire, Pop. 1,652
Lenox SD 800/PK-12
6 Walker St Ste 3 01240 413-637-5550
Dr. Edward Costa, supt. Fax 637-5559
www.lenoxps.org
Lenox Memorial HS 500/6-12
197 East St 01240 413-637-5560
Michael Knybel, prin. Fax 637-5564

Berkshire County Christian S 50/PK-12
PO Box 1980 01240 413-637-2474
Heidi Dickerson, prin.

Leominster, Worcester, Pop. 39,624
Leominster SD 6,200/PK-12
24 Church St 01453 978-534-7700
Jim Jolicoeur, supt. Fax 534-7775
www.leominster.mec.edu/
Leominster Center Technical Education Vo/Tech
122 Granite St 01453 978-534-7735
David Fiandaca, dir. Fax 537-7934
Leominster HS 1,200/9-12
122 Granite St 01453 978-534-7715
Tom Browne, prin. Fax 537-1765
Samoset MS 500/6-8
100 DeCicco Dr 01453 978-534-7725
Colleen LeClair, prin. Fax 466-7421
Sky View MS 900/6-8
500 Kennedy Way 01453 978-534-7780
Timothy Blake, prin. Fax 840-8600

Lexington, Middlesex, Pop. 30,568
Lexington SD 6,400/PK-12
146 Maple St 02420 781-861-2580
Paul Ash Ph.D., supt. Fax 863-5829
lps.lexingtonma.org
Clarke MS 800/6-8
17 Stedman Rd 02421 781-861-2450
Anna Monaco, prin. Fax 674-2043
Diamond MS 700/6-8
99 Hancock St 02420 781-861-2460
Anne Carothers, prin. Fax 274-0174
Lexington HS 2,000/9-12
251 Waltham St 02421 781-861-2320
Laura Lasa, prin. Fax 861-2440

Minuteman Voc Tech SD
758 Marrett Rd 02421 781-861-6500
Dr. Edward Bouquillon, supt. Fax 863-1747
www.minuteman.org
Minuteman Regional Technical HS Vo/Tech
758 Marrett Rd 02421 781-861-6500
Ernest Houle, prin. Fax 863-1747

Lexington Christian Academy 300/6-12
48 Bartlett Ave 02420 781-862-7850
Timothy Russell, head sch Fax 863-8503

Lincoln, Middlesex, Pop. 2,850
Lincoln SD 1,100/PK-8
6 Ballfield Rd 01773 781-259-9409
Rebecca McFall, supt. Fax 259-9246
www.lincnet.org/
Other Schools – See Hanscom AFB

Littleton, Middlesex, Pop. 2,867
Littleton SD 1,600/PK-12
PO Box 1486 01460 978-540-2500
Kelly Clenchy, supt. Fax 486-9581
www.littletonps.org/
Littleton HS 400/9-12
56 King St 01460 978-952-2555
John Harrington, prin. Fax 486-0758
Littleton MS 400/6-8
55 Russell St 01460 978-486-8938
Mark Branco, prin. Fax 952-4547

Longmeadow, Hampden, Pop. 15,594
Longmeadow SD 3,000/PK-12
535 Bliss Rd 01106 413-565-4200
Marie Doyle, supt. Fax 565-4215
sites.longmeadow.k12.ma.us/www/
Glenbrook MS 400/6-8
110 Cambridge Cir 01106 413-565-4250
Daniel Sullivan, prin. Fax 565-4277
Longmeadow HS 1,000/9-12
95 Grassy Gutter Rd 01106 413-565-4220
Lawrence Berte, prin. Fax 565-4233
Williams MS 400/6-8
410 Williams St 01106 413-565-4260
Chris Collins, prin. Fax 565-4254

Bay Path College Post-Sec.
588 Longmeadow St 01106 413-565-1000

Lowell, Middlesex, Pop. 102,517
Lowell SD, 43 Highland St 01852 13,400/PK-12
Jean Franco, supt. 978-674-4324
www.lowell.k12.ma.us/
Butler MS 500/5-8
1140 Gorham St 01852 978-937-8973
Eilish Connaughton, prin. Fax 937-2819
Daley MS 700/5-8
150 Fleming St 01851 978-937-8981
Liam Skinner, prin. Fax 937-7610
Lowell HS 3,400/9-12
50 Father Morissette Blvd 01852 978-937-8900
Ed Rozmiark, hdmstr. Fax 937-8902
Lowell HS Alternative S Alt
125 Smith St 01851 978-970-3318
Cathy Keane, coord. Fax 275-6399
McHugh Alternative MS Alt
73 Woburn St 01852 978-453-1115
Ellen Spiegel, dir. Fax 441-1050
McHugh Alternative S Alt
21 Carter St 01852 978-937-7642
David Cook, coord. Fax 937-7656
Robinson MS 600/5-8
110 June St 01850 978-937-8974
Thad King, prin. Fax 937-8988
Stoklosa MS 700/5-8
560 Broadway St 01854 978-937-7604
Nancy O'Loughlin, prin. Fax 275-6343
Sullivan MS 700/5-8
150 Draper St 01852 978-937-8993
Jacqueline Perrin, prin. Fax 937-3278
Wang MS 700/5-8
365 W Meadow Rd 01854 978-937-7683
Gayle Feeney, prin. Fax 937-7680
Adult Basic Education Program Adult
408 Merrimack St 01854 978-937-8989
Fax 458-9007

Blaine The Beauty Career School Post-Sec.
231 Central St 01852 978-459-9959
Community Christian Academy 200/PK-12
105 Princeton Blvd 01851 978-453-4738
Jennifer Najem, prin. Fax 453-1506
Lincoln Technical Institute Post-Sec.
211 Plain St 01852 978-458-4800
Lowell Academy Hairstyling Institute Post-Sec.
136 Central St 01852 978-453-3235
Lowell Catholic HS 400/9-12
530 Stevens St 01851 978-452-1794
Maryellen DeMarco, prin. Fax 452-5646
University of Massachusetts Lowell Post-Sec.
1 University Ave 01854 978-934-4000

Ludlow, Hampden, Pop. 18,820
Ludlow SD 3,000/PK-12
63 Chestnut St 01056 413-583-8372
Todd Gazda, supt. Fax 583-5666
www.ludlowps.org
Baird MS 700/6-8
1 Rooney Rd 01056 413-583-5685
Sheryl Stanton, prin. Fax 583-5636
Ludlow HS 1,000/9-12
500 Chapin St 01056 413-589-9001
Lisa Nemeth, prin. Fax 583-5637

Jolie Hair and Beauty Academy Post-Sec.
44 Sewall St 01056 413-589-0747

Lunenburg, Worcester, Pop. 1,728
Lunenburg SD 1,200/PK-12
1025 Massachusetts Ave 01462 978-582-4100
Loxi Jo Calmes, supt. Fax 582-4103
www.lunenburgonline.com
Lunenburg HS 500/8-12
1079 Massachusetts Ave 01462 978-582-4115
Brian Spadafino, prin. Fax 582-4153

Twin City Christian S 100/PK-12
194 Electric Ave 01462 978-582-4901
Jack Murray, admin. Fax 582-4978

Lynn, Essex, Pop. 87,864
Lynn SD 13,600/PK-12
90 Commercial St 01905 781-593-1680
Catherine Latham, supt. Fax 477-7487
www.lynnschools.org/
Breed MS 1,200/6-8
90 OCallaghan Way 01905 781-477-7330
Julie Louf, prin. Fax 581-6985
Classical HS 1,400/9-12
235 OCallaghan Way 01905 781-477-7404
Gene Constantino, prin. Fax 477-7212
English HS 1,700/9-12
50 Goodridge St 01902 781-477-7366
Thomas Strangie, prin. Fax 477-7365
Fecteau-Leary JSHS 100/7-12
33 N Common St 01902 781-268-3007
Maura Durgin-Scully, prin. Fax 268-3006
Lynn Vocational Technical Institute Vo/Tech
80 Neptune Blvd 01902 781-477-7431
Diane Paradis, prin. Fax 477-7415
Marshall MS 900/6-8
19 Porter St 01902 781-477-7360
Richard Cowdell, prin. Fax 477-7355
Pickering MS 600/6-8
70 Conomo Ave 01904 781-477-7440
Kevin Rittershaus, prin. Fax 477-7202

St. Mary JSHS 700/7-12
35 Tremont St 01902 781-595-7885
Grace Regan, head sch Fax 595-4471

Lynnfield, Essex, Pop. 11,472
Lynnfield SD 2,300/PK-12
55 Summer St 01940 781-334-5800
Thomas Jefferson Ed.D., supt. Fax 334-5802
www.lynnfield.k12.ma.us/
Lynnfield HS 600/9-12
275 Essex St 01940 781-334-5820
Robert Cleary, prin. Fax 334-7207
Lynnfield MS 800/5-8
505 Main St 01940 781-334-5810
Stephen Ralston, prin. Fax 334-7203

Malden, Middlesex, Pop. 56,660
Malden SD 6,500/PK-12
200 Pleasant St 02148 781-397-7204
David DeRuosi, supt. Fax 397-7276
www.malden.mec.edu
Malden HS 1,800/9-12
77 Salem St 02148 781-397-6001
Dana Brown, prin. Fax 397-7224

Blaine The Beauty Career School Post-Sec.
347 Pleasant St 02148 781-397-7400
Malden Catholic HS 600/9-12
99 Crystal St 02148 781-322-3098
Br. Thomas Puccio, prin. Fax 397-0573
New England Hair Academy Post-Sec.
492 Main St # 500 02148 781-324-6799
Salter School Post-Sec.
2 Florence St 02148 781-324-5454

Manchester, Essex, Pop. 5,286
Manchester Essex Regional SD 1,400/PK-12
PO Box 1407 01944 978-526-4919
Pamela Beaudoin, supt. Fax 526-7585
www.mersd.org
Manchester Essex Regional HS 500/9-12
36 Lincoln St 01944 978-526-4412
Sharon Maguire, prin. Fax 526-2046
Manchester Essex Regional MS 200/6-8
36 Lincoln St 01944 978-526-2022
Catherine Cullinane, prin. Fax 526-2046

Mansfield, Bristol, Pop. 7,170
Mansfield SD 4,800/K-12
2 Park Row 02048 508-261-7500
Brenda Hodges, supt. Fax 261-7509
www.mansfieldschools.com
Mansfield HS 1,500/9-12
250 East St 02048 508-261-7540
Michael Connolly, prin. Fax 339-0259
Qualters MS 1,200/6-8
240 East St 02048 508-261-7530
Zeffro Gianetti, prin. Fax 261-7535

Marblehead, Essex, Pop. 19,576
Marblehead SD 3,200/PK-12
9 Widger Rd 01945 781-639-3141
Gregory Maass, supt. Fax 639-3149
www.marbleheadschools.org
Marblehead HS 1,000/9-12
2 Humphrey St 01945 781-639-3100
Debra Heaton, prin. Fax 639-3105
Marblehead Veterans MS 500/7-8
217 Pleasant St 01945 781-639-3120
Matthew Fox, prin. Fax 639-3130

Marion, Plymouth, Pop. 1,426

Tabor Academy 500/9-12
66 Spring St 02738 508-748-2000
John Quirk, head sch Fax 291-6666

Marlborough, Middlesex, Pop. 36,087
Assabet Valley SD
215 Fitchburg St 01752 508-485-9430
Patrick Collins, supt. Fax 460-3472
www.assabettech.com
Assabet Valley Regional Technical HS Vo/Tech
215 Fitchburg St 01752 508-485-9430
Mark Hollick, prin. Fax 460-3472

Marlborough SD 3,800/PK-12
17 Washington St 01752 508-460-3509
Stephen Dlott Ed.D., supt. Fax 485-1142
www.mps-edu.org
Marlborough HS 1,100/9-12
431 Bolton St 01752 508-460-3500
Craig Hardimon, prin. Fax 460-3501
Whitcomb MS 1,000/5-8
25 Union St 01752 508-460-3502
Mary Murphy, prin. Fax 460-3597

Hillside S 100/5-9
404 Robin Hill St 01752 508-485-2824
David Beecher, hdmstr. Fax 485-4420

Marshfield, Plymouth, Pop. 4,261
Marshfield SD 4,700/PK-12
76 S River St 02050 781-834-5000
Scott Borstel, supt. Fax 834-5070
www.mpsd.org/

Furnace Brook MS 1,100/6-8
500 Furnace St 02050 781-834-5020
Patrick Sullivan, prin. Fax 834-5899
Marshfield HS 1,400/9-12
167 Forest St 02050 781-834-5050
Robert Keuther, prin. Fax 834-5040

Mashpee, Barnstable
Mashpee SD 1,700/K-12
150A Old Barnstable Rd 02649 508-539-1500
Ann Bradshaw, supt. Fax 477-5805
www.mashpee.k12.ma.us
Mashpee HS 500/9-12
500 Old Barnstable Rd 02649 508-539-3600
Jane Day, prin. Fax 539-3607
Mashpee MS 300/7-8
500 Old Barnstable Rd 02649 508-539-3600
Sheila Arnold, prin. Fax 521-1145

Mattapan, See Boston
Boston SD
Supt. — See Boston
Mildred Avenue S 600/3-8
5 Mildred Ave 02126 617-635-1642
Deborah Dancy, prin. Fax 635-1641

Mattapoisett, Plymouth, Pop. 2,949
Old Rochester Regional SD 1,200/7-12
135 Marion Rd 02739 508-758-2772
Douglas White, supt. Fax 758-2802
www.oldrochester.org
Old Rochester Regional HS 700/9-12
135 Marion Rd 02739 508-758-3745
Michael Devoll, prin. Fax 758-3167
Old Rochester Regional JHS 500/7-8
133 Marion Rd 02739 508-758-4928
Kevin Brogioli, prin. Fax 758-6021

Maynard, Middlesex, Pop. 9,932
Maynard SD 1,300/PK-12
12 Bancroft St 01754 978-897-2222
Dr. Robert Gerardi, supt. Fax 897-4610
www.maynardschools.org
Fowler S 500/4-8
3 Tiger Dr 01754 978-897-6700
Jeff Mela, prin. Fax 897-5737
Maynard HS 300/9-12
1 Tiger Dr 01754 978-897-8891
Charles Caragianes, prin. Fax 897-6089

Medfield, Norfolk, Pop. 6,407
Medfield SD 2,900/PK-12
459 Main St Fl 3 02052 508-359-2302
Robert Maguire, supt. Fax 359-9829
www.medfield.net
Blake MS 700/6-8
24 Pound St 02052 508-359-2396
Nathaniel Vaughn, prin. Fax 359-1415
Medfield HS 900/9-12
88R South St 02052 508-359-8385
Robert Parga, prin. Fax 359-2963

Montrose S 200/6-12
29 North St 02052 508-359-2423
Karen Bohlin Ed.D., head sch Fax 359-2597

Medford, Middlesex, Pop. 53,960
Medford SD 4,800/PK-12
489 Winthrop St 02155 781-393-2442
Roy Belson, supt. Fax 393-2322
www.medford.k12.ma.us
Andrews MS 500/6-8
3000 Mystic Valley Pkwy 02155 781-393-2228
Paul D'Alleva, prin. Fax 395-8128
Curtis-Tufts Alternative S 50/Alt
437 Main St 02155 781-393-2343
Anthony Volpe, prin. Fax 393-0699
McGlynn MS 600/6-8
3004 Mystic Valley Pkwy 02155 781-393-2333
Jacob Edwards, prin. Fax 393-5462
Medford HS 1,200/9-12
489 Winthrop St 02155 781-393-2301
John Perella, prin. Fax 395-1468
Medford Vo-Tech HS Vo/Tech
489 Winthrop St 02155 781-393-2260
William Mahoney, prin. Fax 393-2293

Lawrence Memorial/Regis College Post-Sec.
170 Governors Ave 02155 781-306-6600
St. Clement S 200/K-12
579 Boston Ave 02155 617-393-5600
Robert Chevrier, prin. Fax 396-3230
The Elizabeth Grady School of Esthetics Post-Sec.
34 Salem St 02155 781-395-1971
Tufts University Post-Sec.
520 Boston Ave 02155 617-628-5000

Medway, Norfolk, Pop. 9,931
Medway SD 2,600/PK-12
45 Holliston St 02053 508-533-3222
Dr. Judith Evans, supt. Fax 533-3226
www.medwayschools.org
Medway HS 800/9-12
88 Summer St 02053 508-533-3227
Douglas Dias, prin. Fax 533-3246
Medway MS 900/5-8
45 Holliston St 02053 508-533-3230
Armand Pires, prin. Fax 533-3257

Melrose, Middlesex, Pop. 26,480
Melrose SD 3,800/PK-12
360 Lynn Fells Pkwy 02176 781-662-2000
Cyndy Taymore, supt. Fax 979-2149
www.melroseschools.com
Melrose HS 1,000/9-12
360 Lynn Fells Pkwy 02176 781-979-2202
Marianne Farrell, prin. Fax 979-2205

Melrose MS 900/6-8
350 Lynn Fells Pkwy 02176 781-979-2102
Thomas Brow, prin. Fax 979-2104

Mendon, Worcester
Mendon-Upton Regional SD 2,700/PK-12
150 North Ave 01756 508-634-1585
Joseph Maruszczak, supt. Fax 634-1582
mursd.org
Miscoe Hill S 900/5-8
148 North Ave 01756 508-634-1590
Ann Farrell, prin. Fax 634-1576
Other Schools – See Upton

Bethany Christian Academy 100/PK-12
15 Cape Rd 01756 508-634-8171
Cheri McCutchen, dir. Fax 478-4706

Methuen, Essex, Pop. 46,662
Methuen SD 7,100/PK-12
90 Hampshire St 01844 978-722-6000
Judith Scannell, supt. Fax 722-6002
www.methuen.k12.ma.us
Methuen HS 1,800/9-12
1 Ranger Rd 01844 978-722-6041
Jim Giuca, prin Fax 722-6042

Fellowship Christian Academy 100/PK-12
1 Fellowship Way 01844 978-686-9373
Chris Dyer, admin. Fax 685-7466
Presentation of Mary Academy 200/9-12
209 Lawrence St 01844 978-682-9391
Rose Maria Redman, prin. Fax 975-3595

Middleboro, Plymouth, Pop. 7,135
Middleborough SD 3,500/PK-12
30 Forest St 02346 508-946-2000
Dr. Roseli Weiss, supt. Fax 946-2004
www.middleboro.k12.ma.us
Middleboro HS 900/9-12
71 E Grove St 02346 508-946-2010
Paul Branagan, prin. Fax 946-8852
Nichols MS 900/6-8
112 Tiger Dr 02346 508-946-2020
Martin Geoghegan, prin. Fax 946-2019

Middleton, Essex, Pop. 4,921
North Shore Regional Vocational SD
PO Box 806 01949 978-762-0001
Daniel O'Connell, supt. Fax 777-8403
www.nsths.net/
North Shore Technical HS Vo/Tech
PO Box 806 01949 978-762-0001
Brad Morgan, prin. Fax 774-0264

Milford, Worcester, Pop. 23,757
Milford SD 4,200/PK-12
31 W Fountain St 01757 508-478-1100
Robert Tremblay, supt. Fax 478-1459
www.milfordpublicschools.com
Milford HS 1,100/9-12
31 W Fountain St 01757 508-478-1110
Carolyn Banach, prin. Fax 478-1460
Milford MS East 300/8-8
45 Main St 01757 508-478-1170
Nancy Angelini, prin. Fax 634-2381

Millbury, Worcester, Pop. 12,228
Millbury SD 1,800/PK-12
12 Martin St 01527 508-865-9501
Susan Hitchcock, supt. Fax 865-0888
www.millburyschools.org
Millbury JSHS 800/7-12
12 Martin St 01527 508-865-5841
Mandy Vasil, prin. Fax 865-0888

Millis, Norfolk, Pop. 4,081
Millis SD 1,500/PK-12
245 Plain St 02054 508-376-7000
Nancy Gustafson, supt. Fax 376-7020
www.millisps.org
Millis HS 400/9-12
245 Plain St 02054 508-376-7010
Robert Mullaney, prin. Fax 376-7020
Millis MS 400/5-8
245 Plain St 02054 508-376-7014
Andrew Zitoli, prin. Fax 376-7020

Milton, Norfolk, Pop. 26,216
Milton SD 3,900/PK-12
25 Gile Rd 02186 617-696-4808
Mary C. Gormley, supt. Fax 696-5099
www.miltonps.org
Milton HS 1,000/9-12
25 Gile Rd 02186 617-696-4470
James Jette, prin. Fax 696-6990
Pierce MS 800/6-8
451 Central Ave 02186 617-696-4568
Dr. Karen Spaulding, prin. Fax 698-2238

Curry College Post-Sec.
1071 Blue Hill Ave 02186 617-333-0500
Fontbonne Academy 400/9-12
930 Brook Rd 02186 617-696-3241
Mary Ellen Barnes, hdmstr. Fax 696-7688
Milton Academy 1,000/K-12
170 Centre St 02186 617-898-1798
Todd Bland, hdmstr. Fax 898-1700

Monson, Hampden, Pop. 2,101
Monson SD 1,400/PK-12
PO Box 159 01057 413-267-4150
Edward Malvey, supt. Fax 267-9168
www.monsonschools.com
Granite Valley MS 500/5-8
21 Thompson St 01057 413-267-4155
Cheryl Clarke, prin. Fax 267-4624

Monson HS 400/9-12
55 Margaret St 01057 413-267-4589
Andrew Linkenhoker, prin. Fax 267-4157

Montague, Franklin
Gill-Montague SD
Supt. — See Turners Falls
Great Falls MS 300/6-8
224 Turnpike Rd 01351 413-863-7300
Donna Fitzpatrick, prin. Fax 863-7354
Turners Falls HS 300/9-12
222 Turnpike Rd 01351 413-863-7200
Patricia Gardner, prin. Fax 863-7353

Mount Hermon, Franklin

Northfield Mt. Hermon S 600/9-12
1 Lamplighter Way 01354 413-498-3000
Peter Fayroian, hdmstr. Fax 498-3170

Nantucket, Nantucket, Pop. 7,268
Nantucket SD 1,300/PK-12
10 Surfside Rd 02554 508-228-7285
William Cozort, supt. Fax 325-5318
www.npsk.org
Nantucket HS 400/9-12
10 Surfside Rd 02554 508-228-7280
John Buckey, prin. Fax 325-5318
Peirce MS 300/6-8
10 Surfside Rd 02554 508-228-7283
Scott Meadows, prin. Fax 325-7597

Natick, Middlesex, Pop. 30,700
Natick SD 4,700/PK-12
13 E Central St 01760 508-647-6500
Dr. Peter Sanchioni, supt. Fax 647-6506
www.natickps.org/
Kennedy MS 600/5-8
165 Mill St 01760 508-647-6650
Rosemary Vickery, prin. Fax 647-6658
Natick HS 1,300/PK-PK, 9-
15 West St 01760 508-647-6600
Rose Bertucci, prin. Fax 651-7372
Wilson MS 900/5-8
22 Rutledge Rd 01760 508-647-6670
Dr. Tyler Page, prin. Fax 647-6678

Walnut Hill S for the Arts 300/9-12
12 Highland St 01760 508-653-4312
Antonio Viva, head sch Fax 655-3726

Needham, Norfolk, Pop. 28,386
Needham SD 5,400/PK-12
1330 Highland Ave 02492 781-455-0400
Dr. Daniel Gutekanst, supt. Fax 455-0417
www.needham.k12.ma.us/
Pollard MS 800/7-8
200 Harris Ave 02492 781-455-0480
Lisa Chen, prin. Fax 455-0413
Other Schools – See Needham Heights

Franklin W. Olin College of Engineering Post-Sec.
Olin Way 02492 781-292-2300
Haddad MS 200/6-8
110 May St 02492 781-449-0133
Jane Abel, prin. Fax 449-8096
St. Sebastians S 400/7-12
1191 Greendale Ave 02492 781-449-5200
William Burke, hdmstr. Fax 449-5630

Needham Heights, Norfolk
Needham SD
Supt. — See Needham
Needham HS 1,400/9-12
609 Webster St 02494 781-455-0800
Jonathan Pizzi, prin. Fax 449-5111

New Bedford, Bristol, Pop. 86,721
Greater New Bedford Reg Vo/Tech HSD
1121 Ashley Blvd 02745 508-998-3321
Linda Enos, supt. Fax 995-7268
www.gnbvt.edu
Greater New Bedford Reg. Vo Tech HS Vo/Tech
1121 Ashley Blvd 02745 508-998-3321
Michael Murphy, prin. Fax 995-7268

New Bedford SD 12,400/PK-12
455 County St 02740 508-997-4511
Pia Durkin Ph.D., supt. Fax 997-0298
www.newbedfordschools.org
Keith MS 1,000/6-8
225 Hathaway Blvd 02740 508-997-4511
Peter Sykes, prin. Fax 996-2040
New Bedford HS 2,700/9-12
230 Hathaway Blvd 02740 508-997-4511
Andrew Kulak, prin. Fax 991-7483
Normandin MS 1,000/6-8
81 Felton St 02745 508-997-4511
William Burkhead, prin. Fax 995-6975
Roosevelt MS 800/6-8
119 Frederick St 02744 508-997-4511
Margaret Mongiello, prin. Fax 997-1198
Trinity Day Academy 50/Alt
181 Hillman St 02740 508-997-4511
Charles Jodoin, prin. Fax 991-7483
Whaling City Alternative S 50/Alt
455 County St 02740 508-997-4511
Warley Williams, prin.

LaBaron Hairdressing Academy Post-Sec.
281 Union St 02740 508-996-6611
Nazarene Christian Academy 100/PK-12
764 Hathaway Rd 02740 508-992-7944
Rev. Jon Helm, hdmstr. Fax 994-1457
Rob Roy Academy Post-Sec.
1872 Acushnet Ave 02746 508-995-8711
St. Luke's Hospital Post-Sec.
101 Page St 02740 508-997-1525

Salter School | Post-Sec.
950 Kings Hwy Ste 4 02745 | 774-328-3500

Newburyport, Essex, Pop. 17,171
Newburyport SD | 2,300/PK-12
70 Low St 01950 | 978-465-4457
Marc Kerble Ed.D., supt. | Fax 462-3495
www.newburyport.k12.ma.us/
Newburyport HS | 700/9-12
241 High St 01950 | 978-465-4440
Michael Parent, prin. | Fax 465-2198
Nock MS | 500/6-8
70 Low St 01950 | 978-465-4447
Beth Raucci, prin. | Fax 465-4074

Newton, Middlesex, Pop. 83,100
Newton SD
Supt. — See Newtonville
Bigelow MS | 500/6-8
42 Vernon St 02458 | 617-552-7800
Todd Harrison, prin. | Fax 552-7752
Oak Hill MS | 600/6-8
130 Wheeler Rd 02459 | 617-559-9200
Eva Thompson, prin. | Fax 552-5547

Hebrew College | Post-Sec.
160 Herrick Rd 02459 | 617-559-8600
Lasell College | Post-Sec.
1844 Commonwealth Ave 02466 | 617-243-2000
Mt. Alvernia HS | 200/7-12
790 Centre St 02458 | 617-969-2260
Eileen McLaughlin, hdmstr. | Fax 969-4246
New England School of Acupuncture | Post-Sec.
150 California St 02458 | 617-558-1788
Newton Country Day S | 400/5-12
785 Centre St 02458 | 617-244-4246
Sr. Barbara Rogers, hdmstr. | Fax 965-5313

Newton Center, See Newton
Newton SD
Supt. — See Newtonville
Brown MS | 700/6-8
125 Meadowbrook Rd 02459 | 617-559-6900
John Jordan, prin. | Fax 552-7729
Newton South HS | 1,700/9-12
140 Brandeis Rd 02459 | 617-559-6700
Joel Stembridge, prin. | Fax 559-6701

Andover Newton Theological School | Post-Sec.
210 Herrick Rd 02459 | 617-964-1100
Mt. Ida College | Post-Sec.
777 Dedham St 02459 | 617-928-4500
Solomon Schechter Day S Greater Boston | 300/4-8
125 Wells Ave 02459 | 617-928-9100
Arnold Zar-Kessler, head sch | Fax 964-9401

Newtonville, See Newton
Newton SD | 11,900/PK-12
100 Walnut St 02460 | 617-559-6100
David Fleishman, supt. | Fax 559-6101
www3.newton.k12.ma.us/
Day MS | 800/6-8
21 Minot Pl 02460 | 617-559-9100
Brian Turner, prin. | Fax 559-9103
Newton North HS | 1,800/9-12
457 Walnut St 02460 | 617-559-6200
Dr. Jennifer Price, prin. | Fax 559-6204
Other Schools – See Newton, Newton Center

Norfolk, Norfolk
King Philip Regional SD | 2,100/7-12
18 King St 02056 | 508-520-7991
Dr. Elizabeth Zielinski, supt.
www.kingphilip.org
King Philip MS | 800/7-8
18 King St 02056 | 508-541-7324
Dr. Susan Gilson, prin. | Fax 541-3467
Other Schools – See Wrentham

North Adams, Berkshire, Pop. 13,389
North Adams SD | 1,600/PK-12
191 E Main St Ste 1 01247 | 413-662-3225
James E. Montepare, supt. | Fax 662-3212
www.napsk12.org/
Drury HS | 600/8-12
1130 S Church St 01247 | 413-662-3240
Amy Meehan, prin. | Fax 662-3239

Northern Berkshire Vocational Regnl SD
70 Hodges Crossroads 01247 | 413-663-5383
James Brosnan, supt. | Fax 664-9424
www.mccanntech.org
McCann Technical S | Vo/Tech
70 Hodges Crossroads 01247 | 413-663-5383
Justin R. Kratz, prin. | Fax 664-9424

C.H. McCann Technical School | Post-Sec.
70 Hodges Crossroads 01247 | 413-663-5383
Massachusetts College of Liberal Arts | Post-Sec.
375 Church St 01247 | 413-662-5000

Northampton, Hampshire, Pop. 27,865
Northampton SD | 2,700/PK-12
212 Main St Rm 200 01060 | 413-587-1315
Brian Salzer, supt. | Fax 587-1318
www.northampton-k12.us/
Northampton HS | 900/9-12
380 Elm St 01060 | 413-587-1346
Nancy Athas, prin. | Fax 587-1374
Other Schools – See Florence

Northampton-Smith SD
80 Locust St 01060 | 413-587-1414
Jeffrey Peterson, supt. | Fax 587-1405
smith.tec.ma.us
Smith Vocational & Agricultural HS | Vo/Tech
80 Locust St 01060 | 413-587-1414
Tracy Lyon, prin. | Fax 587-1406

Smith College 01063 | Post-Sec.
413-584-2700

North Andover, Essex, Pop. 22,792
North Andover SD | 4,600/PK-12
1600 Osgood St Ste 3059 01845 | 978-794-1503
Kevin Hutchinson, supt. | Fax 794-0231
www.northandoverpublicschools.com
North Andover HS | 1,300/9-12
430 Osgood St 01845 | 978-794-1711
Carla Scuzzarella, prin. | Fax 688-3536
North Andover MS | 1,100/6-8
495 Main St 01845 | 978-794-1870
Joan McQuade, prin. | Fax 794-3619

Brooks S | 400/9-12
1160 Great Pond Rd 01845 | 978-725-6300
John Packard, head sch | Fax 725-6215
Merrimack College | Post-Sec.
315 Turnpike St 01845 | 978-837-5000

North Attleboro, Bristol, Pop. 16,178
North Attleborough SD | 4,700/PK-12
6 Morse St 02760 | 508-643-2100
Suzan Cullen, supt. | Fax 643-2110
www.naschools.net
North Attleboro HS | 1,200/9-12
1 Wilson W Whitty Way 02760 | 508-643-2115
Scott Holcomb, prin. | Fax 643-2173
North Attleboro MS | 1,200/6-8
564 Landry Ave 02760 | 508-643-2130
Victoria Ekk, prin. | Fax 643-2134

Northborough, Worcester, Pop. 6,020
Northborough-Southborough SD
Supt. — See Southborough
Algonquin Regional HS | 1,400/9-12
79 Bartlett St 01532 | 508-351-7010
Thomas Mead, prin. | Fax 393-9226
Melican MS | 600/6-8
145 Lincoln St 01532 | 508-351-7020
Patricia Montimurro, prin. | Fax 351-7006

North Brookfield, Worcester, Pop. 2,236
North Brookfield SD | 600/K-12
10 New School Dr 01535 | 508-867-9821
John Provost Ed.D., supt. | Fax 867-8148
www.nbschools.org
North Brookfield JSHS | 300/7-12
10 New School Dr 01535 | 508-867-7131
William Evans, prin. | Fax 867-3496

North Chelmsford, Middlesex
Chelmsford SD
Supt. — See Chelmsford
Chelmsford HS | 1,600/9-12
200 Richardson Rd 01863 | 978-251-5111
Charles Caliri, prin. | Fax 251-5117

North Dartmouth, Bristol, Pop. 8,000
Dartmouth SD
Supt. — See South Dartmouth
Dartmouth MS | 1,000/6-8
366 Slocum Rd 02747 | 508-997-9333
Darren Doane, prin. | Fax 999-7720

Bishop Stang HS | 800/9-12
500 Slocum Rd 02747 | 508-996-5602
Peter Shaughnessy, prin. | Fax 994-6756
University of Massachusetts Dartmouth | Post-Sec.
285 Old Westport Rd 02747 | 508-999-8000

North Dighton, Bristol
Dighton-Rehoboth Regional SD | 3,200/PK-12
2700 Regional Rd 02764 | 508-252-5000
Dr. Jennifer Wordell, supt. | Fax 252-5024
www.drregional.org
Dighton-Rehoboth Regional HS | 1,000/9-12
2700 Regional Rd 02764 | 508-252-5025
Deborah Sarrey, prin. | Fax 252-5079
Other Schools – See Dighton, Rehoboth

North Eastham, Barnstable, Pop. 1,790
Nauset SD
Supt. — See Orleans
Nauset Regional HS | 1,000/9-12
PO Box 1887 02651 | 508-255-1505
Thomas Conrad, prin. | Fax 255-9701

North Easton, Bristol, Pop. 4,400
Easton SD | 3,700/PK-12
PO Box 359 02356 | 508-230-3200
Dr. Michael Green, supt. | Fax 238-3563
www.easton.k12.ma.us/
Ames HS | 1,200/9-12
100 Lothrop St 02356 | 508-230-3210
Wesley Paul, prin. | Fax 238-7325
Easton MS | 900/6-8
98 Columbus Ave 02356 | 508-230-3222
R. Luke Carroll, prin. | Fax 230-3102

Stonehill College | Post-Sec.
320 Washington St 02357 | 508-565-1000

Northfield, Franklin, Pop. 1,078
Pioneer Valley SD | 1,100/PK-12
97 F Sumner Turner Rd 01360 | 413-498-2911
Dayle Doiron, supt. | Fax 498-0045
www.pioneervalley.k12.ma.us/pvrsd/
Pioneer Valley Regional JSHS | 500/7-12
97 F Sumner Turner Rd 01360 | 413-498-2931
Bill Wehrli, prin. | Fax 498-0184

Redemption Christian Academy | 50/PK-12
PO Box 183 01360 | 855-722-1979
John Massey, admin.

North Quincy, See Quincy
Quincy SD
Supt. — See Quincy
Atlantic MS | 500/6-8
86 Hollis Ave 02171 | 617-984-8727
Maureen MacNeil, prin. | Fax 984-8646
North Quincy HS | 1,400/9-12
316 Hancock St 02171 | 617-984-8744
Robert Shaw, prin. | Fax 984-8647

North Reading, Middlesex, Pop. 12,002
North Reading SD | 2,700/PK-12
Sherman Rd 01864 | 978-664-7810
Kathleen Willis, supt. | Fax 664-0252
www.north-reading.k12.ma.us/
North Reading HS | 700/9-12
191 Park St 01864 | 978-664-7800
Jon Bernard, prin. | Fax 664-7826
North Reading MS | 600/6-8
Sherman Rd 01864 | 978-664-7806
Catherine O'Connell, prin. | Fax 276-0679

Norton, Bristol, Pop. 1,899
Norton SD | 2,800/PK-12
64 W Main St 02766 | 508-285-0100
Christopher Martes, supt. | Fax 285-0199
www.norton.k12.ma.us
Norton HS | 800/9-12
66 W Main St 02766 | 508-285-0160
Megan Lafayette, prin. | Fax 285-0164
Norton MS | 700/6-8
215 W Main St 02766 | 508-285-0140
Michael O'Rourke, prin. | Fax 286-9457

New Testament Christian S | 100/PK-12
1 New Taunton Ave 02766 | 508-285-9771
Lynne Brennan, prin. | Fax 285-6775
Wheaton College | Post-Sec.
26 E Main St 02766 | 508-286-8200

Norwell, Plymouth
Norwell SD | 2,300/PK-12
322 Main St 02061 | 781-659-8800
Matthew Keegan, supt. | Fax 659-8805
www.norwellschools.org
Norwell HS | 600/9-12
18 South St 02061 | 781-659-8810
William Fish, prin. | Fax 659-1824
Norwell MS | 600/6-8
328 Main St 02061 | 781-659-8814
Derek Sulc, prin. | Fax 659-8822

Norwood, Norfolk, Pop. 27,997
Norwood SD | 3,400/PK-12
PO Box 67 02062 | 781-762-6804
James Hayden, supt. | Fax 762-0229
www.norwood.k12.ma.us/
Coakley MS | 800/6-8
PO Box 67 02062 | 781-762-7880
Ann Mitchell, prin. | Fax 255-5630
Norwood HS | 1,000/9-12
PO Box 67 02062 | 781-769-2333
George Usevich, prin. | Fax 762-0826

FINE Mortuary College | Post-Sec.
150 Kerry Pl 02062 | 781-762-1211
ITT Technical Institute | Post-Sec.
333 Providence Hwy 02062 | 781-278-7200
Universal Technical Institute | Post-Sec.
1 Upland Rd Ste 200 02062 | 781-948-2000

Oak Bluffs, Dukes
Martha's Vineyard SD
Supt. — See Vineyard Haven
Martha's Vineyard Regional HS | 700/9-12
PO Box 1385 02557 | 508-693-1033
Stephen Nixon, prin. | Fax 693-1891

Orange, Franklin, Pop. 3,955
Ralph C. Mahar Regional SD | 800/7-12
PO Box 680 01364 | 978-544-2920
Michael Baldassarre, supt. | Fax 544-8383
www.rcmahar.org
Mahar Regional S | 800/7-12
PO Box 680 01364 | 978-544-2542
Ishmael Tabales, prin. | Fax 544-8383

Orleans, Barnstable, Pop. 1,586
Nauset SD | 1,500/6-12
78 Eldridge Park Way 02653 | 508-255-8800
Dr. Richard Hoffmann, supt. | Fax 240-2351
www.nausetschools.org
Nauset Regional MS | 600/6-8
70 S Orleans Rd 02653 | 508-255-0016
Dr. Maxine Minkoff, prin. | Fax 240-1105
Other Schools – See North Eastham

Osterville, Barnstable, Pop. 2,911

Cape Cod Academy | 300/PK-12
50 Osterville-W Barnstable 02655 | 508-428-5400
Phillip Petru, head sch | Fax 428-0701

Oxford, Worcester, Pop. 6,042
Oxford SD | 2,000/PK-12
4 Maple Rd 01540 | 508-987-6050
Allen Himmelberger, supt. | Fax 987-6054
www.oxps.org
Oxford HS | 500/9-12
495 Main St 01540 | 508-987-6081
Kevin Wells, prin. | Fax 987-6083
Oxford MS | 700/5-8
497 Main St 01540 | 508-987-6074
Katherine Hackett, prin. | Fax 987-2588

Palmer, Hampden, Pop. 4,069
Palmer SD | 1,600/PK-12
24 Converse St Ste 1 01069 | 413-283-2650
Thomas Charko, supt. | Fax 283-2655
www.palmerschools.org

Palmer HS 600/8-12
4105 Main St 01069 413-283-6511
Mary Lou Callahan, prin. Fax 283-3476

Pathfinder Vocational-Technical SD
240 Sykes St 01069 413-283-9701
Dr. Gerald Paist, supt. Fax 284-0032
www.pathfindertech.org/
Pathfinder Reg Vocational Technical HS Vo/Tech
240 Sykes St 01069 413-283-9701
Mary Jane Rickson, prin. Fax 284-0032

Paxton, Worcester

Anna Maria College Post-Sec.
50 Sunset Ln 01612 508-849-3330

Peabody, Essex, Pop. 50,101
Peabody SD 6,100/PK-12
21 Johnson St 01960 978-536-6500
Joseph A. Mastrocola, supt. Fax 536-6504
www.peabody.k12.ma.us/
Higgins MS 1,400/6-8
1 King St 01960 978-536-4800
Todd Bucey, prin. Fax 536-4810
Peabody Veterans Memorial HS 1,900/9-12
485 Lowell St 01960 978-536-4500
Edward Sapienza, prin. Fax 535-9578

Bishop Fenwick HS 600/9-12
99 Margin St 01960 978-587-8300
Sr. Catherine Fleming, admin. Fax 587-8309

Pembroke, Plymouth
Pembroke SD 3,400/PK-12
72 Pilgrim Rd 02359 781-829-1178
Frank Hackett, supt. Fax 826-1182
www.pembrokepublicschools.org/
Pembroke Community MS 500/7-8
559 School St 02359 781-294-0911
Donna McGarrigle, prin. Fax 294-0916
Pembroke HS 900/9-12
80 Learning Ln 02359 781-293-9281
Margaret Szostak, prin. Fax 293-2812

Pepperell, Middlesex, Pop. 2,459
North Middlesex SD 4,200/PK-12
45 Main St 01463 978-597-8713
Joan Landers, supt. Fax 597-6534
nmrsd.org
Nissitissit MS 700/5-8
33 Chase Ave 01463 978-433-0114
Diane Gleason, prin. Fax 433-0118
Other Schools – See Townsend

Pittsfield, Berkshire, Pop. 43,503
Pittsfield SD 6,000/PK-12
269 1st St 01201 413-499-9512
Dr. Gordon L. Noseworthy, supt. Fax 448-2643
www.pittsfield.net/
Herberg MS 600/6-8
501 Pomeroy Ave 01201 413-448-9640
Christopher Jacoby, prin. Fax 448-9644
Pittsfield HS 1,000/9-12
300 East St 01201 413-499-9535
Tracey Benson, prin. Fax 442-2540
Reid MS 600/6-8
950 North St 01201 413-448-9620
Morgan Williams, prin. Fax 443-1587
Taconic HS 900/9-12
96 Valentine Rd 01201 413-448-9600
John Vosburgh, prin. Fax 499-4835

Berkshire Community College Post-Sec.
1350 West St 01201 413-499-4660
Berkshire Medical Center Post-Sec.
725 North St 01201 413-447-2144
Mildred Elley School Post-Sec.
505 East St 01201 413-499-8618
Miss Hall's S 200/9-12
PO Box 1166 01202 413-499-1300
Dr. Margaret Jablonski, hdmstr. Fax 448-2994
St. Joseph Central HS 200/9-12
22 Maplewood Ave 01201 413-447-9121
Lillian Quinn, prin. Fax 443-7020

Plymouth, Plymouth, Pop. 7,138
Plymouth SD 8,100/PK-12
253 S Meadow Rd 02360 508-830-4300
Gary Maestas, supt. Fax 746-1873
www.plymouth.k12.ma.us
Plymouth Community IS 1,200/6-8
117 Long Pond Rd 02360 508-830-4450
Brian Palladino, prin. Fax 830-4464
Plymouth North HS 1,100/9-12
41 Obery St 02360 508-830-4400
Kathleen McSweeney, prin. Fax 830-4405
Plymouth South HS 1,400/9-12
490 Long Pond Rd 02360 508-224-7512
Patricia Connors, prin. Fax 224-6765
Plymouth South MS 700/5-8
488 Long Pond Rd 02360 508-224-2725
John Siever, prin. Fax 224-5660

New Testament Christian S 100/K-12
1120 Long Pond Rd 02360 508-888-1889
Dr. Rodd Rodriguez, prin. Fax 833-0920

Quincy, Norfolk, Pop. 89,796
Quincy SD 9,100/PK-12
159 Thomas Burgin Pkwy 02169 617-984-8700
Dr. Richard DeCristofaro, supt. Fax 984-8965
www.quincypublicschools.com
Broad Meadows MS 300/6-8
50 Calvin Rd 02169 617-984-8723
Lawrence Taglieri, prin. Fax 984-8834
Central MS 600/6-8
1012 Hancock St 02169 617-984-8725
Jen Fay-Beers, prin. Fax 984-8661
Point Webster MS 400/5-8
60 Lancaster St 02169 617-984-6600
James McGuire, prin. Fax 984-6609
Quincy HS 1,400/9-12
100 Coddington St 02169 617-984-8751
Frank Santoro, prin. Fax 984-8643
Sterling MS 300/5-8
444 Granite St 02169 617-984-8729
Christine Barrett, prin. Fax 984-8640
Other Schools – See North Quincy

Eastern Nazarene College Post-Sec.
23 E Elm Ave 02170 617-745-3000
Mansfield Beauty School Post-Sec.
200 Parkingway 02169 617-479-1090
Massachusetts School of Barbering Post-Sec.
64 Ross Way 02169 617-770-4444
Quincy College Post-Sec.
1250 Hancock St 02169 617-984-1700
Woodward S 100/6-12
1102 Hancock St 02169 617-773-5610
Carol Andrews, head sch Fax 770-1551

Randolph, Norfolk, Pop. 30,586
Randolph SD 2,600/PK-12
40 Highland Ave 02368 781-961-6205
Dr. Oscar Santos, supt. Fax 961-6295
www.randolph.k12.ma.us/
Randolph Community MS 500/6-8
225 High St 02368 781-961-6243
Helenann Civian, prin. Fax 961-6286
Randolph HS 700/9-12
70 Memorial Pkwy 02368 781-961-6220
Russell Cron, prin. Fax 961-6235

Raynham, Bristol, Pop. 2,100
Bridgewater-Raynham Regional SD
Supt. — See Bridgewater
Raynham MS 700/5-8
420 Titicut Rd 02767 508-977-0504
David Thomson, prin. Fax 977-0659

Reading, Middlesex, Pop. 24,477
Reading SD 4,400/K-12
82 Oakland Rd 01867 781-944-5800
Dr. John Doherty, supt. Fax 942-9149
reading.k12.ma.us/
Coolidge MS 500/6-8
89 Birch Meadow Dr 01867 781-942-9158
Sarah Marchant, prin. Fax 942-9118
Parker MS 600/6-8
45 Temple St 01867 781-944-1236
Douglas Lyons, prin. Fax 942-9008
Reading Memorial HS 1,200/9-12
62 Oakland Rd 01867 781-944-8200
Kevin Higginbottom, prin. Fax 942-5435

Austin Preparatory S 700/6-12
101 Willow St 01867 781-944-4900
Paul Moran, hdmstr. Fax 944-7530

Rehoboth, Bristol
Dighton-Rehoboth Regional SD
Supt. — See North Dighton
Beckwith MS 600/5-8
330R Winthrop St 02769 508-252-5080
Debra Pincince, prin. Fax 252-5082

Revere, Suffolk, Pop. 50,075
Revere SD 6,200/PK-12
101 School St 02151 781-286-8226
Dr. Paul Dakin, supt. Fax 286-8221
www.revereps.mec.edu
Anthony MS 400/6-8
107 Newhall St 02151 781-388-7520
Joanne Willett, prin. Fax 388-7521
Garfield Magnet MS 400/6-8
176 Garfield Ave 02151 781-286-8298
Danielle Mokaba, prin. Fax 286-3557
Revere HS 1,500/9-12
101 School St 02151 781-286-8222
Lourenco Garcia Ed.D., prin. Fax 286-8378
Rumney Marsh Academy 500/6-8
140 American Legion Hwy 02151 781-388-3500
Cindy Evans, prin. Fax 485-8443
Seacoast HS 100/Alt
15 Everard Ave 02151 781-485-2715
Thomas Misci, prin. Fax 485-2718

Rochester, Plymouth
Old Colony Reg Vocational Technical HSD
476 North Ave 02770 508-763-8011
Gary Brown, supt. Fax 763-9821
www.oldcolony.us
Old Colony Reg Vocational Tech HS Vo/Tech
476 North Ave 02770 508-763-8011
Patricia Foskett, prin. Fax 763-9821

Rockland, Plymouth, Pop. 16,123
Rockland SD 1,900/K-12
34 MacKinlay Way 02370 781-878-3893
John Retchless, supt. Fax 982-1483
rocklandschools.org
Rockland HS 600/9-12
52 MacKinlay Way 02370 781-871-0541
Alan Cron, prin. Fax 878-0158
Rogers MS 500/5-8
100 Taunton Ave 02370 781-878-4341
Elizabeth Bohn, prin. Fax 871-8448

Calvary Chapel Academy 100/PK-12
PO Box 409 02370 781-871-1043
Richard Colello, hdmstr. Fax 792-3902

Rockport, Essex, Pop. 4,922
Rockport SD 900/PK-12
24 Jerdens Ln 01966 978-546-1200
Robert Liebow Ph.D., supt. Fax 546-1205
rpk12.org
Rockport HS 300/9-12
24 Jerdens Ln 01966 978-546-1234
Philip Conrad, prin. Fax 546-1205
Rockport MS 200/6-8
26 Jerdens Ln 01966 978-546-1250
Philip Conrad, prin. Fax 546-1205

Roslindale, See Boston
Boston SD
Supt. — See Boston
Irving MS 600/6-8
105 Cummins Hwy 02131 617-635-8072
Arthur Unobskey, prin. Fax 635-9363

Roxbury, See Boston
Boston SD
Supt. — See Boston
Dearborn MS 300/6-8
35 Greenville St 02119 617-635-8412
Jose Duarte, prin. Fax 635-8419
Greater Egleston Community HS 200/9-12
80 School St 02119 617-635-6429
Julie Coles, hdmstr. Fax 635-6469
Hayes S of Music 9-12
55 Malcolm X Blvd 02120 617-635-8973
Gregory Gazzola, dir. Fax 635-6363
Madison Park Technical Vocational HS Vo/Tech
75 Malcolm X Blvd 02120 617 635-8970
Queon Jackson, hdmstr. Fax 635-9831
O'Bryant HS of Mathematics & Science 1,200/7-12
55 Malcolm X Blvd 02120 617-635-9932
Steven Sullivan, hdmstr. Fax 635-7769
Timilty MS 700/6-8
205 Roxbury St 02119 617-635-8109
Valerie Lowe-Barehmi, prin. Fax 635-8115

Roxbury Crossing, See Boston

Roxbury Community College Post-Sec.
1234 Columbus Ave 02120 617-427-0060

Rutland, Worcester, Pop. 2,084
Wachusett Regional SD
Supt. — See Jefferson
Central Tree MS 400/6-8
281 Main St 01543 508-886-0073
Nancy Fournier, prin. Fax 886-0141

Devereux Center in Massachusetts Post-Sec.
PO Box 219 01543 508-886-4746

Salem, Essex, Pop. 40,441
Salem SD 4,600/PK-12
29 Highland Ave 01970 978-740-1212
Stephen Russell, supt. Fax 740-3083
www.salemk12.org/
Collins MS 700/6-8
29 Highland Ave 01970 978-740-1191
Mary Manning, prin. Fax 740-1183
Salem HS 1,200/9-12
77 Willson St 01970 978-740-1123
David Angeramo, prin. Fax 740-1110
Salem Preparatory HS 50/9-12
114 Derby St 01970 978-740-1171
Cheryl Kelly, prin. Fax 740-1171

Salem State University Post-Sec.
352 Lafayette St 01970 978-542-6000

Saugus, Essex, Pop. 26,187
Saugus SD 2,800/PK-12
23 Main St 01906 781-231-5000
Michael Tempesta, supt. Fax 233-9424
www.saugus.k12.ma.us
Belmonte MS 700/6-8
25 Dow St 01906 781-231-5052
Kerry Robbins, prin. Fax 233-5665
Saugus HS 700/9-12
1 Pierce Memorial Dr 01906 781-231-5027
Michael Hashem, prin. Fax 231-5030

Scituate, Plymouth, Pop. 5,135
Scituate SD 3,200/K-12
606 Chief Justice Cushing 02066 781-545-8759
John McCarthy, supt. Fax 545-6291
www.scituate.k12.ma.us/
Gates IS 500/7-8
327 First Parish Rd 02066 781-545-8760
Sarah Shannon, prin. Fax 545-8767
Scituate HS 800/9-12
606 Chief Justice Cushing 02066 781-545-8750
Robert Wargo, prin. Fax 545-8758

Seekonk, Bristol, Pop. 13,046
Seekonk SD 2,100/PK-12
25 Water Ln 02771 508-399-5106
Arlene Bosco, supt. Fax 399-5128
seekonk.sharpschool.com/
Hurley MS 500/6-8
650 Newman Ave 02771 508-761-7570
Fax 336-9630
Seekonk HS 700/9-12
261 Arcade Ave 02771 508-336-7272
Marcia McGovern, prin. Fax 336-8535

MTTI Post-Sec.
1241 Fall River Ave 02771 866-454-6884

Sharon, Norfolk, Pop. 5,546
Sharon SD 3,400/PK-12
75 Mountain St 02067 781-784-1570
Timothy Farmer, supt. Fax 784-1573
www.sharon.k12.ma.us
Sharon HS 1,200/9-12
181 Pond St 02067 781-784-1554
Jose Libano, prin. Fax 784-1550
Sharon MS 800/6-8
75 Mountain St 02067 781-784-1560
Kevin O'Rourke, prin. Fax 784-8432

Sheffield, Berkshire
Southern Berkshire Regional SD — 900/PK-12
PO Box 339 01257 — 413-229-8778
Michael Singleton Ed.D., supt. — Fax 229-2913
sbrsd.org
Mount Everett Regional HS — 400/7-12
PO Box 219 01257 — 413-229-8734
Glenn Devoti, prin. — Fax 229-2044

Berkshire S — 400/9-12
245 N Undermountain Rd 01257 — 413-229-8511
Michael Maher, hdmstr. — Fax 229-1010

Shelburne Falls, Franklin, Pop. 1,695
Mohawk Trail SD — 1,100/PK-12
24 Ashfield Rd 01370 — 413-625-0192
Michael Buoniconti, supt. — Fax 625-0196
www.mohawkschools.org
Mohawk Trail Regional HS — 600/7-12
26 Ashfield Rd 01370 — 413-625-9811
Lynn Dole, prin. — Fax 625-6652

Shirley, Middlesex, Pop. 1,415
Ayer Shirley SD
Supt. — See Ayer
Ayer-Shirley MS — 400/6-8
1 Hospital Rd 01464 — 978-772-8600
Richard McGrath, prin. — Fax 425-0474

Shrewsbury, Worcester, Pop. 25,900
Shrewsbury SD — 5,900/PK-12
100 Maple Ave 01545 — 508-841-8400
Joseph Sawyer, supt. — Fax 841-8490
schools.shrewsbury-ma.gov
Oak MS — 900/7-8
45 Oak St 01545 — 508-841-1200
Ann Jones, prin. — Fax 841-1223
Shrewsbury HS — 1,600/9-12
64 Holden St 01545 — 508-841-8800
Todd Bazydlo, prin. — Fax 841-8858

St. John's HS — 1,000/9-12
378 Main St 01545 — 508-842-8934
Michael Welch, admin. — Fax 842-3670

Somerset, Bristol, Pop. 17,980
Somerset Berkley Regional SD — 1,000/9-12
580 Whetstone Hill Rd 02726 — 508-324-3100
Richard Medeiros, supt. — Fax 324-3104
www.sbregional.org/
Somerset Berkley Regional HS — 1,000/9-12
270 Grandview Ave 02726 — 508-324-3115
Dr. Jahmal Mosley, prin. — Fax 324-3118

Somerset SD — 1,800/PK-8
580 Whetstone Hill Rd 02726 — 508-324-3100
Richard Medeiros, supt. — Fax 324-3104
www.somerset.k12.ma.us/
Somerset MS — 600/6-8
1141 Brayton Ave 02726 — 508-324-3140
Pauline Camara, prin. — Fax 324-3145

Somerville, Middlesex, Pop. 71,913
Somerville SD — 4,800/PK-12
42 Cross St 02145 — 617-625-6600
Anthony Pierantozzi, supt. — Fax 666-1130
www.somerville.k12.ma.us
Full Circle HS — 50/Alt
8 Bonair St 02145 — 617-625-6600
Margaret DePasquale, prin. — Fax 628-6836
Next Wave JHS — 50/Alt
8 Bonair St 02145 — 617-625-6600
Margaret DePasquale, prin. — Fax 628-6837
Somerville HS — 1,300/9-12
81 Highland Ave 02143 — 617-625-6600
John Oteri, hdmstr. — Fax 629-4763

Lincoln Technical Institute — Post-Sec.
5 Middlesex Ave 02145 — 617-776-3500

Southborough, Worcester
Northborough-Southborough SD — 4,800/PK-12
53 Parkerville Rd 01772 — 508-486-5115
Dr. Charles Gobron, supt. — Fax 486-5123
www.nsboro.k12.ma.us/
Trottier MS — 500/6-8
49 Parkerville Rd 01772 — 508-485-2400
Keith Lavoie, prin. — Fax 481-1506
Other Schools – See Northborough

St. Marks S — 300/9-12
25 Marlboro Rd 01772 — 508-786-6000
John Warren, head sch — Fax 786-6109

South Boston, See Boston
Boston SD
Supt. — See Boston
Excel HS — 400/9-12
95 G St 02127 — 617-635-9870
Stephanie Sibley, hdmstr. — Fax 635-9711

Southbridge, Worcester, Pop. 13,631
Southbridge SD — 1,500/PK-12
25 Cole Ave 01550 — 508-764-5415
Basan Nembirkow, supt. — Fax 764-8325
www.southbridge.k12.ma.us/
Southbridge MSHS — 400/6-12
132 Torrey Rd 01550 — 508-764-5450
Gregory Leach, prin. — Fax 318-1687

South Dartmouth, Bristol, Pop. 9,850
Dartmouth SD — 4,000/PK-12
8 Bush St 02748 — 508-997-3391
Ana C. Riley, supt. — Fax 991-4184
dartmouthps.schoolfusion.us/
Dartmouth HS — 1,200/9-12
555 Bakerville Rd 02748 — 508-961-2700
Kerry Lynch, prin. — Fax 910-1410
Other Schools – See North Dartmouth

South Deerfield, Franklin, Pop. 1,861
Frontier Regional SD — 700/7-12
219 Christian Ln 01373 — 413-665-1155
Regina Nash Ed.D., supt. — Fax 665-8506
www.frontierregionalandunion38.com
Frontier Regional JSHS — 700/7-12
113 N Main St 01373 — 413-665-2118
Martha Barrett, prin. — Fax 665-1518

South Dennis, Barnstable, Pop. 3,547
Dennis-Yarmouth SD
Supt. — See South Yarmouth
Wixon MS — 500/4-8
901 Route 134 02660 — 508-398-7695
Carole Eichner, prin. — Fax 398-7608

South Easton, Bristol
Southeastern Regional Voc Tech SD
250 Foundry St 02375 — 508-230-1200
Luis Lopes, supt. — Fax 230-1563
www.sersd.org
Southeastern Regional Vo-Tech HS — Vo/Tech
250 Foundry St 02375 — 508-230-1200
David Wheeler, prin. — Fax 230-1567

Southeastern Technical Institute — Post-Sec.
250 Foundry St 02375 — 508-238-1860

South Hadley, Hampshire, Pop. 5,400
South Hadley SD — 2,100/PK-12
116 Main St Ste 202 01075 — 413-538-5060
Dr. Nicholas D. Young, supt. — Fax 532-6284
www.southhadleyschools.org
Smith MS — 600/5-8
100 Mosier St 01075 — 413-538-5074
Erica Faginski-Stark, prin. — Fax 538-5003
South Hadley HS — 600/9-12
153 Newton St 01075 — 413-538-5063
Sean McNiff, prin. — Fax 532-6538

Mt. Holyoke College — Post-Sec.
50 College St 01075 — 413-538-2000

South Hamilton, Essex, Pop. 2,750

Gordon-Conwell Theological Seminary — Post-Sec.
130 Essex St 01982 — 978-468-7111
Pingree S — 300/9-12
537 Highland St 01982 — 978-468-4415
Dr. Timothy Johnson, head sch — Fax 468-3758

South Lancaster, Worcester, Pop. 1,842

South Lancaster Academy — 100/PK-12
PO Box 1129 01561 — 978-368-8544
Ron Huff, prin. — Fax 365-2244

Southwick, Hampden
Southwick-Tolland-Granville SD — 1,900/PK-12
86 Powder Mill Rd 01077 — 413-569-5391
John Barry, supt. — Fax 569-1711
www.stgrsd.org
Powder Mill MS — 600/5-8
94 Powder Mill Rd 01077 — 413-569-5951
Ronald Peloquin, prin. — Fax 569-1710
Southwick-Tolland Regional HS — 600/9-12
93 Feeding Hills Rd 01077 — 413-569-6171
Pamela Hunter, prin. — Fax 569-1723

South Yarmouth, Barnstable, Pop. 10,789
Dennis-Yarmouth SD — 3,200/PK-12
296 Station Ave 02664 — 508-398-7600
Carol Woodbury, supt. — Fax 398-7622
www.dy-regional.k12.ma.us/
Dennis-Yarmouth Regional HS — 900/8-12
210 Station Ave 02664 — 508-398-7636
Kenneth Jenks, prin. — Fax 398-7635
Other Schools – See South Dennis, West Yarmouth

Spencer, Worcester, Pop. 5,615
Spencer-East Brookfield SD — 2,000/PK-12
306 Main St 01562 — 508-885-8500
Debora Zablocki, supt. — Fax 885-8504
www.seb.mec.edu
Knox Trail JHS — 300/7-8
73 Ash St 01562 — 508-885-8550
Joyce Nelson, prin. — Fax 885-8557
Prouty HS — 500/9-12
302 Main St 01562 — 508-885-8505
Robert O'Brien, prin. — Fax 885-8511

Central Mass School of Massage & Therapy — Post-Sec.
200 Main St 01562 — 508-885-0306

Springfield, Hampden, Pop. 149,577
Springfield SD — 27,400/PK-12
1550 Main St 01103 — 413-787-7100
Daniel Warwick, supt. — Fax 787-6713
www.sps.springfield.ma.us
Balliet MS — Alt
111 Seymour Ave 01109 — 413-787-7284
Chestnut Accelerated MS — 1,000/6-8
355 Plainfield St 01107 — 413-750-2333
Daniel Rossi, prin. — Fax 750-2351
Duggan MS — 400/6-8
1015 Wilbraham Rd 01109 — 413-787-7410
Marisa Mendonsa, prin. — Fax 750-2209
Forest Park MS — 800/6-8
91 School St 01105 — 413-787-7420
Medina Ali, prin. — Fax 787-7419
Kennedy MS — 600/6-8
1385 Berkshire Ave 01151 — 413-787-7510
Bonnie Osgood, prin. — Fax 787-7561
Kiley MS — 800/6-8
180 Cooley St 01128 — 413-787-7240
Christopher Sutton, prin. — Fax 787-7247
Liberty Preparatory Academy — Alt
334 Franklin St 01104 — 413-750-2484
Putnam Vocational Technical HS — Vo/Tech
1300 State St 01109 — 413-787-7424
Gilbert Traverso, prin. — Fax 787-7330
South End MS, 36 Margaret St 01105 — 6-8
Timothy Allen, prin. — 413-750-2442
Springfield Central HS — 2,000/9-12
1840 Roosevelt Ave 01109 — 413-787-7085
Thaddeus Tokarz, prin. — Fax 787-7040
Springfield HS — Alt
140 Wilbraham Ave Ste A 01109 — 413-787-7285
HS of Commerce — 1,300/9-12
415 State St 01105 — 413-787-7220
Charles Grandson, prin. — Fax 787-7041
Springfield HS of Science-Tech — 1,200/9-12
1250 State St 01109 — 413-750-2000
Wedad Saada, prin. — Fax 750-2047
Springfield Public Day MS — Alt
118 Alden St 01109 — 413-787-7261
Rhonda Jacobs, prin.
Springfield Renaissance S — 700/6-12
1170 Carew St 01104 — 413-750-2929
Stephen Mahoney, prin. — Fax 750-2978
STEM Middle Academy — 300/6-8
60 Alton St 01109 — 413-787-6750
Michael Calvanese, prin. — Fax 787-6952
Van Sickle MS — 1,000/6-8
1170 Carew St 01104 — 413-750-2887
Cheryl Despirt, prin. — Fax 750-2972
Adult Education Center — Adult
310 State St 01105 — 413-787-7210
Armando Feliciano, dir.
Other Schools – See Holyoke, Indian Orchard

American International College — Post-Sec.
1000 State St 01109 — 413-737-7000
Branford Hall Career Institute — Post-Sec.
112 Industry Ave 01104 — 413-781-2276
Mansfield Beauty School — Post-Sec.
266 Bridge St 01103 — 413-788-7575
Pioneer Valley Christian S — 300/PK-12
965 Plumtree Rd 01119 — 413-782-8031
Timothy Duff, hdmstr. — Fax 782-8033
Springfield College — Post-Sec.
263 Alden St 01109 — 413-748-3000
Springfield Technical Community College — Post-Sec.
PO Box 9000 01102 — 413-781-7822
Western New England University — Post-Sec.
1215 Wilbraham Rd 01119 — 413-782-3111

Sterling, Worcester
Wachusett Regional SD
Supt. — See Jefferson
Chocksett MS — 400/5-8
40 Boutelle Rd 01564 — 978-422-6552
Anthony Cipro, prin. — Fax 422-7720

Stockbridge, Berkshire
Berkshire Hills SD — 1,400/PK-12
PO Box 617 01262 — 413-298-4017
Dr. Peter Dillon, supt. — Fax 298-4672
www.bhrsd.org
Other Schools – See Great Barrington

Stoneham, Middlesex, Pop. 21,118
Stoneham SD — 2,500/PK-12
149 Franklin St 02180 — 781-279-3800
Dr. Les Olson, supt. — Fax 279-3818
www.stonehamschools.net/
Stoneham HS — 700/9-12
149 Franklin St 02180 — 781-279-3810
Donna Cargill, prin. — Fax 279-2070
Stoneham MS — 600/6-8
101 Central St 02180 — 781-279-3840
Christopher Banos, prin. — Fax 279-3843

Edgewood/Greater Boston Academy — 200/PK-12
108 Pond St 02180 — 781-438-4253
Angela Watson, prin. — Fax 438-6857

Stoughton, Norfolk, Pop. 27,500
Stoughton SD — 3,800/PK-12
232 Pearl St 02072 — 781-344-4000
Marguerite C. Rizzi Ed.D., supt. — Fax 344-6417
www.stoughtonschools.org/
O'Donnell MS — 900/6-8
211 Cushing St 02072 — 781-344-7002
Matt Colantonio, prin. — Fax 297-5263
Stoughton HS — 1,100/9-12
232 Pearl St 02072 — 781-344-7001
Juliette Miller, prin. — Fax 341-6041

Stow, Middlesex
Nashoba Regional SD
Supt. — See Bolton
Hale MS — 300/6-8
55 Hartley Rd 01775 — 978-897-4788
George King, prin. — Fax 897-3631

Sudbury, Middlesex
Lincoln-Sudbury SD — 1,600/9-12
390 Lincoln Rd 01776 — 978-443-9961
Scott Carpenter, supt. — Fax 443-8824
www.lsrhs.net/
Lincoln-Sudbury Regional HS — 1,600/9-12
390 Lincoln Rd 01776 — 978-443-9961
Scott Carpenter, prin. — Fax 443-8824

Sudbury SD — 3,100/PK-8
40 Fairbank Rd Ste C 01776 — 978-639-3211
Anne Wilson, supt. — Fax 443-9001
www.sudbury.k12.ma.us
Curtis MS — 1,100/6-8
22 Pratts Mill Rd 01776 — 978-443-1071
Stephen Lambert, prin. — Fax 443-1098

Willow Hill S — 100/6-12
98 Haynes Rd 01776 — 978-443-2581
Jeffrey Rubin, hdmstr. — Fax 443-7560

Sutton, Worcester
Sutton SD 1,600/PK-12
383 Boston Rd 01590 508-581-1600
Theodore Friend, supt. Fax 865-6463
www.suttonschools.net/
Sutton HS 400/9-12
383 Boston Rd 01590 508-581-1640
Lucille DiLeo, prin. Fax 917-0063
Sutton MS 400/6-8
409 Boston Rd 01590 508-581-1630
Gerard Goyette, prin. Fax 865-6463

Swampscott, Essex, Pop. 13,607
Swampscott SD 2,200/K-12
207 Forest Ave 01907 781-596-8800
Dr. Garry Murphy, supt. Fax 599-2502
www.swampscott.k12.ma.us
Swampscott HS 700/9-12
200 Essex St 01907 781-596-8830
Layne Millington Ed.D., prin. Fax 599-2034
Swampscott MS 700/5-8
207 Forest Ave 01907 781-596-8820
Robert Murphy Ed.D., prin. Fax 593-2126

Marian Court College Post-Sec.
35 Littles Point Rd 01907 781-595-6768

Swansea, Bristol
Swansea SD 2,000/PK-12
1 Gardners Neck Rd 02777 508-675-1195
Robert Monterio, supt. Fax 672-1040
www.swanseaschools.org
Case HS 600/9-12
70 School St 02777 508-675-7483
Brian McCann, prin. Fax 646-4405
Case JHS 500/6-8
195 Main St 02777 508-675-0116
Robert Silveira, prin. Fax 646-4413

New England Christian Academy 200/PK-12
271 Sharps Lot Rd 02777 508-676-3011
Ramona Brown, prin. Fax 646-0392

Taunton, Bristol, Pop. 53,462
Bristol-Plymouth Regional-Tech SD
207 Hart St 02780 508-823-5151
Richard Gross Ed.D., supt. Fax 880-7287
www.bptech.org
Bristol-Plymouth Regional Technical S Vo/Tech
940 County St 02780 508-823-5151
Carolyn Pearson, prin. Fax 822-2687

Taunton SD 7,400/PK-12
215 Harris St 02780 508-821-1100
Dr. Julie Hackett, supt. Fax 821-1177
www.tauntonschools.org
Taunton Alternative HS Alt
120 Cohannet St 02780 508-821-1201
John Cabral, prin. Fax 821-1177
Taunton HS 1,900/8-12
50 Williams St 02780 508-821-1101
Matt Mattos, prin. Fax 821-1362

Coyle & Cassidy HS 600/9-12
2 Hamilton St 02780 508-823-6164
Robert Gay, prin. Fax 823-2530
Rob Roy Academy Post-Sec.
1 School St 02780 508-822-1405
Taunton Catholic MS 200/5-8
61 Summer St 02780 508-822-0491
Dr. Corinne Merritt, prin. Fax 824-0469

Tewksbury, Middlesex, Pop. 11,000
Tewksbury SD 3,900/K-12
139 Pleasant St 01876 978-640-7800
John O'Connor, supt. Fax 640-7804
www.tewksbury.k12.ma.us
Tewksbury Memorial HS 900/9-12
320 Pleasant St 01876 978-640-7825
Brenda Regan, prin. Fax 640-7829
Wynn MS 800/7-8
1 Griffin Way 01876 978-640-7846
John Weir, prin. Fax 640-7850

Electrology Institute of New England Post-Sec.
1501 Main St Ste 50 01876 800-548-6339
Salter School Post-Sec.
515 Woburn St 01876 978-934-9300

Topsfield, Essex, Pop. 2,684
Masconomet SD 2,100/7-12
20 Endicott Rd 01983 978-887-2323
Darrell Lockwood, supt. Fax 887-3573
www.masconomet.org
Masconomet Regional HS 1,300/9-12
20 Endicott Rd 01983 978-887-2323
Pamela Culver, prin. Fax 887-7243
Masconomet Regional MS 800/7-8
20 Endicott Rd 01983 978-887-2323
Dorothy Flaherty, prin. Fax 887-1991

Townsend, Middlesex, Pop. 1,114
North Middlesex SD
Supt. — See Pepperell
Hawthorne Brook MS 600/5-8
64 Brookline St 01469 978-597-6914
Steve Coughlan, prin. Fax 597-0354
North Middlesex Regional HS 1,100/9-12
19 Main St 01469 978-597-8721
Christine Battye, prin. Fax 597-0350

Turners Falls, Franklin, Pop. 4,349
Franklin County Technical SD
82 Industrial Blvd 01376 413-863-9561
James Laverty, supt. Fax 863-2816
www.fcts.org
Franklin County Technical HS Vo/Tech
82 Industrial Blvd 01376 413-863-9561
Richard Martin, prin. Fax 863-2816

Gill-Montague SD 1,100/PK-12
35 Crocker Ave 01376 413-863-9324
Mark Prince, supt. Fax 863-4560
www.gmrsd.org
Other Schools – See Montague

Hallmark Institute of Photography Post-Sec.
PO Box 308 01376 413-863-2478

Tyngsboro, Middlesex
Greater Lowell Technical HSD
250 Pawtucket Blvd 01879 978-441-4800
MaryJo Santoro, supt. Fax 441-5353
www.gltech.org
Greater Lowell Technical HS Vo/Tech
250 Pawtucket Blvd 01879 978-441-4807
Robert Lussier, prin. Fax 441-5353

Tyngsborough SD 1,900/PK-12
50 Norris Rd 01879 978-649-7488
Donald Ciampa, supt. Fax 649-7199
www.tyngsboroughps.org/
Tyngsboro HS 500/9-12
36 Norris Rd 01879 978-649-7571
Michael Woodlock, prin. Fax 649-6530
Tyngsboro MS 500/6-8
50 Norris Rd 01879 978-649-3115
Mary Alise Herrera, prin. Fax 649-8673

Academy of Notre Dame HS 200/9-12
180 Middlesex Rd 01879 978-649-7611
Sr. Patricia Conner, prin. Fax 649-2909

Upton, Worcester, Pop. 2,982
Blackstone Valley Vocational Regional SD
65 Pleasant St 01568 508-529-7758
Dr. Michael F. Fitzpatrick, supt. Fax 529-3079
www.valleytech.k12.ma.us
Blackstone Valley Regional Vo-Tech HS Vo/Tech
65 Pleasant St 01568 508-529-7758
Anthony E. Steele, prin. Fax 529-2403

Mendon-Upton Regional SD
Supt. — See Mendon
Nipmuc Regional HS 700/9-12
90 Pleasant St 01568 508-529-2130
John Clements, prin. Fax 529-2129

Uxbridge, Worcester, Pop. 3,400
Uxbridge SD 1,500/PK-12
21 S Main St 01569 508-278-8648
Kevin Carney, supt. Fax 278-8612
uxbridgeschools.com
McCloskey MS 500/6-8
62 Capron St 01569 508-278-8634
Karen Maguire, prin. Fax 278-8627
Uxbridge HS 400/9-12
300 Quaker Hwy 01569 508-278-8636
Tara Bennett, prin. Fax 278-8627

Vineyard Haven, Dukes, Pop. 1,950
Martha's Vineyard SD 700/9-12
4 Pine St 02568 508-693-2007
James Weiss Ed.D., supt. Fax 693-3190
www.mvyps.org
Other Schools – See Oak Bluffs

Wakefield, Middlesex, Pop. 24,651
Northeast Metro Vocational SD
100 Hemlock Rd 01880 781-246-0810
Theodore Nickole, supt. Fax 246-4919
northeastmetrotech.com
Northeast Metro Regional Vocational HS Vo/Tech
100 Hemlock Rd 01880 781-246-0810
David DiBarri, prin. Fax 246-4919

Wakefield SD 3,400/PK-12
60 Farm St 01880 781-246-6400
Dr. Garry Murphy, supt. Fax 245-9164
www.wakefield.k12.ma.us/
Galvin MS 1,100/5-8
525 Main St 01880 781-246-6410
Mark Bedrosian, prin. Fax 224-5009
Wakefield Memorial HS 900/9-12
60 Farm St 01880 781-246-6440
Kimberly Smith, prin. Fax 246-4714

Walpole, Norfolk, Pop. 5,864
Norfolk County Agricultural SD
400 Main St 02081 508-668-0268
Suzanne Green, supt. Fax 668-0612
www.norfolkaggie.org
Norfolk County Agricultural HS Vo/Tech
400 Main St 02081 508-668-0268
Dr. Tammy Quinn, prin. Fax 668-0612

Walpole SD 4,000/PK-12
135 School St 02081 508-660-7200
Lincoln Lynch Ed.D., supt. Fax 668-1167
www.walpole.k12.ma.us/
Johnson MS 400/6-8
111 Robbins Rd 02081 508-660-7242
Sandra Esmond, prin. Fax 660-7240
Walpole HS 1,100/9-12
275 Common St 02081 508-660-7257
Stephen Imbusch, prin. Fax 850-7958
Other Schools – See East Walpole

Waltham, Middlesex, Pop. 59,317
Waltham SD 4,800/PK-12
617 Lexington St 02452 781-314-5440
Dr. Susan Nicholson, supt. Fax 314-5411
www.walthampublicschools.org/
Kennedy MS 500/6-8
655 Lexington St 02452 781-314-5560
John Cawley, prin. Fax 314-5571
McDevitt MS 500/6-8
75 Church St 02452 781-314-5590
Elizabeth Gavin, prin. Fax 314-5601

Waltham HS 1,400/9-12
617 Lexington St 02452 781-314-5440
Gregory DeMeo, prin. Fax 647-0309

Bentley University Post-Sec.
175 Forest St 02452 781-891-2000
Blaine The Beauty Career School Post-Sec.
314 Moody St 02453 781-899-1500
Brandeis University Post-Sec.
415 South St 02453 781-736-2000
Center for Digital Imaging Arts at BU Post-Sec.
282 Moody St 02453 800-808-2342
Chapel Hill-Chauncy Hall S 200/9-12
785 Beaver St 02452 781-314-0800
Lance Conrad, hdmstr. Fax 894-5205
Gann Academy 300/9-12
333 Forest St 02452 781-642-6800
Marc Baker, hdmstr. Fax 642-6805
Sodexho Marriott Services Post-Sec.
200 5th Ave 02451 800-926-7429

Ware, Hampshire, Pop. 6,031
Ware SD 1,300/PK-12
PO Box 240 01082 413-967-4271
Dr. Mary-Elizabeth Beach, supt. Fax 967-9580
www.warepublicschools.com
Ware JSHS 500/7-12
237 West St 01082 413-967-6234
Marlene DiLeo, prin. Fax 967-9053

Wareham, Plymouth, Pop. 19,232
Wareham SD 3,000/PK-12
54 Marion Rd Ste 1 02571 508-291-3500
Barry Rabinovitch, supt. Fax 291-3578
www.warehamps.org
Wareham Cooperative S 100/Alt
1 Viking Dr 02571 508-291-3526
Kathy Moore-Minkle, prin. Fax 291-3577
Wareham HS 800/9-12
7 Viking Dr 02571 508-291-3510
Scott Palladino, prin. Fax 291-3577
Wareham MS 700/6-8
4 Viking Dr 02571 508-291-3550
Howard Gilmore, prin. Fax 291-3580

Warren, Worcester, Pop. 1,379
Quaboag Regional SD 1,400/PK-12
PO Box 1538 01083 413-436-9256
Brett Kustigian, supt. Fax 436-9738
www.quaboagrsd.org
Quaboag Regional MSHS 600/7-12
PO Box 909 01083 413-436-5991
Greg Myers, prin. Fax 436-9636

Watertown, Middlesex, Pop. 30,947
Watertown SD 2,500/K-12
30 Common St 02472 617-926-7700
Jean Fitzgerald, supt. Fax 923-1234
www.watertown.k12.ma.us
Watertown HS 700/9-12
50 Columbia St 02472 617-926-7760
Steven Watson, hdmstr. Fax 926-7723
Watertown MS 600/6-8
68 Waverley Ave 02472 617-926-7783
James Carter, prin. Fax 926-5407

Cortiva Institute - Boston Post-Sec.
103 Morse St 02472 617-612-6900
Perkins School for the Blind Post-Sec.
175 N Beacon St 02472 617-972-7285
Perkins School for the Blind 200/PK-12
175 N Beacon St 02472 617-924-3434
Steven Rothstein, pres. Fax 926-2027

Wayland, Middlesex, Pop. 2,500
Wayland SD 2,700/K-12
PO Box 408 01778 508-358-3774
Gary Burton, supt. Fax 358-7708
www.wayland.k12.ma.us
Wayland HS 900/9-12
264 Old Connecticut Path 01778 508-358-3705
Patrick Tutwiler, prin. Fax 358-8082
Wayland MS 600/6-8
201 Main St 01778 508-655-6670
Betsy Gavron, prin. Fax 655-2548

Webster, Worcester, Pop. 11,152
Webster SD 1,900/PK-12
PO Box 430 01570 508-943-0104
Barbara Malkas, supt. Fax 943-0315
www.webster-schools.org
Bartlett JSHS 800/7-12
52 Lake Pkwy 01570 508-943-8552
Steven Knowlton, prin. Fax 949-8274

Wellesley, Norfolk, Pop. 27,391
Wellesley SD 4,900/PK-12
40 Kingsbury St 02481 781-446-6210
David Lussier, supt. Fax 446-6207
www.wellesley.k12.ma.us
Wellesley HS 1,300/9-12
50 Rice St 02481 781-446-6290
Andrew Keough, prin. Fax 237-6004
Wellesley MS 1,100/6-8
50 Kingsbury St 02481 781-446-6235
Mark Ito, prin. Fax 446-6208

Dana Hall S 500/6-12
45 Dana Rd 02482 781-235-3010
Caroline Erisman, head sch Fax 237-5949
Massachusetts Bay Community College Post-Sec.
50 Oakland St 02481 781-239-3000
Wellesley College Post-Sec.
106 Central St 02481 781-283-1000

Wendell, Franklin

Lake Grove School-Maple Valley Post-Sec.
PO Box 767 01379 888-585-9007

Linden Hill S, 8 Farley Rd 01379 50/5-10
James McDaniel, hdmstr. 978-544-6888

Wenham, Essex, Pop. 4,212
Hamilton-Wenham SD 2,000/PK-12
5 School St 01984 978-468-5310
Dr. Michael M. Harvey, supt. Fax 468-7889
www.hwschools.net/
Other Schools – See Hamilton

Gordon College Post-Sec.
255 Grapevine Rd 01984 978-927-2300

West Barnstable, Barnstable, Pop. 1,508

Cape Cod Community College Post-Sec.
2240 Iyannough Rd 02668 508-362-2131

Westborough, Worcester, Pop. 3,951
Westborough SD 3,500/PK-12
45 W Main St 01581 508-836-7700
Marianne O'Connor, supt. Fax 836-7704
westborough.ma.schoolwebpages.com
Gibbons MS 600/7-8
20 Fisher St 01581 508-836-7740
John Foley, prin. Fax 836-7744
Westborough HS 1,100/9-12
90 W Main St 01581 508-836-7720
Brian Callaghan, prin. Fax 836-7723

Porter & Chester Institute Post-Sec.
129 Flanders Rd 01581 508-366-0296

West Boylston, Worcester, Pop. 6,611
West Boylston SD 1,000/PK-12
125 Crescent St 01583 508-835-2917
Elizabeth Schaper, supt. Fax 835-8992
www.wbschools.com
West Boylston JSHS 500/6-12
125 Crescent St 01583 508-835-4475
Larry Murphy, prin. Fax 835-3925

Salter College Post-Sec.
184 W Boylston St 01583 508-853-1074

West Bridgewater, Plymouth
West Bridgewater SD 1,300/PK-12
2 Spring St 02379 508-894-1230
Dr. Patricia Oakley, supt. Fax 894-1232
wbridgewaterschools.org
West Bridgewater MSHS 600/7-12
155 W Center St 02379 508-894-1220
Mark Bodwell, prin. Fax 894-1226

Westfield, Hampden, Pop. 40,552
Westfield SD 5,900/PK-12
1029 North Rd 01085 413-572-6403
Dr. Suzanne Scallion, supt. Fax 535-0353
www.schoolsofwestfield.org
North MS 700/6-8
350 Southampton Rd 01085 413-572-6441
Christopher Rogers, prin. Fax 572-1069
South MS 600/6-8
30 W Silver St 01085 413-568-1900
Ronald Rix, prin. Fax 572-4892
Westfield HS 1,600/9-12
177 Montgomery Rd 01085 413-572-6466
Raymond Broderick, prin. Fax 572-6346
Westfield Vocational Technical HS Vo/Tech
33 Smith Ave 01085 413-572-6533
Stefan Czaporowski, prin. Fax 572-6542

St. Mary's Parish HS 100/9-12
27 Bartlett St 01085 413-568-5692
Nichole Nietsche, head sch Fax 562-3501
Westfield State University Post-Sec.
577 Western Ave 01085 413-572-5300

Westford, Middlesex
Nashoba Valley Technical SD
100 Littleton Rd 01886 978-692-4711
Judith Klimkiewicz Ed.D., supt. Fax 392-0570
www.nashobatech.mec.edu
Nashoba Valley Technical HS Vo/Tech
100 Littleton Rd 01886 978-692-4711
Denise Pigeon, prin. Fax 392-0570

Westford SD 5,300/PK-12
23 Depot St 01886 978-692-5560
Everett Olsen, supt. Fax 392-4497
westfordk12.us/
Blanchard MS 600/6-8
14 West St 01886 978-692-5582
Robin Whitney, prin. Fax 692-5598
Stony Brook MS 700/6-8
9 Farmers Way 01886 978-692-2708
Peter Cohen, prin. Fax 692-5391
Westford Academy 1,600/9-12
30 Patten Rd 01886 978-692-5570
James Antonelli, prin. Fax 692-5502

Westhampton, Hampshire
Hampshire SD 800/7-12
19 Stage Rd 01027 413-527-7200
Dr. Craig Jurgensen, supt. Fax 529-9497
www.hr-k12.org/
Hampshire Regional JSHS 800/7-12
19 Stage Rd 01027 413-527-7680
Laurie Hodgdon, prin. Fax 527-1831

West Newbury, Essex
Pentucket SD 3,100/PK-12
22 Main St 01985 978-363-2280
Jeffrey Mulqueen, supt. Fax 363-1165
www.prsd.org
Pentucket Regional HS 800/9-12
24 Main St 01985 978-363-5507
John Seymour, prin. Fax 363-2730
Pentucket Regional MS 500/7-8
20 Main St 01985 978-363-2957
Dr. Debra Lay, prin. Fax 363-2720

Weston, Middlesex, Pop. 10,200
Weston SD 2,300/PK-12
89 Wellesley St 02493 781-786-5200
Dr. Cheryl Maloney, supt. Fax 786-5209
www.westonschools.org/
Weston HS 700/9-12
444 Wellesley St 02493 781-786-5800
Anthony Parker, prin. Fax 786-5829
Weston MS 600/6-8
456 Wellesley St 02493 781-786-5600
John Gibbons, prin. Fax 786-5609

Blessed John XXIII National Seminary Post-Sec.
558 South Ave 02493 781-899-5500
Cambridge S of Weston 300/9-12
45 Georgian Rd 02493 781-642-8600
Jane Moulding, hdmstr. Fax 398-8344
Regis College Post-Sec.
235 Wellesley St 02493 781-768-7000
Rivers S 500/6-12
333 Winter St 02493 781-235-9300
Thomas Olverson, hdmstr. Fax 239-3614

West Peabody, Essex

Covenant Christian Academy 200/PK-12
83 Pine St 01960 978-535-7100

Westport, Bristol, Pop. 13,852
Westport Community SD 1,800/PK-12
17 Main Rd 02790 508-636-1140
Dr. Carlos M. Colley, supt. Fax 636-1146
www.westportschools.org
Westport HS 500/9-12
19 Main Rd 02790 508-636-1050
Cheryl Tutalo, prin. Fax 636-1053
Westport MS 600/5-8
400 Old County Rd 02790 508-636-1090
Alec Ciminello, prin. Fax 636-7413

West Roxbury, See Boston
Boston SD
Supt. — See Boston
Urban Science Academy 300/9-12
1205 VFW Pkwy 02132 617-635-8930
Nicole Gittens, prin. Fax 635-7895

Catholic Memorial HS 700/7-12
235 Baker St 02132 617-469-8000
Richard Chisholm, prin. Fax 325-0888
Roxbury Latin S 300/7-12
101 Saint Theresa Ave 02132 617-325-4920
Kerry Brennan, hdmstr. Fax 325-3585

West Springfield, Hampden, Pop. 27,989
West Springfield SD 3,900/PK-12
26 Central St Ste 33 01089 413-263-3290
Russell Johnston Ph.D., supt. Fax 739-8748
www.wsps.org
West Springfield HS 1,300/9-12
425 Piper Rd 01089 413-263-3400
Michael Richard, prin. Fax 781-4836
West Springfield MS 900/6-8
31 Middle School Dr 01089 413-263-3406
Thomas McNulty, prin. Fax 781-0965

Kay Harvey Hairdressing Academy Post-Sec.
11 Central St 01089 413-732-7117

Westwood, Norfolk, Pop. 12,557
Westwood SD 3,100/PK-12
220 Nahatan St 02090 781-326-7500
John Antonucci Ed.D., supt. Fax 326-8154
www.westwood.k12.ma.us
Thurston MS 700/6-8
850 High St 02090 781-326-7500
Allison Borchers, prin. Fax 326-2709
Westwood HS 900/9-12
200 Nahatan St 02090 781-326-7500
Sean Bevan, prin. Fax 461-8561

Xaverian Brothers HS 900/9-12
800 Clapboardtree St 02090 781-326-6392
Br. Daniel Skala, hdmstr. Fax 320-0458

West Yarmouth, Barnstable, Pop. 5,701
Dennis-Yarmouth SD
Supt. — See South Yarmouth
Mattacheese MS 500/6-8
400 Higgins Crowell Rd 02673 508-778-7979
Ann Knell, prin. Fax 778-7987

Weymouth, Norfolk, Pop. 53,900
Weymouth SD 6,900/PK-12
111 Middle St 02189 781-335-1460
Kenneth Salim, supt. Fax 335-8777
www.weymouthschools.org
Weymouth HS 2,100/9-12
1 Wildcat Way 02190 781-337-7500
Laura Stevenson, prin. Fax 340-2568
Other Schools – See East Weymouth

South Shore Christian Academy 300/PK-12
45 Broad St 02188 781-331-4340
Kristen Jones, dir. Fax 331-9956

Whitinsville, Worcester, Pop. 6,595
Northbridge SD 2,600/PK-12
87 Linwood Ave 01588 508-234-8156
Dr. Nancy Spitulnik, supt. Fax 234-8469
www.nps.org/
Northbridge HS 600/9-12
427 Linwood Ave 01588 508-234-6221
Michael Gauthier, prin. Fax 234-0802
Northbridge MS 800/5-8
171 Linwood Ave 01588 508-234-8718
MaryEllen Mega, prin. Fax 234-9718

Whitinsville Christian S 500/PK-12
279 Linwood Ave 01588 508-234-8211
Lance Engbers, hdmstr. Fax 234-0624

Whitman, Plymouth, Pop. 13,240
Whitman-Hanson SD 4,400/PK-12
610 Franklin St 02382 781-618-7000
Ruth Gilbert-Whitner Ed.D., supt. Fax 618-7099
www.whrsd.k12.ma.us
Whitman-Hanson Regional HS 1,200/9-12
600 Franklin St 02382 781-618-7020
Jeffrey Szymaniak, prin. Fax 618-7099
Whitman MS 500/6-8
100 Corthell Ave 02382 781-618-7035
George Ferro, prin. Fax 618-7091
Other Schools – See Hanson

Wilbraham, Hampden, Pop. 3,882
Hampden-Wilbraham SD 3,600/PK-12
621 Main St 01095 413-596-3884
Martin O'Shea, supt. Fax 599-1328
www.hwrsd.org
Minnechaug Regional HS 1,300/9-12
621 Main St 01095 413-596-9011
Stephen Hale, prin. Fax 596-8907
Wilbraham MS 600/6-8
466 Stony Hill Rd 01095 413-596-9061
Noel Pixley, prin. Fax 596-9382
Other Schools – See Hampden

Cathedral HS 500/8-12
310 Main St 01095 413-782-5285
John Miller, prin. Fax 782-5065
Wilbraham & Monson Academy 400/6-12
423 Main St 01095 413-596-6811
Rodney LaBrecque, hdmstr. Fax 599-1749

Williamstown, Berkshire, Pop. 4,791
Williamstown-Lanesborough SD 1,300/PK-12
1781 Cold Spring Rd 01267 413-458-9582
Dr. Rose Ellis, supt. Fax 458-2856
www.wlschools.org
Mount Greylock Regional JSHS 600/7-12
1781 Cold Spring Rd 01267 413-458-9582
Dr. Jack Kurty, prin. Fax 458-2856

Buxton S 100/9-12
291 South St 01267 413-458-3919
C. William Bennett, dir. Fax 458-9427
Williams College 01267 Post-Sec.
413-597-3131

Wilmington, Middlesex, Pop. 22,011
Wilmington SD 3,700/PK-12
161 Church St 01887 978-694-6000
Joanne Benton, supt. Fax 694-6005
www.wilmington.k12.ma.us
Wilmington HS 1,000/9-12
159 Church St 01887 978-694-6060
Eric Tracy, prin. Fax 694-6074
Wilmington MS 900/6-8
25 Carter Ln 01887 978-694-6080
Christine McMenimen, prin. Fax 694-6085

ITT Technical Institute Post-Sec.
200 Ballardvale St Ste 200 01887 978-658-2636

Winchendon, Worcester, Pop. 4,143
Winchendon SD 1,500/PK-12
175 Grove St 01475 978-297-0031
Dr. Salah E. Khelfaoui, supt. Fax 297-5250
www.winchendonk12.org
Murdock MSHS 800/6-12
3 Memorial Dr 01475 978-297-1256
Steven Meyer, prin. Fax 297-0509

Winchendon S 300/9-12
172 Ash St 01475 978-297-1223
John Kerney, hdmstr. Fax 297-0911

Winchester, Middlesex, Pop. 20,931
Winchester SD 4,300/PK-12
40 Samoset Rd 01890 781-721-7004
William McAlduff, supt. Fax 721-0016
www.winchester.k12.ma.us
McCall MS 1,000/6-8
458 Main St 01890 781-721-7026
Jorge Goncalves, prin. Fax 721-0886
Winchester HS 1,100/9-12
80 Skillings Rd 01890 781-721-7020
Thomas Gwin, prin. Fax 721-7042

Winthrop, Suffolk, Pop. 18,127
Winthrop SD 2,000/PK-12
1 Metcalf Sq 02152 617-846-5500
John Macero, supt. Fax 539-0891
www.winthrop.k12.ma.us
Winthrop HS 500/9-12
400 Main St 02152 617-846-5500
Gail Conlon, prin. Fax 539-0535
Winthrop MS 500/6-8
151 Pauline St 02152 617-846-5507
Martha Kelleher, prin. Fax 539-1115

Woburn, Middlesex, Pop. 37,207
Woburn SD 4,800/PK-12
55 Locust St 01801 781-937-8233
Mark Donovan, supt. Fax 937-0668
woburnpublicschools.com
Joyce MS 500/6-8
55 Locust St 01801 781-937-8233
Thomas Qualey, prin. Fax 937-8279

Kennedy MS 600/6-8
41 Middle St 01801 781-937-8230
Carl Nelson, prin. Fax 937-8223
Woburn Memorial HS 1,400/9-12
88 Montvale Ave 01801 781-937-8210
Joseph Finigan, prin. Fax 937-8216

Catherine Hinds Institute of Esthetics Post-Sec.
300 Wildwood Ave 01801 781-935-3344
Millenium Training Institute Post-Sec.
600 W Cummings Park # 2550 01801 888-388-9981
New England Tractor Trailer Training Sch Post-Sec.
1600 Osgood St 01815 800-333-2888
Porter & Chester Institute Post-Sec.
8 Presidential Way 01801 781-935-1108

Woods Hole, Barnstable, Pop. 767

Woods Hole Oceanographic Institution Post-Sec.
266 Woods Hole Rd 02543 508-289-2252

Worcester, Worcester, Pop. 175,487

Massachusetts Academy of Math & Science 100/11-12
85 Prescott St 01605 508-831-5859
Michael Barney, dir. Fax 831-5880
www.massacademy.org/
Massachusetts Academy of Math & Science 100/11-12
85 Prescott St 01605 508-831-5859
Michael Barney, dir. Fax 831-5880

Worcester SD 23,500/PK-12
20 Irving St 01609 508-799-3115
Dr. Melinda Boone, supt. Fax 799-3119
worcesterschools.org
Burncoat HS 1,100/9-12
179 Burncoat St 01606 508-799-3300
William Foley, prin. Fax 799-8206
Burncoat MS 600/7-8
135 Burncoat St 01606 508-799-3390
Lisa Houlihan, prin. Fax 799-8207
Caradonio New Citizens Center Alt
1407A Main St 01603 508-799-3494
Steven Alzamora, prin. Fax 799-3494
Claremont Academy 400/7-12
15 Claremont St 01610 508-799-3077
Ricci Hall, prin. Fax 799-8202
Creamer Center Alt
120 Granite St 01604 508-799-3476
Timothy Whalen, prin. Fax 799-3459
Doherty Memorial HS 1,300/9-12
299 Highland St 01602 508-799-3270
Sally Maloney, prin. Fax 799-3276
Forest Grove MS 900/7-8
495 Grove St 01605 508-799-3420
Mark Williams, prin. Fax 799-8218
North HS 1,100/9-12
140 Harrington Way 01604 508-799-3370
Lisa Dyer, prin. Fax 799-8252
South Community HS 1,300/9-12
170 Apricot St 01603 508-799-3325
Maureen Binienda, prin. Fax 799-8242
Sullivan MS 800/7-8
140 Apricot St 01603 508-799-3350
Jason DeFalco, prin. Fax 799-8244
University Park Campus S 200/7-12
12 Freeland St 01603 508-799-3591
Daniel St. Louis, prin. Fax 799-8159
Woodward Day S 100/Alt
190 Fremont St 01603 508-799-3513
Angela Moore, dir. Fax 799-3486
Worcester East MS 600/7-8
420 Grafton St 01604 508-799-3430
Rose Dawkins, prin. Fax 799-8251
Worcester Technical HS Vo/Tech
1 Skyline Dr 01605 508-799-1980
Sheila Harrity, prin. Fax 799-1933

Assumption College Post-Sec.
500 Salisbury St 01609 508-767-7000
Bancroft S 600/PK-12
110 Shore Dr 01605 508-853-2640
Scott Reisinger, admin. Fax 853-7824
Bancroft School of Massage Therapy Post-Sec.
333 Shrewsbury St 01604 508-757-7923
Becker College Post-Sec.
61 Sever St 01609 877-523-2537
Clark University Post-Sec.
950 Main St 01610 508-793-7711
College of the Holy Cross Post-Sec.
1 College St 01610 508-793-2011
Hair in Motion Beauty Academy Post-Sec.
6 Park Ave 01605 508-756-6060
Holy Name Central Catholic HS 700/7-12
144 Granite St 01604 508-753-6371
Edward Reynolds, admin. Fax 831-1287
Notre Dame Academy 300/9-12
425 Salisbury St 01609 508-757-6200
Sr. Ann Morrison, prin. Fax 757-7200
Quinsigamond Community College Post-Sec.
670 W Boylston St 01606 508-853-2300
Rob Roy Academy Post-Sec.
150 Pleasant St 01609 508-799-2111
St. Mary HS 100/7-12
50 Richland St 01610 508-753-1170
Thomas Olson, prin. Fax 795-0560
St. Peter-Marian Central HS 700/7-12
781 Grove St 01605 508-852-5555
Matthew Sturgis, admin. Fax 852-7238
University of Massachusetts Medical Sch Post-Sec.
55 Lake Ave N 01655 508-856-8989
Worcester Academy 700/6-12
81 Providence St 01604 508-754-5302
Dexter Morse, hdmstr. Fax 792-1471
Worcester Polytechnic Institute Post-Sec.
100 Institute Rd 01609 508-831-5000
Worcester State University Post-Sec.
486 Chandler St 01602 508-929-8000

Wrentham, Norfolk

King Philip Regional SD
Supt. — See Norfolk
King Philip Regional HS 1,300/9-12
201 Franklin St 02093 508-384-1000
Dr. Lisa Oliveira, prin.

MICHIGAN

MICHIGAN DEPARTMENT OF EDUCATION
608 W Allegan St, Lansing 48933-1524
Telephone 517-373-3324
Fax 517-335-4565
Website http://www.michigan.gov/mde

Superintendent of Public Instruction Michael Flanagan

MICHIGAN BOARD OF EDUCATION
608 W Allegan St, Lansing 48933-1524

President John C. Austin

INTERMEDIATE SCHOOL DISTRICTS (ISD)

Allegan Area ESA
Mark Dobias, supt. 269-673-2161
310 Thomas St, Allegan 49010 Fax 673-2361
www.alleganaesa.org/

Alpena-Montmorency-Alcona ESD
Brian Wilmot, supt. 989-354-3101
2118 US Highway 23 S Fax 356-3385
Alpena 49707
www.amaesd.org

Barry ISD
Jeff Jennette, supt. 269-945-9545
535 W Woodlawn Ave Fax 945-2575
Hastings 49058
www.barryisd.org

Bay-Arenac ISD
Michael Dewey, supt. 989-686-4410
4228 2 Mile Rd, Bay City 48706 Fax 667-3286
www.baisd.net

Berrien RESA
Dr. Kevin Ivers, supt. 269-471-7725
PO Box 364, Berrien Springs 49103 Fax 471-2941
www.berrienresa.org

Branch ISD
Joseph Lopez, supt. 517-279-5730
370 Morse St, Coldwater 49036 Fax 279-5766
www.branch-isd.org

Calhoun ISD
Terance Lunger, supt. 269-781-5141
17111 G Dr N, Marshall 49068 Fax 781-7071
www.calhounisd.org

Charlevoix-Emmet ISD
Richard Diebold, supt. 231-547-9947
8568 Mercer Rd, Charlevoix 49720 Fax 547-5621
www.charemisd.org

Cheboygan-Otsego-Presque Isle ISD
Mary Vratanina, supt. 231-238-9394
6065 Learning Ln Fax 238-8551
Indian River 49749
www.copesd.org/

Clare-Gladwin RESD
Sheryl Presler, supt. 989-386-3851
4041 E Mannsiding Rd Fax 386-3238
Clare 48617
www.cgresd.net/

Clinton County RESA
John Hagel, supt. 989-224-6831
1013 S US Highway 27 Ste A Fax 224-9574
Saint Johns 48879
www.ccresa.org

C.O.O.R. ISD
Robert Jones, supt. 989-275-9555
PO Box 827, Roscommon 48653 Fax 275-5881
www.coorisd.k12.mi.us

Copper Country ISD
Dennis Harbour, supt. 906-482-4250
809 Hecla St, Hancock 49930 Fax 482-1931
www.copperisd.org

Delta-Schoolcraft ISD
Michael Koster, supt. 906-786-9300
2525 3rd Ave S, Escanaba 49829 Fax 786-9318
www.dsisd.k12.mi.us

Dickinson-Iron ISD
Wendy Warmuth, supt. 906-779-2690
1074 Pyle Dr, Kingsford 49802 Fax 779-2669
www.diisd.org

Eastern Upper Peninsula ISD
Daniel Reattoir, supt., PO Box 883 906-632-3373
Sault Sainte Marie 49783 Fax 632-1125
www.eup.k12.mi.us

Eaton ISD
Christine Beardsley, supt. 517-543-5500
1790 Packard Hwy Fax 543-6633
Charlotte 48813
eatonisd.org

Genesee ISD
Lisa Hagel, supt. 810-591-4400
2413 W Maple Ave, Flint 48507 Fax 591-7570
www.geneseeisd.org

Gogebic-Ontonagon ISD
Bruce Mayle, supt. 906-575-3438
PO Box 218, Bergland 49910 Fax 575-3373
www.goisd.org/

Gratiot-Isabella RESD
Jan Amsterburg, supt. 989-875-5101
PO Box 310, Ithaca 48847 Fax 875-7531
www.giresd.net/

Hillsdale ISD
Michael Potts, supt. 517-437-0990
310 W Bacon St, Hillsdale 49242 Fax 439-4388
www.hillsdale-isd.org

Huron ISD
Joseph Murphy, supt. 989-269-6406
1299 S Thomas Rd Ste 1 Fax 269-9218
Bad Axe 48413
www.hisd.k12.mi.us

Ingham ISD
Stanley Kogut, supt. 517-676-1051
2630 W Howell Rd, Mason 48854 Fax 676-1277
www.inghamisd.org

Ionia County ISD
Robert Kjolhede, supt. 616-527-4900
2191 Harwood Rd, Ionia 48846 Fax 527-4731
www.ioniaisd.org/

Iosco RESA
Dana McGrew, supt. 989-362-3006
27 N Rempert Rd Fax 362-9076
Tawas City 48763
www.ioscoresa.net/

Jackson County ISD
Kevin Oxley, supt. 517-768-5200
6700 Browns Lake Rd Fax 787-2026
Jackson 49201
www.jcisd.org

Kalamazoo RESA
Ronald Fuller, supt. 269-250-9200
1819 E Milham Ave, Portage 49002 Fax 250-9205
www.kresa.org

Kent ISD
Kevin Konarska, supt. 616-364-1333
2930 Knapp St NE Fax 364-1488
Grand Rapids 49525
www.kentisd.org

Lapeer County ISD
Steven Zott, supt. 810-664-5917
1996 W Oregon St, Lapeer 48446 Fax 664-1011
www.lcisd.k12.mi.us

Lenawee ISD
Jim Philp, supt. 517-265-2119
4107 N Adrian Hwy, Adrian 49221 Fax 265-9875
www.lisd.us/

Lewis Cass ISD
Robert Colby, supt. 269-445-6204
61682 Dailey Rd, Cassopolis 49031 Fax 445-2981
www.lewiscassisd.org

Livingston ESA
David Campbell, supt. 517-546-5550
1425 W Grand River Ave Fax 546-7047
Howell 48843
www.livingstonesa.org/

Macomb ISD
Michael DeVault, supt. 586-228-3300
44001 Garfield Rd Fax 286-1523
Clinton Township 48038
www.misd.net

Manistee ISD
Scott Crosby, supt. 231-723-4264
772 E Parkdale Ave Fax 398-3036
Manistee 49660
www.manistee.org

Marquette-Alger RESA
Steven Peffers, supt. 906-226-5100
321 E Ohio St, Marquette 49855 Fax 226-5134
www.maresa.org

Mason-Lake ISD
Lawrence Lloyd, supt. 231-757-3716
2130 W US Highway 10 Fax 757-2406
Ludington 49431
www.mloisd.org

Mecosta-Osceola ISD
Curtis Finch, supt., 15760 190th Ave 231-796-3543
Big Rapids 49307 Fax 796-3300
www.moisd.org

Menominee ISD
John Mans, supt. 906-863-5665
1201 41st Ave, Menominee 49858 Fax 863-7776
www.mc-isd.org

Midland County ESA
John Searles, supt. 989-631-5890
3917 Jefferson Ave, Midland 48640 Fax 631-4361
www.mcesa.k12.mi.us

Monroe County ISD
Donald Spencer, supt. 734-242-5799
1101 S Raisinville Rd Fax 242-0567
Monroe 48161
www.monroeisd.us/

Montcalm Area ISD
Dr. Scott Koenigsknecht, supt. 989-831-5261
PO Box 367, Stanton 48888 Fax 831-8727
www.maisd.com

Muskegon Area ISD
David Sipka, supt. 231-777-2637
630 Harvey St, Muskegon 49442 Fax 773-3498
www.muskegonisd.org

Newaygo County RESA
Lori Clark, supt. 231-924-0381
4747 W 48th St, Fremont 49412 Fax 924-8910
www.ncresa.org

Oakland ISD
Vickie Markavitch, supt. 248-209-2000
2111 Pontiac Lake Rd Fax 209-2206
Waterford 48328
www.oakland.k12.mi.us

Oceana ISD
Lawrence Lloyd, supt. 231-873-5651
844 S Griswold St, Hart 49420 Fax 873-5779
www.mloisd.org

Ottawa Area ISD
Karen McPhee, supt. 616-738-8940
13565 Port Sheldon St Fax 738-8946
Holland 49424
www.oaisd.org

Saginaw ISD
Richard Syrek, supt. 989-399-7473
6235 Gratiot Rd, Saginaw Fax 793-1571
www.sisd.cc/

St. Clair County RESA
Dan DeGrow, supt. 810-364-8990
PO Box 1500, Marysville 48040 Fax 364-7474
www.sccresa.org/

St. Joseph County ISD
Barbara Marshall, supt. 269-467-5400
62445 Shimmel Rd Fax 467-4309
Centreville 49032
www.sjcisd.org

Sanilac ISD
Duane Lange Ph.D., supt. 810-648-4700
175 E Aitken Rd, Peck 48466 Fax 648-5784
www.sanilac.k12.mi.us

Shiawassee RESD
John Hagel, supt. 989-743-3471
1025 N Shiawassee St Fax 743-6477
Corunna 48817
www.sresd.org/

Traverse Bay Area ISD
Michael Hill, supt. 231-922-6200
PO Box 6020, Traverse City 49696 Fax 922-6270
www.tbaisd.k12.mi.us

Tuscola ISD
Eugene Pierce, supt. 989-673-2144
1385 Cleaver Rd, Caro 48723 Fax 673-5366
www.tuscolaisd.org/

Van Buren ISD
Jeffrey Mills, supt. 269-674-8091
490 S Paw Paw St Fax 674-8030
Lawrence 49064
www.vbisd.org/

Washtenaw ISD
Scott Menzel, supt. 734-994-8100
PO Box 1406, Ann Arbor 48106 Fax 994-2203
www.wash.k12.mi.us/

Wayne RESA
Christopher Wigent, supt. 734-334-1300
PO Box 807, Wayne 48184 Fax 334-1760
www.resa.net

Wexford-Missaukee ISD
Scott Crosby, supt. 231-876-2260
9907 E 13th St, Cadillac 49601 Fax 876-2261
www.wmisd.org

PUBLIC, PRIVATE AND CATHOLIC SECONDARY SCHOOLS

Ada, Kent
Forest Hills SD
Supt. — See Grand Rapids
Central MS 600/7-8
5810 Ada Dr SE 49301 616-493-8750
Glenn Mitcham, prin. Fax 493-8764
Eastern HS 900/9-12
2200 Pettis Ave NE 49301 616-493-8830
Steve Harvey, prin. Fax 493-8839
Eastern MS 400/7-8
2200 Pettis Ave NE 49301 616-493-8850
David Washburn, prin. Fax 493-8839

Addison, Lenawee, Pop. 592
Addison Community SD 600/K-12
219 N Comstock St 49220 517-547-6123
Steven Guerra, supt. Fax 547-3838
www.addisonschools.org
Addison HS 300/9-12
219 N Comstock St 49220 517-547-6901
Steven Guerra, prin. Fax 547-3838
Addison MS 100/6-8
219 N Comstock St 49220 517-547-6901
Chad VanSickle, admin. Fax 547-3838

Adrian, Lenawee, Pop. 20,608
Adrian SD 3,200/PK-12
785 Riverside Ave Ste 1 49221 517-263-2115
Dr. Christopher Timmis, supt. Fax 265-5381
www.theadrianmaples.com/
Adrian HS 1,000/9-12
785 Riverside Ave 49221 517-263-2181
Kevin Ohrman, prin. Fax 263-0814
Adrian MS 7-8 500/7-8
615 Springbrook Ave 49221 517-263-0543
Nate Parker, prin. Fax 265-5984
McKinley Education Center 100/Alt
726 Elm St 49221 517-263-1332
Derrick Richards, coord. Fax 263-1385

Lenawee ISD 50/
4107 N Adrian Hwy 49221 517-265-2119
Jim Philp, supt. Fax 265-9875
www.lisd.us/
LISD Tech Center Vo/Tech
1372 N Main St 49221 517-265-1704
Ryan Rowe, prin. Fax 263-9433

Madison SD 1,500/PK-12
3498 Treat Hwy 49221 517-263-0741
James Hartley, supt. Fax 265-5635
www.madisonk12.us
Madison HS 400/9-12
3498 Treat Hwy 49221 517-263-0742
Kristin Thomas, prin. Fax 265-1848
Madison MS 300/6-8
3498 Treat Hwy 49221 517-263-0743
Brad Anschuetz, prin. Fax 265-1848

Adrian College Post-Sec.
110 S Madison St 49221 517-265-5161
Fiser's College of Cosmetology Post-Sec.
329 1/2 E Maumee St 49221 517-264-2199
Jackson Community College Post-Sec.
1376 N Main St 49221 517-265-5515
Lenawee Christian S 600/PK-12
111 Wolf Creek Hwy 49221 517-265-7590
Ronald Evans, hdmstr. Fax 265-6558
Siena Heights University Post-Sec.
1247 E Siena Heights Dr 49221 517-263-0731

Alanson, Emmet, Pop. 721
Alanson SD 300/K-12
7400 North St 49706 231-548-2261
Jeffrey Liedel, supt. Fax 548-2132
www.alansonvikings.net
Alanson HS 100/9-12
7400 North St 49706 231-548-2261
Jeffrey Liedel, prin. Fax 548-2132
Alanson MS 100/6-8
7400 North St 49706 231-548-2261
Jeffrey Liedel, admin. Fax 548-2165

Alba, Antrim, Pop. 295
Alba SD 200/PK-12
PO Box 10 49611 231-584-2000
Rich Satterlee, supt. Fax 584-2001
www.albaschool.org/
Alba S 200/PK-12
PO Box 10 49611 231-584-2000
Rich Satterlee, supt. Fax 584-2001

Albion, Calhoun, Pop. 8,323
Albion SD 600/PK-12
225 E Watson St 49224 517-629-9166
Jerri-Lynn Harper, supt. Fax 629-8209
www.albion.k12.mi.us
Albion HS 400/7-12
225 E Watson St 49224 517-629-9421
Derrick Crum, prin. Fax 630-3305

Marshall SD
Supt. — See Marshall
Marshall Alternative HS 100/Alt
14055 26 Mile Rd 49224 517-629-7547
Bob Vaught, dir. Fax 629-7534

Albion College Post-Sec.
611 E Porter St 49224 517-629-1000

Algonac, Saint Clair, Pop. 4,051
Algonac Community SD 1,900/K-12
1216 Saint Clair Blvd 48001 810-794-9364
Michael Sharrow, supt. Fax 794-0040
algonac.k12.mi.us
Algonac HS 700/9-12
5200 Taft Rd 48001 810-794-4911
Brian Brutyn, prin. Fax 794-8876
Algonquin MS 500/6-8
9185 Marsh Rd 48001 810-794-9317
Abraham Leaver, prin. Fax 794-8872

Allegan, Allegan, Pop. 4,893
Allegan Area ESA 50/
310 Thomas St 49010 269-673-2161
Mark Dobias, supt. Fax 673-2361
www.alleganaesa.org/
Allegan Co. Area Technical & Educ. Ctr. Alt
2891 116th Ave 49010 269-673-3121
Linda Blankenship, prin. Fax 686-0327

Allegan SD 2,800/PK-12
550 5th St 49010 269-673-5431
Kevin Harness, supt. Fax 673-5463
www.alleganps.org/
Allegan HS 800/9-12
1560 Lincoln Rd 49010 269-673-7002
Jim Mallard, prin. Fax 686-2486
South Ward Alternative HS 100/Alt
550 5th St 49010 269-673-5433
Laura Feffer, prin. Fax 673-3990
White MS 600/6-8
3300 115th Ave 49010 269-673-2241
James Antoine, prin. Fax 686-0309

Allendale, Ottawa, Pop. 17,229
Allendale SD 1,900/PK-12
10505 Learning Ln 49401 616-892-5570
Daniel Jonker Ed.D., supt. Fax 895-6690
www.allendale.k12.mi.us
Allendale HS 600/9-12
10760 68th Ave 49401 616-892-5585
Dan Remenap, prin. Fax 895-4280
Allendale MS 500/6-8
7161 Pleasant View Ct 49401 616-892-5595
Rocky Thompson, prin. Fax 895-9111
Allendale New Options 100/Alt
6633 Lake Michigan Dr 49401 616-892-5575
Dan Remenap, prin. Fax 892-4668

Grand Valley State University Post-Sec.
1 Campus Dr 49401 616-331-5000

Allen Park, Wayne, Pop. 27,848
Allen Park SD 3,800/K-12
9601 Vine Ave 48101 313-827-2100
Dr. John Sturock, supt. Fax 827-2151
www.apps.k12.mi.us
Allen Park HS 1,200/9-12
18401 Champaign Rd 48101 313-827-1200
Janet Wasko, prin. Fax 827-1231
Allen Park MS 900/6-8
8401 Vine Ave 48101 313-827-2200
Michael Dawson, prin. Fax 827-2251
Community S 200/Alt
14700 Moore Ave 48101 313-827-2660
Tanya Duffy, dir. Fax 827-2661

Baker College of Allen Park Post-Sec.
4500 Enterprise Dr 48101 313-425-3700
Cabrini HS 500/9-12
15305 Wick Rd 48101 313-388-0110
James Wasukanis, prin. Fax 388-1876
Inter City Baptist S 300/K-12
4700 Allen Rd 48101 313-928-6900
James Hubbard, prin. Fax 928-7310
Stautzenberger Institute Post-Sec.
16630 Southfield Rd 48101 313-294-9715

Alma, Gratiot, Pop. 9,259
Alma SD 2,200/PK-12
1500 Pine Ave 48801 989-463-3111
Sonia Lark, supt. Fax 466-2943
www.almaschools.net
Alma HS 600/9-12
1500 Pine Ave 48801 989-463-3111
Donald Everhart, prin. Fax 463-2176
Pavlik MS 500/6-8
1700 Pine Ave 48801 989-463-3111
Sandy Rusell, prin. Fax 466-7612
Alma Adult & Alternative HS Adult
300 Republic Ave 48801 989-463-2488
Liz VanDyke, admin. Fax 466-6814

Gratiot-Isabella RESD
Supt. — See Ithaca
Gratiot Technical Education Center Vo/Tech
327 E Center St 48801 989-466-4832
Fax 466-9734

Alma College Post-Sec.
614 W Superior St 48801 989-463-7111

Almont, Lapeer, Pop. 2,651
Almont Community SD 1,300/K-12
401 Church St 48003 810-798-8561
Joseph Candela, supt. Fax 798-2367
www.almontschools.org
Almont HS 600/9-12
4701 Howland Rd 48003 810-798-8595
Timothy Woelkers, prin. Fax 798-7011
Almont MS 400/5-8
4624 Kidder Rd 48003 810-798-3578
Kimberly VonHiltmayer, prin. Fax 673-9349

Alpena, Alpena, Pop. 10,337
Alpena SD 4,200/K-12
2373 Gordon Rd 49707 989-358-5040
Brent Holcomb, supt. Fax 358-5041
www.alpenaschools.com
ACES/Oxbow Adult/Alternative/Comm Educ 200/Alt
700 Pinecrest St 49707 989-358-5170
Justin Gluesing, dir. Fax 358-5175
Alpena HS 1,400/9-12
3303 S 3rd Ave 49707 989-358-5200
Matt Poli, prin. Fax 358-5205
Thunder Bay JHS 1,000/6-8
3500 S 3rd Ave 49707 989-358-5400
Steve Genschaw, prin. Fax 358-5499

Alpena Community College Post-Sec.
665 Johnson St 49707 989-356-9021

Ann Arbor, Washtenaw, Pop. 109,999
Ann Arbor SD 16,400/PK-12
PO Box 1188 48106 734-994-2200
Dr. Patricia Green, supt. Fax 994-2414
www.aaps.k12.mi.us/
Ann Arbor Technological HS Alt
2800 Stone School Rd 48104 734-997-1237
Tyrone Weeks, prin. Fax 997-1261
Clague MS 700/6-8
2616 Nixon Rd 48105 734-994-1976
Cynthia Leaman, prin. Fax 994-1645
Community HS 500/9-12
401 N Division St 48104 734-994-2025
Jennifer Hein, dean Fax 994-0042
Forsythe MS 700/6-8
1655 Newport Rd 48103 734-994-1985
Janet Schwamb, prin. Fax 994-5749
Huron HS 1,600/9-12
2727 Fuller Rd 48105 734-994-2040
Arthur Williams, prin. Fax 994-2048
Pioneer HS 1,900/9-12
601 W Stadium Blvd 48103 734-994-2120
Kevin Hudson, prin. Fax 994-2198
Scarlett MS 600/6-8
3300 Lorraine St 48108 734-997-1220
Gerald Vazquez, prin. Fax 997-1885
Skyline HS 1,200/9-12
2552 N Maple Rd 48103 734-994-6515
Sulura Jackson, prin. Fax 994-7028
Slauson MS 700/6-8
1019 W Washington St 48103 734-994-2004
Christopher Curtis, prin. Fax 994-1681
Tappan MS 700/6-8
2251 E Stadium Blvd 48104 734-994-2011
Jazz Parks, prin. Fax 997-1873
Other Schools – See Ypsilanti

Cleary University - Washtenaw Campus Post-Sec.
3601 Plymouth Rd 48105 800-686-1883
Concordia University Post-Sec.
4090 Geddes Rd 48105 734-995-7300
Father Gabriel Richard HS 500/9-12
4333 Whitehall Dr 48105 734-662-0496
Brian Wolcott, prin. Fax 662-4133
Greenhills S 500/6-12
850 Greenhills Dr 48105 734-769-4010
Carl Pelofsky, head sch Fax 769-5029
Michigan Islamic Academy 200/PK-12
2301 Plymouth Rd 48105 734-665-8882
Sr. Fayzeh Madani, prin. Fax 665-9058
Ross Medical Education Center Post-Sec.
4741 Washtenaw Ave 48108 734-434-7320
Steiner S of Ann Arbor 100/9-12
2230 Pontiac Trl 48105 734-669-9394
Sandra Greenstone, admin. Fax 669-9396
University of Michigan-Ann Arbor Post-Sec.
1220 Student Activities Bld 48109 734-764-1817
Washtenaw Community College Post-Sec.
4800 E Huron River Dr 48105 734-973-3300

Armada, Macomb, Pop. 1,714
Armada Area SD 2,000/PK-12
74500 Burk St 48005 586-784-2112
Michael Musary, supt. Fax 784-4268
www.armadaschools.org
Armada HS 700/9-12
23655 Armada Center Rd 48005 586-784-2400
Phillip Jankowski, prin. Fax 784-9592
Armada MS 500/6-8
23550 Armada Center Rd 48005 586-784-2500
William Zebelian, prin. Fax 784-8650
Macomb Academy of Arts & Sciences 100/9-12
23211 Prospect Ave 48005 586-784-2150
Blake Prewitt, dir. Fax 784-8688

Ashley, Gratiot, Pop. 562
Ashley Community SD 400/PK-12
PO Box 6 48806 989-847-4000
Tim Hughes, supt. Fax 847-3500
www.ashleyschools.net/
Ashley HS 100/9-12
PO Box 6 48806 989-847-2514
Michael Allison, prin. Fax 847-4204

Ashley MS 100/5-8
PO Box 6 48806 989-846-2514
Michael Allison, prin. Fax 847-4204

Athens, Calhoun, Pop. 1,000
Athens Area SD
Supt. — See East Leroy
Athens JSHS 300/6-12
300 E Holcomb St 49011 269-729-5414
Joe Huepenbecker, prin. Fax 729-9616

Atlanta, Montmorency, Pop. 815
Atlanta Community SD 300/K-12
PO Box 619 49709 989-785-4877
Donald Haskin, supt. Fax 785-2611
www.atlanta.k12.mi.us
Atlanta Community S 300/K-12
PO Box 619 49709 989-785-4877
Donald Haskin, prin. Fax 785-2611

Attica, Lapeer, Pop. 985
Lapeer County ISD
Supt. — See Lapeer
Lapeer County ISD Education Center Vo/Tech
690 N Lake Pleasant Rd 48412 810-664-1124
Dale Moore, prin. Fax 724-7600

Auburn, Bay, Pop. 2,077
Bay City SD
Supt. — See Bay City
Western HS 1,300/9-12
500 W Midland Rd 48611 989-662-4481
Judy Cox, prin. Fax 662-4413
Western MS 900/6-8
500 W Midland Rd 48611 989-662-4489
Amy Bailey, prin. Fax 662-0185

Auburn Hills, Oakland, Pop. 20,778
Avondale SD 3,700/K-12
2940 Waukegan St 48326 248-537-6000
Dr. George Heitsch, supt. Fax 537-6005
www.avondale.k12.mi.us
Avondale HS 1,100/9-12
2800 Waukegan St 48326 248-537-6100
Michelle Imbrunone, prin. Fax 537-6105
Other Schools – See Rochester Hills

Auburn Hills Christian S 200/PK-12
PO Box 214386 48321 248-373-3399
Amy Wickson, prin. Fax 409-2786
Baker College of Auburn Hills Post-Sec.
1500 University Dr 48326 248-340-0600
Oakland Christian S 600/PK-12
3075 Shimmons Rd 48326 248-373-2700
Roger Van Dorp, supt. Fax 373-9255
Oakland Community College Post-Sec.
2900 Featherstone Rd 48326 248-232-4100

Au Gres, Arenac, Pop. 875
Au Gres-Sims SD 400/K-12
PO Box 648 48703 989-876-7150
Jeffrey Collier, supt. Fax 876-6752
www.ags-schools.org
Au Gres-Sims JSHS 200/6-12
PO Box 648 48703 989-876-7157
Chad Zeien, prin. Fax 876-4684

Augusta, Kalamazoo, Pop. 868
Galesburg-Augusta Community SD
Supt. — See Galesburg
Galesburg-Augusta MS 400/5-8
750 W Van Buren St 49012 269-484-2020
Jeremy Mansfield, prin. Fax 731-4138

Bad Axe, Huron, Pop. 3,092
Bad Axe SD 700/K-12
200 N Barrie Rd Ste 100 48413 989-269-9938
Donald Schelke, supt. Fax 269-2739
www.badaxeps.org/
Bad Axe HS 400/8-12
200 N Barrie Rd 48413 989-269-9593
Wayne Brady, prin. Fax 269-6947

Huron ISD 50/
1299 S Thomas Rd Ste 1 48413 989-269-6406
Joseph Murphy, supt. Fax 269-9218
www.hisd.k12.mi.us
Huron Area Technical Center Vo/Tech
1160 S Van Dyke Rd 48413 989-269-9284
Clark Brock, prin. Fax 269-2844

Baldwin, Lake, Pop. 1,141
Baldwin Community SD 600/PK-12
525 4th St 49304 231-745-4791
Stiles Simmons, supt. Fax 745-3240
www.baldwin.k12.mi.us
Baldwin HS 200/9-12
525 4th St 49304 231-745-4683
Calvin Patillo, prin. Fax 745-2898
Baldwin JHS 100/7-8
525 4th St 49304 231-745-4683
Calvin Patillo, prin. Fax 745-2898

Bangor, Van Buren, Pop. 1,809
Bangor SD 1,200/K-12
801 W Arlington St 49013 269-427-6800
Ron Parker, supt. Fax 427-8274
www.bangorvikings.org
Bangor Community Education Alt
12 N Walnut St 49013 269-427-6839
Lynn Johnson, prin. Fax 427-8274
Bangor HS 400/9-12
801 W Arlington St 49013 269-427-6844
Jeff Melvin, prin. Fax 427-6825
Bangor MS 400/5-8
803 W Arlington St 49013 269-427-6824
Jim Greydanus, prin. Fax 427-6892

Baraga, Baraga, Pop. 1,981
Baraga Area SD 500/K-12
210 Lyons St 49908 906-353-6664
Jennifer Lynn, supt. Fax 353-7454
www.baragaschools.org
Baraga JSHS 300/7-12
210 Lyons St 49908 906-353-6661
Jonathan Young, prin. Fax 353-6662

Keweenaw Bay Ojibwa Community College Post-Sec.
PO Box 519 49908 906-353-4600

Bath, Clinton, Pop. 2,052
Bath Community SD 1,000/K-12
PO Box 310 48808 517-641-6721
Jake Huffman, supt. Fax 641-6958
www.bathschools.net/
Bath HS 300/9-12
PO Box 310 48808 517-641-6724
Matt Dodson, prin. Fax 641-7046
Bath MS 200/6-8
PO Box 310 48808 517-641-6781
Lorenda Jonas, prin. Fax 641-4996

Battle Creek, Calhoun, Pop. 50,321
Battle Creek SD 4,900/K-12
3 Van Buren St W 49017 269-965-9500
Dr. Linda Hicks, supt. Fax 965-9474
www.battlecreekpublicschools.org
Battle Creek Central HS 900/10-12
100 Van Buren St W 49017 269-965-9526
Coby Fletcher, prin. Fax 660-5864
Bearcat Success Academy 300/9-9
100 Van Buren St W 49017 269-213-1742
Anita Harvey, prin. Fax 965-9567
Northwestern MS 300/6-8
176 Limit St, 269-965-9607
Bernard Brown, prin. Fax 965-9525
Battle Creek Adult Education Adult
77 Capital Ave NE 49017 269-965-9514
Sharlie Jones, prin. Fax 965-9545
Other Schools – See Springfield

Calhoun ISD
Supt. — See Marshall
Calhoun Area Career Center Vo/Tech
475 Roosevelt Ave E 49017 269-968-2271
Tim Staffen, dir. Fax 968-4344

Harper Creek Community SD 2,600/K-12
7454 B Dr N 49014 269-441-6550
John Severson, supt. Fax 962-6034
www.harpercreek.net
Harper Creek HS 900/9-12
12677 Beadle Lake Rd 49014 269-441-8450
Gary Garland, prin. Fax 441-2206
Harper Creek MS 800/5-8
7290 B Dr N 49014 269-441-4750
Cristina Eyre, prin. Fax 970-4613

Lakeview SD 3,900/K-12
15 Arbor St 49015 269-565-2400
Dave Peterson, supt. Fax 565-2408
www.lakeviewspartans.org
Lakeview HS 1,400/9-12
15060 Helmer Rd S 49015 269-565-3700
Jeffrey Bohl, prin. Fax 565-3708
Lakeview MS 1,200/5-8
300 28th St S 49015 269-565-3900
Michael Norstrom, prin. Fax 565-3908

Pennfield SD 2,100/K-12
8587 Pennfield Rd 49017 269-961-9781
Ben Laser, supt. Fax 961-9799
www.pennfield.net/
Pennfield HS 700/9-12
8587 Pennfield Rd 49017 269-961-9770
Barry Duckham, prin. Fax 441-1274
Pennfield MS 500/6-8
8587 Pennfield Rd 49017 269-961-9784
Michele Herzing, prin. Fax 441-5535

Battle Creek Academy 100/K-12
480 Parkway Dr, 269-965-1278
James Davis, prin. Fax 965-3250
Calhoun Christian S 100/PK-12
20 Woodrow Ave S 49015 269-965-5560
William Spicer, prin. Fax 965-8038
Davenport University Post-Sec.
200 Van Buren St W 49017 269-968-6105
Kambly School/Developmentally Impaired Post-Sec.
1003 North Ave 49017
Kellogg Community College Post-Sec.
450 North Ave 49017 269-965-3931
Robert Miller College Post-Sec.
450 North Ave 49017 269-660-8021
St. Joseph MS 100/6-8
44 25th St N 49015 269-963-4935
Marcy Arnson, prin. Fax 963-0354
St. Philip Catholic Central HS 100/9-12
20 Cherry St 49017 269-963-4503
Tim May, prin. Fax 963-5590
Wright Beauty Academy Post-Sec.
492 Capital Ave SW 49015 269-964-4016

Bay City, Bay, Pop. 33,947
Bangor Township SD 2,500/PK-12
3359 E Midland Rd 48706 989-684-8121
Dr. Shawn Bishop, supt. Fax 684-6000
www.bangorschools.org
Glenn HS 900/9-12
3201 Kiesel Rd 48706 989-684-7510
Tony Bacigalupo, prin. Fax 684-1545
McAuliffe MS 600/6-8
3281 Kiesel Rd 48706 989-686-7640
Diana Tuttle, prin. Fax 686-7633

Bay City SD 8,500/PK-12
910 N Walnut St 48706 989-686-9700
Douglas Newcombe, supt. Fax 686-1047
www.bcschools.net
Central HS 1,400/9-12
1624 Columbus Ave 48708 989-893-9541
Tim Marciniak, prin. Fax 893-0333
Handy MS 1,100/6-8
601 Blend St 48706 989-684-1723
Brian DuFresne, prin. Fax 684-1960
Wenona Center 200/Alt
201 Woodside Ln 48708 989-895-5550
Jerry Lombardo, prin. Fax 895-6517
Other Schools – See Auburn

All Saints Central MSHS 300/6-12
217 S Monroe St 48708 989-892-2533
Brian Campbell, prin. Fax 892-7188
Bayshire Beauty Academy Post-Sec.
917 Saginaw St 48708 989-894-2431

Bear Lake, Manistee, Pop. 281
Bear Lake SD 300/K-12
7748 Cody St 49614 231-864-3133
Marlen Cordes, supt. Fax 864-3434
www.bearlake.k12.mi.us
Bear Lake HS 200/6-12
7748 Cody St 49614 231-864-3133
Sarah Harless, prin. Fax 864-3434

Beaver Island, Charlevoix
Beaver Island Community SD 100/K-12
37895 Kings Hwy 49782 231-448-2744
Riley Justis, supt. Fax 448-2919
www.beaverisland.k12.mi.us
Beaver Island Community S 100/K-12
37895 Kings Hwy 49782 231-448-2744
Riley Justis, prin. Fax 448-2919

Beaverton, Gladwin, Pop. 1,061
Beaverton Rural SD 1,400/K-12
PO Box 529 48612 989-246-3000
Greg Paxton, supt. Fax 435-7631
www.brs.cgresd.net
Beaverton HS 500/9-12
PO Box 529 48612 989-246-3010
Joseph Passalucqua, prin. Fax 246-3366
Beaverton MS 600/4-8
PO Box 529 48612 989-246-3020
Jeffrey Budge, prin. Fax 246-3420

Belding, Ionia, Pop. 5,669
Belding Area SD 2,200/PK-12
850 Hall St 48809 616-794-4700
Sara Shriver, supt. Fax 794-4730
www.bas-k12.org/
Belding HS 700/9-12
850 Hall St 48809 616-794-4900
Brett Zuver, prin. Fax 794-4956
Belding MS 500/6-8
410 Ionia St 48809 616-794-4400
Joel Olson, prin. Fax 794-4420

Bellaire, Antrim, Pop. 1,076
Bellaire SD 500/K-12
204 W Forrest Home Ave 49615 231-533-8141
James Emery, supt. Fax 533-6797
www.bellairepublicschools.com/
Bellaire MSHS 300/6-12
204 W Forrest Home Ave 49615 231-533-8015
James Emery, prin. Fax 533-6797

Belleville, Wayne, Pop. 3,881
Van Buren SD 3,900/PK-12
555 W Columbia Ave 48111 734-697-9123
Michael Van Tassel, supt. Fax 697-6385
www.vanburenschools.net
Belleville HS 1,800/9-12
501 W Columbia Ave 48111 734-697-9133
Abdul Madyun, prin. Fax 697-6551
McBride MS 500/7-8
47097 McBride Ave 48111 734-697-9171
Tim Ottewell, prin. Fax 697-6573

Bellevue, Eaton, Pop. 1,257
Bellevue Community SD 600/K-12
904 W Capital Ave 49021 269-763-9432
Scott Belt, supt. Fax 763-3101
www.bellevue-schools.com/
Bellevue HS 300/6-12
576 Love Hwy 49021 269-763-9413
Monica Burger, prin. Fax 763-3955

Benton Harbor, Berrien, Pop. 9,796
Benton Harbor Area SD 2,100/PK-12
PO Box 1107 49023 269-605-1000
Dr. Leonard Seawood, supt. Fax 605-1043
www.bhas.org
Benton Harbor MSHS 900/8-12
870 Colfax Ave 49022 269-605-1200
Kathy Brooks, prin. Fax 605-1213

Lake Michigan College Post-Sec.
2755 E Napier Ave 49022 269-927-8100

Benzonia, Benzie, Pop. 484
Benzie County Central SD 1,700/K-12
9222 Homestead Rd 49616 231-882-9653
David Micinski, supt. Fax 882-9121
www.benzieschools.net/
Benzie Central HS 500/9-12
PO Box 240 49616 231-882-4497
Peter Olson, prin. Fax 882-5699
Benzie Central MS 300/7-8
9300 Homestead Rd 49616 231-882-4498
David Clasen, prin. Fax 882-7627

Berkley, Oakland, Pop. 14,700
Berkley SD
Supt. — See Oak Park

Anderson MS 600/6-8
3205 Catalpa Dr 48072 248-837-8200
Vince Gigliotti, prin. Fax 546-0696
Berkley HS 1,300/9-12
2325 Catalpa Dr 48072 248-837-8100
Randy Gawel, prin. Fax 544-5860

Berrien Springs, Berrien, Pop. 1,747
Berrien Springs SD 2,000/K-12
PO Box 130 49103 269-471-2891
Dr. James Bermingham, supt. Fax 471-2590
www.homeoftheshamrocks.org
Berrien Springs Discovery Academy 200/Alt
PO Box 130 49103 269-471-2593
William Bergan, prin. Fax 471-8865
Berrien Springs HS 600/9-12
PO Box 130 49103 269-471-1748
David Eichberg, prin. Fax 471-1511
Berrien Springs MS 500/6-8
PO Box 130 49103 269-471-2796
Ryan Pesce, prin. Fax 471-2590

Andrews Academy 200/9-12
8833 Garland Ave 49104 269-471-3138
Robert Overstreet, prin. Fax 471-6368
Andrews University 49104 Post-Sec.
269-471-7771
Griggs University Post-Sec.
8903 US Highway 31 49104 800-782-4769

Bessemer, Gogebic, Pop. 1,874
Bessemer City SD 500/PK-12
301 E Sellar St 49911 906-667-0802
Mark Johnson, supt. Fax 667-0318
www.bessemer.k12.mi.us
Johnston JSHS 200/7-12
100 W Lead St 49911 906-667-0413
Mark Johnson, prin. Fax 667-0320

Beverly Hills, Oakland, Pop. 10,098
Birmingham SD 8,000/PK-12
31301 Evergreen Rd 48025 248-203-3000
Br. Daniel Nerad, supt. Fax 203-3009
www.birmingham.k12.mi.us
Berkshire MS 700/6-8
21707 W 14 Mile Rd 48025 248-203-4702
Jason Clinckscale, prin. Fax 203-4802
Groves HS 1,300/9-12
20500 W 13 Mile Rd 48025 248-203-3530
Cathy Hurley, prin. Fax 203-3636
Other Schools – See Birmingham, Bloomfield Hls

Detroit Country Day MS 400/6-8
22400 Hillview Ln 48025 248-646-7985
Glen Shilling, hdmstr. Fax 646-3459
Detroit Country Day Upper S 700/9-12
22305 W 13 Mile Rd 48025 248-646-7717
Fax 646-2458

Big Rapids, Mecosta, Pop. 10,347
Big Rapids SD 1,700/K-12
21034 15 Mile Rd 49307 231-796-2627
Tim Haist, supt. Fax 592-0639
www.brps.org
Big Rapids HS 700/9-12
21175 15 Mile Rd 49307 231-796-7651
Ron Pincumbe, prin. Fax 592-8505
Big Rapids MS 500/5-8
500 N Warren Ave 49307 231-796-9965
Lenore Weaver, prin. Fax 592-3494
New Directions Alternative HS 50/Alt
14980 215th Ave 49307 231-796-3489
Josh Easler, coord. Fax 592-0644

Mecosta-Osceola ISD 100/
15760 190th Ave 49307 231-796-3543
Curtis Finch, supt. Fax 796-3300
www.moisd.org
Math Science Technology Center Alt
15760 190th Ave 49307 231-796-3543
Jennifer Harrison, dir. Fax 796-3300
Mecosta-Osceola Career Center Vo/Tech
15830 190th Ave 49307 231-796-5805
Stephen Locke, prin. Fax 796-0262

Ferris State University Post-Sec.
1201 S State St 49307 231-591-2000

Birch Run, Saginaw, Pop. 1,524
Birch Run Area SD 1,800/K-12
12400 Church St 48415 989-624-9307
David Bush, supt. Fax 624-8503
www.birchrunschools.org
Birch Run Alternative HS Alt
12400 Church St 48415 989-624-5821
Jennifer Mudge, prin. Fax 624-8507
Birch Run HS 600/9-12
12450 Church St 48415 989-624-9392
Michael Baszler, prin. Fax 624-8502
Greene MS 600/5-8
8225 Main St 48415 989-624-5821
Scott Preston, prin. Fax 624-8507

Birmingham, Oakland, Pop. 19,789
Birmingham SD
Supt. — See Beverly Hills
Derby MS 800/6-8
1300 Derby Rd 48009 248-203-5003
Celeste Nowacki, prin. Fax 203-4948
Seaholm HS 1,300/9-12
2436 W Lincoln St 48009 248-203-3707
Deanna Barash, prin. Fax 203-3706

Roeper S 400/6-12
1051 Oakland Ave 48009 248-203-7300
David Feldman, head sch Fax 203-7310

Blanchard, Isabella
Montabella Community SD
Supt. — See Edmore
Montabella JSHS 400/7-12
1324 N County Line Rd 49310 989-427-5175
Shane Riley, prin. Fax 427-5107

Blissfield, Lenawee, Pop. 3,300
Blissfield Community SD 1,300/K-12
630 S Lane St 49228 517-486-2205
Scott Moellenberndt, supt. Fax 486-5701
www.blissfieldschools.us/
Blissfield HS 400/9-12
630 S Lane St 49228 517-486-2148
Jerry Johnson, prin. Fax 486-4749
Blissfield MS 300/6-8
1305 Beamer Rd 49228 517-486-4420
Chris Rupp, prin. Fax 486-4758

Bloomfield Hls, Oakland, Pop. 3,811
Birmingham SD
Supt. — See Beverly Hills
Birmingham Covington S 600/3-8
1525 Covington Rd, 248-203-4425
Mark Morawski, prin. Fax 203-4433

Bloomfield Hills SD 3,900/PK-12
7273 Wing Lake Rd, 248-341-5400
Robert Glass, supt. Fax 341-5449
www.bloomfield.org
Bloomfield Hills HS 9-12
3456 Lahser Rd, 248-341-5700
Charles Hollerith, prin. Fax 341-5899
Bloomfield Hills MS 700/5-8
4200 Quarton Rd, 248-341-6000
Randy English, prin. Fax 341-6099
Bowers Academy Alt
1223 E Square Lake Rd, 248-341-5985
Bill Boyle, prin. Fax 341-5998
East Hills MS 500/5-8
2800 Kensington Rd, 248-341-6200
Jason Rubel, prin. Fax 341-6299
International Academy 500/9-12
1020 E Square Lake Rd, 248-341-5900
Lynne Gibson, prin. Fax 341-5959
Other Schools – See West Bloomfield

Academy of the Sacred Heart 500/PK-12
1250 Kensington Rd, 248-646-8900
Sr. Bridget Bearss, hdmstr. Fax 646-4143
Brother Rice HS 700/9-12
7101 Lahser Rd, 248-647-2526
Br. Michael Segvich, prin. Fax 647-8170
Cranbrook Academy of Art Post-Sec.
PO Box 801, 248-645-3300
Cranbrook S 1,700/PK-12
PO Box 801, 248-645-3602
Arlyce Seibert, dir. Fax 645-3524
Marian HS 600/9-12
7225 Lahser Rd, 248-644-1750
Sr. Lenore Pochelski, pres. Fax 644-6107

Bloomingdale, Van Buren, Pop. 446
Bloomingdale SD 1,400/K-12
PO Box 217 49026 269-521-3900
Deb Paquette, supt. Fax 521-3907
www.bdalecards.org/
Bloomingdale HS 400/9-12
PO Box 217 49026 269-521-3910
Rick Reo, prin. Fax 521-3915
Bloomingdale MS 300/6-8
PO Box 217 49026 269-521-3950
Patrick Creagan, prin. Fax 521-3958

Boyne City, Charlevoix, Pop. 3,622
Boyne City SD 1,300/K-12
321 S Park St 49712 231-439-8190
Peter Moss M.A., supt. Fax 439-8195
www.boyne.k12.mi.us
Boyne City HS 400/9-12
1035 Boyne Ave 49712 231-439-8100
Karen Jarema M.A., prin. Fax 439-8194
Boyne City MS 400/5-8
1025 Boyne Ave 49712 231-439-8200
Mike Wilson M.A., prin. Fax 439-8233
Other Schools – See Boyne Falls

Boyne Falls, Charlevoix, Pop. 286
Boyne City SD
Supt. — See Boyne City
Boyne Valley Alternative HS 50/Alt
2329 Center St 49713 231-549-7761
Cody Wilcox M.A., admin. Fax 549-7764

Boyne Falls SD 200/K-12
PO Box 356 49713 231-549-2211
Karen Sherwood, admin. Fax 549-2922
www.boynefalls.org
Boyne Falls S 200/K-12
PO Box 356 49713 231-549-2211
Karen Sherwood, admin. Fax 549-2922

Breckenridge, Gratiot, Pop. 1,316
Breckenridge Community SD 800/PK-12
PO Box 217 48615 989-842-3182
Dean Havelka, supt. Fax 842-3625
breck.edzone.net
Breckenridge HS 200/9-12
PO Box 217 48615 989-842-3182
Sheila Pilmore, prin. Fax 842-5761
Breckenridge MS 200/6-8
PO Box 217 48615 989-842-3182
Sheila Pilmore, prin. Fax 842-5761

Brethren, Manistee, Pop. 407
Kaleva Norman Dickson SD 600/K-12
4400 Highbridge Rd 49619 231-477-5353
Marlen Cordes, supt. Fax 477-5240
www.knd.k12.mi.us
Brethren HS 200/9-12
4400 Highbridge Rd 49619 231-477-5355
Jim Wojchiechowski, prin. Fax 477-5242
Brethren MS 100/7-8
4400 Highbridge Rd 49619 231-477-5354
Jim Wojchiechowski, prin. Fax 477-5351

Bridgeport, Saginaw, Pop. 6,811
Bridgeport-Spaulding Community SD 1,000/PK-12
PO Box 657 48722 989-777-1770
Gloria Rubis, supt. Fax 777-4720
www.bscs.k12.mi.us
Bridgeport HS 500/9-12
4691 Bearcat Blvd 48722 989-777-3100
Suzanne Brown, prin. Fax 777-6910

Bridgeport Baptist Academy 100/K-12
PO Box 249 48722 989-777-6811
John Howell, prin. Fax 777-7376

Bridgman, Berrien, Pop. 2,260
Bridgman SD 1,000/PK-12
9964 Gast Rd 49106 269-466-0271
Shane Peters, supt. Fax 466-0221
www.bridgmanschools.com
Bridgman HS 300/9-12
9964 Gast Rd 49106 269-465-6848
Paul Hartsig, prin. Fax 466-0355
Reed MS 300/5-8
10254 California 49106 269-466-0410
Sam Stine, prin. Fax 466-0393

Brighton, Livingston, Pop. 7,364
Brighton Area SD 6,300/K-12
125 S Church St 48116 810-299-4000
Greg Gray, supt. Fax 299-4092
www.brightonk12.com/
Bridge Alternative HS 100/Alt
125 S Church St 48116 810-299-4046
Colleen Deaven, admin.
Brighton HS 2,000/9-12
7878 Brighton Rd 48116 810-299-4100
Gavin Johnson, prin. Fax 299-4111
Scranton MS 1,100/7-8
8415 Maltby Rd 48116 810-299-3700
Mark Wilson, prin. Fax 299-3710

Ross Medical Education Center Post-Sec.
8110 Murphy Dr 48116 810-227-0160

Brimley, Chippewa
Brimley Area SD 500/K-12
7134 S M 221 49715 906-248-3219
Rodney Goehmann, supt. Fax 248-3220
www.eup.k12.mi.us/brimley/
Brimley HS 200/7-12
7134 S M 221 49715 906-248-3218
Brian Reattoir, prin. Fax 248-5339

Bay Mills Community College Post-Sec.
12214 W Lakeshore Dr 49715 906-248-3354

Britton, Lenawee, Pop. 584
Britton Deerfield SD 700/PK-12
201 College Ave 49229 517-451-4581
Charles Pelham, supt. Fax 451-8595
www.bdschools.us
Britton S 500/PK-12
201 College Ave 49229 517-451-4581
John Eisley, prin. Fax 451-8595

Bronson, Branch, Pop. 2,313
Bronson Community SD 1,200/K-12
501 E Chicago St 49028 517-369-3257
James Modert, supt. Fax 369-2802
www.bronson.k12.mi.us
Bronson JSHS 600/6-12
450 E Grant St 49028 517-369-3230
Wesley McCrea, prin. Fax 369-3506

Brooklyn, Jackson, Pop. 1,196
Columbia SD 1,200/K-12
11775 Hewitt Rd 49230 517-592-6641
Lisa Petersen, supt. Fax 592-8090
www.columbiaschooldistrict.org
Columbia Central HS 500/9-12
11775 Hewitt Rd 49230 517-592-6634
David Slusher, prin. Fax 592-8909
Columbia MS 400/5-8
321 School St 49230 517-592-2181
Christi O'Neil, prin. Fax 592-3447
Other Schools – See Clarklake

Brown City, Sanilac, Pop. 1,303
Brown City Community SD 900/K-12
PO Box 160 48416 810-346-2781
Jerry Steigerwald, supt. Fax 346-3762
www.bc.k12.mi.us
Brown City JSHS 400/7-12
PO Box 160 48416 810-346-2781
Barry Markwart, prin. Fax 346-2381

Brownstown, See Flat Rock
Woodhaven-Brownstown SD
Supt. — See Woodhaven
Woodhaven HS 1,200/10-12
24787 Van Horn Rd 48134 734-783-3333
Matthew Czajkowski, prin. Fax 783-3342

Buchanan, Berrien, Pop. 4,325
Buchanan Community SD 1,000/PK-12
401 W Chicago St 49107 269-695-8401
Dr. Andrea Van der Laan, supt. Fax 695-8450
www.buchananschools.com
Buchanan HS 500/8-12
401 W Chicago St 49107 269-695-8403
Sharon Steinke, prin. Fax 695-8451

Buckley, Wexford, Pop. 683
Buckley Community SD 400/K-12
PO Box 38 49620 231-269-3325
Rick Heitmeyer, supt. Fax 269-3833
www.buckleyschools.com

Buckley Community S 400/K-12
PO Box 38 49620 231-269-3325
Todd Kulawiak, prin. Fax 269-3833

Burr Oak, Saint Joseph, Pop. 822
Burr Oak Community SD 300/K-12
PO Box 337 49030 269-489-2213
Terry Conklin, supt. Fax 489-5198
burroak.remc12.k12.mi.us
Burr Oak HS 100/7-12
PO Box 337 49030 269-489-5534
Robert Cary, prin. Fax 489-5198

Burton, Genesee, Pop. 29,312
Atherton Community SD 900/K-12
3354 S Genesee Rd 48519 810-591-9182
John Ploof, supt. Fax 591-1926
www.athertonschools.org
Atherton HS 300/9-12
3354 S Genesee Rd 48519 810-591-9184
Jamie Johnston, prin. Fax 591-9180
Atherton MS 300/4-8
3444 S Genesee Rd 48519 810-591-0604
Jamie Johnston, prin. Fax 591-9456

Bendle SD 1,100/PK-12
3420 Columbine Ave 48529 810-591-2501
John Krolewski, supt. Fax 591-2210
www.bendleschools.org
Bendle HS 300/9-12
2283 E Scottwood Ave 48529 810-591-5103
Scott Williams, prin. Fax 591-2510
Bendle MS 300/6-8
2294 E Bristol Rd 48529 810-591-3385
Pete Gleason, prin. Fax 591-2540

Bentley Community SD 900/K-12
1170 N Belsay Rd 48509 810-591-9100
John Schantz, supt. Fax 591-9102
www.bentleyschools.org
Bentley JSHS 400/7-12
1150 N Belsay Rd 48509 810-591-5811
Rex Hart, prin. Fax 591-9158

Faithway Christian S 100/PK-12
1225 S Center Rd 48509 810-743-0055
Domenic Centofanti, prin. Fax 743-0033
Genesee Christian S 400/PK-12
1223 S Belsay Rd 48509 810-743-3108
Robert Buchalski, prin. Fax 743-3230
St. Thomas More Academy 100/K-12
6456 E Bristol Rd 48519 810-742-2411
Dan Le Blanc, prin. Fax 742-4803

Byron, Shiawassee, Pop. 573
Byron Area SD 1,200/K-12
312 W Maple St 48418 810-266-4881
Tricia Murphy-Alderman, supt. Fax 266-5723
www.byron.k12.mi.us
Byron HS 400/9-12
312 W Maple St 48418 810-266-4620
Frank Trotter, prin. Fax 266-5010
Byron MS 300/6-8
312 W Maple St 48418 810-266-4422
Steve Vowles, prin. Fax 266-4151

Byron Center, Kent, Pop. 5,750
Byron Center SD 3,300/PK-12
8542 Byron Center Ave SW 49315 616-878-6100
Daniel Takens, supt. Fax 878-6120
www.bcpsk12.net
Byron Center HS 1,000/9-12
8500 Burlingame Ave SW 49315 616-878-6600
Scott Joseph, prin. Fax 878-6620
Byron Center West MS 500/7-8
8654 Homerich Ave SW 49315 616-878-6500
John Krajewski, prin. Fax 878-6520

Zion Christian S 300/PK-12
7555 Byron Center Ave SW 49315 616-878-9472
Jason Heerema, admin. Fax 878-9473

Cadillac, Wexford, Pop. 10,183
Cadillac Area SD 2,300/K-12
421 S Mitchell St 49601 231-876-5000
Joann Spry, supt. Fax 876-5021
www.cadillac.k12.mi.us/
Cadillac HS 700/9-12
400 Linden St 49601 231-876-5800
Todd Bruggema, prin. Fax 876-5821
Cadillac JHS 200/7-8
500 Chestnut St 49601 231-876-5700
Dave Champion, prin. Fax 876-5721
Cooley Alternative S 100/Alt
221 Granite St 49601 231-876-5900
Michael Outman, prin. Fax 876-5921

Wexford-Missaukee ISD 50/
9907 E 13th St 49601 231-876-2260
Scott Crosby, supt. Fax 876-2261
www.wmisd.org
Wexford-Missaukee Area Career Tech Vo/Tech
9901 E 13th St 49601 231-876-2200
Fax 876-2212

Baker College of Cadillac Post-Sec.
9600 E 13th St 49601 231-876-3100
Cadillac Heritage Christian S 100/PK-12
1706 Wright St 49601 231-775-4272
William Goodwill, admin. Fax 775-2999

Caledonia, Kent, Pop. 1,496
Caledonia Community SD 4,100/PK-12
9753 Duncan Lake Ave SE 49316 616-891-8185
Randy Rodriguez, supt. Fax 891-9253
www.calschools.org
Caledonia HS 1,300/9-12
9050 Kraft Ave SE 49316 616-891-8129
Jim Glazier, prin. Fax 891-7038
Duncan Lake MS 500/6-8
9757 Duncan Lake Ave SE 49316 616-891-1380
Ryan Graham, prin. Fax 891-8033
Glenmor HS 50/Alt
8948 Kraft Ave SE 49316 616-891-8236
Jim Glazier, admin. Fax 891-8139
Kraft Meadows MS 500/6-8
9230 Kraft Ave SE 49316 616-891-8649
Cary Stamas, prin. Fax 891-7013

Calumet, Houghton, Pop. 716
Calumet-Laurium-Keweenaw SD 1,500/K-12
57070 Mine St 49913 906-337-0311
Darryl Pierce, supt. Fax 337-1406
clkschools.org
Calumet HS 400/9-12
57070 Mine St 49913 906-337-0311
George Twardzik, prin. Fax 337-5405
Horizon Alternative HS 100/Alt
57070 Mine St 49913 906-337-4611
Christopher Davidson, prin. Fax 337-4614
Washington MS 300/6-8
57070 Mine St 49913 906-337-0311
Michael Steber, prin. Fax 337-5406

Camden, Hillsdale, Pop. 510
Camden-Frontier SD 400/K-12
4971 W Montgomery Rd 49232 517-368-5991
Scott Riley, supt. Fax 368-5959
www.cfss.org/
Camden Frontier HS 200/9-12
4971 W Montgomery Rd 49232 517-368-5255
Scott Riley, prin. Fax 368-5959

Canton, Wayne, Pop. 81,500
Plymouth-Canton Community SD
Supt. — See Plymouth
Canton HS 2,100/9-12
8415 N Canton Center Rd 48187 734-416-2850
Carrie Lawler, prin. Fax 416-7531
Discovery MS 1,000/6-8
45083 Hanford Rd 48187 734-416-2880
Roche LaVictor, prin. Fax 416-2895
Plymouth HS 2,100/9-12
8400 N Beck Rd 48187 734-582-5500
Cheri Steckel, prin. Fax 582-5555
Salem HS 2,100/9-12
46181 Joy Rd 48187 734-416-7800
Nancy Laws, prin. Fax 416-7791

ITT Technical Institute Post-Sec.
1905 S Haggerty Rd 48188 734-397-7800
Michigan Institute of Aviation & Tech Post-Sec.
2955 S Haggerty Rd 48188 734-423-2100
Plymouth Christian Academy 600/PK-12
43065 Joy Rd 48187 734-459-3505
Dr. Mark Wood, supt. Fax 459-9997

Capac, Saint Clair, Pop. 1,866
Capac Community SD 1,400/PK-12
PO Box 700 48014 810-395-3710
Dr. Charles C. Smith, supt. Fax 395-4858
www.capacschools.us
Capac JSHS 500/9-12
541 N Glassford St 48014 810-395-3800
Michael Mrozinski, prin. Fax 395-2427
Capac MS 300/6-8
201 N Neeper St 48014 810-395-3750
Fax 395-4098
Crossroads S 50/Alt
403 N Glassford St 48014 810-395-4074
Stewart Sternberg, lead tchr. Fax 395-8237

Carleton, Monroe, Pop. 2,303
Airport Community SD 2,700/PK-12
11270 Grafton Rd 48117 734-654-2414
John Krimmel, supt. Fax 654-4014
www.acspublic.com/
Airport HS 900/9-12
11330 Grafton Rd 48117 734-654-6208
Chris Lukosavich, prin. Fax 654-3005
Wagar MS 700/6-8
11200 Grafton Rd 48117 734-654-6205
Dan Bondy, prin. Fax 654-0057
Other Schools – See Newport

Carney, Menominee, Pop. 190
Carney-Nadeau SD 300/PK-12
PO Box 68 49812 906-639-2171
Claude Siders, supt. Fax 639-2176
www.cnps.us
Carney-Nadeau S 300/PK-12
PO Box 68 49812 906-639-2171
Adam Cocco, prin. Fax 639-2176

Caro, Tuscola, Pop. 4,185
Caro Community SD 1,900/K-12
301 N Hooper St 48723 989-673-3160
Bruce Nelson, supt. Fax 673-6248
www.caro.k12.mi.us
Caro HS 600/9-12
301 N Hooper St 48723 989-673-3165
Mike Joslyn, prin. Fax 673-8707
Caro MS 400/6-8
299 N Hooper St 48723 989-673-3167
JoAnn Nordstrom, prin. Fax 673-1225

Tuscola ISD 200/
1385 Cleaver Rd 48723 989-673-2144
Eugene Pierce, supt. Fax 673-5366
www.tuscolaisd.org/
Tuscola Technology Center Vo/Tech
1401 Cleaver Rd 48723 989-673-5300
Shawn Petri, prin. Fax 673-4228

Carson City, Montcalm, Pop. 1,086
Carson City-Crystal Area SD 1,000/K-12
PO Box 780 48811 989-584-3138
Kevin Murphy, supt. Fax 584-3539
www.carsoncity.k12.mi.us
Carson City-Crystal HS 300/9-12
PO Box 780 48811 989-584-3175
Devin Pringle, prin. Fax 584-3043
Carson City-Crystal MS 400/4-8
PO Box 780 48811 989-584-3903
Charles Larkins, prin. Fax 584-3259

Carsonville, Sanilac, Pop. 513
Carsonville-Port Sanilac SD 600/K-12
100 N Goetze Rd 48419 810-657-9393
Harold Titus, supt. Fax 657-9060
www.carsport.k12.mi.us
Carsonville-Port Sanilac JSHS 300/6-12
100 N Goetze Rd 48419 810-657-9394
Jennifer Richmond, prin. Fax 657-9431
Carsonville-Pt Sanilac Acad Alt Learners 100/Alt
100 N Goetze Rd 48419 810-657-9393
Russell Clark, dir. Fax 657-9060

Casco, Saint Clair
Anchor Bay SD 6,000/K-12
5201 County Line Rd Ste 100 48064 586-725-2861
Leonard Woodside, supt. Fax 727-9059
www.anchorbay.misd.net
Other Schools – See Fair Haven, New Baltimore

Caseville, Huron, Pop. 766
Caseville SD 100/K-12
PO Box 1068 48725 989-856-2940
Dr. Kenneth Ewald, supt. Fax 856-3095
www.caseville.k12.mi.us
Caseville S 100/K-12
PO Box 1068 48725 989-856-7192
Dr. Kenneth Ewald, prin. Fax 856-8641

Cass City, Tuscola, Pop. 2,395
Cass City SD 800/PK-12
4868 Seeger St 48726 989-872-2200
Jeffrey Hartel, supt. Fax 872-5015
www.casscity.k12.mi.us
Cass City HS 400/7-12
4868 Seeger St 48726 989-872-2148
Chad Daniels, prin. Fax 872-2068

Cassopolis, Cass, Pop. 1,687
Cassopolis SD 700/K-12
725 Center St 49031 269-445-0503
Tracy D. Hertsel, supt. Fax 445-0505
www.cassopolis.k12.mi.us
Beatty JSHS 500/7-12
22721 Diamond Cove St 49031 269-445-0540
Bob Sieko, prin. Fax 445-3112

Cedar Lake, Montcalm

Great Lakes Adventist Academy 200/9-12
PO Box 68 48812 989-427-5181
Delwin Garcia, prin. Fax 427-5027

Cedar Springs, Kent, Pop. 3,426
Cedar Springs SD 3,300/PK-12
204 E Muskegon St 49319 616-696-1204
Ron McDermed, supt. Fax 696-3755
www.csredhawks.org
Cedar Springs HS 1,000/9-12
204 E Muskegon St 49319 616-696-1200
Ron Behrenwald, prin. Fax 696-4016
Cedar Springs MS 500/7-8
204 E Muskegon St 49319 616-696-9100
Sue Spahr, prin. Fax 696-3109
New Beginnings HS 100/Alt
204 E Muskegon St 49319 616-696-1203
Stacey Jennette, prin. Fax 696-0296

Cedarville, Mackinac
Les Cheneaux Community SD 100/K-12
PO Box 366 49719 906-484-2256
Amy Scott, supt. Fax 484-2072
lescheneaux.eup.k12.mi.us/site/default.aspx?PageID=1
Cedarville S 100/K-12
PO Box 366 49719 906-484-2256
Amy Scott, prin. Fax 484-7811

Center Line, Macomb, Pop. 8,060
Center Line SD 2,700/PK-12
26400 Arsenal 48015 586-510-2000
Eve Kaltz, supt. Fax 510-2019
www.clps.org
Center Line HS 800/9-12
26300 Arsenal 48015 586-510-2100
John Summerhill, prin. Fax 510-2119
Wolfe MS 700/6-8
8640 McKinley 48015 586-510-2300
Amy Maruca, prin. Fax 510-2319

Central Lake, Antrim, Pop. 931
Central Lake SD 400/K-12
PO Box 128 49622 231-544-3141
Benjamin Williams, supt. Fax 544-2903
clps.k12.mi.us
Central Lake JSHS 200/6-12
PO Box 128 49622 231-544-3341
Michele Derenzy, prin. Fax 544-2903

Centreville, Saint Joseph, Pop. 1,388
Centreville SD 900/K-12
PO Box 158 49032 269-467-5220
Robert Kuhlman, supt. Fax 467-5226
cpschools.org
Centreville HS 300/9-12
PO Box 158 49032 269-467-5210
Dennis Kirby, prin. Fax 467-5214
Centreville JHS 100/7-8
PO Box 158 49032 269-467-5205
Dennis Kirby, prin. Fax 467-5214
Covered Bridge Alternative S 50/Alt
PO Box 158 49032 269-467-5215
Juanita Miller, prin. Fax 467-5227

Glen Oaks Community College Post-Sec.
62249 Shimmel Rd 49032 269-467-9945

Charlevoix, Charlevoix, Pop. 2,468
Charlevoix SD 1,100/K-12
104 E Saint Marys Dr 49720 231-547-3200
Robert Gendron, supt. Fax 547-0556
www.rayder.net
Charlevoix HS 400/9-12
5200 Marion Center Rd 49720 231-547-3222
Suzanne Klinger, prin. Fax 547-3245
Charlevoix MS 300/5-8
108 E Garfield Ave 49720 231-547-3206
Travis Garrett, prin. Fax 547-3244

Charlotte, Eaton, Pop. 8,946
Charlotte SD 2,400/K-12
378 State St 48813 517-541-5100
Dr. Nancy Hipskind, supt. Fax 541-5105
www.charlottenet.org
Charlotte HS 900/9-12
378 State St 48813 517-541-5600
William Barnes, prin. Fax 541-5625
Charlotte MS 500/7-8
1068 Carlisle Hwy 48813 517-541-5700
Wayne Brown, prin. Fax 541-5705

Chassell, Houghton
Chassell Township SD 300/K-12
PO Box 140 49916 906-523-4691
George Stockero, supt. Fax 523-4969
www.chassellschools.org
Chassell Township S 300/K-12
PO Box 140 49916 906-523-4691
George Stockero, supt. Fax 523-4969

Cheboygan, Cheboygan, Pop. 4,714
Cheboygan Area SD 2,000/K-12
PO Box 100 49721 231-627-4436
Mark Dombroski, supt. Fax 627-9105
www.chebschools.com/csd/
Adult/Alternative Education 50/Alt
PO Box 100 49721 231-627-5613
Christopher Ackerman, dir. Fax 597-9433
Cheboygan HS 700/9-12
801 W Lincoln Ave 49721 231-627-7191
Dr. Michele Ackerman, prin. Fax 627-2430
Cheboygan MS 600/5-8
905 W Lincoln Ave 49721 231-627-7103
Linda Chase, prin. Fax 627-4151

Chelsea, Washtenaw, Pop. 4,865
Chelsea SD 2,500/K-12
500 Washington St 48118 734-433-2200
Andrew D. Ingall, supt. Fax 433-2218
www.chelsea.k12.mi.us
Beach MS 600/6-8
445 Mayer Dr 48118 734-433-2202
Nick Angel, prin. Fax 433-2212
Chelsea HS 900/9-12
740 N Freer Rd 48118 734-433-2201
Michael Kapolka, prin. Fax 433-2211

Chesaning, Saginaw, Pop. 2,377
Chesaning UNSD 1,700/K-12
PO Box 95 48616 989-845-7020
Mike McGaugh, supt. Fax 845-3722
www.chesaningschools.net
Chesaning MS 600/5-8
431 N 4th St 48616 989-845-7040
Melinda Scule, prin. Fax 845-5335
Chesaning Union HS 500/9-12
850 N 4th St 48616 989-845-2040
Stephan Clark, prin. Fax 845-2117

Chesterfield, Macomb
L'Anse Creuse SD
Supt. — See Clinton Township
L'Anse Creuse MS East 800/6-8
30300 Hickey Rd 48051 586-493-5200
Mike VanCamp, prin. Fax 493-5205

Clare, Clare, Pop. 3,061
Clare SD 1,600/K-12
201 E State St 48617 989-386-9945
Doniel Pummell, supt. Fax 386-6055
www.clare.k12.mi.us
Clare HS 400/9-12
201 E State St 48617 989-386-7789
Lee Turner, prin. Fax 386-1236
Clare MS 400/5-8
201 E State St 48617 989-386-9979
Steve Newkirk, prin. Fax 386-4008
Pioneer HS 100/Alt
670 Ann Arbor Trl 48617 989-386-3067
Ed Hubel, prin. Fax 386-3274

Clarklake, Jackson, Pop. 400
Columbia SD
Supt. — See Brooklyn
Columbia Options HS 100/Alt
4460 N Lake Rd 49234 517-529-9400
Ralph Piepkow, prin. Fax 529-4853

Clarkston, Oakland, Pop. 980
Clarkston Community SD 8,100/PK-12
6389 Clarkston Rd 48346 248-623-5400
Dr. Rod Rock, supt. Fax 623-5450
ww2.clarkston.k12.mi.us/
Clarkston HS 1,900/10-12
6093 Flemings Lake Rd 48346 248-623-3600
Gary Kaul, prin. Fax 623-3535
Clarkston JHS 1,300/8-9
6595 Waldon Rd 48346 248-623-5600
Adam Kern, prin. Fax 623-5680
Renaissance HS 200/Alt
6558 Waldon Rd 48346 248-623-8060
Billie Pambid, prin. Fax 623-4555

Oakland ISD
Supt. — See Waterford
Oakland Technical Campus NW Vo/Tech
8211 Big Lake Rd 48346 248-922-5800
Chuck Locklear, dean Fax 922-5805

Everest Collegiate HS & Academy 400/PK-12
5935 Clarkston Rd 48348 248-620-3390
Michael Nalepa, pres. Fax 620-3942

Clawson, Oakland, Pop. 11,609
Clawson SD 1,800/K-12
626 Phillips Ave 48017 248-655-4400
Monique Beels, supt. Fax 655-4422
www.clawson.k12.mi.us
Clawson HS 600/9-12
101 John M Ave 48017 248-655-4200
Ryan Sines, prin. Fax 655-4205
Clawson MS 400/6-8
150 John M Ave 48017 248-655-4250
John Dickinson, prin. Fax 655-4251

Academy of Court Reporting Post-Sec.
1055 W Maple Rd 48017 248-435-9030

Climax, Kalamazoo, Pop. 761
Climax-Scotts Community SD 600/PK-12
372 S Main St 49034 269-746-2400
Douglas Newington, supt. Fax 746-4374
www.csschools.net
Climax-Scotts Adult/Alternative Educ 100/Alt
372 S Main St 49034 269-746-2336
J. Eric Adams, prin. Fax 746-2409
Climax-Scotts JSHS 300/6-12
372 S Main St 49034 269-746-2300
Kimberly Kirshman, prin. Fax 746-4142

Clinton, Lenawee, Pop. 2,302
Clinton Community SD 1,100/K-12
341 E Michigan Ave 49236 517-456-6501
David Pray, supt. Fax 456-4324
www.clinton.k12.mi.us/
Clinton HS 400/9-12
340 E Michigan Ave 49236 517-456-6511
Timothy Wilson, prin. Fax 456-2042
Clinton MS 300/6-8
100 E Franklin St 49236 517-456-6507
Donald Dunham, prin. Fax 456-4997

Clinton Township, Macomb, Pop. 95,648
Chippewa Valley SD 14,700/K-12
19120 Cass Ave 48038 586-723-2000
Ron Roberts, supt. Fax 723-2001
www.chippewavalleyschools.org
Algonquin MS 600/6-8
19150 Briarwood Ln 48036 586-723-3500
Walter Kozlowski, prin. Fax 723-3501
Chippewa Valley HS 1,700/10-12
18300 19 Mile Rd 48038 586-723-2300
Dr. Jerry Davisson, prin. Fax 723-2301
Chippewa Valley Ninth Grade Center 9-9
42755 Romeo Plank Rd 48038 586-723-3100
Diane Zatkoff, prin. Fax 723-3101
Mohegan HS 200/Alt
19230 Cass Ave 48038 586-723-2080
Jim Fields, admin. Fax 723-2051
Wyandot MS 1,000/6-8
39490 Garfield Rd 48038 586-723-4200
Darleen Sims, prin. Fax 723-4201
Other Schools – See Macomb

Clintondale Community SD 3,600/PK-12
35100 Little Mack Ave 48035 586-791-6300
George Sassin, supt. Fax 791-6786
seatwaitingforyou.com/
Clintondale Continuing Education Center 1,500/Alt
22280 E Price Dr 48035 586-790-2756
Kenton Rivard, prin. Fax 790-7620
Clintondale HS 600/9-12
35200 Little Mack Ave 48035 586-791-6300
Gregory Green, prin. Fax 790-7645
Clintondale MS 400/6-8
35300 Little Mack Ave 48035 586-791-6300
Ira Hamden, prin. Fax 790-7642

L'Anse Creuse SD 11,700/PK-12
24076 Frederick Pankow Blvd 48036 586-783-6300
Jackie Johnston, supt. Fax 783-6310
www.lc-ps.org
Pankow Center Vo/Tech
24600 Frederick Pankow Blvd 48036 586-783-6570
Amy Gole, prin. Fax 783-6577
Pellerin Center Adult
24001 Frederick Pankow Blvd 48036 586-783-6420
Fax 783-6423
Other Schools – See Chesterfield, Harrison Township, Macomb

Baker College of Clinton Township Post-Sec.
34950 Little Mack Ave 48035 586-791-6610
Faith Christian S 100/PK-12
23130 Remick Dr 48036 586-783-9630
Matt Fenton, prin. Fax 783-9628

Clio, Genesee, Pop. 2,597
Clio Area SD 3,400/PK-12
430 N Mill St 48420 810-591-0500
James Tenbusch, supt. Fax 591-0140
www.clioschools.org
Carter MS 1,100/5-8
300 Rogers Ldg 48420 810-591-0503
Neil Bedell, prin. Fax 591-8148
Clio Alternative Education 100/Alt
420 N Mill St 48420 810-591-4804
John Roark, dir. Fax 591-8193
Clio HS 1,000/9-12
1 Mustang Dr 48420 810-591-1359
Mike Lytle, prin. Fax 591-8169

Coldwater, Branch, Pop. 10,680
Branch ISD 500/
370 Morse St 49036 517-279-5730
Joseph Lopez, supt. Fax 279-5766
www.branch-isd.org
Branch Area Career Center Vo/Tech
366 Morse St 49036 517-279-5721
Michael Hoffner, prin. Fax 279-5777

Coldwater Community SD 2,500/PK-12
401 Sauk River Dr 49036 517-279-5910
Dr. Tina Kerr, supt. Fax 279-7651
www.coldwaterschools.org/
Coldwater HS 900/9-12
275 N Fremont St 49036 517-279-5930
William Milnes, prin. Fax 278-2475
Franklin HS 100/Alt
1011 School Dr 49036 517-279-5900
Janice Storrs, prin. Fax 279-8911
Legg MS 600/6-8
175 Green St 49036 517-279-5940
Jonelle Noble, prin. Fax 279-5945

School of Creative Hair Design Post-Sec.
470 Marshall St 49036 517-279-2355

Coleman, Midland, Pop. 1,211
Coleman Community SD 800/K-12
4823 N Coleman Schools Dr 48618 989-465-6060
Mary Pitchford, supt. Fax 465-9853
www.colemanschools.net
Coleman JSHS 400/7-12
4951 N Lewis Rd 48618 989-465-6171
John Young, prin. Fax 465-9222

Coloma, Berrien, Pop. 1,456
Coloma Community SD 1,800/PK-12
PO Box 550 49038 269-468-2424
Terry Ann Boguth, supt. Fax 468-2440
www.ccs.coloma.org
Coloma JHS 300/8-9
PO Box 550 49038 269-468-2405
Peter Olsen, prin. Fax 468-2428
Coloma SHS 400/10-12
PO Box 550 49038 269-468-2400
David Ehlers, prin. Fax 468-2423

Colon, Saint Joseph, Pop. 1,152
Colon Community SD 600/PK-12
400 Dallas St 49040 269-386-2239
Lloyd Kirby, supt. Fax 432-2577
www.colonschools.org
Colon JSHS 300/6-12
400 Dallas St 49040 269-432-3231
Debra Swartz, prin. Fax 432-9851

Commerce Township, Oakland, Pop. 26,955
Huron Valley SD
Supt. — See Highland
Oak Valley MS 700/6-8
4200 White Oak Trl 48382 248-684-8101
Scott Lindberg, prin. Fax 684-8105

Walled Lake Consolidated SD
Supt. — See Walled Lake
Central HS 1,800/9-12
1600 E Oakley Park Rd 48390 248-956-4700
Charles Morgan, prin. Fax 956-4705
Northern HS 1,600/9-12
6000 Bogie Lake Rd 48382 248-956-5300
Greg Diamond, prin. Fax 956-5305
Smart MS 1,000/6-8
8500 Commerce Rd 48382 248-956-3500
Brian Kaplan, prin. Fax 956-3505

Comstock Park, Kent, Pop. 9,824
Comstock Park SD 2,400/PK-12
101 School St NE 49321 616-254-5001
Ethan Ebenstein, supt. Fax 784-5404
www.cppschools.com
Comstock Park HS 700/9-12
150 6 Mile Rd NE 49321 616-254-5200
Steve Gough, prin. Fax 785-9835
Mill Creek MS 500/6-8
100 Betty St NE 49321 616-254-5100
August Harju, prin. Fax 785-2464

Concord, Jackson, Pop. 1,046
Concord Community SD 800/K-12
PO Box 338 49237 517-524-8850
Terri Mileski, supt. Fax 524-8613
www.concordschools.net
Concord HS 300/9-12
PO Box 338 49237 517-524-8384
Cheryl Price, prin. Fax 524-6196
Concord MS 200/6-8
PO Box 338 49237 517-524-8854
Tony Hutchins, prin. Fax 524-7324

Constantine, Saint Joseph, Pop. 2,015
Constantine SD 1,400/K-12
1 Falcon Dr 49042 269-435-8900
Charles Frisbie, supt. Fax 435-8980
www.constps.org
Constantine HS 400/9-12
1 Falcon Dr 49042 269-435-8920
Christine Barnes, prin. Fax 435-8981
Constantine MS 300/6-8
260 W 6th St 49042 269-435-8940
Ray Bohm, prin. Fax 435-8982

Cooks, Delta
Big Bay de Noc SD 200/PK-12
8928 00.25 Rd 49817 906-644-2773
William Pistulka, supt. Fax 644-2615
www.bigbayschool.com
Big Bay de Noc S 200/PK-12
8928 00.25 Rd 49817 906-644-2773
DeeDee Thill, prin. Fax 644-2615

Coopersville, Ottawa, Pop. 4,215
Coopersville Area SD 2,500/PK-12
198 East St 49404 616-997-3200
Ron Veldman, supt. Fax 997-3214
www.coopersvillebroncos.org/
Coopersville MS 600/6-8
198 East St 49404 616-997-3400
Ryan Pfahler, prin. Fax 997-3414
Coopersville SHS 800/9-12
198 East St 49404 616-997-3500
Pete Bush, prin. Fax 997-3514

Corunna, Shiawassee, Pop. 3,446
Corunna SD 2,300/K-12
124 N Shiawassee St 48817 989-743-6338
Dr. Mark Miller, supt. Fax 743-4474
www.corunna.k12.mi.us
Corunna HS 800/9-12
417 E King St 48817 989-743-3441
Lyle Thomas, prin. Fax 743-5901
Corunna MS 500/6-8
400 N Comstock St 48817 989-743-5641
John Fattal, prin. Fax 743-8761

Covert, Van Buren
Covert SD 600/PK-12
35323 M 140 Hwy 49043 269-764-3701
Michael Alexander, supt. Fax 764-8598
www.covertps.org
Covert HS 200/9-12
35323 M 140 Hwy 49043 269-764-3730
Kristine Simons, prin. Fax 764-3754
Covert MS 100/6-8
35323 M 140 Hwy 49043 269-764-3730
Kristine Simons, prin. Fax 764-3754

Croswell, Sanilac, Pop. 2,419
Croswell-Lexington SD 2,200/PK-12
5407 Peck Rd 48422 810-679-1000
Dr. Kevin Miller, supt. Fax 679-1005
www.croslex.org
Croswell-Lexington HS 700/9-12
5461 Peck Rd 48422 810-679-1500
Theo Kerhoulas, prin. Fax 679-1505
Croswell-Lexington MS 700/5-8
5485 Peck Rd 48422 810-679-1400
Mark Benson, prin. Fax 679-1405

Crystal Falls, Iron, Pop. 1,443
Forest Park SD 500/PK-12
801 Forest Pkwy 49920 906-875-6761
Becky Waters, supt. Fax 875-4660
www.fptrojans.org
Forest Park JSHS 300/6-12
801 Forest Pkwy 49920 906-875-6869
Lisa Olson, prin. Fax 875-4660

Custer, Mason, Pop. 279
Mason County Eastern SD 400/K-12
18 S Main St 49405 231-757-3733
Paul Shoup, supt. Fax 757-9671
mceschools.com
Mason County Eastern JSHS 200/7-12
18 S Main St 49405 231-757-3733
Paul Shoup, prin. Fax 757-9671

Dansville, Ingham, Pop. 554
Dansville SD 900/K-12
PO Box 187 48819 517-623-6120
Amy Hodgson, supt. Fax 623-6719
www.dansville.org
Dansville HS 300/9-12
PO Box 187 48819 517-623-6120
Tania Dupuis, prin. Fax 623-0127
Dansville MS 200/6-8
PO Box 187 48819 517-623-6120
Tania Dupuis, prin. Fax 623-1087

Davison, Genesee, Pop. 5,081
Davison Community SD 5,500/K-12
PO Box 319 48423 810-591-0801
Eric Lieske, supt. Fax 591-7813
www.davisonschools.org/
Alternative Education 200/Alt
1250 N Oak Rd 48423 810-591-1020
David Beamer, dean Fax 591-3784
Davison HS 1,500/9-12
1250 N Oak Rd 48423 810-591-3531
Matt Shanafelt, prin. Fax 591-3555
Davison MS 800/7-8
600 S Dayton St 48423 810-591-0848
Shelly Fenner-Krasny, prin. Fax 591-2754

Faith Baptist S 300/PK-12
7306 E Atherton Rd 48423 810-653-9661
Dr. Larry Nagengast, admin. Fax 658-0087
Waterbrook Christian Academy 100/PK-12
8031 E Court St Ste 2B 48423 810-653-9701
Dean Bowen, admin. Fax 412-5700

Dearborn, Wayne, Pop. 94,259
Dearborn SD 17,200/PK-12
18700 Audette St 48124 313-827-3020
Brian Whiston, supt. Fax 827-3137
www.dearbornschools.org
Bryant MS 700/6-8
460 N Vernon St 48128 313-827-2900
Shannon Peterson, prin. Fax 827-2905
Dearborn HS 1,700/9-12
19501 Outer Dr 48124 313-827-1600
Charles Baughman, prin. Fax 827-1605
Ford HS 1,400/9-12
20601 Rotunda Dr 48124 313-827-1500
Scott Casebolt, prin. Fax 827-1505
Fordson HS 2,400/9-12
13800 Ford Rd 48126 313-827-1400
Youssef Mosallam, prin. Fax 827-1405
Salina IS 500/4-8
2623 Salina St 48120 313-827-6600
Jamel Lawera, prin. Fax 827-6605
Smith MS 600/6-8
23851 Yale St 48124 313-827-2800
Fax 827-2805
Stout MS 600/6-8
18500 Oakwood Blvd 48124 313-827-4600
Julia Maconochie, prin. Fax 827-4605
Woodworth MS 700/6-8
4951 Ternes St 48126 313-827-7100
Maysam Alie-Bazzi, prin. Fax 827-7105
Other Schools – See Dearborn Heights

Divine Child HS 800/9-12
1001 N Silvery Ln 48128 313-562-1990
Margaret Knuth, prin. Fax 562-9361
Everest Institute Post-Sec.
23400 Michigan Ave Ste 200 48124 313-562-4228
Henry Ford Community College Post-Sec.
5101 Evergreen Rd 48128 313-845-9600
ITT Technical Institute Post-Sec.
19855 Outer Dr Ste L10W 48124 313-278-5208
University of Michigan-Dearborn Post-Sec.
4901 Evergreen Rd 48128 313-593-5000

Dearborn Heights, Wayne, Pop. 56,336
Crestwood SD 3,300/PK-12
1501 N Beech Daly Rd 48127 313-278-0903
Dr. Laurine VanValkenburg, supt. Fax 278-4774
www.csdm.k12.mi.us/
Crestwood HS 1,200/9-12
1501 N Beech Daly Rd 48127 313-278-0900
John Tafelski, prin. Fax 792-0205
Riverside MS 1,100/5-8
25900 W Warren St 48127 313-274-0140
Dennis Faletti, prin. Fax 792-0201

Dearborn Heights SD 7 1,900/K-12
20629 Annapolis St 48125 313-278-1900
Jeffrey Bartold, supt. Fax 278-1413
www.district7.net
Annapolis HS 900/9-12
4650 Clippert St 48125 313-278-9870
Dan Scott, prin. Fax 278-1238
Best JHS 800/6-8
22201 Powers Ave 48125 313-278-6200
Jon Znamierowski, prin. Fax 278-2470

Dearborn SD
Supt. — See Dearborn
Berry Career Center Vo/Tech
22586 Ann Arbor Trl 48127 313-827-4800
Winifred Green, prin. Fax 827-4805
Dearborn Ctr for Math Science & Tech Alt
22586 Ann Arbor Trl 48127 313-827-2720
Winifred Green, prin. Fax 827-2725
Dearborn Magnet HS 9-12
22586 Ann Arbor Trl 48127 313-827-4800
Winifred Green, prin.
Ford Early College HS 200/9-12
22586 Ann Arbor Trl 48127 313-317-1588
Majed Fadlallah, prin. Fax 317-2585
Adult & Community Education Adult
22586 Ann Arbor Trl 48127 313-827-1900
Carole Wells, admin. Fax 827-1906

Westwood Community SD 2,100/K-12
3335 S Beech Daly St 48125 313-565-1900
Sue Carnell, supt. Fax 565-3162
www.westwood.k12.mi.us
Robichaud HS 400/9-12
3601 Janet St 48125 313-565-8850
Kellie Cunningham, prin. Fax 565-0304
Westwood New Tech HS 300/9-12
3601 Janet St 48125 313-565-2180
Roderick Wallace, prin. Fax 565-2361
Other Schools – See Inkster

Decatur, Van Buren, Pop. 1,763
Decatur SD 800/K-12
110 Cedar St 49045 269-423-6800
Dr. Elizabeth Godwin, supt. Fax 423-6849
www.raiderpride.org/
Decatur HS 300/9-12
110 Cedar St 49045 269-423-6850
Bill Markovich, prin. Fax 423-6899
Decatur MS 200/6-8
405 N Phelps St 49045 269-423-6900
Bill Markovich, prin. Fax 423-6949

Marcellus Community SD
Supt. — See Marcellus
Volinia Outcome Base S 100/Alt
54080 Gards Prairie Rd 49045 269-782-9716
Donald Price, prin. Fax 782-9789

Deckerville, Sanilac, Pop. 821
Deckerville Community SD 600/K-12
2633 Black River St 48427 810-376-3615
Tricia Pawlowski, supt. Fax 376-3115
www.deckerville.k12.mi.us
Deckerville Community JSHS 300/7-12
2633 Black River St 48427 810-376-3875
Matt Connelly, prin. Fax 376-3115

Delton, Barry, Pop. 851
Delton Kellogg SD 1,500/K-12
327 N Grove St 49046 269-623-9200
Paul Blacken, supt. Fax 623-9269
www.dkschools.org/
Delton Kellogg HS 500/9-12
10425 Panther Pride 49046 269-623-9226
Stewart Schofield, prin. Fax 623-9292
Delton Kellogg MS 400/5-8
6325 Delton Rd 49046 269-623-9251
Diane Talo, prin. Fax 623-9259

De Tour Village, Chippewa, Pop. 312
De Tour Area SD 200/K-12
PO Box 429 49725 906-297-2421
Angela Reed, supt. Fax 297-3403
eup.k12.mi.us/detour/index.html
De Tour JSHS 100/7-12
PO Box 429 49725 906-297-2011
Angela Reed, prin. Fax 297-3403

Detroit, Wayne, Pop. 700,219
Detroit SD 49,800/PK-12
7321 2nd Ave Fl 14 48202 313-873-7450
Barbara Byrd-Bennett, supt. Fax 873-7433
detroitk12.org
Breithaupt Career/Tech S Vo/Tech
9300 Hubbell St 48228 313-866-9550
Charlene Mallory, prin. Fax 866-9605
Carson S for Science & Medicine 9-10
571 Mack Ave 48201 313-494-1805
Brenda Belcher, prin. Fax 494-0992
Cass Technical HS Vo/Tech
2501 2nd Ave 48201 313-263-2000
Lisa Phillips, prin. Fax 263-2001
Clippert Academy 500/5-8
1981 McKinstry St 48209 313-849-5009
Kim Gonzalez, prin. Fax 849-5740
Cody - Academy of Public Leadership 200/9-12
18445 Cathedral St 48228 313-866-9200
Johnathon Matthews, prin. Fax 866-9266
Cody - Detroit Institute of Technology 200/9-12
18445 Cathedral St 48228 313-866-9200
Mary Kovari, prin. Fax 866-9266
Cody - Medicine and Community Health Acd 200/9-12
18445 Cathedral St 48228 313-866-9200
Michelle Parker, prin. Fax 866-9266
Communications & Media Arts HS 500/9-12
14771 Mansfield St 48227 313-866-9300
Donya Odom, prin. Fax 866-9304
Crockett Career/Tech S Vo/Tech
571 Mack Ave 48201 313-494-1805
Brenda Belcher, prin. Fax 494-0992
Davis Aerospace Technical HS Vo/Tech
10200 Erwin St 48234 313-866-5401
Nina Graves-Hicks, prin. Fax 866-5408
Detroit Collegiate Preparatory HS 9-12
2200 W Grand Blvd 48208 313-623-0056
Ricardo Martin, prin.
Detroit Intl Acad for Young Women 600/K-12
9026 Woodward Ave 48202 313-873-3050
Beverly Hibbler, prin. Fax 873-3088
Detroit Lions Alternative S 100/Alt
10101 E Canfield St 48214 313-852-9677
Cheryl White, prin. Fax 852-9676
Detroit S of Arts 700/9-12
123 Selden St 48201 313-494-6000
Ahna Felix-Brown, prin. Fax 494-2129
Douglass Academy for Young Men 300/Alt
2001 W Warren Ave 48208 313-596-3555
Berry Greer, prin. Fax 596-3552
East English Village Preparatory Academy 9-12
17200 Southampton St 48224 313-922-5600
Patricia Murray, prin.
Fisher Magnet Upper Academy 600/5-8
15491 Maddelein St 48205 313-866-7233
Harry Coakley, prin. Fax 866-7329
Golightly Career and Technical Center Vo/Tech
900 Dickerson St 48215 313-822-8820
Betty Edwards, prin. Fax 866-3131
King HS 1,400/9-12
3200 E Lafayette St 48207 313-494-7373
Dr. Deborah Jenkins, prin. Fax 262-9140
Ludington Magnet MS 500/5-8
19501 Berg Rd 48219 313-494-7577
Alora Comer-Maxwell, prin. Fax 494-7707
Northwestern HS 800/9-12
2200 W Grand Blvd 48208 313-596-0700
Belinda Raines, prin. Fax 596-0710
Osborn Academy of Mathematics 200/9-12
11600 E 7 Mile Rd 48205 313-866-0343
Tanya Bowman, prin. Fax 866-0356
Osborn College Preparatory Academy 100/9-12
11600 E 7 Mile Rd 48205 313-866-0343
Calvin Patillo, prin. Fax 866-0356
Osborn Evergreen Acad Design & Alt Enrgy 200/9-12
11600 E 7 Mile Rd 48205 313-866-0343
Felicia Cook, prin. Fax 866-0356
Randolph Career and Technical Center Vo/Tech
17101 Hubbell St 48235 313-494-7100
Cynthia Hough, prin. Fax 494-7114
Renaissance HS 1,100/9-12
6565 W Outer Dr 48235 313-416-4600
Anita Williams, prin. Fax 416-4620
Western International HS 1,500/9-12
1500 Scotten St 48209 313-849-4758
Rodolfo Diaz, prin. Fax 849-4695
West Side Academy of Alternative Ed 300/Alt
4701 McKinley St 48208 313-456-8000
Andrea Ford-Ayler, prin. Fax 456-8001

College for Creative Studies Post-Sec.
201 E Kirby St 48202 313-664-7400
Cornerstone S 500/PK-11
6861 E Nevada St 48234 313-892-1860
Ernestine Sanders, pres. Fax 892-1091
Detroit Cristo Rey HS 9-12
5679 W Vernor Hwy 48209 313-843-2747
Susan Rowe, prin. Fax 843-2750
Detroit Health Department Post-Sec.
1151 Taylor St 48202 313-876-4090
DMC University Laboratories Post-Sec.
4201 Saint Antoine St 48201 313-745-3053
Ecumenical Theological Seminary Post-Sec.
2930 Woodward Ave 48201 313-831-5200
Everest Institute Post-Sec.
300 River Place Dr Ste 1000 48207 313-567-5350
Grace Hospital Post-Sec.
6071 W Outer Dr 48235 313-966-3525
Harper Hospital Post-Sec.
3990 John R St 48201 313-745-9375
Henry Ford Hospital Post-Sec.
2799 W Grand Blvd 48202 313-876-1257
Kaplan Career Institute Post-Sec.
18440 Ford Rd 48228 313-425-4300

Kaplan Career Institute — Post-Sec.
3031 W Grand Blvd Ste 236 48202 — 313-456-8100
Lewis College of Business — Post-Sec.
17370 Meyers Rd 48235 — 313-862-6300
Loyola HS — 200/9-12
15325 Pinehurst St 48238 — 313-861-2407
DeLisa Jones, prin. — Fax 861-4718
Marygrove College — Post-Sec.
8425 W McNichols Rd 48221 — 313-927-1200
Michigan Barber School — Post-Sec.
8988 Grand River Ave # 90 48204 — 313-894-2300
Sacred Heart Major Seminary — Post-Sec.
2701 W Chicago 48206 — 313-883-8500
St. John's Hospital — Post-Sec.
22101 Moross Rd 48236 — 313-343-7531
University of Detroit/Jesuit HS — 800/7-12
8400 S Cambridge Ave 48221 — 313-862-5400
Anthony Trudel, prin. — Fax 862-3299
University of Detroit Mercy — Post-Sec.
4001 W McNichols Rd 48221 — 313-993-1000
Wayne County Community College — Post-Sec.
801 W Fort St 48226 — 313-496-2600
Wayne State University — Post-Sec.
42 W Warren Ave 48201 — 877-978-4636
Westside Christian Academy — 100/PK-12
9540 Bramell 48239 — 313-255-5760
Darryl Ovnanian, prin. — Fax 255-0809

De Witt, Clinton, Pop. 4,434
De Witt SD — 3,000/K-12
PO Box 800, — 517-668-3000
Dr. John Deiter, supt. — Fax 668-3018
www.dewittschools.net/
De Witt HS — 1,000/9-12
PO Box 800, — 517-668-3100
Jody McKean, prin. — Fax 668-3155
De Witt JHS — 500/7-8
PO Box 800, — 517-668-3200
Keith Cravotta, prin. — Fax 668-3255

Dexter, Washtenaw, Pop. 3,976
Dexter Community SD — 3,600/K-12
7714 Ann Arbor St 48130 — 734-424-4100
Dennis Desmarais, supt. — Fax 424-4112
www.dexterschools.org/
Dexter HS — 1,200/9-12
2200 N Parker Rd 48130 — 734-424-4240
Kit Moran, prin. — Fax 424-2747
Mill Creek MS — 600/7-8
7305 Dexter Ann Arbor Rd 48130 — 734-424-4150
Jami Bronson, prin. — Fax 424-4159

Dollar Bay, Houghton, Pop. 1,072
Dollar Bay-Tamarack City SD — 300/K-12
PO Box 371 49922 — 906-482-5800
Jan Quarless, supt. — Fax 487-5931
www.dollarbay.k12.mi.us
Dollar Bay JSHS — 100/7-12
PO Box 371 49922 — 906-482-5812
William Rivest, prin. — Fax 487-5940

Douglas, Allegan, Pop. 1,221
Saugatuck SD — 600/PK-12
PO Box 818 49406 — 269-857-1444
Rolfe Timmerman Ph.D., supt. — Fax 857-1448
www.saugatuckps.com
Other Schools – See Saugatuck

Dowagiac, Cass, Pop. 5,518
Dowagiac UNSD — 2,300/K-12
243 S Front St 49047 — 269-782-4400
Dr. Mark Daniel, supt. — Fax 782-4418
www.dowagiacschools.org
Alternative Education Pathfinders — 100/Alt
501 N Paul St 49047 — 269-782-4471
Fax 782-9748
Dowagiac MS — 500/6-8
57072 Riverside Dr 49047 — 269-782-4440
Matthew Severin, prin. — Fax 782-4449
Union HS — 600/9-12
701 W Prairie Ronde St 49047 — 269-782-4420
Pieter Hoekstra, prin. — Fax 782-9518

Southwestern Michigan College — Post-Sec.
58900 Cherry Grove Rd 49047 — 269-782-1000

Dryden, Lapeer, Pop. 947
Dryden Community SD — 700/K-12
3866 Rochester Rd 48428 — 810-796-9534
Dr. Gary Richards, supt. — Fax 796-3698
www.dryden.k12.mi.us
Dryden JSHS — 400/7-12
3866 Rochester Rd 48428 — 810-796-2266
Richard Duffy, prin. — Fax 796-2510

Dundee, Monroe, Pop. 3,916
Dundee Community SD — 1,600/PK-12
420 Ypsilanti St 48131 — 734-529-2350
Michael Dodge, supt. — Fax 529-5606
www.dundeecommunityschools.org
Dundee HS — 500/9-12
130 Viking Dr 48131 — 734-529-7008
Bryan Schroeder, prin. — Fax 529-7053
Dundee MS — 500/5-8
420 Ypsilanti St 48131 — 734-529-2350
Charles Fuller, prin. — Fax 529-7380
Riverside Academy — 50/Alt
445 Toledo St 48131 — 734-529-3916
Tom Walentowski, dir. — Fax 529-5593

Durand, Shiawassee, Pop. 3,411
Durand Area SD — 1,100/PK-12
310 N Saginaw St 48429 — 989-288-2681
Cindy Weber, supt. — Fax 288-3553
durand.k12.mi.us/
Durand Area HS — 600/8-12
9575 E Monroe Rd 48429 — 989-288-2684
Douglas Lindsay, prin. — Fax 288-2966

East China, Saint Clair, Pop. 3,216
East China SD — 4,800/K-12
1585 Meisner Rd 48054 — 810-676-1000
Ketha Knuth, supt. — Fax 676-1037
www.ecsd.us
Other Schools – See Marine City, Saint Clair

East Jordan, Charlevoix, Pop. 2,312
East Jordan SD — 1,100/K-12
PO Box 399 49727 — 231-536-3131
Jon Hoover, supt. — Fax 536-3310
www.ejps.org/
East Jordan HS — 400/9-12
PO Box 399 49727 — 231-536-2259
Tammy Jackson, prin. — Fax 536-3536
East Jordan MS — 200/6-8
PO Box 399 49727 — 231-536-2823
Matthew Stevenson, prin. — Fax 536-0051

East Lansing, Ingham, Pop. 47,217
East Lansing SD — 3,400/K-12
841 Timberlane St Ste A 48823 — 517-333-7420
David Chapin, supt. — Fax 333-7470
www.elps.us
East Lansing HS — 1,100/9-12
509 Burcham Dr 48823 — 517-333-7500
John Brandenburg, prin. — Fax 333-7559
MacDonald MS — 500/7-8
1601 Burcham Dr 48823 — 517-333-7600
Merem Frierson, prin. — Fax 333-5098

Douglas J Educational Center — Post-Sec.
331 E Grand River Ave 48823 — 517-351-0746
Michigan State Univ - College of Law — Post-Sec.
648 N Shaw Ln Rm 368 48824 — 517-432-6800
Michigan State University — Post-Sec.
250 Administration Bldg 48824 — 517-355-1855

East Leroy, Calhoun
Athens Area SD — 600/K-12
4320 K Dr S 49051 — 269-729-5427
Richard Franklin, supt. — Fax 729-9610
www.athensk12.org
Other Schools – See Athens

Eastpointe, Macomb, Pop. 31,538
East Detroit SD — 2,700/K-12
24685 Kelly Rd 48021 — 586-533-3000
Joanne Lelekatch, supt. — Fax 533-3025
www.eastdetroit.org
East Detroit HS — 1,400/9-12
15501 Couzens Ave 48021 — 586-533-3700
Mary Finnigan, prin. — Fax 533-3709
Kellwood Alternative HS — 100/Alt
23750 David Ave 48021 — 586-533-3900
Christine Nielubowicz, prin. — Fax 533-3909
Kelly MS — 700/6-8
24701 Kelly Rd 48021 — 586-533-3600
Ryan Melrose, prin. — Fax 533-3609

Eaton Rapids, Eaton, Pop. 5,118
Eaton Rapids SD — 2,000/K-12
912 Greyhound Dr 48827 — 517-663-8155
Dr. William DeFrance, supt. — Fax 663-2236
www.erpsk12.org/
Eaton Rapids HS — 900/9-12
800 State St 48827 — 517-663-2231
David Johnson, prin. — Fax 663-5727
Eaton Rapids MS — 400/6-8
815 Greyhound Dr 48827 — 517-663-8151
Elizabeth Lozen, prin. — Fax 663-0625
Greyhound Central Alternative High Schoo — Alt
912 Greyhound Dr 48827 — 517-663-3510
Bill Defrance, prin. — Fax 663-0626

Eau Claire, Berrien, Pop. 604
Eau Claire SD — 700/K-12
6190 W Main St 49111 — 269-461-6947
Mark Costello, supt. — Fax 461-0089
www.eauclaireps.com
Eau Claire HS — 300/9-12
7450 Hochberger Rd 49111 — 269-461-6997
Shane Lausch, prin. — Fax 461-0065
Eau Claire MS — 200/6-8
7450 Hochberger Rd 49111 — 269-461-0083
Tom Ferry, prin. — Fax 461-0082

Eben Junction, Alger
Superior Central SD — 400/K-12
PO Box 148 49825 — 906-439-5531
John Peterson, supt. — Fax 439-5734
superiorcentralschools.org/
Superior Central S — 400/K-12
PO Box 148 49825 — 906-439-5532
William Valima, prin. — Fax 439-5243

Ecorse, Wayne, Pop. 9,214
Ecorse SD — 1,000/PK-12
27225 W Outer Dr 48229 — 313-294-4750
Dr. Emma Epps, supt. — Fax 294-4769
www.eps.k12.mi.us
Advanced Hope Academy — Alt
27225 W Outer Dr 48229 — 313-294-4730
Fax 382-6534
Ecorse Community HS — 400/8-12
27385 W Outer Dr 48229 — 313-294-4700
Kenneth McPhaul, prin. — Fax 294-4709

Edmore, Montcalm, Pop. 1,174
Montabella Community SD — 800/PK-12
PO Box 349 48829 — 989-427-5148
Shelly Millis, supt. — Fax 427-3828
www.montabella.com
Other Schools – See Blanchard

Edwardsburg, Cass, Pop. 1,228
Edwardsburg SD — 2,700/K-12
69410 Section St 49112 — 269-663-3055
Sherman Ostrander, supt. — Fax 663-6485
www.edwardsburgpublicschools.org/
Edwardsburg HS — 800/9-12
69410 Section St 49112 — 269-663-1044
Jeffrey Leslie Ph.D., prin. — Fax 663-8915
Edwardsburg MS — 600/6-8
69410 Section St 49112 — 269-663-1031
Janet MacLean Ph.D., prin. — Fax 663-8638

Elk Rapids, Antrim, Pop. 1,628
Elk Rapids SD — 1,400/K-12
707 E 3rd St 49629 — 231-264-8692
Stephen Prissel, supt. — Fax 264-6538
www.erschools.com
Cherryland MS — 300/6-8
707 E 3rd St 49629 — 231-264-8991
Terry Starr, prin. — Fax 264-9370
Elk Rapids HS — 400/9-12
308 Meguzee Pt 49629 — 231-264-8108
Michael Travis, prin. — Fax 264-0895
Sunrise Academy — Alt
308 Meguzee Pt 49629 — 231-264-5890
Jim Standerfer, prin. — Fax 264-0895

Ellsworth, Antrim, Pop. 341
Ellsworth Community SD — 200/PK-12
9467 Park St 49729 — 231-588-2544
Aaron Gaffney, supt. — Fax 588-6183
www.ellsworth.k12.mi.us/
Ellsworth Community S — 200/PK-12
9467 Park St 49729 — 231-588-2544
Aaron Gaffney, admin. — Fax 588-6183

Elsie, Clinton, Pop. 962
Ovid-Elsie Area SD — 1,800/K-12
8989 E Colony Rd 48831 — 989-834-2271
Ryan Cunningham, supt. — Fax 862-5887
www.ovidelsie.org
Ovid-Elsie HS — 600/9-12
8989 E Colony Rd 48831 — 989-834-2271
Kirk Baese, prin. — Fax 862-4463
Ovid-Elsie MS — 300/7-8
8989 E Colony Rd 48831 — 989-834-2271
Jason Tokar, prin. — Fax 862-4463
Other Schools – See Ovid

Engadine, Mackinac
Engadine Consolidated SD — 300/K-12
W13920 Melville St 49827 — 906-477-6313
Angie McArthur, supt. — Fax 477-6643
www.eup.k12.mi.us/engadine
Engadine Consolidated S — 300/K-12
W13920 Melville St 49827 — 906-477-6351
Kendra Feldhusen, prin. — Fax 477-6643

Erie, Monroe
Mason Consolidated SD — 1,200/PK-12
2400 Mason Eagle Dr 48133 — 734-848-5475
David Drewyor, supt. — Fax 848-2516
www.eriemason.k12.mi.us
Mason HS — 400/9-12
2400 Mason Eagle Dr 48133 — 734-848-5755
Matthew Lukshaitis, prin. — Fax 848-5425
Mason MS — 300/6-8
2400 Mason Eagle Dr 48133 — 734-848-4211
Ben Russow, prin. — Fax 848-0035

Escanaba, Delta, Pop. 12,293
Delta-Schoolcraft ISD — 100/
2525 3rd Ave S 49829 — 906-786-9300
Michael Koster, supt. — Fax 786-9318
www.dsisd.k12.mi.us
Bay Middle College HS/Fitzharris HS — Alt
2001 N Lincoln Rd 49829 — 906-789-5599
Dan Seder, dir.

Escanaba Area SD — 2,000/K-12
1500 Ludington St 49829 — 906-786-5411
Michele Lemire, supt. — Fax 786-4469
www.escanabaschool.com
Escanaba HS — 900/9-12
500 S Lincoln Rd 49829 — 906-786-6521
Doug Leisenring, prin. — Fax 786-2166
Escanaba JHS — 7-8
500 S Lincoln Rd 49829 — 906-786-6521
Darcy Griebel, prin.

Bay College — Post-Sec.
2001 N Lincoln Rd 49829 — 906-786-5802
U.P. Academy of Hair Design — Post-Sec.
1625 Sheridan Rd 49829 — 906-786-5750

Essexville, Bay, Pop. 3,434
Essexville-Hampton SD — 1,600/K-12
303 Pine St 48732 — 989-894-9700
John Mertz, supt. — Fax 894-9705
www.e-hps.net
Cramer JHS — 500/5-8
313 Pine St 48732 — 989-894-9740
James Glasgow, prin. — Fax 894-9720
Garber HS — 600/9-12
213 Pine St 48732 — 989-894-9710
Allen Atkari, prin. — Fax 894-9730

Evart, Osceola, Pop. 1,857
Evart SD — 1,000/PK-12
PO Box 917 49631 — 231-734-5594
Howard Hyde, supt. — Fax 734-2931
www.evart.k12.mi.us/
Evart HS — 300/9-12
6221 95th Ave 49631 — 231-734-5551
Dennis Peacock, prin. — Fax 734-4156
Evart MS — 300/5-8
321 N Hemlock St 49631 — 231-734-4222
Jason O'Dell, prin. — Fax 734-3367

Ewen, Ontonagon
Ewen-Trout Creek SD — 300/K-12
14312 Airport Rd 49925 — 906-988-2350
Loren Vannest, supt. — Fax 988-2864
www.etc.k12.mi.us/

Ewen-Trout Creek JSHS 100/7-12
14312 Airport Rd 49925 906-988-2365
Loren Vannest, prin. Fax 988-2864

Fairgrove, Tuscola, Pop. 559
Akron-Fairgrove SD 300/K-12
PO Box 319 48733 989-693-6163
Stephen Ley, supt. Fax 693-6560
www.akronfairgrove.org
Akron-Fairgrove JSHS 200/7-12
PO Box 319 48733 989-693-6112
Andrew Beauvais, prin. Fax 693-6160

Fair Haven, Saint Clair, Pop. 1,505
Anchor Bay SD
Supt. — See Casco
Anchor Bay HS 1,900/9-12
6319 County Line Rd 48023 586-648-2525
Joseph McDonald, prin. Fax 716-8306

Fairview, Oscoda
Fairview Area SD 200/K-12
1879 E Miller Rd 48621 989-848-7000
Robert Ricketson, supt. Fax 848-7070
www.fairview.k12.mi.us
Fairview S 200/K-12
1879 E Miller Rd 48621 989-848-7009
Robert Ricketson, supt. Fax 848-7070

Farmington, Oakland, Pop. 10,133
Farmington SD 11,500/PK-12
32500 Shiawassee Rd 48336 248-489-3349
Susan Zurvalec, supt. Fax 489-3348
www.farmington.k12.mi.us
Farmington HS 1,400/9-12
32000 Shiawassee Rd 48336 248-489-3455
Julie Kaminski, prin. Fax 489-3474
Other Schools – See Farmington Hills

Farmington Hills, Oakland, Pop. 77,980
Farmington SD
Supt. — See Farmington
Dunckel MS 800/7-8
32800 W 12 Mile Rd 48334 248-489-3577
Allen Archer, prin. Fax 489-3590
East MS 900/7-8
25000 Middlebelt Rd 48336 248-489-3601
Ken Sanders, prin. Fax 489-3606
Farmington Central HS 100/Alt
30415 Shiawassee Rd 48336 248-489-3827
Pat Karas, coord. Fax 489-3380
Harrison HS 1,200/9-12
29995 W 12 Mile Rd 48334 248-489-3499
Jim Myers, prin. Fax 489-3514
North Farmington HS 1,400/9-12
32900 W 13 Mile Rd 48334 248-785-2005
Joe Greene, prin. Fax 855-2060
Farmington Community S Adult
30415 Shiawassee Rd 48336 248-489-3827
Pat Karas, prin. Fax 489-3380

West Bloomfield SD
Supt. — See West Bloomfield
Oakland Early College S 200/9-12
27055 Orchard Lake Rd 48334 248-522-3540
Jennifer Newman, hdmstr. Fax 471-9543

Dorsey School of Business Post-Sec.
33533 W 12 Mile Rd Ste 152 48331 248-994-0133
Mercy HS 800/9-12
29300 W 11 Mile Rd 48336 248-476-8020
Caroline Witte, prin. Fax 476-3691
Michigan Sch of Professional Psychology Post-Sec.
26811 Orchard Lake Rd 48334 248-476-1122
Oakland Community College Post-Sec.
27055 Orchard Lake Rd 48334 248-522-3400

Farwell, Clare, Pop. 865
Farwell Area SD 1,400/K-12
399 E Michigan St 48622 989-588-9917
Carl Seiter, supt. Fax 588-6440
www.farwellschools.net/
Farwell HS 500/9-12
399 E Michigan St 48622 989-588-9913
Dee Yarger, prin. Fax 588-6041
Farwell MS 500/5-8
500 E Ohio St 48622 989-588-9915
Catheryn Gross, prin. Fax 588-3337

Felch, Dickinson
North Dickinson County SD 300/K-12
W6588 State Highway M69 49831 906-542-9281
Angel Inglese, supt. Fax 542-6950
www.go-nordics.com
North Dickinson County S 300/K-12
W6588 State Highway M69 49831 906-542-9281
Angel Inglese, admin. Fax 542-6950

Fennville, Allegan, Pop. 1,373
Fennville SD 1,500/K-12
5 Memorial Dr 49408 269-561-7331
Dirk Weeldreyer, supt. Fax 561-5792
www.fennville.org
Fennville HS 400/9-12
4 Memorial Dr 49408 269-561-7241
Amber Lugten, prin. Fax 561-6901
Fennville MS 300/6-8
1 Memorial Dr 49408 269-561-7341
Kim Zdybel, prin. Fax 561-2143
Pearl Alternative & Adult Education Ctr 100/Alt
5 Memorial Dr 49408 269-561-2343
Amber Lugten, dir. Fax 561-8630

Fenton, Genesee, Pop. 11,554
Fenton Area SD 3,400/K-12
3100 Owen Rd 48430 810-591-4701
Dr. Timothy Jalkanen, supt. Fax 591-4705
www.fenton.k12.mi.us
Fenton HS 1,200/9-12
3200 W Shiawassee Ave 48430 810-591-2600
Mark Suchowski, prin. Fax 591-2605

Schmidt MS - Donaldson 800/6-8
3255 Donaldson Dr 48430 810-591-7700
Heidi Ciesielski, prin. Fax 591-7705

Lake Fenton Community SD 1,800/K-12
11425 Torrey Rd 48430 810-591-4141
Wayne Wright, supt. Fax 591-9866
lake-fenton.schoolfusion.us
Lake Fenton MS 500/6-8
11425 Torrey Rd 48430 810-591-2209
Dan Ferguson, prin. Fax 591-8475
Other Schools – See Linden

Ferndale, Oakland, Pop. 19,252
Ferndale SD 4,000/PK-12
2920 Burdette St 48220 248-586-8651
Gary Meier, supt. Fax 586-8655
www.ferndaleschools.org
Ferndale HS 900/9-12
881 Pinecrest Dr 48220 248-548-8600
Lisa Williams, prin. Fax 586-8620
Ferndale MS 400/7-8
725 Pinecrest Dr 48220 248-541-1783
Dawn Warren, prin. Fax 586-8834
University HS 500/9-12
1244 Paxton St 48220 248-586-8846
George Tomey, prin. Fax 586-8857
Other Schools – See Oak Park

Fife Lake, Grand Traverse, Pop. 434
Forest Area Community SD 600/PK-12
7741 Shippy Rd SW 49633 231-369-4191
Suzanne Cybulla, supt. Fax 369-4153
www.forestarea.k12.mi.us
Forest Area HS 200/9-12
7741 Shippy Rd SW 49633 231-369-2884
Suzanne Cybulla, prin. Fax 369-3646
Forest Area MS 100/6-8
7741 Shippy Rd SW 49633 231-369-2867
Suzanne Cybulla, prin. Fax 369-3618

Flat Rock, Wayne, Pop. 9,628
Flat Rock Community SD 1,900/K-12
28639 Division St 48134 734-535-6500
Joanie Donaldson, supt. Fax 535-6501
www.flatrockschools.org
Flat Rock HS 600/9-12
25600 Seneca St 48134 734-535-6600
Andrew Brodie, prin. Fax 535-6601
Simpson MS 400/6-8
24900 Meadows Ave 48134 734-535-6700
Blaine Armstrong, prin. Fax 535-6701

Flint, Genesee, Pop. 98,869
Beecher Community SD 1,900/PK-12
1020 W Coldwater Rd 48505 810-591-9200
Josha Talison Ed.D., supt. Fax 591-9851
www.beecherschools.org/
Other Schools – See Mount Morris

Carman Ainsworth Community SD 4,200/K-12
G3475 W Court St 48532 810-591-3700
Dr. Steven Tunnicliff, supt. Fax 591-3323
www.carman.k12.mi.us
Carman-Ainsworth HS 1,500/9-12
1300 N Linden Rd 48532 810-591-3240
Rory Mattar, prin. Fax 591-3215
Carman-Ainsworth MS 1,100/6-8
1409 W Maple Ave 48507 810-591-3500
Kevin Summey, prin. Fax 591-3594
Woodland S Alt
G-3493 Beveridge Rd 48532 810-591-3270
Marilyn Korpi, coord. Fax 591-3265

Flint Community SD 7,700/PK-12
923 E Kearsley St 48503 810-760-1000
Linda Thompson, supt. Fax 760-6790
www.flintschools.org
Genessee Area Skill Center Vo/Tech
5081 Torrey Rd 48507 810-760-1444
Chris James, prin. Fax 760-7759
Northern HS 1,000/7-12
G3284 Mackin Rd 48504 810-760-1740
Janice Davis, prin. Fax 760-5009
Northwestern Academy 900/7-12
G2138 W Carpenter Rd 48505 810-760-1780
Cheryl Adkins, prin. Fax 760-6809
Southwestern Classical Academy 600/7-12
1420 W 12th St 48507 810-760-1400
Martin Lyonga, prin. Fax 760-7772
Mott Adult HS Adult
2421 Corunna Rd 48503 810-760-7723
Amy Boyles-Sfetkides, dir. Fax 760-1945

Genesee ISD 1,200/
2413 W Maple Ave 48507 810-591-4400
Lisa Hagel, supt. Fax 591-7570
www.geneseeisd.org
Mott Middle College HS 400/Alt
1401 E Court St Ste 1123 48503 810-232-8530
Chery Wagonlander Ed.D., prin. Fax 232-8660
Other Schools – See Grand Rapids

Kearsley Community SD 2,700/PK-12
4396 Underhill Dr 48506 810-591-8000
Patti Yorks, supt. Fax 591-8421
www.kearsleyschools.org
Armstrong MS 800/6-8
6161 Hopkins Rd 48506 810-591-9929
Casey Killingbeck, prin. Fax 591-9944
Kearsley HS 1,100/9-12
4302 Underhill Dr 48506 810-591-9883
Brian Wiskur, prin. Fax 591-9888

Mount Morris Consolidated SD
Supt. — See Mount Morris
Mount Morris Alternative Education 500/Alt
3400 N Jennings Rd 48504 810-591-9508
Lee Worsham, prin. Fax 591-0658

Westwood Heights SD 900/PK-12
3223 W Carpenter Rd 48504 810-591-0890
Salli Stevens, supt. Fax 591-0898
www.hamadyhawks.net
Hamady Community HS 300/9-12
3223 W Carpenter Rd 48504 810-591-0890
Margaret Green, prin. Fax 591-5140
Hamady MS 200/6-8
3223 W Carpenter Rd 48504 810-591-0895
Margaret Green, prin. Fax 591-5140

Baker College of Flint Post-Sec.
1050 W Bristol Rd 48507 810-766-4000
Davenport University Post-Sec.
4318 Miller Rd 48507 810-732-9977
Flint Institute of Barbering Post-Sec.
3214 Flushing Rd 48504 810-232-4711
Hurley Medical Center Post-Sec.
701 W 8th Ave 48503 810-257-9237
Kettering University Post-Sec.
1700 University Ave 48504 810-762-9500
Mott Community College Post-Sec.
1401 E Court St 48503 810-762-0200
Powers HS 600/9-12
G2040 W Carpenter Rd 48505 810-591-4741
Thomas Furnas, prin. Fax 591-0383
Ross Medical Education Center Post-Sec.
G3630 Miller Rd Ste D 48507 810-230-1100
University of Michigan-Flint Post-Sec.
303 E Kearsley St 48502 810-762-3300

Flushing, Genesee, Pop. 8,256
Flushing Community SD 4,400/PK-12
522 N McKinley Rd 48433 810-591-1180
Timothy Stein, supt. Fax 591-0656
www.flushingschools.org/
Flushing HS 1,500/9-12
5039 Deland Rd 48433 810-591-3770
Jason Melynchek, prin. Fax 591-0693
Flushing MS 700/7-8
8100 Carpenter Rd 48433 810-591-2800
Andrew Schmidt, prin. Fax 591-0148

Fort Gratiot, Saint Clair, Pop. 8,968
Port Huron Area SD
Supt. — See Port Huron
Fort Gratiot MS 700/6-8
3985 Keewahdin Rd 48059 810-984-6544
Debra Ladensack, prin. Fax 385-1624

Fowler, Clinton, Pop. 1,204
Fowler SD 500/PK-12
PO Box 407 48835 989-593-2296
Neil Hufnagel, supt. Fax 593-2358
www.fowlerschools.net
Fowler HS 200/9-12
PO Box 407 48835 989-593-2250
Neil Hufnagel, prin. Fax 593-2358

Most Holy Trinity MS 100/3-8
545 N Maple St 48835 989-593-2616
Anne Hufnagel, prin. Fax 593-2801

Fowlerville, Livingston, Pop. 2,844
Fowlerville Community SD 3,000/K-12
PO Box 769 48836 517-223-6000
Wayne Roedel, supt. Fax 223-6022
www.fowlervilleschools.org
Fowlerville HS 900/9-12
PO Box 769 48836 517-223-6002
Bradford Lusk, prin. Fax 223-6065
Fowlerville JHS 700/6-8
PO Box 769 48836 517-223-6003
Myriah Lillie, prin. Fax 223-6199
Fowlerville Online Learning Academy 50/Alt
PO Box 769 48836 517-223-6239
Grace Damerow, admin. Fax 223-6121

Frankenmuth, Saginaw, Pop. 4,915
Frankenmuth SD 1,200/PK-12
525 E Genesee St 48734 989-652-9958
Mary Anne Ackerman, supt. Fax 652-9780
www.frankenmuth.k12.mi.us/
Frankenmuth HS 500/9-12
525 E Genesee St 48734 989-652-9955
JoLynn Clark, prin. Fax 652-7253
Rittmueller MS 300/5-8
965 E Genesee St 48734 989-652-6119
Kristin Hecht, prin. Fax 652-2921

Frankfort, Benzie, Pop. 1,275
Frankfort-Elberta Area SD 500/K-12
534 11th St 49635 231-352-4641
Thomas Stobie, supt. Fax 352-5066
www.frankfort.k12.mi.us
Frankfort JSHS 200/7-12
534 11th St 49635 231-352-4781
Matt Stapleton, prin. Fax 352-6501

Fraser, Macomb, Pop. 14,229
Fraser SD 5,100/PK-12
33466 Garfield Rd 48026 586-439-7000
David Richards Ph.D., supt. Fax 439-7001
www.fraser.k12.mi.us/
Fraser HS 1,700/9-12
34270 Garfield Rd 48026 586-439-7200
Dr. Michael Lonze, prin. Fax 439-7201
Richards MS 800/7-8
33500 Garfield Rd 48026 586-439-7400
Jessica Carrier, prin. Fax 439-7401

Freeland, Saginaw, Pop. 6,900
Freeland Community SD 1,800/K-12
710 Powley Dr 48623 989-695-5527
Matthew Cairy, supt. Fax 695-5789
www.freeland.k12.mi.us
Freeland HS 600/9-12
8250 Webster Rd 48623 989-695-2586
Jon Good, prin. Fax 695-8022

Freeland MS 300/7-8
8250 Webster Rd 48623 989-692-4032
Rebekah Hornak, prin. Fax 692-4034

Fremont, Newaygo, Pop. 4,037
Fremont SD 2,100/K-12
450 E Pine St 49412 231-924-2350
Jim Hieftje, supt. Fax 924-5264
www.fremont.net
Fremont HS 700/9-12
5421 S Warner Ave 49412 231-924-5300
Scott Sherman, prin. Fax 924-9262
Fremont MS 500/6-8
500 Woodrow St 49412 231-924-0230
Ken Haggart, prin. Fax 924-9149
Quest HS 100/Alt
350 Cedar St 49412 231-924-0470
Tracy Sanchez, dir. Fax 924-9207

Newaygo County RESA 200/
4747 W 48th St 49412 231-924-0381
Lori Clark, supt. Fax 924-8910
www.ncresa.org
Newaygo County Career-Tech Center Vo/Tech
4645 W 48th St 49412 231-924-0380
Kirk Wyers, dir.

Providence Christian HS 100/9-12
5479 W 72nd St 49412 231-924-9780
Steve Witter Ph.D., head sch Fax 924-1676

Fruitport, Muskegon, Pop. 1,081
Fruitport Community SD 2,900/K-12
3255 Pontaluna Rd 49415 231-865-4100
Bob Szymoniak, supt. Fax 865-3393
www.fruitportschools.net
Fruitport HS 900/9-12
357 N 6th Ave 49415 231-865-3101
Lauren Chesney, prin. Fax 865-6351
Fruitport MS 700/6-8
3113 Pontaluna Rd 49415 231-865-3128
Wendy Somers, prin. Fax 865-4086

Calvary Christian S 200/PK-12
5873 Kendra Rd 49415 231-865-2141
Tom Kapanka, admin. Fax 865-8730

Galesburg, Kalamazoo, Pop. 1,969
Galesburg-Augusta Community SD 1,200/PK-12
1076 N 37th St 49053 269-484-2000
Tim Vagts, supt. Fax 484-2001
www.gacsnet.org
Galesburg-Augusta HS 300/9-12
1076 N 37th St 49053 269-484-2010
Fax 484-2011
Other Schools – See Augusta

Garden City, Wayne, Pop. 27,153
Garden City SD 3,300/PK-12
1333 Radcliff St 48135 734-762-8300
Michelle Cline, supt. Fax 762-8530
www.gardencityschools.com
Cambridge HS 400/Alt
28901 Cambridge St 48135 734-762-8430
Susan Ford, prin. Fax 762-8534
Garden City HS 1,500/9-12
6500 Middlebelt Rd 48135 734-762-8350
Derek Fisher, prin. Fax 762-8531
Garden City MS 700/7-8
1851 Radcliff St 48135 734-762-8400
Brian Sumner, prin. Fax 762-8532

Gaylord, Otsego, Pop. 3,564
Gaylord Community SD 3,100/K-12
615 S Elm Ave 49735 989-705-3080
Cheryl Wojtas, supt. Fax 732-6029
www.gaylordschools.com
Gaylord HS 1,100/9-12
90 Livingston Blvd 49735 989-731-0969
Phil Mikulski, prin. Fax 731-2585
Gaylord MS 500/7-8
600 E 5th St 49735 989-731-0848
Gerald Belanger, prin. Fax 732-2632

St. Mary Cathedral S 300/PK-12
321 N Otsego Ave 49735 989-732-5801
Cynthia Pineda, prin. Fax 732-2085

Genesee, Genesee
Genesee SD 800/PK-12
PO Box 220 48437 810-591-1650
Jeff Rohrer, supt. Fax 591-1646
www.geneseeschools.org
Genesee JSHS 400/7-12
7347 N Genesee Rd 48437 810-591-1450
Joseph Perrera, prin. Fax 591-0302

Gibraltar, Wayne, Pop. 4,593
Gibraltar SD
Supt. — See Woodhaven
Carlson HS 1,100/9-12
30550 W Jefferson Ave 48173 734-379-7100
William Stevenson, prin. Fax 379-5444
Shumate MS 900/6-8
30448 W Jefferson Ave 48173 734-379-7600
Brad Coon, prin. Fax 379-2370

Gladstone, Delta, Pop. 4,885
Gladstone Area SD 1,600/PK-12
400 S 10th St 49837 906-428-2417
Dr. Jay Kulbertis, supt. Fax 789-8457
www.gladstoneschools.com
Gladstone HS 500/9-12
2100 State Highway M35 49837 906-428-9200
Brady Downey, prin. Fax 789-8312
Gladstone MS 400/6-8
300 S 10th St 49837 906-428-2295
Dave Ballard, prin. Fax 789-8404

Gladwin, Gladwin, Pop. 2,897
Gladwin Community SD 1,800/K-12
401 N Bowery Ave 48624 989-426-9255
Rick Seebeck, supt. Fax 426-5981
www.gcsnet.org
Gladwin HS 600/9-12
1400 N Spring St 48624 989-426-7341
Paul Zagata, prin. Fax 426-6031
Gladwin JHS 400/6-8
401 N Bowery Ave 48624 989-426-3808
David Beyer, prin. Fax 426-6038

Skeels Christian S 100/PK-12
3956 N M 18 48624 989-426-2054
John Shoaf, dir. Fax 426-4411

Glen Arbor, Leelanau, Pop. 228

Leelanau S 50/9-12
1 Old Homestead Rd 49636 231-334-5800
Matt Ralston, hdmstr. Fax 334-5898

Gobles, Van Buren, Pop. 803
Gobles SD 800/K-12
PO Box 412 49055 269-628-5618
Jeff Rehlander, supt. Fax 628-5306
www.gobles.org/
Gobles HS 300/9-12
PO Box 412 49055 269-628-2113
Phil McAndrew, prin. Fax 628-5306
Gobles MS 100/6-8
PO Box 412 49055 269-628-2113
Chris Miller, dean Fax 628-5306

Gobles Jr. Academy 50/K-10
32110 6th Ave 49055 269-628-2704
Thomas Coffee, prin. Fax 628-7314

Goodrich, Genesee, Pop. 1,851
Goodrich Area SD 2,100/PK-12
8029 Gale Rd 48438 810-591-2250
Scott Bogner, supt. Fax 591-2550
www.goodrich.k12.mi.us
Goodrich HS 700/9-12
8029 Gale Rd 48438 810-591-2251
David St. Aubin, prin. Fax 591-2234
Goodrich MS 500/6-8
7480 Gale Rd 48438 810-591-4210
Steven Vowles, prin. Fax 636-7879

Grand Blanc, Genesee, Pop. 8,062
Grand Blanc Community SD 8,000/PK-12
11920 S Saginaw St 48439 810-591-6000
Dr. Norman M. Abdella, supt. Fax 591-6018
www.grandblancschools.org
Grand Blanc HS 1,900/10-12
12500 Holly Rd 48439 810-591-6638
Jennifer Hammond, prin. Fax 591-6513
Grand Blanc HS West 9-9
1 Jewett Trl 48439 810-591-6350
Jennifer Hammond, prin. Fax 591-6400
Grand Blanc MS East 1,000/6-8
6100 Perry Rd 48439 810-591-4696
Jodi Kruse, prin. Fax 591-0242
Grand Blanc MS West 1,000/6-8
1515 E Reid Rd 48439 810-591-7309
Jeff Neall, prin. Fax 591-0182

Sharps Academy of Hairstyling Post-Sec.
8166 Holly Rd 48439 810-695-6742

Grand Haven, Ottawa, Pop. 10,239
Grand Haven Area SD 4,700/PK-12
1415 S Beechtree St 49417 616-850-5000
Keith Konarska, supt. Fax 850-5010
www.ghaps.org
Central HS 100/Alt
106 S 6th St 49417 616-850-6800
Paul Kunde, prin. Fax 850-6810
Grand Haven HS 1,800/9-12
17001 Ferris St 49417 616-850-6000
Tracy Wilson, prin. Fax 850-6010
Lakeshore MS 400/7-8
900 Cutler St 49417 616-850-6500
Kevin Polston, prin. Fax 850-6510

Grand Ledge, Eaton, Pop. 7,630
Grand Ledge SD 4,900/K-12
220 Lamson St 48837 517-925-5400
Brian Metcalf Ph.D., supt. Fax 925-5409
www.glcomets.net/
Grand Ledge HS 1,700/9-12
820 Spring St 48837 517-925-5815
Steve Gabriel, prin. Fax 925-5829
Hayes MS 800/7-8
12620 Nixon Rd 48837 517-925-5680
Chris Groves, prin. Fax 925-5730

Grand Marais, Alger
Burt Township SD 50/K-12
PO Box 338 49839 906-494-2543
Penny Barney, supt. Fax 494-2522
grandmaraisschools.org/
Burt Township S 50/K-12
PO Box 338 49839 906-494-2521
Penny Barney, prin. Fax 494-2522

Grand Rapids, Kent, Pop. 182,274
East Grand Rapids SD 3,000/K-12
2915 Hall St SE 49506 616-235-3535
Dr. Sara Shubel, supt. Fax 235-6730
www.egrps.org/
East Grand Rapids HS 900/9-12
2211 Lake Dr SE 49506 616-235-7555
Jennifer Fee, prin. Fax 235-7592
East Grand Rapids MS 700/6-8
2425 Lake Dr SE 49506 616-235-7551
J. Peter Stuursma, prin. Fax 235-7587

Forest Hills SD 10,000/K-12
6590 Cascade Rd SE 49546 616-493-8800
Daniel Behm, supt. Fax 493-8552
www.fhps.net
Central HS 1,300/9-12
5901 Hall St SE 49546 616-493-8700
Stephen Passinault, prin. Fax 493-8721
Northern HS 1,000/9-12
3801 Leonard St NE 49525 616-493-8600
Jon Gregory, prin. Fax 493-8644
Northern Hills MS 500/7-8
3775 Leonard St NE 49525 616-493-8650
Nancy Susterka, prin. Fax 493-8686
Other Schools – See Ada

Genesee ISD
Supt. — See Flint
Genessee Early College 9-12
509 N Harrison St 49502 810-591-5115
Sandra Morgan-Jones, prin. Fax 591-2503

Grand Rapids SD 16,800/PK-12
PO Box 117 49501 616-819-2000
Teresa Weatherall Neal M.Ed., supt. Fax 819-3480
www.grps.org/
Academy for Design and Construction 100/9-12
1800 Tremont Blvd NW 49504 616-819-3150
Justin Jennings, prin. Fax 819-3157
Alger MS 400/6-8
921 Alger St SE 49507 616-819-6200
Rodney Brown, prin. Fax 819-6201
Burton MS 500/6-8
2133 Buchanan Ave SW 49507 616-819-2269
Fax 819-2282
City MSHS 700/7-12
1400 Fuller Ave NE 49505 616-819-2380
Michael Pascoe, prin. Fax 819-2496
Creston HS 700/9-12
1720 Plainfield Ave NE 49505 616-819-2424
Troy Wilbon, prin. Fax 819-2427
Ford MS 300/6-8
851 Madison Ave SE 49507 616-819-2640
Stephanie Davis, prin. Fax 819-2660
Grand Rapids Montessori HS 50/9-12
421 Fountain St NE 49503 616-819-2310
Nikki Jones, prin. Fax 819-2400
GRAPCEP Bio-Medical and Engineering S 9-12
1720 Plainfield Ave NE 49505 616-819-2424
Troy Wilbon, prin. Fax 819-2427
Kent Vocational Options Vo/Tech
864 Crahen Ave NE 49525 616-819-2740
Antonette Moore, prin. Fax 819-2747
Ottawa Hills HS 700/9-12
2055 Rosewood Ave SE 49506 616-819-2900
Rodney Lewis, prin. Fax 819-2877
Riverside MS 500/6-8
265 Eleanor St NE 49505 616-819-2969
Donna Boman, prin. Fax 819-2981
School Business Leadership & Entrpnrshp 9-12
2055 Rosewood Ave SE 49506 616-819-2900
Rodney Lewis, prin. Fax 819-2877
School of Business 9-12
1720 Plainfield Ave NE 49505 616-819-2424
Troy Wilbon, prin. Fax 819-2427
School of Health Science and Technology 9-12
421 Fountain St NE 49503 616-819-2310
Mark Frost, prin. Fax 819-2369
Southeast Career Pathways 300/Alt
1356 Jefferson Ave SE 49507 616-819-3088
Chet Huff, prin. Fax 819-2873
Union HS 1,200/9-12
1800 Tremont Blvd NW 49504 616-819-3160
Karl Nelson, prin. Fax 819-3205
University Preparatory Academy 6-11
111 College Ave NE 49503 616-819-1010
Daniel Williams, prin. Fax 819-1011
Westwood MS 500/6-8
1524 Mount Mercy Dr NW 49504 616-819-3322
Arthur Garner, prin. Fax 819-3301

Kelloggsville SD 1,800/PK-12
242 52nd St SE 49548 616-538-7460
Gregory Warsen, supt. Fax 532-1597
www.kvilleps.org
Kelloggsville HS 600/9-12
23 Jean St SW 49548 616-532-1570
Richard Frens, prin. Fax 532-7780
Kelloggsville MS 500/6-8
4650 Division Ave S 49548 616-532-1575
Timothy Reeves, prin. Fax 532-1579
Other Schools – See Wyoming

Kenowa Hills SD 3,200/PK-12
2325 4 Mile Rd NW 49544 616-784-2511
Gerald Hopkins, supt. Fax 784-8323
khps.org
Kenowa Hills HS 1,200/9-12
3825 Hendershot Ave NW 49544 616-784-2400
Katie Pennington, prin. Fax 647-0149
Kenowa Hills MS 800/6-8
3950 Hendershot Ave NW 49544 616-785-3225
Joe Haines, prin. Fax 784-2404

Kent ISD
2930 Knapp St NE 49525 616-364-1333
Kevin Konarska, supt. Fax 364-1488
www.kentisd.org
Kent Career/Technical Center Vo/Tech
1655 E Beltline Ave NE 49525 616-364-8421
John Kraus, prin. Fax 364-9140
Kent Innovation HS 9-12
1655 E Beltline Ave NE 49525 616-363-8010
Kimberly Kimber, prin. Fax 363-8030

Northview SD 3,300/PK-12
4365 Hunsberger Ave NE 49525 616-363-6861
Dr. Michael Paskewicz, supt. Fax 363-9609
www.nvps.net
Crossroads MS 600/7-8
4400 Ambrose Ave NE 49525 616-361-3430
F. Andrew Scogg, prin. Fax 363-7868
East Campus HS 100/Alt
3801 E Beltline Ave NE 49525 616-361-7396
Jamey Vermaat, prin. Fax 361-7398
Northview HS 1,200/9-12
4451 Hunsberger Ave NE 49525 616-363-4857
Mark Thomas, prin. Fax 361-3494

All Saints Academy - MS Campus 100/5-8
1110 4 Mile Rd NE 49525 616-363-7725
Anne Harpold, prin. Fax 363-3086
Aquinas College Post-Sec.
1607 Robinson Rd SE 49506 616-632-8900
Calvin College Post-Sec.
3201 Burton St SE 49546 616-526-6000
Calvin Theological Seminary Post-Sec.
3233 Burton St SE 49546 800-388-6034
Catholic Central HS 800/9-12
319 Sheldon Blvd SE 49503 616-233-5801
Greg Deja, prin. Fax 459-0257
Compass College of Cinematic Arts Post-Sec.
41 Sheldon Blvd SE 49503 616-988-1000
Cornerstone University Post-Sec.
1001 E Beltline Ave NE 49525 616-949-5300
Covenant Christian HS 300/9-12
1401 Ferndale Ave SW, 616-453-5048
Rick Noorman, prin. Fax 453-4277
Davenport University Post-Sec.
6191 Kraft Ave SE 49512 616-698-7111
Empire Beauty School Post-Sec.
1735 4 Mile Rd NE 49525 616-363-9853
Empire Beauty School Post-Sec.
455 Standale Plz NW, 616-735-9680
Everest Institute Post-Sec.
1750 Woodworth St NE 49525 616-364-8464
Grace Bible College Post-Sec.
1011 Aldon St SW 49509 616-538-2330
Grand Rapids Adventist Academy 200/K-12
1151 Oakleigh Rd NW 49504 616-791-9797
Robert Quillin, prin. Fax 791-7242
Grand Rapids Christian HS 1,000/9-12
2300 Plymouth Ave SE 49506 616-574-5500
Jim Primus, prin. Fax 241-3141
Grand Rapids Christian MS 300/5-8
1875 Rosewood Ave SE 49506 616-574-6350
Ashanti Bryant, prin. Fax 574-6316
Grand Rapids Community College Post-Sec.
143 Bostwick Ave NE 49503 616-234-4000
ITT Technical Institute Post-Sec.
3518 Plainfield Ave NE 49525 616-365-4800
Kuyper College Post-Sec.
3333 E Beltline Ave NE 49525 800-511-3749
Legacy Christian West Campus 200/5-8
67 68th St SW 49548 616-455-3860
Vince Bonnema M.A., admin. Fax 455-1960
NorthPointe Christian HS 400/7-12
3101 Leonard St NE 49525 616-942-0350
James Hofman, supt. Fax 942-4647
Plymouth Christian HS 200/7-12
965 Plymouth Ave NE 49505 616-454-9481
James Bazen, prin. Fax 454-7243
Puritan Reformed Theological Seminary Post-Sec.
2965 Leonard St NE 49525 616-977-0599
Ross Medical Education Center Post-Sec.
4528 Breton Rd SE 49508 616-698-3075
South Christian HS 700/9-12
160 68th St SW 49548 616-455-3210
George Guichelaar, prin. Fax 455-8840
Spectrum Health Post-Sec.
100 Michigan St NE 49503 616-391-1605
Taratuta School of Truck Driving Post-Sec.
2215 Oak Indstrl Dr NE #212 49505 616-742-9000
Van Andel Institute Graduate School Post-Sec.
333 Bostwick Ave NE 49503 616-234-5708
West Catholic HS 600/9-12
1801 Bristol Ave NW 49504 616-233-5900
Cynthia Kneibel, prin. Fax 453-4320

Grandville, Kent, Pop. 15,098
Grandville SD 5,700/PK-12
3839 Prairie St SW 49418 616-254-6570
Ronald Caniff, supt. Fax 254-6580
www.grandville.k12.mi.us
Grandville HS 1,900/9-12
4700 Canal Ave SW 49418 616-254-6430
Dr. Randy Morris, prin. Fax 254-6462
Grandville MS 900/7-8
3535 Wilson Ave SW 49418 616-254-6610
Theresa Waterbury, prin. Fax 254-6613

Calvin Christian HS 400/9-12
3750 Ivanrest Ave SW 49418 616-538-0990
Barbara Engbers, prin. Fax 538-9930
Calvin Christian MS 100/7-8
3740 Ivanrest Ave SW 49418 616-531-7400
John Kramer, prin. Fax 531-7402

Grant, Newaygo, Pop. 889
Grant SD 2,100/PK-12
148 Elder St 49327 231-834-5621
Jonathan Whan, supt. Fax 834-7146
www.grantps.net
Grant HS 600/9-12
331 E State Rd 49327 231-834-5622
Dan Simon, prin. Fax 834-8043
Grant Learning Center 200/Alt
331 E State Rd 49327 231-834-5639
Jonathan Whan, supt. Fax 834-8111
Grant MS 600/5-8
96 E 120th St 49327 231-834-5910
Lance Jones, prin. Fax 834-9029

Grass Lake, Jackson, Pop. 1,146
Grass Lake Community SD 1,300/K-12
899 S Union St 49240 517-522-5540
Brad Hamilton, supt. Fax 522-8195
www.grasslakeschools.com
Grass Lake HS 400/9-12
11500 Warrior Trl 49240 517-522-5570
Brian Thompson, prin. Fax 522-5490
Grass Lake MS 300/6-8
1000 Grass Lake Rd 49240 517-522-5550
Jeanene Satterthwaite, prin. Fax 522-4775

Grayling, Crawford, Pop. 1,867
Crawford AuSable SD 1,300/PK-12
1135 N Old 27 49738 989-344-3500
Joseph Powers, supt. Fax 348-6822
www.casdk12.net/
Grayling HS 600/9-12
1135 N Old 27 49738 989-344-3532
Donna Boughner, prin. Fax 348-7799
Grayling MS 400/6-8
500 Spruce St 49738 989-344-3550
Jeffrey Branch, prin. Fax 348-7045

Greenville, Montcalm, Pop. 8,316
Greenville SD 3,700/K-12
1414 Chase St 48838 616-754-3686
Peter Haines, supt. Fax 754-5374
www.greenville.k12.mi.us
Greenville HS 1,200/9-12
111 N Hillcrest St 48838 616-754-3681
Jeffrey Wright, prin. Fax 754-1994
Greenville MS 900/6-8
1321 Chase St 48838 616-754-9361
Leigh Acker, prin. Fax 754-2901

Grosse Ile, Wayne, Pop. 9,781
Grosse Ile Township SD 1,800/K-12
23276 E River Rd 48138 734-362-2555
William Eis, supt. Fax 362-2594
www.gischools.org/
Grosse Ile HS 700/9-12
7800 Grays Dr 48138 734-362-2400
James Stewart, prin. Fax 362-2496
Grosse Ile MS 400/6-8
23270 E River Rd 48138 734-362-2500
David Tucker, prin. Fax 362-2596

Grosse Pointe, Wayne, Pop. 5,336
Grosse Pointe SD 8,200/K-12
389 Saint Clair St 48230 313-432-3000
Dr. Thomas Harwood, supt. Fax 432-3002
www.gpschools.org
Brownell MS 600/6-8
260 Chalfonte Ave 48236 313-432-3900
Dr. Michael Dib, prin. Fax 432-3902
Grosse Pointe North HS 1,300/9-12
707 Vernier Rd 48236 313-432-3200
Tom Tobe, prin. Fax 432-3202
Grosse Pointe South HS 1,600/9-12
11 Grosse Pointe Blvd 48236 313-432-3500
Dr. Matt Outlaw, prin. Fax 432-3502
Parcells MS 700/6-8
20600 Mack Ave 48236 313-432-4600
Cathryn Armstrong, prin. Fax 432-4602
Pierce MS 600/6-8
15430 Kercheval Ave 48230 313-432-4700
Gary Buslepp, prin. Fax 432-4702

University Liggett S 600/PK-12
1045 Cook Rd 48236 313-884-4444
Joseph Healey Ph.D., hdmstr. Fax 884-1775

Gwinn, Marquette, Pop. 1,874
Gwinn Area Community SD 900/K-12
50 W State Highway M35 49841 906-346-9283
Dr. Stephen Piereson, supt. Fax 346-3616
www.gwinn.k12.mi.us
Gwinn HS 400/9-12
50 W State Highway M35 49841 906-346-9247
Kevin Luokkala, prin. Fax 346-0300
Gwinn MS 200/6-8
50 W State Highway M35 49841 906-346-5914
Jacqueline Cole, prin. Fax 346-0300

Hale, Iosco
Hale Area SD 400/K-12
200 W Main St 48739 989-728-7661
Ronald Kraft, supt. Fax 728-2406
www.haleschools.net
Hale S 400/K-12
311 N Washington St 48739 989-728-3551
Richard Reilly, prin. Fax 728-9551

Hamilton, Allegan
Hamilton Community SD 2,600/PK-12
4815 136th Ave 49419 269-751-5148
David Tebo, supt. Fax 751-7116
www.hamiltonschools.us
Hamilton HS 800/9-12
4911 136th Ave 49419 269-751-5185
Doug Braschler, prin. Fax 751-7670
Hamilton MS 600/6-8
4845 136th Ave 49419 269-751-4436
Doug Braschler, prin. Fax 751-8560

Hamtramck, Wayne, Pop. 21,353
Hamtramck SD 2,800/PK-12
PO Box 12012 48212 313-872-9270
Thomas Niczay, supt. Fax 872-8679
www.hamtramck.k12.mi.us
Hamtramck HS 900/9-12
11410 Charest St 48212 313-892-7505
Rebecca Westrate, prin. Fax 892-1990
Kosciuszko MS 400/7-8
2333 Burger St 48212 313-365-4625
Nuo Ivezaj, prin. Fax 365-4760

Al-Ikhlas Training Academy 100/K-12
12555 McDougall St 48212 313-369-0880
Nadir Ahmad, dir. Fax 369-0881

Hancock, Houghton, Pop. 4,572
Hancock SD 800/K-12
501 Campus Dr 49930 906-487-5925
Monica Healy, supt. Fax 487-5216
www.hancockpublicschools.org
Hancock Central HS 200/9-12
501 Campus Dr 49930 906-483-2540
John Sanregret, prin. Fax 483-2539
Hancock MS 200/6-8
501 Campus Dr 49930 906-487-5923
Monica Healy, prin. Fax 487-5924

Finlandia University Post-Sec.
601 Quincy St 49930 906-482-5300

Harbor Beach, Huron, Pop. 1,671
Harbor Beach Community SD 500/K-12
402 S 5th St 48441 989-479-3261
Lawrence Kroswek, supt. Fax 479-9881
www.hbpirates.org
Harbor Beach HS 300/9-12
402 S 5th St 48441 989-479-3261
Michael Hugan, prin. Fax 479-9881
Harbor Beach MS 200/5-8
402 S 5th St 48441 989-479-3261
Lawrence Kroswek, prin. Fax 479-9881

Harbor Springs, Emmet, Pop. 1,169
Harbor Springs SD 1,000/PK-12
800 S State Rd 49740 231-526-4545
Mark Tompkins, supt. Fax 526-4544
www.harborps.org
Harbor Springs HS 300/9-12
500 N Spring St 49740 231-526-4800
Susan Jacobs, prin. Fax 526-4833
Harbor Springs MS 200/6-8
800 S State Rd 49740 231-526-4700
Wil Cwikiel, prin. Fax 526-4760

Harbor Light Christian S 200/PK-12
8333 Clayton Rd 49740 231-347-7859
Gary Urman, head sch Fax 347-7703

Harper Woods, Wayne, Pop. 13,876
Harper Woods SD 1,300/PK-12
20225 Beaconsfield St 48225 313-245-3000
Todd Biederwolf, supt. Fax 839-1249
www.hwschools.org
Harper Woods HS 500/9-12
20225 Beaconsfield St 48225 313-245-3000
Thomas Parker, prin. Fax 839-4360
Harper Woods MS 200/7-8
20225 Beaconsfield St 48225 313-245-3000
Thomas Parker, prin. Fax 839-4360

Harris, Menominee
Bark River-Harris SD 700/K-12
PO Box 350 49845 906-466-9981
Jason Lockwood, supt. Fax 466-0107
www.brhschools.org/
Bark River-Harris JSHS 300/7-12
PO Box 350 49845 906-466-5321
Darren Bray, prin. Fax 466-2925

Harrison, Clare, Pop. 2,058
Harrison Community SD 1,500/K-12
PO Box 529 48625 989-539-7871
Thomas House, supt. Fax 539-7491
www.harrisonschools.com/
Harrison Community Education 50/Alt
PO Box 529 48625 989-539-7194
Richard Foote, dir. Fax 539-4314
Harrison HS 500/9-12
PO Box 529 48625 989-539-7417
Jeremy Thomas, prin. Fax 539-4319
Harrison MS 400/6-8
PO Box 529 48625 989-539-7194
Richard Foote, prin. Fax 539-0460

Mid-Michigan Community College Post-Sec.
1375 S Clare Ave 48625 989-386-6622

Harrison Township, Macomb, Pop. 24,685
L'Anse Creuse SD
Supt. — See Clinton Township
L'Anse Creuse HS 1,800/9-12
38495 LAnse Creuse St 48045 586-783-6400
Stephen Czapski, prin. Fax 783-6408
L'Anse Creuse MS Central 700/6-8
38000 Reimold St 48045 586-783-6430
Andrea Glynn, prin. Fax 783-6437
L'Anse Creuse MS South 600/6-8
34641 Jefferson Ave 48045 586-493-5620
Paul Lasala, prin. Fax 493-5625

Hart, Oceana, Pop. 2,108
Hart SD 1,200/PK-12
301 Johnson St W 49420 231-873-6214
Ron Moag, supt. Fax 873-6244
www.hart.k12.mi.us
Hart HS 400/9-12
300 Johnson St W 49420 231-873-5691
Matthew McDonald, prin. Fax 873-0586
Hart MS 400/5-8
308 Johnson St W 49420 231-873-6320
Kevin Ackley, prin. Fax 873-0245

Hartford, Van Buren, Pop. 2,604
Hartford SD 1,700/PK-12
115 School St 49057 269-621-7000
Andrew Hubbard, supt. Fax 621-3887
www.hpsmi.org
Hartford HS 500/9-12
121 School St 49057 269-621-7100
David Janicki, prin. Fax 621-7160

Hartford MS 300/6-8
141 School St 49057 269-621-7200
Joel Messenger, prin. Fax 621-7260
Southwest Michigan Community S 300/Alt
115 School St 49057 269-621-7102
Cheryl Boothby, prin. Fax 621-3887

Hartland, Livingston
Hartland Consolidated SD
Supt. — See Howell
Hartland HS 1,800/9-12
10635 Dunham Rd 48353 810-626-2200
Ben Mainka, prin. Fax 626-2201
Hartland MS 900/7-8
3250 Hartland Rd 48353 810-626-2400
Steve Livingway, prin. Fax 626-2401

Haslett, Ingham, Pop. 18,726
Haslett SD 2,700/K-12
5593 Franklin St 48840 517-339-8242
Michael Duda, supt. Fax 339-1360
www.haslett.k12.mi.us/
Haslett HS 900/9-12
5450 Marsh Rd 48840 517-339-8249
Bart Wegenke, prin. Fax 339-7353
Haslett MS 600/6-8
1535 Franklin St 48840 517-339-8233
Andy Pridgeon, prin. Fax 339-4837

Hastings, Barry, Pop. 7,265
Hastings Area SD 2,800/PK-12
232 W Grand St 49058 269-948-4400
Todd Geerlings, supt. Fax 948-4425
www.hassk12.org
Hastings HS 900/9-12
520 W South St 49058 269-948-4409
Kevin Riggs, prin. Fax 948-8081
Hastings MS 700/6-8
232 W Grand St 49058 269-948-4404
Christopher Cooley, prin. Fax 945-6101

Barry County Christian S 100/PK-12
2999 McKeown Rd 49058 269-948-2151
Judith Freeman, admin. Fax 948-2795

Hazel Park, Oakland, Pop. 15,715
Hazel Park SD 4,700/PK-12
1620 E Elza Ave 48030 248-658-5200
James D. Meisinger, supt. Fax 544-5443
www.hazelparkschools.org
Hazel Park HS 1,000/9-12
23400 Hughes Ave 48030 248-658-5100
Don Vogt, prin. Fax 544-5389
Hazel Park JHS 700/6-8
22770 Highland Ave 48030 248-658-2300
Douglas Esler, prin. Fax 586-5875
Hazel Park Adult S Adult
420 W 9 Mile Rd 48030 248-658-5600
Kathleen Andre, prin. Fax 544-5447

Hemlock, Saginaw, Pop. 1,446
Hemlock SD 1,100/PK-12
PO Box 260 48626 989-642-5282
Corinne Netzley, supt. Fax 642-2773
www.hemlock.k12.mi.us
Hemlock HS 500/9-12
PO Box 260 48626 989-642-5287
Mike Vondette, prin. Fax 642-5109
Hemlock MS 300/6-8
PO Box 260 48626 989-642-5253
Terry Keyser, prin. Fax 642-8239

Hermansville, Menominee
North Central Area SD 400/PK-12
PO Box 159 49847 906-498-7737
Don Palmer, supt. Fax 498-2235
www.ncajets.org
Other Schools – See Powers

Hesperia, Oceana, Pop. 932
Hesperia Community SD 1,000/K-12
PO Box 338 49421 231-854-6185
Jeffery Haase, supt. Fax 854-1586
www.hesp.net
Hesperia HS 300/9-12
PO Box 338 49421 231-854-6385
Jennifer Kleiner, prin. Fax 854-6070
Hesperia MS 300/5-8
PO Box 338 49421 231-854-6475
Jennifer Kleiner, prin. Fax 854-6096

Highland, Oakland
Huron Valley SD 9,700/PK-12
2390 S Milford Rd 48357 248-684-8000
James Baker, supt. Fax 684-8235
www.huronvalley.k12.mi.us
Harbor HS 100/Alt
5061 N Duck Lake Rd 48356 248-676-8399
Susan Gallagher, dir. Fax 676-8420
Milford HS 1,500/9-12
2380 S Milford Rd 48357 248-684-8091
Kevin McKenna, prin. Fax 684-8094
Other Schools – See Commerce Township, Milford, White Lake

Highland Park, Wayne, Pop. 11,530
Highland Park SD 1,200/PK-12
15900 Woodward Ave 48203 313-957-3000
Edith Hightower, supt. Fax 957-3112
www.resa.net/highlandpark/
Highland Park Community HS 600/9-12
15900 Woodward Ave 48203 313-957-3001
Flinnoia Hall, prin. Fax 868-0483

Hillman, Montmorency, Pop. 696
Hillman Community SD 500/K-12
26042 M 32 S 49746 989-742-2908
Shawn Olson, supt. Fax 742-3376
www.hillmanschools.com
Hillman JSHS 200/7-12
26042 M 32 S 49746 989-742-4538
Michael Leskowich, prin. Fax 742-4536

Hillsdale, Hillsdale, Pop. 8,143
Hillsdale Community SD 1,700/PK-12
30 S Norwood Ave 49242 517-437-4401
Shawn Vondra, supt. Fax 439-4194
www.hillsdaleschools.org
Davis MS 500/5-8
30 N West St 49242 517-439-4326
Erin North, prin. Fax 437-1195
Hillsdale HS 400/9-12
30 S Norwood Ave 49242 517-439-4320
Jeff Terpenning, prin. Fax 437-0377

Hillsdale ISD 50/
310 W Bacon St 49242 517-437-0990
Michael Potts, supt. Fax 439-4388
www.hillsdale-isd.org
Workforce Development & Tech Center Vo/Tech
279 Industrial Dr 49242 517-437-3729
Kevin Leonard, dir. Fax 437-3743

Hillsdale Academy 200/K-12
1 Academy Ln 49242 517-439-8644
Kenneth Calvert, prin. Fax 607-2794
Hillsdale Beauty College Post-Sec.
64 Waldron St 49242 517-437-4670
Hillsdale College Post-Sec.
33 E College St 49242 517-437-7341
Jackson Community College Post-Sec.
PO Box 712 49242 517-437-3343

Holland, Ottawa, Pop. 32,396
Holland SD 4,100/PK-12
156 W 11th St 49423 616-494-2000
Brian Davis, supt. Fax 392-8225
www.hollandpublicschools.org
Holland HS 1,400/8-12
600 Van Raalte Ave 49423 616-494-2200
Deb Feenstra, prin. Fax 393-7534
New Tech HS 100/9-12
45 E 25th St 49423 616-494-2700
Ryan Harrell, contact Fax 928-0581
VR Tech S 200/Alt
461 Van Raalte Ave 49423 616-494-2600
Zach Kapla, coord. Fax 393-7652

Ottawa Area ISD 300/
13565 Port Sheldon St 49424 616-738-8940
Karen McPhee, supt. Fax 738-8946
www.oaisd.org
Careerline Tech Center Vo/Tech
13663 Port Sheldon St 49424 616-738-8950
Dave Searles, dir.

West Ottawa SD 7,400/K-12
1138 136th Ave 49424 616-738-5700
Thomas Martin, supt. Fax 738-5792
www.westottawa.net
Harbor Lights MS 900/6-8
1024 136th Ave 49424 616-786-1000
Dennis White, prin. Fax 786-1091
Macatawa Bay MS 700/6-8
3700 140th Ave 49424 616-786-2000
Michael Fine, prin. Fax 786-2091
West Ottawa HS 2,300/9-12
3685 Butternut Dr 49424 616-994-5000
Todd Tulgestke, prin. Fax 994-5091

Calvary S of Holland 200/PK-12
518 Plasman Ave 49423 616-396-4494
Kevin Alderink, dir. Fax 396-0326
Davenport University Post-Sec.
643 S Waverly Rd 49423 616-395-4600
Holland Christian HS 900/9-12
950 Ottawa Ave 49423 616-820-2905
Troy Stahl, prin. Fax 820-2910
Holland Christian MS 200/7-8
850 Ottawa Ave 49423 616-820-3205
Mark Van Dyke, prin. Fax 820-3210
Hope College Post-Sec.
PO Box 9000 49422 616-395-7000
Western Theological Seminary Post-Sec.
101 E 13th St 49423 616-392-8555

Holly, Oakland, Pop. 5,990
Holly Area SD 3,300/K-12
920 Baird St 48442 248-328-3100
R. Kent Barnes, supt. Fax 328-3145
www.has-k12.org/
Holly HS 1,200/9-12
6161 E Holly Rd 48442 248-328-3200
Peter LoFiego, prin. Fax 328-3211
Holly MS 500/7-8
920 Baird St 48442 248-328-3400
Linda Skrzynski, prin. Fax 328-3404

Adelphian Junior Academy 50/K-10
PO Box 208 48442 248-634-9481
Nancy Danelson, prin. Fax 634-9222

Holt, Ingham, Pop. 23,336
Holt SD 5,700/K-12
5780 Holt Rd 48842 517-694-0401
Dr. Johnny A. Scott, supt. Fax 694-1335
www.hpsk12.net/
EdTrek Alternative Education Center Alt
4610 Spahr St 48842 517-709-3148
Fax 709-3156
Holt JHS 1,000/7-8
1784 Aurelius Rd 48842 517-694-7117
Marshall Perkins, prin. Fax 694-3535
Holt SHS 1,400/10-12
5885 Holt Rd 48842 517-694-2162
Mike Willard, prin. Fax 699-3451
9th Grade Campus 500/9-9
5780 Holt Rd 48842 517-694-4370
Nick Johnson, prin. Fax 694-8362

Holt Lutheran S 100/PK-12
2418 Aurelius Rd 48842 517-694-3182
Traci Backus, prin. Fax 694-6371

Holton, Muskegon
Holton SD 900/PK-12
8897 Holton Duck Lake Rd 49425 231-821-1700
Jason Kennedy, supt. Fax 821-1724
www.holtonschools.com
Holton HS 300/9-12
6477 Syers Rd 49425 231-821-1725
Adam Bayne, prin. Fax 821-1774
Holton MS 200/6-8
6245 Syers Rd 49425 231-821-1775
Adam Bayne, prin. Fax 821-1824

Homer, Calhoun, Pop. 1,660
Homer Community SD 1,000/K-12
403 S Hillsdale St 49245 517-568-4461
Robert Ridgeway, supt. Fax 568-4468
www.homerschools.net
Homer HS 300/9-12
403 S Hillsdale St 49245 517-568-4464
Tom Salow, prin. Fax 568-7125
Homer MS 300/5-8
403 S Hillsdale St 49245 517-568-4456
Scott Salow, prin. Fax 568-4831

Hopkins, Allegan, Pop. 603
Hopkins SD 1,600/K-12
400 S Clark St 49328 269-793-7261
Chris Stephens, supt. Fax 793-3154
www.hpsvikings.org
Hopkins HS 600/9-12
333 S Clark St 49328 269-793-7616
Ken Szczepanski, prin. Fax 793-7085
Hopkins MS 300/6-8
215 S Clark St 49328 269-793-7407
Ken Szczepanski, prin. Fax 793-4086

Horton, Jackson
Hanover-Horton SD 1,300/K-12
10400 Moscow Rd 49246 517-563-0100
John Denney, supt. Fax 563-0150
www.hanoverhorton.org/
Hanover-Horton HS 400/9-12
10000 Moscow Rd 49246 517-563-0101
Dan Draper, prin. Fax 563-0155
Hanover-Horton MS 300/6-8
10000 Moscow Rd 49246 517-563-0102
Denise Bergstrom, prin. Fax 563-9140

Houghton, Houghton, Pop. 7,574
Houghton-Portage Township SD 1,300/K-12
1603 Gundlach Rd 49931 906-482-0451
Doreen Klingbeil, supt. Fax 487-9764
www.hpts.us
Houghton Central HS 400/9-12
1603 Gundlach Rd 49931 906-482-0450
Julie Filpus, prin. Fax 482-5218
Houghton MS 300/6-8
1603 Gundlach Rd 49931 906-482-4871
James Luoma, prin. Fax 483-2566

Michigan Technological University Post-Sec.
1400 Townsend Dr 49931 906-487-1885

Houghton Lake, Roscommon, Pop. 3,390
Houghton Lake Community SD 1,600/PK-12
6001 W Houghton Lake Dr 48629 989-366-2000
Scott Dunsmore, supt. Fax 366-2070
www.hlcsk12.net
Houghton Lake HS 700/8-12
4433 W Houghton Lake Dr 48629 989-366-2005
Brent Cryderman, prin. Fax 366-2071

Houghton Lake Institute of Cosmetology Post-Sec.
PO Box 669 48629 - -

Howard City, Montcalm, Pop. 1,777
Tri County Area SD
Supt. — See Sand Lake
Tri County HS 700/9-12
21338 Kendaville Rd 49329 231-937-4338
Kurt Mabie, prin. Fax 937-5684
Tri County MS 600/6-8
21350 Kendaville Rd 49329 231-937-4318
Fax 937-6319

Howell, Livingston, Pop. 9,332
Hartland Consolidated SD 5,600/K-12
9525 E Highland Rd 48843 810-626-2100
Janet Sifferman, supt. Fax 626-2101
www.hartlandschools.us/
Hartland Alternative Education 100/Alt
9525 E Highland Rd 48843 810-626-2140
Kirk Evenson, prin. Fax 626-2101
Other Schools – See Hartland

Howell SD 8,700/K-12
411 N Highlander Way 48843 517-548-6200
Ronald Wilson, supt. Fax 548-6229
www.howellschools.com
Highlander Way MS 1,100/6-8
511 N Highlander Way 48843 517-548-6252
Melanie Post, prin. Fax 545-1455
Howell HS 2,000/10-12
1200 W Grand River Ave 48843 517-540-8300
Jason Schrock, prin. Fax 545-0136
Howell HS Freshman Campus 700/9-9
1400 W Grand River Ave 48843 517-548-6267
Jason Schrock, prin. Fax 545-1439
Parker MS 900/6-8
400 Wright Rd 48843 517-552-4600
Susan Muntz, prin. Fax 552-0106

Cleary University - Livingston Campus Post-Sec.
3750 Cleary Dr 48843 800-686-1883

Hudson, Lenawee, Pop. 2,276
Hudson Area SD 900/PK-12
781 N Maple Grove Ave 49247 517-448-8912
Michael Osborne Ph.D., supt. Fax 448-8570
www.hudson.k12.mi.us
Hudson Alternative HS 50/Alt
771 N Maple Grove Ave 49247 517-448-8912
Lance Horwath, prin. Fax 448-8975
Hudson Area HS 300/9-12
771 N Maple Grove Ave 49247 517-448-8912
Lance Horwath, prin. Fax 448-8975
Hudson MS 200/6-8
771 N Maple Grove Ave 49247 517-445-8912
Lance Horwath, prin. Fax 448-8975

Hudsonville, Ottawa, Pop. 7,024
Hudsonville SD 5,800/PK-12
3886 Van Buren St 49426 616-669-1740
Nicholas Ceglarek, supt. Fax 669-4878
www.hudsonville.k12.mi.us
Baldwin Street MS 800/6-8
3835 Baldwin St 49426 616-669-7750
David Powers, prin. Fax 669-7755
Hudsonville Freshman Campus 500/9-9
5535 School Ave 49426 616-669-1510
Matt Blood, prin. Fax 669-4895
Hudsonville HS 1,200/10-12
5037 32nd Ave 49426 616-669-1500
Dave Feenstra, prin. Fax 669-4891
Riley Street MS 500/6-8
2745 Riley St 49426 616-896-1920
Bill Ross, prin. Fax 896-1925

Freedom Christian S 300/PK-12
6340 Autumn Dr 49426 616-669-2270
Greg Scheck, hdmstr. Fax 669-2410
Hudsonville Christian MS 300/6-8
3925 Van Buren St 49426 616-669-7487
Mary Broene, prin. Fax 669-2031
Unity Christian HS 700/9-12
3487 Oak St 49426 616-669-1820
Jerry DeGroot, prin. Fax 669-5760

Ida, Monroe
Ida SD 1,600/K-12
3145 Prairie St 48140 734-269-3110
Richard Carsten, supt. Fax 269-2294
www.idaschools.org
Ida HS 500/9-12
3145 Prairie St 48140 734-269-3485
Thomas Dykstra, prin. Fax 269-3495
Ida MS 500/5-8
3143 Prairie St 48140 734-269-2220
Richard Samulak, prin. Fax 269-2576

Imlay City, Lapeer, Pop. 3,545
Imlay City Community SD 2,300/PK-12
634 W Borland Rd 48444 810-724-2765
Dr. Gary Richards, supt. Fax 724-4307
www.imlay.k12.mi.us/
Imlay City HS 700/9-12
1001 Norlin Dr 48444 810-724-9810
Larry Cowger, prin. Fax 724-9897
Imlay City MS 500/6-8
495 W 1st St 48444 810-724-9811
Patrick Brown, prin. Fax 724-9896
Venture HS 100/Alt
2061 S Almont Ave 48444 810-724-9814
Todd Barraco, dean Fax 724-2315

Indian River, Cheboygan, Pop. 1,930
Inland Lakes SD 700/K-12
4363 S Straits Hwy 49749 231-238-6868
Fred Osborn, supt. Fax 238-4181
www.inlandlakes.org
Inland Lakes JSHS 400/5-12
4363 S Straits Hwy 49749 231-238-6868
Melanie Allen, prin. Fax 238-7240

Inkster, Wayne, Pop. 24,504
Inkster SD 2,900/K-12
29115 Carlysle St 48141 734-722-5310
Mischa Bashir, supt. Fax 722-2150
www.inksterschools.org/
Blanchette MS 500/6-8
1771 Henry Ruff Rd 48141 734-326-7041
Beverly Gerhard, prin. Fax 722-5402
Inkster HS 1,400/9-12
3250 Middlebelt Rd 48141 734-326-8519
Latoya Hall King, prin. Fax 467-9698

Westwood Community SD
Supt. — See Dearborn Heights
Tomlinson MS 400/6-8
25912 Annapolis St 48141 313-565-3393
Robert Brooks, prin. Fax 565-0920

Peterson-Warren Academy 100/K-12
PO Box 888 48141 313-565-5808
Juanita Martin, prin. Fax 565-7784

Interlochen, Grand Traverse, Pop. 574

Interlochen Center for the Arts 500/9-12
PO Box 199 49643 231-276-7200
Edward Farraday, prin. Fax 276-7885

Ionia, Ionia, Pop. 11,276
Ionia SD 3,000/PK-12
250 E Tuttle Rd 48846 616-527-9280
Dr. Patricia Batista, supt. Fax 527-8846
www.ioniaschools.org
Ionia HS 900/9-12
250 E Tuttle Rd 48846 616-527-0600
Jack Manciu, prin. Fax 527-8057
Ionia MS 700/6-8
438 Union St 48846 616-527-0040
Cheri Meier, prin. Fax 527-3380
Welch HS 100/Alt
830 Harrison St 48846 616-527-3530
Beth Davis, prin. Fax 527-8012

Iron Mountain, Dickinson, Pop. 7,523
Iron Mountain SD 1,100/PK-12
217 Izzo Marriucci Way 49801 906-779-2600
Tom Jayne, supt. Fax 779-2676
www.imschools.org
Central MS 200/7-8
301 W Hughitt St 49801 906-779-2610
Maryann Boddy, prin. Fax 779-9255
Iron Mountain HS 400/9-12
300 W B St 49801 906-779-2610
Maryann Boddy, prin. Fax 779-2638

Iron River, Iron, Pop. 2,984
West Iron County SD 600/PK-12
601 Garfield Ave 49935 906-265-9218
Christopher Thomson, supt. Fax 265-9736
www.westiron.org
West Iron County JSHS 300/6-12
701 Garfield Ave 49935 906-265-5184
Michael Berutti, prin. Fax 265-9750

Ironwood, Gogebic, Pop. 5,289
Ironwood Area SD 800/PK-12
650 E Ayer St 49938 906-932-0200
Timothy Kolesar, supt. Fax 932-9915
www.ironwood.k12.mi.us/
Wright MSHS 400/7-12
650 E Ayer St 49938 906-932-0932
Michelle Kanipes, prin. Fax 932-3082

Gogebic Community College Post-Sec.
E4946 Jackson Rd 49938 906-932-4231

Ishpeming, Marquette, Pop. 6,339
Ishpeming SD 1 700/K-12
319 E Division St 49849 906-485-5501
Dr. Stephen Piereson, supt. Fax 485-1422
www.ishpemingschools.com
Ishpeming HS 300/9-12
319 E Division St 49849 906-485-1066
Vicki Lempinen, prin. Fax 485-4750
Ishpeming MS 100/5-8
324 E Pearl St 49849 906-485-6341
Vicki Lempinen, prin. Fax 485-5925

NICE Community SD 1,100/K-12
300 S Westwood Dr 49849 906-485-1021
Bryan DeAugustine, supt. Fax 485-4095
www.nice.k12.mi.us/
Westwood HS 300/9-12
300 S Westwood Dr 49849 906-485-1023
David Boase, prin. Fax 485-1530

Ithaca, Gratiot, Pop. 2,877
Gratiot-Isabella RESD
PO Box 310 48847 989-875-5101
Jan Amsterburg, supt. Fax 875-7531
www.giresd.net/
Other Schools – See Alma

Ithaca SD 1,400/PK-12
710 N Union St 48847 989-875-3700
Nathan Bootz, supt. Fax 875-4538
www.ithacaschools.net
Ithaca HS 400/9-12
710 N Union St 48847 989-875-3373
Steven Netzley, prin. Fax 875-2500
Ithaca MS 300/7-8
710 N Union St 48847 989-875-3373
Renee Sopel, prin. Fax 875-2500

Jackson, Jackson, Pop. 31,900
East Jackson Community SD 1,300/K-12
1404 N Sutton Rd 49202 517-764-2090
Patrick Little, supt. Fax 764-6033
www.eastjacksonschools.org/
East Jackson HS 400/9-12
1566 N Sutton Rd 49202 517-764-1700
Brent Cole, prin. Fax 764-6083
East Jackson MS 200/7-8
1566 N Sutton Rd 49202 517-764-6010
Brent Cole, prin. Fax 764-6081

Jackson County ISD 50/
6700 Browns Lake Rd 49201 517-768-5200
Kevin Oxley, supt. Fax 787-2026
www.jcisd.org
Jackson Area Career Center Vo/Tech
6800 Browns Lake Rd 49201 517-768-5200
Patty Horning, prin. Fax 787-2844

Jackson SD 5,600/PK-12
522 Wildwood Ave 49201 517-841-2200
Daniel Evans, supt. Fax 789-8056
www.jpsk12.org/
Jackson HS 1,500/9-12
544 Wildwood Ave 49201 517-841-3700
Barbara Baird-Pauli, prin. Fax 768 5910
MS at Parkside 800/6-8
2400 4th St 49203 517-841-2300
William Patterson, prin. Fax 768-5968
Wilson Academy 300/Alt
310 W Morrell St 49203 517-841-2800
Deven Moore, prin. Fax 783-3582

Napoleon Community SD
Supt. — See Napoleon
Ackerson Lake Community Center 50/Alt
4126 Brooklyn Rd 49201 517-905-5701
Chris Adams, admin. Fax 764-0265

Northwest Community SD 2,800/PK-12
4000 Van Horn Rd 49201 517-817-4700
Geoff Bontrager, supt. Fax 569-2395
www.nwschools.org/
Kidder MS 700/6-8
6700 Rives Junction Rd 49201 517-817-4703
Dan Brooks, prin. Fax 569-2931
Northwest Alternative HS 100/Alt
4100 Van Horn Rd 49201 517-517-4702
Paul Scholz, prin. Fax 569-2870
Northwest HS 900/9-12
4200 Van Horn Rd 49201 517-817-4701
Scott Buchler, prin. Fax 569-2935

Vandercook Lake SD 1,300/K-12
1000 E Golf Ave 49203 517-782-9044
Anthony Hollow, supt. Fax 788-3690
www.vandyschools.org
Vandercook Lake JSHS 700/6-12
1000 E Golf Ave 49203 517-782-8167
Mark Schonhard, prin. Fax 782-3730

Western SD
Supt. — See Parma
Woodville Community Center 200/Alt
3950 Catherine St 49203 517-841-8700
Deborah Batchelder, prin. Fax 841-8807

Baker College of Jackson Post-Sec.
2800 Springport Rd 49202 517-788-7800
Jackson Catholic MS 200/7-8
915 Cooper St 49202 517-784-3385
Anthony Shaughnessy, prin. Fax 782-7883
Jackson Christian MSHS 100/6-12
4200 Lowe Rd 49203 517-783-2658
Todd Barney, prin. Fax 783-4235
Jackson Community College Post-Sec.
2111 Emmons Rd 49201 517-787-0800
Jackson Community College Post-Sec.
3610 Wildwood Ave 49202 517-787-7012
Lumen Christi HS 700/9-12
3483 Spring Arbor Rd 49203 517-787-0630
Christopher Smith, prin. Fax 787-1066

Jenison, Ottawa, Pop. 16,336
Jenison SD 4,500/PK-12
8375 20th Ave 49428 616-457-8890
Thomas TenBrink, supt. Fax 457-8898
www.jpsonline.org/
Jenison HS 1,500/9-12
2140 Bauer Rd 49428 616-457-3400
Dr. Brandon Graham, prin. Fax 457-4070
Jenison JHS 600/7-8
8295 20th Ave 49428 616-457-1402
Brett Cataldo, prin. Fax 457-8090

Johannesburg, Otsego
Johannesburg-Lewiston Area SD 800/K-12
PO Box 69 49751 989-732-1773
Frederick Holt, supt. Fax 732-6556
www.jlas.org
Johannesburg-Lewiston HS 200/9-12
PO Box 69 49751 989-731-4420
Curt Chrencik, prin. Fax 732-6556

Jonesville, Hillsdale, Pop. 2,240
Jonesville Community SD 1,500/PK-12
202 Wright St 49250 517-849-9075
Chellie Broesamle, supt. Fax 849-2434
www.jonesvilleschools.org
Jonesville HS 400/9-12
460 Adrian Rd 49250 517-849-9934
Dustin Scharer, prin. Fax 849-2755
Jonesville MS 300/6-8
401 E Chicago St 49250 517-849-3210
Bryan Playford, prin. Fax 849-3213
Phoenix Alternative S 100/Alt
401 E Chicago St 49250 517-849-7304
Bryan Playford, prin. Fax 849-3213

Kalamazoo, Kalamazoo, Pop. 71,183
Comstock SD 2,200/PK-12
3010 Gull Rd 49048 269-250-8900
Todd Mora, supt. Fax 250-8901
www.comstockps.org
Comstock Compass HS 200/Alt
3010 Gull Rd 49048 269-250-8930
Jay Birchmeier, prin. Fax 250-8931
Comstock HS 600/9-12
2107 N 26th St 49048 269-250-8700
Matthew Montange, prin. Fax 250-8701
Comstock Northeast MS 500/6-8
1423 N 28th St 49048 269-250-8600
Kelley Howard, prin. Fax 250-8601
Adult Education Adult
3010 Gull Rd 49048 269-250-8930
Jay Birchmeier, prin. Fax 250-8931

Kalamazoo RESA
Supt. — See Portage
Valley Center S 50/Alt
3122 Lake St 49048 269-388-9494
Fax 382-8546
Young Adult Program Adult
4606 Croyden Ave 49006 269-250-9600
Deborah Wild, prin. Fax 250-9601

Kalamazoo SD 12,000/K-12
1220 Howard St 49008 269-337-0100
Michael Rice, supt. Fax 337-0149
www.kalamazoopublicschools.com
Alternative Learning Program Alt
1340 Cobb Ave 49007 269-337-0540
Vincent Hodge, prin. Fax 337-1652
Central HS 1,700/9-12
2432 N Drake Rd 49006 269-337-0300
Fax 337-0391
Hillside MS 500/6-8
1941 Alamo Ave 49006 269-337-0570
Scott Millin, prin. Fax 337-1618
Linden Grove MS 800/6-8
4241 Arboretum Pkwy 49006 269-337-1740
Craig McCane, prin. Fax 337-1614
Maple Magnet MS 700/6-8
922 W Maple St 49008 269-337-0730
Fax 337-1633

Milwood Magnet MS 700/6-8
2916 Konkle St 49001 269-337-0670
Craig LeSuer, prin. Fax 337-1628
Norrix HS 1,300/9-12
606 E Kilgore Rd 49001 269-337-0200
Johnny Edwards, prin. Fax 337-1617
Phoenix HS 100/Alt
1411 Oakland Dr 49008 269-337-0760
Mark Hill, prin. Fax 337-1756
Adult Education Program Adult
714 S Westnedge Ave 49007 269-337-0446
Theresa Jacobson, dir. Fax 337-0490

Parchment SD
Supt. — See Parchment
Barclay Hills Education Center Adult
1125 E Mosel Ave 49004 269-488-1470
Kares Hanley, prin. Fax 488-1480

Davenport University Post-Sec.
4123 W Main St 49006 269-382-2835
Everest Institute Post-Sec.
5177 W Main St 49009 269-381-9616
Heritage Christian Academy 300/PK-12
6312 Quail Run Dr 49009 269-372-1400
Jerry Stayton, admin. Fax 372-6018
Kalamazoo Christian HS 300/9-12
2121 Stadium Dr 49008 269-381-2250
B.J. Huizenga, prin. Fax 381-0319
Kalamazoo Christian MS 200/6-8
3333 S Westnedge Ave 49008 269-343-3645
Marc Verkaik, prin. Fax 343-4649
Kalamazoo College Post-Sec.
1200 Academy St 49006 269-337-7000
Kalamazoo Junior Academy 50/K-10
1601 Nichols Rd 49006 269-342-8943
William Crawford, prin. Fax 342-1459
Kalamazoo Valley Community College Post-Sec.
PO Box 4070 49003 269-488-4400
Msgr. Hackett HS 300/9-12
1000 W Kilgore Rd 49008 269-381-2646
Tim Eastman, prin. Fax 381-3919
Western Michigan University Post-Sec.
1903 W Michigan Ave 49008 269-387-1000
West Michigan Coll of Barbering & Beauty Post-Sec.
3200 S Westnedge Ave Ste 1 49008 269-381-4424

Kalkaska, Kalkaska, Pop. 1,989
Kalkaska SD 1,500/PK-12
PO Box 580 49646 231-258-9109
Lee Sandy, supt. Fax 258-4474
www.kpschools.com/
Kalkaska HS 500/9-12
PO Box 580 49646 231-258-9167
Dale Kasza, prin. Fax 258-5188
Kalkaska MS 300/6-8
PO Box 580 49646 231-258-4040
Diane Swoverland, prin. Fax 258-3576
Northside Educational Center 100/Alt
PO Box 580 49646 231-258-5140
Brian Harbour, prin. Fax 258-4940

Kent City, Kent, Pop. 1,047
Kent City Community SD 1,300/PK-12
200 N Clover St 49330 616-678-7714
Mike Weiler, supt. Fax 678-4320
www.kentcityschools.org
Kent City HS 400/9-12
351 N Main St 49330 616-678-4210
Bill Crane, prin. Fax 678-4371
Kent City MS 300/6-8
285 N Main St 49330 616-678-4214
Bill Crane, prin. Fax 678-5099

Algoma Christian S 200/PK-12
PO Box 220 49330 616-678-7480
Terry Yoder, supt. Fax 678-7484

Kentwood, Kent, Pop. 47,105
Kentwood SD 8,500/PK-12
5820 Eastern Ave SE 49508 616-455-4400
Michael Zoerhoff, supt. Fax 455-4476
www.kentwoodps.org
Crestwood MS 600/6-8
2674 44th St SE 49512 616-455-1200
Omar Bakri, prin. Fax 455-2338
East Kentwood Freshman Campus HS 800/9-9
6170 Valley Lane Dr SE 49508 616-698-9292
Michele Siderman, prin. Fax 698-0313
East Kentwood HS 2,000/10-12
6230 Kalamazoo Ave SE 49508 616-698-6700
John Keenoy, prin. Fax 698-2384
Pinewood MS 700/6-8
2100 60th St SE 49508 616-455-1224
Gary Harmon, prin. Fax 455-2054
Valleywood MS 500/6-8
1110 50th St SE 49508 616-538-7670
Mindy Westra, prin. Fax 538-9301
Kentwood Community Education Adult
28 60th St SE 49548 616-261-6166
Rick Hatfield, prin. Fax 261-6170

Kimball, Saint Clair, Pop. 7,247

New Life Christian Academy 200/PK-12
5517 Griswold Rd 48074 810-367-3770
Lee Ann Shimmel, admin. Fax 367-2249

Kinde, Huron, Pop. 445
North Huron SD 400/K-12
21 Main St 48445 989-874-4100
Martin Prout, supt. Fax 874-4109
www.nhuron.org
North Huron JSHS 300/6-12
21 Main St 48445 989-874-4101
Tanya Kramer, prin. Fax 874-4129

Kingsford, Dickinson, Pop. 5,077
Breitung Township SD 1,700/PK-12
2000 W Pyle Dr 49802 906-779-2650
Craig Allen, supt. Fax 779-7703
www.kingsford.org
Kingsford HS 600/9-12
431 Hamilton Ave 49802 906-779-2670
Lyle Smithson, prin. Fax 779-2883
Kingsford MS 400/6-8
445 Hamilton Ave 49802 906-779-2680
David Holmes, prin. Fax 774-1354

Dickinson-Iron ISD 50/
1074 Pyle Dr 49802 906-779-2690
Wendy Warmuth, supt. Fax 779-2669
www.diisd.org
Dickinson-Iron Tech Educ Center Vo/Tech
300 North Blvd 49802 906-779-2697
Paul Bonsall, prin. Fax 779-2087

Kingsley, Grand Traverse, Pop. 1,450
Kingsley Area SD 1,500/K-12
402 Fenton St 49649 231-263-5261
Keith Smith, supt. Fax 263-5282
www.kingsley.k12.mi.us
Kingsley Area HS 500/9-12
402 Fenton St 49649 231-263-5262
Mike Moran, prin. Fax 263-3813
Kingsley Area MS 500/5-8
402 Fenton St 49649 231-263-5262
Vaughn White, prin. Fax 263-4623

Kingston, Tuscola, Pop. 436
Kingston Community SD 600/PK-12
5790 State St 48741 989-683-2294
Matthew Drake, supt. Fax 683-3318
www.kingston.k12.mi.us
Kingston JSHS 300/7-12
5790 State St 48741 989-683-2550
Matthew Drake, supt. Fax 683-2712

Laingsburg, Shiawassee, Pop. 1,260
Laingsburg Community SD 1,300/PK-12
205 S Woodhull Rd 48848 517-651-2705
Matthew Shastal, supt. Fax 651-9075
www.laingsburg.k12.mi.us/
Laingsburg HS 400/9-12
8008 Woodbury Rd 48848 517-651-5091
Christian Morales, prin. Fax 651-9621
Laingsburg MS 300/6-8
112 High St 48848 517-651-5034
Brian Doepker, prin. Fax 651-6213

Lake City, Missaukee, Pop. 830
Lake City Area SD 1,100/K-12
PO Box 900 49651 231-839-4333
Kim Blaszak, supt. Fax 839-5219
www.lakecityschools.net
Lake City HS 400/9-12
PO Box 900 49651 231-839-4331
Tim Peterson, prin. Fax 839-6031
Lake City MS 200/6-8
PO Box 900 49651 231-839-7163
Dave Swanson, prin. Fax 839-6042

Lake Leelanau, Leelanau, Pop. 250

St. Mary S 200/PK-12
PO Box 340 49653 231-256-9636
Megan Glynn, prin. Fax 256-7239

Lake Linden, Houghton, Pop. 992
Lake Linden-Hubbell SD 500/K-12
601 Calumet St 49945 906-296-6211
Craig Sundblad, supt. Fax 296-0943
www.lakelinden.k12.mi.us
Lake Linden Hubbell JSHS 200/7-12
601 Calumet St 49945 906-296-6681
Craig Sundblad, prin. Fax 296-0219

Lake Odessa, Ionia, Pop. 1,980
Lakewood SD
Supt. — See Woodland
Lakewood HS 700/9-12
7223 Velte Rd 48849 616-374-8868
Brian Williams, prin. Fax 374-1477

Lake Orion, Oakland, Pop. 2,917
Lake Orion Community SD 7,700/K-12
315 N Lapeer St 48362 248-693-5400
Marion Ginopolis, supt. Fax 693-5466
www.lakeorion.k12.mi.us/
Lake Orion Community HS 2,500/9-12
495 E Scripps Rd 48360 248-693-5420
Stephen Hawley, prin. Fax 693-5459
Scripps MS 700/6-8
385 E Scripps Rd 48360 248-693-5440
Dan Haas, prin. Fax 693-5301
Waldon MS 600/6-8
2509 Waldon Rd 48360 248-391-1100
Randy Groya, prin. Fax 391-5452
Other Schools – See Oakland

Lake Orion Baptist S 100/K-12
255 E Scripps Rd 48360 248-693-6203
Tony Bryson, prin. Fax 693-6177

Lakeview, Montcalm, Pop. 988
Lakeview Community SD 1,100/PK-12
123 5th St 48850 989-352-6226
Kyle Hamlin, supt. Fax 352-8245
www.lakeviewschools.net
Lakeview HS 500/8-12
9800 Youngman Rd 48850 989-352-7221
Gary Jensen, prin. Fax 352-6320

LAnse, Baraga, Pop. 1,920
L'Anse Area SD 700/K-12
201 N 4th St 49946 906-524-6000
Ray Pasquali, supt. Fax 524-6001
www.lanseschools.org/
L'Anse JSHS 400/7-12
201 N 4th St 49946 906-524-6122
Carrie Meyer, prin. Fax 524-0345

Lansing, Ingham, Pop. 108,750
Lansing SD 8,900/PK-12
519 W Kalamazoo St 48933 517-755-1000
Yvonne Carmel Canul, supt. Fax 755-2009
www.lansingschools.net/
Eastern HS 1,300/7-12
220 N Pennsylvania Ave 48912 517-755-1050
Susan Land, prin. Fax 755-1059
Everett HS 1,400/9-12
3900 Stabler St 48910 517-755-1080
Norman Gear, prin. Fax 755-1089
Sexton HS 700/7-12
102 Mcpherson Ave 48915 517-755-1070
Dr. Sandra Noecker, prin. Fax 755-1079

Waverly Community SD 2,400/PK-12
515 Snow Rd 48917 517-321-7265
Terry Urquhart, supt. Fax 321-8577
www.waverlycommunityschools.net
Waverly HS 1,100/9-12
160 Snow Rd 48917 517-323-3831
Troy Lindley, prin. Fax 323-7714
Waverly MS 500/7-8
620 Snow Rd 48917 517-321-7240
Michael Moreno, prin. Fax 321-5789

American Hotel/Lodging Educational Inst Post-Sec.
2113 N High St 48906 800-390-8399
Career Quest Learning Center Post-Sec.
3215 S Pennsylvania Ave 48910 517-318-3330
Davenport University Post-Sec.
220 E Kalamazoo St 48933 517-484-2600
Greater Lansing Adventist S 100/PK-10
5330 W St Joe Hwy 48917 517-321-5565
Judy Shull, prin. Fax 321-5580
Great Lakes Christian College Post-Sec.
6211 W Willow Hwy 48917 517-321-0242
Lansing Catholic Central HS 500/9-12
501 Marshall St 48912 517-267-2100
Thomas Maloney, prin. Fax 267-2135
Lansing Christian S 600/PK-12
3405 Belle Chase Way 48911 517-882-5779
Fax 882-5849
Lansing Community College Post-Sec.
PO Box 40010 48901 517-483-1957
New Covenant Christian S 100/PK-12
PO Box 80737 48908 517-323-8903
Fred McGlone, prin. Fax 323-0421
Ross Medical Education Center Post-Sec.
4106 W Saginaw Hwy 48917 517-703-9044
Thomas M. Cooley Law School Post-Sec.
PO Box 13038 48901 517-371-5140

Lapeer, Lapeer, Pop. 8,708
Lapeer Community SD 4,600/PK-12
250 2nd St 48446 810-667-2401
Matthew Wandrie, supt. Fax 667-2411
www.lapeerschools.org
Lapeer Community HS 100/Alt
1220 Lake Nepessing Rd 48446 810-667-2453
Kevin Walters, prin. Fax 667-2412
Lapeer East HS 1,100/9-12
933 S Saginaw St 48446 810-667-2418
Scott Roper, prin. Fax 667-2422
Lapeer West HS 1,100/9-12
170 Millville Rd 48446 810-667-2423
Tim Zeeman, prin. Fax 667-2428
Rolland-Warner MS 6-8
3145 W Genesee St 48446 810-538-2334
Jennifer Taylor, prin. Fax 538-3250
Zemmer MS 500/6-8
1920 W Oregon St 48446 810-667-2413
Matt Olson, prin. Fax 667-2483

Lapeer County ISD 50/
1996 W Oregon St 48446 810-664-5917
Steven Zott, supt. Fax 664-1011
www.lcisd.k12.mi.us
Other Schools – See Attica

Health Enrichment Center Post-Sec.
204 E Nepessing St 48446 810-667-9453

Lathrup Village, Oakland, Pop. 3,943
Southfield SD
Supt. — See Southfield
Southfield-Lathrup HS 1,200/9-12
19301 W 12 Mile Rd 48076 248-746-7200
Joseph Spryszak, prin. Fax 746-7488

Lawrence, Van Buren, Pop. 973
Lawrence SD 700/PK-12
650 W Saint Joseph St 49064 269-674-8233
John Overley, supt. Fax 674-8206
www.lawrencetigers.com
Lawrence JSHS 300/7-12
650 W Saint Joseph St 49064 269-674-8232
Duane Fish, prin. Fax 674-8206

Van Buren ISD 50/
490 S Paw Paw St 49064 269-674-8091
Jeffrey Mills, supt. Fax 674-8030
www.vbisd.org/
Van Buren Technology Center Vo/Tech
250 South St 49064 269-674-8091
Fax 674-8954

Lawton, Van Buren, Pop. 1,870
Lawton Community SD 1,000/PK-12
101 Primary Way 49065 269-624-7900
Joseph Trimboli Ed.D., supt. Fax 624-6489
www.lawtoncs.org
Lawton Accelerated Academic Center 50/Alt
101 Primary Way 49065 269-624-7542
Tamara Webster M.Ed., admin.

Lawton HS 300/9-12
101 Primary Way 49065 269-624-7840
Tammy Wilson, prin. Fax 624-6554
Lawton MS 300/6-8
101 Primary Way 49065 269-624-7610
Tim Cerven, prin. Fax 624-5206

Leland, Leelanau, Pop. 377
Leland SD 500/K-12
PO Box 498 49654 231-256-9857
Jason Stowe, supt. Fax 256-9844
www.lelandpublicschools.com
Leland S 500/K-12
PO Box 498 49654 231-256-9857
Charles Gann, prin. Fax 256-9844

LeRoy, Osceola, Pop. 252
Pine River Area SD 800/K-12
17445 Pine River Rd 49655 231-829-3141
Jim Ganger, supt. Fax 829-4410
www.pineriver.org/
Pine River Area HS 400/8-12
17445 Pine River Rd 49655 231-829-3841
Kim Miller, prin. Fax 829-5227

Leslie, Ingham, Pop. 1,824
Leslie SD 1,400/K-12
4141 Hull Rd 49251 517-589-8200
Jeff Manthei, supt. Fax 589-5340
www.lesliek12.net/
Leslie HS 400/9-12
4141 Hull Rd 49251 517-589-9500
Andrew Rogers, prin. Fax 589-5720
Leslie MS 400/5-8
400 Kimball St 49251 517-589-8218
Carol Franz, prin. Fax 589-5714

Lincoln, Alcona, Pop. 335
Alcona Community SD 800/PK-12
PO Box 249 48742 989-736-6212
Shawn Thornton, supt. Fax 736-6261
www.alconaschools.net/
Alcona JSHS 500/7-12
PO Box 249 48742 989-736-8534
Terrence Allison, prin. Fax 736-8495

Lincoln Park, Wayne, Pop. 37,338
Lincoln Park SD 4,100/K-12
1650 Champaign Rd 48146 313-389-0200
Richard Rockwell, supt. Fax 389-1322
www.lincolnparkpublicschools.com
Lincoln Park HS 1,300/9-12
1701 Champaign Rd 48146 313-389-0234
Eric Calvin, prin. Fax 383-5738
Lincoln Park MS 700/6-8
2800 Lafayette Blvd 48146 313-389-0757
Tara Randall, prin. Fax 389-0761

Linden, Genesee, Pop. 3,937
Lake Fenton Community SD
Supt. — See Fenton
Lake Fenton HS 500/9-12
4070 Lahring Rd 48451 810-591-9591
Todd Reynolds, prin. Fax 591-9495

Linden Community SD 3,200/PK-12
7205 Silver Lake Rd 48451 810-591-0980
Edward Koledo, supt. Fax 591-5587
www.lindenschools.org
Linden HS 900/9-12
7201 Silver Lake Rd 48451 810-591-0410
Russ Ciesielski, prin. Fax 591-8014
Linden MS 700/6-8
15425 Lobdell Rd 48451 810-591-0710
Julie Brown, prin. Fax 591-0155

Litchfield, Hillsdale, Pop. 1,359
Litchfield Community SD 300/K-12
210 Williams St 49252 517-542-2388
Anne Riddle, supt. Fax 542-2580
www.lcsmi.org
Litchfield JSHS 200/6-12
210 Williams St 49252 517-542-2386
Anne Riddle, prin. Fax 542-2703

Livonia, Wayne, Pop. 95,640
Clarenceville SD 1,800/PK-12
20210 Middlebelt Rd 48152 248-919-0400
Pamela Swert, supt. Fax 919-0430
www.clarenceville.k12.mi.us
Clarenceville HS 600/9-12
20155 Middlebelt Rd 48152 248-919-0408
Paul Shepich, prin. Fax 919-0438
Clarenceville MS 400/6-8
20210 Middlebelt Rd 48152 248-919-0406
Kathleen Guntzviller, prin. Fax 919-0436

Livonia SD 15,200/PK-12
15125 Farmington Rd 48154 734-744-2500
Dr. Randy Liepa, supt. Fax 744-2571
www.livoniapublicschools.org
Churchill HS 1,900/9-12
8900 Newburgh Rd 48150 734-744-2650
R. Joseph Anderson, prin. Fax 744-2652
Emerson MS 800/7-8
29100 W Chicago St 48150 734-744-2665
Ann Owen, prin. Fax 744-2667
Franklin HS 1,700/9-12
31000 Joy Rd 48150 734-744-2655
Daniel Willenborg, prin. Fax 744-2657
Frost MS 800/7-8
14041 Stark Rd 48154 734-744-2670
Christina Berry, prin. Fax 744-2672
Holmes MS 800/7-8
16200 Newburgh Rd 48154 734-744-2675
Eric Stromberg, prin. Fax 744-2677
Livonia Career/Technical Center Vo/Tech
8985 Newburgh Rd 48150 734-744-2816
Dr. Janet Haas, prin. Fax 744-2817
Stevenson HS 2,100/9-12
33500 6 Mile Rd 48152 734-744-2660
James Gibbons, prin. Fax 744-2662

Other Schools – See Westland

Davenport University Post-Sec.
19499 Victor Pkwy 48152 734-943-2800
Ladywood HS 400/9-12
14680 Newburgh Rd 48154 734-591-1544
Joan Fitzgerald, prin. Fax 591-4214
Madonna University Post-Sec.
36600 Schoolcraft Rd 48150 734-432-5300
Schoolcraft College Post-Sec.
18600 Haggerty Rd 48152 734-462-4400

Lowell, Kent, Pop. 3,710
Lowell Area SD 3,800/K-12
300 High St 49331 616-987-2500
Gregory Pratt, supt. Fax 987-2511
www.lowellschools.com/
Lowell HS 1,200/9-12
11700 Vergennes St 49331 616-987-2900
Amy Pallo, prin. Fax 987-2911
Lowell MS 900/6-8
750 Foreman St 49331 616-987-2800
Dan VanderMeulen, prin. Fax 987-2811
Unity Alternative S 50/Alt
300 High St 49331 616-987-2524
Amy Pallo, prin. Fax 987-2511

Ludington, Mason, Pop. 7,926
Ludington Area SD 2,200/PK-12
809 E Tinkham Ave 49431 231-845-7303
Andrea D. Large, supt. Fax 843-4930
www.lasd.net
DeJonge MS 400/6-8
706 E Tinkham Ave 49431 231-845-3810
Kristi Zimmerman, prin. Fax 845-3814
Ludington HS 700/9-12
508 N Washington Ave 49431 231-845-3880
Dale Horowski, prin. Fax 845-3881
Other Schools – See Scottville

Mason-Lake ISD 100/
2130 W US Highway 10 49431 231-757-3716
Lawrence Lloyd, supt. Fax 757-2406
www.mloisd.org
Mason-Lake-Oceana Math Science Center Alt
2130 W US Highway 10 49431 231-757-3716
Kathy Surd, dir. Fax 757-4208
Other Schools – See Scottville

Mc Bain, Missaukee, Pop. 651
McBain Rural Agricultural SD 1,100/PK-12
107 E Maple St 49657 231-825-2165
Michael Harris, supt. Fax 825-2119
main.mcbain.org/
Mc Bain HS 400/9-12
107 E Maple St 49657 231-825-2412
Joel Bronkema, prin. Fax 825-2119
Mc Bain MS 300/5-8
107 E Maple St 49657 231-825-8041
Kim VanderVlucht, prin. Fax 825-2119

Northern Michigan Christian S 300/PK-12
128 S Martin St 49657 231-825-2492
Rick Klooster, supt. Fax 825-2371

Mackinac Island, Mackinac, Pop. 466
Mackinac Island SD 100/K-12
PO Box 340 49757 906-847-3377
David Waaso, supt. Fax 847-3773
mackinac.eup.k12.mi.us
Mackinac Island S 100/K-12
PO Box 340 49757 906-847-3377
David Waaso, admin. Fax 847-3773

Mackinaw City, Emmet, Pop. 794
Mackinaw City SD 200/PK-12
609 W Central Ave 49701 231-436-8211
Jeffrey Curth, supt. Fax 436-5434
www.mackcity.k12.mi.us
Mackinaw City S 200/PK-12
609 W Central Ave 49701 231-436-8211
Jeffrey Curth, supt. Fax 436-5434

Macomb, Macomb, Pop. 22,714
Chippewa Valley SD
Supt. — See Clinton Township
Dakota HS 1,800/10-12
21051 21 Mile Rd 48044 586-723-2702
Paul Sibley, prin. Fax 723-2701
Dakota Ninth Grade Center 9-9
21055 21 Mile Rd 48044 586-723-3300
Kim Voss, prin. Fax 723-3301
Iroquois MS 1,000/6-8
48301 Romeo Plank Rd 48044 586-723-3700
James Capoferi, prin. Fax 723-3701
Seneca MS 1,300/6-8
47200 Heydenreich Rd 48044 586-723-3900
Todd Distelrath, prin. Fax 723-3901

L'Anse Creuse SD
Supt. — See Clinton Township
L'Anse Creuse HS - North 1,900/9-12
23700 21 Mile Rd 48042 586-493-5270
Greg Dixon, prin. Fax 493-5275
L'Anse Creuse MS North 700/6-8
46201 Fairchild Rd 48042 586-493-5260
John Da Via, prin. Fax 493-5265

Lutheran HS North 600/9-12
16825 24 Mile Rd 48042 586-781-9151
John Reincke, prin. Fax 781-8673

Madison Heights, Oakland, Pop. 28,913
Lamphere SD 2,800/K-12
31201 Dorchester Ave 48071 248-589-1990
Marsha Pando, supt. Fax 589-2618
www.lamphere.k12.mi.us
Lamphere HS 800/9-12
610 W 13 Mile Rd 48071 248-589-3943
Greg Fuller, prin. Fax 589-0240
Page MS 600/6-8
29615 Tawas St 48071 248-589-3428
Douglas Kelley, prin. Fax 545-1870

Madison SD 1,400/K-12
26524 John R Rd 48071 248-399-7800
Randy Seck, supt. Fax 399-2229
www.madisonschools.k12.mi.us/
Madison HS 500/9-12
915 E 11 Mile Rd 48071 248-548-1800
A. Christian Morales, prin. Fax 548-9758
Madison Preparatory HS 200/Alt
27107 Hales St 48071 248-543-5465
Leslie Renne-Kegebein, prin. Fax 543-5844
Wilkinson MS 300/6-8
26524 John R Rd 48071 248-399-0455
Matt Karaffa, prin. Fax 399-1965

Bishop Foley HS 500/9-12
32000 Campbell Rd 48071 248-585-1210
Patricia Domagala, prin. Fax 585-3667
Dorsey School of Business Post-Sec.
30821 Barrington St 48071 248-588-9660
Ross Medical Education Center Post-Sec.
29429 John R Rd 48071 248-548-4389

Mancelona, Antrim, Pop. 1,339
Mancelona SD 1,000/PK-12
PO Box 739 49659 231-587-9764
Jeffery DiRosa, supt. Fax 587-9500
www.mancelonaschools.org/
Mancelona HS 300/9-12
PO Box 739 49659 231-587-8551
Gerald Clark, prin. Fax 587-5401
Mancelona MS 300/5-8
PO Box 739 49659 231-587-9869
Chad Culver, prin. Fax 587-0615

Manchester, Washtenaw, Pop. 2,074
Manchester Community SD 1,200/K-12
410 City Rd 48158 734-428-9711
Cherie Vannatter, supt. Fax 428-9188
www.mcs.k12.mi.us
Manchester HS 400/9-12
20500 Dutch Dr 48158 734-428-7333
Kevin Mowrer, prin. Fax 428-0178
Manchester MS 400/5-8
710 E Main St 48158 734-428-7442
Shanna Spickard, prin. Fax 428-9264

Manistee, Manistee, Pop. 6,070
Manistee Area SD 1,000/PK-12
550 Maple St 49660 231-723-3521
John Chandler, supt. Fax 723-1507
www.honoredstudents.org
Manistee JSHS 500/7-12
525 12th St 49660 231-723-2547
Andy Huber, prin. Fax 398-9277

Manistee Catholic Central S 200/PK-12
1200 US Highway 31 S 49660 231-723-2529
Jan Bigalke, prin. Fax 723-0669

Manistique, Schoolcraft, Pop. 2,986
Manistique Area SD 900/K-12
100 N Cedar St 49854 906-341-4300
Kathy McDonough, supt. Fax 341-2374
www.manistique.k12.mi.us
Manistique HS 300/9-12
100 N Cedar St 49854 906-341-4300
John Shiner, prin. Fax 341-8473
Manistique MS 200/6-8
100 N Cedar St 49854 906-341-4300
John Shiner, prin. Fax 341-8473

Manton, Wexford, Pop. 1,266
Manton Consolidated SD 1,000/K-12
105 5th St 49663 231-824-6411
J. Mark Parsons, supt. Fax 824-4101
www.mantonschools.org
Manton HS 300/9-12
105 5th St 49663 231-824-6411
Char Siddall, prin. Fax 824-6114
Manton MS 300/5-8
105 5th St 49663 231-824-6401
Ryan Hiller, prin. Fax 824-4121

Maple City, Leelanau, Pop. 204
Glen Lake Community SD 800/K-12
3375 W Burdickville Rd 49664 231-334-3061
Joan Groening, supt. Fax 334-6255
www.glenlake.k12.mi.us
Glen Lake JSHS 400/7-12
3375 W Burdickville Rd 49664 231-334-3061
Konrad Molter, prin. Fax 334-6295

Marcellus, Cass, Pop. 1,184
Marcellus Community SD 600/K-12
PO Box 48 49067 269-646-7655
Ronald Herron, supt. Fax 646-2700
www.marcelluscs.org/
Marcellus JSHS 200/5-12
PO Box 48 49067 269-646-5081
Nanette Pauley, prin. Fax 646-5021
Other Schools – See Decatur

Howardsville Christian S 200/PK-12
53441 Bent Rd 49067 269-646-9367
Ric Gilson, admin. Fax 646-7006

Marine City, Saint Clair, Pop. 4,184
East China SD
Supt. — See East China
Marine City HS 700/9-12
1085 Ward St 48039 810-676-1900
William Jedele, prin. Fax 676-1925
Marine City MS 500/6-8
6373 King Rd 48039 810-676-1201
Catherine Woolman, prin. Fax 676-1225

Riverview East HS 100/Alt
6373 King Rd 48039 810-676-1280
Nina Reznich, prin. Fax 676-1285

Cardinal Mooney HS 200/9-12
660 S Water St 48039 810-765-8825
Celeste Conflitti, prin. Fax 765-7164

Marion, Osceola, Pop. 863
Marion SD 500/K-12
PO Box O 49665 231-743-2486
Mort Meier, supt. Fax 743-2890
www.marion.k12.mi.us
Marion JSHS 300/7-12
PO Box O 49665 231-743-2836
Beth Robb, prin. Fax 743-9622

Marlette, Sanilac, Pop. 1,847
Marlette Community SD 1,100/K-12
6230 Euclid St 48453 989-635-7429
Jeriann Patterson, supt. Fax 635-7103
www.marlette.k12.mi.us/
Marlette JSHS 500/7-12
3051 Moore St 48453 989-635-4946
Kyle Wood, prin. Fax 635-5300

Marquette, Marquette, Pop. 20,996
Marquette Area SD 3,000/K-12
1201 W Fair Ave 49855 906-225-4200
William Saunders, supt. Fax 225-5340
www.mapsnet.org
Bothwell MS 900/5-8
1200 Tierney St 49855 906-225-4262
Dan Gannon, prin. Fax 225-4229
Marquette Alternative HS 100/Alt
611 N Front St 49855 906-225-4302
Andrew Crunkleton, admin. Fax 225-4282
Marquette HS 1,000/9-12
1203 W Fair Ave 49855 906-225-4254
Robert Anthony, prin. Fax 225-5370

Father Marquette MS 100/5-8
414 W College Ave 49855 906-226-7912
Maryann Ferns, prin. Fax 225-9962
Marquette General Hospital Post-Sec.
420 W Magnetic St 49855 906-225-3434
Northern Michigan University Post-Sec.
1401 Presque Isle Ave 49855 906-227-1000

Marshall, Calhoun, Pop. 6,978
Calhoun ISD 400/
17111 G Dr N 49068 269-781-5141
Terance Lunger, supt. Fax 781-7071
www.calhounisd.org
Other Schools – See Battle Creek

Marshall SD 2,200/PK-12
100 E Green St 49068 269-781-1257
Dr. Randy Davis, supt. Fax 789-1813
www.marshall.k12.mi.us/
Marshall HS 700/9-12
701 N Marshall Ave 49068 269-781-1252
Daniel Luciani, prin. Fax 781-5304
Marshall MS 500/6-8
100 E Green St 49068 269-781-1251
David Turner, prin. Fax 781-6621
Other Schools – See Albion

Martin, Allegan, Pop. 398
Martin SD 600/PK-12
PO Box 241 49070 269-672-7194
William Miller, supt. Fax 672-7116
www.martinpublicschools.org
Martin JSHS 300/7-12
PO Box 241 49070 269-672-5555
Rich Okoniewski, prin. Fax 672-9263

Marysville, Saint Clair, Pop. 9,889
Marysville SD 2,700/K-12
495 E Huron Blvd 48040 810-364-7731
James Cain, supt. Fax 364-3150
www.marysvilleschools.us/
Marysville HS 800/9-12
555 E Huron Blvd 48040 810-364-7161
Bill Farnsworth, prin. Fax 364-8878
Marysville MS 600/6-8
400 Collard Dr 48040 810-364-6336
John Sazehn, prin. Fax 364-4456

St. Clair County RESA 50/
PO Box 1500 48040 810-364-8990
Dan DeGrow, supt. Fax 364-7474
www.sccresa.org/
Career Technical Center Vo/Tech
PO Box 1500 48040 810-455-1010

Mason, Ingham, Pop. 8,111
Ingham ISD 100/
2630 W Howell Rd 48854 517-676-1051
Stanley Kogut, supt. Fax 676-1277
www.inghamisd.org
Capital Area Career Center Vo/Tech
611 Hagadorn Rd 48854 517-244-1330
Jeffrey Bohl, prin. Fax 676-3602

Mason SD 2,900/K-12
400 S Cedar St 48854 517-676-2484
Mark Dillingham, supt. Fax 676-6058
www.mason.k12.mi.us/
Mason HS 1,000/9-12
1001 S Barnes St 48854 517-676-9055
Lance Delbridge, prin. Fax 244-6412
Mason MS 700/6-8
235 Temple St 48854 517-676-6514
Daniel McConeghy, prin. Fax 676-0287

Mattawan, Van Buren, Pop. 1,954
Mattawan Consolidated SD 3,800/K-12
56720 Murray St 49071 269-668-3361
Patrick Bird Ph.D., supt. Fax 668-2372
www.mattawanschools.org/
Mattawan HS 1,200/9-12
56720 Murray St 49071 269-668-3361
Colin Ripmaster, prin. Fax 668-8245
Mattawan MS 1,000/6-8
56720 Murray St 49071 269-668-3361
Chip Schuman, prin. Fax 668-3188

Mayville, Tuscola, Pop. 933
Mayville Community SD 700/PK-12
6250 Fulton St 48744 989-843-6115
Rhonda Blackburn, supt. Fax 843-6988
www.mayville.k12.mi.us
Mayville HS 300/9-12
6250 Fulton St 48744 989-843-6115
Christopher Kidd, prin. Fax 843-7208
Mayville MS 100/7-8
6210 Fulton St 48744 989-843-6115
Christopher Kidd, prin. Fax 843-7209

Melvindale, Wayne, Pop. 10,396
Melvindale-Northern Allen Park SD 2,700/K-12
18530 Prospect St 48122 313-389-3300
Cora Kelly, supt. Fax 389-3312
www.melnap.k12.mi.us
Melvindale HS 900/9-12
18656 Prospect St 48122 313-389-3320
Shannon Luppino, prin. Fax 389-2072
Strong MS 600/6-8
3303 Oakwood Blvd 48122 313-389-3330
Dr. Kim Soranno-Bond, prin. Fax 389-2077

Memphis, Saint Clair, Pop. 1,172
Memphis Community SD 1,000/K-12
PO Box 201 48041 810-392-2151
Frank Johnson, supt. Fax 392-3614
www.memphisk12.org/
Memphis HS 300/9-12
PO Box 201 48041 810-392-2186
Brad Gudme, prin. Fax 392-2083
Memphis JHS 200/6-8
PO Box 201 48041 810-392-2131
Kenneth Reygaert, prin. Fax 392-2513

Mendon, Saint Joseph, Pop. 857
Mendon Community SD 700/K-12
148 Kirby Rd 49072 269-496-8491
Robert Kuhlman, supt. Fax 496-8234
www.mendonschools.org
Mendon HS 200/9-12
148 Kirby Rd 49072 269-496-8491
Marc Kramer, prin. Fax 496-8234
Mendon MS 200/6-8
148 Kirby Rd 49072 269-496-8491
Marc Kramer, prin. Fax 496-8234

Menominee, Menominee, Pop. 8,500
Menominee Area SD 1,500/PK-12
1230 13th St 49858 906-863-9951
Michael Cattani, supt. Fax 863-1171
www.menomineeschools.org
Menominee Alternative S 50/Alt
1230 13th St 49858 906-863-6990
William Paris, prin.
Menominee HS 600/9-12
2101 18th St 49858 906-863-7814
William Paris, prin. Fax 863-8883
Menominee JHS 200/7-8
2101 18th St 49858 906-863-9929
Alison Granquist, admin. Fax 863-8883

Merrill, Saginaw, Pop. 771
Merrill Community SD 800/PK-12
431 W Alice St 48637 989-643-7261
Sarah Kettelhohn, supt. Fax 643-5570
saginawmerrill.mi.schoolwebpages.com
Merrill HS 300/9-12
431 W Alice St 48637 989-643-7231
Christine Garno, prin. Fax 643-7942
Merrill MS 200/6-8
431 W Alice St 48637 989-643-7231
Christine Garno, prin. Fax 643-7942

Mesick, Wexford, Pop. 390
Mesick Consolidated SD 700/PK-12
PO Box 275 49668 231-885-1200
Mike Corey, supt. Fax 885-1234
www.mesick.org
Mesick JSHS 400/7-12
PO Box 275 49668 231-885-1201
Mike Corey, prin. Fax 885-2554

Michigan Center, Jackson, Pop. 4,596
Michigan Center SD 1,400/PK-12
400 S State St 49254 517-764-5778
Scott Koziol, supt. Fax 764-9607
www.mccardinals.org/
Michigan Center JSHS 700/7-12
400 S State St 49254 517-764-1440
Lisa Falasco, prin. Fax 764-3346

Middleton, Gratiot
Fulton SD 1,000/PK-12
8060 Ely Hwy 48856 989-236-7300
Daymond Grifka, supt. Fax 236-7660
fultonpirates.net
Fulton Alternative Education 200/Alt
8060 Ely Hwy 48856 989-236-5130
Philip Garcia, prin. Fax 236-7301
Fulton HS 200/9-12
8060 Ely Hwy 48856 989-236-7232
Paul Hungerford, prin. Fax 236-7628
Fulton MS 100/7-8
8060 Ely Hwy 48856 989-236-7232
Paul Hungerford, prin. Fax 236-7628

Middleville, Barry, Pop. 3,261
Thornapple-Kellogg SD 2,900/PK-12
10051 Green Lake Rd 49333 269-795-5521
Tom Enslen, supt. Fax 795-5401
www.tkschools.org/
Thornapple-Kellogg HS 900/9-12
3885 Bender Rd 49333 269-795-3394
Tony Koski, prin. Fax 795-5492
Thornapple-Kellogg MS 700/6-8
10375 Green Lake Rd 49333 269-795-3349
Mike Birely, prin. Fax 795-5455

Midland, Midland, Pop. 41,135
Bullock Creek SD 2,000/K-12
1420 S Badour Rd 48640 989-631-9022
Charles Schwedler, supt. Fax 631-2882
www.bcreek.k12.mi.us
Bullock Creek HS 600/9-12
1420 S Badour Rd 48640 989-631-2340
Todd Gorsuch, prin. Fax 835-5467
Bullock Creek MS 400/6-8
644 S Badour Rd 48640 989-631-9260
Shawn Hale, prin. Fax 832-4018

Midland SD 7,900/K-12
600 E Carpenter St 48640 989-923-5001
Michael Sharrow, supt. Fax 923-5003
www.mps.k12.mi.us
Dow HS 1,400/9-12
3901 N Saginaw Rd 48640 989-923-5382
Pam Kastl, prin. Fax 923-5301
Jefferson MS 800/6-8
800 W Chapel Ln 48640 989-923-5873
Steve Poole, prin. Fax 923-5800
Midland HS 1,600/9-12
1301 Eastlawn Dr 48642 989-923-5181
Janet Grief, prin. Fax 923-5100
Northeast MS 800/6-8
1305 E Sugnet Rd 48642 989-923-5772
Jeff Jaster, prin. Fax 923-5780

Calvary Baptist Academy 200/PK-12
6100 Perrine Rd 48640 989-832-3341
Michael Reece, admin. Fax 832-7443
Davenport University Post-Sec.
3555 E Patrick Rd 48642 989-835-5588
Northwood University Post-Sec.
4000 Whiting Dr 48640 989-837-4200

Milan, Monroe, Pop. 5,683
Milan Area SD 2,600/K-12
100 Big Red Dr 48160 734-439-5050
Bryan Girbach, supt. Fax 439-5083
www.milanareaschools.org/
Milan HS 1,000/9-12
200 Big Red Dr 48160 734-439-5000
Ryan McMahon, prin. Fax 439-5084
Milan MS 600/6-8
920 North St 48160 734-439-5200
David Schmittou, prin. Fax 439-5288

Milford, Oakland, Pop. 6,058
Huron Valley SD
Supt. — See Highland
Muir MS 600/6-8
425 George St 48381 248-684-8060
Martin Lindberg, prin. Fax 684-8068

West Highland Christian Academy 100/K-12
1116 S Hickory Ridge Rd 48380 248-887-6698
Jan Grimm, prin. Fax 887-4645

Millington, Tuscola, Pop. 1,059
Millington Community SD 1,100/K-12
8780 Dean Dr 48746 989-871-5227
John Males, supt. Fax 871-5260
www.mcsdistrict.com
Millington Accelerated Learning Center 50/Alt
8537 Gleason St 48746 989-871-5269
Jeffrey Yorke, admin. Fax 871-5249
Millington JSHS 500/7-12
8780 Dean Dr 48746 989-871-5221
Roger Bearss, prin. Fax 871-5244

Mio, Oscoda, Pop. 1,791
Mio-AuSable SD 600/K-12
1110 W 8th St 48647 989-826-2401
Gary Wood, supt. Fax 826-2415
www.mio.k12.mi.us
Mio-AuSable HS 200/9-12
1110 W 8th St 48647 989-826-2481
James Gendernalik, prin. Fax 826-2416
Mio-AuSable MS 200/6-8
1110 W 8th St 48647 989-826-2481
James Gendernalik, prin. Fax 826-2416

Monroe, Monroe, Pop. 20,187
Jefferson SD 2,100/PK-12
2400 N Dixie Hwy 48162 734-289-5550
Craig Haugen, supt. Fax 289-5574
www.jeffersonschools.org
Jefferson HS 700/9-12
5707 Williams Rd 48162 734-289-5555
David Vensel, prin. Fax 289-5595
Jefferson MS 300/7-8
5102 N Stoney Creek Rd 48162 734-289-5565
Stephen Kinsland, prin. Fax 289-5596

Monroe SD 6,500/PK-12
PO Box 733 48161 734-265-3000
Randall Monday, supt. Fax 265-3001
www.monroe.k12.mi.us
Monroe HS 2,000/9-12
901 Herr Rd 48161 734-265-3400
Matthew Cortez, prin. Fax 265-3401
Monroe MS 1,000/7-8
503 Washington St 48161 734-265-4000
Cindy Flynn, prin. Fax 265-4001
Orchard Center HS 200/Alt
1750 Oak St 48161 734-265-3700
Stephanie Cavanaugh, prin. Fax 265-3701

Meadow Montessori S 200/PK-12
1670 S Raisinville Rd 48161 734-241-9496
Catharine Calder, hdmstr. Fax 241-0829

Michigan College of Beauty — Post-Sec.
1020 S Monroe St 48161 — 734-241-8877
Monroe County Community College — Post-Sec.
1555 S Raisinville Rd 48161 — 734-242-7300
St. Mary HS — 400/9-12
108 W Elm Ave 48162 — 734-241-7662
Jenny Biler, prin. — Fax 241-9042
St. Mary S — 100/5-8
151 N Monroe St 48162 — 734-241-3377
Michelle Sontag, prin. — Fax 241-0497

Montague, Muskegon, Pop. 2,329
Montague Area SD — 1,300/PK-12
4882 Stanton Blvd 49437 — 231-893-1515
Nathan Robrahn, supt. — Fax 894-6586
www.montague.k12.mi.us
Chisholm MS — 300/6-8
4700 Stanton Blvd 49437 — 231-894-5617
Curt Hansen, prin. — Fax 894-5728
Montague HS — 400/9-12
4900 Stanton Blvd 49437 — 231-894-2661
Kevin Kruger, prin. — Fax 893-0609

Montrose, Genesee, Pop. 1,644
Montrose Community SD — 1,500/PK-12
PO Box 3129 48457 — 810-591-7267
Mark Kleinhans, supt. — Fax 591-7268
www.montrose.k12.mi.us
Hill-McCloy HS — 400/9-12
PO Box 3129 48457 — 810-591-8822
James Ply, prin. — Fax 591-7281
Kuehn-Haven MS — 500/5-8
PO Box 3129 48457 — 810-591-8832
Linden Bo Moore, prin. — Fax 591-7282
Montrose Choice S — 100/Alt
PO Box 3129 48457 — 810-591-8833
Linden Bo Moore, prin. — Fax 591-7289

Morenci, Lenawee, Pop. 2,192
Morenci Area SD — 700/PK-12
500 Page St 49256 — 517-458-7501
Dr. Michael Osborne, supt. — Fax 458-7821
www.morenci.k12.mi.us
Morenci HS — 200/9-12
788 Coomer St 49256 — 517-458-7502
Kelli Campbell, prin. — Fax 458-7146
Morenci MS — 200/5-8
304 Page St 49256 — 517-458-7506
Kelli Campbell, prin. — Fax 458-3379

Morley, Mecosta, Pop. 490
Morley Stanwood Community SD — 1,100/K-12
4700 Northland Dr 49336 — 231-856-4392
Roger Cole, supt. — Fax 856-4180
www.morleystanwood.org
Morley-Stanwood Alternative S — 50/Alt
151 7th St 49336 — 231-856-0410
James Nelson, prin. — Fax 856-0414
Morley-Stanwood HS — 400/9-12
4700 Northland Dr 49336 — 231-856-4444
James Nelson, prin. — Fax 856-7012
Morley-Stanwood MS — 300/6-8
4700 Northland Dr 49336 — 231-856-4550
Kim Colby, prin. — Fax 856-0136

Morrice, Shiawassee, Pop. 914
Morrice Area SD — 600/K-12
111 E Mason 48857 — 517-625-3142
William Hath, supt. — Fax 625-3866
www.morrice.k12.mi.us
Morrice JSHS — 200/7-12
691 Purdy Ln 48857 — 517-625-3143
William Heath, prin. — Fax 625-8935

Mount Clemens, Macomb, Pop. 15,743
Mount Clemens Community SD — 1,500/PK-12
167 Cass Ave 48043 — 586-469-6100
Deborah Wahlstrom, supt. — Fax 469-5569
www.mtcps.org
Mount Clemens HS — 500/9-12
155 Cass Ave 48043 — 586-461-3400
Michael Bruce, prin. — Fax 469-7058
Mount Clemens JHS — 200/7-8
161 Cass Ave 48043 — 586-461-3300
Michael Bruce, prin. — Fax 469-7066

Mount Morris, Genesee, Pop. 2,972
Beecher Community SD
Supt. — See Flint
Beecher HS — 400/9-12
6255 Neff Rd 48458 — 810-591-9277
Rodney Prewitt, prin. — Fax 591-6911
Beecher MS Academy — 200/7-8
6255 Neff Rd 48458 — 810-591-9277
Rodney Prewitt, prin. — Fax 591-6911
Beecher Adult/Alternative Education — Adult
1149 W Klein St 48458 — 810-591-9218
Eugene Pratt, dir. — Fax 591-5617

Mount Morris Consolidated SD — 2,200/K-12
12356 Walter St 48458 — 810-591-8760
Tricia Hill, supt. — Fax 591-7469
mtmorrisschools.org
Johnson HS — 700/9-12
8041 Neff Rd 48458 — 810-591-2370
Brian Eddy, prin. — Fax 591-3410
Mount Morris JHS — 500/6-8
12356 Walter St 48458 — 810-591-7100
Allen Peter, prin. — Fax 591-7105
Other Schools – See Flint

Mount Pleasant, Isabella, Pop. 25,361
Beal City SD — 700/PK-12
3180 W Beal City Rd 48858 — 989-644-3901
William Chilman, supt. — Fax 644-5847
bealcityschools.net/
Beal City JSHS — 300/7-12
3180 W Beal City Rd 48858 — 989-644-3944
Jeffrey Jackson, prin. — Fax 644-5847

Mount Pleasant SD — 3,500/K-12
720 N Kinney Ave 48858 — 989-775-2300
Michael Pung, supt. — Fax 775-2309
www.mtpleasant.edzone.net
Mount Pleasant Area Technical Center — Vo/Tech
1155 S Elizabeth St 48858 — 989-775-2210
Diane Benford, dir. — Fax 775-2215
Mount Pleasant HS — 1,100/9-12
1155 S Elizabeth St 48858 — 989-775-2200
Brian DeRath, prin. — Fax 773-0631
Oasis/W-A-Y Alternative Education S — 100/Alt
3480 S Isabella Rd 48858 — 989-775-2290
Stacie Zeien, dir. — Fax 772-3165
West IS — 500/7-8
440 S Bradley St 48858 — 989-775-2220
Dana Calkins, prin. — Fax 775-2229
Mount Pleasant Comm & Adult Education — Adult
3480 S Isabella Rd 48858 — 989-775-2370
Mary Murphy, dir. — Fax 773-2374

Shepherd SD
Supt. — See Shepherd
Shepherd MSHS — 100/Alt
3441 S Wise Rd 48858 — 989-773-9473
Lou Ann Schmidt, prin. — Fax 779-0429

Central Michigan University — Post-Sec.
100 Warriner Hall 48859 — 989-774-4000
M.J. Murphy Beauty College — Post-Sec.
201 W Broadway St 48858 — 989-772-2339
Sacred Heart Academy — 200/7-12
316 E Michigan St 48858 — 989-772-1457
Denny Starnes, prin. — Fax 772-1707
Saginaw Chippewa Tribal College — Post-Sec.
2274 Enterprise Dr 48858 — 989-775-4123

Munising, Alger, Pop. 2,289
Munising SD — 700/K-12
810 State Highway M28 W 49862 — 906-387-2251
Pete Kelto, supt. — Fax 387-5416
www.mps-up.com
Munising MSHS — 300/6-12
810 State Highway M28 W 49862 — 906-387-2103
Peter Kelto, prin. — Fax 387-5686

Muskegon, Muskegon, Pop. 37,002
Muskegon Area ISD — 200/
630 Harvey St 49442 — 231-777-2637
David Sipka, supt. — Fax 773-3498
www.muskegonisd.org
Muskegon Area Career Tech Center — Vo/Tech
200 Harvey St 49442 — 231-767-3600
Jeanne Roe, prin. — Fax 767-2692

Muskegon Heights SD — 1,200/PK-12
2603 Leahy St 49444 — 231 830 3200
David Sipka, supt. — Fax 830-3560
www.mhpsnet.org
Muskegon Heights MS — 300/6-8
55 E Sherman Blvd 49444 — 231-830-3600
Andre Johnson, prin. — Fax 830-3572
Other Schools – See Muskegon Heights

Muskegon SD — 3,700/PK-12
349 W Webster Ave 49440 — 231-720-2000
Jon Felske, supt. — Fax 720-2050
www.mpsk12.net/
MCEC — 300/Alt
571 E Apple Ave 49442 — 231-720-2530
Duane Cook, prin. — Fax 720-2593
Muskegon HS — 1,200/9-12
80 W Southern Ave 49441 — 231-720-2800
Corry Lohman, prin. — Fax 720-2811
Muskegon MS — 200/7-8
1150 Amity Ave 49442 — 231-720-3000
Paul Kurdziel, prin. — Fax 720-3025

Oakridge SD — 1,600/PK-12
275 S Wolf Lake Rd 49442 — 231-788-7100
Tom Livezey, supt. — Fax 788-7114
www.oakridgeschools.org
Oakridge HS — 500/9-12
5493 Hall Rd 49442 — 231-788-7300
Jason McVoy, prin. — Fax 788-7314
Oakridge MS — 300/7-8
251 S Wolf Lake Rd 49442 — 231-788-7400
Matthew Berkemeier, prin. — Fax 788-7414

Orchard View SD — 2,600/PK-12
35 S Sheridan Dr 49442 — 231-760-1300
Patricia Walstra, supt. — Fax 760-1323
www.orchardview.org
Orchard View HS — 700/9-12
16 N Quarterline Rd 49442 — 231-760-1400
Dan Bolhuis, prin. — Fax 760-1407
Orchard View MS — 600/6-8
35 S Sheridan Dr 49442 — 231-760-1500
Jim Nielsen, prin. — Fax 760-1506

Reeths-Puffer SD — 3,900/PK-12
991 W Giles Rd 49445 — 231 744-4736
Steve Edwards, supt. — Fax 744-9497
www.reeths-puffer.org
Reeths-Puffer HS — 1,200/9-12
1545 Roberts Rd 49445 — 231-744-1647
Daniel Beckeman, prin. — Fax 744-4796
Other Schools – See North Muskegon

Baker College of Muskegon — Post-Sec.
1903 Marquette Ave 49442 — 231-777-5200
Muskegon Catholic Central HS — 100/7-12
1145 W Laketon Ave 49441 — 231-755-2201
Jim VanBergen, prin. — Fax 755-8615
Muskegon Community College — Post-Sec.
221 S Quarterline Rd 49442 — 231-773-9131
Ross Medical Education Center — Post-Sec.
950 W Norton Ave 49441 — 231-730-9531
Western Michigan Christian HS — 300/9-12
455 E Ellis Rd 49441 — 231-799-9644
Doug Doty, prin. — Fax 798-9018

Muskegon Heights, Muskegon, Pop. 10,491
Muskegon Heights SD
Supt. — See Muskegon
Muskegon Heights HS — 400/9-12
2441 Sanford St 49444 — 231-830-3700
Carla Laws, prin. — Fax 830-3534

Napoleon, Jackson, Pop. 1,230
Napoleon Community SD — 1,500/K-12
PO Box 308 49261 — 517-536-8667
James Graham, supt. — Fax 536-8006
www.napoleonschools.org
Napoleon HS — 400/9-12
PO Box 308 49261 — 517-536-8667
Patrick Dillon, prin. — Fax 536-8007
Napoleon MS — 300/6-8
PO Box 308 49261 — 517-536-8667
Pam Barnes, prin. — Fax 536-8005
Other Schools – See Jackson

Negaunee, Marquette, Pop. 4,500
Negaunee SD — 1,400/PK-12
101 S Pioneer Ave 49866 — 906-475-4157
Jim Derocher, supt. — Fax 475-5107
www.negauneeschools.org/
Negaunee HS — 400/9-12
500 W Arch St 49866 — 906-475-7861
Mark Marana, prin. — Fax 475-7989
Negaunee MS — 300/6-8
102 W Case St 49866 — 906-475-7866
Dan Skewis, prin. — Fax 475-6408

Newaygo, Newaygo, Pop. 1,944
Newaygo SD — 1,700/K-12
PO Box 820 49337 — 231-652-6984
Peggy Mathis, supt. — Fax 652-6505
www.newaygo.net
Newaygo HS — 600/9-12
PO Box 820 49337 — 231-652-1646
Jackie Knight, prin. — Fax 652-3500
Newaygo MS — 400/6-8
PO Box 820 49337 — 231-652-1285
Jackie Knight, prin. — Fax 652-9704

New Baltimore, Macomb, Pop. 11,927
Anchor Bay SD
Supt. — See Casco
Anchor Bay MS North — 900/6-8
52805 Ashley Dr 48047 — 586-725-7373
Tim Brisbois, prin. — Fax 725-6760
Anchor Bay MS South — 600/6-8
48650 Sugarbush Rd 48047 — 586-949-4510
Robin Stanton, prin. — Fax 949-4739
Compass Pointe — 100/Alt
51510 Industrial Dr 48047 — 586-716-7862
Jason Byers, coord. — Fax 716-7864

Newberry, Luce, Pop. 1,471
Tahquamenon Area SD — 600/PK-12
700 Newberry Ave 49868 — 906-293-3226
Alice Walker, supt. — Fax 293-3709
eup.k12.mi.us/tahquamenon
Newberry HS — 300/7-12
700 Newberry Ave 49868 — 906-293-3243
Kris Derusha, prin. — Fax 293-3709

New Boston, Wayne
Huron SD — 2,400/K-12
32044 Huron River Dr 48164 — 734-782-2441
Richard Naughton, supt. — Fax 783-0338
www.huronschools.org
Huron HS — 800/9-12
32044 Huron River Dr 48164 — 734-782-1436
Donovan Rowe, prin. — Fax 783-1534
Renton JHS — 600/6-8
31578 Huron River Dr 48164 — 734-782-2483
Kurt Mrocko, prin. — Fax 783-0327

New Buffalo, Berrien, Pop. 1,853
New Buffalo Area SD — 600/K-12
1112 E Clay St 49117 — 269-469-6010
Mark Westerburg, supt. — Fax 469-3315
www.nbas.org/
New Buffalo HS — 200/9-12
1112 E Clay St 49117 — 269-469-6001
Ronald Hart, prin. — Fax 469-6017
New Buffalo MS — 200/6-8
1112 E Clay St 49117 — 269-469-6003
William Welling, prin. — Fax 469-6017

New Haven, Macomb, Pop. 4,447
New Haven Community SD — 1,200/PK-12
PO Box 482000 48048 — 586-749-5123
Dr. Keith Wunderlich, supt. — Fax 749-6307
newhaven.misd.net/
New Haven HS — 300/9-12
PO Box 482000 48048 — 586-749-5104
Will Timmerman, prin. — Fax 749-8460

New Lothrop, Shiawassee, Pop. 573
New Lothrop Area SD — 800/PK-12
PO Box 339 48460 — 810-638-5091
John Strycker, supt. — Fax 638-7277
www.newlothrop.k12.mi.us
New Lothrop JSHS — 300/7-12
PO Box 339 48460 — 810-638-5054
Anthony Berthiaume, prin. — Fax 638-5057

Newport, Monroe
Airport Community SD
Supt. — See Carleton
Niedermeier Center for Education — 100/Alt
8400 Newport South Rd 48166 — 734-586-2676
Steven Krause, admin. — Fax 586-3342

Lutheran HS South — 100/9-12
8290 N Telegraph Rd 48166 — 734-586-8832
Steven Garrabrant, prin. — Fax 586-7006

Niles, Berrien, Pop. 11,170
Brandywine Community SD 1,200/PK-12
1830 S 3rd St 49120 269-684-7150
John Jarpe Ed.D., supt. Fax 684-8998
www.brandywinebobcats.org
Bell Education Center 50/Alt
1830 S 3rd St 49120 269-683-8805
Michelle Wruble, prin. Fax 684-8998
Brandywine MSHS 400/7-12
1700 Bell Rd 49120 269-683-4800
Patrick Weckel, prin. Fax 683-1186

Niles Community SD 4,300/PK-12
111 Spruce St 49120 269-683-0732
Richard Weigel, supt. Fax 684-6337
www.nilesschools.org
Cedar Lane Alternative S 100/Alt
2301 Niles Buchanan Rd 49120 269-684-9554
John Fonash, prin. Fax 684-9555
Niles HS 1,100/9-12
1441 Eagle St 49120 269-683-2894
Robin Hadrick, prin. Fax 684-9516
Niles New Tech Entrepreneurial Academy 300/9-10
1441 Eagle St 49120 269-683-6031
Jerry Holtgren, dir. Fax 683-1533
Ring Lardner MS 500/7-8
801 N 17th St 49120 269-683-6610
Douglas Langmeyer, prin. Fax 684-9524
Niles Adult Education Adult
111 Spruce St 49120 269-684-4480
Richard Klemm, dir. Fax 684-9548

North Adams, Hillsdale, Pop. 473
North Adams-Jerome SD 400/K-12
4555 Knowles Rd 49262 517-287-4214
Carl Christenson, supt. Fax 287-4722
www.najps.org
North Adams-Jerome JSHS 200/6-12
4555 Knowles Rd 49262 517-287-4214
Carl Christenson, prin. Fax 287-4722

North Branch, Lapeer, Pop. 1,023
North Branch Area SD 2,400/K-12
PO Box 3620 48461 810-688-3570
Thomas English, supt. Fax 688-7010
www.nbbroncos.net
North Branch HS 800/9-12
PO Box 3620 48461 810-688-3001
Mark Hiltunen, prin. Fax 688-8057
North Branch MS 400/7-8
PO Box 3620 48461 810-688-4431
Merideth Collins, prin. Fax 688-4344

North Muskegon, Muskegon, Pop. 3,727
North Muskegon SD 900/K-12
1600 Mills Ave 49445 231-719-4100
Dr. Curt Babcock, supt. Fax 744-0739
www.nmps.k12.mi.us
North Muskegon HS 300/9-12
1507 Mills Ave 49445 231-719-4110
Heidi Christiansen, prin. Fax 719-4156
North Muskegon MS 200/6-8
1507 Mills Ave 49445 231-719-4110
Heidi Christiansen, prin. Fax 719-4156

Reeths-Puffer SD
Supt. — See Muskegon
Reeths-Puffer MS 600/7-8
1911 W Giles Rd 49445 231-744-4721
Simeon Frang, prin. Fax 744-6049

Northport, Leelanau, Pop. 512
Northport SD 200/K-12
PO Box 188 49670 231-386-5153
Jeff Tropf, supt. Fax 386-9838
www.northportps.org/
Northport S 200/K-12
PO Box 188 49670 231-386-5153
Jeff Tropf, supt. Fax 386-9838

Northville, Oakland, Pop. 5,889
Northville SD 7,200/K-12
501 W Main St 48167 248-349-3400
Mary Gallagher, supt. Fax 347-6928
www.northvilleschools.org
Hillside MS 800/6-8
775 N Center St 48167 248-344-8493
James Cracraft, prin. Fax 334-8480
Meads Mill MS 900/6-8
16700 Franklin Rd, 248-344-8435
Sue Meyer, prin. Fax 334-1830
Northville HS 2,200/9-12
45700 6 Mile Rd, 248-344-8420
Rob Watson, prin. Fax 344-8497

Norton Shores, Muskegon, Pop. 23,577
Mona Shores SD 3,800/K-12
121 Randall Rd 49441 231-780-4751
Dave Peden, supt. Fax 780-2099
www.monashores.net
Mona Shores HS 1,400/9-12
1121 Seminole Rd 49441 231-780-4711
Jennifer Bustard, prin. Fax 780-3634
Mona Shores MS 900/6-8
1700 Woodside Rd 49441 231-759-8506
Greg Helmer, prin. Fax 755-0514

Norway, Dickinson, Pop. 2,807
Norway-Vulcan Area SD 800/PK-12
300 Section St 49870 906-563-9552
Louis Steigerwald, supt. Fax 563-5169
www.norway.k12.mi.us
Norway HS 200/9-12
300 Section St 49870 906-563-9542
Joseph Tinti, prin. Fax 563-8708
Vulcan MS 200/5-8
300 Section St 49870 906-563-9563

Novi, Oakland, Pop. 54,165
Novi Community SD 6,700/K-12
25345 Taft Rd 48374 248-449-1200
Dr. Steve Matthews, supt. Fax 449-1219
www.novi.k12.mi.us
Novi HS 2,000/9-12
24062 Taft Rd 48375 248-449-1500
Nicole Carter, prin. Fax 449-1519
Novi MS 1,000/7-8
49000 W 11 Mile Rd 48374 248-449-1600
Stephanie Schriner, prin. Fax 449-1619

Detroit Catholic Central HS 1,100/9-12
27225 Wixom Rd 48374 248-596-3810
Rev. John Huber Ed.D., prin. Fax 596-3811
Franklin Road Christian S 300/K-12
40800 W 13 Mile Rd 48377 248-668-7100
Rev. Timothy Gambino, admin. Fax 668-7101
Sundai Michigan International Academy 300/K-12
24055 Meadowbrook Rd 48375 248-349-5234
Hitoshi Otaka, prin. Fax 349-9488
The Art Institute of Michigan Post-Sec.
28125 Cabot Dr Ste 120 48377 248-675-3800

Oakland, Oakland
Lake Orion Community SD
Supt. — See Lake Orion
Oakview MS 600/6-8
917 Lake George Rd 48363 248-693-0321
John Bernia, prin. Fax 693-5419

Oak Park, Oakland, Pop. 28,448
Berkley SD 4,400/K-12
14700 Lincoln St 48237 248-837-8000
Dennis McDavid, supt. Fax 544-5835
www.berkleyschools.org
Other Schools – See Berkley

Ferndale SD
Supt. — See Ferndale
Center for Advanced Studies & the Arts 11-12
23561 Rosewood St 48237 248-586-8860
Bill James, dir. Fax 414-6508
Ferndale Adult Education Jefferson Ctr Adult
22001 Republic Ave 48237 248-546-6832
Sandra Grosso, admin.

Oak Park SD 3,100/K-12
13900 Granzon St 48237 248-336-7700
Dr. Daveda Colbert, supt. Fax 336-7738
www.oakparkschools.org
NOVA Discipline Academy Alt
22180 Parklawn St 48237 248-336-7650
Derek Faulk, admin.
Oak Park Freshman Institute 200/9-9
22180 Parklawn St 48237 248-336-7780
Pam Vermiglio, prin. Fax 336-7781
Oak Park Preparatory Academy 400/7-8
22180 Parklawn St 48237 248-336-7780
Angela Thomas, prin. Fax 336-7738
Oak Park SHS 900/10-12
13701 Oak Park Blvd 48237 248-336-7740
William Washington, prin. Fax 336-7758

Beth Jacob School for Girls 300/K-12
14390 W 10 Mile Rd 48237 248-544-9070
Esther Gendelman, prin. Fax 544-4662
Lawton Career Institute Post-Sec.
20820 Greenfield Rd 48237 248-569-7559
Yeshiva Gedolah HS 100/9-12
24600 Greenfield Rd 48237 248-968-3360
Mordechai Gold, prin. Fax 968-8613
Yeshiva Gedolah of Greater Detroit Post-Sec.
24600 Greenfield Rd 48237 248-968-3360

Okemos, Ingham, Pop. 20,807
Okemos SD 3,900/K-12
4406 Okemos Rd 48864 517-706-5010
Catherine Ash Ph.D., supt. Fax 349-6235
www.okemosschools.net/
Chippewa MS 600/7-8
4000 Okemos Rd 48864 517-706-4800
Barbara Hoevel, prin. Fax 347-9824
Okemos HS 1,400/9-12
2800 Jolly Rd 48864 517-706-4900
Christine Sermak, prin. Fax 351-2850

Olivet, Eaton, Pop. 1,574
Olivet Community SD 1,500/K-12
255 1st St 49076 269-749-9129
David Campbell, supt. Fax 749-9701
www.olivetschools.org
Olivet HS 500/9-12
255 1st St 49076 269-749-3671
Robert Bobeda, prin. Fax 749-4560
Olivet MS 600/4-8
255 1st St 49076 269-749-9953
Michael Flood, prin. Fax 749-9701

Olivet College Post-Sec.
320 S Main St 49076 269-749-7000

Onaway, Presque Isle, Pop. 861
Onaway Area SD 700/K-12
4549 M 33 49765 989-733-4950
Rod Fullerton, supt. Fax 733-8612
www.onawayschools.com/
Onaway HS 200/9-12
4549 M 33 49765 989-733-4800
Marty Mix, prin. Fax 733-4899
Onaway MS 200/6-8
4549 M 33 49765 989-733-4850
Marty Mix, prin. Fax 733-4899

Onekama, Manistee, Pop. 404
Onekama Consolidated SD 400/K-12
5016 Main St 49675 231-889-4251
Kevin Hughes, supt. Fax 889-3720
www.onekama.k12.mi.us
Onekama MSHS 200/6-12
5016 Main St 49675 231-889-5521
Gina Hagen, prin. Fax 889-9567

Onsted, Lenawee, Pop. 906
Onsted Community SD 1,600/K-12
PO Box 220 49265 517-467-2174
Mark Haag, supt. Fax 467-2026
www.onsted.k12.mi.us
Onsted HS 600/9-12
PO Box 220 49265 517-467-2171
Robert Wright, prin. Fax 467-6910
Onsted MS 400/6-8
PO Box 220 49265 517-467-2168
Thomas Durbin, prin. Fax 467-6907

Ontonagon, Ontonagon, Pop. 1,473
Ontonagon Area SD 500/K-12
701 Parker Ave 49953 906-884-4963
Gray Webber, supt. Fax 884-2742
www.oasd.k12.mi.us
Ontonagon JSHS 300/6-12
701 Parker Ave 49953 906-884-4433
James Bobula, prin. Fax 884-2742

Orchard Lake, Oakland

St. Marys Preparatory HS 500/9-12
3535 Indian Trl 48324 248-683-0530
James Glowacki, prin. Fax 683-1740
SS. Cyril and Methodius Seminary Post-Sec.
3535 Indian Trl 48324 248-683-0310

Ortonville, Oakland, Pop. 1,423
Brandon SD 3,300/K-12
1025 S Ortonville Rd 48462 248-627-1800
Lorrie McMahon, supt. Fax 627-4533
www.brandonschooldistrict.org/
Brandon Education Center 50/Alt
155 E Glass Rd 48462 248-627-1860
Diane Zedan, prin. Fax 627-5079
Brandon HS 1,200/9-12
1025 S Ortonville Rd 48462 248-627-1820
Daniel Stevens, prin. Fax 627-5628
Brandon MS 500/7-8
609 S Ortonville Rd 48462 248-627-1830
Tina Chambers, prin. Fax 627-7201

Oscoda, Iosco, Pop. 877
Oscoda Area SD 700/PK-12
3550 E River Rd 48750 989-739-2033
Scott Moore, supt. Fax 739-2325
www.oscodaschools.org
Oscoda Area HS 400/7-12
3550 E River Rd 48750 989-739-9121
Steve Kennedy, prin. Fax 739-1688

Otisville, Genesee, Pop. 856
LakeVille Community SD 1,700/PK-12
11107 Washburn Rd 48463 810-591-3980
Vickie Luoma, supt. Fax 591-6538
www.lakevilleschools.org/
Lakeville Alternative HS 100/Alt
11107 Washburn Rd 48463 810-591-4050
Brian Titsworth, prin. Fax 631-3961
Lakeville HS 600/9-12
11107 Washburn Rd 48463 810-591-4050
Brian Titsworth, prin. Fax 591-3961
Lakeville MS 400/6-8
11107 Washburn Rd 48463 810-591-3945
Kelli-Ann Fazer, prin. Fax 591-6632

Otsego, Allegan, Pop. 3,879
Otsego SD 2,300/PK-12
400 Sherwood St 49078 269-692-6066
Dennis Patzer, supt. Fax 692-6074
www.otsegops.org
Otsego HS 700/9-12
550 Washington St 49078 269-692-6166
Herve Dardis, prin. Fax 692-6188
Otsego MS 500/6-8
540 Washington St 49078 269-692-6199
Bill Houseman, prin. Fax 692-6228

Ottawa Lake, Monroe
Whiteford Agricultural SD 700/K-12
6655 Consear Rd 49267 734-856-1443
Larry Shilling, supt. Fax 854-6463
www.whiteford.k12.mi.us
Whiteford HS 200/9-12
6655 Consear Rd 49267 734-856-1443
Kelli Tuller, prin. Fax 856-2564
Whiteford MS 200/6-8
6655 Consear Rd 49267 734-856-1443
Kelli Tuller, prin. Fax 856-2564

Ovid, Clinton, Pop. 1,574
Ovid-Elsie Area SD
Supt. — See Elsie
North Community Center 100/Alt
615 N Main St 48866 989-834-2271
Kris Kirby, prin. Fax 834-6108

Owendale, Huron, Pop. 236
Owendale-Gagetown Area SD 200/K-12
7166 E Main St 48754 989-678-4261
James Wencel, supt. Fax 678-4284
www.owengage.org/
Owendale-Gagetown JSHS 100/6-12
7166 E Main St 48754 989-678-4141
Terri Falkenberg, prin. Fax 678-0920

Owosso, Shiawassee, Pop. 14,957
Owosso SD 3,300/PK-12
PO Box 340 48867 989-723-8131
Dr. Andrea Tuttle, supt. Fax 723-7777
www.owosso.k12.mi.us
Lincoln HS 200/Alt
645 Alger Ave 48867 989-725-2839
Karen Van Epps, admin. Fax 729-6706

Owosso HS 1,000/9-12
765 E North St 48867 989-723-8231
Jeff Phillips, prin. Fax 729-5600
Owosso MS 700/6-8
219 N Water St 48867 989-723-3460
Rich Collins, prin. Fax 729-5760

Baker College of Owosso Post-Sec.
1020 S Washington St 48867 989-729-3370

Oxford, Oakland, Pop. 3,399
Oxford Community SD 4,900/K-12
10 N Washington St 48371 248-969-5000
Dr. William Skilling, supt. Fax 969-5016
www.oxfordschools.org/
Crossroads for Youth 100/Alt
930 E Drahner Rd 48371 248-969-1885
Mike Schweig, prin. Fax 969-1833
Oxford HS 1,400/9-12
745 N Oxford Rd 48371 248-969-5100
Todd Dunckley, prin. Fax 969-5145
Oxford MS 1,000/6-8
1420 E Lakeville Rd 48371 248-969-1800
Kenneth Weaver, prin. Fax 969-1840

Painesdale, Houghton
Adams Township SD 400/K-12
PO Box 37 49955 906-482-0599
Tim Keteri, supt. Fax 487-5999
www.adams.k12.mi.us
Jeffers HS 200/7-12
PO Box 37 49955 906-482-0580
Tim Keteri, admin. Fax 487-5999

Paradise, Chippewa
Whitefish Township Community SD 50/K-12
PO Box 58 49768 906-492-3353
John Prescott, supt. Fax 492-3254
whitefish.eup.k12.mi.us/
Whitefish Township S 50/K-12
PO Box 58 49768 906-492-3353
John Prescott, prin. Fax 492-3254

Parchment, Kalamazoo, Pop. 1,738
Parchment SD 1,700/PK-12
520 N Orient St 49004 269-488-1050
Matthew Miller, supt. Fax 488-1060
www.parchmentschools.org
Parchment HS 500/9-12
1916 E G Ave 49004 269-488-1100
Scott Karaptian, prin. Fax 488-1110
Parchment MS 400/6-8
307 N Riverview Dr 49004 269-488-1200
George Stamas, prin. Fax 488-1210
Other Schools – See Kalamazoo

Parma, Jackson, Pop. 755
Western SD 2,900/PK-12
1400 S Dearing Rd 49269 517-841-8100
Michael Smajda, supt. Fax 841-8801
www.westernschools.org/
Western HS 900/9-12
1400 S Dearing Rd 49269 517-841-8200
Sue VanRiper, prin. Fax 841-8282
Western MS 700/6-8
1400 S Dearing Rd 49269 517-841-8300
David Hood, prin. Fax 841-8803
Other Schools – See Jackson

Paw Paw, Van Buren, Pop. 3,443
Paw Paw SD 2,300/K-12
119 Johnson Rd 49079 269-657-8800
Mark Bielang, supt. Fax 657-7292
www.ppps.org
Michigan Avenue Academy 100/Alt
600 E Michigan Ave 49079 269-657-8831
Carol Edinger, prin. Fax 657-7411
Paw Paw HS 700/9-12
30609 E Red Arrow Hwy 49079 269-657-8840
Michael Dahlinger, prin. Fax 655-0009
Paw Paw MS 500/6-8
313 W Michigan Ave 49079 269-657-8870
Jerry McDaniel, prin. Fax 657-5011

Peck, Sanilac, Pop. 624
Peck Community SD 500/K-12
222 E Lapeer St 48466 810-378-5171
Ryle Kiser, supt. Fax 378-5116
www.peck.k12.mi.us
Peck JSHS 300/7-12
222 E Lapeer St 48466 810-378-5501
Ryle Kiser, prin. Fax 378-5116

Pellston, Emmet, Pop. 782
Pellston SD 600/K-12
172 Park St 49769 231-539-8682
William Tebbe, supt. Fax 539-8838
www.pellstonschools.org/
Pellston MSHS 400/5-12
172 Park St 49769 231-539-8801
William Tebbe, prin. Fax 539-8110

Pentwater, Oceana, Pop. 845
Pentwater SD 300/K-12
600 Park St 49449 231-869-4100
Mary Marshall, supt. Fax 869-4535
www.pentwater.k12.mi.us
Pentwater S 300/K-12
600 Park St 49449 231-869-4100
Mary Marshall, prin. Fax 869-4535

Perry, Shiawassee, Pop. 2,154
Perry SD 1,500/PK-12
PO Box 900 48872 517-625-3108
Mike Foster, supt. Fax 625-6256
www.goperry.org
Perry HS 500/9-12
PO Box 900 48872 517-625-3104
Paula Steele, prin. Fax 625-0012
Perry MS 400/5-8
PO Box 900 48872 517-625-6196
Matt Schmidtfranz, prin. Fax 625-0120

Petersburg, Monroe, Pop. 1,129
Summerfield SD 800/K-12
17555 Ida West Rd 49270 734-279-1035
John Hewitt, supt. Fax 279-1448
www.summerfield.k12.mi.us
Summerfield HS 200/9-12
17555 Ida West Rd 49270 734-279-1012
Scott Leach, prin. Fax 279-1018
Summerfield JHS 100/7-8
17555 Ida West Rd 49270 734-279-1012
Scott Leach, prin. Fax 279-1018

Petoskey, Emmet, Pop. 5,571
Petoskey SD 2,800/K-12
1130 Howard St 49770 231-348-2100
John Scholten, supt. Fax 348-2342
www.petoskeyschools.org
Petoskey HS 1,000/9-12
1500 Hill St 49770 231-348-2160
Jim Kanine, prin. Fax 348-2214
Petoskey MS 600/6-8
801 Northmen Dr 49770 231-348-2150
Dan Taylor, prin. Fax 348-2234

North Central Michigan College Post-Sec.
1515 Howard St 49770 231-348-6600

Pickford, Chippewa
Pickford SD 400/K-12
PO Box 278 49774 906-647-6285
Angela Nettleton, supt. Fax 647-3706
pickford.eup.k12.mi.us/
Pickford HS 200/7-12
PO Box 278 49774 906-647-4028
Angela Nettleton, prin. Fax 647-3706

Pigeon, Huron, Pop. 1,203
Elkton-Pigeon-Bay Port Laker SD 900/K-12
6136 Pigeon Rd 48755 989-453-4600
Robert Smith, supt. Fax 453-4609
www.lakerschools.org/
Laker HS 300/9-12
6136 Pigeon Rd 48755 989-453-4600
Brian Keim, prin. Fax 453-4615
Laker MS 200/6-8
6136 Pigeon Rd 48755 989-453-4600
Brian Keim, prin. Fax 453-4609

Pinckney, Livingston, Pop. 2,402
Pinckney Community SD 4,100/K-12
2130 E M 36 48169 810-225-3900
Daniel Danosky, supt. Fax 225-3905
www.pinckneyschools.org/
Pathfinder S 700/7-8
2100 E M 36 48169 810-225-5200
Richard Todd, prin. Fax 225-5205
Pinckney Community HS 1,500/9-12
10255 Dexter Pinckney Rd 48169 810-225-5500
Dr. James Darga, prin. Fax 225-5505

Livingston Christian S 200/PK-12
550 E Hamburg St 48169 734-878-9818
Theodore Nast, admin. Fax 878-9830

Pinconning, Bay, Pop. 1,286
Pinconning Area SD 1,500/PK-12
605 W 5th St 48650 989-879-4556
Michael Vieau, supt. Fax 879-4705
www.pasd.org/
Pinconning Area HS 500/9-12
605 W 5th St 48650 989-879-2311
Andy Kowalczyk, prin. Fax 879-7258
Pinconning Area MS 300/6-8
605 W 5th St 48650 989-879-2311
Keith Wetters, prin. Fax 879-7258

Pittsford, Hillsdale
Pittsford Area SD 600/K-12
9304 Hamilton Rd 49271 517-523-3481
Andrew Shaw, supt. Fax 523-3467
pittsfordk12.org
Pittsford JSHS 300/7-12
9304 Hamilton Rd 49271 517-523-3481
T.G. Cook, prin. Fax 523-2059

Plainwell, Allegan, Pop. 3,755
Plainwell Community SD 2,700/PK-12
600 School Dr 49080 269-685-5823
Susan Wakefield, supt. Fax 685-1108
www.plainwellschools.org
Plainwell HS 900/9-12
684 Starr Rd 49080 269-685-9554
Dr. Jeremy Wright, prin. Fax 685-9064
Plainwell MS 600/6-8
720 Brigham St 49080 269-685-5813
Gary Barton, prin. Fax 685-2099
Renaissance HS 100/Alt
422 Acorn St 49080 269-685-1573
Tammy Glupker, prin. Fax 685-1564

Plymouth, Wayne, Pop. 8,997
Plymouth-Canton Community SD 18,300/K-12
454 S Harvey St 48170 734-416-2700
Dr. Jeremy Hughes, supt. Fax 416-4932
www.pccs.k12.mi.us
Central MS 900/6-8
650 Church St 48170 734-416-2990
Anthony Ruela, prin. Fax 416-7699
East MS 800/6-8
1042 S Mill St 48170 734-416-4950
Scott Burek, prin. Fax 416-4949
Pioneer MS 900/6-8
46081 Ann Arbor Rd W 48170 734-416-2770
Kevin Rhein, prin. Fax 416-7569
Starkweather Center 200/Alt
39750 Joy Rd 48170 734-416-4901
Kevin Lane, coord. Fax 416-6031
West MS 900/6-8
44401 W Ann Arbor Trl 48170 734-416-7550
Clint Smiley, prin. Fax 416-7648
Other Schools – See Canton

Metropolitan SDA Jr Academy 50/1-10
15585 N Haggerty Rd 48170 734-420-4044
Craig Morgan, prin. Fax 420-3710
Moody Theological Seminary Post-Sec.
41550 E Ann Arbor Trl 48170 734-207-9581

Pontiac, Oakland, Pop. 57,635
Oakland ISD
Supt. — See Waterford
Oakland Technical Campus NE Vo/Tech
1371 N Perry St 48340 248-451-2700
Andrea Williams, dean Fax 451-2720

Pontiac SD 5,100/PK-12
47200 Woodward Ave 48342 248-451-6800
Dr. Brian Dougherty, supt. Fax 451-6890
www.pontiac.k12.mi.us
International Technology Academy Vo/Tech
1275 N Perry St 48340 248-451-8010
Suzanne Kavanaugh, prin. Fax 451-8034
Pontiac HS 1,700/9-12
1051 Arlene Ave 48340 248-451-7300
Kwame Stephens, prin. Fax 451-7321
Pontiac MS 700/7-8
1275 N Perry St 48340 248-451-8010
Shana Jackson, prin. Fax 451-8034

Dorsey School of Business Post-Sec.
440 N Telegraph Rd 48341 248-333-1814
Notre Dame Marist Acad - Middle Division 300/6-8
1300 Giddings Rd 48340 248-373-5371
Jill Mistretta, prin. Fax 373-4707
Notre Dame Preparatory HS 700/9-12
1300 Giddings Rd 48340 248-373-5300
Rev. Joseph Hindelang, prin. Fax 373-8024
Oakland County Health Division Post-Sec.
1200 N Telegraph Rd 48341 248-858-1832

Portage, Kalamazoo, Pop. 44,979
Kalamazoo RESA 200/
1819 E Milham Ave 49002 269-250-9200
Ronald Fuller, supt. Fax 250-9205
www.kresa.org
Other Schools – See Kalamazoo

Portage SD 8,300/K-12
8111 S Westnedge Ave 49002 269-323-5000
Mark T. Bielang, supt. Fax 323-5001
www.portageps.org
Northern HS 1,300/9-12
1000 Idaho Ave 49024 269-323-5400
Jim French, prin. Fax 323-5490
North MS 600/6-8
5808 Oregon Ave 49024 269-323-5700
Celeste Shelton-Harris, prin. Fax 323-5790
Portage Central HS 1,400/9-12
8135 S Westnedge Ave 49002 269-323-5200
Eric Alburtus, prin. Fax 323-5290
Portage Central MS 700/6-8
8305 S Westnedge Ave 49002 269-323-5600
Chuck Haskin, prin. Fax 323-5690
West MS 600/6-8
7145 Moorsbridge Rd 49024 269-323-5800
Denny Roehm, prin. Fax 323-5890

Chic University of Cosmetology Post-Sec.
6091 Constitution Blvd 49024 269-329-3333
Wright Beauty Academy Post-Sec.
6666 Lovers Ln 49002 269-321-8708

Port Hope, Huron, Pop. 258
Port Hope Community SD 100/K-12
7840 Portland Rd 48468 989-428-4151
Don Pitts, supt. Fax 428-4153
www.porthope.k12.mi.us
Port Hope Community S 100/K-12
7840 Portland Rd 48468 989-428-4151
Don Pitts, prin. Fax 428-4153

Port Huron, Saint Clair, Pop. 29,088
Port Huron Area SD 9,700/PK-12
PO Box 5013 48061 810-984-3101
H. Ronald Wollen, supt. Fax 984-6606
www.phasd.us/
Central MS 1,000/6-8
200 32nd St 48060 810-984-6533
Michael Palmer, prin. Fax 989-2709
Holland Woods MS 600/6-8
1617 Holland Ave 48060 810-984-6548
Ethan Barden, prin. Fax 989-2713
Port Huron HS 1,500/9-12
2215 Court St 48060 810-984-2611
Ben Brock, prin. Fax 984-6559
Port Huron Northern HS 1,400/9-12
1799 Krafft Rd 48060 810-984-2671
Charles Mossett, prin. Fax 984-2747
Harrison Center Adult
55 15th St 48060 810-455-0029
Gloria Henry, prin. Fax 989-2746
Other Schools – See Fort Gratiot

Baker College of Port Huron Post-Sec.
3403 Lapeer Rd 48060 810-985-7000
Port Huron Hospital Post-Sec.
1221 Pine Grove Ave 48060 810-987-5000
Ross Medical Education Center Post-Sec.
2887 Krafft Rd Ste 700 48060 810-982-0454
St. Clair County Community College Post-Sec.
PO Box 5015 48061 810-984-3881

Portland, Ionia, Pop. 3,841
Portland SD 2,000/K-12
1100 Ionia Rd 48875 517-647-4161
Charles Dumas, supt. Fax 647-2975
www.portlandk12.org
Portland HS 700/9-12
1100 Ionia Rd 48875 517-647-2981
Christine Rockey, prin. Fax 647-1791
Portland MS 500/6-8
745 Storz St 48875 517-647-2985
Kevin Robydek, prin. Fax 647-2820

St. Patrick S 300/PK-12
122 N West St 48875 517-647-7551
Randy Hodge, prin. Fax 647-4545

Posen, Presque Isle, Pop. 228
Posen Consolidated SD 9 300/K-12
PO Box 187 49776 989-766-2573
Dru Milliron, supt. Fax 766-2519
www.posen.k12.mi.us
Posen Consolidated JSHS 100/7-12
PO Box 187 49776 989-766-2471
Dru Milliron, prin. Fax 766-2519

Potterville, Eaton, Pop. 2,560
Potterville SD 900/K-12
420 N High St 48876 517-645-2662
Timothy Donahue, supt. Fax 645-0092
www.pps.k12.mi.us/
Potterville HS 300/9-12
422 N High St 48876 517-645-7609
Julie Klomp, prin. Fax 645-0177
Potterville MS 300/5-8
424 N High St 48876 517-645-4777
Kelly Roe, prin. Fax 645-0091

Powers, Menominee, Pop. 422
North Central Area SD
Supt. — See Hermansville
North Central JSHS 200/7-12
PO Box 601 49874 906-497-5226
Bruce Tapio, prin. Fax 497-5066

Quincy, Branch, Pop. 1,637
Quincy Community SD 1,400/PK-12
1 Educational Pkwy 49082 517-639-7141
Craig Artist, supt. Fax 639-4273
www.quincyschools.org
Quincy HS 400/9-12
18 Colfax St 49082 517-639-9245
David Spalding, prin. Fax 639-3701
Quincy MS 400/5-8
32 Fulton St 49082 517-639-4201
Penny Brockway, prin. Fax 639-3701

Rapid River, Delta
Rapid River SD 400/K-12
10070 US Highway 2 49878 906-474-6411
Jay Kulbertis, supt. Fax 474-9903
www.rapidriver.k12.mi.us
Rapid River JSHS 200/6-12
10070 US Highway 2 49878 906-474-6411
William Warning, prin. Fax 474-9883

Ravenna, Muskegon, Pop. 1,203
Ravenna SD 1,000/K-12
12322 Stafford St 49451 231-853-2231
John Van Loon, supt. Fax 853-2193
www.ravennaschools.org
Ravenna HS 300/9-12
2766 S Ravenna Rd 49451 231-853-2218
Steven Anderson, prin. Fax 853-6981
Ravenna MS 300/5-8
2700 S Ravenna Rd 49451 231-853-2268
Scott Panozzo, prin. Fax 853-2629

Ray, Macomb

Austin Catholic Academy 9-12
24125 26 Mile Rd 48096 586-749-7900
Rev. David Brecht, prin. Fax 749-5217

Reading, Hillsdale, Pop. 1,073
Reading Community SD 900/K-12
223 Strong St 49274 517-283-2166
Chellie Broesamle, supt. Fax 283-3519
www.readingrangers.org
Owens JSHS 500/7-12
301 Chestnut St 49274 517-283-2142
Rick Bailey, prin. Fax 283-3758

Redford, Wayne, Pop. 51,100
Redford Union SD 2,500/K-12
19990 Beech Daly Rd 48240 313-242-6000
Ronald Stoneman, supt. Fax 242-6025
www.redfordu.k12.mi.us
Hilbert MS 700/6-8
26440 Puritan 48239 313-242-4000
Susan Shelton, prin. Fax 242-4005
Redford Union HS 1,100/9-12
17711 Kinloch 48240 313-242-4200
Michael Humitz, prin. Fax 242-4205

South Redford SD 3,200/K-12
26141 Schoolcraft 48239 313-535-4000
Brian Galdes, supt. Fax 535-1059
southredford.net
Pierce MS 700/6-8
25605 Orangelawn 48239 313-937-8880
Christine Hofer, prin. Fax 937-9486
Thurston HS 1,100/9-12
26255 Schoolcraft 48239 313-242-0600
William Simms, prin. Fax 592-0740

Concordia Lutheran S - South Campus 50/5-8
9600 Leverne 48239 313-937-2233
David Kusch, prin. Fax 937-2173

Reed City, Osceola, Pop. 2,371
Reed City Area SD 1,500/K-12
225 W Church Ave 49677 231-832-2201
Steven Westhoff, supt. Fax 832-2202
www.reedcity.k12.mi.us
Reed City HS 500/9-12
225 W Church Ave 49677 231-832-2224
Steven Westhoff, prin. Fax 832-2501
Reed City MS 400/6-8
233 W Church Ave 49677 231-832-6174
Tim Webster, prin. Fax 832-6180

Reese, Tuscola, Pop. 1,450
Reese SD 900/PK-12
PO Box 389 48757 989-868-9864
Keith Wetters, supt. Fax 868-9570
www.reese.k12.mi.us/
Reese HS 400/9-12
PO Box 389 48757 989-868-4191
Brian Galsterer, prin. Fax 868-4091
Reese MS 300/5-8
PO Box 389 48757 989-868-4157
Dave Hurst, prin. Fax 868-1609

Remus, Mecosta
Chippewa Hills SD 1,900/PK-12
3226 Arthur Rd 49340 989-967-2000
Shirley Howard, supt. Fax 967-2009
www.chsd.us
Chippewa Hills HS 600/9-12
3226 Arthur Rd 49340 989-967-2100
Michelle Newman, prin. Fax 967-2109
Chippewa Hills IS 300/7-8
3102 Arthur Rd 49340 989-967-2200
Dr. Bob Grover, prin. Fax 967-2209
Mosaic S 100/Alt
350 E Wheatland Ave 49340 989-967-8150
Dawn Hawley, prin. Fax 967-8385

Republic, Marquette, Pop. 565
Republic-Michigamme SD 100/PK-12
227 Maple St 49879 906-376-2277
Paul Currie, supt. Fax 376-8299
republicmichigamme.maresa.k12.mi.us
Republic-Michigamme S 100/PK-12
227 Maple St 49879 906-376-2277
Paul Currie, supt. Fax 376-8299

Richland, Kalamazoo, Pop. 729
Gull Lake Community SD 2,800/PK-12
11775 E D Ave 49083 269-488-5000
Christopher Rundle, supt. Fax 488-5011
www.gulllakecs.org
Gull Lake HS 1,000/9-12
7753 N 34th St 49083 269-488-5020
Don Eastman, prin. Fax 488-5031
Gull Lake MS 700/6-8
9550 M 89 49083 269-488-5040
David Alban, prin. Fax 488-5041

Richmond, Macomb, Pop. 5,652
Richmond Community SD 1,700/PK-12
35276 Division Rd 48062 586-727-3565
Dr. Linda Olson, supt. Fax 727-2098
www.richmond.misd.net/
Richmond HS 600/9-12
35320 Division Rd 48062 586-727-3225
Deborah Michon, prin. Fax 727-9072
Richmond MS 500/5-8
35250 Division Rd 48062 586-727-7552
Keith Bartels, prin. Fax 727-2545

River Rouge, Wayne, Pop. 7,623
River Rouge SD 1,100/PK-12
1460 Coolidge Hwy 48218 313-297-9600
Derrick Coleman, supt. Fax 297-6525
www.riverrougeschools.org
River Rouge Middle College HS Academy 500/9-12
1460 Coolidge Hwy 48218 313-297-9600
Fax 297-7322
Sabbath MS 200/6-8
340 Frazier St 48218 313-297-9654
Brandon Cox, prin. Fax 297-5695

Riverview, Wayne, Pop. 12,365
Riverview Community SD 2,700/K-12
13425 Colvin St Ste 1, 734-285-9660
Russell Pickell, supt. Fax 285-9822
www.riverviewschools.com
Riverview HS 900/9-12
12431 Longsdorf St, 734-285-7361
Maxine Yetter, prin. Fax 785-6598
Seitz MS 600/6-8
17800 Kennebec St, 734-285-2043
Andrew Zulewski, prin. Fax 285-6649

Detroit Business Institute Post-Sec.
19100 Fort St, 734-479-0660
Richard HS 400/9-12
15325 Pennsylvania Rd, 734-284-1875
Joseph Whalen, prin. Fax 284-9304

Rochester, Oakland, Pop. 12,556
Rochester Community SD 14,700/K-12
501 W University Dr 48307 248-726-3000
Dr. Robert Shaner, supt. Fax 726-3105
www.rochester.k12.mi.us
Other Schools – See Rochester Hills

Oakland University Post-Sec.
2200 N Squirrel Rd 48309 248-370-2100

Rochester Hills, Oakland, Pop. 69,733
Avondale SD
Supt. — See Auburn Hills
Avondale Academy 200/Alt
1435 W Auburn Rd 48309 248-537-6600
Fred Cromie, admin. Fax 537-6605
Avondale MS 800/6-8
1445 W Auburn Rd 48309 248-537-6300
Todd Robinson, prin. Fax 537-6305

Rochester Community SD
Supt. — See Rochester
ACE Alternative S 100/Alt
1440 John R Rd 48307 248-726-5900
Susan Demeniuk, prin. Fax 726-5905
Adams HS 1,500/9-12
3200 W Tienken Rd 48306 248-726-5200
Kevin Cumming, prin. Fax 726-5205
Hart MS 1,100/6-8
6500 Sheldon Rd 48306 248-726-4500
Rachel Guinn, prin. Fax 726-4505
Reuther MS 700/6-8
1430 E Auburn Rd 48307 248-726-4700
Cheryl Gambaro, prin. Fax 726-4705
Rochester HS 1,700/9-12
180 S Livernois Rd 48307 248-726-5400
Charles Rowland, prin. Fax 726-5405
Stony Creek HS 1,700/9-12
575 E Tienken Rd 48306 248-726-5700
Larry Goralski, prin. Fax 726-5705
Van Hoosen MS 800/6-8
1339 N Adams Rd 48306 248-726-4900
Daniel Mooney, prin. Fax 726-4905
West MS 900/6-8
500 Old Perch Rd 48309 248-726-5000
Mike Dillon, prin. Fax 726-5005
RACE Adult
480 E Auburn Rd 48307 248-726-5950
Sean Lively, admin. Fax 726-5955

Holy Family Regional S - South Campus 700/4-8
2633 John R Rd 48307 248-299-3798
Jon Myers, prin. Fax 299-3843
Lutheran HS Northwest 300/9-12
1000 Bagley Dr 48309 248-852-6677
Paul Looker, prin. Fax 852-2667
Rochester College Post-Sec.
800 W Avon Rd 48307 248-218-2000
Rochester Hills Christian S 300/PK-12
3300 S Livernois Rd 48307 248-852-0585
Karen Patton, prin. Fax 852-4757

Rock, Delta
Mid Peninsula SD 200/K-12
5055 Saint Nicholas 31st Rd 49880 906-359-4387
Mary F. Brayak, supt. Fax 359-4167
midpen.dsisd.net/
Mid Peninsula S 200/K-12
5055 Saint Nicholas 31st Rd 49880 906-359-4390
Mary F. Brayak, supt. Fax 359-4167

Rockford, Kent, Pop. 5,617
Rockford SD 7,500/PK-12
350 N Main St 49341 616-863-6320
Michael Shibler Ph.D., supt. Fax 866-1911
www.rockfordschools.org
East Rockford MS 1,000/6-8
8615 9 Mile Rd NE 49341 616-863-6140
Mike Ramm, prin. Fax 863-6565
North Rockford MS 800/6-8
397 E Division St 49341 616-863-6300
Lissa Weidenfeller, prin. Fax 866-5998
River Valley Academy 100/Alt
350 N Main St 49341 616-863-6324
Lisa Jacobs, prin. Fax 866-1911
Rockford Freshman Center 600/9-9
4500 Kroes St NE 49341 616-863-6348
Douglas VanderJagt, prin. Fax 866-7134
Rockford HS 1,900/10-12
4100 Kroes St NE 49341 616-863-6030
Daniel Zang, prin. Fax 866-5997

Rockwood, Wayne, Pop. 3,246
Gibraltar SD
Supt. — See Woodhaven
Downriver HS 50/Alt
33211 Mccann Rd 48173 734-379-7080
Jason Evers, prin. Fax 379-7081

Rogers City, Presque Isle, Pop. 2,809
Rogers City Area SD 600/K-12
1033 W Huron Ave Ste B 49779 989-734-9100
Kathleen Makowski, supt. Fax 734-7428
www.rcas.k12.mi.us
Rogers City MSHS 300/6-12
1033 W Huron Ave 49779 989-734-9170
David O'Bryant, prin. Fax 734-2969

Romeo, Macomb, Pop. 3,511
Romeo Community SD 5,500/K-12
316 N Main St 48065 586-752-0200
Dr. Nancy Campbell, supt. Fax 752-0228
www.romeo.k12.mi.us
Romeo HS 1,900/9-12
11091 32 Mile Rd 48065 586-752-0300
Michael Kaufman, prin. Fax 752-0402
Romeo MS 600/6-8
297 Prospect St 48065 586-752-0240
Brad Martz, prin. Fax 752-0256
Other Schools – See Washington

Romulus, Wayne, Pop. 23,107
Romulus Community SD 3,600/PK-12
36540 Grant St 48174 734-532-1600
Paula Daniels, supt. Fax 532-1611
www.romulus.net
Community HS 200/Alt
15303 Merriman Rd 48174 734-532-1400
Reginald Grantham, prin. Fax 532-1401
Romulus HS 1,100/9-12
9650 Wayne Rd 48174 734-532-1000
Hal Heard, prin. Fax 532-1001
Romulus MS 800/6-8
37300 Wick Rd 48174 734-532-1700
Jason Salhaney, prin. Fax 532-1701

Roscommon, Roscommon, Pop. 1,048
Roscommon Area SD 1,400/K-12
PO Box 825 48653 989-275-6600
Catherine Erickson, supt. Fax 275-8227
www.rapsk12.net
Roscommon HS 500/9-12
PO Box 825 48653 989-275-6675
Ron Alden, prin. Fax 275-6681
Roscommon MS 400/6-8
PO Box 825 48653 989-275-6640
Ron Alden, prin. Fax 275-6609

Kirtland Community College Post-Sec.
10775 N Saint Helen Rd 48653 989-275-5000

Roseville, Macomb, Pop. 46,120
Roseville Community SD 5,300/K-12
18975 Church St 48066 586-445-5505
John Kment, supt. Fax 771-1772
www.rcs.misd.net
Eastland MS 400/6-8
18700 Frank St 48066 586-445-5702
Paul Schummer, prin. Fax 445-5721
Roseville HS 1,800/9-12
17855 Common Rd 48066 586-445-5542
Peter Hedemark, prin. Fax 445-5654
Roseville MS 600/6-8
16250 Martin Rd 48066 586-445-5605
David Rice, prin. Fax 445-5620

Dorsey School of Business Post-Sec.
31542 Gratiot Ave 48066 586-296-3225

Rothbury, Oceana, Pop. 413
Shelby SD
Supt. — See Shelby
Oceana HS 100/Alt
PO Box 36 49452 231-894-5586
Guy Reece, prin. Fax 893-2639

Royal Oak, Oakland, Pop. 56,180
Oakland ISD
Supt. — See Waterford
Oakland Technical Campus SE Vo/Tech
5055 Delemere Ave 48073 248-288-4020
Tammy Brown, dean Fax 288-4071

Royal Oak SD 5,200/PK-12
1123 Lexington Blvd 48073 248-435-8400
Shawn Lewis-Lakin, supt. Fax 435-6170
www.royaloakschools.com
Churchill Community Education Center 200/Alt
707 Girard Ave 48073 248-588-5050
Patrick Wolynski, prin. Fax 588-2881
Royal Oak HS 1,600/9-12
1500 Lexington Blvd 48073 248-435-8500
Jim Moll, prin. Fax 288-8733
Royal Oak MS 1,100/6-8
709 N Washington Ave 48067 248-541-7100
Zoe Marcus, prin. Fax 541-0408

David Pressley School of Cosmetology Post-Sec.
1127 S Washington Ave 48067 248-548-5090
Oakland Community College Post-Sec.
739 S Washington Ave 48067 248-246-2400
Shrine Catholic Academy 100/7-8
3500 W 13 Mile Rd 48073 248-549-2925
Gabrielle Erken, prin. Fax 549-2953
Shrine Catholic HS 300/9-12
3500 W 13 Mile Rd 48073 248-549-2925
Gabrielle Erken, prin. Fax 549-2953
William Beaumont Hospital Post-Sec.
3601 W 13 Mile Rd 48073 248-551-0681

Rudyard, Chippewa
Rudyard Area SD 700/PK-12
PO Box 246 49780 906-478-3771
Anthony Habra, supt. Fax 478-3912
www.rudyard.k12.mi.us
Rudyard HS 200/9-12
PO Box 246 49780 906-478-3771
Mark Pavloski, prin. Fax 478-4101
Rudyard MS 200/7-8
PO Box 246 49780 906-478-3771
Mark Pavloski, prin. Fax 478-4101

Saginaw, Saginaw, Pop. 50,106
Buena Vista SD 600/PK-12
705 N Towerline Rd 48601 989-755-2184
Dr. Deborah Harvill, supt. Fax 755-0286
www.bvsd.us
Buena Vista HS 300/9-12
3945 E Holland Rd 48601 989-754-1493
Brittany Sanford, prin. Fax 758-0915
Phoenix Science & Technology Center 100/4-8
1925 S Outer Dr 48601 989-753-6438
Debra Jackson-Noble, prin. Fax 753-4953

Carrollton SD 2,000/K-12
3211 Carla Dr 48604 989-754-1475
Tim Wilson, supt. Fax 754-1470
www.carrollton.k12.mi.us
Carrollton HS 500/9-12
1235 Mapleridge Rd 48604 989-753-3433
Traci Smith, prin. Fax 754-1041
Carrollton MS 400/6-8
3211 Carla Dr 48604 989-753-9704
Tiffany Peterson, prin. Fax 754-1470
Carrollton Omni Adult Education Adult
479 Shattuck Rd 48604 989-753-3478
Nancy Paris, prin. Fax 754-1470

Saginaw SD 7,700/PK-12
550 Millard St 48607 989-399-6500
Carlton Jenkins Ph.D., supt. Fax 399-6635
www.spsd.net
Daniels MS 500/6-8
1010 Hoyt Ave 48607 989-399-5300
Jimmie Westbrook, prin. Fax 399-5305
Hill HS 1,200/9-12
3115 Mackinaw St 48602 989-399-5800
Nathaniel McClain, prin. Fax 399-5815
Saginaw Arts & Sciences Academy 600/6-12
200 Congress Ave 48602 989-399-5500
Melleretha Johnson, prin. Fax 399-5515
Saginaw Career Complex Vo/Tech
2102 Weiss St 48602 989-399-6150
Jean Farrington, prin. Fax 399-6165
Saginaw HS 700/9-12
3100 Webber St 48601 989-399-6000
Donald Durrett, prin. Fax 399-6015
Thompson MS 700/6-8
3021 Court St 48602 989-399-5600
Mit Foley, prin. Fax 399-5615

Saginaw Township Community SD 5,100/K-12
PO Box 6278 48608 989-797-1800
Douglas Trombley, supt. Fax 797-1801
stcs.org
Heritage HS 1,700/9-12
3465 N Center Rd 48603 989-799-5790
Michael Newman, prin. Fax 799-5159
Mackinaw HS 300/Alt
2775 Shattuck Rd 48603 989-799-8470
Alan Kern, prin. Fax 797-1860
White Pine MS 1,200/6-8
505 N Center Rd, 989-797-1814
Kristen Hecht, prin. Fax 797-1859

Swan Valley SD 1,800/PK-12
8380 OHern Rd 48609 989-921-3701
David Moore, supt. Fax 921-3705
www.swanvalley.k12.mi.us
Swan Valley HS 600/9-12
8400 OHern Rd 48609 989-921-2401
Mat McRae, prin. Fax 921-2405
Swan Valley MS 400/6-8
453 Van Wormer Rd 48609 989-921-2601
Craig Blower, prin. Fax 921-2605

Community Baptist Christian S 100/PK-12
8331 Gratiot Rd 48609 989-781-2340
Douglas Jackson, prin. Fax 781-1344
Davenport University Post-Sec.
5300 Bay Rd 48604 989-799-7800
Dorsey School of Business Post-Sec.
4390 Bay Rd 48603 989-249-1926
Grace Christian S 100/PK-12
4619 Mackinaw Rd 48603 989-793-2129
Sharon Gamber, prin. Fax 793-2125
Michigan Lutheran Seminary 200/9-12
2777 Hardin St 48602 989-793-1041
Rev. Joel Petermann, pres. Fax 793-4213
Nouvel Catholic Central HS 400/9-12
2555 Wieneke Rd 48603 989-791-4330
John Hoving, prin. Fax 797-6603
Ross Medical Education Center Post-Sec.
4300 Fashion Square # 202 48603 989-791-5192
St. Mary's Medical Center Post-Sec.
800 S Washington Ave 48601 989-776-8176
Valley Lutheran HS 400/9-12
3560 McCarty Rd 48603 989-790-1676
Dr. John Brandt, prin. Fax 790-1680

Saint Charles, Saginaw, Pop. 2,035
Saint Charles Community SD 1,100/PK-12
891 W Walnut St 48655 989-865-9961
Michael Wallace, supt. Fax 865-6185
www.stccs.org
Saint Charles HS 400/9-12
881 W Walnut St 48655 989-865-9991
Patricia Sowle, prin. Fax 865-8185
Thurston MS 300/6-8
893 W Walnut St 48655 989-865-9927
Patricia Sowle, prin. Fax 865-2429

Saint Clair, Saint Clair, Pop. 5,422
East China SD
Supt. — See East China
Saint Clair HS 1,000/9-12
2200 Clinton Ave 48079 810-676-1700
Ronald Miller, prin. Fax 676-1725
Saint Clair MS 600/6-8
4335 Yankee Rd 48079 810-676-1800
Michael Alley, prin. Fax 676-1825

Saint Clair Shores, Macomb, Pop. 58,728
Lake Shore SD 3,400/K-12
28850 Harper Ave 48081 586-285-8480
Christopher Loria, supt. Fax 285-8463
www.lakeshoreschools.org
Kennedy MS 800/6-8
23101 Masonic Blvd 48082 586-285-8800
Patrick Donohue, prin. Fax 285-8804
Lake Shore HS 1,100/9-12
22980 E 13 Mile Rd 48082 586-285-8900
Dr. Joseph DiPonio, prin. Fax 285-8904
North Lake Alternative HS 200/Alt
23340 Elmira St 48082 586-285-8780
Mark Adamski, prin. Fax 285-8783

Lakeview SD 3,500/K-12
27575 Harper Ave 48081 586-445-4000
Karl Paulson, supt. Fax 445-4029
www.lakeview.misd.net
Jefferson MS 800/6-8
27900 Rockwood St 48081 586-445-4130
David Lavender, prin. Fax 445-4041
Lakeview HS 1,300/9-12
21100 E 11 Mile Rd 48081 586-445-4045
Brent Case, prin. Fax 445-4072

South Lake SD 2,100/K-12
23101 Stadium Dr 48080 586-435-1600
Pamela Balint, supt. Fax 445-4202
www.solake.org
South Lake HS 700/9-12
21900 E 9 Mile Rd 48080 586-435-1400
Carmen Kennedy, prin. Fax 445-4243
South Lake MS 500/6-8
21621 California St 48080 586-435-1300
Lauren Wells, prin. Fax 778-3151

Saint Ignace, Mackinac, Pop. 2,280
Saint Ignace Area SD 600/K-12
W429 Portage St 49781 906-643-8145
Donald Gustafson, supt. Fax 643-0247
stignace.eup.k12.mi.us/
Lasalle HS 200/9-12
W443 Portage St 49781 906-643-8800
Gregg Fettig, prin. Fax 643-7696
Saint Ignace MS 200/5-8
W429 Portage St 49781 906-643-7822
Kari Visnaw, prin. Fax 643-7873

Saint Johns, Clinton, Pop. 7,721
Saint Johns SD 3,200/K-12
PO Box 230 48879 989-227-4050
Dr. Kenneth Ladouceur, supt. Fax 227-4099
www.sjredwings.org
Saint Johns HS 1,100/9-12
PO Box 230 48879 989-227-4100
Mark Palmer, prin. Fax 227-4199
Saint Johns MS 800/6-8
PO Box 230 48879 989-227-4300
Scott Henry, prin. Fax 227-4399
Wilson Center 100/Alt
PO Box 230 48879 989-227-5200
Dr. Kenneth Ladouceur, prin. Fax 227-5299

Saint Joseph, Berrien, Pop. 8,211
Saint Joseph SD 2,800/K-12
3275 Lincoln Ave 49085 269-926-3100
Ann Cardon, supt. Fax 926-3103
www.sjschools.org/
Saint Joseph HS 1,000/9-12
2521 Stadium Dr 49085 269-926-3200
Jeffrey Runser, prin. Fax 926-3203
Upton MS 700/6-8
800 Maiden Ln 49085 269-926-3400
Chad Mandarino, prin. Fax 926-3403

Lake Michigan Catholic HS 200/9-12
915 Pleasant St 49085 269-983-2511
John Berlin, prin. Fax 983-0883
Lake Michigan Catholic MS 100/6-8
915 Pleasant St 49085 269-983-2511
John Berlin, prin. Fax 983-0883
Michigan Lutheran HS 100/9-12
615 E Marquette Woods Rd 49085 269-429-7861
Matthew Herbst, prin. Fax 429-4428
Twin City Beauty College Post-Sec.
2600 Lincoln Ave 49085 269-428-2900

Saint Louis, Gratiot, Pop. 7,441
Saint Louis SD 1,200/PK-12
113 E Saginaw St 48880 989-681-2545
Steve Brimmer, supt. Fax 681-5894
www.stlouisschools.net
Nurnberger MS 300/6-8
312 Union St 48880 989-681-5155
Wes Johnson, prin. Fax 681-4658
Saint Louis HS 400/9-12
113 E Saginaw St 48880 989-681-2500
Chris Macklin, prin. Fax 681-4535

Saline, Washtenaw, Pop. 8,661
Saline Area SD 5,300/PK-12
7265 N Ann Arbor St 48176 734-429-8000
Scot Graden, supt. Fax 429-8028
www.salineschools.com
Saline Alternative HS 100/Alt
7265 Saline Ann Arbor Rd 48176 734-429-8006
Carol Melcher, prin. Fax 429-8010
Saline HS 1,800/9-12
1300 Campus Pkwy 48176 734-429-8030
Julie Helber, prin. Fax 429-8036
Saline MS 1,200/6-8
7190 N Maple Rd 48176 734-429-8070
David Raft, prin. Fax 429-8076

Washtenaw Christian Academy 200/PK-12
7200 Moon Rd 48176 734-429-7733
Amy Houpt, admin. Fax 944-8343

Sand Creek, Lenawee
Sand Creek Community SD 900/K-12
6518 Sand Creek Hwy 49279 517-436-3108
Steven Laundra, supt. Fax 436-3143
www.sc-aggies.us
Sand Creek JSHS 500/7-12
6518 Sand Creek Hwy 49279 517-436-3124
Steven Laundra, prin. Fax 436-3193

Sand Lake, Montcalm, Pop. 495
Tri County Area SD 2,100/PK-12
PO Box 79 49343 616-636-5454
Allen Cumings M.A., supt. Fax 636-5677
www.tricountyschools.com
Other Schools – See Howard City

Sandusky, Sanilac, Pop. 2,651
Sandusky Community SD 1,100/K-12
191 E Pinetree Ln 48471 810-648-3400
Mike Carmean, supt. Fax 648-5113
www.sandusky.k12.mi.us
Sandusky HS 300/9-12
191 E Pinetree Ln 48471 810-648-3401
Jon Miller, prin. Fax 648-3148
Sandusky MS 300/5-8
395 S Sandusky Rd 48471 810-648-3300
Steve Carlson, prin. Fax 648-5221

Sanford, Midland, Pop. 854
Meridian SD 1,400/PK-12
3361 N Meridian Rd 48657 989-687-3200
Craig Carmoney, supt. Fax 687-3222
merps.org

Meridian Early College HS 400/9-12
3303 N Meridian Rd 48657 989-687-3300
Patrick Malley, prin. Fax 687-3309
Meridian JHS 400/5-8
3475 N Meridian Rd 48657 989-687-3360
Kent Boxey, prin. Fax 687-3364

Saranac, Ionia, Pop. 1,311
Saranac Community SD 800/K-12
88 Pleasant St 48881 616-642-1400
Richard Geiger, supt. Fax 642-1405
www.saranac.k12.mi.us
Saranac JSHS 400/7-12
150 Pleasant St 48881 616-642-1100
Beth Simpson, prin. Fax 642-1105

Saugatuck, Allegan, Pop. 909
Saugatuck SD
Supt. — See Douglas
Saugatuck MSHS 200/6-12
401 Elizabeth St 49453 269-857-2133
Timothy Travis, prin. Fax 857-6145

Sault Sainte Marie, Chippewa, Pop. 13,362
Sault Sainte Marie Area SD 2,400/PK-12
876 Marquette Ave 49783 906-635-6609
Timothy D. Hall Ed.D., supt. Fax 635-6642
sault.eup.k12.mi.us
Malcolm HS 100/Alt
460 W Spruce St 49783 906-635-6638
Sandy Sawyer, prin. Fax 635-3836
Sault Area Career Center Vo/Tech
904 Marquette Ave 49783 906-635-6652
Jo Anne Lussier, dir. Fax 635-6641
Sault Sainte Marie Area HS 900/9-12
904 Marquette Ave 49783 906-635-6605
John Sherry, prin. Fax 635-6641
Sault Sainte Marie MS 600/6-8
684 Marquette Ave 49783 906-635-6604
Dean Paul, prin. Fax 635-3841

Lake Superior State University Post-Sec.
650 W Easterday Ave 49783 906-632-6841

Schoolcraft, Kalamazoo, Pop. 1,506
Schoolcraft Community SD 1,100/K-12
551 E Lyons St 49087 269-488-7390
Dr. Wayne Stitt, supt. Fax 488-7391
www.schoolcraftschools.org
Schoolcraft HS 400/9-12
551 E Lyons St 49087 269-488-7350
Kristin Flynn, prin. Fax 488-7364
Schoolcraft MS 300/6-8
551 E Lyons St 49087 269-488-7300
John Vail, prin. Fax 488-7303

Scottville, Mason, Pop. 1,185
Ludington Area SD
Supt. — See Ludington
Journey JSHS 100/Alt
1916 W US Highway 10 31 49454 231-757-5700
James Bandstra, prin. Fax 757-9744

Mason County Central SD 1,600/PK-12
300 W Broadway Ave 49454 231-757-3713
Jeff Mount, supt. Fax 757-5716
mccschools.com
Mason County Central HS 500/9-12
210 W Broadway Ave 49454 231-757-4748
Brad Jacobs, prin. Fax 757-9084
Mason County Central MS 400/6-8
310 W Beryl St 49454 231-757-3724
Kevin Kimes, prin. Fax 757-4820
Community Education Consortium Adult
300 W Broadway Ave 49454 231-757-3471
Elizabeth Stark, coord. Fax 757-5716

Mason-Lake ISD
Supt. — See Ludington
Mason-Lake ISD Tech Prep Partnership Vo/Tech
3000 N Stiles Rd 49454 231-845-6211
Michael Robinson, admin. Fax 845-8661

West Shore Community College Post-Sec.
3000 N Stiles Rd 49454 231-845-6211

Sebewaing, Huron, Pop. 1,753
Unionville-Sebewaing SD 600/K-12
2203 Wildner Rd 48759 989-883-2360
George Rierson, supt. Fax 883-9021
main.think-usa.org/
Unionville-Sebewaing HS 300/5-12
2203 Wildner Rd 48759 989-883-2534
Todd Laventure, prin. Fax 883-9739

Shelby, Oceana, Pop. 2,029
Shelby SD 1,500/PK-12
525 N State St 49455 231-861-5211
Michael Matiosz, supt. Fax 861-5416
www.shelby.k12.mi.us/
Shelby HS 400/9-12
641 N State St 49455 231-861-4452
Frances Schamber, prin. Fax 861-6867
Shelby MS 300/6-8
525 N State St 49455 231-861-4521
Michael Furnas, prin. Fax 861-0415
Other Schools – See Rothbury

Shelby Township, Macomb, Pop. 69,500
Utica Community SD
Supt. — See Sterling Heights
Eisenhower SHS 2,100/10-12
6500 25 Mile Rd 48316 586-797-1300
Nanette Chesney, prin. Fax 797-1301
Malow JHS 1,200/7-9
6400 25 Mile Rd 48316 586-797-3500
Robert Hock, prin. Fax 797-3501
Shelby JHS 1,300/7-9
51700 Van Dyke Ave 48316 586-797-3700
Lisa McDill, prin. Fax 797-3701

Shepherd, Isabella, Pop. 1,488
Shepherd SD 1,900/K-12
PO Box 219 48883 989-828-5520
Claire Bunker, supt. Fax 828-5679
shepherd.edzone.net:81
Shepherd HS 500/9-12
100 E Hall St 48883 989-828-6601
Douglas Bush, prin. Fax 828-5452
Shepherd MS 400/6-8
150 E Hall St 48883 989-828-6605
Kelly Miscikoski, prin. Fax 828-6578
Other Schools – See Mount Pleasant

Sheridan, Montcalm, Pop. 639

Beth Haven Baptist Academy 100/PK-12
1158 W Carson City Rd 48884 989-291-0555
Kevin Crowell, prin. Fax 527-3122

Sidney, Montcalm
Montcalm Area ISD
Supt. — See Stanton
Montcalm Area Career Center Vo/Tech
1550 W Sidney Rd 48885 989-328-6621
Paula Fortino, prin. Fax 328-2000

Montcalm Community College Post-Sec.
2800 College Dr 48885 989-328-2111

Southfield, Oakland, Pop. 70,027
Southfield SD 7,800/PK-12
24661 Lahser Rd 48033 248-746-8500
Wanda Cook-Robinson Ph.D., supt. Fax 746-8540
www.southfield.k12.mi.us
Levey MS 500/6-8
25300 W 9 Mile Rd, 248-746-8740
Rita Teague, prin. Fax 746-8718
Southfield HS 1,100/9-12
24675 Lahser Rd, 248-746-8600
Michael Horn, prin. Fax 746-8773
Southfield Regional Academic Center 500/Alt
21705 Evergreen Rd 48075 248-746-0012
Marty Bulger, prin. Fax 746-0028
University HS Academy 200/9-12
24815 Lahser Rd, 248-746-4370
Marcia Williams, dean Fax 746-4374
Other Schools – See Lathrup Village

Abcott Institute Post-Sec.
16250 Northland Dr Ste 205 48075 866-532-7699
Akiva Hebrew Day S 300/PK-12
21100 W 12 Mile Rd 48076 248-386-1625
Rabbi Tzvi Klugerman, hdmstr. Fax 386-1632
DeVry University Post-Sec.
26999 Central Park Ste 125 48076 248-213-1610
Everest Institute Post-Sec.
21107 Lahser Rd, 248-799-9933
ITT Technical Institute Post-Sec.
26700 Lahser Rd Ste 100, 248-603-6100
Lawrence Technological University Post-Sec.
21000 W 10 Mile Rd 48075 248-204-4000
Northwestern Technological Institute Post-Sec.
24567 Northwestern Hwy #200 48075 248-358-4006
Oakland Community College Post-Sec.
22322 Rutland Ave 48075 248-233-2700
Providence Hospital Post-Sec.
16001 W 9 Mile Rd 48075 248-424-3000
Southfield Christian S 600/PK-12
28650 Lahser Rd 48034 248-357-3660
Dr. Margie Baldwin, supt. Fax 357-5271
Specs Howard School of Broadcast Arts Post-Sec.
19900 W 9 Mile Rd 48075 248-358-9000
Yeshivas Darchei Torah Girls S 300/K-12
21550 W 12 Mile Rd 48076 248-948-1080
Sharon Kahn, prin. Fax 948-1825

Southgate, Wayne, Pop. 29,584
Southgate Community SD 5,600/K-12
14600 Dix Toledo Rd 48195 734-246-4600
William J. Grusecki, supt. Fax 283-6791
www.sgate.k12.mi.us/
Anderson HS 1,100/10-12
15475 Leroy St 48195 734-246-4611
Michelle Baker-Herring, prin. Fax 246-7840
Davidson MS 800/8-9
15800 Trenton Rd 48195 734-246-4628
Dennis Kemp, prin. Fax 246-7280
Asher Adult & Community Education Adult
14101 Leroy St 48195 734-246-4633
Judy Cock, dir. Fax 246-7244

Dorsey School of Business Post-Sec.
15755 Northline Rd 48195 734-285-5400

South Haven, Van Buren, Pop. 4,285
South Haven SD 2,200/PK-12
554 Green St 49090 269-637-0520
Robert Herrera, supt. Fax 637-3025
www.shps.org
Baseline MS 500/6-8
7357 Baseline Rd 49090 269-637-0530
John Weiss, prin. Fax 639-9689
Mohr HS 700/9-12
600 Elkenburg St 49090 269-637-0502
Craig McCrumb, prin. Fax 637-0516

South Lyon, Oakland, Pop. 11,160
South Lyon Community SD 7,000/PK-12
345 S Warren St 48178 248-573-8127
Dr. William Pearson, supt. Fax 437-8686
www.slcs.us
Centennial MS 800/6-8
62500 9 Mile Rd 48178 248-573-8600
Brian Toth, prin. Fax 573-8611
Millennium MS 900/6-8
61526 9 Mile Rd 48178 248-573-8200
Maureen Altermatt, prin. Fax 573-8231
South Lyon East HS 900/9-12
52200 10 Mile Rd 48178 248-573-8700
Dr. David Phillips, prin. Fax 486-4009
South Lyon HS 1,200/9-12
1000 N Lafayette St 48178 248-573-8150
Chad Scaling, prin. Fax 437-0233

Sparta, Kent, Pop. 4,088
Sparta Area SD 2,600/PK-12
465 S Union St 49345 616-887-8253
Gordie Nickels, supt. Fax 887-9958
www.spartaschools.org
Sparta HS 900/9-12
475 W Spartan Dr 49345 616-887-8213
Matt Spencer, prin. Fax 887-1264
Sparta MS 600/6-8
480 S State St 49345 616-887-8211
Joel Stoner, prin. Fax 887-1080

Spring Arbor, Jackson, Pop. 2,850

Spring Arbor University Post-Sec.
106 E Main St 49283 517-750-1200

Springfield, Calhoun, Pop. 5,036
Battle Creek SD
Supt. — See Battle Creek
Mathematics & Science Center 300/8-12
765 Upton Ave, 269-965-9440
Connie Duncan, admin. Fax 965-9589
Springfield MS 400/6-8
1023 Avenue A, 269-965-9640
William Martin, prin. Fax 962-2486

Spring Lake, Ottawa, Pop. 2,288
Spring Lake SD 2,400/K-12
345 Hammond St 49456 616-846-5500
Dennis Furton, supt. Fax 846-9830
www.springlakeschools.org
Spring Lake HS 800/9-12
16140 148th Ave 49456 616-846-5501
Mike Gilchrist, prin. Fax 847-5855
Spring Lake MS 300/7-8
345 Hammond St 49456 616-846-5502
Aaron West, prin. Fax 847-7913

Springport, Jackson, Pop. 785
Springport SD 800/K-12
PO Box 100 49284 517-857-3495
Randall Cook, supt. Fax 857-4179
springportschools.net
Springport HS, PO Box 100 49284 400/9-12
Tanya Overweg, prin. 517-857-3475
Springport MS 300/6-8
PO Box 100 49284 517-857-3475
Chris Kregel, prin. Fax 857-3251

Standish, Arenac, Pop. 1,487
Standish-Sterling Community SD 1,700/PK-12
3789 Wyatt Rd 48658 989-846-3670
Darren Kroczaleski, supt. Fax 846-7890
www.standish-sterling.org
Standish-Sterling Central HS 600/9-12
2401 Grove Street Rd 48658 989-846-3660
Mark Williams, prin. Fax 846-3666
Standish-Sterling MS 400/6-8
3789 Wyatt Rd 48658 989-846-4526
Gary Roper, prin. Fax 846-4529

Stanton, Montcalm, Pop. 1,397
Central Montcalm SD 1,600/PK-12
PO Box 9 48888 989-831-2000
Kristi Teall, supt. Fax 831-2010
www.central-montcalm.org
Central Montcalm HS 600/9-12
1480 S Sheridan Rd 48888 989-831-2100
Tony Petersen, prin. Fax 831-2110
Central Montcalm MS 500/6-8
1480 S Sheridan Rd 48888 989-831-2200
Tom Torok, prin. Fax 831-2210
Central Montcalm Adult/Community Educ Adult
710 N State St 48888 989-831-2100
Kristi Teall, supt. Fax 831-2110

Montcalm Area ISD 100/
PO Box 367 48888 989-831-5261
Dr. Scott Koenigsknecht, supt. Fax 831-8727
www.maisd.com
Other Schools – See Sidney

Stephenson, Menominee, Pop. 850
Stephenson Area SD 500/K-12
PO Box 509 49887 906-753-2221
Stephen Paliewicz, supt. Fax 753-4676
www.stephenson.k12.mi.us
Stephenson JSHS 200/6-12
PO Box 529 49887 906-753-2222
Jerome Sardina, prin. Fax 753-2326

Sterling Heights, Macomb, Pop. 126,870
Utica Community SD 28,600/PK-12
11303 Greendale Dr 48312 586-797-1000
Christine Johns Ed.D., supt. Fax 797-1001
www.uticak12.org/
Bemis JHS 900/7-8
12500 19 Mile Rd 48313 586-797-2500
Thomas Yaw, prin. Fax 797-2501
Davis JHS 800/7-9
11311 Plumbrook Rd 48312 586-797-2700
Steve Bernier, prin. Fax 797-2701
Ford HS 2,100/9-12
11911 Clinton River Rd 48313 586-797-1600
Steve Beyer, prin. Fax 797-1601
Heritage JHS 600/7-9
37400 Dodge Park Rd 48312 586-797-3100
Scott Waak, prin. Fax 797-3101
Jeanette JHS 900/7-9
40400 Gulliver Dr 48310 586-797-3300
Ken Cucchi, prin. Fax 797-3301

Stevenson SHS 2,000/10-12
39701 Dodge Park Rd 48313 586-797-1900
Steve Pfannes, prin. Fax 797-1901
Utica Advance Path Academy 100/Alt
7600 18 Mile Rd 48314 586-797-7000
Timothy Youngblood, prin. Fax 797-7001
Utica Learning Academy/Adult Education 100/Alt
7600 18 Mile Rd 48314 586-797-6970
Denise Mennucci, admin. Fax 797-6901
Other Schools – See Shelby Township, Utica

Warren Consolidated SD
Supt. — See Warren
Career Prep Center Vo/Tech
12200 15 Mile Rd 48312 586-825-2800
Douglas Babcock, prin. Fax 698-4177
Carleton MS 600/6-8
8900 15 Mile Rd 48312 586-825-2590
Shaun Greene-Beebe, prin. Fax 698-4286
Flynn MS 600/6-8
2899 Fox Hill Dr 48310 586-825-2900
Mary Ann Figurski, prin. Fax 698-4304
Grissom MS 800/6-8
35701 Ryan Rd 48310 586-825-2560
Joseph Konal, prin. Fax 698-4313
Sterling Heights HS 1,500/9-12
12901 15 Mile Rd 48312 586-825-2700
Alison Roberts, prin. Fax 698-4253

Parkway Christian S 500/PK-12
14500 Metropolitan Pkwy 48312 586-446-9900
Lila Place, head sch Fax 446-9904

Stevensville, Berrien, Pop. 1,138
Lakeshore SD 2,900/PK-12
5771 Cleveland Ave 49127 269-428-1400
Julie Powell, admin. Fax 428-1574
www.lakeshoreschools.k12.mi.us
Lakeshore HS 900/9-12
5771 Cleveland Ave 49127 269-428-1402
Michael Mulligan, prin. Fax 428-1423
Lakeshore MS 700/6-8
1459 W John Beers Rd 49127 269-428-1408
Jason Messenger, prin. Fax 428-1571

Stockbridge, Ingham, Pop. 1,207
Stockbridge Community SD 1,500/K-12
305 W Elizabeth St 49285 517-851-7188
Bruce Brown, supt. Fax 851-8334
panthernet.net
Stockbridge HS 500/9-12
416 N Clinton St 49285 517-851-7770
Karl Heidrich, prin. Fax 851-9446
Stockbridge MS 400/6-8
305 W Elizabeth St 49285 517-851-8149
Brad Edwards, prin. Fax 851-8334

Sturgis, Saint Joseph, Pop. 10,748
Sturgis SD 3,300/K-12
107 W West St 49091 269-659-1500
Dr. Thomas Langdon, supt. Fax 659-1584
www.sturgisps.org/
Sturgis HS 1,000/9-12
216 Vinewood Ave 49091 269-659-1515
Ron Ehlers, prin. Fax 659-1532
Sturgis MS 700/6-8
1400 E Lafayette St 49091 269-659-1550
Eric Anderson, prin. Fax 659-1553
Adult Education Center Adult
107 W West St 49091 269-659-1540
Dave Watson, prin. Fax 659-1544

Lake Area Christian S 100/PK-12
63590 Borgert Rd 49091 269-651-5135
Dean Miller, admin. Fax 651-8648

Suttons Bay, Leelanau, Pop. 604
Suttons Bay SD 800/PK-12
PO Box 367 49682 231-271-8604
Michael Murray, supt. Fax 271-8691
www.suttonsbay.k12.mi.us
Suttons Bay Early College S 50/10-12
PO Box 367 49682 231-271-8600
Raphael Rittenhouse, prin. Fax 271-8691
Suttons Bay HS 400/7-12
PO Box 367 49682 231-271-8603
Raphael Rittenhouse, prin. Fax 271-8690

Swartz Creek, Genesee, Pop. 5,666
Swartz Creek Community SD 4,000/PK-12
8354 Cappy Ln 48473 810-591-2300
Dr. Jeff Hall, supt. Fax 591-2784
www.swartzcreek.org
Alternative HS 100/Alt
8197 Miller Rd 48473 810-591-4349
Dave Simancek, prin. Fax 591-4348
Swartz Creek HS 1,200/9-12
1 Dragon Dr 48473 810-591-1800
Sandy Macut, prin. Fax 591-1895
Swartz Creek MS 900/6-8
8230 Crapo St 48473 810-591-1705
Kevin Klaeren, prin. Fax 591-1712

ITT Technical Institute Post-Sec.
6359 Miller Rd 48473 810-628-2500

Tawas City, Iosco, Pop. 1,814
Iosco RESA
27 N Rempert Rd 48763 989-362-3006
Dana McGrew, supt. Fax 362-9076
www.ioscoresa.net/
Career & Technical Education Center Vo/Tech
27 N Rempert Rd 48763 989-362-3006
Fax 362-6905

Tawas Area SD 1,300/K-12
245 W M 55 48763 989-984-2250
Donald Vernon, supt. Fax 984-2253
www.tawas.net
Tawas Area HS 600/8-12
255 W M 55 48763 989-984-2100
Eric Diroff, prin. Fax 984-2106

Taylor, Wayne, Pop. 61,678
Taylor SD 7,500/PK-12
23033 Northline Rd 48180 734-374-1200
Diane Allen, supt. Fax 287-6083
www.taylorschools.net/
Hoover MS 600/7-8
27101 Beverly Rd 48180 313-295-5775
Janice Loomis, prin. Fax 295-8354
Kennedy HS 1,200/9-12
13505 Kennedy Dr 48180 734-374-1229
Michael Wiltse, prin. Fax 374-1676
Taylor Career & Technical Center Vo/Tech
9601 Westlake St 48180 313-295-5750
Edward Buchynski, prin. Fax 291-1090
Titan Alternative HS 100/Alt
9551 Westlake St 48180 313-295-5738
Edward Buchynski, prin. Fax 295-8357
Truman HS 1,300/9-12
11211 Beech Daly Rd 48180 734-946-6555
Tommie Saylor, prin. Fax 946-6590
West MS 700/7-8
10575 William St 48180 313-295-5783
Patricia Kaechele, prin. Fax 291-2203

Baptist Park S 200/PK-12
12501 Telegraph Rd 48180 734-287-2720
Roger Cook, admin. Fax 287-2184
Dorsey School of Business Post-Sec.
23129 Ecorse Rd 48180 313-291-2177
Taylortown School of Beauty Post-Sec.
23129 Ecorse Rd 48180 313-291-2177

Tecumseh, Lenawee, Pop. 8,429
Tecumseh SD 3,000/K-12
212 N Ottawa St 49286 517-424-7318
Dr. Kelly Coffin, supt. Fax 423-3847
tps.k12.mi.us
Tecumseh HS 900/9-12
760 Brown St 49286 517-423-6008
Griff Mills, prin. Fax 423-9644
Tecumseh MS 900/5-8
307 N Maumee St 49286 517-423-1105
Rick Hilderley, prin. Fax 423-1300
Tecumseh Options Program 50/Alt
212 N Ottawa St 49286 517-424-6508
Dr. Kelly Coffin, admin. Fax 424-6407

Tekonsha, Calhoun, Pop. 699
Tekonsha Community SD 200/K-12
245 S Elm St 49092 517-767-4121
Joseph Krause, supt. Fax 767-3465
www.tekonsha.k12.mi.us
Tekonsha JSHS 100/5-12
245 S Elm St 49092 517-767-4121
Joseph Krause, admin. Fax 767-3465

Temperance, Monroe, Pop. 8,433
Bedford SD 4,300/K-12
1623 W Sterns Rd 48182 734-850-6000
Jon White, supt. Fax 850-6099
www.bedford.k12.mi.us
Bedford HS 1,700/9-12
8285 Jackman Rd 48182 734-850-6100
Scott Stalker, prin. Fax 850-6199
Bedford JHS 800/6-8
8405 Jackman Rd 48182 734-850-6200
Roderick Hurley, prin. Fax 850-6299

State Line Christian S 300/K-12
6320 Lewis Ave 48182 734-847-6774
Josh Newbold, prin. Fax 847-4968

Three Oaks, Berrien, Pop. 1,589
River Valley SD 300/PK-12
15480 Three Oaks Rd 49128 269-756-9541
William Kearney, supt. Fax 756-6631
www.rivervalleyschools.org/
River Valley MSHS 200/6-12
15480 Three Oaks Rd 49128 269-756-9541
Cynthia Ursprung, prin. Fax 756-3007

Three Rivers, Saint Joseph, Pop. 7,541
Three Rivers Community SD 2,800/K-12
851 6th Avenue Rd 49093 269-279-1100
Roger Rathburn, supt. Fax 279-5584
www.trschools.org
Three Rivers HS 800/9-12
700 6th Ave 49093 269-279-1120
Jean Logan, prin. Fax 273-8014
Three Rivers MS 600/6-8
1101 Jefferson St 49093 269-279-1130
Chad Cottingham, prin. Fax 279-1139
Barrows Adult Education Adult
416 Washington St 49093 269-279-9581
Judy Wordelman, dean Fax 278-5103

Traverse City, Grand Traverse, Pop. 14,412
Traverse Bay Area ISD
PO Box 6020 49696 231-922-6200
Michael Hill, supt. Fax 922-6270
www.tbaisd.k12.mi.us
TBA Career Tech Center Vo/Tech
880 Parsons Rd 49686 231-922-6273
Fax 922-6364

Traverse City Area SD 9,700/PK-12
412 Webster St 49686 231-933-1700
Stephen Cousins, supt. Fax 933-1721
www.tcaps.net
Traverse City Central HS 1,500/9-12
1150 Milliken Dr 49686 231-933-3500
Rick Vandermolen, prin. Fax 933-3506
Traverse City East MS 900/6-8
1776 3 Mile Rd N 49696 231-933-7300
Steve Urbanski, prin. Fax 933-6998
Traverse City HS 200/Alt
3962 3 Mile Rd N 49686 231-933-5860
Lance Morgan, prin. Fax 933-5885
Traverse City West HS 1,800/9-12
5376 N Long Lake Rd 49685 231-933-7500
Joe Tibaldi, prin. Fax 933-7506
Traverse City West MS 1,200/6-8
3950 Silver Lake Rd 49684 231-933-8200
Pam Alfieri, prin. Fax 933-8205

Davenport University Post-Sec.
2200 Dendrinos Dr Ste 104 49684 231-995-1740
Munson Medical Center Post-Sec.
1105 6th St 49684 231-935-6501
Northwestern Michigan College Post-Sec.
1701 E Front St 49686 231-922-1000
St. Elizabeth Ann Seton MS 200/6-8
1601 3 Mile Rd N 49696 231-932-4810
Tim Shrift, prin. Fax 932-4814
St. Francis of Assisi HS 300/9-12
123 E 11th St 49684 231-946-8038
Erick Chittle, prin. Fax 946-1878
Traverse City Christian S 300/PK-12
753 Emerson Rd 49696 231-929-1747
Anthony Clymer, admin. Fax 929-1831

Trenton, Wayne, Pop. 18,620
Trenton SD 2,700/K-12
2603 Charlton Rd 48183 734-676-8600
Rodney Wakeham, supt. Fax 676-4851
www.trentonschools.com
Arthurs MS 700/6-8
4000 Marian Dr 48183 734-676-8700
Stephanie O'Connor, prin. Fax 676-7364
Trenton HS 1,000/9-12
2601 Charlton Rd 48183 734-692-4530
Michael Doyle Ed.D., prin. Fax 692-4615

Troy, Oakland, Pop. 79,352
Troy SD 11,900/K-12
4400 Livernois Rd 48098 248-823-4000
Dr. Barbara Fowler, supt. Fax 823-4013
www.troy.k12.mi.us
Athens HS 1,700/9-12
4333 John R Rd 48085 248-823-2900
Lara Dixon, prin. Fax 823-2913
Baker MS 700/6-8
1291 Torpey Dr 48083 248-823-4600
Larry Hahn, prin. Fax 823-4613
Boulan Park MS 700/6-8
3570 Northfield Pkwy 48084 248-823-4900
Jo Kwasny, prin. Fax 823-4913
International Academy East 100/9-12
1291 Torpey Dr 48083 248-283-8300
Larson MS 700/6-8
2222 E Long Lake Rd 48085 248-823-4800
Joseph Duda, prin. Fax 823-4813
Niles Community HS 100/Alt
201 W Square Lake Rd 48098 248-823-5100
Richard Machesky, admin.
Smith MS 700/6-8
5835 Donaldson Dr 48085 248-823-4700
Timothy Fulcher, prin. Fax 823-4713
Troy HS 2,000/9-12
4777 Northfield Pkwy 48098 248-823-2700
Mark Dziatczak, prin. Fax 823-2713

Bethany Christian S 300/K-12
2601 John R Rd 48083 248-689-4821
Philip Fitzgerald, prin. Fax 689-3441
Carnegie Institute Post-Sec.
550 Stephenson Hwy Ste 100 48083 248-589-1078
Christian Leadership Academy 200/K-12
3668 Livernois Rd Ste B 48083 248-457-1510
Robin Schmidt, prin. Fax 457-1520
Intl Academy of Design and Technology Post-Sec.
1850 Research Dr 48083 248-457-2700
ITT Technical Institute Post-Sec.
1522 E Big Beaver Rd 48083 248-524-1800
Walsh Coll. Accountancy & Bus. Admin. Post-Sec.
PO Box 7006 48007 248-689-8282

Twining, Arenac, Pop. 180
Arenac Eastern SD 200/PK-12
PO Box 98 48766 989-867-4234
Darren Kroczaleski, supt. Fax 867-4241
www.arenaceastern.org
Arenac Eastern S 200/PK-12
PO Box 98 48766 989-867-4234
Darren Kroczaleski, supt. Fax 867-4241

Ubly, Sanilac, Pop. 853
Ubly Community SD 700/K-12
2020 Union St 48475 989-658-8202
Rocky Aldrich, supt. Fax 658-2361
www.ublyschools.org
Ubly HS 300/7-12
2020 Union St 48475 989-658-8554
Steve Noble, prin. Fax 658-2072

Union City, Branch, Pop. 1,560
Union City Community SD 1,100/PK-12
430 Saint Joseph St 49094 517-741-8091
Patrick Kreger, supt. Fax 741-5205
www.unioncityschools.org/
Union City HS 300/9-12
430 Saint Joseph St 49094 517-741-8561
Christina Feneley, prin. Fax 741-5205
Union City MS 400/5-8
430 Saint Joseph St 49094 517-741-5381
Brandon Bruce, prin. Fax 741-8513

University Center, Bay

Delta College Post-Sec.
1961 Delta Rd 48710 989-686-9000

Saginaw Valley State University — Post-Sec.
7400 Bay Rd 48710 — 989-964-4000

Utica, Macomb, Pop. 4,675
Utica Community SD
Supt. — See Sterling Heights
Eppler JHS — 700/7-9
45461 Brownell St 48317 — 586-797-2900
Brandon Manzella, prin. — Fax 797-2901
Utica SHS — 1,400/10-12
47255 Shelby Rd 48317 — 586-797-2200
Janet Jones, prin. — Fax 797-2201

Vanderbilt, Otsego, Pop. 548
Vanderbilt Area SD — 100/K-12
947 Donovan St 49795 — 989-983-2561
Michelle Kihn, supt. — Fax 983-3051
www.vanderbilt.k12.mi.us
Vanderbilt Area S — 100/K-12
947 Donovan St 49795 — 989-983-2561
Michelle Kihn, supt. — Fax 983-3051

Vassar, Tuscola, Pop. 2,631
Vassar SD — 1,200/PK-12
220 Athletic St 48768 — 989-823-8535
Thomas Palmer, supt. — Fax 823-7823
www.vassar.k12.mi.us
Pioneer Work & Learn Center — 200/Alt
150 Enterprise Dr 48768 — 989-823-9303
Charles Fabbro, prin. — Fax 823-3733
Vassar HS — 500/9-12
220 Athletic St 48768 — 989-823-8534
Paul Wojno, prin. — Fax 823-7823
Vassar JHS — 200/6-8
220 Athletic St 48768 — 989-823-8533
Paul Wojno, prin. — Fax 823-7823

Juniata Christian S — 100/K-12
5656 Washburn Rd 48768 — 989-843-5326
Phil Green, admin.

Vermontville, Eaton, Pop. 745
Maple Valley SD — 1,000/PK-12
11090 Nashville Hwy 49096 — 517-852-9699
Michelle Falcon, supt. — Fax 852-5076
mvs.k12.mi.us
Maple Valley JSHS — 600/6-12
11090 Nashville Hwy 49096 — 517-852-9275
Todd Gonser, prin. — Fax 852-2283
Maple Valley Pathways HS — 50/Alt
11090 Nashville Hwy 49096 — 517-852-2322
Kristine Stewart, prin.

Vestaburg, Montcalm
Vestaburg Community SD — 600/K-12
7188 Avenue B 48891 — 989-268-5353
Jeffrey Beal, supt. — Fax 268-5852
www.vcs-k12.net
Vestaburg JSHS — 200/7-12
7188 Avenue B 48891 — 989-268-5343
Brandon Hubbard, prin. — Fax 268-5246

Vicksburg, Kalamazoo, Pop. 2,854
Vicksburg Community SD — 2,600/PK-12
PO Box 158 49097 — 269-321-1000
Charles Glaes, supt. — Fax 321-1055
www.vicksburgcommunityschools.org/
Vicksburg HS — 800/9-12
501 E Highway St 49097 — 269-321-1100
Keevin O'Neill, prin. — Fax 321-1155
Vicksburg MS — 600/6-8
348 E Prairie St 49097 — 269-321-1300
Laura Kuhlman, prin. — Fax 321-1355

Wakefield, Gogebic, Pop. 1,831
Wakefield-Marenisco SD — 300/K-12
715 Putnam St 49968 — 906-224-9421
Catherine Shamion, supt. — Fax 224-1771
www.wmschools.org
Wakefield-Marenisco S — 300/K-12
715 Putnam St 49968 — 906-224-7211
Catherine Shamion, supt. — Fax 224-1771

Waldron, Hillsdale, Pop. 534
Waldron Area SD — 100/K-12
13380 Waldron Rd 49288 — 517-286-6251
Dr. William Stitt, supt. — Fax 286-6254
www.waldronschools.com
Waldron Area S — 100/K-12
13380 Waldron Rd 49288 — 517-286-6251
Dr. William Stitt, admin. — Fax 286-6254

Walkerville, Oceana, Pop. 238
Walkerville SD — 200/PK-12
145 Lathrop St 49459 — 231-873-4850
Michael Sweet, supt. — Fax 873-5615
www.walkerville.k12.mi.us
Walkerville MS — 6-8
145 Lathrop St 49459 — 231-873-3652
Michael Sweet, prin. — Fax 873-5615
Walkerville MSHS — 100/9-12
145 Lathrop St 49459 — 231-873-3652
Michael Sweet, prin. — Fax 873-5615

Walled Lake, Oakland, Pop. 6,836
Walled Lake Consolidated SD — 14,500/PK-12
850 Ladd Rd Bldg D 48390 — 248-956-2000
Kenneth Gutman M.A., supt. — Fax 956-2123
www.wlcsd.org
Geisler MS — 900/6-8
46720 W Pontiac Trl 48390 — 248-956-2900
Colleen Sturgill, prin. — Fax 956-2905
Western HS — 1,500/9-12
600 Beck Rd 48390 — 248-956-4400
Joe Bell, prin. — Fax 956-4405
Other Schools – See Commerce Township, West Bloomfield, Wixom

Warren, Macomb, Pop. 130,738
Fitzgerald SD — 2,900/PK-12
23200 Ryan Rd 48091 — 586-757-1750
Barbara VanSweden, supt. — Fax 758-0991
www.fitz.k12.mi.us
Chatterton MS — 600/6-8
24333 Ryan Rd 48091 — 586-757-6650
Marcia Dryer, prin. — Fax 758-0928
Fitzgerald HS — 1,000/9-12
23200 Ryan Rd 48091 — 586-757-7070
Carl Schultz, prin. — Fax 757-5536

Van Dyke SD — 2,600/PK-12
23500 Mac Arthur Blvd 48089 — 586-757-6600
Joseph Pius, supt. — Fax 759-9408
www.vdps.net
Lincoln HS — 800/9-12
22900 Federal Ave 48089 — 586-758-8307
Thomas Hill, prin. — Fax 758-8304
Lincoln MS — 700/6-8
22500 Federal Ave 48089 — 586-758-8320
Carol Anthony, prin. — Fax 758-8322

Warren Consolidated SD — 15,700/K-12
31300 Anita Dr 48093 — 586-825-2400
Dr. Robert Livernois, supt. — Fax 698-4095
www.wcskids.net
Beer MS — 700/6-8
3200 Martin Rd 48092 — 586-574-3175
Annette Lauria, prin. — Fax 698-4277
Butcher Community HS — 400/Alt
27500 Cosgrove Dr 48092 — 586-698-4394
Dr. Catherine Neuhoff, prin. — Fax 698-4397
Carter MS — 900/6-8
12000 Masonic Blvd 48093 — 586-825-2620
Amy Hendry, prin. — Fax 698-4295
Cousino HS — 1,800/9-12
30333 Hoover Rd 48093 — 586-574-3100
Stephen Bigelow, prin. — Fax 698-4204
Macomb Math/Science/Tech Center — 8-12
27500 Cosgrove Dr 48092 — 586-698-4394
Dr. Catherine Neuhoff, prin. — Fax 698-4397
Warren-Mott HS — 1,900/9-12
3131 E 12 Mile Rd 48092 — 586-574-3250
John Dignan, prin. — Fax 698-4226
Other Schools – See Sterling Heights

Warren Woods SD — 3,200/K-12
12900 Frazho Rd 48089 — 586-439-4400
Stacey Denewith-Fici, supt. — Fax 353-0544
warrenwoods.misd.net
Warren Woods MS — 800/6-8
13400 E 12 Mile Rd 48088 — 586-439-4403
Jennifer McFarlane, prin. — Fax 574-9830
Warren Woods Tower HS — 1,200/9-12
27900 Bunert Rd 48088 — 586-439-4402
Michael Mackenzie, prin. — Fax 445-8013

Davenport University — Post-Sec.
27650 Dequindre Rd 48092 — 586-558-8700
De La Salle Collegiate HS — 800/9-12
14600 Common Rd 48088 — 586-778-2207
Patrick Adams, prin. — Fax 778-6016
Lawton Career Institute — Post-Sec.
13877 E 8 Mile Rd 48089 — 586-777-7344
Macomb Christian S — 200/PK-12
28501 Lorraine Ave 48093 — 586-751-8980
Dr. Margie Baldwin, supt. — Fax 751-7946
Macomb Community College — Post-Sec.
14500 E 12 Mile Rd 48088 — 586-445-7999
Regina HS — 500/9-12
13900 Masonic Blvd 48088 — 586-585-0500
Ann Diamond, prin. — Fax 585-0507

Washington, Macomb
Romeo Community SD
Supt. — See Romeo
Powell MS — 700/6-8
62100 Jewell Rd 48094 — 586-752-0270
Jeffrey LaPerriere, prin. — Fax 752-0276

Waterford, Oakland, Pop. 74,500
Oakland ISD
2111 Pontiac Lake Rd 48328 — 248-209-2000
Vickie Markavitch, supt. — Fax 209-2206
www.oakland.k12.mi.us
Other Schools – See Clarkston, Pontiac, Royal Oak, Wixom

Waterford SD — 11,000/PK-12
501 N Cass Lake Rd 48328 — 248-682-7800
John Silveri, supt. — Fax 706-4888
www.wsdmi.org
Kettering HS — 1,600/9-12
2800 Kettering Dr 48329 — 248-673-1261
Jeffrey Frankowiak, prin. — Fax 673-1778
Mason MS — 1,300/6-8
3835 W Walton Blvd 48329 — 248-674-2281
Roger Opsommer, prin. — Fax 673-3718
Mott HS — 1,600/9-12
1151 Scott Lake Rd 48328 — 248-674-4134
Craig Blomquist, prin. — Fax 674-2825
Pierce MS — 1,100/6-8
5145 Hatchery Rd 48329 — 248-674-0331
Yvonne Dixon, prin. — Fax 674-4222
Waterford Durant HS — 200/Alt
501 N Cass Lake Rd 48328 — 248-674-3145
Monica Lee, prin. — Fax 674-6320

Michigan College of Beauty — Post-Sec.
5620 Dixie Hwy 48329 — 248-623-9494
Oakland Community College — Post-Sec.
7350 Cooley Lake Rd 48327 — 248-942-3100
Our Lady of the Lakes HS — 300/6-12
5495 Dixie Hwy 48329 — 248-623-0340
Kathy Lewis, prin. — Fax 623-2274

Watersmeet, Gogebic, Pop. 416
Watersmeet Township SD — 200/K-12
PO Box 217 49969 — 906-358-4504
George Peterson, supt. — Fax 358-4713
www.watersmeet.k12.mi.us/
Watersmeet Township S — 200/K-12
PO Box 217 49969 — 906-358-4555
George Peterson, prin. — Fax 358-3036

Watervliet, Berrien, Pop. 1,689
Watervliet SD — 1,300/K-12
450 E Red Arrow Hwy 49098 — 269-463-5566
Kevin Schooley, supt. — Fax 463-6809
www.watervliet.k12.mi.us/
Watervliet HS — 400/9-12
450 E Red Arrow Hwy 49098 — 269-463-4221
Greg Chisek, prin. — Fax 463-6809
Watervliet MS — 300/6-8
450 E Red Arrow Hwy 49098 — 269-463-0342
Dave Armstrong, prin. — Fax 463-0325

Grace Christian S — 200/PK-12
325 N M 140 49098 — 269-463-5545
Jonathan Kohns Ed.D., admin. — Fax 463-5739

Wayland, Allegan, Pop. 3,998
Wayland UNSD — 2,700/PK-12
850 E Superior St 49348 — 269-792-2101
Norman Taylor, supt. — Fax 792-1615
www.wayland.k12.mi.us
Wayland HS — 900/9-12
870 E Superior St 49348 — 269-792-2254
Thomas Cutler, prin. — Fax 792-2116
Wayland Union MS — 400/7-8
701 Wildcat Dr 49348 — 269-792-2306
Carolyn Whyte, prin. — Fax 792-1126

Wayne, Wayne, Pop. 17,081
Wayne-Westland Community SD
Supt. — See Westland
Franklin MS — 900/7-8
33555 Annapolis St 48184 — 734-419-2400
Sandra Brock, prin. — Fax 595-2401
Wayne Memorial HS — 1,800/9-12
3001 4th St 48184 — 734-419-2200
Fax 595-2227

Dorsey School of Business — Post-Sec.
35005 W Michigan Ave 48184 — 734-595-1540
Oakwood - Hospital Annapolis Center — Post-Sec.
33155 Annapolis St 48184 — 734-467-4000

Webberville, Ingham, Pop. 1,262
Webberville Community SD — 500/PK-12
309 E Grand River Rd 48892 — 517-521-3422
Brian Friddle, supt. — Fax 521-4139
www.webbervilleschools.org
Webberville JSHS — 200/6-12
309 E Grand River Rd 48892 — 517-521-3447
Kathy Pierman, prin. — Fax 521-4740

West Bloomfield, Oakland, Pop. 67,200
Bloomfield Hills SD
Supt. — See Bloomfield Hls
Model HS — Alt
3333 W Long Lake Rd 48323 — 248-341-5960
Bill Boyle, prin. — Fax 341-5999
West Hills MS — 600/4-8
2601 Lone Pine Rd 48323 — 248-341-6100
Rob Durecka, prin. — Fax 341-6199

Walled Lake Consolidated SD
Supt. — See Walled Lake
Walnut Creek MS — 900/6-8
7601 Walnut Lake Rd 48323 — 248-956-2400
Carol Lyn McKelvey, prin. — Fax 956-2405

West Bloomfield SD — 6,600/K-12
5810 Commerce Rd 48324 — 248-865-6420
Dr. Gerald Hill, supt. — Fax 865-6481
www.westbloomfield.k12.mi.us
Abbott MS — 800/6-8
3380 Orchard Lake Rd 48324 — 248-865-3670
Amy Hughes, prin. — Fax 865-3671
Orchard Lake MS — 700/6-8
6000 Orchard Lake Rd 48322 — 248-865-4480
Morrison Borders, prin. — Fax 865-4481
West Bloomfield HS — 1,900/9-12
4925 Orchard Lake Rd 48323 — 248-865-6720
Thomas Shelton, prin. — Fax 865-6721
Other Schools – See Farmington Hills

Frankel Jewish Academy — 200/9-12
6600 W Maple Rd 48322 — 248-592-5263
Rabbi Eric Grossman, hdmstr. — Fax 592-0022
Michigan Jewish Institute — Post-Sec.
6890 W Maple Rd 48322 — 248-414-6900

West Branch, Ogemaw, Pop. 2,115
West Branch-Rose City Area SD — 2,100/K-12
PO Box 308 48661 — 989-343-2000
Daniel Cwayna, supt. — Fax 343-2006
www.wbrc.k12.mi.us/
Ogemaw Heights HS — 800/9-12
PO Box 308 48661 — 989-343-2020
Jonathan Good, prin. — Fax 343-2130
Surline MS — 500/5-8
PO Box 308 48661 — 989-343-2140
Patsy Marchel, prin. — Fax 343-2239

Westland, Wayne, Pop. 82,217
Livonia SD
Supt. — See Livonia
Western Wayne Skill Center — Vo/Tech
8075 Ritz Ave 48185 — 734-744-2810
Alphonse DiPaolo, prin. — Fax 744-2811

Wayne-Westland Community SD 12,900/PK-12
36745 Marquette St 48185 734-419-2000
Gregory Baracy Ed.D., supt. Fax 595-2123
www.wwcsd.net/
Ford Career-Technical Center Vo/Tech
36455 Marquette St 48185 734-419-2100
Steven Kay, prin. Fax 595-2127
Glenn HS 2,100/9-12
36105 Marquette St 48185 734-419-2300
David Ingham, prin. Fax 595-2338
Stevenson MS 1,000/7-8
38501 Palmer Rd 48186 734-419-2350
Adam Martin, prin. Fax 595-2692
Tinkham Alternative Education 50/Alt
450 S Venoy Rd 48186 734-419-2436
Bill Swartz, dir. Fax 595-2439
Tinkham Adult and Community Education Adult
450 S Venoy Rd 48186 734-419-2427
Christopher Solano, dir. Fax 595-2439
Other Schools – See Wayne

Huron Valley Lutheran HS 100/9-12
33740 Cowan Rd 48185 734-525-0160
Daniel Schultz, prin. Fax 525-6717
Lutheran HS Westland 200/9-12
33300 Cowan Rd 48185 734-422-2090
Steven Schwecke, prin. Fax 422-8566

Westphalia, Clinton, Pop. 918
Pewamo-Westphalia SD 500/K-12
5101 S Clintonia Rd 48894 989-587-5100
Jason Mellema, supt. Fax 587-5120
www.pwschools.org
Pewamo-Westphalia MSHS 300/6-12
5101 S Clintonia Rd 48894 989-587-5100
Todd Simmons, prin. Fax 587-3550

White Cloud, Newaygo, Pop. 1,346
White Cloud SD 1,100/PK-12
PO Box 1003 49349 231-689-6591
Barry Seabrook, supt. Fax 689-3210
www.whitecloud.net
White Cloud HS 300/9-12
PO Box 1000 49349 231-689-1707
Ed Canning, prin. Fax 689-3349
White Cloud MS 300/6-8
PO Box 1001 49349 231-689-2181
Ed Canning, prin. Fax 689-3339

Whitehall, Muskegon, Pop. 2,657
Whitehall SD 2,100/PK-12
541 E Slocum St 49461 231-893-1005
Jerry McDowell, supt. Fax 894-6450
www.whitehallschools.net
Whitehall HS 700/9-12
3100 White Lake Dr 49461 231-893-1020
Dale McKenzie, prin. Fax 893-2923
Whitehall MS 500/6-8
401 S Elizabeth St 49461 231-893-1030
Bill O'Brien, prin. Fax 894-6844

White Lake, Oakland, Pop. 22,608
Huron Valley SD
Supt. — See Highland
International Academy West HS 9-12
1630 Bogie Lake Rd 48383 248-676-2735
Lynne Gibson, prin. Fax 676-2734
Lakeland HS 1,700/9-12
1630 Bogie Lake Rd 48383 248-676-8320
Paul Gmelin, prin. Fax 676-8382
White Lake MS 600/6-8
1450 Bogie Lake Rd 48383 248-684-8004
Kristin McMurren, prin. Fax 676-8437

White Pigeon, Saint Joseph, Pop. 1,492
White Pigeon Community SD 800/K-12
410 Prairie Ave 49099 269-483-7676
Ronald Drzewicki, supt. Fax 483-2256
www.wpcschools.org
White Pigeon JSHS 400/6-12
410 Prairie Ave 49099 269-483-7679
Jon Keyer, prin. Fax 483-8742

Whitmore Lake, Washtenaw, Pop. 6,301
Whitmore Lake SD 1,100/K-12
8845 Main St 48189 734-449-4464
Kimberley Hart, supt. Fax 449-5336
www.wlps.net/
Whitmore Lake HS 400/9-12
7430 Whitmore Lake Rd 48189 734-449-4461
Tom DeKeyser, prin. Fax 449-5576
Whitmore Lake MS 300/5-8
8877 Main St 48189 734-449-4715
Michael Benczarski, prin. Fax 449-1042

Whittemore, Iosco, Pop. 377
Whittemore-Prescott Area SD 700/PK-12
PO Box 250 48770 989-756-2500
Ted Matuszak, supt. Fax 756-2278
www.wpas.net/
Whittemore-Prescott Area HS 300/9-12
PO Box 250 48770 989-756-2400
Bunny Miller, prin. Fax 756-3363

Williamston, Ingham, Pop. 3,766
Williamston Community SD 1,800/PK-12
418 Highland St 48895 517-655-4361
Narda Murphy, supt. Fax 655-7500
www.gowcs.net
Williamston HS 600/9-12
3939 Vanneter Rd 48895 517-655-2142
Dr. Jeffrey Thoenes, prin. Fax 655-7501
Williamston MS 500/6-8
3845 Vanneter Rd 48895 517-655-4668
Scott Martin, prin. Fax 655-7502

Wilson, Menominee, Pop. 1,391

Wilson SDA Academy 50/1-10
N13925 County Road 551 49896 906-639-2566
Casey Hann, prin. Fax 639-2566

Wixom, Oakland, Pop. 13,242
Oakland ISD
Supt. — See Waterford
Oakland Technical Campus SW Vo/Tech
1000 Beck Rd 48393 248-668-5600
Scott Harris, dean Fax 668-5670

Walled Lake Consolidated SD
Supt. — See Walled Lake
Banks MS 900/6-8
1760 Charms Rd 48393 248-956-2200
Brad Paddock, prin. Fax 956-2205

St. Catherine of Siena Academy 9-12
28200 Napier Rd 48393 248-946-4848
Kathy Tarnacki, prin. Fax 438-1679
Wixom Christian S 100/PK-12
620 N Wixom Rd 48393 248-624-4362
Brad Stille, admin. Fax 624-1068

Wolverine, Cheboygan, Pop. 234
Wolverine Community SD 300/K-12
PO Box 219 49799 231-525-8201
Joe Hart, supt. Fax 525-8591
www.wolverine.k12.mi.us
Wolverine HS 200/7-12
PO Box 219 49799 231-525-9050
Douglas Tippett, prin. Fax 525-8251

Woodhaven, Wayne, Pop. 12,674
Gibraltar SD 3,600/PK-12
19370 Vreeland Rd 48183 734-379-6350
Bruce Burger, supt. Fax 379-6353
www.gibdist.net
Other Schools – See Gibraltar, Rockwood

Woodhaven-Brownstown SD 4,900/K-12
24821 Hall Rd 48183 734-783-3300
Mark Greathead, supt. Fax 783-3316
www.woodhaven.k12.mi.us
Henry MS 700/8-9
24825 Hall Rd 48183 734-362-6100
Molly Mazei, prin. Fax 362-3045
Other Schools – See Brownstown

Woodland, Barry, Pop. 422
Lakewood SD 2,100/K-12
223 W Broadway St 48897 616-374-8043
Michael O'Mara, supt. Fax 374-8858
www.lakewoodps.org
Lakewood MS 500/6-8
8699 Brown Rd 48897 616-374-2400
David Nisbet, prin. Fax 374-2424
Other Schools – See Lake Odessa

Wyandotte, Wayne, Pop. 25,476
Wyandotte SD 4,700/PK-12
PO Box 130 48192 734-759-5000
Dr. Carla Harting, supt. Fax 759-6009
www.wyandotte.org
Roosevelt HS 1,300/9-12
540 Eureka Rd 48192 734-759-5000
Thomas Kell, prin. Fax 759-5009
Wilson MS 1,000/6-8
1275 15th St 48192 734-759-5300
Jason Krajewski, prin. Fax 759-5309

Wyoming, Kent, Pop. 70,258
Godfrey-Lee SD 1,700/PK-12
1324 Burton St SW 49509 616-241-4722
David Britten, supt. Fax 241-4707
www.godfrey-lee.org/
East Lee Campus 100/Alt
982 Lee St SW 49509 616-241-2661
James Jenson, prin. Fax 241-2664
Lee HS 400/9-12
1335 Lee St SW 49509 616-452-3296
Kathryn Curry, prin. Fax 241-4677
Lee MS 400/6-8
1335 Lee St SW 49509 616-452-3298
Kathryn Curry, prin. Fax 241-4677

Godwin Heights SD 2,500/PK-12
15 36th St SW 49548 616-252-2090
William Fetterhoff, supt. Fax 252-2232
www.godwinschools.org
Godwin Heights HS 600/9-12
50 35th St SW 49548 616-252-2050
Chad Tolson, prin. Fax 252-2067
Godwin Heights Learning Center 500/Alt
3529 Division Ave S 49548 616-252-2040
Chad Tolson, dir. Fax 252-2043
Godwin Heights MS 600/5-8
111 36th St SE 49548 616-252-2070
Jeffrey Johnson, dean Fax 252-2075

Kelloggsville SD
Supt. — See Grand Rapids
Discovery Alternative HS 200/Alt
173 54th St SW 49548 616-531-7433
Tammy Savage, prin. Fax 531-6996

Wyoming SD 4,100/PK-12
3575 Gladiola Ave SW, 616-530-7550
Dr. Thomas Reeder, supt. Fax 530-7557
www.wyoming.k12.mi.us
Wyoming HS 900/9-12
1350 Prairie Pkwy SW 49509 616-530-7580
Bradley Perkins, prin. Fax 530-7589
Wyoming JHS 700/7-8
2125 Wrenwood St SW, 616-530-7590
Jon Blackburn, prin. Fax 249-7673

ITT Technical Institute Post-Sec.
1980 Metro Ct SW, 616-406-1200
Potter's House HS 100/9-12
2500 Newport St SW, 616-249-8050
Paul Dull, prin. Fax 249-8555
Tri-Unity Christian HS 100/7-12
2104 44th St SW, 616-532-8827
Deb Blanker, prin. Fax 532-8701
West Michigan Lutheran HS 100/9-12
601 36th St SW 49509 616-455-2200
Robert Patrick, prin. Fax 455-2211

Yale, Saint Clair, Pop. 1,919
Yale SD 2,100/K-12
198 School Dr 48097 810-387-3231
Ken Nicholl, supt. Fax 387-4418
www.ypsd.us/
Yale HS 700/9-12
247 School Dr 48097 810-387-3231
Paul Flynn, prin. Fax 387-9108
Yale JHS 600/6-8
198 School Dr 48097 810-387-3231
Brad Dykstra, prin. Fax 387-9207

Ypsilanti, Washtenaw, Pop. 18,646
Ann Arbor SD
Supt. — See Ann Arbor
Clemente Development Center 100/Alt
4377 Textile Rd 48197 734-997-1236
Benjamin Edmondson, prin. Fax 997-1903

Lincoln Consolidated SD 4,200/PK-12
8970 Whittaker Rd 48197 734-484-7000
Ellen Bonter, supt. Fax 484-1212
www.lincolnk12.org/
Lincoln HS 1,400/9-12
7425 Willis Rd 48197 734-484-7004
Mandy Stewart, prin. Fax 484-7012
Lincoln MS 1,100/6-8
8744 Whittaker Rd 48197 734-484-7033
Christopher Roberts, prin. Fax 484-7088

Ypsilanti Community SD 3,500/PK-12
1885 Packard Rd 48197 734-927-4636
Scott Menzel, supt. Fax 714-1220
www.ycschools.us
Ypsilanti Community MS 400/5-8
235 Spencer Ln 48198 734-714-1400
Ypsilanti HS 1,000/9-12
2095 Packard Rd 48197 734-714-1000
Kelly Mickel, prin. Fax 714-1029

Calvary Christian Academy 200/K-12
1007 Ecorse Rd 48198 734-482-1990
Cathy White, prin. Fax 484-5118
Eastern Michigan University 48197 Post-Sec.
734-487-1849

Zeeland, Ottawa, Pop. 5,407
Zeeland SD 5,900/PK-12
PO Box 110 49464 616-748-3000
Cal De Kuiper, supt. Fax 748-3035
www.zps.org/
Cityside MS 800/6-8
320 E Main Ave 49464 616-748-3200
Sarah Huizenga, prin. Fax 748-3210
Creekside MS 500/6-8
179 W Roosevelt Ave 49464 616-748-3300
Greg Eding, prin. Fax 748-3325
Summit S 50/Alt
3333 96th Ave 49464 616-748-4770
Roberta Brown-Parker, dir. Fax 748-1404
Zeeland East HS 1,100/9-12
3333 96th Ave 49464 616-748-3100
Marc VanSoest, prin. Fax 748-3198
Zeeland West HS 700/9-12
3390 100th Ave 49464 616-748-4500
Colleen Johnson, prin. Fax 748-4505

MINNESOTA

MN DEPARTMENT OF EDUCATION
1500 Highway 36 W, Roseville 55113-4035
Telephone 651-582-8200
Website education.state.mn.us

Commissioner of Education Dr. Brenda Cassellius

PUBLIC, PRIVATE AND CATHOLIC SECONDARY SCHOOLS

Ada, Norman, Pop. 1,681
Ada-Borup SD 2854 500/PK-12
604 W Thorpe Ave 56510 218-784-5300
Michael Kolness, supt. Fax 784-3475
www.ada.k12.mn.us
Ada-Borup JSHS 300/7-12
604 W Thorpe Ave 56510 218-784-5300
Michael Kolness, prin. Fax 784-3475

Adams, Mower, Pop. 779
Southland SD 500 500/K-12
203 NW 2nd St 55909 507-582-3283
Steve Sallee, supt. Fax 582-7813
www.isd500.k12.mn.us
Southland HS 200/9-12
203 NW 2nd St 55909 507-582-3568
Keith Fleming, prin. Fax 582-7813
Southland MS 100/6-8
203 NW 2nd St 55909 507-582-3568
Keith Fleming, prin. Fax 582-7813

Adrian, Nobles, Pop. 1,201
Adrian SD 511 600/PK-12
PO Box 40 56110 507-483-2266
Roger Graff, supt. Fax 483-2342
www.adrianschool.net
Adrian HS 200/9-12
PO Box 40 56110 507-483-2232
Tim Christensen, prin. Fax 483-2375
Adrian MS 100/6-8
PO Box 40 56110 507-483-2232
Tim Christensen, prin. Fax 483-2375

Aitkin, Aitkin, Pop. 2,132
Aitkin SD 1 1,300/PK-12
306 2nd St NW 56431 218-927-2115
Bernie Novak, supt. Fax 927-4234
www.aitkin.k12.mn.us
Aitkin HS 600/7-12
306 2nd St NW 56431 218-927-2115
Chad Pederson, prin. Fax 927-4234

Albany, Stearns, Pop. 2,533
Albany SD 745 1,700/PK-12
PO Box 40 56307 320-845-2171
Steve Dooley, supt. Fax 845-4017
www.albany.k12.mn.us
Albany HS 500/9-12
PO Box 40 56307 320-845-2171
Tim Wege, prin. Fax 845-4017
Albany JHS 300/7-8
PO Box 40 56307 320-845-2171
Charles Griffith, prin. Fax 845-4017

Albert Lea, Freeborn, Pop. 17,797
Albert Lea SD 241 2,700/K-12
211 W Richway Dr 56007 507-379-4800
Dr. Mike Funk, supt. Fax 379-4898
albertlea.k12.mn.us
Albert Lea ALC 100/Alt
211 W Richway Dr 56007 507-379-4850
Nicole Severtson, admin. Fax 379-5498
Albert Lea HS 900/8-12
2000 Tiger Ln 56007 507-379-5340
Jim Wagner, prin. Fax 379-5498

* * *

Riverland Community College Post-Sec.
2200 Riverland Dr 56007 507-379-3300

Albertville, Wright, Pop. 6,921
Saint Michael-Albertville SD 885 4,500/PK-12
11343 50th St NE 55301 763-497-3180
Dr. James Behle, supt. Fax 497-6588
www.stma.k12.mn.us
Saint Michael-Albertville MS West 800/5-8
11343 50th St NE 55301 763-497-4524
Andrew Merfeld, prin. Fax 497-6566
Other Schools – See Saint Michael

Alden, Freeborn, Pop. 654
Alden-Conger ISD 242 500/K-12
PO Box 99 56009 507-874-3240
Brian Grenell, supt. Fax 874-2747
www.alden-conger.org
Alden-Conger HS 200/7-12
PO Box 99 56009 507-874-3240
Brian Shanks, prin. Fax 874-2747

Alexandria, Douglas, Pop. 10,938
Alexandria SD 206 3,800/K-12
PO Box 308 56308 320-762-2141
Rick Lahn, supt. Fax 762-2765
www.alexandria.k12.mn.us
Discovery JHS 900/7-9
510 McKay Ave N 56308 320-762-7900
Matt Aker, prin. Fax 762-8347
Jefferson SHS 900/10-12
1401 Jefferson St 56308 320-762-2142
Chad Duwenhoegger, prin. Fax 762-7749

* * *

Alexandria Technical College Post-Sec.
1601 Jefferson St 56308 320-762-0221

Andover, Anoka, Pop. 30,071
Anoka-Hennepin SD 11
Supt. — See Anoka
Andover HS 1,700/9-12
2115 Andover Blvd NW 55304 763-506-8400
Rhonda Dean, prin. Fax 767-3575
Oak View MS 1,300/6-8
15400 Hanson Blvd NW 55304 763-506-5600
Gary Lundeen, prin. Fax 506-5603

* * *

Legacy Christian Academy 600/PK-12
3037 Bunker Lake Blvd NW 55304 763-427-4595
Steve Larson, pres. Fax 427-3398

Annandale, Wright, Pop. 3,201
Annandale SD 876 1,600/PK-12
PO Box 190 55302 320-274-5602
Steve Niklaus, supt. Fax 274-5978
www.annandale.k12.mn.us
Annandale HS 500/9-12
PO Box 190 55302 320-274-8208
Scot Kerbaugh, prin. Fax 274-2316
Annandale MS 400/6-8
PO Box 190 55302 320-274-8226
Tim Prom, prin. Fax 274-5978

Anoka, Anoka, Pop. 16,703
Anoka-Hennepin SD 11 38,500/K-12
2727 N Ferry St 55303 763-506-1000
Dennis Carlson, supt. Fax 506-1003
www.anoka.k12.mn.us
Anoka HS 2,400/9-12
3939 7th Ave 55303 763-506-6200
Mike Farley, prin. Fax 506-6203
Anoka MS of the Arts - Fred Moore Campus 1,300/7-8
1523 5th Ave 55303 763-506-5000
Jerri McGonigal, prin. Fax 506-6003
Secondary Technical Education Program Vo/Tech
1353 W Highway 10 55303 763-433-4001
Jessica Lipa, dir. Fax 433-4003
Transitions Plus Adult
403 Jackson St Ste 206 55303 763-506-7600
Fax 506-7603
Other Schools – See Andover, Blaine, Champlin, Coon Rapids

* * *

Anoka Technical College Post-Sec.
1355 W Highway 10 55303 763-576-4700

Apple Valley, Dakota, Pop. 47,792
Rosemount-Apple Valley-Eagan ISD 196
Supt. — See Rosemount
Apple Valley HS 1,800/9-12
14450 Hayes Rd 55124 952-431-8200
Steve Degenaar, prin. Fax 431-8744
Area Learning Center 200/Alt
5840 149th St W 55124 952-431-8720
David Schmitz, coord. Fax 431-8722
Eastview HS 2,200/9-12
6200 140th St W 55124 952-431-8900
Randall Peterson, prin. Fax 431-8911
Falcon Ridge MS 1,100/6-8
12900 Johnny Cake Ridge Rd 55124 952-431-8760
Noel Mehus, prin. Fax 431-8770
School of Enviromental Studies 400/11-12
12155 Johnny Cake Ridge Rd 55124 952-431-8750
Dan Bodette, prin. Fax 431-8755
Scott Highlands MS 800/6-8
14011 Pilot Knob Rd 55124 952-423-7581
Daniel Wilharber, prin. Fax 423-7601
Valley MS 900/6-8
900 Garden View Dr 55124 952-431-8300
Dave McKeag, prin. Fax 431-8313

Arden Hills, Ramsey, Pop. 9,377
Mounds View SD 621
Supt. — See Shoreview
Mounds View HS 1,700/9-12
1900 Lake Valentine Rd 55112 651-621-7100
Dr. Jeff Ridlehoover, prin. Fax 621-7105

Arlington, Sibley, Pop. 2,206
Sibley East SD 2310 1,200/PK-12
PO Box 1000 55307 507-964-2292
John Langenbrunner, supt. Fax 964-8224
www.sibleyeast.org/
Sibley East SHS 300/10-12
PO Box 1000 55307 507-964-8235
James Amsden, prin. Fax 964-8245
Other Schools – See Gaylord

Ashby, Grant, Pop. 435
Ashby SD 261 300/PK-12
PO Box 30 56309 218-747-2257
Allan Jensen, supt. Fax 747-2289
www.ashby.k12.mn.us
Ashby JSHS 100/7-12
PO Box 30 56309 218-747-2257
Shane Tappe, prin. Fax 747-2289

* * *

Destiny Academy 50/PK-12
27871 140th Ave 56309 218-747-2646
Stacy Hyttsten, admin. Fax 685-6712

Aurora, Saint Louis, Pop. 1,668
Mesabi East SD 2711 900/PK-12
601 N 1st St W 55705 218-229-3321
Gregg Allen, supt. Fax 229-3736
www.mesabieast.k12.mn.us/
Mesabi East JSHS 400/7-12
601 N 1st St W 55705 218-229-3321
Erik Erie, prin. Fax 229-3736

Austin, Mower, Pop. 24,273
Austin SD 492 4,500/PK-12
401 3rd Ave NW 55912 507-460-1900
David Krenz, supt. Fax 460-1939
www.austin.k12.mn.us
Austin Area Learning Center 100/Alt
301 3rd St NW 55912 507-460-1828
Jason Senne, dir. Fax 460-1810
Austin HS 1,200/9-12
301 3rd St NW 55912 507-460-1800
Bradley Bergstrom, prin. Fax 460-1810
Ellis MS 900/6-8
1700 4th Ave SE 55912 507-460-1500
Katie Berglund, prin. Fax 460-1510

* * *

Pacelli JSHS 100/6-12
311 4th St NW 55912 507-437-3278
Lori Walz, prin. Fax 433-5693
Riverland Community College Post-Sec.
1900 8th Ave NW 55912 507-433-0600

Babbitt, Saint Louis, Pop. 1,456
Saint Louis County SD 2142
Supt. — See Virginia
Northeast Range S 200/PK-12
30 South Dr 55706 218-827-3101
Steve Reznicek, prin. Fax 827-3103

Badger, Roseau, Pop. 364
Badger SD 676 200/PK-12
PO Box 68 56714 218-528-3201
Tom Jerome, supt. Fax 528-3366
www.badger.k12.mn.us/
Badger JSHS 100/7-12
PO Box 68 56714 218-528-3201
Thomas Jerome, prin. Fax 528-3366

Bagley, Clearwater, Pop. 1,356
Bagley SD 162 1,000/PK-12
202 Bagley Ave NW 56621 218-694-6184
Steve Cairns, supt. Fax 694-3221
www.bagley.k12.mn.us/
Bagley JSHS 500/7-12
1130 Main Ave N 56621 218-694-3120
Helen Kennedy, prin. Fax 694-3225

Barnesville, Clay, Pop. 2,545
Barnesville SD 146 800/PK-12
PO Box 189 56514 218-354-2217
Scott Loeslie, supt. Fax 354-7260
www.barnesville.k12.mn.us/
Barnesville JSHS 400/7-12
PO Box 189 56514 218-354-2228
Bryan Strand, prin. Fax 354-2305

Barnum, Carlton, Pop. 583
Barnum SD 91 800/PK-12
3675 County Road 140 55707 218-389-6978
David Bottem, supt. Fax 389-3259
www.barnum.k12.mn.us
Barnum JSHS 300/7-12
3675 County Road 140 55707 218-389-3273
Steve Brandt, prin. Fax 389-3259

Barrett, Grant, Pop. 415
West Central Area SD 2342 600/PK-12
301 County Road 2 56311 320-528-2650
Patrick Westby, supt. Fax 528-2279
www.westcentralareaschools.net
West Central Area Secondary S 300/5-12
301 County Road 2 56311 320-528-2520
Nels Onstad, prin. Fax 528-2609

Battle Lake, Otter Tail, Pop. 865
Battle Lake SD 542 500/K-12
402 W Summit St 56515 218-864-5215
Jeff Drake, supt. Fax 864-0919
www.battlelake.k12.mn.us/

Battle Lake JSHS 200/7-12
402 W Summit St 56515 218-864-5215
Jeff Drake, prin. Fax 864-8651

Baudette, Lake of the Woods, Pop. 1,074
Lake of the Woods SD 390 500/PK-12
PO Box 310 56623 218-634-2735
Jeff Peura, supt. Fax 634-2467
www.blw.k12.mn.us/
Lake of the Woods JSHS 200/7-12
PO Box 310 56623 218-634-2510
Jeff Peura, prin. Fax 634-2750

Baxter, Crow Wing, Pop. 7,503
Brainerd SD 181
Supt. — See Brainerd
Forestview MS 1,900/5-8
12149 Knollwood Dr 56425 218-454-6000
Jonathan Anderson, prin. Fax 454-6687

Lake Region Christian S 200/PK-12
7398 Fairview Rd 56425 218-828-1226
Steve Ogren, prin. Fax 828-1643

Becker, Sherburne, Pop. 4,467
Becker SD 726 2,700/PK-12
12000 Hancock St SE 55308 763-261-4502
Dr. Stephen Malone, supt. Fax 261-4559
www.becker.k12.mn.us
Becker HS 800/9-12
12000 Hancock St SE 55308 763-261-4501
Sandra Logrono, prin. Fax 261-4559
Becker MS 700/6-8
12000 Hancock St SE 55308 763-261-6300
Nancy Helmer, prin. Fax 261-6306

Belgrade, Stearns, Pop. 733
Belgrade-Brooten-Elrosa SD 2364
Supt. — See Brooten
Belgrade-Brooten-Elrosa JSHS 300/7-12
PO Box 339 56312 320-254-8211
Matt Bullard, prin. Fax 254-3784

Belle Plaine, Scott, Pop. 6,520
Belle Plaine SD 716 1,600/PK-12
130 S Willow St 56011 952-873-2400
Dr. Kelly Smith, supt. Fax 873-6909
www.belleplaine.k12.mn.us/
Belle Plaine HS 500/9-12
220 S Market St 56011 952-873-2403
Dave Kreft, prin. Fax 378-2420
Belle Plaine JHS 200/7-8
220 S Market St 56011 952-873-2403
Dave Kreft, prin. Fax 378-2420

Bemidji, Beltrami, Pop. 12,863
Bemidji SD 31 5,000/PK-12
3300 Gillett Dr NW 56601 218-333-3100
James Hess Ed.D., supt. Fax 333-3129
www.bemidji.k12.mn.us
Bemidji Alternative Education Center 50/Alt
3300 Gillett Dr NW 56601 218-333-3299
Tama Wesely, prin. Fax 759-3462
Bemidji HS 1,400/9-12
3300 Gillett Dr NW 56601 218-444-1600
Brian Stefanich, prin. Fax 444-1630
Bemidji MS 1,100/6-8
3300 Gillett Dr NW 56601 218-333-3215
Drew Hildenbrand, prin. Fax 333-3333

Bemidji State University Post-Sec.
1500 Birchmont Dr NE 56601 218-755-2001
Northwest Technical College Post-Sec.
905 Grant Ave SE 56601 218-333-6600
Oak Hills Christian College Post-Sec.
1600 Oak Hills Rd SW 56601 218-751-8670

Benson, Swift, Pop. 3,222
Benson SD 777 700/PK-12
1400 Montana Ave 56215 320-843-2710
Dennis Laumeyer, supt. Fax 843-2262
www.benson.k12.mn.us
Benson Area Learning Center 50/Alt
1400 Montana Ave 56215 320-843-2710
Leah Bloemendaal, dir. Fax 843-2262
Benson HS 300/9-12
1400 Montana Ave 56215 320-843-2710
Dennis Laumeyer, prin. Fax 843-2262
Benson IS 5-8
1400 Montana Ave 56215 320-843-2710
Dennis Laumeyer, prin. Fax 843-2262

Bertha, Todd, Pop. 494
Bertha-Hewitt SD 786 400/K-12
PO Box 8 56437 218-924-2500
Brian Koslofsky, supt. Fax 924-3252
www.bertha-hewitt.k12.mn.us/
Bertha JSHS 200/7-12
PO Box 8 56437 218-924-2500
Mary Merchant, prin. Fax 924-3252

Bigfork, Itasca, Pop. 444
Grand Rapids SD 318
Supt. — See Grand Rapids
Bigfork HS 100/7-12
PO Box 228 56628 218-743-3444
Scott Patrow, prin. Fax 743-3443

Big Lake, Sherburne, Pop. 9,820
Big Lake SD 727 3,500/PK-12
501 Minnesota Ave 55309 763-262-2536
Jonathan Miller, supt. Fax 262-2539
www.biglake.k12.mn.us
Big Lake HS 1,000/9-12
501 Minnesota Ave 55309 763-262-2547
Bob Dockendorf, prin. Fax 262-2543
Big Lake MS 800/6-8
601 Minnesota Ave 55309 763-262-2567
Mark Canton, prin. Fax 262-2563

Birchdale, Koochiching
South Koochiching-Rainy River ISD 363
Supt. — See Northome
Indus JSHS 100/7-12
8560 Highway 11 56629 218-634-2425
Bryan Brown, prin. Fax 634-1334

Blackduck, Beltrami, Pop. 754
Blackduck SD 32 600/PK-12
PO Box 550 56630 218-835-5200
Wallace Schoeb, supt. Fax 835-4491
www.blackduck.k12.mn.us/
Blackduck HS 300/7-12
PO Box 550 56630 218-835-5210
Randy Hansen, prin. Fax 835-5281

Blaine, Anoka, Pop. 55,728
Anoka-Hennepin SD 11
Supt. — See Anoka
Blaine HS 2,900/9-12
12555 University Ave NE 55434 763-506-6500
John Phelps, prin. Fax 506-6503
Roosevelt MS 1,100/6-8
650 125th Ave NE 55434 763-506-5800
Greg Blodgett, prin. Fax 506-5803

Spring Lake Park SD 16
Supt. — See Spring Lake Park
Westwood MS 1,000/6-8
711 91st Ave NE 55434 763-600-5300
Paula Hoff, prin. Fax 600-5313

Globe University MN School of Business Post-Sec.
3680 Pheasant Ridge Dr NE 55449 763-225-8000
Northside Christian S 100/PK-12
804 131st Ave NE 55434 763-755-3993
David Reid, admin. Fax 755-4405
Rasmussen College Post-Sec.
3629 95th Ave NE 55014 763-795-4720
Regency Beauty Academy Post-Sec.
1351 113th Ave NE 55434 763-784-9102

Blooming Prairie, Steele, Pop. 1,975
Blooming Prairie SD 756 700/PK-12
202 4th Ave NW 55917 507-583-4426
Barry Olson, supt. Fax 583-7952
www.blossoms.k12.mn.us
Blooming Prairie JSHS 300/7-12
202 4th Ave NW 55917 507-583-4426
Barry Olson, prin. Fax 583-7952

Bloomington, Hennepin, Pop. 80,538
Bloomington SD 271 10,100/K-12
1350 W 106th St 55431 952-681-6400
Les Fujitake, supt. Fax 681-6401
www.bloomington.k12.mn.us/
Jefferson HS 1,700/9-12
4001 W 102nd St 55437 952-806-7600
Steve Hill, prin. Fax 806-7601
Kennedy HS 1,600/9-12
9701 Nicollet Ave S 55420 952-681-5000
Andrew Beaton, prin. Fax 681-5001
Oak Grove MS 800/6-8
1300 W 106th St 55431 952-681-6600
Brian Ingemann, prin. Fax 681-6601
Olson MS 800/6-8
4551 W 102nd St 55437 952-806-8600
Thomas Lee, prin. Fax 806-8601
Valley View MS 700/6-8
8900 Portland Ave S 55420 952-681-5800
Benjamin Magras, prin. Fax 681-5801

Minneapolis SD 1
Supt. — See Minneapolis
Metropolitan Learning Alliance 100/Alt
141 E Broadway 55425 952-858-9170
Sue Bunting, dir. Fax 858-9181

Academy College Post-Sec.
1101 E 78th St 55420 952-851-0066
Bethany Academy 200/K-12
4300 W 98th St 55437 952-831-8686
Robin Sovine, supt. Fax 831-9568
Empire Beauty School Post-Sec.
9749 Lyndale Ave S 55420 952-881-8662
National American University Post-Sec.
7801 Metro Pkwy Ste 200 55425 952-356-3600
Normandale Community College Post-Sec.
9700 France Ave S 55431 952-358-8200
Northwestern Health Sciences University Post-Sec.
2501 W 84th St 55431 952-888-4777
Rasmussen College Post-Sec.
4400 W 78th St Fl 6 55435 952-545-2000

Blue Earth, Faribault, Pop. 3,328
Blue Earth Area ISD 2860 1,200/K-12
315 E 6th St 56013 507-526-3188
Evan Gough, supt. Fax 526-2432
www.blueearth.k12.mn.us
Blue Earth Area MS 300/6-8
315 E 6th St 56013 507-526-3115
Melissa McGuire, prin. Fax 526-2432
Blue Earth HS 400/9-12
1125 N Grove St 56013 507-526-3201
Richard Schneider, prin. Fax 526-3260

Bluffton, Otter Tail, Pop. 204

SonRise Christian S 50/PK-12
PO Box 65 56518 218-385-3774

Braham, Isanti, Pop. 1,757
Braham SD 314 900/K-12
531 Elmhurst Ave S 55006 320-396-3313
Gregory Winter, supt. Fax 396-3068
www.braham.k12.mn.us
Braham Area JSHS 400/7-12
531 Elmhurst Ave S 55006 320-396-4444
Justin Sawyer, prin. Fax 396-3068

Brainerd, Crow Wing, Pop. 13,204
Brainerd SD 181 6,500/PK-12
804 Oak St 56401 218-454-6900
Steve Razidlo, supt. Fax 454-6901
www.isd181.org/
Brainerd HS South Campus 500/9-9
400 Quince St 56401 218-454-5200
Andrea Rusk, prin. Fax 454-5201
ISD 181 Learning Center 100/Alt
311 10th Ave NE 56401 218-454-5400
Jessica Haapajoki, prin. Fax 454-5401
Brainerd SHS 1,400/10-12
702 S 5th St 56401 218-454-6200
Andrea Rusk, prin. Fax 824-6325
Other Schools – See Baxter

Central Lakes College Post-Sec.
501 W College Dr 56401 218-855-8000
The College of Saint Scholastica Post-Sec.
501 W College Dr 56401 218-855-8006

Brandon, Douglas, Pop. 489
Brandon SD 207 300/PK-12
PO Box 185 56315 320-524-2263
Mark Westby, supt. Fax 524-2228
www.brandon.k12.mn.us
Brandon HS 100/7-12
PO Box 185 56315 320-524-2263
Tom Trisko, prin. Fax 524-2228

Breckenridge, Wilkin, Pop. 3,345
Breckenridge SD 846 700/PK-12
810 Beede Ave 56520 218-643-6822
Rick Bleichner, supt. Fax 641-4035
www.breckenridge.k12.mn.us
Breckenridge HS 300/9-12
710 13th St N 56520 218-643-2694
Ivan Hirst, prin. Fax 643-5229
Breckenridge MS 100/6-8
810 Beede Ave 56520 218-643-6681
Donald Schill, prin. Fax 643-5021

Brooklyn Center, Hennepin, Pop. 28,921
Brooklyn Center SD 286 1,700/PK-12
6500 Humboldt Ave N 55430 763-450-3386
Mark Bonine, supt. Fax 560-2647
brooklyncenterschools.org
Brooklyn Center HS 700/6-12
6500 Humboldt Ave N 55430 763-561-2120
Carly Jarva, prin. Fax 450-3477

Globe University MN School of Business Post-Sec.
5910 Shingle Creek Pkwy 55430 763-566-7777
National American University Post-Sec.
6200 Shingle Creek Pkwy 130 55430 763-852-7500

Brooklyn Park, Hennepin, Pop. 73,081
Osseo SD 279
Supt. — See Maple Grove
Brooklyn JHS 900/7-9
7377 Noble Ave N 55443 763-569-7700
Rob Mendolia, prin. Fax 569-7707
North View Intl Baccalaureate World JHS 600/7-9
5869 69th Ave N 55429 763-585-7200
John Groenke, prin. Fax 585-7210
Osseo Area Learning Center 50/Alt
7300 Boone Ave N 55428 763-391-8890
James Hill, prin. Fax 391-8895
Park Center Intl Baccalaureate World SHS 1,500/10-12
7300 Brooklyn Blvd 55443 763-569-7600
Kelli Parpart, prin. Fax 569-7606

Hennepin Technical College Post-Sec.
9000 Brooklyn Blvd 55445 952-995-1300
Maranatha Christian Academy 700/PK-12
9201 75th Ave N 55428 763-488-7900
Brian Sullivan, admin. Fax 315-7294
North Hennepin Community College Post-Sec.
7411 85th Ave N 55445 763-488-0391
Rasmussen College Post-Sec.
8301 93rd Ave N 55445 763-493-4500

Brooten, Stearns, Pop. 739
Belgrade-Brooten-Elrosa SD 2364 700/PK-12
PO Box 39 56316 320-346-2278
Matt Bullard, supt. Fax 346-2589
www.bbe.k12.mn.us
Other Schools – See Belgrade

Browerville, Todd, Pop. 779
Browerville SD 787 500/PK-12
PO Box 185 56438 320-594-2272
Robert Schaefer, supt. Fax 594-8105
www.browerville.k12.mn.us/
Browerville JSHS 300/7-12
PO Box 185 56438 320-594-2272
Patrick Sutlief, prin. Fax 594-8105

Browns Valley, Traverse, Pop. 577
Browns Valley SD 801 100/PK-8
PO Box N 56219 320-695-2103
Brenda Reed, supt. Fax 695-2868
www.brownsvalley.k12.mn.us/
Browns Valley MS 50/5-8
PO Box N 56219 320-695-2103
Brenda Reed, prin. Fax 695-2868

Buffalo, Wright, Pop. 15,192
Buffalo-Hanover-Montrose SD 5,800/K-12
214 1st Ave NE 55313 763-682-5200
Scott Thielman, supt. Fax 682-8785
www.bhmschools.org
Buffalo Community MS 1,300/6-8
1300 Highway 25 N 55313 763-682-8200
Matt Lubben, prin. Fax 682-8209
Buffalo HS 1,800/9-12
877 Bison Blvd 55313 763-682-8100
Mark Mischke, prin. Fax 682-8118
Phoenix Learning Center 50/Alt
800 8th St NE 55313 763-682-8680
Gretchen Lieb, coord. Fax 682-8681

Burnsville, Dakota, Pop. 58,440
Burnsville-Eagan-Savage ISD 191 9,400/K-12
100 River Ridge Ct 55337 952-707-2000
Randall Clegg, supt. Fax 707-2002
www.isd191.org
Burnsville SHS 2,200/10-12
600 Highway 13 E 55337 952-707-2100
David Helke, prin. Fax 707-2102
Metcalf JHS 600/7-9
2250 Diffley Rd 55337 952-707-2400
Kelly Ronn, prin. Fax 707-2402
Nicollet JHS 600/7-9
400 E 134th St 55337 952-707-2600
Renee Brandner, prin. Fax 707-2602

Other Schools – See Eagan, Savage

Southview Christian S 50/PK-10
15304 County Road 5 55306 952-898-2727
Rayleen Hansen, prin. Fax 898-0457

Butterfield, Watonwan, Pop. 581
Butterfield SD 836 200/K-12
PO Box 189 56120 507-956-2771
Lisa Shellum, supt. Fax 956-3431
butterfield.k12.mn.us/
Butterfield JSHS 100/7-12
PO Box 189 56120 507-956-2771
Lisa Shellum, prin. Fax 956-3431

Byron, Olmsted, Pop. 4,841
Byron SD 531 1,800/PK-12
1887 2nd Ave NW 55920 507-775-2383
Jeffrey Elstad, supt. Fax 775-2385
bears.byron.k12.mn.us
Byron HS 500/9-12
1887 2nd Ave NW 55920 507-775-2301
Michael Duffy, prin. Fax 775-2303
Byron MS 500/5-8
601 4th St NW 55920 507-775-2189
Dr. Richard Jones, prin. Fax 775-2825

Caledonia, Houston, Pop. 2,844
Caledonia SD 299 700/PK-12
511 W Main St 55921 507-725-3389
Benjamin Barton, supt. Fax 725-3558
www.cps.k12.mn.us/
Caledonia Area HS 300/9-12
825 N Warrior Ave 55921 507-725-3316
Paul DeMorett, prin. Fax 725-3319
Caledonia Area MS 100/6-8
825 N Warrior Ave 55921 507-725-3316
Paul DeMorett, prin. Fax 725-3319

Cambridge, Isanti, Pop. 7,948
Cambridge-Isanti SD 911 5,200/PK-12
625A Main St N 55008 763-689-6188
Dr. Raymond Queener, supt. Fax 689-6200
www.cambridge.k12.mn.us
Cambridge-Isanti HS 1,500/9-12
430 8th Ave NW 55008 763-689-6066
Mitchell Clausen, prin. Fax 689-6060
Cambridge MS 600/6-8
31374 Xylite St NE 55008 763-552-6300
Charlie Burroughs, prin. Fax 552-6399
Other Schools – See Isanti

Anoka-Ramsey Community College Post-Sec.
300 Spirit River Dr S 55008 763-433-1100
Cambridge Christian S 200/PK-12
2211 Main St S 55008 763-689-3806
Scott Thune, supt. Fax 689-3807

Campbell, Wilkin, Pop. 158
Campbell-Tintah SD 852 100/PK-12
PO Box 8 56522 218-630-5311
Wayne Olson, supt. Fax 630-5881
www.campbell.k12.mn.us
Campbell-Tintah S 100/PK-12
PO Box 8 56522 218-630-5311
Wayne Olson, admin. Fax 630-5881

Canby, Yellow Medicine, Pop. 1,782
Canby SD 891 500/PK-12
307 1st St W 56220 507-223-2001
Loren Hacker, supt. Fax 223-2011
www.canbymn.org/
Canby JSHS 300/7-12
307 1st St W 56220 507-223-2002
Robert Slaba, prin. Fax 223-2012

Minnesota West Community & Tech College Post-Sec.
1011 1st St W 56220 507-223-7252

Cannon Falls, Goodhue, Pop. 4,027
Cannon Falls SD 252 1,100/PK-12
820 Minnesota St E 55009 507-263-6800
Beth Giese, supt. Fax 263-2555
www.cannonfallsschools.com
Cannon Falls Alternative Learning Center 50/Alt
120 State St W 55009 507-263-6800
Beth Giese, dir. Fax 263-4888
Cannon Falls HS 600/7-12
820 Minnesota St E 55009 507-263-3331
Steve Fredrickson, prin. Fax 263-2515

Carlton, Carlton, Pop. 843
Carlton ISD 93 500/PK-12
PO Box 310 55718 218-384-4225
Peter Haapala, supt. Fax 384-3543
www.carlton.k12.mn.us
Carlton JSHS 300/6-12
PO Box 310 55718 218-384-4226
Becky Connolly, prin. Fax 384-3607

Cass Lake, Cass, Pop. 725
Cass Lake-Bena SD 115 1,100/PK-12
208 Central Ave NW 56633 218-335-2204
Dr. Anita Grace, supt. Fax 335-2614
www.clbs.k12.mn.us
Cass Lake ALC 100/Alt
208 Central Ave NW 56633 218-335-6529
James Chase, prin. Fax 335-8826
Cass Lake-Bena HS 200/9-12
15308 State Highway 371 NW 56633 218-335-2203
John Klinke, prin. Fax 335-7649
Cass Lake-Bena MS 300/5-8
15314 State Highway 371 NW 56633 218-335-7851
Pernell Knutson, prin. Fax 335-1194

Leech Lake Tribal College Post-Sec.
PO Box 180 56633 218-335-4200

Center City, Chisago, Pop. 624

Hazelden Graduate School Post-Sec.
PO Box 11 55012 651-213-4175

Champlin, Hennepin, Pop. 22,615
Anoka-Hennepin SD 11
Supt. — See Anoka
Champlin Park HS 2,900/9-12
6025 109th Ave N 55316 763-506-6800
Michael George, prin. Fax 506-6803
Crossroads West Campus 100/Alt
12439 Champlin Dr 55316 763-433-4500
Nancy Chave, prin. Fax 433-4503
Jackson MS 1,900/6-8
6000 109th Ave N 55316 763-506-5200
Thomas Hagerty, prin. Fax 506-5203

Chanhassen, Carver, Pop. 22,622
Eastern Carver County SD 112
Supt. — See Chaska
Chanhassen HS 1,400/9-12
2200 Lyman Blvd 55317 952-556-3500
Tim Dorway, prin. Fax 556-3509

Chaska, Carver, Pop. 23,347
Eastern Carver County SD 112 8,900/PK-12
11 Peavey Rd 55318 952-556-6100
Dr. Jim Bauck, supt. Fax 556-6109
www.district112.org
Chaska HS 1,100/9-12
545 Pioneer Trl 55318 952-556-7100
David Brecht, prin. Fax 556-7109
Chaska MS East 700/6-8
1600 Park Ridge Dr 55318 952-556-7600
James Bach, prin. Fax 556-7609
Chaska MS West 700/6-8
140 Engler Blvd 55318 952-556-7400
Sheryl Hough, prin. Fax 556-7409
Integrated Arts Academy Alt
11 Peavey Rd 55318 952-556-6100
Jackie Johnston, prin. Fax 556-6109
Pioneer Ridge MS 700/6-8
1085 Pioneer Trl 55318 952-556-7800
Dana Miller, prin. Fax 556-7809
Other Schools – See Chanhassen

Southwest Christian HS 200/9-12
1981 Bavaria Rd 55318 952-556-0040
Dan Beckering, head sch Fax 556-5567

Chatfield, Fillmore, Pop. 2,758
Chatfield SD 227 900/PK-12
205 Union St NE 55923 507-867-4210
Edward Harris, supt. Fax 518-0704
www.chatfield.k12.mn.us
Chatfield JSHS 400/7-12
205 Union St NE 55923 507-867-4210
Randy Paulson, prin. Fax 518-0701

Chisago City, Chisago, Pop. 4,910

Chisago Lakes Baptist S 100/PK-12
9387 Wyoming Trl 55013 651-257-4587

Chisholm, Saint Louis, Pop. 4,873
Chisholm SD 695 700/PK-12
300 3rd Ave SW 55719 218-254-5726
James Varichak, supt. Fax 254-3741
www.chisholm.k12.mn.us
Chisholm HS 300/7-12
301 4th St SW 55719 218-254-5726
Richard Aldrich, prin. Fax 254-1434

Chokio, Stevens, Pop. 399
Chokio-Alberta SD 771 100/K-12
PO Box 68 56221 320-324-7131
Dr. David Baukol, supt. Fax 324-2731
www.chokioalberta.k12.mn.us
Chokio-Alberta S 100/K-12
PO Box 68 56221 320-324-7131
Bill Kehoe, prin. Fax 324-2731

Circle Pines, Anoka, Pop. 4,828
Centennial SD 12 6,500/PK-12
4707 North Rd 55014 763-792-6000
Dr. Keith Dixon, supt. Fax 792-6050
www.isd12.org
Centennial ALC 100/Alt
4203 Woodland Rd 55014 763-398-2960
Tom Breuning, prin. Fax 717-4538
Centennial HS 2,200/9-12
4757 North Rd 55014 763-792-5000
Tom Breuning, prin. Fax 792-5050
Other Schools – See Lino Lakes

Clara City, Chippewa, Pop. 1,350
MACCRAY SD 2180 700/K-12
PO Box 690 56222 320-847-2154
Loren Hacker, supt. Fax 847-3239
www.maccray.k12.mn.us
MACCRAY Alternative Learning 50/Alt
PO Box 690 56222 320-847-3525
Gary Sims, dir. Fax 847-2154
MACCRAY JSHS 300/7-12
PO Box 690 56222 320-847-2478
Gary Sims, prin. Fax 847-3239

Clarissa, Todd, Pop. 674
Eagle Valley SD 2759 300/PK-12
PO Box 468 56440 218-756-3631
Russ Johnson, supt. Fax 738-6493
www.evps.k12.mn.us
Other Schools – See Eagle Bend

Clearbrook, Clearwater, Pop. 513
Clearbrook-Gonvick SD 2311 500/PK-12
16770 Clearwater Lake Rd 56634 218-776-3112
Allen Ralston, supt. Fax 776-3117
www.clearbrook-gonvick.k12.mn.us/
Clearbrook-Gonvick JSHS 200/7-12
16770 Clearwater Lake Rd 56634 218-776-3112
Kristil McDonald, prin. Fax 776-3117

Cleveland, LeSueur, Pop. 714
Cleveland SD 391 200/PK-12
PO Box 310 56017 507-931-5953
Brian Phillips, supt. Fax 931-9088
cleveland.k12.mn.us/
Cleveland S 200/PK-12
PO Box 310 56017 507-931-5953
Dawn Brown, prin. Fax 931-9088

Climax, Polk, Pop. 262
Climax-Shelly SD 592 100/PK-12
PO Box 67 56523 218-857-2385
Norman Baumgarn, supt. Fax 857-3544
www.climax.k12.mn.us
Climax-Shelly S 100/PK-12
PO Box 67 56523 218-857-2385
Nancy Newcomb, prin. Fax 857-3544

Clinton, Big Stone, Pop. 449
Clinton-Graceville-Beardsley SD 2888 400/K-12
PO Box 361 56225 320-325-5282
Bob Vaadeland, supt. Fax 325-5509
www.graceville.k12.mn.us
Other Schools – See Graceville

Cloquet, Carlton, Pop. 11,711
Cloquet SD 94 2,300/K-12
302 14th St 55720 218-879-6721
Ken Scarbrough, supt. Fax 879-6724
www.cloquet.k12.mn.us
Cloquet Area Alternative Education Alt
302 14th St 55720 218-879-0115
Roberta Mondati, prin. Fax 879-6941
Cloquet HS 700/9-12
1000 18th St 55720 218-879-3393
Warren Peterson, prin. Fax 879-6494
Cloquet MS 500/6-8
509 Carlton Ave 55720 218-879-3328
Tom Brenner, prin. Fax 879-4175

Fond du Lac Tribal Community College Post-Sec.
2101 14th St 55720 218-879-0800

Cokato, Wright, Pop. 2,654
Dassel-Cokato SD 466 2,300/PK-12
4852 Reardon Ave SW 55321 320-286-4100
Jeff Powers, supt. Fax 286-4101
www.dc.k12.mn.us
Dassel-Cokato Area Learning Center 50/Alt
4852 Reardon Ave SW 55321 320-286-4100
Jon Nelson, dir. Fax 286-4132
Dassel-Cokato HS 600/9-12
4852 Reardon Ave SW 55321 320-286-4100
Dean Jennissen, prin. Fax 286-4201
Dassel-Cokato MS 700/5-8
4852 Reardon Ave SW 55321 320-286-4100
Brian Franklin, prin. Fax 286-4176

Cold Spring, Stearns, Pop. 3,975
Rocori SD 750 1,900/PK-12
534 5th Ave N 56320 320-685-4901
Scott Staska, supt. Fax 685-4906
www.rocori.k12.mn.us/
Rocori HS 800/9-12
534 5th Ave N 56320 320-685-8683
Mark Jenson, prin. Fax 685-4968
Rocori MS 400/6-8
534 5th Ave N 56320 320-685-3296
Mark Jenson, prin. Fax 685-3448

Coleraine, Itasca, Pop. 1,927
Greenway SD 316
Supt. — See Marble
Greenway HS 300/5-12
PO Box 520 55722 218-245-1287
Anne Champlin, prin. Fax 245-2397

Collegeville, Stearns

St. Johns Preparatory S 300/6-12
PO Box 4000 56321 320-363-3321
Matt Reichert, prin. Fax 525-7737
St. John's University Post-Sec.
PO Box 2000 56321 320-363-2011

Columbia Heights, Anoka, Pop. 18,748
Columbia Heights SD 13 2,900/K-12
1440 49th Ave NE 55421 763-528-4500
Kathy Kelly, supt. Fax 571-9203
www.colheights.k12.mn.us
Columbia Academy 600/6-8
900 49th Ave NE 55421 763-586-4701
Mary Bussman, prin. Fax 528-4707
Columbia Heights HS 1,000/9-12
1400 49th Ave NE 55421 763-528-4600
Joann Karetov, prin. Fax 571-9267

Comfrey, Brown, Pop. 378
Comfrey SD 81 200/K-12
305 Ochre St W 56019 507-877-3491
Allen Hoffman, supt. Fax 877-3492
Comfrey JSHS 100/7-12
305 Ochre St W 56019 507-877-3491
Kirsten Hutchison, prin. Fax 877-3492

Cook, Saint Louis, Pop. 560
Saint Louis County SD 2142
Supt. — See Virginia
North Woods S 200/PK-12
10248 E Olson Rd 55723 218-666-5221
John Metsa, prin. Fax 666-5223

Coon Rapids, Anoka, Pop. 59,722
Anoka-Hennepin SD 11
Supt. — See Anoka
Coon Rapids HS 2,400/9-12
2340 Northdale Blvd NW 55433 763-506-7100
Annette Ziegler, prin. Fax 506-7103
Coon Rapids MS 1,300/6-8
11600 Raven St NW 55433 763-506-4800
Tom Shaw, prin. Fax 506-4803
Crossroads Alternative HS 300/Alt
1313 Coon Rapids Blvd NW 55433 763-506-7400
Nancy Chave, prin. Fax 506-7403
Northdale MS 1,200/6-8
11301 Dogwood St NW 55448 763-506-5400
Laurie Jacklitch, prin. Fax 506-5403

Anoka-Ramsey Community College Post-Sec.
11200 Mississippi Blvd NW 55433 763-433-1100

Cottage Grove, Washington, Pop. 33,853
South Washington County SD 833 17,000/K-12
7362 E Point Douglas Rd S 55016 651-458-6300
Keith Jacobus Ph.D., supt. Fax 458-6318
www.sowashco.k12.mn.us
Alternative Learning Center 100/Alt
8400 E Point Douglas Rd S 55016 651-458-7000
Mike Mahaffey, prin. Fax 458-7015
Cottage Grove MS 1,100/6-8
9775 Indian Blvd S 55016 651-768-6800
Elise Block, prin. Fax 768-6828
Park HS 1,800/9-12
8040 80th St S 55016 651-768-3700
Kerry Timmerman, prin. Fax 768-3705
Other Schools – See Saint Paul Park, Woodbury

Cottonwood, Lyon, Pop. 1,201
Lakeview SD 2167 600/PK-12
PO Box 107 56229 507-423-5164
Chris Fenske, supt. Fax 423-5568
www.lakeview2167.com
Lakeview HS 300/7-12
PO Box 107 56229 507-423-5166
Philip Lienemann, prin. Fax 423-5568

Cromwell, Carlton, Pop. 231
Cromwell-Wright SD 95 300/PK-12
PO Box 7 55726 218-644-3737
Jennifer Backer, supt. Fax 644-3992
www.cromwellwright.k12.mn.us
Cromwell-Wright JSHS 100/7-12
PO Box 7 55726 218-644-3716
Nathan Libbon, prin. Fax 644-3992

Crookston, Polk, Pop. 7,779
Crookston SD 593 1,300/K-12
402 Fisher Ave Ste 593 56716 218-281-5313
Chris Bates, supt. Fax 281-3505
www.crookston.k12.mn.us
Crookston HS 600/7-12
402 Fisher Ave 56716 218-281-2144
Jason Vold, prin. Fax 281-4709
New Paths Area Learning Center 100/Alt
121 E 3rd St 56716 218-281-5864
Sarah Hillier, lead tchr. Fax 281-2386

University of Minnesota Crookston Post-Sec.
2900 University Ave 56716 218-281-6510

Crosby, Crow Wing, Pop. 2,354
Crosby-Ironton SD 182 1,200/PK-12
711 Poplar St 56441 218-545-8801
Jamie Skjeveland, supt. Fax 545-8836
www.ci.k12.mn.us
Crosby-Ironton JSHS 600/7-12
711 Poplar St 56441 218-545-8802
Jim Christenson, prin. Fax 545-8835

Crystal, Hennepin, Pop. 21,394
Minneapolis SD 1
Supt. — See Minneapolis
Fine Arts Interdisciplinary Resource S 500/4-8
3915 Adair Ave N 55422 763-971-4500
Kevin Bennett, prin. Fax 971-4531

Dawson, Lac qui Parle, Pop. 1,527
Dawson-Boyd SD 378 500/PK-12
848 Chestnut St 56232 320-769-2955
Brad Madsen, supt. Fax 769-4502
dawsonboydschools.org/
Dawson-Boyd JSHS 200/7-12
848 Chestnut St 56232 320-769-2955
Keri Bergeson, prin. Fax 769-4502

Deer River, Itasca, Pop. 888
Deer River SD 317 900/PK-12
PO Box 307 56636 218-246-2420
Matt Grose, supt. Fax 246-8948
www.isd317.org
Deer River JSHS 500/6-12
PO Box 307 56636 218-246-8241
Lisa Cooney, prin. Fax 246-8717

Delano, Wright, Pop. 5,379
Delano SD 879 2,300/PK-12
700 Elm Ave E 55328 763-972-3365
Matthew Schoen, supt. Fax 972-6706
www.delano.k12.mn.us
Delano HS 800/9-12
700 Elm Ave E 55328 763-972-3365
Steven Heil, prin. Fax 972-6706
Delano MS 700/5-8
700 Elm Ave E 55328 763-972-3365
Renee Klinkner, prin. Fax 972-6706

Detroit Lakes, Becker, Pop. 8,324
Detroit Lakes SD 22 2,600/PK-12
PO Box 766 56502 218-847-9271
Doug Froke, supt. Fax 847-9273
www.rschooltoday.com
Detroit Lakes ALC 50/Alt
702 Lake Ave 56501 218-847-5687
Lisa Weber, prin. Fax 847-9273
Detroit Lakes HS 800/9-12
1301 Roosevelt Ave 56501 218-847-4401
Steven Morben, prin. Fax 846-1797
Detroit Lakes MS 600/6-8
510 11th Ave 56501 218-847-9228
Michael Suckert, prin. Fax 847-0057

MN State Community & Technical College Post-Sec.
900 Highway 34 E 56501 218-846-3700

Dilworth, Clay, Pop. 3,965
Dilworth-Glyndon-Felton SD 2164 1,400/PK-12
PO Box 188 56529 218-287-2371
Bryan Thygeson, supt. Fax 287-2709
www.dgf.k12.mn.us
Dilworth-Glyndon-Felton MS 200/7-8
PO Box 188 56529 218-287-2148
Shannon Dahlberg, prin. Fax 287-2709
Other Schools – See Glyndon

Dodge Center, Dodge, Pop. 2,647
Triton SD 2125 1,200/PK-12
813 W Highway St 55927 507-374-2192
Robert Kelly, supt. Fax 374-6524
www.triton.k12.mn.us/
Triton HS 300/9-12
813 W Highway St 55927 507-374-6305
Brett Joyce, prin. Fax 374-2447
Triton MS 300/6-8
813 W Highway St 55927 507-633-8676
Craig Schlichting, prin. Fax 633-8673

Duluth, Saint Louis, Pop. 83,742
Duluth ISD 709 7,700/K-12
215 N 1st Ave E 55802 218-336-8752
William Gronseth, supt. Fax 336-8773
www.duluth.k12.mn.us
Area Learning Center/Unity HS 100/Alt
215 N 1st Ave E 55802 218-336-8756
Fax 336-8770
Denfeld HS 1,000/9-12
401 N 44th Ave W 55807 218-336-8830
Tonya Sconiers, prin. Fax 336-8844
East HS 1,400/9-12
301 N 40th Ave E 55804 218-336-8845
Laurie Knapp, prin. Fax 336-8859
Lincoln Park MS 600/6-8
3215 W 3rd St 55806 218-336-8880
Denise Clairmont, prin. Fax 336-8894
Ordean East MS 900/6-8
2900 E 4th St 55812 218-336-8940
Gina Kleive, prin. Fax 336-8949
Adult Basic Education Adult
215 N 1st Ave E 55802 218-336-8790
Beth Tamminen, admin. Fax 336-8791

College of Saint Scholastica Post-Sec.
1200 Kenwood Ave 55811 218-723-6000
Cosmetology Careers Unlimited - Duluth Post-Sec.
121 W Superior St 55802 218-722-7484
Duluth Business University Post-Sec.
4724 Mike Colalillo Dr 55807 218-722-4000
Lake Superior College Post-Sec.
2101 Trinity Rd 55811 218-733-7600
Lakeview Christian Academy 300/PK-12
155 W Central Entrance 55811 218-723-8844
Dr. Todd Benson, head sch Fax 722-7850
Marshall S 500/4-12
1215 Rice Lake Rd 55811 218-727-7266
Karen Snyder, hdmstr. Fax 727-1569
University of Minnesota Duluth Post-Sec.
1049 University Dr 55812 218-726-8000

Eagan, Dakota, Pop. 62,501
Burnsville-Eagan-Savage ISD 191
Supt. — See Burnsville
Burnsville Alternative HS 100/Alt
2140 Diffley Rd 55122 952-707-4077
Janice Porter, prin. Fax 707-4024

Rosemount-Apple Valley-Eagan ISD 196
Supt. — See Rosemount
Black Hawk MS 900/6-8
1540 Deerwood Dr 55122 651-683-8521
Richard Wendorff, prin. Fax 683-8527
Dakota Hills MS 1,200/6-8
4183 Braddock Trl 55123 651-683-6800
Trevor Johnson, prin. Fax 683-6858
Eagan HS 2,200/9-12
4185 Braddock Trl 55123 651-683-6900
Polly Reikowski, prin. Fax 683-6910

Everest Institute Post-Sec.
1000 Blue Gentian Rd 55121 651-688-2145
Rasmussen College Post-Sec.
3500 Federal Dr 55122 651-687-9000
Trinity S at River Ridge 300/7-12
601 River Ridge Pkwy 55121 651-789-2890
Jon Balsbaugh, hdmstr. Fax 789-2891
Twin Cities Argosy University Post-Sec.
1515 Central Pkwy 55121 888-844-2004

Eagle Bend, Todd, Pop. 527
Eagle Valley SD 2759
Supt. — See Clarissa
Eagle Valley JSHS 100/7-12
PO Box 299 56446 218-756-3631
Barry Johnson, admin. Fax 738-6493

East Grand Forks, Polk, Pop. 8,422
East Grand Forks SD 595 1,800/PK-12
PO Box 151 56721 218-773-3494
David Pace, supt. Fax 773-7408
www.egf.k12.mn.us/
Central MS 400/6-8
PO Box 151 56721 218-773-1141
Lon Ellingson, prin. Fax 773-9112
East Grand Forks HS 600/9-12
PO Box 151 56721 218-773-2405
Brian Loer, prin. Fax 773-3070

Northland Community & Technical College Post-Sec.
2022 Central Ave NE 56721 218-793-2800
Sacred Heart HS 100/7-12
122 3rd St NW 56721 218-773-0230
Phillip Meyer, prin. Fax 773-7042

Eden Prairie, Hennepin, Pop. 59,499
Eden Prairie SD 272 9,800/PK-12
8100 School Rd 55344 952-975-7000
Curt Tryggestad Ph.D., supt. Fax 975-7012
www.edenpr.org
Central MS 1,500/7-8
8025 School Rd 55344 952-975-7300
Joe Epping, prin. Fax 975-7320
Eden Prairie HS 3,200/9-12
17185 Valley View Rd 55346 952-975-8000
Conn McCartan, prin. Fax 975-8020
Prairie Center Alternative S 100/Alt
6754 Shady Oak Rd 55344 952-374-5760
Becky Brown, dir. Fax 548-9522

International School of Minnesota 500/PK-12
6385 Beach Rd 55344 952-918-1800
Christi Seiple-Cole, dir. Fax 918-1801
ITT Technical Institute Post-Sec.
8911 Columbine Rd 55347 952-914-5300

Eden Valley, Meeker, Pop. 1,031
Eden Valley-Watkins SD 463 900/PK-12
298 Brooks St N 55329 320-453-2900
Mark Messman, supt. Fax 453-5600
www.evw.k12.mn.us
Eden Valley Secondary S 400/7-12
298 Brooks St N 55329 320-453-2900
Bruce Kiehn, prin. Fax 453-5600

Edgerton, Pipestone, Pop. 1,174
Edgerton SD 581 300/PK-12
PO Box 28 56128 507-442-7881
Roger Graff, supt. Fax 442-8541
edgertonpublic.com
Edgerton JSHS 200/7-12
PO Box 28 56128 507-442-7881
Brian Gilbertson, prin. Fax 442-8541

Southwest Minnesota Christian HS 100/9-12
550 W Elizabeth St 56128 507-442-4471
Paul Bootsma, prin. Fax 442-5801

Edina, Hennepin, Pop. 47,052
Edina SD 273 8,200/K-12
5701 Normandale Rd 55424 952-848-3900
Ric Dressen Ed.D., supt. Fax 848-3901
www.edina.k12.mn.us
Edina SHS 1,900/10-12
6754 Valley View Rd 55439 952-848-3800
Bruce Locklear, prin. Fax 848-3801
South View MS 1,300/6-9
4725 S View Ln 55424 952-848-3700
Beth Russell, prin. Fax 848-3701
Valley View MS 1,300/6-9
6750 Valley View Rd 55439 952-848-3500
Shawn Dudley, prin. Fax 848-3501

DeVry University Post-Sec.
7700 France Ave S Ste 575 55435 952-838-1860

Elgin, Wabasha, Pop. 1,079
Plainview-Elgin-Millville ISD 2899
Supt. — See Plainview
Plainview-Elgin-Millville JHS 200/7-8
70 1st St SE 55932 507-876-2521
Clark Olstad, prin. Fax 876-2110

Elk River, Sherburne, Pop. 22,557
Elk River Area SD 728 11,800/K-12
815 Highway 10 55330 763-241-3400
Dr. Mark Bezek, supt. Fax 241-3407
www.elkriver.k12.mn.us
Elk River HS 1,700/9-12
900 School St NW 55330 763-241-3434
Terry Bizal, prin. Fax 241-3421
Salk MS 700/6-8
11970 Highland Rd NW 55330 763-241-3455
Julie Athman, prin. Fax 241-3456
Sand Community HS 100/Alt
1232 School St NW 55330 763-241-3530
Thomas Hoffman, prin. Fax 241-3532
VandenBerge MS 600/6-8
948 Proctor Ave NW 55330 763-241-3450
Marcia Welch, prin. Fax 241-3552
Other Schools – See Rogers, Zimmerman

Globe University MN School of Business Post-Sec.
11500 193rd Ave NW 55330 763-367-7000

Ellsworth, Nobles, Pop. 460
Ellsworth SD 514 100/PK-12
PO Box 8 56129 507-967-2242
George Berndt, supt. Fax 967-2588
www.ellsworth.mntm.org
Ellsworth S 100/PK-12
PO Box 8 56129 507-967-2151
George Berndt, prin. Fax 967-2588

Ely, Saint Louis, Pop. 3,405
ISD 696 600/PK-12
600 E Harvey St 55731 218-365-6166
Alexis Leitgeb, supt. Fax 365-6138
www.ely.k12.mn.us
Ely Memorial HS 300/7-12
600 E Harvey St 55731 218-365-6166
Laurie Kess, prin. Fax 365-6138

Vermillion Community College Post-Sec.
1900 E Camp St 55731 218-235-2100

Erskine, Polk, Pop. 492
Win-E-Mac SD 2609 400/K-12
23130 345th St SE 56535 218-687-2236
Randy Bruer, supt. Fax 563-2902
www.win-e-mac.k12.mn.us
Win-E-Mac JSHS 200/7-12
23130 345th St SE 56535 218-687-2236
Kevin McKeever, prin. Fax 563-2902

Esko, Carlton, Pop. 1,843
Esko SD 99 1,200/PK-12
PO Box 10 55733 218-879-2969
Aaron Fischer, supt. Fax 879-7490
www.esko.k12.mn.us/
Lincoln JSHS 600/7-12
PO Box 10 55733 218-879-4673
Greg Hexum, prin. Fax 879-7490

Evansville, Douglas, Pop. 609
Evansville SD 208 100/PK-12
PO Box 40 56326 218-948-2241
Mark Westby, supt. Fax 948-2441
www.evansville.k12.mn.us
Evansville JSHS 100/7-12
PO Box 40 56326 218-948-2241
Mark Westby, prin. Fax 948-2441

Eveleth, Saint Louis, Pop. 3,636
Eveleth-Gilbert SD 2154 — 1,000/PK-12
801 Jones St 55734 — 218-744-7700
Deborah Hilde, supt. — Fax 744-4381
www.isd2154.k12.mn.us
Eveleth-Gilbert SHS — 300/9-12
801 Jones St 55734 — 218-744-7706
Danette Seboe, prin. — Fax 744-4381
Other Schools – See Gilbert

Mesabi Range Community & Technical Coll. — Post-Sec.
PO Box 648 55734 — 218-741-3095

Excelsior, Hennepin, Pop. 2,144
Minnetonka SD 276
Supt. — See Minnetonka
Minnetonka West MS — 900/6-8
6421 Hazeltine Blvd 55331 — 952-401-5300
Bill Jacobson, prin. — Fax 401-5350

Eyota, Olmsted, Pop. 1,965
Dover-Eyota SD 533 — 1,100/PK-12
615 South Ave SW 55934 — 507-545-2125
Bruce Klaehn, supt. — Fax 545-2349
www.desch.org
Dover-Eyota JSHS — 300/9-12
615 South Ave SW 55934 — 507-545-2631
Todd Rowekamp, prin. — Fax 545-2218
Dover-Eyota MS — 300/6-8
615 South Ave SW 55934 — 507-545-2631
Todd Rowekamp, prin. — Fax 545-2218

Fairfax, Renville, Pop. 1,227
GFW SD 2365
Supt. — See Gibbon
GFW MS — 300/5-8
300 2nd Ave SE 55332 — 507-426-7251
Ralph Fairchild, prin. — Fax 426-7425

Prairie Lutheran MS — 50/5-8
PO Box 130 55332 — 507-426-7755
Macord Johnson, prin. — Fax 426-8372

Fairmont, Martin, Pop. 10,613
Fairmont Area SD 2752 — 1,300/PK-12
714 Victoria St Ste 103 56031 — 507-238-4234
Joseph Brown, supt. — Fax 235-4050
fairmont.k12.mn.us
Fairmont JSHS — 800/7-12
900 Johnson St 56031 — 507-238-4411
Kim Niss, prin. — Fax 235-4130

Faribault, Rice, Pop. 23,011
Faribault SD 656 — 3,800/PK-12
PO Box 618 55021 — 507-333-6000
Todd Sesker, supt. — Fax 333-6077
www.faribault.k12.mn.us/
Faribault ALC — 100/Alt
PO Box 618 55021 — 507-333-6187
Margaret Gare, dir. — Fax 333-6048
Faribault HS — 1,100/9-12
330 9th Ave SW 55021 — 507-333-6100
Lyle Turtle, prin. — Fax 333-6248
Faribault MS — 900/6-8
704 17th St SW 55021 — 507-333-6300
Troy Prigge, prin. — Fax 333-6400

Bethlehem Academy — 300/7-12
105 3rd Ave SW 55021 — 507-334-3948
Thomas Donlon, prin. — Fax 334-3949
Minnesota School for the Deaf — Post-Sec.
615 Olof Hanson Dr 55021
Shattuck/St. Marys S — 400/6-12
PO Box 218 55021 — 507-333-1500
Nick Stoneman, hdmstr. — Fax 333-1591
South Central College — Post-Sec.
1225 3rd St SW 55021 — 800-422-0391

Farmington, Dakota, Pop. 20,570
Farmington SD 192 — 6,400/PK-12
421 Walnut St 55024 — 651-463-5000
Jay Haugen, supt. — Fax 463-5010
www.farmington.k12.mn.us
Boeckman MS — 700/6-8
800 Denmark Ave 55024 — 651-460-1400
Dan Miller, prin. — Fax 460-1410
Dodge MS — 800/6-8
4200 208th St W 55024 — 651-460-1500
Chris Bussmann, prin. — Fax 460-1510
Farmington HS — 1,700/9-12
20655 Flagstaff Ave 55024 — 651-460-1400
Ben Kusch, prin. — Fax 460-1410
Special Services Center — Alt
510 Walnut St 55024 — 651-463-5020
Carla Nohr Schulz, dir. — Fax 463-5021

Christian Life S — 200/PK-12
6300 212th St W 55024 — 651-463-4545
Rev. Darin Kindle, admin. — Fax 463-8353

Fergus Falls, Otter Tail, Pop. 12,946
Fergus Falls SD 544 — 2,500/PK-12
601 Randolph Ave 56537 — 218-998-0544
Gerald Ness, supt. — Fax 998-3943
www.isd544.org
Area Learning Center — 100/Alt
340 Friberg Ave 56537 — 218-739-2360
Dean Monke, prin. — Fax 998-3952
Fergus Falls HS — 1,300/6-12
601 Randolph Ave 56537 — 218-998-0544
Dean Monke, prin. — Fax 998-3947

Hillcrest Lutheran Academy — 200/7-12
610 Hillcrest Dr 56537 — 218-739-3371
Jeff Isaac M.Ed., prin. — Fax 739-3372
Lutheran Brethren Seminary — Post-Sec.
815 W Vernon Ave 56537 — 218-739-3375
MN State Community & Technical College — Post-Sec.
1414 College Way 56537 — 218-736-1500

Fertile, Polk, Pop. 831
Fertile-Beltrami SD 599 — 500/PK-12
PO Box 648 56540 — 218-945-6933
Brian Clarke, supt. — Fax 945-6934
fertilebeltrami.k12.mn.us
Fertile-Beltrami JSHS — 200/7-12
PO Box 648 56540 — 218-945-6953
Hillary Hornor, prin. — Fax 945-6934

Finlayson, Pine, Pop. 312
East Central SD 2580 — 600/PK-12
61085 State Highway 23 55735 — 320-245-2289
Jack Almos, supt. — Fax 245-5453
www.eastcentral.k12.mn.us
East Central Secondary S — 200/6-12
61085 State Highway 23 55735 — 320-245-2216
Stef Youngberg, prin. — Fax 245-2448
Other Schools – See Sandstone

Fisher, Polk, Pop. 434
Fisher SD 600 — 200/K-12
313 Park Ave 56723 — 218-891-4105
Suraya Driscoll, supt. — Fax 891-4251
www.fisher.k12.mn.us
Fisher JSHS — 100/7-12
313 Park Ave 56723 — 218-891-4905
Suyraya Driscoll, prin. — Fax 891-4251

Floodwood, Saint Louis, Pop. 508
Floodwood SD 698 — 300/PK-12
PO Box 287 55736 — 218-476-2285
Herb Hilinski, supt. — Fax 476-2813
www.floodwood.k12.mn.us/
Floodwood JSHS — 200/7-12
PO Box 287 55736 — 218-476-2285
Daniel Bettin, prin. — Fax 476-2813

Foley, Benton, Pop. 2,576
Foley SD 51 — 1,800/PK-12
PO Box 297 56329 — 320-968-7175
Darrin Strosahl, supt. — Fax 968-8608
foley.k12.mn.us
Foley HS — 500/9-12
PO Box 397 56329 — 320-968-7246
Ryan Luft, prin. — Fax 968-8456
Foley MS — 700/4-8
PO Box 297 56329 — 320-968-6251
Brad Kelvington, prin. — Fax 968-8608

Forest Lake, Washington, Pop. 18,070
Forest Lake SD 831 — 6,700/PK-12
6100 210th St N 55025 — 651-982-8100
Dr. Linda Madsen, supt. — Fax 982-8114
www.flaschools.org
Area Learning Center — 100/Alt
200 4th St SW 55025 — 651-982-3171
Kelly Lessman, prin. — Fax 982-3172
Century JHS — 900/7-9
21395 Goodview Ave N 55025 — 651-982-3000
Dr. Benjamin Lewis, prin. — Fax 982-3017
Forest Lake SHS — 1,600/10-12
6101 Scandia Trl N 55025 — 651-982-8400
Dr. Steve Massey, prin. — Fax 982-8428
Southwest JHS — 600/7-9
943 9th Ave SW 55025 — 651-982-8700
Marc Peterson, prin. — Fax 982-8798

Foreston, Mille Lacs, Pop. 528

Faith Christian S — 100/K-12
11818 160th Ave 56330 — 320-294-5501
Tom Michaud, admin. — Fax 294-5197

Fosston, Polk, Pop. 1,489
Fosston SD 601 — 600/PK-12
301 1st St E 56542 — 218-435-6335
Mark Nohner, supt. — Fax 435-1663
www.fosston.k12.mn.us
Fosston JSHS — 300/7-12
301 1st St E 56542 — 218-435-1909
Patti Johnson, prin. — Fax 435-6340

Frazee, Becker, Pop. 1,295
Frazee-Vergas SD 23 — 900/PK-12
305 N Lake St 56544 — 218-334-3181
Charles Cheney, supt. — Fax 334-3182
www.frazee.k12.mn.us/
Frazee JSHS — 400/7-12
305 N Lake St 56544 — 218-334-3181
Rob Nudell, prin. — Fax 334-4696

Fridley, Anoka, Pop. 26,152
Fridley SD 14 — 2,800/K-12
6000 Moore Lake Dr W 55432 — 763-502-5000
Dr. Peggy Flathmann, supt. — Fax 502-5040
www.fridley.k12.mn.us
Fridley HS — 900/9-12
6000 Moore Lake Dr W 55432 — 763-502-5600
Renee Van Gorp, prin. — Fax 502-5640
Fridley MS — 800/5-8
6100 Moore Lake Dr W 55432 — 763-502-5400
Matthew Boucher, prin. — Fax 502-5440
Fridley Moore Lake Area Learning Center — 100/Alt
6085 7th St NE 55432 — 763-502-5100
Dr. Robert Smith, prin. — Fax 502-5101

Calvin Christian HS — 100/9-12
755 73rd Ave NE 55432 — 763-531-1732
Wendell Schaap, prin. — Fax 531-8075
Totino-Grace HS — 900/9-12
1350 Gardena Ave NE 55432 — 763-571-9116
Julie Michels, prin. — Fax 571-9118

Fulda, Murray, Pop. 1,307
Fulda SD 505 — 400/PK-12
410 N College Ave 56131 — 507-425-2514
Luther Onken, supt. — Fax 425-2001
www.fps.mntm.org
Fulda JSHS — 200/7-12
410 N College Ave 56131 — 507-425-2514
Gregg Slaathaug, prin. — Fax 425-2001

Gaylord, Sibley, Pop. 2,288
Sibley East SD 2310
Supt. — See Arlington
Sibley East JHS — 300/7-9
PO Box 356 55334 — 507-237-3315
Steve Harter, prin. — Fax 237-3300

Gibbon, Sibley, Pop. 764
GFW SD 2365 — 800/PK-12
323 E 11th St 55335 — 507-834-9813
Jeff Bertrang, supt. — Fax 834-6264
www.gfw.k12.mn.us
Other Schools – See Fairfax, Winthrop

Gilbert, Saint Louis, Pop. 1,775
Eveleth-Gilbert SD 2154
Supt. — See Eveleth
Eveleth-Gilbert JHS — 200/7-8
Summit St 55741 — 218-744-7770
Jeffrey Carey, prin. — Fax 744-4381

Glencoe, McLeod, Pop. 5,593
Glencoe-Silver Lake SD 2859 — 1,800/PK-12
1621 16th St E 55336 — 320-864-2499
Chris Sonju, supt. — Fax 864-6320
www.gsl.k12.mn.us
Glencoe-Silver Lake HS — 600/9-12
1621 16th St E 55336 — 320-864-2400
Paul Sparby, prin. — Fax 864-6475
Lincoln JHS — 300/PK-PK, 7-
1621 16th St E 55336 — 320-864-2499
Dan Svoboda, prin. — Fax 864-2475

Glenville, Freeborn, Pop. 641
Glenville-Emmons SD 2886 — 300/K-12
PO Box 38 56036 — 507-448-2889
Jerry Reshetar, supt. — Fax 448-2836
www.geschools.com
Glenville-Emmons JSHS — 200/7-12
230 5th St SE 56036 — 507-448-2889
Jeff Tietje, prin. — Fax 448-2836

Glenwood, Pope, Pop. 2,537
Minnewaska SD 2149 — 900/PK-12
25122 State Highway 28 56334 — 320-239-4820
Greg Schmidt, supt. — Fax 239-1360
www.minnewaska.k12.mn.us
Minnewaska Area HS — 300/7-12
25122 State Highway 28 56334 — 320-239-4800
Lyle Katzenmeyer, prin. — Fax 239-1362
Other Schools – See Starbuck

Glyndon, Clay, Pop. 1,373
Dilworth-Glyndon-Felton SD 2164
Supt. — See Dilworth
Dilworth-Glyndon-Felton HS — 400/9-12
513 Parke Ave S 56547 — 218-498-2263
Terry Karger, prin. — Fax 498-2488

Goodhue, Goodhue, Pop. 1,166
Goodhue SD 253 — 700/PK-12
510 3rd Ave 55027 — 651-923-4447
Michael Redmond, supt. — Fax 923-4083
www.goodhue.k12.mn.us
Goodhue JSHS — 300/7-12
510 3rd Ave 55027 — 651-923-4447
Mike Harvey, prin. — Fax 923-4083

Goodridge, Pennington, Pop. 132
Goodridge SD 561 — 200/K-12
PO Box 195 56725 — 218-378-4133
Galen Clow, supt. — Fax 378-4142
www.goodridge.k12.mn.us/
Goodridge JSHS — 100/7-12
PO Box 195 56725 — 218-378-4133
Dan Boushee, prin. — Fax 378-4142

Graceville, Big Stone, Pop. 577
Clinton-Graceville-Beardsley SD 2888
Supt. — See Clinton
Clinton-Graceville-Beardsley HS — 200/7-12
PO Box 398 56240 — 320-748-7233
Larry Mischke, prin. — Fax 748-7158

Granada, Martin, Pop. 302
Granada - Huntley - East Chain SD 2536 — 200/PK-12
PO Box 17 56039 — 507-447-2211
Dr. Steven Hyde, supt. — Fax 447-2214
www.ghec.k12.mn.us
Granada - Huntley - East Chain JSHS — 100/7-12
PO Box 17 56039 — 507-447-2211
Dr. Steven Hyde, supt. — Fax 447-2214

Grand Marais, Cook, Pop. 1,315
Cook County SD 166 — 300/K-12
101 W 5th St 55604 — 218-387-2271
Beth Schwarz, supt. — Fax 387-1093
www.cookcountyschools.org/
Cook County MSHS — 200/6-12
101 W 5th St 55604 — 218-387-2273
Gwen Carman, prin. — Fax 387-9746

Grand Meadow, Mower, Pop. 1,132
Grand Meadow SD 495 — 400/PK-12
PO Box 68 55936 — 507-754-5318
Jerry Reshetar, supt. — Fax 754-5608
www.gm.k12.mn.us/
Grand Meadow HS — 100/9-12
PO Box 68 55936 — 507-754-5310
Joseph Brown, prin. — Fax 754-5608
Grand Meadow MS — 100/5-8
PO Box 68 55936 — 507-754-5310
Dave Stadum, prin. — Fax 754-5608

Grand Rapids, Itasca, Pop. 10,671
Grand Rapids SD 318 — 3,900/PK-12
820 NW 1st Ave 55744 — 218-327-5700
Joe Silko, supt. — Fax 327-5702
www.isd318.org
Elkington MS — 1,000/5-8
1000 NE 8th Ave 55744 — 218-327-5800
Brent Brunetta, prin. — Fax 327-5801
Grand Rapids Area Learning Center — 100/Alt
409 SE 13th St 55744 — 218-999-9930
Mark Schroeder, prin.
Grand Rapids HS — 1,100/9-12
800 NW Conifer Dr 55744 — 218-327-5760
Jim Smokrovich, prin. — Fax 327-5761

Itaskin Education Center 50/Alt
1880 River Rd 55744 218-322-4129
Brenda Story, prin. Fax 327-2921
Middle Area Learning Center 100/Alt
1000 NE 8th Ave 55744 218-326-5800
Brent Brunetta, prin. Fax 326-5701
Northland Education Center 50/Alt
510 SE 13th St 55744 218-327-2570
Brenda Story, prin.
Other Schools – See Bigfork

Itasca Community College Post-Sec.
1851 E US Highway 169 55744 218-322-2300

Granite Falls, Yellow Medicine, Pop. 2,841
Yellow Medicine East SD 2190 800/K-12
450 9th Ave 56241 320-564-4081
Allen Stoeckman, supt. Fax 564-4781
isd2190.org/
Yellow Medicine East HS 400/6-12
450 9th Ave 56241 320-564-4083
Michael Meihak, prin. Fax 564-4782

Minnesota West Community & Tech College Post-Sec.
1593 11th Ave 56241 320-564-5000

Greenbush, Roseau, Pop. 717
Greenbush-Middle River SD 2683 400/PK-12
PO Box 70 56726 218-782-2231
Tom Jerome, supt. Fax 782-3141
www.middleriver.k12.mn.us/
Greenbush-Middle River HS 100/9-12
PO Box 70 56726 218-782-2232
Eldon Sparby, prin. Fax 782-2165
Other Schools – See Middle River

Grove City, Meeker, Pop. 630
ACGC SD 2396 600/K-12
27250 Minnesota Highway 4 56243 320-857-2271
Sherri Broderius, admin. Fax 857-2989
www.acgc.k12.mn.us
ACGC JSHS 400/5-12
27250 Minnesota Highway 4 56243 320-857-2276
Sherri Broderius, prin. Fax 857-2937

Grygla, Marshall, Pop. 220
Grygla SD 447 200/PK-12
PO Box 18 56727 218-294-6155
Galen Clow, supt. Fax 294-6766
www.grygla.k12.mn.us/
Grygla JSHS 100/7-12
PO Box 18 56727 218-294-6155
Patti Johnson, prin. Fax 294-6766

Hallock, Kittson, Pop. 976
Kittson Central SD 2171 200/PK-12
PO Box 670 56728 218-843-3682
Bob Jaszczak, supt. Fax 843-2856
www.kittson.k12.mn.us
Kittson Central S 100/PK-12
PO Box 670 56728 218-843-3682
Bob Jaszczak, prin. Fax 843-2856

Halstad, Norman, Pop. 582
Norman County West SD 2527
Supt. — See Hendrum
Norman County West JSHS 100/7-12
PO Box 328 56548 218-456-2151
Dave Rufsvold, prin. Fax 456-2193

Hancock, Stevens, Pop. 763
Hancock SD 768 300/K-12
PO Box 367 56244 320-392-5622
Jerry Martinson, supt. Fax 392-5156
hancock.k12.mn.us/
Hancock JSHS 100/7-12
PO Box 367 56244 320-392-5622
Tim Pahl, prin. Fax 392-5156

Harmony, Fillmore, Pop. 1,010
Fillmore Central SD 2198
Supt. — See Preston
Fillmore Central HS 200/7-12
PO Box 599 55939 507-886-6464
Heath Olstad, prin. Fax 886-6642

Hastings, Dakota, Pop. 21,783
Hastings SD 200 4,000/K-12
1000 11th St W 55033 651-480-7000
Tim Collins, supt. Fax 480-7001
www.hastings.k12.mn.us
Hastings HS 1,600/9-12
200 General Sieben Dr 55033 651-480-7470
Mike Johnson, prin. Fax 480-7474
Hastings MS 1,100/5-8
1000 11th St W 55033 651-480-7060
Mark Zuzek, prin. Fax 480-7066

Hawley, Clay, Pop. 2,037
Hawley SD 150 900/K-12
PO Box 608 56549 218-483-4647
Phil Jensen, supt. Fax 483-3510
www.hawley.k12.mn.us/
Hawley JSHS 400/7-12
PO Box 608 56549 218-483-3555
Mike Martin, prin. Fax 483-4802
Spring Prairie S 50/K-12
PO Box 608 56549 218-483-3316
Chris Ellingson, prin. Fax 483-4638

Hayfield, Dodge, Pop. 1,321
Hayfield SD 203 800/PK-12
9 6th Ave SE 55940 507-477-3235
Ron Evjen, supt. Fax 477-3230
www.hayfield.k12.mn.us/
Hayfield JSHS 400/7-12
9 6th Ave SE 55940 507-477-3235
John Howe, prin. Fax 477-3230

Hector, Renville, Pop. 1,148
Buffalo Lake-Hector-Stewart SD 2159 600/PK-12
PO Box 307 55342 320-848-2233
Dr. Rick Clark, supt. Fax 848-2401
www.blhsd.org

Buffalo Lake-Hector-Stewart JSHS 300/6-12
PO Box 307 55342 320-848-2233
David Hansen, prin. Fax 848-2401

Hendricks, Lincoln, Pop. 712
Hendricks SD 402 200/PK-12
PO Box 137 56136 507-275-3116
Bruce Houck, supt. Fax 275-3150
www.lincolnhi.org
Hendricks S 200/PK-12
PO Box 137 56136 507-275-3115
Bruce Houck, supt. Fax 275-3150

Hendrum, Norman, Pop. 307
Norman County West SD 2527 300/PK-12
PO Box 39 56550 218-861-5800
Ollen Church, supt. Fax 861-6223
www.ncw.k12.mn.us
Other Schools – See Halstad

Henning, Otter Tail, Pop. 795
Henning SD 545 400/PK-12
500 School Ave 56551 218-583-2927
Dean Krogstad, supt. Fax 583-2312
www.henning.k12.mn.us
Henning JSHS 200/7-12
500 School Ave 56551 218-583-2927
Thomas Williams, prin. Fax 583-2312

Herman, Grant, Pop. 435
Herman-Norcross SD 264 100/K-12
PO Box 288 56248 320-677-2291
Tom Knoll, supt. Fax 677-2412
herman.mn.schoolwebpages.com
Herman JSHS 50/7-12
PO Box 288 56248 320-677-2291
Tom Knoll, prin. Fax 677-2412

Hermantown, Saint Louis, Pop. 9,290
Hermantown SD 700 2,100/K-12
4307 Ugstad Rd 55811 218-729-9313
Brad Johnson, supt. Fax 729-9315
www.hermantown.k12.mn.us
Hermantown HS 700/9-12
4335 Hawk Circle Dr 55811 218-729-8874
John Muenich, prin. Fax 729-0180
Hermantown MS 800/4-8
4289 Ugstad Rd 55811 218-729-6690
Kerry Juntunen, prin. Fax 729-9890

Hibbing, Saint Louis, Pop. 16,076
Hibbing SD 701 2,400/K-12
800 E 21st St 55746 218-208-0848
Robert Belluzzo, supt. Fax 208-0866
www.hibbing.k12.mn.us
Hibbing HS 1,100/7-12
800 E 21st St 55746 218-208-0841
Mike Finco, prin. Fax 208-0856

Cosmetology Careers Unlimited - Hibbing Post-Sec.
2534 E Beltline 55746 218-263-8354
Hibbing Community College Post-Sec.
1515 E 25th St 55746 218-262-7200
Victory Christian Academy 100/PK-12
4220 3rd Ave W 55746 218-262-6550
Jo Terska, admin. Fax 262-0695

Hill City, Aitkin, Pop. 617
Hill City SD 2 300/PK-12
500 Ione Ave 55748 218-697-2394
Dean Yocum, supt. Fax 697-2594
www.hillcity.k12.mn.us/
Hill City JSHS 100/7-12
500 Ione Ave 55748 218-697-2394
Dean Yocum, prin. Fax 697-2594

Hills, Rock, Pop. 678
Hills-Beaver Creek SD 671 400/PK-12
PO Box 547 56138 507-962-3240
Todd Holthaus, supt. Fax 962-3238
www.hbcpatriots.com
Hills-Beaver Creek JSHS 200/7-12
PO Box 547 56138 507-962-3240
Todd Holthaus, admin. Fax 962-3238

Hinckley, Pine, Pop. 1,722
Hinckley-Finlayson SD 2165 1,000/PK-12
PO Box 308 55037 320-384-6277
Rob Prater, supt. Fax 384-6135
www.hf.k12.mn.us/
Hinckley-Finlayson HS 400/7-12
PO Box 308 55037 320-384-6132
Brian Masterson, prin. Fax 384-6135

Hokah, Houston, Pop. 568
La Crescent-Hokah SD 300
Supt. — See La Crescent
Bluff Country Learning Options 50/Alt
PO Box 476 55941 507-894-4415
Steve Smith, prin. Fax 894-5034

Holdingford, Stearns, Pop. 699
Holdingford SD 738 1,000/PK-12
PO Box 250 56340 320-746-2196
Eric Williams, supt. Fax 746-2274
www.edline.net/pages/Holdingford_Public_Schools
Holdingford JSHS 500/7-12
PO Box 250 56340 320-746-2221
Brian Silbernick, prin. Fax 746-9959

Hopkins, Hennepin, Pop. 17,010
Hopkins SD 270 7,100/K-12
1001 Highway 7 55305 952-988-4000
John Schultz, supt. Fax 988-4020
www.hopkins.k12.mn.us
Other Schools – See Minnetonka

Blake S 1,400/PK-12
110 Blake Rd S 55343 952-988-3400
Dr. Anne Stavney, head sch Fax 988-3455

Houston, Winona, Pop. 978
Houston SD 294 1,900/PK-12
306 W Elm St 55943 507-896-5323
Eric Bartleson, supt. Fax 896-3452
www.houston.k12.mn.us

Houston JSHS 200/7-12
306 W Elm St 55943 507-896-5323
Todd Lundberg, prin. Fax 896-4665

Howard Lake, Wright, Pop. 1,947
Howard Lake-Waverly-Winsted SD 2687 1,100/PK-12
PO Box 708 55349 320-543-3521
Brad Sellner, supt. Fax 543-3590
www.hlww.k12.mn.us
Howard Lake MS 300/5-8
PO Box 708 55349 320-543-3501
Jim Schimelpfenig, prin. Fax 543-3590
Howard Lake-Waverly-Winsted HS 300/9-12
PO Box 708 55349 320-543-4600
Jason Mix, prin. Fax 543-4601

Hutchinson, McLeod, Pop. 14,005
Hutchinson SD 423 2,900/PK-12
30 Glen St NW 55350 320-587-2860
Daron VanderHeiden, supt. Fax 587-4590
www.hutch.k12.mn.us
Crow River ALC 100/Alt
1200 Roberts Rd SW 55350 320-587-2151
Fax 587-8217
Hutchinson HS 800/9-12
1200 Roberts Rd SW 55350 320-587-2151
Patrick Walsh, prin. Fax 587-8217
Hutchinson MS 600/6-8
1365 S Grade Rd SW 55350 320-587-2854
Todd Grina, prin. Fax 587-2857

Maplewood Academy 100/9-12
700 Main St N 55350 320-587-2830
Justin Okimi, prin. Fax 587-5649
Ridgewater College-Hutchinson Campus Post-Sec.
2 Century Ave SE 55350 320-234-8500

International Falls, Koochiching, Pop. 6,261
International Falls SD 361 1,100/PK-12
1515 11th St 56649 218-283-2571
Nordy Nelson, supt. Fax 283-8104
www.isd361.k12.mn.us
Falls HS 600/7-12
1515 11th St 56649 218-283-2571
Tim Everson, prin. Fax 283-2384

Rainy River Community College Post-Sec.
1501 Highway 71 56649 218-285-7722

Inver Grove Heights, Dakota, Pop. 33,073
Inver Grove Heights Community ISD 199 3,600/PK-12
2990 80th St E 55076 651-306-7800
Dr. Deirdre Wells, supt. Fax 306-7295
www.invergrove.k12.mn.us
Inver Grove Heights MS 900/6-8
8167 Cahill Ave 55076 651-306-7200
Gerald Sakala, dir. Fax 306-7152
Simley HS 1,100/9-12
2920 80th St E 55076 651-306-7000
Gerald Sakala, dir. Fax 306-7016

Inver Hills Community College Post-Sec.
2500 80th St E 55076 651-450-3000

Iron, Saint Louis, Pop. 85
Saint Louis County SD 2142
Supt. — See Virginia
Cherry S 200/PK-12
3943 Tamminen Rd 55751 218-258-8991
John Metsa, prin. Fax 258-8993

Isanti, Isanti, Pop. 5,155
Cambridge-Isanti SD 911
Supt. — See Cambridge
Isanti MS 400/6-8
201 Centennial Dr 55040 763-691-8600
Randy Pauly, prin. Fax 691-8662
Minnesota Center S 100/6-8
201 Centennial Dr 55040 763-691-8676
Randy Pauly, prin. Fax 691-8677

Isle, Mille Lacs, Pop. 739
Isle SD 473 500/K-12
PO Box 25 56342 320-676-3146
Michael Conner, supt. Fax 676-3966
www.isle.k12.mn.us
Isle Area Learning Center 50/Alt
PO Box 25 56342 320-676-3721
Jean Novak, coord. Fax 676-3062
Isle JSHS 200/7-12
PO Box 25 56342 320-676-3101
Dean Kapsner, prin. Fax 676-1034

Ivanhoe, Lincoln, Pop. 559
Ivanhoe SD 403 100/PK-12
PO Box 9 56142 507-694-1540
Michelle Mortensen, supt. Fax 694-1125
www.lincolnhi.org
Lincoln S 100/PK-12
PO Box 9 56142 507-694-1540
Michelle Mortensen, admin. Fax 694-1125

Jackson, Jackson, Pop. 3,254
Jackson County Central SD 2895 1,200/PK-12
PO Box 119 56143 507-847-3608
Todd Meyer, supt. Fax 847-3078
www.jccschools.com/
Jackson County Central HS 300/9-12
PO Box 119 56143 507-847-5310
Larry Traetow, prin. Fax 847-3078
Other Schools – See Lakefield

Minnesota West Community & Tech College Post-Sec.
401 West St 56143 507-847-7920

Janesville, Waseca, Pop. 2,234
Janesville-Waldorf-Pemberton SD 2835 600/PK-12
PO Box 389 56048 507-234-5478
Bill Adams, supt. Fax 234-5796
www.jwp.k12.mn.us
Janesville-Waldorf-Pemberton HS 300/6-12
PO Box 389 56048 507-234-5181
Jeremy Erler, prin. Fax 234-5796

Jordan, Scott, Pop. 5,361
Jordan SD 717 1,700/PK-12
500 Sunset Dr 55352 952-492-6200
Kirk Nelson, supt. Fax 492-4445
www.jordan.k12.mn.us
Jordan HS 500/9-12
600 Sunset Dr 55352 952-492-4400
Barb McNulty, prin. Fax 492-4425
Jordan MS 500/5-8
500 Sunset Dr 55352 952-492-2332
Lance Chambers, prin. Fax 492-4450

Karlstad, Kittson, Pop. 759
Tri-County SD 2358 200/PK-12
PO Box 178 56732 218-436-2261
Ron Ruud, supt. Fax 436-2263
www.tricounty.k12.mn.us
Tri-County HS 100/7-12
PO Box 178 56732 218-436-2374
Dave Sorgaard, prin. Fax 436-3422

Kasson, Dodge, Pop. 5,864
Kasson-Mantorville SD 204 2,100/PK-12
101 16th St NE 55944 507-634-1100
Mark D. Matuska, supt. Fax 634-6661
www.komets.k12.mn.us
Kasson-Mantorville HS 600/9-12
101 16th St NE 55944 507-634-2961
Jerry Reker, prin. Fax 634-4745
Kasson-Mantorville MS 700/5-8
1400 5th Ave NE 55944 507-634-4030
Alan Hodge, prin. Fax 634-6485

Kelliher, Beltrami, Pop. 261
Kelliher SD 36 100/PK-12
PO Box 259 56650 218-647-8286
Tim Lutz, supt. Fax 647-8660
www.kelliherschools.org
Kelliher S 100/PK-12
PO Box 259 56650 218-647-8286
Mary Lundin, admin. Fax 647-3110

Kenyon, Goodhue, Pop. 1,804
Kenyon-Wanamingo SD 2172
Supt. — See Wanamingo
Kenyon-Wanamingo HS 200/7-12
400 6th St 55946 507-789-6186
Brent Ashland, prin. Fax 789-6188

Kerkhoven, Swift, Pop. 759
Kerkhoven-Murdock-Sunburg SD 775 600/PK-12
PO Box 168 56252 320-264-1411
Martin Heidelberger, supt. Fax 264-1410
www.kms.k12.mn.us
Kerkhoven JSHS 300/7-12
PO Box 168 56252 320-264-1412
Jeff Keil, prin. Fax 264-1410

Kimball, Stearns, Pop. 750
Kimball SD 739 700/PK-12
PO Box 368 55353 320-398-5585
John Tritabaugh, supt. Fax 398-5595
www.kimball.k12.mn.us/
Kimball JSHS 300/7-12
PO Box 368 55353 320-398-7700
Erik Widvey, prin. Fax 398-7733

La Crescent, Houston, Pop. 4,750
La Crescent-Hokah SD 300 1,300/PK-12
703 S 11th St 55947 507-895-4484
Ron Wilke, supt. Fax 895-8560
www.isd300.k12.mn.us
La Crescent HS 500/9-12
1301 Lancer Blvd 55947 507-895-4481
Rick Wolter, prin. Fax 895-4490
La Crescent MS 400/5-8
1301 Lancer Blvd 55947 507-895-4474
Steve Smith, prin. Fax 895-8597
Other Schools – See Hokah

Lake City, Wabasha, Pop. 4,995
Lake City SD 813 1,300/PK-12
PO Box 454 55041 651-345-2198
Craig Junker, supt. Fax 345-3709
www.lake-city.k12.mn.us
Lincoln JSHS 600/7-12
PO Box 454 55041 651-345-4553
Greg Berge, prin. Fax 345-5894

Lake Crystal, Blue Earth, Pop. 2,527
Lake Crystal Wellcome Memorial SD 2071 800/PK-12
PO Box 160 56055 507-726-2323
Tom Farrell, supt. Fax 726-2334
www.isd2071.k12.mn.us
Lake Crystal Wellcome Memorial HS 400/7-12
PO Box 160 56055 507-726-2110
Linda Isebrand, prin. Fax 726-2283

Lake Elmo, Washington, Pop. 7,919
Stillwater Area SD 834
Supt. — See Stillwater
Oak-Land JHS 1,000/7-9
820 Manning Ave N 55042 651-351-8500
Andy Fields, prin. Fax 351-8505

Rasmussen College Post-Sec.
8565 Eagle Point Cir 55042 651-259-6600

Lakefield, Jackson, Pop. 1,687
Jackson County Central SD 2895
Supt. — See Jackson
Jackson County Central MS 300/6-8
PO Box 338 56150 507-662-6625
Kari Wilkinson, prin. Fax 662-5083

Lake Park, Becker, Pop. 774
Lake Park Audubon ISD 2889 600/K-12
PO Box 479 56554 218-238-5914
Dale Hogie, supt. Fax 201-0886
www.lakeparkaudubon.com
Lake Park Audubon JSHS 300/7-12
PO Box 479 56554 218-238-5916
Kevin Ricke, prin. Fax 201-0886

Lakeville, Dakota, Pop. 54,640
Lakeville Area SD 194 10,600/K-12
8670 210th St W 55044 952-232-2000
Dr. Lisa Snyder, supt. Fax 469-6054
www.isd194.k12.mn.us
Century MS 900/6-8
18610 Ipava Ave 55044 952-232-2300
Fax 469-6103
Kenwood Trail MS 800/6-8
19455 Kenwood Trl 55044 952-232-3800
Kate Eisenthal, prin. Fax 469-3508
Lakeville Area Learning Center 100/Alt
20950 Howland Ave W 55044 952-232-2080
Clifford Skagen, prin. Fax 469-7171
Lakeville North HS 1,800/9-12
19600 Ipava Ave 55044 952-232-3600
Marne Berkvam, prin. Fax 469-3367
Lakeville South HS 1,900/9-12
21135 Jacquard Ave 55044 952-232-3300
Scott Douglas, prin. Fax 469-8383
McGuire MS 900/6-8
21220 Holyoke Ave 55044 952-232-2200
Joshua Alexander, prin. Fax 469-7224

Globe University MN School of Business Post-Sec.
17685 Juniper Path 55044 952-892-9000
Glory Academy 50/PK-12
25170 Dodd Blvd 55044 952-985-3659
Rev. Cheryl Engelman, prin.

Lamberton, Redwood, Pop. 817
Red Rock Central SD 2884 400/PK-12
PO Box 278 56152 507-752-7361
Dr. John Brennan, supt. Fax 752-6133
www.rrcnet.org
Red Rock Central HS 200/6-12
PO Box 278 56152 507-752-7361
Phil Goetstouwers, prin. Fax 752-6133

Lancaster, Kittson, Pop. 340
Lancaster SD 356 200/PK-12
401 Central Ave S 56735 218-762-5400
Bradley Homstad, supt. Fax 762-5512
www.lancaster.k12.mn.us/
Lancaster JSHS 100/7-12
401 Central Ave S 56735 218-762-5400
Bradley Homstad, admin. Fax 762-5512

Lanesboro, Fillmore, Pop. 743
Lanesboro SD 229 300/PK-12
100 Kirkwood St E 55949 507-467-2229
Jeff Boggs, supt. Fax 467-3026
www.lanesboro.k12.mn.us
Lanesboro JSHS 200/7-12
100 Kirkwood St E 55949 507-467-2229
Brett Clarke, prin. Fax 467-3026

Laporte, Hubbard, Pop. 104
Laporte SD 306 200/PK-12
315 Main St W 56461 218-224-2288
Harvey Johnson, supt. Fax 224-2905
www.laporte.k12.mn.us
Laporte JSHS 100/7-12
315 Main St W 56461 218-224-2288
Kim Goodwin, prin. Fax 224-2905

Le Center, LeSueur, Pop. 2,491
Tri-City United ISD 2905
Supt. — See Montgomery
Tri-City United LeCenter MS 200/5-8
150 W Tyrone St 56057 507-357-6802
Dave Dooley, prin. Fax 357-4825

Le Roy, Mower, Pop. 926
Le Roy-Ostrander SD 499 300/PK-12
PO Box 1000 55951 507-324-5743
Steve Sallee, supt. Fax 324-5149
www.leroy.k12.mn.us
Le Roy-Ostrander JSHS 100/7-12
PO Box 1000 55951 507-324-5741
Aaron Hungerholt, prin. Fax 324-5149

Lester Prairie, McLeod, Pop. 1,714
Lester Prairie SD 424 400/PK-12
131 Hickory St N 55354 320-395-2521
Mike McNulty, supt. Fax 395-4204
www.lp.k12.mn.us
Lester Prairie JSHS 200/6-12
131 Hickory St N 55354 320-395-2521
Jeremy Schmidt, prin. Fax 395-4204

Le Sueur, LeSueur, Pop. 4,019
Le Sueur-Henderson SD 2397 700/PK-12
115 1/2 N 5th St Ste 200 56058 507-665-4600
Richard Hanson, supt. Fax 665-6858
www.isd2397.org
Le Sueur-Henderson MSHS 400/6-12
901 Ferry St 56058 507-665-5800
Kevin Enerson, prin. Fax 665-6012
Ziebarth Alternative Learning Center 50/Alt
706 Turril St 56058 507-665-4620
Becki Hawkins, prin. Fax 665-4187

Lewiston, Winona, Pop. 1,612
Lewiston-Altura SD 857 800/PK-12
100 County Road 25 55952 507-523-2191
Jeff Apse, supt. Fax 523-3460
www.lewalt.k12.mn.us
Lewiston-Altura JSHS 400/7-12
100 County Road 25 55952 507-523-2191
Mitch Schiltz, prin. Fax 523-2286

Lindstrom, Chisago, Pop. 4,380
Chisago Lakes SD 2144 3,500/PK-12
13750 Lake Blvd 55045 651-213-2000
Dr. Michael McLoughlin, supt. Fax 213-2050
www.chisagolakes.k12.mn.us
Chisago Lakes HS 1,100/9-12
13750 Lake Blvd 55045 651-213-2500
David Ertl, prin. Fax 213-2550
Chisago Lakes MS 800/6-8
13750 Lake Blvd 55045 651-213-2400
Jodi Otte, prin. Fax 213-2051

Lino Lakes, Anoka, Pop. 19,895
Centennial SD 12
Supt. — See Circle Pines
Centennial MS 1,600/6-8
399 Elm St 55014 763-792-5400
Robert Stevens, prin. Fax 792-5450

Litchfield, Meeker, Pop. 6,688
Litchfield SD 465 1,700/PK-12
114 N Holcombe Ave Ste 100 55355 320-693-2444
Dan Frazier, supt. Fax 593-6528
www.litchfield.k12.mn.us
Litchfield HS 500/9-12
901 N Gilman Ave 55355 320-693-2424
Patrick Devine, prin. Fax 593-3308
Litchfield MS 400/6-8
340 E 10th St 55355 320-693-2441
Patrick Devine, prin. Fax 593-3485

Little Canada, Ramsey, Pop. 9,560
Roseville Area SD 623
Supt. — See Roseville
Roseville Area MS 800/7-8
15 County Road B2 E 55117 651-482-5280
Dr. Juanita Hoskins, prin. Fax 482-5299

Little Falls, Morrison, Pop. 8,197
Little Falls SD 482 2,400/PK-12
1001 5th Ave SE 56345 320-632-2002
Stephen Jones, supt. Fax 632-2012
www.lfalls.k12.mn.us
Little Falls Community HS 700/9-12
1001 5th Ave SE 56345 320-616-2200
Tim Bjorge, prin. Fax 616-2210
Little Falls Community MS 500/6-8
1000 1st Ave NE 56345 320-616-4200
Nathan Swenson, prin. Fax 616-4210

Mary of Lourdes MS 100/5-8
205 3rd St NW 56345 320-632-6742
Maria Heymans-Becker, prin. Fax 632-3556

Littlefork, Koochiching, Pop. 646
Littlefork-Big Falls SD 362 200/PK-12
700 Main St 56653 218-278-6614
Fred Seybert, supt. Fax 278-6615
www.isd362.k12.mn.us
Littlefork-Big Falls S 200/PK-12
700 Main St 56653 218-278-6614
Christopher Bachmeier, prin. Fax 278-6615

Long Lake, Hennepin, Pop. 1,729
Orono SD 278 2,800/K-12
685 N Old Crystal Bay Rd 55356 952-449-8300
Dr. Karen Orcutt, supt. Fax 449-8399
www.orono.k12.mn.us
Orono HS 900/9-12
795 N Old Crystal Bay Rd 55356 952-449-8400
Dave Benson, prin. Fax 449-8449
Orono MS 700/6-8
800 N Old Crystal Bay Rd 55356 952-449-8450
Dr. Patricia Wroten, prin. Fax 449-8453

Long Prairie, Todd, Pop. 3,383
Long Prairie-Grey Eagle SD 2753 1,000/PK-12
205 2nd St S 56347 320-732-2194
Jon Kringen, supt. Fax 732-3791
www.lpge.k12.mn.us/
Long Prairie-Grey Eagle HS 400/9-12
510 9th St NE 56347 320-732-2194
Paul Weinzierl, prin. Fax 732-6470
Long Prairie MS 200/6-8
205 2nd St S 56347 320-732-2194
Paul Weinzierl, prin. Fax 732-2844

Luverne, Rock, Pop. 4,679
Luverne SD 2184 1,200/PK-12
709 N Kniss Ave 56156 507-283-8088
Gary Fisher, supt. Fax 283-9681
www.isd2184.net/
Luverne Alternative Program 50/Alt
709 N Kniss Ave 56156 507-283-0075
Gary Fisher, prin. Fax 283-9681
Luverne HS 300/9-12
709 N Kniss Ave 56156 507-283-4491
Ryan Johnson, prin. Fax 283-9681
Luverne MS 300/6-8
709 N Kniss Ave 56156 507-283-4491
Ryan Johnson, prin. Fax 283-9681

Lyle, Mower, Pop. 544
Lyle SD 497 200/PK-12
700 E 2nd St 55953 507-325-4146
Joe Guanella, supt. Fax 325-4611
www.lyle.k12.mn.us
Lyle HS 100/6-12
700 E 2nd St 55953 507-325-2201
Joe Guanella, prin. Fax 325-4611

Mabel, Fillmore, Pop. 777
Mabel-Canton SD 238 300/PK-12
316 W Fillmore 55954 507-493-5423
Michael Moriarty, supt. Fax 493-5425
www.mabelcanton.k12.mn.us/
Mabel-Canton JSHS 100/7-12
316 W Fillmore 55954 507-493-5422
Jeffrey Nolte, prin. Fax 493-5425

Mc Gregor, Aitkin, Pop. 390
McGregor ISD 4 400/PK-12
PO Box 160 55760 218-768-2111
Paul Grams, supt. Fax 768-3901
www.mcgregor.k12.mn.us
McGregor JSHS 200/7-12
PO Box 160 55760 218-768-2111
Robert Staska, prin. Fax 768-3802

Madelia, Watonwan, Pop. 2,301
Madelia SD 837 500/PK-12
320 Buck Ave SE 56062 507-642-3232
Brian Grenell, supt. Fax 642-3622
www.madelia.k12.mn.us
Madelia JSHS 300/7-12
320 Buck Ave SE 56062 507-642-3232
Allan Beyer, prin. Fax 642-3622

Madison, Lac qui Parle, Pop. 1,527
Lac Qui Parle Valley SD 2853 800/PK-12
2860 291st Ave 56256 320-752-4800
Renae Tostenson, supt. Fax 752-4401
www.lqpv.org
Lac Qui Parle Valley HS 400/7-12
2860 291st Ave 56256 320-752-4800
Scott Sawatsky, prin. Fax 752-4401

Mahnomen, Mahnomen, Pop. 1,108
Mahnomen SD 432 600/PK-12
PO Box 319 56557 218-935-2211
Jeff Bisek, supt. Fax 935-5921
www.mahnomen.k12.mn.us/
Mahnomen Area Learning Center 50/Alt
PO Box 319 56557 218-935-2346
Sandra Haddeland, dir. Fax 935-5921
Mahnomen JSHS 300/7-12
PO Box 319 56557 218-935-2213
Ramona Miller, prin. Fax 935-5921

White Earth Tribal and Community College Post-Sec.
124 1st St SW 56557 218-935-0417

Mahtomedi, Washington, Pop. 7,538
Mahtomedi SD 832 3,200/K-12
1520 Mahtomedi Ave 55115 651-407-2000
Dr. Mark Larson, supt. Fax 407-2025
www.mahtomedi.k12.mn.us
Mahtomedi HS 1,200/9-12
8000 75th St N 55115 651-407-2100
Kathe Nickleby, prin. Fax 407-2125
Mahtomedi MS 800/6-8
8100 75th St N 55115 651-407-2200
Dr. Mike Neubeck, prin. Fax 407-2225

Mankato, Blue Earth, Pop. 38,565
Mankato SD 77 7,300/K-12
PO Box 8741 56002 507-387-1868
Sheri Allen, supt. Fax 387-4257
www.isd77.k12.mn.us
Central Freedom S 50/Alt
110 Fulton St 56001 507-387-2794
Kathleen Johnson, prin. Fax 387-7737
Central HS 100/Alt
110 Fulton St 56001 507-387-3047
Kathleen Johnson, prin. Fax 387-7737
Mankato East HS 900/9-12
2600 Hoffman Rd 56001 507-387-5671
Jeff Dahline, prin. Fax 387-7927
Mankato East JHS 500/7-8
2600 Hoffman Rd 56001 507-345-6625
Rich Dahman, prin. Fax 387-2890
Mankato West HS 1,100/9-12
1351 S Riverfront Dr 56001 507-387-3461
Brian Gersich, prin. Fax 345-1502
Other Schools – See North Mankato

Bethany Lutheran College Post-Sec.
700 Luther Dr 56001 507-344-7000
Immanuel Lutheran S 100/K-12
421 N 2nd St 56001 507-345-3027
Karl Olmanson, prin. Fax 345-1562
Loyola HS 200/9-12
145 Good Counsel Dr 56001 507-388-2997
Shelley Schutz, prin. Fax 388-3081
Loyola IS Fitzgerald Campus 4-8
110 N 5th St 56001 507-388-9344
William Schumacher, prin. Fax 388-2750
Minnesota State University Mankato Post-Sec.
309 Wigley Administrtn Ctr 56001 507-389-1866
Rasmussen College Post-Sec.
130 Saint Andrews Dr 56001 507-625-6556

Maple Grove, Hennepin, Pop. 60,235
Osseo SD 279 20,700/PK-12
11200 93rd Ave N 55369 763-391-7000
Kate Maguire, supt. Fax 391-7070
www.district279.org
Maple Grove JHS 1,700/7-9
7000 Hemlock Ln N 55369 763-315-7600
Laurel Anderson, prin. Fax 315-7601
Maple Grove SHS 1,700/10-12
9800 Fernbrook Ln N 55369 763-391-8700
Sara Vernig, prin. Fax 391-8701
Other Schools – See Brooklyn Park, Osseo

Heritage Christian Academy 500/PK-12
15655 Bass Lake Rd 55311 763-463-2200
Tonya Scott, pres. Fax 463-2299

Maple Lake, Wright, Pop. 2,037
Maple Lake SD 881 1,000/PK-12
PO Box 760 55358 320-963-3171
Mark Redemske, supt. Fax 963-3170
www.maplelake.k12.mn.us
Maple Lake JSHS 500/7-12
PO Box 820 55358 320-963-3171
David J. Hansen, prin. Fax 963-3170

Mapleton, Blue Earth, Pop. 1,738
Maple River SD 2135 1,100/PK-12
PO Box 515 56065 507-524-3918
Dan Anderson, supt. Fax 524-4882
www.isd2135.k12.mn.us/
Maple River HS 300/9-12
PO Box 515 56065 507-524-3918
Todd Griepentrog, prin. Fax 524-4919
Maple River MS 200/6-8
PO Box 515 56065 507-524-3918
Todd Griepentrog, prin. Fax 524-3638

Maplewood, Ramsey, Pop. 37,068
North St. Paul-Maplewood-Oakdale SD 622
Supt. — See North Saint Paul
Glenn MS 800/6-8
1560 County Road B E 55109 651-748-6300
Mike Redmond, prin. Fax 748-6391
Harmony Learning Center 100/Alt
1961 County Road C E 55109 651-748-6200
Joe Richter, admin. Fax 748-7486
Maplewood MS 800/6-8
2410 Holloway Ave E 55109 651-748-6500
Jill Miklausich, prin. Fax 748-6591

Hill-Murray HS 900/7-12
2625 Larpenteur Ave E 55109 651-777-1376
David Meyer, prin. Fax 748-2444

Marble, Itasca, Pop. 685
Greenway SD 316 700/PK-12
201 Kate St 55764 218-247-7306
Mark Adams, supt. Fax 245-6612
www.isd316.org
Other Schools – See Coleraine

Nashwauk-Keewatin SD 319 600/PK-12
PO Box 170 55764 218-247-7306
Mark Adams, supt.
www.isd319.org
Other Schools – See Nashwauk

Marshall, Lyon, Pop. 13,459
Marshall SD 413 2,100/K-12
401 S Saratoga St 56258 507-537-6924
Klint Willert, supt. Fax 537-6931
www.swmn.org
Marshall HS 800/9-12
400 Tiger Dr 56258 507-537-6920
Brian Jones, prin. Fax 537-6933
Marshall MS 500/5-8
401 S Saratoga St 56258 507-537-6938
Mary Kay Thomas, prin. Fax 537-6942
MEC Learning Alternatives 50/Alt
1420 E College Dr 56258 507-537-6210
Jeremy Williams, prin. Fax 537-7609

Southwest Minnesota State University Post-Sec.
1501 State St 56258 507-537-7678

Mayer, Carver, Pop. 1,725

Mayer Lutheran HS 300/9-12
305 5th St NE 55360 952-657-2251
Kevin Wilaby, prin. Fax 657-2344

Mazeppa, Wabasha, Pop. 837
Zumbrota-Mazeppa SD 2805 900/PK-12
343 3rd Ave NE 55956 507-732-1400
Tony Simons, supt. Fax 732-1401
www.zmschools.us/
Other Schools – See Zumbrota

Medford, Steele, Pop. 1,228
Medford ISD 763 800/PK-12
750 2nd Ave SE 55049 507-451-5250
Rich Dahman, supt. Fax 451-6474
www.medford.k12.mn.us
Medford JSHS 400/7-12
750 2nd Ave SE 55049 507-451-5250
Jeff Sampson, prin. Fax 451-6474

Melrose, Stearns, Pop. 3,582
Melrose SD 740 1,300/PK-12
546 N 5th Ave E 56352 320-256-4224
Tom Rich, supt. Fax 256-4311
www.melrose.k12.mn.us
Melrose HS 500/9-12
546 N 5th Ave E 56352 320-256-4224
Chad Doetkott, prin. Fax 256-4311
Melrose MS 300/6-8
546 N 5th Ave E 56352 320-256-4224
Randy Bergquist, prin. Fax 256-4311

Menahga, Wadena, Pop. 1,296
Menahga SD 821 800/PK-12
PO Box 160 56464 218-564-4141
Mary Klamm, supt. Fax 564-5401
www.menahga.k12.mn.us
Menahga JSHS 300/7-12
PO Box 160 56464 218-564-4141
Daniel Stifter, prin. Fax 564-5401

Mendota Heights, Dakota, Pop. 10,905
West St. Paul-Mendota Hts-Eagan SD 197 4,400/PK-12
1897 Delaware Ave 55118 651-403-7000
Dr. Nancy Allen-Mastro, supt. Fax 403-7010
isd197.org
Friendly Hills MS 600/5-8
701 Mendota Heights Rd 55120 651-403-7600
Joni Hagebock, prin. Fax 403-7610
Sibley HS 1,400/9-12
1897 Delaware Ave 55118 651-403-7100
Dr. Robin Percival, prin. Fax 403-7110
Other Schools – See West Saint Paul

Brown College Post-Sec.
1345 Mendota Heights Rd 55120 651-905-3400
Convent of the Visitation S 600/PK-12
2455 Visitation Dr 55120 651-683-1700
Dawn Nichols, hdmstr. Fax 454-7144
Le Cordon Bleu College of Culinary Arts Post-Sec.
1315 Mendota Heights Rd 55120 651-675-4700
St. Thomas Academy 700/7-12
949 Mendota Heights Rd 55120 651-454-4570
Thomas Mich Ph.D., hdmstr. Fax 454-4574

Middle River, Marshall, Pop. 301
Greenbush-Middle River SD 2683
Supt. — See Greenbush
Greenbush-Middle River JHS 100/6-8
PO Box 130 56737 218-222-3310
Sharon Schultz, prin. Fax 222-3314

Milaca, Mille Lacs, Pop. 2,899
Milaca SD 912 1,900/PK-12
500 Highway 23 W 56353 320-982-7210
Jerry Hansen, supt. Fax 982-7179
www.milaca.k12.mn.us/
Milaca ALC 50/Alt
305 3rd Ave NW 56353 320-982-7249
Betsy Hoover, prin. Fax 982-7290
Milaca HS 800/7-12
500 Highway 23 W 56353 320-982-7206
Damian Patnode, prin. Fax 983-3566

Milroy, Redwood, Pop. 251
Milroy SD 635 100/PK-8
PO Box 10 56263 507-336-2563
Wade McKittrick, supt. Fax 336-2568
www.milroy.k12.mn.us/
Milroy JHS 50/7-8
PO Box 10 56263 507-336-2563
Wade McKittrick, prin. Fax 336-2568

Minneapolis, Hennepin, Pop. 368,444
Minneapolis SD 1 32,800/PK-12
1250 W Broadway Ave 55411 612-668-0000
Bernadeia Johnson, supt. Fax 668-0195
www.mpls.k12.mn.us
Anthony MS 700/6-8
5757 Irving Ave S 55419 612-668-3240
Jackie Hanson, prin. Fax 668-3250
Anwatin MS 600/6-8
256 Upton Ave S 55405 612-668-2450
VaNita Miller, prin. Fax 668-2460
Broadway Alternative HS 100/Alt
3017 E 31st St 55406 612-668-4700
Jean Neuman, dir. Fax 668-4710
Cityview Performing Arts Magnet S 100/7-8
3350 N 4th St 55412 612-668-2270
Pao Vue, prin. Fax 668-2280
Edison HS 900/9-12
700 22nd Ave NE 55418 612-668-1300
Carla Steinbach, prin. Fax 668-1320
Field Community MS 500/5-8
4645 4th Ave S 55419 612-668-3640
Steve Norlin-Weaver, prin. Fax 668-3661
Fine Arts Interdisciplinary Resource S 500/K-12
10 S 10th St 55403 612-752-7100
Kevin Bennett, prin. Fax 752-7150
Henry HS 1,100/9-12
4320 Newton Ave N 55412 612-668-2000
Latanya Daniels, prin. Fax 668-1993
Lake Harriet Community Upper ES 600/3-8
4912 Vincent Ave S 55410 612-668-3310
Mary Rynchek, prin. Fax 668-3320
Lake Nokomis S - Keewaydin Campus 300/4-8
5209 30th Ave S 55417 612-668-4670
Martha Spriggs, prin. Fax 668-4680
MPS Metro St. Joseph's S 100/Alt
1121 E 46th St 55407 612-290-3512
Kristi Ward, admin. Fax 827-9571
North Academy of Arts & Communication 9-9
1500 James Ave N 55411 612-668-1700
Shawn Harris-Berry, prin. Fax 668-1770
Northeast MS 500/6-8
2955 Hayes St NE 55418 612-668-1500
Padmini Udupa, prin. Fax 668-1510
North HS 200/10-12
1500 James Ave N 55411 612-668-1700
David Branch, prin. Fax 668-1770
Olson MS 300/6-8
1607 51st Ave N 55430 612-668-1640
Karon Cunningham, prin. Fax 668-1650
Roosevelt HS 900/9-12
4029 28th Ave S 55406 612-668-4800
Michael Bradley, prin. Fax 668-4810
Sanford MS 600/6-8
3524 42nd Ave S 55406 612-668-4900
Meredith Davis, prin. Fax 668-4910
South HS 2,000/9-12
3131 19th Ave S 55407 612-668-4300
Cecilia Saddler, prin. Fax 668-4310
Southwest HS 1,800/9-12
3414 W 47th St 55410 612-668-3030
Bill Smith, prin. Fax 668-3080
Stadium View S 100/Alt
510 Park Ave 55415 612-348-7740
Larry Lucio, prin. Fax 596-9989
Washburn HS 1,000/9-12
201 W 49th St 55419 612-668-3400
Carol Markham-Cousins, prin. Fax 668-3410
Wellstone International HS 100/Alt
4029 28th Ave S 55406 612-668-5070
Fax 668-5080
Other Schools – See Bloomington, Crystal

Art Institutes International Minnesota Post-Sec.
15 S 9th St 55402 612-332-3361
Art Instruction Schools Post-Sec.
3400 Technology Dr 55418 800-801-6940
Augsburg College Post-Sec.
2211 Riverside Ave 55454 612-330-1000
Aveda Institute Post-Sec.
400 Central Ave SE 55414 612-378-7404
Bais Yaakov HS of the Twin Cities 50/9-12
4221 Sunset Blvd 55416 952-915-9117
Sarah Gibber, prin. Fax 915-9116
Blake S - Northrop Campus 500/9-12
511 Kenwood Pkwy 55403 952-988-3700
Dr. Anne Stavney, head sch Fax 988-3705
Breck S 1,200/PK-12
123 Ottawa Ave N 55422 763-381-8100
Edward Kim, hdmstr. Fax 381-8288
Brown College Post-Sec.
5951 Earle Brown Dr 55430 763-279-2400
Capella University Post-Sec.
225 S 6th St Fl 9 55402 888-227-3552
Cristo Rey Jesuit HS 9-12
2924 4th Ave S 55408 612-545-9700
Jeb Myers, prin. Fax 276-0142
De La Salle HS 700/9-12
1 De La Salle Dr 55401 612-676-7600
James Benson, prin.
Dunwoody College of Technology Post-Sec.
818 Dunwoody Blvd 55403 612-374-5800
Globe University Post-Sec.
80 S 8th St 55402 612-455-3000
Hennepin County Medical Center Post-Sec.
701 Park Ave 55415 612-347-2352
Herzing University Post-Sec.
5700 W Broadway Ave 55428 763-535-3000
Institute of Production and Recording Post-Sec.
312 Washington Ave N 55401 612-375-1900
ITT Technical Institute Post-Sec.
6120 Earle Brown Dr Ste 100 55430 763-549-5900
Minneapolis College of Art & Design Post-Sec.
2501 Stevens Ave 55404 612-874-3700

Minneapolis Community and Tech College Post-Sec.
1501 Hennepin Ave 55403 612-659-6000
Minneapolis Media Institute Post-Sec.
4100 W 76th St 55435 866-701-1310
Minneapolis VA Medical Center Post-Sec.
1 Veterans Dr 55417 612-725-2000
Minnehaha Academy 500/9-12
3100 W River Pkwy 55406 612-729-8321
Dr. Donna Harris, pres. Fax 728-7787
North Central University Post-Sec.
910 Elliot Ave 55404 612-343-4400
North Memorial Medical Center Post-Sec.
3300 Oakdale Ave N 55422 763-520-5200
Summit Academy OIC Post-Sec.
935 Olson Memorial Hwy 55405 612-377-0150
University of Minnesota Twin Cities Post-Sec.
231 Pillsbury Dr SE 55455 612-625-5000
Walden University Post-Sec.
100 Washington Ave S # 900 55401 612-338-7224
Woodcrest Baptist Academy 200/PK-12
6875 University Ave NE 55432 763-571-6410
Loren Isaacs, admin. Fax 571-3978

Minneota, Lyon, Pop. 1,386
Minneota SD 414 500/K-12
PO Box 98 56264 507-872-6532
Dan Deltte, supt. Fax 872-5172
www.minneotaschools.org/
Minneota JSHS 200/7-12
PO Box 98 56264 507-872-6175
Harlen Ulrich, prin. Fax 872-6494

Minnetonka, Hennepin, Pop. 48,748
Hopkins SD 270
Supt. — See Hopkins
Hopkins HS 1,800/10-12
2400 Lindbergh Dr 55305 952-988-4500
Patty Johnson, prin. Fax 988-4716
Hopkins North JHS 900/7-9
10700 Cedar Lake Rd 55305 952-988-4800
Becky Melville, prin. Fax 988-4869
Hopkins West JHS 800/7-9
3830 Baker Rd 55305 952-988-4400
Shirley Gregoire, prin. Fax 988-4477

Minnetonka SD 276 8,600/K-12
5621 County Road 101 55345 952-401-5000
Dr. Dennis Peterson, supt. Fax 401-5083
www.minnetonka.k12.mn.us
Minnetonka East MS 900/6-8
17000 Lake Street Ext 55345 952-401-5200
Pete Dymit, prin. Fax 401-5268
Minnetonka HS 2,800/9-12
18301 Highway 7 55345 952-401-5700
David Adney, prin. Fax 401-5709
Other Schools – See Excelsior

Minnetonka Christian Academy 100/K-12
3500 Williston Rd 55345 952-935-4497
Matthew Jakobsons, prin. Fax 935-4498

Minnetrista, Hennepin, Pop. 6,316
Westonka SD 277 2,200/PK-12
5901 Sunnyfield Rd E 55364 952-491-8000
Kevin Borg, supt. Fax 491-8012
www.westonka.k12.mn.us
Other Schools – See Mound

Montevideo, Chippewa, Pop. 5,317
Montevideo SD 129 1,300/PK-12
2001 William Ave 56265 320-269-8833
Dr. Luther Heller, supt. Fax 269-8834
www.montevideoschools.com
Montevideo HS 500/8-12
1501 William Ave 56265 320-269-6446
Bruce Bergeson, prin. Fax 321-8960

Montgomery, LeSueur, Pop. 2,910
Tri-City United ISD 2905 1,400/PK-12
101 2nd St NE Ste 3 56069 507-364-8100
Teri Preisler, supt. Fax 364-8103
www.tcu2905.us
Tri-City United HS 300/9-12
700 4th St NW 56069 507-364-8111
Alan Fitterer, prin. Fax 364-8410
Tri-City United MS 200/5-8
101 2nd St NE Ste 2 56069 507-364-8118
Deb Dwyer, dir. Fax 364-8412
Other Schools – See Le Center

Monticello, Wright, Pop. 12,521
Monticello SD 882 3,900/PK-12
302 Washington St 55362 763-272-2000
James Johnson, supt. Fax 272-2009
www.monticello.k12.mn.us
Monticello HS 1,200/9-12
5225 School Blvd 55362 763-272-3000
Joel Lundin, prin. Fax 272-3009
Monticello MS 1,000/6-8
800 E Broadway St 55362 763-272-2100
Jeff Scherber, prin. Fax 272-2109

Moorhead, Clay, Pop. 37,202
Moorhead Area SD 152 5,300/K-12
2410 14th St S 56560 218-284-3330
Lynne Kovash Ed.D., supt. Fax 284-3332
www.moorhead.k12.mn.us
Horizon MS 1,300/6-8
3601 12th Ave S 56560 218-284-7300
Lori Lockhart, prin. Fax 284-7333
Moorhead HS 1,500/9-12
2300 4th Ave S 56560 218-284-2300
Dave Lawrence, prin. Fax 284-2333
Red River Area Learning Center 100/Alt
1100 32nd Ave S 56560 218-284-2200
Deb Pender-Tilleraas, dir. Fax 284-2233

Concordia College Post-Sec.
901 8th St S 56562 218-299-4000
Globe University MN School of Business Post-Sec.
2777 34th St S 56560 218-422-1000
MN State Community & Technical College Post-Sec.
1900 28th Ave S 56560 218-299-6500
Minnesota State University Moorhead Post-Sec.
1104 7th Ave S 56563 218-477-4000

Park Christian S 400/PK-12
300 17th St N 56560 218-236-0500
Kent Hannestad, pres. Fax 236-7301
Rita's Moorhead Beauty College Post-Sec.
1024 Center Ave 56560 218-236-7201

Moose Lake, Carlton, Pop. 2,729
Moose Lake SD 97 700/PK-12
PO Box 489 55767 218-485-4435
Robert Indihar, supt. Fax 485-8110
www.mooselake.k12.mn.us
Moose Lake JSHS 400/7-12
PO Box 489 55767 218-485-4622
Billie Jo Steen, prin. Fax 485-8681

Mora, Kanabec, Pop. 3,511
Mora SD 332 1,800/PK-12
400 Maple Ave E 55051 320-679-6200
Craig Schultz, supt. Fax 679-6209
www.mora.k12.mn.us
Mora HS 800/7-12
400 Maple Ave E 55051 320-679-6220
Brent Nelson, prin. Fax 679-6238

Morgan, Redwood, Pop. 873
Cedar Mountain SD 2754 500/K-12
PO Box 188 56266 507-249-5990
Robert Tews, supt. Fax 249-3149
www.cms.mntm.org/
Cedar Mountain JSHS 300/6-12
PO Box 188 56266 507-249-5888
Jeremy Schultz, prin. Fax 249-3149

Morris, Stevens, Pop. 5,158
Morris SD 769 1,000/PK-12
201 S Columbia Ave 56267 320-589-4840
Scott Monson, supt. Fax 585-2208
www.morris.k12.mn.us
Morris Area JSHS 500/7-12
201 S Columbia Ave 56267 320-589-4400
Craig Peterson, prin. Fax 589-3203

University of Minnesota Morris Post-Sec.
600 E 4th St 56267 320-589-6035

Morristown, Rice, Pop. 973
Waterville-Elysian-Morristown SD 2143
Supt. — See Waterville
Waterville-Elysian-Morristown JHS 100/7-8
PO Box 278 55052 507-685-4222
Bernardine Sauter, prin. Fax 685-2420

Cannon Valley Lutheran HS 50/9-12
PO Box 346 55052 507-685-2636
Andrew Boll, admin. Fax 685-4502

Motley, Morrison, Pop. 649
Staples-Motley ISD 2170
Supt. — See Staples
Motley-Staples MS 300/6-8
PO Box 268 56466 218-352-6315
Justin Sperling, prin. Fax 352-6508

Mound, Hennepin, Pop. 8,930
Westonka SD 277
Supt. — See Minnetrista
Mound-Westonka HS 900/8-12
5905 Sunnyfield Rd E 55364 952-491-8100
Keith Randklev, prin. Fax 491-8103

Mounds View, Ramsey, Pop. 11,818
Mounds View SD 621
Supt. — See Shoreview
Edgewood MS 600/6-8
5100 Edgewood Dr 55112 651-621-6600
Penny Howard, prin. Fax 621-6605

Mountain Iron, Saint Louis, Pop. 2,818
Mountain Iron-Buhl SD 712 500/PK-12
5720 Marble Ave 55768 218-735-8271
John Klarich, supt. Fax 735-8244
www.mib.k12.mn.us
Mountain Iron-Buhl JSHS 200/7-12
5720 Marble Ave 55768 218-735-8271
Angie Williams, prin. Fax 735-8217

Mountain Lake, Cottonwood, Pop. 2,081
Mountain Lake SD 173 500/PK-12
PO Box 400 56159 507-427-2325
William Strom, supt. Fax 427-3047
www.mountainlake.k12.mn.us
Mountain Lake JSHS 200/7-12
PO Box 400 56159 507-427-2325
Pamela Anderson, prin. Fax 427-3047

Mountain Lake Christian S 100/PK-12
PO Box 478 56159 507-427-2010
Dr. Bob Windel, admin. Fax 427-3123

Nashwauk, Itasca, Pop. 964
Nashwauk-Keewatin SD 319
Supt. — See Marble
Nashwauk JSHS 300/7-12
400 2nd St 55769 218-885-1280
Jeff Britten, prin. Fax 885-2910

Nevis, Hubbard, Pop. 379
Nevis SD 308 300/PK-12
PO Box 138 56467 218-652-3500
Steven Rassier, supt. Fax 652-3505
www.nevis.k12.mn.us
Nevis S 300/PK-12
PO Box 138 56467 218-652-3500
John Strom, prin. Fax 652-3505

New Brighton, Ramsey, Pop. 20,903
Mounds View SD 621
Supt. — See Shoreview
Area Learning Center 100/Alt
2101 14th St NW 55112 651-621-6200
Julie Wikelius, prin. Fax 621-6205
Highview MS 800/6-8
2300 7th St NW 55112 651-621-6700
Sheila Eller, prin. Fax 621-6705

Irondale HS 1,600/9-12
2425 Long Lake Rd 55112 651-621-6800
Scott Gengler, prin. Fax 621-6805

United Theological Seminary/Twin Cities Post-Sec.
3000 5th St NW 55112 651-633-4311

Newfolden, Marshall, Pop. 366
Marshall County Central SD 441 400/K-12
PO Box 189 56738 218-874-8530
Scott Vedbraaten, supt. Fax 874-8581
www.newfolden.k12.mn.us/
Marshall County Central HS 200/7-12
PO Box 189 56738 218-874-7225
Ryan Johnson, prin. Fax 874-8581

New Hope, Hennepin, Pop. 19,669
Robbinsdale SD 281 11,700/K-12
4148 Winnetka Ave N 55427 763-504-8000
Aldo Sicoli, supt. Fax 504-8979
www.rdale.org
Robbinsdale Cooper HS 1,900/9-12
8230 47th Ave N 55428 763-504-8500
Michael Favor, prin. Fax 504-8531
Other Schools – See Plymouth, Robbinsdale

New London, Kandiyohi, Pop. 1,247
New London-Spicer SD 345 1,400/K-12
101 4th Ave SW 56273 320-354-2252
Paul Carlson, supt. Fax 354-9001
nls.k12.mn.us
New London-Spicer HS 500/9-12
101 4th Ave SW 56273 320-354-2252
Kevin Acquard, prin. Fax 354-9001
New London-Spicer MS 400/5-8
101 4th Ave SW 56273 320-354-2252
Trish Perry, prin. Fax 354-4244

New Prague, Scott, Pop. 7,228
New Prague Area SD 721 3,700/PK-12
410 Central Ave N 56071 952-758-1700
Tim Dittberner, supt. Fax 758-1799
www.np.k12.mn.us
New Prague HS 1,200/9-12
221 12th St NE 56071 952-758-1200
Lonnie Seifert, prin. Fax 758-1299
New Prague MS 900/6-8
721 Central Ave N 56071 952-758-1400
Brad Gregor, prin. Fax 758-1499

New Richland, Waseca, Pop. 1,198
NRHEG SD 2168 1,000/PK-12
306 Ash Ave S 56072 507-465-3205
Kevin Wellen, supt. Fax 465-8633
www.nrheg.k12.mn.us
NRHEG HS 400/7-12
306 Ash Ave S 56072 507-465-3205
Paul Cyr, prin. Fax 465-8633

New Ulm, Brown, Pop. 13,436
New Ulm ISD 88 2,000/PK-12
15 N State St 56073 507-359-8401
Jeff Bertrang, supt. Fax 359-8406
www.newulm.k12.mn.us
New Ulm HS 900/7-12
414 S Payne St 56073 507-359-8420
Mark Bergmann, prin. Fax 359-8432

Cathedral HS 200/7-12
600 N Washington St 56073 507-354-4511
Peter Roufs, prin. Fax 354-5711
Martin Luther College Post-Sec.
1995 Luther Ct 56073 507-354-8221
Minnesota Valley Lutheran HS 200/9-12
45638 561st Ave 56073 507-354-6851
Tim Plath, prin. Fax 354-6854

New York Mills, Otter Tail, Pop. 1,166
New York Mills SD 553 700/PK-12
PO Box 218 56567 218-385-4201
Todd Cameron, supt. Fax 385-2551
www.nymills.k12.mn.us
New York Mills JSHS 300/7-12
PO Box 218 56567 218-385-4211
Blaine Novak, prin. Fax 385-2551

Nicollet, Nicollet, Pop. 1,085
Nicollet SD 507 100/K-12
PO Box 108 56074 507-232-3411
Jack Eustice, supt. Fax 232-3536
www.isd507.k12.mn.us
Nicollet S 100/K-12
PO Box 108 56074 507-232-3411
Jennifer Baumgartner, prin. Fax 232-3536

North Branch, Chisago, Pop. 9,994
North Branch Area ISD 138 3,400/PK-12
PO Box 370 55056 651-674-1000
Dr. Deb Henton, supt. Fax 674-1010
www.northbranch.k12.mn.us
North Branch Area Learning Center 50/Alt
PO Box 370 55056 651-674-1050
David Treichel, dir. Fax 674-1060
North Branch HS 1,000/9-12
PO Box 370 55056 651-674-1500
Coleman McDonough, prin. Fax 674-1510
North Branch MS 1,100/5-8
PO Box 370 55056 651-674-1300
Todd Tetzlaff, prin. Fax 674-1310

Northfield, Rice, Pop. 19,624
Northfield SD 659 3,800/PK-12
1400 Division St S 55057 507-663-0629
L. Chris Richardson Ph.D., supt. Fax 663-0611
www.nfld.k12.mn.us
Northfield HS 1,300/9-12
1400 Division St S 55057 507-663-0630
Joel Leer, prin. Fax 645-3455
Northfield MS 900/6-8
2200 Division St S 55057 507-663-0650
Jeff Pesta, prin. Fax 663-0660

Carleton College Post-Sec.
1 N College St 55057 507-222-4000

Laura Baker School Post-Sec.
211 Oak St 55057 507-645-8866
St. Olaf College Post-Sec.
1520 Saint Olaf Ave 55057 507-786-2222

North Mankato, Nicollet, Pop. 13,239
Mankato SD 77
Supt. — See Mankato
Dakota Meadows JHS 600/7-8
1900 Howard Dr W 56003 507-387-5077
Carmen Strahan, prin. Fax 387-1119

South Central College Post-Sec.
1920 Lee Blvd 56003 507-389-7200

Northome, Koochiching, Pop. 196
South Koochiching-Rainy River ISD 363 400/K-12
PO Box 465 56661 218-897-5275
Jerry Struss, supt. Fax 897-5280
www.northome.k12.mn.us
Northome JSHS 100/7-12
PO Box 465 56661 218-897-5275
Travis Hensch, prin. Fax 897-5280
Other Schools – See Birchdale

Northrop, Martin, Pop. 227

Luther HS 100/9-12
PO Box 228 56075 507-436-5249
Rebecca Oerman, prin. Fax 436-5240

North Saint Paul, Ramsey, Pop. 11,176
North St. Paul-Maplewood-Oakdale SD 622 10,400/K-12
2520 12th Ave E 55109 651-748-7622
Patricia Phillips, supt. Fax 748-7413
www.isd622.org/
North HS 2,000/9-12
2416 11th Ave E 55109 651-748-6000
Greg Nelson, prin. Fax 748-6091
Other Schools – See Maplewood, Oakdale

Norwood Young America, Carver, Pop. 3,521
Central ISD 108 1,000/PK-12
PO Box 247 55368 952-467-7000
Brian Corlett, supt. Fax 467-7003
www.central.k12.mn.us
Central HS 400/9-12
PO Box 247 55368 952-467-7100
Tom Erickson, prin. Fax 467-7103
Central MS 200/6-8
PO Box 247 55368 952-467-7200
Ron Erpenbach, prin. Fax 467-7203

Oakdale, Washington, Pop. 26,751
North St. Paul-Maplewood-Oakdale SD 622
Supt. — See North Saint Paul
Skyview Community MS 800/6-8
1100 Heron Ave N 55128 651-702-8000
Chris Hester, prin. Fax 702-8091
Tartan HS 1,800/9-12
828 Greenway Ave N 55128 651-702-8600
Adam Ehrmantraut, prin. Fax 702-8799

Ogilvie, Kanabec, Pop. 366
Ogilvie SD 333 600/PK-12
333 School Dr 56358 320-272-5000
Kathy Belsheim, supt. Fax 272-5072
www.ogilvie.k12.mn.us
Ogilvie JSHS 300/7-12
333 School Dr 56358 320-272-5000
Jake Nelson, prin. Fax 272-5072

Okabena, Jackson, Pop. 186
Heron Lake-Okabena SD 330 300/PK-12
PO Box 97 56161 507-853-4507
Ann Wendorff, supt. Fax 853-4642
www.ssc.mntm.org
Heron Lake-Okabena HS 200/7-12
PO Box 97 56161 507-853-4507
Ann Wendorff, prin. Fax 853-4642

Oklee, Red Lake, Pop. 424
Red Lake County Central ISD 2906 400/PK-12
PO Box 100 56742 218-796-5136
James Guetter, supt. Fax 796-5139
Red Lake County Central HS 200/7-12
PO Box 100 56742 218-796-5136
Randy Pederson, prin. Fax 796-5139

Olivia, Renville, Pop. 2,461
BOLD SD 2534 700/K-12
701 9th St S 56277 320-523-1031
John Dotson, supt. Fax 523-2399
www.bold.k12.mn.us
BOLD JSHS 400/7-12
701 9th St S 56277 320-523-1031
Brian Gauer, prin. Fax 523-5410

Onamia, Mille Lacs, Pop. 845
Onamia SD 480 600/K-12
35465 125th Ave 56359 320-532-4174
John Varner, supt. Fax 532-4658
www.onamia.k12.mn.us
Kokesh Area Learning Center 50/Alt
35465 125th Ave 56359 320-532-6831
Larry Ronglien, prin. Fax 532-5683
Onamia JSHS 300/7-12
35465 125th Ave 56359 320-532-4174
Larry Ronglien, prin. Fax 532-4974

Ortonville, Big Stone, Pop. 1,887
Ortonville SD 2903 300/PK-12
200 Trojan Dr 56278 320-839-6181
Jeffrey Taylor, supt. Fax 839-3708
www.ortonville.k12.mn.us
Ortonville S 300/PK-12
200 Trojan Dr 56278 320-839-6181
Joel Stattelman, prin. Fax 839-2499

Osakis, Douglas, Pop. 1,728
Osakis SD 213 700/PK-12
PO Box X 56360 320-859-2191
John Peterka, supt. Fax 859-2835
www.osakis.k12.mn.us
Osakis JSHS 400/5-12
PO Box X 56360 320-859-2191
Tim Roggenbuck, prin. Fax 859-2835

Osseo, Hennepin, Pop. 2,385
Osseo SD 279
Supt. — See Maple Grove
Osseo JHS 1,300/7-9
10223 93rd Ave N 55369 763-391-8800
Brian Chance, prin. Fax 391-8801
Osseo SHS 1,600/10-12
317 2nd Ave NW 55369 763-391-8500
Bob Perdaems, prin. Fax 391-8501

Owatonna, Steele, Pop. 25,301
Owatonna SD 761 4,700/K-12
515 W Bridge St 55060 507-444-8600
Peter Grant, supt. Fax 444-8688
www.owatonna.k12.mn.us/
Owatonna HS 1,600/9-12
333 E School St 55060 507-444-8810
Mark Randall, prin. Fax 444-8999
Owatonna JHS 600/7-8
500 15th St NE 55060 507-444-8710
Jason Hunt, prin. Fax 444-8799
Rose Alternative Learning Center 100/Alt
134 E Vine St 55060 507-455-1302
Jane Tapper, prin. Fax 455-1253

Parkers Prairie, Otter Tail, Pop. 1,009
Parkers Prairie ISD 547 500/PK-12
PO Box 46 56361 218-338-6011
Thomas Ames, supt. Fax 338-4077
www.isd547.com
Parkers Prairie JSHS 300/7-12
PO Box 46 56361 218-338-6011
Carey Johnson, prin. Fax 338-4077

Park Rapids, Hubbard, Pop. 3,639
Park Rapids SD 309 1,500/PK-12
301 Huntsinger Ave 56470 218-237-6500
Lance Bagstad, supt. Fax 237-6519
www.parkrapids.k12.mn.us
Century MS 400/5-8
501 Helten Ave 56470 218-237-6300
Joleen de la Hunt, prin. Fax 237-6349
Park Rapids Area HS 500/9-12
401 Huntsinger Ave 56470 218-237-6400
Jeff Johnson, admin. Fax 237-6401

Paynesville, Stearns, Pop. 2,410
Paynesville SD 741 800/PK-12
217 W Mill St 56362 320-243-3410
Robert Huot, supt. Fax 243-7525
www.paynesvilleschools.com/
Paynesville MSHS 300/6-12
795 W State Highway 23 56362 320-243-3761
Loric Floura, prin. Fax 243-4534

Pelican Rapids, Otter Tail, Pop. 2,413
Pelican Rapids SD 548 900/PK-12
PO Box 642 56572 218-863-5910
Deborah Wanek, supt. Fax 863-5915
www.pelicanrapids.k12.mn.us
Pelican Rapids JSHS 500/7-12
PO Box 642 56572 218-863-5910
Brian Korf, prin. Fax 863-5915

Pequot Lakes, Crow Wing, Pop. 2,149
Pequot Lakes SD 186 1,500/PK-12
30805 Olson St 56472 218-568-4996
Rick Linnell, supt. Fax 568-5259
pequotlakes.k12.mn.us/
Pequot Lakes HS 500/9-12
30805 Olson St 56472 218-568-9210
Chip Rankin, prin. Fax 568-9250
Pequot Lakes MS 400/5-8
30805 Olson St 56472 218-568-9357
Susan Sergent, prin. Fax 568-9202

Perham, Otter Tail, Pop. 2,944
Perham-Dent SD 549 1,400/PK-12
200 5th St SE 56573 218-346-4501
Mitch Anderson, supt. Fax 346-4506
www.perham.k12.mn.us
Perham Area Learning Center 50/Alt
520 1st Ave S 56573 218-346-6502
Fred Sailer, prin. Fax 346-4506
Perham HS 500/9-12
200 5th St SE 56573 218-346-6500
Ehren Zimmerman, prin. Fax 346-6504
Prairie Wind MS 400/5-8
480 Coney St W 56573 218-346-1700
Scott Bjerke, prin. Fax 346-1704

Peterson, Fillmore, Pop. 199
Rushford-Peterson SD 239
Supt. — See Rushford
Rushford-Peterson MS 200/6-8
PO Box 8 55962 507-875-2238
Luke Lutterman, prin. Fax 875-2316

Pierz, Morrison, Pop. 1,383
Pierz SD 484 1,100/PK-12
112 Kamnic St 56364 320-468-6458
George Weber, supt. Fax 468-6408
www.pierz.k12.mn.us
Healy JSHS 600/7-12
112 Kamnic St 56364 320-468-6458
Karrie Boser, prin. Fax 468-6408

Pillager, Cass, Pop. 463
Pillager SD 116 900/PK-12
323 E 2nd St 56473 218-746-3772
Chuck Arns, supt. Fax 746-4236
www.isd116.org
Pillager JSHS 400/7-12
323 E 2nd St 56473 218-746-3557
Scott Doss, prin. Fax 746-3406

Pine City, Pine, Pop. 3,072
Pine City SD 578 1,600/K-12
1400 Main St S 55063 320-629-4010
Wayne Gilman, supt. Fax 629-4070
www.pinecity.k12.mn.us
Pine City Area Learning Center 50/Alt
1400 Main St S 55063 320-629-4112
George Johnson, prin. Fax 629-3571
Pine City JSHS 700/7-12
1400 Main St S 55063 320-629-4112
Troy Anderson, prin. Fax 629-4105

Pine Technical College Post-Sec.
900 4th St SE 55063 320-629-5100

Pine Island, Goodhue, Pop. 3,224
Pine Island SD 255 700/K-12
PO Box 398 55963 507-356-4849
Tammy Berg-Beniak, supt. Fax 356-8827
www.pineisland.k12.mn.us
Pine Island HS 400/9-12
PO Box 398 55963 507-356-4849
Kevin Cardille, prin. Fax 356-4130

Pine River, Cass, Pop. 928
Pine River-Backus SD 2174 900/PK-12
PO Box 610 56474 218-587-4720
Catherine Bettino, supt. Fax 587-4120
www.prbschools.org
Pine River Area Learning Center 100/Alt
PO Box 610 56474 218-587-3131
Sue Peet, prin. Fax 587-3130
Pine River-Backus HS 400/7-12
PO Box 610 56474 218-587-4425
Trent Langemo, prin. Fax 587-3108

Pipestone, Pipestone, Pop. 4,229
Pipestone Area SD 2689 1,200/PK-12
1401 7th St SW 56164 507-825-5861
Jim Lentz, supt. Fax 825-6718
pas.k12.mn.us
Pipestone HS 300/9-12
1401 7th St SW 56164 507-825-5861
Cory Strasser, prin. Fax 825-6729
Pipestone MS 300/5-8
1401 7th St SW 56164 507-825-5861
Cory Strasser, prin. Fax 825-6729

Minnesota West Community & Tech College Post-Sec.
1314 N Hiawatha Ave 56164 507-825-6800

Plainview, Wabasha, Pop. 3,322
Plainview-Elgin-Millville ISD 2899 1,500/PK-12
500 W Broadway 55964 507-534-3651
Gary Kuphal, supt. Fax 534-3907
www.pem.k12.mn.us/
Plainview-Elgin-Millville HS 500/9-12
500 W Broadway 55964 507-534-3128
Bill Ihrke, prin. Fax 534-0174
Other Schools – See Elgin

Plymouth, Hennepin, Pop. 69,055
Robbinsdale SD 281
Supt. — See New Hope
Plymouth MS 1,300/6-8
10011 36th Ave N 55441 763-504-7100
Bruce Beidelman, prin. Fax 504-7131
Robbinsdale Armstrong HS 2,100/9-12
10635 36th Ave N 55441 763-504-8800
David Dahl, prin. Fax 504-8831

Wayzata SD 284 10,300/PK-12
210 County Road 101 N 55447 952-745-5000
Dr. Chace Anderson, supt. Fax 745-5091
www.wayzata.k12.mn.us
Wayzata Central MS 900/6-8
305 Vicksburg Ln N 55447 763-745-6000
Clark Doten, prin. Fax 745-6091
Wayzata East MS 700/6-8
12000 Ridgemount Ave W 55441 763-745-6200
Paul Paetzel, prin. Fax 745-6291
Wayzata HS 3,200/9-12
4955 Peony Ln N, 763-745-6600
Michael Trewick, prin. Fax 745-6691
Other Schools – See Wayzata

Central Baptist Theological Seminary Post-Sec.
900 Forestview Ln N 55441 763-417-8250
Globe University MN School of Business Post-Sec.
1455 County Road 101 N 55447 763-476-2000
Providence Academy 900/PK-12
15100 Schmidt Lake Rd, 763-258-2500
Dr. Todd Flanders, hdmstr. Fax 258-2501
West Lutheran HS 100/9-12
3350 Harbor Ln N 55447 763-509-9378
Merlin Meitner, prin. Fax 509-0861

Preston, Fillmore, Pop. 1,314
Fillmore Central SD 2198 500/PK-12
PO Box 50 55965 507-765-3845
Richard Keith, supt. Fax 765-3636
www.fillmorecentral.k12.mn.us/
Other Schools – See Harmony

Princeton, Mille Lacs, Pop. 4,614
Princeton SD 477 3,400/PK-12
706 1st St 55371 763-389-2422
Dr. Julia Espe, supt. Fax 389-9142
www.princeton.k12.mn.us
Princeton HS 1,000/9-12
807 8th Ave S 55371 763-389-4101
Peter Olson, prin. Fax 389-5816
Princeton MS 800/6-8
1100 4th Ave N 55371 763-389-6704
Dan Voce, prin. Fax 389-6737

Prinsburg, Kandiyohi, Pop. 492

Central Minnesota Christian S 300/PK-12
PO Box 98 56281 320-978-8700
Peter Van Der Puy, supt. Fax 978-6797

Prior Lake, Scott, Pop. 22,273
Prior Lake - Savage Area SD 719 7,000/K-12
4540 Tower St SE 55372 952-226-0000
Dr. Sue Ann Gruver, supt. Fax 226-0059
www.priorlake-savage.k12.mn.us

Bridges Area Learning Center — Alt
15875 Franklin Trl SE 55372 — 952-226-0840
Dave Brown, dean
Hidden Oaks MS — 900/6-8
15855 Fish Point Rd SE 55372 — 952-226-0700
Sasha Kuznetsov, prin. — Fax 226-0749
Twin Oaks MS — 700/6-8
15860 Fish Point Rd SE 55372 — 952-226-0500
Dr. Dan Edwards, prin. — Fax 226-0549
Other Schools – See Savage

Proctor, Saint Louis, Pop. 3,021
Proctor SD 704 — 1,800/PK-12
131 9th Ave 55810 — 218-628-4934
John Engelking, supt. — Fax 628-4937
www.proctor.k12.mn.us
Jedlicka MS — 400/6-8
131 9th Ave 55810 — 218-628-4926
Nancy Litman, prin. — Fax 628-4932
Proctor HS — 600/9-12
131 9th Ave 55810 — 218-628-4926
Nancy Litman, prin. — Fax 628-4931

Randolph, Dakota, Pop. 430
Randolph SD 195 — 600/PK-12
PO Box 38 55065 — 507-263-2151
Michael Kelley, supt. — Fax 645-5950
www.randolph.k12.mn.us
Randolph JSHS — 300/7-12
PO Box 38 55065 — 507-263-2151
Benjamin Fisher, prin. — Fax 645-5950

Redlake, Beltrami, Pop. 1,719
Red Lake SD 38 — 1,200/PK-12
PO Box 499 56671 — 218-679-3353
Steve Wymore, supt. — Fax 679-2321
www.redlake.k12.mn.us
Red Lake Alternative Learning Center — 50/Alt
PO Box 499 56671 — 218-679-3733
Everett Arnold, prin. — Fax 679-2717
Red Lake HS — 300/9-12
PO Box 499 56671 — 218-679-3733
Ramona Gehlert, prin. — Fax 679-2717
Red Lake MS — 200/6-8
PO Box 499 56671 — 218-679-2700
Susan Ninham, prin. — Fax 679-2733

Red Lake Falls, Red Lake, Pop. 1,407
Red Lake Falls SD 630 — 400/PK-12
PO Box 399 56750 — 218-253-2139
Joel Young, supt. — Fax 253-2135
www.redlakefalls.k12.mn.us
LaFayette JSHS — 200/7-12
PO Box 399 56750 — 218-253-2163
Brad Kennett, prin. — Fax 253-4480

Red Wing, Goodhue, Pop. 16,138
Red Wing SD 256 — 2,800/K-12
2451 Eagle Ridge Dr 55066 — 651-385-4500
Karsten Anderson, supt. — Fax 385-4510
www.redwing.k12.mn.us
Red Wing Alternative Learning Center — 100/Alt
154 Tower View Dr 55066 — 651-388-8963
Brian Cashman, prin. — Fax 385-8619
Red Wing HS — 1,100/8-12
2451 Eagle Ridge Dr 55066 — 651-385-4600
Beth Borgen, prin. — Fax 385-4610

Minnesota State College Southeast Tech. — Post-Sec.
308 Pioneer Rd 55066 — 651-385-6300

Redwood Falls, Redwood, Pop. 5,083
Redwood Area SD 2897 — 1,200/PK-12
100 George Ramseth Dr 56283 — 507-644-3531
Rick Ellingworth, supt. — Fax 644-3057
redwood.mntm.org
Redwood Valley Alternative S — Alt
100 George Ramseth Dr 56283 — 507-644-3531
Margie Buckley, dir. — Fax 644-3057
Redwood Valley HS — 400/9-12
100 George Ramseth Dr 56283 — 507-644-3511
Rick Jorgenson, prin. — Fax 644-3057
Redwood Valley MS — 300/5-8
100 George Ramseth Dr 56283 — 507-644-3521
Wade Mathers, prin. — Fax 644-3057

Remer, Cass, Pop. 366
Northland Community SD 118 — 400/PK-12
316 Main St E Rm 200 56672 — 218-566-2351
Daniel Parent, supt. — Fax 566-2053
www.isd118.k12.mn.us
Northland HS — 200/7-12
316 Main St E Rm 300 56672 — 218-566-2352
Joe Akre, prin. — Fax 566-3199

Renville, Renville, Pop. 1,277
Renville County West SD 2890 — 200/K-12
PO Box 338 56284 — 320-329-8362
Lance Bagstad, supt. — Fax 329-3271
www.rcw.k12.mn.us
Renville County West S — 200/K-12
PO Box 338 56284 — 320-329-8368
Jeff Wilson, prin. — Fax 329-8191

Richfield, Hennepin, Pop. 34,223
Richfield SD 280 — 3,900/K-12
7001 Harriet Ave 55423 — 612-798-6000
Robert Slotterback, supt. — Fax 798-6057
www.richfield.k12.mn.us
Richfield HS — 1,200/9-12
7001 Harriet Ave 55423 — 612-798-6100
Jason Wenschlag, prin. — Fax 798-6127
Richfield MS — 800/6-8
7461 Oliver Ave S 55423 — 612-798-6400
Brian Zambreno, prin. — Fax 798-6427

Academy of Holy Angels — 800/9-12
6600 Nicollet Ave 55423 — 612-798-2600
Heidi Foley, prin. — Fax 798-2610
Adler Graduate School — Post-Sec.
1550 E 78th St 55423 — 612-861-7554
Blessed Trinity S - Nicollet Campus — 200/4-8
6720 Nicollet Ave 55423 — 612-869-5200
Patrick O'Keefe, prin. — Fax 767-2191

Globe University MN School of Business — Post-Sec.
1401 W 76th St Ste 500 55423 — 612-861-2000

Robbinsdale, Hennepin, Pop. 13,450
Robbinsdale SD 281
Supt. — See New Hope
Robbinsdale MS — 1,400/6-8
3730 Toledo Ave N 55422 — 763-504-4800
John Cook, prin. — Fax 504-4831

Rochester, Olmsted, Pop. 104,165
Rochester ISD 535 — 15,000/PK-12
615 7th St SW 55902 — 507-328-3000
Michael Munoz, supt. — Fax 328-4212
www.rochester.k12.mn.us
Adams MS — 1,000/6-8
1525 31st St NW 55901 — 507-328-5700
LaShawn Ray, prin. — Fax 280-4726
Century HS — 1,400/9-12
2525 Viola Rd NE 55906 — 507-328-5100
Chris Fogarty, prin. — Fax 328-5045
Friedell MS — 400/6-8
1200 S Broadway 55904 — 507-328-5650
Monica Bowler, prin. — Fax 328-5635
Golden Hill Education Center — 200/Alt
2220 3rd Ave SE 55904 — 507-328-3999
Gordon Ziebart, admin.
Kellogg MS, 503 17th St NE 55906 — 900/6-8
Dwight Jennings, prin. — 507-328-5800
Marshall HS — 1,600/9-12
1510 14th St NW 55901 — 507-328-5400
Tim Limberg, prin. — Fax 328-5295
Mayo HS, 1420 11th Ave SE 55904 — 1,700/9-12
Tom Olson, prin. — 507-328-5500
Rochester Area Learning Center — 100/Alt
2220 3rd Ave SE 55904 — 507-328-4373
Gordon Ziebart, prin.
Willow Creek MS — 1,000/6-8
2425 11th Ave SE 55904 — 507-328-5900
Nancy Denzer, prin. — Fax 328-5905
Hawthorne Adult Literacy Center — Adult
700 4th Ave SE 55904 — 507-328-4440
Julie Nigon, admin. — Fax 287-2643

Crossroads College — Post-Sec.
920 Mayowood Rd SW 55902 — 507-288-4563
Globe University MN School of Business — Post-Sec.
2521 Pennington Dr NW 55901 — 507-536-9500
Lourdes HS — 400/9-12
621 W Center St 55902 — 507-289-3991
Suzanne Lagerwaard, prin. — Fax 289-4008
Mayo Graduate School — Post-Sec.
200 1st St SW 55905 — 507-538-1160
Mayo Medical School — Post-Sec.
200 1st St SW 55905 — 507-284-2316
Mayo School of Health Sciences — Post-Sec.
200 1st St SW Bldg 11 55905 — 507-284-3678
Rochester Community & Technical College — Post-Sec.
851 30th Ave SE 55904 — 507-285-7210
Rochester Community & Technical College — Post-Sec.
1926 Collegeview Rd E 55904 — 800-247-1296
St. John the Evangelist S — 300/5-8
424 W Center St 55902 — 507-282-5248
Erin Widman, prin. — Fax 282-1343
St. Mary's Hospital/Mayo Medical Center — Post-Sec.
1216 2nd St NW 55901 — 507-255-5221
Schaeffer Academy — 400/K-12
2700 Schaeffer Ln NE 55906 — 507-286-1050
Keith Phillips, hdmstr. — Fax 282-3823
The College of Saint Scholastica — Post-Sec.
221 1st Ave SW Ste 100 55902 — 507-424-0144
University of Minnesota Rochester — Post-Sec.
111 S Broadway Ste 300 55904 — 800-947-0117

Rockford, Wright, Pop. 4,215
Rockford Area ISD 883 — 1,500/PK-12
6051 Ash St 55373 — 763-477-9165
Paul Durand, supt. — Fax 477-5833
www.rockford.k12.mn.us
Rockford HS — 500/9-12
7600 County Road 50 55373 — 763-477-5846
Ryan Jensen, prin. — Fax 477-6123
Rockford MS Center for Environmental Std — 300/6-8
6051 Ash St 55373 — 763-477-5831
Amy Denneson, prin. — Fax 477-5832

Rogers, Hennepin, Pop. 8,439
Elk River Area SD 728
Supt. — See Elk River
Rogers HS — 1,200/9-12
21000 141st Ave N 55374 — 763-274-3140
Roman Pierskalla, prin. — Fax 274-3141
Rogers MS — 1,000/6-8
20855 141st Ave N 55374 — 763-241-3550
Jason Paurus, prin. — Fax 241-3518

Roseau, Roseau, Pop. 2,615
Roseau SD 682 — 1,300/PK-12
509 3rd St NE 56751 — 218-463-1471
Larry Guggisberg, supt. — Fax 463-3243
www.roseau.k12.mn.us/
Roseau JSHS — 600/7-12
509 3rd St NE 56751 — 218-463-2770
Dave Reaves, prin. — Fax 463-3658

Rosemount, Dakota, Pop. 21,334
Rosemount-Apple Valley-Eagan ISD 196 — 26,900/K-12
3455 153rd St W 55068 — 651-423-7700
Jane Berenz, supt. — Fax 423-7633
www.district196.org
Rosemount HS — 2,100/9-12
3335 142nd St W 55068 — 651-423-7501
John Wollersheim, prin. — Fax 423-7511
Rosemount MS — 1,200/6-8
3135 143rd St W 55068 — 651-423-7570
Mary Thompson, prin. — Fax 423-7664
Other Schools – See Apple Valley, Eagan

Dakota Co. Technical College — Post-Sec.
1300 145th St E 55068 — 651-423-8301
First Baptist S — 200/PK-12
14400 Diamond Path W 55068 — 651-423-2272
Dr. David Clear, supt. — Fax 423-8844

Roseville, Ramsey, Pop. 32,857
Roseville Area SD 623 — 6,500/K-12
1251 County Road B2 W 55113 — 651-635-1600
Dr. John Thein, supt. — Fax 635-1659
www.isd623.org
Fairview Alternative HS — 100/Alt
1910 County Road B W 55113 — 651-604-3800
Laura Freer, prin. — Fax 604-3801
Roseville Area HS — 2,100/9-12
1240 County Road B2 W 55113 — 651-635-1660
Jenny Loeck, prin. — Fax 635-1699
Other Schools – See Little Canada

American Academy of Acupuncture — Post-Sec.
1925 County Road B2 W 55113 — 651-631-0204
Concordia Academy — 400/9-12
2400 Dale St N 55113 — 651-484-8429
Dr. Tim Berner, prin. — Fax 484-0594
Minneapolis Business College — Post-Sec.
1711 County Road B W 55113 — 651-636-7406
National American University — Post-Sec.
1550 Highway 36 W 55113 — 651-855-6300

Rothsay, Wilkin, Pop. 493
Rothsay SD 850 — 100/PK-12
123 2nd St NW 56579 — 218-867-2117
Warren Schmidt, supt. — Fax 867-2376
www.rothsay.k12.mn.us
Rothsay S — 100/PK-12
123 2nd St NW 56579 — 218-867-2116
Staci Allmaras, prin. — Fax 867-2376

Round Lake, Nobles, Pop. 376
Round Lake SD 516 — 100/7-12
445 Harrison St 56167 — 507-945-8123
Cornelius Smit, supt. — Fax 945-8124
www.rlb.mntm.org
Round Lake JSHS — 100/7-12
445 Harrison St 56167 — 507-945-8123
Raymond Hassing, prin. — Fax 945-8124

Royalton, Morrison, Pop. 1,237
Royalton SD 485 — 800/PK-12
PO Box 5 56373 — 320-584-4000
Dr. Jon Ellerbusch, supt. — Fax 584-4249
www.royalton.k12.mn.us
Royalton JSHS — 300/7-12
PO Box 5 56373 — 320-584-4000
Joel Swenson, prin. — Fax 584-4242

Rush City, Chisago, Pop. 3,060
Rush City SD 139 — 900/K-12
PO Box 566 55069 — 320-358-4855
Vern Koepp, supt. — Fax 358-1351
www.rushcity.k12.mn.us
Rush City HS — 400/7-12
PO Box 566 55069 — 320-358-4795
Brent Stavig, prin. — Fax 358-1261

Rushford, Fillmore, Pop. 1,721
Rushford-Peterson SD 239 — 500/PK-12
PO Box 627 55971 — 507-864-7785
Charles Ehler, supt. — Fax 864-2085
www.r-pschools.com
Rushford-Peterson HS — 200/9-12
PO Box 627 55971 — 507-864-7786
Shane McBroom, prin. — Fax 864-2085
Other Schools – See Peterson

Russell, Lyon, Pop. 338
R T R ISD 2902
Supt. — See Tyler
R T R MS — 100/6-8
PO Box 310 56169 — 507-823-4371
James Burns, prin. — Fax 823-4657

Saint Anthony, Hennepin, Pop. 8,057
Saint Anthony-New Brighton SD 282 — 1,800/PK-12
3303 33rd Ave NE 55418 — 612-706-1000
William Robert Laney, supt. — Fax 706-1020
www.stanthony.k12.mn.us
Saint Anthony MS — 400/6-8
3303 33rd Ave NE 55418 — 612-706-1032
Renee Corneille, prin. — Fax 706-1040
Saint Anthony Village HS — 700/9-12
3303 33rd Ave NE 55418 — 612-706-1102
Wayne Terry, prin. — Fax 706-1140

Saint Bonifacius, Hennepin, Pop. 2,257

Crown College — Post-Sec.
8700 College View Dr 55375 — 952-446-4100

Saint Charles, Winona, Pop. 3,695
Saint Charles SD 858 — 1,000/PK-12
600 E 6th St 55972 — 507-932-4420
Mark Roubinek, supt. — Fax 932-4700
www.scschools.net
Saint Charles HS — 500/7-12
600 E 6th St 55972 — 507-932-4420
Ben Bernard, prin. — Fax 932-4700

Saint Clair, Blue Earth, Pop. 859
Saint Clair SD 75 — 600/PK-12
PO Box 99 56080 — 507-245-3501
Tom Bruels, supt. — Fax 245-3517
www.isd75.k12.mn.us/
Saint Clair JSHS — 300/7-12
PO Box 99 56080 — 507-245-3027
Dustin Bosshart, prin. — Fax 245-3517

Saint Cloud, Stearns, Pop. 64,343
Saint Cloud Area SD 742 — 9,300/PK-12
1000 44th Ave N 56303 — 320-253-9333
Willie Jett, supt. — Fax 529-4343
www.isd742.org
Apollo HS — 1,300/9-12
1000 44th Ave N 56303 — 320-253-1600
Charles Eisenreich, prin. — Fax 253-8475
North JHS — 700/6-8
1212 29th Ave N 56303 — 320-251-2159
Robert Huot, prin. — Fax 251-7350
Saint Cloud ALC — 300/Alt
809 12th St N 56303 — 320-251-4963
Adam Holm, prin. — Fax 251-4173

South JHS 800/6-8
1120 15th Ave S 56301 320-251-1322
George Nolan, prin. Fax 251-2911
Technical HS 1,400/9-12
233 12th Ave S 56301 320-252-2231
Roger Ziemann, prin. Fax 252-0257

Cathedral HS 700/7-12
PO Box 1579 56302 320-251-3421
Lynn Grewing, prin. Fax 253-5576
Model College of Hair Design Post-Sec.
201 8th Ave S 56301 320-253-4222
Rasmussen College Post-Sec.
226 Park Ave S 56301 320-251-5600
Saint Cloud Christian S 200/K-12
430 3rd Ave NE 56304 320-252-8182
Chad Schneider, admin. Fax 656-9678
St. Cloud Hospital Post-Sec.
1406 6th Ave N 56303 320-255-5666
St. Cloud State University Post-Sec.
720 4th Ave S 56301 320-308-0121
St. Cloud Technical & Community College Post-Sec.
1540 Northway Dr 56303 320-308-5000
The College of Saint Scholastica Post-Sec.
4150 2nd St S Ste 330 56301 320-529-6663

Saint Francis, Anoka, Pop. 7,077
Saint Francis SD 15 5,200/K-12
4115 Ambassador Blvd NW 55070 763-753-7040
Edward Saxton, supt. Fax 753-4693
www.stfrancis.k12.mn.us
Crossroads S & Vocational Center 50/Alt
4111 Ambassador Blvd NW 55070 763-753-7120
Keri Neubauer, prin. Fax 753-1385
Saint Francis HS 1,700/9-12
3325 Bridge St NW 55070 763-213-1500
Paul Neubauer, prin. Fax 213-1693
Saint Francis MS 1,200/6-8
23026 Ambassador Blvd NW 55070 763-213-8500
Dale Johnson, prin. Fax 753-3821
Community Education Adult
4115 Ambassador Blvd NW 55070 763-753-7041
Tom Larson, dir. Fax 753-4693

Saint James, Watonwan, Pop. 4,579
Saint James SD 840 900/PK-12
PO Box 509 56081 507-375-5974
Becky Cselovszki, supt. Fax 375-7143
www.stjames.k12.mn.us
Saint James JSHS 500/6-12
1001 10th Ave N 56081 507-375-3381
Ted Simon, prin. Fax 375-4371

Saint Joseph, Stearns, Pop. 6,430

College of Saint Benedict Post-Sec.
37 College Ave S 56374 320-363-5011

Saint Louis Park, Hennepin, Pop. 43,914
Saint Louis Park SD 283 4,300/K-12
6425 W 33rd St 55426 952-928-6000
Robert Metz, supt. Fax 928-6020
www.slpschools.org
Saint Louis Park HS 1,400/9-12
6425 W 33rd St 55426 952-928-6100
Robert Metz, prin. Fax 928-6113
Saint Louis Park MS 900/6-8
2025 Texas Ave S 55426 952-928-6300
Les Bork, prin. Fax 928-6383

Anthem College Post-Sec.
5100 Gamble Dr Ste 200 55416 952-417-2200
Benilde-St. Margarets HS 1,200/7-12
2501 Highway 100 S 55416 952-927-4176
Dr. Sue Skinner, prin. Fax 920-8889
Groves Academy 200/1-12
3200 Highway 100 S 55416 952-920-6377
John Alexander, head sch Fax 920-2068
Health System Minnesota/Methodist Hosp. Post-Sec.
6500 Excelsior Blvd 55426 952-993-3601

Saint Michael, Wright, Pop. 16,153
Saint Michael-Albertville SD 885
Supt. — See Albertville
Saint Michael-Albertville HS 1,400/9-12
5800 Jamison Ave NE 55376 763-497-2192
Bob Driver, prin. Fax 497-6590
Saint Michael-Albertville MS East 5-8
4862 Naber Ave NE 55376 763-497-2655
Jennifer Kelly, prin. Fax 497-6591

Saint Paul, Ramsey, Pop. 275,178
Saint Paul SD 625 33,400/PK-12
360 Colborne St 55102 651-767-8100
Valeria Silva, supt. Fax 293-8586
www.spps.org
Battle Creek MS 700/7-8
2121 N Park Dr 55119 651-293-8960
Jocelyn Sims, prin. Fax 293-8866
Central HS 2,200/9-12
275 Lexington Pkwy N 55104 651-744-4900
Mary Mackbee, prin. Fax 293-5433
Como Park HS 1,600/9-12
740 Rose Ave W 55117 651-293-8800
Dan Mesick, prin. Fax 293-8806
Creative Arts HS 100/9-12
65 Kellogg Blvd E 55101 651-292-3480
Dr. Valerie Littles-Butler, prin. Fax 292-3484
Farnsworth Aerospace Magnet MS 600/5-8
1000 Walsh St 55106 651-293-8880
Hamilton Bell, prin. Fax 293-8888
Harding HS 2,100/9-12
1540 6th St E 55106 651-793-4700
Doug Revsbeck, prin. Fax 293-8912
Highland Park HS 1,500/9-12
1015 Snelling Ave S 55116 651-293-8940
Winston Tucker, prin. Fax 293-8939
Highland Park MS 600/6-8
975 Snelling Ave S 55116 651-293-8950
Charlene Hoff, prin. Fax 293-8953
Humboldt JSHS 900/7-12
30 Baker St E 55107 651-293-8600
Mike Sodomka, prin. Fax 293-8605
Johnson HS 1,700/9-12
1349 Arcade St 55106 651-293-8890
Astein Osei, prin. Fax 293-8895
LEAP HS 400/9-12
631 Albert St N 55104 651-228-7706
Rose Santos, prin. Fax 228-7711
Linwood Monroe Arts Plus MS 400/PK-PK, 4-
810 Palace Ave 55102 651-293-8690
Beth Behnke, prin. Fax 293-8699
Murray JHS 800/7-8
2200 Buford Ave 55108 651-293-8740
Tim Williams, prin. Fax 293-8742
Open World Learning Community S 200/7-12
65 Kellogg Blvd E 55101 651-293-8670
Valerie Littles-Butler, prin. Fax 293-5308
Parks HS 200/Alt
1212 University Ave W 55104 651-744-1212
Michael Thompson, prin. Fax 744-1208
Ramsey JHS 600/7-8
1700 Summit Ave 55105 651-293-8860
Nancy Flynn, prin. Fax 298-1587
Washington Technology Magnet JSHS 800/7-12
1495 Rice St 55117 651-293-8830
Mike McCollor, prin. Fax 228-4331
Hubbs Center for Lifelong Learning Adult
1030 University Ave W 55104 651-290-4822
Kristine Halling, admin. Fax 290-4785

Bethel Seminary Post-Sec.
3949 Bethel Dr 55112 651-638-6288
Bethel University Post-Sec.
3900 Bethel Dr 55112 651-638-6400
Christ's Household of Faith S 100/PK-12
355 Marshall Ave 55102 651-265-3400
Dennis Bluhm, prin. Fax 227-9813
College of Saint Scholastica Post-Sec.
340 Cedar St Ste 50 55101 651-298-1015
College of Visual Arts Post-Sec.
344 Summit Ave 55102 651-757-4000
Concordia University-St. Paul Post-Sec.
275 Syndicate St N 55104 651-641-8278
Cretin-Derham Hall HS 1,300/9-12
550 Albert St S 55116 651-690-2443
Mona Schmitz, prin. Fax 696-3394
Empire Beauty School Post-Sec.
1905 Suburban Ave 55119 651-209-6930
Hamline University Post-Sec.
1536 Hewitt Ave 55104 651-523-2800
Luther Seminary Post-Sec.
2481 Como Ave 55108 800-588-4373
Macalester College Post-Sec.
1600 Grand Ave 55105 651-696-6000
McNally Smith College of Music Post-Sec.
19 Exchange St E 55101 651-291-0177
Metropolitan State University Post-Sec.
700 7th St E 55106 651-793-1300
Mounds Park Academy 600/PK-12
2051 Larpenteur Ave E 55109 651-777-2555
Michael Downs, hdmstr. Fax 777-8633
Northwestern College Post-Sec.
3003 Snelling Ave N 55113 651-631-5100
St. Agnes S 500/K-12
530 Lafond Ave 55103 651-925-8700
James Morehead, prin. Fax 925-8708
Saint Catherine University Post-Sec.
2004 Randolph Ave 55105 651-690-6000
St. Paul Academy & Summit S 600/6-12
1712 Randolph Ave 55105 651-698-2451
Bryn Roberts, hdmstr. Fax 698-6787
St. Paul College Post-Sec.
235 Marshall Ave 55102 651-846-1600
University of St. Thomas Post-Sec.
2115 Summit Ave 55105 651-962-5000
William Mitchell College of Law Post-Sec.
875 Summit Ave 55105 651-227-9171

Saint Paul Park, Washington, Pop. 5,176
South Washington County SD 833
Supt. — See Cottage Grove
Oltman MS 700/6-8
1020 3rd St 55071 651-768-3500
Becky Schroeder, prin. Fax 768-3555

Hope Christian Academy 100/PK-12
920 Holley Ave Ste 2 55071 651-459-6438
Randy Krussow, prin. Fax 769-2108

Saint Peter, Nicollet, Pop. 11,009
Saint Peter SD 508 1,500/K-12
100 Lincoln Dr 56082 507-934-5703
Dr. Jeffrey Olson, supt. Fax 934-2805
www.stpeterschools.org
Saint Peter MSHS 500/7-12
100 Lincoln Dr 56082 507-934-4210
Paul Peterson, prin. Fax 934-4783

Gustavus Adolphus College Post-Sec.
800 W College Ave 56082 507-933-8000

Sandstone, Pine, Pop. 2,776
East Central SD 2580
Supt. — See Finlayson
Crossroads Learning Center 100/Alt
130 Oriole St E Ste 2 55072 320-245-3070
Stef Youngberg, dir. Fax 245-3075

Harvest Christian S 50/PK-12
PO Box 646 55072 320-245-5330
Jack Allen, admin. Fax 245-5330

Sartell, Stearns, Pop. 15,661
Sartell-St Stephen SD 748 3,600/PK-12
212 3rd Ave N 56377 320-656-3715
Dr. Joe Hill, supt. Fax 656-3765
www.sartell.k12.mn.us
Sartell HS 1,000/9-12
748 7th St N 56377 320-656-0748
Brenda Steve, prin. Fax 656-5296
Sartell MS 1,100/5-8
627 3rd Ave N 56377 320-253-2200
Michael Spanier, prin. Fax 253-1403

Sauk Centre, Stearns, Pop. 4,294
Sauk Centre SD 743 700/PK-12
903 State Rd 56378 320-352-2284
Dan Brooks, supt. Fax 352-3404
www.isd743.k12.mn.us
Sauk Centre Secondary S 300/7-12
903 State Rd 56378 320-352-2856
Belinda Selfors, prin. Fax 352-3404

Sauk Rapids, Benton, Pop. 12,559
Sauk Rapids-Rice SD 47 3,800/PK-12
1833 Osauka Rd 56379 320-253-4703
Dr. Daniel Bittman, supt. Fax 255-1914
www.isd47.org
Sauk Rapids-Rice HS 1,200/9-12
1835 Osauka Rd 56379 320-253-4700
Erich Martens, prin. Fax 258-1717
Sauk Rapids-Rice MS 900/6-8
901 1st St S 56379 320-654-9073
Larry Stracke, prin. Fax 259-8909
Hillside ECFE & ABE Adult
30 4th Ave S 56379 320-255-8910
Julie Midas, dir. Fax 258-1197

Savage, Scott, Pop. 26,220
Burnsville-Eagan-Savage ISD 191
Supt. — See Burnsville
Eagle Ridge JHS 700/7-9
13955 Glendale Rd 55378 952-707-2800
Don Leake, prin. Fax 707-2802

Prior Lake - Savage Area SD 719
Supt. — See Prior Lake
Prior Lake HS 2,200/9-12
7575 150th St W 55378 952-226-8600
Dave Lund, prin. Fax 226-8649

Sebeka, Wadena, Pop. 700
Sebeka SD 820 500/PK-12
PO Box 249 56477 218-837-5101
Dave Fjeldheim, supt. Fax 837-5967
www.sebeka.k12.mn.us
Sebeka JSHS 300/7-12
PO Box 249 56477 218-837-5101
Dave Fjeldheim, prin. Fax 837-5967

Shakopee, Scott, Pop. 36,163
Shakopee SD 720 6,500/K-12
505 Holmes St S 55379 952-496-5000
Dr. Rod Thompson, supt. Fax 496-5056
www.shakopee.k12.mn.us
Shakopee JHS 1,000/8-9
200 10th Ave E 55379 952-496-5752
Christopher Endicott, prin. Fax 496-5755
Shakopee SHS 1,400/10-12
100 17th Ave W 55379 952-496-5152
Kim Swift, prin. Fax 496-5155
Tokata Learning Center Alt
1110 Shakopee Town Sq 55379 952-496-5982
Dr. Chris Hergenrader, prin.

Globe University MN School of Business Post-Sec.
1200 Shakopee Town Sq 55379 952-345-1200

Sherburn, Martin, Pop. 1,125
Martin County West SD 2448
Supt. — See Welcome
Martin County West HS 200/9-12
16 W 5th St 56171 507-764-4671
David Traetow, prin. Fax 764-4691

Shoreview, Ramsey, Pop. 24,520
Mounds View SD 621 9,800/K-12
350 Highway 96 W 55126 651-621-6000
Dan Hoverman, supt. Fax 621-6046
www.moundsviewschools.org
Chippewa MS 900/6-8
5000 Hodgson Rd 55126 651-621-6400
Dr. Mona Fadness, prin. Fax 621-6405
Other Schools – See Arden Hills, Mounds View, New Brighton

Silver Bay, Lake, Pop. 1,866
Lake Superior SD 381
Supt. — See Two Harbors
Kelley JSHS 200/7-12
137 Banks Blvd 55614 218-226-4437
Joe Nicklay, prin. Fax 226-4860

Slayton, Murray, Pop. 2,140
Murray County Central SD 2169 800/PK-12
2420 28th St 56172 507-836-6183
Luther Onken, supt. Fax 836-6375
www.mcc.mntm.org
Murray County Central JSHS 300/7-12
2420 28th St 56172 507-836-6184
Joe Meyer, prin. Fax 836-6375

Sleepy Eye, Brown, Pop. 3,585
Sleepy Eye SD 84 600/PK-12
400 4th Ave SW 56085 507-794-7903
John Cselovszki, supt. Fax 794-5404
www.sleepyeyeschools.com
Sleepy Eye JSHS 300/7-12
400 4th Ave SW 56085 507-794-7904
Shane Laffen, prin. Fax 794-5404

St. Mary JSHS 200/7-12
104 Saint Marys St NW 56085 507-794-4121
Jerry Neubauer, prin. Fax 794-4841

South Saint Paul, Dakota, Pop. 19,660
South St. Paul SD 6 3,200/PK-12
104 5th Ave S 55075 651-457-9400
Dr. Dave Webb, supt. Fax 457-9485
www.sspps.org
Community Learning Center 100/Alt
151 6th St E 55075 651-450-9966
Kathleen Johnson, dir. Fax 306-3666
South Saint Paul HS 1,300/7-12
700 2nd St N 55075 651-457-9408
Butch Moening, prin. Fax 457-9455

Springfield, Brown, Pop. 2,141
Springfield SD 85 — 600/PK-12
12 Burns Ave 56087 — 507-723-4283
Keith Kottke, supt. — Fax 723-6407
www.springfield.mntm.org/
Springfield JSHS — 300/7-12
12 Burns Ave 56087 — 507-723-4288
Pat Moriarty, prin. — Fax 723-4447

Spring Grove, Houston, Pop. 1,322
Spring Grove SD 297 — 300/K-12
PO Box 626 55974 — 507-498-3221
Rachel Udstuen, supt. — Fax 498-3470
www.springgrove.k12.mn.us
Spring Grove JSHS — 100/7-12
PO Box 626 55974 — 507-498-3223
Nancy Gulbranson, prin. — Fax 498-3470

Spring Lake Park, Anoka, Pop. 6,217
Spring Lake Park SD 16 — 4,500/K-12
1415 81st Ave NE 55432 — 763-600-5000
Dr. Jeff Ronneberg, supt. — Fax 600-5582
www.springlakeparkschools.org
Spring Lake Park HS — 1,300/9-12
1100 81st Ave NE 55432 — 763-600-5100
Jane Stevenson, prin. — Fax 600-5113
Other Schools – See Blaine

Empire Beauty School — Post-Sec.
8205 University Ave NE 55432 — - -

Spring Valley, Fillmore, Pop. 2,458
Kingsland SD 2137 — 700/PK-12
705 N Section Ave 55975 — 507-346-7276
John McDonald, supt. — Fax 346-7278
www.kingsland.k12.mn.us
Kingsland JSHS — 300/7-12
705 N Section Ave 55975 — 507-346-7276
Jim Hecimovich, prin. — Fax 346-7278

Staples, Todd, Pop. 2,930
Staples-Motley ISD 2170 — 1,300/PK-12
202 Pleasant Ave NE 56479 — 218-894-5400
Mark Schmitz, supt. — Fax 894-1828
www.isd2170.k12.mn.us/
Staples-Motley HS — 500/9-12
401 Centennial Ln 56479 — 218-894-2431
Ryan Luft, prin. — Fax 894-2434
Other Schools – See Motley

Central Lakes College — Post-Sec.
1830 Airport Rd 56479 — 218-894-5100

Starbuck, Pope, Pop. 1,289
Minnewaska SD 2149
Supt. — See Glenwood
Minnewaska Alternative Options S — Alt
500 John St 56381 — 320-239-2257
Diane Cordes, prin. — Fax 239-1420

Stephen, Marshall, Pop. 657
Stephen-Argyle Central SD 2856 — 400/PK-12
PO Box 68 56757 — 218-478-3315
Chris Mills, supt. — Fax 478-3537
www.sac.k12.mn.us/
Stephen JSHS — 200/7-12
PO Box 68 56757 — 218-478-3314
Mark Kroulik, prin. — Fax 478-3537

Stewartville, Olmsted, Pop. 5,872
Stewartville SD 534 — 1,900/PK-12
440 6th Ave SW 55976 — 507-533-1438
Dr. David Thompson, supt. — Fax 533-4012
ssd.k12.mn.us
Stewartville HS — 500/9-12
440 6th Ave SW 55976 — 507-533-1600
Bruce Hoff, prin. — Fax 533-4143
Stewartville MS — 400/6-8
440 6th Ave SW 55976 — 507-533-1666
Steven Gibbs, prin. — Fax 533-1021

Stillwater, Washington, Pop. 17,911
Stillwater Area SD 834 — 8,300/K-12
1875 Greeley St S 55082 — 651-351-8301
Corey Lunn, supt. — Fax 351-8380
www.stillwater.k12.mn.us
St. Croix Valley ALC — 100/Alt
5640 Memorial Ave N 55082 — 651-351-8464
Don Kirkpatrick, prin. — Fax 351-8465
Stillwater Area SHS — 2,100/10-12
5701 Stillwater Blvd N 55082 — 651-351-8040
Don Johnson, prin. — Fax 351-8049
Stillwater JHS — 1,000/7-9
523 Marsh St W 55082 — 651-351-6905
Chuck Ochocki, prin. — Fax 351-6999
Other Schools – See Lake Elmo

Swanville, Morrison, Pop. 348
Swanville SD 486 — 400/PK-12
PO Box 98 56382 — 320-547-5100
Gene Harthan, supt. — Fax 547-2576
www.swanville.k12.mn.us/
Molly Creek ALC — 50/Alt
PO Box 98 56382 — 320-547-9930
Cy Durand, prin. — Fax 547-2576
Swanville JSHS — 200/7-12
PO Box 98 56382 — 320-547-5101
Dennis Saurer, prin. — Fax 547-2576

Taylors Falls, Chisago, Pop. 960

Valley Christian S — 50/PK-12
661B West St 55084 — 651-465-3333
Gary Peterson, admin. — Fax 465-3323

Thief River Falls, Pennington, Pop. 8,403
Thief River Falls SD 564 — 2,000/PK-12
230 Labree Ave S 56701 — 218-681-8711
Laine Larson, supt. — Fax 681-2905
www.trf.k12.mn.us
Franklin MS — 500/6-8
300 Spruce Ave S 56701 — 218-681-8813
Bob Wayne, prin. — Fax 681-4771
Lincoln HS — 600/9-12
101 Knight Ave S 56701 — 218-681-7432
Shane Zutz, prin. — Fax 681-4510
Northwest Area Learning Center — 50/Alt
230 Labree Ave 56701 — 218-681-8711
Loren Leake, prin. — Fax 681-4686

Northland Community & Technical College — Post-Sec.
1101 Highway 1 E 56701 — 218-683-8800

Tower, Saint Louis, Pop. 489
Saint Louis County SD 2142
Supt. — See Virginia
Tower-Soudan S — 100/PK-12
PO Box 469 55790 — 218-753-4040
Kevin Abrahamson, prin. — Fax 753-6461

Tracy, Lyon, Pop. 2,129
Tracy SD 2904 — 800/PK-12
934 Pine St 56175 — 507-629-5500
Loy Woelber, supt. — Fax 629-5507
tracy.k12.mn.us
Tracy JSHS — 400/7-12
934 Pine St 56175 — 507-629-5500
Chad Anderson, prin. — Fax 629-5507

Trimont, Martin, Pop. 740
Martin County West SD 2448
Supt. — See Welcome
Martin County West JHS — 100/7-8
PO Box 408 56176 — 507-639-2081
Allison Schmidt, prin. — Fax 639-2091

Truman, Martin, Pop. 1,111
Truman SD 458 — 300/K-12
PO Box 276 56088 — 507-776-2111
Tom Ames, supt. — Fax 776-3379
www.truman.k12.mn.us
Truman JSHS — 200/7-12
PO Box 276 56088 — 507-776-2111
Tate Jerome, prin. — Fax 776-3379

Twin Valley, Norman, Pop. 807
Norman County East SD 2215 — 300/PK-12
PO Box 420 56584 — 218-584-5151
Mark Lundin, supt. — Fax 584-5170
nce.k12.mn.us/
Norman County East HS — 200/7-12
PO Box 420 56584 — 218-584-5151
Mark Lundin, prin. — Fax 584-5170

Two Harbors, Lake, Pop. 3,693
Lake Superior SD 381 — 1,400/PK-12
1640 Highway 2 55616 — 218-834-8201
Bill Crandall, supt. — Fax 834-8239
www.isd381.k12.mn.us/
Two Harbors JSHS — 600/6-12
1640 Highway 2 Ste 100 55616 — 218-834-8201
Brett Archer, prin. — Fax 834-5513
Other Schools – See Silver Bay

Tyler, Lincoln, Pop. 1,129
R T R ISD 2902 — 500/PK-12
PO Box 659 56178 — 507-247-5913
Fr. Bruce Houck, supt. — Fax 247-3876
www.rtrschools.org
R T R HS — 200/9-12
PO Box 659 56178 — 507-247-5911
Pam Bush, prin. — Fax 247-3876
Other Schools – See Russell

Ulen, Clay, Pop. 535
Ulen-Hitterdal SD 914 — 300/K-12
PO Box 389 56585 — 218-596-8853
Allen Zenor, supt. — Fax 596-8610
www.ulenhitterdal.k12.mn.us
Ulen-Hitterdal JSHS — 100/7-12
PO Box 389 56585 — 218-596-8853
Kent Henrickson, prin. — Fax 596-8610

Underwood, Otter Tail, Pop. 340
Underwood SD 550 — 600/PK-12
100 Southern Ave E 56586 — 218-826-6101
Dr. Jeremiah Olson, supt. — Fax 826-6310
www.underwood.k12.mn.us
Underwood JSHS — 300/7-12
100 Southern Ave E 56586 — 218-826-6102
John Hamann, prin. — Fax 826-6310

Upsala, Morrison, Pop. 425
Upsala SD 487 — 400/PK-12
PO Box 190 56384 — 320-573-2174
Gery Arndt, supt. — Fax 573-2173
www.upsala.k12.mn.us/
Upsala JSHS — 200/7-12
PO Box 190 56384 — 320-573-2176
Verne Capelle, prin. — Fax 573-2173

Verndale, Wadena, Pop. 586
Verndale SD 818 — 500/PK-12
411 SW Brown St 56481 — 218-445-5184
Paul Brownlow, supt. — Fax 445-5185
www.verndale.k12.mn.us
Verndale JSHS — 200/7-12
411 SW Brown St 56481 — 218-445-5184
Thomas Ritters, prin. — Fax 445-5185

Victoria, Carver, Pop. 7,244

Holy Family HS — 600/9-12
8101 Kochia Ln 55386 — 952-443-4659
Kathie Brown, prin. — Fax 443-1822

Virginia, Saint Louis, Pop. 8,491
Saint Louis County SD 2142 — 500/PK-12
1701 N 9th Ave 55792 — 218-749-8130
Teresa Strong, supt. — Fax 749-8133
www.isd2142.k12.mn.us/
Other Schools – See Babbitt, Cook, Iron, Tower
Virginia SD 706 — 1,600/PK-12
411 S 5th Ave 55792 — 218-742-3901
Deron Stender, supt. — Fax 742-3960
vmps.org
Virginia Secondary S — 800/7-12
411 S 5th Ave 55792 — 218-742-3916
Laverne Hakly, prin. — Fax 741-8522

Mesabi Range Community & Technical Coll. — Post-Sec.
1001 Chestnut St W 55792 — 218-741-3095

Wabasha, Wabasha, Pop. 2,493
Wabasha-Kellogg SD 811 — 600/PK-12
2113 Hiawatha Dr E 55981 — 651-565-3559
Jim Freihammer, supt. — Fax 565-2769
www.wabasha-kellogg.k12.mn.us/
Wabasha-Kellogg JSHS — 300/7-12
2113 Hiawatha Dr E 55981 — 651-565-3559
Rob Stewart, prin. — Fax 565-2769

Wabasso, Redwood, Pop. 691
Wabasso SD 640 — 400/PK-12
PO Box 69 56293 — 507-342-5114
Wade McKittrick, supt. — Fax 342-5203
www.wabassoschool.com
Wabasso JSHS — 200/7-12
PO Box 69 56293 — 507-342-5114
Wade McKittrick, prin. — Fax 342-5203

Waconia, Carver, Pop. 10,592
Waconia SD 110 — 3,300/PK-12
512 Industrial Blvd 55387 — 952-442-0600
Nancy Rajanen, supt. — Fax 442-0609
www.waconia.k12.mn.us
Clearwater MS — 1,000/5-8
1650 Community Dr 55387 — 952-442-0650
Peter Gustafson, prin. — Fax 442-0659
Waconia HS — 1,000/9-12
1400 Community Dr 55387 — 952-442-0670
Mark Fredericksen, prin. — Fax 442-0679

Wadena, Wadena, Pop. 4,023
Wadena-Deer Creek SD 2155 — 1,000/PK-12
600 Colfax Ave SW 56482 — 218-632-2155
Virginia Dahlstrom, supt. — Fax 632-2199
www.wdc2155.k12.mn.us
Wadena-Deer Creek HS — 500/7-12
600 Colfax Ave SW 56482 — 218-632-2300
Tyler Church, prin. — Fax 632-2399

MN State Community & Technical College — Post-Sec.
405 Colfax Ave SW 56482 — 218-631-7800

Waite Park, Stearns, Pop. 6,543

Globe University MN School of Business — Post-Sec.
1201 2nd St S 56387 — 320-257-2000
Regency Beauty Institute — Post-Sec.
110 2nd St S 56387 — 320-251-0500

Walker, Cass, Pop. 910
Walker-Hackensack-Akeley SD 113 — 800/PK-12
PO Box 4000 56484 — 218-547-1311
Dr. Mary Stetz, supt. — Fax 547-4298
www.wha.k12.mn.us
Walker-Hackensack-Akeley HS — 400/7-12
PO Box 4000 56484 — 218-547-4210
Peggy Novak, prin. — Fax 547-4297

Wanamingo, Goodhue, Pop. 1,081
Kenyon-Wanamingo SD 2172 — 700/PK-12
225 3rd Ave 55983 — 507-824-2211
Jeff Evert, supt. — Fax 824-2212
www.kw.k12.mn.us
Other Schools – See Kenyon

Warren, Marshall, Pop. 1,554
Warren-Alvarado-Oslo SD 2176 — 400/PK-12
224 E Bridge Ave 56762 — 218-745-5393
Dr. Ronald Bratlie, supt. — Fax 745-5886
www.wao.k12.mn.us
Warren-Alvarado-Oslo JSHS — 200/7-12
224 E Bridge Ave 56762 — 218-745-4646
Wade Johnson, prin. — Fax 745-7658

Warroad, Roseau, Pop. 1,740
Warroad SD 690 — 800/PK-12
510 Cedar Ave NW 56763 — 218-386-1472
Craig Oftedahl, supt. — Fax 386-1909
www.warroad.k12.mn.us
Border Area Learning Center — 50/Alt
510 Cedar Ave NW 56763 — 218-386-3385
Maureen Stodgell, prin. — Fax 386-1909
Warroad JSHS — 500/7-12
510 Cedar Ave NW 56763 — 218-386-1820
Brad Nash, prin. — Fax 386-1909

Waseca, Waseca, Pop. 9,257
Waseca SD 829 — 1,600/PK-12
501 Elm Ave E 56093 — 507-835-2500
Brian Dietz, supt. — Fax 835-1161
www.waseca.k12.mn.us
Waseca Alternative Learning Center — 50/Alt
501 Elm Ave E 56093 — 507-835-5588
Daryl Kehler, coord. — Fax 835-1724
Waseca JSHS — 600/7-12
1717 2nd St NW 56093 — 507-835-5470
Jeanne Swanson, prin. — Fax 835-1724

Watertown, Carver, Pop. 4,128
Watertown-Mayer SD 111 — 1,600/PK-12
1001 Highway 25 Shls NW 55388 — 952-955-0480
Dave Marlette, supt. — Fax 955-0481
www.wm.k12.mn.us
Watertown-Mayer HS — 500/9-12
1001 Highway 25 Shls NW 55388 — 952-955-0600
Bob Hennen, prin. — Fax 955-0601
Watertown-Mayer MS — 300/6-8
1001 Highway 25 Shls NW 55388 — 952-955-0400
Nick Guertin, prin. — Fax 955-0481

Waterville, LeSueur, Pop. 1,853
Waterville-Elysian-Morristown SD 2143 900/PK-12
500 Paquin St E 56096 507-362-4432
Joel Whitehurst, supt. Fax 362-4561
www.wem.k12.mn.us/
Waterville-Elysian-Morristown HS 300/9-12
500 Paquin St E 56096 507-362-4431
John Kaplan, prin. Fax 362-4561
Other Schools – See Morristown

Waubun, Mahnomen, Pop. 324
Waubun SD 435 600/PK-12
PO Box 98 56589 218-473-6171
Brandon Lunak, supt. Fax 473-6191
www.waubun.k12.mn.us
Waubun JSHS 300/7-12
PO Box 98 56589 218-473-6173
Eric Martinez, prin. Fax 473-6190

Wayzata, Hennepin, Pop. 3,646
Wayzata SD 284
Supt. — See Plymouth
Wayzata West MS 700/6-8
149 Barry Ave N 55391 952-745-6400
Susan Sommerfeld, prin. Fax 745-6491

Welcome, Martin, Pop. 686
Martin County West SD 2448 700/K-12
PO Box 268 56181 507-728-8276
Allison Schmidt, supt. Fax 728-8278
www.martin.k12.mn.us
Other Schools – See Sherburn, Trimont

Wells, Faribault, Pop. 2,325
United South Central SD 2134 700/PK-12
250 2nd Ave SW 56097 507-553-3134
Jerry Jensen, supt. Fax 553-5929
www.usc.k12.mn.us
United South Central JSHS 300/7-12
250 2nd Ave SW 56097 507-553-5819
Kelly Schlaak, prin. Fax 553-5929

Westbrook, Cottonwood, Pop. 737
Westbrook-Walnut Grove SD 2898 500/PK-12
PO Box 129 56183 507-274-5450
Loy Woelber, supt. Fax 274-6113
www.walnut.mntm.org/
Westbrook-Walnut Grove JHHS 200/7-12
PO Box 129 56183 507-274-5450
William Richards, prin. Fax 858-2329

West Saint Paul, Dakota, Pop. 19,105
West St. Paul-Mendota Hts-Eagan SD 197
Supt. — See Mendota Heights
Heritage MS 700/5-8
121 Butler Ave W 55118 651-403-7400
Chris Hiti, prin. Fax 403-7410

St. Croix Lutheran MSHS 400/6-12
1200 Oakdale Ave 55118 651-455-1521
Richard Gibson, prin. Fax 451-3968

Wheaton, Traverse, Pop. 1,408
Wheaton Area SD 803 400/PK-12
1700 3rd Ave S 56296 320-563-8283
Daniel Posthumus, supt. Fax 563-4218
www.wheaton.k12.mn.us
Wheaton JSHS 300/6-12
1700 3rd Ave S 56296 320-563-8282
Russ Armstrong, prin. Fax 563-4218

White Bear Lake, Ramsey, Pop. 23,270
White Bear Lake Area SD 624 7,900/PK-12
4855 Bloom Ave 55110 651-407-7500
Dr. Michael Lovett, supt. Fax 407-7566
www.whitebear.k12.mn.us
Central MS 1,000/6-8
4857 Bloom Ave 55110 651-653-2888
Dr. Noel Schmidt, prin. Fax 653-2885
Sunrise Park MS 800/6-8
2399 Cedar Ave 55110 651-653-2700
Dr. Bob McDowell, prin. Fax 653-2716
White Bear Lake Area HS - North Campus 1,200/9-10
5045 Division Ave 55110 651-653-2920
Donald Bosch, prin. Fax 653-2630
White Bear Lake Area HS - South Campus 1,200/11-12
3551 McKnight Rd N 55110 651-773-6200
Timothy Wald, prin. Fax 773-6215
White Bear Lake Area Learning Center 100/Alt
2449 Orchard Ln 55110 651-773-6400
Gretchen Harriman, admin. Fax 773-6402

Century College Post-Sec.
3300 Century Ave N 55110 651-779-3200

Willmar, Kandiyohi, Pop. 19,385
Willmar SD 347 4,000/K-12
611 5th St SW 56201 320-231-8500
Jerry Kjergaard, supt. Fax 231-1061
www.willmar.k12.mn.us
Willmar HS 1,200/9-12
2701 30th St NE 56201 320-231-8300
Paul Schmitz, prin. Fax 231-8460
Willmar MS 900/6-8
201 Willmar Ave SE 56201 320-214-6000
Mark Miley, prin. Fax 235-1254
Wilmar Alternative Programs 100/Alt
611 5th St SW 56201 320-231-8300
Paul Schmitz, prin. Fax 846-8460

Community Christian S 200/PK-12
1300 19th Ave SW 56201 320-235-0592
John Chapin, admin. Fax 235-0620
Rice Memorial Hospital Post-Sec.
301 Becker Ave SW 56201 320-231-4530
Ridgewater College Post-Sec.
PO Box 1097 56201 320-222-5200

Willow River, Pine, Pop. 405
Willow River SD 577 400/PK-12
PO Box 66 55795 218-372-3131
Scott Anderson, supt. Fax 372-3132
www.willowriver.k12.mn.us
Willow River ALP 50/Alt
PO Box 66 55795 218-372-3131
Scott Anderson, prin. Fax 372-3132
Willow River JSHS 200/5-12
PO Box 66 55795 218-372-3131
Matt Hosmer, prin. Fax 372-3132

Windom, Cottonwood, Pop. 4,585
Windom SD 177 1,000/K-12
PO Box 177 56101 507-831-6901
Wayne Wormstadt, supt. Fax 831-6919
www.windom.k12.mn.us
Windom Area HS 300/9-12
PO Box 177 56101 507-831-6910
Lance Northey, prin. Fax 831-6909
Windom MS 400/4-8
PO Box 177 56101 507-831-6910
Wayland Denny, prin. Fax 831-6909

Winona, Winona, Pop. 27,243
Winona Area SD 861 3,200/PK-12
903 Gilmore Ave 55987 507-494-0861
Dr. Scott Hannon, supt. Fax 494-0863
www.winona.k12.mn.us
Winona ALC 100/Alt
1299 W 3rd St 55987 507-494-1460
Mark Winter, prin. Fax 494-1465
Winona HS 1,100/9-12
901 Gilmore Ave 55987 507-494-1504
Kelly Halvorsen, prin. Fax 494-1501
Winona MS 1,000/5-8
1570 Homer Rd 55987 507-494-1000
Mark Anderson, prin. Fax 494-1002

Cotter HS 300/9-12
1115 W Broadway St 55987 507-453-5000
Sandra Blank, prin. Fax 453-5006
Cotter JHS 100/7-8
1115 W Broadway St 55987 507-453-5000
David Forney, dir. Fax 453-5006
Hope Lutheran HS 50/9-12
253 Liberty St 55987 507-474-7799
Rocky Sandcork, admin. Fax 452-8992
Minnesota State College Southeast Tech. Post-Sec.
PO Box 409 55987 507-453-2700
St. Mary's University of Minnesota Post-Sec.
700 Terrace Hts 55987 507-452-4430
Winona State University Post-Sec.
PO Box 5838 55987 507-457-5000

Winsted, McLeod, Pop. 2,341

Holy Trinity HS 100/7-12
PO Box 38 55395 320-485-2182
Bill Tschida, prin. Fax 485-4283

Winthrop, Sibley, Pop. 1,386
GFW SD 2365
Supt. — See Gibbon
GFW HS 300/9-12
1001 N Cottonwood St 55396 507-647-5382
Steven Schauberger, prin. Fax 647-4329

Woodbury, Washington, Pop. 60,529
South Washington County SD 833
Supt. — See Cottage Grove
East Ridge HS 1,600/9-12
4200 Pioneer Dr 55129 651-768-2300
Aaron Harper, prin. Fax 768-2305
Lake MS 1,100/6-8
3133 Pioneer Dr 55125 651-768-6400
Molly Roeske, prin. Fax 768-6428
Woodbury HS 1,800/9-12
2665 Woodlane Dr 55125 651-768-4400
Linda Plante, prin. Fax 768-4411
Woodbury MS 900/6-8
1425 School Dr 55125 651-768-4500
Kari Lopez, prin. Fax 768-4567

Globe University Post-Sec.
8089 Globe Dr 55125 651-730-5100
New Life Academy 700/PK-12
6758 Bailey Rd 55129 651-459-4121
Cade Lambert, head sch Fax 459-6194

Worthington, Nobles, Pop. 12,573
Worthington SD 518 2,500/PK-12
1117 Marine Ave 56187 507-372-2172
John Landgaard, supt. Fax 372-2174
www.isd518.net
Worthington Area Learning Center 100/Alt
117 11th Ave 56187 507-372-1322
Nate Hanson, prin. Fax 372-1361
Worthington HS 700/9-12
1211 Clary St 56187 507-376-6121
Paul Karelis, prin. Fax 372-4304
Worthington MS 700/5-8
1401 Crailsheim Dr 56187 507-376-4174
Jeff Luke, prin. Fax 372-1424

Minnesota West Community & Tech College Post-Sec.
1450 Collegeway 56187 507-372-3400

Wrenshall, Carlton, Pop. 390
Wrenshall SD 100 400/PK-12
207 Pioneer Dr 55797 218-384-4274
Kimberly Belcastro, supt. Fax 384-4293
www.wrenshall.k12.mn.us/
Wrenshall JSHS 200/7-12
207 Pioneer Dr 55797 218-384-4274
Sue Frank, prin. Fax 384-4293

Zimmerman, Sherburne, Pop. 5,145
Elk River Area SD 728
Supt. — See Elk River
Zimmerman MSHS 600/6-12
25900 4th St W 55398 763-241-3505
Marco Voce, prin. Fax 241-3506

Zumbrota, Goodhue, Pop. 3,200
Zumbrota-Mazeppa SD 2805
Supt. — See Mazeppa
Zumbrota-Mazeppa HS 400/9-12
705 Mill St 55992 507-732-7395
Erick Enger, prin. Fax 732-4511
Zumbrota-Mazeppa MS 200/7-8
705 Mill St 55992 507-732-7395
Erick Enger, prin. Fax 324-4511

MISSISSIPPI

MISSISSIPPI DEPARTMENT OF EDUCATION
359 N West St, Jackson 39201-1502
Telephone 601-359-1750
Fax 601-359-3242
Website http://www.mde.k12.ms.us

Superintendent of Education Lynn J. House Ph.D

MISSISSIPPI BOARD OF EDUCATION
359 N West St Ste 309, Jackson 39201-1502

Chairperson Dr. O. Wayne Gann

PUBLIC, PRIVATE AND CATHOLIC SECONDARY SCHOOLS

Aberdeen, Monroe, Pop. 5,561
Aberdeen SD 1,100/PK-12
PO Box 607 39730 662-369-4682
Robert Strebeck, contact Fax 369-0987
www.asdms.us
Aberdeen HS 500/9-12
PO Box 607 39730 662-369-8933
Demond Radcliff, prin. Fax 369-6004
Shivers MS 200/6-8
PO Box 607 39730 662-369-6241
Bobby Taylor, prin. Fax 369-3207

Monroe County SD
Supt. — See Amory
Monroe County Technical Center Vo/Tech
50057 Airport Rd 39730 662-369-7845
Steve Cantrell, dir. Fax 369-9607

Ackerman, Choctaw, Pop. 1,499
Choctaw County SD 1,400/PK-12
PO Box 398 39735 662-285-4022
Stewart Beard, supt. Fax 285-4049
www.choctaw.k12.ms.us/
Ackerman JSHS 400/7-12
393 E Main St 39735 662-285-4101
Shane Burton, prin. Fax 285-4149
Choctaw County Career & Technology Ctr Vo/Tech
PO Box 775 39735 662-285-4160
Ronda Huffman, prin. Fax 285-4199

Amory, Monroe, Pop. 7,262
Amory SD 1,800/K-12
PO Box 330 38821 662-256-5991
Tony Cook, supt. Fax 256-6302
www.amoryschools.com/
Amory Career and Technical Center Vo/Tech
PO Box 330 38821 662-256-7601
Andy Cantrell, dir. Fax 256-1649
Amory HS 500/9-12
PO Box 330 38821 662-256-5753
David Poss, prin. Fax 256-5754
Amory MS 400/6-8
700 2nd Ave N 38821 662-256-5658
Ken Byars, prin. Fax 256-6304

Monroe County SD 2,200/K-12
PO Box 209 38821 662-257-2176
Scott Cantrell, supt. Fax 257-2181
www.mcsd.us
Advanced Learning Center 10-12
52251 Highway 25 S 38821 662-256-2495
Billy Loague, prin. Fax 256-2731
Hatley S 1,000/K-12
60286 Hatley Rd 38821 662-256-4563
Van Pearson, prin. Fax 256-5626
Other Schools – See Aberdeen, Hamilton, Smithville

Anguilla, Sharkey, Pop. 721
South Delta SD
Supt. — See Rolling Fork
South Delta MS 200/6-8
PO Box 487 38721 662-873-6535
Mark Beechem, prin. Fax 873-6073

Arcola, Washington, Pop. 359

Deer Creek S 200/PK-12
PO Box 376 38722 662-827-5165

Ashland, Benton, Pop. 566
Benton County SD 1,300/K-12
PO Box 247 38603 662-224-6252
Jack Gadd, supt. Fax 224-3607
www.benton.k12.ms.us
Ashland HS 100/9-12
PO Box 187 38603 662-224-6247
Dr. Lakimberly Hobson, prin. Fax 224-3614
Ashland JHS 100/6-8
PO Box 368 38603 662-224-6485
Rosie Ladd, prin. Fax 224-3609
Benton County Regional Vocational Center Vo/Tech
PO Box 754 38603 662-224-3108
Merri Gadd, dir. Fax 224-3629
Other Schools – See Hickory Flat

Avon, Washington
Western Line SD 2,000/PK-12
PO Box 50 38723 662-335-7186
Larry Green, supt. Fax 378-2285
www.westernline.org
Riverside HS 400/7-12
PO Box 80 38723 662-335-4527
Donald Coleman, prin. Fax 334-1797
Other Schools – See Greenville

Baldwyn, Lee, Pop. 3,256
Baldwyn SD 900/K-12
107 W Main St 38824 662-365-1000
Ronnie Hill, supt. Fax 365-1003
baldwyn.ms.schoolwebpages.com/
Baldwyn HS 300/9-12
512 N Fourth St 38824 662-365-1020
Adam Lindsey, prin. Fax 365-1028
Baldwyn MS 300/5-8
452 N Fourth St 38824 662-365-1015
Danny Ramsey, prin. Fax 365-1029

Bassfield, Jefferson Davis, Pop. 253
Jefferson Davis County SD
Supt. — See Prentiss
Bassfield JSHS 400/7-12
PO Box 370 39421 601-943-5391
John Daley, prin. Fax 943-5790

Batesville, Panola, Pop. 7,385
South Panola SD 4,500/PK-12
209 Boothe St 38606 662-563-9361
Tim Wilder, supt. Fax 563-6077
www.spsd.k12.ms.us
Batesville JHS 900/6-8
507 Tiger Dr 38606 662-563-4503
Lorenzo Grimes, prin. Fax 563-6038
South Panola HS 1,100/9-12
601 Tiger Dr 38606 662-563-4756
Roy Balentine, prin. Fax 563-8993

North Delta S 400/PK-12
330 Green Wave Ln 38606 662-563-4536
John Howell, hdmstr. Fax 563-5690

Bay Saint Louis, Hancock, Pop. 9,056
Bay St. Louis-Waveland SD 1,500/K-12
201 Carroll Ave 39520 228-467-6621
Dr. Rebecca Ladner, supt. Fax 467-1230
www.bwsd.org/
Bay HS 500/9-12
750 Blue Meadow Rd 39520 228-467-6611
Dr. Andy Parker, prin. Fax 466-0883
Bay-Waveland MS 400/6-8
600 Pine St 39520 228-463-0315
Dr. Cherie Labat, prin. Fax 463-2681
Crossroads Learning Center Alt
750 Blue Meadow Rd 39520 228-467-4536
Myron Labatt, prin. Fax 467-5575

Our Lady Academy 200/7-12
222 S Beach Blvd 39520 228-467-7048
Tiffany Lindmark, prin. Fax 467-1666
St. Stanislaus College Prep S 400/7-12
304 S Beach Blvd 39520 228-467-9057
Patrick McGrath, prin. Fax 466-2972

Bay Springs, Jasper, Pop. 1,763
West Jasper Consolidated SD 1,500/K-12
PO Box 610 39422 601-764-2280
Warren Woodrow, supt. Fax 764-4490
wjsd-mississippi.schoolloop.com/
Bay Springs HS 200/9-12
PO Box 389 39422 601-764-4151
James Raborn, prin. Fax 764-6445
Bay Springs MS 300/5-8
PO Box 587 39422 601-764-3378
Tracy Adcock, prin. Fax 764-2329
Other Schools – See Stringer

Sylva-Bay Academy 300/K-12
PO Box J 39422 601-764-2157
Richard Shoemake, hdmstr. Fax 764-6755

Belden, Lee

Tupelo Christian Preparatory S 400/PK-12
5440 Endville Rd 38826 662-844-8604
Brian Benscoter, hdmstr. Fax 823-6972

Belmont, Tishomingo, Pop. 2,002
Tishomingo County Special Municipal SD
Supt. — See Iuka
Belmont S 1,000/K-12
PO Box 250 38827 662-454-7924
Mark Hood, prin. Fax 454-7611

Belzoni, Humphreys, Pop. 2,229
Humphreys County SD 1,400/K-12
PO Box 678 39038 662-247-6000
Fax 247-6004
Humphreys County HS 500/9-12
PO Box 658 39038 662-247-6040
Fax 247-6044
Humphreys JHS 200/6-8
700 Cohn St 39038 662-247-6050
Fax 247-6054
Randle Career and Technical Ctr Vo/Tech
PO Box 672 39038 662-247-6030
Jimmie Hurst, prin. Fax 247-6034

Humphreys Academy 200/K-12
PO Box 179 39038 662-247-1572
Mac Abernathy, hdmstr. Fax 247-2776

Benoit, Bolivar, Pop. 477
Benoit SD 300/PK-12
PO Box 189 38725 662-742-3287
Dr. Beverly Culley, supt. Fax 742-3149
www.benoit.k12.ms.us/
Brooks S 300/PK-12
PO Box 8 38725 662-742-3257
Barbara Flore, prin. Fax 742-3493

Benton, Yazoo

Benton Academy 200/K-12
PO Box 308 39039 662-673-9722
Cindy Shipp, prin. Fax 673-9090

Biloxi, Harrison, Pop. 42,823
Biloxi Public SD 5,000/K-12
PO Box 168 39533 228-374-1810
Arthur McMillan, supt. Fax 435-6289
www.biloxischools.net
Biloxi HS 1,400/9-12
1845 Richard Dr 39532 228-435-6105
Pamela Manners, prin. Fax 435-6353
Biloxi JHS 1,100/6-8
1424 Father Ryan Ave 39530 228-435-1421
Dennis Penton, prin. Fax 435-1426
Lopez S Alt
140 Saint John Ave 39530 228-432-7783
Dr. Alice Duggan, prin. Fax 374-6909

Harrison County SD
Supt. — See Gulfport
D'Iberville HS 1,200/9-12
15625 Lamey Bridge Rd 39532 228-392-2678
Cheryle Broadus, prin. Fax 392-7807

Cedar Lake Christian Academy 300/PK-12
11555 Cedar Lake Rd 39532 228-392-6279
Rev. Billy Wise, hdmstr. Fax 396-2006
St. Patrick HS 7-12
18300 Saint Patrick Rd 39532 228-702-0500
J. Renee McDaniel, prin. Fax 702-0511
Virginia College Post-Sec.
920 Cedar Lake Rd 39532 228-546-9100
William Carey University Post-Sec.
19640 Highway 67 39532 228-702-1775

Blue Mountain, Tippah, Pop. 901
South Tippah SD
Supt. — See Ripley
Blue Mountain S 300/K-12
408 W Mill St 38610 662-685-4706
Eddie Conner, prin. Fax 685-4706

Blue Mountain College Post-Sec.
PO Box 160 38610 662-685-4771

Blue Springs, Union, Pop. 228
Union County SD
Supt. — See New Albany
East Union S 800/K-12
1548 Highway 9 S 38828 662-534-6920
Ray Kennedy, prin. Fax 534-6542

Bogue Chitto, Lincoln, Pop. 518
Lincoln County SD
Supt. — See Brookhaven
Bogue Chitto S 600/K-12
385 Monticello St 39629 601-734-2723
Mickey Myers, prin. Fax 734-6020

Bolton, Hinds, Pop. 565
Hinds County SD
Supt. — See Raymond
Main Street Restart S Alt
130 Champion Hill Rd 39041 601-866-2642
Kim Davenport, prin. Fax 866-4414

Booneville, Prentiss, Pop. 8,634
Booneville SD 1,200/K-12
201 N 1st St 38829 662-728-2171
Todd English, supt. Fax 728-4940
boonevilleschools.org
Booneville HS 400/9-12
300 W George E Allen Dr # B 38829 662-728-5445
Terry King, prin. Fax 728-2953
Booneville MS 400/5-8
300 W George E Allen Dr # B 38829 662-728-5843
Brad Mixon, prin. Fax 728-2427

Prentiss County SD 2,000/K-12
PO Box 179 38829 662-728-4911
Randle Downs, supt. Fax 728-2000
www.prentiss.k12.ms.us/
Jumpertown S 300/K-12
717 Highway 4 W 38829 662-728-6378
Anthony Michael, prin. Fax 728-9420
Prentiss County Vocational Technical S Vo/Tech
302 W George E Allen Dr 38829 662-728-9259
Kim Green, dir. Fax 728-9259
Thrasher S 400/K-12
167 County Road 1040 38829 662-728-5233
Rivers Stroup, prin. Fax 728-8107
Other Schools – See New Site, Wheeler

Northeast Mississippi Community College Post-Sec.
101 Cunningham Blvd 38829 662-728-7751

Brandon, Rankin, Pop. 21,524
Rankin County SD 18,300/K-12
PO Box 1359 39043 601-825-5590
Dr. Lynn Weathersby, supt. Fax 825-2618
www.rcsd.ms
Alternative Education Center Alt
200 School Rd 39042 601-824-0334
Harry Hill, prin. Fax 825-2988
Brandon HS 1,500/9-12
3090 Highway 18 39042 601-825-2201
Buddy Bailey, prin. Fax 591-1037
Brandon MS 1,200/6-8
408 S College St 39042 601-825-5998
Kalvin Robinson, prin. Fax 825-8402
Other Schools – See Florence, Flowood, Pelahatchie, Puckett, Richland, Sandhill

Brookhaven, Lincoln, Pop. 12,389
Brookhaven SD 2,900/K-12
PO Box 540 39602 601-833-6661
Dr. Lisa Karmacharya, supt. Fax 833-4154
www.brookhaven.k12.ms.us
Alexander JHS 400/7-8
713 Beauregard St 39601 601-833-7549
Rod Henderson, prin. Fax 835-5467
Brookhaven HS 800/9-12
PO Box 532 39602 601-833-4498
David Martin, prin. Fax 823-3792
Brookhaven Technical Center Vo/Tech
325 E Court St 39601 601-833-8335
Jackie Martin, dir. Fax 835-3985

Lincoln County SD 3,000/K-12
PO Box 826 39602 601-835-0011
Terry Brister, supt. Fax 833-3030
lcsd.k12.ms.us/
Enterprise S 800/K-12
1601 Highway 583 SE 39601 601-833-7284
Shannon Eubanks, prin. Fax 835-1261
Star S 900/K-12
1880 Highway 550 NW 39601 601-833-3473
Robin Case, prin. Fax 833-1254
West Lincoln S 700/K-12
948 Jackson Liberty Dr SW 39601 601-833-4600
Jason Case, prin. Fax 833-9909
Other Schools – See Bogue Chitto

Brookhaven Academy 500/PK-12
943 Brookway Blvd Ext 39601 601-833-4041
Julie Wright, hdmstr. Fax 833-1846

Brooklyn, Forrest
Forrest County Agricultural HSD
215 Old Highway 49 E 39425 601-582-4102
Dr. Jerry Morgan, supt. Fax 545-9483
aggies.myownpage.net
Forrest County Agricultural HS Vo/Tech
215 Old Highway 49 E 39425 601-582-4741
Loren Harris, prin. Fax 582-9031

Bruce, Calhoun, Pop. 1,918
Calhoun County SD
Supt. — See Pittsboro
Bruce HS 400/7-12
PO Box 248 38915 662-983-3350
Michael Gillespie, prin. Fax 983-3356

Byhalia, Marshall, Pop. 1,278
Marshall County SD
Supt. — See Holly Springs
Byhalia HS 500/9-12
278 Highway 309 N 38611 662-838-2206
Charles LeSure, prin. Fax 838-2218
Byhalia MS 400/6-8
172 Highway 309 N 38611 662-838-2591
Landon Pollard, prin. Fax 838-5141

Caledonia, Lowndes, Pop. 1,021
Lowndes County SD
Supt. — See Columbus
Caledonia HS 600/9-12
111 Confederate Dr 39740 662-356-2001
Randy Barnett, prin. Fax 356-2036
Caledonia MS 500/6-8
105 Confederate Dr 39740 662-356-2042
Karen Pittman, prin. Fax 356-2045

Calhoun City, Calhoun, Pop. 1,755
Calhoun County SD
Supt. — See Pittsboro
Calhoun Career & Technical Center Vo/Tech
PO Box 1573 38916 662-628-1143
Kyle Clark, admin. Fax 628-1123
Calhoun City HS 200/9-12
PO Box 559 38916 662-628-5112
Mike Ray, prin. Fax 628-6240
Calhoun City MS 200/5-8
PO Box 1546 38916 662-628-1890
Stacia Parker, prin. Fax 628-1896

Calhoun Academy 200/PK-12
PO Box C 38916 662-412-2087
Cameron Wright, hdmstr. Fax 412-2081

Camden, Madison
Madison County SD
Supt. — See Flora
Jackson HS 300/9-12
2000 Loring Rd 39045 662-468-2531
George Jones, prin. Fax 468-2748

Canton, Madison, Pop. 13,125
Canton SD 3,300/K-12
403 Lincoln St 39046 601-859-4110
Dwight Luckett, supt. Fax 859-4023
www.cantonschools.net
Canton Career Center Vo/Tech
487 N Union Street Ext 39046 601-859-3984
W.K. Luckett, dir. Fax 859-1115
Canton Educational Services Center Alt
529 Mace St 39046 601-859-5010
Jacqueline Griffin, prin. Fax 859-5011
Canton HS 900/9-12
634 Finney Rd 39046 601-859-5325
Shirley Sanders, prin. Fax 859-2554
Nichols MS 700/6-8
529 Mace St 39046 601-859-3741
Tina Manning, prin. Fax 859-6561
Porter MS 6-8
Finney Rd 39046 601-407-1820

Madison County SD
Supt. — See Flora
Madison County Academic Options Center Alt
1633 W Peace St 39046 601-859-0367
Chris Perritt, prin. Fax 859-0374
Northeast Madison MS 200/6-8
820 Sulphur Springs Rd 39046 601-855-2406
Kelvin Griffin, prin. Fax 859-7615

Canton Academy 300/K-12
PO Box 116 39046 601-859-5231
Steve Simpson, head sch Fax 859-5232

Carriere, Pearl River
Pearl River County SD 3,000/K-12
7441 Highway 11 39426 601-798-7744
Alan Lumpkin, supt. Fax 798-3527
www.prc.k12.ms.us/
Pearl River Central Alternative Educ Alt
461 Burgetown Rd 39426 601-798-6852
Lori Burkett, dir. Fax 799-4355
Pearl River Central HS 900/9-12
7407 Highway 11 39426 601-798-1986
Stacy Baudoin, prin. Fax 798-0068
Pearl River Central MS 700/6-8
7391 Highway 11 39426 601-798-5654
Missy Holston, prin. Fax 798-2822

Carrollton, Carroll, Pop. 190
Carroll County SD 900/K-12
PO Box 256 38917 662-237-9276
Billy Ferguson, supt. Fax 237-9703
www.ccsd.ms
Other Schools – See North Carrollton

Carroll Academy 400/PK-12
PO Box 226 38917 662-237-6858

Carson, Jefferson Davis
Jefferson Davis County SD
Supt. — See Prentiss
Davis County Voc-Tech Center Vo/Tech
PO Box 70 39427 601-792-5005
Dr. Thomas Johnson, dir. Fax 792-2511

Carthage, Leake, Pop. 5,025
Leake County SD 2,200/K-12
PO Box 478 39051 601-267-4579
Patrick Posey, supt. Fax 267-5283
www.leakesd.org
Leake Central HS 400/9-12
704 N Jordan St 39051 601-267-7713
J.B. Norwood, prin. Fax 267-3738
Leake Central JHS 300/6-8
801 Martin Luther King Dr 39051 601-267-8909
Peggy Marble, prin. Fax 267-5902

Leake County Career & Technical Center Vo/Tech
703 N West St 39051 601-267-8442
Glenda Holleyman, prin. Fax 267-5150
Other Schools – See Walnut Grove

Infinity Career College Post-Sec.
305B Highway 16 W 39051 601-267-3678

Centreville, Wilkinson, Pop. 1,683
Wilkinson County SD
Supt. — See Woodville
Winans MS 300/6-8
PO Box 610 39631 601-645-0008
Fax 645-0170

Centreville Academy 400/K-12
PO Box 70 39631 601-645-5912

Charleston, Tallahatchie, Pop. 2,183
East Tallahatchie Consolidated SD 1,300/K-12
411 E Chestnut St 38921 662-647-5524
Ellis Smith, supt. Fax 647-3720
www.etsd.k12.ms.us
Charleston HS 400/9-12
411 E Chestnut St 38921 662-647-5359
Marshall Whittemore, prin. Fax 647-3724
Charleston MS 300/6-8
411 E Chestnut St 38921 662-647-2115
Sammie Armstrong, prin.

Strider Academy 100/K-12
3698 MS Highway 32 Central 38921 662-647-5833
David Arrington, hdmstr. Fax 647-5702

Clarksdale, Coahoma, Pop. 17,884
Clarksdale Municipal SD 3,400/PK-12
PO Box 1088 38614 662-627-8500
Dennis Dupree, supt. Fax 627-8542
www.cmsd.k12.ms.us/
Clarksdale HS 900/9-12
PO Box 1088 38614 662-627-8530
Dr. Manika Kemp, prin. Fax 627-8549
Higgins MS 300/6-8
PO Box 1088 38614 662-627-8550
Edwin Robinson, prin. Fax 627-8543
Keen Vocational Center Vo/Tech
PO Box 1088 38614 662-627-8580
Kenisha Shelton, dir. Fax 627-8582
Oakhurst MS 400/6-8
PO Box 1088 38614 662-627-8560
Valencia Rhodes, prin. Fax 627-8512
Shaw S of Excellence Alt
PO Box 1088 38614 662-627-8595
Fax 627-8552

Coahoma Agricultural HSD 200/9-12
3240 Friars Point Rd 38614 662-624-9424
Dr. Vivian Presley, supt. Fax 624-4315
caho.k12.ms.us
Coahoma Agricultural HS 200/9-12
3240 Friars Point Rd 38614 662-624-8045
I.D. Thompson Ed.D., prin. Fax 621-4672

Coahoma County SD 1,400/K-12
PO Box 820 38614 662-624-5448
Pauline Rhoads, supt. Fax 624-5512
www.coahoma.k12.ms.us
Coahoma County JSHS 500/7-12
1535 Lee Dr 38614 662-627-7378
James Bryant, prin. Fax 627-4516

Coahoma Community College Post-Sec.
3240 Friars Point Rd 38614 662-627-2571
Lee Academy 500/PK-12
415 Lee Dr 38614 662-627-7891

Cleveland, Bolivar, Pop. 12,236
Cleveland SD 3,100/PK-12
305 Merritt Dr 38732 662-843-3529
Jacquelyn Thigpen Ed.D., supt. Fax 843-9731
www.cleveland.k12.ms.us
Cleveland Career Development & Tech Ctr. Vo/Tech
601 3rd St 38732 662-843-8818
Monica Mitchell, dir. Fax 846-0308
Cleveland HS 500/9-12
300 W Sunflower Rd 38732 662-843-2460
Steven Craddock, prin. Fax 843-2455
East Side HS 300/9-12
601 Lucy Seaberry Blvd 38732 662-843-2338
Dr. Randy Grierson, prin. Fax 843-1900
Green JHS 400/7-8
305 N Bolivar Ave 38732 662-843-2456
Archie Mitchell, prin. Fax 843-6820
Robinson Achievement Center Alt
607 3rd St 38732 662-846-6478
Dianne Hill, prin. Fax 846-7125
Smith MS 200/7-8
715 S Martin Luther King Dr 38732 662-843-4355
Morgan Dean, prin. Fax 843-7334

Bayou Academy 300/PK-12
PO Box 417 38732 662-843-3708
Delta State University Post-Sec.
1003 W Sunflower Rd 38733 662-846-3000

Clinton, Hinds, Pop. 24,956
Clinton SD 4,500/K-12
PO Box 300 39060 601-924-7533
Phillip Burchfield Ed.D., supt. Fax 924-6345
www.clintonpublicschools.com
Clinton Career Complex Vo/Tech
713 Lakeview Dr 39056 601-924-0247
Brett Robinson, prin. Fax 924-1168
Clinton HS 1,000/10-12
401 Arrow Dr 39056 601-924-5656
Dr. Eddie Peasant, prin. Fax 924-4622
Clinton JHS 700/7-8
711 Lakeview Dr 39056 601-924-0619
Anthony Goins, prin. Fax 924-7703

Sumner Hill JHS 400/9-9
400 W Northside Dr 39056 601-924-5510
Bobby Hathorn, prin. Fax 924-4182

Mississippi College Post-Sec.
200 W College St 39058 601-925-3000
Mount Salus Christian S 200/K-12
PO Box 240 39060 601-924-5863

Coffeeville, Yalobusha, Pop. 891
Coffeeville SD 600/K-12
96 Mississippi St 38922 662-675-8941
Eddie Anderson, supt. Fax 675-5004
www.coffeevilleschools.org/
Coffeeville HS 200/8-12
96 Mississippi St 38922 662-675-8904
Fletcher Harges, prin. Fax 675-8905

Coldwater, Tate, Pop. 1,663
Tate County SD
Supt. — See Senatobia
Coldwater HS 300/6-12
PO Box 1050 38618 662-622-5511
Robert Skipper, prin. Fax 622-7601
Independence HS 500/8-12
3184 Highway 305 38618 662-233-4691
Steve Hurdle, prin. Fax 233-2214
Senatobia/Tate Vocational-Technical Ctr Vo/Tech
165 W Central Ave 38618 662-622-5142
Richard Hartley, dir. Fax 622-7005

Collins, Covington, Pop. 2,566
Covington County SD 3,100/K-12
PO Box 1269 39428 601-765-4457
Clay Anglin, supt. Fax 765-4102
www.cov.k12.ms.us
Carver MS 300/5-8
PO Box 757 39428 601-765-4908
Pauline Fairley, prin. Fax 765-4100
Collins HS 300/9-12
PO Box 1479 39428 601-765-3203
Bryan Hoda, prin. Fax 765-4116
Covington County Alternative S 50/Alt
PO Box 1269 39428 601-765-1465
Jake Kyzar, prin. Fax 765-4102
Covington County Vocational Ctr Vo/Tech
PO Box 1268 39428 601-765-8253
Cecil Easterling, dir. Fax 765-6360
Other Schools – See Mount Olive, Seminary

Collinsville, Lauderdale, Pop. 1,932
Lauderdale County SD
Supt. — See Meridian
West Lauderdale HS 600/9-12
9916 W Lauderdale Rd 39325 601-737-2277
Kevin Cheatham, prin. Fax 737-2377
West Lauderdale MS 700/5-8
9916 W Lauderdale Rd 39325 601-737-8689
Linda Dulaney, prin. Fax 737-5145

Columbia, Marion, Pop. 6,495
Columbia SD 1,800/K-12
613 Bryan Ave 39429 601-736-2366
Marietta James Ed.D., supt. Fax 736-2653
www.columbiaschools.org
Columbia HS 500/9-12
1009 Broad St 39429 601-736-5334
Sheila Burbridge, prin. Fax 731-1068
Jefferson MS 400/6-8
611 Owens St 39429 601-736-2786
Raymond Powell, prin. Fax 731-3762

Marion County SD 2,400/PK-12
1010 Highway 13 N Ste 2 39429 601-736-7193
Craig Robbins, supt. Fax 736-6274
www.marionk12.org
East Marion JSHS 400/7-12
527 E Marion School Rd 39429 601-736-3006
John Taylor, prin. Fax 736-8215
Loftin Career and Technology Ctr Vo/Tech
1140 Highway 13 S 39429 601-736-6095
Dr. Jan Sears, prin. Fax 731-2077
Other Schools – See Foxworth

Columbia Academy 500/K-12
1548 Highway 98 E 39429 601-736-6418

Columbus, Lowndes, Pop. 23,393
Columbus Municipal SD 3,500/PK-12
PO Box 1308 39703 662-241-7400
Dr. Martha Liddell, supt. Fax 241-7453
www.columbuscityschools.org/
CMSD Alternative S Alt
924 20th St N 39701 662-241-7250
Tamela Barr, dir. Fax 241-7252
Columbus HS 1,200/9-12
215 Hemlock St 39702 662-241-7200
Jill Savely, prin. Fax 241-7205
Columbus MS 6-8
175 Highway 373 39705 662-241-7300
Freda Dismukes, prin. Fax 241-7305
McKellar Technology Center Vo/Tech
810 N Browder St 39702 662-241-7290
Christopher Bray, dir. Fax 241-7293

Lowndes County SD 5,000/K-12
1053 Highway 45 S 39701 662-244-5000
Lynn Wright, supt. Fax 244-5043
www.lowndes.k12.ms.us/
New Hope HS 800/9-12
3419 New Hope Rd 39702 662-244-4701
Matthew Smith, prin. Fax 244-4725
New Hope MS 600/6-8
462 Center Rd 39702 662-244-4740
Sam Allison, prin. Fax 244-4758
West Lowndes HS 200/9-12
644 S Frontage Rd 39701 662-328-1369
Charles Jackson, prin. Fax 327-3353
West Lowndes MS 100/6-8
1380 Motley Rd 39701 662-244-5060
Cynthia McMath, prin. Fax 327-4857

Other Schools – See Caledonia

Heritage Academy 600/K-12
623 Willowbrook Rd 39705 662-327-1556
Mississippi University for Women Post-Sec.
1100 College St 39701 662-329-4750

Como, Panola, Pop. 1,273
North Panola SD
Supt. — See Sardis
North Panola Career & Technical Center Vo/Tech
601 Railroad St 38619 662-526-5804
Carolyn Shaw, dir. Fax 526-5868
North Panola JHS 300/6-8
526 Compress Rd 38619 662-526-5938
Dr. Ella Walker, prin. Fax 526-5990

Corinth, Alcorn, Pop. 14,398
Alcorn SD 3,500/PK-12
PO Box 1420 38835 662-286-5591
Gina Rogers Smith, admin. Fax 286-7766
www.alcorn.k12.ms.us
Alcorn Alternative S Alt
2101 Norman Rd 38834 662-284-3359
Randy Holt, admin. Fax 284-4950
Alcorn Career & Technology Center Vo/Tech
2101 Norman Rd 38834 662-286-7727
Richard Turner, admin. Fax 286-5674
Biggersville JSHS 200/7-12
571 Highway 45 38834 662-286-3542
Gary Johnson, admin. Fax 286-3023
Kossuth HS 500/9-12
15 County Road 604 38834 662-286-3653
Matt Smith, admin. Fax 286-3507
Kossuth MS 500/5-8
17 County Road 604 38834 662-286-7093
Dr. James Vansandt, admin. Fax 286-6837
Other Schools – See Glen

Corinth SD 1,700/PK-12
1204 N Harper Rd 38834 662-287-2425
Edward Lee Childress Ed.D., supt. Fax 286-1885
www.corinth.k12.ms.us
Corinth HS 500/9-12
1310 N Harper Rd 38834 662-286-1000
Russ Elam, prin. Fax 286-1003
Corinth MS 300/5-8
1000 E 5th St 38834 662-286-1261
Nathan Hall, prin. Fax 287-0296

ICS The Wright Beauty College Post-Sec.
2077 Highway 72 E Anx 38834 662-287-0944

Crawford, Oktibbeha, Pop. 634
Oktibbeha County SD
Supt. — See Starkville
East Oktibbeha County HS 200/7-12
1699 Moor High Rd 39743 662-272-5660
Dr. Helen Kennard, prin. Fax 272-5603

Crystal Springs, Copiah, Pop. 5,021
Copiah County SD
Supt. — See Hazlehurst
Crystal Springs HS 500/9-12
201 Newton St 39059 601-892-4791
Michael Evans, prin. Fax 892-2071
Crystal Springs MS 600/4-8
2092 S Pat Harrison Dr 39059 601-892-2722
Donald Regan, prin. Fax 892-9949

Decatur, Newton, Pop. 1,826
Newton County SD 1,900/K-12
PO Box 97 39327 601-635-2317
J.O. Amis, supt. Fax 635-4025
www.newton.k12.ms.us
East Central Alternative S Alt
PO Box 579 39327 601-635-2118
Sal LaBue, prin. Fax 635-5659
Newton Co. Career and Technical Center Vo/Tech
PO Box 742 39327 601-635-4138
Ken Stringer, dir. Fax 635-4024
Newton County HS 1,000/6-12
PO Box 278 39327 601-635-2718
Brian Foster, prin. Fax 635-4045

East Central Community College Post-Sec.
PO Box 129 39327 601-635-2111
Newton County Academy 200/PK-12
PO Box 25 39327 601-635-2756

De Kalb, Kemper, Pop. 1,156
Kemper County SD 1,100/PK-12
PO Box 219 39328 601-743-2657
Jackie Pollock, supt. Fax 743-9297
kemper.k12.ms.us/
Kemper County HS 500/7-12
PO Box 429 39328 601-743-5292
Calvin Melton, prin. Fax 743-5952
Stennis Vocational Complex Vo/Tech
PO Box 549 39328 601-743-5226
Monica Westerfield, dir. Fax 743-2351

Kemper Academy 200/K-12
149 Walnut Ave 39328 601-743-2232
Pete McCleskey, admin. Fax 743-9627

D'Iberville, Harrison, Pop. 9,203
Harrison County SD
Supt. — See Gulfport
D'Iberville MS 700/4-8
3320 Warrior Dr 39540 228-392-1746
Dana Trochessett, prin. Fax 392-9948

Drew, Sunflower, Pop. 1,923
Sunflower County SD
Supt. — See Indianola
Drew Hunter MS 100/7-8
10 Swoope Rd 38737 662-745-8529
Edgar Holman, prin. Fax 745-8529

North Sunflower Academy 100/K-12
148 Academy Rd 38737 662-756-4573
Janet Ray, head sch Fax 756-2580

Dundee, Tunica
Tunica County SD
Supt. — See Tunica
TCS Alternative S Alt
12910 Old Highway 61 S 38626 662-363-0147
Glen Newson, prin. Fax 363-0610

Durant, Holmes, Pop. 2,658
Durant SD 500/K-12
5 W Madison St 39063 662-653-3175
Louise Sanders-Tate, supt. Fax 653-6151
durant.k12.ms.us
Durant S 500/K-12
PO Box 669 39063 662-653-3429
Fax 653-3472

Holmes County SD
Supt. — See Lexington
Williams-Sullivan HS 200/9-12
14494 Highway 51 39063 662-653-6262
Valerie Bankhead, prin. Fax 653-6519

Ecru, Pontotoc, Pop. 882
Pontotoc County SD
Supt. — See Pontotoc
North Pontotoc HS 500/9-12
8324 Highway 15 N 38841 662-489-5612
Roger Smith, prin. Fax 489-2985
North Pontotoc MS 300/7-8
8324 Highway 15 N 38841 662-489-2479
roger smith, prin. Fax 489-7068

Ellisville, Jones, Pop. 4,419
Jones County SD 8,300/K-12
5204 Highway 11 N 39437 601-649-5201
Thomas Parker, supt. Fax 649-1613
www.jones.k12.ms.us/
South Jones JSHS 1,200/7-12
313 Anderson St 39437 601-477-8451
Tommy Branch, prin. Fax 477-3505
Other Schools – See Laurel

Jones County Junior College Post-Sec.
900 S Court St 39437 601-477-4000

Enterprise, Clarke, Pop. 526
Enterprise SD 900/PK-12
503 S River Rd 39330 601-659-7965
Rita Windham, supt. Fax 659-3254
www.esd.k12.ms.us/
Enterprise HS 200/9-12
501 S River Rd 39330 601-659-4435
Mike Weathers, prin. Fax 659-3274
Enterprise MS 300/5-8
105 Short St 39330 601-659-7722
Steven Gunn, prin. Fax 659-7722

Ethel, Attala, Pop. 416
Attala County SD
Supt. — See Kosciusko
Ethel JSHS 300/7-12
PO Box 340 39067 662-674-5673
Michael Ray, prin. Fax 674-5817

Eupora, Webster, Pop. 2,169
Webster County SD 1,800/PK-12
95 Clark Ave 39744 662-258-5921
Jack Treloar, supt. Fax 258-3134
www.webstercountyschools.org
Eupora HS 400/7-12
65 Clark Ave 39744 662-258-4041
Laci Knight, prin. Fax 258-4716
Webster County Career & Technology Ctr Vo/Tech
605 Hall Rd 39744 662-258-8206
Phil Ferguson, dir. Fax 258-6769
Other Schools – See Maben

Falkner, Tippah, Pop. 510
North Tippah SD
Supt. — See Tiplersville
Falkner JSHS 200/7-12
20350 Highway 15 38629 662-837-7892
Fax 837-8800

Fayette, Jefferson, Pop. 1,609
Jefferson County SD 1,600/PK-12
PO Box 157 39069 601-786-3721
Tracy M. Cook, supt. Fax 786-8441
www.jcpsd.net
Jefferson County Alternative S 200/Alt
468 Highway 33 39069 601-786-3900
Harry Brown, prin. Fax 786-2273
Jefferson County HS 500/9-12
2277 Main St 39069 601-786-3919
Barbara Lewis, prin. Fax 786-6002
Jefferson County JHS 200/7-8
468 Highway 33 39069 601-786-3900
LaRondrial Barnes, prin. Fax 786-2273
Jefferson County Vocational Center Vo/Tech
205 Industrial Park Rd 39069 601-786-3642
David Perry, prin. Fax 786-2271

Flora, Madison, Pop. 1,878
Madison County SD 11,400/PK-12
PO Box 159 39071 601-879-3000
Dr. Ronnie McGehee, supt. Fax 879-3039
www.madison-schools.com/
Other Schools – See Camden, Canton, Madison, Ridgeland

Tri-County Academy 300/PK-12
PO Box K 39071 601-879-8517
Mark Johnson, hdmstr. Fax 879-3373

Florence, Rankin, Pop. 4,112
Rankin County SD
Supt. — See Brandon

Florence HS 700/9-12
232 Highway 469 N 39073 601-845-2205
Tony Martin, prin. Fax 845-3752
Florence MS 500/6-8
123 Beverly Dr 39073 601-845-2862
Beverly Weathersby, prin. Fax 845-2114
McLaurin JSHS 600/7-12
130 Tiger Dr 39073 601-845-2247
Bill Lenington, prin. Fax 845-1170

Flowood, Rankin, Pop. 7,724
Rankin County SD
Supt. — See Brandon
Northwest HS 1,500/9-12
5805 Highway 25 39232 601-992-2242
Dr. Charles Frazier, prin. Fax 992-6005
Northwest MS 1,300/6-8
1 Paw Print Pl 39232 601-992-1329
Jacob McEwen, prin. Fax 992-1347

Hartfield Academy 300/PK-12
1240 Luckney Rd 39232 601-992-5333
Rick Burslem, hdmstr. Fax 992-5320

Forest, Scott, Pop. 5,620
Forest Municipal SD 1,500/K-12
325 Cleveland St 39074 601-469-3250
Dr. Joseph White, supt. Fax 469-3101
www.forest.k12.ms.us/
Forest HS 400/9-12
511 Cleveland St 39074 601-469-3255
Kim Shoemaker, prin. Fax 469-8250
Hawkins MS 500/5-8
803 E Oak St 39074 601-469-1474
Harry Bates, prin. Fax 469-8251

Scott County SD 3,700/K-12
100 E First St 39074 601-469-3861
Bingham Moncrief, supt. Fax 469-3874
www.scott.k12.ms.us
Forest/Scott County Career & Tech Ctr Vo/Tech
521 Cleveland St 39074 601-469-2913
Michael Wade, dir. Fax 469-2917
Scott Central S 900/K-12
2415 Old Jackson Rd 39074 601-469-4883
Debbie Herring, prin. Fax 469-3746
Other Schools – See Lake, Morton, Sebastopol

Foxworth, Marion, Pop. 592
Marion County SD
Supt. — See Columbia
West Marion JSHS 600/7-12
2 W Marion St 39483 601-736-6381
Rusty Rutland, prin. Fax 731-7937

French Camp, Choctaw, Pop. 172

French Camp Academy 200/9-12
1 Fine Pl 39745 662-547-6113
Rusty McKnight, prin. Fax 547-6302

Fulton, Itawamba, Pop. 3,914
Itawamba County SD 3,100/PK-12
605 S Cummings St 38843 662-862-2159
Michael Nanney, supt. Fax 862-4713
www.itawamba.k12.ms.us/
Itawamba Agricultural HS 600/9-12
11900 Highway 25 S 38843 662-862-3104
Trae Wiygul, prin. Fax 862-5494
Itawamba County Vocational Center Vo/Tech
200 Vo Tech Rd 38843 662-862-3137
Gary Hamm, prin. Fax 862-3138
Other Schools – See Mantachie, Tremont

Itawamba Community College Post-Sec.
602 W Hill St 38843 662-862-8000

Gallman, Copiah

Copiah Academy 600/K-12
PO Box 125 39077 601-892-3770

Gautier, Jackson, Pop. 18,202
Pascagoula SD
Supt. — See Pascagoula
Gautier HS 900/9-12
4307 Gautier Vancleave Rd 39553 228-522-8783
Boyd West, prin. Fax 522-8788
Gautier MS 700/7-8
1920 Graveline Rd 39553 228-522-8806
Christy Reimsnyder, prin. Fax 522-8813

Mississippi Gulf Coast Community College Post-Sec.
PO Box 100 39553 228-497-9602

Glen, Alcorn, Pop. 409
Alcorn SD
Supt. — See Corinth
Alcorn Central HS 400/9-12
8 County Road 254 38846 662-286-8720
Tim Littlejohn, admin. Fax 286-8720
Alcorn Central MS 400/5-8
8A County Road 254 38846 662-286-3674
Nellie Massengill, admin. Fax 286-6712

Goodman, Holmes, Pop. 1,376

Holmes Community College Post-Sec.
PO Box 369 39079 662-472-2312

Greenville, Washington, Pop. 34,233
Greenville SD 6,100/K-12
PO Box 1619 38702 662-334-7000
Dr. Leeson Taylor, supt. Fax 334-2902
Coleman MS 800/6-8
400 Dr Martin L King Blvd 38701 662-334-7035
Dianne Zanders, prin. Fax 334-7040
Darling Achievement Center 50/Alt
242 S Broadway St 38701 662-334-7141
Charles Brady, prin. Fax 334-7023
Greenville Technical Center Vo/Tech
350 S Raceway Rd 38703 662-334-7171
Sherry Jackson, prin. Fax 334-2848
Greenville-Weston SHS 1,300/10-12
419 E Robert Shaw St 38701 662-334-7077
Melvin Brown, prin. Fax 334-7060
Solomon MS 600/6-8
556 Bowman Blvd 38701 662-334-7050
Samuel Evans, prin. Fax 334-7053
Weston 9th Grade Academy 500/9-9
901 Archer St 38701 662-334-7081
Tommy Molden, prin. Fax 334-7091

Western Line SD
Supt. — See Avon
O'Bannon HS 400/7-12
PO Box 5816 38704 662-335-2637
Derrick Cook, prin. Fax 334-1689

Delta Beauty College Post-Sec.
697 Delta Pl 38701 662-332-0587
Greenville Christian S 100/K-12
PO Box 4398 38704 662-332-0946
Fax 332-0948
St. Joseph HS 200/7-12
1501 V F W Rd 38701 662-378-9711
Paul Artman, prin. Fax 378-3496
Washington S 800/PK-12
1605 E Reed Rd 38703 662-334-4096
Rodney Brown, hdmstr. Fax 332-0434

Greenwood, LeFlore, Pop. 15,124
Greenwood SD 2,800/PK-12
401 Howard St 38930 662-453-4231
Dr. Montelle Greene, supt. Fax 455-7409
www.greenwood.k12.ms.us/
Greenwood Alternative S Alt
410 Main St 38930 662-455-8989
Kenneth Pulley, dir. Fax 455-7433
Greenwood Career and Technical Ctr Vo/Tech
616 Sycamore Ave 38930 662-455-7414
David Taylor, dir. Fax 455-8979
Greenwood HS 700/9-12
1209 Garrard Ave 38930 662-455-7450
Percy Powell, prin. Fax 455-7468
Greenwood MS 400/7-8
1200 Garrard Ave 38930 662-455-3661
Chiqueta Daniels, prin. Fax 455-5559

Leflore County SD 2,700/K-12
1901 Highway 82 W 38930 662-453-8566
Dr. Viola Williams-McCaskill, supt. Fax 459-7265
www.leflorecountyschools.org
East MS 400/4-8
208 Meadowbrook Rd 38930 662-453-9182
Jackie Lewis, prin. Fax 451-7734
Elzy HS 600/7-12
604 Elzy Ave 38930 662-453-9677
Jacqueline Boyd, prin. Fax 455-0139
Leflore County Vocational Center Vo/Tech
PO Box 1158 38935 662-453-7706
Charles Streeter, prin. Fax 453-7733
Other Schools – See Itta Bena

Infinity Career College Post-Sec.
502 Howard St 38930 662-451-5546
Pillow Academy 800/PK-12
69601 Highway 82 W 38930 662-453-1266

Grenada, Grenada, Pop. 12,980
Grenada SD 4,200/K-12
PO Box 1940 38902 662-226-1606
Dr. David Daigneault, supt. Fax 226-7994
www.gsd.k12.ms.us/
Grenada HS 1,200/9-12
1875 Fairground Rd 38901 662-226-8844
Jerry Williams, prin. Fax 227-6109
Grenada MS 1,000/6-8
28 Jones Rd 38901 662-226-5135
Lyle Williams, prin. Fax 227-6106
Grenada Vocational Complex Vo/Tech
2035 Jackson Ave 38901 662-226-5969
Dr. Cliff Craven, prin. Fax 226-5992
Tie Plant S Alt
809 Tie Plant Rd 38901 662-226-3311
Dr. Sandra Howell, prin. Fax 226-8388

Academy of Hair Design #1 Post-Sec.
2003B Commerce St 38901 662-226-2462
Kirk Academy 400/PK-12
PO Box 1008 38902 662-226-2791
Dr. Randy Poss, hdmstr. Fax 226-9066

Gulfport, Harrison, Pop. 66,180
Gulfport SD 5,700/K-12
2001 Pass Rd 39501 228-865-4600
Glen East, supt. Fax 865-1918
www.gulfportschools.org/
Bayou View MS 800/6-8
212 43rd St 39507 228-865-4633
Dean Scarbrough, prin. Fax 867-1967
Gulfport Central MS 600/6-8
1310 42nd Ave 39501 228-870-1035
Dr. Mike Battle, prin. Fax 870-1041
Gulfport HS 1,600/9-12
100 Perry St 39507 228-896-7525
Michael Lindsey, prin. Fax 896-8281
Gulfport Vocational Annex S Vo/Tech
100 Perry St 39507 228-896-6011
David Fava, dir. Fax 896-7686
Learning Center Alt
1215 Church St 39507 228-897-6045
Vicki Williams, prin. Fax 897-6053
Harrison County SD 13,600/K-12
11072 Highway 49 39503 228-539-6500
Henry Arledge, supt. Fax 539-6507
www.harrison.k12.ms.us/
Harrison Central HS 1,600/9-12
15600 School Rd 39503 228-832-2610
Averie Bush, prin. Fax 832-7433
Harrison County Alternative S Alt
11072 Highway 49 39503 228-539-5956
Joycelyn Moody, prin. Fax 539-5959
Harrison County Vocational Complex Vo/Tech
15600 School Rd 39503 228-832-6652
Russell Clark, prin. Fax 539-5965
North Gulfport 8th Grade S 400/8-8
4715 Illinois Ave 39501 228-864-8944
Regina Watts, prin. Fax 863-7326
West Harrison HS 1,000/9-12
10399 County Farm Rd 39503 228-539-8900
Sherry Washburn, prin. Fax 539-8910
Other Schools – See Biloxi, D'Iberville

Blue Cliff College Post-Sec.
12251 Bernard Pkwy 39503 228-896-9727
Chris' Beauty College Post-Sec.
1265 Pass Rd 39501 228-864-2920
Christian Collegiate Academy 200/PK-12
12200 Dedeaux Rd 39503 228-832-4585
Infinity Career College Post-Sec.
319 Pass Rd 39507 228-864-4663
Miller-Motte Technical College Post-Sec.
12121 Highway 49 39503 228-273-3400
Mississippi Gulf Coast Community College Post-Sec.
2226 Switzer Rd 39507 228-896-3355

Guntown, Lee, Pop. 2,042
Lee County SD
Supt. — See Tupelo
Guntown MS 800/6-8
PO Box 8 38849 662-348-8800
Steven Havens, prin. Fax 348-8810

Hamilton, Monroe, Pop. 450
Monroe County SD
Supt. — See Amory
Hamilton S 700/K-12
40201 Hamilton Rd 39746 662-343-8307
Tim Dickerson, prin. Fax 343-5813

Hattiesburg, Forrest, Pop. 45,409
Forrest County SD 2,400/K-12
400 Forrest St 39401 601-545-6055
Brian Freeman, supt. Fax 545-6054
www.forrest.k12.ms.us/
North Forrest JSHS 400/7-12
693 Eatonville Rd 39401 601-545-9304
Larry Johnson, prin. Fax 545-9318

Hattiesburg SD 3,900/K-12
PO Box 1569 39403 601-582-5078
James Q. Bacchus, supt. Fax 582-6666
www.hattiesburgpsd.com
Bethune Alternative Center Alt
610 Dumas Ave 39401 601-584-6311
Dr. Vanessa Lofton, prin. Fax 583-7322
Burger MS 600/7-8
174 WSF Tatum Drive Ext 39401 601-582-0536
Dr. Robert Williams, prin. Fax 582-0572
Hattiesburg HS 900/9-12
301 Hutchinson Ave 39401 601-544-0811
Jermain Brown, prin. Fax 544-8946

Lamar County SD
Supt. — See Purvis
Oak Grove HS 1,500/9-12
5198 Old Highway 11 39402 601-264-7232
Helen Price, prin. Fax 264-0160
Oak Grove MS 1,300/6-8
2543 Old Highway 24 39402 601-264-4634
Patrick Gray, prin. Fax 264-0160

Antonelli College Post-Sec.
1500 N 31st Ave 39401 601-583-4100
Forrest General Hospital Post-Sec.
6051 U S Highway 49 39401 601-288-4201
Hattiesburg Radiology Group Post-Sec.
5000 W 4th St 39402 601-288-4241
Presbyterian Christian S 1,000/PK-12
221 Bonhomie Rd 39401 601-582-4956
Sacred Heart S 600/PK-12
608 Southern Ave 39401 601-583-8683
Brian McCrory, prin. Fax 583-8684
University of Southern Mississippi Post-Sec.
118 College Dr 39406 601-266-1000
William Carey University Post-Sec.
498 Tuscan Ave 39401 601-318-6051

Hazlehurst, Copiah, Pop. 3,977
Copiah County SD 2,800/PK-12
254 W Gallatin St 39083 601-894-1341
Rickey Clopton, supt. Fax 894-2634
www.copiah.ms/
Other Schools – See Crystal Springs, Wesson

Hazlehurst CSD 1,500/PK-12
119 Robert McDaniel Dr 39083 601-894-1152
Fax 894-3170
www.hazlehurst.k12.ms.us
Hazlehurst HS 400/9-12
101 S Haley St 39083 601-894-2489
Will Russell, prin. Fax 894-3120
Hazlehurst MS 400/5-8
112 School Dr 39083 601-894-3463
Nyisha Wells, prin. Fax 894-2629

Heidelberg, Jasper, Pop. 716
East Jasper Consolidated SD 1,000/K-12
PO Box E 39439 601-787-3281
Dr. Gwendolyn Page, supt. Fax 787-3410
www.eastjasper.k12.ms.us

Heidelberg HS 300/9-12
PO Box M 39439 601-787-3414
Kevin Jones, prin. Fax 787-3416
Heidelberg JHS 200/7-8
PO Box M 39439 601-787-3665
Marie Parker, prin. Fax 787-3045

Heidelberg Academy 200/K-12
PO Box Q 39439 601-787-4589
Fax 787-3371

Hernando, DeSoto, Pop. 13,952
DeSoto County SD 30,100/K-12
5 E South St 38632 662-429-5271
Milton Kuykendall, supt. Fax 429-4198
www.desotocountyschools.org
Hernando HS 1,000/9-12
805 Dilworth Ln 38632 662-429-4170
Freddie Joseph, prin. Fax 429-6269
Hernando MS 900/6-8
700 Dilworth Ln 38632 662-429-4154
Rob Chase, prin. Fax 429-4189
Other Schools – See Horn Lake, Lake Cormorant, Olive Branch, Southaven

Hickory Flat, Benton, Pop. 592
Benton County SD
Supt. — See Ashland
Hickory Flat S 700/K-12
1005 Spruce St 38633 662-333-7731
Barry Goolsby, prin. Fax 333-4127

Hollandale, Washington, Pop. 2,691
Hollandale SD 600/K-12
PO Box 128 38748 662-827-2276
James Johnson-Waldington, supt. Fax 827-5261
www.hollandale.k12.ms.us
Simmons JSHS 200/7-12
PO Box 428 38748 662-827-2228
Randy Grierson, prin. Fax 827-2231

Holly Springs, Marshall, Pop. 7,662
Holly Springs SD 1,400/PK-12
840 Highway 178 E 38635 662-252-2183
Dr. Irene Walton Turnage, supt. Fax 252-7718
www.hssd.k12.ms.us
Holly Springs Career & Technical Center Vo/Tech
410 E Falconer Ave 38635 662-252-2071
Cravin Turnage, dir. Fax 252-7719
Holly Springs HS 500/9-12
165 N Walthall St 38635 662-252-4371
Cedric Richardson, prin. Fax 252-7720
Holly Springs JHS 200/7-8
325 E Falconer Ave 38635 662-252-7737
Letashia White, prin. Fax 252-7751

Marshall County SD 2,800/K-12
158 E College Ave 38635 662-252-4271
Jerry Moore, supt. Fax 252-5129
www.marshallcountysd.org/
Byers HS 200/9-12
4178 Highway 72 38635 662-851-7826
Sonya Cross, prin. Fax 851-4027
Other Schools – See Byhalia, Potts Camp

Infinity Career College Post-Sec.
960 Highway 4 E 38635 662-252-2600
Marshall Academy 300/PK-12
100 Academy Dr 38635 662-252-3449
Tommy C. Gunn, hdmstr. Fax 252-4510
Rust College Post-Sec.
150 Rust Ave 38635 662-252-8000

Horn Lake, DeSoto, Pop. 25,611
DeSoto County SD
Supt. — See Hernando
Desoto County Alternative Center Alt
6870 Center St E 38637 662-253-0017
Jay Baird, prin. Fax 253-0013
Horn Lake HS 1,300/9-12
3360 Church Rd 38637 662-393-5273
Andy Orr, prin. Fax 393-5275
Horn Lake MS 1,200/6-8
6125 Hurt Rd 38637 662-393-7443
Lucy Hasselman, prin. Fax 342-5039

Delta Technical College Post-Sec.
6550 Interstate Dr # D 38637 662-280-1443

Houlka, Chickasaw, Pop. 621
Chickasaw County SD 600/PK-12
PO Box 480 38850 662-568-3333
Dr. Betsy Collums, supt. Fax 568-2993
chickasaw.k12.ms.us/
Houlka S 600/PK-12
510 Griffin Ave 38850 662-568-2772
Jerry Seago, prin. Fax 568-7931

Houston, Chickasaw, Pop. 3,580
Houston SD 1,800/K-12
PO Box 351 38851 662-456-3332
Dr. Steve Coker, supt. Fax 456-5259
www.houston.k12.ms.us
Houston HS 500/9-12
PO Box 568 38851 662-456-3320
Buz Boyer, prin. Fax 456-3527
Houston MS 400/6-8
PO Box 192 38851 662-456-5174
Tony Horton, prin. Fax 456-2254
Houston Vocational Center Vo/Tech
PO Box 608 38851 662-456-3748
Beverly James, dir. Fax 456-5172

Indianola, Sunflower, Pop. 10,634
Indianola SD 2,200/K-12
702 Highway 82 E 38751 662-884-1200
Dr. King Rush, supt. Fax 887-7042
www.indianolaschools.org/
Gentry HS 600/10-12
801 BB King Rd 38751 662-884-1240
Gared Watkins, prin. Fax 887-7410
Indianola Academic Achievement Center Alt
300 Jefferson St 38751 662-884-1278
Perry Reed, prin. Fax 887-3038
Indianola Career & Technical Center Vo/Tech
801 BB King Rd 38751 662-884-6000
Dr. Valerie Simpson, dir. Fax 887-7087
Merritt MS 500/7-9
705 Kinlock Rd 38751 662-884-1270
Glenda Shedd, prin. Fax 887-5247

Sunflower County SD 2,000/K-12
PO Box 70 38751 662-887-4919
Charles Barron, admin. Fax 887-7051
www.sunflower.k12.ms.us/
Other Schools – See Drew, Inverness, Moorhead, Ruleville

Indianola Academy 500/PK-12
PO Box 967 38751 662-887-2025
Sammy Henderson, hdmstr. Fax 887-3117
Restoration Ministries Christian Academy 100/PK-12
PO Box 1001 38751 662-887-2040
Richard Jenkins, admin. Fax 887-2040

Inverness, Sunflower, Pop. 1,017
Sunflower County SD
Supt. — See Indianola
Ruleville Central HS 300/9-12
PO Box 228 38753 662-265-5752
Darron Edwards, prin. Fax 265-0027

Itta Bena, LeFlore, Pop. 2,046
Leflore County SD
Supt. — See Greenwood
Leflore County HS 500/7-12
PO Box 564 38941 662-254-7762
Julius Lucas, prin. Fax 254-7530

Mississippi Valley State University Post-Sec.
14000 Highway 82 W 38941 662-254-9041

Iuka, Tishomingo, Pop. 2,992
Tishomingo County Special Municipal SD 3,200/K-12
1620 Paul Edmondson Dr 38852 662-423-3206
Ben McClung, supt. Fax 424-9820
www.tishomingo.k12.ms.us
Iuka MS 400/5-8
507 W Quitman St 38852 662-423-3316
Christy Holly, prin. Fax 423-2426
Tishomingo County HS 600/9-12
701 Highway 72 38852 662-423-7300
Dr. Eddie Britton, prin. Fax 423-7307
Other Schools – See Belmont, Tishomingo

Jackson, Hinds, Pop. 172,074
Jackson SD 29,300/PK-12
PO Box 2338 39225 601-960-8700
Dr. Cedrick Gray, supt. Fax 960-8713
www.jackson.k12.ms.us
Bailey APAC MS 200/6-8
1900 N State St 39202 601-960-5343
Christi Hollinghead, prin. Fax 592-2496
Blackburn MS 400/6-8
1311 W Pearl St 39203 601-960-5329
Marietta Carter, prin. Fax 360-2601
Brinkley MS 400/6-8
3535 Albermarle Rd 39213 601-987-3573
Dr. Leroy Pope, prin. Fax 987-3746
Callaway HS 1,100/9-12
601 Beasley Rd 39206 601-987-3535
Clyde Speaks, prin. Fax 987-3729
Capital City Alternative S Alt
2221 Boling St 39213 601-713-2376
Marie Harris, prin. Fax 987-3727
Cardozo MS 500/6-8
3180 McDowell Road Ext 39204 601-346-5635
Dr. Josephine Kelly, prin. Fax 373-0286
Chastain MS 800/6-8
4650 Manhattan Rd 39206 601-987-3550
Victor Ellis, prin. Fax 987-4930
Forest Hill HS 1,300/9-12
2607 Raymond Rd 39212 601-371-4313
Dr. Kimberly Warfield, prin. Fax 371-4379
Hardy MS 500/6-8
545 Ellis Ave 39209 601-960-5362
Antonius Caldwell, prin. Fax 360-2686
Hill HS 1,200/9-12
2185 Fortune St 39204 601-960-5354
Bobby Brown, prin. Fax 360-2625
Jackson Career Development Center Vo/Tech
2703 First Ave 39209 601-960-5322
Dr. Brenda Jackson, prin. Fax 960-5411
Kirksey MS, 5677 Highland Dr 39206 400/6-8
Dr. Edward Buck, prin. 601-987-8360
Lanier HS 800/9-12
833 Maple St 39203 601-960-5369
Dr. Shemeka McClung, prin. Fax 960-4047
Murrah HS 1,400/9-12
1400 Murrah Dr 39202 601-960-5380
Dr. Freddrick Murray, prin. Fax 360-2622
Northwest Jackson MS 600/6-8
7020 Highway 49 N 39213 601-987-3609
Chinelo Evans, prin. Fax 987-4975
Peeples MS 600/6-8
290 Treehaven Dr 39212 601-346-5660
Larry Holmes, prin. Fax 371-4722
Powell MS 600/6-8
3655 Livingston Rd 39213 601-987-3580
Dr. Valerie Bradley, prin. Fax 987-3583
Power APAC 200/4-12
1120 Riverside Dr 39202 601-960-5387
Dr. Marlynn Martin, prin. Fax 968-5157
Provine HS 1,000/9-12
2400 Robinson St 39209 601-960-5393
Laketia Marshall-Thomas, prin. Fax 360-2606
Rowan MS 200/6-8
136 E Ash St 39202 601-960-5349
Dr. Shimelle Mayers, prin. Fax 960-4046
Siwell Road MS 800/6-8
1983 N Siwell Rd 39209 601-923-2550
Larry Armstrong, prin. Fax 923-2570
Whitten MS 700/6-8
210 Daniel Lake Blvd 39212 601-371-4309
Anthony Moore, prin. Fax 371-4728
Wingfield HS 1,100/9-12
1985 Scanlon Dr 39204 601-371-4350
Cynthia Armstrong, prin. Fax 371-4734

Academy of Hair Design #3 Post-Sec.
1815 Terry Rd 39204 601-372-9800
Antonelli College Post-Sec.
2323 Lakeland Dr 39232 601-362-9991
Belhaven University Post-Sec.
1500 Peachtree St 39202 601-968-5940
Christ Missionary & Industrial S 200/PK-12
3910 Main St 39213 601-366-6413
Fax 366-5152
Education Center S 200/K-12
PO Box 55509 39296 601-982-2812
Deborah Stamper, prin. Fax 982-2827
Healthcare Institute of Jackson Post-Sec.
405 Briarwood Dr Ste 110 39206 601-956-3940
Hillcrest Christian S 500/K-12
4060 S Siwell Rd 39212 601-372-0149
Dr. Tom Prather, hdmstr Fax 371-8061
Hinds Community College Nursing/Alld Hlt Post-Sec.
1750 Chadwick Dr 39204 601-376-4800
Jackson Academy 1,300/PK-12
PO Box 14978 39236 601-362-9676
Dr. Pat Taylor, hdmstr. Fax 364-5722
Jackson Preparatory S 800/6-12
PO Box 4940 39296 601-939-8611
Susan Lindsay, head sch Fax 936-4068
Jackson State University Post-Sec.
1440 J R Lynch St 39217 601-979-2100
Magnolia College of Cosmetology Post-Sec.
4725 I 55 N 39206 601-362-6940
Millsaps College Post-Sec.
1701 N State St 39210 601-974-1000
Mississippi Baptist Medical Center Post-Sec.
1225 N State St 39202 601-968-5130
Mississippi College Post-Sec.
151 E Griffith St 39201 601-925-7100
Mississippi School for the Blind Post-Sec.
1252 Eastover Dr 39211 601-984-8000
Mississippi School for the Deaf Post-Sec.
1253 Eastover Dr 39211 601-984-8001
Reformed Theological Seminary Post-Sec.
5422 Clinton Blvd 39209 601-923-1600
St. Dominic-Jackson Memorial Hospital Post-Sec.
969 Lakeland Dr 39216 601-364-6935
Traxler School of Hair Post-Sec.
2821 Suncrest Dr 39212 601-371-3253
University of Mississippi Medical Center Post-Sec.
2500 N State St 39216 601-984-1000
Virginia College Post-Sec.
4795 I 55 N 39206 601-977-0960
Wesley Biblical Seminary Post-Sec.
787 E Northside Dr 39206 601-366-8880

Kilmichael, Montgomery, Pop. 698
Montgomery County SD
Supt. — See Winona
Montgomery County HS 200/7-12
PO Box 278 39747 662-262-5535
Lewis Zeigler, prin. Fax 262-4218

Kiln, Hancock, Pop. 2,194
Hancock County SD 4,900/K-12
17304 Highway 603 39556 228-255-0376
Alan Dedeaux, supt. Fax 255-0378
www.hancock.k12.ms.us
Hancock County Career Technical Center Vo/Tech
7180 Stennis Airport Rd 39556 228-467-3568
Dr. Rick Saucier, dir. Fax 466-4944
Hancock HS 1,300/9-12
7084 Stennis Airport Rd 39556 228-467-2251
Rhett Ladner, prin. Fax 467-2689
Hancock MS 1,000/6-8
7070 Stennis Airport Rd 39556 228-467-1889
Dane Aube, prin. Fax 467-2812

Kosciusko, Attala, Pop. 7,358
Attala County SD 1,100/PK-12
100 Courthouse Ste 3 39090 662-289-2801
Bryan Weaver, supt. Fax 289-2804
www.attala.k12.ms.us/
Kosciusko-Attala County Voc Complex Vo/Tech
450 Highway 12 E 39090 662-289-2689
Fax 289-2701
Other Schools – See Ethel, Sallis

Kosciusko SSD 2,300/PK-12
229 W Washington St 39090 662-289-4771
Tony McGee, supt. Fax 289-1177
www.ksd.k12.ms.us/
Kosciusko Alternative S Alt
229 W Washington St 39090 662-289-1188
Dwayne Cade, prin. Fax 289-1177
Kosciusko HS 600/9-12
229 W Washington St 39090 662-289-2424
Jonathan Carnes, prin. Fax 289-8767
Kosciusko JHS 500/6-8
229 W Washington St 39090 662-289-3737
Roger Hill, prin. Fax 289-1177

Lake, Newton, Pop. 321
Scott County SD
Supt. — See Forest
Lake HS 200/9-12
24442 Highway 80 39092 601-775-3248
Shane Phillips, prin. Fax 775-3861
Lake MS 200/5-8
1770 E Scott Rd 39092 601-775-3614
Clay Purvis, prin. Fax 775-8830

Lake Cormorant, DeSoto
DeSoto County SD
Supt. — See Hernando
Lake Cormorant HS 800/9-12
10201 Star Landing Rd 38641 662-996-3060
Rhonda Guice, prin. Fax 996-2520
Lake Cormorant MS 700/6-8
3203 Wilson Mill Rd 38641 662-781-0778
Jeff Morgan, prin. Fax 781-0688

Laurel, Jones, Pop. 18,408
Jones County SD
Supt. — See Ellisville
Jones County Career & Tech Center Vo/Tech
2409 Moose Dr 39440 601-425-2378
Patsy Reon, prin. Fax 425-2349
Northeast Jones JSHS 1,000/7-12
68 Northeast Dr 39443 601-425-2347
Cooper Pope, prin. Fax 649-1736
Pine Belt Educational Center Alt
923B Sawmill Rd 39440 601-428-8080
Mike Moore, prin.
West Jones JSHS 1,300/7-12
254 Springhill Rd 39443 601-729-8144
Lynn Lyon, prin. Fax 729-8148

Laurel SD 3,000/PK-12
PO Box 288 39441 601-649-6391
Dr. Chuck Benigno, supt. Fax 649-6398
www.laurelschools.org
Laurel HS 700/9-12
1100 W 12th St 39440 601-649-4145
Carl Day, prin. Fax 426-2347
Laurel MS 700/6-8
1600 Grandview Dr 39440 601-428-5312
Jeannine Agee, prin. Fax 426-6775

Laurel Christian S 500/PK-12
PO Box 8425 39441 601-649-4190
Mississippi College of Beauty Culture Post-Sec.
732 Sawmill Rd 39440 601-428-7127
Southeastern Baptist College Post-Sec.
4229 Highway 15 N 39440 601-426-6346

Leakesville, Greene, Pop. 893
Greene County SD 2,100/K-12
PO Box 1329 39451 601-394-2364
Richard Fleming, supt. Fax 394-5542
www.greene.k12.ms.us/
Greene County HS 600/9-12
4336 High School Rd 39451 601-394-5290
Scott Bray, prin. Fax 394-4878
Greene County Vo-Tech Complex Vo/Tech
173 Vo Tech Rd 39451 601-394-2973
Tom Wallace, prin. Fax 394-5953
Leakesville JHS 400/5-8
620 Main St 39451 601-394-2495
Amanda Dearman, prin. Fax 394-5690

Learned, Hinds, Pop. 92

Rebul Academy 100/PK-12
5257 Learned Rd 39154 601-885-6802
Jack Rice, hdmstr. Fax 885-9550

Leland, Washington, Pop. 4,449
Leland SD 1,000/PK-12
408 4th St 38756 662-686-5000
Glenda Triplett-Jackson, supt. Fax 686-5029
leland.schoolfusion.us/
Leland HS 300/9-12
404 E 3rd St 38756 662-686-5020
Hosea Haywood, prin. Fax 686-5027
Leland School Park MS 300/5-8
200 Milam St 38756 662-686-5017
Arthur Johnson, prin. Fax 686-5042
Leland Vocational Center Vo/Tech
E Deer Creek Dr 38756 662-686-5025
Kermit McAdory, dir. Fax 686-5024

Lexington, Holmes, Pop. 1,722
Holmes County SD 3,100/PK-12
PO Box 630 39095 662-834-2175
Powell Rucker, supt. Fax 834-9060
www.holmescountyschools.com
Holmes County Career & Technical Center Vo/Tech
PO Box 390 39095 662-834-3052
Frank Kimes, prin. Fax 834-3053
Marshall HS 300/9-12
12572 Highway 12 39095 662-235-5113
Reginald Barnes, prin. Fax 235-5551
McClain HS 500/9-12
PO Box 270 39095 662-834-2172
Sherrod Miller, prin. Fax 834-2709
McClain MS 300/6-8
PO Box 270 39095 662-834-0875
Aleen Benson, prin. Fax 834-0617
Other Schools – See Durant, Tchula

Central Holmes Christian S 200/PK-12
130 Robert E Lee Dr 39095 662-834-3011
Kristi Hager, hdmstr. Fax 834-1011

Liberty, Amite, Pop. 726
Amite County SD 800/K-12
PO Box 378 39645 601-657-4361
Scotty Whittington, supt. Fax 657-4291
www.amite.k12.ms.us/
Amite County HS 300/9-12
PO Box 328 39645 601-657-8920
Celdric McDowell, prin. Fax 657-4044
Amite County Vocational Educational S Vo/Tech
PO Box 770 39645 601-657-8081
Augustus Russ, prin. Fax 657-8098

Amite School Center 300/K-12
PO Box 354 39645 601-657-8896
Paul Hayles, hdmstr. Fax 657-4642

Long Beach, Harrison, Pop. 14,545
Long Beach SD 2,900/K-12
19148 Commission Rd 39560 228-864-1146
Carrolyn Hamilton, supt. Fax 863-3196
www.lbsdk12.com
Long Beach HS 900/9-12
300 E Old Pass Rd 39560 228-863-6945
Peter Dabbs, prin. Fax 864-8961
Long Beach MS 400/7-8
204 N Cleveland Ave 39560 228-864-3370
Dr. Tim Holland, prin. Fax 867-1789

University of Southern Mississippi Post-Sec.
730 E Beach Blvd 39560 228-865-4500

Lorman, Jefferson

Alcorn State University Post-Sec.
1000 Alcorn Dr 39096 601-877-6100

Louisville, Winston, Pop. 6,587
Louisville Municipal SD 2,400/PK-12
PO Box 909 39339 662-773-3411
Dr. William Wade, supt. Fax 773-4013
louisville.k12.ms.us/
Eiland MS 200/7-8
508 Camille Ave 39339 662-773-9001
James Brooks, prin. Fax 773-4016
Louisville HS 500/9-12
200 Ivy Ave 39339 662-773-3431
Kyle Hammond, prin. Fax 773-4017
Waiya S 500/K-12
13937 Highway 397 39339 662-773-6770
David Luke, prin. Fax 773-6764
Winston-Louisville Career & Tech Center Vo/Tech
204 Ivy Ave 39339 662-773-6152
James Webb, dir. Fax 773-9572
Other Schools – See Noxapater

Grace Christian S 100/PK-12
173 McLeod Rd 39339 662-773-8524
James Gregory, hdmstr. Fax 773-4308
Winston Academy 500/PK-12
PO Box 545 39339 662-773-3569

Lucedale, George, Pop. 2,907
George County SD 4,200/PK-12
5152 Main St 39452 601-947-6993
Debbie Harrell, supt. Fax 947-8805
www.gcsd.us
George County HS 1,200/9-12
9284 Old 63 S 39452 601-947-3116
Kiley Hughes, prin. Fax 947-1076
George County MS 700/7-8
330 Church St 39452 601-947-3106
Stewart Hurley, prin. Fax 947-6004

Lumberton, Lamar, Pop. 2,065
Lumberton SD 700/K-12
PO Box 551 39455 601-796-2441
Dr. Robert Walker, supt. Fax 796-2051
www.lumberton.k12.ms.us/
Lumberton HS 200/9-12
PO Box 551 39455 601-796-2451
Dennis Holder, prin. Fax 796-7907

Bass Memorial Academy 100/9-12
6433 U S Highway 11 39455 601-794-8561
Phil Wilhelm, prin. Fax 517-1815

Maben, Webster, Pop. 864
Oktibbeha County SD
Supt. — See Starkville
West Oktibbeha County HS 200/7-12
PO Box 506 39750 662-263-8106
Leonardo Thompson, prin. Fax 263-5440

Webster County SD
Supt. — See Eupora
East Webster HS 400/7-12
195 Old Cumberland Rd 39750 662-263-5321
Bill Brand, prin. Fax 263-4518

Mc Comb, Pike, Pop. 12,696
McComb SD 3,000/PK-12
PO Box 868 39649 601-684-4661
Cederick Ellis Ph.D., supt. Fax 249-4732
www.mccomb.k12.ms.us
Business & Technology Complex Vo/Tech
1003 Virginia Ave 39648 601-684-5288
Robert Biggs, dir. Fax 249-2454
Denman JHS 400/7-8
1211 Louisiana Ave 39648 601-684-2387
James Brown, prin. Fax 249-3564
McComb HS 800/9-12
310 7th St 39648 601-684-5678
Robert Lamkin, prin. Fax 249-4737
Summit Learning Center Adult
411A Saint Augustine Ave 39648 601-684-4306
Alvin Hogan, dir. Fax 684-4308

Parklane Academy 900/K-12
1115 Parklane Dr 39648 601-684-8113
Jack Henderson, admin. Fax 684-4166
SW Mississippi Regional Medical Center Post-Sec.
PO Box 1307 39649 601-249-1807

Macon, Noxubee, Pop. 2,760
Noxubee County SD 2,000/PK-12
PO Box 540 39341 662-726-4527
Kevin Jones Ed.D., supt. Fax 726-2809
www.noxcnty.k12.ms.us
Liddell MS 500/5-8
PO Box 229 39341 662-726-4880
Wendi Dancy-Clark, prin. Fax 726-5044
Noxubee County HS 600/9-12
PO Box 490 39341 662-726-4428
Dr. Hattie Thomas, prin. Fax 726-5048
Noxubee County Vocational Center Vo/Tech
PO Box 266 39341 662-726-4225
Dr. Annie Snow, dir. Fax 726-2804
Other Schools – See Shuqualak

Central Academy 200/PK-12
PO Box 231 39341 662-726-4817

Madden, Leake

Leake Academy 600/PK-12
PO Box 128 39109 601-267-4461

Madison, Madison, Pop. 23,961
Madison County SD
Supt. — See Flora
Germantown HS 9-12
200 Calhoun Pkwy 39110 601-859-6150
Ted Poore, prin. Fax 859-6075
Germantown MS 600/6-8
202 Calhoun Pkwy 39110 601-859-0376
Richard Burge, prin. Fax 859-1302
Madison Career & Tech Center Vo/Tech
142 Calhoun Pkwy 39110 601-859-6847
Aimee Brown Ph.D., dir. Fax 859-0372
Madison Central HS 1,600/10-12
1417 Highland Colony Pkwy 39110 601-856-7121
Austin Brown, prin. Fax 853-2712
Madison MS 1,200/6-8
1365 Mannsdale Rd 39110 601-605-4171
Dee Walsh, prin. Fax 853-2254
Scott S 600/9-9
200 Crawford St 39110 601-605-0054
Sean Brewer, prin. Fax 898-5017

ITT Technical Institute Post-Sec.
382 Galleria Pkwy Ste 100 39110 601-607-4500
Madison Ridgeland Academy 900/PK-12
7601 Old Canton Rd 39110 601-856-4455
Tommy Thompson, hdmstr. Fax 853-3835
St. Joseph Catholic HS 500/7-12
PO Box 2027 39130 601-898-4800
Keith Barnes, prin. Fax 898-4689

Magee, Simpson, Pop. 4,347
Simpson County SD
Supt. — See Mendenhall
Magee HS 500/9-12
501 Choctaw St E 39111 601-849-2263
George Huffman, prin. Fax 849-6201
Magee MS 600/5-8
413 Choctaw St E Ste 100 39111 601-849-3334
William Trammell, prin. Fax 849-6130
Simpson County Achievement Center Alt
177 Simpson Highway 149 39111 601-849-6135
Greg Paes, prin. Fax 849-6137

Magnolia, Pike, Pop. 2,410
South Pike SD 1,900/K-12
250 W Bay St 39652 601-783-0430
Dr. Estes Taplin, supt. Fax 783-6733
www.southpike.org
South Pike Career & Technical Center Vo/Tech
252 W Bay St 39652 601-783-0438
Rochelle Collins, dir. Fax 783-3491
South Pike HS 500/9-12
205 W Myrtle St 39652 601-783-0420
Lisa Davis, prin. Fax 783-4179
South Pike JHS 300/7-8
275 W Myrtle St 39652 601-783-0425
Iscinova Gray, prin. Fax 783-2272

Mantachie, Itawamba, Pop. 1,139
Itawamba County SD
Supt. — See Fulton
Mantachie HS 7-12
PO Box 38 38855 662-282-4276
Jeff Credille, prin. Fax 282-4270

Marks, Quitman, Pop. 1,725
Quitman County SD 1,300/K-12
PO Box E 38646 662-326-7046
Dr. Brenda Hobson, supt. Fax 326-3694
www.qcschools.org
Palmer HS 400/9-12
PO Box 350 38646 662-326-5191
Carl Palmer, prin. Fax 326-8918
Quitman County MS 400/5-8
PO Box 290 38646 662-326-6871
Cynthia Washington, prin. Fax 326-6300
Quitman County Vocational HS Vo/Tech
PO Box 117 38646 662-326-8427
Robert Skipper, dir. Fax 326-8430

Delta Academy 200/PK-12
PO Box 70 38646 662-326-8164

Meadville, Franklin, Pop. 448
Franklin County SD 1,500/PK-12
PO Box 605 39653 601-384-2340
Ray Carlock, supt. Fax 384-2393
www.franklincountyschoolsms.com
Franklin County Career & Technical Ctr Vo/Tech
PO Box 155 39653 601-384-5889
Jack Hollingsworth, prin. Fax 384-5578
Franklin County HS 400/9-12
PO Box 666 39653 601-384-2965
Marion Bilbo, prin. Fax 384-2498
Franklin County MS 300/6-8
236 Edison St S 39653 601-384-2441
Chris Kent, prin. Fax 384-2085

Mendenhall, Simpson, Pop. 2,477
Simpson County SD 4,200/K-12
111 Education Ln 39114 601-847-8000
Glenn Harris, supt. Fax 847-8001
www.simpson.k12.ms.us
Mendenhall HS 700/9-12
207 Circle Dr 39114 601-847-2411
John James, prin. Fax 847-8002

Mendenhall JHS 500/5-8
733 Dixie Ave 39114 601-847-2296
Janice Skiffer, prin. Fax 847-7175
Simpson County Technical Center Vo/Tech
3415 Simpson Highway 49 39114 601-847-4000
Dr. Kay Berry, prin. Fax 847-8011
Other Schools – See Magee

Simpson County Academy 500/K-12
124 Academy Cir 39114 601-847-1394
David Granville, admin. Fax 847-1338

Meridian, Lauderdale, Pop. 40,816
Lauderdale County SD 6,400/PK-12
PO Box 5498 39302 601-693-1683
Randy Hodges, supt. Fax 485-1748
www.lauderdale.k12.ms.us
Clarkdale HS 300/9-12
7000 Highway 145 39301 601-693-4463
Cheryl Thomas, prin. Fax 693-6329
Clarkdale MS 300/5-8
7000 Highway 145 39301 601-693-4463
Roy McNeill, prin. Fax 693-4463
Northeast Lauderdale HS 600/9-12
702 Briarwood Rd 39305 601-679-8523
Rob Calcote, prin. Fax 679-7515
Northeast MS 700/5-8
7763 Highway 39 39305 601-483-3532
Billy Burnham, prin. Fax 485-0846
Southeast HS 400/9-12
2362 Long Creek Rd 39301 601-483-5501
Dwane Taylor, prin. Fax 483-6347
Southeast MS 400/5-8
2535 Old Highway 19 SE 39301 601-485-5751
Marcus Irby, prin. Fax 485-2302
Other Schools – See Collinsville

Meridian SD 6,100/PK-12
1019 25th Ave 39301 601-484-4977
Dr. Alvin Taylor, supt. Fax 482-6286
www.mpsd.k12.ms.us
Carver MS 400/6-8
900 44th Ave 39307 601-484-4482
Tiffany Plott, prin. Fax 484-3011
Collins Career & Tech Center Vo/Tech
2640 24th Ave 39305 601-483-3331
Terry Moore, dir. Fax 484-5173
Magnolia MS 400/6-8
1350 24th St 39301 601-484-4060
Angela McQuarley, prin. Fax 484-5179
Marion Park Complex Alt
2815 25th St 39301 601-484-4977
Beverly Pennington, dir. Fax 482-6286
Meridian HS 1,700/9-12
2320 32nd St 39305 601-482-3191
Victor Hubbard, prin. Fax 483-5502
Northwest MS 500/6-8
4400 32nd St 39307 601-484-4094
Jackie McFarland, prin. Fax 484-5180

Calvary Christian S 200/PK-12
3917 7th St 39307 601-483-2305
Curt Pouncey, hdmstr. Fax 482-5376
Final Touch Beauty School Post-Sec.
5700 N Hills St 39307 601-485-7733
Lamar S 500/PK-12
544 Lindley Rd 39305 601-482-1345
Meridian Community College Post-Sec.
910 Highway 19 N 39307 601-483-8241
Pentecostal Christian Academy 50/K-12
PO Box 1390 39302 601-693-7375
Fred Summerville, supt. Fax 693-7347
Russell Christian Academy 400/PK-12
1844D Highway 11 And 80 39301 601-484-5888

Mississippi State, Oktibbeha, Pop. 3,939

Mississippi State University Post-Sec.
PO Box J 39762 662-325-2323

Mize, Smith, Pop. 339
Smith County SD
Supt. — See Raleigh
Mize S 700/K-12
PO Box 187 39116 601-733-2242
Chuck Jones, prin. Fax 733-9649

Monticello, Lawrence, Pop. 1,561
Lawrence County SD 2,100/K-12
346 Thomas E Jolly Dr W 39654 601-587-2506
Tammy Fairburn, supt. Fax 587-2221
www.lawrence.k12.ms.us
Lawrence County HS 600/9-12
PO Box 488 39654 601-587-4910
Daryl Scoggin, prin. Fax 587-5001
Lawrence County Technology & Career Ctr Vo/Tech
PO Box 578 39654 601-587-9346
Angela Calcote, dir. Fax 587-2980
Paige MS 300/5-8
1570 W Broad St 39654 601-587-2128
Cassie Bridges, prin. Fax 587-7178

Mooreville, Lee, Pop. 646
Lee County SD
Supt. — See Tupelo
Mooreville HS 400/9-12
PO Box 180 38857 662-842-6859
Lee Bruce, prin. Fax 841-5988
Mooreville MS 300/6-8
PO Box 180 38857 662-680-4894
Roman Doty, prin. Fax 680-4896

Moorhead, Sunflower, Pop. 2,399
Sunflower County SD
Supt. — See Indianola
Moorhead MS 100/6-8
PO Box 749 38761 662-246-5680
Dr. Cassandra Banks, prin. Fax 246-5080

Mississippi Delta Community College Post-Sec.
PO Box 668 38761 662-246-6322

Morton, Scott, Pop. 3,416
Scott County SD
Supt. — See Forest
Jack Upper MS 400/5-8
PO Box 500 39117 601-732-6977
Marsha Purvis, prin. Fax 732-2242
Morton HS 400/9-12
238 E Fourth Ave 39117 601-732-6210
Dr. William Shaw, prin. Fax 732-8086

Moss Point, Jackson, Pop. 13,562
Jackson County SD
Supt. — See Vancleave
East Central HS 800/9-12
21700 Slider Rd 39562 228-588-7000
James Hughey, prin. Fax 588-7045
East Central MS 700/6-8
5404 Hurley Wade Rd 39562 228-588-7009
R. L. Watson, prin. Fax 588-7043

Moss Point SD 2,700/PK-12
4924 Church St 39563 228-475-0691
Maggie Griffin Ph.D., supt. Fax 474-3302
www.mosspointschools.org/
Magnolia JHS 400/7-8
4924 Church St 39563 228-475-1429
Joanne Pettaway, prin. Fax 475-2684
Moss Point Alternative Learning Center Alt
4924 Church St 39563 228-475-3543
Durand Payton, prin. Fax 474-3395
Moss Point HS 900/9-12
4924 Church St 39563 228-475-5721
Jeff Mumford, prin. Fax 474-3305
Moss Point Vocational Center Vo/Tech
4924 Church St 39563 228-475-1233
Paulette Briscoe, dir.

Mound Bayou, Bolivar, Pop. 1,532
Mound Bayou SD 600/K-12
201 Green St 38762 662-741-2555
William Crockett, supt. Fax 741-2726
mbpsd.com/
Kennedy Memorial HS 300/7-12
204 N Edwards Ave 38762 662-741-2510
Dr. Wanda Stringer, prin. Fax 741-2246

Mount Olive, Covington, Pop. 971
Covington County SD
Supt. — See Collins
Mt. Olive S 500/K-12
PO Box 309 39119 601-797-3939
Joe Welch, prin. Fax 797-3980

Myrtle, Union, Pop. 482
Union County SD
Supt. — See New Albany
Myrtle S 700/K-12
1008 Hawk Ave 38650 662-988-2416
Vince Jordan, prin. Fax 988-2001
West Union S 600/K-12
1610 State Road 30 W 38650 662-534-6745
Jamey Wright, prin. Fax 534-6716

Natchez, Adams, Pop. 15,630
Natchez-Adams SD 2,800/PK-12
10 Homochitto St 39120 601-445-2800
Dr. Frederick Hill, supt. Fax 445-2818
www.natchez.k12.ms.us
Central Alternative S Alt
208 Lynda Lee Dr 39120 601-445-2941
Edward Reed, prin. Fax 445-2498
Fallin Career & Technology Center Vo/Tech
315 Sgt Prentiss Dr 39120 601-445-2902
Linda Grafton, prin. Fax 445-2967
Morgantown MS 300/6-8
101 Cottage Home Dr 39120 601-445-2917
Roberta Phipps, prin. Fax 445-2912
Natchez HS 700/10-12
319 Sgt Prentiss Dr 39120 601-445-2864
Cleveland Moore, prin. Fax 445-2870
9th Grade Academy 300/9-9
319 Sgt Prentiss Dr 39120 601-445-2864
Sekufele Lewanika, admin. Fax 445-4353

Adams County Christian S 400/PK-12
300 Chinquapin Ln 39120 601-442-1422
David King, hdmstr. Fax 442-1477
Cathedral Unit S 600/PK-12
701 N Dr ML King Jr St 39120 601-442-2531
Patrick Sanguinetti, prin. Fax 442-0960
Copiah-Lincoln Community College Post-Sec.
11 Co Lin Cir 39120 601-442-9111
Trinity Episcopal Day S 300/PK-12
1 Mallan G Morgan Dr 39120 601-442-5424
Les Hegwood, hdmstr. Fax 442-3216

Nettleton, Itawamba, Pop. 1,982
Nettleton SD 1,300/K-12
PO Box 409 38858 662-963-2151
Russell Taylor, supt. Fax 963-7407
www.nettletonschools.com/
Nettleton HS 400/9-12
PO Box 409 38858 662-963-2306
Melissa Thomas, prin. Fax 963-7407
Nettleton JHS 300/6-8
PO Box 409 38858 662-963-7400
Marshall Johnson, prin. Fax 963-1525

New Albany, Union, Pop. 7,897
New Albany SD 2,200/PK-12
301 State Highway 15 N 38652 662-534-1800
Jackie Ford, supt. Fax 534-3608
www.newalbany.k12.ms.us
New Albany HS 600/9-12
201 State Highway 15 N 38652 662-534-1805
Lance Evans, prin. Fax 534-1817
New Albany MS 500/6-8
400 Apple St 38652 662-534-1820
Damon Ladner, prin. Fax 534-1819
New Albany/S. Tippah/Union Co. Alt S Alt
915 Denmill Rd 38652 662-538-4100
Minerva Graham, dir. Fax 538-4102
New Albany Vocational Complex Vo/Tech
203 State Highway 15 N 38652 662-534-1810
John Ferrell, dir. Fax 534-1811

Union County SD 2,700/K-12
PO Box 939 38652 662-534-1960
Ken Basil, supt. Fax 534-1961
www.union.k12.ms.us
Ingomar S 600/K-12
1384 County Road 101 38652 662-534-2680
Kenny Roberts, prin. Fax 534-3624
Other Schools – See Blue Springs, Myrtle

New Augusta, Perry, Pop. 638
Perry County SD 1,300/K-12
PO Box 137 39462 601-964-3211
Dr. Scott Dearman, supt. Fax 964-8204
www.perry.k12.ms.us/
Perry Central HS 400/9-12
9899 Highway 98 39462 601-964-3235
Titus Hines, prin. Fax 964-8273
Perry County Vocational Tech Center Vo/Tech
PO Box 138 39462 601-964-8282
Rex Buckhaults, admin. Fax 964-8562

New Site, Prentiss
Prentiss County SD
Supt. — See Booneville
New Site HS 300/9-12
1020 Highway 4 E 38859 662-728-5205
Paul Henry, prin. Fax 728-1965

Newton, Newton, Pop. 3,349
Newton Municipal SD 1,000/K-12
205 School St 39345 601-683-2451
Dr. Virginia Young, supt. Fax 683-7131
www.nmsd.k12.ms.us
Newton HS 300/9-12
PO Box 150 39345 601-683-2232
Vicky Hood, prin. Fax 683-6808
Newton Municipal Career Center Vo/Tech
203 W First St 39345 601-683-6338
Tracy Dearing, prin. Fax 683-2283
Pilate MS 300/5-8
521 E Church St 39345 601-683-3926
Tammy Bell, prin. Fax 683-7139

North Carrollton, Carroll, Pop. 470
Carroll County SD
Supt. — See Carrollton
George HS 300/9-12
PO Box 398 38947 662-237-4701
Joey Carpenter, prin. Fax 237-4522
George MS 300/6-8
PO Box 398 38947 662-237-4701
Coretta Green, prin. Fax 237-9742

Noxapater, Winston, Pop. 468
Louisville Municipal SD
Supt. — See Louisville
Noxapater S 400/K-12
220 W Alice St 39346 662-724-4241
Glenn Stevens, prin. Fax 724-4240

Ocean Springs, Jackson, Pop. 17,087
Jackson County SD
Supt. — See Vancleave
St. Martin HS 1,100/9-12
11300 Yellow Jacket Rd 39564 228-875-8418
Dina Holland, prin. Fax 875-8426
St. Martin MS 800/6-8
10800 Yellow Jacket Rd 39564 228-818-4833
Stephanie Gruich, prin. Fax 818-0198

Ocean Springs SD 4,500/K-12
PO Box 7002 39566 228-875-7706
Dr. Bonita Coleman-Potter, supt. Fax 875-7708
www.ossdms.org/
Career & Technical Education Center Vo/Tech
PO Box 7002 39566 228-872-3411
Dr. Jan Griffin, dir. Fax 872-7865
Keys Alternative Education Center Alt
PO Box 7002 39566 228-872-0031
Jon Wilson, prin. Fax 875-7745
Ocean Springs HS 1,600/9-12
PO Box 7002 39566 228-875-0333
David Baggett, prin. Fax 875-7404
Ocean Springs MS 800/7-8
PO Box 7002 39566 228-872-6210
Jerry Twiggs, prin. Fax 872-9850

Day Spa Career College Post-Sec.
3900 Bienville Blvd 39564 228-875-4809

Okolona, Chickasaw, Pop. 2,664
Okolona SSD 700/K-12
105 N Church St 38860 662-447-2353
Mr. James Malone, supt. Fax 447-9955
okolona.k12.ms.us/
Okolona JSHS 300/7-12
404 Winter St 38860 662-447-2362
Tami Doss, prin. Fax 447-3306
Okolona Vocational Complex Vo/Tech
605 N Church St 38860 662-447-3331
Amy Anderson, dir. Fax 447-2721

Olive Branch, DeSoto, Pop. 33,067
DeSoto County SD
Supt. — See Hernando
Center Hill HS 800/9-12
13250 Kirk Rd 38654 662-890-2490
George Loper, prin. Fax 890-2458
Center Hill MS 800/6-8
8756 Forest Hill Irene Ln 38654 662-892-6800
Doug Payne, prin. Fax 892-6810

Desoto County Career Tech East — Vo/Tech
8890 Deerfield Dr 38654 — 662-893-0855
Beth Turner, prin. — Fax 893-0853
Lewisburg HS — 700/9-12
1755 Craft Rd 38654 — 662-890-6708
James Brady, prin. — Fax 890-6202
Lewisburg MS — 600/6-8
1711 Craft Rd 38654 — 662-892-5050
Chris Fleming, prin. — Fax 892-5060
Olive Branch HS — 1,200/9-12
9366 E Sandidge Rd 38654 — 662-893-3344
Kyle Brigance, prin. — Fax 893-3353
Olive Branch MS — 900/6-8
6530 Blocker St 38654 — 662-895-4610
Jerry Floate, prin. — Fax 895-7358

Oxford, Lafayette, Pop. 18,701
Lafayette County SD — 2,500/PK-12
100 Commodore Dr 38655 — 662-234-3271
Dr. Adam Pugh, supt. — Fax 236-3019
www.gocommodores.org
Lafayette HS — 700/9-12
160 Commodore Dr 38655 — 662-234-3614
Patrick Robinson, prin. — Fax 234-3856
Lafayette MS — 600/6-8
102 Commodore Dr 38655 — 662-234-1664
Chris Chism, prin. — Fax 232-8736
Oxford/Lafayette School of Applied Tech — Vo/Tech
134 Highway 7 S 38655 — 662-234-9469
Marybeth Lowrey, prin. — Fax 236-2496

Oxford SD — 3,600/PK-12
224 Bramlett Blvd 38655 — 662-234-3541
Brian Harvey, supt. — Fax 232-2862
www.oxford.k12.ms.us
Oxford HS — 900/9-12
222 Bramlett Blvd 38655 — 662-234-1562
Mike Martin, prin. — Fax 232-1862
Oxford Learning Center — Alt
399 N 5th St 38655 — 662-234-3588
Dr. Charles Dodson, dir. — Fax 236-1052
Oxford MS — 800/6-8
501 Mrtin Luther King Jr Dr 38655 — 662-234-2288
Jeff Clay, prin. — Fax 234-0235

Regents S of Oxford — 200/PK-12
14 County Road 130 38655 — 662-232-1945
Dr. Michael Johnson, hdmstr. — Fax 232-8818

Pascagoula, Jackson, Pop. 22,125
Pascagoula SD — 6,500/K-12
PO Box 250 39568 — 228-938-6491
Wayne Rodolfich, supt. — Fax 938-6528
www.psd.ms
Applied Technology Center — Vo/Tech
2602 Market St 39567 — 228-938-6579
Pat Taylor, dir. — Fax 938-6597
Colmer MS — 600/7-8
3112 Eden St 39581 — 228-938-6473
Dr. Myrick Nicks, prin. — Fax 938-6593
Opportunity Center — Alt
1520 Tucker Ave 39567 — 228-938-6222
Dr. Shannon Vincent, prin — Fax 938-6210
Pascagoula HS — 1,100/9-12
1716 Tucker Ave 39567 — 228-938-6443
Ronald Roberts, prin. — Fax 938-6445
Other Schools – See Gautier

Resurrection Catholic MSHS — 200/7-12
520 Watts Ave 39567 — 228-762-3353
Marcia McKenna, prin. — Fax 769-1226

Pass Christian, Harrison, Pop. 4,509
Pass Christian SD — 1,600/K-12
6457 Kiln Delisle Rd 39571 — 228-255-6200
Beth John, supt. — Fax 255-6204
www.pc.k12.ms.us/
Pass Christian HS — 500/9-12
720 W North St 39571 — 228-452-2008
Meridith Bang, prin. — Fax 452-6128
Pass Christian MS — 400/6-8
280 W Second St 39571 — 228-452-5220
Joe Nelson, prin. — Fax 452-5221

Pearl, Rankin, Pop. 24,692
Pearl SD — 3,900/K-12
3375 Highway 80 E 39208 — 601-932-7921
Raymond Morgigno Ph.D., supt. — Fax 932-7929
www.pearl.k12.ms.us/
Pearl HS — 1,100/9-12
500 Pirates Cv 39208 — 601-932-7931
Dr. Lundy Brantley, prin. — Fax 932-7992
Pearl JHS — 900/6-8
200 Mary Ann Dr 39208 — 601-932-7952
Dr. Jessica Broome, prin. — Fax 932-7998

Academy of Hair Design #4 — Post-Sec.
3167 Highway 80 E 39208 — 601-939-4441
Park Place Christian Academy — 400/PK-12
201 Park Place Dr 39208 — 601-939-6229
Jeremy Nicholas, head sch — Fax 939-3276

Pelahatchie, Rankin, Pop. 1,321
Rankin County SD
Supt. — See Brandon
Pelahatchie JSHS — 300/7-12
PO Box 569 39145 — 601-854-8135
Shane Sanders, prin. — Fax 854-8638

East Rankin Academy — 800/PK-12
PO Box 509 39145 — 601-854-5691
Robert Gates M.Ed., admin. — Fax 854-5893

Perkinston, Stone

Mississippi Gulf Coast Community College — Post-Sec.
PO Box 548 39573 — 601-928-5211

Petal, Forrest, Pop. 10,310
Petal SD — 3,900/K-12
115 E Central Ave 39465 — 601-545-3002
Dr. John Buchanan, supt. — Fax 584-4700
www.petalschools.com
Petal HS — 1,100/9-12
1145 Highway 42 39465 — 601-583-3538
Steve Simmons, prin. — Fax 545-1229
Petal MS — 600/7-8
203 Highway 42 39465 — 601-584-6301
Michael Hogan, prin. — Fax 584-4716

Pheba, Clay

Hebron Christian S — 200/K-12
6230 Henryville Rd 39755 — 662-494-7513
William Cotton, prin. — Fax 494-1002

Philadelphia, Neshoba, Pop. 7,347
Neshoba County SD — 3,200/K-12
PO Box 338 39350 — 601-656-3752
Tommy Dearing, supt. — Fax 656-3789
www.neshoba.k12.ms.us/
Neshoba Central HS — 900/9-12
1125 Golf Course Rd 39350 — 601-656-3654
John Bowen, prin. — Fax 656-1588
Neshoba Central MS — 800/6-8
1000 Saint Francis Dr 39350 — 601-656-4636
Tommy Holland, prin. — Fax 389-2989

Philadelphia SD — 1,200/K-12
248 Byrd Ave N 39350 — 601-656-2955
Terry Larabee Ph.D., supt. — Fax 656-3141
www.phillytornadoes.com
Philadelphia HS — 300/9-12
248 Byrd Ave N 39350 — 601-656-2672
Jason Gentry, prin. — Fax 656-2273
Philadelphia MS — 200/7-8
248 Byrd Ave N 39350 — 601-656-6439
Chris Kennedy, prin. — Fax 656-5328

Picayune, Pearl River, Pop. 10,684
Picayune SD — 3,400/K-12
706 Goodyear Blvd 39466 — 601-798-3230
Dean Shaw, supt. — Fax 798-1742
www.pcu.k12.ms.us/
Center for Alternative Education — Alt
900 Third St 39466 — 601-799-0684
Daphnie Beebe, prin. — Fax 799-0325
Picayune JHS — 500/7-8
702 Goodyear Blvd 39466 — 601-798-5449
James Williams, prin. — Fax 799-4715
Picayune Memorial HS — 1,000/9-12
800 Fifth Ave 39466 — 601-798-1380
Kent Kirkland, prin. — Fax 798-4705
PMHS Career & Technology Center — Vo/Tech
600 Goodyear Blvd 39466 — 601-798-7601
Christie Pinero, prin. — Fax 799-4711

Piney Woods, Rankin

Piney Woods S — 200/9-12
PO Box 57 39148 — 601-845-2214
Dr. Reginald T.W. Nichols, pres. — Fax 845-6977

Pittsboro, Calhoun, Pop. 200
Calhoun County SD — 2,500/PK-12
119 W Main St 38951 — 662-412-3152
Mike Moore, supt. — Fax 412-3157
www.calhoun.k12.ms.us/
Other Schools – See Bruce, Calhoun City, Vardaman

Plantersville, Lee, Pop. 1,140
Lee County SD
Supt. — See Tupelo
Plantersville MS — 200/5-8
PO Box 129 38862 — 662-842-4690
Bill Horton, prin. — Fax 791-0491

Pontotoc, Pontotoc, Pop. 5,537
Pontotoc CSD — 2,200/K-12
140 Education Dr 38863 — 662-489-3336
Karen Tutor, supt. — Fax 489-7932
www.pontotoc.k12.ms.us
Pontotoc HS — 700/9-12
123 N Main St 38863 — 662-489-1275
Eddie Moore, prin. — Fax 489-5255
Pontotoc JHS — 300/7-8
132 N Main St 38863 — 662-489-8360
Cedric Graham, prin. — Fax 489-8947

Pontotoc County SD — 3,100/PK-12
285 Highway 15 S 38863 — 662-489-3932
Kenneth Roye, supt. — Fax 489-3922
www.pcsd.k12.ms.us/
Pontotoc Ridge Career & Technolog Center — Vo/Tech
354 Ridge Dr 38863 — 662-489-1826
Phil Ryan, dir. — Fax 489-0704
South Pontotoc HS — 500/9-12
1523 S Pontotoc Rd 38863 — 662-489-5925
Tim West, prin. — Fax 489-8598
South Pontotoc MS — 300/6-8
1523 S Pontotoc Rd 38863 — 662-489-5925
Jimmy Flake, prin. — Fax 489-6252
Other Schools – See Ecru

Poplarville, Pearl River, Pop. 2,824
Poplarville SSD — 2,100/PK-12
302 Julia St 39470 — 601-795-8477
Carl Merritt, supt. — Fax 795-0712
www.poplarvilleschools.org/
Poplarville Career Development Center — Vo/Tech
9 Career Center Cir 39470 — 601-795-8343
Marlene Cole, prin. — Fax 795-1353
Poplarville HS — 600/9-12
1 Hornet Dr 39470 — 601-795-8424
Gary Malley, prin. — Fax 795-1345
Poplarville MS — 500/6-8
6 Spirit Dr 39470 — 601-795-1350
Leah Stevens, prin. — Fax 795-1351

Pearl River Community College — Post-Sec.
101 Highway 11 N 39470 — 601-403-1000

Port Gibson, Claiborne, Pop. 1,561
Claiborne County SD — 1,700/PK-12
404 Market St 39150 — 601-437-4232
Rev. Elijah Brown D.D., supt. — Fax 437-4409
www.claiborne.k12.ms.us/
Clairborne Co. Voc Educational Complex — Vo/Tech
PO Box 47 39150 — 601-437-4251
Nathaniel Martin, dir. — Fax 437-3099
Port Gibson HS — 500/9-12
159 Old Highway 18 39150 — 601-437-4190
Curtis Ross, prin. — Fax 437-3803
Port Gibson MS — 400/6-8
PO Box 567 39150 — 601-437-4251
Dr. Onedia Butler, prin. — Fax 437-3099

Oakland Collegiate S — 100/7-12
124 McComb Ave 39150 — 601-437-8855
John Gardner West, pres. — Fax 437-3212

Potts Camp, Marshall, Pop. 520
Marshall County SD
Supt. — See Holly Springs
Potts Camp S — 400/4-12
7050 Church St 38659 — 662-333-6354
Leigh Anne Sanderson, prin. — Fax 333-7023

Prentiss, Jefferson Davis, Pop. 1,069
Jefferson Davis County SD — 1,600/K-12
PO Box 1197 39474 — 601-792-4267
Ike Haynes, supt. — Fax 792-2251
www.jeffersondavis.k12.ms.us
Prentiss JSHS — 500/7-12
PO Box 1168 39474 — 601-792-4646
Cathy Anderson, prin. — Fax 792-8149
Other Schools – See Bassfield, Carson

Prentiss Christian S — 300/K-12
PO Box 1287 39474 — 601-792-8549
Fax 792-2560

Puckett, Rankin, Pop. 315
Rankin County SD
Supt. — See Brandon
Puckett Attendance Center — 300/7-12
PO Box 40 39151 — 601-825-5742
Robert Crain, prin. — Fax 825-9838

Purvis, Lamar, Pop. 2,145
Lamar County SD — 8,900/K-12
PO Box 609 39475 — 601-794-1030
Ben Burnett, supt. — Fax 794-1012
www.lamarcountyschools.org
Jefferson-Todd Alternative Education Ctr — Alt
424 Martin Luther King Dr 39475 — 601-794-8121
Brian Stewart, prin. — Fax 794-2005
Lamar County Vo Tech Center — Vo/Tech
41 College Dr 39475 — 601-794-8298
Tina Byrd, prin. — Fax 794-1026
Purvis HS — 500/9-12
PO Box 1089 39475 — 601-794-2708
Billy Ellzey, prin. — Fax 794-2150
Purvis MS — 400/6-8
PO Box 549 39475 — 601-794-1068
Jackie Cuevas, prin. — Fax 794-1069
Other Schools – See Hattiesburg, Sumrall

Lamar Christian S — 300/PK-12
62 Purvis Oloh Rd 39475 — 601-794-0016
Glenn Swan, admin. — Fax 794-3726

Quitman, Clarke, Pop. 2,307
Quitman SD — 2,000/PK-12
104 E Franklin St 39355 — 601-776-2186
Dr. Suzanne Hawley, supt. — Fax 776-1051
www.quitmanschools.org
Clarke County Vocational Center — Vo/Tech
910 N Archusa Ave 39355 — 601-776-5219
Mark Hudson, dir. — Fax 776-5219
Quitman HS — 600/9-12
210 S Jackson Ave 39355 — 601-776-3341
Michael McDonald, prin. — Fax 776-6136
Quitman JHS — 500/6-8
501 W Lynda St 39355 — 601-776-6243
Roger Satcher, prin. — Fax 776-1288

Raleigh, Smith, Pop. 1,457
Smith County SD — 2,900/K-12
PO Box 308 39153 — 601-782-4296
Fax 782-9895
smithcountyschools.net
Raleigh HS — 600/7-12
491 Magnolia Dr 39153 — 601-782-4261
Miles Butler, prin. — Fax 782-4359
Smith County Career Center — Vo/Tech
469 Magnolia Dr 39153 — 601-782-4211
Hollis Blackwell, dir. — Fax 782-9842
Other Schools – See Mize, Taylorsville

Raymond, Hinds, Pop. 1,915
Hinds County SD — 6,400/PK-12
13192 Highway 18 39154 — 601-857-5222
Dr. Stephen Handley, supt. — Fax 857-8548
www.hinds.k12.ms.us/
Carver MS — 200/6-8
417 Palestine St 39154 — 601-857-5006
Dr. Bill Hardin, prin. — Fax 857-4935
Hinds County Career Center — Vo/Tech
PO Box 789 39154 — 601-857-5536
Patricia Ashmore, prin. — Fax 857-2212
Raymond HS — 600/9-12
14050 Highway 18 39154 — 601-857-8016
Shakinna Patterson, prin. — Fax 857-2007
Other Schools – See Bolton, Terry

Central Hinds Academy 400/K-12
2894 Raymond Bolton Rd 39154 601-857-5568
Bobby Allen, hdmstr. Fax 857-5082
Hinds Community College Post-Sec.
PO Box 1100 39154 601-857-5261

Richland, Rankin, Pop. 6,844
Rankin County SD
Supt. — See Brandon
Richland HS 800/7-12
1202 Highway 49 S 39218 601-939-5144
Richard Sutton, prin. Fax 939-7631

Richton, Perry, Pop. 1,058
Richton SD 700/K-12
PO Box 568 39476 601-788-6581
Dr. Noal Cochran, supt. Fax 788-9391
www.richtonschools.com
Richton JSHS 300/7-12
PO Box 568 39476 601-788-9608
David Shepard, prin. Fax 788-6390

Ridgeland, Madison, Pop. 23,769
Madison County SD
Supt. — See Flora
Olde Towne MS 600/6-8
210 Sunnybrook Rd 39157 601-898-8730
Allen Lawrence, prin. Fax 853-8108
Ridgeland HS 800/9-12
586 Sunnybrook Rd 39157 601-898-5023
Sharon Summers, prin. Fax 853-7822

Delta Technical College Post-Sec.
113 Marketridge Dr 39157 601-206-5200
St. Andrew's Episcopal S 700/5-12
370 Old Agency Rd 39157 601-853-6000
Dr. George Penick, hdmstr. Fax 853-6001
Veritas S K-12
1202 Highland Colony Pkwy 39157 601-713-1555
Dr. David Ritter, hdmstr. Fax 605-1306

Ripley, Tippah, Pop. 5,308
South Tippah SD 2,600/K-12
402 Greenlee Dr 38663 662-837-7156
Frank Campbell, supt. Fax 837-1362
www.stippah.k12.ms.us/
Pine Grove S 600/K-12
3510A County Road 600 38663 662-837-7789
Clint Stroupe, prin. Fax 837-8179
Ripley HS 500/9-12
720 S Clayton St 38663 662-837-7583
Jeff Palmer, prin. Fax 837-0118
Ripley MS 600/5-8
718 S Clayton St 38663 662-837-7959
James Storey, prin. Fax 837-0251
Tippah Career & Technology Center Vo/Tech
PO Box 533 38663 662-837-9798
Tony Elliott, dir. Fax 837-8833
Other Schools – See Blue Mountain

Foster's Cosmetology College Post-Sec.
PO Box 66 38663 662-837-9334

Rolling Fork, Sharkey, Pop. 2,129
South Delta SD 1,000/PK-12
PO Box 219 39159 662-873-4302
Sammie Ivy, supt. Fax 873-6114
www.southdelta.k12.ms.us/
South Delta HS 300/9-12
303 Parkway Ave 39159 662-873-4308
Katie Jones, prin. Fax 873-6106
South Delta Vocational S Vo/Tech
285 Maple St 39159 662-873-2029
Beverly Wilson, prin. Fax 873-4194
Other Schools – See Anguilla

Sharkey Issaquena Academy 300/K-12
272 Academy Dr 39159 662-873-4241
Mike Brown, admin. Fax 873-4637

Rosedale, Bolivar, Pop. 1,864
West Bolivar SD 900/K-12
PO Box 189 38769 662-759-3525
Henry Phillips, supt. Fax 759-6795
www.wbsd.k12.ms.us
Barnes Vocational Center Vo/Tech
PO Box 160 38769 662-759-3791
Eddie Culley, prin. Fax 759-6795
West Bolivar HS 300/9-12
PO Box 398 38769 662-759-3346
Joseph Griffin, prin. Fax 759-6795
West Bolivar MS 300/5-8
PO Box 159 38769 662-759-3743
Dr. Nehru Brown, prin. Fax 759-6795

Ruleville, Sunflower, Pop. 2,980
Sunflower County SD
Supt. — See Indianola
Ruleville MS 200/7-8
250 Oscar St 38771 662-756-4698
Miskia Davis, prin. Fax 756-4902

Sallis, Attala, Pop. 134
Attala County SD
Supt. — See Kosciusko
Mc Adams JSHS 200/7-12
6315 Attala Road 4167 39160 662-289-3838
Jackie Sandifer, prin. Fax 289-7181

Saltillo, Lee, Pop. 4,701
Lee County SD
Supt. — See Tupelo
Saltillo HS 800/9-12
PO Box 460 38866 662-869-5466
Tim DeVaughn, prin. Fax 869-7229

Sandhill, Rankin
Rankin County SD
Supt. — See Brandon

Pisgah HS 400/7-12
PO Box 70 39161 601-829-1138
Dr. Norman Session, prin. Fax 829-1753

Sarah, Tate
Tate County SD
Supt. — See Senatobia
Strayhorn HS 400/7-12
86 Mustang Dr 38665 662-562-9246
John Shows, prin. Fax 562-9249

Sardis, Panola, Pop. 1,686
North Panola SD 1,600/K-12
470 Highway 51 S 38666 662-487-2305
Robert King, supt. Fax 487-2050
www.northpanolaschools.org
North Panola HS 500/9-12
500 Highway 51 N 38666 662-487-1070
Jamone Edwards, prin. Fax 487-2052
Other Schools – See Como

Scooba, Kemper, Pop. 727

East Mississippi Community College Post-Sec.
PO Box 158 39358 662-476-8442

Sebastopol, Scott, Pop. 272
Scott County SD
Supt. — See Forest
Sebastopol Attendance Center 600/K-12
PO Box 86 39359 601-625-8654
Randi Stewart, prin. Fax 625-9426

Seminary, Covington, Pop. 314
Covington County SD
Supt. — See Collins
Seminary HS 400/9-12
PO Box 34 39479 601-722-3220
Brad Skeen, prin. Fax 722-9543
Seminary MS 400/5-8
PO Box 34 39479 601-722-4510
Dwight Yates, prin. Fax 722-4463

Senatobia, Tate, Pop. 8,076
Senatobia Municipal SD 1,900/K-12
104 McKie St 38668 662-562-4897
Jay Foster, supt. Fax 562-4996
www.senatobiaschools.com
Senatobia JSHS 800/7-12
221 Warrior Dr 38668 662-562-4230
Bradley Roberson, prin. Fax 562-6659
Tate County Optional Learning Center Alt
403 W Gilmore St 38668 662-562-5193
Robert Downing, prin. Fax 562-4996

Tate County SD 2,900/K-12
107 Court St 38668 662-562-5861
Jamer Malone, supt. Fax 562-8516
www.tcsd.k12.ms.us/
Other Schools – See Coldwater, Sarah

Infinity Career College Post-Sec.
562 W Main St Ste B 38668 662-562-8010
Magnolia Heights S 700/K-12
1 Chiefs Dr 38668 662-562-4491
Northwest Mississippi Community College Post-Sec.
4975 Highway 51 N 38668 662-562-3200

Shannon, Lee, Pop. 1,726
Lee County SD
Supt. — See Tupelo
Shannon HS 700/9-12
PO Box 8 38868 662-767-9566
Bill Rosenthal, prin. Fax 767-2847
Shannon MS 300/6-8
PO Box 8 38868 662-767-3986
Keith Steele, prin. Fax 767-9981

Shaw, Bolivar, Pop. 1,947
Shaw SD 500/K-12
PO Box 510 38773 662-754-2611
Dr. Cederick Ellis, supt. Fax 754-2612
www.shawschools.k12.ms.us
Shaw HS 200/9-12
PO Box 510 38773 662-754-2611
L'Kenna Whitehead, prin. Fax 754-4418

Shelby, Bolivar, Pop. 2,225
North Bolivar SD 700/K-12
PO Box 28 38774 662-398-4000
Jesse King, supt. Fax 398-7884
www.nbsd.k12.ms.us/
Broad Street HS 200/9-12
PO Box 149 38774 662-398-4040
Lisa Davis, prin. Fax 398-5900
Shelby MS 200/5-8
PO Box 28 38774 662-398-4020
Fredrick Ford, prin. Fax 398-4039

Shuqualak, Noxubee, Pop. 499
Noxubee County SD
Supt. — See Macon
Reed Resource Center 100/Alt
PO Box 29 39361 662-793-4544
Holli Jenkins, prin. Fax 793-4793

Smithville, Monroe, Pop. 930
Monroe County SD
Supt. — See Amory
Smithville S 600/K-12
60017 Highway 23 38870 662-651-4276
Chad O'Brian, prin. Fax 651-4163

Southaven, DeSoto, Pop. 48,244
DeSoto County SD
Supt. — See Hernando
Desoto Central HS 1,500/9-12
2911 Central Pkwy 38672 662-536-3612
Cory Uselton, prin. Fax 536-3623
Desoto Central MS 1,200/6-8
2611 Central Pkwy 38672 662-349-6660
Duane Case, prin. Fax 349-1045

DeSoto County Career Tech West Vo/Tech
847 Rasco Rd W 38671 662-393-6211
Paul Chrestman, dir. Fax 393-5708
Southaven HS 1,700/9-12
735 Rasco Rd W 38671 662-393-9300
Shane Jones, prin. Fax 996-1574
Southaven MS 1,500/6-8
899 Rasco Rd W 38671 662-280-0422
Levi Williams, prin. Fax 280-3613

Northwest Mississippi Community College Post-Sec.
5197 WE Ross Pkwy 38671 662-342-1570
Southern Baptist Educational Center 1,100/PK-12
7400 Getwell Rd 38672 662-349-3096
David Manley, pres. Fax 349-4962

Starkville, Oktibbeha, Pop. 23,580
Oktibbeha County SD 900/PK-12
106 W Main St 39759 662-323-1472
James Covington, supt. Fax 323-9614
www.oktibbeha.k12.ms.us
Other Schools – See Crawford, Maben

Starkville SD 3,300/K-12
401 Greensboro St 39759 662-324-4050
Dr. Lewis Holloway, supt. Fax 324-4068
www.starkville.k12.ms.us
Armstrong MS 900/6-8
303 McKee St 39759 662-324-4070
Elizabeth Mosley, prin. Fax 324-4075
Millsaps Career & Tech Center Vo/Tech
803 Louisville St 39759 662-324-4170
Ray New, prin. Fax 324-4103
Overstreet S Alt
307 S Jackson St 39759 662-324-4090
Julie Kennedy, prin. Fax 324-4162
Starkville HS 1,000/9-12
603 Yellow Jacket Dr 39759 662-324-4130
Keith Fennell, prin. Fax 324-4128

Starkville Academy 700/PK-12
505 Academy Rd 39759 662-323-7814
John Stephens, head sch Fax 323-5480
Starkville Christian S 200/PK-12
303 Lynn Ln 39759 662-323-7453
Rev. Randall Witbeck, prin. Fax 323-7571

Steens, Lowndes

Immanuel Christian S 300/PK-12
6405 Military Rd 39766 662-328-7888
Bob Williford, admin. Fax 328-7750

Stringer, Jasper
West Jasper Consolidated SD
Supt. — See Bay Springs
Stringer S 600/K-12
PO Box 68 39481 601-428-5508
Jon Will, prin. Fax 426-6760

Summit, Pike, Pop. 1,702
North Pike SD 2,400/K-12
1036 Jaguar Trl 39666 601-276-2216
Dr. Ben Cox, supt. Fax 276-3666
npsd.k12.ms.us/
North Pike HS 700/9-12
1022 Jaguar Trl 39666 601-276-2175
Scott Hallmark, prin. Fax 276-2720
North Pike MS 800/5-8
2034 Highway 44 NE 39666 601-684-3283
Janice Samuels, prin. Fax 684-3269

Southwest Mississippi Community College Post-Sec.
1156 College Dr 39666 601-276-2000

Sumner, Tallahatchie, Pop. 316
West Tallahatchie SD
Supt. — See Webb
North Delta Alternative S Alt
300 Jennings St 38957 662-375-8392
Tony Young, prin. Fax 375-0069

Sumrall, Lamar, Pop. 1,412
Lamar County SD
Supt. — See Purvis
Sumrall HS 500/9-12
PO Box 187 39482 601-758-4730
Tess Smith, prin. Fax 758-0512
Sumrall MS 400/6-8
1217 Highway 42 39482 601-758-4416
Jamie Jones, prin. Fax 758-4148

Taylorsville, Smith, Pop. 1,344
Smith County SD
Supt. — See Raleigh
Taylorsville HS 500/6-12
PO Box 8 39168 601-785-6942
Jeff Duvall, prin. Fax 785-9711

Tchula, Holmes, Pop. 2,088
Holmes County SD
Supt. — See Lexington
Holmes County Learning Center Alt
PO Box 387 39169 662-235-5637
Dr. Charles Robinson, prin. Fax 235-5639
Mileston MS 200/6-8
147 Head Start Rd 39169 662-235-5026
Linda Sanders, prin. Fax 235-5136

Terry, Hinds, Pop. 1,052
Hinds County SD
Supt. — See Raymond
Byram MS 1,000/6-8
2009 Byram Bulldog Blvd 39170 601-372-4597
David Campbell, prin. Fax 346-2383
Terry HS 1,300/9-12
235 W Beasley St 39170 601-878-5905
Dr. Bill Sellers, prin. Fax 878-2782

Tiplersville, Tippah
North Tippah SD 1,300/K-12
24111 Highway 15 38674 662-223-4384
Junior Wooten, supt. Fax 223-5379
www.ntippah.k12.ms.us
Other Schools – See Falkner, Walnut

Tishomingo, Tishomingo, Pop. 335
Tishomingo County Special Municipal SD
Supt. — See Iuka
Tishomingo County Alternative S Alt
1421 Highway 25 N 38873 662-438-6864
Nancy Parker, prin. Fax 424-9820
Tishomingo County Vocational Center Vo/Tech
1421 Highway 25 38873 662-438-6689
John Taylor, dir. Fax 438-6777

Tougaloo, Hinds

Tougaloo College Post-Sec.
500 W County Line Rd 39174 601-977-7700

Tremont, Itawamba, Pop. 462
Itawamba County SD
Supt. — See Fulton
Tremont Attendance Center 300/K-12
PO Box 9 38876 662-652-3391
Michael Cates, prin. Fax 652-3994

Tunica, Tunica, Pop. 1,021
Tunica County SD 2,200/PK-12
PO Box 758 38676 662-363-2811
Bernard Chandler, supt. Fax 363-3061
www.tunicak12.org
Rosa Fort HS 500/9-12
PO Box 997 38676 662-363-1343
Derrick Dace, prin. Fax 363-4222
Tunica MS 500/6-8
PO Box 967 38676 662-363-4224
Dr. Bacardi Harris, prin. Fax 357-1058
Williams Career and Technical Ctr Vo/Tech
PO Box 2618 38676 662-363-2051
Dianne Daley, dir. Fax 363-2052
Other Schools – See Dundee

Tunica Institute of Learning S 200/K-12
PO Box 966 38676 662-363-1051
Fax 363-2037

Tupelo, Lee, Pop. 34,140
Lee County SD 6,800/K-12
1280 College View St 38804 662-841-9144
Jimmy Weeks, supt. Fax 680-6012
www.leecountyschools.us/
Other Schools – See Guntown, Mooreville, Plantersville, Saltillo, Shannon

Tupelo SD 7,200/PK-12
PO Box 557 38802 662-841-8850
Dr. Gearl Loden, supt. Fax 841-8887
www.tupeloschools.com/
Tupelo HS 2,100/9-12
4125 Cliff Gookin Blvd 38801 662-841-8970
Jason Harris, prin. Fax 841-8987
Tupelo MS 1,100/7-8
1009 Varsity Dr 38801 662-840-8780
Dr. Kristy Luse, prin. Fax 840-1831

Creations College of Cosmetology Post-Sec.
PO Box 2635 38803 662-844-9264
North Mississippi Medical Center Post-Sec.
830 S Gloster St 38801 662-841-3136

Tylertown, Walthall, Pop. 1,598
Walthall County SD 2,400/K-12
814A Morse Ave 39667 601-876-3401
Danny McCallum, supt. Fax 876-6982
www.wcsd.k12.ms.us/
Dexter S 200/K-12
927 Highway 48 E 39667 601-876-3985
Allen Dyess, prin. Fax 876-5410
Salem S 500/K-12
881 Highway 27 N 39667 601-876-2580
Charles Boyd, prin. Fax 876-4155
Tylertown JSHS 700/7-12
204 High School Rd 39667 601-876-3370
Rebecca Bull, prin. Fax 876-3122
Walthall County Career & Tech Center Vo/Tech
803 Ball Ave 39667 601-222-1500
Wade Carney, dir. Fax 222-1506

Union, Newton, Pop. 1,954
Union SD 900/PK-12
PO Box 445 39365 601-774-9579
Dr. Michael McInnis, supt. Fax 774-0600
www.unioncity.k12.ms.us/
Union HS 200/9-12
101 Forest St 39365 601-774-8257
Brett Rigby, prin. Fax 774-9600
Union MS 300/5-8
115 James St 39365 601-774-5303
Loretta White, prin. Fax 774-9607

University, Lafayette, Pop. 4,155

University of Mississippi Post-Sec.
PO Box 1848 38677 662-915-7211

Utica, Hinds, Pop. 817
Hinds County Agricultural HSD
PO Box 1089 39175 601-885-7047
Dr. Clyde Muse, supt. Fax 885-2676
www.hindsahs.k12.ms.us/
Hinds County Agricultural HS Vo/Tech
PO Box 1089 39175 601-885-7083
Robert Strong, prin. Fax 885-2676

Vancleave, Jackson, Pop. 5,787
Jackson County SD 9,200/K-12
PO Box 5069 39565 228-826-1757
Dr. Barry Amacker, supt. Fax 826-2165
www.jcsd.k12.ms.us/
Jackson County Technology Center Vo/Tech
12425 Highway 57 39565 228-826-5944
Diane Novak, prin. Fax 826-4209
Vancleave HS 700/9-12
12424 Highway 57 39565 228-826-4701
Todd Knight, prin. Fax 826-5066
Vancleave MS 600/6-8
4725 Bull Dog Ln 39565 228-826-5902
Jill Davis, prin. Fax 826-1421
Other Schools – See Moss Point, Ocean Springs

Vardaman, Calhoun, Pop. 1,309
Calhoun County SD
Supt. — See Pittsboro
Vardaman HS 200/7-12
PO Box 193 38878 662-682-7574
Porter Casey, prin. Fax 682-7743

Vicksburg, Warren, Pop. 23,676
Vicksburg Warren SD 8,700/PK-12
1500 Mission 66 39180 601-638-5122
Dr. Liz Swinford, supt. Fax 631-2819
www.vwsd.k12.ms.us/
Center for Alternative Programs Alt
1315 Grove St 39183 601-636-2539
Lee Dixon, prin. Fax 631-2856
Vicksburg HS 1,100/9-12
3701 Drummond St 39180 601-636-2914
Derrick Reed, prin. Fax 631-2885
Vicksburg JHS 600/7-8
1533 Baldwin Ferry Rd 39180 601-636-1966
Antonio Cooper, prin. Fax 631-2830
Warren Central HS 1,200/9-12
1000 Highway 27 39180 601-638-2539
James Creel, prin. Fax 631-2937
Warren Central JHS 800/7-8
1630 Baldwin Ferry Rd 39180 601-638-3981
Cedric Magee, prin. Fax 631-2839

Hinds Community College Post-Sec.
755 Highway 27 39180 601-629-6801
Porters Chapel Academy 200/K-12
3460 Porters Chapel Rd 39180 601-638-3733
Pam Wilbanks, hdmstr. Fax 638-6311
St. Aloysius MSHS 200/7-12
1900 Grove St 39183 601-636-2256
Michele Connelly, prin. Fax 631-0430

Walnut, Tippah, Pop. 762
North Tippah SD
Supt. — See Tiplersville
Walnut S 500/K-12
280 Commerce Ave 38683 662-223-6471
Fax 223-5275

Walnut Grove, Leake, Pop. 1,907
Leake County SD
Supt. — See Carthago
Leake County HS 300/7-12
PO Box 159 39189 601-253-2393
Timothy Chambers, prin. Fax 253-0100

Water Valley, Yalobusha, Pop. 3,370
Water Valley SD 1,200/K-12
PO Box 788 38965 662-473-1203
Kim Chrestman, supt. Fax 473-1225
www.wvsd.k12.ms.us
Water Valley JSHS 500/7-12
PO Box 647 38965 662-473-2468
Dr. Glenn Kitchens, prin. Fax 473-1444

Waynesboro, Wayne, Pop. 4,998
Wayne County SD 3,500/K-12
810 Chickasawhay St 39367 601-735-4871
Ben Graves, supt. Fax 735-4872
www.wayne.k12.ms.us
Wayne County HS 1,000/9-12
1325 Azalea Dr 39367 601-735-2851
Dr. Cathy Davis, prin. Fax 735-1389
Wayne County Vocational Center Vo/Tech
800 Collins St 39367 601-735-5036
Bobby Jones, prin. Fax 735-6326
Waynesboro MS 500/5-8
155 Wayne St 39367 601-735-3159
Tyrone Marshall, prin. Fax 735-6316

Wayne Academy 200/K-12
PO Box 308 39367 601-735-2921
Wendell Barr, admin. Fax 735-2117

Webb, Tallahatchie, Pop. 557
West Tallahatchie SD 800/K-12
PO Box 129 38966 662-375-9291
Dr. P.B. Cole, supt. Fax 375-9294
www.westtallahatchie.net/
West Tallahatchie HS 400/7-12
PO Box 130 38966 662-375-8829
Lawrence Hudson, prin. Fax 375-7402
Other Schools – See Sumner

Wesson, Copiah, Pop. 1,907
Copiah County SD
Supt. — See Hazlehurst
Wesson S 1,100/K-12
1048 Grove St 39191 601-643-2221
Marilyn Phillips, prin. Fax 643-2458

Copiah-Lincoln Community College Post-Sec.
PO Box 649 39191 601-643-5101

West Point, Clay, Pop. 11,257
West Point SD 3,200/PK-12
PO Box 656 39773 662-494-4242
Burnell McDonald, supt. Fax 494-8605
www.westpoint.k12.ms.us/
Fifth Street JHS 500/7-8
PO Box 776 39773 662-494-2191
Jermaine Taylor, prin. Fax 494-2432
West Point Career and Technology Center Vo/Tech
1253 E Church Hill Rd 39773 662-494-6176
Patrick Ray, prin. Fax 495-2426
West Point HS 1,000/9-12
950 S Eshman Ave 39773 662-494-5083
Mario Williss, prin. Fax 494-0969

Gibson's Barber & Beauty College Post-Sec.
PO Box 990 39773 662-494-5444
Oak Hill Academy 500/PK-12
800 N Eshman Ave 39773 662-494-5043

Wheeler, Prentiss
Prentiss County SD
Supt. — See Booneville
Wheeler S 200/K-12
PO Box 98 38880 662-365-2629
Todd Swinney, prin. Fax 365-2535

Wiggins, Stone, Pop. 4,345
Stone County SD 2,700/K-12
214 Critz St N 39577 601-928-7247
Gwen Miller, supt. Fax 928-5122
stoneweb.stone.k12.ms.us
Stone HS 700/9-12
400 Border Ave E 39577 601-928-5492
Hope Hendry, prin. Fax 928-6874
Stone MS 600/6-8
532 Central Ave E 39577 601-928-4876
Dr. Shauna Breland, prin. Fax 928-6440

Vardaman Street Christian Academy 100/PK-12
908 Frontage Dr W 39577 601-528-5454
Dr. Eugene Anderson, admin.

Winona, Montgomery, Pop. 5,020
Montgomery County SD 300/K-12
PO Box 687 38967 662-283-4533
Michael Hood, supt. Fax 283-4584
www.mcsdms.net
Other Schools – See Kilmichael

Winona SD 1,200/K-12
218 Fairground St 38967 662-283-3731
Randle Poss Ph.D., supt. Fax 283-1003
www.winonaschools.net/
Winona Career and Technical Center Vo/Tech
300 N Applegate St 38967 662-283-3601
Lance VanHorn, prin. Fax 283-9807
Winona HS 500/7-12
301 Fairground St 38967 662-283-1244
Charlie Parkerson, prin. Fax 283-4267

Winona Christian S 300/PK-12
1014 S Applegate St 38967 662-283-1169

Woodville, Wilkinson, Pop. 1,088
Wilkinson County SD 1,400/PK-12
PO Box 785 39669 601-888-3582
Timothy Scott, supt. Fax 888-3133
wilkinsoncounty.schoolinsites.com/
King Vocational Complex Vo/Tech
PO Box 1193 39669 601-888-4394
Kimberly Jackson, prin. Fax 888-4740
Wilkinson County HS 400/9-12
522 Pinckneyville Rd 39669 601-888-4228
Ougrett Brumfield, prin. Fax 888-4736
Other Schools – See Centreville

Wilkinson County Christian Academy 300/K-12
2420 US Highway 61 S 39669 601-888-4313

Yazoo City, Yazoo, Pop. 11,345
Yazoo City Municipal SD 2,400/PK-12
1133 Calhoun Ave 39194 662-746-2125
Dr. Arthur Cartlidge, supt. Fax 746-9210
www.yazoocity.k12.ms.us/
Woolfolk MS 600/5-8
209 E Fifth St 39194 662-746-2904
Elease Lee, prin. Fax 746-8609
Yazoo City Alternative S Alt
1318 Grand Ave 39194 662-746-0985
John Holmes, prin.
Yazoo City HS 800/9-12
1825 Dr Mrtn Lthr Kng Jr Dr 39194 662-746-2378
Reginald Barnes, prin. Fax 746-3779
Yazoo City Vocational Center Vo/Tech
1825 Dr Mrtn Lthr Kng Jr Dr 39194 662-746-7642
Gregg Giles, dir. Fax 746-0991

Yazoo County SD 1,700/K-12
PO Box 1088 39194 662-746-4672
Rebecca Fisher, supt. Fax 746-9270
www.yazoo.k12.ms.us
Yazoo County HS 500/9-12
6789 Highway 49 Frontage Rd 39194 662-746-1492
Tom Taylor, prin. Fax 746-1593
Yazoo County JHS 200/7-8
6781 Highway 49 Frontage Rd 39194 662-746-1596
Gloria Jamison, prin. Fax 746-1616

Manchester Academy 400/PK-12
2132 Gordon Ave 39194 662-746-5913

MISSOURI

MISSOURI DEPARTMENT OF EDUCATION
PO Box 480, Jefferson City 65102-0480
Telephone 573-751-4212
Fax 573-751-1179
Website http://www.dese.mo.gov

Commissioner of Education Chris Nicastro

MISSOURI BOARD OF EDUCATION
PO Box 480, Jefferson City 65102-0480

President Peter Herschend

PUBLIC, PRIVATE AND CATHOLIC SECONDARY SCHOOLS

Adrian, Bates, Pop. 1,663
Adrian R-III SD 800/PK-12
PO Box 98 64720 816-297-2710
Dr. Kirk Eidson, supt. Fax 297-2980
www.adrian.k12.mo.us/
Adrian JSHS 400/6-12
PO Box 98 64720 816-297-4460
Don Lile, prin. Fax 297-4598

Advance, Stoddard, Pop. 1,340
Advance R-IV SD 400/PK-12
PO Box 370 63730 573-722-3581
Stan Seiler, supt. Fax 722-9886
www.advance.k12.mo.us
Advance JSHS 200/7-12
PO Box 370 63730 573-722-3584
Shana Kight, prin. Fax 722-5479

Albany, Gentry, Pop. 1,720
Albany R-III SD 400/PK-12
101 W Jefferson St 64402 660-726-3911
John Rinehart, supt. Fax 726-5841
www.albany.k12.mo.us
Albany HS 100/9-12
101 W Jefferson St 64402 660-726-3912
Timothy Beydler, prin. Fax 726-5841
Albany MS 100/6-8
101 W Jefferson St 64402 660-726-3912
Timothy Beydler, prin. Fax 726-5841

Alma, Lafayette, Pop. 395
Santa Fe R-X SD 400/K-12
PO Box 197 64001 660-674-2238
Dr. Gini Barnett, supt. Fax 674-2239
santafechiefs.k12.mo.us
Santa Fe HS 200/7-12
PO Box 197 64001 660-674-2236
Tom Burton, prin. Fax 674-2760

Alton, Oregon, Pop. 847
Alton R-IV SD 700/K-12
RR 2 Box 2180 65606 417-778-7216
Sheila Wheeler, supt. Fax 778-6394
www.alton.k12.mo.us/
Alton HS 400/7-12
RR 2 Box 2180 65606 417-778-7215
Eric Allen, prin. Fax 778-7851

Amoret, Bates, Pop. 185
Miami R-I SD 200/K-12
RR 1 Box 418 64722 660-267-3480
Dennis Dahman, supt. Fax 267-3630
www.miami-eagles.k12.mo.us/
Miami JSHS 100/7-12
RR 1 Box 418 64722 660-267-3484
Dr. Daniel Johnson, prin. Fax 267-3630

Anderson, McDonald, Pop. 1,900
McDonald County R-I SD 3,800/PK-12
100 Mustang Dr 64831 417-845-3321
Dr. Mark Stanton, supt. Fax 845-6972
www.mcdonaldco.k12.mo.us/
Anderson MS 200/7-8
135 Mustang Dr 64831 417-845-1805
Ken Anders, prin. Fax 845-7406
McDonald County HS 1,000/9-12
100 Mustang Dr 64831 417-845-3322
Kim Harrell, prin. Fax 845-8467
Other Schools – See Noel, Pineville

Annapolis, Iron, Pop. 343
South Iron R-I SD 300/PK-12
210 School St 63620 573-598-4241
Donald Wakefield, supt. Fax 598-4210
www.schoolweb.missouri.edu/southiron.k12.mo.us/
South Iron JSHS 200/7-12
210 School St 63620 573-598-4241
Joseph Jackson, prin. Fax 598-4210

Appleton City, Saint Clair, Pop. 1,108
Appleton City R-II SD 300/K-12
408 W 4th St 64724 660-476-2161
Dr. Steve Beckett, supt. Fax 476-5564
appletoncity.k12.mo.us/
Appleton City HS 200/6-12
408 W 4th St 64724 660-476-2118
Kevin Mitchell, prin. Fax 476-5564

Archie, Cass, Pop. 1,157
Archie R-V SD 600/PK-12
302 W State Route A 64725 816-293-5312
Dr. Sean Smith, supt. Fax 293-5712
www.archie.k12.mo.us/
Archie JSHS 300/7-12
302 W State Route A 64725 816-293-5312
Jeff Kramer, prin. Fax 293-5712

Arnold, Jefferson, Pop. 20,546
Fox C-6 SD 11,400/PK-12
745 Jeffco Blvd 63010 636-296-8000
Dr. Dianne Critchlow, supt. Fax 282-5170
www.fox.k12.mo.us
Fox HS 1,700/9-12
751 Jeffco Blvd 63010 636-296-5210
Dr. Kevin Rossiter, prin. Fax 282-6980
Fox MS 500/7-8
743 Jeffco Blvd 63010 636-296-5077
Aaron Wilken, prin. Fax 282-5171
Ridgewood MS 500/7-8
1401 Ridgewood School Rd 63010 636-282-1459
Jamie Lavanchy, prin. Fax 282-5193
Other Schools – See Barnhart, Imperial

ITT Technical Institute Post-Sec.
1930 Meyer Drury Dr 63010 636-464-6600
Metro Business College Post-Sec.
2132 Tenbrook Rd 63010 636-296-9300

Ash Grove, Greene, Pop. 1,452
Ash Grove R-IV SD 700/PK-12
100 N Maple Ln 65604 417-751-2534
Dr. Don Christensen, supt. Fax 751-2283
www.ashgrove.k12.mo.us
Ash Grove JSHS 400/7-12
100 N Maple Ln 65604 417-751-2330
Christopher Thompson, prin. Fax 751-2889

Ashland, Boone, Pop. 3,660
Southern Boone County R-I SD 1,500/PK-12
PO Box 168 65010 573-657-2147
Charlotte Miller, supt. Fax 657-5513
ashland.k12.mo.us
Southern Boone County HS 500/9-12
PO Box 168 65010 573-657-2144
Dale Van Deven, prin. Fax 657-9035
Southern Boone County MS 300/6-8
PO Box 168 65010 573-657-2146
Kevin Kiley, prin. Fax 657-5519

Atlanta, Macon, Pop. 377
Atlanta C-3 SD 200/K-12
PO Box 367 63530 660-239-4212
William Perkins, supt. Fax 239-4205
www.atlanta.k12.mo.us/
Atlanta JSHS 100/7-12
PO Box 367 63530 660-239-4211
William Perkins, prin. Fax 239-4205

Aurora, Lawrence, Pop. 7,398
Aurora R-VIII SD 2,100/PK-12
409 W Locust St 65605 417-678-3373
Dan Decker, supt. Fax 678-4043
www.aurorar8.org
Aurora HS 600/9-12
305 W Prospect St 65605 417-678-3355
Kevin Kultgen, prin. Fax 678-2905
Aurora JHS 400/7-8
500 W Olive St 65605 417-678-3630
Allison Murphy-Pope, prin. Fax 678-2487

Ava, Douglas, Pop. 2,954
Ava R-I SD 1,400/PK-12
PO Box 338 65608 417-683-4717
Dr. Brian Wilson, supt. Fax 683-6329
www.avaschools.k12.mo.us/
Ava HS 500/9-12
PO Box 338 65608 417-683-5747
Teresa Nash, prin. Fax 683-2306
Ava MS 400/5-8
PO Box 338 65608 417-683-3835
Mike Henry, prin. Fax 683-9101

Ava Victory Academy 100/PK-12
PO Box 608 65608 417-683-6630
Teresa Bruffett, admin. Fax 683-1402

Bakersfield, Ozark, Pop. 240
Bakersfield R-IV SD 400/PK-12
PO Box 38 65609 417-284-7333
Amy Britt, supt. Fax 284-7335
www.bakersfield.k12.mo.us
Bakersfield JSHS 200/6-12
PO Box 38 65609 417-284-7333
Troy Wiesner, prin. Fax 284-7335

Ballwin, Saint Louis, Pop. 29,903
Parkway C-2 SD
Supt. — See Chesterfield
Parkway South HS 1,900/9-12
801 Hanna Rd 63021 314-415-7700
Dr. Patrice Aitch, prin. Fax 415-7712
Parkway West HS 1,300/9-12
14653 Clayton Rd 63011 314-415-7500
Dr. Jeremy Mitchell, prin. Fax 415-7534

Rockwood R-VI SD
Supt. — See Eureka
Crestview MS 1,200/6-8
16025 Clayton Rd 63011 636-207-2520
Dr. Jill Scheulen, prin. Fax 207-2529
Lafayette HS 2,000/9-12
17050 Clayton Rd 63011 636-733-4100
John Shaughnessy, prin. Fax 458-7219
Selvidge MS 700/6-8
235 New Ballwin Rd 63021 636-207-2622
Sean Stryhal, prin. Fax 207-2632

Grabber School of Hair Design Post-Sec.
14557 Manchester Rd 63011 636-227-4440

Barnard, Nodaway, Pop. 221
South Nodaway County R-IV SD 200/PK-12
209 Morehouse St 64423 660-652-3221
Dr. Kyle Collins, supt. Fax 652-3413
www.southnodaway.k12.mo.us/
South Nodaway JSHS 100/7-12
209 Morehouse St 64423 660-652-3727
Shawn Emerson, prin. Fax 652-3411

Barnhart, Jefferson, Pop. 5,631
Fox C-6 SD
Supt. — See Arnold
Antonia MS 6-8
6798 Saint Lukes Church Rd 63012 636-282-6970
Joe Willis, prin. Fax 282-6971

Bell City, Stoddard, Pop. 438
Bell City R-II SD 200/K-12
25254 Walnut St 63735 573-733-4444
Matthew Asher, supt. Fax 733-4114
www.bellcity.k12.mo.us/
Bell City JSHS 100/7-12
25254 Walnut St 63735 573-733-4444
Lincoln Scherer, prin. Fax 733-4114

Belle, Maries, Pop. 1,518
Maries County R-II SD 800/K-12
PO Box 819 65013 573-859-3800
Dr. Patrick Call, supt. Fax 859-3883
www.mariesr2.org
Belle HS 200/9-12
PO Box 819 65013 573-859-6114
Danielle Tuepker, prin. Fax 859-6122
Other Schools – See Bland

Belton, Cass, Pop. 22,497
Belton SD 124 5,100/PK-12
110 W Walnut St 64012 816-489-7000
Dr. Andrew Underwood, supt. Fax 489-7005
www.beltonschools.org
Belton HS 1,000/10-12
107 Pirate Pkwy 64012 816-348-1036
Fred Skretta, prin. Fax 348-1516
Belton HS Freshman Center 400/9-9
801 W North Ave 64012 816-348-1726
Dr. Denise Gaynor, prin. Fax 348-1727

Yeokum MS 700/7-8
613 Mill St 64012 816-348-1042
Dr. Michele Norman, prin. Fax 348-1534

Heartland Christian S 200/PK-12
810 S Cedar St 64012 816-331-1000
Claire Baker, prin. Fax 322-2782

Benton, Scott, Pop. 855
Scott County R-IV SD 1,000/PK-12
4035 State Highway 77 63736 573-545-3541
Don Moore, supt. Fax 545-3929
kelly.k12.mo.us/
Kelly HS 300/9-12
4035 State Highway 77 63736 573-545-3541
Dan Hecht, prin. Fax 545-4485
Scott County MS 200/6-8
4035 State Highway 77 63736 573-545-3541
Michael Eftink, prin. Fax 545-4386

Berkeley, Saint Louis, Pop. 8,830
Ferguson-Florissant R-II SD
Supt. — See Florissant
Berkeley MS 300/7-8
8300 Frost Ave 63134 314-524-3883
Steven Lawler, prin. Fax 524-3885

Vatterott College - NorthPark Post-Sec.
8580 Evans Ave 63134 314-264-1000

Bernie, Stoddard, Pop. 1,930
Bernie R-XIII SD 500/PK-12
516 W Main Ave 63822 573-293-5333
Doug Ruck, supt. Fax 293-5731
www.bernie.k12.mo.us
Bernie JSHS 200/7-12
516 W Main Ave 63822 573-293-5334
Bryce Matthews, prin. Fax 293-6124

Bethany, Harrison, Pop. 3,262
South Harrison County R-II SD 900/PK-12
PO Box 445 64424 660-425-8044
Donald Wilburn, supt. Fax 425-7050
www.shr2.k12.mo.us
North Central Career Center Vo/Tech
PO Box 445 64424 660-425-2196
Billy Pottorff, dir. Fax 425-2197
South Harrison County R-II HS 300/7-12
PO Box 445 64424 660-425-8051
Dennis Eastin, prin. Fax 425-7447

Bevier, Macon, Pop. 711
Bevier C-4 SD 200/K-12
400 Bloomington St 63532 660-773-6611
Joan Patrick, supt. Fax 773-6955
bevierc-4.com
Bevier HS 100/9-12
400 Bloomington St 63532 660-773-5213
Lisa Borden, prin. Fax 773-6964

Billings, Christian, Pop. 1,023
Billings R-IV SD 400/PK-12
118 W Mount Vernon Rd 65610 417-744-2623
Cynthia Brandt, supt. Fax 744-4545
www.billings.k12.mo.us
Billings HS 200/7-12
118 W Mount Vernon Rd 65610 417-744-2551
Roger Cavener, prin. Fax 744-4545

Bismarck, Saint Francois, Pop. 1,531
Bismarck R-V SD 600/PK-12
PO Box 257 63624 573-734-6111
Chuck Hasty, supt. Fax 734-2957
www.bismarckr5.org
Bismarck JSHS 300/7-12
PO Box 257 63624 573-734-6111
Jason King, prin. Fax 734-2957

Black, Reynolds
Lesterville R-IV SD
Supt. — See Lesterville
Lesterville Ranch Campus 50/Alt
525 County Road 816 63625 573-269-4207
Mary Balderas, prin. Fax 269-4277

Black Jack, Saint Louis, Pop. 6,797
Hazelwood SD
Supt. — See Florissant
Hazelwood Central MS 700/6-8
13450 Old Jamestown Rd 63033 314-953-7400
Yolander Pittman, prin. Fax 953-7413

Bland, Gasconade, Pop. 534
Maries County R-II SD
Supt. — See Belle
Maries County MS 200/5-8
PO Box 10 65014 573-646-3912
Samantha White, prin. Fax 646-3148

Bloomfield, Stoddard, Pop. 1,925
Bloomfield R-XIV SD 800/PK-12
505 Court St 63825 573-568-4564
Toni Hill, supt. Fax 568-4565
www.bloomfieldschooldistrict.blogspot.com/
Bloomfield HS 200/9-12
505 Court St 63825 573-568-2146
Dustin Hicks, prin. Fax 568-2147
Bloomfield MS 200/7-8
505 Court St 63825 573-568-4283
Dustin Hicks, prin. Fax 568-4286

Blue Eye, Stone, Pop. 163
Blue Eye R-V SD 700/PK-12
PO Box 105 65611 417-779-5332
Dan Ray, supt. Fax 779-2151
www.blueeye.k12.mo.us
Blue Eye HS 300/9-12
PO Box 105 65611 417-779-5331
Ben Johnson, prin. Fax 779-2151
Blue Eye MS 200/5-8
PO Box 105 65611 417-779-4299
Craig Linson, prin. Fax 779-4526

Blue Springs, Jackson, Pop. 51,123
Blue Springs R-IV SD 14,000/K-12
1801 NW Vesper St 64015 816-224-1300
Dr. Paul Kinder, supt. Fax 224-1310
www.bssd.net
Blue Springs Freshman Center 1,100/9-9
2103 NW Vesper St 64015 816-224-1325
Brandon Martin, prin. Fax 224-1344
Blue Springs HS 1,700/10-12
2000 NW Ashton Dr 64015 816-229-3459
David Adams, prin. Fax 229-1025
Blue Springs South HS 1,400/10-12
1200 SE Adams Dairy Pkwy 64014 816-224-1315
Dr. Randy Dowell, prin. Fax 224-1324
Brittany Hill MS 800/6-8
2701 NW 1st St 64014 816-224-1700
Dallas Truex, prin. Fax 224-1704
Moreland Ridge MS 1,000/6-8
900 SW Bishop Dr 64015 816-224-1800
Kevin Grover, prin. Fax 224-1805
Sunny Vale MS 800/6-8
3930 S R D Mize Rd 64015 816-224-1330
Steve Goddard, prin. Fax 224-1309
Valley View HS Alt
5000 NW Valley View Rd 64015 816-224-4388
Charlie Weber, prin. Fax 224-1374
Other Schools – See Lees Summit

House of Heavilin Beauty College Post-Sec.
2000 SW State Route 7 64014 816-229-9000
Plaza Heights Christian Academy 200/PK-12
1500 SW Clark Rd 64015 816-228-0670
Chuck Lawson, admin. Fax 229-4092

Bolivar, Polk, Pop. 10,153
Bolivar R-I SD 2,900/PK-12
524 W Madison St 65613 417-326-5291
Dr. Steve Morgan, supt. Fax 326-3562
www.bolivarschools.org
Bolivar HS 900/9-12
1401 Highway D 65613 417-326-5228
Dr. David Geurin, prin. Fax 326-4325
Bolivar MS 600/6-8
604 W Jackson St 65613 417-326-3811
Shane Dublin, prin. Fax 326-8277

Bolivar Technical College Post-Sec.
2001 W Broadway St Ste 2 65613 417-777-5062
Southwest Baptist University Post-Sec.
1600 University Ave 65613 417-328-5281

Bonne Terre, Saint Francois, Pop. 6,797
North St. Francois County R-I SD 3,100/PK-12
300 Berry Rd 63628 573-431-3300
Dr. Yancy Poorman, supt. Fax 350-2077
www.ncsd.k12.mo.us/
North St. Francois County HS 900/9-12
7151 Raider Rd 63628 573-431-3300
Lance Sprenkle, prin. Fax 358-0021
Unitec Career Center Vo/Tech
7163 Raider Rd 63628 573-431-3300
Larry Kekec, dir. Fax 358-3577
Other Schools – See Desloge

Boonville, Cooper, Pop. 8,135
Boonville R-I SD 1,500/K-12
736 Main St 65233 660-882-7474
Mark Ficken, supt. Fax 882-5721
www.boonville.k12.mo.us/
Boonslick Technical Education Center Vo/Tech
1694 W Ashley Rd 65233 660-882-5306
Karen Brosi, dir. Fax 882-3269
Boonville HS 500/9-12
1690 W Ashley Rd 65233 660-882-7426
Jeff Brackman, prin. Fax 882-3368
Elliott MS 300/6-8
700 Main St 65233 660-882-6649
Shelli Adams, prin. Fax 882-8646

Bosworth, Carroll, Pop. 302
Bosworth R-V SD 100/PK-12
102 E Eldridge St 64623 660-534-7311
Lachrissa Smith, supt. Fax 534-7409
www.bosworthr-v.k12.mo.us/
Bosworth JSHS 100/7-12
102 E Eldridge St 64623 660-534-7311
Todd Park, prin. Fax 534-7409

Bourbon, Crawford, Pop. 1,624
Crawford County R-I SD 1,000/PK-12
1444 S Old Highway 66 65441 573-732-4426
Patricia Thompson, supt. Fax 732-4545
crawford.mo.schoolwebpages.com
Bourbon HS 300/9-12
1500 S Old Highway 66 65441 573-732-5615
Dena Smith, prin. Fax 732-4407
Bourbon MS 300/5-8
363 Jost St 65441 573-732-4424
Deena Swyers, prin. Fax 732-4425

Bowling Green, Pike, Pop. 5,265
Bowling Green R-I SD 1,300/K-12
700 W Adams St 63334 573-324-5441
Darin Powell, supt. Fax 324-2439
www.bgschools.k12.mo.us
Bowling Green HS 500/9-12
700 W Adams St 63334 573-324-5341
Brad Kurz, prin. Fax 324-3011
Bowling Green MS 300/6-8
700 W Adams St 63334 573-324-2181
Kimberlee Pafford, prin. Fax 324-3292

Bradleyville, Taney, Pop. 84
Bradleyville R-I SD 200/PK-12
PO Box 20 65614 417-796-2288
Joe Combs, supt. Fax 796-2289
Bradleyville JSHS 200/7-12
PO Box 20 65614 417-796-2288
Robert Comer, prin. Fax 796-2289

Branson, Taney, Pop. 10,302
Branson R-IV SD 4,500/PK-12
1756 Bee Creek Rd 65616 417-334-6541
Dr. Doug Hayter, supt. Fax 332-2510
www.branson.k12.mo.us
Branson HS 1,400/9-12
935 Buchanan Rd 65616 417-334-6511
Chip Arnette, prin. Fax 335-4889
Branson JHS 700/7-8
263 Buccaneer Dr 65616 417-334-3087
Bryan Bronn, prin. Fax 336-3913

Brashear, Adair, Pop. 264
Adair County R-II SD 200/K-12
205 W Dewey St 63533 660-323-5272
Shelly Shipman, supt. Fax 323-5250
brashear.k12.mo.us
Adair County R-II HS 100/7-12
205 W Dewey St 63533 660-323-5272
Brent Doolin, prin. Fax 323-5250

Braymer, Caldwell, Pop. 864
Braymer C-4 SD 300/PK-12
400 Bobcat Ave 64624 660-645-2284
Don Regan, supt. Fax 645-2780
www.braymerbobcats.org
Braymer JSHS 100/7-12
400 Bobcat Ave 64624 660-645-2284
Mitchel Barnes, prin. Fax 645-2780

Breckenridge, Caldwell, Pop. 364
Breckenridge R-I SD 100/PK-12
400 W Colfax St 64625 660-644-5715
Brent Skinner, supt. Fax 644-5710
Breckenridge HS 50/7-12
400 W Colfax St 64625 660-644-5715
Brent Skinner, prin. Fax 644-5710

Brentwood, Saint Louis, Pop. 7,905
Brentwood SD 800/K-12
1201 Hanley Industrial Ct 63144 314-962-4507
David Faulkner, supt. Fax 962-7302
www.brentwood.k12.mo.us
Brentwood HS 300/9-12
2221 High School Dr 63144 314-962-3837
Dr. Edward M. Johnson, prin. Fax 963-3166
Brentwood MS 200/6-8
9127 White Ave 63144 314-962-8238
Dr. Andrew Loiterstein, prin. Fax 968-8724

Missouri College Post-Sec.
1405 S Hanley Rd 63144 314-768-7800

Brighton, Polk
Pleasant Hope R-VI SD
Supt. — See Pleasant Hope
Pleasant Hope Ranch S 100/4-12
5545 N Highway 13 65617 417-376-3000
Gloria Bailey, dir. Fax 376-3575

Bronaugh, Vernon, Pop. 241
Bronaugh R-VII SD 200/PK-12
527 E 6th St 64728 417-922-3211
Lyle Best, supt. Fax 922-3308
www.bronaughschools.net/
Bronaugh JSHS 100/7-12
527 E 6th St 64728 417-922-3211
Geoff Stewart, prin. Fax 922-3308

Brookfield, Linn, Pop. 4,463
Brookfield R-III SD 1,100/PK-12
124A N Pershing Dr 64628 660-258-7443
Dr. Paul Barger, supt. Fax 258-4711
www.brookfield.k12.mo.us
Brookfield HS 300/9-12
124 N Pershing Dr 64628 660-258-7242
Vicki Enyart, prin. Fax 258-2871
Brookfield MS 300/5-8
126 N Pershing Dr 64628 660-258-7335
Melinda Wilbeck, prin. Fax 258-2190
Linn County Area Career Tech Center Vo/Tech
122 N Pershing Dr 64628 660-258-2682
Carey Smith, dir. Fax 258-3875

Broseley, Butler
Twin Rivers R-X SD 900/K-12
PO Box 146 63932 573-328-4321
Mike Stevenson, supt. Fax 328-1070
www.tr10.us/
Twin Rivers HS 300/9-12
PO Box 146 63932 573-328-4730
Jerry Stockton, prin. Fax 328-1511

Brunswick, Chariton, Pop. 841
Brunswick R-II SD 200/PK-12
1008 County Rd 65236 660-548-3550
Robert Kottman, supt. Fax 548-3029
www.brunswick.k12.mo.us
Brunswick JSHS 100/7-12
1008 County Rd 65236 660-548-3771
Cara Engelbrecht, prin. Fax 548-3072

Bucklin, Linn, Pop. 465
Bucklin R-II SD 100/K-12
26832 Highway 129 64631 660-695-3555
Steve Coulson, supt. Fax 695-3345
www.bucklin.k12.mo.us/
Bucklin R-II S 100/K-12
26832 Highway 129 64631 660-695-3225
Steve Coulson, prin. Fax 695-3345

Buffalo, Dallas, Pop. 3,038
Dallas County R-I SD 1,800/PK-12
309 W Commercial St 65622 417-345-2222
Robin Ritchie, supt. Fax 345-8446
www.dallasr1.k12.mo.us/
Buffalo HS 600/9-12
500 W Main St 65622 417-345-2223
Debby Dryer, prin. Fax 345-8495
Buffalo MS 500/5-8
926 Truman 65622 417-345-2335
Matt Nimmo, prin. Fax 345-5968
Other Schools – See Louisburg

Bunceton, Cooper, Pop. 348
Cooper County R-IV SD 100/K-12
500 E Main St 65237 660-427-5347
John Thompson, supt. Fax 427-5348
bunceton.k12.mo.us
Bunceton JSHS 100/7-12
500 E Main St 65237 660-427-5415
Maurice Guerin, prin. Fax 427-5348

Bunker, Reynolds, Pop. 405
Bunker R-III SD 200/K-12
PO Box 365 63629 573-689-2507
Jane Reeves, supt. Fax 689-1268
www.bunkerr3.k12.mo.us/
Bunker JSHS 100/7-12
PO Box 365 63629 573-689-2211
Rob Harlow, prin. Fax 689-2011

Burlington Junction, Nodaway, Pop. 533
West Nodaway R-I SD 300/PK-12
PO Box 260 64428 660-725-4613
Nancy Greeley, supt. Fax 725-4300
www.wnrockets.com/
West Nodaway JSHS 100/7-12
PO Box 260 64428 660-725-3317
Jeremy Ingraham, prin. Fax 725-4300

Butler, Bates, Pop. 4,155
Ballard R-II SD 200/K-12
RR 1 Box 497 64730 816-297-2656
John Siebeneck, supt. Fax 297-4002
www.ballardr2.net
Ballard JSHS 100/7-12
RR 1 Box 497 64730 816-297-2656
Jimmie Barton, prin. Fax 297-4002

Butler R-V SD 1,000/PK-12
420 S Fulton St 64730 660-679-0653
Alan Stauffacher, supt. Fax 620-3010
www.butlerr5.org/
Butler JSHS 400/7-12
420 S Fulton St 64730 660-679-6121
Steve Hubbard, prin. Fax 679-4378

Cabool, Texas, Pop. 2,104
Cabool R-IV SD 800/PK-12
PO Box 613 65689 417-962-3153
Dr. Wesley Davis, supt. Fax 962-5043
www.cabool.k12.mo.us
Cabool HS 200/9-12
PO Box 613 65689 417-962-3153
Brad Shockley, prin. Fax 962-5663
Cabool MS 300/5-8
PO Box 613 65689 417-962-3153
Cheryl Manning, prin. Fax 962-5043

Cadet, Washington
Kingston SD K-14 800/K-12
10047 Diamond Rd 63630 573-438-4982
Dr. Gary Milner, supt.
www.kingston.k12.mo.us/
Kingston HS 300/9-12
10047 Diamond Rd 63630 573-438-4982
Thomas Gotsch, prin.
Kingston MS 200/6-8
10047 Diamond Rd 63630 573-438-4982
Alex McCaul, prin.

Cainsville, Harrison, Pop. 285
Cainsville R-I SD 100/PK-12
PO Box 108 64632 660-893-5213
Richard Smith, supt. Fax 893-5713
cainsville.k12.mo.us
Cainsville JSHS 50/7-12
PO Box 108 64632 660-893-5214
Kristi Reeder, prin. Fax 893-5713

Cairo, Randolph, Pop. 287
Northeast Randolph County R-IV SD 400/PK-12
301 W Martin St 65239 660-263-2788
Richard Morelock, supt. Fax 263-5735
www.ner4schools.org
Northeast JSHS 200/6-12
301 W Martin St 65239 660-263-2788
Greg Taylor, prin. Fax 263-5735

Caledonia, Washington, Pop. 130
Valley R-VI SD 300/K-12
1 Viking Dr 63631 573-779-3446
Brad Crocker, supt. Fax 779-3505
www.valley.k12.mo.us/
Valley JSHS 200/7-12
1 Viking Dr 63631 573-779-3515
Brad Crocker, prin. Fax 779-3346

Calhoun, Henry, Pop. 463
Calhoun R-VIII SD 200/K-12
409 S College St 65323 660-694-3422
Daniel Roberts, supt. Fax 694-3501
calhoun.k12.mo.us/
Calhoun JSHS 100/7-12
409 S College St 65323 660-694-3412
Janette Lawson, prin. Fax 694-3941

California, Moniteau, Pop. 4,221
Moniteau County R-I SD 1,300/K-12
211 S Owen St Ste B 65018 573-796-2145
Dwight Sanders, supt. Fax 796-6123
www.californiak12.org/
California HS 400/9-12
1501 W Buchanan St 65018 573-796-4911
Mike Hight, prin. Fax 796-4503
California MS 300/6-8
211 S Owen St 65018 573-796-2146
Matt Abernathy, prin. Fax 796-8257

Camdenton, Camden, Pop. 3,647
Camdenton R-III SD 4,300/PK-12
PO Box 1409 65020 573-346-9213
Timothy Hadfield, supt. Fax 346-9211
camdentonschools.schoolwires.net/
Camdenton HS 1,300/9-12
PO Box 1409 65020 573-346-9232
Brett Thompson, prin. Fax 346-9238
Camdenton MS 600/7-8
PO Box 1409 65020 573-346-9257
Sean Kirksey, prin. Fax 346-9288
Lake Career & Technical Center Vo/Tech
PO Box 1409 65020 573-346-9260
Dr. Gail White, dir. Fax 346-9284

Cameron, Clinton, Pop. 9,834
Cameron R-I SD 1,800/PK-12
423 N Chestnut St 64429 816-632-2170
Dr. Matt Robinson, supt. Fax 632-2612
www.cameronschools.org/
Cameron HS 500/9-12
1022 S Chestnut St 64429 816-632-2129
Don Gerber, prin. Fax 632-1634
Cameron MS 500/5-8
915 Park Ave 64429 816-632-2185
Jay Albright, prin. Fax 632-3752
Turning Point Alt
423 N Chestnut St 64429 816-632-8491
Chad Snyder, dir. Fax 632-7431

Campbell, Dunklin, Pop. 1,968
Campbell R-II SD 600/PK-12
801 S State Highway 53 63933 573-246-2133
Jay Thornton, supt. Fax 246-3212
www.campbell.k12.mo.us
Campbell JSHS 300/7-12
801 S State Highway 53 63933 573-246-2576
Jeremy Siebert, prin. Fax 246-2890

Canton, Lewis, Pop. 2,342
Canton R-V SD 600/PK-12
200 S 4th St 63435 573-288-5216
W.A. Anderson, supt. Fax 288-5442
canton.k12.mo.us/
Canton JSHS 300/7-12
200 S 4th St 63435 573-288-5216
Jesse Uhlmeyer, prin. Fax 288-5442

Culver-Stockton College Post-Sec.
1 College Hl 63435 573-288-6000

Cape Girardeau, Cape Girardeau, Pop. 37,082
Cape Girardeau SD 63 4,100/PK-12
301 N Clark St 63701 573-335-1867
Dr. James Welker, supt. Fax 335-1820
cape.k12.mo.us
Alternative Education Center Alt
301 N Spring St 63701 573-335-5939
Scott McMullen, admin. Fax 335-6041
Cape Girardeau Career & Technology Ctr. Vo/Tech
1080 S Silver Springs Rd 63703 573-334-0826
Rich Payne, dir. Fax 334-5930
Central HS 1,200/9-12
1000 S Silver Springs Rd 63703 573-335-8228
Dr. Mike Cowan, prin. Fax 334-1114
Central JHS 600/7-8
205 Caruthers St 63701 573-334-2923
Carla Fee, prin. Fax 332-8746

Cape Girardeau Career & Technical School Post-Sec.
1080 S Silver Springs Rd 63703 573-334-0826
Eagle Ridge Christian S 100/PK-12
4210 State Highway K 63701 573-339-1335
Janice Margrabe, admin. Fax 339-1390
Metro Business College Post-Sec.
1732 N Kings Highway St 63701 573-334-9181
Notre Dame Regional HS 500/9-12
265 Notre Dame Dr 63701 573-335-6772
Br. David Migliorino, prin. Fax 335-3458
Southeast Hospital College of Nursing Post-Sec.
2001 William St # 2 63703 573-334-6825
Southeast Missouri State University Post-Sec.
1 University Plz 63701 573-651-2000

Cardwell, Dunklin, Pop. 704
Southland C-9 SD 400/PK-12
500 S Main St 63829 573-654-3574
Kim Campbell, supt. Fax 654-3575
southland.k12.mo.us
Southland JSHS 100/7-12
500 S Main St 63829 573-654-3531
Johnny McMinn, prin. Fax 654-3534

Carl Junction, Jasper, Pop. 7,264
Carl Junction R-I SD 3,400/PK-12
206 S Roney St 64834 417-649-7026
Dr. Phillip Cook, supt. Fax 649-6594
www.cj.k12.mo.us
Carl Junction Alternative S 50/Alt
206 S Roney St 64834 417-649-5731
Cyndy Giebler, dir. Fax 649-5751
Carl Junction HS 900/9-12
206 S Roney St 64834 417-649-7081
David Pyle, prin. Fax 649-5791
Carl Junction JHS 500/7-8
206 S Roney St 64834 417-649-7246
Scott Sawyer, prin. Fax 649-0022
Carl Junction Satellite 50/Alt
206 S Roney St 64834 417-627-1541
Cindy Jackson, dir. Fax 627-1525

Carrollton, Carroll, Pop. 3,737
Carrollton R-VII SD 1,000/PK-12
300 E 9th St 64633 660-542-2769
Dr. Judith DeLany, supt. Fax 542-3416
www.trojans.k12.mo.us/
Carrollton Area Career Center Vo/Tech
305 E 10th St 64633 660-542-0000
George Eiserer, dir. Fax 542-0600
Carrollton HS 300/9-12
300 E 9th St 64633 660-542-1276
Susan Finlayson, prin. Fax 542-1903
Carrollton MS 300/5-8
300 E 9th St 64633 660-542-3472
Brent Dobbins, prin. Fax 542-3169

Carthage, Jasper, Pop. 14,047
Carthage R-IX SD 4,300/PK-12
710 Lyon St 64836 417-359-7000
Dr. Blaine Henningsen, supt. Fax 359-7004
www.carthage.k12.mo.us
Carthage HS 1,200/9-12
2600 S River St 64836 417-359-7020
Kandy Frazier, prin. Fax 359-7037
Carthage JHS 600/7-8
714 S Main St 64836 417-359-7050
Jenny Bogle, prin. Fax 359-7057
Carthage Technical Center North Campus Vo/Tech
609 S River St 64836 417-359-7095
Eddie Stephens, dir. Fax 359-7419
Carthage Technical Center South Campus Vo/Tech
1100 E Airport Dr 64836 417-359-7026
Eddie Stephens, dir. Fax 359-7098

Caruthersville, Pemiscot, Pop. 6,073
Caruthersville SD 18 1,300/PK-12
1711 Ward Ave 63830 573-333-6100
J.J. Bullington, supt. Fax 333-6108
www.cps18.org
Caruthersville HS 300/9-12
1708 Ward Ave 63830 573-333-6110
John Jones, prin. Fax 333-6117
Caruthersville MS 300/6-8
1705 Ward Ave 63830 573-333-6120
Stephanie McGraw, prin. Fax 333-1835

Cassville, Barry, Pop. 3,224
Cassville R-IV SD 1,900/PK-12
1501 Main St 65625 417-847-2221
Richard Asbill, supt. Fax 847-4009
cassville.k12.mo.us/
Cassville HS 600/9-12
1501 Main St 65625 417-847-3137
Chris Redmon, prin. Fax 847-5111
Cassville MS 400/6-8
1501 Main St 65625 417-847-3136
Terry Jamieson, prin. Fax 847-3156

Cedar Hill, Jefferson, Pop. 1,703
Northwest R-I SD
Supt. — See High Ridge
Northwest HS 2,100/9-12
6005 Cedar Hill Rd 63016 636-274-0555
Brad Snell, prin. Fax 274-2076

Center, Ralls, Pop. 502
Ralls County R-II SD 700/PK-12
21622 Highway 19 63436 573-267-3397
Deanette Jarman, supt. Fax 267-3538
rallsr2.k12.mo.us/
Twain HS 200/9-12
21622 Highway 19 63436 573-267-3397
Jake Moss, prin. Fax 267-3538
Twain JHS 200/6-8
21622 Highway 19 63436 573-267-3397
Delores Woodhurst, prin. Fax 267-3538

Centerview, Johnson, Pop. 266
Johnson County R-VII SD 600/PK-12
92 NW State Route 58 64019 660-656-3316
Julie Dill, supt. Fax 656-3633
www.crestridge.org
Crest Ridge HS 200/9-12
92 NW State Route 58 64019 660-656-3391
Marlon Dyer, prin. Fax 656-3633
Crest Ridge MS 200/6-8
92 NW State Route 58 64019 660-656-3843
Marlon Dyer, prin. Fax 656-3633

Centralia, Boone, Pop. 3,976
Centralia R-VI SD 1,400/PK-12
635 S Jefferson St 65240 573-682-3561
Darin Ford, supt. Fax 682-2181
www.centralia.k12.mo.us
Boren MS 300/6-8
110 N Jefferson St 65240 573-682-2617
Vincent Matlick, prin. Fax 682-1500
Centralia HS 400/9-12
849 S Jefferson St 65240 573-682-3508
Dave Meyers, prin. Fax 682-2749

Sunnydale Adventist Academy 100/9-12
6818 Audrain Road 9139 65240 573-682-2164

Chadwick, Christian
Chadwick R-I SD 200/K-12
PO Box 274 65629 417-634-3588
Dana Comstock, supt. Fax 634-2668
www.chadwick.k12.mo.us/
Chadwick JSHS 100/7-12
PO Box 274 65629 417-634-3588
Darin Meinders, contact Fax 634-4040

Chaffee, Scott, Pop. 2,925
Chaffee R-II SD 600/PK-12
517 W Yoakum Ave 63740 573-887-3532
Ken Latham, supt. Fax 887-3926
chaffee.k12.mo.us
Chaffee JSHS 300/7-12
517 W Yoakum Ave 63740 573-887-3226
Brad Blackman, prin. Fax 887-3926

Chamois, Osage, Pop. 395
Osage County R-I SD 200/K-12
614 S Poplar St 65024 573-763-5666
Michael Bumgarner, supt. Fax 763-5686
www.chamois.k12.mo.us
Chamois JSHS 100/7-12
614 S Poplar St 65024 573-763-5393
Brad Strobel, prin. Fax 763-5686

Charleston, Mississippi, Pop. 5,882
Charleston R-I SD 1,100/PK-12
PO Box 39 63834 573-683-3776
Tony Watkins, supt. Fax 683-2909
charlestonr1.org
Charleston HS 300/9-12
PO Box 39 63834 573-683-3761
James Grasdorf, prin. Fax 683-2907
Charleston MS 200/6-8
PO Box 39 63834 573-683-3346
Christopher Stanfield, prin. Fax 683-2930

Chesterfield, Saint Louis, Pop. 46,860
Parkway C-2 SD 17,500/PK-12
455 N Woods Mill Rd 63017 314-415-8100
Keith Marty, supt. Fax 415-8009
www.parkwayschools.net/
Parkway Central HS 1,300/9-12
369 N Woods Mill Rd 63017 314-415-7900
Tim McCarthy, prin. Fax 415-7913
Parkway Central MS 900/6-8
471 N Woods Mill Rd 63017 314-415-7800
Dr. Michael Baugus, prin. Fax 415-7834
Parkway West MS 800/6-8
2312 Baxter Rd 63017 314-415-7400
Linda Lelonek, prin. Fax 415-7409
Other Schools – See Ballwin, Creve Coeur, Manchester

Rockwood R-VI SD
Supt. — See Eureka
Marquette HS 2,200/9-12
2351 Clarkson Rd 63017 636-891-6000
Dr. Greg Mathison, prin. Fax 537-4319

Barat Academy 200/9-12
17815 Wild Horse Creek Rd 63005 636-300-5500
Debra Watson, pres. Fax 300-5501
Logan College of Chiropractic Post-Sec.
1851 Schoettler Rd 63017 800-533-9210
Missouri Torah Institute 9-12
14550 Ladue Rd 63017 314-594-0462
St. Joseph's Institute for the Deaf Post-Sec.
1809 Clarkson Rd 63017 636-532-3211
Westminster Christian Academy 900/7-12
800 Maryville Centre Dr 63017 314-997-2900
James Marsh, hdmstr. Fax 997-2903

Chilhowee, Johnson, Pop. 315
Chilhowee R-IV SD 200/PK-12
101 Highway 2 64733 660-678-2511
Jeff Blackford, supt. Fax 678-5711
www.chilhowee.k12.mo.us
Chilhowee JSHS 100/7-12
101 Highway 2 64733 660-678-4511
Bonnie Parsons, prin. Fax 678-5711

Chillicothe, Livingston, Pop. 9,375
Chillicothe R-II SD 1,900/K-12
PO Box 530 64601 660-646-4566
Dr. Roger Barnes, supt. Fax 646-6508
www.chillicotheschools.org/
Chillicothe HS 600/9-12
2801 Hornet Rd 64601 660-646-0700
Brian Sherrow, prin. Fax 646-7106
Chillicothe MS 400/6-8
1529 Calhoun St 64601 660-646-1916
Steve Haley, prin. Fax 646-5065
Grand River Tech S Vo/Tech
1200 Fair St 64601 660-646-3414
Ron Wolf, prin. Fax 646-3568

Chillicothe Beauty Academy Post-Sec.
505 Elm St 64601 660-646-4198

Clarksville, Pike, Pop. 436
Pike County R-III SD 500/PK-12
28176 Highway WW 63336 573-242-3546
Mark Harvey, supt. Fax 485-2393
cloptonhawks.com
Clopton JSHS 300/7-12
28176 Highway WW 63336 573-242-3546
Larry Lagemann, prin. Fax 485-2393
Other Schools – See Eolia

Clarkton, Dunklin, Pop. 1,265
Clarkton C-4 SD 300/PK-12
PO Box 637 63837 573-448-3712
Philip Harrison, supt. Fax 448-5182
www.clarktonschools.org/
Clarkton JSHS 200/7-12
PO Box 637 63837 573-448-3712
Scottie Blackburn, prin. Fax 448-3226

Clayton, Saint Louis, Pop. 15,572
Clayton SD 2,600/PK-12
2 Mark Twain Cir 63105 314-854-6000
Dr. Sharmon Wilkinson, supt. Fax 854-6094
www.claytonschools.net
Clayton HS 800/9-12
1 Mark Twain Cir 63105 314-854-6600
Dr. Dan Gutchewsky, prin. Fax 854-6793
Wydown MS 600/6-8
6500 Wydown Blvd 63105 314-854-6400
Mary Ann Goldberg, prin. Fax 854-6491

Cleveland, Cass, Pop. 645
Midway R-I SD 500/K-12
5801 State Route 2 64734 816-250-2994
Gordon Myers, supt. Fax 899-2823
www.midwayk12.net
Midway JSHS 200/7-12
5801 State Route 2 64734 816-250-2994
Doug Dahman, prin. Fax 899-2823

Clever, Christian, Pop. 2,109
Clever R-V SD 300/PK-12
103 S Public Ave 65631 417-743-4800
Richard Henson, supt. Fax 743-4802
www.clever.k12.mo.us
Clever HS 300/9-12
6800 State Highway 14 W 65631 417-743-4830
Robert Parker, prin. Fax 743-4832

Clifton Hill, Randolph, Pop. 111
Westran R-I SD
Supt. — See Huntsville
Westran MS 100/6-8
622 Harlan St 65244 660-261-4511
Mike Aulbur, prin. Fax 261-4292

Climax Springs, Camden, Pop. 124
Climax Springs R-IV SD 200/PK-12
119 Nort Dr 65324 573-347-3905
Nathan Barb, supt. Fax 347-9931
csprings.k12.mo.us
Climax Springs JSHS 100/7-12
119 Nort Dr 65324 573-347-2351
Mary Gerriets, prin. Fax 347-2394

Clinton, Henry, Pop. 8,864
Clinton SD 124 1,800/PK-12
701 S 8th St 64735 660-885-2237
Craig Eaton, supt. Fax 885-7033
clinton.k12.mo.us
Clinton HS 600/9-12
701 S 8th St 64735 660-885-2247
Dr. Bryan Pettengill, prin. Fax 885-2012
Clinton MS 400/6-8
701 S 8th St 64735 660-885-3353
Andy Ford, prin. Fax 885-4826
Clinton Technical S Vo/Tech
701 S 8th St 64735 660-885-6101
Dan Wallace, dir. Fax 885-6789

Cole Camp, Benton, Pop. 1,108
Cole Camp R-I SD 700/K-12
500 S Keeney St 65325 660-668-4427
Perry Gorrell, supt. Fax 668-4703
colecamp.schoolwires.net
Cole Camp HS 200/9-12
500 S Keeney St 65325 660-668-3751
Brandon Harding, prin. Fax 668-4703
Cole Camp MS 200/5-8
500 S Keeney St 65325 660-668-3502
Tyler Clark, prin. Fax 668-4703

Columbia, Boone, Pop. 105,254
Columbia SD 93 17,300/PK-12
1818 W Worley St 65203 573-214-3400
Dr. Chris Belcher, supt. Fax 214-3401
www.columbia.k12.mo.us/
Columbia Area Career Ctr Vo/Tech
4203 S Providence Rd 65203 573-214-3800
Linda Rawlings, dir. Fax 214-3801
Douglass HS 200/Alt
310 N Providence Rd 65203 573-214-3680
Eryca Neville, prin. Fax 214-3681
Hickman SHS 1,900/10-12
1104 N Providence Rd 65203 573-214-3000
Dr. Tracey Conrad, prin. Fax 214-3057
Jefferson JHS 800/8-9
713 Rogers St 65201 573-214-3210
Gregery Caine, prin. Fax 214-3211
Oakland JHS 800/8-9
3405 Oakland Pl 65202 573-214-3220
Helen Porter, prin. Fax 214-3221
Rock Bridge SHS 1,800/10-12
4303 S Providence Rd 65203 573-214-3100
Mark Maus, prin. Fax 214-3109
West JHS 900/8-9
401 Clinkscales Rd 65203 573-214-3230
Dr. Sandra Logan, prin. Fax 214-3231

Bryan University Post-Sec.
3215 Lemone Industrial Blvd 65201 573-777-5550
Christian Fellowship S 300/PK-12
4600 Christian Fellowship 65203 573-445-8565
Dr. Rick Mueller, admin. Fax 445-8564
Columbia Beauty Academy Post-Sec.
503 E Nifong Blvd 65201 573-445-6611
Columbia College Post-Sec.
1001 Rogers St 65216 573-875-8700
Columbia Independent S 400/PK-12
1801 N Stadium Blvd 65202 573-777-9250
Scott Gibson, hdmstr. Fax 777-9251
Jerry's School of Hairstyling Post-Sec.
1001 Royal Birkdale Dr 65203 573-449-7527
Stephens College Post-Sec.
1200 E Broadway 65215 800-876-7207
Tolton HS 9-12
3351 E Gans Rd 65201 573-445-7700
Kristie Wolfe, prin. Fax 445-7703
University of Missouri Post-Sec.
228 Jesse Hall 65211 573-882-2121

Conception, Nodaway, Pop. 209

Conception Seminary College Post-Sec.
PO Box 502 64433 660-944-3105

Conception Junction, Nodaway, Pop. 198
Jefferson C-123 SD 200/PK-12
37614 US Highway 136 64434 660-944-2316
Rob Dowis, supt. Fax 944-2315
Jefferson JSHS 100/7-12
37614 US Highway 136 64434 660-944-2316
Tim Jermain, prin. Fax 944-2315

Concordia, Lafayette, Pop. 2,425
Concordia R-II SD 500/PK-12
PO Box 879 64020 660-463-7235
Mary Beth Scherer, supt. Fax 463-1326
www.concordia.k12.mo.us
Concordia JSHS 200/7-12
PO Box 879 64020 660-463-2246
Troy Marnholtz, prin. Fax 463-4081

St. Paul Lutheran HS 200/9-12
PO Box 719 64020 660-463-2238
Bill Lemmons, prin. Fax 463-7621

Conway, Laclede, Pop. 768
Laclede County R-I SD 800/K-12
726 W Jefferson Ave 65632 417-589-2951
Dr. Chris Berger, supt. Fax 589-3202
www.conwayschooldistrict.com
Conway HS 300/9-12
726 W Jefferson Ave 65632 417-589-2941
Ricky Lowrance, prin. Fax 589-2500
Conway JHS 100/7-8
726 W Jefferson Ave 65632 417-589-8147
Jeanie White, prin. Fax 589-2500

Cooter, Pemiscot, Pop. 468
Cooter R-IV SD 300/K-12
PO Box 218 63839 573-695-3312
William Crowder, supt. Fax 695-3073
cooter.k12.mo.us
Cooter JHSS 200/7-12
PO Box 218 63839 573-695-4972
Clay Snider, prin. Fax 695-3073

Cottleville, Saint Charles, Pop. 3,037

Patsy & Rob's Academy of Beauty Post-Sec.
5065 Highway N 63304 636-447-0650
St. Charles Community College Post-Sec.
4601 Mid Rivers Mall Dr 63376 636-922-8000

Craig, Holt, Pop. 248
Craig R-III SD 50/K-12
402 N Ward St 64437 660-683-5351
Michael Leach, supt. Fax 683-5769
www.craigr3school.com
Craig R-III S 50/K-12
402 N Ward St 64437 660-683-5431
Ken Grove, prin. Fax 683-5769

Crane, Stone, Pop. 1,443
Crane R-III SD 800/PK-12
PO Box 405 65633 417-723-5300
Travis Shaw, supt. Fax 723-5551
www.crane.k12.mo.us
Crane HS 200/9-12
PO Box 405 65633 417-723-5383
Grant Stock, prin. Fax 723-5551
Crane MS 200/5-8
PO Box 405 65633 417-723-8177
Kurt Stumpff, prin. Fax 723-5551

Creighton, Cass, Pop. 347
Sherwood Cass R-VIII SD 900/PK-12
PO Box 98 64739 660-499-2834
Dr. Tim Gallagher, supt. Fax 499-2624
Sherwood HS 300/9-12
PO Box 98 64739 660-499-2239
William Stackhouse, prin. Fax 499-2258
Sherwood MS 200/6-8
PO Box 98 64739 660-499-2239
Brenda Koch, prin. Fax 499-2585

Creve Coeur, Saint Louis, Pop. 17,490
Parkway C-2 SD
Supt. — See Chesterfield
Fern Ridge HS 100/Alt
13157 N Olive Spur Rd 63141 314-415-6900
Dr. Becky Warren, prin. Fax 415-6912
Parkway Northeast MS 1,000/6-8
181 Coeur De Ville Dr 63141 314-415-7100
Kim Brandon Ed.D., prin. Fax 415-7113
Parkway North HS 1,500/9-12
12860 Fee Fee Rd, Saint Louis MO 63146
314-415-7600
Dr. Jenny Marquart, prin. Fax 415-7614

Crocker, Pulaski, Pop. 1,094
Crocker R-II SD 600/PK-12
PO Box 488 65452 573-736-5000
Dr. Jim Bogle, supt. Fax 736-5924
www.crockerschools.org
Crocker JSHS 200/7-12
PO Box 488 65452 573-736-5000
Tami Bobbitt, prin. Fax 736-2801

Crystal City, Jefferson, Pop. 4,757
Crystal City SD 47 700/K-12
1100 Mississippi Ave 63019 636-937-4411
Ronald Swafford, supt. Fax 937-2512
www.crystal.k12.mo.us/
Crystal City HS 300/7-12
1100 Mississippi Ave 63019 636-937-2005
Robert Linderer, prin. Fax 937-2075

National Academy of Beauty Arts Post-Sec.
137 Twin City Mall 63019 636-931-7100

Cuba, Crawford, Pop. 3,311
Crawford County R-II SD 1,400/K-12
1 Wildcat Pride Dr 65453 573-885-2534
Johnny Thompson, supt. Fax 885-3900
www.cuba.k12.mo.us/
Cuba HS 400/9-12
1 Wildcat Pride Dr 65453 573-885-2534
Jon Earnhart, prin. Fax 885-7726
Cuba MS 400/5-8
1 Wildcat Pride Dr 65453 573-885-2534
Marie Shoemaker, prin. Fax 885-6278

Curryville, Pike, Pop. 217

Pike County Christian S K-12
PO Box 96 63339 573-324-2700
Frank Welch, admin. Fax 324-2700

Dadeville, Dade, Pop. 228
Dadeville R-II SD 100/K-12
PO Box 188 65635 417-995-2201
Matt Bushey, supt. Fax 995-2110
Dadeville JSHS 100/6-12
PO Box 188 65635 417-995-2201
Cassy Farmer, prin. Fax 995-2110

Dearborn, Platte, Pop. 488
North Platte County R-I SD 600/PK-12
212 W 6th St 64439 816-450-3511
Dr. Jeffrey Sumy, supt. Fax 992-8727
www.nppanthers.org
North Platte HS 200/9-12
212 W 6th St 64439 816-450-3344
Karl Matt, prin. Fax 992-8955
North Platte JHS 100/7-8
212 W 6th St 64439 816-450-3350
Janey Hoeffner, prin. Fax 992-3665

Deepwater, Henry, Pop. 430
Lakeland R-III SD 400/PK-12
12530 Lakeland School Dr 64740 417-644-2223
Mitch Towne, supt. Fax 644-2316
www.lakeland.k12.mo.us
Lakeland JSHS 200/7-12
12530 Lakeland School Dr 64740 417-644-2223
Steve Ritter, prin. Fax 644-2316

Deering, Pemiscot, Pop. 130
Delta C-7 SD 200/K-12
PO Box 297 63840 573-757-6648
Kenny Copley, supt. Fax 757-9691
www.schoolweb.missouri.edu/deltac7.k12.mo.us/
Delta C-7 JSHS 100/7-12
PO Box 297 63840 573-757-6611
Nathan Baker, prin. Fax 757-9691

De Kalb, Buchanan, Pop. 219
Buchanan County R-IV SD 300/PK-12
702 Main St 64440 816-685-3160
Lane Novinger, supt. Fax 685-3203
www.bcr4.k12.mo.us/
De Kalb JSHS 200/7-12
702 Main St 64440 816-685-3211
Travis Dittemore, prin. Fax 685-3156

Delta, Cape Girardeau, Pop. 421
Delta R-V SD 300/PK-12
PO Box 787 63744 573-794-2500
Nate Crowden, supt. Fax 794-2504
www.deltar5schools.com
Delta JSHS 200/7-12
PO Box 787 63744 573-794-2511
James Gloth, prin. Fax 794-2504

Desloge, Saint Francois, Pop. 4,987
North St. Francois County R-I SD
Supt. — See Bonne Terre
North County MS 500/7-8
406 E Chestnut St 63601 573-431-3300
Brenda Medley, prin. Fax 431-5203

De Soto, Jefferson, Pop. 6,303
Desoto SD 73 3,000/PK-12
610 Vineland School Rd 63020 636-586-1000
Dr. Trisha Burkeen, supt. Fax 586-1009
www.desoto.k12.mo.us
De Soto HS 1,000/9-12
815 Amvets Dr 63020 636-586-1050
Dan Hoehn, prin. Fax 586-1059
De Soto JHS 400/7-8
731 Amvets Dr 63020 636-586-1030
Cooper Tucker, prin. Fax 586-1039

Dexter, Stoddard, Pop. 7,773
Dexter R-XI SD 2,000/PK-12
1031 Brown Pilot Ln 63841 573-614-1000
Dr. Thomas Sharp, supt. Fax 614-1002
dexter.k12.mo.us/
Dexter HS 600/9-12
1101 W Grant St 63841 573-614-1030
Corey Mouser, prin. Fax 614-1032
Hill MS 500/6-8
1107 Brown Pilot Ln 63841 573-614-1010
Scott Kruse, prin. Fax 614-1012

Diamond, Newton, Pop. 880
Diamond R-IV SD 900/K-12
PO Box 68 64840 417-325-5186
Dr. Patricia Wilson, supt. Fax 325-5338
www.diamondwildcats.org/
Diamond HS 300/9-12
PO Box 68 64840 417-325-5188
Brian Lee, prin. Fax 325-5331
Diamond MS 300/5-8
PO Box 68 64840 417-325-5336
Danny DeWitt, prin. Fax 325-5333

Dixon, Pulaski, Pop. 1,508
Dixon R-I SD 1,100/PK-12
106 W 4th St 65459 573-759-7163
Duane Doyle, supt. Fax 759-2506
www.dixonr1.com
Dixon HS 300/9-12
106 W 4th St 65459 573-759-7163
Lyndel Whittle, prin. Fax 759-3625
Dixon MS 200/6-8
106 W 4th St 65459 573-759-7163
Mark Parker, prin. Fax 759-6627

Doniphan, Ripley, Pop. 1,976
Doniphan R-I SD 1,600/PK-12
309 Pine St 63935 573-996-3667
Dan Schlief, supt. Fax 996-5865
www.doniphanr1.k12.mo.us
Current River Career Center Vo/Tech
301 E Spring St 63935 573-996-3667
Penny Fowler, dir. Fax 996-7838
Doniphan HS 500/9-12
5 Ball Park Rd 63935 573-996-3667
Ron McCutchen, prin. Fax 996-3739
Doniphan MS 400/6-8
651 E Summit St 63935 573-996-3667
Jason Rose, prin. Fax 996-4525

Dora, Ozark
Dora R-III SD 300/PK-12
PO Box 14 65637 417-261-2346
Steve Richards, supt. Fax 261-2673
www.dora.org
Dora JSHS 200/7-12
PO Box 14 65637 417-261-2263
Rick Luna, prin. Fax 261-2673

Drexel, Bates, Pop. 952
Drexel R-IV SD 300/K-12
PO Box 860 64742 816-657-4715
Bill Johnston, supt. Fax 657-4798
www.drexel.k12.mo.us/
Drexel HS 200/7-12
PO Box 860 64742 816-619-2287
Ken Shipps, prin. Fax 657-4798

Eagleville, Harrison, Pop. 315
North Harrison R-III SD 200/PK-12
12023 Fir St 64442 660-867-5222
Troy Clawson, supt. Fax 867-5263
www.nhr3.net
North Harrison County JSHS 100/7-12
12023 Fir St 64442 660-867-5221
Mike Schmidli, prin. Fax 867-5263

Earth City, Saint Louis

Everest College Post-Sec.
3420 Rider Trl S 63045 314-739-7333
ITT Technical Institute Post-Sec.
3640 Corporate Trail Dr 63045 314-298-7800
Midwest Institute - Earth City Post-Sec.
4260 Shoreline Dr 63045 314-344-4440

Easton, Buchanan, Pop. 228
East Buchanan County C-1 SD
Supt. — See Gower
East Buchanan MS 200/6-8
301 N County Park Rd 64443 816-473-2451
David Elms, prin. Fax 473-2604

East Prairie, Mississippi, Pop. 3,146
East Prairie R-II SD 1,100/PK-12
PO Box 10 63845 573-649-3562
Scott Downing, supt. Fax 649-5455
eastprairie.org/
East Prairie HS 300/9-12
PO Box 10 63845 573-649-3564
Steve Douglas, prin. Fax 649-3208
East Prairie JHS 200/7-8
210 E Washington St 63845 573-649-9368
Amanda Hall, prin. Fax 649-9370

Edina, Knox, Pop. 1,171
Knox County R-I SD 500/PK-12
RR 3 Box 59 63537 660-397-2228
Andy Turgeon, supt. Fax 397-3998
www.knox.k12.mo.us/
Knox County JSHS 300/6-12
RR 3 Box 59 63537 660-397-2231
Richard Johnson, prin. Fax 397-3282

Eldon, Miller, Pop. 4,478
Eldon R-I SD 1,900/PK-12
112 S Pine St 65026 573-392-8000
Matt Davis, supt. Fax 392-8080
www.eldon.k12.mo.us/
Eldon Career Center Vo/Tech
112 S Pine St 65026 573-392-8060
Willard Haley, dir. Fax 392-9154
Eldon HS 600/9-12
101 S Pine St 65026 573-392-8010
Kris Harwood, prin. Fax 392-5057
Eldon MS 300/7-8
1400 N Grand Ave 65026 573-392-8020
Shaun Fischer, prin. Fax 392-9151

El Dorado Springs, Cedar, Pop. 3,534
El Dorado Springs R-II SD 1,200/PK-12
901 S Grand Ave 64744 417-876-3112
Mark Koca, supt. Fax 876-2128
www.eldo.k12.mo.us/
El Dorado Springs HS 400/9-12
901 S Grand Ave 64744 417-876-3112
David Hedrick, prin. Fax 876-2128
El Dorado Springs MS 300/6-8
901 S Grand Ave 64744 417-876-3112
Brad Steward, prin. Fax 876-2128

El Dorado Christian S 100/PK-12
1600 S Ohio St 64744 417-876-2201
Amy Castor, prin. Fax 876-4913

Ellington, Reynolds, Pop. 979
Southern Reynolds County R-II SD 500/PK-12
1 School St 63638 573-663-3591
Dr. Mike Redlich, supt. Fax 663-2412
www.ellington.k12.mo.us/
Southern Reynolds County HS 200/7-12
1 School St 63638 573-663-2291
Dr. Tim Hager, prin. Fax 663-2155

Ellsinore, Carter, Pop. 444
East Carter County R-II SD 800/PK-12
24 S Herren Ave 63937 573-322-5625
Dr. Richard Sullivan, supt. Fax 322-8586
www.ecarter.k12.mo.us
East Carter County R-II HS 200/9-12
24 S Herren Ave 63937 573-322-5653
Robert Eudaley, prin. Fax 322-5720
East Carter County R-II MS 200/6-8
24 S Herren Ave 63937 573-322-5420
Theresa Kearbey, prin. Fax 322-5420

Elsberry, Lincoln, Pop. 1,898
Elsberry R-II SD 800/PK-12
PO Box 106 63343 573-898-5554
Dr. Tim Reller, supt. Fax 898-3140
schoolweb.missouri.edu/elsberry.k12.mo.us/
Cannon MS 200/5-8
PO Box 106 63343 573-898-5554
Jason Miller, prin. Fax 898-5825
Elsberry HS 200/9-12
PO Box 106 63343 573-898-5554
Steve Hill, prin. Fax 898-9132

Eminence, Shannon, Pop. 585
Eminence R-I SD 300/PK-12
PO Box 730 65466 573-226-3251
Armand Spurgin, supt. Fax 226-3250
www.redwingsk12.org/
Eminence JSHS 100/7-12
PO Box 730 65466 573-226-3252
Armand Spurgin, prin. Fax 226-3211

Eolia, Pike, Pop. 513
Pike County R-III SD
Supt. — See Clarksville
Pike-Lincoln Technical Center Vo/Tech
PO Box 38 63344 573-485-2900
Martin Hanley, dir. Fax 485-2388

Essex, Stoddard, Pop. 469
Richland R-I SD 300/K-12
24456 State Highway 114 63846 573-283-5332
Frank Killian, supt. Fax 283-5798
www.richland.k12.mo.us/
Richland JSHS 100/7-12
24456 State Highway 114 63846 573-283-5332
Cynthia Rhodes, prin. Fax 283-5798

Eugene, Cole, Pop. 159
Cole County R-V SD 700/K-12
14803 Highway 17 65032 573-498-4000
Dawna Burrow, supt. Fax 498-4090
www.coler-v.k12.mo.us/
Eugene JSHS 400/7-12
14803 Highway 17 65032 573-498-4001
Jerry Braschler, prin. Fax 498-4091

Eureka, Saint Louis, Pop. 10,033
Rockwood R-VI SD 22,800/PK-12
111 E North St 63025 636-733-2000
Dr. Bruce Borchers, supt. Fax 938-2251
www.rockwood.k12.mo.us
Eureka HS 1,900/9-12
4525 Highway 109 63025 636-733-3100
Deborah Asher, prin. Fax 938-2411
Individualized Learning Center Alt
500 N Central Ave 63025 636-733-2100
Matthew Dieckhaus, admin. Fax 938-2346
Other Schools – See Ballwin, Chesterfield, Fenton, Glencoe

Everton, Dade, Pop. 310
Everton R-III SD 100/K-12
211 E School St 65646 417-535-2221
Dr. Karl Janson, supt. Fax 535-4105
www.evertontigers.org
Everton HS 100/9-12
211 E School St 65646 417-535-2221
Rory Mauschbaugh, prin. Fax 535-4105
Everton MS 6-8
211 E School St 65646 417-535-2221
Dana Dreier, prin. Fax 535-4105

Excelsior Springs, Clay, Pop. 10,839
Excelsior Springs SD 40 3,000/PK-12
PO Box 248 64024 816-630-9200
Dr. John Lacy, supt. Fax 630-9203
essd40.com
Excelsior Springs Career Ctr Vo/Tech
PO Box 248 64024 816-630-9240
Dr. Chris Lake, dir. Fax 630-9245
Excelsior Springs HS 800/9-12
PO Box 248 64024 816-630-9210
Vincent Spallo, prin. Fax 630-9227
Excelsior Springs MS 600/6-8
PO Box 248 64024 816-630-9230
Chris Hubbuch, prin. Fax 630-9236
Excelsior Springs Technical HS 200/Alt
PO Box 248 64024 816-630-5501
Tom Mayfield, prin. Fax 637-1806

Martinez School of Cosmetology Post-Sec.
248 1/2 E Broadway St 64024 816-630-3900

Exeter, Barry, Pop. 762
Exeter R-VI SD 400/K-12
101 Locust St 65647 417-835-2922
Dr. Ernest Raney, supt. Fax 835-3201
www.exeter.k12.mo.us/
Exeter HS 100/9-12
101 Locust St 65647 417-835-3745
Robert Taylor, prin. Fax 835-3201

Fairfax, Atchison, Pop. 634
Fairfax R-III SD 200/PK-12
500 E Main St 64446 660-686-2421
Ed Defenbaugh, supt. Fax 686-2848
www.fairfaxk12mo.us/

Fairfax JSHS 100/7-12
500 E Main St 64446 660-686-2851
Dustin Barnes, prin. Fax 686-3436

Fair Grove, Greene, Pop. 1,384
Fair Grove R-X SD 1,100/PK-12
PO Box 367 65648 417-759-2233
Dr. John Link, supt. Fax 759-7150
www.fairgrove.k12.mo.us
Fair Grove HS 400/9-12
PO Box 367 65648 417-759-2554
Mike Bell, prin. Fax 759-7685
Fair Grove MS 300/5-8
PO Box 367 65648 417-759-2556
Chris Stallings, prin. Fax 759-9053

Fair Play, Polk, Pop. 467
Fair Play R-II SD 400/PK-12
301 N Walnut St 65649 417-654-2231
Renee Sagaser, supt. Fax 654-5028
www.fairplay.k12.mo.us/
Fair Play JSHS 200/7-12
301 N Walnut St 65649 417-654-2232
Derek Banwart, prin. Fax 654-3503

Farmington, Saint Francois, Pop. 16,061
Farmington R-VII SD 3,900/PK-12
PO Box 570 63640 573-701-1300
Natalie Thomas Ph.D., supt. Fax 701-1309
www.farmington.k12.mo.us
Farmington HS 1,200/9-12
1 Black Knight Dr 63640 573-701-1310
Matt Ruble, prin. Fax 701-1329
Farmington MS 600/7-8
506 S Fleming St 63640 573-701-1330
Dorothy Winslow, prin. Fax 701-1339
Midwest Learning Center 50/Alt
608 Pine St 63640 573-701-1385
Jerry Will, lead tchr. Fax 701-1388

Mineral Area Regional Medical Center Post-Sec.
1212 Weber Rd 63640 573-756-4581
National Academy of Beauty Arts Post-Sec.
670 Walton Dr 63640 573-756-2730

Faucett, Buchanan
Mid-Buchanan County R-V SD 700/K-12
3221 State Route H SE 64448 816-238-1646
John James, supt. Fax 238-4150
www.midbuchanan.k12.mo.us
Mid-Buchanan JSHS 300/7-12
3221 State Route H SE 64448 816-238-1646
Dave Rapp, prin. Fax 238-2484

Fayette, Howard, Pop. 2,632
Fayette R-III SD 500/PK-12
705 Lucky St 65248 660-248-2153
Tamara Kimball Ed.D., supt. Fax 248-3702
www.fayette.k12.mo.us/
Fayette HS 200/9-12
510 N Cleveland St 65248 660-248-2124
Corey Felter, prin. Fax 248-2120

Central Methodist University Post-Sec.
411 Central Methodist Sq 65248 660-248-3391

Fenton, Saint Louis, Pop. 3,976
Rockwood R-VI SD
Supt. — See Eureka
Rockwood South MS 1,000/6-8
1628 Hawkins Rd 63026 636-861-7723
Dr. Linda Miller, prin. Fax 861-7730
Rockwood Summit HS 1,300/9-12
1780 Hawkins Rd 63026 636-891-6800
Renee Trotier, prin. Fax 861-7717

Anthem College Post-Sec.
645 Gravois Bluffs Blvd 63026 888-852-7272
Brown Mackie College Post-Sec.
2 Soccer Park Rd 63026 636-651-3290
Midwest Institute Post-Sec.
964 S Highway Dr 63026 314-965-8363
St. Louis College of Health Careers Post-Sec.
1297 N Highway Dr 63026 636-529-0000

Ferguson, Saint Louis, Pop. 20,785

St. Louis Community College Post-Sec.
3400 Pershall Rd 63135 314-513-4200

Festus, Jefferson, Pop. 11,379
Festus R-VI SD 3,100/K-12
1515 Midmeadow Ln 63028 636-937-4920
Dr. Randy Sheriff, supt. Fax 937-8525
www.festus.k12.mo.us
Festus HS 900/9-12
501 Westwind Dr 63028 636-937-5410
Karen Biehle, prin. Fax 937-8048
Festus MS 500/7-8
1717 W Main St 63028 636-937-5417
Tina Thebeau, prin. Fax 937-4171

Jefferson County R-VII SD 900/PK-12
1250 Dooling Hollow Rd 63028 636-937-7940
Clint Johnston, supt. Fax 937-9189
www.jr7.k12.mo.us/
Danby-Rush Tower MS 200/6-8
1250 Dooling Hollow Rd 63028 636-937-9188
Cynthia Holdinghausen, admin. Fax 937-9189
Jefferson County HS 200/9-12
7 Blue Jay Way 63028 636-933-6900
David Haug, prin. Fax 933-2663

St. Pius X HS 300/9-12
1030 Saint Pius Dr 63028 636-931-7488
Karen DeCosty, pres. Fax 931-7487

Florissant, Saint Louis, Pop. 50,980
Ferguson-Florissant R-II SD 12,500/PK-12
1005 Waterford Dr 63033 314-506-9000
Dr. Arteveld McCoy, supt. Fax 506-9010
www.fergflor.org
Cross Keys MS 800/7-8
14205 Cougar Dr 63033 314-506-9700
Jeremy Van Pelt, prin. Fax 506-9701
McCluer HS 1,400/9-12
1896 S New Florissant Rd 63031 314-506-9400
Gary Spiller, prin. Fax 506-9401
McCluer North HS 1,800/9-12
705 Waterford Dr 63033 314-506-9200
Dr. Shane Hopper, prin. Fax 506-9201
Student Support Center 200/Alt
1555 Derhake Rd 63033 314-839-5959
Mark Weller, prin. Fax 839-7536
Other Schools – See Berkeley, Saint Louis

Hazelwood SD 18,100/PK-12
15955 New Halls Ferry Rd 63031 314-953-5000
Dr. Steve Price, supt. Fax 953-5085
www.hazelwoodschools.org/
Hazelwood Central HS 2,200/9-12
15875 New Halls Ferry Rd 63031 314-953-5400
Dr. Cheryol Mitchell, prin. Fax 953-5413
Hazelwood North MS 800/6-8
4420 Vaile Ave 63034 314-953-7500
Dr. Laurie Birkenmeier, prin. Fax 953-7513
Hazelwood Northwest MS 800/6-8
1605 Shackelford Rd 63031 314-953-5500
Willicia Hobbs, prin. Fax 953-5513
Other Schools – See Black Jack, Hazelwood, Saint Louis

Special SD of St. Louis County
Supt. — See Saint Louis
North Technical HS Vo/Tech
1700 Derhake Rd 63033 314-989-7600
Mike Powers, prin. Fax 989-7665

Missouri Sch. of Barbering & Hairstyling Post-Sec.
1125 N Highway 67 63031 314-839-0310
North County Christian S 300/PK-12
845 Dunn Rd 63031 314-972-6227
Dr. Greg Clark, admin. Fax 972-6220
St. Louis Christian College Post-Sec.
1360 Grandview Dr 63033 314-837-6777
Urshan Graduate School of Theology Post-Sec.
704 Howdershell Rd 63031 314-921-9290

Fordland, Webster, Pop. 792
Fordland R-III SD 600/PK-12
1230 School St 65652 417-738-2296
Richard Spacek, supt. Fax 767-4483
www.fordland.k12.mo.us
Fordland HS 200/9-12
1248 School St 65652 417-738-2212
Judy Kindall, prin. Fax 767-2240
Fordland MS 100/6-8
1230 School St 65652 417-738-2119
Vanessa Criger, prin. Fax 767-4483

Forsyth, Taney, Pop. 2,219
Forsyth R-III SD 1,200/PK-12
PO Box 187 65653 417-546-6384
Dr. Brent Blevins, supt. Fax 546-2204
www.forsythr3.k12.mo.us/
Forsyth HS 400/9-12
PO Box 187 65653 417-546-6383
Neale Richardson, prin. Fax 546-5987
Forsyth MS 400/5-8
PO Box 187 65653 417-546-6382
Sandra Goss, prin. Fax 546-6943

Fredericktown, Madison, Pop. 3,947
Fredericktown R-I SD 1,900/PK-12
704 E Highway 72 63645 573-783-2570
Dr. Kelly Burlison, supt. Fax 783-7045
www.fpsk12.org/
Fredericktown HS 600/9-12
805 E Highway 72 63645 573-783-3628
G. Brett Reutzel, prin. Fax 783-8224
Fredericktown MS 400/6-8
805A E Highway 72 63645 573-783-6555
Scott Sikes, prin. Fax 783-8079

Fulton, Callaway, Pop. 12,513
Fulton SD 58 2,100/K-12
2 Hornet Dr 65251 573-590-8000
Dr. Jacque Cowherd, supt. Fax 590-8090
www.fulton.k12.mo.us/
Fulton HS 700/9-12
1 Hornet Dr 65251 573-590-8100
Dr. Jason Whitt, prin. Fax 590-8190
Fulton MS 500/6-8
403 E 10th St 65251 573-590-8200
Christopher Crain, prin. Fax 590-8290

Missouri School for the Deaf Post-Sec.
505 E 5th St 65251 573-592-4000
Westminster College Post-Sec.
501 Westminster Ave 65251 573-642-3361
William Woods University Post-Sec.
1 University Ave 65251 573-642-2251

Gainesville, Ozark, Pop. 761
Gainesville R-V SD 600/K-12
422 Bulldog Dr 65655 417-679-4260
Joe Donley, supt. Fax 679-4270
gainesville.mo.schoolwebpages.com
Gainesville HS 300/7-12
422 Bulldog Dr 65655 417-679-4200
Aaron Dalton, prin. Fax 679-4270

Galena, Stone, Pop. 437
Galena R-II SD 500/PK-12
PO Box 286 65656 417-357-6027
Daniel Humble, supt. Fax 357-0058
www.galena.k12.mo.us/
Galena JSHS 200/7-12
PO Box 286 65656 417-357-6618
Misty Townsend, prin. Fax 357-8444

Gallatin, Daviess, Pop. 1,762
Gallatin R-V SD 700/PK-12
602 S Olive St 64640 660-663-2171
Dennis Croy, supt. Fax 663-2559
gallatin.k12.mo.us
Gallatin JSHS 300/7-12
602 S Olive St 64640 660-663-2171
Chris Elbert, prin. Fax 663-2559

Galt, Grundy, Pop. 246
Grundy County R-V SD 200/K-12
PO Box 6 64641 660-673-6511
Robert Deaver, supt. Fax 673-6523
Grundy County JSHS 100/7-12
PO Box 6 64641 660-673-6511
Randy Huffman, prin. Fax 673-6523

Garden City, Cass, Pop. 1,626

Training Center Christian S 100/PK-12
PO Box 200 64747 816-773-8367
Richard Williams, supt. Fax 862-6052

Gideon, New Madrid, Pop. 1,088
Gideon SD 37 300/PK-12
PO Box 227 63848 573-448-3911
Dr. David Hollingshead, supt. Fax 448-5197
gideon.k12.mo.us/
Gideon JSHS 200/7-12
PO Box 227 63848 573-448-3471
Keenan Buchanan, prin. Fax 448-3868

Gilman City, Daviess, Pop. 381
Gilman City R-IV SD 100/PK-12
141 Lindsey Ave 64642 660-876-5221
David Cross, supt. Fax 876-5553
www.gilman.k12.mo.us
Gilman City JSHS 100/7-12
141 Lindsey Ave 64642 660-876-5221
Roger Alley, prin. Fax 876-5553

Gladstone, Clay, Pop. 24,544
North Kansas City SD 74
Supt. — See Kansas City
Antioch MS 900/6-8
2100 NE 65th St 64118 816-413-6200
Robert Russell, prin. Fax 413-6205

Paris II Educational Center Post-Sec.
6840 N Oak Trfy 64118 816-468-6666

Glasgow, Howard, Pop. 1,085
Glasgow SD 300/PK-12
860 Randolph St 65254 660-338-2012
Michael Reynolds, supt. Fax 338-2610
Glasgow JSHS 200/7-12
860 Randolph St 65254 660-338-2012
Sonya Fuemmeler, prin. Fax 338-2610

Glencoe, Saint Louis
Rockwood R-VI SD
Supt. — See Eureka
LaSalle Springs MS 900/6-8
3300 Highway 109 63038 636-938-2425
Deborah Brandt, prin. Fax 938-2434
Rockwood Valley MS 800/6-8
1220 Babler Park Dr 63038 636-458-7324
Dr. Andrew Loiterstein, prin. Fax 458-7325
Wildwood MS 800/6-8
17401 Manchester Rd 63038 636-458-7360
Dr. Allison Klouse, prin. Fax 458-7372

Golden City, Barton, Pop. 757
Golden City R-III SD 300/PK-12
1208 Walnut St 64748 417-537-4900
Kevin Baldwin, supt. Fax 537-8717
Golden City JSHS 100/7-12
1208 Walnut St 64748 417-537-8311
Stephen Brigham, prin. Fax 537-8717

Gower, Buchanan, Pop. 1,511
East Buchanan County C-1 SD 700/K-12
100 Smith St 64454 816-424-6466
Paul Mensching, supt. Fax 424-3511
www.ebs.k12.mo.us/
East Buchanan HS 200/9-12
100 Smith St 64454 816-424-6460
Scott Antle, prin. Fax 424-6410
Other Schools – See Easton

Graham, Nodaway, Pop. 171
Nodaway-Holt R-VII SD 200/PK-12
318 S Taylor St 64455 660-939-2137
Karma Coleman, supt. Fax 939-2200
www.nodholt.k12.mo.us
Nodaway-Holt JSHS 100/7-12
318 S Taylor St 64455 660-939-2135
Terry Petersen, prin. Fax 939-2201

Grain Valley, Jackson, Pop. 12,604
Grain Valley R-V SD 3,400/PK-12
PO Box 304 64029 816-847-5006
Roy Moss Ph.D., supt. Fax 229-4831
www.grainvalley.k12.mo.us
Grain Valley HS 900/9-12
PO Box 304 64029 816-847-5000
Beth Mulvey, prin. Fax 847-5002
Grain Valley North MS 6-8
PO Box 304 64029 816-994-4800
Theresa Nelson, prin. Fax 994-4899
Grain Valley South MS 600/6-8
PO Box 304 64029 816-229-3499
Jeff Scalfaro, prin. Fax 847-5017

Granby, Newton, Pop. 2,075
East Newton County R-VI SD 1,600/PK-12
22808 E Highway 86 64844 417-472-6231
Todd McCrackin, supt. Fax 472-3500
www.eastnewton.org
East Newton HS 500/9-12
22876 E Highway 86 64844 417-472-6238
Scott Charlton, prin. Fax 472-7129

Grandview, Jackson, Pop. 23,651
Grandview C-4 SD 3,800/PK-12
13015 10th St 64030 816-316-5000
Dr. Ralph Teran, supt. Fax 316-5050
www.csd4.k12.mo.us
C.A.I.R. Alt
1001 Main St 64030 816-316-5150
Lori DeAnda, prin. Fax 316-5151
Grandview HS 1,000/9-12
2300 High Grove Rd 64030 816-316-5800
Steve Scraggs, prin. Fax 316-5898
Grandview MS 500/6-8
12650 Manchester Ave 64030 816-316-5600
Jennifer Price, prin. Fax 316-5699

Grandview Christian S 100/K-12
12340 Grandview Rd 64030 816-767-8630
Dale Hanson, supt. Fax 763-5029

Grant City, Worth, Pop. 858
Worth County R-III SD 400/PK-12
510 East Ave 64456 660-564-3389
Mike Rennells, supt. Fax 564-2193
wc.k12.mo.us/index.html
Worth County JSHS 200/7-12
510 East Ave 64456 660-564-2218
Jon Adwell, prin. Fax 564-2193

Green City, Sullivan, Pop. 647
Green City R-I SD 300/PK-12
301 Northeast St 63545 660-874-4128
Donnie Campbell, supt. Fax 874-4515
www.greencity.k12.mo.us/
Green City JSHS 100/7-12
301 Northeast St 63545 660-874-4127
Laura Olmstead, prin. Fax 874-5010

Greenfield, Dade, Pop. 1,342
Greenfield R-IV SD 400/K-12
410 College St 65661 417-637-5321
Jeffery Davis, supt. Fax 637-5805
greenfield.k12.mo.us/
Greenfield JSHS 200/7-12
410 College St 65661 417-637-5328
Jeff Davis, prin. Fax 637-5530

Green Ridge, Pettis, Pop. 466
Green Ridge R-VIII SD 400/K-12
PO Box 70 65332 660-527-3315
Cara Easter, supt. Fax 527-3299
greenridge.k12.mo.us
Green Ridge JSHS 200/7-12
PO Box 70 65332 660-527-3315
Eric Rehmer, prin. Fax 527-3299

Greenville, Wayne, Pop. 503
Greenville R-II SD 800/PK-12
PO Box 320 63944 573-224-3844
Dr. Andrew Rogers, supt. Fax 224-3412
bears.k12.mo.us
Greenville HS 200/9-12
PO Box 320 63944 573-224-3618
Rick Rainwater, prin. Fax 224-3580
Greenville JHS 100/7-8
PO Box 320 63944 573-224-3833
Rick Rainwater, prin. Fax 224-3580

Hale, Carroll, Pop. 409
Hale R-I SD 200/PK-12
PO Box 248 64643 660-565-2417
Clinton Heussner, supt. Fax 565-2418
Hale JSHS 100/7-12
PO Box 248 64643 660-565-2417
Hollie Burnside, prin. Fax 565-2418

Half Way, Polk, Pop. 165
Halfway R-III SD 300/K-12
2150 Highway 32 65663 417-445-2351
Tim Boatwright, supt. Fax 445-2026
www.halfwayschools.org
Halfway JSHS 100/7-12
2150 Highway 32 65663 417-445-2211
Tammy Highley, prin. Fax 445-3330

Hallsville, Boone, Pop. 1,463
Hallsville R-IV SD 1,300/PK-12
421 Hwy 124 E 65255 573-696-5512
John Robertson, supt. Fax 696-3606
www.hallsville.org/
Hallsville HS 400/9-12
421 Hwy 124 E 65255 573-696-5512
Robert Plourde, prin. Fax 696-1482
Hallsville MS 300/6-8
421 Hwy 124 E 65255 573-696-5512
Clinton Hague, prin. Fax 696-7238

Hamilton, Caldwell, Pop. 1,790
Hamilton R-II SD 700/K-12
PO Box 130 64644 816-583-2134
Troy Ford, supt. Fax 583-2139
www.hamilton.k12.mo.us/
Hamilton MS 200/6-8
PO Box 130 64644 816-583-2173
Dave Richman, prin. Fax 583-2686
Penney HS 200/9-12
PO Box 130 64644 816-583-2136
Tim Schieber, prin. Fax 583-2319

Hannibal, Marion, Pop. 17,465
Hannibal SD 60 3,600/PK-12
4650 McMasters Ave 63401 573-221-1258
Rich Stilley, supt. Fax 221-2994
www.hannibal.k12.mo.us
Hannibal Career & Technical Center Vo/Tech
4550 McMasters Ave 63401 573-221-4430
Roger McGregor, dir. Fax 221-7971
Hannibal HS 1,000/9-12
4500 Mcmasters Ave 63401 573-221-2733
Ryan Sharkey, prin. Fax 221-9511
Hannibal MS 800/6-8
4700 Mcmasters Ave 63401 573-221-5840
Blane Mundle, prin. Fax 221-7779

Hannibal Area Voc. Technical School Post-Sec.
4550 McMasters Ave 63401 573-221-4430
Hannibal-LaGrange University Post-Sec.
2800 Palmyra Rd 63401 573-221-3675

Hardin, Ray, Pop. 565
Hardin-Central C-2 SD 200/K-12
PO Box 548 64035 660-398-4394
Martin Griffin, supt. Fax 398-4396
www.hardin-central.org
Hardin-Central JSHS 100/7-12
PO Box 548 64035 660-398-4394
Rodney Clodfelter, prin. Fax 398-4396

Harrisburg, Boone, Pop. 260
Harrisburg R-VIII SD 600/K-12
1000 S Harris St 65256 573-875-5604
Lynn Proctor, supt. Fax 875-8877
www.harrisburg.k12.mo.us
Harrisburg HS 200/9-12
801 S Harris St 65256 573-875-5602
Lesa Rapert, prin. Fax 443-1559
Harrisburg MS 100/7-8
233 S Harris St 65256 573-817-5857
Steve Combs, prin. Fax 875-8936

Harrisonville, Cass, Pop. 9,864
Harrisonville R-IX SD 2,700/PK-12
503 S Lexington St 64701 816-380-2727
Dr. Bryan McDonald, supt. Fax 380-3134
www.harrisonvilleschools.org/
Cass Career Center Vo/Tech
1600 E Elm St 64701 816-380-3253
Gina Smith, dir. Fax 884-3179
Harrisonville HS 900/9-12
1504 E Elm St 64701 816-380-3273
Andy Campbell, prin. Fax 380-5853
Harrisonville MS 600/6-8
601 S Highland Dr 64701 816-380-7654
Chris Grantham, prin. Fax 884-5733

Harrisonville Christian S West Campus 100/5-8
1202 S Commercial St 64701 816-884-6499
Al Sancken, admin. Fax 887-2093

Hartville, Wright, Pop. 610
Hartville R-II SD 800/PK-12
PO Box 460 65667 417-741-7676
Mark Piper, supt. Fax 741-7746
www.hartville.k12.mo.us
Hartville JSHS 300/7-12
PO Box 460 65667 417-741-7676
Scott Keith, prin. Fax 741-7746

Hayti, Pemiscot, Pop. 2,893
Hayti R-II SD 900/PK-12
PO Box 469 63851 573-359-6500
Thomas Tucker, supt. Fax 359-6502
hayti.k12.mo.us
Hayti HS 400/7-12
PO Box 469 63851 573-359-6500
Jackie Johnson, prin. Fax 359-6504

Pemiscot County Special SD
1317 State Highway 84 63851 573-359-0021
Sandra Manley, supt. Fax 359-6525
Pemiscot County Career & Tech Center Vo/Tech
1317 State Highway 84 63851 573-359-2601
James White, dir. Fax 359-1317

Hazelwood, Saint Louis, Pop. 25,088
Hazelwood SD
Supt. — See Florissant
Hazelwood West HS 2,300/9-12
1 Wildcat Ln 63042 314-953-5800
Dennis Newell, prin. Fax 953-5813
Hazelwood West MS 800/6-8
12834 Missouri Bottom Rd 63042 314-953-5800
Tony Brooks, prin. Fax 953-5813

Herculaneum, Jefferson, Pop. 3,429
Dunklin R-V SD 1,500/K-12
497 Joachim Ave 63048 636-479-5200
Stan Stratton, supt. Fax 479-6208
www.dunklin.k12.mo.us
Herculaneum HS 400/9-12
1 Black Cat Dr 63048 636-479-5200
Dr. John Crabtree, prin. Fax 479-2051
Senn-Thomas MS 300/6-8
200 Senn Tomas Dr 63048 636-479-5200
Jeremy Davidson, prin. Fax 479-7219

Hermann, Gasconade, Pop. 2,399
Gasconade County R-I SD 1,100/K-12
170 Blue Pride Dr 65041 573-486-2116
Dr. Chris Neale, supt. Fax 486-3032
www.hermann.k12.mo.us
Hermann HS 400/9-12
176 Bearcat Xing 65041 573-486-5425
Gary Leimkuehler, prin. Fax 486-3058
Hermann MS 400/4-8
164 Blue Pride Dr 65041 573-486-3121
Chip Stutzman, prin. Fax 486-5106

Hermitage, Hickory, Pop. 457
Hermitage R-IV SD 300/PK-12
PO Box 327 65668 417-745-6418
Shelly Aubuchon, supt. Fax 745-6475
www.hermitage.k12.mo.us/
Hermitage HS 100/9-12
PO Box 327 65668 417-745-6417
Ed Vest, prin. Fax 745-6475
Hermitage MS 100/6-8
PO Box 327 65668 417-745-6417
Ed Vest, prin. Fax 745-6475

Higbee, Randolph, Pop. 552
Higbee R-VIII SD 200/K-12
PO Box 128 65257 660-456-7277
Ronald Hay, supt. Fax 456-7278
www.higbeeschool.com/
Higbee JSHS 100/7-12
PO Box 128 65257 660-456-7206
Jamey Fuemmeler, prin. Fax 456-7207

Higginsville, Lafayette, Pop. 4,706
Lafayette County C-1 SD 1,000/PK-12
805 W 31st St 64037 660-584-3631
David Figg, supt. Fax 584-2622
huskers.k12.mo.us
Lafayette County HS 300/9-12
807a W 31st St 64037 660-584-3661
Todd Whitney, prin. Fax 584-8666
Lafayette County MS 200/6-8
807b W 31st St 64037 660-584-7161
Gary Wheeler, prin. Fax 584-6080

Highlandville, Christian, Pop. 898
Spokane R-VII SD 800/PK-12
167 Kentling Ave 65669 417-443-2200
Daryl Bernskoetter, supt. Fax 443-2205
www.spokane.k12.mo.us
Other Schools – See Spokane

High Ridge, Jefferson, Pop. 4,270
Northwest R-I SD 6,000/K-12
2843 Community Ln 63049 636-677-3473
Dr. Paul Ziegler, supt. Fax 677-5480
www.nwr1.k12.mo.us/
Woodridge MS 200/6-8
2109 Gravois Rd 63049 636-677-3577
Kim Quentin, prin. Fax 677-5581
Other Schools – See Cedar Hill, House Springs

Hillsboro, Jefferson, Pop. 2,784
Grandview R-II SD 800/K-12
11470 State Road C 63050 636-944-3941
Dr. Michael Brown, supt. Fax 944-5239
www.grandviewr2.com
Grandview HS 300/9-12
11470 State Road C 63050 636-944-3390
Matthew Zoph, prin. Fax 944-3515
Grandview MS 200/6-8
11470 State Road C 63050 636-944-3931
James Keeling, prin. Fax 944-5239

Hillsboro R-III SD 3,600/K-12
20 Hawk Dr 63050 636-789-0060
Beverly Schonhoff Ph.D., supt. Fax 789-3216
www.hillsboro.k12.mo.us/
Hillsboro Alternative S 50/Alt
10486 Business 21 63050 636-789-0000
Melissa Hildebrand, prin. Fax 789-2773
Hillsboro HS 1,200/9-12
123 Leon Hall Pkwy 63050 636-789-0010
Cathy Freeman, prin. Fax 789-3211
Hillsboro JHS 600/7-8
12 Hawk Dr 63050 636-789-0020
Heath Allison, prin. Fax 789-3212

Christian Outreach S 50/PK-12
4450 Outreach Dr 63050 636-797-3466
Shirley Keener, prin.
Jefferson College Post-Sec.
1000 Viking Dr 63050 636-797-3000

Holcomb, Dunklin, Pop. 633
Holcomb R-III SD 600/PK-12
PO Box 190 63852 573-792-3113
Mr. Ashley McMillian, supt. Fax 792-3118
www.holcombschools.com/
Holcomb JSHS 300/7-12
PO Box 190 63852 573-792-3362
Matt Hodges, prin. Fax 792-3631

Holden, Johnson, Pop. 2,201
Holden R-III SD 1,400/PK-12
1612 S Main St 64040 816-732-5568
Wade Schroeder, supt. Fax 732-4336
schoolweb.missouri.edu/holden.k12.mo.us/
Holden HS 400/9-12
1901 S Main St 64040 816-732-5523
Ginger Jones, prin. Fax 732-4142
Holden MS 300/6-8
301 Eagle Dr 64040 816-732-4125
Dr. Mike Hough, prin. Fax 732-2009

Hollister, Taney, Pop. 4,346
Hollister R-V SD 800/PK-12
1914 State Highway BB 65672 417-243-4005
Dr. Timothy Taylor, supt. Fax 334-2663
www.hollister.k12.mo.us/
Hollister HS 500/9-12
2112 State Highway BB 65672 417-243-4045
Sean Woods, prin. Fax 336-2240
Hollister MS 100/6-8
1798 State Highway BB 65672 417-243-4035
Josh Holt, prin. Fax 336-5263

Trinity Christian Academy 100/PK-12
119 Myrtle Ave 65672 417-334-7084
Fax 334-1794

Hopkins, Nodaway, Pop. 530
North Nodaway County R-VI SD 200/PK-12
705 E Barnard St 64461 660-778-3411
James Simmelink, supt. Fax 778-3210
www.nnr6.org/
North Nodaway County JSHS 100/6-12
705 E Barnard St 64461 660-778-3315
Travis Dimmitt, prin. Fax 778-3210

Hornersville, Dunklin, Pop. 654
Senath-Hornersville C-8 SD
Supt. — See Senath
Senath-Hornersville MS 200/5-8
601 School St 63855 573-737-2455
Chad Morgan, prin. Fax 737-2456

House Springs, Jefferson
Northwest R-I SD
Supt. — See High Ridge
Valley MS 1,100/6-8
4300 Gravois Rd 63051 636-671-3470
Geoff Macy, prin. Fax 671-0948

Houston, Texas, Pop. 2,038
Houston R-I SD 1,100/PK-12
423 W Pine St 65483 417-967-3024
Scott Dill, supt. Fax 967-4887
www.houston.k12.mo.us
Houston HS 400/9-12
423 W Pine St 65483 417-967-3024
Charlie Malam, prin. Fax 967-3669
Houston MS 200/6-8
423 W Pine St 65483 417-967-3024
Jeremie Akins, prin. Fax 967-5481

Texas County Techical College Post-Sec.
6915 Highway 63 65483 417-967-5466

Hughesville, Pettis, Pop. 182
Pettis County R-V SD 300/K-12
16215 Highway H 65334 660-827-0772
Sharee Norfleet, supt. Fax 827-7162
www.northwest.k12.mo.us
Northwest JSHS 200/7-12
16215 Highway H 65334 660-827-0774
Travis Moore, prin. Fax 827-7162

Humansville, Polk, Pop. 1,030
Humansville R-IV SD 400/K-12
300 N Oak St 65674 417-754-2535
Dr. Ryan Nowlin, supt. Fax 754-8565
www.humansville.k12.mo.us
Humansville HS 200/7-12
300 N Oak St 65674 417-754-2219
Tammy Erwin, prin. Fax 754-8565

Hume, Bates, Pop. 331
Hume R-VIII SD 200/PK-12
PO Box 402 64752 660-643-7411
David Quick, supt. Fax 643-7506
Hume JSHS 100/7-12
PO Box 402 64752 660-643-7411
Kenny Otto, prin. Fax 643-7506

Huntsville, Randolph, Pop. 1,540
Westran R-I SD 700/PK-12
228 Huntsville Ave 65259 660-277-4429
Dr. Kelly Shelby, supt. Fax 277-4420
westran.k12.mo.us/
Westran HS 200/9-12
601 Hornet Ln 65259 660-277-4415
Mike Nagel, prin. Fax 277-4644
Other Schools – See Clifton Hill

Hurley, Stone, Pop. 177
Hurley R-I SD 200/K-12
PO Box 248 65675 417-369-3271
Dr. Doug Arnold, supt. Fax 369-2212
www.hurley.k12.mo.us/
Hurley JSHS 100/6-12
PO Box 248 65675 417-369-3271
Joey Little, prin. Fax 369-2202

Iberia, Miller, Pop. 730
Iberia R-V SD 800/PK-12
201 Pemberton Dr 65486 573-793-6818
Dr. Tamara Kimball, supt. Fax 793-6821
www.iberia.k12.mo.us/
Iberia HS 400/7-12
201 Pemberton Dr 65486 573-793-2228
Tara Luttrell, prin. Fax 793-2946

Imperial, Jefferson, Pop. 4,673
Fox C-6 SD
Supt. — See Arnold
Seckman HS 1,800/9-12
2800 Seckman Rd 63052 636-282-1485
Don Grimshaw, prin. Fax 282-5177
Seckman MS 500/7-8
2840 Seckman Rd 63052 636-296-5707
Tammy Cardona, prin. Fax 296-5707

Windsor C-1 SD 3,000/K-12
6208 US Highway 61/67 63052 636-464-4400
Dr. Joel Holland, supt. Fax 464-4454
windsorc1sd.schoolwires.com/
Windsor HS 900/9-12
6208 US Highway 61/67 63052 636-464-4429
Jeff Buscher, prin. Fax 464-4456
Windsor MS 700/6-8
6208 US Highway 61/67 63052 636-464-4417
Mike Rickermann, prin. Fax 464-4473

Independence, Jackson, Pop. 113,065
Fort Osage R-I SD 4,700/K-12
2101 N Twyman Rd 64058 816-650-7000
Mark Enderle, supt. Fax 650-3888
www.fortosage.net
Career & Technology Center Vo/Tech
2101 N Twyman Rd 64058 816-650-7180
Mike Pantleo, dir. Fax 650-7195
Ft. Osage HS 1,400/9-12
2101 N Twyman Rd 64058 816-650-7030
Jason Snodgrass, prin. Fax 650-7088
Osage Trail MS 800/7-8
2101 N Twyman Rd 64058 816-650-7151
John Schuler, prin. Fax 650-7152

Independence SD 30 14,300/PK-12
201 N Forest Ave 64050 816-521-5300
Dr. Jim Hinson, supt. Fax 521-5680
www.isdschools.org/
Bingham MS 600/6-8
1716 S Speck Rd 64057 816-521-5490
Corey Willich, prin. Fax 521-5631
Bridger MS 900/6-8
18200 E State Route 78 64057 816-521-5375
Kirsten Clemons, prin. Fax 521-5632
Chrisman HS 1,500/9-12
1223 N Noland Rd 64050 816-521-5355
Mike Becker, prin. Fax 521-5606
Independence Academy 100/Alt
600 W Mechanic Ave 64050 816-521-5505
Chad Bruton, prin. Fax 521-5613
Nowlin MS 700/6-8
2800 S Hardy Ave 64052 816-521-5380
Dr. Dale Wolff, prin. Fax 521-5633
Pioneer Ridge MS 800/6-8
1656 S Speck Rd 64057 816-521-5385
Dr. Michael Weishaar, prin. Fax 521-5630
Truman HS 1,600/9-12
3301 S Noland Rd 64055 816-521-5350
Kristel Barr, prin. Fax 521-5604
Van Horn HS 700/9-12
1109 S Arlington Ave 64053 816-521-5360
Dr. Greg Netzer, prin. Fax 521-5610

Graceland University Post-Sec.
1401 W Truman Rd 64050 816-833-0524
Independence College of Cosmetology Post-Sec.
815 W 23rd St 64055 816-252-4247
Metropolitan Community Coll - Blue River Post-Sec.
20301 E State Route 78 64057 816-604-6500
National American University Post-Sec.
3620 Arrowhead Ave 64057 816-353-4554

Ironton, Iron, Pop. 1,442
Arcadia Valley R-II SD 1,000/PK-12
750 Park Dr 63650 573-546-9700
Jim Carver Ed.D., supt. Fax 546-7314
www.avr2.org
Arcadia Valley Career Tech Vo/Tech
650 Park Dr 63650 573-546-9700
Steve Pursley, dir. Fax 546-6956
Arcadia Valley HS 300/9-12
520 Park Dr 63650 573-546-9700
Brian Beard, prin. Fax 546-3934
Arcadia Valley MS 300/5-8
550 Park Dr 63650 573-546-9700
Kent Huddleston, prin. Fax 546-7304

Jackson, Cape Girardeau, Pop. 13,577
Jackson R-II SD 4,900/PK-12
614 E Adams St 63755 573-243-9501
Dr. Ron Anderson, supt. Fax 243-9503
www.jacksonr2schools.com
Hawkins JHS 700/8-9
210 N West Ln 63755 573-243-9533
Cory Crosnoe, prin. Fax 243-9584
Jackson SHS 1,100/10-12
315 S Missouri St 63755 573-243-9513
Vince Powell, prin. Fax 243-9524

Saxony Lutheran HS 200/9-12
2004 Saxony Ln 63755 573-204-7555
Craig Ernstmeyer, prin. Fax 204-7445

Jameson, Daviess, Pop. 124
North Daviess R-III SD 100/PK-12
413 E 2nd St 64647 660-828-4123
Becky Morris, supt. Fax 828-4122
northdaviess.webs.com
North Daviess JSHS 50/7-12
413 E 2nd St 64647 660-828-4123
Gregg Hartley, prin. Fax 828-4122

Jamesport, Daviess, Pop. 506
Tri-County R-VII SD 200/K-12
904 W Auberry Grv 64648 660-684-6118
Phillip Fox, supt. Fax 684-6218
Tri-County HS 100/7-12
904 W Auberry Grv 64648 660-684-6116
Bryan McArthur, prin. Fax 684-6218

Jamestown, Moniteau, Pop. 378
Jamestown C-1 SD 200/K-12
222 School St 65046 660-849-2141
Fax 849-2600
www.jamestown.k12.mo.us
Jamestown C-I JSHS 100/7-12
222 School St 65046 660-849-2141
Steven McDannold, prin. Fax 849-2600

Jasper, Jasper, Pop. 913
Jasper County R-V SD 500/K-12
201 W Mercer St 64755 417-394-2416
Rick Stark, supt. Fax 394-2394
www.jasper.k12.mo.us/
Jasper County JSHS 200/7-12
201 W Mercer St 64755 417-394-2511
Jeff Jones, prin. Fax 394-2394

Jefferson City, Cole, Pop. 42,185
Jefferson City SD 8,900/PK-12
315 E Dunklin St 65101 573-659-3000
Brian Mitchell, supt. Fax 659-3807
www.jcschools.us/
Jefferson City HS 1,900/10-12
609 Union St 65101 573-659-3050
Jeff Dodson, prin. Fax 659-3153
Jefferson MS 900/6-8
1201 Fairgrounds Rd 65109 573-659-3250
Roberta Hubbs, prin. Fax 659-3259
Lewis and Clark MS 900/6-8
325 Lewis and Clark Dr 65101 573-659-3200
Sherri Thomas, prin. Fax 659-3209
Nichols Career Center Vo/Tech
605 Union St 65101 573-659-3100
Sharon Longan, dir. Fax 659-3154
Simonsen Ninth Grade Center 700/9-9
501 E Miller St 65101 573-659-3125
Tammy Ridgeway, admin. Fax 659-7362

Helias Catholic HS 800/9-12
1305 Swifts Hwy 65109 573-635-6139
Sr. Jean Dietrich, prin. Fax 635-5615
Lincoln University Post-Sec.
820 Chestnut St 65101 573-681-5000
Merrell Univ of Beauty Arts & Science Post-Sec.
1101 Southwest Blvd Ste R 65109 573-635-4433
Metro Business College Post-Sec.
210 El Mercado Plz 65109 573-635-6600
Nichols Career Center Post-Sec.
605 Union St 65101 573-659-3100

Jennings, Saint Louis, Pop. 14,545
Jennings SD 2,800/PK-12
2559 Dorwood Dr 63136 314-653-8000
Tiffany Anderson, supt. Fax 653-8030
www.jenningsk12.net/
Jennings HS 900/9-12
8850 Cozens Ave 63136 314-653-8100
Vara Burgdorf, prin. Fax 653-8102
Jennings JHS 400/7-8
8831 Cozens Ave 63136 314-653-8150
GeNita Williams, prin. Fax 653-8168

Joplin, Jasper, Pop. 48,394
Joplin R-VIII SD 7,600/PK-12
PO Box 128 64802 417-625-5200
Dr. C.J. Huff, supt. Fax 625-5210
www.joplinschools.org
East MS 500/6-8
PO Box 128 64802 417-625-5280
James Sexson, prin. Fax 625-5284
Franklin Tech S Vo/Tech
PO Box 128 64802 417-625-5260
David Rockers, dir. Fax 625-5266
Joplin HS 2,200/9-12
PO Box 128 64802 417-625-5230
Dr. Kerry Sachetta, prin. Fax 625-5238
North MS 600/6-8
PO Box 128 64802 417-625-5270
Brandon Eggleston, prin. Fax 625-5273
South MS 700/6-8
PO Box 128 64802 417-625-5250
Stephen Gilbreth, prin. Fax 625-5256

College Heights Christian S 600/PK-12
4311 Newman Rd 64801 417-782-4114
Nelson Horton, supt. Fax 659-9092
Franklin Technology - MSSU Post-Sec.
3950 Newman Rd 64801 417-659-4400
Jefferson Independent Day S 300/PK-12
3401 Newman Rd 64801 417-781-5124
Laura McDonald, head sch Fax 781-1949
McAuley Catholic HS 100/9-12
930 S Pearl Ave 64801 417-624-9320
Gene Koester, prin. Fax 626-8334
Messenger College Post-Sec.
300 E 50th St 64804 417-624-7070
Missouri Southern State University Post-Sec.
3950 Newman Rd 64801 417-625-9300
New Dimensions School of Hair Design Post-Sec.
705 Illinois Ave Ste 12 64801 417-782-2875
Ozark Christian College Post-Sec.
1111 N Main St 64801 417-626-1234
St. John's Regional Medical Center Post-Sec.
2727 Mc Clelland Blvd 64804 417-781-2727
St. Peter MS 100/6-8
802 Byers Ave 64801 417-624-5605
Greg Emory, prin. Fax 624-6254
Vatterott College - Joplin Post-Sec.
809 Illinois Ave 64801 417-781-5633
Wichita Technical Institute - Joplin Post-Sec.
1715 N Range Line Rd 64801 417-206-9115

Kahoka, Clark, Pop. 2,063
Clark County R-I SD 1,000/PK-12
427 W Chestnut St 63445 660-727-2377
Ritchie Kracht, supt. Fax 727-2035
www.clarkcounty.k12.mo.us/
Clark County HS 300/9-12
680 E Main St 63445 660-727-2205
Jason Harper, prin. Fax 727-2245
Clark County MS 200/6-8
384 N Jefferson St 63445 660-727-3319
Jason Church, prin. Fax 727-3363

Shiloh Christian S 50/K-12
RR 1 Box 68A 63445 573-853-4430
Ken Penfield, admin. Fax 853-4432

Kansas City, Jackson, Pop. 447,224
Center SD 58 2,500/PK-12
8701 Holmes Rd 64131 816-349-3300
Dr. Robert Bartman, supt. Fax 349-3431
www.center.k12.mo.us
Center Alternative S Alt
8434 Paseo Blvd 64131 816-349-3662
Dr. Sharon Nibbelink, prin. Fax 349-3667
Center HS 700/9-12
8715 Holmes Rd 64131 816-349-3330
Beth Heide, prin. Fax 349-3427
Center MS 500/6-8
326 E 103rd St 64114 816-612-4000
Linda Williams, prin. Fax 612-4053

Hickman Mills C-I SD 4,400/K-12
9000 Old Santa Fe Rd 64138 816-316-7000
Barbara Tate, supt. Fax 316-7020
www.hickmanmills.org
Hickman Mills JHS 300/8-9
9010 Old Santa Fe Rd 64138 816-316-7300
Jan Davis, prin. Fax 316-8009
Ruskin HS 500/10-12
7000 E 111th St Ste 46 64134 816-316-7400
Chad Ryerson, prin. Fax 316-7475

Kansas City SD 33 14,300/PK-12
1211 McGee St 64106 816-418-7000
Dr. Stephen Green, supt. Fax 418-7631
www.kcpublicschools.org/
African-Centered College Prep K-12
3500 E Meyer Blvd 64132 816-418-1028
Joseph Williams, prin.
Central HS 600/7-12
3221 Indiana Ave 64128 816-418-2000
Linda Collins, prin. Fax 418-2027
East HS 1,100/7-12
1924 Van Brunt Blvd 64127 816-418-3130
Thomas Herrera, prin. Fax 418-3162
Lincoln College Prep HS 1,000/6-12
2111 Woodland Ave 64108 816-418-3000
Jonathan Richard, prin. Fax 418-3015
Manual Career & Tech Center Vo/Tech
1215 E Truman Rd 64106 816-418-5200
Jack Bitzenburg, prin. Fax 418-5220
Northeast HS 1,100/7-12
415 Van Brunt Blvd 64124 816-418-3300
Michael Burns, prin. Fax 418-3310
Paseo Academy of Performing Arts 700/7-12
4747 Flora Ave 64110 816-418-2275
Dennis Walker, prin. Fax 418-2300
Southwest Early College Campus 300/7-12
6512 Wornall Rd 64113 816-418-1800
Edwin Richardson, prin. Fax 418-1837

North Kansas City SD 74 19,100/PK-12
2000 NE 46th St 64116 816-413-5000
Todd White Ed.D., supt. Fax 413-5005
www.nkcschools.org
Career & Technical Education Vo/Tech
1950 NE 46th St 64116 816-413-5058
Renee Freers, dir. Fax 413-5015
Eastgate MS 700/6-8
4700 NE Parvin Rd 64117 816-413-5800
Chris McCann, prin. Fax 413-5805
Maple Park MS 800/6-8
5300 N Bennington Ave 64119 816-413-5700
Kevin Kooi, prin. Fax 413-5705
New Mark MS 1,000/6-8
515 NE 106th St 64155 816-413-6300
Terri Stirlen, prin. Fax 413-6305
Northgate MS 800/6-8
2117 NE 48th St 64118 816-413-6100
Steve St. Louis, prin. Fax 413-6105
Oak Park HS 1,400/9-12
825 NE 79th Ter 64118 816-413-5300
Joseph Hesman, prin. Fax 413-5305
Staley HS 1,300/9-12
2800 NE Shoal Creek Pkwy 64156 816-413-4100
Clark Mershon, prin. Fax 413-4105
Winnetonka HS 1,400/9-12
5815 NE 48th St 64119 816-413-5500
Matt Lindsey, prin. Fax 413-5505
Other Schools – See Gladstone, North Kansas City

Park Hill SD 11,200/PK-12
7703 NW Barry Rd 64153 816-359-4000
Dr. Scott Springston, supt. Fax 359-4049
www.parkhill.k12.mo.us
Congress MS 800/7-8
8150 N Congress Ave 64152 816-359-4230
Dr. Timothy Todd, prin. Fax 359-4219
Jones Education Center 50/Alt
7642 N Green Hills Rd 64151 816-359-4510
Stephanie Amaya, prin. Fax 359-4519
Lakeview MS 700/7-8
6720 NW 64th St 64151 816-359-4220
Dr. Becky Kiefer, prin. Fax 359-4229
Park Hill HS 1,700/9-12
7701 NW Barry Rd 64153 816-359-4110
Dr. J. Bradford Kincheloe, prin. Fax 359-4119
Other Schools – See Riverside

Platte County R-III SD
Supt. — See Platte City
Barry S 500/3-8
2001 NW 87th Ter 64154 816-436-9623
Rebecca Henshaw, prin. Fax 468-6046

Raytown C-2 SD
Supt. — See Raytown
Raytown MS 900/6-8
4900 Pittman Rd 64133 816-268-7360
Dr. Georgetta May, prin. Fax 268-7365

Achieve Test Prep Post-Sec.
2300 Main St Fl 9 64108 816-399-4556
Anthem College Post-Sec.
9001 State Line Rd 64114 888-852-7272
ARAMARK Healthcare Support Services SW Post-Sec.
1000 Carondelet Dr 64114 816-943-2146
Archbishop O'Hara HS 400/9-12
9001 James A Reed Rd 64138 816-763-4800
John O'Connor, prin. Fax 763-0156
Aviation Institute of Maintenance Post-Sec.
4100 Raytown Rd 64129 816-753-9920
Avila University Post-Sec.
11901 Wornall Rd 64145 816-942-8400
Barstow S 700/PK-12
11511 State Line Rd 64114 816-942-3255
Shane Foster, hdmstr. Fax 942-3227
Blue Ridge Christian S 200/PK-12
8524 Blue Ridge Blvd 64138 816-358-0950
Larry Becker, supt. Fax 358-1138
Calvary Bible College & Theological Sem Post-Sec.
15800 Calvary Rd 64147 816-322-0110
Concorde Career College Post-Sec.
3239 Broadway St 64111 816-531-5223
Cristo Rey Kansas City HS 300/9-12
211 W Linwood Blvd 64111 816-457-6044
Kathleen Hanlon, pres. Fax 457-6046
DeVry University Post-Sec.
11224 Holmes Rd 64131 816-943-7300
DeVry University Post-Sec.
1100 Main St Ste 118 64105 816-221-1300
Everest College Post-Sec.
1740 W 92nd St 64114 816-423-8600
Grantham University Post-Sec.
7200 NW 86th St 64153 800-955-2527
Heritage College Post-Sec.
1200 E 104th St Ste 300 64131 816-942-5474
House of Heavilin Beauty College Post-Sec.
5720 Troost Ave 64110 816-523-2471
ITT Technical Institute Post-Sec.
9150 E 41st Ter 64133 816-276-1400
Kansas City Academy 100/6-12
7933 Main St 64114 816-444-5225
Kathy Baldwin-Heitman, prin. Fax 444-8354
Kansas City Art Institute Post-Sec.
4415 Warwick Blvd 64111 816-472-4852
KC Univ. of Medicine and Biosciences Post-Sec.
1750 Independence Ave 64106 816-654-7000
L'Ecole Culinaire Post-Sec.
310 Ward Pkwy 64112 866-205-2521
Lutheran HS 100/9-12
12411 Wornall Rd 64145 816-241-5478
Cary Stelmachowicz Ed.D., dir. Fax 876-2069
Metropolitan Comm College - Penn Valley Post-Sec.
3201 Southwest Traffic Way 64111 816-604-4000
Metropolitan Community Coll - Bus & Tech Post-Sec.
1775 Universal Ave 64120 816-604-5200
Metropolitan Community Coll-Maple Woods Post-Sec.
2601 NE Barry Rd 64156 816-604-3000
Midwestern Baptist Theological Seminary Post-Sec.
5001 N Oak Trfy 64118 816-414-3700
Nazarene Theological Seminary Post-Sec.
1700 E Meyer Blvd 64131 816-268-5400
Northland Christian S 300/PK-12
4214 NW Cookingham Rd 64164 816-464-0555
Richard Rice, prin. Fax 464-0578
Notre Dame De Sion HS 400/9-12
10631 Wornall Rd 64114 816-942-3282
Natalie McDonough, prin. Fax 942-4052
Pembroke Hill S - Ward Pkwy Campus 700/6-12
5121 State Line Rd 64112 816-936-1200
Dr. Steve J. Bellis, head sch Fax 936-1208
Pinnacle Career Institute Post-Sec.
1001 E 101st Ter Ste 325 64131 816-331-5700
Pinnacle Career Institute Post-Sec.
11500 N Ambassador Dr 64153 816-268-3499
Research College of Nursing Post-Sec.
2525 E Meyer Blvd 64132 816-995-2800
Research Medical Center Post-Sec.
2316 E Meyer Blvd 64132 816-276-4101
Rockhurst HS 1,100/9-12
9301 State Line Rd 64114 816-363-2036
Gregory Harkness, prin. Fax 363-3764
Rockhurst University Post-Sec.
1100 Rockhurst Rd 64110 816-501-4000
St. Luke's College of Health Sciences Post-Sec.
624 Westport Rd 64111 816-932-6700
St. Paul School of Theology Post-Sec.
5123 E Truman Rd 64127 816-483-9600
St. Pius X HS 400/9-12
1500 NE 42nd Ter 64116 816-453-3450
Joseph Monachino, prin. Fax 452-7099
St. Teresa Academy 500/9-12
5600 Main St 64113 816-501-0011
Barbara McCormick M.S., prin. Fax 523-0232
Strayer University Post-Sec.
10450 Holmes Rd Ste 100 64131 816-489-4500
Truman Medical Center Post-Sec.
2301 Holmes St 64108 816-556-3153
University of Missouri - Kansas City Post-Sec.
5100 Rockhill Rd 64110 816-235-1000
Vatterott College - Kansas City Post-Sec.
4131 N Corrington Ave 64117 816-861-1000

Kearney, Clay, Pop. 8,257
Kearney R-I SD 3,700/K-12
1002 S Jefferson St 64060 816-628-4116
Dr. Bill Nicely, supt. Fax 628-4074
www.kearney.k12.mo.us
Kearney HS 900/10-12
715 E 19th St 64060 816-628-4585
David Schwarzenbach, prin. Fax 628-3383
Kearney JHS 600/8-9
2215 S Campus St 64060 816-628-2650
Andy Gustafson, prin. Fax 628-1938

Kennett, Dunklin, Pop. 10,740
Kennett SD 39 2,100/PK-12
510 College Ave 63857 573-717-1100
Chris Wilson, supt. Fax 717-1016
www.kennett.k12.mo.us
Kennett Career & Technology Center Vo/Tech
1400 W Washington St 63857 573-717-1123
Terry Bruce, dir. Fax 717-1386
Kennett HS 500/9-12
1400 W Washington St 63857 573-717-1120
David Gilmore, prin. Fax 717-1016
Kennett MS 500/6-8
510 College Ave 63857 573-717-1105
Ward Billings, prin. Fax 717-1106

Keytesville, Chariton, Pop. 471
Keytesville R-III SD 200/PK-12
27247 Highway 5 65261 660-288-3767
Tracy Bottoms, supt. Fax 288-3110
keytesville.k12.mo.us
Keytesville R-III HS 100/7-12
27247 Highway 5 65261 660-288-3767
Rena Roth, prin. Fax 288-3110

King City, Gentry, Pop. 1,004
King City R-I SD 400/PK-12
PO Box 189 64463 660-535-4319
Bruce Skogland, supt. Fax 535-4765
www.kingcity.k12.mo.us
King City JSHS 100/7-12
PO Box 189 64463 660-535-4319
Dottie Stoll, prin. Fax 535-4765

Kingdom City, Callaway, Pop. 127
North Callaway County R-I SD 1,200/PK-12
2690 US Highway 54 65262 573-386-2214
Dr. Bryan Thomsen, supt. Fax 386-2169
nc.k12.mo.us
North Callaway HS 400/9-12
2700 US Highway 54 65262 573-386-2211
Matt Boyer, prin. Fax 386-2403

Kingsville, Johnson, Pop. 264
Kingsville R-I SD 100/K-12
PO Box 7 64061 816-597-3422
Kevin Coleman, supt. Fax 597-3702
www.kingsville.k12.mo.us/
Kingsville S 100/K-12
PO Box 7 64061 816-597-3422
Lorna Warren, prin. Fax 597-3702

Kirbyville, Taney, Pop. 203
Kirbyville R-VI SD 300/K-8
6225 E State Highway 76 65679 417-337-8913
Carless Osbourn, supt. Fax 348-0794
www.kirbyville.k12.mo.us/
Kirbyville MS 200/4-8
6225 E State Highway 76 65679 417-348-0444
Amy Burton, prin. Fax 348-0525

Kirksville, Adair, Pop. 17,170
Kirksville R-III SD 2,600/PK-12
1901 E Hamilton St 63501 660-665-7774
Patrick Williams, supt. Fax 665-1448
www.kirksville.k12.mo.us
Kirksville Area Technical Center Vo/Tech
1103 Cottage Grove Ave 63501 660-665-2865
Sheryl Ferguson, prin. Fax 626-1477
Kirksville HS 800/9-12
1300 Cottage Grove Ave 63501 660-665-4631
Randy Mikel, prin. Fax 626-1439
Kirksville MS 500/6-8
1515 Cottage Grove Ave 63501 660-665-3793
Dr. Michael Mitchell, prin. Fax 626-1418

Kirksville Coll. of Osteopathic Medicine Post-Sec.
800 W Jefferson St 63501 660-626-2237
School of Health Management Post-Sec.
800 W Jefferson St 63501 877-626-5577
Still Univ MO Sch of Dentistry & Oral Hl Post-Sec.
800 W Jefferson St 63501 866-626-2878
Truman State University Post-Sec.
100 E Normal Ave 63501 660-785-4000

Kirkwood, Saint Louis, Pop. 27,112
Kirkwood R-VII SD 5,100/K-12
11289 Manchester Rd 63122 314-213-6101
Dr. Tom Williams, supt. Fax 984-0002
www.kirkwoodschools.org
Kirkwood HS 1,700/9-12
801 W Essex Ave 63122 314-213-6110
Dr. Michael Havener, prin. Fax 984-4412
Nipher MS 600/6-8
700 S Kirkwood Rd 63122 314-213-6180
Dr. Michele Condon, prin. Fax 213-6178
North Kirkwood MS 600/6-8
11287 Manchester Rd 63122 314-213-6170
Tim Cochran, prin. Fax 213-6177

St. Louis Community College - Meramec Post-Sec.
11333 Big Bend Rd 63122 314-984-7500
Ursuline Academy 600/9-12
341 S Sappington Rd 63122 314-984-2800
Mark Michalski, prin. Fax 966-3396

Knob Noster, Johnson, Pop. 2,592
Knob Noster R-VIII SD 1,400/PK-12
401 E Wimer St 65336 660-563-3186
Dr. Jaret Tomlinson, supt. Fax 563-3026
knobnoster.k12.mo.us/
Knob Noster HS 400/9-12
504 S Washington Ave 65336 660-563-2283
Connie Morris, prin. Fax 563-3384
Knob Noster MS 300/6-8
211 E Wimer St 65336 660-563-2260
Brett Hieronymus, prin. Fax 563-3274

Koshkonong, Oregon, Pop. 200
Oregon-Howell R-III SD 200/K-12
PO Box 398 65692 417-867-5601
Robert Casteel, supt. Fax 867-3757
koshkonong.k12.mo.us/
Koshkonong JSHS 100/7-12
PO Box 398 65692 417-867-5601
Stan Elliott, prin. Fax 867-3757

Laddonia, Audrain, Pop. 512
Community R-VI SD 300/PK-12
35063 Highway BB 63352 573-492-6223
Cheryl Mack, supt. Fax 492-6268
www.cr6.net/
Community HS 200/6-12
35063 Highway BB 63352 573-492-6222
Dale Marshall, prin. Fax 492-6407

Lake Ozark, Camden, Pop. 1,563
School of the Osage R-II SD 1,900/PK-12
PO Box 1960 65049 573-365-4091
Dr. Brent Depee', supt. Fax 365-5748
www.osage.k12.mo.us
Other Schools – See Osage Beach

Lamar, Barton, Pop. 4,398
Lamar R-I SD 1,300/PK-12
202 W 7th St 64759 417-682-3527
Dr. Dennis Wilson, supt. Fax 682-6013
www.lamar.k12.mo.us
Lamar Career & Technical Center Vo/Tech
202 W 7th St 64759 417-682-3384
Dr. Traci Pattison, dir. Fax 682-3420
Lamar HS 400/9-12
202 W 7th St 64759 417-682-5571
Jennifer Beem, prin. Fax 681-0328
Lamar MS 300/6-8
202 W 7th St 64759 417-682-3548
Alan Ray, prin. Fax 682-3420

La Monte, Pettis, Pop. 1,113
La Monte R-IV SD 400/PK-12
301 S Washington St 65337 660-347-5439
Joan Twidwell, supt. Fax 347-5467
lamonte.k12.mo.us/
La Monte JSHS 200/7-12
301 S Washington St 65337 660-347-5439
Jana Fleckenstine, prin. Fax 347-5467

La Plata, Macon, Pop. 1,336
La Plata R-II SD 300/PK-12
201 W Moore St 63549 660-332-7001
Dr. Craig Noah, supt. Fax 332-7929
laplata.k12.mo.us
La Plata JSHS 200/7-12
201 W Moore St 63549 660-332-7001
Steve Safley, prin. Fax 332-7656

Laquey, Pulaski
Laquey R-V SD 700/PK-12
PO Box 130 65534 573-765-3716
Randy Caffey, supt. Fax 765-4052
www.laquey.k12.mo.us/
Laquey R-V HS 200/9-12
PO Box 130 65534 573-765-4051
Eric Shaw, prin. Fax 765-5608
Laquey R-V MS 200/6-8
PO Box 130 65534 573-765-3129
Jamie Roberts, prin. Fax 765-4086

Lathrop, Clinton, Pop. 2,052
Lathrop R-II SD 800/K-12
700 East St 64465 816-528-7500
Chris Fine, supt. Fax 528-7514
lathropschools.com
Lathrop HS 300/9-12
102 N School Dr 64465 816-528-7400
Robert Bowers, prin. Fax 528-7456
Lathrop MS 200/6-8
612 Center St 64465 816-528-7600
Kurtis Jensen, prin. Fax 528-7637

Lawson, Ray, Pop. 2,441
Lawson R-XIV SD 1,200/PK-12
PO Box 157 64062 816-580-7277
Roger Schmitz, supt. Fax 296-7723
lawsoncardinals.org/
Lawson HS 400/9-12
PO Box 157 64062 816-580-7270
Don Edwards, prin. Fax 296-3048
Lawson MS 400/5-8
PO Box 157 64062 816-580-7279
Tammy Dunn, prin. Fax 296-3164

Leadwood, Saint Francois, Pop. 1,274
West St. Francois County R-IV SD 1,000/PK-12
1124 Main St 63653 573-562-7535
Stacy Stevens, supt. Fax 562-7510
westco.k12.mo.us/
West County MS 200/6-8
1124 Main St 63653 573-562-7544
Kevin Coffman, prin. Fax 562-7510
Other Schools – See Park Hills

Lebanon, Laclede, Pop. 14,144
Lebanon R-III SD 4,700/PK-12
1310 E Route 66 65536 417-532-9141
Dr. Duane Widhalm, supt. Fax 532-9492
www.lebanon.k12.mo.us
Lebanon Alternative S Alt
1015 N Jefferson Ave 65536 417-533-3824
Katie Mitchell, dir.
Lebanon JHS 600/7-8
500 N Adams Ave 65536 417-532-9121
Tom Merriott, prin. Fax 533-3805
Lebanon SHS 1,500/9-12
777 Brice St 65536 417-532-9144
Kevin Lowery, prin. Fax 532-3386
Lebanon Technology Career Center Vo/Tech
757 Brice St 65536 417-532-5494
Keith Davis, dir. Fax 532-4510

Lees Summit, Jackson, Pop. 89,308
Blue Springs R-IV SD
Supt. — See Blue Springs
Delta Woods MS 800/6-8
4401 NE Lakewood Way 64064 816-795-5830
Steve Cook, prin. Fax 795-5839

Lee's Summit R-VII SD 17,800/PK-12
301 NE Tudor Rd 64086 816-986-1000
Dr. David McGehee, supt. Fax 986-1170
www.leesummit.k12.mo.us
Campbell MS 900/7-8
1201 NE Colbern Rd 64086 816-986-3175
Dr. Vicki Porter, prin. Fax 986-3245
Lee's Summit HS 1,900/9-12
400 SE Blue Pkwy 64063 816-986-2000
Dr. John Faulkenberry, prin. Fax 986-2095
Lee's Summit North HS 1,900/9-12
901 NE Douglas St 64086 816-986-3000
Lisa Jacques, prin. Fax 986-3170
Lee's Summit West HS 1,700/9-12
2600 SW Ward Rd 64082 816-986-4000
Dr. David Sharp, prin. Fax 986-4115

Pleasant Lea MS 900/7-8
630 SW Persels Rd 64081 816-986-1175
Janette Miller, prin. Fax 986-1225
Summit Lakes MS 900/7-8
3500 SW Windemere Dr 64082 816-986-1375
Dr. David Carlson, prin. Fax 986-1435
Summit Ridge Academy Alt
2620 SW Ward Rd 64082 816-986-4120
Burt Whaley, prin. Fax 986-4135
Summit Technical Academy Vo/Tech
777 NW Blue Pkwy 64086 816-524-3366
Elaine Metcalf, prin. Fax 524-1436

Metropolitan Community Coll - Longview Post-Sec.
500 SW Longview Rd 64081 816-604-2000
Summit Christian Academy 700/PK-12
1500 SW Jefferson St 64081 816-525-1480
Linda Harrelson, admin. Fax 525-5402

Leeton, Johnson, Pop. 557
Leeton R-X SD 400/PK-12
500 N Main St 64761 660-653-2301
Susan Crooks, supt. Fax 653-4315
www.leeton.k12.mo.us/
Leeton HS 100/9-12
500 N Main St 64761 660-653-4314
Jim Newland, prin. Fax 653-4315
Leeton MS 100/6-8
500 N Main St 64761 660-653-4314
Jim Newland, prin. Fax 653-4315

Leopold, Bollinger
Leopold R-III SD 200/K-12
PO Box 39 63760 573-238-2211
Keenan Kinder, supt. Fax 238-9868
schoolweb.missouri.edu/leopold.k12.mo.us/
Leopold JSHS 100/7-12
PO Box 39 63760 573-238-2211
Matt Britt, prin. Fax 283-9868

Lesterville, Reynolds
Lesterville R-IV SD 300/PK-12
PO Box 120 63654 573-637-2201
Earlene Fox, supt. Fax 637-2279
www.lesterville.k12.mo.us/
Lesterville JSHS 100/7-12
PO Box 120 63654 573-637-2201
James Watts, prin. Fax 637-2279
Other Schools – See Black

Lewistown, Lewis, Pop. 532
Lewis County C-1 SD 1,000/PK-12
21504 State Highway 6 63452 573-209-3217
Jacqueline Ebeling, supt. Fax 209-3318
www.lewis.k12.mo.us
Highland JSHS 500/7-12
21504 State Highway 6 63452 573-209-3215
Alan Koch, prin. Fax 209-3469

Lexington, Lafayette, Pop. 4,541
Lexington R-V SD 900/PK-12
2323 High School Dr Ste A 64067 660-259-4369
Brad MacLaughlin, supt. Fax 259-4992
www.lexington.k12.mo.us
Lexington HS 300/9-12
2309 Aull Ln 64067 660-259-4391
Marlin Roach, prin. Fax 259-2166
Lexington MS 300/5-8
1111 S 24th St 64067 660-259-4611
Joy Grimes, prin. Fax 259-2538
Lex La-Ray Tech Ctr Vo/Tech
2323 High School Dr 64067 660-259-2264
Sarrah Dobson, dir. Fax 259-6262
Student Success Center Alt
2309 Aull Ln 64067 660-259-6676
Marlin Roach, prin. Fax 259-3639

Wentworth Military Academy Post-Sec.
1880 Washington Ave 64067 800-962-7682
Wentworth Military Academy 100/9-12
1880 Washington Ave 64067 660-259-2221
Col. Bill Sellers, pres. Fax 259-2677

Liberal, Barton, Pop. 739
Liberal R-II SD 500/PK-12
PO Box 38 64762 417-843-5115
William Harvey, supt. Fax 843-6698
www.liberal.k12.mo.us/
Liberal HS 100/9-12
PO Box 38 64762 417-843-2125
Anthony Robertson, prin. Fax 843-2403
Liberal MS 100/6-8
PO Box 38 64762 417-843-6033
Margaret Ruddick, prin. Fax 843-2403

Liberty, Clay, Pop. 28,451
Liberty SD 53 10,500/PK-12
650 Conistor Ln 64068 816-736-5300
Mike Brewer, supt. Fax 736-5306
www.liberty.k12.mo.us
Liberty Academy Alt
8 Victory Ln 64068 816-736-5470
Robert Cordell, dir. Fax 736-5471
Liberty JHS 800/8-9
600 W Kansas St 64068 816-736-5380
Scott Carr, prin. Fax 736-5384
Liberty North HS 10-12
1000 NE 104th St 64068 816-736-5500
Martin Jacobs, prin. Fax 736-5535
Liberty SHS 1,700/10-12
200 Blue Jay Dr 64068 816-736-5340
April Adams, prin. Fax 736-5345
South Valley JHS 800/8-9
800 Midjay Dr 64068 816-736-7300
Dr. Julie Moore, prin. Fax 736-7301

William Jewell College Post-Sec.
500 College Hl 64068 816-781-7700

Licking, Texas, Pop. 3,111
Licking R-VIII SD 900/PK-12
125 College Ave 65542 573-674-2911
Dr. John Hood, supt. Fax 674-4064
www.licking.k12.mo.us/
Licking JSHS 400/7-12
125 College Ave 65542 573-674-2711
Stephen Denbow, prin. Fax 674-2142

Lincoln, Benton, Pop. 1,178
Lincoln R-II SD 500/K-12
PO Box 39 65338 660-547-3514
Kevin Smith, supt. Fax 547-3729
www.lincoln.k12.mo.us/
Lincoln JSHS 200/7-12
PO Box 39 65338 660-547-3514
Marc Spunaugle, prin. Fax 547-3729

Linn, Osage, Pop. 1,447
Osage County R-II SD 700/PK-12
1212 E Main St 65051 573-897-4200
Shawn Poyser, supt. Fax 897-3768
www.linn.k12.mo.us
Linn JSHS 300/6-12
1212 E Main St 65051 573-897-4216
Lorie Winslow, prin. Fax 897-4570

Linn State Technical College Post-Sec.
1 Technology Dr 65051 573-897-5000

Lockwood, Dade, Pop. 928
Lockwood R-I SD 400/PK-12
400 W 4th St 65682 417-232-4513
Bill Rogers, supt. Fax 232-4187
www.lockwoodschools.org/
Lockwood HS 100/9-12
400 W 4th St 65682 417-232-4513
Dennis Cornish, prin. Fax 232-4187

Lone Jack, Jackson, Pop. 1,030
Lone Jack C-6 SD 600/PK-12
201 W Lne Jack Lees Smmt Rd 64070816-697-3539
Bryan Prewitt, admin. Fax 697-8869
www.lonejackc6.net
Lone Jack JSHS 300/7-12
313 S Bynum Rd 64070 816-697-2215
Matthew Tarwater, admin. Fax 566-3128

Louisburg, Dallas, Pop. 116
Dallas County R-I SD
Supt. — See Buffalo
Dallas County Career Center Vo/Tech
PO Box 100 65685 417-752-3491
Lester Abel, prin. Fax 752-3493

Louisiana, Pike, Pop. 3,291
Louisiana R-II SD 700/PK-12
3321 Georgia St 63353 573-754-4261
Richard Boaden, supt. Fax 754-4319
www.schoolweb.missouri.edu/louisiana.k12.mo.us
Louisiana HS 200/9-12
3321 Georgia St 63353 573-754-6181
Todd Smith, prin. Fax 754-5964
Louisiana MS 200/6-8
3321 Georgia St 63353 573-754-5340
Chuck Tophinke, prin. Fax 754-5377

Ludlow, Livingston, Pop. 131
Southwest Livingston County R-I SD 200/PK-12
4944 Highway DD 64656 660-738-4433
Cinthia Barnes, supt. Fax 738-4441
www.southwestr1.org/
Southwest Livingston County JSHS 100/7-12
4944 Highway DD 64656 660-738-4433
Tom Smith, prin. Fax 738-4115

Macks Creek, Camden, Pop. 238
Macks Creek R-V SD 300/PK-12
245 State Rd N 65786 573-363-5909
Joshua Phillips, supt. Fax 363-0127
mcreek.k12.mo.us/
Macks Creek JSHS 100/7-12
245 State Rd N 65786 573-363-5911
Doug Kempker, prin. Fax 363-5981

Macon, Macon, Pop. 5,339
Macon County R-I SD 1,300/PK-12
702 N Missouri St 63552 660-385-5719
Dr. Charles Stockton, supt. Fax 385-7179
www.macon.k12.mo.us/
Family Literacy Center Alt
204 Crescent Dr 63552 660-385-2061
Shandra Clark, dir. Fax 385-5893
Macon Area Vocational Technical S Vo/Tech
702 N Missouri St 63552 660-385-2158
Peter Claas, dir. Fax 385-3667
Macon County HS 400/9-12
702 N Missouri St 63552 660-385-5748
Jeffrey Haley, prin. Fax 385-2746
Macon County MS 300/6-8
702 N Missouri St 63552 660-385-2189
Dustin Fanning, prin. Fax 385-7230

Madison, Monroe, Pop. 551
Madison C-3 SD 300/PK-12
309 S Thomas St 65263 660-291-5115
Fred Weibling, supt. Fax 291-5006
www.madison.k12.mo.us
Madison JSHS 100/7-12
309 S Thomas St 65263 660-291-4515
Patricia Vessar, prin. Fax 291-5006

Malden, Dunklin, Pop. 4,199
Malden R-I SD 1,100/PK-12
505 Burkhart St 63863 573-276-5794
Kenneth Cook, supt. Fax 276-5796
www.malden.k12.mo.us/
Malden JSHS 500/7-12
505 Burkhart St 63863 573-276-4546
Jerri Hardy, prin. Fax 276-4548

Malta Bend, Saline, Pop. 249
Malta Bend R-V SD 100/K-12
PO Box 10 65339 660-595-2371
Charles Marcum, supt. Fax 595-2430
mbtigers.com
Malta Bend JSHS 100/6-12
PO Box 10 65339 660-595-2371
Charles Marcum, prin. Fax 595-2430

Manchester, Saint Louis, Pop. 17,723
Parkway C-2 SD
Supt. — See Chesterfield
Parkway South MS 600/6-8
760 Woods Mill Rd 63011 314-415-7200
Craig Fenner, prin. Fax 415-7213
Parkway Southwest MS 700/6-8
701 Wren Ave 63021 314-415-7300
Dr. Craig Maxwell, prin. Fax 415-7334

Heritage Classical Christian Academy 7-12
625 Meramec Station Rd 63021 636-394-8063
Jason Wood, dir. Fax 394-8067
Kennedy HS 300/9-12
500 Woods Mill Rd 63011 636-227-5900
Mary Hey, prin. Fax 227-0298

Mansfield, Wright, Pop. 1,287
Mansfield R-IV SD 700/PK-12
316 W Ohio St 65704 417-924-8458
Nate Moore, supt. Fax 924-3427
www.mansfieldschool.net
Mansfield HS 200/9-12
315 W Ohio St 65704 417-924-3236
Richard Wylie, prin. Fax 924-8789
Mansfield JHS 200/6-8
316 W Ohio St 65704 417-924-8625
Gary Greene, prin. Fax 924-8789

Maplewood, Saint Louis, Pop. 7,766
Maplewood Richmond Heights SD 1,200/PK-12
7539 Manchester Rd 63143 314-644-4400
Karen Hall, supt. Fax 781-3160
www.mrhsd.org/
Maplewood Richmond Heights HS 300/9-12
7539 Manchester Rd 63143 314-644-4401
Kevin Grawer, prin. Fax 644-3681
Other Schools – See Saint Louis

Marble Hill, Bollinger, Pop. 1,464
Woodland R-IV SD 900/K-12
RR 5 Box 3210 63764 573-238-3343
Jennings Wilkinson, supt. Fax 238-2153
www.woodland.k12.mo.us/
Woodland HS 300/9-12
RR 5 Box 3210 63764 573-238-2663
Shawn Kinder, prin. Fax 238-0186
Woodland MS 300/5-8
RR 5 Box 3210 63764 573-238-2656
Ed Siebenhuener, prin. Fax 238-0133

Marceline, Linn, Pop. 2,210
Marceline R-V SD 600/PK-12
400 E Santa Fe Ave 64658 660-376-3371
Gabe Edgar, supt. Fax 376-6001
www.marcelineschools.org
Marceline HS 200/9-12
314 E Santa Fe Ave 64658 660-376-2411
Matt Finch, prin. Fax 376-6016
Marceline MS 100/6-8
314 E Santa Fe Ave 64658 660-376-2411
Matt Finch, prin. Fax 376-6016

Marionville, Lawrence, Pop. 2,171
Marionville R-IX SD 800/PK-12
PO Box 409 65705 417-258-7755
Dr. Larry Brown, supt. Fax 258-2564
www.marionville.us/
Marionville HS 200/9-12
PO Box 409 65705 417-258-2521
Mark Estep, prin. Fax 258-7637
Marionville MS 200/6-8
PO Box 409 65705 417-258-2531
Shane Moseman, prin. Fax 258-2564

Marquand, Madison, Pop. 203
Marquand-Zion R-VI SD 200/K-12
205 E Morley 63655 573-783-3388
John Boyd, supt. Fax 783-3067
Marquand-Zion JSHS 100/7-12
205 E Morley 63655 573-783-3388
John Boyd, prin. Fax 783-3067

Marshall, Saline, Pop. 12,591
Marshall SD 2,500/K-12
860 W Vest St 65340 660-886-7414
Ryan Huff, supt. Fax 886-5641
www.marshallschools.com/
Bueker MS 700/5-8
565 S Odell Ave 65340 660-886-6833
Lance Tobin, prin. Fax 886-7529
Marshall HS 800/9-12
805 S Miami Ave 65340 660-886-2244
Royal Peterson, prin. Fax 886-2669
Saline County Career Ctr Vo/Tech
900 W Vest St 65340 660-886-6958
Derek Lark, dir. Fax 886-3092

Missouri Valley College Post-Sec.
500 E College St 65340 660-831-4000

Marshfield, Webster, Pop. 6,529
Marshfield R-I SD 3,100/PK-12
170 State Highway DD 65706 417-859-2120
Dr. Mark Mayo, supt. Fax 859-2193
marshfieldbluejays.org/
Marshfield HS 900/9-12
370 State Highway DD 65706 417-859-2120
Randy Luebbert, prin. Fax 859-7756
Marshfield JHS 700/6-8
660 N Locust St 65706 417-859-2120
Jeff Curley, prin. Fax 859-4970

Maryland Heights, Saint Louis, Pop. 26,834
Pattonville R-III SD
Supt. — See Saint Ann
Pattonville Heights MS 500/6-8
195 Fee Fee Rd 63043 314-213-8033
Scot Mosher, prin. Fax 213-8633
Pattonville HS 1,800/9-12
2497 Creve Coeur Mill Rd 63043 314-213-8051
Joe Dobrinic Ed.D., prin. Fax 213-8651

Anthem College Post-Sec.
13723 Riverport Dr Ste 103 63043 888-852-7272

Maryville, Nodaway, Pop. 11,837
Maryville R-II SD 1,400/PK-12
1429 S Munn Ave 64468 660-562-3255
Larry Linthacum, supt. Fax 562-4113
www.maryville.k12.mo.us/
Maryville HS 500/9-12
1503 S Munn Ave 64468 660-562-3511
Jason Eggers, prin. Fax 562-4822
Maryville MS 400/5-8
525 W South Hills Dr 64468 660-562-3244
Kevin Pitts, prin. Fax 562-4138
Northwest Technical S Vo/Tech
1515 S Munn Ave 64468 660-562-3022
Jim Cassity, dir. Fax 562-2010

Northwest Missouri State University Post-Sec.
800 University Dr 64468 660-562-1212

Maysville, DeKalb, Pop. 1,100
Maysville R-I SD 600/K-12
PO Box 68 64469 816-449-2308
Robert Smith, supt. Fax 449-5678
maysville.k12.mo.us/
Maysville JSHS 300/7-12
PO Box 68 64469 816-449-2308
Alan Hutchcraft, prin. Fax 449-5610

Meadville, Linn, Pop. 461
Meadville R-IV SD 200/K-12
PO Box 217 64659 660-938-4111
Ron Holcer, supt. Fax 938-4100
Meadville JSHS 100/7-12
PO Box 217 64659 660-938-4112
Ronald Holcer, prin. Fax 938-4100

Memphis, Scotland, Pop. 1,807
Scotland County R-I SD 600/PK-12
438 W Lovers Ln 63555 660-465-8531
David Shalley, supt. Fax 465-8636
scotland.k12.mo.us/
Scotland County JSHS 300/7-12
606 W Lovers Ln 63555 660-465-8901
Ryan Bergeson, prin. Fax 465-7715

Mendon, Chariton, Pop. 171
Northwestern R-I SD 200/PK-12
PO Box 43 64660 660-272-3201
Ron Garber, supt. Fax 272-3419
Northwestern HS 100/7-12
PO Box 43 64660 660-272-3201
Eric Hoyt, prin. Fax 272-3738

Mercer, Mercer, Pop. 315
North Mercer County R-III SD 200/PK-12
PO Box 648 64661 660-382-4214
Dan Owens, supt. Fax 382-4236
www.northmercer.k12.mo.us
Mercer JSHS 100/7-12
PO Box 648 64661 660-382-4214
Kim Palmer, prin. Fax 382-4239

Mexico, Audrain, Pop. 11,278
Mexico SD 59 2,400/PK-12
2101 Lakeview Rd 65265 573-581-3773
Kevin Freeman, supt. Fax 581-1794
www.mexicoschools.net
Hart Career Center Vo/Tech
905 N Wade St 65265 573-581-5684
Dr. Mickie Shank, dir. Fax 581-7084
Mexico Education Center Alt
905 N Wade St 65265 573-581-5529
Chris Denham, dir. Fax 581-1794
Mexico HS 800/9-12
639 N Wade St 65265 573-581-4296
Dr. Terry Robinson, prin. Fax 581-3788
Mexico MS 500/6-8
1200 W Boulevard St 65265 573-581-4664
Deb Haag, prin. Fax 581-8440

Missouri Military Academy 300/6-12
204 N Grand St 65265 573-581-1776
Charles McGeorge, pres. Fax 581-0081

Milan, Sullivan, Pop. 1,949
Milan C-2 SD 700/PK-12
373 S Market St 63556 660-265-4414
Kimberly K. Johnson, supt. Fax 265-4315
www.milan.k12.mo.us/
Milan HS 200/9-12
373 S Market St 63556 660-265-4415
Leah Stein, prin. Fax 265-4315
Milan MS 200/5-8
373 S Market St 63556 660-265-4421
Eric Eckhoff, prin. Fax 265-4315

Miller, Lawrence, Pop. 697
Miller R-II SD 600/K-12
110 W 6th St 65707 417-452-3515
Tracey Hankins, supt. Fax 452-2709
www.millerschools.org/
Miller JSHS 300/7-12
110 W 6th St 65707 417-452-3271
Kern Sorrell, prin. Fax 452-2310

Moberly, Randolph, Pop. 13,647
Moberly SD 2,400/K-12
926 Kwix Rd 65270 660-269-2600
Gena McCluskey, supt. Fax 269-2611
moberly.k12.mo.us/
Moberly Area Technical Center Vo/Tech
1623 Gratz Brown St 65270 660-269-2690
Mike Barner, dir. Fax 269-2692
Moberly HS 800/9-12
1625 Gratz Brown St 65270 660-269-2660
Aaron Vitt, prin. Fax 263-5977
Moberly MS 500/6-8
920 Kwix Rd 65270 660-269-2680
Wes Land, prin. Fax 269-8519
North Central Regional Alt. S Alt
200 Porter St 65270 660-269-8800
Debbie Young, dir. Fax 269-8576

Central Christian College of the Bible Post-Sec.
911 E Urbandale Dr 65270 660-263-3900
Moberly Area Community College Post-Sec.
101 College Ave 65270 660-263-4110

Mokane, Callaway, Pop. 182
South Callaway County R-II SD 900/PK-12
10135 State Road C 65059 573-676-5225
Mary Battles, supt. Fax 676-5134
www.sc.k12.mo.us/
South Callaway HS 300/9-12
10135 State Road C 65059 573-676-5211
Heather Helsel, prin. Fax 676-5132
South Callaway MS 200/5-8
10135 State Road C 65059 573-676-5216
Gary Bonsall, prin. Fax 676-5347

Monett, Barry, Pop. 8,746
Monett R-I SD 2,400/PK-12
900 E Scott St 65708 417-235-7422
Brad Hanson, supt. Fax 235-1415
monett.schoolfusion.us/
Monett HS 600/9-12
1 David Sippy Dr 65708 417-235-5445
David Steward, prin. Fax 235-7884
Monett MS 400/7-8
710 9th St 65708 417-235-6228
Dr. Jonathan Apostol, prin. Fax 235-3278
Southwest Area Career Center Vo/Tech
2 David Sippy Dr 65708 417-235-7022
Russ Moreland, dir. Fax 235-8270

Monroe City, Monroe, Pop. 2,481
Monroe City R-I SD 700/PK-12
401 US Highway 24/36 E 63456 573-735-4631
James Masters, supt. Fax 735-2413
monroe.k12.mo.us/
Monroe City MS 200/5-8
430 N Washington St 63456 573-735-4742
Joshua Klusmeyer, prin. Fax 735-2413
Monroe City R-I HS 300/9-12
401 US Highway 24/36 E 63456 573-735-4626
Ryan Watson, prin. Fax 735-2413

Montgomery City, Montgomery, Pop. 2,792
Montgomery County R-II SD 1,400/PK-12
418 N Highway 19 63361 573-564-2278
Michael Gray, supt. Fax 564-6182
www.mc-wildcats.org
Montgomery County HS 400/9-12
394 N Highway 19 63361 573-564-2213
John Hixson, prin. Fax 564-3516
Montgomery County MS 300/6-8
418 N Highway 19 63361 573-564-2253
Madonna Pund, prin. Fax 564-6182

Montrose, Henry, Pop. 383
Montrose R-XIV SD 100/K-12
307 E 2nd St 64770 660-693-4812
Richard Wells, supt. Fax 693-4594
Montrose R-XIV HS 50/9-12
307 E 2nd St 64770 660-693-4812
Richard Wells, admin. Fax 693-4594

Morrisville, Polk, Pop. 377
Marion C. Early R-V SD 700/PK-12
5309 S Main Ave 65710 417-376-2255
Eric Kurre, supt. Fax 376-3243
mceonline.net
Early JSHS 400/6-12
5309 S Main Ave 65710 417-376-2216
Leane McNay, prin. Fax 376-7622

Moscow Mills, Lincoln, Pop. 2,430
Troy R-III SD
Supt. — See Troy
Ninth Grade Center 500/9-9
80 Elm Tree Rd 63362 636-366-4450
Chris Chaney, prin. Fax 366-4451

Mound City, Holt, Pop. 1,154
Mound City R-II SD 200/PK-12
708 Nebraska St 64470 660-442-3737
Ken Eaton, supt. Fax 442-5941
mndcty.k12.mo.us
Mound City HS 100/9-12
708 Nebraska St 64470 660-442-5429
Korey Miles, prin. Fax 442-5941

Mountain Grove, Wright, Pop. 4,721
Mountain Grove R-III SD 1,500/K-12
PO Box 806 65711 417-926-3177
Bridget Williams, supt. Fax 926-4564
www.mg.k12.mo.us
Mountain Grove HS 400/9-12
PO Box 806 65711 417-926-3177
Marcie Stumpff, prin. Fax 926-1702
Mountain Grove MS 400/5-8
PO Box 806 65711 417-926-3177
J.T. Hale, prin. Fax 926-1673

Ozark Mountain Technical Center — Vo/Tech
PO Box 806 65711 — 417-926-3177
Robert Higgins, dir. — Fax 926-6858

Mountain View, Howell, Pop. 2,694
Mountain View-Birch Tree R-III SD — 1,300/PK-12
PO Box 464 65548 — 417-934-2020
Jerry Nicholson, supt. — Fax 934-5404
mvbt.k12.mo.us/
Liberty HS — 400/9-12
PO Box 464 65548 — 417-934-2020
John Daniels, prin. — Fax 934-1329
Liberty MS — 300/6-8
PO Box 464 65548 — 417-934-2020
Walt Belcher, prin. — Fax 934-1329

Mount Vernon, Lawrence, Pop. 4,491
Mt. Vernon R-V SD — 1,500/K-12
731 S Landrum St 65712 — 417-466-7573
Russ Cruzan, supt. — Fax 466-7058
Mount Vernon HS — 500/9-12
400 W Highway 174 65712 — 417-466-7526
Scott Cook, prin. — Fax 466-4307
Mount Vernon MS — 400/6-8
731 S Landrum St 65712 — 417-466-3137
Robert Senninger, prin. — Fax 466-7058

Myrtle, Oregon
Couch R-I SD — 300/PK-12
RR 1 Box 1187 65778 — 417-938-4211
Allen Moss, supt. — Fax 938-4267
www.couch.k12.mo.us/
Couch JSHS — 200/7-12
RR 1 Box 1187 65778 — 417-938-4212
Sherry McMasters, prin. — Fax 938-4267

Naylor, Ripley, Pop. 602
Naylor R-II SD — 400/K-12
RR 2 Box 512 63953 — 573-399-2505
Sherry Burns, supt. — Fax 399-2874
schoolweb.missouri.edu/naylor.k12.mo.us/
Naylor JSHS — 200/7-12
RR 2 Box 512 63953 — 573-399-2506
Terry Arnold, prin. — Fax 399-2388

Neelyville, Butler, Pop. 467
Neelyville R-IV SD — 600/PK-12
PO Box 8 63954 — 573-989-3813
Brad Hagood, supt. — Fax 989-3434
www.neelyville.k12.mo.us
Neelyville JSHS — 300/7-12
PO Box 8 63954 — 573-989-3815
Justin Dobbins, prin. — Fax 989-6322

Neosho, Newton, Pop. 11,282
Neosho R-V SD — 4,400/PK-12
511 S Neosho Blvd 64850 — 417-451-8600
Dan Decker, supt. — Fax 451-8604
www.neosho.k12.mo.us
Neosho HS — 1,300/9-12
511 S Neosho Blvd 64850 — 417-451-8670
Darren Cook, prin — Fax 451-8605
Neosho JHS — 300/8-8
511 S Neosho Blvd 64850 — 417-451-8660
Jenifer Cryer, prin — Fax 451-8687

Crowder College — Post-Sec.
601 Laclede Ave 64850 — 417-451-3223
Neosho Beauty College — Post-Sec.
116 N Wood St 64850 — 417-451-7216
Neosho Christian S — 100/K-12
903 W South St 64850 — 417-451-1941
Lawrence Sanders M.S., supt. — Fax 451-4059
Ozark Christian Academy — 50/K-12
PO Box 786 64850 — 417-451-1100
Joyce Prihoda, prin. — Fax 451-9902

Nevada, Vernon, Pop. 8,266
Nevada R-V SD — 2,500/PK-12
811 W Hickory St 64772 — 417-448-2000
Dr. David Stephens, supt. — Fax 448-2006
www.nevada.k12.mo.us
Nevada HS — 700/9-12
800 W Hickory St 64772 — 417-448-2020
Debra Workman, prin. — Fax 448-1923
Nevada MS — 600/6-8
900 N Olive St 64772 — 417-448-2040
Jodie McNeley, prin. — Fax 448-2048
Nevada Regional Tech-Center — Vo/Tech
900 W Ashland St 64772 — 417-448-2090
Dr. Phillip Witt, dir. — Fax 448-2092

Cottey College — Post-Sec.
1000 W Austin Blvd 64772 — 417-667-8181

Newark, Knox, Pop. 88

Heartland Christian College — Post-Sec.
500 New Creation Rd N 63458 — 660-284-4800

New Bloomfield, Callaway, Pop. 652
New Bloomfield R-III SD — 700/PK-12
307 Redwood Dr 65063 — 573-491-3700
David Tramel, supt. — Fax 491-3772
www.nb.k12.mo.us
New Bloomfield JSHS — 300/6-12
307 Redwood Dr 65063 — 573-491-3700
Jeremy Davidson, prin. — Fax 491-3696

Newburg, Phelps, Pop. 466
Newburg R-II SD — 500/PK-12
PO Box C 65550 — 573-762-9653
John Westerman, supt. — Fax 762-3040
www.newburg.k12.mo.us
Newburg JSHS — 200/7-12
PO Box C 65550 — 573-762-2331
Steve Guffey, prin. — Fax 762-0140

New Cambria, Macon, Pop. 195
Macon County R-IV SD — 100/K-12
PO Box 70 63558 — 660-226-5615
John Dunham, supt. — Fax 226-5618
www.mcr4.k12.mo.us/
Macon County JSHS — 100/7-12
PO Box 70 63558 — 660-226-5615
Carol Burstert, prin. — Fax 226-5618

New Franklin, Howard, Pop. 1,064
New Franklin R-I SD — 500/PK-12
412 W Broadway 65274 — 660-848-2141
Dr. David Haggard, supt. — Fax 848-2226
www.nfranklin.k12.mo.us/
New Franklin MSHS — 200/6-12
412 W Broadway 65274 — 660-848-2314
Benji Dorson, prin. — Fax 848-3071

New Haven, Franklin, Pop. 2,057
New Haven SD — 500/K-12
100 Park Dr 63068 — 573-237-3231
Kyle Kruse, supt. — Fax 237-5959
newhaven.mo.schoolwebpages.com
New Haven HS — 200/9-12
100 Park Dr 63068 — 573-237-2629
Timothy Strobel, prin. — Fax 237-5959
New Haven MS — 100/7-8
100 Park Dr 63068 — 573-237-2900
Timothy Strobel, prin. — Fax 237-5959

New Madrid, New Madrid, Pop. 3,072
New Madrid County R-I SD — 1,600/PK-12
310 US Highway 61 63869 — 573-688-2161
Dr. Cindy Amick, supt. — Fax 688-2169
www.newmadridco.k12.mo.us/
Central HS — 500/9-12
310 US Highway 61 63869 — 573-688-2165
Gerald Murphy, prin. — Fax 688-2169
Central MS — 400/6-8
308 US Highway 61 63869 — 573-688-2176
Thomas Drummond, prin. — Fax 688-2245
New Madrid R-I Tech Skills Center — Vo/Tech
310 US Highway 61 63869 — 573-688-2161
John Garner, dir. — Fax 688-2169

Newtown, Sullivan, Pop. 178
Newtown-Harris R-III SD — 100/PK-12
306 N Main St 64667 — 660-794-2245
B. Copple, supt. — Fax 794-2730
www.nhtigers.k12.mo.us/
Newtown-Harris JSHS — 100/7-12
306 N Main St 64667 — 660-794-2245
Misty Foster, prin. — Fax 794-2730

Niangua, Webster, Pop. 404
Niangua R-V SD — 300/PK-12
301 Rumsey St 65713 — 417-473-6101
T.J. Bransfield, supt. — Fax 473-6124
www.nianguaschools.net
Niangua JSHS — 100/7-12
301 Rumsey St 65713 — 417-473-6101
T.J. Bransfield, prin. — Fax 473-6124

Nixa, Christian, Pop. 18,053
Nixa SD — 5,200/PK-12
301 S Main St 65714 — 417-875-5400
Dr. Stephen Kleinsmith, supt. — Fax 449-3190
www.nixapublicschools.net
Nixa HS — 1,600/9-12
514 S Nicholas Rd 65714 — 417-724-3500
Mark McGehee, prin. — Fax 724-3515
Nixa JHS — 800/7-8
205 North St 65714 — 417-875-5430
Lori Wilson, prin. — Fax 875-5426
SCORE Learning Center — Alt
1398 W Mount Vernon St 65714 — 417-724-4080
Cheryl Huson, prin. — Fax 724-4088

Noel, McDonald, Pop. 1,745
McDonald County R-I SD
Supt. — See Anderson
Noel ES — 400/3-8
318 Sulphur St 64854 — 417-475-3302
Angela Brewer, prin. — Fax 475-6516

Norborne, Carroll, Pop. 697
Norborne R-VIII SD — 200/PK-12
PO Box 192 64668 — 660-593-3319
Dr. Roger Feagan, supt. — Fax 593-3657
www.norborneschools.com/
Norborne HS — 100/6-12
PO Box 192 64668 — 660-593-3319
Roger Stone, prin. — Fax 593-3657

Normandy, Saint Louis, Pop. 4,907
Normandy SD
Supt. — See Saint Louis
Normandy MS — 700/6-8
7855 Natural Bridge Rd 63121 — 314-493-0500
GeNita Williams, prin. — Fax 493-0560

North Kansas City, Clay, Pop. 4,094
North Kansas City SD 74
Supt. — See Kansas City
North Kansas City HS — 1,500/9-12
620 E 23rd Ave 64116 — 816-413-5900
Dr. Dan Wartick, prin. — Fax 413-5905

North Kansas City Hospital — Post-Sec.
2800 Clay Edwards Dr 64116 — 816-691-2000

Norwood, Wright, Pop. 654
Norwood R-I SD — 400/K-12
675 N Hawk St 65717 — 417-746-4101
Shannon Crain, supt. — Fax 746-9950
www.norwood.k12.mo.us/
Norwood HS — 200/6-12
675 N Hawk St 65717 — 417-746-4101
Kevin Johnson, prin. — Fax 746-9950

Novinger, Adair, Pop. 454
Adair County R-I SD — 300/K-12
600 Rombauer Ave 63559 — 660-488-6411
William Lake, supt. — Fax 488-5400
www.novinger.k12.mo.us
Adair County JSHS — 100/7-12
600 Rombauer Ave 63559 — 660-488-6411
Penny Copelin, prin. — Fax 488-5400

Oak Grove, Jackson, Pop. 7,672
Oak Grove R-VI SD — 2,100/PK-12
601 SE 12th St 64075 — 816-690-4156
Freddie Doherty, supt. — Fax 690-3031
www.oakgrove.k12.mo.us
Oak Grove HS — 700/9-12
605 SE 12th St 64075 — 816-690-4152
Adam Salmon, prin. — Fax 690-5666
Oak Grove MS — 500/6-8
401 SE 12th St 64075 — 816-690-4154
Tracy Kemp, prin. — Fax 690-3976

Oak Ridge, Cape Girardeau, Pop. 236
Oak Ridge R-VI SD — 300/K-12
PO Box 10 63769 — 573-266-3218
Dr. Gerald Landewee, supt. — Fax 266-0133
www.showme.net/ork12/
Oak Ridge JSHS — 200/7-12
PO Box 10 63769 — 573-266-3630
Allan Horrell, prin. — Fax 266-0133

Odessa, Lafayette, Pop. 5,180
Odessa R-VII SD — 2,100/K-12
701 S 3rd St 64076 — 816-633-5316
Robert Brinkley, supt. — Fax 633-8582
www.odessa.k12.mo.us/
Odessa HS — 600/9-12
713 S 3rd St 64076 — 816-633-5533
John McGraw, prin. — Fax 633-7506
Odessa MS — 500/6-8
607 S 5th St 64076 — 816-633-1500
Sherry Billings, prin. — Fax 633-7101

O Fallon, Saint Charles, Pop. 77,920
Ft. Zumwalt R-II SD — 18,700/K-12
110 Virgil St 63366 — 636-272-6620
Dr. Bernard DuBray, supt. — Fax 980-1946
www.fz.k12.mo.us
Ft. Zumwalt North HS — 1,400/9-12
1230 Tom Ginnever Ave 63366 — 636-272-4447
Joe Sutton, prin. — Fax 272-6124
Ft. Zumwalt North MS — 900/6-8
210 Virgil St 63366 — 636-281-2356
Dr. Tim Jamieson, prin. — Fax 281-0005
Ft. Zumwalt West HS — 2,100/9-12
1251 Turtle Creek Dr 63366 — 636-379-0300
Neil Berry, prin. — Fax 281-0202
Ft. Zumwalt West MS — 1,500/6-8
150 Waterford Crossing Dr, — 636-272-6690
Jennifer Waters, prin. — Fax 272-6361
Hope HS — 100/Alt
307 W Pitman St 63366 — 636-379-5300
Kim Bertram, prin. — Fax 379-5909
Other Schools – See Saint Peters

Wentzville R-IV SD
Supt. — See Wentzville
Frontier MS — 1,100/6-8
9233 Highway DD, — 636-625-1026
Phil Ragusky, prin. — Fax 625-1094

Living Word Christian MSHS — 500/6-12
1145 Tom Ginnever Ave 63366 — 636-978-1680
Patrick Turner, supt. — Fax 978-5024
St. Dominic HS — 700/9-12
31 Saint Dominic Dr 63366 — 636-240-8303
Janet Eaton, prin. — Fax 240-9884

Oran, Scott, Pop. 1,284
Oran R-III SD — 400/K-12
PO Box 250 63771 — 573-262-2330
Mitchell Wood, supt. — Fax 262-2330
www.oran.k12.mo.us
Oran JSHS — 200/7-12
PO Box 250 63771 — 573-262-3345
Adam Friga, prin. — Fax 262-2289

Oregon, Holt, Pop. 851
South Holt County R-I SD — 200/K-12
201 S Barbour St 64473 — 660-446-2282
Bob Ottman, supt. — Fax 446-2312
www.southholtr1.com
South Holt County JSHS — 100/7-12
201 S Barbour St 64473 — 660-446-3454
Pat Ryan, prin. — Fax 446-2312

Orrick, Ray, Pop. 827
Orrick R-XI SD — 400/PK-12
100 Kirkham St 64077 — 816-770-0094
Aerin O'Dell, supt. — Fax 496-2306
www.orrick.k12.mo.us
Orrick JSHS — 200/7-12
100 Kirkham St 64077 — 816-770-3327
Scott Archibald, prin. — Fax 496-3829

Osage Beach, Miller, Pop. 4,299
School of the Osage R-II SD
Supt. — See Lake Ozark
Osage HS — 600/9-12
636 Highway 42 65065 — 573-348-0115
Mike Williams, prin. — Fax 348-9774
Osage MS — 400/6-8
635 Highway 42 65065 — 573-552-8326
Tony Slack, prin. — Fax 552-8322

Osborn, DeKalb, Pop. 422
Osborn R-0 SD — 100/K-12
275 Clinton Ave 64474 — 816-675-2217
Laurie Mefford, supt. — Fax 675-2222
schoolweb.missouri.edu/osborn.k12.mo.us/

Osborn JSHS 100/7-12
275 Clinton Ave 64474 816-675-2217
Troy Stemberger, prin. Fax 675-2222

Osceola, Saint Clair, Pop. 924
Osceola SD 500/PK-12
76 SE Highway WW 64776 417-646-8143
Aron Bennett, supt. Fax 646-8075
www.osceola.k12.mo.us
Osceola JSHS 300/7-12
76 SE Highway WW 64776 417-646-8144
Dustin Schubert, prin. Fax 646-8549

Otterville, Cooper, Pop. 446
Otterville R-VI SD 300/K-12
PO Box 177 65348 660-366-4391
Matt Unger, supt. Fax 366-4293
Otterville JSHS 100/7-12
PO Box 177 65348 660-366-4621
Kim Oelrichs, prin. Fax 366-4293

Overland, Saint Louis, Pop. 15,614
Ritenour SD
Supt. — See Saint Louis
Ritenour HS 1,900/9-12
9100 Saint Charles Rock Rd 63114 314-493-6105
Anthony Robinson, prin. Fax 429-6725
Ritenour MS 700/6-8
2500 Marshall Ave 63114 314-493-6250
Ken Roumpos, prin. Fax 429-6726

Owensville, Gasconade, Pop. 2,647
Gasconade County R-II SD 1,800/PK-12
PO Box 536 65066 573-437-2177
Dr. Chuck Garner, supt. Fax 437-5808
owensville.k12.mo.us
Owensville HS 600/9-12
PO Box 536 65066 573-437-2174
Kurt Keller, prin. Fax 437-7174
Owensville MS 400/6-8
PO Box 536 65066 573-437-2172
Teresa Ragan, prin. Fax 437-6704

Ozark, Christian, Pop. 17,472
Ozark R-VI SD 5,400/K-12
PO Box 166 65721 417-582-5900
Dr. Gordon Pace, supt. Fax 582-5960
www.ozark.k12.mo.us
Ozark HS 1,500/9-12
PO Box 166 65721 417-582-5901
Dr. Sam Taylor, prin. Fax 582-5944
Ozark JHS 800/7-8
PO Box 166 65721 417-582-4701
Jeff Simpson, prin. Fax 582-4714

Pacific, Franklin, Pop. 6,911
Meramec Valley R-III SD 3,400/PK-12
126 N Payne St 63069 636-271-1400
Randy George, supt. Fax 271-1406
www.mvr3.k12.mo.us/
Pacific HS 1,000/9-12
425 Indian Warpath Dr 63069 636-627-1414
Tom Sauvage, prin. Fax 257-8340
Riverbend S 300/8-8
2085 Highway N 63069 636-271-1481
Ketina Armstrong, prin. Fax 271-8080

Palmyra, Marion, Pop. 3,541
Palmyra R-I SD 1,200/K-12
PO Box 151 63461 573-769-2066
Eric Churchwell, supt. Fax 769-4218
www.palmyra.k12.mo.us
Palmyra HS 400/9-12
PO Box 151 63461 573-769-2067
Kenneth Holstine, prin. Fax 769-1013
Palmyra MS 400/5-8
PO Box 151 63461 573-769-2174
Kirt Malone, prin. Fax 769-4227

Paris, Monroe, Pop. 1,208
Paris R-II SD 500/PK-12
740 Cleveland St 65275 660-327-4112
Chris Johnson, supt. Fax 327-4290
paris.k12.mo.us/site/
Paris HS 200/9-12
25686 Business Highway 24 65275 660-327-4111
Matt Smith, prin. Fax 327-6220
Paris JHS 100/7-8
25678 Business Highway 24 65275 660-327-4563
Matt Smith, prin. Fax 327-4782

Park Hills, Saint Francois, Pop. 8,642
Central R-III SD 2,000/PK-12
200 High St 63601 573-431-2616
Dr. Desmond Mayberry, supt. Fax 431-2107
www.centralr3.org
Central HS 600/9-12
116 Rebel Dr 63601 573-431-2616
Brad Coleman, prin. Fax 431-0700
Central MS 400/6-8
801 Columbia St 63601 573-431-2616
Mike Harlow, prin. Fax 431-5393

West St. Francois County R-IV SD
Supt. — See Leadwood
West County HS 300/9-12
768 Highway M 63601 573-562-7521
Eric Moyers, prin. Fax 562-7510

Mineral Area College Post-Sec.
PO Box 1000 63601 573-431-4593

Parkville, Platte, Pop. 5,415

Park University Post-Sec.
8700 NW River Park Dr 64152 816-741-2000

Patton, Bollinger
Meadow Heights R-II SD 500/K-12
RR 1 Box 2365 63662 573-866-0060
Andrew B. Comstock, supt. Fax 866-3240
Meadow Heights JSHS 300/7-12
RR 1 Box 2365 63662 573-866-2924
Mitchell Nanney, prin. Fax 866-2219

Pattonsburg, Daviess, Pop. 346
Pattonsburg R-II SD 200/PK-12
PO Box 200 64670 660-367-2111
Johnnie Silkett, supt. Fax 367-4205
schoolweb.missouri.edu/pattonsburg.k12.mo.us/
Pattonsburg JSHS 100/7-12
PO Box 200 64670 660-367-2111
Chris Hodge, prin. Fax 367-4205

Peculiar, Cass, Pop. 4,532
Raymore-Peculiar R-II SD 6,500/PK-12
PO Box 789 64078 816-892-1300
Dr. Kari Monsees, supt. Fax 892-1380
www.raypec.k12.mo.us
Raymore-Peculiar Academy 400/Alt
PO Box 789 64078 816-892-1528
Jim Brown, prin. Fax 892-1501
Raymore-Peculiar HS 1,800/9-12
PO Box 789 64078 816-892-1400
Steven Miller, prin. Fax 892-1401
Other Schools – See Raymore

Perryville, Perry, Pop. 8,127
Perry County SD 32 2,300/K-12
326 College St 63775 573-547-7500
Kevin Dunn, supt. Fax 547-8572
www.perryville.k12.mo.us
Perry County MS 700/5-8
326 College St 63775 573-547-7500
Velda Haertling, prin. Fax 547-1962
Perryville Area Career Center Vo/Tech
326 College St 63775 573-547-7500
Steve King, dir. Fax 517-0396
Perryville HS 800/9-12
326 College St 63775 573-547-7500
Lee Gattis, prin. Fax 517-0592

St. Vincent JSHS 300/7-12
210 S Waters St 63775 573-547-2560
Dr. Patricia Hensley, pres. Fax 547-1722

Philadelphia, Marion
Marion County R-II SD 200/K-12
2905 Highway D 63463 573-439-5913
Dianna Hoenes, supt. Fax 439-5914
www.marion.k12.mo.us/
Marion County JSHS 100/7-12
2905 Highway D 63463 573-439-5913
Dianna Hoenes, admin. Fax 439-5914

Piedmont, Wayne, Pop. 1,960
Clearwater R-I SD 1,100/PK-12
RR 4 Box 1004 63957 573-223-7426
Blane Keel, supt. Fax 223-2932
Clearwater HS 300/9-12
RR 4 Box 1004 63957 573-223-4524
Paul D'Amico, prin. Fax 223-3208
Clearwater MS 300/5-8
RR 4 Box 1004 63957 573-223-7724
Michael Keller, prin. Fax 223-3117

Lighthouse Christian Academy 50/7-12
PO Box 100 63957 573-223-2025
Larry Musgrave, pres. Fax 223-2105

Pierce City, Lawrence, Pop. 1,276
Pierce City R-VI SD 700/PK-12
300 N Myrtle St 65723 417-476-2555
Dr. Aaron Cornman, supt. Fax 476-5213
schoolweb.missouri.edu/piercecity.k12.mo.us/
Pierce City HS 200/9-12
300 N Myrtle St 65723 417-476-2515
Steve Garner, prin. Fax 476-3516
Pierce City MS 200/6-8
300 N Myrtle St 65723 417-476-2842
Gayla DeGraffenreid, prin. Fax 476-5405

Pilot Grove, Cooper, Pop. 759
Pilot Grove C-4 SD 300/PK-12
107 School St 65276 660-834-6915
D.J. Leverton, supt. Fax 834-6925
www.schoolweb.missouri.edu/pilotgrovec4.k12.mo.us/
Pilot Grove HS 100/9-12
107 School St 65276 660-834-4415
Randall Glenn, prin. Fax 834-4401
Pilot Grove MS 100/6-8
107 School St 65276 660-834-4415
Randall Glenn, prin. Fax 834-4401

Pineville, McDonald, Pop. 780
McDonald County R-I SD
Supt. — See Anderson
Pineville ES 200/3-8
202 E 8th St 64856 417-223-4346
Tamra Kester, prin. Fax 223-4195

Plato, Texas, Pop. 109
Plato R-V SD 700/PK-12
PO Box A 65552 417-458-3333
Ben Yocom, supt. Fax 458-4706
www.plato.k12.mo.us/
Plato HS 400/6-12
PO Box A 65552 417-458-4980
Charles Crain, prin. Fax 458-4706

Platte City, Platte, Pop. 4,565
Platte County R-III SD 3,600/PK-12
998 Platte Falls Rd 64079 816-858-5420
Dr. Mike Reik, supt. Fax 858-5593
www.plattecountyschooldistrict.com/
Northland Career Center Vo/Tech
1801 Branch St 64079 816-858-5505
Brian Noller, dir. Fax 858-3278
Platte City MS 600/6-8
900 Pirate Dr 64079 816-858-2036
Chris Miller, prin. Fax 858-3748
Platte County HS 1,000/9-12
1501 Branch St 64079 816-858-2822
Patrick Martin, prin. Fax 858-5140
Other Schools – See Kansas City

Plattsburg, Clinton, Pop. 2,263
Clinton County R-III SD 800/PK-12
800 W Frost St 64477 816-539-2183
Dr. Marcus Stucker, supt. Fax 539-2412
ccr3.k12.mo.us
Clinton County R-III MS 200/6-8
800 W Frost St 64477 816-539-3920
Andy McNeely, prin. Fax 539-2412
Plattsburg HS 200/9-12
800 W Frost St 64477 816-539-2184
Zach McMains, prin. Fax 539-3315

Pleasant Hill, Cass, Pop. 7,996
Pleasant Hill R-III SD 2,200/PK-12
318 Cedar St 64080 816-540-3161
Dr. Wesley Townsend, supt. Fax 540-5135
www.pleasanthillschools.com
Pleasant Hill HS 700/9-12
1 Rooster Way 64080 816-540-3111
Paul Canaan, prin. Fax 987-6084
Pleasant Hill MS 300/7-8
1301 E Myrtle St 64080 816-540-2149
Jenny Bell, prin. Fax 987-2017

Pleasant Hope, Polk, Pop. 604
Pleasant Hope R-VI SD 900/PK-12
PO Box 387 65725 417-267-2850
Scott Ireland, supt. Fax 267-4373
www.phr6.com
Pleasant Hope HS 300/9-12
PO Box 387 65725 417-267-2271
Brent Offerdahl, prin. Fax 267-5007
Pleasant Hope MS 300/5-8
PO Box 387 65725 417-267-7701
Michael Smith, prin. Fax 267-9221
Other Schools – See Brighton

Point Lookout, Taney

College of the Ozarks Post-Sec.
PO Box 17 65726 417-334-6411

Polo, Caldwell, Pop. 552
Polo R-VII SD 400/K-12
300 W School St 64671 660-354-2326
Dr. Beverly Deis, supt. Fax 354-2910
polo.k12.mo.us/
Polo HS 100/9-12
300 W School St 64671 660-354-2524
Kyle Ross, prin. Fax 354-2738
Polo MS 100/5-8
300 W School St 64671 660-354-2200
Monica Palmer, prin. Fax 354-3162

Poplar Bluff, Butler, Pop. 16,562
Poplar Bluff R-I SD 5,000/PK-12
1110 N Westwood Blvd 63901 573-785-7751
Chris Hon, supt. Fax 785-0336
www.r1schools.org
Poplar Bluff HS 1,400/9-12
1300 Victory Ln 63901 573-785-6471
Michael Kiehne, prin. Fax 785-6471
Poplar Bluff JHS 700/7-8
550 N Westwood Blvd 63901 573-785-5602
Bob Case, prin. Fax 785-5004
Technical Career Center Vo/Tech
3203 Oak Grove Rd 63901 573-785-2248
Jean Winston, prin. Fax 785-4168

Three Rivers Community College Post-Sec.
2080 Three Rivers Blvd 63901 573-840-9600

Portageville, New Madrid, Pop. 3,162
Portageville SD 800/PK-12
904 King Ave 63873 573-379-3855
Michael Allred, supt. Fax 379-5817
www.portageville.k12.mo.us
Portageville HS 200/9-12
904 King Ave 63873 573-379-3819
Jeff Bullock, prin. Fax 379-3159
Portageville MS 200/6-8
902 King Ave 63873 573-379-3853
Jim Bidewell, prin. Fax 379-3159

Potosi, Washington, Pop. 2,627
Potosi R-III SD 2,400/PK-12
400 N Mine St 63664 573-438-5485
Randy Davis, supt. Fax 438-5487
www.potosir3.org/
Evans MS 400/7-8
303 S Lead St 63664 573-438-2101
Dan Beckwith, prin. Fax 438-4635
Potosi HS 700/9-12
1 Trojan Dr 63664 573-438-2156
Nathan Hostetler, prin. Fax 438-2269

Prairie Home, Cooper, Pop. 279
Prairie Home R-V SD 200/K-12
301 Highway 87 65068 660-841-5296
Barbara Bancroft, supt. Fax 841-5513
www.prairiehome.k12.mo.us/
Prairie Home HS 100/7-12
301 Highway 87 65068 660-841-5296
Patrick Tray, prin. Fax 841-5513

Princeton, Mercer, Pop. 1,164
Princeton R-V SD 400/PK-12
1008 E Coleman St 64673 660-748-3211
Terry Mayfield, supt. Fax 748-3212
www.tigertown.k12.mo.us/
Princeton JSHS 200/7-12
1008 E Coleman St 64673 660-748-3490
Angie Ormsby, prin. Fax 748-3212

Purdin, Linn, Pop. 189
Linn County R-I SD 100/PK-12
PO Box 130 64674 660-244-5045
Ryan Livingston, supt. Fax 244-5025
www.linnr1.k12.mo.us
Linn County S 100/PK-12
PO Box 130 64674 660-244-5035
Candi Gray, prin. Fax 244-5025

Purdy, Barry, Pop. 1,081
Purdy R-II SD 700/K-12
PO Box 248 65734 417-442-3216
Dr. Steven Chancellor, supt. Fax 442-3963
www.purdyk12.com
Purdy HS 200/9-12
PO Box 248 65734 417-442-3215
Robert Vice, prin. Fax 442-3632
Purdy MS 200/5-8
PO Box 248 65734 417-442-7066
Janet Boys, prin. Fax 442-7067

Puxico, Stoddard, Pop. 867
Puxico R-VIII SD 900/PK-12
481 N Bedford St 63960 573-222-3762
Kyle Dare, supt. Fax 222-3137
www.puxico.k12.mo.us
Mingo/Puxico Technical HS Vo/Tech
481 N Bedford St 63960 573-222-2675
Fax 222-3137
Puxico HS 200/9-12
481 N Bedford St 63960 573-222-3175
Cindy Crabb, prin. Fax 222-2375
Puxico JHS 200/6-8
481 N Bedford St 63960 573-222-3058
Jason Hill, prin. Fax 222-6373

Queen City, Schuyler, Pop. 595
Schuyler County R-I SD 600/PK-12
1170 Highway 63 63561 660-766-2204
Robert Amen, supt. Fax 766-2400
www.schuyler.k12.mo.us
Schuyler County R-I HS 200/7-12
1170 Highway 63 63561 660-766-2424
Kyle Windy, prin. Fax 766-2646

Ravenwood, Nodaway, Pop. 439
Northeast Nodaway County R-V SD 200/PK-12
PO Box 206 64479 660-937-3112
Jeff Mehlenbacher Ed.D., supt. Fax 937-3110
www.ihigh.com/northeastnodaway
Northeast Nodaway HS 100/7-12
PO Box 206 64479 660-937-3125
Linda Mattson, prin. Fax 937-3110

Raymore, Cass, Pop. 18,776
Raymore-Peculiar R-II SD
Supt. — See Peculiar
Raymore-Peculiar East MS 1,000/7-8
17509 E State Route 58 64083 816-388-4000
David Mitchell, prin. Fax 388-4001

House of Heavilin Beauty College Post-Sec.
800 W Foxwood Dr 64083 816-767-8000

Raytown, Jackson, Pop. 28,561
Raytown C-2 SD 8,600/PK-12
6608 Raytown Rd 64133 816-268-7000
Dr. Allan Markley, supt. Fax 268-7019
www.raytownschools.org/
Herndon Career Center Vo/Tech
11501 E State Route 350 64138 816-268-7140
Cheryl Reichert, dir. Fax 268-7149
Raytown Alternative S Alt
10750 E State Route 350 64138 816-268-7180
Lori Forte, prin. Fax 268-7185
Raytown Central MS 600/6-8
10601 E 59th St 64133 816-268-7050
Jaime Sadich, prin. Fax 268-7055
Raytown HS 1,400/9-12
6019 Blue Ridge Blvd 64133 816-268-7300
Dr. Chad Bruton, prin. Fax 268-7315
Raytown South HS 1,300/9-12
8211 Sterling Ave 64138 816-268-7330
Dr. Kevin Overfelt, prin. Fax 268-7345
Raytown South MS 600/6-8
8401 E 83rd St 64138 816-268-7380
Randy Thomas, prin. Fax 268-7385
Other Schools – See Kansas City

Reeds Spring, Stone, Pop. 896
Reeds Spring R-IV SD 2,000/PK-12
20281 State Highway 413 65737 417-272-8173
Dr. Michael Mason, supt. Fax 272-8656
www.wolves.k12.mo.us
Gibson Technical Center Vo/Tech
386 W State Highway 76 65737 417-272-3271
Nick Thieman, dir. Fax 272-1529
New Horizons Alternative S Alt
386 W State Highway 76 65737 417-272-3271
Nick Thieman, dir. Fax 272-1529
Reeds Spring HS 600/9-12
20277 State Highway 413 65737 417-272-8171
Steve Levingston, prin. Fax 272-1481
Reeds Spring MS 300/7-8
21016 Main St 65737 417-272-8245
Travis Kite, prin. Fax 272-8490

Republic, Greene, Pop. 14,495
Republic R-III SD 4,300/PK-12
518 N Hampton Ave 65738 417-732-3605
Chance Wistrom, supt. Fax 732-3609
www.republicschools.org
Republic HS 1,200/9-12
4370 S Repmo Dr 65738 417-732-3650
Daren Harris Ed.D., prin. Fax 732-3659
Republic MS 1,000/6-8
1 Tiger Dr 65738 417-732-3640
Mike Linehan, prin. Fax 732-3649

Rich Hill, Bates, Pop. 1,356
Rich Hill R-IV SD 400/K-12
703 N 3rd St 64779 417-395-2418
Glenn Niffen, supt. Fax 395-2407
www.richhill.k12.mo.us/
Rich Hill HS 200/7-12
703 N 3rd St 64779 417-395-4191
David Rotert, prin. Fax 395-2407

Richland, Pulaski, Pop. 1,803
Richland R-IV SD 600/PK-12
714 E Jefferson Ave 65556 573-765-3241
Joe Ridgeway, supt. Fax 765-5552
www.bcar.k12.mo.us
Richland HS 200/9-12
714 E Jefferson Ave 65556 573-765-3711
Doug Smith, prin. Fax 765-5552
Richland JHS 100/7-8
714 E Jefferson Ave 65556 573-765-3711
Michele Hedges, prin. Fax 765-5552

Richmond, Ray, Pop. 5,691
Richmond R-XVI SD 1,600/PK-12
1017 E Main St 64085 816-776-6912
Dr. Damon Kizzire, supt. Fax 776-5554
richmond.k12.mo.us
Richmond HS 500/9-12
451 E South St 64085 816-776-2226
John Parker, prin. Fax 776-8748
Richmond MS 400/6-8
715 S Wellington St 64085 816-776-5841
Fax 776-2788

Ridgeway, Harrison, Pop. 462
Ridgeway R-V SD 100/PK-12
305 Main St 64481 660-872-6813
Dr. Regina Knott, supt. Fax 872-6230
Ridgeway JSHS 50/7-12
305 Main St 64481 660-872-6813
Sharon Hendren, prin. Fax 872-6230

Risco, New Madrid, Pop. 338
Risco R-II SD 200/K-12
PO Box 17 63874 573-396-5568
Amy Baker, supt. Fax 396-5503
www.risco.k12.mo.us/
Risco JSHS 100/7-12
PO Box 17 63874 573-396-5568
Ron Cross, prin. Fax 396-5503

Riverside, Platte, Pop. 2,836
Park Hill SD
Supt. — See Kansas City
Park Hill South HS 1,600/9-12
4500 NW River Park Dr 64150 816-359-4120
Dr. Dale Longenecker, prin. Fax 359-4129

Rock Port, Atchison, Pop. 1,303
Rock Port R-II SD 300/K-12
600 S Nebraska St 64482 660-744-6298
Alan Kerr, supt. Fax 744-5539
Rock Port JSHS 200/7-12
600 S Nebraska St 64482 660-744-6296
Craig Walker, prin. Fax 744-5539

Rogersville, Greene, Pop. 3,000
Logan-Rogersville R-VIII SD 2,300/PK-12
100 E Front St 65742 417-753-2891
Dr. Michael J. Tucker, supt. Fax 753-3063
logrog.net/
Logan-Rogersville HS 700/9-12
4700 S State Highway 125 65742 417-753-2813
Dr. Teresa McKenzie, prin. Fax 753-3960
Logan-Rogersville MS 300/7-8
8225 E Farm Road 174 65742 417-753-2896
Toby Kite, prin. Fax 753-3182

Rolla, Phelps, Pop. 19,067
Rolla SD 31 4,100/PK-12
500A Forum Dr 65401 573-458-0100
Dr. Aaron Zalis, supt. Fax 458-0105
rolla.k12.mo.us
Rolla JHS 600/8-9
1360 Soest Rd 65401 573-458-0130
Monica Fulton, prin. Fax 458-0135
Rolla SHS 1,000/10-12
900 Bulldog Run 65401 573-458-0140
Dr. Jim Pritchett, prin. Fax 458-0147
Rolla Technical Center Vo/Tech
500 Forum Dr 65401 573-458-0160
Paula Hass, dir. Fax 458-0164
Rolla Technical Institute Vo/Tech
1304 E 10th St 65401 573-458-0150
Lucas Chapman, dir. Fax 458-0155

Metro Business College Post-Sec.
1202 E State Route 72 65401 573-364-8464
Missouri University of Science & Tech Post-Sec.
1870 Miner Cir 65409 573-341-4111
Salem College of Hairstyling Post-Sec.
1051 Kingshighway St Ste 1 65401 573-368-3136

Rosendale, Andrew, Pop. 143
North Andrew County R-VI SD 400/K-12
9120 Highway 48 64483 816-567-2965
Jim Shultz, supt. Fax 567-2096
schoolweb.missouri.edu/nandrew.k12.mo.us/
North Andrew HS 100/9-12
9120 Highway 48 64483 816-567-2525
Shannon Nolte, prin. Fax 567-2096
North Andrew MS 100/6-8
9120 Highway 48 64483 816-567-2525
Shannon Nolte, prin. Fax 567-2096

Russellville, Cole, Pop. 799
Cole County R-I SD 700/PK-12
13600 Route C 65074 573-782-3534
Jerry Hobbs, supt. Fax 782-3545
www.cole.k12.mo.us
Cole County R-I HS 200/9-12
13600 Route C 65074 573-782-3313
Heath Waters, prin. Fax 782-3262
Cole County R-I MS 200/6-8
13111 Park St 65074 573-782-4915
Karen Ponder, prin. Fax 782-3775

Saint Albans, Franklin

Fulton S at St. Albans 100/PK-12
PO Box 78 63073 636-458-6688
Kara Douglass, hdmstr. Fax 458-6660

Saint Ann, Saint Louis, Pop. 12,679
Pattonville R-III SD 5,600/PK-12
11097 Saint Charles Rock Rd 63074 314-213-8500
Dr. Michael Fulton, supt. Fax 213-8601
www.psdr3.org
Holman MS 600/6-8
11055 Saint Charles Rock Rd 63074 314-213-8032
Teisha Ashford, prin. Fax 213-8632
Other Schools – See Maryland Heights

Ritenour SD
Supt. — See Saint Louis
Hoech MS 800/6-8
3312 Ashby Rd 63074 314-493-6200
Tim Streicher, prin. Fax 426-3837

American Trade School Post-Sec.
3925 Industrial Dr 63074 314-423-1900
Patsy & Rob's Academy of Beauty Post-Sec.
18 Northwest Plz 63074 314-298-8808

Saint Charles, Saint Charles, Pop. 64,512
Francis Howell R-III SD 20,100/PK-12
4545 Central School Rd. 63304 636-851-4000
Dr. Pam Sloan, supt. Fax 851-4093
www.fhsdschools.org
Barnwell MS 800/6-8
1035 Jungs Station Rd 63303 636-851-4100
David Eckhoff, prin. Fax 851-4095
Heritage Landing Alternative Program Alt
1400 Gettysburg Lndg 63303 636-851-5300
Jennifer Bracken, prin. Fax 851-4130
Hollenbeck MS 700/6-8
4555 Central School Rd 63304 636-851-5400
Woody Borgschulte, prin. Fax 851-4132
Howell Central HS 1,900/9-12
5199 Highway N 63304 636-851-4600
Sonny Arnel, prin. Fax 851-4111
Howell HS 1,800/9-12
7001 S Highway 94 63304 636-851-4700
Dave Wedlock, prin. Fax 851-4116
Howell North HS 1,900/9-12
2549 Hackmann Rd 63303 636-851-4900
Darlene Jones, prin. Fax 851-6199
Howell Union HS 100/Alt
1405 Highway D 63304 636-851-5000
Krisandra Worley, prin. Fax 851-4127
Saeger MS 800/6-8
5201 Highway N 63304 636-851-5600
Brian Schick, prin. Fax 851-4138
Other Schools – See Weldon Spring

Orchard Farm R-V SD 1,300/PK-12
2165 Highway V 63301 636-250-5000
Dr. Daniel Dozier, supt. Fax 250-5444
www.ofsd.k12.mo.us
Orchard Farm HS 400/9-12
2165 Highway V 63301 636-250-5400
Brian Smith, prin. Fax 250-5425
Orchard Farm MS 400/6-8
2165 Highway V 63301 636-250-5300
Dr. Wade Steinhoff, prin. Fax 250-5306

St. Charles R-VI SD 5,500/PK-12
400 N 6th St 63301 636-443-4000
Dr. Jeff Marion, supt. Fax 443-4001
www.stcharles.k12.mo.us
Hardin MS 800/7-8
1950 Elm St 63301 636-443-4300
Dr. Ed Gettemeier, prin. Fax 443-4301
Lewis & Clark Career Center Vo/Tech
2400 Zumbehl Rd 63301 636-443-4950
Kathy Frederking, dir. Fax 443-4951
St. Charles HS 900/9-12
725 N Kingshighway St 63301 636-443-4100
Jeff Walker, prin. Fax 443-4101
St. Charles West HS 800/9-12
3601 Droste Rd 63301 636-443-4200
Dr. Kim Fitterling, prin. Fax 443-4201
Success Campus Alternative S Alt
1600 Waverly St 63301 636-443-4890
Laurie Juergensen, prin. Fax 443-4891

Duchesne HS 500/9-12
2550 Elm St 63301 636-946-6767
Fritz Long, prin. Fax 946-6267
Lewis & Clark Career Center Post-Sec.
2400 Zumbehl Rd 63301 636-443-4950
Lindenwood University Post-Sec.
209 S Kingshighway St 63301 636-949-2000
Missouri Tech Post-Sec.
1690 Country Club Dr 63303 636-573-9300
Vatterott College - St. Charles Post-Sec.
3550 W Clay St 63301 636-940-4100

Saint Clair, Franklin, Pop. 4,665
St. Clair R-XIII SD 2,300/K-12
905 Bardot St 63077 636-629-3500
Dr. Michael Murphy, supt. Fax 629-4466
stclair.fesdev.org
Saint Clair HS 800/9-12
1015 High School Dr 63077 636-629-3500
Kevin Hillman, prin. Fax 629-1979
Saint Clair JHS 500/6-8
925 High School Dr 63077 636-629-3500
Steven Weinhold, prin. Fax 629-1363

Sainte Genevieve, Sainte Genevieve, Pop. 4,356
St. Genevieve County R-II SD 1,900/K-12
375 N 5th St 63670 573-883-4500
Shelley Jokerst, supt. Fax 883-5957
www.stegen.k12.mo.us
Sainte Genevieve HS 700/9-12
715 Washington St 63670 573-883-4500
Chris Hoehne, prin. Fax 883-5957
Sainte Genevieve MS 400/6-8
211 N 5th St 63670 573-883-4500
Julie Flieg, prin. Fax 883-5957

Valle Catholic HS 100/9-12
40 N 4th St 63670 573-883-7496
Dr. Mark Gilligan, prin. Fax 883-9142

Saint Elizabeth, Miller, Pop. 334
St. Elizabeth R-IV SD 100/PK-12
PO Box 68 65075 573-493-2246
Toni Taylor, supt. Fax 493-2380
www.ste.k12.mo.us
Saint Elizabeth S 100/PK-12
PO Box 68 65075 573-493-2246
Crintina Wald, prin. Fax 493-2380

Saint James, Phelps, Pop. 4,150
St. James R-I SD 1,700/PK-12
122 E Scioto St 65559 573-265-2300
Joy Tucker, supt. Fax 265-6126
www.stjschools.org/
St. James HS 500/9-12
101 E Scioto St 65559 573-265-2300
Keith McCarthy, prin. Fax 265-3652
St. James MS 400/6-8
1 Tiger Dr 65559 573-265-2300
Kaaren Lepper, prin. Fax 265-6302

Saint John, Saint Louis, Pop. 6,331
Ritenour SD
Supt. — See Saint Louis
Ritenour Adult Learning Center Adult
8762 Saint Charles Rock Rd 63114 314-426-7900
JaVonda Quinn, dir. Fax 429-4348

Saint Joseph, Buchanan, Pop. 74,914
St. Joseph SD 11,800/PK-12
925 Felix St 64501 816-671-4000
Dr. Melody Smith, supt. Fax 671-4470
www.sjsd.k12.mo.us
Benton HS 900/9-12
5655 S 4th St 64504 816-671-4030
Dr. Jeanette Westfall, prin. Fax 671-4036
Bode MS 500/7-8
720 N Noyes Blvd 64506 816-671-4050
Roberta Dias, prin. Fax 671-4473
Central HS 1,600/9-12
2602 Edmond St 64501 816-671-4080
Marlie Williams, prin. Fax 671-4474
Colgan Alternative Resource Center 300/Alt
3510 Frederick Ave 64506 816-671-4072
Michele Thomason, dir. Fax 671-4022
Hillyard Technical Center Vo/Tech
3434 Faraon St 64506 816-671-4170
Regenia Briggs, dir. Fax 671-4479
Lafayette HS 900/9-12
412 E Highland Ave 64505 816-671-4220
Dr. Tyran Sumy, prin. Fax 671-4480
Robidoux MS 300/7-8
4212 Saint Joseph Ave 64505 816-671-4350
Precious Kurth, prin. Fax 671-4487
Spring Garden MS 400/7-8
5802 S 22nd St 64503 816-671-4380
Lara Gilpin, prin. Fax 671-4489
Truman MS 500/7-8
3227 Olive St Ste 45 64507 816-671-4400
Sandy Steggall, prin. Fax 671-4491
Webster Learning Center Alt
1211 N 18th St 64501 816-671-4020
Fax 671-4471

American College of Technology Post-Sec.
2700 N Belt Hwy 64506 816-279-7000
Bishop Le Blond HS 200/9-12
3529 Frederick Ave 64506 816-279-1629
Dr. Solon Haynes, prin. Fax 279-5488
Missouri Western State University Post-Sec.
4525 Downs Dr 64507 816-271-4200
St. Joseph Christian S 300/PK-12
5401 Gene Field Rd 64506 816-279-1555
Lydia Zuidema, supt. Fax 279-4574
Vatterott College - Saint Joseph Post-Sec.
3709 N Belt Hwy 64506 816-558-7500

Saint Louis, Saint Louis, Pop. 312,138
Affton SD 101 2,500/PK-12
8701 MacKenzie Rd 63123 314-638-8770
Dr. Steve Brotherton, supt. Fax 631-2548
www.affton.k12.mo.us
Affton HS 900/9-12
8309 MacKenzie Rd 63123 314-638-6330
Dr. Susan Jackson, prin. Fax 633-5990
Rogers MS 500/6-8
7550 MacKenzie Rd 63123 314-351-9679
Jeff Remelius, prin. Fax 351-6381

Bayless SD 1,400/PK-12
4530 Weber Rd 63123 314-256-8600
Ronald J. Tucker, supt. Fax 544-6315
baylessk12.org
Bayless HS 500/9-12
4532 Weber Rd 63123 314-256-8660
Patrick McEvoy, prin. Fax 544-6315
Bayless MS 200/6-8
4530 Weber Rd 63123 314-256-8690
Doug Harness, prin. Fax 544-6315

Ferguson-Florissant R-II SD
Supt. — See Florissant
Ferguson MS 600/7-8
701 January Ave 63135 314-506-9600
Susan Kelly, prin. Fax 506-9601
McCluer South - Berkeley HS 600/9-12
201 Brotherton Ln 63135 314-506-9800
Betty Fagan, prin. Fax 506-9801

Hancock Place SD 1,700/PK-12
9417 S Broadway 63125 314-544-1300
Dr. Kevin Carl, supt. Fax 631-3752
hancock.k12.mo.us
Hancock Place HS 500/9-12
229 W Ripa Ave 63125 314-544-1200
Dr. Cathy Lorenz, prin. Fax 544-6427
Hancock Place MS 300/6-8
243 W Ripa Ave 63125 314-544-6423
Scott Wilkerson, prin. Fax 544-6470

Hazelwood SD
Supt. — See Florissant
Hazelwood East HS 1,500/9-12
11300 Dunn Rd 63138 314-953-5600
Dr. Jacqueline Kelly, prin. Fax 953-5613
Hazelwood East MS 500/6-8
1865 Dunn Rd 63138 314-953-5700
Dr. Gary Jansen, prin. Fax 953-5713
Hazelwood Southeast MS 700/6-8
918 Prigge Rd 63138 314-953-7700
Chauncey Granger, prin. Fax 953-7713

Ladue SD 3,900/PK-12
9703 Conway Rd 63124 314-994-7080
Dr. Marsha Chappelow, supt. Fax 994-0441
www.ladueschools.net
Ladue MS 900/6-8
9701 Conway Rd 63124 314-993-3900
Dr. Vicki Van Laere, prin. Fax 997-8736
Watkins HS 1,200/9-12
1201 S Warson Rd 63124 314-993-6447
Dr. Bridget Hermann, prin. Fax 994-1467

Lindbergh R-VIII SD 5,700/PK-12
4900 S Lindbergh Blvd 63126 314-729-2480
Dr. Jim Simpson, supt. Fax 729-2482
www.lindberghschools.ws/
Lindbergh HS 2,000/9-12
4900 S Lindbergh Blvd 63126 314-729-2410
Dr. Ron Helms, prin. Fax 729-2412
Sperreng MS 1,300/6-8
12111 Tesson Ferry Rd 63128 314-729-2420
Mark Eggers, prin. Fax 729-2422
Truman MS 800/6-8
12225 Eddie and Park Rd 63127 314-729-2470
Dr. Tara Sparks, prin. Fax 729-2472

Maplewood Richmond Heights SD
Supt. — See Maplewood
Maplewood Richmond Heights MS 200/7-8
7539 Manchester Rd 63143 314-644-4406
Dr. Robert Dillon, prin. Fax 781-4629

Mehlville R-IX SD 10,700/K-12
3120 Lemay Ferry Rd 63125 314-467-5000
Dr. Eric Knost, supt. Fax 467-5099
www.mehlvilleschooldistrict.com
Bernard MS 700/6-8
1054 Forder Rd 63129 314-467-6600
Lori Sullivan, prin. Fax 467-6699
Buerkle MS 600/6-8
623 Buckley Rd 63125 314-467-6800
John Weber, prin. Fax 467-6899
Mehlville HS 1,900/9-12
3200 Lemay Ferry Rd 63125 314-467-6000
Dr. Denise Swanger, prin. Fax 467-6099
Oakville HS 1,800/9-12
5557 Milburn Rd 63129 314-467-7000
Jan Kellerman, prin. Fax 467-7099
Oakville MS 700/6-8
5950 Telegraph Rd 63129 314-467-7400
Mike Salsman, prin. Fax 467-7499
Washington MS 500/6-8
5165 Ambs Rd 63128 314-467-7600
Adam Smith, prin. Fax 467-7699

Normandy SD 3,400/PK-12
3855 Lucas and Hunt Rd 63121 314-493-0400
Dr. Tyrone McNichols, supt. Fax 493-0475
www.normandysd.org
Normandy HS 1,200/9-12
6701 Saint Charles Rock Rd 63133 314-493-0600
Derrick Mitchell, prin. Fax 493-0668
Normandy Positive Alt Learning Center 100/Alt
6834 Normandale Dr 63121 314-493-0280
Cherron L. White, prin. Fax 493-0258
Other Schools – See Normandy

Ritenour SD 6,100/PK-12
2420 Woodson Rd 63114 314-493-6010
Dr. Chris Kilbride, supt. Fax 426-7144
www.ritenour.k12.mo.us
Other Schools – See Overland, Saint Ann, Saint John

Riverview Gardens SD 6,300/PK-12
1370 Northumberland Dr 63137 314-869-2505
Dr. Clive Coleman, supt. Fax 388-6002
www.rgsd.k12.mo.us
Central MS 800/6-8
9800 Patricia Barkalow Dr 63137 314-867-2603
Michael Wallace, prin. Fax 388-6029
Riverview Gardens HS 1,500/9-12
1218 Shepley Dr 63137 314-869-4700
Jason Roberts, prin. Fax 388-6020
Westview MS 700/6-8
1950 Nemnich Rd 63136 314-867-0410
Valeska Hill, prin. Fax 388-6050

Special SD of St. Louis County 2,800/10-12
12110 Clayton Rd 63131 314-989-8100
John Cary, supt. Fax 989-8440
www.ssdmo.org/
South Technical HS Vo/Tech
12721 W Watson Rd 63127 314-989-7400
Dave Baker, prin. Fax 989-7503
Other Schools – See Florissant

St. Louis City SD 24,200/PK-12
801 N 11th St 63101 314-231-3720
Dr. Kelvin Adams, supt. Fax 345-2661
www.slps.org/
Beaumont HS 700/9-12
3836 Natural Bridge Ave 63107 314-533-2410
Michael Brown, prin. Fax 244-1712
Busch MS of Character & Athletics 300/6-8
5910 Clifton Ave 63109 314-352-1043
Robert Lescher, prin. Fax 244-1729
Carnahan HS of the Future 400/9-12
4041 S Broadway 63118 314-457-0582
Bruce Green, prin. Fax 457-9741
Carr Lane Visual & Performing Art MS 600/6-8
1004 N Jefferson Ave 63106 314-231-0413
Perry Anselman, prin. Fax 244-1733
Central Visual and Performing Arts HS 500/9-12
3125 S Kingshighway Blvd 63139 314-771-2772
Dr. Amy Phillips, prin. Fax 771-0135
Cleveland NJROTC Academy 300/9-12
4939 Kemper Ave 63139 314-776-1301
Susan Viviano, prin. Fax 244-1747
College Prep HS at Madison Alt
1118 S 7th St 63104 314-932-5711
Charmyn Baker, prin. Fax 244-1948
Compton-Drew ILC MS 500/6-8
5130 Oakland Ave 63110 314-652-9282
Susan Reid, prin. Fax 244-1756
Fanning MS Community Education Center 400/6-8
3417 Grace Ave 63116 314-772-1038
Cornelius Green, prin. Fax 244-1766
Fresh Start Academy North Alt
4248 Cottage Ave 63113 314-531-2220
Stanley Green, prin. Fax 244-1930
Gateway MST Prep S 500/6-8
1200 N Jefferson Ave 63106 314-241-2295
Aisha Grace, prin. Fax 241-7698
Gateway STEM HS 1,200/9-12
5101 McRee Ave 63110 314-776-3300
Dr. Elizabeth Bender, prin. Fax 776-8267
Langston MS 300/6-8
5511 Wabada Ave 63112 314-383-2908
Lanetra Thomas, prin. Fax 385-4632
Long MS Community Education Center 300/6-8
5028 Morganford Rd 63116 314-481-3440
Brenda Smith, prin. Fax 481-7329
L'Ouverture Academy 300/6-8
3021 Hickory St 63104 314-664-3579
Lisa Nuyens, prin. Fax 664-7955
McKinley Classical Junior Academy 200/7-8
2156 Russell Blvd 63104 314-773-0027
Earl Williams, prin. Fax 771-9749
McKinley Classical Leadership Academy 9-12
2156 Russell Blvd 63104 314-773-0027
Earl Williams, prin. Fax 244-1834
Metro Academic & Classical HS 300/9-12
4015 McPherson Ave 63108 314-534-3894
Wilfred Moore Ph.D., prin. Fax 531-4894
Miller Career Academy Vo/Tech
1000 N Grand Blvd 63106 314-371-0394
Stephen Warmack, prin. Fax 371-1311
Northwest Academy of Law 300/9-12
5140 Riverview Blvd 63120 314-385-4774
Valerie Carter-Thomas, prin. Fax 385-3651
Nottingham CAJT Vo/Tech
4915 Donovan Ave 63109 314-481-4095
Brian O'Connor, prin. Fax 244-1730
Roosevelt HS 1,000/9-12
3230 Hartford St 63118 314-776-6040
Crystal Gale, prin. Fax 244-1861
Soldan International Studies HS 700/9-12
918 Union Blvd 63108 314-367-9222
Dr. Thomas Cason, prin. Fax 367-1898
Sumner Magnet HS 600/9-12
4248 Cottage Ave 63113 314-371-1048
Trista Harper, prin. Fax 531-9852
Vashon HS 700/9-12
3035 Cass Ave 63106 314-533-9487
Derrick Mitchell, prin. Fax 533-7540
Yeatman-Liddell MS 300/6-8
4265 Athlone Ave 63115 314-261-8132
James Harris, prin. Fax 389-4613

Webster Groves SD
Supt. — See Webster Groves
Hixson MS 600/7-8
630 S Elm Ave 63119 314-963-6450
Jason Heisserer, prin. Fax 918-4624

Achieve Test Prep Post-Sec.
1810 Craig Rd Ste 213 63146 314-288-0702
Aquinas Institute of Theology Post-Sec.
23 S Spring Ave 63108 314-256-8800
Bais Yaakov HS of St. Louis 50/9-12
700 N and South Rd 63130 314-863-9230
Bishop DuBourg HS 700/9-12
5850 Eichelberger St 63109 314-832-3030
Bridget Timoney, prin. Fax 832-0529
Block Yeshiva HS 100/9-12
1146 N Warson Rd 63132 314-872-8701
Rabbi Gabriel Munk, prin. Fax 872-8703
Burroughs S 600/7-12
755 S Price Rd 63124 314-993-4040
Andy Abbott, head sch Fax 993-6458
Cardinal Ritter College Prep HS 300/9-12
701 N Spring Ave 63108 314-446-5500
Michael Blackshear, prin. Fax 446-5570
Chamberlain College of Nursing Post-Sec.
11830 Westline Indtrl # 106 63146 314-991-6200

Chaminade College Preparatory S 800/6-12
425 S Lindbergh Blvd 63131 314-993-4400
Dr. Louis Peters, prin. Fax 993-4403
Christian Academy of Greater St. Louis 100/PK-12
11050 N Warson Rd 63114 314-429-7070
Carla Payne, admin. Fax 426-8601
Christian Brothers College HS 800/9-12
1850 De La Salle Dr 63141 314-985-6100
Br. David Poos, prin. Fax 985-6101
Concordia Seminary Post-Sec.
801 Seminary Pl 63105 314-505-7000
Cor Jesu Academy 600/9-12
10230 Gravois Rd 63123 314-842-1546
Sr. Kathleen Coonan, prin. Fax 842-6061
Court Reporting Institute Post-Sec.
7730 Carondelet Ave Ste 400 63105 888-208-6780
Covenant Theological Seminary Post-Sec.
12330 Conway Rd 63141 800-264-8064
Crossroads S 200/7-12
500 De Baliviere Ave 63112 314-367-8085
Clark Daggett, hdmstr. Fax 367-9711
De LaSalle MS 100/6-8
4145 Kennerly Ave 63113 314-531-9820
Phillip Pusateri, prin. Fax 531-4820
De Smet Jesuit HS 1,100/9-12
233 N New Ballas Rd 63141 314-567-3500
Dr. Gregory Densberger, prin. Fax 567-1519
DeVry University Post-Sec.
11830 Westline Indstrl #100 63146 866-831-3882
DVA Medical Center Post-Sec.
1 Jefferson Barracks Rd 63125 314-894-6631
Elaine Steven Beauty College Post-Sec.
10420 W Florissant Ave 63136 314-868-8196
ex'treme Institute by Nelly Post-Sec.
800 N 3rd St 63102 888-669-0633
Fontbonne University Post-Sec.
6800 Wydown Blvd 63105 314-862-3456
Goldfarb School of Nursing Barnes-Jewish Post-Sec.
4483 Duncan Ave 63110 314-454-7055
Harris-Stowe State University Post-Sec.
3026 Laclede Ave 63103 314-340-3300
Healing Arts Center Post-Sec.
2601 S Big Bend Blvd 63143 314-647-8080
Hickey College Post-Sec.
940 W Port Plz Ste 101 63146 314-434-2212
IHM Health of EMS Post-Sec.
2500 Abbott Pl 63143 314-768-1234
IHM Health Studies Center Post-Sec.
3663 Lindell Blvd 63108 314-768-1000
Incarnate Word Academy 500/9-12
2788 Normandy Dr 63121 314-725-5850
Molly Grumich, prin. Fax 725-2308
Jefferson S 100/7-12
4100 S Lindbergh Blvd 63127 314-843-4151
Dr. Lisa Holekamp, head sch Fax 843-3527
Kenrick School of Theology Post-Sec.
5200 Glennon Dr 63119 314-792-6100
L'Ecole Academy Post-Sec.
9200 Olive Blvd Ste 108 63132 314-264-1999
L'Ecole Culinaire Post-Sec.
9811 S 40 Dr 63124 314-587-2433
Logos S 100/6-12
9137 Old Bonhomme Rd 63132 314-997-7002
Dr. Kathleen Boyd-Fenger, hdmstr. Fax 997-6848
Loyola Academy 100/6-8
3851 Washington Blvd 63108 314-531-9091
Katherine Petron, prin. Fax 531-3603
Lutheran HS North 400/9-12
5401 Lucas and Hunt Rd 63121 314-389-3100
Tim Brackman, prin. Fax 389-3103
Lutheran HS South 500/9-12
9515 Tesson Ferry Rd 63123 314-631-1400
Brian Ryherd, prin. Fax 631-7762
Lutheran School of Nursing Post-Sec.
3547 S Jefferson Ave 63118 314-577-5850
Marian MS 100/5-8
4130 Wyoming St 63116 314-771-7674
Christy Toben, prin. Fax 771-7679
Mary Institute/St. Louis Country Day S 1,200/PK-12
101 N Warson Rd 63124 314-993-5100
Lisa Lyle, hdmstr. Fax 995-7470
Maryville University of St. Louis Post-Sec.
650 Maryville University Dr 63141 314-529-9300
Missouri Baptist University Post-Sec.
1 College Park Dr 63141 314-434-1115
Missouri School for the Blind Post-Sec.
3815 Magnolia Ave 63110 314-776-4320
National Academy of Beauty Arts Post-Sec.
157 Concord Plz 63128 314-842-3616
Nerinx Hall HS 600/9-12
530 E Lockwood Ave 63119 314-968-1505
Jane Kosash, prin. Fax 968-0604
Notre Dame HS 300/9-12
320 E Ripa Ave 63125 314-544-1015
Sr. Michelle Emmerich, prin. Fax 544-8003
Parks College of St. Louis University Post-Sec.
3450 Lindell Blvd 63103 314-977-8203
Principia S 500/PK-12
13201 Clayton Rd 63131 314-434-2100
Marilyn Wallace, hdmstr. Fax 275-3583
Ranken Technical College Post-Sec.
4431 Finney Ave 63113 314-371-0236
Rosati-Kain HS 400/9-12
4389 Lindell Blvd 63108 314-533-8513
Judy Mohan, prin. Fax 533-1618
St. Elizabeth Academy 200/9-12
3401 Arsenal St 63118 314-771-5134
Christina Cheak, prin. Fax 771-3528
St. John Vianney HS 600/9-12
1311 S Kirkwood Rd 63122 314-965-4853
Dr. Timothy Dilg, prin. Fax 965-1950
St. Joseph Academy 600/9-12
2307 S Lindbergh Blvd 63131 314-965-7205
Sr. Pat Dunphy, prin. Fax 965-9114
St. Louis College of Health Careers Post-Sec.
909 S Taylor Ave 63110 314-652-0300
St. Louis College of Pharmacy Post-Sec.
4588 Parkview Pl 63110 314-367-8700

St. Louis Community College- Forest Park Post-Sec.
5600 Oakland Ave 63110 314-644-9100
St. Louis Hair Academy Post-Sec.
3701 Kossuth Ave 63107 314-533-3125
St. Louis Priory S 400/7-12
500 S Mason Rd 63141 314-434-3690
Rev. Linus Dolce, hdmstr. Fax 576-7800
St. Louis University Post-Sec.
221 N Grand Blvd 63103 800-758-3678
St. Louis University HS 1,100/9-12
4970 Oakland Ave 63110 314-531-0330
Dr. John Moran, prin. Fax 531-3441
St. Mary's HS 400/9-12
4701 S Grand Blvd 63111 314-481-8400
Kevin Hacker M.D., prin. Fax 481-3670
Stevens Institute of Business & Arts Post-Sec.
1521 Washington Ave 63103 800-871-0949
Strayer University Post-Sec.
1600 S Brentwood Blvd # 300 63144 314-817-9100
Tower Grove Christian S 300/PK-12
4257 Magnolia Ave 63110 314-776-6473
Michael Gregory, admin. Fax 776-4867
Trinity Catholic HS 400/9-12
1720 Redman Rd 63138 314-741-1333
Nancy Lydon, prin. Fax 741-1335
University of Missouri - Saint Louis Post-Sec.
1 University Blvd 63121 314-516-5000
Villa Duchesne/Oak Hill JSHS 400/7-12
801 S Spoede Rd 63131 314-432-2021
Douglas Lowney, prin. Fax 432-0199
Visitation Academy 600/PK-12
3020 N Ballas Rd 63131 314-625-9100
Mary Ellen Schraeder, hdmstr. Fax 432-7210
Washington University in St. Louis Post-Sec.
1 Brookings Dr 63130 314-935-5000
Webster University Post-Sec.
470 E Lockwood Ave 63119 314-968-6900
Whitfield S 500/6-12
175 S Mason Rd 63141 314-434-5141
John Delautre, pres. Fax 434-6193

Saint Peters, Saint Charles, Pop. 51,692
Ft. Zumwalt R-II SD
Supt. — See O Fallon
DuBray MS 900/6-8
100 DuBray Dr 63376 636-279-7979
Mike Anderson, prin. Fax 278-4749
Ft. Zumwalt East HS 1,300/9-12
600 First Executive Ave 63376 636-477-2400
Dr. Henry St. Pierre, prin. Fax 926-3345
Ft. Zumwalt South HS 1,300/9-12
8050 Mexico Rd 63376 636-978-1212
Dr. Kevin Keltner, prin. Fax 980-1745
Ft. Zumwalt South MS 1,000/6-8
300 Knaust Rd 63376 636-281-0776
Dr. Monte Massey, prin. Fax 281-0006

Le Cordon Bleu College of Culinary Arts Post-Sec.
7898 Veterans Memorial Pkwy 63376 866-863-2061
Lutheran HS of St. Charles County 300/9-12
5100 Mexico Rd 63376 636-928-5100
David Schlesselman, dir. Fax 928-8451

Salem, Dent, Pop. 4,859
Salem R-80 SD 1,400/K-12
1409 W Rolla Rd 65560 573-729-6642
Stephen Carvajal, supt. Fax 729-8493
www.salem.k12.mo.us/
Salem HS 600/9-12
1400 Tiger Pride Dr 65560 573-729-2222
John Smith, prin. Fax 729-7408
Salem JHS 200/7-8
1400 Tiger Pride Dr 65560 573-729-4261
Bobbie Jo Lewis, prin. Fax 729-2720

Salisbury, Chariton, Pop. 1,601
Salisbury R-IV SD 500/K-12
PO Box 314 65281 660-388-6699
Todd Willhite, supt. Fax 388-6753
www.salisbury.k12.mo.us/
Salisbury JSHS 200/7-12
PO Box 314 65281 660-388-6442
J.W. Brandt, prin. Fax 388-5651

Sarcoxie, Jasper, Pop. 1,304
Sarcoxie R-II SD 800/K-12
101 S 17th St 64862 417-548-3134
Dr. Kevin Goddard, supt. Fax 548-6165
www.sarcoxie.k12.mo.us/
Sarcoxie JSHS 400/6-12
101 S 17th St 64862 417-548-2153
Philip Lewis, prin. Fax 548-7193

Savannah, Andrew, Pop. 5,020
Savannah R-III SD 2,300/K-12
408 W Market St 64485 816-324-3144
Dr. David Brax, supt. Fax 324-5594
www.savannahr3.com
Savannah HS 700/9-12
701 State Rte E 64485 816-324-3128
Zac Coughlin, prin. Fax 324-6536
Savannah MS 600/6-8
10500 State Route T 64485 816-324-3126
Leisa Blair, prin. Fax 324-6397

Scott City, Scott, Pop. 4,518
Scott City R-I SD 900/K-12
3000 Main St 63780 573-264-2381
Diann Bradshaw-Ulmer, supt. Fax 264-2206
scschools.k12.mo.us/
Scott City HS 300/9-12
3000 Main St 63780 573-264-2138
Michael Johnson, prin. Fax 264-2608
Scott City MS 300/5-8
3000 Main St 63780 573-264-2139
Michael Umfleet, prin. Fax 264-2599

Sedalia, Pettis, Pop. 20,824
Sedalia SD 200 3,900/PK-12
2806 Matthew Dr 65301 660-829-6450
Bradley Pollitt, supt. Fax 827-8938
www.sedalia200.org
Smith-Cotton HS 1,000/10-12
2010 Tiger Pride Blvd 65301 660-851-5300
Wade Norton, prin. Fax 851-5393
Smith-Cotton JHS 300/7-9
312 E Broadway Blvd 65301 660-829-6300
Jason Curry, prin. Fax 829-6409

American College of Hair Design Post-Sec.
125 Duke Rd 65301 660-827-3295
Sacred Heart HS 100/9-12
416 W 3rd St 65301 660-827-3800
Dr. Mark Register, prin. Fax 827-3806
State Fair Community College Post-Sec.
3201 W 16th St 65301 660-530-5800

Senath, Dunklin, Pop. 1,752
Senath-Hornersville C-8 SD 800/PK-12
PO Box 370 63876 573-738-2669
Larry Wood, supt. Fax 738-9845
www.shs.k12.mo.us/
Senath-Hornersville HS 200/9-12
PO Box 370 63876 573-738-2661
Kevin Reddick, prin. Fax 738-3481
Other Schools – See Hornersville

Seneca, Newton, Pop. 2,214
Seneca R-VII SD 1,300/PK-12
914 Frisco St 64865 417-776-3426
Steve Wilmoth, supt. Fax 776-2177
schoolweb.missouri.edu/seneca.k12.mo.us/
Seneca HS 500/9-12
914 Frisco St 64865 417-776-3926
Willie Ng, prin. Fax 776-1878
Seneca JHS 200/7-8
914 Frisco St 64865 417-776-3911
Tony Simmons, prin. Fax 776-2673

Seymour, Webster, Pop. 1,885
Seymour R-II SD 800/PK-12
416 E Clinton Ave 65746 417-935-2287
Bruce Denney, supt. Fax 935-4060
www.seymourschool.net
Seymour HS 300/9-12
625 E Clinton Ave 65746 417-935-4508
Aaron Gray, prin. Fax 935-4539
Seymour MS 200/6-8
501 E Clinton Ave 65746 417-935-4626
Brian Bell, prin. Fax 935-2848

Shelbina, Shelby, Pop. 1,695
Shelby County R-IV SD 600/PK-12
4154 Highway 36 63468 573-588-4961
Rick Roberts, supt. Fax 588-2490
www.cardinals.k12.mo.us
South Shelby MSHS 200/6-12
4154 Highway 36 63468 573-588-4163
Deacon Windsor, prin. Fax 588-2490

Shelbyville, Shelby, Pop. 547
North Shelby SD 300/PK-12
3071 Highway 15 63469 573-633-2410
Paul Sulser, supt. Fax 633-2138
www.nshelby.k12.mo.us
North Shelby JSHS 100/7-12
3071 Highway 15 63469 573-633-2410
Harold Eckler, prin. Fax 633-2138

Sheldon, Vernon, Pop. 525
Sheldon R-VIII SD 200/PK-12
100 E Gene Lathrop Dr 64784 417-884-5113
Tim Judd, supt. Fax 884-5331
www.sheldon.k12.mo.us
Sheldon JSHS 100/7-12
100 E Gene Lathrop Dr 64784 417-884-5111
Jason Irwin, prin. Fax 884-5331

Sikeston, Scott, Pop. 16,008
Scott County Central SD 400/PK-12
20794 US Highway 61 63801 573-471-2686
Alvin McFerren, supt. Fax 471-2029
scottcentral.k12.mo.us
Scott County Central JSHS 200/7-12
20794 US Highway 61 63801 573-471-2001
Rich Thomas M.Ed., prin. Fax 471-2004

Sikeston R-6 SD 3,300/K-12
1002 Virginia St 63801 573-472-2581
Thomas Williams, supt. Fax 472-2584
www.sikeston.k12.mo.us
Sikeston 7th and 8th Grade Center 500/7-8
1002 Virginia St 63801 573-471-1720
Jodi Glidewell, prin. Fax 472-8884
Sikeston Career & Technology Center Vo/Tech
1002 Virginia St 63801 573-471-5442
Chad King, dir. Fax 472-8861
Sikeston HS 1,000/9-12
1002 Virginia St 63801 573-472-8850
Tim Regenold, prin. Fax 472-8857

Silex, Lincoln, Pop. 187
Silex R-I SD 400/K-12
PO Box 46 63377 573-384-5227
Elaine Henderson, supt. Fax 384-5996
schoolweb.missouri.edu/silex.k12.mo.us/
Silex JSHS 200/7-12
PO Box 46 63377 573-384-5227
Dr. Bruce Werkmeister, prin. Fax 384-5996

Slater, Saline, Pop. 1,827
Slater SD 400/PK-12
515 Elm St 65349 660-529-2278
Dr. Terry Lorenz, supt. Fax 529-2279
www.slaterpublicschools.net
Slater HS 100/9-12
515 Elm St 65349 660-529-3133
Dr. Terry Lorenz, prin. Fax 529-3134

Smithton, Pettis, Pop. 561
Smithton R-VI SD 600/K-12
505 S Myrtle Ave 65350 660-343-5316
Diedrick Kahrs Ed.D., supt. Fax 343-5389
smithton.k12.mo.us
Smithton HS 300/7-12
505 S Myrtle Ave 65350 660-343-5318
Jonathan Petersen M.S., prin. Fax 343-5389

Smithville, Clay, Pop. 8,290
Smithville R-II SD 2,400/PK-12
655 S Commercial Ave 64089 816-532-0406
Dr. George Curry, supt. Fax 532-4192
www.smithville.k12.mo.us/
Smithville HS 800/9-12
645 S Commercial Ave 64089 816-532-0405
Dr. Rudy Papenfuhs, prin. Fax 532-4193
Smithville MS 600/6-8
675 S Commercial Ave 64089 816-532-1122
Matt Teeter, prin. Fax 532-3210

Sparta, Christian, Pop. 1,734
Sparta R-III SD 700/PK-12
PO Box 160 65753 417-634-4284
Dr. Joff Hyatt, supt. Fax 634-3156
www.sparta.k12.mo.us/
Sparta HS 200/9-12
PO Box 160 65753 417-634-3224
Fax 634-0091
Sparta MS 200/5-8
PO Box 160 65753 417-634-5518
Shawn Poyser, prin. Fax 634-0091

Spokane, Christian, Pop. 175
Spokane R-VII SD
Supt. — See Highlandville
Spokane HS 200/9-12
PO Box 218 65754 417-443-3502
Jim Millsap, prin. Fax 443-7714
Spokane MS 200/6-8
PO Box 220 65754 417-443-3506
Pamila Rowe, prin. Fax 443-2069

Springfield, Greene, Pop. 154,799
Springfield R-XII SD 24,400/PK-12
1359 E Saint Louis St 65802 417-523-0000
Dr. Norman Ridder, supt. Fax 523-0196
www.springfieldpublicschoolsmo.org/
AIMS MS, 1518 E Dale St 65803 Alt
Cathy Clark, coord. 417-523-4200
Bailey Alternative HS Alt
501 W Central St 65802 417-523-2700
Justin Dickenson, coord. Fax 523-2795
Carver MS 800/6-8
3325 W Battlefield St 65807 417-523-6800
Dr. Dan O'Reilly, prin. Fax 523-6895
Central HS 1,600/6-12
423 E Central St 65802 417-523-9600
Ron Snodgrass, prin. Fax 523-9695
Cherokee MS 800/6-8
420 E Farm Road 182 65810 417-523-7200
Bill Powers, prin. Fax 523-7295
Glendale HS 1,300/9-12
2727 S Ingram Mill Rd 65804 417-523-8900
Dr. Matt Pearce, prin. Fax 523-8995
Hickory Hills MS 500/6-8
4650 E State Highway YY 65802 417-523-7100
Kelly Allison, prin. Fax 523-7195
Hillcrest HS 1,100/9-12
3319 N Grant Ave 65803 417-523-8000
Garry Moore, prin. Fax 523-8095
Jarrett MS 500/6-8
840 S Jefferson Ave 65806 417-523-6600
Teresa Wise, prin. Fax 523-6695
Kickapoo HS 1,700/9-12
3710 S Jefferson Ave 65807 417-523-8500
David Schmitz, prin. Fax 523-8595
OTC Middle College Alt
1001 E Chestnut Expy 65802 417-447-7500
Dr. LaRaine Bauer, prin.
Parkview HS 1,500/9-12
516 W Meadowmere St 65807 417-523-9200
Eric Ramsey, prin. Fax 523-9295
Pershing MS 700/6-8
2120 S Ventura Ave 65804 417-523-2400
Dr. Natalie Cauldwell, prin. Fax 523-2495
Pipkin MS 600/6-8
1215 N Boonville Ave 65802 417-523-6000
Dr. Tim Zeigler, prin. Fax 523-6195
Pleasant View MS 300/6-8
2210 E State Highway AA 65803 417-523-2100
Donna Aldrich, prin. Fax 523-2395
Reed MS 400/6-8
2000 N Lyon Ave 65803 417-523-6300
Dr. Debbie Grega, prin. Fax 523-6395
Study MS 400/6-8
2343 W Olive St 65802 417-523-6502
Jim Harvey, prin. Fax 523-6495

Assemblies of God Theological Seminary Post-Sec.
1435 N Glenstone Ave 65802 417-268-1000
Baptist Bible College Post-Sec.
628 E Kearney St 65803 800-228-5754
Bryan University Post-Sec.
4255 S Nature Center Way 65804 417-862-5700
Central Bible College Post-Sec.
3000 N Grant Ave 65803 800-831-4222
Cox College Post-Sec.
1423 N Jefferson Ave 65802 417-269-3401
Drury University Post-Sec.
900 N Benton Ave 65802 417-873-7879
Evangel University Post-Sec.
1111 N Glenstone Ave 65802 417-865-2811
Everest College Post-Sec.
1010 W Sunshine St 65807 417-864-7220
Global University Post-Sec.
1211 S Glenstone Ave 65804 417-862-9533
Greenwood Laboratory S 300/K-12
901 S National Ave, 417-836-5124
Dr. Janice Duncan, dir. Fax 836-8449
ITT Technical Institute Post-Sec.
3216 S National Ave 65807 417-877-4800
Missouri College of Cosmetology North Post-Sec.
2555 W Kearney St 65803 417-866-2786
Missouri State University Post-Sec.
901 S National Ave, 417-836-5000
New Covenant Academy 400/PK-12
3304 S Cox Ave 65807 417-887-9848
Matthew Searson, admin. Fax 887-2419
Ozarks Technical Community College Post-Sec.
1001 E Chestnut Expy 65802 417-447-7500
Professional Massage Training Center Post-Sec.
229 E Commercial St 65803 417-863-7682
St. John's Regional Health Center Post-Sec.
1235 E Cherokee St 65804 417-885-2845
St. John's School of Nursing Post-Sec.
4431 S Fremont Ave 65804 417-885-2098
School of Professional Psychology Post-Sec.
2885 W Battlefield St 65807 417-823-3477
Southwest Baptist University Post-Sec.
4431 S Fremont Ave 65804 417-820-2069
Springfield Catholic HS 300/9-12
2340 S Eastgate Ave 65809 417-887-8817
Dr. Amy DeMelo, prin. Fax 885-1165
Springfield SDA S 50/K-10
704 S Belview Ave 65802 417-862-0833
Vatterott College - Springfield Post-Sec.
3850 S Campbell Ave 65807 417-831-8116

Stanberry, Gentry, Pop. 1,181
Stanberry R-II SD 400/PK-12
610 N Park St 64489 660-783-2136
Dr. Bruce Johnson, supt. Fax 783-2177
www.sr2.k12.mo.us/
Stanberry JSHS 200/7-12
610 N Park St 64489 660-783-2163
Danny Johnson, prin. Fax 783-2177

Steele, Pemiscot, Pop. 2,134
South Pemiscot County R-V SD 700/K-12
611 Beasley Rd 63877 573-695-4426
Chris Moore, supt. Fax 695-4427
www.southpemiscot.com/
South Pemiscot HS 300/7-12
611 Beasley Rd 63877 573-695-3342
Glenn Carter, prin. Fax 695-7461

Steelville, Crawford, Pop. 1,631
Steelville R-III SD 900/PK-12
PO Box 339 65565 573-775-2175
Mike Whittaker, supt. Fax 775-2179
steelville.k12.mo.us
Steelville HS 300/9-12
PO Box 339 65565 573-775-2144
Tana Booker, prin. Fax 775-5050
Steelville MS 300/5-8
PO Box 339 65565 573-775-2176
John Bunch, prin. Fax 775-2591

Stewartsville, DeKalb, Pop. 741
Stewartsville C-2 SD 200/K-12
902 Buchanan St 64490 816-669-3792
Paul Perry, supt. Fax 669-8125
www.stewartsville.k12.mo.us
Stewartsville JSHS 100/7-12
902 Buchanan St 64490 816-669-3258
Chris Gagnon, prin. Fax 669-8125

Stockton, Cedar, Pop. 1,789
Stockton R-I SD 1,100/K-12
PO Box 190 65785 417-276-5143
Shannon Snow, supt. Fax 276-3765
www.stockton.k12.mo.us/
Stockton HS 300/9-12
PO Box 190 65785 417-276-8806
Michael Postlewait, prin. Fax 276-8584
Stockton MS 400/5-8
PO Box 190 65785 417-276-5141
Bill Crabtree, prin. Fax 276-6389

Stoutland, Laclede, Pop. 192
Stoutland R-II SD 500/PK-12
7584 State Road T 65567 417-286-3711
Eric Cooley, supt. Fax 286-3153
www.stoutlandschools.com
Stoutland JSHS 200/7-12
7584 State Road T 65567 417-286-3711
Sara Light, prin. Fax 286-3981

Stover, Morgan, Pop. 1,079
Morgan County R-I SD 500/PK-12
701 N Oak St 65078 573-377-2217
John French, supt. Fax 377-2211
mcr1.stovermo.com/
Morgan County R-I HS 200/7-12
701 N Oak St 65078 573-377-2218
Michael Marriott, prin. Fax 377-2952

Strafford, Greene, Pop. 2,311
Strafford R-VI SD 1,200/K-12
201 W McCabe St 65757 417-736-7000
John Collins, supt. Fax 736-7016
straffordschools.net
Strafford HS 400/9-12
201 W McCabe St 65757 417-736-7000
Brett Soden, prin. Fax 736-7020
Strafford MS 400/5-8
211 W McCabe St 65757 417-736-7000
Marcia Chadwell, prin. Fax 736-7019

Sturgeon, Boone, Pop. 864
Sturgeon R-V SD 400/K-12
210 W Patton St 65284 573-687-3515
Shawn Schultz, supt. Fax 687-2116
www.sturgeon.k12.mo.us/
Sturgeon HS 100/9-12
210 W Patton St 65284 573-687-3512
Greg Buescher, prin. Fax 687-3441
Sturgeon MS 100/5-8
210 W Patton St 65284 573-687-2155
Brandee Brown, prin. Fax 687-1226

Sullivan, Franklin, Pop. 7,019
Sullivan SD 2,200/PK-12
138 Taylor St 63080 573-468-5171
Dr. Thomas Allen, supt. Fax 468-7720
www.eagles.k12.mo.us
Sullivan HS 700/9-12
1073 E Vine St 63080 573-468-5181
Dr. Jennifer Schmidt, prin. Fax 860-3524
Sullivan MS 500/6-8
1156 Elmont Rd 63080 573-468-5191
Matt Parker, prin. Fax 860-2326

Summersville, Texas, Pop. 492
Summersville R-II SD 400/PK-12
PO Box 198 65571 417-932-4045
Merlyn Johnson, supt. Fax 932-5360
www.sville.k12.mo.us
Summersville JSHS 200/7-12
PO Box 198 65571 417-932-4929
Jon Johnson, prin. Fax 932-4178

Sunset Hills, Saint Louis, Pop. 8,388

Vatterott College - Sunset Hills Post-Sec.
12900 Maurer Industrial Dr 63127 314-843-4200

Sweet Springs, Saline, Pop. 1,457
Sweet Springs R-VII SD 500/PK-12
600 E Marshall St 65351 660-335-4860
Donna Wright, admin. Fax 335-4378
sweetsprings.k12.mo.us/
Sweet Springs JSHS 200/7-12
600 E Marshall St 65351 660-335-6341
David Reinke, admin. Fax 335-6379

Tarkio, Atchison, Pop. 1,576
Tarkio R-I SD 300/K-12
312 S 11th St 64491 660-736-4161
Tim Lenz, supt. Fax 736-4546
www.tarkio.k12.mo.us
Tarkio JSHS 200/7-12
312 S 11th St 64491 660-736-4118
Doug Miller, prin. Fax 736-4546

Thayer, Oregon, Pop. 2,197
Thayer R-II SD 700/PK-12
401 E Walnut St 65791 417-264-7261
Jeffrey Chappell, supt. Fax 264-4608
thayer.k12.mo.us/
Thayer JSHS 300/7-12
401 E Walnut St 65791 417-264-7261
Michael Hess, prin. Fax 264-4608

Theodosia, Ozark, Pop. 239
Lutie R-VI SD 200/K-12
HC 4 Box 4775 65761 417-273-4274
Scot Young, supt. Fax 273-4171
www.schoolweb.missouri.edu/lutie.k12.mo.us
Lutie JSHS 100/7-12
HC 4 Box 4775 65761 417-273-4274
Elaine Butler, prin. Fax 273-4171

Tina, Carroll, Pop. 154
Tina-Avalon R-II SD 200/PK-12
11896 Highway 65 64682 660-622-4211
Jana Holcer, supt. Fax 622-4210
tinaavalon.k12.mo.us/
Tina-Avalon JSHS 100/7-12
11896 Highway 65 64682 660-622-4212
David Probasco, prin. Fax 622-4210

Tipton, Moniteau, Pop. 3,237
Tipton R-VI SD 600/K-12
305 US Highway 50 E 65081 660-433-5520
Scott Jarvis, supt. Fax 433-5241
tipton.k12.mo.us/
Tipton HS 300/7-12
305 US Highway 50 E 65081 660-433-5528
Allee Ellen, prin. Fax 433-2419

Trenton, Grundy, Pop. 5,941
Trenton R-IX SD 1,200/K-12
1607 Normal St 64683 660-359-3994
Becky Albrecht, supt. Fax 359-3995
www.trentonr9.k12.mo.us/
Trenton HS 400/9-12
1415 Oklahoma Ave 64683 660-359-2291
Dan Wiebers, prin. Fax 359-4073
Trenton MS 400/5-8
1417 Oklahoma Ave 64683 660-359-4328
Jamie Oram, prin. Fax 359-6554

North Central Missouri College Post-Sec.
1301 Main St 64683 660-359-3948

Troy, Lincoln, Pop. 10,315
Troy R-III SD 6,200/PK-12
951 W College St 63379 636-462-6098
Mark Penny, supt. Fax 528-2411
www.troy.k12.mo.us
Buchanan HS 1,400/10-12
1190 Old Cap Au Gris Rd 63379 636-528-4618
Stephen Hunter, prin. Fax 528-5164
New Horizons HS Alt
41 Clonts Field Dr 63379 636-528-7667
Amy Salvo, prin. Fax 528-2411
Troy MS 1,400/6-8
713 W College St 63379 636-528-7057
Jerry Raines, prin. Fax 528-2199
Other Schools – See Moscow Mills

Tuscumbia, Miller, Pop. 203
Miller County R-III SD 200/K-12
PO Box 1 65082 573-369-2375
Dr. Jeff Koonce, supt. Fax 369-2833
www.tuscumbialions.k12.mo.us
Tuscumbia HS 100/9-12
PO Box 1 65082 573-369-2375
Jason Price, prin. Fax 369-2833

Union, Franklin, Pop. 10,024
Union R-XI SD 3,000/K-12
PO Box 440 63084 636-583-8626
Steve Bryant, supt. Fax 583-2403
union.k12.mo.us
Union HS 1,000/9-12
PO Box 440 63084 636-583-2513
Doug Cuneio, prin. Fax 583-4203
Union MS 400/7-8
PO Box 440 63084 636-583-5855
Ty Crain, prin. Fax 583-6156

East Central College Post-Sec.
1964 Prairie Dell Rd 63084 636-584-6551

Union Star, DeKalb, Pop. 430
Union Star R-II SD 100/K-12
6132 NW State Route Z 64494 816-593-2294
Rick Calloway, supt. Fax 593-4427
www.usr2.com
Union Star JSHS 100/6-12
6132 NW State Route Z 64494 816-593-2294
Chris Turpin, prin. Fax 593-4427

Unionville, Putnam, Pop. 1,843
Putnam County R-I SD 800/PK-12
803 S 20th St 63565 660-947-3361
Heath Halley, supt. Fax 947-2912
www.putnamcountyr1.net
Putnam County HS 200/9-12
803 S 20th St 63565 660-947-2481
Jeremy Watt, prin. Fax 947-2912
Putnam County MS 200/6-8
802 S 18th St 63565 660-947-3237
Andrew Garber, prin. Fax 947-2912

University City, Saint Louis, Pop. 34,413
School District of University City 2,500/PK-12
8136 Groby Rd 63130 314-290-4000
Joylynn Pruitt, supt. Fax 725-7692
www.ucityschools.org
Brittany Woods MS 500/6-8
8125 Groby Rd 63130 314-290-4280
Jamie Jordan, prin. Fax 997-1786
Lieberman Learning Center Alt
8136 Groby Rd 63130 314-290-4330
Chris Blumenhorst, prin. Fax 432-4478
University City HS 900/9-12
7401 Balson Ave 63130 314-290-4100
Michael Maclin, prin. Fax 290-4120

Urbana, Hickory, Pop. 412
Hickory County R-I SD 500/K-12
RR 1 Box 838 65767 417-993-4241
Mark Boem, supt. Fax 993-4269
www.skylineschools.info
Skyline HS 300/7-12
RR 1 Box 838 65767 417-993-4226
Randall Dougherty, prin. Fax 993-5947

Valley Park, Saint Louis, Pop. 6,786
Valley Park SD 1,100/PK-12
1 Main St 63088 636-923-3500
Dave Knes, supt. Fax 861-1002
www.vp.k12.mo.us
Valley Park HS 300/9-12
1 Main St 63088 636-923-3613
Randall Fidler, prin. Fax 225-0542
Valley Park MS 200/6-8
1 Main St 63088 636-923-3624
Dr. Tad Savage, prin. Fax 225-1529

Van Buren, Carter, Pop. 813
Van Buren R-I SD 500/PK-12
PO Box 550 63965 573-323-4281
Sonia Kuessner, supt. Fax 323-4297
schoolweb.missouri.edu/vanburen.k12.mo.us
Van Buren HS 300/6-12
PO Box 550 63965 573-323-4295
Mark Wood, prin. Fax 323-4295

Vandalia, Audrain, Pop. 3,832
Van-Far R-I SD 600/PK-12
2200 W US Highway 54 63382 573-594-6111
Chris Felmlee, supt. Fax 594-2878
www.vf.k12.mo.us
Van-Far JSHS 300/7-12
2200 W US Highway 54 63382 573-594-6442
Cindy Pirch, prin. Fax 594-3054

Verona, Lawrence, Pop. 608
Verona R-VII SD 400/K-12
PO Box 7 65769 417-498-2274
Tony L. Simmons, supt. Fax 498-6590
verona.k12.mo.us
Verona JSHS 200/7-12
PO Box 7 65769 417-498-6775
Terry Winton, prin. Fax 498-6045

Versailles, Morgan, Pop. 2,421
Morgan County R-II SD 1,400/PK-12
913 W Newton St 65084 573-378-4231
Dr. Joyce Ryerson, supt. Fax 378-5714
www.mcr2.k12.mo.us/
Morgan County HS 400/9-12
913 W Newton St 65084 573-378-4697
Kent Chamberlain, prin. Fax 378-2704
Morgan County MS 300/6-8
913 W Newton St 65084 573-378-5432
Travis Troyer, prin. Fax 378-6610

Viburnum, Iron, Pop. 688
Iron County C-4 SD 400/K-12
PO Box 368 65566 573-244-5422
Deron Gibbs, supt. Fax 244-5424
www.ironc4.k12.mo.us
Viburnum JSHS 200/7-12
PO Box 368 65566 573-244-5521
Clay LaRue, prin. Fax 244-3410

Vienna, Maries, Pop. 605
Maries County R-I SD 500/PK-12
PO Box 218 65582 573-422-3304
Mark Pottorff, supt. Fax 422-3185
www.mariesr1.k12.mo.us
Vienna HS 300/7-12
PO Box 218 65582 573-422-3363
Warren Ripley, prin. Fax 422-3185

Villa Ridge, Franklin, Pop. 2,605

Crosspoint Christian S 100/PK-12
PO Box 100 63089 636-742-5380
Joshua Haveman, admin. Fax 742-5917

Walker, Vernon, Pop. 266
Northeast Vernon County R-I SD 200/PK-12
216 E Leslie Ave 64790 417-465-2221
Charles Naas, supt. Fax 465-2388
www.nevcknights.org
Northeast Vernon County R-I HS 100/7-12
216 E Leslie Ave 64790 417-465-2221
Chris Hudson, prin. Fax 465-2388

Walnut Grove, Greene, Pop. 659
Walnut Grove R-V SD 300/K-12
PO Box 187 65770 417-788-2543
Gwenda Barton, supt. Fax 788-1254
www.wgtigers.com
Walnut Grove JSHS 100/7-12
PO Box 187 65770 417-788-2543
Christina Bowers, prin. Fax 788-1254

Wardell, Pemiscot, Pop. 423
North Pemiscot County R-I SD 300/K-12
PO Box 38 63879 573-628-3471
Terry Hamilton, supt. Fax 628-3472
www.northpem.k12.mo.us
North Pemiscot County JSHS 100/6-12
PO Box 38 63879 573-628-3465
Bill Hoffmann, prin. Fax 628-3418

Wardsville, Cole, Pop. 1,489
Blair Oaks R-II SD 1,100/K-12
6124 Falcon Ln 65101 573-636-2020
Dr. James Jones, supt. Fax 636-2202
www.blairoaks.k12.mo.us
Blair Oaks HS 400/9-12
6124 Falcon Ln 65101 573-635-8514
Gary Verslues, prin. Fax 635-6327
Blair Oaks MS 300/5-8
6124 Falcon Ln 65101 573-634-2053
Julia Gampher, prin. Fax 636-3509

Warrensburg, Johnson, Pop. 18,253
Warrensburg R-VI SD 2,600/PK-12
PO Box 638 64093 660-747-7823
Dr. Scott Patrick, supt. Fax 747-9615
www.warrensburgr6.org
Reese S Alt
301 W Market St 64093 660-747-2496
Leslie Brown, dir. Fax 747-2579
Warrensburg Area Career Center Vo/Tech
205 S Ridgeview Dr 64093 660-747-2283
Rusty Sproat, dir. Fax 747-3778
Warrensburg HS 1,000/9-12
1411 S Ridgeview Dr 64093 660-747-2262
Simone Dillingham, prin. Fax 747-8731
Warrensburg MS 700/6-8
640 E Gay St 64093 660-747-5612
Jim Elliott, prin. Fax 747-8779

University of Central Missouri Post-Sec.
PO Box 800 64093 660-543-4111

Warrenton, Warren, Pop. 7,746
Warren County R-III SD 3,000/PK-12
302 Kuhl Ave 63383 636-456-6901
Dr. Thomas Muzzey, supt. Fax 456-7687
www.warrencor3.org
Black Hawk MS 700/6-8
300 Kuhl Ave 63383 636-456-6903
Steve Barnes, prin. Fax 456-1445
Warrenton HS 900/9-12
803 Pinckney St 63383 636-456-6902
Jeremy Way, prin. Fax 456-5771

Warsaw, Benton, Pop. 2,107
Warsaw R-IX SD 1,300/PK-12
PO Box 248 65355 660-438-7120
Dr. James Haley, supt. Fax 438-5028
www.warsaw.k12.mo.us/
Boise MS 300/6-8
PO Box 1750 65355 660-438-9079
Eric Findley, prin. Fax 438-2209
Warsaw HS 400/9-12
PO Box 248 65355 660-438-7351
Amie Breshears, prin. Fax 438-3749

Washburn, Barry, Pop. 418
Southwest R-V SD 800/PK-12
529 E Pineville Rd 65772 417-826-5410
Robert Walker, supt. Fax 826-5603
www.swr5.k12.mo.us
Southwest HS 300/9-12
529 E Pineville Rd 65772 417-826-5413
Tosha Watson, prin. Fax 826-5603
Southwest MS 300/5-8
529 E Pineville Rd 65772 417-826-5050
Beverly Bonner, prin. Fax 826-5603

Washington, Franklin, Pop. 13,819
Washington SD 4,200/PK-12
220 Locust St 63090 636-231-2000
Dr. Lori VanLeer, supt. Fax 239-3315
www.washington.k12.mo.us
Four Rivers Career Center Vo/Tech
1978 Image Dr 63090 636-231-2100
Randy Kosark, dir. Fax 239-0791
Washington HS 1,400/9-12
600 Blue Jay Dr 63090 636-231-2200
Dr. Frank Wood, prin. Fax 231-2165
Washington MS 600/7-8
401 E 14th St 63090 636-231-2300
Ron Millheiser, prin. Fax 231-2305

St. Francis Borgia Regional HS 500/9-12
1000 Borgia Dr 63090 636-239-7871
Dr. Brad Heger, prin. Fax 239-1198

Waynesville, Pulaski, Pop. 4,531
Waynesville R-VI SD 5,600/PK-12
200 Fleetwood Dr 65583 573-842-2097
Dr. Judene Blackburn, supt. Fax 433-2967
waynesville.k12.mo.us
Waynesville Career Center Vo/Tech
400 GW Ln 65583 573-774-6106
Laura McVay, dir. Fax 774-3355
Waynesville HS 1,700/9-12
200 GW Ln 65583 573-774-6401
Courtney Long, prin. Fax 774-2393
Waynesville MS 900/7-8
1001 Historic 66 W 65583 573-842-2550
John Fluhrer, prin. Fax 774-6089

Central College of Cosmetology Post-Sec.
PO Box 463 65583 573-336-3888

Weaubleau, Hickory, Pop. 411
Weaubleau R-III SD 400/PK-12
509 N Center St 65774 417-428-3317
Eric Wilken, supt. Fax 428-3521
www.weaubleau.k12.mo.us/
Weaubleau HS 200/7-12
509 N Center St 65774 417-428-3368
Rodney Delmont, prin. Fax 428-3004

Webb City, Jasper, Pop. 10,693
Webb City R-VII SD 4,100/PK-12
411 N Madison St 64870 417-673-6000
Anthony Rossetti, supt. Fax 673-6007
www.wccards.k12.mo.us/
Webb City HS 1,200/9-12
621 N Madison St 64870 417-673-6010
Tim Davied, prin. Fax 673-6017
Webb City JHS 600/7-8
807 W 1st St 64870 417-673-6030
Angie Broadus, prin. Fax 673-6037

Webster Groves, Saint Louis, Pop. 22,645
Webster Groves SD 4,500/PK-12
400 E Lockwood Ave 63119 314-961-1233
Dr Sarah Riss, supt. Fax 963-6411
www.webster.k12.mo.us
Webster Groves HS 1,300/9-12
100 Selma Ave 63119 314-963-6400
Dr. Jon Clark, prin. Fax 963-6483
Other Schools – See Saint Louis

Eden Theological Seminary Post-Sec.
475 E Lockwood Ave 63119 314-961-3627
Holy Cross Academy Annunciation S 50/6-8
16 W Glendale Rd 63119 314-961-7712
Michael Biggs, prin. Fax 961-2157

Weldon Spring, Saint Charles, Pop. 5,401
Francis Howell R-III SD
Supt. — See Saint Charles
Bryan MS 900/6-8
605 Independence Rd 63304 636-851-5800
Mark Delaney, prin. Fax 851-6208
Howell MS 900/6-8
825 OFallon Rd 63304 636-851-4800
Ted Huff, prin. Fax 851-4121

Wellington, Lafayette, Pop. 797
Wellington-Napoleon R-IX SD 400/K-12
PO Box 280 64097 816-934-2531
Jeff Ruskey, supt. Fax 934-8649
www.well-nap.k12.mo.us/
Wellington-Napoleon JSHS 200/7-12
PO Box 280 64097 816-240-2621
Kenneth Holland, prin. Fax 934-8649

Wellsville, Montgomery, Pop. 1,206
Wellsville Middletown R-I SD 400/PK-12
900 Burlington St 63384 573-684-2428
Pete Nasir, supt. Fax 684-2018
wmr1.k12.mo.us/
Wellsville JSHS 200/7-12
900 Burlington St 63384 573-684-2017
Duane Bennett, prin. Fax 684-2018

Wentzville, Saint Charles, Pop. 28,539
Wentzville R-IV SD 11,900/K-12
1 Campus Dr 63385 636-327-3800
Dr. Terry Adams, supt. Fax 327-8611
www.wentzville.k12.mo.us
Holt HS 1,600/9-12
600 Campus Dr 63385 636-327-3876
John Waters, prin. Fax 327-3953
Timberland HS 1,800/9-12
559 E Highway N 63385 636-327-3988
Nathan Hoven, prin. Fax 327-3922
Wentzville MS 1,000/6-8
405 Campus Dr 63385 636-327-3815
Dr. Kelly Mantz, prin. Fax 327-3954
Wentzville South MS 700/6-8
561 E Highway N 63385 636-327-3928
Scott Swift, prin. Fax 327-3955

Other Schools – See O Fallon

Midwest University — Post-Sec.
851 Parr Rd 63385 — 636-327-4645

Weston, Platte, Pop. 1,614
West Platte County R-II SD — 600/K-12
1103 Washington St 64098 — 816-640-2236
Gerrod Wheeler, supt. — Fax 386-2104
www.wprii.k12.mo.us
West Platte County JSHS — 300/7-12
1103 Washington St 64098 — 816-640-2292
Stanley Coulson, prin. — Fax 386-2293

Westphalia, Osage, Pop. 382
Osage County R-III SD — 800/K-12
PO Box 37 65085 — 573-455-2375
Joe Scott, supt. — Fax 455-9884
www.fatimacomets.org
Fatima JSHS — 500/7-12
PO Box 37 65085 — 573-455-2550
Chuck Woody, prin. — Fax 455-9884

West Plains, Howell, Pop. 11,780
West Plains R-VII SD — 2,500/PK-12
305 Valley View Dr 65775 — 417-256-6150
John Mulford, supt. — Fax 256-8616
www.zizzers.org
South Central Career Center — Vo/Tech
407 W Thornburgh St 65775 — 417-256-6152
Jim Laughary, dir. — Fax 256-5786
West Plains HS — 1,200/9-12
602 E Olden St 65775 — 417-256-6150
Jack Randolph, prin. — Fax 256-8908
West Plains MS — 600/5-8
730 E Olden St 65775 — 417-256-6150
Scott Smith, prin. — Fax 256-8907

Missouri State University - West Plains — Post-Sec.
128 Garfield Ave 65775 — 417-255-7255

Wheatland, Hickory, Pop. 358
Wheatland R-II SD — 300/PK-12
PO Box 68 65779 — 417-282-6433
David McQuerter, supt. — Fax 282-5733
wheatland.mo.schoolwebpages.com/
Wheatland JSHS — 200/7-12
PO Box 68 65779 — 417-282-5833
Matt Gunter, prin. — Fax 282-5733

Wheaton, Barry, Pop. 680
Wheaton R-III SD — 500/PK-12
PO Box 249 64874 — 417-652-3914
Dr. Lance Massey, supt. — Fax 652-7355
www.wheatonbulldogs.org/
Wheaton JSHS — 200/7-12
PO Box 249 64874 — 417-652-7249
Mike Evans, prin. — Fax 652-7355

Wildwood, Saint Louis, Pop. 35,007

Saint Louis Community College - Wildwood — Post-Sec.
2645 Generations Dr 63040 — 636-422-2000

Willard, Greene, Pop. 5,200
Willard R-II SD — 4,400/PK-12
460 Kime St 65781 — 417-742-2584
Dr. Kent Medlin, supt. — Fax 742-2586
www.willard.k12.mo.us
Willard HS — 1,200/9-12
515 E Jackson St 65781 — 417-742-3524
Curt Graves, prin. — Fax 742-3667
Willard MS — 700/7-8
205 S Miller Rd 65781 — 417-742-2588
Amy Sims, prin. — Fax 742-3505

Willow Springs, Howell, Pop. 2,140
Willow Springs R-IV SD — 1,300/PK-12
215 W 4th St 65793 — 417-469-3260
Derrick Hutsell, supt. — Fax 469-5127
www.willowspringsschool.com/
Willow Springs HS — 300/9-12
215 W 4th St 65793 — 417-469-2114
Jimalee James, prin. — Fax 469-2507
Willow Springs MS — 400/5-8
215 W 4th St 65793 — 417-469-3211
Philip Pietroburgo, prin. — Fax 469-1229

Windsor, Henry, Pop. 2,866
Henry County R-I SD — 700/PK-12
210 North St 65360 — 660-647-3533
Kevin Sandlin, supt. — Fax 647-2711
henrycountyr1.k12.mo.us
Windsor JSHS — 300/7-12
210 North St 65360 — 660-647-3106
Cindy Hawkins, prin. — Fax 647-3218

Winfield, Lincoln, Pop. 1,383
Winfield R-IV SD — 1,500/K-12
701 W Elm St 63389 — 636-668-8188
Dr. Jim Chandler, supt. — Fax 668-8641
www.winfield.k12.mo.us
Winfield HS — 500/9-12
701 W Elm St 63389 — 636-668-8130
Nick Heggemann, prin. — Fax 566-6455
Winfield MS — 300/6-8
701 W Elm St 63389 — 636-668-8001
Tom McCracken, prin. — Fax 668-6044

Winona, Shannon, Pop. 1,311
Winona R-III SD — 500/PK-12
PO Box 248 65588 — 573-325-8101
Scott Lindsey, supt. — Fax 325-8447
www.winona.k12.mo.us
Winona HS — 200/9-12
PO Box 248 65588 — 573-325-8101
Gilbert Miley, prin. — Fax 325-4700

Winston, Daviess, Pop. 258
Winston R-VI SD — 200/PK-12
PO Box 38 64689 — 660-749-5331
Brian Robinson, supt. — Fax 749-5432
www.winston.k12.mo.us
Winston JSHS — 100/7-12
PO Box 38 64689 — 660-749-5456
Eric Lewis, prin. — Fax 749-5432

Wright City, Warren, Pop. 3,037
Wright City R-II SD — 1,500/PK-12
90 Bell Rd 63390 — 636-745-7200
Dr. Chris Gaines, supt. — Fax 745-3613
www.wrightcity.k12.mo.us/
Wright City HS — 500/9-12
520 Westwoods Rd 63390 — 636-745-7500
Shawn Brown, prin. — Fax 745-7518
Wright City MS — 300/6-8
100 Bell Rd 63390 — 636-745-7300
Deborah Stukey, prin. — Fax 745-7304

Zalma, Bollinger, Pop. 122
Zalma R-V SD — 200/K-12
HC 2 Box 184 63787 — 573-722-5504
Darryl Sauer, supt. — Fax 722-9870
www.zalma.k12.mo.us/
Zalma JSHS — 100/7-12
HC 2 Box 184 63787 — 573-722-3320
Gerard Vandeven, prin. — Fax 722-9870

MONTANA

MONTANA OFFICE OF PUBLIC INSTRUCTION
PO Box 202501, Helena 59620-2501
Telephone 406-444-3095
Fax 406-444-2893
Website opi.mt.gov

State Superintendent of Public Instruction   Denise Juneau

MONTANA BOARD OF EDUCATION
PO Box 200601, Helena 59620-0601

Chairperson   Patty Myers

COUNTY SUPERINTENDENTS OF SCHOOLS

Beaverhead County Office of Education
Linda Marsh, supt. 406-683-3737
2 S Pacific St Ste 7, Dillon 59725 Fax 683-3769
Big Horn County Office of Education
Sandy Watts, supt. 406-665-9823
PO Box 908, Hardin 59034 Fax 665-9823
Blaine County Office of Education
Lisa Stroh, supt. 406-357-3270
PO Box 819, Chinook 59523 Fax 357-2199
Broadwater County Office of Education
Rhonda Nelson, supt. 406-266-9215
515 Broadway St, Townsend 59644 Fax 266-3674
Carbon County Office of Education
Jerry Scott, supt. 406-446-1301
PO Box 116, Red Lodge 59068 Fax 446-9155
Carter County Office of Education
Marilyn Hutchinson, supt. 406-775-8721
PO Box 352, Ekalaka 59324 Fax 775-8703
Cascade County Office of Education
Jamie Bailey, supt. 406-454-6776
121 4th St N Ste 1A Fax 454-6778
Great Falls 59401
Chouteau County Office of Education
Rick Cook, supt. 406-622-3242
PO Box 459, Fort Benton 59442 Fax 622-3028
Custer County Office of Education
Doug Ellingson, supt. 406-874-3421
1010 Main St, Miles City 59301 Fax 874-3452
Daniels County Office of Education
Patricia McDonnell, supt. 406-487-2651
PO Box 67, Scobey 59263 Fax 487-5432
Dawson County Office of Education
Steve Engebretson, supt. 406-377-3963
207 W Bell St, Glendive 59330 Fax 377-2022
Deer Lodge County Office of Education
Michael O'Rourke, supt. 406-563-9178
800 Main St, Anaconda 59711 Fax 563-5476
Fallon County Office of Education
Brenda Wood, supt. 406-778-8182
PO Box 846, Baker 59313 Fax 778-2048
Fergus County Office of Education
Rhonda Long, supt. 406-535-3136
712 W Main St, Lewistown 59457 Fax 535-2819
Flathead County Office of Education
Marcia Sheffels, supt. 406-758-5720
935 1st Ave W, Kalispell 59901 Fax 758-5850
Gallatin County Office of Education
Mary Ellen Fitzgerald, supt. 406-582-3090
311 W Main St Rm 107 Fax 582-3093
Bozeman 59715
Garfield County Office of Education
Jessica McWilliams, supt. 406-557-6115
PO Box 28, Jordan 59337 Fax 557-6115
Glacier County Office of Education
Darryl Omsberg, supt. 406-873-2295
1210 E Main St, Cut Bank 59427 Fax 873-9103
Golden Valley County Office of Education
Craig Mattheis, supt. 406-568-2342
107 Kemp St, Ryegate 59074 Fax 568-2428
Granite County Office of Education
Jo Ann Husbyn, supt. 406-859-7024
PO Box 520, Philipsburg 59858 Fax 859-3817
Hill County Office of Education
Diane McLean, supt. 406-265-5481
315 4th St, Havre 59501 Fax 265-5487
Jefferson County Office of Education
Garry Pace, supt. 406-225-4114
PO Box H, Boulder 59632 Fax 225-4149
Judith Basin County Office of Education
Julie Peevey, supt. 406-566-2277
PO Box 307, Stanford 59479 Fax 566-2211
Lake County Office of Education
Gale Decker, supt. 406-883-7262
106 4th Ave E, Polson 59860 Fax 883-7283
www.lakecounty-mt.org/schools
Lewis & Clark County Office of Education
Marsha Davis, supt. 406-447-8344
316 N Park Ave Ste 221 Fax 447-8398
Helena 59623
Liberty County Office of Education
Rachel Ghekiere, supt. 406-759-5216
PO Box 684, Chester 59522 Fax 759-5996
Lincoln County Office of Education
Ron Higgins, supt. 406-283-2450
418 Mineral Ave, Libby 59923 Fax 283-2453
Madison County Office of Education
Judi Osborn, supt. 406-843-4217
PO Box 247, Virginia City 59755 Fax 843-5261
McCone County Office of Education
Jackie Becker, supt. 406-485-3590
PO Box 180, Circle 59215 Fax 485-2689
Meagher County Office of Education
Helen Hanson, supt., PO Box 354 406-547-3612
White Sulphur Springs 59645 Fax 547-3388
Mineral County Office of Education
Mary Yarnall, supt. 406-822-3529
PO Box 100, Superior 59872 Fax 822-3579
Missoula County Office of Education
Erin Lipkind, supt. 406-258-3349
438 W Spruce St, Missoula 59802 Fax 258-3973
Musselshell County Office of Education
Kathryn Pfister, supt. 406-323-1470
506 Main St, Roundup 59072 Fax 323-3303
Park County Office of Education
Ed Barich, supt., 414 E Callender St 406-222-4148
Livingston 59047 Fax 222-4199
Petroleum County Office of Education
Ashley Obrigewitch, supt. 406-429-5551
PO Box 226, Winnett 59087 Fax 429-6328
Phillips County Office of Education
Vivian Taylor, supt. 406-654-2010
PO Box 138, Malta 59538 Fax 654-1213
Pondera County Office of Education
Jo Stone, supt. 406-271-4055
20 4th Ave SW Ste 307 Fax 271-4070
Conrad 59425
Powder River County Office of Education
Charlotte Miller, supt. 406-436-2488
PO Box 718, Broadus 59317 Fax 436-2151
Powell County Office of Education
Jules Waber, supt. 406-846-9719
409 Missouri Ave Fax 846-3891
Deer Lodge 59722
Prairie County Office of Education
Jamie Smith, supt. 406-635-5577
PO Box 566, Terry 59349 Fax 635-5576
Ravalli County Office of Education
Michael Williams, supt. 406-375-6522
215 S 4th St Ste B, Hamilton 59840 Fax 375-6554
Richland County Office of Education
Gail Anne Staffanson, supt. 406-433-1608
201 W Main St, Sidney 59270 Fax 433-3731
Roosevelt County Office of Education
Pat Stennes, supt. 406-653-6266
400 2nd Ave S, Wolf Point 59201 Fax 653-6203
Rosebud County Office of Education
Joby Parker, supt. 406-346-2537
PO Box 407, Forsyth 59327 Fax 346-7319
Sanders County Office of Education
Kathy McEldery, supt. 406-826-4288
PO Box 519, Plains 59859 Fax 826-4299
Sheridan County Office of Education
June Johnson, supt. 406-765-3403
100 W Laurel Ave Fax 765-2609
Plentywood 59254
Silver Bow County Office of Education
Cathy Maloney, supt. 406-497-6215
155 W Granite St, Butte 59701 Fax 497-6328
Stillwater County Office of Education
Judy Martin, supt. 406-322-8057
PO Box 1139, Columbus 59019 Fax 322-1118
Sweet Grass County Office of Education
Susan Metcalf, supt. 406-932-5147
PO Box 1310, Big Timber 59011 Fax 932-5112
Teton County Office of Education
Diane Inbody, supt. 406-466-2907
PO Box 610, Choteau 59422 Fax 466-2138
Toole County Office of Education
Boyd Jackson, supt. 406-424-8322
226 1st St S, Shelby 59474 Fax 424-8321
Treasure County Office of Education
Kathleen Thomas, supt. 406-342-5545
PO Box 429, Hysham 59038 Fax 342-5445
Valley County Office of Education
Lynne Nyquist, supt. 406-228-6226
501 Court Sq Ste 2 Fax 228-9027
Glasgow 59230
Wheatland County Office of Education
Susan Beley, supt. 406-632-4816
PO Box 637, Harlowton 59036 Fax 632-4880
Wibaux County Office of Education
Patricia Zinda, supt. 406-796-2481
PO Box 199, Wibaux 59353 Fax 796-2625
Yellowstone County Office of Education
Max Lenington, supt. 406-256-6933
PO Box 35022, Billings 59107 Fax 256-6930
www.co.yellowstone.mt.us

PUBLIC, PRIVATE AND CATHOLIC SECONDARY SCHOOLS

Absarokee, Stillwater, Pop. 1,134
Absarokee SD 300/PK-12
327 S Woodard Ave 59001 406-328-4583
Dustin Sturm, supt. Fax 328-4077
www.absarokee.k12.mt.us/
Absarokee HS 100/9-12
327 S Woodard Ave 59001 406-328-4583
Dustin Sturm, prin. Fax 328-4077
Absarokee MS 50/7-8
327 S Woodard Ave 59001 406-328-4583
Dustin Sturm, prin. Fax 328-4077

Alberton, Mineral, Pop. 415
Alberton SD 200/PK-12
PO Box 330 59820 406-722-4413
James Baldwin, supt. Fax 722-3040
Alberton HS 100/9-12
PO Box 330 59820 406-722-3381
Chris Clevenger, prin. Fax 722-3040
Alberton MS 50/7-8
PO Box 330 59820 406-722-4413
Chris Clevenger, prin. Fax 722-3040

Anaconda, Deer Lodge, Pop. 9,095
Anaconda SD 1,100/PK-12
1410 W Park Ave 59711 406-563-6361
Dr. Tom Darnell, supt. Fax 563-7763
www.anacondaschools.org/
Anaconda HS 400/9-12
515 Main St 59711 406-563-5269
Paul Furthmyre, prin. Fax 563-5260
Moodry JHS 300/6-8
219 E 3rd St 59711 406-563-6242
Sue Meredith, prin. Fax 563-5093

Arlee, Lake, Pop. 605
Arlee SD 400/K-12
72220 Fyant St 59821 406-726-3216
George Linthicum, supt. Fax 360-8531
www.arlee.k12.mt.us/
Arlee HS 100/9-12
72220 Fyant St 59821 406-726-3216
James Taylor, prin. Fax 726-3940
Arlee JHS 100/7-8
72220 Fyant St 59821 406-726-3216
James Taylor, prin. Fax 726-3940

Ashland, Rosebud, Pop. 799
Ashland ESD 100/PK-8
PO Box 17 59003 406-784-2568
Jennifer Smith, supt. Fax 784-6138

Ashland MS 50/7-8
PO Box 17 59003 406-784-2568
Jennifer Smith, prin. Fax 784-6138

St. Labre Catholic HS 100/9-12
PO Box 216 59003 406-784-4500
Bart Bailey, prin. Fax 784-4565
St. Labre Catholic MS 100/5-8
PO Box 216 59003 406-784-4500
Jack Gion, prin. Fax 784-4565

Augusta, Lewis and Clark, Pop. 305
Augusta SD 100/PK-12
PO Box 307 59410 406-562-3384
Larry Markuson, supt. Fax 562-3898
Augusta HS 50/9-12
PO Box 307 59410 406-562-3384
Larry Markuson, prin. Fax 562-3898
Augusta MS 50/7-8
PO Box 307 59410 406-562-3384
Larry Markuson, prin. Fax 562-3898

Bainville, Roosevelt, Pop. 202
Bainville SD 100/PK-12
PO Box 177 59212 406-769-2321
Brandy Hanson, supt. Fax 769-3291
www.bainvilleschool.k12.mt.us
Bainville HS 50/9-12
PO Box 177 59212 406-769-2321
Rhiannon Beery, prin. Fax 769-3291
Bainville MS 50/7-8
PO Box 177 59212 406-769-2321
Rhiannon Beery, prin. Fax 769-3291

Baker, Fallon, Pop. 1,723
Baker SD 400/PK-12
PO Box 659 59313 406-778-3574
Donald Schillinger, supt. Fax 778-2785
www.baker.k12.mt.us/
Baker HS 100/9-12
PO Box 659 59313 406-778-3329
David Breitbach, prin. Fax 778-2785
Baker JHS 50/7-8
PO Box 659 59313 406-778-3329
David Breitbach, prin. Fax 778-2785

Belfry, Carbon, Pop. 215
Belfry SD 50/PK-12
PO Box 210 59008 406-664-3319
Jason Olson, supt. Fax 664-3274
Belfry HS 50/9-12
PO Box 210 59008 406-664-3319
Dale Freeman, prin. Fax 664-3274
Belfry MS 50/7-8
PO Box 210 59008 406-664-3319
Dale Freeman, prin. Fax 664-3274

Belgrade, Gallatin, Pop. 7,233
Belgrade SD 3,100/PK-12
PO Box 166 59714 406-924-2006
Candy Lubansky, supt. Fax 388-0122
www.belgrade.k12.mt.us
Belgrade HS 900/9-12
303 N Hoffman St 59714 406-924-2513
Russ McDaniel, prin. Fax 388-4633
Belgrade MS 400/7-8
410 Triple Crown St 59714 406-924-2258
Julie Mickolio, prin. Fax 388-8894

Belt, Cascade, Pop. 585
Belt SD 300/PK-12
PO Box 197 59412 406-277-3351
Kathleen Prody, supt. Fax 277-4466
www.beltschool.com
Belt HS 100/9-12
PO Box 197 59412 406-277-3351
Kyle Paulson, prin. Fax 277-4466
Belt MS 50/7-8
PO Box 197 59412 406-277-3351
Kyle Paulson, prin. Fax 277-4466

Bigfork, Flathead, Pop. 4,196
Bigfork SD 700/K-12
PO Box 188 59911 406-837-7400
Cynthia Clary, supt. Fax 837-7407
www.bigforkschools.org
Bigfork HS 300/9-12
PO Box 188 59911 406-837-7420
Matthew Porrovecchio, prin. Fax 837-7245
Bigfork MS 100/7-8
PO Box 188 59911 406-837-7412
Matthew Jensen, prin. Fax 837-7438

Swan River ESD 200/K-8
1205 Swan Hwy 59911 406-837-4528
Fax 837-4055
Swan River MS 50/7-8
1205 Swan Hwy 59911 406-837-4528
Marc Bunker, prin. Fax 837-4055

Big Sandy, Chouteau, Pop. 583
Big Sandy SD 200/PK-12
PO Box 570 59520 406-378-2501
Sonny Broesder, supt. Fax 378-2275
Big Sandy HS 50/9-12
PO Box 570 59520 406-378-2502
Sonny Broesder, prin. Fax 378-2275
Big Sandy JHS 50/7-8
PO Box 570 59520 406-378-2502
Sonny Broesder, prin. Fax 378-2275

Big Sky, Gallatin, Pop. 2,277
Big Sky SD
Supt. — See Gallatin Gateway
Lone Peak HS 50/9-12
PO Box 161280 59716 406-995-4281
Jerry House, prin. Fax 995-2161

Big Timber, Sweet Grass, Pop. 1,599
Big Timber ESD 300/PK-8
PO Box 887 59011 406-932-5939
Mark Ketcham, supt. Fax 932-4069
www.bigtimber-gs.k12.mt.us
Big Timber MS 100/7-8
PO Box 887 59011 406-932-5939
Mark Ketcham, prin. Fax 932-4069

Sweet Grass County HSD 200/9-12
PO Box 886 59011 406-932-5993
Alvin Buerkle, supt. Fax 932-5982
www.sgchs.com/
Sweet Grass County HS 200/9-12
PO Box 886 59011 406-932-5993
Kip Ryan, prin. Fax 932-5982

Billings, Yellowstone, Pop. 101,668
Billings SD 15,700/PK-12
415 N 30th St 59101 406-281-5065
Terry Bouck, supt. Fax 281-6179
www.billingsschools.org/
Billings HS 1,700/9-12
425 Grand Ave 59101 406-281-5400
Dennis Holmes, prin. Fax 281-6174
Billings West HS 1,900/9-12
2201 Saint Johns Ave 59102 406-281-5600
David Cobb, prin. Fax 655-3100
Career Center Vo/Tech
3723 Central Ave 59102 406-281-5340
Scott Anderson, prin. Fax 655-3096
Castle Rock MS 700/7-8
1441 Governors Blvd 59105 406-281-5800
Shaun Harrington, prin. Fax 254-1116
James MS 500/7-8
1200 30th St W 59102 406-281-6100
Lance Orner, prin. Fax 281-6178
Lewis & Clark MS 600/7-8
1315 Lewis Ave 59102 406-281-5900
Steve Pomroy, prin. Fax 281-6177
Riverside MS 500/7-8
3700 Madison Ave 59101 406-281-6000
Sharon Tietema, prin. Fax 255-3534
Skyview HS 1,500/9-12
1775 High Sierra Blvd 59105 406-281-5200
Debra Black, prin. Fax 255-3507
Adult & Basic Education Adult
415 N 30th St 59101 406-281-5001
Josh Middleton, prin. Fax 281-6827

Canyon Creek ESD 200/PK-8
3139 Duck Creek Rd 59101 406-656-4471
Brent Lipp, supt. Fax 655-1031
www.canyoncreekschool.org
Canyon Creek MS 50/7-8
3139 Duck Creek Rd 59101 406-656-4471
Brent Lipp, prin. Fax 655-1031

Elder Grove ESD 300/K-8
1532 S 64th St W 59106 406-656-2893
Justin Klebe, supt. Fax 651-4346
www.eldergrove.k12.mt.us/
Elder Grove MS 100/5-8
1532 S 64th St W 59106 406-656-2893
Nathan Schmitz, prin. Fax 651-1987

Elysian ESD 200/PK-8
6416 Elysian Rd 59101 406-656-4101
Lucas Larson, supt. Fax 656-9941
elysianschool.org
Elysian MS 50/7-8
6416 Elysian Rd 59101 406-656-4101
Lucas Larson, prin. Fax 656-9941

Lockwood ESD 1,200/PK-8
1932 US Highway 87 E 59101 406-252-6022
Tobin Novasio, supt. Fax 259-2502
www.lockwoodschool.org/
Lockwood MS 300/6-8
1932 US Highway 87 E 59101 406-259-0154
Gordon Klasna, prin. Fax 259-3832

Billings Central Catholic HS 300/9-12
3 Broadwater Ave 59101 406-245-6651
Sheldon Hanser, prin. Fax 259-3124
Billings Christian S 200/PK-12
4519 Grand Ave 59106 406-656-9484
Paul Waggoner, prin. Fax 655-4880
City College MSU Billings Post-Sec.
3803 Central Ave 59102 406-247-3000
Montana State University - Billings Post-Sec.
1500 University Dr 59101 406-657-2011
Rocky Mountain College Post-Sec.
1511 Poly Dr 59102 406-657-1000
SAGE Technical Service Truck Driving Sch Post-Sec.
3044 Hesper Rd 59102 800-545-4546
St. Francis Upper S 200/6-8
205 N 32nd St 59101 406-259-5037
Jim Stanton, prin. Fax 259-7981
St. Vincent's Hospital & Health Center Post-Sec.
PO Box 35200 59107 406-657-7102

Bonner, Missoula, Pop. 1,669
Bonner ESD 400/PK-8
PO Box 1004 59823 406-258-6151
Doug Ardiana, supt. Fax 258-6153
www.bonner.k12.mt.us
Bonner MS 100/7-8
PO Box 1004 59823 406-258-6151
Jon Fimmel, prin. Fax 258-6153

Potomac ESD 100/PK-8
29750 Potomac Rd 59823 406-244-5581
Fax 244-5840
www.potomacschoolmontana.us/
Potomac MS 50/7-8
29750 Potomac Rd 59823 406-244-5581
Tim Johnson, prin. Fax 244-5840

Boulder, Jefferson, Pop. 1,141
Boulder ESD 200/PK-8
PO Box 1346 59632 406-225-3316
Maria Pace, supt. Fax 225-9218
www.bgs.k12.mt.us/
Boulder MS 50/7-8
PO Box 1346 59632 406-225-3316
Maria Pace, prin. Fax 225-9218

Jefferson HSD 200/9-12
PO Box 838 59632 406-225-3740
Jim Whealon, supt. Fax 225-3289
www.jhs.k12.mt.us
Jefferson HS 200/9-12
PO Box 838 59632 406-225-3317
Jim Whealon, prin. Fax 225-3289

Box Elder, Hill, Pop. 80
Box Elder SD 400/PK-12
PO Box 205 59521 406-352-4195
Robert Heppner, supt. Fax 352-3830
Box Elder HS 100/9-12
PO Box 205 59521 406-352-4195
Darin Hannum, prin. Fax 352-3830
Box Elder MS 100/7-8
PO Box 205 59521 406-352-4195
Darin Hannum, prin. Fax 352-3830

Rocky Boy SD 600/PK-12
81 Mission Taylor Rd 59521 406-395-4291
Voyd St. Pierre, supt. Fax 395-4829
www.rockyboy.k12.mt.us
Rocky Boy HS 200/9-12
81 Mission Taylor Rd 59521 406-395-4270
Lewis Reese, prin. Fax 395-4829
Rocky Boy MS 100/7-8
81 Mission Taylor Rd 59521 406-395-4270
Lewis Reese, prin. Fax 395-4829

Stone Child College Post-Sec.
8294 Upper Box Elder Rd 59521 406-395-4875

Bozeman, Gallatin, Pop. 36,568
Anderson ESD 200/PK-8
10040 Cottonwood Rd 59718 406-587-1305
Jeff Blessum, supt. Fax 587-2501
www.andersonmt.org/
Anderson MS 50/7-8
10040 Cottonwood Rd 59718 406-587-1305
Jeff Blessum, prin. Fax 587-2501

Bozeman SD 5,400/PK-12
404 W Main St 59715 406-522-6000
Robert Watson, supt. Fax 522-6065
www.bsd7.org
Bozeman HS 1,800/9-12
205 N 11th Ave 59715 406-522-6200
Ken Gibson, prin. Fax 522-6222
Chief Joseph MS 600/6-8
4255 Kimberwicke St 59718 406-522-6300
Brian Ayers, prin. Fax 522-6306
Hyalite MS 100/6-8
3600 W Babcock St 59718 406-582-6800
Mike Van Buren, prin. Fax 582-6850
Sacajawea MS 600/6-8
3525 S 3rd Rd 59715 406-522-6470
Gordon Grissom, prin. Fax 522-6474

LaMotte ESD 100/PK-8
841 Bear Canyon Rd 59715 406-586-2838
Fax 586-8626
www.lamotteschool.com
LaMotte MS 50/7-8
841 Bear Canyon Rd 59715 406-586-2838
LeeAnn Burke, prin. Fax 585-8626

Monforton ESD 200/PK-8
6001 Monforton School Rd 59718 406-586-1557
Darren Strauch, supt. Fax 587-5049
www.monfortonschool.org/
Monforton MS 100/7-8
6001 Monforton School Rd 59718 406-586-1557
Darren Strauch, prin. Fax 587-5049

Academy of Cosmetology Post-Sec.
133 W Mendenhall St 59715 406-587-1265
Headwaters Academy 50/6-8
418 W Garfield St 59715 406-585-9997
Larry Bartel, head sch Fax 585-9992
Heritage Christian S 200/PK-12
4310 Durston Rd 59718 406-587-9311
Ethel Gray, admin. Fax 587-1838
Montana Bible College Post-Sec.
3625 S 19th Ave 59718 406-586-3585
Montana State University Post-Sec.
PO Box 172190 59717 406-994-0211
Mt. Ellis Academy 100/9-12
3641 Bozeman Trail Rd 59715 406-587-5178
Bruce Lane, prin. Fax 587-5170
Petra Academy 100/K-12
4720 Classical Way 59718 406-582-8165
Todd Hicks, hdmstr. Fax 556-8777

Bridger, Carbon, Pop. 700
Bridger SD 200/PK-12
429 W Park Ave 59014 406-662-3533
Bill Phillips, supt. Fax 662-3076
www.bridger.k12.mt.us
Bridger HS 100/9-12
429 W Park Ave 59014 406-662-3533
Bill Phillips, prin. Fax 662-3076
Bridger MS 50/7-8
106 N 4th St 59014 406-662-3588
Patrick Cates, prin. Fax 662-3520

Broadus, Powder River, Pop. 457
Broadus SD 200/PK-12
PO Box 500 59317 406-436-2658
Jim Hansen, supt. Fax 436-2660
www.broadus.net/

Powder River County District HS 100/7-12
PO Box 500 59317 406-436-2658
Rosalie Lunby, prin. Fax 436-2660

Broadview, Yellowstone, Pop. 191
Broadview SD 200/PK-12
PO Box 147 59015 406-667-2337
Rob Osborne, supt. Fax 667-2195
www.broadview.k12.mt.us/
Broadview HS 100/9-12
PO Box 147 59015 406-667-2337
Rob Osborne, prin. Fax 667-2195
Broadview MS 50/7-8
PO Box 147 59015 406-667-2337
Rob Osborne, prin. Fax 667-2195

Brockton, Roosevelt, Pop. 255
Brockton SD 100/PK-12
PO Box 198 59213 406-786-3311
Jeff Ralston, supt. Fax 786-3377
www.brockton.k12.mt.us/
Brockton HS 50/9-12
PO Box 198 59213 406-786-3311
Jeff Ralston, prin. Fax 786-3377
Gilligan MS 50/7-8
PO Box 198 59213 406-786-3311
Jeff Ralston, prin. Fax 786-3377

Browning, Glacier, Pop. 998
Browning SD 1,900/PK-12
PO Box 610 59417 406-338-2715
Mary Johnson, supt. Fax 338-3200
www.bps.k12.mt.us/
Browning HS 500/9-12
PO Box 610 59417 406-338-2745
John Salois, prin. Fax 338-2844
Browning MS 200/7-8
PO Box 610 59417 406-338-2725
Julie Hayes, prin. Fax 338-5320

Blackfeet Community College Post-Sec.
PO Box 819 59417 406-338-5441
De LaSalle Blackfeet S 100/4-8
PO Box 1489 59417 406-338-5290
Roonie Leittem-Murrell, prin. Fax 338-7900

Butte, Silver Bow, Pop. 32,958
Butte SD 4,300/PK-12
111 N Montana St 59701 406-533-2500
Judy Jonart, supt. Fax 533-2525
www.butte.k12.mt.us
Butte HS 1,400/9-12
401 S Wyoming St 59701 406-533-2200
John Metz, prin. Fax 533-2277
East MS 600/7-8
2600 Grand Ave 59701 406-533-2600
Larry Driscoll, prin. Fax 533-2670

Butte Academy of Beauty Culture Post-Sec.
303 W Park St 59701 406-723-8565
Butte Central HS 100/9-12
9 S Idaho St 59701 406-782-6761
Tim Norbeck, prin. Fax 723-3873
Capstone Christian Academy 50/K-12
PO Box 3074 59702 406-782-7777
Kirk Pugsley, prin. Fax 782-7777
Highlands College of Montana Tech Post-Sec.
25 Basin Creek Rd 59701 406-496-3707
Montana Tech of the University of MT Post-Sec.
1300 W Park St 59701 406-496-4101

Cascade, Cascade, Pop. 673
Cascade SD 300/PK-12
PO Box 529 59421 406-468-9383
Lou Ann Gay, supt. Fax 468-2212
www.cascade.k12.mt.us
Cascade HS 100/9-12
PO Box 529 59421 406-468-9383
Dave Malloy, prin. Fax 468-2212
Cascade JHS 50/7-8
PO Box 529 59421 406-468-9383
Dave Malloy, prin. Fax 468-2212

Charlo, Lake, Pop. 328
Charlo SD 300/PK-12
PO Box 10 59824 406-644-2206
Thom Peck, supt. Fax 644-2400
www.charlo.k12.mt.us/
Charlo HS 100/9-12
PO Box 10 59824 406-644-2206
Steve Love, prin. Fax 644-2400
Charlo MS 50/7-8
PO Box 10 59824 406-644-2206
Steve Love, prin. Fax 644-2400

Chester, Liberty, Pop. 830
Chester-Joplin-Inverness SD 300/PK-12
PO Box 550 59522 406-759-5108
Rita Chvilicek, supt. Fax 759-5867
www.cji.k12.mt.us
Chester-Joplin-Inverness HS 100/9-12
PO Box 550 59522 406-759-5108
Pam Graff, prin. Fax 759-5867
Chester-Joplin-Inverness MS 50/7-8
PO Box 550 59522 406-759-5108
Pam Graff, prin. Fax 759-5867

Chinook, Blaine, Pop. 1,183
Chinook SD 400/PK-12
PO Box 1059 59523 406-357-2628
Jay Eslick, supt. Fax 357-2238
www.chinookschools.org
Chinook HS 100/9-12
PO Box 1059 59523 406-357-2236
Matt Molyneaux, prin. Fax 357-2238
Chinook MS 100/7-8
PO Box 1059 59523 406-357-2237
Matt Molyneaux, prin. Fax 357-2238

Choteau, Teton, Pop. 1,646
Choteau SD 400/PK-12
204 7th Ave NW 59422 406-466-5303
Kevin St. John, supt. Fax 466-5305
www.choteauschools.net
Choteau HS 200/9-12
204 7th Ave NW 59422 406-466-5303
Nate Achenbach, prin. Fax 466-5305
Choteau MS 100/7-8
204 7th Ave NW 59422 406-466-5303
Nate Achenbach, prin. Fax 466-5305

Circle, McCone, Pop. 606
Circle SD 200/PK-12
PO Box 99 59215 406-485-2545
Gary Fisher, supt. Fax 485-2332
Circle HS 100/9-12
PO Box 99 59215 406-485-3600
Gary Fisher, prin. Fax 485-2332
Redwater MS 50/7-8
PO Box 99 59215 406-485-2140
Helen Murphy, prin. Fax 485-2332

Clancy, Jefferson, Pop. 1,638
Clancy ESD 300/PK-8
PO Box 209 59634 406-933-5575
Bruce Dunkle, supt. Fax 933-5715
www.clancy.k12.mt.us/
Clancy MS 100/7-8
PO Box 209 59634 406-933-5575
Bruce Dunkle, prin. Fax 933-5715

Montana City ESD 400/K-8
11 McClellan Creek Rd 59634 406-442-6779
Tony Kloker, supt. Fax 443-8875
montanacity.schoolwires.com
Montana City MS 100/6-8
11 McClellan Creek Rd 59634 406-442-6779
Stephanie Thennis, prin. Fax 443-8875

Clinton, Missoula, Pop. 1,018
Clinton ESD 200/PK-8
PO Box 250 59825 406-825-3113
Tom Stack, supt. Fax 825-3114
www.clintoncougars.com
Clinton MS 100/7-8
PO Box 250 59825 406-825-3113
Julie Espinosa, prin. Fax 825-3114

Clyde Park, Park, Pop. 288
Shields Valley SD 200/PK-12
405 1st St E 59018 406-578-2535
Erik Wilkerson, supt. Fax 578-2176
www.shieldsvalleyschools.org/
Shields Valley HS 100/9-12
405 1st St E 59018 406-686-4621
Alex Ator, prin. Fax 686-4937
Shields Valley MS 50/7-8
405 1st St E 59018 406-686-4621
Alex Ator, prin. Fax 686-4937

Colstrip, Rosebud, Pop. 2,118
Colstrip SD 600/PK-12
PO Box 159 59323 406-748-4699
Dan Schmidt, supt. Fax 748-2268
colstrip.schoolwires.net
Brattin MS 100/6-8
PO Box 159 59323 406-748-4699
Justin Helvik, prin. Fax 748-3143
Colstrip HS 200/9-12
PO Box 159 59323 406-748-4699
Dennis Davenport, prin. Fax 748-2517

Columbia Falls, Flathead, Pop. 4,562
Columbia Falls SD 2,000/PK-12
PO Box 1259 59912 406-892-6550
Michael Nicosia, supt. Fax 892-6552
www.sd6.k12.mt.us
Columbia Falls HS 700/9-12
PO Box 1259 59912 406-892-6500
Scott Gaiser, prin. Fax 892-6583
Columbia Falls JHS 400/6-8
PO Box 1259 59912 406-892-6530
Dave Wick, prin. Fax 892-6528

Deer Park ESD 100/PK-8
2105 Middle Rd 59912 406-892-5388
Marcia Sheffels, supt. Fax 892-3504
www.deerpark.k12.mt.us/
Deer Park MS 50/7-8
2105 Middle Rd 59912 406-892-5388
Dan Block, lead tchr. Fax 892-3504

Columbus, Stillwater, Pop. 1,857
Columbus SD 600/PK-12
433 N 3rd St 59019 406-322-5373
Allan Sipes, supt. Fax 322-5028
www.columbus.k12.mt.us
Columbus HS 200/9-12
433 N 3rd St 59019 406-322-5373
George McKay, prin. Fax 322-5028
Columbus MS 200/6-8
415 N 3rd St 59019 406-322-5375
Ron Osborne, prin. Fax 322-5376

Conrad, Pondera, Pop. 2,522
Conrad SD 500/PK-12
215 S Maryland St 59425 406-278-5521
Craig Barringer, supt. Fax 278-3630
www.conradschools.org
Conrad HS 200/9-12
308 S Illinois St 59425 406-278-3285
Ken Larson, prin. Fax 278-3806
Utterback MS 50/6-8
201 S Maryland St 59425 406-278-3227
Tara Thielman, prin. Fax 278-3228

Corvallis, Ravalli, Pop. 945
Corvallis SD 1,300/PK-12
PO Box 700 59828 406-961-4211
Monte Silk, supt. Fax 961-5144
www.corvallis.k12.mt.us
Corvallis HS 500/9-12
PO Box 700 59828 406-961-3201
Jason Wirt, prin. Fax 961-4894
Corvallis JHS 200/7-8
PO Box 700 59828 406-961-3007
Rich Durgin, prin. Fax 961-5144

Crow Agency, Big Horn, Pop. 1,597

Little Big Horn College Post-Sec.
PO Box 370 59022 406-638-3100

Culbertson, Roosevelt, Pop. 690
Culbertson SD 300/PK-12
PO Box 459 59218 406-787-6246
Larry Crowder, supt. Fax 787-6244
www.culbertsonschool.com
Culbertson HS 100/9-12
PO Box 459 59218 406-787-6241
Mike Olson, prin. Fax 787-6244
Culbertson MS 50/7-8
PO Box 459 59218 406-787-6241
Mike Olson, prin. Fax 787-6244

Custer, Yellowstone, Pop. 158
Custer SD 100/PK-12
PO Box 69 59024 406-856-4117
Bart Hawkins, supt. Fax 856-4206
www.custerschools.org
Custer HS 50/9-12
PO Box 69 59024 406-856-4117
Bart Hawkins, prin. Fax 856-4206
Custer MS 50/7-8
PO Box 69 59024 406-856-4117
Bart Hawkins, prin. Fax 856-4206

Cut Bank, Glacier, Pop. 2,736
Cut Bank SD 600/PK-12
101 3rd Ave SE 59427 406-873-2229
Wade Johnson, supt. Fax 873-4691
www.cutbankschools.net
Cut Bank HS 200/9-12
101 3rd Ave SE 59427 406-873-5629
Peter Hamilton, prin. Fax 873-4691
Cut Bank MS 100/6-8
101 3rd Ave SE 59427 406-873-4421
Gail Hofstad, prin. Fax 873-4691

Darby, Ravalli, Pop. 697
Darby SD 400/PK-12
209 School Dr 59829 406-821-1305
Loyd Rennaker, supt. Fax 821-4977
www.darby.k12.mt.us/
Darby HS 100/9-12
209 School Dr 59829 406-821-3252
Jennifer Burdette, prin. Fax 821-4977
Darby MS 100/7-8
209 School Dr 59829 406-821-3252
Jennifer Burdette, prin. Fax 821-4977

Deer Lodge, Powell, Pop. 3,077
Deer Lodge ESD 400/PK-8
444 Montana Ave 59722 406-846-1553
Rodney Simpson, supt. Fax 846-1599
Duvall MS 100/7-8
444 Montana Ave 59722 406-846-1684
Rick Chrisman, prin. Fax 846-1599

Powell County HSD 300/9-12
709 Missouri Ave 59722 406-846-2757
Rick Duncan, supt. Fax 846-2759
www.pchs.dl.k12.mt.us
Powell County HS 300/9-12
709 Missouri Ave 59722 406-846-2757
Kerry Glisson, prin. Fax 846-2759

Denton, Fergus, Pop. 253
Denton SD 100/PK-12
PO Box 1048 59430 406-567-2270
Jan Cahill, supt. Fax 567-2559
www.denton.k12.mt.us/
Denton HS 50/9-12
PO Box 1048 59430 406-567-2270
Jan Cahill, prin. Fax 567-2559
Denton JHS 50/7-8
PO Box 1048 59430 406-567-2270
Jan Cahill, prin. Fax 567-2559

Dillon, Beaverhead, Pop. 4,039
Beaverhead County HSD 400/9-12
104 N Pacific St 59725 406-683-2361
Fred Chouinard, supt. Fax 683-5263
bchsmt.schoolwires.com
Beaverhead County HS 400/9-12
104 N Pacific St 59725 406-683-2361
Fred Chouinard, admin. Fax 683-5263

Dillon ESD 600/PK-8
22 Cottom Dr 59725 406-683-4311
Glen Johnson, supt. Fax 683-4312
www.dillonelem.k12.mt.us/
Dillon MS 200/6-8
14 Cottom Dr 59725 406-683-2368
Randy Shipman, prin. Fax 683-2369

University of Montana Western Post-Sec.
710 S Atlantic St 59725 406-683-7331

Dixon, Sanders, Pop. 184
Dixon ESD 100/PK-8
PO Box 10 59831 406-246-3566
Mark Faroni, admin. Fax 246-3379
dixonschool.net
Dixon MS 50/7-8
PO Box 10 59831 406-246-3566
Mark Faroni, prin. Fax 246-3379

Dodson, Phillips, Pop. 121
Dodson SD 100/PK-12
PO Box 278 59524 406-383-4362
Dollyann Willcutt, supt. Fax 383-4489
Dodson HS 50/9-12
PO Box 278 59524 406-383-4362
Dollyann Willcutt, prin. Fax 383-4489
Dodson MS 50/7-8
PO Box 278 59524 406-383-4362
Dollyann Willcutt, prin. Fax 383-4489

Drummond, Granite, Pop. 304
Drummond SD 200/K-12
PO Box 349 59832 406-288-3281
Donn Livoni, supt. Fax 288-3299
Drummond HS 100/9-12
PO Box 349 59832 406-288-3281
Rick Parke, prin. Fax 288-3299
Drummond MS 50/7-8
PO Box 349 59832 406-288-3281
Rick Parke, prin. Fax 288-3299

Dutton, Teton, Pop. 311
Dutton/Brady SD 100/PK-12
101 2nd St NE 59433 406-476-3424
D.K. Brooks, supt. Fax 476-3342
duttonbradyps.schoolwires.net/site/default.aspx?page
l
Dutton/Brady HS 50/9-12
101 2nd St NE 59433 406-476-3424
D.K. Brooks, prin. Fax 476-3342
Dutton/Brady MS 50/7-8
101 2nd St NE 59433 406-476-3201
Tim Dolphay, prin. Fax 476-3342

East Helena, Lewis and Clark, Pop. 1,919
East Helena ESD 1,100/PK-8
PO Box 1280 59635 406-227-7700
Ron Whitmoyer, supt. Fax 227-5534
www.ehps.k12.mt.us
East Valley MS 400/6-8
PO Box 1280 59635 406-227-7740
Dan Rispens, prin. Fax 227-9730

Helena Christian S 100/K-12
3384 Canyon Ferry Rd 59635 406-442-3821
Mike Dellwo, prin. Fax 442-0341

Ekalaka, Carter, Pop. 327
Ekalaka SD 100/PK-12
PO Box 458 59324 406-775-8601
Allison Hardin, supt. Fax 775-8766
www.ekalaka.net
Carter County HS 50/9-12
PO Box 458 59324 406-775-8767
Allison Hardin, prin. Fax 775-8766
Ekalaka MS 50/7-8
PO Box 458 59324 406-775-8767
Allison Hardin, prin. Fax 775-8766

Ennis, Madison, Pop. 828
Ennis SD 300/PK-12
PO Box 517 59729 406-682-4258
John Overstreet, supt. Fax 682-7751
www.ennisschools.org
Ennis HS 100/9-12
PO Box 517 59729 406-682-4258
John Sullivan, prin. Fax 682-7751
Ennis MS 50/7-8
PO Box 517 59729 406-682-4237
Brian Hilton, prin. Fax 682-7752

Eureka, Lincoln, Pop. 1,015
Eureka SD 800/PK-12
PO Box 2000 59917 406-297-5650
Jim Mepham, supt. Fax 297-2644
www.lchigh.net
Eureka MS 200/5-8
PO Box 2000 59917 406-297-5600
Trevor Utter, prin. Fax 297-5653
Lincoln County HS 300/9-12
PO Box 2000 59917 406-297-5700
Joel Graves, prin. Fax 297-5714

Fairfield, Teton, Pop. 690
Fairfield SD 300/PK-12
PO Box 399 59436 406-467-2103
Les Meyer, supt. Fax 467-2554
www.fairfield.k12.mt.us/
Fairfield HS 100/9-12
PO Box 399 59436 406-467-2528
Dustin Gordon, prin. Fax 467-2554
Fairfield MS 50/7-8
PO Box 399 59436 406-467-2425
Dustin Gordon, prin. Fax 467-2554

Greenfield ESD 50/PK-8
590 Mt Highway 431 59436 406-467-2433
Fax 467-3138
Greenfield MS 50/7-8
590 Mt Highway 431 59436 406-467-2433
Paul Wilson, prin. Fax 467-3138

Fairview, Richland, Pop. 832
Fairview SD 300/PK-12
PO Box 467 59221 406-742-5265
Matt Schriver, supt. Fax 742-3336
fschool.org
Fairview HS 100/9-12
PO Box 467 59221 406-742-5265
Luke Kloker, prin. Fax 742-3336
Fairview MS 50/7-8
PO Box 467 59221 406-742-5265
Luke Kloker, prin. Fax 742-8265

Florence, Ravalli, Pop. 755
Florence-Carlton SD 800/PK-12
5602 Old US Highway 93 59833 406-273-6751
John McGee, supt.
www.florence.k12.mt.us
Florence-Carlton HS 300/9-12
5602 Old US Highway 93 59833 406-273-6301
Daniel Grabowska, prin. Fax 273-2643
Florence-Carlton MS 100/7-8
5602 Old US Highway 93 59833 406-273-0587
Audrey Backus, prin. Fax 273-0545

Forsyth, Rosebud, Pop. 1,757
Forsyth SD 400/PK-12
PO Box 319 59327 406-346-2796
David Shreeve, supt. Fax 346-7455
www.forsyth.k12.mt.us
Forsyth HS 100/9-12
PO Box 319 59327 406-346-2796
Doug Roberts, prin. Fax 346-9219
Forsyth MS 100/7-8
PO Box 319 59327 406-346-2796
Doug Roberts, prin. Fax 346-9219

Fort Benton, Chouteau, Pop. 1,439
Ft. Benton SD 300/PK-12
PO Box 399 59442 406-622-5691
Scott Chauvet, supt. Fax 622-5691
www.fortbenton.k12.mt.us/
Fort Benton HS 100/9-12
PO Box 399 59442 406-622-3213
Scott Chauvet, prin. Fax 622-5691
Fort Benton JHS 50/7-8
PO Box 399 59442 406-622-3213
Scott Chauvet, prin. Fax 622-5691

Frazer, Valley, Pop. 360
Frazer SD 100/PK-12
PO Box 488 59225 406-695-2241
Corrina Guardipee, supt. Fax 695-2243
www.frazer.k12.mt.us
Frazer HS 50/9-12
PO Box 488 59225 406-695-2241
Melanie Blount, prin. Fax 695-2243
Frazer MS 50/7-8
PO Box 488 59225 406-695-2241
Melanie Blount, prin. Fax 695-2243

Frenchtown, Missoula, Pop. 1,780
Frenchtown SD 1,000/PK-12
PO Box 117 59834 406-626-2600
Randy Cline, supt. Fax 626-2605
www.ftsd.org
Frenchtown HS 400/9-12
PO Box 117 59834 406-626-2670
Rory Weishaar, prin. Fax 626-2676
Frenchtown MS 200/7-8
PO Box 117 59834 406-626-2650
Jacob Haynes, prin. Fax 626-2654

Froid, Roosevelt, Pop. 181
Froid SD 100/K-12
PO Box 218 59226 406-766-2343
Roger Britton M.Ed., supt. Fax 766-2206
Froid HS 50/9-12
PO Box 218 59226 406-766-2342
Roger Britton M.Ed., prin. Fax 766-2206
Froid MS 50/7-8
PO Box 218 59226 406-766-2342
Roger Britton M.Ed., prin. Fax 766-2206

Fromberg, Carbon, Pop. 437
Fromberg SD 100/PK-12
PO Box 189 59029 406-668-7611
Teri Harris, supt. Fax 668-7669
www.fromberg.k12.mt.us
Fromberg HS 50/9-12
PO Box 189 59029 406-668-7315
Teri Harris, prin. Fax 668-7669
Fromberg MS 50/7-8
PO Box 189 59029 406-668-7315
Teri Harris, prin. Fax 668-7669

Gallatin Gateway, Gallatin, Pop. 845
Big Sky SD 200/PK-12
45465 Gallatin Rd 59730 406-995-4281
Jerry House, supt. Fax 995-2161
www.bssd72.org
Ophir MS 50/7-8
45465 Gallatin Rd 59730 406-995-4281
Jerry House, prin. Fax 995-2161
Other Schools – See Big Sky

Gallatin Gateway ESD 200/PK-8
PO Box 265 59730 406-763-4415
Kim DeBruycker, supt. Fax 763-4886
www.gallatingatewayschool.com
Gallatin Gateway MS 50/7-8
PO Box 265 59730 406-763-4415
Kim DeBruycker, prin. Fax 763-4886

Gardiner, Park, Pop. 871
Gardiner SD 200/PK-12
510 Stone St 59030 406-848-7261
J.T. Stroder, supt. Fax 848-9489
Gardiner HS 100/9-12
510 Stone St 59030 406-848-7261
Thomas Gauthier, prin. Fax 848-9489
Gardiner MS 50/7-8
510 Stone St 59030 406-848-7563
Thomas Gauthier, prin. Fax 848-9489

Geraldine, Chouteau, Pop. 255
Geraldine SD 100/PK-12
PO Box 347 59446 406-737-4371
Chad Fordyce, supt. Fax 737-4478
www.geraldine.k12.mt.us/
Geraldine HS 50/9-12
PO Box 347 59446 406-737-4371
Chad Fordyce, prin. Fax 737-4478
Geraldine MS 50/7-8
PO Box 347 59446 406-737-4371
Chad Fordyce, prin. Fax 737-4478

Geyser, Judith Basin, Pop. 87
Geyser SD 58 50/PK-12
PO Box 70 59447 406-735-4368
Dale Bernard, supt. Fax 735-4452
geyser.k12.mt.us
Geyser HS 50/9-12
PO Box 70 59447 406-735-4368
Dale Bernard, admin. Fax 735-4452
Geyser MS 50/7-8
PO Box 70 59447 406-735-4368
Dale Bernard, admin. Fax 735-4452

Glasgow, Valley, Pop. 3,170
Glasgow SD 800/PK-12
PO Box 28 59230 406-228-2406
Robert Connors, supt. Fax 228-2407
www.glasgow.k12.mt.us/
Glasgow HS 200/9-12
PO Box 28 59230 406-228-2485
Margaret Markle, prin. Fax 228-4061
Glasgow MS 100/7-8
PO Box 28 59230 406-228-2485
Margaret Markle, prin. Fax 228-4061

Glendive, Dawson, Pop. 4,857
Glendive SD 1,100/PK-12
PO Box 701 59330 406-377-5293
Ross Farber, supt. Fax 377-6212
www.glendiveschools.com
Dawson County HS 300/9-12
PO Box 701 59330 406-377-5265
Bruce Clausen, prin. Fax 377-8206
Washington MS 200/6-8
PO Box 701 59330 406-377-2356
Dinny Bennett, prin. Fax 377-2357

Dawson Community College Post-Sec.
300 College Dr 59330 406-377-3396

Grass Range, Fergus, Pop. 109
Grass Range SD 100/PK-12
PO Box 58 59032 406-428-2122
Barbara Solf, supt. Fax 428-2235
www.grps.k12.mt.us
Grass Range HS 50/9-12
PO Box 58 59032 406-428-2341
Barbara Solf, prin. Fax 428-2235
Grass Range MS 50/7-8
PO Box 58 59032 406-428-2122
Barbara Solf, prin. Fax 428-2235

Great Falls, Cascade, Pop. 56,542
Great Falls SD 10,500/PK-12
PO Box 2429 59403 406-268-6001
Cheryl Crawley, supt. Fax 268-6002
www.gfps.k12.mt.us
East MS 800/7-8
4040 Central Ave 59405 406-268-6500
Shelly Fagenstrom, prin. Fax 268-6524
Great Falls HS 1,600/9-12
1900 2nd Ave S 59405 406-268-6250
Fred Anderson, prin. Fax 268-6256
North MS 700/7-8
2601 8th St NE 59404 406-268-6525
Jane Gregiore, prin. Fax 268-6575
Paris Gibson Education Center 300/Alt
2400 Central Ave 59401 406-268-6600
Drew Uecker, prin. Fax 268-6603
Russell HS 1,500/9-12
228 17th Ave NW 59404 406-268-6100
Dick Kloppel, prin. Fax 268-6109

Benefits Health Care-West Campus Post-Sec.
PO Box 5013 59403 406-727-3333
Dahl's College of Beauty Post-Sec.
718 Central Ave 59401 406-454-3453
Foothills Community Christian S 200/PK-12
2210 5th Ave N 59401 406-452-5276
John Peterson, admin. Fax 452-8606
Great Falls Central Catholic HS 100/9-12
2800 18th Ave S 59405 406-216-3344
Vickie Donisthorpe, prin. Fax 216-3343
Great Falls College Montana State Univ Post-Sec.
2100 16th Ave S 59405 406-771-4300
Montana School for the Deaf and Blind Post-Sec.
3911 Central Ave 59405 406-771-6000
University of Great Falls Post-Sec.
1301 20th St S 59405 800-856-9544

Hamilton, Ravalli, Pop. 4,256
Hamilton SD 1,600/PK-12
217 Daly Ave 59840 406-363-2280
Tom Korst, supt. Fax 363-1843
www.hsd3.org
Hamilton HS 500/9-12
327 Fairgrounds Rd 59840 406-375-6060
Kevin Conwell, prin. Fax 375-6076
Hamilton MS 400/6-8
209 S 5th St 59840 406-363-2121
Dan Kimzey, prin. Fax 363-7032

Hardin, Big Horn, Pop. 3,345
Hardin SD 1,700/PK-12
585 W John Deere Rd 59034 406-665-9300
Albert Peterson, supt. Fax 665-9338
www.hardin.k12.mt.us
Hardin HS 500/9-12
702 N Terry Ave 59034 406-665-6300
Rob Hankins, prin. Fax 665-1909
Hardin MS 400/6-8
611 5th St W 59034 406-665-6300
Scott Brokaw, prin. Fax 665-1409

Harlem, Blaine, Pop. 770
Harlem SD 500/PK-12
PO Box 339 59526 406-353-2289
Rhonda Baker, supt. Fax 353-2674
www.harlem-hs.k12.mt.us

Harlem HS 200/9-12
PO Box 339 59526 406-353-2287
Mary Fear, prin. Fax 353-2339
Harlem MS 100/7-8
PO Box 339 59526 406-353-2287
Mary Fear, prin. Fax 353-2339

Aaniiih Nakoda College Post-Sec.
PO Box 159 59526 406-353-2607

Harlowton, Wheatland, Pop. 971
Harlowton SD 300/PK-12
PO Box 288 59036 406-632-4822
Andrew Begger, supt. Fax 632-4416
www.harlowton.k12.mt.us/
Harlowton HS 100/9-12
PO Box 288 59036 406-632-4324
Gregg Wasson, prin. Fax 632-4416
Hillcrest MS 50/7-8
PO Box 288 59036 406-632-4361
Gregg Wasson, prin. Fax 632-4416

Harrison, Madison, Pop. 137
Harrison SD 100/PK-12
PO Box 7 59735 406-685-3428
Fred Hofman, supt. Fax 685-3430
www.hhswildcats.com
Harrison HS 50/9-12
PO Box 7 59735 406-685-3428
Fred Hofman, prin. Fax 685-3430
Harrison MS 50/7-8
PO Box 7 59735 406-685-3428
Fred Hofman, prin. Fax 685-3430

Havre, Hill, Pop. 8,979
Havre SD 1,900/K-12
PO Box 7791 59501 406-265-4356
Andy Carlson, supt. Fax 265-8460
www.havre.k12.mt.us/
Havre HS 600/9-12
PO Box 7791 59501 406-265-6731
Craig Mueller, prin. Fax 265-3217
Havre MS 400/6-8
1441 11th St W 59501 406-265-9613
Dustin Kraske, prin. Fax 265-4414

Montana State University - Northern Post-Sec.
PO Box 7751 59501 406-265-3700

Hays, Blaine, Pop. 831
Hays-Lodge Pole SD 200/PK-12
PO Box 110 59527 406-673-3120
Margrett Campbell, supt. Fax 673-3294
www.hays.schoolaccess.net
Hays-Lodge Pole HS 100/9-12
PO Box 110 59527 406-673-3120
Juanita Cole, prin. Fax 673-3415
Hays-Lodge Pole MS 50/7-8
PO Box 110 59527 406-673-3120
Juanita Cole, prin. Fax 673-3274

Heart Butte, Pondera, Pop. 576
Heart Butte SD 200/PK-12
PO Box 259 59448 406-338-3344
Gerald Gray, supt. Fax 338-5832
www.heartbutteschool.com
Heart Butte HS 50/9-12
PO Box 259 59448 406-338-3344
Gerald Gray, prin. Fax 338-5832
Heart Butte MS 50/7-8
PO Box 259 59448 406-338-2200
Gerald Gray, prin. Fax 338-5832

Helena, Lewis and Clark, Pop. 27,530
Helena SD 8,100/PK-12
55 S Rodney St 59601 406-324-2001
Kent Kultgen, supt. Fax 324-2035
www.helena.k12.mt.us
Anderson MS 1,000/6-8
1200 Knight St 59601 406-324-2800
Bruce Campbell, prin. Fax 324-2801
Capital HS 1,400/9-12
100 Valley Dr 59601 406-324-2500
Elisabeth Hudnutt, prin. Fax 324-2501
Helena HS 1,700/9-12
1300 Billings Ave 59601 406-324-2200
Steve Thennis, prin. Fax 324-2201
Helena MS 700/6-8
1025 N Rodney St 59601 406-324-1000
Josh McKay, prin. Fax 324-1001
Project for Alternative Programs Alt
1325 Poplar St 59601 406-324-1631
Frank Jobe, prin. Fax 324-1645

Carroll College Post-Sec.
1601 N Benton Ave 59625 406-447-4300
Helena College University of Montana Post-Sec.
1115 N Roberts St 59601 406-447-6900

Highwood, Chouteau, Pop. 174
Highwood SD 100/PK-12
160 West St S 59450 406-733-2081
Becky Aaring, supt. Fax 733-2671
www.highwood.k12.mt.us
Highwood HS 50/9-12
160 West St S 59450 406-733-2081
Becky Aaring, prin. Fax 733-2671
Highwood MS 50/6-8
160 West St S 59450 406-733-2081
Becky Aaring, prin. Fax 733-2671

Hinsdale, Valley, Pop. 212
Hinsdale SD 100/PK-12
PO Box 398 59241 406-364-2314
Julie Gaffney, supt. Fax 364-2205
Hinsdale HS 50/9-12
PO Box 398 59241 406-364-2314
Julie Gaffney, admin. Fax 364-2205
Hinsdale MS 50/7-8
PO Box 398 59241 406-364-2314
Julie Gaffney, admin. Fax 364-2205

Hobson, Judith Basin, Pop. 215
Hobson SD 100/PK-12
PO Box 410 59452 406-423-5483
Colby Fitzgerald, supt. Fax 423-5260
www.hobson.k12.mt.us/
Hobson HS 50/9-12
PO Box 410 59452 406-423-5483
Fax 423-5260
Hobson MS 50/7-8
PO Box 410 59452 406-423-5483
Fax 423-5260

Hot Springs, Sanders, Pop. 493
Hot Springs SD 200/PK-12
PO Box 1005 59845 406-741-3285
Kevin Meredith, supt. Fax 741-3287
Hot Springs HS 100/9-12
PO Box 1005 59845 406-741-2962
Kevin Meredith, prin. Fax 741-3287
Hot Springs MS 50/7-8
PO Box 1005 59845 406-741-2962
Kevin Meredith, prin. Fax 741-3287

Hysham, Treasure, Pop. 299
Hysham SD 100/PK-12
PO Box 272 59038 406-342-5237
Larry Fink, supt. Fax 342-5257
Hysham HS 50/9-12
PO Box 272 59038 406-342-5237
Larry Fink, prin. Fax 342-5257
Hysham MS 50/7-8
PO Box 272 59038 406-342-5237
Larry Fink, prin. Fax 342-5257

Joliet, Carbon, Pop. 592
Joliet SD 400/PK-12
PO Box 590 59041 406-962-3541
Jeff Bermes, supt. Fax 962-3958
www.jolietschools.org/
Joliet HS 100/9-12
PO Box 590 59041 406-962-3541
Marilyn Vukonich, prin. Fax 962-3958
Joliet MS 100/7-8
PO Box 590 59041 406-962-3541
Marilyn Vukonich, prin. Fax 962-3958

Jordan, Garfield, Pop. 342
Jordan SD 200/PK-12
PO Box 409 59337 406-557-2259
Jennifer O'Connor, supt. Fax 557-2778
Garfield County HS 50/9-12
PO Box 409 59337 406-557-2259
Jennifer O'Connor, prin. Fax 557-2778
Jordan MS 50/7-8
PO Box 409 59337 406-557-2259
Jennifer O'Connor, prin. Fax 557-2778

Judith Gap, Wheatland, Pop. 125
Judith Gap SD 50/PK-12
PO Box 67 59453 406-473-2211
Annette Hart, supt. Fax 473-2250
www.judithgap.k12.mt.us/
Judith Gap HS 50/9-12
PO Box 67 59453 406-473-2211
Annette Hart, prin. Fax 473-2250
Judith Gap MS 50/7-8
PO Box 67 59453 406-473-2211
Annette Hart, prin. Fax 473-2250

Kalispell, Flathead, Pop. 19,453
Cayuse Prairie ESD 200/PK-8
897 Lake Blaine Rd 59901 406-756-4560
Amy Piazzola, supt. Fax 756-4570
cayuseprairie.com
Cayuse Prairie MS 50/7-8
897 Lake Blaine Rd 59901 406-756-4560
Amy Piazzola, prin. Fax 756-4570

Evergreen ESD 800/PK-8
18 W Evergreen Dr 59901 406-751-1111
Joel Voytoski, supt. Fax 752-2307
www.evergreensd50.com
Evergreen JHS 200/7-8
18 W Evergreen Dr 59901 406-751-1131
Kim Anderson, prin. Fax 751-1134

Fair-Mont-Egan ESD 200/PK-8
797 Fairmont Rd 59901 406-755-7072
Christine Anthony, admin. Fax 755-7077
fair.mt.schoolwebpages.com
Fair-Mont-Egan MS 50/7-8
797 Fairmont Rd 59901 406-755-7072
Christine Anthony, prin. Fax 755-7077

Helena Flats SD 15 200/K-8
1000 Helena Flats Rd 59901 406-257-2301
Gary Weitz, supt. Fax 257-2304
helenaflats.org
Helena Flats MS 50/7-8
1000 Helena Flats Rd 59901 406-257-2301
Ann Minckler, prin. Fax 257-2304

Kalispell SD 5,600/PK-12
233 1st Ave E 59901 406-751-3434
Dr. Darlene Schottle, supt. Fax 751-3416
www.sd5.k12.mt.us
Flathead HS 1,400/9-12
644 4th Ave W 59901 406-751-3500
Peter Fusaro, prin. Fax 751-3505
Glacier HS 1,300/9-12
375 Wolfpack Way 59901 406-758-8600
Callie Langohr, prin. Fax 758-8602
Kalispell MS 1,000/6-8
205 Northwest Ln 59901 406-751-3800
Tryg Johnson, prin. Fax 751-3805

Smith Valley ESD 200/K-8
2901 US Highway 2 W 59901 406-756-4535
Laili Komenda, admin. Fax 756-4534
www.smithvalleyschool.org
Smith Valley MS 50/7-8
2901 US Highway 2 W 59901 406-756-4535
Laili Komenda, prin. Fax 756-4534

West Valley ESD 500/PK-8
2290 Farm To Market Rd 59901 406-755-7239
Cal Ketchum, supt. Fax 755-7300
www.westvalleyschool.com
West Valley MS 100/6-8
2290 Farm To Market Rd 59901 406-755-7239
Dan Anderson, prin. Fax 755-7300

Flathead Valley Community College Post-Sec.
777 Grandview Dr 59901 406-756-3822
Stillwater Christian S 300/PK-12
255 FFA Dr 59901 406-752-4400
Daniel Makowski, supt. Fax 755-4061

Kila, Flathead, Pop. 375
Kila ESD 100/PK-8
PO Box 40 59920 406-257-2428
Fax 755-6663
www.kilaschool.com/
Kila MS 50/7-8
PO Box 40 59920 406-257-2428
Jason Christy, prin. Fax 755-6663

Lambert, Richland
Lambert SD 100/PK-12
PO Box 260 59243 406-774-3333
William Colter, supt. Fax 774-3335
Lambert HS 50/9-12
PO Box 260 59243 406-774-3333
William Colter, prin. Fax 774-3335
Lambert MS 50/7-8
PO Box 260 59243 406-774-3333
William Colter, prin. Fax 774-3335

Lame Deer, Rosebud, Pop. 2,025
Lame Deer SD 500/PK-12
PO Box 96 59043 406-477-6305
Bryan Kott, supt. Fax 477-6535
www.lamedeer.k12.mt.us/
Lame Deer HS 100/9-12
PO Box 96 59043 406-477-8900
Frank NoRunner, prin. Fax 477-8906
Lame Deer MS 100/7-8
PO Box 96 59043 406-477-8900
Frank NoRunner, prin. Fax 477-8906

Chief Dull Knife College Post-Sec.
PO Box 98 59043 406-477-6215

Laurel, Yellowstone, Pop. 6,588
Laurel SD 1,900/PK-12
410 Colorado Ave 59044 406-628-8623
Tim Bronk, supt. Fax 628-8625
www.laurel.k12.mt.us
Laurel HS 600/9-12
203 E 8th St 59044 406-628-7911
Karen Fox, prin. Fax 628-3558
Laurel MS 600/5-8
725 Washington Ave 59044 406-628-6919
Andrea Meiers, prin. Fax 628-3350

Lavina, Golden Valley, Pop. 177
Lavina SD 100/PK-12
PO Box 290 59046 406-636-2761
Steven Schwartz, supt. Fax 636-4911
www.edline.net/pages/lavina_k-12_schools
Lavina HS 50/9-12
PO Box 290 59046 406-636-2761
Steven Schwartz, prin. Fax 636-4911
Lavina MS 50/7-8
PO Box 290 59046 406-636-2761
Steven Schwartz, prin. Fax 636-4911

Lewistown, Fergus, Pop. 5,800
Lewistown SD 1,200/PK-12
215 7th Ave S 59457 406-535-8777
Jason Butcher, supt. Fax 535-7292
www.lewistown.k12.mt.us
Fergus HS 400/9-12
215 7th Ave S 59457 406-535-2321
Jerry Feller, prin. Fax 535-3835
Lewistown JHS 200/7-8
215 7th Ave S 59457 406-535-5419
Tim Majerus, prin. Fax 535-2300

Libby, Lincoln, Pop. 2,579
Libby SD 800/PK-12
724 Louisiana Ave 59923 406-293-8811
Kirby Maki, supt. Fax 293-8812
www.libbyschools.org
Libby JSHS 400/7-12
150 Education Way 59923 406-293-8802
Rik Rewerts, prin. Fax 293-3927

Lima, Beaverhead, Pop. 213
Lima SD 100/PK-12
PO Box 186 59739 406-276-3571
Dr. W. Blair Wilding, supt. Fax 276-3495
www.lima.k12.mt.us
Lima HS 50/9-12
PO Box 186 59739 406-276-3571
Dr. W. Blair Wilding, prin. Fax 276-3495
Lima MS 50/7-8
PO Box 186 59739 406-276-3571
Dr. W. Blair Wilding, prin. Fax 276-3495

Lincoln, Lewis and Clark, Pop. 993
Lincoln SD 200/PK-12
PO Box 39 59639 406-362-4201
Kathy Heisler, supt. Fax 362-4030
www.lincolnlynx.com

Lincoln HS 100/9-12
PO Box 39 59639 406-362-4201
Laurie Maughan, prin. Fax 362-4030
Lincoln MS 50/7-8
PO Box 39 59639 406-362-4201
Laurie Maughan, prin. Fax 362-4030

Livingston, Park, Pop. 6,921
Arrowhead ESD 75 100/K-8
1489 E River Rd 59047 406-333-4359
Debbra House, supt. Fax 333-4975
Arrowhead MS 50/7-8
1489 E River Rd 59047 406-333-4359
Debbra House, prin. Fax 333-4975

Livingston SD 1,100/K-12
132 S B St 59047 406-222-0861
Rich Moore Ph.D., supt. Fax 222-7323
www.livingston.k12.mt.us
Park HS 500/9-12
102 View Vista Dr 59047 406-222-0448
Lynne Scalia, prin. Fax 222-9404
Sleeping Giant MS 300/6-8
301 View Vista Dr 59047 406-222-3292
Lisa Rosburg, prin. Fax 222-3512

Pine Creek ESD 50/PK-8
2575 E River Rd 59047 406-222-0059
Fax 222-0059
pinecreekschool.com
Pine Creek MS 50/7-8
2575 E River Rd 59047 406-222-0059
Leah Shannon, lead tchr. Fax 222-0059

Lodge Grass, Big Horn, Pop. 414
Lodge Grass SD 300/PK-12
PO Box 810 59050 406-639-2304
John Small, supt. Fax 639-2388
lodgegrass.k12.mt.us
Lodge Grass HS 100/9-12
PO Box 810 59050 406-639-2385
Scott Gion, prin. Fax 639-2066
Lodge Grass MS 100/7-8
PO Box 810 59050 406-639-2333
Scott Gion, prin. Fax 639-2388

Lolo, Missoula, Pop. 3,815
Lolo ESD 600/PK-8
11395 US Highway 93 S 59847 406-273-0451
Michael Magone, supt. Fax 273-2628
www.lolo.k12.mt.us
Lolo MS 200/5-8
11395 US Highway 93 S 59847 406-273-6141
Dave Hansen M.Ed., prin. Fax 273-2628

Woodman ESD 100/K-8
18470 Lolo Creek Rd 59847 406-273-6770
Fax 273-6659
Woodman MS 50/7-8
18470 Lolo Creek Rd 59847 406-273-6770
Louise Rhode, prin. Fax 273-6659

Lustre, Valley

Lustre Christian HS 50/9-12
294 Lustre Rd 59225 406-392-5735
Wes Young, admin. Fax 392-5765

Malta, Phillips, Pop. 1,893
Malta SD 500/PK-12
PO Box 670 59538 406-654-1871
Kris Kuehn, supt. Fax 654-2205
www.malta.k12.mt.us/
Malta HS 200/9-12
PO Box 670 59538 406-654-2002
Scott King, prin. Fax 654-2226
Malta JHS 100/6-8
PO Box 670 59538 406-654-2225
Shawn Bleth, prin. Fax 654-2226

Manhattan, Gallatin, Pop. 1,493
Manhattan SD 500/PK-12
PO Box 425 59741 406-284-6460
Jim Notaro, supt. Fax 284-6853
www.manhattan.k12.mt.us
Manhattan HS 200/9-12
PO Box 425 59741 406-284-3341
Bob Moore, prin. Fax 284-3104
Manhattan MS 100/7-8
PO Box 425 59741 406-284-3250
Scott Schumacher, prin. Fax 284-4122

Manhattan Christian S 300/PK-12
8000 Churchill Rd 59741 406-282-7261
Patrick DeJong, supt. Fax 282-7701

Marion, Flathead, Pop. 853
Marion ESD 100/PK-8
205 Gopher Ln 59925 406-854-2333
Fax 854-2690
www.marionschoolmt.com
Marion MS 50/7-8
205 Gopher Ln 59925 406-854-2333
Justin Barnes, prin. Fax 854-2690

Medicine Lake, Sheridan, Pop. 215
Medicine Lake SD 100/PK-12
PO Box 265 59247 406-789-2211
Tiffani Anderson, supt. Fax 789-2213
www.medicinelake.k12.mt.us/
Medicine Lake HS 50/9-12
PO Box 265 59247 406-789-2211
Tiffani Anderson, prin. Fax 789-2213
Medicine Lake MS 50/7-8
PO Box 265 59247 406-789-2211
Tiffani Anderson, prin. Fax 789-2213

Melstone, Musselshell, Pop. 96
Melstone SD 100/PK-12
PO Box 97 59054 406-358-2352
Kelly Haaland, supt. Fax 358-2346
Melstone HS 50/9-12
PO Box 97 59054 406-358-2352
Kelly Haaland, prin. Fax 358-2346
Melstone MS 50/7-8
PO Box 97 59054 406-358-2352
Kelly Haaland, prin. Fax 358-2346

Miles City, Custer, Pop. 8,282
Miles City SD 1,600/PK-12
1604 Main St 59301 406-234-3840
Keith Campbell, supt. Fax 234-3147
www.milescity.k12.mt.us
Custer County District HS 500/9-12
20 S Center Ave 59301 406-234-4920
Jamie Ogolin, prin. Fax 234-4923
Washington MS 200/7-8
210 N 9th St 59301 406-234-2084
Derrick Tvedt, prin. Fax 234-7403

Miles Community College Post-Sec.
2715 Dickinson St 59301 406-874-6100

Missoula, Missoula, Pop. 65,061
DeSmet ESD 100/PK-8
6355 Padre Ln 59808 406-549-4994
Fax 549-6731
www.desmet.k12.mt.us
DeSmet MS 50/7-8
6355 Padre Ln 59808 406-549-4994
Shelley Andres, prin. Fax 549-6731

Hellgate ESD 1,300/PK-8
2385 Flynn Ln 59808 406-728-5626
Dr. Doug Reisig, supt. Fax 728-5636
www.hellgate.k12.mt.us
Hellgate MS 400/6-8
2385 Flynn Ln 59808 406-721-2452
Nancy Singleton, prin. Fax 728-0967

Missoula SD 1 8,400/K-12
215 S 6th St W 59801 406-728-2400
Alex Apostle, supt. Fax 542-4009
www.mcps.k12.mt.us
Big Sky HS 1,000/9-12
3100 South Ave W 59804 406-728-2401
Trevor Laboski, prin. Fax 549-4616
Hellgate HS 1,300/9-12
900 S Higgins Ave 59801 406-728-2402
Lisa Hendrix, prin. Fax 728-2496
Meadow Hill MS 400/6-8
4210 S Reserve St 59803 406-542-4045
Christina Stevens, prin. Fax 721-4418
Porter MS 500/6-8
2510 W Central Ave 59804 406-542-4060
Julie Hainline, prin. Fax 542-4098
Sentinel HS 1,200/9-12
901 South Ave W 59801 406-728-2403
Tom Blakely, prin. Fax 329-5959
Washington MS 600/6-8
645 W Central Ave 59801 406-542-4085
Paul Johnson, prin. Fax 721-7346
Willard Alternative Learning Center Alt
901 S 6th St W 59801 406-542-4073
Jane Bennett, admin. Fax 327-6965
Other Schools – See Seeley Lake

Target Range ESD 400/PK-8
4095 South Ave W 59804 406-549-9239
Corey Austin, supt. Fax 728-8841
www.target.k12.mt.us
Target Range MS 100/6-8
4095 South Ave W 59804 406-549-9239
Barb Johnson, prin. Fax 728-8841

Loyola Sacred Heart HS 200/9-12
320 Edith St 59801 406-549-6101
Kathy Schneider, prin. Fax 542-1432
Missoula College University of Montana Post-Sec.
909 South Ave W 59801 406-243-7882
Modern Beauty School Post-Sec.
2700 Paxson St Ste G 59801 406-721-1800
St. Patrick Hospital Post-Sec.
PO Box 4587 59806 406-543-7271
University of Montana Post-Sec.
32 Campus Dr 59812 406-243-0211
Valley Christian S 200/PK-12
2526 Sunset Ln 59804 406-549-0482
Chris Martineau, prin. Fax 549-5047

Moore, Fergus, Pop. 188
Moore SD 100/PK-12
509 Highland Ave 59464 406-374-2231
Denise Chrest, supt. Fax 374-2490
www.moore.k12.mt.us
Moore HS 50/9-12
509 Highland Ave 59464 406-374-2231
Denise Chrest, admin. Fax 374-2490
Moore MS 50/7-8
509 Highland Ave 59464 406-374-2231
Denise Chrest, admin. Fax 374-2490

Nashua, Valley, Pop. 284
Nashua SD 100/PK-12
PO Box 170 59248 406-746-3411
Jennifer Cunningham, supt. Fax 746-3458
www.nashua.k12.mt.us
Nashua HS 50/9-12
PO Box 170 59248 406-746-3411
Jennifer Cunningham, prin. Fax 746-3458
Nashua MS 50/7-8
PO Box 170 59248 406-746-3411
Jennifer Cunningham, prin. Fax 746-3458

Noxon, Sanders, Pop. 210
Noxon SD 200/PK-12
300 Noxon Ave 59853 406-847-2442
Jackie Branum, supt. Fax 847-2232
noxonschools.com
Noxon HS 100/9-12
300 Noxon Ave 59853 406-847-2442
Joshua Patterson, prin. Fax 847-2232
Noxon MS 50/7-8
300 Noxon Ave 59853 406-847-2442
Jackie Branum, prin. Fax 847-2232

Opheim, Valley, Pop. 83
Opheim SD 50/PK-12
PO Box 108 59250 406-762-3214
Ed Ray, supt. Fax 762-3348
sites.google.com/site/opheimschool/Home
Opheim HS 50/9-12
PO Box 108 59250 406-762-3214
Ed Ray, prin. Fax 762-3348
Opheim MS 50/7-8
PO Box 108 59250 406-762-3214
Ed Ray, prin. Fax 762-3348

Pablo, Lake, Pop. 2,090

Salish Kootenai College Post-Sec.
PO Box 70 59855 406-275-4800

Park City, Stillwater, Pop. 973
Park City SD 300/PK-12
PO Box 278 59063 406-633-2350
Patrick Audet, supt. Fax 633-2913
parkcityschools.org
Park City HS 100/9-12
PO Box 278 59063 406-633-2350
Jared Delaney, prin. Fax 633-2913
Park City MS 100/7-8
PO Box 278 59063 406-633-2350
Jared Delaney, prin. Fax 633-2913

Philipsburg, Granite, Pop. 808
Philipsburg SD 200/PK-12
PO Box 400 59858 406-859-3232
Mike Cutler, supt. Fax 859-3674
pburg.k12.mt.us
Granite HS 100/9-12
PO Box 400 59858 406-859-3232
Mike Cutler, prin. Fax 859-3674
Philipsburg MS 50/7-8
PO Box 400 59858 406-859-3232
Mike Cutler, prin. Fax 859-3674

Plains, Sanders, Pop. 1,024
Plains SD 400/PK-12
PO Box 549 59859 406-826-8600
Thomas Chisholm, supt. Fax 826-4439
www.plainsschools.net/
Plains HS 200/9-12
PO Box 549 59859 406-826-8600
Larry McDonald, prin. Fax 826-4439
Plains MS 100/7-8
PO Box 549 59859 406-826-8600
Larry McDonald, prin. Fax 826-4439

Plentywood, Sheridan, Pop. 1,706
Plentywood SD 300/PK-12
100 E Laurel Ave 59254 406-765-1803
Joe Bennett, supt. Fax 765-1195
www.plentywood.k12.mt.us/
Plentywood HS 100/9-12
100 E Laurel Ave 59254 406-765-1803
Matt Torix, prin. Fax 765-1195
Plentywood MS 50/7-8
100 E Laurel Ave 59254 406-765-1803
Rob Pedersen, prin. Fax 765-1195

Plevna, Fallon, Pop. 160
Plevna SD 100/PK-12
PO Box 158 59344 406-772-5666
Jule Walker, supt. Fax 772-5548
www.plevna.k12.mt.us/
Plevna HS 50/9-12
PO Box 158 59344 406-772-5666
Jule Walker, prin. Fax 772-5548
Plevna MS 50/7-8
PO Box 158 59344 406-772-5666
Jule Walker, prin. Fax 772-5548

Polson, Lake, Pop. 4,155
Polson SD 1,700/K-12
111 4th Ave E 59860 406-883-6355
Dr. Linda E. Reksten, supt. Fax 883-6345
www.polson.k12.mt.us
Polson HS 500/9-12
111 4th Ave E 59860 406-883-6351
Rex Weltz, prin. Fax 883-6330
Polson MS 300/7-8
111 4th Ave E 59860 406-883-6335
Brian Adams, prin. Fax 883-6334

Mission Valley Christian Academy 100/PK-12
38907 Mt Highway 35 59860 406-883-6858
Chris Bumgarner, dir. Fax 883-6860

Poplar, Roosevelt, Pop. 787
Poplar SD 700/PK-12
PO Box 458 59255 406-768-6600
James Rickley, supt. Fax 768-6800
www.poplar.k12.mt.us/
Poplar HS 200/9-12
PO Box 458 59255 406-768-6830
Rayna Hartz, prin. Fax 768-6803
Poplar JHS 100/5-8
PO Box 458 59255 406-768-6730
Brant Flath, prin. Fax 768-6802

Fort Peck Community College Post-Sec.
PO Box 398 59255 406-768-6300

Power, Teton, Pop. 174
Power SD 100/PK-12
PO Box 155 59468 406-463-2251
Loren Dunk, supt. Fax 463-2360
www.power.k12.mt.us/

Power HS — 100/9-12
PO Box 155 59468 — 406-463-2251
Loren Dunk, prin. — Fax 463-2360
Power MS — 50/7-8
PO Box 155 59468 — 406-463-2251
Loren Dunk, prin. — Fax 463-2360

Pryor, Big Horn, Pop. 610
Pryor SD — 100/PK-12
PO Box 229 59066 — 406-259-7329
Dan McGee, supt. — Fax 245-8938
www.pryor.k12.mt.us
Plenty Coups HS — 50/9-12
PO Box 229 59066 — 406-259-7329
Dan McGee, prin. — Fax 245-8938
Pryor MS — 50/7-8
PO Box 229 59066 — 406-259-7329
Dan McGee, prin. — Fax 245-8938

Ramsay, Silver Bow
Ramsay ESD — 100/K-8
PO Box 105 59748 — 406-782-5470
Fax 723-8905
Ramsay MS — 50/7-8
PO Box 105 59748 — 406-782-5470
Rosemary Garvey, prin. — Fax 723-8905

Rapelje, Stillwater
Rapelje SD — 100/K-12
PO Box 89 59067 — 406-663-2215
Jerry Thompson, supt. — Fax 663-2299
www.rapelje.k12.mt.us/
Rapelje HS — 50/9-12
PO Box 89 59067 — 406-663-2215
Jerry Thompson, prin. — Fax 663-2299
Rapelje MS — 50/7-8
PO Box 89 59067 — 406-663-2215
Jerry Thompson, prin. — Fax 663-2299

Red Lodge, Carbon, Pop. 2,091
Red Lodge SD — 500/PK-12
PO Box 1090 59068 — 406-446-2110
Mark Brajcich, supt. — Fax 446-2037
redlodge.schoolwires.com/
Red Lodge HS — 200/9-12
PO Box 1090 59068 — 406-446-1903
Rex Ternan, prin. — Fax 446-3953
Roosevelt JHS — 100/6-8
PO Box 1090 59068 — 406-446-2110
John Fitzgerald, prin. — Fax 446-3975

Reed Point, Stillwater, Pop. 186
Reed Point SD — 100/PK-12
PO Box 338 59069 — 406-326-2245
Dwain Haggard, supt. — Fax 326-2339
www.reedpoint.k12.mt.us/
Reed Point HS — 50/9-12
PO Box 338 59069 — 406-326-2245
Dwain Haggard, prin. — Fax 326-2339
Reed Point MS — 50/7-8
PO Box 338 59069 — 406-326-2245
Dwain Haggard, prin. — Fax 326-2339

Richey, Dawson, Pop. 177
Richey SD — 100/PK-12
PO Box 60 59259 — 406-773-5680
Brad Moore, supt. — Fax 773-5554
www.richey.k12.mt.us/
Richey HS — 50/9-12
PO Box 60 59259 — 406-773-5523
Brad Moore, prin. — Fax 773-5554
Richey MS — 50/7-8
PO Box 60 59259 — 406-773-5680
Brad Moore, prin. — Fax 773-5554

Roberts, Carbon, Pop. 354
Roberts SD — 100/K-12
PO Box 78 59070 — 406-445-2421
Elliott Crump, supt. — Fax 445-2506
www.roberts.k12.mt.us
Roberts HS — 50/9-12
PO Box 78 59070 — 406-445-2421
Elliott Crump, prin. — Fax 445-2506
Roberts MS — 50/7-8
PO Box 78 59070 — 406-445-2421
Elliott Crump, prin. — Fax 445-2506

Ronan, Lake, Pop. 1,691
Ronan SD — 1,300/PK-12
421 Andrew St NW 59864 — 406-676-3390
Andrew Holmlund, supt. — Fax 676-3392
www.ronank12.edu/
Ronan HS — 300/9-12
421 Andrew St NW 59864 — 406-676-3390
Kevin Kenelty, prin. — Fax 676-3330
Ronan MS — 300/6-8
421 Andrew St NW 59864 — 406-676-3390
Mark Johnston, prin. — Fax 676-2852

Rosebud, Rosebud, Pop. 111
Rosebud SD — 100/PK-12
PO Box 38 59347 — 406-347-5353
Matt Kleinsasser, supt. — Fax 347-5544
www.rosebudschooldist.com/
Rosebud HS — 50/9-12
PO Box 38 59347 — 406-347-5353
Matt Kleinsasser, prin. — Fax 347-5544
Rosebud MS — 50/7-8
PO Box 38 59347 — 406-347-5353
Matt Kleinsasser, prin. — Fax 347-5544

Roundup, Musselshell, Pop. 1,766
Roundup SD — 600/PK-12
700 3rd St W 59072 — 406-323-1507
Chad Sealey, supt. — Fax 323-1927
www.roundup.k12.mt.us
Roundup HS — 200/9-12
525 6th Ave W 59072 — 406-323-2402
Dana Quenzer, prin. — Fax 323-1583
Roundup MS — 100/7-8
525 6th Ave W 59072 — 406-323-2402
Dana Quenzer, prin. — Fax 323-1583

Roy, Fergus, Pop. 108
Roy SD — 50/PK-12
PO Box 9 59471 — 406-464-2511
Lori Goodell, supt. — Fax 464-2561
www.roy.k12.mt.us
Roy HS — 50/9-12
PO Box 9 59471 — 406-464-2511
Lori Goodell, prin. — Fax 464-2561
Roy MS — 50/7-8
PO Box 9 59471 — 406-464-2511
Lori Goodell, prin. — Fax 464-2561

Rudyard, Hill, Pop. 252
North Star SD — 200/K-12
PO Box 129 59540 — 406-355-4481
Ken Halverson, supt. — Fax 355-4532
www.northstar.k12.mt.us
North Star HS — 50/9-12
PO Box 129 59540 — 406-355-4481
Ken Halverson, prin. — Fax 355-4532
North Star MS — 50/7-8
PO Box 129 59540 — 406-355-4481
Ken Halverson, prin. — Fax 355-4532

Ryegate, Golden Valley, Pop. 241
Ryegate SD — 100/K-12
PO Box 129 59074 — 406-568-2211
Carl Somers, supt. — Fax 568-2528
Ryegate HS — 50/9-12
PO Box 129 59074 — 406-568-2211
Carl Somers, prin. — Fax 568-2528
Ryegate MS — 50/7-8
PO Box 129 59074 — 406-568-2211
Carl Somers, prin. — Fax 568-2528

Saco, Phillips, Pop. 189
Saco SD — 100/PK-12
PO Box 298 59261 — 406-527-3531
Gordon Hahn, supt. — Fax 527-3479
www.sacoschools.k12.mt.us
Saco HS — 50/9-12
PO Box 298 59261 — 406-527-3531
Gordon Hahn, prin. — Fax 527-3479
Saco MS — 50/7-8
PO Box 298 59261 — 406-527-3531
Gordon Hahn, prin. — Fax 527-3479

Saint Ignatius, Lake, Pop. 774
St. Ignatius SD — 500/PK-12
PO Box 1540 59865 — 406-745-3811
Robert Lewandowski, supt. — Fax 745-4421
www.stignatiusschools.org/
St. Ignatius HS — 200/9-12
PO Box 1540 59865 — 406-745-3811
Jason Sargent, prin. — Fax 745-4060
St. Ignatius MS — 100/6-8
PO Box 1540 59865 — 406-745-3811
Jason Sargent, prin. — Fax 745-4060

Saint Regis, Mineral, Pop. 301
Saint Regis SD — 200/PK-12
PO Box 280 59866 — 406-649-2311
Janet Hanson, supt. — Fax 649-2788
sites.google.com/site/stregisk12mtus/
Saint Regis HS — 50/9-12
PO Box 280 59866 — 406-649-2311
Tammy Demein, prin. — Fax 649-2788
Saint Regis MS — 50/7-8
PO Box 280 59866 — 406-649-2311
Tammy Demein, prin. — Fax 649-2788

Sand Coulee, Cascade, Pop. 209
Centerville SD — 300/PK-12
PO Box 100 59472 — 406-736-5167
Dennis Gerke, supt. — Fax 736-5210
www.centerville.k12.mt.us/
Centerville HS — 100/9-12
PO Box 100 59472 — 406-736-5167
Matthew McCale, prin. — Fax 736-5210
Centerville MS — 50/7-8
PO Box 100 59472 — 406-736-5167
Matthew McCale, prin. — Fax 736-5210

Savage, Richland
Savage SD — 100/PK-12
PO Box 110 59262 — 406-776-2317
Tyler Arlint, supt. — Fax 776-2260
www.savagepublicschool.com
Savage HS — 50/9-12
PO Box 110 59262 — 406-776-2317
Tyler Arlint, prin. — Fax 776-2260
Savage MS — 50/7-8
PO Box 110 59262 — 406-776-2317
Tyler Arlint, prin. — Fax 776-2260

Scobey, Daniels, Pop. 996
Scobey SD — 300/PK-12
PO Box 10 59263 — 406-487-2202
Dave Selvig, supt. — Fax 487-2204
Scobey HS — 100/9-12
PO Box 10 59263 — 406-487-2202
George Rider, prin. — Fax 487-2204
Scobey MS — 50/7-8
PO Box 10 59263 — 406-487-2202
George Rider, prin. — Fax 487-2204

Seeley Lake, Missoula, Pop. 1,625
Missoula SD 1
Supt. — See Missoula
Seeley-Swan HS — 100/9-12
PO Box 416 59868 — 406-677-2224
Kathleen Pecora, prin. — Fax 677-2949
Seeley Lake ESD 34 — 200/PK-8
PO Box 840 59868 — 406-677-2265
Chris Stout, supt. — Fax 677-2264
www.sleonline.org
Seeley Lake MS — 50/7-8
PO Box 840 59868 — 406-677-2265
Chris Stout, prin. — Fax 677-2264

Shelby, Toole, Pop. 3,316
Shelby SD — 500/PK-12
1010 Oilfield Ave 59474 — 406-434-2622
Matt Genger, supt. — Fax 434-2959
www.shelbypublicschools.org/
Shelby HS — 200/9-12
1001 Valley St 59474 — 406-424-8910
Shawn Clark, prin. — Fax 434-7273
Shelby MS — 100/7-8
1001 Valley St 59474 — 406-424-8910
Shawn Clark, prin. — Fax 434-7273

Shepherd, Yellowstone, Pop. 501
Shepherd SD — 800/PK-12
PO Box 8 59079 — 406-373-5461
Dan Jamieson, supt. — Fax 373-5284
www.shepherd.k12.mt.us/
Shepherd HS — 300/9-12
PO Box 8 59079 — 406-373-5300
Kenneth Poepping, prin. — Fax 373-5342
Shepherd MS — 100/7-8
PO Box 8 59079 — 406-373-5873
Richard Hash, prin. — Fax 373-5648

Sheridan, Madison, Pop. 623
Sheridan SD — 200/PK-12
PO Box 586 59749 — 406-842-5302
Kim Harding, supt. — Fax 842-5391
www.sheridan.k12.mt.us/
Sheridan HS — 100/9-12
PO Box 586 59749 — 406-842-5401
Rod Stout, prin. — Fax 842-5856
Sheridan MS — 50/7-8
PO Box 586 59749 — 406-842-5302
Rod Stout, prin. — Fax 842-5391

Sidney, Richland, Pop. 5,107
Sidney SD — 1,100/K-12
200 3rd Ave SE 59270 — 406-433-4080
Dan Farr, supt. — Fax 433-4358
www.sidney.k12.mt.us/
Sidney HS — 400/9-12
200 3rd Ave SE 59270 — 406-433-2330
Dan Peters, prin. — Fax 433-2481
Sidney MS — 300/6-8
200 3rd Ave SE 59270 — 406-433-4050
Kelly Johnson, prin. — Fax 433-4052

Simms, Cascade, Pop. 343
Sun River Valley SD — 300/PK-12
PO Box 380 59477 — 406-264-5111
Dave Marzolf, supt. — Fax 264-5189
www.srvs.k12.mt.us
Simms HS — 100/9-12
PO Box 380 59477 — 406-264-5110
Thad Kaiser, prin. — Fax 264-5189

Somers, Flathead, Pop. 1,095
Somers ESD — 600/PK-8
PO Box 159 59932 — 406-857-3661
Paul Jenkins, supt. — Fax 857-3144
www.somersdist29.org
Somers MS — 200/6-8
PO Box 159 59932 — 406-857-3661
Lori Schieffer, prin. — Fax 857-3144

Stanford, Judith Basin, Pop. 400
Stanford SD — 100/PK-12
PO Box 506 59479 — 406-566-2265
Nancy Coleman, supt. — Fax 566-2772
www.stanford.k12.mt.us/
Stanford HS — 50/9-12
PO Box 506 59479 — 406-566-2265
Nancy Coleman, prin. — Fax 566-2772
Stanford MS — 50/7-8
PO Box 506 59479 — 406-566-2265
Nancy Coleman, prin. — Fax 566-2772

Stevensville, Ravalli, Pop. 1,781
Lone Rock ESD — 300/PK-8
1112 Three Mile Creek Rd 59870 — 406-777-3314
David Cluff, supt. — Fax 777-2770
www.lonerockschool.org/
Lone Rock MS — 100/7-8
1112 Three Mile Creek Rd 59870 — 406-777-3314
Tamara Lysons, prin. — Fax 777-2770

Stevensville SD — 1,000/PK-12
300 Park St 59870 — 406-777-5481
David Whitesell, supt. — Fax 258-1241
www.stevensvilleschool.net/
Stevensville HS — 400/9-12
300 Park St 59870 — 406-777-5481
Brian Gum, prin. — Fax 258-1243
Stevensville JHS — 200/7-8
300 Park St 59870 — 406-777-5533
Bob Connors, prin. — Fax 258-1242

Sunburst, Toole, Pop. 361
Sunburst SD 2 — 200/K-12
PO Box 710 59482 — 406-937-2811
Tim Tharp, supt. — Fax 937-2828
www.sunburstschools.net/
Sunburst HS — 100/9-12
PO Box 710 59482 — 406-937-2811
Tim Tharp, prin. — Fax 937-2828
Sunburst MS — 50/7-8
PO Box 710 59482 — 406-937-2816
Dan Nau, prin. — Fax 937-4444

Superior, Mineral, Pop. 795
Superior SD 300/PK-12
PO Box 400 59872 406-822-3600
Wayne Stanley, supt. Fax 822-3601
www.sd3.k12.mt.us/
Superior HS 100/9-12
PO Box 400 59872 406-822-4851
Allan Labbe, prin. Fax 822-4396
Superior MS 50/7-8
PO Box 400 59872 406-822-4851
Allan Labbe, prin. Fax 822-4396

Terry, Prairie, Pop. 589
Terry SD 200/PK-12
PO Box 187 59349 406-635-5533
Casey Klasna, supt. Fax 635-5705
www.terry.k12.mt.us/
Terry HS 100/9-12
PO Box 187 59349 406-635-5533
Casey Klasna, prin. Fax 635-5705
Terry MS 50/7-8
PO Box 187 59349 406-635-5595
Casey Klasna, prin. Fax 635-5705

Thompson Falls, Sanders, Pop. 1,286
Thompson Falls SD 500/PK-12
PO Box 129 59873 406-827-3323
Jerry Pauli, supt. Fax 827-3020
www.thompsonfalls.net
Thompson Falls HS 200/9-12
PO Box 129 59873 406-827-3561
Jason Slater, prin. Fax 827-9463
Thompson Falls MS 100/7-8
PO Box 129 59873 406-827-3593
Maureen Simonson, prin. Fax 827-0306

Three Forks, Gallatin, Pop. 1,859
Three Forks SD 600/PK-12
212 E Neal St 59752 406-285-3216
Jerry Breen, supt. Fax 285-3216
www.tfschools.com
Three Forks HS 200/9-12
210 E Neal St 59752 406-285-3224
Robert DoBell, prin. Fax 285-3503
Three Forks MS 100/7-8
210 E Neal St 59752 406-285-3224
Robert DoBell, prin. Fax 285-3503

Townsend, Broadwater, Pop. 1,847
Townsend SD 700/PK-12
201 N Spruce St 59644 406-441-3454
Andrea Johnson, supt. Fax 441-3457
townsendps.schoolwires.com
Broadwater HS 200/9-12
201 N Spruce St 59644 406-441-3430
Beez Lucero, prin. Fax 441-3466
Townsend MS 100/7-8
201 N Spruce St 59644 406-441-3431
Brad Racht, prin. Fax 441-3475

Trout Creek, Sanders, Pop. 235
Trout Creek ESD 100/PK-8
4 School Ln 59874 406-827-3629
Fax 827-4185
www.troutcreekeagles.org/
Trout Creek MS 50/7-8
4 School Ln 59874 406-827-3629
Daisy Carlsmith, lead tchr. Fax 827-4185

Troy, Lincoln, Pop. 913
Troy SD 400/PK-12
PO Box 867 59935 406-295-4606
Dan Wendt, supt. Fax 295-4802
troymtk-12.us/
Troy HS 200/9-12
PO Box 867 59935 406-295-4520
Jacob Francom, prin. Fax 295-5371
Troy MS 100/7-8
PO Box 867 59935 406-295-4520
Jacob Francom, prin. Fax 295-5371

Turner, Blaine, Pop. 56
Turner SD 100/K-12
PO Box 40 59542 406-379-2315
Russ McKenna, supt. Fax 379-2398
www.turner.k12.mt.us
Turner HS 50/9-12
PO Box 40 59542 406-379-2219
Russ McKenna, prin. Fax 379-2398
Turner MS 50/7-8
PO Box 40 59542 406-379-2219
Russ McKenna, prin. Fax 379-2398

Twin Bridges, Madison, Pop. 367
Twin Bridges SD 300/PK-12
PO Box 419 59754 406-684-5657
Chad Johnson, supt. Fax 684-5458
www.twinbridges.k12.mt.us
Twin Bridges HS 100/9-12
PO Box 419 59754 406-684-5657
Chad Johnson, prin. Fax 684-5458
Twin Bridges MS 50/7-8
PO Box 419 59754 406-684-5613
Aaron Griffin, prin. Fax 684-5458

Ulm, Cascade, Pop. 714
Ulm ESD 100/PK-8
PO Box 189 59485 406-866-3313
Fax 866-3209
Ulm MS 50/7-8
PO Box 189 59485 406-866-3313
Lauri Ingebrigtson, prin. Fax 866-3209

Valier, Pondera, Pop. 489
Valier SD 200/PK-12
PO Box 528 59486 406-279-3613
Matthew Hauk, supt. Fax 279-3764
valier.k12.mt.us
Valier HS 100/9-12
PO Box 528 59486 406-279-3613
Matthew Hauk, prin. Fax 279-3764
Valier MS 50/7-8
PO Box 508 59486 406-279-3314
Jackie Christiaens, prin. Fax 279-3510

Vaughn, Cascade, Pop. 628
Vaughn ESD 100/PK-8
PO Box 279 59487 406-965-2231
Dean Jardee, admin. Fax 965-3703
www.vaughnschool.com/
Vaughn MS 50/7-8
PO Box 279 59487 406-965-2231
Dean Jardee, prin. Fax 965-3703

Victor, Ravalli, Pop. 724
Victor SD 400/PK-12
425 4th Ave 59875 406-642-3221
Lance Pearson, supt. Fax 642-3446
www.victor.k12.mt.us/
Victor HS 100/9-12
425 4th Ave 59875 406-642-3221
Danny Johnston, prin. Fax 642-3446
Victor MS 100/6-8
425 4th Ave 59875 406-642-3221
Danny Johnston, prin. Fax 642-3446

Westby, Sheridan, Pop. 166
Westby SD 100/PK-12
PO Box 109 59275 406-385-2225
Tony Holecek, supt. Fax 385-2430
www.westbyschool.k12.mt.us/
Westby HS 50/9-12
PO Box 109 59275 406-385-2225
Tony Holecek, prin. Fax 385-2430
Westby MS 50/7-8
PO Box 109 59275 406-385-2225
Tony Holecek, prin. Fax 385-2430

West Yellowstone, Gallatin, Pop. 1,235
West Yellowstone SD 200/PK-12
PO Box 460 59758 406-646-7617
Lael Calton, supt. Fax 646-7232
www.westyellowstone.k12.mt.us
West Yellowstone HS 100/9-12
PO Box 460 59758 406-646-7617
Terry Falcon, prin. Fax 646-7232
West Yellowstone MS 50/7-8
PO Box 460 59758 406-646-7617
Terry Falcon, prin. Fax 646-7232

Whitefish, Flathead, Pop. 6,250
Olney-Bissell ESD 100/PK-8
5955 Farm To Market Rd 59937 406-862-2828
Fax 862-2838
Bissell MS 50/7-8
5955 Farm to Market Rd 59937 406-862-2828
Lona Everett, prin. Fax 862-2838

Whitefish SD 1,600/PK-12
600 2nd St E 59937 406-862-8640
Kate Orozco, supt. Fax 862-1507
www.wfps.k12.mt.us
Whitefish HS 500/9-12
600 2nd St E 59937 406-862-8600
Kerry Drown, prin. Fax 862-2586
Whitefish Independent HS Alt
600 2nd St E 59937 406-862-8688
Kerry Drown, prin. Fax 862-8689
Whitefish MS 600/5-8
600 2nd St E 59937 406-862-8650
Josh Branstetter, prin. Fax 862-8664

Whitehall, Jefferson, Pop. 1,005
Whitehall SD 400/PK-12
PO Box 1109 59759 406-287-3455
Kimberly Kingston, supt. Fax 287-3843
whitehall.schoolwires.com/
Whitehall HS 200/9-12
PO Box 1109 59759 406-287-3862
Britt McLean, dean Fax 287-3843
Whitehall JHS 100/7-8
PO Box 1109 59759 406-287-3882
Nate Lant, prin. Fax 287-5508

White Sulphur Springs, Meagher, Pop. 922
White Sulphur Springs SD 200/PK-12
PO Box C 59645 406-547-3751
Andrew Lind, supt. Fax 547-3922
www.whitesulphur.k12.mt.us/
White Sulphur Springs HS 100/9-12
PO Box C 59645 406-547-3351
David Stuhlberg, prin. Fax 547-2407
White Sulphur Springs MS 50/7-8
PO Box C 59645 406-547-3351
David Stuhlberg, prin. Fax 547-2407

Whitewater, Phillips, Pop. 62
Whitewater SD 50/PK-12
PO Box 46 59544 406-674-5418
Darin Cummings, supt. Fax 674-5460
www.whitewater.k12.mt.us
Whitewater HS 50/9-12
PO Box 46 59544 406-674-5417
Darin Cummings, prin. Fax 674-5460
Whitewater MS 50/7-8
PO Box 46 59544 406-674-5417
Darin Cummings, prin. Fax 674-5460

Wibaux, Wibaux, Pop. 582
Wibaux SD 100/PK-12
121 F St N 59353 406-796-2474
Terry Quintus, supt. Fax 796-2259
wchs.k12.mt.us/
Wibaux HS 50/9-12
121 F St N 59353 406-795-2474
Terry Quintus, prin. Fax 795-2259
Wibaux JHS 50/7-8
121 F St N 59353 406-796-2474
Janet Huisman, prin. Fax 796-2259

Willow Creek, Gallatin, Pop. 206
Willow Creek SD 100/PK-12
PO Box 189 59760 406-285-6991
Bonnie Lauer, supt. Fax 285-6923
www.willowcreek.k12.mt.us/
Willow Creek HS 50/9-12
PO Box 189 59760 406-285-6991
Bonnie Lauer, prin. Fax 285-6923
Willow Creek MS 50/7-8
PO Box 189 59760 406-285-6991
Bonnie Lauer, prin. Fax 285-6923

Winifred, Fergus, Pop. 207
Winifred SD 100/PK-12
PO Box 109 59489 406-462-5349
Roy Goodell, supt. Fax 462-5477
www.winifred.k12.mt.us
Winifred HS 50/9-12
PO Box 109 59489 406-462-5420
Roy Goodell, prin. Fax 462-5477
Winifred MS 50/7-8
PO Box 109 59489 406-462-5349
Roy Goodell, prin. Fax 462-5477

Winnett, Petroleum, Pop. 182
Winnett SD 100/PK-12
PO Box 167 59087 406-429-2251
Dr. Clay Dunlap, supt. Fax 429-7631
Winnett HS 50/9-12
PO Box 167 59087 406-429-2251
Dr. Clay Dunlap, prin. Fax 429-7631
Winnett MS 50/7-8
PO Box 167 59087 406-429-2251
Dr. Clay Dunlap, prin. Fax 429-7631

Wolf Point, Roosevelt, Pop. 2,478
Frontier ESD 100/PK-8
6996 Roy St 59201 406-653-7083
Christine Eggar, supt. Fax 653-2508
Frontier MS 50/7-8
6996 Roy St 59201 406-653-2501
Christine Eggar, admin. Fax 653-2508

Wolf Point SD 900/PK-12
213 6th Ave S 59201 406-653-2361
Eileen Karge, supt. Fax 653-3405
wolfpoint.k12.mt.us
Wolf Point HS 200/9-12
213 6th Ave S 59201 406-653-1200
Joseph Paine, prin. Fax 653-3104
Wolf Point JHS 100/7-8
213 6th Ave S 59201 406-653-1200
Kim Hanks, prin. Fax 653-3104

Worden, Yellowstone, Pop. 573
Huntley Project SD 700/PK-12
1477 Ash St 59088 406-967-2540
Wes Coy, supt. Fax 967-3059
www.huntley.k12.mt.us/
Huntley Project HS 200/9-12
1477 Ash St 59088 406-967-2540
Mark Wandle, prin. Fax 967-2589
Huntley Project MS 100/7-8
1477 Ash St 59088 406-967-2540
Frank Hollowell, prin. Fax 967-3054

Wyola, Big Horn, Pop. 212
Wyola ESD 100/PK-8
PO Box 66 59089 406-343-2722
Jason Cummins, supt. Fax 343-5901
www.wyola.k12.mt.us
Wyola MS 50/7-8
PO Box 66 59089 406-343-2722
Jason Cummins, prin. Fax 343-5901

NEBRASKA

NEBRASKA DEPARTMENT OF EDUCATION
PO Box 94987, Lincoln 68509-4987
Telephone 402-471-2295
Fax 402-471-0117
Website http://www.education.ne.gov/

Commissioner of Education — Dr. Scott Swisher

NEBRASKA BOARD OF EDUCATION
PO Box 94987, Lincoln 68509-4987

President — Jim Scheer

EDUCATIONAL SERVICE UNITS (ESU)

ESU 1
Robert Uhing, admin. — 402-287-2061
211 10th St, Wakefield 68784 — Fax 287-2065
www.esu1.org/

ESU 2
David Ludwig, admin. — 402-721-7710
PO Box 649, Fremont 68026 — Fax 721-7712
www.esu2.org/

ESU 3
Dr. Gil Kettelhut, admin. — 402-597-4800
6949 S 110th St, La Vista 68128 — Fax 597-4808
www2.esu3.org/esu3/

ESU 4
Jon Fisher, admin. — 402-274-4354
919 16th St, Auburn 68305 — Fax 274-4356
www.esu4.org/

ESU 5
Brian Gegg, admin. — 402-223-5277
900 W Court St, Beatrice 68310 — Fax 223-5279
www.esu5.org/

ESU 6
Dr. Dan Shoemake, admin. — 800-327-0091
210 5th St, Milford 68405 — Fax 761-3279
www.esu6.org/

ESU 7
Dr. Norman Ronell, admin. — 402-564-5753
2657 44th Ave, Columbus 68601 — Fax 563-1121
www.esu7.org

ESU 8
Randall Peck, admin. — 402-887-5041
PO Box 89, Neligh 68756 — Fax 887-4604
www.esu8.org/

ESU 9
Kraig Lofquist, admin. — 402-463-5611
PO Box 2047, Hastings 68902 — Fax 463-9555
www.esu9.org/

ESU 10
Wayne Bell, admin. — 308-237-5927
PO Box 850, Kearney 68848 — Fax 237-5920
www.esu10.org/

ESU 11
Paul Tedesco, admin. — 308-995-6585
PO Box 858, Holdrege 68949 — Fax 995-6587
www.esu11.org/

ESU 13
Dr. Jeff West, admin. — 308-635-3696
4215 Avenue I, Scottsbluff 69361 — Fax 635-0680
www.esu13.org/

ESU 15
Paul Calvert, admin. — 308-334-5160
PO Box 398, Trenton 69044 — Fax 334-5581
www.esu15.org

ESU 16
Margene Beatty, admin. — 308-284-8481
PO Box 915, Ogallala 69153 — Fax 284-8483
www.esu16.org/

ESU 17
Dennis Radford, admin. — 402-387-1420
207 N Main St, Ainsworth 69210 — Fax 387-1028
www.esu17.org/

ESU 18
Steve Joel Ed.D., supt. — 402-436-1610
PO Box 82889, Lincoln 68501 — Fax 436-1620
www.lps.org/

ESU 19
Dr. John Mackiel, admin. — 402-557-2002
3215 Cuming St, Omaha 68131 — Fax 557-2019
esu19.org/

PUBLIC, PRIVATE AND CATHOLIC SECONDARY SCHOOLS

Adams, Gage, Pop. 572
Freeman SD — 400/PK-12
PO Box 259 68301 — 402-988-2525
Randy Page, supt. — Fax 988-3475
www.freemanpublicschools.org/
Freeman JSHS — 200/7-12
PO Box 259 68301 — 402-988-2525
Bob Michl, prin. — Fax 988-3475

Ainsworth, Brown, Pop. 1,710
Ainsworth SD — 500/K-12
PO Box 65 69210 — 402-387-2333
Darrell Peterson, supt. — Fax 387-0525
www.ainsworthschools.org/
Ainsworth HS — 200/9-12
PO Box 65 69210 — 402-387-2082
Richard Gilson, prin. — Fax 387-0525
Ainsworth MS — 100/5-8
PO Box 65 69210 — 402-387-2082
Richard Gilson, prin. — Fax 387-0525

Albion, Boone, Pop. 1,646
Boone Central SD — 600/K-12
PO Box 391 68620 — 402-395-2134
Cory Worrell, supt. — Fax 395-2137
www.boonecentral.esu7.org/
Boone Central HS — 200/9-12
PO Box 391 68620 — 402-395-2134
Darrell Barnes, prin. — Fax 395-2137
Other Schools – See Petersburg

Allen, Dixon, Pop. 375
Allen Consolidated SD — 200/K-12
PO Box 190 68710 — 402-635-2484
Don Schmidt, supt. — Fax 635-2331
allenweb.esu1.org/
Allen JSHS — 100/7-12
PO Box 190 68710 — 402-635-2484
Lana Oswald, prin. — Fax 635-2331

Alliance, Box Butte, Pop. 8,339
Alliance SD — 1,600/K-12
1604 Sweetwater Ave 69301 — 308-762-5475
Troy Unzicker, supt. — Fax 762-8249
apschools.schoolfusion.us
Alliance HS — 500/9-12
1604 Sweetwater Ave 69301 — 308-762-3359
Patrick Jones, prin. — Fax 762-7683
Alliance MS — 400/5-8
1604 Sweetwater Ave 69301 — 308-762-3079
Katie White, prin. — Fax 762-7302

Western Nebraska Community College — Post-Sec.
1750 Sweetwater Ave 69301 — 308-763-2000

Alma, Harlan, Pop. 1,129
Alma SD — 300/K-12
PO Box 170 68920 — 308-928-2131
Jon Davis, supt. — Fax 928-2763
almacardinals.org
Alma JSHS — 100/7-12
PO Box 170 68920 — 308-928-2131
Galen Kronhofman, prin. — Fax 928-2763

Amherst, Buffalo, Pop. 248
Amherst SD — 300/K-12
PO Box 8 68812 — 308-826-3131
Tom Moore, supt. — Fax 826-4865
amherst.k12.ne.us/
Amherst JSHS — 100/7-12
PO Box 8 68812 — 308-826-3131
Roger Thomsen, prin. — Fax 826-4865

Ansley, Custer, Pop. 440
Ansley SD — 200/K-12
PO Box 370 68814 — 308-935-1121
Michael McCabe, supt. — Fax 935-9103
Ansley JSHS — 100/7-12
PO Box 370 68814 — 308-935-1121
Lance Bristol, prin. — Fax 935-9103

Arapahoe, Furnas, Pop. 1,013
Arapahoe SD — 300/K-12
PO Box 360 68922 — 308-962-5458
Larry Weaver, supt. — Fax 962-7481
Arapahoe HS — 100/7-12
PO Box 360 68922 — 308-962-5458
Daren Hatch, prin. — Fax 962-7481

Arcadia, Valley, Pop. 309
Arcadia SD — 100/K-12
PO Box 248 68815 — 308-789-6522
Michael McCabe, supt. — Fax 789-6214
www.arcadiapublicschools.org/
Arcadia JSHS — 100/7-12
PO Box 248 68815 — 308-789-6522
Jess Underwood, prin. — Fax 789-6214

Arlington, Washington, Pop. 1,239
Arlington SD — 600/K-12
PO Box 580 68002 — 402-478-4173
Lynn Johnson, supt. — Fax 478-4176
www.apseagles.org
Arlington JSHS — 300/7-12
PO Box 580 68002 — 402-478-4171
Andrew Farber, prin. — Fax 478-4176

Arnold, Custer, Pop. 592
Arnold SD — 100/K-12
PO Box 399 69120 — 308-848-2226
Patrick Osmond, supt. — Fax 848-2201
blog.arnold.k12.ne.us
Arnold JSHS — 100/7-12
PO Box 399 69120 — 308-848-2226
Dawn Lewis, prin. — Fax 848-2201

Arthur, Arthur, Pop. 117
Arthur County SD — 100/K-12
PO Box 145 69121 — 308-764-2253
Gregory East, supt. — Fax 764-2206
Arthur County JSHS — 50/7-12
PO Box 145 69121 — 308-764-2253
Barry Schaeffer, prin. — Fax 764-2206

Ashland, Saunders, Pop. 2,429
Ashland-Greenwood SD — 900/PK-12
1225 Clay St 68003 — 402-944-2128
Dr. Zach Kassebaum, supt. — Fax 944-3310
www.agps.org/
Ashland-Greenwood HS — 300/9-12
1842 Furnas St 68003 — 402-944-2114
Brad Jacobsen, prin. — Fax 944-2116
Ashland-Greenwood MS — 100/7-8
1842 Furnas St 68003 — 402-944-2114
Brad Jacobsen, prin. — Fax 944-2116

Atkinson, Holt, Pop. 1,242
West Holt SD — 300/K-12
PO Box 457 68713 — 402-925-2848
Bill McAllister, supt. — Fax 925-2177
westholt.esu8.org
West Holt HS — 200/7-12
PO Box 457 68713 — 402-925-2848
Kevin Young, prin. — Fax 925-2177

Auburn, Nemaha, Pop. 3,425
Auburn SD — 900/PK-12
1713 J St 68305 — 402-274-4830
Kevin Reiman, supt. — Fax 274-5227
www.auburnpublicschools.org/
Auburn HS — 300/9-12
1713 J St 68305 — 402-274-4328
Vernon Golladay, prin. — Fax 274-5434
Auburn MS — 200/6-8
1713 J St 68305 — 402-274-4027
Vernon Golladay, prin. — Fax 274-4147

Aurora, Hamilton, Pop. 4,447
Aurora SD — 1,200/K-12
300 L St 68818 — 402-694-6923
Damon McDonald, supt. — Fax 694-5097
aurorahuskies.us
Aurora HS — 400/9-12
300 L St 68818 — 402-694-6968
Douglas Kittle, prin. — Fax 694-2573
Aurora MS — 300/6-8
300 L St 68818 — 402-694-6915
Kenneth Thiele, prin. — Fax 694-3815

Axtell, Kearney, Pop. 718
Axtell Community SD 200/K-12
PO Box 97 68924 308-743-2415
Steven Wickham, supt. Fax 743-2417
axtell.k12.ne.us
Axtell JSHS 100/7-12
PO Box 97 68924 308-743-2415
Bill Gilbreath, prin. Fax 743-2417

Bancroft, Cuming, Pop. 482
Bancroft-Rosalie SD 200/K-12
PO Box 129 68004 402-648-3336
Jon Cerny, supt. Fax 648-3338
www.bancroft-rosalie.org/
Bancroft JSHS 100/7-12
PO Box 129 68004 402-648-3336
Mike Sjuts, prin. Fax 648-3338

Bartlett, Wheeler, Pop. 117
Wheeler Central SD 100/PK-12
PO Box 68 68622 308-654-3273
Gary Klahn, supt. Fax 654-3237
Wheeler Central JSHS 100/7-12
PO Box 68 68622 308-654-3273
Gary Klahn, prin. Fax 654-3237

Bartley, Red Willow, Pop. 282
Southwest SD 179 300/PK-12
PO Box 187 69020 308-692-3223
Clayton Waddle, supt. Fax 692-3221
www.swpschools.org/
Southwest JSHS 100/7-12
PO Box 187 69020 308-692-3223
Matt Springer, prin. Fax 692-3221

Bassett, Rock, Pop. 618
Rock County SD 200/K-12
PO Box 448 68714 402-684-3411
David Zumbahlen, supt. Fax 684-3671
Rock County HS 100/7-12
PO Box 448 68714 402-684-3411
Steve Camp, prin. Fax 684-3671

Battle Creek, Madison, Pop. 1,202
Battle Creek SD 400/K-12
PO Box 100 68715 402-675-6905
Jay Bellar, supt. Fax 675-1038
bcps.esu8.org/
Battle Creek JSHS 200/7-12
PO Box 100 68715 402-675-3705
Jeff Heimes, prin. Fax 675-1038

Bayard, Morrill, Pop. 1,198
Bayard SD 400/K-12
PO Box 607 69334 308-586-1700
Travis Miller, supt. Fax 586-1638
www.bayardpublicschools.org/
Bayard JSHS 200/7-12
PO Box 607 69334 308-586-1700
Thomas Perlinski, prin. Fax 586-1638

Beatrice, Gage, Pop. 12,303
Beatrice SD 2,100/PK-12
320 N 5th St 68310 402-223-1500
Pat Nauroth, supt. Fax 223-1509
www.beatricepublicschools.org
Beatrice HS 700/9-12
600 Orange Blvd 68310 402-223-1515
Jason Sutter, prin. Fax 223-1510
Beatrice MS 500/6-8
215 N 5th St 68310 402-223-1545
John Jarosh, prin. Fax 223-1547

Joseph's College of Beauty Post-Sec.
618 Court St 68310 402-223-3588
Southeast Community College Post-Sec.
4771 W Scott Rd 68310 402-228-3468

Bellevue, Sarpy, Pop. 48,571
Bellevue SD 9,600/PK-12
1600 Highway 370 68005 402-293-4000
Frank Harwood, supt. Fax 293-5002
www.bellevuepublicschools.org
Bellevue East HS 1,500/9-12
1401 High School Dr 68005 402-293-4150
Brad Stueve, prin. Fax 293-4259
Bellevue West HS 1,700/9-12
1501 Thurston Ave 68123 402-293-4040
Kevin Rohlfs, prin. Fax 293-4149
Fontenelle MS 500/7-8
701 Kayleen Dr 68005 402-293-4360
Doug Schaefer, prin. Fax 293-4450
Lewis & Clark MS 500/7-8
13502 S 38th St 68123 402-898-8760
Dr. Mike Smith, prin. Fax 898-9018
Mission MS 400/7-8
2202 Washington St 68005 402-293-4260
Jenny Powell, prin. Fax 293-4350

Bellevue University Post-Sec.
1000 Galvin Rd S 68005 402-293-2000
Cornerstone Christian S 200/K-10
3704 370 Plz 68123 402-292-1030
Teri Schrag M.A., admin. Fax 292-1030

Benkelman, Dundy, Pop. 937
Dundy County-Straton SD 300/PK-12
PO Box 586 69021 308-423-2738
James Kent, supt. Fax 423-2711
204.234.184.9/
Dundy County Stratton HS 100/9-12
PO Box 586 69021 308-423-2738
Phil Truax, prin. Fax 423-2711

Bennington, Douglas, Pop. 1,439
Bennington SD 1,300/K-12
11620 N 156th St 68007 402-238-3044
Dr. Terry Haack, supt. Fax 238-2185
www.benningtonschools.org/
Bennington JSHS 500/7-12
16610 Bennington Rd 68007 402-238-2447
Stan Turner, prin. Fax 238-2950

Bertrand, Phelps, Pop. 742
Bertrand SD 200/K-12
PO Box 278 68927 308-472-3427
Dr. Dennis Shipp, supt. Fax 472-3429
Bertrand JSHS 100/7-12
PO Box 278 68927 308-472-3427
Kevin Buxton, prin. Fax 472-3429

Big Springs, Deuel, Pop. 393
South Platte SD 200/K-12
PO Box 457 69122 308-889-3622
David Spencer, supt. Fax 889-3523
manzana.esu16.org/groups/southplatte
South Platte HS 100/7-12
PO Box 457 69122 308-889-3622
Rodney Gaston, prin. Fax 889-3523

Blair, Washington, Pop. 7,886
Blair Community SD 2,300/PK-12
PO Box 288 68008 402-426-2610
Rex Pfeil, supt. Fax 426-3110
www.blairschools.org/
Blair HS 700/9-12
PO Box 288 68008 402-426-4941
Thomas Anderson, prin. Fax 426-4949
Otte Blair MS 500/6-8
PO Box 288 68008 402-426-3678
Chris Stogdill, prin. Fax 426-1788

Bloomfield, Knox, Pop. 1,011
Bloomfield SD 200/PK-12
PO Box 308 68718 402-373-4800
Robert Marks, supt. Fax 373-2712
www.bloomfieldschools.net/
Bloomfield JSHS 100/7-12
PO Box 308 68718 402-373-4800
Rusty Kluender, prin. Fax 373-2712

Blue Hill, Webster, Pop. 925
Blue Hill SD 400/K-12
PO Box 217 68930 402-756-2085
Joel Ruybalid, supt. Fax 756-2086
www.bluehillschools.org/
Blue Hill JSHS 200/7-12
PO Box 217 68930 402-756-3043
Rodney Olson, prin. Fax 756-3044

Boys Town, Douglas, Pop. 727

Boys Town HS 400/9-12
13727 Flanagan Blvd 68010 402-498-1800
Robert Gehringer, supt. Fax 498-3246

Brady, Lincoln, Pop. 425
Brady SD 200/K-12
PO Box 68 69123 308-584-3317
William Porter, supt. Fax 584-3725
Brady JSHS 100/7-12
PO Box 68 69123 308-584-3317
Bruce Hird, prin. Fax 584-3725

Brainard, Butler, Pop. 330
East Butler SD 400/K-12
PO Box 36 68626 402-545-2081
James Koontz, supt. Fax 545-2023
www.ebutler.esu7.org/eastbutler.html
Brainard JSHS 200/7-12
PO Box 36 68626 402-545-2081
Shawn Biltoft, prin. Fax 545-2023

Bridgeport, Morrill, Pop. 1,536
Bridgeport SD 63 500/K-12
PO Box 430 69336 308-262-1470
Dave Miller, supt. Fax 262-0444
www.bridgeportschools.org/
Bridgeport JSHS 200/7-12
PO Box 430 69336 308-262-0346
Matt Asche, prin. Fax 262-1284

Broken Bow, Custer, Pop. 3,500
Broken Bow SD 800/K-12
323 N 7th Ave 68822 308-872-6821
Mark Sievering, supt. Fax 872-2751
www.bbps.org/
Broken Bow HS 300/9-12
323 N 7th Ave 68822 308-872-2475
Ken Kujath, prin. Fax 872-6296
Broken Bow MS 200/6-8
322 N 9th Ave 68822 308-872-6441
Ken Kujath, prin. Fax 872-2528

Bruning, Thayer, Pop. 279
Bruning-Davenport USD
Supt. — See Davenport
Bruning-Davenport HS 50/9-12
PO Box 70 68322 402-353-4685
Patrick Moore, prin. Fax 353-4445

Burwell, Garfield, Pop. 1,207
Burwell SD 400/PK-12
PO Box 670 68823 308-346-4150
Daniel Bird, supt. Fax 346-5430
www.burwellpublicschools.org/
Burwell JSHS 200/7-12
PO Box 670 68823 308-346-4150
David Owen, prin. Fax 346-5430

Cairo, Hall, Pop. 780
Centura SD 500/PK-12
PO Box 430 68824 308-485-4258
Julie Otero, supt. Fax 485-4780
www.centura.k12.ne.us/
Centura JSHS 200/7-12
PO Box 430 68824 308-485-4258
Tammy Holcomb, prin. Fax 485-4780

Callaway, Custer, Pop. 533
Callaway SD 200/K-12
101 N Needham St 68825 308-836-2272
Patrick Osmond, supt. Fax 836-2771
blog.callaway.k12.ne.us/school/
Callaway JSHS 100/7-12
101 N Needham St 68825 308-836-2272
Jane Brown, prin. Fax 836-2771

Cambridge, Furnas, Pop. 1,055
Cambridge SD 300/K-12
PO Box 100 69022 308-697-3322
Robert Gregory, supt. Fax 697-4880
cambridge.k12.ne.us/
Cambridge JSHS 200/7-12
PO Box 100 69022 308-697-3322
Michael Shoff, prin. Fax 697-4880

Cedar Bluffs, Saunders, Pop. 604
Cedar Bluffs SD 200/PK-12
PO Box 66 68015 402-628-2060
Harlan Ptomey, supt. Fax 628-2108
www.cedarbluffsschools.org/
Cedar Bluffs JSHS 100/7-12
PO Box 66 68015 402-628-2080
Harlan Ptomey, supt. Fax 628-2108

Cedar Rapids, Boone, Pop. 382
Cedar Rapids SD 100/K-12
408 W Dayton St 68627 308-358-0640
Joan Carraher, supt. Fax 358-0211
www.cedar.esu7.org/
Cedar Rapids JSHS 100/7-12
408 W Dayton St 68627 308-358-0640
Christopher Kuncl, prin. Fax 358-0211

Central City, Merrick, Pop. 2,899
Central City SD 700/PK-12
PO Box 57 68826 308-946-3055
Candace Conradt, supt. Fax 946-3149
centralcityschoolsne.org/
Central City HS 200/9-12
PO Box 57 68826 308-946-3086
Shawn McDiffett, prin. Fax 946-2954
Central City MS 200/5-8
PO Box 57 68826 308-946-3056
Darron Arlt, prin. Fax 946-2124

Nebraska Christian S 200/PK-12
1847 Inskip Ave 68826 308-946-3836
Joshua Cumpston, admin. Fax 946-3837

Chadron, Dawes, Pop. 5,665
Chadron SD 600/K-12
602 E 10th St 69337 308-432-0700
Dr. Caroline Winchester, supt. Fax 432-0702
www.chadronschools.org/
Chadron HS 300/9-12
901 Cedar St 69337 308-432-0707
Jerry Mack, prin. Fax 432-0723
Chadron MS 200/5-8
551 E 6th St 69337 308-432-0708
Nichlas Dressel, prin. Fax 432-0720

Pine Ridge Job Corps
Supt. — None
Pine Ridge Job Corps Vo/Tech
15710 Highway 385 69337 308-432-3316
Brian Kizer, prin. Fax 432-4145

Chadron State College Post-Sec.
1000 Main St 69337 308-432-6000

Chambers, Holt, Pop. 268
Chambers SD 100/K-12
PO Box 218 68725 402-482-5233
Gary Klahn, supt. Fax 482-5234
chambers.esu8.org/
Chambers JSHS 100/7-12
PO Box 218 68725 402-482-5233
Justin Frederick, prin. Fax 482-5234

Chappell, Deuel, Pop. 921
Creek Valley SD 300/K-12
PO Box 608 69129 308-874-2911
Ted Classen, supt. Fax 874-2602
creekvalleystorm.com/
Creek Valley HS 100/9-12
PO Box 608 69129 308-874-3310
Patrick Ningen, prin. Fax 874-2604
Other Schools – See Lodgepole

Clarks, Merrick, Pop. 363
High Plains Community SD
Supt. — See Polk
High Plains MS 100/6-8
PO Box 205 68628 308-548-2216
Karyee LeSuer, prin. Fax 548-2120

Clarkson, Colfax, Pop. 655
Clarkson SD 100/K-12
PO Box 140 68629 402-892-3454
Rich Lemburg, supt. Fax 892-3455
sites.esu7.org/clarkson/
Clarkson S 100/K-12
PO Box 140 68629 402-892-3454
Rich Lemburg, prin. Fax 892-3455

Cody, Cherry, Pop. 150
Cody-Kilgore SD 100/K-12
PO Box 216 69211 402-823-4190
Clarence Chessmore, supt. Fax 823-4275
www.esu17.org/~codyhtml/
Cody-Kilgore JSHS 100/7-12
PO Box 216 69211 402-823-4190
Clarence Chessmore, prin. Fax 823-4275

Coleridge, Cedar, Pop. 470
Coleridge Community SD 100/K-12
PO Box 37 68727 402-283-4844
Randall Klooz, supt. Fax 283-4230
coleridge.esu1.org/
Coleridge JSHS 50/9-12
PO Box 37 68727 402-283-4844
Adam Zellmer, admin. Fax 283-4230

Laurel-Concord SD
Supt. — See Laurel
Laurel-Concord MS 5-8
203 S Main St 68727 402-283-4844
Stephanie Petersen, prin. Fax 283-4230

Columbus, Platte, Pop. 21,922
Columbus SD 3,600/K-12
PO Box 947 68602 402-563-7000
Dr. Troy Loeffelholz, supt. Fax 563-7005
www.columbuspublicschools.org
Columbus HS 1,100/9-12
2200 26th St 68601 402-563-7050
Steve Woodside, prin. Fax 563-7058
Columbus MS 800/6-8
2410 16th St 68601 402-563-7060
Douglas Kluth, prin. Fax 563-7068

Lakeview Community SD 600/K-12
3744 83rd St 68601 402-563-2345
Russ Freeman, supt. Fax 564-5209
www.lakeview.esu7.org/
Lakeview JSHS 300/7-12
3744 83rd St 68601 402-563-2345
Steve Borer, prin. Fax 564-5209

Central Community College Post-Sec.
PO Box 1027 68602 402-564-7132
Scotus Central Catholic JSHS 400/7-12
1554 18th Ave 68601 402-564-7165
Wayne Morfeld, prin. Fax 564-6004

Cook, Johnson, Pop. 316
Johnson County Central SD
Supt. — See Tecumseh
Johnson County Central MS 100/6-8
PO Box 255 68329 402-864-4181
Rich Bacon, prin. Fax 864-2074

Cozad, Dawson, Pop. 3,959
Cozad Community SD 1,000/PK-12
1910 Meridian Ave 69130 308-784-2745
John Grinde, supt. Fax 784-2784
www.cozadschools.org
Cozad Alternative Ed Center Alt
1910 Meridian Ave 69130 308-784-2745
William Beckenhauer, prin. Fax 784-2784
Cozad HS 300/9-12
1710 Meridian Ave 69130 308-784-2744
William Beckenhauer, prin. Fax 784-2728
Cozad MS 200/6-8
1810 Meridian Ave 69130 308-784-2746
Brian Regelin, prin. Fax 784-2606

Crawford, Dawes, Pop. 968
Crawford SD 200/PK-12
908 5th St 69339 308-665-1537
Dick Lesher, supt. Fax 665-1909
www.cpsrams.org/
Crawford JSHS 100/7-12
908 5th St 69339 308-665-1531
Liz Baker, prin. Fax 665-1483

Creighton, Knox, Pop. 1,135
Creighton SD 300/K-12
PO Box 10 68729 402-358-3663
Jeff Jensen, supt. Fax 358-3804
creighton.esu1.org/
Creighton Community JSHS 200/4-12
PO Box 10 68729 402-358-3663
Brent Harrill, prin. Fax 358-3804

Crete, Saline, Pop. 6,858
Crete SD 1,600/K-12
920 Linden Ave 68333 402-826-5855
Kyle McGowan, supt. Fax 826-5120
www.creteschools.com
Crete HS 500/9-12
1500 E 15th St 68333 402-826-5811
Tim Conway, prin. Fax 826-2701
Crete MS 500/5-8
1700 Glenwood Ave 68333 402-826-5844
Steve Teget, prin. Fax 826-7789

Doane College Post-Sec.
1014 Boswell Ave 68333 402-826-2161

Crofton, Knox, Pop. 722
Crofton Community SD 300/K-12
PO Box 429 68730 402-388-2440
Randall Anderson, supt. Fax 388-4265
www.croftonschools.com/
Crofton JSHS 200/7-12
PO Box 429 68730 402-388-2440
Todd Strom, prin. Fax 388-4265

Curtis, Frontier, Pop. 926
Medicine Valley SD 200/K-12
PO Box 9 69025 308-367-4106
Alan Garey, supt. Fax 367-4108
www.mvraiders.org/
Medicine Valley JSHS 100/7-12
PO Box 9 69025 308-367-4106
Steven Gleisberg, prin. Fax 367-4108

University of Nebraska NE Coll of Tech Post-Sec.
404 E 7th St 69025 308-367-4124

Dalton, Cheyenne, Pop. 312
Leyton SD 200/K-12
PO Box 297 69131 308-377-2303
Fax 377-2304
www.leytonwarriors.org
Leyton HS 100/9-12
PO Box 297 69131 308-377-2303
James McGown, prin. Fax 377-2304

Davenport, Thayer, Pop. 289
Bruning-Davenport USD 200/PK-12
PO Box 190 68335 402-364-2225
Trudy Clark, supt. Fax 364-2477
www.bruningdavenport.org/
Bruning-Davenport MS 50/5-8
PO Box 190 68335 402-364-2225
Trudy Clark, prin. Fax 364-2477
Other Schools – See Bruning

David City, Butler, Pop. 2,884
David City SD 700/PK-12
750 D St 68632 402-367-4590
Jerry Phillips, supt. Fax 367-3479
www.davidcitypublicschools.org/
David City JSHS 300/7-12
750 D St 68632 402-367-3187
Bill Lentz, prin. Fax 367-3479

Aquinas HS 200/6-12
PO Box 149 68632 402-367-3175
David McMahon, prin. Fax 367-3176

Daykin, Jefferson, Pop. 166
Meridian SD 200/K-12
PO Box 190 68338 402-446-7265
Russ Gade, supt. Fax 446-7246
www.meridianmustangs.org
Meridian JSHS 100/7-12
PO Box 190 68338 402-446-7265
Tammi Mans, prin. Fax 446-7246

Deshler, Thayer, Pop. 745
Deshler SD 200/K-12
PO Box 547 68340 402-365-7272
Dr. Al Meier, supt. Fax 365-7560
www.deshlerpublicschools.org
Deshler JSHS 100/7-12
PO Box 547 68340 402-365-7272
Jack Waite, prin. Fax 365-7560

De Witt, Saline, Pop. 509
Tri County SD 400/K-12
72520 Highway 103 68341 402-683-2037
Russell Finken, supt. Fax 683-2116
www.tricountyschools.org
Tri County JSHS 200/7-12
72520 Highway 103 68341 402-683-2015
Matthew Uher, prin. Fax 683-2116

Doniphan, Hall, Pop. 824
Doniphan-Trumbull SD 500/K-12
PO Box 300 68832 402-845-2282
Kirk Russell, supt. Fax 845-6688
www.dtcardinals.org
Doniphan-Trumbull JSHS 200/7-12
PO Box 300 68832 402-845-6531
Phillip Picquet, prin. Fax 845-6688

Dorchester, Saline, Pop. 580
Dorchester SD 200/K-12
PO Box 7 68343 402-946-2781
Mitch Kubicek, supt. Fax 946-6271
www.dorchesterschool.org
Dorchester JSHS 100/7-12
PO Box 7 68343 402-946-2781
Duane Dohmon, prin. Fax 946-6271

Dunning, Blaine, Pop. 103
Sandhills SD 100/K-12
PO Box 29 68833 308-538-2224
Dale Hafer, supt. Fax 538-2228
blog.sandhills.k12.ne.us/
Dunning JSHS 100/7-12
PO Box 29 68833 308-538-2224
Dale Hafer, prin. Fax 538-2228

Elba, Howard, Pop. 212
Elba SD 100/PK-12
PO Box 100 68835 308-863-2228
Mikal Shalikow, supt. Fax 863-2329
www.elba.k12.ne.us
Elba JSHS 100/7-12
PO Box 100 68835 308-863-2228
Mikal Shalikow, supt. Fax 863-2329

Elgin, Antelope, Pop. 656
Elgin SD 100/K-12
PO Box 399 68636 402-843-2455
Daniel Polk, supt. Fax 843-2475
elgineagles.org/
Elgin HS 50/9-12
PO Box 399 68636 402-843-2457
Adam Patrick, prin. Fax 843-2475

Pope John XXIII Central Catholic HS 100/7-12
PO Box 179 68636 402-843-5325
Betty Getzfred, prin. Fax 843-2297

Elkhorn, Douglas, Pop. 8,192
Elkhorn SD 4,700/PK-12
20650 Glenn St 68022 402-289-2579
Steve Baker, supt. Fax 289-2585
www.elkhornweb.org/
Elkhorn HS 800/9-12
1401 Veterans Dr 68022 402-289-4239
Dan Radicia, prin. Fax 289-4383
Elkhorn MS 500/6-8
3200 N 207th Plz 68022 402-289-2428
Michael Tomjack, prin. Fax 289-1639
Elkhorn Valley View MS 6-8
1313 S 208th St 68022 402-289-0362
Chad Soupir, prin.
Other Schools – See Omaha

Mt. Michael Benedictine HS 200/9-12
22520 Mount Michael Rd 68022 402-289-2541
Dr. David Peters, head sch Fax 289-4539

Elm Creek, Buffalo, Pop. 896
Elm Creek SD 300/K-12
PO Box 490 68836 308-856-4300
Dean Tickle, supt. Fax 856-4907
www.elmcreek.k12.ne.us/
Elm Creek JSHS 200/7-12
PO Box 490 68836 308-856-4300
Cynthia Baum, prin. Fax 856-4907

Elwood, Gosper, Pop. 693
Elwood SD 200/K-12
PO Box 107 68937 308-785-2491
Richard Einspahr, supt. Fax 785-2322
elwood.k12.ne.us
Elwood JSHS 100/7-12
PO Box 107 68937 308-785-2491
Kyle Hemmerling, prin. Fax 785-2322

Emerson, Dakota, Pop. 834
Emerson-Hubbard SD 300/K-12
PO Box 9 68733 402-695-2621
David Jones, supt. Fax 695-2622
emersonhubbardschools.org/
Emerson-Hubbard JSHS 100/7-12
PO Box 9 68733 402-695-2636
Mark Koch, prin. Fax 695-2637

Eustis, Frontier, Pop. 399
Eustis-Farnham SD 200/K-12
PO Box 9 69028 308-486-3991
Steve Sampy, supt. Fax 486-5350
www.efknights.org
Eustis-Farnham HS 100/7-12
PO Box 9 69028 308-486-3991
Paul Pistulka, prin. Fax 486-5659

Ewing, Holt, Pop. 385
Ewing SD 100/K-12
PO Box 98 68735 402-626-7235
Ted Hillman, supt. Fax 626-7236
ewing.ne.schoolwebpages.com
Ewing JSHS 100/7-12
PO Box 98 68735 402-626-7235
Greg Appleby, prin. Fax 626-7236

Exeter, Fillmore, Pop. 589
Exeter-Milligan SD 200/PK-12
PO Box 139 68351 402-266-5911
Paul Sheffield, supt. Fax 266-4811
www.emwolves.org/
Exeter-Milligan JSHS 100/7-12
PO Box 139 68351 402-266-5911
Lindley Schlueter, prin. Fax 266-4811

Fairbury, Jefferson, Pop. 3,893
Fairbury SD 1,000/PK-12
703 K St 68352 402-729-6104
Frederick Helmink, supt. Fax 729-6392
www.fairburyjeffs.org/
Fairbury JSHS 400/7-12
1501 9th St 68352 402-729-6116
Jeff Vetter, prin. Fax 729-6275

Fairfield, Clay, Pop. 385
South Central Nebraska Unified SD 700/PK-12
30671 Highway 14 68938 402-726-2151
Randall Gilson, supt. Fax 726-2208
southcentralusd.us/
Sandy Creek JSHS 200/7-12
30671 Highway 14 68938 402-726-2151
Jason Searle, prin. Fax 726-2208
Other Schools – See Nelson

Fairmont, Fillmore, Pop. 560
Fillmore Central SD
Supt. — See Geneva
Fillmore Central MS 100/5-8
PO Box 157 68354 402-268-3411
Steven Adkisson, prin. Fax 268-3491

Falls City, Richardson, Pop. 4,224
Falls City SD 900/PK-12
PO Box 129 68355 402-245-2825
Dr. Tim Heckenlively, supt. Fax 245-2022
www.fctigers.org/
Falls City HS 300/9-12
1400 Fulton St 68355 402-245-2116
Gale Dunkhas, prin. Fax 245-5050
Falls City MS 200/6-8
PO Box 129 68355 402-245-3455
Rick Johnson, prin. Fax 245-2022

Sacred Heart S 200/K-12
1820 Fulton St 68355 402-245-4151
Doug Goltz, prin. Fax 245-5217

Firth, Lancaster, Pop. 580
Norris SD 160 2,100/PK-12
25211 S 68th St 68358 402-791-0000
Dr. John Skretta, supt. Fax 791-0025
www.norris160.org
Norris HS 600/9-12
25211 S 68th St 68358 402-791-0010
Ryan Ruhl, prin. Fax 791-0027
Norris MS 600/5-8
25211 S 68th St 68358 402-791-0020
MaryJo Rupert, prin. Fax 791-0029

Fort Calhoun, Washington, Pop. 895
Fort Calhoun SD 600/K-12
PO Box 430 68023 402-468-5596
Donald Johnson, supt. Fax 468-5593
www.fortcalhounschools.org/
Fort Calhoun JSHS 300/7-12
PO Box 430 68023 402-468-5591
Jerry Green, prin. Fax 468-5593

Franklin, Franklin, Pop. 993
Franklin SD 300/K-12
1001 M St 68939 308-425-6283
Ken Schroeder, supt. Fax 425-6553
franklin.k12.ne.us
Franklin JSHS 200/7-12
1001 M St 68939 308-425-6283
Ken Schroeder, prin. Fax 425-6553

Fremont, Dodge, Pop. 26,088
Fremont SD 4,000/PK-12
130 E 9th St 68025 402-727-3000
Dr. Stephen Sexton, supt. Fax 727-3002
www.fpsweb.org

Fremont HS | 1,400/9-12
1750 N Lincoln Ave 68025 | 402-727-3050
Chuck Story, prin. | Fax 727-3033
Fremont Learning Center | 100/Alt
130 E 9th St 68025 | 402-727-3180
Lea Adler, lead tchr. | Fax 727-3085
Fremont MS | 600/7-8
540 Johnson Rd 68025 | 402-727-3100
Gale Hamilton, prin. | Fax 727-3963

Archbishop Bergan JSHS | 200/6-12
545 E 4th St 68025 | 402-721-9683
Ron Beacom, prin. | Fax 721-5366
Midland University | Post-Sec.
900 N Clarkson St 68025 | 402-721-5408

Friend, Saline, Pop. 1,022
Friend SD | 300/K-12
PO Box 67 68359 | 402-947-2781
Michael Moody, supt. | Fax 947-2026
www.friend.esu6.org/
Friend JSHS | 200/7-12
PO Box 67 68359 | 402-947-2781
Ben Dempsey, prin. | Fax 947-2026

Fullerton, Nance, Pop. 1,303
Fullerton SD | 300/K-12
PO Box 520 68638 | 308-536-2431
Jeffrey Anderson, supt. | Fax 536-2432
Fullerton HS | 100/9-12
PO Box 520 68638 | 308-536-2431
Pat Larsen, prin. | Fax 536-2432

Geneva, Fillmore, Pop. 2,199
Fillmore Central SD | 500/K-12
1410 L St 68361 | 402-759-4955
Mark Norvell, supt. | Fax 759-4038
www.fcps.esu6.org/
Fillmore Central HS | 200/9-12
1410 L St 68361 | 402-759-3141
James Rose, prin. | Fax 759-4038
Other Schools – See Fairmont

Genoa, Nance, Pop. 992
Twin River SD | 500/K-12
PO Box 640 68640 | 402-993-2274
Donald Graff, supt. | Fax 993-7718
www.esu7.org/~trweb/
Twin River JSHS | 200/7-12
PO Box 640 68640 | 402-993-2911
Terry Gray, prin. | Fax 993-7718

Gering, Scotts Bluff, Pop. 8,397
Gering SD | 2,000/PK-12
1800 8th St 69341 | 308-436-3125
Don Hague, supt. | Fax 436-4301
www.geringschools.net
Gering Freshman Academy | 9-9
800 Q St 69341 | 308-436-4255
Kraig Weyrich, prin.
Gering JHS | 300/7-8
800 Q St 69341 | 308-436-3123
Dora Olivares, prin. | Fax 436-6010
Gering SHS | 500/10-12
1500 U St 69341 | 308-436-3121
Eldon Hubbard, prin. | Fax 436-4214

Gibbon, Buffalo, Pop. 1,809
Gibbon SD | 600/K-12
PO Box 790 68840 | 308-468-6555
Larry Witt, supt. | Fax 468-5164
www.gibbonpublic.org
Gibbon JSHS | 300/7-12
PO Box 790 68840 | 308-468-5721
Loreda Miller, prin. | Fax 468-5164

Giltner, Hamilton, Pop. 348
Giltner SD | 200/K-12
PO Box 160 68841 | 402-849-2238
Larry Lambert, supt. | Fax 849-2440
www.giltner.k12.ne.us/
Giltner JSHS | 100/7-12
PO Box 160 68841 | 402-849-2238
Kurt Polt, prin. | Fax 849-2440

Gordon, Sheridan, Pop. 1,571
Gordon-Rushville SD | 700/PK-12
PO Box 530 69343 | 308-282-1322
Merrell Nelsen, supt. | Fax 282-2207
www.grmustangs.org
Gordon-Rushville HS | 200/9-12
PO Box 530 69343 | 308-282-1322
Lori Liggett, prin. | Fax 282-2207
Other Schools – See Rushville

Gothenburg, Dawson, Pop. 3,547
Gothenburg SD | 900/K-12
1322 Avenue I 69138 | 308-537-3651
Michael Teahon, supt. | Fax 537-3965
gothenburg.k12.ne.us
Gothenburg JSHS | 400/7-12
1322 Avenue I 69138 | 308-537-3651
Randy Evans, prin. | Fax 537-3965

Grand Island, Hall, Pop. 47,867
Grand Island SD | 9,200/PK-12
PO Box 4904 68802 | 308-385-5900
Robert Winter Ed.D., supt. | Fax 385-5949
www.gips.org
Barr MS | 700/6-8
602 W Stolley Park Rd 68801 | 308-385-5875
Brian Kort, prin. | Fax 385-5880
Grand Island HS | 2,100/9-12
2124 N Lafayette Ave 68803 | 308-385-5950
Jeff Gilbertson, prin. | Fax 385-5966
Success Academy | Alt
1912 N Lafayette Ave 68803 | 308-385-5885
Kenneth Defrank, dir. | Fax 385-5608
Walnut MS | 800/6-8
1600 N Custer Ave 68803 | 308-385-5990
Rod Foley, prin. | Fax 385-5992
Westridge MS | 400/6-8
4111 W 13th St 68803 | 308-385-5886
Brad Wolfe, prin. | Fax 385-5003

Northwest SD | 1,300/K-12
2710 N North Rd 68803 | 308-385-6398
Matthew Fisher, supt. | Fax 385-6393
www.ginorthwest.org/
Northwest HS | 700/9-12
2710 N North Rd 68803 | 308-385-6394
Tim Krupicka, prin. | Fax 385-6393

Central Catholic MSHS | 300/6-12
1200 Ruby Ave 68803 | 308-384-2440
John Golka, prin. | Fax 389-3274
Central Community College | Post-Sec.
PO Box 4903 68802 | 308-398-4222
Heartland Lutheran HS | 100/9-12
3900 W Husker Hwy 68803 | 308-385-3900
Rev. Kurt Busskohl, prin. | Fax 381-7415
Joseph's College of Beauty | Post-Sec.
305 W 3rd St 68801 | 308-381-8848

Grant, Perkins, Pop. 1,163
Perkins County SD | 400/K-12
PO Box 829 69140 | 308-352-4735
Tobin Buchanan, supt. | Fax 352-4769
www.pcs.k12.ne.us/
Perkins County HS | 100/9-12
PO Box 829 69140 | 308-352-4735
Dean Friedel, prin. | Fax 352-4769
Other Schools – See Madrid

Perkins County Christian S | 50/K-10
PO Box 322 69140 | 308-352-8309
Jarret Malmkar, pres. | Fax 352-4505

Greeley, Greeley, Pop. 461
Greeley-Wolbach SD | 100/PK-12
PO Box 160 68842 | 308-428-3145
Amy Malander, supt. | Fax 428-5395
greeley-wolbach.k12.ne.us
Greeley-Wolbach JSHS | 100/7-12
PO Box 160 68842 | 308-428-3145
Todd Beck, prin. | Fax 428-5395

Gretna, Sarpy, Pop. 4,403
Gretna SD | 3,100/PK-12
11717 S 216th St 68028 | 402-332-3265
Dr. Kevin Riley, supt. | Fax 332-5833
www.gretnadragons.org
Gretna HS | 700/9-12
11717 S 216th St 68028 | 402-332-3936
Roger Miller, prin. | Fax 332-4119
Gretna MS | 700/6-8
11717 S 216th St 68028 | 402-332-3048
Harvey Birky, prin. | Fax 332-2931

Hampton, Hamilton, Pop. 420
Hampton SD | 200/K-12
458 5th St 68843 | 402-725-3117
Holly Herzberg, supt. | Fax 725-3334
www.hampton.k12.ne.us/
Hampton JSHS | 100/7-12
458 5th St 68843 | 402-725-3116
Kyle Gunderson, prin. | Fax 725-3334

Harrisburg, Banner, Pop. 96
Banner County SD | 200/K-12
PO Box 5 69345 | 308-436-5263
Lana Sides, supt. | Fax 436-5252
www.bannercountyschool.org
Banner County JSHS | 100/7-12
PO Box 5 69345 | 308-436-5263
Heath Johnson, prin. | Fax 436-5252

Harrison, Sioux, Pop. 247
Sioux County SD | 100/K-12
PO Box 38 69346 | 308-668-2415
Brett Gies, supt. | Fax 668-2260
www.siouxcountyschools.org/
Sioux County HS | 50/9-12
PO Box 38 69346 | 308-668-2415
Barry Swisher, prin. | Fax 668-2260

Hartington, Cedar, Pop. 1,550
Hartington SD | 300/K-12
PO Box 75 68739 | 402-254-3947
Randall Anderson, supt. | Fax 254-3945
hartington.esu1.org/
Hartington JSHS | 100/7-12
PO Box 75 68739 | 402-254-3947
Russell Flamig, prin. | Fax 254-3945

Cedar Catholic JSHS | 200/7-12
PO Box 15 68739 | 402-254-3906
Terry Kathol, prin. | Fax 254-3976

Harvard, Clay, Pop. 1,002
Harvard SD | 300/K-12
PO Box 100 68944 | 402-772-2171
Michael Derr, supt. | Fax 772-2204
Harvard JSHS | 100/7-12
PO Box 100 68944 | 402-772-2171
Brent Williamson, prin. | Fax 772-2204

Hastings, Adams, Pop. 24,622
Adams Central SD | 800/K-12
PO Box 1088 68902 | 402-463-3285
Shawn Scott, supt. | Fax 463-6344
adamscentral.us
Adams Central JSHS | 500/7-12
PO Box 1088 68902 | 402-463-3285
David Barrett, prin. | Fax 463-6344

Hastings SD | 3,500/PK-12
1924 W A St 68901 | 402-461-7500
Craig Kautz, supt. | Fax 461-7509
www.hastingspublicschools.org/
Hastings HS | 900/9-12
1100 W 14th St 68901 | 402-461-7550
Jay Opperman, prin. | Fax 461-7535
Hastings MS | 700/6-8
201 N Marian Rd 68901 | 402-461-7520
David Essink, prin. | Fax 461-7650

Central Community College | Post-Sec.
PO Box 1024 68902 | 402-463-9811
Hastings College | Post-Sec.
PO Box 269 68902 | 402-463-2402
Joseph's College of Beauty | Post-Sec.
828 W 2nd St 68901 | 402-463-1357
Mary Lanning Healthcare Radiology Sch | Post-Sec.
715 N Saint Joseph Ave 68901 | 402-461-5177
St. Cecilia MSHS | 300/6-12
521 N Kansas Ave 68901 | 402-462-2105
Rev. Lee Jirovsky, prin. | Fax 462-2106

Hayes Center, Hayes, Pop. 214
Hayes Center SD | 100/K-12
PO Box 8 69032 | 308-286-5600
Ron Howard, supt. | Fax 286-5629
www.hccardinals.org
Hayes Center JSHS | 100/7-12
PO Box 8 69032 | 308-286-5600
Ron Howard, prin. | Fax 286-5629

Hay Springs, Sheridan, Pop. 560
Hay Springs SD | 100/PK-12
PO Box 280 69347 | 308-638-4434
Steven Pummel, supt. | Fax 638-7500
www.hshawks.com/
Hay Springs HS | 50/9-12
PO Box 280 69347 | 308-638-4434
Steve Pummel, prin. | Fax 638-7500
Hay Springs MS | 50/6-8
PO Box 280 69347 | 308-638-4434
Steve Pummel, prin. | Fax 638-7500

Hebron, Thayer, Pop. 1,566
Thayer Central Community SD | 400/K-12
PO Box 9 68370 | 402-768-6117
Drew Harris, supt. | Fax 768-6110
www.thayercentral.org/
Thayer Central HS | 200/7-12
PO Box 9 68370 | 402-768-6117
Tom Kiburz, prin. | Fax 768-6110

Hemingford, Box Butte, Pop. 793
Hemingford SD | 400/PK-12
PO Box 217 69348 | 308-487-3328
Casper Ningen, supt. | Fax 487-5215
www.hemingfordschools.org/
Hemingford JSHS | 200/7-12
PO Box 217 69348 | 308-487-3328
Peggy Foster, prin. | Fax 487-5215

Henderson, York, Pop. 988
Heartland Community SD | 300/K-12
1501 Front St 68371 | 402-723-4434
Brad Best, supt. | Fax 723-4431
www.heartlandschools.org/
Heartland Community JSHS | 200/7-12
1501 Front St 68371 | 402-723-4434
Tim Carr, prin. | Fax 723-4431

Hershey, Lincoln, Pop. 650
Hershey SD | 500/PK-12
PO Box 369 69143 | 308-368-5574
Dr. Michael Cunning, supt. | Fax 368-5570
www.hpspanthers.org
Hershey JSHS | 200/7-12
PO Box 369 69143 | 308-368-5573
Michael Troxel, prin. | Fax 368-5571

Hildreth, Franklin, Pop. 376
Wilcox-Hildreth SD
Supt. — See Wilcox
Wilcox-Hildreth MS | 100/6-8
PO Box 157 68947 | 308-938-3825
Steven Dennis, prin. | Fax 938-5335

Holdrege, Phelps, Pop. 5,459
Holdrege SD | 1,100/K-12
PO Box 2002 68949 | 308-995-8663
Todd Hilyard, supt. | Fax 995-6956
www.thedusters.org/
Holdrege HS | 400/9-12
PO Box 2002 68949 | 308-995-6558
Robert Drews, prin. | Fax 995-8662
Holdrege MS | 300/5-8
PO Box 2002 68949 | 308-995-5421
Russell Baker, prin. | Fax 995-4970

Homer, Dakota, Pop. 542
Homer Community SD | 400/PK-12
PO Box 340 68030 | 402-698-2377
Cheryll Malcom, supt. | Fax 698-2379
homerweb.esu1.org/
Homer JSHS | 200/7-12
PO Box 340 68030 | 402-698-2377
Randy Pirner, prin. | Fax 698-2379

Hooper, Dodge, Pop. 820
Logan View SD | 300/K-12
2163 County Road G 68031 | 402-654-3317
Jeremy Klein, supt. | Fax 654-3699
www.loganview.org/
Logan View JSHS | 300/7-12
2163 County Road G 68031 | 402-654-3317
Rochelle Clausen, prin. | Fax 654-3699

Howells, Colfax, Pop. 557
Howells-Dodge SD | 200/K-12
PO Box 159 68641 | 402-986-1621
Thomas McMahon, supt. | Fax 986-1261
howellspublicschools.org/
Howells JSHS | 100/7-12
PO Box 159 68641 | 402-986-1621
Tom Ridder, prin. | Fax 986-1261

Humboldt, Richardson, Pop. 874
Humboldt Table Rock Steinauer SD 70 400/PK-12
810 Central Ave 68376 402-862-2235
Clinton Kimbrough, supt. Fax 862-3135
www.htrstitans.net
Humboldt Table Rock Steinauer HS 100/9-12
810 Central Ave 68376 402-862-2151
Lisa Othmer, prin. Fax 862-2152
Other Schools – See Table Rock

Humphrey, Platte, Pop. 758
Humphrey SD 67 300/PK-12
PO Box 278 68642 402-923-1230
Greg Sjuts, supt. Fax 923-1235
www.humphrey.esu7.org/
Humphrey JSHS 100/7-12
PO Box 278 68642 402-923-1230
Marty Moser, prin. Fax 923-1235

St. Francis S 200/K-12
300 S 7th St 68642 402-923-0818
Jennifer Dunn, prin. Fax 923-1590

Hyannis, Grant, Pop. 178
Hyannis Area SD 100/K-12
PO Box 286 69350 308-458-2202
Daniel Hoesing, supt. Fax 458-2227
disteleven.org/
Hyannis JSHS 100/7-12
PO Box 286 69350 308-458-2202
Bruce Parish, prin. Fax 458-2227

Imperial, Chase, Pop. 2,057
Chase County SD 600/K-12
PO Box 577 69033 308-882-4304
Dr. Brad Schoeppey, supt. Fax 882-5629
chasecountyschools.org
Chase County HS 300/7-12
PO Box 577 69033 308-882-4304
Michael Sorensen, prin. Fax 882-5629

Johnson, Nemaha, Pop. 325
Johnson-Brock SD 300/K-12
PO Box 186 68378 402-868-5235
Jeffrey Kochler, supt. Fax 868-4785
www.johnsonbrock.esu6.org/
Johnson JSHS 100/7-12
PO Box 186 68378 402-868-5235
Jacquelyn Kelsay, prin. Fax 868-4785

Kearney, Buffalo, Pop. 30,426
Kearney SD 5,100/PK-12
310 W 24th St 68845 308-698-8000
Dr. Brian Maher, supt. Fax 698-8001
www.kearneypublicschools.org/
Horizon MS 500/6-8
915 W 35th St 68845 308-698-8120
Kipp Petersen, prin. Fax 698-8143
Kearney HS 1,500/9-12
3610 6th Ave 68845 308-698-8060
Dr. Jay Dostal, prin. Fax 698-8061
Sunrise MS 500/6-8
4611 N Ave 68847 308-698-8150
Lance Fuller, prin. Fax 698-8152

Joseph's of Kearney Sch of Hair Design Post-Sec.
2213 Central Ave 68847 308-234-6594
Kearney Catholic HS 300/6-12
PO Box 1866 68848 308-234-2610
Terrence Torson, prin. Fax 234-4986
University of Nebraska at Kearney Post-Sec.
905 W 25th St 68849 308-865-8526

Kenesaw, Adams, Pop. 876
Kenesaw SD 300/K-12
PO Box 129 68956 402-752-3215
William Troshynski, supt. Fax 752-3579
www.kenesawschools.org/
Kenesaw JSHS 100/7-12
PO Box 129 68956 402-752-3215
Robby Thompson, prin. Fax 752-3579

Kimball, Kimball, Pop. 2,447
Kimball SD 500/PK-12
901 S Nadine St 69145 308-235-2188
Marshall Lewis, supt. Fax 235-3269
kimball.k12.ne.us/
Kimball JSHS 200/7-12
901 S Nadine St 69145 308-235-4861
Eugene Hanks, prin. Fax 235-4128

Laurel, Cedar, Pop. 959
Laurel-Concord SD 200/K-12
PO Box 8 68745 402-256-3133
Richard Patton, supt. Fax 256-9465
www.lccschool.org
Laurel-Concord HS 100/7-12
PO Box 8 68745 402-256-3731
Adam Zellmer, prin. Fax 256-9465
Other Schools – See Coleridge

La Vista, Sarpy, Pop. 15,366
Papillion-La Vista SD
Supt. — See Papillion
La Vista JHS 700/7-8
7900 Edgewood Blvd 68128 402-898-0436
Thomas Furby, prin. Fax 898-0442

Leigh, Colfax, Pop. 404
Leigh Community SD 100/K-12
PO Box 98 68643 402-487-3301
Dr. Michael Montgomery, supt. Fax 487-3341
www.esu7.org/~leiweb/
Leigh JSHS 100/7-12
PO Box 98 68643 402-487-2228
Jarred Royal, prin. Fax 487-2607

Lewellen, Garden, Pop. 223
Garden County SD
Supt. — See Oshkosh
Garden County JHS 50/5-8
504 W Hwy 26 69147 308-778-5561
Jason Spady, prin. Fax 778-5568

Lewiston, Pawnee, Pop. 68
Lewiston SD 200/K-12
306 Tiger Ave 68380 402-865-4675
Rick Kentfield, supt. Fax 865-4875
www.lewistonschool.org/
Lewiston JSHS 100/7-12
306 Tiger Ave 68380 402-865-4675
Fred Ivey, prin. Fax 865-4875

Lexington, Dawson, Pop. 10,140
Lexington SD 2,900/PK-12
PO Box 890 68850 308-324-4681
John Hakonson Ed.D., supt. Fax 324-2528
www.lexschools.org
Lexington HS 800/9-12
705 W 13th St 68850 308-324-4691
Kyle Hoehner, prin. Fax 324-7224
Lexington MS 600/6-8
1100 N Washington St 68850 308-324-2349
Scott West, prin. Fax 324-6612

Lincoln, Lancaster, Pop. 251,784
Lincoln SD 35,900/PK-12
PO Box 82889 68501 402-436-1000
Stephen Joel Ed.D., supt. Fax 436-1084
www.lps.org/
Bryan Community S 100/Alt
300 S 48th St 68510 402-436-1308
Mindy Roberts, prin. Fax 458-1381
Culler MS 400/6-8
5201 Vine St 68504 402-436-1210
Gary Czapla, prin. Fax 458-3210
Dawes MS 600/6-8
5130 Colfax Ave 68504 402-436-1211
Angela Zabawa, prin. Fax 458-3211
Goodrich MS 700/6-8
4600 Lewis Ave 68521 402-436-1213
Rachelle Conner, prin. Fax 458-3213
Irving MS 900/6-8
2745 S 22nd St 68502 402-436-1214
Hugh McDermott, prin. Fax 458-3214
Lefler MS 600/6-8
1100 S 48th St 68510 402-436-1215
Kelly Schrad, prin. Fax 458-3215
Lincoln East HS 1,500/9-12
1000 S 70th St 68510 402-436-1302
Susan Cassata, prin. Fax 436-1325
Lincoln HS 1,700/9-12
2229 J St 68510 402-436-1301
Dr. Michael Wortman, prin. Fax 458-1540
Lincoln Northeast HS 1,500/9-12
2635 N 63rd St 68507 402-436-1303
Kurt Glathar, prin. Fax 436-1345
Lincoln North Star HS 1,900/9-12
5801 N 33rd St 68504 402-436-1305
Vann Price, prin. Fax 436-1054
Lincoln Southeast HS 1,800/9-12
2930 S 37th St 68506 402-436-1304
Brent Toalson, prin. Fax 436-1357
Lincoln Southwest HS 1,900/9-12
7001 S 14th St 68512 402-436-1306
Rob Slauson, prin. Fax 436-1085
Lux MS 900/6-8
7800 High St 68506 402-436-1220
William Bucher, prin. Fax 458-3292
Mickle MS 800/6-8
2500 N 67th St 68507 402-436-1216
Gene Thompson, prin. Fax 458-3216
Park MS 700/6-8
855 S 8th St 68508 402-436-1212
Ryan Zabawa, prin. Fax 458-3212
Pound MS 700/6-8
4740 S 45th St 68516 402-436-1217
Dr. Christopher Deibler, prin. Fax 458-3217
Schoo MS 800/6-8
700 Penrose Dr 68521 402-436-1222
Bill Schulenberg, prin. Fax 458-3222
Scott MS 900/6-8
2200 Pine Lake Rd 68512 402-436-1218
Dave Knudsen, prin. Fax 458-3218

Bryan College of Health Science Post-Sec.
5035 Everett St 68506 402-481-3801
College of Hair Design Post-Sec.
304 S 11th St 68508 402-477-4040
College of Hair Design - East Post-Sec.
9000 Andermatt Dr 68526 402-477-4040
College View Academy 100/PK-12
5240 Calvert St 68506 402-483-1181
Joseph's College of Beauty Post-Sec.
2637 O St 68510 402-435-2333
Kaplan University Post-Sec.
1821 K St 68508 402-474-5315
Lincoln Christian S 600/PK-12
5801 S 84th St 68516 402-488-8888
Mark Wilson, supt. Fax 488-6617
Lincoln Lutheran MSHS 400/6-12
1100 N 56th St 68504 402-467-5404
Scott Ernstmeyer, dir. Fax 467-5405
Lincoln Pius X HS 1,100/9-12
6000 A St 68510 402-488-0931
Thomas Korta, prin. Fax 488-1061
Myotherapy Institute Post-Sec.
4001 Pioneer Woods Dr 68506 402-421-7410
Nebraska Wesleyan University Post-Sec.
5000 Saint Paul Ave 68504 800-541-3818
Parkview Christian S 200/PK-12
4400 N 1st St 68521 402-474-8309
Harold Scott, supt.
Southeast Community College Post-Sec.
8800 O St 68520 402-471-3333
Union College Post-Sec.
3800 S 48th St 68506 402-486-2600
University of Nebraska Post-Sec.
14th & R Sts 68588 402-472-7211

Lindsay, Platte, Pop. 253

Holy Family S 100/1-12
PO Box 158 68644 402-428-3455
Neely Moser, prin. Fax 428-3231

Litchfield, Sherman, Pop. 262
Litchfield SD 100/K-12
PO Box 167 68852 308-446-2244
Scott Maline, supt. Fax 446-2244
blog.litchfield.k12.ne.us
Litchfield JSHS 100/7-12
PO Box 167 68852 308-446-2244
Jeffrey Smith, prin. Fax 446-2244

Lodgepole, Cheyenne, Pop. 315
Creek Valley SD
Supt. — See Chappell
Creek Valley MS 100/5-8
PO Box 158 69149 308-483-5252
Katherine Urbanek, prin. Fax 483-5251

Loomis, Phelps, Pop. 377
Loomis SD 200/K-12
PO Box 250 68958 308-876-2111
Nathan Stineman, supt. Fax 876-2372
Loomis JSHS 100/7-12
PO Box 250 68958 308-876-2111
Nicole Hardwick, prin. Fax 876-2372

Louisville, Cass, Pop. 1,086
Louisville SD 500/K-12
PO Box 489 68037 402-234-3585
Gregory Shepard, supt. Fax 234-2141
www.lpslions.org
Louisville HS 200/9-12
PO Box 489 68037 402-234-3585
Brett Schwartz, prin. Fax 234-2141
Louisville MS 100/6-8
PO Box 489 68037 402-234-3585
Brett Schwartz, prin. Fax 234-2141

Loup City, Sherman, Pop. 1,023
Loup City SD 300/K-12
PO Box 628 68853 308-745-0120
Tom Hinrichs, supt. Fax 745-0130
www.loupcity.k12.ne.us/
Loup City HS 100/7-12
PO Box 628 68853 308-745-0548
Nicholas Hodge, prin. Fax 745-0130

Lynch, Boyd, Pop. 241
Lynch SD 100/K-12
PO Box 98 68746 402-569-2081
Ted Hillman, supt. Fax 569-2091
lynch.esu8.org/
Lynch JSHS 100/7-12
PO Box 98 68746 402-569-2081
Ted Hillman, prin. Fax 569-2091

Lyons, Burt, Pop. 845
Lyons-Decatur Northeast SD 300/PK-12
PO Box 526 68038 402-687-2363
Fred Hansen, supt. Fax 687-2472
www.lyonsdecaturschools.org/
Northeast JSHS 100/7-12
PO Box 526 68038 402-687-2349
Andrew Cronin, prin. Fax 687-2472

Mc Cook, Red Willow, Pop. 7,616
Mc Cook SD 1,500/PK-12
700 W 7th St 69001 308-345-2510
Grant Norgaard, supt. Fax 345-2511
www.mccookbison.org/
Mc Cook Alternative Education 50/Alt
N Highway 83 69001 308-345-5631
Jeff Gross, prin. Fax 345-6134
Mc Cook HS 500/9-12
600 W 7th St 69001 308-345-5422
Jerome Smith, prin. Fax 345-5477
Mc Cook JHS 300/6-8
800 W 7th St 69001 308-345-6940
Dennis Berry, prin. Fax 345-6941

Mid-Plains Community College Post-Sec.
1205 E 3rd St 69001 308-345-8100

Mc Cool Junction, York, Pop. 409
Mc Cool Junction SD 300/K-12
PO Box 278 68401 402-724-2231
Curtis Cogswell, supt. Fax 724-2232
www.mccool.esu6.org/
Mc Cool Junction JSHS 100/7-12
PO Box 278 68401 402-724-2231
Dade McDonald, prin. Fax 724-2232

Macy, Thurston, Pop. 1,021
UMO N HO N Nation SD 400/PK-12
PO Box 280 68039 402-837-5622
Tom Carlstrom, supt. Fax 837-5245
macyweb.esu1.org/
UMO N HO N Nation HS 100/9-12
PO Box 280 68039 402-837-5622
Broderick Steed, prin. Fax 837-5245
UMO N HO N Nation MS 100/6-8
PO Box 280 68039 402-837-5622
Stacie Hardy, prin. Fax 837-5245

Nebraska Indian Community College Post-Sec.
PO Box 428 68039 402-494-2311

Madison, Madison, Pop. 2,422
Madison SD 500/K-12
PO Box 450 68748 402-454-3336
Alan Ehlers, supt. Fax 454-2238
madison.esu8.org/
Madison HS 200/9-12
PO Box 450 68748 402-454-3336
Jim Crilly, prin. Fax 454-2238
Madison MS 100/6-8
PO Box 450 68748 402-454-3336
Jim Crilly, prin. Fax 454-2238

Madrid, Perkins, Pop. 231
Perkins County SD
Supt. — See Grant
Perkins County JHS 100/6-8
501 S Ford Ave 69150 308-326-4201
Terry Prante, prin. Fax 326-4231

Malcolm, Lancaster, Pop. 378
Malcolm SD 500/K-12
10004 NW 112th St 68402 402-796-2151
Ryan Terwilliger, supt. Fax 796-2178
www.malcolmschools.org
Malcolm JSHS 200/7-12
10002 NW 112th St 68402 402-796-2151
Greg Adams, prin. Fax 796-2189

Maxwell, Lincoln, Pop. 309
Maxwell SD 300/PK-12
PO Box 188 69151 308-582-4585
Dan Twarling, supt. Fax 582-4584
www.maxwell.k12.ne.us
Maxwell JSHS 100/7-12
PO Box 188 69151 308-582-4585
Aubrey Boucher, prin. Fax 582-4584

Maywood, Frontier, Pop. 257
Maywood SD 100/K-12
PO Box 46 69038 308-362-4223
Michael Williams, supt. Fax 362-4454
www.maywoodtigers.org
Maywood JSHS 100/7-12
PO Box 46 69038 308-362-4223
Michael Williams, prin. Fax 362-4454

Mead, Saunders, Pop. 567
Mead SD 200/K-12
PO Box 158 68041 402-624-2745
Dr. Dale Rawson, supt. Fax 624-2001
www.meadpublicschools.org/
Mead JSHS 100/7-12
PO Box 158 68041 402-624-3435
P.J. Quinn, prin. Fax 624-2069

Merna, Custer, Pop. 361
Anselmo-Merna SD 100/K-12
PO Box 68 68856 308-643-2224
Mike Davis, supt. Fax 643-2243
blog.anselmo-merna.k12.ne.us/anselmomerna/
Anselmo-Merna S 100/K-12
PO Box 68 68856 308-643-2224
Darrin Max, prin. Fax 643-2243

Milford, Seward, Pop. 2,066
Milford SD 700/PK-12
PO Box C 68405 402-761-3321
Kevin Wingard, supt. Fax 761-3322
www.milfordpublicschools.org/
Milford JSHS 300/7-12
PO Box C 68405 402-761-2525
Brandon Mowinkel, prin. Fax 761-2663

Southeast Community College Post-Sec.
600 State St 68405 402-761-2131

Minatare, Scotts Bluff, Pop. 808
Minatare SD 200/K-12
PO Box 425 69356 308-783-1232
Tim Cody, supt. Fax 783-2982
www.minatareschools.com/
Minatare JSHS 100/7-12
PO Box 425 69356 308-783-1733
Kyle Metzger, prin. Fax 783-2982

Minden, Kearney, Pop. 2,907
Minden SD 800/PK-12
PO Box 301 68959 308-832-2440
Melissa Wheelock, supt. Fax 832-2567
minden.k12.ne.us
Jones MS 300/4-8
PO Box 301 68959 308-832-2338
John Osgood, prin. Fax 832-3236
Minden HS 200/9-12
PO Box 301 68959 308-832-2254
Don Hosick, prin. Fax 832-1892
Minden Success Center 50/Alt
PO Box 301 68959 308-832-1992

Mitchell, Scotts Bluff, Pop. 1,691
Mitchell SD 700/K-12
1819 19th Ave 69357 308-623-1707
Kent Halley, supt. Fax 623-1330
www.mpstigers.com
Mitchell JSHS 300/7-12
1819 19th Ave 69357 308-623-1707
Heath Peters, prin. Fax 623-1330

Morrill, Scotts Bluff, Pop. 916
Morrill SD 400/PK-12
PO Box 486 69358 308-247-3414
Nicholas Schafer, supt. Fax 247-2196
www.morrillpublicschools.org
Morrill JSHS 200/7-12
PO Box 486 69358 308-247-2149
Kent Swearingen, prin. Fax 247-2196

Mullen, Hooker, Pop. 506
Mullen SD 200/K-12
PO Box 127 69152 308-546-2223
Jeffery Hoesing, supt. Fax 546-2209
Mullen JSHS 100/7-12
PO Box 127 69152 308-546-2223
Michael Kvanvig, prin. Fax 546-2209

Murdock, Cass, Pop. 236
Elmwood-Murdock SD 400/K-12
300 Wyoming St 68407 402-867-2341
Daniel Novak, supt. Fax 867-2009
www.elm.esu3.org/
Elmwood-Murdock JSHS 200/7-12
300 Wyoming St 68407 402-867-2341
Tim Allemang, prin. Fax 867-2009

Murray, Cass, Pop. 456
Conestoga SD 600/PK-12
PO Box 184 68409 402-235-2992
Beth Johnsen, supt. Fax 227-2992
www.conestogacougars.org/
Conestoga JSHS 300/7-12
PO Box 40 68409 402-235-2271
David Friedli, prin. Fax 235-2421
Other Schools – See Nehawka

Nebraska City, Otoe, Pop. 7,192
Nebraska City SD 1,400/PK-12
215 N 12th St 68410 402-873-6033
Dr. Jeffrey Edwards, supt. Fax 873-6030
www.nebcityps.org/education
Nebraska City HS 400/9-12
141 Steinhart Park Rd 68410 402-873-3360
Brian Hoover, prin. Fax 873-3831
Nebraska City MS 300/6-8
909 1st Corso 68410 402-873-5591
Craig Taylor, prin. Fax 873-5641

Lourdes Central S 200/6-12
412 2nd Ave 68410 402-873-6154
Rev. Mark Cyza, prin. Fax 873-3154
Nebraska School for Visually Handicapped Post-Sec.
PO Box 129 68410

Nehawka, Cass, Pop. 204
Conestoga SD
Supt. — See Murray
Conestoga Alternative S Alt
PO Box 187 68413 402-227-2935
Robin Frost, prin.

Neligh, Antelope, Pop. 1,591
Neligh-Oakdale SD 400/K-12
PO Box 149 68756 402-887-4166
Kim Lingenfelter, supt. Fax 887-5322
Neligh-Oakdale JSHS 200/7-12
PO Box 149 68756 402-887-4166
George Loofe, prin. Fax 887-5322

Nelson, Nuckolls, Pop. 480
South Central Nebraska Unified SD
Supt. — See Fairfield
Lawrence/Nelson JSHS 100/7-12
PO Box 368 68961 402-225-3371
Craig McLey, prin. Fax 225-5431

Newcastle, Dixon, Pop. 325
Newcastle SD 100/K-12
PO Box 187 68757 402-355-2231
Joseph Lefdal, supt. Fax 355-2635
newcastle.esu1.org/
Newcastle HS 50/9-12
PO Box 187 68757 402-355-2231
Joseph Lefdal, prin. Fax 355-2635
Newcastle MS 50/5-8
PO Box 187 68757 402-355-2231
Joseph Lefdal, prin. Fax 355-2635

Newman Grove, Madison, Pop. 715
Newman Grove SD 200/K-12
PO Box 370 68758 402-447-2721
Loren Pokorny, supt. Fax 447-2445
newman.esu8.org/
Newman Grove JSHS 100/7-12
PO Box 370 68758 402-447-6294
Beth Nelson, prin. Fax 447-2445

Niobrara, Knox, Pop. 360
Niobrara SD 100/K-12
PO Box 310 68760 402-857-3323
Margaret Sandoz, supt. Fax 857-3877
teacherweb.esu1.org/NiobraraPublicSchools/
Niobrara JSHS 100/5-12
PO Box 310 68760 402-857-3322
Angie Guenther, prin. Fax 857-3716

Santee SD 100/K-12
206 Frazier Ave E 68760 402-857-2741
Paul Sellon, supt. Fax 857-2743
santeeweb.esu1.org/
Santee HS 50/9-12
206 Frazier Ave E 68760 402-857-2741
Kevin Finkey, prin. Fax 857-2743

Norfolk, Madison, Pop. 23,882
Norfolk SD 3,900/PK-12
PO Box 139 68702 402-644-2500
Marlene Uhing Ed.D., supt. Fax 644-2506
www.norfolkpublicschools.org/
Alternatives for Success 50/Alt
PO Box 139 68702 402-844-3515
Fax 844-3515
Norfolk JHS 600/7-8
PO Box 139 68702 402-644-2516
Michael Hart, prin. Fax 644-2519
Norfolk SHS 1,200/9-12
PO Box 139 68702 402-644-2529
James Lake, prin. Fax 644-2538

Joseph's College of Beauty Post-Sec.
202 W Madison Ave 68701 402-371-3358
Lutheran HS Northeast 200/9-12
2010 N 37th St 68701 402-379-3040
Paul Leckband, prin. Fax 379-8340
Norfolk Catholic JSHS 300/7-12
2300 W Madison Ave 68701 402-371-2784
Jeff Bellar, prin. Fax 379-2929
Northeast Community College Post-Sec.
PO Box 469 68702 402-371-2020

North Bend, Dodge, Pop. 1,172
North Bend Central SD 500/K-12
PO Box 160 68649 402-652-3268
Dan Endorf, supt. Fax 652-8348
www.nbtigers.org/
North Bend Central JSHS 200/7-12
PO Box 160 68649 402-652-3268
Brenda Petersen, prin. Fax 652-8348

North Platte, Lincoln, Pop. 24,455
North Platte SD 4,200/PK-12
PO Box 1557 69103 308-535-7100
Marty Bassett, supt. Fax 535-5300
www.nppsd.org
Adams MS 700/6-8
1200 McDonald Rd 69101 308-535-7112
Jeff Steinbeck, prin. Fax 535-5309
Learning Center 50/Alt
1400 N Madison Ave 69101 308-535-5311
Mike Brownawell, prin. Fax 535-5311
Madison MS 200/6-8
1400 N Madison Ave 69101 308-535-7126
Danny McMurtry, prin. Fax 535-5303
North Platte HS 1,100/9-12
1220 W 2nd St 69101 308-535-7105
Mike Brownawell, prin. Fax 535-7111

Joseph's College of Beauty Post-Sec.
1620 E 4th St 69101 308-532-4664
Mid-Plains Community College Post-Sec.
601 W State Farm Rd 69101 308-535-3600
Mid-Plains Community College Post-Sec.
1101 Halligan Dr 69101 308-535-3600
St. Patrick HS 200/7-12
PO Box 970 69103 308-532-1874
Mark Skillstead, prin. Fax 532-8015

Oakland, Burt, Pop. 1,227
Oakland Craig SD 400/K-12
309 N Davis Ave 68045 402-685-5661
Joe Peitzmeier, supt. Fax 685-5697
web.ocknights.org
Oakland Craig HS 100/9-12
309 N Davis Ave 68045 402-685-5661
Rusty Droescher, prin. Fax 685-5697
Oakland Craig JHS 100/7-8
309 N Davis Ave 68045 402-685-5661
Rusty Droescher, prin. Fax 685-5697

Odell, Gage, Pop. 299
Diller-Odell SD 200/K-12
PO Box 188 68415 402-766-4171
Michael Meyerle, supt. Fax 766-4211
www.dillerodell.org/
Diller-Odell JSHS 100/7-12
PO Box 188 68415 402-766-4210
Christopher Prososki, prin. Fax 766-4211

Ogallala, Keith, Pop. 4,669
Ogallala SD 1,000/PK-12
205 E 6th St 69153 308-284-4060
Carl Dietz, supt. Fax 284-3981
www.opsd.org/
Ogallala HS 300/9-12
602 E G St 69153 308-284-4029
Troy Lurz, prin. Fax 284-3869
Ogallala MS 200/6-8
205 E 6th St 69153 308-284-4478
Traci Rezac, prin. Fax 284-8129

Omaha, Douglas, Pop. 399,005
Elkhorn SD
Supt. — See Elkhorn
Elkhorn Ridge MS 700/6-8
17880 Marcy St 68118 402-334-9302
Kevin Riggert, prin. Fax 334-9378
Elkhorn South HS 9-12
20303 Blue Sage Pkwy 68130 402-289-0616
Mark Kalvoda, prin. Fax 289-1523

Millard SD 21,900/PK-12
5606 S 147th St 68137 402-715-8200
Dr. Keith Lutz, supt. Fax 715-8409
www.mpsomaha.org
Andersen MS 800/6-8
15404 Adams St 68137 402-715-8440
Jeff Alfrey, prin. Fax 715-8410
Beadle MS 900/6-8
18201 Jefferson St 68135 402-715-6100
John Southworth, prin. Fax 715-6140
Horizon HS 100/Alt
5300 George B Lake Pkwy, 402-715-8470
Angie Craft, prin. Fax 715-6196
Kiewit MS 900/6-8
15650 Howard St 68118 402-715-1470
Heather Phipps, prin. Fax 715-1490
Millard Central MS 800/6-8
12801 L St 68137 402-715-8225
Beth Fink, prin. Fax 715-8574
Millard North HS 2,500/9-12
1010 S 144th St 68154 402-715-1365
Brian Begley, prin. Fax 715-1336
Millard North MS 800/6-8
2828 S 139th St 68144 402-715-1280
Scott Ingwerson, prin. Fax 715-1275
Millard South HS 2,000/9-12
14905 Q St 68137 402-715-8268
Curtis Case, prin. Fax 715-6160
Millard West HS 2,200/9-12
5710 S 176th Ave 68135 402-715-6000
Greg Tiemann, prin. Fax 715-6060
Russell MS 900/6-8
5304 S 172nd St 68135 402-715-8500
Mitch Mollring, prin. Fax 715-8368

Omaha SD 46,900/PK-12
3215 Cuming St 68131 402-557-2222
Virginia Moon, supt. Fax 557-2019
www.ops.org
Benson HS 1,500/9-12
5120 Maple St 68104 402-557-3000
Anita Harkins-Baldwin, prin. Fax 557-3039
Beveridge Magnet MS 800/7-8
1616 S 120th St 68144 402-557-4000
Dr. David Lavender, prin. Fax 557-4009
Blackburn HS A Alt
2606 Hamilton St 68131 402-344-3385
Fred Marisett, dir. Fax 344-3724

Blackburn HS B Alt
5141 F St 68117 402-898-1568
Fred Marisett, dir. Fax 344-3724
Bryan HS 1,800/9-12
4700 Giles Rd 68157 402-557-3100
Robert Aranda, prin. Fax 557-3139
Bryan MS 700/7-8
8210 S 42nd St 68147 402-557-4100
Darren Rasmussen, prin. Fax 557-4129
Buffet Magnet MS 700/5-8
14101 Larimore Ave 68164 402-561-6160
Dr. Ed Bonnett, prin. Fax 561-6170
Burke HS 2,200/9-12
12200 Burke Blvd 68154 402-557-3200
Dr. Deborah Frison, prin. Fax 557-3239
Career Center Vo/Tech
3230 Burt St 68131 402-557-3700
Timothy Hoffman, dir. Fax 557-2629
Central HS 2,500/9-12
124 N 20th St 68102 402-557-3300
Dr. Keith Bigsby, prin. Fax 557-3339
Davis MS 6-8
8050 N 129th Ave 68142 402-557-4502
Dan Bartels, prin. Fax 502-9108
Hale MS 300/7-8
6143 Whitmore St 68152 402-557-4200
Susan Colvin, prin. Fax 557-4229
King Science Magnet MS 400/5-8
3720 Florence Blvd 68110 402-557-3720
Steve Eubanks, prin. Fax 557-4459
Lewis & Clark MS 500/7-8
6901 Burt St 68132 402-557-4300
Dr. Lisa Sterba, prin. Fax 557-4309
Marrs Magnet MS 500/5-8
5619 S 19th St 68107 402-557-4400
Bryan Dunne, prin. Fax 557-4429
McMillan Magnet MS 700/7-8
3802 Redick Ave 68112 402-557-4500
Daniel Bartels, prin. Fax 557-4509
Monroe MS 500/7-8
5105 Bedford Ave 68104 402-557-4600
Boris Moore, prin. Fax 557-4609
Morton Magnet MS 700/5-8
4606 Terrace Dr 68134 402-557-4700
Matt Brandl, prin. Fax 557-4709
Norris MS 700/7-8
2235 S 46th St 68106 402-557-4800
Ruben Cano, prin. Fax 557-4809
Omaha North HS Magnet 2,000/9-12
4410 N 36th St 68111 402-557-3400
Gene Haynes, prin. Fax 557-3439
Omaha Northwest HS 1,200/9-12
8204 Crown Point Ave 68134 402-557-3500
Herman Colvin, prin. Fax 557-3539
Omaha South HS 2,000/9-12
4519 S 24th St 68107 402-557-3600
Cara Riggs, prin. Fax 557-3639
Parrish S Alt
4469 Farnam St 68131 402-554-8460
Dr. Bonnie Perry-Adams, prin. Fax 554-1639

Westside Community SD 6,000/PK-12
909 S 76th St 68114 402-390-2100
Dr. Blane McCann, supt. Fax 390-2120
www.westside66.org
Westside Career Center Vo/Tech
3534 S 108th St 68144 402-390-8214
Maria Neesman, admin. Fax 390-8212
Westside HS 1,900/9-12
8701 Pacific St 68114 402-343-2600
Maryanne Ricketts, prin. Fax 343-2608
Westside MS 900/7-8
8601 Arbor St 68124 402-390-6464
Russ Olsen, prin. Fax 390-6454

Alegent Health School of Radiologic Tech Post-Sec.
7500 Mercy Rd 68124 402-398-5527
Bishop Clarkson Memorial Hospital Post-Sec.
4350 Dewey Ave 68105 402-552-3203
Brownell-Talbot S 500/PK-12
400 N Happy Hollow Blvd 68132 402-556-3772
Dr. Sylvia Rodriguez Vargas, head sch Fax 553-2994
Capitol School of Hairstyling - West Post-Sec.
10803 John Galt Blvd 68137 402-333-3329
Clarkson College Post-Sec.
101 S 42nd St 68131 402-552-3100
College of Saint Mary Post-Sec.
7000 Mercy Rd 68106 402-399-2400
Concordia Lutheran JSHS 200/7-12
15656 Fort St 68116 402-445-4000
Matthew Korte, prin. Fax 965-9310
Creighton Preparatory S 1,000/9-12
7400 Western Ave 68114 402-393-1190
John Naatz, prin. Fax 343-1889
Creighton University Post-Sec.
2500 California Plz 68178 402-280-2700
Duchesne Academy 300/9-12
3601 Burt St 68131 402-558-3800
Laura Hickman, prin. Fax 558-0051
Grace University Post-Sec.
1311 S 9th St 68108 402-449-2800
Gross HS 400/9-12
7700 S 43rd St 68147 402-734-2000
John Schultz, prin. Fax 734-4270
Immanuel Medical Center Post-Sec.
6901 N 72nd St 68122 402-572-2270
ITT Technical Institute Post-Sec.
1120 N 103rd Plz Ste 200 68114 402-331-2900
Jesuit MS 100/4-8
2311 N 22nd St 68110 402-346-4464
Troy Wharton, prin. Fax 341-1817
Kaplan University Post-Sec.
5425 N 103rd St 68134 402-572-8500
Marian HS 700/9-12
7400 Military Ave 68134 402-571-2618
Susan Toohey, hdmstr. Fax 571-1952
Mercy HS 400/9-12
1501 S 48th St 68106 402-553-9424
Carolyn Jaworski, prin. Fax 553-0394
Metropolitan Community College Post-Sec.
PO Box 3777 68103 402-457-2400
Metropolitan Community College- Ft Omaha Post-Sec.
PO Box 3777 68103 402-457-2400
Metropolitan Community Coll- Elkhorn Vly Post-Sec.
PO Box 3777 68103 402-457-2400
Nebraska Methodist College Post-Sec.
720 N 87th St 68114 402-354-7000
Omaha Christian Academy 200/PK-12
10244 Wiesman Dr 68134 402-399-9565
Dr. Victor Fordyce, supt. Fax 399-0248
Omaha School of Massage Therapy Post-Sec.
9748 Park Dr 68127 402-331-3694
Roncalli HS 300/9-12
6401 Sorensen Pkwy 68152 402-571-7670
Chad Holtz, prin. Fax 571-3216
Skutt Catholic HS 700/9-12
3131 S 156th St 68130 402-333-0818
Jon Burt, prin. Fax 333-1790
The Creative Center Post-Sec.
10850 Emmet St 68164 402-898-1000
Universal College of Healing Arts Post-Sec.
8702 N 30th St 68112 402-556-4456
University of Nebraska Medical Center Post-Sec.
987020 Nebraska Medical Ctr 68198 402-559-4000
University of Nebraska Omaha Post-Sec.
6001 Dodge St 68182 402-554-2800
Vatterott College - Omaha Post-Sec.
11818 I St 68137 402-891-9411
Xenon International Academy Post-Sec.
8516 Park Dr 68127 402-393-2933

O Neill, Holt, Pop. 3,676
O'Neill SD 700/PK-12
PO Box 230 68763 402-336-3775
Amy Shane, supt. Fax 336-4890
www.oneillpublicschools.org
O'Neill JSHS 400/7-12
PO Box 230 68763 402-336-1544
Steven Brosz, prin. Fax 336-1105

St. Mary S 200/PK-12
326 E Benton St 68763 402-336-4455
Walter Dupre, prin. Fax 336-1281

Ord, Valley, Pop. 2,094
Ord SD 500/K-12
320 N 19th St 68862 308-728-5013
Jason Alexander, supt. Fax 728-5108
www.ordps.org/
Ord JSHS 200/7-12
1800 K St 68862 308-728-3241
Mark Hagge, prin. Fax 728-5108

Osceola, Polk, Pop. 874
Osceola SD 300/K-12
PO Box 198 68651 402-747-3121
Steve Rinehart, supt. Fax 747-3041
www.edline.net/pages/Osceola_Public_School/
Osceola HS 100/9-12
PO Box 198 68651 402-747-3121
Darren Schmidt, prin. Fax 747-3041
Osceola MS 100/6-8
PO Box 198 68651 402-747-3121
Darren Schmidt, prin. Fax 747-3041

Oshkosh, Garden, Pop. 869
Garden County SD 200/K-12
PO Box 230 69154 308-772-3242
Paula Sissel, supt. Fax 772-3039
www.gardencountyschools.org/
Garden County HS 100/9-12
PO Box 230 69154 308-772-3242
Jason Spady, prin. Fax 772-3039
Other Schools – See Lewellen

Osmond, Pierce, Pop. 774
Osmond SD 200/K-12
PO Box 458 68765 402-748-3777
David Hamm, supt. Fax 748-3210
www.osmondtigers.org
Osmond JSHS 100/7-12
PO Box 458 68765 402-748-3777
Michael Brown, prin. Fax 748-3210

Overton, Dawson, Pop. 592
Overton SD 300/PK-12
PO Box 310 68863 308-987-2424
Mark Aten, supt. Fax 987-2349
www.ovr.esu10.k12.ne.us/
Overton JSHS 100/7-12
PO Box 310 68863 308-987-2424
Brian Fleischman, prin. Fax 987-2349

Oxford, Furnas, Pop. 773
Southern Valley SD 400/K-12
43739 Highway 89 68967 308-868-2222
Chuck Lambert, supt. Fax 868-2223
blog.southern-valley.k12.ne.us
Southern Valley JSHS 200/7-12
43739 Highway 89 68967 308-868-2222
Darren Tobey, prin. Fax 868-2223

Palmer, Merrick, Pop. 470
Palmer SD 200/K-12
PO Box 248 68864 308-894-3065
Gary Monter, supt. Fax 894-8245
www.palmertigers.org
Palmer JSHS 100/7-12
PO Box 248 68864 308-894-3065
Gary Monter, prin. Fax 894-8245

Palmyra, Otoe, Pop. 536
Palmyra OR 1 SD 400/K-12
PO Box 130 68418 402-780-5327
Robert Hanger, supt. Fax 780-5328
www.district or1.org/
Palmyra JSHS 200/7-12
PO Box 130 68418 402-780-5327
David Bottrell, prin. Fax 780-5328

Papillion, Sarpy, Pop. 18,478
Papillion-La Vista SD 10,100/PK-12
420 S Washington St 68046 402-537-6200
Fax 537-6216
www.paplv.org
Ideal S Alt
1104 Applewood Dr 68046 402-898-0485
Pat Zalesky, admin. Fax 898-0486
Papillion JHS 700/7-8
423 S Washington St 68046 402-898-0424
Brent Holder, prin. Fax 898-0430
Papillion-La Vista HS 1,500/9-12
402 E Centennial Rd 68046 402-898-0400
Jerry Kalina, prin. Fax 898-0415
Papillion-La Vista South HS 1,600/9-12
10799 Highway 370 68046 402-829-4600
Dr. Enid Schonewise, prin. Fax 827-1330
Other Schools – See La Vista

Nebraska Christian College Post-Sec.
12550 S 114th St 68046 402-935-9400

Pawnee City, Pawnee, Pop. 861
Pawnee City SD 300/K-12
PO Box 393 68420 402-852-2988
Stephen Grizzle, supt. Fax 852-2993
www.pawneecityschool.com
Pawnee City JSHS 100/7-12
PO Box 393 68420 402-852-2988
Donald Jacobs, prin. Fax 852-2993

Paxton, Keith, Pop. 521
Paxton Consolidated SD 200/K-12
PO Box 368 69155 308-239-4283
Delbert Dack, supt. Fax 239-4359
www.paxton.k12.ne.us/
Paxton JSHS 100/7-12
PO Box 368 69155 308-239-4283
Sheri Chittenden, prin. Fax 239-4359

Pender, Thurston, Pop. 991
Pender SD 300/PK-12
609 Whitney St 68047 402-385-3244
Jason Dolliver, supt. Fax 385-2285
www.penderschools.org/
Pender JSHS 200/7-12
609 Whitney St 68047 402-385-3244
Kelly Ballinger, prin. Fax 385-3342

Peru, Nemaha, Pop. 853

Peru State College Post-Sec.
PO Box 10 68421 800-742-4412

Petersburg, Boone, Pop. 329
Boone Central SD
Supt. — See Albion
Boone Central MS 100/6-8
PO Box 240 68652 402-386-5302
Jimmy Feeney, prin. Fax 386-5464

Pierce, Pierce, Pop. 1,757
Pierce SD 700/K-12
201 N Sunset St 68767 402-329-4677
Kendall Steffensen, supt. Fax 329-4678
www.piercepublic.org/
Pierce JSHS 300/7-12
201 N Sunset St 68767 402-329-6217
Mark Brahmer, prin. Fax 329-4678

Pilger, Stanton, Pop. 343
Wisner-Pilger SD
Supt. — See Wisner
Wisner-Pilger MS 100/7-8
PO Box 325 68768 402-396-3566
Mark Porter, prin. Fax 396-3566

Plainview, Pierce, Pop. 1,240
Plainview SD 300/K-12
PO Box 638 68769 402-582-4993
Richard Alt, supt. Fax 582-4665
www.plainviewschools.org/
Plainview JSHS 200/7-12
PO Box 638 68769 402-582-4991
Patty Novicki, prin. Fax 582-4665

Plattsmouth, Cass, Pop. 6,376
Plattsmouth SD 1,800/PK-12
1912 E Highway 34 68048 402-296-3361
Dr. Richard Hasty, supt. Fax 296-2667
www.pcsd.org
Plattsmouth HS 600/9-12
1916 E Highway 34 68048 402-296-3322
Jeffery Wiles, prin. Fax 296-3342
Plattsmouth MS 500/5-8
1724 8th Ave 68048 402-296-3174
Mark Smith, prin. Fax 296-2910

Pleasanton, Buffalo, Pop. 340
Pleasanton SD 200/PK-12
PO Box 190 68866 308-388-2041
Ronald Wymore, supt. Fax 388-5502
pleasanton.k12.ne.us
Pleasanton JSHS 100/7-12
PO Box 190 68866 308-388-2041
James Westland, prin. Fax 388-5502

Polk, Polk, Pop. 321
High Plains Community SD 200/K-12
PO Box 29 68654 402-765-2271
Stan Hendricks, supt. Fax 765-2272
www.hpcstorm.org
High Plains HS 100/9-12
PO Box 29 68654 402-765-3331
Cameron Hudson, prin. Fax 765-3332
Other Schools – See Clarks

Ponca, Dixon, Pop. 947
Ponca SD 400/K-12
PO Box 568 68770 402-755-5700
Joan Reznicek, supt. Fax 755-5773
www.poncaschool.org/

Ponca JSHS — 200/7-12
PO Box 568 68770 — 402-755-5701
Michelle Rinas, prin. — Fax 755-5773

Potter, Cheyenne, Pop. 337
Potter-Dix SD — 200/K-12
PO Box 189 69156 — 308-879-4434
Kevin Thomas, supt. — Fax 879-4566
www.pdcoyotes.com
Potter-Dix JSHS — 100/7-12
PO Box 189 69156 — 308-879-4434
Don Frenzen, prin. — Fax 879-4566

Ralston, Douglas, Pop. 5,872
Ralston SD — 3,200/PK-12
8545 Park Dr 68127 — 402-331-4700
Dr. Mark Adler, supt. — Fax 331-4843
www.ralstonschools.org/
Ralston HS — 1,000/9-12
8969 Park Dr 68127 — 402-331-7373
Steve Schrad, prin. — Fax 898-3511
Ralston MS — 400/7-8
8202 Lakeview St 68127 — 402-331-4701
Jason Buckingham, prin. — Fax 331-5376

Randolph, Cedar, Pop. 943
Randolph SD 45 — 300/K-12
PO Box 755 68771 — 402-337-0252
David Hamm, supt. — Fax 337-0235
www.randolphpublic.org/
Randolph JSHS — 100/7-12
PO Box 755 68771 — 402-337-0252
Dennis Bazata, prin. — Fax 337-0235

Ravenna, Buffalo, Pop. 1,347
Ravenna SD — 400/K-12
PO Box 8400 68869 — 308-452-3249
Dwaine Uttecht, supt. — Fax 452-3172
www.ravenna.k12.ne.us/
Ravenna JSHS — 200/7-12
PO Box 8400 68869 — 308-452-3249
Corey Fisher, prin. — Fax 452-3172

Raymond, Lancaster, Pop. 163
Raymond Central SD — 600/K-12
1800 W Agnew Rd 68428 — 402-785-2615
Paul Hull, supt. — Fax 785-2097
www.rcentral.org
Raymond JSHS — 300/7-12
1800 W Agnew Rd 68428 — 402-785-2685
Kolin Haecker, prin. — Fax 785-7070

Red Cloud, Webster, Pop. 1,006
Red Cloud Community SD — 200/K-12
334 N Cherry St 68970 — 402-746-3413
Brian Hof, supt. — Fax 746-3690
www.redcloud.k12.ne.us/
Washington JSHS — 100/7-12
121 W 7th Ave 68970 — 402-746-2818
Marlyn Washburn, prin. — Fax 746-2817

Rising City, Butler, Pop. 373
Shelby-Rising City SD
Supt. — See Shelby
Shelby-Rising City MS — 6-8
PO Box 160 68658 — 402-542-2216
William Curry, prin. — Fax 542-2265

Roseland, Adams, Pop. 235
Silver Lake SD — 200/K-12
PO Box 8 68973 — 402-756-6611
Mel Crowe, supt. — Fax 756-6613
www.silverlakemustangs.org
Silver Lake JSHS — 100/7-12
PO Box 8 68973 — 402-756-6611
Kenneth Mahoney, prin. — Fax 756-6613

Royal, Antelope, Pop. 63
Nebraska USD 1 — 300/PK-12
PO Box 98 68773 — 402-893-2068
Dale Martin, supt. — Fax 893-9949
neunified1.esu8.org/
Other Schools – See Verdigre

Rushville, Sheridan, Pop. 866
Gordon-Rushville SD
Supt. — See Gordon
Gordon-Rushville MS — 100/6-8
PO Box 590 69360 — 308-327-2491
Casey Slama, prin. — Fax 327-2504

Saint Edward, Boone, Pop. 704
Saint Edward SD — 100/K-12
PO Box C 68660 — 402-678-2282
Kevin Lyons, supt. — Fax 678-2284
Saint Edward JSHS — 100/7-12
PO Box C 68660 — 402-678-2282
Kevin Lyons, prin. — Fax 678-2284

Saint Paul, Howard, Pop. 2,270
Saint Paul SD — 500/K-12
PO Box 325 68873 — 308-754-4433
John Poppert, supt. — Fax 754-5374
www.stpaul.k12.ne.us/
Saint Paul JSHS — 200/7-12
PO Box 325 68873 — 308-754-4433
Jennifer Hagen, prin. — Fax 754-5374

Sargent, Custer, Pop. 524
Sargent SD — 200/K-12
PO Box 366 68874 — 308-527-4119
Wayne Ruppert, supt. — Fax 527-3332
blog.sargent.k12.ne.us
Sargent JSHS — 100/7-12
PO Box 366 68874 — 308-527-4119
Cory Grint, prin. — Fax 527-3332

Schuyler, Colfax, Pop. 6,165
Schuyler Community SD — 1,000/PK-12
401 Adam St 68661 — 402-352-3527
Robin Stevens, supt. — Fax 352-5552
schuylercommunityschools.org
Schuyler Central HS — 400/9-12
401 Adam St 68661 — 402-352-3527
Greg Pavlik, prin. — Fax 352-5552
Schuyler MS — 300/6-8
200 W 10th St 68661 — 402-352-5514
Stephen Grammer, prin. — Fax 352-2644

Scotia, Greeley, Pop. 317
North Loup Scotia SD — 200/K-12
PO Box 307 68875 — 308-245-3201
Jim Duval, supt. — Fax 245-9133
blog.northloupscotia.k12.ne.us
Scotia JSHS — 100/7-12
PO Box 307 68875 — 308-245-3201
Zane Young, prin. — Fax 245-9133

Scottsbluff, Scotts Bluff, Pop. 14,885
Scottsbluff SD — 2,900/PK-12
1722 1st Ave 69361 — 308-635-6200
Rick Myles, supt. — Fax 635-6217
www.sbps.net/
Bluffs MS — 600/6-8
23rd and Broadway 69361 — 308-635-6270
Andrew Dick, prin. — Fax 635-6271
Scottsbluff HS — 800/9-12
313 E 27th St 69361 — 308-635-6230
Michael Halley, prin. — Fax 635-6240

Regional West Medical Center — Post-Sec.
4021 Avenue B 69361 — 308-635-3711
Western Nebraska Community College — Post-Sec.
1601 E 27th St 69361 — 308-635-3606

Scribner, Dodge, Pop. 841
Scribner-Snyder SD — 200/K-12
PO Box L 68057 — 402-664-2568
Ginger Meyer, supt. — Fax 664-2708
www.sstrojans.esu2.org/
Scribner-Snyder JSHS — 100/7-12
PO Box L 68057 — 402-664-2567
Brad Stithem, prin. — Fax 664-2407

Seward, Seward, Pop. 6,883
Seward SD — 1,400/PK-12
410 South St 68434 — 402-643-2941
Greg Barnes, supt. — Fax 643-4986
www.sewardpublicschools.org
Seward HS — 500/9-12
532 Northern Heights Dr 68434 — 402-643-2988
Chad Denker, prin. — Fax 643-2599
Seward MS — 400/5-8
237 S 3rd St 68434 — 402-643-2986
Kirk Gottschalk, prin. — Fax 643-6686

Concordia University — Post-Sec.
800 N Columbia Ave 68434 — 402-643-3651
Saint Gregory the Great Seminary — Post-Sec.
800 Fletcher Rd 68434 — 402-643-4052

Shelby, Polk, Pop. 707
Shelby-Rising City SD — 200/K-12
PO Box 218 68662 — 402-527-5946
Larry Stick, supt. — Fax 527-5133
www.shelby.esu7.org
Shelby-Rising City HS — 100/9-12
PO Box 218 68662 — 402-527-5946
Larry Stick, prin. — Fax 527-5133
Other Schools – See Rising City

Shelton, Buffalo, Pop. 1,053
Shelton SD — 300/K-12
PO Box 610 68876 — 308-647-6742
Brian Redinger, supt. — Fax 647-5233
www.sheltonbulldogs.org
Shelton JSHS — 100/7-12
PO Box 610 68876 — 308-647-5459
Edward Lowe, prin. — Fax 647-5233

Shickley, Fillmore, Pop. 338
Shickley SD — 50/PK-12
PO Box 407 68436 — 402-627-3375
Bryce Jorgenson, supt. — Fax 627-2003
www.shickleypublicschool.com
Shickley S — 50/PK-12
PO Box 407 68436 — 402-627-3375
Derek Ippensen, prin. — Fax 627-2003

Sidney, Cheyenne, Pop. 6,700
Sidney SD — 1,300/K-12
1101 21st Ave 69162 — 308-254-5855
Jay Ehler, supt. — Fax 254-5756
www.sidneyraiders.org
Sidney HS — 300/9-12
1101 19th Ave 69162 — 308-254-5893
Chris Arent, prin. — Fax 254-5992
Sidney MS — 200/7-8
1122 19th Ave 69162 — 308-254-5853
Brandon Ross, prin. — Fax 254-1130

Western Nebraska Community College — Post-Sec.
371 College Dr 69162 — 308-254-5450

South Sioux City, Dakota, Pop. 13,178
South Sioux City SD — 3,600/K-12
PO Box 158 68776 — 402-494-2425
Dr. Vernon Fisher, supt. — Fax 494-3916
www.ssccardinals.org/
South Sioux City HS — 1,100/9-12
3301 G St 68776 — 402-494-2433
Ed Akins, prin. — Fax 494-2464
South Sioux City MS — 900/6-8
3625 G St 68776 — 402-494-3061
Tom McGuire, prin. — Fax 494-8427

Spalding, Greeley, Pop. 485
Spalding SD — 100/K-12
PO Box 220 68665 — 308-497-2431
Stephanie Wlaschin, supt. — Fax 497-2141
sites.spalding.k12.ne.us/
Spalding JSHS — 100/7-12
PO Box 220 68665 — 308-497-2431
Stephanie Wlaschin, prin. — Fax 497-2141

Spalding Academy — 100/K-12
PO Box 310 68665 — 308-497-2103
Amy McKay, prin. — Fax 497-2105

Spencer, Boyd, Pop. 452
West Boyd SD — 200/K-12
PO Box 109 68777 — 402-589-2040
Duane Lechtenberg, supt. — Fax 589-2041
www.westboyd.com/
West Boyd - Spencer Attendance Center — 100/5-12
PO Box 109 68777 — 402-589-1333
Duane Lechtenberg, prin. — Fax 589-1142

Springfield, Sarpy, Pop. 1,494
Springfield Platteview Community SD — 1,000/PK-12
14801 S 108th St 68059 — 402-592-1300
Brett Richards, supt. — Fax 597-8551
www.springfieldplatteview.org
Platteview Central JHS — 200/7-8
14801 S 108th St 68059 — 402-339-5052
Darin Johnson, prin. — Fax 339-3166
Platteview HS — 300/9-12
14801 S 108th St 68059 — 402-339-3606
Angela Simpson, prin. — Fax 339-3751

Springview, Keya Paha, Pop. 242
Keya Paha County SD — 100/K-12
PO Box 219 68778 — 402-497-3501
Rodger Lenhard, supt. — Fax 497-4321
keyapahacountyschools.org/
Keya Paha County HS — 50/9-12
PO Box 219 68778 — 402-497-3501
Rodger Lenhard, prin. — Fax 497-4321

Stanton, Stanton, Pop. 1,562
Stanton Community SD — 500/K-12
PO Box 749 68779 — 402-439-2233
Michael J. Sieh Ed.D., supt. — Fax 439-2270
www.scs-ne.org/
Stanton MSHS — 200/7-12
PO Box 749 68779 — 402-439-2250
David Cunningham, prin. — Fax 439-2270

Stapleton, Logan, Pop. 305
Stapleton SD — 200/PK-12
PO Box 128 69163 — 308-636-2252
Leroy Sayer, supt. — Fax 636-2618
Stapleton JSHS — 100/7-12
PO Box 128 69163 — 308-636-2252
Adam Boettcher, prin. — Fax 636-2618

Sterling, Johnson, Pop. 476
Sterling SD — 200/K-12
PO Box 39 68443 — 402-866-4761
Larry Harnisch, supt. — Fax 866-4771
www.sterlingjets.org/
Sterling HS — 100/9-12
PO Box 39 68443 — 402-866-4761
Ryun Theobald, prin. — Fax 866-4771
Sterling MS — 50/6-8
PO Box 39 68443 — 402-866-4761
Ryun Theobald, prin. — Fax 866-4771

Stromsburg, Polk, Pop. 1,155
Cross County Community SD — 400/PK-12
PO Box 525 68666 — 402-764-5521
Brent Hollinger, supt. — Fax 764-8294
crosscountyschools.com/
Cross County MSHS — 200/6-12
PO Box 525 68666 — 402-764-5521
Ron Nickel, prin. — Fax 764-8294

Stuart, Holt, Pop. 586
Stuart SD — 200/K-12
PO Box 99 68780 — 402-924-3302
Robert Hanzlik, supt. — Fax 924-3676
stuart.esu8.org/
Stuart JSHS — 100/7-12
PO Box 99 68780 — 402-924-3302
Robert Hanzlik, prin. — Fax 924-3676

Sumner, Dawson, Pop. 234
Sumner-Eddyville-Miller SD — 200/K-12
PO Box 126 68878 — 308-752-2925
Jeffery Walbrun, supt. — Fax 752-2600
www.semmustangs.org
SEM JSHS — 100/7-12
PO Box 126 68878 — 308-752-2925
Jeffrey Walburn, supt. — Fax 752-2600

Superior, Nuckolls, Pop. 1,929
Superior SD — 300/K-12
PO Box 288 68978 — 402-879-3258
Charles Isom, supt. — Fax 879-3022
Superior JSHS — 200/7-12
PO Box 288 68978 — 402-879-3257
Robert Cook, prin. — Fax 879-3022

Sutherland, Lincoln, Pop. 1,283
Sutherland SD — 400/PK-12
PO Box 217 69165 — 308-386-4656
Dan Keyser, supt. — Fax 386-2426
www.spssailors.org/
Sutherland JSHS — 100/7-12
PO Box 217 69165 — 308-386-4656
Dustin Mitchell, prin. — Fax 386-2426

Sutton, Clay, Pop. 1,500
Sutton SD — 400/PK-12
PO Box 590 68979 — 402-773-5569
Dana Wiseman, supt. — Fax 773-5578
www.suttonpublicschool.org
Sutton JSHS — 200/7-12
PO Box 590 68979 — 402-773-4303
Brandy Thompson, prin. — Fax 773-5578

Syracuse, Otoe, Pop. 1,933
Syracuse-Dunbar-Avoca SD 600/K-12
PO Box P 68446 402-269-2381
Bradley Buller, supt. Fax 269-2224
www.sdarockets.org/
Syracuse HS 200/9-12
PO Box P 68446 402-269-2381
Joy Stilmock, prin. Fax 269-3028
Syracuse MS 100/7-8
PO Box P 68446 402-269-2388
Michael Wentz, prin. Fax 269-2402

Table Rock, Pawnee, Pop. 267
Humboldt Table Rock Steinauer SD 70
Supt. — See Humboldt
Humboldt Table Rock Steinauer MS 100/4-8
PO Box F 68447 402-839-2085
Kari Cover, prin. Fax 839-2088

Taylor, Loup, Pop. 190
Loup County SD 100/K-12
PO Box 170 68879 308-942-6115
Wayne Ruppert, supt. Fax 942-6248
blog.loupcounty.k12.ne.us/school/
Loup County JSHS 50/7-12
PO Box 170 68879 308-942-6115
Ken Sheets, prin. Fax 942-6248

Tecumseh, Johnson, Pop. 1,665
Johnson County Central SD 500/PK-12
PO Box 338 68450 402-335-3320
Jack Moles, supt. Fax 335-3346
jccentral.org/
Johnson County Central HS 100/9-12
PO Box 338 68450 402-335-3328
Rick Lester, prin. Fax 335-3346
Other Schools – See Cook

Tekamah, Burt, Pop. 1,725
Tekamah-Herman SD 600/PK-12
112 N 13th St 68061 402-374-2157
Brandon Lavaley, supt. Fax 374-2155
www.tekamah.esu2.org/
Tekamah JSHS 200/7-12
112 N 13th St 68061 402-374-2156
Daniel Gross, prin. Fax 374-2155

Thedford, Thomas, Pop. 188
Thedford SD 100/PK-12
PO Box 248 69166 308-645-2230
Henry Eggert, supt. Fax 645-2618
Thedford HS 100/7-12
PO Box 248 69166 308-645-2614
Henry Eggert, supt. Fax 645-2618

Tilden, Madison, Pop. 942
Elkhorn Valley SD 300/PK-12
PO Box 430 68781 402-368-5301
Keith Leckron, supt. Fax 368-5338
www.elkhornvalleyschools.org
Elkhorn Valley JSHS 100/7-12
PO Box 430 68781 402-368-5301
Darin Hahne, prin. Fax 368-5338

Trenton, Hitchcock, Pop. 557
Hitchcock County SD 300/PK-12
PO Box 368 69044 308-334-5575
Mike Apple, supt. Fax 334-5381
www.hcfalcons.org/
Hitchcock County HS 100/7-12
PO Box 368 69044 308-334-5575
Mike Apple, prin. Fax 334-5381

Tryon, McPherson, Pop. 153
McPherson County SD 100/K-12
PO Box 38 69167 308-587-2262
Joseph Sherwood, supt. Fax 587-2571
McPherson County HS 50/9-12
PO Box 38 69167 308-587-2262
Debra Brownfield, prin. Fax 587-2571

Utica, Seward, Pop. 859
Centennial SD 500/PK-12
PO Box 187 68456 402-534-2291
Tim DeWaard, supt. Fax 534-2291
www.centennialbroncos.org
Centennial JSHS 200/7-12
PO Box 187 68456 402-534-2321
Colin Bargen, prin. Fax 534-2291

Valentine, Cherry, Pop. 2,652
Valentine SD 600/K-12
431 N Green St 69201 402-376-2730
Jamie Isom, supt. Fax 376-2736
www.valentinecommunityschools.org/
Valentine HS 200/9-12
431 N Green St 69201 402-376-2730
Dave Renning, prin. Fax 376-2736
Valentine MS 100/6-8
239 N Wood St 69201 402-376-3367
Jeff Sayer, prin. Fax 376-3386

Valley, Douglas, Pop. 1,851
Douglas County West Community SD 600/K-12
PO Box 378 68064 402-359-2583
Dr. Dan Schnoes, supt. Fax 359-4371
www.dcwest.org/
Douglas County West HS 200/9-12
PO Box 378 68064 402-359-2121
Jim Knott, prin. Fax 359-2893
Other Schools – See Waterloo

Verdigre, Knox, Pop. 565
Nebraska USD 1
Supt. — See Royal
Verdigre S 100/PK-12
201 S 3rd St 68783 402-668-2275
Chuck Kucera, prin. Fax 668-2276

Waco, York, Pop. 233

Nebraska Lutheran HS 100/9-12
203 Kendall St 68460 402-728-5236
Craig Charron, prin. Fax 728-5433

Wahoo, Saunders, Pop. 4,441
Wahoo SD 900/PK-12
2201 N Locust St 68066 402-443-3051
Galen Boldt, supt. Fax 443-4731
www.wahooschools.org/
Wahoo HS 300/9-12
2201 N Locust St 68066 402-443-4332
Jason Libal, prin. Fax 443-4731
Wahoo MS 200/6-8
2201 N Locust St 68066 402-443-3101
John Harris, prin. Fax 443-4731

Bishop Neumann Central HS 300/7-12
202 S Linden St 68066 402-443-4151
Rev. Jeremy Hazuka, prin. Fax 443-5551

Wakefield, Dixon, Pop. 1,440
Wakefield SD 400/K-12
PO Box 330 68784 402-287-2012
Mark Bejot, supt. Fax 287-2014
www.wakefieldschools.org/
Wakefield JSHS 200/7-12
PO Box 330 68784 402-287-2012
Jason Heitz, prin. Fax 287-2014

Wallace, Lincoln, Pop. 360
Wallace SD 65 R 200/K-12
151 N Wallace Rd 69169 308-387-4323
Todd Porter, supt. Fax 387-4322
whs.esu16.org/Administration.html
Wallace JSHS 100/7-12
151 N Wallace Rd 69169 308-387-4323
Kelly Erickson, prin. Fax 387-4322

Walthill, Thurston, Pop. 761
Walthill SD 300/K-12
PO Box 3C 68067 402-846-5432
Ed Stansberry, supt. Fax 846-5029
walthweb.esu1.org/
Walthill JSHS 100/7-12
PO Box 3C 68067 402-846-5432
Joseph Ross, prin. Fax 846-5029

Waterloo, Douglas, Pop. 837
Douglas County West Community SD
Supt. — See Valley
Douglas County West MS 200/5-8
800 N Front St 68069 402-779-2646
Jeremy Travis, prin. Fax 779-2534

Wauneta, Chase, Pop. 575
Wauneta-Palisade SD 100/K-12
PO Box 368 69045 308-394-5700
Randy Geier, supt. Fax 394-5962
www.waunetapalisade.org/
Wauneta-Palisade HS 100/9-12
PO Box 368 69045 308-394-5650
Troy Holmberg, prin. Fax 394-5962
Wauneta Palisade JHS 50/7-8
PO Box 368 69045 308-394-5650
Troy Holmberg, prin. Fax 394-5962

Wausa, Knox, Pop. 629
Wausa SD 200/K-12
PO Box 159 68786 402-586-2255
Robert Marks Ed.D., supt. Fax 586-2406
wausaweb.esu1.org/
Wausa JSHS 100/7-12
PO Box 159 68786 402-586-2255
Bradley Hoesing, prin. Fax 586-2406

Waverly, Lancaster, Pop. 3,253
Waverly SD 145 1,800/K-12
PO Box 426 68462 402-786-2321
Dr. Bill Heimann, supt. Fax 786-2799
www.dist145schools.org/
Waverly HS 600/9-12
PO Box 426 68462 402-786-2765
Ryan Ricenbaw, prin. Fax 786-2799
Waverly MS 400/6-8
PO Box 426 68462 402-786-2348
Gary Cooper, prin. Fax 786-2782

Wayne, Wayne, Pop. 5,585
Wayne SD 400/K-12
611 W 7th St 68787 402-375-3150
Mark Lenihan, supt. Fax 375-5251
www.wayneschools.org
Wayne JSHS 300/7-12
611 W 7th St 68787 402-375-3150
Mark Hanson, prin. Fax 375-5251

Wayne State College Post-Sec.
1111 Main St 68787 402-375-7000

Weeping Water, Cass, Pop. 1,042
Weeping Water SD 400/PK-12
PO Box 206 68463 402-267-2445
Dr. Ken Heinz, supt. Fax 267-5217
www.weepingwaterps.org/
Weeping Water JSHS 200/7-12
PO Box 206 68463 402-267-2445
Gary Wockenfuss, prin. Fax 267-5217

West Point, Cuming, Pop. 3,356
West Point SD 800/PK-12
1200 E Washington St 68788 402-372-5860
Theodore De Turk, supt. Fax 372-5458
www.wpcadets.org/
West Point-Beemer JSHS 400/7-12
1200 E Washington St 68788 402-372-5546
Daniel Weddle, prin. Fax 372-2252

Guardian Angels/Central Catholic HS 100/7-12
419 E Decatur St 68788 402-372-5326
Matthew Richardson, prin. Fax 372-5327

Wilber, Saline, Pop. 1,843
Wilber-Clatonia SD 600/PK-12
PO Box 487 68465 402-821-2266
Ray Collins, supt. Fax 821-3013
www.wilber-clatonia.org/
Wilber-Clatonia JSHS 300/7-12
PO Box 487 68465 402-821-2508
Evan Wieseman, prin. Fax 821-3013

Wilcox, Kearney, Pop. 354
Wilcox-Hildreth SD 200/K-12
PO Box 190 68982 308-478-5265
Steven Dennis, supt. Fax 478-5260
Wilcox-Hildreth HS 100/9-12
PO Box 190 68982 308-478-5265
Victor Young, prin. Fax 478-5260
Other Schools – See Hildreth

Winnebago, Thurston, Pop. 756
Winnebago SD 400/K-12
PO Box KK 68071 402-878-2224
Dan Fehringer, supt. Fax 878-2472
winnebago.esu1.org/
Winnebago HS 100/7-12
PO Box KK 68071 402-878-2224
Chris Bernard, prin. Fax 878-2472

Little Priest Tribal College Post-Sec.
PO Box 270 68071 402-878-2380

Winside, Wayne, Pop. 419
Winside SD 200/K-12
PO Box 158 68790 402-286-4466
Jeffrey Messersmith, supt. Fax 286-4466
winside.esu1.org/
Winside JSHS 100/7-12
PO Box 158 68790 402-286-4465
Erik Kravig, prin. Fax 286-4466

Wisner, Cuming, Pop. 1,154
Wisner-Pilger SD 400/K-12
PO Box 580 68791 402-529-3249
Alan Harms, supt. Fax 529-3477
www.wisnerpilger.org/
Wisner HS 200/9-12
PO Box 580 68791 402-529-3249
Christopher Uttecht, prin. Fax 529-3477
Other Schools – See Pilger

Wood River, Hall, Pop. 1,319
Wood River Rural SD 500/K-12
PO Box 518 68883 308-583-2249
Cynthia Huff, supt. Fax 583-2395
www.woodriver.k12.ne.us/
Wood River Rural HS 200/9-12
PO Box 518 68883 308-583-2249
Terry Zessin, prin. Fax 583-2395
Wood River Rural MS 100/6-8
PO Box 518 68883 308-583-2249
Cynthia Huff, prin. Fax 583-2395

Wymore, Gage, Pop. 1,431
Southern SD 1 400/K-12
PO Box 237 68466 402-645-3326
Gene Haddix, supt. Fax 645-8049
www.southernschools.org
Southern JSHS 200/7-12
PO Box 237 68466 402-645-3326
Jeff Murphy, prin. Fax 645-8049

Wynot, Cedar, Pop. 165
Wynot SD 100/K-12
PO Box 157 68792 402-357-2121
Joseph Lefdal, supt. Fax 357-2524
www.wynotpublicschools.org
Wynot HS 100/9-12
PO Box 157 68792 402-357-2121
Richard Higgins, prin. Fax 357-2524
Wynot MS 50/5-8
PO Box 157 68792 402-357-2121
Richard Higgins, prin. Fax 357-2524

York, York, Pop. 7,673
York SD 1,200/PK-12
2918 N Delaware Ave 68467 402-362-6655
Mike Lucas, supt. Fax 362-6943
www.yorkpublic.org/
York HS 400/9-12
1005 Duke Dr 68467 402-362-6655
Mitch Bartholomew, prin. Fax 362-2994
York MS 300/6-8
1730 N Delaware Ave 68467 402-362-6655
Brian Tonniges, prin. Fax 362-6831

York College Post-Sec.
1125 E 8th St 68467 402-363-5600

Yutan, Saunders, Pop. 1,169
Yutan SD 400/K-12
1200 2nd St 68073 402-625-2243
Kevin Johnson, supt. Fax 625-2812
www.teacherweb.com/NE/YutanPublicSchools/Home/sdhp1.aspx
Yutan JSHS 200/7-12
1200 2nd St 68073 402-625-2241
Timothy McNamara, prin. Fax 625-2812

NEVADA

NEVADA DEPARTMENT OF EDUCATION
700 E Fifth St, Carson City 89701-5096
Telephone 775-687-9200
Fax 775-687-9101
Website http://www.doe.nv.gov/

Superintendent of Instruction Dale Erquiaga

NEVADA BOARD OF EDUCATION
700 E Fifth St, Carson City 89701-5096

President Stavan Corbett

PUBLIC, PRIVATE AND CATHOLIC SECONDARY SCHOOLS

Alamo, Lincoln, Pop. 1,045
Lincoln County SD
Supt. — See Panaca
Pahranagat Valley JSHS 100/7-12
PO Box 298 89001 775-725-3321
Mike Strong, prin. Fax 725-3334

Austin, Lander, Pop. 191
Lander County SD
Supt. — See Battle Mountain
Austin S 50/K-12
PO Box 160 89310 775-964-2467
Michelle Caramella, prin. Fax 964-1206

Battle Mountain, Lander, Pop. 3,594
Lander County SD 1,100/PK-12
PO Box 1300 89820 775-635-2886
Jim Squibb, supt. Fax 635-5347
www.lander.k12.nv.us
Battle Mountain HS 400/9-12
PO Box 1330 89820 775-635-5436
Collin Belnap, prin. Fax 635-5459
Battle Mountain JHS 200/7-8
PO Box 1360 89820 775-635-2415
Michelle Caramella, prin. Fax 635-6118
Other Schools – See Austin

Beatty, Nye, Pop. 983
Nye County SD
Supt. — See Tonopah
Beatty HS 100/9-12
PO Box 806 89003 775-553-2595
Gary Flood, prin. Fax 553-2887

Boulder City, Clark, Pop. 14,662
Clark County SD
Supt. — See Las Vegas
Boulder City HS 700/9-12
1101 5th St 89005 702-799-8200
Kent Roberts, prin. Fax 799-8230
Garrett MS 500/6-8
1200 Avenue G 89005 702-799-8290
Jamey Hood, prin. Fax 799-8252

Caliente, Lincoln, Pop. 1,102
Lincoln County SD
Supt. — See Panaca
Bastian HS 100/7-12
PO Box 1088 89008 775-726-3140
Dr. Ken Higbee, prin. Fax 726-3371

Carlin, Elko, Pop. 2,339
Elko County SD
Supt. — See Elko
Carlin S 100/K-12
PO Box 730 89822 775-754-6317
Janice Alexander, prin. Fax 754-2175

Carson City, Carson City, Pop. 54,098
Carson City SD 7,700/K-12
PO Box 603 89702 775-283-2000
Richard Stokes, supt. Fax 283-2090
www.carsoncityschools.com
Carson HS 2,200/9-12
1111 N Saliman Rd 89701 775-283-1600
Ron Beck, prin. Fax 283-1790
Carson MS 1,100/6-8
1140 W King St 89703 775-283-2800
Dan Sadler, prin. Fax 283-2890
Eagle Valley MS 600/6-8
4151 E Fifth St 89701 775-283-2600
Lee Conley, prin. Fax 283-2690
Pioneer Alternative HS 200/Alt
225 E Park St 89706 775-283-1300
Jason Zona, prin. Fax 283-1390

Carson City Beauty Academy Post-Sec.
1851 S Roop St Ste 100 89701 775-885-9853
Sierra Lutheran HS 100/9-12
3601 Romans Rd 89705 775-267-1921
Brian Underwood, admin. Fax 267-6580
Western Nevada College Post-Sec.
2201 W College Pkwy 89703 775-445-3000

Dayton, Lyon, Pop. 8,727
Lyon County SD
Supt. — See Yerington
Dayton HS 800/9-12
335 Dayton Valley Rd 89403 775-246-6240
Tim Logan, prin. Fax 246-6245
Dayton IS 600/6-8
315 Dayton Valley Rd 89403 775-246-6250
Linda Flaherty, prin. Fax 246-6253

Dyer, Esmeralda, Pop. 249

Deep Springs College Post-Sec.
HC 72 Box 45001 89010 760-872-2000

Elko, Elko, Pop. 17,970
Elko County SD 8,500/K-12
PO Box 1012 89803 775-738-5196
Jeff Zander, supt. Fax 738-5857
www.ecsdnv.net
Adobe MS 700/7-8
3375 Jennings Way 89801 775-738-3375
Colby Corbitt, prin. Fax 738-3860
Elko HS 1,300/9-12
987 College Ave 89801 775-738-7281
Mike Altenburg, prin. Fax 738-9616
Adult HS Adult
PO Box 1012 89803 775-753-2233
Anna Bolin, lead tchr. Fax 753-2257
Other Schools – See Carlin, Jackpot, Owyhee, Spring Creek, Wells, West Wendover

---

Great Basin College Post-Sec.
1500 College Pkwy 89801 775-738-8493

Ely, White Pine, Pop. 4,185
White Pine County SD 1,400/K-12
1135 Avenue C 89301 775-289-4851
Bob Dolezal, supt. Fax 289-3999
www.whitepine.k12.nv.us
White Pine HS 400/9-12
1800 Bobcat Dr 89301 775-289-4811
Adam Young, prin. Fax 289-1542
White Pine MS 300/6-8
844 Aultman St 89301 775-289-4841
Aaron Hansen, prin. Fax 289-1565
Other Schools – See Lund

Eureka, Eureka, Pop. 600
Eureka County SD 200/K-12
PO Box 249 89316 775-237-5373
Ben Zunino, supt. Fax 237-5014
www.eureka.k12.nv.us
Eureka County JSHS 100/7-12
PO Box 237 89316 775-237-5361
Ken Fujii, prin. Fax 237-5113

Fallon, Churchill, Pop. 8,201
Churchill County SD 3,700/PK-12
690 S Maine St 89406 775-423-5184
Dr. Bus Scharmann, supt. Fax 423-0583
www.churchill.k12.nv.us
Churchill County HS 1,300/9-12
1222 S Taylor St 89406 775-423-2181
Kevin Lords, prin. Fax 423-8968
Churchill County MS 600/7-8
650 S Maine St 89406 775-423-7701
Scott Meihack, prin. Fax 423-8010

Fernley, Lyon, Pop. 18,657
Lyon County SD
Supt. — See Yerington
Fernley HS 900/9-12
1300 US Highway 95A S 89408 775-575-3400
Kent Jones, prin. Fax 575-3406
Silverland MS 7-8
1100 Jasmine Ln 89408 775-575-1575
Ryan Cross, prin. Fax 575-1566
Fernley Adult Education Center Adult
1300 US Highway 95A S 89408 775-575-3409
Kathleen Jameson, prin. Fax 575-3399

Gabbs, Nye, Pop. 259
Nye County SD
Supt. — See Tonopah
Gabbs S 50/PK-12
PO Box 147 89409 775-285-2692
Jerri Kerns, prin. Fax 285-2381

Gardnerville, Douglas, Pop. 5,526
Douglas County SD
Supt. — See Minden
Carson Valley MS 800/7-9
1477 US Highway 395 N 89410 775-782-2265
Bob Been, prin. Fax 782-7341
Pau-Wa-Lu MS 600/7-9
701 Long Valley Rd, 775-265-6100
Keith Lewis, prin. Fax 265-1653

Gerlach, Washoe, Pop. 206
Washoe County SD
Supt. — See Reno
Gerlach S 50/K-12
555 E Sunset Blvd 89412 775-557-2326
Rick Taylor, prin. Fax 557-2587

Hawthorne, Mineral, Pop. 3,168
Mineral County SD 300/PK-12
PO Box 1540 89415 775-945-2403
Chris Schultz, supt. Fax 945-3709
www.mineral.k12.nv.us
Hawthorne JHS 100/7-8
PO Box 1060 89415 775-945-3332
Walt Hackford, prin. Fax 945-3371
Mineral County HS 200/9-12
PO Box 938 89415 775-945-3332
Walt Hackford, prin. Fax 945-3371

Henderson, Clark, Pop. 247,241
Clark County SD
Supt. — See Las Vegas
Basic HS 2,500/9-12
400 Palo Verde Dr 89015 702-799-8000
David Bechtel, prin. Fax 799-8966
Brown JHS 900/6-8
307 Cannes St 89015 702-799-8900
Gregory Misel, prin. Fax 799-3511
Burkholder MS 800/6-8
355 W Van Wagenen St 89015 702-799-8080
Jessie Phee, prin. Fax 799-8088
College of Southern Nevada HS-South 100/11-12
700 College Dr, 702-651-3080
Dennis Birr, prin. Fax 651-3075
Coronado HS 3,100/9-12
1001 Coronado Center Dr 89052 702-799-6800
Lee Koelliker, prin. Fax 799-6839
Foothill HS 2,600/9-12
800 College Dr, 702-799-3500
Jeanne Donadio, prin. Fax 799-3524
Greenspun JHS 1,400/6-8
140 N Valle Verde Dr 89074 702-799-0920
Warren McKay, prin. Fax 799-0925
Green Valley HS 2,900/9-12
460 N Arroyo Grande Blvd 89014 702-799-0950
Jeffrey Horn, prin. Fax 799-0717
Liberty HS 2,000/9-12
3700 Liberty Heights Ave 89052 702-799-2270
Jeffrey Geihs, prin. Fax 799-6858
Mannion MS 1,800/6-8
155 E Paradise Hills Dr, 702-799-3020
David Erbach, prin. Fax 799-3501
Miller MS 1,800/6-8
2400 Cozy Hill Cir 89052 702-799-2260
Nicole Lehman-Donadio, prin. Fax 799-1309
Webb MS 1,800/6-8
2200 Reunion Ave 89052 702-799-1305
Paula Naegle, prin. Fax 799-1310
White MS 1,400/6-8
1661 Galleria Dr 89014 702-799-0777
Jesse Welsh, prin. Fax 799-7690

College of Southern Nevada Post-Sec.
700 College Dr, 702-651-3000
DeVry University Post-Sec.
2490 Paseo Verde Pkwy #150 89074 702-933-9700
Euphoria Inst of Beauty Arts & Sciences Post-Sec.
11041 S Eastern Ave Ste 112 89052 702-932-8111
Everest College Post-Sec.
170 N Stephanie St 89074 702-567-1920

Green Valley Christian S 600/PK-12
711 N Valle Verde Dr 89014 702-454-4056
Deborah Ingalls, prin. Fax 454-6275
Henderson International S 300/K-12
1165 Sandy Ridge Ave 89052 702-818-2100
Seth Ahlborn, hdmstr. Fax 616-2065
Intl Academy of Design and Technology Post-Sec.
2495 Village View Dr 89074 702-990-0150
ITT Technical Institute Post-Sec.
168 N Gibson Rd 89014 702-558-5404
Lake Mead Christian Academy 600/PK-12
540 E Lake Mead Pkwy 89015 702-565-5831
Gayle Blakeley, admin. Fax 566-6206
Nevada State College Post-Sec.
1125 Nevada State Dr, 702-992-2000
Roseman University of Health Sciences Post-Sec.
11 Sunset Way 89014 702-990-4433
The Art Institute of Las Vegas Post-Sec.
2350 Corporate Cir 89074 702-369-9944

Incline Village, Washoe, Pop. 8,627
Washoe County SD
Supt. — See Reno
Incline HS 300/9-12
499 Village Blvd 89451 775-832-4260
Stacey Cooper, prin. Fax 832-4208
Incline MS 200/6-8
931 Southwood Blvd 89451 775-832-4220
Kathleen Watty, prin. Fax 832-4210

Sierra Nevada College-Lake Tahoe Post-Sec.
999 Tahoe Blvd 89451 775-831-1314

Indian Springs, Clark, Pop. 947
Clark County SD
Supt. — See Las Vegas
Indian Springs HS 100/9-12
PO Box 1088 89018 702-799-0932
Brian Wiseman, prin. Fax 879-3142
Indian Springs MS 100/6-8
400 Sky Rd 89018 702-799-0932
Brian Wiseman, prin. Fax 879-3142
Indian Springs Adult HS Adult
PO Box 208 89070 702-879-1029
Robert Tarter, prin. Fax 486 3398

Jackpot, Elko, Pop. 1,175
Elko County SD
Supt. — See Elko
Jackpot S 100/K-12
PO Box 463 89825 775-755-2374
Brian Messmer, prin. Fax 755-2291

Las Vegas, Clark, Pop. 562,567
Clark County SD 307,400/PK-12
5100 W Sahara Ave 89146 702-799-5000
Dwight Jones, supt. Fax 799-5125
www.ccsd.net/
Academy for Individualized Study 300/Alt
3050 E Flamingo Rd 89121 702-799 8630
Anita Wilbur, admin. Fax 799-0169
Advance Technologies Academy 1,100/9-12
2501 Vegas Dr 89106 702-799 7870
Karen Diamond, prin. Fax 799-0656
Arbor View HS 2,700/9-12
7500 Whispering Sands Dr 89131 702-799-6660
Kevin McPartlin, prin. Fax 799-6669
Bailey MS 1,300/6-8
2500 N Hollywood Blvd 89156 702-799-4811
Teri Knepp, prin. Fax 799-4807
Becker MS 1,400/6-8
9151 Pinewood Hills Dr 89134 702-799-4460
Amy Smith, prin. Fax 799-4470
Biltmore Continuation S 100/Alt
801 Veterans Memorial Dr 89101 702-799-7880
Michael Sharapan, prin. Fax 799-7889
Bonanza HS 2,200/9-12
6665 Del Rey Ave 89146 702-799-4000
Northey Henderson, prin. Fax 799-4078
Brinley MS 900/6-8
2480 Maverick St 89108 702-799-4550
Sharon Beatty, prin. Fax 799-4549
Burk Horizon/Southwest Sunset HS 300/Alt
4560 W Harmon Ave 89103 702-799-8150
Derek Bellow, prin. Fax 799-1207
Cadwallader MS 1,600/6-8
7775 Elkhorn Rd 89131 702-799-6692
Kathryn Singer, prin. Fax 799-4536
Canarelli MS 1,600/6-8
7808 S Torrey Pines Dr 89139 702-799-1340
Kathy Mead, prin. Fax 799-5715
Cannon JHS 900/6-8
5850 Euclid St 89120 702-799-5600
Elmer Manzanares, prin. Fax 799-5644
Cashman MS 1,500/6-8
4622 W Desert Inn Rd 89102 702-799-5880
Misti Taton, prin. Fax 799-5947
Centennial HS 3,000/9-12
10200 Centennial Pkwy 89149 702-799-3440
Trent Day, prin. Fax 799-3443
Chaparral HS 2,400/9-12
3850 Annie Oakley Dr 89121 702-799-7580
David Wilson, prin. Fax 799-0776
Cimarron-Memorial HS 2,700/9-12
2301 N Tenaya Way 89128 702-799-4400
Joseph Caruso, prin. Fax 799-4425
Clark HS 2,700/9-12
4291 Pennwood Ave 89102 702-799-5800
Jillyn Pendleton, prin. Fax 799-5813
College of Southern Nevada HS-West 200/11-12
6375 W Charleston Blvd 89146 702-651-5030
Dennis Birr, prin. Fax 651-5035
Cortney JHS 1,200/6-8
5301 E Hacienda Ave 89122 702-799-2400
David Rose, prin. Fax 799-2407
Cowan Behavior JSHS 100/Alt
5300 E Russell Rd 89122 702-799-6380
Gina Piccolo, prin. Fax 799-6388
Cowan Sunset Program 100/Alt
5300 E Russell Rd 89122 702-799-6370
Anita Williams, prin. Fax 799-6377
Del Sol HS 2,100/9-12
3100 E Patrick Ln 89120 702-799-6830
Lisandra Primas, prin. Fax 799-2235
Desert Oasis HS 2,000/9-12
6600 W Erie Ave 89141 702-799-6881
Emil Wozniak, prin. Fax 799-6888
Desert Pines HS 2,300/9-12
3800 Harris Ave 89110 702-799-2196
Timothy Stephens, prin. Fax 799-2198
Durango HS 2,300/9-12
7100 W Dewey Dr 89113 702-799-5850
Kristy Keller, prin. Fax 799-5855
East Career & Technical Academy Vo/Tech
6705 Vegas Valley Dr 89142 702-799-8888
Glenda Goetting, prin. Fax 799-8899
Eldorado HS 1,600/9-12
1139 Linn Ln 89110 702-799-7200
Danielle Miller, prin. Fax 799-7255
Escobedo MS 1,200/6-8
9501 Echelon Point Dr 89149 702-799-4560
Stefanie Machin, prin. Fax 799-4568
Faiss MS 1,200/6-8
9525 W Maule Ave 89148 702-799-6850
Eduardo Zaldivar, prin. Fax 799-6852
Fertitta MS 1,400/6-8
9905 W Mesa Vista Ave 89148 702-799-1900
Elizabeth Cano, prin. Fax 799-5688
Fremont Professional Development MS 900/6-8
1100 E Saint Louis Ave 89104 702-799-5558
Ann Brown, prin. Fax 799-5566
Garside JHS 1,200/6-8
300 S Torrey Pines Dr 89107 702-799-4245
Scarlett Perryman, prin. Fax 799-4296
Gibson MS 1,000/6-8
3900 W Washington Ave 89107 702-799-4700
Linda Archambault, prin. Fax 799-4705
Global Community HS 200/Alt
3801 E Washington Ave 89110 702-799-8850
John Anzalone, prin. Fax 799-8898
Guinn MS 800/6-8
4150 S Torrey Pines Dr 89103 702-799-5900
Georgia Taton, prin. Fax 799-5905
Harney MS 1,800/6-8
1580 S Hollywood Blvd 89142 702-799-3240
Susan Echols, prin. Fax 799-3286
Hyde Park MS 1,700/6-8
900 Hinson St 89107 702-799-4260
Kimberly Bauman, prin. Fax 799-0348
Johnson JHS 1,200/6-8
7701 Ducharme Ave 89145 702-799-4480
Terry Ann Sobrero, prin. Fax 799 4497
Keller MS 1,300/6-8
301 Fogg St 89110 702-799-3220
Karen Smallwood, prin. Fax 799-3226
Knudson MS 1,300/6-8
2400 Atlantic St 89104 702-799-7470
Monica Cortez, prin. Fax 799-0157
Las Vegas Academy/Intl Stud/Perf/Vis Art 1,600/9-12
315 S 7th St 89101 702-799-7800
Scott Walker, prin. Fax 799-7948
Las Vegas HS 2,900/9-12
6500 E Sahara Ave 89142 702-799-0180
Debbie Brockett, prin. Fax 799-0192
Lawrence JHS 1,400/6-8
4410 S Juliano Rd 89147 702-799-2540
Bevelyn Smothers, prin. Fax 799-2563
Leavitt MS 1,500/6-8
4701 Quadrel St 89129 702-799-4699
Keith Wipperman, prin. Fax 799-4528
Lied MS 1,400/6-8
5350 W Tropical Pkwy 89130 702-799-4620
Kimberly Bass-Davis, prin. Fax 799-4626
Mack MS 1,400/6-8
4250 Karen Ave 89121 702-799-2005
Teresa Holden, prin. Fax 799-2412
Martin MS 1,400/6-8
200 N 28th St 89101 702-799-7922
Mary Hafner, prin. Fax 799-7959
Molasky JHS 1,500/6-8
7801 W Gilmore Ave 89129 702-799-3400
Daron Heilman, prin. Fax 799-3407
Monaco MS 1,300/6-8
1870 N Lamont St 89115 702-799-3670
Lisa Medina, prin. Fax 799-3202
Morris Behavior JSHS 50/Alt
3801 E Washington Ave 89110 702-855-7820
John Anzalone, prin. Fax 855-7879
Morris Sunset E HS 100/Alt
3801 E Washington Ave 89110 702-799-8880
Randy Pagel, prin. Fax 799-8898
Northwest Career & Technical Academy 1,900/9-12
8200 W Tropical Pkwy 89149 702-799-4640
Frank Pesce, prin. Fax 799-4644
O'Callaghan MS 1,400/6-8
1450 Radwick Dr 89110 702-799-7340
Merry Sillitoe, prin. Fax 799-8870
Orr MS 900/6-8
1562 E Katie Ave 89119 702-799-5573
George Leavens, prin. Fax 799-0297
Palo Verde HS 2,800/9-12
333 S Pavilion Center Dr 89144 702-799-1450
Daniel Phillips, prin. Fax 799-1455
Peterson Behavior JSHS 100/Alt
10250 Centennial Pkwy 89149 702-799-6610
Scott Fligor, prin. Fax 799-6604
Rancho HS 3,000/9-12
1900 Searles Ave 89101 702-799-7000
James Kuzma, prin. Fax 799-8316
Robison MS 1,100/6-8
825 Marion Dr 89110 702-799-7300
Elena Baker, prin. Fax 799-7302
Rogich MS 1,800/6-8
235 N Pavilion Center Dr 89144 702-799-6040
Susan Harrison, prin. Fax 799-6094
Saville MS 1,600/6-8
8101 N Torrey Pines Dr 89131 702-799-3460
Joy Lea, prin. Fax 799-4511
Sawyer MS 1,300/6-8
5450 Redwood St 89118 702-799-5980
Kim Friel, prin. Fax 799-5969
Schofield MS 1,300/6-8
8625 Spencer St 89123 702-799-2290
Arthur Adams, prin. Fax 799-5717
Shadow Ridge HS 2,300/9-12
5050 Brent Ln 89131 702-799-6699
Thomas Barberini, prin. Fax 799-4698
Sierra Vista HS 2,100/9-12
8100 W Robindale Rd 89113 702-799-6820
Shawn Boyle, prin. Fax 799-6847
Silverado HS 2,500/9-12
1650 Silver Hawk Ave 89123 702-799-5790
Kim Grytdahl, prin. Fax 799-5744
Silvestri JHS 1,500/6-8
1055 E Silverado Ranch Blvd, 702-799-2240
Robert Mars, prin. Fax 799-2247
South Continuation HS 100/Alt
1801 S Maryland Pkwy 89104 702-799-2070
Thomas Gerbracht, prin. Fax 799-2089
Southeast Career Tech Academy Vo/Tech
5710 Mountain Vista St 89120 702-799-7500
Richard Arguello, prin. Fax 799-2007
Southwest Behavior JSHS 100/Alt
6480 Fairbanks Rd 89103 702-799-5904
Caryl Suzuki, prin. Fax 799-1294
Southwest Career & Tech Academy Vo/Tech
7050 W Shelbourne Ave 89113 702-799-5766
Felicia Nemcek, prin. Fax 799-5751
Spring Mountain JSHS 100/Alt
PO Box 252 89125 702-455-5555
Frank Cooper, prin. Fax 382-6035
Spring Valley HS 2,300/9-12
3750 S Buffalo Dr 89147 702-799-2580
Robert Gerye, prin. Fax 799-1288
Sunrise Mountain HS 2,400/9-12
2575 Los Feliz St 89156 702-799-7207
John Barlow, prin. Fax 799-7212
Tarkanian MS 1,300/6-8
5800 W Pyle Ave 89141 702-799-6801
Darren Sweikert, prin. Fax 799-6805
Valley HS 3,000/9-12
2839 Burnham Ave, 702-799-5450
Deann Burnett, prin. Fax 799-1074
Veterans Tribute Career Technical Acad 600/9-12
2531 Vegas Dr 89106 702-799-4710
Tammy Bofelli, prin. Fax 799-4722
Von Tobel MS 1,100/6-8
2436 N Pecos Rd 89115 702-799-7280
Rogelio Gonzalez, prin. Fax 799-7286
West Career & Technical Academy 9-12
11945 W Charleston Blvd 89135 702-799-4340
Monte Bay, prin. Fax 799-4355
Western HS 2,300/9-12
4601 W Bonanza Rd 89107 702-799-4080
Neddy Alvarez, prin. Fax 799-4104
West Prep S 1,300/K-12
2050 Saphire Stone Ave 89106 702-799-3120
Michael Piccininni, prin. Fax 799-1858
Woodbury MS 900/6-8
3875 E Harmon Ave 89121 702-799-7660
Greg Snelling, prin. Fax 799-0805
Other Schools – See Boulder City, Henderson, Indian Springs, Laughlin, Logandale, Mesquite, North Las Vegas, Overton, Sandy Valley

---

Academy of Hair Design Post-Sec.
5191 W Charleston Blvd #150 89146 702-878-1185
Adelson Educational Campus 400/PK-12
9700 Hillpointe Rd 89134 702-255-4500
Paul Schiffman, hdmstr. Fax 255-7232
American Heritage Academy 200/PK-12
6126 S Sandhill Rd 89120 702-949-5614
Laurel Beckstead, hdmstr. Fax 949-0273
American Institute of Medical Sonography Post-Sec.
5450 W Sahara Ave Ste 320 89146 702-369-4216
Anthem Institute Post-Sec.
2320 S Rancho Dr 89102 702-385-6700
Associated Pathologist Laboratories Post-Sec.
4230 Burnham Ave 89119 702-733-7866
Bishop Gorman HS 1,200/9-12
5959 S Hualapai Way 89148 702-732-1945
Kevin Kiefer, prin. Fax 732-2856
Calvary Chapel Christian S 600/PK-12
7175 W Oquendo Rd 89113 702-248-8879
James Davis, supt. Fax 220-8694
Carrington College Post-Sec.
5740 S Eastern Ave Ste 140 89119 702-688-4300
College of Southern Nevada Post-Sec.
6375 W Charleston Blvd 89146 702-651-5000
Euphoria Inst of Beauty Arts & Sciences Post-Sec.
6578 N Decatur Blvd Ste 200 89131 702-360-8111
Euphoria Inst of Beauty Arts & Sciences Post-Sec.
9340 W Sahara Ave Ste 205 89117 702-341-8111
Faith Lutheran MSHS 1,400/6-12
2015 S Hualapai Way 89117 702-804-4400
Steven Buuck Ph.D., admin. Fax 804-4488
Institute of Professional Careers Post-Sec.
4472 S Eastern Ave 89119 702-734-9900
John Fish Jewelry School Post-Sec.
933 E Sahara Ave Ste B5 89104 702-731-3686
Kaplan College Post-Sec.
3535 W Sahara Ave 89102 702-368-2338
Le Cordon Bleu College of Culinary Arts Post-Sec.
1451 Center Crossing Rd 89144 702-365-7690
Liberty Baptist Academy 200/K-12
6501 W Lake Mead Blvd 89108 702-647-4522
John Shorer, admin. Fax 647-8083
Marinello School of Beauty Post-Sec.
5001 E Bonanza Rd Ste 110 89110 702-796-6200
Meadows S 900/PK-12
8601 Scholar Ln 89128 702-254-1610
Henry Chanin, hdmstr. Fax 254-2452

Montessori Visions Academy 100/PK-12
3551 E Sunset Rd 89120 702-451-9801
Lori Bossy M.Ed., admin. Fax 451-0049
Mountain View Christian S 500/PK-12
3900 E Bonanza Rd 89110 702-452-1300
Dr. Crystal McClanahan, supt. Fax 452-0499
Oasis Christian Academy 100/PK-12
5220 E Russell Rd 89122 702-777-0800
Pima Medical Institute Post-Sec.
3333 E Flamingo Rd 89121 702-458-9650
Southern Nevada Univ of Cosmetology Post-Sec.
3315 E Russell Rd Ste A4 89120 702-458-6333
Trinity International S 200/K-12
700 E Saint Louis Ave 89104 702-732-3957
Maria Cochrane, admin. Fax 784-0192
University of Nevada Las Vegas Post-Sec.
4505 S Maryland Pkwy 89154 702-895-3011
Word of Life Christian Academy 300/PK-12
3520 N Buffalo Dr 89129 702-645-1180
Rev. Kelly Marchello, prin. Fax 396-0293

Laughlin, Clark, Pop. 7,092
Clark County SD
Supt. — See Las Vegas
Laughlin MSHS 400/6-12
1900 Cougar Dr 89029 702-298-1996
Lynne Ruegamer, prin. Fax 298-5493

Logandale, Clark
Clark County SD
Supt. — See Las Vegas
Moapa Valley HS 600/9-12
2400 St Joseph St 89021 702-397-2611
Grant Hanevold, prin. Fax 397-2892

Lovelock, Pershing, Pop. 1,824
Pershing County SD 700/K-12
PO Box 389 89419 775-273-7819
Daniel Fox, supt. Fax 273-2668
www.pershing.k12.nv.us
Pershing County HS 200/9-12
PO Box 990 89419 775-273-2625
Russell Fecht, prin. Fax 273-2163
Pershing County MS 200/6-8
PO Box 1020 89419 775-273-1200
Richard Tree, prin. Fax 273-3191

Lund, White Pine, Pop. 277
White Pine County SD
Supt. — See Ely
Lund JSHS 50/7-12
PO Box 129 89317 775-238-5200
Jolynn Maynard, prin. Fax 238-0208

Mc Dermitt, Humboldt, Pop. 172
Humboldt County SD
Supt. — See Winnemucca
Mc Dermitt JSHS 100/7-12
PO Box 98 89421 775-532-8761
Dustin Christean, prin. Fax 532-8017

Mesquite, Clark, Pop. 15,069
Clark County SD
Supt. — See Las Vegas
Hughes MS 600/6-8
550 Hafen Ln 89027 702-346-3250
Maurice Perkins, prin. Fax 346-3095
Virgin Valley HS 700/9-12
820 Valley View Dr 89027 702-346-2780
Clifford Hughes, prin. Fax 346-7265

Minden, Douglas, Pop. 2,948
Douglas County SD 6,200/K-12
1638 Mono Ave 89423 775-782-5134
Lisa Noonan Ed.D., supt. Fax 782-3162
www.dcsd.k12.nv.us
Douglas HS 1,400/10-12
1670 State Route 88 89423 775-782-5136
Marty Swisher, prin. Fax 782-7039
Other Schools – See Gardnerville, Zephyr Cove

North Las Vegas, Clark, Pop. 207,375
Clark County SD
Supt. — See Las Vegas
Bridger MS 1,300/6-8
2505 N Bruce St 89030 702-799-7185
Deanna Jaskolski, prin. Fax 799-7074
Canyon Springs HS 2,500/9-12
350 E Alexander Rd 89032 702-799-1870
Ronnie Guerzon, prin. Fax 799-1876
Cheyenne HS 2,400/9-12
3200 W Alexander Rd 89032 702-799-4830
April Key, prin. Fax 799-4856
College of Southern Nevada HS-East 100/11-12
3200 E Cheyenne Ave 89030 702-651-4070
Dennis Birr, prin. Fax 651-4627
Cram MS 1,500/6-8
1900 W Deer Springs Way 89084 702-799-7020
Lori Sarabyn, prin. Fax 799-8346
Findlay MS 1,500/6-8
333 W Tropical Pkwy 89031 702-799-3160
Ken Sobaszek, prin. Fax 799-3169
Jeffrey Behavior JSHS 100/Alt
602 W Brooks Ave 89030 702-799-8375
Frances Hall, prin. Fax 799-8369
Johnston MS 1,400/6-8
5855 Lawrence St, 702-799-7001
Lisa Rustand, prin. Fax 799-7010
Legacy HS 2,800/9-12
150 W Deer Springs Way 89084 702-799-1777
Tammy Malich, prin. Fax 799-1701
Mojave HS 2,100/9-12
5302 Goldfield St 89031 702-799-0432
Antonio Rael, prin. Fax 799-0437
Sedway MS 1,400/6-8
3465 Engelstad St 89032 702-799-3880
Zachary Robbins, prin. Fax 799-1785
Smith MS 900/6-8
1301 E Tonopah Ave 89030 702-799-7080
Brett Booth, prin. Fax 799-7195

Swainston MS 1,300/6-8
3500 W Gilmore Ave 89032 702-799-4860
Lori Desiderato, prin. Fax 799-4806
Washington Continuation S 50/Alt
1901 White St 89030 702-799-8320
Margaret Harmon, prin. Fax 799-8322
Desert Rose Adult HS Adult
444 W Brooks Ave 89030 702-799-6240
Sandra Ransel, prin. Fax 799-8371

American Institute of Technology Post-Sec.
4020 E Lone Mountain Rd, 702-644-1234
College of Southern Nevada Post-Sec.
3200 E Cheyenne Ave 89030 702-651-4000
ITT Technical Institute Post-Sec.
3825 W Cheyenne Ave Ste 600 89032 702-240-0967

Overton, Clark
Clark County SD
Supt. — See Las Vegas
Lyon MS 400/6-8
179 S Anderson St 89040 702-397-8610
Roderick Adams, prin. Fax 397-2754

Owyhee, Elko, Pop. 941
Elko County SD
Supt. — See Elko
Owyhee S 100/K-12
PO Box 100 89832 775-757-3400
Joseph Mirich, prin. Fax 757-3663

Pahrump, Nye, Pop. 35,299
Nye County SD
Supt. — See Tonopah
Clarke MS 1,100/6-8
4201 N Blagg Rd 89060 775-727-5546
Tim Wombaker, prin. Fax 727-7104
Pahrump Valley HS 1,400/9-12
501 E Calvada Blvd 89048 775-727-7737
Max Bufe, prin. Fax 727-7722
Pathways Innovative Education 100/Alt
484 West St 89048 775-751-6822
Karen Hills, prin. Fax 751-6829

Panaca, Lincoln, Pop. 955
Lincoln County SD 900/K-12
PO Box 118 89042 775-728-4471
Nykki Holton, supt. Fax 728-4435
lcsdnv.com
Lincoln County HS 200/9-12
PO Box 268 89042 775-728-4481
Marty Soderborg, prin. Fax 728-4484
Meadow Valley MS 100/7-8
PO Box 567 89042 775-728-4655
Marty Soderborg, prin. Fax 728-4302
Other Schools – See Alamo, Caliente

Reno, Washoe, Pop. 217,361
State Supported Schools
Supt. — None
Davidson Academy of Nevada 100/5-12
PO Box 9119 89507 775-682-5800
Colleen Harsin, dir. Fax 682-5801

Washoe County SD 63,100/PK-12
PO Box 30425 89520 775-348-0200
Pedro Martinez, supt. Fax 348-0304
www.washoecountyschools.org
Academy of Arts Careers and Technology Vo/Tech
380 Edison Way 89502 775-861-4418
Robert Sullivan, prin. Fax 861-4415
Billinghurst MS 700/7-8
6685 Chesterfield Ln 89523 775-746-5870
Ken Cervantes, prin. Fax 746-5875
Clayton MS 600/7-8
1295 Wyoming Ave 89503 775-746-5860
Bruce Meissner, prin. Fax 746-5864
Cold Springs MS 900/5-8
18235 Cody Ct, 775-677-5433
Roberta Duval, prin. Fax 677-5439
Damonte Ranch HS 1,300/9-12
10500 Rio Wrangler Pkwy, 775-851-5656
Denise Hausauer, prin. Fax 851-5663
Depoali MS 1,200/6-8
9300 Wilbur May Pkwy, 775-852-6700
Juliana Annand, prin. Fax 852-6701
Galena HS 1,400/9-12
3600 Butch Cassidy Dr 89511 775-851-5630
Tom Brown, prin. Fax 851-5607
Hare Occupational Center Vo/Tech
350 Hunter Lake Dr 89509 775-857-4947
Hug HS 1,400/9-12
2880 Sutro St 89512 775-333-5300
Lauren Baxter, prin. Fax 333-5312
McQueen HS 1,900/9-12
6055 Lancer St 89523 775-746-5880
John Carlson, prin. Fax 747-6883
North Valleys HS 2,200/9-12
1470 E Golden Valley Rd 89506 775-677-5499
Jeana Curtis, prin. Fax 677-5497
O'Brien MS 700/7-8
10500 Stead Blvd 89506 775-677-5420
Mary Green, prin. Fax 677-5423
Pine MS 800/7-8
4800 Neil Rd 89502 775-689-2550
Brad Boudreau, prin. Fax 689-2539
Reno HS 1,700/9-12
395 Booth St 89509 775-333-5050
Kris Hackbusch, prin. Fax 333-5058
Swope MS 700/7-8
901 Keele Dr 89509 775-333-5330
George Brown, prin. Fax 333-5083
Traner MS 500/7-8
1700 Carville Dr 89512 775-333-5130
Chad Lindeen, prin. Fax 333-5135
Truckee Meadows Community College HS 200/11-12
7000 Dandini Blvd 89512 775-674-7660
Susan Mayes-Smith, admin. Fax 674-7931

Vaughn MS 500/7-8
1200 Bresson Ave 89502 775-333-5160
Dr. Ginny Knowles, prin. Fax 333-5118
Washoe Innovations HS 500/9-12
777 W 2nd St 89503 775-333-5150
Frank Selvaggio, prin. Fax 333-5122
Washoe Inspire Academy Alt
1155 Corporate Blvd 89502 775-857-3181
Taylor Harper, admin. Fax 337-3182
Wooster HS 1,600/9-12
1331 E Plumb Ln 89502 775-333-5100
Leah Keuscher, prin. Fax 333-5108
Other Schools – See Gerlach, Incline Village, Sparks

Bishop Manogue HS 600/9-12
110 Bishop Manogue Dr 89511 775-336-6000
Tim Jaureguito, prin. Fax 336-6015
Carrington College Post-Sec.
5580 Kietzke Ln 89511 775-686-2494
Church Academy 50/K-12
1205 N McCarran Blvd 89512 775-329-5848
Dan Moriarty, admin. Fax 329-3360
Morrison University Post-Sec.
10315 Professional Cir #201, 888-852-7272
Sage Ridge S 200/5-12
2515 Crossbow Ct 89511 775-852-6222
Sierra Nevada HS 600/9-12
14175 Mount Charleston St 89506 775-709-0051
Joseph Reading Ph.D., prin. Fax 789-1091
Truckee Meadows Community College Post-Sec.
7000 Dandini Blvd 89512 775-673-7000
University of Nevada Reno Post-Sec.
1664 N Virginia St 89557 775-784-1110

Round Mountain, Nye
Nye County SD
Supt. — See Tonopah
Round Mountain JSHS 100/6-12
PO Box 1427 89045 775-377-2690
James Fitch, prin. Fax 377-1239

Sandy Valley, Clark, Pop. 1,978
Clark County SD
Supt. — See Las Vegas
Sandy Valley HS 100/9-12
HC 31 Box 111 89019 702-723-1800
Gerald Cornell, prin. Fax 723-1802
Sandy Valley MS 100/6-8
HC 31 Box 111 89019 702-723-1800
Gerald Cornell, prin. Fax 723-1802

Silver Springs, Lyon, Pop. 5,112
Lyon County SD
Supt. — See Yerington
Silver Stage HS 400/9-12
3755 W Spruce Ave 89429 775-577-5071
Patrick Peters, prin. Fax 577-5079

Smith, Lyon, Pop. 1,033
Lyon County SD
Supt. — See Yerington
Smith Valley S 200/K-12
20 Day Ln 89430 775-465-2332
M. Gradillas, prin. Fax 465-2681

Sparks, Washoe, Pop. 87,304
Washoe County SD
Supt. — See Reno
Dilworth MS 600/7-8
255 Prater Way 89431 775-353-5740
Laura Peterson, prin. Fax 353-5584
Mendive MS 900/7-8
1900 Whitewood Dr 89434 775-353-5990
Scott Grange, prin. Fax 353-5994
Reed HS 2,200/9-12
1350 Baring Blvd 89434 775-353-5700
Mary Vesco, prin. Fax 353-5708
Shaw MS 1,100/7-8
600 Eagle Canyon Dr, 775-425-7777
Gina Leonhard, prin. Fax 425-7779
Spanish Springs HS 2,400/9-12
1065 Eagle Canyon Dr, 775-425-7733
Tasha Fuson, prin. Fax 425-7735
Sparks HS 1,200/9-12
820 15th St 89431 775-353-5550
Wanda Shakeenab, prin. Fax 353-5514
Sparks MS 800/7-8
2275 18th St 89431 775-353-5770
Kevin Carroll, prin. Fax 353-5585

Career College of Northern Nevada Post-Sec.
1421 Pullman Dr 89434 775-856-2266
Excel Christian S 100/K-12
850 Baring Blvd 89434 775-356-9995
Lisa Cross, admin. Fax 356-9527
Milan Institute Post-Sec.
950 Industrial Way 89431 775-348-7200

Spring Creek, Elko, Pop. 12,111
Elko County SD
Supt. — See Elko
Spring Creek HS 900/9-12
14550 Lamoille Hwy 89815 775-753-5575
Keith Walz, prin. Fax 753-5956
Spring Creek MS 600/6-8
14650 Lamoille Hwy 89815 775-777-1688
Tim Giere, prin. Fax 777-1738

Spring Creek Christian Academy 50/K-12
285 Spring Creek Pkwy 89815 775-777-1222
Patrick Herman, prin.

Tonopah, Nye, Pop. 2,418
Nye County SD 5,100/PK-12
PO Box 113 89049 775-482-6258
Dale Norton, supt. Fax 482-8573
www.nye.k12.nv.us

Tonopah HS 200/9-12
PO Box 1349 89049 775-482-3698
Alvin Eiseman, prin. Fax 482-3635
Other Schools – See Beatty, Gabbs, Pahrump, Round Mountain

Virginia City, Storey, Pop. 832
Storey County SD 400/PK-12
PO Box C 89440 775-847-0983
Dr. Robert Slaby, supt. Fax 847-0989
www.storey.k12.nv.us
Virginia City HS 100/9-12
PO Box C 89440 775-847-0992
Richard Schrank, prin. Fax 847-0994
Virginia City MS 100/6-8
PO Box C 89440 775-847-0980
Todd Hess, prin. Fax 847-0913

Wells, Elko, Pop. 1,257
Elko County SD
Supt. — See Elko
Wells S 100/K-12
PO Box 338 89835 775-752-3837
Donna Webster, prin. Fax 752-2470

West Wendover, Elko, Pop. 4,333
Elko County SD
Supt. — See Elko
West Wendover JSHS 300/7-12
PO Box 3830 89883 775-664-3940
Craig Kyllonen, prin. Fax 664-3944

Winnemucca, Humboldt, Pop. 7,277
Humboldt County SD 3,300/K-12
310 E 4th St 89445 775-623-8100
Dr. David Jensen, supt. Fax 623-8102
www.humboldt.k12.nv.us
Leighton Hall Alt
310 E 4th St 89445 775-623-6382
Deborah Watts, prin. Fax 623-6386
Lowry HS 1,000/9-12
5375 Kluncy Canyon Rd 89445 775-623-8130
Deborah Watts, prin. Fax 623-8185
Winnemucca JHS 500/7-8
451 Reinhart St 89445 775-623-8120
Janet Kennedy, prin. Fax 623-8208
Other Schools – See Mc Dermitt

Yerington, Lyon, Pop. 2,993
Lyon County SD 7,500/K-12
25 E Goldfield Ave 89447 775-463-6800
Keith Savage, supt. Fax 463-6808
www.lyon.k12.nv.us
Yerington HS 500/9-12
114 Pearl St 89447 775-463-6822
Jerry Ogolin, prin. Fax 463-6828
Yerington IS 400/5-8
215 Pearl St 89447 775-463-6833
Sean Moyle, prin. Fax 463-6840
Other Schools – See Dayton, Fernley, Silver Springs, Smith

Zephyr Cove, Douglas, Pop. 557
Douglas County SD
Supt. — See Minden
Whittell HS 200/7-12
PO Box 677 89448 775-588-2446
Crespin Esquivel, prin. Fax 588-2443

NEW HAMPSHIRE

NEW HAMPSHIRE DEPT. OF EDUCATION
101 Pleasant St, Concord 03301-3852
Telephone 603-271-3494
Fax 603-271-1953
Website http://www.education.nh.gov/

Commissioner of Education Virginia Barry

NEW HAMPSHIRE BOARD OF EDUCATION
101 Pleasant St, Concord 03301-3852

Chairperson Tom Raffio

SCHOOL ADMINISTRATIVE UNITS (SAU)

SAU 1
Dr. Richard Bergeron, supt. 603-924-3336
106 Hancock Rd Fax 924-6707
Peterborough 03458
www.conval.edu/

SAU 2
Mary Ellen Ormond, supt. 603-279-7947
103 Main St Ste 2, Meredith 03253 Fax 279-3044
www.sau2.k12.nh.us/

SAU 3
Corinne Cascadden, supt. 603-752-6500
183 Hillside Ave, Berlin 03570 Fax 752-2528
www.sau3.org/

SAU 4
Dr. Marie Ross, supt. 603-744-5555
20 N Main St, Bristol 03222 Fax 744-6659
www.sau4.org

SAU 5
James Morse, supt. 603-868-5100
36 Coe Dr, Durham 03824 Fax 868-6668
www.orcsd.org

SAU 6
Middleton McGoodwin Ed.D., supt. 603-543-4200
165 Broad St, Claremont 03743 Fax 543-4244
www.sau6.k12.nh.us/

SAU 7
Robert Mills, supt. 603-237-5571
21 Academy St, Colebrook 03576 Fax 237-5126

SAU 8
Dr. Christine Rath, supt. 603-225-0811
38 Liberty St, Concord 03301 Fax 226-2187
www.concordnhschools.net

SAU 9
Dr. Carl Nelson, supt. 603-447-8368
176A Main St, Conway 03818 Fax 447-8497
www.sau9.org

SAU 10
Laura Nelson, supt. 603-432-1210
18 S Main St, Derry 03038 Fax 432-1264
www.derry.k12.nh.us

SAU 11
Dr. Jean Briggs-Badger, supt. 603-516-6800
61 Locust St Ste 409, Dover 03820 Fax 516-6809
www.dover.k12.nh.us

SAU 12
Dr. Nathan Greenberg, supt. 603-432-6920
268C Mammoth Rd Fax 425-1049
Londonderry 03053
www.londonderry.org

SAU 13
Louis Goscinski, supt. 603-323-5088
881A Tamworth Rd Fax 323-5093
Tamworth 03886
sau13.weebly.com

SAU 14
Barbara Munsey, supt. 603-679-5402
213 Main St, Epping 03042 Fax 679-1237
www.sau14.org

SAU 15
Dr. Charles Littlefield, supt. 603-622-3731
90 Farmer Rd, Hooksett 03106 Fax 669-4352
www.sau15.net

SAU 16
Michael Morgan, supt. 603-775-8653
30 Linden St, Exeter 03833 Fax 775-8673
www.sau16.org/

SAU 17
Dr. Brian Blake, supt. 603-642-3688
178 Main St, Kingston 03848 Fax 642-7885
web.sau17.org

SAU 18
Dr. Maureen Ward, supt. 603-934-3108
119 Central St, Franklin 03235 Fax 934-3462
www.franklin.k12.nh.us

SAU 19
Brian Balke, supt. 603-497-4818
11 School St, Goffstown 03045 Fax 497-8425
www.goffstown.k12.nh.us

SAU 20
Paul Bousquet, supt. 603-466-3632
123 Main St, Gorham 03581 Fax 466-3870
www.sau20.org/

SAU 21
Robert Sullivan Ed.D., supt. 603-926-8992
2 Alumni Dr, Hampton 03842 Fax 926-5157
www.sau21.org/sau

SAU 23
Bruce Labs, supt. 603-787-2113
2975 Dartmouth College Hwy Fax 787-2118
North Haverhill 03774
www.sau23.org

SAU 24
Dr. Lorraine Tacconi-Moore, supt. 603-428-3269
258 Western Ave, Henniker 03242 Fax 428-6545
www.sau24.org

SAU 25
Timothy Mayes, supt. 603-472-3755
103 County Rd, Bedford 03110 Fax 472-2567
www.sau25.net/

SAU 26
Marjorie Chiafery, supt. 603-424-6200
36 McElwain St, Merrimack 03054 Fax 424-6229
www.merrimack.k12.nh.us

SAU 27
Brian Cochrane, supt. 603-578-3570
1 Highlander Ct, Litchfield 03052 Fax 578-1267
www.litchfieldsd.org

SAU 28
Dr. Henry LaBranche, supt. 603-425-1976
PO Box 510, Windham 03087 Fax 425-1719
www.sau28.org

SAU 29
Wayne Woolridge, supt. 603-357-9002
193 Maple Ave, Keene 03431 Fax 357-9012
www.sau29.org

SAU 30
Robert Champlin, supt. 603-524-5710
PO Box 309, Laconia 03247 Fax 528-8442
www2.laconiaschools.org/sau/

SAU 31
Dr. James Hayes, supt. 603-659-5020
186A Main St, Newmarket 03857 Fax 659-5022
www.newmarket.k12.nh.us

SAU 32
Gregory Vogt, supt. 603-469-3442
92 Bonner Rd, Meriden 03770 Fax 469-3985
www.plainfieldschool.org

SAU 33
Ellen Small, supt. 603-895-4299
43 Harriman Hill Rd Fax 895-0147
Raymond 03077
www.sau33.com

SAU 34
Dr. Robert Hassett, supt. 603-464-4466
PO Box 2190, Deering 03244 Fax 464-4053
www.hdsd.org

SAU 35
Paul MacMillan, supt. 603-444-3925
260 Cottage St Ste C Fax 444-6299
Littleton 03561
www.sau35.k12.nh.us

SAU 36
Harry Fensom, supt. 603-837-9363
14 King Sq, Whitefield 03598 Fax 837-2326
www.sau36.org

SAU 37
Thomas Brennan Ph.D., supt. 603-624-6300
195 McGregor St Ste 201 Fax 624-6337
Manchester 03102
www.mansd.org

SAU 39
Peter Warburton, supt. 603-673-2690
PO Box 849, Amherst 03031 Fax 672-1786
www.sprise.com/

SAU 40
Robert Suprenant, supt. 603-673-2202
100 West St, Milford 03055 Fax 673-2237
sau40.com

SAU 41
Susan Hodgdon, supt. 603-465-7118
PO Box 1588, Hollis 03049 Fax 465-3933
www.sau41.org

SAU 42
Mark Conrad, supt. 603-966-1000
PO Box 687, Nashua 03061 Fax 594-4350
www.nashua.edu

SAU 43
Irwin Sussman, supt. 603-863-3540
9 Depot St Ste 2, Newport 03773 Fax 863-5368
www.sau43.org

SAU 44
Dr. Michael Ludwell, supt. 603-942-1290
23 Mountain Ave Unit A Fax 942-1295
Northwood 03261
sau44.org

SAU 45
Susan Noyes, supt., PO Box 419 603-476-5247
Moultonborough 03254 Fax 476-8009
sau45.org

SAU 46
Dr. Michael Martin, supt. 603-753-6561
105 Community Dr Fax 753-6023
Penacook 03303
sau46.mvsd.k12.nh.us

SAU 47
James O'Neill, supt. 603-532-8100
81 Fitzgerald Dr Unit 2 Fax 532-8165
Jaffrey 03452
www.sau47.org

SAU 48
Mark Halloran, supt. 603-536-1254
47 Old Ward Bridge Rd Fax 536-3545
Plymouth 03264
www.sau48.org

SAU 49
John Robertson, supt. 603-569-1658
PO Box 190, Wolfeboro Falls 03896 Fax 569-6983
www.govwentworth.k12.nh.us

SAU 50
Dr. George Cushing, supt. 603-422-9572
48 Post Rd, Greenland 03840 Fax 422-9575
www.sau50.org

SAU 51
Dr. John Freeman, supt. 603-435-5526
23 Oneida St Unit 1 Fax 435-5331
Pittsfield 03263
pittsfield-nh.com/sau/district-2/district

SAU 52
Edward McDonough, supt. 603-431-5080
1 Junkins Ave Unit 402 Fax 431-6753
Portsmouth 03801
www.cityofportsmouth.com/school/

SAU 53
Helene Bickford, supt. 603-485-5188
267 Pembroke St, Pembroke 03275 Fax 485-9529
www.sau53.org

SAU 54
Michael Hopkins, supt. 603-332-3678
150 Wakefield St Ste 8 Fax 335-7367
Rochester 03867
www.rochesterschools.com

SAU 55
Dr. Earl Metzler, supt. 603-382-6119
30 Greenough Rd, Plaistow 03865 Fax 382-3334
www.timberlane.net/sau/

SAU 56
Jeni Mosca, supt. 603-692-4450
51 W High St, Somersworth 03878 Fax 692-9100
www.sau56.org

SAU 57
Michael Delahanty, supt. 603-893-7040
38 Geremonty Dr, Salem 03079 Fax 893-7080
www.sau57.org

SAU 58
Carl Ladd, supt. 603-636-1437
15 Preble St, Groveton 03582 Fax 636-6102
www.sau58.org

SAU 59
Dr. Tammy Davis, supt. 603-286-4116
433 W Main St, Northfield 03276 Fax 286-7402
www.winnisquam.k12.nh.us/Sau/index.htm

SAU 60
Dr. Debra Livingston, supt. 603-826-7756
PO Box 600, Charlestown 03603 Fax 826-4430
www.sau60.org
SAU 61
Steve Welford, supt. 603-755-2627
60 Charles St, Farmington 03835 Fax 755-9334
www.sau61.org
SAU 62
Patrick Andrew, supt. 603-632-5563
PO Box 789, Enfield 03748 Fax 632-4181
www.mascoma.k12.nh.us
SAU 63
Donald LaPlante, supt. 603-878-8100
PO Box 1149, Wilton 03086 Fax 654-6691
www.sau63.org
SAU 64
Jay McIntire, supt. 603-652-0262
18 Commerce Way, Milton 03851 Fax 652-0250
www.sau64.org
SAU 65
Jerome Frew, supt. 603-526-2051
114 Cougar Ct, New London 03257 Fax 526-2145
www.kearsarge.org
SAU 66
Steven Chamberlin, supt. 603-746-5186
204 Maple St, Contoocook 03229 Fax 746-5714
www.hopkintonschools.org
SAU 67
Dr. Dean Cascadden, supt. 603-224-4728
32 White Rock Hill Rd, Bow 03304 Fax 224-4111
www.bownet.org
SAU 68
Judith McGann, supt. 603-745-2051
PO Box 846, Lincoln 03251 Fax 745-2351
www.lin-wood.org
SAU 70
Franklyn Bass, supt. 603-643-6050
41 Lebanon St Ste 2 Fax 643-3073
Hanover 03755
www.sau70.org/
SAU 71
Dr. Michele Munson, supt. 603-863-2420
29 School Rd, Lempster 03605 Fax 863-2451
www.gl.k12.nh.us/SAU.html
SAU 72
William Lander, supt. 603-875-7890
252 Suncook Valley Rd Fax 875-0391
Alton 03809
www.alton.k12.nh.us

SAU 73
Kent Hemingway, supt. 603-527-9215
2 Belknap Mountain Rd Fax 527-9216
Gilford 03249
www.sau73.org/
SAU 74
Gail Kushner, supt. 603-664-2715
77 Ramsdell Ln, Barrington 03825 Fax 664-2609
www.barrington.k12.nh.us
SAU 75
Jacqueline Guillette, supt. 603-863-9689
PO Box 287, Grantham 03753 Fax 863-9684
www.grantham.k12.nh.us
SAU 76
Dr. Michael Harris, supt. 603-795-4431
PO Box 117, Lyme 03768 Fax 795-9407
www.lymeschool.org
SAU 77
Thomas McGuire, admin. 603-638-2800
PO Box 130, Monroe 03771 Fax 638-2031
www.monroeschool77.com
SAU 78
Brenda Needham, supt. 603-353-2170
10 School Dr, Orford 03777 Fax 353-2189
www.rivendellschool.org
SAU 79
John Fauci, supt. 603-267-9097
PO Box 309, Gilmanton 03237 Fax 267-9498
www.gilmanton.k12.nh.us
SAU 80
Maria Dreyer, supt. 603-267-9223
58 School St, Belmont 03220 Fax 267-9225
www.sau80.org
SAU 81
Bryan Lane, supt. 603-886-1235
20 Library St, Hudson 03051 Fax 886-1236
www.sau81.org
SAU 82
James Gaylord, supt. 603-887-3621
22 Murphy Dr, Chester 03036 Fax 887-7586
www.chesteracademy.org/
SAU 83
Michelle Langa, supt. 603-895-6903
5 Hall Rd Unit 1, Fremont 03044 Fax 895-6905
www.sau83.org
SAU 84
Dr. Keith Pfeifer, supt. 603-444-5215
102 School St, Littleton 03561 Fax 444-3015
www.littletonschools.org/
SAU 85
Brendan Minnihan, supt. 603-763-4627
70 Lower Main St, Sunapee 03782 Fax 763-4718
www.sunapeeschools.org

SAU 86
John Fauci, supt., PO Box 250 603-435-1510
Center Barnstead 03225 Fax 435-1511
www.barnstead.k12.nh.us
SAU 87
Betsey Cox-Buteau, supt. 603-721-0160
16 School St, Greenville 03048 Fax 721-0175
www.sau.mascenic.org
SAU 88
Dr. Gail Paludi, supt. 603-448-1634
20 Seminary Hl Fax 448-0602
West Lebanon 03784
www.sau88.net
SAU 89
James McCormick, supt. 603-878-2962
13 Darling Hill Rd, Mason 03048 Fax 878-3439
mason.sau89.org
SAU 90
Kathleen Murphy, supt. 603-926-4560
6 Marston Way, Hampton 03842 Fax 926-5070
www.sau90.org/
SAU 91
Kenneth Dassau, supt. 603-239-8061
1 Village Rd, Surry 03431 Fax 239-7593
SAU 92
David Crisafulli, supt. 603-336-5728
PO Box 27, Hinsdale 03451 Fax 336-5731
sau92.org/
SAU 93
Dr. Leo Corriveau, supt. 603-352-6955
600 Old Homestead Hwy Fax 358-6708
Swanzey 03446
www.mrsd.org
SAU 94
James Lewis, supt. 603-239-8061
PO Box 46, Winchester 03470 Fax 239-7593
www.wnhsd.org
SAU 97
Kathleen Vizard, supt. 603-356-5535
91 Samuel Hale Dr Fax 356-5535
Hales Location 03860
SAU 98
Jennifer Fish, supt. 603-246-3321
136 County Farm Rd Fax 246-8117
West Stewartstown 03597
SAU 201
David Smith, hdmstr. 603-942-5531
907 1st NH Tpke Fax 942-7537
Northwood 03261
coebrown.org
SAU 202
Mary Anderson, hdmstr. 603-437-5200
5 Pinkerton St, Derry 03038 Fax 432-5328
www.pinkertonacademy.net
SAU 301
Robert Cullison, supt. 603-875-8600
242 Suncook Valley Rd Fax 875-8200
Alton 03809
www.pmhschool.com

PUBLIC, PRIVATE AND CATHOLIC SECONDARY SCHOOLS

Allenstown, Merrimack
Allenstown SD
Supt. — See Pembroke
Dupont MS 100/6-8
10 1/2 School St 03275 603-485-4474
Lynn Allen, prin. Fax 485-1806

Alstead, Cheshire
Fall Mountain Regional SD
Supt. — See Charlestown
Vilas MS 100/5-8
82 Mechanic St 03602 603-835-6351
Gail Rowe, prin. Fax 835-2052

Alton, Belknap, Pop. 499
Prospect Mountain SD 500/9-12
242 Suncook Valley Rd 03809 603-875-3800
Robert L. Cullison M.Ed., supt. Fax 875-8200
www.pmhschool.com
Prospect Mountain HS 500/9-12
242 Suncook Valley Rd 03809 603-875-3800
James Fitzpatrick, prin. Fax 875-8200

Amherst, Hillsborough, Pop. 612
Amherst SD 1,500/K-8
PO Box 849 03031 603-673-2690
Peter Warburton, supt. Fax 672-1786
www.sprise.com
Amherst MS 800/5-8
PO Box 966 03031 603-673-8944
Porter Dodge, prin. Fax 673-6774

Souhegan Cooperative SD 900/9-12
PO Box 849 03031 603-673-2690
Peter Warburton, supt. Fax 672-1786
www.sprise.com/shs/
Souhegan Cooperative HS 900/9-12
PO Box 1152 03031 603-673-9940
Rob Scully, prin. Fax 673-0318

Andover, Merrimack

Proctor Academy 400/9-12
PO Box 500 03216 603-735-6000
Michael Henriques, head sch Fax 735-5129

Antrim, Hillsborough, Pop. 1,376
Contoocook Valley SD
Supt. — See Peterborough
Great Brook MS 300/5-8
16 School St 03440 603-588-6630
James Elder, prin. Fax 588-3207

Barrington, Strafford
Barrington SD 800/PK-8
77 Ramsdell Ln 03825 603-664-2715
Gail Kushner, supt. Fax 664-2609
www.barrington.k12.nh.us
Barrington MS 400/5-8
51 Haley Dr 03825 603-664-2127
Michael Powers, prin. Fax 664-5739

Bedford, Hillsborough
Bedford SD 4,400/PK-12
103 County Rd 03110 603-472-3755
Timothy Mayes, supt. Fax 472-2567
www.sau25.net/
Bedford HS 1,300/9-12
47 Nashua Rd Unit B 03110 603-310-9000
William Hagen, prin. Fax 472-3024
Lurgio MS 800/7-8
47 Nashua Rd Unit A 03110 603-310-9100
Edward Joyce, prin. Fax 472-5090

Michael's School of Hair Design Post-Sec.
79 S River Rd Ste 6 03110 603-668-4300

Belmont, Belknap, Pop. 1,272
Shaker Regional SD 1,400/PK-12
58 School St 03220 603-267-9223
Maria Dreyer, supt. Fax 267-9225
www.sau80.org
Belmont HS 500/9-12
255 Seavey Rd 03220 603-267-6525
Dan Clary, prin. Fax 267-5962
Belmont MS 400/5-8
38 School St 03220 603-267-9220
Aaron Pope, prin. Fax 267-9228

Berlin, Coos, Pop. 9,890
Berlin SD 1,200/K-12
183 Hillside Ave 03570 603-752-6500
Corinne Cascadden, supt. Fax 752-2528
www.sau3.org/
Berlin HS 500/9-12
550 Willard St 03570 603-752-4122
Gary Bisson, prin. Fax 752-8566
Berlin MS 200/6-8
200 State St 03570 603-752-5311
Daniel Record, prin. Fax 752-8580
Berlin Regional Vocational Center Vo/Tech
550 Willard St 03570 603-752-4122
Roland Pinette, prin. Fax 752-8566

White Mountains Community College Post-Sec.
2020 Riverside Dr 03570 603-752-1113

Bethlehem, Grafton, Pop. 962
Profile SD
Supt. — See Littleton
Profile HS 200/9-12
691 Profile Rd 03574 603-823-7411
Michael Kelley, prin. Fax 823-7490
Profile JHS 100/7-8
691 Profile Rd 03574 603-823-7411
Michael Kelley, prin. Fax 823-7490

White Mountain S 100/9-12
371 W Farm Rd 03574 603-444-2928
Timothy Breen Ph.D., hdmstr. Fax 444-1258

Bow, Merrimack
Bow SD 1,500/PK-12
32 White Rock Hill Rd 03304 603-224-4728
Dr. Dean Cascadden, supt. Fax 224-4111
www.bownet.org
Bow HS 600/9-12
32 White Rock Hill Rd 03304 603-228-2210
John House-Myers, prin. Fax 228-2212
Bow Memorial MS 500/5-8
20 Bow Center Rd 03304 603-225-3212
Adam Osburn, prin. Fax 228-2228

Bristol, Grafton, Pop. 1,657
Newfound Area SD 1,300/PK-12
20 N Main St 03222 603-744-5555
Dr. Marie Ross, supt. Fax 744-6659
www.sau4.org
Newfound Memorial MS 300/6-8
155 N Main St 03222 603-744-8162
Eric Chase, prin. Fax 744-8037
Newfound Regional HS 500/9-12
150 Newfound Rd 03222 603-744-6006
Michael O'Malley, prin. Fax 744-2526

Canaan, Grafton, Pop. 511
Mascoma Valley Regional SD
Supt. — See Enfield
Indian River S 400/5-8
45 Royal Rd 03741 603-632-4357
Kevin Towle, prin. Fax 632-4262
Mascoma Valley Regional HS 400/9-12
27 Royal Rd 03741 603-632-4308
James Collins, prin. Fax 632-5419

Cardigan Mountain S 200/6-9
62 Alumni Dr 03741 603-523-4321
David McCusker, hdmstr. Fax 523-7227

Candia, Rockingham

Remington HS 50/9-12
PO Box 473 03034 603-483-5664
Jeffrey Philbrick, hdmstr. Fax 483-4811

Charlestown, Sullivan, Pop. 1,173
Fall Mountain Regional SD 1,700/PK-12
PO Box 600 03603 603-826-7756
Dr. Debra Livingston, supt. Fax 826-4430
www.sau60.org
Charlestown MS 200/6-8
PO Box 325 03603 603-826-7711
Paula Southard-Stevens, prin. Fax 826-3102
Other Schools – See Alstead, Langdon, Walpole

Claremont, Sullivan, Pop. 13,132
Claremont SD 1,900/K-12
165 Broad St 03743 603-543-4200
Middleton McGoodwin Ed.D., supt. Fax 543-4244
www.sau6.k12.nh.us
Claremont MS 500/6-8
107 South St 03743 603-543-4250
Paulette Fitzgerald, prin. Fax 543-4289
Stevens HS 600/9-12
175 Broad St 03743 603-543-4220
Frank Sprague, prin. Fax 542-2805
Sugar River Valley Regional Technical Ct Vo/Tech
111 South St 03743 603-543-4291
Joel Schneid, dir. Fax 543-4296

Claremont Christian Academy 50/K-12
97 Maple Ave 03743 603-542-8759
Adam Barton, dir. Fax 542-8759
River Valley Community College Post-Sec.
1 College Dr 03743 603-542-7744

Colebrook, Coos, Pop. 1,376
Colebrook SD 400/K-12
21 Academy St 03576 603-237-5571
Robert Mills, supt. Fax 237-5126
www.colebrook.k12.nh.us
Colebrook Academy 100/9-12
13 Academy St 03576 603-237-8351
Joanne Melanson, prin. Fax 237-5717

Pittsburg SD 100/K-12
21 Academy St 03576 603-237-5571
Robert Mills, supt. Fax 237-5126
Other Schools – See Pittsburg

Concord, Merrimack, Pop. 41,988
Concord SD 4,500/PK-12
38 Liberty St 03301 603-225-0811
Dr. Christine Rath, supt. Fax 226-2187
www.concordnhschools.net
Concord HS 1,800/9-12
170 Warren St 03301 603-225-0800
Gene Connolly, prin. Fax 223-2054
Concord Regional Technical Center Vo/Tech
170 Warren St 03301 603-225-0800
Steve Rothenberg, admin. Fax 223-2050
Rundlett MS 1,100/6-8
144 South St 03301 603-225-0862
Thomas Sica, prin. Fax 226-3288

Bishop Brady HS 400/9-12
25 Columbus Ave 03301 603-224-7418
Trevor Bonat, prin. Fax 228-6664
Concord Academy of Hair Design Post-Sec.
20 S Main St 03301 603-224-2211
Concord Christian Academy 200/PK-12
PO Box 3664 03302 603-228-8888
Dean Whiteway, hdmstr. Fax 226-9696
Franklin Pierce University Post-Sec.
5 Chenell Dr 03301 603-228-1155
Granite State College Post-Sec.
25 Hall St 03301 603-228-3000
Hesser College Post-Sec.
16 Foundry St Ste 201 03301 603-225-9200
NHTI - Concord's Community College Post-Sec.
31 College Dr 03301 603-271-6484
St. Paul's S 500/9-12
325 Pleasant St 03301 603-229-4600
Michael Hirschfeld, dir. Fax 229-4892
Trinity Christian S 200/PK-12
80 Clinton St 03301 603-225-5410
Peter Flint, prin. Fax 225-3235
University of New Hampshire Sch of Law Post-Sec.
2 White St 03301 603-228-1541

Contoocook, Merrimack, Pop. 1,432
Hopkinton SD 1,000/PK-12
204 Maple St 03229 603-746-5186
Steven Chamberlin, supt. Fax 746-5714
www.hopkintonschools.org
Hopkinton HS 300/9-12
297 Park Ave 03229 603-746-4167
Christopher Kelley, prin. Fax 746-5109
Hopkinton MS 200/7-8
297 Park Ave 03229 603-746-4167
Christopher Kelley, prin. Fax 746-5109

Conway, Carroll, Pop. 1,799
Conway SD 1,900/K-12
176A Main St 03818 603-447-8368
Dr. Carl Nelson, supt. Fax 447-8497
www.sau9.org
Kennett MS 300/7-8
176 Main St 03818 603-447-6364
Kevin Richard, prin. Fax 447-6842
Other Schools – See North Conway

Deering, Hillsborough
Hillsboro-Deering Cooperative SD 1,400/PK-12
2300 2nd NH Tpke 03244 603-464-4466
Dr. Robert Hassett, supt. Fax 464-4053
www.hdsd.org
Other Schools – See Hillsborough

Derry, Rockingham, Pop. 21,640
Derry Cooperative SD 3,700/PK-8
18 S Main St 03038 603-432-1210
Laura Nelson, supt. Fax 432-1264
www.derry.k12.nh.us
Hood Memorial MS 800/6-8
5 Hood Rd 03038 603-432-1224
Austin Garofalo, prin. Fax 432-1227
West Running Brook MS 600/6-8
1 W Running Brook Ln 03038 603-432-1250
Leslie Saucier, prin. Fax 432-1243

Pinkerton Academy 3,200/9-12
5 Pinkerton St 03038 603-437-5200
Mary Anderson, hdmstr. Fax 432-5328
www.pinkertonacademy.net
Pinkerton Academy 3,200/9-12
5 Pinkerton St 03038 603-437-5200
Mary Anderson, hdmstr. Fax 432-5328

Dover, Strafford, Pop. 29,321
Dover SD 4,100/PK-12
61 Locust St Ste 409 03820 603-516-6800
Dr. Jean Briggs Badger, supt. Fax 516-6809
www.dover.k12.nh.us
Dover Career Technical Center Vo/Tech
25 Alumni Dr 03820 603-516-6976
Jim Amara, dir. Fax 516-6975
Dover HS 1,500/9-12
25 Alumni Dr 03820 603-516-6900
Christine Boston, prin. Fax 516-6926
Dover MS 1,100/5-8
16 Daley Dr 03820 603-516-7200
Kim Lyndes, prin. Fax 516-5747

Portsmouth Christian Academy 600/PK-12
20 Seaborne Dr 03820 603-742-3617
Dennis Runey, hdmstr. Fax 750-0490
St. Thomas Aquinas HS 700/9-12
197 Dover Point Rd 03820 603-742-3206
Kevin Collins, prin. Fax 749-7822

Dublin, Cheshire

Dublin S 100/9-12
PO Box 522 03444 603-563-8584
Bradford Bates, head sch Fax 563-7121

Durham, Strafford, Pop. 10,187
Oyster River Cooperative SD 2,000/K-12
36 Coe Dr 03824 603-868-5100
James Morse Ed.D., supt. Fax 868-6668
www.orcsd.org
Oyster River HS 700/9-12
55 Coe Dr 03824 603-868-2375
Todd Allen, prin. Fax 868-2049
Oyster River MS 600/5-8
1 Coe Dr 03824 603-868-2155
Jay Richard, prin. Fax 868-3469

University of New Hampshire 03824 Post-Sec.
603-862-1234

Enfield, Grafton, Pop. 1,510
Mascoma Valley Regional SD 1,400/PK-12
PO Box 789 03748 603-632-5563
Patrick Andrew, supt. Fax 632-4181
www.mascoma.k12.nh.us/
Other Schools – See Canaan

Epping, Rockingham, Pop. 1,654
Epping SD 1,000/PK-12
213 Main St 03042 603-679-5402
Barbara Munsey, supt. Fax 679-1237
www.sau14.org
Epping HS 300/9-12
21 Academy St 03042 603-679-5472
Kyle Repucci, prin. Fax 679-2966
Epping MS 200/6-8
33 Prescott Rd 03042 603-679-2544
Kyle Repucci, prin. Fax 679-5514

Exeter, Rockingham, Pop. 9,087
Exeter Region Cooperative SD 3,000/6-12
30 Linden St 03833 603-775-8653
Michael Morgan, supt. Fax 775-8673
www.sau16.org/
Exeter HS 1,700/9-12
1 Blue Hawk Dr 03833 603-775-8400
Sean Kiley, prin. Fax 395-2499
Seacoast School of Tech Vo/Tech
40 Linden St 03833 603-775-8958
Margaret Callahan, prin. Fax 775-8983
Other Schools – See Stratham

Phillips Exeter Academy 1,000/9-12
20 Main St 03833 603-772-4311
Thomas Hassan, prin. Fax 777-4384

Farmington, Strafford, Pop. 3,815
Farmington SD 1,400/PK-12
60 Charles St 03835 603-755-2627
Steve Welford, supt. Fax 755-9334
www.sau61.org
Farmington HS 400/9-12
40 Thayer Dr 03835 603-755-2811
Matthew Jozokos, prin. Fax 755-3252
Wilson Memorial MS 600/4-8
51 School St 03835 603-755-2181
Steve Woodward, prin. Fax 755-9473

Franklin, Merrimack, Pop. 8,346
Franklin SD 1,100/PK-12
119 Central St 03235 603-934-3108
Dr. Maureen Ward, supt. Fax 934-3462
www.franklin.k12.nh.us
Franklin HS 400/9-12
115 Central St 03235 603-934-5441
Richard Towne, prin. Fax 934-7445
Franklin MS 400/5-8
200 Sanborn St 03235 603-934-5828
Kevin Barbour, prin. Fax 934-2432

Gilford, Belknap
Gilford SD 1,300/K-12
2 Belknap Mountain Rd 03249 603-527-9215
Kent Hemingway, supt. Fax 527-9216
www.sau73.org/
Gilford HS 600/9-12
88 Alvah Wilson Rd 03249 603-524-7135
Peter Sawyer, prin. Fax 524-3867
Gilford MS 400/5-8
72 Alvah Wilson Rd 03249 603-527-2460
Marcia Ross, prin. Fax 527-2461

Goffstown, Hillsborough, Pop. 14,621
Goffstown SD 3,000/PK-12
11 School St 03045 603-497-4818
Brian Balke, supt. Fax 497-8425
www.goffstown.k12.nh.us
Goffstown Area HS 1,200/9-12
27 Wallace Rd 03045 603-497-4841
Frank McBride, prin. Fax 497-5257
Mountain View MS 900/5-8
41 Lauren Ln 03045 603-497-8288
James Hunt, prin. Fax 497-4987

Gorham, Coos, Pop. 1,579
Gorham Randolph Shelburne Cooperative SD 500/K-12
123 Main St 03581 603-466-3632
Paul Bousquet, supt. Fax 466-3870
www.sau20.org/
Gorham HS 200/9-12
120 Main St 03581 603-466-2776
Keith Parent, prin. Fax 466-3111
Gorham MS 100/6-8
120 Main St 03581 603-466-2776
Keith Parent, prin. Fax 466-3111

Greenland, Rockingham
Rye SD 500/PK-8
48 Post Rd 03840 603-422-9572
Dr. George Cushing, supt. Fax 422-9575
www.sau50.org
Other Schools – See Rye

Greenville, Hillsborough, Pop. 1,101
Mascenic Regional SD 900/PK-12
16 School St 03048 603-721-0160
Betsey Cox-Buteau, supt. Fax 721-0175
www.sau.mascenic.org
Other Schools – See New Ipswich

Groveton, Coos, Pop. 1,110
Northumberland SD 300/K-12
15 Preble St 03582 603-636-1437
Carl Ladd, supt. Fax 636-6102
www.sau58.org
Groveton MSHS 100/6-12
65 State St 03582 603-636-1619
Pierre Couture, prin. Fax 636-9752

Hampstead, Rockingham
Hampstead SD
Supt. — See Plaistow
Hampstead MS 400/5-8
28 School St 03841 603-329-6743
Patricia Grassbaugh, prin. Fax 329-4120

Hampton, Rockingham, Pop. 9,556
Hampton SD 1,300/PK-8
6 Marston Way 03842 603-926-4560
Kathleen Murphy, supt. Fax 926-5070
www.sau90.org
Hampton Academy 400/6-8
29 Academy Ave 03842 603-926-2000
David O'Connor, prin. Fax 926-1855

Seabrook SD 700/PK-8
2 Alumni Dr 03842 603-926-8992
Robert Sullivan Ed.D., supt. Fax 926-5157
www.sau21.org/sau
Other Schools – See Seabrook

Winnacunnet Cooperative SD 1,200/9-12
2 Alumni Dr 03842 603-926-8992
Robert Sullivan Ed.D., supt. Fax 926-5157
www.sau21.org/sau
Winnacunnet HS 1,200/9-12
1 Alumni Dr 03842 603-926-3395
William McGowan, prin. Fax 926-5418

Hampton Falls, Rockingham

Heronfield Academy 100/6-8
356 Exeter Rd 03844 603-772-9093
Martha Shepardson-Killam, head sch

Hanover, Grafton, Pop. 8,321
Dresden SD 1,200/6-12
41 Lebanon St Ste 2 03755 603-643-6050
Franklyn Bass, supt. Fax 643-3073
www.sau70.org/
Hanover HS 700/9-12
41 Lebanon St Ste 1 03755 603-643-3431
Justin Campbell, prin. Fax 643-0661
Richmond MS 400/6-8
63 Lyme Rd 03755 603-643-6040
James Nourse, prin. Fax 643-0662

Dartmouth College 03755 Post-Sec.
603-646-1110

Henniker, Merrimack, Pop. 1,723
John Stark Regional SD 800/9-12
258 Western Ave 03242 603-428-3269
Dr. Lorraine Tacconi-Moore, supt. Fax 428-6545
www.sau24.org
Other Schools – See Weare

Weare SD 1,100/PK-8
258 Western Ave 03242 603-428-3269
Dr. Lorraine Tacconi-Moore, supt. Fax 428-6545
www.sau24.org
Other Schools – See Weare

New England College Post-Sec.
98 Bridge St 03242 603-428-2211

Hillsborough, Hillsborough, Pop. 1,929
Hillsboro-Deering Cooperative SD
Supt. — See Deering
Hillsboro-Deering HS 500/9-12
12 Hillcat Dr 03244 603-464-1130
James O'Rourke, prin. Fax 464-4028
Hillsboro-Deering MS 300/6-8
6 Hillcat Dr 03244 603-464-1120
Patricia Barry, prin. Fax 464-5759

Hinsdale, Cheshire, Pop. 1,534
Hinsdale SD 600/PK-12
PO Box 27 03451 603-336-5728
Dr. David Crisafulli, supt. Fax 336-5731
sau92.org
Hinsdale HS 200/9-12
49 School St 03451 603-336-5984
Ann Freitag, prin. Fax 336-7497
Hinsdale MS 100/6-8
49 School St 03451 603-336-5984
Ann Freitag, prin. Fax 336-7497

Holderness, Grafton

Holderness S 300/9-12
33 Chapel Ln 03245 603-536-1257
Phillip Peck, head sch Fax 536-1267

Hollis, Hillsborough
Hollis/Brookline Cooperative SD 1,300/7-12
PO Box 1588 03049 603-465-7118
Susan Hodgdon, supt. Fax 465-3933
www.sau41.org
Hollis/Brookline HS 900/9-12
24 Cavalier Ct 03049 603-465-2269
Cynthia Matte, prin. Fax 465-2485
Hollis/Brookline MS 400/7-8
25 Main St 03049 603-465-2223
Robert Thompson, prin. Fax 465-7523

Hooksett, Merrimack, Pop. 4,079
Hooksett SD 1,500/PK-8
90 Farmer Rd 03106 603-622-3731
Dr. Charles Littlefield, supt. Fax 669-4352
www.sau15.net
Cawley MS 500/6-8
89 Whitehall Rd 03106 603-518-5047
Matthew Benson, prin. Fax 518-5086

Hopkinton, Merrimack

Beech Hill S, 20 Beech Hill Rd 03229 50/6-8
Rick Johnson, head sch 603-715-5129

Hudson, Hillsborough, Pop. 7,236
Hudson SD 4,300/PK-12
20 Library St 03051 603-886-1235
Bryan K. Lane, supt. Fax 886-1236
www.sau81.org
Alvirne HS 1,400/9-12
200 Derry Rd 03051 603-886-1260
Steven Beals, prin. Fax 595-1525
Hudson Memorial MS 1,000/6-8
1 Memorial Dr 03051 603-886-1240
Susan Nadeau, prin. Fax 883-1252
Palmer Vocational Tech Center Vo/Tech
200 Derry Rd 03051 603-886-1260
Karen Worthen, dir. Fax 595-1513

Continental Academie of Hair Design Post-Sec.
PO Box 370 03051 603-889-1614

Jaffrey, Cheshire, Pop. 2,700
Jaffrey-Rindge Cooperative SD 1,600/PK-12
81 Fitzgerald Dr Unit 2 03452 603-532-8100
James O'Neill, supt. Fax 532-8165
www.sau47.org
Conant HS 500/9-12
3 Conant Way 03452 603-532-8131
John Barth, prin. Fax 532-8102
Jaffrey-Rindge MS 300/6-8
1 Conant Way 03452 603-532-8122
Ryan Earley, prin. Fax 532-8124

Keene, Cheshire, Pop. 23,106
Keene SD 3,400/PK-12
193 Maple Ave 03431 603-357-9002
Wayne Woolridge, supt. Fax 357-9012
www.sau29.org
Cheshire Career Center Vo/Tech
43 Arch St 03431 603-352-0640
Jim Logan, prin. Fax 357-9061
Keene HS 1,600/9-12
43 Arch St 03431 603-352-0640
Lynne Wagner, prin. Fax 357-1512
Keene MS 600/6-8
167 Maple Ave 03431 603-357-9020
Dorothy Frazier, prin. Fax 357-9045

Antioch University New England Post-Sec.
40 Avon St 03431 603-357-3122
Keene Beauty Academy Post-Sec.
800 Park Ave 03431 603-357-3736
Keene State College Post-Sec.
229 Main St 03435 603-352-1909
Monadnock Waldorf S 200/PK-12
98 S Lincoln St 03431 603-357-4442

Kingston, Rockingham
Sanborn Regional SD 1,900/PK-12
178 Main St 03848 603-642-3688
Dr. Brian Blake, supt. Fax 642-7885
web.sau17.org
Sanborn Regional HS 700/9-12
17 Danville Rd 03848 603-642-3341
Brian Stack, prin. Fax 642-6947
Other Schools – See Newton

Laconia, Belknap, Pop. 15,741
Laconia SD 2,200/PK-12
PO Box 309 03247 603-524-5710
Robert Champlin, supt. Fax 528-8442
www2.laconiaschools.org
Huot Technical Center Vo/Tech
345 Union Ave 03246 603-528-8693
Scott Davis, prin. Fax 524-5711
Laconia HS 700/9-12
345 Union Ave 03246 603-524-3350
James McCollum, prin. Fax 528-8683
Laconia MS 500/6-8
150 McGrath St 03246 603-524-4632
Eric Johnson, prin. Fax 528-8675

Empire Beauty School Post-Sec.
556 Main St 03246 603-524-8777
Laconia Christian S 100/PK-12
1386 Meredith Center Rd 03246 603-524-3250
Rick Duba, head sch Fax 524-3285
Lakes Region Community College Post-Sec.
379 Belmont Rd 03246 603-524-3207

Langdon, Sullivan
Fall Mountain Regional SD
Supt. — See Charlestown
Fall Mountain Regional HS 600/9-12
134 Fmrhs Rd 03602 603-835-6318
Thomas Ronning, prin. Fax 835-6254
Fall Mountain Regional Vocational Center Vo/Tech
134 Fmrhs Rd 03602 603-835-6319
Cindy Allen, prin. Fax 835-6254

Lebanon, Grafton, Pop. 12,877
Lebanon SD
Supt. — See West Lebanon
Lebanon HS 700/9-12
195 Hanover St 03766 603-448-2055
Nancy Parsons, prin. Fax 448-0605
Lebanon MS 300/5-8
3 Moulton Ave 03766 603-448-3056
Martha Langill, prin. Fax 448-0616

Lebanon College Post-Sec.
15 Hanover St 03766 603-448-2445
Upper Valley Teacher Institute Post-Sec.
194 Dartmouth College Hwy 03766 603-678-4888

Lincoln, Grafton, Pop. 991
Lincoln-Woodstock Cooperative SD 100/K-12
PO Box 846 03251 603-745-2051
Judith McGann, supt. Fax 745-2351
www.lin-wood.org
Lin-Wood S 100/K-12
72 Linwood Dr 03251 603-745-2214
Robert Nelson, prin. Fax 745-6797

Lisbon, Grafton, Pop. 967
Lisbon Regional SD
Supt. — See Littleton
Lisbon Regional S 100/K-12
24 Highland Ave 03585 603-838-5506
Stephen Sexton, prin. Fax 838-5012

Litchfield, Hillsborough
Litchfield SD 1,600/PK-12
1 Highlander Ct 03052 603-578-3570
Brian Cochrane Ph.D., supt. Fax 578-1267
www.litchfieldsd.org
Campbell HS 500/9-12
1 Highlander Ct 03052 603-546-0300
Laura Rothhaus, prin. Fax 546-0310
Litchfield MS 500/5-8
19 McElwain Dr 03052 603-424-0566
Thomas Lecklider, prin. Fax 424-1296

Tabernacle Christian S 100/K-12
242 Derry Rd 03052 603-883-6310
Fax 883-2413

Littleton, Grafton, Pop. 4,350
Lisbon Regional SD 100/K-12
260 Cottage St Ste C 03561 603-444-3925
Paul MacMillan, supt. Fax 444-6299
www.sau35.k12.nh.us
Other Schools – See Lisbon

Littleton SD 800/K-12
102 School St 03561 603-444-5215
Dr. Keith Pfeifer, supt. Fax 444-3015
www.littletonschools.org/
Bronson JHS 100/7-8
159 Oak Hill Ave 03561 603-444-5601
Sikander Rashid, prin. Fax 444-3009
Gallen Regional Vocational Center Vo/Tech
140 High St 03561 603-444-5186
Alan Smith, prin. Fax 444-0167
Littleton HS 300/9-12
159 Oak Hill Ave 03561 603-444-5601
Sikander Rashid, prin. Fax 444-3009

Profile SD 300/7-12
260 Cottage St Ste C 03561 603-444-3925
Paul MacMillan, supt. Fax 444-6299
www.sau35.k12.nh.us
Other Schools – See Bethlehem

Londonderry, Rockingham, Pop. 10,903
Londonderry SD 5,000/PK-12
268C Mammoth Rd 03053 603-432-6920
Dr. Nathan Greenberg, supt. Fax 425-1049
www.londonderry.org
Londonderry HS 1,700/9-12
295 Mammoth Rd 03053 603-432-6941
Jason Parent, prin. Fax 425-1022
Londonderry MS 1,200/6-8
313 Mammoth Rd 03053 603-432-6925
Richard Zacchilli, prin. Fax 432-0714

Manchester, Hillsborough, Pop. 107,082
Manchester SD 15,700/PK-12
195 McGregor St Ste 201 03102 603-624-6300
Thomas Brennan Ph.D., supt. Fax 624-6337
www.mansd.org
Hillside MS 900/6-8
112 Reservoir Ave 03104 603-624-6352
Brendan McCafferty, prin. Fax 628-6049
Manchester Central HS 2,200/9-12
207 Lowell St 03104 603-624-6363
Ronald Mailhot, prin. Fax 624-6376
Manchester Memorial HS 2,000/9-12
1 Crusader Way 03103 603-624-6378
Arthur Adamakos, prin. Fax 628-6009
Manchester School of Tech Vo/Tech
530 S Porter St 03103 603-624-6490
Karen White, dir. Fax 628-6146
Manchester West HS 1,400/9-12
9 Notre Dame Ave 03102 603-624-6384
John Rist, prin. Fax 628-6153
McLaughlin MS 800/6-8
290 S Mammoth Rd 03109 603-628-6247
William Krantz, prin. Fax 628-6274
Parkside MS 700/6-8
75 Parkside Ave 03102 603-624-6356
Forrest Ransdell, prin. Fax 624-6355
Southside MS 900/6-8
140 S Jewett St 03103 603-624-6359
Marilyn Azevedo, prin. Fax 624-6361

Derryfield S 400/6-12
2108 River Rd 03104 603-669-4524
Dr. Mary Halpin Carter, hdmstr. Fax 641-9521
Franklin Pierce University Post-Sec.
670 N Commercial St Ste 206 03101 603-626-4972
Hesser College Post-Sec.
3 Sundial Ave 03103 603-668-6660
Manchester Community College Post-Sec.
1066 Front St 03102 603-206-8000
Mount Zion Christian S 100/PK-12
132 Titus Ave 03103 603-606-7930
Robert Carter, hdmstr. Fax 606-7935
New England EMS Institute Post-Sec.
1 Elliot Way 03103 603-628-2220
New Hampshire Institute of Art Post-Sec.
148 Concord St 03104 603-623-0313
St. Anselm College Post-Sec.
100 Saint Anselms Dr 03102 603-641-7000
St. Joseph Regional JHS 200/7-8
148 Belmont St 03103 603-624-4811
Denis Mailloux, prin. Fax 624-6670
Southern New Hampshire University Post-Sec.
2500 N River Rd 03106 603-626-9100
Trinity HS 400/9-12
581 Bridge St 03104 603-668-2910
Denis Mailloux, prin. Fax 668-2913
University of New Hampshire Post-Sec.
400 Commercial St 03101 603-641-4321

Meredith, Belknap, Pop. 1,695
Inter-Lakes Cooperative SD 1,100/PK-12
103 Main St Ste 2 03253 603-279-7947
Mary Ellen Ormond, supt. Fax 279-3044
www.interlakes.org/
Inter-Lakes HS 400/9-12
1 Laker Ln 03253 603-279-6162
Patricia Kennelly, prin. Fax 279-5302
Inter-Lakes MS 300/5-8
1 Laker Ln 03253 603-279-5312
Everett Bennett, prin. Fax 279-5310

Meriden, Sullivan

Kimball Union Academy 300/9-12
57 Main St 03770 603-469-2100
Michael Schafer, hdmstr. Fax 469-2041

Merrimack, Hillsborough, Pop. 22,156
Merrimack SD 4,300/PK-12
36 McElwain St 03054 603-424-6200
Marjorie Chiafery, supt. Fax 424-6229
www.merrimack.k12.nh.us
Merrimack HS 1,500/9-12
38 McElwain St 03054 603-424-6204
Kenneth Johnson, prin Fax 424-6230
Merrimack MS 700/7-8
31 Madeline Bennett Ln 03054 603-424-6289
Deborah Woolflein, prin. Fax 423-1109

South Merrimack Christian Academy 300/PK-12
517 Boston Post Rd 03054 603-880-6832
Brian Burbach, hdmstr. Fax 598-7085
Thomas More College of Liberal Arts Post-Sec.
6 Manchester St 03054 603-880-8308

Milford, Hillsborough, Pop. 8,681
Milford SD 2,800/PK-12
100 West St 03055 603-673-2202
Robert Suprenant, supt. Fax 673-2237
milfordk12.org
Milford Applied Technology Center Vo/Tech
100 West St 03055 603-673-4201
Rosie Deloge, dir. Fax 673-4202
Milford HS 1,000/9-12
100 West St 03055 603-673-4201
Bradford Craven Ph.D., prin. Fax 673-4201

Milford MS 600/6-8
33 Osgood Rd 03055 603-673-5221
Anthony DeMarco, prin. Fax 673-5221

Milton, Strafford, Pop. 560
Milton SD 600/K-12
18 Commerce Way Unit 1 03851 603-652-0262
Michael Tursi, supt. Fax 652-0250
www.sau64.org
Nute HS 200/9-12
22 Elm St 03851 603-652-4591
Aaron Bronson, prin. Fax 652-9926
Nute JHS 100/6-8
22 Elm St 03851 603-652-4591
Aaron Bronson, prin. Fax 652-9926

Moultonborough, Carroll
Moultonborough SD 700/PK-12
PO Box 419 03254 603-476-5247
Susan Noyes, supt. Fax 476-8009
sau45.org
Moultonborough Academy 100/7-8
PO Box 228 03254 603-476-5517
Andrew Coppinger, prin. Fax 476-5153
Moultonborough Academy 200/9-12
PO Box 228 03254 603-476-5517
Andrew Coppinger, prin. Fax 476-5153

Nashua, Hillsborough, Pop. 84,540
Nashua SD 12,100/PK-12
PO Box 687 03061 603-966-1000
Mark Conrad, supt. Fax 594-4350
www.nashua.edu
Elm Street MS 1,200/6-8
117 Elm St 03060 603-594-4322
Colette Valade, prin. Fax 594-4370
Fairgrounds MS 800/6-8
27 Cleveland St 03060 603-594-4393
John Nelson, prin. Fax 594-4355
Nashua HS North 1,900/9-12
10 Chuck Druding Dr 03063 603-589-6400
David Ryan, prin. Fax 589-6449
Nashua HS South 2,000/9-12
36 Riverside Dr 03062 603-589-4311
Keith Richard, prin. Fax 589-8722
Nashua Technology Center Vo/Tech
10 Chuck Druding Dr 03063 603-589-6883
Marianne Dustin, dir. Fax 589-6899
Pennichuck MS 700/6-8
207 Manchester St 03064 603-594-4308
Lynne Joseph, prin. Fax 594-4413

Bishop Guertin HS 900/9-12
194 Lund Rd 03060 603-889-4107
Linda Brodeur, prin. Fax 889-0701
Daniel Webster College Post-Sec.
20 University Dr 03063 800-325-6876
Hesser College Post-Sec.
410 Amherst St 03063 603-883-0404
Nashua Catholic Regional JHS 200/7-8
6 Bartlett Ave 03064 603-883-6707
Glenda McFadden, prin. Fax 594-8955
Nashua Christian Academy 200/PK-12
55 Franklin St 03064 603-889-8892
Christine Urban, hdmstr. Fax 821-7451
Nashua Community College Post-Sec.
505 Amherst St 03063 603-882-6923
Rivier College Post-Sec.
420 S Main St 03060 603-888-1311
St. Joseph School of Nursing Post-Sec.
5 Woodward Ave 03060 603-594-2567

New Hampton, Belknap, Pop. 350

New Hampton S 300/9-12
70 Main St 03256 603-677-3400
Andrew Menke, head sch Fax 677-3482

New Ipswich, Hillsborough
Mascenic Regional SD
Supt. — See Greenville
Boynton MS 400/5-8
500 Turnpike Rd 03071 603-878-4800
Thomas Starratt, prin. Fax 878-0525
Mascenic Regional HS 400/9-12
175 Turnpike Rd 03071 603-878-1113
Trevor Courtney, prin. Fax 878-3344

New London, Merrimack, Pop. 1,397
Kearsarge Regional SD 2,000/PK-12
114 Cougar Ct 03257 603-526-2051
Jerome Frew, supt. Fax 526-2145
www.kearsarge.org
Other Schools – See North Sutton

Colby-Sawyer College Post-Sec.
541 Main St 03257 603-526-3000

Newmarket, Rockingham, Pop. 5,181
Newmarket SD 800/PK-12
186A Main St 03857 603-659-5020
Dr. James Hayes, supt. Fax 659-5022
www.newmarket.k12.nh.us
Newmarket Central JSHS 300/6-12
213 S Main St 03857 603-659-3271
Christopher Andriski, prin. Fax 659-5304

Newport, Sullivan, Pop. 4,688
Newport SD 1,000/K-12
9 Depot St Ste 2 03773 603-863-3540
Irwin Sussman, supt. Fax 863-5368
www.sau43.org
Newport HS 400/9-12
245 N Main St 03773 603-863-2414
Linda Sutton, prin. Fax 863-0887
Newport MS 100/7-8
245 N Main St 03773 603-863-2414
Linda Sutton, prin. Fax 863-0887

Sugar River Valley Reg Voc Ctr Vo/Tech
243 N Main St 03773 603-863-3759
Marcie Ouellette, dir. Fax 863-7104

Newton, Rockingham
Sanborn Regional SD
Supt. — See Kingston
Sanborn Regional MS 400/6-8
31 W Main St Ste A 03858 603-382-6226
Alexander Rutherford, prin. Fax 382-9771

North Conway, Carroll, Pop. 2,311
Conway SD
Supt. — See Conway
Kennett HS 900/9-12
409 Eagles Way 03860 603-356-4343
Cornelius Moylan, prin. Fax 356-3927
Mt. Washington Vly Career/Technical Ctr Vo/Tech
409 Eagles Way 03860 603-356-4370
Neal Moylan, prin. Fax 356-4373

North Haverhill, Grafton
Haverhill Cooperative SD 800/PK-12
2975 Dartmouth College Hwy 03774 603-787-2113
Bruce Labs, supt. Fax 787-2118
www.sau23.org
Haverhill Cooperative MS 300/4-8
175 Morrill Dr 03774 603-787-2100
Brent Walker, prin. Fax 787-6117
Other Schools – See Woodsville

North Sutton, Merrimack
Kearsarge Regional SD
Supt. — See New London
Kearsarge Regional HS 700/9-12
PO Box 182 03260 603-927-4261
Jim Daley, prin. Fax 927-4453
Kearsarge Regional MS 500/6-8
PO Box 269 03260 603-927-2100
James Spadaro, prin. Fax 927-4731

Northwood, Rockingham
Coe-Brown Northwood Academy 700/9-12
907 1st NH Tpke 03261 603-942-5531
David Smith, hdmstr. Fax 942-7537
www.coebrown.org
Coe-Brown Northwood Academy 700/9-12
907 1st NH Tpke 03261 603-942-5531
David Smith, hdmstr. Fax 942-7537

Orford, Grafton
Rivendell Interstate SD 500/PK-12
10 School Dr 03777 603-353-2170
Brenda Needham, supt. Fax 353-2189
www.rivendellschool.org
Rivendell Academy 200/7-12
2972 Route 25A 03777 603-353-4321
Keri Gelenian, prin. Fax 353-4414

Pelham, Hillsborough
Pelham SD
Supt. — See Windham
Pelham HS 600/9-12
85 Marsh Rd 03076 603-635-2115
Dr. Dorothy Mohr, prin. Fax 635-3994
Pelham Memorial MS 600/6-8
59 Marsh Rd 03076 603-635-2321
Stephen Secor, prin. Fax 635-2369

Pembroke, Merrimack, Pop. 6,561
Allenstown SD 400/K-8
267 Pembroke St 03275 603-485-5188
Helene Bickford, supt. Fax 485-9529
www.sau53.org
Other Schools – See Allenstown

Pembroke SD 1,700/K-12
267 Pembroke St 03275 603-485-5188
Helene Bickford, supt. Fax 485-9529
www.sau53.org
Pembroke Academy 900/9-12
209 Academy Rd 03275 603-485-7881
Michael Reardon, prin. Fax 485-1824
Three Rivers MS 400/5-8
243 Academy Rd 03275 603-485-9539
Deborah Bulkley, prin. Fax 485-1829

Penacook, See Concord
Merrimack Valley SD 2,700/PK-12
105 Community Dr 03303 603-753-6561
Dr. Michael Martin, supt. Fax 753-6023
fc.mvsd.k12.nh.us/
Merrimack Valley HS 900/9-12
106 Village St 03303 603-753-4311
Michael Jette, prin. Fax 753-6423
Merrimack Valley MS 600/6-8
14 Allen St 03303 603-753-6336
Patricia Severence, prin. Fax 753-8107

Peterborough, Hillsborough, Pop. 3,075
Contoocook Valley SD 2,600/PK-12
106 Hancock Rd 03458 603-924-3336
Dr. Richard Bergeron, supt. Fax 924-6707
www.conval.edu
Applied Technology Center Region 14 Vo/Tech
182 Hancock Rd 03458 603-371-0310
Brian Pickering, dir. Fax 924-9176
ConVal Regional HS 900/9-12
184 Hancock Rd 03458 603-924-3869
Brian Pickering, prin. Fax 924-9176
South Meadow MS 500/5-8
108 Hancock Rd 03458 603-924-7105
Richard Dunning, prin. Fax 924-2064
Other Schools – See Antrim

Well S 100/K-12
360 Middle Hancock Rd 03458 603-924-6908

Pittsburg, Coos
Pittsburg SD
Supt. — See Colebrook

Pittsburg HS 50/9-12
12 School St 03592 603-538-6536
Heather Zybas, prin. Fax 538-6996

Pittsfield, Merrimack, Pop. 1,547
Pittsfield SD 600/PK-12
23 Oneida St Unit 1 03263 603-435-5526
Dr. John Freeman, supt. Fax 435-5331
pittsfield-nh.com/sau
Pittsfield HS 200/9-12
23 Oneida St 03263 603-435-6701
Bob Bickford, prin. Fax 435-7087
Pittsfield MS 100/7-8
23 Oneida St 03263 603-435-6701
Bob Bickford, prin. Fax 435-7087

Plaistow, Rockingham
Hampstead SD 1,000/PK-8
30 Greenough Rd 03865 603-382-6119
Dr. Earl Metzler, supt. Fax 382-3334
www.hampstead.k12.nh.us
Other Schools – See Hampstead

Timberlane Regional SD 4,300/PK-12
30 Greenough Rd 03865 603-382-6119
Dr. Earl Metzler, supt. Fax 382-3334
www.timberlane.net/
Timberlane Regional HS 1,400/9-12
36 Greenough Rd 03865 603-382-6541
Donald Woodworth, prin. Fax 382-8086
Timberlane Regional MS 1,000/6-8
44 Greenough Rd 03865 603-382-7131
Michael Hogan, prin. Fax 382-2781

Plymouth, Grafton, Pop. 4,412
Pemi-Baker Regional SD 700/9-12
47 Old Ward Bridge Rd 03264 603-536-1254
Mark Halloran, supt. Fax 536-3545
www.sau48.org
Plymouth Applied Technology Center Vo/Tech
86 Old Ward Bridge Rd 03264 603-536-1444
Randy Cleary, prin. Fax 536-9086
Plymouth Regional HS 700/9-12
86 Old Ward Bridge Rd 03264 603-536-1444
Bruce Parsons, prin. Fax 536-9086

Plymouth State University Post-Sec.
17 High St 03264 603-535-5000

Portsmouth, Rockingham, Pop. 20,315
Portsmouth SD 2,700/PK-12
1 Junkins Ave Unit 402 03801 603-431-5080
Edward McDonough, supt. Fax 431-6753
www.cityofportsmouth.com/school/
Portsmouth Career-Tech Center 19 Vo/Tech
50 Andrew Jarvis Dr 03801 603-436-7100
Diane Canada, prin. Fax 436-6793
Portsmouth HS 1,100/9-12
50 Andrew Jarvis Dr 03801 603-436-7100
Jeffrey Collins, prin. Fax 427-2320
Portsmouth MS 500/6-8
155 Parrott Ave 03801 603-436-5781
John Stokel, prin. Fax 427-2326

Franklin Pierce University Post-Sec.
73 Corporate Dr 03801 603-433-2000
Great Bay Community College Post-Sec.
320 Corporate Dr 03801 603-427-7600
Hesser College Post-Sec.
170 Commerce Way 03801 603-436-5300
Portsmouth Beauty School of Hair Design Post-Sec.
140 Congress St 03801 603-436-7775

Raymond, Rockingham, Pop. 2,815
Raymond SD 1,500/PK-12
43 Harriman Hill Rd 03077 603-895-4299
Ellen Small, supt. Fax 895-0147
www.sau33.com/
Gove MS 500/5-8
1 Stephen K Batchelder Pkwy 03077 603-895-3394
Michael Chouinard, prin. Fax 895-9856
Raymond HS 400/9-12
45 Harriman Hill Rd 03077 603-895-6616
James Beitler, prin. Fax 895-1582

Rindge, Cheshire

Franklin Pierce University Post-Sec.
40 University Dr 03461 603-899-4000
Hampshire Country S 50/3-12
28 Patey Cir 03461 603-899-3325
Bernd Foecking, hdmstr. Fax 899-6521
Meeting S 50/11-11
120 Thomas Rd 03461 603-899-3366
Jacqueline Stillwell, hdmstr. Fax 899-6216

Rochester, Strafford, Pop. 29,277
Rochester SD 4,500/PK-12
150 Wakefield St Ste 8 03867 603-332-3678
Michael Hopkins, supt. Fax 335-7367
www.rochesterschools.com
Carlson Academy 100/Alt
150 Wakefield St Ste 8 03867 603-332-3678
Kathy Dubois, dir. Fax 335-7367
Creteau Regional Technology Center Vo/Tech
140 Wakefield St 03867 603-335-7351
Dave Robbins, dir. Fax 335-7365
Rochester MS 1,000/6-8
47 Brock St 03867 603-332-4090
Valerie McKenney, prin. Fax 332-9384
Spaulding HS 1,500/9-12
130 Wakefield St 03867 603-332-0757
Robert Seaward, prin. Fax 330-0251

Rye, Rockingham
Rye SD
Supt. — See Greenland

Rye JHS 200/6-8
501 Washington Rd 03870 603-964-5591
Christopher Pollet, prin. Fax 964-3881

Salem, Rockingham, Pop. 27,400
Salem SD 4,600/PK-12
38 Geremonty Dr 03079 603-893-7040
Michael Delahanty, supt. Fax 893-7080
www.sau57.org
Center for Career & Technical Education Vo/Tech
44 Geremonty Dr 03079 603-893-7073
Chris Dodge, prin. Fax 898-0208
Salem HS 1,700/9-12
44 Geremonty Dr 03079 603-893-7069
Tracy Collyer, prin. Fax 893-7087
Woodbury MS 1,100/6-8
206 Main St 03079 603-893-7055
Brad St. Laurent, prin. Fax 898-0634

Hesser College Post-Sec.
11 Manor Pkwy 03079 603-898-3480

Sanbornton, Belknap

Sant Bani S 200/K-12
19 Ashram Rd 03269 603-934-4240
Kent Bicknell Ed.D., prin. Fax 934-2970

Seabrook, Rockingham
Seabrook SD
Supt. — See Hampton
Seabrook MS 300/5-8
256 Walton Rd 03874 603-474-9221
Leslie Shepard, prin. Fax 474-8020

Somersworth, Strafford, Pop. 11,470
Somersworth SD 1,600/PK-12
51 W High St 03878 603-692-4450
Jeni Mosca, supt. Fax 692-9100
www.sau56.org/somersworth-school-district/home
Somersworth Career Technical Center Vo/Tech
18 Cemetery Rd 03878 603-692-2242
Dr. Bette Chamberlain, dir. Fax 692-9116
Somersworth HS 600/9-12
11 Memorial Dr 03878 603-692-2431
Sharon Lampros, prin. Fax 692-7326
Somersworth MS 500/5-8
7 Memorial Dr 03878 603-692-2126
Dana Hilliard, prin. Fax 692-9101

Empire Beauty School Post-Sec.
362 Route 108 03878 603-692-1515
Tri-City Christian Academy 300/PK-12
150 W High St 03878 603-692-2093
Paul Edgar, admin. Fax 692-6305

Stratham, Rockingham
Exeter Region Cooperative SD
Supt. — See Exeter
Cooperative MS 1,300/6-8
100 Academic Way 03885 603-775-8700
William Furbush, prin. Fax 775-0151

Sunapee, Sullivan
Sunapee SD 500/K-12
70 Lower Main St 03782 603-763-4627
Brendan Minnihan, supt. Fax 763-4718
www.sunapeeschools.org
Sunapee HS 100/9-12
10 North Rd 03782 603-763-5615
Sean Moynihan, prin. Fax 763-3055
Sunapee MS 100/6-8
10 North Rd 03782 603-763-5615
Sean Moynihan, prin. Fax 763-3055

Mount Royal Academy 100/PK-12
26 Seven Hearths Ln 03782 603-763-9010
David Thibault, hdmstr. Fax 763-5390

Swanzey, Cheshire
Monadnock Regional SD 1,800/PK-12
600 Old Homestead Hwy 03446 603-352-6955
Dr. Leo Corriveau, supt. Fax 358-6708
www.mrsd.org
Monadnock Regional HS 600/9-12
580 Old Homestead Hwy 03446 603-352-6575
Jed Butterfield, prin. Fax 355-1209
Monadnock Regional MS 300/7-8
580 Old Homestead Hwy 03446 603-352-6575
Jed Butterfield, prin. Fax 357-6520

Tilton, Belknap, Pop. 3,081
Winnisquam Regional SD 1,500/PK-12
433 W Main St 03276 603-286-4116
Dr. Tammy Davis, supt. Fax 286-7402
www.winnisquam.k12.nh.us
Winnisquam Regional HS 500/9-12
435 W Main St 03276 603-286-4531
Robert Pedersen, prin. Fax 286-2006
Winnisquam Regional MS 400/6-8
76 Winter St 03276 603-286-7143
Robert Seaward, prin. Fax 286-7410

Tilton S 200/9-12
30 School St 03276 603-286-4342
James Clements, hdmstr. Fax 286-3137

Walpole, Cheshire, Pop. 595
Fall Mountain Regional SD
Supt. — See Charlestown
Walpole MS 200/5-8
PO Box 549 03608 603-756-4728
Samuel Jacobs, prin. Fax 756-3343

Warner, Merrimack, Pop. 440

College of St. Mary Magdalen Post-Sec.
511 Kearsarge Mountain Rd 03278 603-456-2656

Weare, Hillsborough
John Stark Regional SD
Supt. — See Henniker
Stark Regional HS 800/9-12
618 N Stark Hwy 03281 603-529-7675
Chris Mosca, prin. Fax 529-4646

Weare SD
Supt. — See Henniker
Weare MS 500/5-8
16 East Rd 03281 603-529-7555
Mark Willis, prin. Fax 529-0464

West Lebanon, See Lebanon
Lebanon SD 1,500/PK-12
20 Seminary Hl 03784 603-448-1634
Dr. Gail Paludi, supt. Fax 448-0602
www.sau88.net
Other Schools – See Lebanon

Franklin Pierce University Post-Sec.
24 Airport Rd Ste 19 03784 603-298-5549
New England School of Hair Design Post-Sec.
12 Interchange Dr 03784 603-298-5199

Whitefield, Coos, Pop. 1,128
White Mountains Regional SD 1,300/PK-12
14 King Sq 03598 603-837-9363
Harry Fensom, supt. Fax 837-2326
www.sau36.org
White Mountains Regional HS 400/9-12
PO Box 338 03598 603-837-2528
Michael Berry, prin. Fax 837-3811
White Mountains Reg/Voc HS Vo/Tech
PO Box 338 03598 603-837-2528
Lori Lane, dir. Fax 837-3811

Wilton, Hillsborough, Pop. 1,150
Wilton-Lyndeborough SD 600/PK-12
PO Box 1149 03086 603-878-8100
Donald LaPlante Ed.D., supt. Fax 654-6691
www.sau63.org
Wilton-Lyndeborough HS 200/9-12
PO Box 255 03086 603-654-6123
Brian Bagley, prin. Fax 654-2104
Wilton-Lyndeborough MS 100/6-8
PO Box 255 03086 603-654-6123
Brian Bagley, prin. Fax 654-2104

High Mowing S 100/9-12
222 Isaac Frye Hwy 03086 603-654-2391
Rea Taylor Gill, dir. Fax 654-6588

Windham, Rockingham
Pelham SD 2,100/PK-12
PO Box 510 03087 603-425-1976
Dr. Henry LaBranche, supt. Fax 425-1719
www.pelhamsd.org
Other Schools – See Pelham

Windham SD 2,400/PK-12
PO Box 510 03087 603-425-1976
Dr. Henry LaBranche, supt. Fax 425-1719
www.windhamsd.org
Windham HS 500/9-12
64 London Bridge Rd 03087 603-537-2400
Tom Murphy, prin. Fax 537-2499
Windham MS 600/6-8
112 Lowell Rd Ste A 03087 603-893-2636
Daniel Moulis, prin. Fax 870-9007

Wolfeboro, Carroll, Pop. 2,811
Governor Wentworth Regional SD 2,500/PK-12
140 Pine Hill Rd 03894 603-569-1658
John Robertson, supt. Fax 569-6983
www.govwentworth.k12.nh.us
Kingswood Regional HS 800/9-12
396 S Main St 03894 603-569-2055
Guy Donnelly, prin. Fax 569-8104
Kingswood Regional MS 400/7-8
404 S Main St 03894 603-569-3689
Kirkland Ross, prin. Fax 569-8113
Lakes Region Technology Center Vo/Tech
384 S Main St 03894 603-569-4361
Stephen Guyer, prin. Fax 569-9243

Brewster Academy 400/9-12
80 Academy Dr 03894 603-569-1600
Dr. Michael Cooper, head sch Fax 569-7199

Woodsville, Grafton, Pop. 1,115
Haverhill Cooperative SD
Supt. — See North Haverhill
Woodsville HS 300/9-12
9 High St 03785 603-747-2781
Robert Jones, prin. Fax 747-2766

NEW JERSEY

NEW JERSEY DEPARTMENT OF EDUCATION
PO Box 500, Trenton 08625-0500
Telephone 609-292-4469
Fax 609-777-4099
Website http://www.state.nj.us/education

Commissioner of Education Chris Cerf

NEW JERSEY BOARD OF EDUCATION
PO Box 500, Trenton 08625-0500

President Arcelio Aponte

COUNTY SUPERINTENDENTS OF SCHOOLS

Atlantic County Office of Education
Thomas Dowd, supt. 609-625-0004
6260 Old Harding Hwy Ste 1 Fax 625-6539
Mays Landing 08330
www.aclink.org/education/

Bergen County Office of Education
Robert Gilmartin, supt. 201-336-6875
1 Bergen County Plz Rm 350 Fax 336-6880
Hackensack 07601

Burlington County Office of Education
Peggy Nicoloti, supt. 609-265-5060
PO Box 6000, Westampton 08060 Fax 265-5922

Camden County Office of Education
Peggy Nicoloti, supt. 856-401-2400
PO Box 200, Blackwood 08012 Fax 401-2410
www.camdencounty.com/education

Cape May County Office of Education
Dr. Richard Stepura, supt. 609-465-1283
4 Moore Rd Fax 465-2094
Cape May Court House
www.capemaycountygov.net/

Cumberland County Office of Education
Richard Stepura, supt. 856-451-0211
19 Landis Ave, Bridgeton 08302 Fax 455-9523
www.co.cumberland.nj.us/

Essex County Office of Education
Thomas Dowd, supt. 973-395-4677
7 Glenwood Ave Ste 404 Fax 395-4696
East Orange 07017

Gloucester County Office of Education
Robert Bumpus, supt. 856-686-8370
254 County House Rd Fax 423-5296
Clarksboro 08020
www.co.gloucester.nj.us

Hudson County Office of Education
Monica Tone, supt. 201-369-5290
595 County Ave Bldg 3 Fax 369-5288
Secaucus 07094
www.hcstonline.org/main/hcdoe/Home.aspx

Hunterdon County Office of Education
Jeffrey Scott, supt. 908-788-1414
PO Box 2900, Flemington 08822 Fax 788-1457
www.co.hunterdon.nj.us/schools.htm

Mercer County Office of Education
Dr. Samuel Stewart, supt. 609-588-5884
1075 Old Trenton Rd Fax 588-5878
Trenton 08690
nj.gov/counties/mercer/departments/schools/index.html

Middlesex County Office of Education
Dr. Patrick Piegari, supt. 732-249-2900
1460 Livingston Ave Fax 296-0683
North Brunswick 08902

Monmouth County Office of Education
Carol Morris, supt. 732-431-7816
60 Neptune Blvd Fl 2 Fax 577-0679
Neptune 07753

Morris County Office of Education
Dr. Kathleen Serafino, supt. 973-285-8332
PO Box 900, Morristown 07963 Fax 285-8341

Ocean County Office of Education
Dr. Bruce Greenfield, supt. 732-929-2078
212 Washington St Fax 506-5336
Toms River 08753
www.co.ocean.nj.us/OCSchools/MainPage.aspx

Passaic County Office of Education
Robert Gilmartin, supt. 973-569-2110
501 River St, Paterson 07524 Fax 754-0241

Salem County Office of Education
Michael Elwell, supt. 856-339-8611
94 Market St, Salem 08079 Fax 935-6290

Somerset County Office of Education 908-541-5700
, PO Box 3000, Somerville 08876 Fax 722-6902
www.co.somerset.nj.us/schools/

Sussex County Office of Education
Barry Worman, supt. 973-579-6996
262 White Lake Rd, Sparta 07871 Fax 579-6476
www.sussex.nj.us/

Union County Office of Education
Dr. Carmen Centuolo, supt. 908-654-9860
300 North Ave E, Westfield 07090 Fax 654-9869

Warren County Office of Education
Thomas Gross, supt. 908-475-6030
537 Oxford St, Belvidere 07823 Fax 475-6035
www.co.warren.nj.us/edu.html

PUBLIC, PRIVATE AND CATHOLIC SECONDARY SCHOOLS

Aberdeen, Monmouth, Pop. 17,038
Matawan-Aberdeen Regional SD 3,700/PK-12
1 Crest Way 07747 732-705-4000
David Healy, supt.
www.marsd.org/
Matawan Regional HS 1,100/9-12
450 Atlantic Ave 07747 732-705-5200
Michele Ruscavage, prin. Fax 566-2404
Other Schools – See Cliffwood

Monmouth County Vocational SD
Supt. — See Freehold
Aberdeen Vocational S Vo/Tech
450 Atlantic Ave 07747 732-566-5599
Joseph Diver, prin. Fax 566-2392

Absecon, Atlantic, Pop. 8,239
Absecon CSD 700/K-8
800 Irelan Ave 08201 609-641-5375
James Giaquinto, supt. Fax 641-8692
www.abseconschools.org
Attales MS 200/5-8
800 Irelan Ave Ste 1 08201 609-641-5375
Andrew Weber, prin. Fax 641-8692

Holy Spirit HS 800/9-12
500 S New Rd 08201 609-646-3000
Susan Dennen, prin. Fax 646-1770

Adelphia, Monmouth

Talmudical Academy of New Jersey Post-Sec.
Route 524 07710 732-431-1600
Talmudical Academy of NJ 50/9-12
PO Box 7 07710 732-431-1600

Allendale, Bergen, Pop. 6,407
Allendale SD 900/PK-8
100 Brookside Ave 07401 201-327-2020
Michael Barcadepone, supt. Fax 785-9735
www.allendaleschoolsnj.com
Brookside MS 600/4-8
100 Brookside Ave 07401 201-327-2020
Bruce Winkelstein, prin. Fax 825-6553

Northern Highlands Regional HSD 1,300/9-12
298 Hillside Ave 07401 201-327-8700
John Keenan, supt. Fax 327-5274
www.northernhighlands.org
Northern Highlands Regional HS 1,300/9-12
298 Hillside Ave 07401 201-327-8700
Joseph Occhino, prin. Fax 327-3370

Allentown, Monmouth, Pop. 1,798
Upper Freehold Regional SD 2,300/PK-12
27 High St 08501 609-259-7292
Dr. Richard Fitzpatrick, supt. Fax 259-0881
www.ufrsd.net
Allentown HS 1,100/9-12
27 High St 08501 609-259-2160
Connie Embley, prin. Fax 259-0390
Upper Freehold Regional MS 500/5-8
27 High St 08501 609-259-7369
Mark Guterl, prin. Fax 208-1411

Annandale, Hunterdon, Pop. 1,653
North Hunterdon/Voorhees Regional HSD 2,700/9-12
1445 State Route 31 S 08801 908-735-2846
Dr. Charles Shaddow, supt. Fax 735-6914
www.nhvweb.net
North Hunterdon HS 1,700/9-12
1445 State Route 31 S 08801 908-735-5191
Michael Hughes, prin. Fax 735-6447
Other Schools – See Glen Gardner

Asbury, Hunterdon, Pop. 273
Bethlehem Township SD 500/K-8
940 Iron Bridge Rd 08802 908-537-4044
Dr. Edward Keegan, admin. Fax 537-4309
www.btschools.org
Hoppock MS 200/6-8
280 Asbury West Portal Rd 08802 908-479-6336
Jane Smith, prin. Fax 479-1021

Asbury Park, Monmouth, Pop. 15,693
Asbury Park SD 1,200/PK-12
603 Mattison Ave Ste 3 07712 732-776-2606
Dr. Denise Lowe, supt. Fax 774-8067
www.asburypark.k12.nj.us
Alternative S Alt
605 Asbury Ave 07712 732-988-4140
Ernest Whittaker, prin. Fax 988-2037
Asbury Park HS 400/9-12
1003 Sunset Ave 07712 732-776-2638
Reginald Mirthil, prin. Fax 776-3119
Asbury Park MS 300/5-8
1200 Bangs Ave 07712 732-776-2559
Dr. Antonio Lewis, prin. Fax 776-7503

Monmouth County Vocational SD
Supt. — See Freehold
Culinary Education Center Vo/Tech
101 Drury Ln 07712 732-988-3299
Michael Sirianni, prin. Fax 776-8096

Atco, Camden
Winslow Township SD 5,000/PK-12
40 Cooper Folly Rd 08004 856-767-2850
Dr. H. Major Poteat, supt. Fax 767-4782
www.winslow-schools.com
Winslow Township HS 1,500/9-12
10 Cooper Folly Rd 08004 856-767-1850
Nython Carter, prin. Fax 767-5670
Winslow Township MS 800/7-8
30 Cooper Folly Rd 08004 856-767-7222
Stella Nwanguma, prin. Fax 767-5411

Atlantic City, Atlantic, Pop. 38,716
Atlantic City SD 6,100/PK-12
1300 Atlantic Ave 08401 609-343-7200
Donna Haye, supt. Fax 345-3268
www.acboe.org/
Atlantic City HS 2,200/9-12
1400 N Albany Ave 08401 609-343-7300
Oscar Torres, prin. Fax 343-7345
Atlantic City HS - East Alt
117 N Indiana Ave 08401 609-343-7360
Charles Wilson, prin. Fax 343-7408

Audubon, Camden, Pop. 8,746
Audubon SD 1,400/PK-12
350 Edgewood Ave 08106 856-547-7695
Edward Wasilewski Ed.D., supt. Fax 546-8550
www.audubonschools.org/
Audubon JSHS 800/7-12
350 Edgewood Ave 08106 856-547-7695
John Ross, prin. Fax 547-4073

Avalon, Cape May, Pop. 1,326
Avalon SD 50/5-8
235 32nd St 08202 609-967-7544
Stacey Tracy, supt. Fax 967-3109
www.avesnj.org/
Avalon ES 50/5-8
235 32nd St 08202 609-967-7544
Stacey Tracy, supt. Fax 967-3109

Avenel, Middlesex, Pop. 16,588
Woodbridge Township SD
Supt. — See Woodbridge
Avenel MS 600/6-8
85 Woodbine Ave 07001 732-596-4210
Joseph Short, prin. Fax 574-0573

Barnegat, Ocean, Pop. 2,775
Barnegat Township SD 3,100/PK-12
550 Barnegat Blvd N 08005 609-698-5800
Karen Wood, supt. Fax 698-6638
www.barnegatschools.com

Barnegat HS 900/9-12
180 Bengal Blvd 08005 609-660-7510
Dr. Joseph Saxton, prin. Fax 660-7598
Brackman MS 800/6-8
600 Barnegat Blvd N 08005 609-698-5880
Stephen Nichol, prin. Fax 698-7965

Barrington, Camden, Pop. 6,884
Barrington Borough SD 600/PK-8
311 Reading Ave 08007 856-547-8467
Anthony Arcodia, supt. Fax 547-5533
www.barringtonschools.net/
Woodland MS 300/5-8
I School Ln 08007 856-547-8402
David Zucker, prin. Fax 522-1248

Castle Academy 200/PK-12
60 E Gloucester Pike 08007 856-546-5901

Basking Ridge, Somerset, Pop. 4,000
Bernards Township SD 5,500/K-12
101 Peachtree Rd 07920 908-204-2600
Nick Markarian, supt. Fax 766-7641
www.bernardsboe.com/
Annin MS 1,400/6-8
70 Quincy Rd 07920 908-204-2610
Karen Hudock, prin. Fax 204-0244
Ridge HS 1,700/9-12
268 S Finley Ave 07920 908-204-2585
Frank Howlett, prin. Fax 204-2582

Pingry S 700/7-12
131 Martinsville Rd 07920 908-647-5555
Nathaniel Conard, hdmstr. Fax 647-3703

Bayonne, Hudson, Pop. 61,671
Bayonne SD 8,800/PK-12
669 Avenue A 07002 201-858-5800
Patricia McGeehan Ed.D., supt. Fax 858-6289
www.bboed.org
Bayonne HS 2,400/9-12
667 Avenue A 07002 201-858-5900
Richard Baccarella, prin. Fax 858-6263

Bayonne Hospital School of Nursing Post-Sec.
29 E 29th St 07002 201-339-9656
Holy Family Academy 200/9-12
239 Avenue A 07002 201-339-7341
Mary Tremitiedi, prin. Fax 339-9295
Marist HS 400/9-12
1241 Kennedy Blvd 07002 201-437-4544
Alice Miesnik, prin. Fax 437-6013
Yeshiva Gedola of Bayonne 100/9-12
747 Avenue C 07002 201-339-7187

Bayville, Ocean
Central Regional SD 1,900/7-12
509 Forest Hills Pkwy 08721 732-269-1100
Dr. T. Parlapanides, supt. Fax 237-8872
www.centralreg.k12.nj.us
Central Regional HS 1,300/9-12
509 Forest Hills Pkwy 08721 732-269-1100
Dr. Douglas Corbett, prin. Fax 269-7723
Central Regional MS 600/7-8
509 Forest Hills Pkwy 08721 732-269-1100
Dr. Dennis Driber, prin. Fax 269-7723

Beachwood, Ocean, Pop. 10,934
Toms River Regional SD
Supt. — See Toms River
Toms River IS South 1,000/6-8
1675 Pinewald Rd 08722 732-505-3900
Paul Gluck, prin. Fax 818-7512

Belleville, Essex, Pop. 36,300
Belleville SD 4,600/K-12
102 Passaic Ave 07109 973-450-3500
Joseph Picardo, supt. Fax 450-3504
www.bellevilleschools.org
Belleville HS 1,400/9-12
100 Passaic Ave 07109 973-450-3500
Russell Pagano, prin. Fax 450-3196
Belleville MS 700/7-8
279 Washington Ave 07109 973-450-3500
Dora Cavallio, prin. Fax 450-5001

Eastern International College Post-Sec.
251 Washington Ave 07109 973-751-9051

Bellmawr, Camden, Pop. 11,414
Bellmawr Borough SD 1,100/PK-8
256 Anderson Ave 08031 856-931-3620
Annette Castiglione, supt. Fax 931-9326
bellmawrschools.org
Bell Oaks MS 500/5-8
256 Anderson Ave 08031 856-931-6273
Anthony Farinelli, prin. Fax 931-9326

Belmar, Monmouth, Pop. 5,731

Mesivta Keser Torah Post-Sec.
503 11th Ave 07719 732-367-4259
Mesivta Keser Torah 100/9-12
503 11th Ave 07719 732-681-5656
St. Rose HS 600/9-12
607 7th Ave 07719 732-681-2858
Sr. Kathy Nace, prin. Fax 280-2745

Belvidere, Warren, Pop. 2,652
Belvidere SD 800/K-12
809 Oxford St 07823 908-475-6600
Dirk Swaneveld, supt. Fax 475-6619
www.belvideresd.org
Belvidere HS 500/9-12
809 Oxford St 07823 908-475-4025
Chris Carrubba, prin. Fax 475-1685
Oxford Street MS 200/4-8
807 Oxford St 07823 908-475-4001
Sandra Szabocsik, prin. Fax 475-6619

Bergenfield, Bergen, Pop. 26,177
Bergenfield SD 3,200/K-12
225 W Clinton Ave 07621 201-385-8801
Dr. Michael Kuchar, supt. Fax 384-2914
www.bergenfield.org/
Bergenfield HS 1,200/9-12
80 S Prospect Ave 07621 201-385-8600
James Fasano, prin. Fax 439-0978
Brown MS 800/6-8
130 S Washington Ave 07621 201-385-8847
Shana Wright, prin. Fax 385-0219

Berkeley Heights, Union, Pop. 11,980
Berkeley Heights SD 2,100/PK-12
345 Plainfield Ave 07922 908-464-1718
Judith Rattner, supt. Fax 464-1728
www.bhpsnj.org/
Columbia MS 600/6-8
345 Plainfield Ave 07922 908-464-1600
Frank Geiger, prin. Fax 464-0017
Livingston HS 700/9-12
175 Watchung Blvd 07922 908-464-3100
Scott McKinney, prin. Fax 464-7508

Bernardsville, Somerset, Pop. 7,613
Somerset Hills SD 2,100/PK-12
25 Olcott Ave 07924 908-204-1930
Dr. Frances Wood, supt. Fax 953-0699
www.shsd.org/
Bernards HS 800/9-12
25 Olcott Ave 07924 908-204-1930
Scott Neigel, prin. Fax 766-8223
Bernardsville MS 600/5-8
141 Seney Dr 07924 908-204-1916
Dr. Lynn Kratz, prin. Fax 953-2184

Blackwood, Camden, Pop. 4,485
Black Horse Pike Regional SD 4,100/9-12
580 Erial Rd 08012 856-227-4106
John Golden, supt. Fax 227-6835
www.bhprsd.org
Highland HS 1,100/9-12
450 Erial Rd 08012 856-227-4100
Elizabeth Petitte, prin. Fax 227-3619
Other Schools – See Erial, Runnemede

Gloucester Township SD 7,000/K-8
17 Erial Rd 08012 856-227-1400
John Bilodeau, supt. Fax 228-1422
www.gloucestertownshipschools.org/
Glen Landing MS 800/6-8
85 Little Gloucester Rd 08012 856-227-3534
Suzanne Schultes, prin. Fax 228-5260
Lewis MS 600/6-8
875 Erial Rd 08012 856-227-8400
Theodore Otten, prin. Fax 228-5130
Other Schools – See Sicklerville

Camden County College Post-Sec.
PO Box 200 08012 856-227-7200
Pennco Tech Post-Sec.
99 Erial Rd 08012 856-232-0310

Blairstown, Warren
North Warren Regional SD 1,100/7-12
PO Box 410 07825 908-362-9342
Brian Fogelson Ed.D., supt. Fax 362-8744
www.northwarren.org
North Warren Regional MSHS 1,100/7-12
PO Box 410 07825 908-362-8211
Louis Melchor, prin. Fax 362-7353

Blair Academy 500/9-12
PO Box 600 07825 908-362-6121
T. Chandler Hardwick, admin. Fax 362-7945

Bloomfield, Essex, Pop. 48,200
Bloomfield Township SD 5,700/PK-12
155 Broad St 07003 973-680-8500
Jason Bing, supt. Fax 680-8274
www.bloomfield.k12.nj.us
Bloomfield HS 1,800/9-12
160 Broad St 07003 973-680-8600
Christopher Jennings, prin. Fax 680-8684
Bloomfield MS 900/7-8
60 Huck Rd 07003 973-680-8620
Salvatore Goncalves, prin. Fax 338-6523
Bridges Academy 50/Alt
280 Davey St 07003 973-680-8686
Kerry DiGiacinto, prin. Fax 429-7960

Essex County Vocational Technical SD
Supt. — See Newark
Essex Co. Vocational Tech HS Bloomfield Vo/Tech
209 Franklin St 07003 973-412-2206
Eric Love, prin. Fax 412-2096

Bloomfield College Post-Sec.
467 Franklin St 07003 973-748-9000
Concorde School of Hair Design Post-Sec.
15 Ward St 07003 973-680-0099

Bloomingdale, Passaic, Pop. 7,587
Bloomingdale SD 600/PK-8
225 Glenwild Ave 07403 973-838-3282
Frank Buglione, supt. Fax 838-6397
www.bloomingdaleschools.org
Bergen MS 300/5-8
225 Glenwild Ave 07403 973-838-4835
Frank Verducci, prin. Fax 283-1893

Bogota, Bergen, Pop. 7,987
Bogota SD 1,100/PK-12
1 Henry C Luthin Pl 07603 201-441-4800
Dr. Letizia Pantoliano, supt. Fax 489-5759
www.bogotaboe.com
Bogota JSHS 600/7-12
2 Henry C Luthin Pl 07603 201-441-4808
Linda Gatusso, prin. Fax 441-4849

Boonton, Morris, Pop. 8,097
Boonton SD 800/PK-12
434 Lathrop Ave 07005 973-335-3994
Dr. Christine Johnson, supt. Fax 335-8281
www.boontonschools.org
Boonton HS 600/9-12
306 Lathrop Ave 07005 973-335-9700
Jacalyn Richardson, prin. Fax 402-5135

Bordentown, Burlington, Pop. 3,853
Bordentown Regional SD 2,100/K-12
318 Ward Ave 08505 609-298-0025
Dr. Constance Bauer, supt. Fax 298-2515
www.bordentown.k12.nj.us
Bordentown Regional HS 700/9-12
318 Ward Ave 08505 609-298-0025
Patrick Lynch, prin. Fax 298-2515
Bordentown Regional MS 500/6-8
50 Dunns Mill Rd 08505 609-298-0674
Robert Walder, prin. Fax 291-1929

Bound Brook, Somerset, Pop. 10,250
Bound Brook Borough SD 1,500/PK-12
337 W 2nd St 08805 732-356-2500
Dr. Edward Hoffman, supt. Fax 271-9097
www.bbrook.org
Bound Brook HS 500/9-12
111 W Union Ave 08805 732-652-7950
Dr. Daniel Gallagher, prin. Fax 356-6445
Smalley MS 300/6-8
163 Cherry Ave 08805 732-652-7940
Edward Gordon, prin. Fax 271-4879

Branchburg, Somerset
Branchburg Township SD 1,400/PK-8
240 Baird Rd 08876 908-722-3335
Dr. Carol Kelley, supt. Fax 526-6144
www.branchburg.k12.nj.us
Branchburg Central MS 600/6-8
220 Baird Rd 08876 908-526-1415
Matthew Barbosa, prin. Fax 526-7486

Raritan Valley Community College Post-Sec.
118 Larmington Rd 08876 908-526-1200

Brick, Ocean, Pop. 78,300
Brick Township SD 9,400/PK-12
101 Hendrickson Ave 08724 732-785-3000
Dr. Walter Uszenski, supt. Fax 840-9089
www.brickschools.org/
Brick Township HS 1,400/9-12
346 Chambersbridge Rd 08723 732-262-2500
Dennis Filippone, prin. Fax 920-5907
Brick Township Memorial HS 1,800/9-12
2001 Lanes Mill Rd 08724 732-785-3090
Dr. Richard Caldes, prin. Fax 458-2748
Lake Riviera MS 1,000/6-8
171 Beaverson Blvd 08723 732-785-3000
Dr. Alyce Anderson, prin. Fax 477-0392
Veteran's Memorial MS 1,300/6-8
105 Hendrickson Ave 08724 732-785-3030
Renee Kotsianas, prin. Fax 458-9777

Ocean County Vocational SD
Supt. — See Toms River
Ocean County Voc-Tech S - Brick Vo/Tech
350 Chambersbridge Rd 08723 732-286-5670
Lynn Sauer, prin. Fax 920-0108

Capri Institute of Hair Design Post-Sec.
268 Brick Blvd 08723 732-920-3600
Star Career Academy Post-Sec.
150 Brick Blvd 08723 732-451-9710

Bridgeton, Cumberland, Pop. 24,883
Bridgeton SD 4,900/PK-12
PO Box 657 08302 856-455-8030
Dr. Thomasina Jones, supt. Fax 451-0815
www.bridgeton.k12.nj.us/
Bridgeton HS 1,100/9-12
111 N West Ave 08302 856-455-8030
Lynn Williams, prin. Fax 455-0486
ExCEL S 6-8
398 N Pearl St 08302 856-455-8030
Isaias Garza, lead tchr. Fax 459-0280

Cumberland County Technical SD
601 Bridgeton Ave 08302 856-451-9000
Dr. Dina Elliott, supt. Fax 453-1118
www.cumberland.tec.nj.us
Cumberland Co. Technical Education Ctr Vo/Tech
601 Bridgeton Ave 08302 856-451-9000
Patrick Cruet, prin. Fax 453-1118

Cumberland Regional SD 1,300/9-12
65 Love Ln 08302 856-451-9400
William Stonis, supt. Fax 455-9750
www.crhsd.org/
Cumberland Regional HS 1,300/9-12
90 Silver Lake Rd 08302 856-451-9400
John Mitchell, prin. Fax 455-8514

Cumberland Co. Tech. Education Center Post-Sec.
601 Bridgeton Ave 08302 856-451-9000
Devereux New Jersey Center for Autism Post-Sec.
198 Roadstown Rd 08302 856-599-6411

Bridgewater, Somerset, Pop. 36,400
Bridgewater-Raritan Regional SD 8,800/PK-12
PO Box 6030 08807 908-685-2777
Fax 231-8496
www.brrsd.k12.nj.us
Bridgewater-Raritan HS 2,900/9-12
PO Box 6569 08807 908-231-8660
Brett Charleston, prin. Fax 231-0467
Bridgewater-Raritan MS 1,400/7-8
PO Box 6933 08807 908-231-8661
Nancy Iatesta, prin. Fax 575-0847

Somerset County Vocational SD
PO Box 6350 08807 908-526-8900
Chrys Harttraft, supt. Fax 704-0784
www.scvths.org/
Somerset County Vo-Tech HS Vo/Tech
PO Box 6350 08807 908-526-8900
Diane Ziegler, prin. Fax 704-0784

Brigantine, Atlantic, Pop. 9,281
Brigantine CSD 700/PK-8
PO Box 947 08203 609-266-7671
Dr. William Gussie, supt. Fax 266-4748
www.brigantineschools.org/
Brigantine North MS 200/5-8
PO Box 947 08203 609-266-3603
Brian Pruitt, prin. Fax 266-7062

Brookside, Morris
Mendham Township SD 800/K-8
PO Box 510 07926 973-543-7107
Dr. Salvatore Constantino, supt. Fax 543-5537
www.mendhamtwp.org
Mendham Township MS 400/5-8
PO Box 510 07926 973-543-2505
Dr. Patrick Ciccone, prin. Fax 543-0701

Budd Lake, Morris, Pop. 8,814
Mt. Olive Township SD 4,300/K-12
89 US Highway 46 07828 973-691-4008
Larrie Reynolds Ph.D., supt. Fax 691-4022
www.mtoliveboe.org
Mt. Olive MS 1,100/6-8
160 Wolfe Rd 07828 973-691-4006
Dr. Tracey Severns, prin. Fax 691-4029
Other Schools – See Flanders

Buena, Atlantic, Pop. 4,524
Buena Regional SD 1,800/PK-12
PO Box 309 08310 856-697-0800
Walter Whitaker, supt. Fax 697-4963
www.buena.k12.nj.us/
Buena Regional HS 800/9-12
125 Weymouth Rd 08310 856-697-2400
Moses White, prin. Fax 697-4701
Buena Regional MS 500/6-8
175 Weymouth Rd 08310 856-697-0100
Karen Santoro, prin. Fax 697-9580

Burlington, Burlington, Pop. 9,602
Burlington CSD 1,800/PK-12
518 Locust Ave 08016 609-387-5874
Patricia Doloughty, supt. Fax 386-6971
www.burlington-nj.net
Burlington City JSHS 700/7-12
100 Blue Devil Way 08016 609-387-5800
Julian Jenkins, prin. Fax 387-4287

Burlington Township SD 3,900/PK-12
PO Box 428 08016 609-387-3955
Dr. Christopher Manno, supt. Fax 239-2192
www.burltwpsch.org/
BTMS @ Springside 1,000/6-8
1600 Burlington Byp 08016 609-699-4021
Lawrence Penny, prin. Fax 699-4022
Burlington Township HS 1,200/9-12
610 Fountain Ave 08016 609-387-1713
Phillip Brownridge, prin. Fax 387-0439

Doane Academy 200/PK-12
350 Riverbank 08016 609-386-3500
John McGee, hdmstr. Fax 386-5878
Institute of Logistical Management Post-Sec.
PO Box 427 08016 609-747-1515
Life Center Academy 300/PK-12
2045 Columbus Rd 08016 609-499-2100
Rev. Paul Graban, hdmstr. Fax 499-4905

Butler, Morris, Pop. 7,440
Butler SD 1,100/K-12
38 Bartholdi Ave 07405 973-492-2000
Mario Cardinale, supt. Fax 492-1016
www.butlerboe.org
Butler HS 500/9-12
38 Bartholdi Ave 07405 973-492-2000
Martin Wall, prin. Fax 492-8672
Butler MS 200/5-8
30 Pearl Pl 07405 973-492-2079
Andrea Vladichak, prin. Fax 492-9774

Morris County Vocational SD
Supt. — See Denville
Academy for Law & Public Safety Vo/Tech
Bartholdi Ave 07405 973-492-2000
Scott Moffitt, prin.

Caldwell, Essex, Pop. 7,489
Caldwell-West Caldwell SD
Supt. — See West Caldwell
Cleveland MS 600/6-8
36 Academy Rd 07006 973-228-9115
James Brown, prin. Fax 228-7471

Caldwell College Post-Sec.
120 Bloomfield Ave 07006 973-618-3000
Mt. St. Dominic Academy 300/9-12
3 Ryerson Ave 07006 973-226-0660
Sr. Frances Sullivan, head sch Fax 226-2693

Califon, Hunterdon, Pop. 1,050
Lebanon Township SD 700/PK-8
70 Bunnvale Rd 07830 908-638-4521
Jason R. Kornegay, supt. Fax 638-5511
www.lebtwpk8.org
Woodglen MS 300/5-8
70 Bunnvale Rd 07830 908-638-4111
Michael Rubright, prin. Fax 638-8418

Tewksbury Township SD 700/PK-8
173 County Road 517 07830 908-439-2010
Dr. James Gamble, supt. Fax 439-2655
www.tewksburyschools.org
Old Turnpike MS 400/PK-PK, 5-
171 County Road 517 07830 908-439-2010
Kenneth Wark, prin. Fax 439-3160

Camden, Camden, Pop. 76,282
Camden CSD 10,000/PK-12
201 N Front St 08102 856-966-2000
Reuben Mills, supt. Fax 966-2138
www.camden.k12.nj.us
Brimm Medical Arts HS 200/9-12
1626 Copewood St 08103 856-966-2500
Herbert Simons, prin. Fax 966-2489
Camden HS 600/9-12
1700 Park Blvd 08103 856-966-5100
James Thompson, prin. Fax 966-4756
Creative Arts Morgan Village Academy 100/6-12
990 Morgan St 08104 856-966-8955
Davida Coe-Brockington, prin. Fax 964-9759
East Camden MS 300/6-8
3064 Stevens St 08105 856-966-5111
Sharif Daaliya, prin. Fax 964-9791
Met East HS 100/9-12
1656 Kaighns Ave 08103 856-966-8950
Timothy Jenkins, prin. Fax 966-2388
Pyne Poynt MS 300/6-8
800 Erie St 08102 856-966-5360
Brian Medley, prin. Fax 964-8462
Wilson HS 800/9-12
3100 Federal St 08105 856-966-5300
Lisa Thomas, prin. Fax 966-4755
Riggs Adult Learning Center Adult
1656 Kaighns Ave 08103 856-966-5223
Timothy Jenkins, prin. Fax 541-8671

Cooper Hospital/Univ Medical Center Post-Sec.
1 Cooper Plz # 217 08103 856-342-2416
Our Lady of Lourdes School of Nursing Post-Sec.
1600 Haddon Ave 08103 856-757-3729
Rowan University Post-Sec.
200 N Broadway 08102 856-361-2900
Rutgers-The State University of N.J. Post-Sec.
303 Cooper St 08102 856-225-1766
West Jersey Health System Post-Sec.
1000 Atlantic Ave 08104 856-342-4600

Cape May, Cape May, Pop. 3,525
Lower Cap May Regional SD 1,500/7-12
687 Route 9 08204 609-884-3475
Jack Pfizenmayer, supt. Fax 884-0546
lcmrschool.org/lcm/home.html
Lower Cape May Regional HS 1,000/9-12
687 Route 9 08204 609-884-3475
Joe Castellucci, prin. Fax 884-0546
Teitelman MS 500/7-8
687 Route 9 08204 609-884-3475
Greg Lasher, prin. Fax 884-0546

Cape May Court House, Cape May, Pop. 5,227
Cape May County Technical SD
188 Crest Haven Rd, 609-465-2161
Dr. Nancy M. Hudanich, supt. Fax 465-3069
www.capemaytech.com
Cape May County Tech HS Vo/Tech
188 Crest Haven Rd, 609-465-2161
Michael Adams, prin. Fax 465-4504
Cape May County Tech Evening HS Adult
188 Crest Haven Rd, 609-465-2161
Rusty Miller, dir.

Dennis Township SD 500/K-8
601 Hagan Rd, 609-861-2821
Mark Miller, supt. Fax 861-1833
dennistwpschools.org
Other Schools – See Dennisville

Middle Township SD 2,600/PK-12
216 S Main St, 609-465-1800
Michael Kopakowski, supt. Fax 463-1979
www.middletwp.k12.nj.us
Middle Township HS 900/9-12
300 E Atlantic Ave, 609-465-1852
Richard Falletta, prin. Fax 465-3415
Middle Township MS 4 500/6-8
300 E Pacific Ave, 609-465-1834
Amos Kraybill, prin. Fax 465-5524

Burdette Tomlin Memorial Hospital Post-Sec.
2 Stone Harbor Blvd, 609-463-2180
Cape Christian Academy 100/PK-12
10 Oyster Rd, 609-465-4132
John Spriggs, admin. Fax 465-0170
Cape May County Technical Institute Post-Sec.
188 Crest Haven Rd, 609-465-2161

Carneys Point, Salem, Pop. 7,250
Penns Grove-Carneys Point Regional SD
Supt. — See Penns Grove
Penns Grove HS 600/9-12
334 Harding Hwy 08069 856-299-6300
Joseph Sottosanti, prin. Fax 299-5192

Salem Community College Post-Sec.
460 Hollywood Ave 08069 856-299-2100

Carteret, Middlesex, Pop. 22,279
Carteret Borough SD 3,600/PK-12
599 Roosevelt Ave 07008 732-541-8960
Kevin Ahearn, supt. Fax 541-0433
www.carteretschools.org
Carteret HS 1,000/9-12
199 Washington Ave 07008 732-541-8960
Lamont Repollet, prin. Fax 969-4004
Carteret MS 800/6-8
300 Carteret Ave 07008 732-541-8960
Mary Spiga, prin. Fax 541-0483

Cedar Grove, Essex, Pop. 12,053
Cedar Grove Township SD 1,600/K-12
520 Pompton Ave 07009 973-239-1550
Dr. Gene Polles, supt. Fax 239-2994
www.cedargrove.k12.nj.us
Cedar Grove HS 500/9-12
90 Rugby Rd 07009 973-239-6400
Michael Fetherman, admin. Fax 857-9833
Cedar Grove Memorial MS 500/5-8
500 Ridge Rd 07009 973-239-5233
Richard Mangili, prin.

Chatham, Morris, Pop. 8,814
School District of the Chathams 3,900/K-12
58 Meyersville Rd 07928 973-457-2520
Dr. Michael LaSusa, supt. Fax 457-2481
www.chatham-nj.org/coin
Chatham HS 1,100/9-12
255 Lafayette Ave 07928 973-457-2505
Darren Groh, prin. Fax 635-8670
Chatham MS 1,000/6-8
480 Main St 07928 973-457-2506
Jill Gihorski, prin. Fax 457-2492

Cherry Hill, Camden, Pop. 70,100
Cherry Hill Township SD 11,400/K-12
PO Box 5015 08034 856-429-5600
Dr. Maureen Reusche, supt. Fax 354-1864
www.cherryhill.k12.nj.us
Beck MS 900/6-8
950 Cropwell Rd 08003 856-424-4505
Dr. Dennis Perry, prin. Fax 424-8602
Carusi MS 1,000/6-8
315 Roosevelt Dr 08002 856-667-1220
Dr. Kirk Rickansrud, prin. Fax 779-0613
Cherry Hill HS - East 2,100/9-12
1750 Kresson Rd 08003 856-424-2222
Dr. John O'Breza, prin. Fax 424-0637
Cherry Hill HS - West 1,500/9-12
2101 Chapel Ave W 08002 856-663-8006
Dr. Joseph Meloche, prin. Fax 663-5746
Malberg Alternative HS 50/Alt
45 Ranoldo Ter 08034 856-427-4311
Dr. Neil Burti, prin. Fax 427-0017
Rosa International MS 800/6-8
485 Browning Ln 08003 856-616-8787
Ed Canzanese, prin. Fax 616-0904

Anthem Institute Post-Sec.
2100 Route 38 08002 856-755-4800
Camden Catholic HS 800/9-12
300 Cuthbert Blvd 08002 856-663-2247
Heather Crisci, prin. Fax 661-0632
Empire Beauty School Post-Sec.
2100 State Highway #38 08002 856-667-8887
Harris School of Business Post-Sec.
1 Mall Dr Ste 700 08002 856-662-5300
Kings Christian S 300/PK-12
5 Carnegie Plz 08003 856-489-6720
John Walsh, prin. Fax 489-6727

Chester, Morris, Pop. 1,618
Chester SD 1,300/K-8
415 State Route 24 Ste 11 07930 908-879-7373
Dr. Christina Van Woert, supt. Fax 879-5887
www.chester-nj.org
Black River MS 500/6-8
133 North Rd 07930 908-879-6363
Robert Mullen, prin. Fax 879-9085

West Morris Regional HSD 2,700/9-12
10 S Four Bridges Rd 07930 908-879-6404
Mackey Pendergrast, supt. Fax 879-8861
www.wmrhsd.org
West Morris Central HS 1,400/9-12
259 Bartley Rd 07930 908-879-5212
Stephen Ryan, prin. Fax 879-2741
Other Schools – See Mendham

Chesterfield, Burlington

Meadow View Junior Academy 100/K-10
241 Bordentown Chstrfeld Rd, 609-298-1122
M. Saint-Ulysse, prin. Fax 298-7550

Cinnaminson, Burlington, Pop. 14,583
Cinnaminson Township SD 2,300/K-12
PO Box 224 08077 856-829-7600
Dr. Salvatore Illuzzi, supt. Fax 786-9618
www.cinnaminson.com
Cinnaminson HS 700/9-12
1197 Riverton Rd 08077 856-829-7770
Darlene Llewellyn, prin. Fax 829-7777
Cinnaminson MS 500/6-8
312 N Fork Landing Rd 08077 856-786-8012
Frank Goulburn, prin. Fax 786-1860

Clark, Union, Pop. 14,629
Clark Township SD 2,300/PK-12
365 Westfield Ave 07066 732-574-9600
Kenneth Knops, supt. Fax 574-1456
www.clarkschools.org
Johnson HS 800/9-12
365 Westfield Ave 07066 732-382-0910
Richard Delmonaco, prin. Fax 382-5957
Kumpf MS 500/6-8
59 Mildred Ter 07066 732-381-0400
Jennifer Feeley, prin. Fax 381-0262

Mother Seton Regional HS 400/9-12
Valley Rd 07066 732-382-1952
Sr. Regina Martin, prin. Fax 382-4725

Clayton, Gloucester, Pop. 7,923
Clayton SD 1,200/PK-12
350 E Clinton St 08312 856-881-8700
David Lindenmuth, supt. Fax 863-8196
www.clayton.k12.nj.us
Clayton HS 300/9-12
55 Pop Kramer Blvd 08312 856-881-8701
Nikolaos Koutsogiannis, prin. Fax 863-0808
Clayton MS 200/6-8
55 Pop Kramer Blvd 08312 856-881-8702
Dennis Haynes, prin. Fax 863-0808

Cliffside Park, Bergen, Pop. 22,965
Cliffside Park SD 2,200/PK-12
525 Palisade Ave 07010 201-313-2310
Michael Romagnino, supt. Fax 943-7050
www.cliffsidepark.edu

Cliffside Park HS 900/9-12
64 Riverview Ave 07010 201-313-2370
Lorraine Morrow, prin. Fax 313-7961

Cliffwood, Monmouth, Pop. 1,500
Matawan-Aberdeen Regional SD
Supt. — See Aberdeen
Matawan Aberdeen MS 800/6-8
469 Matawan Ave 07721 732-705-5400
Cory Radisch, prin. Fax 765-0894

Clifton, Passaic, Pop. 82,465
Clifton SD, 745 Clifton Ave 07013 10,400/K-12
Richard Tardalo, supt. 973-470-2300
www.clifton.k12.nj.us
Clifton HS 3,300/9-12
333 Colfax Ave 07013 973-470-2312
Michael McGinley, prin. Fax 458-9290
Columbus MS 1,100/6-8
350 Piaget Ave 07011 973-470-2360
Patricia DeLotto, prin. Fax 470-2365
Wilson MS 1,300/6-8
1400 Van Houten Ave 07013 973-470-2348
Maria Romeo, prin. Fax 470-2607

Garfield SD
Supt. — See Garfield
Garfield Auxiliary MSHS 100/Alt
43 Clifton Ave 07011 973-272-7465
Dr. Charles Bonanno, prin. Fax 253-5696

American Institute Post-Sec.
346 Lexington Ave 07011 973-340-9500
Capri Institute of Hair Design Post-Sec.
1595 Main Ave 07011 973-772-4610
Dover Business College Post-Sec.
600 Getty Ave 07011 973-546-0123
Mesivta of Clifton 9-12
338 Delawanna Ave 07014 973-779-4800
Star Career Academy Post-Sec.
1231 Main Ave 07011 973-928-1700

Clinton, Hunterdon, Pop. 2,686
Clinton Township SD
Supt. — See Lebanon
Clinton Township MS 500/7-8
34 Grayrock Rd 08809 908-238-9141
John Grebeck, prin. Fax 238-9376

Closter, Bergen, Pop. 8,270
Closter SD 1,100/PK-8
340 Homans Ave 07624 201-768-3001
Joanne Newberry, supt. Fax 768-1903
closterpublicschools.schoolwires.net
Tenakill MS 600/5-8
275 High St 07624 201-768-1332
Danielle DaGiau, prin. Fax 784-0726

Collingswood, Camden, Pop. 13,647
Collingswood Borough SD 1,800/PK-12
200 Lees Ave 08108 856-962-5700
Dr. Scott Oswald, supt. Fax 962-5723
www.collingswood.k12.nj.us/
Collingswood HS 800/9-12
424 W Collings Ave 08108 856-962-5701
Edward Hill, prin. Fax 962-5565
Collingswood MS 400/6-8
414 W Collings Ave 08108 856-962-5702
Dr. John McMullin, prin. Fax 962-5751

Colonia, Middlesex, Pop. 17,529
Woodbridge Township SD
Supt. — See Woodbridge
Colonia HS 1,400/9-12
180 East St 07067 732-726-7060
Kenneth Pace, prin. Fax 574-2575
Colonia MS 600/6-8
100 Delaware Ave 07067 732-396-7000
Cynthia Lagunovich, prin. Fax 574-0772

Colts Neck, Monmouth
Colts Neck Township SD 1,200/K-8
70 Conover Rd 07722 732-946-0055
Fredrik Oberkehr Ed.D., supt. Fax 858-8583
www.coltsneckschools.org
Cedar Drive MS 500/6-8
73 Cedar Dr 07722 732-946-0055
Colin Rigby, prin. Fax 462-4108

Freehold Regional HSD
Supt. — See Englishtown
Colts Neck HS 1,500/9-12
59 Five Points Rd 07722 732-761-0190
Keith Land, prin. Fax 761-0193

Columbus, Burlington
Northern Burlington County Regional SD 1,900/7-12
160 Mansfield Rd E 08022 609-298-3900
Dr. James Sarruda, supt. Fax 298-3154
www.nburlington.com
Northern Burlington County Regional HS 1,200/9-12
160 Mansfield Rd E 08022 609-298-3900
Craig Wigley, prin. Fax 298-8563
Northern Burlington County Regional JHS 700/7-8
180 Mansfield Rd E 08022 609-298-3900
Andrew Kearns, prin. Fax 291-1563

Convent Station, Morris

Academy of St. Elizabeth 200/9-12
PO Box 297 07961 973-605-3200
Sr. Patricia Costello, prin.

Cranbury, Middlesex, Pop. 2,142

Gentle Healing School of Massage Post-Sec.
1274 S River Rd 08512 609-409-2700

Cranford, Union, Pop. 22,624
Cranford Township SD 3,700/K-12
132 Thomas St 07016 908-709-6202
Dr. Gayle Carrick, supt. Fax 272-7735
www.cranfordschools.org
Cranford HS 1,100/9-12
201 W End Pl 07016 908-709-6272
Rui Dionisio, prin. Fax 276-6552
Orange Avenue S 800/3-8
901 Orange Ave 07016 908-709-6257
Michelle Vella, prin. Fax 272-3025

Union County College Post-Sec.
1033 Springfield Ave 07016 908-709-7000

Cream Ridge, Monmouth

New Jersey United Christian Academy 100/6-12
73 Holmes Mill Rd 08514 609-738-2121
Robert Pupchik, prin. Fax 738-2151

Cresskill, Bergen, Pop. 8,463
Cresskill SD 1,700/K-12
1 Lincoln Dr 07626 201-227-7791
Dr. Loretta Bellina, supt. Fax 567-7976
www.cboek12.org
Cresskill HS 600/9-12
1 Lincoln Dr 07626 201-567-7791
Michael Burke, prin. Fax 567-0028
Cresskill MS 400/6-8
1 Lincoln Dr 07626 201-227-7791
Michael Burke, prin. Fax 567-0028

Delanco, Burlington, Pop. 3,316
Delanco Township SD 400/K-8
1301 Burlington Ave 08075 856-461-1905
Barbara Behnke, supt. Fax 461-1627
www.delanco.com
Walnut Street MS 100/6-8
411 Walnut St 08075 856-461-0874
Ronald Pettie, admin. Fax 461-6903

Delran, Burlington, Pop. 13,178
Delran Township SD 2,800/PK-12
52 Hartford Rd 08075 856-461-6800
Dr. Patricia Camp, supt. Fax 461-6125
www.delranschools.org/
Delran HS 900/9-12
50 Hartford Rd 08075 856-461-6100
Daniel Finkle, prin. Fax 764-6177
Delran MS 600/6-8
905 S Chester Ave 08075 856-461-8822
Dr. Melanie Goodwin, prin. Fax 461-0311

Holy Cross HS 700/9-12
5035 Route 130 08075 856-461-5400
Dennis Guida, prin. Fax 461-0323

Demarest, Bergen, Pop. 4,792
Demarest SD 700/K-8
568 Piermont Rd 07627 201-768-6060
Michael Fox, supt. Fax 767-9122
demarestsd.schoolwires.net/
Demarest MS 300/5-8
568 Piermont Rd 07627 201-768-6061
Michael Fox, prin. Fax 768-9122

Northern Valley Regional HSD 2,600/9-12
162 Knickerbocker Rd 07627 201-768-2200
Dr. Christopher Nagy, supt. Fax 768-9488
www.nvnet.org
Northern Valley Regional HS 1,200/9-12
150 Knickerbocker Rd 07627 201-768-3200
Dr. Bruce Sabatini, prin. Fax 768-5438
Other Schools – See Old Tappan

Academy of the Holy Angels 500/9-12
315 Hillside Ave 07627 201-768-7822
Jennifer Moran, prin. Fax 768-6933

Dennisville, Cape May
Dennis Township SD
Supt. — See Cape May Court House
Dennis Township S 400/3-8
PO Box 363 08214 609-861-2821
Dr. Joseph LaRosa, prin. Fax 861-5229

Denville, Morris, Pop. 13,812
Denville Township SD 1,900/PK-8
400 Morris Ave Ste 279 07834 973-983-6530
Catherine Mozak, supt. Fax 784-4778
www.denville.org
Valleyview MS 700/6-8
320 Diamond Spring Rd 07834 973-983-6535
Paul Iantosca, prin. Fax 627-0632

Morris County Vocational SD
400 E Main St 07834 973-627-4600
Scott Moffitt, supt. Fax 627-6979
www.mcvts.org
Morris County School of Technology Vo/Tech
400 E Main St 07834 973-627-4600
Scott Moffitt, prin. Fax 627-4958
Other Schools – See Butler, Rockaway

Morris Catholic HS 500/9-12
200 Morris Ave 07834 973-627-6660
Steven Kramer, prin. Fax 627-4351

Deptford, Gloucester
Deptford Township SD 4,200/PK-12
2022 Good Intent Rd 08096 856-232-2700
Gary Loudenslager, supt. Fax 227-7473
www.deptford.k12.nj.us/
Deptford Township HS 1,100/9-12
575 Fox Run Rd 08096 856-232-2713
Gary Swenson, prin. Fax 374-9145
Other Schools – See Sewell

Dover, Morris, Pop. 17,974
Dover Town SD 2,900/PK-12
100 Grace St 07801 973-989-2000
Robert Becker, supt. Fax 989-1662
district.dover-nj.org
Dover HS 800/9-12
100 Grace St 07801 973-989-2010
Delvis Rodriguez, prin. Fax 989-1662
Dover MS 400/7-8
302 E McFarlan St 07801 973-989-2040
Robert Franks, prin. Fax 361-2117

Dover Business College Post-Sec.
1 W Blackwell St 07801 973-285-8400
Joe Kubert Sch of Cartoon & Graphic Arts Post-Sec.
37 Myrtle Ave 07801 973-361-1327

Dumont, Bergen, Pop. 17,212
Dumont SD 2,700/PK-12
25 Depew St 07628 201-387-1600
Emanuele Triggiano, supt. Fax 387-0259
www.dumontnj.org
Dumont HS 900/9-12
101 New Milford Ave 07628 201-387-3000
Michael Parent, prin. Fax 387-8461

Dunellen, Middlesex, Pop. 7,100
Dunellen SD 1,100/K-12
400 High St 08812 732-968-3226
Pio Pennisi, supt. Fax 968-3513
www.dunellenschools.org/
Dunellen HS 300/9-12
411 1st St 08812 732-968-0885
Paul Lynch, prin. Fax 968-3138
Lincoln MS 300/6-8
400 Dunellen Ave 08812 732-968-0885
Robert Altmire, prin. Fax 424-1359

East Brunswick, Middlesex, Pop. 47,400
East Brunswick Township SD 8,300/PK-12
760 State Route 18 08816 732-613-6705
Dr. Patrick Piegari, supt. Fax 698-9871
www.ebnet.org
Churchill JHS 1,400/8-9
18 Norton Rd 08816 732-613-6800
Mark Sutor, prin. Fax 257-0087
East Brunswick SHS 2,200/10-12
380 Cranbury Rd 08816 732-613-6904
Dr. Michael Vinella, prin. Fax 254-1938

Middlesex County Vocational SD
PO Box 1070 08816 732-257-3300
Brian Loughlin, supt. Fax 651-0618
www.mcvts.net
East Brunswick Vocational HS Vo/Tech
PO Box 1070 08816 732-254-8700
Jeffrey Bicsko, prin. Fax 613-9608
Adult HS - East Brunswick Adult
112 Rues Ln 08816 732-257-7715
Jeffrey Bicsko, admin. Fax 613-9608
Other Schools – See Edison, Perth Amboy, Piscataway, Woodbridge

East Hanover, Morris, Pop. 9,926
East Hanover Township SD 1,100/PK-8
20 School Ave 07936 973-887-2112
Dr. Joseph Ricca, supt. Fax 887-2773
www.easthanoverschools.org/
East Hanover MS 400/6-8
477 Ridgedale Ave 07936 973-887-8810
Stacie Costello, prin. Fax 887-5079

Hanover Park Regional HSD 1,400/9-12
75 Mount Pleasant Ave 07936 973-887-0320
Carol Grossi, supt. Fax 887-9247
www.hpreg.org
Hanover Park HS 800/9-12
63 Mount Pleasant Ave 07936 973-887-0300
Thomas Callanan, prin. Fax 515-7680
Other Schools – See Whippany

East Orange, Essex, Pop. 62,841
East Orange SD 8,100/PK-12
715 Park Ave 07017 973-266-5760
Dr. Gloria Scott, supt. Fax 678-4865
www.eastorange.k12.nj.us
East Orange Campus HS 1,400/10-12
344 Prospect St 07017 973-266-7300
Dr. Kelvin Harris, prin. Fax 266-7368
East Orange Campus STEM Academy 500/9-9
129 Renshaw Ave 07017 973-266-5900
Dr. Nicholas Del Tufo, prin. Fax 266-3473
Fresh Start Academy Vo/Tech
74 Halsted St 07018 973-266-2957
Dr. Neville Matadine, prin. Fax 674-4226
Tyson Comm MSHS Prfrmg/Fine Arts 800/6-12
161 Elmwood Ave 07018 973-414-8600
Dr. Stephen Cowan, prin. Fax 395-3888
Tyson Communty HS of Fine & Perfrmg Arts 9-12
35 Winans St 07017 973-414-8600
Dr. Stephen Cowan, prin. Fax 395-3888

Ahlus Sunnah S 200/PK-12
215 N Oraton Pkwy 07017 973-672-4121
Qamarudin Hosein, admin. Fax 672-3919
Best Care Training Institute Post-Sec.
68 S Harrison St 07017 973-673-3900
National Career Institute Post-Sec.
134 Evergreen Pl Fl 2 07018 973-678-3901

East Rutherford, Bergen, Pop. 8,757
Carlstadt-East Rutherford Regional HSD 500/9-12
120 Paterson Ave 07073 201-935-3007
Dr. Gary Bowen, supt. Fax 935-5639
www.bectonhs.org/
Becton Regional HS 500/9-12
120 Paterson Ave 07073 201-935-3007
Kevin O'Leary, prin. Fax 935-5639

East Rutherford SD 700/PK-8
100 Uhland St 07073 201-804-3100
Dr. Gary Bowen, supt. Fax 804-3131
www.erboe.net/
Faust MS 200/5-8
100 Uhland St 07073 201-804-3110
Henry Srednicki Ph.D., prin. Fax 804-3131

East Windsor, Mercer, Pop. 22,353
East Windsor Regional SD
Supt. — See Hightstown

Kreps MS 1,200/6-8
5 Kent Ln 08520 609-443-7767
Lori Stein, prin. Fax 443-8972

Eatontown, Monmouth, Pop. 12,304
Eatontown SD 1,000/PK-8
5 Grant Ave 07724 732-542-1310
Scott McCue, supt. Fax 578-0017
www.eatontown.org
Memorial MS 200/7-8
7 Grant Ave 07724 732-542-5013
Ronald Danielson, prin. Fax 389-1364

Edgewater Park, Burlington, Pop. 8,388
Edgewater Park Township SD 800/PK-8
25 Washington Ave 08010 609-877-2124
Cheryl Smith, supt. Fax 877-4235
www.edgewaterpark.k12.nj.us
Ridgeway MS 300/5-8
300 Delanco Rd 08010 609-871-3434
Joseph Corn, prin. Fax 871-2434

Edison, Middlesex, Pop. 99,500
Edison Township SD 14,000/PK-12
312 Pierson Ave 08837 732-452-4900
Dr. Richard O'Malley, supt. Fax 452-4993
www.edison.k12.nj.us
Adams MS 800/6-8
1081 New Dover Rd 08820 732-452-2920
Joan Valentine, prin. Fax 452-2922
Edison HS 2,000/9-12
50 Boulevard of Eagles 08817 732-650-5200
Charles Ross, prin. Fax 650-5259
Hoover MS 800/6-8
174 Jackson Ave 08837 732-452-2940
Brian McGrath, prin. Fax 452-2950
Jefferson MS 800/6-8
450 Division St 08817 732-650-5290
Antoinette Emden, prin. Fax 652-5295
Stevens HS 2,200/9-12
855 Grove Ave 08820 732-452-2800
Gail Pawlikowski, prin. Fax 452-2863
Wilson MS 800/6-8
50 Woodrow Wilson Dr 08820 732-452-2870
Patricia Cotoia, prin. Fax 452-2876

Middlesex County Vocational SD
Supt. — See East Brunswick
Academy of Science and Technology Vo/Tech
100 Technology Dr 08837 732-452-2600
Dr. Linda Russo, prin. Fax 906-8421

Bishop George Ahr HS 900/9-12
1 Tingley Ln 08820 732-549-1108
Sr. Donna Trukowski, prin. Fax 494-2229
Lincoln Technical Institute Post-Sec.
1697 Oak Tree Rd 08820 732-548-8798
Middlesex County College Post-Sec.
2600 Woodbridge Ave 08837 732-548-6000
PC AGE Career Institute Post-Sec.
145 Talmadge Rd Ste 19 08817 732-287-3622
Rabbi Jacob Joseph School Post-Sec.
1 Plainfield Ave 08817 732-985-6533
Rabbi Jacob Joseph S 100/9-12
1 Plainfield Ave 08817 732-985-6533
Rabbi Yitzchok Weintraub, dir. Fax 985-6553
Wardlaw-Hartridge S 400/PK-12
1295 Inman Ave 08820 908-754-1882
Andrew Webster, hdmstr. Fax 754-9678

Egg Harbor City, Atlantic, Pop. 4,134
Egg Harbor City SD 400/PK-8
730 Havana Ave 08215 609-965-1034
John Gilly, supt. Fax 965-6719
www.ehcs.k12.nj.us
Egg Harbor City Community S 200/4-8
730 Havana Ave 08215 609-965-1034
Jack Griffith, prin. Fax 965-4742

Greater Egg Harbor Regional HSD
Supt. — See Mays Landing
Cedar Creek HS 9-12
1701 New York Ave 08215 609-593-3560
James Reina, prin. Fax 593-3570

Pilgrim Academy 400/PK-12
PO Box 322 08215 609-965-2866
Christopher Storr, hdmstr. Fax 965-3379

Egg Harbor Township, Atlantic
Egg Harbor Township SD 7,700/PK-12
13 Swift Ave 08234 609-646-7911
Dr. Scott McCartney, supt. Fax 383-8749
www.eht.k12.nj.us
Alder Avenue MS 800/6-8
25 Alder Ave 08234 609-383-3366
Joseph Marinelli, prin. Fax 383-1492
Eagle Academy Alt
3515 Bargaintown Rd 08234 609-926-1235
Earl Smith, prin. Fax 926-1095
Egg Harbor Township HS 2,500/9-12
24 High School Dr 08234 609-653-0100
Terry Charlton, prin. Fax 927-8844
Fernwood Avenue MS 900/6-8
4034 Fernwood Ave 08234 609-383-3355
James Battersby, prin. Fax 383-0628

Atlantic Christian S 300/PK-12
391 Zion Rd 08234 609-653-1199
Karen Newman, prin. Fax 653-1435
Star Career Academy Post-Sec.
3003 English Creek Ave #212 08234 609-407-2999
Trocki Hebrew Academy 50/PK-12
6814 Black Horse Pike 08234 609-383-8484

Elizabeth, Union, Pop. 122,789
Elizabeth SD 21,800/PK-12
500 N Broad St 07208 908-436-5000
Pablo Munoz, supt. Fax 436-6133
www.elizabeth.k12.nj.us
Dwyer Technology Academy 900/9-12
123 Pearl St 07202 908-436-6565
Christopher Van Vliet, prin.
Edison Career & Technical Academy 700/9-12
625 Summer St 07202 908-436-6800
Jeffrey Roszkowski, prin. Fax 436-6780
Elizabeth HS Lower Academy 400/9-10
425 Grier Ave 07202 908-436-6180
Michael Cummings, admin.
Elizabeth HS Upper Academy 300/11-12
447 Richmond St 07202 908-436-5870
Michael Cummings, admin. Fax 436-5861
Halsey Leadership Academy 1,000/9-12
641 South St 07202 908-436-6600
Stephen Williams, prin.
Hamilton Preparatory Academy 700/9-12
310 Cherry St 07208 908-436-6100
George Mikros, prin. Fax 436-6082
Jefferson Arts Academy 900/9-12
27 Martin Luther King Plz 07201 908-436-6767
Michael Ojeda, prin. Fax 436-6733

Benedictine Academy 200/9-12
840 N Broad St 07208 908-352-0670
Sr. Germaine Fritz, pres. Fax 352-0698
Drake College of Business Post-Sec.
125 Broad St 07201 908-352-5509
Elizabeth General Medical Center School Post-Sec.
925 E Jersey St 07201 908-965-7390
Jewish Educational Center - Bruriah HS 300/7-12
35 North Ave 07208 908-355-4850
Rabbi Elazar Teitz, dean Fax 351-5420
Rav Teitz Mesivta Academy 200/6-12
330 Elmora Ave 07208 908-355-4850
Chanie Moskowitz, prin. Fax 355-3140
St. Mary of the Assumption HS 200/9-12
237 S Broad St 07202 908-352-4350
Janet Malko, prin. Fax 352-2359
Union County College Post-Sec.
40 W Jersey St Fl 8 07202 908-965-6000
Yeshivas Be'er Yitzchok Post-Sec.
1391 North Ave 07208 908-354-6057

Elmwood Park, Bergen, Pop. 19,032
Elmwood Park SD 2,300/K-12
60 E 53rd St 07407 201-796-8700
Dr. Richard Tomko, supt. Fax 794-6677
www.epps.org/
Memorial HS 700/9-12
375 River Dr 07407 201-796-8700
David Warner, prin. Fax 797-1405
Memorial MS 500/6-8
375 River Dr 07407 201-796-8700
Anthony Grieco, prin. Fax 797-1405

Elwood, Atlantic, Pop. 1,395
Mullica Township SD 700/PK-8
PO Box 318 08217 609-561-3868
Dr. Brenda Harring-Marro, supt. Fax 561-7133
www.mullica.k12.nj.us
Mullica Township MS 300/5-8
PO Box 318 08217 609-561-3868
Matt Mazzoni, prin. Fax 561-7133

Emerson, Bergen, Pop. 7,299
Emerson SD 1,200/PK-12
131 Main St 07630 201-599-4178
Philip Nisonoff, supt. Fax 599-4160
www.emerson.k12.nj.us
Emerson JSHS 500/7-12
131 Main St 07630 201-262-4447
Dr. Paula Valenti, prin. Fax 262-1041

Englewood, Bergen, Pop. 26,555
Englewood CSD 2,800/PK-12
274 Knickerbocker Rd 07631 201-862-6000
Dr. Donald Carlisle, supt. Fax 569-6099
www.epsd.org
Dismus MS 400/7-8
325 Tryon Ave 07631 201-862-6025
Lamarr Thomas, prin. Fax 833-9103
Morrow Alternative S 100/Alt
83 W Demarest Ave 07631 201-862-6249
Joseph Bell, prin. Fax 871-5931
Morrow HS 1,000/9-12
274 Knickerbocker Rd 07631 201-862-6039
Peter Elbert, prin. Fax 833-9620

Dwight-Englewood S 900/PK-12
315 E Palisade Ave 07631 201-569-9500
Dr. Rodney DeJarnett, head sch Fax 569-1676
Englewood Hospital & Medical Center Post-Sec.
350 Engle St 07631 201-894-3002
Yeshiva Ohr Simcha of Englewood 100/9-12
101 W Forest Ave 07631 201-816-1800

Englewood Cliffs, Bergen, Pop. 5,175
Englewood Cliffs SD 400/PK-8
143 Charlotte Pl 07632 201-567-7292
Dominic Mucci, supt. Fax 567-2738
www.englewoodcliffs.org
Upper S 200/3-8
143 Charlotte Pl 07632 201-567-6151
Maria Narcisi, prin. Fax 541-8672

St. Peter's College Post-Sec.
Hudson Terrace 07632 201-761-7480

Englishtown, Monmouth, Pop. 1,825
Freehold Regional HSD 11,700/9-12
11 Pine St 07726 732-792-7300
Charles Sampson, supt. Fax 446-9126
www.frhsd.com
Manalapan HS 1,900/9-12
20 Church Ln 07726 732-792-7200
Adam Angelozzi, prin. Fax 446-4981
Other Schools – See Colts Neck, Farmingdale, Freehold, Marlboro

Manalapan-Englishtown Regional SD 5,100/PK-8
54 Main St 07726 732-786-2500
John Marciante Ph.D., supt. Fax 786-2542
www.mers.k12.nj.us
Other Schools – See Manalapan

Erial, Camden, Pop. 2,500
Black Horse Pike Regional SD
Supt. — See Blackwood
Timber Creek Regional HS 1,400/9-12
501 Jarvis Rd 08081 856-232-9703
Mae Robinson, prin. Fax 232-5267

Divers Academy International Post-Sec.
1500 Liberty Pl 08081 856-404-6100

Ewing, Mercer, Pop. 36,000
Ewing Township SD 3,500/K-12
2099 Pennington Rd 08618 609-538-9800
Michael Nitti, supt. Fax 538-0041
www.ewing.k12.nj.us
Ewing HS 1,100/9-12
900 Parkway Ave 08618 609-538-9800
Rodney Logan Ed.D., prin. Fax 882-8172
Fisher MS 900/6-8
1325 Lower Ferry Rd 08618 609-538-9800
Barbara Brower, prin. Fax 637-9753

Mercer County Technical SD
Supt. — See Trenton
Rubino Academy Alt
11 Buttonwood Dr 08638 609-882-3200
Henry Krzeczkowski, prin. Fax 882-2128

College of New Jersey Post-Sec.
2000 Pennington Rd 08618 609-771-1855
Villa Victoria Academy - Upper 100/9-12
376 W Upper Ferry Rd 08628 609-882-1700
Sr. Lesley Draper, prin. Fax 882-8421

Fairfield, Essex, Pop. 7,615
Essex Regional Educ Services Commission 50/6-12
369 Passaic Ave 07004 973-405-6262
Dr. Jacqueline Young, supt. Fax 405-6555
www.eresc.com/
Essex Campus Academy 50/Alt
369 Passaic Ave 07004 973-575-0469
David Pinkney, prin. Fax 575-0136
Other Schools – See Newark, Passaic

StenoTech Career Institute Post-Sec.
20 Just Rd 07004 888-783-6685

Fair Haven, Monmouth, Pop. 6,047
Fair Haven Borough SD 1,000/PK-8
224 Hance Rd 07704 732-747-2294
Nelson Ribon, supt. Fax 747-7441
www.fairhaven.edu
Knollwood MS 600/4-8
224 Hance Rd 07704 732-747-0320
Nelson Ribon, prin. Fax 747-7441

Fair Lawn, Bergen, Pop. 32,055
Fair Lawn SD 4,500/K-12
37-01 Fair Lawn Ave 07410 201-794-5500
Bruce Watson, supt. Fax 797-9296
www.fairlawnschools.org/
Fair Lawn HS 1,500/9-12
14-00 Berdan Ave 07410 201-794-5450
James Marcella, prin. Fax 794-8107
Jefferson MS 700/6-8
35-01 Morlot Ave 07410 201-703-2240
Sherrie Galofaro, prin. Fax 475-9185
Memorial MS 400/6-8
12-00 1st St 07410 201-794-5470
Scott Helfand, prin. Fax 703-2237

Artistic Academy of Hair Design Post-Sec.
21 S Broadway 07410 201-794-3502

Fairview, Bergen, Pop. 13,423
Fairview SD 1,100/PK-8
130 Hamilton Ave 07022 201-943-1699
Dr. Louis DeLisio, supt. Fax 941-1195
fairviewps.org
Lincoln S 600/4-8
140 Anderson Ave 07022 201-943-0560
Lea Turro, prin. Fax 943-7154

Farmingdale, Monmouth, Pop. 1,307
Freehold Regional HSD
Supt. — See Englishtown
Howell HS 2,200/9-12
405 Squankum Yellowbrook Rd 07727732-919-2131
Zina Duerbig, prin. Fax 919-1964

Howell Township SD 5,600/K-8
200 Squankum Yellowbrook Rd 07727732-751-2480
Dr. Enid Golden, supt. Fax 919-1060
www.howell.k12.nj.us
Howell Township MS North 600/6-8
501 Squankum Yellowbrook Rd 07727732-919-0095
Paul Farley, prin. Fax 919-1008
Other Schools – See Freehold, Howell

Flanders, Morris, Pop. 1,200
Mt. Olive Township SD
Supt. — See Budd Lake
Mt. Olive HS 1,100/9-12
18 Corey Rd 07836 973-927-2208
Kevin Stansberry, prin. Fax 927-2204

Flemington, Hunterdon, Pop. 4,482
Flemington-Raritan Regional SD 3,500/PK-8
50 Court St 08822 908-284-7561
Gregory Nolan, supt. Fax 284-7514
www.frsd.k12.nj.us/
Case MS 800/7-8
301 Case Blvd 08822 908-284-5100
Robert Castellano, prin. Fax 284-5144

Hudson County Schools of Technology
Supt. — See North Bergen
Hunterdon County Adult S Vo/Tech
8 Bartles Corner Rd Ste 2 08822 201-778-1119
Christina Shockley, dir.

Hunterdon Central Regional SD 2,900/9-12
84 State Route 31 08822 908-782-5727
Christina Steffner, supt. Fax 284-7138
www.hcrhs.k12.nj.us
Hunterdon Central Regional HS 2,900/9-12
84 State Route 31 08822 908-782-5727
Suzanne Cooley, prin. Fax 284-7138

Hunterdon County Vocational SD
8 Bartles Corner Rd Ste 2 08822 908-788-1119
Dr. Kimberly Metz, supt. Fax 806-4839
www.hcpolytech.org
Hunterdon County Vocational S - Bartles Vo/Tech
8 Bartles Corner Rd 08822 908-806-3855
Dan Kerr, prin.
Hunterdon County Vocational S - Central Vo/Tech
10 Junction Rd 08822 908-284-1444
Dan Kerr, prin. Fax 284-9824

Florence, Burlington, Pop. 4,260
Florence Township SD 1,500/K-12
201 Cedar St 08518 609-499-4600
Donna Ambrosius, supt. Fax 499-9679
www.florence.k12.nj.us
Florence Township Memorial HS 400/9-12
1050 Cedar Ln 08518 609-499-4620
John Cogan, prin. Fax 499-3424
Riverfront S 600/4-8
500 E Front St 08518 609-499-4647
Theresa Elias, prin. Fax 499-8356

Florham Park, Morris, Pop. 11,496
Florham Park SD 1,000/PK-8
PO Box 39 07932 973-822-3880
Dr. William Ronzitti, supt. Fax 822-0716
www.fpks.org
Ridgedale MS 400/6-8
71 Ridgedale Ave 07932 973-822-3855
Mark Majeski, prin. Fax 822-7963

Fords, Middlesex, Pop. 14,870
Woodbridge Township SD
Supt. — See Woodbridge
Fords MS 700/6-8
100 Fanning St 08863 732-596-4200
Glenn Lottmann, prin. Fax 417-2159

Forked River, Ocean, Pop. 5,199
Lacey Township SD
Supt. — See Lanoka Harbor
Lacey Township MS 700/7-8
660 Denton Ave 08731 609-242-2100
James Handschuch, prin. Fax 242-2114

Fort Lee, Bergen, Pop. 34,777
Fort Lee SD 3,500/K-12
2175 Lemoine Ave 07024 201-585-4612
Steven Engravalle, supt. Fax 585-0691
www.flboe.com/
Cole MS 500/7-8
467 Stillwell Ave 07024 201-585-4660
Robert Kravitz, prin. Fax 585-1688
Fort Lee HS 1,000/9-12
3000 Lemoine Ave 07024 201-585-4675
Priscilla Church, prin. Fax 585-2296

Franklin Lakes, Bergen, Pop. 10,458
Franklin Lakes SD 1,400/PK-8
490 Pulis Ave 07417 201-891-1856
Dr. Frank Romano, supt. Fax 891-9333
www.franklinlakes.k12.nj.us/
Franklin Avenue MS 500/6-8
755 Franklin Ave 07417 201-891-0202
Joseph Keiser, prin. Fax 848-5190

Ramapo Indian Hills Regional HSD
Supt. — See Oakland
Ramapo HS 1,100/9-12
331 George St 07417 201-891-1500
Dr. Louis Moore, prin. Fax 891-6844

Franklinville, Gloucester
Delsea Regional SD 1,700/7-12
242 Fries Mill Rd 08322 856-694-0100
Dr. Piera Gravenor, supt. Fax 694-4417
www.delsearegional.us/
Delsea Regional HS 1,100/9-12
PO Box 405 08322 856-694-0100
Paul Berardelli, prin. Fax 694-2046
Delsea Regional MS 500/7-8
PO Box 405 08322 856-694-0100
Jill Bryfogle, prin. Fax 694-4417

Freehold, Monmouth, Pop. 11,870
Freehold Borough SD 1,300/PK-8
280 Park Ave 07728 732-761-2100
Rocco Tomazic Ed.D., supt. Fax 462-8954
www.freeholdboro.k12.nj.us
Freehold IS 400/6-8
280 Park Ave 07728 732-761-2156
Ronnie Dougherty, prin. Fax 761-2181

Freehold Regional HSD
Supt. — See Englishtown
Freehold Borough HS 1,500/9-12
2 Robertsville Rd 07728 732-431-8360
Linda Jewell, prin. Fax 577-8228
Freehold Township HS 2,500/9-12
281 Elton Adelphia Rd 07728 732-431-8460
Elizabeth Higley, prin. Fax 780-5314

Freehold Township SD 4,200/PK-8
384 W Main St 07728 732-866-8400
Ross Kasun Ed.D., supt. Fax 761-1809
www.freeholdtwp.k12.nj.us/
Barkalow MS 800/6-8
498 Stillwells Corner Rd 07728 732-431-4403
John Soviero, prin. Fax 294-5560
Eisenhower MS 800/6-8
279 Burlington Rd 07728 732-431-3910
Dianne Brethauer, prin. Fax 294-7180

Howell Township SD
Supt. — See Farmingdale
Memorial MS 400/6-8
485 Adelphia Rd 07728 732-919-1085
Dr. Laurie Bandlow, prin. Fax 751-0325

Monmouth County Vocational SD
PO Box 5033 07728 732-431-7942
Timothy McCorkell, supt. Fax 409-6736
www.mcvsd.org
Biotechnology HS Vo/Tech
5000 Kozloski Rd 07728 732-431-6443
Linda Eno, prin. Fax 409-6736
Freehold Vocational S Vo/Tech
21 Robertsville Rd 07728 732-462-7570
Joseph Diver, prin. Fax 294-0569
Monmouth County Career Center Vo/Tech
1000 Kozloski Rd 07728 732-431-3773
Thomas Sansevero, prin. Fax 409-7292
Other Schools – See Aberdeen, Asbury Park, Hazlet, Highlands, Keyport, Lincroft, Long Branch, Middletown, Neptune, Tinton Falls, Wall

Frenchtown, Hunterdon, Pop. 1,362
Delaware Valley Regional HSD 1,000/9-12
19 Senator Stout Rd 08825 908-996-2131
Elizabeth Nastus Ed.D., supt. Fax 996-4527
www.dvrhs.org
Delaware Valley Regional HS 1,000/9-12
19 Senator Stout Rd 08825 908-996-2131
Nicholas Romanetz, prin. Fax 996-6653

Galloway, Atlantic
Galloway Township SD 3,300/PK-8
101 S Reeds Rd 08205 609-748-1250
Annette Giaquinto Ed.D., supt. Fax 748-1796
www.gtps.k12.nj.us
Galloway Township MS 800/7-8
100 S Reeds Rd 08205 609-748-1250
Sharon Kurtz, prin. Fax 748-8926

Greater Egg Harbor Regional HSD
Supt. — See Mays Landing
Absegami HS 1,900/9-12
201 S Wrangleboro Rd 08205 609-652-1372
Jeri-Lynn Gatto Ed.D., prin. Fax 652-0139

Richard Stockton College of New Jersey Post-Sec.
101 Vera King Farris Dr 08205 609-652-1776

Garfield, Bergen, Pop. 30,041
Garfield SD 4,400/PK-12
34 Outwater Ln 07026 973-340-5000
Nicholas Perrapato, supt. Fax 340-4620
www.garfield.k12.nj.us/
Garfield HS 1,000/9-12
500 Palisade Ave 07026 973-340-5010
Dora D'Amico, prin. Fax 546-8430
Garfield MS 900/6-8
175 Lanza Ave 07026 973-272-7020
Anna Sciacca, prin. Fax 340-1767
Other Schools – See Clifton

Gibbstown, Gloucester, Pop. 3,693
Greenwich Township SD 500/PK-8
415 Swedesboro Rd 08027 856-224-4920
Stephen Derkoski, supt. Fax 224-5761
www.greenwich.k12.nj.us
Nehaunsey MS 200/5-8
415 Swedesboro Rd 08027 856-224-4920
Alisa Whitcraft, prin. Fax 224-5765

Gillette, Morris
Long Hill Township SD 900/K-8
759 Valley Rd 07933 908-647-1200
Rene Rovtar Ed.D., supt. Fax 647-1200
www.longhill.org
Other Schools – See Stirling

Gladstone, Somerset, Pop. 2,086

Gill St. Bernard's S 700/PK-12
PO Box 604 07934 908-234-1611
Sid Rowell, hdmstr. Fax 234-1712

Glassboro, Gloucester, Pop. 18,158
Glassboro SD 2,100/PK-12
560 Bowe Blvd 08028 856-652-2700
Dr. Mark Silverstein, supt. Fax 881-0884
www.glassboroschools.us
Glassboro Adult HS Alt
560 Bowe Blvd 08028 856-652-2700
Robin Boyd, contact
Glassboro HS 600/9-12
550 Bowe Blvd 08028 856-652-2700
Santina Haldeman, prin. Fax 307-1189
Glassboro IS 300/7-8
202 Delsea Dr N 08028 856-652-2700
Santina Haldeman, prin. Fax 881-3751

Rowan University Post-Sec.
201 Mullica Hill Rd 08028 856-256-4000

Glen Gardner, Hunterdon, Pop. 1,684
North Hunterdon/Voorhees Regional HSD
Supt. — See Annandale
Voorhees HS 1,100/9-12
256 County Road 513 08826 908-638-6116
Ronald Peterson, prin. Fax 638-8689

Glen Ridge, Essex, Pop. 7,336
Glen Ridge SD 1,900/PK-12
12 High St 07028 973-429-8302
John Mucciolo Ph.D., supt. Fax 429-5750
www.glenridge.org
Glen Ridge HS 800/7-12
200 Ridgewood Ave 07028 973-429-8303
Dirk Phillips, prin. Fax 429-3531

Glen Rock, Bergen, Pop. 11,424
Glen Rock SD 2,400/K-12
620 Harristown Rd 07452 201-445-7700
Raymond J. Albano, supt. Fax 389-5019
www.glenrocknj.org/

Glen Rock HS 700/9-12
600 Harristown Rd 07452 201-445-7700
John Arlotta, prin. Fax 389-5015
Glen Rock MS 600/6-8
400 Hamilton Ave 07452 201-445-7700
Edward Thompson, prin. Fax 389-5042

Gloucester City, Camden, Pop. 11,306
Gloucester City SD 1,900/PK-12
520 Cumberland St 08030 856-456-7000
Joseph Rafferty, supt. Fax 742-8815
www.gcsd.k12.nj.us
Gloucester City JSHS 800/7-12
1300 Market St 08030 856-456-7000
Dr. Jack Don, prin. Fax 456-2348
Gloucester City Adult HS Adult
1300 Market St 08030 856-456-7000
Victoria Ernst, prin. Fax 742-8570

Gloucester Catholic HS 700/7-12
333 Ridgeway St 08030 856-456-4400
John Colman, prin. Fax 456-0506
P.B. Cosmetology Education Centre Post-Sec.
110 Monmouth St 08030 856-456-4927

Great Meadows, Warren, Pop. 303
Great Meadows Regional SD 800/K-8
PO Box 74 07838 908-637-6576
David C. Mango, supt. Fax 637-6356
www.gmrsd.com
Great Meadows Regional MS 300/6-8
273 US Highway 46 07838 908-637-4584
Israel Marmolejos, prin. Fax 637-4492

Green Brook, Somerset
Green Brook Township SD 1,000/PK-8
132 Jefferson Ave 08812 732-968-1171
Dr. Richard Labbe, supt. Fax 968-1869
www.gbtps.org
Green Brook MS 600/4-8
132 Jefferson Ave 08812 732-968-1051
Linda Pollard, prin. Fax 752-1086

Hackensack, Bergen, Pop. 42,163
Bergen County Vocational SD
Supt. — See Paramus
Bergen County Academies Vo/Tech
200 Hackensack Ave 07601 201-343-6000
Russell Davis, prin. Fax 996-6955
Bergen Co. Adult & Continuing Education Adult
200 Hackensack Ave 07601 201-343-6000
James Smith, prin.

Hackensack SD 4,100/PK-12
191 2nd St 07601 201-646-7830
Joseph Abate, supt. Fax 646-7827
www.hackensackschools.org
Hackensack HS 1,800/9-12
135 1st St 07601 201-646-7900
James Montesano, prin. Fax 646-7922
Hackensack MS 600/5-8
360 Union St 07601 201-646-7842
David Petrella, prin. Fax 646-7840

Academy of Massage Therapy Post-Sec.
321 Main St 07601 201-568-3220
Center for Allied Health & Nursing Educ Post-Sec.
387 Main St 07601 201-489-5836
Hackensack Univ Medical Center Post-Sec.
30 Prospect Ave 07601 201-996-2000
HoHokus-Hackensack School of Business Post-Sec.
250 Moore St 07601 201-488-9400
Parisian Academy Post-Sec.
21 Passaic St 07601 201-487-2203

Hackettstown, Warren, Pop. 9,581
Hackettstown SD 1,800/PK-12
PO Box 465 07840 908-850-6500
David C. Mango, supt. Fax 852-0286
www.hackettstown.org
Hackettstown HS 900/9-12
701 Warren St 07840 908-852-8150
John Sarcone, prin. Fax 852-6214
Hackettstown MS 400/5-8
500 Washington St 07840 908-852-8554
Marie Griffin, prin. Fax 850-6544

Centenary College Post-Sec.
400 Jefferson St 07840 908-852-1400

Haddonfield, Camden, Pop. 11,436
Haddonfield Borough SD 2,400/PK-12
1 Lincoln Ave 08033 856-429-7510
Dr. Richard Perry, supt. Fax 429-6015
www.haddonfield.k12.nj.us
Haddonfield Memorial HS 800/9-12
401 Kings Hwy E 08033 856-429-3960
Chuck Klaus, prin. Fax 795-8910
Haddonfield MS 500/6-8
5 Lincoln Ave 08033 856-429-5851
Dr. Gino Priolo, prin. Fax 429-2006

Paul VI HS 1,200/9-12
901 Hopkins Rd Ste B 08033 856-858-4900
Sr. Marianne McCann, prin. Fax 858-6832

Haddon Heights, Camden, Pop. 7,379
Haddon Heights SD 1,300/PK-12
316A 7th Ave 08035 856-547-1412
Michael Adams, supt. Fax 547-3868
hhsd.k12.nj.us
Haddon Heights JSHS 800/7-12
301 2nd Ave 08035 856-547-1920
Ron Corn, prin. Fax 547-6808

Baptist Regional S 200/K-12
300 Station Ave 08035 856-547-2996
Lynn Conahan, admin. Fax 547-6584

Haledon, Passaic, Pop. 8,172
Passaic County Manchester Regional HSD 800/9-12
70 Church St 07508 973-389-2820
Dr. Richard Ney, supt. Fax 956-8805
www.mrhs.net
Manchester Regional HS 800/9-12
70 Church St 07508 973-389-2820
Dr. Richard Ney, admin. Fax 956-8805

Hamburg, Sussex, Pop. 3,209
Hardyston Township SD 500/PK-8
183 Wheatsworth Rd 07419 973-823-7000
Richard Corbett, supt. Fax 823-7010
www.htps.org
Hardyston MS 200/5-8
183 Wheatsworth Rd 07419 973-823-7000
Richard Corbett, prin. Fax 823-7011

Wallkill Valley Regional SD 800/9-12
10 Grumm Rd 07419 973-827-4100
Edward Bolcar, supt. Fax 827-8318
www.wallkill.k12.nj.us
Wallkill Valley Regional HS 800/9-12
10 Grumm Rd 07419 973-827-4100
Edward Bolcar, prin. Fax 827-8318

Hamilton, Mercer
Hamilton Township SD 11,900/K-12
90 Park Ave 08690 609-631-4100
Dr. James Parla, supt. Fax 631-4103
www.hamilton.k12.nj.us
Crockett MS 800/6-8
2631 Kuser Rd 08691 609-631-4149
Roger Bigos, prin. Fax 631-4116
Grice MS 900/6-8
901 Whitehorse Hamilton Sq 08610 609-631-4152
David Innocenzi, prin. Fax 631-4119
Hamilton East-Steinert HS 1,500/9-12
2900 Klockner Rd 08690 609-631-4150
Kelly Mattis, prin. Fax 631-4117
Hamilton North-Nottingham HS 1,300/9-12
1055 Klockner Rd 08619 609-631-4161
Michael Giambelluca, prin. Fax 631-4129
Hamilton West-Watson HS 1,300/9-12
2720 S Clinton Ave 08610 609-631-4168
Katherine Taylor, prin. Fax 631-4137
Reynolds MS 1,000/6-8
2145 Yrdvll Hamilton Squ Rd 08690 609-631-4162
Gary Mattia, prin. Fax 631-4130
Accredited Evening HS Adult
90 Park Ave 08690 609-631-4100
Dr. Michael Gilbert, prin. Fax 631-4106

Trenton Catholic Academy 200/9-12
175 Leonard Ave 08610 609-586-3705
Michele Neves, prin. Fax 586-6584

Hammonton, Atlantic, Pop. 14,622
Hammonton SD 3,400/PK-12
566 Old Forks Rd 08037 609-567-7000
Dr. Dan Blachford, supt. Fax 561-3567
www.hammontonps.org/
Hammonton HS 1,300/9-12
566 Old Forks Rd 08037 609-567-7000
Thomas Ramsay, prin. Fax 567-5985
Hammonton MS 800/6-8
75 N Liberty St 08037 609-567-7007
Gene Miller, prin. Fax 561-3974

St. Joseph HS 300/9-12
328 Vine St 08037 609-561-8700
Lynn Domenico, prin. Fax 561-8701

Hampton, Hunterdon, Pop. 1,385
Union Township SD 500/PK-8
165 Perryville Rd 08827 908-735-5511
Jeffrey Bender, supt. Fax 735-6657
www.uniontwpschool.org
Union Township MS 200/5-8
165 Perryville Rd 08827 908-735-5511
Frances Suchovic, prin. Fax 735-6657

Harrison, Hudson, Pop. 13,212
Harrison SD 1,900/K-12
501 Hamilton St 07029 973-483-4627
James P. Doran Ed.D., supt. Fax 484-7484
www.harrison.k12.nj.us
Harrison HS 600/9-12
800 Hamilton St 07029 973-482-5050
Ronald Shields, prin. Fax 412-8729
Washington MS 400/6-8
1 N 5th St 07029 973-483-2285
Donna McBride, dir. Fax 482-3625

Hasbrouck Heights, Bergen, Pop. 11,674
Hasbrouck Heights SD 1,700/PK-12
379 Boulevard 07604 201-288-6150
Dr. Mark Porto, supt. Fax 288-0289
www.hhschools.org
Hasbrouck Heights HS 500/9-12
365 Boulevard 07604 201-393-8164
Linda Simmons, prin. Fax 288-2083
Hasbrouck Heights MS 400/6-8
365 Boulevard 07604 201-393-8164
Joseph Mastropietro, prin. Fax 288-2083

Haskell, See Wanaque

Institute for Therapeutic Massage Post-Sec.
1069 Ringwood Ave Ste 315 07420 973-839-6131

Hawthorne, Passaic, Pop. 18,585
Hawthorne SD 2,400/K-12
445 Lafayette Ave 07506 973-427-1300
Robert Mooney, supt. Fax 427-1757
www.hawthorne.k12.nj.us
Hawthorne HS 700/9-12
160 Parmelee Ave 07506 973-423-6415
Barry Cohen, prin. Fax 423-6422
Lincoln MS 600/6-8
230 Hawthorne Ave 07506 973-423-6460
John Peraino, prin. Fax 427-5393

Hawthorne Christian Academy 400/K-12
2000 State Rt 208 07506 973-423-3331
Donald Klingen, prin. Fax 238-1718
Roman Academy of Beauty Culture Post-Sec.
431 Lafayette Ave 07506 973-423-2223

Hazlet, Monmouth, Pop. 21,976
Hazlet Township SD 3,200/PK-12
421 Middle Rd 07730 732-264-8402
Dr. Bernard Bragen, supt. Fax 264-1599
www.hazlet.org
Hazlet MS 500/7-8
1639 Union Ave 07730 732-264-0940
Christine McCoid, prin. Fax 264-0571
Raritan HS 1,000/9-12
419 Middle Rd 07730 732-264-8411
William Smith, prin. Fax 264-3214

Monmouth County Vocational SD
Supt. — See Freehold
Hazlet Vocational S Vo/Tech
417 Middle Rd 07730 732-264-4995
James Johnson, prin. Fax 264-3846

Hibernia, Morris, Pop. 200
Rockaway Township SD 2,400/K-8
PO Box 500 07842 973-627-8200
Dr. Deborah Grefe, supt. Fax 627-7968
Other Schools – See Rockaway

High Bridge, Hunterdon, Pop. 3,609
High Bridge SD 400/PK-8
50 Thomas St 08829 908-638-4103
Dr. Gregory Hobaugh, supt. Fax 638-4211
www.hbschools.org
High Bridge MS 100/6-8
50 Thomas St 08829 908-638-4101
Dr. Gregory Hobaugh, prin. Fax 638-4211

Highland Park, Middlesex, Pop. 13,661
Highland Park SD 1,400/PK-12
435 Mansfield St 08904 732-572-6990
Frances Wood Ed.D., supt. Fax 393-1174
www.hpschools.net/
Highland Park HS 400/9-12
102 N 5th Ave 08904 732-572-2400
Frederick Williams, prin. Fax 819-7041
Highland Park MS 300/6-8
330 Wayne St 08904 732-572-2400
Michael Lassiter, prin. Fax 819-7041

Reenas Bais Yaakov 9-12
1131 Raritan Ave 08904 732-985-5646
Chaya Eidelman, prin. Fax 985-5660

Highlands, Monmouth, Pop. 4,929
Henry Hudson Regional SD 400/7-12
1 Grand Tour 07732 732-872-0900
Christopher Rooney, supt. Fax 708-1409
www.henryhudsonreg.k12.nj.us
Hudson Regional JSHS 400/7-12
1 Grand Tour 07732 732-872-0900
Lenore Kingsmore, prin. Fax 708-1409

Monmouth County Vocational SD
Supt. — See Freehold
Marine Academy of Science & Technology Vo/Tech
305 Mast Way 07732 732-291-0995
Paul Christopher, prin. Fax 291-9367

Hightstown, Mercer, Pop. 5,390
East Windsor Regional SD 4,800/PK-12
25A Leshin Ln 08520 609-443-7717
Edward Forsthoffer, supt. Fax 443-7704
www.eastwindsorregionalschools.com
Hightstown HS 1,300/9-12
25 Leshin Ln 08520 609-443-7738
Alix Arvizu, prin. Fax 443-7880
Other Schools – See East Windsor

Peddie S 500/9-12
201 S Main St 08520 609-944-7500
John Green, head sch Fax 944-7901

Hillsborough, Somerset
Hillsborough Township SD 7,200/PK-12
379 S Branch Rd 08844 908-431-6600
Dr. Jorden Schiff, supt. Fax 369-8286
www.htps.us
Hillsborough HS 2,400/9-12
466 Raider Blvd 08844 908-874-4200
Karen Bingert, prin. Fax 874-3762
Hillsborough MS 1,200/7-8
260 Triangle Rd 08844 908-874-3420
Dr. Joseph Trybulski, prin. Fax 874-3492

Hillsdale, Bergen, Pop. 10,123
Hillsdale SD 1,400/PK-8
32 Ruckman Rd 07642 201-664-4512
Richard Spirito, supt. Fax 664-9049
www.hillsdaleschools.com
White MS 600/5-8
120 Magnolia Ave 07642 201-664-0286
Dr. Noreen Hajinlian, prin. Fax 664-2715

Pascack Valley Regional HSD
Supt. — See Montvale
Pascack Valley HS 1,200/9-12
200 Piermont Ave 07642 201-358-7060
Thomas DeMaio, prin. Fax 358-7102

Hillside, Union, Pop. 21,044
Hillside Township SD 2,200/PK-12
195 Virginia St 07205 908-352-7664
Dr. Frank Deo, supt. Fax 282-5831
www.hillsidek12.org
Hillside HS 800/9-12
1085 Liberty Ave 07205 908-352-7664
Dr. Christine Sidwa, prin. Fax 352-4246
Krumbiegel MS 400/6-8
145 Hillside Ave 07205 908-352-7664
Alphonsus Platt, prin. Fax 282-5840

Hoboken, Hudson, Pop. 49,047
Hoboken SD, 158 4th St 07030 1,700/PK-12
Dr. Mark Toback, supt. 201-356-3600
www.hoboken.k12.nj.us
Hoboken HS 700/8-12
900 Clinton St 07030 201-356-3700
Robin Piccapietra, prin. Fax 356-3704

Cortiva Institute - Hoboken Post-Sec.
2 Hudson Pl Ste 2 07030 201-215-6440
Hudson S 200/5-12
601 Park Ave 07030 201-659-8335
Suellen Newman, dir. Fax 222-3669
Stevens Institute of Technology Post-Sec.
Castle Point on Hudson 07030 201-216-5000

Holmdel, Monmouth
Holmdel Township SD 2,600/K-12
65 McCampbell Rd 07733 732-946-1800
Barbara Duncan, supt. Fax 946-1875
www.holmdelschools.org
Holmdel HS 800/9-12
36 Crawfords Corner Rd 07733 732-946-1832
William Loughran, prin. Fax 946-0093
Satz MS 600/7-8
24 Crawfords Corner Rd 07733 732-946-1808
Arthur Howard, prin. Fax 834 0089

St. John Vianney HS 1,000/9-12
540A Line Rd 07733 732-739-0800
Steven DiMezza, prin. Fax 739-0843

Hopatcong, Sussex, Pop. 14,950
Hopatcong Borough SD 1,900/K-12
PO Box 1029 07843 973-398-8801
Dr. Charles Maranzano, supt. Fax 398-1961
www.hopatcongschools.org/
Hopatcong HS 700/9-12
PO Box 1029 07843 973-398-8803
Fax 398-9048
Hopatcong MS 500/6-8
PO Box 1029 07843 973-398-8804
Emil Binotto, prin. Fax 398-4184

Howell, Monmouth
Howell Township SD
Supt. — See Farmingdale
Howell Township MS South 600/6-8
1 Kuzminski Way 07731 732-836-1327
Thomas Feaster, prin. Fax 836-0698

Yeshivas Emek Hatorah 50/9-12
395 Kent Rd 07731 732-367-1289

Irvington, Essex, Pop. 60,600
Irvington Township SD 6,300/PK-12
1 University Pl 07111 973-399-6800
Dr. Neely Hackett, supt. Fax 372-3724
www.irvington.k12.nj.us
Irvington HS, 1253 Clinton Ave 07111 1,400/9-12
Burnett Davis, prin. 973-399-6897
Union Avenue MS 800/6-8
427 Union Ave 07111 973-399-6885
Cheryl Chester, prin. Fax 373-0734
University MS 700/6-8
255 Myrtle Ave 07111 973-399-6879
Shakuur Sabuur, prin. Fax 351-1025
Irvington Adult HS Adult
255 Myrtle Ave 07111 973-399-6879
John Severs, prin.

Iselin, Middlesex, Pop. 18,174
Woodbridge Township SD
Supt. — See Woodbridge
Iselin MS 600/6-8
900 Woodruff St 08830 732-602-8450
Dr. Jared Rumage, prin. Fax 750-4861
Kennedy Memorial HS 1,300/9-12
200 Washington Ave 08830 732-602-8650
Michael Cilento, prin. Fax 634-1112

Sanford-Brown Institute Post-Sec.
675 US Highway 1 S Fl 2 08830 732-634-1131

Jackson, Ocean, Pop. 800
Jackson Township SD 9,400/PK-12
151 Don Connor Blvd 08527 732-833-4600
Thomas Gialanella, supt. Fax 833-4609
www.jacksonsd.org
Goetz MS 1,300/6-8
835 Patterson Rd 08527 732-833-4610
Dr. Faith Lessig, prin. Fax 833-4749
Jackson Liberty HS 1,400/9-12
125 N Hope Chapel Rd 08527 732-833-4700
Maureen Butler, prin. Fax 415-7099
Jackson Memorial HS 1,700/9-12
101 Don Connor Blvd 08527 732-833-4670
Kevin DiEugenio, prin. Fax 833-4629
McAuliffe MS 1,000/6-8
35 S Hope Chapel Rd 08527 732-833-4701
Robert Rotante, prin. Fax 833-4729

Ocean County Vocational SD
Supt. — See Toms River
Ocean County Voc-Tech S - Jackson Vo/Tech
850 Toms River Rd 08527 732-286-5665
Lillian Zavattieri, prin. Fax 928-0490

Jamesburg, Middlesex, Pop. 5,804
Jamesburg SD 700/PK-8
13 Augusta St 08831 732-521-0303
Dr. Gail Verona, supt. Fax 521-1267
www.jamesburg.org
Breckwedel MS 200/6-8
13 Augusta St 08831 732-521-0303
Dr. Gail Verona, prin. Fax 521-1267

Jersey City, Hudson, Pop. 239,244
Hudson County Schools of Technology
Supt. — See North Bergen
County Prep HS Vo/Tech
525 Montgomery St 07302 201-631-6302
Barbara Mendolla, prin.

Explore 2000 Vo/Tech
525 Montgomery St 07302 201-631-6396
Fax 369-5562

Jersey City SD 27,600/PK-12
346 Claremont Ave 07305 201-915-6202
Dr. Marcia Lyles, supt. Fax 915-6084
www.jcboe.org/

Academy I 400/Alt
209 Bergen Ave 07305 201-915-6500
Grace Moriarty, prin. Fax 435-9224

Conwell MS 800/6-8
107 Bright St 07302 201-946-5740
Joanna Veloz, prin. Fax 209-1293

Dickinson HS 2,400/9-12
2 Palisade Ave 07306 201-714-4400
Arlene Farrell, prin. Fax 792-2292

Ferris HS 1,600/9-12
35 Colgate St 07302 201-915-6660
Jaime Morales, prin. Fax 451-6067

Infinity Institute 7-12
193 Old Bergen Rd 07305 201-915-1404
Treniere Dobson, prin. Fax 433-9456

Liberty HS 200/Alt
299 Sip Ave 07306 201-714-4373
Larry Odoms, prin. Fax 369-3714

Lincoln HS 1,000/9-12
60 Crescent Ave 07304 201-915-6700
Cheryle Richardson-Evans, prin. Fax 435-4493

McNair Academic HS 700/9-12
123 Coles St 07302 201-418-7618
Edward Slattery, prin. Fax 792-1498

Nolan MS 400/6-8
88 Gates Ave 07305 201-915-6570
Susan Decker, prin. Fax 369-3749

Snyder HS 1,100/9-12
239 Bergen Ave 07305 201-915-6600
Belinda Mays-Stokes, prin. Fax 435-5019

Williams MS 800/6-8
222 Laidlaw Ave 07306 201-714-8342
Edwin Rivera, prin. Fax 659-6457

Anthem Institute Post-Sec.
40 Journal Sq 07306 201-876-3800

Christ Hospital School of Nursing Post-Sec.
176 Palisade Ave 07306 201-795-8360

Christ Hospital School of Radiography Post-Sec.
176 Palisade Ave 07306 201-795-8246

Eastern International College Post-Sec.
3000 John F Kennedy # 310 07306 201-216-9901

Full Will of God Christian Academy 50/1-12
84 Martin Luther King Jr Dr 07305 201-433-6278
Roberta Glee-Stevens, head sch Fax 938-1481

Hudson Catholic Regional HS 400/9-12
790 Bergen Ave 07306 201-332-5970
Richard Garibell, prin. Fax 332-6373

Hudson County Community College Post-Sec.
70 Sip Ave 07306 201-714-7100

Natural Motion Institute of Hair Design Post-Sec.
2800 John F Kennedy Blvd 07306 201-659-0303

New Jersey City University Post-Sec.
2039 John F Kennedy Blvd 07305 201-200-2000

PC AGE Career Institute Post-Sec.
2815 John F Kennedy Blvd #3 07306 201-761-0144

St. Anthony HS 200/9-12
175 8th St 07302 201-653-5143
Charles Tortorello, prin. Fax 653-8120

St. Dominic Academy 500/9-12
2572 John F Kennedy Blvd 07304 201-434-5938
Barbara Griffin, head sch Fax 434-2603

St. Peter Preparatory S 900/9-12
144 Grand St 07302 201-434-4400
James DeAngelo, prin. Fax 547-2341

St. Peter's College Post-Sec.
2641 John F Kennedy Blvd 07306 201-761-6000

The Institute for Health Education Post-Sec.
600 Pavonia Ave Ste 1 07306 201-217-1113

Keansburg, Monmouth, Pop. 9,873

Keansburg Borough SD 1,600/PK-12
100 Palmer Pl 07734 732-787-2007
Gerald North, supt. Fax 495-6714
www.keansburg.k12.nj.us

Bolger MS 400/5-8
100 Palmer Pl 07734 732-787-2007
Eric Platt, prin. Fax 495-7906

Keansburg HS 400/9-12
140 Port Monmouth Rd 07734 732-787-2007
Robert Adams, prin. Fax 495-5401

Kearny, Hudson, Pop. 39,579

Kearny SD 5,000/PK-12
100 Davis Ave 07032 201-955-5000
Ronald Bolandi, supt. Fax 955-0544
www.kearnyschools.com/

Kearny HS 1,700/9-12
336 Devon St 07032 201-955-5048
Fax 998-9653

Kearny Christian Academy 100/PK-12
22 Wilson Ave 07032 201-998-0788
Jane Botelho, admin. Fax 998-1102

Kenilworth, Union, Pop. 7,800

Kenilworth SD 1,300/PK-12
426 Boulevard 07033 908-276-5936
Sylvan Hershey, supt. Fax 709-7315
www.kenilworthschools.com

Brearley MSHS 700/7-12
401 Monroe Ave 07033 908-931-9696
Brian Luciani, prin. Fax 931-1618

Capri Institute of Hair Design Post-Sec.
660 N Michigan Ave 07033 908-964-1330

Keyport, Monmouth, Pop. 7,124

Keyport SD 1,100/PK-12
370 Broad St 07735 732-212-6100
Lisa Savoia, supt. Fax 212-6115
www.kpsdschools.org

Keyport JSHS 500/8-12
351 Broad St 07735 732-212-6100
Michael Waters, prin. Fax 212-6145

Monmouth County Vocational SD
Supt. — See Freehold

Keyport Vocational S Vo/Tech
280 Atlantic St 07735 732-739-0592
Joseph Diver, prin. Fax 739-1470

Kinnelon, Morris, Pop. 10,145

Kinnelon Borough SD 1,800/K-12
109 Kiel Ave 07405 973-838-1418
Diane DiGiuseppe, supt. Fax 838-5527
kinnelonpublicschools.org/

Kinnelon HS 500/9-12
121 Kinnelon Rd 07405 973-838-5500
Dr. Wayne Merckling, prin. Fax 838-0261

Miller MS 500/6-8
117 Kiel Ave 07405 973-838-5250
John Hynes, prin. Fax 283-0390

Lake Hopatcong, Morris, Pop. 3,000

Jefferson Township SD 3,400/PK-12
31 State Route 181 07849 973-663-5780
Joseph Kraemer, supt. Fax 663-2790
www.jefftwp.org/
Other Schools – See Oak Ridge

Lakehurst, Ocean, Pop. 2,552

Ocean County Vocational SD
Supt. — See Toms River

Ocean County Voc-Tech S - Navy Lakehurst Vo/Tech
PO Box 1125 08733 732-286-5678
Karen Homiek, prin. Fax 657-4500

Lakewood, Ocean, Pop. 53,516

Lakewood Township SD 4,000/K-12
1771 Madison Ave Ste B 08701 732-364-2400
Laura Winters, supt. Fax 905-3687
www.lakewoodpiners.org

Lakewood HS 1,100/9-12
855 Somerset Ave 08701 732-905-3502
Marcy Paturzo, prin. Fax 905-0895

Lakewood MS 600/6-8
755 Somerset Ave 08701 732-905-3600
Richard Fastnacht, prin. Fax 905-3695

Achieve Test Prep Post-Sec.
1072 Madison Ave 08701 732-719-2353

Bais Kaila Torah Prep HS 300/9-12
PO Box 952 08701 732-370-4300

Bais Medrash Toras Chesed Post-Sec.
901 Monmouth Ave 08701 732-364-1220

Bais Shaindel HS 500/9-12
685 River Ave 08701 732-363-7074

Bais Yaakov HS 400/9-12
277 James St 08701 732-370-8200

Beth Medrash Govoha Post-Sec.
617 6th St 08701 732-367-1060

Calvary Academy 300/PK-12
1133 E County Line Rd 08701 732-363-3633
Melissa Payne, head sch Fax 363-7337

Georgian Court University Post-Sec.
900 Lakewood Ave 08701 732-987-2200

Lakewood Cheder S 7-8
520 James St 08701 732-370-6460

Lakewood Cheder S Bais Faga 1,200/3-8
350 Courtney Rd 08701 732-363-5070

Mesivta Keren HaTorah 100/9-12
1083 Brook Rd 08701 732-942-7300

Mesivta of Lakewood 50/8-12
415 6th St 08701 732-905-8370

Oros Bais Yaakov 9-12
50 Lapsley Ln 08701 732-370-6049

Yeshiva Bais Aharon 50/9-12
1430 14th St 08701 732-367-7604

Yeshiva Chayei Olam 9-12
14 11th St E 08701 732-363-1267

Yeshiva Gedola Ohr HaTalmud 50/9-12
PO Box 826 08701 732-364-7062

Yeshivas Bais Pinchos 100/9-12
1951 New Central Ave 08701 732-367-2880

Yeshiva Toras Chaim Post-Sec.
1027 Ridge Ave 08701 732-414-2834

Yeshiva Toras Chaim 9-12
999 Ridge Ave 08701 732-942-3090

Yeshiva Yesodei Hatorah Post-Sec.
2 Yesodei Ct 08701 732-370-3360

Lambertville, Hunterdon, Pop. 3,873

South Hunterdon Regional HSD 400/7-12
301 Mt Airy Harbourton Rd 08530 609-397-2060
Joanne Calabro, supt. Fax 397-2366
www.shrhs.org

South Hunterdon Regional HS 400/7-12
301 Mt Airy Harbourton Rd 08530 609-397-2060
Mark Collins, prin. Fax 397-2366

Lanoka Harbor, Ocean

Lacey Township SD 4,300/PK-12
200 Western Blvd 08734 609-971-2000
Sandra Brower, supt. Fax 242-9406
www.laceyschools.org

Lacey Township HS 1,400/9-12
73 Haines St 08734 609-971-2020
James Handschuch, prin. Fax 242-0873
Other Schools – See Forked River

Laurel Springs, Camden, Pop. 1,884

Empire Beauty School Post-Sec.
1305 Blackwood Clementon Rd 08021
856-435-8100

Lawrenceville, Mercer, Pop. 3,814

Lawrence Township SD 3,900/PK-12
2565 Princeton Pike 08648 609-671-5500
Crystal Edwards Ed.D., supt. Fax 883-4225
www.ltps.org

Lawrence HS 1,100/9-12
2525 Princeton Ave 08648 609-671-5510
Jonathan Dauber, prin. Fax 671-3411

Lawrence MS 600/7-8
2455 Princeton Pike 08648 609-671-5520
Mindy Milavsky, prin. Fax 671-3421

Fortis Institute Post-Sec.
2572 US Highway 1 Ste 100 08648 609-512-2560

Lawrenceville S 800/9-12
PO Box 6008 08648 609-896-0400
Elizabeth Duffy, hdmstr. Fax 895-2217

Notre Dame HS 1,300/9-12
601 Lawrence Rd 08648 609-882-7900
Mary Liz Ivins, prin. Fax 882-5723

Rider University Post-Sec.
2083 Lawrenceville Rd 08648 609-896-5000

Lebanon, Hunterdon, Pop. 1,334

Clinton Township SD 1,700/PK-8
PO Box 362 08833 908-236-7235
Dr. Drucilla Clark, supt. Fax 236-6358
www.ctsd.k12.nj.us
Other Schools – See Clinton

Hunterdon Co. Educational Services Comm. 50/7-12
51 Sawmill Rd 08833 908-439-4280
Dennis Cox, supt. Fax 439-2270
www.hcesc.com

ESC Academy Tewksbury Campus 50/Alt
51 Sawmill Rd 08833 908-439-3703
Andrea Romano, dir. Fax 439-3701

Leonardo, Monmouth, Pop. 2,725

Middletown Township SD 10,000/PK-12
834 Leonardville Rd Fl 2 07737 732-671-3850
Dr. William George, supt. Fax 615-9351
mtps.schoolwires.net

Bayshore MS 700/6-8
834 Leonardville Rd 07737 732-291-1380
Carol Force, prin.
Other Schools – See Middletown, Port Monmouth

Leonia, Bergen, Pop. 8,727

Leonia SD 1,700/PK-12
570 Grand Ave 07605 201-302-5200
Joanne Megargee, supt. Fax 947-4782
www.leoniaschools.org

Leonia HS 600/9-12
100 Christie Heights St 07605 201-302-5200
Edward Bertolini, prin. Fax 461-8957

Leonia MS 400/6-8
500 Broad Ave 07605 201-302-5200
Dr. Nicholas Bernice, prin. Fax 461-1510

Lincoln Park, Morris, Pop. 10,363

Lincoln Park Borough SD 800/PK-8
92 Ryerson Rd 07035 973-696-5500
James Grube, supt. Fax 696-9273
www.lincolnparkboe.org

Lincoln Park MS 400/5-8
90 Ryerson Rd 07035 973-696-5520
Michael Meyer, prin. Fax 872-8930

Craig HS 100/9-12
200 Comly Rd 07035 973-305-8085
Dr. Eric Caparulo, hdmstr. Fax 305-8086

Lincroft, Monmouth, Pop. 6,069

Monmouth County Vocational SD
Supt. — See Freehold

High Technology HS Vo/Tech
PO Box 119 07738 732-842-8444
Kevin Bals, prin. Fax 219-9418

Brookdale Community College Post-Sec.
765 Newman Springs Rd 07738 732-224-2345

Christian Brothers Academy 1,000/9-12
850 Newman Springs Rd 07738 732-747-1959
Peter Santanello, prin. Fax 747-1643

Linden, Union, Pop. 39,711

Linden SD 5,700/PK-12
2 E Gibbons St 07036 908-486-2800
Danny Robertozzi Ed.D., supt. Fax 486-6331
www.linden.k12.nj.us

Linden HS 1,800/9-12
121 W Saint Georges Ave 07036 908-486-5432
Antoinette Modrak, prin. Fax 486-3242

McManus MS 700/6-8
300 Edgewood Rd 07036 908-486-7751
Kcyronne Zahir, prin. Fax 587-0607

Soehl MS 600/6-8
300 E Henry St 07036 908-486-0550
Joseph Picaro, prin. Fax 486-3478

Sinai Christian Academy 100/PK-12
2301 Grier Ave 07036 908-486-2006
Kathleen Salardino, prin. Fax 925-9258

Yeshiva Gedolah Zichron Leyma Post-Sec.
1000 Orchard Ter 07036 908-587-0502

Lindenwold, Camden, Pop. 17,154

Lindenwold SD 2,200/PK-12
801 Egg Harbor Rd 08021 856-783-0276
Geraldine Carroll, supt. Fax 435-5887
www.lindenwold.k12.nj.us/

Lindenwold HS 500/9-12
801 Egg Harbor Rd 08021 856-741-0320
Peter Brandt, prin. Fax 741-0350

Lindenwold MS 600/5-8
40 White Horse Ave 08021 856-346-3330
Kasha Giddins, prin. Fax 346-0554

Linwood, Atlantic, Pop. 6,996

Linwood CSD 900/PK-8
51 Belhaven Ave 08221 609-926-6700
Thomas Baruffi Ed.D., supt. Fax 926-6705
www.linwoodschools.org/

Belhaven MS 400/5-8
51 Belhaven Ave 08221 609-926-6700
Frank Rudnesky Ed.D., prin. Fax 926-6705

Mainland Regional HSD 1,500/9-12
1301 Oak Ave 08221 609-927-4151
Dr. Thomas Baruffi, supt. Fax 927-1942
www.mainlandregional.net
Mainland Regional HS 1,500/9-12
1301 Oak Ave 08221 609-927-4151
Mark Marrone, prin. Fax 927-1942

Harris School of Business Post-Sec.
1201 New Rd Ste 226 08221 609-927-4310

Little Egg Harbor Township, Ocean, Pop. 13,333
Pinelands Regional SD 1,700/7-12
PO Box 248, 609-296-3106
Dr. Robert Blake, supt. Fax 294-9519
www.pinelandsregional.org/
Pinelands Regional HS 900/10-12
PO Box 248, 609-296-3106
Thomas Normile, prin. Fax 296-6905
Pinelands Regional JHS 800/7-9
PO Box 248, 609-296-3106
Frank Pschorr, prin. Fax 296-2626

Little Falls, Passaic, Pop. 11,294
Little Falls Township SD 900/K-8
560 Main St 07424 973-256-1034
William Petrick, supt. Fax 256-6542
www.lfnjschools.org/
Little Falls MS 1 400/5-8
32 Stevens Ave 07424 973-256-1033
Philip Ligus, prin. Fax 785-4857

Passaic Valley Regional HSD 1 1,300/9-12
100 E Main St 07424 973-890-2500
Dr. Viktor Joganow, supt. Fax 890-0512
www.pvhs.k12.nj.us
Passaic Valley Regional HS 1,300/9-12
100 E Main St 07424 973-890-2500
Dr. Viktor Joganow, supt. Fax 890-0512

Little Silver, Monmouth, Pop. 5,876
Little Silver Borough SD 800/PK-8
124 Willow Dr 07739 732-741-2188
Dr. Carolyn Kossack, supt. Fax 741-3644
www.littlesilverschools.org
Markham Place MS 400/5-8
95 Markham Pl 07739 732-741-7112
Dennis Morolda, prin. Fax 741-3562

Red Bank Regional HSD 1,000/9-12
101 Ridge Rd 07739 732-842-8000
Dr. James Stefankiewicz, supt. Fax 842-8504
www.rbrhs.org/
Red Bank Regional HS 1,000/9-12
101 Ridge Rd 07739 732-842-8000
Risa Clay, prin. Fax 842-4868

Livingston, Essex, Pop. 27,500
Livingston Township SD 5,600/PK-12
11 Foxcroft Dr 07039 973-535-8000
Dr. Brad Draeger, supt. Fax 535-1254
www.livingston.org
Heritage MS 900/7-8
20 Foxcroft Dr 07039 973-535-8000
Patricia Boland, prin. Fax 597-9492
Livingston HS 1,700/9-12
30 Robert H Harp Dr 07039 973-535-8000
Mark Stern, prin. Fax 994-4297

Kushner Yeshiva HS 200/9-12
110 S Orange Ave 07039 973-597-1115
Newark Academy 600/6-12
91 S Orange Ave 07039 973-992-7000
Donald Austin, hdmstr. Fax 992-8962
St. Barnabas Medical Center Post-Sec.
94 Old Short Hills Rd 07039 973-533-5628

Lodi, Bergen, Pop. 23,608
Lodi SD 3,200/PK-12
8 Hunter St 07644 973-778-4620
Frank Quatrone, supt. Fax 778-6393
www.lodi.k12.nj.us
Jefferson MS 800/6-8
75 1st St 07644 973-478-8662
Robert Sciolaro, prin. Fax 478-0358
Lodi HS 900/9-12
99 Putnam St 07644 973-478-6100
Frank D'Amico, prin. Fax 478-4012

Felician College Post-Sec.
262 S Main St 07644 201-559-6000
Immaculate Conception HS 200/9-12
258 S Main St 07644 973-773-2400
Joseph Azzolino, prin. Fax 614-0893

Long Branch, Monmouth, Pop. 29,197
Long Branch SD 4,700/PK-12
540 Broadway 07740 732-571-2868
Michael Salvatore, supt. Fax 229-0797
www.longbranch.k12.nj.us
Academy of Alternative Programs Alt
375 Exchange Pl 07740 732-728-9090
Carmen Vega, prin. Fax 728-1579
Long Branch HS 1,100/9-12
404 Indiana Ave 07740 732-229-7300
Vincent Muscillo, prin. Fax 229-2825
Long Branch MS 800/6-8
350 Indiana Ave 07740 732-229-5533
Michael Viturello, prin. Fax 229-4894

Monmouth County Vocational SD
Supt. — See Freehold
Long Branch Vocational S Vo/Tech
255 W End Ave 07740 732-229-3019
Joseph Diver, prin. Fax 229-5727

Ma'or Yeshiva HS for Boys 100/9-12
250 Park Ave 07740 732-222-4797
Rabbi Reuven Semah, dean Fax 222-5457
Monmouth Medical Center Post-Sec.
300 2nd Ave 07740 732-222-5200

Long Valley, Morris, Pop. 1,859
Washington Township SD 2,600/PK-8
53 W Mill Rd 07853 908-876-4172
Jeffrey Mohre, supt. Fax 876-9392
www.wtschools.org
Long Valley MS 1,000/6-8
51 W Mill Rd 07853 908-876-3434
Mark Ippolito, prin. Fax 876-3436

Lumberton, Burlington
Lumberton Township SD 1,600/K-8
33 Municipal Dr 08048 609-267-1406
Joseph Miller, supt. Fax 267-0002
www.lumberton.k12.nj.us/
Lumberton MS 600/6-8
30 Dimsdale Dr 08048 609-265-0123
Patricia Hutchinson, prin. Fax 265-0476

Lyndhurst, Bergen, Pop. 18,262
Lyndhurst Township SD 1,500/K-12
420 Fern Ave 07071 201-438-5683
Dr. Tracey Stellato, supt. Fax 896-2118
www.lyndhurstschools.net
Jefferson S 100/4-8
336 Lake Ave 07071 201-896-2065
Robert Giangeruso, prin. Fax 933-3112
Lincoln S 200/4-8
281 Ridge Rd 07071 201-438-5683
Joseph Vastola, prin. Fax 438-5786
Lyndhurst HS 700/9-12
400 Weart Ave 07071 201-896-2100
Dr. Jean Gordon, prin. Fax 896-2088
Roosevelt S 200/4-8
530 Stuyvesant Ave 07071 201-896-2068
Peter Strumolo, prin. Fax 933-3143

Madison, Morris, Pop. 15,563
Madison SD 2,300/PK-12
359 Woodland Rd 07940 973-593-3100
Dr. Michael Rossi, supt. Fax 301-2170
www.madisonpublicschools.org
Madison HS 800/9-12
170 Ridgedale Ave 07940 973-593-3117
Greg Robertson, prin. Fax 593-3141
Madison JHS 500/6-8
285 Main St 07940 973-593-3149
Nicole Sherrin, prin. Fax 966-1908

Drew University Post-Sec.
36 Madison Ave 07940 973-408-3000
Fairleigh Dickinson University Post-Sec.
285 Madison Ave 07940 973-443-8500

Mahwah, Bergen, Pop. 17,905
Mahwah Township SD 3,300/PK-12
60 Ridge Rd 07430 201-762-2400
C. Lauren Schoen, supt. Fax 529-1287
www.mahwah.k12.nj.us
Mahwah HS 1,100/9-12
50 Ridge Rd 07430 201-762-2300
John Pascale, prin. Fax 512-0949
Ramapo Ridge MS 800/6-8
150 Ridge Rd 07430 201-762-2380
Brian Miller, prin. Fax 529-6790

Lincoln Technical Institute Post-Sec.
70 McKee Dr 07430 201-529-1414
National Tax Training School Post-Sec.
PO Box 767 07430 201-684-0828
Ramapo College of New Jersey Post-Sec.
505 Ramapo Valley Rd 07430 201-684-7500

Manahawkin, Ocean, Pop. 2,289
Ocean County Vocational SD
Supt. — See Toms River
Ocean County Voc-Tech S - MATES Vo/Tech
195 Cedar Bridge Rd 08050 609-978-8439
Alison Carroll, prin. Fax 978-8540

Southern Regional SD 3,000/7-12
105 Cedar Bridge Rd 08050 609-597-9481
Craig Henry, supt. Fax 978-0298
www.srsd.net
Southern Regional HS 1,000/9-10
600 N Main St 08050 609-597-9481
Eric Wilhelm, prin. Fax 978-5375
Southern Regional HS 900/11-12
90 Cedar Bridge Rd 08050 609-597-9481
Eric Wilhelm, prin. Fax 978-5357
Southern Regional MS 1,000/7-8
75 Cedar Bridge Rd 08050 609-597-9481
Lorraine Airey, prin. Fax 978-8209
Adult Evening HS Adult
105 Cedar Bridge Rd 08050 609-597-9481
Susan Craig, coord. Fax 978-5352

Manalapan, Monmouth
Manalapan-Englishtown Regional SD
Supt. — See Englishtown
Manalapan-Englishtown MS 1,300/7-8
155 Millhurst Rd 07726 732-786-2650
Robert Williams, prin. Fax 786-2660

Manasquan, Monmouth, Pop. 5,870
Manasquan SD 1,600/PK-12
169 Broad St 08736 732-528-8800
Robert Mahon, supt. Fax 223-6286
www.manasquanschools.org
Manasquan HS 1,000/9-12
167 Broad St 08736 732-528-8820
Richard Coppola, prin. Fax 528-0316

Manchester, Ocean
Manchester Township SD
Supt. — See Whiting
Manchester Township HS 1,100/9-12
101 S Colonial Dr 08759 732-657-2121
Alex George, prin. Fax 657-2781
Manchester Township MS 600/6-8
2759 Ridgeway Rd 08759 732-657-1717
Nancy Driber, prin. Fax 657-0326

Manville, Somerset, Pop. 10,188
Manville Borough SD 1,300/K-12
410 Brooks Blvd 08835 908-231-8500
Dr. Johanna Ruberto, supt. Fax 707-3963
www.manvilleschools.org
Batcho IS, 100 N 13th Ave 08835 300/6-8
Michael Magliacano, prin. 908-231-8521
Manville HS 400/9-12
1100 Brooks Blvd 08835 908-231-6806
Dr. James Brunn, prin. Fax 231-8532

Maple Shade, Burlington, Pop. 19,211
Maple Shade Township SD 1,900/K-12
170 Frederick Ave 08052 856-779-1750
Michael Livengood, supt. Fax 779-1054
www.mapleshade.org/
Maple Shade JSHS 800/7-12
180 Frederick Ave 08052 856-779-2880
Scott Arnauer, prin. Fax 779-8849

Maplewood, Essex, Pop. 21,756
South Orange-Maplewood SD 6,300/K-12
525 Academy St 07040 973-762-5600
Dr. Brian Osborne, supt. Fax 378-9464
www.somsd.k12.nj.us
Columbia HS 1,800/9-12
17 Parker Ave 07040 973-762-5600
Dr. Lovie Lilly, prin. Fax 378-7607
Maplewood MS 700/6-8
7 Burnett St 07040 973-378-7660
Jeffrey Truppo, prin. Fax 378-5247
Other Schools – See South Orange

Margate City, Atlantic, Pop. 6,302
Margate City SD 500/K-8
8103 Winchester Ave 08402 609-822-2080
Theresa DeFranco, supt. Fax 822-3399
www.margateschools.org
Tighe MS 200/5-8
7804 Amherst Ave 08402 609-822-2353
Michelle Carney-Ray, prin. Fax 822-8456

Marlboro, Monmouth
Freehold Regional HSD
Supt. — See Englishtown
Marlboro HS 2,000/9-12
95 N Main St 07746 732-617-8393
Shaun Boylan, prin. Fax 972-6615

Marlboro Township SD 5,600/PK-8
1980 Township Dr 07746 732-972-2000
Dr. David Abbott, supt. Fax 972-2003
www.marlboro.k12.nj.us
Marlboro MS 1,100/6-8
355 County Road 520 07746 732-972-2100
Patricia Nieliwocki, prin. Fax 972-6765
Other Schools – See Morganville

Marlton, Burlington, Pop. 9,983
Evesham Township SD 4,500/PK-8
25 S Maple Ave 08053 856-983-1800
John Scavelli, supt. Fax 983-2939
www.evesham.k12.nj.us
DeMasi MS 700/6-8
199 Evesboro Medford Rd 08053 856-988-0777
Irene Romanelli, prin. Fax 596-1571
Marlton MS 1,000/6-8
150 Tomlinson Mill Rd 08053 856-988-0684
Gary Hoffman, prin. Fax 988-9327

Lenape Regional HSD
Supt. — See Shamong Township
Cherokee HS 2,200/9-12
120 Tomlinson Mill Rd 08053 856-983-5140
Donna Charlesworth, prin. Fax 596-6495

Achieve Test Prep Post-Sec.
1 Eves Dr 08053 609-529-8589
ITT Technical Institute Post-Sec.
9000 Lincoln Dr E Ste 100 08053 856-396-3500
The School of Court Reporting Post-Sec.
1002 Lincoln Dr W Ste F 08053 856-988-0800

Matawan, Monmouth, Pop. 8,609
Old Bridge Township SD 9,200/K-12
4207 Highway 516 07747 732-566-1000
Dr. Tim Brennan, supt.
www.oldbridgeadmin.org
Old Bridge HS 3,000/9-12
4209 Highway 516 07747 732-290-3900
David Cittadino, prin. Fax 566-1263
Other Schools – See Old Bridge

Mays Landing, Atlantic, Pop. 2,098
Atlantic County Vocational SD
5080 Atlantic Ave 08330 609-625-2249
Dr. Philip Guenther, supt. Fax 625-2876
Atlantic County Alternative HS Alt
1450 19th St 08330 609-625-2249
Jamie Moscony, prin.
Atlantic County Institute of Technology Vo/Tech
5080 Atlantic Ave 08330 609-625-2249
Ronald DeFelice, prin. Fax 625-0707

Greater Egg Harbor Regional HSD 3,300/9-12
1824 Dr Dennis Foreman Dr 08330 609-625-1456
Steven Ciccariello Ed.D., supt. Fax 625-0045
www.gehrhsd.net/
Oakcrest HS 1,400/9-12
1824 Dr Dennis Foreman Dr 08330 609-909-2600
Daniel Money, prin. Fax 625-0872
Other Schools – See Egg Harbor City, Galloway

Hamilton Township SD 3,000/PK-8
1876 Dr Dennis Foreman Dr 08330 609-476-6300
Michelle Cappelluti Ed.D., supt. Fax 625-4847
www.hamiltonschools.org
Davies MS 900/6-8
1876 Dr Dennis Foreman Dr 08330 609-476-6242
Stephen Santilli, prin.

Atlantic Cape Community College Post-Sec.
5100 Black Horse Pike 08330 609-343-5000

Maywood, Bergen, Pop. 9,373
Maywood SD 900/PK-8
452 Maywood Ave 07607 201-845-9114
Michael Jordan, supt. Fax 845-7146
www.maywoodschools.org
Maywood Avenue MS 500/4-8
452 Maywood Ave 07607 201-845-9110
Michael Jordan, prin. Fax 291-1917

Medford, Burlington
Burlington Co. Institute of Technology
Supt. — See Mount Holly
Burlington Co. Institute of Technology Vo/Tech
10 Hawkin Rd 08055 609-654-0200
Frank Ranelli Ed.D., prin. Fax 654-1081

Lenape Regional HSD
Supt. — See Shamong Township
Lenape HS 1,900/9-12
235 Hartford Rd 08055 609-654-5111
Anthony Cattani, prin. Fax 953-6779
Shawnee HS 1,600/9-12
600 Tabernacle Rd 08055 609-654-7544
Matthew Campbell, prin. Fax 654-5611

Medford Township SD 3,000/PK-8
137 Hartford Rd 08055 609-654-6416
Joseph Del Rossi Ed.D., supt. Fax 654-7436
www.medford.k12.nj.us/
Medford Township Memorial MS 700/7-8
55 Mill St 08055 609-654-7707
Shawn Ryan, prin. Fax 654-7297

Medford Lakes, Burlington, Pop. 4,117
Medford Lakes Borough SD 500/PK-8
135 Mudjekeewis Trl 08055 609-654-0991
Walter Bowyer, supt. Fax 654-7629
www.medford-lakes.k12.nj.us
Neeta S 400/3-8
44 Neeta Trl 08055 609-654-5155
Carole Ramage, prin. Fax 953-8258

Mendham, Morris, Pop. 4,930
Mendham Borough SD 700/PK-8
12 Hilltop Rd 07945 973-543-2295
Dr. Thomas Butler, supt. Fax 543-2805
www.mendhamboro.org
Mountain View MS 300/5-8
100 Dean Rd 07945 973-543-7075
James Bigsby, prin. Fax 543-7993

West Morris Regional HSD
Supt. — See Chester
West Morris Mendham HS 1,300/9-12
65 E Main St 07945 973-543-2501
Michael Matyas, prin. Fax 543-6950

Assumption College for Sisters Post-Sec.
350 Bernardsville Rd 07945 973-543-6528

Metuchen, Middlesex, Pop. 13,256
Metuchen SD 1,900/PK-12
16 Simpson Pl 08840 732-321-8700
Vincent Caputo, supt. Fax 321-6567
www.metuchenschools.org
Edgar MS 600/5-8
49 Brunswick Ave 08840 732-321-8770
Katherine Glutz, prin. Fax 452-0571
Metuchen HS 500/9-12
400 Grove Ave 08840 732-321-8743
Bruce Peragallo, prin. Fax 549-6415

St. Joseph HS 800/9-12
145 Plainfield Rd 08840 732-549-7600
John Anderson, prin. Fax 549-0664

Middlesex, Middlesex, Pop. 13,451
Middlesex Borough SD 2,000/K-12
300 John F Kennedy Dr 08846 732-317-6000
Dr. James C. Baker, supt. Fax 317-6006
www.middlesex.k12.nj.us
Mauger MS 800/4-8
Fisher Ave 08846 732-317-6000
Robert Heidt, prin. Fax 317-6002
Middlesex HS 700/9-12
300 John F Kennedy Dr 08846 732-317-6000
Joseph Sabato, prin. Fax 317-6008

Middletown, Monmouth, Pop. 24,000
Middletown Township SD
Supt. — See Leonardo
Middletown HS North 1,600/9-12
63 Tindall Rd 07748 732-706-6061
Patricia Cartier, prin. Fax 706-6067
Middletown HS South 1,400/9-12
900 Nutswamp Rd 07748 732-706-6111
Patrick Rinella, prin. Fax 706-8058
Thompson MS 1,000/6-8
1001 Middletown Lincroft Rd 07748 732-671-2212
Anne Facendo, prin.

Monmouth County Vocational SD
Supt. — See Freehold
Middletown Vocational S Vo/Tech
2 Swartzel Dr 07748 732-671-0650
Joseph Diver, prin. Fax 671-7455

Mater Dei Prep HS 400/9-12
538 Church St 07748 732-671-9100
Steve Sciarappa, prin. Fax 671-9214

Midland Park, Bergen, Pop. 7,021
Midland Park Borough SD 700/PK-12
250 Prospect St 07432 201-444-1400
Marie Cirasella Ed.D., supt. Fax 444-3051
www.midlandparkschools.k12.nj.us
Midland Park HS 400/7-12
250 Prospect St 07432 201-444-7400
Nicholas Capuano, prin. Fax 444-0352

Millburn, Essex, Pop. 18,630
Millburn Township SD 4,900/PK-12
434 Millburn Ave 07041 973-376-3600
Dr. James Crisfield, supt. Fax 912-9396
www.millburn.org
Millburn HS, 462 Millburn Ave 07041 1,500/9-12
Dr. William Miron, prin. 973-564-7130
Millburn MS 1,200/6-8
25 Old Short Hills Rd 07041 973-379-2600
Michael Cahill, prin. Fax 912-0939

Milburn School for Hearing Handicapped Post-Sec.
Spring & Willow Sts 07041 973-376-9439

Millstone Township, Monmouth
Millstone Township SD 1,500/PK-8
5 Dawson Ct, 732-786-0950
Scott Feder, supt. Fax 792-0951
www.millstone.k12.nj.us/
Millstone Township MS 600/6-8
5 Dawson Ct, 732-786-0950
Karen Barry, prin. Fax 786-0953

Milltown, Middlesex, Pop. 6,830
Milltown SD 700/K-8
80 Violet Ter 08850 732-214-2360
Dr. Linda Madison, supt. Fax 214-2376
www.milltownps.org
Kilmer S 300/5-8
21 W Church St 08850 732-214-2370
Janet Ferlazzo, prin. Fax 214-2378

Millville, Cumberland, Pop. 27,693
Millville SD 5,800/PK-12
PO Box 5010 08332 856-293-2000
Dr. David Gentile, supt. Fax 293-9852
mps.millvillenj.gov/pages/Millville_Public_Schools
Alternative S Alt
200 N Wade Blvd 08332 856-327-6058
Harry Tillotson, prin. Fax 825-2543
Lakeside MS 1,100/6-8
2 N Sharp St 08332 856-293-2420
Thomas Denning, prin. Fax 825-7588
Memorial HS 700/9-10
504 E Broad St 08332 856-327-6072
Al Johnson, prin. Fax 825-4480
Millville SHS 1,100/10-12
200 N Wade Blvd 08332 856-327-6040
Kathleen Procopio, prin. Fax 293-1342

Monmouth Junction, Middlesex, Pop. 2,829
South Brunswick Township SD
Supt. — See North Brunswick
Crossroads North MS 1,000/6-8
635 Georges Rd 08852 732-329-4191
Mark Daniels, prin. Fax 329-1905
Crossroads South MS 1,100/6-8
195 Major Rd 08852 732-329-4633
W. Glenn Famous, prin. Fax 329-1906
South Brunswick HS 2,100/9-12
750 Ridge Rd 08852 732-329-4044
Peter Varela, prin. Fax 274-1237

Noor-Ul-Iman S 500/PK-12
4137 US Highway 1 08852 732-329-1306

Monroe Township, Middlesex
Monroe Township SD 4,700/PK-12
423 Buckelew Ave 08831 732-521-2111
Dr. Kenneth Hamilton, supt. Fax 521-2719
www.monroe.k12.nj.us
Monroe Township HS 1,700/9-12
200 Schoolhouse Rd 08831 732-521-2882
Robert Goodall, prin. Fax 521-2976
Monroe Township MS 900/6-8
1629 Perrineville Rd 08831 732-521-6042
Chari Chanley, prin. Fax 521-2846

Montclair, Essex, Pop. 39,200
Montclair SD 6,000/K-12
22 Valley Rd 07042 973-509-4000
Dr. Penny MacCormack, supt. Fax 509-0586
www.montclair.k12.nj.us/
Glenfield MS 700/6-8
25 Maple Ave 07042 973-509-4172
Charles Miller, prin. Fax 509-4179
Montclair HS 1,900/9-12
100 Chestnut St 07042 973-509-4100
James Earle, prin. Fax 509-4098
Renaissance MS 200/6-8
176 N Fullerton Ave 07042 973-509-5741
Dr. Barbara Weller, prin. Fax 509-5752
Other Schools – See Upper Montclair

Eastern School of Acupuncture Post-Sec.
427 Bloomfield Ave Ste 301 07042 973-746-8717
Immaculate Conception HS 200/9-12
33 Cottage Pl 07042 973-744-7445
Joann Degnan, prin. Fax 744-3926
Lacordaire Academy 100/9-12
155 Lorraine Ave 07043 973-744-1156
Brian Morgan, hdmstr. Fax 783-9521
Montclair Kimberley Academy 400/4-8
201 Valley Rd 07042 973-746-9800
Thomas Nammack, hdmstr. Fax 509-7950
Montclair Kimberley Academy - Upper S 400/9-12
6 Lloyd Rd 07042 973-783-8300
Thomas Nammack, hdmstr. Fax 744-4051
Montclair State University Post-Sec.
1 Normal Ave 07043 973-655-4000
Mountainside Hospital Post-Sec.
1 Bay Ave 07042 973-429-6850

Montvale, Bergen, Pop. 7,749
Montvale SD 1,000/PK-8
47 Spring Valley Rd 07645 201-391-1662
Dr. Darren Petersen, supt. Fax 391-8935
www.montvalek8.org
Fieldstone MS 400/5-8
47 Spring Valley Rd 07645 201-391-9000
Mark Maire, prin. Fax 391-8935

Pascack Valley Regional HSD 2,000/9-12
46 Akers Ave 07645 201-358-7004
P. Erik Gundersen, supt. Fax 505-4858
www.pascack.k12.nj.us
Pascack Hills HS 800/9-12
225 W Grand Ave 07645 201-358-7020
Glenn de Marrais, prin. Fax 358-7019
Other Schools – See Hillsdale

St. Joseph Regional HS 500/9-12
40 Chestnut Ridge Rd 07645 201-391-3300
Barry Donnelly, prin. Fax 391-8073

Montville, Morris, Pop. 15,600
Montville Township SD 4,200/K-12
86 River Rd 07045 973-331-7100
Dr. Paul Fried, supt. Fax 316-4640
montville.net
Lazar MS 1,000/6-8
123 Changebridge Rd 07045 973-331-7140
Sharon Carr, prin. Fax 331-9279
Montville Township HS 1,400/9-12
100 Horseneck Rd 07045 973-331-7100
Dr. Frank Calabria, prin. Fax 334-0753

Trinity Christian S 200/K-12
160 Changebridge Rd 07045 973-334-1785
Douglas Prol, head sch Fax 334-9282

Moorestown, Burlington, Pop. 13,242
Moorestown Township SD 4,100/K-12
803 N Stanwick Rd 08057 856-778-6600
Brien Betze, supt. Fax 235-0961
www.mtps.com
Allen III MS 700/7-8
801 N Stanwick Rd 08057 856-778-6620
Carole Butler, prin. Fax 727-9309
Moorestown HS 1,400/9-12
350 Bridgeboro Rd 08057 856-778-6610
Andrew Seibel, prin. Fax 722-8983

Lincoln Technical Institute Post-Sec.
308 W Route 38 Ste 2 08057 856-722-9333
Moorestown Friends S 700/PK-12
110 E Main St 08057 856-235-2900
Laurence Van Meter, hdmstr. Fax 235-6684

Morganville, Monmouth, Pop. 4,962
Marlboro Township SD
Supt. — See Marlboro
Marlboro Memorial MS 1,100/6-8
71 Nolan Rd 07751 732-972-7115
Dr. Joanmarie Penney, prin. Fax 972-7118

Morris Plains, Morris, Pop. 5,456
Morris Plains SD 600/PK-8
500 Speedwell Ave 07950 973-538-1650
Dr. Ernest Palestis, supt. Fax 540-1983
morrisplainsschooldistrict.org
Borough MS 400/3-8
500 Speedwell Ave 07950 973-538-1650
Sean Dolan, prin. Fax 538-8367

Parsippany-Troy Hills Township SD
Supt. — See Parsippany
Parsippany Hills HS 1,100/9-12
20 Rita Dr 07950 973-682-2815
Lewis Ludwig, prin. Fax 682-2855

Morris Catholic JHS 50/6-8
238 Speedwell Ave 07950 973-539-7267
Deborah Duane, prin.

Morristown, Morris, Pop. 18,125
Morris SD 4,800/K-12
31 Hazel St 07960 973-292-2300
Thomas Ficarra, supt. Fax 292-2057
www.morrisschooldistrict.org
Frelinghuysen MS 1,000/6-8
10 Jane Way 07960 973-292-2200
Mark Manning, prin. Fax 292-2458
Morristown HS 1,500/9-12
50 Early St 07960 973-292-2000
Ethel Minchello, prin. Fax 539-5573

College of Saint Elizabeth Post-Sec.
2 Convent Rd 07960 973-290-4000
Delbarton S 500/7-12
230 Mendham Rd 07960 973-538-3231
Br. Paul Diveny, hdmstr. Fax 538-8836
Morristown-Beard S 500/6-12
70 Whippany Rd 07960 973-539-3032
Peter Caldwell, hdmstr. Fax 539-1590
Morristown Memorial Hospital Post-Sec.
100 Madison Ave 07960 973-971-5177
Rabbinical College of America Post-Sec.
226 Sussex Ave 07960 973-267-9404
Villa Walsh Academy 300/7-12
455 Western Ave 07960 973-538-3680
Sr. Patricia Pompa, prin. Fax 538-6733

Mountain Lakes, Morris, Pop. 4,079
Mountain Lakes SD 1,600/K-12
400 Boulevard 07046 973-334-8280
Dr. Anne Mucci, supt. Fax 334-2316
www.mlschools.org
Briarcliff MS 300/6-8
93 Briarcliff Rd 07046 973-334-0342
Constance Sakala, prin. Fax 334-6857
Mountain Lakes HS 700/9-12
96 Powerville Rd 07046 973-334-8400
Jeremy Davies, prin. Fax 334-3550

Craig S 100/3-8
15 Tower Hill Rd 07046 973-334-4375
Dr. Eric Caparulo, hdmstr. Fax 334-2861

Mountainside, Union, Pop. 6,605
Mountainside SD 800/PK-8
1497 Woodacres Dr 07092 908-232-3232
Dr. Nancy Lubarsky, admin. Fax 232-1743
www.mountainsideschools.org
Deerfield ES 500/3-8
302 Central Ave 07092 908-232-8828
Kimberly Richards, prin. Fax 232-7338

Mount Arlington, Morris, Pop. 4,979
Mount Arlington SD 300/K-8
446 Howard Blvd 07856 973-770-7140
Jane Mullins Jameson, supt. Fax 398-3614
www.mtarlingtonschools.org
Mount Arlington MS 200/3-8
235 Howard Blvd 07856 973-398-4400
Jeffrey Grillo, prin. Fax 398-5726

Mount Ephraim, Camden, Pop. 4,636
Mount Ephraim Borough SD 500/PK-8
225 W Kings Hwy 08059 856-931-7807
Leslie Koller, supt. Fax 931-5831
mtephraimschools.org/
Kershaw MS 200/5-8
125 S Black Horse Pike 08059 856-931-1634
Michael Hunter, prin. Fax 931-5831

Mount Holly, Burlington, Pop. 10,639
Burlington Co. Institute of Technology
695 Woodlane Rd 08060 609-267-4226
Donald Lucas Ed.D., supt. Fax 267-9788
www.bcit.cc/
Burlington Co. Institute of Technology Vo/Tech
695 Woodlane Rd 08060 609-267-4226
Joseph Venuto, prin. Fax 267-3752
Other Schools – See Medford

Mount Holly Township SD 700/PK-8
331 Levis Dr 08060 609-267-7108
Dr. Eric Hibbs, supt. Fax 702-9082
www.mtholly.k12.nj.us
Holbein MS 200/6-8
333 Levis Dr 08060 609-267-7200
Roy Rakszawski, prin. Fax 702-9775

Rancocas Valley Regional HSD 2,000/9-12
520 Jacksonville Rd 08060 609-267-0830
Dr. Gerard Jellig, supt. Fax 702-0167
www.rvrhs.com/
Rancocas Valley Regional HS 2,000/9-12
520 Jacksonville Rd 08060 609-267-0830
Dr. Gerard Jellig, prin. Fax 702-0167
Other Schools – See Pemberton

Burlington County Inst. of Technology Post-Sec.
695 Woodlane Rd 08060 609-267-4226

Mount Laurel, Burlington
Mount Laurel Township SD 4,000/K-8
330 Mount Laurel Rd 08054 856-235-3387
Dr. Antoinette Rath, supt. Fax 235-1837
www.mtlaurelschools.org
Harrington MS 1,000/7-8
514 Mount Laurel Rd 08054 856-234-1610
Kathleen Haines, prin. Fax 222-9754

Heritage Christian Academy 100/PK-12
530 Union Mill Rd 08054 856-234-1145
Ronald Hamilton, prin. Fax 222-9699

Mullica Hill, Gloucester, Pop. 3,933
Clearview Regional HSD 2,400/7-12
420 Cedar Rd 08062 856-223-2765
John Horchak, supt. Fax 478-0409
www.clearviewregional.edu
Clearview Regional HS 1,500/9-12
625 Breakneck Rd 08062 856-223-2790
Keith Brook, prin. Fax 478-6705
Clearview Regional MS 900/7-8
595 Jefferson Rd 08062 856-223-2740
Robin Bazzel, prin. Fax 223-9068

Neptune, Monmouth, Pop. 4,773
Monmouth County Vocational SD
Supt. — See Freehold
CLASS Academy Alt
105 Neptune Blvd 07753 732-431-7245
Earl Moore, prin. Fax 897-1676
Monmouth Co. Acad of Allied Health & Sci Vo/Tech
2325 Heck Ave 07753 732-775-0058
Paul Mucciarone, prin. Fax 775-6646

Neptune Township SD 4,200/PK-12
60 Neptune Blvd 07753 732-776-2000
David Mooij, supt. Fax 897-7595
www.neptune.k12.nj.us/
Neptune HS 1,300/9-12
55 Neptune Blvd 07753 732-776-2200
Richard Allen, prin. Fax 776-2253
Neptune MS 800/6-8
2300 Heck Ave 07753 732-776-2200
Mark Alfone, prin. Fax 776-2254

Jersey Shore Medical Center Post-Sec.
1945 State Route 33 07753 732-776-4603

Newark, Essex, Pop. 268,973
Essex County Vocational Technical SD
60 Nelson Pl 1 North 07102 973-412-2069
Dr. Michael Pennella, supt. Fax 412-5910
www.essextech.org
Essex Co. Vocational Tech HS - N 13th St Vo/Tech
300 N 13th St 07107 973-412-2203
Patricia Clark-Jeter, prin. Fax 412-2098
Essex Co. Vocational Tech - Newark Tech Vo/Tech
91 W Market St 07103 973-412-2204
Oge Denis, prin. Fax 412-2094
Other Schools – See Bloomfield, West Caldwell

Essex Regional Educ Services Commission
Supt. — See Fairfield
Sojourn HS Alt
80 Duryea St 07103 973-484-4858
Dr. Jacqueline Young, prin. Fax 268-3511

Newark SD 35,600/PK-12
2 Cedar St 07102 973-733-7360
Cami Anderson, supt. Fax 733-6834
www.nps.k12.nj.us/
American History HS 300/9-12
74 Montgomery St 07103 973-733-6903
Robert Gregory, prin. Fax 456-7086
Arts HS 500/9-12
550 Martin Luther King Jr 07102 973-733-7391
Lynn Jackson, prin. Fax 483-5524
Bard HS Early College 9-12
321 Bergen St 07103 973-733-8353
John Weinstein, prin.
Barringer HS 1,200/9-12
90 Parker St 07104 973-268-5125
Shonda Davis, prin. Fax 268-5322
Camden MS, 321 Bergen St 07103 200/5-8
LaConte Hill, prin. 973-733-8351
Central HS 700/9-12
246 18th Ave 07108 973-733-6897
Ras Baraka, prin. Fax 733-8212
Chancellor Avenue MS 300/3-8
321 Chancellor Ave 07112 973-705-3870
Jose Fuentes, prin. Fax 733-6841
East Side HS 1,100/9-12
238 Van Buren St 07105 973-465-4900
Dr. Mario Santos, prin. Fax 465-4936
Fast Track Success Academy 200/6-12
200 Washington St 07102 973-733-8765
Dannete Miller, prin.
Newark Bridges HS 9-12
321 Bergen St 07103 973-733-7343
Shenette Gray, prin.
Newark Early College HS 6-12
66 Muhammad Ali Ave 07108 973-733-7594
Carynne Conover, prin.
Newark Innovation Academy 800/Alt
190 Muhammad Ali Ave 07108 973-733-7382
Keria Blue, dir.
Newark Leadership Academy 9-12
301 W Kinney St 07103 973-733-6773
Semone Morant, prin.
Newark Vocational S Vo/Tech
301 W Kinney St 07103 973-733-7018
Dr. Kimberly Honnick, prin. Fax 242-5431
Science Park MSHS 800/7-12
260 Norfolk St 07103 973-733-8689
Lamont Thomas, prin. Fax 733-8236
Shabazz HS 700/9-12
80 Johnson Ave 07108 973-733-6760
Gemar Mills, prin. Fax 430-9163
Technology HS Vo/Tech
187 Broadway 07104 973-481-5962
Mona Dana, prin. Fax 268-5464
University JSHS 500/7-12
55 Clinton Pl 07108 973-351-2010
Henry McNair, prin. Fax 351-2003
Weequahic HS 600/9-12
279 Chancellor Ave 07112 973-705-3900
John Tonero, prin. Fax 923-4095
West Side HS 800/9-12
403 S Orange Ave 07103 973-733-6977
Dara Gronau, prin.
Newark Evening HS Adult
403 S Orange Ave 07103 973-733-7256
LaShawn Gibson-Burney, prin.

Berkeley College Post-Sec.
536 Broad St 07102 973-642-3888
Bethel Christian Academy 100/K-12
580 Mount Prospect Ave 07104 973-484-6646
Fax 484-5328
Christ the King Preparatory S 9-12
239 Woodside Ave 07104 973-483-0033
Cynthia Bielskie, prin. Fax 481-0693
Drake College of Business Post-Sec.
800 Broad St 07102 973-645-1333
Essex County College Post-Sec.
303 University Ave 07102 973-877-3000
Link Community S 100/7-8
23 Pennsylvania Ave 07114 973-642-0529
Maria Pilar Paradiso J.D., head sch Fax 642-1978
New Community Workforce Development Ctr. Post-Sec.
201 Bergen St 07103 973-824-6484
New Jersey Institute of Technology Post-Sec.
University Heights 07102 973-596-3000
New Testament S 50/PK-12
511 Orange St 07107 973-268-1310
Mollie Haynes, admin. Fax 268-1310
Pillar College Post-Sec.
60 Park Pl Ste 701 07102 973-803-5000
Rutgers-The State University of N.J. Post-Sec.
249 University Ave 07102 973-353-5568
St. Benedict Preparatory S 600/7-12
520 Martin Luther King Jr 07102 973-643-4800
Rev. Edwin Leahy, hdmstr. Fax 643-6922
St. Vincent Academy 300/9-12
228 W Market St 07103 973-622-1613
Sr. June Favata, dir. Fax 622-1128
Seton Hall University School of Law Post-Sec.
1 Newark Ctr 07102 973-642-8500
Star Career Academy Post-Sec.
550 Broad St 07102 973-639-0789
University of Medicine & Dentistry of NJ Post-Sec.
65 Bergen St 07107 973-972-4400

New Brunswick, Middlesex, Pop. 54,229
New Brunswick SD 6,700/PK-12
PO Box 2683 08903 732-745-5300
Richard Kaplan, supt. Fax 745-5459
www.nbps.k12.nj.us
New Brunswick HS 1,400/9-12
1000 Somerset St 08901 732-745-5300
Janene Rodriguez, prin. Fax 214-1215
New Brunswick MS 1,100/6-8
1125 Livingston Ave 08901 732-745-5300
Kathy Antoine-Smith, prin. Fax 565-7630
Adult HS Adult
268 Baldwin St 08901 732-846-5300
Marlene Lederman, prin. Fax 745-5325

New Brunswick Theological Seminary Post-Sec.
17 Seminary Pl 08901 732-247-5241
Rutgers-The State University of N.J. Post-Sec.
57 US Highway 1 08901 732-932-4636

New Egypt, Ocean, Pop. 2,476
Plumsted Township SD 1,700/PK-12
117 Evergreen Rd 08533 609-758-6800
Karen Jones Ed.D., supt. Fax 758-6808
www.newegypt.us
New Egypt HS 600/9-12
117 Evergreen Rd 08533 609-758-6800
Thomas Farrell, prin. Fax 758-5683
New Egypt MS 400/6-8
115 Evergreen Rd 08533 609-758-6800
Andrea Caldes, prin. Fax 758-5538

Newfield, Gloucester, Pop. 1,534

Our Lady of Mercy Academy 200/9-12
1001 Main Rd 08344 856-697-2008
Sr. Grace Marie, prin. Fax 697-2887

New Milford, Bergen, Pop. 16,071
New Milford SD 2,000/K-12
145 Madison Ave 07646 201-261-2952
Michael Polizzi, supt. Fax 261-8018
www.newmilfordschools.org
New Milford HS 700/9-12
1 Snyder Cir 07646 201-262-0172
Eric Sheninger, prin. Fax 262-4445
Owens MS 500/6-8
470 Marion Ave 07646 201-265-8661
Whitney Perro, prin. Fax 265-5680

New Providence, Union, Pop. 12,002
New Providence SD 2,200/PK-12
356 Elkwood Ave 07974 908-464-9050
David Miceli Ed.D., supt. Fax 464-9041
www.npsd.k12.nj.us
New Providence HS 600/9-12
35 Pioneer Dr 07974 908-464-4700
Paul Casarico, prin. Fax 464-8556
New Providence MS 300/7-8
35 Pioneer Dr 07974 908-464-9161
Scott Hough, prin. Fax 464-5927

Newton, Sussex, Pop. 7,865
Andover Regional SD 500/K-8
707 Limecrest Rd 07860 973-383-3746
Vicki J. Pede, supt. Fax 579-3972
www.andoverregional.org
Long Pond S 300/5-8
707 Limecrest Rd 07860 973-940-1234
T. Jon Sinclair, prin. Fax 579-2690

Kittatinny Regional SD 1,100/7-12
77 Halsey Rd 07860 973-383-1800
Craig Hutcheson, supt. Fax 383-6218
www.krhs.net
Kittatinny Regional JSHS 1,100/7-12
77 Halsey Rd 07860 973-383-1800
Chris Angelillo, prin. Fax 383-4392

Newton SD 1,500/PK-12
57 Trinity St 07860 973-383-1900
Dr. G. Kennedy Greene, supt. Fax 383-5378
www.newtonnj.org
Halsted Street MS 200/6-8
59 Halsted St 07860 973-383-7440
Jeffrey Waldron, prin. Fax 383-7432
Newton HS 800/9-12
44 Ryerson Ave 07860 973-383-7573
James Tasker, prin. Fax 383-1153

Sussex County Community College Post-Sec.
1 College Hill Rd 07860 973-300-2100

North Arlington, Bergen, Pop. 15,146
North Arlington SD 1,600/PK-12
222 Ridge Rd 07031 201-991-6800
Dr. Oliver Stringham, supt. Fax 991-1656
www.narlington.k12.nj.us
North Arlington HS 500/9-12
222 Ridge Rd 07031 201-991-6800
Louis Manuppelli, prin. Fax 991-0188
North Arlington MS 300/6-8
45 Beech St 07031 201-991-6800
Daniel DiGuglielmo, prin. Fax 246-0703

Queen of Peace HS 500/9-12
191 Rutherford Pl 07031 201-998-8227
Br. Larry Lavallee, prin. Fax 998-3040

North Bergen, Hudson, Pop. 59,000
Hudson County Schools of Technology
8511 Tonnelle Ave 07047 201-662-6700
Frank Gargiulo, supt.
www.hcstonline.org
High Tech HS Vo/Tech
2000 85th St 07047 201-662-6801
Dr. Joseph Giammarella, dir. Fax 854-4129
Other Schools – See Flemington, Jersey City

North Bergen SD 7,300/PK-12
7317 Kennedy Blvd 07047 201-868-1000
Robert Dandorph, supt. Fax 295-2747
www.northbergen.k12.nj.us/
North Bergen HS 2,400/9-12
7417 Kennedy Blvd 07047 201-295-2800
Paschal Tennaro, prin. Fax 295-2873

North Brunswick, Middlesex, Pop. 37,400
North Brunswick Township SD 5,600/PK-12
PO Box 6016 08902 732-289-3000
Dr. Brian Zychowski, supt. Fax 297-8567
www.nbtschools.org
Linwood MS 1,200/6-8
25 Linwood Pl 08902 732-289-3600
Brian Brotschul, prin. Fax 247-7033
North Brunswick Township HS 1,700/9-12
98 Raider Rd 08902 732-289-3700
Peter Clark, prin. Fax 821-8342

South Brunswick Township SD 8,100/K-12
231 Black Horse Ln 08902 732-297-7800
Gary McCartney Ed.D., supt. Fax 297-8456
www.sbschools.org
Other Schools – See Monmouth Junction

Anthem Institute Post-Sec.
651 US Highway 1 08902 855-331-7764
DeVry University Post-Sec.
630 US Highway 1 08902 732-729-3532

North Caldwell, Essex, Pop. 6,124
West Essex Regional SD 1,600/7-12
65 W Greenbrook Rd 07006 973-228-1200
Barbara Longo, supt. Fax 228-0559
www.westex.org
West Essex HS 1,000/9-12
65 W Greenbrook Rd 07006 973-228-1200
Gary Suda, prin. Fax 364-1872
West Essex MS 600/7-8
65 W Greenbrook Rd 07006 973-228-1200
David Montgomery, prin. Fax 228-5852

Northfield, Atlantic, Pop. 8,484
Northfield CSD 1,000/K-8
2000 New Rd 08225 609-407-4000
Janice Fipp Ed.D., supt. Fax 646-0608
northfield.groupfusion.net
Northfield Community MS 500/5-8
2000 New Rd 08225 609-407-4008
Glenn Robbins, prin. Fax 641-2646

North Haledon, Passaic, Pop. 8,332
North Haledon SD 700/K-8
515 High Mountain Rd 07508 973-427-1220
John Petrelli, supt. Fax 427-4357
nhschools.net
High Mountain MS 300/5-8
515 High Mountain Rd 07508 973-427-1220
Melissa Tait M.A., prin. Fax 427-7685

Eastern Christian HS 300/9-12
50 Oakwood Ave 07508 973-427-0900
Joel Eucker, prin. Fax 427-3716
Mary Help of Christians Academy 200/9-12
659 Belmont Ave 07508 973-790-6200
Sr. Lise Parent, prin. Fax 790-6125

North Plainfield, Somerset, Pop. 21,559
North Plainfield Borough SD 3,200/PK-12
33 Mountain Ave 07060 908-769-6060
Dr. Marilyn E. Birnbaum, supt. Fax 755-5490
www.nplainfield.org
North Plainfield HS 1,500/7-12
34 Wilson Ave 07060 908-769-6000
Jerard Stephenson, prin. Fax 769-6032

Robert Fiance Beauty School Post-Sec.
121 Watchung Ave 07060 908-754-4247

Nutley, Essex, Pop. 27,400
Nutley SD 3,700/K-12
315 Franklin Ave 07110 973-661-8798
Russell Lazovick, supt. Fax 320-8476
www.nutleyschools.org
Nutley HS 1,200/9-12
300 Franklin Ave 07110 973-661-8832
Denis Williams, prin. Fax 661-3664
Walker MS 600/7-8
325 Franklin Ave 07110 973-661-8871
Keith Cortright, prin. Fax 661-3775

Abundant Life Academy 400/PK-12
390 Washington Ave 07110 973-667-9700
John Kuebler, head sch Fax 667-1278
Hohokus School - RETS Nutley Post-Sec.
103 Park Ave 07110 973-661-0600

Oakhurst, Monmouth, Pop. 3,965
Ocean Township SD 3,800/PK-12
163 Monmouth Rd 07755 732-531-5600
John Lysko, supt. Fax 531-3874
www.ocean.k12.nj.us
Ocean Township HS 1,300/9-12
550 W Park Ave 07755 732-531-5650
Kelly Weldon, prin. Fax 571-4009
Other Schools – See Ocean

Oakland, Bergen, Pop. 12,608
Oakland SD 1,700/K-8
315 Ramapo Valley Rd 07436 201-337-6156
Dr. Jeffrey Feifer, supt. Fax 405-1237
www.oaklandschoolsnj.org/
Valley MS 600/6-8
71 Oak St 07436 201-337-8185
Gregg Desiderio, prin. Fax 337-7089

Ramapo Indian Hills Regional HSD 2,300/9-12
131 Yawpo Ave 07436 201-416-8100
Dr. Lauren Schoen, supt. Fax 416-8123
www.rih.org
Indian Hills HS 1,200/9-12
97 Yawpo Ave 07436 201-337-0100
Albert Evangelista, prin. Fax 337-1031
Other Schools – See Franklin Lakes

Barnstable Academy 100/5-12
8 Wright Way 07436 201-651-0200
Lizanne Coyne, admin. Fax 337-9797

Oak Ridge, Passaic
Jefferson Township SD
Supt. — See Lake Hopatcong
Jefferson Township HS 1,000/9-12
1010 Weldon Rd 07438 973-697-3535
Karl Mundi, prin. Fax 208-8409
Jefferson Township MS 700/6-8
1000 Weldon Rd 07438 973-697-1980
Jeanne Howe, prin. Fax 697-1348

Ocean, Monmouth, Pop. 26,700
Ocean Township SD
Supt. — See Oakhurst
Ocean Township IS 1,200/5-8
1200 W Park Ave 07712 732-531-5630
Larry Kostula, prin. Fax 493-1891

Concorde School of Hair Design Post-Sec.
1458 State Route 35 07712 732-918-0505
Deal Yeshiva 300/K-12
1515 Logan Rd 07712 732-663-1717
Hillel Yeshiva HS 200/9-12
1027 Deal Rd 07712 732-493-0420
Rabbi Howard Bald, hdmstr. Fax 493-2718
Ilan HS 100/9-12
1200 Roseld Ave 07712 732-517-1111
Raizi Chechik, head sch Fax 663-0194

Ocean City, Cape May, Pop. 11,545
Ocean City SD 2,000/K-12
501 Atlantic Ave Ste 1 08226 609-399-5150
Dr. Kathleen Taylor, supt. Fax 399-4656
www.oceancityschools.org/
Ocean City HS 1,200/9-12
501 Atlantic Ave 08226 609-399-1290
Dr. Matthew Jamison, prin. Fax 399-1966
Ocean City IS 500/4-8
1801 Bay Ave 08226 609-399-5611
Geoffrey Haines, prin. Fax 398-7089

Oceanport, Monmouth, Pop. 5,763
Oceanport Borough SD 600/PK-8
2 Maple Pl 07757 732-544-8588
Andrew Orefice, supt. Fax 544-0386
www.oceanport.k12.nj.us
Maple Place MS 300/5-8
2 Maple Pl 07757 732-229-0267
Matthew Howell, prin. Fax 229-0961

Old Bridge, Middlesex, Pop. 23,304
Old Bridge Township SD
Supt. — See Matawan
Salk MS 1,000/6-8
155 W Greystone Rd 08857 732-360-4519
William Rezes, prin. Fax 251-1690
Sandburg MS 1,200/6-8
3439 Highway 516 08857 732-360-4400
Joseph Marinzoli, prin. Fax 360-0676

Calvary Christian S 200/PK-12
123 White Oak Ln 08857 732-479-0700
Eric Morris, prin. Fax 679-1948
Yeshiva Tiferes Naftoli of Central NJ 100/9-12
8998 State Route 18 08857 732-446-5841

Old Tappan, Bergen, Pop. 5,680
Northern Valley Regional HSD
Supt. — See Demarest
Northern Valley Regional HS 1,400/9-12
100 Central Ave 07675 201-784-1600
Fred Hessler, prin. Fax 768-7724

Old Tappan SD 800/K-8
277 Old Tappan Rd 07675 201-664-1421
William Ward Ed.D., supt. Fax 664-4418
www.oldtappanschools.org/
DeWolf MS 400/5-8
275 Old Tappan Rd 07675 201-664-1475
Dennis Rossi, prin. Fax 664-8101

Oradell, Bergen, Pop. 7,880
River Dell Regional SD
Supt. — See River Edge
River Dell Regional HS 1,000/9-12
55 Pyle St 07649 201-599-7240
Lorraine Brooks, prin. Fax 599-2294

Bergen Catholic HS 700/9-12
1040 Oradell Ave 07649 201-261-1844
Timothy McElhinney, prin. Fax 599-9507

Orange, Essex, Pop. 33,300
Orange Township SD 3,400/PK-12
451 Lincoln Ave 07050 973-677-4000
Ronald Lee, supt. Fax 677-0486
www.orange.k12.nj.us
Career & Innovation Academy of Orange Vo/Tech
123 Cleveland St 07050 973-677-4000
Jason Belton, prin.
Orange HS 700/9-12
400 Lincoln Ave 07050 973-677-4050
Faith Alcantara, prin. Fax 677-4069
Orange Preparatory Academy 300/7-8
400 Central Ave 07050 973-677-4135
Darrell Medley, prin. Fax 677-2439

Palisades Park, Bergen, Pop. 19,390
Palisades Park SD 1,400/PK-12
410 2nd St 07650 201-947-3550
Dr. Mark Hayes, supt. Fax 947-4079
www.palpkschools.org/
Palisades Park HS 500/8-12
1 Veterans Plz 07650 201-941-1100
Nicholas Cipriano, prin. Fax 947-1280

Palmyra, Burlington, Pop. 7,223
Palmyra Borough SD 900/PK-12
301 Delaware Ave 08065 856-786-9300
Brian McBride, supt. Fax 829-9638
www.palmyra.k12.nj.us
Delaware Avenue S 50/Alt
301 Delaware Ave 08065 856-829-4777
Joseph Martin, admin. Fax 829-9638

Palmyra HS 400/7-12
311 W 5th St 08065 856-786-9400
Joseph Martin, prin. Fax 786-3014

Paramus, Bergen, Pop. 25,735
Bergen County Vocational SD
327 E Ridgewood Ave 07652 201-343-6000
Dr. Howard Lerner, supt. Fax 225-9182
bcts.bergen.org
Bergen County Technical HS - Paramus Vo/Tech
285 Pascack Rd 07652 201-343-6000
Carole Terrizzi, prin. Fax 996-6935
Other Schools – See Hackensack, Teterboro

Paramus SD 4,000/K-12
145 Spring Valley Rd 07652 201-261-7800
Kenneth Rota, supt. Fax 261-5861
www.paramusschools.org/ppsd/
East Brook MS 600/5-8
190 Spring Valley Rd 07652 201-261-7800
Thomas LoBue, prin. Fax 262-1541
Paramus HS 1,300/9-12
99 E Century Rd 07652 201-261-7800
Anthony Panico, prin. Fax 261-3833
West Brook MS 700/5-8
560 Roosevelt Blvd 07652 201-261-7800
Carla Alvarez, prin. Fax 652-0376

Bergen Community College Post-Sec.
400 Paramus Rd 07652 201-447-7100
Berkeley College Post-Sec.
64 E Midland Ave 07652 201-967-9667
Capri Institute of Hair Design Post-Sec.
615 Winters Ave 07652 201-599-0880
DeVry University Post-Sec.
81 E State Rt 4 Ste 102 07652 201-556-2840
Frisch S 600/9-12
120 W Century Rd 07652 201-267-9100
Dr. Kalman Stein, prin. Fax 261-9340
Lincoln Technical Institute Post-Sec.
240 Bergen Town Ctr 07652 201-845-6868
Paramus Catholic HS 1,600/9-12
425 Paramus Rd 07652 201-445-6465
James Vail, pres. Fax 445-3952

Park Ridge, Bergen, Pop. 8,566
Park Ridge SD 1,300/PK-12
2 Park Ave 07656 201-573-6000
Dr. Robert Gamper, supt. Fax 391-6511
www.parkridge.k12.nj.us
Park Ridge HS 600/7-12
2 Park Ave 07656 201-573-6000
Patricia Bucci, prin. Fax 930-4874

Parlin, Middlesex
Sayreville SD
Supt. — See South Amboy
Sayreville MS 1,300/6-8
800 Washington Rd 08859 732-525-5288
Donna Jakubik, prin. Fax 727-5621
Sayreville War Memorial HS 1,700/9-12
820 Washington Rd 08859 732-525-5253
James Brown, prin. Fax 316-0720

Parsippany, Morris, Pop. 51,000
Parsippany-Troy Hills Township SD 7,000/PK-12
292 Parsippany Rd 07054 973-263-7250
LeRoy Seitz Ed.D., supt. Fax 263-7230
www.pthsd.k12.nj.us/
Brooklawn MS 800/6-8
250 Beachwood Rd 07054 973-428-7551
Eileen Hoehne, prin. Fax 781-0309
Central MS 800/6-8
1620 US Highway 46 07054 973-263-7125
Dr. Norman Francis, prin. Fax 402-1579
Parsippany HS 1,000/9-12
309 Baldwin Rd 07054 973-263-7001
Dr. Natalie Betz, prin. Fax 263-7347
Other Schools – See Morris Plains

Anthem Institute Post-Sec.
959 US Highway 46 07054 855-331-7765
Parsippany Christian S 200/PK-12
PO Box 5365 07054 973-539-7012
Rev. Philip Thibault, admin. Fax 539-2527

Passaic, Passaic, Pop. 69,000
Essex Regional Educ Services Commission
Supt. — See Fairfield
Essex HS Adult
188 1st St 07055 973-815-1389
Kimberly Brucale, prin. Fax 815-1635

Passaic CSD 12,400/PK-12
PO Box 388 07055 973-470-5500
Dr. Lawrence Everet, supt. Fax 470-8984
www.passaic-city.k12.nj.us
Lincoln MS 1,600/7-8
291 Lafayette Ave 07055 973-470-5504
Steve Cruz, prin. Fax 470-5128
Passaic HS 2,600/9-12
170 Paulison Ave 07055 973-470-5600
Tobias Weissman, prin. Fax 470-5135

Passaic Co. Education Services Comm.
Supt. — See Wayne
Hope Academy 100/Alt
209 Hope Ave 07055 973-928-1509
Irene LeFebvre Ed.D., dir. Fax 928-1505

Bais Yaakov of Passaic HS 200/9-12
181 Pennington Ave 07055 973-365-0100
Collegiate S 100/PK-12
22 Kent Ct 07055 973-777-1714
Mesivta Tiferes Rav Zvi Aryeh Zemel 100/9-12
15 Temple Pl 07055 973-594-9001

Paterson, Passaic, Pop. 143,991
Paterson SD 18,900/PK-12
90 Delaware Ave 07503 973-321-1000
Dr. Donnie Evans, supt. Fax 321-0470
www.paterson.k12.nj.us

Bosco Technology Academy 300/7-8
202 Union Ave 07502 973-321-1000
Joseph Andriulli, prin. Fax 321-0587
Destiny Academy, 45 Smith St 07505 Alt
Jalyn Lyde, prin. 973-321-2530
Eastside HS Operations 9-12
150 Park Ave 07501 973-321-2487
Zatiti Moody, prin. Fax 321-0517
Eastside HS S of Culinary Arts Hosp Trsm 600/9-12
150 Park Ave 07501 973-321-2489
Edgard Nieves, prin. Fax 321-0517
Eastside HS S of Government/Public Admin 500/9-12
150 Park Ave 07501 973-321-2488
Karen Johnson, prin. Fax 321-0517
Eastside HS S of Information and Tech 500/9-12
150 Park Ave 07501 973-321-2490
Vivian Gaines, prin. Fax 321-0517
Great Falls Academy 9-12
11 22nd Ave 07513 973-321-2380
Andre McCollum, prin. Fax 321-2387
HARP Academy 9-12
175 Main St 07505 973-321-0561
Isabelle Grassi, admin. Fax 321-0565
International HS 400/9-12
200 Grand St 07501 973-321-2280
Robina Puryear-Castro, prin. Fax 321-2283
Kennedy HS Academy of Arch & Const Trade 9-12
127 Preakness Ave 07522 973-321-0504
Pedro Valdes, admin. Fax 321-0507
Kennedy HS Academy of Bus Tech Mktg 9-12
127 Preakness Ave 07522 973-321-0505
Kyle Brunson, admin. Fax 321-0507
Kennedy HS Academy of Sci Tech Eng Math 9-12
127 Preakness Ave 07522 973-321-0507
Kathleen Kellett, prin. Fax 321-0507
Kennedy HS Acad of Education & Training 9-12
127 Preakness Ave 07522 973-321-2461
Maryanne Perrotta, admin. Fax 321-0507
Kennedy HS Operations 9-12
127 Preakness Ave 07522 973-321-0500
Amod Field, prin. Fax 321-0507
Morgan Academy of Trans & Engineering 9-12
200 Grand St 07501 973-321-2540
Danyel Cicarelli, admin. Fax 321-2547
New Roberto Clemente S 300/6-8
482 Market St 07501 973-321-0240
Edward Cisneros, prin. Fax 321-0247
PANTHER Academy 9-12
201 Memorial Dr 07505 973-321-2290
Bonnie Miele, admin. Fax 321-2297
Parks HS of Fine & Performing Arts 200/9-12
413 12th Ave 07514 973-321-0520
Christine Lewis, prin. Fax 321-0527
Paterson City S 7 200/5-8
106 Ramsey St 07501 973-321-0070
JoAnne Cardillo, prin. Fax 321-0077
Sports Business and Public Safety Acad 9-12
47 State St 07501 973-321-2392
Sham Bacchus, admin. Fax 321-2396
YES Academy Alt
45 Smith St 07505 973-321-0570
Nicole Payne, prin. Fax 321-0577
Silk City 2000 Academy/Adult S Adult
151 Ellison St 07505 973-321-0760
Sebastian Calabria, prin. Fax 321-0767

HoHoKus Sch of Trade/Technical Sciences Post-Sec.
634 Market St 07513 800-646-9353
Madison Avenue Baptist Academy 200/K-12
900 Madison Ave 07501 973-279-5800
Jay Harvey, admin. Fax 684-6289
Passaic County Community College Post-Sec.
1 College Blvd 07505 973-684-6868

Paulsboro, Gloucester, Pop. 5,820
Paulsboro SD 1,200/PK-12
662 N Delaware St 08066 856-423-2222
Dr. Frank Scambia, supt. Fax 423-4602
www.paulsboro.k12.nj.us/
Paulsboro JSHS 600/7-12
670 N Delaware St 08066 856-423-2222
Paul Morina, prin. Fax 423-8915

Pemberton, Burlington, Pop. 1,373
Pemberton Township SD 3,800/PK-12
PO Box 228 08068 609-893-8141
Dr. Michael Gorman, supt. Fax 894-0933
www.pemberton.k12.nj.us
Fort/Newcomb MS 600/6-8
301 Fort Dix Rd 08068 609-893-8141
Mary Hutchinson, prin. Fax 894-9287
Pemberton Township HS 1,100/9-12
148 Arneys Mount Rd 08068 609-893-8141
Christine Vespe, prin. Fax 894-0126

Rancocas Valley Regional HSD
Supt. — See Mount Holly
Burlington County Alternative HS 50/Alt
601 Pemberton Browns Mills 08068 609-894-9311
Camille Rosenberg, dir. Fax 894-9372

Burlington County College Post-Sec.
601 Pemberton Brown Mill Rd 08068 609-894-9311

Pennington, Mercer, Pop. 2,560
Hopewell Valley Regional SD 3,900/PK-12
425 S Main St 08534 609-737-4000
Dr. Tom Smith, supt. Fax 737-1418
www.hvrsd.org/
Central HS 1,200/9-12
259 Pennington Titusville 08534 609-737-4003
Michael Daher, prin. Fax 737-1581
Timberlane MS 1,000/6-8
51 Timberlane Dr 08534 609-737-4004
Tony Suozzo, prin. Fax 737-2718

Mercer County Technical SD
Supt. — See Trenton
Sypek Center Vo/Tech
129 Bull Run Rd 08534 609-737-9785
Mary Smith Jones, prin. Fax 737-3951

Pennington S 500/6-12
112 W Delaware Ave 08534 609-737-1838
Stephanie Townsend, hdmstr. Fax 730-1405

Pennsauken, Camden, Pop. 35,900
Camden County Technical Schools
Supt. — See Sicklerville
Camden County Technical S - Pennsauken Vo/Tech
6008 Browning Rd 08109 856-663-1040
Patricia Fitzgerald, prin. Fax 655-8011

Pennsauken Township SD 4,900/PK-12
1695 Hylton Rd 08110 856-662-8505
Marilyn Martinez Ed.D., supt. Fax 663-5865
www.pennsauken.net
Pennsauken HS 1,400/9-12
800 Hylton Rd 08110 856-662-8500
Dennis Vinson, prin. Fax 910-2612
Phifer MS 700/7-8
8201 Park Ave 08109 856-662-8511
Monroe Logan, prin. Fax 486-1422
Washington Alternative S Alt
1641 Derousse Ave 08110 856-662-0877
Richard Bonkowski, admin. Fax 662-8185

Bishop Eustace Prep S 800/9-12
5552 Marlton Pike 08109 856-662-2160
Cyril Bleistine, prin. Fax 662-0802
Omega Institute Post-Sec.
7050 Kaighns Ave 08109 856-663-4299

Penns Grove, Salem, Pop. 4,982
Penns Grove-Carneys Point Regional SD 2,200/PK-12
100 Iona Ave 08069 856-299-4250
Joseph Massare Ed.D., supt. Fax 299-5226
www.pennsgrove.k12.nj.us
Penns Grove MS 500/6-8
351 E Maple Ave 08069 856-299-0576
Jean Spinelli, prin. Fax 299-4378
Other Schools – See Carneys Point

Pennsville, Salem, Pop. 11,771
Pennsville Township SD 1,800/PK-12
30 Church St 08070 856-540-6200
Dr. Michael Brodzik, supt. Fax 678-7565
www.psdnet.org/
Pennsville Memorial HS 500/9-12
110 S Broadway 08070 856-540-6220
Matthew McFarland, prin. Fax 678-2715
Pennsville MS 400/6-8
4 William Penn Ave 08070 856-540-6240
Sheila Burris, prin. Fax 678-2908

Salem County Christian Academy 200/PK-12
104 Sparks Ave 08070 856-678-9464
Eddie Riley, admin. Fax 678-3696

Perth Amboy, Middlesex, Pop. 50,388
Middlesex County Vocational SD
Supt. — See East Brunswick
Perth Amboy Vocational HS Vo/Tech
457 High St 08861 732-376-6300
Robert Fuller, prin. Fax 376-6391

Perth Amboy SD 10,100/PK-12
178 Barracks St 08861 732-376-6200
Dr. Janine Caffrey, supt. Fax 826-1644
www.paps.net/
McGinnis MS 1,400/5-8
271 State St 08861 732-376-6040
Dr. Myrna Garcia, prin. Fax 376-6047
Perth Amboy HS 2,400/9-12
300 Eagle Ave 08861 732-376-6030
Dr. Nestor Collazo, prin. Fax 376-6275
Shull MS 1,300/5-8
380 Hall Ave 08861 732-376-6060
Lorraine Morgan, prin. Fax 376-6067
Perth Amboy Adult HS Adult
178 Barracks St 08861 732-376-6240
Dr. Senovia Robles, prin. Fax 376-6245

Perth Amboy Catholic Upper S 100/4-8
500 State St 08861 732-826-1598
Sr. Mary Rebecca Piatek, prin. Fax 826-7063
Raritan Bay Medical Center Post-Sec.
530 New Brunswick Ave 08861 732-324-5232
Robert Fiance Beauty Academy Post-Sec.
312 State St 08861 732-442-6007

Petersburg, See Woodbine
Upper Township SD 1,400/PK-8
525 Perry Rd 08270 609-628-3500
Vincent Palmieri, supt. Fax 628-2002
upperschools.org/
Upper Township MS 500/6-8
525 Perry Rd 08270 609-628-3500
Ken Barth, prin. Fax 628-3506

Phillipsburg, Warren, Pop. 14,597
Lopatcong Township SD 900/PK-8
263 State Route 57 08865 908-859-0800
Dr. William Caldwell, supt. Fax 213-1339
www.lopatsd.org
Lopatcong MS 400/5-8
321 Stonehenge Dr 08865 908-213-2955
Jeanene Dutt, prin. Fax 213-0373

Phillipsburg SD 3,500/PK-12
445 Marshall St 08865 908-454-3400
George M. Chando, supt. Fax 213-2424
www.pburgsd.net/
Phillipsburg Alternative HS Alt
20 Fairview Ave 08865 908-213-2688
Kyle Rovi, dir. Fax 213-2708
Phillipsburg Alternative Learning S Alt
445 Marshall St 08865 908-213-2651
Kyle Rovi, dir. Fax 454-2479
Phillipsburg HS 1,600/9-12
200 Hillcrest Blvd 08865 908-454-6551
Gregory Troxell, prin. Fax 213-2427
Phillipsburg MS 500/6-8
525 Warren St 08865 908-454-5577
Richard Kistler, prin. Fax 213-2546

Pilesgrove, Salem
Salem County Vocational Technical SD
880 Route 45 08098 856-769-0101
Dr. Loren Thomas, supt. Fax 769-3602
www.scvts.org/
Salem County Career & Technical HS Vo/Tech
880 Route 45 08098 856-769-0101
Jason Helder, prin. Fax 769-4214

Pine Hill, Camden, Pop. 9,944
Pine Hill Borough SD 1,700/PK-12
1003 Turnerville Rd 08021 856-783-6900
Dr. Kenneth Koczur, supt. Fax 783-2955
www.pinehill.k12.nj.us
Overbrook HS 700/9-12
1200 Turnerville Rd 08021 856-767-8000
Paul Harmelin, prin. Fax 767-3082
Pine Hill MS 300/6-8
1100 Turnerville Rd 08021 856-210-0200
Kathleen Klemick, prin. Fax 210-0195

Piscataway, Middlesex, Pop. 48,900
Middlesex County Vocational SD
Supt. — See East Brunswick
Piscataway Vocational HS Vo/Tech
21 Suttons Ln 08854 732-985-0717
Dr. Joseph Armstead, prin. Fax 985-7717

Piscataway Township SD 7,000/PK-12
PO Box 1332 08855 732-572-2289
Robert Copeland, supt. Fax 777-1361
www.piscatawayschools.org/
Conackamack MS 500/6-8
5205 Witherspoon St 08854 732-699-1577
Donna White, prin. Fax 699-0118
Piscataway Township HS 2,200/9-12
100 Behmer Rd 08854 732-981-0700
Dr. Michael Wanko, prin. Fax 981-1985
Quibbletown MS 600/6-8
99 Academy St 08854 732-752-0444
Deidre Ortiz, prin. Fax 752-5798
Schor MS 600/6-8
243 N Randolphville Rd 08854 732-752-4457
Richard Hueston, prin. Fax 424-9445

An-Noor Academy 300/PK-12
120 Ethel Rd W Ste A 08854 732-287-1530
StenoTech Career Institute Post-Sec.
262 Old New Brunswick Rd 08854 732-562-1200
Timothy Christian S 500/K-12
2008 Ethel Rd 08854 732-985-0300
Dr. Hubert Hartzler, supt. Fax 985-8008

Pitman, Gloucester, Pop. 8,890
Pitman SD 1,400/PK-12
420 Hudson Ave 08071 856-589-2145
Dr. Patrick McAleer, supt. Fax 582-5465
www.pitman.k12.nj.us
Pitman HS 400/9-12
225 Linden Ave 08071 856-589-2121
Dr. Cherie Lombardo, prin. Fax 589-8855
Pitman MS 400/6-8
138 E Holly Ave 08071 856-589-0636
Eileen Salmon, prin. Fax 589-2289

Pittsgrove, Salem
Pittsgrove Township SD 1,600/PK-12
1076 Almond Rd 08318 856-358-3094
Henry Bermann, supt. Fax 358-6020
www.pittsgrove.org
Pittsgrove Township MS 400/6-8
1082 Almond Rd 08318 856-358-8529
Priscilla Ocasio-Jimenez, prin. Fax 358-2686
Schalick HS 500/9-12
718 Centerton Rd 08318 856-358-2054
Donna Meyers, prin. Fax 358-7063

Pittstown, Hunterdon
Alexandria Township SD 600/PK-8
557 County Road 513 08867 908-996-6811
Dr. Matthew Jennings, supt. Fax 996-7029
www.alexandriaschools.org
Alexandria MS 400/4-8
557 County Road 513 08867 908-996-6811
David Pawlowski, prin. Fax 996-7963

Plainfield, Union, Pop. 48,849
Plainfield SD 6,000/PK-12
1200 Myrtle Ave 07063 908-731-4335
Anna Belin-Pyles, supt. Fax 731-4336
www.plainfieldnjk12.org
Hubbard MS 300/6-8
661 W 8th St 07060 908-731-4320
Kwame Asante, prin. Fax 731-4315
Maxson MS 300/6-8
920 E 7th St 07062 908-731-4310
Joi Bethea, prin. Fax 731-4306
Obama Acad for Academic & Civic Dvlpmnt 100/Alt
1200 Myrtle Ave 07063 908-731-4270
Kevin Stansbury, prin.
Plainfield Academy for the Arts 200/7-12
1700 W Front St 07063 908-731-4421
Angela Bento, prin.
Plainfield HS 1,300/9-12
950 Park Ave 07060 908-731-4390
Otis Brown, prin. Fax 731-4394

---

du Cret School of the Arts Post-Sec.
1030 Central Ave 07060 908-757-7171
Koinonia Academy 300/K-12
1040 Plainfield Ave 07060 908-668-9002
Hendrick Soule, admin. Fax 668-9883
Muhlenberg - Snyder Schools Post-Sec.
Park Avenue And Randolph Rd 07061 908-668-2400
New Covenant Christian Academy 50/K-12
315 W 7th St 07060 908-756-3322
Stephanie DeGeneste, admin. Fax 756-3302
Union County College Post-Sec.
232 E 2nd St 07060 908-412-3599

Plainsboro, Middlesex
West Windsor-Plainsboro Regional SD
Supt. — See West Windsor
Community MS 1,200/6-8
95 Grovers Mill Rd 08536 609-716-5300
Gerard Dalton, prin. Fax 716-5333
West Windsor-Plainsboro HS North 1,500/9-12
90 Grovers Mill Rd 08536 609-716-5100
Michael Zapicchi, prin. Fax 716-5142

Pleasantville, Atlantic, Pop. 19,789
Pleasantville SD 3,100/PK-12
PO Box 960 08232 609-383-6800
Dr. Garnell Bailey, supt. Fax 677-8101
www.pps-nj.us/
Pleasantville HS 800/9-12
701 Mill Rd 08232 609-383-6900
Stephen Townsend, prin. Fax 383-9934
Pleasantville MS 600/6-8
801 Mill Rd 08232 609-383-6800
Briggitte White, prin. Fax 677-0852

Shore Beauty School Post-Sec.
103 W Washington Ave 08232 609-645-3635

Point Pleasant, Ocean, Pop. 18,265
Point Pleasant Borough SD 3,000/PK-12
2100 Panther Path 08742 732-701-1900
Vincent Smith, supt. Fax 892-8403
www.pointpleasant.k12.nj.us/
Memorial MS 700/6-8
808 Laura Herbert Dr 08742 732-701-1900
Gary Floyd, prin. Fax 892-0984
Point Pleasant Borough HS 1,000/9-12
808 Laura Herbert Dr 08742 732-701-1900
Linda Rocco, prin. Fax 892-1252

Pt Pleas Bch, Ocean, Pop. 4,621
Point Pleasant Beach SD 1,000/PK-12
299 Cooks Ln 08742 732-899-8840
Dr. John Ravally, supt. Fax 899-1730
ptbeach.com
Point Pleasant Beach HS 500/9-12
700 Trenton Ave 08742 732-899-1817
Terri King, prin. Fax 899-1145

Pompton Lakes, Passaic, Pop. 10,956
Pompton Lakes SD 1,400/K-12
237 Van Ave 07442 973-835-4334
Dr. Paul Amoroso, supt. Fax 835-1748
www.plps-k12.org
Lakeside MS 300/6-8
316 Lakeside Ave 07442 973-835-2221
Jake Herninko, prin. Fax 835-8088
Pompton Lakes HS 500/9-12
44 Lakeside Ave 07442 973-835-7100
Vincent Przybylinski, prin. Fax 835-1054

Pompton Plains, Morris
Pequannock Township SD 2,300/K-12
538 Newark Pompton Tpke 07444 973-616-6040
Dr. Victor Hayek, supt. Fax 616-6043
www.pequannock.org
Pequannock Township HS 700/9-12
85 Sunset Rd 07444 973-616-6000
Frank Ingargiola, prin. Fax 616-6029
Pequannock Valley MS 600/6-8
493 Newark Pompton Tpke 07444 973-616-6050
Richard Hayzler, prin. Fax 616-8370

Chancellor Academy 100/6-12
PO Box 338 07444 973-835-4989
Kevin McNaught, dir. Fax 835-0768
Netherlands Reformed Christian S 200/PK-12
164 Jacksonville Rd 07444 973-628-7400
John VanDerBrink, prin. Fax 628-0461

Port Monmouth, Monmouth, Pop. 3,791
Middletown Township SD
Supt. — See Leonardo
Thorne MS, 70 Murphy Rd 07758 800/6-8
Thomas Olausen, prin. 732-787-1220

Port Norris, Cumberland, Pop. 1,319
Commercial Township SD 600/PK-8
1308 North Ave 08349 856-785-0840
John Saporito, supt. Fax 785-2354
www.commercial.k12.nj.us
Port Norris MS 200/6-8
PO Box 670 08349 856-785-1611
Robert Domico, prin. Fax 785-2556

Pottersville, Hunterdon

Purnell S 100/9-12
PO Box 500 07979 908-439-2154
Ayanna Hill-Gill, hdmstr. Fax 439-2090

Princeton, Mercer, Pop. 11,896
Princeton SD 3,300/PK-12
25 Valley Rd 08540 609-806-4220
Judith Wilson, supt. Fax 806-4221
www.princetonk12.org
Princeton HS 1,400/9-12
151 Moore St 08540 609-806-4280
Gary Snyder, prin. Fax 806-4281
Witherspoon MS 700/6-8
217 Walnut Ln 08540 609-806-4270
Jason Burr, prin. Fax 806-4271

Achieve Test Prep Post-Sec.
100 Overlook Ctr 08540 609-964-0772
American Boychoir S 50/4-8
75 Mapleton Rd 08540 609-924-5858
Fax 924-5812
Hun S of Princeton 500/6-12
176 Edgerstoune Rd 08540 609-921-7600
Jonathan Brougham, hdmstr. Fax 683-4410
Princeton Day S 900/PK-12
PO Box 75 08542 609-924-6700
Paul Stellato, hdmstr. Fax 924-8944
Princeton Theological Seminary Post-Sec.
PO Box 821 08542 609-921-8300
Princeton University 08544 Post-Sec.
609-258-3000
Raritan Valley Flying School Post-Sec.
41 Airpark Rd 08540 609-921-3100
Stuart Country Day S 600/PK-12
1200 Stuart Rd 08540 609-921-2330
Dr. Patty Fagin, hdmstr. Fax 497-0784

Princeton Junction, Mercer, Pop. 2,407
West Windsor-Plainsboro Regional SD
Supt. — See West Windsor
Grover MS 1,100/6-8
10 Southfield Rd 08550 609-716-5250
Bev Krocker, prin. Fax 716-5270

Rahway, Union, Pop. 26,740
Rahway SD 3,300/PK-12
1138 Kline Pl 07065 732-396-1000
Edward Yergalonis, supt. Fax 396-1391
www.rahway.net
Rahway HS 1,100/9-12
1012 Madison Ave 07065 732-396-1090
John Farinella, prin. Fax 396-2630
Rahway MS 600/7-8
1138 Kline Pl 07065 732-396-1025
Alan Johnson, prin. Fax 396-2633

Ramsey, Bergen, Pop. 14,315
Ramsey SD 3,000/K-12
266 E Main St 07446 201-785-2300
Bruce DeYoung, supt. Fax 934-6623
www.ramsey.k12.nj.us
Ramsey HS 1,000/9-12
256 E Main St 07446 201-785-2300
Dr. Michael Thumm, prin. Fax 818-2656
Smith MS 800/6-8
73 Monroe St 07446 201-785-2313
Stacie Poelstra, prin. Fax 785-2320

Don Bosco Prep HS 900/9-12
492 N Franklin Tpke 07446 201-327-8003
John Stanczak, prin. Fax 327-3397
Eastwick College Post-Sec.
10 S Franklin Tpke 07446 201-327-8877

Randolph, Morris, Pop. 19,974
Randolph Township SD 5,200/PK-12
25 Schoolhouse Rd 07869 973-361-0808
Dr. David Browne, supt. Fax 361-2405
www.rtnj.org
Randolph HS 1,700/9-12
511 Millbrook Ave 07869 973-361-2400
Debbie Iosso, prin. Fax 361-1661
Randolph MS 1,200/6-8
507 Millbrook Ave 07869 973-366-8700
Carol Strowbridge Ed.D., prin. Fax 361-6501

County College of Morris Post-Sec.
214 Center Grove Rd 07869 973-328-5000

Red Bank, Monmouth, Pop. 11,983
Red Bank Borough SD 900/PK-8
76 Branch Ave 07701 732-758-1500
Dr. Laura Morana, supt. Fax 212-1356
www.rbb.k12.nj.us
Red Bank MS 400/4-8
101 Harding Rd 07701 732-758-1500
Maria Iozzi, prin. Fax 758-1518

Red Bank Catholic HS 1,000/9-12
112 Broad St 07701 732-747-1774
Robert Abatemarco, prin. Fax 747-1936

Richland, Atlantic

St. Augustine Prep S 700/9-12
PO Box 279 08350 856-697-2600
Rev. Donald Reilly, prin. Fax 697-8389

Ridgefield, Bergen, Pop. 10,875
Ridgefield SD 1,300/1-12
555 Chestnut St 07657 201-945-9236
Dr. Harry Groveman, supt. Fax 945-7830
www.ridgefieldschools.com
Ridgefield Memorial HS 500/9-12
555 Walnut St 07657 201-945-4455
Dr. Tamika DePass, prin. Fax 945-3505
Slocum/Skewes ES 500/3-8
650 Prospect Ave 07657 201-943-4299
Janet Seabold, prin. Fax 943-9527

Ridgefield Park, Bergen, Pop. 12,530
Ridgefield Park SD 2,000/K-12
712 Lincoln Ave 07660 201-641-0800
Christopher R. Onorato, supt. Fax 641-2203
www.rpps.net
Ridgefield Park JSHS 1,100/7-12
1 Ozzie Nelson Dr 07660 201-440-1440
James Donohue, prin. Fax 641-6861

Ridgewood, Bergen, Pop. 24,497
Ridgewood Village SD 5,700/PK-12
49 Cottage Pl 07450 201-670-2700
Dr. Daniel Fishbein, supt. Fax 670-2668
www.ridgewood.k12.nj.us
Franklin MS 700/6-8
335 N Van Dien Ave 07450 201-670-2780
Anthony Orsini, prin. Fax 670-3382
Ridgewood HS 1,700/9-12
627 E Ridgewood Ave 07450 201-670-2800
Dr. Thomas Gorman, prin. Fax 444-7008
Washington MS 700/6-8
155 Washington Pl 07450 201-670-2790
Dr. Katie Kashmanian, prin. Fax 670-3290

Valley Hospital Post-Sec.
223 N Van Dien Ave 07450 201-447-8002

Ringwood, Passaic, Pop. 11,996
Ringwood SD 1,200/K-8
121 Carletondale Rd 07456 973-962-7028
Hugh Beattie, supt. Fax 962-9211
www.ringwoodschools.org/
Ryerson MS 400/6-8
130 Valley Rd 07456 973-962-7063
Paul Scutti, prin. Fax 962-6905

River Edge, Bergen, Pop. 11,204
River Dell Regional SD 1,600/7-12
230 Woodland Ave 07661 201-599-7206
Patrick Fletcher, supt. Fax 261-3809
www.riverdell.org/
River Dell MS 500/7-8
230 Woodland Ave 07661 201-599-7250
Richard Freedman, prin. Fax 599-2202
Other Schools – See Oradell

Riverside, Burlington, Pop. 7,974
Riverside Township SD 1,400/PK-12
112 E Washington St 08075 856-461-1255
Robin A. Ehrich, supt. Fax 461-5168
www.riverside.k12.nj.us
Riverside HS 400/9-12
112 E Washington St 08075 856-461-1255
Todd Pae, prin. Fax 461-7277
Riverside MS 300/6-8
112 E Washington St 08075 856-461-1255
Michael W. Mongon, prin. Fax 461-0182

River Vale, Bergen, Pop. 9,410
River Vale SD 1,400/K-8
609 Westwood Ave 07675 201-358-4000
Dr. Matthew Murphy, supt. Fax 358-8319
www.rivervaleschools.com/
Holdrum MS 500/6-8
393 Rivervale Rd 07675 201-358-4016
Jayellen Jenkins, prin. Fax 358-8427

Robbinsville, Mercer, Pop. 2,974
Robbinsville SD 2,700/PK-12
155 Robbinsville Edinburg 08691 609-632-0910
Steven Mayer, supt. Fax 371-7964
www.robbinsville.k12.nj.us
Pond Road MS 1,100/4-8
150 Pond Rd 08691 609-632-0940
Paul Gizzo, prin. Fax 918-9011
Robbinsville HS 800/9-12
155 Robbinsville Edinburg 08691 609-632-0950
Molly Avery, prin. Fax 371-7961

Rockaway, Morris, Pop. 6,360
Morris County Vocational SD
Supt. — See Denville
Academy for Math Science & Engineering Vo/Tech
520 W Main St 07866 973-664-2301
Scott Moffitt, prin.

Morris Hills Regional SD 2,800/9-12
48 Knoll Dr 07866 973-664-2291
James Jencarelli, supt. Fax 627-6588
mhrd.org
Morris Hills HS 1,100/9-12
520 W Main St 07866 973-664-2309
Joseph Cacciaguida, prin. Fax 983-7461
Morris Knolls HS 1,600/9-12
50 Knoll Dr 07866 973-664-2200
William Cleffi, prin. Fax 586-3550
Morris Hills Adult HS Adult
48 Knoll Dr 07866 973-664-2232
Scott Gambale, coord. Fax 627-6588

Rockaway Borough SD 700/PK-8
103 E Main St 07866 973-625-8600
Dr. Brian Purzak, supt. Fax 625-7355
www.rockboro.org/
Jefferson MS, 95 E Main St 07866 400/4-8
Dr. Brian Purzak, prin. 973-625-8603

Rockaway Township SD
Supt. — See Hibernia
Copeland MS 900/6-8
100 Lakeshore Dr 07866 973-627-2465
F. Scott Allshouse, prin. Fax 983-1843

Roselle, Union, Pop. 20,670
Roselle Borough SD 1,800/PK-12
710 Locust St 07203 908-298-2040
Dr. Kevin West, supt. Fax 298-3353
www.roselleschools.org
Clark HS 800/9-12
122 E 6th Ave 07203 908-298-2004
Rashon Mickens, prin. Fax 259-0782
Wilday JHS 200/7-8
400 Brooklawn Ave 07203 908-298-2066
Dr. Josue Falaise, prin. Fax 298-2068

Roselle Catholic HS 600/9-12
350 Raritan Rd 07203 908-245-2350
Dr. Robert Stickles, prin. Fax 241-3869

Roselle Park, Union, Pop. 13,111
Roselle Park SD 1,900/K-12
510 Chestnut St 07204 908-245-1197
Patrick Spagnoletti, supt. Fax 245-1226
www.rpsd.org/
Roselle Park HS 600/9-12
185 W Webster Ave 07204 908-241-4550
Sarah Costa, prin. Fax 245-6609
Roselle Park MS 500/6-8
57 W Grant Ave 07204 908-245-1634
Jeannine Grasso, prin. Fax 245-7491

Rumson, Monmouth, Pop. 7,054
Rumson Borough SD 1,000/K-8
60 Forrest Ave 07760 732-842-4747
Dr. Maryrose Caulfield-Sloan, supt. Fax 842-4877
www.rumsonschool.org/
Forrestdale MS 600/4-8
60 Forrest Ave 07760 732-842-0383
Jennifer Gibbons, prin. Fax 219-9458

Rumson-Fair Haven Regional HSD 1,000/9-12
74 Ridge Rd 07760 732-842-1597
Dr. Peter Righi, supt. Fax 842-3139
www.rumsonfairhaven.org
Rumson-Fair Haven HS 1,000/9-12
74 Ridge Rd 07760 732-842-1597
Tracy Handerhan, prin. Fax 741-1712

Runnemede, Camden, Pop. 8,357
Black Horse Pike Regional SD
Supt. — See Blackwood
Triton HS 1,500/9-12
250 Schubert Ave 08078 856-939-4500
Dr. Daniel Mackie, prin. Fax 939-4724

Runnemede Borough SD 800/PK-8
505 W 3rd Ave 08078 856-931-5365
Dr. Nancy Ward, supt. Fax 931-4446
www.runnemedeschools.org/
Volz MS, 505 W 3rd Ave 08078 500/PK-PK, 4-
Mark Iannucci, prin. 856-931-5353

Rutherford, Bergen, Pop. 17,647
Rutherford SD, 176 Park Ave 07070 2,400/K-12
Dr. Rosemary Jones, supt. 201-438-7675
www.rutherfordschools.org
Pierrepont S 500/4-8
70 E Pierrepont Ave 07070 201-438-7675
Joan Carrion, prin. Fax 842-0452
Rutherford HS 700/9-12
56 Elliott Pl 07070 201-438-7675
Jack Hurley, prin. Fax 438-7293
Union S 500/4-8
359 Union Ave 07070 201-438-7675
Kenneth Polakowski, prin. Fax 804-8248

St. Mary HS 300/9-12
64 Chestnut St 07070 201-933-5220
Roy Corso, prin. Fax 933-0834
Yeshivas Mesillah 6-8
185 Montross Ave 07070 201-372-0020

Saddle Brook, Bergen, Pop. 13,296
Saddle Brook Township SD 1,700/K-12
355 Mayhill St 07663 201-843-2880
Dr. Kathryn Fedina, supt. Fax 843-0216
www.saddlebrookschools.org/
Saddle Brook MSHS 800/7-12
355 Mayhill St Ste 1 07663 201-843-2880
Jim Sarto, prin. Fax 843-4305

Saddle River, Bergen, Pop. 3,086

Saddle River Day S 400/K-12
147 Chestnut Ridge Rd 07458 201-327-4050
Eileen Lambert, hdmstr. Fax 327-6161

Salem, Salem, Pop. 4,985
Salem CSD 1,200/PK-12
205 Walnut St 08079 856-935-3800
Dr. Amiot Michel, supt. Fax 935-6977
www.salemnj.org
Salem HS 400/9-12
219 Walnut St 08079 856-935-3900
Dr. Gregory Dunham, prin. Fax 935-3288
Salem MS 400/3-8
51 New Market St 08079 856-935-2700
John Mulhorn, prin. Fax 935-2284

Salem County Special Services SD
Supt. — See Woodstown
Alternative S Alt
118 Walnut St 08079 856-935-7552
Frank Maurer, prin. Fax 935-7618

Scotch Plains, Union, Pop. 21,160
Scotch Plains-Fanwood SD 5,400/PK-12
2280 Evergreen Ave 07076 908-232-6161
Dr. Margaret Hayes, supt. Fax 889-1769
www.spfk12.org
Park MS 900/5-8
580 Park Ave 07076 908-322-4445
Lisa Rebimbas, prin. Fax 561-5929
Scotch Plains-Fanwood HS 1,500/9-12
641 Westfield Rd 07076 908-889-8600
Dr. David Heisey, prin. Fax 889-8254
Terrill MS 800/5-8
1301 Terrill Rd 07076 908-322-5215
Dr. Kevin Holloway, prin. Fax 322-6813

Union Co. Educational Services Comm SD
Supt. — See Westfield
Hillcrest Academy North Campus 100/Alt
2630 Plainfield Ave 07076 908-233-9366
John Marquet, prin. Fax 301-9093

Union County Vocational-Technical SD
1776 Raritan Rd 07076 908-889-8288
Peter A. Capodice, supt. Fax 889-4336
www.ucvts.tec.nj.us
Academy for Allied Health Sciences Vo/Tech
1776 Raritan Rd 07076 908-889-8288
Dr. Scott Rubin, prin. Fax 889-4734
Academy for Information Technology Vo/Tech
1776 Raritan Rd 07076 908-889-8288
Gloria Griffith, prin. Fax 889-6831
Academy for Performing Arts Vo/Tech
1776 Raritan Rd 07076 908-889-8288
Dr. Scott Rubin, prin. Fax 889-1666
Union County Magnet HS Vo/Tech
1776 Raritan Rd 07076 908-889-8288
Gwendolyn Ryan, prin. Fax 889-3196
Union County Vo-Tech HS Vo/Tech
1776 Raritan Rd 07076 908-889-8288
Jeffrey Lerner, prin. Fax 889-4399

Union Catholic Regional HS 800/9-12
1600 Martine Ave 07076 908-889-1600
Sr. Percylee Hart, prin. Fax 889-7867

Seabrook, Cumberland, Pop. 1,405
Upper Deerfield Township SD 800/PK-8
1369 Highway 77 08302 856-455-2267
Dr. Peter Koza, supt. Fax 453-7077
www.udts.org
Woodruff MS 300/6-8
1385 Highway 77 08302 856-455-2267
Dr. Peter Koza, prin. Fax 453-7077

Secaucus, Hudson, Pop. 15,983
Secaucus SD 2,100/PK-12
PO Box 1496 07096 201-974-2004
Cynthia Randina, supt. Fax 974-1911
www.sboe.org
Secaucus HS 600/9-12
11 Millridge Rd 07094 201-974-2033
Dr. Robert Berckes, prin. Fax 974-0026
Secaucus MS 300/7-8
11 Millridge Rd 07094 201-974-2022
Robert Daniello, prin. Fax 974-2006

Sewell, Gloucester
Deptford Township SD
Supt. — See Deptford
Monongahela MS 600/7-8
890 Bankbridge Rd 08080 856-415-9540
Arthur Dietz, prin. Fax 464-9284

Gloucester County Vocational SD
1360 Tanyard Rd 08080 856-468-1445
Michael Dicken, supt. Fax 468-3397
www.gcit.org
Gloucester Co. Institute of Technology Vo/Tech
1360 Tanyard Rd 08080 856-468-1445
Dr. Gina Mateka, prin. Fax 468-1035
Adult Regional HS Adult
1360 Tanyard Rd 08080 856-468-1445
Dr. Gina Mateka, prin.

Washington Township SD 6,700/PK-12
206 E Holly Ave 08080 856-589-6644
Robert Goldschmidt, supt. Fax 582-1918
www.wtps.org
Bunker Hill MS 600/6-8
372 Pitman Downer Rd 08080 856-881-7007
Dr. Mark Ebner, prin. Fax 881-5414
Chestnut Ridge MS 600/6-8
641 Hurffville Crosskeys Rd 08080 856-582-3535
James Barnes, prin. Fax 589-0683
Orchard Valley MS 700/6-8
238 Pitman Downer Rd 08080 856-582-5353
Stevan Gregor, prin. Fax 589-0197
Washington Township HS 2,300/9-12
519 Hurffville Crosskeys Rd 08080 856-589-8500
Joseph Bollendorf, prin. Fax 218-0991

Gloucester County Christian S 400/PK-12
151 Golf Club Rd 08080 856-589-1665
Donald Netz, prin. Fax 582-4989
Gloucester County College Post-Sec.
1400 Tanyard Rd 08080 856-468-5000

Shamong Township, Burlington, Pop. 5,765
Lenape Regional HSD 7,000/9-12
93 Willow Grove Rd 08088 609-268-2000
Dr. Carol Birnbohm, supt. Fax 268-6642
www.lrhsd.org/
Other Schools – See Marlton, Medford, Tabernacle

Shamong Township SD 900/K-8
295 Indian Mills Rd 08088 609-268-0120
Dolores M. Szymanski Ed.D., supt. Fax 268-1229
www.ims.k12.nj.us
Indian Mills Memorial MS 400/5-8
295 Indian Mills Rd 08088 609-268-0440
Timothy Carroll, prin. Fax 268-1229

Short Hills, Essex, Pop. 12,919

Winston S 100/3-8
30 East Ln 07078 973-379-4114
Dr. Peter Lewis, hdmstr. Fax 379-3984

Sicklerville, Camden
Camden County Technical Schools
343 Berlin Cross Keys Rd 08081 856-767-7000
Timothy Bell, supt. Fax 767-3589
www.ccts.info
Camden County Technical S - Gloucester Vo/Tech
343 Berlin Cross Keys Rd 08081 856-767-7000
Dr. Teri Stallone, prin. Fax 767-3638
Other Schools – See Pennsauken

Gloucester Township SD
Supt. — See Blackwood
Mullen MS 1,100/6-8
1400 Sicklerville Rd 08081 856-875-8777
Timothy Trow, prin. Fax 875-0902

Technical Institute of Camden County Post-Sec.
343 Berlin Cross Keys Rd 08081 856-767-7000

Skillman, Somerset, Pop. 236
Montgomery Township SD 5,000/K-12
1014 Route 601 08558 609-466-7600
Nancy Gartenberg, supt. Fax 466-0944
www.mtsd.k12.nj.us
Montgomery HS 1,700/9-12
1016 Route 601 08558 609-466-7602
Paul Popadiuk, prin. Fax 466-0243
Montgomery Upper MS 900/7-8
375 Burnt Hill Rd 08558 609-466-7604
Cory Delgado, prin. Fax 874-7045

Somerdale, Camden, Pop. 5,010
Sterling HSD 900/9-12
801 W Preston Ave Ste B 08083 856-784-1287
Dr. Jack McCulley, supt. Fax 435-1530
www.sterling.k12.nj.us
Sterling HS 900/9-12
501 S Warwick Rd 08083 856-784-1333
Mark Napoleon, prin. Fax 784-7661

Somerset, Somerset, Pop. 21,468
Franklin Township SD 7,600/PK-12
1755 Amwell Rd 08873 732-873-2400
Edward Seto, supt.
www.franklinboe.org
Franklin HS 2,000/9-12
500 Elizabeth Ave 08873 732-302-4200
James Bevere, prin. Fax 302-4212
Franklin MS 1,000/7-8
415 Francis St 08873 732-249-6410
RaShawn Adams, prin. Fax 246-0770

Rutgers Preparatory S 700/PK-12
1345 Easton Ave 08873 732-545-5600
Dr. Steven Loy, hdmstr. Fax 214-1819

Somers Point, Atlantic, Pop. 10,546

Shore Memorial Hospital Post-Sec.
Shore Rd 08244 609-653-3545

Somerville, Somerset, Pop. 11,787
Somerville Borough SD 2,300/K-12
51 W Cliff St 08876 908-218-4100
Dr. Timothy Purnell, supt. Fax 526-9668
www.somervillenjk12.org
Somerville HS 1,300/9-12
222 Davenport St 08876 908-218-4108
Gerard Foley, prin. Fax 707-0971
Somerville MS 300/6-8
51 W Cliff St 08876 908-218-4107
Georgette Boulegeris, prin. Fax 575-9526

Immaculata HS 800/9-12
240 Mountain Ave 08876 908-722-0200
Mary Smith, prin. Fax 218-7765

South Amboy, Middlesex, Pop. 8,493
Sayreville SD 5,700/K-12
150 Lincoln St 08879 732-525-5200
Dr. Frank Alfano, supt. Fax 727-5769
www.sayrevillek12.net/
Other Schools – See Parlin

South Amboy SD 1,000/PK-12
240 John St 08879 732-525-2100
Robert Sheedy, supt. Fax 727-0730
www.saboe.k12.nj.us/
South Amboy MSHS 400/7-12
200 Gvrnr Hrold G Hffmn Plz 08879 732-316-7669
Dr. Patrick McCabe, prin. Fax 721-0054

Cardinal McCarrick HS 300/9-12
310 Augusta St 08879 732-721-0748
Dr. Karen Juliano, prin. Fax 727-7018

Southampton, Burlington
Southampton Township SD 800/K-8
177 Main St 08088 609-859-2256
Michael Harris, supt. Fax 859-1542
www.southampton.k12.nj.us
Southampton Township MS 3 300/6-8
100 Warrior Way 08088 609-859-2256
Jennifer Horner, prin. Fax 801-0754

South Orange, Essex, Pop. 16,390
South Orange-Maplewood SD
Supt. — See Maplewood
South Orange MS 700/6-8
70 N Ridgewood Rd 07079 973-378-2772
Joseph Uglialoro, prin. Fax 378-2775

Marylawn of the Oranges Academy 200/9-12
445 Scotland Rd 07079 973-762-9222
Christine Lopez, prin. Fax 378-7975
Seton Hall University Post-Sec.
400 S Orange Ave 07079 973-761-9000

South Plainfield, Middlesex, Pop. 22,711
South Plainfield SD 3,600/K-12
125 Jackson Ave 07080 908-754-4620
Stepehn Genco Ed.D., supt. Fax 822-2453
www.spboe.org
South Plainfield HS 1,200/9-12
200 Lake St 07080 908-754-4620
James Pedersen, prin. Fax 756-7659
South Plainfield MS 600/7-8
2201 Plainfield Ave 07080 908-754-4620
Kevin Hajduk, admin. Fax 791-1152
Adult HS Adult
125 Jackson Ave 07080 908-754-4620
Nicole Pormilli, admin. Fax 561-2859

Avtech Institute of Technology Post-Sec.
50 Cragwood Rd Ste 350 07080 908-222-2833
Central Career School Post-Sec.
126 Corporate Blvd 07080 908-412-8600
Everest Institute Post-Sec.
5000 Hadley Rd Ste 100 07080 908-222-9300
Lincoln Technical Institute Post-Sec.
901 Hadley Rd 07080 800-305-3487

South River, Middlesex, Pop. 15,456
South River SD 2,300/PK-12
15 Montgomery St 08882 732-613-4000
Michael Pfister, supt. Fax 613-4756
www.srivernj.org
South River HS 700/9-12
11 Montgomery St 08882 732-613-4014
Kevin Kidney, prin. Fax 613-4044
South River MS 500/6-8
3 Montgomery St 08882 732-613-4073
Lisa Wargo, prin. Fax 698-9305

Sparta, Sussex, Pop. 15,157
Sparta Township SD 3,400/PK-12
18 Mohawk Ave 07871 973-729-7886
Dennis Tobin, supt. Fax 729-0576
www.sparta.org
Sparta HS 1,200/9-12
70 W Mountain Rd 07871 973-729-6191
Daniel Johnson Ed.D., prin. Fax 729-3258

Sparta MS 1,000/6-8
350 Main St 07871 973-729-3151
Douglas Layman, prin. Fax 729-0573

Sussex County Technical SD
105 N Church Rd 07871 973-383-6700
Gus Modla, supt. Fax 383-4272
www.sussex.tec.nj.us
Sussex County Technical S Vo/Tech
105 N Church Rd 07871 973-383-6700
Gus Modla, prin. Fax 383-4272

Pope John XXIII HS 900/9-12
28 Andover Rd 07871 973-729-6125
Gloria Shope, prin. Fax 729-3487
Veritas Christian Academy 50/9-12
385 Houses Corner Rd 07871 973-579-6333
Dr. Eric Mindrebo, admin. Fax 579-6293

Spotswood, Middlesex, Pop. 8,141
Spotswood SD 1,800/PK-12
105 Summerhill Rd 08884 732-723-2236
Anthony Vaz, supt. Fax 251-7666
www.spotswood.k12.nj.us
Spotswood HS 800/9-12
105 Summerhill Rd 08884 732-723-2202
Thomas Calder, prin. Fax 251-7666
Spotswood Memorial MS 300/6-8
115 Summerhill Rd 08884 732-723-2227
Pamela Slevin, prin. Fax 251-7666

Springfield, Union, Pop. 13,420
Springfield SD 2,000/PK-12
PO Box 210 07081 973-376-1025
Michael Davino, supt. Fax 912-9229
www.springfieldschools.com
Dayton HS 500/9-12
139 Mountain Ave 07081 973-376-1025
Elizabeth Cresci, prin. Fax 376-4570
Gaudineer MS 400/6-8
75 S Springfield Ave 07081 973-376-1025
Timothy Kielty, prin. Fax 376-3259

Stanhope, Sussex, Pop. 3,550
Byram Township SD 1,000/K-8
12 Mansfield Dr 07874 973-347-1019
Dr. Bryan Hensz, supt. Fax 347-9001
www.byramschools.org
Byram IS 500/5-8
12 Mansfield Dr 07874 973-347-1019
Thomas Barnard, prin. Fax 347-9001

Lenape Valley Regional HSD 800/9-12
PO Box 578 07874 973-347-7600
Paul DiRupo, admin. Fax 691-0164
www.lvhs.org
Lenape Valley Regional HS 800/9-12
PO Box 578 07874 973-347-7600
Edward Braun, prin. Fax 347-2536

Stewartsville, Warren, Pop. 346
Greenwich Township SD 900/PK-8
101 Wyndham Farm Blvd 08886 908-859-2022
Maria Eppolite, supt. Fax 859-4522
www.gtsd.net/pub/
Stewartsville MS 300/6-8
101 Wyndham Farm Blvd 08886 908-859-2023
Stephanie Snyder, prin. Fax 859-1809

Stirling, Morris
Long Hill Township SD
Supt. — See Gillette
Central MS 300/6-8
90 Central Ave 07980 908-647-2311
George Villar, prin. Fax 647-0610

Stratford, Camden, Pop. 6,903
Stratford Borough SD 800/PK-8
111 Warwick Rd 08084 856-783-2555
Dr. Albert Brown, supt. Fax 309-0304
www.stratford.k12.nj.us
Yellin MS 500/4-8
111 Warwick Rd 08084 856-783-1094
Thomas Attanasi, prin. Fax 309-0304

Stratford Classical Christian Academy 100/K-12
710 W Laurel Rd 08084 856-882-7222
Jim Luchs, supt. Fax 882-7226

Succasunna, Morris, Pop. 9,054
Roxbury Township SD 4,100/PK-12
42 N Hillside Ave 07876 973-584-6099
Dr. Patrick Tierney, supt. Fax 252-1434
www.roxbury.org
Eisenhower MS 700/7-8
47 Eyland Ave 07876 973-584-2973
Scott Shaw, prin. Fax 584-4529
Roxbury HS 1,500/9-12
1 Bryant Dr 07876 973-584-1200
Jeffrey Swanson, prin. Fax 584-7584

American Christian S 200/PK-12
126 S Hillside Ave 07876 973-584-6616
Kristen Brennan, hdmstr. Fax 584-0686

Summit, Union, Pop. 21,055
Summit CSD 3,900/PK-12
14 Beekman Ter 07901 908-918-2100
Dr. Nathan Parker, supt. Fax 273-3656
www.summit.k12.nj.us
Summit HS 1,000/9-12
125 Kent Place Blvd 07901 908-273-1494
Paul Sears, prin. Fax 273-2832
Summit MS 1,000/6-8
272 Morris Ave 07901 908-273-1190
Matt Block, prin. Fax 273-8320

Kent Place S 600/PK-12
42 Norwood Ave 07901 908-273-0900
Susan Bosland, hdmstr. Fax 273-9390
Oak Knoll S of the Holy Child 600/K-12
44 Blackburn Rd 07901 908-522-8100
Timothy Saburn, head sch Fax 277-1838

Oratory Preparatory S 300/7-12
1 Beverly Rd 07901 908-273-1084
Robert Costello, head sch Fax 273-5505

Sussex, Sussex, Pop. 2,089
High Point Regional SD 1,100/9-12
299 Pidgeon Hill Rd 07461 973-875-3101
Terrance Brennan Ed.D., supt. Fax 875-0904
www.hpregional.org
High Point Regional HS 1,100/9-12
299 Pidgeon Hill Rd 07461 973-875-3101
Thomas Costello, prin. Fax 875-2756

Sussex-Wantage Regional SD 1,200/PK-8
27 Bank St 07461 973-875-3175
Jeanne Apryasz, supt. Fax 875-7175
www.swregional.org
Sussex MS 400/6-8
10 Loomis Ave 07461 973-875-4138
Kevin Lipton, prin. Fax 875-6790

Tabernacle, Burlington
Lenape Regional HSD
Supt. — See Shamong Township
Seneca HS 1,300/9-12
110 Carranza Rd 08088 609-268-4600
Jeffrey Spector, prin. Fax 268-4635

Tabernacle Township SD 800/K-8
132 New Rd 08088 609-268-0153
George Rafferty, supt. Fax 268-1006
www.tabernacle.k12.nj.us
Olson MS 400/5-8
132 New Rd 08088 609-268-0153
Susan Grosser, prin. Fax 268-1006

Teaneck, Bergen, Pop. 39,500
Teaneck SD 3,800/PK-12
1 Merrison St 07666 201-833-5510
Barbara Pinsak, supt. Fax 837-9468
www.teaneckschools.org/
Franklin MS 500/5-8
1315 Taft Rd 07666 201-833-5450
Dr. Lennox Small, prin. Fax 862-2465
Jefferson MS 600/5-8
655 Teaneck Rd 07666 201-833-5471
Angela Davis, prin. Fax 833-3983
Teaneck HS 1,300/9-12
100 Elizabeth Ave 07666 201-833-5400
Dennis Heck, prin. Fax 833-5403

Fairleigh Dickinson University Post-Sec.
1000 River Rd 07666 201-692-2000
Holy Name Hospital School of Nursing Post-Sec.
690 Teaneck Rd 07666 201-833-3005
Ma'ayanot Yeshiva HS for Girls 300/9-12
1650 Palisade Ave 07666 201-833-4307
Rachel Feldman, admin. Fax 833-0816
Torah Academy of Bergen County 300/9-12
1600 Queen Anne Rd 07666 201-837-7696
Arthur Poleyeff, prin. Fax 837-9027

Tenafly, Bergen, Pop. 14,170
Tenafly SD 3,600/K-12
500 Tenafly Rd 07670 201-816-4500
Lynn Trager, supt. Fax 816-4521
www.tenafly.k12.nj.us
Tenafly HS 1,200/9-12
19 Columbus Dr 07670 201-816-6600
Dr. Dora Kontogiannis, prin. Fax 871-9184
Tenafly MS 800/6-8
10 Sunset Ln 07670 201-816-4900
Dr. Ann Powell, prin. Fax 569-0327

Teterboro, Bergen, Pop. 61
Bergen County Vocational SD
Supt. — See Paramus
Bergen County Technical HS - Teterboro Vo/Tech
504 State Rt 46 07608 201-343-6000
David Tankard, prin. Fax 996-6925

Teterboro School of Aeronautics Post-Sec.
80 Moonachie Ave 07608 201-288-6300

Tinton Falls, Monmouth, Pop. 17,575
Monmouth County Vocational SD
Supt. — See Freehold
KIVA HS Vo/Tech
537 Tinton Ave 07724 732-542-5455
Denise Kebeck, prin. Fax 544-8018

Monmouth Regional HSD 1,100/9-12
1 Norman J Field Way 07724 732-542-1170
Charles Ford, supt. Fax 542-5815
www.monmouthregional.net
Monmouth Regional HS 1,100/9-12
1 Norman J Field Way 07724 732-542-1170
Andrew Teeple, prin. Fax 542-5815

Monmouth-Ocean Ed. Serv. Comm. SD 50/6-12
900 Hope Rd, 732-695-7800
Timothy Nogueira, supt.
www.moesc.org/
Regional Alternative S "Choices" 50/Alt
100 Tornillo Way Ste 1, 732-389-5555
Linda Phillips, prin. Fax 542-0302

Tinton Falls SD 1,500/K-8
658 Tinton Ave 07724 732-460-2400
John Russo, supt. Fax 542-1158
www.tfs.k12.nj.us
Tinton Falls MS 500/6-8
674 Tinton Ave 07724 732-542-0775
Linda Balogh, prin. Fax 542-8723

Ranney S 800/PK-12
235 Hope Rd 07724 732-542-4777
Lawrence Sykoff Ed.D., hdmstr. Fax 544-1629

Toms River, Ocean, Pop. 87,576
Ocean County Vocational SD
137 Bey Lea Rd 08753 732-240-6414
William Hoey, supt. Fax 505-8929
www.ocvts.org
Ocean County Voc-Tech S - Toms River Vo/Tech
1299 Old Freehold Rd 08753 732-473-3100
Jo-Ann Price, prin. Fax 349-9788
Other Schools – See Brick, Jackson, Lakehurst, Manahawkin, Waretown

Toms River Regional SD 15,900/K-12
1144 Hooper Ave 08753 732-505-5510
Frank Roselli, supt. Fax 505-9330
www.trschools.com
Toms River HS - East 1,600/9-12
1225 Raider Way 08753 732-505-5666
Anne Baldi, prin. Fax 270-0909
Toms River HS - North 2,200/9-12
1245 Old Freehold Rd 08753 732-505-5702
Edward Keller, prin. Fax 341-6249
Toms River HS - South 1,400/9-12
55 Hyers St 08753 732-505-5738
Leonard Stanziano, prin. Fax 341-1321
Toms River IS East 1,400/6-8
1519 Hooper Ave 08753 732-505-5777
Bryan Madigan, prin. Fax 286-1290
Toms River IS North 1,300/6-8
150 Intermediate North Way 08753 732-505-5800
Lynn Fronzak, prin. Fax 286-1291
Other Schools – See Beachwood

Monsignor Donovan HS 1,000/9-12
711 Hooper Ave 08753 732-349-8801
Dr. Edward Gere, prin. Fax 349-8956
Ocean County College Post-Sec.
PO Box 2001 08754 732-255-0400
Performance Training Institute Post-Sec.
1012 Cox Cro Rd 08755 732-505-9119

Totowa, Passaic, Pop. 10,662
Totowa SD 1,000/PK-8
10 Crews St 07512 973-956-0010
Dr. Vincent Varcadipane, supt. Fax 956-9859
www.totowa.k12.nj.us
Washington Park MS 700/3-8
10 Crews St 07512 973-956-0010
John Vanderberg, prin. Fax 389-2270

Trenton, Mercer, Pop. 83,491
Mercer County Technical SD
1085 Old Trenton Rd 08690 609-586-2129
Dr. Kimberly J. Schneider, supt. Fax 586-8966
www.mcts.edu
Assunpink Center Vo/Tech
1085 Old Trenton Rd 08690 609-586-5144
S. Lucille Jones, prin. Fax 586-1709
Career Prep Vo/Tech
1200 Old Trenton Rd 08690 609-586-3550
Dana Hico DoPugh, admin. Fax 586-4985
Health Careers Center Vo/Tech
1070 Klockner Rd 08619 609-587-7640
Sharon Nemeth, prin. Fax 587-3304
Adult Evening S Adult
1085 Old Trenton Rd 08690 609-586-5146
Peter Frascella, prin. Fax 586-1709
Other Schools – See Ewing, Pennington

Trenton SD 8,300/PK-12
108 N Clinton Ave 08609 609-656-4900
Francisco Duran, supt. Fax 989-2682
www.trenton.k12.nj.us
Dunn MS 400/6-8
401 Dayton St 08611 609-656-4700
Addie Daniels-Lane, prin. Fax 989-1478
Munoz-Rivera MS Alt
400 N Montgomery St 08618 609-656-4840
William Tracy, prin.
Trenton Central HS 1,400/9-12
400 Chambers St 08609 609-278-7260
Marc Maurice, prin. Fax 989-2940
Trenton Central HS - West 400/9-12
1001 W State St 08618 609-656-4770
Brenda Torrence, prin. Fax 989-2925
Daylight/Twilight HS Adult
135 E Hanover St 08608 609-656-4850
Hope Grant, prin. Fax 656-6062

Harris School of Business Post-Sec.
3620 Quakerbridge Rd 08619 609-586-9104
Helene Fuld Medical Center Post-Sec.
750 Brunswick Ave 08638 609-394-3174
Marie Katzenbach School for the Deaf Post-Sec.
PO Box 535 08625 609-530-3100
Mercer Medical Center Post-Sec.
PO Box 1658 08607 609-394-4050
St. Francis Medical Center Post-Sec.
601 Hamilton Ave 08629 609-599-5000
Thomas Edison State College Post-Sec.
101 W State St 08608 609-984-1100

Union, Union, Pop. 55,000
Township of Union SD 7,400/PK-12
2369 Morris Ave 07083 908-851-3000
Dr. Patrick Martin, supt. Fax 851-9688
www.twpunionschools.org
Burnet MS 1,100/6-8
1000 Caldwell Ave 07083 908-851-6490
Raymond Salvatore, prin. Fax 687-2645
Kawameeh MS 700/6-8
490 David Ter 07083 908-851-6570
Jason Malanda, prin. Fax 687-5741
Union HS 2,400/9-12
2350 N 3rd St 07083 908-851-6500
Edward Gibbons, prin. Fax 687-5204

European Academy of Cosmetology Post-Sec.
1126 Morris Ave 07083 908-686-4422
Healthcare Training Institute Post-Sec.
1969 Morris Ave 07083 908-851-7711
Kean University Post-Sec.
1000 Morris Ave 07083 908-737-5326

Lincoln Technical Institute — Post-Sec.
2299 Vauxhall Rd 07083 — 908-964-7800

Union City, Hudson, Pop. 65,896
Union City SD — 8,100/PK-12
3912 32nd St 07087 — 201-348-5851
Stanley Sanger, supt. — Fax 330-1736
www.union-city.k12.nj.us/
Emerson MS — 1,300/6-8
318 18th St 07087 — 201-348-5900
Michael Celebrano, prin. — Fax 864-2262
Marti Freshman Academy — 500/9-9
1800 Summit Ave 07087 — 201-348-5400
Joseph Polinik, prin. — Fax 348-5405
Union City HS — 1,000/10-12
2500 Kennedy Blvd 07087 — 201-330-8678
John Bennetti, prin. — Fax 330-8736
Union Hill MS — 600/7-8
3808 Hudson Ave 07087 — 201-348-5808
Victoria Dickson, prin. — Fax 867-4205
Adult Learning Center — Adult
400 38th St 07087 — 201-348-5868
Oscar Cordero, prin. — Fax 348-5659

Mesivta Sanz Hudson County S — 300/K-12
3400 New York Ave 07087 — 201-867-8690
Miftaahul Uloom Academy — 200/PK-12
501 15th St 07087 — 201-223-9920
Syed Kamram Qadri, prin. — Fax 223-9921
Rising Star Academy — 200/PK-11
4613 Cottage Pl 07087 — 201-758-5590
Dr. Hala Shehadeh, prin. — Fax 758-5589

Upper Montclair, Essex, Pop. 11,116
Montclair SD
Supt. — See Montclair
Mt. Hebron MS — 600/6-8
173 Bellevue Ave 07043 — 973-509-4220
Dr. Jill Sack, prin. — Fax 509-4218

Upper Saddle River, Bergen, Pop. 8,104
Upper Saddle River SD — 1,400/PK-8
395 W Saddle River Rd 07458 — 201-961-6500
Dr. Monica Browne, supt. — Fax 934-4923
www.usrschoolsk8.com
Cavallini MS — 500/6-8
392 W Saddle River Rd 07458 — 201-961-6400
James McCusker, prin. — Fax 236-9662

Ventnor City, Atlantic, Pop. 10,474
Ventnor City SD — 1,000/PK-8
400 N Lafayette Ave 08406 — 609-487-7900
Robert Baker, supt. — Fax 822-0150
www.veccnj.org/
Ventnor MS — 400/5-8
400 N Lafayette Ave 08406 — 609-487-7900
Robert Baker, prin. — Fax 823-4036

Vernon, Sussex
Vernon Township SD — 2,800/PK-12
PO Box 99 07462 — 973-764-2900
Dr. John Alfieri, supt. — Fax 764-0033
www.vtsd.com
Glen Meadow MS — 300/7-8
PO Box 516 07462 — 973-764-8981
Rosemary Gebhardt, prin. — Fax 764-3295
Vernon Township HS — 1,100/9-12
PO Box 800 07462 — 973-764-2960
Timothy Dunnigan, prin. — Fax 764-2961

Verona, Essex, Pop. 13,597
Verona SD — 2,100/K-12
121 Fairview Ave 07044 — 973-571-2029
Steven Forte, supt. — Fax 571-6779
www.veronaschools.org
Verona HS — 600/9-12
151 Fairview Ave 07044 — 973-571-6750
Glenn Cesa, prin. — Fax 571-6765
Whitehorne MS — 600/5-8
600 Bloomfield Ave 07044 — 973-571-6751
Yvette McNeal, prin. — Fax 571-6767

Vineland, Cumberland, Pop. 59,740
Vineland CSD — 9,100/PK-12
625 E Plum St 08360 — 856-794-6700
Dr. Mary Gruccio, supt. — Fax 794-9464
www.vineland.org/index.php
Cunningham Alternative S — 100/Alt
315 S East Ave 08360 — 856-794-6937
Fax 507-8744
Landis MS — 500/6-8
61 W Landis Ave 08360 — 856-794-6925
Hope Johnson, prin. — Fax 507-8763
Rossi MS — 500/6-8
2572 Palermo Ave 08361 — 856-794-6961
Tammy Monahan, prin. — Fax 507-8786
Veterans Memorial MS — 500/6-8
424 S Main Rd 08360 — 856-794-6918
Joseph Camardo, prin. — Fax 507-8759
Vineland HS North — 1,400/9-10
3010 E Chestnut Ave 08361 — 856-794-6800
Mario Olsen, prin. — Fax 507-8781
Vineland HS South — 1,100/11-12
2880 E Chestnut Ave 08361 — 856-794-6800
Dr. Thomas McCann, prin. — Fax 507-8751
Wallace MS — 400/6-8
688 N Mill Rd 08360 — 856-362-8887
Dr. Juanita Davis, prin. — Fax 362-8980

Achieve Test Prep — Post-Sec.
313 W Landis Ave 08360 — 856-457-3881
Cumberland Christian S — 300/PK-12
1100 W Sherman Ave 08360 — 856-696-1600
David Hobbs, hdmstr. — Fax 696-0631
Cumberland County College — Post-Sec.
PO Box 1500 08362 — 856-691-8600
Sacred Heart HS — 400/9-12
15 N East Ave 08360 — 856-691-4491
Dr. Albert Monillas, prin. — Fax 563-1644

Voorhees, Camden, Pop. 946
Eastern Camden County Regional HSD — 1,000/9-12
PO Box 2500 08043 — 856-784-4441
Dr. Harold Melleby, supt. — Fax 627-7894
www.eastern.k12.nj.us
Eastern HS — 1,000/9-12
PO Box 2500 08043 — 856-784-4441
Robert Tull, prin. — Fax 784-1322

Voorhees Township SD — 3,100/PK-8
329 Route 73 08043 — 856-751-8446
Raymond Brosel, supt. — Fax 751-3666
www.voorhees.k12.nj.us/
Voorhees MS — 1,100/6-8
1000 Holly Oak Dr 08043 — 856-795-2025
Diane Young, prin. — Fax 795-4611

Harris School of Business — Post-Sec.
401 White Horse Rd Ste 200 08043 — 856-309-3701
Rizzieri Aveda School — Post-Sec.
8200 Town Center Blvd 08043 — 856-988-8600

Waldwick, Bergen, Pop. 9,513
Waldwick SD — 1,500/PK-12
155 Summit Ave 07463 — 201-445-3131
Dr. Patricia M. Raupers, supt. — Fax 445-0584
www.waldwick.k12.nj.us/
Waldwick HS — 400/9-12
155 Wyckoff Ave 07463 — 201-652-9000
Kevin Carroll, prin. — Fax 652-5053
Waldwick MS — 400/6-8
155 Wyckoff Ave 07463 — 201-652-9000
Michael J. Meyers, prin. — Fax 652-5053

Waldwick SDA S — 100/PK-12
70 Wyckoff Ave 07463 — 201-652-6078
Ruth Nino, prin. — Fax 652-4652

Wall, Monmouth, Pop. 5,201
Monmouth County Vocational SD
Supt. — See Freehold
Communications HS of Monmouth Co. — Vo/Tech
1740 New Bedford Rd 07719 — 732-681-1010
James Gleason, prin. — Fax 681-6780

Wall Township SD — 4,000/PK-12
PO Box 1199 07719 — 732-556-2000
Stephanie Bilenker, supt. — Fax 556-2101
www.wall.k12.nj.us
Wall HS — 1,300/9-12
PO Box 1199 07719 — 732-556-2047
Rosaleen Sirchio, prin. — Fax 556-2104
Wall IS — 1,000/6-8
PO Box 1199 07719 — 732-556-2500
Gary Azzolini, prin. — Fax 556-2535

Cortiva Institute - Wall — Post-Sec.
1985 State Route 34 07719 — 732-282-0100

Wallington, Bergen, Pop. 11,200
Wallington SD — 1,200/K-12
32 Pine St 07057 — 973-777-4421
Albert Pecora, supt. — Fax 614-9391
www.wboe.org
Wallington JSHS — 500/7-12
234 Main Ave 07057 — 973-777-0808
Dr. Joseph Pompeo, prin. — Fax 777-1434

Wanaque, Passaic, Pop. 10,935
Lakeland Regional HSD — 1,100/9-12
205 Conklintown Rd 07465 — 973-835-1900
Anthony Riscica, supt. — Fax 835-2834
www.lakeland.k12.nj.us
Lakeland Regional HS — 1,100/9-12
205 Conklintown Rd 07465 — 973-835-1900
Anthony Riscica, prin. — Fax 835-6369

Waretown, Ocean, Pop. 1,552
Ocean County Vocational SD
Supt. — See Toms River
Ocean County Voc-Tech S - Waretown — Vo/Tech
423 Wells Mill Rd 08758 — 609-286-5660
Thomas McInerney, prin. — Fax 693-1514

Warren, Somerset
Warren Township SD — 2,100/K-8
213 Mount Horeb Rd 07059 — 732-753-5300
Dr. Tami Crader, supt. — Fax 560-8801
www.warrentboe.org
Warren MS — 800/6-8
100 Old Stirling Rd 07059 — 908-753-5300
Robert Comba, prin. — Fax 753-4789

Watchung Hills Regional SD — 2,100/9-12
108 Stirling Rd 07059 — 908-647-4800
Dr. Frances Strumsland, supt. — Fax 647-4852
www.whrhs.org
Watchung Hills Regional HS — 2,100/9-12
108 Stirling Rd 07059 — 908-647-4800
Dr. George Alexis, prin. — Fax 647-4852

Washington, Warren, Pop. 6,336
Warren County Vocational SD
1500 State Route 57 W 07882 — 908-689-0122
Robert Glowacky, admin. — Fax 689-7699
www.wctech.org
Warren County Vo-Tech Institute — Vo/Tech
1500 State Route 57 W 07882 — 908-689-0122
Robert Glowacky, dir. — Fax 689-7699

Warren Hills Regional HSD — 1,900/7-12
89 Bowerstown Rd 07882 — 908-689-3143
Dr. Thomas Altonjy, supt. — Fax 689-4814
www.warrenhills.org
Warren Hills Regional HS — 1,200/9-12
41 Jackson Valley Rd 07882 — 908-689-3050
Earl Clymer, prin. — Fax 689-9640
Warren Hills Regional MS — 600/7-8
64 Carlton Ave 07882 — 908-689-0750
Patricia Hetrick, prin. — Fax 689-3663

Warren County Community College — Post-Sec.
475 State Route 57 W 07882 — 908-835-9222

Washington Township, Bergen, Pop. 9,245
Westwood Regional SD — 2,100/K-12
701 Ridgewood Rd 07676 — 201-664-0880
Geoffrey Zoeller Ed.D., supt. — Fax 664-7642
www.wwrsd.org/
Westwood Regional JSHS — 1,000/8-12
701 Ridgewood Rd 07676 — 201-664-0880
Dr. Matthew Certo, prin. — Fax 722-1542

Immaculate Heart Academy — 800/9-12
500 Van Emburgh Ave 07676 — 201-445-6800
Patricia Molloy, prin. — Fax 445-7416

Watchung, Somerset, Pop. 5,662
Watchung Borough SD — 700/PK-8
1 Dr Parenty Way 07069 — 908-755-8121
Dr. Barbara Resko, supt. — Fax 755-6946
www.watchungschools.com
Valley View MS — 300/5-8
50 Valleyview Rd 07069 — 908-755-4422
Mary Nunn, prin. — Fax 755-4035

Mt. St. Mary Academy — 400/9-12
1645 US Highway 22 07069 — 908-757-0108
Sr. Lisa Gambacorto, dir. — Fax 756-5751

Wayne, Passaic, Pop. 55,000
Passaic Co. Education Services Comm. — 100/7-12
45 Reinhardt Rd 07470 — 973-614-8585
Diana Lobosco, supt. — Fax 614-1334
www.pcesc.org
Preakness Academy — Alt
1006 Hamburg Tpke 07470 — 973-614-8585
Irene LeFebvre Ed.D., admin. — Fax 614-1334
Other Schools – See Passaic

Passaic County Technical Institute
45 Reinhardt Rd 07470 — 973-790-6000
Diana Lobosco, supt.
www.pcti.tec.nj.us
Passaic County Technical Institute — Vo/Tech
45 Reinhardt Rd 07470 — 973-389-4259
Dr. Michael Parent, prin. — Fax 389-2049
Passaic County Adult HS — Adult
45 Reinhardt Rd 07470 — 973-389-4101
John DePalma, admin.

Wayne Township SD — 8,400/K-12
50 Nellis Dr 07470 — 973-633-3000
Dr. Raymond Gonzalez, supt. — Fax 628-8058
www.wayneschools.com
Schuyler-Colfax MS — 800/6-8
1500 Hamburg Tpke 07470 — 973-633-3130
Frank Markowick, prin. — Fax 633-3195
Washington MS — 600/6-8
68 Lenox Rd 07470 — 973-633-3140
Jack Leonard, prin. — Fax 633-7590
Wayne Hills HS — 1,300/9-12
272 Berdan Ave 07470 — 973-317-2000
Maureen Weir, prin. — Fax 633-2589
Wayne MS — 700/6-8
201 Garside Ave 07470 — 973-389-2120
Michael Ben-David, prin. — Fax 389-2130
Wayne Valley HS — 1,500/9-12
551 Valley Rd 07470 — 973-633-3067
Robert Reis, prin. — Fax 633-3082

Achieve Test Prep — Post-Sec.
40 Galesi Dr 07470 — 973-321-3217
De Paul Catholic HS — 900/9-12
1512 Alps Rd 07470 — 973-694-3702
Anthony Sciaino, prin. — Fax 633-5381
Fortis Institute — Post-Sec.
201 Willowbrook Blvd 07470 — 973-837-1818
William Paterson University — Post-Sec.
300 Pompton Rd 07470 — 973-720-2000

Weehawken, Hudson, Pop. 12,385
Weehawken Township SD — 1,200/PK-12
53 Liberty Pl 07086 — 201-422-6120
Kevin McLellan, supt.
www.weehawken.k12.nj.us
Weehawken JSHS — 500/7-12
53 Liberty Pl 07086 — 201-422-6130
Dr. Peter Olivieri, prin.

Westampton, Burlington, Pop. 60,004
Westampton Township SD — 800/PK-8
700 Rancocas Rd 08060 — 609-267-2053
Virginia Grossman, supt. — Fax 267-2760
www.westamptonschools.org
Westampton MS — 300/PK-PK, 5-
700 Rancocas Rd 08060 — 609-267-2722
Matthew Andris, prin. — Fax 702-9017

West Berlin, Camden, Pop. 3,000
Berlin Township SD — 600/PK-8
225 Grove Ave 08091 — 856-767-9480
Dr. Leonard Fitts, supt. — Fax 767-8235
www.btwpschools.org
Eisenhower MS — 300/4-8
235 Grove Ave 08091 — 856-767-0203
Leslie Koller, prin. — Fax 767-7992

West Caldwell, Essex, Pop. 10,422
Caldwell-West Caldwell SD — 2,500/K-12
104 Gray St 07006 — 973-228-6979
James Heinegg, supt. — Fax 228-8716
www.cwcboe.org/
Caldwell HS — 800/9-12
265 Westville Ave 07006 — 973-228-6981
Kevin Barnes, prin. — Fax 228-1116
Other Schools – See Caldwell

Essex County Vocational Technical SD
Supt. — See Newark
Essex Co. Vocational Tech - W Caldwell — Vo/Tech
620 Passaic Ave 07006 — 973-412-2205
Chetram Singh, prin. — Fax 412-2090

Essex County College — Post-Sec.
730 Bloomfield Ave 07006 — 973-877-6590

West Deptford, Gloucester, Pop. 19,380
West Deptford Township SD 2,900/PK-12
675 Grove Rd 08066 856-848-4300
Kevin Kitchenman, supt. Fax 845-5743
www.wdeptford.k12.nj.us/
West Deptford HS 900/9-12
1600 Crown Point Rd, 856-848-6110
Dr. Brian Gismondi, prin. Fax 845-5774
West Deptford MS 1,000/5-8
675 Grove Rd 08066 856-848-1200
Michael Fanelli, prin. Fax 848-2325

Westfield, Union, Pop. 29,789
Union Co. Educational Services Comm SD 100/9-12
45 Cardinal Dr 07090 908-233-9317
William Presutti, supt. Fax 233-7432
www.ucesc.org/
Hillcrest Academy South Campus 100/Alt
1571 Lamberts Mill Rd 07090 908-654-8558
Jason Balsamello, prin. Fax 233-2954
Other Schools – See Scotch Plains

Westfield SD 6,300/PK-12
302 Elm St 07090 908-789-4400
Dr. Margaret Dolan, supt. Fax 789-4192
www.westfieldnjk12.org
Edison IS 800/6-8
800 Rahway Ave 07090 908-789-4470
Matthew Bolton, prin. Fax 789-1506
Roosevelt IS 700/6-8
301 Clark St 07090 908-789-4560
Stewart Carey, prin. Fax 789-4193
Westfield HS 1,800/9-12
550 Dorian Rd 07090 908-789-4500
Peter Renwick, prin. Fax 789-4230

West Long Branch, Monmouth, Pop. 8,009
Shore Regional HSD 700/9-12
132 State Route 36 07764 732-222-9300
Renae LaPrete, supt. Fax 222-8849
www.shoreregional.org
Shore Regional HS 700/9-12
132 State Route 36 07764 732-222-9300
Vincent DalliCardillo, prin. Fax 222-8849

West Long Branch SD 500/PK-8
135 Locust Ave 07764 732-222-5900
Thomas Farrell, supt. Fax 222-9325
www.wlbschools.com
Antonides S 300/4-8
135 Locust Ave 07764 732-222-5900
Jessica Shaw, prin. Fax 222-8154

Monmouth University Post-Sec.
400 Cedar Ave 07764 732-571-3400

West Milford, Passaic, Pop. 26,600
West Milford Township SD 3,800/PK-12
46 Highlander Dr 07480 973-697-1700
Dr. James McLaughlin, supt. Fax 697-8351
www.wmtps.org
Macopin MS 700/7-8
70 Highlander Dr 07480 973-697-5691
Mary Reinhold, prin. Fax 697-0301
West Milford HS 1,300/9-12
67 Highlander Dr 07480 973-697-1701
Paul Gorski, prin. Fax 208-0912

Westmont, Camden, Pop. 5,500
Haddon Township SD 1,800/PK-12
500 Rhoads Ave 08108 856-869-7700
Cheryl Simone Ed.D., supt. Fax 854-7792
www.haddontwpschools.com/
Haddon Township HS 500/9-12
406 Memorial Ave 08108 856-869-7750
Gary O'Brien, prin. Fax 869-7764
Rohrer MS 400/6-8
101 MacArthur Blvd 08108 856-869-7750
Kevin Rooney, prin. Fax 869-7772

West New York, Hudson, Pop. 49,199
West New York SD 6,500/PK-12
6028 Broadway 07093 201-553-4000
John Fauta, supt. Fax 865-2725
www.wnyschools.net
Memorial HS 1,700/9-12
5501 Park Ave 07093 201-553-4110
Scott Wohlrab, prin. Fax 864-2151
West New York MS 600/7-8
201 57th St 07093 201-563-4160
Israel Rodriguez, prin. Fax 863-6698

Robert Fiance Beauty School Post-Sec.
5518 Bergenline Ave 07093 201-866-4000

West Orange, Essex, Pop. 45,500
West Orange SD 6,300/PK-12
179 Eagle Rock Ave 07052 973-669-5400
James O'Neill, supt. Fax 669-1432
www.woboe.org
Liberty MS 500/7-8
1 Kelly Dr 07052 973-243-2007
Robert Klemt, prin. Fax 243-2743
Roosevelt MS 400/7-8
36 Gilbert Pl 07052 973-669-5373
Lionel Hush, prin. Fax 243-9807
West Orange HS 2,000/9-12
51 Conforti Ave 07052 973-669-5301
Hayden Moore, prin. Fax 669-1260

Golda Och Academy 400/6-12
1418 Pleasant Valley Way 07052 973-602-3600
Joyce Raynor Ph.D., hdmstr. Fax 669-0034
Seton Hall Preparatory HS 900/9-12
120 Northfield Ave 07052 973-325-6624
Rev. Michael Kelly, hdmstr. Fax 325-6652

Westville, Gloucester, Pop. 4,234

St. John of God Community Services Post-Sec.
1145 Delsea Dr 08093 856-848-4700

West Windsor, Mercer
West Windsor-Plainsboro Regional SD 9,500/K-12
PO Box 505 08550 609-716-5000
Victoria Kniewel Ed.D., supt. Fax 716-5012
www.ww-p.org
West Windsor-Plainsboro HS South 1,600/9-12
346 Clarksville Rd 08550 609-716-5050
Dennis Lepold, prin. Fax 716-5092
Other Schools – See Plainsboro, Princeton Junction

Mercer County Community College Post-Sec.
1200 Old Trenton Rd 08550 609-586-4800
Mercer County Community College Post-Sec.
1200 Old Trenton Rd 08550 609-586-4800

Wharton, Morris, Pop. 6,390
Wharton Borough SD 700/K-8
137 E Central Ave 07885 973-361-2592
Dennis Mack, supt. Fax 895-2187
www.wbps.org/
MacKinnon MS 200/6-8
137 E Central Ave 07885 973-361-1253
Christopher Herdman, prin. Fax 361-4805

Whippany, Morris
Hanover Park Regional HSD
Supt. — See East Hanover
Whippany Park HS 600/9-12
165 Whippany Rd 07981 973-887-3004
John Manning, prin. Fax 887-0451

Hanover Township SD 1,500/K-8
61 Highland Ave 07981 973-515-2404
Scott Pepper, supt. Fax 540-1023
www.hanovertwpschools.com/
Memorial JHS 600/6-8
61 Highland Ave 07981 973-515-2427
Michael Wasko, prin. Fax 515-2481

Abundant Life Christian S 100/PK-12
43 S Jefferson Rd 07981 973-463-9455
Angela Fernandez, admin. Fax 463-9677

White House Station, Hunterdon, Pop. 2,066
Readington Township SD 2,000/PK-8
PO Box 807 08889 908-534-2195
Dr. Barbara Sargent, supt. Fax 349-3042
www.readington.k12.nj.us
Readington MS 800/6-8
PO Box 700 08889 908-534-2113
Sharon Moffat, prin. Fax 534-6802

Whiting, Ocean
Manchester Township SD 3,100/K-12
121 Route 539 08759 732-350-5900
David Trethaway, supt. Fax 350-0436
www.manchestertwp.org
Other Schools – See Manchester

Wildwood, Cape May, Pop. 5,246
Wildwood CSD 800/PK-12
4300 Pacific Ave 08260 609-522-7922
Dennis Anderson, supt. Fax 523-1014
www.edline.net/pages/Wildwood_PSD
Wildwood HS 300/9-12
4300 Pacific Ave 08260 609-522-7922
Christopher Armstrong, prin. Fax 522-7914
Wildwood MS 100/6-8
4300 Pacific Ave 08260 609-522-7922
Christopher Armstrong, prin. Fax 522-7914

Wildwood Catholic HS 200/9-12
1500 Central Ave 08260 609-522-7257
Anthony Degatano, prin. Fax 522-2453

Williamstown, Gloucester, Pop. 15,255
Monroe Township SD 5,800/PK-12
75 E Academy St 08094 856-629-6400
Charles Earling, supt. Fax 262-2499
www.monroetwp.k12.nj.us
Williamstown HS 1,800/9-12
700 N Tuckahoe Rd 08094 856-262-8200
Paul Deal, prin. Fax 262-0869
Williamstown MS 1,800/5-8
561 Clayton Rd 08094 856-629-7444
Dana Mericle, prin. Fax 875-6757

Willingboro, Burlington, Pop. 32,400
Willingboro Township SD 3,700/PK-12
440 Beverly Rancocas Rd 08046 609-835-8600
Dr. Ronald G. Taylor, supt. Fax 835-3880
www.willingboroschools.org/
Levitt MS 600/Alt
50 Salem Rd 08046 609-835-8900
Ebonee Markham, prin. Fax 835-3974
Memorial MS 300/6-8
451 Van Sciver Pkwy 08046 609-835-8700
Ellis Brown, prin. Fax 835-1457
Willingboro HS 900/9-12
20 S John F Kennedy Way 08046 609-835-8800
Nadine Tribbett, prin. Fax 835-8877
Adult HS, 50 Salem Rd 08046 Adult
Harold Shafer, dir. 609-835-3810

Strayer University Post-Sec.
300 Willingboro Way # 125 08046 609-835-6000

Woodbridge, Middlesex, Pop. 18,933
Middlesex County Vocational SD
Supt. — See East Brunswick
Acad for Allied Health & Biomed Science Vo/Tech
1 Convery Blvd 07095 732-634-5858
Alex Guzman, prin. Fax 632-7073

Woodbridge Township SD 12,400/PK-12
PO Box 428 07095 732-750-3200
Dr. Robert Zega, supt. Fax 750-3493
www.woodbridge.k12.nj.us
Woodbridge HS 1,400/9-12
25 Samuel Lupo Pl 07095 732-602-8600
Steven Caroscio, prin. Fax 602-8612
Woodbridge MS 400/6-8
525 Barron Ave 07095 732-602-8690
Gary Kuzniak, prin. Fax 855-0326
Other Schools – See Avenel, Colonia, Fords, Iselin

Achieve Test Prep Post-Sec.
1480 US Highway 9 N 07095 732-750-2321
Berkeley College Post-Sec.
430 Rahway Ave 07095 732-750-1800

Woodbury, Gloucester, Pop. 9,869
Woodbury SD 1,400/PK-12
25 N Broad St 08096 856-853-0123
Joseph Jones, supt. Fax 853-0704
www.woodburysch.com
Woodbury JSHS 800/6-12
25 N Broad St 08096 856-853-0123
Denise Dunham, prin. Fax 853-2684

Woodbury Heights, Gloucester, Pop. 3,021
Gateway Regional SD 800/7-12
775 Tanyard Rd, 856-848-8172
Shannon Whalen Ed.D., supt. Fax 848-2049
www.gatewayhs.com
Gateway Regional MSHS 800/7-12
775 Tanyard Rd, 856-848-8200
Steven Hindman, prin. Fax 251-9813

Woodcliff Lake, Bergen, Pop. 5,674
Woodcliff Lake SD 800/PK-8
134 Woodcliff Ave 07677 201-930-5600
Lauren Barbelet, supt. Fax 930-0488
www.woodcliff-lake.com
Woodcliff MS 300/6-8
134 Woodcliff Ave 07677 201-930-5600
Robert Lombardy, prin. Fax 391-7932

Woodland Park, Passaic
Woodland Park SD 1,100/K-8
853 McBride Ave, 973-317-7700
Elaine Baldwin, supt. Fax 317-7773
wpschools.org
Memorial MS 500/5-8
15 Memorial Dr, 973-317-7750
Charles Silverstein, prin. Fax 317-7753

Berkeley College Post-Sec.
44 Rifle Camp Rd, 973-278-5400

Wood Ridge, Bergen, Pop. 7,540
Wood-Ridge SD 1,100/K-12
89 Hackensack St 07075 201-933-6777
Beth Ebler, supt. Fax 804-9204
www.wood-ridgeschools.org
Ostrovsky MS 300/6-8
540 Windsor Rd 07075 201-933-6777
Robert Recchione, prin. Fax 939-0259
Wood-Ridge HS 300/9-12
258 Hackensack St 07075 201-933-6777
Dr. Sue DeNobile, prin. Fax 939-1195

Woodstown, Salem, Pop. 3,420
Salem County Special Services SD 50/6-12
PO Box 126 08098 856-769-0101
Dr. Mark Jones, supt.
www.scsssd.org/
Other Schools – See Salem

Woodstown-Pilesgrove Regional SD 1,600/PK-12
135 East Ave 08098 856-769-0144
Thomas Coleman, supt. Fax 769-4549
www.woodstown.org
Woodstown HS 800/9-12
140 East Ave 08098 856-769-0144
Dr. Scott Hoopes, prin. Fax 769-4102
Woodstown MS 400/6-8
15 Lincoln Ave 08098 856-769-0144
John Fargnoli, prin. Fax 769-3872

Woolwich, Gloucester
Kingsway Regional SD 2,200/7-12
213 Kings Hwy 08085 856-467-4600
Dr. James Lavender, supt. Fax 467-5382
www.kingsway.k12.nj.us
Kingsway Regional HS 1,500/9-12
201 Kings Hwy 08085 856-467-3300
Craig Stephenson, prin. Fax 241-1932
Kingsway Regional MS 700/7-8
203 Kings Hwy 08085 856-467-3300
Troy Walton, prin. Fax 467-2703

Wyckoff, Bergen, Pop. 15,372
Wyckoff Township SD 2,300/PK-8
241 Morse Ave 07481 201-848-5700
Richard Kuder, supt. Fax 848-5695
www.wyckoffps.org/
Eisenhower MS 800/6-8
344 Calvin Ct 07481 201-848-5750
Christopher Iasiello, prin. Fax 848-5682

Eastern Christian MS 200/5-8
518 Sicomac Ave 07481 201-891-3663
Andrew Culp, prin.

NEW MEXICO

NEW MEXICO PUBLIC EDUCATION DEPARTMENT

300 Don Gaspar Ave, Santa Fe 87501-2786
Telephone 505-827-5800
Fax 505-827-6696
Website http://www.sde.state.nm.us

Secretary of Education Hanna Skandara

NEW MEXICO PUBLIC EDUCATION COMMISSION

300 Don Gaspar Ave, Santa Fe 87501-2744

Chairperson Andrew Garrison

REGIONAL EDUCATION COOPS (REC) & REGIONAL CENTER COOPS (RCC)

Central REC 5
Nina Tafoya, dir. 505-889-3412
PO Box 37440, Albuquerque 87176 Fax 889-3422
www.crecnm.org/
High Plains REC 3
Stephen Aguirre, dir. 575-445-7090
101 N 2nd St, Raton 87740 Fax 445-7663
hprec.com
Northeast REC 4
Jim Abreu, dir. 505-426-2085
PO Box 927, Las Vegas 87701 Fax 454-1473
www.rec4.com
Northwest REC 2
Kim Mizell, dir. 575-756-1274
PO Box 113, Chama 87520 Fax 756-1278
www.nwrec2.org
Pecos Valley REC 8
Lena Trujillo-Chavez, dir. 575-748-6100
PO Box 155, Artesia 88211 Fax 748-6160
www.pvrec8.com/
REC 6
Patti Harrelson, dir. 575-562-4455
1500 S Avenue K, Portales 88130 Fax 562-4460
www.rec6.net
REC 7
Belinda Morris, dir. 575-393-0755
315 E Clinton St, Hobbs 88240 Fax 393-0249
hobbsschools.net/department/regional_education_cooperative_7
REC 9
Cathy Jones, dir. 575-257-2368
237 Service Rd, Ruidoso 88345 Fax 257-2141
rec9nm.org
Southwest REC 10
Bruce Hegwer, dir., PO Box 4075 575-894-7589
Truth or Consequences 87901 Fax 894-7584
www.swrecnm.org

PUBLIC, PRIVATE AND CATHOLIC SECONDARY SCHOOLS

Alamogordo, Otero, Pop. 29,463
Alamogordo SD 6,200/PK-12
PO Box 650 88311 575-812-6000
Dr. George Straface, supt. Fax 812-6003
www.aps4kids.org
Academy Del Sol 200/10-12
PO Box 650 88311 575-812-5500
Linda Carr, prin. Fax 812-5503
Alamogordo HS 1,700/9-12
PO Box 650 88311 575-812-6500
Darian Jaramillo, prin. Fax 812-6503
Chaparral MS 700/6-8
PO Box 650 88311 575-812-6300
Bertha Garza, prin. Fax 812-6303
Mountain View MS 500/6-8
PO Box 650 88311 575-812-6400
Mike Farley, prin. Fax 812-6403
Other Schools – See Holloman AFB

Legacy Christian Academy 100/PK-12
2907 Thunder Rd 88310 575-434-0352
Cindy McKee, dir. Fax 437-1320
New Mexico School Visually Handicapped Post-Sec.
1900 N White Sands Blvd 88310 575-437-3505
New Mexico State University Post-Sec.
2400 Scenic Dr 88310 575-439-3600
Olympian University of Cosmetology Post-Sec.
1810 10th St 88310 575-437-2221

Albuquerque, Bernalillo, Pop. 534,167
Albuquerque SD 93,300/PK-12
PO Box 25704 87125 505-880-3700
Winston Brooks, supt. Fax 872-8855
ww2.aps.edu
Adams MS 800/6-8
5401 Glenrio Rd NW 87105 505-831-0400
Holly Gurule, prin. Fax 836-7760
Albuquerque HS 1,700/9-12
800 Odelia Rd NE 87102 505-843-6400
Tim McCorkle, prin. Fax 848-9432
Atrisco Heritage Academy 1,700/9-12
10800 Dennis Chavez Blvd SW 87121 505-243-1458
Antonio Gonzales, prin. Fax 873-1041
Career Enrichment Ctr Vo/Tech
807 Mountain Rd NE 87102 505-247-3658
Nikki Dennis, prin. Fax 848-9421
Carter MS 1,200/6-8
8901 Bluewater Rd NW 87121 505-833-7540
Rick Braden, prin. Fax 833-7559
Cibola HS 1,900/9-12
1510 Ellison Dr NW 87114 505-897-0110
Elena Salazar, prin. Fax 897-4251
Cleveland MS 700/6-8
6910 Natalie Ave NE 87110 505-881-9227
Susan Labarge, prin. Fax 881-9441
Del Norte HS 1,200/9-12
5323 Montgomery Blvd NE 87109 505-883-7222
Jo Sloan, prin. Fax 880-3965
Desert Ridge MS 1,000/6-8
8400 Barstow St NE 87122 505-857-9282
Troy Hughes, prin. Fax 857-0201
Early College Academy 200/9-12
807 Mountain Rd NE 87102 505-878-6181
Nikki Dennis, prin. Fax 848-9421
Eisenhower MS 900/6-8
11001 Camero Ave NE 87111 505-292-2530
Rosalind Deasy, prin. Fax 291-6884
Eldorado HS 1,900/9-12
11300 Montgomery Blvd NE 87111 505-296-4871
Martin Sandoval, prin. Fax 291-6809
Freedom HS 100/Alt
5200 Cutler Ave NE 87110 505-884-6012
Vivia Sparkler, prin. Fax 880-3979
Garfield MS 400/6-8
3501 6th St NW 87107 505-344-1647
David Lynch, prin. Fax 344-6562
Grant MS 700/6-8
1111 Easterday Dr NE 87112 505-299-2113
Paul Roney, prin. Fax 291-6881
Harrison MS 800/6-8
3912 Isleta Blvd SW 87105 505-877-1279
Kevin Cummings, prin. Fax 877-6797
Hayes MS 400/6-8
1100 Texas St NE 87110 505-265-7741
Tracy Straub, prin. Fax 260-6108
Highland HS 1,700/9-12
4700 Coal Ave SE 87108 505-265-3711
Scott Elder, prin. Fax 348-8503
Hillerman MS 900/6-8
8101 Rainbow Blvd NW 87114 505-792-0698
Renee Salazar, prin. Fax 792-2322
Hoover MS 600/6-8
12015 Tivoli Ave NE Ste A 87111 505-298-6896
Kathy Alexander, prin. Fax 291-6883
Jackson MS 600/6-8
10600 Indian School Rd NE 87112 505-299-7377
Ann Piper, prin. Fax 291-6887
Jefferson MS 900/6-8
712 Girard Blvd NE 87106 505-255-8691
Pam Meyer, prin. Fax 268-2334
Johnson MS 1,000/6-8
6811 Taylor Ranch Rd NW 87120 505-898-1492
Mike Bachicha, prin. Fax 898-7150
Kennedy MS 500/6-8
721 Tomasita St NE 87123 505-298-6701
Ed Bortot, prin. Fax 291-6879
La Cueva HS 2,100/9-12
7801 Wilshire Ave NE 87122 505-823-2327
Todd Resch, prin. Fax 857-0177
Madison MS 800/6-8
3501 Moon St NE 87111 505-299-4735
Marcia Johnson, prin. Fax 323-9512
Manzano HS 1,900/9-12
12200 Lomas Blvd NE 87112 505-559-2200
Therese Carroll, prin. Fax 291-6854
McKinley MS 600/6-8
4500 Comanche Rd NE 87110 505-881-9390
Mary Cade, prin. Fax 880-3968
Monroe MS 1,000/6-8
6100 Paradise Blvd NW 87114 505-897-0101
Vernon Martinez, prin. Fax 897-2371
New Futures S 200/Alt
5400 Cutler Ave NE 87110 505-883-5680
Jinx Baskerville, prin. Fax 880-3977
Nex+Gen Academy 200/9-12
5323 Montgomery Blvd NE 87109 505-878-6400
Michael Stanton, prin.
Polk MS 500/6-8
2220 Raymac Rd SW 87105 505-877-6444
Eva Vigil, prin. Fax 877-1618
Pyle MS 700/6-8
1820 Valdora Rd SW 87105 505-877-3770
James Lujan, prin. Fax 873-8540
Rio Grande HS 1,600/9-12
2300 Arenal Rd SW 87105 505-873-0220
Yvonne Garcia, prin. Fax 873-8523
Sandia HS 2,000/9-12
7801 Candelaria Rd NE 87110 505-294-1511
Katy Harvey, prin. Fax 291-6878
School on Wheels 100/Alt
129 Hartline Ave SW 87105 505-243-2395
Stan Pena, prin. Fax 243-5180
Sierra Alternative HS 50/Alt
5200 Cutler Ave NE 87110 505-884-6012
Vivia Sparkler, prin. Fax 880-3979
Taylor MS 600/6-8
8200 Guadalupe Trl NW 87114 505-898-3666
Michael Bateson, prin. Fax 897-5165
Truman MS 1,300/6-8
9400 Benavides Rd SW 87121 505-836-3030
Judith Martin-Tafoya, prin. Fax 836-7745
Valley HS 1,500/9-12
1505 Candelaria Rd NW 87107 505-345-9021
Anthony Griego, prin. Fax 761-8429
Van Buren MS 600/6-8
700 Louisiana Blvd SE 87108 505-268-3833
Cardinal Rieger, prin. Fax 260-6104
Vision Quest Alternative MS 50/Alt
5401 Glenrio Rd NW 87105 505-352-0343
Adele Evans, prin. Fax 352-0343
Volcano Vista HS 2,100/9-12
8100 Rainbow Blvd NW 87114 505-890-0343
Valerie Atencio, prin. Fax 792-4805
Washington MS 500/6-8
1101 Park Ave SW 87102 505-764-2000
Blanca Lopez, prin. Fax 764-2022
West Mesa HS 1,700/9-12
6701 Fortuna Rd NW 87121 505-831-6993
Ben Santistevan, prin. Fax 836-7756
Wilson MS 500/6-8
1138 Cardenas Dr SE 87108 505-268-3961
Marco Harris, prin. Fax 260-2000
Other Schools – See Los Ranchos, Tijeras

Albuquerque Academy 1,100/6-12
6400 Wyoming Blvd NE 87109 505-828-3200
Andrew Watson, head sch Fax 828-3320
ATI Career Training Center Post-Sec.
4575 San Mateo NE Ste G130 87109 505-903-7055
Aveda Institute New Mexico Post-Sec.
1816 Central Ave SW 87104 505-294-5333
Bosque S 500/6-12
4000 Learning Rd NW 87120 505-898-6388
Billy Handmaker, hdmstr. Fax 922-0392
Brookline College Post-Sec.
4201 Central Ave NW Ste J 87105 505-880-2877
Brown Mackie College Post-Sec.
10500 Copper Ave NE 87123 505-559-5200
Calvary Christian Academy 200/PK-12
12820 Indian School Rd NE 87112 505-842-8681
Tara Urquidez, prin. Fax 842-8746
Carrington College Post-Sec.
1001 Menaul Blvd NE 87107 505-634-5236
Central New Mexico Community College Post-Sec.
525 Buena Vista Dr SE 87106 505-224-3000

DeWolff Coll of Hairstyling\Cosmetology — Post-Sec.
1500 Eubank Blvd NE 87112 — 505-296-4100
Evangel Christian Academy — 300/PK-12
4501 Montgomery Blvd NE 87109 — 505-883-4674
Graceway Christian Academy — 200/PK-12
1621 Arizona St NE 87110 — 505-262-0969
Dr. John Adams, supt. — Fax 262-0996
Hope Christian S — 1,400/PK-12
8005 Louisiana Blvd NE 87109 — 505-822-8868
Tom Morris, dir. — Fax 822-8260
ITT Technical Institute — Post-Sec.
5100 Masthead St NE 87109 — 505-828-1114
Menaul S — 200/6-12
301 Menaul Blvd NE 87107 — 505-345-7727
National American University — Post-Sec.
4775 Indian Sch Rd NE #200 87110 — 505-348-3700
National American University — Post-Sec.
10131 Coors Blvd NW Ste I1 87114 — 800-895-9904
New Life Baptist Academy — 200/PK-12
6900 Los Volcanes Rd NW 87121 — 505-352-2628
Lillie Allen, prin. — Fax 352-2684
Olympian University of Cosmetology — Post-Sec.
6300 San Mateo Blvd NE # J 87109 — 505-765-1044
Pima Medical Institute — Post-Sec.
4400 Cutler Ave NE 87110 — 505-881-1234
St. Pius X HS — 900/9-12
5301 Saint Josephs Dr NW 87120 — 505-831-8400
Barbara Rothweiler, prin. — Fax 831-8413
Sandia Preparatory S — 700/6-12
532 Osuna Rd NE 87113 — 505-338-3000
Steven Albert, hdmstr. — Fax 338-3099
Southwest Acupuncture College — Post-Sec.
7801 Academy Rd NE 87109 — 505-888-8898
Southwestern Indian Polytechnic Inst. — Post-Sec.
9169 Coors Blvd NW 87120 — 505-346-2347
Southwest University of Visual Arts — Post-Sec.
5000 Marble Ave NE 87110 — 505-254-7575
Universal Therapeutic Massage Institute — Post-Sec.
3410 Aztec Rd NE 87107 — 505-888-0020
University of New Mexico — Post-Sec.
PO Box 4895 87196 — 505-277-0111
University of Phoenix-NM Division — Post-Sec.
5700 Pasadena Ave NE 87113 — 505-821-4800
Victory Christian S — 100/K-12
220 El Pueblo Rd NW 87114 — 505-898-3060
Glenn Frey, supt. — Fax 898-6690

Animas, Hidalgo, Pop. 225
Animas SD — 200/PK-12
PO Box 85 88020 — 575-548-2299
Betsy Ward, supt. — Fax 548-2388
www.animask12.net
Animas HS — 100/7-12
PO Box 90 88020 — 575-548-2296
Jacque Davenport, lead tchr. — Fax 548-2388

Anthony, Dona Ana, Pop. 9,342
Gadsden ISD
Supt. — See Sunland Park
Desert Pride Academy — 300/Alt
PO Box 70 88021 — 575-882-0142
George Foster, prin. — Fax 882-4926
Gadsden HS — 1,700/9-12
6301 Highway 28 88021 — 575-882-6300
Lucia Servin, prin. — Fax 882-2370
Gadsden MS — 800/7-8
1301 Washington St 88021 — 575-882-2372
Veronica Quinones, prin. — Fax 882-5227

Anton Chico, Guadalupe, Pop. 188
Santa Rosa Consolidated SD
Supt. — See Santa Rosa
Anton Chico MS — 50/6-8
PO Box 169 87711 — 575-427-6038
Danielle Esquibel, prin. — Fax 427-4246

Artesia, Eddy, Pop. 11,178
Artesia SD — 3,600/PK-12
1106 W Quay Ave 88210 — 575-746-3585
Dr. Crit Caton, supt. — Fax 746-6232
www.bulldogs.org
Artesia HS — 700/10-12
1006 W Richardson Ave 88210 — 575-746-9816
Thad Phipps, prin. — Fax 746-4365
Artesia Park JHS — 500/8-9
1508 W Cannon Ave 88210 — 575-746-9892
Cody Skinner, prin. — Fax 746-4462

Aztec, San Juan, Pop. 6,640
Aztec Municipal SD — 3,200/PK-12
1118 W Aztec Blvd 87410 — 505-334-9474
Kirk Carpenter, supt. — Fax 334-9861
www.aztec.k12.nm.us
Aztec HS — 900/9-12
500 E Chaco St 87410 — 505-334-9414
Warman Hall, prin. — Fax 599-4387
Koogler MS — 700/6-8
455 N Light Plant Rd 87410 — 505-334-6102
Rick Espinoza, prin. — Fax 599-4385
Vista Nueva HS — 100/Alt
315 S Ash St Ste 100 87410 — 505-334-3831
Melissa Maestas, prin. — Fax 334-1427

Bayard, Grant, Pop. 2,310
Cobre Consolidated SD — 1,400/PK-12
PO Box 1000 88023 — 575-537-4010
George Peru, supt. — Fax 537-5455
www.cobre.k12.nm.us
Cobre HS — 400/9-12
PO Box 749 88023 — 575-537-4020
Johnny Benavidez, prin. — Fax 537-5503
Snell MS — 200/7-8
PO Box 729 88023 — 575-537-4030
Sharon Miller, prin. — Fax 537-3358

Belen, Valencia, Pop. 7,165
Belen Consolidated SD — 4,700/PK-12
520 N Main St 87002 — 505-966-1000
Ron Marquez, supt. — Fax 966-1050
www.beleneagles.org
Belen HS — 1,300/9-12
520 N Main St 87002 — 505-966-1300
Christopher Hotchkiss, prin. — Fax 966-1350
Belen Infinity HS — 100/Alt
520 N Main St 87002 — 505-966-1520
Buddy Dillow, prin. — Fax 966-1524
Belen MS — 700/7-8
520 N Main St 87002 — 505-966-1600
Sheila Armijo, prin. — Fax 966-1650

Bernalillo, Sandoval, Pop. 8,231
Bernalillo SD — 2,400/PK-12
224 N Camino Del Pueblo 87004 — 505-867-2317
Allan Tapia, supt. — Fax 867-7850
www.bernalillo.bps.k12.nm.us
Bernalillo HS — 900/9-12
250 Isidora Sanchez 87004 — 505-867-2388
Keith Cowan, prin. — Fax 867-7826
Bernalillo MS — 500/6-8
485 Camino don Tomas 87004 — 505-867-3309
Nolan Correa, prin. — Fax 867-7819

Bloomfield, San Juan, Pop. 7,953
Bloomfield SD — 3,100/PK-12
325 N Bergin Ln 87413 — 505-632-3316
Joe Rasor, supt. — Fax 632-4371
www.bsin.k12.nm.us
Bloomfield HS — 700/9-12
520 N 1st St 87413 — 505-634-3400
Cody Diehl, prin. — Fax 634-3413
Brown Secondary S — 100/Alt
924 S Bloomfield Blvd 87413 — 505-634-3940
Troy Webb, prin. — Fax 634-3950
Mesa Alta JHS — 500/7-8
329 N Bergin Ln 87413 — 505-632-4350
Jessica Sledzinski, prin. — Fax 634-3835

Capitan, Lincoln, Pop. 1,465
Capitan Municipal SD — 500/PK-12
PO Box 278 88316 — 575-354-8500
Shirley Crawford, supt. — Fax 354-8505
www.capitan.k12.nm.us
Capitan HS — 200/9-12
PO Box 278 88316 — 575-354-8503
Jerrett Perry, prin. — Fax 354-8508
Capitan MS — 100/6-8
PO Box 278 88316 — 575-354-8502
Jerrett Perry, prin. — Fax 354-8507

Carlsbad, Eddy, Pop. 25,808
Carlsbad Municipal SD — 5,700/K-12
408 N Canyon St 88220 — 575-234-3300
Gary Perkowski, supt. — Fax 234-3367
www.carlsbad.k12.nm.us
Alta Vista MS — 600/6-8
408 N Canyon St 88220 — 575-234-3316
Mark Barela, prin. — Fax 234-3478
Carlsbad HS — 1,600/9-12
408 N Canyon St 88220 — 575-234-3319
Mark Driskell, prin. — Fax 234-3393
Leyva MS — 800/6-8
408 N Canyon St 88220 — 575-234-3318
Mark McAlister, prin. — Fax 234-3452

Eddy County Beauty College — Post-Sec.
1115 W Mermod St 88220 — 575-885-4545
New Mexico State University — Post-Sec.
1500 University Dr 88220 — 575-234-9200

Carrizozo, Lincoln, Pop. 975
Carrizozo Municipal SD — 200/PK-12
PO Box 99 88301 — 575-648-2346
Patti Nesbitt, supt. — Fax 648-2216
www.carrizozoschools.org
Carrizozo HS — 100/9-12
PO Box 99 88301 — 575-648-2346
Patti Nesbitt, prin. — Fax 648-3255
Carrizozo MS — 50/5-8
PO Box 99 88301 — 575-648-2346
Patti Nesbitt, prin. — Fax 648-3255

Casa Blanca, Cibola
Grants-Cibola County SD
Supt. — See Grants
Laguna Acoma JSHS — 300/7-12
PO Box 689 87007 — 505-285-2670
Tom Trujillo, prin. — Fax 552-7184

Chaparral, Dona Ana, Pop. 14,528
Gadsden ISD
Supt. — See Sunland Park
Chaparral HS — 1,100/9-12
800 S County Line Dr, — 575-824-6700
Mark Rupcich, prin. — Fax 824-5081
Chaparral MS — 600/7-8
290 E Lisa Dr, — 575-824-4847
Marti Muela, prin. — Fax 824-4045

Cimarron, Colfax, Pop. 1,000
Cimarron Municipal SD — 300/K-12
125 N Collison Ave 87714 — 575-376-2445
Adan Estrada, supt. — Fax 376-2442
cimarronschools.org
Cimarron HS — 100/9-12
125 N Collison Ave 87714 — 575-376-2241
Letitia Martinez, prin. — Fax 376-2428
Cimarron MS — 50/5-8
125 N Collison Ave 87714 — 575-376-2512
Bonnie Lightfoot, prin. — Fax 376-2217
Other Schools – See Eagle Nest

Clayton, Union, Pop. 2,951
Clayton Municipal SD — 600/PK-12
323 S 5th St 88415 — 575-374-9611
Dr. Nelda Isaacs, supt. — Fax 374-9881
www.claytonschools.us
Clayton HS — 200/9-12
323 S 5th St 88415 — 575-374-2596
Gary Miller, prin. — Fax 374-6012
Clayton JHS — 100/7-8
323 S 5th St 88415 — 575-374-9543
Marvin Martin, prin. — Fax 374-9469

Cliff, Grant, Pop. 288
Silver Consolidated SD
Supt. — See Silver City
Cliff JSHS — 100/7-12
PO Box 9 88028 — 575-535-2051
Clayton Ellwanger, prin. — Fax 535-2054

Cloudcroft, Otero, Pop. 659
Cloudcroft Municipal SD — 300/PK-12
PO Box 198 88317 — 575-601-4416
Travis Dempsey, supt. — Fax 235-1668
www.cmsbears.org
Cloudcroft HS — 100/9-12
PO Box 198 88317 — 575-601-4416
Roman Renteria, prin. — Fax 405-0833

Clovis, Curry, Pop. 36,950
Clovis Municipal SD — 8,800/PK-12
PO Box 19000 88102 — 575-769-4300
Terry Myers, supt. — Fax 769-4333
www.clovis-schools.org/
Clovis Freshman HS — 600/9-9
1400 Cameo St 88101 — 575-769-4400
Diana Russell, prin. — Fax 769-4403
Clovis SHS — 1,700/10-12
1900 N Thornton St 88101 — 575-769-4350
Wayne Marshall, prin. — Fax 769-4366
Marshall MS — 600/7-8
100 Commerce Way 88101 — 575-769-4410
Jay Brady, prin. — Fax 769-4413
Yucca MS — 600/7-8
1500 Sycamore St 88101 — 575-769-4420
Loran Hill, prin. — Fax 769-4421

Clovis Christian Schools - West Campus — 50/9-12
PO Box 608 88102 — 575-763-5311
Ladona Clayton Ed.D., supt. — Fax 763-4469
Clovis Community College — Post-Sec.
417 Schepps Blvd 88101 — 575-769-2811

Corona, Lincoln, Pop. 169
Corona Municipal SD — 100/PK-12
PO Box 258 88318 — 575-849-1911
Travis Lightfoot, supt. — Fax 849-2026
www.cpscardinals.org
Corona HS — 50/7-12
PO Box 258 88318 — 575-849-1911
Rick Cogdill, prin. — Fax 849-2026

Corrales, Sandoval, Pop. 8,197

Sandia View Academy — 50/9-12
65 Sandia View Ln 87048 — 505-898-0717
Fax 897-7053

Crownpoint, McKinley, Pop. 2,253
Gallup-McKinley County SD
Supt. — See Gallup
Crownpoint HS — 400/9-12
PO Box 700 87313 — 505-721-1600
George Bickert, prin. — Fax 721-1699
Crownpoint MS — 200/6-8
PO Box 1110 87313 — 505-786-5663
Deloria Chapo, prin. — Fax 721-5499

Navajo Technical College — Post-Sec.
PO Box 849 87313 — 505-786-4100

Cuba, Sandoval, Pop. 717
Cuba ISD — 600/PK-12
PO Box 70 87013 — 575-289-3211
Vicki Smith, supt. — Fax 289-3314
cuba.k12.nm.us/
Cuba HS — 300/9-12
PO Box 70 87013 — 575-289-3211
Randy Houk, prin. — Fax 289-3314
Cuba MS — 100/6-8
PO Box 70 87013 — 575-289-3211
Ed Painter, prin. — Fax 289-3314

Deming, Luna, Pop. 14,749
Deming SD — 5,500/PK-12
1001 S Diamond Ave 88030 — 575-546-8841
Harvielee Moore, supt. — Fax 546-8517
www.demingps.org
Deming HS — 1,600/9-12
1100 S Nickel St 88030 — 575-546-2678
Janean Garney, prin. — Fax 544-0918
Red Mountain MS — 800/7-8
2100 Highway 418 SW 88030 — 575-546-0668
Robin Parnell, prin. — Fax 546-9263

Des Moines, Union, Pop. 140
Des Moines Municipal SD — 100/K-12
PO Box 38 88418 — 575-278-2611
Stacy Diller, supt. — Fax 278-2617
www.desmoines.k12.nm.us/
Des Moines JSHS — 50/7-12
PO Box 38 88418 — 575-278-2611
Stacy Diller, supt. — Fax 278-2617

Dexter, Chaves, Pop. 1,260
Dexter Consolidated SD — 1,100/PK-12
PO Box 159 88230 — 575-734-5420
Patricia Parsons, supt. — Fax 734-6813
www.dexterdemons.org
Dexter HS — 300/9-12
PO Box 159 88230 — 575-734-5420
Eddie Ward, prin. — Fax 734-6709
Dexter MS — 200/6-8
PO Box 159 88230 — 575-734-5414
Lesa Dodd, prin. — Fax 734-6811

Dora, Roosevelt, Pop. 133
Dora Consolidated SD 300/PK-12
PO Box 327 88115 575-477-2216
Steve Barron, supt. Fax 477-2464
www.doraschools.com
Dora JSHS 200/7-12
PO Box 327 88115 575-477-2216
Brandon Hays, prin. Fax 477-2464

Dulce, Rio Arriba, Pop. 2,716
Dulce ISD 600/K-12
PO Box 547 87528 575-759-3225
James Lesher, supt. Fax 759-3533
www.dulceschools.com/
Dulce HS 200/9-12
PO Box 547 87528 575-759-2959
Manuel Valdez, prin. Fax 759-3535
Dulce MS 100/5-8
PO Box 547 87528 575-759-3225
Joyce Lindauer, prin. Fax 759-3533

Eagle Nest, Colfax, Pop. 289
Cimarron Municipal SD
Supt. — See Cimarron
Eagle Nest MS 100/5-8
PO Box 287 87718 575-377-6991
Lee Mills, prin. Fax 377-3646

Edgewood, Santa Fe, Pop. 3,663
Moriarty-Edgewood SD
Supt. — See Moriarty
Edgewood MS 300/7-8
17 Venus Rd W 87015 505-832-5880
Dr. Barbara Gradner, prin. Fax 281-7210

Elida, Roosevelt, Pop. 195
Elida Municipal SD 100/K-12
PO Box 8 88116 575-274-6211
Jim Daugherty, supt. Fax 274-6213
www.elidaschools.net/
Elida JSHS 100/7-12
PO Box 8 88116 575-274-6211
Larry Gregory, prin. Fax 274-6213

El Rito, Rio Arriba, Pop. 781

Northern New Mexico Community College Post-Sec.
PO Box 160 87530 575-581-4110

Espanola, Rio Arriba, Pop. 10,179
Espanola SD 4,400/PK-12
714 Calle Don Diego 87532 505-753-2254
Daniel Trujillo Ph.D., supt. Fax 747-3514
www.k12espanola.org
Espanola Valley HS 1,000/9-12
714 Calle Don Diego 87532 505-753-7357
Hoyt Mutz, prin. Fax 753-6177
Vigil MS 600/7-8
714 Calle Don Diego 87532 505-753-1348
Robert Archuleta, prin. Fax 747-3083

McCurdy S 300/PK-12
261 S McCurdy Rd 87532 505-753-7221
Northern New Mexico College Post-Sec.
921 N Paseo De Onate 87532 505-747-2100

Estancia, Torrance, Pop. 1,626
Estancia Municipal SD 800/PK-12
PO Box 68 87016 505-384-2001
Audie Brown, supt. Fax 384-2015
www.estancia.k12.nm.us
Estancia HS 200/9-12
PO Box 68 87016 505-384-2002
Lane Widner, prin. Fax 384-2015
Estancia MS 100/7-8
PO Box 68 87016 505-384-2003
Denise Smythe, prin. Fax 384-2015

Liberty Ranch Christian S 50/1-12
Blue Grass Rd Ste 3 87016 505-384-2530
Mary Bragg, admin. Fax 384-2530

Eunice, Lea, Pop. 2,893
Eunice SD 600/PK-12
PO Box 129 88231 575-394-2524
Dwain Haynes, supt. Fax 394-3006
www.eunice.org/
Caton MS 100/6-8
PO Box 129 88231 575-394-3338
Christy Boyd, prin. Fax 394-3661
Eunice HS 200/9-12
PO Box 129 88231 575-394-2332
Gary Frazier, prin. Fax 394-3140

Farmington, San Juan, Pop. 44,787
Farmington Municipal SD 10,600/PK-12
PO Box 5850 87499 505-324-9840
Janel Ryan, supt. Fax 599-8806
district.fms.k12.nm.us
Farmington HS 1,400/9-12
2200 N Sunset Ave 87401 505-324-0352
Tim Kienitz, prin. Fax 599-8832
Heights MS 700/6-8
3700 College Blvd 87402 505-599-8611
Kristi Burns, prin. Fax 599-8673
Hermosa MS 600/6-8
1500 E 25th St 87401 505-599-8612
Mark Harris, prin. Fax 599-8681
Mesa View MS 600/6-8
4451 Wildflower Mesa Dr 87401 505-599-8622
Kim Salazar, prin. Fax 599-8646
Piedra Vista HS 1,300/9-12
5700 College Blvd 87402 505-599-8880
Ann Gattis, prin. Fax 599-8891
Rocinante HS 200/Alt
3250 E 30th St 87402 505-599-8627
Bob Rank, prin. Fax 599-8731

Tibbetts MS 500/6-8
3500 Twin Peaks Blvd 87401 505-599-8613
Karen Brown, prin. Fax 599-8675

San Juan College Post-Sec.
4601 College Blvd 87402 505-326-3311

Floyd, Roosevelt, Pop. 133
Floyd Municipal SD 200/PK-12
PO Box 65 88118 575-478-2211
Paul Benoit, supt. Fax 478-2811
www.floydbroncos.com/
Floyd HS 100/9-12
PO Box 65 88118 575-478-2211
Damon Terry, prin. Fax 478-2811
Floyd MS 100/5-8
PO Box 65 88118 575-478-2211
Damon Terry, prin. Fax 478-2811

Fort Sumner, DeBaca, Pop. 1,008
Fort Sumner Municipal SD 300/PK-12
PO Box 387 88119 575-355-7734
Patricia Miller, supt. Fax 355-7716
www.ftsumnerk12.com/
Fort Sumner HS 100/9-12
PO Box 387 88119 575-355-2231
Sean Wootton, prin. Fax 355-7663
Fort Sumner MS 100/6-8
PO Box 387 88119 575-355-2231
Sean Wootton, prin. Fax 355-7663

Gallina, Rio Arriba, Pop. 280
Jemez Mountain SD 200/K-12
PO Box 230 87017 575-638-5419
Manuel Medrano, supt. Fax 638-5571
www.jmsk12.com/
Coronado MSHS 100/6-12
PO Box 230 87017 575-638-5549
Athena Trujillo, prin. Fax 638-5571

Gallup, McKinley, Pop. 21,028
Gallup-McKinley County SD 12,000/PK-12
PO Box 1318 87305 505-722-1000
Ray Arsenault, supt. Fax 721-1199
www.gmcs.k12.nm.us/
Chief Manuelito MS 600/6-8
1325 Rico St 87301 505-721-5600
Dan Horsley, prin. Fax 721-5699
Gallup Central HS 200/Alt
325 Marguerite St 87301 505-721-2400
Don Sparks, prin. Fax 721-2499
Gallup HS 1,200/9-12
1055 Rico St 87301 505-721-2500
Mike Butkovich, prin. Fax 721-2556
Gallup MS 400/6-8
1001 S Grandview Dr 87301 505-721-2700
Peggy Taylor, prin. Fax 721-2799
Kennedy MS 600/6-8
600 S Boardman Ave 87301 505-721-3100
Jack McFarland, prin. Fax 721-3199
Miyamura HS 1,100/9-12
680 Boardman Ave 87301 505-721-1900
Frank Chiapetti, prin. Fax 721-1999
Other Schools – See Crownpoint, Navajo, Pueblo Pintado, Ramah, Thoreau, Tohatchi

---

Gallup Catholic HS 100/9-12
515 Park Ave 87301 505-722-6089
Barbara Kozeliski, prin. Fax 879-3130
University of New Mexico - Gallup Post-Sec.
705 Gurley Ave 87301 505-863-7500

Grady, Curry, Pop. 103
Grady Municipal SD 100/PK-12
PO Box 71 88120 575-357-2192
Ted Trice, supt. Fax 357-2000
www.gradyschool.com/
Grady HS 50/9-12
PO Box 71 88120 575-357-2192
Alicia Rush, prin. Fax 357-2000
Grady MS 50/6-8
PO Box 71 88120 575-357-2192
Alicia Rush, prin. Fax 357-2000

Grants, Cibola, Pop. 9,030
Grants-Cibola County SD 3,500/PK-12
PO Box 8 87020 505-285-2600
Kilino Marquez, supt. Fax 285-2628
www.gccs.cc/
Grants HS 900/9-12
500 Mountain Rd 87020 505-285-2651
Alton Autrey, prin. Fax 285-2661
Los Alamitos MS 500/7-8
1100 Mount Taylor Ave 87020 505-285-2683
Joan Gilmore, prin. Fax 285-2692
Other Schools – See Casa Blanca

New Mexico State University Post-Sec.
1500 N 3rd St 87020 505-287-6678

Hagerman, Chaves, Pop. 1,250
Hagerman Municipal SD 400/PK-12
PO Box B 88232 575-752-3254
Steven Starkey, supt. Fax 752-3255
bobcat.net
Hagerman HS 100/9-12
PO Box B 88232 575-752-3283
Michael Chavez, prin. Fax 752-3306
Hagerman MS 100/6-8
PO Box B 88232 575-752-2002
Michael Chavez, prin. Fax 752-0241

Hatch, Dona Ana, Pop. 1,642
Hatch Valley SD 1,300/K-12
PO Box 790 87937 575-267-8200
Linda Hale, supt. Fax 267-8202
www.hatchschools.net

Hatch Valley HS 400/9-12
PO Box 790 87937 575-267-8230
Carmen Garcia, prin. Fax 267-8235
Hatch Valley MS 300/6-8
PO Box 790 87937 575-267-8250
Daniel Montoya, prin. Fax 267-8255

Hobbs, Lea, Pop. 33,769
Hobbs Municipal SD 7,800/PK-12
PO Box 1030 88241 575-433-0100
T.J. Parks, supt. Fax 433-0142
www.hobbsschools.net
Freshman HS 600/9-9
1401 E Sanger St 88240 575-433-0300
Dawni Nelson, prin. Fax 433-1109
Heizer MS 6-8
101 E Stanolind Rd 88240 575-433-1100
Zeke Kaney, prin. Fax 433-1101
Highland MS 600/6-8
2500 N Jefferson St 88240 575-433-1200
Ron Haggerton, prin. Fax 433-1203
Hobbs Alternative Learning Center 100/Alt
PO Box 1030 88241 575-433-0226
Lorna Jackson, prin. Fax 433-0229
Hobbs HS 1,600/10-12
800 N Jefferson St 88240 575-433-0200
Jeff Cearley, prin. Fax 433-0203
Houston MS 600/6-8
300 N Houston St 88240 575-433-1300
Donna Jones, prin. Fax 433-1303

New Mexico Junior College Post-Sec.
1 Thunderbird Cir 88240 505-392-4510
University of the Southwest Post-Sec.
6610 N Lovington Hwy 88240 575-392-6561

Holloman AFB, Otero, Pop. 2,857
Alamogordo SD
Supt. — See Alamogordo
Holloman MS 200/6-8
381 1st St 88330 575-812-6200
Maria Showalter, prin. Fax 812-6203

Hondo, Lincoln
Hondo Valley SD 200/K-12
PO Box 55 88336 575-653-4411
Andrea Nieto, supt. Fax 653-4414
www.hondoschools.org
Hondo HS 100/7-12
PO Box 55 88336 575-653-4411
Andrea Nieto, admin. Fax 653-4414

House, Quay, Pop. 68
House Municipal SD 100/K-12
PO Box 673 88121 575-279-7353
Lecil Richards, supt. Fax 279-6201
www.houseschools.net
House JSHS 50/7-12
PO Box 673 88121 575-279-7353
Lecil Richards, prin. Fax 279-6201
Learning Center Alt
PO Box 673 88121 575-279-7322
Lecil Richards, prin. Fax 279-6093

Jal, Lea, Pop. 2,030
Jal SD 400/PK-12
PO Box 1386 88252 575-395-2101
Israel Carrera, supt. Fax 395-2146
www.jalnm.org
Jal JSHS 100/7-12
PO Box 1386 88252 575-395-2277
Keith Bausman, prin. Fax 395-3177

Jemez Pueblo, Sandoval, Pop. 1,783
Jemez Valley SD 500/PK-12
8501 Highway 4 87024 575-834-7391
David Atencio, supt. Fax 834-7394
www.jvps.org
Jemez Valley HS 100/9-12
8501 Highway 4 87024 575-834-7392
Brad Parker, prin. Fax 834-7676
Jemez Valley MS 100/6-8
8501 Highway 4 87024 575-834-7393
Laura Mijares, prin. Fax 834-3311

Kirtland, San Juan, Pop. 7,619
Central Consolidated SD 22
Supt. — See Shiprock
Kirtland Central HS 800/9-12
550 Road 6100 87417 505-598-5881
Shawna Becenti, prin. Fax 598-9712
Kirtland MS 500/7-8
538 Road 6100 87417 505-598-6114
Randy Mason, prin. Fax 598-9582

Lake Arthur, Chaves, Pop. 422
Lake Arthur Municipal SD 100/PK-12
PO Box 98 88253 575-365-2000
Michael Grossman, supt. Fax 365-2002
www.la-panthers.org/
Lake Arthur HS 50/9-12
PO Box 98 88253 575-365-2000
Dale Ballard, prin. Fax 365-2002
Lake Arthur MS 50/6-8
PO Box 98 88253 575-365-2000
Dale Ballard, prin. Fax 365-2002

Las Cruces, Dona Ana, Pop. 96,217
Las Cruces SD 25,000/PK-12
505 S Main St Ste 249 88001 575-527-5807
Stan Rounds, supt. Fax 527-5972
www.lcps.k12.nm.us
Arrowhead Park Early College HS 9-12
505 S Main St Ste 249 88001 575-527-9540
Jennifer Amis, prin.
Camino Real MS 800/6-8
505 S Main St Ste 249 88001 575-527-6030
Ralph Ramos, prin. Fax 527-6031

Centennial HS 9-12
505 S Main St Ste 249 88001 575-527-9330
Michael Montoya, prin.
Las Cruces HS 2,400/9-12
505 S Main St Ste 249 88001 575-527-9400
Jed Hendee, prin. Fax 527-9767
Lynn MS 700/6-8
505 S Main St Ste 249 88001 575-527-9445
Mary Nunez, prin. Fax 527-9454
Mayfield HS 2,300/9-12
505 S Main St Ste 249 88001 575-527-9415
Jo Beth Hawk, prin. Fax 527-9420
Mesa MS 400/6-8
505 S Main St Ste 249 88001 575-527-9510
Gabe Jacquez, prin. Fax 527-9511
Onate HS 2,100/9-12
505 S Main St Ste 249 88001 575-527-9430
David Day, prin. Fax 527-9444
Picacho MS 800/6-8
505 S Main St Ste 249 88001 575-527-9455
Cindy Baker, prin. Fax 527-9459
Sierra MS 900/6-8
505 S Main St Ste 249 88001 575-527-9640
Brenda Lewis, prin. Fax 527-9768
Vista MS 800/6-8
505 S Main St Ste 249 88001 575-527-9465
Wendi Hammond, prin. Fax 527-9470
Zia MS 900/6-8
505 S Main St Ste 249 88001 575-527-9475
Heather Kingery, prin. Fax 527-9479
Other Schools – See Mesilla, White Sands

Las Cruces Catholic S 300/PK-12
1331 N Miranda St 88005 575-526-2517
Connie Limon, prin. Fax 524-0544
Mesilla Valley Christian S 500/K-12
3850 Stern Dr 88001 575-525-8515
Dr. John Foreman, supt. Fax 526-2713
New Mexico State Univ. Dona Ana Branch Post-Sec.
2800 Sonoma Ranch Blvd 88011 575-527-7500
New Mexico State University Post-Sec.
PO Box 30001 88003 575-646-0111
Olympian University of Cosmetology Post-Sec.
1460 Missouri Ave # 5 88001 575-523-7181
Vista College Post-Sec.
850 N Telshor Blvd Ste F 88011 866-442-4197

Las Vegas, San Miguel, Pop. 13,609
Las Vegas City SD 1,900/PK-12
901 Douglas Ave 87701 505-454-5700
Sheryl McNellis Martinez, supt. Fax 454-5716
cybercardinal.com/
Memorial MS 400/6-8
901 Douglas Ave 87701 505-454-5710
Martina Tapia, prin. Fax 426-0303
Robertson HS 500/9-12
901 Douglas Ave 87701 505-454-5770
Darlene Ulibarri, prin. Fax 425-6852

West Las Vegas SD 1,400/K-12
179 Bridge St 87701 505-426-2300
Gene Parson, supt. Fax 426-2318
www.wlvs.k12.nm.us/
West Las Vegas HS 500/9-12
179 Bridge St 87701 505-426-2500
John Bustos, prin. Fax 426-2501
West Las Vegas MS 300/6-8
179 Bridge St 87701 505-426-2541
Julianna Trujillo, prin. Fax 426-2542
W Las Vegas Schools Family Partnership 100/Alt
179 Bridge St 87701 505-426-2535
Anna Valdez, prin. Fax 426-2526
Other Schools – See Ribera

Luna Community College Post-Sec.
366 Luna Dr 87701 505-454-2500
New Mexico Highlands University Post-Sec.
PO Box 9000 87701 505-425-7511

La Union, Dona Ana, Pop. 1,103

Calvary West Christian HS 50/9-12
7048 McNutt Rd 88021 575-589-1433
Elizabeth Gonzales, admin.

Logan, Quay, Pop. 1,034
Logan Municipal SD 300/PK-12
PO Box 67 88426 575-487-2252
Johnnie Cain, supt. Fax 487-9479
logan.echalk.com
Logan HS 100/9-12
PO Box 67 88426 575-487-2252
Craig Terry, prin. Fax 487-9479
Logan MS 50/6-8
PO Box 67 88426 575-487-2252
Craig Terry, prin. Fax 487-9479

Lordsburg, Hidalgo, Pop. 2,787
Lordsburg Municipal SD 600/PK-12
PO Box 430 88045 575-542-9361
Randy Piper, supt. Fax 542-9364
www.lmsed.org
Dugan-Tarango MS 100/7-8
1352 Hardin St 88045 575-542-9806
Terry Bentley, prin. Fax 542-9811
Lordsburg HS 200/9-12
501 W 4th St 88045 575-542-3782
Greg Lelvis, prin. Fax 542-3712

Los Alamos, Los Alamos, Pop. 11,762
Los Alamos SD 3,400/PK-12
PO Box 90 87544 505-663-2222
Eugene Schmidt, supt. Fax 663-3247
www.laschools.net
Los Alamos HS 1,100/9-12
1300 Diamond Dr 87544 505-663-2510
Sandra Warnock, prin. Fax 662-6846
Los Alamos MS 500/7-8
2101 Hawk Dr 87544 505-663-2375
Rex Kilburn, prin. Fax 662-4270

University of New Mexico - Los Alamos Post-Sec.
4000 University Dr 87544 505-662-5919

Los Lunas, Valencia, Pop. 14,610
Los Lunas SD 8,200/PK-12
PO Box 1300 87031 505-865-9636
Bernard Saiz, supt. Fax 865-7766
www.llschools.net/
Century Alternative HS 100/Alt
PO Box 1300 87031 505-866-2453
Wilson Holland, prin. Fax 866-8064
Los Lunas HS 1,400/9-12
PO Box 1300 87031 505-865-4646
Dan Padilla, prin. Fax 565-2847
Los Lunas MS 800/7-8
PO Box 1300 87031 505-865-7273
Victoria Baca, prin. Fax 865-9742
Valencia HS 1,000/9-12
PO Box 1300 87031 505-565-8755
Andrew Saiz, prin. Fax 565-8762
Valencia MS 500/7-8
PO Box 1300 87031 505-865-1750
Ron Hendrix, prin. Fax 866-8921

University of New Mexico - Valencia Post-Sec.
280 La Entrada Rd 87031 505-925-8500

Los Ranchos, Bernalillo
Albuquerque SD
Supt. — See Albuquerque
Taft MS 500/6-8
620 Schulte Rd NW, 505-344-4389
Steve Scully, prin. Fax 761-8440

Loving, Eddy, Pop. 1,402
Loving Municipal SD 600/PK-12
PO Box 98 88256 575-745-2000
Jesse Fuentes, supt. Fax 745-2002
www.lovingschools.com
Loving HS 200/9-12
PO Box 98 88256 575-745-2020
Dr. Ann Lynn McIlroy, prin. Fax 745-2002
Loving MS 200/6-8
PO Box 98 88256 575-745-2050
Judy Groh, prin. Fax 745-2052

Lovington, Lea, Pop. 10,904
Lovington Municipal SD 3,300/PK-12
18 W Washington Ave 88260 575-739-2200
Darin Manes, supt. Fax 739-2205
www.lovingtonschools.net/
Freshman Academy 200/9-9
701 W Avenue K 88260 575-739-2260
Robert Brown, prin. Fax 739-2261
Lovington SHS 600/10-12
701 W Avenue K 88260 575-739-2230
Robert Brown, prin. Fax 739-2242
New Hope Alternative HS 100/Alt
601 N 5th St 88260 575-739-2415
Mark Mapes, prin. Fax 739-2417
Taylor MS 500/7-8
700 S 11th St 88260 575-739-2435
Pam Quinones, prin. Fax 739-2438

Magdalena, Socorro, Pop. 910
Magdalena Municipal SD 500/PK-12
PO Box 24 87825 575-854-2241
Mike Chambers, supt. Fax 854-2294
www.magdalena.k12.nm.us
Magdalena HS 100/9-12
PO Box 629 87825 575-854-2241
Kim Ortiz, prin. Fax 854-2294
Magdalena MS 100/6-8
PO Box 629 87825 575-854-2241
Kim Ortiz, prin. Fax 854-2294

Maxwell, Colfax, Pop. 243
Maxwell Municipal SD 100/PK-12
PO Box 275 87728 575-375-2371
Dr. Charles Harrison, supt. Fax 375-2375
www.maxwellp12.com/
Maxwell HS 50/9-12
PO Box 275 87728 575-375-2371
Fax 375-2375
Maxwell MS 50/7-8
PO Box 275 87728 575-375-2371
Fax 375-2375

Melrose, Curry, Pop. 637
Melrose SD 200/PK-12
PO Box 275 88124 575-253-4269
Jamie Widner, supt. Fax 253-4291
www.melroseschools.org
Melrose JSHS 100/7-12
PO Box 275 88124 575-253-4267
Dickle Roybal, prin. Fax 253-4291

Mesilla, Dona Ana, Pop. 2,164
Las Cruces SD
Supt. — See Las Cruces
San Andres HS 200/Alt
2355 Avenida de Mesilla 88046 575-527-6058
Kathryn Davis, prin. Fax 527-9736

Montezuma, San Miguel

United World College USA 200/11-12
PO Box 248 87731 505-454-4200
Lisa Darling, pres. Fax 454-4274

Mora, Mora, Pop. 656
Mora ISD 500/K-12
PO Box 179 87732 575-387-3101
Tom Sullivan, supt. Fax 387-3111
mora.k12.nm.us
Garcia MS 100/6-8
PO Box 687 87732 575-387-3128
Pauline Duran, prin. Fax 387-3126
Mora HS 100/9-12
PO Box 180 87732 575-387-3122
Danny Chavez, prin. Fax 387-3121

Moriarty, Torrance, Pop. 1,873
Moriarty-Edgewood SD 3,400/PK-12
PO Box 2000 87035 505-832-4471
Fax 832-4472
www.mesd.us
Moriarty HS 1,000/9-12
PO Box 2000 87035 505-832-4254
Stephanie West, prin. Fax 832-4939
Moriarty MS 200/7-8
PO Box 2000 87035 505-832-6200
Robert Adams, prin. Fax 832-5919
Other Schools – See Edgewood

Mosquero, Harding, Pop. 93
Mosquero Municipal SD 50/K-12
PO Box 258 87733 575-673-2271
Bill Ward, supt. Fax 673-2305
www.mosquero.net
Mosquero JSHS 50/7-12
PO Box 258 87733 575-673-2271
Bill Ward, prin. Fax 673-2305

Mountainair, Torrance, Pop. 908
Mountainair SD 200/PK-12
PO Box 456 87036 505-847-2333
Jay Mortensen, supt. Fax 847-2843
www.mountainairpublicschools.com
Mountainair HS 100/6-12
PO Box 456 87036 505-847-2211
Bryan Craven, prin. Fax 847-2843

Navajo, McKinley, Pop. 1,626
Gallup-McKinley County SD
Supt. — See Gallup
Navajo MS 100/6-8
PO Box 1287 87328 505-777-2390
Colleen Bowman, prin. Fax 721-5399
Navajo Pine HS 200/9-12
PO Box 1286 87328 505-777-2288
Pauletta White, prin. Fax 721-3699

Newcomb, San Juan, Pop. 335
Central Consolidated SD 22
Supt. — See Shiprock
Newcomb HS 300/9-12
PO Box 7927 87455 505-696-3417
Raul Sanchez, prin. Fax 696-3265
Newcomb MS 200/6-8
PO Box 7927 87455 505-696-3434
Toni Purrachio, prin. Fax 696-3430

Ojo Caliente, Taos
Mesa Vista Consolidated SD 400/PK-12
PO Box 309 87549 575-583-2645
Ernesto Valdez, supt. Fax 583-2815
www.mesavista.org
Mesa Vista HS 100/9-12
PO Box 50 87549 575-583-2275
Ricardo Snachez, prin. Fax 583-9133
Mesa Vista MS 100/7-8
PO Box 50 87549 575-583-2275
Ricardo Sanchez, prin. Fax 583-9133

Pecos, San Miguel, Pop. 1,378
Pecos ISD 700/PK-12
PO Box 368 87552 505-757-4700
Fred Trujillo, supt. Fax 757-8721
www.pecos.k12.nm.us
Pecos HS 200/9-12
PO Box 368 87552 505-757-4720
June Boles, prin. Fax 757-2772
Pecos MS 200/6-8
PO Box 368 87552 505-757-4620
June Boles, prin. Fax 757-2561

Penasco, Taos, Pop. 584
Penasco ISD 500/K-12
PO Box 520 87553 575-587-2230
Dr. Theresa Baca-Watson, supt. Fax 587-2513
www.penasco.k12.nm.us
Penasco HS 200/9-12
PO Box 520 87553 575-587-2503
Ray Maestas, prin. Fax 587-9910
Penasco MS 100/7-8
PO Box 520 87553 575-587-2503
Ray Maestas, prin. Fax 587-9910

Portales, Roosevelt, Pop. 12,080
Portales Municipal SD 2,800/PK-12
501 S Abilene Ave 88130 575-356-7000
Randy Fowler, supt. Fax 356-4377
www.portalesschools.com
Portales HS 800/9-12
201 S Knoxville St 88130 575-356-7015
Melvin Nusser, prin. Fax 356-8082
Portales JHS 400/7-8
700 E 3rd St 88130 575-356-7045
Steve Harris, prin. Fax 359-0826

Eastern New Mexico University Post-Sec.
1500 S Avenue K 88130 575-562-1011

Pueblo Pintado, McKinley, Pop. 187
Gallup-McKinley County SD
Supt. — See Gallup
Tse' Yi Gai HS 100/9-12
118 Counselor Rd 87013 505-721-5500
Christopher Spade, prin. Fax 721-5599

Quemado, Catron, Pop. 224
Quemado ISD 200/K-12
PO Box 128 87829 575-773-4700
Bill Green, supt. Fax 773-4717
www.quemadoschools.org

Quemado JSHS 100/7-12
PO Box 128 87829 575-773-4700
Valerie Brea, prin. Fax 773-4717

Questa, Taos, Pop. 1,751
Questa ISD 400/K-12
PO Box 440 87556 575-586-0421
Dr. Lillian Torrez, supt. Fax 586-0531
www.qisd-nm.schoolloop.com
Questa HS 100/9-12
PO Box 529 87556 575-586-1604
Valerie Trujillo, prin. Fax 586-2282
Questa JHS 100/7-8
PO Box 529 87556 575-586-1604
Valerie Trujillo, prin. Fax 586-2282

Ramah, McKinley, Pop. 354
Gallup-McKinley County SD
Supt. — See Gallup
Ramah MSHS 200/6-12
PO Box 849 87321 505-783-4211
Rex Morris, prin. Fax 721-3699

Ranchos de Taos, Taos, Pop. 2,481

University of New Mexico - Taos Post-Sec.
1157 County Road 110 87557 575-737-6200

Raton, Colfax, Pop. 6,809
Raton SD 1,300/PK-12
PO Box 940 87740 575-445-9111
David Willden, supt. Fax 445-5641
www.ratonschools.org
Raton HS 400/9-12
1535 Tiger Cir 87740 575-445-3541
JoAnne Johnson, prin. Fax 445-2237
Raton MS 300/6-8
500 S 3rd St 87740 575-445-9881
Hector Cavazos, prin. Fax 445-3682

Rehoboth, McKinley

Rehoboth Christian S 400/PK-12
PO Box 41 87322 505-863-4412
Carol Bremer-Bennett, dir. Fax 863-2185

Reserve, Catron, Pop. 285
Reserve ISD 200/K-12
PO Box 350 87830 575-533-6241
Loren Cushman, supt. Fax 533-6647
www.reserveschools.com
Reserve JSHS 100/7-12
PO Box 350 87830 575-533-6242
Cindy Shellhorn, prin. Fax 533-6900

Ribera, San Miguel, Pop. 415
West Las Vegas SD
Supt. — See Las Vegas
Valley MS 50/6-8
PO Box 519 87560 505-426-2581
Cathy Lucero, prin. Fax 426-2582

Rio Rancho, Sandoval, Pop. 85,293
Rio Rancho SD 16,700/PK-12
500 Laser Rd NE 87124 505-896-0667
Dr. V. Sue Cleveland, supt. Fax 896-0662
www.rrps.net
Cleveland HS 2,200/9-12
4800 Laban Rd NE, 505-938-0300
Scott Affentranger, prin. Fax 338-3474
Eagle Ridge MS 800/6-8
800 Fruta Rd NE 87124 505-892-6630
Sarah Poutsch, prin. Fax 892-6909
Independence HS 200/Alt
421 Quantum Rd NE 87124 505-338-4658
Myra Roosevelt, prin. Fax 892-9742
Lincoln MS 1,000/6-8
2287 Lema Rd SE 87124 505-892-1100
Debby Morrell, prin. Fax 892-9728
Mountain View MS 900/6-8
4101 Montreal Loop NE, 505-867-0711
Julie Arnold, prin. Fax 867-7901
Rio Rancho HS 2,400/9-12
301 Loma Colorado Blvd NE 87124 505-896-5600
Richard Von Ancken, prin. Fax 896-5901
Rio Rancho MS 1,200/6-8
1600 Loma Colorado Blvd NE, 505-891-5335
Lynda Kitts, prin. Fax 891-1180

University of New Mexico West Post-Sec.
2600 College Ave NE, 505-925-8669

Roswell, Chaves, Pop. 47,742
Roswell ISD 10,200/PK-12
PO Box 1437 88202 575-627-2500
Tom Burrris, supt. Fax 627-2512
www.risd.k12.nm.us
Berrendo MS 700/6-8
800 Marion Richards Rd 88201 575-627-2775
Susan Martin, prin. Fax 625-8248
Goddard HS 1,100/9-12
701 E Country Club Rd 88201 575-627-4800
Brian Luck, prin. Fax 627-4856
Mesa MS 500/6-8
1601 E Bland St 88203 575-627-2800
Jennifer Cole, prin. Fax 625-8263
Mountain View MS 400/6-8
312 E Mountain View Rd 88203 575-627-2825
Glenda Beckham, prin. Fax 625-8260
Roswell HS 1,400/9-12
500 W Hobbs St 88203 575-637-3200
Ruben Bolanos, prin. Fax 637-3250
Sierra MS 600/6-8
615 S Sycamore Ave 88203 575-627-2850
Rhonda Martinez, prin. Fax 625-8283
University HS 200/Alt
25 W Martin St 88203 575-627-2750
Laura Herrera, prin. Fax 625-8278

Aladdin Beauty College Post-Sec.
108 S Union Ave 88203 575-623-6331
Eastern New Mexico University Post-Sec.
PO Box 6000 88202 575-624-7000
Gateway Christian S 200/PK-12
PO Box 1642 88202 575-622-9710
Rick Rapp, admin. Fax 622-9739
New Mexico Military Institute Post-Sec.
101 W College Blvd 88201 575-622-6250
New Mexico Military Institute 400/9-12
101 W College Blvd 88201 575-624-8001
Jerry Grizzle Ph.D., pres. Fax 624-8025

Roy, Harding, Pop. 234
Roy Municipal SD 50/PK-12
PO Box 430 87743 575-485-2242
Nino Esquivel, supt. Fax 485-2497
www.roy-nm-schools.org/
Roy JSHS 50/7-12
PO Box 430 87743 575-485-2242
Nino Esquivel, prin. Fax 485-2497

Ruidoso, Lincoln, Pop. 7,928
Ruidoso Municipal SD 2,200/PK-12
200 Horton Cir 88345 575-257-4051
Dr. George Bickert, supt. Fax 257-4150
www.ruidososchools.org/
Ruidoso HS 600/9-12
200 Horton Cir 88345 575-258-4910
Pauline Staski, prin. Fax 258-3516
Ruidoso MS 500/6-8
200 Horton Cir 88345 575-630-7800
George Heaton, prin. Fax 258-5809

San Jon, Quay, Pop. 209
San Jon Municipal SD 100/PK-12
PO Box 5 88434 575-576-2466
Colin Taylor, supt. Fax 576-2772
www.sanjonschools.com/
San Jon HS 100/9-12
PO Box 5 88434 575-576-2466
Fax 576-2772
San Jon MS 50/6-8
PO Box 5 88434 575-576-2466
Fax 576-2772

Santa Fe, Santa Fe, Pop. 66,849
Pojoaque Valley SD 1,800/PK-12
1574 State Road 502 87506 505-455-2282
Adan Delgado, supt. Fax 455-7152
pvs.k12.nm.us/
Pojoaque Valley HS 700/9-12
1574 State Road 502 87506 505-455-2234
Albert Martinez, prin. Fax 455-3471
Pojoaque Valley MS 400/7-8
1574 State Road 502 87506 505-455-2238
Vera Trujillo, prin. Fax 455-3392

Santa Fe SD 12,200/PK-12
610 Alta Vista St 87505 505-467-2000
Dr. Joel Boyd, supt. Fax 995-3300
www.sfps.info
Capital HS 1,100/9-12
4851 Paseo Del Sol 87507 505-467-1000
Melanie Romero, prin. Fax 995-3311
Capshaw MS 500/7-8
351 W Zia Rd 87505 505-467-4300
David Bibiano, prin. Fax 989-5439
De Vargas MS 500/7-8
1720 Llano St 87505 505-467-3300
Diane Garcia-Piro, prin. Fax 995-3307
Ortiz MS 700/6-8
4164 S Meadows Rd 87507 505-467-2300
Steve Baca, prin. Fax 989-5597
Santa Fe HS 1,500/9-12
2100 Yucca St 87505 505-467-2400
Leslie Kilmer, prin. Fax 467-2992
SER/SFPS Career Academy 100/Alt
1604 Agua Fria St 87505 505-467-1900
Dr. Cynthia Sanchez, prin. Fax 995-3394

Desert Academy 200/7-12
7300 Old Santa Fe Trl 87505 505-992-8284
Terry Passalacqua, hdmstr. Fax 992-8270
Institute of American Indian Arts Post-Sec.
83 Avan NU PO 87508 505-424-2300
Mission Viejo Christian Academy 200/PK-11
4601 Mission Bnd 87507 505-474-8080
Bernadette Shanaberger, prin. Fax 474-8082
New Mexico School for the Deaf Post-Sec.
1060 Cerrillos Rd 87505 505-827-6739
St. John's College Post-Sec.
1160 Camino De Cruz Blanca 87505 505-984-6000
St. Michael HS 800/7-12
100 Siringo Rd 87505 505-983-7353
Sam Govea, prin. Fax 982-8722
Santa Fe Community College Post-Sec.
6401 S Richards Ave 87508 505-428-1000
Santa Fe Preparatory S 300/7-12
1101 Camino De Cruz Blanca 87505 505-982-1829
James Leonard, hdmstr. Fax 982-2897
Santa Fe University of Art and Design Post-Sec.
1600 Saint Michaels Dr 87505 505-473-6011
Sante Fe Waldorf S 200/PK-12
26 Puesta Del Sol 87508 505-983-9727
Beverly Amico, admin. Fax 983-7416
Southwest Acupuncture College Post-Sec.
1622 Galisteo St 87505 505-438-8884
Southwestern College Post-Sec.
PO Box 4788 87502 505-471-5756

Santa Rosa, Guadalupe, Pop. 2,827
Santa Rosa Consolidated SD 600/PK-12
344 S 4th St 88435 575-472-3171
Ted Hern, supt. Fax 472-5609
www.srlions.com
Santa Rosa HS 200/9-12
717 S 3rd St 88435 575-472-3422
Richard Perea, prin. Fax 472-3169
Santa Rosa MS 100/6-8
116 Camino de Vida 88435 575-472-3633
Joseph Salas, prin. Fax 472-0663
Other Schools – See Anton Chico

Santa Teresa, Dona Ana, Pop. 4,240
Gadsden ISD
Supt. — See Sunland Park
Santa Teresa HS 1,300/9-12
100 Airport Rd 88008 575-589-5300
Kathryn Harper, prin. Fax 589-5311
Santa Teresa MS 600/7-8
4800 McNutt Rd 88008 575-874-7200
Rosa Lovelace, prin. Fax 589-2780

Anamarc College Post-Sec.
2660 Airport Rd 88008 575-589-3158

Shiprock, San Juan, Pop. 8,162
Central Consolidated SD 22 6,600/PK-12
PO Box 1199 87420 505-368-4984
Donald Levinski, supt. Fax 368-5232
www.ccsdnm.org/
Career Prep Alternative HS 200/Alt
PO Box 1199 87420 505-368-4980
Joyce Rock, prin. Fax 368-5307
Shiprock HS 700/9-12
PO Box 3578 87420 505-368-5161
Rick Edwards, prin. Fax 368-5796
Tse' Bit'ai MS 500/6-8
PO Box 1703 87420 505-368-4741
Greg Rockhold, prin. Fax 368-5105
Other Schools – See Kirtland, Newcomb

Silver City, Grant, Pop. 10,166
Silver Consolidated SD 3,000/PK-12
2810 N Swan St 88061 575-956-2000
Dick Pool, supt. Fax 956-2039
www.silverschools.org/
La Plata MS 600/6-8
3500 N Silver St 88061 575-956-2060
Wayne Mendonca, prin. Fax 956-2098
Opportunity HS 100/Alt
600 E 32nd St 88061 575-956-2140
Gary Koger, prin. Fax 956-2149
Silver HS 700/9-12
3200 N Silver St 88061 575-956-2158
David Carrillo, prin. Fax 388-2927
Other Schools – See Cliff

Western New Mexico University Post-Sec.
PO Box 680 88062 575-538-6011

Socorro, Socorro, Pop. 8,907
Socorro Consolidated SD 1,900/K-12
700 Franklin St 87801 575-835-0300
Dr. Randall K. Earwood, supt. Fax 835-1682
www.socorro.k12.nm.us/
Sarracino MS 300/6-8
PO Box X 87801 575-835-0283
Manual Molina, prin. Fax 835-0360
Socorro HS 500/9-12
PO Box 1367 87801 575-835-0700
Jennifer Molina, admin. Fax 835-0704

New Mexico Institute Mining & Technology Post-Sec.
801 Leroy Pl 87801 575-835-5434

Springer, Colfax, Pop. 1,037
Springer Municipal SD 200/K-12
PO Box 308 87747 575-483-3432
Freda Daugherty, supt. Fax 483-2387
www.springerschools.org
Springer HS 100/7-12
PO Box 308 87747 575-483-3464
Fax 483-3970

Sunland Park, Dona Ana, Pop. 14,071
Gadsden ISD 14,200/PK-12
4950 McNutt Rd 88008 575-882-6200
Efren Yturralde, supt. Fax 882-6229
www.gisd.k12.nm.us
Other Schools – See Anthony, Chaparral, Santa Teresa

International School Post-Sec.
PO Box 1919 88063 800-743-1414

Taos, Taos, Pop. 5,592
Taos Municipal SD 2,700/PK-12
310 Camino De La Placita 87571 575-758-5200
Rod Weston Ed.D., supt. Fax 758-5298
www.taosschools.org/
Taos HS 700/9-12
134 Cervantes St 87571 575-751-8000
Robert Trujillo, prin. Fax 751-8001
Taos MS 500/6-8
235 Paseo Del Canon E 87571 575-737-6000
Alfred Cordova, prin. Fax 737-6001

National College of Midwifery Post-Sec.
209 State Road 240 87571 575-758-8914

Tatum, Lea, Pop. 793
Tatum Municipal SD 300/PK-12
PO Box 685 88267 575-398-4455
Buddy Little, supt. Fax 398-8220
www.tatumschools.org/
Tatum JSHS 100/7-12
PO Box 685 88267 575-398-4555
Greg Slover, prin. Fax 398-4450

Texico, Curry, Pop. 1,118
Texico Municipal SD 600/PK-12
PO Box 237 88135 575-482-3801
Miles Mitchell, supt. Fax 482-3650
www.texicoschools.com

Texico HS 200/9-12
PO Box 237 88135 575-482-3305
Richard Estes, prin. Fax 482-3650
Texico MS 100/6-8
PO Box 237 88135 575-482-9520
Dennis Roch, prin. Fax 482-3650

Thoreau, McKinley, Pop. 1,831
Gallup-McKinley County SD
Supt. — See Gallup
Thoreau HS 400/9-12
PO Box 969 87323 505-721-4500
Monique Siedschlag, prin. Fax 721-4599
Thoreau MS 200/6-8
PO Box 787 87323 505-721-4600
Alberta Nozie, prin. Fax 721-4699

Tierra Amarilla, Rio Arriba, Pop. 379
Chama Valley ISD 300/PK-12
PO Box 10 87575 575-588-7285
Anthony Casados, supt. Fax 588-7860
www.chamaschools.com/
Escalante MSHS 100/7-12
PO Box 157 87575 575-588-7201
Eric Martinez, prin. Fax 588-7911

Tijeras, Bernalillo, Pop. 534
Albuquerque SD
Supt. — See Albuquerque
Roosevelt MS 400/6-8
11799 New Mexico 337 87059 505-281-3316
Cee Kay Nation, prin. Fax 281-5120

Tohatchi, McKinley, Pop. 799
Gallup-McKinley County SD
Supt. — See Gallup
Tohatchi HS 300/9-12
PO Box 248 87325 505-733-2206
Ethel Manuelito, prin. Fax 721-4899
Tohatchi MS 200/6-8
PO Box 322 87325 505-721-4900
Tammy Somers, prin. Fax 721-4999

Truth or Consequences, Sierra, Pop. 6,359
Truth or Consequences Municipal SD 1,400/PK-12
180 N Date St 87901 575-894-8150
Dr. Craig Cummins, supt. Fax 894-7532
www.torcschools.net
Hot Springs HS 400/9-12
180 N Date St 87901 575-894-8350
Patti Nesbitt, prin. Fax 894-0471
Truth or Consequences MS 300/6-8
180 N Date St 87901 575-894-8380
Dr. Renee Garcia, prin. Fax 894-0606

AppleTree Education Center 100/PK-12
1300 S Broadway St 87901 575-894-5646
Rebecca Dow, dir. Fax 894-0132

Tucumcari, Quay, Pop. 5,279
Tucumcari SD 1,100/PK-12
PO Box 1046 88401 575-461-3910
Aaron McKinney, supt. Fax 461-3554
www.gorattlers.org
Tucumcari HS 300/9-12
1100 S 7th St 88401 575-461-3830
Nicole Lesley, prin. Fax 461-3769
Tucumcari MS 200/6-8
914 S 5th St 88401 575-461-2310
Roberta Segura, prin. Fax 461-8610

Mesalands Community College Post-Sec.
911 S 10th St 88401 575-461-4413

Tularosa, Otero, Pop. 2,782
Tularosa Municipal SD 900/K-12
504 1st St 88352 575-585-8800
Brenda Vigil, supt. Fax 585-4439
www.tularosak12.us
Tularosa HS 300/9-12
504 1st St 88352 575-585-8866
John J. Marrujo, prin. Fax 585-8112
Tularosa MS 100/7-8
504 1st St 88352 575-585-8803
Sergio Castanon, prin. Fax 585-4739

Vaughn, Guadalupe, Pop. 444
Vaughn Municipal SD 100/PK-12
PO Box 489 88353 575-584-2283
Dr. Susan Wilkinson-Davis, supt. Fax 584-2355
www.vaughn.k12.nm.us/
Vaughn JSHS 50/7-12
PO Box 489 88353 575-584-2283
Lynda Spencer, prin. Fax 584-2355

Wagon Mound, Mora, Pop. 312
Wagon Mound SD 100/K-12
PO Box 158 87752 575-666-3000
Albert Martinez, supt. Fax 666-9001
www.wm.k12.nm.us
Wagon Mound JSHS 50/7-12
PO Box 158 87752 575-666-3001
Albert Martinez, prin. Fax 666-9001

White Sands, Dona Ana, Pop. 1,564
Las Cruces SD
Supt. — See Las Cruces
White Sands MS 100/6-8
290 Picatinny 88002 575-674-1241
Tom Bulger, prin. Fax 674-1515

Zuni, McKinley, Pop. 5,857
Zuni SD 1,000/K-12
PO Box A 87327 505-782-5511
Hayes A. Lewis, supt. Fax 782-5505
www.zpsd.org
Twin Buttes HS 100/9-12
PO Box 680 87327 505-782-4446
Roberta Tayah, prin. Fax 782-4944
Zuni HS 400/9-12
PO Box 550 87327 505-782-4451
Mike Hyatt, prin. Fax 782-5551
Zuni MS 200/6-8
PO Box E 87327 505-782-5561
Ophelia Barber, prin. Fax 782-5563

NEW YORK

NEW YORK EDUCATION DEPARTMENT
89 Washington Ave, Albany 12234-1000
Telephone 518-474-3852
Fax 518-473-4909
Website http://www.nysed.gov

Commissioner of Education John King

NEW YORK BOARD OF REGENTS
89 Washington Ave, Albany 12234-1000

Chancellor Merryl Tisch

BOARDS OF COOPERATIVE EDUCATIONAL SERVICES (BOCES)

Broome-Deleware-Tioga BOCES
Allen Buyck, supt. 607-766-3802
435 Glenwood Rd Fax 763-3215
Binghamton 13905
www.btboces.org/

Capital Region BOCES
Br. Charles Dedrick, supt. 518-862-4900
900 Watervliet Shaker Rd Fax 862-4903
Albany 12205
www.capregboces.org

Cattaraugus/Allegany/Erie/Wyoming BOCES
Dr. Robert Olczak, supt. 585-376-8246
1825 Windfall Rd, Olean 14760 Fax 376-8452
caew-boces.wnyric.org/

Cayuga/Onondaga BOCES
William Speck, supt. 315-253-0361
1879 W Genesee Street Rd Fax 252-6493
Auburn 13021
cayboces.org

Champlain Valley Educational Services
Craig King, supt. 518-561-0100
PO Box 455, Plattsburgh 12901 Fax 562-1471
www.cves.org/

Delaware/Chenango/Madison/Otsego BOCES
Bill Tammaro, supt. 607-335-1233
6678 County Road 32 Fax 334-9848
Norwich 13815
www.dcmoboces.com

Dutchess BOCES
Dr. John Pennoyer, supt. 845-486-4800
5 Boces Rd, Poughkeepsie 12601 Fax 486-4981
www.dcboces.org

Eastern Suffolk BOCES
Dr. Thomas Rogers, supt. 631-289-2200
201 Sunrise Hwy, Patchogue 11772 Fax 289-2381
www.esboces.org/

Erie 1 BOCES
Donald Ogilvie, supt. 716-821-7000
355 Harlem Rd Fax 821-7242
West Seneca 14224
www.erie1boces.org

Erie 2-Chautauqua-Cattaraugus BOCES
Robert Guiffreda, supt. 716-549-4454
8685 Erie Rd, Angola 14006 Fax 549-1758
www.e2ccb.org

Franklin-Essex-Hamilton BOCES
Stephen Shafer, supt. 518-483-6420
PO Box 28, Malone 12953 Fax 483-2178
www.fehb.org/

Genesee Valley BOCES
Dr. Michael Glover, supt. 585-658-7900
80 Munson St, Le Roy 14482 Fax 658-7910
www.gvboces.org

Greater Southern Tier BOCES
Dr. Horst Graefe, supt. 607-962-3175
9579 Vocational Dr Fax 962-1579
Painted Post 14870
www.gstboces.org/index.cfm

Hamilton-Fulton-Montgomery BOCES
Dr. Patrick Michel, supt. 518-736-4300
2755 State Highway 67 Fax 762-4724
Johnstown 12095
www.hfmboces.org

Herkimer-Fulton-Hamilton-Otsego BOCES
Mark Vivacqua, supt. 315-867-2023
352 Gros Blvd, Herkimer 13350 Fax 867-2002
www.herkimer-boces.org

Jefferson-Lewis-Hmltn-Hrkmr-Oneida BOCES
Jack Boak, supt. 315-779-7000
20104 State Route 3 Fax 785-8300
Watertown 13601
www.boces.com/

Madison-Oneida BOCES
Jacklin Starks, supt. 315-361-5500
PO Box 168, Verona 13478 Fax 361-5595
www.moboces.org

Monroe 1 BOCES
Daniel White, supt. 585-383-2200
41 OConnor Rd, Fairport 14450 Fax 383-6404
www.monroe.edu/

Monroe 2 - Orleans BOCES
JoAnne Antonacci, supt. 585-352-2400
3599 Big Ridge Rd Fax 352-2442
Spencerport 14559
www.monroe2boces.org

Nassau BOCES
Dr. Thomas Rogers, supt. 516-396-2200
PO Box 9195, Garden City 11530 Fax 997-8742
www.nassauboces.org

Oneida-Herkimer-Madison BOCES
Howard Mettelman, supt. 315-793-8561
PO Box 70, New Hartford 13413 Fax 793-8541
www.oneida-boces.org/

Onondaga-Cortland-Madison BOCES
Dr. Jessica Cohen, supt. 315-433-2602
PO Box 4754, Syracuse 13221 Fax 437-4816
www.ocmboces.org/

Orange-Ulster BOCES
Dr. John Pennoyer, supt. 845-291-0100
53 Gibson Rd, Goshen 10924 Fax 291-0118
www.ouboces.org/

Orleans-Niagara BOCES
Dr. Clark Godshall, supt. 800-836-7510
4232 Shelby Basin Rd Fax 798-1317
Medina 14103
www.onboces.org

Oswego BOCES
Jay Boak, supt. 315-963-4222
179 County Route 64 Fax 963-7131
Mexico 13114
www.oswegoboces.org/

Otsego-Northern Catskills BOCES
Nicholas Savin, supt. 607-588-6291
2020 Jump Brook Rd, Stamford
www.oncboces.org

Putnam Northern Westchester BOCES
Dr. James Langlois, supt. 914-248-2300
200 BOCES Dr Fax 248-2308
Yorktown Heights 10598
www.pnwboces.org

Questar III BOCES
James Baldwin, supt. 518-477-8771
10 Empire State Blvd Fax 477-9833
Castleton on Hudson 12033
www.questar.org

Rockland BOCES
Dr. Mary Marsico, supt. 845-627-4701
65 Parrott Rd, West Nyack 10994 Fax 624-1764
www.rocklandboces.org/

St. Lawrence-Lewis BOCES
Thomas Burns, supt. 315-386-4504
139 State Street Rd, Canton 13617 Fax 386-3395
www.sllboces.org/

Southern Westchester BOCES
James Langlois Ed.D., supt. 914-937-3820
17 Berkley Dr, Rye Brook 10573 Fax 937-7850
www.swboces.org/

Sullivan County BOCES
Lawrence Thomas, supt. 845-295-4015
6 Wierk Ave, Liberty 12754 Fax 292-8694
www.scboces.org

Tompkins-Seneca-Tioga BOCES
Dr. Ellen O'Donnell, supt. 607-257-1551
555 Warren Rd, Ithaca 14850 Fax 257-2825
www.tstboces.org/

Ulster BOCES
Charles Khoury, supt. 845-255-3040
175 State Route 32 N Fax 255-7942
New Paltz 12561
www.ulsterboces.org/

Washington-Srtg-Warren-Hmltn-Essex BOCES
Dr. James Dexter, supt. 518-746-3310
1153 Burgoyne Ave Ste 2 Fax 746-3309
Fort Edward 12828
wswheboces.org/

Wayne-Finger Lakes BOCES
Dr. Joseph Marinelli, supt. 315-332-7284
131 Drumlin Ct, Newark 14513 Fax 332-7425
www.wflboces.org/wflboces/index.cfm

Western Suffolk BOCES
Michael Mensch, admin. 631-549-4900
507 Deer Park Rd, Dix Hills 11746 Fax 423-1821
www.wsboces.org/

PUBLIC, PRIVATE AND CATHOLIC SECONDARY SCHOOLS

Accord, Ulster, Pop. 551

Rondout Valley Central SD 1,600/K-12
PO Box 9 12404 845-687-2400
Rosario Agostaro, supt. Fax 687-9577
www.rondout.k12.ny.us

Rondout Valley HS 800/9-12
PO Box 9 12404 845-687-2400
Andrew Davenport, prin. Fax 687-7665

Rondout Valley JHS 300/7-8
PO Box 9 12404 845-687-2400
Andrew Davenport, prin. Fax 687-8980

Adams, Jefferson, Pop. 1,752

South Jefferson Central SD
Supt. — See Adams Center

Clarke MS 500/6-8
11060 US Route 11 13605 315-232-4531
Tom O'Brien, prin. Fax 232-4620

South Jefferson HS 600/9-12
11060 US Route 11 13605 315-232-4531
Karen Denny, prin. Fax 232-3728

Adams Center, Jefferson, Pop. 1,533

South Jefferson Central SD 1,900/K-12
13180 US Route 11 13606 315-583-6104
Jamie Moesel, supt. Fax 583-6381
www.spartanpride.org
Other Schools – See Adams

Addison, Steuben, Pop. 1,744

Addison Central SD 1,100/PK-12
7 Cleveland Dr 14801 607-359-2244
Joseph DioGuardi, supt. Fax 359-2246
www.addisoncsd.org/

Addison MSHS 400/8-12
1 Colwell St 14801 607-359-2241
Jennifer Crane, prin. Fax 359-3443

Afton, Chenango, Pop. 818

Afton Central SD 600/K-12
PO Box 5 13730 607-639-8229
Elizabeth Briggs, supt. Fax 639-1801
www.afton.stier.org

Afton JSHS 300/6-12
PO Box 5 13730 607-639-8202
David Glover, prin. Fax 639-8257

Airmont, Rockland, Pop. 8,483

Mesifta Beth Shraga S 100/9-12
28 N Saddle River Rd, 845-356-1980

Monsey Beis Chaya Mushka 100/9-12
27 S Monsey Rd, 845-634-7400
Rabbi Dovid Kagan, prin. Fax 634-7422

Rabbinical College Beth Shraga Post-Sec.
28 N Saddle River Rd, 845-356-1980

Toras Chaim 50/9-12
1 Regina Rd, 845-352-9126

Akron, Erie, Pop. 2,833

Akron Central SD 1,500/K-12
47 Bloomingdale Ave 14001 716-542-5010
Kevin Shanley, supt. Fax 542-5018
www.akronschools.org

Akron HS 500/9-12
47 Bloomingdale Ave 14001 716-542-5030
Joseph Lucenti, prin. Fax 542-5018
Akron MS 300/6-8
47 Bloomingdale Ave 14001 716-542-5040
Joseph Caprio, prin. Fax 542-5018

Albany, Albany, Pop. 94,773
Albany CSD 8,700/PK-12
1 Academy Park 12207 518-475-6000
Dr. M. Vanden Wyngaard, supt. Fax 475-6009
www.albanyschools.org
Abrookin Career & Tech Center Vo/Tech
99 Kent St 12206 518-475-6400
Bryan Cartwright, admin. Fax 475-6402
Albany HS 2,500/9-12
700 Washington Ave 12203 518-475-6200
Cecily Wilson, prin. Fax 475-6202
Hackett MS 600/6-8
45 Delaware Ave 12202 518-475-6475
Michael Paolino, prin. Fax 475-6477
Myers MS 700/6-8
100 Elbel Ct 12209 518-475-6425
Kimberly Wilkins, prin. Fax 475-6427
Alternative Learning Center Adult
50 Lark St 12210 518-475-6525
Sophia Newell, prin. Fax 475-6527

South Colonie Central SD 5,400/PK-12
102 Loralee Dr 12205 518-869-3576
Jonathan Buhner, supt. Fax 869-6517
www.southcolonieschools.org
Colonie Central HS 1,900/9-12
1 Raider Blvd 12205 518-459-1220
David Wetzel, prin. Fax 459-8524
Lisha Kill MS 700/5-8
68 Waterman Ave 12205 518-456-2306
Joseph Guardino, prin. Fax 452-8165
Sand Creek MS 900/5-8
329 Sand Creek Rd 12205 518-459-1333
David Perry, prin. Fax 459-1404

Academy of the Holy Names 300/7-12
1075 New Scotland Rd 12208 518-438-7895
Mary Ann Vigliante, prin. Fax 438-7368
Albany Academies 500/PK-12
135 Academy Rd 12208 518-429-2300
Douglas North Ph.D., head sch Fax 427-7016
Albany Academy for Girls 400/PK-12
140 Academy Rd 12208 518-429-2300
Douglas North Ph.D., head sch Fax 463-5096
Albany College of Pharmacy & Health Sci Post-Sec.
106 New Scotland Ave 12208 888-203-8010
Albany Law School Post-Sec.
80 New Scotland Ave 12208 518-445-2311
Albany Medical College Post-Sec.
47 New Scotland Ave Code 3 12208 518-262-5521
Bishop Maginn HS 200/9-12
99 Slingerland St 12202 518-463-2247
Joseph Salamack, head sch Fax 463-9880
Branford Hall Career Institute Post-Sec.
500 New Karner Rd 12205 518-456-4464
Bryant & Stratton College Post-Sec.
1259 Central Ave 12205 518-437-1802
Center for Natural Wellness School Post-Sec.
3 Cerone Commercial Dr 12205 518-489-4026
Christian Brothers Academy 300/6-12
12 Airline Dr 12205 518-452-9809
James Schlegel, prin. Fax 452-9804
College of Saint Rose Post-Sec.
432 Western Ave 12203 800-637-8556
Excelsior College Post-Sec.
7 Columbia Cir 12203 518-464-8500
ITT Technical Institute Post-Sec.
13 Airline Dr 12205 518-452-9300
La Salle S 100/6-12
391 Western Ave 12203 518-242-4731
Bill Wolff, dir. Fax 242-4747
Maimonides Hebrew Day S 100/PK-12
404 Partridge St 12208 518-453-9363
Marcia Rosenfield, prin. Fax 453-9362
Maria College of Albany Post-Sec.
700 New Scotland Ave 12208 518-438-3111
Memorial Hospital School of Nursing Post-Sec.
600 Northern Blvd 12204 518-471-3260
Mildred Elley School Post-Sec.
855 Central Ave 12206 518-786-0855
Orlo School of Hair Design & Cosmetology Post-Sec.
232 N Allen St 12206 518-459-7832
The New School of Radio & Television Post-Sec.
7 Harriman Campus Rd 12206 518-438-7682
University at Albany SUNY Post-Sec.
1400 Washington Ave 12222 518-442-3300

Albertson, Nassau, Pop. 5,037
Herricks UFD
Supt. — See New Hyde Park
Herricks MS 1,000/6-8
7 Hilldale Dr 11507 516-305-8600
Joan Keegan, prin. Fax 248-3281

Albion, Orleans, Pop. 5,876
Albion Central SD 2,200/PK-12
324 East Ave 14411 585-589-2056
Michael Bonnewell, supt. Fax 589-2059
www.albionk12.org/
Bergerson MS, 254 East Ave 14411 500/6-8
Daniel Monacelli, prin. 585-589-2020
D'Amico HS, 302 East Ave 14411 700/9-12
Leslie Stauss, prin. 585-589-2040

Alden, Erie, Pop. 2,590
Alden Central SD 1,400/K-12
13190 Park St 14004 716-937-9116
Adam Stoltman, supt. Fax 937-7132
www.aldenschools.org
Alden HS 600/9-12
13190 Park St 14004 716-937-9116
Kevin Ryan, prin. Fax 937-1740
Alden MS 400/4-8
13250 Park St 14004 716-937-9116
William MacCowan, prin. Fax 937-3563

Alexander, Genesee, Pop. 501
Alexander Central SD 900/PK-12
3314 Buffalo St 14005 585-591-1551
Kathleen Maerten, supt. Fax 591-2257
www.alexandercsd.org
Alexander MSHS 500/6-12
3314 Buffalo St 14005 585-591-1551
Shannon Whitcombe, prin. Fax 591-1098

Alexandria Bay, Jefferson, Pop. 1,066
Alexandria Central SD 700/PK-12
34 Bolton Ave 13607 315-482-9971
Robert Wagoner, supt. Fax 482-9973
www.alexandriacentral.org
Alexandria Central JSHS 300/7-12
34 Bolton Ave 13607 315-482-5113
Julie Ludwig, prin. Fax 482-9973

Alfred, Allegany, Pop. 4,085

Alfred State College Post-Sec.
10 Upper College Dr 14802 800-425-3733
Alfred University Post-Sec.
1 Saxon Dr 14802 607-871-2111

Allegany, Cattaraugus, Pop. 1,807
Allegany-Limestone Central SD 1,300/PK-12
3131 Five Mile Rd 14706 716-375-6600
Dr. Karen Geelan, supt. Fax 375-6629
www.alli.wnyric.org
Allegany-Limestone HS 400/9-12
3131 Five Mile Rd 14706 716-375-6600
Kevin Straub, prin. Fax 375-6630
Allegany-Limestone MS 300/6-8
3131 Five Mile Rd 14706 716-375-6600
Michael Martel, prin. Fax 375-6630

Almond, Allegany, Pop. 460
Alfred-Almond Central SD 600/PK-12
6795 State Route 21 14804 607-276-6500
Richard Calkins, supt. Fax 276-6556
www.aacs.wnyric.org
Alfred-Almond JSHS 300/7-12
6795 State Route 21 14804 607-276-6555
Susan Bain-Lucey, prin. Fax 276-6556

Amenia, Dutchess, Pop. 935
Webutuck Central SD 700/PK-12
PO Box 405 12501 845-373-4100
James Gratto, supt. Fax 373-4102
www.webutuckschools.org/
Brooks IS 200/4-8
PO Box 405 12501 845-373-4114
Jay Curtis, prin. Fax 373-4126
Webutuck HS 300/9-12
PO Box 405 12501 845-373-4106
Ken Sauer, prin. Fax 373-8529

Kildonan S 100/2-12
425 Morse Hill Rd 12501 845-373-8111
Kevin Pendergast, hdmstr. Fax 373-9793

Amherst, Erie, Pop. 45,800
Amherst Central SD 2,900/K-12
55 Kings Hwy 14226 716-362-3000
Dr. Laura Chabe, supt. Fax 362-3022
amherstschools.org
Amherst Central HS 900/9-12
4301 Main St 14226 716-362-8100
Gregory Pigeon, prin. Fax 836-4972
Amherst MS 600/6-8
55 Kings Hwy 14226 716-362-7100
Michael Cornell, prin. Fax 836-0193

Sweet Home Central SD 3,500/PK-12
1901 Sweet Home Rd 14228 716-250-1402
Anthony Day, supt. Fax 250-1374
www.sweethomeschools.com
Sweet Home HS 1,200/9-12
1901 Sweet Home Rd 14228 716-250-1200
Joleen Reinholz, prin. Fax 250-1362
Sweet Home MS 800/6-8
4150 Maple Rd 14226 716-250-1450
Marty Pizur, prin. Fax 250-1490

Daemen College Post-Sec.
4380 Main St 14226 716-839-8225

Amityville, Suffolk, Pop. 9,408
Amityville UFD, 150 Park Ave 11701 2,900/PK-12
Dr. John Williams, supt. 631-565-6019
www.amityvilleufsd.org/
Amityville Memorial HS 700/10-12
250 Merrick Rd 11701 631-565-6100
Dr. Mary DeRose, prin.
Miles MS, 501 Route 110 11701 600/7-9
Michele Darby, prin. 631-565-6200

Island Drafting & Technical Institute Post-Sec.
128 Broadway 11701 631-691-8733

Amsterdam, Montgomery, Pop. 18,256
Broadalbin-Perth Central SD
Supt. — See Broadalbin
Broadalbin-Perth MS 400/6-8
1870 County Highway 107 12010 518-954-2700
Wayne Bell, prin. Fax 954-2709

Greater Amsterdam SD 3,700/K-12
11 Liberty St 12010 518-843-3180
Thomas Perillo, supt. Fax 842-0012
www.gasd.org
Amsterdam HS 1,200/9-12
140 Saratoga Ave 12010 518-843-4932
David Ziskin, prin. Fax 843-5432
Lynch MS 800/6-8
55 Brandt Pl 12010 518-843-3716
Fax 843-6287

Andes, Delaware, Pop. 250
Andes Central SD 100/PK-12
PO Box 248 13731 845-676-3167
Robert Chakar Ed.D., supt. Fax 676-3181
www.andescentralschool.org
Andes Central S 100/PK-12
PO Box 248 13731 845-676-3166
Robert Chakar Ed.D., admin. Fax 676-3181

Andover, Allegany, Pop. 1,032
Andover Central SD 400/PK-12
PO Box G 14806 607-478-8491
William Berg, supt. Fax 478-8833
www.andovercsd.org/
Andover S 400/PK-12
PO Box G 14806 607-478-8491
Jon Morris, prin. Fax 478-8833

Angola, Erie, Pop. 2,096
Lake Shore Central SD 2,500/K-12
959 Beach Rd 14006 716-926-2200
James E. Przepasniak, supt. Fax 549-6407
www.lakeshorecsd.org
Lake Shore MS 600/6-8
8855 Erie Rd 14006 716-549-2302
Erich Reidell, prin. Fax 549-4374
Lake Shore SHS 900/9-12
959 Beach Rd 14006 716-549-2301
Julie Hoerner, prin. Fax 549-4033

Annandale on Hudson, Dutchess

Bard College Post-Sec.
PO Box 5000 12504 845-758-6822

Ardsley, Westchester, Pop. 4,379
Ardsley UFD 2,000/K-12
500 Farm Rd 10502 914-693-6300
Dr. Lauren Allan, supt. Fax 693-8340
www.ardsleyschools.org
Ardsley HS 700/9-12
300 Farm Rd 10502 914-693-6300
Dr. James Haubner, prin. Fax 693-6822
Ardsley MS 600/5-8
700 Ashford Ave 10502 914-693-7564
Edgar McIntosh, prin. Fax 693-7896

Arkport, Steuben, Pop. 839
Arkport Central SD 600/K-12
35 East Ave 14807 607-295-7471
Glenn Niles, supt. Fax 295-7473
www.stev.net
Arkport Central S 600/K-12
35 East Ave 14807 607-295-9823
Caitlin Dewey, prin. Fax 295-7473

Armonk, Westchester, Pop. 4,278
Byram Hills Central SD 2,700/K-12
10 Tripp Ln 10504 914-273-4082
Dr. William Donohue, supt. Fax 273-2516
www.byramhills.org
Byram Hills HS 900/9-12
12 Tripp Ln Ste 1 10504 914-273-9200
Christopher Borsari, prin. Fax 273-2067
Crittenden MS 700/6-8
10 MacDonald Ave 10504 914-273-4250
Dr. H. Evan Powderly, prin. Fax 273-4618

Astoria, See New York
NYC Department of Education
Supt. — See New York
Academy for New Americans 200/6-8
3014 30th St 11102 718-932-5876
Betty Cartagena, prin. Fax 932-5990
IS 10 900/6-8
4511 31st Ave 11103 718-278-7054
Clemente Lopes, prin. Fax 274-1578
Baccalaureate S for Global Education 400/7-12
3412 36th Ave 11106 718-361-5275
Kelly Johnson, prin. Fax 361-5395
Long Island City HS 3,500/9-12
1430 Broadway 11106 718-545-7095
Vivian Selenikas, prin. Fax 545-2980
Sinatra HS 700/9-12
3512 35th Ave 11106 718-361-9920
Donna Finn, prin. Fax 361-9995

Empire Beauty School Post-Sec.
3815 Broadway 11103 718-726-8383
St. Demetrios Greek American S 600/PK-12
3003 30th Dr 11102 718-728-1754
St. John's Prep HS 1,300/9-12
2121 Crescent St 11105 718-721-7200
William Higgins, prin. Fax 545-9385

Athol Springs, Erie

St. Francis HS 500/9-12
4129 Lake Shore Rd 14010 716-627-1200
Thomas Braunscheidel, pres. Fax 627-4610

Attica, Wyoming, Pop. 2,513
Attica Central SD 1,500/K-12
3338 E Main Street Rd 14011 585-591-0400
Bryce Thompson, supt. Fax 591-2681
www.atticacsd.org
Attica HS 500/9-12
3338 E Main Street Rd 14011 585-591-0400
Kenneth Hammel, prin. Fax 591-4484
Attica MS 500/5-8
3338 E Main Street Rd 14011 585-591-0400
Paul Clark, prin. Fax 591-4496

Auburn, Cayuga, Pop. 26,874
Auburn CSD 3,600/K-12
78 Thornton Ave 13021 315-255-8800
Constance Evelyn, supt. Fax 255-8855
district.auburn.cnyric.org
Auburn HS 1,400/9-12
250 Lake Ave 13021 315-255-8300
Brian Morgan, prin. Fax 255-8357
Auburn JHS 300/7-8
191 Franklin St 13021 315-255-8480
David Oliver, prin. Fax 255-8495

Cayuga Community College Post-Sec.
197 Franklin St 13021 315-255-1743

Aurora, Cayuga, Pop. 708
Southern Cayuga Central SD 400/PK-12
2384 State Route 34B 13026 315-364-7211
Patrick Jensen, supt. Fax 364-7863
www.southerncayuga.org
Southern Cayuga JSHS 200/7-12
2384 State Route 34B 13026 315-364-7111
Luke Carnicelli, prin. Fax 364-8207

Wells College Post-Sec.
PO Box 500 13026 315-364-3266

Averill Park, Rensselaer, Pop. 1,668
Averill Park Central SD 3,300/K-12
146 Gettle Rd 12018 518-674-7050
Dr. James Hoffman, supt. Fax 674-3802
www.averillpark.k12.ny.us/
Algonquin MS 800/6-8
333 NY Highway 351 12018 518-674-7100
Robert Messia, prin. Fax 674-0671
Averill Park HS 1,100/9-12
146 Gettle Rd 12018 518-674-7000
Colleen Gomes, prin. Fax 674-7046

Avoca, Steuben, Pop. 933
Avoca Central SD 500/K-12
PO Box G 14809 607-566-2221
Richard Yochem, supt. Fax 566-2398
www.avocacsd.org/
Avoca Central S 500/K-12
PO Box G 14809 607-566-2221
Matthew Pfleegor, prin. Fax 566-8384

Avon, Livingston, Pop. 3,354
Avon Central SD 1,000/K-12
191 Clinton St 14414 585-226-2455
Bruce Amey, supt. Fax 226-8202
www.avoncsd.org
Avon HS 300/9-12
245 Clinton St 14414 585-226-2455
Barbara Zelazny, prin. Fax 226-8202
Avon MS 300/5-8
191 Clinton St 14414 585-226-2455
Jennifer Miller, prin. Fax 226-8202

Babylon, Suffolk, Pop. 11,970
Babylon UFD 1,800/K-12
50 Railroad Ave 11702 631-893-7925
Richard Rozakis, supt. Fax 893-7935
www.babylonschools.org
Babylon JSHS 800/7-12
50 Railroad Ave 11702 631-893-7910
Al Cirone, prin. Fax 893-7936

Bainbridge, Chenango, Pop. 1,346
Bainbridge-Guilford Central SD 800/PK-12
18 Juliand St 13733 607-967-6321
Dr. Don Wheeler, supt. Fax 967-4231
www.bgcsd.org
Bainbridge-Guilford HS 300/7-12
18 Juliand St 13733 607-967-6323
William Zakrajsek, prin. Fax 967-4231

Baldwin, Nassau, Pop. 23,329
Baldwin UFD 4,800/K-12
960 Hastings St 11510 516-377-9271
Dr. James Mapes, supt. Fax 377-9421
www.baldwinschools.org/
Baldwin HS 1,700/9-12
841 Ethel T Kloberg Dr 11510 516-377-9204
Susan Knors, prin. Fax 377-9208
Baldwin MS 1,300/6-8
3211 Schreiber Pl 11510 516-377-9321
Timothy Mayer, prin. Fax 377-9432

Baldwinsville, Onondaga, Pop. 7,290
Baldwinsville Central SD 5,700/K-12
29 E Oneida St 13027 315-638-6043
Jeanne Dangle, supt. Fax 638-6041
www.bville.org
Baker HS 1,400/10-12
29 E Oneida St 13027 315-638-6008
Robert Edwards, prin. Fax 638-6150
Durgee JHS 900/8-9
29 E Oneida St 13027 315-638-6086
Bonnie VanBenschoten, prin. Fax 638-6168

Baldwinsville Christian Academy 100/PK-12
7312 Van Buren Rd 13027 315-638-1069
Richard Auwarter, admin. Fax 638-4207

Ballston Spa, Saratoga, Pop. 5,283
Ballston Spa Central SD 4,200/K-12
70 Malta Ave 12020 518-884-7195
Joseph Dragone Ph.D., supt. Fax 884-7101
www.bscsd.org
Ballston Spa HS 1,400/9-12
220 Ballston Ave 12020 518-884-7150
Kristi Jensen, prin. Fax 884-7199
Ballston Spa MS 1,000/6-8
210 Ballston Ave 12020 518-884-7200
Pamela Motler, prin. Fax 884-7234

John Pauls Hair Nails & Skin Care Inst Post-Sec.
2144 Saratoga Ave 12020 518-583-3700

Bardonia, Rockland, Pop. 4,047

Albertus Magnus HS 500/9-12
798 Route 304 10954 845-623-8842
Joseph Troy, pres. Fax 623-0009

Barker, Niagara, Pop. 527
Barker Central SD 700/PK-12
1628 Quaker Rd 14012 716-795-3832
Dr. Roger Klatt, supt. Fax 795-3394
barkercsd.net
Barker JSHS 300/7-12
1628 Quaker Rd 14012 716-795-3201
Barbara Converso, prin. Fax 795-3911

Barrytown, Dutchess

Unification Theological Seminary Post-Sec.
30 Seminary Dr 12507 845-752-3000

Batavia, Genesee, Pop. 15,019
Batavia CSD 1,600/PK-12
260 State St 14020 585-343-2480
Christopher J. Dailey, supt. Fax 344-8204
www.bataviacsd.org
Batavia HS 700/9-12
260 State St 14020 585-343-2480
Scott Wilson, prin. Fax 344-8609
Batavia MS 500/5-8
96 Ross St 14020 585-343-2480
Sandra Griffin, prin. Fax 344-8626

Continental School of Beauty Culture Post-Sec.
215 Main St 14020 585-344-0886
Genesee Community College Post-Sec.
1 College Rd 14020 585-343-0055
New York State School for the Blind Post-Sec.
2A Richmond Ave 14020
Notre Dame HS 200/9-12
73 Union St 14020 585-343-2783
Dr. Joseph Scanlon, prin. Fax 343-7323

Bath, Steuben, Pop. 5,678
Bath Central SD 1,700/PK-12
25 Ellas Ave 14810 607-776-3301
Patrick Kelley, supt. Fax 776-5021
www.bathcsd.org
Haverling HS 500/9-12
25 Ellas Ave 14810 607-776-4107
Randy Brzezinski, prin. Fax 776-5021
Lyon MS 600/4-8
25 Ellas Ave 14810 607-776-2170
Michael Siebert, prin. Fax 776-1470

Bayport, Suffolk, Pop. 8,813
Bayport-Blue Point UFD 2,500/K-12
189 Academy St 11705 631-472-7860
Vincent Butera Ed.D., supt. Fax 472-7873
www.bbpschools.org/
Bayport-Blue Point HS 800/9-12
200 Snedecor Ave 11705 631-472-7800
Timothy Hearney Ed.D., prin. Fax 472-7814
Young MS 600/6-8
602 Sylvan Ave 11705 631-472-7820
Susan Haske, prin. Fax 472-7849

Bay Shore, Suffolk, Pop. 25,685
Bay Shore UFD 5,700/K-12
75 Perkal St 11706 631-968-1100
Peter Dion Ph.D., supt. Fax 968-4131
www.bayshoreschools.org
Bay Shore HS 1,900/9-12
155 3rd Ave 11706 631-968-1157
Robert Pashkin, prin. Fax 968-2332
Bay Shore MS 1,300/6-8
393 Brook Ave 11706 631-968-1210
Dr. LaQuita Outlaw, prin. Fax 968-2342

Brentwood UFD
Supt. — See Brentwood
West MS 800/6-8
2030 Udall Rd 11706 631-434-2371
Matthew Gengler, prin. Fax 242-3992

Bayside, See New York
NYC Department of Education
Supt. — See New York
Bayside HS 3,600/9-12
3224 Corporal Kennedy St 11361 718-229-7600
Michael Athy, prin. Fax 423-9566
MS 158 1,100/6-8
4635 Oceania St 11361 718-423-8100
Marie Nappi, prin. Fax 423-8135
Bell Academy 300/6-8
1825 212th St 11360 718-428-0587
Cheryl Quatrano, prin. Fax 428-0237

CUNY Queensborough Community College Post-Sec.
22205 56th Ave, Oakland Gardens NY 11364
718-631-6262

Beacon, Dutchess, Pop. 15,060
Beacon CSD 3,300/PK-12
10 Education Dr 12508 845-838-6900
Harvey Hilburgh, supt. Fax 838-6905
www.beaconcityk12.org/
Beacon HS 1,100/9-12
101 Matteawan Rd 12508 845-838-6900
Dr. Joannes Sieverding, prin. Fax 838-0796
Rombout MS 700/6-8
84 Matteawan Rd 12508 845-838-6900
Sherrill Lazarus, prin. Fax 231-0474

Beaver Falls, Lewis
Beaver River Central SD 900/K-12
9508 Artz Rd 13305 315-346-1211
Leueen Smithling, supt. Fax 346-6775
www.brcsd.org
Beaver River HS 300/9-12
9508 Artz Rd 13305 315-346-1211
Rebecca Dunckel-King, prin. Fax 346-6775
Beaver River MS 200/6-8
9508 Artz Rd 13305 315-346-1211
Christine LaBare, prin. Fax 346-6775

Bedford, Westchester, Pop. 1,810
Bedford Central SD 4,300/K-12
632 S Bedford Rd 10506 914-241-6000
Dr. Jere Hochman, supt. Fax 241-6004
www.bcsdny.org
Fox Lane HS 1,300/9-12
PO Box 390 10506 914-241-6085
Dr. Joel Adelberg, prin. Fax 241-6064
Other Schools – See Mount Kisco

Rippowam Cisqua S 200/5-9
439 Cantitoe St 10506 914-244-1250
Fax 244-1245

Bedford Hills, Westchester, Pop. 2,942

Yeshiva & Mesivta Ohel Shmuel 50/11-12
165 Haines Rd Stop 1 10507 914-241-2700

Belfast, Allegany, Pop. 823
Belfast Central SD 400/PK-12
1 King St 14711 585-365-9940
Judy May, supt. Fax 365-2648
www.belfast.wnyric.org
Belfast Central S 400/PK-12
1 King St 14711 585-365-8285
Michael Roche, prin. Fax 365-2648

Belle Harbor, Queens

Yeshiva Mercaz Hatorah of Belle Harbor 100/9-12
505 Beach 129th St 718-474-3064

Bellerose, Queens, Pop. 1,168
NYC Department of Education
Supt. — See New York
HS of Teaching Liberal Arts & Science 1,200/9-12
7420 Commonwealth Blvd 11426 718-736-7100
Jae Hyun-Cho, dir. Fax 736-7117

Belleville, Jefferson, Pop. 225
Belleville Henderson Central SD 500/PK-12
PO Box 158 13611 315-846-5826
Rick Moore, supt. Fax 846-5617
www.bhpanthers.org
Belleville Henderson Central S 500/PK-12
PO Box 158 13611 315-846-5121
Scott Storey, prin. Fax 846-5617

Bellmore, Nassau, Pop. 16,044
Bellmore-Merrick Central HSD
Supt. — See North Merrick
Grand Avenue MS 1,000/7-8
2301 Grand Ave 11710 516-992-1100
Carlo Conte, prin. Fax 679-5068
Kennedy HS 1,300/9-12
3000 Bellmore Ave 11710 516-992-1400
Lorraine Poppe, prin. Fax 826-0526
Mepham HS 1,300/9-12
2401 Camp Ave 11710 516-992-1500
Michael Harrington, prin. Fax 785-7590

Bellport, Suffolk, Pop. 2,050
South Country Central SD
Supt. — See East Patchogue
Bellport MS 1,000/6-8
35 Kreamer St 11713 631-730-1657
Brian Ginty, prin. Fax 286-4460

Belmont, Allegany, Pop. 950
Genesee Valley Central SD 600/PK-12
1 Jaguar Dr 14813 585-268-7900
Dr. Brian Schmitt, supt. Fax 268-7990
www.genvalley.org
Genesee Valley HS 200/7-12
1 Jaguar Dr 14813 585-268-7900
Mia O'Brien, prin. Fax 268-7990

Bemus Point, Chautauqua, Pop. 360
Bemus Point Central SD 800/PK-12
PO Box 468 14712 716-386-2375
Michael Mansfield, supt. Fax 386-2376
www.bemusptcsd.org
Maple Grove JSHS 400/6-12
PO Box 468 14712 716-386-2855
Julie Verdonik, prin. Fax 386-2376

Bergen, Genesee, Pop. 1,158
Byron-Bergen Central SD 700/PK-12
6917 W Bergen Rd 14416 585-494-1220
Casey Kosiorek, supt. Fax 494-2613
www.bbschools.org/
Byron-Bergen JSHS 300/6-12
6917 W Bergen Rd 14416 585-494-1220
Aaron Johnson, prin. Fax 494-2613

Berne, Albany
Berne-Knox-Westerlo Central SD 800/K-12
1738 Helderberg Trl 12023 518-872-1293
Dr. Paul Dorward, supt. Fax 872-2031
www.bkwschools.org
Berne-Knox-Westerlo JSHS 500/7-12
1738 Helderberg Trl 12023 518-872-1482
Brian Corey, prin. Fax 872-2083

Bethpage, Nassau, Pop. 16,246
Bethpage UFD 3,000/K-12
10 Cherry Ave 11714 516-644-4000
Terrence Clark, supt. Fax 931-8783
www.bethpagecommunity.com/Schools/
Bethpage HS 1,000/9-12
10 Cherry Ave 11714 516-644-4100
Michael Spence, prin. Fax 937-6076

Kennedy MS 700/6-8
500 Broadway 11714 516-644-4200
David Schneider, prin. Fax 937-0540

Plainedge UFD
Supt. — See North Massapequa
Plainedge MS 800/6-8
200 Stewart Ave 11714 516-992-7650
Anthony DeRiso, prin. Fax 992-7645

Briarcliffe College Post-Sec.
1055 Stewart Ave 11714 516-918-3600

Binghamton, Broome, Pop. 45,574
Binghamton CSD 5,700/PK-12
PO Box 2126 13902 607-762-8100
Marion Martinez, supt. Fax 762-8112
www.binghamtonschools.org
Binghamton HS 1,600/9-12
31 Main St 13905 607-762-8200
Roxie Oberg, prin. Fax 762-6072
East MS 600/6-8
167 E Frederick St 13904 607-762-8300
Michael O'Branski, prin. Fax 762-8398
West MS 700/6-8
W Middle Ave 13905 607-763-8400
Michael Holly, prin. Fax 763-8429

Chenango Forks Central SD 1,300/PK-12
1 Gordon Dr 13901 607-648-7543
Lloyd Peck, supt. Fax 648-7560
www.cforks.org
Chenango Forks HS 500/9-12
1 Gordon Dr 13901 607-648-7544
John Hillis, prin. Fax 648-7568
Chenango Forks MS 400/6-8
1 Gordon Dr 13901 607-648-7576
Lorraine Pourby, prin. Fax 648-2767

Chenango Valley Central SD 1,800/PK-12
221 Chenango Bridge Rd 13901 607-762-6800
David Gill, supt. Fax 762-6890
www.cvcsd.stier.org/
Chenango Valley HS 500/9-12
221 Chenango Bridge Rd 13901 607-762-6900
Terrence Heller, prin. Fax 779-4777
Chenango Valley MS 300/7-8
221 Chenango Bridge Rd 13901 607-762-6902
Eric Attleson, prin. Fax 779-4784

Binghamton University SUNY Post-Sec.
4400 Vestal Pkwy 13902 607-777-2000
Broome Community College Post-Sec.
PO Box 1017 13902 607-778-5000
Ridley-Lowell Business & Technical Inst. Post-Sec.
116 Front St 13905 607-724-2941
Seton Catholic Central HS 300/7-12
70 Seminary Ave 13905 607-723-5307
Richard Bucci, prin. Fax 723-4601

Blauvelt, Rockland, Pop. 5,591
South Orangetown Central SD 3,400/K-12
160 Van Wyck Rd 10913 845-680-1050
Dr. Ken Mitchell, supt. Fax 680-1900
www.socsd.org
South Orangetown MS 800/6-8
160 Van Wyck Rd 10913 845-680-1100
Karen Tesik, prin. Fax 680-1905
Other Schools – See Orangeburg

Bloomfield, Ontario, Pop. 1,335
Bloomfield Central SD 1,000/PK-12
45 Maple Ave Ste A 14469 585-657-6121
Michael Midey, supt. Fax 657-6060
www.bloomfieldcsd.org
Bloomfield HS 300/9-12
1 Oakmount Ave 14469 585-657-6121
Nancy Gerstner, prin. Fax 657-4771
Bloomfield MS 200/6-8
1 Oakmount Ave 14469 585-657-6121
Nancy Gerstner, prin. Fax 657-4771

Bohemia, Suffolk, Pop. 10,114
Connetquot Central SD 6,700/K-12
780 Ocean Ave 11716 631-244-2215
Dr. Alan Groveman, supt. Fax 589-0683
www.connetquot.k12.ny.us/
Connetquot HS 2,100/9-12
190 7th St 11716 631-244-2226
Gregory Murtha, prin. Fax 244-2287
Other Schools – See Oakdale, Ronkonkoma

Branford Hall Career Institute Post-Sec.
565 Johnson Ave 11716 631-471-9100

Boiceville, Ulster
Onteora Central SD 1,500/K-12
PO Box 300 12412 845-657-6383
Dr. Phyllis McGill, supt. Fax 657-8742
onteora.schoolwires.com/
Onteora HS 600/9-12
PO Box 300 12412 845-657-2373
Lance Edelman, prin. Fax 657-8430
Onteora MS 200/7-8
PO Box 300 12412 845-657-2373
Jennifer O'Connor, prin. Fax 657-7763

Bolivar, Allegany, Pop. 1,040
Bolivar-Richburg Central SD 900/PK-12
100 School St 14715 585-928-2561
John Marshall, supt. Fax 928-2411
www.brcs.wnyric.org
Bolivar-Richburg JSHS 500/6-12
100 School St 14715 585-928-2561
Tim Houseknecht, prin. Fax 928-1368

Bolton Landing, Warren, Pop. 501
Bolton Central SD 200/PK-12
PO Box 120 12814 518-644-2400
Raymond Ciccarelli, supt. Fax 644-2124
www.boltoncsd.org
Bolton Central S 200/PK-12
PO Box 120 12814 518-644-2400
Michael Graney, prin. Fax 644-2124

Boonville, Oneida, Pop. 2,065
Adirondack Central SD 1,400/PK-12
110 Ford St 13309 315-942-9200
David Hubman, supt. Fax 942-5522
www.adirondackcsd.org
Adirondack HS 400/9-12
8181 State Route 294 13309 315-942-9250
Edward Niznik, prin. Fax 942-9254
Adirondack MS 300/6-8
8181 State Route 294 13309 315-942-9202
Patricia Thomas, prin. Fax 942-9211

Bradford, Schuyler
Bradford Central SD 300/K-12
2820 State Route 226 14815 607-583-4616
Wendy Field, supt. Fax 583-4013
www.bradfordcsd.org
Bradford Central S 300/K-12
2820 State Route 226 14815 607-583-4616
Mary Ordway, prin. Fax 583-4013

Brasher Falls, Saint Lawrence, Pop. 656
Brasher Falls Central SD 1,100/PK-12
PO Box 307 13613 315-389-5131
Stephan Vigliotti, supt. Fax 389-5245
bfcsd.org
St. Lawrence Central HS 400/9-12
PO Box 307 13613 315-389-5131
Tracy Davison, prin. Fax 389-5245
St. Lawrence Central MS 300/5-8
PO Box 307 13613 315-389-5131
Christoper Rose, prin. Fax 389-4185

Breesport, Chemung, Pop. 625

Twin Tiers Christian Academy 100/7-12
PO Box K 14816 607-739-3619
Cary Shaw, admin. Fax 739-3619

Brentwood, Suffolk, Pop. 59,660
Brentwood UFD 16,700/PK-12
52 3rd Ave 11717 631-434-2323
Joseph Bond, supt. Fax 273-6575
www.bufsd.org/
Brentwood Freshman Center 1,200/9-9
33 Leahy Ave 11717 631-434-2541
Felicia Thomas-Williams, prin. Fax 434-2549
Brentwood SHS 3,700/10-12
2 6th Ave 11717 631-434-2204
Richard Loeschner, prin. Fax 434-2206
East MS 900/6-8
70 Hilltop Dr 11717 631-434-2473
John Callan, prin. Fax 434-2171
North MS 1,000/6-8
350 Wicks Rd 11717 631-434-2356
Luis Velazquez, prin. Fax 952-9249
South MS 800/6-8
785 Candlewood Rd 11717 631-434-2341
Dergre Escobores Ed.D., prin. Fax 434-2560
Other Schools – See Bay Shore

Long Island University Post-Sec.
100 2nd Ave 11717 631-273-5112
Suffolk County Community College Grant Post-Sec.
1001 Crooked Hill Rd 11717 631-851-6700

Brewster, Putnam, Pop. 2,362
Brewster Central SD 2,900/K-12
30 Farm To Market Rd 10509 845-279-8000
Dr. Jane Sandbank, supt. Fax 279-3510
www.brewsterschools.org
Brewster HS 1,200/9-12
50 Foggintown Rd 10509 845-279-5051
Dr. Joseph Castagnola, prin. Fax 279-6730
Wells MS 900/6-8
570 Route 312 10509 845-279-3702
Michelle Gosh, prin. Fax 279-7634

Briarcliff Manor, Westchester, Pop. 7,748
Briarcliff Manor UFD 1,600/K-12
45 Ingham Rd 10510 914-941-8880
Neal Miller, supt. Fax 941-2177
www.briarcliffschools.org
Briarcliff Manor HS 600/9-12
444 Pleasantville Rd 10510 914-769-6299
James Kaishian, prin. Fax 769-2509
Briarcliff MS 400/6-8
444 Pleasantville Rd 10510 914-769-6343
Susan Howard, prin. Fax 769-6375

Bridgehampton, Suffolk, Pop. 1,736
Bridgehampton UFD 200/PK-12
PO Box 3021 11932 631-537-0271
Dr. Lois Favre, supt. Fax 537-9038
www.bridgehampton.k12.ny.us/
Bridgehampton S 200/PK-12
PO Box 3021 11932 631-537-0271
John Pryor, prin. Fax 537-0443

Broadalbin, Fulton, Pop. 1,305
Broadalbin-Perth Central SD 1,800/PK-12
20 Pine St 12025 518-954-2500
Stephen Tomlinson, supt. Fax 954-2509
www.bpcsd.org
Broadalbin-Perth HS 600/9-12
100 Bridge St 12025 518-954-2600
Margaret Blowers, prin. Fax 954-2609
Other Schools – See Amsterdam

Brockport, Monroe, Pop. 8,227
Brockport Central SD 3,800/K-12
40 Allen St 14420 585-637-1810
Lesli Myers Ed.D., supt. Fax 637-0165
www.bcs1.org
Brockport HS 1,300/9-12
40 Allen St 14420 585-637-1877
Dana Boshnack, prin. Fax 637-1867
Oliver MS 900/6-8
40 Allen St 14420 585-637-1860
Melody Martinez-Davis, prin. Fax 637-1869

SUNY College at Brockport Post-Sec.
350 New Campus Dr 14420 585-395-2211

Brocton, Chautauqua, Pop. 1,467
Brocton Central SD 600/K-12
138 W Main St 14716 716-792-9121
John Hertlein, supt. Fax 792-9965
www.broctoncsd.org
Brocton MSHS 300/6-12
138 W Main St 14716 716-792-2190
Jason Delcamp, prin. Fax 792-2246

Bronx, See New York
NYC Department of Education
Supt. — See New York
Academy for Language and Technology 400/9-12
1700 Macombs Rd 10453 718-731-0219
Arisleyda Urena, prin. Fax 731-2031
Academy for Personal Leadership 300/6-8
120 E 184th St 10468 718-220-3139
Angelo Ledda, prin. Fax 220-6018
Academy of Applied Math & Technology 200/6-8
345 Brook Ave 10454 718-292-3883
Vincent Gassetto, prin. Fax 292-4473
Academy of Public Relations 200/6-8
778 Forest Ave 10456 718-665-8866
Amy Andino, prin. Fax 401-0051
Acad for Scholarship & Entrepreneurship 600/6-12
921 E 228th St 10466 718-696-3840
Zenobia White, prin. Fax 696-3841
Accion Academy 200/6-8
1825 Prospect Ave 10457 718-294-0514
Nikole Booker, prin. Fax 294-3869
Addams Academic Careers HS Vo/Tech
900 Tinton Ave 10456 718-292-4513
Joel DiBartolomeo, prin. Fax 292-1947
Archimedes Academy 400/6-12
456 White Plains Rd 10473 718-617-5046
Miriam Lazar, prin. Fax 617-7395
Aspire Preparatory MS 500/6-8
2441 Wallace Ave 10467 718-231-6592
Steven Cobb, prin. Fax 231-6591
Astor Collegiate Academy 500/9-12
925 Astor Ave 10469 718-944-3419
Sandra Burgos, prin. Fax 944-3638
Baychester MS 6-8
3750 Baychester Ave 10466 718-547-1890
Shawn Mangar, prin. Fax 547-1895
Belmont Preparatory HS 400/9-12
500 E Fordham Rd 10458 718-733-4559
Stephen Gumbs, prin. Fax 295-3655
Blueprint MS 100/6-8
1111 Pugsley Ave 10472 718-822-2780
Tyneka Harrington, prin. Fax 822-2279
Bronck Academy 200/6-8
400 E Fordham Rd 10458 718-365-2502
Brenda Gonzalez, prin. Fax 365-3892
Bronx Academy of Health Careers 400/9-12
800 E Gun Hill Rd 10467 718-696-3340
Dawn Santiago, prin. Fax 696-3380
Bronx Aerospace Academy 400/9-12
800 E Gun Hill Rd 10467 718-696-6010
Barbara Kirkweg, prin. Fax 696-6030
Bronx Arena HS 300/Alt
1440 Story Ave 10473 718-860-5060
Ty Cesene, prin. Fax 860-5058
Bronx Bridges HS 100/9-12
1980 Lafayette Ave 10473 718-829-2984
Pablo Villavicencio, prin. Fax 829-2987
Bronx Career and College Preparatory HS Vo/Tech
800 Home St 10456 718-542-4011
Kizhaya Roberts, prin. Fax 542-4377
Bronx Center for Science & Mathematics 400/9-12
1363 Fulton Ave 10456 718-992-7089
Edward Tom, prin. Fax 590-1052
Bronx Community HS 200/Alt
1980 Lafayette Ave 10473 718-892-1026
Flora Greenaway, prin. Fax 892-6941
Bronx Compass HS 9-12
1980 Lafayette Ave 10473 718-828-1206
Stacy McCoy, prin.
Bronxdale HS 100/9-12
925 Astor Ave 10469 718-944-3655
Carolyne Quintana, prin. Fax 944-3662
Bronx Dance Academy 300/6-8
3617 Bainbridge Ave 10467 718-515-0410
Sandra Sanchez, prin. Fax 515-0345
Bronx Design and Construction Academy 9-12
333 E 151st St 10451 718-402-7690
Matthew Williams, prin. Fax 402-4216
Bronx Early College Academy 400/6-12
250 E 164th St 10456 718-681-8287
Yvette Rivera, prin. Fax 681-8650
Bronx Engineering & Technology Academy 400/9-12
99 Terrace View Ave Rm 544 10463 718-563-6678
Karalyne Sperling, prin. Fax 741-5263
Bronx Envision Academy 9-12
1619 Boston Rd 10460 718-589-1590
Emily Shu, prin. Fax 589-1595
Bronx Expeditionary Learning HS 400/9-12
240 E 172nd St 10457 718-410-4077
D. White, prin. Fax 293-9567
Bronx Green MS 400/6-8
2441 Wallace Ave 10467 718-325-6593
Charles Johnson, prin. Fax 325-3625
Bronx Guild HS 300/9-12
1980 Lafayette Ave 10473 718-597-1587
Sam Decker, prin. Fax 597-1371
Bronx Haven HS 100/Alt
333 E 151st St 10451 718-292-3638
Lucinda Mendez, prin. Fax 292-6065
Bronx Health Sciences HS 300/9-12
750 Baychester Ave 10475 718-862-4406
Miriam Rivas, prin. Fax 862-4410

HS for Contemporary Arts 500/9-12
800 E Gun Hill Rd 10467 718-944-5610
Francisco Sanchez, prin. Fax 944-5650
HS for Energy and Technology 9-12
2474 Crotona Ave 10458 718-733-3080
Ignazio Accardi, prin.
HS for Language and Innovation 9-12
925 Astor Ave 10469 718-944-3625
Julie Nariman, prin. Fax 944-3641
Bronx HS for Law & Community Service 400/9-12
500 E Fordham Rd 10458 718-733-5274
Michael Barakate, prin. Fax 295-3631
HS for Teaching & Professions 500/9-12
2780 Reservoir Ave 10468 718-329-7380
Jason Maass, prin. Fax 365-7984
HS for Violin & Dance 300/9-12
1110 Boston Rd 10456 718-842-0687
Franklin Sim, prin. Fax 589-9849
Bronx HS for Visual Arts 400/9-12
2040 Antin Pl 10462 718-319-5160
G. Jones, prin. Fax 319-5165
Bronx HS for Writing & Communication 400/9-12
800 E Gun Hill Rd 10467 718-944-5660
Terri Grey, prin. Fax 944-5690
HS of American Studies 400/9-12
2925 Goulden Ave 10468 718-329-2144
Alessandro Weiss, prin. Fax 329-0792
Bronx HS of Business 400/9-12
240 E 172nd St 10457 718-410-4060
Vincent Rodriguez, prin. Fax 992-5760
HS of Computers & Technology 600/9-12
800 E Gun Hill Rd 10467 718-696-3930
Bruce Abramowitz, prin. Fax 696-3950
Bronx HS of Science 3,000/9-12
75 W 205th St 10468 718-817-7700
Valerie Reidy, prin. Fax 733-7951
HS of World Cultures 400/9-12
1300 Boynton Ave 10472 718-860-8120
Dr. Ramon Namnum, prin. Fax 893-7152
IS 117 800/6-8
1865 Morris Ave 10453 718-583-7750
Delise Jones, prin. Fax 583-7658
IS 129 600/6-8
2055 Mapes Ave 10460 718-933-5976
Raymond Granda, prin. Fax 933-8132
IS 181 600/6-8
800 Baychester Ave 10475 718-904-5600
Christopher Warnock, prin. Fax 904-5620
IS 190 200/6-8
1550 Crotona Park E 10460 718-620-9423
Diana Santiago, prin. Fax 620-9927
IS 206 400/5-8
2280 Aqueduct Ave 10468 718-584-1570
David Neering, prin. Fax 584-7928
IS 219 400/6-8
3630 3rd Ave 10456 718-681-7093
Dominic Cipollone, prin. Fax 681-7324
IS 224 400/6-8
345 Brook Ave 10454 718-665-9804
Sojourner Welch, prin. Fax 665-0078
IS 229 200/6-8
275 Harlem River Park Brg 10453 718-583-6266
Dr. Ezra Matthias, prin. Fax 583-6325
IS 232 400/6-8
1700 Macombs Rd 10453 718-583-7007
Neifi Acosta, prin. Fax 583-4864
IS 254 500/6-8
2452 Washington Ave 10458 718-220-8700
Wilfred Heymans, prin. Fax 220-4881
IS 303 300/6-8
1700 Macombs Rd 10453 718-583-5466
Patricia Bentley, prin. Fax 583-2463
IS 313 400/6-10
1600 Webster Ave 10457 718-583-1736
Lauren Wilkens, prin. Fax 299-5559
IS 318 400/6-8
1919 Prospect Ave 10457 718-294-8504
Maria Lopez, prin. Fax 901-0778
IS 339 800/6-8
1600 Webster Ave 10457 718-583-6767
Kim Outerbridge, prin. Fax 583-0281
Bronx International HS 400/9-12
1110 Boston Rd 10456 718-620-1053
Joaquin Vega, prin. Fax 620-1056
JHS 22 600/6-8
270 E 167th St 10456 718-681-6850
Linda Rosenbury, prin. Fax 681-6895
JHS 80 700/6-8
149 E Mosholu Pkwy N 10467 718-405-6300
Emmanuel Polanco, prin. Fax 405-6324
JHS 98 500/6-8
1619 Boston Rd 10460 718-589-8200
Claralee Irobunda, prin. Fax 589-8179
JHS 118 1,200/6-8
577 E 179th St 10457 718-584-2330
Elizabeth Lawrence, prin. Fax 584-7763
JHS 123 500/6-8
1025 Morrison Ave 10472 718-328-2105
Tyra Williams, prin. Fax 328-8561
JHS 125 700/6-8
1111 Pugsley Ave 10472 718-822-5186
Lori Anne Evanko, prin. Fax 239-3121
JHS 127 700/6-8
1560 Purdy St 10462 718-892-8600
Harry Sherman, prin. Fax 892-8300
JHS 131 900/6-8
885 Bolton Ave 10473 718-991-7490
Ed Leotta, prin. Fax 328-6705
JHS 144 1,000/6-8
2545 Gunther Ave 10469 718-379-7400
Jeremy Cavinoff, prin. Fax 320-7135
JHS 145 500/5-8
1000 Teller Ave 10456 718-681-7219
Robert Hannibal, prin. Fax 681-6913
JHS 151 300/6-8
250 E 156th St 10451 718-292-0260
Socorro Rivera, prin. Fax 292-5704

JHS 162 700/6-8
600 Saint Anns Ave 10455 718-292-0880
Maryann Manzolillo, prin. Fax 292-5735
Bronx Lab S 500/9-12
800 E Gun Hill Rd 10467 718-696-3700
Christopher Lagares, prin. Fax 696-3730
Bronx Latin S 400/6-12
800 Home St 10456 718-991-6349
Annette Fiorentino, prin. Fax 991-6627
Bronx Leadership Academy 700/9-12
1710 Webster Ave 10457 718-299-4274
Kenneth Gaskins, prin. Fax 299-4707
Bronx Leadership Academy II 400/9-12
730 Concourse Vlg W 10451 718-292-7171
Katherine Callaghan, prin. Fax 292-2355
Bronx Mathematics Preparatory S 400/6-8
456 White Plains Rd 10473 718-542-5063
Anya Munce, prin. Fax 542-5236
MS 101 500/6-8
2750 Lafayette Ave 10465 718-829-6372
Jared Rosoff, prin. Fax 829-6594
MS 142 800/6-8
3750 Baychester Ave 10466 718-231-0100
Lajuan White, prin. Fax 231-3046
MS 180 700/6-8
700 Baychester Ave 10475 718-904-5650
Frank Uzzo, prin. Fax 904-5655
MS 203 300/6-8
339 Morris Ave 10451 718-292-1052
William Hewlett, prin. Fax 292-5765
MS 223 500/6-8
360 E 145th St 10454 718-292-8627
Ramon Gonzalez, prin. Fax 292-7435
MS 301 300/6-8
890 Cauldwell Ave 10456 718-585-2950
Benjamin Basile, prin. Fax 401-2567
MS 302 700/6-8
681 Kelly St 10455 718-292-6070
Liza Ortiz, prin. Fax 401-2958
MS 390 400/6-8
1930 Andrews Ave 10453 718-583-5501
Robert Mercedes, prin. Fax 583-5556
Bronx MSHS for Medical Science 400/6-12
240 E 172nd St 10457 718-410-4040
William Quintana, prin. Fax 992-4129
Bronx Park MS 6-8
2441 Wallace Ave 10467 718-652-6090
Bronx Regional HS 300/Alt
1010 Rev James A Polite Ave 10459 718-991-2020
Colin Thomas, prin. Fax 617-0257
S for Tourism and Hospitality 9-12
900 Tinton Ave 10456 718-401-4214
David Martin, prin.
Bronx S Law Government & Justice 700/6-12
244 E 163rd St 10451 718-410-3430
Meisha Ross-Porter, prin. Fax 410-3950
Bronx S of Law & Finance 400/9-12
99 Terrace View Ave Rm 804 10463 718-561-0113
Jessica Goring, prin. Fax 561-0595
Bronx S of Young Leaders 400/6-8
40 W Tremont Ave 10453 718-583-4146
Serapha Cruz, prin. Fax 583-4292
Bronx Studio S 400/6-12
928 Simpson St 10459 718-893-5158
David Vazquez, prin. Fax 893-5982
Bronx Theatre HS 400/9-12
99 Terrace View Ave Rm 716 10463 718-329-2902
Charles Gallo, prin. Fax 329-0433
Bronxwood Preparatory Academy 400/9-12
921 E 228th St 10466 718-696-3820
Janet Gallardo, prin. Fax 696-3821
Bronx Writing Academy 500/6-8
270 E 167th St 10456 718-293-9048
Kamar Samuels, prin. Fax 293-9748
Chaifetz Transfer HS 200/Alt
778 Forest Ave 10456 718-402-2429
Anne Fennelly, prin. Fax 402-3120
Cinema S 100/9-12
1551 E 172nd St 10472 718-620-2560
Rex Bobbish, prin. Fax 620-2561
Clinton HS 4,400/9-12
100 W Mosholu Pkwy S 10468 718-543-1000
Geraldine Ambrosio, prin. Fax 548-0036
Collegiate Institute of Math & Science 500/9-12
925 Astor Ave 10469 718-944-3635
Shadia Alvarez, prin. Fax 652-3525
Columbus HS 1,200/9-12
925 Astor Ave 10469 718-944-3400
Lisa Fuentes, prin. Fax 519-1565
Community S for Social Justice 300/9-12
350 Gerard Ave 10451 718-402-8481
Sue-Ann Rosch, prin. Fax 402-8650
Comprehensive Model S Project-MS 327 400/6-9
1501 Jerome Ave 10452 718-861-0852
Manuel Ramirez, prin. Fax 993-2990
Cornerstone Academy for Social Action MS 200/6-8
3441 Steenwick Ave 10475 718-794-7970
Jamaal Bowman, prin. Fax 794-7981
Creston Academy 200/6-8
125 E 181st St 10453 718-367-5035
Pamela Edwards, prin. Fax 367-5176
Crotona Academy HS 100/Alt
639 Saint Anns Ave 10455 718-402-8378
Anthony Harris, prin. Fax 402-8446
Crotona International HS 9-12
2474 Crotona Ave 10458 718-561-8701
Jesseca Long, prin. Fax 561-8707
Cruz Bronx HS of Music 400/9-12
2780 Reservoir Ave 10468 718-329-8550
Dr. William Rodriguez, prin. Fax 329-8559
Curie HS 500/9-12
120 W 231st St 10463 718-432-6491
Rodney Fisher, prin. Fax 796-7051
Discovery HS 500/9-12
2780 Reservoir Ave 10468 718-733-3872
Rolando Rivera, prin. Fax 733-3621
Dodge Career & Technology HS Vo/Tech
2474 Crotona Ave 10458 718-584-2700
Frank Giaimo, prin. Fax 584-7490

Douglas Academy V 300/6-8
2111 Crotona Ave 10457 718-561-1617
Deborah Cimini, prin. Fax 561-2184
Douglass Academy III 400/8-12
3630 3rd Ave 10456 718-538-9726
Rahesha Amon, prin. Fax 538-9796
Dreamyard Preparatory S 300/9-12
240 E 172nd St 10457 718-410-4242
Alicia Wargo, prin. Fax 410-4312
Eagle Academy for Young Men 500/9-12
4143 3rd Ave 10457 718-466-8000
Jonathan Foy, prin. Fax 466-8090
East Bronx Academy for the Future 600/6-12
1716 Southern Blvd 10460 718-861-8641
Sarah Scrogin, prin. Fax 861-8634
East Fordham Academy for the Arts 200/6-8
120 E 184th St 10468 718-220-4185
Tanicia Williams, prin. Fax 220-5976
Emolior Academy 200/6-8
1970 W Farms Rd 10460 718-842-2670
Derick Spaulding, prin. Fax 842-2857
English Language Learners Academy 200/9-12
99 Terrace View Ave 10463 718-220-1889
Norma Vega, prin. Fax 220-8758
Entrada Academy 300/6-8
977 Fox St 10459 718-378-1649
Socorro Diaz, prin. Fax 378-4707
Eximius College Preparatory Academy 300/9-12
1363 Fulton Ave 10456 718-992-7154
Jonathan Daly, prin. Fax 590-1081
Explorations Academy 400/9-12
1619 Boston Rd 10460 718-893-6173
Susana Hernandez, prin. Fax 893-6439
Fordham HS for the Arts 400/9-12
500 E Fordham Rd 10458 718-733-4656
Iris Blige, prin. Fax 295-3605
Fordham Leadership Academy 500/9-12
500 E Fordham Rd 10458 718-733-5024
Maryann Tucker, prin. Fax 295-3674
Foreign Langugage Academy\Global Study 400/9-12
470 Jackson Ave 10455 718-585-4024
Leba Augone, prin. Fax 585-4239
Forward School of Creative Writing 300/6-8
3710 Barnes Ave 10467 718-652-0519
Adrienne Phifer, prin. Fax 652-0428
Gateway S of Environmental Research 500/9-12
1980 Lafayette Ave 10473 718-824-9327
Cliff Siegel, prin. Fax 824-4368
Giordano MS 1,000/6-8
2502 Lorillard Pl 10458 718-584-1660
Anna Maria Giordano, prin. Fax 584-7968
Global Enterprise HS 400/9-12
925 Astor Ave 10469 718-944-3548
Sandra Maldonado, prin.
Globe S for Environmental Research 500/6-8
3710 Barnes Ave 10467 718-994-1395
Matthew Angell, prin. Fax 994-1316
Gompers Career & Technical HS Vo/Tech
455 Southern Blvd 10455 718-665-0950
Joyce Kittrell, prin. Fax 292-3164
Hamer Freedom HS 500/9-12
1021 Jennings St 10460 718-861-0521
Nancy Mann, prin. Fax 861-0619
Hamer MS 200/6-8
1001 Jennings St 10460 718-860-2707
Lorraine Chanon, prin. Fax 860-3212
Health Opportunities HS 600/9-12
350 Gerard Ave 10451 718-401-1826
Julie McHedlishvili, prin. Fax 401-1632
Hostos-Lincoln Academy 600/6-12
600 Saint Anns Ave 10455 718-402-5640
Nick Paarlberg, prin. Fax 518-4321
Hunts Point S 400/6-8
730 Bryant Ave 10474 718-328-1972
Sonya Johnson, prin. Fax 328-7330
Institute for Law and Public Policy 400/9-12
1440 Story Ave 10473 718-860-5110
Grismaldy Laboy-Wilson, prin. Fax 860-5081
In-Tech Academy 1,100/6-12
2975 Tibbett Ave 10463 718-432-4300
Yvette Allen, prin. Fax 432-4310
International Community HS 400/9-12
345 Brook Ave 10454 718-665-4128
Berena Cabarcas, prin. Fax 665-4547
International S for Liberal Arts 600/6-12
2780 Reservoir Ave 10468 718-329-8570
Francine Cruz, prin. Fax 329-8572
KAPPA 400/5-8
3630 3rd Ave 10456 718-590-5455
Sheri Warren, prin. Fax 681-4266
KAPPA 400/9-12
500 E Fordham Rd 10458 718-933-1247
Panorea Panagiosoulis, prin. Fax 933-1568
KAPPA III S 200/6-8
2055 Mapes Ave 10460 718-561-3580
Elisa Alvarez, prin. Fax 561-3719
Kelly HS 500/9-12
965 Longwood Ave 10459 718-860-1242
Antonio Arocho, prin. Fax 860-1934
Kennedy HS 1,100/9-12
99 Terrace View Ave 10463 718-817-7400
Lisa Luft, prin. Fax 562-5132
Kingsbridge International HS 500/9-12
2780 Reservoir Ave 10468 718-329-8580
Ronald Newlon, prin. Fax 329-8582
Leadership Institute 300/9-12
1701 Fulton Ave 10457 718-299-7490
Marta Colon, prin.
Lehman HS 3,900/9-12
3000 E Tremont Ave 10461 718-904-4200
R. Lobianco, prin. Fax 904-4285
Levin HS for Media & Communications 400/9-12
240 E 172nd St 10457 718-992-3709
Nasib Hoxha, prin. Fax 992-4170
Marble Hill HS for International Studies 400/9-12
99 Terrace View Ave Rm 822 10463 718-561-0973
Kirsten Larson, prin. Fax 561-5612

Metropolitan HS 300/9-12
1180 Rev James A Polite Ave 10459 718-991-4634
Carla Theodorou, prin. Fax 542-7294
Metropolitan Soundview HS 9-12
1300 Boynton Ave 10472 718-860-8240
Michael Lanaghan, prin. Fax 860-8232
Millenium Art Academy 500/9-12
1980 Lafayette Ave 10473 718-824-0978
Herman Guy, prin. Fax 824-0963
Monroe Academy for Business & Law 400/9-12
1300 Boynton Ave 10472 718-860-8140
Charles Ogundimu, prin. Fax 893-3262
Monroe Academy for Visual Arts & Design 500/9-12
1300 Boynton Ave 10472 718-860-8160
Richard Massel, prin. Fax 860-8110
Morris Academy for Collaborative Studies 400/9-12
1110 Boston Rd 10456 718-542-3700
Charles Osewalt, prin. Fax 542-3958
Mott Hall Bronx HS 400/9-12
1595 Bathgate Ave 10457 718-466-6800
Kathryn Malloy, prin. Fax 466-6801
Mott Hall Community S 200/6-8
650 Hollywood Ave 10465 718-829-3254
Jennie Garrison, prin. Fax 829-3859
Mott Hall III 300/6-8
560 Crotona Park S 10456 718-842-6138
Jorisis Stupart, prin. Fax 842-6348
Mott Hall V 400/6-12
1551 E 172nd St 10472 718-620-8160
Peter Oroszlany, prin. Fax 620-8161
Mott Haven Community HS 9-12
455 Southern Blvd 10455 718-665-8512
Helene Spadaccini, prin.
Mott Haven Village Prep HS 400/9-12
701 Saint Anns Ave 10455 718-402-0571
William Doyle, prin. Fax 665-2363
Neruda Academy 400/9-12
1980 Lafayette Ave 10473 718-824-1682
Sabrina Cook, prin. Fax 824-1663
New Day Academy 300/6-12
800 Home St 10456 718-542-1155
Mara Ganeles, prin. Fax 589-8067
New Explorers HS 300/9-12
730 Concourse Vlg W 10451 718-292-4150
Jake Hobson, prin. Fax 292-5887
New Millenium Business Academy 200/6-8
1000 Teller Ave 10456 718-588-8308
Dorald Bastian, prin. Fax 681-6913
New S for Leadership and Journalism 700/6-8
120 W 231st St 10463 718-601-2869
Dolores Peterson, prin. Fax 601-2867
New World HS 400/9-12
921 E 228th St 10466 718-696-3800
Fausto Salazar, prin. Fax 696-3801
One World MS 6-8
3750 Baychester Ave 10466 718-515-6780
Patricia Wynne, prin. Fax 515-6785
Pan American International HS 300/9-12
1300 Boynton Ave 10472 718-991-7238
Bridgit Bye, prin. Fax 991-7872
Pantoja Preparatory Academy 400/6-12
1980 Lafayette Ave 10473 718-824-3152
Nancy Diaz, prin. Fax 824-3543
Patri MS 600/6-8
2225 Webster Ave 10457 718-584-1295
Gracela Abadia, prin. Fax 584-1358
Peace & Diversity Academy 300/9-12
1180 Rev James A Polite Ave 10459 718-991-1855
Andrew Turay, prin. Fax 991-2998
Pelham Academy of Academics 200/6-8
2441 Wallace Ave 10467 718-881-3136
Anthony Rivera, prin. Fax 881-3413
Pelham Gardens MS 6-8
2545 Gunther Ave 10469 718-320-8712
Pelham Preparatory Academy 500/9-12
925 Astor Ave 10469 718-944-3401
Carlos Santiago, prin. Fax 944-3479
Performance Conservatory HS 400/9-12
1619 Boston Rd 10460 718-991-0860
Ulynis Fridie, prin. Fax 991-5258
PULSE HS 200/Alt
560 E 179th St 10457 718-294-0230
Carol Wiggins, prin. Fax 584-7809
Renaissance HS of Musical Theater 500/9-12
3000 E Tremont Ave 10461 718-430-6390
Maria Herrera, prin. Fax 430-6308
Riverdale/Kingsbridge Academy 1,300/6-12
660 W 237th St 10463 718-796-8516
Lori O'Mara, prin. Fax 796-8657
Rucker S of Community Research 300/9-12
965 Longwood Ave 10459 718-860-1053
Sharif Rucker, prin. Fax 860-1321
Schomburg Satellite Academy 100/Alt
1010 Rev James A Polite Ave 10459 718-542-2700
Marsha Vernon, prin. Fax 589-3710
School for Community Research & Learning 200/10-12
1980 Lafayette Ave 10473 347-892-2054
Jacqueline Boswell, prin. Fax 892-3580
School for Excellence HS 400/9-12
1110 Boston Rd 10456 718-860-1385
Carmen Brown, prin. Fax 860-4882
School for Inquiry & Social Justice 300/6-8
1025 Morrison Ave 10472 718-860-4181
Andrea Cyprys, prin. Fax 860-4163
School of Diplomacy 400/6-8
3710 Barnes Ave 10467 718-994-1028
Sean Licata, prin.
School of Performing Arts 300/6-8
977 Fox St 10459 718-589-4844
Maiysha Etienne, prin. Fax 589-7998
Science and Technology Academy 200/6-8
250 E 164th St 10456 718-293-4017
Dr. Patrick Awosogba, prin. Fax 293-7396
Smith Career and Tech HS Vo/Tech
333 E 151st St 10451 718-993-5000
Evan Schwartz, prin. Fax 292-1944
Soundview Acad for Culture & Scholarship 200/6-8
885 Bolton Ave 10473 718-991-4027
William Frackelton, prin. Fax 991-4807

South Bronx Academy for Applied Media 300/6-8
778 Forest Ave 10456 718-401-0059
Roshone Ault, prin. Fax 401-0577
South Bronx Preparatory HS 600/6-12
360 E 145th St 10454 718-292-2211
Ellen Flanagan, prin. Fax 292-2172
Theatre Arts Production Company S 500/6-12
2225 Webster Ave 10457 718-584-0832
Ron Link, prin. Fax 584-5102
Truman HS 2,000/9-12
750 Baychester Ave 10475 718-904-5400
Sana Nasser, prin. Fax 904-5502
University Heights HS 300/9-12
701 Saint Anns Ave 10455 718-292-0578
Hazel Roseboro, prin. Fax 292-4276
Urban Assembly Academy Civic Engagement 300/6-8
650 Hollywood Ave 10465 718-822-0126
Mary Sheppard, prin. Fax 822-1049
Urban Assembly Acad History/Citizenship 200/10-12
240 E 172nd St 10457 718-293-6768
Avis Terrol, prin. Fax 293-4084
Urban Assembly Bronx Academy of Letters 600/6-12
339 Morris Ave 10451 718-401-4891
Jeffrey Garrett, prin. Fax 401-6626
Urban Assembly Math & Science MSHS 600/6-12
1595 Bathgate Ave 10457 718-466-7800
David Krulwich, prin. Fax 466-7801
Urban Assembly S for Careers in Sports 400/9-12
730 Concourse Vlg W 10451 718-292-7110
Johanny Garcia, prin. Fax 993-1567
Urban Assembly S Wildlife Conservation 300/6-12
2024 Mohegan Ave 10460 718-991-2695
Mark Ossenheimer, prin. Fax 991-2980
Urban Institute of Mathematics 300/6-8
650 Hollywood Ave 10465 718-823-6042
Jennifer Joynt, prin. Fax 823-6347
Urban Science Academy 400/5-8
1000 Teller Ave 10456 718-588-8221
Patrick Kelly, prin. Fax 588-8263
Validus Preparatory Academy 400/9-12
1595 Bathgate Ave 10457 718-466-4000
Javier Ocampo, prin. Fax 466-4001
West Bronx Academy for the Future 600/6-12
500 E Fordham Rd 10458 718-563-7139
Wilper Morales, prin. Fax 563-7362
Westchester Square Academy 9-12
3000 E Tremont Ave 10461 718-904-5050
Sara Dingledy, prin.
Wings Academy 500/9-12
1122 E 180th St 10460 718-597-1751
Wayne Cox, prin. Fax 931-8366
Womans Academy of Excellence 300/9-12
456 White Plains Rd 10473 718-542-0740
Arnette Crocker, prin. Fax 542-0841
Young Scholars Academy 400/6-8
3710 Barnes Ave 10467 718-325-5834
Jeanette Vargas, prin. Fax 325-5676
Young Womens Leadership S of the Bronx 6-8
1865 Morris Ave 10453 718-731-2590
Lemarie Laureano, prin.

Academy of Mt. St. Ursula 300/9-12
330 Bedford Park Blvd 10458 718-364-5353
Lisa Harrison, prin. Fax 364-2354
All Hallows HS 600/9-12
111 E 164th St 10452 718-293-4545
Sean Sullivan, prin. Fax 410-8298
Aquinas HS 700/9-12
685 E 182nd St 10457 718-367-2113
Sr. Catherine Rose Quigley, prin. Fax 295-5864
Bronx Lebanon Hospital Center Post-Sec.
1650 Grand Concourse 10457 718-518-1800
Cardinal Hayes HS 900/9-12
650 Grand Concourse 10451 718-292-6100
William Lessa, prin. Fax 292-9178
Cardinal Spellman HS 1,400/9-12
1 Cardinal Spellman Pl 10466 718-881-8000
Daniel O'Keefe, prin. Fax 515-6615
College of New Rochelle Post-Sec.
332 E 149th St 10451 718-665-1310
College of New Rochelle Post-Sec.
755 Co Op City Blvd 10475 718-320-0300
CUNY Bronx Community College Post-Sec.
2155 University Ave 10453 718-289-5100
CUNY Hostos Community College Post-Sec.
500 Grand Concourse 10451 718-518-4444
CUNY Lehman College Post-Sec.
250 Bedford Park Blvd W 10468 718-960-8000
Ethical Culture Fieldston S 1,000/6-12
3901 Fieldston Rd 10471 718-329-7300
Dr. John Love, prin. Fax 329-7305
Fordham Preparatory HS 900/9-12
441 E Fordham Rd 10458 718-367-7500
Robert Gomprecht, prin. Fax 367-7598
Fordham University Post-Sec.
441 E Fordham Rd 10458 718-817-1000
Lavelle School/Blind-Visually Impaired Post-Sec.
E 221 St & Paulding Ave 10469
Mann S 1,800/PK-12
231 W 246th St 10471 718-432-4000
Dr. Thomas Kelly, hdmstr. Fax 548-2089
Mercy College Post-Sec.
1200 Waters Pl 10461 800-637-2969
Monroe College Post-Sec.
2501 Jerome Ave 10468 718-933-6700
Monsignor Scanlan HS 600/9-12
915 Hutchinson River Pkwy 10465 718-430-0100
Emily Padilla-Bradley, prin. Fax 892-8845
Montefiore Medical Center Post-Sec.
111 E 210th St 10467 718-920-4001
Mt. St. Michael Academy 800/6-12
4300 Murdock Ave 10466 718-515-6400
Br. Steve Schlitte, prin. Fax 994-7729
New York Institute for Special Education Post-Sec.
999 Pelham Pkwy N 10469 718-519-7000
Our Saviour Lutheran S 300/PK-12
1734 Williamsbridge Rd 10461 718-792-5665
John Schmidt, prin. Fax 409-3877

Preston HS 600/9-12
2780 Schurz Ave 10465 718-863-9134
Jane Grendell, prin. Fax 863-6125
Riverdale Country S 700/6-12
5250 Fieldston Rd 10471 718-549-8810
Dominic Randolph, hdmstr. Fax 519-2795
St. Barnabas HS 200/9-12
425 E 240th St 10470 718-325-8800
Sr. Joan Faraone, prin. Fax 325-8820
St. Catharine Academy 700/9-12
2250 Williamsbridge Rd 10469 718-882-2882
Sr. Anne Welch, prin. Fax 231-9099
St. Ignatius Academy 100/5-8
740 Manida St 10474 718-861-9084
John Omernik, prin. Fax 861-9096
St. Raymond Girls Academy 400/9-12
1725 Castle Hill Ave 10462 718-824-4220
Sr. Mary Ann D'Antonio, prin. Fax 829-3571
St. Raymond HS for Boys 800/9-12
2151 Saint Raymonds Ave 10462 718-824-5050
Br. Daniel Gardner, prin. Fax 863-8808
Salanter Akiba Riverdale HS 400/9-12
503 W 259th St 10471 718-548-2727
Rabbi Tully Harcsztark, prin. Fax 548-4400
SUNY Maritime College Post-Sec.
6 Pennyfield Ave 10465 718-409-7200
Veterans Affairs Medical Center Post-Sec.
130 W Kingsbridge Rd 10468 718-579-1640
Yeshiva of the Telshe Alumni Post-Sec.
4904 Independence Ave 10471 718-601-3523

Bronxville, Westchester, Pop. 6,193
Bronxville UFD 1,500/K-12
177 Pondfield Rd 10708 914-395-0500
Dr. David Quattrone, supt. Fax 961-2364
www.bronxville.k12.ny.us
Bronxville HS 400/9-12
177 Pondfield Rd 10708 914-395-0500
Terence Barton, prin. Fax 395-0513
Bronxville MS 300/6-8
177 Pondfield Rd 10708 914-395-0500
Dr. Thomas Wilson, prin. Fax 771-6223

Concordia College Post-Sec.
171 White Plains Rd 10708 914-337-9300
Sarah Lawrence College Post-Sec.
1 Mead Way 10708 914-337-0700

Brookfield, Madison
Brookfield Central SD 200/PK-12
PO Box 60 13314 315-899-3323
Robert Service, supt. Fax 899-8902
www.brookfieldcsd.org
Brookfield Central S 200/PK-12
PO Box 60 13314 315-899-3323
Kathleen Donovan, prin. Fax 899-8902

Brookhaven, Suffolk, Pop. 3,414
South Country Central SD
Supt. — See East Patchogue
Bellport HS 1,400/9-12
205 Beaver Dam Rd 11719 631-730-1575
Tim Hogan, prin. Fax 286-5336

Brooklyn, See New York
NYC Department of Education
Supt. — See New York
Academy for College Preparation 600/6-12
911 Flatbush Ave 11226 718-564-2566
Doris Unger, prin. Fax 564-2567
Academy for Conservation & Environment 200/9-12
6565 Flatlands Ave 11236 718-968-4101
Eugene Mazzola, prin. Fax 968-4296
Academy for Environmental Leadership 400/9-12
400 Irving Ave 11237 718-381-7100
Nilda Gomez-Katz, prin. Fax 628-6965
Academy for Health Careers 100/9-12
150 Albany Ave 11213 718-773-0128
Deonne Martin, prin. Fax 773-0648
Academy for Young Writers 400/9-12
1065 Elton St 11239 718-688-7230
Courtney Winkfield, prin. Fax 688-7236
Academy of Hospitality & Tourism 300/9-12
911 Flatbush Ave 11226 718-564-2580
Adam Brier, prin. Fax 564-2581
Academy of Innovative Technology 300/9-12
999 Jamaica Ave 11208 718-827-2469
Cynthia Fowlkes, prin. Fax 827-4013
Academy of Urban Planning 500/9-12
400 Irving Ave 11237 718-381-7100
Rodney Orji, prin. Fax 418-0314
Acorn Community HS 700/9-12
561 Grand Ave 11238 718-789-2258
Andrea Piper, dir. Fax 789-2260
All City Leadership Academy 200/6-12
1474 Gates Ave 11237 718-381-9653
Elvis Estevez, prin. Fax 381-9680
Arts & Media Preparatory Academy 200/9-12
905 Winthrop St 11203 718-773-3908
Robert Hall, prin. Fax 773-7274
Aspirations Diploma Plus HS 300/Alt
1495 Herkimer St 11233 718-498-5257
Shermila Bharat, prin. Fax 498-7170
Automotive HS Vo/Tech
50 Bedford Ave 11222 718-218-9301
Catherina Lafergola, prin. Fax 599-4351
Banneker Academy 800/9-12
77 Clinton Ave 11205 718-797-3702
Deonca Renee, prin. Fax 797-3862
Barton HS Vo/Tech
901 Classon Ave 11225 718-636-4900
Richard Forman, prin. Fax 857-3688
Bedford Academy HS 400/9-12
1119 Bedford Ave 11216 718-398-3061
Adofo Muhammad, prin. Fax 636-3819
Bedford - Stuyvesant Prep HS 100/Alt
832 Marcy Ave 11216 718-622-4310
Darryl Rascoe, prin. Fax 398-4381

Boys & Girls HS 1,900/9-12
1700 Fulton St 11213 718-467-1700
Bernard Gassaway, prin. Fax 221-0645

Brooklyn Academy HS 200/Alt
832 Marcy Ave 11216 718-638-4235
Charon Hall, prin. Fax 638-0051

Brooklyn Academy of Global Finance 100/9-12
125 Stuyvesant Ave 11221 718-574-3126
Dannielle Darbee, prin. Fax 574-3681

Brooklyn Acad of Science & Environment 400/9-12
883 Classon Ave 11225 718-230-6363
Veronica Peterson, prin. Fax 230-6370

Brooklyn Bridge Academy 200/Alt
6565 Flatlands Ave 11236 718-968-1689
Max Paul, prin. Fax 968-1678

Brooklyn College Academy 600/7-12
350 Coney Island Ave 11218 718-951-5941
Nick Mazzarella, prin. Fax 951-4441

Brooklyn Collegiate S 500/7-12
2021 Bergen St 11233 718-922-1145
Amote Sias, prin. Fax 922-2347

Brooklyn Community HS of Arts & Media 500/9-12
300 Willoughby Ave 11205 718-230-5748
James O'Brien, prin. Fax 230-3050

Brooklyn Democracy Academy 200/Alt
985 Rockaway Ave 11212 718-342-6348
Andrew Brown, prin. Fax 342-6708

Brooklyn Frontiers HS 9-12
112 Schermerhorn St 11201 718-722-4727
Alona Cohen Ph.D., prin. Fax 722-7919

Brooklyn Generation S 300/9-12
6565 Flatlands Ave 11236 718-968-4200
Lydia Bomani, prin. Fax 444-5419

HS for Civil Rights 400/9-12
400 Pennsylvania Ave 11207 718-922-6289
Michael Steele, prin. Fax 922-7253

HS for Global Citizenship 400/9-12
883 Classon Ave 11225 718-230-6300
Michelle Rochon, prin. Fax 230-6301

Brooklyn HS for Law & Technology 400/9-12
1396 Broadway 11221 718-919-1256
Michael Prayor, prin. Fax 852-4593

HS for Medical Professions 300/9-12
1600 Rockaway Pkwy 11236 718-290-8700
Joseph Scarmato, prin. Fax 290-8705

HS for Public Service 400/9-12
600 Kingston Ave 11203 718-756-5325
Ben Shuldiner, prin. Fax 363-3206

HS for Service & Learning 400/9-12
911 Flatbush Ave 11226 718-564-2551
Peter Fabianski, prin. Fax 564-2552

Brooklyn HS for the Arts 700/9-12
345 Dean St 11217 718-855-2412
Margaret Berman, prin. Fax 852-8734

HS for Youth & Community Development 400/9-12
911 Flatbush Ave 11226 718-564-2470
Pamela Washington, prin. Fax 564-2471

HS Innovation in Advertising 200/9-12
1600 Rockaway Pkwy 11236 718-290-8760
Adaleza Michelena, prin. Fax 290-8766

Brooklyn HS Leadership Community Service 200/Alt
300 Willoughby Ave 11205 718-638-3062
Georgia Kouriampalis, prin. Fax 638-3404

HS of Enterprise - Business & Tech 900/9-12
850 Grand St 11211 718-387-2800
Holger Carrillo, prin. Fax 387-2748

HS of Sports Management 300/9-12
2630 Benson Ave 11214 718-333-7650
Robin Pitts, prin. Fax 333-7675

HS of Telecommunications Arts & Tech 1,300/9-12
350 67th St 11220 718-759-3400
Philip Weinberg, prin. Fax 759-3490

Brooklyn Institute For Liberal Arts 9-12
600 Kingston Ave 11203 718-221-1097
Ann-Marie Henry-Stephens, prin.

IS 30 300/6-8
415 Ovington Ave 11209 718-491-5684
Carol Heeraman, prin. Fax 491-0071

IS 68 900/6-8
956 E 82nd St 11236 718-241-4800
Merve Williams, prin. Fax 241-5582

IS 96 900/6-8
99 Avenue P 11204 718-236-1344
Denise Levinsky, prin. Fax 236-2397

IS 98 1,200/6-8
1401 Emmons Ave 11235 718-891-9005
Maria Timo, prin. Fax 646-7250

IS 136 500/6-8
4004 4th Ave 11232 718-965-3333
Eric Sackler, prin. Fax 965-9567

IS 171 900/5-8
528 Ridgewood Ave 11208 718-647-0111
Barbara Kendall, prin. Fax 827-5834

IS 211 800/6-8
1001 E 100th St 11236 718-251-4411
Carolyn James, prin. Fax 241-2503

IS 228 800/6-8
228 Avenue S 11223 718-375-7635
Dominick D'Angelo, prin. Fax 376-1209

IS 281 1,300/6-8
8787 24th Ave 11214 718-996-6706
Maria Bender, prin. Fax 996-4186

IS 285 900/6-8
5909 Beverley Rd 11203 718-451-2200
Frederick Underwood, prin. Fax 451-0229

IS 296 400/7-8
125 Covert St 11207 718-574-0288
Diana Devito, prin. Fax 574-1368

IS 303 700/6-8
501 West Ave 11224 718-996-0100
Fax 996-3785

IS 318 1,700/6-8
101 Walton St 11206 718-782-0589
Leander Windley, prin. Fax 384-7715

IS 340 300/6-8
227 Sterling Pl 11238 718-857-5516
Jean Williams, prin. Fax 230-5479

IS 347 500/5-8
35 Starr St 11221 718-821-4248
John Barbella, prin. Fax 821-1332

IS 349 500/6-8
35 Starr St 11221 718-418-6389
Rogelio Parris, prin. Fax 418-6146

IS 364 400/6-8
1426 Freeport Loop 11239 718-642-3007
Dale Kelly, prin. Fax 642-8516

IS 381 400/6-8
1599 E 22nd St 11210 718-252-0058
Mary Harrington, prin. Fax 252-0035

IS 392 300/5-8
104 Sutter Ave 11212 718-498-2491
Shirley Massey, prin. Fax 346-2804

Brooklyn International HS 400/9-12
49 Flatbush Avenue Ext 11201 718-643-9315
Pamela Taranto, prin. Fax 643-9516

JHS 14 600/6-8
2424 Batchelder St 11235 718-743-0220
Anne Tully, prin. Fax 769-8632

JHS 50 500/6-8
183 S 3rd St 11211 718-387-4184
Denise Jamison, prin. Fax 302-2320

JHS 57 200/6-8
125 Stuyvesant Ave 11221 718-574-2357
Celeste Douglas, prin. Fax 453-0577

JHS 62 1,200/6-8
700 Cortelyou Rd 11218 718-941-5450
Barry Kevorkian, prin. Fax 693-7433

JHS 78 1,100/6-8
1420 E 68th St 11234 718-763-4701
Anthony Cusumano, prin. Fax 251-3439

JHS 88 900/6-8
544 7th Ave 11215 718-788-4482
Ailene Altman-Mitchell, prin. Fax 768-0213

JHS 162 600/6-8
1390 Willoughby Ave 11237 718-821-4860
Barbara DeMartino, prin. Fax 821-1728

JHS 166 500/6-8
800 Van Siclen Ave 11207 718-649-0765
Maria Ortega, prin. Fax 927-2172

JHS 201 1,500/6-8
8010 12th Ave 11228 718-833-9363
Madeleine Brennan, prin. Fax 836-1786

JHS 218 600/6-8
370 Fountain Ave 11208 718-647-9050
Valena Woodley, prin. Fax 827-5839

JHS 220 1,300/6-8
4812 9th Ave 11220 718-633-8200
Loretta Witek, prin. Fax 871-7466

JHS 223 600/6-8
4200 16th Ave 11204 718-438-0155
Andrew Frank, prin. Fax 871-7477

JHS 227 1,300/6-8
6500 16th Ave 11204 718-256-8218
Brenda Champion, prin. Fax 234-6204

JHS 234 1,800/6-8
1875 E 17th St 11229 718-645-1334
Susan Schaeffer, prin. Fax 645-7759

JHS 259 1,400/6-8
7305 Fort Hamilton Pkwy 11228 718-833-1000
Janice Geary, prin. Fax 833-3419

JHS 278 1,000/6-8
1925 Stuart St 11229 718-375-3523
Debra Garofalo, prin. Fax 998-7324

JHS 291 700/6-8
231 Palmetto St 11221 718-574-0361
Jacqueline Rosado, prin. Fax 574-1360

JHS 292 700/6-8
301 Vermont St 11207 718-498-6562
Gloria Nandan, prin. Fax 345-3327

JHS 302 1,000/6-8
350 Linwood St 11208 718-647-9500
Lisa Linder, prin. Fax 827-3294

JHS 383 1,000/5-8
1300 Greene Ave 11237 718-574-0390
Jeanette Smith, prin. Fax 574-1366

Brooklyn Lab S 300/9-12
999 Jamaica Ave 11208 718-235-3592
Renel Piton, prin. Fax 235-4028

Brooklyn Latin S 300/9-12
325 Bushwick Ave 11206 718-366-0154
Jason Griffiths, prin. Fax 381-3012

MS 35 200/6-8
272 MacDonough St 11233 718-574-2345
Jackie Charles-Marcus, prin. Fax 452-1273

MS 51 1,100/6-8
350 5th Ave 11215 718-369-7603
Lenore Berner, prin. Fax 499-4948

MS 61 1,100/6-8
400 Empire Blvd 11225 718-774-1002
Sandra Taylor, prin. Fax 467-4335

MS 113 900/6-8
300 Adelphi St 11205 718-834-6734
Dawnique Daughtry, prin. Fax 596-2802

MS 246 600/6-8
72 Veronica Pl 11226 718-282-5230
Bently Warrington, prin. Fax 284-6429

MS 266 200/6-8
62 Park Pl 11217 718-857-2291
Glenda Esperance, prin. Fax 857-2347

MS 267 300/6-8
800 Gates Ave 11221 718-574-2318
Patricia King, prin. Fax 574-2320

MS 571 200/6-8
80 Underhill Ave 11238 718-638-1740
Santosha Troutman, prin. Fax 638-0295

MS 582 300/6-8
207 Bushwick Ave 11206 718-456-8218
Brian Walsh, prin. Fax 456-8220

MS 584 200/6-8
130 Rochester Ave 11213 718-604-1380
Gilleyan Hargrove, prin. Fax 604-3784

MS 596 200/6-8
300 Willoughby Ave 11205 718-230-3273
Lisa Reiter, prin. Fax 230-0173

MS for Academic and Social Excellence 200/6-8
1224 Park Pl 11213 718-774-0105
Andrea Whitehurst, prin. Fax 774-0298

MS for Art and Philosophy 400/6-8
1084 Lenox Rd 11212 718-342-7563
Neil McNeill, prin. Fax 342-8131

MS for the Arts 400/6-8
790 E New York Ave 11203 718-773-3343
Daniqua Brooks, prin. Fax 773-4168

MS of Marketing & Legal Studies 300/6-8
905 Winthrop St 11203 718-773-7343
Jameela Horton-Ball, prin. Fax 773-7946

Brooklyn Preparatory HS 400/9-12
257 N 6th St 11211 718-486-2550
Noah Lansner, prin. Fax 486-2505

Brooklyn S for Collaborative Studies 700/6-12
610 Henry St 11231 718-923-4750
Alyce Barr, prin. Fax 923-4730

Brooklyn S for Global Studies 400/6-12
284 Baltic St 11201 718-694-9741
Joseph O'Brien, prin. Fax 694-9745

Brooklyn School for Math and Research 9-12
400 Irving Ave 11237 718-381-7100
Perry Rainey, prin. Fax 381-9897

Brooklyn S for Music & Theater 400/9-12
883 Classon Ave 11225 718-230-6250
Pamela Dorcely, prin. Fax 230-6262

S of Business Finance Entrepreneurship 200/6-8
125 Stuyvesant Ave 11221 718-602-3271
Glyn Marryshow, prin. Fax 602-3274

Brooklyn Studio Secondary S 900/6-12
8310 21st Ave 11214 718-266-5032
Andrea Ciliotta, prin. Fax 266-5093

Brooklyn Technical HS 5,100/9-12
29 Fort Greene Pl 11217 718-804-6400
Randy Asher, prin. Fax 260-9245

Brooklyn Theatre Arts HS 300/9-12
6565 Flatlands Ave 11236 917-968-1072
David Ward, prin. Fax 968-1065

Brownsville Academy HS 200/Alt
1150 E New York Ave 11212 718-778-7305
Lashawn Robinson, prin. Fax 778-7385

Brownsville Collaborative MS 6-8
85 Watkins St 11212 718-495-1202

Bushwick Community HS 400/Alt
231 Palmetto St 11221 718-443-3083
Llermi Gonzalez, prin. Fax 443-4757

Bushwick HS for Social Justice 400/9-12
400 Irving Ave 11237 718-381-7100
Lucas Cooke, prin. Fax 418-0192

Bushwick Leaders HS 500/9-12
797 Bushwick Ave 11221 718-919-4212
Catherine Reilly, prin. Fax 574-1103

Campos Secondary S 800/6-12
215 Heyward St 11206 718-302-7900
Eric Fraser, prin. Fax 302-7979

Carson HS for Coastal Studies 500/9-12
521 West Ave 11224 718-265-0329
Ed Wilensky, prin. Fax 372-2514

Cobble Hill S of American Studies 700/9-12
347 Baltic St 11201 718-403-9544
Annamaria Mule, prin. Fax 403-9553

Conselyea Preparatory S 400/6-8
208 N 5th St 11211 718-486-6211
Maria Masullo, prin. Fax 486-6771

Cultural Academy for Arts and Sciences 200/9-12
5800 Tilden Ave 11203 718-968-6630
Diane Varano, prin. Fax 968-6635

Cypress Hills Collegiate Preparatory S 400/9-12
999 Jamaica Ave 11208 718-647-1672
Any Yager, prin. Fax 647-6719

Dewey HS 2,600/9-12
50 Avenue X 11223 718-373-6400
Kathleen Elvin, prin. Fax 266-4385

Douglas Academy IV 400/7-12
1014 Lafayette Ave 11221 718-574-2820
Elvin Crespo, prin. Fax 574-2821

Douglas Academy VII HS 400/9-12
226 Bristol St 11212 718-485-3789
Jessica Endlich, prin. Fax 922-2761

Douglass Academy VIII MS 200/6-8
1400 Pennsylvania Ave 11239 718-642-4305
Yolanda Martin, prin. Fax 642-4537

Eagle Academy for Young Men II 200/6-10
1137 Herkimer St 11233 718-495-0863
Rashad Meade, prin. Fax 732-2129

East Brooklyn Community HS 200/9-12
9517 Kings Hwy 11212 718-927-6880
Patrick McGillicuddy, prin. Fax 927-6885

East Flatbush Community Research S 200/6-8
905 Winthrop St 11203 718-773-3059
Daveida Daniel, prin. Fax 773-3827

East NY Family Academy 400/6-12
2057 Linden Blvd 11207 718-927-0012
Sheila Richards, prin. Fax 927-0411

East New York MS of Excellence 100/6-8
605 Shepherd Ave 11208 718-257-4061
Malik Small, prin. Fax 257-4738

Ebbets Field MS 400/6-8
46 McKeever Pl 11225 718-941-5097
Margaret Baker, prin. Fax 284-7973

EBC-HS for Public Service 700/9-12
1155 Dekalb Ave 11221 718-452-3440
Shawn Brown, prin. Fax 452-3603

Edmonds Learning Center II 200/6-8
430 Howard Ave 11233 718-467-0306
Michele Luard, prin. Fax 953-0682

El Puente Academy for Peace & Justice 200/Alt
250 Hooper St 11211 718-387-1125
Wanda Vazquez, prin. Fax 387-4229

Ericsson MS 300/6-8
424 Leonard St 11222 718-782-2527
Marcos Bausch, prin. Fax 302-2319

Essence MS 200/6-8
590 Sheffield Ave 11207 718-272-8371
Claudy Makelele, prin. Fax 272-8372

Evers Preparatory S 1,000/6-12
1186 Carroll St 11225 718-703-5400
Dr. Michael Wiltshire, prin. Fax 703-5600

Expeditionary Learning S for Comm Leader 200/9-12
2630 Benson Ave 11214 718-333-7700
David O'Hara, prin. Fax 333-7725
FDNY S for Fire & Life Safety 400/9-12
400 Pennsylvania Ave 11207 718-922-0389
James Anderson, prin. Fax 922-0593
Fort Greene Preparatory Academy 100/6-8
100 Clermont Ave 11205 718-254-9401
Paula Lettiere, prin. Fax 254-9407
Ft. Hamilton HS 4,400/9-12
8301 Shore Rd 11209 718-748-1537
Kaye Houlihan, prin. Fax 836-3955
Foundations Academy 200/9-12
70 Tompkins Ave 11206 718-302-5092
Jimmy Molina, prin. Fax 599-1369
Freedom Academy 300/9-12
116 Nassau St 11201 718-694-8357
Alyson Forde, prin. Fax 694-8360
Gibran International Academy 50/8-9
362 Schermerhorn St 11217 718-237-2502
Winston Hamann, prin. Fax 488-1724
Goldstein - Sciences HS 1,000/9-12
1830 Shore Blvd 11235 718-368-8500
Scott Hughes, prin. Fax 368-8555
Gotham Professional Arts Academy 300/9-12
265 Ralph Ave 11233 718-455-0746
Alexander White, prin. Fax 574-3971
Grady Career & Tech HS Vo/Tech
25 Brighton 4th Rd 11235 718-332-5000
Geraldine Maione, prin. Fax 332-2544
Green S Academy for Environmental Career 400/9-12
223 Graham Ave 11206 718-599-1207
Cara Tait, prin. Fax 387-7945
Hudde IS 1,100/6-8
2500 Nostrand Ave 11210 718-253-3700
Elena O'Sullivan, prin. Fax 253-0356
International Arts & Business HS 500/9-12
600 Kingston Ave 11203 718-467-7400
Angelo Marra, prin. Fax 604-3029
International HS at Lafayette 300/9-12
2630 Benson Ave 11214 718-333-7860
Jon Harriman, prin. Fax 333-7861
International HS at Prospect Heights 400/9-12
883 Classon Ave 11225 718-230-6333
Nedda DeCastro, prin. Fax 230-6322
It Takes a Village Academy 400/9-12
5800 Tilden Ave 11203 718-629-2307
Marina Vinitskaya, prin. Fax 629-6162
James MS of Science 200/6-8
76 Riverdale Ave 11212 718-498-5276
Kiersten Ward, prin. Fax 498-5361
KAPPA V S, 985 Rockaway Ave 11212 300/6-8
Thomas Mullin, prin. 718-922-4690
Kingsborough Early College S 400/6-12
2630 Benson Ave 11214 718-333-7850
Connie Hamilton, prin. Fax 333-7875
Liberation Diploma Plus 200/9-12
2865 W 19th St 11224 718-946-6812
April Leong, prin. Fax 946-6825
Life Academy HS for Film and Music 200/9-12
2630 Benson Ave 11214 718-333-7750
Lisa Farraiola, prin. Fax 333-7775
Lincoln HS 2,600/9-12
2800 Ocean Pkwy 11235 718-333-7400
Ari Hoogenboom, prin. Fax 946-5035
Lyons Community S 500/6-12
223 Graham Ave 11206 718-782-0918
Taeko Onishi, prin. Fax 782-5283
Madiba Prep MS 6-8
1014 Lafayette Ave 11221 718-574-2804
Sharon Stephens, prin.
Madison HS 3,200/9-12
3787 Bedford Ave 11229 718-758-7200
Joseph Gogliormella, prin. Fax 758-7341
Math & Science Exploratory S 500/6-8
345 Dean St 11217 718-330-9328
Dawn Faraj, prin. Fax 330-0944
Maxwell Career and Technical HS Vo/Tech
145 Pennsylvania Ave 11207 718-345-9100
Jocelyn Babette, prin. Fax 345-5470
McAuliffe S 1,000/6-8
1171 65th St 11219 718-236-3394
Justin Berman, prin. Fax 236-3638
McKinney S of the Arts 500/6-12
101 Park Ave 11205 718-834-6760
Paula Holmes, prin. Fax 834-6776
Metropolitan Corporate Academy 300/9-12
362 Schermerhorn St 11217 718-222-6200
Lennel George, prin. Fax 222-6296
Metropolitan Diploma Plus HS 200/Alt
985 Rockaway Ave 11212 718-342-6249
Meri Yallowitz, prin. Fax 342-6329
Midwood HS 4,000/9-12
2839 Bedford Ave 11210 718-724-8500
David Cohen, prin. Fax 724-8515
Millennium Brooklyn HS 9-12
237 7th Ave 11215 718-832-4333
Lisa Gioe, prin. Fax 499-2126
Mott Hall Bridges MS 100/6-8
210 Chester St 11212 718-345-6912
Nadia Lopez, prin. Fax 345-6918
Mott Hall IV, 1137 Herkimer St 11233 300/6-8
Thomas McBryde, prin. 718-485-5240
Multicultural HS 400/9-12
999 Jamaica Ave 11208 718-827-2796
Alexandra Hernandez, prin. Fax 827-3970
Murrow HS 4,000/9-12
1600 Avenue L 11230 718-258-9283
Allen Barge, prin. Fax 252-2611
New Heights MS 6-8
790 E New York Ave 11203 718-467-4501
New Horizons S 200/6-8
317 Hoyt St 11231 718-330-9227
Deanna Sinito, dir. Fax 330-9251
New Utrecht HS 3,200/9-12
1601 80th St 11214 718-232-2500
Maureen Goldfarb, prin. Fax 259-5526

New Voices S of Academic & Creative Arts 500/6-8
330 18th St 11215 718-965-0390
Frank Giordano, prin. Fax 965-0603
Olympus Academy 200/Alt
755 E 100th St 11236 718-272-1926
P.J. Murray, prin. Fax 272-5713
Parkside Preparatory Academy 400/6-8
655 Parkside Ave 11226 718-462-6992
Adrienne Spencer, prin. Fax 284-7717
Park Slope Collegiate S 400/6-12
237 7th Ave 11215 718-832-4300
Jill Bloomberg, prin. Fax 788-8127
Pathways in Technology Early College HS 9-12
150 Albany Ave 11213 718-221-1593
Rashid Davis, prin. Fax 221-1781
Performing Arts & Technology HS 400/9-12
400 Pennsylvania Ave 11207 718-922-0762
Reginald Richardson, prin. Fax 922-0953
Perkins Academy Vo/Tech
50 Bedford Ave 11222 718-388-7721
Jocelyn Santana, prin. Fax 388-7793
Progress HS 1,000/9-12
850 Grand St 11211 718-387-0228
William Jusino, prin. Fax 782-0911
Public S 332 300/3-8
51 Christopher Ave 11212 718-495-7805
Mickisha Goss, prin. Fax 495-7708
Robeson HS 600/9-12
150 Albany Ave 11213 718-774-0300
Ronald Wells, prin. Fax 467-3692
Roosevelt HS 3,400/9-12
5800 20th Ave 11204 718-621-8800
Steven Demarco, prin. Fax 232-9513
Satellite East 200/6-8
344 Monroe St 11216 718-789-4251
Kim McPherson, prin. Fax 789-4823
Satellite III S 200/7-8
170 Gates Ave 11238 718-789-5835
Beatrice Thompson, prin. Fax 789-5814
Satellite West MS 200/6-8
209 York St 11201 718-834-6774
Suzanne Joseph, prin. Fax 834-2979
School for Classics 200/9-12
370 Fountain Ave 11208 718-277-1069
Janice Ross, prin. Fax 277-1873
School for Democracy & Leadership 400/6-12
600 Kingston Ave 11203 718-771-4865
James Olearchek, prin. Fax 771-5847
School for Human Rights 400/6-12
600 Kingston Ave 11203 718-771-4793
Michael Alexander, prin. Fax 771-4815
School for International Studies 500/6-12
284 Baltic St 11201 718-330-9390
Jillian Juman, prin. Fax 875-7522
School for Legal Studies 800/9-12
850 Grand St 11211 718-387-2800
Monica Ortiz, prin. Fax 387-3281
School of Integrated Learning 300/6-8
1224 Park Pl 11213 718-774-0362
Monique Campbell, prin. Fax 774-0521
Science and Medicine MS 200/6-8
965 E 107th St 11236 718-688-6400
Ingrid Thomas-Clark, prin. Fax 688-6401
Science Skills Center HS 600/9-12
49 Flatbush Avenue Ext 11201 718-243-9413
Dahilia McGregor, prin. Fax 243-9399
Science Technology & Research HS 500/6-12
911 Flatbush Ave 11226 718-564-2540
Dr. Eric Blake, prin. Fax 564-2541
Secondary S for Journalism 300/8-12
237 7th Ave 11215 718-832-4201
Jodi Radwell, prin. Fax 832-0273
Secondary S for Law 500/8-12
237 7th Ave 11215 718-832-4250
Oneatha Swinton, prin. Fax 499-3947
Sheepshead Bay HS 2,100/9-12
3000 Avenue X 11235 718-332-2003
John Omahoney, prin. Fax 648-9349
South Brooklyn Community HS 200/9-12
173 Conover St 11231 718-237-8902
Jean Foley, dir. Fax 422-1927
Spring Creek Community S 6-12
1065 Elton St 11239 718-935-3605
Christina Koza, prin.
Stroud MS 100/6-8
750 Classon Ave 11238 718-638-3067
Tricia Delauney, prin. Fax 638-3515
Sunset Park HS 700/9-12
153 35th St 11232 718-840-1900
Corinne Vinal, prin. Fax 840-1925
Sunset Park Prep MS 500/6-8
4004 4th Ave 11232 718-965-3331
Lola Padin, prin. Fax 965-3330
Teachers Preparatory HS 600/6-12
226 Bristol St 11212 718-498-2605
Carmen Simon, prin. Fax 345-8069
Transit Tech HS Vo/Tech
1 Wells St 11208 718-647-5204
Neil Harris, prin. Fax 647-4458
Twain Gifted & Talented S 1,300/6-8
2401 Neptune Ave 11224 718-266-0814
Karen Ditolla, prin. Fax 266-1693
Upper S @ PS 25 200/6-8
787 Lafayette Ave 11221 718-574-6032
Ativia Sandusky, prin. Fax 602-2357
Urban Action Academy 200/9-12
1600 Rockaway Pkwy 11236 718-290-8720
Abe Correa, prin. Fax 290-8721
Urban Assembly Institute Math & Science 400/6-12
283 Adams St 11201 718-260-2300
Kiri Soares, prin. Fax 260-2301
Urban Assembly S for Criminal Justice 300/6-12
4200 16th Ave 11204 718-438-3893
Mariela Graham, prin. Fax 438-3527
Urban Assembly S for Law & Justice 500/9-12
283 Adams St 11201 718-858-1160
Shannon Curran, prin. Fax 858-4733

Urban Assembly S for Music & Art 400/9-12
49 Flatbush Avenue Ext 11201 718-858-0249
Paul Thompson, prin. Fax 858-0492
Urban Assembly S for Urban Environment 100/6-8
70 Tompkins Ave 11206 718-599-0371
Kourtney Boyd, prin. Fax 388-0872
Victory Collegiate HS 300/9-12
6565 Flatlands Ave 11236 718-968-1530
Marcel Deans, prin. Fax 968-1526
WATCH HS 400/9-12
400 Pennsylvania Ave 11207 718-922-0650
Kim Wanliss, prin. Fax 922-0709
W.E.B. DuBois Academic HS 300/9-12
402 Eastern Pkwy 11225 718-773-7765
Catherine Hartnett, prin. Fax 773-7849
West Brooklyn Community HS 200/10-12
1053 41st St 11219 718-686-1444
Gloria Rosario, prin. Fax 686-1189
Westinghouse Career & Tech HS Vo/Tech
105 Johnson St 11201 718-625-6130
Janine Kieran, prin. Fax 596-9434
Williamsburg HS Architecture & Design 400/9-12
257 N 6th St 11211 718-388-1260
Gill Cornell, prin. Fax 486-2580
Williamsburg Preparatory S 500/9-12
257 N 6th St 11211 718-302-2306
Michael Shadrick, prin. Fax 302-3726
Young Womens Leadership S of Brooklyn 200/6-12
223 Graham Ave 11206 718-387-5641
Talana Bradley, prin.

Access Careers Post-Sec.
25 Elm Pl Ste 201 11201 718-643-9060
Adelphi Academy of Brooklyn 100/PK-12
8515 Ridge Blvd 11209 718-238-3308
Dr. Roy Blash, pres. Fax 238-2894
Al-Noor S 600/PK-12
675 4th Ave 11232 718-768-7181
Abdulhakeem Alhasel, prin. Fax 768-7088
ASA Inst of Business & Computer Tech Post-Sec.
81 Willoughby St 11201 718-522-9073
Bais Brocha Stolin Karlin 500/PK-12
4314 10th Ave 11219 718-853-1222
Bais Esther S 300/PK-12
1353 50th St 11219 718-436-1234
Bais Rochel HS 900/9-12
68 Harrison Ave 11211 718-963-9287
Leah Schorr, prin. Fax 963-9571
Bais Rochel S of Boro Park 400/K-12
5301 14th Ave 11219 718-438-7822
Bais Ruchel D'Satmar 3-12
84 Sandford St 11205 718-422-0375
Bais Sarah Girls S 800/PK-12
6101 16th Ave 11204 718-871-7571
Bais Tziporah S 400/PK-12
1449 39th St 11218 718-436-8336
Bais Yaakov Academy 900/PK-12
1213 Elm Ave 11230 718-339-4747
Rabbi Avrohom Greenberg, prin. Fax 998-5766
Bais Yaakov Adas Yereim 300/PK-12
563 Bedford Ave 11211 718-302-7500
Bais Yaakov Adas Yereim 300/PK-12
1169 43rd St 11219 718-686-8580
Bais Yaakov D'Chassidei Gur 500/PK-12
1975 51st St 11204 718-338-5600
Bais Yaakov D'Rav Meir HS 9-12
98 Lawrence Ave 11230 718-633-1232
Bay Ridge Preparatory S 400/K-12
8101 Ridge Blvd 11209 718-833-9090
Dr. Charles Fasano, hdmstr. Fax 833-6680
Be'er Hagolah Institutes 600/K-12
671 Louisiana Ave 11239 718-642-6800
Beikvei Hatzoin S 100/PK-12
31 Division Ave 11249 718-486-6363
Beis Chaya Mushka 200/PK-12
1505 Carroll St 11213 718-756-0770
Rabbi Levi Plotkin, prin. Fax 221-1878
Belz Girls S 900/PK-12
600 McDonald Ave 11218 718-871-0500
Berkeley Carroll S 500/5-12
181 Lincoln Pl 11217 718-534-6550
Robert Vitalo, head sch Fax 398-3640
Berkeley College Post-Sec.
255 Duffield St 11201 718-637-8600
Beth Chana S 300/1-12
712 Bedford Ave 11206 718-935-1845
Beth HaMedrash Shaarei Yosher Post-Sec.
4102 16th Ave # 10 11204 718-854-2290
Beth Hamedrash Shaarei Yosher 50/9-12
4102 16th Ave 11204 718-854-2290
Beth Hatalmud Rabbinical College Post-Sec.
2127 82nd St 11214 718-259-2525
Beth Jacob HS 700/9-12
4420 15th Ave 11219 718-851-2255
Beth Rivkah HS 500/9-12
310 Crown St 11225 718-735-0400
Bet Yaakov Ateret Torah HS 100/9-12
2166 Coney Island Ave 11223 718-382-7002
Bishop Ford Central Catholic HS 1,000/9-12
500 19th St 11215 718-360-2500
Sam Sued, prin. Fax 360-2595
Bishop Kearney HS 700/9-12
2202 60th St 11204 718-236-6363
Sr. Thomasine Stagnitta, prin. Fax 236-7784
Bishop Loughlin Memorial HS 800/9-12
357 Clermont Ave 11238 718-857-2700
James Dorney, prin. Fax 398-4227
Bnos Menachem S for Girls 400/PK-12
739 E New York Ave 11203 718-493-1100
Bnos Yaakov Educational Center 600/1-12
62 Harrison Ave 11211 718-387-7905
Bnos Yaakov Pupa 900/PK-12
1402 40th St 11218 718-851-0316
Bnos Yisroel Viznitz S 400/PK-12
12 Franklin Ave 11249 718-330-0222
Bnos Zion of Bobov 1,400/PK-12
5000 14th Ave 11219 718-438-3080

Bobover Yeshiva Bnei Zion S 50/6-8
1533 48th St 11219 718-435-8033
Boricua College Post-Sec.
186 N 6th St 11211 718-782-2200
Brooklyn Amity S 300/PK-12
3867 Shore Pkwy 11235 718-891-6100
Cengiz Karabekmez, prin. Fax 891-6841
Brooklyn Friends S 800/PK-12
375 Pearl St 11201 718-852-1029
Dr. Larry Weiss, head sch Fax 643-4868
Brooklyn Hospital Post-Sec.
121 Dekalb Ave 11201 718-250-8005
Brooklyn Law School Post-Sec.
250 Joralemon St 11201 718-625-2200
Career & Educational Consultants Post-Sec.
270 Flatbush Avenue Ext 11201 718-858-8500
Career Institute of Health & Technology Post-Sec.
340 Flatbush Avenue Ext 11201 718-422-1212
Central Yeshiva Tomchei Tmimim Lubavitz Post-Sec.
841 Ocean Pkwy 11230 718-434-0784
Charles Stuart School of Locksmithing Post-Sec.
1420 Kings Hwy 11229 718-339-2640
Chatzar Hakodesh Sanz-Klausenberg 700/PK-12
4511 14th Ave 11219 718-436-1248
Christian Heritage Academy 300/PK-12
1100 E 42nd St 11210 718-377-9406
Rev. Albert Delmadge, hdmstr. Fax 338-9870
College of New Rochelle Post-Sec.
1368 Fulton St 11216 718-638-2500
Cope Institute Post-Sec.
4006 18th Ave 11218 718-506-0500
Cristo Rey Brooklyn HS 9-12
2 Aberdeen St 11207 718-455-3555
Christine Roman, prin. Fax 455-3556
CUNY Brooklyn College Post-Sec.
2900 Bedford Ave 11210 718-951-5000
CUNY Kingsborough Community College Post-Sec.
2001 Oriental Blvd 11235 718-368-5000
CUNY Medgar Evers College Post-Sec.
1650 Bedford Ave 11225 718-270-4900
CUNY New York City College of Technology Post-Sec.
300 Jay St 11201 718-260-5000
Darkei Noam Rabbinical College Post-Sec.
2822 Avenue J 11210 718-338-6464
EDP School of Computer Programming Post-Sec.
1601 Voorhies Ave 11235 718-332-6469
Educational Institute Oholei Torah 100/9-12
667 Eastern Pkwy 11213 718-363-0019
Elite HS 100/9-12
2115 Benson Ave 11214 718-373-0960
Followers of Jesus S 100/1-12
3065 Atlantic Ave 11208 718-235-5493
James Gochnauer, prin. Fax 484-1477
Fontbonne Hall Academy 500/9-12
9901 Shore Rd 11209 718-748-2244
Sr. Dolores Crepeau, prin. Fax 745-3841
Gamla College Post-Sec.
1213 Elm Ave 11230 718-339-4747
Gerer Mesivta Bais Yisroel 100/9-12
5407 16th Ave 11204 718-854-8777
Hair Design Institute at Fifth Avenue Post-Sec.
6711 5th Ave 11220 718-745-1000
Harma Religious Institute Yeshiva HS 200/12-12
30 Lancaster Ave 11223 718-743-3141
Institute of Design and Construction Post-Sec.
141 Willoughby St 11201 718-855-3661
Kehilath Yakov Rabbinical Seminary Post-Sec.
638 Bedford Ave 11249 718-963-1212
Learning Institute for Beauty Sciences Post-Sec.
2384 86th St 11214 718-373-2400
Long Island University Post-Sec.
1 University Plz 11201 718-488-1000
Lubavitcher S Chabad 200/PK-12
841 Ocean Pkwy 11230 718-859-7600
Machon Bais Yaakov S 400/9-12
1683 42nd St 11204 718-972-7900
Machzikei Hadath Rabbinical College Post-Sec.
5407 16th Ave 11204 718-854-8777
Magen David Yeshiva HS 500/9-12
7801 Bay Pkwy 11214 718-331-4002
Manhattan School of Computer Technology Post-Sec.
931 Coney Island Ave 11230 212-349-9768
Masores Bais Yaakov S 800/PK-12
1395 Ocean Ave 11230 718-692-2424
McAuley HS 300/9-12
710 E 37th St 11203 718-462-7282
Margaret Lake, prin. Fax 462-7284
Me'orot Bais Yaakov 50/9-12
1797 Coney Island Ave 11230 718-627-3158
Merkaz Bnos - Career Institute Post-Sec.
2115 Benson Ave 11214 718-234-4000
Merkaz Bnos HS 100/9-12
1400 W 6th St 11204 718-259-5600
Mesivta Eastern Parkway Rabbinical Sem. Post-Sec.
510 Dahill Rd 11218 718-438-1002
Mesivta Eitz Chaim S 300/9-12
1577 48th St 11219 718-438-2018
Mesivta Imrei Yosef Spinka 400/9-12
1460 56th St 11219 718-851-1600
Mesivta Lev Bonim 100/9-12
8700 Avenue K 11236 718-444-5996
Mesivta Nachlas Yakov of Adas Yereim 100/9-12
185 Wilson St 11211 718-388-1751
Mesivta Nesivos Hatalmud 8-12
PO Box 190432 11219 718-972-0804
Rabbi Samuel Wolner, admin. Fax 972-5825
Mesivta of Manhattan Beach 50/9-11
59 W End Ave 11235 718-368-1333
Rabbi Chaim Zelikovitz, prin. Fax 368-1969
Mesivta Sholom Shachne 100/9-12
129 Elmwood Ave 11230 718-252-6333
Mesivta Tiferes Elimelech S 50/9-12
4407 12th Ave 11219 718-854-3062
Mesivta Torah Vodaath Seminary Post-Sec.
425 E 9th St 11218 718-941-8000
Mesivta Veretzky 100/9-12
1102 Avenue L 11230 718-258-3888

Mesivta Yeshiva Rabbi Chaim Berlin 200/9-12
1585 Coney Island Ave 11230 718-377-8400
Rabbi Yosef Landsberg, prin. Fax 377-5883
Mesivta Zichron Eliezer S 50/9-12
1543 E 9th St 11230 718-336-9629
Mikdash Shelomo HS 50/8-12
1532 E 10th St 11230 718-382-1152
Mirrer Yeshiva Central Institute Post-Sec.
1795 Ocean Pkwy 11223 718-645-0536
Mirrer Yeshiva Mesivta HS 200/9-12
1795 Ocean Pkwy 11223 718-375-0771
Mosdos Bnos Frima 300/PK-10
1377 42nd St 11219 718-972-7666
Mosdos Chasidei Square 300/K-12
1373 43rd St 11219 718-436-2550
Nazareth Regional HS 400/9-12
475 E 57th St 11203 718-763-1100
Providentia Quiles, prin. Fax 629-5382
Nefesh Academy 200/PK-12
1750 E 18th St 11229 718-339-9880
New Vistas Academy 200/PK-12
PO Box 100796 11210 718-421-1786
New York Methodist Hospital Post-Sec.
1401 Kings Hwy 11229 718-780-3706
Packer Collegiate Institute 1,000/PK-12
170 Joralemon St 11201 718-250-0221
Dr. Bruce Dennis, hdmstr. Fax 250-0271
Poly Prep Country Day S 800/5-12
9216 7th Ave 11228 718-836-9800
David Harman, hdmstr. Fax 921-5112
Polytechnic Institute of New York Univ. Post-Sec.
6 Metrotech Ctr 11201 718-260-3600
Pratt Institute Post-Sec.
200 Willoughby Ave 11205 718-636-3600
Prospect Park Bnos Leah HS 300/9-12
1604 Avenue R 11229 718-376-3337
Rabbinical Academy Mesivta Rabbi Chaim Post-Sec.
1605 Coney Island Ave 11230 718-377-0777
Rabbinical Coll. Bobovr Yeshiva Bnei Zn. Post-Sec.
1577 48th St 11219 718-438-2018
Rabbinical College Ch' San Sofer Post-Sec.
1876 50th St 11204 718-236-1171
Rabbinical College Ohr Shimon Yisroel Post-Sec.
215 Hewes St 11211 718-855-4092
Rabbinical Seminary Adas Yereim Post-Sec.
185 Wilson St 11211 718-388-1751
Rabbinical Seminary M'Kor Chaim Post-Sec.
1571 55th St 11219 718-851-0183
St. Ann's S 1,100/PK-12
129 Pierrepont St 11201 718-522-1660
Vincent Tompkins, hdmstr. Fax 522-2599
St. Edmund Preparatory HS 700/9-12
2474 Ocean Ave 11229 718-743-6100
John Lorenzetti, prin. Fax 743-5243
St. Francis College Post-Sec.
180 Remsen St 11201 718-522-2300
St. Joseph HS 300/9-12
80 Willoughby St 11201 718-624-3618
Sr. Joan Gallagher, prin. Fax 624-2792
St. Joseph's College New York Post-Sec.
245 Clinton Ave 11205 718-940-5300
St. Saviour HS 300/9-12
588 6th St 11215 718-768-4406
Sr. Valeria Belanger, prin. Fax 369-2688
Shalsheles Bais Yaakov S 100/1-12
4421 15th Ave 11219 718-436-1122
Sinai Academy 50/9-12
2025 79th St 11214 718-256-7400
Soille Bais Yaakov HS 100/9-12
1492 E 12th St 11230 718-769-8160
SUNY Downstate Medical Center Post-Sec.
450 Clarkson Ave 11203 718-270-1000
Talmudical Seminary of Bobov Post-Sec.
5120 New Utrecht Ave 11219 718-854-8700
Talmudical Seminary Oholei Torah Post-Sec.
667 Eastern Pkwy 11213 718-774-5050
Talmud Torah Imrei Chaim 600/PK-12
1824 53rd St 11204 718-234-2000
Tichon Bnot Rachel HS 100/9-12
1950 E 7th St 11223 718-382-1555
Tomer Dvora HS 300/9-12
5801 16th Ave 11204 718-633-4125
Torah Academy HS of Brooklyn 50/9-12
2066 E 9th St 11223 718-339-8844
Rabbi Avi Davidowitz, prin. Fax 339-9701
Torah Temimah Talmudical Seminary Post-Sec.
507 Ocean Pkwy 11218 718-853-8500
United Lubavitcher Yeshiva 100/9-12
PO Box 130347 11213 718-735-6607
Rabbi Menachem Minsky, prin. Fax 778-7161
United Talmudical Academy 400/7-9
1346 53rd St 11219 718-438-7038
United Talmudical Seminary Post-Sec.
191 Rodney St 11211 718-963-9770
Xaverian HS 1,100/9-12
7100 Shore Rd 11209 718-836-7100
Kevin McCormack, admin. Fax 836-7114
Yeshiva and Kollel Harbotzas Torah Post-Sec.
1049 E 15th St 11230 718-692-0208
Yeshiva & Mesivta Torah Temimah 600/PK-12
555 Ocean Pkwy 11218 718-853-8500
Rabbi Yaakov Applegrad, dir. Fax 438-5779
Yeshiva Beis Meir 200/9-12
1327 38th St 11218 718-437-5844
Yeshiva Bnos Ahavas Yisroel 600/K-12
2 Lee Ave 11211 718-388-0848
Yeshiva Chanoch Lenaar 50/8-12
876 Eastern Pkwy 11213 718-774-8456
Yeshiva Chemdas Yisroel Kerem 200/10-12
1149 38th St 11218 718-686-5500
Yeshiva Ch'san Sofer - Mesivta M'shmuel 300/PK-12
1876 50th St 11204 718-236-1171
Yeshiva Congregation Toras Yufa S 100/10-10
1056 54th St 11219 718-436-5683
Yeshiva Darchai Menachem 50/4-12
432 Rutland Rd 11203 718-953-2919
Rabbi Eyal Bension, dir. Fax 666-2919
Yeshiva Derech Chaim Post-Sec.
1573 39th St 11218 718-438-5476

Yeshiva Derech HaTorah 300/PK-10
2810 Nostrand Ave 11229 718-258-4441
Yeshiva Gedolah Bais Yisroel Post-Sec.
2002 Avenue J 11210 718-258-7400
Yeshiva Gedolah Imrei Yosef D'Spinka Post-Sec.
1466 56th St 11219 718-851-8721
Yeshiva Gedolah of Midwood 100/11-12
201 Avenue F 11218 718-853-2400
Yeshiva Gedolah Ohr Yisrael Post-Sec.
2899 Nostrand Ave 11229 718-382-8702
Yeshiva Karlin Stolin Post-Sec.
1818 54th St 11204 718-232-7800
Yeshiva Kehilath Yaakov 700/PK-10
183 Wilson St Ste 136 11211 718-486-7934
Yeshiva Ketana of Bensonhurst 200/PK-10
2025 67th St 11204 718-236-4100
Yeshiva Ketana Toldos Yaakov 100/9-12
87 Heyward St 11206 718-852-0502
Yeshiva Machzikei Hadas Belz 1,000/PK-12
1601 42nd St 11204 718-436-4445
Yeshiva Mesivta Arugath Habosem 400/K-12
40 Lynch St 11206 718-237-4500
Yeshiva Mesivta Karlin Stolin 600/PK-12
1818 54th St 11204 718-232-7800
Yeshiva Mesivta Tiferes Yisroel S 700/K-12
1271 E 35th St 11210 718-258-9006
Yeshiva Mesivta Torah Vodaath 400/K-12
425 E 9th St 11218 718-941-8000
Yeshiva Mikdash Melech Post-Sec.
1326 Ocean Pkwy 11230 718-339-1090
Yeshiva Minchas Eluzar S 50/9-12
4706 14th Ave 11219 718-438-7633
Yeshiva M'Kor Chaim 50/9-12
1571 55th St 11219 718-851-0183
Yeshiva Nesivos Chaim 50/9-12
221 Avenue F 11218 718-633-4760
Yeshiva of Brooklyn-Girls 700/PK-12
1470 Ocean Pkwy 11230 718-376-3775
Yeshiva of Flatbush Joel Braverman HS 700/9-12
1609 Avenue J 11230 718-377-1100
Yeshiva of Machzikai Hadas Post-Sec.
1301 47th St 11219 718-853-2442
Yeshiva of Nitra Rabbinical College Post-Sec.
194 Division Ave 11211 718-387-0422
Yeshiva R'tzahd S 400/5-8
8700 Avenue K 11236 718-444-5996
Yeshivas Boyan Tiferes Mordechai Shlomo 400/PK-12
1205 44th St 11219 718-435-6060
Yeshivas Novominsk Post-Sec.
1690 60th St 11204 718-438-2727
Yeshivas Novominsk-Kol Yehuda 200/9-12
1690 60th St 11204 718-438-2727
Rabbi Yisroel Schwebel, admin. Fax 438-2472
Yeshivas Tiferes Avos 50/9-12
1960 Schenectady Ave 11234 718-252-0801
Yeshivas Vyelipol HS 100/9-12
860 E 27th St 11210 718-951-1800
Yeshivat Ateret Torah 700/PK-12
901 Quentin Rd 11223 718-375-7100
Yeshiva Tiferes Shmiel D'Aleksander 100/9-12
PO Box 190738 11219 718-438-1818
Yeshiva Toldos Yitzchok Bnei Mordechai 300/K-10
1413 45th St 11219 718-633-4802
Yeshiva Toras Emes Kamenitz 500/PK-12
1904 Avenue N 11230 718-375-0900
Yeshivat Or Hatorah S 50/9-12
2119 Homecrest Ave 11229 718-645-4645
Yeshivat Shaare Torah Boys S 100/PK-12
1202 Avenue P 11229 718-645-6676
Yeshivat Shaare Torah Girls HS 100/9-12
1768 Ocean Ave 11230 718-382-4000
Sarah Wadler, prin. Fax 382-7999
Yeshiva Yesode Hatorah 50/9-12
620 Bedford Ave 11249 718-802-1613
Zvi Dov Roth Academy 100/7-12
3300 Kings Hwy 11234 718-338-6921

Brookville, Nassau, Pop. 3,435

Long Island Lutheran Middle & HS 600/6-12
131 Brookville Rd 11545 516-626-1700
Dr. David Hahn, head sch Fax 622-7459
Long Island University Post-Sec.
720 Northern Blvd 11548 516-299-2000

Brushton, Franklin, Pop. 466

Brushton-Moira Central SD 800/PK-12
758 County Route 7 12916 518-529-8942
Beverly Ouderkirk, supt. Fax 529-6062
www.bmcsd.org
Brushton-Moira Central HS 500/5-12
758 County Route 7 12916 518-529-7342
Nenette Greeno, prin. Fax 529-6062

Buffalo, Erie, Pop. 254,867

Buffalo CSD 31,500/PK-12
712 City Hall 14202 716-816-3500
Pamela Brown, supt. Fax 851-3535
www.buffaloschools.org/
Public HS 195 900/5-12
186 E North St 14204 716-816-4230
Dr. William Kresse, prin. Fax 888-7145
Public HS 200 800/9-12
2885 Main St 14214 716-816-4250
Carlos Alvarez, prin. Fax 838-7490
Public HS 204 700/9-12
370 Lafayette Ave 14213 716-816-4340
Naomi Cerre, prin. Fax 888-7096
Public HS 205 800/9-12
51 Ontario St 14207 716-816-4360
Denise Clarke, prin. Fax 871-6046
Public HS 206 800/9-12
150 Southside Pkwy 14220 716-816-4828
Theresa Schuta, prin. Fax 828-4905
Public HS 212 400/9-12
320 Porter Ave 14201 716-816-4380
Michael O'Brien, prin. Fax 888-7181

Public HS 301 Vo/Tech
400 Kensington Ave 14214 716-816-4450
Brian Wiesinger, prin. Fax 838-7546
Public HS 302 500/9-12
70 W Chippewa St 14202 716-816-3018
James Weimer, prin. Fax 851-3017
Public HS 304 1,100/9-12
256 S Elmwood Ave 14201 716-816-3888
Sabatino Cimato, prin. Fax 851-3890
Public HS 305 Vo/Tech
1500 Elmwood Ave 14207 716-816-4480
Crystal Barton, prin. Fax 897-6073
Public HS 307 600/9-12
820 Northampton St 14211 716-816-4520
Casey Young, prin. Fax 897-8130
Public HS 415 9-12
290 Main St Fl 4 14202 716-851-3763
Susan Doyle, prin. Fax 851-3766
Public JSHS 131 7-12
1369 Broadway St 14212 716-816-3270
Michael Mogavero, prin. Fax 897-8027
Public JSHS 197 400/5-12
101 Hertel Ave 14207 716-816-4500
Rose Schneider, prin. Fax 871-6007
Public MS 66 400/5-8
780 Parkside Ave 14216 716-816-3440
Maria Fasolino, prin. Fax 838-7448
Public MSHS 192 5-12
450 Masten Ave 14209 716-816-4220
Jody Covington, prin. Fax 888-7136
Public MSHS 198 400/5-12
333 Clinton St 14204 716-816-4300
Kevin Eberle, prin. Fax 851-3863
Public S 59 500/3-8
100 Poplar Ave 14211 716-816-3370
Denisca Thompson, prin. Fax 897-8049
Public S 76 400/3-8
3005 Elmwood Ave 14217 716-816-3848
Donna Jackson, prin. Fax 851-3853
Public S 156 500/5-12
319 Suffolk St 14215 716-816-4330
Michael Geuber, prin. Fax 838-7530

Cheektowago-Sloan UFD 1,500/PK-12
166 Halstead Ave 14212 716-891-6402
Andrea Galenski, supt. Fax 891-6435
www.sloanschools.org
Other Schools – See Cheektowaga

Kenmore-Tonawanda UFSD 7,700/K-12
1500 Colvin Blvd 14223 716-874-8400
Mark Mondanaro, supt. Fax 874-8621
www.kenton.k12.ny.us/
Franklin MS 500/6-8
540 Parkhurst Blvd 14223 716-874-8404
Kevin Kruger, prin. Fax 874-8480
Hoover MS 700/6-8
249 Thorncliff Rd 14223 716-874-8405
Carmelina Persico, prin. Fax 874-8470
Kenmore West HS 1,500/9-12
33 Highland Pkwy 14223 716-874-8401
Dean Johnson, prin. Fax 874-8527
Other Schools – See Kenmore, Tonawanda

Bishop Timon-St. Jude HS 300/9-12
601 McKinley Pkwy 14220 716-826-3610
Thomas Sullivan, prin. Fax 824-5833
Bryant & Stratton College Post-Sec.
465 Main St Ste 400 14203 716-884-9120
Buffalo Academy of the Sacred Heart 400/9-12
3860 Main St 14226 716-834-2101
Jennifer Demert, hdmstr. Fax 834-2944
Buffalo Seminary 200/9-12
205 Bidwell Pkwy 14222 716-885-6780
Jody Douglass, hdmstr. Fax 885-6785
Canisius College Post-Sec.
2001 Main St 14208 716-883-7000
Canisius HS 800/9-12
1180 Delaware Ave 14209 716-882-0466
Timothy Fitzgerald, prin. Fax 883-1870
Continental School of Beauty Culture Post-Sec.
326 Kenmore Ave 14223 716-833-5016
Darul-Uloom Al Madania 200/PK-10
182 Sobieski St 14212 716-892-2606
Fax 892-6621
D'Youville College Post-Sec.
320 Porter Ave 14201 716-829-8000
Erie Community College City Post-Sec.
121 Ellicott St 14203 716-842-2770
Holy Angels Academy 300/9-12
24 Shoshone St 14214 716-834-7120
Kathleen Tedesco, prin. Fax 834-7128
Medaille College Post-Sec.
18 Agassiz Cir 14214 716-880-2000
Mt. Mercy Academy 300/9-12
88 Red Jacket Pkwy 14220 716-825-8796
Margaret Staszak, prin. Fax 825-0976
Nardin Academy 500/9-12
135 Cleveland Ave 14222 716-881-6262
Rebecca Reeder, prin. Fax 881-0086
National Tractor Trailer School Post-Sec.
175 Katherine St 14210 716-849-6887
Nativity Miguel MS 100/5-8
21 Davidson Ave 14215 716-836-5188
Fr. Edward Durkin, prin. Fax 836-5189
New York Institute of Massage Post-Sec.
PO Box 645 14231 716-633-0355
Nichols S 600/5-12
1250 Amherst St 14216 716-332-6300
Fax 875-2169
St. Mary's School for the Deaf Post-Sec.
2253 Main St 14214
Salvatore Sch of Hospitality & Business Post-Sec.
6681 Transit Rd 14221 716-827-4300
SUNY Buffalo State College Post-Sec.
1300 Elmwood Ave 14222 716-878-4000
SUNY Educational Opportunity Center Post-Sec.
465 Washington St 14203 716-849-6725

Trocaire College Post-Sec.
360 Choate Ave 14220 716-826-1200
University at Buffalo SUNY Post-Sec.
12 Capen Hall 14260 716-645-2000
Villa Maria College of Buffalo Post-Sec.
240 Pine Ridge Rd 14225 716-896-0700

Burnt Hills, Saratoga
Burnt Hills-Ballston Lake Central SD
Supt. — See Glenville
Burnt Hills-Ballston Lake HS 1,200/9-12
88 Lake Hill Rd 12027 518-399-9141
Maryellen Symer, prin. Fax 399-4341
O'Rourke MS 800/6-8
173 Lake Hill Rd 12027 518-399-9141
Colleen Wolff, prin. Fax 384-2588

Burt, Niagara
Newfane Central SD 1,600/PK-12
6048 Godfrey Rd 14028 716-778-6850
Christine Tibbetts, supt. Fax 778-6852
www.newfane.wnyric.org
Other Schools – See Newfane

Cairo, Greene, Pop. 1,375
Cairo-Durham Central SD 1,400/K-12
PO Box 780 12413 518-622-8534
Joel Pollak, supt. Fax 622-9566
www.cairodurham.org/
Cairo-Durham HS 500/9-12
PO Box 598 12413 518-622-8543
Anthony Taibi, prin. Fax 622-8857
Cairo-Durham MS 400/6-8
PO Box 1139 12413 518-622-0490
Nathan Farrell, prin. Fax 622-0493

Caledonia, Livingston, Pop. 2,169
Caledonia-Mumford Central SD 1,000/PK-12
PO Box 150 14423 585-538-3400
Robert Molisani, supt. Fax 538-3450
www.cal-mum.org
Caledonia-Mumford HS 300/9-12
PO Box 150 14423 585-538-3483
Merritt Holly, prin. Fax 538-3470
Caledonia-Mumford MS 200/6-8
PO Box 150 14423 585-538-3482
Paul Estabrooks, prin. Fax 538-3430

Cambridge, Washington, Pop. 1,844
Cambridge Central SD 900/K-12
58 S Park St 12816 518-677-2653
Vince Canini, supt. Fax 677-3889
www.cambridgecsd.org
Cambridge HS 400/7-12
24 S Park St 12816 518-677-8527
Tammy Silvernell, prin. Fax 677-3246

Camden, Oneida, Pop. 2,211
Camden Central SD 2,400/PK-12
51 3rd St 13316 315-245-4075
Dr. Jeffrey Bryant, supt. Fax 245-1622
www.camdenschools.org
Camden HS 800/9-12
55 Oswego St 13316 315-245-3168
Heather Wieland, prin. Fax 245-4173
Camden MS 600/6-8
32 Union St 13316 315-245-0080
Mary Walker, prin. Fax 245-0083

Camillus, Onondaga, Pop. 1,196
West Genesee Central SD 5,000/K-12
300 Sanderson Dr 13031 315-487-4562
Dr. Christopher Brown, supt. Fax 487-2999
www.westgenesee.org
Camillus MS 500/6-8
5525 Ike Dixon Rd 13031 315-672-3159
Beth Lozier, prin. Fax 672-3309
West Genesee HS 1,700/9-12
5201 W Genesee St 13031 315-487-4601
Dr. Barry Copeland, prin. Fax 487-4582
West Genesee MS 700/6-8
500 Sanderson Dr 13031 315-487-4615
Stephen Dunham, prin. Fax 487-4618

Campbell, Steuben, Pop. 695
Campbell-Savona Central SD 900/K-12
8455 County Route 125 14821 607-527-9800
Kathleen Hagenbuch, supt. Fax 527-8363
www.cscsd.org
Campbell-Savona JSHS 500/7-12
8455 County Route 125 14821 607-527-9800
Lisa Hawken, prin. Fax 527-8363

Canaan, Columbia
Berkshire UFD 100/7-12
13640 State Route 22 12029 518-781-3500
Bruce Potter, supt. Fax 781-4890
www.berkshirefarm.org
Berkshire JSHS 100/Alt
13640 State Route 22 12029 518-781-3500
Greg Pasos, prin. Fax 781-4890

Canajoharie, Montgomery, Pop. 2,208
Canajoharie Central SD 1,000/PK-12
136 Scholastic Way 13317 518-673-6302
Deborah Grimshaw, supt. Fax 673-3177
www.canajoharieschools.org
Canajoharie HS 300/9-12
136 Scholastic Way 13317 518-673-6330
David Barnes, prin. Fax 673-3177
Canajoharie MS 200/6-8
25 School District Rd 13317 518-673-6320
Douglas Morrissey, prin. Fax 673-5557

Canandaigua, Ontario, Pop. 10,383
Canandaigua CSD 3,800/K-12
143 N Pearl St 14424 585-396-3700
Lynne H. Erdle, supt. Fax 396-7306
www.canandaiguaschools.org/
Canandaigua Academy 1,300/9-12
435 East St 14424 585-396-3800
Vernon Tenney, prin. Fax 396-3806
Canandaigua MS 900/6-8
215 Granger St 14424 585-396-3850
Brian Nolan, prin. Fax 396-3863

Finger Lakes Community College Post-Sec.
3325 Marvin Sands Dr 14424 585-394-3500

Canaseraga, Allegany, Pop. 544
Canaseraga Central SD 300/K-12
PO Box 230 14822 607-545-6421
Kelly Houck, supt. Fax 545-6265
www.ccsdny.org/
Canaseraga S 300/K-12
PO Box 230 14822 607-545-6421
Mike Gill, prin. Fax 545-6265

Canastota, Madison, Pop. 4,723
Canastota Central SD 1,500/K-12
120 Roberts St 13032 315-697-2025
Frederick Bragan, supt. Fax 697-6368
www.canastotacsd.org
Canastota JSHS 700/7-12
101 Roberts St 13032 315-697-2003
William LaClair, prin. Fax 697-6314

USC The Business College Post-Sec.
PO Box 462 13032 315-697-8200

Candor, Tioga, Pop. 840
Candor Central SD 800/K-12
PO Box 145 13743 607-659-5010
Jeffrey Kisloski, supt. Fax 659-7112
candor.org
Candor JSHS 400/7-12
PO Box 145 13743 607-659-5020
Wayne Aman, prin. Fax 659-4692

Canisteo, Steuben, Pop. 2,260
Canisteo-Greenwood Central SD 900/PK-12
84 Greenwood St 14823 607-698-4225
Jeffrey Matteson, supt. Fax 698-2833
www.cg.wnyric.org
Canisteo-Greenwood HS 300/9-12
84 Greenwood St 14823 607-698-4225
Michael Wright, prin. Fax 698-9125
Canisteo-Greenwood MS 300/5-8
120 Greenwood St 14823 607-698-4225
Fax 698-2244

Canton, Saint Lawrence, Pop. 6,213
Canton Central SD 1,200/PK-12
99 State St 13617 315-386-8561
William Gregory, supt. Fax 386-1323
www.ccsdk12.org/
McKenney MS 400/5-8
99 State St 13617 315-386-8561
Jennifer Rurak, prin. Fax 386-1323
Williams HS 400/9-12
99 State St 13617 315-386-8561
Mark Passamonte, prin. Fax 386-1323

St. Lawrence University Post-Sec.
23 Romoda Dr 13617 315-229-5011
SUNY Canton Post-Sec.
34 Cornell Dr 13617 315-386-7011

Carle Place, Nassau, Pop. 4,914
Carle Place UFD 1,400/K-12
168 Cherry Ln 11514 516-622-6442
David Flatley, supt. Fax 622-6447
www.cps.k12.ny.us
Carle Place MSHS 700/7-12
168 Cherry Ln 11514 516-622-6431
Thomas DePaola, prin. Fax 622-6587

Carmel, Putnam, Pop. 4,800
Carmel Central SD
Supt. — See Patterson
Carmel HS 1,600/9-12
30 Fair St 10512 845-225-8441
Kevin Carroll, prin. Fax 228-2308
Fischer MS 1,400/5-8
281 Fair St 10512 845-228-2300
William Manfredonia, prin. Fax 228-2304

Carthage, Jefferson, Pop. 3,663
Carthage Central SD 3,500/K-12
25059 Woolworth St 13619 315-493-5000
Peter Turner, supt. Fax 493-5069
www.carthagecsd.org
Carthage HS 1,000/9-12
36500 State Route 26 13619 315-493-5030
Joseph Sedita, prin. Fax 493-5039
Carthage MS 1,100/5-8
21986 Cole Rd 13619 315-493-5020
Peter Stratton, prin. Fax 493-5029

Castleton on Hudson, Rensselaer, Pop. 1,464
Schodack Central SD 1,000/K-12
1216 Maple Hill Rd 12033 518-732-2297
Robert Horan, supt. Fax 732-7710
www.schodack.k12.ny.us/
Maple Hill HS 400/9-12
1216 Maple Hill Rd 12033 518-732-7701
Ron Agostinoni, prin. Fax 732-0494
Maple Hill MS 200/6-8
1477 S Schodack Rd 12033 518-732-7736
Michael Bennett, prin. Fax 732-0493

Cato, Cayuga, Pop. 516
Cato-Meridian Central SD 1,000/PK-12
2851 State Route 370 13033 315-626-3439
W. Noel Patterson, supt. Fax 626-2888
www.catomeridian.org/
Cato-Meridian HS 300/9-12
2851 State Route 370 13033 315-626-3317
Danielle Mahoney, prin. Fax 626-2551
Cato-Meridian MS 300/5-8
2851 State Route 370 13033 315-626-3319
Sean Gleason, prin. Fax 626-2327

Catskill, Greene, Pop. 3,926
Catskill Central SD 1,700/PK-12
343 W Main St 12414 518-943-4696
Kathleen Farrell Ph.D., supt. Fax 943-7116
www.catskillcsd.org
Catskill HS 600/9-12
341 W Main St 12414 518-943-2300
Selma Friedman Ed.D., prin. Fax 943-1451
Catskill MS 400/6-8
345 W Main St 12414 518-943-5665
Marielena Davis, prin. Fax 943-3001

Cattaraugus, Cattaraugus, Pop. 997
Cattaraugus-Little Valley Central SD 800/PK-12
25 N Franklin St 14719 716-257-5293
Jon Peteson, supt. Fax 257-5298
www.cattlv.wnyric.org/
Cattaraugus-Little Valley HS 300/9-12
25 N Franklin St 14719 716-257-3483
Aaron Wolfe, prin. Fax 257-5108
Cattaraugus-Little Valley MS 200/5-8
25 N Franklin St 14719 716-257-3483
Anthony Giannicchi, prin. Fax 257-5108

Cazenovia, Madison, Pop. 2,807
Cazenovia Central SD 1,700/K-12
31 Emory Ave 13035 315-655-1317
Robert Dubik, supt. Fax 655-1375
www.caz.cnyric.org
Cazenovia JSHS 700/8-12
31 Emory Ave 13035 315-655-1314
Eric Schnabl, prin. Fax 655-1371

Cazenovia College 13035 Post-Sec.
800-654-3210

Cedarhurst, Nassau, Pop. 6,500
Lawrence UFD
Supt. — See Lawrence
Lawrence HS 1,000/9-12
2 Reilly Rd 11516 516-295-8000
Dr. Jennifer Lagnado, prin. Fax 295-2754

Hebrew Academy of Five Towns HS 300/9-12
635 Central Ave 11516 516-569-3807
Naomi Lippman, prin. Fax 374-5761

Centereach, Suffolk, Pop. 31,131
Middle Country Central SD 10,600/PK-12
8 43rd St 11720 631-285-8005
Dr. Roberta Gerold, supt. Fax 738-2719
www.mccsd.net
Centereach HS 1,700/9-12
14 43rd St 11720 631-285-8100
Thomas Bell, prin. Fax 285-8101
Dawnwood MS 1,200/6-8
10 43rd St 11720 631-285-8200
Linda Peyser, prin. Fax 285-8201
Selden MS 1,200/6-8
22 Jefferson Ave 11720 631-285-8400
Barbara Phillipson, prin. Fax 285-8401
Other Schools – See Selden

Our Savior New American S 200/PK-12
140 Mark Tree Rd 11720 631-588-2757
Dolores Reade, prin. Fax 588-2617

Center Moriches, Suffolk, Pop. 7,447
Center Moriches UFD 1,600/K-12
529 Main St 11934 631-878-0052
Russell Stewart, supt. Fax 878-4326
www.cmschools.org
Center Moriches HS 600/9-12
311 Frowein Rd 11934 631-878-0092
Edward Casswell, prin. Fax 878-1796
Center Moriches MS 400/6-8
311 Frowein Rd 11934 631-878-2519
Patricia Cunningham, prin. Fax 878-0362

Burket Christian S 100/PK-12
34 Oak St 11934 631-878-1727
Dominick Scibetta, prin. Fax 878-8968

Central Islip, Suffolk, Pop. 33,583
Central Islip UFD 6,600/PK-12
50 Wheeler Rd 11722 631-348-5112
Dr. Craig Carr, supt. Fax 348-0366
www.cischools.org
Central Islip HS 1,900/9-12
85 Wheeler Rd 11722 631-348-5078
Dr. Franklin Caesar, prin. Fax 342-0161
Reed MS 900/7-8
200 Half Mile Rd 11722 631-348-5066
Brett MacMonigle, prin. Fax 348-5159

Central Square, Oswego, Pop. 1,828
Central Square Central SD 4,400/K-12
642 S Main St 13036 315-668-4220
Joseph Menard, supt. Fax 676-4437
www.cssd.org
Central Square MS 1,000/6-8
248 US Route 11 13036 315-668-4269
Concetta Galvan, prin. Fax 668-8410
Moore HS 1,500/9-12
44 School Dr 13036 315-668-4231
David Furletti, prin. Fax 668-4346

Central Valley, Orange, Pop. 1,929
Monroe-Woodbury Central SD 7,400/K-12
278 Route 32 10917 845-460-6200
Edward Mehrhof, supt. Fax 460-6080
www.mw.k12.ny.us
Monroe-Woodbury HS 2,400/9-12
155 Dunderberg Rd 10917 845-460-7000
David Bernsley, prin. Fax 460-7090
Monroe-Woodbury MS 1,700/6-8
199 Dunderberg Rd 10917 845-460-6400
John Kaste, prin. Fax 460-6044

Champlain, Clinton, Pop. 1,086
Northeastern Clinton Central SD 1,300/K-12
103 State Route 276 12919 518-298-8242
Gerald Blair, supt. Fax 298-4293
www.nccscougar.org/
Northeastern Clinton HS 500/9-12
103 State Route 276 12919 518-298-8638
Stephen Gratto, prin. Fax 298-4293
Northeastern Clinton MS 300/6-8
103 State Route 276 12919 518-298-8681
Thomas Brandell, prin. Fax 298-4293

Chappaqua, Westchester, Pop. 1,404
Chappaqua Central SD 4,100/K-12
PO Box 21 10514 914-238-7200
Dr. Lyn Mckay, supt. Fax 238-7231
www.ccsd.ws
Bell MS 700/5-8
50 Senter St 10514 914-238-6170
Martin Fitzgerald, prin. Fax 238-2085
Greeley HS 1,300/9-12
70 Roaring Brook Rd 10514 914-861-9400
Robert Rhodes, prin. Fax 238-4291
Seven Bridges MS 600/5-8
PO Box 22 10514 914-666-7330
Martha Zornow, prin. Fax 666-7306

Chateaugay, Franklin, Pop. 824
Chateaugay Central SD 500/K-12
PO Box 904 12920 518-497-6420
Wayne Walbridge, supt. Fax 497-3170
www.chateaugay.org/
Chateaugay JSHS 300/7-12
PO Box 904 12920 518-497-6611
Donna Andre, prin. Fax 497-3170

Chatham, Columbia, Pop. 1,720
Chatham Central SD 1,200/K-12
50 Woodbridge Ave 12037 518-392-1501
Cheryl Nuciforo, supt. Fax 392-2413
www.chathamcentralschools.com/
Chatham HS 500/9-12
50 Woodbridge Ave 12037 518-392-4142
John Thorsen, prin. Fax 392-0908
Chatham MS 300/6-8
50 Woodbridge Ave 12037 518-392-1560
Annemarie Barkman, prin. Fax 392-1559

Chaumont, Jefferson, Pop. 611
Lyme Central SD 400/PK-12
PO Box 219 13622 315-649-2417
Karen Donahue, supt. Fax 649-2663
www.lymecsd.org
Lyme Central S 400/PK-12
PO Box 219 13622 315-649-2417
Barry Davis, prin. Fax 649-2663

Chazy, Clinton, Pop. 555
Chazy Central UFD 500/K-12
609 Miner Farm Rd 12921 518-846-7135
John Fairchild, supt. Fax 846-8322
www.chazy.org
Chazy Central Rural JSHS 300/7-12
609 Miner Farm Rd 12921 518-846-7135
John Fairchild, prin. Fax 846-8322

Cheektowaga, Erie, Pop. 74,096
Cheektowaga Central SD 2,300/PK-12
3600 Union Rd 14225 716-686-3606
Dennis Kane, supt. Fax 681-5232
www.cheektowagacentral.org
Cheektowaga Central HS 700/9-12
3600 Union Rd 14225 716-686-3602
Susan Cain, prin. Fax 686-3619
Cheektowaga Central MS 500/6-8
3600 Union Rd 14225 716-686-3660
Brian Bridges, prin. Fax 686-3669

Cheektowaga-Maryvale UFD 2,200/PK-12
1050 Maryvale Dr 14225 716-631-7407
Deborah Ziolkowski, supt. Fax 635-4699
www.maryvale.wnyric.org
Maryvale HS 700/9-12
1050 Maryvale Dr 14225 716-631-7481
Renee Salvadore, prin. Fax 631-7404
Maryvale MS 500/6-8
1050 Maryvale Dr 14225 716-631-7425
Jeffrey Barthelme, prin. Fax 631-7499

Cheektowaga-Sloan UFD
Supt. — See Buffalo
Kennedy HS 500/9-12
305 Cayuga Creek Rd 14227 716-891-6407
Kevin Kazmierczak, prin. Fax 891-6430
Kennedy MS 400/6-8
305 Cayuga Creek Rd 14227 716-897-7300
Gretchen Cercone, prin. Fax 891-6430

Cleveland Hill UFD 1,100/PK-12
105 Mapleview Dr 14225 716-836-7200
Jon MacSwan, supt. Fax 836-0675
www.clevehill.wnyric.org/
Cleveland Hill HS 500/9-12
105 Mapleview Dr 14225 716-836-7200
Jill Sherman, prin. Fax 836-7741
Cleveland Hill MS 400/6-8
105 Mapleview Dr 14225 716-836-7200
Andrea Kersten, prin. Fax 836-7741

Cherryplain, Rensselaer
Berlin Central SD 700/PK-12
17400 Route 22 12040 518-658-2690
Dr. Stephen Young, supt. Fax 658-3822
www.berlincentral.org/
Berlin Central JSHS 300/6-12
17400 Route 22 12040 518-658-2515
Dr. Cathie Allain, prin. Fax 658-2535

Cherry Valley, Otsego, Pop. 511
Cherry Valley-Springfield Central SD 500/PK-12
PO Box 485 13320 607-264-9332
Robert Miller, supt. Fax 264-9023
www.cvscs.org
Cherry Valley-Springfield JSHS 300/6-12
PO Box 485 13320 607-264-9012
Kevin Keane, prin. Fax 264-3458

Chester, Orange, Pop. 3,852
Chester UFD 1,100/K-12
64 Hambletonian Ave 10918 845-469-5052
Sean Michel, supt. Fax 469-2377
chesterufsd.org
Chester Academy 600/6-12
64 Hambletonian Ave 10918 845-469-2231
Leslie Hyatt, prin. Fax 469-3547

Chestertown, Warren, Pop. 671
North Warren Central SD 500/PK-12
6110 State Route 8 12817 518-494-3015
Joseph Murphy, supt. Fax 494-2929
www.northwarren.k12.ny.us
North Warren Central S 500/PK-12
6110 State Route 8 12817 518-494-3015
Theresa Andrew, prin. Fax 494-2929

Chestnut Ridge, Rockland, Pop. 7,763
East Ramapo Central SD
Supt. — See Spring Valley
Chestnut Ridge MS 500/7-8
892 Chestnut Ridge Rd 10977 845-577-6300
Maria Vergez, prin. Fax 426-1063

Green Meadow Waldorf S 400/PK-12
307 Hungry Hollow Rd 10977 845-356-2514
Bill Pernice, admin. Fax 356-2921

Chittenango, Madison, Pop. 5,016
Chittenango Central SD 2,200/K-12
1732 Fyler Rd 13037 315-687-2850
Michael Schiedo, supt. Fax 687-2841
www.chittenangoschools.org
Chittenango HS 800/9-12
150 Genesee St 13037 315-687-2900
Derek Sajnog, prin. Fax 687-2924
Chittenango MS 500/6-8
1732 Fyler Rd 13037 315-687-2800
Thomas Piatti, prin. Fax 687-2801

Churchville, Monroe, Pop. 1,935
Churchville-Chili Central SD 4,100/K-12
139 Fairbanks Rd 14428 585-293-1800
Dr. Pamela Kissel, supt. Fax 293-1013
www.cccsd.org
Churchville-Chili MS 1,300/5-8
139 Fairbanks Rd 14428 585-293-4541
Giulio Bosco, prin. Fax 293-4516
Churchville-Chili SHS 1,000/10-12
5786 Buffalo Rd 14428 585-293-4540
Bill Geraci, prin. Fax 293-4508
9th Grade Academy 300/9-9
137 Fairbanks Rd 14428 585-293-4546
Mary Leach, admin. Fax 293-4521

Cicero, Onondaga
North Syracuse Central SD
Supt. — See North Syracuse
Cicero-North Syracuse SHS 2,200/10-12
6002 State Route 31 13039 315-218-4100
Melissa Julian, prin. Fax 218-4185

Cincinnatus, Cortland
Cincinnatus Central SD 600/K-12
2809 Cincinnatus Rd 13040 607-863-4069
Steven Hubbard, supt. Fax 863-4109
www.cc.cnyric.org/
Cincinnatus HS 200/9-12
2809 Cincinnatus Rd 13040 607-863-3200
Joseph Mack, prin. Fax 863-4559
Cincinnatus MS 200/5-8
2809 Cincinnatus Rd 13040 607-863-3200
Joseph Mack, prin. Fax 863-4559

Circleville, Orange, Pop. 1,350
Pine Bush Central SD
Supt. — See Pine Bush
Circleville MS 600/6-8
PO Box 143 10919 845-744-2031
Lisa Hankinson, prin. Fax 361-3811

Clarence, Erie, Pop. 2,634
Clarence Central SD 5,000/K-12
9625 Main St 14031 716-407-9100
Geoffrey Hicks, supt. Fax 407-9126
www.clarenceschools.org
Clarence HS 1,700/9-12
9625 Main St 14031 716-407-9020
Kenneth Smith, prin. Fax 407-9061
Clarence MS 1,200/6-8
10150 Greiner Rd 14031 716-407-9200
Robert Moore, prin. Fax 407-9229

Clayton, Jefferson, Pop. 1,959
Thousand Islands Central SD 1,100/K-12
PO Box 100 13624 315-686-5594
Frank House, supt. Fax 686-5511
www.1000islandsschools.org
Thousand Islands HS 300/9-12
PO Box 100 13624 315-686-5594
Joseph Gilfus, prin. Fax 654-5039
Thousand Islands MS 300/6-8
PO Box 100 13624 315-686-5594
Debra Percy, prin. Fax 654-5038

Clifton Park, Saratoga
Shenendehowa Central SD 9,800/K-12
5 Chelsea Pl 12065 518-881-0600
L. Oliver Robinson, supt. Fax 371-9393
www.shenet.org/

Acadia MS 800/6-8
970 Route 146 Ste 54 12065 518-881-0450
Jonathan Burns, prin. Fax 371-3981
Gowana MS 800/6-8
970 Route 146 Ste 55 12065 518-881-0460
Robin Gawrys, prin. Fax 383-1490
Koda MS 800/6-8
970 Route 146 Ste 59 12065 518-881-0470
Sean Gnat, prin. Fax 383-1532
Shenendehowa HS West 700/9-9
970 Route 146 Ste 56 12065 518-881-0330
Donald Flynt, prin. Fax 383-5768
Shenendehowa SHS East 2,300/10-12
970 Route 146 12065 518-881-0310
Donald Flynt, prin. Fax 383-1670

Clifton Springs, Ontario, Pop. 2,111
Phelps-Clifton Springs Central SD 1,400/K-12
1490 State Route 488 14432 315-548-6420
Michael Ford, supt. Fax 548-6429
www.midlakes.org
Midlakes MSHS 600/7-12
1554 State Route 488 14432 315-548-6300
Jamie Farr, prin. Fax 548-6319

Climax, Greene

Grapeville Christian S 100/K-12
2416 County Route 26 12042 518-966-5037
Nicole Orsino, admin. Fax 966-5498

Clinton, Oneida, Pop. 1,917
Clinton Central SD 1,400/K-12
75 Chenango Ave 13323 315-557-2253
Matthew Reilly, supt. Fax 853-8727
www.ccs.edu
Clinton HS 500/9-12
75 Chenango Ave 13323 315-557-2232
Matthew Lee, prin. Fax 853-1424
Clinton MS 300/6-8
75 Chenango Ave 13323 315-557-2260
Shaun Carney, prin. Fax 853-8727

Hamilton College Post-Sec.
198 College Hill Rd 13323 315-859-4011

Clinton Corners, Dutchess

Upton Lake Christian S 100/PK-12
PO Box 63 12514 845-266-3497
Dietlind Hoiem, admin. Fax 266-3828

Clintonville, Clinton
Au Sable Valley Central SD 1,200/K-12
1273 Route 9N 12924 518-834-2845
Paul Savage, supt. Fax 834-2843
www.avcs.org
Au Sable Valley HS 400/9-12
1490 Route 9N 12924 518-834-2800
Aimee Defayette, prin. Fax 834-2847
Au Sable Valley MS 200/7-8
1490 Route 9N 12924 518-834-2800
Philip Mero, prin. Fax 834-2847

Clyde, Wayne, Pop. 2,017
Clyde-Savannah Central SD 700/K-12
215 Glasgow St 14433 315-902-3000
Theresa Pulos, supt. Fax 923-2560
www.clydesavannah.org/
Clyde-Savannah HS 300/9-12
215 Glasgow St 14433 315-902-3050
Dr. Craig Pawlak, prin. Fax 923-7906
Clyde-Savannah MS 100/5-8
215 Glasgow St 14433 315-902-3200
Belinda Crowe, prin. Fax 923-2560

Clymer, Chautauqua
Clymer Central SD 500/PK-12
8672 E Main St 14724 716-355-4444
Karen Moon, supt. Fax 355-2200
www.clymercsd.org
Clymer Central S 500/PK-12
8672 E Main St 14724 716-355-4444
Edward Bailey, prin. Fax 355-4467

Cobleskill, Schoharie, Pop. 4,593
Cobleskill-Richmondville Central SD 2,000/K-12
155 Washington Ave 12043 518-234-4032
Lynn Macan, supt. Fax 234-7721
www.crcs.k12.ny.us/
Golding MS 500/6-8
193 Golding Dr 12043 518-234-8368
Scott McDonald, prin. Fax 234-1018
Other Schools – See Richmondville

SUNY Cobleskill Post-Sec.
State Route 7 12043 518-255-5011

Cohoes, Albany, Pop. 15,737
Cohoes CSD 2,000/K-12
7 Bevan St 12047 518-237-0100
Robert Libby, supt. Fax 237-2912
www.cohoes.org
Cohoes HS 600/9-12
1 Tiger Cir 12047 518-237-9100
Joseph Rajczak, prin. Fax 238-0169
Cohoes MS 400/6-8
7 Bevan St 12047 518-237-4131
Daniel Martinelli, prin. Fax 237-2253
Page Avenue S, 21 Page Ave 12047 Alt
Erin Hill, prin. 518-237-0990

Cold Spring, Putnam, Pop. 1,981
Haldane Central SD 900/K-12
15 Craigside Dr 10516 845-265-9254
Dr. Mark Villanti, supt. Fax 265-9213
www.haldaneschool.org
Haldane HS 300/9-12
15 Craigside Dr 10516 845-265-9254
Brian Alm, prin. Fax 265-3510

Cold Spring Harbor, Suffolk, Pop. 5,024
Cold Spring Harbor Central SD 2,000/K-12
75 Goose Hill Rd 11724 631-367-8800
Judith Wilansky Ed.D., supt. Fax 367-3108
www.csh.k12.ny.us
Cold Spring Harbor JSHS 1,000/7-12
82 Turkey Ln 11724 631-367-6900
Jay Matuk, prin. Fax 692-8016

Watson School of Biological Sciences Post-Sec.
1 Bungtown Rd 11724 516-367-6890

College Point, See New York

St. Agnes Academic HS 300/9-12
1320 124th St 11356 718-353-6276
Sr. Joan Martin, prin. Fax 353-6068

Colton, Saint Lawrence, Pop. 343
Colton-Pierrepont Central SD 200/PK-12
4921 State Highway 56 13625 315-262-2100
Joseph Kardash, supt. Fax 262-2644
www.cpcs.us/
Colton-Pierrepont Central S 200/PK-12
4921 State Highway 56 13625 315-262-2100
James Nee, prin. Fax 262-2644

Commack, Suffolk, Pop. 35,739
Commack UFD
Supt. — See East Northport
Commack HS, 1 Scholar Ln 11725 2,500/9-12
Catherine Nolan, prin. 631-912-2100
Commack MS 1,900/6-8
700 Vanderbilt Pkwy 11725 631-858-3500
Anthony Davidson, prin.

Long Island Business Institute Post-Sec.
6500 Jericho Tpke Ste 202 11725 631-499-7100

Congers, Rockland, Pop. 8,213

Rockland Country Day S 100/PK-12
34 Kings Hwy 10920 845-268-6802
Kimberly Morcate, head sch Fax 268-4644

Conklin, Broome
Susquehanna Valley Central SD 1,700/K-12
PO Box 200 13748 607-775-0170
Gerardo Tagliaferri, supt. Fax 775-4575
www.svsabers.org/
Stank MS 400/6-8
1040 Conklin Rd 13748 607-775-0303
Roland Doig, prin. Fax 775-9142
Susquehanna Valley HS 600/9-12
1040 Conklin Rd 13748 607-775-0304
David Daniels, prin. Fax 775-4575

Cooperstown, Otsego, Pop. 1,834
Cooperstown Central SD 600/K-12
39 Linden Ave 13326 607-547-5364
C.J. Hebert, supt. Fax 547-5100
www.cooperstowncs.org/
Cooperstown JSHS 200/7-12
39 Linden Ave 13326 607-547-8181
Michael Cring, prin. Fax 547-5100

Copenhagen, Lewis, Pop. 796
Copenhagen Central SD 500/PK-12
PO Box 30 13626 315-688-4411
Scott Connell, supt. Fax 688-2001
www.ccsknights.org/
Copenhagen Central S 500/PK-12
PO Box 30 13626 315-688-4411
Nadine O'Shaughnessy, prin. Fax 688-2001

Copiague, Suffolk, Pop. 22,652
Copiague UFD 4,700/K-12
2650 Great Neck Rd 11726 631-842-4015
Charles Leunig, supt. Fax 841-4614
www.copiague.k12.ny.us/
Copiague MS 1,100/6-8
2650 Great Neck Rd 11726 631-842-4011
Andrew Lagnado, prin. Fax 841-4630
O'Connell - Copiague HS 1,500/9-12
1100 Dixon Ave 11726 631-842-4010
Jeanette Altruda, prin. Fax 841-4642

Corfu, Genesee, Pop. 702
Pembroke Central SD 1,000/PK-12
PO Box 308 14036 585-599-4525
Matthew Calderon, supt. Fax 599-4213
www.pembroke.k12.ny.us
Pembroke JSHS 500/7-12
PO Box 308 14036 585-599-4525
Keith Palmer, prin. Fax 599-4213

Corinth, Saratoga, Pop. 2,505
Corinth Central SD 1,100/K-12
105 Oak St 12822 518-654-2601
Dr. Daniel Starr, supt. Fax 654-6266
www.corinthcsd.com/
Corinth HS 400/9-12
105 Oak St 12822 518-654-9005
Brian Testani, prin. Fax 654-6132
Corinth MS 300/6-8
105 Oak St 12822 518-654-9005
Lisa Meade, prin. Fax 654-2129

Corning, Steuben, Pop. 10,950
Corning CSD
Supt. — See Painted Post
Corning Free Academy MS 500/6-8
11 W 3rd St 14830 607-936-3788
Richard Kimble, prin. Fax 654-2809
Corning-Painted Post East HS 900/9-12
201 Cantigney St 14830 607-936-3746
Robin Sheehan, prin. Fax 654-2787
Corning - Painted Post HS Learning Ctr 50/Alt
1 Academic Dr 14830 607-962-9283
Frank Barber, prin.

Northside Blodgett MS 600/6-8
143 Princeton Ave 14830 607-936-3791
Jeffrey Marchionda, prin. Fax 654-2798

Corning Christian Academy 200/PK-12
11 Aisne St 14830 607-962-4220
Richard Cornfield, admin. Fax 962-4410
Corning Community College Post-Sec.
1 Academic Dr 14830 607-962-9011

Cornwall, Orange, Pop. 11,270
Cornwall Central SD
Supt. — See Cornwall on Hudson
Cornwall Central MS 1,000/5-8
122 Main St 12518 845-534-8009
Kate Polumbo, prin. Fax 534-7809

Cornwall on Hudson, Orange, Pop. 2,955
Cornwall Central SD 3,400/K-12
24 Idlewild Ave 12520 845-534-8009
Timothy Rehm, supt. Fax 534-9032
www.cornwallschools.com
Other Schools – See Cornwall, New Windsor

New York Military Academy 100/7-12
78 Academy Ave 12520 845-534-3710
Jeffrey Coverdale, supt. Fax 534-7121
Storm King S 100/8-12
314 Mountain Rd 12520 845-534-7892
Helen Chinitz, hdmstr. Fax 534-2709

Corona, See New York
NYC Department of Education
Supt. — See New York
HS for Arts & Business 800/9-12
10525 Horace Harding Expy 11368 718-271-8383
Ana Bruakov, prin. Fax 271-7196
IS 61 2,200/6-8
9850 50th Ave 11368 718-760-3233
Joseph Lisa, prin. Fax 760-5220

Cortland, Cortland, Pop. 18,830
Cortland CSD 2,700/K-12
1 Valley View Dr 13045 607-758-4100
Michael J. Hoose, supt. Fax 758-4128
www.cortlandschools.org
Cortland JSHS 1,200/7-12
8 Valley View Dr 13045 607-758-4100
Greg Santoro, prin. Fax 758-4119

Cortland Christian Academy 100/PK-12
15 West Rd 13045 607-756-5838
Craig Miller, admin. Fax 756-7716
SUNY College at Cortland Post-Sec.
PO Box 2000 13045 607-753-2011

Cortlandt Manor, See Peekskill
Hendrick Hudson Central SD
Supt. — See Montrose
Blue Mountain MS 600/6-8
7 Furnace Woods Rd 10567 914-257-5700
John Owens, prin. Fax 257-5701
Lakeland Central SD
Supt. — See Shrub Oak
Panas HS 1,000/9-12
300 Croton Ave 10567 914-739-2823
Susan Strauss, prin. Fax 739-3545

Ohr Hameir Seminary Tifereth Israel HS 100/9-12
141 Furnace Woods Rd 10567 914-736-1500
Ohr HaMeir Theological Seminary Post-Sec.
141 Furnace Woods Rd 10567 914-736-1500

Coxsackie, Greene, Pop. 2,765
Coxsackie-Athens Central SD 1,500/K-12
24 Sunset Blvd 12051 518-731-1710
Randall Squier, supt. Fax 731-1729
www.coxsackie-athens.org
Coxsackie-Athens HS 500/9-12
24 Sunset Blvd 12051 518-731-1800
Heath Hanley, prin. Fax 731-1809
Coxsackie-Athens MS 400/5-8
24 Sunset Blvd 12051 518-731-1850
David Proper, prin. Fax 731-1859

Craryville, Columbia
Taconic Hills Central SD 1,500/PK-12
73 County Route 11A 12521 518-325-2810
Dr. Neil Howard, supt.
www.taconichills.k12.ny.us/
Taconic Hills HS 500/9-12
73 County Route 11A 12521 518-325-2840
Marie Digirolamo, prin. Fax 325-2845
Taconic Hills MS 300/6-8
73 County Route 11A 12521 518-325-2830
Sandra Gardner, prin. Fax 325-2835

Cross River, Westchester
Katonah-Lewisboro UFD
Supt. — See Goldens Bridge
Jay HS 1,300/9-12
60 N Salem Rd 10518 914-763-7200
John Goetz, prin. Fax 763-7494
Jay MS 900/6-8
40 N Salem Rd 10518 914-763-7500
Rich Leprine, prin. Fax 763-7665

Croton on Hudson, Westchester, Pop. 7,883
Croton-Harmon UFD 1,700/K-12
10 Gerstein St 10520 914-271-4793
Edward Fuhrman, supt. Fax 271-8685
www.croton-harmonschools.org
Croton-Harmon HS 600/9-12
36 Old Post Rd S 10520 914-271-2147
Alan Capasso, prin. Fax 271-6643
Van Cortlandt MS 500/5-8
3 Glen Pl 10520 914-271-2191
Dr. Barbara Ulm, prin. Fax 271-6618

Crown Point, Essex
Crown Point Central SD 300/PK-12
PO Box 35 12928 518-597-4200
Shari Brannock, supt. Fax 597-4121
cpcsteam.org/
Crown Point Central S 300/PK-12
PO Box 35 12928 518-597-3285
Agatha Mace, prin. Fax 597-4121

Cuba, Allegany, Pop. 1,561
Cuba-Rushford Central SD 800/K-12
5476 Route 305 14727 585-968-2650
Carlos Gildemeister, supt. Fax 968-2651
www.crcs.wnyric.org/
Cuba-Rushford HS 300/9-12
5476 Route 305 14727 585-968-2650
Carrie Bold, prin. Fax 968-2651
Cuba-Rushford MS 200/6-8
5476 Route 305 14727 585-968-2650
Andrew Rantz, prin. Fax 968-2651

Cutchogue, Suffolk, Pop. 3,330
Mattituck-Cutchogue UFD 1,400/1-12
385 Depot Ln 11935 631-298-4242
James McKenna, supt. Fax 298-8573
www.mufsd.com/cms/
Other Schools – See Mattituck

Dannemora, Clinton, Pop. 3,874
Saranac Central SD 1,600/K-12
32 Emmons St 12929 518-565-5600
Kenneth Cringle, supt. Fax 565-5617
www.saranac.org
Other Schools – See Saranac

Dansville, Livingston, Pop. 4,671
Dansville Central SD 1,300/K-12
284 Main St 14437 585-335-4000
Dr. Paul Alioto, supt. Fax 335-4002
www.dansvillecsd.org
Dansville HS 600/7-12
282 Main St 14437 585-335-4010
Michael Falzoi, prin. Fax 335-4080

Davenport, Delaware
Charlotte Valley Central SD 400/PK-12
15611 State Highway 23 13750 607-278-5511
Mark Dupra, supt. Fax 278-5900
www.charlottevalleycs.org
Charlotte Valley S 400/PK-12
15611 State Highway 23 13750 607-278-5511
David Slater, prin. Fax 278-5900

Deer Park, Suffolk, Pop. 27,209
Deer Park UFD 4,400/PK-12
1881 Deer Park Ave 11729 631-274-4000
Eva Demyen, supt. Fax 242-6762
www.deerparkschools.org/
Deer Park HS 1,300/9-12
1 Falcon Pl 11729 631-274-4100
James Cummings, prin. Fax 254-0237
Frost MS 1,000/6-8
450 Half Hollow Rd 11729 631-274-4200
Eliana Levey, prin. Fax 242-0035

De Kalb Junction, Saint Lawrence, Pop. 515
Hermon-DeKalb Central SD 400/PK-12
709 E DeKalb Rd 13630 315-347-3442
Ann Adams, supt. Fax 347-3817
www.hdcsk12.org
Hermon-DeKalb Central S 400/PK-12
709 E DeKalb Rd 13630 315-347-3442
Mark White, prin. Fax 347-3817

Delanson, Schenectady, Pop. 371
Duanesburg Central SD 700/K-12
133 School Rd 12053 518-895-2279
Christine Crowley, supt. Fax 895-2626
www.duanesburg.org/
Duanesburg JSHS 300/6-12
163 School Rd 12053 518-895-2355
Beth DeLuke, prin. Fax 895-9971

Delhi, Delaware, Pop. 3,025
Delaware Academy Central SD at Delhi 600/K-12
2 Sheldon Dr 13753 607-746-1300
Jason Thomson, supt. Fax 746-6028
www.delhischools.org
Delaware Academy MSHS 300/6-12
2 Sheldon Dr 13753 607-746-1300
Laurie Alberti, prin. Fax 746-1324

SUNY Delhi Post-Sec.
2 Main St 13753 607-746-4000

Delmar, Albany, Pop. 8,360
Bethlehem Central SD 4,800/K-12
700 Delaware Ave 12054 518-439-7098
Dr. Thomas Douglas, supt. Fax 475-0352
bcsd.k12.ny.us
Bethlehem Central HS 1,700/9-12
700 Delaware Ave 12054 518-439-4921
Scott Landry, prin. Fax 439-2837
Bethlehem Central MS 1,200/6-8
332 Kenwood Ave 12054 518-439-7460
Mike Klugman, prin. Fax 475-0092

Depew, Erie, Pop. 15,147
Depew UFD 2,000/K-12
591 Terrace Blvd 14043 716-686-5105
Jeffrey Rabey, supt. Fax 686-5101
www.depewschools.org/
Depew HS 700/9-12
5201 Transit Rd 14043 716-686-5095
Carol Townsend, prin. Fax 686-5094
Depew MS 500/6-8
5201 Transit Rd 14043 716-686-5050
Joseph D'Amato, prin. Fax 686-5057

Deposit, Delaware, Pop. 1,641
Deposit Central SD 600/PK-12
171 2nd St 13754 607-467-5380
Ed Shirkey, supt. Fax 467-5535
www.depositcsd.org/
Deposit HS 200/9-12
171 2nd St 13754 607-467-2197
Theresa Rajner, prin. Fax 467-5504
Deposit MS 100/7-8
171 2nd St 13754 607-467-2197
Theresa Rajner, prin. Fax 467-5504

DeRuyter, Madison, Pop. 552
De Ruyter Central SD 400/PK-12
711 Railroad St 13052 315-852-3400
Charles Walters, supt. Fax 852-3446
www.deruytercentral.org/
De Ruyter Central JSHS 200/6-12
711 Railroad St 13052 315-852-3400
Dr. Karen Genzel, prin. Fax 852-3404

De Witt, Onondaga, Pop. 8,244
Jamesville-DeWitt Central SD 2,900/K-12
PO Box 606 13214 315-445-8304
Dr. Alice Kendrick, supt. Fax 445-8477
www.jamesvilledewitt.org
Jamesville-DeWitt HS 900/9-12
PO Box 606 13214 315-445-8340
Paul Gasparini, prin. Fax 445-8307
Other Schools – See Jamesville

Manlius Pebble Hill S 600/PK-12
5300 Jamesville Rd 13214 315-446-2452
D. Scott Wiggins, hdmstr. Fax 446-2620

Dexter, Jefferson, Pop. 1,036
General Brown Central SD 1,500/K-12
PO Box 500 13634 315-779-2300
Stephan J. Vigliotti, supt. Fax 639-6916
www.gblions.org
Brown JSHS 700/7-12
17643 Cemetery Rd 13634 315-779-2300
Tina Heckman, prin. Fax 639-3444

Dix Hills, Suffolk, Pop. 26,364
Half Hollow Hills Central SD 9,800/K-12
525 Half Hollow Rd 11746 631-592-3000
Kelly Fallon, supt. Fax 592-3900
www.hhh.k12.ny.us
Candlewood MS 1,100/6-8
1200 Carlls Straight Path 11746 631-592-3300
Andrew Greene, prin. Fax 592-3921
Half Hollow Hills HS East 1,800/9-12
50 Vanderbilt Pkwy 11746 631-592-3100
Dr. Jeffery Woodberry, prin. Fax 592-3907
Half Hollow Hills HS West 1,400/9-12
375 Wolf Hill Rd 11746 631-592-3200
Wayne Ebanks, prin. Fax 592-3923
Other Schools – See Melville

Five Towns College Post-Sec.
305 N Service Rd 11746 631-656-2110
Upper Room Christian S 200/K-12
722 Deer Park Rd 11746 631-242-5359
Dr. Gregory Eck, prin. Fax 242-5418

Dobbs Ferry, Westchester, Pop. 10,650
Dobbs Ferry UFD 1,400/K-12
505 Broadway 10522 914-693-1506
Dr. Lisa Brady, dir. Fax 693-1787
www.dfsd.org
Dobbs Ferry HS 400/9-12
505 Broadway 10522 914-693-7645
John Falino, prin. Fax 693-5227
Dobbs Ferry MS 300/6-8
505 Broadway 10522 914-693-7640
Patrick Mussolini, prin. Fax 693-5229

Greenburgh-North Castle UFD 400/7-12
71 Broadway 10522 914-693-4309
Dr. Edward Placke, supt. Fax 693-8030
greenburghnorthcastleschools.com/
Other Schools – See New Windsor

Masters S 600/5-12
49 Clinton Ave 10522 914-479-6400
Dr. Maureen Fonseca, hdmstr. Fax 693-1230
Mercy College Post-Sec.
555 Broadway 10522 800-637-2969

Dolgeville, Herkimer, Pop. 2,188
Dolgeville Central SD 700/PK-12
38 Slawson St 13329 315-429-3155
Christine Reynolds, supt. Fax 429-8473
www.dolgeville.org
Dolgeville Central MS 100/5-8
38 Slawson St 13329 315-429-3155
Melissa Hoskey, prin. Fax 429-8473
Green HS 200/9-12
38 Slawson St 13329 315-429-3155
Timothy Jenny, prin. Fax 429-8473

Dover Plains, Dutchess, Pop. 1,293
Dover UFD 1,600/K-12
2368 Route 22 12522 845-832-4500
Michael Tierney, supt. Fax 832-4511
www.doverschools.org
Dover HS 500/9-12
2368 Route 22 12522 845-832-4520
Brian Timm, prin. Fax 832-3924
Dover MS 400/6-8
2368 Route 22 12522 845-832-4521
Patricia Rizzo, prin. Fax 832-3924

Downsville, Delaware, Pop. 606
Downsville Central SD 300/PK-12
PO Box J 13755 607-363-2100
Roger Adams, supt. Fax 363-2105
www.dcseagles.org
Downsville Central S 300/PK-12
PO Box J 13755 607-363-2111
Timothy McNamara, prin. Fax 363-2105

Dryden, Tompkins, Pop. 1,854
Dryden Central SD 1,100/PK-12
PO Box 88 13053 607-844-5361
Sandra Sherwood, supt. Fax 844-4733
dcsd-ny.schoolloop.com
Dryden HS 600/9-12
PO Box 88 13053 607-844-8694
Brett Fingland, prin. Fax 844-9004
Dryden MS 400/6-8
PO Box 88 13053 607-844-8694
John Birmingham, prin. Fax 844-5174

Tompkins Cortland Community College Post-Sec.
PO Box 139 13053 607-844-8211

Dundee, Yates, Pop. 1,714
Dundee Central SD 800/K-12
55 Water St 14837 607-243-5533
Kathy Ring, supt. Fax 243-7912
www.dundeecs.org
Dundee JSHS 400/7-12
55 Water St 14837 607-243-5534
Chris Arnold, prin. Fax 243-7912

Dunkirk, Chautauqua, Pop. 12,328
Dunkirk CSD 2,000/K-12
620 Marauder Dr 14048 716-366-9300
Gary Cerne, supt. Fax 366-9399
www.dunkirkcsd.org
Dunkirk HS 600/9-12
75 W 6th St 14048 716-366-9390
Steve O'Brien, prin. Fax 366-0321
Dunkirk MS 400/6-8
525 Eagle St 14048 716-366-9380
David Boyda, prin. Fax 366-9357

East Amherst, Erie
Williamsville Central SD 10,400/K-12
PO Box 5000 14051 716-626-8000
Dr. Scott Martzloff, supt. Fax 626-8089
www.williamsvillek12.org
Casey MS 700/5-8
105 Casey Rd 14051 716-626-8585
Francis McGreevy, prin. Fax 626-8562
Transit MS 1,000/5-8
8730 Transit Rd 14051 716-626-8701
Daniel Walh, prin. Fax 626-8796
Williamsville East HS 1,100/9-12
151 Paradise Rd 14051 716-626-8404
Scott Taylor, prin. Fax 626-8408
Other Schools – See Williamsville

East Aurora, Erie, Pop. 6,180
East Aurora UFD 1,900/K-12
430 Main St 14052 716-687-2302
Brian Russ, supt. Fax 652-8581
eastauroraschools.org/
East Aurora HS 700/9-12
1003 Center St 14052 716-687-2505
Dr. James Hoagland, prin. Fax 687-2552
East Aurora MS 600/5-8
430 Main St 14052 716-687-2453
Mark Mambretti, prin. Fax 652-8581

Christ the King Seminary Post-Sec.
PO Box 607 14052 716-652-8900

Eastchester, Westchester, Pop. 19,285
Eastchester UFD 3,100/K-12
580 White Plains Rd 10709 914-793-6130
Dr. Marilyn Terranova, supt. Fax 793-9006
district.eastchesterschools.org
Eastchester HS 900/9-12
2 Stewart Pl 10709 914-793-6130
Dr. Jeffrey Capuano, prin. Fax 793-9000
Eastchester MS 700/6-8
550 White Plains Rd 10709 914-793-6130
Dr. Walter Moran, prin. Fax 793-1699

Tuckahoe UFD 1,000/K-12
65 Siwanoy Blvd 10709 914-337-6600
Dr. Barbara Nuzzi, supt. Fax 337-3072
www.tuckahoeschools.org
Tuckahoe HS 300/9-12
65 Siwanoy Blvd 10709 914-337-5376
Bart Linehan Ed.D., prin. Fax 337-5168
Tuckahoe MS 200/6-8
65 Siwanoy Blvd 10709 914-337-5376
Dr. Timothy Mundell, prin. Fax 337-5236

East Elmhurst, See New York
NYC Department of Education
Supt. — See New York
IS 227 1,400/5-8
3202 Junction Blvd 11369 718-335-7500
William Fahey, prin. Fax 779-7186

Monsignor McClancy Memorial HS 500/9-12
7106 31st Ave 11370 718-898-3800
James Carey, prin. Fax 898-3929

East Greenbush, Rensselaer, Pop. 4,416
East Greenbush Central SD 4,300/K-12
29 Englewood Ave 12061 518-207-2500
Angela Nagle Ph.D., supt. Fax 477-4833
www.egcsd.org
Columbia HS 1,500/9-12
962 Luther Rd 12061 518-207-2000
John Sawchuk, prin. Fax 207-2009
Goff MS 1,000/6-8
35 Gilligan Rd 12061 518-207-2430
Matthew Sloane, prin. Fax 477-2667

East Hampton, Suffolk, Pop. 1,079
East Hampton UFD 1,800/K-12
4 Long Ln 11937 631-329-4100
Richard Burns, supt. Fax 324-0109
www.ehufsd.org
East Hampton HS 1,000/9-12
2 Long Ln 11937 631-329-4130
Adam Fine, prin. Fax 329-4210
East Hampton MS 300/6-8
76 Newtown Ln 11937 631-329-4116
Dr. Charles Soriano, prin. Fax 329-4187

Ross S 300/5-12
18 Goodfriend Dr 11937 631-907-5000
Gregg Maloberti, head sch Fax 329-6830

East Meadow, Nassau, Pop. 37,572
East Meadow UFD
Supt. — See Westbury
East Meadow HS 1,600/9-12
101 Carman Ave 11554 516-228-5331
Richard Howard, prin. Fax 228-5339
Woodland MS 1,200/6-8
690 Wenwood Dr 11554 516-564-6523
James Lethbridge, prin. Fax 564-6519

East Moriches, Suffolk, Pop. 5,179
East Moriches UFD 700/K-8
9 Adelaide Ave 11940 631-878-0162
Dr. Charles Russo, supt. Fax 878-0186
emoschools.org/
East Moriches MS 300/5-8
9 Adelaide Ave 11940 631-878-0162
Thomas Colletti, prin. Fax 874-0096

East Northport, Suffolk, Pop. 19,969
Commack UFD 7,500/K-12
480 Clay Pitts Rd 11731 631-912-2000
Dr. Donald James, supt. Fax 266-2406
www.commack.k12.ny.us
Other Schools – See Commack

Northport-East Northport UFD
Supt. — See Northport
East Northport MS 700/6-8
1075 5th Ave 11731 631 262-6770
Pasquale DeStefano, prin. Fax 262-6773

East Patchogue, Suffolk, Pop. 22,129
South Country Central SD 4,600/PK-12
189 N Dunton Ave 11772 631-730-1510
Dr. Howard Koenig, supt. Fax 286-6394
www.southcountry.org/
Other Schools – See Bellport, Brookhaven

East Rochester, Monroe, Pop. 6,434
East Rochester UFD 1,200/PK 12
222 Woodbine Ave 14445 585-248-6302
Richard Stutzman, supt. Fax 586-3254
www.erschools.org
East Rochester JSHS 500/7 12
200 Woodbine Ave 14445 585-248-6350
Fax 248-6383

East Rockaway, Nassau, Pop. 9,736
East Rockaway UFD 1,300/K-12
443 Ocean Ave 11518 516-887-8300
Lisa J. Ruiz, supt. Fax 887-8308
www.eastrockawayschools.org
East Rockaway JSHS 600/7-12
443 Ocean Ave 11518 516-887-8300
Joseph Spero, prin. Fax 887-8308

East Setauket, See Setauket
Three Village Central SD
Supt. — See Stony Brook
Melville HS 1,800/10-12
380 Old Town Rd 11733 631-730-4900
Alan Baum, prin. Fax 730-4901

East Syracuse, Onondaga, Pop. 2,961
East Syracuse Minoa Central SD 3,500/PK-12
407 Fremont Rd 13057 315-434-3012
Dr. Donna DeSiato, supt. Fax 434-3020
www.esmschools.org
East Syracuse Minoa Central HS 1,100/9-12
6400 Fremont Rd 13057 315-434-3300
Grenardo Avellino, prin. Fax 434-3335
Pine Grove MS 800/6-8
6318 Fremont Rd 13057 315-434-3050
Kelly Sajnog, prin. Fax 434-3070

Bishop Grimes JSHS 400/7-12
6653 Kirkville Rd 13057 315-437-0356
Marc Crouse, prin. Fax 437-0358

Eden, Erie, Pop. 3,494
Eden Central SD 1,700/PK-12
3150 Schoolview Rd 14057 716-992-3629
Ronald Buggs, supt. Fax 992-3656
www.edencsd.org/
Eden JSHS 900/7 12
3150 Schoolview Rd 14057 716-992-3641
Marc Graff, prin. Fax 992-3652

Edmeston, Otsego, Pop. 650
Edmeston Central SD 500/PK-12
PO Box 5129 13335 607-965-8931
Brian Hunt, supt. Fax 965-8942
edmestoncentralschool.net
Edmeston Central S 500/PK-12
PO Box 5129 13335 607-965-8931
Martha Winsor, prin. Fax 965-8942

Elba, Genesee, Pop. 668
Elba Central SD 500/K-12
PO Box 370 14058 585-757-9967
Jerome Piwko, supt. Fax 757-2713
www.elbacsd.org
Elba JSHS 200/7-12
PO Box 370 14058 585-757-9967
Dr. Chris Salinas, prin. Fax 757-6683

Eldred, Sullivan
Eldred Central SD 700/PK-12
PO Box 249 12732 845-456-1100
Robert M. Dufour, supt. Fax 557-3672
www.eldred.k12.ny.us/
Eldred Central JSHS 300/7-12
PO Box 249 12732 845-456-1100
Scott Krebs, prin. Fax 557-3672

Elizabethtown, Essex
Elizabethtown-Lewis Central SD 300/K-12
PO Box 158 12932 518-873-6371
Paul Scott, supt. Fax 873-9552
elcsd.org
Elizabethtown-Lewis Central S 300/K-12
PO Box 158 12932 518-873-6371
Jennifer Bull, prin. Fax 873-9552

Ellenburg Depot, Clinton
Northern Adirondack Central SD 900/K-12
PO Box 164 12935 518-594-7060
Laura Marlow, supt. Fax 594-7255
www.nacs1.org/
Northern Adirondack MSHS 500/6-12
PO Box 164 12935 518-594-3962
Michael Loughman, prin. Fax 594-7255

Ellenville, Ulster, Pop. 3,954
Ellenville Central SD 1,600/PK-12
28 Maple Ave 12428 845-647-0100
Lisa Wiles, supt. Fax 647-0105
www.ecs.k12.ny.us
Ellenville HS 500/9-12
28 Maple Ave 12428 845-647-0123
Carl Pabon, prin. Fax 647-5972
Ellenville MS 400/6-8
28 Maple Ave 12428 845-647-0126
Angela Urbina, prin. Fax 647-0230

Ellicottville, Cattaraugus, Pop. 371
Ellicottville Central SD 500/K-12
5873 Route 219 S 14731 716-699-2368
Mark Ward, supt. Fax 699-6017
www.ellicottvillecentral.com/
Ellicottville MSHS 300/6-12
5873 Route 219 S 14731 716-699-2316
Robert Miller, prin. Fax 699-5423

Elma, Erie
Iroquois Central SD 2,600/K-12
PO Box 32 14059 716-652-3000
Douglas Scofield, supt. Fax 652-9305
www.iroquoiscsd.org
Iroquois HS 900/9-12
PO Box 32 14059 716-652-3000
Dennis Kenney, prin. Fax 995-2440
Iroquois MS 600/6-8
PO Box 32 14059 716-652-3000
Ross Esslinger, prin. Fax 995-2335

Elmhurst, See New York
NYC Department of Education
Supt. — See New York
Civic Leadership Academy 300/9-12
4510 94th St 11373 718-271-1487
Phuong Nguyen, prin. Fax 271-3408
IS 5 1,500/6-9
5040 Jacobus St 11373 718-205-6788
Michael Dantona, prin. Fax 429-6518
Maspeth HS 9-12
5440 74th St 11373 718-803-7100
Khurshid Mutakabbir, prin. Fax 803-7105
Newtown HS 2,900/9-12
4801 90th St 11373 718-595-8400
John Ficalora, prin. Fax 699-8584
Pan American International HS 300/9-12
4510 94th St 11373 718-271-3602
Minerva Zanca, prin. Fax 271-4041
VOYAGES Preparatory S 200/9-12
4510 94th St 11373 718-271-7851
Joan Klingsberg, prin. Fax 271-8549

Cathedral Prep Seminary 200/9-12
5625 92nd St 11373 718-592-6800
Rev. Fred Marano, prin. Fax 592-5574
Jewish Institute of Queens 400/PK-12
6005 Woodhaven Blvd 11373 718-426-9369
Jennifer Seideman, prin. Fax 446-2071

Elmira, Chemung, Pop. 27,883
Elmira CSD 4,700/PK-12
951 Hoffman St 14905 607-735-3000
Joseph Hochreiter, supt. Fax 735-3009
www.elmiracityschools.com
Broadway MS 500/7-8
1000 Broadway St 14904 607-735-3300
Brian LeBaron, prin. Fax 735-3309
Davis MS 500/7-8
610 Lake St 14901 607-735-3400
John Kohena, prin. Fax 735-3409
Elmira Free Academy 900/9-12
933 Hoffman St 14905 607-735-3100
John Wood, prin. Fax 735-3109
Southside HS 1,100/9-12
777 S Main St 14904 607-735-3200
Christopher Krantz, prin. Fax 735-3209

Arnot-Ogden Medical Center Post-Sec.
600 Roe Ave 14905 607-737-4289
Arnot-Ogden Medical Center Post-Sec.
600 Roe Ave 14905 607-737-4153
Elmira Business Institute Post-Sec.
303 N Main St 14901 800-843-1812
Elmira Christian Academy 100/PK-12
235 E Miller St 14904 607-734-7195
Martin Douglass, prin. Fax 734-7195
Elmira College Post-Sec.
1 Park Pl 14901 607-735-1800

Notre Dame HS 200/7-12
1400 Maple Ave 14904 607-734-2267
Sr. Nancy Kelly, prin. Fax 737-8903

Elmira Heights, Chemung, Pop. 4,011
Elmira Heights Central SD 1,000/K-12
2083 College Ave 14903 607-734-7114
Mary Beth Fiore, supt. Fax 734-7134
www.heightsschools.com
Cohen MS 300/6-8
100 Robinwood Ave 14903 607-734-5078
Dawn Hanrahan, prin. Fax 734-9382
Edison HS 300/9-12
2083 College Ave 14903 607-733-5604
Lisa Kelly, prin. Fax 737-7976

Elmont, Nassau, Pop. 32,024
Sewanhaka Central HSD
Supt. — See Floral Park
Elmont Memorial HS 1,900/7-12
555 Ridge Rd 11003 516-488-9200
John Capozzi, prin. Fax 488-5560

Elmsford, Westchester, Pop. 4,549
Elmsford UFD 1,000/PK-12
98 S Goodwin Ave 10523 914-592-6632
Gladys Pagan-Baxter, supt. Fax 592-2181
www.elmsd.org
Hamilton JSHS 400/7-12
98 S Goodwin Ave 10523 914-592-7311
Marc Baiocco, prin. Fax 592-2881

Elwood, Suffolk, Pop. 11,032
Elwood UFD
Supt. — See Greenlawn
Elwood/Glenn HS 800/9-12
478 Elwood Rd 11731 631-266-5410
Dr. Vincent Mulieri, prin. Fax 368-5038
Elwood MS 700/6-8
478 Elwood Rd 11731 631-266-5420
Dr. Hugh Gigante, prin. Fax 266-3987

Endicott, Broome, Pop. 12,995
Union-Endicott Central SD 3,300/K-12
1100 E Main St 13760 607-757-2111
Dr. Suzanne McLeod, supt. Fax 757-2809
www.uek12.org
Snapp MS 600/6-8
101 S Loder Ave 13760 607-757-2156
Catherine Kacyvenski, prin. Fax 658-7117
Union-Endicott HS 1,300/9-12
1200 E Main St 13760 607-757-2181
Steven DiStefano, prin. Fax 757-2592

Endwell, Broome, Pop. 11,248
Maine-Endwell Central SD 2,500/K-12
712 Farm To Market Rd 13760 607-754-1400
Jason Van Fossen, supt. Fax 754-1650
www.me.stier.org/
Maine-Endwell HS 800/9-12
750 Farm To Market Rd 13760 607-748-8070
Thomas Burkhardt, prin. Fax 786-8209
Maine-Endwell MS 600/6-8
1119 Farm To Market Rd 13760 607-786-8271
Richard Otis, prin. Fax 786-5137

Fabius, Onondaga, Pop. 352
Fabius-Pompey Central SD 800/K-12
1211 Mill St 13063 315-683-5301
Timothy Ryan, supt. Fax 683-5827
www.fabiuspompey.org
Fabius-Pompey MSHS 500/6-12
1211 Mill St 13063 315-683-5811
Robert Hughes, prin. Fax 683-5569

Fairport, Monroe, Pop. 5,283
Fairport Central SD 6,500/K-12
38 W Church St 14450 585-421-2000
Dr. Jon Hunter, supt. Fax 421-3421
www.fairport.org
Brown MS 900/6-8
665 Ayrault Rd 14450 585-421-2065
David Dunn, prin. Fax 421-2136
Fairport HS 1,600/10-12
1 Dave Paddock Way 14450 585-421-2100
Joseph Fantigrossi, prin. Fax 421-4645
Minerva-Deland JHS 500/9-9
140 Hulburt Rd 14450 585-421-2030
Pam Ciranni, prin. Fax 421-1985
Perrin MS 800/6-8
85 Potter Pl 14450 585-421-2080
Brett Provenzano, prin. Fax 421-2097

Falconer, Chautauqua, Pop. 2,402
Falconer Central SD 1,300/PK-12
2 East Ave N 14733 716-665-6624
Stephen Penhollow, supt. Fax 665-9265
www.falconerschools.org
Falconer MSHS 700/6-12
2 East Ave N 14733 716-665-6624
Jeffrey Jordan, prin. Fax 665-9265

Fallsburg, Sullivan
Fallsburg Central SD 1,400/PK-12
PO Box 124 12733 845-434-5884
Dr. Ivan Katz, supt. Fax 434-8346
www.fallsburgcsd.net/
Fallsburg HS 600/7-12
PO Box 124 12733 845-434-6800
Michael Williams, prin. Fax 434-0418

Farmingdale, Nassau, Pop. 8,087
Farmingdale UFD 6,000/K-12
50 Van Cott Ave 11735 516-752-6510
John Lorentz, supt.
www.farmingdaleschools.org
Farmingdale HS 2,000/9-12
150 Lincoln St 11735 516-752-6600
Glen Zakian, prin. Fax 454-6196
Howitt MS 1,400/6-8
70 Van Cott Ave 11735 516-752-6519
Luis Pena, prin. Fax 752-2004

Farmingdale State College SUNY — Post-Sec.
2350 Broadhollow Rd 11735 — 631-420-2000

Farmingville, Suffolk, Pop. 15,238
Sachem Central SD
Supt. — See Ronkonkoma
Sachem HS East — 2,400/9-12
177 Granny Rd 11738 — 631-716-8200
Louis Antonetti, prin. — Fax 716-8207

Far Rockaway, See New York
NYC Department of Education
Supt. — See New York
Academy of Medical Technology — 400/6-12
821 Bay 25th St 11691 — 718-471-3571
Jose Merced, prin. — Fax 471-0314
Douglass Academy VI HS — 400/9-12
821 Bay 25th St 11691 — 718-471-2154
Linda Alfred, prin. — Fax 471-2890
MS 53 — 500/6-8
1045 Nameoke St 11691 — 718-471-6900
Shawn Rux, prin. — Fax 471-6955
KAPPA VI — 300/6-8
821 Bay 25th St 11691 — 718-471-6934
Gary Dumornay, prin. — Fax 471-6938
Queens HS for Info. Research & Tech. — 200/9-12
821 Bay 25th St 11691 — 718-868-2978
Magaly Hicks, prin. — Fax 868-1653
Village Academy — 200/6-8
1045 Nameoke St 11691 — 718-471-6042
Doris Lee, prin. — Fax 471-6243

Beis Medrash Heichal Dovid — Post-Sec.
211 Beach 17th St 11691 — 718-868-2300
Global Business Institute — Post-Sec.
1931 Mott Ave 11691 — 718-327-2220
Mesivta Chaim Shlomo S — 300/9-12
211 Beach 17th St 11691 — 718-868-2300
Tichon Meir Moshe S — 100/9-12
613 Beach 9th St 11691 — 718-327-6645
Torah Academy HS for Girls — 300/9-12
636 Lanett Ave 11691 — 718-327-1300
Yeshiva Darchei Torah S — 1,600/PK-12
257 Beach 17th St 11691 — 718-868-2300
Yeshiva of Far Rockaway — Post-Sec.
802 Hicksville Rd 11691 — 718-327-7600
Yeshiva of Far Rockaway S — 200/9-12
802 Hicksville Rd 11691 — 718-327-7600
Rabbi Aaron Brafman, prin. — Fax 327-1430
Yeshiva Zidvon Aryeh — Post-Sec.
2242 Baysumter Ave 11691 — 516-295-5700

Fayetteville, Onondaga, Pop. 4,326
Fayetteville-Manlius Central SD
Supt. — See Manlius
Wellwood MS — 700/5-8
700 S Manlius St 13066 — 315-692-1300
Melissa Corbin, prin. — Fax 692-1049

Fillmore, Allegany, Pop. 603
Fillmore Central SD — 700/K-12
104 W Main St 14735 — 585-567-2251
Rabo Root, supt. — Fax 567-2541
www.fillmorecsd.org/fillmorecsd/site/default.asp
Fillmore Central S — 700/K-12
104 W Main St 14735 — 585-567-2289
Kyle Faulkner, prin. — Fax 567-2541

Fishers Island, Suffolk, Pop. 231
Fishers Island UFD — 100/PK-12
78 Greenwood Rd Ste 600 06390 — 631-788-7444
Charles Meyers, supt. — Fax 788-5562
www.fischool.com
Fishers Island S — 100/PK-12
78 Greenwood Rd Ste 600 06390 — 631-788-7444
Charles Meyers, admin. — Fax 788-5562

Floral Park, Nassau, Pop. 15,623
NYC Department of Education
Supt. — See New York
Altman MS — 1,000/6-8
8114 257th St 11004 — 718-831-4000
Jeffrey Slivko, prin. — Fax 831-4008

Sewanhaka Central HSD — 8,400/7-12
77 Landau Ave 11001 — 516-488-9800
Dr. Ralph Ferrie, supt. — Fax 488-7738
www.sewanhaka.k12.ny.us/
Floral Park Memorial HS — 1,400/7-12
210 Locust St 11001 — 516-488-9300
Kathleen Sottile, prin. — Fax 394-5079
Sewanhaka HS — 1,600/7-12
500 Tulip Ave 11001 — 516-488-9600
Debra Lidowsky, prin. — Fax 488-9215
Other Schools – See Elmont, Franklin Square, New Hyde Park

Florida, Orange, Pop. 2,798
Florida UFD — 800/K-12
PO Box 757 10921 — 845-651-3095
Diane Munro, supt. — Fax 651-6801
www.floridaufsd.org
Seward Institute — 500/6-12
PO Box 757 10921 — 845-651-4038
Michael Rheaume, prin. — Fax 651-7166

Flushing, See New York
NYC Department of Education
Supt. — See New York
Bowne HS — 3,500/9-12
6325 Main St 11367 — 718-263-1919
Howie Kwait, prin. — Fax 575-4069
East-West S of International Studies — 600/6-12
4621 Colden St 11355 — 718-353-0009
Benjamin Sherman, prin. — Fax 353-3772
Flushing HS — 3,000/9-12
3501 Union St 11354 — 718-888-7500
Magdalen Radovich, prin. — Fax 886-4255
IS 25 — 800/6-8
3465 192nd St 11358 — 718-961-3480
Maryellen Beirne, prin. — Fax 358-1563
IS 237 — 1,200/6-8
4621 Colden St 11355 — 718-353-6464
Judith Friedman, prin. — Fax 460-6427
IS 250 — 400/6-8
15840 76th Rd 11366 — 718-591-9000
Vincent Randazzo, prin. — Fax 591-2340
Flushing International HS — 400/9-12
14480 Barclay Ave 11355 — 718-463-2348
Lara Evangelista, prin. — Fax 463-3514
JHS 185 — 1,100/6-8
14726 25th Dr 11354 — 718-445-3232
Theresa Mshar, prin. — Fax 359-5352
JHS 189 — 800/6-8
14480 Barclay Ave 11355 — 718-359-6676
Cindy Diaz-Burgos, prin. — Fax 358-0155
JHS 216 — 1,200/6-8
6420 175th St 11365 — 718-358-2005
Reginald Landeau, prin. — Fax 358-2070
Harris HS — 1,100/9-12
14911 Melbourne Ave 11367 — 718-575-5580
Anthony Barbetta, prin. — Fax 575-1366
Kennedy Community HS — 700/9-12
7540 Parsons Blvd 11366 — 718-969-5510
Beshir Abdellatif, prin. — Fax 969-5524
Lewis HS — 4,100/9-12
5820 Utopia Pkwy 11365 — 718-281-8200
Musa Shama, prin. — Fax 746-2017
North Queens Community HS — 200/9-12
14125 77th Rd 11367 — 718-380-1650
Winston McCarthy, prin. — Fax 380-2189
Queens Academy HS — 400/10-12
13811 35th Ave 11354 — 718-463-3111
Beverly Short, prin. — Fax 886-5015
World Journalism Preparatory S — 600/6-12
3465 192nd St 11358 — 718-461-2219
Cynthia Schneider, prin. — Fax 461-2633

CUNY Queens College — Post-Sec.
6530 Kissena Blvd 11367 — 718-997-5000
Holy Cross HS — 1,000/9-12
2620 Francis Lewis Blvd 11358 — 718-886-7250
Joseph Giannuzzi, prin. — Fax 886-7257
Long Island Business Institute — Post-Sec.
13618 39th Ave 11354 — 718-939-5100
Mesivta Yesodei Yeshurun — 100/9-12
14151 71st Ave 11367 — 718-261-4738
New York Medical Career Training Center — Post-Sec.
3609 Main St Fl 5 11354 — 718-460-4340
Rabbinical Seminary Chofetz Chaim HS — 100/9-12
7601 147th St 11367 — 718-263-1445
Rabbinical Seminary of America — Post-Sec.
7601 147th St 11367 — 718-268-4700
St. Pauls School of Nursing — Post-Sec.
3050 Whitestone Expy # 400 11354 — 718-357-0500
Vaughn College of Aeronautics and Tech — Post-Sec.
8601 23rd Ave 11369 — 718-429-6600
Windsor S — 100/6-12
3702 Main St Ste 4 11354 — 718-359-8300
James Seery, prin. — Fax 359-1876

Fonda, Montgomery, Pop. 787
Fonda-Fultonville Central SD — 1,400/K-12
PO Box 1501 12068 — 518-853-4415
Dr. Raymond Colucciello, supt. — Fax 853-4461
www.fondafultonvilleschools.org
Fonda-Fultonville HS — 500/9-12
PO Box 1501 12068 — 518-853-3182
David Halloran, prin. — Fax 853-1239
Fonda-Fultonville MS — 400/5-8
PO Box 1501 12068 — 518-853-4747
Elizabeth Donovan, prin. — Fax 853-4498

Forest Hills, See New York
NYC Department of Education
Supt. — See New York
Forest Hills HS — 3,900/9-12
6701 110th St 11375 — 718-268-3137
Saul Gootnick, prin. — Fax 793-7850
JHS 190 — 800/6-8
6817 Austin St 11375 — 718-830-4970
Marilyn Grant, prin. — Fax 830-3566
Metropolitan Expeditionary Learning S — 200/6-12
9130 Metropolitan Ave 11375 — 718-286-3500
Daman McCord, prin. — Fax 286-3501
Queens Metropolitan HS — 400/9-12
9130 Metropolitan Ave 11375 — 718-286-3600
Marci Levy-Mcguire, prin. — Fax 286-3601

ACE Computer Training Center — Post-Sec.
10919 72nd Rd Ste 4F 11375 — 718-575-3223
Bramson ORT College — Post-Sec.
6930 Austin St 11375 — 718-261-5800
Ezra Academy — 100/7-12
11945 Union Tpke 11375 — 718-263-5500
Francine Hirschman, prin. — Fax 520-9424
Kew-Forest S — 200/PK-12
11917 Union Tpke 11375 — 718-268-4667
Mark Fish, hdmstr. — Fax 268-9121

Forestville, Chautauqua, Pop. 686
Forestville Central SD — 600/K-12
12 Water St 14062 — 716-965-2742
Charles Leichner, supt. — Fax 965-2117
www.forestville.com
Forestville Central JSHS — 300/6-12
4 Academy St 14062 — 716-965-2711
Charles Leichner, prin. — Fax 965-2102

Fort Ann, Washington, Pop. 482
Fort Ann Central SD — 500/K-12
1 Catherine St 12827 — 518-639-5594
Maureen VanBuren, supt. — Fax 639-8911
www.fortannschool.org/
Fort Ann S — 500/K-12
1 Catherine St 12827 — 518-639-5594
Dan Ward, prin. — Fax 639-8911

Fort Covington, Franklin
Salmon River Central SD — 1,600/PK-12
637 County Route 1 12937 — 518-358-6610
Jane Collins, supt. — Fax 358-3492
www.srk12.org/
Salmon River HS — 400/9-12
637 County Route 1 12937 — 518-358-6620
Alison Benedict, prin. — Fax 358-9787
Salmon River MS — 200/6-8
637 County Route 1 12937 — 518-358-6650
Tammy Russell, prin. — Fax 358-6510

Fort Edward, Washington, Pop. 3,335
Fort Edward UFD — 500/PK-12
220 Broadway 12828 — 518-747-4594
Jeffery Ziegler, supt. — Fax 747-4289
www.fortedward.org
Fort Edward S — 500/PK-12
220 Broadway 12828 — 518-747-4594
Thomas McGurl, prin. — Fax 747-4289

Hudson Falls Central SD — 2,200/K-12
1153 Burgoyne Ave 12828 — 518-747-2121
Mark Doody, supt. — Fax 747-0951
www.hfcsd.org
Other Schools – See Hudson Falls

Fort Montgomery, Orange, Pop. 1,512
Highland Falls Ft. Montgomery Central SD — 900/K-12
21 Morgan Farm Rd 10922 — 845-446-9575
Dr. Debra Jackson, supt. — Fax 446-3321
www.hffmcsd.org/
O'Neill HS — 500/9-12
21 Morgan Rd 10922 — 845-446-4914
Louis Trombetta, prin. — Fax 446-2123
Other Schools – See Highland Falls

Fort Plain, Montgomery, Pop. 2,284
Fort Plain Central SD — 900/PK-12
25 High St 13339 — 518-993-4000
Douglas Burton, supt. — Fax 993-3393
www.fortplain.org
Fort Plain JSHS — 400/7-12
1 West St 13339 — 518-993-4000
Deborah Larrabee, prin. — Fax 993-2897

Frankfort, Herkimer, Pop. 2,561
Frankfort-Schuyler Central SD — 700/K-12
605 Palmer St 13340 — 315-894-5083
Robert Reina, supt. — Fax 895-7011
www.frankfort-schuyler.org
Frankfort-Schuyler Central JSHS — 400/6-12
605 Palmer St 13340 — 315-895-7461
John Bubb, prin. — Fax 895-4032

Franklin, Delaware, Pop. 368
Franklin Central SD — 300/PK-12
PO Box 888 13775 — 607-829-3551
Gordon Daniels, supt. — Fax 829-2101
www.franklincsd.org
Franklin Central S — 300/PK-12
PO Box 888 13775 — 607-829-3551
James Harter, prin. — Fax 829-2101

Franklin Square, Nassau, Pop. 28,887
Sewanhaka Central HSD
Supt. — See Floral Park
Carey HS — 1,900/7-12
230 Poppy Ave 11010 — 516-539-9400
Valerie Angelillo, prin. — Fax 538-1791

Valley Stream Central HSD
Supt. — See Valley Stream
Valley Stream North HS — 1,200/7-12
750 Herman Ave 11010 — 516-564-5510
Clifford Odell, prin. — Fax 564-5539

Franklinville, Cattaraugus, Pop. 1,715
Franklinville Central SD — 700/K-12
31 N Main St 14737 — 716-676-8029
Michelle Spasiano, supt. — Fax 676-8041
tbafcs.org
Franklinville JSHS — 400/7-12
31 N Main St 14737 — 716-676-8060
Thomas Kopp, prin. — Fax 676-2798

Fredonia, Chautauqua, Pop. 11,103
Fredonia Central SD — 1,600/PK-12
425 E Main St 14063 — 716-679-1581
Paul DiFonzo, supt. — Fax 679-1555
www.fredonia.wnyric.org
Fredonia HS — 500/9-12
425 E Main St 14063 — 716-679-1581
Todd Crandall, prin. — Fax 672-8687
Fredonia MS — 500/5-8
425 E Main St 14063 — 716-679-1581
Andrew Ludwig, prin. — Fax 672-2686

SUNY Fredonia — Post-Sec.
280 Central Ave 14063 — 716-673-3111

Freeport, Nassau, Pop. 41,960
Freeport UFD — 6,600/PK-12
235 N Ocean Ave 11520 — 516-867-5200
Dr. Kishore Kuncham, supt. — Fax 623-4759
www.freeportschools.org
Dodd MS — 900/7-8
25 Pine St 11520 — 516-867-5280
John O'Mard, prin. — Fax 379-6794
Freeport HS — 2,100/9-12
50 S Brookside Ave 11520 — 516-867-5300
Linda Carter, prin. — Fax 379-7592

De LaSalle S — 50/5-8
87 Pine St 11520 — 516-379-8660
Kathleen Boniello, prin. — Fax 379-8806

Freeville, Tompkins, Pop. 511
George Junior Republic UFD — 200/7-12
24 McDonald Rd 13068 — 607-844-6343
Brad Herman, supt. — Fax 844-3410

George Junior Republic S | 200/Alt
24 McDonald Rd 13068 | 607-844-6365
Sonia Apker, prin. | Fax 844-3410

Fresh Meadows, See New York
NYC Department of Education
Supt. — See New York
Queens S of Inquiry | 500/6-12
15840 76th Rd 11366 | 718-380-6929
Meredith Inbal, prin. | Fax 380-6809

St. Francis Prep S | 2,700/9-12
6100 Francis Lewis Blvd 11365 | 718-423-8810
Br. Leonard Conway, prin. | Fax 504-7668

Frewsburg, Chautauqua, Pop. 1,879
Frewsburg Central SD | 900/PK-12
PO Box 690 14738 | 716-569-7041
Danielle O'Connor, supt. | Fax 569-7050
www.frewsburgcsd.org/
Frewsburg JSHS | 400/7-12
PO Box 690 14738 | 716-569-7055
Scott Cooper, prin. | Fax 569-7050

Friendship, Allegany, Pop. 1,208
Friendship Central SD | 400/PK-12
46 W Main St 14739 | 585-973-3534
Judy May, supt. | Fax 973-2023
www.friendship.wnyric.org/
Friendship Central S | 400/PK-12
46 W Main St 14739 | 585-973-3311
Judy May, supt. | Fax 973-2023

Fulton, Oswego, Pop. 11,719
Fulton CSD | 3,600/K-12
167 S 4th St 13069 | 315-593-5510
William Lynch, supt. | Fax 598-6351
www.fulton.cnyric.org/
Bodley HS | 1,100/9-12
6 Gillard Dr 13069 | 315-593-5400
Donna Parkhurst, prin. | Fax 593-5427
Fulton JHS | 500/7-8
129 Curtis St 13069 | 315-593-5440
Ryan Lanigan, prin. | Fax 593-5459

Gainesville, Wyoming, Pop. 228
Letchworth Central SD | 1,000/K-12
5550 School Rd 14066 | 585-493-5450
Joseph Backer, supt. | Fax 493-2762
www.letchworth.k12.ny.us/
Letchworth HS | 300/9-12
5550 School Rd 14066 | 585-493-2571
Matthew Wilkins, prin. | Fax 493-2762
Letchworth MS | 300/5-8
5550 School Rd 14066 | 585-493-2592
Paula Roberts-Mighells, prin. | Fax 493-2762

Galway, Saratoga, Pop. 200
Galway Central SD | 800/K-12
5317 Sacandaga Rd 12074 | 518-882-1033
William Scott, supt.
www.galwaycsd.org/
Galway JSHS | 400/7-12
5317 Sacandaga Rd 12074 | 518-882-1221
Michael Healey, prin. | Fax 882-5250

Garden City, Nassau, Pop. 22,129
Garden City UFD | 4,100/K-12
56 Cathedral Ave 11530 | 516-478-1000
Dr. Robert Feirsen, supt. | Fax 294-5631
www.gardencity.k12.ny.us
Garden City HS | 1,200/9-12
170 Rockaway Ave 11530 | 516-478-2000
Nanine McLaughlin, prin. | Fax 294-2639
Garden City MS | 1,000/6-8
98 Cherry Valley Ave 11530 | 516-478-3000
Dr. Peter Osroff, prin. | Fax 294-0732

Adelphi University | Post-Sec.
PO Box 701 11530 | 516-877-3000
Career Institute of Health & Technology | Post-Sec.
200 Garden City Plz Ste 519 11530 | 516-877-1225
Nassau Community College | Post-Sec.
1 Education Dr 11530 | 516-572-7501
Sanford-Brown Institute | Post-Sec.
711 Stewart Ave Ste 2 11530 | 516-247-2900
Waldorf S of Garden City | 400/PK-12
225 Cambridge Ave 11530 | 516-742-3434
Susan Braun, admin. | Fax 742-3457

Garden City Park, Nassau, Pop. 7,612
Mineola UFD
Supt. — See Mineola
Mineola HS | 800/9-12
10 Armstrong Rd 11040 | 516-237-2600
Edward Escobar, prin. | Fax 739-4765

Garnerville, See West Haverstraw
North Rockland Central SD | 5,400/K-12
65 Chapel St 10923 | 845-942-3000
Ileana Eckert, supt. | Fax 942-3175
www.nrcsd.org
Other Schools – See Thiells

Geneseo, Livingston, Pop. 7,881
Geneseo Central SD | 900/K-12
4050 Avon Rd 14454 | 585-243-3450
Timothy Hayes, supt. | Fax 243-9481
www.geneseocsd.org/
Geneseo MSHS | 500/6-12
4050 Avon Rd 14454 | 585-243-3450
Michael Salatel, prin. | Fax 243-9481

SUNY Geneseo | Post-Sec.
1 College Cir 14454 | 585-245-5000

Geneva, Ontario, Pop. 12,783
Geneva CSD | 2,200/PK-12
400 W North St 14456 | 315-781-0400
Trina Smith Newton, supt. | Fax 781-4193
www.genevacsd.org
Geneva HS | 700/9-12
101 Carter Rd 14456 | 315-781-0402
Greg Baker, prin. | Fax 781-0695
Geneva MS | 500/6-8
101 Carter Rd 14456 | 315-781-0404
Carmine Calabria, prin. | Fax 781-0694

Hobart & William Smith Colleges | Post-Sec.
300 Pulteney St 14456 | 315-781-3000

Germantown, Columbia
Germantown Central SD | 600/K-12
123 Main St 12526 | 518-537-6280
Susan L. S. Brown, supt. | Fax 537-6283
www.germantowncsd.org
Germantown Central HS | 300/7-12
123 Main St 12526 | 518-537-6281
Karol Harlow, prin. | Fax 537-6893

Getzville, Erie, Pop. 2,300

Bryant & Stratton College | Post-Sec.
3650 Millersport Hwy 14068 | 716-625-6300
ITT Technical Institute | Post-Sec.
PO Box 327 14068 | 716-689-2200

Ghent, Columbia, Pop. 556

Hawthorne Valley Waldorf S | 200/PK-12
330 County Route 21C 12075 | 518-672-7092
Caroline Geisler, chrpsn. | Fax 672-8006

Gilbertsville, Otsego, Pop. 397
Gilbertsville-Mount Upton Central SD | 400/PK-12
693 State Highway 51 13776 | 607-783-2207
Glenn Hamilton, supt. | Fax 783-2254
www.gmucsd.org/
Gilbertsville-Mount Upton JSHS | 200/6-12
693 State Highway 51 13776 | 607-783-2207
Annette Hammond, prin. | Fax 783-2254

Gilboa, Schoharie
Gilboa-Conesville Central SD | 400/K-12
132 Wyckoff Rd 12076 | 607-588-7541
Ruth Reeve, supt. | Fax 588-6820
www.gilboa-conesville.k12.ny.us/
Gilboa-Conesville Central S | 400/K-12
132 Wyckoff Rd 12076 | 607-588-7909
Kathryn Allen, prin. | Fax 588-6820

Glen Cove, Nassau, Pop. 26,520
Glen Cove CSD | 3,100/PK-12
150 Dosoris Ln 11542 | 516-801-7010
Dr. Joseph Laria, supt. | Fax 801-7019
www.glencove.k12.ny.us
Finley MS | 700/6-8
1 Forest Ave 11542 | 516-801-7510
Nelson Iocolano, prin. | Fax 801-7519
Glen Cove HS | 1,000/9-12
150 Dosoris Ln 11542 | 516-801-7610
Dr. Joseph Hinton, prin. | Fax 801-7619

Solomon Schechter HS of Long Island | 300/6-12
27 Cedar Swamp Rd 11542 | 516-656-5500
Cindy Dolgin, head sch | Fax 656-9822
Webb Institute | Post-Sec.
298 Crescent Beach Rd 11542 | 516-671-2213

Glendale, See New York
NYC Department of Education
Supt. — See New York
IS 119 | 1,000/6-8
7401 78th Ave 11385 | 718-326-8261
Dr. Jeanne Fagan, prin. | Fax 456-9523

Glen Head, Nassau, Pop. 4,626
North Shore Central SD
Supt. — See Sea Cliff
North Shore HS | 900/9-12
450 Glen Cove Ave 11545 | 516-277-7000
Albert Cousins, prin. | Fax 277-7001
North Shore MS | 700/6-8
505 Glen Cove Ave 11545 | 516-277-7300
Marc Ferris, prin. | Fax 277-7301

Glens Falls, Warren, Pop. 14,415
Glens Falls CSD | 1,800/PK-12
15 Quade St 12801 | 518-792-1212
Paul Jenkins, supt. | Fax 792-1538
www.gfsd.org
Glens Falls HS | 800/9-12
10 Quade St 12801 | 518-792-6564
Mark Stratton, prin. | Fax 743-1164
Glens Falls MS | 500/5-8
20 Quade St 12801 | 518-793-3418
Christopher Reed, prin. | Fax 793-4888

Adirondack Beauty School | Post-Sec.
108 Dix Ave 12801 | 518-745-1646
Glens Falls Hospital | Post-Sec.
100 Park St 12801 | 518-792-3151

Glenville, Schenectady
Burnt Hills-Ballston Lake Central SD | 3,300/K-12
50 Cypress Dr 12302 | 518-399-9141
Patrick McGrath, supt. | Fax 399-1882
www.bhbl.org
Other Schools – See Burnt Hills

Gloversville, Fulton, Pop. 15,362
Gloversville CSD | 3,100/PK-12
234 Lincoln St 12078 | 518-775-5700
Michael Vanyo, supt. | Fax 725-8793
www.gloversvilleschools.org
Gloversville HS | 900/9-12
199 Lincoln St 12078 | 518-775-5710
Richard DeMallie, prin. | Fax 773-3674
Gloversville MS | 700/6-8
234 Lincoln St 12078 | 518-775-5720
James Christopher, prin. | Fax 773-9865

Goldens Bridge, Westchester, Pop. 1,609
Katonah-Lewisboro UFD | 3,800/K-12
186 Waccabuc Rd 10526 | 914-763-7000
Dr. Paul Kreutzer, supt. | Fax 763-7035
www.klschooldistrict.org/
Other Schools – See Cross River

Goshen, Orange, Pop. 5,361
Goshen Central SD | 2,900/K-12
227 Main St 10924 | 845-615-6720
Daniel Connor, supt. | Fax 615-6725
www.gcsny.org
Goshen Central HS | 1,000/9-12
222 Scotchtown Rd 10924 | 845-615-6100
Kurtis Kotes, prin. | Fax 615-6116
Hooker MS | 600/6-8
41 Lincoln Ave 10924 | 845-615-6300
William Rolon, prin. | Fax 615-6310

Burke Catholic HS | 600/9-12
80 Fletcher St 10924 | 845-294-5481
John Dolan, prin. | Fax 294-7957

Gouverneur, Saint Lawrence, Pop. 3,883
Gouverneur Central SD | 1,600/PK-12
133 E Barney St 13642 | 315-287-4870
Lauren French, supt. | Fax 287-4736
www.gcsk12.org
Gouverneur MS | 300/6-8
113 E Barney St 13642 | 315-287-1903
Steven Coffin, prin. | Fax 287-2666
Gouverneur HS | 500/9-12
113 E Barney St 13642 | 315-287-1900
Cory Wood, prin. | Fax 287-7963

Gowanda, Cattaraugus, Pop. 2,660
Gowanda Central SD | 1,400/PK-12
10674 Prospect St 14070 | 716-532-3325
Charles Rinaldi, supt. | Fax 995-2154
www.gowcsd.com
Gowanda HS | 400/9-12
10674 Prospect St 14070 | 716-532-3325
Dr. Robert Anderson, prin. | Fax 995-2108
Gowanda MS | 400/5-8
10674 Prospect St 14070 | 716-532-3325
David Smith, prin. | Fax 995-2127

Grahamsville, Sullivan
Tri-Valley Central SD | 1,200/PK-12
34 Moore Hill Rd 12740 | 845-985-2296
Thomas Palmer, supt. | Fax 985-0310
www.trivalleycsd.org
Tri-Valley Secondary S | 600/7-12
34 Moore Hill Rd 12740 | 845-985-2296
Robert Peters, prin. | Fax 985-7903

Grand Island, Erie
Grand Island Central SD | 3,100/K-12
1100 Ransom Rd 14072 | 716-773-8800
Teresa Lawrence Ph.D., supt. | Fax 773-8843
www.k12.ginet.org/
Connor MS | 800/6-8
1100 Ransom Rd 14072 | 716-773-8830
Jerry Parisi, prin. | Fax 773-8983
Grand Island HS | 1,000/9-12
1100 Ransom Rd 14072 | 716-773-8820
Daniel Quartley, prin. | Fax 773-8951

Granville, Washington, Pop. 2,523
Granville Central SD | 1,300/PK-12
58 Quaker St 12832 | 518-642-1051
Mark Bessen, supt. | Fax 642-2491
www.granvillecsd.org
Granville JSHS | 700/7-12
58 Quaker St 12832 | 518-642-1051
James Donnelly, prin. | Fax 642-4544

Great Neck, Nassau, Pop. 9,663
Great Neck UFD | 6,400/PK-12
345 Lakeville Rd 11020 | 516-441-4001
Dr. Thomas P. Dolan, supt. | Fax 441-4994
www.greatneck.k12.ny.us
Great Neck South MS | 800/6-8
349 Lakeville Rd 11020 | 516-441-4600
Dr. James Welsch, prin. | Fax 441-4690
Miller Great Neck North HS | 1,000/9-12
35 Polo Rd 11023 | 516-441-4700
Bernard Kaplan, prin. | Fax 441-4795
Sherman Great Neck North MS | 700/6-8
77 Polo Rd 11023 | 516-441-4500
Dr. Anael Alston, prin. | Fax 773-4841
Shine Great Neck South HS | 1,300/9-12
341 Lakeville Rd 11020 | 516-441-4800
Susan Elliott, prin. | Fax 773-8279
Village S | 50/Alt
614 Middle Neck Rd 11023 | 516-441-4900
Stephen Goldberg, prin. | Fax 441-4909

North Shore Hebrew Academy | 200/6-8
26 Old Mill Rd 11023 | 516-487-9163
Rabbi Yeshayahu E. Greenfeld M.A., dean | Fax 829-3933

Greene, Chenango, Pop. 1,564
Greene Central SD | 1,100/K-12
40 S Canal St 13778 | 607-656-4161
Jonathan Retz, supt. | Fax 656-9362
www.greenecsd.org
Greene HS | 400/9-12
40 S Canal St 13778 | 607-656-4161
James Walters, prin. | Fax 656-8872
Greene MS | 300/6-8
40 S Canal St 13778 | 607-656-4161
Jim Walters, prin. | Fax 656-4520

Green Island, Albany, Pop. 2,545
Green Island UFD | 300/K-12
171 Hudson Ave 12183 | 518-273-1422
Dr. Michael Mugits, supt. | Fax 270-0818
www.greenisland.org

Heatly S — 300/K-12
171 Hudson Ave 12183 — 518-273-1422
Erin Peteani, prin. — Fax 270-0818

Greenlawn, Suffolk, Pop. 13,492
Elwood UFD — 2,600/K-12
100 Kenneth Ave 11740 — 631-266-5400
Peter Scordo, supt. — Fax 368-2338
www.elwood.k12.ny.us
Other Schools – See Elwood

Harborfields Central SD — 3,600/K-12
2 Oldfield Rd 11740 — 631-754-5320
Diana Todaro, supt. — Fax 261-0068
www.harborfieldscsd.net
Harborfields HS — 1,100/9-12
98 Taylor Ave 11740 — 631-754-5360
Dr. Rory Manning, prin. — Fax 754-3751
Oldfield MS — 900/6-8
2 Oldfield Rd 11740 — 631-754-5310
Joanne Giordano, prin. — Fax 754-2677

Greenport, Suffolk, Pop. 2,155
Greenport UFD — 600/K-12
720 Front St 11944 — 631-477-1950
Michael Comanda, supt. — Fax 593-8951
www.gufsd.org/
Greenport JSHS — 300/7-12
720 Front St 11944 — 631-477-1950
Leonard Skuggevik, prin. — Fax 593-8954

Greenville, Greene, Pop. 9,528
Greenville Central SD — 1,200/K-12
4982 State Route 81 12083 — 518-966-5070
Cheryl Dudley, supt.
www.greenville.k12.ny.us
Greenville HS — 400/9-12
4976 State Route 81 12083 — 518-966-5070
Michael Laster, prin.
Greenville MS — 300/6-8
4976 State Route 81 12083 — 518-966-5070
Brian Reeve, prin.

Greenwich, Washington, Pop. 1,754
Greenwich Central SD — 1,100/K-12
10 Gray Ave 12834 — 518-692-9542
Matthias Donnelly, supt. — Fax 692-9547
www.greenwichcsd.org/
Greenwich JSHS — 500/7-12
10 Gray Ave 12834 — 518-692-9542
George Niesz, prin. — Fax 692-8503

Groton, Tompkins, Pop. 2,324
Groton Central SD — 1,000/PK-12
400 Peru Rd 13073 — 607-898-5301
James Abrams, supt. — Fax 898-4647
www.grotoncs.org
Groton HS — 300/9-12
400 Peru Rd 13073 — 607-898-5802
William Congdon, prin. — Fax 898-5824
Groton MS — 200/6-8
400 Peru Rd 13073 — 607-898-5803
Jeffrey Evener, prin. — Fax 898-5824

Guilderland, Albany
Guilderland Central SD
Supt. — See Guilderland Center
Farnsworth MS — 1,200/6-8
6072 State Farm Rd 12084 — 518-456-6010
Mary Summermatter, prin. — Fax 456-3747

Guilderland Center, Albany
Guilderland Central SD — 5,200/K-12
PO Box 18 12085 — 518-456-6200
Marie Whiles Ph.D., supt. — Fax 456-1152
www.guilderlandschools.org/
Guilderland HS — 1,800/9-12
PO Box 37 12085 — 518-861-8591
Thomas Lutsic, prin. — Fax 861-5874
Other Schools – See Guilderland

Hamburg, Erie, Pop. 9,357
Frontier Central SD — 5,000/K-12
5120 Orchard Ave 14075 — 716-926-1711
James Bodziak, supt. — Fax 926-1776
www.frontier.wnyric.org
Frontier HS — 1,600/9-12
4432 Bay View Rd 14075 — 716-926-1720
Jeffrey Sortisio, prin. — Fax 646-2195
Frontier MS — 1,200/6-8
2751 Amsdell Rd 14075 — 716-926-1730
Barbara Shea, prin. — Fax 646-2207

Hamburg Central SD — 3,900/PK-12
5305 Abbott Rd 14075 — 716-646-3220
Steven Achramovitch, supt. — Fax 646-3209
www.hamburgschools.org/
Hamburg HS — 1,200/9-12
4111 Legion Dr 14075 — 716-646-3300
Michael Gallagher, prin. — Fax 646-3028
Hamburg MS — 900/6-8
360 Division St 14075 — 716-646-3250
Jennifer Giallella, prin. — Fax 646-6380

Hilbert College — Post-Sec.
5200 S Park Ave 14075 — 716-649-7900
Immaculata Academy — 200/9-12
5138 S Park Ave 14075 — 716-649-6161
Jill Monaco, prin. — Fax 646-1782

Hamilton, Madison, Pop. 4,131
Hamilton Central SD — 600/PK-12
47 W Kendrick Ave 13346 — 315-824-6330
Dr. Diana Bowers, supt. — Fax 824-6314
www.hamiltoncentral.org/
Hamilton JSHS — 300/6-12
47 W Kendrick Ave 13346 — 315-824-6320
William Dowsland, prin. — Fax 824-6314

Colgate University — Post-Sec.
13 Oak Dr 13346 — 315-228-1000

Hammond, Saint Lawrence, Pop. 278
Hammond Central SD — 300/PK-12
PO Box 185 13646 — 315-324-5931
Douglas H. McQueer, supt. — Fax 324-6057
hammond.sllboces.org/
Hammond Central S — 300/PK-12
PO Box 185 13646 — 315-324-5931
Douglas H. McQueer, supt. — Fax 324-6057

Hammondsport, Steuben, Pop. 654
Hammondsport Central SD — 500/K-12
8272 Main Street Ext 14840 — 607-569-5200
Kyle Bower, supt. — Fax 569-5212
www.hammondsportcsd.org
Hammondsport JSHS — 300/7-12
8272 Main Street Ext 14840 — 607-569-5287
Tad Rounds, prin. — Fax 569-5279

Hampton Bays, Suffolk, Pop. 13,462
Hampton Bays UFD — 1,600/PK-12
86 Argonne Rd E 11946 — 631-723-2100
Lars Clemensen, supt. — Fax 723-2109
www.hbschools.us
Hampton Bays HS — 600/9-12
88 Argonne Rd E 11946 — 631-723-2110
Chris Richardt, prin. — Fax 723-2120
Hampton Bays MS — 300/5-8
70 Ponquogue Ave 11946 — 631-723-4700
Dennis Schug, prin. — Fax 723-4900

Hancock, Delaware, Pop. 1,014
Hancock Central SD — 400/PK-12
67 Education Ln 13783 — 607-637-1301
Dr. Terrance Dougherty, supt. — Fax 637-2512
hancock.stier.org
Hancock JSHS — 300/5-12
67 Education Ln 13783 — 607-637-1306
Brenton Taylor, prin. — Fax 637-2512

Hannibal, Oswego, Pop. 547
Hannibal Central SD — 1,600/PK-12
928 Cayuga St 13074 — 315-564-7900
Donna J. Fountain, supt. — Fax 564-7263
www.hannibalcsd.org/
Hannibal HS — 500/9-12
928 Cayuga St 13074 — 315-564-7910
Dr. Brian Schmitt, prin. — Fax 564-7973
Kenney MS — 400/5-8
928 Cayuga St 13074 — 315-564-7955
Patrick Keefe, prin. — Fax 564-7509

Harpursville, Broome
Harpursville Central SD — 900/PK-12
PO Box 147 13787 — 607-693-8101
Kathleen Wood, supt. — Fax 693-1480
www.hcs.stier.org/
Harpursville JSHS — 400/7-12
PO Box 147 13787 — 607-693-8105
Michael Rullo, prin. — Fax 693-1480

Harrison, Westchester, Pop. 26,975
Harrison Central SD — 3,500/K-12
50 Union Ave 10528 — 914-630-3021
Louis Wool, supt. — Fax 835-5893
www.harrisoncsd.org
Harrison HS — 1,000/9-12
255 Union Ave 10528 — 914-630-3095
Dr. James Ruck, prin. — Fax 835-5471
Klein MS — 800/6-8
50 Union Ave 10528 — 914-630-3033
Scott Fried, prin. — Fax 777-1346

Harrisville, Lewis, Pop. 623
Harrisville Central SD — 400/PK-12
14371 Pirate Ln 13648 — 315-543-2707
Rolf Waters, supt. — Fax 543-2360
www.hcsk12.org/
Harrisville JSHS — 200/6-12
14371 Pirate Ln 13648 — 315-543-2920
Robert Finster, prin. — Fax 543-2360

Hartford, Washington
Hartford Central SD — 500/PK-12
4704 State Route 149 12838 — 518-632-5931
Thomas Abraham, supt. — Fax 632-5231
www.hartfordcsd.org
Hartford Central HS — 300/6-12
4704 State Route 149 12838 — 518-632-5923
Andrew Cook, prin. — Fax 632-5231

Hartsdale, Westchester, Pop. 5,198
Greenburgh Central SD — 1,700/PK-12
475 W Hartsdale Ave 10530 — 914-761-6000
Ronald Ross, supt. — Fax 761-2354
www.greenburghcsd.org
Woodlands HS — 500/9-12
475 W Hartsdale Ave 10530 — 914-761-6052
Will Washington, prin. — Fax 761-6951
Woodlands MS — 200/7-8
475 W Hartsdale Ave 10530 — 914-761-6052
Brodrick Spencer, prin. — Fax 686-0445

Maria Regina HS — 500/9-12
500 W Hartsdale Ave 10530 — 914-761-3300
Robert Fazio, prin. — Fax 761-0860
Solomon Schechter S of Westchester — 500/6-12
555 W Hartsdale Ave 10530 — 914-948-8333

Hastings on Hudson, Westchester, Pop. 7,663
Greenburgh-Graham UFD — 300/1-12
1 S Broadway 10706 — 914-478-1106
Amy Goodman, supt. — Fax 478-0904
www.greenburgh-graham.org
King HS — 200/9-12
1 S Broadway 10706 — 914-478-1161
Paul Tobin, prin. — Fax 478-2321

Hastings-on-Hudson UFD — 1,600/K-12
27 Farragut Ave 10706 — 914-478-6200
Dr. Roy Montesano, supt. — Fax 478-6209
www.hastings.k12.ny.us
Farragut MS — 500/5-8
27 Farragut Ave 10706 — 914-478-6230
Gail Kipper, prin. — Fax 478-6314
Hastings HS — 500/9-12
1 Mount Hope Blvd 10706 — 914-478-6250
Louis Adipietro, prin. — Fax 478-7842

Hauppauge, Suffolk, Pop. 20,653
Hauppauge UFD — 4,000/K-12
PO Box 6006 11788 — 631-761-8208
Patricia Sullivan-Kriss, supt. — Fax 265-3649
www.hauppauge.k12.ny.us
Hauppauge HS — 1,300/9-12
PO Box 6006 11788 — 631-761-8302
Christine O'Connor, prin. — Fax 979-0926
Hauppauge MS — 1,000/6-8
PO Box 6006 11788 — 631-761-8230
Maryann Fletcher, prin. — Fax 265-9546

Learning Institute for Beauty Sciences — Post-Sec.
544 Route 111 11788 — 631-724-0440

Hempstead, Nassau, Pop. 52,895
Hempstead UFD — 6,100/PK-12
185 Peninsula Blvd 11550 — 516-292-7111
Susan Johnson, supt. — Fax 292-9471
www.hempsteadschools.org/
Hempstead HS — 1,600/9-12
201 President St 11550 — 516-292-7111
Dr. Jonetta Hill, prin. — Fax 292-7770
HYPE Academy, 100 Main St 11550 — Alt
Angela Maynard, admin. — 516-307-9645
Schultz MS — 1,200/6-8
70 Greenwich St 11550 — 516-292-7111
Henry Williams, prin. — Fax 483-2549

Uniondale UFD
Supt. — See Uniondale
Lawrence Road MS — 700/6-8
50 Lawrence Rd 11550 — 516-918-1500
Dexter Hodge, prin. — Fax 565-5023

Franklin Career Institute — Post-Sec.
91 N Franklin St 11550 — 516-481-4444
Hofstra University — Post-Sec.
100 Hofstra University 11549 — 516-463-6600
Learning Institute for Beauty Sciences — Post-Sec.
173A Fulton Ave 11550 — 516-483-6259
Sacred Heart Academy — 900/9-12
47 Cathedral Ave 11550 — 516-483-7383
Sr. Joanne Forker, prin. — Fax 483-1016
Suburban Technical School — Post-Sec.
175 Fulton Ave 11550 — 516-481-6660

Henrietta, Monroe
Rush-Henrietta Central SD — 5,500/K-12
2034 Lehigh Station Rd 14467 — 585-359-5012
Dr. J. Kenneth Graham, supt. — Fax 359-5045
www.rhnet.org
Ninth Grade Academy — 400/9-9
2000 Lehigh Station Rd 14467 — 585-359-5550
Timothy Heaphy, prin. — Fax 359-5559
Roth MS — 700/6-8
4000 E Henrietta Rd 14467 — 585-359-5108
Denise Zeh, prin. — Fax 359-5164
Rush-Henrietta HS — 1,400/10-12
1799 Lehigh Station Rd 14467 — 585-359-5208
Beth Patton, prin. — Fax 359-5290
Other Schools – See West Henrietta

Herkimer, Herkimer, Pop. 7,636
Herkimer Central SD — 1,200/K-12
801 W German St 13350 — 315-866-2230
Gary Tutty, supt. — Fax 866-2234
www.herkimercsd.org/
Herkimer JSHS — 600/7-12
801 W German St 13350 — 315-866-2230
Terry Dangle, prin. — Fax 866-8595

Herkimer County Community College — Post-Sec.
100 Reservoir Rd 13350 — 315-866-0300

Heuvelton, Saint Lawrence, Pop. 711
Heuvelton Central SD — 600/PK-12
PO Box 375 13654 — 315-344-2414
Susan Todd, supt. — Fax 344-2349
heuvelton.schoolfusion.us
Heuvelton Central S — 600/PK-12
PO Box 375 13654 — 315-344-2414
Michael Warden, prin. — Fax 344-2349

Hewlett, Nassau, Pop. 6,722
Hewlett-Woodmere UFD
Supt. — See Woodmere
Hewlett HS, 60 Everit Ave 11557 — 1,100/9-12
Thomas Russo, prin. — 516-792-4100
Woodmere MS — 700/6-8
1170 Peninsula Blvd 11557 — 516-792-4368
Richard Berkowitz, prin.

Abraham HS for Girls — 300/9-12
291 Meadowview Ave 11557 — 516-374-7195
Helen Spirn, prin. — Fax 374-2532

Hicksville, Nassau, Pop. 40,674
Hicksville UFD — 5,300/PK-12
200 Division Ave 11801 — 516-733-2105
Maureen Bright, supt. — Fax 733-6584
www.hicksvillepublicschools.com
Hicksville HS — 1,800/9-12
180 Division Ave 11801 — 516-733-2201
Brijinder Singh, prin. — Fax 733-6626
Hicksville MS — 1,200/6-8
215 Jerusalem Ave 11801 — 516-733-2261
Mara Jorisch, prin. — Fax 733-6528

Holy Trinity Diocesan HS 1,400/9-12
98 Cherry Ln 11801 516-433-2900
Gene Fennell, prin. Fax 433-2827

Highland, Ulster, Pop. 5,534
Highland Central SD 1,900/K-12
320 Pancake Hollow Rd 12528 845-691-1000
Deborah Haab, supt. Fax 691-1039
www.highland-k12.org/
Highland HS 600/9-12
320 Pancake Hollow Rd 12528 845-691-1020
Pete Harris, prin. Fax 691-1038
Highland MS 500/6-8
71 Main St 12528 845-691-1080
Daniel Seyler-Wetzel, prin. Fax 691-1083

Highland Falls, Orange, Pop. 3,773
Highland Falls Ft. Montgomery Central SD
Supt. — See Fort Montgomery
Highland Falls MS 300/5-8
PO Box 287 10928 845-446-4761
Bethany Negersmith, prin. Fax 446-0858

Hillburn, Rockland, Pop. 844
Ramapo Central SD 4,700/K-12
45 Mountain Ave 10931 845-357-7783
Douglas Adams, supt. Fax 357-5707
www.ramapocentral.org
Other Schools – See Suffern

Mesivta Ohr Naftoli 100/9-12
275 Route 17 10931 845-357-5609

Hilton, Monroe, Pop. 5,826
Hilton Central SD 4,400/K-12
225 West Ave 14468 585-392-1000
David Dimbleby, supt. Fax 392-1038
www.hilton.k12.ny.us
Hilton HS 1,400/9-12
400 East Ave 14468 585-392-1000
Brian Bartalo, prin. Fax 392-1052
Williams MS 700/7-8
200 School Ln 14468 585-392-1000
Tim Dobbertin, prin. Fax 392-1054

Hinsdale, Cattaraugus
Hinsdale Central SD 400/K-12
3701 Main St 14743 716-557-2227
Judi McCarthy, supt. Fax 557-2259
www.hinsdalebobcats.org/hinsdale
Hinsdale Central S 400/K-12
3701 Main St 14743 716-557-2227
Laurie Cuddy, prin. Fax 557-2259

Holbrook, Suffolk, Pop. 26,920
Sachem Central SD
Supt. — See Ronkonkoma
Seneca MS 800/6-8
850 Main St 11741 631-471-1850
Gemma Salvia, prin. Fax 471-1840

Holland, Erie, Pop. 1,197
Holland Central SD 700/PK-12
11720 Partridge Rd 14080 716-537-8200
Cathy Fabiatos, supt. Fax 537-2453
www.holland.wnyric.org
Holland HS 300/7-12
103 Canada St 14080 716-537-8221
Carl Guidotti, prin. Fax 537-8233

Holland Patent, Oneida, Pop. 456
Holland Patent Central SD 1,600/PK-12
9601 Main St 13354 315-865-7221
Kathleen Davis, supt. Fax 865-4057
www.hpschools.org/
Holland Patent Central HS 500/9-12
9601 Main St 13354 315-865-8154
John Egresits, prin. Fax 865-4069
Holland Patent MS 400/6-8
9601 Main St 13354 315-865-8152
Charles Pratt, prin. Fax 865-7243

Holley, Orleans, Pop. 1,790
Holley Central SD 1,200/K-12
3800 N Main Street Rd 14470 585-638-6316
Robert D'Angelo, supt. Fax 638-7409
www.holleycsd.org
Holley JSHS 600/7-12
3800 N Main Street Rd 14470 585-638-6335
Susan Cory, prin. Fax 638-7925

Hollis, See New York
NYC Department of Education
Supt. — See New York
Cambria Heights Academy 100/9-12
18804 91st Ave 11423 718-776-2815
Melissa Menake, prin. Fax 776-2818
IS 238 1,600/6-8
8815 182nd St 11423 718-297-9821
Peter Leddy, prin. Fax 658-5288

Wang Yeshiva University HS for Girls 300/9-12
8686 Palo Alto St 11423 718-479-8550
C.B. Neugroschl, hdmstr. Fax 479-8686

Holtsville, Suffolk, Pop. 19,502
Sachem Central SD
Supt. — See Ronkonkoma
Sagamore MS 800/6-8
57 Division St 11742 631-696-8600
Steve Siciliano, prin. Fax 696-8620
Sequoya MS 1,000/6-8
750 Waverly Ave 11742 631-207-7100
Frank Panasci, prin. Fax 207-7115

Homer, Cortland, Pop. 3,225
Homer Central SD 2,000/K-12
PO Box 500 13077 607-749-7241
Nancy Ruscio, supt. Fax 749-2312
www.homercentral.org
Homer HS 700/9-12
80 S West St 13077 607-749-7246
Doug VanEtten, prin. Fax 749-2312
Homer JHS 400/6-8
58 Clinton St 13077 607-749-1230
Tom Turck, prin. Fax 749-1238

Honeoye, Ontario, Pop. 571
Honeoye Central SD 700/K-12
PO Box 170 14471 585-229-4125
David C. Bills, supt. Fax 229-5633
www.honeoye.org
Honeoye MSHS 500/6-12
PO Box 170 14471 585-229-5171
Mike Mead, prin. Fax 229-4879

Honeoye Falls, Monroe, Pop. 2,631
Honeoye Falls-Lima Central SD 2,500/K-12
20 Church St 14472 585-624-7000
Philip Burrows, supt. Fax 624-7003
www.hflcsd.org/
Honeoye Falls-Lima HS 900/9-12
83 East St 14472 585-624-7051
David Roth, prin. Fax 624-7118
Honeoye Falls-Lima MS 600/6-8
619 Quaker Meeting House Rd 14472 585-624-7100
Shawn Williams, prin. Fax 624-7121

Hoosick, Rensselaer

Hoosac S 100/8-12
PO Box 9 12089 518-686-7331
Dean Foster, hdmstr. Fax 686-3370

Hoosick Falls, Rensselaer, Pop. 3,451
Hoosick Falls Central SD 1,200/K-12
PO Box 192 12090 518-686-7012
Kenneth Facin, supt. Fax 686-9060
www.hoosickfallscsd.org/
Hoosick Falls HS 600/7-12
PO Box 192 12090 518-686-7321
Stacy Vadney, prin. Fax 686-7452

Hopewell Junction, Dutchess, Pop. 354
Wappingers Central SD
Supt. — See Wappingers Falls
Jay HS 2,200/9-12
2012 Route 52 12533 845-897-6700
Dwight Bonk, prin. Fax 897-6719

Hornell, Steuben, Pop. 8,357
Hornell CSD 1,800/K-12
25 Pearl St 14843 607-324-1302
Doug Wyant, supt. Fax 324-4060
www.hornellcityschools.com
Hornell JHS 400/7-9
134 Seneca St 14843 607-324-1303
Theodore Illi, prin. Fax 324-3421
Hornell SHS 400/10-12
134 Seneca St 14843 607-324-1303
Tony Gill, prin. Fax 324-3702

St. James Mercy Hospital Post-Sec.
411 Canisteo St 14843 607-324-3900

Horseheads, Chemung, Pop. 6,375
Horseheads Central SD 4,200/PK-12
1 Raider Ln 14845 607-739-5601
Dr. Ralph Marino, supt. Fax 795-2405
www.horseheadsdistrict.com/
Horseheads HS 1,300/9-12
401 Fletcher St 14845 607-795-2500
Karen Donahue, prin. Fax 795-2505
Horseheads MS 600/7-8
950 Sing Sing Rd 14845 607-739-6357
Ronald Holloway, prin. Fax 795-2525

Houghton, Allegany, Pop. 1,665

Houghton Academy 200/6-12
9790 Thayer St 14744 585-567-8115
Scott Frazier, hdmstr. Fax 567-8048
Houghton College Post-Sec.
1 Willard Ave 14744 585-567-9200

Hudson, Columbia, Pop. 6,373
Hudson CSD 2,000/PK-12
215 Harry Howard Ave 12534 518-828-4360
Maria J. Suttmeier, supt. Fax 697-8777
www.hudsoncityschooldistrict.com/
Hudson HS 600/9-12
215 Harry Howard Ave 12534 518-828-4132
Thomas Gavin, prin. Fax 697-8418
Hudson JHS 300/7-8
215 Harry Howard Ave 12534 518-828-4360
Derek Reardon, prin. Fax 697-8522

Columbia-Greene Community College Post-Sec.
4400 State Route 23 12534 518-828-4181

Hudson Falls, Washington, Pop. 7,173
Hudson Falls Central SD
Supt. — See Fort Edward
Hudson Falls HS 700/9-12
80 E La Barge St 12839 518-747-2121
James Bennefield, prin. Fax 746-9033
Hudson Falls MS 500/6-8
131 Notre Dame St 12839 518-747-2121
Todd Gonyeau, prin. Fax 746-2790

Huntington, Suffolk, Pop. 17,836
Huntington UFD
Supt. — See Huntington Station
Finley MS 700/7-8
20 Greenlawn Rd 11743 631-673-2020
John Amato, prin. Fax 425-4746
Huntington HS 1,300/9-12
188 Oakwood Rd 11743 631-673-2003
Dr. Carmela Leonardi, prin. Fax 425-4730

Seminary of the Immaculate Conception Post-Sec.
440 W Neck Rd 11743 631-423-0483

Huntington Station, Suffolk, Pop. 32,344
Huntington UFD 4,400/K-12
50 Tower St 11746 631-673-2038
James Polansky, supt. Fax 423-3447
www.hufsd.edu/
Other Schools – See Huntington

South Huntington UFD 5,500/K-12
60 Weston St 11746 631-812-3070
David P. Bennardo Ed.D., supt. Fax 812-3075
www.shufsd.org
Stimson MS 900/7-8
401 Oakwood Rd 11746 631-812-3700
Edwin Smith, prin. Fax 812-3737
Whitman HS 1,800/9-12
301 W Hills Rd 11746 631-812-3800
Kathleen Acker, prin. Fax 812-3838

St. Anthony HS 2,500/9-12
275 Wolf Hill Rd 11747 631-271-2020
Br. Gary Cregan, prin. Fax 547-6820

Hurley, Ulster, Pop. 3,401

Coleman HS 200/9-12
430 Hurley Ave 12443 845-338-2750
James Lyons, prin. Fax 338-0250

Hyde Park, Dutchess, Pop. 1,897
Hyde Park Central SD 3,800/K-12
PO Box 2033 12538 845-229-4000
Dr. Greer Fischer, supt. Fax 229-4056
www.hpcsd.org
Haviland MS 900/6-8
PO Box 721 12538 845-229-4030
Eric Shaw, prin. Fax 229-2475
Other Schools – See Staatsburg on Hudson

Culinary Institute of America Post-Sec.
1946 Campus Dr 12538 845-452-9600

Ilion, Herkimer, Pop. 7,948
Central Valley Community SD 1,400/K-12
111 Frederick St 13357 315-894-9934
Cosimo Tangorra, supt. Fax 894-2716
www.ilioncsd.org
Central Valley Academy 500/9-12
111 Frederick St 13357 315-895-7471
Renee Rudd, prin. Fax 894-5255
Other Schools – See Mohawk

Indian Lake, Hamilton
Indian Lake Central SD 100/K-12
6345 Nys Route 30 12842 518-648-5024
Mark Brand, supt. Fax 648-6346
www.ilcsd.org
Indian Lake Central S 100/K-12
6345 Nys Route 30 12842 518-648-5024
David Snide, prin. Fax 648-6346

Irvington, Westchester, Pop. 6,319
Irvington UFD 1,800/K-12
6 Dows Ln 10533 914-591-8500
Dr. Kristopher Harrison, supt. Fax 591-3064
www.irvingtonschools.org
Irvington HS 600/9-12
40 N Broadway 10533 914-591-8648
David Cohen, prin. Fax 591-6714
Irvington MS 400/6-8
40 N Broadway 10533 914-591-9494
David Sottile, prin. Fax 591-8535

Island Park, Nassau, Pop. 4,586
Island Park UFD 700/K-8
150 Trafalgar Blvd 11558 516-434-2600
Dr. Rosmarie T. Bovino, supt. Fax 431-7550
www.ips.k12.ny.us
Island Park/Lincoln Orens MS 300/5-8
150 Trafalgar Blvd 11558 516-434-2630
John Barnes, prin. Fax 431-7550

Islip, Suffolk, Pop. 18,391
Islip UFD 3,300/K-12
215 Main St 11751 631-650-8210
Susan Schnebel, supt. Fax 650-8218
www.islipufsd.org/
Islip HS 1,200/9-12
2508 Union Blvd 11751 631-650-8305
Dr. Eileen Rossman, prin. Fax 650-8308
Islip MS 800/6-8
211 Main St 11751 631-650-8505
Dr. Timothy Martin, prin. Fax 650-8508

Islip Terrace, Suffolk, Pop. 5,327
East Islip UFD 4,300/PK-12
1 Craig B Gariepy Ave 11752 631-224-2000
Linda Rozzi, supt. Fax 581-1617
www.eischools.org
East Islip HS 1,600/9-12
1 Redmen St 11752 631-224-2100
William Brennen, prin. Fax 581-4410
East Islip MS 1,100/6-8
100 Redmen St 11752 631-224-2170
Mark Bernard, prin. Fax 859-3745

Ithaca, Tompkins, Pop. 28,833
Ithaca CSD 5,300/PK-12
400 Lake St 14850 607-274-2101
Dr. Luvelle Brown, supt. Fax 274-2271
www.icsd.k12.ny.us
Boynton MS 600/6-8
1601 N Cayuga St 14850 607-274-2241
Diane Carruthers, prin. Fax 274-2357
De Witt MS 500/6-8
560 Warren Rd 14850 607-257-3222
Mac Knight, prin. Fax 266-3502

Ithaca HS 1,300/9-12
1401 N Cayuga St 14850 607-274-2145
Jarrett Powers, prin. Fax 277-3061
Lehman Alternative Community S 300/Alt
111 Chestnut St 14850 607-274-2183
Joe Greenberg, prin. Fax 274-2351

Cornell University Post-Sec.
410 Thurston Ave 14850 607-255-2000
Ithaca College Post-Sec.
953 Danby Rd 14850 607-274-3011

Jackson Heights, See New York
NYC Department of Education
Supt. — See New York
IS 145 2,000/6-8
3334 80th St 11372 718-457-1242
Delores Beckham, prin. Fax 335-0601
IS 230 900/6-8
7310 34th Ave 11372 718-335-7648
Sharon Terry, prin. Fax 335-7513

Garden S 300/PK-12
3316 79th St 11372 718-335-6363
Dr. Richard Marotta, hdmstr Fax 565-1169
Plaza College Post-Sec.
7409 37th Ave 11372 718-779-1430

Jamaica, See New York
NYC Department of Education
Supt. — See New York
Basie MS 700/6-8
13325 Guy R Brewer Blvd 11434 718-723-6200
Omotayo Cineus, prin. Fax 527-1675
Business/Computer Applications S 400/9-12
20701 116th Ave 11411 718-978-2807
Lynne Callender, prin. Fax 978-3402
Edison Career & Tech HS Vo/Tech
16565 84th Ave 11432 718-297-6580
Moses Ojeda, prin. Fax 658-0365
Hillcrest HS 3,300/9-12
16005 Highland Ave 11432 718-658-5407
Steven Duch, prin. Fax 739-5137
Hillside Arts & Letters Academy 100/9-12
16701 Gothic Dr 11432 718-658-1249
Matthew Ritter, prin. Fax 658-1613
Humanities & the Arts Magnet HS 500/9-12
20701 116th Ave 11411 718-978-2135
Rosemarie O'Mard, prin. Fax 978-2309
Jamaica Gateway to the Sciences 9-12
16701 Gothic Dr 11432 718-480-2689
Caren Taylor, prin. Fax 480-2697
Jamaica HS 1,200/9-12
16701 Gothic Dr 11432 718-739-5942
Enric Kendall, prin. Fax 739-4826
HS for Community Leadership 100/9-12
16701 Gothic Dr 11432 718-558-9801
Carlos Borrero, prin. Fax 558-9807
HS for Law Enforcement & Public Safety 500/9-12
11625 Guy R Brewer Blvd 11434 718-977-4800
Diahann Malcolm, dir. Fax 977-4802
JHS 8 700/6-8
10835 167th St 11433 718-739-6883
Angela Green, prin. Fax 526-2727
JHS 217 1,400/6-8
8505 144th St 11435 718-657-1120
Patrick Burns, prin. Fax 291-3668
Law 400/9-12
20701 116th Ave 11411 718-978-6432
Donna White, prin. Fax 978-6749
Martin HS 1,200/9-12
15610 Baisley Blvd 11434 718-528-2920
Gillian Smith, prin. Fax 276-1846
Math Science Research & Tech Magnet HS 400/9-12
20701 116th Ave 11411 718-978-1837
Jose Cruz, prin. Fax 978-2063
Queens Collegiate HS 300/6-12
16701 Gothic Dr 11432 718-658-4016
Jaime Dubei, prin. Fax 658-5149
Queens Gateway to the Health Sciences 600/6-12
16020 Goethals Ave 11432 718-969-3155
Judy Henry, prin. Fax 969-3552
Queens HS for Science 400/9-12
9450 159th St 11433 718-657-3181
David Marmor, prin. Fax 657-2579
Queens Satellite HS for Opportunity Alt
16202 Hillside Ave 11432 718-657-3920
Mark Melkonian, prin. Fax 658-2309
York Early College Academy 400/6-12
10835 167th St 11433 718-262-8547
Deborah Burnett, prin. Fax 558-4257
Young Womens Leadership S 500/6-12
15091 87th Rd 11432 718-725-0402
Avionne Gumbs, prin. Fax 725-0390

Al-Iman S 100/PK-12
8989 Van Wyck Expy 11435 718-297-6520
Fax 658-5530
Allen School Post-Sec.
16318 Jamaica Ave 11432 888-620-6745
Archbishop Molloy HS 1,500/9-12
8353 Manton St 11435 718-441-2100
Br. Thomas Schady, prin. Fax 849-8251
CUNY York College Post-Sec.
9420 Guy R Brewer Blvd 11451 718-262-2000
Jon Louis School of Beauty Post-Sec.
9114 Merrick Blvd 11432 718-658-6240
Louis Academy 900/9-12
17621 Wexford Ter 11432 718-297-2120
Sr. Kathleen McKinney, prin. Fax 739-0037
New York Automotive & Diesel Institute Post-Sec.
17818 Liberty Ave 11433 718-658-0006
St. John's University Post-Sec.
8000 Utopia Pkwy 11439 718-990-2000

Jamestown, Chautauqua, Pop. 30,116
Jamestown CSD 4,700/PK-12
197 Martin Rd 14701 716-483-4420
Daniel Kathman, supt. Fax 483-4421
www.jamestown.wnyric.org
Jamestown HS 1,400/9-12
350 E 2nd St 14701 716-483-3470
Mike McElrath Ph.D., prin. Fax 483-4399
Jefferson MS 500/5-8
195 Martin Rd 14701 716-483-4411
Carm Proctor, prin. Fax 483-4273
Persell MS 500/5-8
375 Baker St 14701 716-483-4406
Philip Cammarata, prin. Fax 483-4417
Washington MS 500/5-8
159 Buffalo St 14701 716-483-4413
Melissa Emerson, prin. Fax 483-4268

Southwestern Central SD 1,400/PK-12
600 Hunt Rd 14701 716-484-1136
Daniel George, supt. Fax 484-1139
swcs.wnyric.org/
Southwestern HS 500/9-12
600 Hunt Rd 14701 716-664-6273
Michael Cipolla, prin. Fax 484-1167
Southwestern MS 300/6-8
600 Hunt Rd 14701 716-664-6270
Richard Rybicki, prin. Fax 487-0855

Bethel Baptist Christian Academy 100/K-12
200 Hunt Rd 14701 716-484-7420
Herb Hotchkiss, chrpsn. Fax 484-0087
Jamestown Business College Post-Sec.
PO Box 429 14702 716-664-5100
Jamestown Community College Post-Sec.
PO Box 20 14702 716-338-1000
Woman's Christian Assoc. Hospital Post-Sec.
207 Foote Ave 14701 716-664-8110

Jamesville, Onondaga
Jamesville-DeWitt Central SD
Supt. — See De Witt
Jamesville-DeWitt MS 900/5-8
6280 Randall Rd 13078 315-445-8360
Peter Smith, prin. Fax 445-8421

Jasper, Steuben
Jasper-Troupsburg Central SD 600/PK-12
PO Box 81 14855 607-792-3675
Chad Groff, supt. Fax 792-3749
www.jtcsd.org
Jasper-Troupsburg JSHS 300/7-12
PO Box 81 14855 607-792-3675
Christopher Parker, prin. Fax 792-3749

Jefferson, Schoharie
Jefferson Central SD 300/K-12
1332 State Route 10 12093 607-652-7821
Carl Mummenthey, supt. Fax 652-7806
www.jeffersoncs.org
Jefferson Central S 300/K-12
1332 State Route 10 12093 607-652-7821
Eric Whipple, prin. Fax 652-7806

Jeffersonville, Sullivan, Pop. 355
Sullivan West Central SD 1,300/PK-12
PO Box 308 12748 845-482-4610
Dr. Nancy Hackett, supt. Fax 482-3022
www.swcsd.org/
Other Schools – See Lake Huntington

Jericho, Nassau, Pop. 13,391
Jericho UFD 3,000/K-12
99 Old Cedar Swamp Rd 11753 516-203-3600
Henry Grishman, supt. Fax 933-2047
www.jerichoschools.org
Jericho HS 1,200/9-12
99 Old Cedar Swamp Rd 11753 516-203-3610
Joe Prisinzano, prin. Fax 681-2895
Jericho MS 700/6-8
99 Old Cedar Swamp Rd 11753 516-203-3620
Donald Gately, prin. Fax 681-8984

Johnson City, Broome, Pop. 14,676
Johnson City Central SD 2,600/K-12
666 Reynolds Rd 13790 607-763-1230
Mary Kay Frys, supt. Fax 729-2767
www.jcschools.com
Johnson City HS 800/9-12
666 Reynolds Rd 13790 607-763-1256
Kimberly Beukema, prin. Fax 763-1211
Johnson City MS 600/6-8
601 Columbia Dr 13790 607-763-1240
Joseph Guccia, prin. Fax 763-1297

Davis College Post-Sec.
400 Riverside Dr 13790 607-729-1581
United Health Services Hospital Post-Sec.
33-57 Harrison St 13790 607-763-6000

Johnstown, Fulton, Pop. 8,615
Johnstown CSD 1,900/PK-12
1 Sir Bills Cir Ste 101 12095 518-762-4611
Robert DeLilli, supt. Fax 762-6379
www.johnstownschools.org/
Johnstown HS 700/9-12
1 Sir Bills Cir 12095 518-762-4661
Michael Beatty, prin. Fax 736-1489
Knox JHS 300/7-8
400 S Perry St 12095 518-762-3711
Michael Satterlee, prin. Fax 762-2775

Fulton-Montgomery Community College Post-Sec.
2805 State Highway 67 12095 518-762-4651

Jordan, Onondaga, Pop. 1,356
Jordan-Elbridge Central SD 1,100/K-12
PO Box 902 13080 315-689-8500
James Froio, supt. Fax 689-0084
www.jecsd.org
Jordan-Elbridge HS 500/9-12
PO Box 901 13080 315-689-8510
Mary Madonna, prin. Fax 689-1985
Jordan-Elbridge MS 300/5-8
PO Box 1150 13080 315-689-8520
David Shafer, prin. Fax 689-6524

Jordanville, Herkimer

Holy Trinity Orthodox Seminary Post-Sec.
PO Box 36 13361 315-858-0945

Katonah, Westchester, Pop. 1,654

Harvey S 300/6-12
260 Jay St 10536 914-232-3161
Barry Fenstermacher, hdmstr. Fax 232-6034
Montfort Academy 50/9-12
99 Valley Rd 10536 914-767-0325
Dr. Jacqueline Lofaro, head sch Fax 767-0735

Keene Valley, Essex
Keene Central SD 200/K-12
PO Box 67 12943 518-576-4555
Cynthia Ford-Johnston, supt. Fax 576-4599
www.keenecentralschool.org
Keene Central S 200/K-12
PO Box 67 12943 518-576-4555
Daniel Mayberry, prin. Fax 576-4599

Kendall, Orleans
Kendall Central SD 800/K-12
1932 Kendall Rd 14476 585-659-2741
Julie Christensen, supt. Fax 659-8903
www.kendallschools.org
Kendall JSHS 400/7-12
16887 Roosevelt Hwy 14476 585-659-2706
Carol D'Agostino, prin. Fax 659-8988

Kenmore, Erie, Pop. 15,148
Kenmore-Tonawanda UFSD
Supt. — See Buffalo
Kenmore MS 600/6-8
155 Delaware Rd 14217 716-874-8403
Elaine Thomas, prin. Fax 874-8650

Mt. St. Mary Academy 300/9-12
3756 Delaware Ave 14217 716-877-1358
Dawn Riggie, prin. Fax 877-0548
St. Joseph Collegiate Institute 800/9-12
845 Kenmore Ave 14223 716-874-4024
Jeffery Hazel, prin. Fax 874-4956

Keuka Park, Yates, Pop. 1,126

Keuka College Post-Sec.
141 Central Ave 14478 315-279-5000

Kew Garden Hills, See New York

Shaarey B'nos Chayil - Shevach HS 200/9-12
7509 Main St, 718-263-0525

Kew Gardens, See New York

Yeshiva Shaar Hatorah-Grodno 100/9-12
11706 84th Ave 11418 718-846-1940

Kings Park, Suffolk, Pop. 17,098
Kings Park Central SD 3,900/K-12
180 Lawrence Rd 11754 631-269-3310
Dr. Susan Agruso, supt. Fax 269-0750
www.kpcsd.org/
Kings Park HS 1,300/9-12
200 Route 25A 11754 631-269-3345
Lino Bracco, prin. Fax 269-7472
Rogers MS 1,000/6-8
97 Old Dock Rd 11754 631-269-3369
John Craig, prin. Fax 269-3282

Kings Point, Nassau, Pop. 4,807

United States Merchant Marine Academy Post-Sec.
300 Steamboat Rd 11024 516-726-5800

Kingston, Ulster, Pop. 22,973
Kingston CSD 6,700/PK-12
61 Crown St 12401 845-339-3000
Dr. Paul Padalino, supt. Fax 339-2249
www.kingstoncityschools.org/
Bailey MS 800/6-8
Merilina Ave Ext 12401 845-943-3940
Julie Linton, prin. Fax 338-6312
Kingston HS 2,200/9-12
403 Broadway 12401 845-331-1970
Adrian Manual, prin. Fax 331-1628
Other Schools – See Lake Katrine

Gloden Hall Health Care Center Post-Sec.
Golden Hill Dr 12401 845-339-4540

Lackawanna, Erie, Pop. 17,629
Lackawanna CSD 1,900/PK-12
245 S Shore Blvd 14218 716-827-6767
Nicholas Korach, supt. Fax 827-6710
www.lackawannaschools.org
Lackawanna HS 600/9-12
550 Martin Rd 14218 716-827-6727
Bruce Axelson, prin. Fax 827-6724
Lackawanna MS 200/7-8
550 Martin Rd 14218 716-827-6704
Matthew McKenna, prin. Fax 827-6784

La Fargeville, Jefferson, Pop. 577
La Fargeville Central SD 600/PK-12
PO Box 138 13656 315-658-2241
Susan Whitney, supt. Fax 658-4223
www.lafargevillecsd.org

La Fargeville Central HS 300/7-12
PO Box 138 13656 315-658-2241
Travis Hoover, prin. Fax 658-4223

La Fayette, Onondaga
La Fayette Central SD 900/PK-12
5955 US Route 20 13084 315-677-9728
Peter Tigh, supt. Fax 677-3372
www.lafayetteschools.org
Big Picture S Alt
5940 Feather Dr 13084 315-504-1000
Susan Osborn, prin. Fax 504-1004
La Fayette JSHS 400/7-12
3122 US Route 11 13084 315-677-5506
Jennifer Blossey, prin. Fax 677-5507

Lagrangeville, Dutchess
Arlington Central SD 9,700/K-12
144 Todd Hill Rd 12540 845-486-4460
Dr. Lorenzo Licopoli, supt. Fax 486-4457
www.arlingtonschools.org
Arlington HS 3,400/9-12
1157 Route 55 12540 845-486-4860
Paul Fanuele, prin. Fax 486-4879
Lagrange MS 900/6-8
110 Stringham Rd 12540 845-486-4880
Eric Schetter, prin. Fax 486-8863
Union Vale MS 900/6-8
1657 E Noxon Rd 12540 845-223-8600
Stephen Kerins, prin. Fax 223-8610
Other Schools – See Poughkeepsie

Lake George, Warren, Pop. 894
Lake George Central SD 1,000/K-12
381 Canada St 12845 518-668-5456
Patrick Dee, supt. Fax 668-2285
www.lkgeorge.org
Lake George JSHS 500/7-12
381 Canada St 12845 518-668-5452
Francis Cocozza, prin. Fax 668-2285

Lake Grove, Suffolk, Pop. 11,039

Lake Grove School Post-Sec.
PO Box 712 11755 888-585-9007

Lake Huntington, Sullivan
Sullivan West Central SD
Supt. — See Jeffersonville
Sullivan West JSHS 700/7-12
PO Box 309 12752 845-932-8401
Margaret Tenbus, prin. Fax 932-8425

Lake Katrine, Ulster, Pop. 2,330
Kingston CSD
Supt. — See Kingston
Miller MS 700/6-8
65 Fording Place Rd 12449 845-943-3941
Jo Burruby, prin. Fax 382-6069

Lake Luzerne, Warren, Pop. 1,220
Hadley-Luzerne Central SD 900/PK-12
PO Box 200 12846 518-696-2378
Paul Berry, supt. Fax 696-5884
www.hlcs.org
Hadley-Luzerne HS 300/9-12
PO Box 200 12846 518-696-2112
Beecher Baker, prin. Fax 696-2356
Townsend MS 400/3-8
PO Box 200 12846 518-696-2378
Patrick Cronin, prin. Fax 696-2485

Lake Placid, Essex, Pop. 2,496
Lake Placid Central SD 700/K-12
50 Cummings Rd 12946 518-523-2475
Dr. Roger Carania, supt. Fax 523-4901
lpds-ny.schoolloop.com
Lake Placid JSHS 400/6-12
34 School St 12946 518-523-2474
Dana Wood, prin. Fax 523-2896

Mountain Lake Children's Residence Post-Sec.
386 River Rd 12946 888-585-9007
National Sports Academy 100/8-12
821 Mirror Lake Dr 12946 518-523-3460
Dr. Jeffrey Pratt Beedy, hdmstr. Fax 523-3488
North Country S 100/4-9
4382 Cascade Rd 12946 518-523-9329
David Hochschartner, head sch Fax 523-4858
Northwood S 200/9-12
PO Box 1070 12946 518-523-3357
Edward Good, hdmstr. Fax 523-3405

Lake Ronkonkoma, Suffolk, Pop. 19,855
Sachem Central SD
Supt. — See Ronkonkoma
Sachem HS North 2,400/9-12
212 Smith Rd 11779 631-471-1400
John Dolan, prin. Fax 471-1408
Samoset MS 900/6-8
51 School St 11779 631-471-1700
James Horan, prin. Fax 471-1706

Lancaster, Erie, Pop. 10,243
Lancaster Central SD 6,000/K-12
177 Central Ave 14086 716-686-3201
Edward Myszka, supt. Fax 686-3350
lancasterschools.org
Lancaster HS 2,000/9-12
1 Forton Dr 14086 716-686-3250
Cesar Marchioli, prin. Fax 686-3347
Lancaster MS 1,000/7-8
148 Aurora St 14086 716-686-3220
Peter Kruszynski, prin. Fax 686-3223

St. Mary HS 300/9-12
142 Laverack Ave 14086 716-683-4824
Rebecca Kranz, prin. Fax 683-4996

Lansing, Tompkins, Pop. 3,411
Lansing Central SD 1,200/K-12
284 Ridge Rd 14882 607-533-3020
Dr. Stephen Grimm, supt. Fax 533-3602
www.lcsd.k12.ny.us/
Lansing HS 400/9-12
300 Ridge Rd 14882 607-533-3020
Eric Hartz, prin. Fax 533-4612
Lansing MS 400/5-8
6 Ludlowville Rd 14882 607-533-3020
Jamie Thomas, prin. Fax 533-3543

Larchmont, Westchester, Pop. 5,760
Mamaroneck UFD
Supt. — See Mamaroneck
Hommocks MS 1,100/6-8
10 Hommocks Rd 10538 914-220-3300
Seth Weitzman, prin. Fax 220-3315

Latham, Albany, Pop. 10,131
North Colonie Central SD 5,400/K-12
91 Fiddlers Ln 12110 518-785-8591
D. Joseph Corr, supt. Fax 785-5504
www.northcolonie.org
Shaker HS 2,000/9-12
445 Watervliet Shaker Rd 12110 518-785-5511
Richard Murphy, prin. Fax 783-5905
Shaker JHS 900/7-8
475 Watervliet Shaker Rd 12110 518-785-1341
Russell Moore, prin. Fax 783-8877

John Paolo's Exteme Beauty Institute Post-Sec.
638 Columbia St Ext Ste 1 12110 518-783-0808

Laurelton, See New York
NYC Department of Education
Supt. — See New York
Collaborative Arts MS 6-8
14500 Springfield Blvd 11413 718-977-6181
Tammy Holloway, prin.
Community Voices MS 6-8
14500 Springfield Blvd 11413 718-977-6180
Tamra Collins, prin. Fax 977-6182
IS 231 900/6-8
14500 Springfield Blvd 11413 718-276-5140
Emmanuel Lubin, prin. Fax 276-2259

Laurens, Otsego, Pop. 259
Laurens Central SD 300/K-12
PO Box 301 13796 607-432-2050
Romona Wenck, supt. Fax 432-4388
laurenscs.org
Laurens Central S 300/K-12
PO Box 301 13796 607-432-2050
Bill Dorritie, prin. Fax 432-4388

Lawrence, Nassau, Pop. 6,454
Lawrence UFD 3,000/PK-12
PO Box 477 11559 516-295-7030
Gary Schall, supt. Fax 239-7164
www.lawrence.org
Lawrence MS 900/5-8
195 Broadway 11559 516-295-7000
George Akst, prin. Fax 295-7196
Other Schools – See Cedarhurst

Hebrew Academy of Five Towns MS 300/6-8
44 Frost Ln 11559 516-569-6352
Rabbi Dovid Kupchik, prin. Fax 569-6457
Mesivta Ateres Yaakov HS 200/9-12
131 Washington Ave 11559 516-374-6465
Rambam Mesivta 200/9-12
15 Frost Ln 11559 516-371-5824
Rabbi Yotav Eliach, prin. Fax 371-4706
Shor Yoshuv Rabbinical College Post-Sec.
1 Cedarlawn Ave 11559 516-239-9002

Le Roy, Genesee, Pop. 4,322
Le Roy Central SD 1,300/PK-12
2 Trigon Park 14482 585-768-8133
Kim Cox, supt. Fax 768-8929
www.leroycsd.org
Le Roy JSHS 600/7-12
9300 S Street Rd 14482 585-768-8131
Joseph Englebert, prin. Fax 768-8929

Levittown, Nassau, Pop. 51,176
Island Trees UFD 2,600/K-12
74 Farmedge Rd 11756 516-520-2100
Dr. Charles Murphy, supt. Fax 520-2113
www.islandtrees.org
Island Trees HS 900/9-12
59 Straight Ln 11756 516-520-2135
Nicholas Grande, prin. Fax 520-9199
Island Trees Memorial MS 800/5-8
45 Wantagh Ave 11756 516-520-2157
Roger Bloom, prin. Fax 520-2168

Levittown UFD 7,400/K-12
150 Abbey Ln 11756 516-520-8300
Dr. James Grossane, supt. Fax 520-8314
www.levittownschools.com
Division Avenue HS 1,100/9-12
120 Division Ave 11756 516-520-8350
Dr. Francesco Lanni, prin. Fax 520-8364
MacArthur HS 1,500/9-12
3369 N Jerusalem Rd 11756 516-520-8450
Kathleen Valentino, prin. Fax 520-8466
Salk MS 1,000/6-8
3359 N Jerusalem Rd 11756 516-520-8470
John Zampaglione, prin. Fax 520-8479
Wisdom Lane MS 800/6-8
120 Center Ln 11756 516-520-8370
John Avena, prin. Fax 520-8380

Hunter Business School Post-Sec.
3601 Hempstead Tpke 11756 516-796-1000

Liberty, Sullivan, Pop. 4,273
Liberty Central SD 1,600/PK-12
115 Buckley St 12754 845-292-6990
Edward Rhine, supt. Fax 292-1164
www.libertyk12.org
Liberty HS 500/9-12
125 Buckley St 12754 845-292-5400
Jack Strassman, prin. Fax 292-7262
Liberty MS 400/5-8
145 Buckley St 12754 845-292-5400
Jack Strassman, prin. Fax 292-5691

Lido Beach, Nassau, Pop. 2,865
Long Beach CSD 4,000/PK-12
235 Lido Blvd 11561 516-897-2000
David Weiss, supt. Fax 897-2107
www.lbeach.org
Long Beach HS 1,300/9-12
322 Lagoon Dr W 11561 516-897-2012
Dr. Gaurav Passi, prin. Fax 897-2052
Long Beach MS 900/6-8
239 Lido Blvd 11561 516-897-2166
Michele Natali Ed.D., prin. Fax 897-2145

Lincolndale, Westchester, Pop. 1,500
Somers Central SD
Supt. — See Somers
Somers HS 1,000/9-12
PO Box 640 10540 914-248-8585
Mark Bayer, prin. Fax 248-8186

Ives S 200/7-11
PO Box 600 10540 914-248-7474

Lindenhurst, Suffolk, Pop. 26,920
Lindenhurst UFD 6,500/K-12
PO Box 621 11757 631-867-3000
Richard Nathan, supt. Fax 867-3008
www.lindenhurstschools.org
Lindenhurst HS 2,400/9-12
300 Charles St 11757 631-867-3700
Daniel Giordano, prin. Fax 867-3708
Lindenhurst MS 1,600/6-8
350 S Wellwood Ave 11757 631-867-3500
Frank Naccarato, prin. Fax 867-3508

Lisbon, Saint Lawrence
Lisbon Central SD 600/PK-12
6866 County Route 10 13658 315-393-4951
Erin Woods, supt. Fax 393-7666
lisboncs.schoolwires.com
Lisbon Central S 600/PK-12
6866 County Route 10 13658 315-393-4951
Eric Burke, prin. Fax 393-7666

Little Falls, Herkimer, Pop. 4,870
Little Falls CSD 1,200/K-12
15 Petrie St 13365 315-823-1470
Louis Patrei, supt. Fax 823-0321
www.lfcsd.org
Little Falls HS 400/9-12
1 High School Rd 13365 315-823-1167
Bart Tooley, prin. Fax 823-1200
Little Falls MS 300/6-8
1 High School Rd 13365 315-823-4300
Brian Coleman, prin. Fax 823-3920

Little Neck, See New York
NYC Department of Education
Supt. — See New York
JHS 67 900/6-8
5160 Marathon Pkwy 11362 718-423-8138
Zoi McGrath, prin. Fax 423-8281

Liverpool, Onondaga, Pop. 2,310
Liverpool Central SD 6,800/K-12
195 Blackberry Rd 13090 315-622-7900
Mark F. Potter, supt. Fax 622-7115
www.liverpool.k12.ny.us
Chestnut Hill MS 300/7-8
204 Saslon Park Dr 13088 315-453-0245
Peter Ianzito, prin. Fax 453-0278
Liverpool HS 1,800/10-12
4338 Wetzel Rd 13090 315-453-1500
Anthony Davis, prin. Fax 453-1246
Liverpool MS 400/7-8
720 7th St 13088 315-453-0258
Joseph Mussi, prin. Fax 453-0281
Ninth Grade Annex 9-9
4340 Wetzel Rd 13090 315-453-1275
Judy Campolieta, prin. Fax 453-1247
Soule Road MS 500/7-8
8340 Soule Rd 13090 315-453-1283
Amanda Caldwell, prin. Fax 453-1286

Bryant & Stratton College Post-Sec.
8687 Carling Rd 13090 315-652-6500
ITT Technical Institute Post-Sec.
235 Greenfield Pkwy 13088 315-461-8000
National Tractor Trailer School Post-Sec.
4650 Buckley Rd 13088 315-451-2430

Livingston Manor, Sullivan, Pop. 1,201
Livingston Manor Central SD 500/PK-12
PO Box 947 12758 845-439-4400
Dr. Deborah Fox, supt. Fax 439-4717
lmcs.k12.ny.us
Livingston Manor JSHS 200/7-12
PO Box 947 12758 845-439-4400
Sandra Johnson, prin. Fax 439-4717

Livonia, Livingston, Pop. 1,405
Livonia Central SD 1,400/PK-12
PO Box E 14487 585-346-4000
Matthew Cole, supt. Fax 346-6145
www.livoniacsd.org
Livonia HS 600/9-12
PO Box E 14487 585-346-4040
Karen Bennett, prin. Fax 346-9605

Livonia MS 300/6-8
PO Box E 14487 585-346-4050
Chuck D'Imperio, prin. Fax 346-6835

Loch Sheldrake, Sullivan

SUNY Sullivan County Community College Post-Sec.
112 College Rd 12759 845-434-5750

Lockport, Niagara, Pop. 20,480
Lockport CSD 4,100/PK-12
130 Beattie Ave 14094 716-478-4800
Michelle T. Bradley, supt. Fax 478-4863
www.lockportschools.org
Lockport HS 1,600/9-12
250 Lincoln Ave 14094 716-478-4450
Frank Movalli, prin. Fax 478-4498
Lockport Opportunity Projects Alt
319 West Ave 14094 716-478-4626
Russell Buckley, prin. Fax 478-4634
North Park JHS 400/7-8
160 Passaic Ave 14094 716-478-4700
Ryan Schoenfeld, prin. Fax 478-4705

Starpoint Central SD 2,800/K-12
4363 Mapleton Rd 14094 716-210-2352
Dr. C. Douglas Whelan, supt. Fax 210-2355
www.starpointcsd.org/
Starpoint HS 900/9-12
4363 Mapleton Rd 14094 716-210-2300
Gil Licata, prin. Fax 210-2334
Starpoint MS 700/6-8
4363 Mapleton Rd 14094 716-210-2200
James Bryer, prin. Fax 210-2233

Locust Valley, Nassau, Pop. 3,370
Locust Valley Central SD 2,200/K-12
22 Horse Hollow Rd 11560 516-277-5000
Dr. Anna Hunderfund, supt. Fax 277-5098
www.lvcsd.k12.ny.us/
Locust Valley HS 700/9-12
99 Horse Hollow Rd 11560 516-277-5100
Dr. Kieran McGuire, prin. Fax 277-5108
Locust Valley MS 500/6-8
99 Horse Hollow Rd 11560 516-277-5200
H. Thomas Hogan, prin. Fax 277-5208

Friends Academy 700/PK-12
270 Duck Pond Rd 11560 516-676-0393
William Morris, hdmstr. Fax 393-4276
Portledge S 400/PK-12
355 Duck Pond Rd 11560 516-750-3100
Simon Owen-Williams, head sch Fax 674-7063

Long Beach, Nassau, Pop. 32,689

Mesivta of Long Beach 100/9-12
205 W Beech St 11561 516-255-4700
Rabbinical College of Long Island Post-Sec.
205 W Beech St 11561 516-255-4700

Long Island City, See New York
NYC Department of Education
Supt. — See New York
Academy for Careers in TV & Film 300/9-12
3641 28th St 11106 718-472-0536
Mark Dunetz, prin. Fax 472-0490
Academy of American Studies 700/9-12
2804 41st Ave 11101 718-361-8786
William Bassell, prin. Fax 361-8832
Academy of Finance & Enterprise 400/9-12
3020 Thomson Ave 11101 718-389-3623
Victoria Armano, prin. Fax 389-3724
Aviation Career & Technical HS Vo/Tech
4530 36th St 11101 718-361-2032
Deno Charalambous, prin. Fax 784-8654
Bard HS Early College II 500/9-12
3020 Thomson Ave 11101 718-361-3133
Valerie Thomson, prin. Fax 361-6742
Bryant HS 3,000/9-12
4810 31st Ave 11103 718-721-5404
Namita Dwarka, prin. Fax 728-3478
Information Technology HS 900/9-12
2116 44th Rd 11101 718-937-4270
Joseph Reed, dir. Fax 937-5236
International HS at Laguardia College 500/9-12
4535 Van Dam St 11101 718-392-3433
John Starkey, prin. Fax 392-3443
HS of Applied Communication 400/9-12
3020 Thomson Ave 11101 718-389-3163
Daniel Korb, prin. Fax 389-3427
IS 141 1,000/6-8
3711 21st Ave 11105 718-278-6403
Miranda Pavlou, prin. Fax 278-2884
IS 204 700/6-8
3641 28th St 11106 718-937-1463
Yvonne Leimsider, prin. Fax 937-7964
Middle College HS 500/9-12
4535 Van Dam St 11101 718-392-3330
Linda Siegmund, prin. Fax 392-3315
Newcomers HS 1,000/9-12
2801 41st Ave 11101 718-937-6005
Orlando Sarmiento, prin. Fax 937-6316
Queens Vocational HS Vo/Tech
3702 47th Ave 11101 718-937-3010
Melissa Burg, prin. Fax 392-8397
Shanker S for Visual & Performing Arts 600/6-8
3151 21st St 11106 718-274-8316
Alexander Angueira, prin. Fax 278-6512
Wagner HS 600/7-12
4707 30th Pl 11101 718-472-5671
Ann Seifullah, prin. Fax 472-9117
Young Womens Leadership S 400/6-12
2315 Newtown Ave 11102 718-267-2839
Laura Mitchell, prin. Fax 728-0218

Berk Trade School Post-Sec.
3309 Queens Blvd Fl 2 11101 718-729-0909
Briarcliffe College Post-Sec.
3030 Thomson Ave 11101 516-918-3900
CUNY LaGuardia Community College Post-Sec.
31-10 Thompson Ave 11101 718-482-7200
Evangel Christian S 500/PK-12
3921 Crescent St 11101 718-937-9600
Rev. Robert Johansson, hdmstr. Fax 937-1613
Industrial Management & Training Inst Post-Sec.
4382 Vernon Blvd 11101 718-786-9298
New York School for Medical Dental Asst. Post-Sec.
3310 Queens Blvd 11101 718-793-2330

Long Lake, Hamilton, Pop. 541
Long Lake Central SD 100/PK-12
PO Box 217 12847 518-624-2147
Mary Dickerson, supt. Fax 624-3896
www.longlakecsd.org/
Long Lake Central S 100/PK-12
PO Box 217 12847 518-624-2147
Mary Dickerson, prin. Fax 624-3896

Loudonville, Albany, Pop. 10,822

Loudonville Christian S 300/PK-12
374 Loudon Rd 12211 518-434-6051
Kathryn Hills M.Ed., admin. Fax 935-2258
Siena College Post-Sec.
515 Loudon Rd 12211 518-783-2300

Lowville, Lewis, Pop. 3,442
Lowville Central SD 1,400/K-12
7668 N State St 13367 315-376-9000
Cheryl Steckly, supt. Fax 376-1933
www.lacs-ny.org
Lowville HS 400/9-12
7668 N State St 13367 315-376-9015
Daniel Cushing, prin. Fax 376-1933
Lowville MS 300/6-8
7668 N State St 13367 315-376-9010
Scott Exford, prin. Fax 376-9011

Lynbrook, Nassau, Pop. 19,147
Lynbrook UFD 2,900/K-12
111 Atlantic Ave 11563 516-887-0253
Melissa Burak, supt. Fax 887-3263
www.lynbrook.k12.ny.us
Lynbrook HS 1,000/9-12
9 Union Ave 11563 516-887-0200
Joseph Rainis, prin. Fax 887-8079
Lynbrook North MS 300/6-8
529 Merrick Rd 11563 516-887-0282
Sean Fallon, prin. Fax 887-0286
Lynbrook South MS 400/6-8
333 Union Ave 11563 516-887-0266
Margaret Ronai Ed.D., prin. Fax 887-0268

Lyndonville, Orleans, Pop. 823
Lyndonville Central SD 700/PK-12
PO Box 540 14098 585-765-3101
Jason Smith, supt. Fax 765-2106
www.lyndonvillecsd.org/
Webber MSHS 300/7-12
PO Box 540 14098 585-765-3162
Aaron Slack Ed.D., prin. Fax 765-2106

Lyons, Wayne, Pop. 3,527
Lyons Central SD 800/K-12
10 Clyde Rd 14489 315-946-2200
Denise Dzikowski, supt. Fax 946-2205
www.lyonscsd.org
Lyons MSHS 300/7-12
10 Clyde Rd 14489 315-946-2220
Nelson Kise, prin. Fax 946-2221

Mc Graw, Cortland, Pop. 1,031
Mc Graw Central SD 500/K-12
PO Box 556 13101 607-836-3636
Mary Curcio, supt. Fax 836-3635
www.mcgrawschools.org
Mc Graw JSHS 300/6-12
PO Box 556 13101 607-836-3600
Mark Dimorier, prin. Fax 836-3635

Madison, Madison, Pop. 304
Madison Central SD 400/K-12
7303 State Route 20 13402 315-893-1878
Perry Dewey, supt. Fax 893-7111
www.madisoncentralny.org
Madison Central S 400/K-12
7303 State Route 20 13402 315-893-1878
Dana Chapman, prin. Fax 893-7111

Madrid, Saint Lawrence, Pop. 751
Madrid-Waddington Central SD 700/K-12
PO Box 67 13660 315-322-5746
Lynn Roy, supt. Fax 322-4462
www.mwcsk12.org
Madrid-Waddington JSHS 400/6-12
PO Box 67 13660 315-322-5746
Bryan Harmer, prin. Fax 322-4462

Mahopac, Putnam, Pop. 8,268
Mahopac Central SD 4,900/K-12
179 E Lake Blvd 10541 845-628-3415
Thomas Manko, supt. Fax 628-5502
www.mahopac.k12.ny.us
Mahopac HS 1,700/9-12
421 Baldwin Place Rd 10541 845-628-3256
Adam Pease, prin. Fax 628-4380
Mahopac MS 1,200/6-8
425 Baldwin Place Rd 10541 845-621-1330
Ira Gurkin, prin. Fax 628-5847

Malone, Franklin, Pop. 5,853
Malone Central SD 2,400/PK-12
PO Box 847 12953 518-483-7800
Jerry Griffin, supt. Fax 483-3071
www.malonecsd.org
Franklin Academy HS 900/9-12
42 Huskie Ln 12953 518-483-7807
Lori Tourville, prin. Fax 483-7813
Malone MS 500/6-8
15 Francis St 12953 518-483-7801
James Knight, prin. Fax 483-9497

Malverne, Nassau, Pop. 8,420
Malverne UFD 1,600/K-12
301 Wicks Ln 11565 516-887-6405
Dr. James Hunderfund, supt. Fax 596-2910
www.malverne.k12.ny.us
Herber MS 400/6-8
75 Ocean Ave 11565 516-887-6444
Steven Gilhuley, prin. Fax 596-0525
Malverne HS 600/9-12
80 Ocean Ave 11565 516-887-6420
Dr. Vincent Romano, prin. Fax 887-6479

Mamaroneck, Westchester, Pop. 18,587
Mamaroneck UFD 5,000/PK-12
1000 W Boston Post Rd 10543 914-220-3000
Dr. Robert Shaps, supt. Fax 220-3010
www.mamkschools.org
Mamaroneck HS 1,500/9-12
1000 W Boston Post Rd 10543 914-220-3100
Elizabeth Clain, prin. Fax 220-3115
Other Schools – See Larchmont

Rye Neck UFD 1,200/K-12
310 Hornidge Rd 10543 914-777-5200
Dr. Peter Mustich, supt. Fax 777-5201
www.ryeneck.k12.ny.us/
Rye Neck HS 400/9-12
300 Hornidge Rd 10543 914-777-5200
Dr. Barbara Ferraro, prin. Fax 777-4801
Rye Neck MS 300/5-8
300 Hornidge Rd 10543 914-777-5200
Eric Lutinski, prin. Fax 777-4701

French-American S of NY 800/PK-12
525 Fenimore Rd 10543 914-250-0400
Robert Leonhardt, hdmstr.
Westchester Hebrew HS 100/9-12
856 Orienta Ave 10543 914-698-0806

Manhasset, Nassau, Pop. 7,968
Manhasset UFD 3,200/K-12
200 Memorial Pl 11030 516-267-7700
Charles Cardillo, supt. Fax 627-1618
www.manhasset.k12.ny.us
Manhasset HS 900/9-12
200 Memorial Pl 11030 516-267-7600
Dean Schlanger, prin. Fax 627-4604
Manhasset MS 500/7-8
200 Memorial Pl 11030 516-267-7500
Dean Schlanger, prin. Fax 627-8157

Elmezzi Graduate School of Molecular Med Post-Sec.
350 Community Dr 11030 718-562-3467
St. Mary HS 900/9-12
51 Clapham Ave 11030 516-627-2711
Jonathan Kramer, prin. Fax 627-3209

Manlius, Onondaga, Pop. 4,642
Fayetteville-Manlius Central SD 4,500/K-12
8199 E Seneca Tpke 13104 315-692-1200
Dr. Corliss Kaiser, supt. Fax 692-1227
www.fmschools.org
Eagle Hill MS 700/5-8
4645 Enders Rd 13104 315-692-1400
Maureen McCrystal, prin. Fax 692-1046
Fayetteville-Manlius HS 1,600/9-12
8201 E Seneca Tpke 13104 315-692-1900
Raymond Kilmer, prin. Fax 692-1028
Other Schools – See Fayetteville

Manorville, Suffolk, Pop. 14,172
Eastport-South Manor Central SD 3,900/K-12
149 Dayton Ave 11949 631-874-6720
Mark Nocero, supt. Fax 878-6308
www.esmonline.org
Eastport/South Manor JSHS 1,900/7-12
543 Moriches Middle Isle Rd 11949 631-874-6500
Joseph Steimel, prin. Fax 874-6787

Marathon, Cortland, Pop. 912
Marathon Central SD 800/PK-12
PO Box 339 13803 607-849-3251
Rebecca Stone, supt. Fax 849-3305
www.marathonschools.org/
Marathon JSHS 400/7-12
PO Box 339 13803 607-849-3251
Douglas Pasquerella, prin. Fax 849-3305

Marcellus, Onondaga, Pop. 1,781
Marcellus Central SD 1,900/K-12
2 Reed Pkwy 13108 315-673-6000
Dr. Craig Tice, supt. Fax 673-1727
marcellusschools.org
Driver MS 800/4-8
2 Reed Pkwy 13108 315-673-6200
Michael Dardaris, prin. Fax 673-1727
Marcellus HS 600/9-12
1 Mustang Hl 13108 315-673-6300
John Durkee, prin. Fax 673-0312

Marcy, Oneida, Pop. 8,685
Whitesboro Central SD
Supt. — See Yorkville
Whitesboro HS 1,200/9-12
6000 State Route 291 13403 315-266-3200
Jeff Kuhn, prin. Fax 266-3223

Margaretville, Delaware, Pop. 595
Margaretville Central SD 400/K-12
PO Box 319 12455 845-586-2647
Anthony Albanese, supt. Fax 586-2949
www.margaretvillecs.org
Margaretville Central S 400/K-12
PO Box 319 12455 845-586-2647
Linda Taylor, prin. Fax 586-2949

Marion, Wayne, Pop. 1,490
Marion Central SD 900/K-12
4034 Warner Rd 14505 315-926-2300
Kathryn Wegman, supt. Fax 926-5797
www.marioncs.org/
Marion JSHS 400/7-12
4034 Warner Rd 14505 315-926-4228
Duane Perry, prin. Fax 926-3114

Marlboro, Ulster, Pop. 3,611
Marlboro Central SD 1,600/K-12
1510 Route 9W 12542 845-236-5814
Raymond Castellani, supt.
www.marlboroschools.org
Marlboro Central HS 700/9-12
50 Cross Rd 12542 845-236-5810
Roseanne Collins-Judon, prin. Fax 236-2638
Marlboro MS 500/6-8
1375 Route 9W 12542 845-236-5842
Debra Clinton, prin. Fax 236-3634

Maspeth, See New York
NYC Department of Education
Supt. — See New York
IS 73 1,500/6-8
7002 54th Ave 11378 718-639-3817
Camillo Turriciano, prin. Fax 429-5162

Luther S 300/9-12
6002 Maspeth Ave 11378 718-894-4000
Randal Gast, prin. Fax 894-1469

Massapequa, Nassau, Pop. 21,527
Massapequa UFD 8,000/K-12
4925 Merrick Rd 11758 516-308-5000
Charles Sulc, supt.
www.msd.k12.ny.us
Berner MS, 50 Carman Mill Rd 11758 1,300/7-8
Jason Esposito, prin. 516-308-5700
Massapequa HS 2,000/10-12
4925 Merrick Rd 11758 516-308-5900
Dr. Barbara Williams, prin.
Massapequa HS Ames Campus 700/9-9
198 Baltimore Ave 11758 516-308-5800
Patrick DiClemente, prin.

Plainedge UFD
Supt. — See North Massapequa
Plainedge HS 1,100/9-12
241 Wyngate Dr 11758 516-992-7550
Robert Amster, prin. Fax 992-7545

Massena, Saint Lawrence, Pop. 10,748
Massena Central SD 2,900/PK-12
84 Nightengale Ave 13662 315-764-3700
Roger Clough, supt. Fax 764-3701
www.mcs.k12.ny.us
Alternative Education S 100/Alt
84 Nightengale Ave 13662 315-764-3700
Jeremy Siddon, prin.
Leary JHS 500/7-8
84 Nightengale Ave 13662 315-764-3720
Jesse Coburn, prin. Fax 764-3723
Massena HS 900/9-12
84 Nightengale Ave 13662 315-764-3710
Patrick Farrand, prin. Fax 764-3719

Mastic Beach, Suffolk, Pop. 12,605
William Floyd UFD 9,100/K-12
240 Mastic Beach Rd 11951 631-874-1100
Dr. Paul Casciano, supt. Fax 281-3047
www.wfsd.k12.ny.us
Floyd HS 3,100/9-12
240 Mastic Beach Rd 11951 631-874-1120
Barbara Butler, prin. Fax 874-1540
Paca MS 1,000/6-8
338 Blanco Dr 11951 631-874-1414
Ed Plaia, prin. Fax 874-1561
Other Schools – See Moriches

Mattituck, Suffolk, Pop. 4,155
Mattituck-Cutchogue UFD
Supt. — See Cutchogue
Mattituck-Cutchogue JSHS 800/7-12
15125 Main Rd 11952 631-298-8460
Shawn Petretti, prin. Fax 298-8544

Mayfield, Fulton, Pop. 827
Mayfield Central SD 1,000/PK-12
27 School St 12117 518-661-8207
Paul Williamsen, supt. Fax 661-7666
www.mayfieldk12.com/
Mayfield JSHS 500/7-12
27 School St 12117 518-661-8200
Robert Husain, prin. Fax 661-7666

Mayville, Chautauqua, Pop. 1,698
Chautauqua Lake Central SD 800/PK-12
100 N Erie St 14757 716-753-5808
Benjamin Spitzer, supt. Fax 753-5813
www.clake.org
Chautauqua Lake Central Secondary S 400/7-12
100 N Erie St 14757 716-753-5882
Joshua Liddell, prin. Fax 753-5886

Mechanicville, Saratoga, Pop. 5,096
Mechanicville CSD 1,100/K-12
25 Kniskern Ave 12118 518-664-5727
Dr. Michael McCarthy, supt. Fax 514-2101
www.mechanicville.org/
Mechanicville JSHS 400/6-12
25 Kniskern Ave 12118 518-664-9888
Kevin Kolakowski, prin. Fax 514-2107

Medford, Suffolk, Pop. 23,778
Patchogue-Medford UFD
Supt. — See Patchogue
Oregon MS, 109 Oregon Ave 11763 600/6-9
James Bertsch, prin. 631-687-6800
Patchogue-Medford HS 2,000/10-12
181 Buffalo Ave 11763 631-687-6500
Randy Rusielewicz Ed.D., prin.

Hunter Business School Post-Sec.
3247 Route 112 Ste 3 11763 631-736-7360

Medina, Orleans, Pop. 5,905
Medina Central SD 1,000/PK-12
1 Mustang Dr 14103 585-798-2700
Jeffrey Evoy, supt. Fax 798-5676
www.medinacsd.org
Medina HS 600/8-12
2 Mustang Dr 14103 585-798-2700
Mark Kruzynski, prin. Fax 798-2787

Orleans County Christian S 50/K-12
PO Box 349 14103 585-798-2992
Linda Strickland, admin. Fax 798-3766

Melville, Suffolk, Pop. 18,680
Half Hollow Hills Central SD
Supt. — See Dix Hills
West Hollow MS 1,500/6-8
250 Old East Neck Rd 11747 631-592-3400
Milton Strong, prin. Fax 592-3922

SBI Campus Post-Sec.
320 S Service Rd 11747 631-370-3300

Merrick, Nassau, Pop. 21,879
Bellmore-Merrick Central HSD
Supt. — See North Merrick
Calhoun HS 1,400/9-12
1786 State St 11566 516-992-1300
David Seinfeld, prin. Fax 867-7390
Merrick Avenue MS 900/7-8
1870 Merrick Ave 11566 516-992-1200
Meador Pratt, prin. Fax 867-6391

Grace Christian Academy 100/K-12
36 Smith St 11566 516-379-2223
Stephen Schultz, hdmstr. Fax 771-8063

Mexico, Oswego, Pop. 1,597
Mexico Central SD 2,300/PK-12
16 Fravor Rd Ste A 13114 315-963-8400
Robert Pritchard, supt. Fax 963-5801
www.mexico.cnyric.org
Mexico HS 800/9-12
3338 Main St 13114 315-963-8400
Donald Root, prin. Fax 963-8887
Mexico MS 700/5-8
16 Fravor Rd 13114 315-963-8400
Kim Holliday, prin. Fax 963-3848

Middleburgh, Schoharie, Pop. 1,471
Middleburgh Central SD 900/PK-12
PO Box 606 12122 518-827-3625
Michele Weaver, supt. Fax 827-6632
www.middleburgh.k12.ny.us
Middleburgh HS 300/9-12
PO Box 850 12122 518-827-3600
Lorianne Petrosino, prin. Fax 827-5192
Middleburgh MS 200/6-8
PO Box 850 12122 518-827-3600
Michael Teator, prin. Fax 827-9533

Middle Island, Suffolk, Pop. 10,280
Longwood Central SD 9,100/K-12
35 Yaphank Middle Island Rd 11953 631-345-2172
Dr. Michael Lonergan, supt. Fax 345-2166
www.longwood.k12.ny.us
Longwood HS 2,900/9-12
100 Longwood Rd 11953 631-345-9200
Maria Castro Ed.D., prin. Fax 345-9279
Longwood JHS 1,400/7-8
198 Longwood Rd 11953 631-345-2701
Levi McIntyre, prin. Fax 345-9281

Middleport, Niagara, Pop. 1,807
Royalton-Hartland Central SD 1,500/PK-12
54 State St 14105 716-735-2000
Kevin McDonald, supt. Fax 735-3660
www.royhart.org/
Royalton-Hartland HS 500/9-12
54 State St 14105 716-735-2000
Gary Bell, prin. Fax 735-6128
Royalton-Hartland MS 500/5-8
78 State St 14105 716-735-2000
John Fisgus, prin. Fax 735-0047

Middletown, Orange, Pop. 27,256
Middletown CSD 5,900/K-12
223 Wisner Ave 10940 845-326-1193
Dr. Kenneth Eastwood, supt. Fax 326-1215
www.middletowncityschools.org/
Middletown HS 2,100/9-12
20 Gardner Ave Ext 10940 845-326-1600
Ann Hall, prin. Fax 326-1605
Monhagen MS 800/6-8
555 County Highway 78 10940 845-326-1700
Tracey Sorrentino, prin. Fax 326-1701
Twin Towers MS 800/6-8
112 Grand Ave 10940 845-326-1650
Gordon Dean, prin. Fax 326-1651

Beauty School of Middletown Post-Sec.
225 Dolson Ave Ste 100 10940 845-343-2171
Harmony Christian S 200/PK-12
1790 Route 211 E 10941 845-692-5353
Kevin Barry, admin. Fax 692-7140
SUNY Orange County Community College Post-Sec.
115 South St 10940 845-344-6222

Middle Village, See New York

Christ the King Regional HS 1,100/9-12
6802 Metropolitan Ave 11379 718-366-7400
Peter Mannarino, prin. Fax 366-1165

Milford, Otsego, Pop. 406
Milford Central SD 400/K-12
PO Box 237 13807 607-286-3341
Peter Livshin, supt. Fax 286-7879
www.schoolworld.milfordcentral.org/
Milford Central S 400/K-12
PO Box 237 13807 607-286-3349
Michael Miller, prin. Fax 286-7879

Millbrook, Dutchess, Pop. 1,439
Millbrook Central SD 1,200/K-12
PO Box AA 12545 845-677-4200
Dr. R. Lloyd Jaeger, supt. Fax 677-4206
www.millbrookcsd.org/
Millbrook HS, PO Box AA 12545 400/9-12
Sandra Intrien, prin. 845-677-2510
Millbrook MS 300/6-8
PO Box AA 12545 845-677-4210
Dr. Phyllis Armori, prin. Fax 677-6913

Millbrook S 300/9-12
131 Millbrook School Rd 12545 845-677-8261
Drew Casertano, hdmstr. Fax 677-8598

Miller Place, Suffolk, Pop. 12,218
Miller Place UFD 3,000/K-12
7 Memorial Dr 11764 631-474-2700
Dr. Marianne Higuera, supt. Fax 474-0686
www.millerplace.k12.ny.us
Miller Place HS 1,000/9-12
15 Memorial Dr 11764 631-474-2723
Kevin Slavin, prin. Fax 474-1734
North Country Road MS 800/6-8
191 N Country Rd 11764 631-474-2710
Matthew Clark, prin. Fax 474-5178

Mill Neck, Nassau, Pop. 979

Mill Neck Lutheran School Post-Sec.
Frost Mill Rd B12 11765

Millwood, Westchester, Pop. 1,000

Yeshiva Kehilath Yaakov 50/11-12
PO Box 501 10546 914-762-3010

Mineola, Nassau, Pop. 18,445
Mineola UFD 2,600/PK-12
121 Jackson Ave 11501 516-237-2000
Dr. Michael Nagler, supt. Fax 237-2008
www.mineola.k12.ny.us
Mineola MS 600/6-8
200 Emory Rd 11501 516-237-2500
Matthew Gaven, prin. Fax 739-4129
Other Schools – See Garden City Park

Chaminade HS 1,700/9-12
340 Jackson Ave 11501 516-742-5555
Br. Joseph Bellizzi, prin. Fax 742-1989
NY College Traditional Chinese Medicine Post-Sec.
155 1st St 11501 516-739-1545
Winthrop University Hospital Post-Sec.
259 1st St 11501 516-663-2201

Mohawk, Herkimer, Pop. 2,697
Central Valley Community SD
Supt. — See Ilion
Jarvis MS 100/7-8
28 Grove St 13407 315-866-2620
Melissa Hoskey, prin. Fax 867-2909

Monroe, Orange, Pop. 8,240
Greenwood Lake UFD 500/K-8
1247 Lakes Rd 10950 845-477-7395
Dr. Richard Brockel, supt. Fax 477-7398
www.gwlufsd.org/
Greenwood Lake MS 300/4-8
1247 Lakes Rd 10950 845-986-8624
Matthew Lawrence, prin. Fax 782-2004

Kiryas Joel Village UFSD 50/PK-12
48 Bakertown Rd Ste 401 10950 845-782-2300
Joel Petlin, supt. Fax 782-4176
Kiryas Joel Village S 50/PK-12
1 Dinev Ct 10950 845-782-7510
Jehudah Halpern, prin. Fax 782-5849

UTA Mesivta of Kiryas Joel Post-Sec.
PO Box 2009, 845-783-9901
UTA of Kiryas Joel 2,600/K-12
PO Box 477, 845-783-5800

Monsey, Rockland, Pop. 18,318

Ateres Bais Yaakov 400/PK-12
236 Cherry Ln 10952 845-368-2200
Rabbi Aaron Fink, dean Fax 368-2210
Bais Malka Girls S of Belz 400/PK-12
PO Box 977 10952 845-354-9500
Bais Shifra Miriam S 300/K-12
PO Box 682 10952 845-356-0061
Bais Yaakov HS of Spring Valley 400/9-12
11 Smolley Dr 10952 845-356-3113
Bais Yaakov of Ramapo HS 100/9-12
16 Hershel Ter 10952 845-356-0580
Beth Medrash Meor Yitzchok Post-Sec.
65 Dykstras Way E 10952 845-426-3488
Beth Rochel School for Girls 100/K-12
145 Saddle River Rd 10952 845-352-5000
Bnos Yisroel Girls S of Viznitz 2,100/1-12
1 School Ter 10952 845-731-3700
Kol Yaakov Torah Center Post-Sec.
29 W Maple Ave 10952 845-425-3863
Mesivta Yesodei Yisroel 100/9-12
51 Carlton Rd 10952 845-425-2520
Mesivta Ziev Hatorah 50/9-12
PO Box 814 10952 845-426-6868
Monsey Academy for Girls 50/9-12
27 Remsen Ave 10952 845-918-1220

Ohr Somayach Monsey — Post-Sec.
244 Route 306 10952 — 845-425-1370
Yeshiva and Kolel Bais Medrash Elyon — Post-Sec.
73 Main St 10952 — 845-356-7064
Yeshiva Beth David S — 600/K-12
PO Box 136 10952 — 845-352-3100
Yeshiva D'Monsey Rabbinical College — Post-Sec.
2 Roman Blvd 10952 — 845-426-3276
Yeshiva Gedolah Bais Yisroel — 50/12-12
4 Solond Rd 10952 — 845-258-7400
Fax 258-2394
Yeshiva Gedolah Kesser Torah — Post-Sec.
28 Cedar Ln 10952 — 845-406-4308
Yeshiva Gedola of South Monsey — 100/9-12
260 Saddle River Rd 10952 — 845-356-4030
Yeshiva Ohel Torah — 9-12
91 College Rd 10952 — 845-371-3740
Yeshiva Shaar Ephraim S — 200/9-12
PO Box 253 10952 — 845-426-3110
Yeshivath Viznitz — Post-Sec.
PO Box 446 10952 — 845-731-3700
Yeshiva Viznitz — 2,500/PK-12
15 Elyon Rd 10952 — 845-356-1010

Montgomery, Orange, Pop. 3,752
Valley Central SD — 4,800/K-12
944 State Route 17K 12549 — 845-457-2400
Richard M. Hooley Ed.D., supt. — Fax 457-4319
www.vcsd.k12.ny.us
Valley Central HS — 1,600/9-12
1175 State Route 17K 12549 — 845-457-2400
Jayme Ginda-Baxter, prin. — Fax 457-4056
Valley Central MS — 1,100/6-8
1189 State Route 17K 12549 — 845-457-2400
Ned Hayes, prin. — Fax 457-4311

Monticello, Sullivan, Pop. 6,485
Monticello Central SD — 3,200/K-12
237 Forestburgh Rd 12701 — 845-794-7700
Daniel Teplesky, supt. — Fax 794-7710
www.monticelloschools.net
Kaiser MS — 700/6-8
45 Breakey Ave 12701 — 845-794-7700
Nichole Horler, prin. — Fax 796-3099
Monticello HS — 1,000/9-12
39 Breakey Ave 12701 — 845-794-7700
Lori Orestano-James, prin. — Fax 794-8133

Montrose, Westchester, Pop. 2,689
Hendrick Hudson Central SD — 2,600/K-12
61 Trolley Rd 10548 — 914-257-5100
Joseph Hochreiter, supt. — Fax 257-5121
www.henhudschools.org/
Hendrick Hudson HS — 800/9-12
2166 Albany Post Rd 10548 — 914-257-5800
James Mackin, prin. — Fax 257-5801
Other Schools – See Cortlandt Manor

Moravia, Cayuga, Pop. 1,274
Moravia Central SD — 900/K-12
PO Box 1189 13118 — 315-497-2670
Michelle Brantner, supt. — Fax 497-2260
www.moraviaschool.org/
Moravia JSHS — 500/7-12
PO Box 1189 13118 — 315-497-2670
Greg Jenne, prin. — Fax 497-3852

Moriches, Suffolk, Pop. 2,802
William Floyd UFD
Supt. — See Mastic Beach
Floyd MS — 1,000/6-8
630 Moriches Middle Island 11955 — 631-874-5505
Carolyn Schick, prin. — Fax 878-7690

Morris, Otsego, Pop. 573
Morris Central SD — 400/PK-12
PO Box 40 13808 — 607-263-6100
Matthew Sheldon, supt. — Fax 263-2483
morriscs.org
Morris Central S — 400/PK-12
PO Box 40 13808 — 607-263-6100
Katharine Smith, prin. — Fax 263-2483

Morristown, Saint Lawrence, Pop. 395
Morristown Central SD — 400/K-12
PO Box 217 13664 — 315-375-8814
David Glover, supt. — Fax 375-8604
mcsd.schoolfusion.us/
Morristown Central S — 400/K-12
PO Box 217 13664 — 315-375-8814
Jeff Durant, prin. — Fax 375-8604

Morrisville, Madison, Pop. 2,159
Morrisville-Eaton Central SD — 800/PK-12
PO Box 990 13408 — 315-684-9300
Michael Drahos, supt. — Fax 684-9399
www.m-ecs.org
Morrisville-Eaton MSHS — 400/7-12
PO Box 990 13408 — 315-684-9121
Christopher Brewer, prin. — Fax 684-9192

SUNY College of Agriculture & Technology — Post-Sec.
PO Box 901 13408 — 315-684-6000

Mountain Dale, Sullivan, Pop. 200

Yeshiva Zichron Mayir — 12-12
5 Ronald Tawil Way 12763 — 845-434-5328

Mount Kisco, Westchester, Pop. 10,701
Bedford Central SD
Supt. — See Bedford
Fox Lane MS — 1,000/6-8
S Bedford Rd 10549 — 914-241-6126
Anne Marie Berardi, prin. — Fax 241-6129

Yeshiva Farm Settlement S — 400/9-12
PO Box 1050 10549 — 914-666-9702

Mount Morris, Livingston, Pop. 2,942
Mount Morris Central SD — 500/K-12
30 Bonadonna Ave 14510 — 585-658-2568
Dawn Mirand, supt. — Fax 658-4814
www.mtmorriscsd.org
Mount Morris JSHS — 200/7-12
30 Bonadonna Ave 14510 — 585-658-3331
Tom Kelleher, prin. — Fax 658-4814

Mount Sinai, Suffolk, Pop. 11,989
Mount Sinai UFD — 2,600/K-12
118 N Country Rd 11766 — 631-870-2550
Enrico Crocetti, supt. — Fax 473-0905
www.mtsinai.k12.ny.us
Mount Sinai HS — 800/9-12
1 Gertrude Goodman Dr 11766 — 631-870-2800
Robert Grable, prin. — Fax 928-3668
Mount Sinai MS — 800/5-8
114 N Country Rd 11766 — 631-870-2700
Peter Pramataris, prin. — Fax 928-3129

Mount Vernon, Westchester, Pop. 64,673
Mount Vernon CSD — 8,400/PK-12
165 N Columbus Ave 10553 — 914-665-5000
Judith Johnson, supt. — Fax 665-6077
www.mtvernoncsd.org/
Davis MS — 800/7-8
350 Gramatan Ave 10552 — 914-665-5120
Murdisia Orr, prin. — Fax 665-5128
Longfellow MS — 400/7-8
624 S 3rd Ave 10550 — 914-665-5151
Sheila Burns-Owens, prin. — Fax 665-5152
Mandela Community HS at Columbus — 200/Alt
250 Gramatan Ave 10550 — 914-665-5160
Vijay Giles, prin. — Fax 665-5159
Mount Vernon HS — 1,500/9-12
100 California Rd 10552 — 914-665-5300
Ronald Gonzalez, prin. — Fax 665-5281
Thornton HS, 121 S 6th Ave 10550 — 800/9-12
Sharon Bradley, prin. — 914-358-2740

Hopfer School of Nursing — Post-Sec.
53 Valentine St 10550 — 914-361-6472
Westchester School of Beauty Culture — Post-Sec.
6 Gramatan Ave 10550 — 914-699-2344

Munnsville, Madison, Pop. 470
Stockbridge Valley Central SD — 500/K-12
PO Box 732 13409 — 315-495-4400
Dr. Patrick Curtin, supt. — Fax 495-4492
www.stockbridgevalley.org
Stockbridge Valley Central S — 500/K-12
PO Box 732 13409 — 315-495-4550
Mary Anne Iritz, prin. — Fax 495-4492

Nanuet, Rockland, Pop. 17,600
Nanuet UFD — 2,300/K-12
101 Church St 10954 — 845-627-9888
Dr. Mark McNeill, supt. — Fax 624-5338
www.nanuetsd.org
Barr MS — 700/5-8
143 Church St 10954 — 845-627-4040
Roger Guccione, prin. — Fax 624-3138
Nanuet HS — 700/9-12
103 Church St 10954 — 845-627-9804
Dr. Vin Carella, prin. — Fax 624-5520

Capri Cosmetology Learning Center — Post-Sec.
251 W Route 59 10954 — 845-623-6339

Naples, Ontario, Pop. 1,024
Naples Central SD — 800/PK-12
136 N Main St 14512 — 585-374-7900
Kimberle Ward, supt. — Fax 374-5859
www.naples.k12.ny.us
Naples HS — 400/7-12
136 N Main St 14512 — 585-374-7905
Matthew Frahm, prin. — Fax 374-5859

Nedrow, Onondaga, Pop. 2,167
Onondaga Central SD — 900/PK-12
4466 S Onondaga Rd 13120 — 315-552-5000
Joseph Rotella, supt. — Fax 492-4650
www.ocs.cnyric.org
Onondaga JSHS — 400/7-12
4479 S Onondaga Rd 13120 — 315-552-5020
Helen Q. White, prin. — Fax 552-5027

Nesconset, Suffolk, Pop. 13,284
Smithtown Central SD
Supt. — See Smithtown
Great Hollow MS — 1,000/6-8
150 Southern Blvd 11767 — 631-382-2800
John Scomillio, prin. — Fax 382-2807

Newark, Wayne, Pop. 8,894
Newark Central SD — 2,200/PK-12
100 E Miller St Ste 5 14513 — 315-332-3217
Henry Hann, supt. — Fax 332-3523
newarkcsd.schoolwires.com/
Newark HS — 700/9-12
625 Peirson Ave 14513 — 315-332-3242
Kevin Whitaker, prin. — Fax 332-3567
Newark MS — 500/6-8
701 Peirson Ave 14513 — 315-332-3295
Mark Miller, prin. — Fax 332-3584

Newark Valley, Tioga, Pop. 980
Newark Valley Central SD — 1,200/K-12
PO Box 547 13811 — 607-642-3221
Ryan Dougherty, supt. — Fax 642-8821
www.nvcs.stier.org/
Newark Valley HS — 500/8-12
68 Wilson Creek Rd 13811 — 607-642-8665
Diane Arbes, prin. — Fax 642-5292

New Berlin, Chenango, Pop. 1,014
Unadilla Valley Central SD — 900/PK-12
PO Box F 13411 — 607-847-7500
Robert Mackey, supt. — Fax 847-6924
www.uvstorm.org
Unadilla Valley HS — 300/9-12
PO Box F 13411 — 607-847-7500
Franklin Johnson, prin. — Fax 847-8045
Unadilla Valley MS — 200/6-8
PO Box F 13411 — 607-847-7500
Franklin Johnson, prin. — Fax 847-8045

Newburgh, Orange, Pop. 28,122
Newburgh Enlarged CSD — 11,100/PK-12
124 Grand St 12550 — 845-563-3500
Ralph Pizzo, supt. — Fax 563-3501
www.newburghschools.org
Newburgh Free Academy — 3,400/9-12
201 Fullerton Ave 12550 — 845-563-5400
Maxine Nodel, prin. — Fax 563-5405
Newburgh Free Academy North — 700/9-12
301 Robinson Ave 12550 — 845-563-8400
Maxine Nodel, prin. — Fax 563-8409
South MS — 600/6-8
33 Monument St 12550 — 845-563-7000
Michael Ragusa, prin. — Fax 563-7019
Other Schools – See New Windsor

Cronin Presentation Academy — 100/5-8
69 Bay View Ter 12550 — 845-567-0708
Sr. Yliana Hernandez, prin. — Fax 567-0709
Mt. St. Mary College — Post-Sec.
330 Powell Ave 12550 — 845-561-0800

New City, Rockland, Pop. 32,957
Clarkstown Central SD — 9,000/K-12
62 Old Middletown Rd 10956 — 845-639-6418
J. Thomas Morton Ed.D., supt. — Fax 639-6488
www.ccsd.edu
Clarkstown North HS — 1,500/9-12
151 Congers Rd 10956 — 845-639-6504
Harry Leonardatos, prin. — Fax 638-6916
Other Schools – See West Nyack

Newcomb, Essex
Newcomb Central SD — 100/PK-12
PO Box 418 12852 — 518-582-3341
Clark Hults, supt. — Fax 582-2163
www.newcombcsd.org
Newcomb Central S — 100/PK-12
PO Box 418 12852 — 518-582-3341
Clark Hults, prin. — Fax 582-2163

Newfane, Niagara, Pop. 3,772
Newfane Central SD
Supt. — See Burt
Newfane HS — 600/9-12
6273 Charlotteville Rd 14108 — 716-778-6551
Thomas Stack, prin. — Fax 778-6590
Newfane MS — 400/5-8
6273 Charlotteville Rd 14108 — 716-778-6452
Thomas Adams, prin. — Fax 778-6460

Newfield, Tompkins
Newfield Central SD — 900/PK-12
247 Main St 14867 — 607-564-9955
Dr. Cheryl Thomas, supt. — Fax 564-0055
www.newfieldschools.org
Newfield HS — 300/9-12
247 Main St 14867 — 607-564-9955
Barry Derfel, prin. — Fax 564-3624
Newfield MS — 200/6-8
247 Main St 14867 — 607-564-9955
Catherine Griggs, prin. — Fax 564-3403

New Hartford, Oneida, Pop. 1,828
New Hartford Central SD — 2,600/K-12
33 Oxford Rd 13413 — 315-624-1218
Robert Nole, supt. — Fax 724-8940
www.newhartfordschools.org
New Hartford SHS — 600/10-12
33 Oxford Rd 13413 — 315-624-1214
Jennifer Spring, prin. — Fax 738-9209
Perry JHS — 700/7-9
9499 Weston Rd 13413 — 315-738-9300
Keith Levatino, prin. — Fax 738-9349

New Hyde Park, Nassau, Pop. 9,473
Herricks UFD — 4,000/K-12
999 Herricks Rd 11040 — 516-305-8900
Dr. John Bierwirth, supt. — Fax 248-3108
www.herricks.org/
Herricks HS — 1,400/9-12
100 Shelter Rock Rd 11040 — 516-305-8700
Dr. Jane Modoono, prin. — Fax 248-3282
Other Schools – See Albertson

Sewanhaka Central HSD
Supt. — See Floral Park
New Hyde Park Memorial HS — 1,700/7-12
500 Leonard Blvd 11040 — 516-488-9500
Dr. Richard Faccio, prin. — Fax 488-9506

New Lebanon, Columbia
New Lebanon Central SD — 500/K-12
14665 State Route 22 12125 — 518-794-9016
Karen McGraw, supt. — Fax 766-5574
www.newlebanoncsd.org
New Lebanon JSHS — 200/7-12
14665 State Route 22 12125 — 518-794-7600
Leslie Whitcomb, prin. — Fax 766-6265

Darrow S — 100/9-12
110 Darrow Rd 12125 — 518-794-6000
Nancy Wolf, hdmstr. — Fax 794-7065

New Paltz, Ulster, Pop. 6,646
New Paltz Central SD — 2,200/K-12
196 Main St 12561 — 845-256-4020
Maria Rice, supt. — Fax 256-4025
www.newpaltz.k12.ny.us
New Paltz Central HS — 700/9-12
196 Main St 12561 — 845-256-4100
Barbara Clinton, prin. — Fax 256-4109

New Paltz MS 500/6-8
196 Main St 12561 845-256-4200
Dr. Richard Wiesenthal, prin. Fax 256-4209

SUNY College at New Paltz Post-Sec.
1 Hawk Dr 12561 845-257-7869

Newport, Herkimer, Pop. 637
West Canada Valley Central SD 700/K-12
PO Box 360 13416 315-845-6800
John Banek, supt. Fax 845-8652
www.westcanada.org/
West Canada Valley JSHS 400/7-12
PO Box 360 13416 315-845-6802
Frank Sutliff, prin. Fax 845-8652

New Rochelle, Westchester, Pop. 75,662
New Rochelle CSD 10,800/PK-12
515 North Ave 10801 914-576-4300
Richard Organisciak, supt. Fax 632-4144
www.nred.org
Leonard MS 1,200/6-8
25 Gerada Ln 10804 914-576-4339
Dr. Velma Whiteside, prin. Fax 576-4784
New Rochelle HS 3,400/9-12
265 Clove Rd 10801 914-576-4502
Don Conetta, prin. Fax 576-4284
Young MS 1,100/6-8
270 Centre Ave 10805 914-576-4360
Anthony Bongo, prin. Fax 632-2738

College of New Rochelle Post-Sec.
29 Castle Pl 10805 914-654-5000
Iona College Post-Sec.
715 North Ave 10801 914-633-2000
Iona Preparatory S 800/9-12
255 Wilmot Rd 10804 914-632-0714
Maureen Kiers, prin. Fax 632-9760
Monroe College Post-Sec.
434 Main St 10801 914-632-5400
Salesian HS 500/9-12
148 E Main St 10801 914-632-0248
John Flaherty, prin. Fax 632-5426
Thornton-Donovan S 200/K-12
100 Overlook Cir 10804 914-632-8836
Douglas Fleming, hdmstr. Fax 576-7936
Ursuline HS 700/9-12
1354 North Ave 10804 914-636-3950
Eileen Davidson, prin. Fax 636-3949

New Square, Rockland, Pop. 6,907

Avir Yaakov Girl's S 1,200/K-12
15 Roosevelt Ave 10977 845-354-0874

New Windsor, Orange, Pop. 8,717
Cornwall Central SD
Supt. — See Cornwall on Hudson
Cornwall Central HS 1,200/9-12
10 Dragon Dr 12553 845-534-8009
Nancy Noonan, prin. Fax 565-2754

Greenburgh-North Castle UFD
Supt. — See Dobbs Ferry
Kaplan Career Academy 12553 Alt
Jason Gerard, prin. 914-693-3030

Newburgh Enlarged CSD
Supt. — See Newburgh
Heritage MS 700/6-8
405 Union Ave 12553 845-563-3750
Raul Rodriguez, prin. Fax 563-3759

New York, New York, Pop. 7,965,821
NYC Department of Education 965,200/PK-12
52 Chambers St 10007 718-935-2000
Dennis Walcott, chncllr.
schools.nyc.gov/
Academy for Environmental Science 200/10-12
410 E 100th St 10029 212-860-5854
Irma Garceau, prin. Fax 860-6008
Academy for Social Action 400/6-12
509 W 129th St 10027 212-234-3102
Rhokeisha Ford, prin. Fax 234-8597
Academy for Software Engineering 9-12
40 Irving Pl 10003 – Seung Yu, prin. 212-253-3299
American Sign Language S 200/9-12
223 E 23rd St 10010 917-326-6668
Watfa Shama, prin. Fax 326-6688
Art & Design HS 1,300/9-12
231 E 56th St 10022 212-752-4340
Eric Strauss, prin. Fax 752-4945
Baldwin S 300/Alt
351 W 18th St 10011 212-627-2812
Christine Olson, prin. Fax 627-9803
Ballet Tech / S for Dance 100/4-8
890 Broadway Fl 3 10003 212-254-1803
Roy O'Neill, prin. Fax 477-5048
Bard HS Early College 600/9-12
525 E Houston St 10002 212-995-8479
Michael Lerner, prin. Fax 777-4702
Baruch College Campus HS 400/9-12
55 E 25th St 10010 212-683-7440
Alicia Katz, prin. Fax 683-7338
Bayard Rustin HS for the Humanities 500/9-12
351 W 18th St 10011 212-675-5350
Lisa Ostrom, prin. Fax 255-5701
Beacon HS 1,200/9-12
227 W 61st St 10023 212-245-2807
Ruth Lacey, prin. Fax 245-2179
Bergtraum HS 2,400/9-12
411 Pearl St 10038 212-964-9610
Lottie Almonte, prin. Fax 732-6622
Bread & Roses Integrated Arts HS 500/9-12
6 Edgecombe Ave 10030 212-926-4152
Rodney Lofton, prin. Fax 926-4317
Business of Sports S 200/9-12
439 W 49th St 10019 212-246-2183
Joshua Solomon, prin. Fax 246-2913

Cascade HS 200/Alt
198 Forsyth St 10002 646-654-1261
Paul Rotondo, prin. Fax 654-1742
Central Park East HS 400/9-12
1573 Madison Ave 10029 212-860-5929
Bennett Lieberman, prin. Fax 860-2938
Chelsea Career & Technical Education HS Vo/Tech
131 Avenue of the Americas 10013 212-925-1080
Brian Rosenblum, prin. Fax 941-7934
Choir Academy of Harlem 300/6-12
2005 Madison Ave 10035 212-289-6227
Dr. Ellen Harris, prin. Fax 289-4195
City As School HS 600/Alt
16 Clarkson St 10014 212-337-6800
Alan Cheng, prin. Fax 337-6875
City College Academy of the Arts 500/6-12
4600 Broadway 10040 212-567-3164
Bernadette Drysdale, prin. Fax 567-3958
Coalition S for Social Change 400/Alt
2351 1st Ave 10035 212-831-5153
John Sullivan, prin. Fax 831-5951
Collaborative Academy of Science 300/6-8
220 Henry St 10002 212-227-0762
Judith DeLosSantos, prin. Fax 577-9785
College Academy 600/9-12
549 Audubon Ave 10040 212-927-1841
Peter Sloman, prin. Fax 927-2388
Columbia Secondary S 400/6-12
425 W 123rd St 10027 212-666-1278
Miriam Nightengale, prin. Fax 666-3805
Community Action S - MS 258 200/6-8
154 W 93rd St 10025 212-678-5888
John Curry, prin. Fax 961-1613
Community Health Academy of the Heights 500/6-12
512 W 182nd St 10033 212-568-3401
Mark House, prin. Fax 928-1716
Douglas Academy 1,500/6-12
2581 7th Ave 10039 212-491-4107
Joseph Gates, prin. Fax 491-4414
Douglass Academy II 400/6-12
215 W 114th St 10026 212-865-9260
Osei Owusu-Afriyie, prin. Fax 865-9281
East Side Community HS 600/6-12
420 E 12th St 10009 212-460-8467
Mark Federman, prin. Fax 260-9657
East Side MS 400/6-8
331 E 91st St 10128 212-360-0114
David Getz, prin. Fax 360-0121
Esperanza Preparatory Academy 200/6-8
240 E 109th St 10029 212-722-6507
Alex Estrella, prin. Fax 722-6717
Essex Street Academy 300/9-12
350 Grand St 10002 347-475-4773
Erin Carstensen, prin. Fax 674-2058
Facing History S 400/9-12
525 W 50th St 10019 718-757-2680
Dana Panagot, prin. Fax 757-2156
Food & Finance HS 400/9-12
525 W 50th St 10019 212-586-2943
Roger Turgeon, prin. Fax 586-4205
Forsyth Satellite Academy 9-12
198 Forsyth St 10002 212-677-8900
Ingrid Haynes, prin. Fax 260-3063
Global Learning Collaborative 200/9-12
145 W 84th St 10024 212-877-1103
Karla Chiluiza, prin. Fax 877-1138
Global Neighborhood Secondary S 200/6-8
240 E 109th St 10029 212-289-4204
Luis Genao, prin. Fax 289-4301
Global Technology Preparatory S 100/6-8
160 E 120th St 10035 212-722-1395
Chrystina Russell, prin. Fax 722-5864
Gramercy Arts HS 500/9-12
40 Irving Pl 10003 212-253-7076
Denise Di'Carlo, prin. Fax 253-8095
Green HS of Teaching 600/9-12
26 Broadway 10004 646-826-8174
Nigel Pugh, prin. Fax 826-8175
Harbor Heights MS 200/6-8
306 Fort Washington Ave 10033 212-568-6052
Monica Klehr, prin. Fax 568-7959
Harlem Renaissance HS 200/9-12
22 E 128th St 10035 212-996-3795
Nadv Ziemer, prin. Fax 996-4354
Harvest Collegiate HS 9-12
34 W 14th St 10011 212-242-3384
Catherine Burch, prin.
Health Professions & Human Services HS 1,700/9-12
345 E 15th St 10003 212-780-9175
Robert Gentile, prin. Fax 979-7261
Henry Street S for International Studies 400/6-12
220 Henry St 10002 212-406-9411
Christine Loughlin, prin. Fax 406-9417
Heritage S 300/9-12
1680 Lexington Ave 10029 212-828-2858
Dyanand Sugrim, prin. Fax 828-2861
Hudson HS of Learning Technologies 100/9-12
351 W 18th St 10011 212-488-3330
Nancy Amling, prin. Fax 488-3335
Humanities Preparatory S 200/9-12
351 W 18th St 10011 212-929-4433
Jeannie Ferrari, prin. Fax 929-4445
Independence HS 400/Alt
850 10th Ave 10019 212-262-8067
Ron Smolkin, prin. Fax 262-8110
Innovation Diploma Plus 200/Alt
145 W 84th St 10024 212-724-2039
Casey Jones, prin. Fax 724-2765
Institute for Collaborative Education 500/6-12
345 E 15th St 10003 212-475-7972
Peter Karp, prin. Fax 475-0459
International HS at Union Square 100/9-12
40 Irving Pl 10003 212-533-2560
Gaylea Silvers, prin. Fax 228-2946
Irving HS 1,200/9-12
40 Irving Pl 10003 212-674-5000
Sarah Hernandez, prin. Fax 673-9569

KAPPA IV S 200/6-8
6 Edgecombe Ave 10030 212-690-4963
Juan Vives, prin. Fax 690-8056
Kennedy-Onassis HS 700/9-12
120 W 46th St 10036 212-391-0041
Edward Demeo, prin. Fax 391-1293
La Guardia HS 2,500/9-12
100 Amsterdam Ave 10023 212-496-0700
Kim Bruno, prin. Fax 724-5748
Landmark HS 400/9-12
351 W 18th St 10011 212-647-7410
Caron Pinkus, prin. Fax 647-7416
Lazarus HS 200/Alt
100 Hester St 10002 212-925-5017
Melody Kellogg, prin. Fax 925-5920
Leadership & Public Service HS 600/9-12
90 Trinity Pl 10006 212-346-0007
Philip Santos, prin. Fax 346-0612
Legacy S for Integrated Studies 400/9-12
34 W 14th St 10011 212-645-1980
Arleen Liquori, prin. Fax 645-2596
Liberty HS 400/Alt
250 W 18th St 10011 212-691-0934
Melodee Khristan, prin. Fax 727-1369
Life Science Secondary S 700/6-12
320 E 96th St 10128 212-348-1694
Genevieve Stanislaus, prin. Fax 348-4293
Lower East Side Prep S 600/Alt
145 Stanton St 10002 212-505-6366
Martha Polin, prin. Fax 260-0813
Lower Manhattan Arts Academy 300/9-12
350 Grand St 10002 212-505-0143
John Wenk, prin. Fax 674-8021
Lower Manhattan Community MS 200/6-8
26 Broadway 10004 212-826-8100
Kelly McGuire, prin. Fax 826-8101
Luperon HS of Science & Math 500/9-12
501 W 165th St 10032 212-928-1202
Juan Villar, prin. Fax 928-1309
Manhattan Academy for Arts & Language 100/9-12
111 E 33rd St 10016 212-576-0502
Siv Boletsis, prin. Fax 576-0518
Manhattan Bridges HS 500/9-12
525 W 50th St 10019 212-757-5274
Mirza Sanchez-Medina, prin. Fax 757-5411
Manhattan Business Academy 200/9-12
351 W 18th St 10011 212-647-1983
Karen Polsonetti, prin. Fax 647-1989
Manhattan Center for Science/Math 1,700/9-12
280 Pleasant Ave 10029 212-876-4639
Jose Jimenez, prin. Fax 996-5946
Manhattan/Hunter Science HS 400/9-12
122 Amsterdam Ave 10023 212-501-1235
Susan Kreisman, prin. Fax 501-1171
Manhattan International HS 300/9-12
317 E 67th St, 212-517-6728
Gladys Rodriguez, prin. Fax 517-7147
Manhattan Theatre Lab HS 400/9-12
122 Amsterdam Ave 10023 212-362-2075
Lisa Ostrom, prin. Fax 362-9031
Manhattan Village Academy 400/9-12
43 W 22nd St 10010 212-242-8752
Hector Geager, prin. Fax 242-7630
Marshall Academy 600/6-12
200 W 135th St 10030 212-283-8055
Sean Davenport, prin. Fax 283-8109
Marte Valle HS 400/9-12
145 Stanton St 10002 212-473-8152
Mimi Fortunato, prin. Fax 475-7588
McCourt HS 100/9-12
145 W 84th St 10024 917-362-2015
Danielle Salzberg, prin. Fax 362-5926
Milk HS 100/9-12
2 Astor Pl 10003 212-477-1555
Daphne Perrini, prin. Fax 674-8650
Millenium HS 600/9-12
75 Broad St 10004 212-825-9008
Colin McEvoy, prin. Fax 825-9095
Mott Hall HS 400/9-12
6 Edgecombe Ave 10030 212-690-5501
Altagracia Villalona, prin. Fax 690-5047
Mott Hall II 300/6-8
234 W 109th St 10025 212-678-2960
Ana Tornatore, prin. Fax 222-0560
Mott Hall S 400/6-8
71 Convent Ave 10027 212-281-5028
Cynthia Arndt, prin. Fax 491-3451
Murray Hill Academy 100/9-12
111 E 33rd St 10016 212-696-0195
Anita Felix, prin. Fax 696-2498
New Design HS 400/9-12
350 Grand St 10002 212-475-4148
Scott Conti, prin. Fax 674-2128
New Design MS 6-8
625 W 133rd St 10027 212-281-6339
Daniel Black, prin. Fax 281-6674
New Explorations Science Tech/Math S 1,600/K-12
111 Columbia St 10002 212-677-5190
Dr. Olga Livanis, prin. Fax 260-8124
Newton MS for Science Math Tech 400/6-8
260 Pleasant Ave 10029 212-860-6006
Lisa Nelson, prin. Fax 987-4197
HS for Arts Imagination & Inquiry 500/9-12
122 Amsterdam Ave 10023 212-799-4064
Stephen Noonan, prin. Fax 799-4171
HS for Dual Language & Asian Studies 300/9-12
350 Grand St 10002 212-475-4097
Li Yan, prin. Fax 674-1392
HS for Environmental Studies 1,400/9-12
444 W 56th St 10019 212-262-8113
Shirley Matthews, prin. Fax 262-0702
HS for Excellence and Innovation 100/9-12
650 Academy St 10034 212-569-1022
Tyona Washington, prin. Fax 569-1190
HS for Health Careers & Science 700/9-12
549 Audubon Ave 10040 212-927-1841
Harris Marmor, prin. Fax 927-2179

HS for Language and Diplomacy 200/9-12
40 Irving Pl 10003 212-253-2480
Santiago Mayol, prin. Fax 253-2539
HS for Law Advocacy & Community Justice 500/9-12
122 Amsterdam Ave 10023 212-501-1201
Doreen Conwell, prin. Fax 501-1195
HS for Law & Public Service 600/9-12
549 Audubon Ave 10040 212-927-2380
Nicholas Politis, prin. Fax 781-9516
HS for Math Science Engineering 400/9-12
240 Convent Ave 10031 212-281-6490
Crystal Bonds, prin. Fax 281-6918
HS for Media & Communications 600/9-12
549 Audubon Ave 10040 212-927-1841
Ronni Michelen, prin. Fax 927-2326
HS of Arts & Technology 600/9-12
122 Amsterdam Ave 10023 212-501-1198
Anne Geiger, prin. Fax 441-3693
HS of Economic & Finance 800/9-12
100 Trinity Pl 10006 212-346-0708
Michael Stanzione, prin. Fax 346-0712
HS of Fashion Industries 1,600/9-12
225 W 24th St 10011 212-255-1235
Daryl Blank, prin. Fax 255-4756
HS of Graphic Communication Arts 1,700/9-12
439 W 49th St 10019 212-245-5925
Brendon Lyons, prin. Fax 265-1552
HS of Hospitality Management 400/9-12
525 W 50th St 10019 212-586-1819
Matthew Corallo, prin. Fax 586-2713
IS 195 400/6-8
625 W 133rd St 10027 212-690-5848
Rashaunda Shaw, prin. Fax 690-5999
IS 218 400/6-8
4600 Broadway 10040 212-567-2322
June Barnett, prin. Fax 569-7421
IS 286 300/6-8
509 W 129th St 10027 212-690-5972
Qadir Dixon, prin. Fax 694-4124
IS 289 300/6-8
201 Warren St 10282 212-571-9268
Ellen Foote, prin. Fax 587-6610
IS 528 300/6-8
180 Wadsworth Ave 10033 212-740-4900
Kristy Dela Cruz, prin. Fax 781-7302
JHS 13 300/6-8
1573 Madison Ave 10029 212-860-8935
Jacob Michelman, prin. Fax 860-5933
JHS 52 700/6-8
650 Academy St 10034 212-567-9162
Sal Fernandez, prin. Fax 942-4952
JHS 54 800/6-8
103 W 107th St 10025 212-678-2861
Dr. Elana Elster, prin. Fax 316-0883
JHS 104 1,000/6-8
330 E 21st St 10010 212-674-4545
Rosemarie Gaetani, prin. Fax 477-2205
JHS 143 600/6-8
511 W 182nd St 10033 212-927-7739
Lakisha Luke, prin. Fax 781-5539
JHS 167 1,200/6-8
220 E 76th St 10021 212-535-8610
Jennifer Rehn, prin. Fax 472-9385
MS 45 300/6-8
2351 1st Ave 10035 212-860-5838
Alexa Sorden, prin. Fax 860-5837
MS 131 700/6-8
100 Hester St 10002 212-219-1204
Phyllis Tam, prin. Fax 925-6386
MS 224 300/6-8
410 E 100th St 10029 212-860-6047
Liliana Sarro, prin. Fax 410-0678
MS 243 200/5-8
100 W 84th St 10024 212-799-1477
Elaine Schwartz, prin. Fax 579-9728
MS 245 400/6-8
100 W 77th St 10024 917-441-0873
Henry Zymeck, prin. Fax 678-5908
MS 247 200/6-8
32 W 92nd St 10025 212-799-2653
Claudia Aguirre, prin. Fax 579-2407
MS 250 200/6-8
735 W End Ave 10025 212-866-6313
Jeanne Rotunda, dir. Fax 678-5295
MS 255 400/6-8
319 E 19th St 10003 212-614-8785
Rhonda Perry, prin. Fax 614-0095
MS 256 200/6-8
154 W 93rd St 10025 212-222-2857
Jeffrey Perl, prin. Fax 531-0586
MS 260 300/6-8
425 W 33rd St 10001 212-695-9114
Jonathan Levin, prin. Fax 695-9611
MS 319 600/6-8
21 Jumel Pl 10032 212-923-3827
Ysidro Abreu, prin. Fax 923-3676
MS 322 500/6-8
4600 Broadway 10040 212-304-0853
Fax 567-3016
MS 324 400/6-8
21 Jumel Pl 10032 212-923-4057
Janet Heller, prin. Fax 923-4626
MS 326 400/6-8
401 W 164th St 10032 917-521-1875
Sharon Weissbrot, prin. Fax 521-1750
MS 328 400/6-8
401 W 164th St 10032 917-521-2508
Olga Quiles, prin. Fax 521-7797
NYC iSchool 300/9-12
131 Avenue of the Americas 10013 917-237-7300
Isora Bailey, prin. Fax 219-0743
NYC Lab HS for Collaborative Studies 500/9-12
333 W 17th St 10011 212-691-6119
Brooke Jackson, prin. Fax 691-2147
NYC Lab MS for Collaborative Studies 600/6-8
333 W 17th St 10011 212-691-6119
Megan Adams, prin. Fax 691-6219

NYC Museum S 400/9-12
333 W 17th St 10011 212-675-6206
Darlene Miller, dir. Fax 675-6524
Pace HS 400/9-12
100 Hester St 10002 212-334-4663
Yvette Sy, prin. Fax 334-4919
Park East HS 400/9-12
230 E 105th St 10029 212-831-1517
Xiomara Rodriguez, prin. Fax 348-6097
Professional Performing Arts HS 500/6-12
328 W 48th St 10036 212-247-8652
Keith Ryan, prin. Fax 247-7514
Quest to Learn S 100/6-9
351 W 18th St 10011 212-488-3645
Elisa Aragon, prin.
Randolph HS 1,400/9-12
443 W 135th St 10031 212-926-0113
David Fanning, prin. Fax 281-2726
Renaissance School of the Arts 200/6-8
319 E 117th St 10035 212-369-1564
Tammy Pate-Spears, prin. Fax 369-1693
Repertory Company HS for Theatre Arts 200/9-12
123 W 43rd St 10036 212-382-1875
Michael Mehmet, prin. Fax 382-2306
Reynolds West Side HS 500/Alt
140 W 102nd St 10025 212-678-7300
Jean McTavish, prin. Fax 678-7380
Roosevelt HS 500/9-12
411 E 76th St 10021 212-772-1220
Demitri Saliani, prin. Fax 772-1440
Satellite Academy 300/Alt
120 W 30th St 10001 646-674-2800
Steve Zbaida, prin.
School for Cooperative Technical Ed. Alt
321 E 96th St 10128 212-369-8800
John Windlund, prin. Fax 876-9290
School for Global Leaders 200/6-8
145 Stanton St 10002 212-260-5375
Carry Chan, prin. Fax 260-7386
School of the Future 700/6-12
127 E 22nd St 10010 212-475-8086
Stacy Goldstein, admin. Fax 475-9273
Stuyvesant HS 3,300/9-12
345 Chambers St 10282 212-312-4800
Jie Zhang, prin. Fax 587-3874
Talent Unlimited HS 500/9-12
317 E 67th St, 212-737-1530
Linda Hamil, prin. Fax 737-2863
Technology Arts & Sciences Studio 200/6-8
185 1st Ave 10003 212-982-1836
George Morgan, prin. Fax 982-0528
Thomas HS 1,700/9-12
111 E 33rd St 10016 212-576-0500
Philip Martin, prin. Fax 545-9648
Tompkins Square MS 400/6-8
600 E 6th St 10009 212-995-1430
Sonhando Estwick, prin. Fax 979-1341
Union Square Academy for Health Science 9-12
40 Irving Pl 10003 212-253-3110
Bernardo Ascona, prin.
Unity Center for Urban Technologies 200/9-12
111 E 33rd St 10016 212-576-0530
Fausto DeLaRosa, prin. Fax 576-0562
University Neighborhood HS 500/9-12
200 Monroe St 10002 212-962-4341
Elizabeth Collins, prin. Fax 267-5611
University Nieghborhood MS 100/6-8
220 Henry St 10002 212-267-5701
Laura Peynado, prin. Fax 349-8224
Urban Academy Laboratory HS 200/9-12
317 E 67th St, 212-570-5284
Herb Mack, prin. Fax 570-5366
Urban Assembly Academy Government & Law300/9-12
350 Grand St 10002 212-505-0745
David Glasner, prin. Fax 674-8021
Urban Assembly for Media Studies HS 300/9-12
122 Amsterdam Ave 10023 212-501-1110
Cordelia Veve, prin. Fax 580-0156
Urban Assembly Gateway S for Technology 9-12
439 W 49th St 10019 212-246-1041
April McCoy, prin. Fax 246-2654
Urban Assembly Inst for New Technologies 100/6-8
509 W 129th St 10027 212-690-5977
Jeffrey Chetirko, prin. Fax 690-5980
Urban Assembly New York Harbor S Vo/Tech
10 South St Slip 7 10004 347-675-9403
Edward Biedermann, prin. Fax 458-0801
Urban Assembly S Design & Construction 400/9-12
525 W 50th St 10019 212-586-0981
Mathew Willoughby, prin. Fax 586-1731
Urban Assembly S for Green Careers 200/9-12
145 W 84th St 10024 212-787-1189
A. Rathmann-Noonan, prin. Fax 787-1455
Urban Assembly S for Performing Arts 300/9-12
509 W 129th St 10027 212-234-4631
Fia Davis, prin. Fax 234-4975
Urban Assembly S of Business 400/9-12
26 Broadway 10004 212-668-0169
Patricia Minaya, prin. Fax 668-0635
Vanguard HS 400/9-12
317 E 67th St, 212-517-5175
William Klann, prin. Fax 517-5334
Wadleigh Arts HS 500/6-12
215 W 114th St 10026 212-749-5800
Tyee Chin, prin. Fax 749-6463
Washington Hts. Expeditionary Learning S 500/6-12
511 W 182nd St 10033 212-781-0524
Brett Kimmel, prin. Fax 781-0742
West Prep Academy 100/6-8
150 W 105th St 10025 212-362-1674
Roberto Padilla, prin. Fax 362-2794
Young Womens Leadership HS 500/6-12
105 E 106th St 10029 212-289-7593
Althea Bradshaw-Tyson, prin. Fax 289-7728
Manhattan Comprehensive Night & Day HS Adult
240 2nd Ave 10003 212-353-2010
Michael Toice, prin. Fax 353-1673

Other Schools – See Astoria, Bayside, Bellerose, Bronx, Brooklyn, Corona, East Elmhurst, Elmhurst, Far Rockaway, Floral Park, Flushing, Forest Hills, Fresh Meadows, Glendale, Hollis, Jackson Heights, Jamaica, Laurelton, Little Neck, Long Island City, Maspeth, Oakland Gardens, Ozone Park, Queens Village, Rego Park, Richmond Hill, Ridgewood, Rockaway Park, Saint Albans, South Ozone Park, Springfield Gardens, Staten Island, Whitestone, Woodside

---

ABI School of Barbering and Cosmetology Post-Sec.
252 W 29th St 10001 212-290-2289
Achieve Test Prep Post-Sec.
5 Penn Plz Ste 1975 10001 917-267-0711
AMDA College & Conservatory Post-Sec.
211 W 61st St 10023 212-787-5300
American Academy McAllister Institute Post-Sec.
619 W 54th St Fl 2 10019 212-757-1190
American Academy of Dramatic Arts Post-Sec.
120 Madison Ave 10016 800-463-8990
American University in Cairo Post-Sec.
420 5th Ave Fl 3 10018 212-730-8800
Anthem Institute Post-Sec.
498 Fashion Ave Fl 17 10018 212-659-2116
Apex Technical School Post-Sec.
635 Avenue of the Americas 10011 212-645-3300
Bank Street College of Education Post-Sec.
610 W 112th St 10025 212-875-4400
Barnard College Post-Sec.
3009 Broadway 10027 212-854-5262
Bellevue Hospital Center Post-Sec.
462 1st Ave 10016 212-561-4132
Berkeley College Post-Sec.
3 E 43rd St 10017 212-986-4343
Birch Wathen Lenox S 600/K-12
210 E 77th St, 212-861-0404
Frank Carnabuci, hdmstr. Fax 879-3388
Boricua College Post-Sec.
3755 Broadway 10032 212-694-1000
Brearley S 700/K-12
610 E 83rd St 10028 212-744-8582
Jane Fried, hdmstr. Fax 472-8020
Browning S 400/K-12
52 E 62nd St, 212-838-6280
Dr. Stephen Clement, hdmstr. Fax 355-5602
Calhoun S 500/2-12
433 W End Ave 10024 212-497-6500
Steven Nelson, admin. Fax 497-6530
Cathedral HS 600/9-12
350 E 56th St 10022 212-688-1545
Maria Spagnuolo, prin. Fax 754-2024
Chapin S 700/K-12
100 E End Ave 10028 212-744-2335
Patricia Hayot Ph.D., hdmstr. Fax 535-8138
Christie's Education Post-Sec.
11 W 42nd St Fl 8 10036 212-355-1501
College of New Rochelle Post-Sec.
125 Barclay St 10007 212-815-1710
College of New Rochelle Post-Sec.
144 W 125th St 10027 212-662-7500
Collegiate S 600/K-12
260 W 78th St 10024 212-812-8500
Lee Levison, hdmstr. Fax 812-8524
Columbia Grammar & Preparatory S 1,200/PK-12
5 W 93rd St 10025 212-749-6200
Richard Soghoian, hdmstr. Fax 865-4278
Columbia University Post-Sec.
2960 Broadway 10027 212-854-1754
Connelly Center for Education 100/5-8
220 E 4th St 10009 212-982-2287
Shalonda Neeley, prin. Fax 982-0547
Convent of the Sacred Heart S 700/PK-12
1 E 91st St 10128 212-722-4745
Dr. Joseph Ciancaglini, hdmstr. Fax 996-1784
Cooper Union Post-Sec.
30 Cooper Sq 10003 212-353-4100
County Univ. Sch. of Dental & Oral Surg. Post-Sec.
630 W 168th St 10032
Cristo Rey HS 300/9-12
112 E 106th St 10029 212-996-7000
William Ford, prin. Fax 427-7444
CUNY Bernard M. Baruch College Post-Sec.
1 Bernard Baruch Way 10010 646-312-1000
CUNY Borough/Manhattan Comm. College Post-Sec.
199 Chambers St 10007 212-220-8000
CUNY City College Post-Sec.
160 Convent Ave 10031 212-650-7000
CUNY Graduate Center Post-Sec.
365 5th Ave 10016 212-817-7000
CUNY Hunter College Post-Sec.
695 Park Ave, 212-772-4000
CUNY John Jay College Criminal Justice Post-Sec.
899 10th Ave 10019 212-237-8000
Dalton S 1,300/K-12
108 E 89th St 10128 212-423-5200
Ellen Stein, hdmstr. Fax 423-5259
De La Salle Academy 200/6-8
202 W 97th St 10025 212-316-5840
Br. Brian Carty, pres. Fax 316-5998
DeVry College Post-Sec.
180 Madison Ave Ste 900 10016 212-312-4300
Dominican Academy 200/9-12
44 E 68th St, 212-744-0195
Sr. Barbara Kane, prin. Fax 744-0375
Dwight S 800/PK-12
291 Central Park W 10024 212-724-6360
Dianne Drew, head sch Fax 874-4232
Fashion Institute of Technology Post-Sec.
227 W 27th St 10001 212-217-7999
Fordham University Post-Sec.
113 W 60th St 10023 212-636-6000
Friends Seminary 800/K-12
222 E 16th St 10003 212-979-5030
Robert Lauder, prin. Fax 979-5034
Gemological Institute of America Post-Sec.
270 Madison Ave Fl 2 10016 800-366-8519

General Theological Seminary Post-Sec.
440 W 21st St 10011 212-243-5150
Global Business Institute Post-Sec.
145 E 125th St 10035 212-663-1500
Globe Institute of Technology Post-Sec.
500 7th Ave 10018 212-349-4330
Grace Church HS 9-12
46 Cooper Sq 10034 212-475-5610
George Davison, head sch
Hebrew Union College Post-Sec.
1 W 4th St 10012 212-674-5300
Helene Fuld College of Nursing Post-Sec.
24 E 120th St Ste 3 10035 212-616-7200
Heschel HS 300/9-12
20 W End Ave 10023 212-246-7717
Roanna Shorofsky, hdmstr. Fax 246-7686
Heschel MS 100/6-8
30 W End Ave 10023 212-595-7087
Roanna Shorofsky, hdmstr. Fax 489-1990
Hewitt S 500/K-12
45 E 75th St 10021 212-288-1919
Joan Lonergan, hdmstr. Fax 472-7531
Hunter College Campus S 300/K-12
71 E 94th St 10128 212-860-1267
Randy Collins, dir. Fax 289-2209
Institute of Audio Research Post-Sec.
64 University Pl 10003 212-677-7590
Jewish Theological Seminary of America Post-Sec.
3080 Broadway 10027 212-678-8000
Juilliard School Post-Sec.
60 Lincoln Center Plz 10023 212-799-5000
Keller Graduate School Post-Sec.
120 W 45th St Fl 6 10036 212-556-0002
LaSalle Academy 400/9-12
215 E 6th St 10003 212-475-8940
William Macatee Ed.D., prin. Fax 529-3598
La Scuola D'Italia Gueglealmo Marconi S 200/PK-12
12 E 96th St 10128 212-369-3290
Anna Fiore, prin. Fax 369-1164
Learning Institute for Beauty Sciences Post-Sec.
22 W 34th St 10001 212-695-4555
Leman Manhattan Preparatory S 500/PK-12
41 Broad St 10004 212-232-0266
Drew Alexander, hdmstr. Fax 232-0284
Lia Schorr Inst of Cosmetic Skin Care Post-Sec.
686 Lexington Ave 10022 212-486-9541
LIM College Post-Sec.
12 E 53rd St 10022 212-752-1530
Lookstein Upper S 500/9-12
60 E 78th St, 212-774-8070
Rabbi Jay Goldmintz Ed.D., hdmstr. Fax 774-8099
Louis Gerstner Graduate Sch Biomed Sci Post-Sec.
1275 York Ave Ste 441, 646-888-6639
Loyola HS 200/9-12
980 Park Ave 10028 212-288-3522
James Lyness, hdmstr. Fax 861-1021
LREI Little Red School House & Irwin HS 400/PK-12
272 6th Ave 10014 212-477-5316
Philip Kassen, dir Fax 677 9150
Lycee Francais De New York 1,300/PK-12
505 E 75th St 10021 212-369-1400
Sean Lynch, hdmstr Fax 439-4200
Lyceum Kennedy S 200/PK-11
225 E 43rd St 10017 212-681-1877
Dr. Laurent Bonardi, head sch Fax 681-1922
Make-Up Designory Post-Sec.
375 W Broadway 10012 212-925-9250
Mandl School College of Allied Health Post-Sec.
254 W 54th St Fl 9 10019 212-247-3434
Manhattan HS for Girls 200/9-12
154 E 70th St 10021 212-737-6800
Tsivia Yanofsky, prin. Fax 737-0766
Manhattan Institute Post-Sec.
255 5th Ave 10016 347-220-8181
Manhattan School of Music Post-Sec.
120 Claremont Ave 10027 212-749-2802
Marymount Manhattan College Post-Sec.
221 E 71st St 10021 212-517-0400
Marymount S 600/PK-12
1026 5th Ave 10028 212-744-4486
Concepcion Alvar, hdmstr. Fax 744-0163
Mercy College - Manhattan Campus Post-Sec.
66 W 35th St 10001 800-637-2969
Mesivta Tifereth Jerusalem of America Post-Sec.
1417 E Broadway 10002 212-964-2830
Mesivta Tifereth Jerusalem S 200/K-12
145 E Broadway 10002 212-964-2830
Metropolitan College of New York Post-Sec.
431 Canal St 10013 212-343-1234
Micropower Career Institute Post-Sec.
137 W 25th St 10001 212-279-2550
Mildred Elley School Post-Sec.
25 Broadway Fl 16 10004 212-380-9004
Mother Cabrini HS 300/9-12
701 Fort Washington Ave 10040 212-923-3540
Kerry Schmid, prin. Fax 781-2051
Mount Sinai Icahn School of Medicine Post-Sec.
1 Gustave L Levy Pl 10029 212-241-6500
New York Academy of Art Post-Sec.
111 Franklin St 10013 212-966-0300
New York Career Institute Post-Sec.
11 Park Pl Fl 4 10007 212-962-0002
New York College of Podiatric Medicine Post-Sec.
53 E 124th St 10035 212-410-8000
New York Eye & Ear Infirmary Post-Sec.
310 E 14th St 10003 212-979-4375
New York Institute of Photography Post-Sec.
211 E 43rd St Ste 2402 10017 212-867-8260
New York Inst. of English and Business Post-Sec.
248 W 35th St 10001 212-725-9400
New York International Beauty School Post-Sec.
500 8th Ave Rm 803 10018 212-868-7171
New York Law School Post-Sec.
185 W Broadway 10013 212-431-2100
New York Presbyterian Hospital Post-Sec.
525 E 68th St, 212-746-4000
New York School of Interior Design Post-Sec.
170 E 70th St 10021 212-472-1500

New York Theological Seminary Post-Sec.
475 Riverside Dr Ste 500 10115 212-870-1211
New York University Post-Sec.
70 Washington Sq S 10012 212-998-1212
Nightingale-Bamford S 600/K-12
20 E 92nd St 10128 212-289-5020
Paul Burke, head sch Fax 876-1045
Northeastern Academy 100/9-12
532 W 215th St 10034 212-569-4800
James Bennett, prin. Fax 569-6145
Notre Dame HS 300/9-12
327 W 13th St 10014 212-620-5575
Jaclyn Brilliant, prin. Fax 620-0432
Pace University Post-Sec.
1 Pace Plz 10038 212-346-1200
Pacific College of Oriental Medicine Post-Sec.
915 Broadway Fl 2 10010 212-982-3456
Phillips Beth Israel School of Nursing Post-Sec.
776 Ave of Americas Fl 4 10001 212-614-6110
Professional Business College Post-Sec.
408 Broadway Fl 2 10013 212-226-7300
Professional Children's S 200/6-12
132 W 60th St 10023 212-582-3116
Dr. James Dawson, head sch Fax 956-3295
Rabbi Haskel Lookstein MS 200/5-8
114 E 85th St 10028 212-774-8040
Morah Smadar Seinfed, hdmstr. Fax 774-8069
Rabbi Isaac Elchanan Theological Sem. Post-Sec.
2540 Amsterdam Ave 10033 212-568-7400
Regis HS 500/9-12
55 E 84th St 10028 212-288-1100
Dr. Gary Tocchet, prin. Fax 794-1221
Relay Graduate School of Education Post-Sec.
40 W 20th St Fl 7 10011 212-228-1888
Richard Gilder Graduate School Post-Sec.
Central Park W at 79th St 10024 212-769-5055
Rockefeller University Post-Sec.
1230 York Ave, 212-327-8000
SAE Institute of Technology Post-Sec.
1293 Broadway Fl 9 10001 212-944-9121
St. George Academy HS 100/9-12
215 E 6th St 10003 212-473-3323
Rev. Peter Shyshka, prin. Fax 534-0819
St. Jean Baptiste HS 300/9-12
173 E 75th St 10021 212-288-1645
Sr. Maria Cassano, prin. Fax 288-6540
St. Thomas Choir S 50/3-8
202 W 58th St 10019 212-247-3311
Rev. Charles Wallace, hdmstr. Fax 247-3393
St. Vincent Ferrer HS 500/9-12
151 E 65th St, 212-535-4680
Sr. Gail Morgan, prin. Fax 988-3455
St. Vincent's Hospital & Medical Center Post-Sec.
153 W 11th St 10011 212-604-7500
Sanford Brown Institute Post-Sec.
120 E 16th St Fl 4 10003 646-313-4510
School for the Deaf Post-Sec.
225 E 23rd St 10010
School of Visual Arts Post-Sec.
209 E 23rd St 10010 212-592-2000
Sheffield School of Interior Design Post-Sec.
211 E 43rd St 10017 212-661-7270
Sotheby's Institute of Art Post-Sec.
570 Lexington Ave Fl 6 10022 212-517-3929
Spanish-American Institute Post-Sec.
215 W 43rd St 10036 212-840-7111
Spence S 700/K-12
22 E 91st St 10128 212-289-5940
Bodie Brizendine, hdmstr. Fax 860-2652
Star Career Academy Post-Sec.
154 W 14th St 10011 212-675-6655
Steiner Upper S 100/7-12
15 E 78th St, 212-879-1101
Joshua Eisen, admin. Fax 794-1554
Stevenson S 100/8-12
24 W 74th St 10023 212-787-6400
Douglas Herron M.A., head sch Fax 873-1872
Studio Jewelers Post-Sec.
32 E 31st St 10016 212-686-1944
SUNY College of Optometry Post-Sec.
33 W 42nd St 10036 212-938-4000
Swedish Institute College of Health Sci Post-Sec.
226 W 26th St Fl 5 10001 212-924-5900
Teachers College of Columbia University Post-Sec.
525 W 120th St 10027 212-678-3000
Technical Career Institute Post-Sec.
320 W 31st St 10001 212-594-4000
The Art Institute of New York City Post-Sec.
11 Beach St 10013 212-226-5500
The Institute of Culinary Education Post-Sec.
50 W 23rd St 10010 212-847-0711
The International Culinary Center Post-Sec.
462 Broadway 10013 212-219-8890
The King's College Post-Sec.
350 5th Ave Ste 1500 10118 212-659-7200
The New School Post-Sec.
66 W 12th St 10011 212-229-5600
Touro College Post-Sec.
27 W 23rd St 10010 212-463-0400
Trevor Day S 400/6-12
1 W 88th St 10024 212-426-3384
Pamela Clarke, hdmstr. Fax 873-8520
Trinity S 1,000/K-12
139 W 91st St 10024 212-873-1650
John Allman, hdmstr. Fax 799-3417
Tri-State College of Acupuncture Post-Sec.
80 8th Ave Ste 400 10011 212-242-2255
Ultrasound Diagnostic School Post-Sec.
120 E 16th St Fl 2 10003 212-645-9116
U.N. International S 1,500/K-12
2450 FDR Dr 10010 212-684-7400
David Shapiro, dir. Fax 779-2259
Union Theological Seminary Post-Sec.
3041 Broadway 10027 212-662-7100
Weill Cornell Medical College Post-Sec.
1300 York Ave, 212-746-5454
Wood Tobe-Coburn School Post-Sec.
8 E 40th St 10016 212-686-9040

Xavier HS 1,000/9-12
30 W 16th St 10011 212-924-7900
Michael LiVigni, hdmstr. Fax 924-0303
Yeshiva Rabbi S.R. Hirsch 300/PK-12
91 Bennett Ave 10033 212-568-6200
Yeshiva University Post-Sec.
500 W 185th St 10033 212-960-5400
Yeshiva University HS 600/9-12
500 W 185th St 10033 212-960-5400
Richard Joel, pres.
Yeshiva University HS for Boys 300/9-12
2540 Amsterdam Ave 10033 212-960-5337
Rabbi Michael Taubes, admin. Fax 960-0027
York Prep S 400/6-12
40 W 68th St 10023 212-362-0400
Ronald Stewart, hdmstr. Fax 362-7424

New York Mills, Oneida, Pop. 3,298
New York Mills UFD 600/K-12
1 Marauder Blvd 13417 315-768-8127
Kathy Houghton, supt. Fax 768-3521
www.newyorkmills.org
New York Mills JSHS 300/7-12
1 Marauder Blvd 13417 315-768-8124
Gary Hadfield, prin. Fax 768-3521

Niagara Falls, Niagara, Pop. 48,343
Niagara Falls CSD 7,200/PK-12
630 66th St 14304 716-286-4205
Cynthia Bianco, supt. Fax 286-4283
www.nfschools.net/
Gaskill Preparatory S 500/7-8
910 Hyde Park Blvd 14301 716-278-5820
Robert Bradley, prin. Fax 278-5829
La Salle Preparatory S 500/7-8
7436 Buffalo Ave 14304 716-278-5880
James Spanbauer, prin. Fax 278-5899
Niagara Falls HS 2,200/9-12
4455 Porter Rd 14305 716-278-5800
Joseph Colburn, prin. Fax 286-7964

Niagara-Wheatfield Central SD 4,300/PK-12
6700 Schultz St 14304 716-215-3003
James Knowles, supt. Fax 215-3039
www.nwcsd.k12.ny.us
Other Schools – See Sanborn

Cheryl Fell's School of Business Post-Sec.
2541 Military Rd 14304 716-297-2750
Niagara Catholic JSHS 100/7-12
520 66th St 14304 716-283-8771
Robert DiFrancesco, prin. Fax 283-8774
St. Dominic Savio MS 100/6-8
504 66th St 14304 716-215-1461
Rose Mary Buccaglia, prin. Fax 215-1465

Niagara University, Niagara

Niagara University Post-Sec.
PO Box 2011 14109 716-285-1212

North Babylon, Suffolk, Pop. 17,252
North Babylon UFD 4,900/K-12
5 Jardine Pl 11703 631-620-7000
Patricia Godek, supt. Fax 321-3295
www.northbabylonschools.net/
Moses MS 1,200/6-8
250 Phelps Ln 11703 631-620-7300
Kathleen Hartnett, prin. Fax 587-2619
North Babylon HS 1,600/9-12
1 Phelps Ln 11703 631-620-7100
Raymond Williams, prin. Fax 321-3327

North Collins, Erie, Pop. 1,203
North Collins Central SD 600/PK-12
2045 School St 14111 716-337-0101
Benjamin Halsey, supt. Fax 337-3457
www.northcollins.com
North Collins JSHS 300/7-12
2045 School St 14111 716-337-0101
Annie Metcalf, prin. Fax 337-3457

North Creek, Warren, Pop. 613
Johnsburg Central SD 300/K-12
PO Box 380 12853 518-251-2814
Michael Markwica, supt. Fax 251-2562
www.johnsburgcsd.org
Johnsburg Central S 300/K-12
PO Box 380 12853 518-251-3504
Nadine Kearney, prin. Fax 251-2562

North Massapequa, Nassau, Pop. 17,762
Plainedge UFD 3,400/K-12
241 Wyngate Dr 11758 516-992-7455
Dr. Edward Salina, supt. Fax 992-7446
www.plainedgeschools.org
Other Schools – See Bethpage, Massapequa

North Merrick, Nassau, Pop. 12,143
Bellmore-Merrick Central HSD 6,000/7-12
1260 Meadowbrook Rd 11566 516-992-1000
Dr. Henry Kiernan, supt. Fax 623-0151
www.bellmore-merrick.k12.ny.us
Other Schools – See Bellmore, Merrick

Northport, Suffolk, Pop. 7,346
Northport-East Northport UFD 6,300/K-12
PO Box 210 11768 631-262-6604
Dr. Marylou McDermott, supt. Fax 262-6607
web.northport.k12.ny.us/
Northport HS 2,100/9-12
154 Laurel Hill Rd 11768 631-262-6652
Irene McLaughlin, prin. Fax 262-6736
Northport MS 800/6-8
11 Middleville Rd 11768 631-262-6750
Timothy Hoss, prin. Fax 262-6793
Other Schools – See East Northport

Northport VA Medical Center Post-Sec.
79 Middleville Rd 11768 631-261-4400

North Salem, Westchester
North Salem Central SD 1,300/K-12
230 June Rd 10560 914-669-5414
Dr. Kenneth Freeston, supt. Fax 669-8753
www.northsalemschools.org/
North Salem MSHS 700/6-12
230 June Rd 10560 914-669-5414
Dr. Patricia Cyganovich, prin. Fax 669-5663

North Syracuse, Onondaga, Pop. 6,697
North Syracuse Central SD 9,600/PK-12
5355 W Taft Rd 13212 315-218-2100
Kim Faucette, supt. Fax 218-2185
www.nscsd.org
North Syracuse JHS 1,500/8-9
5353 W Taft Rd 13212 315-218-3600
Constance Turose, prin. Fax 218-3685
Other Schools – See Cicero

North Tonawanda, Niagara, Pop. 31,199
North Tonawanda CSD 3,500/K-12
175 Humphrey St 14120 716-807-3599
Gregory Woytila, supt. Fax 807-3525
www.ntschools.org/
North Tonawanda HS 1,300/9-12
405 Meadow Dr 14120 716-807-3600
James Fisher, prin. Fax 807-3639
North Tonawanda MS 600/7-8
1500 Vanderbilt Ave 14120 716-807-3700
Lisa Colburn, prin. Fax 807-3701

Christian Academy of Western New York 200/PK-12
621 Payne Ave 14120 716-433-1652
Patricia Poeller, admin. Fax 478-7979

Northville, Fulton, Pop. 1,084
Northville Central SD 500/PK-12
PO Box 608 12134 518-863-7000
Kathy Dougherty, supt. Fax 863-7011
northvillecsd.k12.ny.us
Northville MSHS 300/6-12
PO Box 608 12134 518-863-7000
Michael Healey, prin. Fax 863-7011

Norwich, Chenango, Pop. 7,042
Norwich CSD 2,100/PK-12
89 Midland Dr 13815 607-334-1600
Gerard O'Sullivan, supt. Fax 336-8652
www.norwichcsd.org/
Norwich HS 700/9-12
89 Midland Dr 13815 607-334-1600
Fax 334-6680
Norwich MS 500/6-8
89 Midland Dr 13815 607-334-1600
Scott Ryan, prin. Fax 334-6210

Norwood, Saint Lawrence, Pop. 1,621
Norwood-Norfolk Central SD 900/K-12
7852 State Highway 56 13668 315-353-9951
Elizabeth Kirnie, supt. Fax 353-2467
www.nncsk12.org/
Norwood HS 300/9-12
7852 State Highway 56 13668 315-353-6631
Robin Fetter, prin. Fax 353-2480
Norwood-Norfolk MS 300/5-8
7852 State Highway 56 13668 315-353-6674
Jon Sovay, prin.

Nunda, Livingston, Pop. 1,354
Keshequa Central SD 800/PK-12
PO Box 517 14517 585-468-2541
Donald Covell, supt. Fax 468-3814
www.keshequa.org
Keshequa HS 300/9-12
PO Box 517 14517 585-468-2541
Matt Hopkins, prin. Fax 468-5493
Keshequa MS 200/6-8
PO Box 517 14517 585-468-2541
Matt Hopkins, prin. Fax 468-5493

Nyack, Rockland, Pop. 6,636
Nyack UFD 2,900/K-12
13A Dickinson Ave 10960 845-353-7000
James Montesano Ed.D., supt. Fax 353-7019
www.nyackschools.com
Nyack MS 700/6-8
98 S Highland Ave 10960 845-353-7200
Kevin Brentnall, prin. Fax 353-0506
Other Schools – See Upper Nyack

Alliance Theological Seminary Post-Sec.
350 N Highland Ave 10960 845-353-2020
Nyack College Post-Sec.
1 S Boulevard 10960 845-358-1710

Oakdale, Suffolk, Pop. 7,925
Connetquot Central SD
Supt. — See Bohemia
Oakdale-Bohemia Road MS 800/6-8
60 Oakdale Bohemia Rd 11769 631-244-2268
Susanne Bailey, prin. Fax 563-6167

Dowling College Post-Sec.
150 Idle Hour Blvd 11769 631-244-3000

Oakfield, Genesee, Pop. 1,789
Oakfield-Alabama Central SD 900/PK-12
7001 Lewiston Rd 14125 585-948-5211
Mark Alexander, supt. Fax 948-9362
www.oahornets.org
Oakfield-Alabama MSHS 400/7-12
7001 Lewiston Rd 14125 585-948-5211
Lynn Muscarella, prin. Fax 948-9362

Oakland Gardens, See New York
NYC Department of Education
Supt. — See New York
Cardozo HS 4,100/9-12
5700 223rd St 11364 718-279-6500
Gerald Martori, prin. Fax 631-7880
JHS 74 900/6-8
6115 Oceania St 11364 718-631-6800
Anthony Armstrong, prin. Fax 631-6899

Midrash L'man Achai 100/7-12
6745 215th St 11364 718-225-4003

Oceanside, Nassau, Pop. 31,810
Oceanside UFD 5,900/PK-12
145 Merle Ave 11572 516-678-1215
Dr. Herb Brown, supt. Fax 678-7503
www.oceansideschools.org
Castleton Academy HS 100/Alt
145 Merle Ave 11572 516-678-7593
Dorie Ciulla, prin. Fax 678-7594
Oceanside HS 1,900/9-12
3160 Skillman Ave 11572 516-678-7526
Mark Secaur, prin. Fax 678-6790
Oceanside MS 900/7-8
186 Alice Ave 11572 516-678-8518
Allison Glickman-Rogers, prin. Fax 594-2365

Hochstim School of Radiography Post-Sec.
PO Box 9007 11572 516-763-2030

Odessa, Schuyler, Pop. 582
Odessa-Montour Central SD 700/PK-12
300 College Ave 14869 607-594-3341
James Frame, supt. Fax 594-3976
www.omschools.org
Odessa-Montour JSHS 400/7-12
300 College Ave 14869 607-594-3341
Christopher Wood, prin. Fax 594-3438

Ogdensburg, Saint Lawrence, Pop. 10,977
Ogdensburg CSD 1,600/K-12
1100 State St 13669 315-393-0900
Timothy Vernsey, supt. Fax 393-2767
www.ogdensburgk12.org/
Ogdensburg Free Academy 800/7-12
1100 State St 13669 315-393-0900
Cynthia Centofanti, prin. Fax 393-7412

Old Forge, Herkimer, Pop. 747
Town of Webb UFD 300/K-12
PO Box 38 13420 315-369-3222
Rex Germer, supt. Fax 369-6216
www.towschool.org
Town of Webb S 300/K-12
PO Box 38 13420 315-369-3222
John Swick, prin. Fax 369-6216

Old Westbury, Nassau, Pop. 4,556
East Williston UFD 1,800/K-12
11 Bacon Rd 11568 516-333-1630
Dr. Elaine Kanas, supt. Fax 333-1937
www.ewsdonline.org/
Wheatley HS, 11 Bacon Rd 11568 800/8-12
Dr. Sean Feeney, prin. 516-333-7804

Westbury UFD 4,400/PK-12
2 Hitchcock Ln 11568 516-876-5016
Mary A. Lagnado, supt. Fax 876-5187
www.westburyschools.org
Westbury HS 1,200/9-12
1 Post Rd 11568 516-876-5047
Manuel Arias, prin. Fax 876-5079
Other Schools – See Westbury

New York Institute of Technology Post-Sec.
PO Box 8000 11568 516-686-1000
SUNY College at Old Westbury Post-Sec.
PO Box 210 11568 516-876-3000

Olean, Cattaraugus, Pop. 14,023
Olean CSD 1,800/PK-12
410 W Sullivan St 14760 716-375-8018
Colleen Taggerty Ed.D., supt. Fax 375-8047
www.oleanschools.org
Olean HS 600/8-12
410 W Sullivan St 14760 716-375-8010
Barbara Lias, prin. Fax 375-8048

Archbishop Walsh Academy 100/9-12
208 N 24th St 14760 585-372-8122
Mykal Karl, prin. Fax 372-6707
Continental School of Beauty Culture Post-Sec.
517 N Barry St 14760 716-372-5095
Jamestown Community College- Cattaraugus Post-Sec.
PO Box 5901 14760 716-376-7500
Olean Business Institute Post-Sec.
301 N Union St 14760 716-372-7978

Olmstedville, Essex
Minerva Central SD 100/K-12
PO Box 39 12857 518-251-2000
Timothy Farrell, supt. Fax 251-2395
www.minervasd.org/
Minerva Central S 100/K-12
PO Box 39 12857 518-251-2000
Heidi Kelly, prin. Fax 251-2395

Oneida, Madison, Pop. 11,232
Oneida CSD 2,200/PK-12
PO Box 327 13421 315-363-2550
Ronald Spadafora, supt. Fax 363-6728
www.oneidacsd.org/
Oneida HS 700/9-12
560 Seneca St 13421 315-363-6901
Brian Gallagher, prin. Fax 366-0619
Other Schools – See Wampsville

Oneonta, Otsego, Pop. 13,601
Oneonta CSD 1,600/PK-12
31 Center St 13820 607-433-8200
David Rowley, supt. Fax 433-8290
oneontacsd.org
Oneonta HS 600/9-12
130 East St 13820 607-433-8243
Nancy Osborn, prin. Fax 433-8204
Oneonta MS 300/7-8
130 East St 13820 607-433-8262
Kevin Johnson, prin. Fax 433-8203

Hartwick College Post-Sec.
PO Box 4020 13820 607-431-4000
Lighthouse Christian Academy 50/PK-12
12 Grove St 13820 607-432-2031
Chris Cleveland, admin. Fax 432-3403
SUNY College at Oneonta Post-Sec.
108 Ravine Pkwy 13820 607-436-3500
USC The Business College Post-Sec.
17 Elm St 13820 607-432-7003

Ontario Center, Wayne
Wayne Central SD 2,400/K-12
PO Box 155 14520 315-524-1000
Renee Garrett, supt. Fax 524-1049
www.wayne.k12.ny.us
Armstrong MS 600/6-8
PO Box 155 14520 315-524-1080
Pamela Tatro, prin. Fax 524-1119
Beneway HS 800/9-12
PO Box 155 14520 315-524-1050
Michael Pullen, prin. Fax 524-1079

Orangeburg, Rockland, Pop. 4,400
South Orangetown Central SD
Supt. — See Blauvelt
Tappan Zee HS 1,100/9-12
15 Dutch Hill Rd 10962 845-680-1600
Dr. Jennifer Amos, prin. Fax 680-1950

Dominican College of Blauvelt Post-Sec.
470 Western Hwy 10962 845-359-7800
Long Island University-Hudson Grad Ctr Post-Sec.
70 Route 340 10962 845-359-7200

Orchard Park, Erie, Pop. 3,209
Orchard Park Central SD 5,100/K-12
3330 Baker Rd 14127 716-209-6280
Matthew McGarrity, supt. Fax 209-6353
www.opschools.org
Orchard Park HS 1,600/9-12
4040 Baker Rd 14127 716-209-6242
Jonathan Wolf, prin. Fax 209-6451
Orchard Park MS 1,200/6-8
60 S Lincoln Ave 14127 716-209-6227
David Lilleck, prin. Fax 209-6338

Bryant & Stratton College Post-Sec.
200 Red Tail 14127 716-677-9500
Erie Community College South Post-Sec.
4041 Southwestern Blvd 14127 716-648-5400

Oriskany, Oneida, Pop. 1,381
Oriskany Central SD 700/K-12
PO Box 539 13424 315-768-2058
Gregory Kelahan, supt. Fax 768-1733
www.oriskanycsd.org
Oriskany JSHS 300/7-12
PO Box 539 13424 315-768-2063
Daniel Myers, prin. Fax 768-4496

Ossining, Westchester, Pop. 24,636
Ossining UFD 4,500/PK-12
190 Croton Ave 10562 914-941-7700
Dr. Phyllis Glassman, supt. Fax 941-7291
www.ossiningufsd.org/
Dorner MS 900/6-8
Van Cortlandt Ave 10562 914-762-5740
Regina Cellio, prin. Fax 762-5246
Ossining HS 1,300/9-12
29 S Highland Ave 10562 914-762-5760
Joshua Mandel, prin. Fax 762-4011

Oswego, Oswego, Pop. 17,912
Oswego CSD 4,100/K-12
120 E 1st St Ste 1 13126 315-341-2000
William Crist, supt. Fax 341-2910
www.oswego.org
Oswego HS 1,400/9-12
2 Buccaneer Blvd 13126 315-341-2200
Brian Hartwell, prin. Fax 341-2920
Oswego MS 600/7-8
100 Mark Fitzgibbons Dr 13126 315-341-2300
Mary Fierro, prin. Fax 341-2390

SUNY at Oswego Post-Sec.
7060 State Route 104 13126 315-312-2500

Otego, Otsego, Pop. 991
Otego-Unadilla Central SD 800/K-12
2641 State Highway 7 13825 607-988-5038
Charles Molloy, supt. Fax 988-1039
www.unatego.stier.org/
Unatego HS 400/9-12
2641 State Highway 7 13825 607-988-5098
Julie Lambiaso, prin. Fax 988-1050
Unatego MS 200/6-8
2641 State Highway 7 13825 607-988-5036
Patricia Hoyt, prin. Fax 988-5058

Ovid, Seneca, Pop. 592
South Seneca Central SD 800/PK-12
7263 Main St 14521 607-869-9636
Janie Nusser, supt. Fax 532-8540
www.southseneca.com/
South Seneca HS 300/9-12
7263 Main St 14521 607-869-9636
Steve Zielinski, prin. Fax 869-9553
South Seneca MS 200/6-8
7263 Main St 14521 607-869-9636
Steve Zielinski, prin. Fax 532-8540

Owego, Tioga, Pop. 3,824
Owego-Apalachin Central SD 2,100/PK-12
36 Talcott St 13827 607-687-6224
Dr. William Russell, supt. Fax 687-6313
www.oacsd.org

Owego-Apalachin MS 500/6-8
3 Sheldon Guile Blvd 13827 607-687-6248
Thomas Beatty, prin. Fax 687-6593
Owego Free Academy 700/9-12
1 Sheldon Guile Blvd 13827 607-687-6230
Heath Georgia, prin. Fax 687-6244

Oxford, Chenango, Pop. 1,425
Oxford Academy & Central SD 800/PK-12
PO Box 192 13830 607-843-2025
Dr. David S. Richards, supt. Fax 843-3241
www.oxac.org
Oxford Academy HS 300/9-12
PO Box 192 13830 607-843-2025
Janet Laytham, prin. Fax 843-3231
Oxford Academy MS 300/5-8
PO Box 192 13830 607-843-2025
Kathleen Hansen, prin. Fax 843-3241

Oyster Bay, Nassau, Pop. 6,598
Oyster Bay-East Norwich Central SD 1,600/PK-12
1 McCouns Ln 11771 516-624-6505
Dr. Phyllis Harrington, supt. Fax 624-6520
obenschools.org
Oyster Bay JSHS 700/7-12
150 E Main St 11771 516-624-6524
Dr. Dennis O'Hara, prin. Fax 624-6684

St. Dominic HS 400/9-12
110 Anstice St 11771 516-922-4888
Denise Smith, prin. Fax 922-4898

Ozone Park, See New York
NYC Department of Education
Supt. — See New York
Adams HS 3,300/9-12
10101 Rockaway Blvd 11417 718-322-0500
Daniel Scanlon, prin. Fax 738-9077
Goddard HS of Communication Arts & Tech. 400/9-12
13830 Lafayette St 11417 718-848-8357
Joseph Birgeles, prin. Fax 848-8579
HS for Construction Engineering & Arch 900/9-12
9406 104th St 11416 718-846-6280
Lakesha Gordon, prin. Fax 846-6283
JHS 202 1,100/6-8
13830 Lafayette St 11417 718-848-0001
William Fitzgerald, prin. Fax 848-8082
JHS 210 2,000/6-8
9311 101st Ave 11416 718-845-5942
Rosalyn Allman-Manning, prin. Fax 845-4037
MS 137 2,000/6-8
10915 98th St 11417 718-659-0471
Laura Mastrogiovanni, prin. Fax 659-4594

Painted Post, Steuben, Pop. 1,780
Corning CSD 5,300/K-12
165 Charles St 14870 607-936-3704
Michael Ginalski, supt. Fax 654-2735
www.corningareaschools.com
Corning-Painted Post West HS 1,000/9-12
201 Victory Hwy 14870 607-936-3794
Robin Sheehan, prin. Fax 654-2771
Other Schools – See Corning

Palmyra, Wayne, Pop. 3,491
Palmyra-Macedon Central SD 2,000/K-12
151 Hyde Pkwy 14522 315-597-3401
Robert Ike, supt. Fax 597-3898
www.palmaccsd.org
Palmyra-Macedon HS 700/9-12
151 Hyde Pkwy 14522 315-597-3420
Andrew Wahl, prin. Fax 597-3425
Palmyra-Macedon MS 500/6-8
163 Hyde Pkwy 14522 315-597-3450
Darcy Smith, prin. Fax 597-3460

East Palmyra Christian S 100/PK-12
2023 E Palmyra Port Gibson 14522 315-597-4400
Keith Vanderzwan, prin. Fax 597-9717

Panama, Chautauqua, Pop. 475
Panama Central SD 600/PK-12
41 North St 14767 716-782-2455
Bert Lictus, supt. Fax 782-4674
www.pancent.org
Panama Central S 300/7-12
41 North St 14767 716-782-2455
Emily Harvey, prin. Fax 782-4674

Parish, Oswego, Pop. 445
Altmar-Parish-Williamstown Central SD 900/PK-12
PO Box 97 13131 315-625-5251
Gerry Hudson, supt. Fax 625-7952
www.apw.cnyric.org
Altmar-Parish-Williamstown JSHS 500/7-12
PO Box 97 13131 315-625-5222
Jamie Coppola, prin. Fax 625-4638

Parishville, Saint Lawrence, Pop. 641
Parishville-Hopkinton Central SD 500/PK-12
PO Box 187 13672 315-265-4642
Darin Saiff, supt. Fax 268-1309
phcs.neric.org
Parishville-Hopkinton JSHS 200/7-12
PO Box 187 13672 315-265-4642
Robert Stewart, prin. Fax 268-1309

Patchogue, Suffolk, Pop. 11,620
Patchogue-Medford UFD 7,500/PK-12
241 S Ocean Ave 11772 631-687-6380
Michael Locantore, supt.
www.pmschools.org
Saxton MS, 121 Saxton St 11772 800/6-9
Manuel Sanzone, prin. 631-687-6700
South Ocean MS 500/6-9
225 S Ocean Ave 11772 631-687-6600
Linda Pickford, prin.
Other Schools – See Medford

Briarcliffe College Post-Sec.
225 W Main St 11772 631-654-5300
St. Joseph's College New York Post-Sec.
155 W Roe Blvd 11772 631-687-5100

Patterson, Putnam
Carmel Central SD 4,600/K-12
PO Box 296 12563 845-878-2094
James Ryan Ed.D., supt. Fax 878-2566
www.carmelschools.org
Other Schools – See Carmel

Paul Smiths, Franklin, Pop. 664

Paul Smith's College Post-Sec.
PO Box 265 12970 518-327-6227

Pavilion, Genesee, Pop. 644
Pavilion Central SD 800/K-12
7014 Big Tree Rd 14525 585-584-3115
Kenneth Ellison, supt. Fax 584-3421
www.pavilioncsd.org
Pavilion JSHS 500/6-12
7014 Big Tree Rd 14525 585-584-3070
Dr. Sheila Eigenbrod, prin. Fax 584-3421

Pawling, Dutchess, Pop. 2,332
Pawling Central SD 1,400/K-12
515 Route 22 12564 845-855-4600
Michael Mahoney, supt. Fax 855-4659
www.pawlingschools.org
Pawling HS 400/9-12
30 Wagner Dr 12564 845-855-4620
Helen Callan, prin. Fax 855-4617
Pawling MS 400/5-8
80 Wagner Dr 12564 845-855-4653
Allan Lipsky, prin. Fax 855-4134

Trinity-Pawling S 300/7-12
700 Route 22 12564 845-855-3100
Archibald Smith, admin. Fax 855-3816

Pearl River, Rockland, Pop. 15,720
Pearl River UFD 2,600/K-12
135 W Crooked Hill Rd 10965 845-620-3900
John Morgano, supt. Fax 620-3927
www.pearlriver.org
Pearl River HS 1,100/8-12
275 E Central Ave 10965 845-620-3800
William Furdon, prin. Fax 620-3852

Iona College Rockland Graduate Center Post-Sec.
PO Box 1522 10965 845-620-1350

Peekskill, Westchester, Pop. 22,929
Peekskill CSD 3,000/PK-12
1031 Elm St 10566 914-737-3300
Dr. Lorenzo Licopoli, supt. Fax 737-3912
www.peekskillcsd.org
Peekskill HS 900/9-12
1072 Elm St 10566 914-737-0201
Frederick Hutchinson, prin. Fax 737-2550
Peekskill MS 600/6-8
212 Ringgold St 10566 914-737-4542
Dr. David Fine, prin. Fax 737-3253

Northern Westchester Sch of Hairdressing Post-Sec.
19 Bank St 10566 914-739-8400

Pelham, Westchester, Pop. 6,710
Pelham UFD 2,800/K-12
18 Franklin Pl 10803 914-738-3434
Peter Giarrizzo, supt. Fax 738-7223
www.pelhamschools.org
Pelham Memorial HS 800/9-12
575 Colonial Ave 10803 914-738-8110
Jeannine Clark, prin. Fax 738-8122
Pelham MS 700/6-8
28 Franklin Pl 10803 914-738-8190
Dr. Robert Roelle, prin. Fax 738-8132

Penfield, Monroe, Pop. 30,219
Penfield Central SD
Supt. — See Rochester
Bay Trail MS 1,100/6-8
1760 Scribner Rd 14526 585-249-6450
Winton Buddington, prin. Fax 248-0735
Penfield HS 1,500/9-12
25 High School Dr 14526 585-249-6700
Thomas Putnam Ed.D., prin. Fax 248-2810

Finney S 300/K-12
2070 Five Mile Line Rd 14526 585-387-3770
Michael VanLeeuwen, pres. Fax 387-3771

Penn Yan, Yates, Pop. 5,081
Penn Yan Central SD 1,700/PK-12
1 School Dr 14527 315-536-3371
David Hamilton, supt. Fax 536-0068
www.pycsd.org
Penn Yan Academy 600/9-12
305 Court St 14527 315-536-4408
David Pullen, prin. Fax 536-0341
Penn Yan MS 400/6-8
515 Liberty St 14527 315-536-3366
Howard Dennis, prin. Fax 536-7769

Perry, Wyoming, Pop. 3,633
Perry Central SD 900/PK-12
33 Watkins Ave 14530 585-237-0270
Dr. William Stavisky, supt. Fax 237-6172
www.perry.k12.ny.us
Perry HS 300/9-12
33 Watkins Ave 14530 585-237-0270
Joshua Audsley, prin. Fax 237-6350
Perry MS 300/5-8
50 Olin Ave 14530 585-237-0270
Katherine Waite, prin. Fax 237-3483

Peru, Clinton, Pop. 1,580
Peru Central SD 1,900/K-12
PO Box 68 12972 518-643-6000
Dr. Patrick Brimstein, supt. Fax 643-2043
www.perucsd.org
Peru HS 700/7-12
PO Box 68 12972 518-643-6400
Christopher Mazzella, prin. Fax 643-6438

Philadelphia, Jefferson, Pop. 1,192
Indian River Central SD 4,000/PK-12
32735 County Route 29 Ste B 13673 315-642-3441
James Kettrick, supt. Fax 642-3738
www.ircsd.org/
Indian River HS 900/9-12
32925 US Route 11 13673 315-642-3427
Troy Decker, prin. Fax 642-5658
Indian River MS 800/6-8
32735 County Route 29 Ste A 13673 315-642-0125
Nancy Taylor-Schmitt, prin. Fax 642-0802

Phoenix, Oswego, Pop. 2,343
Phoenix Central SD 1,900/K-12
116 Volney St 13135 315-695-1555
Judy Belfield, supt. Fax 695-1201
www.phoenixcsd.org
Birdlebough HS 700/9-12
552 Main St 13135 315-695-1631
Gregory Molloy, prin. Fax 695-1618
Dillon MS 500/6-8
116 Volney St 13135 315-695-1521
Susan Anderson, prin. Fax 695-1523

Pine Bush, Orange, Pop. 1,744
Pine Bush Central SD 5,700/PK-12
PO Box 700 12566 845-744-2031
Philip Steinberg, supt. Fax 744-6189
www.pinebushschools.org
Crispell MS 800/6-8
PO Box 780 12566 845-744-2031
John Boyle, prin. Fax 744-2261
Pine Bush HS 1,900/9-12
PO Box 670 12566 845-744-2031
Aaron Hopmayer, prin. Fax 744-3488
Other Schools – See Circleville

AEF Chapel Field S 200/PK-12
211 Fleury Rd 12566 845-778-1881
William Spanjer, prin. Fax 778-5841

Pine Plains, Dutchess, Pop. 1,324
Pine Plains Central SD 1,100/K-12
2829 Church St 12567 518-398-7181
Linda Kaumeyer, supt. Fax 398-6592
www.ppcsd.org/
Stissing Mountain HS 400/9-12
2829 Church St 12567 518-398-7181
Tara Sherman, prin. Fax 398-6592
Stissing Mountain MS 200/6-8
2829 Church St 12567 518-398-7181
James DiDonna, prin. Fax 398-6592

Pittsford, Monroe, Pop. 1,344
Pittsford Central SD 6,000/K-12
75 Barker Rd 14534 585-267-1000
Mary Alice Price, supt. Fax 267-1088
www.pittsfordschools.org
Barker Road MS 700/6-8
75 Barker Rd 14534 585-267-1800
Gerald Eckert, prin. Fax 385-5960
Calkins Road MS 700/6-8
1899 Calkins Rd 14534 585-267-1900
Scott Reinhart, prin. Fax 264-0053
Pittsford-Mendon HS 1,000/9-12
472 Mendon Rd 14534 585-267-1600
Karl Thielking, prin. Fax 267-1679
Pittsford Sutherland HS 1,000/9-12
55 Sutherland St 14534 585-267-1100
Elizabeth Konar, prin. Fax 381-7687

Plainview, Nassau, Pop. 25,853
Plainview-Old Bethpage Central SD 5,000/K-12
106 Washington Ave 11803 516-434-3001
Dr. Lorna R. Lewis, supt. Fax 937-6303
www.pobschools.org
Mattlin MS 800/5-8
100 Washington Ave 11803 516-434-3250
Dean Mittleman, prin. Fax 937-6431
Plainview-Old Bethpage/JFK HS 1,600/9-12
50 Kennedy Dr 11803 516-434-3125
James Murray, prin. Fax 937-6433
Plainview-Old Bethpage MS 800/5-8
121 Central Park Rd 11803 516-434-3308
John McNamara, prin. Fax 349-4777

Plattsburgh, Clinton, Pop. 19,572
Beekmantown Central SD
Supt. — See West Chazy
Beekmantown HS 600/9-12
6944 Route 22 12901 518-563-8787
Diane Fox, prin. Fax 563-8789
Beekmantown MS 400/6-8
6944 Route 22 12901 518-563-8690
Elaine Dixon, prin. Fax 563-8691

Plattsburgh CSD 1,900/PK-12
49 Broad St 12901 518-957-6002
James Short, supt. Fax 561-6605
www.plattscsd.org/
Plattsburgh HS 600/9-12
1 Clifford Dr 12901 518-561-7500
Glenn Hurlock, prin. Fax 561-1895
Stafford MS 400/6-8
15 Broad St 12901 518-563-6800
Patricia Amo, prin. Fax 563-8520

Champlain Valley Physicians Hospital Post-Sec.
75 Beekman St 12901 518-561-2000

New Life Christian Academy 50/PK-10
164 Prospect Ave 12901 518-563-2842
Rev. James Miller, admin. Fax 563-8331
Seton Catholic Central JSHS 200/7-12
206 New York Rd 12903 518-561-4031
Catherine Russell, prin. Fax 563-1193
SUNY Clinton Community College Post-Sec.
136 Clinton Point Dr 12901 518-562-4200
SUNY College at Plattsburgh Post-Sec.
101 Broad St 12901 518-564-2000

Pleasantville, Westchester, Pop. 6,927
Pleasantville UFD 1,800/K-12
60 Romer Ave 10570 914-741-1400
Mary Fox-Alter, supt. Fax 741-1499
www.pleasantvilleschools.com
Pleasantville HS 600/9-12
60 Romer Ave 10570 914-741-1420
Dawn Bartz, prin. Fax 741-2546
Pleasantville MS 600/5-8
40 Romer Ave 10570 914-741-1450
Vivian Ossowski, prin. Fax 741-1476

Pace University Post-Sec.
861 Bedford Rd 10570 914-773-3200

Poland, Herkimer, Pop. 505
Poland Central SD 700/PK-12
74 Cold Brook St 13431 315-826-7900
Laura Dutton, supt. Fax 826-7516
www.polandcs.org
Poland JSHS 400/6-12
74 Cold Brook St 13431 315-826-7900
Jason Mitchell, prin. Fax 826-7516

Port Byron, Cayuga, Pop. 1,272
Port Byron Central SD 1,000/K-12
30 Maple Ave 13140 315-776-5728
Neil O'Brien, supt. Fax 776-4050
pbcschools.org
West HS 500/7-12
30 Maple Ave 13140 315-776-4598
Shawn Bissetta, prin. Fax 776-4050

Port Chester, Westchester, Pop. 28,517
Port Chester-Rye UFD
Supt. — See Rye Brook
Port Chester HS 1,200/9-12
1 Tamarack Rd 10573 914-934-7950
Dr. Mitchell Combs, prin. Fax 934-2998
Port Chester MS 900/6-8
113 Bowman Ave 10573 914-934-7930
Patrick Swift, prin. Fax 934-7886

Port Henry, Essex, Pop. 1,181
Moriah Central SD 1,100/PK-12
39 Viking Ln 12974 518-546-3301
William Larrow, supt. Fax 546-7895
www.moriahk12.org/
Moriah JSHS 300/7-12
39 Viking Ln 12974 518-546-3301
Alison Burch, prin. Fax 546-7895

Port Jefferson, Suffolk, Pop. 7,650
Port Jefferson UFD 1,300/PK-12
550 Scraggy Hill Rd 11777 631-791-4500
Dr. Kenneth Bossert, supt. Fax 476-4409
www.portjeffschools.org
Port Jefferson MS 300/6-8
350 Old Post Rd 11777 631-791-4400
Antonio Santana, prin. Fax 476-4430
Vandermuelen HS 400/9-12
350 Old Post Rd 11777 631-791-4400
Dr. Matthew Murphy, prin. Fax 476-4408

Port Jefferson Station, Suffolk, Pop. 7,762
Comsewogue SD 3,900/K-12
290 Norwood Ave 11776 631-474-8100
Joseph Rella, supt. Fax 474-3568
www.comsewogue.org/
Comsewogue HS 1,300/9-12
565 Bicycle Path 11776 631-474-8178
Joseph Coniglione, prin. Fax 474-8175
Kennedy MS 800/6-8
200 Jayne Blvd 11776 631-474-8160
Michael Fama, prin. Fax 474-8176

Port Jervis, Orange, Pop. 8,515
Port Jervis CSD 3,000/K-12
9 Thompson St 12771 845-858-3100
Thomas Bongiovi, supt. Fax 856-1885
www.pjschools.org
Port Jervis HS 1,000/9-12
10 Route 209 12771 845-858-3100
Andrew Marotta, prin. Fax 858-2895
Port Jervis MS 500/7-8
118 E Main St 12771 845-858-3100
Jean Lain, prin. Fax 858-2893

Portville, Cattaraugus, Pop. 993
Portville Central SD 900/PK-12
PO Box 790 14770 585-933-6000
Thomas Simon, supt. Fax 933-6774
www.portville.wnyric.org/
Portville JSHS 400/7-12
PO Box 790 14770 585-933-6705
Lawrence Welty, prin. Fax 933-6774

Port Washington, Nassau, Pop. 15,596
Port Washington UFD 5,000/K-12
100 Campus Dr 11050 516-767-5000
Dr. Kathleen Mooney, supt. Fax 767-5007
www.portnet.k12.ny.us
Schreiber HS 1,600/9-12
101 Campus Dr 11050 516-767-5800
Ira Pernick, prin. Fax 767-5807
Weber MS 1,100/6-8
52 Campus Dr 11050 516-767-5500
Marilyn Rodahan, prin. Fax 767-5507

Potsdam, Saint Lawrence, Pop. 9,246
Potsdam Central SD 1,400/PK-12
29 Leroy St 13676 315-265-2000
Patrick Brady, supt. Fax 265-2048
www.potsdam.k12.ny.us
Kingston MS 400/5-8
29 Leroy St 13676 315-265-2000
Mark Bennett, prin. Fax 265-8103
Potsdam HS 500/9-12
29 Leroy St 13676 315-265-2000
Joann Chambers, prin. Fax 265-8134

Clarkson University Post-Sec.
8 Clarkson Ave 13676 315-268-6400
SUNY College at Potsdam Post-Sec.
44 Pierrepont Ave 13676 315-267-2000

Pottersville, Warren, Pop. 420

Word of Life Bible Institute Post-Sec.
PO Box 129 12860 518-494-4723

Poughkeepsie, Dutchess, Pop. 31,635
Arlington Central SD
Supt. — See Lagrangeville
Arlington MS 600/6-8
601 Dutchess Tpke 12603 845-486-4480
Richard Carroll, prin. Fax 486-4446

Poughkeepsie CSD 4,200/K-12
11 College Ave 12603 845-451-4900
Dr. Laval Wilson, supt. Fax 451-4955
www.poughkeepsieschools.org/
Poughkeepsie HS 1,200/9-12
70 Forbus St 12603 845-451-4850
Edgar Glascott, prin. Fax 451-4853
Poughkeepsie MS 1,000/6-8
55 College Ave 12603 845-451-4800
Phee Simpson, prin. Fax 451-4836

Spackenkill UFD 1,300/K-12
15 Croft Rd 12603 845-463-7800
Dr. Lois Powell, supt. Fax 463-7804
www.spackenkillschools.org/
Spackenkill HS 600/9-12
112 Spackenkill Rd 12603 845-463-7810
Steven Malkischer, prin. Fax 463-7826
Todd MS 400/6-8
11 Croft Rd 12603 845-463-7830
Michael Murphy, prin. Fax 463-7832

Dutchess Community College Post-Sec.
53 Pendell Rd 12601 845-431-8000
Faith Christian Academy 200/PK-12
254 Spackenkill Rd 12603 845-462-0266
Alexander Averin, hdmstr. Fax 462-1561
Marist College Post-Sec.
3399 North Rd 12601 845-575-3000
Oakwood Friends S 200/6-12
22 Spackenkill Rd 12603 845-462-4200
Peter Baily, head sch Fax 462-4251
Our Lady of Lourdes HS 700/9-12
131 Boardman Rd 12603 845-463-0400
Fr. John Lagiovane, prin. Fax 463-0174
Poughkeepsie Day S 300/PK-12
260 Boardman Rd 12603 845-462-7600
Josie Holford, head sch Fax 462-7603
Ridley-Lowell Business & Technical Inst. Post-Sec.
26 S Hamilton St 12601 845-471-0330
Tabernacle Christian Academy 100/K-12
155 Academy St 12601 845-454-2792
Timothy Hostetter, prin. Fax 483-0926
Vassar College Post-Sec.
124 Raymond Ave 12604 845-437-7000

Prattsburgh, Steuben, Pop. 649
Prattsburg Central SD 400/PK-12
1 Academy St 14873 607-522-3795
Joseph Rumsey, supt. Fax 522-6221
www.prattsburghcsd.org/
Prattsburg Central S 400/PK-12
1 Academy St 14873 607-522-3795
Joseph Rumsey, supt. Fax 522-6221

Pulaski, Oswego, Pop. 2,352
Pulaski Central SD 900/PK-12
2 Hinman Rd 13142 315-298-5188
Dr. Marshall Marshall, supt. Fax 298-4390
www.pacs.cnyric.org
Pulaski HS 400/9-12
4624 Salina St 13142 315-298-5103
Jay Altobello, prin. Fax 298-2371
Pulaski MS 7-8
4624 Salina St 13142 315-298-6001
Jean Lynch, prin. Fax 298-2371

Purchase, See Harrison

Keio Academy of New York 300/9-12
3 College Rd 10577 914-694-4825
Masashi Notsu, hdmstr. Fax 694-4830
Long Island University Post-Sec.
735 Anderson Hill Rd 10577 800-472-3548
Manhattanville College Post-Sec.
2900 Purchase St 10577 914-694-2200
SUNY Purchase College Post-Sec.
735 Anderson Hill Rd 10577 914-251-6000

Putnam Valley, Putnam
Putnam Valley Central SD 1,800/K-12
146 Peekskill Hollow Rd 10579 845-528-8143
Dr. Fran Wills, supt. Fax 528-0274
www.pvcsd.org
Putnam Valley HS 600/9-12
146 Peekskill Hollow Rd 10579 845-526-7847
Vincent Burruano, prin. Fax 528-4456
Putnam Valley MS 600/5-8
142 Peekskill Hollow Rd 10579 845-528-8101
Edward Hallisey, prin. Fax 528-8145

Queensbury, Warren
Queensbury UFD 3,600/K-12
429 Aviation Rd 12804 518-824-5600
Dr. Douglas Huntley, supt. Fax 793-4476
www.queensburyschool.org/
Queensbury HS 1,200/9-12
409 Aviation Rd 12804 518-824-4626
Damian Switzer, prin. Fax 824-4680
Queensbury MS 900/6-8
455 Aviation Rd 12804 518-824-3610
Richard Keys, prin. Fax 824-3682

SUNY Adirondack Post-Sec.
640 Bay Rd 12804 518-743-2200

Queens Village, See New York
NYC Department of Education
Supt. — See New York
Nuzzi IS 1,100/6-8
21310 92nd Ave 11428 718-465-0651
Karleen Comrie, prin. Fax 264-1246
Van Buren HS 2,500/9-12
23017 Hillside Ave 11427 718-776-4728
Sam Sochet, prin. Fax 217-6287

Randolph, Cattaraugus, Pop. 1,268
Randolph Central SD 1,000/PK-12
18 Main St 14772 716-358-7005
Kimberly Moritz, supt. Fax 358-7072
www.randolphcsd.org/
Randolph JSHS 500/7-12
18 Main St 14772 716-358-7007
Laurie Sanders, prin. Fax 358-7072

Ravena, Albany, Pop. 3,205
Ravena-Coeymans-Selkirk Central SD 2,000/PK-12
15 Mountain Rd 12143 518-756-5200
Alan McCartney, supt. Fax 767-2644
www.rcscsd.org
Ravena-Coeymans-Selkirk HS 600/9-12
2025 US Route 9W 12143 518-756-5200
Brian Bailey, prin. Fax 756-3534
Ravena-Coeymans-Selkirk MS 500/5-8
2025 US Route 9W 12143 518-756-5200
Pam Black, prin. Fax 756-1988

Red Creek, Wayne, Pop. 530
Red Creek Central SD 900/K-12
PO Box 190 13143 315-754-2010
David Sholes, supt. Fax 754-8169
www.rccsd.org
Red Creek HS 300/9-12
PO Box 190 13143 315-754-2040
Timothy Gaffney, prin. Fax 754-2068
Red Creek MS 200/6-8
PO Box 190 13143 315-754-2070
Matthew Vanorman, prin. Fax 754-2077

Red Hook, Dutchess, Pop. 1,942
Red Hook Central SD 2,200/K-12
9 Mill Rd 12571 845-758-2241
Paul Finch Ed.D., supt. Fax 758-3366
www.redhookcentralschools.org/
Linden Avenue MS 500/6-8
65 W Market St 12571 845-758-2241
Dr. Katie Zahedi, prin. Fax 758-0688
Red Hook HS 800/9-12
103 W Market St 12571 845-758-2241
Roy Paisley, prin. Fax 758-0482

Devereux Center in New York Post-Sec.
40 Devereux Way 12571 845-758-1899

Rego Park, See New York
NYC Department of Education
Supt. — See New York
JHS 157 1,000/6-9
6355 102nd St 11374 718-830-4910
Vincent Suraci, prin. Fax 830-4993

Metropolitan Learning Institute Post-Sec.
9777 Queens Blvd Ste 900 11374 718-897-0482

Remsen, Oneida, Pop. 502
Remsen Central SD 500/PK-12
PO Box 406 13438 315-831-3797
Carl Klossner, supt. Fax 831-2172
www.remsencsd.org/
Remsen JSHS 200/7-12
PO Box 406 13438 315-831-3851
Dale Turner, prin. Fax 831-2172

Rensselaer, Rensselaer, Pop. 9,055
Rensselaer CSD 1,100/PK-12
25 Van Rensselaer Dr 12144 518-465-7509
Sally Ann Shields, supt. Fax 436-0479
www.rcsd.k12.ny.us
Rensselaer JSHS 500/7-12
25 Van Rensselaer Dr 12144 518-436-8561
Karen Urbanski, prin. Fax 436-8563

Doane Stuart S 300/PK-12
199 Washington Ave 12144 518-465-5222
Lisa Brown, head sch Fax 465-5230

Retsof, Livingston, Pop. 330
York Central SD 800/K-12
PO Box 102 14539 585-243-1730
Dr. Daniel Murray, supt. Fax 243-5269
www.yorkcsd.org/
York MSHS 500/6-12
PO Box 102 14539 585-243-1730
David Sylvester, prin. Fax 243-5269

Rhinebeck, Dutchess, Pop. 2,623
Rhinebeck Central SD 1,200/K-12
PO Box 351 12572 845-871-5520
Joseph Phelan, supt. Fax 876-4276
www.rhinebeckcsd.org/

Bulkeley MS 300/6-8
PO Box 351 12572 845-871-5500
John Kemnitzer, prin. Fax 871-5553
Rhinebeck HS 400/9-12
PO Box 351 12572 845-871-5500
Dr. Edwin Davenport, prin. Fax 876-8755

Richfield Springs, Otsego, Pop. 1,252
Richfield Springs Central SD 500/K-12
PO Box 631 13439 315-858-0610
Robert Barraco, supt. Fax 858-2440
www.richfieldcsd.org
Richfield Springs Central S 500/K-12
PO Box 631 13439 315-858-0610
Therijo Climenhaga, prin. Fax 858-2440

Richmond Hill, See New York
NYC Department of Education
Supt. — See New York
Richmond Hill HS 2,900/9-12
8930 114th St 11418 718-846-3335
Wayne Anderson, prin. Fax 847-0980

Yeshiva Shaar HaTorah - Grodno Post-Sec.
8396 117th St 11418 718-846-1940

Richmondville, Schoharie, Pop. 910
Cobleskill-Richmondville Central SD
Supt. — See Cobleskill
Cobleskill-Richmondville HS 600/9-12
1353 State Route 7 12149 518-234-3565
Melissa Ausfeld, prin. Fax 234-1018

Ridgewood, See New York
NYC Department of Education
Supt. — See New York
Cleveland HS 2,400/9-12
2127 Himrod St 11385 718-381-9600
Denise Vittor, prin. Fax 417-8457
IS 77 1,100/6-8
976 Seneca Ave 11385 718-366-7120
Joseph Miller, prin. Fax 456-9512
IS 93 1,300/6-8
6656 Forest Ave 11385 718-821-4882
Edward Santos, prin. Fax 456-9521

Midway Paris Beauty School Post-Sec.
5440 Myrtle Ave 11385 718-418-2790

Riverdale, See New York

College of Mount Saint Vincent Post-Sec.
6301 Riverdale Ave 10471 718-405-3267
Manhattan College Post-Sec.
4513 Manhattan College Pkwy 10471 718-862-8000
Yeshiva of Telshe Alumni 100/9-12
4904 Independence Ave 10471 718-601-3523
Yeshiva Ohavei Torah 100/9-12
450 W 250th St 10471 718-432-2600

Riverhead, Suffolk, Pop. 12,979
Riverhead Central SD 4,900/K-12
700 Osborn Ave 11901 631-369-6700
Nancy Carney, supt. Fax 369-6816
www.riverhead.net
Riverhead HS 1,500/9-12
700 Harrison Ave 11901 631-369-6723
David Wicks, prin. Fax 369-5164
Riverhead MS 700/7-8
600 Harrison Ave 11901 631-369-6759
Andrea Pekar, prin. Fax 369-6829

Central Suffolk Hospital Post-Sec.
1300 Roanoke Ave 11901 631-548-6000
Long Island University Post-Sec.
121 Speonk Riverhead Rd 11901 631-287-8010
McGann-Mercy HS 500/7-12
1225 Ostrander Ave 11901 631-727-5900
Carl Semmler, prin. Fax 369-7328
Suffolk County Community College Post-Sec.
121 Speonk Riverhead Rd 11901 631-548-2500

Rochester, Monroe, Pop. 203,996
Brighton Central SD 3,500/K-12
2035 Monroe Ave 14618 585-242-5080
Dr. Kevin McGowan, supt. Fax 242-5164
www.bcsd.org
Brighton HS 1,200/9-12
1150 Winton Rd S 14618 585-242-5000
Thomas Hall, prin. Fax 242-7364
Twelve Corners MS 900/6-8
2643 Elmwood Ave 14618 585-242-5100
Rob Thomas, prin. Fax 242-2540

East Irondequoit Central SD 3,100/K-12
600 Pardee Rd 14609 585-339-1210
Susan Allen, supt. Fax 339-1219
www.eicsd.k12.ny.us/
East Irondequoit MS 700/6-8
155 Densmore Rd 14609 585-339-1400
Mark Anson, prin. Fax 339-1409
Eastridge HS 1,000/9-12
2350 E Ridge Rd 14622 585-339-1450
Mary Grow, prin. Fax 339-1459

Gates-Chili Central SD 4,400/K-12
3 Spartan Way 14624 585-247-5050
Carol Stehm, supt. Fax 340-1072
www.gateschili.org
Gates-Chili HS 1,600/9-12
1 Spartan Way 14624 585-247-5050
Timothy Clasgens, prin. Fax 340-5518
Gates-Chili MS 1,000/6-8
2 Spartan Way 14624 585-247-5050
Lisa Buckshaw, prin. Fax 340-5532

Greece Central SD 10,800/PK-12
750 Maiden Ln 14615 585-966-2000
Barbara Deane-Williams, supt. Fax 581-8203
www.greece.k12.ny.us
Arcadia HS 1,200/9-12
120 Island Cottage Rd 14612 585-966-3000
Lesley Flick, prin. Fax 966-3039
Arcadia MS 800/6-8
130 Island Cottage Rd 14612 585-966-3300
Linda Pickering, prin. Fax 966-3339
Athena HS 1,300/9-12
800 Long Pond Rd 14612 585-966-4000
Jason Gianotti, prin. Fax 966-4039
Athena MS 900/6-8
800 Long Pond Rd 14612 585-966-8800
David Richardson, prin. Fax 966-4039
Odyssey Academy 800/Alt
750 Maiden Ln 14615 585-966-5500
Susan Meier, prin. Fax 966-5539
Olympia HS 1,100/9-12
1139 Maiden Ln 14615 585-966-5000
Christina Sloane, prin. Fax 966-5039

Penfield Central SD 4,600/K-12
2590 Atlantic Ave 14625 585-249-5700
Stephen L. Grimm Ed.D., supt. Fax 248-8412
www.penfield.edu
Other Schools – See Penfield

Rochester CSD 29,000/PK-12
131 W Broad St 14614 585-262-8100
Dr. Bolgen Vargas, supt. Fax 262-8381
www.rcsdk12.org/
All City HS 1,000/Alt
180 Ridgeway Ave 14615 585-458-2110
Sandra Jordan, prin. Fax 277-0077
BioScience & Health Careers HS 400/9-12
950 Norton St 14621 585-324-3730
Carol Jones, prin. Fax 336-8018
Brown HS of Constructn & Design 200/9-12
655 Colfax St 14606 585-324-9770
David Grant, prin.
Charlotte HS 700/9-12
175 Martin St 14605 585-663-7070
Michael Allen, prin. Fax 621-0275
East HS 1,700/7-12
1801 E Main St 14609 585-288-3130
Anibal Soler, prin. Fax 654-1066
Global Media Arts HS @ Franklin 200/9-12
950 Norton St 14621 585-324-3720
Carol Jones, prin. Fax 336-5549
Integrated Arts & Technology HS 7-12
950 Norton St 14621 585-324-3750
Kevin Klein, prin.
Intl Finance & Economic Dev Career HS 200/9-12
950 Norton St 14621 585-324-3725
Carol Jones, prin. Fax 336-5562
Leadership Academy for Young Men 9-12
655 Colfax St 14606 585-324-7760
Wakili Moore, prin.
Monroe HS 1,100/7-12
164 Alexander St 14607 585-232-1530
Armando Ramirez, prin. Fax 262-8965
Northeast College Preparatory HS 500/7-12
940 Fernwood Park 14609 585-324-9273
Dr. Mary Aronson, prin.
Northwest College Preparatory HS 400/7-12
940 Fernwood Park 14609 585-324-9289
Toyia Wilson, prin.
Public S 58 500/K-10
950 Norton St 14621 585-325-6170
Sheelarani Webster, prin. Fax 262-8964
Rochester Early College International HS 9-12
200 Genesee St 14611 585-324-9010
Marlene Blocker, prin.
S of Business Finance & Entrepreneurship 200/10-12
655 Colfax St 14606 585-324-9781
Joseph Baldino, prin.
Rochester STEM HS 9-12
655 Colfax St 14606 585-324-9760
Kathleen Denaro, prin.
School of Applied Technology at Edison Vo/Tech
655 Colfax St 14606 585-324-9781
Joseph Baldino, prin.
School of Engineering & Manufacturing 300/10-12
655 Colfax St 14606 585-324-9782
Joseph Baldino, prin.
School of Imaging & Information Tech Vo/Tech
655 Colfax St 14606 585-324-9794
Joseph Baldino, prin.
School of the Arts 1,200/7-12
45 Prince St 14607 585-242-7682
Brenda Pacheco, prin. Fax 256-6580
School Without Walls Commencement Acad 300/10-12
480 Broadway 14607 585-546-6732
Idonia Owens, prin. Fax 262-8947
School Without Walls Foundation Academy 200/7-9
111 Clinton Ave N 14604 585-324-3111
Uma Metha, prin.
Thomas HS 200/8-8
625 Scio St 14605 585-262-8850
Bonnie Atkins, prin. Fax 262-8872
Vanguard Collegiate HS 100/9-12
950 Norton St 14621 585-324-3760
Carol Jones, prin.
Wilson Foundation Academy 600/K-K, 5-8
200 Genesee St 14611 585-463-4100
Dr. Deasure Matthew, prin. Fax 463-4103
Wilson Magnet HS Commencement Academy 1,100/9-12
501 Genesee St 14611 585-328-3440
Pamela Rutland, prin. Fax 464-6153
Young Adult Evening HS Adult
625 Scio St 14605 585-262-8850
Lisa Young, prin.

West Irondequoit Central SD 3,800/K-12
321 List Ave 14617 585-342-5500
Jeffrey Crane, supt. Fax 266-1556
www.westirondequoit.org
Dake MS 600/7-8
350 Cooper Rd 14617 585-342-2140
Matthew Schrage, prin. Fax 336-3034
Irondequoit HS 1,300/9-12
260 Cooper Rd 14617 585-336-2914
Patrick McCue, prin. Fax 336-2929

Allendale Columbia S 400/PK-12
519 Allens Creek Rd 14618 585-381-4560
Michael Gee, head sch Fax 383-1191
Aquinas Institute 900/7-12
1127 Dewey Ave 14613 585-254-2020
Theodore Mancini, prin. Fax 254-7401
Bishop Kearney HS 500/7-12
125 Kings Hwy S 14617 585-342-4000
Julie Locey, prin. Fax 342-4694
Bryant & Stratton College Post-Sec.
854 Long Pond Rd 14612 585-720-0660
Bryant & Stratton College Post-Sec.
1225 Jeffson Rd 14623 585-292-5627
Colgate Rochester Crozer Divinity School Post-Sec.
1100 Goodman St S 14620 585-271-1320
Continental School Post-Sec.
633 Jefferson Rd 14623 585-272-8060
David Hochstein School of Music & Dance Post-Sec.
50 Plymouth Ave N 14614 585-454-4596
Destiny Christian S 100/PK-12
1876 Elmwood Ave 14620 585-473-1680
Lavonda Lofton, prin. Fax 473-2112
Everest Institute Post-Sec.
1630 Portland Ave 14621 585-266-0430
Harley S 500/PK-12
1981 Clover St 14618 585-442-1770
Valerie Myntti, head sch Fax 442-5758
McQuaid Jesuit HS 800/7-12
1800 Clinton Ave S 14618 585-473-1130
Fr. James Coughlin, prin. Fax 256-6171
Monroe Community College Post-Sec.
1000 E Henrietta Rd 14623 585-292-2000
Nazareth College of Rochester Post-Sec.
4245 East Ave 14618 585-389-2525
Northeastern Seminary Post-Sec.
2265 Westside Dr 14624 585-594-6800
Northstar Christian Academy 300/PK-12
332 Spencerport Rd 14606 585-429-5530
Rob Johnson, prin. Fax 429-7913
Onondaga School of Therapeutic Massage Post-Sec.
302 Goodman St N 14607 585-241-0070
Ora Academy 50/9-12
600 East Ave 14607 585-271-8711
Rabbi Eliezer Lehrer, hdmstr. Fax 271-8158
Our Lady of Mercy HS 700/7-12
1437 Blossom Rd 14610 585-288-7120
Terence Quinn, prin. Fax 288-7966
Roberts Wesleyan College Post-Sec.
2301 Westside Dr 14624 585-594-6000
Rochester General Hospital Post-Sec.
1425 Portland Ave 14621 585-338-4430
Rochester Institute of Technology (NTID) Post-Sec.
52 Lomb Memorial Dr 14623 585-475-6400
Rochester Institute of Technology Post-Sec.
1 Lomb Memorial Dr 14623 585-475-2411
Rochester School for the Deaf Post-Sec.
1545 Saint Paul St 14621 585-544-1240
St. Bernard's Sch of Theology & Ministry Post-Sec.
120 French Rd 14618 585-271-3657
St. John Fisher College Post-Sec.
3690 East Ave 14618 585-385-8000
Shear Ego Intl School of Hair Design Post-Sec.
525 Titus Ave 14617 585-342-0070
Siena Catholic Academy 300/7-8
2617 East Ave 14610 585-381-1220
Vincent Tata, prin. Fax 381-1223
Talmudical Institute of Upstate New York Post-Sec.
769 Park Ave 14607 585-473-2810
Talmudical Institute of Upstate New York 50/9-12
769 Park Ave 14607 585-473-2810
University of Rochester Post-Sec.
500 Joseph C Wilson Blvd 14627 585-275-2121

Rockaway Park, See New York
NYC Department of Education
Supt. — See New York
Beach Channel HS 1,100/9-12
10000 Beach Channel Dr 11694 718-945-6900
Dr. David Morris, prin. Fax 474-7682
Channel View S for Research 600/6-12
10000 Beach Channel Dr 11694 718-634-1970
Patricia Tubridy, prin. Fax 634-2896
Rockaway Collegiate HS 9-12
10000 Beach Channel Dr 11694 718-634-3031
Robert Young, prin. Fax 634-3043
Rockaway Park HS for Environmental Sust 100/9-12
10000 Beach Channel Dr 11694 718-318-6170
Jennifer Connolly, prin. Fax 318-6176
Scholars Academy 1,000/6-12
320 Beach 104th St 11694 718-474-6918
Brian O'Connell, prin. Fax 945-8958
Waterside S for Leadership 100/6-8
190 Beach 110th St 11694 718-634-1128
Linda Munro, prin. Fax 634-1185

Rockville Centre, Nassau, Pop. 23,734
Rockville Centre UFD 3,500/K-12
128 Shepherd St 11570 516-255-8957
Dr. William Johnson, supt. Fax 255-8810
www.rvcschools.org
South Side HS 1,100/9-12
140 Shepherd St 11570 516-255-8944
Dr. Carol Burris, prin. Fax 766-7934
South Side MS 800/6-8
67 Hillside Ave 11570 516-255-8976
Shelagh McGinn, prin. Fax 763-0914

Mercy Medical Center — Post-Sec.
PO Box 9024 11571 — 516-705-2525
Molloy College — Post-Sec.
PO Box 5002 11571 — 516-678-5000

Rocky Point, Suffolk, Pop. 13,836
Rocky Point UFD — 3,400/K-12
90 Rocky Point Yaphank Rd 11778 — 631-744-1600
Dr. Michael Ring, supt. — Fax 849-7557
www.rockypointschools.org
Rocky Point HS — 1,000/9-12
82 Rocky Point Yaphank Rd 11778 — 631-744-1604
John DeBenedetto, prin. — Fax 209-0204
Rocky Point MS — 800/6-8
76 Rocky Point Yaphank Rd 11778 — 631-744-1603
Scott O'Brien Ed.D., prin. — Fax 886-0000

Rome, Oneida, Pop. 32,943
Rome CSD — 5,300/PK-12
409 Bell Rd S 13440 — 315-338-6500
Jeffrey P. Simons, supt. — Fax 334-7409
www.romecsd.org
Rome Free Academy — 1,600/9-12
95 Dart Cir 13441 — 315-334-7203
Mark Benson, prin. — Fax 334-7236
Strough MS — 800/7-8
801 Laurel St 13440 — 315-338-5201
Tracy O'Rourke, prin. — Fax 334-7465

New York State School for the Deaf — Post-Sec.
401 Turin St 13440
Rome Catholic S — 300/PK-12
800 Cypress St 13440 — 315-336-6190
Michael Powers, prin. — Fax 336-6194

Romulus, Seneca, Pop. 400
Romulus Central SD — 500/PK-12
5705 State Route 96 14541 — 866-810-0345
Nancy Zimar, supt. — Fax 869-5961
www.rcs.k12.ny.us
Romulus Central HS — 100/9-12
5705 State Route 96 14541 — 866-810-0345
Lynn Rhone, prin. — Fax 869-5961

Ronkonkoma, Suffolk, Pop. 18,816
Connetquot Central SD
Supt. — See Bohemia
Ronkonkoma MS — 800/6-8
501 Peconic St 11779 — 631-467-6000
Charles Morea, prin. — Fax 467-6003

Sachem Central SD — 14,700/K-12
51 School St 11779 — 631-471-1336
James Nolan, supt. — Fax 471-1341
www.sachem.edu
Other Schools – See Farmingville, Holbrook, Holtsville, Lake Ronkonkoma

Roosevelt, Nassau, Pop. 15,891
Roosevelt UFD — 2,800/PK-12
335 E Clinton Ave 11575 — 516-345-7000
Robert-Wayne Harris, supt. — Fax 345-7326
www.rooseveltufsd.com/
Roosevelt HS — 800/9-12
1 Wagner Ave 11575 — 516-345-7200
Dr. Stephen Strachan, prin. — Fax 345-7790
Roosevelt MS — 600/6-8
335 E Clinton Ave 11575 — 516-345-7700
Michael Jones, prin. — Fax 345-7791

Roscoe, Sullivan, Pop. 539
Roscoe Central SD — 200/PK-12
PO Box 429 12776 — 607-498-4126
John Evans, supt. — Fax 498-5609
www.roscoe.k12.ny.us
Roscoe Central S — 200/PK-12
PO Box 429 12776 — 607-498-4126
Janice Phillips, prin. — Fax 498-6015

Roslyn, Nassau, Pop. 2,718
Roslyn UFD — 3,300/PK-12
PO Box 367 11576 — 516-801-5000
Dr. Dan Brenner, supt. — Fax 801-5008
www.roslynschools.org
Other Schools – See Roslyn Heights

Mesivta of Roslyn — 50/9-12
2 Shelter Rock Rd 11576 — 516-877-2131

Roslyn Heights, Nassau, Pop. 6,383
Roslyn UFD
Supt. — See Roslyn
Roslyn HS — 1,100/9-12
475 Round Hill Rd 11577 — 516-801-5100
Scott Andrews, prin. — Fax 801-5108
Roslyn MS — 800/6-8
375 Locust Ln 11577 — 516-801-5200
Jack Palmadesso, prin. — Fax 801-5208

Roxbury, Delaware
Roxbury Central SD — 300/PK-12
53729 State Highway 30 12474 — 607-326-4151
Thomas O'Brien, supt. — Fax 326-4154
www.roxburycs.org
Roxbury Central S — 300/PK-12
53729 State Highway 30 12474 — 607-326-4151
Eric Windover, prin. — Fax 326-4154

Rushville, Ontario, Pop. 661
Marcus Whitman Central SD — 1,000/K-12
4100 Baldwin Rd 14544 — 585-554-4848
Michael Chirco, supt. — Fax 554-4882
www.mwcsd.org/
Whitman HS — 500/9-12
4100 Baldwin Rd 14544 — 585-554-6441
Jennifer Taft, prin. — Fax 554-5201
Whitman MS — 300/6-8
4100 Baldwin Rd 14544 — 585-554-6442
Clayton Cole, prin. — Fax 554-3414

Russell, Saint Lawrence
Edwards-Knox Central SD — 600/PK-12
PO Box 630 13684 — 315-562-8330
Suzanne Kelly, supt. — Fax 562-2477
www.ekcsk12.org
Edwards-Knox JSHS — 300/7-12
PO Box 630 13684 — 315-562-8131
Michelle Varian, prin. — Fax 562-8139

Rye, Westchester, Pop. 15,489
Rye CSD — 3,200/K-12
411 Theodore Fremd Ste 100S 10580 — 914-967-6100
Dr. Frank Alvarez, supt. — Fax 967-6957
www.ryeschools.org/
Rye HS — 900/9-12
1 Parsons St 10580 — 914-967-6100
Patricia Taylor, prin. — Fax 967-4380
Rye MS — 800/6-8
3 Parsons St 10580 — 914-967-6100
Dr. Ann Edwards, prin. — Fax 921-6189
Rye S of Leadership — Alt
324 Midland Ave 10580 — 914-760-1462
Paul Blank, coord.

Rye Country Day S — 900/PK-12
Cedar St 10580 — 914-967-1417
Scott Nelson, hdmstr. — Fax 967-1418
School of the Holy Child — 300/5-12
2225 Westchester Ave 10580 — 914-967-5622
Ann Sullivan, hdmstr. — Fax 967-7210

Rye Brook, Westchester, Pop. 9,207
Blind Brook-Rye UFD — 1,500/K-12
390 N Ridge St 10573 — 914-937-3600
William Stark, supt. — Fax 937-5871
www.blindbrook.org
Blind Brook HS — 400/9-12
840 King St 10573 — 914-937-3600
Patricia Lambert, prin. — Fax 937-4509
Blind Brook MS — 400/6-8
840 King St 10573 — 914-937-3600
Todd Richard, prin. — Fax 937-4509

Port Chester-Rye UFD — 4,100/K-12
113 Bowman Ave 10573 — 914-934-7900
Dr. Edward Kliszus, supt. — Fax 934-0727
www.portchesterschools.org
Other Schools – See Port Chester

Sackets Harbor, Jefferson, Pop. 1,431
Sackets Harbor Central SD — 500/K-12
PO Box 290 13685 — 315-646-3575
Frederick Hall, supt. — Fax 646-1038
www.sacketspatriots.org/
Sackets Harbor Central S — 500/K-12
PO Box 290 13685 — 315-646-3575
Jennifer Gaffney, prin. — Fax 646-1038

Sag Harbor, Suffolk, Pop. 2,139
Sag Harbor UFD — 1,000/PK-12
200 Jermain Ave 11963 — 631-725-5300
Dr. Carl Bonuso, supt. — Fax 725-5330
www.sagharborschools.org
Pierson MSHS — 500/6-12
200 Jermain Ave 11963 — 631-725-5302
Jeff Nichols, prin. — Fax 725-5314

Saint Albans, See New York
NYC Department of Education
Supt. — See New York
Pathways College Preparatory S — 500/6-12
10989 204th St 11412 — 718-454-4957
Kimberly Mitchell, prin. — Fax 454-4892
IS 192 — 700/6-8
10989 204th St 11412 — 718-479-5540
Harriett Diaz, prin. — Fax 217-4645

Saint Bonaventure, Cattaraugus, Pop. 2,013

St. Bonaventure University — Post-Sec.
3261 W State Rd 14778 — 585-375-2000

Saint James, Suffolk, Pop. 13,215
Smithtown Central SD
Supt. — See Smithtown
Nesaquake MS — 800/6-8
479 Edgewood Ave 11780 — 631-382-5100
Kevin Simmons, prin. — Fax 382-5107
Smithtown HS East — 1,700/9-12
10 School St 11780 — 631-382-2700
Edwin Thompson, prin. — Fax 382-2707

Knox S — 100/6-12
541 Long Beach Rd 11780 — 631-686-1600
Thad Gaebelein, hdmstr. — Fax 686-1650

Saint Johnsville, Montgomery, Pop. 1,719
Oppenheim-Ephratah Central SD — 400/PK-12
6486 State Highway 29 13452 — 518-568-2014
Laura Campione Lawrence, supt. — Fax 568-2941
www.oecs.k12.ny.us/DistrictInformation/index.htm
Oppenheim-Ephratah-Saint Johnsville HS — 200/9-12
44 Center St 13452 — 518-568-2011
Fax 568-2797

Saint Regis Falls, Franklin, Pop. 456
Saint Regis Falls Central SD — 300/PK-12
PO Box 309 12980 — 518-856-9421
Beverly Ouderkirk, supt. — Fax 856-0142
stregisfallscsd.org/
Saint Regis Falls S — 300/PK-12
PO Box 309 12980 — 518-856-9421
Marc Czadzeck, prin. — Fax 856-0142

Salamanca, Cattaraugus, Pop. 5,605
Salamanca City Central SD — 1,000/PK-12
50 Iroquois Dr 14779 — 716-945-2403
Robert Breidenstein, supt. — Fax 945-3964
www.salamancany.org/
Salamanca JSHS — 300/7-12
50 Iroquois Dr 14779 — 716-945-2404
Ann Anderson, prin. — Fax 945-5983

Salem, Washington, Pop. 930
Salem Central SD — 600/K-12
PO Box 517 12865 — 518-854-7855
Thomas McGowan, supt. — Fax 854-3957
salemcsd.org/
Salem JSHS — 300/7-12
PO Box 517 12865 — 518-854-7600
Fax 854-3957

Sanborn, Niagara, Pop. 1,620
Niagara-Wheatfield Central SD
Supt. — See Niagara Falls
Niagara-Wheatfield HS — 1,300/9-12
2292 Saunders Settlement Rd 14132 — 716-215-3100
Tim Carter, prin. — Fax 215-3125
Town MS — 900/6-8
2292 Saunders Settlement Rd 14132 — 716-215-3150
Dr. Laura Palka, prin. — Fax 215-3160

SUNY Niagara County Community College — Post-Sec.
3111 Saunders Settlement Rd 14132 — 716-614-6200

Sandy Creek, Oswego, Pop. 769
Sandy Creek Central SD — 900/PK-12
PO Box 248 13145 — 315-387-3445
Stewart Amell, supt. — Fax 387-2196
www.sccs.cnyric.org/
Sandy Creek HS — 300/9-12
PO Box 248 13145 — 315-387-3445
Maureen Shiel, prin. — Fax 387-2196
Sandy Creek MS — 200/6-8
PO Box 248 13145 — 315-387-3445
Carolyn Shirley, prin. — Fax 387-2196

Saranac, Clinton
Saranac Central SD
Supt. — See Dannemora
Saranac HS — 600/9-12
PO Box 8 12981 — 518-565-5800
Jonathan Parks, prin. — Fax 565-5809
Saranac MS — 300/6-8
PO Box 8 12981 — 518-565-5700
Jeffrey Durant, prin. — Fax 565-5706

Saranac Lake, Franklin, Pop. 5,317
Saranac Lake Central SD — 1,300/PK-12
79 Canaras Ave 12983 — 518-891-5460
Gerald Goldman, supt. — Fax 891-5140
saranaclakecs.org/
Saranac Lake HS — 500/9-12
79 Canaras Ave 12983 — 518-891-4450
Bruce VanWeelden, prin. — Fax 891-6813
Saranac Lake MS — 300/6-8
79 Canaras Ave 12983 — 518-891-4221
Patricia Kenyon, prin. — Fax 891-6615

SUNY North Country Community College — Post-Sec.
PO Box 89 12983 — 518-891-2915

Saratoga Springs, Saratoga, Pop. 26,062
Saratoga Springs CSD — 6,800/K-12
3 Blue Streak Blvd 12866 — 518-583-4700
Michael Piccirillo, supt. — Fax 584-6624
www.saratogaschools.org
Maple Ave MS — 1,600/6-8
515 Maple Ave 12866 — 518-587-4551
Stuart Byrne, prin. — Fax 587-5759
Saratoga Springs HS — 2,100/9-12
1 Blue Streak Blvd 12866 — 518-587-6690
Brett Miller, prin. — Fax 583-1671

Saratoga Central Catholic HS — 200/7-12
247 Broadway 12866 — 518-587-7070
Steve Lombard, prin. — Fax 587-0678
Skidmore College — Post-Sec.
815 N Broadway 12866 — 518-580-5000
SUNY Empire State College — Post-Sec.
2 Union Ave 12866 — 518-587-2100
Waldorf S of Saratoga Springs — 200/PK-12
122 Regent St 12866 — 518-587-0549
Katherine Scharff, admin. — Fax 581-1466

Saugerties, Ulster, Pop. 3,876
Saugerties Central SD — 2,500/K-12
PO Box A 12477 — 845-247-6550
Seth Turner, supt. — Fax 246-8364
www.saugerties.k12.ny.us
Saugerties JSHS — 1,000/7-12
PO Box A 12477 — 845-247-6650
Thomas Averill, prin. — Fax 246-4312

Woodstock Day S — 200/PK-12
1430 Glasco Tpke 12477 — 845-246-3744
Dr. Jim Handlin, hdmstr. — Fax 246-0053

Sauquoit, Oneida
Sauquoit Valley Central SD — 1,100/K-12
2601 Oneida St 13456 — 315-839-6311
Ronald Wheelock, supt. — Fax 839-5352
www.svcsd.org
Sauquoit Valley HS — 400/9-12
2601 Oneida St 13456 — 315-839-6316
Zane Mahar, prin. — Fax 839-6397
Sauquoit Valley MS — 200/6-8
2601 Oneida St 13456 — 315-839-6371
Peter Madden, prin. — Fax 839-6390

Sayville, Suffolk, Pop. 16,715
Sayville UFD — 3,300/K-12
99 Greeley Ave 11782 — 631-244-6510
Dr. Walter Schartner, supt. — Fax 244-6504
www.sayville.k12.ny.us
Sayville MS — 800/6-8
291 Johnson Ave 11782 — 631-244-6650
Thomas Murray, prin. — Fax 244-6655
Other Schools – See West Sayville

Scarsdale, Westchester, Pop. 16,786
Edgemont UFD 1,900/K-12
300 White Oak Ln 10583 914-472-7768
Dr. Victoria S. Kniewel, supt. Fax 472-6846
www.edgemont.org/
Edgemont JSHS 900/7-12
200 White Oak Ln 10583 914-725-1500
Devan Ganeshananthan, prin. Fax 725-1057

Scarsdale UFD 4,800/K-12
2 Brewster Rd Ste 2 10583 914-721-2410
Dr. Michael McGill, supt. Fax 722-2822
www.scarsdaleschools.k12.ny.us
Scarsdale HS 1,400/9-12
1057 Post Rd 10583 914-721-2450
Kenneth Bonamo, prin. Fax 721-2549
Scarsdale MS 1,200/6-8
134 Mamaroneck Rd 10583 914-721-2600
Michael McDermott, prin. Fax 721-2655

Schaghticoke, Rensselaer, Pop. 588
Hoosic Valley Central SD 1,100/K-12
2 Pleasant Ave 12154 518-753-4450
Douglas Kelley, supt. Fax 753-7665
www.hoosicvalley.k12.ny.us/
Hoosic Valley HS 400/9-12
1548 State Route 67 12154 518-753-4432
Amy Goodell, prin. Fax 753-7491
Hoosic Valley MS 400/5-8
1548 State Route 67 12154 518-753-4432
Amy Goodell, prin. Fax 753-7491

Schenectady, Schenectady, Pop. 59,889
Mohonasen Central SD 3,000/K-12
2072 Curry Rd 12303 518-356-8200
Dr. Kathleen Spring, supt. Fax 356-8247
www.mohonasen.org
Draper MS 700/6-8
2070 Curry Rd 12303 518-356-8350
Debra Male, prin. Fax 356-8359
Mohonasen HS 1,100/9-12
2072 Curry Rd 12303 518-356-8300
David Collins, prin. Fax 356-8309

Niskayuna Central SD 4,200/K-12
1239 Van Antwerp Rd 12309 518-377-4666
Susan Kay Salvaggio, supt. Fax 377-4074
www.niskyschools.org
Iroquois MS 600/6-8
2495 Rosendale Rd 12309 518-377-2233
Vicki Wyld, prin. Fax 377-2219
Niskayuna HS 1,400/9-12
1626 Balltown Rd 12309 518-382-2521
John Rickert, prin. Fax 382-2539
Van Antwerp MS 400/6-8
2253 Story Ave 12309 518-370-1243
Luke Rakoczy, prin. Fax 370-4610

Schalmont Central SD 1,600/K-12
4 Sabre Dr 12306 518-355-9200
Carol Pallas, supt. Fax 355-9203
www.schalmont.org
Schalmont HS 700/9-12
1 Sabre Dr 12306 518-355-6110
Terence Nash, prin. Fax 355-8720
Schalmont MS 400/5-8
2 Sabre Dr 12306 518-355-6255
Matthew Morgan, prin. Fax 355-5329

Schenectady CSD 8,900/PK-12
108 Education Dr 12303 518-370-8100
Laurence Spring, supt. Fax 370-8173
www.schenectady.k12.ny.us
Mont Pleasant MS 600/7-8
1121 Forest Rd 12303 518-370-8160
Michael Bush, prin. Fax 881-3562
Schenectady HS 2,800/9-12
1445 The Plz 12308 518-881-2044
Diane Wilkinson, prin. Fax 370-8169
Steinmetz Career and Leadership Academy Vo/Tech
880 Oakwood Ave 12303 518-370-8183
Gregory Fields, prin. Fax 881-3602

Ellis Hospital School of Nursing Post-Sec.
1101 Nott St 12308 518-243-4471
Mid-America Baptist Theological Seminary Post-Sec.
2810 Curry Rd 12303 518-355-4000
Modern Welding School Post-Sec.
1842 State St 12304 518-374-1216
Notre Dame-Bishop Gibbons HS 300/6-12
2600 Albany St 12304 518-393-3131
Ninette Kondratowicz, prin. Fax 370-3817
SUNY Schenectady County Community Coll. Post-Sec.
78 Washington Ave 12305 518-381-1200
Troy School of Beauty Culture Post-Sec.
101 Deanna Ct 12309 518-273-7741
Union College Post-Sec.
807 Union St 12308 518-388-6000
Union Graduate College Post-Sec.
80 Nott Ter 12308 518-631-9900

Schenevus, Otsego, Pop. 543
Schenevus Central SD 300/K-12
159 Main St 12155 607-638-5530
Thomas Jennings, supt. Fax 638-5600
www.schenevuscs.org/
Schenevus Central S 300/K-12
159 Main St 12155 607-638-5881
Coleen Lewis, prin. Fax 638-5600

Schoharie, Schoharie, Pop. 912
Schoharie Central SD 900/K-12
PO Box 430 12157 518-295-6600
Brian Sherman, supt. Fax 295-8178
www.schoharie.k12.ny.us
Schoharie JSHS 400/7-12
PO Box 430 12157 518-295-6601
Stacey DeLaney, prin. Fax 295-8161

Schroon Lake, Essex, Pop. 817
Schroon Lake Central SD 200/K-12
PO Box 338 12870 518-532-7164
Bonnie Finnerty, supt. Fax 532-0284
www.schroonschool.org
Schroon Lake Central S 200/K-12
PO Box 338 12870 518-532-7164
Bonnie Finnerty, prin. Fax 532-0284

Schuylerville, Saratoga, Pop. 1,376
Schuylerville Central SD 1,800/K-12
14 Spring St 12871 518-695-3255
Ryan Sherman Ed.D., supt. Fax 695-6491
www.schuylervilleschools.org
Schuylerville HS 600/9-12
14 Spring St 12871 518-695-3255
Matthew Sickles, prin. Fax 695-3103
Schuylerville MS 500/6-8
14 Spring St 12871 518-695-3255
Mary Kate Elsworth, prin. Fax 695-6491

Scio, Allegany, Pop. 604
Scio Central SD 400/PK-12
3968 Washington St 14880 585-593-5076
Tracie Preston, supt. Fax 593-3468
scio.schooltools.us/
Scio Central S 400/PK-12
3968 Washington St 14880 585-593-5510
Matthew Hopkins, prin. Fax 593-0653

Scotia, Schenectady, Pop. 7,607
Scotia-Glenville Central SD 2,600/K-12
900 Preddice Pkwy 12302 518-382-1215
Susan Swartz, supt. Fax 386-4336
www.sgcsd.net
Scotia-Glenville HS 800/9-12
1 Tartan Way 12302 518-382-1231
Peter Bednarek, prin. Fax 386-4303
Scotia-Glenville MS 600/6-8
10 Prestige Pkwy 12302 518-382-1263
Robert Cosmer, prin. Fax 386-4303

Mekeel Christian Academy 300/K-12
36-38 Sacandaga Rd 12302 518-370-4272
Yvonne Gormley, prin. Fax 370-4778

Scottsville, Monroe, Pop. 1,964
Wheatland-Chili Central SD 700/K-12
13 Beckwith Ave 14546 585-889-6246
Dr. Deborah Leh, supt. Fax 889-6284
www.wheatland.k12.ny.us
Wheatland-Chili MSHS 400/6-12
940 North Rd 14546 585-889-6245
Brad Zilliox, prin. Fax 889-6217

Sea Cliff, Nassau, Pop. 4,948
North Shore Central SD 2,900/K-12
112 Franklin Ave 11579 516-277-7800
Edward Melnick, supt. Fax 277-7801
www.northshoreschools.org/
Other Schools – See Glen Head

Seaford, Nassau, Pop. 15,154
Seaford UFD 2,500/K-12
1600 Washington Ave 11783 516-592-4000
Brian Conboy, supt. Fax 592-4049
www.seaford.k12.ny.us
Seaford HS 800/9-12
1575 Seamans Neck Rd 11783 516-592-4300
Scott Bersin, prin. Fax 592-4399
Seaford MS 600/6-8
3940 Sunset Ave 11783 516-592-4200
Dan Smith, prin. Fax 592-4299

Selden, Suffolk, Pop. 19,540
Middle Country Central SD
Supt. — See Centereach
Newfield HS 1,600/9-12
145 Marshall Dr 11784 631-285-8300
Dr. Theodore Fulton, prin. Fax 285-8301

SUNY Suffolk County Community College Post-Sec.
533 College Rd 11784 631-451-4000

Seneca Falls, Seneca, Pop. 6,593
Seneca Falls Central SD 1,300/K-12
PO Box 268 13148 315-568-5500
Robert McKeveny, supt. Fax 712-0535
www.sfcs.k12.ny.us/
Mynderse Academy 400/9-12
105 Troy St 13148 315-568-5500
Anthony Ferrara, prin. Fax 712-0523
Seneca Falls MS 300/6-8
95 Troy St 13148 315-568-5500
Kevin Rhinehart, prin. Fax 712-0524

New York Chiropractic College Post-Sec.
2360 State Route 89 13148 315-568-3000

Setauket, Suffolk, Pop. 15,248
Three Village Central SD
Supt. — See Stony Brook
Gelinas JHS 900/7-9
25 Mud Rd 11733 631-730-4700
Gustave Hueber, prin. Fax 730-4706

Sharon Springs, Schoharie, Pop. 550
Sharon Springs Central SD 300/K-12
PO Box 218 13459 518-284-2266
Patterson Green, supt. Fax 284-9033
www.sharonsprings.org/
Sharon Springs Central S 300/K-12
PO Box 218 13459 518-284-2267
Patterson Green, prin. Fax 284-9075

Shelter Island, Suffolk, Pop. 1,316
Shelter Island UFD 200/K-12
PO Box 2015 11964 631-749-0302
Dr. Michael Hynes, supt. Fax 749-1262
www.shelterisland.k12.ny.us
Shelter Island Central S 200/K-12
PO Box 2015 11964 631-749-0302
Dr. Michael Hynes, prin. Fax 749-1262

Sherburne, Chenango, Pop. 1,358
Sherburne-Earlville Central SD 1,400/K-12
15 School St 13460 607-674-7300
Gayle Hellert, supt. Fax 674-9742
secsd.org
Sherburne-Earlville HS 500/9-12
13 School St 13460 607-674-7380
Kyle McFarland, prin. Fax 674-7368
Sherburne-Earlville MS 300/6-8
13 School St 13460 607-674-7350
Jolene Emhoff, prin. Fax 674-7392

Sherman, Chautauqua, Pop. 717
Sherman Central SD 500/PK-12
PO Box 950 14781 716-761-6122
Kaine Kelly, supt. Fax 761-6119
www.sherman.wnyric.org
Sherman HS 200/7-12
PO Box 950 14781 716-761-6121
Michael Ginestre, prin. Fax 761-6119

Shoreham, Suffolk, Pop. 528
Shoreham-Wading River Central SD 2,700/K-12
250B Route 25A 11786 631-821-8100
Steven Cohen Ph.D., admin. Fax 929-3001
www.swrschools.org
Prodell MS 600/6-8
100 Randall Rd 11786 631-821-8212
Dr. Linda Anthony, prin. Fax 821-8275
Shoreham-Wading River HS 900/9-12
250A Route 25A 11786 631-821-8264
Dan Holtzman, prin. Fax 821-8162

Shortsville, Ontario, Pop. 1,429
Manchester-Shortsville Central SD 900/PK-12
1506 State Route 21 14548 585-289-3964
Robert Leiby, supt. Fax 289-6660
www.redjacket.org
Red Jacket HS 300/9-12
1506 State Route 21 14548 585-289-3966
James Niedermeier, prin. Fax 289-4755
Red Jacket MS 200/6-8
1506 State Route 21 14548 585-289-3967
Charlene Harvey, prin. Fax 289-8715

Shrub Oak, Westchester, Pop. 1,970
Lakeland Central SD 6,200/K-12
1086 E Main St 10588 914-245-1700
Dr. George Stone, supt. Fax 245-1589
www.lakelandschools.org
Lakeland HS 1,100/9-12
1349 E Main St 10588 914-528-0600
Lorrie Yurish, prin. Fax 528-0521
Other Schools – See Cortlandt Manor, Yorktown Heights

Sidney, Delaware, Pop. 3,846
Sidney Central SD 1,000/K-12
95 W Main St 13838 607-563-2135
William Christensen, supt. Fax 563-2386
www.sidneycsd.org
Sidney HS 400/9-12
95 W Main St 13838 607-561-7703
Eben Bullock, prin. Fax 563-1800
Sidney MS 200/6-8
13 Pearl St E 13838 607-561-7702
Robert Hansen, prin. Fax 563-7242

Silver Creek, Chautauqua, Pop. 2,618
Silver Creek Central SD 1,000/K-12
1 Dickinson St 14136 716-934-2603
Daniel G. Ljiljanich, supt. Fax 934-7983
www.silvercreek.wnyric.org/
Silver Creek HS 300/9-12
1 Dickinson St 14136 716-934-2603
James Klubek, prin. Fax 934-2103
Silver Creek MS 200/6-8
1 Dickinson St 14136 716-934-2603
Paula Troutman, prin. Fax 934-3760

Sinclairville, Chautauqua, Pop. 578
Cassadaga Valley Central SD 1,000/PK-12
PO Box 540 14782 716-962-5155
Scott Smith, supt. Fax 962-5976
cvweb.wnyric.org
Cassadaga Valley HS 400/9-12
PO Box 540 14782 716-962-8581
Tara DiDomenico, prin. Fax 962-5788
Cassadega Valley MS 300/6-8
PO Box 540 14782 716-962-8581
Rich Siegel, prin. Fax 962-5788

Skaneateles, Onondaga, Pop. 2,428
Skaneateles Central SD 1,600/K-12
45 E Elizabeth St 13152 315-291-2221
Judith Pastel, supt. Fax 685-0347
www.skanschools.org
Skaneateles HS 500/9-12
49 E Elizabeth St 13152 315-291-2231
Georgette Hoskins, prin. Fax 291-2250
Skaneateles MS 400/6-8
35 East St 13152 315-291-2241
Timothy Chiavara, prin. Fax 291-2267

Slate Hill, Orange
Minisink Valley Central SD 4,400/K-12
PO Box 217 10973 845-355-5110
John Latini, supt. Fax 355-5119
www.minisink.com
Minisink Valley HS 1,500/9-12
PO Box 217 10973 845-355-5150
Kenneth Hauck, prin. Fax 355-5198
Minisink Valley MS 1,000/6-8
PO Box 217 10973 845-355-5200
Michael Giardina, prin. Fax 355-5205

Sleepy Hollow, Westchester, Pop. 9,977
Tarrytown UFD — 2,700/PK-12
200 N Broadway 10591 — 914-631-9404
Dr. Christopher P. Clouet, supt. — Fax 332-6283
www.tufsd.org
Sleepy Hollow HS — 800/9-12
210 N Broadway 10591 — 914-631-8838
Carol Conklin-Spillane, prin. — Fax 332-6219
Sleepy Hollow MS — 600/6-8
210 N Broadway 10591 — 914-332-6275
Elizabeth Lopez, prin. — Fax 332-6219

Smithtown, Suffolk, Pop. 27,100
Smithtown Central SD — 10,400/K-12
26 New York Ave 11787 — 631-382-2000
Dr. Anthony Annunziato, supt. — Fax 382-2010
www.smithtown.k12.ny.us
Accompsett MS — 800/6-8
660 Meadow Rd 11787 — 631-382-2300
John Nocero, prin. — Fax 382-2307
Smithtown HS West — 1,700/9-12
100 Central Rd 11787 — 631-382-2905
John Coady, prin. — Fax 382-2910
Other Schools – See Nesconset, Saint James

Smithtown Christian S — 600/PK-12
1 Higbie Dr 11787 — 631-265-3334
Rev. Roger Erdvig M.Ed., supt. — Fax 265-1079

Snyder, Erie

Park S of Buffalo — 300/PK-12
4625 Harlem Rd 14226 — 716-839-1242
Christopher Lauricella, hdmstr. — Fax 839-2014

Sodus, Wayne, Pop. 1,754
Sodus Central SD — 1,200/PK-12
PO Box 220 14551 — 315-483-5201
Martin Cox, supt. — Fax 483-4755
www.soduscsd.org
Sodus HS — 400/9-12
PO Box 220 14551 — 315-483-5285
Eugene Hoskins, prin. — Fax 483-6168
Sodus MS — 400/5-8
PO Box 220 14551 — 315-483-5281
Heather Uetz, prin. — Fax 483-5291

Solvay, Onondaga, Pop. 6,416
Solvay UFD — 1,500/K-12
103 3rd St 13209 — 315-468-1111
Lawrence Wright, supt. — Fax 468-2755
www.solvayschools.org
Solvay HS — 600/9-12
600 Gertrude Ave 13209 — 315-468-2551
Jay Tinklepaugh, prin. — Fax 484-1404
Other Schools – See Syracuse

Somers, Westchester
Somers Central SD — 3,400/K-12
250 Route 202 10589 — 914-277-2400
Dr. Raymond Blanch, supt. — Fax 277-2409
www.somersschools.org/
Somers MS — 900/6-8
250 Route 202 10589 — 914-277-3399
Jeffrey Getman, prin. — Fax 277-2236
Other Schools – See Lincolndale

Kennedy HS — 600/9-12
54 Route 138 10589 — 914-232-5061
Rev. Mark Vaillancourt Ph.D., prin. — Fax 232-3416

Southampton, Suffolk, Pop. 3,057
Southampton UFD — 1,600/PK-12
70 Leland Ln 11968 — 631-591-4500
Dr. J. Richard Boyes, supt. — Fax 287-2870
www.southamptonschools.org
Southampton HS — 600/9-12
141 Narrow Ln 11968 — 631-591-4600
Dr. Brian Zahn, prin. — Fax 283-6313
Southampton IS — 400/5-8
70 Leland Ln 11968 — 631-591-4700
Timothy Frazier, prin. — Fax 283-6899

South Dayton, Chautauqua, Pop. 607
Pine Valley Central SD — 700/PK-12
7755 Route 83 14138 — 716-988-3293
Pete Morgante, supt. — Fax 988-3243
www.pval.org/
Pine Valley Central JSHS — 300/7-12
7827 Route 83 14138 — 716-988-3276
Cathy Fabiatos, prin. — Fax 988-3139

South Fallsburg, Sullivan, Pop. 2,810

Yeshiva Gedola Zichron Moshe — 50/9-12
PO Box 580 12779 — 845-434-5240
Yeshivath Zichron Moshe — Post-Sec.
PO Box 580 12779 — 845-434-5240

South Glens Falls, Saratoga, Pop. 3,492
South Glens Falls Central SD — 3,200/PK-12
6 Bluebird Rd 12803 — 518-793-9617
Michael Patton, supt. — Fax 761-0723
www.sgfallssd.org/
South Glens Falls HS — 1,000/9-12
42 Merritt Rd 12803 — 518-792-9987
Carla Biviano, prin. — Fax 792-5412
Winch MS — 800/6-8
99 Hudson St 12803 — 518-792-5891
Mark Fish, prin. — Fax 793-9505

South Kortright, Delaware
South Kortright Central SD — 400/PK-12
PO Box 113 13842 — 607-538-9111
Patricia Norton-White, supt. — Fax 538-9205
www.skcs.org
South Kortright Central S — 400/PK-12
PO Box 113 13842 — 607-538-9111
Patricia Norton-White, admin. — Fax 538-9205

Southold, Suffolk, Pop. 5,696
Southold UFD — 900/K-12
PO Box 470 11971 — 631-765-5400
David Gamberg, supt. — Fax 765-5086
www.southoldufsd.net/
Southold JSHS — 500/7-12
PO Box 470 11971 — 631-765-5081
William Galati, prin. — Fax 765-5086

South Otselic, Chenango
Otselic Valley Central SD — 400/K-12
PO Box 161 13155 — 315-653-7218
Richard Hughes, supt. — Fax 653-7500
www.ovcs.org/
Otselic Valley JSHS — 200/7-12
PO Box 161 13155 — 315-653-7218
Daniel Henner, prin. — Fax 653-7500

South Ozone Park, See New York
NYC Department of Education
Supt. — See New York
JHS 226 — 1,500/6-8
12110 Rockaway Blvd 11420 — 718-843-2260
Rushell White, prin. — Fax 835-6317

Al-Ihsan Academy — 500/PK-12
PO Box 200215 11420 — 718-322-3154

South Wales, Erie

Gow S — 100/7-12
PO Box 85 14139 — 716-652-3450
M. Bradley Rogers, hdmstr. — Fax 652-3457

Sparkill, Rockland, Pop. 1,536

St. Thomas Aquinas College — Post-Sec.
125 Route 340 10976 — 845-398-4000

Spencer, Tioga, Pop. 744
Spencer-Van Etten Central SD — 1,000/PK-12
PO Box 307 14883 — 607-589-7100
Dr. Joseph Morgan, supt. — Fax 589-3010
www.svecsd.org/
Spencer-Van Etten HS — 400/9-12
PO Box 307 14883 — 607-589-7140
Melissa Jewell, prin. — Fax 589-3010
Spencer-Van Etten MS — 300/5-8
PO Box 369 14883 — 607-589-7120
Eric Knolles, prin. — Fax 589-3020

North Spencer Christian Academy — 100/PK-12
721 Ithaca Rd 14883 — 607-589-6366
L. Ed Brown, admin. — Fax 589-4455

Spencerport, Monroe, Pop. 3,553
Spencerport Central SD — 3,900/K-12
71 Lyell Ave 14559 — 585-349-5000
Michael Crumb, supt. — Fax 349-5011
www.spencerportschools.org
Cosgrove MS — 1,000/6-8
2749 Spencerport Rd 14559 — 585-349-5300
Ned Dale, prin. — Fax 349-5346
Spencerport HS — 1,300/9-12
2707 Spencerport Rd 14559 — 585-349-5200
Sean McCabe, prin. — Fax 349-5266

Springfield Gardens, See New York
NYC Department of Education
Supt. — See New York
Carver HS for the Sciences — 400/9-12
14310 Springfield Blvd 11413 — 718-525-6439
Dr. Janice Sutton, prin. — Fax 525-6482
Excelsior Preparatory HS — 500/9-12
14310 Springfield Blvd 11413 — 718-525-6507
Lillie Lucas, prin. — Fax 525-6276
Preparatory Academy for Writers — 400/6-12
14310 Springfield Blvd 11413 — 718-949-8405
Charles Anderson, prin. — Fax 525-8495
Queens Preparatory Academy — 400/9-12
14310 Springfield Blvd 11413 — 718-712-2304
Tashon Haywood, prin. — Fax 712-3273
IS 59 — 700/6-8
13255 Ridgedale St 11413 — 718-527-3501
Carleton Gordon, prin. — Fax 276-1364

Spring Valley, Rockland, Pop. 30,786
East Ramapo Central SD — 7,000/K-12
105 S Madison Ave 10977 — 845-577-6000
Dr. Joel Klein, supt. — Fax 577-6168
www.eram.k12.ny.us
Ramapo HS — 1,400/9-12
400 Viola Rd 10977 — 845-577-6400
Sherrill Murray-Lazarus, prin. — Fax 426-1124
Spring Valley HS — 1,100/9-12
361 W Route 59 10977 — 845-577-6500
Karen Pinel, prin. — Fax 426-1127
Other Schools – See Chestnut Ridge, Suffern

Bais Malka HS of Belz — 100/9-12
111 Union Rd 10977 — 845-371-0020
Bais Yaakov D'Rav Hirsch — 100/9-12
235 N Main St 10977 — 845-371-6750
Be'er Yaakov Talmudic Seminary — Post-Sec.
12 Jefferson Ave 10977 — 845-362-3053
Mesivta Shaarei Arazim — 100/9-12
52 S Main St 10977 — 845-426-6401
Sunbridge Institute — Post-Sec.
285 Hungry Hollow Rd 10977 — 845-425-0055
United Talmudical Academy — 1,500/K-12
89 S Main St 10977 — 845-425-0392
Yeshiva Avir Yaakov — 3,100/PK-12
766 N Main St 10977 — 845-362-6600
Yeshiva Bais Hachinuch — 100/3-8
50A S Main St Ste 8 10977 — 845-354-3805
Yeshiva Degel Hatorah — 200/K-12
111 Maple Ave 10977 — 845-356-4610
Yeshiva Tzoin Yosef-Pupa — 300/PK-12
15 Widman Ct 10977 — 845-371-1220
Yeshiva Zichron Yaakov — 50/9-12
720 Union Rd 10977 — 845-362-4990

Springville, Erie, Pop. 4,257
Springville-Griffith Inst. Central SD — 2,100/K-12
307 Newman St 14141 — 716-592-3230
Dr. Paul Connelly, supt. — Fax 592-3209
www.springvillegi.org/
Griffith Institute HS — 700/9-12
290 N Buffalo St 14141 — 716-592-3202
Vincent Vanderlip, prin. — Fax 592-3297
Griffith Institute MS — 500/6-8
267 Newman St 14141 — 716-592-3203
Michael Retzlaff, prin. — Fax 592-3268

Staatsburg on Hudson, Dutchess, Pop. 372
Hyde Park Central SD
Supt. — See Hyde Park
Roosevelt HS — 1,400/9-12
156 S Cross Rd 12580 — 845-229-4020
Barbara Marrine, prin. — Fax 229-4029

Stamford, Delaware, Pop. 1,103
Stamford Central SD — 400/K-12
1 River St 12167 — 607-652-7301
Catherine Graves, supt. — Fax 652-3446
stamfordcs.org/
Stamford Central S — 400/K-12
1 River St 12167 — 607-652-7301
Ruth Ehrets, prin. — Fax 652-3446

Star Lake, Saint Lawrence, Pop. 799
Clifton-Fine Central SD — 300/PK-12
11 Hall Ave 13690 — 315-848-3333
Susan Shene, supt. — Fax 848-3350
www.cfeagles.org
Clifton-Fine JSHS — 200/7-12
11 Hall Ave 13690 — 315-848-3333
Susan Shene, prin. — Fax 848-3350

Staten Island, See New York
NYC Department of Education
Supt. — See New York
Concord HS — 200/Alt
109 Rhine Ave 10304 — 718-447-1274
Ron Gorsky, prin. — Fax 442-6276
CSI HS for International Studies — 500/9-12
100 Essex Dr 10314 — 718-370-6900
Joseph Canale, prin. — Fax 370-6915
Curtis HS — 2,600/9-12
105 Hamilton Ave 10301 — 718-390-1800
Aurelia Curtis, prin. — Fax 556-4800
Marsh Ave S for Expeditionary Learning — 400/6-8
100 Essex Dr 10314 — 718-370-6850
Jessica Jenkins-Milona, prin. — Fax 370-6860
McCown Expeditionary Learning S — 300/9-12
100 Essex Dr 10314 — 718-370-6950
Traci Frey, prin. — Fax 370-6960
McKee Career and Technical HS — Vo/Tech
290 Saint Marks Pl 10301 — 718-420-2600
Sharon Henry, prin. — Fax 981-8776
New Dorp HS — 2,500/9-12
465 New Dorp Ln 10306 — 718-667-8686
Deirdre DeAngelis, prin. — Fax 987-4889
Petrides S — 1,300/K-12
715 Ocean Ter 10301 — 718-815-0186
Joanne Buckheit, prin. — Fax 815-9638
Port Richmond HS — 2,300/9-12
85 Saint Josephs Ave 10302 — 718-420-2100
Tim Gannon, prin. — Fax 981-6203
IS 2 — 900/6-8
333 Midland Ave 10306 — 718-987-5336
Adrienne Stallone, prin. — Fax 987-6937
IS 7 — 1,200/6-8
1270 Huguenot Ave 10312 — 718-697-8488
Dr. Nora Derosa-Karby, prin. — Fax 967-0809
IS 24 — 1,400/6-8
225 Cleveland Ave 10308 — 718-982-4700
Lenny Santamaria, prin. — Fax 356-5834
IS 27 — 1,100/6-8
11 Clove Lake Pl 10310 — 718-981-8800
Tracey Kornish, prin. — Fax 815-4677
IS 34 — 1,100/6-8
528 Academy Ave 10307 — 718-477-4500
John Boyle, prin. — Fax 227-4074
IS 49 — 900/6-8
101 Warren St 10304 — 718-727-6040
Linda Hill, prin. — Fax 876-8207
IS 51 — 1,000/6-8
20 Houston St 10302 — 718-981-0502
Nicholas Mele, prin. — Fax 815-3957
IS 61 — 1,300/6-8
445 Castleton Ave 10301 — 718-727-8481
Susan Tronolone, prin. — Fax 447-2112
IS 72 — 1,600/6-8
33 Ferndale Ave 10314 — 718-698-5757
Peter Macellari, prin. — Fax 761-5928
IS 75 — 1,300/6-8
455 Huguenot Ave 10312 — 718-356-0130
Kenneth Zapata, prin. — Fax 984-5302
Staten Island Tech HS — Vo/Tech
485 Clawson St 10306 — 718-667-3222
Vincent Maniscalco, prin. — Fax 987-5872
Tottenville HS — 3,800/9-12
100 Luten Ave 10312 — 718-668-8800
John Tuminaro, prin. — Fax 317-0962
Wagner HS — 3,100/9-12
1200 Manor Rd 10314 — 718-698-4200
Gary Giordano, prin. — Fax 698-5213

Career School of New York — Post-Sec.
350 Saint Marks Pl 10301 — 718-420-6440
CUNY College of Staten Island — Post-Sec.
2800 Victory Blvd 10314 — 718-982-2000
Francis HS — 200/9-12
4240 Amboy Rd 10308 — 718-967-0400
Fax 227-7766
Monsignor Farrell HS — 1,200/9-12
2900 Amboy Rd 10306 — 718-987-2900
Msgr. Edmund Whalen, prin. — Fax 987-4241

Moore Catholic HS 800/9-12
100 Merrill Ave 10314 718-761-9200
Robert Manisero, prin. Fax 982-7779
Notre Dame Academy 500/9-12
134 Howard Ave 10301 718-447-8878
Kathryn Jaenicke, prin. Fax 447-2926
St. John's University Post-Sec.
300 Howard Ave 10301 718-390-4500
St. John Villa Academy 600/9-12
25 Landis Ave 10305 718-442-6240
Barbara Logan, prin. Fax 447-6729
St. Joseph by the Sea HS 400/9-12
5150 Hylan Blvd 10312 718-984-6500
Fr. Michael Reilly, prin. Fax 984-6503
St. Joseph Hill Academy 400/9-12
850 Hylan Blvd 10305 718-447-1374
Angela Ferrando, prin. Fax 447-3041
St. Pauls School of Nursing Post-Sec.
2 Teleport Dr Ste 203 10311 718-816-6470
St. Peter's Boys HS 600/9-12
200 Clinton Ave 10301 718-447-1676
John Fodera, prin. Fax 447-4027
St. Vincent's Medical Center Post-Sec.
355 Bard Ave 10310 718-876-2413
Sisters of Charity Medical Center Post-Sec.
75 Vanderbilt Ave 10304 718-818-6470
Staten Island Academy 400/PK-12
715 Todt Hill Rd 10304 718-987-8100
Albert Cauz, hdmstr. Fax 979-7641
Wagner College Post-Sec.
1 Campus Rd 10301 718-390-3100
Yeshiva & Mesvita of Staten Island 100/9-12
1870 Drumgoole Rd E 10309 718-356-4323

Stillwater, Saratoga, Pop. 1,707
Stillwater Central SD 1,100/K-12
1068 Hudson Ave 12170 518-373-6100
Stan Maziejka, supt. Fax 664-9134
www.scsd.org/
Stillwater HS 400/9-12
1068 Hudson Ave 12170 518-373-6100
Mario Fernandez, prin. Fax 664-1832
Stillwater MS 300/5-8
1068 Hudson Ave 12170 518-373-6100
Patti Morris, prin. Fax 664-1832

Stone Ridge, Ulster, Pop. 1,136

SUNY Ulster Post-Sec.
491 Cottekill Rd 12484 845-687-5000

Stony Brook, Suffolk, Pop. 13,574
Three Village Central SD 7,300/K-12
100 Suffolk Ave 11790 631-730-4000
Cheryl Pedisich, supt. Fax 474-7784
www.threevillagecsd.org
Murphy JHS 900/7-9
351 Oxhead Rd 11790 631-730-4800
Vincent Vizzo, prin. Fax 730-4801
Other Schools – See East Setauket, Setauket

Stony Brook S 300/7-12
1 Chapman Pkwy 11790 631-751-1800
Joshua Crane, head sch Fax 751-3449
Stony Brook University SUNY Post-Sec.
118 Administration 11794 631-632-6000

Suffern, Rockland, Pop. 10,548
East Ramapo Central SD
Supt. — See Spring Valley
Pomona MS 700/7-8
101 Pomona Rd 10901 845-577-6200
Christine Alfonso, prin. Fax 577-6245

Ramapo Central SD
Supt. — See Hillburn
Suffern HS 1,500/9-12
49 Viola Rd 10901 845-357-3800
Patrick Breen, prin. Fax 357-5035
Suffern MS 1,100/6-8
80 Hemion Rd 10901 845-357-7400
Brian Fox, prin. Fax 357-4563

Salvation Army School Officer Training Post-Sec.
201 Lafayette Ave 10901 845-368-7200
SUNY Rockland Community College Post-Sec.
145 College Rd 10901 845-574-4000
Yeshiva Ohr Reuven 100/9-12
259 Grandview Ave 10901 845-362-8362
Rabbi Bezalel Rudinsky, prin. Fax 354-4830
Yeshiva Shaarei Torah 100/9-12
91 Carlton Rd W 10901 845-352-3431
Yeshiva Shaarei Torah of Rockland Post-Sec.
91 Carlton Rd W 10901 845-352-3431

Syosset, Nassau, Pop. 18,544
Syosset Central SD, 99 Pell Ln 11791 6,600/K-12
Dr. Carole Hankin, supt. 516-364-5600
www.syosset.k12.ny.us
South Woods MS, 99 Pell Ln 11791 800/6-8
Michelle Burget, prin. 516-364-5621
Syosset HS, 70 Southwoods Rd 11791 2,200/9-12
Dr. Giovanni Durante, prin. 516-364-5675
Thompson MS, 98 Ann Dr 11791 800/6-8
James Kassebaum, prin. 516-364-5760

New York College of Health Professions Post-Sec.
6801 Jericho Tpke 11791 800-922-7337
Our Lady of Mercy Academy 500/9-12
815 Convent Rd 11791 516-921-1047
Joan Gordon, prin. Fax 921-3634
Star Career Academy Post-Sec.
125 Michael Dr 11791 516-364-4344

Syracuse, Onondaga, Pop. 138,722
Solvay UFD
Supt. — See Solvay
Solvay MS 500/4-8
299 Bury Dr 13209 315-487-7061
James Werbeck, prin. Fax 484-1444

Syracuse CSD 18,800/K-12
1025 Erie Blvd W 13204 315-435-4161
Sharon Contreras, supt. Fax 435-4015
www.syracusecityschools.com/
Clary MS 400/6-8
100 Amidon Dr 13205 315-435-4411
Pamela Odom, prin. Fax 435-5832
Corcoran HS 1,400/9-12
919 Glenwood Ave 13207 315-435-4321
Leo Cosgrove, prin. Fax 435-4024
Danforth MS 500/6-8
309 W Brighton Ave 13205 315-435-4535
Patricia Clark, prin. Fax 435-6208
Expeditionary Learning S 100/6-8
4942 S Salina St 13205 315-435-6416
Rebecca Groat, prin. Fax 435-4880
Fowler HS 1,100/9-12
227 Magnolia St 13204 315-435-4376
James Palumbo, prin. Fax 435-6313
Grant MS 600/6-8
2400 Grant Blvd 13208 315-435-4433
Dean DeSantis, prin. Fax 435-4856
Henninger HS 1,600/9-12
600 Robinson St 13206 315-435-4343
Robert DiFlorio, prin. Fax 435-6277
Institute of Technology at Syracuse Cntr Vo/Tech
258 E Adams St 13202 315-435-4300
Matthews Williams, prin. Fax 435-5816
Johnson Vocational Center Vo/Tech
573 E Genesee St 13202 315-435-4135
John Dittmann, prin. Fax 435-6599
Lincoln MS 500/6-8
1613 James St 13203 315-435-4450
Kevin Burns, prin. Fax 435-4455
Nottingham HS 1,300/9-12
3100 E Genesee St 13224 315-435-4380
David Maynard, prin. Fax 435-4177
Westside Academy at Blodgett 200/6-8
312 Oswego St 13204 315-435-4386
Alton Hicks, prin. Fax 435-4539
Johnson Adult & Continuing Education Ctr Adult
573 E Genesee St 13202 315-435-4135
Kathryn Lent, coord. Fax 435-5875

Westhill Central SD 1,700/K-12
400 Walberta Rd 13219 315-426-3218
Casey Barduhn, supt. Fax 488-6411
www.westhillschools.org/
Onondaga Hill MS 600/5-8
4860 Onondaga Rd 13215 315-426-3400
Mark Bednarski, prin. Fax 492-0156
Westhill HS 600/9-12
4501 Onondaga Blvd 13219 315-426-3100
Lee Roscoe, prin. Fax 475-0319

Bishop Ludden JSHS 400/7-12
815 Fay Rd 13219 315-468-2591
Michael Sandore, prin. Fax 468-0097
Bryant & Stratton College Post-Sec.
953 James St 13203 315-472-6603
Christian Brothers Academy 800/7-12
6245 Randall Rd 13214 315-446-5960
Br. Joseph Jozwiak, prin. Fax 446-3393
Crouse Hospital College of Nursing Post-Sec.
736 Irving Ave 13210 315-470-7481
Faith Heritage S 300/PK-12
3740 Midland Ave 13205 315-469-7777
Neal Capone, head sch Fax 492-7440
Le Moyne College Post-Sec.
1419 Salt Springs Rd 13214 315-445-4100
Living Word Academy 200/PK-12
6101 Court Street Rd 13206 315-437-6744
Philip Mastroleo, prin. Fax 437-6766
Onondaga School of Therapeutic Massage Post-Sec.
719 E Genesee St 13210 315-424-1159
Phillips Hairstyling Institute Post-Sec.
709 E Genesee St 13210 315-422-9656
St. Joseph's Hospital College of Nursing Post-Sec.
206 Prospect Ave 13203 315-448-5040
Simmons Institute of Funeral Service Post-Sec.
1828 South Ave 13207 315-475-5142
SUNY College Environ. Science - Forestry Post-Sec.
1 Forestry Dr 13210 315-470-6500
SUNY Onondaga Community College Post-Sec.
4585 W Seneca Tpke 13215 315-498-2622
SUNY Upstate Medical University Post-Sec.
750 E Adams St 13210 315-464-5540
Syracuse University 13244 Post-Sec.
315-443-1870

Tannersville, Greene, Pop. 531
Hunter-Tannersville Central SD 400/PK-12
PO Box 1018 12485 518-589-5400
Dr. Patrick Sweeney, supt. Fax 589-5403
www.htcsd.org/
Tannersville MSHS 200/7-12
PO Box 1018 12485 518-589-5880
Simon Williams, prin. Fax 589-7071

Tarrytown, Westchester, Pop. 11,035

Hackley S 800/K-12
293 Benedict Ave 10591 914-366-2642
Walter Johnson, hdmstr. Fax 366-2636

Thiells, Rockland, Pop. 4,970
North Rockland Central SD
Supt. — See Garnerville
Fieldstone MS 600/7-8
100 Fieldstone Dr 10984 845-942-7900
Anthony Zollo, prin. Fax 942-7910
North Rockland HS 2,000/9-12
106 Hammond Rd 10984 845-942-3300
Michael Gill, prin. Fax 942-3365

Thornwood, Westchester, Pop. 3,718
Mount Pleasant Central SD 2,000/K-12
825 Westlake Dr 10594 914-769-5500
Dr. Susan Guiney, supt. Fax 769-3733
www.mtplcsd.org
Westlake HS 600/9-12
825 Westlake Dr 10594 914-769-8311
Keith Schenker, prin. Fax 769-0596
Westlake MS 500/6-8
825 Westlake Dr 10594 914-769-8540
Dr. Robert Hendrickson, prin. Fax 769-8550

Ticonderoga, Essex, Pop. 3,342
Ticonderoga Central SD 900/K-12
5 Calkins Pl 12883 518-585-7400
John McDonald, supt. Fax 585-2682
www.ticonderogak12.org
Ticonderoga HS 300/9-12
5 Calkins Pl 12883 518-585-7400
Michael Graney, prin. Fax 585-4076
Ticonderoga MS 200/6-8
116 Alexandria Ave 12883 518-585-7442
John Donohue, prin. Fax 585-2716

SUNY North Country Community College Post-Sec.
11 Hawkeye Trl 12883 518-585-4454

Tioga Center, Tioga
Tioga Central SD 900/K-12
PO Box 241 13845 607-687-8000
Scot Taylor, supt. Fax 687-8007
www.tiogacentral.org
Tioga HS 300/9-12
PO Box 241 13845 607-687-8001
Margo Martin, prin. Fax 687-8010
Tioga MS 300/5-8
PO Box 241 13845 607-687-8004
Willard Cook, prin. Fax 687-6910

Tonawanda, Erie, Pop. 14,988
Kenmore-Tonawanda UFSD
Supt. — See Buffalo
Kenmore East HS 1,100/9-12
350 Fries Rd 14150 716-874-8402
Patrick Heyden, prin. Fax 874-8443

Tonawanda CSD 1,300/PK-12
100 Hinds St 14150 716-694-7784
Mary Beth Scullion, supt. Fax 695-8738
www.tonawandacsd.org
Tonawanda MSHS 400/6-12
600 Fletcher St 14150 716-694-7660
James Newton, prin. Fax 743-8839

Cardinal O'Hara HS 200/9-12
39 Ohara Rd 14150 716-695-2600
Mary Holzerland, prin. Fax 692-8697
MarJon School of Beauty Culture Post-Sec.
1154 Niagara Falls Blvd 14150 716-836-6240

Troy, Rensselaer, Pop. 48,315
Brunswick Central SD 1,300/K-12
3992 State Highway 2 12180 518-279-4600
Dr. Angelina Bergin, supt. Fax 279-4588
www.brittonkill.k12.ny.us
Tamarac MSHS 800/6-12
3992 State Highway 2 12180 518-279-4600
Richard Pogue, prin. Fax 279-3888

Lansingburgh Central SD 2,400/K-12
576 5th Ave 12182 518-233-6850
Cynthia DeDominick, supt. Fax 235-7436
www.lansingburgh.org
Knickerbacker MS 600/6-8
320 7th Ave 12182 518-233-6811
Shaun Paolino, prin. Fax 238-2518
Lansingburgh HS 800/9-12
320 7th Ave 12182 518-233-6806
Frank Macri, prin. Fax 233-6826

Troy CSD 4,100/PK-12
2920 5th Ave 12180 518-328-5052
Dr. Brian Howard, supt. Fax 271-5229
www.troy.k12.ny.us/
Doyle MS 500/7-8
475 1st St 12180 518-328-5301
Brian Dunn, prin. Fax 274-8160
Public S 1 Alt
2920 5th Ave 12180 518-328-5473
James Canfield, prin. Fax 271-5229
Troy HS 1,300/9-12
1950 Burdett Ave 12180 518-328-5401
Joseph Mariano, prin. Fax 274-2341

Catholic Central HS 500/7-12
625 7th Ave 12182 518-235-7100
Christopher Bott, prin. Fax 237-1796
La Salle Institute 400/6-12
174 Williams Rd 12180 518-283-2500
Br. Carl Malacalza, prin. Fax 283-6265
Oakwood Christian S 100/PK-12
260 Oakwood Ave 12182 518-271-0526
Rev. James DuJack, admin. Fax 270-1659
Redemption Christian Academy 100/PK-12
PO Box 753 12181 518-272-6679
John Massey, dir. Fax 270-8039
Rensselaer Polytechnic Institute Post-Sec.
110 8th St 12180 518-276-6000
Samaritan Hospital School of Nursing Post-Sec.
2215 Burdett Ave 12180 518-271-3285
SUNY Hudson Valley Community College Post-Sec.
80 Vandenburgh Ave 12180 518-629-4822
The Sage Colleges Post-Sec.
65 1st St 12180 518-244-2000
Willard S 300/9-12
285 Pawling Ave 12180 518-833-1300
Trudy Hall, hdmstr. Fax 833-1800

Trumansburg, Tompkins, Pop. 1,761
Trumansburg Central SD 1,200/K-12
100 Whig St 14886 607-387-7551
Michael McGuire, supt. Fax 387-2807
www.tburg.k12.ny.us
Dickerson HS 400/9-12
100 Whig St 14886 607-387-7551
Jon Koeng, prin. Fax 387-2807
Doig MS 300/5-8
100 Whig St 14886 607-387-7551
Francisco Paler-Large, prin. Fax 387-2807

Tuckahoe, Westchester, Pop. 6,361

St. Vladimir's Orthodox Theological Sem. Post-Sec.
575 Scarsdale Rd 10707 914-961-8313

Tully, Onondaga, Pop. 852
Tully Central SD 1,000/K-12
20 State St 13159 315-696-6204
Kraig Pritts, supt. Fax 883-1343
www.tullyschools.org/
Tully JSHS 600/7-12
20 State St 13159 315-696-6235
Mary Ann Murphy, prin. Fax 696-6237

Tupper Lake, Franklin, Pop. 3,639
Tupper Lake Central SD 800/K-12
294 Hosley Ave 12986 518-359-3371
Seth McGowan, supt. Fax 359-7862
www.tupperlakecsd.net/
Tupper Lake MSHS 400/7-12
25 Chaney Ave 12986 518-359-3322
Seth McGowan, prin. Fax 359-7862

Turin, Lewis, Pop. 232
South Lewis Central SD 900/PK-12
PO Box 10 13473 315-348-2500
Douglas Premo, supt. Fax 348-2510
www.southlewis.org
South Lewis HS 400/9-12
PO Box 40 13473 315-348-2520
Jennifer Myers, prin. Fax 348-2510
South Lewis MS 200/5-8
PO Box 70 13473 315-348-2570
Philomena Goss, prin. Fax 348-2510

Tuxedo Park, Orange, Pop. 598
Tuxedo UFD 600/K-12
PO Box 2002 10987 845-351-4799
Carol Lomascolo, supt. Fax 351-5296
tuxedoschooldistrict.com
Baker HS 400/9-12
PO Box 2002 10987 845-351-4786
Denis Petrilak, prin. Fax 351-4823

Uniondale, Nassau, Pop. 24,253
Uniondale UFD 6,200/K-12
933 Goodrich St 11553 516-560-8800
William Lloyd Ph.D., supt. Fax 292-2659
www.uniondaleschools.org
Turtle Hook MS 700/6-8
975 Jerusalem Ave 11553 516-918-1300
Dr. Donald Humphrey, prin. Fax 505-2533
Uniondale HS 2,000/9-12
933 Goodrich St 11553 516-560-8831
Florence Simmons, prin. Fax 564-8464
Other Schools – See Hempstead

Hebrew Academy of Nassau County 400/7-12
215 Oak St 11553 516-538-8161
Rabbi Shlomo Adelman, prin. Fax 489-1142
Institute of Allied Medical Professions Post-Sec.
333 Earle Ovington Ste 305 11553 516-450-3110
Kellenberg Memorial HS 2,600/6-12
1400 Glenn Curtiss Blvd 11553 516-292-0200
Br. Ken Hoagland, prin. Fax 292-0877

Union Springs, Cayuga, Pop. 1,182
Union Springs Central SD 900/K-12
239 Cayuga St 13160 315-889-4101
Linda Rice, supt. Fax 889-4108
www.uscsd.info/
Union Springs HS 300/9-12
239 Cayuga St 13160 315-889-4110
Charles Walker, prin. Fax 889-4118
Union Springs MS 100/7-8
239 Cayuga St 13160 315-889-4112
Thomas Eldridge, prin. Fax 889-4118

Union Springs Academy 100/9-12
PO Box 524 13160 315-889-7314
Wayne Edwards, prin. Fax 889-7188

Upper Nyack, Rockland, Pop. 2,003
Nyack UFD
Supt. — See Nyack
Nyack HS 900/9-12
360 Christian Herald Rd 10960 845-353-7100
Nicole Saieva, prin. Fax 353-7119

Utica, Oneida, Pop. 60,287
Utica CSD 9,600/K-12
106 Memorial Pkwy 13501 315-792-2210
Bruce Karam, supt. Fax 792-2200
www.uticacsd.org/
Donovan MS 1,000/6-8
1701 Noyes St 13502 315-792-2006
Ann Marie Palladino, prin. Fax 792-2077
Kennedy MS 1,100/6-8
500 Deerfield Dr E 13502 315-368-6641
Joshua Gifford, prin.
Proctor HS, 1203 Hilton Ave 13501 2,600/9-12
Steven Falchi, prin. 315-368-6400

Faxton-St. Luke's Healthcare Post-Sec.
PO Box 479 13503 315-624-6136
Mohawk Valley Community College Post-Sec.
1101 Sherman Dr 13501 315-792-5400
Notre Dame JSHS 400/7-12
2 Notre Dame Ln 13502 315-724-5118
Sr. Anna Collins, prin. Fax 724-9460
Pratt MWP Post-Sec.
310 Genesee St 13502 800-755-8920
St. Elizabeth College of Nursing Post-Sec.
2215 Genesee St 13501 315-798-8144
SUNY Institute of Technology Utica/Rome Post-Sec.
100 Seymour Rd 13502 315-792-7500
USC The Business College Post-Sec.
201 Bleecker St 13501 315-733-2300
Utica College Post-Sec.
1600 Burrstone Rd 13502 315-792-3111

Valatie, Columbia, Pop. 1,798
Ichabod Crane Central SD 1,700/K-12
PO Box 820 12184 518-758-7575
George Zini, supt. Fax 758-7579
www.ichabodcrane.org/
Crane HS 700/9-12
PO Box 820 12184 518-758-7575
William Schneider, prin. Fax 758-2181
Crane MS 500/6-8
PO Box 820 12184 518-758-7575
Tim Farley, prin. Fax 758-1405

Valhalla, Westchester, Pop. 3,081
Valhalla UFD 1,600/K-12
316 Columbus Ave 10595 914-683-5040
Dr. Brenda Myers, supt. Fax 683-5075
www.valhallaschools.org/
Valhalla HS 400/9-12
300 Columbus Ave 10595 914-683-5014
Jonathan Thomas, prin. Fax 683-5003
Valhalla MS 400/6-8
300 Columbus Ave 10595 914-683-5011
Steven Garcia, prin. Fax 683-5003

New York Medical College Post-Sec.
40 Sunshine Cottage Rd 10595 914-594-4000
SUNY Westchester Community College Post-Sec.
75 Grasslands Rd 10595 914-606-6600

Valley Stream, Nassau, Pop. 36,423
Valley Stream Central HSD 4,600/7-12
1 Kent Rd 11580 516-872-5601
Dr. Bill Heidenreich, supt. Fax 872-5658
www.vschsd.org
Valley Stream Central HS 1,100/10-12
135 Fletcher Ave 11580 516-561-4410
Dr. Joseph Pompilio, prin. Fax 561-4490
Valley Stream Memorial JHS 1,000/7-9
320 Fletcher Ave 11580 516-872-7710
Anthony Mignella, prin. Fax 872-7711
Valley Stream South HS 1,300/7-12
150 Jedwood Pl 11581 516-791-0310
Maureen Henry, prin. Fax 791-0305
Other Schools – See Franklin Square

Business Informatics Center Post-Sec.
134 S Central Ave 11580 516-561-0050
Valley Stream Christian Academy 200/K-12
12 E Fairview Ave 11580 516-823-0022
Leslie Fowley, supt. Fax 823-0228

Van Hornesville, Herkimer
Van Hornesville-Owen D. Young Central SD 200/K-12
PO Box 125 13475 315-858-0729
James Picolla, supt. Fax 858-2019
Young Central S 200/K-12
PO Box 125 13475 315-858-0729
James Picolla, supt. Fax 858-2019

Verona, Oneida, Pop. 837
Vernon-Verona-Sherrill Central SD 2,100/PK-12
PO Box 128 13478 315-829-2520
Martha Group, supt. Fax 829-4949
www.vvsschools.org
Vernon-Verona-Sherrill HS 700/9-12
PO Box 128 13478 315-829-2520
Andy Brown, prin. Fax 829-4465
Vernon-Verona-Sherrill MS 300/7-8
PO Box 128 13478 315-829-2520
Carrie Hodkinson, prin. Fax 829-5966

Vestal, Broome, Pop. 5,000
Vestal Central SD 3,700/K-12
201 Main St 13850 607-757-2241
Mark LaRoach, supt. Fax 757-2227
www.vestal.k12.ny.us/
Vestal HS 1,200/9-12
205 Woodlawn Dr 13850 607-757-2281
Catherine Hepler, prin. Fax 757-2301
Vestal MS 900/6-8
600 S Benita Blvd 13850 607-757-2331
Ann Marie Loose, prin. Fax 757-2229

Elmira Business Institute Post-Sec.
4100 Vestal Rd 13850 607-729-8915
Ross Corners Christian Academy 200/PK-12
2101 Owego Rd 13850 607-748-3301
Toby Wyse, admin. Fax 748-3301

Victor, Ontario, Pop. 2,645
Victor Central SD 4,300/PK-12
953 High St 14564 585-924-3252
Dr. Dawn Santiago-Marullo, supt. Fax 742-7090
www.victorschools.org
Victor HS 1,300/9-12
953 High St 14564 585-924-3252
Yvonne O'Shea, prin. Fax 924-9536
Victor JHS 600/7-8
953 High St 14564 585-924-3252
Carl Christensen, prin. Fax 924-9535

Voorheesville, Albany, Pop. 2,770
Voorheesville Central SD 1,200/K-12
432 New Salem Rd 12186 518-765-3313
Teresa Snyder Ed.D., supt. Fax 765-2751
vcsd.neric.org/
Bouton HS 400/9-12
432 New Salem Rd 12186 518-765-3314
Imran Abassi, prin. Fax 765-5547
Voorheesville MS 300/6-8
432 New Salem Rd 12186 518-765-3314
James Franchini, prin. Fax 765-3842

Wallkill, Ulster, Pop. 2,258
Wallkill Central SD 3,400/K-12
PO Box 310 12589 845-895-7100
William Hecht, supt. Fax 895-3630
www.wallkillcsd.k12.ny.us
Borden MS 600/7-8
PO Box 310 12589 845-895-7175
Marjorie Anderson, prin. Fax 895-8036
Wallkill HS 1,200/9-12
PO Box 310 12589 845-895-7150
Michael Rydell, prin. Fax 895-8003

Walton, Delaware, Pop. 3,059
Walton Central SD 1,400/K-12
47-49 Stockton Ave 13856 607-865-4116
Dr. George Mack, supt. Fax 865-8568
www.waltoncsd.org
Mack MS 600/6-8
47-49 Stockton Ave 13856 607-865-4116
Michael MacDonald, prin. Fax 865-8568
O'Neill HS 300/9-12
47-49 Stockton Ave 13856 607-865-4116
Michael MacDonald, prin. Fax 865-6130

Walworth, Wayne
Gananda Central SD 1,100/K-12
1500 Dayspring Rdg 14568 315-986-3521
Shawn VanScoy Ed.D., supt. Fax 986-2003
www.gananda.org
Gananda / Cirillo HS 400/9-12
1500 Dayspring Rdg 14568 315-986-3521
Kelly Van Laeken, prin. Fax 986-2003
Gananda MS 300/6-8
1500 Dayspring Rdg 14568 315-986-3521
Matthew Mahoney, prin. Fax 986-2003

Wampsville, Madison, Pop. 531
Oneida CSD
Supt. — See Oneida
Shortell MS 400/7-8
PO Box 716 13163 315-363-1050
Robin Price, prin. Fax 366-0622

Wantagh, Nassau, Pop. 18,699
Wantagh UFD 3,500/K-12
3301 Beltagh Ave 11793 516-781-8000
Maureen Goldberg, supt. Fax 781-6076
www.wantaghschools.org
Wantagh HS 1,200/9-12
3297 Beltagh Ave 11793 516-679-6402
Dr. Carolyn Breivogel, prin. Fax 679-6432
Wantagh MS 900/6-8
3299 Beltagh Ave 11793 516-679-6350
Dawn Matrochano, prin. Fax 679-6311

Wappingers Falls, Dutchess, Pop. 5,339
Wappingers Central SD 12,300/K-12
167 Myers Corners Rd 12590 845-298-5000
Marco Pochintesta, supt. Fax 298-5041
www.wappingersschools.org
Ketcham HS 2,000/9-12
99 Myers Corners Rd 12590 845-298-5100
G. Thomas Stella, prin. Fax 298-5099
Orchard View Alternative HS 50/Alt
167 Myers Corners Rd 12590 845-298-5000
Rodger Dettay, prin.
Van Wyck JHS 1,600/6-8
6 Hillside Lake Rd 12590 845-227-1700
Steve Shuchat, prin. Fax 227-1748
Wappingers Falls JHS 900/7-8
30 Major MacDonald Way 12590 845-298-5200
Terrence Thompson, prin. Fax 298-5156
Other Schools – See Hopewell Junction

Warrensburg, Warren, Pop. 3,071
Warrensburg Central SD 800/K-12
103 Schroon River Rd 12885 518-623-2861
Timothy Lawson, supt. Fax 623-2436
www.wcsd.org/
Warrensburg JSHS 400/7-12
103 Schroon River Rd 12885 518-623-2862
Doug Duell, prin. Fax 623-5089

Warsaw, Wyoming, Pop. 3,438
Warsaw Central SD 1,000/K-12
153 W Buffalo St 14569 585-786-8000
Thomas Cox, supt. Fax 786-8008
www.warsaw.k12.ny.us/
Warsaw MSHS 500/6-12
81 W Court St 14569 585-786-8000
Christopher Swiatek, prin. Fax 786-3193

Warwick, Orange, Pop. 6,603
Warwick Valley Central SD 4,000/K-12
PO Box 595 10990 845-987-3000
Dr. Ray Bryant, supt. Fax 987-1147
www.warwickvalleyschools.com
Warwick Valley HS 1,500/9-12
PO Box 595 10990 845-987-3050
Richard Linkens, prin. Fax 987-8982
Warwick Valley MS 1,000/6-8
PO Box 595 10990 845-987-3100
Cindy Leandro, prin. Fax 986-6942

Washingtonville, Orange, Pop. 5,806
Washingtonville Central SD 4,400/K-12
52 W Main St 10992 845-497-4000
Roberta Greene, supt. Fax 496-2330
www.ws.k12.ny.us
Washingtonville HS 1,600/9-12
54 W Main St 10992 845-497-4000
Brian Connolly, prin. Fax 496-2212
Washingtonville MS 1,100/6-8
38 W Main St 10992 845-497-4000
Teresa Thompson, prin. Fax 496-2099

Waterford, Saratoga, Pop. 1,958
Waterford-Halfmoon UFD 800/K-12
125 Middletown Rd 12188 518-237-0800
Timothy Lange, supt. Fax 237-7335
www.whufsd.org
Waterford-Halfmoon HS 400/7-12
125 Middletown Rd 12188 518-237-0800
Debra Cardnuto, prin. Fax 237-7335

Waterloo, Seneca, Pop. 5,097
Waterloo Central SD 1,600/K-12
109 Washington St 13165 315-539-1500
Terry MacNabb, supt. Fax 539-1504
www.waterloocsd.org
Waterloo HS 600/9-12
96 Stark St 13165 315-539-1550
Jeramy Clingerman, prin. Fax 539-1536
Waterloo MS 400/6-8
65 Center St 13165 315-539-1540
Michael Ferrara, prin. Fax 539-1534

Watertown, Jefferson, Pop. 26,112
Watertown CSD 4,200/K-12
1351 Washington St 13601 315-785-3700
Terry Fralick, supt. Fax 785-6855
www.watertowncsd.org
Case MS 600/7-8
1237 Washington St 13601 315-785-3870
Terry Gonseth, prin. Fax 785-3731
Watertown HS 1,200/9-12
1335 Washington St 13601 315-785-3800
Joseph McGrath, prin. Fax 785-3733

Faith Fellowship Christian S 100/PK-12
131 Moore Ave 13601 315-782-9342
Theodore Curinga, prin. Fax 786-0309
Immaculate Heart Central JSHS 300/7-12
1316 Ives St 13601 315-788-4670
Lisa Parsons, prin. Fax 788-4672
Jefferson Community College Post-Sec.
1220 Coffeen St 13601 315-786-2200
Samaritan Medical Center Post-Sec.
830 Washington St 13601 315-785-4000

Waterville, Oneida, Pop. 1,551
Waterville Central SD 800/K-12
381 Madison St 13480 315-841-3900
Charles Chafee, supt. Fax 841-3939
www.watervilleschools.org/
Waterville JSHS 400/6-12
381 Madison St 13480 315-841-3800
Jon Thummler, prin. Fax 841-3838

Watervliet, Albany, Pop. 9,992
Watervliet CSD 1,400/K-12
1245 Hillside Dr 12189 518-629-3200
Dr. Lori Caplan, supt. Fax 629-3265
vliet.neric.org/
Watervliet JSHS 700/7-12
1245 Hillside Dr 12189 518-629-3200
Ryan Groat, prin. Fax 273-1707

Watkins Glen, Schuyler, Pop. 1,826
Watkins Glen Central SD 1,100/PK-12
303 12th St 14891 607-535-3220
Thomas Phillips, supt. Fax 535-4629
www.wgcsd.org
Watkins Glen Central HS 400/9-12
301 12th St 14891 607-535-3210
David Warren, prin. Fax 535-4629
Watkins Glen MS 300/6-8
200 10th St 14891 607-535-3230
Kai D'Alleva, prin. Fax 535-4532

Waverly, Tioga, Pop. 4,388
Waverly Central SD 1,100/PK-12
15 Frederick St 14892 607-565-2841
Joseph Yelich, supt. Fax 565-4997
www.waverlyschools.com/
Waverly HS 500/9-12
1 Frederick St 14892 607-565-8101
Kim Forero, prin. Fax 565-4997
Waverly MS 200/6-8
1 Frederick St 14892 607-565-3410
Kim Forero, prin. Fax 565-4997

Wayland, Steuben, Pop. 1,852
Wayland-Cohocton Central SD 1,600/PK-12
2350 State Route 63 14572 585-728-2211
Michael Wetherbee, supt. Fax 728-3566
www.wccsk12.org
Wayland-Cohocton HS 500/9-12
2350 State Route 63 14572 585-728-2366
William Whyte, prin. Fax 728-2425
Wayland-Cohocton MS 400/5-8
2350 State Route 63 14572 585-728-2551
Eileen Feinman, prin. Fax 728-3556

Webster, Monroe, Pop. 5,251
Webster Central SD 8,800/K-12
119 South Ave 14580 585-265-3600
Adele Bovard, supt. Fax 265-6561
www.websterschools.org
Spry MS 1,000/6-8
119 South Ave 14580 585-265-6500
David Swinson, prin. Fax 265-6512
Thomas HS 1,500/9-12
800 Five Mile Line Rd 14580 585-670-8000
Glenn Widor, prin. Fax 671-1884
Webster Schroeder HS 1,500/9-12
875 Ridge Rd 14580 585-670-5000
Joseph Pustulka, prin. Fax 671-8681
Willink MS 1,000/6-8
900 Publishers Pkwy 14580 585-670-1030
Jim Gindling, prin. Fax 671-1978

Webster Christian S 200/PK-12
675 Holt Rd 14580 585-872-5150
Keith Bell, admin. Fax 872-5932

Weedsport, Cayuga, Pop. 1,803
Weedsport Central SD 800/K-12
2821 E Brutus Street Rd 13166 315-834-6637
Shaun O'Connor, supt.
www.weedsport.org
Weedsport JSHS 400/6-12
2821 E Brutus Street Rd 13166 315-834-6652
Carrie Widrick, prin. Fax 834-8693

Wells, Hamilton
Wells Central SD 200/PK-12
PO Box 300 12190 518-924-6000
Thomas Sincavage, supt. Fax 924-9246
wellscsd.com/
Wells Central S 200/PK-12
PO Box 300 12190 518-924-6000
Thomas Sincavage, prin. Fax 924-9246

Wellsville, Allegany, Pop. 4,622
Wellsville Central SD 1,300/K-12
126 W State St 14895 585-596-2170
Kimberly Mueller, supt. Fax 596-2177
www.wellsville.wnyric.org
Wellsville HS 400/9-12
126 W State St 14895 585-596-2188
Mary VanEtten, prin. Fax 596-2180
Wellsville MS 300/6-8
126 W State St 14895 585-596-2144
Mary Ellen O'Connell, prin. Fax 596-2142

West Babylon, Suffolk, Pop. 42,432
West Babylon UFD 4,400/K-12
10 Farmingdale Rd 11704 631-376-7000
Anthony Cacciola, supt. Fax 376-7019
www.wbschools.org
West Babylon HS 1,500/9-12
500 Great East Neck Rd 11704 631-376-7101
Dr. Ellice Vassallo, prin. Fax 376-7119
West Babylon JHS 1,000/6-8
200 Old Farmingdale Rd 11704 631-376-7201
Scott Payne, prin. Fax 376-7209

Commercial Driver Training School Post-Sec.
600 Patton Ave 11704 631-249-1330

Westbury, Nassau, Pop. 14,820
East Meadow UFD 7,300/K-12
718 The Plain Rd 11590 516-478-5776
Louis DeAngelo, supt. Fax 478-5779
www.eastmeadow.k12.ny.us
Clarke HS 800/9-12
740 Edgewood Dr 11590 516-876-7450
Timothy Voels, prin. Fax 876-7416
Clarke MS 600/6-8
740 Edgewood Dr 11590 516-876-7401
Stacey Breslin, prin. Fax 876-7407
Other Schools – See East Meadow

Westbury UFD
Supt. — See Old Westbury
Westbury MS 900/6-8
455 Rockland St 11590 516-876-5082
David Zimbler, prin. Fax 876-5141

West Chazy, Clinton, Pop. 516
Beekmantown Central SD 2,000/PK-12
37 Eagle Way 12992 518-563-8250
Scott Amo, supt. Fax 563-8132
www.bcsdk12.org
Other Schools – See Plattsburgh

Westfield, Chautauqua, Pop. 3,195
Westfield Central SD 700/K-12
203 E Main St 14787 716-326-2151
David Davison, supt. Fax 326-2195
www.wacs.wnyric.org/
Westfield HS 300/9-12
203 E Main St 14787 716-326-2151
Ivana Hite, prin. Fax 326-2157
Westfield MS 200/6-8
203 E Main St 14787 716-326-2151
Ivana Hite, prin. Fax 326-2157

Westhampton Beach, Suffolk, Pop. 1,702
Westhampton Beach UFD 1,800/K-12
340 Mill Rd 11978 631-288-3800
Mike Radday, supt. Fax 288-8351
www.westhamptonbeach.k12.ny.us
Westhampton Beach HS 1,000/9-12
49 Lilac Rd 11978 631-288-3800
Christopher Herr, prin. Fax 288-3915
Westhampton Beach MS 400/6-8
340 Mill Rd 11978 631-288-3800
Charisse Miller, prin. Fax 288-5496

West Harrison, Westchester

Fordham Westchester Post-Sec.
400 Westchester Ave 10604 914-332-8295

West Hempstead, Nassau, Pop. 18,467
West Hempstead UFD 2,200/K-12
252 Chestnut St 11552 516-390-3100
John Hogan, supt. Fax 489-1776
www.whufsd.com/
West Hempstead HS 900/9-12
400 Nassau Blvd 11552 516-390-3214
Daniel Rehman, prin. Fax 489-1769
West Hempstead MS 500/6-8
450 Nassau Blvd 11552 516-390-3160
Marcia Murray, prin. Fax 489-8946

West Henrietta, Monroe
Rush-Henrietta Central SD
Supt. — See Henrietta
Burger MS 500/6-8
639 Erie Station Rd 14586 585-359-5308
Greg Lane, prin. Fax 359-5333
Vollmer Alternative Center 100/Alt
159 Telephone Rd 14586 585-359-5520
Curt Diesenberg, dir. Fax 359-5523

West Islip, Suffolk, Pop. 28,075
West Islip UFD 4,600/K-12
100 Sherman Ave 11795 631-893-3200
Bernadette Burns, supt. Fax 893-3212
www.wi.k12.ny.us
Beach Street MS 600/6-8
17 Beach St 11795 631-893-3310
Andrew O'Farrell, prin. Fax 893-3318
Udall Road MS 600/6-8
900 Udall Rd 11795 631-893-3290
Daniel Marquardt, prin. Fax 893-3301
West Islip HS 1,800/9-12
1 Lions Path 11795 631-893-3250
Dr. Anthony Bridgeman, prin. Fax 893-3318

St. John the Baptist Diocesan HS 1,700/9-12
1170 Montauk Hwy 11795 631-587-8000
Nan Doherty, prin. Fax 587-8996

Westmoreland, Oneida, Pop. 420
Westmoreland Central SD 1,000/K-12
PO Box 430 13490 315-557-2614
Rocco Migliori, supt. Fax 853-4602
www.westmorelandschool.org
Westmoreland HS 300/9-12
PO Box 430 13490 315-557-2616
Joshua Saxton, prin. Fax 557-2672
Westmoreland MS 300/5-8
PO Box 430 13490 315-557-2618
Joanne Shelmidine, prin. Fax 557-2760

West Nyack, Rockland, Pop. 3,385
Clarkstown Central SD
Supt. — See New City
Clarkstown South HS 1,500/9-12
31 Demarest Mill Rd 10994 845-624-3400
James Vitale, prin. Fax 623-5470
Festa MS 2,200/6-8
30 Parrott Rd 10994 845-639-6339
Dianne Basso, prin. Fax 634-5874

West Point, Orange, Pop. 6,475

United States Military Academy Post-Sec.
646 Swift Rd 10996 845-938-4041

Westport, Essex, Pop. 508
Westport Central SD 300/K-12
25 Sisco St 12993 518-962-8244
Dr. John Gallagher, supt. Fax 962-4571
www.westportcs.org
Westport Central S 300/K-12
25 Sisco St 12993 518-962-8244
Michele Friedman, prin Fax 962-4571

West Sayville, Suffolk, Pop. 4,972
Sayville UFD
Supt. — See Sayville
Sayville HS 1,100/9-12
20 Brook St 11796 631-244-6600
Ronald Hoffer, prin. Fax 244-6779

West Seneca, Erie, Pop. 44,393
West Seneca Central SD 6,900/K-12
1397 Orchard Park Rd 14224 716-677-3101
Mark Crawford, supt. Fax 677-3104
www.wscschools.org/
Alternative Learning Center 50/Alt
900 Mill Rd 14224 716-677-3695
William Maloney, prin. Fax 677-3804
East MS 400/7-8
1445 Center Rd 14224 716-677-3530
Vincent Dell'Oso, prin. Fax 674-1046
West MS 700/7-8
395 Center Rd 14224 716-677-3500
Brian Graham, prin. Fax 675-6134
West Seneca East HS 900/9-12
4760 Seneca St 14224 716-677-3300
Jonathan Cervoni, prin. Fax 677-2933
West Seneca West HS 1,300/9-12
3330 Seneca St 14224 716-677-3350
John Brinker, prin. Fax 674-3551

Continental School of Beauty Culture Post-Sec.
1050 Union Rd 14224 716-675-8205
West Seneca Christian S 100/PK-12
511 Union Rd 14224 716-674-1820
Dr. Orlando Buria, admin. Fax 674-4894

West Valley, Cattaraugus, Pop. 518
West Valley Central SD 300/PK-12
PO Box 290 14171 716-942-3293
Eric Lawton, supt. Fax 942-3440
www.wvalley.wnyric.org
West Valley Central S 300/PK-12
PO Box 290 14171 716-942-3293
Daniel Amodeo, prin. Fax 942-3440

West Winfield, Herkimer, Pop. 820
Mount Markham CSD 1,200/K-12
500 Fairground Rd 13491 315-822-2824
Casey Barduhn, supt. Fax 822-6162
www.mmcsd.org
Mount Markham HS 400/9-12
500 Fairground Rd 13491 315-822-2900
Russell Kissinger, prin. Fax 822-3486
Mount Markham MS 400/5-8
500 Fairground Rd 13491 315-822-2870
Dawn Yerkie, prin. Fax 822-6125

Whitehall, Washington, Pop. 2,580
Whitehall Central SD 800/K-12
87 Buckley Rd 12887 518-499-1772
James Watson, supt. Fax 499-1759
www.railroaders.net
Whitehall JSHS 400/7-12
87 Buckley Rd 12887 518-499-1770
Kelly McHugh, prin. Fax 499-1759

White Plains, Westchester, Pop. 55,780
White Plains CSD 6,900/K-12
5 Homeside Ln 10605 914-422-2000
Chris Clouet, supt. Fax 422-2024
www.wpcsd.k12.ny.us
White Plains HS 2,200/9-12
550 North St 10605 914-422-2182
Ellen Doherty, prin. Fax 422-2196
White Plains MS - Eastview Campus 6-8
350 Main St 10601 914-422-2223
Joseph Cloherty, prin. Fax 422-2222
White Plains MS - Highlands Campus 1,500/6-8
128 Grandview Ave 10605 914-422-2092
Jonathan Brown, prin. Fax 422-2273

Academy of Our Lady of Good Counsel HS 300/9-12
52 N Broadway 10603 914-949-0178
Sr. Laura Donovan, prin. Fax 682-3531
Archbishop Stepinac HS 600/9-12
950 Mamaroneck Ave 10605 914-946-4800
Paul Carty, prin. Fax 684-2591
Berkeley College Post-Sec.
99 Church St 10601 914-694-1122
German S New York 400/K-12
50 Partridge Rd 10605 914-940-6513
Ulrich Weghoff, head sch Fax 948-6529
Music Conservatory of Westchester Post-Sec.
216 Central Ave 10606 914-761-3715
New York School for the Deaf Post-Sec.
555 Knollwood Rd 10603
Pace University Post-Sec.
1 Martine Ave 10606 914-442-2000
Pace University School of Law Post-Sec.
78 N Broadway 10603 914-422-4000
Sanford-Brown Institute Post-Sec.
333 Westchester Ave 10604 914-874-2500
The College of Westchester Post-Sec.
325 Central Ave 10606 914-948-4442
Windward S 300/5-9
40 W Red Oak Ln 10604 914-949-6968
Dr. John Russell, hdmstr. Fax 949-8220

Whitesboro, Oneida, Pop. 3,727
Whitesboro Central SD
Supt. — See Yorkville
Whitesboro MS 500/7-8
75 Oriskany Blvd 13492 315-266-3100
Christopher Staats, prin. Fax 768-9770

Whitestone, See New York
NYC Department of Education
Supt. — See New York
JHS 194 1,100/6-8
15460 17th Ave 11357 718-746-0818
Jennifer Miller, prin. Fax 746-7618

Lincoln Technical Institute Post-Sec.
1530 Petracca Pl 11357 718-640-9800

Whitesville, Allegany
Whitesville Central SD 300/K-12
692 Main St 14897 607-356-3301
Charles Cutler, supt. Fax 356-3598
www.whitesville.wnyric.org
Whitesville Central S 300/K-12
692 Main St 14897 607-356-3301
Tammy Emery, prin. Fax 356-3598

Whitney Point, Broome, Pop. 945
Whitney Point Central SD 1,500/PK-12
PO Box 249 13862 607-692-8202
Patricia Follette, supt. Fax 692-4434
www.wpcsd.org
Tioughnioga Riverside Academy 600/4-8
PO Box 249 13862 607-692-8232
Laura Chestnut, prin. Fax 692-8283
Whitney Point HS 400/9-12
PO Box 249 13862 607-692-8201
Bruce Tytler, prin. Fax 692-8256

Williamson, Wayne, Pop. 2,435
Williamson Central SD 1,100/K-12
PO Box 900 14589 315-589-9661
Maria Ehresman, supt. Fax 589-7611
www.williamsoncentral.org
Williamson HS 400/9-12
PO Box 900 14589 315-589-9621
Douglas Lauf, prin. Fax 589-8310
Williamson MS 300/5-8
PO Box 900 14589 315-589-9665
John Fulmer, prin. Fax 589-8314

Williamsville, Erie, Pop. 5,229
Williamsville Central SD
Supt. — See East Amherst
Heim MS 600/5-8
175 Heim Rd 14221 716-626-8600
Valerie Keipper, prin. Fax 626-8626
Mill MS 900/5-8
505 Mill St 14221 716-626-8300
Michael Calandra, prin. Fax 626-8326
Williamsville North HS 1,400/9-12
1595 Hopkins Rd 14221 716-626-8505
Petrina Neureuter, prin. Fax 626-8597
Williamsville South HS 1,000/9-12
5950 Main St 14221 716-626-8200
Fax 626-8207

Christian Central Academy 400/K-12
39 Academy St 14221 716-634-4821
Nurline Lawrence, hdmstr. Fax 634-5851
Erie Community College North Post-Sec.
6205 Main St 14221 716-634-0800
Leon Studio One School of Hair Design Post-Sec.
5221 Main St 14221 716-631-3878

Willsboro, Essex, Pop. 740
Willsboro Central SD 300/PK-12
PO Box 180 12996 518-963-4456
Stephen Broadwell, supt. Fax 963-7577
www.willsborocsd.org/
Willsboro Central S 300/PK-12
PO Box 180 12996 518-963-4456
Stephen Broadwell, prin. Fax 963-7577

Wilson, Niagara, Pop. 1,249
Wilson Central SD 1,300/PK-12
PO Box 648 14172 716-751-9341
Dr. Michael Wendt, supt. Fax 751-6556
www.wilson.wnyric.org/
Wilson HS 500/9-12
PO Box 648 14172 716-751-9341
Daniel Johnson, prin. Fax 751-9597
Wilson MS 300/6-8
PO Box 648 14172 716-751-9341
Phillip Incorvaia, prin. Fax 751-9597

Windham, Greene, Pop. 359
Windham-Ashland-Jewett Central SD 400/K-12
PO Box 429 12496 518-734-3400
John Wiktorko, supt. Fax 734-6050
www.wajcs.org/
Windham-Ashland Central S 400/K-12
PO Box 429 12496 518-734-3400
Kerry Overbaugh, prin. Fax 734-6050

Windsor, Broome, Pop. 903
Windsor Central SD 1,800/K-12
1191 State Route 79 13865 607-655-8216
Jason Andrews, supt. Fax 655-3553
www.windsor-csd.org
Windsor Central HS 600/9-12
1191 State Route 79 13865 607-655-8250
Jeffrey Salasny, prin. Fax 655-3622
Windsor MS 400/6-8
213 Main St 13865 607-655-8247
Kevin Strahley, prin. Fax 655-3760

Wolcott, Wayne, Pop. 1,683
North Rose-Wolcott Central SD 1,000/K-12
11631 Salter Colvin Rd 14590 315-594-3141
John Walker, supt. Fax 594-2352
www.nrwcs.org/
North Rose-Wolcott HS 500/9-12
11631 Salter Colvin Rd 14590 315-594-3100
Paul Benz, prin. Fax 594-6235
North Rose-Wolcott MS 300/5-8
5957 New Hartford St 14590 315-594-3130
Michele Sullivan, prin. Fax 594-3120

Woodbourne, Sullivan

Hamesivta 50/9-12
Hasbrouck Rd 12788 845-369-3360
Rabbi Moshe Ginsburg, prin. Fax 382-8863

Woodmere, Nassau, Pop. 17,006
Hewlett-Woodmere UFD 3,000/PK-12
1 Johnson Pl 11598 516-792-4800
Dr. Joyce Bisso, supt. Fax 374-8185
www.hewlett-woodmere.net
Other Schools – See Hewlett

Davis Renov Stahler Yeshiva HS for Boys 300/9-12
700 Ibsen St 11598 516-295-7700
Dr. Gerald Kirshenbaum, prin. Fax 295-2929
Lawrence Woodmere Academy 300/PK-12
336 Woodmere Blvd 11598 516-374-9000
Alan Bernstein, hdmstr. Fax 374-4707

Woodside, See New York
NYC Department of Education
Supt. — See New York
IS 125 1,700/5-8
4602 47th Ave 11377 718-937-0320
Judy Mittler, prin. Fax 361-2451

Greater New York Academy 200/9-12
4132 58th St 11377 718-639-1752
Lillian Mitchell M.Ed., prin. Fax 639-8992
Razi S 400/PK-12
5511 Queens Blvd 11377 718-779-0711
Dr. Ghassan Elcheikhali, prin. Fax 779-0103

Worcester, Otsego, Pop. 1,097
Worcester Central SD 400/K-12
198 Main St 12197 607-397-8785
William Diamond, supt. Fax 397-8464
www.worcestercs.org
Worcester Central S 400/K-12
198 Main St 12197 607-397-8785
Shelly Hilts, prin. Fax 397-9454

Wyandanch, Suffolk, Pop. 11,382
Wyandanch UFD 2,100/PK-12
1445 Straight Path 11798 631-870-0400
Dr. Pless Dickerson, supt. Fax 870-0404
www.wufsd.net/
Olive MS 400/6-8
140 Garden City Ave 11798 631-870-0525
Kester Hodge, prin. Fax 870-0533
Wyandanch Memorial HS 500/9-12
54 S 32nd St 11798 631-870-0450
Paul Sibblies, prin. Fax 870-0459

Yonkers, Westchester, Pop. 192,139
Yonkers CSD 24,200/PK-12
1 Larkin Ctr 10701 914-376-8000
Bernard Pierorazio, supt. Fax 376-8062
www.yonkerspublicschools.org
Early College HS 9-12
631 Tuckahoe Rd 10710 914-376-8118
Maximo Catala, prin. Fax 793-4971
Gorton HS 1,200/9-12
100 Shonnard Pl 10703 914-376-8350
Gail Joyner-White, prin. Fax 376-8377
Lincoln HS 1,200/9-12
375 Kneeland Ave 10704 914-376-8400
Edwin Quezada, prin. Fax 376-8414
Palisade Preparatory S 400/7-12
201 Palisade Ave 10703 914-376-8177
Dr. Michelle Yazurio, prin. Fax 376-8484
Riverside HS 800/9-12
565 Warburton Ave 10701 914-376-8425
Steve Murphy, prin. Fax 376-8475
Roosevelt SHS 200/12-12
631 Tuckahoe Rd 10710 914-376-8500
Jade Sharp, prin. Fax 779-7632
Saunders Trades & Tech HS 1,200/9-12
183 Palmer Rd 10701 914-376-8150
Steve Mazzola, prin. Fax 376-8154
Yonkers Montessori Academy 1,100/PK-12
160 Woodlawn Ave 10704 914-376-8540
Eileen Rivera-Shapiro, prin. Fax 376-8552
Yonkers MSHS 1,100/7-12
150 Rockland Ave 10705 914-376-8191
Jane Wermuth, prin. Fax 376-4856
Pathways to Success Adult
75 Riverdale Ave 10701 914-376-8600
Susan Naber, prin. Fax 376-0541

Cochran School of Nursing Post-Sec.
967 N Broadway 10701 914-964-4296
Sacred Heart HS 400/9-12
34 Convent Ave 10703 914-965-3114
Rev. Maurice Moreau, head sch Fax 965-4510
St. Joseph's Seminary Post-Sec.
201 Seminary Ave 10704 914-968-6200

Yorkshire, Cattaraugus, Pop. 1,167
Yorkshire-Pioneer Central SD 2,400/K-12
PO Box 579 14173 585-492-9300
Sharon Huff Ed.D., supt. Fax 492-9360
www.pioneerschools.org/
Pioneer HS 800/9-12
PO Box 639 14173 585-492-9328
Mark Schultz, prin. Fax 492-1825
Pioneer MS 700/5-8
PO Box 619 14173 585-492-9375
Melissa Prorok, prin. Fax 492-9372

Yorktown Heights, Westchester, Pop. 1,760
Lakeland Central SD
Supt. — See Shrub Oak
Lakeland-Copper Beech MS 1,500/6-8
3401 Old Yorktown Rd 10598 914-245-1885
Vanessa DeFonce, prin. Fax 245-1259

Yorktown Central SD 3,800/K-12
2725 Crompond Rd 10598 914-243-8000
Dr. Ralph Napolitano, supt. Fax 243-8002
www.yorktown.org/
Strang MS 900/6-8
2701 Crompond Rd 10598 914-243-8100
Linda Grimm, prin. Fax 243-0016
Yorktown Alternative HS Alt
2729 Crompond Rd 10598 914-243-8011
James Emanuele, dir. Fax 962-8357
Yorktown HS 1,300/9-12
2727 Crompond Rd 10598 914-243-8050
Joseph DeGennaro, prin. Fax 245-9256

Mercy College Post-Sec.
2651 Strang Blvd 10598 800-637-2969
Soundview Preparatory S 100/6-12
370 Underhill Ave 10598 914-962-2780
Glyn Hearn, head sch Fax 302-2769

Yorkville, Oneida, Pop. 2,659
Whitesboro Central SD 3,500/K-12
PO Box 304 13495 315-266-3300
David Langone, supt. Fax 768-9730
www.wboro.org
Other Schools – See Marcy, Whitesboro

Youngstown, Niagara, Pop. 1,918
Lewiston-Porter Central SD 2,200/K-12
4061 Creek Rd 14174 716-286-7266
Chris Roser, supt. Fax 754-2755
www.lew-port.com
Lewiston-Porter HS 800/9-12
4061 Creek Rd 14174 716-286-7263
Paul Casseri, prin. Fax 286-7852
Lewiston-Porter MS 500/6-8
4061 Creek Rd 14174 716-286-7201
Dean Ramirez, prin. Fax 286-7204

NORTH CAROLINA

NORTH CAROLINA DEPT. PUBLIC INSTRUCTION
301 N Wilmington St, Raleigh 27601-1058
Telephone 919-807-3300
Fax 919-807-3445
Website http://www.dpi.state.nc.us

Superintendent of Public Instruction June Atkinson

NORTH CAROLINA BOARD OF EDUCATION
301 N Wilmington St, Raleigh 27601-1058

Chairperson William Harrison

PUBLIC, PRIVATE AND CATHOLIC SECONDARY SCHOOLS

Aberdeen, Moore, Pop. 6,182
Moore County SD
Supt. — See Carthage
Southern MS 700/6-8
717 Johnson St 28315 910-693-1550
Herb Hanson, prin. Fax 693-1544

Advance, Davie, Pop. 1,117
Davie County SD
Supt. — See Mocksville
Ellis MS 600/6-8
144 William Ellis Dr 27006 336-998-2007
Alicia Holman, prin. Fax 998-6249

Ahoskie, Hertford, Pop. 4,982
Hertford County SD
Supt. — See Winton
Hertford County Early College HS 100/9-12
109 Community College Rd 27910 252-332-7788
Joanne Jones, prin. Fax 332-3605
Hertford County HS 800/9-12
1500 1st St W 27910 252-332-4096
James Futrell, prin. Fax 332-6176

Ahoskie Christian S 200/PK-12
500 Kiwanis St 27910 252-332-2764
Elaine Pool, prin. Fax 332-2492
Ridgecroft S 300/PK-12
PO Box 1008 27910 252-332-2964
Fax 332-7586
Roanoke-Chowan Community College Post-Sec.
109 Community College Rd 27910 252-862-1200

Albemarle, Stanly, Pop. 15,632
Stanly County SD 7,300/PK-12
1000 N 1st St Ste 4 28001 704-961-3000
Dr. Terry Griffin, supt. Fax 961-3099
www.stanlycountyschools.org
Albemarle HS 500/9-12
311 Park Ridge Rd 28001 704-961-3000
Karen Nixon, prin. Fax 961-3099
Albemarle MS 400/6-8
1811 Badin Rd 28001 704-961-3400
David Grice, prin. Fax 961-3499
Stanly Academy Learning Center 50/Alt
1121 Austin St 28001 704-961-4500
Mike Campbell, prin. Fax 961-4599
Stanly Early College HS 200/9-12
141 College Dr 28001 704-991-0128
Amy Blake-Lewis, dean Fax 991-0109
Other Schools – See Locust, New London, Norwood, Oakboro

Stanly Community College Post-Sec.
141 College Dr 28001 704-982-0121

Andrews, Cherokee, Pop. 1,715
Cherokee County SD
Supt. — See Murphy
Andrews HS 300/9-12
50 High School Dr 28901 828-321-5415
Virginia Haynes, prin. Fax 321-3986
Andrews MS 200/6-8
2750 Business 19 28901 828-321-5762
John Higdon, prin. Fax 321-2009

Angier, Harnett, Pop. 4,289
Harnett County SD
Supt. — See Lillington
Harnett Central HS 1,400/9-12
2911 Harnett Central Rd 27501 919-639-6161
Chris Mace, prin. Fax 639-3642
Harnett Central MS 1,200/6-8
2529 Harnett Central Rd 27501 919-639-6000
Linwood Smith, prin. Fax 639-9617

Apex, Wake, Pop. 36,623
Wake County SD
Supt. — See Raleigh
Apex HS 2,300/9-12
1501 Laura Duncan Rd 27502 919-387-2208
Matthew Wight, prin. Fax 387-3023
Apex MS 1,100/6-8
400 E Moore St 27502 919-387-2181
Dr. Camille Hedrick, prin. Fax 387-2203
Lufkin Road MS 1,000/6-8
1002 Lufkin Rd, 919-387-4465
Karen Sinders, prin. Fax 363-1095
Middle Creek HS 1,800/9-12
123 Middle Creek Park Ave, 919-773-3838
Thomas Dixon, prin. Fax 773-3880
Salem MS 1,100/6-8
6150 Old Jenks Rd, 919-363-1870
Herbert Ellzey, prin. Fax 363-1876
West Lake MS 1,300/6-8
4600 W Lake Rd, 919-662-2900
Dell Edwards, prin. Fax 662-2906

Archdale, Randolph, Pop. 11,273

Mount Calvary Christian S 100/K-12
6551 Weant Rd 27263 336-434-6800

Arden, Buncombe
Buncombe County SD
Supt. — See Asheville
Valley Springs MS 800/6-8
224 Long Shoals Rd 28704 828-654-1785
Eddie Burchfiel, prin. Fax 654-1789

Christ S 200/8-12
500 Christ School Rd 28704 828-684-6232
Paul Krieger, hdmstr. Fax 684-2745

Asheboro, Randolph, Pop. 24,567
Asheboro CSD 4,700/PK-12
PO Box 1103 27204 336-625-5104
Dr. Diane Frost, supt. Fax 625-9238
www.asheboro.k12.nc.us
Asheboro HS 1,300/9-12
1221 S Park St 27203 336-625-6185
Dr. Brian Toth, prin. Fax 625-9320
North Asheboro MS 500/6-8
1861 N Asheboro School Rd 27203 336-672-1900
Candace Call, prin. Fax 672-6267
South Asheboro MS 600/6-8
523 W Walker Ave 27203 336-629-4141
Charlie Lyons, prin. Fax 629-3761

Randolph County SD 18,700/K-12
2222 S Fayetteville St # C 27205 336-318-6100
Donald Andrews, supt. Fax 318-6155
www.randolph.k12.nc.us
Randolph Early College HS 300/9-12
629 Industrial Park Ave 27205 336-625-1137
Cathy Waddell, prin. Fax 625-3186
Southwestern Randolph HS 1,200/9-12
1641 Hopewell Friends Rd 27205 336-381-7747
Shon Hildreth, prin. Fax 381-7743
Southwestern Randolph MS 600/6-8
1509 Hopewell Friends Rd 27205 336-381-3900
Edwina Ashworth, prin. Fax 381-3905
Other Schools – See Climax, Liberty, Ramseur, Randleman, Trinity

---

Fayetteville Street Christian S 100/K-12
151 W Pritchard St 27203 336-629-1383
David Jeffreys, admin. Fax 629-0067
Neighbors Grove Christian Academy 100/K-12
1928 N Fayetteville St 27203 336-672-1147
Randy Haithcock, admin. Fax 672-5500
Randolph Community College Post-Sec.
629 Industrial Park Ave 27205 336-633-0200

Asheville, Buncombe, Pop. 81,334
Asheville CSD 3,600/PK-12
85 Mountain St 28801 828-350-7000
Allen Johnson, supt. Fax 255-5131
www.asheville.k12.nc.us
Asheville HS 900/9-12
419 Mcdowell St 28803 828-350-2500
Carol Ray, prin. Fax 255-5316
Asheville MS 700/6-8
197 S French Broad Ave 28801 828-350-6200
Cynthia Sellinger, prin. Fax 255-5311

Buncombe County SD 24,500/K-12
175 Bingham Rd 28806 828-255-5921
Dr. Tony Baldwin, supt. Fax 255-5923
www.buncombe.k12.nc.us/
Buncombe County Early College S 200/9-12
340 Victoria Rd 28801 828-232-4123
Bonnie Johnston, prin. Fax 232-4165
Buncombe County Middle College HS 100/Alt
340 Victoria Rd 28801 828-232-4123
Bonnie Johnston, prin. Fax 232-4165
Erwin HS 1,400/9-12
60 Lees Creek Rd 28806 828-232-4251
Dr. Jim Brown, prin. Fax 251-2893
Erwin MS 700/7-8
20 Erwin Hills Rd 28806 828-232-4264
Joel Hathaway, prin. Fax 253-4267
Reynolds HS 1,400/9-12
1 Rocket Dr 28803 828-298-2500
Doris Sellers, prin. Fax 298-2002
Reynolds MS 600/6-8
2 Rocket Dr 28803 828-298-7484
Jamie Laws, prin. Fax 298-7503
Roberson HS 1,500/9-12
250 Overlook Rd 28803 828-654-1765
Amy Rhoney, prin. Fax 654-1768
Other Schools – See Arden, Black Mountain, Candler, Fletcher, Swannanoa, Weaverville

---

Asheville Buncombe Technical Comm. Coll. Post-Sec.
340 Victoria Rd 28801 828-254-1921
Asheville S 300/9-12
360 Asheville School Rd 28806 828-254-6345
Archibald Montgomery, hdmstr. Fax 210-6109
Carolina Day S 600/PK-12
1345 Hendersonville Rd 28803 828-274-0757
Thomas Trigg, head sch Fax 274-0756
Daoist Traditions Coll of Chinese Med Post-Sec.
382 Montford Ave 28801 828-225-3993
Montreat College Post-Sec.
29 Turtle Creek Dr 28803 828-667-5044
North Asheville Christian S 200/PK-12
20 Reynolds Mountain Blvd 28804 828-645-8053
Susie Hepler, admin. Fax 645-4542
Providence Christian Academy 100/PK-12
48 Woodland Hills Rd 28804 828-658-8964
Larry Basinger, prin. Fax 658-8965
South College Post-Sec.
140 Sweeten Creek Rd 28803 828-398-2500
Temple Baptist S 200/PK-12
985 1/2 Patton Ave 28806 828-252-3712
William Spence, prin. Fax 254-5119
University of North Carolina Post-Sec.
1 University Hts 28804 828-251-6600
Warren Wilson College Post-Sec.
PO Box 9000 28815 828-298-3325

Ayden, Pitt, Pop. 4,853
Pitt County SD
Supt. — See Greenville
Ayden-Grifton HS 700/9-12
7653 NC 11 S 28513 252-746-4183
Marty Baker, prin. Fax 746-2120
Ayden MS 400/6-8
192 3rd St 28513 252-746-3672
Jeff Theus, prin. Fax 746-9923

Bailey, Nash, Pop. 561
Nash-Rocky Mount SD
Supt. — See Nashville
Southern Nash HS 1,300/9-12
6446 Southern Nash High Rd 27807 252-451-8520
Dr. Mark Cockrell, prin. Fax 478-5953

Bakersville, Mitchell, Pop. 450
Mitchell County SD 1,900/K-12
72 Ledger School Rd 28705 828-766-2220
Dr. Richard Spurling, supt. Fax 766-2221
www.mcsnc.org
Bowman MS 200/5-8
410 S Mitchell Ave 28705 828-688-2752
Stacie Burleson, prin. Fax 688-6002
Mitchell HS 600/9-12
416 Ledger School Rd 28705 828-766-3400
Mark Woody, prin. Fax 688-4847
Other Schools – See Spruce Pine

Banner Elk, Avery, Pop. 1,011

Lees-McRae College | Post-Sec.
PO Box 128 28604 | 828-898-5241

Barco, Currituck
Currituck County SD
Supt. — See Currituck
Currituck County HS | 1,000/9-12
4203 Caratoke Hwy 27917 | 252-453-0014
Diane Newbern, prin. | Fax 453-0017
Currituck County MS | 400/6-8
4263 Caratoke Hwy 27917 | 252-453-2171
Rhonda James-Davis, prin. | Fax 453-0019

Battleboro, Edgecombe, Pop. 559
Edgecombe County SD
Supt. — See Tarboro
Phillips MS | 200/6-8
4371 Battleboro Leggett Rd 27809 | 252-446-2031
Lisa Howell, prin. | Fax 446-1629

Nash-Rocky Mount SD
Supt. — See Nashville
Red Oak MS | 1,000/6-8
3170 Red Oak Battleboro Rd 27809 | 252-462-2000
Chad Thompson, prin. | Fax 451-5510

Bayboro, Pamlico, Pop. 1,250
Pamlico County SD | 1,500/PK-12
507 Anderson Dr 28515 | 252-745-4171
Dr. Wanda Dawson, supt. | Fax 745-4172
www.pamlico.k12.nc.us
Pamlico County HS | 500/9-12
601 Main St 28515 | 252-745-3151
Henry Rice, prin. | Fax 745-3153
Pamlico County MS | 300/6-8
15526 NC Highway 55 28515 | 252-745-4061
Lisa Jackson, prin. | Fax 745-5583

Bear Creek, Chatham
Chatham County SD
Supt. — See Pittsboro
Chatham Central HS | 500/9-12
14950 NC 902 Hwy 27207 | 919-837-2251
Mitch Stensland, prin. | Fax 837-2975

Beaufort, Carteret, Pop. 3,948
Carteret County SD | 8,600/PK-12
107 Safrit Dr 28516 | 252-728-4583
Dr. Daniel Novey, supt. | Fax 728-3028
www.carteretcountyschools.org
Beaufort MS | 300/6-8
100 Carraway Dr 28516 | 252-728-4520
Greg Guthrie, prin. | Fax 728-3392
East Carteret HS | 600/9-12
3263 US Highway 70 E 28516 | 252-728-3514
April Lilley, prin. | Fax 728-3487
Other Schools – See Morehead City, Newport

Belhaven, Beaufort, Pop. 1,666

Pungo Christian Academy | 200/PK-12
983 W Main St 27810 | 252-943-2678
Marcy Morgan, head sch | Fax 943-3292

Belmont, Gaston, Pop. 9,916
Gaston County SD
Supt. — See Gastonia
Belmont MS | 700/6-8
110 N Central Ave 28012 | 704-825-9619
Mark Schultz, prin. | Fax 825-6951
South Point HS | 1,300/9-12
906 S Point Rd 28012 | 704-825-3351
Gary Ford, prin. | Fax 825-2820

Belmont Abbey College | Post-Sec.
100 Belmont Mount Holly Rd 28012 | 888-222-0110

Benson, Johnston, Pop. 3,270
Johnston County SD
Supt. — See Smithfield
Benson MS | 400/5-8
1600 N Wall St 27504 | 919-894-3889
Sheila Singleton, prin. | Fax 894-1551
McGee's Crossroads MS | 800/6-8
13353 NC Highway 210 27504 | 919-894-6003
Chad Jewett, prin. | Fax 894-6007
West Johnston HS | 1,800/9-12
5935 Raleigh Rd 27504 | 919-934-7333
Paula Coates, prin. | Fax 934-6906

Bessemer City, Gaston, Pop. 5,262
Gaston County SD
Supt. — See Gastonia
Bessemer City HS | 600/9-12
119 Yellow Jacket Rd 28016 | 704-629-2258
James Montgomery, prin. | Fax 629-2775
Bessemer City MS | 600/6-8
525 Ed Wilson Rd 28016 | 704-629-3281
Rebecca Wilson, prin. | Fax 629-4501

Bethel, Pitt, Pop. 1,573
Pitt County SD
Supt. — See Greenville
North Pitt HS | 1,000/9-12
5659 NC Highway 11 N 27812 | 252-825-0054
Mike King, prin. | Fax 825-1310

Beulaville, Duplin, Pop. 1,278
Duplin County SD
Supt. — See Kenansville
East Duplin HS | 900/9-12
394 N NC 111 Hwy 28518 | 910-298-4535
Scott Ballard, prin. | Fax 298-2021

Biscoe, Montgomery, Pop. 1,683
Montgomery County SD
Supt. — See Troy
East MS | 500/6-8
1834 US Highway 220 Alt S 27209 | 910-428-3278
Della Ingram, prin. | Fax 428-1279
East Montgomery HS | 600/9-12
157 Eagle Ln 27209 | 910-428-9641
Heather Seawell, prin. | Fax 428-1197

Black Mountain, Buncombe, Pop. 7,683
Buncombe County SD
Supt. — See Asheville
Owen HS | 900/9-12
99 Lake Eden Rd 28711 | 828-686-3852
Margaret Turner, prin. | Fax 686-8442

Montreat College | Post-Sec.
PO Box 1267 28711 | 828-669-8012

Bladenboro, Bladen, Pop. 1,726
Bladen County SD
Supt. — See Elizabethtown
Bladenboro MS | 400/5-8
910 S Main St 28320 | 910-863-3232
Randi Harrelson, prin. | Fax 863-4683
West Bladen HS | 800/9-12
1600 NC 410 Hwy 28320 | 910-862-2130
Toni Warrick, prin. | Fax 862-3328

Boiling Springs, Cleveland, Pop. 4,581

Gardner-Webb University | Post-Sec.
PO Box 997 28017 | 704-406-4000

Bolivia, Brunswick, Pop. 139
Brunswick County SD | 12,200/PK-12
35 Referendum Dr NE 28422 | 910-253-2900
Dr. Edward Pruden, supt. | Fax 253-2983
www.bcswan.net
Brunswick County Academy | 100/Alt
1109 Old Ocean Hwy 28422 | 910-754-9593
Stephanie Smith, prin. | Fax 754-9594
Brunswick County Early College HS | 200/9-12
60 College Rd NE 28422 | 910-754-8565
Dr. Cheryl Skaggs, prin. | Fax 754-8567
Other Schools – See Leland, Shallotte, Southport, Supply

Boone, Watauga, Pop. 16,843
Watauga County SD | 4,400/PK-12
PO Box 1790 28607 | 828-264-7190
Dr. David Kafitz, supt. | Fax 264-7196
www.watauga.k12.nc.us
Watauga HS | 1,400/9-12
300 Go Pioneers Dr 28607 | 828-264-2407
Marshall Gasperson, prin. | Fax 264-9030

Appalachian State University | Post-Sec.
Asu Sta 28608 | 828-262-2000

Boonville, Yadkin, Pop. 1,215
Yadkin County SD
Supt. — See Yadkinville
Starmount HS | 700/9-12
2516 Longtown Rd 27011 | 336-468-2891
Junior Luffman, prin. | Fax 468-6434
Starmount MS | 400/7-8
2626 Longtown Rd 27011 | 336-468-6833
Rick Swaim, prin. | Fax 468-6838

Bostic, Rutherford, Pop. 382
Rutherford County SD
Supt. — See Forest City
East Rutherford MS | 600/6-8
259 E Church St 28018 | 828-245-3750
Jo Oliver, prin. | Fax 245-1491

Brevard, Transylvania, Pop. 7,401
Transylvania County SD | 3,600/K-12
225 Rosenwald Ln 28712 | 828-884-6173
Dr. Jeffrey McDaris, supt. | Fax 884-9524
www.tcsnc.org
Brevard HS | 700/9-12
609 Country Club Rd 28712 | 828-884-4103
| Fax 885-7355
Brevard MS | 500/6-8
400 Fisher Rd 28712 | 828-884-2091
Kerry Putnam, prin. | Fax 883-3150
Davidson River S | 100/Alt
970 Ecusta Rd 28712 | 828-884-9567
Donna Wilde, prin. | Fax 862-5347
Other Schools – See Rosman

Brevard College | Post-Sec.
1 Brevard College Dr 28712 | 828-883-8292

Browns Summit, Guilford
Guilford County SD
Supt. — See Greensboro
Brown Summit MS | 200/6-8
4720 E NC Highway 150 27214 | 336-656-0432
Deborah Mott, prin. | Fax 656-0439

Bryson City, Swain, Pop. 1,399
Swain County SD | 2,000/PK-12
PO Box 2340 28713 | 828-488-3129
Sam Pattillo, supt. | Fax 488-8510
www.swain.k12.nc.us
Swain County HS | 600/9-12
1415 Fontana Rd 28713 | 828-488-2152
Mark Sale, prin. | Fax 488-0523
Swain County MS | 600/PK-PK, 6-
135 Arlington Ave 28713 | 828-488-3480
Brandon Suttn, prin. | Fax 488-0949

Buies Creek, Harnett, Pop. 2,881

Campbell University | Post-Sec.
PO Box 567 27506 | 910-893-1200

Bunn, Franklin, Pop. 340
Franklin County SD
Supt. — See Louisburg
Bunn HS | 900/9-12
PO Box 146 27508 | 919-496-3975
Robin Faulkner, prin. | Fax 496-6943
Bunn MS | 700/6-8
4742 NC 39 Hwy S 27508 | 919-496-7700
Roosevelt Alston, prin. | Fax 496-1404

Burgaw, Pender, Pop. 3,819
Pender County SD | 7,900/PK-12
925 Penderlea Hwy 28425 | 910-259-2187
Dr. Terri Cobb, supt. | Fax 259-0133
www.pendercountyschools.net/
Burgaw MS | 200/6-8
500 S Wright St 28425 | 910-259-0149
Darren Lafon, prin. | Fax 259-0150
Pender Early College HS | 200/9-12
100 Industrial Dr 28425 | 910-259-7925
Edith Skipper, prin. | Fax 259-7174
Pender HS | 600/9-12
5380 NC Highway 53 W 28425 | 910-259-0162
Craig Baker, prin. | Fax 259-0166
West Pender MS | 200/6-8
10750 NC Highway 53 W 28425 | 910-283-5626
| Fax 283-9537
Other Schools – See Hampstead, Rocky Point

Burlington, Alamance, Pop. 49,060
Alamance-Burlington SD | 22,600/PK-12
1712 Vaughn Rd 27217 | 336-570-6060
Dr. Lillie Cox, supt. | Fax 570-6218
www.abss.k12.nc.us
Broadview MS | 700/6-8
2229 Broadview Dr 27217 | 336-570-6195
Reginald Davis, prin. | Fax 570-6202
Career and Technical Education Center | Vo/Tech
2550 Buckingham Rd 27217 | 336-570-6092
Heather Blackmon, prin. | Fax 570-6093
Cummings HS | 900/9-12
2200 N Mebane St 27217 | 336-570-6100
Emmet Alexander, prin. | Fax 570-6107
Turrentine MS | 900/6-8
1710 Edgewood Ave 27215 | 336-570-6150
Brian Williams, prin. | Fax 570-6210
Williams HS | 1,200/9-12
1307 S Church St 27215 | 336-570-6161
Joe Ferrell, prin. | Fax 570-6214
Other Schools – See Elon, Graham, Mebane

Burlington Christian Academy | 700/PK-12
621 E 6th St 27215 | 336-227-0288
Michael Brown, admin. | Fax 570-1314
Elon S | 100/9-12
408 W Davis St 27215 | 336-395-8550
Killian Barefoot, hdmstr. | Fax 395-8551

Burnsville, Yancey, Pop. 1,680
Yancey County SD | 2,300/K-12
PO Box 190 28714 | 828-682-6101
Dr. Tony Tipton, supt. | Fax 682-7110
www.yanceync.net
Cane River MS | 200/6-8
1128 Cane River School Rd 28714 | 828-682-2202
Alton Robinson, prin. | Fax 682-3754
East Yancey MS | 300/6-8
285 Georges Fork Rd 28714 | 828-682-2281
Rick Tipton, prin. | Fax 682-3513
Mountain Heritage HS | 700/9-12
PO Box 70 28714 | 828-682-6103
Kevin Huskins, prin. | Fax 682-4287

Butner, Granville, Pop. 7,466
Granville County SD
Supt. — See Oxford
Butner-Stem MS | 500/6-8
501 E D St 27509 | 919-575-9429
Andre Ross, prin. | Fax 575-5894

Buxton, Dare, Pop. 1,259
Dare County SD
Supt. — See Nags Head
Cape Hatteras S of Coastal Studies | 300/6-12
PO Box 948 27920 | 252-995-5730
Jean Taylor, prin. | Fax 995-6161

Camden, Camden, Pop. 580
Camden County SD | 2,000/PK-12
174 NC Highway 343 N 27921 | 252-335-0831
Melvin Hawkins, supt. | Fax 331-2300
www.camden.k12.nc.us
Camden County HS | 400/9-12
103 US Highway 158 W 27921 | 252-338-0114
Billie Berry, prin. | Fax 331-6792
Camden MS | 300/7-8
248 Scotland Rd 27921 | 252-338-3349
Ernest Cooley, prin. | Fax 331-2253
CamTech HS | 200/9-12
103 US Highway 158 W Ste A 27921 | 252-335-7219
Ina Lane, prin. | Fax 335-4219

Cameron, Moore, Pop. 274
Moore County SD
Supt. — See Carthage
New Century MS | 500/6-8
1577 Union Church Rd 28326 | 910-947-1301
Robin Calcutt, prin. | Fax 947-1227
Union Pines HS | 1,200/9-12
1981 Union Church Rd 28326 | 910-947-5511
Robin Lea, prin. | Fax 947-5117

Candler, Buncombe
Buncombe County SD
Supt. — See Asheville
Enka HS | 1,300/9-12
475 Enka Lake Rd 28715 | 828-670-5000
Edwin Spivey, prin. | Fax 670-5007
Enka MS | 1,100/6-8
390 Asbury Rd 28715 | 828-670-5010
Thomas Keever, prin. | Fax 670-5015

Mt. Pisgah Academy | 100/9-12
75 Academy Dr 28715 | 828-667-2535
Rick Anderson, prin. | Fax 667-0657

Canton, Haywood, Pop. 4,165
Haywood County SD
Supt. — See Waynesville
Canton MS 600/6-8
60 Penland St 28716 828-646-3467
Travis Collins, prin. Fax 646-3478
Pisgah HS 1,000/9-12
1 Black Bear Dr 28716 828-646-3440
Greg Bailey, prin. Fax 648-8618

Carrboro, Orange, Pop. 19,067
Chapel Hill-Carrboro CSD
Supt. — See Chapel Hill
Carrboro HS 900/9-12
201 Rock Haven Rd 27510 919-918-2200
LaVerne Mattocks, prin. Fax 918-2507

Carthage, Moore, Pop. 2,154
Moore County SD 11,900/PK-12
PO Box 1180 28327 910-947-2976
Dr. Aaron Spence, supt. Fax 947-3011
www.ncmcs.org
Crain's Creek MS 6-8
4631 Union Church Rd 28327 910-245-3796
Rose Cooper, prin. Fax 245-7312
Pinckney Academy 50/Alt
PO Box 1180 28327 910-947-2603
Kelvin Watson, prin. Fax 947-2404
Other Schools – See Aberdeen, Cameron, Robbins, Southern Pines, West End

Cary, Wake, Pop. 131,955
Wake County SD
Supt. — See Raleigh
Cary HS 2,300/9-12
638 Walnut St 27511 919-460-3549
Douglas Thilman, prin. Fax 460-3573
Davis Drive MS 1,200/6-8
2101 Davis Dr 27519 919-387-3033
Karen Summers, prin. Fax 387-3039
East Cary MS 800/6-8
1111 SE Maynard Rd 27511 919-466-4377
Kerry Chisnall, prin. Fax 466-4388
Green Hope HS 2,000/9-12
2500 Carpenter Upchurch Rd 27519 919-380-3700
James Hedrick, prin. Fax 380-3712
Mills Park MS 6-8
441 Mills Park Dr 27519 919-466-1500
Robert Smith, prin. Fax 466-1522
Panther Creek HS 2,300/9-12
6770 McCrimmon Pkwy 27519 919-463-8656
Rodney Nelson, prin. Fax 463-8666
Reedy Creek MS 900/6-8
930 Reedy Creek Rd 27513 919-460-3504
Therman Flowers, prin. Fax 460-3391
West Cary MS 700/6-8
1000 Evans Rd 27513 919-460-3528
Wanza Cole, prin. Fax 460-3540

Cary Academy 800/6-12
1500 N Harrison Ave 27513 919-677-3873
Mitch McGuigan, hdmstr. Fax 677-4002
Cary Christian S 000/K-12
1330 Old Apex Rd 27513 919-303-2560
ITT Technical Institute Post-Sec.
5520 Dillard Dr Ste 100 27518 919-233-2520
Miller-Motte College Post-Sec.
2205 Walnut St 27518 919-532-7171
Shepherds Theological Seminary Post-Sec.
6051 Tryon Rd 27518 919-573-5350

Cashiers, Jackson, Pop. 156
Jackson County SD
Supt. — See Sylva
Blue Ridge Early College 100/7-12
95 Bobcat Dr 28717 828-743-2646
Jason Watson, prin. Fax 743-5320

Castle Hayne, New Hanover, Pop. 1,182
New Hanover County SD
Supt. — See Wilmington
Holly Shelter MS 600/6-8
3921 Roger Haynes Dr 28429 910-602-4046
Dr. Sherry Pinto, prin. Fax 602-4045
Wilmington Early College HS 200/9-12
4500 Blue Clay Rd 28429 910-362-7789
Ivy Murrain, prin. Fax 362-7424

Catawba, Catawba, Pop. 599
Catawba County SD
Supt. — See Newton
Bandys HS 900/9-12
5040 E Bandys Xrd 28609 828-241-3171
Todd Black, prin. Fax 241-9402
Catawba Rosenwald S 50/Alt
403 6th Ave SW 28609 828-241-2734
Tim Conaway, prin. Fax 241-4999

Cerro Gordo, Columbus, Pop. 201
Columbus County SD
Supt. — See Whiteville
West Columbus HS 500/9-12
PO Box 130 28430 910-654-6111
Jeffrey Greene, prin. Fax 654-4082

Chadbourn, Columbus, Pop. 1,832
Columbus County SD
Supt. — See Whiteville
Chadbourn MS 200/6-8
801 W Smith St 28431 910-654-4300
Georgia Spaulding, prin. Fax 654-6809

Chapel Hill, Orange, Pop. 55,802
Chapel Hill-Carrboro CSD 11,600/PK-12
750 S Merritt Mill Rd 27516 919-967-8211
Dr. Tom Forcella, supt. Fax 933-4560
www.chccs.k12.nc.us
Chapel Hill HS 1,300/9-12
1709 High School Rd 27516 919-929-2106
Salura Jackson, prin. Fax 929-2455
East Chapel Hill HS 1,400/9-12
500 Weaver Dairy Rd 27514 919-969-2482
Eileen Tully, prin. Fax 969-2492
Grey Culbreth MS 700/6-8
225 Culbreth Rd 27516 919-929-7161
Beverly Rudolph, prin. Fax 969-2412
McDougle MS 700/6-8
900 Old Fayetteville Rd 27516 919-933-1556
Debra Scott, prin. Fax 969-2433
Phillips MS 700/6-8
606 N Estes Dr 27514 919-929-2188
Jonathan Enns, prin. Fax 969-2477
Phoenix Academy HS 50/Alt
750 S Merritt Mill Rd 27516 919-918-2300
John Williams, prin. Fax 933-4560
Smith MS 700/6-8
9201 Seawell School Rd 27516 919-918-2145
Phil Holmes, prin. Fax 918-2079
Other Schools – See Carrboro

Chatham County SD
Supt. — See Pittsboro
Pollard MS 500/6-8
185 Granite Mill Blvd 27516 919-969-0070
Dr. Justin Batholomew, prin.

Emerson Waldorf S 200/PK-12
6211 New Jericho Rd 27516 919-967-1858
Fax 967-2732
University of North Carolina 27599 Post-Sec.
919-962-2211
University of North Carolina Hospitals Post-Sec.
101 Manning Dr 27514 919-966-5111

Charlotte, Mecklenburg, Pop. 715,605
Charlotte/Mecklenburg County SD 124,200/PK-12
PO Box 30035 28230 980-343-6270
Dr. Heath Morrison, supt. Fax 343-7135
www.cms.k12.nc.us/
Albemarle Road MS 800/6-8
6900 Democracy Dr 28212 980-343-6420
Toni Perry, prin. Fax 343-6501
Berry Academy of Technology Vo/Tech
1430 Alleghany St 28208 980-343-5992
Curtis Carroll, prin. Fax 343-5994
Biotechnolgy Health & Public Admin @ OHS 400/9-12
4301 Sandy Porter Rd Ste E 28273 980-343-1110
Angela Bozeman, prin. Fax 343-1114
Carmel MS 1,200/6-8
5001 Camilla Dr 28226 980-343-6705
Mark Angerer, prin. Fax 343-6749
Cato Middle College HS 100/11-12
8120 Grier Rd 28215 980-343-1452
Joseph Burch, prin. Fax 343-1453
Cochrane Colegiate Academy 600/6-12
6200 Starhaven Dr 28215 980-343-6460
Josh Bishop, prin. Fax 343-6521
Community House MS 1,500/6-8
9500 Community House Rd 28277 980-343-0689
Jamie Brooks, prin. Fax 343-0691
Coulwood MS 800/6-8
500 Kentberry Dr 28214 980-343-0090
Rachel Goldberg, prin. Fax 343-6142
East Mecklenburg HS 1,800/9-12
6800 Monroe Rd 28212 980-343-6430
Richard Parker, prin. Fax 343-6437
Eastway MS 900/6-8
1501 Norland Rd 28205 980-343-6410
Anne Brinkley, prin. Fax 343-6406
Garinger HS 700/9-12
1100 Eastway Dr 28205 980-343-6450
Kondra Rattley, prin. Fax 343-1475
Graham MS 1,200/6-8
1800 Runnymede Ln 28211 980-343-5810
Robert Folk, prin. Fax 343-5868
Harding University HS 900/9-12
2001 Alleghany St 28208 980-343-6007
Alicisa Johnson, prin. Fax 343-6015
Hawthorne HS Alt
1411 Hawthorne Ln 28205 980-343-6011
Sheila Ijames, prin. Fax 343-5609
Independence HS 2,000/9-12
1967 Patriot Dr 28227 980-343-6900
Amy Dellinger, prin. Fax 343-6907
Intl Business & Communication HS 400/9-12
4301 Sandy Porter Rd Ste C 28273 980-343-1104
Dr. Jeffrey Crook, prin. Fax 343-1108
Intl Studies & Global Economics HS 400/9-12
4301 Sandy Porter Rd Ste A 28273 980-343-1113
Barry Burford, prin. Fax 343-1102
Kell HS 2,200/9-12
10220 Ardrey Kell Rd 28277 980-343-0860
David Switzer, prin. Fax 343-0862
Kennedy MS 600/6-8
4000 Gallant Ln 28273 980-343-5540
Kevin Sudimack, prin. Fax 343-5412
King MS 800/6-8
500 Bilmark Ave 28213 980-343-0698
Jennifer Dean, prin. Fax 343-0700
Mallard Creek HS 2,100/9-12
3825 Johnston Oehler Rd 28269 980-343-1341
Nancy Hicks-Brightwell, prin. Fax 343-1342
Martin MS 1,200/6-8
7800 IBM Dr 28262 980-343-5382
Ayinde Rudolph, prin. Fax 343-5135
Math Engineering Tech/Science S @ OHS 400/9-12
4301 Sandy Porter Rd Ste B 28273 980-343-1101
Richard Reynolds, prin. Fax 343-1105
McClintock MS 600/6-8
2101 Rama Rd 28212 980-343-6425
Paul Williams, prin. Fax 343-6509
Military & Global Leadrshp Acad @ Davis K-12
3351 Griffith St 28203 980-343-0006
Lawrance Mayes, prin. Fax 343-1735
Myers Park HS 2,700/9-12
2400 Colony Rd 28209 980-343-5800
Tom Spivey, prin. Fax 343-5803
Northridge MS 900/6-8
7601 the Plz 28215 980-343-5015
Raymond Barnes, prin. Fax 343-5174
Northwest S of the Arts 1,000/6-12
1415 Beatties Ford Rd 28216 980-343-5500
Melody Sears, prin. Fax 343-5593
Performance Learning Center 100/Alt
1400 N Graham St 28206 980-343-1118
Tracey Pickard, prin. Fax 343-1117
Piedmont IB MS 900/6-8
1241 E 10th St 28204 980-343-5435
Deirdra Gardner, prin. Fax 343-5557
Providence HS 2,100/9-12
1800 Pineville Matthews Rd 28270 980-343-5390
Tracey Harrill, prin. Fax 343-3956
Quail Hollow MS 900/6-8
2901 Smithfield Church Rd 28210 980-343-3620
Rachael Neill, prin. Fax 343-3622
Randolph MS 1,000/6-8
4400 Water Oak Rd 28211 980-343-6700
Jackie Menser, prin. Fax 343-6741
Ranson MS 1,200/6-8
5850 Statesville Rd 28269 980-343-6800
Allison Harris, prin. Fax 343-6796
Renaissance S @ Olympic 400/9-12
4301 Sandy Porter Rd Ste D 28273 980-343-1107
Sonya Cason McInnis, prin. Fax 343-1111
Ridge Road MS 1,200/6-8
7260 Highland Creek Pkwy 28269 980-344-3410
Jametta Martin-Tanner, prin. Fax 343-1835
Robinson MS 1,100/6-8
5925 Ballantyne Commons Pky 28277 980-343-6944
Kathleen Fox, prin. Fax 343-6947
Sedgefield MS 500/6-8
2700 Dorchester Pl 28209 980-343-5840
Robert Ellyson, prin. Fax 343-5862
South Charlotte MS 900/6-8
8040 Strawberry Ln 28277 980-343-3670
Lisa Bowen, prin. Fax 343-3725
South Mecklenburg HS 2,000/9-12
8900 Park Rd 28210 980-343-3600
Dr. Maureen Furr, prin. Fax 343-3607
Southwest MS 1,300/6-8
13624 Steele Creek Rd 28273 980-343-5006
Barry Blair, prin. Fax 343-3239
Turning Point Academy 300/Alt
2300 W Sugar Creek Rd 28262 980-343-5231
Valoria Burch, prin. Fax 343-6808
Vance HS 1,800/9-12
7600 IBM Dr 28262 980-343-5284
Melissa Dunlap, prin. Fax 343-5286
Waddell Language Academy 1,100/K-12
7030 Nations Ford Rd 28217 980-343-5815
Ynez Olshausen, prin. Fax 343-5854
West Charlotte HS 1,700/9-12
2219 Senior Dr 28216 980-343-6060
John Wall, prin. Fax 343-6049
West Mecklenburg HS 2,200/9-12
7400 Tuckaseegee Rd 28214 980-343-6080
Eric Ward, prin. Fax 343-6079
Whitewater MS 600/6-8
1520 Belmeade Dr 28214 980-344-3400
Dr. Valarie Williams, prin. Fax 344-1814
Other Schools – See Cornelius, Huntersville, Matthews, Mint Hill

---

Art Institute of Charlotte Post-Sec.
2110 Water Ridge Pkwy 28217 704-357-8020
Brisbane Academy Preparatory S 100/PK-12
5901 Statesville Rd 28269 704-598-5208
Christopher Crooks, dir. Fax 597-0792
Brookstone College of Business Post-Sec.
10125 Berkeley Place Dr 28262 704-547-8600
Carolina School of Broadcasting Post-Sec.
3435 Performance Rd 28214 704-395-9272
Carolinas College of Health Sciences Post-Sec.
PO Box 32861 28232 704-355-5043
Central Piedmont Community College Post-Sec.
PO Box 35009 28235 704-330-2722
Charlotte Catholic HS 1,400/9-12
7702 Pineville Matthews Rd 28226 704-543-1127
Jerry Healy, prin. Fax 543-1217
Charlotte Christian S 1,000/PK-12
7301 Sardis Rd 28270 704-366-5657
Barry Giller, head sch Fax 366-5678
Charlotte Country Day S 1,600/PK-12
1440 Carmel Rd 28226 704-943-4500
Mark Reed, hdmstr. Fax 943-4536
Charlotte Islamic Academy 100/K-12
4301 Shamrock Dr 28215 704-537-1772
Dr. Abdel Jebbar-Lamti, prin. Fax 537-1702
Charlotte Latin S 1,400/PK-12
9502 Providence Rd 28277 704-846-1100
Arch McIntosh, hdmstr. Fax 846-1712
Charlotte School of Law Post-Sec.
2145 Suttle Ave 28208 704-971-8500
Charlotte United Christian Academy 200/PK-12
7640 Wallace Rd 28212 704-537-0331
Janet Atwell, prin. Fax 537-0568
Countryside Montessori HS 100/7-12
4125 Johnston Oehler Rd 28269 704-936-5580
Heide Putt, admin. Fax 936-5599
Crosland S 100/K-12
5146 Parkway Plaza Blvd 28217 704-365-5490
Maria M. Leahy, head sch Fax 365-3240
DeVry University Post-Sec.
2015 Ayrsley Town Blvd #109 28273 704-362-2345
Dudley Beauty College Post-Sec.
1950 John McDonald Ave 28216 704-392-2564
ECPI University Post-Sec.
4800 Airport Center Pkwy 28208 704-399-1010
Hairstyling Institute of Charlotte Post-Sec.
209B S Kings Dr 28204 704-334-5511
Hickory Grove Christian S 1,000/K-12
6050 Hickory Grove Rd 28215 704-531-4008
G.T. Freeman, head sch Fax 531-3509
Holy Trinity Catholic MS 900/6-8
3100 Park Rd 28209 704-527-7822
Kevin Parks, prin. Fax 525-7288
ITT Technical Institute Post-Sec.
4135 Southstream Blvd # 200 28217 704-423-3100

ITT Technical Institute — Post-Sec.
10926 David Taylor Dr # 100 28262 — 704-548-2300
Johnson & Wales University — Post-Sec.
801 W Trade St 28202 — 980-598-1000
Johnson C. Smith University — Post-Sec.
100 Beatties Ford Rd 28216 — 704-378-1000
King's College — Post-Sec.
322 Lamar Ave 28204 — 704-372-0266
Mercy School of Nursing — Post-Sec.
701 Forest Point Cir Ste B 28273 — 704-512-2010
Montreat College — Post-Sec.
212 S Tryon St Ste 1700 28202 — 828-669-8012
New Life Theological Seminary — Post-Sec.
3117 Whiting Ave 28205 — 704-334-6882
Northside Christian Academy — 600/PK-12
333 Jeremiah Blvd 28262 — 704-599-9015
Tony Fajardo, hdmstr. — Fax 921-1384
Pfeiffer University — Post-Sec.
4701 Park Rd 28209 — 704-945-7320
Presbyterian Hospital — Post-Sec.
PO Box 33549 28233 — 704-384-4141
Providence Day S — 1,500/PK-12
5800 Sardis Rd 28270 — 704-887-6000
Glyn Cowlishaw, hdmstr. — Fax 887-7042
Queens University of Charlotte — Post-Sec.
1900 Selwyn Ave 28274 — 704-337-2200
Reformed Theological Seminary — Post-Sec.
2101 Carmel Rd 28226 — 704-366-5066
Renaissance Christian S of Excellence — 50/PK-12
7209 E W T Harris Blvd # J 28227 — 704-323-5938
Southeastern Institute — Post-Sec.
5250 77 Center Dr Ste 100 28217 — 704-527-4979
United Faith Christian Academy — 300/PK-12
8617 Providence Rd 28277 — 704-541-1742
Esther Feather, head sch — Fax 540-7926
Universal College of Beauty — Post-Sec.
1701 W Trade St 28216 — 704-333-6969
University of North Carolina — Post-Sec.
9201 University City Blvd 28223 — 704-687-2000
Victory Christian Center S — 300/PK-12
1501 Carrier Dr 28216 — 704-391-7339
Michael Pratt, prin. — Fax 391-0494

Cherryville, Gaston, Pop. 5,683
Gaston County SD
Supt. — See Gastonia
Chavis MS — 500/6-8
103 S Chavis Dr 28021 — 704-435-6045
Bryan Denton, prin. — Fax 435-6168
Cherryville HS — 700/9-12
313 Ridge Ave 28021 — 704-435-4506
Derrick Jackson, prin. — Fax 435-4989

China Grove, Rowan, Pop. 3,516
Rowan-Salisbury County SD
Supt. — See Salisbury
China Grove MS — 600/6-8
1013 N Main St 28023 — 704-857-7038
Linda Johnson, prin. — Fax 857-6650
South Rowan HS — 1,000/9-12
1655 Patterson St 28023 — 704-857-1161
Dr. Don Knox, prin. — Fax 855-1420

Chocowinity, Beaufort, Pop. 806
Beaufort County SD
Supt. — See Washington
Chocowinity MS — 400/5-8
3831 US Highway 17 S 27817 — 252-946-6191
Dale Cole, prin. — Fax 975-3812
Southside HS — 500/9-12
5700 NC Highway 33 E 27817 — 252-940-1881
Rick Anderson, prin. — Fax 940-1888

Claremont, Catawba, Pop. 1,328
Catawba County SD
Supt. — See Newton
Bunker Hill HS — 900/9-12
4675 Oxford School Rd 28610 — 828-241-3355
Jeff Taylor, prin. — Fax 241-9401
Mill Creek MS — 500/7-8
1041 Shiloh Rd 28610 — 828-241-2711
Rob Rucker, prin. — Fax 241-2743
River Bend MS — 500/7-8
4670 Oxford School Rd 28610 — 828-241-2754
Donna Heavner, prin. — Fax 241-2820

Clarkton, Bladen, Pop. 821
Bladen County SD
Supt. — See Elizabethtown
Clarkton MS of Discovery — 400/6-8
PO Box 127 28433 — 910-647-6531
Stephanie Ensminger, prin. — Fax 647-6671

Clayton, Johnston, Pop. 15,821
Johnston County SD
Supt. — See Smithfield
Clayton HS — 1,800/9-12
600 S Fayetteville St 27520 — 919-553-4064
Clint Eaves, prin. — Fax 553-2563
Clayton MS — 800/6-8
490 Guy Rd 27520 — 919-553-5811
Stephen Baker, prin. — Fax 553-6978
Cleveland HS — 9-12
1892 Polenta Rd 27520 — 919-934-2455
Anne Meredith, prin. — Fax 934-2414
Riverwood MS — 1,000/6-8
204 Athletic Club Blvd, — 919-359-2769
Phillip Lee, prin. — Fax 359-1519

Clemmons, Forsyth, Pop. 18,375
Winston-Salem/Forsyth SD
Supt. — See Winston Salem
West Forsyth HS — 1,900/9-12
1735 Lewisville Clemmons Rd 27012 — 336-712-4400
Charles McAninch, prin. — Fax 712-4416

Climax, Guilford
Randolph County SD
Supt. — See Asheboro
Providence Grove HS — 800/9-12
5555 Mack Lineberry Rd 27233 — 336-685-0728
Rick Dawes, prin. — Fax 685-0731

Clinton, Sampson, Pop. 8,488
Clinton CSD — 3,200/PK-12
300 Westover Rd 28328 — 910-592-3132
Stuart Blount, supt. — Fax 592-2011
www.clinton.k12.nc.us
Clinton HS — 800/9-12
340 Indian Town Rd 28328 — 910-592-2067
Dr. Steven Miller, prin. — Fax 299-5164
Sampson MS — 700/6-8
1201 W Elizabeth St 28328 — 910-592-3327
Greg Dirks, prin. — Fax 592-6185

Sampson County SD — 8,100/PK-12
PO Box 439 28329 — 910-592-1401
Dr. Ethan Lenker, supt. — Fax 590-2445
www.sampson.k12.nc.us
Sampson Early College HS — 200/9-12
PO Box 318 28329 — 910-592-8081
Susan Westerbeck, prin. — Fax 592-8048
Union MS — 500/6-8
455 River Rd 28328 — 910-592-4547
Lynn Prescott, prin. — Fax 592-4211
Other Schools – See Dunn, Newton Grove, Roseboro, Rose Hill, Salemburg

---

Sampson Community College — Post-Sec.
PO Box 318 28329 — 910-592-8081

Clyde, Haywood, Pop. 1,216
Haywood County SD
Supt. — See Waynesville
Central Haywood HS — 100/9-12
3215 Broad St 28721 — 828-627-9944
Jeff Haney, prin. — Fax 627-0709
Haywood Early College HS — 100/9-12
185 Freedlander Dr 28721 — 828-565-4000
Doris Greene, prin. — Fax 565-4074

Haywood Christian Academy — 100/PK-12
1400 Old Clyde Rd 28721 — 828-627-0229
Msgr. Blake Stanbery, hdmstr. — Fax 880-8447
Haywood Community College — Post-Sec.
185 Freedlander Dr 28721 — 828-627-4500

Columbia, Tyrrell, Pop. 886
Tyrrell County SD — 600/PK-12
PO Box 328 27925 — 252-796-1121
Dr. Michael Dunsmore, supt. — Fax 796-1492
www.tyrrell.k12.nc.us
Columbia HS — 200/9-12
PO Box 419 27925 — 252-796-8161
Marcia Manning, prin. — Fax 796-0143
Columbia MS — 100/6-8
PO Box 839 27925 — 252-796-0369
Jana Rawls, prin. — Fax 796-3639

Columbus, Polk, Pop. 981
Polk County SD — 2,500/PK-12
PO Box 638 28722 — 828-894-3051
William Miller, supt. — Fax 894-8153
www.polkschools.org
Polk County HS — 700/9-12
1681 NC 108 Hwy E 28722 — 828-894-2525
Mary Feagan, prin. — Fax 894-2093
Other Schools – See Mill Spring

Concord, Cabarrus, Pop. 77,521
Cabarrus County SD — 27,400/PK-12
PO Box 388 28026 — 704-786-6191
Dr. Barry Shepherd, supt. — Fax 786-6141
www.cabarrus.k12.nc.us
Cabarrus County Opportunity S — 50/Alt
120 Marsh Ave NW 28025 — 704-793-1736
Beverly Mack, prin. — Fax 793-1740
Cabarrus-Kannapolis Early College HS — 100/9-12
1531 Trinity Church Rd 28027 — 704-260-0227
Vance Fishback, prin. — Fax 260-0229
Central Cabarrus HS — 1,200/9-12
505 Highway 49 S 28025 — 704-786-0125
Lynn Rhymer, prin. — Fax 920-7164
Concord HS — 1,200/9-12
481 Burrage Rd NE 28025 — 704-786-4161
Carla Black, prin. — Fax 782-7539
Concord MS — 900/6-8
1500 Gold Rush Dr 28025 — 704-786-4121
Susan Owens, prin. — Fax 782-8632
Cox Mill HS — 1,100/9-12
1355 Cox Mill Rd 28027 — 704-788-6700
Todd Smith, prin. — Fax 788-1112
Fries MS — 1,000/6-8
133 Stonecrest Cir SW 28027 — 704-788-4140
Dr. Kecia Coln, prin. — Fax 784-2086
Griffin MS — 700/6-8
7650 Griffins Gate Dr SW 28025 — 704-455-4700
Kristy Bullock, prin. — Fax 454-4780
Harris Road MS — 1,500/6-8
1251 Patriot Plantation 28027 — 704-782-2002
Raymond Aldridge, prin. — Fax 262-4298
Northwest Cabarrus HS — 1,000/9-12
5130 NW Cabarrus Dr 28027 — 704-788-4111
Mike Jolley, prin. — Fax 723-4114
Northwest Cabarrus MS — 900/6-8
5140 NW Cabarrus Dr 28027 — 704-788-4135
Tim Farrar, prin. — Fax 784-2649
Performance Learning Center — 100/9-12
133 Stonecrest Cir SW 28027 — 704-795-7074
Dr. James Williams, prin. — Fax 795-5994
Robinson HS — 1,500/9-12
300 Pitts School Rd SW 28027 — 704-788-4500
Gregory Hall, prin. — Fax 723-4352
Winkler MS — 6-8
4501 Weddington Rd NW 28027 — 704-786-2000
Dr. Mary Roth, prin. — Fax 786-2002
Other Schools – See Harrisburg, Mount Pleasant

Cabarrus College of Health Sciences — Post-Sec.
401 Medical Park Dr 28025 — 704-403-1555
Cannon S — 800/PK-12
5801 Poplar Tent Rd 28027 — 704-786-8171
Matthew Gossage, hdmstr. — Fax 788-7779

CFA Academy — 500/K-12
154 Warren C Coleman Blvd N 28027 — 704-793-4750
Frank Cantadore, hdmstr. — Fax 793-4784
Covenant Classical S — 200/PK-12
3200 Patrick Henry Dr NW 28027 — 704-792-1854
Greg Hardie, hdmstr. — Fax 792-2102
Empire Beauty School — Post-Sec.
10075 Weddington Road Ext 28027 — 800-575-5983

Connelly Sprngs, Burke
Burke County SD
Supt. — See Morganton
East Burke HS — 1,000/9-12
3695 E Burke Blvd, — 828-397-5541
Debbie Jennings, prin. — Fax 397-7652
East Burke MS — 800/6-8
3519 Miller Bridge Rd, — 828-397-7446
Shane Mace, prin. — Fax 397-1086

Conover, Catawba, Pop. 8,005
Newton-Conover CSD
Supt. — See Newton
Newton-Conover MS — 600/6-8
873 Northern Dr NW 28613 — 828-464-4221
Kim Kaylor, prin. — Fax 464-5238

Tri-City Christian S — 200/PK-12
PO Box 1690 28613 — 828-465-0475
Debbie Hedrick, admin. — Fax 466-3749

Conway, Northampton, Pop. 825
Northampton County SD
Supt. — See Jackson
Conway MS — 400/5-8
400 E Main St 27820 — 252-585-0312
Oliver Holley, prin. — Fax 585-0335
Northampton County HS — 400/9-12
750 NCHS Rd 27820 — 252-585-0627
Felisha Whitaker, prin. — Fax 585-9019

Cornelius, Mecklenburg, Pop. 24,533
Charlotte/Mecklenburg County SD
Supt. — See Charlotte
Bailey MS — 1,300/6-8
11900 Bailey Rd 28031 — 980-343-1068
Chad Thomas, prin. — Fax 343-1069
Hough HS — 1,500/9-12
12420 Bailey Rd 28031 — 980-344-0514
Dr. Terri Cockerham, prin. — Fax 343-2215

Phoenix Montessori Academy — 100/PK-10
17609 Old Statesville Rd 28031 — 704-892-7536
India Adams, head sch — Fax 892-8481

Cramerton, Gaston, Pop. 4,105
Gaston County SD
Supt. — See Gastonia
Cramerton MS — 900/6-8
601 Cramer Mountain Rd 28032 — 704-824-2907
Amy Holbrook, prin. — Fax 824-0228

Cramerton Christian Academy — 300/K-12
426 Woodlawn Ave 28032 — 704-824-2840
Fax 824-9642

Creedmoor, Granville, Pop. 4,037
Granville County SD
Supt. — See Oxford
Granville Early College S — 100/9-12
701 N Crescent Dr 27522 — 919-528-5583
Chris Ham, prin. — Fax 528-5584
Hawley MS — 700/6-8
PO Box 68 27522 — 919-528-0091
Frank Wiggins, prin. — Fax 528-0051
South Granville HS of ITL — 500/9-12
701 N Crescent Dr 27522 — 919-528-5533
Katherine Fuerst, prin. — Fax 528-5577
South Granville S of Health & Life Sci — 400/9-12
701 N Crescent Dr 27522 — 919-528-5532
Lisa Tusa, prin. — Fax 528-5575

Creswell, Washington, Pop. 268
Washington County SD
Supt. — See Plymouth
Creswell JSHS — 200/7-12
PO Box 188 27928 — 252-797-4766
Sharon Cherry, prin. — Fax 797-4651

Cullowhee, Jackson, Pop. 6,135

Western Carolina University — Post-Sec.
University Dr 28723 — 828-227-7211

Currituck, Currituck
Currituck County SD — 3,600/PK-12
2958 Caratoke Hwy 27929 — 252-232-2223
Allison Sholar, supt. — Fax 232-3655
www.currituck.k12.nc.us
Knapp Early College HS — 200/9-12
2966 Caratoke Hwy 27929 — 252-232-3107
Stephen Basnight, prin. — Fax 232-3923
Other Schools – See Barco, Moyock

Dallas, Gaston, Pop. 4,415
Gaston County SD
Supt. — See Gastonia
Friday MS — 700/6-8
1221 Ratchford Dr 28034 — 704-922-5297
Crystal Houser, prin. — Fax 922-9841
North Gaston HS — 1,100/9-12
1133 Ratchford Dr 28034 — 704-922-5285
Judy Moore, prin. — Fax 922-7486

Gaston College — Post-Sec.
201 Highway 321 S 28034 — 704-922-6200

Danbury, Stokes, Pop. 189
Stokes County SD — 7,100/PK-12
PO Box 50 27016 — 336-593-8146
Ronnie Mendenhall, supt. — Fax 593-2041
www.stokes.k12.nc.us

North Stokes HS 400/9-12
1350 N Stokes School Rd 27016 336-593-8134
Nathan Rasey, prin. Fax 593-8882
Other Schools – See King, Lawsonville, Walnut Cove

Davidson, Mecklenburg, Pop. 10,776

Davidson College Post-Sec.
PO Box 7171 28035 704-894-2000
Davidson Day S 400/PK-12
750 Jetton St 28036 704-237-5200
Bonnie Cotter, hdmstr. Fax 896-5535
Lake Norman Christian S 100/K-10
PO Box 4267 28036 704-987-9811
Sarah Beam, prin. Fax 896-5875
Woodlawn S 200/K-12
PO Box 549 28036 704-895-8653

Deep Run, Lenoir
Lenoir County SD
Supt. — See Kinston
South Lenoir HS 800/9-12
3355 Old Hwy 11 28525 252-568-6161
James Saint-Amand, prin. Fax 568-6015

Delco, Columbus, Pop. 332
Columbus County SD
Supt. — See Whiteville
Acme-Delco MS 100/6-8
PO Box 40 28436 910-655-3200
Christy Brown, prin. Fax 655-6865

Denton, Davidson, Pop. 1,618
Davidson County SD
Supt. — See Lexington
South Davidson HS 500/9-12
14956 S NC Highway 109 27239 336-242-5700
Mike Lawson, prin. Fax 242-5702
South Davidson MS 400/6-8
14954 S NC Highway 109 27239 336-242-5705
Loretta Fulbright, prin. Fax 242-5707

Denver, Lincoln, Pop. 2,276
Lincoln County SD
Supt. — See Lincolnton
East Lincoln HS 900/9-12
6471 Highway 73 28037 704-736-1860
Tim Woody, prin. Fax 483-6751
North Lincoln MS 700/6-8
1503 Amity Church Rd 28037 704-736-0262
Chris Kolasinski, prin. Fax 736-9812

Dobson, Surry, Pop. 1,569
Surry County SD 7,900/PK-12
PO Box 364 27017 336-386-8211
Dr. Travis Reeves, supt. Fax 386-4279
www.surry.k12.nc.us/
Central MS 700/6-8
PO Box 768 27017 336-386-4018
Neil Atkins, prin. Fax 386-4371
Surry Central HS 800/9-12
PO Box 8 27017 336-386-8842
Kevin Via, prin. Fax 386-4424
Surry Early College HS 300/9-12
630 S Main St 27017 336-386-3621
Celia Hodges, prin. Fax 386-3629
Other Schools – See Mount Airy, Pilot Mountain

Surry Community College Post-Sec.
630 S Main St 27017 336-386-8121

Drexel, Burke, Pop. 1,832
Burke County SD
Supt. — See Morganton
Hallyburton Academy 100/6-12
205 S Main St 28619 828-437-4184
Teresa DeHart, prin. Fax 437-0655

Dublin, Bladen, Pop. 329

Bladen Community College Post-Sec.
PO Box 266 28332 910-879-5500

Dudley, Wayne
Wayne County SD
Supt. — See Goldsboro
Brogden MS 500/5-8
3761 US 117 Alt 28333 919-705-6010
Sylvester Townsend, prin. Fax 705-6000
Southern Wayne HS 1,000/9-12
124 Walter Fulcher Rd 28333 919-705-6060
Dr. John Boldt, prin. Fax 731-5982

Dunn, Harnett, Pop. 9,078
Harnett County SD
Supt. — See Lillington
Coats-Erwin MS 700/6-8
2833 NC Highway 55 E 28334 910-230-0300
Whit Bradham, prin. Fax 230-0306
Dunn MS 400/6-8
1301 Meadow Lark Rd 28334 910-892-1017
Tina Tasker, prin. Fax 892-7923

Sampson County SD
Supt. — See Clinton
Midway MS 600/6-8
1115 Roberts Grove Rd 28334 910-567-5879
John Goode, prin. Fax 567-5131

Heritage Bible College Post-Sec.
PO Box 1628 28335 910-892-3178

Durham, Durham, Pop. 223,352
Durham County SD 32,100/PK-12
PO Box 30002 27702 919-560-2000
Dr. Eric Becoats, supt. Fax 560-2422
www.dpsnc.net
Brogden MS 700/6-8
1001 Leon St 27704 919-560-3906
Renee Trapp, prin. Fax 560-3957
Carrington MS 1,200/6-8
227 Milton Rd 27712 919-560-3916
Holly Emmanuel, prin. Fax 560-3522
Chewning MS 500/6-8
5001 Red Mill Rd 27704 919-560-3914
John Williams, prin. Fax 477-9189
City of Medicine Academy 200/9-12
4100 N Roxboro St 27704 919-560-2001
Elizabeth Shearer, prin. Fax 477-3128
Clement Early College HS 300/9-12
1801 Fayetteville St 27707 919-560-2696
Gloria Woods-Weaks, prin. Fax 560-2698
Durham S of the Arts 1,400/6-12
400 N Duke St 27701 919-560-3926
David Hawks, prin. Fax 560-2217
Githens MS 1,000/6-8
4800 Old Chapel Hill Rd 27707 919-560-3966
Tonya Williams, prin. Fax 560-3454
Hillside HS 1,300/9-12
3727 Fayetteville St 27707 919-560-3925
Dr. William Logan, prin. Fax 560-2312
Hillside New Tech HS Vo/Tech
3727 Fayetteville St 27707 919-560-9183
Dr. William Logan, prin. Fax 560-3686
Holton Career & Resource Center Vo/Tech
401 N Driver St 27703 919-560-2219
Danny Gilford, prin. Fax 237-5669
Jordan HS 1,800/9-12
6806 Garrett Rd 27707 919-560-3912
Jerome Leathers, prin. Fax 560-2620
Lakeview S 200/Alt
3507 Dearborn Dr 27704 919-560-2520
Jeffery Dockery, prin. Fax 560-2446
Lakewood Montessori S 6-8
700 Watts St 27701 919-560-3947
Sheldon Reynolds, prin. Fax 560-3949
Lowes Grove MS 600/6-8
4418 S Alston Ave 27713 919-560-3946
Kathleen Kirkpatrick, prin. Fax 560-2102
Lucas MS, 923 Snow Hill Rd 27712 6-8
Tom Seckler, prin. 919-560-3843
Middle College HS at DTCC 100/11-12
1616 Cooper St Bldg Newton 27703 919-536-7203
Dr. Charles Nolan, prin. Fax 536-7294
Neal MS 600/6-8
201 Baptist Rd 27704 919-560-3955
Jill Hall, prin. Fax 560-3451
Northern HS 1,500/9-12
117 Tom Wilkinson Rd 27712 919-560-3956
Kathryn Bonner, prin. Fax 479-3001
Pearson MS 300/6-8
600 E Umstead St 27701 919-560-2208
Valerie Griffin-Puryear, prin. Fax 560-3802
Performance Learning Center 200/9-12
401 N Driver St 27703 919-560-9190
Danny Gilfort, prin. Fax 560-2214
Riverside HS 1,900/9-12
3218 Rose of Sharon Rd 27712 919-560-3965
Jackie Tobias, prin. Fax 560-3798
Rogers-Herr MS 600/6-8
911 W Cornwallis Rd 27707 919-560-3970
Michael Fuga, prin. Fax 560-2439
Shepard MS 400/6-8
2401 Dakota St 27707 919-560-3938
Ericka Boone, prin. Fax 560-3945
Southern HS 1,000/9-12
800 Clayton Rd 27703 919-560-3968
Kenneth Barnes, prin. Fax 560-2445
Southern S of Engineering 200/9-12
800 Clayton Rd 27703 919-560-9184
Darneise Massey, prin. Fax 560-3848

Apex School of Theology Post-Sec.
2945 S Miami Blvd Ste 114 27703 919-572-1625
Art Institute of Raleigh - Durham Post-Sec.
410 Blackwell St Ste 200 27701 919-317-3050
Carolina Friends S 500/PK-12
4809 Friends School Rd 27705 919-383-6602
Mike Hanas, prin. Fax 383-6009
Cresset Christian Academy 300/PK-12
3707 Garrett Rd 27707 919-489-2655
Greg Hardy, admin. Fax 354-8009
Duke University 27708 Post-Sec.
919-684-8111
Durham Academy 400/5-8
3116 Academy Rd 27707 919-489-9118
Jon Meredith, prin. Fax 489-9110
Durham Academy 400/9-12
3601 Ridge Rd 27705 919-493-9595
Edward Costello, hdmstr. Fax 489-7356
Durham Technical Community College Post-Sec.
1637 E Lawson St 27703 919-536-7200
Fellowship Baptist Academy 200/PK-12
515 Southerland St 27703 919-596-9331
Paul Moolenaar, prin.
Hill Center 100/K-12
3200 Pickett Rd 27705 919-489-7464
Sharon Maskel Ed.D., dir. Fax 489-7466
ITT Technical Institute Post-Sec.
3518 Westgate Dr Ste 150 27707 919-401-1400
Liberty Christian S 300/K-12
3864 Guess Rd 27705 919-471-5522
Fax 620-6870
Mt. Zion Christian Academy 200/K-12
3519 Fayetteville St 27707 919-688-4245
Peggy McIlwain, prin. Fax 688-2201
North Carolina Central University Post-Sec.
1801 Fayetteville St 27707 919-560-6100
Trinity S of Durham & Chapel Hill 500/PK-12
4011 Pickett Rd 27705 919-402-8262
Dr. Peter T. Denton, hdmstr. Fax 402-0762

East Bend, Yadkin, Pop. 604
Yadkin County SD
Supt. — See Yadkinville
Forbush HS 1,000/9-12
1525 Falcon Rd 27018 336-961-4644
Dr. Chris Nichols, prin. Fax 961-2575
Forbush MS 500/7-8
1431 Falcon Rd 27018 336-961-6360
Kelly Mabe, prin. Fax 961-6370

East Flat Rock, Henderson, Pop. 4,872
Henderson County SD
Supt. — See Hendersonville
East Henderson HS 1,000/9-12
110 Old Upward Rd 28726 828-697-4768
Scott Rhodes, prin. Fax 698-6123
Flat Rock MS 800/6-8
191 Preston Ln 28726 828-697-4775
Jeff Roper, prin. Fax 698-6124

Eden, Rockingham, Pop. 15,244
Rockingham County SD 14,000/PK-12
511 Harrington Hwy 27288 336-627-2600
Dr. Rodney Shotwell, supt. Fax 627-2660
www.rock.k12.nc.us
Holmes MS 900/6-8
211 N Pierce St 27288 336-623-9791
Brenda Nordan, prin. Fax 627-0075
Morehead HS 1,000/9-12
134 N Pierce St 27288 336-627-7731
Al Royster, prin. Fax 623-5462
Other Schools – See Madison, Mayodan, Reidsville, Wentworth

Edenton, Chowan, Pop. 4,952
Edenton/Chowan County SD 2,400/PK-12
PO Box 206 27932 252-482-4436
Allan Smith, supt. Fax 482-7309
www.edenton-chowan.net
Holmes HS 700/9-12
PO Box 409 27932 252-482-8426
Sheila Evans, prin. Fax 482-2010
Other Schools – See Tyner

Efland, Orange, Pop. 722
Orange County SD
Supt. — See Hillsborough
Gravelly Hill MS 500/6-8
4819 W Ten Rd 27243 919-732-8126
Marcus Gause, prin. Fax 245-4055

Elizabeth City, Pasquotank, Pop. 18,282
Elizabeth City/Pasquotank County SD 6,200/PK-12
1200 Halstead Blvd 27909 252-335-2981
Linwood Williams, supt. Fax 335-0974
www.ecpps.k12.nc.us
Elizabeth City MS 700/6-8
1066 Northside Rd 27909 252-335-2974
Cynthia Morris, prin. Fax 335-1751
Northeastern HS 900/9-12
963 Oak Stump Rd 27909 252-335-2932
Ron Payne, prin. Fax 335-1005
Pasquotank County HS 800/9-12
1064 Northside Rd 27909 252-337-6880
Amy Fyffe, prin. Fax 337-6890
River Road MS 700/6-8
1701 River Rd 27909 252-333-1454
LeVar Mizelle, prin. Fax 331-1339
Trigg Community HS 100/Alt
1004 Parkview Dr 27909 252-335-1765
Ainslie Jones, prin. Fax 337-6740

Albemarle S 100/K-12
1210 US Highway 17 S 27909 252-338-0883
Billy Stallings, prin. Fax 338-1222
College of the Albemarle Post-Sec.
PO Box 2327 27906 252-335-0821
Elizabeth City State University Post-Sec.
1704 Weeksville Rd 27909 252-335-3400
Mid Atlantic Christian University Post-Sec.
715 N Poindexter St 27909 252-334-2000
Victory Christian S 200/PK-12
684 Old Hertford Hwy 27909 252-264-2011
R.L. Parker, admin. Fax 264-4155

Elizabethtown, Bladen, Pop. 3,534
Bladen County SD 5,300/PK-12
PO Box 37 28337 910-862-4136
Robert Taylor, supt. Fax 862-4277
www.bladen.k12.nc.us/
East Bladen HS 700/9-12
5600 NC Highway 87 E 28337 910-645-2500
John McMillan, prin. Fax 645-2509
Elizabethtown MS 400/5-8
PO Box 639 28337 910-862-4071
Adell Baldwin, prin. Fax 862-7426
Other Schools – See Bladenboro, Clarkton, Tar Heel

Elkin, Surry, Pop. 3,953
Elkin CSD 1,200/PK-12
202 W Spring St 28621 336-835-3135
Dr. Randy Bledsoe, supt. Fax 835-3376
www.elkin.k12.nc.us
Elkin HS 400/9-12
334 Elk Spur St 28621 336-835-3858
Joel Hoyle, prin. Fax 835-3253
Elkin MS 200/7-8
300 Elk Spur St 28621 336-835-3175
Pam Colbert, prin. Fax 835-1427

Elk Park, Avery, Pop. 449
Avery County SD
Supt. — See Newland
Cranberry MS 200/6-8
6230 N US Highway 19E 28622 828-733-2932
Matthew Bentley, prin. Fax 733-6863

Ellerbe, Richmond, Pop. 1,027
Richmond County SD
Supt. — See Hamlet
Ellerbe MS 200/6-8
128 W Ballard St 28338 910-652-3231
Melvin Ingram, prin. Fax 652-3106

Elm City, Wilson, Pop. 1,289
Wilson County SD
Supt. — See Wilson

Elm City MS 500/6-8
215 Church St E 27822 252-236-4148
Eddie Doll, prin. Fax 236-3754

Elon, Alamance, Pop. 9,262
Alamance-Burlington SD
Supt. — See Burlington
Western Alamance HS 1,200/9-12
1731 N NC Highway 87 27244 336-538-6020
Todd Stephan, prin. Fax 538-6014
Western Alamance MS 900/6-8
2100 Eldon Dr 27244 336-538-6010
Gregory Holland, prin. Fax 538-6012

Elon University Post-Sec.
2700 Campus Box 27244 336-278-2000

Enfield, Halifax, Pop. 2,522
Halifax County SD
Supt. — See Halifax
Enfield MS 400/6-8
13723 Highway 481 27823 252-445-5455
Jacqueline Williams, prin. Fax 445-3885

Erwin, Harnett, Pop. 4,318
Harnett County SD
Supt. — See Lillington
Triton HS 1,400/9-12
215 Maynard Lake Rd 28339 910-897-8121
Chip Mangum, prin. Fax 897-3148

Cape Fear Christian Academy 300/PK-12
138 Erwin Chapel Rd 28339 910-897-5423
Karen Parker, hdmstr. Fax 897-2150

Fair Bluff, Columbus, Pop. 944
Columbus County SD
Supt. — See Whiteville
Columbus Career & Coll Acad - Fair Bluff 9-12
685 Academy St 28439 910-649-7622
Nicky Hobbs, prin. Fax 649-6506

Fairmont, Robeson, Pop. 2,595
Robeson County SD
Supt. — See Lumberton
Fairgrove MS 300/4-8
1953 Fairgrove Rd 28340 910-628-8290
Charles Locklear, prin. Fax 628-6181
Fairmont HS 700/9-12
5419 Old Stage Rd 28340 910-628-6727
Ronald Prater, prin. Fax 628-0652
Fairmont MS 500/5-8
402 Iona St 28340 910-628-4363
Avery Brooks, prin. Fax 628-0335

Falcon, Cumberland, Pop. 249

Falcon Christian Academy 50/6-12
7569 West St 28342 910-980-1065
Renee McLamb, head sch Fax 980-1161

Farmville, Pitt, Pop. 4,617
Pitt County SD
Supt. — See Greenville
Farmville Central HS 800/9-12
PO Box 209 27828 252-753-5138
Brad Johnston, prin. Fax 753-7873
Farmville MS 700/6-8
3914 Grimmersburg St 27828 252-753-2116
Dr. Lionel Kato, prin. Fax 753-7995

Fayetteville, Cumberland, Pop. 191,875
Cumberland County SD 52,400/PK-12
PO Box 2357 28302 910-678-2300
Dr. Frank Till, supt. Fax 678-2339
www.ccs.k12.nc.us
Abbott MS 1,000/6-8
590 Winding Creek Rd 28305 910-323-2201
Scott Pope, prin. Fax 485-0841
Britt HS 1,800/9-12
7403 Rockfish Rd 28306 910-429-2800
Denise Garison, prin. Fax 429-2810
Byrd HS 1,300/9-12
1624 Ireland Dr 28304 910-484-8121
Dan Krumanocker, prin. Fax 323-4127
Byrd MS 700/7-8
1616 Ireland Dr 28304 910-483-3101
David Edwards, prin. Fax 483-3741
Cape Fear HS 1,600/9-12
4762 Clinton Rd, 910-483-0191
Lee Spruill, prin. Fax 483-1679
Chesnutt MS 700/6-8
2121 Skibo Rd 28314 910-867-9147
Tonjai Robertson, prin. Fax 868-3695
Cross Creek Early College HS 200/9-12
1200 Murchison Rd 28301 910-672-1499
Patsy Patrick, prin. Fax 672-1590
Cumberland International Early College S 9-12
1200 Murchison Rd 28301 910-672-2830
Lavette McMillan, prin. Fax 672-2849
Fuller Performance Learning Center 100/9-12
314 Jasper St 28301 910-488-6262
Vernon Lowery, prin. Fax 488-3633
Griffin MS 1,300/6-8
5551 Fisher Rd 28304 910-424-7678
Mike Mangum, prin. Fax 424-7602
Howard Health & Life Sciences HS 200/9-12
1608 Camden Rd 28306 910-485-1634
Joy Williams, prin. Fax 483-5754
Jeralds MS 600/6-8
2517 Ramsey St 28301 910-822-2570
Maria Pierce-Ford, prin. Fax 822-1534
Jones Alternative S Alt
117 Quincy St 28301 910-437-5829
Dorothy Fisher, prin. Fax 437-5971
Lewis Chapel MS 800/6-8
2150 Skibo Rd 28314 910-864-1407
Sheldon Harvey, prin. Fax 864-8298
Massey Hill Classical HS 400/9-12
1062 Southern Ave 28306 910-485-8761
Mark Culbreath, prin. Fax 485-7950
New Century International MS 6-8
5551 Fisher Rd 28304 910-487-2001
Tonya Page, prin. Fax 487-2009
Pine Forest HS 1,500/9-12
525 Andrews Rd 28311 910-488-2384
Jane Fields, prin. Fax 488-0790
Pine Forest MS 1,000/6-8
6901 Ramsey St 28311 910-488-2711
Bill Starks, prin. Fax 630-2357
Ramsey Street Alternative MS 50/Alt
500 Fisher St 28301 910-483-5656
Reggie Pinkney, prin. Fax 483-3076
Ross Classical JSHS 800/6-12
3200 Ramsey St 28301 910-488-8415
Thomas Hatch, prin. Fax 488-6209
Sanford HS 1,400/9-12
2301 Fort Bragg Rd 28303 910-484-1151
David Haggerty, prin. Fax 484-7203
Seventy-First Academy of Arts HS 1,700/9-12
6764 Raeford Rd 28304 910-867-3116
Vanessa Alford, prin. Fax 867-1445
Seventy-First Classical MS 500/6-8
6830 Raeford Rd 28304 910-864-0092
Patricia Ramos, prin. Fax 487-8547
Smith HS 1,100/9-12
1800 Seabrook Rd 28301 910-483-0153
Melody Chalmers, prin. Fax 483-7696
Westover HS 1,200/9-12
277 Bonanza Dr 28303 910-864-0190
Thomas Benson, prin. Fax 864-5924
Westover MS 700/6-8
275 Bonanza Dr 28303 910-864-0813
Myron Williams, prin. Fax 864-7906
Williams MS 1,200/6-8
4644 Clinton Rd, 910-483-8222
Steven Morris, prin. Fax 483-4831
Other Schools – See Hope Mills, Spring Lake

Bal-Perazim Christian Academy 100/PK-12
4921 Bragg Blvd 28303 910-487-4220
Morris Braxton D.D.S., hdmstr. Fax 864-3451
Berean Baptist Academy 400/PK-12
518 Glensford Dr 28314 910-868-2511
Carolina Bible College Post-Sec.
817 S McPherson Church Rd 28303 910-323-5614
Cornerstone Christian Academy 200/PK-12
3000 Scotty Hill Rd 28303 910-867-1166
Fayetteville Academy 400/PK-12
3200 Cliffdale Rd 28303 910-868-5131
Ray Quesnel, head sch Fax 868-7351
Fayetteville Beauty College Post-Sec.
3442 Bragg Blvd 28303 910-487-0227
Fayetteville Christian S 600/PK-12
1422 Ireland Dr 28304 910-483-3905
Tammi Peters, admin. Fax 483-6966
Fayetteville State University Post-Sec.
1200 Murchison Rd 28301 910-672-1111
Fayetteville Technical Community College Post-Sec.
PO Box 35236 28303 910-678-8400
Freedom Christian Academy 300/PK-12
3130 Gillespie St 28306 910-485-7777
Joan Dayton, prin. Fax 485-7757
Grace College of Divinity Post-Sec.
5117 Cliffdale Rd 28314 910-221-2224
Harvest Preparatory Academy 50/PK-12
PO Box 2391 28302 910-483-6838
Rosa Herman, admin. Fax 433-2364
Liberty Christian Academy 300/PK-12
6548 Rockfish Rd 28306 910-424-1205
Duncan Edge, admin. Fax 424-8049
Methodist University Post-Sec.
5400 Ramsey St 28311 910-630-7000
Miller-Motte College Post-Sec.
3725 Ramsey St 28311 910-354-1900
Mitchell's Hairstyling Academy Post-Sec.
222 Tallywood Shopping Ctr 28303 910-485-6310
New Life Christian Academy 100/PK-12
1420 Hoke Loop Rd 28314 910-868-9640
Shelia Wilson, prin. Fax 868-3300
Northwood Temple Academy 400/PK-12
4200 Ramsey St 28311 910-822-7711
Jonathon Good, head sch Fax 488-7299
Trinity Christian S 200/K-12
3727 Rosehill Rd 28311 910-488-6779
Dennis Vandevender, prin. Fax 488-2729
Village Christian Academy 800/K-12
908 S McPherson Church Rd 28303 910-483-5500
Dr. Gene Hales, supt. Fax 483-5335

Flat Rock, Henderson, Pop. 3,091
Henderson County SD
Supt. — See Hendersonville
Henderson County Early College HS 100/9-12
120 Alumni Way 28731 828-697-4561
Beth Caudle, prin. Fax 697-4564

Blue Ridge Community College Post-Sec.
180 W Campus Dr 28731 828-694-1700

Fletcher, Henderson, Pop. 7,049
Buncombe County SD
Supt. — See Asheville
Cane Creek MS 800/6-8
570 Lower Brush Creek Rd 28732 828-628-0824
Robin Board, prin. Fax 628-9833

Fletcher Academy 100/9-12
PO Box 5440 28732 828-209-6800
Terry Pottle, prin. Fax 209-6809
Veritas Christian Academy 400/PK-12
17 Cane Creek Rd 28732 828-681-0546
Kay Belknap, hdmstr. Fax 681-0547

Forest City, Rutherford, Pop. 7,281
Rutherford County SD 8,800/PK-12
382 W Main St 28043 828-288-2200
Dr. Janet Mason, supt. Fax 288-2490
www.rcsnc.org/
Chase HS 800/9-12
1603 Chase High Rd 28043 828-245-7668
Greg Lovelace, prin. Fax 248-3584
Chase MS 700/6-8
840 Chase High Rd 28043 828-247-1044
La'Ronda Whiteside, prin. Fax 247-0551
East Rutherford HS 800/9-12
PO Box 668 28043 828-245-6424
Brad Teague, prin. Fax 247-0039
Rutherford Opportunity Center Alt
140 Old Caroleen Rd 28043 828-248-5294
Tim Torvinen, prin. Fax 248-5297
Other Schools – See Bostic, Rutherfordton, Spindale

Four Oaks, Johnston, Pop. 1,883
Johnston County SD
Supt. — See Smithfield
Four Oaks MS 500/6-8
1475 Boyette Rd 27524 919-963-4022
David Cobb, prin. Fax 963-4123
South Johnston HS 1,200/9-12
10381 US Highway 301 S 27524 919-894-3146
Eddie Price, prin. Fax 894-3229

Franklin, Macon, Pop. 3,786
Macon County SD 3,700/K-12
1202 Old Murphy Rd 28734 828-524-3314
Dr. Jim Duncan, supt. Fax 524-5938
www.macon.k12.nc.us
Franklin HS 1,000/9-12
100 Panther Dr 28734 828-524-6467
Chris Baldwin, prin. Fax 524-0684
Macon Early College HS 100/9-12
77 Siler Farm Rd 28734 828-369-7331
Todd Gibbs, prin. Fax 349-9692
Macon MS 600/7-8
1345 Wells Grove Rd 28734 828-524-3766
Scot Maslin, prin. Fax 349-3900
Union Academy 100/Alt
158 Union School Rd 28734 828-369-1277
Kris Reis, prin. Fax 524-2859
Other Schools – See Highlands, Topton

Trimont Christian Academy 100/PK-12
98 Promise Ln 28734 828-369-6756
Fax 524-0622

Franklinton, Franklin, Pop. 1,988
Franklin County SD
Supt. — See Louisburg
Franklinton HS 900/9-12
910 Cedar Creek Rd 27525 919-494-2332
Charles Fuller, prin. Fax 494-5140

Fremont, Wayne, Pop. 1,228
Wayne County SD
Supt. — See Goldsboro
Norwayne MS 1,100/6-8
1394 Norwayne School Rd 27830 919-242-3414
Mario Re, prin. Fax 242-3418

Fuquay Varina, Wake, Pop. 17,531
Wake County SD
Supt. — See Raleigh
Fuquay-Varina HS 2,000/9-12
201 Bengal Dr 27526 919-557-2511
Edward McFarland, prin. Fax 557-2512
Fuquay-Varina MS 900/6-8
109 N Ennis St 27526 919-557-2727
William Holley, prin. Fax 557-2732

Hilltop Christian S 300/K-12
10212 Fayetteville Rd 27526 919-552-5612
Travis Moots, prin. Fax 552-3189

Garner, Wake, Pop. 25,256
Johnston County SD
Supt. — See Smithfield
Cleveland MS 1,000/6-8
2323 Cornwallis Rd 27529 919-553-7500
Kendrick Byrd, prin. Fax 553-7798

Wake County SD
Supt. — See Raleigh
East Garner MS 1,200/6-8
6301 Jones Sausage Rd 27529 919-662-2339
Cathy Williams, prin. Fax 662-2357
Garner Magnet HS 2,300/9-12
2101 Spring Dr 27529 919-662-2379
Drew Cook, prin. Fax 662-2397
North Garner MS 1,100/6-8
720 Powell Dr 27529 919-662-2434
Gregory Butler, prin. Fax 662-5637

Gaston, Northampton, Pop. 1,141
Northampton County SD
Supt. — See Jackson
Gaston MS 400/5-8
152 Hurricane Ln 27832 252-537-1910
Barbara Stephenson, prin. Fax 537-9028
Northampton County Alternative S 50/Alt
152 Hurricane Ln 27832 252-537-1910
Barbara Drummond, prin.

Gastonia, Gaston, Pop. 70,333
Gaston County SD 31,900/PK-12
PO Box 1397 28053 704-866-6100
L. Reeves McGlohon, supt. Fax 866-6321
www.gaston.k12.nc.us/
Ashbrook HS 1,300/9-12
2222 S New Hope Rd 28054 704-866-6600
Joey Clinton, prin. Fax 866-6203
Forestview HS 1,300/9-12
5545 Union Rd 28056 704-861-2625
Chad Carper, prin. Fax 853-3323
Grier MS 700/6-8
1622 E Garrison Blvd 28054 704-866-6086
Torben Ross, prin. Fax 866-6116
Highland School of Technology Vo/Tech
1600 N Morris St 28052 704-810-8818
Lee Dedmon, prin. Fax 866-6105

Huss HS 1,100/9-12
1518 Edgefield Ave 28052 704-866-6610
Denece Farris, prin. Fax 866-6103
Southwest MS 900/6-8
1 Roadrunner Dr 28052 704-866-6290
Glynis Brooks, prin. Fax 866-6293
Warlick S 100/Alt
1316 Spencer Mountain Rd 28054 704-824-3012
Harrison Conyers, prin. Fax 824-0918
York-Chester MS 400/6-8
601 S Clay St 28052 704-866-6297
Mike Grimmer, prin. Fax 866-6319
Other Schools – See Belmont, Bessemer City, Cherryville, Cramerton, Dallas, Lowell, Mount Holly, Stanley

---

Gaston Christian S 900/PK-12
1625 Lowell Bethesda Rd 28056 704-349-5020
Dr. Marc Stout, hdmstr. Fax 349-5029
Gaston Day S 500/PK-12
2001 Gaston Day School Rd 28056 704-864-7744
Dr. Richard Rankin, hdmstr. Fax 865-3813
Victory Christian Academy 100/K-12
310 Carolina Ave 28052 704-865-7132
Fax 867-1731

Gatesville, Gates, Pop. 318
Gates County SD 1,900/PK-12
PO Box 125 27938 252-357-1113
Dr. Barry Williams, supt. Fax 357-0207
coserver.gates.k12.nc.us/
Central MS 500/6-8
362 US Highway 158 W 27938 252-357-0470
Tammy Boone, prin. Fax 357-1319
Gates County HS 600/9-12
88 US Highway 158 W 27938 252-357-0720
Tammi Ward, prin. Fax 357-2058

Gibsonville, Guilford, Pop. 6,318
Guilford County SD
Supt. — See Greensboro
Eastern Guilford HS 1,200/9-12
415 Peeden Dr 27249 336-449-6311
Marilyn Foley, prin. Fax 449-7392
Eastern MS 900/6-8
435 Peeden Dr 27249 336-449-4255
Sarah Matthews, prin. Fax 449-0728

Goldsboro, Wayne, Pop. 35,562
Wayne County SD 19,500/PK-12
PO Box 1797 27533 919-731-5900
Dr. Steven Taylor, supt. Fax 705-6199
www.waynecountyschools.org
Dillard MS 600/5-8
1101 Devereaux St 27530 919-580-9360
Sonja Emerson, prin. Fax 736-1121
Eastern Wayne HS 1,000/9-12
1135 E New Hope Rd 27534 919-751-7120
Eugene Byrd, prin. Fax 751-7107
Eastern Wayne MS 700/6-8
3518 Central Heights Rd 27534 919-751-7110
Catherine Eubanks, prin. Fax 751-7114
Goldsboro HS 600/9-12
901 Beech St 27530 919-731-5930
Tonya Faison, prin. Fax 731-5914
Greenwood MS 500/5-8
3209 E Ash St 27534 919-751-7100
Rolanda Best, prin. Fax 751-7201
Rosewood HS 500/9-12
900 Rosewood Rd 27530 919-705-6050
Dean Sauls, prin. Fax 705-6055
Rosewood MS 400/6-8
541 NC 581 Hwy S 27530 919-736-5050
Kevin Smith, prin. Fax 736-5055
Wayne Early Middle College HS 200/9-12
3000 Wayne Memorial Dr 27534 919-739-7070
Lee Johnson, prin. Fax 581-1011
Wayne MSHS Academy 100/Alt
801 Lionel St 27530 919-580-3608
Carole Battle, prin. Fax 731-5495
Wayne S of Engineering 300/6-12
700 N Herman St 27530 919-734-0070
Gary Hales, prin. Fax 731-0072
Other Schools – See Dudley, Fremont, Mount Olive, Pikeville, Seven Springs

---

Faith Christian Academy 400/PK-12
1200 W Grantham St 27530 919-734-8701
Walter Sloan, prin. Fax 734-9658
Mitchell's Hairstyling Academy Post-Sec.
1021 N Spence Ave 27534 919-778-8200
Wayne Christian S 400/PK-12
1201 Patetown Rd 27530 919-735-5605
Lynn Mooring M.Ed., admin. Fax 735-5229
Wayne Community College Post-Sec.
PO Box 8002 27533 919-735-5151
Wayne Country Day S 300/PK-12
480 Country Day Rd 27530 919-736-1045
Todd Anderson, head sch Fax 583-9493

Graham, Alamance, Pop. 13,906
Alamance-Burlington SD
Supt. — See Burlington
Alamance-Burlington Middle College HS 100/9-12
PO Box 8000 27253 336-506-4001
Bonnie Roane, prin. Fax 506-4004
Graham HS 800/9-12
903 Trollinger Rd 27253 336-570-6440
Charlotte Holmes, prin. Fax 570-6446
Graham MS 700/6-8
311 E Pine St 27253 336-570-6460
Ronald Villines, prin. Fax 570-6464
Ray Street Academy Alt
609 Ray St 27253 336-570-6644
Darrell Thomas, prin.
Southern Alamance HS 1,500/9-12
631 Southern High School Rd 27253 336-570-6400
Teresa Faucette, prin. Fax 570-6404
Southern Alamance MS 800/6-8
771 Southern High School Rd 27253 336-570-6500
Heather Ward, prin. Fax 570-6504

Alamance Christian S 300/PK-12
PO Box 838 27253 336-578-0318
Dr. Robert Hodges, admin. Fax 578-7200
Alamance Community College Post-Sec.
PO Box 8000 27253 336-578-2002

Granite Falls, Caldwell, Pop. 4,669
Caldwell County SD
Supt. — See Lenoir
Caldwell County Gateway S 100/Alt
1889 Dudley Shoals Rd 28630 828-396-8373
Libby Carter, prin. Fax 396-7960
Granite Falls MS 700/6-8
90 N Main St 28630 828-396-2341
Bill Schreiber, prin. Fax 396-7072

Grantsboro, Pamlico, Pop. 679

Pamlico Community College Post-Sec.
PO Box 185 28529 252-249-1851

Greensboro, Guilford, Pop. 263,264
Guilford County SD 72,900/PK-12
PO Box 880 27402 336-370-8100
Maurice Green, supt. Fax 370-8299
www.gcsnc.com/
Academy at Lincoln 700/4-8
1016 Lincoln St 27401 336-370-3471
Anita Stewart, prin. Fax 370-3480
Academy at Smith 200/9-12
2225 S Holden Rd 27407 336-316-5866
David Miller, prin. Fax 294-7313
Allen MS 700/6-8
1108 Glendale Dr 27406 336-294-7325
Curtis Adair, prin. Fax 294-7315
Aycock MS 600/6-8
811 Cypress St 27405 336-370-8110
Keisha McMillan, prin. Fax 370-8044
Dudley HS 1,500/9-12
1200 Lincoln St 27401 336-370-8130
Jesse Pratt, prin. Fax 370-8979
Early College at Guilford 200/9-12
5608 W Friendly Ave 27410 336-316-2860
Dr. Bobby Hayes, prin. Fax 316-2858
Greenboro Middle College HS 100/11-12
815 W Market St 27401 336-370-8300
Jamie King, prin. Fax 370-8918
Grimsley HS 1,700/9-12
801 Westover Ter 27408 336-370-8180
Gregory Newlin, prin. Fax 370-8194
Guilford MS 700/4-8
320 Lindley Rd 27410 336-316-5833
Cynthia Kremer, prin. Fax 316-5837
Hairston MS 600/6-8
3911 Naco Rd 27401 336-378-8280
Rydell Harrison, prin. Fax 370-8153
Henderson Newcomers S 200/Alt
411 Friendway Rd 27410 336-316-5883
Candice Wright, prin. Fax 316-7092
High School Ahead Academy 100/Alt
329 College Rd 27410 336-294-7640
Michelle Hayes, prin. Fax 294-7643
Jackson MS 400/6-8
2200 Ontario St 27403 336-294-7350
Lance Stokes, prin. Fax 294-7316
Kernodle MS 1,000/6-8
3600 Drawbridge Pkwy 27410 336-545-3717
Thea McHam, prin. Fax 545-3714
Kiser MS 800/6-8
716 Benjamin Pkwy 27408 336-370-8240
Sharon McCants, prin. Fax 370-8248
Mendenhall MS 1,000/6-8
205 Willoughby Blvd 27408 336-545-2000
Marshall Matson, prin. Fax 545-2004
Middle College HS @ Bennett 100/9-12
610 Gorrell St 27406 336-517-1832
Esther Coble, prin. Fax 517-2120
Middle College HS @ GTCC Greensboro 9-12
3505 E Wendover Ave 27405 336-375-2466
Rodney Boone, prin. Fax 375-2469
Middle College HS @ NC A&T 100/9-12
1601 E Market St 27411 336-691-0941
Eric Hines, prin. Fax 691-0952
Middle College HS @ UNCG 9-12
1408 Walker Ave 27412 336-334-3662
Angela Polk-Jones, prin. Fax 334-5503
Northern HS 1,300/9-12
7101 Spencer Dixon Rd 27455 336-643-8449
William Laine, prin. Fax 644-2589
Northern MS 1,000/6-8
616 Simpson Calhoun Rd 27455 336-605-3342
Dr. Sam Misher, prin. Fax 643-8435
Northwest HS 1,900/9-12
5240 NW School Rd 27409 336-605-3300
Ralph Kitley, prin. Fax 605-3314
Northwest MS 1,000/6-8
5300 NW School Rd 27409 336-605-3333
Richard Thomae, prin. Fax 605-3325
Page HS 1,900/9-12
201 Alma Pinnix Dr 27405 336-370-8200
Patrice Faison, prin. Fax 370-8219
SCALE - Greensboro 50/Alt
116 Pisgah Church Rd 27455 336-545-2031
Russell Woodward, prin. Fax 545-2035
Smith HS 1,200/9-12
2407 S Holden Rd 27407 336-294-7300
Dr. Noah Rogers, prin. Fax 294-7313
Southeast HS 1,300/9-12
4530 SE School Rd 27406 336-674-4300
Charles Blanchard, prin. Fax 674-4290
Southeast MS 1,000/6-8
4825 Woody Mill Rd 27406 336-674-4280
Karen Burress, prin. Fax 674-4276
Southern HS 1,100/9-12
5700 Drake Rd 27406 336-674-4250
James Gibson, prin. Fax 674-4254
Southern MS 700/6-8
5747 Drake Rd 27406 336-674-4266
Kevin Wheat, prin. Fax 674-4278
STEM Early College at NC A&T 9-12
402 Laurel St 27411 336-274-7167
Stacey Alston, prin. Fax 370-8580
Twilight S 100/Alt
116 Pisgah Church Rd 27455 336-282-6797
Pandora Bell, prin.
Weaver Academy 300/9-12
300 S Spring St 27401 336-370-8282
Johncarlos Miller, prin. Fax 370-8287
Western HS 1,300/9-12
409 Friendway Rd 27410 336-316-5800
Pete Kashubara, prin. Fax 316-5813
Other Schools – See Browns Summit, Gibsonville, High Point, Jamestown, Mc Leansville

---

American Hebrew Academy 200/9-12
4334 Hobbs Rd 27410 336-217-7100
Dr. Gary Grandon, prin. Fax 217-7011
Bennett College Post-Sec.
900 E Washington St 27401 336-273-4431
Brookstone College of Business Post-Sec.
424 Gallimore Dairy Rd St A 27409 336-668-2627
Caldwell Academy 700/K-12
2900 Horse Pen Creek Rd 27410 336-665-1161
Mark Guthrie, hdmstr. Fax 665-1178
Carolina Graduate School of Divinity Post-Sec.
PO Box 7148 27417 336-315-8660
ECPI University Post-Sec.
7802 Airport Center Dr 27409 336-665-1400
Greensboro College Post-Sec.
815 W Market St 27401 336-272-7102
Greensboro Day S 900/PK-12
5401 Lawndale Dr 27455 336-288-8590
Mark Hale, head sch Fax 282-2905
Guilford College Post-Sec.
5800 W Friendly Ave 27410 336-316-2000
Hope Academy, PO Box 10616 27404 5-9
Dayna Carr, admin. 336-303-0436
Leon's Beauty School Post-Sec.
1305 Coliseum Blvd 27403 336-274-4601
Moses H. Cone Memorial Hospital Post-Sec.
1200 N Elm St 27401 336-574-7881
New Garden Friends S 300/PK-12
1128 New Garden Rd 27410 336-299-0964
David Tomlin, head sch Fax 292-0347
Noble Academy 200/K-12
3310 Horse Pen Creek Rd 27410 336-282-7044
Linda Hale, head sch Fax 282-2048
North Carolina A&T State University Post-Sec.
1601 E Market St 27411 336-334-7500
Shining Light Academy 100/PK-12
4530 W Wendover Ave 27409 336-299-9688
Mark Lenington M.A., prin. Fax 299-6126
University of North Carolina Post-Sec.
PO Box 26170 27402 336-334-5000
Vandalia Christian S 700/PK-12
3919 Pleasant Garden Rd 27406 336-379-8380
Dr. Mark Weatherford, admin. Fax 379-8671

Greenville, Pitt, Pop. 82,822
Pitt County SD 23,300/PK-12
1717 W 5th St 27834 252-830-4200
Dr. Beverly Emory, supt. Fax 830-4239
www.pitt.k12.nc.us/
Aycock MS 600/6-8
1325 Red Banks Rd 27858 252-756-4181
Jennifer Poplin, prin. Fax 756-2408
Conley HS 1,400/9-12
2006 Worthington Rd 27858 252-756-3440
Mary Carter, prin. Fax 756-3028
Eppes MS 400/6-8
1100 S Elm St 27858 252-757-2160
Rebecca Beaulieu, prin. Fax 757-2163
Hope MS 700/6-8
2995 Mills Rd 27858 252-355-7071
Mike Pollard, prin. Fax 355-6055
Rose HS 1,600/9-12
600 W Arlington Blvd 27834 252-321-3640
Charlie Langley, prin. Fax 321-3653
Wellcome MS 400/6-8
3101 N Memorial Dr 27834 252-752-5938
Maurice Harris, prin. Fax 752-1685
Other Schools – See Ayden, Bethel, Farmville, Winterville

East Carolina University Post-Sec.
1000 E 5th St 27858 252-328-6131
Greenville Christian Academy 300/K-12
1621 Greenville Blvd SW 27834 252-756-0939
Paul Aynes, prin.
John Paul II Catholic HS 9-12
PO Box 4431 27836 252-215-1224
John Donohue, prin.
Miller-Motte College Post-Sec.
1021 WH Smith Blvd Ste 102 27834 252-215-2000
Mitchell's Hairstyling Academy Post-Sec.
426 E Arlington Blvd 27858 252-756-3050
Oakwood S 300/PK-12
4000 MacGregor Downs Rd 27834 252-931-0760
Robert Peterson, hdmstr. Fax 931-0964
Pitt Community College Post-Sec.
PO Box 7007 27835 252-493-7200
Pope John Paul II HS 9-12
3250 Dickinson Avenue Ext 27834 252-215-1224
Glenn Joyner, prin.
Trinity Christian S 400/PK-12
3111 Golden Rd 27858 252-758-0037

Halifax, Halifax, Pop. 232
Halifax County SD 4,000/PK-12
PO Box 468 27839 252-583-5111
Dr. Elease Frederick, supt. Fax 583-1474
www.halifax.k12.nc.us/
Southeast Halifax HS 500/9-12
16683 NC Highway 125 27839 252-445-2027
Pamela Chamblee, prin. Fax 445-3463
Other Schools – See Enfield, Littleton, Roanoke Rapids

Weldon CSD
Supt. — See Weldon
Weldon MS 200/5-8
4489 US Highway 301 27839 252-536-2571
Cynthia Byrd, prin. Fax 536-3485

Hallsboro, Columbus, Pop. 457
Columbus County SD
Supt. — See Whiteville
Hallsboro MS 300/6-8
PO Box 248 28442 910-646-4192
Adam Thompson, prin. Fax 646-5072

Hamlet, Richmond, Pop. 6,381
Richmond County SD 7,300/PK-12
PO Box 1259 28345 910-582-5860
Dr. George Norris, supt. Fax 582-7921
www.richmond.k12.nc.us
Hamlet MS 600/6-8
1406 Mcdonald Ave 28345 910-582-7903
Jim Butler, prin. Fax 582-5730
Richmond County 9th Grade Academy 600/9-9
804 County Home Rd 28345 910-582-7800
Pam Patterson, prin. Fax 582-7804
Richmond Early College HS 100/9-12
1042 W Hamlet Ave 28345 910-410-1022
Michael Chapman, prin.
Other Schools – See Ellerbe, Rockingham

Richmond Community College Post-Sec.
PO Box 1189 28345 910-410-1700

Hampstead, Pender, Pop. 4,028
Pender County SD
Supt. — See Burgaw
Topsail HS 1,100/9-12
245 N Saint Johns Church Rd 28443 910-270-2755
Donald Simmons, prin. Fax 270-9290
Topsail MS 800/6-8
17445 US Highway 17 N 28443 910-270-2612
James Klingensmith, prin. Fax 270-3190

Harrells, Sampson, Pop. 202

Harrells Christian Academy 400/K-12
PO Box 88 28444 910-532-4575
Marcus Skipper, hdmstr. Fax 532-2958

Harrisburg, Cabarrus, Pop. 11,315
Cabarrus County SD
Supt. — See Concord
Hickory Ridge HS 1,400/9-12
7321 Raging Ridge Rd 28075 704-454-7300
Dan Meehan, prin. Fax 454-7330
Hickory Ridge MS 6-8
7336 Raging Ridge Rd 28075 704-455-1331
James Carroll, prin. Fax 455-1338

Havelock, Craven, Pop. 19,878
Craven County SD
Supt. — See New Bern
Early College EAST HS 9-12
104 Middle School Ln 28532 252-444-5194
Allan Quinn, prin. Fax 444-5129
Havelock HS 1,200/9-12
101 Webb Blvd 28532 252-444-5112
Jeffrey Murphy, prin. Fax 444-5112
Havelock MS 500/6-8
102 High School Dr 28532 252-444-5125
Tabari Wallace, prin. Fax 444-5129
Tucker Creek MS 600/6-8
200 Sermons Blvd 28532 252-444-7200
Angie Franks, prin. Fax 444-7206

Hayesville, Clay, Pop. 309
Clay County SD 1,400/PK-12
PO Box 178 28904 828-389-8513
Dr. Mark Leek, supt. Fax 389-3437
www.clayschools.org/
Hayesville HS 400/9-12
205 Yellow Jacket Dr 28904 828-389-6532
Keith Nuckols, prin. Fax 389-6251
Hayesville MS 400/5-8
135 School Dr 28904 828-389-9924
Mickey Noe, prin. Fax 389-1706

Hays, Wilkes, Pop. 1,835
Wilkes County SD
Supt. — See North Wilkesboro
North Wilkes HS 700/9-12
PO Box 430 28635 336-957-8601
Eric Barker, prin. Fax 957-4787

Henderson, Vance, Pop. 15,184
Vance County SD 7,000/PK-12
PO Box 7001 27536 252-492-2127
Ronald E. Gregory, supt. Fax 438-6119
www.vcs.k12.nc.us
Eaton-Johnson MS 800/6-8
500 N Beckford Dr 27536 252-438-5017
Dr. Larry Webb, prin. Fax 738-0250
Henderson MS 800/6-8
219 Charles St 27536 252-492-0054
Dr. John Hargrove, prin. Fax 430-8588
Northern Vance HS 1,100/9-12
293 Warrenton Rd 27537 252-492-6041
Dr. Michael Applewhite, prin. Fax 492-5938
Southern Vance HS 800/9-12
925 Garrett Rd 27537 252-430-6000
Stephanie Ayscue, prin. Fax 430-0308
Vance County Early College HS 200/9-12
PO Box 917 27536 252-738-3580
Michael Bullard, prin. Fax 438-3128
Western Vance Secondary S 100/Alt
2785 Poplar Creek Rd 27537 252-438-8407
Eric Pierce, prin. Fax 438-4957

Crossroads Christian S 300/PK-12
PO Box 249 27536 252-431-1333
Jonathan Capps, hdmstr. Fax 431-0333
Kerr-Vance Academy 500/PK-12
700 Vance Academy Rd 27537 252-492-0018
Vance-Granville Community College Post-Sec.
PO Box 917 27536 252-492-2061
Victory Christian S 100/K-12
PO Box 592 27536 252-492-6079
Rev. Ricky Easter, prin. Fax 492-4683

Hendersonville, Henderson, Pop. 12,877
Henderson County SD 13,400/K-12
414 4th Ave W 28739 828-697-4733
David L. Jones, supt. Fax 697-5541
www.henderson.k12.nc.us
Apple Valley MS 900/6-8
43 Fruitland Rd 28792 828-697-4545
Marcie Wilson, prin. Fax 698-6119
Balfour Education Center 100/Alt
2529 Asheville Hwy 28791 828-697-4629
Kent Parent, prin. Fax 698-6130
Hendersonville HS 700/9-12
1 Bearcat Blvd 28791 828-697-4802
W. Robert Wilkins, prin. Fax 698-6126
Hendersonville MS 500/6-8
825 N Whitted St 28791 828-697-4800
Jenny Moreno, prin. Fax 698-6127
North Henderson HS 1,000/9-12
35 Fruitland Rd 28792 828-697-4500
Frank Edney, prin. Fax 698-6129
Rugby MS 900/6-8
3345 Haywood Rd 28791 828-891-6566
Bill Reedy, prin. Fax 891-6589
West Henderson HS 1,100/9-12
3600 Haywood Rd 28791 828-891-6571
R. Dean Jones, prin. Fax 891-6590
Other Schools – See East Flat Rock, Flat Rock

Hendersonville Christian S 100/PK-12
708 S Grove St 28792 828-692-0556

Hertford, Perquimans, Pop. 2,119
Perquimans County SD 1,800/PK-12
PO Box 337 27944 252-426-5741
Dr. Dwayne Stallings, supt. Fax 426-4913
www.pcs.k12.nc.us
Perquimans County HS 500/9-12
PO Box 398 27944 252-426-5778
Chante Lassiter, prin. Fax 426-7614
Other Schools – See Winfall

Hickory, Catawba, Pop. 39,263
Catawba County SD
Supt. — See Newton
Arndt MS 700/7-8
3350 34th Street Dr NE 28601 828-256-9545
Angela Williams, prin. Fax 256-6748
Catawba Valley Early College HS 400/9-12
2550 US Highway 70 SE 28602 828-485-2980
Heather Benfield, prin. Fax 485-2981
St. Stephens HS 1,200/9-12
3205 34th Street Dr NE 28601 828-256-9841
DeAnna Taylor, prin. Fax 256-7159

Hickory CSD 4,400/PK-12
432 4th Ave SW 28602 828-322-2855
Dr. Walter Hart, supt. Fax 322-1834
www.hickoryschools.net
Grandview MS 400/6-8
451 Catawba Valley Blvd 28602 828-328-2289
Dr. Vanessa Howerton, prin. Fax 328-2992
Hickory Career and Arts Magnet HS 100/Alt
409 8th Ave NE 28601 828-328-6738
David Coyne, prin. Fax 328-8539
Hickory HS 1,000/9-12
1234 3rd St NE 28601 828-322-5860
Ann Stalnaker, prin. Fax 326-7101
Northview MS 500/6-8
302 28th Ave NE 28601 828-327-6300
Stephanie Dischiavi, prin. Fax 327-6367

Catawba Valley Community College Post-Sec.
2550 US Highway 70 SE 28602 828-327-7000
Hickory Christian Academy 300/K-12
3260 6th Street Dr NW 28601 828-324-5405
Tracy Robinson, hdmstr. Fax 324-4353
Lenoir-Rhyne College Post-Sec.
625 7th Ave NE 28601 828-328-1741
Tabernacle Christian S 100/PK-12
1225 29th Avenue Dr NE 28601 828-324-9936

Hiddenite, Alexander, Pop. 532
Alexander County SD
Supt. — See Taylorsville
East Alexander MS 700/6-8
1285 White Plains Rd 28636 828-632-7565
Rosanna Whisnant, prin. Fax 632-4508

Highlands, Macon, Pop. 908
Macon County SD
Supt. — See Franklin
Highlands S 400/K-12
PO Box 940 28741 828-526-2147
Brian Jetter, prin. Fax 526-0615

High Point, Guilford, Pop. 102,180
Guilford County SD
Supt. — See Greensboro
Academy at HP Central 9-12
700 Chestnut Dr 27262 336-885-7905
Quincy Williams, prin. Fax 885-7927
Andrews HS 900/9-12
1920 McGuinn Dr 27265 336-819-2800
Rodney Wilds, prin. Fax 887-5585
Ferndale MS 800/6-8
701 Ferndale Blvd 27262 336-819-2855
Angela Jackson, prin. Fax 885-2854
High Point Central HS 1,300/9-12
801 Ferndale Blvd 27262 336-819-2825
Robert Christina, prin. Fax 819-2991
Middle College HS @ GTCC High Point 100/9-12
901 S Main St 27260 336-819-4111
Charlos Smith-Banks, prin. Fax 819-4116
Penn-Griffin School for the Arts 600/6-12
825 E Washington Dr 27260 336-819-2870
Shelley Nixon-Greene, prin. Fax 889-4841
Pruett SCALE Academy Alt
900 W English Rd 27262 336-878-5380
Ken Wheat, prin. Fax 889-7625
Southwest HS 1,400/9-12
4364 Barrow Rd 27265 336-819-2970
George Allen Parker, prin. Fax 454-5175
Southwest MS 1,100/6-8
4368 Barrow Rd 27265 336-819-2985
Joseph Caraher, prin. Fax 454-4015
Welborn Academy of Science & Technology 500/6-8
1710 McGuinn Dr 27265 336-819-2880
N. Brewington-McCormick, prin. Fax 819-2878

Hayworth Christian S 200/PK-12
PO Box 5448 27262 336-882-3126
Vicki Beale, admin. Fax 882-9157
High Point Christian Academy 700/PK-12
800 Phillips Ave 27262 336-841-8702
Richard Hardee, hdmstr. Fax 841-8850
High Point University Post-Sec.
833 Montlieu Ave 27262 336-841-9000
ITT Technical Institute Post-Sec.
4050 Piedmont Pkwy 27265 336-819-5900
Laurel University Post-Sec.
1215 Eastchester Dr 27265 336-887-3000
Tri-City Christian Academy 100/PK-12
8000 Clinard Farms Rd 27265 336-665-9822
Peter Cousins, prin. Fax 665-9834
Wesleyan Christian Academy 1,000/PK-12
1917 N Centennial St 27262 336-884-3333
Dr. Rob Brown, hdmstr. Fax 884-8232
Westchester Country Day S 400/PK-12
2045 N Old Greensboro Rd 27265 336-869-2128
Cobb Atkinson, head sch Fax 869-6685

Hillsborough, Orange, Pop. 5,962
Orange County SD 7,200/K-12
200 E King St 27278 919-732-8126
Del Burns Ed.D., supt. Fax 732-8120
www.orange.k12.nc.us
Cedar Ridge HS 1,000/9-12
1125 New Grady Brown Sch Rd 27278 919-245-4000
John Wheeler, prin. Fax 245-4010
Orange HS 1,200/9-12
500 Orange High School Rd 27278 919-732-6133
Jason Johnson, prin. Fax 644-7699
Partnership Academy S 50/Alt
1006 Storey Ln 27278 919-245-4030
Paige Marsh, prin. Fax 245-4035
Stanback MS 600/6-8
3700 NC Highway 86 S 27278 919-644-3200
Gloria Jones, prin. Fax 644-3226
Stanford MS 600/6-8
308 Orange High School Rd 27278 919-732-6121
Anne Purcell, prin. Fax 732-6910
Other Schools – See Efland

Hobgood, Halifax, Pop. 346

Hobgood Academy 200/K-12
201 S Beech St 27843 252-826-4116
William Whitehurst, hdmstr. Fax 826-2265

Holly Ridge, Onslow, Pop. 1,230
Onslow County SD
Supt. — See Jacksonville
Dixon HS 700/9-12
160 Dixon School Rd 28445 910-347-2958
Vikki Childress, prin. Fax 347-3932
Dixon MS 600/6-8
200 Dixon School Rd 28445 910-347-2738
Jay Strope, prin. Fax 347-4399

Holly Springs, Wake, Pop. 24,092
Wake County SD
Supt. — See Raleigh
Holly Grove MS 6-8
1401 Avent Ferry Rd 27540 919-567-4177
Kenneth Proulx, prin. Fax 567-4159
Holly Ridge MS 1,000/6-8
950 Holly Springs Rd 27540 919-577-1335
Brian Pittman, prin. Fax 577-1379
Holly Springs HS 2,000/9-12
5329 Cass Holt Rd 27540 919-577-1444
Timothy Locklair, prin. Fax 577-1742

Hope Mills, Cumberland, Pop. 14,573
Cumberland County SD
Supt. — See Fayetteville
Grays Creek HS 1,200/9-12
5301 Celebration Dr 28348 910-424-8589
Vernon Aldridge, prin. Fax 424-7411
Grays Creek MS 900/6-8
5151 Celebration Dr 28348 910-483-4124
Sara Whitaker, prin. Fax 483-5296
Hope Mills MS 700/6-8
4975 Cameron Rd 28348 910-425-5106
Cherie Graham, prin. Fax 423-5887
South View HS 1,800/9-12
4184 Elk Rd 28348 910-425-8181
Yolanda Nash, dir. Fax 425-2962
South View MS 800/6-8
4100 Elk Rd 28348 910-424-3131
Terrence McAllister, prin. Fax 424-2402

Hubert, Onslow
Onslow County SD
Supt. — See Jacksonville
Onslow County Learning Center Alt
PO Box 158 28539 910-326-2305
Felicia Walton, dir. Fax 326-2208

Hudson, Caldwell, Pop. 3,744
Caldwell County SD
Supt. — See Lenoir

Caldwell County Career Center HS Vo/Tech
2857 Hickory Blvd 28638 828-759-4640
Brian Suddreth, prin. Fax 759-4672
Caldwell Early College HS 300/9-12
2859 Hickory Blvd 28638 828-759-4636
Candis Hagaman, prin. Fax 759-4666
Hudson MS 900/6-8
291 Pine Mountain Rd 28638 828-728-4281
Bill Griffin, prin. Fax 726-8157
South Caldwell HS 1,600/9-12
7035 Spartan Dr 28638 828-396-2188
Michael Peake, prin. Fax 396-5929

Caldwell Community Coll. & Tech. Inst. Post-Sec.
2855 Hickory Blvd 28638 828-726-2200
Harris Chapel Christian Academy 50/K-12
1444 Cajah Mountain Rd 28638 828-728-3721
Allen Norrod, prin. Fax 728-2375
Heritage Christian S 100/K-12
239 Mount Herman Rd 28638 828-726-0055
Robert Setzer, prin.

Huntersville, Mecklenburg, Pop. 45,893
Charlotte/Mecklenburg County SD
Supt. — See Charlotte
Alexander MS 600/6-8
12201 Hambright Rd 28078 980-343-3830
Angela Richardson, prin. Fax 343-3851
Bradley MS 1,200/6-8
13345 Beatties Ford Rd 28078 980-343-5750
Laura Rosenbach, prin. Fax 343-5743
Hopewell HS 1,800/9-12
11530 Beatties Ford Rd 28078 980-343-5988
Michael Jones, prin. Fax 343-5990
North Mecklenburg HS 1,700/9-12
11201 Old Statesville Rd 28078 980-343-3840
Matthew Hayes, prin. Fax 343-3845

SouthLake Christian Academy 900/PK-12
13820 Hagers Ferry Rd 28078 704-949-2200
Dr. C. Wayne Parker, hdmstr. Fax 949-2203

Indian Trail, Union, Pop. 32,854
Union County SD
Supt. — See Monroe
Porter Ridge HS 1,500/9-12
2839 Ridge Rd 28079 704-292-7662
Sam Basden, prin. Fax 296-9733
Porter Ridge MS 1,300/6-8
2827 Ridge Rd 28079 704-225-7555
Bashawn Harris, prin. Fax 226-9844
Sun Valley MS 1,200/6-8
1409 Wesley Chapel Rd 28079 704-296-3009
Vicki Merritt, prin. Fax 296-3045

Central Academy at Lake Park 100/K-12
3624 Lake Park Rd 28079 704-882-6267
Dr. Terry Moffitt, hdmstr. Fax 882-4651
Metrolina Christian Academy 1,000/PK-12
PO Box 1460 28079 704-882-3375
Rev. Rick Calloway, hdmstr. Fax 882-0631

Iron Station, Lincoln, Pop. 736
Lincoln County SD
Supt. — See Lincolnton
East Lincoln MS 600/6-8
4137 Highway 73 28080 704-732-0761
Rusty Saine, prin. Fax 732-4456

Jackson, Northampton, Pop. 512
Northampton County SD 2,400/PK-12
PO Box 158 27845 252-534-1371
Dr. Eric Bracy, supt. Fax 534-4631
www.northampton.k12.nc.us
Other Schools – See Conway, Gaston

Jacksonville, Onslow, Pop. 67,399
Onslow County SD 23,200/PK-12
PO Box 99 28541 910-455-2211
Dr. Kathy Spencer, supt. Fax 455-1965
www.onslow.k12.nc.us
Hunters Creek MS 800/6-8
4040 Hunters Trl 28546 910-353-2147
Jocelyn Cassidy, prin. Fax 353-7939
Jacksonville Commons MS 700/6-8
315 Commons Dr S 28546 910-346-6888
Gail Pylant, prin. Fax 938-1682
Jacksonville HS 1,100/9-12
1021 Henderson Dr 28540 910-989-2048
Donna Lynch, prin. Fax 989-2046
New Bridge MS 500/6-8
401 New Bridge St 28540 910-346-5144
Chris Barnes, prin. Fax 346-5402
Northside HS 800/9-12
365 Commons Dr S 28546 910-455-4868
Maria Johnson, prin. Fax 455-4987
Northwoods Park MS 700/6-8
904 Sioux Dr 28540 910-347-1202
Dennie Fidalgo, prin. Fax 347-0713
Southwest HS 700/9-12
1420 Burgaw Hwy 28540 910-455-4888
Tim Foster, prin. Fax 455-3949
Southwest MS 500/6-8
3000 Furia Dr 28540 910-455-1105
Steve Clark, prin. Fax 455-4082
White Oak HS 1,100/9-12
1001 Piney Green Rd 28546 910-455-1541
Jane Dennis, prin. Fax 938-2302
Other Schools – See Holly Ridge, Hubert, Richlands, Swansboro

---

Cheveux School Hair Design and Hairport Post-Sec.
4781 Gum Branch Rd Ste 1 28540 910-455-5767
Coastal Carolina Community College Post-Sec.
444 Western Blvd 28546 910-455-1221
Jacksonville Christian Academy 200/K-12
919 Gum Branch Rd 28540 910-347-2358
Rev. Larry Haggard, prin. Fax 347-3138

Living Water Christian S 200/K-12
3980 Gum Branch Rd 28540 910-938-7017
Barbara Koebbe, prin. Fax 938-7025
Miller-Motte College Post-Sec.
1291 Hargett St Ste A 28540 910-478-4300

Jamestown, Guilford, Pop. 3,331
Guilford County SD
Supt. — See Greensboro
Jamestown MS 1,100/6-8
301 Haynes Rd 27282 336-819-2100
Denise Richmond, prin. Fax 454-6734
Middle College HS @ GTCC - Jamestown 200/9-12
601 High Point Rd 27282 336-819-2957
Loretta Rowland-Kitley, prin. Fax 819-2961
Ragsdale HS 1,400/9-12
1000 Lucy Ragsdale Rd 27282 336-454-7400
Kathy Rogers, prin. Fax 454-6767

Guilford Technical Community College Post-Sec.
PO Box 309 27282 336-334-4822

Jamesville, Martin, Pop. 479
Martin County SD
Supt. — See Williamston
Jamesville MS 100/6-8
1215 Saint Andrews St 27846 252-792-4428
Dennis Hart, prin. Fax 809-4812

Jefferson, Ashe, Pop. 1,599
Ashe County SD 3,300/PK-12
PO Box 604 28640 336-246-7175
Dr. Travis Reeves, supt. Fax 246-7609
www.ashe.k12.nc.us/
Other Schools – See Warrensville, West Jefferson

Kannapolis, Cabarrus, Pop. 41,850
Kannapolis CSD 5,200/PK-12
100 Denver St 28083 704-938-1131
Dr. Pam Cain, supt. Fax 933-6370
www.kcs.k12.nc.us
Brown HS 1,400/9-12
415 E 1st St 28083 704-932-6125
Kevin Garay, prin. Fax 933-1862
Kannapolis MS 800/7-8
1445 Oakwood Ave 28081 704-932-4102
Bridgette Reese, prin. Fax 932-4104

Franklin Heights Christian Academy 200/K-12
526 Wright Ave 28083 704-933-8348
Blenda Snodderly, admin. Fax 932-9470

Kenansville, Duplin, Pop. 849
Duplin County SD 9,100/PK-12
PO Box 128 28349 910-296-1521
Dr. Austin Obasohan, supt. Fax 296-1396
www.duplinschools.net
Duplin Early College HS 200/9-12
PO Box 128 28349 910-296-1136
Felicia Brown, prin. Fax 296-0348
Smith MS 300/6-8
PO Box 369 28349 910-296-0309
Jackie Arthur, prin. Fax 296-0086
Other Schools – See Beulaville, Mount Olive, Rose Hill, Teachey, Warsaw

---

James Sprunt Community College Post-Sec.
PO Box 398 28349 910-296-2500

Kenly, Johnston, Pop. 1,330
Johnston County SD
Supt. — See Smithfield
North Johnston HS 700/9-12
PO Box 339 27542 919-284-2031
Tim Harrell, prin. Fax 284-6224

Kernersville, Forsyth, Pop. 22,718
Winston-Salem/Forsyth SD
Supt. — See Winston Salem
East Forsyth HS 2,000/9-12
2500 W Mountain St 27284 336-703-6735
Patricia Gainey, prin. Fax 727-8546
East Forsyth MS 800/6-8
810 Bagley Rd 27284 336-703-6765
Dossie Poteat, prin. Fax 607-8531
Glenn HS 1,500/9-12
1600 Union Cross Rd 27284 336-771-4500
Brad Craddock, prin. Fax 771-4507
Kernersville MS 800/6-8
110 Brown Rd 27284 336-996-5566
Sharon Porter, prin. Fax 996-1966
Southeast MS 1,100/6-8
1200 Old Salem Rd 27284 336-996-5848
Stephanie Gentry, prin. Fax 996-0148

Bishop McGuiness HS 600/9-12
1725 NC Highway 66 S 27284 336-564-1010
George Repass, prin. Fax 564-1060
Dudley Cosmetology University Post-Sec.
900 E Mountain St 27284 336-996-2030
First Christian Academy 200/PK-12
1130 N Main St 27284 336-996-1660
Bonnie McDaniel, admin. Fax 996-6511

Kill Devil Hills, Dare, Pop. 6,558
Dare County SD
Supt. — See Nags Head
First Flight HS 800/9-12
100 Veterans Dr 27948 252-449-7000
Arty Tillett, prin. Fax 449-7004
First Flight MS 600/6-8
109 Veterans Dr 27948 252-441-8888
John Donlan, prin. Fax 441-7694

King, Stokes, Pop. 6,843
Stokes County SD
Supt. — See Danbury
Chestnut Grove MS 800/6-8
2185 Chestnut Grove Rd 27021 336-983-2106
Karen Boles, prin. Fax 983-2725

Meadowbrook Academy 100/Alt
817 Meadowbrook Dr 27021 336-985-3224
David Hicks, prin. Fax 985-3568
West Stokes HS 1,000/9-12
1400 Priddy Rd 27021 336-983-2099
Tony George, prin. Fax 983-6076

Calvary Christian S 200/PK-12
748 Spainhour Rd 27021 336-983-3743
Sid Main, admin. Fax 983-8426

Kings Mountain, Cleveland, Pop. 10,130
Cleveland County SD
Supt. — See Shelby
Kings Mountain HS 1,300/9-12
500 Phifer Rd 28086 704-734-5647
Ronny Funderburke, prin. Fax 734-1723
Kings Mountain MS 700/7-8
1000 Phifer Rd 28086 704-476-8340
Dr. Brian Hunnell, prin. Fax 734-5615

Grace Christian Academy 100/K-10
260 Range Rd 28086 704-734-0509
Leigh Renn, prin.

Kinston, Lenoir, Pop. 21,394
Lenoir County SD 9,300/PK-12
PO Box 729 28502 252-527-1109
Dr. Stephen Mazingo, supt. Fax 527-6884
www.lenoir.k12.nc.us
Kinston HS 900/9-12
2601 N Queen St 28501 252-527-8067
Angela Bryant, prin. Fax 527-4090
Lenoir County Early College HS 200/9-12
231 Hwy 58 S 28504 252-233-6870
Jason Miller, prin. Fax 233-6879
Rochelle MS 500/6-8
301 N Rochelle Blvd 28501 252-527-4290
Nicholas Harvey, prin. Fax 527-6498
Sampson S 100/Alt
2529 Cedar Dell Ln 28504 252-527-4264
Diane Heath, prin. Fax 527-7631
Woodington MS 700/6-8
4939 Hwy 258 S 28504 252-527-9570
Teresa George, prin. Fax 527-3883
Other Schools – See Deep Run, La Grange

Arendell Parrott Academy 800/PK-12
PO Box 1297 28503 252-522-4222
Hugh Pollock, admin. Fax 522-0672
Bethel Christian Academy 400/PK-12
1936 Banks School Rd 28504 252-522-4636
Douglas K. Phillips, admin. Fax 523-7290
Lenoir Community College Post-Sec.
PO Box 188 28502 252-527-6223
Lenoir Memorial Hospital Post-Sec.
100 Airport Rd 28501 252-522-7797

Knightdale, Wake, Pop. 11,083
Wake County SD
Supt. — See Raleigh
Knightdale HS 1,800/9-12
100 Bryan Chalk Ln 27545 919-217-5350
Carla Jernigan, prin. Fax 217-5356

La Grange, Lenoir, Pop. 2,845
Lenoir County SD
Supt. — See Kinston
Frink MS 600/6-8
102 Martin Luther King Jr 28551 252-566-3326
Tina Letchworth, prin. Fax 566-4027
North Lenoir HS 1,000/9-12
2400 Institute Rd 28551 252-527-9184
Gil Respess, prin. Fax 527-8672

Lake Waccamaw, Columbus, Pop. 1,463
Columbus County SD
Supt. — See Whiteville
Boys and Girls Homes S 50/Alt
PO Box 250 28450 910-646-3088
Michael Mobley, prin. Fax 646-4934
East Columbus HS 600/9-12
PO Box 401 28450 910-646-4094
Bobby Vaughan, prin. Fax 646-3779

Landis, Rowan, Pop. 3,094
Rowan-Salisbury County SD
Supt. — See Salisbury
Corriher-Lipe MS 600/6-8
214 W Rice St 28088 704-857-7946
Dr. Beverly Pugh, prin. Fax 855-2670

Lasker, Northampton, Pop. 119

Northeast Academy 200/PK-12
210 E Church St 27845 252-539-2461
Russell Leake, hdmstr. Fax 539-3919

Laurel Hill, Scotland, Pop. 1,230
Scotland County SD
Supt. — See Laurinburg
Carver MS 500/6-8
18601 Fieldcrest Rd 28351 910-462-4669
Amber Alford-Watkins, prin. Fax 462-4674

Laurinburg, Scotland, Pop. 15,644
Scotland County SD 4,900/PK-12
322 S Main St 28352 910-276-1138
Rick Stout, supt. Fax 277-4310
www.scotland.k12.nc.us
Scotland Early College S 100/9-12
1700 Dogwood Mile St 28352 910-277-3951
Joe Critcher, prin. Fax 277-5020
Scotland HS 400/9-12
1000 W Church St 28352 910-276-7370
Greg Batten, prin. Fax 277-4444
Shaw Academy 200/Alt
18700 Old Wire Rd 28352 910-277-4316
John Teal, prin. Fax 277-4319

Spring Hill MS 500/6-8
22801 Airbase Rd 28352 910-369-0590
Beth Ammons, prin. Fax 369-0595
Sycamore Lane MS 500/6-8
2100 Sycamore Ln 28352 910-277-4350
Rick Singletary, prin. Fax 277-4321
Other Schools – See Laurel Hill

Christ the Cornerstone Academy 100/K-12
10401 McColl Rd 28352 910-277-0077
Billy Storms, admin. Fax 277-8682
St. Andrews University Post-Sec.
1700 Dogwood Mile St 28352 910-277-5555
Scotland Christian Academy 300/K-12
10300 McColl Rd 28352 910-276-7722
Phillip Cline, hdmstr. Fax 277-2735

Lawndale, Cleveland, Pop. 596
Cleveland County SD
Supt. — See Shelby
Burns HS 1,100/9-12
307 E Stagecoach Trl 28090 704-538-7403
Dr. Aaron Allen, prin. Fax 538-3895
Burns MS 900/6-8
215 Shady Grove Rd 28090 704-538-3126
Ann Caldwell, prin. Fax 538-3944

Lawsonville, Stokes
Stokes County SD
Supt. — See Danbury
Piney Grove MS 400/6-8
3415 Piney Grove Church Rd 27022 336-593-4000
Roger Tucker, prin. Fax 593-4003

Leland, Brunswick, Pop. 13,291
Brunswick County SD
Supt. — See Bolivia
Leland MS 800/6-8
927 Old Fayetteville Rd NE 28451 910-371-3030
Patricia Underwood, prin. Fax 371-0647
North Brunswick HS 900/9-12
114 Scorpion Dr 28451 910-371-2261
Sheila Grady, prin. Fax 371-0879

Lenoir, Caldwell, Pop. 17,882
Caldwell County SD 12,700/PK-12
1914 Hickory Blvd SW 28645 828-728-8407
Dr. Steve Stone, supt. Fax 728-0012
www.caldwellschools.com
Gamewell MS 600/6-8
3210 Gamewell School Rd 28645 828-754-6204
Chris Greene, prin. Fax 754-6278
Hibriten HS 900/9-12
1350 Panther Trl SE 28645 828-758-7376
David Colwell, prin. Fax 758-9708
Lenoir MS 500/6-8
332 Greenhaven Dr NW 28645 828-758-2500
Lisa Vaughn, prin. Fax 758-1570
West Caldwell HS 900/9-12
300 W Caldwell Dr 28645 828-758-5583
Jeff Link, prin. Fax 754-2783
Other Schools – See Granite Falls, Hudson

Lewisville, Forsyth, Pop. 12,465

Forsyth Country Day S 900/PK-12
5501 Shallowford Rd 27023 336-945-3151
Dr. Nan Wodarz, hdmstr. Fax 945-2907

Lexington, Davidson, Pop. 18,479
Davidson County SD 20,300/PK-12
PO Box 2057 27293 336-249-8182
Dr. Fred Mock, supt. Fax 249-1062
www.davidson.k12.nc.us
Central Davidson HS 1,000/9-12
2747 NC Highway 47 27292 336-357-2920
Tabitha Broadway, prin. Fax 357-5175
Central Davidson MS 800/6-8
2591 NC Highway 47 27292 336-357-2310
Deana Coley, prin. Fax 357-5965
Davidson County HS 100/Alt
2065 E Holly Grove Rd 27292 336-242-1459
James Fitzgerald, prin. Fax 242-1465
North Davidson HS 1,600/9-12
7227 Old US Highway 52 27295 336-731-8431
Emily Lipe, prin. Fax 731-2642
North Davidson MS 1,200/6-8
333 Critcher Dr 27295 336-731-2331
Angie Kiger, prin. Fax 731-2328
Tyro MS 700/6-8
2946 Michael Rd 27295 336-853-7795
Debbie Hill, prin. Fax 853-7357
West Davidson HS 800/9-12
200 Dragon Dr 27295 336-853-8082
Travis Smith, prin. Fax 853-7315
Other Schools – See Denton, Thomasville, Winston Salem

Lexington CSD 3,100/1-12
1010 Fair St 27292 336-242-1527
Richard Kriesky, supt. Fax 249-3206
lexcs.org
Lexington HS 800/9-12
26 Penry St 27292 336-242-1574
Travis Taylor, prin. Fax 242-1285
Lexington MS 600/6-8
100 W Hemstead St 27292 336-242-1557
Rosa Lovelace, prin. Fax 242-1372

Davidson County Community College Post-Sec.
PO Box 1287 27293 336-249-8186
Sheets Memorial Christian S 300/PK-12
307 Holt St 27292 336-249-4224
Ethan Woodward, head sch Fax 249-6985
Union Grove Christian S 400/PK-12
2295 Union Grove Rd 27295 336-764-3105
Peter Steinhaus, admin. Fax 764-8657

Liberty, Randolph, Pop. 2,592
Randolph County SD
Supt. — See Asheboro
Northeastern Randolph MS 700/6-8
3493 Ramseur Julian Rd 27298 336-622-5808
Tracy Dawes, prin. Fax 622-5868

Lillington, Harnett, Pop. 3,141
Harnett County SD 19,400/K-12
PO Box 1029 27546 910-893-8151
Tom Frye, supt. Fax 893-4279
www.harnett.k12.nc.us/
STAR Academy 100/Alt
PO Box 1029 27546 910-893-4072
Ron Avery, prin. Fax 893-3421
Western Harnett HS 1,300/9-12
10637 NC 27 W 27546 919-499-5113
Stan Williams, prin. Fax 499-1537
Western Harnett MS 1,000/6-8
11135 NC 27 W 27546 919-499-4497
Walter McPherson, prin. Fax 499-1788
Other Schools – See Angier, Dunn, Erwin, Spring Lake

Lincolnton, Lincoln, Pop. 10,295
Lincoln County SD 11,900/PK-12
PO Box 400 28093 704-732-2261
Sherry Hoyle Ed.D., supt. Fax 736-4280
www.lincoln.k12.nc.us
Asbury S 50/Alt
221 Salem Church Rd 28092 704-736-4766
Ted Shiver, prin. Fax 736-4183
Lincoln County School of Technology Vo/Tech
1 Timpken Dr 28092 704-732-4084
Mitch Sherrill, prin. Fax 735-8292
Lincolnton HS 900/9-12
803 N Aspen St 28092 704-735-3089
Tony Worley, prin. Fax 736-4234
Lincolnton MS 700/6-8
2361 Startown Rd 28092 704-735-1120
Scott Carpenter, prin. Fax 732-6811
North Lincoln HS 1,000/9-12
2737 Lee Lawing Rd 28092 704-736-1969
Marty Helton, prin. Fax 736-1966
West Lincoln HS 1,000/9-12
172 Shoal Rd 28092 704-736-9453
Dr. Cale Sain, prin. Fax 276-2004
West Lincoln MS 700/6-8
260 Shoal Rd 28092 704-276-1760
Diana Carpenter, prin. Fax 276-2293
Other Schools – See Denver, Iron Station

Littleton, Halifax, Pop. 660
Halifax County SD
Supt. — See Halifax
Northwest HS 700/9-12
8492 NC Highway 48 27850 252-586-4125
Dr. Marvin Bradley, prin. Fax 586-6240

Locust, Stanly, Pop. 2,907
Stanly County SD
Supt. — See Albemarle
West Stanly MS 100/6-8
339 Running Creek Church Rd 28097 704-961-3600
Damon Rhodes, prin. Fax 961-3699

Carolina Christian S 300/PK-12
PO Box 399 28097 704-888-4332
Adam Thomas, hdmstr. Fax 888-4492

Louisburg, Franklin, Pop. 3,311
Franklin County SD 8,600/PK-12
53 W River Rd 27549 919-496-2600
Dr. Eddie Ingram, supt. Fax 496-2104
www.fcschools.net
Franklin County Early College HS 100/9-12
8150 NC 56 Hwy 27549 919-496-1055
Jim Harris, prin. Fax 496-1033
Louisburg HS 700/9-12
201 Allen Ln 27549 919-496-3725
Freda Clifton, prin. Fax 496-2505
Terrell Lane MS 500/6-8
101 Terrell Ln 27549 919-496-1855
Novella Brown, prin. Fax 496-1370
Other Schools – See Bunn, Franklinton, Youngsville

Louisburg College Post-Sec.
501 N Main St 27549 919-496-2521

Lowell, Gaston, Pop. 3,488
Gaston County SD
Supt. — See Gastonia
Holbrook MS 800/6-8
418 S Church St 28098 704-824-2381
Jessica McGee, prin. Fax 824-4529

Lucama, Wilson, Pop. 1,093
Wilson County SD
Supt. — See Wilson
Springfield MS 500/6-8
5551 Wiggins Mill Rd 27851 252-239-1347
Pattie Barnes, prin. Fax 239-1686

Lumberton, Robeson, Pop. 21,026
Robeson County SD 23,900/PK-12
PO Box 2909 28359 910-671-6000
Dr. Johnny Hunt, supt. Fax 671-6024
www.robeson.k12.nc.us
Early College HS 200/9-12
5170 N Fayetteville Rd 28360 910-737-5232
Shelia Gasque, prin. Fax 737-5231
Littlefield MS 800/4-8
9674 NC Highway 41 N 28358 910-671-6065
Kendall Hamilton, prin. Fax 671-6068
Lumberton HS 2,100/9-12
3901 Fayetteville Rd 28358 910-671-6050
Larry Obeda, prin. Fax 671-4399
Lumberton JHS 600/7-8
82 Marion Rd 28358 910-735-2108
Erika McComb, prin. Fax 671-4350
Robeson County Career Center Vo/Tech
PO Box 2909 28359 910-671-6095
Mark Smith, prin. Fax 671-6097
Other Schools – See Fairmont, Maxton, Orrum, Pembroke, Red Springs, Rowland, Saint Pauls

---

Antioch Christian Academy 300/K-12
5071 Old Whiteville Rd 28358 910-735-1011
James Coleman, prin. Fax 737-6301
Robeson Community College Post-Sec.
PO Box 1420 28359 910-272-3700

Mc Leansville, Guilford, Pop. 1,014
Guilford County SD
Supt. — See Greensboro
Northeast HS 1,100/9-12
6700 Mcleansville Rd 27301 336-375-2500
Fabby Williams, prin. Fax 375-2520
Northeast MS 800/6-8
6720 Mcleansville Rd 27301 336-375-2525
Karen Williams, prin. Fax 375-2534

Madison, Rockingham, Pop. 2,190
Rockingham County SD
Supt. — See Eden
Western Rockingham MS 700/6-8
915 Ayersville Rd 27025 336-548-2168
Duane Hensley, prin. Fax 548-1799

Maiden, Catawba, Pop. 3,281
Catawba County SD
Supt. — See Newton
Maiden HS 800/9-12
600 W Main St 28650 828-428-8197
Dwayne Finger, prin. Fax 428-8341
Maiden MS 500/7-8
518 N C Ave 28650 828-428-2326
Nan VanHoy, prin. Fax 428-5389

Manteo, Dare, Pop. 1,400
Dare County SD
Supt. — See Nags Head
Dare County Alternative S 50/Alt
205 N Highway 64/264 27954 252-473-3141
Teresa Twyne, prin. Fax 473-1638
Manteo HS 500/9-12
829 Wingina St 27954 252-473-5841
John Luciano, prin. Fax 473-2263
Manteo MS 300/6-8
1000 US Highway 64 and 264 27954 252-473-5549
Terry McGinnis, prin. Fax 473-2612

Marion, McDowell, Pop. 7,708
McDowell County SD 6,400/K-12
PO Box 130 28752 828-652-4535
Dr. Gerri Martin, supt. Fax 659-2238
www.mcdowell.k12.nc.us/
Alternative Education Center Alt
176 Lukin St 28752 828-652-1040
Tracy Widmann, dir. Fax 652-9840
East McDowell JHS 600/7-9
676 State St 28752 828-652-7711
Charles Gaffigan, prin. Fax 652-1469
McDowell Early College 200/9-12
54 College Dr 28752 828-659-0411
Lisa Robinson, prin. Fax 659-0469
McDowell HS 1,300/9-12
600 McDowell High Dr 28752 828-652-7920
Ben Talbert, prin. Fax 652-1101
West McDowell JHS 800/7-9
346 W McDowell Jr High Sch 28752 828-652-3390
Vicki Webb, prin. Fax 659-1964

McDowell Technical Community College Post-Sec.
54 College Dr 28752 828-652-6021
New Manna Christian S 100/K-12
PO Box 1085 28752 828-652-7729
Anthony Shirley, prin. Fax 652-7729

Marshall, Madison, Pop. 859
Madison County SD 2,600/K-12
5738 US 25/70 Hwy 28753 828-649-9276
Ronald Wilcox Ed.D., supt. Fax 649-9334
www.madisonk12.net
Madison HS 700/9-12
5740 US 25/70 Hwy 28753 828-649-2876
Steve Bowlin, prin. Fax 649-0104
Madison MS 600/6-8
95 Upper Brush Creek Rd 28753 828-649-2269
Dr. Barbara Tipton, prin. Fax 649-9015
Other Schools – See Mars Hill

Mars Hill, Madison, Pop. 1,829
Madison County SD
Supt. — See Marshall
Madison Early College HS 100/9-12
PO Box 999 28754 828-689-9552
David Robinson, prin. Fax 689-9644

Mars Hill College Post-Sec.
PO Box 370 28754 866-642-4968

Marshville, Union, Pop. 2,366
Union County SD
Supt. — See Monroe
East Union MS 800/6-8
6010 W Marshville Blvd 28103 704-290-1540
Dr. Kenneth Hoover, prin. Fax 624-9302
Forest Hills HS 900/9-12
100 Forest Hills School S 28103 704-233-4001
Dr. Kevin Plue, prin. Fax 233-4003

Matthews, Mecklenburg, Pop. 26,705
Charlotte/Mecklenburg County SD
Supt. — See Charlotte
Butler HS 2,200/9-12
1810 Matthews Mint Hill Rd 28105 980-343-6300
Will Leach, prin. Fax 343-6315
Crestdale MS 1,000/6-8
940 Sam Newell Rd 28105 980-343-5755
Rhonda Houston, prin. Fax 343-5761
Mint Hill MS 1,300/6-8
11501 Idlewild Rd 28105 980-343-5439
Steve Drye, prin. Fax 343-5442

Union County SD
Supt. — See Monroe
Weddington HS 1,200/9-12
4901 Weddington Rd 28104 704-708-5530
Jonathan Bowers, prin. Fax 708-6218
Weddington MS 1,100/6-8
5903 Deal Rd 28104 704-814-9772
Steven Wray, prin. Fax 814-9775

Bible Baptist Christian S 100/PK-12
2724 Margaret Wallace Rd 28105 704-535-1694
Damian Ahrens, prin. Fax 536-1289
Carmel Christian S 400/K-12
1145 Pineville Matthews Rd 28105 704-849-9723
J. Van Wade, hdmstr. Fax 847-9908
Covenant Day S 800/PK-12
800 Fullwood Rd 28105 704-847-2385
Mark Davis, hdmstr. Fax 708-6137
Empire Beauty School Post-Sec.
11032 E Independence Blvd 28105 800-575-5983
Grace Academy 400/K-12
3645 Pleasant Plains Rd 28104 704-234-0292
Southern Evangelical Seminary Post-Sec.
3000 Tilley Morris Rd 28105 704-847-5600

Maxton, Robeson, Pop. 2,397
Robeson County SD
Supt. — See Lumberton
Townsend MS 200/5-8
105 Carolina St 28364 910-844-5086
Eric Sanders, prin. Fax 844-4292

Mayodan, Rockingham, Pop. 2,444
Rockingham County SD
Supt. — See Eden
McMichael HS 1,000/9-12
6845 NC Highway 135 27027 336-427-5165
Leigh Jones, prin. Fax 427-5776

Mebane, Alamance, Pop. 11,146
Alamance-Burlington SD
Supt. — See Burlington
Eastern Alamance HS 1,100/9-12
4040 Mebane Rogers Rd 27302 919-563-5991
Dave Ebert, prin. Fax 563-6114
Hawfields MS 700/6-8
1951 S NC Highway 119 27302 919-563-5303
Amy Walker, prin. Fax 563-1351
Woodlawn MS 600/6-8
3970 Mebane Rogers Rd 27302 919-563-3222
Andrew Brehler, prin. Fax 563-6807

Merry Hill, Bertie

Lawrence Academy 200/PK-12
PO Box 70 27957 252-482-4748
Thomas Gregory, hdmstr. Fax 482-2215

Micro, Johnston, Pop. 438
Johnston County SD
Supt. — See Smithfield
North Johnston MS 600/6-8
PO Box 69 27555 919-284-3374
Jarvis Ellis, prin. Fax 284-3399

Millers Creek, Wilkes, Pop. 2,085
Wilkes County SD
Supt. — See North Wilkesboro
West Wilkes HS 700/9-12
6598 Boone Trl 28651 336-973-4503
Wayne Sheperd, prin. Fax 973-7323

Millers Creek Christian S 100/PK-12
PO Box 559 28651 336-838-2517
April Huffman, admin. Fax 838-2546

Mill Spring, Polk
Polk County SD
Supt. — See Columbus
Polk County MS 500/6-8
321 Wolverine Trl 28756 828-894-2215
Hank Utz, prin. Fax 894-0191

Mint Hill, Mecklenburg, Pop. 22,306
Charlotte/Mecklenburg County SD
Supt. — See Charlotte
Northeast MS 900/6-8
5960 Brickstone Dr 28227 980-343-6920
Alicia McCree, prin. Fax 343-3264
Rocky River HS 100/9-12
10505 Clear Creek Cmmrc Dr 28227 980-344-0409
Brandy Nelson, prin. Fax 343-2135

Misenheimer, Stanly, Pop. 712

Pfeiffer University Post-Sec.
48380 US Highway 52 28109 800-338-2060

Mocksville, Davie, Pop. 4,904
Davie County SD 6,600/PK-12
220 Cherry St 27028 336-751-5921
Dr. Darrin Hartness, supt. Fax 751-9013
www.davie.k12.nc.us
Central Davie Academy 50/Alt
160 Campbell Rd 27028 336-751-5712
Beth Weatherman, prin. Fax 751-5719
Davie County Early College HS 200/9-12
1211 Salisbury Rd 27028 336-753-0888
Melissa Lynch, prin. Fax 753-1192
Davie County HS 1,800/9-12
1200 Salisbury Rd 27028 336-751-5905
Jinda Haynes, prin. Fax 751-4597
North Davie MS 500/6-8
497 Farmington Rd 27028 336-998-5555
Jennifer Custer, prin. Fax 998-7233
South Davie MS 500/6-8
700 Hardison St 27028 336-751-5941
Keith Whitaker, prin. Fax 751-5656
Other Schools – See Advance

Trinity Baptist Academy 100/K-12
2722 US Highway 601 S 27028 336-284-2404

Monroe, Union, Pop. 32,321
Union County SD 38,800/PK-12
400 N Church St 28112 704-296-0766
Mary Ellis, supt. Fax 282-2171
www.ucps.k12.nc.us
Central Academy of Technology and Arts 9-12
600 Brewer Dr 28112 704-296-3088
Dr. Shaun Poole, prin. Fax 296-3090
Monroe HS 800/9-12
1 High School Dr 28112 704-296-3130
Brad Breedlove, prin. Fax 296-3138
Monroe MS 900/6-8
601 E Sunset Dr 28112 704-296-3120
Dr. Mike Harvey, prin. Fax 296-3122
Parkwood HS 1,000/9-12
3220 Parkwood School Rd 28112 704-764-2900
Jan Hollis, prin. Fax 764-2907
Parkwood MS 800/6-8
3219 Parkwood School Rd 28112 704-764-2910
Kimberly Chinnis, prin. Fax 764-2914
Piedmont HS 1,000/9-12
3006 Sikes Mill Rd 28110 704-753-2810
Jonathan Tyson, prin. Fax 753-2817
Piedmont MS 1,000/6-8
2816 Sikes Mill Rd 28110 704-753-2840
Dr. Anne Radke, prin. Fax 753-2846
Sun Valley HS 1,400/9-12
5211 Old Charlotte Hwy 28110 704-296-3020
Janice Burns, prin. Fax 296-3029
Union County Early College HS 300/9-12
4209A Old Charlotte Hwy 28110 704-290-1565
Jane Wade, prin. Fax 282-0956
Other Schools – See Indian Trail, Marshville, Matthews, Waxhaw

---

Shining Light Baptist Academy 100/PK-12
2541 Old Charlotte Hwy 28110 704-283-1480
Tim Cruse, admin. Fax 289-4945
Tabernacle Christian S 100/K-12
2900 Walkup Ave 28110 704-283-4395
Stephen Leonard, admin.

Montreat, Buncombe, Pop. 715

Montreat College Post-Sec.
PO Box 1267 28757 800-622-6968

Mooresville, Iredell, Pop. 32,023
Iredell-Statesville SD
Supt. — See Statesville
Brawley MS 700/6-8
132 Swift Arrow Dr 28117 704-664-4430
Jimmie Dancy, prin. Fax 664-9846
Lake Norman HS 1,900/9-12
186 Doolie Rd 28117 704-799-8555
Todd Griffin, prin. Fax 799-1512
Lakeshore MS 600/6-8
244 Lakeshore School Dr 28117 704-799-0187
Jim Gaghan, prin. Fax 663-6431
Mount Mourne IB S 500/6-9
1431 Mecklenburg Hwy 28115 704-892-4711
Boen Nutting, prin. Fax 892-3804

Mooresville Graded SD 5,500/PK-12
305 N Main St 28115 704-658-2530
Dr. Mark Edwards, supt. Fax 663-3005
www.mgsd.k12.nc.us
Mooresville HS 1,600/9-12
659 E Center Ave 28115 704-658-2580
Michael Royal, prin. Fax 664-4381
Mooresville MS 800/7-8
233 Kistler Farm Rd 28115 704-658-2720
Carrie Tulbert, prin. Fax 664-5101
Woods Adv Tech / Arts Center Vo/Tech
574 W McLelland Ave 28115 704-658-2500
Devry Gibbs, prin. Fax 664-5102

Christ the King HS 9-12
753 Oak Ridge Farm Hwy 28115 704-799-4400
Daniel Dolan, prin. Fax 799-4404
Mooresville Christian Academy 100/K-12
PO Box 114 28115 704-663-4690
NASCAR Technical Institute Post-Sec.
220 Byers Creek Rd 28117 704-658-1950

Moravian Falls, Wilkes, Pop. 1,870
Wilkes County SD
Supt. — See North Wilkesboro
Central Wilkes MS 700/6-8
3541 S NC Highway 16 28654 336-667-7453
Ryan McCreary, prin. Fax 667-5825

Morehead City, Carteret, Pop. 8,439
Carteret County SD
Supt. — See Beaufort
Bridges Alternative S 50/Alt
140 Vashti Dr 28557 252-808-3040
Regi Bolen, admin. Fax 726-5245
Morehead City MS 500/6-8
400 Barbour Rd 28557 252-726-1126
Al Roberson, prin. Fax 726-4980
West Carteret HS 1,200/9-12
4700 Country Club Rd 28557 252-726-1176
Carolyn Heller, prin. Fax 726-6290

Carteret Community College Post-Sec.
3505 Arendell St 28557 252-222-6000

Morganton, Burke, Pop. 16,462
Burke County SD 13,800/PK-12
PO Box 989 28680 828-439-4312
Larry Putnam, supt. Fax 439-4314
www.burke.k12.nc.us
Burke Middle College HS 100/11-12
1001 Burkemont Ave 28655 828-448-3175
Tim Davis, prin. Fax 442-6172

Freedom HS 1,200/9-12
511 Independence Blvd 28655 828-433-1310
Mike Swan, prin. Fax 439-8420
Johnson MS 500/6-8
701 Lenoir Rd 28655 828-430-7340
Darrin Foddrell, prin. Fax 430-4801
Liberty MS 700/6-8
529 Enola Rd 28655 828-437-1330
Mike Holden, prin. Fax 432-2124
Patton HS 1,100/9-12
701 Enola Rd 28655 828-433-3000
Kathy Amos, prin. Fax 433-3001
Table Rock MS 600/6-8
1581 NC 126 28655 828-437-5212
Wendi Barber, prin. Fax 439-5702
Other Schools – See Connelly Sprngs, Drexel, Valdese

North Carolina School for the Deaf Post-Sec.
517 W Fleming Dr 28655 828-433-2971
Western Piedmont Community College Post-Sec.
1001 Burkemont Ave 28655 828-438-6000

Morrisville, Wake, Pop. 17,983

DeVry University Post-Sec.
1600 Perimeter Park Dr #100 27560 919-463-1380
Pfeiffer University Post-Sec.
2880 Slater Rd Ste 100 27560 919-941-2920
The Chef's Acadmey Post-Sec.
2001 Carrington Mill Blvd 27560 919-313-4715

Mount Airy, Surry, Pop. 10,205
Mt. Airy CSD 1,700/PK-12
130 Rawley Ave 27030 336-786-8355
Dr. Gregory Little, supt. Fax 786-7553
www.mtairy.k12.nc.us
Mount Airy HS 500/9-12
1011 N South St 27030 336-789-5147
Sandy George, prin. Fax 719-2341
Mount Airy MS 400/6-8
249 Hamburg St 27030 336-789-9021
Bryan Taylor, prin. Fax 789-6074

Surry County SD
Supt. — See Dobson
Gentry MS 400/6-8
1915 W Pine St 27030 336-786-4155
Paige Badgett, prin. Fax 786-6863
Meadowview MS 400/6-8
1282 Mckinney Rd 27030 336-789-0276
Denny Barr, prin. Fax 789-0449
North Surry HS 900/9-12
2440 W Pine St 27030 336-789-5055
Bill Goins, prin. Fax 786-8630

Northern Hospital of Surry County Post-Sec.
PO Box 1101 27030 336-719-7124

Mount Gilead, Montgomery, Pop. 1,163
Montgomery County SD
Supt. — See Troy
West MS 500/6-8
129 NC Highway 109 S 27306 910-572-9378
Joan Frye, prin. Fax 572-2114
West Montgomery HS 600/9-12
147 Warrior Rd 27306 910-439-6191
Jack Cagle, prin. Fax 439-4600

Mount Holly, Gaston, Pop. 13,424
Gaston County SD
Supt. — See Gastonia
East Gaston HS 1,500/9-12
1744 Lane Rd 28120 704-827-7251
Cristi Bostic, prin. Fax 827-5974
Mount Holly MS 800/6-8
124 S Hawthorne St 28120 704-827-4811
Jennifer Reep, prin. Fax 822-1049

Mount Olive, Wayne, Pop. 4,528
Duplin County SD
Supt. — See Kenansville
North Duplin JSHS 500/7-12
1388 W NC 403 Hwy 28365 919-658-3051
Connie Harrell, prin. Fax 658-9971

Wayne County SD
Supt. — See Goldsboro
Mount Olive MS 500/5-8
309 Wooten St 28365 919-658-7320
Tammy Keel, prin. Fax 658-7325

Mt. Olive College Post-Sec.
634 Henderson St 28365 919-658-2502

Mount Pleasant, Cabarrus, Pop. 1,645
Cabarrus County SD
Supt. — See Concord
Mount Pleasant HS 900/9-12
700 Walker Rd 28124 704-436-9321
Edith Saycwich, prin. Fax 436-3179
Mount Pleasant MS 600/6-8
8325 Highway 49 N 28124 704-436-9302
Danah Wilson, prin. Fax 436-6112

Mount Ulla, Rowan
Rowan-Salisbury County SD
Supt. — See Salisbury
West Rowan HS 1,100/9-12
8050 NC Highway 801 28125 704-278-9233
Dr. Jamie Durant, prin. Fax 278-9733

Moyock, Currituck, Pop. 3,696
Currituck County SD
Supt. — See Currituck
Moyock MS 500/6-8
216 Survey Rd 27958 252-435-2566
Phil Walls, prin. Fax 435-2576

Murfreesboro, Hertford, Pop. 2,786
Hertford County SD
Supt. — See Winton

Hertford County MS 400/7-8
1850 NC Highway 11 27855 252-398-4091
Dr. Vatera Slade, prin. Fax 398-5570

Chowan University Post-Sec.
1 University Pl 27855 252-398-6500

Murphy, Cherokee, Pop. 1,590
Cherokee County SD 3,600/PK-12
911 Andrews Rd 28906 828-837-2722
Dr. Stephen Lane, supt. Fax 837-5799
www.cherokee.k12.nc.us
Hiwassee Dam HS 200/9-12
267 Blue Eagle Cir 28906 828-644-5916
Tom Graham, prin. Fax 644-9463
Mountain Youth S 50/Alt
4533 Martins Creek Rd 28906 828-837-6775
Bill Gaither, prin. Fax 837-7979
Murphy HS 500/9-12
234 High School Cir 28906 828-837-2426
Boyd Shields, prin. Fax 837-2555
Murphy MS 300/6-8
65 Middle School Dr 28906 828-837-0160
Barry McClure, prin. Fax 837-5814
Tri-County Early College HS 100/9-12
4600 E US Highway 64 Alt 28906 828-835-4208
Alissa Cheek, prin. Fax 835-4319
Other Schools – See Andrews

Murphy Adventist Christian S 50/PK-12
1584 Old Ranger Rd 28906 828-837-5857
Jessie Zollinger, lead tchr. Fax 835-9300
Tri-County Community College Post-Sec.
21 Campus Cir 28906 828-837-6810

Nags Head, Dare, Pop. 2,716
Dare County SD 5,000/PK-12
PO Box 1508 27959 252-480-8888
Dr. Sue Burgess, supt. Fax 480-8889
www.darecountyschoolsonline.com
Other Schools – See Buxton, Kill Devil Hills, Manteo

Nakina, Columbus
Columbus County SD
Supt. — See Whiteville
Nakina MS 6-8
9822 Seven Creeks Hwy 28455 910-642-8301
Richard Gore, prin. Fax 642-3287

Nashville, Nash, Pop. 5,285
Nash-Rocky Mount SD 17,100/PK-12
930 Eastern Ave 27856 252-459-5220
Dr. Anthony Jackson, supt. Fax 459-6403
www.nrms.k12.nc.us
Nash Central MS 600/6-8
1638 S 1st St 27856 252-459-5292
Craig Harris, prin. Fax 459-5297
Other Schools – See Bailey, Battleboro, Rocky Mount, Spring Hope

New Bern, Craven, Pop. 28,922
Craven County SD 15,000/PK-12
3600 Trent Rd 28562 252-514-6300
Dr. Lane Mills, supt. Fax 514-6351
www.craven.k12.nc.us
Craven Early College HS 200/9-12
800 College Ct 28562 252-637-5706
Todd Bradley, prin. Fax 637-4459
Fields MS 600/6-8
2000 Dr M L King Jr Blvd 28560 252-514-6438
Thomasine Hassell, prin. Fax 514-6443
MacDonald MS 900/6-8
3127 Elizabeth Ave 28562 252-514-6450
Nancy Gaskill, prin. Fax 514-6456
New Bern HS 1,800/9-12
4200 Academic Dr 28562 252-514-6400
Jerry Simmons, prin. Fax 514-6412
West Craven MS 800/6-8
515 NW Craven Middle School 28562 252-514-6488
Francis Altman, prin. Fax 514-6491
Other Schools – See Havelock, Vanceboro

Calvary Baptist Church S 100/K-12
PO Box 1089 28563 252-633-5410
Fax 633-4340
Craven Community College Post-Sec.
800 College Ct 28562 252-638-7200
Epiphany S 200/5-12
2301 Trent Rd 28562 252-638-0122
Saul Hillel Benjamin, head sch Fax 288-5464

Newland, Avery, Pop. 690
Avery County SD 2,300/PK-12
775 Cranberry St 28657 828-733-6006
David Burleson, supt. Fax 733-8943
www.averyschools.net
Avery County MS 300/6-8
PO Box 729 28657 828-733-0145
Ricky Ward, prin. Fax 733-3506
Leadership & Public Service Academy 300/9-12
401 High School Rd 28657 828-733-0151
Mark Garrett, prin. Fax 733-1742
STEM Academy 300/9-12
401 High School Rd 28657 828-733-0151
Kim Davis, prin. Fax 733-1742
Viking & Challenge Academy 200/9-12
401 High School Rd 28657 828-733-0151
Monet Samuelson, prin. Fax 733-1742
Other Schools – See Elk Park

New London, Stanly, Pop. 599
Stanly County SD
Supt. — See Albemarle
North Stanly HS 700/9-12
40206 US Highway 52 N 28127 704-961-4600
Joy Hathcock, prin. Fax 961-4699
North Stanly MS 50/6-8
36605 Old Salisbury Rd 28127 704-961-3700
Anne Watson, prin. Fax 961-3799

Newport, Carteret, Pop. 4,038
Carteret County SD
Supt. — See Beaufort
Broad Creek MS 600/6-8
2382 Highway 24 28570 252-247-3135
Dr. Cathy Tomon, prin. Fax 247-5114
Croatan HS 900/9-12
3355 Highway 24 28570 252-393-7022
Joseph Poletti, prin. Fax 393-1223
Newport MS 500/6-8
500 E Chatham St 28570 252-223-3482
Michael McKay, prin. Fax 223-4914

Gramercy Christian S 200/K-12
8170 Highway 70 28570 252-223-5199
Kirk Nielsen, admin. Fax 223-2359

Newton, Catawba, Pop. 12,714
Catawba County SD 17,300/PK-12
PO Box 1010 28658 828-464-8333
Dr. Dan Brigman, supt. Fax 464-0925
www.catawbaschools.net/
Foard HS 1,100/9-12
3407 Plateau Rd 28658 704-462-1496
Chris Gibbs, prin. Fax 462-1988
Jacobs Fork MS 600/7-8
3431 Plateau Rd 28658 704-462-1827
Jeff Isenhour, prin. Fax 462-1600
Other Schools – See Catawba, Claremont, Hickory, Maiden

Newton-Conover CSD 2,900/PK-12
605 N Ashe Ave 28658 828-464-3191
Dr. David Stegall, supt. Fax 466-0063
www.nccs.k12.nc.us
Discovery HS 9-12
605 N Ashe Ave 28658 828-464-3191
John Robinson, prin. Fax 466-0063
Newton-Conover HS 800/9-12
338 W 15th St 28658 828-465-0920
Kevin Campbell, prin. Fax 464-1412
Other Schools – See Conover

Newton Grove, Sampson, Pop. 561
Sampson County SD
Supt. — See Clinton
Hobbton HS 500/9-12
12201 Hobbton Hwy 28366 910-594-0242
Wesley Johnson, prin. Fax 594-1115
Hobbton MS 400/6-8
12081 Hobbton Hwy 28366 910-594-1420
Kevin Hunter, prin. Fax 594-0049
Midway HS 700/9-12
15274 Spiveys Corner Hwy 28366 910-567-6664
Stuart Daughtery, prin. Fax 567-5989

Norlina, Warren, Pop. 1,094

Norlina Christian S 100/PK-12
PO Box 757 27563 252-456-3385
David Spence, prin. Fax 456-3354

North Wilkesboro, Wilkes, Pop. 4,150
Wilkes County SD 10,400/PK-12
613 Cherry St 28659 336-667-1121
Dr. Marty Hemric, supt. Fax 667-5971
www.wilkes.k12.nc.us
North Wilkes MS 600/6-8
2776 Yellow Banks Rd 28659 336-696-2724
David Johnson, prin. Fax 696-4183
Other Schools – See Hays, Millers Creek, Moravian Falls, Ronda, Wilkesboro

Wilkes Regional Medical Center Post-Sec.
PO Box 609 28659 336-651-8433

Norwood, Stanly, Pop. 2,351
Stanly County SD
Supt. — See Albemarle
South Stanly HS 500/9-12
40488 S Stanly School Rd 28128 704-961-4100
Shawn Britt, prin. Fax 961-4199
South Stanly MS 400/6-8
12492 Cottonville Rd 28128 704-961-5700
Daniel Goodman, prin. Fax 961-5799

Oakboro, Stanly, Pop. 1,840
Stanly County SD
Supt. — See Albemarle
West Stanly HS 900/9-12
306 E Red Cross Rd 28129 704-961-5200
Kimberly Page, prin. Fax 961-5299

Oak Ridge, Guilford, Pop. 6,114

Oak Ridge Military Academy 100/7-12
PO Box 498 27310 336-643-4131
David Johnson, pres. Fax 643-1797

Ocracoke, Hyde, Pop. 942
Hyde County SD
Supt. — See Swanquarter
Ocracoke S 100/PK-12
PO Box 189 27960 252-928-3251
Laura Kelly, prin. Fax 928-5380

Olin, Iredell
Iredell-Statesville SD
Supt. — See Statesville
North Iredell HS 1,200/9-12
156 Raider Rd 28660 704-876-4191
Teresa Evans, prin. Fax 876-3241
North Iredell MS 600/6-8
2467 Jennings Rd 28660 704-876-4802
David Ivey, prin. Fax 876-6190

Orrum, Robeson, Pop. 91
Robeson County SD
Supt. — See Lumberton
Orrum MS 300/5-8
PO Box 129 28369 910-628-6285
Cynthia Lewis, prin. Fax 628-8408

Oxford, Granville, Pop. 8,335
Granville County SD 8,800/PK-12
101 Delacroix St 27565 919-693-4613
Dr. Timothy Farley, supt. Fax 693-7391
www.gcs.k12.nc.us/
Northern Granville MS 400/6-8
3144 Webb School Rd 27565 919-693-1483
Jackie Harris, prin. Fax 693-1716
Potter MS 400/6-8
200 Taylor St 27565 919-693-3914
Julie Finch, prin. Fax 693-2896
Webb HS 700/9-12
3200 Webb School Rd 27565 919-693-2521
Calvin Timberlake, prin. Fax 693-2589
Webb S of Health & Life Sciences 300/9-12
3200 Webb School Rd 27565 919-693-6411
Reggie Brooks, prin. Fax 693-6079
Other Schools – See Butner, Creedmoor, Stem

Pantego, Beaufort, Pop. 178

Terra Ceia Christian S 200/PK-12
4428 Christian School Rd 27860 252-943-2485
Jon Postma, prin. Fax 944-0458

Pembroke, Robeson, Pop. 2,870
Robeson County SD
Supt. — See Lumberton
Pembroke MS 700/6-8
PO Box 1148 28372 910-522-5013
Darlene Cummings, prin. Fax 522-1562
Swett HS 1,600/9-12
PO Box 1210 28372 910-521-3253
Antonio Wilkins, prin. Fax 521-2956

University of North Carolina Post-Sec.
PO Box 1510 28372 910-521-6000

Pfafftown, Forsyth
Winston-Salem/Forsyth SD
Supt. — See Winston Salem
Reagan HS 1,700/9-12
3750 Transou Rd 27040 336-703-6776
Frank Martin, prin. Fax 922-1752

Pikeville, Wayne, Pop. 673
Wayne County SD
Supt. — See Goldsboro
Aycock HS 1,200/9-12
PO Box 159 27863 919-242-3400
Dr. Earl Moore, prin. Fax 242-6994

Pilot Mountain, Surry, Pop. 1,458
Surry County SD
Supt. — See Dobson
East Surry HS 600/9-12
801 W Main St 27041 336-368-2251
Diane Beane, prin. Fax 368-3035
Pilot Mountain MS 500/6-8
543 Old Westfield Rd 27041 336-368-2641
Lorrie Sawyers, prin. Fax 368-3935

Pinehurst, Moore, Pop. 12,981

Sandhills Community College Post-Sec.
3395 Airport Rd 28374 910-692-6185

Pinetops, Edgecombe, Pop. 1,369
Edgecombe County SD
Supt. — See Tarboro
South Edgecombe MS 400/6-8
230 Pinetops Crisp Rd 27864 252-827-5083
Kevin Cutler, prin. Fax 827-2811
SouthWest Edgecombe HS 900/9-12
5912 NC 43 N 27864 252-827-5016
Marc Whichard, prin. Fax 827-2815

Pinetown, Beaufort, Pop. 155
Beaufort County SD
Supt. — See Washington
Northside HS 500/9-12
7868 Free Union Church Rd 27865 252-943-6341
Charles Clark, prin. Fax 943-6344

Pittsboro, Chatham, Pop. 3,666
Chatham County SD 7,800/PK-12
PO Box 128 27312 919-542-3626
Robert Logan, supt. Fax 542-1380
www.chatham.k12.nc.us
Horton MS 400/5-8
PO Box 639 27312 919-542-2303
Mattie Smith, prin. Fax 542-7099
Northwood HS 1,000/9-12
310 Northwood School Rd 27312 919-542-4181
Chris Blice, prin. Fax 542-4934
Other Schools – See Bear Creek, Chapel Hill, Siler City

Plymouth, Washington, Pop. 3,841
Washington County SD 1,800/PK-12
802 Washington St 27962 252-793-5171
Dr. Valerie Bridges, supt. Fax 793-5062
www.washingtonco.k12.nc.us/
Plymouth HS 500/9-12
PO Box 827 27962 252-793-3031
Jamie Liverman, prin. Fax 793-3986
Other Schools – See Creswell, Roper

Polkton, Anson, Pop. 3,338
Anson County SD
Supt. — See Wadesboro
Anson Early College S 100/9-12
680 Highway 74 W 28135 704-272-5395
Deborah Davis, prin. Fax 272-6155

South Piedmont Community College Post-Sec.
PO Box 126 28135 704-272-5324

Princeton, Johnston, Pop. 1,179
Johnston County SD
Supt. — See Smithfield
Princeton JSHS 900/6-12
PO Box 38 27569 919-936-5011
W. Kirk Denning, prin. Fax 936-2962

Raeford, Hoke, Pop. 4,467
Hoke County SD 8,300/PK-12
PO Box 370 28376 910-875-4106
Dr. Freddie Williamson, supt. Fax 875-3362
www.hcs.k12.nc.us
East Hoke MS 1,000/6-8
4702 Fayetteville Rd 28376 910-875-5048
Erica Fortenberry, prin. Fax 875-9307
Hoke County HS 1,800/9-12
505 S Bethel Rd 28376 910-875-2156
Roger Edwards, prin. Fax 904-1644
SandHoke Early College HS 200/9-12
1110 E Central Ave 28376 910-878-5806
Colleen Pegram, prin. Fax 878-5807
Turlington JSHS 50/Alt
116 W Prospect Ave 28376 910-875-2583
Krista Friedrich, prin. Fax 875-3012
West Hoke MS 900/6-8
200 NC Highway 211 28376 910-875-3411
Mary McLeod, prin. Fax 875-0332

Raleigh, Wake, Pop. 395,376
Wake County SD 139,100/PK-12
PO Box 28041 27611 919-850-1600
Dr. Donna Hargens, supt. Fax 850-1819
www.wcpss.net
Athens Drive HS 1,900/9-12
1420 Athens Dr 27606 919-233-4050
William Crockett, prin. Fax 233-4054
Broughton HS 2,200/9-12
723 Saint Marys St 27605 919-856-7810
Stephen Mares, prin. Fax 856-7822
Carnage MS 1,100/6-8
1425 Carnage Dr 27610 919-856-7600
David Schwenker, prin. Fax 856-7619
Carroll MS 700/6-8
4520 Six Forks Rd 27609 919-881-1370
Cynthia Keech, prin. Fax 881-5016
Centennial MS 600/6-8
1900 Main Campus Dr 27606 919-233-4217
Edye Bryant, prin. Fax 233-4268
Daniels MS 1,100/6-8
2816 Oberlin Rd 27608 919-881-4860
Elizabeth Battle, prin. Fax 881-1418
Dillard Drive MS 1,200/6-8
5200 Dillard Dr 27606 919-233-4228
Jacob Bryant, prin. Fax 854-1615
Durant Road MS 1,400/6-8
10401 Durant Rd 27614 919-870-4098
Fred Sawyer, prin. Fax 518-0021
East Millbrook MS 1,200/6-8
3801 Spring Forest Rd 27616 919-850-8755
Andrew Livengood, prin. Fax 850-8770
East Wake MS 1,000/6-8
2700 Old Milburnie Rd 27604 919-266-8500
Nancy Allen, prin. Fax 266-8506
Enloe HS 2,700/9-12
128 Clarendon Cres 27610 919-856-7918
Scott Lyons, prin. Fax 856-7917
Leesville Road HS 2,400/9-12
8409 Leesville Rd 27613 919-870-4250
Anthony Muttillo, prin. Fax 870-4287
Leesville Road MS 1,300/6-8
8405 Leesville Rd 27613 919-870-4141
Patti Hamler, prin. Fax 870-4166
Ligon MS 1,100/6-8
706 E Lenoir St 27601 919-856-7929
Gretta Dula, prin. Fax 856-3745
Martin MS 1,000/6-8
1701 Ridge Rd 27607 919-881-4970
Diann Kearney, prin. Fax 881-1416
Millbrook HS 2,400/9-12
2201 Spring Forest Rd 27615 919-850-8787
Dana King, prin. Fax 850-8803
Moore Square Museums MS 500/6-8
301 S Person St 27601 919-664-5737
Kengie Bass, prin. Fax 856-8194
Mt. Vernon Redirection S 100/Alt
5418 Chapel Hill Rd 27607 919-233-4313
Robert Gupton, prin. Fax 233-4006
Phillips HS 200/Alt
1923 Milburnie Rd 27610 919-856-7710
Frederick McNary, prin. Fax 856-7763
River Oaks MS 50/Alt
4700 New Bern Ave 27610 919-231-5600
Luther Thomas, prin. Fax 231-5607
Sanderson HS 1,900/9-12
5500 Dixon Dr 27609 919-881-4800
Gregory Decker, prin. Fax 881-5006
Southeast Raleigh HS 1,700/9-12
2600 Rock Quarry Rd 27610 919-856-2800
Gerald Pickett, prin. Fax 856-2827
Wake Early College of Health & Sciences 200/9-12
2901 Holston Ln 27610 919-212-5800
Lisa Whitaker, prin. Fax 212-5810
Wake Early College STEM HS 9-9
1220 Varsity Dr 27606 919-515-2255
Robert Matheson, prin. Fax 515-2157
Wakefield HS 2,600/9-12
2200 Wakefield Pines Dr 27614 919-562-3600
Tripp Crayton, prin. Fax 562-3623
Wakefield MS 1,200/6-8
2300 Wakefield Pines Dr 27614 919-562-3500
James Sposato, prin. Fax 562-3527
Wake Young Mens Leadership Academy 6-12
3851 Spring Forest Rd 27616 919-431-2244
Ian Soloman, prin. Fax 431-2264
West Millbrook MS 1,000/6-8
8115 Strickland Rd 27615 919-870-4050
Kelly Aman, prin. Fax 870-4064
Young Womens Leadership Academy 6-12
301 Ashe Ave 27606
Teresa Pierrie, prin.
Other Schools – See Apex, Cary, Fuquay Varina, Garner, Holly Springs, Knightdale, Rolesville, Wake Forest, Wendell, Zebulon

---

Adventist Christian Academy of Raleigh 50/K-12
4805 Dillard Dr 27606 919-233-1300
Fax 235-1640
Body of Christ Christian Academy 100/PK-12
4501 Spring Forest Rd 27616 919-872-3622
Fax 872-7661
Cardinal Gibbons HS 1,200/9-12
1401 Edwards Mill Rd 27607 919-834-1625
Jason Curtis, prin. Fax 834-9771
ECPI University Post-Sec.
4101 Doie Cope Rd 27613 919-571-0057
Friendship Christian S 300/PK-12
5510 Falls of Neuse Rd 27609 919-872-2133
Ric Nelson, admin. Fax 872-7451
GRACE Christian HS 200/7-12
1101 Buck Jones Rd 27606 919-747-2020
Don Payne, head sch Fax 747-2021
Living Arts College @ Sch of Comm Arts Post-Sec.
3000 Wakefield Crossing Dr 27614 800-288-7442
Meredith College Post-Sec.
3800 Hillsborough St 27607 919-760-8600
Miller-Motte College Post-Sec.
3901 Capital Blvd Ste 151 27604 919-723-2820
Neuse Christian Academy 200/K-12
7600 Falls of Neuse Rd 27615 919-844-6496
Penny Hill, admin. Fax 861-6819
North Carolina State University Post-Sec.
PO Box 7001 27695 919-515-2011
North Raleigh Christian Academy 1,400/K-12
7300 Perry Creek Rd 27616 919-573-7900
Dr. S.L. Sherrill, supt. Fax 573-7901
Raleigh Christian Academy 400/PK-12
2110 Trawick Rd 27604 919-872-2215
Dwight Ausley, admin. Fax 861-1000
Ravenscroft S 1,200/PK-12
7409 Falls of Neuse Rd 27615 919-847-0900
Doreen Kelly, hdmstr. Fax 846-2135
St. Augustine's University Post-Sec.
1315 Oakwood Ave 27610 919-516-4000
St. David's S 600/K-12
3400 White Oak Rd 27609 919-782-3331
Kevin Lockerbie, hdmstr. Fax 571-3330
St. Mary's S 200/9-12
900 Hillsborough St 27603 919-424-4000
Dr. Monica Gillespie, head sch Fax 424-4137
Shaw University Post-Sec.
118 E South St 27601 919-546-8200
Strayer University Post-Sec.
8701 Wadford Dr 27616 919-878-9900
Trinity Academy of Raleigh 300/K-12
10224 Baileywick Rd 27613 919-786-0114
Steve Pond, prin. Fax 786-0621
Upper Room Christian Academy 400/PK-12
3330 Idlewood Village Dr 27610 919-829-6250
John Amanchukwu, hdmstr. Fax 829-6103
Wake Christian Academy 900/K-12
5500 Wake Academy Dr 27603 919-772-6264
Mike Woods, admin. Fax 779-0918
Wake Technical Community College Post-Sec.
9101 Fayetteville Rd 27603 919-866-5000
William Peace University Post-Sec.
15 E Peace St 27604 919-508-2000
Word of God Christian Academy 200/K-12
3000 Rock Quarry Rd 27610 919-834-8200
Vern Parsons, prin. Fax 899-3640

Ramseur, Randolph, Pop. 1,657
Randolph County SD
Supt. — See Asheboro
Eastern Randolph HS 800/9-12
390 Eastern Randolph Rd 27316 336-824-2351
Stephanie Bridges, prin. Fax 824-6164
Southeastern Randolph MS 700/6-8
5302 Foushee Rd 27316 336-824-6700
Larry Chappell, prin. Fax 824-6705

Faith Christian S 300/PK-12
5449 Brookhaven Rd 27316 336-824-4156
Todd Daniel, prin. Fax 824-1012

Randleman, Randolph, Pop. 4,054
Randolph County SD
Supt. — See Asheboro
Randleman HS 900/9-12
4396 Tigers Den Rd 27317 336-498-2682
Karen Simmons, prin. Fax 498-2609
Randleman MS 800/6-8
800 High Point St 27317 336-498-2606
Dennis Hamilton, prin. Fax 498-8015

Red Springs, Robeson, Pop. 3,362
Robeson County SD
Supt. — See Lumberton
Red Springs HS 700/9-12
509 N Vance St 28377 910-843-4211
Larry Brooks, prin. Fax 843-2025
Red Springs MS 500/5-8
302 W 2nd Ave 28377 910-843-3883
Karen Brooks-Floyd, prin. Fax 843-3765

Macdonald Academy 200/PK-12
200 N College St 28377 910-843-4995

Reidsville, Rockingham, Pop. 14,244
Rockingham County SD
Supt. — See Eden
Reidsville HS 900/9-12
1901 S Park Dr 27320 336-349-6361
Charles Perkins, prin. Fax 349-3205
Reidsville MS 600/6-8
1903 S Park Dr 27320 336-342-4726
Erselle Young, prin. Fax 342-9434
Rockingham County HS 1,100/9-12
180 High School Rd 27320 336-634-3220
Richie Weaver, prin. Fax 342-7794
Rockingham County MS 900/6-8
182 High School Rd 27320 336-616-0073
Joe Baez, prin. Fax 616-0870
S.C.O.R.E Center 50/Alt
401 Moss St 27320 336-634-3209
Curtis Gore, prin. Fax 634-3260

Community Baptist S 200/PK-12
509 Triangle Rd 27320 336-342-5991
Jim Scott, prin. Fax 342-7180

Richlands, Onslow, Pop. 1,464
Onslow County SD
Supt. — See Jacksonville
Richlands HS 1,000/9-12
PO Box 218 28574 910-324-4191
Darin Cloninger, prin. Fax 324-6688
Trexler MS 800/6-8
PO Box 188 28574 910-324-4414
Lynn Jackson, prin. Fax 324-3963

Roanoke Rapids, Halifax, Pop. 15,565
Halifax County SD
Supt. — See Halifax
Davie MS 400/6-8
4391 US Highway 158 27870 252-519-0300
Victor Fenner, prin. Fax 519-0222

Roanoke Rapids CSD 3,100/PK-12
536 Hamilton St 27870 252-519-7100
Dr. Dennis Sawyer, supt. Fax 535-5919
www.rrgsd.org
Chaloner MS 600/6-8
2100 Virginia Ave 27870 252-519-7600
Thomas Davis, prin. Fax 537-9947
Roanoke Rapids HS 900/9-12
800 Hamilton St 27870 252-519-7200
Robert Hurley, prin. Fax 537-3606

Halifax Academy 400/PK-12
1400 Three Bridges Rd 27870 252-537-8527
Glenn Wiggs, hdmstr. Fax 308-0555

Robbins, Moore, Pop. 1,085
Moore County SD
Supt. — See Carthage
Elise MS 200/6-8
180 W Elm St 27325 910-948-2421
Brenda Cassady, prin. Fax 948-4112
North Moore HS 600/9-12
PO Box 9 27325 910-464-3105
Jenny Purvis, prin. Fax 464-6016

Robbinsville, Graham, Pop. 615
Graham County SD 1,200/PK-12
52 Moose Branch Rd 28771 828-479-3413
Clark Carringer, supt. Fax 479-9844
www.grahamcountyschools.org
Robbinsville HS 400/9-12
301 Sweetwater Rd 28771 828-479-3330
David Matheson, prin. Fax 479-9859
Robbinsville MS 200/7-8
301 Sweetwater Rd Ste B 28771 828-479-8488
Kevin White, prin. Fax 479-9847

Robersonville, Martin, Pop. 1,478
Martin County SD
Supt. — See Williamston
South Creek HS 500/9-12
21077 NC Highway 903 27871 252-795-4081
James Guard, prin. Fax 795-4187
South Creek MS 400/6-8
21230 NC Highway 903 27871 252-795-3910
Jan Wagner, prin. Fax 795-3890

Rockingham, Richmond, Pop. 9,384
Richmond County SD
Supt. — See Hamlet
Leak Street HS 100/Alt
377 Mizpah Rd 28379 910-997-9797
Susan Brigman, prin. Fax 997-8170
Richmond SHS 1,400/10-12
PO Box 1748 28380 910-997-9812
Keith McKenzie, prin. Fax 997-9816
Rockingham MS 700/6-8
415 Wall St 28379 910-997-9827
Julian Carter, prin. Fax 997-9859
Rohanen MS 300/6-8
252 School St 28379 910-997-9839
Hal Shuler, prin. Fax 997-8172

Temple Christian S 200/K-12
165 Airport Rd 28379 910-997-3179

Rockwell, Rowan, Pop. 2,077

Rockwell Christian S 100/K-12
PO Box 609 28138 704-279-8854
Dr. John Houghton, admin. Fax 279-1442

Rocky Mount, Edgecombe, Pop. 56,654
Edgecombe County SD
Supt. — See Tarboro
West Edgecombe MS 400/6-8
6301 Nobles Mill Pond Rd 27801 252-446-2030
Donita Gregory, prin. Fax 446-1592

Nash-Rocky Mount SD
Supt. — See Nashville
Edwards MS 700/6-8
720 Edwards St 27803 252-937-9025
Chris Sivills, prin. Fax 446-5527
Nash Central HS 1,200/9-12
4279 Nash Central High Rd 27804 252-451-2860
Gail Powers, prin. Fax 451-1279
Nash-Rocky Mount Early College HS 200/9-12
530 N Old Carriage Rd 27804 252-451-2890
Chris Catalano, prin. Fax 443-0068
Northern Nash HS 1,200/9-12
4230 Green Hills Rd 27804 252-937-9040
Chip Hodges, prin. Fax 443-5448

Parker MS 500/6-8
1500 E Virginia St 27801 252-977-3486
Dr. Anthony Nottingham, prin. Fax 446-5756
Rocky Mount HS 1,200/9-12
1400 Bethlehem Rd 27803 252-937-9050
Leon Farrow, prin. Fax 443-6686
Tar River Academy Alt
224 S Pearl St 27804 252-451-2875
Brian Hopkins, prin. Fax 985-4336

Faith Christian S 400/PK-12
1333 Faith Christian Dr 27803 252-443-3700
Edward Bunn, hdmstr. Fax 443-2456
Falls Road Baptist Church S 200/PK-12
113 Trevathan St 27804 252-977-2401
Jonathan Wright, prin. Fax 977-3493
Nash Community College Post-Sec.
522 N Old Carriage Rd 27804 252-443-4011
North Carolina Wesleyan College Post-Sec.
3400 N Wesleyan Blvd 27804 252-985-5100
Rocky Mount Academy 400/PK-12
1313 Avondale Ave 27803 252-443-4126
Beth Covolo, head sch Fax 937-7922

Rocky Point, Pender, Pop. 1,566
Pender County SD
Supt. — See Burgaw
Cape Fear MS 500/6-8
1886 NC Highway 133 28457 910-602-3334
Christopher Madden, prin. Fax 602-3036
Trask HS 700/9-12
14328 NC Highway 210 28457 910-602-6810
Fax 602-6662

Rolesville, Wake, Pop. 3,697
Wake County SD
Supt. — See Raleigh
Rolesville MS 6-8
4700 Burlington Mills Rd 27571 919-570-2260
Dhedra Lassiter, prin. Fax 570-2270

Ronda, Wilkes, Pop. 410
Wilkes County SD
Supt. — See North Wilkesboro
East Wilkes HS 500/9-12
13315 Elkin Highway 268 28670 336-651-7200
Jodi Weatherman, prin. Fax 835-9298
East Wilkes MS 400/6-8
2202 Macedonia Church Rd 28670 336-928-9800
Ramona Hemric, prin. Fax 957-8734

Roper, Washington, Pop. 608
Washington County SD
Supt. — See Plymouth
Washington County Union MS 300/6-8
PO Box 309 27970 252-793-2835
Kevin Cutler, prin. Fax 793-4411

Roseboro, Sampson, Pop. 1,167
Sampson County SD
Supt. — See Clinton
Roseboro-Salemburg MS 400/6-8
PO Box 976 28382 910-525-4764
Sheila Peterson, prin. Fax 525-3471

Rose Hill, Duplin, Pop. 1,619
Duplin County SD
Supt. — See Kenansville
Charity MS 500/6-8
PO Box 70 28458 910-289-3323
Janice Wynn, prin. Fax 289-2064

Sampson County SD
Supt. — See Clinton
Union HS 500/9-12
1189 Kader Merritt Rd 28458 910-532-6300
Edward Holmes, prin. Fax 532-6350

Rosman, Transylvania, Pop. 567
Transylvania County SD
Supt. — See Brevard
Rosman HS 400/9-12
749 Pickens Hwy 28772 828-862-4284
Brian Weaver, prin. Fax 885-5572
Rosman MS 300/6-8
2770 Old Rosman Hwy 28772 828-862-4286
Greg Carter, prin. Fax 885-5573

Rowland, Robeson, Pop. 1,020
Robeson County SD
Supt. — See Lumberton
Rowland MS 200/6-8
408 W Chapel St 28383 910-422-3983
Shanita Wooten, prin. Fax 422-8369
South Robeson HS 500/9-12
3268 S Robeson Rd 28383 910-422-3987
Christopher Clark, prin. Fax 422-3221

Roxboro, Person, Pop. 8,217
Person County SD 5,000/PK-12
304 S Morgan St Ste 25 27573 336-599-2191
Dr. Tom Daly, supt. Fax 599-2194
www.person.k12.nc.us
Northern MS 500/6-8
1935 Carver Dr, 336-599-6344
Chris Tomasic, prin. Fax 598-9207
Person County Learning Academy Alt
361 Virgilina Rd 27573 336-322-1021
Joan Kister, dir. Fax 322-1029
Person HS 1,500/9-12
1010 Ridge Rd 27573 336-599-8321
Jarrod Dennis, prin. Fax 599-6583
Southern MS 600/6-8
209 Southern Middle School 27573 336-599-6995
Harriett Tillett, prin. Fax 503-0587

Piedmont Community College Post-Sec.
PO Box 1197 27573 336-599-1181
Roxboro Christian Academy 100/K-12
PO Box 1357 27573 336-599-0208
Lynn Bowen, prin. Fax 599-0209

Rutherfordton, Rutherford, Pop. 4,144
Rutherford County SD
Supt. — See Forest City
R-S Central HS 1,000/9-12
PO Box 1119 28139 828-287-3304
Phil Rogers, prin. Fax 286-2024
R-S MS 700/6-8
545 Charlotte Rd 28139 828-286-4461
Dr. Keith Silver, prin. Fax 286-4882

Saint Pauls, Robeson, Pop. 1,997
Robeson County SD
Supt. — See Lumberton
Saint Pauls HS 900/9-12
648 N Old Stage Rd 28384 910-865-4177
Hoyt McCormick, prin. Fax 865-3736
Saint Pauls MS 500/6-8
526 W Shaw St 28384 910-865-4070
Isabel Jones, prin. Fax 865-1599

Salemburg, Sampson, Pop. 427
Sampson County SD
Supt. — See Clinton
Lakewood HS 500/9-12
245 Lakewood School Rd 28385 910-525-5171
Monty Strickland, prin. Fax 525-3344

Salisbury, Rowan, Pop. 33,082
Rowan-Salisbury County SD 18,600/PK-12
PO Box 2349 28145 704-636-7500
Dr. Judy Grissom, supt. Fax 630-6129
www.rss.k12.nc.us
East Rowan HS 1,100/9-12
175 Saint Luke Church Rd 28146 704-279-5232
G. Kelly Sparger, prin. Fax 279-4549
Erwin MS 1,000/6-8
170 Saint Luke Church Rd 28146 704-279-7265
Kristi Rhone, prin. Fax 279-7954
Henderson Independent HS 100/8-12
1215 N Main St 28144 704-639-3103
Dr. Chris Vecchione, prin. Fax 639-3118
Knox MS 600/6-8
1625 W Park Rd 28144 704-633-2922
Terrence Snider, prin. Fax 638-3538
Rowan County Early College S 200/9-12
PO Box 1595 28145 704-216-3873
Dr. Cynthia Misenheimer, prin. Fax 216-2942
Salisbury HS 900/9-12
500 Lincolnton Rd 28144 704-636-1221
Dr. Avis Williams, prin. Fax 639-3029
Southeast MS 700/6-8
1570 Peeler Rd 28146 704-638-5561
David Miller, prin. Fax 638-5719
West Rowan MS 700/6-8
5925 Statesville Blvd 28147 704-633-4775
Nancy Barkemeyer, prin. Fax 633-3157
Other Schools – See China Grove, Landis, Mount Ulla, Spencer

Catawba College Post-Sec.
2300 W Innes St 28144 800-228-2922
Hood Theological Seminary Post-Sec.
1810 Lutheran Synod Dr 28144 704-636-6882
Livingstone College Post-Sec.
701 W Monroe St 28144 704-216-6000
North Hills Christian S 300/PK-12
2970 W Innes St 28144 704-636-3005
Matthew Mitchell, admin. Fax 636-3597
Rowan-Cabarrus Community College Post-Sec.
1333 Jake Alexander Blvd S 28146 704-216-7222

Sanford, Lee, Pop. 27,645
Lee County SD 9,800/PK-12
PO Box 1010 27331 919-774-6226
Andy Bryan Ed.D., supt. Fax 776-4954
www.lee.k12.nc.us
Bragg Street Academy 100/Alt
504 Bragg St 27330 919-775-2686
Jolanda Jordan, prin. Fax 774-1429
East Lee MS 600/6-8
1337 Broadway Rd 27332 919-776-8441
Shannon Shuey, prin. Fax 774-7451
Lee County HS 1,400/9-12
1708 Nash St 27330 919-776-7541
Kenna Wilson, prin. Fax 718-7170
Lee Early College 300/9-12
1105 Kelly Dr 27330 919-718-7259
Robert Biehl, prin. Fax 718-7519
SanLee MS 800/6-8
2309 Tramway Rd 27332 919-708-7227
Betsy Bridges, prin. Fax 718-2875
Southern Lee HS 1,100/9-12
2301 Tramway Rd 27332 919-718-2400
Gary Moore, prin. Fax 718-2410
West Lee MS 700/6-8
3301 Wicker St 27330 919-775-7351
Melvin Marshall, prin. Fax 776-3694

Central Carolina Community College Post-Sec.
1105 Kelly Dr 27330 919-775-5401
Grace Christian S 300/K-12
PO Box 1408 27331 919-774-4415
William Carver, hdmstr. Fax 718-6777
Lee Christian S 400/PK-12
3220 Keller Andrews Rd 27330 919-708-5115
Dr. Stephen Coble, prin. Fax 708-6933

Selma, Johnston, Pop. 5,974
Johnston County SD
Supt. — See Smithfield
Selma MS 400/5-8
1533 US Highway 301 N 27576 919-965-2555
John Bell, prin. Fax 202-0116

Seven Springs, Wayne, Pop. 109
Wayne County SD
Supt. — See Goldsboro
Spring Creek JSHS 900/6-12
4340 Indian Springs Rd 28578 919-751-7160
Steve Clingan, prin. Fax 751-7202

Shallotte, Brunswick, Pop. 3,616
Brunswick County SD
Supt. — See Bolivia
Shallotte MS 600/6-8
225 Village Rd SW 28470 910-754-6882
Paul Price, prin. Fax 754-3108
West Brunswick HS 1,400/9-12
550 Whiteville Rd NW 28470 910-754-4338
Brockton Ahrens, prin. Fax 754-3110

Shannon, Robeson, Pop. 263

Native American Bible College Post-Sec.
PO Box 248 28386 910-843-5304

Shelby, Cleveland, Pop. 19,999
Cleveland County SD 15,400/PK-12
130 S Post Rd Ste 2 28152 704-476-8000
Dr. Bruce Boyles, supt. Fax 476-8300
www.clevelandcountyschools.org
Cleveland Early College HS 100/9-12
137 S Post Rd 28152 704-476-8200
Dr. Anita Ware, prin. Fax 476-8300
Crest HS 1,200/9-12
800 Old Boiling Springs Rd 28152 704-482-5354
Gary Blake, prin. Fax 482-1187
Crest MS of Technology 1,000/6-8
315 Beaver Dam Church Rd 28152 704-482-0343
Amy Jones, prin. Fax 487-0378
Shelby HS 1,000/9-12
230 E Dixon Blvd 28152 704-482-3409
Jennifer Walker, prin. Fax 487-2869
Shelby MS 500/7-8
1480 S Dekalb St 28152 704-476-8328
Tim Quattlebaum, prin. Fax 487-2889
Turning Point Academy 100/Alt
910 S Post Rd 28152 704-487-6128
Rodney Borders, prin. Fax 487-6375
Other Schools – See Kings Mountain, Lawndale

Cleveland Community College Post-Sec.
137 S Post Rd 28152 704-669-6000

Siler City, Chatham, Pop. 7,749
Chatham County SD
Supt. — See Pittsboro
Chatham MS 400/5-8
2025 S 2nd Avenue Ext 27344 919-663-2414
Tracy Fowler, prin. Fax 663-2871
Jordan-Matthews HS 700/9-12
910 E Cardinal St 27344 919-742-2916
Martin McDonald, prin. Fax 742-2201
SAGE Academy 100/Alt
501 M L King Jr Blvd 27344 919-663-5899
Bobby Dixon, prin. Fax 663-3827

Smithfield, Johnston, Pop. 10,815
Johnston County SD 30,800/PK-12
PO Box 1336 27577 919-934-6031
Edward Croom Ed.D., supt. Fax 934-6035
www.johnston.k12.nc.us
Johnston County Early College Academy 100/9-9
PO Box 1336 27577 919-464-2314
Brandon Garland, prin. Fax 464-2315
Johnston County Middle College HS 100/10-12
PO Box 1336 27577 919-464-2303
Barretta Haynes, prin. Fax 464-2300
Smithfield MS 800/6-8
1455 Buffalo Rd 27577 919-934-4696
Jennifer Moore, prin. Fax 934-7552
Smithfield-Selma HS 1,400/9-12
700 E Booker Dairy Rd 27577 919-934-5191
Michael Taylor, prin. Fax 934-3001
South Campus Community S 50/Alt
PO Box 1336 27577 919-934-6481
Ersaleen Creech, prin. Fax 938-3555
Other Schools – See Benson, Clayton, Four Oaks, Garner, Kenly, Micro, Princeton, Selma, Wendell

---

Johnston Community College Post-Sec.
PO Box 2350 27577 919-934-3051

Snow Hill, Greene, Pop. 1,577
Greene County SD 2,600/PK-12
301 Kingold Blvd 28580 252-747-3425
Dr. Patrick Miller, supt. Fax 747-5942
www.gcsedu.org/
Greene Central HS 800/9-12
140 School Dr 28580 252-747-3814
Don Marr, prin. Fax 747-5972
Greene County MS 800/6-8
485 Middle School Rd 28580 252-747-8191
Dr. Lori Garrison, prin. Fax 747-8696
Greene Early College HS 100/9-12
818 Hwy 91 28580 252-747-9044
Patrick Greene, prin. Fax 747-9046

Southern Pines, Moore, Pop. 12,175
Moore County SD
Supt. — See Carthage
Pinecrest HS 2,100/9-12
250 Voit Gilmore Rd 28387 910-692-6554
Joel County, prin. Fax 692-0606

Calvary Christian S 100/K-12
400 S Bennett St 28387 910-692-8311
Dwight Creech, admin. Fax 692-1992
O'Neal S 400/PK-12
PO Box 290 28388 910-692-6920
Alan Barr, hdmstr. Fax 692-6930

Southport, Brunswick, Pop. 2,791
Brunswick County SD
Supt. — See Bolivia
South Brunswick HS 1,100/9-12
280 Cougar Rd 28461 910-845-2204
Vicky Snyder, prin. Fax 845-8974
South Brunswick MS 800/6-8
100 Cougar Rd 28461 910-845-2771
David Ruth, prin. Fax 845-8972

Sparta, Alleghany, Pop. 1,751
Alleghany County SD 1,600/PK-12
85 Peachtree St 28675 336-372-4345
Dr. Jeff Cox, supt. Fax 372-4204
www.alleghany.k12.nc.us
Alleghany HS 400/9-12
404 Trojan Ave 28675 336-372-4554
Chris Barnes, prin. Fax 372-2680

Spencer, Rowan, Pop. 3,207
Rowan-Salisbury County SD
Supt. — See Salisbury
North Rowan HS 700/9-12
300 N Whitehead Ave 28159 704-636-4420
Darrell McDowell, prin. Fax 639-3033
North Rowan MS 500/6-8
512 Charles St 28159 704-639-3018
Alexis Cowan, prin. Fax 639-3099

Spindale, Rutherford, Pop. 4,228
Rutherford County SD
Supt. — See Forest City
Rutherford Early College HS 200/9-12
PO Box 804 28160 828-395-1464
Jeremiah McCluney, prin. Fax 288-0285

Isothermal Community College Post-Sec.
PO Box 804 28160 828-286-3636
Word of Faith Christian S 100/K-12
207 Old Flynn Rd 28160 828-286-3772
Jane Whaley, admin.

Spring Hope, Nash, Pop. 1,294
Nash-Rocky Mount SD
Supt. — See Nashville
Southern Nash MS 1,100/6-8
5301 S NC Highway 581 27882 252-937-9020
Carina Bryant, prin. Fax 478-4861

Spring Lake, Cumberland, Pop. 11,305
Cumberland County SD
Supt. — See Fayetteville
Spring Lake MS 400/6-8
612 Spring Ave 28390 910-497-1175
Derek McCoy, prin. Fax 497-1598

Harnett County SD
Supt. — See Lillington
Overhills HS 1,600/9-12
2495 Ray Rd 28390 910-436-1436
Dr. Kylon Middleton, prin. Fax 436-0413
Overhills MS 1,100/6-8
2711 Ray Rd 28390 910-436-0009
Joan Wicker, prin. Fax 436-0948

Spruce Pine, Mitchell, Pop. 2,151
Mitchell County SD
Supt. — See Bakersville
Harris MS 300/6-8
121 Harris St 28777 828-766-3340
Rodney Slagle, prin. Fax 765-1595
Mayland Early College HS 100/9-12
200 Mayland Ln 28777 828-765-7351
Angela Burleson, prin. Fax 765-0720

Altapass Christian S 50/K-12
3631 Altapass Hwy 28777 828-765-0660
Debbie McKinney, prin. Fax 765-0660
Mayland Community College Post-Sec.
PO Box 547 28777 828-765-7351
Tri County Christian S 50/K-12
207 Pinebridge Ave 28777 828-765-2969
Teresa Young B.A., prin. Fax 765-0569

Stanley, Gaston, Pop. 3,517
Gaston County SD
Supt. — See Gastonia
Stanley MS 600/6-8
317 Hovis Rd 28164 704-263-2941
George Conner, prin. Fax 263-0993

Stantonsburg, Wilson, Pop. 782
Wilson County SD
Supt. — See Wilson
Speight MS 400/6-8
5514 Old Stantonsburg Rd 27883 252-238-3983
Valerie Budd, prin. Fax 238-2104

Statesville, Iredell, Pop. 24,072
Iredell-Statesville SD 20,900/K-12
PO Box 911 28687 704-872-8931
Brady Johnson, supt. Fax 871-2834
www.iss.k12.nc.us
Collaborative College for Technology 200/9-12
500 W Broad St 28677 704-978-5450
Keith Gentle, prin. Fax 878-3330
East Iredell MS 500/6-8
590 Chestnut Grove Rd 28625 704-872-4666
Jimmy Elliott, prin. Fax 873-6602
Monticello S 100/Alt
435 Monticello Rd 28625 704-872-5297
Beth Bradley, prin. Fax 924-8814
Northview IB S 400/6-9
625 N Carolina Ave 28677 704-873-7354
Tim Ivey, prin. Fax 873-6149
Pressly S 100/Alt
222 Knox St 28677 704-872-7606
Sheila Alston, prin. Fax 838-0839
South Iredell HS 900/9-12
299 Old Mountain Rd 28677 704-528-4536
Aron Gabriel, prin. Fax 528-0882
Statesville HS 1,100/9-12
474 N Center St 28677 704-873-3491
Garriot Rose, prin. Fax 878-6195
Statesville MS 400/6-8
321 Clegg St 28677 704-872-2135
Billy Thompson, prin. Fax 871-9279
Visual & Performing Arts HS 9-12
474 N Center St 28677 704-978-0034
Lisa Miller, prin. Fax 978-0035
West Iredell HS 1,000/9-12
213 Warrior Dr 28625 704-873-2181
Todd Holden, prin. Fax 873-0356
West Iredell MS 800/6-8
303 Watermelon Rd 28625 704-873-2887
Lucille Asbury, prin. Fax 881-0582
Other Schools – See Mooresville, Olin, Troutman

Crossroads Christian S of Statesville 50/PK-PK, 4-
1950 Salisbury Hwy 28677 704-871-1515
Anne Wooten, admin.
Mitchell Community College Post-Sec.
500 W Broad St 28677 704-878-3200
Southview Christian S 100/K-12
625 Wallace Springs Rd 28677 704-872-9554
Walter Wagner, prin. Fax 872-4359
Statesville Christian S 300/PK-12
1210 Museum Rd 28625 704-873-9511
Dirk Mroczek, hdmstr. Fax 873-0841

Stem, Granville, Pop. 446
Granville County SD
Supt. — See Oxford
Granville Central HS 700/9-12
2043 Sanders Rd 27581 919-528-5530
Brian Mathis, prin. Fax 528-5574

Sugar Grove, Watauga

Jung Tao School of Chinese Medicine Post-Sec.
207 Dale Adams Rd 28679 828-297-4181

Supply, Brunswick
Brunswick County SD
Supt. — See Bolivia
Cedar Grove MS 500/6-8
750 Grove Trl SW 28462 910-846-3400
Rhonda Benton, prin. Fax 846-3401

Brunswick Community College Post-Sec.
PO Box 30 28462 910-755-7300

Swannanoa, Buncombe, Pop. 4,465
Buncombe County SD
Supt. — See Asheville
Community HS 200/Alt
235 Old US 70 Hwy 28778 828-686-7734
Clifford Owens, prin. Fax 686-7834
Owen MS 600/6-8
730 Old US 70 Hwy 28778 828-686-7739
Gayland Welborn, prin. Fax 686-7938

Asheville Christian Academy 600/PK-12
PO Box 1089 28778 828-581-2200
Dr. William George, head sch Fax 581-2218

Swanquarter, Hyde, Pop. 313
Hyde County SD 400/PK-12
PO Box 217 27885 252-926-3281
Dr. Randolph Latimore, supt. Fax 926-3083
www.hyde.k12.nc.us/
Hyde County Early College HS 50/6-12
20346 US Highway 264 27885 252-926-1098
Thomas Midgette, prin. Fax 926-0700
Other Schools – See Ocracoke

Swansboro, Onslow, Pop. 2,580
Onslow County SD
Supt. — See Jacksonville
Swansboro HS 1,000/9-12
161 Queens Creek Rd 28584 910-326-4300
Christine Andre, prin. Fax 326-1674
Swansboro MS 900/6-8
1240 W Corbett Ave 28584 910-326-3601
Brendan Gartner, prin. Fax 326-5848

Sylva, Jackson, Pop. 2,551
Jackson County SD 3,600/PK-12
398 Hospital Rd 28779 828-586-2311
Dr. Michael Murray, supt. Fax 586-5450
www.jcps.k12.nc.us
Jackson County Early College 100/9-12
447 College Dr 28779 828-339-4235
Raylene Bryson, prin.
School of Alternatives 100/Alt
3770 Skyland Dr 28779 828-586-4328
Dr. Beverly VanHook, prin. Fax 586-2490
Smoky Mountain HS 800/9-12
100 Smoky Mountain Dr 28779 828-586-2177
Jake Buchanan, prin. Fax 586-2374
Other Schools – See Cashiers

Southwestern Community College Post-Sec.
447 College Dr 28779 828-339-4000

Tabor City, Columbus, Pop. 2,463
Columbus County SD
Supt. — See Whiteville
South Columbus HS 800/9-12
40 Stallion Dr 28463 910-653-4073
Eddie Beck, prin. Fax 653-9461
Tabor City MS 200/6-8
701 W 6th St 28463 910-653-3637
Dianna Bellamy, prin. Fax 653-2093

Tarboro, Edgecombe, Pop. 11,342
Edgecombe County SD 7,400/PK-12
PO Box 7128 27886 252-641-2600
John Farrelly, supt. Fax 641-5714
www.ecps.us/
Edgecombe Early College HS 100/9-12
2009 W Wilson St 27886 252-823-5166
Dr. Katrenna Rich, prin. Fax 823-2053
Martin MS 400/7-8
400 E Johnston St 27886 252-641-5710
Bernadine Lewis, prin. Fax 641-5713
North Edgecombe HS 400/9-12
7589 NC Highway 33 NW 27886 252-823-3562
Robert Batts, prin. Fax 823-7847
Tarboro HS 700/9-12
1400 W Howard Ave 27886 252-823-4284
Dr. Michael Turner, prin. Fax 823-0862
Other Schools – See Battleboro, Pinetops, Rocky Mount

Edgecombe Community College Post-Sec.
2009 W Wilson St 27886 252-823-5166

Tar Heel, Bladen, Pop. 115
Bladen County SD
Supt. — See Elizabethtown
Tar Heel MS 300/5-8
PO Box 128 28392 910-862-2475
Clarissa Kelly, prin. Fax 872-5599

Taylorsville, Alexander, Pop. 2,066
Alexander County SD 5,500/PK-12
700 Liledoun Rd 28681 828-632-7001
Dr. Brock Womble, supt. Fax 632-8862
www.alexander.k12.nc.us
Alexander Central HS 1,700/9-12
223 School Dr 28681 828-632-7063
Doug Rhoney, prin. Fax 632-5387
West Alexander MS 600/6-8
85 Bulldog Ln 28681 828-495-4611
Dr. Chad Maynor, prin. Fax 495-3527
Other Schools – See Hiddenite

Teachey, Duplin, Pop. 375
Duplin County SD
Supt. — See Kenansville
Wallace-Rose Hill HS 500/9-12
602 High School Rd 28464 910-285-7501
M.D. Guthrie, prin. Fax 285-1116

Thomasville, Davidson, Pop. 26,312
Davidson County SD
Supt. — See Lexington
Brown MS 800/6-8
1140 Kendall Mill Rd 27360 336-475-8845
Randy Holmes, prin. Fax 475-3842
Davidson Early College HS 100/9-12
297 DCCC Rd 27360 336-242-5686
Dr. Larry Allred, prin. Fax 242-5688
East Davidson HS 1,000/9-12
1408 Lake Rd 27360 336-476-4814
Billy Hunt, prin. Fax 476-2982
Ledford HS 1,200/9-12
140 Jesse Green Rd 27360 336-769-9671
Jonathan Brown, prin. Fax 769-0650
Ledford MS 1,000/6-8
3954 N NC Highway 109 27360 336-476-4816
Sloan Denny, prin. Fax 476-1479

Thomasville CSD 2,500/PK-12
400 Turner St 27360 336-474-4200
Keith Tobin, supt. Fax 475-0356
www.tcs.k12.nc.us
Thomasville HS 700/9-12
410 Unity St 27360 336-474-4250
Deboy Beamon, prin. Fax 476-7430
Thomasville MS 600/6-8
400 Unity St 27360 336-474-4120
Matthew Pugh, prin. Fax 472-5081

Carolina Christian Academy 100/K-12
367 Academy Dr 27360 336-472-8950
Daniel Lee, prin. Fax 472-8920

Topton, Macon
Macon County SD
Supt. — See Franklin
Nantahala S 100/K-12
213 Winding Stairs Rd 28781 828-321-4388
James Bryan, prin. Fax 321-4834

Trenton, Jones, Pop. 270
Jones County SD 1,300/PK-12
320 W Jones St 28585 252-448-2531
Michael Bracy, supt. Fax 448-1394
www.jonesnc.net
Jones HS 300/9-12
1490 NC Highway 58 S 28585 252-448-2451
Christopher Meadows, prin. Fax 448-1034
Jones MS 200/7-8
190 Old New Bern Rd 28585 252-448-3956
Michael White, prin. Fax 448-1044

Trinity, Randolph, Pop. 6,568
Randolph County SD
Supt. — See Asheboro
Archdale-Trinity MS 800/7-8
PO Box 232 27370 336-431-2589
Andrea Haynes, prin. Fax 431-1809
Trinity HS 700/9-12
5746 Trinity High School Dr 27370 336-861-6870
Brad Phillips, prin. Fax 861-8613
Uwharrie MS 400/6-8
1463 Pleasant Union Rd 27370 336-241-3900
Kenneth Cox, prin. Fax 241-3904
Wheatmore HS 800/9-12
3678 Finch Farm Rd 27370 336-476-1500
Eric Johnson, prin. Fax 476-1520

Troutman, Iredell, Pop. 2,323
Iredell-Statesville SD
Supt. — See Statesville
Troutman MS 400/6-8
305 Rumple St 28166 704-528-5137
Jeff James, prin. Fax 528-4006

Troy, Montgomery, Pop. 3,135
Montgomery County SD 4,300/PK-12
PO Box 427 27371 910-576-6511
Dr. Dale Ellis, supt. Fax 576-2044
www.montgomery.k12.nc.us
Montgomery Learning Academy 100/Alt
310 S Main St 27371 910-572-1161
Todd Beane, prin. Fax 572-2362
Other Schools – See Biscoe, Mount Gilead

Montgomery Community College Post-Sec.
1011 Page St 27371 910-576-6222
Wescare Christian Academy 100/K-12
1368 NC Hwy 134 N 27371 910-572-2270
Ann Morgan, admin. Fax 572-2257

Tyner, Chowan
Edenton/Chowan County SD
Supt. — See Edenton
Chowan MS 500/6-8
2845 Virginia Rd 27980 252-221-4131
Tanya Turner, prin. Fax 221-8033

Valdese, Burke, Pop. 4,425
Burke County SD
Supt. — See Morganton
Draughn HS 800/9-12
709 Lovelady Rd NE 28690 828-879-4200
Emily Garrison, prin. Fax 879-4201
Heritage MS 600/6-8
1951 Enon Rd 28690 828-874-0731
Ross Rumbaugh, prin. Fax 879-6330

Vanceboro, Craven, Pop. 972
Craven County SD
Supt. — See New Bern
West Craven HS 1,100/9-12
2600 Streets Ferry Rd 28586 252-244-3200
Karen Barrow, prin. Fax 244-3207

Wadesboro, Anson, Pop. 5,742
Anson County SD 3,800/K-12
320 Camden Rd 28170 704-694-4417
Dr. Gregory Firn, supt. Fax 694-7470
www.ansonschools.org/
Anson Academy 100/Alt
320 Camden Rd 28170 704-994-9284
Preston Waddell, prin. Fax 944-9104
Anson HS 800/9-12
96 Anson High School Rd 28170 704-694-9301
Charles Murphy, prin. Fax 694-4570
Anson MS 500/7-8
832 US Highway 52 N 28170 704-694-3945
Joshua McLaurin, prin. Fax 694-5209
Anson New Technology HS 100/9-12
118 W Ashe St 28170 704-694-7447
Chris Stinson, prin. Fax 694-7447
Other Schools – See Polkton

Wake Forest, Wake, Pop. 29,480
Wake County SD
Supt. — See Raleigh
Heritage HS 9-12
1150 Forestville Rd 27587 919-570-5600
Mark Savage, prin. Fax 570-5650
Heritage MS 1,400/6-8
3400 Rogers Rd 27587 919-562-6204
Christopher McCabe, prin. Fax 562-6227
Wake Forest-Rolesville HS 2,100/9-12
420 Stadium Dr 27587 919-554-8611
Thomas Dixon, prin. Fax 554-8617
Wake Forest-Rolesville MS 1,200/6-8
1800 S Main St 27587 919-554-8440
Stacey Weddle, prin. Fax 554-8435

Southeastern Baptist Theological Sem. Post-Sec.
PO Box 1889 27588 919-761-2100
Thales Academy of Wake Forest JHS 100/6-9
3121 Heritage Trade Dr #104 27587 919-435-2715
Melissa Edwards, admin. Fax 453-0484

Walkertown, Forsyth, Pop. 4,605
Winston-Salem/Forsyth SD
Supt. — See Winston Salem
Walkertown MSHS 600/6-12
5240 Sullivantown Rd 27051 336-703-4151
Piper Hendrix, prin. Fax 595-1372

Walnut Cove, Stokes, Pop. 1,407
Stokes County SD
Supt. — See Danbury
Southeastern Stokes MS 500/6-8
1044 N Main St 27052 336-591-4371
Rhonda Jackson, prin. Fax 591-8164
South Stokes HS 700/9-12
1100 S Stokes High Dr 27052 336-994-2995
Rich Pekar, prin. Fax 994-2608
Stokes Early College HS 100/9-12
1165 Dodgetown Rd 27052 336-593-5402
Kim Marion, prin. Fax 593-2501

Warrensville, Ashe
Ashe County SD
Supt. — See Jefferson
Ashe County MS 500/7-8
PO Box 259 28693 336-384-3591
Earl Pennington, prin. Fax 384-2112

Warrenton, Warren, Pop. 855
Warren County SD 2,600/PK-12
PO Box 110 27589 252-257-3184
Dr. Ray Spain, supt. Fax 257-5357
www.warrenk12nc.org/
Warren County HS 500/9-12
149 Campus Dr 27589 252-257-4413
Warren Keith Bell, prin. Fax 257-1019
Warren County MS 600/6-8
118 Campus Dr 27589 252-257-3751
Wray Cannaday, prin. Fax 257-4532
Warren Early College HS 100/9-12
PO Box 110 27589 252-738-3598
Ryan Hurley, prin. Fax 257-5357
Warren New Tech HS 200/9-12
219 US Highway 158 Byp 27589 252-257-3767
Iris Dethmers, prin. Fax 257-1266

Warsaw, Duplin, Pop. 3,022
Duplin County SD
Supt. — See Kenansville
Kenan HS 500/9-12
1241 NC Highway 24 50 28398 910-293-4218
Michael Holton, prin. Fax 293-6744
Warsaw MS 200/6-8
738 W College St 28398 910-293-7997
Kenneth Houston, prin. Fax 293-7397

Washington, Beaufort, Pop. 9,614
Beaufort County SD 7,200/PK-12
321 Smaw Rd 27889 252-946-6593
Dr. Donald Phipps, supt. Fax 946-3255
www.beaufort.k12.nc.us
B.C. Education Technical Center 100/Alt
820 N Bridge St 27889 252-946-5382
Will Bryant, prin. Fax 946-7964
Beaufort County Early College HS 100/9-12
5337 US Highway 264 E 27889 252-940-6227
Emily Pake, prin. Fax 975-2752
Jones MS 800/6-8
4105 Market Street Ext 27889 252-946-0874
Tracey Nixon, prin. Fax 946-7604
Washington HS 1,000/9-12
400 Slatestone Rd 27889 252-946-0858
Russell Holloman, prin. Fax 946-9633
Other Schools – See Chocowinity, Pinetown

Beaufort County Community College Post-Sec.
PO Box 1069 27889 252-946-6194

Waxhaw, Union, Pop. 9,622
Union County SD
Supt. — See Monroe
Cuthbertson HS 1,000/9-12
1400 Cuthbertson Rd 28173 704-296-0105
Kim Warr, prin. Fax 843-3565
Cuthbertson MS 1,000/6-8
1520 Cuthbertson Rd 28173 704-296-0107
Scott Sofsian, prin. Fax 243-1673
Marvin Ridge HS 1,300/9-12
2825 Crane Rd 28173 704-290-1520
Tim Connor, prin. Fax 243-0012
Marvin Ridge MS 1,200/6-8
2831 Crane Rd 28173 704-290-1510
Scott Broome, prin. Fax 243-0153
South Providence Alternative S 100/Alt
500 S Providence St 28173 704-290-1580
Barry Ross, prin. Fax 843-5708

Waynesville, Haywood, Pop. 9,753
Haywood County SD 7,700/K-12
1230 N Main St 28786 828-456-2400
Anne Garrett, supt. Fax 456-2438
www.haywood.k12.nc.us
Bethel MS 300/6-8
630 Sonoma Rd 28786 828-646-3442
Shawn Parris, prin. Fax 648-6259
Tuscola HS 1,100/9-12
564 Tuscola School Rd 28786 828-456-2408
Dale McDonald, prin. Fax 456-2434
Waynesville MS 900/6-8
495 Brown Ave 28786 828-456-2403
Trevor Putnam, prin. Fax 452-7905
Other Schools – See Canton, Clyde

Weaverville, Buncombe, Pop. 3,037
Buncombe County SD
Supt. — See Asheville
North Buncombe HS 1,200/9-12
890 Clarks Chapel Rd 28787 828-645-4221
Jack Evans, prin. Fax 645-4367
North Buncombe MS 600/7-8
51 N Buncombe School Rd 28787 828-645-7944
Sherry Barnette, prin. Fax 645-2509

Weldon, Halifax, Pop. 1,616
Weldon CSD 1,100/PK-12
301 Mulberry St 27890 252-536-4821
Dr. Elie Bracy, supt. Fax 536-3062
district.weldoncityschools.org/
Roanoke Valley Early College 100/9-12
100 College Dr Bldg 600 27890 252-536-6364
Dr. Monica Smith-Woofter, prin.
Weldon HS 300/9-12
415 County Rd 27890 252-536-4829
Michelle Burton, prin. Fax 536-0168
Other Schools – See Halifax

Halifax Community College Post-Sec.
PO Box 809 27890 252-536-4221

Wendell, Wake, Pop. 5,709
Johnston County SD
Supt. — See Smithfield
Archer Lodge MS 900/6-8
740 Wendell Rd 27591 919-553-0714
Betsy Huddleston, prin. Fax 553-8540
Corinth Holders HS 9-12
6875 Applewhite Rd 27591 919-365-4306
Charles Ferrell, prin. Fax 365-4344

Wake County SD
Supt. — See Raleigh
East Wake HS of Health Science 400/9-12
5101 Rolesville Rd 27591 919-365-2652
Martha McCaskill, prin. Fax 365-2717
East Wake S of Arts Education Global Std 400/9-12
5101 Rolesville Rd 27591 919-365-2642
Ericka Lucas, prin. Fax 365-2717
East Wake S of Engineering Systems 400/9-12
5101 Rolesville Rd 27591 919-365-2629
Sebastian Shipp, prin. Fax 365-2628
East Wake S of Integrated Technology 300/9-12
5101 Rolesville Rd 27591 919-365-2625
Ritchie Bazzell, prin. Fax 365-2658
Wendell MS 900/6-8
3409 NC 97 Hwy 27591 919-365-1667
Mary Castleberry, prin. Fax 365-1686

Wentworth, Rockingham, Pop. 2,774
Rockingham County SD
Supt. — See Eden
Rockingham County Early College HS 200/9-12
310 Wrenn Memorial Rd 27375 336-342-4261
Diane Hill, prin. Fax 349-9986

Rockingham Community College Post-Sec.
PO Box 38 27375 336-342-4261

West End, Moore
Moore County SD
Supt. — See Carthage
West Pine MS 800/6-8
144 Archie Rd 27376 910-673-1464
Dr. Candace Turk, prin. Fax 673-1272

West Jefferson, Ashe, Pop. 1,280
Ashe County SD
Supt. — See Jefferson
Ashe County HS 900/9-12
PO Box 450 28694 336-846-2400
Jason Krider, prin. Fax 846-2411

Whiteville, Columbus, Pop. 5,303
Columbus County SD 6,400/PK-12
PO Box 729 28472 910-642-5168
Alan Faulk, supt. Fax 640-1010
www.columbus.k12.nc.us/
Columbus Career & College Acad - SCC 9-12
PO Box 151 28472 910-642-7141
Nicky Hobbs, prin. Fax 642-7693
Other Schools – See Cerro Gordo, Chadbourn, Delco, Fair Bluff, Hallsboro, Lake Waccamaw, Nakina, Tabor City

Whiteville CSD 2,300/PK-12
PO Box 609 28472 910-642-4116
Dr. C.T. Hager, supt. Fax 642-0564
www.whiteville.k12.nc.us
Central MS 600/6-8
310 S Mrtn Lthr King Jr Ave 28472 910-642-3546
Chris Burton, prin. Fax 642-7484
North Whiteville Academy 50/Alt
310 S Martin Luther King Jr 28472 910-914-4161
Susan Smith, dir. Fax 914-4164
Whiteville HS 600/9-12
413 N Lee St 28472 910-914-4189
Jes Sealey, prin. Fax 914-4186

Carolina Adventist Academy 50/K-12
PO Box 1937 28472 910-640-0855
Karen Taylor, prin. Fax 640-1062
Columbus Christian Academy 200/K-12
PO Box 1100 28472 910-642-6196
Sam Hinson, admin. Fax 642-3066
Southeastern Community College Post-Sec.
PO Box 151 28472 910-642-7141

Wilkesboro, Wilkes, Pop. 3,340
Wilkes County SD
Supt. — See North Wilkesboro
West Wilkes MS 600/6-8
1677 N NC Highway 16 28697 336-973-1700
Dion Stocks, prin. Fax 973-7423
Wilkes Central HS 900/9-12
1179 Moravian Falls Rd 28697 336-667-5277
Michelle Shepherd, prin. Fax 667-2091
Wilkes Early College HS 100/9-12
1328 S Collegiate Dr # 800 28697 336-838-6247
Christopher Jones, prin.

Wilkes Community College Post-Sec.
PO Box 120 28697 336-838-6100

Williamston, Martin, Pop. 5,452
Martin County SD 3,300/PK-12
300 N Watts St 27892 252-792-1575
Dr. Ron Melchiorre, supt. Fax 792-1965
martin.sharpschool.net/
Riverside HS 9-12
1260 Godwin Dr 27892 252-792-7881
Clay Wagner, prin. Fax 809-4807
Riverside MS 400/6-8
2920 US Highway 17 27892 252-792-1111
Ronald Byrd, prin. Fax 792-6644
Other Schools – See Jamesville, Robersonville

Martin Community College Post-Sec.
1161 Kehukee Park Rd 27892 252-792-1521

Wilmington, New Hanover, Pop. 104,394
New Hanover County SD 24,200/PK-12
6410 Carolina Beach Rd 28412 910-763-5431
Dr. Tim Markley, supt. Fax 254-4479
www.nhcs.net
Ashley HS 1,700/9-12
555 Halyburton Memorial Pky 28412 910-790-2360
Kenneth Bowen, prin. Fax 790-2356
Bear Early College HS 200/9-12
630 MacMillan Ave N 28403 910-350-1387
Philip Sutton, prin. Fax 350-1392
Hoggard HS 1,800/9-12
4305 Shipyard Blvd 28403 910-350-2072
Eric Pfirman, prin. Fax 350-2066
Laney HS 1,800/9-12
2700 N College Rd 28405 910-350-2089
Allen O'Briant, prin. Fax 350-2083
Mosley Performance Learning Center 50/9-12
3702 Princess Place Dr 28405 910-251-6161
Dr. Jerry Oates, prin. Fax 251-6022
Murray MS 800/6-8
655 Halyburton Memorial Pky 28412 910-790-2363
Patrick McCarty, prin. Fax 790-2351
Myrtle Grove MS 800/6-8
901 Piner Rd 28409 910-350-2100
Sam Highsmith, prin. Fax 350-2104
New Hanover HS 1,600/9-12
1307 Market St 28401 910-251-6100
Todd Finn, prin. Fax 251-6114
Noble MS 600/6-8
6520 Market St 28405 910-350-2112
Wade Smith, prin. Fax 350-2109
Roland-Grise MS 900/6-8
4412 Lake Ave 28403 910-350-2136
William Hatch, prin. Fax 350-2133

Trask MS 700/6-8
2900 N College Rd 28405 910-350-2142
Sharon Dousharm, prin. Fax 350-2144
Williston MS 700/6-8
401 S 10th St 28401 910-815-6906
Dr. Sherry Veasey, prin. Fax 815-6904
Other Schools – See Castle Hayne

Cape Fear Academy 600/PK-12
3900 S College Rd 28412 910-791-0287
Donald Berger, hdmstr. Fax 791-0290
Cape Fear Community College Post-Sec.
411 N Front St 28401 910-362-7000
Coastal Christian HS 100/9-12
1150 the Kings Hwy 28409 910-395-9995
Gabriel Pethtel, admin. Fax 395-9901
College of Wilmington Post-Sec.
3500 Oleander Dr Ste 1111 28403 910-763-4418
Miller-Motte College Post-Sec.
5000 Market St 28405 910-392-4660
New Hanover Regional Medical Center Post-Sec.
2131 S 17th St 28401 910-343-7074
University of North Carolina Post-Sec.
601 S College Rd 28403 910-962-3000
Wilmington Christian Academy 800/PK-12
1401 N College Rd 28405 910-791-4248
Barren Nobles M.S., admin. Fax 791-4276

Wilson, Wilson, Pop. 48,488
Wilson County SD 12,200/PK-12
PO Box 2048 27894 252-399-7700
Sean Bulson, supt. Fax 399-2776
www.wilsonschoolsnc.net
Beddingfield HS 900/9-12
4510 Old Stantonsburg Rd 27893 252-399-7880
Nelson Johnston, prin. Fax 399-7850
Daniels Learning Center 100/Alt
723 Elvie St S 27893 252-399-7900
Anita Wright, prin. Fax 399-7892
Darden MS 300/6-8
1665 Lipscomb Rd E 27893 252-206-4973
Fate Franks, prin. Fax 206-1508
Fike HS 1,200/9-12
500 Harrison Dr N 27893 252-399-7905
Dr. Steve Ellis, prin. Fax 399-7893
Forest Hills MS 600/6-8
1210 Forest Hills Rd NW 27896 252-399-7913
Joyce Best, prin. Fax 399-7894
Hunt HS 1,300/9-12
4559 Lamm Rd SW 27893 252-399-7930
Jerry Simmons, prin. Fax 399-7897
Toisnot MS 500/6-8
1301 Corbett Ave N 27893 252-399-7973
Michael Kennedy, prin. Fax 399-7749
Wilson Early College Academy 100/9-12
PO Box 4305 27893 252-291-1195
Robin Gasque, prin. Fax 243-7148
Other Schools – See Elm City, Lucama, Stantonsburg

Barton College Post-Sec.
PO Box 5000 27893 252-399-6300
Community Christian S 400/PK-12
5160 Packhouse Rd 27896 252-399-1376
Paula Webb, admin. Fax 243-6973
Eastern North Carolina Sch. for the Deaf Post-Sec.
1311 US Highway 301 S 27893 252-237-2450
Greenfield S 300/PK-12
3351 NC Highway 42 W 27893 252-237-8046
Fax 237-1825
Mitchell's Hairstyling Academy Post-Sec.
2620 Forest Hills Rd #A 27893 252-243-3158
Wilson Christian Academy 500/PK-12
PO Box 3818 27895 252-237-8064
Wilson Community College Post-Sec.
PO Box 4305 27893 252-291-1195

Windsor, Bertie, Pop. 3,573
Bertie County SD 2,900/PK-12
PO Box 10 27983 252-794-6000
Elaine White, supt. Fax 794-9727
www.bertie.k12.nc.us
Bertie Early College HS 100/9-12
819B Governors Rd 27983 252-794-2150
Andrew Harris, prin. Fax 794-3407
Bertie HS 600/9-12
715 US Highway 13 N 27983 252-794-3034
Calvin Moore, prin. Fax 794-1932
Bertie MS 600/6-8
652 US Highway 13 N 27983 252-794-2143
Carson Watford, prin. Fax 794-4024
Bertie STEM HS 200/9-12
715 US Highway 13 N 27983 252-794-5820
Deborah Carroll, prin. Fax 794-5815

Bethel Assembly Christian Academy 200/PK-12
105 Askewville Bryant St 27983 252-794-4034

Winfall, Perquimans, Pop. 587
Perquimans County SD
Supt. — See Hertford
Perquimans County MS 400/6-8
PO Box 39 27985 252-426-7355
Fax 426-1424

Wingate, Union, Pop. 3,424

Wingate University Post-Sec.
220 N Camden Rd 28174 704-233-8000

Winston Salem, Forsyth, Pop. 225,143
Davidson County SD
Supt. — See Lexington
Oak Grove MS 6-8
1771 Hoy Long Rd 27107 336-249-8182
Chris Johnston, prin. Fax 474-8257

Winston-Salem/Forsyth SD 51,400/PK-12
PO Box 2513 27102 336-727-2816
Dr. Donald Martin, supt. Fax 661-6572
wsfcs.k12.nc.us
Atkins Academic Technology HS 9-12
3605 Old Greensboro Rd 27101 336-703-6754
Joe Childers, prin. Fax 748-3565
Career Center Vo/Tech
910 Highland Ct 27101 336-727-8181
Dr. Dennis Moser, prin. Fax 727-7607
Carter HS Vo/Tech
851 Highland Ct 27101 336-703-4119
Donna Horton, prin. Fax 631-1885
Carver HS 600/9-12
3545 Carver School Rd 27105 336-727-2987
Ronald Travis, prin. Fax 727-8211
Clemmons MS 800/6-8
3785 Fraternity Church Rd 27127 336-774-4677
Sandra Hunter, prin. Fax 774-4678
Early College of Forsyth County 9-12
2100 Silas Creek Pkwy 27103 336-757-3290
Frances Cook, prin. Fax 734-7467
Flat Rock MS, 4648 Ebert Rd 27127 800/6-8
Becky Hodges, prin. 336-703-6762
Forsyth Middle College HS 100/9-12
2100 Silas Creek Pkwy 27103 336-734-7437
William Wynn, prin.
Hanes MS 1,100/6-8
2900 Indiana Ave 27105 336-727-2252
Melita Wise, prin. Fax 727-3207
Jacket Academy 100/9-12
3545 Carver School Rd 27105 336-727-2772
Ronald Travis, prin.
Jefferson MS 1,200/6-8
3500 Sally Kirk Rd 27106 336-774-4630
Brad Royal, prin. Fax 774-4635
Kennedy HS 50/9-12
890 E 11th St 27101 336-703-4143
Leslie Atcher, prin. Fax 727-8559
Kingswood S 50/Alt
1001 Reynolda Rd 27104 336-703-4128
Ted Burcaw, prin.
Main Street Academy Alt
2700 S Main St 27127 336-771-4500
Spencer Hardy, prin. Fax 771-4706
Meadowlark MS 1,000/6-8
301 Meadowlark Dr 27106 336-922-1700
Sharon Richardson, prin. Fax 922-1745
Mineral Springs MS 500/6-8
4559 Ogburn Ave 27105 336-703-6733
Danyelle Parker, prin. Fax 661-4857
Mt. Tabor HS 1,700/9-12
342 Petree Rd 27106 336-703-6700
Ed Weiss, prin. Fax 774-4606
North Forsyth HS 1,200/9-12
5705 Shattalon Dr 27105 336-661-4880
Rodney Bass, prin. Fax 661-4869
Northwest MS 900/6-8
5501 Murray Rd 27106 336-924-5126
Ingrid Medlock, prin. Fax 924-5128
Paisley MS 700/6-10
1400 Grant Ave 27105 336-727-2775
Dr. Gary Cone, prin. Fax 727-8315
Parkland HS 1,400/9-12
1600 Brewer Rd 27127 336-771-4700
Dr. Tim Lee, prin. Fax 771-4703
Philo-Hill MS 300/6-8
410 Haverhill St 27127 336-703-4165
Mark Hairston, prin. Fax 771-4737
Reynolds HS 1,700/9-12
301 N Hawthorne Rd 27104 336-703-4145
David Small, prin. Fax 727-2053
Wiley MS 500/6-8
1400 W Northwest Blvd 27104 336-727-2378
Sean Gaillard, prin. Fax 727-8412
Winston-Salem Preparatory Academy 400/6-12
1215 N Cameron Ave 27101 336-703-6732
Richard Watts, prin. Fax 727-2931
Other Schools – See Clemmons, Kernersville, Pfafftown, Walkertown

---

Calvary Baptist Day S 800/PK-12
5000 Country Club Rd 27104 336-765-5546
Guy Hipp, head sch Fax 714-5577
Carolina Christian College Post-Sec.
PO Box 777 27102 336-774-0900
First Assembly Christian S 300/PK-12
3730 University Pkwy 27106 336-759-7762
Dr. Liz Ashby, admin. Fax 896-7667
Forsyth Technical Community College Post-Sec.
2100 Silas Creek Pkwy 27103 336-723-0371
Gospel Light Christian S 500/PK-12
4940 Gospel Light Church Rd 27101 336-722-6100
Living Arts Institute Post-Sec.
1100 S Stratford Rd 27103 336-774-7600
Piedmont Baptist College & Graduate Sch Post-Sec.
420 S Broad St 27101 336-725-8344
Salem Academy 200/9-12
500 E Salem Ave 27101 336-721-2643
Karl Sjolund, head sch Fax 917-5340
Salem Baptist Christian S 400/PK-12
429 S Broad St 27101 336-725-6113
Martha Drake, hdmstr. Fax 725-8455
Salem College Post-Sec.
601 S Church St 27101 800-327-2536
University of NC School of the Arts Post-Sec.
1533 S Main St 27127 336-770-3399
Wake Forest University Post-Sec.
1834 Wake Forest Rd 27109 336-758-5000
Winston-Salem Barber School Post-Sec.
1531 Silas Creek Pkwy 27127 336-724-1459
Winston-Salem State University Post-Sec.
601 S Mrtn Lther King Jr Dr 27110 336-750-2000
Woodland Baptist Christian S 200/PK-12
1175 Bethania Rural Hall Rd 27106 336-969-2088

Winterville, Pitt, Pop. 9,094
Pitt County SD
Supt. — See Greenville
Cox MS 1,100/6-8
2657 Church St 28590 252-756-3105
Tracy Cole, prin. Fax 756-1081
South Central HS 1,600/9-12
570 Forlines Rd 28590 252-321-3232
Julie Cary, prin. Fax 321-7909

Winton, Hertford, Pop. 760
Hertford County SD 3,300/PK-12
PO Box 158 27986 252-358-1761
Dr. Michael Perry, supt. Fax 358-4745
www.hertford.k12.nc.us
Brown Student Development Center 50/Alt
102 C S Brown Dr 27986 252-358-2852
Keisha Peele, prin. Fax 358-0121
Other Schools – See Ahoskie, Murfreesboro

Yadkinville, Yadkin, Pop. 2,941
Yadkin County SD 6,100/PK-12
121 Washington St 27055 336-679-2051
Dr. Stewart Hobbs, supt. Fax 679-4013
www.yadkin.k12.nc.us
Yadkin Early College HS 200/9-12
121 Washington St 27055 336-679-4600
Tracy Kimmer, prin. Fax 679-3210
Yadkin Success Academy 50/Alt
733 E Main St 27055 336-679-4888
Mary Catherine Berry, prin. Fax 679-6623
Other Schools – See Boonville, East Bend

Yanceyville, Caswell, Pop. 1,971
Caswell County SD 3,000/PK-12
PO Box 160 27379 336-694-4116
Dr. Douglas Barker, supt. Fax 694-5154
www.caswell.k12.nc.us/
Bartlett Yancey HS 900/9-12
PO Box 190 27379 336-694-4212
Dr. Precilla Stone, prin. Fax 694-5285
Dillard MS 700/6-8
PO Box 310 27379 336-694-4941
Lamont Dixon, prin. Fax 694-6353

Youngsville, Franklin, Pop. 1,142
Franklin County SD
Supt. — See Louisburg
Cedar Creek MS 800/6-8
2228 Cedar Creek Rd 27596 919-554-4848
Dr. Laverne Daniels, prin. Fax 570-5143

American Institute of Applied Science Post-Sec.
100 Hunter Pl 27596 919-554-2500

Zebulon, Wake, Pop. 4,340
Wake County SD
Supt. — See Raleigh
Zebulon MS 600/6-8
1000 Shepard School Rd 27597 919-404-3630
Dalphine Perry, prin. Fax 404-3651

Heritage Christian Academy 100/K-12
615 Mack Todd Rd 27597 919-269-6915
Joel Dupree, admin.

NORTH DAKOTA

NORTH DAKOTA DEPT. OF PUBLIC INSTRUCTION
600 E Boulevard Ave, Bismarck 58505-0601
Telephone 701-328-2260
Fax 701-328-2461
Website http://www.dpi.state.nd.us

Superintendent of Public Instruction Kirsten Baesler

NORTH DAKOTA BOARD OF EDUCATION
600 E Boulevard Ave, Bismarck 58505-0601

COUNTY SUPERINTENDENTS OF SCHOOLS

Adams County Office of Education
Patricia Carroll, supt. 701-567-4363
PO Box 589, Hettinger 58639 Fax 567-2910

Barnes County Office of Education
Beth Didier, supt. 701-845-6666
230 4th St NW Rm 202
Valley City 58072

Benson County Office of Education
Lucia Jacobson, supt. 701-473-5370
PO Box 347, Minnewaukan 58351 Fax 473-5571

Billings County Office of Education
Joan Jurgens, supt. 701-623-4377
PO Box 168, Medora 58645 Fax 623-4896

Bottineau County Office of Education
Ann Monson, supt. 701-228-2035
314 5th St W Ste 8A Fax 228-3658
Bottineau 58318

Bowman County Office of Education
Christine Septon, supt. 701-523-3478
PO Box 380, Bowman 58623 Fax 523-3428

Burke County Office of Education
Jeanine Jensen, supt. 701-377-2861
PO Box 310, Bowbells 58721 Fax 377-2020

Burleigh County Office of Education
Karen Kautzmann, supt. 701-667-3315
210 2nd Ave NW, Mandan 58554 Fax 667-3348
www.co.burleigh.nd.us

Cass County Office of Education
Mike Montplaisir, supt. 701-241-5627
PO Box 2806, Fargo 58108 Fax 241-5728
www.casscountynd.gov

Cavalier County Office of Education
Dawn Roppel, supt. 701-256-2229
901 3rd St Ste 11, Langdon 58249 Fax 256-2546

Dickey County Office of Education
Deborah Anderson, supt. 701-349-3249
PO Box 148, Ellendale 58436 Fax 349-4639

Divide County Office of Education
Sherlock Hirning, supt. 701-965-6313
PO Box G, Crosby 58730 Fax 965-6004

Dunn County Office of Education
Tracey Dolezal, supt. 701-573-4448
PO Box 105, Manning 58642 Fax 573-4444

Eddy County Office of Education
Tracy Henningsgard, supt. 701-947-2434
524 Central Ave Ste 301 Fax 947-2279
New Rockford 58356

Emmons County Office of Education
Florence Plienis, supt. 701-254-4802
PO Box 188, Linton 58552 Fax 254-4802

Foster County Office of Education
Roger Schlotman, supt. 701-652-1200
PO Box 104, Carrington 58421 Fax 652-2173

Golden Valley County Office of Education
Virginia Bares, supt. 701-872-4543
PO Box 35, Beach 58621 Fax 872-4383
www.beachnd.com

Grand Forks County Office of Education
David Godfread, supt. 701-795-2777
500 Stanford Rd Fax 795-2770
Grand Forks 58203

Grant County Office of Education
Kelly Bachmeier, supt. 701-622-3263
210 2nd Ave W, Carson 58529 Fax 622-3717

Griggs County Office of Education
Janet Tenneson, supt. 701-797-3117
PO Box 511, Cooperstown 58425

Hettinger County Office of Education
Sheila Steiner, supt. 701-824-2500
336 Pacific Ave, Mott 58646 Fax 824-2717

Kidder County Office of Education
Angela Haverkamp, supt. 701-475-2632
PO Box 66, Steele 58482 Fax 475-2202

La Moure County Office of Education
Mike Johnson, supt. 701-883-5301
PO Box 128, LaMoure 58458 Fax 883-4240

Logan County Office of Education
Gary Schumacher, supt. 701-754-2756
PO Box 7, Napoleon 58561 Fax 754-2270

McHenry County Office of Education
Maxine Rognlien, supt. 701-537-5642
407 Main St S, Towner 58788 Fax 537-5969

McIntosh County Office of Education
Coreen Schumacher, supt. 701-684-7631
PO Box 290, Ashley 58413 Fax 288-3671

McKenzie County Office of Education
Carol Kieson, supt. 701-444-3456
201 5th St NW Ste 523 Fax 444-4113
Watford City 58854
www.mckenziecounty.net

McLean County Office of Education
Lori Foss, supt. 701-462-8541
PO Box 1108, Washburn 58577 Fax 462-3542

Mercer County Office of Education
Gontran Langowski, supt. 701-748-3300
1021 Arthur St, Stanton 58571

Morton County Office of Education
Karen Kautzmann, supt. 701-667-3315
210 2nd Ave NW, Mandan 58554 Fax 667-3348
www.co.morton.nd.us/

Mountrail County Office of Education
Joan Hollekim, supt. 701-628-2145
PO Box 69, Stanley 58784 Fax 628-3975

Nelson County Office of Education
Sharon Young, supt. 701-247-2472
210 B Ave W, Lakota 58344 Fax 247-2943

Oliver County Office of Education
Judith Hintz, supt. 701-794-8721
PO Box 188, Center 58530 Fax 794-3476

Pembina County Office of Education
Linda Schlittenhard, supt. 701-265-4231
301 Dakota St W Unit 11 Fax 265-4876
Cavalier 58220

Pierce County Office of Education
Karin Fursather, supt. 701-776-5225
240 2nd St SE Ste 6, Rugby 58368 Fax 776-5707

Ramsey County Office of Education
Lisa Diseth, supt. 701-662-7023
524 4th Ave NE, Devils Lake 58301 Fax 662-7049

Ransom County Office of Education
Suzanne Anderson, supt. 701-683-6117
PO Box 112, Lisbon 58054

Renville County Office of Education
LeAnn Pollman, supt. 701-756-6301
PO Box 68, Mohall 58761 Fax 756-6391

Richland County Office of Education
Harris Bailey, supt. 701-642-7702
418 2nd Ave N Ofc 15 Fax 642-7701
Wahpeton 58075

Rolette County Office of Education
Dwane Getzlaff, supt. 701-477-5265
PO Box 939, Rolla 58367 Fax 477-6339

Sargent County Office of Education
Sherry Hosford, supt. 701-724-6241
355 Main St S Ste 1, Forman 58032 Fax 724-6244

Sheridan County Office of Education
Shirley Murray, supt. 701-363-2205
PO Box 439, Mc Clusky 58463 Fax 363-2953

Sioux County Office of Education
Barb Hettich, supt. 701-854-3481
PO Box L, Fort Yates 58538 Fax 854-3854

Slope County Office of Education
Kathy Walser, supt. 701-879-6277
PO Box MM, Amidon 58620 Fax 879-6278

Stark County Office of Education
Kay Haag, supt. 701-456-7630
PO Box 130, Dickinson 58602 Fax 456-7634

Steele County Office of Education
Linda Leadbetter, supt. 701-524-2110
PO Box 275, Finley 58230 Fax 524-1715

Stutsman County Office of Education
Casey Bradley, supt. 701-252-9035
511 2nd Ave SE Ste 102 Fax 251-1603
Jamestown 58401

Towner County Office of Education
Wayne Lingen, supt. 701-968-4346
PO Box 603, Cando 58324 Fax 968-4342

Traill County Office of Education
Rebecca Braaten, supt. 701-636-4458
PO Box 429, Hillsboro 58045 Fax 636-5418

Walsh County Office of Education
Kris Molde, supt. 701-352-2851
600 Cooper Ave, Grafton 58237 Fax 352-3340

Ward County Office of Education
Jodi Johnson, supt. 701-857-6495
PO Box 5005, Minot 58702 Fax 857-6424

Wells County Office of Education
Janelle Rudel, supt. 701-547-3521
PO Box 37, Fessenden 58438 Fax 547-3719

Williams County Office of Education
Patti Ogurchak, supt. 701-577-4580
PO Box 2047, Williston 58802 Fax 577-4579

PUBLIC, PRIVATE AND CATHOLIC SECONDARY SCHOOLS

Alexander, McKenzie, Pop. 220

Alexander SD 2 100/K-12
PO Box 66 58831 701-828-3334
Michael Klabo, supt. Fax 828-3134
www.alexander.k12.nd.us/

Alexander HS 50/7-12
PO Box 66 58831 701-828-3335
Michael Klabo, prin. Fax 828-3134

Ashley, McIntosh, Pop. 736

Ashley SD 9 100/K-12
703 W Main St 58413 701-288-3456
Brad Webster, supt. Fax 288-3457
www.ashley.k12.nd.us/

Ashley HS 100/7-12
703 W Main St 58413 701-288-3456
Jason Schmidt, prin. Fax 288-3457

Beach, Golden Valley, Pop. 1,013

Beach SD 3 300/K-12
PO Box 368 58621 701-872-4161
Larry Helvik, supt. Fax 872-3801
www.beach.k12.nd.us

Beach JSHS 200/7-12
PO Box 368 58621 701-872-4161
Brandt Gaugler, prin. Fax 872-3801

Belcourt, Rolette, Pop. 2,055

Belcourt SD 7 1,600/K-12
PO Box 440 58316 701-477-6471
Dr. Lana DeCoteau, supt. Fax 477-6470
www.belcourt.k12.nd.us

Turtle Mountain Community HS 600/9-12
PO Box 440 58316 701-477-6471
Melvin Laducer, prin. Fax 477-8821

Turtle Mountain Community MS 400/6-8
PO Box 440 58316 701-477-6471
Louis Dauphinais, prin. Fax 477-3973

Turtle Mountain Community College Post-Sec.
PO Box 340 58316 701-477-7862

Belfield, Stark, Pop. 793

Belfield SD 13 200/K-12
PO Box 97 58622 701-575-4275
Darrel Remington, supt. Fax 575-8533
www.belfield.k12.nd.us/

Belfield JSHS 100/7-12
PO Box 97 58622 701-575-4275
Jeffrey Lamprecht, prin. Fax 575-8533

Berthold, Ward, Pop. 449

Lewis and Clark SD 161 400/PK-12
PO Box 185 58718 701-453-3484
Brian Nelson, supt. Fax 453-3488
www.lewisandclark.k12.nd.us/

Berthold HS 100/9-12
PO Box 185 58718 701-453-3484
Margaret Person, prin. Fax 453-3488

Other Schools – See Makoti

Beulah, Mercer, Pop. 3,078
Beulah SD 27 700/K-12
204 5th St NW 58523 701-873-2237
Robert Lech, supt. Fax 873-5273
www.beulah.k12.nd.us
Beulah HS 300/9-12
204 5th St NW 58523 701-873-2261
Todd Kaylor, prin. Fax 873-5273
Beulah MS 200/5-8
1700 Central Ave N 58523 701-873-4325
Stacy Murschel, prin. Fax 873-2844

Binford, Griggs, Pop. 183
Midkota SD 7 100/K-12
PO Box 38 58416 701-676-2511
Gilbert Black, supt. Fax 676-2510
www.midkotaschools.com
Other Schools – See Glenfield

Bismarck, Burleigh, Pop. 60,375
Bismarck SD 1 10,500/PK-12
806 N Washington St 58501 701-323-4000
Tamara Uselman, supt. Fax 355-4001
www.bismarckschools.org
Bismarck Career & Technical Center Vo/Tech
1221 College Dr 58501 701-323-4340
Dale Hoerauf, prin. Fax 323-4345
Bismarck SHS 1,300/10-12
800 N 8th St 58501 701-323-4800
Michael Cary, prin. Fax 323-4805
Century SHS 1,100/10-12
1000 E Century Ave 58503 701-323-4900
Steve Madler, prin. Fax 323-4905
Horizon MS 900/7-9
500 Ash Coulee Dr 58503 701-323-4550
Sherry Heaton, prin. Fax 323-4555
Simle MS 900/7-9
1215 N 19th St 58501 701-323-4600
Russ Riehl, prin. Fax 323-4605
South Central Alternative S 100/Alt
806 N Washington St 58501 701-323-4520
Tom Schmidt, prin. Fax 323-4525
Wachter MS 800/7-9
1107 S 7th St 58504 701-323-4650
Brian Beehler, prin. Fax 323-4655
Adult Learning Center Adult
1200 College Dr 58501 701-323-4530
Dale Hoerauf, prin. Fax 323-4535

Bismarck State College Post-Sec.
PO Box 5587 58506 701-224-5400
Dakota Adventist Academy 50/9-12
15905 Sheyenne Cir 58503 701-258-9000
Dr. Gerald Coy, prin. Fax 258-0110
Medcenter One College of Nursing Post-Sec.
512 N 7th St 58501 701-323-6271
Medcenter One Health System Post-Sec.
222 N 7th St 58501 701-222-5413
Rasmussen College Post-Sec.
1701 E Century Ave 58503 701-530-9600
R.D. Hairstyling College Post-Sec.
1320 Tacoma Ave 58504 701-223-8804
St. Alexius Medical Center Post-Sec.
PO Box 5510 58506 701-224-7600
St. Marys Central HS 300/9-12
1025 N 2nd St 58501 701-223-4113
Tom Eberle, prin. Fax 223-8629
Shiloh Christian S 400/PK-12
1915 Shiloh Dr 58503 701-221-2104
Morgan Forness, admin. Fax 224-8221
United Tribes Technical College Post-Sec.
3315 University Dr 58504 701-255-3285
University of Mary Post-Sec.
7500 University Dr 58504 701-255-7500

Bottineau, Bottineau, Pop. 2,163
Bottineau SD 1 600/K-12
301 Brander St 58318 701-228-2266
Jason Kersten, supt. Fax 228-2021
www.bottineau.k12.nd.us/
Bottineau JSHS 300/7-12
301 Brander St 58318 701-228-2266
Joel Bickford, prin. Fax 228-2021

Dakota College at Bottineau Post-Sec.
105 Simrall Blvd 58318 701-228-2277

Bowbells, Burke, Pop. 335
Bowbells SD 14 100/K-12
PO Box 279 58721 701-377-2396
Celeste Thingvold, supt. Fax 377-2399
www.bowbells.k12.nd.us
Bowbells HS 50/7-12
PO Box 279 58721 701-377-2396
Celeste Thingvold, supt. Fax 377-2399

Bowman, Bowman, Pop. 1,641
Bowman County SD 1 400/K-12
PO Box H 58623 701-523-3283
Tony Duletski, supt. Fax 523-3849
www.bowman.k12.nd.us
Bowman HS 100/9-12
PO Box H 58623 701-523-3283
Wayne Olson, prin. Fax 523-3849

Buxton, Traill, Pop. 323
Central Valley SD 3 100/K-12
1556 Highway 81 NE 58218 701-847-2220
Jeremy Brandt, supt. Fax 847-2407
www.centralvalley.k12.nd.us/
Central Valley S 100/K-12
1556 Highway 81 NE 58218 701-847-2220
Frank Justin, prin. Fax 847-2407

Cando, Towner, Pop. 1,101
North Star SD 10 300/PK-12
PO Box 489 58324 701-968-4416
Jeff Hagler, supt. Fax 968-4418
www.northstar.k12.nd.us//index.html
North Star HS 100/9-12
PO Box 489 58324 701-968-4416
Nancy Reiser, prin. Fax 968-4418

Carrington, Foster, Pop. 2,050
Carrington SD 49 500/PK-12
PO Box 48 58421 701-652-3136
Dr. Brian Duchscherer, supt. Fax 652-1243
www.carrington.k12.nd.us/
Carrington JSHS 300/7-12
PO Box 48 58421 701-652-3136
David Nowatzki, prin. Fax 652-1243

Casselton, Cass, Pop. 2,310
Central Cass SD 17 800/K-12
802 5th St N 58012 701-347-5352
Mark Weston, supt. Fax 347-5354
www.central-cass.k12.nd.us/
Central Cass HS 300/9-12
802 5th St N 58012 701-347-5352
Steve Lorentzen, prin. Fax 347-5354
Central Cass MS 200/6-8
802 5th St N 58012 701-347-5352
Pete Pogatshnik, prin. Fax 347-5354

Cavalier, Pembina, Pop. 1,278
Cavalier SD 6 400/K-12
PO Box 410 58220 701-265-8417
Jeff Manley, supt. Fax 265-8106
www.cavalierschool.org
Cavalier HS 100/9-12
PO Box 410 58220 701-265-8417
Sandy Laxdal, prin. Fax 265-8106

Center, Oliver, Pop. 569
Center-Stanton SD 1 200/K-12
PO Box 248 58530 701-794-8778
Curt Pierce, supt. Fax 794-3659
www.center.k12.nd.us/
Center-Stanton HS 100/7-12
PO Box 248 58530 701-794-8778
Tracy Peterson, prin. Fax 794-3659

Colfax, Richland, Pop. 121
Richland SD 44 300/K-12
PO Box 49 58018 701-372-3713
Les Dale, supt. Fax 372-3718
www.richland.k12.nd.us
Richland JSHS 100/7-12
PO Box 49 58018 701-372-3713
Bruce Anderson, prin. Fax 372-3718

Cooperstown, Griggs, Pop. 983
Griggs County Central SD 18 300/K-12
1207 Foster Ave NE 58425 701-797-3114
Wade Faul, supt. Fax 797-3130
www.griggs-co.k12.nd.us/
Griggs County Central HS 100/9-12
1207 Foster Ave NE 58425 701-797-3114
Travis Jordan, admin. Fax 797-3130

Crosby, Divide, Pop. 1,064
Divide County SD 1 200/PK-12
PO Box G 58730 701-965-6313
Dr. Sherlock Hirning, supt. Fax 965-6004
www.divide-co.k12.nd.us/
Divide County JSHS 100/7-12
PO Box G 58730 701-965-6392
Dr. Travis Frank, prin. Fax 965-6942

Crystal, Pembina, Pop. 137
Valley-Edinburg SD 118
Supt. — See Edinburg
Valley-Edinburg ES 50/5-8
PO Box 129 58222 701-657-2163
Andrew Currie, prin. Fax 657-2150

Des Lacs, Ward, Pop. 201
United SD 7 600/PK-12
PO Box 117 58733 701-725-4334
Clarke Ranum, supt. Fax 725-4375
www.united.k12.nd.us/
Des Lacs Burlington HS 200/9-12
PO Box 117 58733 701-725-4334
Andrew Gilbertson, prin. Fax 725-4375

Devils Lake, Ramsey, Pop. 6,910
Devils Lake SD 1 1,700/PK-12
1601 College Dr N 58301 701-662-7640
Scott Privratsky, supt. Fax 662-7646
www.dlschools.org/
Central MS 500/5-8
325 7th St NE 58301 701-662-7664
Jared Schlenker, prin. Fax 662-7649
Devils Lake HS 600/9-12
1601 College Dr N 58301 701-662-1200
Ryan Hanson, prin. Fax 662-1208
Lake Area Career & Technology Center Vo/Tech
205 16th St NW 58301 701-662-7650
Christa Brodina, dir. Fax 662-7658

Lake Region State College Post-Sec.
1801 College Dr N 58301 701-662-1600

Dickinson, Stark, Pop. 17,565
Dickinson SD 1 2,600/PK-12
444 4th St W 58601 701-456-0002
Dr. Douglas Sullivan, supt. Fax 456-0035
www.dickinson.k12.nd.us
Dickinson HS 800/9-12
979 13th Ave W 58601 701-456-0030
Ron Dockter, prin. Fax 456-0019
Hagen JHS 300/7-8
402 4th St W 58601 701-456-0020
Marcus Lewton, prin. Fax 456-0044
Southwest Community HS Adult
1173 3rd Ave W Ste 37 58601 701-456-0042
Jay Hepperle, prin. Fax 456-0042

Dickinson State University Post-Sec.
291 Campus Dr 58601 701-483-2507
Trinity HS 200/7-12
PO Box 1177 58602 701-483-6081
Carter Fong, prin. Fax 483-1450

Drake, McHenry, Pop. 270
Drake SD 57 100/7 12
PO Box 256 58736 701-465-3732
Steven Heim, supt. Fax 465-3634
Drake/Anamoose HS 100/7-12
PO Box 256 58736 701-465-3732
Travis Engen, prin. Fax 465-3634

Drayton, Pembina, Pop. 819
Drayton SD 19 200/PK-12
108 S 5th St 58225 701-454-3324
Hy Schlieve, supt. Fax 454-3485
www.drayton.k12.nd.us/
Drayton JSHS 100/7-12
108 S 5th St 58225 701-454-3324
Fax 454-3485

Dunseith, Rolette, Pop. 742
Dunseith SD 1 400/K-12
PO Box 789 58329 701-244-0480
Pat Brenden, supt. Fax 244-5129
www.dunseith.k12.nd.us/
Dunseith HS 200/7-12
PO Box 789 58329 701-244-5249
David Sjol, prin. Fax 244-9708

Edgeley, LaMoure, Pop. 562
Edgeley SD 3 200/K-12
PO Box 37 58433 701-493-2292
Richard Diegel, supt. Fax 493-2411
www.edgeley.k12.nd.us/
Edgeley HS 100/7-12
PO Box 37 58433 701-493-2292
Todd Kosel, prin. Fax 493-2411

Edinburg, Walsh, Pop. 192
Valley-Edinburg SD 118 100/K-12
PO Box 6 58227 701-993-8312
John Olstad, supt. Fax 993-8313
www.edinburg.k12.nd.us
Valley-Edinburg HS 50/9-12
PO Box 6 58227 701-993-8312
Larry Larson, prin. Fax 993-8313
Other Schools – See Crystal

Edmore, Ramsey, Pop. 179
Edmore SD 2 100/7-12
PO Box 188 58330 701-644-2281
Francis Schill, supt. Fax 644-2222
www.adams-edmore.k12.nd.us
Edmore JSHS 100/7-12
PO Box 188 58330 701-644-2281
Matt Ford, prin. Fax 644-2222

Elgin, Grant, Pop. 638
Elgin - New Leipzig SD 49 100/K-12
PO Box 70 58533 701-584-2374
Kyle Edgerton, supt. Fax 584-3018
www.elgin.k12.nd.us
Grant County HS 100/9-12
PO Box 70 58533 701-584-2374
Terry Bentz, prin. Fax 584-3018

Ellendale, Dickey, Pop. 1,371
Ellendale SD 40 400/K-12
PO Box 400 58436 701-349-3232
Jeff Fastnacht, supt. Fax 349-3447
www.ellendale.k12.nd.us
Ellendale JSHS 200/7-12
PO Box 400 58436 701-349-3232
Matthew Herman, prin. Fax 349-3447

Trinity Bible College Post-Sec.
50 6th Ave S 58436 701-349-3621

Enderlin, Ransom, Pop. 884
Enderlin Area SD 24 300/K-12
410 Bluff St 58027 701-437-2240
Tom Rettig, supt. Fax 437-2242
www.enderlin.k12.nd.us/
Enderlin Area HS 200/7-12
410 Bluff St 58027 701-437-2240
Timothy Michaelson, prin. Fax 437-2242

Fairmount, Richland, Pop. 360
Fairmount SD 18 100/K-12
PO Box 228 58030 701-474-5469
Ron Stahlecker, supt. Fax 474-5862
www.fairmount.k12.nd.us/
Fairmount HS 100/7-12
PO Box 228 58030 701-474-5469
Jay Townsend, prin. Fax 474-5862

Fargo, Cass, Pop. 103,464
Fargo SD 1 10,000/PK-12
415 4th St N 58102 701-446-1000
Dr. Jeff Schatz, supt. Fax 446-1200
www.fargo.k12.nd.us/
Davies HS 9-12
7150 25th St S 58104 701-446-5600
Troy Cody, prin. Fax 446-5910
Discovery MS 800/6-8
1717 40th Ave S 58104 701-446-3300
Dr. Linda Davis, prin. Fax 446-3599
Eielson MS 800/6-8
1601 13th Ave S 58103 701-446-1700
Brad Larson, prin. Fax 446-1799
Fargo North HS 1,100/9-12
801 17th Ave N 58102 701-446-2400
Andrew Dahlen, prin. Fax 446-2799

Fargo South HS — 1,600/10-12
1840 15th Ave S 58103 — 701-446-2000
Todd Bertsch, prin. — Fax 446-2399
Franklin MS — 700/6-8
1420 8th St N 58102 — 701-446-3600
John Nelson, prin. — Fax 446-3899
Wilson HS — 100/Alt
1305 9th Ave S 58103 — 701-446-2800
David Burkman, prin. — Fax 446-2899
Evaluation & Training Center — Adult
424 9th Ave S 58103 — 701-241-4858
Terry Paulson, prin. — Fax 241-4896

Josef's School of Hair Design — Post-Sec.
627 NP Ave N 58102 — 701-235-0011
Moler Barber College of HairStyling — Post-Sec.
16 8th St S 58103 — 701-232-6773
North Dakota State University — Post-Sec.
PO Box 6050 58108 — 701-231-8011
Oak Grove Lutheran HS — 300/6-12
124 N Terrace N 58102 — 701-373-7100
Darrin Roach, prin. — Fax 237-4217
Rasmussen College — Post-Sec.
4012 19th Ave SW 58103 — 701-277-3889
Shanley HS — 300/9-12
5600 25th St S 58104 — 701-893-3200
Sean Safranski, prin. — Fax 893-3277
Sullivan MS — 200/6-8
5600 25th St S 58104 — 701-893-3200
Sean Safranski, prin. — Fax 893-3277

Fessenden, Wells, Pop. 475
Fessenden-Bowdon SD 25 — 100/K-12
PO Box 67 58438 — 701-547-3296
Nancy Bollingberg, supt. — Fax 547-3125
www.fessenden.k12.nd.us/
Fessenden-Bowdon HS — 100/9-12
PO Box 67 58438 — 701-547-3296
Warren Strand, prin. — Fax 547-3125

Finley, Steele, Pop. 440
Finley-Sharon SD 19 — 100/K-12
PO Box 448 58230 — 701-524-2420
Jeff Larson, supt. — Fax 524-2588
www.finley.k12.nd.us/
Finley-Sharon HS — 100/7-12
PO Box 448 58230 — 701-524-2420
Marvin Goplen, prin. — Fax 524-2588

Flasher, Morton, Pop. 229
Flasher SD 39 — 200/K-12
PO Box 267 58535 — 701-597-3355
Martin Bratrud, supt. — Fax 597-3781
www.flasher.k12.nd.us/
Flasher HS — 100/7-12
PO Box 267 58535 — 701-597-3355
Martin Bratrud, prin. — Fax 597-3781

Fordville, Walsh, Pop. 211
Fordville-Lankin SD 5 — 50/K-12
PO Box 127 58231 — 701-229-3297
Michael O'Brien, supt. — Fax 229-3231
www.fordville-lankin.k12.nd.us/
Fordville Lankin HS — 50/7-12
PO Box 127 58231 — 701-229-3297
Michael O'Brien, prin. — Fax 229-3231

Forman, Sargent, Pop. 501
Sargent Central SD 6 — 200/K-12
575 5th St SW 58032 — 701-724-3205
Michael Campbell, supt. — Fax 724-3559
www.sargent.k12.nd.us
Sargent Central HS — 100/7-12
575 5th St SW 58032 — 701-724-3205
Wade Crissman, prin. — Fax 724-3559

Fort Totten, Benson, Pop. 1,233
Fort Totten SD 30 — 200/9-12
PO Box 239 58335 — 701-766-1400
Jeff Olson, supt. — Fax 766-1475
Four Winds Community HS — 200/9-12
PO Box 239 58335 — 701-766-1400
John Lohnes, prin. — Fax 766-1475

Cankdeska Cikana Community College — Post-Sec.
PO Box 269 58335 — 701-766-4415

Fort Yates, Sioux, Pop. 181
Fort Yates SD 4 — 200/6-8
9189 Highway 24 58538 — 701-854-2142
Wayne Trottier, supt. — Fax 854-7488
Fort Yates MS — 200/6-8
9189 Highway 24 58538 — 701-854-3819
Tomi Kuntz, prin. — Fax 854-7467

Sitting Bull College — Post-Sec.
9299 Highway 24 58538 — 701-854-8000

Gackle, Logan, Pop. 308
Gackle-Streeter SD 56 — 100/K-12
PO Box 375 58442 — 701-485-3692
Duke Larson, supt. — Fax 485-3620
www.gacklestreeter.k12.nd.us/
Gackle-Streeter HS — 50/7-12
PO Box 375 58442 — 701-485-3692
Kurt Hayes, prin. — Fax 485-3620

Garrison, McLean, Pop. 1,428
Garrison SD 51 — 300/PK-12
PO Box 249 58540 — 701-463-2818
Steve Brannan, supt. — Fax 463-2067
www.garrison.k12.nd.us/
Garrison JSHS — 200/7-12
PO Box 249 58540 — 701-463-2818
Jim Upgren, prin. — Fax 463-2067

Glenburn, Renville, Pop. 368
Glenburn SD 26 — 200/K-12
PO Box 138 58740 — 701-362-7426
Brian Wolf, supt. — Fax 362-7349
www.glenburn.k12.nd.us/
Glenburn HS — 100/7-12
PO Box 138 58740 — 701-362-7426
Larry Derr, prin. — Fax 362-7349

Glenfield, Foster, Pop. 91
Midkota SD 7
Supt. — See Binford
Midkota HS — 100/7-12
PO Box 98 58443 — 701-785-2126
Gilbert Black, prin. — Fax 785-2226

Glen Ullin, Morton, Pop. 794
Glen Ullin SD 48 — 200/K-12
PO Box 548 58631 — 701-348-3590
Heather Hertz, supt. — Fax 348-3084
www.glen-ullin.k12.nd.us
Glen Ullin JSHS — 100/7-12
PO Box 548 58631 — 701-348-3590
Peter Remboldt, prin. — Fax 348-3084

Goodrich, Sheridan, Pop. 98
Goodrich SD 16 — 50/K-12
PO Box 159 58444 — 701-884-2469
Rodney Scherbenske, supt. — Fax 884-2496
Goodrich HS — 50/7-12
PO Box 159 58444 — 701-884-2469
Rodney Scherbenske, prin. — Fax 884-2496

Grafton, Walsh, Pop. 4,231
Grafton SD 3 — 800/K-12
1548 School Rd 58237 — 701-352-1930
Jack Maus, supt. — Fax 352-1943
www.grafton.k12.nd.us/
Grafton Central MS — 300/5-8
725 Griggs Ave 58237 — 701-352-1930
Jeff Rerick, prin. — Fax 352-1120
Grafton HS — 300/9-12
1548 School Rd 58237 — 701-352-1930
Darren Albrecht, prin. — Fax 352-1943
North Valley Area Career & Tech — Vo/Tech
1540 School Rd 58237 — 701-352-3705
Mark Wagner, dir. — Fax 352-3170

Grand Forks, Grand Forks, Pop. 51,662
Grand Forks SD 1 — 6,900/PK-12
PO Box 6000 58206 — 701-746-2200
Dr. Larry P. Nybladh, supt. — Fax 772-7739
www.gfschools.org
Central HS — 1,000/9-12
115 N 4th St 58203 — 701-746-2375
Buck Kasowski, prin. — Fax 746-2387
Community Alternative HS — 100/Alt
500 Stanford Rd 58203 — 701-795-2777
Terry Bohan, prin. — Fax 795-2770
Red River HS — 1,100/9-12
2211 17th Ave S 58201 — 701-746-2400
Kris Arason, prin. — Fax 746-2406
Schroeder MS — 500/6-8
800 32nd Ave S 58201 — 701-746-2330
Catherine Gillach, prin. — Fax 746-2332
South MS — 600/6-8
1999 47th Ave S 58201 — 701-746-2345
Nancy Dutot, prin. — Fax 746-2355
Valley MS — 400/6-8
2100 5th Ave N 58203 — 701-746-2360
Barry Lentz, prin. — Fax 746-2363
Other Schools – See Grand Forks AFB

Josef's School of Hair Design — Post-Sec.
2011 S Washington St 58201 — 701-772-2728
North Dakota School for the Blind — Post-Sec.
500 Stanford Rd 58203
University of North Dakota — Post-Sec.
264 Centennial Dr 58202 — 701-777-3000

Grand Forks AFB, Grand Forks, Pop. 2,246
Grand Forks SD 1
Supt. — See Grand Forks
Twining S — 100/4-8
1422 Louisiana St 58204 — 701-787-5100
Dr. Mary Koopman, prin. — Fax 787-5143

Granville, McHenry, Pop. 241
TGU SD 60
Supt. — See Towner
TGU Granville HS — 100/7-12
210 6th St SW 58741 — 701-728-6641
Tonya Hunskor, prin. — Fax 728-6386

Grenora, Williams, Pop. 241
Grenora SD 99 — 100/K-12
PO Box 38 58845 — 701-694-2711
Troy Walters, supt. — Fax 694-2717
www.grenora.k12.nd.us/
Grenora HS — 50/7-12
PO Box 38 58845 — 701-694-2711
Troy Walters, prin. — Fax 694-2717

Gwinner, Sargent, Pop. 749
North Sargent SD 3 — 200/K-12
PO Box 289 58040 — 701-678-2492
Randall Cale, supt. — Fax 678-2311
www.northsargent.k12.nd.us
North Sargent HS — 100/7-12
PO Box 289 58040 — 701-678-2492
Randal Brockman, prin. — Fax 678-2311

Halliday, Dunn, Pop. 185
Halliday SD 19 — 50/K-12
PO Box 188 58636 — 701-938-4391
Kyle Christensen, supt. — Fax 938-4373
www.halliday.k12.nd.us/
Halliday HS — 50/9-12
PO Box 188 58636 — 701-938-4391
Kyle Christensen, prin. — Fax 938-4373

Hankinson, Richland, Pop. 903
Hankinson SD 8 — 300/K-12
PO Box 220 58041 — 701-242-7516
Chad Benson, supt. — Fax 242-7434
www.hankinson.k12.nd.us/
Hankinson HS — 100/7-12
PO Box 220 58041 — 701-242-7138
Kent Dennis, prin. — Fax 242-7434

Harvey, Wells, Pop. 1,771
Harvey SD 38 — 400/K-12
811 Burke Ave 58341 — 701-324-2265
Daniel Stutlien, supt. — Fax 324-4414
www.harvey.k12.nd.us/
Harvey HS — 100/7-12
200 North St E 58341 — 701-324-2267
Daniel Stutlien, prin. — Fax 324-2424

Hatton, Traill, Pop. 763
Hatton Eielson SD 7 — 200/K-12
PO Box 200 58240 — 701-543-3455
Kevin Rogers, supt. — Fax 543-3459
www.hatton.k12.nd.us/
Hatton Eielson HS — 100/7-12
PO Box 200 58240 — 701-543-3455
Lucas Soine, prin. — Fax 543-3459

Hazelton, Emmons, Pop. 234
Hazelton-Moffit-Braddock SD 6 — 100/K-12
PO Box 209 58544 — 701-782-6231
Brandt Dick, supt. — Fax 782-6245
www.hmb.k12.nd.us/
Hazelton-Moffit-Braddock HS — 100/7-12
PO Box 209 58544 — 701-782-6231
Matt Scherbenske, prin. — Fax 782-6245

Hazen, Mercer, Pop. 2,396
Hazen SD 3 — 600/PK-12
PO Box 487 58545 — 701-748-2345
Michael Ness, supt. — Fax 748-2342
www.hazen.k12.nd.us
Hazen HS — 200/9-12
PO Box 487 58545 — 701-748-2345
Ed Boger, prin. — Fax 748-2342
Hazen MS — 100/6-8
PO Box 487 58545 — 701-748-6649
Ed Boger, prin. — Fax 748-6650

Hebron, Morton, Pop. 732
Hebron SD 13 — 200/K-12
PO Box Q 58638 — 701-878-4442
Kevin Nelson, supt. — Fax 878-4345
www.hebron.k12.nd.us/
Hebron HS — 100/7-12
PO Box Q 58638 — 701-878-4442
Stephanie Hochhalter, prin. — Fax 878-4345

Hettinger, Adams, Pop. 1,214
Hettinger SD 13 — 300/PK-12
PO Box 1188 58639 — 701-567-5315
Adam Hill, supt. — Fax 567-5094
www.hettinger.k12.nd.us
Hettinger HS — 100/7-12
PO Box 1188 58639 — 701-567-4502
Kevin Morast, prin. — Fax 567-2796

Hillsboro, Traill, Pop. 1,587
Hillsboro SD 9 — 400/K-12
PO Box 579 58045 — 701-636-4360
Paula Pederson, supt. — Fax 636-4362
www.hillsborok12.com
Hillsboro JSHS — 200/7-12
PO Box 579 58045 — 701-636-4360
Terry Baesler, prin. — Fax 636-4362

Hope, Steele, Pop. 258
Hope SD 10 — 100/7-12
PO Box 100 58046 — 701-945-2473
Jeff Watts, supt. — Fax 945-2511
www.hope-page.k12.nd.us/
Hope-Page HS — 100/7-12
PO Box 100 58046 — 701-945-2473
Dale Krueger, prin. — Fax 945-2511

Hunter, Cass, Pop. 255
Northern Cass SD 97 — 500/K-12
16021 18th St SE 58048 — 701-874-2322
Wayne Ulven, supt. — Fax 874-2422
www.northerncass.k12.nd.us
Northern Cass HS — 200/7-12
16021 18th St SE 58048 — 701-874-2322
Ryan Lyson, prin. — Fax 874-2422

Inkster, Grand Forks, Pop. 47
Midway SD 128 — 200/K-12
3202 33rd Ave NE, — 701-869-2432
Roger Abbe, supt. — Fax 869-2688
midway.nd.schoolwebpages.com
Midway HS — 100/9-12
3202 33rd Ave NE, — 701-869-2432
George Lee, prin. — Fax 869-2688

Jamestown, Stutsman, Pop. 15,252
Jamestown SD 1 — 2,100/PK-12
PO Box 269 58402 — 701-252-1950
Robert Toso, supt. — Fax 251-2011
www.jamestown.k12.nd.us
Jamestown HS — 700/9-12
PO Box 269 58402 — 701-952-4003
William Nold, prin. — Fax 252-8580
Jamestown MS — 500/6-8
PO Box 269 58402 — 701-252-0317
Gail Wold, prin. — Fax 252-3310
James Valley Area Vo-Tech Center — Vo/Tech
PO Box 269 58402 — 701-252-8841
John Lynch, prin. — Fax 252-3646

Jamestown College — Post-Sec.
6000 College Ln 58405 — 701-252-3467

Kenmare, Ward, Pop. 1,084
Kenmare SD 28 300/K-12
PO Box 667 58746 701-385-4996
Duane Mueller, supt. Fax 385-4390
www.kenmare.k12.nd.us/
Kenmare JSHS 100/7-12
PO Box 667 58746 701-385-4996
Robert Thom, prin. Fax 385-4390

Kensal, Stutsman, Pop. 163
Kensal SD 19 50/K-12
803 1st Ave 58455 701-435-2484
Tom Tracy, supt. Fax 435-2486
www.kensal.k12.nd.us/
Kensal HS 50/7-12
803 1st Ave 58455 701-435-2484
Matthew Lokemoen, prin. Fax 435-2486

Killdeer, Dunn, Pop. 734
Killdeer SD 16 400/PK-12
PO Box 579 58640 701-764-5877
Gary Wilz, supt. Fax 764-5648
www.killdeer.k12.nd.us
Killdeer HS 200/7-12
PO Box 579 58640 701-764-5877
Steve Quintus, prin. Fax 764-5648

Kindred, Cass, Pop. 678
Kindred SD 2 600/K-12
255 Dakota St 58051 701-428-3177
Steve Hall, supt. Fax 428-3149
www.kindred.k12.nd.us/
Kindred HS 300/7-12
255 Dakota St 58051 701-428-3177
Kent Packer, prin. Fax 428-3736

Kulm, LaMoure, Pop. 352
Kulm SD 7 100/PK-12
PO Box G 58456 701-647-2303
Thomas Nitschke, supt. Fax 647-2304
www.kulm.k12.nd.us/
Kulm JSHS 100/7-12
PO Box G 58456 701-647-2303
Derrick Bopp, prin. Fax 647-2457

Lakota, Nelson, Pop. 665
Lakota SD 66 200/K-12
PO Box 388 58344 701-247-2992
Joe Harder, supt. Fax 247-2910
www.lakota.k12.nd.us
Lakota JSHS 100/7-12
PO Box 388 58344 701-247-2992
Joe Harder, prin. Fax 247-2910

LaMoure, LaMoure, Pop. 884
La Moure SD 8 300/K-12
PO Box 656 58458 701-883-5396
Mitch Carlson, supt. Fax 883-5144
www.lamoure.k12.nd.us/
La Moure JSHS 100/7-12
PO Box 656 58458 701-883-5397
Andrew DelaBarre, prin. Fax 883-5144

Langdon, Cavalier, Pop. 1,855
Langdon Area SD 23 300/PK-12
715 14th Ave 58249 701-256-5291
Rich Rogers, supt. Fax 256-2606
lhs.utma.com/
Langdon Area JSHS 100/7-12
715 14th Ave 58249 701-256-5291
Daryl Timian, prin. Fax 256-2606

Larimore, Grand Forks, Pop. 1,320
Larimore SD 44 400/PK-12
PO Box 769 58251 701-343-2366
Dr. Roger Abbe, supt. Fax 343-2908
www.larimore.k12.nd.us/
Larimore JSHS 200/7-12
PO Box 769 58251 701-343-2366
Dave Wheeler, prin. Fax 343-2908

Leeds, Benson, Pop. 425
Leeds SD 6 100/PK-12
PO Box 189 58346 701-466-2461
Charles Dunlop, supt. Fax 466-2422
Leeds JSHS 50/9-12
PO Box 189 58346 701-466-2461
Charles Dunlop, prin. Fax 466-2422

Lidgerwood, Richland, Pop. 649
Lidgerwood SD 28 200/PK-12
PO Box 468 58053 701-538-7341
Tony Grubb, supt. Fax 538-4483
www.lidgerwood.k12.nd.us/
Lidgerwood HS 100/7-12
PO Box 468 58053 701-538-7341
Tony Grubb, prin. Fax 538-4483

Lignite, Burke, Pop. 154
Burke Central SD 36 100/K-12
PO Box 91 58752 701-933-2821
Sherry Lalum, supt. Fax 933-2823
www.burkecentral.k12.nd.us
Burke Central HS 50/7-12
PO Box 91 58752 701-933-2821
Erika Landro, prin. Fax 933-2823

Linton, Emmons, Pop. 1,084
Linton SD 36 300/PK-12
PO Box 970 58552 701-254-4138
Alan Bjornson, supt. Fax 254-4313
www.linton.k12.nd.us
Linton HS 100/9-12
PO Box 970 58552 701-254-4717
Alan Bjornson, prin. Fax 254-4313

Lisbon, Ransom, Pop. 2,132
Lisbon SD 19 600/K-12
PO Box 593 58054 701-683-4106
Steven Johnson, supt. Fax 683-4414
www.lisbon.k12.nd.us/
Lisbon HS 200/9-12
PO Box 593 58054 701-683-4106
Patrick Adair, prin. Fax 683-4414
Lisbon MS 200/5-8
PO Box 593 58054 701-683-4108
Elinor Meckle, prin. Fax 683-4111

Mc Clusky, Sheridan, Pop. 368
McClusky SD 19 100/K-12
PO Box 499 58463 701-363-2470
Robert Tollefson, supt. Fax 363-2239
mcclusky.nd.schoolwebpages.com/
McClusky JSHS 50/7-12
PO Box 499 58463 701-363-2470
Daniel Klemisch, prin. Fax 363-2239

Maddock, Benson, Pop. 380
Maddock SD 9 200/K-12
PO Box 398 58348 701-438-2531
Kimberly Anderson, supt. Fax 438-2620
Maddock HS 100/9-12
PO Box 398 58348 701-438-2531
Kimberly Anderson, prin. Fax 438-2620

Makoti, Ward, Pop. 149
Lewis and Clark SD 161
Supt. — See Berthold
North Shore HS 50/7-12
PO Box 127 58756 701-726-5591
Lori Ostrem, prin. Fax 726-5701

Mandan, Morton, Pop. 18,009
Mandan SD 1 3,300/K-12
901 Division St NW 58554 701-751-6500
Dr. Mike Bitz, supt. Fax 751-6674
www.mandan.k12.nd.us
Mandan HS 1,000/9-12
905 8th Ave NW 58554 701-751-6501
Mark Andresen, prin. Fax 751-6675
Mandan MS 800/6-8
2901 12th Ave NW 58554 701-751-6502
Ryan Leingang, prin. Fax 751-6682

Marion, LaMoure, Pop. 131
Litchville Marion SD 46 100/PK-12
PO Box 159 58466 701-669-2262
Steven Larson, supt. Fax 669-2316
www.litchville-marion.k12.nd.us/
Litchville-Marion JSHS 100/7-12
PO Box 159 58466 701-669-2261
Marc Ritteman, prin. Fax 669-2316

Max, McLean, Pop. 324
Max SD 50 200/K-12
PO Box 297 58759 701-679-2685
Craig M. Eraas, supt. Fax 679-2245
www.max.k12.nd.us/
Max HS 100/7-12
PO Box 297 58759 701-679-2685
David McQueen, prin. Fax 679-2245

Mayville, Traill, Pop. 1,819
May Port CG SD 14 500/K-12
900 Main St W 58257 701-788-2281
Michael Bradner, supt. Fax 788-2959
www.mayportcg.com/
Mayville-Portland CG HS 200/9-12
900 Main St W 58257 701-788-2281
Scott Ulland, prin. Fax 788-2959
Mayville-Portland CG MS 100/6-8
900 Main St W 58257 701-788-2281
Jeffrey Houdek, prin. Fax 788-2959

Mayville State University Post-Sec.
330 3rd St NE 58257 800-437-4104

Medina, Stutsman, Pop. 298
Medina SD 3 200/PK-12
PO Box 547 58467 701-486-3121
Brian Christopherson, supt. Fax 486-3138
www.medina.k12.nd.us/
Medina JSHS 100/7-12
PO Box 547 58467 701-486-3121
Brian Christopherson, admin. Fax 486-3138

Milnor, Sargent, Pop. 648
Milnor SD 2 200/K-12
PO Box 369 58060 701-427-5237
Diann Aberle M.Ed., supt. Fax 427-5304
www.milnor.k12.nd.us/
Milnor HS 100/7-12
PO Box 369 58060 701-427-5237
Ned Clooten, prin. Fax 427-5304

Minnewaukan, Benson, Pop. 217
Minnewaukan SD 5 200/K-12
PO Box 348 58351 701-473-5306
Myron Jury, supt. Fax 473-5420
www.minnewaukan.k12.nd.us/
Minnewaukan HS 50/7-12
PO Box 348 58351 701-473-5306
Ronald Carlson, prin. Fax 473-5420

Minot, Ward, Pop. 39,893
Minot SD 1 7,200/PK-12
215 2nd St SE 58701 701-857-4400
Mark Vollmer, supt. Fax 857-4432
www.minot.k12.nd.us/
Central Campus HS 1,000/9-10
215 1st St SE 58701 701-857-4660
Keith Altendorf, prin. Fax 857-4636
Hill MS 700/6-8
1000 6th St SW 58701 701-857-4477
Cindy Mau, prin. Fax 857-4479
Magic City Campus HS 900/11-12
1100 11th Ave SW 58701 701-857-4500
Scott Faul, prin. Fax 857-4521
Northwest ND Career & Technical Center Vo/Tech
1100 11th Ave SW 58701 701-420-1804
Pam Stroklund, dir.
Ramstad MS 600/6-8
420 3rd Ave SW 58701 701-857-4466
Ione Sautner, prin. Fax 857-4464
Souris River Campus Alternative HS 300/Alt
1510 University Ave W 58703 701-857-4496
Ned Strand, prin. Fax 857-4508
Other Schools – See Minot AFB

Bishop Ryan HS 300/6-12
316 11th Ave NW 58703 701-852-4004
Darwin Routledje, prin. Fax 839-4651
Headquarters Academy of Hair Design Post-Sec.
108 Main St S 58701 701-852-8329
Minot State University Post-Sec.
500 University Ave W 58707 701-858-3000
Our Redeemer's Christian S 300/PK-12
700 16th Ave SE 58701 701-839-0772
Charles Strand, admin. Fax 858-0994
Trinity Medical Center Post-Sec.
3 Burdick Expy 58701 701-857-5000

Minot AFB, Ward, Pop. 5,179
Minot SD 1
Supt. — See Minot
Memorial MS 100/7-8
1 Rocket Rd 58704 701-727-3300
Tom Holtz, prin. Fax 727-3303

Minto, Walsh, Pop. 603
Minto SD 20 200/PK-12
PO Box 377 58261 701-248-3479
Linda Lutovsky, supt. Fax 248-3001
www.minto.k12.nd.us/
Minto HS 100/7-12
PO Box 377 58261 701-248-3479
Randy Rice, prin. Fax 248-3001

Mohall, Renville, Pop. 775
Mohall-Lansford-Sherwood SD 1 300/PK-12
PO Box 187 58761 701-756-6660
Kelly Taylor, supt. Fax 756-6549
www.mls.k12.nd.us//index.html
MLS - Mohall HS 200/7-12
PO Box 187 58761 701-756-6660
Lenora Stevenson, prin. Fax 756-6549

Montpelier, Stutsman, Pop. 87
Montpelier SD 14 100/PK-12
214 7th Ave 58472 701-489-3348
Mary Steele, supt. Fax 489-3349
www.montpelier.k12.nd.us
Montpelier HS 100/7-12
214 7th Ave 58472 701-489-3348
Jerry Waagen, prin. Fax 489-3349

Mott, Hettinger, Pop. 709
Mott-Regent SD 1 200/K-12
205 Dakota Ave 58646 701-824-2795
Myron Schweitzer, supt. Fax 824-2249
mott.nd.schoolwebpages.com/
Mott / Regent HS 100/7-12
205 Dakota Ave 58646 701-824-2795
David Libis, prin. Fax 824-2249

Munich, Cavalier, Pop. 209
Munich SD 19 100/K-12
PO Box 39 58352 701-682-5321
Dean Ralston, supt. Fax 682-5323
www.munich.k12.nd.us/
Munich HS 50/7-12
PO Box 39 58352 701-682-5321
Daniel Ludrigson, prin. Fax 682-5323

Napoleon, Logan, Pop. 791
Napoleon SD 2 300/K-12
PO Box 69 58561 701-754-2244
Elroy Burkle, supt. Fax 754-2233
www.napoleon.k12.nd.us/
Napoleon HS 100/7-12
PO Box 69 58561 701-754-2244
Robert Dietchman, prin. Fax 754-2233

Newburg, Bottineau, Pop. 110
Newburg - United SD 54 100/PK-12
PO Box 427 58762 701-272-6151
Jason Kertsen, supt. Fax 272-6117
www.newburg.k12.nd.us/
Newburg United HS 50/7-12
PO Box 427 58762 701-272-6151
Bob Beaudrie, prin. Fax 272-6117

New England, Hettinger, Pop. 588
New England SD 9 200/K-12
PO Box 307 58647 701-579-4160
Kelly Rasch, supt. Fax 579-4462
www.new-england.k12.nd.us
New England HS 100/7-12
PO Box 307 58647 701-579-4160
Lawrence Lechler, prin. Fax 579-4462

New Rockford, Eddy, Pop. 1,375
New Rockford-Sheyenne SD 2 300/K-12
437 1st Ave N 58356 701-947-5036
Jill Louters, supt. Fax 947-2195
www.newrockford.k12.nd.us/
New Rockford HS 200/7-12
437 1st Ave N 58356 701-947-5036
A.J. Benz, prin. Fax 947-2195

New Salem, Morton, Pop. 936
New Salem-Almont SD 49 300/PK-12
PO Box 378 58563 701-843-7610
Michael Severson, supt. Fax 843-7011
www.newsalem.k12.nd.us/
New Salem-Almont HS 200/7-12
PO Box 378 58563 701-843-7610
Bruce Schumacher, prin. Fax 843-7011

New Town, Mountrail, Pop. 1,853
New Town SD 1 800/K-12
PO Box 700 58763 701-627-3650
Marc Bluestone, supt. Fax 627-3689
www.new-town.k12.nd.us/
New Town HS 200/9-12
PO Box 700 58763 701-627-3658
John Gartner, prin. Fax 627-3689
New Town MS 200/6-8
PO Box 700 58763 701-627-3660
Andy Decoteau, prin. Fax 627-3689

Fort Berthold Community College Post-Sec.
PO Box 490 58763 701-627-4738

Northwood, Grand Forks, Pop. 931
Northwood SD 129 200/K-12
420 Trojan Rd 58267 701-587-5221
Keith Arneson, supt. Fax 587-5423
Northwood HS 100/7-12
420 Trojan Rd 58267 701-587-5221
Daniel Azure, prin. Fax 587-5423

Oakes, Dickey, Pop. 1,836
Oakes SD 41 500/PK-12
804 Main Ave 58474 701-742-3234
Arthur Conklin, supt. Fax 742-2812
www.oakes.k12.nd.us
Oakes JSHS 300/7-12
804 Main Ave 58474 701-742-3234
Donald Warren, prin. Fax 742-2812
Other Schools – See Wahpeton

Park River, Walsh, Pop. 1,393
Park River SD 78 300/K-12
PO Box 240 58270 701-284-7164
Kirk Ham, supt. Fax 284-7936
www.parkriver.k12.nd.us/
Park River HS 100/7-12
PO Box 240 58270 701-284-7164
Aaron Schramm, prin. Fax 284-7936

Parshall, Mountrail, Pop. 852
Parshall SD 3 300/PK-12
PO Box 158 58770 701-862-3129
Dr. John Weidner, supt. Fax 862-3801
www.parshall.k12.nd.us
Parshall JSHS 100/7-12
PO Box 158 58770 701-862-3129
Mark Grueneich, prin. Fax 862-3801

Pembina, Pembina, Pop. 576
North Border SD 100
Supt. — See Walhalla
North Border Pembina HS 50/9-12
155 S 3rd St 58271 701-825-6261
Jeff Carpenter, prin. Fax 825-6645
North Border Pembina MS 50/7-8
155 S 3rd St 58271 701-825-6261
Jeff Carpenter, prin. Fax 825-6645

Petersburg, Nelson, Pop. 192
Dakota Prairie SD 1 300/K-12
PO Box 37 58272 701-345-8233
Janet Edlund, supt. Fax 345-8251
www.dakotaprairie.k12.nd.us/
Dakota Prairie HS 100/7-12
PO Box 37 58272 701-345-8233
Jay Slade, prin. Fax 345-8251

Pingree, Stutsman, Pop. 59
Pingree-Buchanan SD 10 100/K-12
111 Lincoln Ave 58476 701-252-5563
Richard Bailey, supt. Fax 252-2245
www.pingree.k12.nd.us/
Pingree Buchanan JSHS 100/7-12
111 Lincoln Ave 58476 701-252-5563
Richard Bailey, prin. Fax 252-2245

Powers Lake, Burke, Pop. 279
Powers Lake SD 27 100/K-12
PO Box 346 58773 701-464-5432
Tim Holte, supt. Fax 464-5435
www.powerslake.k12.nd.us/
Powers Lake JSHS 50/7-12
PO Box 346 58773 701-464-5432
Tim Holte, prin. Fax 464-5435

Ray, Williams, Pop. 585
Nesson SD 2 200/K-12
PO Box 564 58849 701-568-3301
Benjamin Schafer, supt. Fax 568-3302
www.ray.k12.nd.us
Ray HS 100/7-12
PO Box 564 58849 701-568-3301
Arley Larson, prin. Fax 568-3302

Richardton, Stark, Pop. 528
Richardton-Taylor SD 34 200/K-12
PO Box 289 58652 701-974-2111
Brent Bautz, supt. Fax 974-2161
www.richardton-taylor.k12.nd.us
Richardton-Taylor HS 100/7-12
PO Box 289 58652 701-974-2111
Russell Ziegler, prin. Fax 974-2161

Rogers, Barnes, Pop. 46
Barnes County North SD 7
Supt. — See Spiritwood
North Central HS 100/7-12
10860 20 1/2 St SE 58479 701-646-6202
Daren Christianson, prin. Fax 646-6566

Rolette, Rolette, Pop. 566
Rolette SD 29 100/K-12
PO Box 97 58366 701-246-3595
Wade Sherwin, supt. Fax 246-3452
www.rolettepublicschools.com
Rolette JSHS 50/7-12
PO Box 97 58366 701-246-3595
Brandon Strong, prin. Fax 246-3452

Rolla, Rolette, Pop. 1,226
Mt. Pleasant SD 4 200/PK-12
201 5th St NE 58367 701-477-3151
Kevin Baumgarn, supt. Fax 477-5001
www.rolla.k12.nd.us
Mt. Pleasant HS 100/7-12
201 5th St NE 58367 701-477-3151
Randy Loing, prin. Fax 477-5001

Rugby, Pierce, Pop. 2,841
Rugby SD 5 600/PK-12
1123 S Main Ave 58368 701-776-5201
Michael McNeff, supt. Fax 776-5091
www.rugby.k12.nd.us/
North Central Area Career & Tech Ctr Vo/Tech
1123 S Main Ave 58368 701-776-7208
Kathy McCracken, dir. Fax 776-5091
Rugby JSHS 300/7-12
1123 S Main Ave 58368 701-776-5201
Jared Blikre, prin. Fax 776-5091

Saint John, Rolette, Pop. 309
Saint John SD 3 400/K-12
PO Box 200 58369 701-477-5651
Donald Davis, supt. Fax 477-8195
www.stjohn.k12.nd.us
Saint John HS 100/9-12
PO Box 200 58369 701-477-5651
Nathan Jensen, prin. Fax 477-8195

Saint Thomas, Pembina, Pop. 330
Saint Thomas SD 43 100/K-12
PO Box 150 58276 701-257-6424
Darren Albrecht, supt. Fax 257-6461
www.stthomas.k12.nd.us
Saint Thomas HS 50/7-12
PO Box 150 58276 701-257-6424
David Hanson, prin. Fax 257-6461

Sawyer, Ward, Pop. 354
Sawyer SD 16 100/K-12
101 2nd St W 58781 701-624-5167
Heather Schilling, supt. Fax 624-5482
www.sawyer.k12.nd.us/
Sawyer HS 100/7-12
101 2nd St W 58781 701-624-5167
Heather Schilling, prin. Fax 624-5482

Scranton, Bowman, Pop. 279
Scranton SD 33 100/K-12
PO Box 126 58653 701-275-8897
John Pretzer, supt. Fax 275-6221
www.scrantonpublicschool.homestead.com/
Scranton HS 100/7-12
PO Box 126 58653 701-275-8266
John Pretzer, prin. Fax 275-6221

Selfridge, Sioux, Pop. 151
Selfridge SD 8 100/K-12
PO Box 45 58568 701-422-3353
James Gross, supt. Fax 422-3348
Selfridge HS 50/7-12
PO Box 45 58568 701-422-3353
James Gross, prin. Fax 422-3348

Solen, Sioux, Pop. 73
Solen SD 3 100/K-12
PO Box 128 58570 701-445-3331
Judy Zins, supt. Fax 445-3323
Solen HS 100/7-12
PO Box 128 58570 701-445-3331
Judy Zins, prin. Fax 445-3323

South Heart, Stark, Pop. 298
South Heart SD 9 200/K-12
PO Box 159 58655 701-677-5671
Riley Mattson, supt. Fax 677-5616
www.southheart.k12.nd.us/
South Heart HS 100/7-12
PO Box 159 58655 701-677-5671
Scott Jung, prin. Fax 677-5616

Spiritwood, Stutsman, Pop. 18
Barnes County North SD 7 300/PK-12
PO Box 37 58481 701-646-6202
Doug Jacobson, supt. Fax 646-6566
www.barnescountynorth.k12.nd.us/
Other Schools – See Rogers, Wimbledon

Stanley, Mountrail, Pop. 1,448
Stanley SD 2 500/K-12
PO Box 10 58784 701-628-3811
Dr. Kent Hjelmstad, supt. Fax 628-3358
www.stanley.k12.nd.us/
Stanley JSHS 200/7-12
PO Box 10 58784 701-628-2342
Kevin Hoherz, prin. Fax 628-3358

Starkweather, Ramsey, Pop. 114
Starkweather SD 44 100/PK-12
PO Box 45 58377 701-292-4381
Dean Ralston, supt. Fax 292-5714
www.starkweather.k12.nd.us/
Starkweather HS 50/7-12
PO Box 45 58377 701-292-4381
Dennis Dockter, prin. Fax 292-5714

Steele, Kidder, Pop. 715
Kidder County SD 1 400/K-12
PO Box 380 58482 701-475-2243
Ken Miller, supt. Fax 475-2737
www.steele-dawson.k12.nd.us/
Steele-Dawson HS 200/7-12
PO Box 380 58482 701-475-2243
Darnell Schmidt, prin. Fax 475-2737
Other Schools – See Tappen

Strasburg, Emmons, Pop. 408
Strasburg SD 15 100/K-12
PO Box 308 58573 701-336-2667
Mary Larson, prin. Fax 336-7490
www.strasburg.k12.nd.us/
Strasburg JSHS 100/7-12
PO Box 308 58573 701-336-2667
Brandon Strong, prin. Fax 336-7490

Surrey, Ward, Pop. 914
Surrey SD 41 400/PK-12
PO Box 40 58785 701-839-8867
Kevin Klassen, supt. Fax 838-8822
www.surrey.k12.nd.us
Surrey HS 200/7-12
PO Box 40 58785 701-838-3282
David Gerding, prin. Fax 838-1262

Tappen, Kidder, Pop. 197
Kidder County SD 1
Supt. — See Steele
Tappen HS 50/9-12
PO Box 127 58487 701-327-4256
Tom Six, prin. Fax 327-4255

Thompson, Grand Forks, Pop. 982
Thompson SD 61 400/K-12
424 3rd St 58278 701-599-2765
Jason Schwabe, prin. Fax 599-2819
www.thompson.k12.nd.us
Thompson HS 200/7-12
424 3rd St 58278 701-599-2765
Jason Schwabe, prin. Fax 599-2819

Tioga, Williams, Pop. 1,208
Tioga SD 15 300/K-12
PO Box 279 58852 701-664-2333
D'Wayne Johnston, supt. Fax 664-3356
www.tioga.k12.nd.us
Tioga HS 100/7-12
PO Box 279 58852 701-664-3606
Brodie Odegaard, prin. Fax 664-3356

Tower City, Cass, Pop. 251
Maple Valley SD 4 200/K-12
PO Box 168 58071 701-749-2570
Roger Mulvaney, supt. Fax 749-2313
www.maple-valley.k12.nd.us/
Maple Valley HS 100/7-12
PO Box 168 58071 701-749-2570
Gary Milbrandt, prin. Fax 749-2313

Towner, McHenry, Pop. 528
TGU SD 60 300/PK-12
PO Box 270 58788 701-537-5414
Debby Marshall, supt. Fax 537-5413
www.granville.k12.nd.us
TGU Towner HS 100/9-12
PO Box 270 58788 701-537-5414
Wade Schock, prin. Fax 537-5413
Other Schools – See Granville

Trenton, Williams
Eight Mile SD 6 200/K-12
PO Box 239 58853 701-774-8221
Stephen Cascaden, supt. Fax 774-8040
www.eight-mile.k12.nd.us
Eight Mile HS 100/9-12
PO Box 239 58853 701-774-8221
Mary Paul, prin. Fax 774-8040

Turtle Lake, McLean, Pop. 570
Turtle Lake - Mercer SD 72 200/K-12
PO Box 160 58575 701-448-2365
Gaillord Peltier, supt. Fax 448-2368
www.tlm.k12.nd.us/
Turtle Lake Mercer HS 100/7-12
PO Box 160 58575 701-448-2365
Daren Kurle, prin. Fax 448-2368

Underwood, McLean, Pop. 762
Underwood SD 8 200/PK-12
PO Box 100 58576 701-442-3201
Brandt Dick, supt. Fax 442-3704
www.underwood.k12.nd.us/
Underwood HS 100/7-12
PO Box 100 58576 701-442-3201
Lee Weisgarber, prin. Fax 442-3704

Valley City, Barnes, Pop. 6,490
Valley City SD 2 1,100/PK-12
460 Central Ave N 58072 701-845-0483
Dean Koppelman, supt. Fax 845-4109
www.valley-city.k12.nd.us
Sheyenne Valley Area Career & Tech Ctr. Vo/Tech
801 Valley Ave SE 58072 701-845-0256
Jeffrey Bopp, prin. Fax 845-0003
Valley City HS 400/9-12
460 Central Ave N 58072 701-845-0483
Kristi Brandt, prin. Fax 845-2762
Valley City JHS 200/7-8
460 Central Ave N 58072 701-845-0483
Dan Larson, prin. Fax 845-2762

Valley City State University Post-Sec.
101 College St SW 58072 800-532-8641

Velva, McHenry, Pop. 1,077
Velva SD 1 400/K-12
PO Box 179 58790 701-338-2022
Sr. Steven Swiontek, supt. Fax 338-2023
velva.nd.schoolwebpages.com/
Velva HS 200/7-12
PO Box 179 58790 701-338-2022
Ryan Harty, prin. Fax 338-2023

Wahpeton, Richland, Pop. 7,637
Oakes SD 41
Supt. — See Oakes
SE Rgn Career & Tech-Oakes Ctr Vo/Tech
2101 9th St N 58075 701-742-3248
Dan Rood, dir. Fax 742-3152

Wahpeton SD 37 1,200/PK-12
PO Box 10 58074 701-642-6741
Rick Jacobson, supt. Fax 642-4908
www.wahpeton.k12.nd.us
SE Region Career & Tech-Wahpeton Ctr Vo/Tech
PO Box 10 58074 701-642-8701
Dan Rood, dir. Fax 642-3811
Wahpeton HS 400/9-12
PO Box 10 58074 701-642-2604
Clark Gripentrog, prin. Fax 642-1330
Wahpeton MS 300/6-8
PO Box 10 58074 701 642 6687
Beverly Jacobson, prin. Fax 642-5622

North Dakota State College of Science Post-Sec.
800 6th St N 58076 800-342-4325

Walhalla, Pembina, Pop. 969
North Border SD 100 400/K-12
PO Box 558 58282 701-549-3751
Dr. Paul Stremick, supt. Fax 549-3753
www.northborder.k12.nd.us
North Border Walhalla HS 100/9-12
PO Box 558 58282 701-549-3751
Shon Horgan, prin. Fax 549-3753
Other Schools – See Pembina

Warwick, Benson, Pop. 65
Warwick SD 29 300/PK-12
210 4th Ave 58381 701-294-2561
Dean Dauphinais, supt. Fax 294-2626
www.warwick.k12.nd.us
Warwick HS 100/7-12
210 4th Ave 58381 701-294-2561
Dean Dauphinais, prin. Fax 294-2626

Washburn, McLean, Pop. 1,238
Washburn SD 4 200/K-12
PO Box 280 58577 701-462-3228
Brad Rinas, supt. Fax 462-3561
www.washburn.k12.nd.us
Washburn HS 100/7-12
PO Box 280 58577 701-462-3221
Glen Weinmann, prin. Fax 462-3561

Watford City, McKenzie, Pop. 1,714
McKenzie County SD 1 600/K-12
PO Box 589 58854 701-444-3626
Steven Holen, supt. Fax 444-6345
www.watford-city.k12.nd.us/
Watford City JSHS 300/7-12
PO Box 589 58854 701-444-3624
Jay Diede, prin. Fax 444-3612

Johnson Corners Christian Academy 50/K-12
11008 Highway 23 58854 701-675-2359
Adrian Timmons, admin. Fax 675-2357

West Fargo, Cass, Pop. 25,407
West Fargo SD 6 7,100/PK-12
207 Main Ave W 58078 701-356-2000
Dr. David Flowers, supt. Fax 356-2009
www.west-fargo.k12.nd.us
Cheney MS 1,400/6-8
825 17th Ave E 58078 701-356-2090
Don Lennon, prin. Fax 356-2099
Community HS Alt
109 3rd St E 58078 701-356-2008
Dr. Thomas Gravel, prin. Fax 234-9305
Liberty MS 700/6-8
801 36th Ave E 58078 701-356-2671
Denise Jonas, prin. Fax 356-2679
Sheyenne HS 500/9-10
800 40th Ave E 58078 701-356-2160
Dr. Greg Grooters, prin. Fax 356-2169
West Fargo HS 1,500/10-12
801 9th St E 58078 701-356-2050
Jennifer Fremstad, prin. Fax 356-2060

Westhope, Bottineau, Pop. 415
Westhope SD 17 100/K-12
PO Box 406 58793 701-245-6444
John Gruenberg, supt. Fax 245-6418
www.westhope.k12.nd.us/
Westhope HS 100/7-12
PO Box 406 58793 701-245-6444
John Gruenberg, prin. Fax 245-6418

Williston, Williams, Pop. 14,321
Williston SD 1 2,600/K-12
PO Box 1407 58802 701-572-1580
Dr. Viola LaFontaine, supt. Fax 572-3547
www.williston.k12.nd.us
Williston HS 800/9-12
PO Box 1407 58802 701-572-0967
Chris Kittleson, prin. Fax 572-5449
Williston MS 400/7-8
PO Box 1407 58802 701-572-5618
Marcia Bartok, prin. Fax 774-3109

Trinity Christian S 200/PK-12
2419 9th Ave W 58801 701-774-9056
Ed Crawford, dir. Fax 774-3158
Williston State College Post-Sec.
1410 University Ave 58801 701-774-4200

Wilton, McLean, Pop. 705
Wilton SD 1 200/K-12
PO Box 249 58579 701-734-6559
Craig Johnson, supt. Fax 734-6944
www.wilton.k12.nd.us
Wilton HS 100/7-12
PO Box 249 58579 701-734-6331
Richard Bjerklie, prin. Fax 734-6944

Wimbledon, Barnes, Pop. 210
Barnes County North SD 7
Supt. — See Spiritwood
Wimbledon Courtenay HS 100/7-12
PO Box 255 58492 701-435-2494
Joan Klein, prin. Fax 435-2365

Wing, Burleigh, Pop. 148
Wing SD 28 100/K-12
PO Box 130 58494 701-943-2319
John Jankowski, supt. Fax 943-2318
www.wing.k12.nd.us
Wing HS 50/7-12
PO Box 130 58494 701-943-2319
John Jankowski, prin. Fax 943-2318

Wishek, McIntosh, Pop. 999
Wishek SD 19 200/PK-12
PO Box 247 58495 701-452-2892
Jim Eiseman, supt. Fax 452-4273
www.wishek.k12.nd.us
Wishek JSHS 100/7-12
PO Box 247 58495 701-452-2892
Yvonne Engelhart, prin. Fax 452-4273

Wolford, Pierce, Pop. 36
Wolford SD 1 50/K-12
PO Box 478 58385 701-583-2387
Larry Zavada, supt. Fax 583-2519
www.wolford.k12.nd.us/
Wolford HS 50/7-12
PO Box 478 58385 701-583-2387
Joel Braaten, prin. Fax 583-2519

Wyndmere, Richland, Pop. 423
Wyndmere SD 42 200/K-12
PO Box 190 58081 701-439-2287
Chris Swenson, supt. Fax 439-2804
Wyndmere HS 100/7-12
PO Box 190 58081 701-439-2287
Scott Strenge, prin. Fax 439-2804

Zeeland, McIntosh, Pop. 86
Zeeland SD 4 100/K-12
PO Box 2 58581 701-423-5429
Corbley Ogren, supt. Fax 423-5465
www.zeeland.k12.nd.us/
Zeeland HS 50/7-12
PO Box 2 58581 701-423-5429
Corbley Ogren, prin. Fax 423-5465

OHIO

OHIO DEPARTMENT OF EDUCATION
25 S Front St, Columbus 43215-4183
Telephone 877-644-6338
Website http://www.ode.state.oh.us

Superintendent of Public Instruction Dr. Richard Ross

OHIO BOARD OF EDUCATION
25 S Front St, Columbus 43215-4176

President Debe Terhar

EDUCATIONAL SERVICE CENTERS (ESC)

Allen County ESC
Brian Rockhold, supt. 419-222-1836
1920 Slabtown Rd, Lima 45801 Fax 224-0718
www.allencountyesc.org/

Ashtabula County ESC
John Rubesich, supt. 440-576-9023
PO Box 186, Jefferson 44047 Fax 576-3065
www.acesc.k12.oh.us

Athens-Meigs Counties ESC
Ricky Edwards, supt. 740-797-0064
21 Birge Dr, Chauncey 45719 Fax 797-0070
www.athensmeigs.org

Auglaize County ESC
Ann Harvey, supt. 419-738-3422
1045 Dearbaugh Ave Ste 2 Fax 738-1267
Wapakoneta 45895
www.auglaizeesc.org

Brown County ESC
James Frazier, supt. 937-378-6118
325 W State St, Georgetown 45121 Fax 378-4286
brown.k12.oh.us

Butler County ESC
Jon Graft, supt. 513-887-3710
400 N Erie Hwy Ste A Fax 887-3709
Hamilton 45011
www.bcesc.org

Clark County ESC
Stacia Smith, supt., 25 W Pleasant St 937-325-7671
Springfield 45506 Fax 325-9915
www.clarkesc.org/

Clermont County ESC
Jeff Weir, supt. 513-735-8300
2400 Clermont Center Dr Fax 735-8371
Batavia 45103
www.ccesc.org/

Columbiana County ESC
Anna Vaughn, supt. 330-424-9591
38720 Saltwell Rd, Lisbon 44432 Fax 424-9481
www.ccesc.k12.oh.us/

Darke County ESC
Michael Gray, supt. 937-548-4915
5279 Education Dr Fax 548-8920
Greenville 45331
www.darke.k12.oh.us

East Central Ohio ESC- New Philadelphia
Kevin Spears, supt., 834 E High Ave 330-308-9939
New Philadelphia 44663 Fax 308-0964
www.ecoesc.org

ESC of Central Ohio
Bart Anderson, supt. 614-445-3750
2080 Citygate Dr, Columbus 43219 Fax 445-3767
www.escofcentralohio.org

ESC of Cuyahoga County
Dr. Robert Mengerink, supt. 216-524-3000
5811 Canal Rd, Valley View 44125 Fax 524-3683
www.esc-cc.org/

ESC of Lake Erie West
Sandra C. Frisch, supt. 419-245-4150
2275 Collingwood Blvd Fax 245-4186
Toledo 43620
www.esclakeeriewest.org

ESC of Lorain County
Dr. Thomas Rockwell, supt. 440-324-5777
1885 Lake Ave, Elyria 44035 Fax 324-7355
www.loraincountyesc.org

Fairfield County ESC
Daniel Montgomery, supt. 740-653-3193
955 Liberty Dr, Lancaster 43130 Fax 653-4053
faircoesc.org/

Gallia-Vinton Counties ESC
Denise Shockley, supt. 740-245-0593
PO Box 178, Rio Grande 45674 Fax 245-0596
www.galliavintonesc.org

Geauga County ESC
Matthew Galemmo, supt. 440-279-1700
470 Center St Bldg 2 Fax 286-7106
Chardon 44024
www.geaugaesc.org

Greene County ESC
Terry Thomas, supt., 360 E Enon Rd 937-767-1303
Yellow Springs 45387 Fax 767-1025
www.greeneesc.org

Hamilton County ESC
David Distel, supt. 513-674-4251
11083 Hamilton Ave Fax 742-5525
Cincinnati 45231
www.hcesc.org/

Hancock County ESC
Larry Busdeker, supt. 419-422-7525
7746 County Road 140 Fax 422-8766
Findlay 45840
hancockesc.org

Hardin County ESC
Christine Jeffers, supt. 419-674-2288
1211 W Lima St Ste A Fax 675-3309
Kenton 43326
www.hardinesc.org

Jefferson County ESC
Joy Howell, supt., 2023 Sunset Blvd 740-283-3347
Steubenville 43952 Fax 283-2709
www.jcesc.k12.oh.us/

Knox County ESC
Timm Mackley, supt. 740-393-6767
308 Martinsburg Rd Fax 393-6812
Mount Vernon 43050
www.kcesc.org

Lake County ESC
Dr. Brian Bontempo, supt. 440-350-2563
382 Blackbrook Rd Fax 350-2566
Painesville 44077
www.esc-lc.org/

Lawrence County ESC
Dr. James Payne, supt. 740-532-4223
111 S 4th St, Ironton 45638 Fax 532-7226
www.lawrencecountyesc.com

Licking County ESC
Dr. Nelson McCray, supt. 740-349-6084
675 Price Rd NE, Newark 43055 Fax 349-6107
www.lcesc.org/

Logan County ESC
Joyce Roberts, supt. 937-599-5195
121 S Opera St Fax 599-1959
Bellefontaine 43311
www.loganesc.k12.oh.us/

Madison-Champaign Counties ESC
Dr. Daniel Kaffenbarger, supt. 937-484-1557
1512 S US Highway 68 J100 Fax 484-1571
Urbana 43078
www.mccesc.k12.oh.us

Mahoning County ESC
Ronald Iarussi, supt. 330-965-7828
100 DeBartolo Pl Ste 220 Fax 965-7902
Youngstown 44512
www.mahoningesc.org/

Medina County ESC
William Koran, supt. 330-723-6393
124 W Washington St Fax 723-0573
Medina 44256
www.medina-esc.org/

Mercer County ESC
Andrew Smith, supt. 419-586-6628
441 E Market St, Celina 45822 Fax 586-3377
www.mercercountyesc.org/

Miami County ESC
Tom Dunn, supt. 937-339-5100
2000 W Stanfield Rd, Troy 45373 Fax 339-3256
www.miami.k12.oh.us/

Mid-Ohio ESC
Linda Keller, supt. 419-774-5520
890 W 4th St Ste 100 Fax 774-5523
Mansfield 44906
www.moesc.net/

Montgomery County ESC
Frank DePalma, supt. 937-225-4598
200 S Keowee St, Dayton 45402 Fax 496-7426
www.mcesc.org/

Muskingum Valley ESC
Richard Murray, supt. 740-452-4518
205 N 7th St, Zanesville 43701 Fax 455-6702
www.mvesc.k12.oh.us/

North Central Ohio ESC
James Lahoski, supt. 419-447-2927
928 W Market St Ste A, Tiffin 44883 Fax 447-2825
www.ncoesc.org/

North Point ESC
William Lally, supt. 419-627-3900
2900 Columbus Ave Fax 627-3999
Sandusky 44870
www.npesc.org

Northwest Ohio ESC
Darren Jenkins, supt. 567-444-4800
PO Box 250, Archbold 43502 Fax 444-4802
www.nwoesc.k12.oh.us

Ohio Valley ESC
Chris Keylor, supt. 740-439-3558
128 E 8th St, Cambridge 43725 Fax 439-0012
www.ovesc.k12.oh.us

Perry-Hocking Counties ESC
David Branch, supt. 740-342-3502
1605 Airport Rd Fax 342-1961
New Lexington 43764
www.perryhockingesc.org

Pickaway County ESC
Tyrus Ankrom, supt. 740-474-7529
2050 Stoneridge Dr Fax 474-7251
Circleville 43113
pickawayesc.org/

Portage County ESC
Dewey Chapman, supt. 330-297-1436
326 E Main St, Ravenna 44266 Fax 297-1113
www.portage-esc.org

Preble County ESC
Kevin Turner, supt. 937-456-1187
597 Hillcrest Dr, Eaton 45320 Fax 456-3253
www.preblecountyesc.com

Putnam County ESC
Dr. Jan Osborn, supt. 419-523-5951
124 Putnam Pkwy, Ottawa 45875 Fax 523-6126
putnam.noacsc.org/

Ross-Pike Counties ESC
Steve Martin, supt. 740-702-3120
475 Western Ave Ste E Fax 702-3123
Chillicothe 45601
rpesd.org

Shelby County ESC
Heather Neer, supt. 937-498-1354
129 E Court St, Sidney 45365 Fax 498-4850
www.scesc.k12.oh.us

South Central Ohio ESC
Lowell Howard, supt. 740-354-7761
522 Glenwood Ave Fax 353-1882
New Boston 45662
www.scoesc.org

Southern Ohio ESC
Anthony Long, supt. 937-382-6921
3321 Airborne Rd Fax 383-3171
Wilmington 45177
southernohioesc.org

Stark County ESC
Larry Morgan, supt. 330-492-8136
2100 38th St NW, Canton 44709 Fax 492-6381
www.starkcountyesc.org/

Summit County ESC
Linda Fuline, supt. 330-945-5600
420 Washington Ave Ste 200 Fax 920-1734
Cuyahoga Falls 44221
www.cybersummit.org/

Tri-County ESC
Eugene Linton, supt. 330-345-6771
741 Winkler Dr, Wooster 44691 Fax 345-7622
www.youresc.k12.oh.us/

Trumbull County ESC
Michael Hanshaw, supt. 330-505-2800
6000 Youngstown Warren Rd Fax 505-2814
Niles 44446
www.trumbull.k12.oh.us

Warren County ESC
John Lazares, supt. 513-695-2900
1879 Deerfield Rd, Lebanon 45036 Fax 695-2961
www.warrencountyesc.com/

Western Buckeye ESC
Brian Gerber, supt. 419-399-4711
PO Box 176, Paulding 45879 Fax 399-3346
www.wbesc.org/

Wood County ESC
Kyle Kanuckel, supt. 419-354-9010
1867 N Research Dr Fax 354-1146
Bowling Green 43402
www.wcesc.org/

PUBLIC, PRIVATE AND CATHOLIC SECONDARY SCHOOLS

Aberdeen, Brown, Pop. 1,615
Ripley-Union-Lewis-Huntington Local SD
Supt. — See Ripley
Ripley-Union-Lewis-Huntington MS 400/5-8
2300 Rains Eitel Rd 45101 937-795-8001
Chris Smith, prin. Fax 795-8035

Ada, Hardin, Pop. 5,849
Ada EVD 900/K-12
725 W North Ave 45810 419-634-6421
Dr. Suzanne Darmer, supt. Fax 634-0311
www.ada.k12.oh.us
Ada JSHS 400/7-12
725 W North Ave 45810 419-634-2746
Robin VanBuskirk, prin. Fax 634-4153

Ohio Northern University Post-Sec.
525 S Main St 45810 419-772-2000

Akron, Summit, Pop. 192,922
Akron CSD 22,200/K-12
70 N Broadway St 44308 330-761-1661
David James, supt. Fax 761-3225
www.akronschools.com
Akron Alternative Academy 300/Alt
77 W Thornton St 44311 330-761-1609
Rebecca Green-Pallotta, admin. Fax 761-1349
Akron Early College HS 400/9-12
225 S Main St 44325 330-972-6450
Marilyn Bennett, prin. Fax 972-5305
Akron Opportunity Center 100/Alt
77 W Thornton St 44311 330-761-1604
Rebecca Green-Pallotta, prin. Fax 761-1344
Buchtel HS 700/7-12
1040 Copley Rd 44320 330-873-3300
Sonya Gordon, prin. Fax 873-3307
East Community Learning Center 1,200/7-12
80 Brittain Rd 44305 330-761-7920
Felisha Gould, prin. Fax 784-1859
Ellet HS 1,100/9-12
309 Woolf Ave 44312 330-794-4120
Michelle Marquess-Kearns, prin. Fax 794-4130
Firestone HS 1,300/9-12
333 Rampart Ave 44313 330-873-3315
Larry Petry, prin. Fax 873-3318
Garfield HS 1,000/9-12
435 N Firestone Blvd 44301 330-773-6831
Frank Kalain, prin. Fax 773-3403
Hyre Community Learning Center 800/6-8
2443 Wedgewood Dr 44312 330-761-7930
Cynthia Wilhite, prin. Fax 761-7932
Innes Community Learning Center 700/6-8
1999 East Ave 44314 330-761-7900
Jennifer Moff, prin. Fax 848-5212
Jennings Community Learning Center 600/6-8
227 E Tallmadge Ave 44310 330-761-2002
Rochelle Brown-Hall, prin. Fax 761-2611
Kenmore HS 800/9-12
2140 13th St SW 44314 330-848-4141
Ginelle Rasnick, prin. Fax 848-5270
Kent MS 600/6-8
1445 Hammel St 44306 330-773-7631
Anthony Lane, prin. Fax 773-6442
Litchfield MS 600/6-8
630 Mull Ave 44313 330-873-3330
Dyan Floyd, prin. Fax 873-3337
Miller South S for Visual & Perform Arts 500/4-8
1055 East Ave 44307 330-761-1765
Dawn Wilson, prin. Fax 761-1764
National Inventors Hall of Fame S - STEM 300/5-8
199 S Broadway St 44308 330-761-3195
Traci Buckner, prin. Fax 761-5576
North HS 700/9-12
985 Gorge Blvd 44310 330-761-2665
Addie Veasley, prin. Fax 761-2661
STEM HS 9-12
123 S Forge St 44308 330-761-7965
Larry Johnson, prin. Fax 761-7966
Evening HS Adult
435 N Firestone Blvd 44301 330-773-6831
Minnie Carter-Page, coord. Fax 773-3403

Coventry Local SD 1,400/K-12
2910 S Main St 44319 330-644-8489
Russell Chaboudy, supt. Fax 644-0159
www.coventryschools.org/
Coventry HS 600/9-12
3089 Manchester Rd 44319 330-644-3004
Cynthia McDonald, prin. Fax 644-4222
Coventry MS 200/6-8
3257 Cormany Rd 44319 330-644-2232
Tina Norris, prin. Fax 644-0331

Manchester Local SD 1,500/K-12
6075 Manchester Rd 44319 330-882-6926
Sam Reynolds, supt. Fax 882-0013
www.panthercountry.org/
Other Schools – See New Franklin

Springfield Local SD 2,400/PK-12
2410 Massillon Rd 44312 330-798-1111
William Stauffer, supt. Fax 798-1161
www.springfieldspartans.org/
Springfield HS 700/9-12
2966 Sanitarium Rd 44312 330-798-1002
Cynthia Frola, admin. Fax 798-1162
Spring Hill JHS 400/7-8
660 Lessig Ave 44312 330-798-1003
Cynthia Frola, admin. Fax 798-1163

Akron General Medical Center Post-Sec.
400 Wabash Ave 44307 330-846-6548
Archbishop Hoban HS 900/9-12
1 Holy Cross Blvd 44306 330-773-6658
Dr. Mary Anne Beiting, prin. Fax 773-9100
Brown Mackie College Post-Sec.
755 White Pond Dr Ste 101 44320 330-869-3600
Children's Hospital & Medical Center Post-Sec.
1 Perkins Sq 44308 330-379-8293
Cooperative Medical Technology Program Post-Sec.
1 Perkins Sq 44308 330-543-8720
Gerber Akron Beauty School Post-Sec.
1915 W Market St Ste 800 44313 330-867-6200
Herzing University Akron Post-Sec.
1600 S Arlington St Ste 100 44306 330-724-1600
ITT Technical Institute Post-Sec.
3428 W Market St 44333 330-865-8600
Mogadore Christian Academy 50/1-12
3603 Carper Ave 44312 330-628-8482
Pamela Wise, prin. Fax 628-2677
National Institute of Massotherapy Post-Sec.
3681 Manchester Rd Ste 304 44319 330-867-1996
North Akron Catholic S 100/6-8
1570 Creighton Ave 44310 330-633-1383
Michael Capitena, prin. Fax 633-4512
Ohio College of Massotherapy Post-Sec.
225 Heritage Woods Dr 44321 330-665-1084
Our Lady of the Elms MSHS 200/7-12
1375 W Exchange St 44313 330-867-0880
Dr. Ruth Friedman, prin. Fax 864-6488
St. Vincent-St. Mary HS 700/9-12
15 N Maple St 44303 330-253-9113
David Rathz, hdmstr. Fax 996-0020
University of Akron Post-Sec.
302 Buchtel Mall 44325 330-972-7111

Albany, Athens, Pop. 825
Alexander Local SD 1,200/PK-12
6091 Ayers Rd 45710 740-698-8831
Jeff Cullum, supt. Fax 698-2038
www.alexanderschools.org/
Alexander JSHS 400/7-12
6125 School Rd 45710 740-698-8831
Frank Doudna, prin. Fax 698-3614

Alliance, Stark, Pop. 21,573
Alliance CSD 2,900/PK-12
200 Glamorgan St 44601 330-821-2100
Peter Basil, supt. Fax 821-0202
www.alliancecityschools.org/
Alliance HS 900/9-12
400 Glamorgan St 44601 330-829-2245
Shawn Jackson, prin. Fax 823-4920
Alliance MS 600/6-8
3205 S Union Ave 44601 330-829-2254
Jarred Zapolnik, prin. Fax 823-0872

Marlington Local SD 2,500/K-12
10320 Moulin Ave NE 44601 330-823-7458
Joe Knoll, supt. Fax 823-7759
www.marlingtonlocal.org
Marlington HS 800/9-12
10450 Moulin Ave NE 44601 330-823-1300
Sam Pepper, prin. Fax 829-1986
Marlington MS 600/6-8
10325 Moulin Ave NE 44601 330-823-7566
Adam McKenzie, prin. Fax 823-7594

University of Mount Union Post-Sec.
1972 Clark Ave 44601 800-992-6682

Amanda, Fairfield, Pop. 725
Amanda-Clearcreek Local SD 1,700/K-12
328 E Main St 43102 740-969-7250
David Gaul, supt. Fax 969-7620
www.amanda.k12.oh.us
Amanda-Clearcreek HS 500/9-12
328 E Main St 43102 740-969-7251
Michael Edwards, prin. Fax 969-7669
Amanda-Clearcreek MS 400/6-8
328 E Main St 43102 740-969-7252
Patricia Haughn, prin. Fax 969-7638

Amherst, Lorain, Pop. 11,868
Amherst EVD 3,300/PK-12
185 Forest St 44001 440-988-4406
Steven Sayers, supt. Fax 988-4413
www.amherst.k12.oh.us
Amherst JHS 700/7-8
548 Milan Ave 44001 440-988-0324
Ryan Coleman, prin. Fax 988-0328
Steele HS 1,400/9-12
450 Washington St 44001 440-988-4433
Michael May, prin. Fax 988-5087

Andover, Ashtabula, Pop. 1,129
Pymatuning Valley Local SD 1,300/K-12
PO Box 1180 44003 440-293-6488
Mike Candela, supt. Fax 293-7654
www.pvschools.k12.oh.us/
Pymatuning Valley HS 500/9-12
PO Box 1180 44003 440-293-6263
Daniel Jackson, prin. Fax 293-7214
Pymatuning Valley MS 400/5-8
PO Box 1180 44003 440-293-6981
Andrew Kuthy, prin. Fax 293-7237

Anna, Shelby, Pop. 1,544
Anna Local SD 1,300/K-12
PO Box 169 45302 937-394-2011
Andrew Bixler, supt. Fax 394-7658
www.anna.k12.oh.us
Anna HS 400/9-12
PO Box 169 45302 937-394-2011
Rick Russell, prin. Fax 394-7658
Anna MS 300/6-8
PO Box 169 45302 937-394-2011
Cynthia Endsley, prin. Fax 394-7658

Ansonia, Darke, Pop. 1,168
Ansonia Local SD 700/K-12
PO Box 279 45303 937-337-4000
James Atchley, supt. Fax 337-9520
www.ansonia.k12.oh.us/
Ansonia HS 200/9-12
PO Box 279 45303 937-337-5591
Stephen Garman, prin. Fax 337-9520
Ansonia MS 100/7-8
PO Box 279 45303 937-337-5591
Stephen Garman, prin. Fax 337-9520

Antwerp, Paulding, Pop. 1,725
Antwerp Local SD 600/K-12
303 S Harrmann Rd 45813 419-258-5421
Patricia Ross, supt. Fax 258-4041
www.aw.noacsc.org
Antwerp Local HS 200/9-12
303 S Harrmann Rd 45813 419-258-5421
Michael Bute, prin. Fax 258-4041
Antwerp Local MS 100/7-8
303 S Harrmann Rd 45813 419-258-5421
Michael Bute, prin. Fax 258-4041

Apple Creek, Wayne, Pop. 1,169
Southeast Local SD 1,600/PK-12
9048 Dover Rd 44606 330-698-3001
James J. Ritchie, supt. Fax 698-5000
www.southeast.k12.oh.us
Lea MS 200/7-8
9130 Dover Rd 44606 330-698-3151
Patti Arnold, prin. Fax 698-1922
Waynedale HS 400/9-12
9050 Dover Rd 44606 330-698-3071
Richard Roth, prin. Fax 698-1432

Arcadia, Hancock, Pop. 583
Arcadia Local SD 500/K-12
19033 State Route 12 44804 419-894-6431
Laurie Walles, supt. Fax 894-6970
www.noacsc.org/hancock/ad/
Arcadia JSHS 200/7-12
19033 State Route 12 44804 419-894-6431
Cathy Schroll, prin. Fax 894-6970

Arcanum, Darke, Pop. 2,116
Arcanum Butler Local SD 900/PK-12
2011 Trojan Ave 45304 937-692-5174
John Stephens, supt. Fax 692-5959
www.arcanum-butler.k12.oh.us
Arcanum HS 300/9-12
2011 Trojan Ave 45304 937-692-5174
Jason Stephan, prin. Fax 692-8865
Butler MS 200/5-8
2011 Trojan Ave 45304 937-692-5174
Kirby Tipple, prin. Fax 692-8865

Franklin Monroe Local SD 700/K-12
8639 Oakes Rd 45304 937-947-1212
Jeff Patrick, supt. Fax 947-1372
www.franklin-monroe.k12.oh.us/
Franklin Monroe JSHS 300/7-12
8591 Oakes Rd 45304 937-947-1328
Jason Wood, prin. Fax 947-1371

Archbold, Fulton, Pop. 4,305
Archbold Area Local SD 1,200/K-12
600 Lafayette St 43502 419-446-2728
Joe Long, supt. Fax 445-8536
www.archbold.k12.oh.us
Archbold HS 400/9-12
600 Lafayette St 43502 419-445-5579
Royal Short, prin. Fax 445-8536
Archbold MS 400/5-8
306 Stryker St 43502 419-446-2726
Matthew Shields, prin. Fax 445-8402

Four County Career Center SD 419-267-3331
22900 State Route 34 43502 Fax 267-2346
Tim Meister, supt.
www.fourcounty.net
Four County Career Center Vo/Tech
22900 State Route 34 43502 419-267-3331
Rick Bachman, prin. Fax 267-2346

Northwest State Community College Post-Sec.
22600 State Route 34 43502 419-267-5511

Arlington, Hancock, Pop. 1,451
Arlington Local SD 600/K-12
PO Box 260 45814 419-365-5121
Kevin Haught, supt. Fax 365-1282
www.noacsc.org/hancock/ag
Arlington JSHS 300/7-12
PO Box 260 45814 419-365-5121
Teri Kubbs, prin. Fax 365-1282

Ashland, Ashland, Pop. 20,088
Ashland CSD 3,300/K-12
PO Box 160 44805 419-289-1117
Douglas Marrah, supt. Fax 289-9534
www.ashlandcityschools.org/
Ashland HS 1,100/9-12
1440 King Rd 44805 419-289-7968
Thomas Marquette, prin. Fax 289-8218
Ashland MS 500/7-8
345 Cottage St 44805 419-289-7966
Mike Heimann, prin. Fax 289-2303

Ashland County-West Holmes JVSD 419-289-3313
1783 State Route 60 44805 Fax 289-3729
Michael McDaniel, supt.
www.acwhcc.org
Ashland Co. - West Holmes JVS Career Ctr Vo/Tech
1783 State Route 60 44805 419-289-3313
Rodney Cheyney, prin. Fax 289-3729

Crestview Local SD 1,200/K-12
1575 State Route 96 44805 419-895-1700
William Seder, supt. Fax 895-1733
www.crestviewschools.net
Crestview HS 300/9-12
1575 State Route 96 44805 419-895-1700
Scott Will, prin. Fax 895-3103
Crestview MS 500/4-8
1575 State Route 96 44805 419-895-1700
Eric Yetter, prin. Fax 895-1733

Mapleton Local SD 900/K-12
635 County Road 801 44805 419-945-2188
John Marks, supt. Fax 945-8133
www.mapleton.k12.oh.us/
Mapleton HS 300/9-12
1 Mountie Dr 44805 419-945-2188
Joe Morabito, prin. Fax 945-8166
Mapleton MS 200/6-8
1 Mountie Dr 44805 419-945-2188
Andrew Mangun, prin. Fax 945-8166

Ashland County-West Holmes Career Center Post-Sec.
1783 State Route 60 44805 419-289-3313
Ashland University Post-Sec.
401 College Ave 44805 419-289-4142

Ashtabula, Ashtabula, Pop. 18,304
Ashtabula Area CSD 2,800/PK-12
2630 W 13th St 44004 440-992-1200
Joseph Donatone, supt. Fax 992-1209
www.aacs.net
Lakeside HS 1,100/9-12
6600 Sanborn Rd 44004 440-993-2522
Donald Rapose, prin. Fax 993-2647
Lakeside JHS 600/7-8
6620 Sanborn Rd 44004 440-993-2618
Kathleen Reichert, prin. Fax 992-2647

Buckeye Local SD 1,600/K-12
3436 Edgewood Dr 44004 440-998-4411
Joseph Spiccia, supt. Fax 992-8369
www.buckeyeschools.info/
Braden MS 300/6-8
3436 Edgewood Dr 44004 440-998-0550
Bill Billington, prin.
Edgewood HS 600/9-12
2428 Blake Rd 44004 440-997-5301
Karl Williamson, prin. Fax 998-6143

Kent State University at Ashtabula Post-Sec.
3300 Lake Rd W 44004 440-964-3322
St. John S 100/K-12
7911 Depot Rd 44004 440-997-5531
Nicholas Perkoski, prin. Fax 998-1661

Ashville, Pickaway, Pop. 4,045
Teays Valley Local SD 3,600/PK-12
385 Circleville Ave 43103 740-983-5000
Jeff Sheets, supt. Fax 983-5035
www.tvsd.us/
Teays Valley East MS 500/6-8
655 Viking Way 43103 740-983-5000
Shannon Helser, prin. Fax 983-5037
Teays Valley HS 1,000/9-12
3887 State Route 752 43103 740-983-5000
John Keel, prin. Fax 983-5074
Other Schools – See Commercial Point

Athens, Athens, Pop. 23,284
Athens CSD
Supt. — See The Plains
Athens MS 400/7-8
51 W State St 45701 740-593-7107
Paul Grippa, prin. Fax 594-6506

Ohio University Post-Sec.
120 Chubb Hall 45701 740-593-1000

Attica, Seneca, Pop. 880
Seneca East Local SD 800/K-12
13343 E US Highway 224 44807 419-426-7041
Michael Wank, supt. Fax 426-5514
www.seneca-east.k12.oh.us/
Seneca East JSHS 300/7-12
13343 E US Highway 224 44807 419-426-3312
Don Vogt, prin. Fax 426-5400

Atwater, Portage, Pop. 754
Waterloo Local SD 1,200/K-12
1464 Industry Rd 44201 330-947-2664
Andrew Hill, supt. Fax 947-2847
www.viking.portage.k12.oh.us
Waterloo HS 400/9-12
1464 Industry Rd 44201 330-947-2124
Nick Hulea, prin. Fax 947-1911
Waterloo MS 300/6-8
1464 Industry Rd 44201 330-947-0033
Matt Montgomery, prin. Fax 947-4073

Aurora, Portage, Pop. 15,422
Aurora CSD 2,800/PK-12
102 E Garfield Rd 44202 330-562-6106
Russell Bennett, supt. Fax 562-4892
www.aurora-schools.org
Aurora HS 1,000/9-12
109 W Pioneer Trl 44202 330-562-3501
Mike Roberto, prin. Fax 562-3588
Harmon MS 700/6-8
130 Aurora Hudson Rd 44202 330-562-3375
Mark Abramovich, prin. Fax 562-4796

Austinburg, Ashtabula, Pop. 512

Grand River Academy 100/9-12
PO Box 222 44010 440-275-2811
Tim Viands, hdmstr. Fax 275-1825

Austintown, Mahoning, Pop. 31,500

Hair Academy Post-Sec.
6000 Mahoning Ave 44515 330-792-6504

Avon, Lorain, Pop. 20,897
Avon Local SD 3,900/K-12
35573 Detroit Rd 44011 440-937-4680
Mike Laub, supt. Fax 937-4688
www.avonlocalschools.org/
Avon HS 1,000/9-12
37545 Detroit Rd 44011 440-934-6171
Kristina Buller, prin. Fax 934-5450
Avon MS 600/7-8
3075 Stoney Ridge Rd 44011 440-934-3800
Dr. Craig Koehler, prin. Fax 934-3803

Avon Lake, Lorain, Pop. 22,318
Avon Lake CSD 3,700/K-12
175 Avon Belden Rd 44012 440-933-6210
Robert Scott, supt. Fax 933-6711
www.avonlakecityschools.org
Avon Lake HS 1,200/9-12
175 Avon Belden Rd 44012 440-933-6290
Joanie Walker Ed.D., prin. Fax 930-2798
Learwood MS 600/7-8
340 Lear Rd 44012 440-933-8142
Jane Ramsay, prin. Fax 933-8406

Bainbridge, Ross, Pop. 838
Paint Valley Local SD 1,000/K-12
7454 US Highway 50 W 45612 740-634-2826
Timothy Winland, supt. Fax 634-2890
paintvalleylocalschools.org
Paint Valley HS 300/9-12
7454 US Highway 50 W 45612 740-634-3582
Casey Smith, prin. Fax 634-3518
Paint Valley MS 200/6-8
7454 US Highway 50 W 45612 740-634-3512
Heather Bowles, prin. Fax 634-3459

Baltimore, Fairfield, Pop. 2,921
Liberty Union-Thurston Local SD 1,300/K-12
1108 S Main St 43105 740-862-4171
Paul Mathews, supt. Fax 862-2015
www.libertyunion.org
Liberty Union HS 400/9-12
500 W Washington St 43105 740-862-4107
Ed Miller, prin. Fax 862-4100
Liberty Union MS 400/5-8
994 S Main St 43105 740-862-4126
Tim Turner, prin. Fax 862-0239

Barberton, Summit, Pop. 25,978
Barberton CSD 1,700/K-12
479 Norton Ave 44203 330-753-1025
Patti Cleary, supt. Fax 848-0884
www.barbertonschools.org
Barberton HS 1,200/9-12
555 Barber Rd 44203 330-753-1084
Jeff Ramnytz, prin. Fax 848-5517
Barberton MS 400/5-8
477 4th St NW 44203 330-745-9950
Joyce Walker, prin. Fax 745-9962

Barnesville, Belmont, Pop. 4,130
Barnesville EVD 1,100/K-12
210 W Church St 43713 740-425-3615
Randy Lucas, supt. Fax 425-5000
www.barnesville.k12.oh.us/
Barnesville HS 300/9-12
910 Shamrock Dr 43713 740-425-3617
Jeff Crosier, prin. Fax 425-9254
Barnesville MS 300/5-8
970 Shamrock Dr 43713 740-425-3116
Julie Erwin, prin. Fax 425-9204

Olney Friends S 100/9-12
61830 Sandy Ridge Rd 43713 740-425-3655
Charlie Szumilas, head sch Fax 425-3202

Bascom, Seneca, Pop. 390
Hopewell-Loudon Local SD 900/K-12
PO Box 400 44809 419-937-2216
Nichole Jiran, supt. Fax 937-2516
www.hlschool.org/
Hopewell-Loudon Local JSHS 400/7-12
PO Box 400 44809 419-937-2216
Bill Dobbins, prin. Fax 937-2516

Batavia, Clermont, Pop. 1,482
Batavia Local SD 2,000/K-12
2400 Clermont Center Dr 45103 513-732-2343
Jill Grubb, supt. Fax 732-3221
www.bataviaschools.org
Batavia HS 500/9-12
1 Bulldog Pl 45103 513-732-2341
Jamie Corrill, prin. Fax 732-9740
Batavia MS 600/5-8
800 Bauer Ave 45103 513-732-9534
Susan Hakel, prin. Fax 732-3696

Clermont County ESC
2400 Clermont Center Dr 45103 513-735-8300
Jeff Weir, supt. Fax 735-8371
www.ccesc.org/
Other Schools – See Williamsburg

Clermont Northeastern Local SD 1,600/K-12
2792 US Highway 50 45103 513-625-5478
Ralph Shell, supt. Fax 625-6080
www.cneschools.org
Clermont Northeastern HS 500/9-12
5327 Hutchinson Rd 45103 513-625-1211
John Eckert, prin. Fax 625-3328
Clermont Northeastern MS 400/6-8
2792 US Highway 50 45103 513-625-1211
Heather Powell, prin. Fax 625-3325

West Clermont Local SD
Supt. — See Cincinnati
Amelia HS 1,100/9-12
1351 Clough Pike 45103 513-947-7400
Keith Hickman, prin. Fax 753-2419
Amelia MS 1,000/6-8
1341 Clough Pike 45103 513-947-7500
Keith Hickman, prin. Fax 753-7851

University of Cincinnati Post-Sec.
4200 Clermont College Dr 45103 513-732-5200

Bath, Summit
Revere Local SD
Supt. — See Richfield
Revere HS 1,000/9-12
3420 Everett Rd 44210 330-659-6111
Phil King, prin. Fax 659-6407
Revere MS 700/6-8
PO Box 339 44210 330-666-4155
Judy Myers, prin. Fax 659-3795

Bay Village, Cuyahoga, Pop. 15,468
Bay Village CSD 2,500/K-12
377 Dover Center Rd 44140 440-617-7300
Clinton Keener, supt. Fax 617-7301
www.bayvillageschools.com
Bay HS 800/9-12
29230 Wolf Rd 44140 440-617-7400
Jason Martin, prin. Fax 617-7401
Bay MS 800/5-8
27725 Wolf Rd 44140 440-617-7600
Sean McAndrews, prin. Fax 617-7601

Beachwood, Cuyahoga, Pop. 11,798
Beachwood CSD 1,600/PK-12
24601 Fairmount Blvd 44122 216-464-2600
Dr. Richard Markwardt, supt. Fax 292-2340
www.beachwoodschools.org/
Beachwood HS 700/9-12
25100 Fairmount Blvd 44122 216-831-2080
Edward Klein, prin. Fax 292-4169
Beachwood MS 300/6-8
2860 Richmond Rd 44122 216-831-0355
Linda LoGalbo, prin. Fax 831-1891

Fuchs Mizrachi S 400/PK-12
26600 Shaker Blvd 44122 216-932-0220

Beallsville, Monroe, Pop. 400
Switzerland of Ohio Local SD
Supt. — See Woodsfield
Beallsville JSHS 200/7-12
PO Box 262 43716 740-926-1302
Micah Fuchs, prin. Fax 926-1394

Beaver, Pike, Pop. 431
Eastern Local SD 800/PK-12
1170 Tile Mill Rd 45613 740-226-4851
Neil Leist, supt. Fax 226-1331
www.ep.k12.oh.us
Eastern HS 200/9-12
1170 Tile Mill Rd 45613 740-226-1544
Matt Hines, prin. Fax 226-6322
Eastern MS 200/6-8
1170 Tile Mill Rd 45613 740-226-1544
Matt Hines, prin. Fax 226-6322

Beavercreek, Greene, Pop. 44,171
Beavercreek CSD 7,900/PK-12
3040 Kemp Rd 45431 937-426-1522
Dr. William McGlothlin, supt. Fax 429-7517
www.beavercreek.k12.oh.us/
Ankeney MS 900/6-8
4085 Shakertown Rd 45430 937-429-7567
James Rhoades, prin. Fax 429-7685
Beavercreek HS 2,500/9-12
2660 Dayton Xenia Rd 45434 937-429-7547
Marian West, prin. Fax 429-7546
Ferguson MS 1,000/6-8
2680 Dayton Xenia Rd 45434 937-429-7577
Brad Wolgast, prin. Fax 429-7686

Bedford, Cuyahoga, Pop. 12,768
Bedford CSD 3,700/PK-12
475 Northfield Rd 44146 440-439-1500
Sherman Micsak, supt. Fax 439-4850
www.bedford.k12.oh.us
Bedford HS 1,200/9-12
481 Northfield Rd 44146 440-439-4848
Samuel Vawters, prin. Fax 439-4627
Other Schools – See Bedford Heights

St. Peter Chanel HS 300/9-12
480 Northfield Rd 44146 440-232-5900
Sr. Maria Berlec, pres. Fax 232-9283

Bedford Heights, Cuyahoga, Pop. 10,538
Bedford CSD
Supt. — See Bedford
Heskett MS 600/7-8
5771 Perkins Rd 44146 440-439-4450
Virginia Golden, prin. Fax 786-3572

Bellaire, Belmont, Pop. 4,190
Bellaire Local SD 1,300/K-12
340 34th St 43906 740-676-1826
Tony Scott, supt. Fax 671-6002
www.bellaire.k12.oh.us
Bellaire HS 300/9-12
349 35th St 43906 740-676-3652
Stephen Romey, prin. Fax 671-6004
Bellaire MS 400/5-8
54555 Neffs Bellaire Rd 43906 740-676-1635
Derrick McAfee, prin. Fax 676-3014

St. John Central HS 100/9-12
3625 Guernsey St 43906 740-676-4932
Sheila Blackmore, prin. Fax 676-4934

Bellbrook, Greene, Pop. 6,854
Bellbrook-Sugarcreek Local SD 2,600/PK-12
3757 Upper Bellbrook Rd 45305 937-848-6251
Dr. Keith St. Pierre, supt. Fax 848-5018
www.sugarcreek.k12.oh.us
Bellbrook HS 800/9-12
3737 Upper Bellbrook Rd 45305 937-848-3737
Christopher Baker, prin. Fax 848-5016
Bellbrook MS 600/6-8
3600 Feedwire Rd 45305 937-848-2141
Jenness Sigman, prin. Fax 848-2152

Bellefontaine, Logan, Pop. 12,899
Bellefontaine CSD 2,600/K-12
820 Ludlow Rd 43311 937-593-9060
Beth Harman, supt. Fax 599-1346
www.bellefontaine.k12.oh.us/
Bellefontaine HS 800/9-12
555 E Lake Ave 43311 937-593-0545
Christine Galvin, prin. Fax 593-0575
Bellefontaine MS 600/6-8
509 N Park St 43311 937-593-9010
Shanel Henry, prin. Fax 593-9030

Benjamin Logan Local SD 1,800/K-12
4740 County Road 26 43311 937-593-9211
Lori Lytle, supt. Fax 599-4059
www.benlogan.k12.oh.us
Logan HS 600/9-12
6609 State Route 47 E 43311 937-592-1666
Mark Butler, prin. Fax 599-4061
Logan MS 600/5-8
4626 County Road 26 43311 937-599-2386
Deb Johnson, prin. Fax 599-4062

Ohio Hi-Point Career Center
2280 State Route 540 43311 937-599-3010
Jeffrey Price, supt. Fax 599-2318
www.ohiohipoint.com
Ohio Hi-Point Career Center Vo/Tech
2280 State Route 540 43311 937-599-3010
Fax 599-2318

Bellevue, Huron, Pop. 8,079
Bellevue CSD 2,000/PK 12
125 North St 44811 419-484-5000
Kim Schubert, supt. Fax 483-0723
www.bellevueschools.org
Bellevue HS 700/9-12
200 Oakland Ave 44811 419-484-5070
Nate Artino, prin. Fax 483-7157
Bellevue MS 500/6-8
1035 Castalia St 44811 419-484-5060
John Bollinger, prin. Fax 484-5096

Bellville, Richland, Pop. 1,888
Clear Fork Valley Local SD 1,800/K-12
92 Hines Ave 44813 419-886-3855
Matthew Dill, supt. Fax 886-2237
www.clearfork.k12.oh.us
Clear Fork HS 500/9-12
987 State Route 97 E 44813 419-886-2601
Brian Brown, prin. Fax 886-4749
Clear Fork MS 400/6-8
987 State Route 97 E 44813 419-886-3111
Steve Bloir, prin. Fax 886-4749

Belmont, Belmont, Pop. 449
Union Local SD 1,500/PK-12
66779 Belmont Morristown Rd 43718 740-782-1978
H. Kirk Glasgow, supt. Fax 782-1212
www.ulschools.com
Union Local HS 400/9-12
66779 Belmont Morristown Rd 43718 740-782-1181
Joel Davia, prin. Fax 782-1346
Union Local MS 400/6-8
66859 Belmont Morristown Rd 43718 740-782-1388
Ben Porter, prin. Fax 782-1474

Beloit, Mahoning, Pop. 960
West Branch Local SD 1,900/K-12
14277 S Main St 44609 330-938-9324
Dr. Scott Weingart, supt. Fax 938-6815
www.westbranch.k12.oh.us
West Branch HS 700/9-12
14277 S Main St 44609 330-938-2183
Brian Coffee, prin. Fax 938-4444
West Branch MS 600/5-8
14409 Beloit Snodes Rd 44609 330-938-4300
Roger Kitzmiller, prin. Fax 938-4301

Belpre, Washington, Pop. 6,292
Belpre CSD 1,000/K-12
2014 Rockland Ave 45714 740-423-9511
Tony Dunn, supt. Fax 423-3050
www.belpre.k12.oh.us
Belpre JSHS 400/7-12
612 3rd St 45714 740-423-3000
Dennis Eichinger, prin. Fax 423-3003

Berea, Cuyahoga, Pop. 18,699
Berea CSD 3,700/PK-12
390 Fair St 44017 216-898-8300
Michael Sheppard, supt. Fax 898-8551
www.berea.k12.oh.us
Berea-Midpark HS 800/10-12
165 E Bagley Rd 44017 216-898-8900
Vincenzo Ruggiero, prin. Fax 898-8558
Other Schools – See Middleburg Heights

Baldwin-Wallace University Post-Sec.
275 Eastland Rd 44017 440-826-2900

Berlin, Holmes, Pop. 892
East Holmes Local SD 1,800/K-12
PO Box 182 44610 330-893-2610
Joseph Edinger, supt. Fax 893-2838
www.eastholmesschools.org
Hiland JSHS 400/7-12
PO Box 275 44610 330-893-2626
Matthew Johnson, prin. Fax 893-3570

Other Schools – See Charm

Berlin Center, Mahoning
Western Reserve Local SD 800/K-12
13850 W Akron Canfield Rd 44401 330-547-4100
Jeffrey Zatchok, supt. Fax 547-9302
www.westernreserve.k12.oh.us
Western Reserve S 800/K-12
13850 W Akron Canfield Rd 44401 330-547-4100
Jeffrey Zatchok, supt. Fax 547-9302

Berlin Heights, Erie, Pop. 698
Edison Local SD
Supt. — See Milan
Edison MS 300/4-8
20 Center St 44814 419-588-2078
Bethany Stipp, prin. Fax 588-3212

Bethel, Clermont, Pop. 2,658
Bethel-Tate Local SD 1,800/K-12
675 W Plane St 45106 513-734-2271
Melissa Kircher, supt. Fax 734-4792
www.betheltate.org
Bethel-Tate HS 500/9-12
3420 State Route 125 45106 513-734-2271
Susen Arn, prin. Fax 734-1355
Bethel-Tate MS 400/6-8
649 W Plane St 45106 513-734-2271
Steve Gill, prin. Fax 734-0888

U.S. Grant JVSD
718 W Plane St 45106 513-734-6222
Lisa Tuttle-Huff, supt. Fax 734-4758
www.grantcareer.com
Grant Career Center Vo/Tech
718 W Plane St 45106 513-734-6222
Barry L. Daulton, prin. Fax 734-4758

Bettsville, Seneca, Pop. 659
Bettsville Local SD 100/K-12
PO Box 6 44815 419-986-5166
Gregg Pettit, supt. Fax 986-6039
www.bettsville.k12.oh.us/
Bettsville S 100/K-12
PO Box 6 44815 419-986-5166
Michelle Dantuono, prin. Fax 986-6039

Beverly, Washington, Pop. 1,285
Fort Frye Local SD 1,000/K-12
PO Box 1149 45715 740-984-2497
Thomas Gibbs, supt. Fax 984-8784
www.fortfrye.k12.oh.us
Ft. Frye JSHS 500/7-12
PO Box 1089 45715 740-984-2376
Susan Rauch, prin. Fax 984-4361

Bexley, Franklin, Pop. 12,740
Bexley CSD 2,100/K-12
348 S Cassingham Rd 43209 614-231-7611
Dr. Michael Johnson, supt. Fax 231-8448
www.bexleyschools.org
Bexley HS 700/9-12
326 S Cassingham Rd 43209 614-231-4591
Harley Williams, prin. Fax 338-2087
Bexley MS 300/7-8
300 S Cassingham Rd 43209 614-237-4277
Jason Caudill, prin. Fax 338-2090

Bidwell, Gallia
Gallia County Local SD
Supt. — See Gallipolis
River Valley HS 400/9-12
8785 State Route 160 45614 740-446-2926
Timothy Edwards, prin. Fax 446-7382
River Valley MS 400/6-8
8779 State Route 160 45614 740-446-8399
David Moore, prin. Fax 441-3038

Blanchester, Clinton, Pop. 4,195
Blanchester Local SD 1,700/PK-12
951 Cherry St 45107 937-783-3523
Brian Ruckel, supt. Fax 783-2990
www.blanchester.k12.oh.us/
Blanchester HS 500/9-12
953 Cherry St 45107 937-783-2461
Rick Hosler, prin. Fax 783-5666
Blanchester MS 400/6-8
955 Cherry St 45107 937-783-3642
Joel King, prin. Fax 783-3477

Bloomdale, Wood, Pop. 675
Elmwood Local SD 1,300/PK-12
7650 Jerry City Rd 44817 419-655-2583
Tony Borton, supt. Fax 655-3995
www.elmwood.k12.oh.us
Elmwood HS 400/9-12
7650 Jerry City Rd 44817 419-655-2583
Tom Bentley, prin. Fax 655-2153
Elmwood MS 400/5-8
7650 Jerry City Rd 44817 419-655-2583
Dean Bell, prin. Fax 655-2153

Bloomingdale, Jefferson, Pop. 200
Jefferson County JVSD
1509 County Road 22A 43910 740-264-5545
Dale Edwards, supt. Fax 264-3144
www.jcjvs.k12.oh.us
Jefferson County Vocational S Vo/Tech
1509 County Road 22A 43910 740-264-5545
Todd Phillipson, prin. Fax 264-3144

Blue Ash, Hamilton, Pop. 11,860

Hondros College Post-Sec.
4675 Cornell Rd Ste 175 45241 513-247-9711
University of Cincinnati Post-Sec.
9555 Plainfield Rd 45236 513-745-5600

Bluffton, Allen, Pop. 4,072
Bluffton EVD 1,100/K-12
102 S Jackson St 45817 419-358-5901
Gregory Denecker, supt. Fax 358-4871
www.blufftonschools.org
Bluffton HS 300/9-12
106 W College Ave 45817 419-358-7941
Michael Minnig, prin. Fax 358-6586
Bluffton MS 300/6-8
116 S Jackson St 45817 419-358-7961
Dean Giesige, prin. Fax 358-4871

Bluffton University Post-Sec.
1 University Dr 45817 419-358-3000

Botkins, Shelby, Pop. 1,145
Botkins Local SD 300/K-12
PO Box 550 45306 937-693-4241
Connie Schneider, supt. Fax 693-2557
www.botkins.k12.oh.us
Botkins S 300/K-12
PO Box 550 45306 937-693-4241
Jeff McPheron, prin. Fax 693-2557

Bowerston, Harrison, Pop. 397
Conotton Valley Union Local SD
Supt. — See Sherrodsville
Connotton Valley JSHS 200/7-12
7205 Cumberland Rd SW 44695 740-269-2711
Jerry Herman, prin. Fax 269-4405

Bowling Green, Wood, Pop. 29,467
Bowling Green CSD 2,900/PK-12
137 Clough St 43402 419-352-3576
Ann McVey, supt. Fax 352-1701
www.bgcs.k12.oh.us
Bowling Green HS 900/9-12
530 W Poe Rd 43402 419-354-0100
Jeff Dever, prin. Fax 354-1839
Bowling Green MS 500/7-8
1079 Fairview Ave 43402 419-354-0200
Joseph Zabowski, prin. Fax 353-1958

Bowling Green Christian Academy 200/PK-12
1165 Haskins Rd 43402 419-354-2422
Wendie Cuckler, prin. Fax 354-0232
Bowling Green State University Post-Sec.
110 McFall Ctr 43403 419-372-2531

Bradford, Darke, Pop. 1,831
Bradford EVD 600/K-12
760 Railroad Ave 45308 937-448-2770
David Warvel, supt. Fax 448-2493
www.bradford.k12.oh.us/
Bradford JSHS 300/6-12
750 Railroad Ave 45308 937-448-2719
P.J. Burgett, prin. Fax 448-2742

Brecksville, Cuyahoga, Pop. 13,500
Brecksville-Broadview Heights CSD 4,300/K-12
6638 Mill Rd 44141 440-740-4000
Scot Prebles, supt. Fax 740-4004
www.bbhcsd.org
Other Schools – See Broadview Heights

Cuyahoga Valley Career Center
8001 Brecksville Rd 44141 440-526-5200
Dr. Celena Roebuck, supt. Fax 746-8298
www.cvccworks.com
Cuyahoga Valley Career Center Vo/Tech
8001 Brecksville Rd 44141 440-526-5200
Mike Hall, prin. Fax 746-8299

Stautzenberger College Post-Sec.
8001 Katherine Blvd 44141 440-838-1999

Bridgeport, Belmont, Pop. 1,773
Bridgeport EVD 800/PK-12
55781 National Rd 43912 740-635-1713
Ted Downing, supt. Fax 635-6003
www.bevs.k12.oh.us/
Bridgeport HS 300/9-12
55707 Industrial Dr 43912 740-635-0853
Rob Zitzelsberger, prin. Fax 635-6008
Bridgeport MS 200/5-8
55707 Industrial Dr 43912 740-635-0853
Anne Haverty, prin. Fax 635-6003

Bristolville, Trumbull
Bristol Local SD 700/K-12
PO Box 260 44402 330-889-3882
Chrisopher Dray, supt. Fax 889-2529
www.bristol.k12.oh.us
Bristol HS 300/7-12
PO Box 260 44402 330-889-2621
Tracey Ryser, prin. Fax 889-2529

Broadview Heights, Cuyahoga, Pop. 19,168
Brecksville-Broadview Heights CSD
Supt. — See Brecksville
Brecksville-Broadview Heights HS 1,600/9-12
6380 Mill Rd 44147 440-740-4700
Joseph Mueller, prin. Fax 740-4704
Brecksville-Broadview Heights MS 1,100/6-8
6376 Mill Rd 44147 440-740-4400
Patrick Farrell, prin. Fax 740-4404

Vatterott College Post-Sec.
5025 E Royalton Rd 44147 440-526-1660

Brookfield, Trumbull
Brookfield Local SD 1,100/K-12
614 Bedford Rd SE 44403 330-448-4930
Tim Saxton, supt. Fax 448-5026
www.brookfield.k12.oh.us
Brookfield HS 400/9-12
614 Bedford Rd SE 44403 330-448-3001
Velina Taylor, prin. Fax 448-8016

Brookfield MS 400/5-8
614 Bedford Rd SE 44403 330-448-3003
Shari Baxter, prin. Fax 448-5028

Brooklyn, Cuyahoga, Pop. 10,955
Brooklyn CSD 1,200/K-12
9200 Biddulph Rd 44144 216-485-8110
Cynthia Walker, supt. Fax 485-8118
www.brooklyn.k12.oh.us/
Brooklyn HS 500/8-12
9200 Biddulph Rd 44144 216-485-8163
Antoinette Hostetler, prin. Fax 485-8124

Brookville, Montgomery, Pop. 5,844
Brookville Local SD 1,400/K-12
75 June Pl 45309 937-833-2181
Timothy Hopkins, supt. Fax 833-2787
www.brookvilleschools.org
Brookville HS 400/9-12
1 Blue Pride Dr 45309 937-833-6761
Christopher Bronner, prin. Fax 833-6302
Brookville IS 600/4-8
2 Blue Pride Dr 45309 937-833-6731
Amy Anyanwu, prin. Fax 833-6756

Brunswick, Medina, Pop. 33,855
Brunswick CSD 7,200/PK-12
3643 Center Rd 44212 330-225-7731
Michael Mayell, supt. Fax 273-0507
www.bcsoh.org
Brunswick HS 2,200/9-12
3581 Center Rd 44212 330-225-7731
Michael Draves, prin. Fax 225-5393
Edwards MS 500/6-8
1497 Pearl Rd 44212 330-225-7731
Heidi Armentrout, prin. Fax 273-0519
Visintainer MS 500/6-8
1459 Pearl Rd 44212 330-225-7731
Brian Sharosky, prin. Fax 273-0400
Willetts MS 700/6-8
1045 Hadcock Rd 44212 330-225-7731
Brian Miller, prin. Fax 273-0222

Bryan, Williams, Pop. 8,426
Bryan CSD 2,000/PK-12
1350 Fountain Grove Dr 43506 419-636-6973
Diana Savage, supt. Fax 633-6280
www.bryan.k12.oh.us
Bryan HS 600/9-12
150 S Portland St 43506 419-636-4536
Steve Alspaugh, prin. Fax 633-6281
Bryan MS 800/4-8
1301 Center St 43506 419-636-6766
Chad Bassett, prin. Fax 633-6282

Fountain City Christian S 50/K-12
PO Box 150 43506 419-636-2333
Troy Cummins, admin. Fax 636-2888

Bucyrus, Crawford, Pop. 12,227
Bucyrus CSD 1,600/PK-12
170 Plymouth St 44820 419-562-4045
Kevin Kimmel, supt. Fax 562-3990
www.bucyrusschools.org
Bucyrus HS 400/9-12
900 W Perry St 44820 419-562-7721
Matthew Henderson, prin. Fax 562-7819
Bucyrus MS 300/6-8
455 Redman Way 44820 419-562-0003
John Massara, admin. Fax 562-1773

Wynford Local SD 1,100/PK-12
3288 Holmes Center Rd 44820 419-562-7828
Steve Mohr, supt. Fax 562-7825
www.wynford.k12.oh.us
Wynford HS 200/10-12
3288 Holmes Center Rd 44820 419-562-7828
Jeffrey Holbrook, prin. Fax 562-7825
Wynford JHS 300/7-9
3288 Holmes Center Rd 44820 419-562-7828
Jeffrey Holbrook, prin. Fax 562-7825

Burton, Geauga, Pop. 1,446
Berkshire Local SD 1,100/K-12
PO Box 364 44021 440-834-3380
Douglas DeLong, supt.
www.berkshire.k12.oh.us
Berkshire JSHS, PO Box 365 44021 600/7-12
Steve Reedy, prin. 440-834-3380

Kent State University-Geauga Campus Post-Sec.
14111 Claridon Troy Rd 44021 440-834-4187

Byesville, Guernsey, Pop. 2,409
Rolling Hills Local SD
Supt. — See Cambridge
Meadowbrook HS 500/9-12
58615 Marietta Rd 43723 740-685-2566
Keith Arnold, prin. Fax 685-2797
Meadowbrook MS 500/6-8
58607 Marietta Rd 43723 740-685-2561
J.P. Wray, admin. Fax 685-2628

Cadiz, Harrison, Pop. 3,237
Belmont-Harrison Area JVSD
Supt. — See Saint Clairsville
Harrison Career Center Vo/Tech
82500 Cadiz Jewett Rd 43907 740-942-2148
Larry Bossell, lead tchr. Fax 695-4866

Harrison Hills CSD 1,200/PK-12
730 Peppard Ave 43907 740-942-7800
George Ash, supt. Fax 942-7808
www.hhcsd.org/
Harrison Central JSHS 700/7-12
440 E Market St 43907 740-942-7700
Mark Kowalski, prin. Fax 942-7705

Caldwell, Noble, Pop. 1,727
Caldwell EVD 800/K-12
516 Fairground St 43724 740-732-5637
William Brelsford, supt. Fax 732-7303
www.caldwell.k12.oh.us/
Caldwell HS, 516 Fairground St 43724 200/9-12
Robert Podlasiak, prin. 740-732-5634

Caledonia, Marion, Pop. 572
River Valley Local SD 2,000/K-12
197 Brocklesby Rd 43314 740-725-5400
Thomas Shade, supt. Fax 725-5499
www.rivervalley.k12.oh.us
River Valley HS 500/9-12
4280 Marion Mount Gilead Rd 43314 740-725-5800
David Coleman, prin. Fax 725-5899
River Valley MS 500/6-8
4334 Marion Mount Gilead Rd 43314 740-725-5700
Donald Gliebe, prin. Fax 725-5799

Cambridge, Guernsey, Pop. 10,324
Cambridge CSD 2,200/K-12
6111 Fairdale Dr 43725 740-439-5021
Dennis Dettra, supt. Fax 439-3796
www.cambridge.k12.oh.us/
Cambridge HS 600/9-12
1401 Deerpath Dr 43725 740-435-1100
Scott Eldredge, prin. Fax 435-1101
Cambridge MS 600/6-8
1400 Deerpath Dr 43725 740-435-1140
Duane Poland, prin. Fax 435-1141

Rolling Hills Local SD 1,700/K-12
60851 Southgate Rd 43725 740-432-6952
Ryan Caldwell, supt. Fax 432-6523
www.rollinghills.k12.oh.us
Other Schools – See Byesville

Camden, Preble, Pop. 2,033
Preble Shawnee Local SD 1,400/PK-12
124 Bloomfield St 45311 937-452-3323
Dale Robertson, supt. Fax 452-3926
www.preble-shawnee.k12.oh.us
Preble Shawnee JSHS 600/7-12
5495 Somers Gratis Rd 45311 937-787-3541
Dianna Whitis, prin. Fax 787-3664

Campbell, Mahoning, Pop. 8,033
Campbell CSD 1,100/K-12
280 6th St 44405 330-799-8777
Thomas Robey, supt. Fax 799-0875
Memorial HS 300/8-12
280 6th St 44405 330-799-1515
Jacquelyn Hampton, prin. Fax 799-6390

Canal Fulton, Stark, Pop. 5,390
Northwest Local SD 2,100/K-12
2309 Locust St S 44614 330-854-2291
Dr. Michael Shreffler, supt. Fax 854-3591
www.northwest.sparcc.org/
Northwest HS 600/9-12
8580 Erie Ave NW 44614 330-854-2205
Eric Bornstine, prin. Fax 854-2030
Northwest MS 500/6-8
8614 Erie Ave NW 44614 330-854-3303
Larry Tausch, prin. Fax 854-5883

Canal Winchester, Franklin, Pop. 6,995
Canal Winchester Local SD 3,500/K-12
100 Washington St 43110 614-837-4533
James Sotlar, supt. Fax 833-2165
www.cwschools.org
Canal Winchester HS 1,000/9-12
300 Washington St 43110 614-833-2157
Kirk Henderson, prin. Fax 833-2163
Canal Winchester MS 900/6-8
7155 Parkview Dr 43110 614-833-2151
Cassandra Miller, prin. Fax 833-2173

Harvest Preparatory S 600/PK-12
PO Box 400 43110 614-382-1111
Jack Johnson M.A., supt. Fax 382-1143

Canfield, Mahoning, Pop. 7,448
Canfield Local SD 3,000/K-12
100 Wadsworth St 44406 330-533-3303
Alex Geordan, supt. Fax 533-6827
www.canfieldschools.net/
Canfield HS 1,000/9-12
100 Cardinal Dr 44406 330-533-5507
John Tullio, prin. Fax 533-1919
Canfield Village MS 900/5-8
42 Wadsworth St 44406 330-533-4019
Joseph Maroni, prin. Fax 702-7064

Mahoning County Career & Technical Ctr
7300 N Palmyra Rd 44406 330-729-4000
Dr. Roan Craig, supt. Fax 729-4050
www.mahoningctc.com
Mahoning County Career & Technical Ctr Vo/Tech
7300 N Palmyra Rd 44406 330-729-4000
Jane Hogan, dir. Fax 729-4015

South Range Local SD 1,300/K-12
11300 Columbiana Canfield 44406 330-549-5226
Dennis J. Dunham, supt. Fax 549-4740
www.southrange.k12.oh.us/
South Range HS 400/9-12
11300 Columbiana Canfield 44406 330-549-2163
Stephen Rohan, prin. Fax 549-4083
South Range MS 400/5-8
11300 Columbiana Canfield 44406 330-549-4071
Daniel Szolek, prin. Fax 549-4073

Canton, Stark, Pop. 69,508
Canton CSD 9,900/PK-12
305 McKinley Ave NW 44702 330-438-2500
Chris Smith, supt. Fax 430-4230
www.ccsdistrict.org
Choices Alternative S 200/Alt
401 14th St SE 44707 330-451-3300
Timothy Henderson, prin. Fax 451-3301
Connections Academy 50/Alt
401 14th St SE 44707 330-456-1189
Tim Henderson, prin. Fax 580-2404
Crenshaw MS 400/7-8
2525 19th St NE 44705 330-454-7717
Wanda Grubbs, prin. Fax 588-2120
Early College Academy 7-8
1510 Clarendon Ave NW 44708 330-438-2736
Micki Senter, prin.
Early College HS 9-12
231 McKinley Ave NW 44702 330-458-3950
Ken Brunner, prin. Fax 458-3980
Hartford MS 200/7-8
1824 3rd St SE 44707 330-453-6012
Sandy Womack, prin. Fax 453-5096
Lehman MS 700/7-8
1400 Broad Ave NW 44708 330-456-1963
Jeanne McNeal, prin. Fax 456-8121
McKinley HS 1,600/9-12
2323 17th St NW 44708 330-438-2712
Chet Lenartowicz, prin. Fax 580-2712
Passages HS Alt
401 14th St SE 44707 330-438-2678
Timothy Henderson, prin. Fax 438-2679
Timken HS 1,000/9-12
521 Tuscarawas St W 44702 330-438-2602
Corey Grubbs, prin. Fax 580-3508

Canton Local SD 2,300/PK-12
4526 Ridge Ave SE 44707 330-484-8010
Kim Redmond, supt. Fax 484-8032
www.cantonlocal.org
Canton South HS 900/9-12
600 Faircrest St SE 44707 330-484-8000
Todd Osborn, prin. Fax 484-8013
Faircrest Memorial MS 700/5-8
616 Faircrest St SW 44706 330-484-8015
Gay Welker, prin. Fax 484-8033

Plain Local SD 5,900/K-12
901 44th St NW 44709 330-492-3500
Brent May, supt. Fax 493-5542
www.plainlocal.org/
Glenoak HS 2,000/9-12
1801 Schneider St NE 44721 330-491-3800
Ken Faye, prin. Fax 491-3801
Glenwood MS 600/6-8
1015 44th St NW 44709 330-491-3780
Jerad Buck, prin. Fax 491-3781
Oakwood MS 700/6-8
2300 Schneider St NE 44721 330-491-3790
Brian Matthews, prin. Fax 491-3791

Aultman College Nursing and Health Sci Post-Sec.
2600 6th St SW 44710 330-363-6347
Brown Mackie College Post-Sec.
4300 Munson St NW 44718 330-494-1214
Central Catholic HS 500/9-12
4824 Tuscarawas St W 44708 330-478-2131
David Oates, prin. Fax 478-6086
Heritage Christian S 200/PK-12
2107 6th St SW 44706 330-452-8271
Charles Riddle A.B., admin. Fax 452-0672
Malone University Post-Sec.
2600 Cleveland Ave NW 44709 330-471-8100
National Beauty College Post-Sec.
4642 Cleveland Ave NW 44709 330-499-9444
National College Post-Sec.
4736 Dressler Rd NW 44718 330-492-5300
Timken Mercy Medical Center Post-Sec.
1320 Mercy Dr NW 44708 330-489-1001

Cardington, Morrow, Pop. 2,023
Cardington-Lincoln Local SD 1,100/K-12
121 Nichols St 43315 419-864-3691
Brian Petrie, supt. Fax 864-0946
www.cardington.k12.oh.us
Cardington-Lincoln HS 300/9-12
349 Chesterville Ave 43315 419-864-2691
Joseph Mills, prin. Fax 864-9515
Cardington-Lincoln JHS 200/7-8
349 Chesterville Ave 43315 419-864-0609
Joseph Mills, admin. Fax 864-3168

Carey, Wyandot, Pop. 3,640
Carey EVD 900/K-12
357 E South St 43316 419-396-7922
Mark Vehre, supt. Fax 396-3158
careyevs.schoolwires.com/
Carey JSHS 400/7-12
357 E South St 43316 419-396-7638
Peter Cole, prin. Fax 396-3158

Carlisle, Warren, Pop. 4,885
Carlisle Local SD 1,700/PK-12
724 Fairview Dr 45005 937-746-0710
Larry Hook, supt. Fax 746-0438
www.carlisleindians.org
Carlisle HS 400/9-12
250 Jamaica Rd 45005 937-746-4481
Matt Bishop, prin. Fax 746-6578
Chamberlain MS 400/6-8
720 Fairview Dr 45005 937-746-3227
Dan Turner, prin. Fax 746-0519

Carroll, Fairfield, Pop. 510
Bloom-Carroll Local SD 1,500/K-12
PO Box 338 43112 614-837-6560
Lynn Landis, supt. Fax 756-4221
www.bloomcarroll.net
Bloom-Carroll HS 500/9-12
5240 Plum Rd 43112 740-756-4317
Bob Richards, prin. Fax 756-9525
Bloom-Carroll MS 400/5-8
PO Box 338 43112 740-756-9231
Mark Fenik, prin. Fax 756-7466

Eastland-Fairfield Career & Technical SD
Supt. — See Groveport
Fairfield Career Center — Vo/Tech
3985 Coonpath Rd 43112 — 614-837-9443
Shelley Groves, dir. — Fax 837-9447

Carrollton, Carroll, Pop. 3,218
Carrollton EVD — 2,400/PK-12
252 3rd St NE 44615 — 330-627-2181
David Quattrochi, supt. — Fax 627-2182
www.carrolltonschools.org
Bell-Herron MS — 600/6-8
252 3rd St NE 44615 — 330-627-7188
Tricia Green, prin. — Fax 627-8429
Carrollton HS — 700/9-12
252 3rd St NE 44615 — 330-627-2134
David Davis, prin. — Fax 627-8103

Casstown, Miami, Pop. 267
Miami East Local SD — 1,200/K-12
3825 N State Route 589 45312 — 937-335-7505
Dr. Todd Rappold, supt. — Fax 335-6309
www.miamieast.k12.oh.us
Miami East HS — 300/9-12
3925 N State Route 589 45312 — 937-335-7070
Tim Williams, prin. — Fax 440-9581
Miami East JHS — 300/6-8
4025 N State Route 589 45312 — 937-335-5439
Allen Mack, prin. — Fax 332-7927

Castalia, Erie, Pop. 846
Margaretta Local SD — 1,100/K-12
305 S Washington St 44824 — 419-684-5322
Edward Kurt, supt. — Fax 684-9003
www.margaretta.k12.oh.us/
Margaretta JSHS — 600/6-12
209 Lowell St 44824 — 419-684-5351
Troy Roth, prin. — Fax 684-5632

Firelands Christian Academy — 100/K-11
3809 Maple Ave 44824 — 419-684-8642
Rusty Yost, pres. — Fax 684-5378

Cedarville, Greene, Pop. 3,956
Cedar Cliff Local SD — 600/K-12
PO Box 45 45314 — 937-766-6000
Dr. David Baits, supt. — Fax 766-4717
www.cedarcliffschools.org
Cedarville MSHS — 300/6-12
PO Box 45 45314 — 937-766-1871
Virginia Potter, prin. — Fax 766-5211

Cedarville University — Post-Sec.
251 N Main St 45314 — 937-766-2211

Celina, Mercer, Pop. 10,225
Celina CSD — 2,300/K-12
585 E Livingston St 45822 — 419-586-8300
Jesse Steiner, supt. — Fax 586-7046
www.celinaschools.org
Celina HS — 1,000/9-12
715 E Wayne St 45822 — 419-586-8300
Phil Metz, prin. — Fax 584-0307
Celina MS — 400/7-8
615 Holly St 45822 — 419-586-8300
Ann Esselstein, prin. — Fax 586-9166

Mercer County ESC
441 E Market St 45822 — 419-586-6628
Andrew Smith, supt. — Fax 586-3377
www.mercercountyesc.org/
Mercer County Alternative HS — Alt
441 E Market St 45822 — 419-584-0186

Wright State University — Post-Sec.
7600 Lake Campus Dr 45822 — 419-586-0300

Centerburg, Knox, Pop. 1,748
Centerburg Local SD — 1,100/K-12
119 S Preston St 43011 — 740-625-6346
Mike Hebenthal, supt. — Fax 625-9939
www.centerburgschools.org/
Centerburg HS — 300/9-12
3782 Columbus Rd 43011 — 740-625-6055
Ryan Gallwitz, prin. — Fax 625-5799
Centerburg MS — 300/6-8
3782 Columbus Rd 43011 — 740-625-6055
Ryan Gallwitz, prin. — Fax 625-5799

Centerville, Montgomery, Pop. 23,528
Centerville CSD — 8,300/PK-12
111 Virginia Ave 45458 — 937-433-8841
Tom Henderson Ph.D., supt. — Fax 438-6057
www.centerville.k12.oh.us
Centerville HS — 2,800/9-12
500 E Franklin St 45459 — 937-439-3500
Jon Wesney, prin. — Fax 439-3574
Magsig MS — 600/6-8
192 W Franklin St 45459 — 937-433-0965
Stacey Westendorf, prin. — Fax 433-5256
Tower Heights MS — 600/6-8
195 N Johanna Dr 45459 — 937-434-0383
Clint Freese, prin. — Fax 434-3033
Other Schools – See Dayton

Fortis College — Post-Sec.
555 E Alex Bell Rd 45459 — 937-433-3410
Spring Valley Academy — 300/PK-12
1461 E Spring Valley Pike 45458 — 937-433-0790
Vern Biloff, prin. — Fax 433-0914

Chagrin Falls, Cuyahoga, Pop. 4,089
Chagrin Falls EVD — 2,000/PK-12
400 E Washington St 44022 — 440-247-4363
Robert Hunt, supt. — Fax 247-5883
www.chagrinschools.org
Chagrin Falls HS — 600/9-12
400 E Washington St 44022 — 440-247-2072
Steven Ast, prin. — Fax 247-2071
Chagrin Falls MS — 300/7-8
342 E Washington St 44022 — 440-247-4746
David Wessel, prin. — Fax 247-4855

Kenston Local SD — 2,900/K-12
17419 Snyder Rd 44023 — 440-543-9677
Robert Lee, supt. — Fax 543-8634
www.kenstonlocal.com
Kenston HS — 1,100/9-12
9500 Bainbridge Rd 44023 — 440-543-9821
Jeremy McDevitt, prin. — Fax 543-9021
Kenston MS — 700/6-8
17425 Snyder Rd 44023 — 440-543-8241
Patricia Brockway, prin. — Fax 543-4851

English Nanny and Governess School — Post-Sec.
37 S Franklin St 44022 — 440-247-0600

Chardon, Geauga, Pop. 5,091
Chardon Local SD — 3,100/K-12
428 North St 44024 — 440-285-4052
Joseph Bergant, supt. — Fax 285-7229
www.chardon.k12.oh.us
Chardon HS — 1,100/9-12
151 Chardon Ave 44024 — 440-285-4057
Andrew Fetchik, prin. — Fax 285-9463
Chardon MS — 700/6-8
424 North St 44024 — 440-285-4062
Steven Kofol, prin. — Fax 286-0461

Notre Dame-Cathedral Latin HS — 700/9-12
13000 Auburn Rd 44024 — 440-286-6226
Joseph Waler, prin. — Fax 286-7199

Charm, Holmes
East Holmes Local SD
Supt. — See Berlin
Wise ES, PO Box 159 44617 — 100/5-8
Jon Wilson, prin. — 330-893-2505

Chesapeake, Lawrence, Pop. 736
Chesapeake Union EVD — 1,400/K-12
10183 County Road 1 45619 — 740-867-3135
Jerry McConnell, supt. — Fax 867-3136
www.peake.k12.oh.us
Chesapeake HS — 400/9-12
10181 County Road 1 45619 — 740-867-5958
Joseph Rase, prin. — Fax 867-1130
Chesapeake MS — 400/5-8
10335 County Road 1 45619 — 740-867-3972
John Hayes, prin. — Fax 867-1120

Lawrence County JVSD
11627 State Route 243 45619 — 740-867-6641
Stephen Dodgion, supt. — Fax 867-1317
www.collins-cc.edu/
Collins Career Center — Vo/Tech
11627 State Route 243 45619 — 740-867-6641
Stephen Dodgion, supt. — Fax 867-1317

Collins Career Center — Post-Sec.
11627 State Route 243 45619 — 740-867-6641

Chesterland, Geauga, Pop. 2,498
West Geauga Local SD — 2,300/K-12
8615 Cedar Rd 44026 — 440-729-5900
Geoff Palmer, supt. — Fax 729-5939
www.westg.org/
West Geauga HS — 900/9-12
13401 Chillicothe Rd 44026 — 440-729-5950
Jay Bishop, prin. — Fax 729-5959
West Geauga MS — 500/6-8
8611 Cedar Rd 44026 — 440-729-5940
James Kish, prin. — Fax 729-5909

Chillicothe, Ross, Pop. 21,171
Chillicothe CSD — 2,900/K-12
235 Cherry St 45601 — 740-775-4250
Jon Saxton, supt. — Fax 775-4270
www.ccsd.us/
Chillicothe HS — 900/9-12
421 Yoctangee Pkwy 45601 — 740-702-2287
Jeff Fisher, prin. — Fax 773-1097
Chillicothe MS Site 1 — 400/7-8
381 Yoctangee Pkwy 45601 — 740-773-2241
Aaron Brown, prin. — Fax 774-9482

Huntington Local SD — 1,200/K-12
188 Huntsman Rd 45601 — 740-663-5892
Jerry Mowery, supt. — Fax 663-6078
www.hunt.k12.oh.us/
Huntington HS — 300/9-12
188 Huntsman Rd 45601 — 740-663-2230
Keith Stevenson, prin. — Fax 663-5042
Huntington MS — 300/6-8
188 Huntsman Rd 45601 — 740-663-6079
Alice Kellough, prin. — Fax 663-6080

Pickaway-Ross County JVSD
895 Crouse Chapel Rd 45601 — 740-642-1200
Dennis Franks, supt. — Fax 642-1399
www.pickawayross.com
Pickaway-Ross Career & Technology Center — Vo/Tech
895 Crouse Chapel Rd 45601 — 740-642-1200
Shara Cochenour, prin. — Fax 642-1399

Southeastern Local SD — 1,200/K-12
2003 Lancaster Rd 45601 — 740-774-2003
Brian Justice, supt. — Fax 774-1687
www.sepanthers.k12.oh.us/
Southeastern HS — 300/9-12
2003 Lancaster Rd 45601 — 740-774-2003
Leonard Steyer, prin. — Fax 774-1684
Southeastern MS — 400/5-8
2003 Lancaster Rd 45601 — 740-774-2003
Zachary Pfeifer, prin. — Fax 774-1684

Union-Scioto Local SD — 2,100/K-12
1565 Egypt Pike 45601 — 740-773-4102
Dwight Garrett, supt. — Fax 775-2852
www.unioto.k12.oh.us
Unioto HS — 600/9-12
14193 Pleasant Valley Rd 45601 — 740-773-4105
James Osborne, prin. — Fax 774-9158
Unioto JHS — 400/7-8
160 Moundsville Rd 45601 — 740-773-5211
Ron Lovely, prin. — Fax 772-2974

Zane Trace Local SD — 1,600/K-12
946 State Route 180 45601 — 740-775-1355
Richard Spindler, supt. — Fax 773-0249
www.zanetrace.org
Zane Trace HS — 500/9-12
946 State Route 180 45601 — 740-775-1809
Todd Holdren, prin. — Fax 775-1301
Zane Trace MS — 500/5-8
946 State Route 180 45601 — 740-773-9854
Bret Mavis, prin. — Fax 773-9998

Daymar College — Post-Sec.
1410 Industrial Dr 45601 — 740-774-6300
Ohio University — Post-Sec.
PO Box 629 45601 — 740-774-7200
Recording Workshop — Post-Sec.
455 Massieville Rd 45601 — 740-663-1000

Cincinnati, Hamilton, Pop. 289,429
Cincinnati CSD, PO Box 5381 45201 — 30,700/PK-12
Mary Ronan, supt. — 513-363-0000
www.cps-k12.org
Aiken College & Career HS — 400/9-12
2240 Baltimore Ave 45225 — 513-363-6700
Carlos Blair, prin. — Fax 363-6720
Clark Montessori JSHS — 700/7-12
3030 Erie Ave 45208 — 513-363-7100
Rupashree Townsend, prin. — Fax 363-7120
Dater HS — 800/7-12
2146 Ferguson Rd 45238 — 513-363-7200
Stephen Sippel, prin. — Fax 363-7220
Gamble Montessori HS — 300/7-12
5425 Winton Ridge Ln 45232 — 513-363-2600
Jack Jose, prin. — Fax 363-2620
Hughes STEM HS — 400/7-12
2515 Clifton Ave 45219 — 513-363-7400
Dorothy James, prin. — Fax 363-7420
Oyler S — 700/PK-12
2121 Hatmaker St 45204 — 513-363-4100
Craig Hockenberry, prin. — Fax 363-4120
Riverview East Academy — 500/PK-12
3555 Kellogg Ave 45226 — 513-363-3400
Charlene Myers, prin. — Fax 363-3420
School for Creative & Performing Arts — 1,400/K-12
108 W Central Pkwy 45202 — 513-363-8000
Steve Brokamp, prin. — Fax 363-8020
Shroder HS — 700/7-12
5030 Duck Creek Rd 45227 — 513-363-6900
Larry Williams, prin. — Fax 363-6920
Taft Information Technology HS — 500/9-12
420 Ezzard Charles Dr 45214 — 513-363-8200
Kelly Rozelle, prin. — Fax 363-8220
Walnut Hills JSHS — 2,200/7-12
3250 Victory Pkwy 45207 — 513-363-8400
Jeff Brokamp, prin. — Fax 363-8420
Western Hills University HS — 700/7-12
2144 Ferguson Rd 45238 — 513-363-8900
Stephanie Morton, prin. — Fax 363-8920
Withrow University HS — 800/9-12
2488 Madison Rd 45208 — 513-363-9200
Sharon Johnson, prin. — Fax 363-9220
Woodward Career Technical HS — Vo/Tech
7005 Reading Rd 45237 — 513-363-9300
Shauna Murphy, prin. — Fax 363-9320

Deer Park Community CSD — 1,200/K-12
4131 Matson Ave 45236 — 513-891-0222
Jeff Langdon, supt. — Fax 891-2930
www.deerparkcityschools.org
Deer Park JSHS — 500/7-12
8351 Plainfield Rd 45236 — 513-891-0010
Larry Knapp, prin. — Fax 891-3845

Finneytown Local SD — 1,500/K-12
8916 Fontainebleau Ter 45231 — 513-728-3700
Dr. Alan Robertson, supt. — Fax 931-0986
www.finneytown.org
Finneytown Secondary Campus — 800/7-12
8916 Fontainebleau Ter 45231 — 513-931-0712
Jack Fisher, prin. — Fax 728-7230

Forest Hills Local SD — 7,500/PK-12
7550 Forest Rd 45255 — 513-231-3600
Dallas Jackson Ed.D., supt. — Fax 231-3830
www.foresthills.edu
Anderson HS — 1,300/9-12
7560 Forest Rd 45255 — 513-232-2772
Michael Broadwater, prin. — Fax 232-3146
Nagel MS — 1,100/7-8
1500 Nagel Rd 45255 — 513-474-5407
John Vander Meer, prin. — Fax 474-5584
Turpin HS — 1,100/9-12
2650 Bartels Rd 45244 — 513-232-7770
Peggy Johnson, prin. — Fax 232-9047

Great Oaks Institute of Technology
3254 E Kemper Rd 45241 — 513-771-8840
Dr. Roberta White, supt. — Fax 771-6575
www.greatoaks.com/
Diamond Oaks CDC — Vo/Tech
6375 Harrison Ave 45247 — 513-574-1300
Nancy Mulvey, prin. — Fax 574-3953
Scarlet Oaks CDC — Vo/Tech
3254 E Kemper Rd 45241 — 513-771-8810
Julie Woodward, prin. — Fax 771-4928
Other Schools – See Milford, Wilmington

Indian Hill EVD 2,000/K-12
6855 Drake Rd 45243 513-272-4500
Dr. Mark Miles, supt. Fax 272-4756
www.ih.k12.oh.us
Indian Hill HS 700/9-12
6865 Drake Rd 45243 513-272-4550
Antonio Shelton, prin. Fax 272-4557
Indian Hill MS 500/6-8
6845 Drake Rd 45243 513-272-4642
Joshua Kauffman, prin. Fax 272-4690

Lockland Local SD
Supt. — See Lockland
Arlington Heights Academy 100/Alt
607 Carthage Ave 45215 513-563-5000
Chuck Soule, prin. Fax 761-3408

Madeira CSD 1,500/PK-12
7465 Loannes Dr 45243 513-985-6070
Stephen Kramer, supt. Fax 985-6072
www.madeiracityschools.org
Madeira HS 400/9-12
7465 Loannes Dr 45243 513-891-8222
Tom Olson, prin. Fax 985-6089
Madeira MS 400/5-8
6612 Miami Ave 45243 513-561-5555
Robert Kramer, prin. Fax 272-4145

Mariemont CSD 1,600/K-12
2 Warrior Way 45227 513-272-7500
Paul Imhoff, supt. Fax 527-3436
www.mariemontschools.org
Mariemont HS 400/9-12
1 Warrior Way 45227 513-272-7600
Jim Renner, prin. Fax 527-5991
Mariemont JHS 300/7-8
3847 Southern Ave 45227 513-272-7300
Keith Koehne, prin. Fax 527-3432

Mt. Healthy CSD
Supt. — See Mount Healthy
Mt. Healthy HS 800/9-12
8101 Hamilton Ave 45231 513-729-0130
Marlon Styles, prin. Fax 728-4695
Mt. Healthy JHS 500/7-8
8101 Hamilton Ave 45231 513-742-0666
Marlon Styles, prin. Fax 742-2797

North College Hill CSD 1,500/PK-12
1731 Goodman Ave 45239 513-931-8181
Gary Gellert, supt. Fax 728-4774
www.nchcityschools.org
North College Hill HS 400/9-12
1620 W Galbraith Rd 45239 513-728-4783
Ann Brinkley, prin. Fax 728-4784
North College Hill MS 500/5-8
1624 W Galbraith Rd 45239 513-728-4785
Jennifer Moeller, prin. Fax 728-4786

Northwest Local SD 8,300/PK-12
3240 Banning Rd 45239 513-923-1000
Richard Glatfelter, supt. Fax 923-3644
www.nwlsd.org
Colerain HS 2,000/9-12
8801 Cheviot Rd 45251 513-385-6424
Maureen Heintz, prin. Fax 741-5032
Colerain MS 600/6-8
4700 Poole Rd 45251 513-385-8490
Chris Shisler, prin. Fax 385-6685
Northwest HS 1,000/9-12
10761 Pippin Rd 45231 513-851-7300
Todd Bowling, prin. Fax 742-6376
Pleasant Run MS 800/6-8
11770 Pippin Rd 45231 513-851-2400
David Maine, prin. Fax 851-7071
White Oak MS 800/6-8
3130 Jessup Rd 45239 513-741-4300
Dustin Gehring, prin. Fax 741-0717

Oak Hills Local SD 7,800/K-12
6325 Rapid Run Rd 45233 513-574-3200
Todd Yohey, supt. Fax 598-2947
ohlsd.us
Bridgetown MS 600/6-8
3900 Race Rd 45211 513-574-3511
Adam Taylor, prin. Fax 574-6689
Delhi MS 600/6-8
5280 Foley Rd 45238 513-922-8400
Daniel Beckenhaupt, prin. Fax 922-8472
Oak Hills HS 2,500/9-12
3200 Ebenezer Rd 45248 513-922-2300
Jeff Brandt, prin. Fax 922-4900
Rapid Run MS 600/6-8
6345 Rapid Run Rd 45233 513-467-0300
Tiffany Brennan, prin. Fax 467-0333

Princeton CSD 5,500/PK-12
3900 Cottingham Dr 45241 513-864-1000
Dr. William Pack, supt. Fax 864-1008
www.princeton.k12.oh.us
Princeton Community MS 1,100/6-8
11157 Chester Rd 45246 513-864-2000
Maureen Durham, prin. Fax 864-2091
Princeton HS 1,600/9-12
11080 Chester Rd 45246 513-864-1500
William Sprankles, prin. Fax 864-1591

Sycamore Community CSD 5,300/PK-12
5959 Hagewa Dr 45242 513-686-1700
Dr. Adrienne James, supt. Fax 791-4873
www.sycamoreschools.org
Sycamore HS 1,800/9-12
7400 Cornell Rd 45242 513-686-1770
Chris Davis, prin. Fax 489-7425
Sycamore JHS 800/7-8
5757 Cooper Rd 45242 513-686-1760
Brian Wallace, prin. Fax 891-3162

West Clermont Local SD 8,800/K-12
4350 Aicholtz Rd 45245 513-943-5000
Dr. Gary Brooks, supt. Fax 752-6158
www.westcler.k12.oh.us
Glen Este HS 1,300/9-12
4342 Glen Este Wthmsvlle Rd 45245 513-947-7600
John Spieser, prin. Fax 943-7090
Glen Este MS 1,000/6-8
4342 Glen Este Wthmsvlle Rd 45245 513-947-7700
John Spieser, prin. Fax 753-3462
Other Schools – See Batavia

Winton Woods CSD 3,500/PK-12
1215 W Kemper Rd 45240 513-619-2300
Jim Smith, supt. Fax 619-2309
www.wintonwoods.org
Academy of Global Studies @ Winton Woods 200/9-10
1231 W Kemper Rd 45240 513-619-2420
Dr. Terri Holden, prin. Fax 619-2417
Winton Woods HS 1,000/9-12
1231 W Kemper Rd 45240 513-619-2420
Dr. Terri Holden, prin. Fax 619-2417
Winton Woods MS 500/7-8
147 Farragut Rd 45218 513-619-2440
Lisa Votaw, prin. Fax 619-2452

Aldersgate Christian Academy 100/K-12
1810 Young St 45202 513-763-6655
William Marshall, prin. Fax 763-6643
Antonelli College Post-Sec.
124 E 7th St 45202 513-241-4338
Archbishop McNicholas HS 700/9-12
6536 Beechmont Ave 45230 513-231-3500
Patty Beckert, prin. Fax 231-1351
Art Academy of Cincinnati Post-Sec.
1212 Jackson St 45202 513-562-6262
Art Institute of Ohio - Cincinnati Post-Sec.
8845 Governors Hill Dr #100 45249 513-833-2400
Athenaeum of Ohio Post-Sec.
6616 Beechmont Ave 45230 513-231-2223
Bacon HS 500/9-12
4320 Vine St 45217 513-641-1300
Steve Schad, prin. Fax 641-0498
Beckfield College Post-Sec.
225 Pictoria Dr Ste 200 45246 513-671-1920
Brown Mackie College Post-Sec.
1011 Glendale Milford Rd 45215 513-771-2424
Christ College of Nursing & Heath Sci Post-Sec.
2139 Auburn Ave 45219 513-585-2401
Cincinnati Christian University Post-Sec.
2700 Glenway Ave 45204 513-244-8100
Cincinnati College of Mortuary Science Post-Sec.
645 W North Bend Rd 45224 888-377-8433
Cincinnati Country Day S 900/PK-12
6905 Given Rd 45243 513-561-7298
Dr. Robert Macrae, hdmstr. Fax 527-7600
Cincinnati Hills Christian Academy HS 400/9-12
11525 Snider Rd 45249 513-247-0900
Dr. Dean Nicholas, prin. Fax 247-0982
Cincinnati Hills Christian Academy MS 400/5-8
11300 Snider Rd 45249 513-247-0900
Fax 247-9362
Cincinnati State Technical & Comm Coll Post-Sec.
3520 Central Pkwy 45223 513-569-1500
College of Mount Saint Joseph Post-Sec.
5701 Delhi Rd 45233 513-244-4200
DePaul Cristo Rey HS 100/9-12
1133 Clifton Hills Ave 45220 513-861-0600
Andrew Farfsing, prin.
DeVry University Post-Sec.
8800 Governors Hill Dr #100 45249 513-583-5000
Elder HS 900/9-12
3900 Vincent Ave 45205 513-921-3744
Thomas Otten, prin. Fax 921-8123
Fortis College Post-Sec.
11499 Chester Rd Ste 200 45246 513-771-2795
God's Bible School and College Post-Sec.
1810 Young St 45202 513-721-7944
Good Samaritan Coll of Nursing/Alld Hlth Post-Sec.
375 Dixmyth Ave 45220 513-862-2743
Hebrew Union College Post-Sec.
3101 Clifton Ave 45220 513-221-1875
International Academy of Hair Design Post-Sec.
8419 Colerain Ave 45239 513-741-4777
La Salle HS 800/9-12
3091 N Bend Rd 45239 513-741-3000
Thomas Luebbe, prin. Fax 741-2666
Lincoln College of Technology Post-Sec.
149 Northland Blvd 45246 513-874-0432
Marinello-Eastern Hills Academy Post-Sec.
7681 Beechmont Ave 45255 513-231-8621
McAuley HS 700/9-12
6000 Oakwood Ave 45224 513-681-1800
Nicole Brainard, prin. Fax 681-1802
Miami Valley Christian Academy 300/PK-12
6830 School St 45244 513-272-6822
Shawn Baker, head sch Fax 272-3711
Moeller HS 900/9-12
9001 Montgomery Rd 45242 513-791-1680
Blane Collison, prin. Fax 792-3343
Moler-Hollywood Beauty Academy Post-Sec.
6142 Montgomery Rd 45213 513-621-5262
Mother of Mercy HS 500/9-12
3036 Werk Rd 45211 513-661-2740
Dave Mueller, prin. Fax 661-1842
National College Post-Sec.
6871 Steger Dr 45237 513-761-1291
Ohio Center for Broadcasting Post-Sec.
6703 Madison Rd 45227 513-271-6060
Ohio Mid-Western College Post-Sec.
19 Triangle Park Dr 45246 513-772-9888
Purcell-Marian HS 400/9-12
2935 Hackberry St 45206 513-751-1230
Paul Ramstetter, prin. Fax 751-1395
Reg Inst for Torah & Secular Studies 50/9-12
2209 Losantiville Ave 45237 513-631-0083
Rabbi E. Dzialoszynski, prin. Fax 631-0947

Ross Inst of Medical & Dental Technology Post-Sec.
11590 Century Blvd Ste 210 45246 513-851-8500
St. Rita School for the Deaf Post-Sec.
1720 Glendale Milford Rd 45215 513-771-7600
St. Ursula Academy 700/9-12
1339 E Mcmillan St 45206 513-961-3410
Craig Maliborski, prin. Fax 961-3856
St. Xavier HS 1,500/9-12
600 W North Bend Rd 45224 513-761-7600
Bill Sandquist, prin. Fax 842-1610
Seton HS 500/9-12
3901 Glenway Ave 45205 513-471-2600
Donna Brigger, prin. Fax 471-0529
Seven Hills S 1,100/PK-12
5400 Red Bank Rd 45227 513-728-2400
Christopher Garten, hdmstr. Fax 728-2409
Sevenstar Academy 2,200/6-12
3630 Park 42 Dr 45241 513-612-1029
Dr. R. Mark Beadle, admin. Fax 618-3334
Summit Country Day S 1,100/PK-12
2161 Grandin Rd 45208 513-871-4700
Richard Wilson, hdmstr. Fax 871-6558
The AIC College of Design Post-Sec.
1171 E Kemper Rd 45246 513-751-1206
Tri County Beauty College Post-Sec.
111 W Kemper Rd 45246 513-671-8340
Union Institute and University Post-Sec.
440 E McMillan St 45206 513-861-6400
University of Cincinnati Post-Sec.
2600 Clifton Ave 45220 513-556-6000
Ursuline Academy 700/9-12
5535 Pfeiffer Rd 45242 513-791-5791
Tom Barhorst, prin. Fax 791-5802
Western Hills Sch of Beauty & Hair Dsgn. Post-Sec.
6490 Glenway Ave 45211 513-574-3818
Xavier University Post-Sec.
3800 Victory Pkwy 45207 513-745-3000

Circleville, Pickaway, Pop. 13,083
Circleville CSD 1,800/PK-12
388 Clark Dr 43113 740-474-4340
Kirk McMahon, supt. Fax 474-6600
www.circlevillecityschools.org/
Circleville HS 600/9-12
380 Clark Dr 43113 740-474-4846
Chris Thornsley, prin. Fax 474-3987
Everts MS 500/6-8
520 S Court St 43113 740-474-2345
Kevin Fox, prin. Fax 477-6384

Logan Elm Local SD 1,700/K-12
9579 Tarlton Rd 43113 740-474-7501
Tim Williams, supt. Fax 477-6525
www.loganelmschools.com/
Logan Elm HS 600/9-12
9575 Tarlton Rd 43113 740-474-7503
Shawn Haughn, prin. Fax 477-3592
McDowell-Exchange JHS 400/7-8
9579 Tarlton Rd 43113 740-474-7538
Marsha Waidelich, prin. Fax 474-8539

Ohio Christian University Post-Sec.
1476 Lancaster Pike 43113 740-474-8896

Clarksville, Clinton, Pop. 544
Clinton-Massie Local SD 1,800/PK-12
2556 Lebanon Rd 45113 937-289-2471
Michael Sander Ed.D., supt. Fax 289-3313
www.clinton-massie.k12.oh.us
Clinton-Massie HS 500/9-12
2556 Lebanon Rd 45113 937-289-2109
Randy Dunlap, prin. Fax 289-7019
Clinton-Massie MS 400/6-8
2556 Lebanon Rd 45113 937-289-2932
Greg Grove, prin. Fax 289-8100

Clayton, Montgomery, Pop. 12,864
Miami Valley Career Technology Center
6800 Hoke Rd 45315 937-837-7781
Nicholas Weldy, supt. Fax 837-5318
www.mvctc.com
Miami Valley Career Tech Center Vo/Tech
6800 Hoke Rd 45315 937-837-7781
Kristy Taylor, prin. Fax 837-1594
Other Schools – See Dayton

Northmont CSD
Supt. — See Englewood
Northmont HS 1,600/9-12
4916 National Rd 45315 937-832-6000
George Caras, prin. Fax 832-6001
Northmont MS 900/7-8
4810 National Rd 45315 937-832-6500
John Stekli, prin. Fax 832-6501

Cleveland, Cuyahoga, Pop. 388,662
Cleveland Municipal SD 38,700/PK-12
1380 E 6th St 44114 216-574-8000
Dr. Eugene Sanders, supt. Fax 574-8193
www.cmsdnet.net
Adams College Board 9-12
3817 Martin Luther King Jr 44105 216-491-5700
Donald Jolly, prin. Fax 295-4645
Adams Financial Services Academy 9-12
3817 Martin Luther King Jr 44105 216-491-5700
Donald Jolly, prin. Fax 295-4645
Adams Ninth Grade Academy 9-9
3817 Martin Luther King Jr 44105 216-491-5700
Damon Holmes, prin. Fax 295-4645
Addams Business Careers Academy 400/9-12
2373 E 30th St 44115 216-623-8900
Ann McGhee, prin. Fax 621-3910
Addams Design Lab Early College HS 200/9-12
2373 E 30th St 44115 216-621-5064
Eric Juli, prin. Fax 623-3772
Cleveland S of the Arts @ Harry Davis 600/6-12
10700 Churchill Ave 44106 216-791-2496
Andrew Koonce, prin. Fax 421-7689

Collinwood College Board Academy 9-12
15210 Saint Clair Ave 44110 216-268-6052
Kevin Payton, prin. Fax 268-6057
Collinwood Interior & Fashion Design 9-12
15210 Saint Clair Ave 44110 216-268-6125
Kevin Payton, prin. Fax 268-6057
Collinwood Teaching Professions Academy 9-12
15210 Saint Clair Ave 44110 216-268-0175
Marsha Curtis, prin. Fax 268-6057
Downtown Educational Center 6-12
9300 Quincy Ave 44106 216-443-4902
Wayne Marok, prin. Fax 443-4903
East Technical Community Wrap Around 9-12
2439 E 55th St 44104 216-432-4554
Paul Hoover, prin. Fax 431-4631
East Technical Engineering Academy 9-12
2439 E 55th St 44104 216-432-4558
Christy Nickerson, prin. Fax 431-4631
East Tech Ninth Grade Academy 200/9-9
2439 E 55th St 44104 216-426-7075
Byron Hopkins, prin. Fax 361-3279
Facing History New Tech HS @ Mooney 9-9
3213 Montclair Ave 44109 216-838-8600
Marc Engoglia, prin. Fax 838-8610
Ginn Academy 300/9-12
655 E 162nd St 44110 216-531-4466
Nicholas Petty, prin. Fax 531-2874
Glenville Health Exercise Sports Academy 9-12
650 E 113th St 44108 216-268-6000
Doris Redic, prin. Fax 541-7666
Glenville Ninth Grade Academy 9-9
650 E 113th St 44108 216-268-6000
David Reiman, prin. Fax 541-7666
Glenville Programming/Software Academy 9-12
650 E 113th St 44108 216-268-6000
Teresa Conley, prin. Fax 541-7666
Hay Architecture & Design Academy 300/9-12
2075 Stokes Blvd 44106 216-229-0100
Tianna Maxey, prin. Fax 229-0072
Hay Early College Academy 200/9-12
2075 Stokes Blvd 44106 216-229-0200
Carol Lockhart, prin. Fax 229-0087
Hayes Technical HS Vo/Tech
4600 Detroit Ave 44102 216-631-1528
Phillip Schwenk, prin. Fax 634-2175
Hay Science & Medicine Academy 400/9-12
2075 Stokes Blvd 44106 216-229-0070
Edward Weber, prin. Fax 339-3242
Health Career Academy - MLK Campus 300/9-12
1651 E 71st St 44103 216-426-7079
Cynthia Hanish, prin. Fax 431-8690
High Tech Academy 10-12
2900 Community College Ave 44115 216-987-3549
Stacy Hutchinson, prin. Fax 987-4397
Jefferson Ninth Grade Academy 9-9
3145 W 46th St 44102 216-404-5120
Rhonda Saegert, prin. Fax 404-5490
Kennedy Entertainment Marketing Acad 9-12
17100 Harvard Ave 44128 216-921-1450
Mary Miller, prin. Fax 295-2455
Kennedy Interactive Media Academy 9-12
17100 Harvard Ave 44128 216-921-1450
Maryum Spencer-Sims, prin. Fax 295-2455
Kennedy Ninth Grade Academy 1,000/9-12
17100 Harvard Ave 44128 216-921-1450
Jason Tidmore, prin. Fax 295-2455
Law & Municipal Careers Academy - MLK 300/9-12
1651 E 71st St 44103 216-431-6858
Cynthia Hanish M.Ed., prin. Fax 431-5180
Lincoln West Community Wraparound 9-12
3202 W 30th St 44109 216-634-2414
Maria Carlson, prin. Fax 634-2403
Lincoln West Programming & Software 9-12
3202 W 30th St 44109 216-634-2421
James Shepherd, prin. Fax 634-2403
Lincoln West World Cultures Academy 9-12
3202 W 30th St 44109 216-631-1505
Dr. Irene Javier, prin. Fax 634-2403
Marshall 9th Grade Academy @ Hawthorne 9-9
3575 W 130th St 44111 216-889-4000
Lisa Williams-Locklear, prin.
Marshall HS 1,400/9-12
13501 Terminal Ave 44135 216-858-6000
Luther Johnson, prin. Fax 476-4458
MC2 STEM 9th Grade S 9-9
601 Erieside Ave 44114 216-858-1267
Feowin Mackinnon, prin. Fax 858-1264
MC2 STEM 10th Grade S 10-10
1975 Noble Rd Bldg 336 44112 216-744-1512
Adam Flowers-Sinclair, prin. Fax 744-1530
MC2 STEM 11th & 12th Grade S 400/11-12
1740 E 32nd St 44114 216-592-6875
Jeffrey McClellan, prin. Fax 592-6879
Morgan S of Science 200/9-12
4016 Woodbine Ave 44113 216-281-6188
Kimberly Harris, prin. Fax 634-2113
New Tech East @ East Technical 9-12
2439 E 55th St 44104 216-361-3116
Ryan Durr, prin. Fax 361-3282
New Tech West @ Max Hayes 9-12
4600 Detroit Ave 44102 216-281-1030
Erin Frew, prin. Fax 281-1055
Rhodes HS 1,300/9-12
5100 Biddulph Ave 44144 216-459-4200
Charlene Hilliard, prin. Fax 459-3133
School of One @ Nathaniel Hawthorne 9-12
3575 W 130th St 44111 216-659-4049
Wayne Marok, prin.
SuccessTech Academy 200/9-12
1440 Lakeside Ave E 44114 216-523-8463
Sara Kidner, prin. Fax 523-8464
Young Academy 300/2-12
17900 Harvard Ave 44128 216-283-5220
Karen Byron-Johnson, prin. Fax 295-3547
Other Schools – See Newburgh Heights

Mayfield CSD
Supt. — See Mayfield Heights
CEVEC Vo/Tech
1111 Som Center Rd 44124 440-995-7450
Cheryl Schwartz, prin. Fax 646-1117

Orange CSD 2,300/PK-12
32000 Chagrin Blvd 44124 216-831-8600
Dr. Nancy Wingenbach, supt. Fax 831-8029
www.orangeschools.org
Brady MS 500/6-8
32000 Chagrin Blvd 44124 216-831-1521
Brian Frank, prin. Fax 839-1335
Orange HS 800/9-12
32000 Chagrin Blvd 44124 216-831-8581
Dr. Paul Lucas, prin. Fax 831-2595

Benedictine HS 400/9-12
2900 Martin Luther King Jr 44104 216-421-2080
Joseph Gressock, prin. Fax 421-0107
Bryant & Stratton College Post-Sec.
3121 Euclid Ave 44115 216-771-1700
Calvary Chapel Academy 50/K-12
6770 Brookpark Rd 44129 216-351-7995
Linda Gaiser, prin. Fax 351-2530
Case Western Reserve University Post-Sec.
10900 Euclid Ave 44106 216-368-2000
Chamberlain College of Nursing Post-Sec.
6700 Euclid Ave Ste 201 44103 216-361-6005
Chancellor University Post-Sec.
3921 Chester Ave 44114 216-391-6937
Cleveland Central Catholic HS 500/9-12
6550 Baxter Ave 44105 216-441-4700
Sr. Allison Gusdanovic, prin. Fax 441-8353
Cleveland Clinic Center Allied Health Post-Sec.
9500 Euclid Ave 44195 216-986-4312
Cleveland Institute Dental Medical Asst. Post-Sec.
2450 Prospect Ave E 44115 216-241-2930
Cleveland Institute of Art Post-Sec.
11141 East Blvd 44106 216-421-7000
Cleveland Institute of Electronics Post-Sec.
1776 E 17th St 44114 216-781-9400
Cleveland Institute of Music Post-Sec.
11021 East Blvd 44106 216-791-5000
Cleveland State University Post-Sec.
2121 Euclid Ave 44115 216-687-2000
Cleveland Veterans Affairs Medical Ctr Post-Sec.
10701 East Blvd 44106 216-421-3028
Cuyahoga Community College Post-Sec.
2900 Community College Ave 44115 800-954-8742
Fairview General Hospital Post-Sec.
18101 Lorain Ave 44111 216-476-7000
John Carroll University Post-Sec.
1 John Carroll Blvd 44118 216-397-1886
Kaplan Career Institute Post-Sec.
8720 Brookpark Rd 44129 216-485-0900
Laura/Alvin Siegal Coll Judaic Studies Post-Sec.
26500 Shaker Blvd 44122 216-464-4050
Lincoln College of Technology Post-Sec.
1700 E 13th St 44114 216-706-6481
Meridia Health System Post-Sec.
17325 Euclid Ave 44112 440-446-8260
MetroHealth Medical Center Post-Sec.
2500 Metrohealth Dr 44109 216-459-5700
Notre Dame College Post-Sec.
4545 College Rd 44121 216-381-1680
Ohio Center for Broadcasting Post-Sec.
9885 Rockside Rd Ste 160 44125 216-503-5900
Ohio Technical College Post-Sec.
1374 E 51st St 44103 216-881-1700
Remington College Post-Sec.
14445 Broadway Ave 44125 216-475-7520
St. Ignatius HS 1,500/9-12
1911 W 30th St 44113 216-651-0222
Dan Bradesca, prin. Fax 961-2564
St. Joseph Academy 600/9-12
3430 Rocky River Dr 44111 216-251-6788
James Cantwel, prin. Fax 251-5809
St. Luke's Medical Center Post-Sec.
2351 E 22nd St 44115 216-368-7000
St. Martin de Porres HS 400/9-12
6111 Lausche Ave 44103 216-881-1689
Mary Ann Vogel, prin. Fax 881-8303
Sanford-Brown College Post-Sec.
17535 Rosbough Blvd Ste 100 44130 440-202-3232
Southwest General Hospital Post-Sec.
18697 Bagley Rd 44130 440-816-6801
Villa Angela-St. Joseph HS 400/9-12
18491 Lake Shore Blvd 44119 216-481-8414
David Csank, prin. Fax 486-1035

Cleveland Heights, Cuyahoga, Pop. 44,828
Cleveland Hts - University Hts CSD
Supt. — See University Heights
Cleveland Heights HS 1,900/9-12
13263 Cedar Rd 44118 216-371-7101
Joseph Bagatti, admin. Fax 371-6506
Monticello MS 400/6-8
3665 Monticello Blvd 44121 216-371-6520
Brian Sharosky, prin. Fax 397-5967
Roxboro MS 600/6-8
2400 Roxboro Rd 44106 216-371-7440
Patrick McNichols, prin. Fax 397-3857

Beaumont HS 400/9-12
3301 N Park Blvd 44118 216-321-2954
Mary Whelan, prin. Fax 321-3947
Hebrew Academy of Cleveland 800/PK-12
1860 S Taylor Rd 44118 216-321-5838
Rabbi Simcha Dessler, dir. Fax 932-4597
Lutheran HS East 100/9-12
3565 Mayfield Rd 44118 216-382-6100
Chris Steinmann, prin. Fax 382-6119
Mosdos Ohr HaTorah S - Boys 400/PK-12
1508 Warrensville Center Rd 44121 216-382-6248
Mosdos Ohr HaTorah S - Girls 200/PK-12
1700 S Taylor Rd 44118 216-321-1547

Cleves, Hamilton, Pop. 3,191
Three Rivers Local SD 500/PK-12
401 N Miami Ave 45002 513-941-6400
Dr. Rhonda Bohannon, supt. Fax 941-1102
www.threeriversschools.org
Taylor HS 500/7-12
56 Cooper Rd 45002 513-467-3200
Craig Spite, prin. Fax 467-0138

Clyde, Sandusky, Pop. 6,212
Clyde-Green Springs EVD 2,300/K-12
106 S Main St 43410 419-547-0588
David Stubblebine, supt. Fax 547-8644
www.clyde.k12.oh.us
Clyde HS 700/9-12
1015 Race St 43410 419-547-9511
Joe Webb, prin. Fax 547-7593
McPherson MS 500/6-8
4230 Limerick Rd 43410 419-547-9150
Rachael Aldrich, prin. Fax 547-9173

Coal Grove, Lawrence, Pop. 2,141
Dawson-Bryant Local SD 1,100/K-12
222 Lane St 45638 740-532-6451
George York, supt. Fax 533-6019
db.k12.oh.us
Dawson-Bryant HS 300/9-12
1 Hornet Ln 45638 740-532-6345
Steven Easterling, prin. Fax 533-6013
Dawson-Bryant MS 300/6-8
1 Hornet Ln 45638 740-533-6008
Michael Eicher, prin. Fax 533-6002

Coldwater, Mercer, Pop. 4,401
Coldwater EVD 1,500/K-12
310 N 2nd St 45828 419-678-2611
Richard Seas, supt. Fax 678-3100
cw.noacsc.org
Coldwater HS 500/9-12
310 N 2nd St 45828 419-678-4821
Charles Tackett, prin. Fax 678-3100
Coldwater MS 400/5-8
310 N 2nd St 45828 419-678-3331
Bill Ruane, prin. Fax 678-3100

Collins, Huron, Pop. 625
Western Reserve Local SD 1,200/K-12
3765 State Route 20 44826 419-660-8508
Rodge Wilson, supt. Fax 660-8429
www.western-reserve.org
Western Reserve HS 400/9-12
3841 State Route 20 44826 419-668-8470
Lisa Border, prin. Fax 663-5916
Western Reserve MS 200/7-8
3841 State Route 20 44826 419-668-1924
Lisa Border, prin. Fax 663-2521

Columbiana, Columbiana, Pop. 6,337
Columbiana EVD 900/PK-12
700 Columbiana Waterford Rd 44408 330-482-5352
Donald Mook, supt. Fax 482-5361
www.columbiana.k12.oh.us
Columbiana HS 300/9-12
700 Columbiana Waterford Rd 44408 330-482-3818
Lance Hostetler, prin. Fax 482-5360
South Side MS 300/6-8
720 Columbiana Waterford Rd 44408 330-482-5354
David Buzzard, prin. Fax 482-6332

Crestview Local SD 1,200/K-12
44100 Crestview Rd Ste A 44408 330-482-5526
John Dilling, supt. Fax 482-5367
www.crestviewlocal.k12.oh.us/
Crestview HS 300/9-12
44100 Crestview Rd Ste B 44408 330-482-4744
Lynda Dickson, prin. Fax 482-5369
Crestview MS 400/5-8
44100 Crestview Rd Ste C 44408 330-482-4648
Jeff Richardson, prin. Fax 482-5374

Heartland Christian S 300/PK-12
28 Pittsburgh St 44408 330-482-2331
Eric Hosler, admin. Fax 482-2413

Columbia Station, Lorain
Columbia Local SD 1,000/K-12
25796 Royalton Rd 44028 440-236-5008
Graig Bansek, supt. Fax 236-8817
www.columbia.k12.oh.us/
Columbia HS 300/9-12
14168 W River Rd 44028 440-236-5001
Sean Lynch, prin. Fax 236-3081
Columbia MS 300/5-8
13646 W River Rd 44028 440-236-5741
Kathi Maxwell, prin. Fax 236-9274

Columbus, Franklin, Pop. 762,045
Columbus CSD 49,500/PK-12
270 E State St 43215 614-365-5000
Gene Harris Ph.D., supt. Fax 365-5689
www.columbus.k12.oh.us/
Africentric Early College S 600/6-12
300 E Livingston Ave 43215 614-365-8675
Ernest West, prin. Fax 365-8908
Arts Impact MS at Everett 500/Alt
680 Jack Gibbs Blvd 43215 614-365-5558
Nicole Edwards, prin. Fax 365-5561
Beechcroft HS 800/9-12
6100 Beechcroft Rd 43229 614-365-5364
Anthony Alston, prin. Fax 365-6963
Briggs HS 1,100/9-12
2555 Briggs Rd 43223 614-365-5915
Marcy Drafts, prin. Fax 365-6964
Brookhaven HS 700/9-12
4077 Karl Rd 43224 614-365-5985
Duane Bland, prin. Fax 365-6965
Buckeye MS 600/6-8
2950 Parsons Ave 43207 614-365-5417
Stephanie Patton, prin. Fax 365-5895

Centennial HS 800/9-12
1441 Bethel Rd 43220 614-365-5491
Frances Hershey, prin. Fax 365-6967
Champion MS 300/6-8
284 N 22nd St 43203 614-365-6082
Edmund Baker, prin. Fax 365-6080
Columbus Alternative HS 600/Alt
2632 McGuffey Rd 43211 614-365-6006
Sharee Wells, prin. Fax 365-6300
Columbus Downtown HS 100/9-12
364 S 4th St 43215 614-365-2283
Dave Mangas, dir. Fax 365-2287
Columbus Global Academy 500/6-12
2001 Hamilton Ave 43211 614-365-8811
Kimberly Normand, prin. Fax 365-6909
Columbus International HS 9-12
100 E Arcadia Ave 43202 614-365-4054
Ameer El-Malawany, prin. Fax 365-8582
Dominion MS 500/6-8
330 E Dominion Blvd 43214 614-365-6020
Dorothy Flanagan, prin. Fax 365-6018
East HS 700/9-12
1500 E Broad St 43205 614-365-6096
Monique Jacquet, prin. Fax 365-6966
Eastmoor Academy HS 700/9-12
417 S Weyant Ave 43213 614-365-6158
Alesia Gillison, prin. Fax 365-6960
Fort Hayes Arts and Academics S 600/9-12
546 Jack Gibbs Blvd 43215 614-365-6681
Milton Ruffin, prin. Fax 365-5620
Fort Hayes Career Center Vo/Tech
546 Jack Gibbs Blvd 43215 614-365-6681
Milton Ruffin, dir. Fax 365-8582
Hilltonia MS 600/6-8
2345 W Mound St 43204 614-365-5937
Donna LeBeau, prin. Fax 365-8015
Independence HS 800/9-12
5175 Refugee Rd 43232 614-365-5372
Christopher Qualls, prin. Fax 365-8286
Johnson Park MS 400/6-8
1130 S Waverly St 43227 614-365-6501
Kevin Kinne, prin. Fax 365-8698
Linden-McKinley STEM HS 800/7-12
1320 Duxberry Ave 43211 614-365-5583
Tiffany Chavers, prin. Fax 365-6968
Marion-Franklin HS 800/9-12
1265 Koebel Rd 43207 614-365-5432
Pamela Diggs, prin. Fax 365-6625
Medina MS 500/6-8
1425 Huy Rd 43224 614-365-6050
Charmaine Tinker, prin. Fax 365-8136
Mifflin HS 700/9-12
3245 Oak Spring St 43219 614-365-5466
Jonathan Stevens, prin. Fax 365-6628
Mifflin MS 600/6-8
3000 Agler Rd 43219 614-365-5474
Amanda Harding, prin. Fax 365-5477
Monroe Alternative MS 400/Alt
474 N Monroe Ave 43203 614-365-6124
Kevin Freeman, prin. Fax 365-8389
Northland HS 1,100/9-12
1919 Northcliff Dr 43229 614-365-5342
Daniel Martin, prin. Fax 365-6479
Ridgeview MS 500/6-8
4241 Rudy Rd 43214 614-365-5506
Natalie James, prin. Fax 365-5505
Sherwood MS 500/6-8
1400 Shady Lane Rd 43227 614-365-5393
Ray Caruthers, prin. Fax 365-8351
South HS 500/9-12
1160 Ann St 43206 614-365-5541
Colon Lewis, prin. Fax 365-5538
Starling MS 300/6-8
120 S Central Ave 43222 614-365-5945
Melanie McGue, prin. Fax 365-5942
Walnut Ridge HS 800/9-12
4841 E Livingston Ave 43227 614-365-5400
Todd Walker, prin. Fax 365-5662
Wedgewood MS 500/6-8
3800 Briggs Rd 43228 614-365-5947
Vincent Coleman, prin. Fax 365-5950
West HS 1,000/9-12
179 S Powell Ave 43204 614-365-5956
Jason Johnson, prin. Fax 365-6970
Westmoor MS 500/6-8
3001 Valleyview Dr 43204 614-365-5974
William Doermann, prin. Fax 365-6705
Whetstone HS 1,000/9-12
4405 Scenic Dr 43214 614-365-6060
Janet Routzong, prin. Fax 365-6971
Woodward Park MS 900/6-8
5151 Karl Rd 43229 614-365-5354
Timothy Donahue, prin. Fax 365-5357
Yorktown MS 500/6-8
5600 E Livingston Ave 43232 614-365-5408
Maria Stockard, prin. Fax 365-5411

Grandview Heights CSD 900/PK-12
1587 W 3rd Ave 43212 614-481-3600
Edward O'Reilly, supt. Fax 481-3648
www.grandviewschools.org/
Edison Intermediate MS 300/4-8
1240 Oakland Ave 43212 614-481-3630
Robert Baeslack, prin. Fax 481-3628
Grandview Heights HS 300/9-12
1587 W 3rd Ave 43212 614-481-3620
Dawn Sayre, prin. Fax 481-3648

Hamilton Local SD 3,100/PK-12
775 Rathmell Rd 43207 614-491-8044
Christopher T. Lester, supt. Fax 491-8323
www.hamiltonrangers.org
Hamilton Alternative Academy 100/Alt
775 Rathmell Rd 43207 614-491-8044
Allyson Price, dir. Fax 491-5564
Hamilton MS 500/7-8
755 Rathmell Rd 43207 614-491-8044
Jeff Endres, prin. Fax 491-0260
Hamilton Township HS 800/9-12
1105 Rathmell Rd 43207 614-491-8044
James Miller, prin. Fax 492-1495

South-Western CSD
Supt. — See Grove City
Finland MS 600/7-8
1825 Finland Ave 43223 614-801-3600
Paul Smathers, prin. Fax 278-6334
Franklin Heights HS 1,200/9-12
1001 Demorest Rd 43204 614-801-3200
Ronald Meyer, prin. Fax 278-6303
Norton MS 500/7-8
215 Norton Rd 43228 614-801-3700
Tresa Davis, prin. Fax 870-5528

Whitehall CSD
Supt. — See Whitehall
Rosemore MS 600/6-8
4800 Langley Ave 43213 614-417-5200
Mark Trace, prin. Fax 417-5201

Worthington CSD
Supt. — See Worthington
McCord MS 500/7-8
1500 Hard Rd 43235 614-450-4000
Michael Kuri, prin. Fax 883-3560
Worthington Kilbourne HS 1,300/9-12
1499 Hard Rd 43235 614-450-6400
Angie Adrean, prin. Fax 450-6560

American Inst. of Alternative Medicine Post-Sec.
6685 Doubletree Ave 43229 614-825-6255
American School of Technology Post-Sec.
2100 Morse Rd # 4599 43229 614-436-4820
Arthur James Cancer Hospital Post-Sec.
300 W 10th Ave 43210 614-293-5485
Bexley Hall Seminary Post-Sec.
583 Sheridan Ave 43209 614-231-3095
Bishop Hartley HS 700/9-12
1285 Zettler Rd 43227 614-237-5421
Mike Winters, prin. Fax 237-3809
Bishop Ready HS 400/9-12
707 Salisbury Rd 43204 614-276-5263
Celene Seamen, prin. Fax 276-5116
Bishop Watterson HS 1,100/9-12
99 E Cooke Rd 43214 614-268-8671
Marian Hutson, prin. Fax 268-0551
Bradford School Post-Sec.
2469 Stelzer Rd 43219 614-416-6200
Capital University Post-Sec.
1 College and Main 43209 614-236-6011
Chamberlain College of Nursing Post-Sec.
1350 Alum Creek Dr 43209 614-252-8890
Columbus College of Art and Design Post-Sec.
60 Cleveland Ave 43215 614-224-9101
Columbus School for Girls 600/PK-12
56 S Columbia Ave 43209 614-252-0781
Elizabeth Lee, hdmstr. Fax 252-0571
Columbus State Community College Post-Sec.
550 E Spring St 43215 614-287-5353
Columbus Torah Academy 200/K-12
181 Noe Bixby Rd 43213 614-864-0299
Rabbi Zvi Kahn, hdmstr. Fax 864-2119
DeVry University Post-Sec.
1350 Alum Creek Dr 43209 614-253-7291
DeVry University Post-Sec.
8800 Lyra Dr Ste 120 43240 614-854-7500
Franklin University Post-Sec.
201 S Grant Ave 43215 614-797-4700
ITT Technical Institute Post-Sec.
4717 Hilton Corporate Dr 43232 614-868-2000
Kaplan College Post-Sec.
2745 Winchester Pike 43232 614-456-4600
Miami-Jacobs Career College Post-Sec.
150 E Gay St Fl 15 43215 614-221-7770
Mt. Carmel College of Nursing Post-Sec.
127 S Davis Ave 43222 614-234-5800
National College Post-Sec.
5665 Forest Hills Blvd 43231 614-212-2800
Nationwide Beauty Academy Post-Sec.
5300 Westpointe Plaza Dr 43228 614-921-9109
Ohio Business College Post-Sec.
1880 E Dublin Granville Rd 43229 614-891-5030
Ohio Center for Broadcasting Post-Sec.
5330 E Main St Ste 200 43213 614-655-5250
Ohio Dominican University Post-Sec.
1216 Sunbury Rd 43219 614-251-4500
Ohio School for the Deaf Post-Sec.
500 Morse Rd 43214
Ohio State College of Barber Styling Post-Sec.
4614 E Broad St 43213 614-868-1015
Ohio State Sch of Cosmetology Northland Post-Sec.
4390 Karl Rd 43224 614-263-1861
Ohio State School for the Blind Post-Sec.
5220 N High St 43214
Ohio State School of Cosmetology East Post-Sec.
1720 E Broad St 43203 614-868-1601
Ohio State University Post-Sec.
154 W 12th Ave 43210 614-292-6446
Ohio State University Hospitals Post-Sec.
450 W 10th Ave 43210 614-293-5555
Pontifical College Josephinum Post-Sec.
7625 N High St 43235 614-885-5585
St. Charles Preparatory S 600/9-12
2010 E Broad St 43209 614-252-6714
Jim Lower, prin. Fax 251-6800
St. Francis De Sales HS 900/9-12
4212 Karl Rd 43224 614-267-7808
Dan Garrick, prin. Fax 265-3375
Spa School Post-Sec.
5050 N High St 43214 614-888-1092
Tree of Life Christian HS - Northridge 400/6-12
935 Northridge Rd 43224 614-263-2688
Lynn Tolley, admin. Fax 263-6450
Trinity Lutheran Seminary Post-Sec.
2199 E Main St 43209 614-235-4136
Valor Christian College Post-Sec.
PO Box 800 43216 800-940-9422
Wellington S 600/PK-12
3650 Reed Rd 43220 614-457-7883
Rob Brisk, hdmstr. Fax 442-3286

Columbus Grove, Putnam, Pop. 2,103
Columbus Grove Local SD 900/K-12
201 W Cross St 45830 419-659-2639
George Verhoff, supt. Fax 659-5134
cg.noacsc.org
Columbus Grove HS 300/9-12
201 W Cross St 45830 419-659-2156
Scott Hummel, prin. Fax 659-5134
Columbus Grove MS 300/5-8
201 W Cross St 45830 419-659-2631
James Kincaid, prin. Fax 659-5134

Commercial Point, Pickaway, Pop. 1,557
Teays Valley Local SD
Supt. — See Ashville
Teays Valley West MS 400/6-8
200 Grove Run Rd 43116 740-983-5000
Michael Kauffeld, prin. Fax 983-5040

Concord, Lake
Auburn Vocational SD
8140 Auburn Rd 44077 440-357-7542
Margaret Lynch, supt. Fax 357-0310
www.auburncc.org
Auburn Career Center Vo/Tech
8140 Auburn Rd 44077 440-357-7542
MaryAnn Bittner, prin. Fax 357-0310

Conneaut, Ashtabula, Pop. 12,629
Conneaut Area CSD 1,900/PK-12
400 Mill St Ste B 44030 440-593-7200
Kent Houston, supt. Fax 593-6253
www.cacsk12.org
Conneaut HS 600/9-12
381 Mill St 44030 440-593-7210
Dawn Zappitelli, prin. Fax 593-6899
Conneaut MS 500/6-8
230 Gateway Ave 44030 440-593-7240
Joel Taylor, prin. Fax 593-6289

Continental, Putnam, Pop. 1,147
Continental Local SD 400/K-12
5211 State Route 634 45831 419-596-3671
Joel Mengerink, supt. Fax 596-3861
www.cn.noacsc.org
Continental JSHS 100/7-12
5211 State Route 634 45831 419-596-3871
Joel Mengerink, prin. Fax 596-2651

Convoy, Van Wert, Pop. 1,077
Crestview Local SD 900/K-12
531 E Tully St 45832 419-749-9100
Mike Estes, supt. Fax 749-4235
www.crestviewknights.com/
Crestview HS 300/9-12
531 E Tully St 45832 419-749-9100
Mike Biro, prin. Fax 749-4235
Crestview MS 100/7-8
531 E Tully St 45832 419-749-9100
Dave Bowen, prin. Fax 749-2484

Copley, Summit, Pop. 11,130
Copley-Fairlawn CSD 3,300/PK-12
3797 Ridgewood Rd 44321 330-664-4800
Brian Poe, supt. Fax 664-4811
www.copley-fairlawn.org
Copley-Fairlawn MS 1,100/5-8
1531 S Cleveland Massillon 44321 330-664-4875
Kathleen Ashcroft, prin. Fax 664-4912
Copley HS 1,100/9-12
3807 Ridgewood Rd 44321 330-664-4822
Aaron Sable, prin. Fax 664-4951

Corning, Perry, Pop. 572
Southern Local SD 800/K-12
10397 State Route 155 SE 43730 740-394-2402
Greg Holbert, supt. Fax 394-2083
www.spsd.k12.oh.us
Miller HS 400/7-12
10397 State Route 155 SE 43730 740-394-2426
Scott Christman, prin. Fax 394-2083

Cortland, Trumbull, Pop. 7,046
Lakeview Local SD 1,800/K-12
300 Hillman Dr 44410 330-637-8741
Robert Wilson, supt. Fax 282-4260
www.lakeviewlocal.org
Lakeview HS 700/8-12
300 Hillman Dr 44410 330-637-4921
Rich Stevens, prin. Fax 638-8812

Maplewood Local SD 900/K-12
2414 Greenville Rd 44410 330-637-7506
Perry Nicholas, supt. Fax 637-6616
www.maplewood.k12.oh.us/
Maplewood HS 200/9-12
2414 Greenville Rd 44410 330-637-8466
Gordon Hitchcock, prin. Fax 637-0496
Maplewood MS 300/5-8
4174 Greenville Rd 44410 330-924-2431
Elizabeth Goerig, prin. Fax 924-5151

Coshocton, Coshocton, Pop. 11,049
Coshocton CSD 1,700/PK-12
1207 Cambridge Rd 43812 740-622-1901
Dr. David Hire, supt. Fax 623-5803
www.coshoctonredskins.com/
Coshocton JSHS 700/7-12
1205 Cambridge Rd 43812 740-622-9433
Grant Fauver, prin. Fax 623-0774

Coshocton County JVSD
23640 Airport Rd 43812 740-622-0211
Deborah Kapp-Salupo, supt. Fax 623-4651
www.coshoctoncareers.org
Coshocton County Career Center Vo/Tech
23640 Airport Rd 43812 740-622-0211
Eddie Dovenbarger, prin. Fax 623-4651

Coshocton Christian S 50/K-12
23891 Airport Rd 43812 740-622-5052
Joseph Hedstrom, admin. Fax 622-9244

Covington, Miami, Pop. 2,556
Covington EVD 800/K-12
25 N Grant St 45318 937-473-2249
David Larson, supt. Fax 473-3730
www.covington.k12.oh.us
Covington HS 200/9-12
807 Chestnut St 45318 937-473-3746
Ken Miller, prin. Fax 473-3435
Covington MS 200/6-8
25 N Grant St 45318 937-473-2833
Josh Long, prin. Fax 473-8189

Craig Beach, Mahoning, Pop. 1,144

TDDS Technical Institute Post-Sec.
PO Box 506 44429 330-538-2216

Crestline, Crawford, Pop. 4,534
Colonel Crawford Local SD
Supt. — See North Robinson
Crawford IS 200/6-8
5444 Crestline Rd 44827 419-562-7529
April Bond, prin. Fax 562-3319

Crestline EVD 700/K-12
PO Box 350 44827 419-683-3647
Dave Heflinger, supt. Fax 683-2330
www.crestline.k12.oh.us
Crestline HS 300/7-12
7854 Oldfield Rd 44827 419-683-3647
Douglas Potts, prin. Fax 683-9063

Creston, Wayne, Pop. 2,138
Norwayne Local SD 1,200/PK-12
350 S Main St 44217 330-435-6382
Larry Acker, supt. Fax 435-4633
www.norwaynelocal.k12.oh.us
Norwayne HS 400/9-12
350 S Main St 44217 330-435-6384
Douglas Zimmerly, prin. Fax 435-4633
Norwayne MS 300/6-8
350 S Main St 44217 330-435-1195
Karen O'Hare, prin. Fax 435-4633

Crooksville, Perry, Pop. 2,512
Crooksville EVD 800/PK-12
4065 School Dr 43731 740-982-7040
Kyle Newton, supt. Fax 982-3551
www.crooksville.k12.oh.us/
Crooksville HS 300/8-12
4075 Ceramic Way 43731 740-982-7015
Casey Coffey, prin. Fax 982-3086

Crown City, Gallia, Pop. 412
Gallia County Local SD
Supt. — See Gallipolis
South Gallia MSHS 200/7-12
55 Rebel Dr 45623 740-256-1054
Scot West, prin. Fax 256-6399

Cuyahoga Falls, Summit, Pop. 48,868
Cuyahoga Falls CSD 5,000/K-12
PO Box 396 44222 330-926-3800
Dr. Todd Nichols, supt. Fax 920-1074
www.cfalls.org
Bolich MS 700/6-8
2630 13th St 44223 330-926-3801
John Musat, prin. Fax 920-3737
Cuyahoga Falls HS 1,600/9-12
2300 4th St 44221 330-926-3808
Anne Alfano, prin. Fax 916-6013
Roberts MS 500/6-8
3333 Charles St 44221 330-926-3809
Allison Bogdan, prin. Fax 920-3748

Cuyahoga Valley Christian Academy 900/7-12
4687 Wyoga Lake Rd 44224 330-929-0575
Mike Bova, hdmstr. Fax 929-0156
Fortis College Post-Sec.
2545 Bailey Rd 44221 330-923-9959
Walsh Jesuit HS 900/9-12
4550 Wyoga Lake Rd 44224 330-929-4205
Mark Hassman, prin. Fax 929-9749

Cuyahoga Heights, Cuyahoga, Pop. 635
Cuyahoga Heights Local SD 900/PK-12
4820 E 71st St 44125 216-429-5700
Joseph Bergant, supt. Fax 341-3737
www.cuyhts.org
Cuyahoga Heights HS 300/9-12
4820 E 71st St 44125 216-429-5707
Tom Evans, prin. Fax 429-5706
Cuyahoga Heights MS 200/6-8
4840 E 71st St 44125 216-429-5757
Tom Evans, prin. Fax 429-5735

Dalton, Wayne, Pop. 1,798
Dalton Local SD 800/K-12
PO Box 514 44618 330-828-2267
Scott Beatty, supt. Fax 828-2800
www.dalton.k12.oh.us
Dalton IS 200/5-8
PO Box 514 44618 330-828-2405
Shelly Menuez, prin. Fax 828-2801
Dalton Local HS 300/9-12
PO Box 514 44618 330-828-2261
Larry Case, prin. Fax 828-2904

Danville, Knox, Pop. 1,035
Danville Local SD 700/K-12
PO Box 30 43014 740-599-6116
Dan Harper, supt. Fax 599-5417
www.danville.k12.oh.us/
Danville HS 200/9-12
PO Box 30 43014 740-599-6116
Ed Honabarger, prin. Fax 599-5418
Danville MS 100/7-8
PO Box 30 43014 740-599-6116
Ed Honabarger, prin. Fax 599-5904

Dayton, Montgomery, Pop. 137,548
Centerville CSD
Supt. — See Centerville
Watts MS 700/6-8
7056 McEwen Rd 45459 937-434-0370
Brian Miller, prin. Fax 434-2907

Dayton CSD 14,300/PK-12
115 S Ludlow St 45402 937-542-3000
Lori Ward, supt. Fax 542-3188
www.dps.k12.oh.us
Belmont HS 900/7-12
2615 Wayne Ave 45420 937-542-6460
Kenneth Kraemer, prin. Fax 542-6461
Dunbar HS 600/9-12
1400 Albritton Dr 45417 937-542-6760
Marlayna Randolph, prin. Fax 542-6761
Gardendale Academy 100/Alt
1733 N Gettysburg Ave 45417 937-542-4450
Cheryl Owens, prin. Fax 542-4451
Longfellow Academy 200/Alt
245 Salem Ave 45406 937-542-6910
Bettylene Mulligan, prin. Fax 542-6911
Marshall HS 600/9-12
4447 Hoover Ave 45417 937-542-6610
Sharon Goins, prin. Fax 542-6611
Meadowdale HS 600/9-12
3873 Whitestone Ct 45416 937-542-7030
Melanie Walter, prin. Fax 542-7031
Ponitz Career Center Vo/Tech
741 Washington St 45402 937-542-7180
David White, prin. Fax 542-7181
Stivers S for the Arts 900/7-12
1313 E 5th St 45402 937-542-7380
Erin Dooley, prin. Fax 542-7381
Wogaman S 300/4-8
920 McArthur Ave 45417 937-542-5890
Marvis Meeks, prin. Fax 542-5891

Jefferson Township Local SD 400/K-12
2625 S Union Rd 45417 937-835-5682
Dr. Richard Gates, supt. Fax 835-5955
www.jeffersontwp.k12.oh.us/
Jefferson HS 200/7-12
2701 S Union Rd 45417 937-295-5691
Gerry Griffith, prin. Fax 835-5693

Mad River Local SD 3,500/PK-12
801 Old Harshman Rd 45431 937-259-6606
Necia Nicholas, supt. Fax 259-6607
www.madriverschools.org
Mad River MS 500/7-8
1801 Harshman Rd 45424 937-237-4265
Laurie Plank, prin. Fax 237-4273
Stebbins HS 1,100/9-12
1900 Harshman Rd 45424 937-237-4250
Brian Honeycutt, prin. Fax 237-4262

Miami Valley Career Technology Center
Supt. — See Clayton
Miami Valley Career Tech Alternative S Alt
1133 S Edwin C Moses Blvd 45417 937-226-1741
Jay Byrne, prin. Fax 226-1788

Northridge Local SD 1,000/K-12
2011 Timber Ln 45414 937-278-5885
David Jackson, supt. Fax 276-8351
www.northridgeschools.org/
Northridge HS 500/7-12
2251 Timber Ln 45414 937-275-7469
Tim Whitestone, prin. Fax 275-8434

Oakwood CSD 2,100/PK-12
20 Rubicon Rd 45409 937-297-5332
Mary Jo Scalzo Ph.D., supt. Fax 297-5345
www.oakwood.k12.oh.us
Oakwood HS 700/9-12
1200 Far Hills Ave 45419 937-297-5325
Paul Waller, prin. Fax 297-5348
Oakwood JHS 400/7-8
1200 Far Hills Ave 45419 937-297-5328
Dan Weckstein, prin. Fax 297-7807

Bishop Leibold Consolidated S East 300/4-8
6666 Springboro Pike 45449 937-434-9343
Paul Beyerle, prin. Fax 436-3048
Carousel Beauty College Post-Sec.
125 E 2nd St 45402 937-223-3572
Carroll HS 900/9-12
4524 Linden Ave 45432 937-253-8188
Matt Sableski, prin. Fax 258-7001
Chaminade-Julienne HS 700/9-12
505 S Ludlow St 45402 937-461-3740
John Marshall, prin. Fax 461-6256
Creative Images-Matrix Design Academy Post-Sec.
7535 Poe Ave 45414 937-454-1200
DeVry University Post-Sec.
3610 Pentagon Blvd Ste 100 45431 937-320-3200
East Dayton Christian S 500/PK-12
999 Spinning Rd 45431 937-252-5400
Stacie Auvil, prin. Fax 258-4099
International College of Broadcasting Post-Sec.
6 S Smithville Rd 45431 937-258-8251
ITT Technical Institute Post-Sec.
3325 Stop 8 Rd 45414 937-264-7700
Kaplan College Post-Sec.
2800 E River Rd 45439 937-294-6155

Lincoln College of Technology Post-Sec.
111 W 1st St 45402 937-224-0061
Miami-Jacobs Career College Post-Sec.
110 N Patterson Blvd 45402 937-222-7337
Miami Valley Hospital Post-Sec.
1 Wyoming St 45409 937-223-6192
Miami Valley S 500/PK-12
5151 Denise Dr 45429 937-434-4444
Peter Benedict, hdmstr. Fax 434-1033
Sinclair Community College Post-Sec.
444 W 3rd St 45402 800-315-3000
United Theological Seminary Post-Sec.
4501 Denlinger Rd 45426 937-529-2201
University of Dayton Post-Sec.
300 College Park Ave 45469 937-229-1000
Wright State University Post-Sec.
3640 Colonel Glenn Hwy 45435 937-775-3333

Defiance, Defiance, Pop. 16,265
Ayersville Local SD 800/K-12
28046 Watson Rd 43512 419-395-1111
Tod Hug, supt. Fax 395-9990
www.ayersville.org
Ayersville JSHS 400/7-12
28046 Watson Rd 43512 419-395-1111
Jeremy Kuhlman, prin. Fax 395-2566

Defiance CSD 2,500/K-12
629 Arabella St 43512 419-782-0070
Michael Struble, supt. Fax 782-4395
www.defcity.org/
Defiance HS 700/9-12
1755 Palmer Dr 43512 419-784-2777
Robert Morton, prin. Fax 784-0102
Defiance MS 600/6-8
629 Arabella St 43512 419-782-0050
Richard Peters, prin. Fax 782-0060

Northeastern Local SD 1,100/K-12
5921 Domersville Rd 43512 419-497-3461
James Roach, supt. Fax 497-3401
www.tinora.org
Tinora HS 300/9-12
5921 Domersville Rd 43512 419-497-2621
Philip Nofziger, prin. Fax 497-3401
Tinora JHS 200/7-8
5921 Domersville Rd 43512 419-497-2361
G. Kent Adams, prin. Fax 497-3401

Defiance College Post-Sec.
701 N Clinton St 43512 419-784-4010

De Graff, Logan, Pop. 1,275
Riverside Local SD 700/K-12
2096 County Road 24 S 43318 937-585-5981
Scott Mann, supt. Fax 585-4599
www.riverside.k12.oh.us
Riverside JSHS 300/7-12
2096 County Road 24 S 43318 937-585-5981
Andrew McGill, prin. Fax 585-4599

Delaware, Delaware, Pop. 33,899
Buckeye Valley Local SD 1,900/K-12
679 Coover Rd 43015 740-369-8735
Mark Tingley, supt. Fax 363-7654
www.buckeyevalley.k12.oh.us
Buckeye Valley HS 700/9-12
901 Coover Rd 43015 740-363-1349
Andrew Miller, prin. Fax 363-9380
Buckeye Valley MS 500/5-8
683 Coover Rd 43015 740-363-6626
Jason Spencer, prin. Fax 363-4483

Delaware Area Career Center
4565 Columbus Pike 43015 740-548-0708
Mary Beth Freeman, supt. Fax 548-0710
www.delawareareacc.org
Delaware Area Career Center North Campus Vo/Tech
1610 State Route 521 43015 740-363-1993
Mary Titus, prin. Fax 362-6461
Delaware Area Career Center South Campus Vo/Tech
4565 Columbus Pike 43015 740-548-0708
Dale Hayes, prin. Fax 548-0710
Delaware Area Career Ctr Adult Education Adult
4565 Columbus Pike 43015 740-201-3206
Scott Palmer, prin. Fax 549-1397

Delaware CSD 5,000/K-12
248 N Washington St 43015 740-833-1100
Paul Craft, supt. Fax 833-1149
www.dcs.k12.oh.us
Dempsey MS 700/7-8
599 Pennsylvania Ave 43015 740-833-1800
Andrew Hatton, prin. Fax 833-1899
Hayes HS 1,300/9-12
289 Euclid Ave 43015 740-833-1010
Ric Stranges, prin. Fax 833-1099

Delaware Christian S 300/PK-12
45 Belle Ave 43015 740-363-8425
Gordon McDonald, admin. Fax 203-2117
Methodist Theological School in Ohio Post-Sec.
3081 Columbus Pike 43015 740-363-1146
Ohio Wesleyan University Post-Sec.
61 S Sandusky St 43015 740-368-2000

Delphos, Allen, Pop. 7,017
Delphos CSD 1,100/K-12
234 N Jefferson St 45833 419-692-2509
Frank Sukup, supt. Fax 692-2653
www.dl.noacsc.org/
Jefferson HS 300/9-12
901 Wildcat Ln 45833 419-695-1786
John Edinger, prin. Fax 692-2287
Jefferson MS 300/6-8
227 N Jefferson St 45833 419-695-2523
Terry Moreo, prin. Fax 692-2302

St. John HS 300/9-12
515 E 2nd St 45833 419-692-5371
Donald Huysman, prin. Fax 879-6874

Delta, Fulton, Pop. 3,070
Pike-Delta-York Local SD 1,300/K-12
504 Fernwood St 43515 419-822-3391
Jay LeFevre, supt. Fax 822-4478
www.pdys.org
Pike-Delta-York HS 400/9-12
605 Taylor St 43515 419-822-8247
Martin Friess, prin. Fax 822-2826
Pike-Delta-York MS 400/5-8
1101 Panther Pride Dr 43515 419-822-9118
Dennis Ford, prin. Fax 822-8490

Dennison, Tuscarawas, Pop. 2,624
Claymont CSD 2,100/PK-12
201 N 3rd St 44621 740-922-5478
Ryan Delaney, supt. Fax 922-7325
www.claymontschools.org
Other Schools – See Uhrichsville

Diamond, Portage
Southeast Local SD
Supt. — See Ravenna
Southeast MS 500/6-8
8540 Tallmadge Rd 44412 330-654-1950
James Ries, prin. Fax 654-9110

Dillonvale, Jefferson, Pop. 660
Buckeye Local SD 1,500/PK-12
6899 State Route 150 43917 740-769-7395
Mark Miller, supt. Fax 769-2361
buckeye.omeresa.net/
Other Schools – See Rayland

Dola, Hardin, Pop. 136
Hardin Northern Local SD 500/K-12
11589 State Route 81 45835 419-759-2331
Doug Roberts, supt. Fax 759-2581
www.hn.k12.oh.us/
Hardin Northern JSHS 200/7-12
11589 State Route 81 45835 419-759-3515
Joe Hoelzle, prin. Fax 759-2581

Dover, Tuscarawas, Pop. 12,639
Dover CSD 2,600/K-12
219 W 6th St 44622 330-364-1906
Robert Hamm, supt. Fax 343-7070
www.dover.k12.oh.us/
Dover HS 700/9-12
520 N Walnut St 44622 330-364-7148
Karie McCrate, prin. Fax 364-7142
Dover MS 700/6-8
2131 N Wooster Ave 44622 330-364-7121
Ronald Bond, prin. Fax 364-7127

Doylestown, Wayne, Pop. 3,018
Chippewa Local SD 1,400/K-12
56 N Portage St 44230 330-658-6368
David Fischer, supt. Fax 658-5842
www.chippewa.k12.oh.us
Chippewa HS 400/9-12
100 Valley View Rd 44230 330-658-2011
Shawn Bramen, prin. Fax 658-3339
Chippewa MS 400/5-8
257 High St 44230 330-658-2214
Sandy Stebly, prin. Fax 658-5842

Dresden, Muskingum, Pop. 1,503
Tri-Valley Local SD 3,100/K-12
36 E Muskingum Ave 43821 740-754-1572
Mark Neal, supt. Fax 754-6400
www.tvschools.org
Tri-Valley HS 900/9-12
46 E Muskingum Ave 43821 740-754-2921
James Pottmeyer, prin. Fax 754-6409
Tri-Valley MS 500/7-8
1358 Main St 43821 740-754-3531
Chad Shawger, prin. Fax 754-1879

Dublin, Franklin, Pop. 40,967
Dublin CSD 14,000/K-12
7030 Coffman Rd 43017 614-764-5913
Dr. David Axner, supt. Fax 761-5856
www.dublinschools.net
Davis MS 900/6-8
2400 Sutter Pkwy 43016 614-761-5820
Brian Lidle, prin. Fax 761-5893
Dublin Coffman HS 1,900/9-12
6780 Coffman Rd 43017 614-764-5900
Mike Ulring, prin. Fax 764-5925
Dublin Jerome HS 1,200/9-12
8300 Hyland Croy Rd 43016 614-873-7377
Cathy Sankey, prin. Fax 873-7340
Dublin Scioto HS 1,200/9-12
4000 Hard Rd 43016 614-717-2464
Donis Toler, prin. Fax 717-2484
Grizzell MS 700/6-8
8705 Avery Rd 43017 614-718-8600
Dr. Dustin Miller, prin. Fax 761-6514
Karrer MS 800/6-8
7245 Tullymore Dr 43016 614-873-0459
Rick Weininger, prin. Fax 873-1492
Sells MS 900/6-8
150 W Bridge St 43017 614-764-5919
Rich Baird, prin. Fax 764-5923

Duncan Falls, Muskingum, Pop. 873
Franklin Local SD 2,100/PK-12
PO Box 428 43734 740-674-5203
Sharon McDermott, supt. Fax 674-5214
www.franklin-local.k12.oh.us
Philo HS 500/9-12
4000 Millers Ln 43734 740-674-4355
Troy Dawson, prin. Fax 674-5202
Other Schools – See Philo

East Canton, Stark, Pop. 1,566
Osnaburg Local SD 900/PK-12
310 Browning Ct N 44730 330-488-1609
Melissa Marconi, supt. Fax 488-4001
ecweb.sparcc.org
East Canton HS 300/9-12
310 Browning Ct N 44730 330-488-0316
Erica Knowles, prin. Fax 488-4015
East Canton MS 200/6-8
310 Browning Ct N 44730 330-488-0316
Erica Knowles, prin. Fax 488-4015

East Cleveland, Cuyahoga, Pop. 17,585
East Cleveland CSD 3,300/PK-12
1843 Stanwood Rd 44112 216-268-6600
Myrna Loy Corley, supt. Fax 268-6676
www.east-cleveland.k12.oh.us
Heritage MS 500/7-8
14410 Terrace Rd 44112 216-268-6610
Kamal Chatman, prin. Fax 268-6676
Shaw HS 1,300/9-12
15320 Euclid Ave 44112 216-268-6500
Deborah Moore, prin. Fax 268-6676

Huron School of Nursing Post-Sec.
13951 Terrace Rd 44112 216-761-7990

Eastlake, Lake, Pop. 18,364
Willoughby-Eastlake CSD
Supt. — See Willoughby
Eastlake MS 500/6-8
35972 Lake Shore Blvd 44095 440-942-5696
Michael Chokshi, prin. Fax 918-8973
North HS 1,400/9-12
34041 Stevens Blvd 44095 440-975-3666
Jennifer Chauby, prin. Fax 975-3671

Bryant & Stratton College Post-Sec.
35350 Curtis Blvd Ste 100 44095 440-510-1112

East Liverpool, Columbiana, Pop. 10,871
East Liverpool CSD 2,200/K-12
810 W 8th St 43920 330-385-7132
James Herring, supt. Fax 382-7673
www.elcsd.k12.oh.us
East Liverpool HS 700/9-12
100 Maine Blvd 43920 330-386-8750
Randy Taylor, prin. Fax 386-8753
East Liverpool JHS 300/7-8
100 Maine Blvd 43920 330-386-8750
Randy Taylor, prin. Fax 386-8753

American Spirit Academy 100/PK-12
46682 Florence St 43920 330-385-5588
Susan Mackall, hdmstr. Fax 385-1267
Kent State University-East Liverpool Post-Sec.
400 E 4th St 43920 330-385-3805
Ohio Valley College of Technology Post-Sec.
15258 State Route 170 43920 330-385-1070

East Palestine, Columbiana, Pop. 4,696
East Palestine CSD 1,100/PK-12
200 W North Ave 44413 330-426-4191
George Fisk, supt. Fax 426-9592
www.myepschools.org
East Palestine HS 400/9-12
360 W Grant St 44413 330-426-9401
Laura Griffiths, prin. Fax 426-5105
East Palestine MS 300/6-8
320 W Grant St 44413 330-426-9451
Carol Vollnogle, prin. Fax 426-5118

Eaton, Preble, Pop. 8,276
Eaton Community SD 2,200/K-12
307 N Cherry St 45320 937-456-1107
Bradley Neavin, supt. Fax 472-1057
www.eaton.k12.oh.us
Eaton HS 600/9-12
600 Hillcrest Dr 45320 937-456-1141
Scott Couch, prin. Fax 456-1143
Eaton MS 500/6-8
311 N Cherry St 45320 937-456-2286
Kern Carpenter, prin. Fax 456-9687

Edgerton, Williams, Pop. 1,997
Edgerton Local SD 600/PK-12
111 E River St 43517 419-298-2112
Andy Morr, supt. Fax 298-1322
www.edgerton.k12.oh.us/
Edgerton HS 300/7-12
111 E River St 43517 419-298-2331
Roger Cade, prin. Fax 298-1322

Edon, Williams, Pop. 823
Edon-Northwest Local SD 400/K-12
802 W Indiana St 43518 419-272-3213
Edward Ewers, supt. Fax 272-2240
www.edon.k12.oh.us/
Edon HS 200/7-12
802 W Indiana St 43518 419-272-3113
David Kennedy, prin. Fax 272-2240

Elida, Allen, Pop. 1,868
Elida Local SD 2,000/K-12
4380 Sunnydale St 45807 419-331-4155
Don Diglia, supt. Fax 331-1656
home.elida.k12.oh.us/
Elida HS 700/9-12
401 E North St 45807 419-331-4115
Greg Leeth, prin. Fax 339-3523
Elida MS 600/5-8
4500 Sunnydale St 45807 419-331-2505
Dave Morman, prin. Fax 331-6822

Elmore, Ottawa, Pop. 1,392
Woodmore Local SD 1,100/PK-12
PO Box 701 43416 419-862-1060
Linda Bringman, supt. Fax 862-1951
www.woodmore.k12.oh.us
Woodmore JSHS 500/7-12
633 Fremont St 43416 419-862-2721
Jim Kieper, prin. Fax 862-3835

Elyria, Lorain, Pop. 52,588
Elyria CSD 6,700/PK-12
42101 Griswold Rd 44035 440-284-8000
Paul Rigda, supt. Fax 284-0678
www.elyriaschools.org
Early College HS 9-12
1005 Abbe Rd N 44035 440-366-4720
Dianne Quinn, prin.
Eastern Heights MS 600/6-8
528 Garford Ave 44035 440-284-8015
Dr. Kimberly Benetto, prin. Fax 323-0827
Elyria HS 2,000/9-12
601 Middle Ave 44035 440-284-8300
Dr. Thomas Jama, prin. Fax 323-2543
Northwood MS 600/6-8
700 Gulf Rd 44035 440-284-8016
James Wall, prin. Fax 284-1546
Westwood MS 500/6-8
42350 Adelbert St 44035 440-284-8017
Theresa Lengel, prin. Fax 284-1055

Elyria Catholic HS 500/9-12
725 Gulf Rd 44035 440-365-1821
Amy Butler, prin. Fax 365-7536
First Baptist Christian S 100/PK-12
11400 Lagrange Rd 44035 440-458-5185
Brenda Milam, prin. Fax 458-8717
Lorain County Community College Post-Sec.
1005 Abbe Rd N 44035 440-365-5222
Open Door Christian S 500/PK-12
8287 W Ridge Rd 44035 440-322-6386
Dr. Jonathan Burton, pres. Fax 284-6033

Englewood, Montgomery, Pop. 13,133
Northmont CSD 5,300/K-12
4001 Old Salem Rd 45322 937-832-5000
Dr. Sarah Zatik, supt. Fax 832-5001
www.northmontschools.com/
Other Schools – See Clayton

Enon, Clark, Pop. 2,391
Greenon Local SD 1,900/K-12
500 S Xenia Dr 45323 937-864-1202
Daniel Bennett, supt. Fax 864-2470
www.greenon.k12.oh.us
Indian Valley MS 600/5-8
510 S Xenia Dr 45323 937-864-7348
Richard Quisenberry, prin. Fax 864-6009
Other Schools – See Springfield

Etna, Licking, Pop. 1,187
Southwest Licking Local SD
Supt. — See Pataskala
Watkins Memorial HS 1,100/9-12
8868 Watkins Rd SW, 740-927-3846
Ben Richards, prin. Fax 964-0088
Watkins MS 900/6-8
8808 Watkins Rd SW, 740-927-5767
Kasey Rathburn, prin. Fax 927-2337

Euclid, Cuyahoga, Pop. 47,840
Euclid CSD 5,100/K-12
651 E 222nd St 44123 216-261-2900
Keith Bell, supt. Fax 261-3120
www.euclid.k12.oh.us
Euclid Central MS 600/6-8
20701 Euclid Ave 44117 216-797-5300
Mike Mennel, prin. Fax 797-5333
Euclid HS 2,200/9-12
711 E 222nd St 44123 216-797-7800
Dr. Charlie Smialek, prin. Fax 797-7900
Forest Park MS 700/6-8
27000 Elinore Ave 44132 216-797-4700
Tina Elliott, prin. Fax 797-4710

Fairborn, Greene, Pop. 31,321
Fairborn CSD 4,600/PK-12
306 E Whittier Ave 45324 937-878-3961
Dave Scarberry, supt. Fax 879-8180
www.fairborn.k12.oh.us
Baker MS 900/6-8
200 Lincoln Dr 45324 937-878-4681
Deb Hauberg, prin. Fax 879-8193
Fairborn HS 1,200/9-12
900 E Dayton Yellow Springs 45324 937-879-3611
Eugene Lolli, prin. Fax 879-8190

Hondros College Post-Sec.
1810 Successful Dr 45324 937-879-1940

Fairfield, Butler, Pop. 41,547
Fairfield CSD 8,900/K-12
211 Donald Dr 45014 513-829-6300
Paul Otten, supt. Fax 829-0148
www.fairfieldcityschools.com
Fairfield Freshman HS 800/9-9
5050 Dixie Hwy 45014 513-829-8300
Katie Pospisil, prin. Fax 829-4733
Fairfield MS 1,500/7-8
1111 Nilles Rd 45014 513-829-4433
Dr. Kristilynn Turney, prin. Fax 829-6480
Fairfield SHS 2,100/10-12
8800 Holden Blvd 45014 513-942-2999
David Helms, prin. Fax 942-3288

Moler-Hollywood Beauty Academy Post-Sec.
5951 Boymel Dr Ste S 45014 513-874-5116

Fairport Harbor, Lake, Pop. 3,058
Fairport Harbor EVD 500/K-12
329 Vine St 44077 440-354-5400
Domenic Paolo, supt. Fax 354-1724
www.fairport.k12.oh.us/

Fairport Harding JSHS 300/6-12
329 Vine St 44077 440-354-3592
Thomas Fazekas, prin. Fax 354-5426

Fairview Park, Cuyahoga, Pop. 16,640
Fairview Park CSD 1,700/PK-12
21620 Mastick Rd 44126 440-331-5500
Brion Deitsch, supt. Fax 356-3545
www.fairviewparkschools.org
Fairview HS 600/9-12
4507 W 213th St 44126 440-356-3500
Brady Sheets, prin. Fax 356-3529
Mayer MS 200/7-8
21200 Campus Dr 44126 440-356-3510
Ray Mohr, prin. Fax 895-2191

Fairview Academy Post-Sec.
22610 Lorain Rd 44126 440-734-5555

Farmersville, Montgomery, Pop. 991
Valley View Local SD
Supt. — See Germantown
Valley View JHS 300/7-8
202 Jackson St 45325 937-696-2591
Dan Dodds, prin. Fax 696-1007

Fayette, Fulton, Pop. 1,278
Fayette Local SD 400/K-12
400 E Gamble Rd 43521 419-237-2573
Erik Belcher, supt. Fax 237-3125
www.fayette.k12.oh.us
Fayette JSHS 200/7-12
400 E Gamble Rd 43521 419-237-2114
Dan Feasel, prin. Fax 237-4306

Fayetteville, Brown, Pop. 329
Fayetteville-Perry Local SD 900/PK-12
551 S Apple St 45118 513-875-2423
Raegan White, supt. Fax 875-2703
www.fp.k12.oh.us
Fayetteville-Perry HS 300/9-12
501 S Apple St 45118 513-875-3520
David Tatman, prin. Fax 875-4512
Fayetteville-Perry MS 200/6-8
521 S Apple St 45118 513-875-2829
David Tatman, prin. Fax 875-4200

Chatfield College Post-Sec.
20918 State Route 251 45118 513-875-3344

Felicity, Clermont, Pop. 815
Felicity-Franklin Local SD 1,000/PK-12
PO Box 619 45120 513-876-2113
Glenn Moore, supt. Fax 876-2519
www.felicityschools.org/
Felicity-Franklin Local HS 300/9-12
PO Box 619 45120 513-876-2113
Amy Shrock, prin. Fax 876-2560
Felicity-Franklin Local MS 300/5-8
PO Box 619 45120 513-876-2113
Joe Pfeffer, prin. Fax 876-2519

Findlay, Hancock, Pop. 40,536
Findlay CSD 4,700/K-12
1100 Broad Ave 45840 419-425-8212
Dr. Dean Wittwer, supt. Fax 425-8203
www.findlaycityschools.org
Donnell MS, 301 Baldwin Ave 45840 6-8
Don Williams, prin. 419-425-8370
Findlay HS 2,100/9-12
1200 Broad Ave 45840 419-425-8279
Victoria Swartz, prin. Fax 427-5448
Glenwood MS 400/6-8
1715 N Main St 45840 419-425-8373
David Alvarado, prin. Fax 427-5455
Millstream Career Center Vo/Tech
1150 Broad Ave 45840 419-425-8293
Chris Renn, prin. Fax 420-7199

Hancock County ESC
7746 County Road 140 45840 419-422-7525
Larry Busdeker, supt. Fax 422-8766
hancockesc.org
Hancock Alternative Opportunity HS Alt
7746 County Road 140 45840 419-422-7525
Fax 422-8766

Liberty-Benton Local SD 1,200/K-12
9190 County Road 9 45840 419-422-8526
Jim Kanable, supt. Fax 422-5108
www.noacsc.org/hancock/lb/
Liberty-Benton HS 400/9-12
9190 County Road 9 45840 419-424-5351
Brenda Frankart, prin. Fax 422-5108
Liberty Benton MS 300/6-8
9050 W State Route 12 45840 419-422-9166
Bruce Otley, prin. Fax 420-9237

Brown Mackie College Post-Sec.
1700 Fostoria Ave Ste 100 45840 419-423-2211
Owens Community College Post-Sec.
3200 Bright Rd 45840 567-429-3500
University of Findlay Post-Sec.
1000 N Main St 45840 800-548-0932
Winebrenner Theological Seminary Post-Sec.
950 N Main St 45840 419-434-4200

Fort Jennings, Putnam, Pop. 485
Jennings Local SD 400/K-12
PO Box 98 45844 419-286-2238
Nicholas Langhals, supt. Fax 286-2240
jennings.noacsc.org/
Fort Jennings JSHS 200/7-12
PO Box 98 45844 419-286-2238
Nicholas Langhals, prin. Fax 286-2240

Fort Loramie, Shelby, Pop. 1,478
Fort Loramie Local SD 800/K-12
PO Box 26 45845 937-295-3931
Daniel Holland, supt. Fax 295-2758
www.loramie.k12.oh.us/
Fort Loramie JSHS 400/7-12
PO Box 290 45845 937-295-3342
Justin Firks, prin. Fax 295-2758

Fort Recovery, Mercer, Pop. 1,410
Fort Recovery Local SD 1,100/PK-12
PO Box 604 45846 419-375-4139
Michelle Vaughn, supt. Fax 375-1058
www.fortrecoveryschools.org
Fort Recovery HS 300/9-12
PO Box 604 45846 419-375-4111
Jeffrey Hobbs, prin. Fax 375-2039
Fort Recovery MS 200/6-8
865 Sharpsburg Rd 45846 419-375-2815
Matt Triplett, prin. Fax 375-1126

Fostoria, Seneca, Pop. 12,940
Fostoria CSD 1,900/PK-12
500 Parkway Dr 44830 419-435-8163
Steven J. Pritts, supt. Fax 436-4109
www.fostoriaschools.org/
Fostoria JSHS 700/7-12
1001 Park Ave 44830 419-436-4110
Tom Grine, prin. Fax 436-4118

St. Wendelin S 200/PK-12
533 N Countyline St 44830 419-435-8144
Michael Amlin, prin. Fax 436-4042

Frankfort, Ross, Pop. 1,038
Adena Local SD 1,200/K-12
3367 County Road 550 45628 740-998-4633
David Warne, supt. Fax 998-4632
adena.k12.oh.us/
Adena HS 400/9-12
3367 County Road 550 45628 740-998-2313
Craig Kerns, prin. Fax 998-2317
Adena MS 300/6-8
3367 County Road 550 45628 740-998-2313
Craig Kerns, prin. Fax 998-2317

Franklin, Warren, Pop. 11,585
Franklin CSD 2,800/K-12
150 E 6th St 45005 937-746-1699
Arnol Elam, supt. Fax 743-8620
www.franklincityschools.com
Franklin HS 700/9-12
750 E 4th St 45005 937-743-8610
David Riegel, prin. Fax 743-8625
Franklin JHS 400/7-8
136 E 6th St 45005 937-743-8630
Jeremy Ward, prin. Fax 743-8635

Fenwick HS 500/9-12
4855 State Route 122 45005 513-423-0723
Trevor Block, prin. Fax 420-8690
Middletown Christian S 500/PK-12
3011 Union Rd 45005 513-423-4542
Mark Spradling, supt. Fax 261-6841

Franklin Furnace, Scioto, Pop. 1,641
Green Local SD 400/PK-12
4070 Gallia Pike 45629 740-354-9221
Sandra Mers, supt. Fax 355-8975
www.green.k12.oh.us
Green JSHS 200/7-12
4057 Gallia Pike 45629 740-354-9150
Joseph Emnett, prin. Fax 355-4094

Fredericktown, Knox, Pop. 2,475
Fredericktown Local SD 900/K-12
117 Columbus Rd 43019 740-694-2956
Matthew W. Chrispin, supt. Fax 694-0956
www.fredericktownschools.com
Fredericktown MSHS 300/6-12
111 Stadium Dr 43019 740-694-2726
Douglas Potts, prin. Fax 694-1294

Freeport, Harrison, Pop. 360

Antrim Mennonite S 50/K-12
20360 Cadiz Rd 43973 740-489-5161
Titus Lapp, prin.

Fremont, Sandusky, Pop. 16,145
Fremont CSD 4,100/K-12
500 W State St Ste A 43420 419-332-6454
Dr. Traci McCaudy, supt. Fax 334-5454
www.fremontschools.net
Fremont MS 600/7-8
1250 North St 43420 419-332-5569
Anthony Walker, prin. Fax 334-5494
Fremont Ross SHS 1,200/9-12
1100 North St 43420 419-332-8221
Jose Hernandez, prin. Fax 334-5450

Vanguard-Sentinel JVSD
1306 Cedar St 43420 419-332-2626
Gregory Edinger, supt. Fax 334-4308
www.vscc.k12.oh.us/
Technology Center Vo/Tech
1220 Cedar St Ste C 43420 419-334-5698
Fax 334-2609
Vanguard Career Center Vo/Tech
1306 Cedar St 43420 419-332-2626
Jim Rutter, dir. Fax 334-5692
Other Schools – See Tiffin

Bishop Hoffman HS 200/9-12
702 Croghan St 43420 419-332-9947
Tim Cullen, supt. Fax 332-4945
Bishop Hoffman S - St. Joseph Campus 100/4-8
716 Croghan St 43420 419-332-5161
Cathy Krupp, prin. Fax 332-7299

Terra State Community College Post-Sec.
2830 Napoleon Rd 43420 419-334-8400

Gahanna, Franklin, Pop. 32,425
Gahanna-Jefferson CSD 7,200/K-12
160 S Hamilton Rd 43230 614-471-7065
Francis R. Scruci, supt. Fax 478-5568
www.gahannaschools.org
Gahanna MS East 500/6-8
730 Clotts Rd 43230 614-478-5550
Brad Barboza, prin. Fax 478-5544
Gahanna MS South 500/6-8
349 Shady Spring Dr 43230 614-337-3730
Kristen Groves, prin. Fax 337-3734
Gahanna MS West 600/6-8
350 N Stygler Rd 43230 614-478-5570
Brett Harmon, prin. Fax 337-3771
Lincoln HS 2,300/9-12
140 S Hamilton Rd 43230 614-478-5500
Dwight Carter, prin. Fax 337-3769

Columbus Academy 1,100/PK-12
4300 Cherry Bottom Rd 43230 614-475-2311
John Mackenzie, admin. Fax 475-0396
Everest Institute Post-Sec.
825 Tech Center Dr 43230 614-322-3414
Gahanna Christian Academy 500/PK-12
817 N Hamilton Rd 43230 614-471-9270
Ruth Bischoff, supt. Fax 471-9201

Galena, Delaware, Pop. 644
Olentangy Local SD
Supt. — See Lewis Center
Berkshire MS 6-8
2869 S 3 Bs and K Rd 43021 740-657-5200
Carla Baker, prin. Fax 657-5299

Galion, Crawford, Pop. 10,395
Galion CSD 1,900/PK-12
470 Portland Way N 44833 419-468-3432
Dr. Kathleen Jenney, supt. Fax 468-4333
www.galionschools.org
Galion HS 400/9-12
472 Portland Way N 44833 419-468-6500
Fritz Caudle, prin. Fax 468-4333
Galion MS 400/6-8
474 Portland Way N 44833 419-468-3134
Andrew Johnson, prin. Fax 468-4333

Northmor Local SD 800/K-12
5247 County Road 29 44833 419-946-8861
Brent Winand Ed.D., supt. Fax 947-6255
www.northmor.k12.oh.us
Northmor HS 500/7-12
7819 State Route 19 44833 419-946-3946
Chad Redmon, prin. Fax 947-7545

Gallipolis, Gallia, Pop. 3,534
Gallia County Local SD 2,200/K-12
230 Shawnee Ln 45631 740-446-7917
Dr. Charla Evans, supt. Fax 446-3187
gallialocal.org
Other Schools – See Bidwell, Crown City

Gallipolis CSD 2,200/PK-12
61 State St 45631 740-446-3211
Roger Mace, supt. Fax 446-6433
www.gc.k12.oh.us
Clay Alternative S 50/Alt
340 4th Ave 45631 740-446-3214
Gallia Academy HS 600/9-12
2855 Centenary Rd 45631 740-446-3212
Tim Massie, prin. Fax 446-3436
Gallia Academy MS 500/6-8
340 4th Ave 45631 740-446-3214
Craig Wright, prin. Fax 446-2493

Gallipolis Career College Post-Sec.
1176 Jackson Pike # 312 45631 740-446-4367
Gallipolis State Institute 45631 Post-Sec.
Ohio Valley Christian S 100/PK-12
1100 4th Ave 45631 740-446-0374
Patrick O'Donnell, admin. Fax 446-3961

Galloway, Franklin
South-Western CSD
Supt. — See Grove City
Westland HS 1,600/9-12
146 Galloway Rd 43119 614-851-7000
John Rathburn, prin. Fax 870-5531

Gambier, Knox, Pop. 2,300

Kenyon College Post-Sec.
1 Kenyon College 43022 740-427-5000

Garfield Heights, Cuyahoga, Pop. 28,281
Garfield Heights CSD 3,900/K-12
5640 Briarcliff Dr 44125 216-475-8100
Terrance Olszewski, supt. Fax 475-1824
www.garfieldheightscityschools.com
Garfield Heights HS 1,400/9-12
4900 Turney Rd 44125 216-662-2800
Tammy Hager, prin. Fax 271-6183
Garfield Heights MS 900/6-8
12000 Maple Leaf Dr 44125 216-475-8105
Christopher Hanke, prin. Fax 475-8146

Archbishop Lyke S - St. Timothy Campus 200/5-8
4351 E 131st St 44105 216-581-3517
Margarete Smith, prin. Fax 581-6204
Trinity HS 400/9-12
12425 Granger Rd 44125 216-581-1644
Linda Bacho, prin. Fax 581-9348

Garrettsville, Portage, Pop. 2,303
James A. Garfield Local SD 1,500/K-12
10235 State Route 88 44231 330-527-4336
Charles Klamer, supt. Fax 527-5941
garfield.sparcc.org/
Garfield HS 400/9-12
10233 State Route 88 44231 330-527-4341
Jennifer Mulhern, prin. Fax 527-5636
Garfield MS 200/7-8
10231 State Route 88 44231 330-527-2151
Donald Long, prin. Fax 527-2601

Gates Mills, Cuyahoga, Pop. 2,236

Gilmour Academy 700/PK-12
34001 Cedar Rd 44040 440-473-8090
Br. Robert Lavelle, hdmstr. Fax 473-8010
Hawken S 400/9-12
PO Box 8002 44040 440-423-4446
D. Scott Looney, head sch Fax 423-2960

Geneva, Ashtabula, Pop. 6,134
Geneva CSD 2,600/K-12
135 S Eagle St 44041 440-466-4831
Mary Zappitelli, supt. Fax 466-0908
www.genevaschools.org/
Geneva HS 800/9-12
1301 S Ridge Rd E 44041 440-466-4831
Doug Wetherholt, prin. Fax 466-8547
Geneva MS 600/6-8
839 Sherman St 44041 440-466-4831
Steve Candela, prin. Fax 466-5692

Genoa, Ottawa, Pop. 2,309
Genoa Area Local SD 1,100/K-12
2810 N Genoa Clay Center Rd 43430 419-855-7741
Dennis Mock, supt. Fax 855-4030
www.genoaschools.com
Genoa Area HS 400/9-12
2980 N Genoa Clay Center Rd 43430 419-855-7741
Kevin Katafias, prin. Fax 855-7739
Genoa Area MS 300/6-8
2950 N Genoa Clay Center Rd 43430 419-855-7741
Kevin Katafias, prin. Fax 855-7784

Georgetown, Brown, Pop. 4,266
Georgetown EVD 1,000/PK-12
1043 Mount Orab Pike 45121 937-378-3730
Thomas Durbin, supt. Fax 378-2219
www.gtown.k12.oh.us/
Georgetown JSHS 500/7-12
987 Mount Orab Pike 45121 937-378-6730
Jerry Underwood, prin. Fax 378-2442

Southern Hills JVSD
9193 Hamer Rd 45121 937-378-6131
Kevin Kratzer, supt. Fax 378-4577
www.shctc.k12.oh.us
Southern Hills Career & Technical Center Vo/Tech
9193 Hamer Rd 45121 937-378-6131
Tim Chadwell, prin. Fax 378-4577

Germantown, Montgomery, Pop. 5,508
Valley View Local SD 1,900/PK-12
64 Comstock St 45327 937-855-6581
Fax 855-0266
www.valleyview.k12.oh.us
Valley View HS 600/9-12
6027 Frmrsvll Germantn Pike 45327 937-855-4116
Todd Kozarec, prin. Fax 855-4739
Other Schools – See Farmersville

Germantown Christian S 100/PK-12
9440 Eby Rd 45327 937-855-7334
Rhonda Jerman, admin. Fax 855-7746

Gibsonburg, Sandusky, Pop. 2,557
Gibsonburg EVD 1,100/PK-12
301 S Sunset Ave 43431 419-637-2479
Thomas Peiffer, supt. Fax 637-3029
www.gibsonburg.k12.oh.us/
Gibsonburg HS 300/9-12
740 S Main St 43431 419-637-2873
Thom Loomis, prin. Fax 637-2046
Gibsonburg MS 300/6-8
740 S Main St 43431 419-637-7954
Danny Kissell, prin. Fax 637-2046

Girard, Trumbull, Pop. 9,767
Girard CSD 1,700/K-12
704 E Prospect St 44420 330-545-2596
David Cappuzzello, supt. Fax 545-2597
www.girardcityschools.org/
Girard HS 500/9-12
1244 Shannon Rd 44420 330-545-5431
William Ryser, prin. Fax 545-5440
Girard JHS 300/7-8
1244 Shannon Rd 44420 330-545-5431
Jennifer Santangelo, dean Fax 545-5440

Glouster, Athens, Pop. 1,756
Trimble Local SD 800/PK-12
1 Tomcat Dr 45732 740-767-4444
Dr. Kimberly Jones, supt. Fax 767-4901
trimble.k12.oh.us
Trimble HS 200/9-12
1 Tomcat Dr 45732 740-767-3434
Matt Curtis, prin. Fax 767-4901
Trimble MS 300/5-8
18500 Jacksonville Rd 45732 740-767-2810
Deborah Koons, prin. Fax 767-9523

Gnadenhutten, Tuscarawas, Pop. 1,282
Indian Valley Local SD 1,800/K-12
PO Box 171 44629 740-254-4334
G. Ira Wentworth, supt. Fax 254-9271
www.ivschools.org/
Indian Valley HS 500/9-12
PO Box 130 44629 740-254-4262
Troy Page, prin. Fax 254-4911
Other Schools – See Tuscarawas

Goshen, Clermont
Goshen Local SD 2,500/PK-12
6694 Goshen Rd 45122 513-722-2222
Darrell Edwards, supt. Fax 722-3767
www.goshenlocalschools.org
Goshen HS 700/9-12
6707 Goshen Rd 45122 513-722-2227
Nick Inabnitt, prin. Fax 722-2247
Goshen MS 600/6-8
6692 Goshen Rd 45122 513-722-2226
Tina Reichert, prin. Fax 722-2246

Grafton, Lorain, Pop. 6,573
Midview Local SD 3,300/K-12
1010 Vivian Dr 44044 440-926-3737
John Kuhn, supt. Fax 926-2675
www.midviewk12.org
Midview HS 1,100/9-12
38199 Capel Rd 44044 440-748-2124
Thomas Faska, prin. Fax 748-5277
Midview MS 600/7-8
12865 Grafton Rd 44044 440-748-2122
John Brown, prin. Fax 748-0411

Granville, Licking, Pop. 5,563
Granville EVD 2,500/K-12
PO Box 417 43023 740-587-8101
Jeff Brown, supt. Fax 587-8191
www.granville.k12.oh.us/
Granville HS 800/9-12
248 New Burg St 43023 740-587-8105
Ryan Bernath, prin. Fax 587-8195
Granville MS 400/7-8
210 New Burg St 43023 740-587-8104
Lisa Sealover-Ormond, prin. Fax 587-8194

Denison University Post-Sec.
100 W College St 43023 740-587-0810
Granville Christian Academy 2,300/K-12
1820 Newark Granville Rd 43023 740-587-4423
Jennifer Haga, admin. Fax 587-4776

Green Camp, Marion, Pop. 363
Elgin Local SD
Supt. — See Marion
Elgin JHS 200/7-8
PO Box 214 43322 740-528-2320
Michael Malcolm, prin. Fax 528-2618

Greenfield, Highland, Pop. 4,562
Greenfield EVD 2,100/PK-12
200 N 5th St 45123 937-981-2152
Terrence Fouch, supt. Fax 981-4395
greenfield.k12.oh.us
Greenfield MS 500/6-8
200 N 5th St 45123 937-981-2197
Howard Zody, prin. Fax 981-0417
McClain HS 500/9-12
200 N 5th St 45123 937-981-7731
Dan Strain, prin. Fax 981-4395

Greenville, Darke, Pop. 13,080
Greenville CSD 2,800/K-12
215 W 4th St 45331 937-548-3185
Douglas Fries, supt. Fax 548-6943
www.greenville.k12.oh.us
Greenville HS 900/9-12
100 Greenwave Way 45331 937-548-4188
Ken Neff, prin. Fax 548-3082
Greenville JHS 400/7-8
131 Central Ave 45331 937-548-3202
Christian Mortensen, prin. Fax 548-3315

Greenwich, Huron, Pop. 1,472
South Central Local SD 800/PK-12
3305 Greenwich Angling Rd 44837 419-752-3815
David Brand, supt. Fax 752-0182
www.south-central.org
South Central HS 200/9-12
3305 Greenwich Angling Rd 44837 419-752-3354
Wayne Hinkle, prin. Fax 752-6927
South Central MS 200/5-8
3291 Greenwich Angling Rd 44837 419-752-0011
Fax 752-8705

Grove City, Franklin, Pop. 34,836
South-Western CSD 20,300/PK-12
3805 Marlane Dr 43123 614-801-3000
Dr. Bill Wise, supt. Fax 871-2781
www.swcs.us
Brookpark MS 600/7-8
2803 Southwest Blvd 43123 614-801-3500
Neil Britton, prin. Fax 871-6512
Central Crossing HS 1,700/9-12
4500 Big Run South Rd 43123 614-801-6500
Jill Burke, prin. Fax 801-6690
Grove City HS 1,900/9-12
4750 Hoover Rd 43123 614-801-3300
Michael Starner, prin. Fax 871-6563
Jackson MS 600/7-8
2271 Holton Rd 43123 614-801-3800
Emily Jablonka, prin. Fax 801-3818
Pleasant View MS 800/7-8
7255 Kropp Rd 43123 614-801-3900
Thom Gamertsfelder, prin. Fax 870-5530
South-Western Career Academy Vo/Tech
4750 Big Run South Rd 43123 614-801-3400
Shirley Moore, prin. Fax 801-6138
Other Schools – See Columbus, Galloway

Grove City Christian S 700/K-12
4750 Hoover Rd 43123 614-875-3000
Rebecca Jeffries, prin. Fax 875-8933
Harrison College Post-Sec.
3880 Gateway Lakes Dr 43123 614-539-8800

Groveport, Franklin, Pop. 5,240
Eastland-Fairfield Career & Technical SD
4300 Amalgamated Pl 43125 614-836-4530
Bonnie Hopkins, supt. Fax 836-0203
www.eastland-fairfield.com
Eastland Career Center Vo/Tech
4465 S Hamilton Rd 43125 614-836-5725
Nelson Karshner, dir. Fax 836-4525
Adult Workforce Development Adult
4300 Amalgamated Pl Ste 100 43125 614-836-4541
Angela Ward, dir. Fax 836-0203
Other Schools – See Carroll

Groveport Madison Local SD 5,500/K-12
5940 Clyde Moore Dr 43125 614-492-2520
Bruce Hoover, supt. Fax 492-2532
www.gocruisers.org
Groveport Madison HS 1,500/9-12
4475 S Hamilton Rd 43125 614-836-4964
Aric Thomas, prin. Fax 836-4690
Groveport Madison JHS 500/8-8
751 Main St 43125 614-836-4957
John Hurd, prin. Fax 836-4999

Eastland Career Center Post-Sec.
4465 S Hamilton Rd 43125 614-836-5725
Madison Christian S 500/PK-12
3565 Bixby Rd 43125 614-497-3456
Debbie Ostrander, admin. Fax 497-3057

Hamilton, Butler, Pop. 60,903
Butler Technology/Career Development SD
3603 Hamilton Middletown Rd 45011 513-868-1911
Brett Smith, supt. Fax 868-9348
www.butlertech.org
Lee Career Technology Center Vo/Tech
3603 Hamilton Middletown Rd 45011 513-868-6300
Lisa Tuttle-Huff, prin. Fax 868-1701
Options Arts Academy Alt
101 S Monument Ave 45011 513-863-8898
Erin Schilling, coord. Fax 863-8865
Other Schools – See Monroe

Hamilton CSD 9,400/PK-12
PO Box 627 45012 513-887-5000
Janet Baker, supt. Fax 868-4473
www.hamiltoncityschools.com/
Garfield MS 800/7-8
250 N Fair Ave 45011 513-887-5035
Brandon Stanfill, prin. Fax 887-4700
Hamilton Freshman HS 600/9-9
2260 NW Washington Blvd 45013 513-896-3400
Jeff Miller, prin. Fax 896-3402
Hamilton HS 1,900/10-12
1165 Eaton Ave 45013 513-868-7700
Doug Leist, prin. Fax 887-4810
Wilson MS 600/7-8
714 Eaton Ave 45013 513-887-5170
Sheryl Burk, prin. Fax 887-5068

New Miami Local SD 700/K-12
600 Seven Mile Ave 45011 513-863-0833
David Gibson, supt. Fax 863-0497
www.new-miami.k12.oh.us
New Miami HS 200/9-12
600 Seven Mile Ave 45011 513-863-4917
Michael Howton, prin. Fax 896-3956
New Miami MS 200/6-8
600 Seven Mile Ave 45011 513-863-4917
Michael Howton, prin. Fax 863-3956

Ross Local SD 2,800/PK-12
3371 Hamilton Cleves Rd 45013 513-863-1253
Greg Young, supt. Fax 863-6250
www.rossrams.com
Ross HS 900/9-12
3601 Hamilton Cleves Rd 45013 513-863-1252
Lani Wildow, prin. Fax 863-8340
Ross MS 800/5-8
3425 Hamilton Cleves Rd 45013 513-863-1251
Christopher Saylor, prin. Fax 863-0066

Badin HS 500/9-12
571 Hamilton New London Rd 45013 513-863-3993
Brian Pendergest, prin. Fax 785-2844
Cincinnati Christian Schools - JSHS Cmps 400/7-12
7474 Morris Rd 45011 513-892-8500
Debbie Enos, prin. Fax 892-0516
Miami University-Hamilton Campus Post-Sec.
1601 University Blvd 45011 513-785-3000

Hamler, Henry, Pop. 573
Patrick Henry Local SD 1,000/PK-12
6900 State Route 18 43524 419-274-5451
Thomas L. Taylor, supt. Fax 274-1641
www.patrickhenry.k12.oh.us/
Henry HS 300/9-12
6900 State Route 18 43524 419-274-3015
Josh Biederstedt, prin. Fax 274-8365
Henry MS 300/5-8
E050 County Road 7 43524 419-274-3431
Jennifer Ripke, prin. Fax 274-1890

Hammondsville, Jefferson
Edison Local SD 1,500/PK-12
14890 State Route 213 43930 330-532-3199
Bill Beattie, supt. Fax 532-2860
www.edisonlocal.k12.oh.us/
Other Schools – See Richmond

Hannibal, Monroe, Pop. 405
Switzerland of Ohio Local SD
Supt. — See Woodsfield
River HS 200/9-12
PO Box 37 43931 740-483-1358
Ed Trifonoff, prin. Fax 483-2321

Hanoverton, Columbiana, Pop. 408
United Local SD 1,300/K-12
8143 State Route 9 44423 330-223-1521
Steven Viscounte, supt. Fax 223-2363
www.united.k12.oh.us
United JSHS 600/7-12
8143 State Route 9 44423 330-223-7102
William Young, prin. Fax 223-2363

Harrison, Hamilton, Pop. 9,812
Southwest Local SD 3,300/K-12
230 S Elm St 45030 513-367-4139
Chris Brown, supt. Fax 367-2287
www.southwestschools.org
Harrison HS 1,000/9-12
9860 West Rd 45030 513-367-4169
Davis Baker, prin. Fax 367-7251
Harrison MS 600/7-8
9830 West Rd 45030 513-367-4831
Christian Tracy, prin. Fax 367-0370

Harrod, Allen, Pop. 415
Allen East Local SD 1,100/K-12
9105 Harding Hwy 45850 419-648-3333
Michael Richards, supt. Fax 648-5282
www.ae.k12.oh.us
Allen East HS 500/7-12
9105 Harding Hwy 45850 419-649-6311
Keith Baumgartner, prin. Fax 649-8900

Hartville, Stark, Pop. 2,894
Lake Local SD
Supt. — See Uniontown
Lake MS 900/6-8
12001 Market Ave N 44632 330-877-4290
Brian Reed, prin. Fax 877-1384

Lake Center Christian S 600/PK-12
12893 Kaufman Ave NW 44632 330-877-2049
Matthew McMullen, supt. Fax 877-2040

Haviland, Paulding, Pop. 213
Wayne Trace Local SD 900/PK-12
4915 US Route 127 45851 419-263-2415
Steve Arnold, supt. Fax 263-2377
www.waynetrace.org
Wayne Trace JSHS 400/7-12
4915 US Route 127 45851 419-399-4100
Greg Leeth, prin. Fax 622-3037

Heath, Licking, Pop. 10,088
Heath CSD 1,700/K-12
107 Lancaster Dr 43056 740-522-2816
Tom Forman, supt. Fax 522-4697
www.heath.k12.oh.us/
Heath HS 500/9-12
300 Licking View Dr 43056 740-788-3300
Ellis Booth, prin. Fax 788-3322
Heath MS 500/6-8
310 Licking View Dr 43056 740-788-3200
Jeffrey Hempleman, prin. Fax 788-3209

Hebron, Licking, Pop. 2,293
Lakewood Local SD 2,000/K-12
PO Box 70 43025 740-928-5878
Jay Gault, supt. Fax 928-3152
www.lakewoodlocal.k12.oh.us/
Lakewood HS 600/9-12
PO Box 70 43025 740-928-4526
Larry Bevard, prin. Fax 928-3731
Lakewood MS 500/6-8
PO Box 70 43025 740-928-8330
Patti Pickering, prin. Fax 928-5627

Hicksville, Defiance, Pop. 3,540
Hicksville EVD 900/PK-12
958 E High St 43526 419-542-7665
Keith Countryman, supt. Fax 542-8534
www.hicksvilleschools.org/
Hicksville JSHS 400/7-12
958 E High St 43526 419-542-7636
Charles Life, prin. Fax 542-8534

Highland Heights, Cuyahoga, Pop. 8,256

ATS Institute of Technology Post-Sec.
325 Alpha Park 44143 440-449-1700

Highland Hills, Cuyahoga, Pop. 1,115

Cuyahoga Community College Post-Sec.
4250 Richmond Rd 44122 800-954-8742

Hilliard, Franklin, Pop. 27,909
Hilliard CSD 15,400/PK-12
5323 Cemetery Rd 43026 614-921-7000
Dale McVey, supt. Fax 921-7001
www.hilliardschools.org
Hilliard Bradley HS 1,400/9-12
2800 Walker Rd 43026 614-921-7400
David Stewart, prin. Fax 921-7401
Hilliard Darby HS 1,400/9-12
4200 Leppert Rd 43026 614-921-7300
Ryan McClure, prin. Fax 921-7301
Hilliard Davidson HS 1,700/9-12
5100 Davidson Rd 43026 614-921-7200
John Bandow, prin. Fax 921-7201
Hilliard Heritage MS 700/7-8
5670 Scioto Darby Rd 43026 614-921-7500
Joyce Brickley, prin. Fax 921-7501
Hilliard Memorial MS 800/7-8
5600 Scioto Darby Rd 43026 614-921-7600
Barry Bay, prin. Fax 921-7601
Hilliard Weaver MS 900/7-8
4600 Avery Rd 43026 614-921-7700
Craig Vroom, prin. Fax 921-7701

ITT Technical Institute Post-Sec.
3781 Park Mill Run Dr 43026 614-771-4888

Hillsboro, Highland, Pop. 6,439
Hillsboro CSD 2,600/PK-12
39 Willetsville Pike 45133 937-393-3475
Rick Earley, supt. Fax 393-5841
www.hcs-k12.org/
Hillsboro HS 700/9-12
550 US Highway 62 45133 937-393-3485
Jason Snively, prin. Fax 393-5842
Hillsboro MS 700/6-8
550 US Highway 62 45133 937-393-9877
Shanon Coblentz, prin. Fax 393-5843

Hillsboro Christian Academy 100/K-12
8230 US Highway 50 45133 937-393-8422
Connie Sears, admin. Fax 393-4963
Southern State Community College Post-Sec.
100 Hobart Dr 45133 937-393-3431

Hiram, Portage, Pop. 1,376

Hiram College Post-Sec.
PO Box 67 44234 330-569-3211

Holgate, Henry, Pop. 1,102
Holgate Local SD 400/K-12
801 Joe E Brown Ave 43527 419-264-5141
Kelly Meyers, supt. Fax 264-1965
www.holgate.k12.oh.us
Holgate JSHS 200/6-12
801 Joe E Brown Ave 43527 419-264-2521
Gary Dulle, prin. Fax 264-1965

Holland, Lucas, Pop. 1,746
Springfield Local SD 3,700/K-12
6900 Hall St 43528 419-867-5600
Kathryn Hott, supt. Fax 867-5700
www.springfieldlocalschools.net
Springfield HS 1,000/9-12
1470 S Mccord Rd 43528 419-867-5633
Steve Gwin, prin. Fax 867-5618
Springfield MS 900/6-8
7001 Madison Ave 43528 419-867-5644
Dana Falkenberg, prin. Fax 867-5732

Houston, Shelby
Hardin-Houston Local SD 800/PK-12
5300 Houston Rd 45333 937-295-3010
Larry Claypool, supt. Fax 295-3737
www.houston.k12.oh.us
Houston JSHS 400/7-12
5300 Houston Rd 45333 937-295-3010
Ryan Maier, prin. Fax 295-3737

Howard, Knox, Pop. 239
East Knox Local SD 1,000/K-12
23201 Coshocton Rd 43028 740-599-7493
Stephen Larcomb, supt. Fax 599-5863
www.ekschools.com
East Knox HS 300/9-12
23227 Coshocton Rd 43028 740-599-7000
Don Sullivan, prin. Fax 599-2922
East Knox MS 200/5-8
23081 Coshocton Rd 43028 740-599-7000
Lisa Brown, prin. Fax 599-6397

Hubbard, Trumbull, Pop. 7,784
Hubbard EVD 2,100/K-12
108 Orchard Ave 44425 330-534-1921
Richard Buchenic, supt. Fax 534-0522
www.hubbard.k12.oh.us/
Hubbard HS 700/9-12
350 Hall Ave 44425 330-534-1921
Ronald Garrett, prin. Fax 534-6191
Hubbard MS 600/5-8
250 Hall Ave 44425 330-534-1921
Dr. Phil Latessa, prin. Fax 534-6191

Huber Heights, Montgomery, Pop. 36,793
Huber Heights CSD 4,900/PK-12
5954 Longford Rd 45424 937-237-6300
Susan Gunnell, supt. Fax 237-6307
www.huberheightscityschools.org/
Wayne HS 1,900/9-12
5400 Chambersburg Rd 45424 937-233-6431
Reva Cosby, prin. Fax 237-6321
Weisenborn JHS 500/7-8
6061 Troy Pike 45424 937-237-6350
Tom Heid, prin. Fax 237-7491

Carousel of Miami Valley Beauty College Post-Sec.
7809 Waynetowne Blvd 45424 937-233-8818

Hudson, Summit, Pop. 21,988
Hudson CSD 4,800/PK-12
2400 Hudson Aurora Rd 44236 330-653-1200
Phillip Herman, supt. Fax 653-1474
www.hudson.edu
Hudson HS 1,700/9-12
2500 Hudson Aurora Rd 44236 330-653-1416
Brian Wilch, prin. Fax 653-1481
Hudson MS 1,200/6-8
77 N Oviatt St 44236 330-653-1316
Dr. Kim Cockley, prin. Fax 653-1368

Western Reserve Academy 400/9-12
115 College St 44236 330-650-4400
Christopher Burner, head sch Fax 650-9754

Hunting Valley, Cuyahoga, Pop. 696

University S 400/9-12
2785 Som Center Rd 44022 216-831-2200
Stephen Murray, hdmstr. Fax 831-0402

Huntsburg, Geauga

Hershey Montessori S 7-9
11530 Madison Rd 44046 440-636-6290
Paula Leigh-Doyle, prin. Fax 636-5665

Huron, Erie, Pop. 7,058
Huron CSD 1,500/PK-12
712 Cleveland Rd E 44839 419-433-1234
Dennis Muratori, supt. Fax 433-7095
www.huronhs.com
Huron HS 500/9-12
710 Cleveland Rd W 44839 419-433-1234
Scott Matheny, prin. Fax 433-2339
McCormick JHS 300/7-8
325 Ohio St 44839 419-433-1234
Chad Carter, prin. Fax 433-8427

Bowling Green State University Post-Sec.
1 University Dr 44839 419-433-5560

Independence, Cuyahoga, Pop. 7,078
Independence Local SD 1,100/PK-12
7733 Stone Rd 44131 216-642-5850
Stephen Marlow, supt. Fax 642-3482
www.independence.k12.oh.us
Independence HS 400/9-12
6001 Archwood Rd 44131 216-642-5860
William McGuinness, prin. Fax 642-5886
Independence MS 300/5-8
6111 Archwood Rd 44131 216-642-5865
Benjamin Hegedish, prin. Fax 520-7002

Kent State Univ Coll of Podiatric Med Post-Sec.
6000 Rockside Woods Blvd N 44131 216-231-3300
Miami-Jacobs Career College Post-Sec.
6400 Rockside Rd 44131 216-834-1400

Ironton, Lawrence, Pop. 10,894
Ironton CSD 1,500/K-12
105 S 5th St 45638 740-532-4133
Dean Nance, supt. Fax 532-2314
www.tigertown.com
Ironton HS 400/9-12
1701 S 7th St 45638 740-532-3911
Joseph Rowe, prin. Fax 533-6027
Ironton MS 300/6-8
302 Delaware St 45638 740-532-3347
Toben Schreck, prin. Fax 532-3077

Rock Hill Local SD 1,600/PK-12
2325 County Road 26 Unit A 45638 740-532-7030
Wesley Hairston, supt. Fax 532-7043
rockhill.org
Rock Hill HS 400/9-12
2415 County Road 26 45638 740-533-7012
Glenn Hopper, prin. Fax 533-7015
Rock Hill MS 400/6-8
2171 County Road 26 45638 740-532-7026
Michael Hairston, prin. Fax 532-7028

Ohio University Southern Campus Post-Sec.
1804 Liberty Ave 45638 740-533-4600
St. Joseph Central HS 100/7-12
912 S 6th St 45638 740-532-0485
James Mains, prin. Fax 532-3699

Irwin, Union

Rosedale Bible College Post-Sec.
2270 Rosedale Rd 43029 740-857-1311

Jackson, Jackson, Pop. 6,292
Jackson CSD 2,400/K-12
450 Vaughn St 45640 740-286-6442
Phil Howard, supt. Fax 286-6445
www.jcs.k12.oh.us
Jackson HS 700/9-12
500 Vaughn St 45640 740-286-7575
Joseph Hemsley, prin. Fax 286-8197
Jackson MS 600/6-8
21 Tropic St 45640 740-286-7586
Mark Broermann, prin. Fax 286-8637

Daymar College Post-Sec.
980 E Main St 45640 740-286-1554

Jackson Center, Shelby, Pop. 1,444
Jackson Center Local SD 400/PK-12
PO Box 849 45334 937-596-6053
William Reichert, supt. Fax 596-6490
www.jackson-center.k12.oh.us
Jackson Center JSHS 200/4-12
PO Box 849 45334 937-596-6149
William Reichert, prin. Fax 596-6490

Jamestown, Greene, Pop. 1,954
Greeneview Local SD 1,200/PK-12
4 S Charleston Rd 45335 937-675-2728
Joe Parish, supt. Fax 675-6807
www.greeneview.k12.oh.us
Greeneview MS 400/5-8
4990 Cottonville Rd 45335 937-675-9391
Mary Beth Minear, prin. Fax 675-6866
Greenview HS 400/9-12
4710 Cottonville Rd 45335 937-675-9711
Isaac Seevers, prin. Fax 675-6805

Jefferson, Ashtabula, Pop. 3,086
Ashtabula County JVSD
1565 State Route 167 44047 440-576-6015
Dr. Jerome Brockway, supt. Fax 576-6502
atech.edu
A-Tech Vo/Tech
1565 State Route 167 44047 440-576-6015
Jon Whipple, prin. Fax 576-6502

Jefferson Area Local SD 1,900/K-12
121 S Poplar St 44047 440-576-9180
John Montanaro, supt. Fax 576-9876
www.jefferson.k12.oh.us/
Jefferson Area HS 600/9-12
207 W Mulberry St 44047 440-576-4731
Jeremy Huber, prin. Fax 576-7344

Jefferson Area JHS 300/7-8
207 W Mulberry St 44047 440-576-1736
Richard Hoyson, prin. Fax 576-3082

Jeromesville, Ashland, Pop. 562

Hillsdale Local SD 1,000/K-12
485 Township Road 1902 44840 419-368-8231
Steve Dickerson, supt. Fax 368-7504
www.hillsdale.k12.oh.us/

Hillsdale HS 300/9-12
485 Township Road 1902 44840 419-368-6841
Kevin Reidy, prin. Fax 368-7504

Hillsdale MS 300/5-8
PO Box 57 44840 419-368-4911
Tim Keib, prin. Fax 368-3613

Johnstown, Licking, Pop. 4,591

Johnstown-Monroe Local SD 1,600/K-12
441 S Main St 43031 740-967-6846
Thomas Slater, supt. Fax 967-1106
www.johnstown.k12.oh.us/

Adams MS 400/6-8
80 W Maple St 43031 740-967-8766
Debbie Seibel, prin. Fax 967-0051

Johnstown-Monroe HS 500/9-12
401 S Oregon St 43031 740-967-2721
Kim Jakeway, prin. Fax 967-1140

Northridge Local SD 1,400/K-12
6097 Johnstown Utica Rd 43031 740-967-6631
John Shepard, supt. Fax 967-5022
northridge.k12.oh.us

Northridge HS 400/9-12
6066 Johnstown Utica Rd 43031 740-967-6651
Amy Anderson, prin. Fax 967-6958

Northridge MS 400/6-8
6066 Johnstown Utica Rd 43031 740-967-6671
Robin Elliott, prin. Fax 967-7083

Kalida, Putnam, Pop. 1,534

Kalida Local SD 600/K-12
PO Box 269 45853 419-532-3534
Don Horstman, supt. Fax 532-2277
www.kalida.k12.oh.us

Kalida JSHS 400/6-12
PO Box 269 45853 419-532-3529
Chris Pfahler, prin. Fax 532-3582

Kansas, Sandusky, Pop. 179

Lakota Local SD 800/PK-12
5200 County Road 13 44841 419-986-6650
David Danhoff, supt. Fax 986-6651
www.lakota-sandusky.k12.oh.us

Lakota HS 300/9-12
5200 County Road 13 44841 419-986-6620
Sherry Sprow, prin. Fax 986-6621

Lakota MS 200/5-8
5200 County Road 13 44841 419-986-6630
Norman Elchert, prin. Fax 986-6631

Kelleys Island, Erie, Pop. 311

Kelleys Island Local SD 50/K-12
PO Box 349 43438 419-746-2730
Phil Thiede, supt. Fax 746-2271
www.kelleys.k12.oh.us/

Kelleys Island S 50/K-12
PO Box 349 43438 419-746-2730
Phil Thiede, prin. Fax 746-2271

Kent, Portage, Pop. 28,086

Kent CSD 3,700/PK-12
321 N Depeyster St 44240 330-676-7600
Dr. Joseph Giancola, supt. Fax 677-6166
www.kentschools.net

Central HS 9-12
200 N Mantua St 44240 330-676-4181
Tim King, dean Fax 676-4303

Roosevelt HS 1,400/9-12
1400 N Mantua St 44240 330-673-9595
Bob Klinar, prin. Fax 673-9217

Stanton MS 800/6-8
1175 Hudson Rd 44240 330-673-6693
Anthony Horton, prin. Fax 673-1561

Kent State University Post-Sec.
PO Box 5190 44242 330-672-3000

Northcoast Medical Training Academy Post-Sec.
1832 St Rd 59 44240 330-678-6600

Kenton, Hardin, Pop. 8,149

Kenton CSD 1,900/PK-12
222 W Carrol St 43326 419-673-0775
Jennifer Penczarski, supt. Fax 673-3180
www.kentoncityschools.org

Kenton HS 500/9-12
200 Harding Ave 43326 419-673-1286
Rick Abbott, prin. Fax 675-5200

Kenton MS 400/6-8
300 Oriental St 43326 419-673-1237
Kirk Cameron, prin. Fax 673-1626

Kettering, Montgomery, Pop. 55,018

Kettering CSD 7,700/PK-12
3750 Far Hills Ave 45429 937-499-1430
Dr. James Schoenlein, supt. Fax 499-1465
www.ketteringschools.org

Kettering-Fairmont HS 2,400/9-12
3301 Shroyer Rd 45429 937-499-1601
Dan Von Handorf, prin. Fax 499-1661

Kettering MS 1,000/6-8
3000 Glengarry Dr 45420 937-499-1550
Dr. Douglas Cozad, prin. Fax 499-1598

Van Buren JHS 700/6-8
3775 Shroyer Rd 45429 937-499-1800
Matthew Rugh, prin. Fax 499-1820

Archbishop Alter HS 700/9-12
940 E David Rd 45429 937-434-4434
Lourdes Lambert, prin. Fax 434-0507

Carousel Beauty College Post-Sec.
3076 Woodman Dr 45420 937-298-5752

Kettering College of Medical Arts Post-Sec.
3737 Southern Blvd 45429 937-395-8601

National College Post-Sec.
1837 Woodman Center Dr 45420 937-299-9450

School of Advertising Art Post-Sec.
1725 E David Rd 45440 877-300-9866

Kidron, Wayne, Pop. 938

Central Christian S 200/PK-12
PO Box 9 44636 330-857-7311
Gene Miller, admin. Fax 857-7331

Kings Mills, Warren, Pop. 1,300

Kings Local SD 3,800/K-12
PO Box 910 45034 513-398-8050
Valerie Browning, supt. Fax 229-7590
www.kingslocal.net/

Kings HS 1,100/9-12
5500 Columbia Rd 45034 513-398-8050
Doug Mader, prin. Fax 459-2941

Kings JHS 600/7-8
5620 Columbia Rd 45034 513-398-8050
Tim Spinner, prin. Fax 459-2951

Kinsman, Trumbull

Joseph Badger Local SD 900/PK-12
7119 State Route 7 44428 330-876-2800
Dr. David Bair, supt. Fax 876-2811
www.joseph-badger.k12.oh.us/

Badger HS 300/9-12
7119 State Route 7 44428 330-876-2820
Edwin Baldwin, prin. Fax 876-2821

Badger MS 300/5-8
7119 State Route 7 44428 330-876-2840
Robert Moon, prin. Fax 876-2841

Kirtland, Lake, Pop. 6,804

Kirtland Local SD 1,200/K-12
9252 Chillicothe Rd 44094 440-256-3311
Stephen G. Barrett, supt. Fax 256-3831
www.kirtlandschools.org

Kirtland HS 400/9-12
9150 Chillicothe Rd 44094 440-256-3366
Dr. Lynn Campbell, prin. Fax 256-1042

Kirtland MS 300/6-8
9152 Chillicothe Rd 44094 440-256-3358
Scott A. Amstutz, prin. Fax 256-3928

Lakeland Community College Post-Sec.
7700 Clocktower Dr 44094 440-525-7000

LaGrange, Lorain, Pop. 2,072

Keystone Local SD 1,500/K-12
PO Box 65 44050 440-355-5131
Jay Arbaugh, supt. Fax 355-6052
www.keystonelocalschools.org/

Keystone HS 500/9-12
580 Opportunity Way 44050 440-355-5132
Franco Gallo, prin. Fax 355-6017

Keystone MS 400/6-8
PO Box 65 44050 440-355-5133
Timothy Jenkins, prin. Fax 355-6678

Lakeside, Ottawa, Pop. 691

Danbury Local SD 500/PK-12
9451 E Harbor Rd 43440 419-798-5185
Daniel Parent, supt. Fax 798-2260
www.danbury.k12.oh.us

Danbury HS 100/9-12
9451 E Harbor Rd 43440 419-798-4037
Mike Cole, prin. Fax 798-2262

Danbury MS 200/5-8
9451 E Harbor Rd 43440 419-798-2258
Joe Miller, prin. Fax 798-2259

Lakewood, Cuyahoga, Pop. 50,830

Lakewood CSD 5,900/K-12
1470 Warren Rd 44107 216-529-4000
Jeffrey Patterson, supt. Fax 228-8327
www.lakewoodcityschools.org

Garfield MS 600/6-8
13114 Detroit Ave 44107 216-529-4241
Mark Walter, prin. Fax 529-4146

Harding MS 600/6-8
16601 Madison Ave 44107 216-529-4261
Joseph Niemantsverdriet, prin. Fax 529-4708

Lakewood HS 1,900/9-12
14100 Franklin Blvd 44107 216-529-4028
Keith Ahearn, prin. Fax 529-4459

Lakewood College Post-Sec.
12900 Lake Ave Ste 3A 44107 800-517-0857

St. Edward HS 800/9-12
13500 Detroit Ave 44107 216-221-3776
Dr. Gregg Good, prin. Fax 221-4609

Virginia Marti College of Art & Design Post-Sec.
11724 Detroit Ave 44107 216-221-8584

Lancaster, Fairfield, Pop. 38,140

Fairfield Union Local SD 1,600/K-12
6417 Cincinnati Zanesvll NE 43130 740-536-7384
James Herd, supt. Fax 536-9132
www.fairfield-union.k12.oh.us/

Fairfield Union HS 600/9-12
6675 Cincinnati Zansvll NE 43130 740-536-7306
Dale Ferbrache, prin. Fax 536-7911

Rushville MS 300/5-8
6409 Cincinnati Zanesvll NE 43130 740-536-7249
Scott Philabaum, prin. Fax 536-7211

Lancaster CSD 5,900/K-12
345 E Mulberry St 43130 740-687-7300
Steve Wigton, supt. Fax 687-7303
www.lancaster.k12.oh.us

Ewing JHS 700/6-8
825 E Fair Ave 43130 740-687-7347
Steve Poston, prin. Fax 687-3446

Lancaster HS 1,600/9-12
1312 Granville Pike 43130 740-681-7500
Jack Greathouse, prin. Fax 681-7505

Sherman JHS 700/6-8
701 Union St 43130 740-687-7344
Scott Burre, prin. Fax 687-3443

Daymar College Post-Sec.
1579 Victor Rd NW 43130 740-687-6126

Fairfield Christian Academy 600/PK-12
1965 N Columbus St 43130 740-654-2889
Ed Reck, supt. Fax 654-7689

Fisher Catholic HS 300/9-12
1803 Granville Pike 43130 740-654-1231
Sean Kenney, pres. Fax 654-1233

Ohio University Post-Sec.
1570 Granville Pike 43130 740-654-6711

Latham, Pike

Western Local SD 800/K-12
PO Box 130 45646 740-493-3113
Terry Leeth, supt. Fax 493-2065
www.westernlocalschools.com/

Western JSHS 300/7-12
PO Box 130 45646 740-493-2514
Brock Brewster, prin. Fax 493-8513

Leavittsburg, Trumbull, Pop. 1,932

LaBrae Local SD 1,500/K-12
1001 N Leavitt Rd 44430 330-898-0800
Anthony J. Calderone, supt. Fax 898-6112
www.labrae.k12.oh.us/

LaBrae HS 400/9-12
1001 N Leavitt Rd 44430 330-898-0800
Jeff Starkey, prin. Fax 898-7808

LaBrae MS 400/6-8
1001 N Leavitt Rd 44430 330-898-0800
Martin Kelly, prin. Fax 898-7808

Lebanon, Warren, Pop. 19,670

Lebanon CSD 5,400/PK-12
700 Holbrook Ave 45036 513-934-5770
Mark North, supt. Fax 932-5906
www.lebanon.k12.oh.us

Lebanon HS 1,500/9-12
1916 Drake Rd 45036 513-934-5100
Scott Butler, prin. Fax 933-2150

Lebanon JHS 900/7-8
160 Miller Rd 45036 513-934-5300
Ian Frank, prin. Fax 932-9436

Warren County ESC
1879 Deerfield Rd 45036 513-695-2900
John Lazares, supt. Fax 695-2961
www.warrencountyesc.com/

Warren County Alternative S Alt
3527 N State Route 48 45036 513-695-2994
Patrick Pare, prin. Fax 695-1836

Warren County JVSD
3525 N State Route 48 45036 513-932-5677
Margaret Hess, supt. Fax 934-0121
www.mywccc.org/

Warren County Career Center Vo/Tech
3525 N State Route 48 45036 513-932-5677
Margaret Hess, supt. Fax 932-3810

Leesburg, Highland, Pop. 1,294

Fairfield Local SD 900/K-12
11611 State Route 771 45135 937-780-2221
William Garrett, supt. Fax 780-6900
www.fairfield-highland.k12.oh.us

Fairfield HS 200/9-12
11611 State Route 771 45135 937-780-2966
Stephen Hackett, prin. Fax 780-2841

Fairfield MS 300/5-8
11611 State Route 771 45135 937-780-2977
Stephen Hackett, prin. Fax 780-2841

Lees Creek, Clinton

East Clinton Local SD
Supt. — See Sabina

East Clinton MS 300/6-8
PO Box 19, 937-584-9267
Robbin Luck, prin. Fax 584-9558

Leetonia, Columbiana, Pop. 1,931

Leetonia EVD 700/K-12
450 Walnut St 44431 330-427-6594
Robert Mehno, supt. Fax 427-1136
www.leetonia.k12.oh.us

Leetonia HS 200/9-12
450 Walnut St 44431 330-427-2115
Troy Radinsky, prin. Fax 427-6904

Leetonia MS 200/5-8
450 Walnut St 44431 330-427-2444
Troy Radinsky, prin. Fax 427-2549

Leipsic, Putnam, Pop. 2,076

Leipsic Local SD 600/K-12
232 Oak St 45856 419-943-2165
Greg Williamson, supt. Fax 943-4331
www.lp.noacsc.org

Leipsic HS 300/6-12
232 Oak St 45856 419-943-2164
Larry Black, prin. Fax 943-2185

Lewisburg, Preble, Pop. 1,788

Tri-County North Local SD 900/K-12
PO Box 40 45338 937-962-2671
William Derringer, supt. Fax 962-4731
tricounty.oh.schoolwebpages.com/

Tri-County North HS 200/9-12
PO Box 610 45338 937-962-2675
Doug Dunham, prin. Fax 833-4860
Tri-County North MS 300/5-8
PO Box 699 45338 937-962-2631
Joseph Finkbine, prin. Fax 833-4860

Lewis Center, Delaware, Pop. 300
Olentangy Local SD 15,800/PK-12
814 Shanahan Rd Ste 100 43035 740-657-4050
Dr. Wade Lucas, supt. Fax 657-4099
www.olentangy.k12.oh.us
Olentangy HS 1,200/9-12
675 Lewis Center Rd 43035 740-657-4100
Thomas McDonnell, prin. Fax 657-4199
Olentangy Orange HS 1,200/9-12
2840 E Orange Rd 43035 740-657-5100
Todd Meyer, prin. Fax 657-5199
Olentangy Orange MS 1,100/6-8
2680 E Orange Rd 43035 740-657-5300
Scott Cunningham, prin. Fax 657-5399
Olentangy Shanahan MS 900/6-8
814 Shanahan Rd 43035 740-657-4300
Josh McDaniels, prin. Fax 657-4398
Other Schools – See Galena, Powell

Lewistown, Logan, Pop. 220
Indian Lake Local SD 1,800/K-12
6210 State Route 235 N 43333 937-686-8601
Patrick O'Donnell, supt. Fax 686-8421
www.indianlake.k12.oh.us
Indian Lake HS 500/9-12
6210 State Route 235 N 43333 937-686-8851
Denny Shaner, prin. Fax 686-0024
Indian Lake MS 600/5-8
8920 County Road 91 43333 937-686-8833
Misha Boyer-Monnin, prin. Fax 686-8993

Lexington, Richland, Pop. 4,768
Lexington Local SD 2,500/K-12
103 Clever Ln 44904 419-884-2132
J. Michael Ziegelhofer, supt. Fax 884-3129
www.lexington.k12.oh.us
Lexington HS 800/9-12
103 Clever Ln 44904 419-884-1111
Jeremy Secrist, prin. Fax 884-3129
Lexington JHS 400/7-8
90 Frederick St 44904 419-884-2112
Taylor Gerhardt, prin. Fax 884-0134

Liberty Center, Henry, Pop. 1,169
Liberty Center Local SD 800/PK-12
PO Box 434 43532 419-533-5011
Kristi Thompson, supt. Fax 533-5036
www.libertycenterschools.org
Liberty Center HS 400/7-12
PO Box 434 43532 419-533-6641
Mel Rentschler, prin. Fax 533-6108

Liberty Twp, Butler
Lakota Local SD 17,500/PK-12
5572 Princeton Rd 45011 513-874-5505
Dr. Karen Mantia, supt. Fax 644-1167
www.lakotaonline.com
Lakota East Freshman HS 9-9
7630 Bethany Rd 45044 513-588-7700
Stacy Millburg, prin. Fax 759-2024
Lakota East SHS 1,900/10-12
6840 Lakota Ln 45044 513-755-7211
Suzanna Davis, prin. Fax 759-8633
Lakota Plains JHS 800/7-8
5500 Princeton Rd 45011 513-644-1130
Kim Wade, prin. Fax 644-1135
Liberty JHS 800/7-8
7055 Dutchland Pkwy 45044 513-777-4420
Eric Bauman, prin. Fax 777-7950
Other Schools – See West Chester

Lima, Allen, Pop. 37,107
Allen County ESC
1920 Slabtown Rd 45801 419-222-1836
Brian Rockhold, supt. Fax 224-0718
www.allencountyesc.org/
Allen County Alternative HS Alt
1920 Slabtown Rd 45801 419-222-1836
Mitch Black, admin. Fax 222-2107

Apollo JVSD
3325 Shawnee Rd 45806 419-998-2908
Judy Wells, supt. Fax 998-2929
www.apollocareercenter.com
Apollo Career Center Vo/Tech
3325 Shawnee Rd 45806 419-998-2908
Fax 998-2929

Bath Local SD 1,800/K-12
2650 Bible Rd 45801 419-221-0807
Dale Lewellen, supt. Fax 221-0983
www.bathwildcats.org
Bath HS 500/9-12
2850 Bible Rd 45801 419-221-0366
Richard Gross, prin. Fax 221-0766
Bath MS 600/5-8
2700 Bible Rd 45801 419-221-1839
Bradley Clark, prin. Fax 221-2431

Lima CSD 3,700/PK-12
755 Saint Johns Ave 45804 419-996-3400
Jill Ackerman, supt. Fax 996-3401
www.limacityschools.org
Lima Alternative S 50/Alt
1 Spartan Way 45801 419-996-3000
Fran Mort, prin. Fax 996-3001
HS for Multiple Intelligences 400/9-12
1 Spartan Way 45801 419-996-3000
Alison Vangorder, prin. Fax 996-3001
Lima Performance Based HS 400/9-12
1 Spartan Way 45801 419-996-3000
Douglas Kent, prin. Fax 996-3001
Lima West MS 200/7-8
503 N Cable Rd 45805 419-996-3150
Steven Carr, prin. Fax 996-3151
Progressive Academy HS 400/9-12
1 Spartan Way 45801 419-996-3000
Timothy Fitzpatrick, prin. Fax 996-3001

Perry Local SD 800/K-12
2770 E Breese Rd 45806 419-221-2770
Omer Schroeder, supt. Fax 224-6215
mycommodores.org
Perry HS 300/7-12
2770 E Breese Rd 45806 419-221-2773
Nicholas Weingart, prin. Fax 224-6215

Shawnee Local SD 2,400/K-12
3255 Zurmehly Rd 45806 419-998-8031
Michael Lamb, supt. Fax 998-8050
www.limashawnee.com
Shawnee HS 700/9-12
3333 Zurmehly Rd 45806 419-998-8000
Don Wade, prin. Fax 998-8026
Shawnee MS 800/5-8
3235 Zurmehly Rd 45806 419-998-8057
Judy Gephart, prin. Fax 222-6572

James A. Rhodes State Coll Post-Sec.
4240 Campus Dr 45804 419-995-8020
Liberty Christian S 50/PK-12
801 Bellefontaine Ave 45801 419-229-6266
Br. Nadine Wagner, admin. Fax 229-6266
Lima Central Catholic HS 400/9-12
720 S Cable Rd 45805 419-222-4276
Walter Klimaski, pres. Fax 222-6933
Ohio State Beauty Academy Post-Sec.
1760 N Eastown Rd 45807 419-229-7896
Ohio State University-Lima Campus Post-Sec.
4240 Campus Dr 45804 419-995-8600
Temple Christian S 200/PK-12
982 Brower Rd 45801 419-227-1644
Bruce Bowman, admin. Fax 227-6635
University of Northwestern Ohio Post-Sec.
1441 N Cable Rd 45805 419-998-3120

Lisbon, Columbiana, Pop. 2,802
Beaver Local SD 2,000/K-12
13093 State Route 7 44432 330-385-6831
Kent C. Polen, supt. Fax 386-8711
www.beaver.k12.oh.us/
Beaver Local HS 600/9-12
13187 State Route 7 44432 330-386-8700
Thomas Cunningham, prin. Fax 386-8720
Beaver Local MS 700/5-8
13052 State Route 7 44432 330-386-8707
Connie Shive, prin. Fax 382-0317

Columbiana County JVSD
9364 State Route 45 44432 330-424-9561
Willard Adkins, supt. Fax 424-9719
Columbiana County Joint Vocational SHS Vo/Tech
9364 State Route 45 44432 330-424-9561
Curtis Kaiser, prin. Fax 424-9719

Lisbon EVD 1,000/PK-12
317 N Market St 44432 330-424-7714
Donald Thompson, supt. Fax 424-0135
www.lisbon.k12.oh.us/
Anderson JSHS 500/6-12
260 W Pine St 44432 330-424-3215
Joseph Siefke, prin. Fax 424-1004

Lockland, Hamilton, Pop. 3,333
Lockland Local SD 600/K-12
210 N Cooper Ave 45215 513-563-5000
Dr. Dan Lawler, supt. Fax 563-9611
www.locklandschools.org
Lockland HS 100/9-12
249 W Forrer St 45215 513-563-5000
Greg Rulon, prin. Fax 733-0800
Lockland MS 100/6-8
249 W Forrer St 45215 513-563-5000
Greg Rulon, prin. Fax 733-0800
Other Schools – See Cincinnati

Lodi, Medina, Pop. 2,720
Cloverleaf Local SD 2,600/PK-12
8525 Friendsville Rd 44254 330-948-2500
Daryl Kubilus, supt. Fax 948-1034
www.cloverleaflocal.org/
Cloverleaf HS 900/9-12
8525 Friendsville Rd 44254 330-721-3526
Rose Marie Torma, prin. Fax 721-3559
Other Schools – See Seville

Logan, Hocking, Pop. 7,087
Logan-Hocking Local SD 3,900/PK-12
2019 E Front St 43138 740-385-8517
Stephen Stirn, supt. Fax 385-3683
www.lhsd.k12.oh.us
Logan HS 1,100/9-12
14470 State Route 328 43138 740-385-2069
Jim Robinson, prin. Fax 385-9564
Logan-Hocking MS 1,200/5-8
1 Middleschool Dr 43138 740-385-8764
Brice Frasure, prin. Fax 385-9547

London, Madison, Pop. 9,615
London CSD 2,100/PK-12
380 Elm St 43140 740-852-5700
Thomas Ben, supt. Fax 845-3282
www.london.k12.oh.us/
London HS 600/9-12
336 Elm St 43140 740-852-5705
Chad Eisler, prin. Fax 852-3284
London MS 500/6-8
270 Keny Blvd 43140 740-852-5700
Adelle Faulkner, prin. Fax 845-1279
Madison-Plains Local SD 900/K-12
55 Linson Rd 43140 740-852-0290
Bernie Hall, supt. Fax 852-5895
www.mplsd.org/
Madison-Plains HS 400/9-12
800 Linson Rd 43140 740-852-0364
Chris Clark, prin. Fax 852-3046
Madison-Plains JHS 300/6-8
803 Linson Rd 43140 740-852-1707
Fax 852-6351

Lorain, Lorain, Pop. 62,074
Clearview Local SD 1,700/PK-12
4700 Broadway 44052 440-233-5412
Stanley Mounts, supt. Fax 233-6034
www.clearviewschools.org
Clearview HS 600/9-12
4700 Broadway 44052 440-233-6313
Dr. Thomas Jama, prin. Fax 233-6311
Durling MS 500/5-8
100 N Ridge Rd W 44053 440-233-6869
Jerome Davis, prin. Fax 233-6204

Lorain CSD 5,500/PK-12
2350 Pole Ave 44052 440-233-2271
Tom Tucker, supt. Fax 282-9151
www.lorainschools.org
Credit Recovery Academy Alt
2321 Fairless Dr 44055 440-277-7261
Nikole Davis, prin. Fax 277-5566
Longfellow MS 300/7-8
305 Louisiana Ave 44052 440-288-1002
Christine Miller, prin. Fax 288-1149
Lorain HS 2,000/9-12
2270 E 42nd St 44055 440-277-1176
Diane Conibear, prin. Fax 277-1163
New Beginnings Academy 100/Alt
3200 Clinton Ave 44055 440-277-8157
Steve Meggitt, prin. Fax 277-7354
Wilson MS 400/7-8
2700 Washington Ave 44052 440-246-1020
Michael Scott, prin. Fax 246-1016

Northern Institute of Cosmetology Post-Sec.
667 Broadway 44052 440-244-4282

Lore City, Guernsey, Pop. 322
East Guernsey Local SD
Supt. — See Old Washington
Buckeye Trail HS 300/9-12
65555 Wintergreen Rd 43755 740-489-5005
Marcia Lucas, prin. Fax 489-9839
Buckeye Trail MS 300/6-8
65553 Wintergreen Rd 43755 740-489-5100
Lonnie Caudill, prin. Fax 489-9049

Loudonville, Ashland, Pop. 2,623
Loudonville-Perrysville EVD 900/PK-12
210 E Main St 44842 419-994-3912
John Miller, supt. Fax 994-5528
www.lpschools.k12.oh.us
Loudonville JSHS 300/7-12
421 Campus Ave 44842 419-994-4101
John Lance, prin. Fax 994-3485

Louisville, Stark, Pop. 9,114
Louisville CSD 2,500/K-12
407 E Main St 44641 330-875-1666
Steve Milano, supt. Fax 875-7673
www.leopard.sparcc.org
Louisville HS 900/9-12
1201 S Nickelplate St 44641 330-875-1438
Stephen Milano, prin. Fax 875-7606
Louisville MS 800/6-8
1300 S Chapel St 44641 330-875-5597
Jason Greathouse, prin. Fax 875-7620

Good Shepherd S 50/1-12
8700 Edison St 44641 330-935-0623
Rev. Gary Spencer, admin. Fax 935-0700
St. Thomas Aquinas HS 300/9-12
2121 Reno Dr 44641 330-875-1631
Joseph Vagedes, prin. Fax 875-8469

Loveland, Hamilton, Pop. 11,848
Loveland CSD 4,700/PK-12
757 S Lebanon Rd 45140 513-683-5600
John Marschhausen Ph.D., supt. Fax 683-5697
www.lovelandschools.org/
Loveland HS 1,300/9-12
1 Tiger Trl 45140 513-683-1920
Chris Kloesz, prin. Fax 677-7952
Loveland MS 700/7-8
801 S Lebanon Rd 45140 513-683-3100
Chris Burke, prin. Fax 677-7986

Lowellville, Mahoning, Pop. 1,148
Lowellville Local SD 600/K-12
52 Rocket Pl 44436 330-536-6318
Rocco Nero, supt. Fax 536-8221
www.lowellville.k12.oh.us/
Lowellville JSHS 300/7-12
52 Rocket Pl 44436 330-536-8426
Rocco Nero, prin. Fax 536-8468

Lucas, Richland, Pop. 605
Lucas Local SD 600/K-12
84 Lucas North Rd 44843 419-892-2338
Steven Dickerson, supt. Fax 892-1138
www.lucascubs.org
Lucas HS 200/8-12
5 1st Ave 44843 419-892-2338
Eric Teague, prin. Fax 892-1138

Lucasville, Scioto, Pop. 2,738
Scioto County Career Technical Center
951 Vern Riffe Dr 45648 740-259-5522
Stan Jennings, supt. Fax 259-1553
www.sciototech.org

Scioto County Career Technical Center Vo/Tech
951 Vern Riffe Dr 45648 740-259-5522
Stan Jennings, supt. Fax 259-1553

Valley Local SD 1,100/K-12
1821 State Route 728 45648 740-259-3115
Carl McCrory, supt. Fax 259-2314
www.valleyls.org/
Valley HS 300/9-12
1821 State Route 728 45648 740-259-5551
Lisa Harley, prin. Fax 259-2314
Valley MS, 393 Indian Dr 45648 300/5-8
Lisa Harley, prin. 740-259-2651

Lynchburg, Highland, Pop. 1,486
Lynchburg-Clay Local SD 1,200/PK-12
PO Box 515 45142 937-364-2338
Shane Shope, supt. Fax 364-2339
www.lynchclay.k12.oh.us
Lynchburg-Clay HS 300/9-12
6762 State Route 134 45142 937-364-2250
Linda Hatten, prin. Fax 364-6133
Lynchburg-Clay MS 300/6-8
8250 State Route 134 45142 937-364-2811
Casey Smith, prin. Fax 364-2159

Lyndhurst, Cuyahoga, Pop. 13,838
South Euclid-Lyndhurst CSD 4,400/K-12
5044 Mayfield Rd 44124 216-691-2000
Linda Reid, supt. Fax 691-2298
www.sel.k12.oh.us
Brush HS 1,700/9-12
4875 Glenlyn Rd 44124 216-691-2065
Kenya Harrington, prin. Fax 691-2064
Memorial JHS 700/7-8
1250 Professor Rd 44124 216-691-2141
Kathybel Ortiz, prin. Fax 691-2159

Cleveland Institute Dental Medical Asst. Post-Sec.
5564 Mayfield Rd 44124 440-473-6273
Inner State Beauty School Post-Sec.
5150 Mayfield Rd 44124 440-442-4500

Mc Arthur, Vinton, Pop. 1,685
Vinton County Local SD 2,400/PK-12
307 W High St 45651 740-596-5218
Rick Brooks, supt. Fax 596-3142
www.vinton.k12.oh.us/
Vinton County HS 700/9-12
63910 US Highway 50 45651 740-596-5258
Kevin Waddell, prin. Fax 596-3003
Vinton County MS 500/6-8
63780 Locker Plant Rd 45651 740-596-5243
Stephen Roach, prin. Fax 596-3815

Mc Comb, Hancock, Pop. 1,624
Mc Comb Local SD 700/PK-12
PO Box 877 45858 419-293-3979
Michael Lamb, supt. Fax 293-2412
www.noacsc.org/hancock/mb
Mc Comb Local HS 300/9-12
PO Box 877 45858 419-293-3853
Jeremy Herr, prin. Fax 293-3107
Mc Comb Local MS 100/7-8
PO Box 877 45858 419-293-3979
Heath Huffman, lead tchr. Fax 293-2412

Mc Connelsville, Morgan, Pop. 1,738
Morgan Local SD 2,100/PK-12
PO Box 509 43756 740-962-2782
Lori Snyder-Lowe, supt. Fax 962-4931
www.mlsd.k12.oh.us/
Morgan HS 600/9-12
800 Raider Dr 43756 740-962-2944
Anita Eldridge, prin. Fax 962-6005
Morgan JHS 300/7-8
820 Junior Raider Dr 43756 740-962-2833
Timothy Hopkins, prin. Fax 962-3389

Mc Dermott, Scioto, Pop. 428
Northwest Local SD 1,600/K-12
800 Mohawk Dr 45652 740-259-5558
A. Todd Jenkins, supt. Fax 259-3476
www.nwmohawks.net
Northwest HS 400/9-12
914 Mohawk Dr 45652 740-259-2366
Rick Scarberry, prin. Fax 259-8544
Northwest MS 400/6-8
692 Mohawk Dr 45652 740-259-2528
Gregory Tipton, prin. Fax 259-5731

Mc Donald, Trumbull, Pop. 3,227
McDonald Local SD 900/K-12
600 Iowa Ave 44437 330-530-8051
Ken Halbert, supt. Fax 530-7041
www.mcdonald.k12.oh.us
McDonald JSHS 400/7-12
600 Iowa Ave 44437 330-530-8051
Gary Carkido, prin. Fax 530-7034

Macedonia, Summit, Pop. 11,001
Nordonia Hills CSD
Supt. — See Northfield
Nordonia HS 1,400/9-12
8006 S Bedford Rd 44056 330-468-4601
Casey Wright, prin. Fax 468-0045

Mc Guffey, Hardin, Pop. 491
Upper Scioto Valley Local SD 600/K-12
PO Box 305 45859 419-757-3231
Dennis Recker, supt. Fax 757-0135
usv.k12.oh.us
Upper Scioto Valley HS 200/9-12
PO Box 305 45859 419-757-3231
Craig Hurley, prin. Fax 757-0135
Upper Scioto Valley MS 100/7-8
PO Box 305 45859 419-757-3231
Craig Hurley, prin. Fax 757-0135

Madison, Lake, Pop. 3,130
Madison Local SD 3,300/K-12
6741 N Ridge Rd 44057 440-428-2166
Dr. Roger Goudy, supt. Fax 428-9379
www.madisonschools.net/
Madison HS 1,100/9-12
3100 Burns Rd 44057 440-428-2161
William Fisher, prin. Fax 428-2165
Madison MS 800/6-8
1941 Red Bird Rd 44057 440-428-1196
Thomas Brady, prin. Fax 428-9389

Magnolia, Stark, Pop. 965
Sandy Valley Local SD 1,100/PK-12
5362 State Route 183 NE 44643 330-866-3339
David Janofa, supt. Fax 866-5238
cardweb.stark.k12.oh.us/
Sandy Valley MSHS 500/6-12
5130 State Route 183 NE 44643 330-866-9371
Brian Garrett, prin. Fax 866-2490

Maineville, Warren, Pop. 962
Little Miami Local SD 2,900/PK-12
7247 Zoar Rd 45039 513-899-2264
Gregory Power, supt. Fax 899-3244
www.littlemiamischools.com
Other Schools – See Morrow

Malvern, Carroll, Pop. 1,175
Brown Local SD 700/K-12
401 W Main St 44644 330-863-1170
Connie Griffin, supt. Fax 863-1172
www.brownlocalschools.com/
Malvern HS 200/9-12
401 W Main St 44644 330-863-1355
Jane Swinderman, prin. Fax 863-1366
Malvern MS 200/6-8
401 W Main St 44644 330-863-1355
Jane Swinderman, prin. Fax 863-1915

Manchester, Adams, Pop. 1,976
Manchester Local SD 800/PK-12
130 Wayne Frye Dr 45144 937-549-4777
Robert Ralstin, supt. Fax 549-4744
www.mlsd.us
Manchester HS 300/7-12
130 Wayne Frye Dr 45144 937-549-4777
James Wilkins, prin. Fax 549-2872

Mansfield, Richland, Pop. 46,379
Madison Local SD 2,900/PK-12
1379 Grace St 44905 419-589-2600
Lee Kaple, supt. Fax 589-3653
www.mlsd.net/
Madison Comprehensive HS 900/9-12
600 Esley Ln 44905 419-589-2112
Rob Peterson, prin. Fax 589-2533
Madison JHS 500/7-8
690 Ashland Rd 44905 419-522-0471
Tom Wolff, prin. Fax 522-1463

Mansfield CSD 3,200/PK-12
PO Box 1448 44901 419-525-6400
Dan Freund, supt. Fax 525-6415
www.tygerpride.com
Mansfield HS 1,000/9-12
124 N Linden Rd 44906 419-525-6369
Brad Callender, prin. Fax 524-2210
Mansfield Integrated Learning Center 100/Alt
150 W 5th St 44902 419-525-6305
Robert Singleton, prin. Fax 525-6304
Mansfield MS 7-8
124 N Linden Rd 44906 419-525-6307
Jason Goings, prin. Fax 525-6306

Mansfield Christian S 500/PK-12
500 Logan Rd 44907 419-756-5651
Dr. Cy Smith, supt. Fax 756-7470
North Central State College Post-Sec.
2441 Kenwood Cir 44906 419-755-4800
Ohio State University-Mansfield Campus Post-Sec.
1760 University Dr 44906 419-755-4011
St. Peter HS 300/7-12
104 W 1st St 44902 419-524-0979
Tressa Reith, prin. Fax 524-3336
Temple Christian S 200/K-12
752 Stewart Rd N 44905 419-589-9707
Paul Baird, prin. Fax 589-7213

Mantua, Portage, Pop. 1,029
Crestwood Local SD 2,100/PK-12
4565 W Prospect St 44255 330-274-8511
Joseph Iacano, supt. Fax 274-3710
www.crestwood.sparcc.org/
Crestwood HS 700/9-12
10919 Main St 44255 330-274-2214
Arden Sommers, prin. Fax 274-3150
Crestwood MS 500/6-8
10880 John Edward Dr 44255 330-274-2249
Julie Schmidt, prin. Fax 274-3705

Maple Heights, Cuyahoga, Pop. 22,680
Maple Heights CSD 3,600/PK-12
5740 Lawn Ave 44137 216-587-6100
Dr. Charles Keenan, supt. Fax 518-2674
www.mapleschools.com/
Maple Heights HS 1,200/9-12
5445 West Blvd 44137 216-438-6400
Mariel Sallee, prin.
Milkovich MS 600/6-8
19800 Stafford Ave 44137 216-438-6000
Susan Harvey, prin. Fax 587-4523

Marengo, Morrow, Pop. 330
Highland Local SD 1,300/K-12
6506 State Route 229 43334 419-768-2206
Bill Dodds, supt. Fax 768-3115
www.highland.k12.oh.us/
Highland HS 500/9-12
1300 State Route 314 43334 419-768-3101
Nate Huffman, prin. Fax 768-3560
Highland MS 400/6-8
6506 State Route 229 43334 419-768-2781
Rob Terrill, prin. Fax 768-2742

Maria Stein, Mercer
Marion Local SD 900/K-12
7956 State Route 119 45860 419-925-4294
Michael Pohlman, supt. Fax 925-0212
marionlocal.org
Marion Local HS 300/9-12
1901 State Route 716 45860 419-925-4597
Tim Goodwin, prin. Fax 925-5111

Marietta, Washington, Pop. 13,848
Marietta CSD 2,800/K-12
111 Academy Dr 45750 740-374-6500
Harry Fleming, supt. Fax 374-6506
mariettacityschools.k12.oh.us
Marietta HS 800/9-12
208 Davis Ave 45750 740-374-6540
William Lee, prin. Fax 376-2462
Marietta MS 700/6-8
242 N 7th St 45750 740-374-6530
William Hampton, prin. Fax 374-6531

Washington County JVSD
21740 State Route 676 45750 740-373-2766
Dennis Blatt, supt. Fax 373-9026
www.thecareercenter.net
Washington County Career Center Vo/Tech
21740 State Route 676 45750 740-373-2766
Dennis Blatt, supt. Fax 373-9026

Marietta College Post-Sec.
215 5th St 45750 740-376-4000
Memorial Hospital Post-Sec.
401 Matthew St 45750 740-374-1412
Valley Beauty School Post-Sec.
113 Wildwood Dr 45750 740-373-3617
Washington State Community College Post-Sec.
710 Colegate Dr 45750 740-374-8716

Marion, Marion, Pop. 36,113
Elgin Local SD 1,200/K-12
4616 Larue Prospect Rd W 43302 740-382-1101
Bruce Gast, supt. Fax 382-1672
www.elginschools.org
Elgin HS 400/9-12
1239 Keener Rd S 43302 740-383-5118
Chad Cunningham, prin. Fax 383-4225
Other Schools – See Green Camp

Marion CSD 4,300/PK-12
420 Presidential Dr Ste B 43302 740-387-3300
James Barney, supt. Fax 223-4400
www.marioncityschools.org/
Grant MS 1,000/6-8
420 Presidential Dr 43302 740-223-4900
Amy Wood, prin. Fax 223-4820
Harding HS 1,000/9-12
1500 Harding Hwy E 43302 740-223-4700
Carol Bebout, prin. Fax 223-4705

Pleasant Local SD 1,200/K-12
1107 Owens Rd W 43302 740-389-4476
Dr. John Bruno, supt. Fax 389-6985
www.pleasant.treca.org
Pleasant HS 400/9-12
1101 Owens Rd W 43302 740-389-2389
Brian Sparling, prin. Fax 389-3904
Pleasant MS 300/6-8
3507 Smeltzer Rd 43302 740-389-5167
Lane Warner, prin. Fax 389-5111

Tri-Rivers Career Center
2222 Marion Mount Gilead Rd 43302 740-389-4681
Charles Speelman, supt. Fax 389-2963
www.tririvers.com
Tri-Rivers Career Center Vo/Tech
2222 Marion Mount Gilead Rd 43302 740-389-4681
Larry Hickman, dir. Fax 389-2963

Marion General Hospital Post-Sec.
1000 McKinley Park Blvd 43302 740-383-8700
Marion Technical College Post-Sec.
1467 Mount Vernon Ave 43302 740-389-4636
Ohio State University-Marion Post-Sec.
1465 Mount Vernon Ave 43302 740-389-6786

Martins Ferry, Belmont, Pop. 6,765
Martins Ferry CSD 1,500/K-12
5001 Ayers Lime Stone Rd 43935 740-633-1732
Dirk Fitch, supt. Fax 633-5666
www.mfcsd.k12.oh.us
Martins Ferry HS 400/9-12
5000 Ayers Lime Stone Rd 43935 740-633-0684
Jeff Oberdick, prin. Fax 635-6103
Martins Ferry MS 500/5-8
5000 Ayers Lime Stone Rd 43935 740-633-9741
Mike Delatore, prin. Fax 635-6107

Speiro Academy, 500 N 5th St 43935 50/1-12
Susan Cline, prin. 740-738-0203

Marysville, Union, Pop. 21,701
Marysville EVD 5,300/K-12
1000 Edgewood Dr 43040 937-644-8105
Diane Mankins, supt. Fax 644-1849
www.marysville.k12.oh.us
Bunsold MS 800/7-8
14198 State Route 4 43040 937-642-1721
Kathy McKinniss, prin. Fax 642-2170
Marysville HS 1,600/9-12
800 Amrine Mill Rd 43040 937-642-0010
Matt Chrispin, prin. Fax 642-2033

Mason, Warren, Pop. 30,202
Mason CSD 10,100/PK-12
211 N East St 45040 513-398-0474
Dr. Gail Kist, supt. Fax 398-4554
www.masonohioschools.com
Mason HS 3,100/9-12
6100 S Mason Montgomery Rd 45040 513-398-5025
Melinda McCarty, prin. Fax 336-6823
Mason MS 1,800/7-8
6370 S Mason Montgomery Rd 45040 513-398-9035
Tonya McCall, prin. Fax 459-0904

Hondros College Post-Sec.
4605 Duke Dr Ste 115 45040 513-247-9711
Mars Hill Academy 200/K-12
4230 Aero Dr 45040 513-770-3223
Roger Wismer, hdmstr. Fax 770-3443

Massillon, Stark, Pop. 31,305
Jackson Local SD 5,800/K-12
7602 Fulton Dr NW 44646 330-830-8000
Chris DiLoreto, supt. Fax 830-8008
jackson.stark.k12.oh.us
Jackson HS 1,900/9-12
7600 Fulton Dr NW 44646 330-837-3501
Monica Myers, prin. Fax 830-8069
Jackson Memorial MS 1,400/6-8
7355 Mudbrook Rd NW 44646 330-830-8034
Paul Salvino, prin. Fax 830-8068

Massillon CSD 3,400/PK-12
930 17th St NE 44646 330-830-3900
Richard Goodright, supt. Fax 830-0953
www.massillonschools.org
Massillon JHS 600/7-8
250 29th St NW 44647 330-830-3902
Jennifer Allerding, prin. Fax 830-3952
Washington HS 1,200/9-12
1 Paul E Brown Dr SE 44646 330-830-1800
Brad Warner, prin. Fax 832-1954

Perry Local SD 3,500/PK-12
4201 13th St SW 44646 330-477-8121
Marty Bowe, supt. Fax 478-6184
www.perrylocal.org/
Edison MS 400/7-8
4201 13th St SW 44646 330-478-6167
Diane Kittelberger, prin. Fax 477-4612
Perry HS 1,300/9-12
3737 13th St SW 44646 330-477-3486
Don Gregoire, prin. Fax 478-6180

Stark County Area JVSD
2800 Richville Dr SE 44646 330-832-9856
Cynthia Smythe, dir. Fax 832-9850
www.drage.stark.k12.oh.us
Drage Career-Technical Center Vo/Tech
2800 Richville Dr SE 44646 330-832-9856
John Walker, admin. Fax 832-9850

Tuslaw Local SD 900/PK-12
1835 Manchester Ave NW 44647 330-837-7813
Alan Osler, supt. Fax 837-7804
www.tuslaw.sparcc.org/
Tuslaw HS 400/9-12
1847 Manchester Ave NW 44647 330-837-7800
Melissa Marconi, prin. Fax 837-6016
Tuslaw MS 500/5-8
1723 Manchester Ave NW 44647 330-837-7807
David Ryder, prin. Fax 837-6015

Massillon Christian S 100/K-12
965 Overlook Ave SW 44647 330-833-1039
Rebecca Hartline, prin. Fax 830-5981

Maumee, Lucas, Pop. 14,100
Maumee CSD 1,900/K-12
716 Askin St 43537 419-893-3200
Gregory Smith, supt. Fax 891-5387
www.maumee.k12.oh.us
Gateway MS 600/6-8
900 Gibbs St 43537 419-893-3386
Angela Rose, prin. Fax 893-2263
Maumee HS 900/9-12
1147 Saco St 43537 419-893-8778
Larry Caffro, prin. Fax 893-5621

Hondros College Post-Sec.
1750 Indian Wood Cir # 140 43537 419-887-1721
ITT Technical Institute Post-Sec.
1656 Henthorne Dr Ste B 43537 419-861-6500
Stautzenberger College Post-Sec.
1796 Indian Wood Cir 43537 419-866-0261

Mayfield, Cuyahoga, Pop. 3,423
Mayfield CSD
Supt. — See Mayfield Heights
Mayfield HS 2,100/9-12
6116 Wilson Mills Rd 44143 440-995-6900
Tony Loewer, prin. Fax 995-6805

Mayfield Heights, Cuyahoga, Pop. 18,836
Mayfield CSD 4,300/K-12
1101 SOM Center Rd 44124 440-995-6800
Keith Kelly, supt. Fax 995-7205
www.mayfieldschools.org
Mayfield MS 600/6-8
1123 SOM Center Rd 44124 440-995-7800
Paul Destino, prin. Fax 995-7805
Other Schools – See Cleveland, Mayfield

Mechanicsburg, Champaign, Pop. 1,610
Mechanicsburg EVD 900/K-12
60 High St 43044 937-834-2453
Dr. Dan Kaffenbarger, supt. Fax 834-3954
www.mechanicsburg.k12.oh.us
Mechanicsburg HS 400/7-12
60 High St 43044 937-834-2453
Scott Wasserman, prin. Fax 834-7103

Medina, Medina, Pop. 26,154
Buckeye Local SD 2,300/PK-12
3044 Columbia Rd 44256 330-722-8257
Dr. Brian J. Williams, supt. Fax 722-5793
www.buckeyeschools.org
Buckeye HS 700/9-12
3084 Columbia Rd 44256 330-722-3604
Charles Vrabel, prin. Fax 722-8257
Buckeye JHS 400/7-8
3024 Columbia Rd 44256 330-725-0118
Jeff Smith, prin. Fax 722-8257

Highland Local SD 3,300/PK-12
3880 Ridge Rd 44256 330-239-1901
Catherine Aukerman, supt. Fax 239-2456
www.highlandschools.org
Highland HS 1,000/9-12
4150 Ridge Rd 44256 330-239-1901
Dana Addis, prin. Fax 239-2807
Highland MS 800/6-8
3880 Ridge Rd 44256 330-239-1901
John Deuber, prin. Fax 239-2487

Medina CSD 7,500/PK-12
140 W Washington St 44256 330-636-3010
David Knight, supt. Fax 764-3501
www.mcsoh.org
Claggett MS 900/6-8
420 E Union St 44256 330-636-3600
Thomas Hellickson, prin. Fax 725-9349
Medina HS 2,200/9-12
777 E Union St 44256 330-636-3200
Bryan Farson, prin. Fax 764-3521
Root MS 800/6-8
333 W Sturbridge Dr 44256 330-636-3500
Chad Wise, prin. Fax 764-1471

Medina County JVSD
1101 W Liberty St 44256 330-725-8461
Michael Larson, supt. Fax 725-5870
www.mcjvs.edu
Medina County Career Center Vo/Tech
1101 W Liberty St 44256 330-725-8461
Steven Chrisman, prin. Fax 725-5870

Hamrick School Post-Sec.
1156 Medina Rd 44256 330-239-2229
Medina County Career Center Post-Sec.
1101 W Liberty St 44256 330-725-8461

Mentor, Lake, Pop. 46,722
Mentor EVD 8,000/K-12
6451 Center St 44060 440-255-4444
Matthew Miller, supt. Fax 255-4622
www.mentorschools.org
Memorial MS 700/6-8
8979 Mentor Ave 44060 440-974-2250
Kathy Burnett, prin. Fax 974-2259
Mentor HS 2,800/9-12
6477 Center St 44060 440-974-5300
William Wade, prin. Fax 974-5216
Ridge MS 500/6-8
7860 Johnnycake Ridge Rd 44060 440-974-5400
Megan Kinsey, prin. Fax 974-5285
Shore MS 700/6-8
5670 Hopkins Rd 44060 440-257-8750
Douglas Baker, prin. Fax 257-8761

Brown Aveda Institute Post-Sec.
8816 Mentor Ave 44060 440-255-9494
Cleveland Institute Dental Medical Asst. Post-Sec.
5733 Hopkins Rd 44060 440-946-9530
Lake Catholic HS 800/9-12
6733 Reynolds Rd 44060 440-578-1020
Robert Kumazec, prin. Fax 974-9087

Metamora, Fulton, Pop. 623
Evergreen Local SD 1,200/K-12
14544 County Road 6 43540 419-644-3521
James Wyse, supt. Fax 644-6070
www.evergreen.k12.oh.us
Evergreen HS 400/9-12
14544 County Road 6 43540 419-644-2951
Mark Basilius, prin. Fax 644-6070
Evergreen MS 300/6-8
14544 County Road 6 43540 419-644-2331
Thomas Shafer, prin. Fax 644-9203

Miamisburg, Montgomery, Pop. 19,876
Miamisburg CSD 4,400/PK-12
540 Park Ave 45342 937-866-3381
Dr. David Vail, supt. Fax 865-5250
www.miamisburgcityschools.org
Miamisburg HS 1,500/9-12
1860 Belvo Rd 45342 937-866-0771
Craig Morris, prin. Fax 865-5267
Miamisburg MS 6-8
8668 Miamisburg Springboro 45342 937-865-0011
Erin Wheat, prin. Fax 865-0114

Dayton Barber College Post-Sec.
2741 Lyons Rd Ste C 45342 937-222-9101
Dayton Christian S 1,000/PK-12
9391 Washington Church Rd 45342 937-291-7201
Robert Elliott, pres. Fax 291-7202
Miamisburg Christian Academy 50/K-12
8500 S Union Rd 45342 937-866-6226
Fax 866-0112

Middleburg Heights, Cuyahoga, Pop. 15,799
Berea CSD
Supt. — See Berea
Middleburg Heights JHS 300/7-9
7000 Paula Dr 44130 216-676-8400
Paul Kish, prin. Fax 676-2070

Polaris JVSD
7285 Old Oak Blvd 44130 440-891-7600
Bob Timmons, supt. Fax 243-3952
www.polaris.edu
Polaris Career Center Vo/Tech
7285 Old Oak Blvd 44130 440-891-7600
Gerald Lanning, prin. Fax 243-3952

Middlefield, Geauga, Pop. 2,651
Cardinal Local SD 1,300/K-12
PO Box 188 44062 440-632-0261
Scott Hunt Ed.D., supt. Fax 632-5886
www.cardinalschools.org
Cardinal HS 400/9-12
PO Box 7 44062 440-632-0264
James Howard, prin. Fax 632-1734
Cardinal MS 300/6-8
PO Box 879 44062 440-632-0263
James Millet, prin. Fax 632-0294

Middleport, Meigs, Pop. 2,488

Mid Valley Christian S 50/PK-12
500 N 2nd Ave 45760 740-992-6249
Melissa Dailey, admin. Fax 992-6249

Middletown, Butler, Pop. 47,397
Madison Local SD 1,200/PK-12
1324 Middletown Eaton Rd 45042 513-420-4750
Curtis Philpot, supt. Fax 420-4781
www.madisonmohawks.org/
Madison JSHS 700/7-12
5797 W Alexandria Rd 45042 513-420-4760
Justin Smith, prin. Fax 420-4914

Middletown CSD 5,800/PK-12
1515 Girard Ave 45044 513-423-0781
Greg Rasmussen, supt. Fax 420-4579
www.middletowncityschools.com
Middleton MS 500/7-8
1415 Girard Ave 45044 513-420-4528
Michael Valenti, prin. Fax 420-4527
Middletown HS 1,700/9-12
601 N Breiel Blvd 45042 513-420-4500
Carmela Cotter, prin. Fax 420-4648

Carousel Beauty College Post-Sec.
633 S Breiel Blvd 45044 513-422-2962
Miami University-Middletown Campus Post-Sec.
4200 N University Blvd 45042 513-727-3200
Middletown Regional Hospital Post-Sec.
PO Box 428810 45042 513-420-5100

Milan, Erie, Pop. 1,356
EHOVE JVSD
316 Mason Rd W 44846 419-499-4663
Sharon Mastroianni, supt. Fax 499-4076
www.ehove.net
EHOVE Career Center Vo/Tech
316 Mason Rd W 44846 419-499-4663
Rod Smith, prin. Fax 499-4076

Edison Local SD 1,100/PK-12
140 S Main St 44846 419-499-4272
Thomas Roth, supt. Fax 499-4859
www.edisonchargers.org/
Edison HS 500/9-12
2603 State Route 113 E 44846 419-499-4652
Jeffrey Goodwin, prin. Fax 499-2035
Other Schools – See Berlin Heights

Milford, Clermont, Pop. 6,599
Great Oaks Institute of Technology
Supt. — See Cincinnati
Live Oaks CDC Vo/Tech
5956 Buckwheat Rd 45150 513-575-1900
Dan Cox, prin. Fax 575-0805

Milford EVD 6,400/PK-12
777 Garfield Ave 45150 513-831-1314
Dr. Robert Farrell, supt. Fax 831-3208
www.milfordschools.org
Milford HS 1,800/9-12
1 Eagles Way 45150 513-831-2990
Mark Lutz, prin. Fax 831-9714
Milford JHS 1,000/7-8
5735 Pleasant Hill Rd 45150 513-831-1900
Kelli Ellison, prin. Fax 248-3451

St. Andrew/St. Elizabeth Ann Seton S 200/5-8
555 Main St 45150 513-831-5277
Tom Devolve, prin. Fax 831-8436

Milford Center, Union, Pop. 776
Fairbanks Local SD 900/K-12
11158 State Route 38 43045 937-349-3731
Bob Humble, supt. Fax 349-8885
www.fairbanks.k12.oh.us/
Fairbanks HS 300/9-12
11158 State Route 38 43045 937-349-3721
Tom Montgomery, prin. Fax 349-2011
Fairbanks MS 100/7-8
11158 State Route 38 43045 937-349-6841
Tom Montgomery, prin. Fax 349-2013

Millbury, Wood, Pop. 1,191
Lake Local SD 1,300/PK-12
28090 Lemoyne Rd 43447 419-661-6690
Jim Witt, supt. Fax 661-6678
www.lakeschools.org
Lake HS 400/8-12
28080 Lemoyne Rd 43447 419-661-6640
Lee Herman, prin. Fax 661-6650

Miller City, Putnam, Pop. 137
Miller City-New Cleveland Local SD 400/K-12
PO Box 38 45864 419-876-3172
Kerry Johnson, supt. Fax 876-3849
web.ml.noacsc.org/

Miller City-New Cleveland HS 100/9-12
PO Box 38 45864 419-876-3173
Kerry Johnson, prin. Fax 876-2020
Miller City-New Cleveland MS 100/6-8
PO Box 38 45864 419-876-3174
Cathy Burgei, prin. Fax 876-2020

Millersburg, Holmes, Pop. 2,985
West Holmes Local SD 2,500/K-12
28 W Jackson St 44654 330-674-3546
Kristie Pipes-Perone, supt. Fax 674-1177
www.westholmes.k12.oh.us
West Holmes HS 800/9-12
10909 State Route 39 44654 330-674-6085
William Sterling, prin. Fax 674-0818
West Holmes MS 600/6-8
10901 State Route 39 44654 330-674-4761
Jeff Woods, prin. Fax 674-2311

Gospel Haven Academy 100/K-12
6871 State Route 241 44654 330-674-0752
Galen Kauffman, prin. Fax 674-0752

Millersport, Fairfield, Pop. 1,033
Walnut Township Local SD 600/K-12
11850 Lancaster St 43046 740-467-2802
Randy Cotner, supt. Fax 467-3494
www.walnuttsd.org
Millersport JSHS 300/7-12
11850 Lancaster St 43046 740-467-2929
Jeff Stought, prin. Fax 467-3494

Mineral Ridge, Trumbull, Pop. 3,840
Weathersfield Local SD 1,000/K-12
3750 Main St 44440 330-652-0287
Damon Dohar, supt. Fax 544-7476
www.weathersfield.k12.oh.us/
Mineral Ridge HS 300/9-12
1334 Seaborn St 44440 330-652-1451
Lew Lowery, prin. Fax 505-9374
Mineral Ridge MS 300/5-8
3750 Main St 44440 330-652-2120
William Koppel, prin. Fax 544-7476

Minerva, Stark, Pop. 3,671
Minerva Local SD 1,900/K-12
406 East St 44657 330-868-4332
Joe Chaddock, supt. Fax 868-4731
minerva.web1.schoolpointe.com/
Minerva HS 600/9-12
501 Almeda Ave 44657 330-868-4134
Michael Riley, prin. Fax 868-5973
Minerva MS 500/6-8
600 E Line St 44657 330-868-4497
Gary Chaddock, prin. Fax 868-3144

Minford, Scioto, Pop. 684
Minford Local SD 1,500/K-12
PO Box 204 45653 740-820-3896
Mark Wilcheck, supt. Fax 820-3334
www.minfordfalcons.net/
Minford HS 400/9-12
PO Box 204 45653 740-820-3445
Barbara Dever, prin. Fax 820-4484
Minford MS 600/4-8
PO Box 204 45653 740-820-2181
Kevin Lloyd, prin. Fax 820-2191

Mingo Junction, Jefferson, Pop. 3,405
Indian Creek Local SD
Supt. — See Wintersville
Indian Creek MS 300/6-8
110 Steuben St 43938 740-266-2916
John Belt, prin. Fax 535-9100

Minster, Auglaize, Pop. 2,793
Minster Local SD 500/K-12
50 E 7th St 45865 419-628-3397
Brenda Boeke, supt. Fax 628-2482
www.minster.k12.oh.us
Minster JSHS 300/7-12
100 E 7th St 45865 419-628-2324
Michael Lee, prin. Fax 628-2495

Mogadore, Summit, Pop. 3,799
Field Local SD 2,400/K-12
2900 State Route 43 44260 330-673-2659
David Heflinger, supt. Fax 673-0270
www.fieldlocalschools.org
Field HS 700/9-12
2900 State Route 43 44260 330-673-9591
Michael Harris, prin. Fax 677-2520
Field MS, 1379 Saxe Rd 44260 600/6-8
Susan Blake, prin. 330-673-4176

Mogadore Local SD 700/K-12
1 S Cleveland Ave 44260 330-628-9946
Dr. Christina Dinklocker, supt. Fax 628-6661
www.mogadore.net
Mogadore JSHS 300/7-12
130 S Cleveland Ave 44260 330-628-9943
Russ Swartz, prin. Fax 628-6657

Monclova, Lucas

Monclova Christian Academy 100/K-12
PO Box 15 43542 419-866-7630
Neil Black, prin. Fax 868-1062

Monroe, Butler, Pop. 12,294
Butler Technology/Career Development SD
Supt. — See Hamilton
Natural Science Center Vo/Tech
640 Hamilton Lebanon Rd E 45050 513-539-0818
Chad Packer, prin. Fax 539-1129

Monroe Local SD 1,900/PK-12
500 Yankee Rd 45050 513-539-2536
Dr. Phillip Cagwin, supt. Fax 539-2648
www.monroelocalschools.com/
Monroe JSHS 600/7-12
220 Yankee Rd 45050 513-539-8471
Robert Leahy, prin. Fax 539-8474

Monroeville, Huron, Pop. 1,379
Monroeville Local SD 600/K-12
101 West St 44847 419-465-2610
David Stubblebine, supt. Fax 465-4263
www.monroevilleschools.org/
Monroeville JSHS 300/7-12
101 West St 44847 419-465-2531
James Kaczor, prin. Fax 465-4580

Montpelier, Williams, Pop. 4,026
Montpelier EVD 1,000/PK-12
PO Box 193 43543 419-485-6700
Jamison Grime, supt. Fax 485-3676
www.montpelier-k12.org/
Montpelier JSHS 400/7-12
PO Box 193 43543 419-485-6700
Su Thorop, prin. Fax 485-6700

Morral, Marion, Pop. 394
Ridgedale Local SD 700/K-12
3103 Hillman Ford Rd 43337 740-382-6065
Robert Britton, supt. Fax 383-6538
www.ridgedale.k12.oh.us/
Ridgedale JSHS 400/6-12
3165 Hillman Ford Rd 43337 740-382-6065
Brian Napper, prin. Fax 387-8525

Morrow, Warren, Pop. 1,164
Little Miami Local SD
Supt. — See Maineville
Little Miami HS 900/9-12
3001 E US Highway 22 and 3 45152 513-899-3781
Erica Kramer, prin. Fax 899-4912
Little Miami JHS 300/7-8
5290 Morrow Cozaddale Rd 45152 513-899-3408
Ryan Cherry, prin. Fax 899-2048

Mount Blanchard, Hancock, Pop. 482
Riverdale Local SD 800/K-12
20613 State Route 37 45867 419-694-4994
Eric Hoffman, supt. Fax 694-6465
www.riverdale.k12.oh.us
Riverdale HS 300/9-12
20613 State Route 37 45867 419-694-2211
Terry Huffman, prin. Fax 694-5008
Riverdale MS 200/6-8
20613 State Route 37 45867 419-694-2211
Terry Huffman, prin. Fax 694-5008

Mount Gilead, Morrow, Pop. 3,594
Mt. Gilead EVD 1,200/K-12
145 N Cherry St 43338 419-946-1646
Jeffrey Thompson, supt. Fax 946-3651
www.mgschools.org
Mount Gilead HS 400/9-12
338 W Park Ave 43338 419-947-6065
Debra Clauss, prin. Fax 946-3263
Mount Gilead MS 300/6-8
324 W Park Ave 43338 419-947-9517
Rick Nabors, prin. Fax 947-9518

Gilead Christian S South Campus 100/7-12
3613 Township Road 115 43338 419-946-5990
Aimee Horton, supt. Fax 946-1103

Mount Healthy, Hamilton, Pop. 5,926
Mt. Healthy CSD 1,400/K-12
7615 Harrison Ave 45231 513-729-0077
Lori Handler, supt. Fax 728-4692
www.mthcs.org
Other Schools – See Cincinnati

Mount Orab, Brown, Pop. 3,635
Western Brown Local SD 3,300/K-12
524 W Main St 45154 937-444-2044
Peggy McKinney, supt. Fax 444-4303
www.wb.k12.oh.us
Mount Orab MS 700/5-8
472 W Main St 45154 937-444-2529
Sabrina Armstrong, prin. Fax 444-4268
Western Brown HS 900/9-12
476 W Main St 45154 937-444-2544
Heather Cooper, prin. Fax 444-4355

Mount Vernon, Knox, Pop. 16,729
Knox County JVSD
306 Martinsburg Rd 43050 740-397-5820
Bernadette Pachmayer, supt. Fax 397-7040
www.knoxcc.org
Knox County Career Center Vo/Tech
306 Martinsburg Rd 43050 740-397-5820
Fax 397-7040

Mt. Vernon CSD 4,000/PK-12
300 Newark Rd 43050 740-397-7422
Steve Short, supt. Fax 397-5949
www.mvcsd.us/
Mount Vernon HS 1,100/9-12
300 Martinsburg Rd 43050 740-393-5900
Kathy Kasler, prin. Fax 397-6018
Mount Vernon MS 900/6-8
298 Martinsburg Rd 43050 740-392-6867
Gary Hankins, prin. Fax 392-3369

Christian Star Academy 50/K-12
7 E Sugar St 43050 740-393-0251
Suzanne Feasel, admin. Fax 393-0067
Knox County Career Center Post-Sec.
306 Martinsburg Rd 43050 740-397-5820
Mount Vernon Academy 100/9-12
PO Box 311 43050 740-397-5411
Mt. Vernon Nazarene University Post-Sec.
800 Martinsburg Rd 43050 740-392-6868

Mowrystown, Highland, Pop. 359
Bright Local SD 600/PK-12
PO Box 299 45155 937-442-3114
Dee Wright, supt. Fax 442-6655
www.brightlocalschools.com
Whiteoak JSHS 200/7-12
PO Box 299 45155 937-442-2241
Michael Roades, prin. Fax 442-2111

Munroe Falls, Summit, Pop. 4,951
Stow-Munroe Falls CSD
Supt. — See Stow
Kimpton MS 900/7-8
380 N River Rd 44262 330-689-5288
Jim Saxer, prin. Fax 686-4718

Napoleon, Henry, Pop. 8,677
Napoleon Area CSD 1,900/K-12
701 Briarheath Ave Ste 108 43545 419-599-7015
Dr. Stephen R. Fogo, supt. Fax 599-7035
www.napoleonareaschools.org/
Napoleon HS 600/9-12
701 Briarheath Ave Ste 123 43545 419-599-1050
Ryan Wilde, prin. Fax 599-8537
Napoleon MS 400/6-8
303 W Main St 43545 419-592-6991
Matthew Dietrich, prin. Fax 599-7638

Navarre, Stark, Pop. 1,939
Fairless Local SD 1,600/K-12
11885 Navarre Rd SW 44662 330-767-3577
Broc Bidlack, supt. Fax 767-3298
www.falcon.stark.k12.oh.us/
Fairless HS 500/9-12
11885 Navarre Rd SW 44662 330-767-3444
Dr. Larry Chambliss, prin. Fax 767-3447
Fairless JHS 400/6-8
11836 Navarre Rd SW 44662 330-767-4293
Theodore George, prin. Fax 767-3807

Nelsonville, Athens, Pop. 5,295
Nelsonville-York CSD 1,300/PK-12
2 Buckeye Dr 45764 740-753-4441
Charles McClelland, supt. Fax 753-1968
www.nelsonvilleyork.k12.oh.us/
Nelsonville-York HS 300/9-12
1 Buckeye Dr 45764 740-753-4441
Elise Stephan, prin. Fax 753-1420
Nelsonville-York MS 200/7-8
3 Buckeye Dr 45764 740-753-4441
Joseph Malesick, prin. Fax 753-1087

Tri-County Career Center
15676 State Route 691 45764 740-753-3511
William Wittman, supt. Fax 753-5376
www.tricountyhightech.com
Tri-County Career Center Vo/Tech
15676 State Route 691 45764 740-753-3511
Connie Altier, prin. Fax 753-5132
Tri-County Adult Career Center Adult
15676 State Route 691 45764 740-753-5465
Kim McKinley, dir.

Hocking College Post-Sec.
3301 Hocking Pkwy 45764 740-735-3591

New Albany, Franklin, Pop. 7,553
New Albany - Plain Local SD 4,300/K-12
55 N High St 43054 614-855-2040
April Domine, supt. Fax 855-2043
www.new-albany.k12.oh.us
New Albany HS 1,200/9-12
7600 Fodor Rd 43054 614-413-8300
Mark White, prin. Fax 413-8301
New Albany MS 1,000/6-8
6600 E Dublin Granville Rd 43054 614-413-8500
Kip Greenhill, prin. Fax 413-8501

Newark, Licking, Pop. 46,372
Career & Technology Educational Centers
150 Price Rd 43055 740-364-2832
Joyce Malainy, supt. Fax 364-2815
www.c-tec.edu/
Career & Technology Educational Center Vo/Tech
150 Price Rd 43055 740-364-2832
Mary Andrews, dir. Fax 364-2815

Licking Valley Local SD 2,000/K-12
1379 Licking Valley Rd 43055 740-763-3525
David Hile, supt. Fax 763-0471
www.lickingvalley.k12.oh.us/
Licking Valley HS 600/9-12
100 Hainsview Dr 43055 740-763-3721
Wes Weaver, prin. Fax 763-0847
Licking Valley MS 500/6-8
1379 Licking Valley Rd 43055 740-763-3396
Scott Beery, prin. Fax 763-2612

Newark CSD 6,100/PK-12
621 Mount Vernon Rd 43055 740-670-7000
Douglas Ute, supt. Fax 670-7009
www.newarkcityschools.org
Heritage MS 400/6-8
600 Arlington Ave 43055 740-670-7110
Tom Suriano, prin. Fax 670-7119
Liberty MS 500/6-8
1055 Evans Blvd 43055 740-670-7320
Diane Henry, prin. Fax 670-7329
Newark HS 1,400/9-12
314 Granville St 43055 740-670-7400
J. Mark Fullen, prin. Fax 670-7409
Wilson MS 400/6-8
805 W Church St 43055 740-670-7120
John Davis, prin. Fax 670-7129

Central Ohio Technical College Post-Sec.
1179 University Dr 43055 740-366-9494

Newark Catholic HS 300/9-12
1 Green Wave Dr 43055 740-344-3594
Beth Hill, prin. Fax 344-0421
Ohio State University-Newark Post-Sec.
1179 University Dr 43055 740-366-3321

New Boston, Scioto, Pop. 2,223
New Boston Local SD 400/PK-12
522 Glenwood Ave 45662 740-456-4626
Mike Staggs, supt. Fax 456-5252
www.newboston.k12.oh.us
Glenwood HS 200/7-12
522 Glenwood Ave 45662 740-456-4559
Melinda Burnside, prin. Fax 456-5252

Daymar College Post-Sec.
3879 Rhodes Ave 45662 740-456-4124

New Bremen, Auglaize, Pop. 2,950
New Bremen Local SD 900/K-12
901 E Monroe St 45869 419-629-2443
Howard Overman, supt. Fax 629-0115
www.newbremenschools.org
New Bremen HS 300/9-12
901 E Monroe St 45869 419-629-8606
Brian Pohl, prin. Fax 629-0115
New Bremen MS 200/5-8
202 S Walnut St 45869 419-629-2373
Jason Schrader, prin. Fax 629-8113

Newburgh Heights, Cuyahoga, Pop. 2,102
Cleveland Municipal SD
Supt. — See Cleveland
Washington Park Environmental Studies 100/9-12
3875 Washington Park Blvd 44105 216-441-8070
Alisa Lawson-McKinnie, prin. Fax 441-8038

Newbury, Geauga
Newbury Local SD 600/K-12
14775 Auburn Rd 44065 440-564-5501
Richard Wagner, supt. Fax 564-9460
www.newburyschools.org/
Newbury JSHS 300/7-12
14775 Auburn Rd 44065 440-564-2281
Trista Linden-Warren, prin. Fax 564-9788

New Carlisle, Clark, Pop. 5,735
Tecumseh Local SD 2,200/K-12
9760 W National Rd 45344 937-845-3576
Dr. Bradley Martin, supt. Fax 845-4453
www.tecumseh.k12.oh.us
Tecumseh HS 1,000/9-12
9830 W National Rd 45344 937-845-4500
Ivan Gehret, prin. Fax 845-4547
Tecumseh MS 800/6-8
10000 W National Rd 45344 937-845-4465
Brian Dixon, prin. Fax 845-4484

Newcomerstown, Tuscarawas, Pop. 3,763
Newcomerstown EVD 1,100/K-12
702 S River St 43832 740-498-8373
Jeffrey Staggs, supt. Fax 498-8375
www.nctschools.org
Newcomerstown HS 300/9-12
659 Beaver St 43832 740-498-5111
Matthew Fockler, prin. Fax 498-4994
Newcomerstown MS 200/6-8
325 W State St 43832 740-498-8151
Jason Peoples, prin. Fax 498-4991

New Concord, Muskingum, Pop. 2,459
East Muskingum Local SD 2,100/K-12
13505 John Glenn School Rd 43762 740-826-7655
Jill Johnson, supt. Fax 826-7194
www.east-muskingum.k12.oh.us
East Muskingum MS 500/6-8
13120 John Glenn School Rd 43762 740-826-7631
Robert Baier, prin. Fax 826-4392
Glenn HS 600/9-12
13115 John Glenn School Rd 43762 740-826-7641
Steve Brooks, prin. Fax 826-3039

Muskingum University Post-Sec.
163 Stormont St 43762 740-826-8211

New Franklin, Stark
Manchester Local SD
Supt. — See Akron
Manchester HS 500/9-12
437 W Nimisila Rd, 330-882-3291
James France, prin. Fax 882-5642
Manchester MS 500/5-8
760 W Nimisila Rd, 330-882-3812
James Miller, prin. Fax 882-2013

New Knoxville, Auglaize, Pop. 875
New Knoxville Local SD 400/K-12
PO Box 476 45871 419-753-2431
Kim Waterman, supt. Fax 753-2333
www.nk.k12.oh.us
New Knoxville HS 100/7-12
PO Box 476 45871 419-753-2431
Linda Tebbe, prin. Fax 753-2333

New Lebanon, Montgomery, Pop. 3,918
New Lebanon Local SD 1,100/K-12
320 S Fuls Rd 45345 937-687-1301
Dr. Barbara Curry, supt. Fax 687-7321
www.newlebanon.k12.oh.us/
Dixie HS 300/9-12
300 S Fuls Rd 45345 937-687-1366
Dr. Greg Williams, prin. Fax 687-7074
Dixie MS 300/5-8
200 S Fuls Rd 45345 937-687-3508
Dr. Gary Schomburg, prin. Fax 687-7705

New Lexington, Perry, Pop. 4,679
New Lexington CSD 1,800/K-12
PO Box 630 43764 740-342-4133
Tonya Foster-Sherburne, supt. Fax 342-6051
nlpanthers.org
New Lexington HS 500/9-12
PO Box 630 43764 740-342-3528
Robert Dodd, prin. Fax 342-4765
New Lexington MS 400/6-8
PO Box 630 43764 740-342-4128
Anette Losco, prin. Fax 342-6071

New London, Huron, Pop. 2,415
New London Local SD 1,000/PK-12
2 Wildcat Dr 44851 419-929-8433
Bradley Romano, supt. Fax 929-4108
www.newlondon.k12.oh.us/
New London HS 300/9-12
1 Wildcat Dr 44851 419-929-1586
Cosetta Adkins, prin. Fax 929-9513
New London MS 200/7-8
1 Wildcat Dr 44851 419-929-5409
Cosetta Adkins, prin. Fax 929-9513

New Madison, Darke, Pop. 886
Tri-Village Local SD 800/K-12
PO Box 31 45346 937-996-6261
Josh Sagester, supt. Fax 996-5537
www.tri-village.k12.oh.us
Tri-Village JSHS 300/7-12
PO Box 31 45346 937-996-1511
Lee Morris, prin. Fax 996-0307

New Matamoras, Washington, Pop. 879
Frontier Local SD 600/K-12
44870 State Route 7 45767 740-865-3473
Bruce Kidder, supt. Fax 865-2010
www.flsd.k12.oh.us/
Frontier MSHS 200/7-12
44870 State Route 7 45767 740-865-3441
Jack Mental, prin. Fax 865-2011

New Middletown, Mahoning, Pop. 1,611
Springfield Local SD 1,100/K-12
PO Box 549 44442 330-542-2929
Debra Mettee, supt. Fax 542-9453
www.springfieldlocal.us/
Springfield HS 300/9-12
11335 Youngstown Pittsburgh 44442 330-542-3626
Anthony De Felice, prin. Fax 542-9453
Springfield IS 400/5-8
11333 Youngstown Pittsburgh 44442 330-542-3624
David Malone, prin. Fax 542-2159

New Paris, Preble, Pop. 1,607
National Trail Local SD 1,100/K-12
6940 Oxford Gettysburg Rd 45347 937-437-3333
Jeff Parker, supt. Fax 437-7865
www.nationaltrail.k12.oh.us/
National Trail HS 300/9-12
6940 Oxford Gettysburg Rd 45347 937-437-3333
Bob Fischer, prin. Fax 437-8270
National Trail MS 300/5-8
6940 Oxford Gettysburg Rd 45347 937-437-3333
Mark Wiseman, prin. Fax 437-7306

New Philadelphia, Tuscarawas, Pop. 17,008
Buckeye JVSD
545 University Dr NE 44663 330-339-2288
Roger Bond, supt. Fax 339-5159
buckeyecareercenter.org/
Buckeye Career Center Vo/Tech
545 University Dr NE 44663 330-339-2288
Tom Hackenbracht, prin. Fax 339-5159

New Philadelphia CSD 2,900/K-12
248 Front Ave SW 44663 330-364-0600
Bob Alsept, supt. Fax 364-9310
www.npschools.org
New Philadelphia HS 800/9-12
343 Ray Ave NW 44663 330-364-0644
Dr. Doug Baker, prin. Fax 364-0633
Welty MS 700/6-8
315 4th St NW 44663 330-364-0645
Eric Jurkovic, prin. Fax 364-0677

Kent State University- Tuscarawas Campus Post-Sec.
330 University Dr NE 44663 330-339-3391
Tuscarawas Central Catholic HS 200/7-12
777 3rd St NE 44663 330-343-3302
Scott Power, prin. Fax 343-6388

New Richmond, Clermont, Pop. 2,535
New Richmond EVD 2,300/K-12
212 Market St 45157 513-553-2616
Adam Bird, supt. Fax 553-6431
www.nrschools.org
New Richmond HS 700/9-12
1131 Bethel New Richmond Rd 45157513-553-3191
Mark Bailey, prin. Fax 553-2531
New Richmond MS 400/7-8
1135 Bethel New Richmond Rd 45157513-553-3161
Court Lilly, prin. Fax 553-6412

New Riegel, Seneca, Pop. 248
New Riegel Local SD 400/K-12
44 N Perry St 44853 419-595-2256
Elaine Nye, supt. Fax 595-2901
newriegelschools.org/
New Riegel JSHS 200/7-12
44 N Perry St 44853 419-595-2256
David Rombach, prin. Fax 595-2901

Newton Falls, Trumbull, Pop. 4,737
Newton Falls EVD 1,000/K-12
909 1/2 Milton Blvd 44444 330-872-5445
Paul Woodard, supt. Fax 872-3351
www.newton-falls.k12.oh.us/
Falls Learning Academy Alt
907 Milton Blvd 44444 330-872-5121
John Crowder, prin.
Newton Falls JSHS 400/7-12
907 Milton Blvd 44444 330-872-5121
John Crowder, prin. Fax 872-3351

New Washington, Crawford, Pop. 962
Buckeye Central Local SD 700/K-12
938 S Kibler St 44854 419-492-2864
Tara Meyerink, supt. Fax 492-2039
www.buckeye-central.org
Buckeye Central HS 200/9-12
938 S Kibler St 44854 419-492-2266
Jay Zeiter, prin. Fax 492-2039
Buckeye Central MS 200/5-8
938 S Kibler St 44854 419-492-1035
Nannette Chorba, prin. Fax 492-2039

Niles, Trumbull, Pop. 18,878
Niles CSD 2,300/K-12
100 West St 44446 330-652-2509
Frank Danso, supt. Fax 652-3522
www.nilescityschools.org/
McKinley HS 700/9-12
616 Dragon Dr 44446 330-652-9968
Mark Lucas, prin. Fax 505-0755
Niles MS 600/6-8
411 Brown St 44446 330-652-5656
Samuel Reigle, prin. Fax 652-9158

ETI Technical College of Niles Post-Sec.
2076 Youngstown Warren Rd 44446 330-652-9919
Raphael's School of Beauty Culture Post-Sec.
1324 Youngstown Warren Rd 44446 330-652-1559
Victory Christian S 100/K-12
2053 Pleasant Valley Rd 44446 330-539-9827
Colleen McCullough, prin. Fax 539-9828

North Baltimore, Wood, Pop. 3,396
North Baltimore Local SD 700/K-12
201 S Main St 45872 419-257-3531
Marlene North, supt. Fax 257-2008
www.nbls.org/
North Baltimore HS 200/9-12
2012 Tiger Dr 45872 419-257-3531
Dr. Bob Falkenstein, prin. Fax 257-2008
North Baltimore MS 100/7-8
2012 Tiger Dr 45872 419-257-3531
Dr. Bob Falkenstein, prin. Fax 257-2008

North Bloomfield, Trumbull
Bloomfield-Mespo Local SD 300/K-12
2077 Park West Rd 44450 440-685-4710
Russell McQuaide, supt. Fax 685-4751
www.bloomfield-mespo.org/
Bloomfield MSHS 100/6-12
2077 Park West Rd 44450 440-685-4711
Steve Kobus, prin. Fax 685-4751

North Canton, Stark, Pop. 17,236
North Canton CSD 3,600/K-12
525 7th St NE 44720 330-497-5600
Michael Hartenstein, supt. Fax 497-5618
www.northcantonschools.org
Hoover HS 1,700/9-12
525 7th St NE 44720 330-497-5620
Anthony Pallija, prin. Fax 497-5606
North Canton MS 1,100/6-8
605 Fair Oaks Ave SW 44720 330-497-5635
Marjorie McDougal, prin. Fax 497-5659

Kent State University at Stark Post-Sec.
6000 Frank Ave NW 44720 330-499-9600
Stark State College Post-Sec.
6200 Frank Ave NW 44720 330-494-6170
Walsh University Post-Sec.
2020 E Maple St 44720 330-490-7090

North Eaton, Lorain

Christian Community S 200/K-12
35716 Royalton Rd 44044 440-748-6224
Richard Willis, hdmstr. Fax 748-1007

Northfield, Summit, Pop. 3,593
Nordonia Hills CSD 4,000/K-12
9370 Olde 8 Rd 44067 330-467-0580
Joseph Clark, supt. Fax 468-0152
www.nordoniaschools.org
Nordonia MS 700/7-8
73 Leonard Ave 44067 330-467-0584
David Wessel, prin. Fax 468-6719
Other Schools – See Macedonia

North Jackson, Mahoning
Jackson-Milton Local SD 800/K-12
13910 Mahoning Ave 44451 330-538-3232
Kirk Baker, supt. Fax 538-6297
www.jacksonmilton.k12.oh.us/
Jackson-Milton HS 300/9-12
13910 Mahoning Ave 44451 330-538-3308
David Vega, prin. Fax 538-0821
Jackson-Milton MS 100/7-8
13910 Mahoning Ave 44451 330-538-3308
David Vega, prin. Fax 538-0821

North Lewisburg, Union, Pop. 1,449
Triad Local SD 1,000/K-12
7920 Brush Lake Rd 43060 937-826-4961
Matt Sheridan, supt. Fax 826-3281
www.triad.k12.oh.us
Triad HS 300/9-12
8099 Brush Lake Rd 43060 937-826-3771
Kyle Huffman, prin. Fax 826-2002
Triad MS 300/5-8
7941 Brush Lake Rd 43060 937-826-3071
Duane Caudill, prin. Fax 826-1000

North Olmsted, Cuyahoga, Pop. 32,229
North Olmsted CSD 4,200/PK-12
27425 Butternut Ridge Rd 44070 440-779-3576
Michael Zalar Ph.D., supt. Fax 779-3505
www.northolmstedschools.org

North Olmsted HS 1,400/9-12
5755 Burns Rd 44070 440-779-8825
Jeffrey Stanton, prin. Fax 777-2216
North Olmsted MS 600/7-8
27351 Butternut Ridge Rd 44070 440-779-8501
Tom Dreiling, prin. Fax 779-8510

Remington College Post-Sec.
26350 Brookpark Rd 44070 440-777-2560

North Randall, Cuyahoga, Pop. 1,013

PowerSport Institute Post-Sec.
21210 Emery Rd 44128 216-587-5000

North Ridgeville, Lorain, Pop. 29,069
North Ridgeville CSD 4,000/K-12
5490 Mills Creek Ln 44039 440-327-4444
Larry Brown, supt. Fax 327-9774
www.nrcs.k12.oh.us
North Ridgeville HS 1,100/9-12
34600 Bainbridge Rd 44039 440-327-1992
Patricia Bahr, prin. Fax 327-4056
North Ridgeville MS 900/6-8
35895 Center Ridge Rd 44039 440-353-1180
Amy Peck, prin. Fax 353-1144

Lake Ridge Academy 300/K-12
37501 Center Ridge Rd 44039 440-327-1175
Carol Klimas, pres. Fax 327-3641

North Robinson, Crawford, Pop. 201
Colonel Crawford Local SD 700/PK-12
PO Box 7 44856 419-562-4666
Todd Martin, supt. Fax 562-3304
www.cck12.org
Crawford HS 300/9-12
PO Box 7 44856 419-562-4666
Jake Bruner, prin. Fax 562-3304
Other Schools – See Crestline

North Royalton, Cuyahoga, Pop. 30,115
North Royalton CSD 4,600/PK-12
6579 Royalton Rd 44133 440-237-8800
Greg Gurka, supt. Fax 582-7336
www.northroyaltonsd.org
North Royalton HS 1,700/9-12
14713 Ridge Rd 44133 440-582-7801
Mic Becerra, prin. Fax 582-7337
North Royalton MS 1,400/5-8
14709 Ridge Rd 44133 440-582-9120
Melissa Vojta, prin. Fax 582-7229

Northwood, Wood, Pop. 5,174
Northwood Local SD 600/PK-12
500 Lemoyne Rd 43619 419-691-3888
Gregory Clark, supt. Fax 697-2470
www.northwood.k12.oh.us
Northwood HS 300/7-12
700 Lemoyne Rd 43619 419-691-4651
Jason Kozina, prin. Fax 691-2846

Norton, Summit, Pop. 11,968
Norton CSD 2,600/PK-12
4128 Cleveland Massillon Rd 44203 330-825-0863
David Dunn, supt. Fax 825-0929
www.norton.k12.oh.us
Norton HS 800/9-12
4108 Cleveland Massillon Rd 44203 330-825-7300
Ryan Shanor, prin. Fax 825-4275
Norton MS 800/5-8
3390 Cleveland Massillon Rd 44203 330-825-5607
Joyce Gerber, prin. Fax 825-1461

Norwalk, Huron, Pop. 16,729
Norwalk CSD 2,200/PK-12
134 Benedict Ave 44857 419-668-2779
Dennis Doughty, supt. Fax 663-3302
www.norwalk-city.k12.oh.us
Norwalk HS 900/9-12
350 Shady Lane Dr 44857 419-660-6500
Brad Cooley, prin. Fax 668-4719
Norwalk MS 500/7-8
64 Christie Ave 44857 419-668-8370
Corey Ream, prin. Fax 668-6622

Norwalk Catholic - St. Paul JSHS 300/7-12
93 E Main St 44857 419-668-3005
James Tokarsky, prin. Fax 668-6417

Norwood, Hamilton, Pop. 18,788
Norwood CSD 1,900/PK-12
2132 Williams Ave Ste 1 45212 513-924-2500
Rob Amodio, supt. Fax 396-6420
www.norwoodschools.org
Norwood HS 600/9-12
2020 Sherman Ave 45212 513-924-2800
Brad Winterod, prin. Fax 396-5559
Norwood MS 300/7-8
2060 Sherman Ave 45212 513-924-2700
Kathy Sabo, prin. Fax 396-5537

Cornerstone Christian Academy 50/PK-12
PO Box 12824 45212 513-351-7900
Dr. Phyllis Wilson, dir. Fax 351-7900
ITT Technical Institute Post-Sec.
4750 Wesley Ave 45212 513-531-8300

Oak Harbor, Ottawa, Pop. 2,732
Benton Carroll Salem Local SD 1,100/K-12
11685 W State Route 163 43449 419-898-6210
Dr. Guy Parmigian, supt. Fax 898-4303
www.bcssd.com
Oak Harbor HS 500/8-12
11661 W State Route 163 43449 419-898-6216
Keith Thorbahn, prin. Fax 898-0116

Oak Hill, Jackson, Pop. 1,527
Oak Hill Union Local SD 1,300/PK-12
205 Western Ave 45656 740-682-7595
Michael A. McCoy, supt. Fax 682-6998
www.oakhill.k12.oh.us
Oak Hill MSHS 700/6-12
5063 State Route 93 45656 740-682-7055
Randall Layton, prin. Fax 682-6075

Oberlin, Lorain, Pop. 7,787
Firelands Local SD
Supt. — See South Amherst
Firelands HS 600/9-12
10643 Vermilion Rd 44074 440-965-4255
Richard Reighley, prin. Fax 965-5296

Lorain County JVSD
15181 State Route 58 44074 440-774-1051
Dr. Glenn Faircloth, supt. Fax 774-2144
www.lcjvs.com/
Burton Vocational Center HS Vo/Tech
15181 State Route 58 44074 440-774-1051
Jill Petitti, prin. Fax 774-6421

Oberlin CSD 1,100/PK-12
153 N Main St 44074 440-774-1458
John Schroth, supt. Fax 774-4492
ocs.schoolwires.net/site/default.aspx?pageid=1
Langston MS 300/6-8
150 N Pleasant St 44074 440-775-7961
John Crecelius, prin. Fax 776-4520
Oberlin HS 300/9-12
281 N Pleasant St 44074 440-774-1295
William Baylis, prin. Fax 774-5099

Oberlin College Post-Sec.
101 N Professor St 44074 440-775-8121

Old Fort, Seneca, Pop. 185
Old Fort Local SD 500/K-12
PO Box 64 44861 419-992-4291
Jude Meyers, supt. Fax 992-4293
www.old-fort.k12.oh.us/
Old Fort JSHS 200/7-12
PO Box 64 44861 419-992-4291
Thomas Weaver, prin. Fax 992-4293

Old Washington, Guernsey, Pop. 277
East Guernsey Local SD 1,100/K-12
PO Box 128 43768 740-489-5190
Richard Hall, supt. Fax 489-9813
www.eguernsey.k12.oh.us
Other Schools – See Lore City

Olmsted Falls, Cuyahoga, Pop. 8,919
Olmsted Falls CSD 3,800/PK-12
PO Box 38010 44138 440-427-6000
Dr. Jim Lloyd, supt. Fax 427-6010
www.ofcs.net
Olmsted Falls HS 1,200/9-12
26939 Bagley Rd 44138 440-427-6100
Holly Schafer, prin. Fax 427-6110
Olmsted Falls MS 900/6-8
27045 Bagley Rd 44138 440-427-6200
Mark Kurz, prin. Fax 427-6210

Ontario, Richland, Pop. 6,103
Ontario Local SD 1,300/PK-12
457 Shelby Ontario Rd, 419-747-4311
Lisa Carmichael, supt. Fax 747-6859
www.ontarioschools.org
Ontario HS 500/9-12
467 Shelby Ontario Rd, 419-529-3969
Chris Smith, prin. Fax 529-5649
Ontario MS 400/6-8
447 Shelby Ontario Rd, 419-529-5507
Julie Brokaw, prin. Fax 529-7058

Oregon, Lucas, Pop. 20,036
ESC of Lake Erie West
Supt. — See Toledo
Shuer Learning Center 100/Alt
4955 Seaman Rd 43616 419-698-1501
Fax 698-1457

Oregon CSD 3,600/K-12
5721 Seaman Rd 43616 419-693-0661
Mike Zalar, supt. Fax 698-6016
www.oregoncityschools.org
Clay HS 1,300/9-12
5665 Seaman Rd 43616 419-693-0665
Jeff Thompson, prin. Fax 698-6047
Eisenhower MS 500/6-8
331 N North Curtice Rd 43616 419-836-8498
Rebecca Bihn, prin. Fax 836-2005
Fassett MS 500/6-8
3025 Starr Ave 43616 419-693-0455
Tim Holcombe, prin. Fax 698-6048

Cardinal Stritch HS 300/9-12
3225 Pickle Rd 43616 419-693-0465
Tim Malone, prin. Fax 697-2816
St. Charles Hospital Post-Sec.
2600 Navarre Ave 43616 419-698-7341
Toledo Academy of Beauty Culture - East Post-Sec.
3341 Navarre Ave 43616 419-693-7257

Orrville, Wayne, Pop. 8,182
Orrville CSD 1,500/PK-12
815 N Ella St 44667 330-682-4651
James Ritchie, supt. Fax 682-0073
www.orrville.k12.oh.us
Orrville HS 400/9-12
841 N Ella St 44667 330-682-4661
Philip Hatton, prin. Fax 682-4662
Orrville MS 500/5-8
801 Mineral Springs St 44667 330-682-1791
David Sovacool, prin. Fax 682-2743

Kingsway Christian S 200/K-12
11138 Old Lincoln Way E 44667 330-683-0012
Lynette Duplain M.Ed., admin. Fax 683-0017
University of Akron-Wayne College Post-Sec.
1901 Smucker Rd 44667 330-683-2010

Orwell, Ashtabula, Pop. 1,614
Grand Valley Local SD 1,400/K-12
111 W Grand Valley Ave # A 44076 440-437-6260
Dr. William Nye, supt. Fax 437-1025
www.grand-valley.k12.oh.us
Grand Valley HS 400/9-12
111 W Grand Valley Ave # C 44076 440-437-6260
Doug Hitchcock, prin. Fax 437-1025
Grand Valley MS 500/5-8
111 W Grand Valley Ave # D 44076 440-437-6260
Lowell Moodt, prin. Fax 437-1025

Ottawa, Putnam, Pop. 4,436
Ottawa-Glandorf Local SD 1,500/K-12
630 Glendale Ave 45875 419-523-5261
Kevin Brinkman, supt. Fax 523-5978
og.noacsc.org/
Ottawa-Glandorf HS 600/9-12
630 Glendale Ave 45875 419-523-5702
Jayson Selgo, prin. Fax 523-6346

Putnam County ESC
124 Putnam Pkwy 45875 419-523-5951
Dr. Jan Osborn, supt. Fax 523-6126
putnam.noacsc.org/
Putnam County Alternative Center Alt
7374 State Route 109 45875 419-523-0026
Fax 523-0046

Ottawa Hills, Lucas, Pop. 4,439
Ottawa Hills Local SD 1,000/K-12
3600 Indian Rd, 419-536-6371
Dr. Kevin Miller, supt. Fax 534-5380
www.ottawahillsschools.org/
Ottawa Hills JSHS 500/7-12
2532 Evergreen Rd, 419-534-5376
Ben McMurray, prin. Fax 534-5384

Ottoville, Putnam, Pop. 974
Ottoville Local SD 500/K-12
PO Box 248 45876 419-453-3356
Scott Mangas, supt. Fax 453-3367
www.ottovilleschools.org
Ottoville JSHS 200/7-12
PO Box 248 45876 419-453-3358
Wilbur Altenburger, prin. Fax 453-3367

Oxford, Butler, Pop. 20,904
Talawanda CSD 3,000/PK-12
131 W Chestnut St 45056 513-273-3333
Kelly Spivey, supt. Fax 273-3113
www.talawanda.net/
Talawanda HS 900/9-12
101 W Chestnut St 45056 513-273-3200
Vicki Brunn, prin. Fax 273-3203
Talawanda MS 700/6-8
4030 Oxford Reily Rd 45056 513-273-3300
Mike Malone, prin. Fax 273-3303

Miami University Post-Sec.
501 E High St 45056 513-529-1809

Painesville, Lake, Pop. 18,851
Lake County ESC
382 Blackbrook Rd 44077 440-350-2563
Dr. Brian Bontempo, supt. Fax 350-2566
www.esc-lc.org/
Other Schools – See Willoughby

Painesville City Local SD 3,400/PK-12
58 Jefferson St 44077 440-392-5060
John Shepard, supt. Fax 392-5089
www.pcls.net
Harvey HS 800/9-12
200 W Walnut Ave 44077 440-392-5110
Van McWreath, prin. Fax 392-5119
Heritage MS 600/6-8
135 Cedarbrook Dr 44077 440-392-5250
Melissa DeAngelis, prin. Fax 392-5259

Riverside Local SD 5,000/K-12
585 Riverside Dr 44077 440-352-0668
James Kalis, supt. Fax 639-1959
www.riversidelocalschools.com
Riverside JSHS 1,900/8-12
585 Riverside Dr 44077 440-352-3341
Peter Hliatzos, prin. Fax 352-0695

Lake Erie College Post-Sec.
391 W Washington St 44077 440-296-1856

Pandora, Putnam, Pop. 1,146
Pandora-Gilboa Local SD 600/K-12
410 Rocket Rdg 45877 419-384-3227
Todd Schmutz, supt. Fax 384-3230
www.pg.noacsc.org
Pandora-Gilboa HS 200/9-12
410 Rocket Rdg 45877 419-384-3225
Jeffrey Wise, prin. Fax 384-3230
Pandora-Gilboa MS 200/5-8
410 Rocket Rdg 45877 419-384-3225
Jodi Schroeder, prin. Fax 384-3230

Parma, Cuyahoga, Pop. 80,516
Parma CSD 10,300/PK-12
5311 Longwood Ave 44134 440-842-5300
Dr. Jeffrey Graham, supt. Fax 885-8304
www.parmacityschools.org/
Greenbriar MS 600/7-8
11810 Huffman Rd 44130 440-885-2370
Frank Spisak, prin. Fax 885-8353
Normandy HS 1,300/9-12
2500 W Pleasant Valley Rd 44134 440-885-2400
Dr. Brad Ritchey, prin. Fax 885-2402

Parma HS 1,500/9-12
6285 W 54th St 44129 440-885-2300
Chad Coffman, prin. Fax 888-0358
Shiloh MS 700/7-8
2303 Grantwood Dr 44134 440-885-8485
Nicola Discenza, prin. Fax 885-8486
Other Schools – See Parma Heights, Seven Hills

Bryant & Stratton College Post-Sec.
12955 Snow Rd 44130 216-265-3151
Padua Franciscan HS 900/9-12
6740 State Rd 44134 440-845-2444
David Stec, prin. Fax 845-5710
Parma Community General Hospital Post-Sec.
7007 Powers Blvd 44129 440-743-3000

Parma Heights, Cuyahoga, Pop. 20,381
Parma CSD
Supt. — See Parma
Valley Forge HS 1,500/9-12
9999 Independence Blvd 44130 440-885-2330
Janine Andrzejewski, prin. Fax 885-8412

Cuyahoga Community College Post-Sec.
11000 W Pleasant Valley Rd 44130 800-954-8742
Holy Name HS 700/9-12
6000 Queens Hwy 44130 440-886-0300
Benjamin Farmer, prin. Fax 886-1267

Pataskala, Licking, Pop. 14,629
Licking Heights Local SD 3,400/K-12
6539 Summit Rd SW 43062 740-927-6926
Dr. Philip Wagner, supt. Fax 927-9043
www.licking-heights.k12.oh.us/
Licking Heights Central MS 800/6-8
6565 Summit Rd SW 43062 740-927-3365
Terrance Hubbard, prin. Fax 927-5845
Licking Heights HS 800/9-12
4000 Mink St SW 43062 740-927-9046
Mark White, prin. Fax 927-3197

Southwest Licking Local SD 3,600/K-12
927 South St Unit A 43062 740-927-3941
Robert Jennell, supt. Fax 927-4648
www.swl.k12.oh.us
Other Schools – See Etna

Liberty Christian Academy 300/PK-12
10447 Refugee Rd SW 43062 740-964-2211
LaVonne McIlrath, admin. Fax 964-2311

Paulding, Paulding, Pop. 3,557
Paulding EVD 1,600/PK-12
405 N Water St 45879 419-399-4656
Patricia Ross, supt. Fax 399-2404
www.pauldingschools.org/
Paulding HS 400/9-12
405 N Water St 45879 419-399-4656
Todd Harmon, prin. Fax 399-2404
Paulding MS 300/6-8
405 N Water St 45879 419-399-4656
David Stallkamp, prin. Fax 399-2404

Western Buckeye ESC
PO Box 176 45879 419-399-4711
Brian Gerber, supt. Fax 399-3346
www.wbesc.org/
ACE Academy Alt
PO Box 176 45879 419-399-4649

Peebles, Adams, Pop. 1,762
Adams County/Ohio Valley Local SD
Supt. — See West Union
Peebles HS 500/7-12
25719 State Route 41 45660 937-587-2681
Linda Naylor, prin. Fax 587-5236

Pemberville, Wood, Pop. 1,357
Eastwood Local SD 1,300/K-12
4800 Sugar Ridge Rd 43450 419-833-6411
Brent Welker, supt. Fax 833-4915
www.eastwood.k12.oh.us/
Eastwood HS 500/9-12
4900 Sugar Ridge Rd 43450 419-833-3611
Jeff Hill, prin. Fax 833-6014
Eastwood MS 400/5-8
4800 Sugar Ridge Rd 43450 419-833-6011
John Obrock, prin. Fax 833-7454

Peninsula, Summit, Pop. 560
Woodridge Local SD 2,000/K-12
4411 Quick Rd 44264 330-928-9074
Walter Davis, supt. Fax 928-1542
www.woodridge.k12.oh.us/
Woodridge HS 700/9-12
4440 Quick Rd 44264 330-929-3191
Joel Morgan, prin. Fax 928-5036
Woodridge MS 500/6-8
4451 Quick Rd 44264 330-928-7420
Jesse Hosford, prin. Fax 928-5645

Pepper Pike, Cuyahoga, Pop. 5,884

Ursuline College Post-Sec.
2550 Lander Rd 44124 440-449-4200

Perry, Lake, Pop. 1,647
Perry Local SD 1,800/K-12
4325 Manchester Rd 44081 440-259-3881
Jack Thompson Ph.D., supt. Fax 259-3607
www.perry-lake.org
Perry HS 600/9-12
1 Success Blvd 44081 440-259-3511
Todd Porcello, prin. Fax 259-9290
Perry MS 500/6-8
2 Learning Ln 44081 440-259-3026
Robert Knisely, prin. Fax 259-5149

Perrysburg, Wood, Pop. 20,359
Penta Career Center
9301 Buck Rd 43551 419-666-1120
Ron Matter, supt. Fax 666-6049
www.pentacareercenter.org
Penta Career Center Vo/Tech
9301 Buck Rd 43551 419-666-1120
Jeffrey Kurtz, prin. Fax 666-6049

Perrysburg SD 4,500/K-12
140 E Indiana Ave 43551 419-874-9131
Thomas Hosler, supt. Fax 872-8820
www.perrysburgschools.net
Perrysburg HS 1,300/9-12
13385 Roachton Rd 43551 419-874-3181
Dr. Michael Short, prin. Fax 872-8813
Perrysburg JHS 1,100/6-8
550 E South Boundary St 43551 419-874-9193
Dale Wiltse, prin. Fax 872-8812

Healing Arts Institute Post-Sec.
340 3 Meadows Dr 43551 419-874-4496

Pettisville, Fulton, Pop. 497
Pettisville Local SD 500/PK-12
PO Box 53001 43553 419-446-2705
Stephen Switzer, supt. Fax 445-2992
blackbirds.pettisville.k12.oh.us/
Pettisville JSHS 200/7-12
PO Box 53001 43553 419-446-2705
Michael Lane, prin. Fax 445-2992

Philo, Muskingum, Pop. 726
Franklin Local SD
Supt. — See Duncan Falls
Philo JHS 500/6-8
PO Box 178 43771 740-674-5210
Rob Preston, prin. Fax 674-5217

Pickerington, Fairfield, Pop. 17,708
Pickerington Local SD 10,500/K-12
90 N East St 43147 614-833-2110
Rob Walker, supt. Fax 833-2143
www.pickerington.k12.oh.us
Pickerington HS Central 1,600/9-12
300 Opportunity Way 43147 614-548-1800
Zachary Howard, prin. Fax 548-1810
Pickerington HS North 1,800/9-12
7800 Refugee Rd 43147 614-830-2700
Kiya Hunt, prin. Fax 833-3660
Pickerington Lakeview JHS 900/7-8
12445 Ault Rd 43147 614-830-2200
Jeff Clark, prin. Fax 834-3267
Pickerington Ridgeview JHS 900/7-8
130 Hill Rd S 43147 614-548-1700
Susan Caudill, prin. Fax 548-1710

Piketon, Pike, Pop. 2,150
Pike County Area JVSD
PO Box 577 45661 740-289-2721
Eric Meredith, supt. Fax 289-4243
www.pikectc.org
Rifle Career Technology Center Vo/Tech
PO Box 577 45661 740-289-2721
Shon Tackett, dir. Fax 289-2527

Scioto Valley Local SD 1,400/K-12
PO Box 600 45661 740-289-4456
Dr. Todd Burkitt, supt. Fax 289-3065
www.piketon.k12.oh.us/
Piketon JSHS 600/7-12
1414 Piketon Rd 45661 740-289-2254
Jeff Reuter, prin. Fax 289-1514

Pioneer, Williams, Pop. 1,360
North Central Local SD 600/PK-12
400 E Baubice St 43554 419-737-2392
Kenneth Boyer, supt. Fax 737-3361
www.northcentralschool.org
North Central JSHS 300/7-12
400 E Baubice St 43554 419-737-2366
Fax 737-2531

Piqua, Miami, Pop. 19,922
Piqua CSD 3,500/K-12
719 E Ash St 45356 937-773-4321
Richard Hanes, supt. Fax 778-4518
www.piqua.org
Piqua HS 1,000/9-12
1 Indian Trl 45356 937-773-6314
Anthony Lyons, prin. Fax 778-4514
Piqua JHS 600/7-8
1 Tomahawk Trl 45356 937-778-2997
Jeff Clark, prin. Fax 773-3574

Upper Valley JVSD
8811 Career Dr 45356 937-778-1980
Dr. Nancy Luce, supt. Fax 778-0103
www.uppervalleycc.org
Upper Valley Career Center Vo/Tech
8811 Career Dr 45356 937-778-1980
Jason Haak, dir. Fax 778-4677

Edison State Community College Post-Sec.
1973 Edison Dr 45356 937-778-8600
Piqua Catholic S - North 100/4-8
503 W North St 45356 937-773-1564
Joshua Bornhorst, prin. Fax 773-0380

Plain City, Madison, Pop. 4,160
Jonathan Alder Local SD 2,200/PK-12
9200 US Highway 42 S 43064 614-873-5621
Gary Chapman, supt. Fax 873-8462
www.alder.k12.oh.us
Alder HS 600/9-12
9200 US Highway 42 S 43064 614-873-4642
Phil Harris, prin. Fax 873-4252
Alder JHS 300/7-8
6440 Kilbury Huber Rd 43064 614-873-4635
Chris Piper, prin. Fax 873-0845

Tolles Career & Technical Center
7877 US Highway 42 S 43064 614-873-4666
Kimberly Wilson, supt. Fax 873-8761
www.tollestech.com
Tolles Career & Technical Center Vo/Tech
7877 US Highway 42 S 43064 614-873-4666
Connie Strebe, dir. Fax 873-6909

Pleasant Hill, Miami, Pop. 1,191
Newton Local SD 600/K-12
PO Box 803 45359 937-676-2002
Pat McBride, supt. Fax 676-2054
www.newton.k12.oh.us/
Newton JSHS 200/7-12
PO Box 803 45359 937-676-2002
Danielle Davis, prin. Fax 676-2397

Pleasant Plain, Warren, Pop. 153

Village Christian S 200/PK-12
PO Box 48 45162 513-877-2143

Plymouth, Huron, Pop. 1,844
Plymouth-Shiloh Local SD 700/K-12
365 Sandusky St 44865 419-687-4733
James Metcalf, supt. Fax 687-1541
plymouth.schoolwires.com/plymouth/site/
Plymouth HS 200/9-12
400 Trux St 44865 419-687-8200
John Hart, prin. Fax 687-8175
Shiloh MS 200/6-8
400 Trux St 44865 419-687-8200
Bradley Turson, prin. Fax 687-8175

Poland, Mahoning, Pop. 2,537
Poland Local SD 2,300/K-12
3199 Dobbins Rd 44514 330-757-7000
Donald Dailey, supt. Fax 757-2390
www.polandbulldogs.com/
Poland MS 400/7-8
47 College St 44514 330-757-7003
Mark Covell, prin. Fax 757-2390
Poland Seminary HS 800/9-12
3199 Dobbins Rd 44514 330-757-7018
Kevin Snyder, prin. Fax 757-2390

Pomeroy, Meigs, Pop. 1,809
Meigs Local SD 1,900/K-12
41765 Pomeroy Pike 45769 740-992-2153
Rusty Bookman, supt. Fax 992-7814
www.meigslocalschools.org/
Meigs HS 600/9-12
42091 Pomeroy Pike 45769 740-992-2158
Steve Ohlinger, prin. Fax 992-5839
Meigs MS 400/6-8
42353 Charles Chancey Dr 45769 740-992-3058
Vickie Jones, prin. Fax 992-6952

Port Clinton, Ottawa, Pop. 5,954
Port Clinton CSD 1,700/K-12
811 Jefferson St 43452 419-732-2102
Patrick Adkins, supt. Fax 734-4527
www.pccsd.net/
Port Clinton HS 500/9-12
821 Jefferson St 43452 419-734-2147
Gary Steyer, prin. Fax 734-4276
Port Clinton MS 400/6-8
807 Jefferson St 43452 419-734-4448
Carrie Sanchez, prin. Fax 734-4440

Portsmouth, Scioto, Pop. 19,655
Clay Local SD 300/PK-12
44 Clay High St 45662 740-354-6645
Anthony Mantell, supt. Fax 354-5746
clay.k12.oh.us/
Clay MSHS 300/7-12
44 Clay High St 45662 740-354-6644
Todd Warnock, prin. Fax 354-6105

Portsmouth CSD 2,000/PK-12
724 Findlay St 45662 740-354-5663
Gary Dutey, supt. Fax 355-4496
www.portsmouthtrojans.org
Portsmouth JSHS 700/7-12
1225 Gallia St 45662 740-353-2398
Douglas Poage, prin. Fax 354-3494

Washington-Nile Local SD
Supt. — See West Portsmouth
Portsmouth West HS 400/9-12
15332 US Highway 52 45663 740-858-1103
Anthony Bazler, prin. Fax 858-1110

Notre Dame JSHS 200/7-12
2220 Sunrise Ave 45662 740-353-0719
Kathy Milligan, prin. Fax 353-2526
Paramount Beauty Academy Post-Sec.
PO Box 1444 45662 740-353-2436
Shawnee State University Post-Sec.
940 2nd St 45662 740-351-4778

Powell, Delaware, Pop. 11,313
Olentangy Local SD
Supt. — See Lewis Center
Olentangy Hyatts MS 700/6-8
6885 Sawmill Pkwy 43065 740-657-5400
Kathy McFarland, prin. Fax 657-5499
Olentangy Liberty HS 1,500/9-12
3584 Home Rd 43065 740-657-4200
Randy Wright, prin. Fax 657-4299
Olentangy Liberty MS 800/6-8
7940 Liberty Rd N 43065 740-657-4400
Michelle Blackley, prin. Fax 657-4499

Village Academy 400/PK-12
284 S Liberty St 43065 614-841-0050
Susan Lasley, head sch Fax 841-0501

Proctorville, Lawrence, Pop. 565
Fairland Local SD 1,700/K-12
228 Private Drive 10010 45669 740-886-3100
Roni Hayes, supt. Fax 886-7253
fairland.k12.oh.us/
Fairland HS 500/9-12
812 County Road 411 45669 740-886-3250
Chad Belville, prin. Fax 886-6738
Fairland MS 400/6-8
7875 County Road 107 45669 740-886-3200
Aaron Lewis, prin. Fax 886-5125

Put in Bay, Ottawa, Pop. 138
Put-in-Bay Local SD 100/K-12
PO Box 659 43456 419-285-3614
Steven Poe, supt. Fax 285-2137
www.put-in-bay.k12.oh.us
Put-in-Bay JSHS 50/7-12
PO Box 659 43456 419-285-3614
Steven Poe, supt. Fax 285-2137

Racine, Meigs, Pop. 665
Southern Local SD 700/K-12
920 Elm St 45771 740-949-2669
Tony Deem, supt. Fax 949-3309
www.southernlocalmeigs.org/
Southern HS 200/9-12
920 Elm St 45771 740-949-2611
Daniel Otto, prin. Fax 949-2456

Ravenna, Portage, Pop. 11,455
Maplewood Career Center
7075 State Route 88 44266 330-296-2892
Randy Griffith, supt. Fax 296-5680
www.mwood.cc
Maplewood Career Center Vo/Tech
7075 State Route 88 44266 330-296-2892
Craig Morgan, dir. Fax 296-5680

Ravenna CSD 2,600/K-12
507 E Main St 44266 330-296-9679
Dennis Honkala, supt. Fax 297-4158
www.ravenna.portage.k12.oh.us
Brown MS 700/6-8
228 S Scranton St 44266 330-296-3849
Tara Reis, prin. Fax 297-4146
Ravenna HS 800/9-12
6589 N Chestnut St 44266 330-296-3844
Lorie Marozzi, prin. Fax 296-1855

Southeast Local SD 1,500/K-12
8245 Tallmadge Rd 44266 330-654-5841
Tom Harrison, supt. Fax 654-9110
www.sepirates.org
Southeast HS 600/9-12
8423 Tallmadge Rd 44266 330-654-1960
Robert Dunn, prin. Fax 654-9110
Other Schools – See Diamond

Fortis College Post-Sec.
653 Enterprise Pkwy 44266 330-297-7319

Rawson, Hancock, Pop. 564
Cory-Rawson Local SD 500/K-12
3930 County Road 26 45881 419-963-3415
Robert Hlasko, supt. Fax 963-4400
cory-rawson.k12.oh.us
Cory-Rawson HS 200/7-12
3930 County Road 26 45881 419-963-2611
Mark Willeke, prin. Fax 963-4400

Rayland, Jefferson, Pop. 413
Buckeye Local SD
Supt. — See Dillonvale
Buckeye HS 600/9-12
10692 State Route 150 43943 740-859-2196
Coy Sudvary, prin. Fax 859-2857
Buckeye JHS 7-8
10692 State Route 150 43943 740-859-2196
Grant Williams, prin. Fax 859-2857

Reading, Hamilton, Pop. 10,188
Reading Community CSD 1,600/K-12
1301 Bonnell St 45215 513-554-1800
L. Scott Inskeep, supt. Fax 483-6754
www.readingschools.org
Reading Community HS 400/9-12
810 E Columbia Ave 45215 513-733-4422
Charles LaFata, prin. Fax 483-6766
Reading Community MS 400/6-8
230 Halker Ave 45215 513-842-5151
Robert Longworth, prin. Fax 842-5146

Mt. Notre Dame HS 700/9-12
711 E Columbia Ave 45215 513-821-3044
Larry Mock, hdmstr. Fax 821-6068

Reedsville, Meigs
Eastern Local SD 800/K-12
50008 State Route 681 45772 740-667-6079
Scot Gheen, supt. Fax 667-3978
www.easternlocal.com
Eastern HS 200/9-12
38900 State Route 7 45772 740-985-3329
Shawn Bush, prin. Fax 985-3778
Eastern MS 200/5-8
38850 State Route 7 45772 740-985-3304
Shawn Bush, prin. Fax 985-3304

Reynoldsburg, Franklin, Pop. 34,685
Reynoldsburg CSD 4,500/K-12
7244 E Main St 43068 614-501-1020
Stephen Dackin, supt. Fax 501-1050
www.reyn.org/
Baldwin Road JHS 400/7-8
2300 Baldwin Pl 43068 614-367-1600
Scott Bennett, prin. Fax 367-1625
BELL Academy 9-12
6699 E Livingston Ave 43068 614-501-4000
Erica Dodson, prin.
ENCORE Academy 9-12
8579 Summit Rd 43068 614-501-2300
Katy Myers, prin.
eSTEM Academy 200/9-12
6699 E Livingston Ave 43068 614-501-4000
Marcy Ramond, prin.
HS2 Academy 9-12
6699 E Livingston Ave 43068 614-501-4000
Anne Baldwin, prin. Fax 575-3098
Waggoner Road JHS 600/7-8
360 Waggoner Rd 43068 614-501-5700
Chris Brooks, prin. Fax 501-5700

New Life S of Excellence 50/K-12
PO Box 461 43068 740-919-4526
Dr. Anne Harris, admin.

Richfield, Summit, Pop. 3,610
Revere Local SD 2,800/K-12
3496 Everett Rd 44286 330-666-4155
Randy Boroff, supt. Fax 659-3127
www.revereschools.org/
Other Schools – See Bath

Richmond, Jefferson, Pop. 480
Edison Local SD
Supt. — See Hammondsville
Edison HS 500/7-12
9890 State Route 152 43944 740-765-4313
Matt Morrison, prin. Fax 765-4961

Richmond Heights, Cuyahoga, Pop. 10,347
Richmond Heights Local SD 700/PK-12
447 Richmond Rd 44143 216-692-0086
Robert Moore Ed.D., supt.
www.richmondheightsschools.org
Richmond Heights MSHS 300/7-12
447 Richmond Rd 44143 216-692-0094
Jason Tidmore, prin. Fax 692-8495

Richwood, Union, Pop. 2,209
North Union Local SD 1,500/PK-12
12920 State Route 739 43344 740-943-2509
Dr. Rick Smith, supt. Fax 943-2534
www.n-union.k12.oh.us
North Union HS 400/9-12
401 N Franklin St 43344 740-943-3012
Diana Martin, prin. Fax 943-2046
North Union MS 400/6-8
12555 Mulvane Rd 43344 740-943-2369
Matt Burggraf, prin. Fax 943-9279

Ridgeway, Hardin, Pop. 337
Ridgemont Local SD 600/PK-12
PO Box 86 43345 937-354-2441
Emmy Davis, supt. Fax 354-2194
www.ridgemont.k12.oh.us
Ridgemont JSHS 200/7-12
162 E Hale St 43345 937-363-2701
Joseph Becker, prin. Fax 363-2066

Rio Grande, Gallia, Pop. 808
Gallia-Jackson-Vinton JVSD
PO Box 157 45674 740-245-5334
Daniel Lewis, supt. Fax 245-9465
bhcc.k12.oh.us/
Buckeye Hills Career Center Vo/Tech
PO Box 157 45674 740-245-5334
Daniel Lewis, dir. Fax 245-9465

University of Rio Grande Post-Sec.
218 N College Ave 45674 740-245-5353

Ripley, Brown, Pop. 1,713
Ripley-Union-Lewis-Huntington Local SD 1,100/K-12
PO Box 85 45167 937-392-4396
Linda Naylor, supt. Fax 392-7003
www.ripley.k12.oh.us
Ripley-Union-Lewis-Huntington HS 300/9-12
1317 S 2nd St 45167 937-392-4384
Susie Skinner, prin. Fax 392-7017
Other Schools – See Aberdeen

Rittman, Wayne, Pop. 6,392
Rittman EVD 1,000/K-12
100 Saurer St 44270 330-927-7400
James Ritchie, supt. Fax 927-7405
www.rittman.k12.oh.us/
Rittman HS 300/8-12
50 Saurer St 44270 330-927-7141
Nick Evans, prin. Fax 927-7145

Rockford, Mercer, Pop. 1,102
Parkway Local SD 1,100/PK-12
400 Buckeye St 45882 419-363-3045
Gregory Puthoff, supt. Fax 363-2595
www.parkwayschools.org/
Parkway HS 300/9-12
400 Buckeye St 45882 419-363-3045
Brian Fortkamp, prin. Fax 363-2596
Parkway MS 300/5-8
400 Buckeye St 45882 419-363-3045
Brian Woods, prin. Fax 363-2597

Rocky River, Cuyahoga, Pop. 19,974
Rocky River CSD 2,600/K-12
1101 Morewood Pkwy 44116 440-333-6000
Michael Shoaf, supt. Fax 356-6014
www.rrcs.org
Rocky River HS 900/9-12
20951 Detroit Rd 44116 440-356-6800
Debra Bernard, prin. Fax 331-2189
Rocky River MS 600/6-8
1631 Lakeview Ave 44116 440-356-6870
Megan Rose, prin. Fax 356-6881

Lutheran HS West 400/9-12
3850 Linden Rd 44116 440-333-1660
Dale Wolfgram, prin. Fax 333-1729
Magnificat HS 800/9-12
20770 Hilliard Blvd 44116 440-331-1572
Sr. Carol Smith, pres. Fax 331-7257

Rootstown, Portage
Rootstown Local SD 1,200/K-12
4140 State Route 44 44272 330-325-9911
Andrew Hawkins, supt. Fax 325-4105
rootstown.sparcc.org
Rootstown HS 300/9-12
4140 State Route 44 44272 330-325-7911
Michael Ferguson, prin. Fax 325-8506
Rootstown MS 300/6-8
4140 State Route 44 44272 330-325-9956
Robert Campbell, prin. Fax 325-8505

Northeastern Ohio Medical University Post-Sec.
PO Box 95 44272 800-686-2511

Rossford, Wood, Pop. 6,225
Rossford EVD 1,700/K-12
601 Superior St 43460 419-666-2010
William McFarland, supt. Fax 661-2856
www.rossfordschools.org/
Rossford HS 500/9-12
701 Superior St 43460 419-666-5262
Tony Brashear, prin. Fax 661-2831
Rossford JHS 300/7-8
651 Superior St 43460 419-666-5254
Lester Pierson, prin. Fax 661-2890

Russia, Shelby, Pop. 636
Russia Local SD 500/K-12
100 School St 45363 937-295-3454
Steve Rose, supt. Fax 526-0045
www.russiaschool.org
Russia JSHS 200/7-12
100 School St 45363 937-295-3454
Nicholas Wilker, prin. Fax 526-9519

Sabina, Clinton, Pop. 2,532
East Clinton Local SD 1,400/PK-12
97 Astro Way 45169 937-584-2461
Gary West, supt. Fax 584-2817
www.eastclinton.org/
East Clinton HS 400/9-12
PO Box 19 45169 937-584-2474
Betsy Wyatt, prin. Fax 584-4842
Other Schools – See Lees Creek

Saint Bernard, Hamilton, Pop. 4,269
St. Bernard-Elmwood Place CSD 900/PK-12
105 Washington Ave 45217 513-482-7121
Dr. Mimi Webb, supt. Fax 641-0066
www.sbepschools.org
Saint Bernard-Elmwood Place JSHS 400/7-12
4615 Tower Ave 45217 513-482-7100
Alison Gates, prin. Fax 641-4878

Saint Clairsville, Belmont, Pop. 5,119
Belmont-Harrison Area JVSD
110 Fox Shannon Pl 43950 740-695-9130
Richard Schoene, supt. Fax 695-5340
bhccenters.com
Belmont Career Center Vo/Tech
110 Fox Shannon Pl 43950 740-695-9130
Mike Saffell, prin. Fax 695-5330
Other Schools – See Cadiz

St. Clairsville-Richland CSD 1,600/PK-12
108 Woodrow Ave 43950 740-695-1624
Walter Skaggs, supt. Fax 695-1627
www.stcschools.com
St. Clairsville HS 500/9-12
102 Woodrow Ave 43950 740-695-1584
Walter Skaggs, prin. Fax 695-2513
St. Clairsville MS 500/5-8
104 Woodrow Ave 43950 740-695-1591
Mike McKeever, prin. Fax 695-2317

Belmont College Post-Sec.
120 Fox Shannon Pl 43950 740-695-9500
East Richland Christian S 100/PK-12
67888 Friends Church Rd 43950 740-695-2281
April Woods, admin. Fax 695-9659
Ohio University Post-Sec.
45425 National Rd W 43950 740-695-1720

Saint Henry, Mercer, Pop. 2,423
St. Henry Consolidated Local SD 1,000/K-12
391 E Columbus St 45883 419-678-4834
Rodney Moorman, supt. Fax 678-1724
sthenryschools.org
Saint Henry HS 300/9-12
391 E Columbus St 45883 419-678-4834
Eric Rosenbeck, prin. Fax 678-1724
Saint Henry MS 300/5-8
381 E Columbus St 45883 419-678-4834
Julie Garke, prin. Fax 678-1724

Saint Marys, Auglaize, Pop. 8,208
St. Marys CSD 2,300/K-12
100 W Spring St 45885 419-394-4312
Shawn Brown, supt. Fax 394-5638
sm.k12.oh.us
St. Marys Memorial HS 800/9-12
2250 State Route 66 45885 419-394-4011
Dave Lewis, prin. Fax 394-1932
St. Marys MS 500/6-8
2250 State Route 66 45885 419-394-2112
Mary Miller, prin. Fax 394-1932

Grand Lake Christian S 100/PK-12
1001 Holly St Ste A 45885 419-300-9001
David Wilson, supt. Fax 300-9001

Saint Paris, Champaign, Pop. 2,056
Graham Local SD 2,200/PK-12
370 E Main St 43072 937-663-4123
Norm Glismann, supt. Fax 663-4670
www.grahamlocalschools.org
Graham HS 600/9-12
7800 US Highway 36 43072 937-663-4127
Joe Hurst, prin. Fax 663-0396
Graham MS 500/6-8
9644 US Highway 36 43072 937-663-5339
Adam Kunkle, prin. Fax 663-4674

Salem, Columbiana, Pop. 12,168
Salem CSD 2,100/K-12
1226 E State St 44460 330-332-0316
Tom Bratten, supt. Fax 332-8936
www.salemquakers.org
Salem HS 700/9-12
1200 E 6th St 44460 330-332-8905
Joseph Shivers, prin. Fax 332-8943
Salem JHS 300/7-8
1200 E 6th St 44460 330-332-8914
Sean Kirkland, prin. Fax 332-8923

Allegheny Wesleyan College Post-Sec.
2161 Woodsdale Rd 44460 330-337-6403
Kent State University-Salem Campus Post-Sec.
2491 State Route 45 S 44460 330-332-0361
Salem Wesleyan Academy 100/K-12
1095 Newgarden Ave 44460 330-332-4819
Dan Forrider, prin. Fax 332-4819

Salineville, Columbiana, Pop. 1,294
Southern Local SD 900/K-12
38095 State Route 39 43945 330-679-2343
John Wilson, supt. Fax 679-0193
www.southern.k12.oh.us
Southern Local JSHS 400/7-12
38095 State Route 39 43945 330-679-2305
Dallas Saunders, prin. Fax 679-3005

Sandusky, Erie, Pop. 24,586
Perkins Local SD 2,300/K-12
3714 Campbell St Ste B 44870 419-625-0484
James Gunner Ed.D., supt. Fax 621-2052
www.perkinsschools.org
Briar MS 600/6-8
3700 South Ave 44870 419-625-0132
Stephen Finn, prin. Fax 625-0523
Perkins HS 700/9-12
3714 Campbell St 44870 419-625-1252
Mark Dahlmann, prin. Fax 621-2057

Sandusky CSD 2,900/K-12
407 Decatur St 44870 419-626-6940
Eugene Sanders Ph.D., supt. Fax 621-2784
www.scs-k12.net
Compass Academy Alt
318 Columbus Ave 44870 419-627-3969
Fax 627-3996
Sandusky Career Center Vo/Tech
2130 Hayes Ave 44870 419-984-1000
Nancy Zechman, dir. Fax 621-2893
Sandusky HS 1,000/9-12
2130 Hayes Ave 44870 419-984-1068
Dan Poggiali, prin. Fax 621-2751
Sandusky MS 7-8
2130 Hayes Ave 44870 419-984-1180
Venice Slaughter, prin. Fax 621-2824

Firelands Regional Medical Center Post-Sec.
1912 Hayes Ave 44870 419-557-7110
Ohio Business College Post-Sec.
5202 Timber Commons Dr 44870 419-627-8345
Sandusky Central Catholic HS 200/7-12
410 W Jefferson St 44870 419-626-1892
Mike Savona, prin. Fax 621-2252

Sarahsville, Noble, Pop. 166
Noble Local SD 1,000/PK-12
20977 Zep Rd E 43779 740-732-2084
Daniel Doyle, supt. Fax 732-7669
www.gozeps.org/
Shenandoah HS 300/9-12
49346 Seneca Lake Rd 43779 740-732-2361
Justin Denius, prin. Fax 732-6479

Seaman, Adams, Pop. 934
Adams County/Ohio Valley Local SD
Supt. — See West Union
North Adams HS 500/7-12
96 Green Devil Dr 45679 937-386-2528
Greg Grooms, prin. Fax 386-2888

Sebring, Mahoning, Pop. 4,362
Sebring Local SD 600/K-12
510 N 14th St 44672 330-938-6165
Christopher Lewis, supt. Fax 938-4701
www.sebring.k12.oh.us/
McKinley JSHS 300/7-12
225 E Indiana Ave 44672 330-938-2963
Chris Corbi, prin. Fax 938-4702

Senecaville, Guernsey, Pop. 454
Mid-East Career & Technology Centers
Supt. — See Zanesville
Mid-East Career & Tech Center - Buffalo Vo/Tech
57090 Vocational Rd 43780 740-685-2516
Daniel Coffman, dir. Fax 685-2518

Seven Hills, Cuyahoga, Pop. 11,709
Parma CSD
Supt. — See Parma
Hillside MS 500/7-8
1 Educational Park Dr 44131 440-885-2373
Tiffany Stropko, prin. Fax 885-8448

DeVry University Post-Sec.
4141 Rockside Rd Ste 110 44131 216-328-8754
Hondros College Post-Sec.
4100 Rockside Rd 44131 216-524-1143

Seville, Medina, Pop. 2,268
Cloverleaf Local SD
Supt. — See Lodi
Cloverleaf MS 500/6-8
7500 Buffham Rd 44273 330-721-3607
Jamie Lormeau, admin. Fax 721-3619

Shadyside, Belmont, Pop. 3,765
Shadyside Local SD 800/PK-12
3890 Lincoln Ave 43947 740-676-3121
Terry Brinker, supt. Fax 676-6616
www.shadyside.k12.oh.us
Shadyside JSHS 400/7-12
3890 Lincoln Ave 43947 740-676-3235
John Haswell, prin. Fax 676-6616

Shaker Heights, Cuyahoga, Pop. 27,675
Shaker Heights CSD 5,500/PK-12
15600 Parkland Dr 44120 216-295-1400
Mark Freeman, supt. Fax 295-4340
www.shaker.org
Shaker Heights HS 1,800/9-12
15911 Aldersyde Dr 44120 216-295-4200
Michael Griffith, prin. Fax 295-4277
Shaker Heights MS 900/7-8
20600 Shaker Blvd 44122 216-295-4100
Danny Young, prin. Fax 295-4129

Hathaway Brown S 900/PK-12
19600 N Park Blvd 44122 216-932-4214
William Christ, hdmstr. Fax 371-1501
Laurel S 700/PK-12
1 Lyman Cir 44122 216-464-1441
Ann V. Klotz, head sch Fax 464-8995

Sharonville, Hamilton, Pop. 13,127

Miami-Jacobs Career College Post-Sec.
2 Crowne Pointe Ct Ste 100 45241 866-324-4375

Sheffield Lake, Lorain, Pop. 8,982
Sheffield-Sheffield Lake CSD 1,900/K-12
1824 Harris Rd 44054 440-949-6181
Will Folger, supt. Fax 949-4204
www.sheffield.k12.oh.us
Other Schools – See Sheffield Vlg

Sheffield Vlg, Lorain
Sheffield-Sheffield Lake CSD
Supt. — See Sheffield Lake
Brookside HS 600/9-12
1812 Harris Rd 44054 440-949-4220
Michael Cook, prin. Fax 949-4204
Sheffield MS 400/6-8
1919 Harris Rd 44054 440-949-4228
James Kohler, prin. Fax 949-4204

Ohio Business College Post-Sec.
5095 Waterford Dr 44035 888-514-3126

Shelby, Richland, Pop. 9,228
Pioneer Career & Technology Center
27 Ryan Rd 44875 419-347-7926
Glenna Cannon, supt. Fax 347-4709
www.pctc.k12.oh.us/
Pioneer Career & Technology Center Vo/Tech
27 Ryan Rd 44875 419-347-7744
Fax 347-4977

Shelby CSD 1,500/K-12
PO Box 31 44875 419-342-3520
Tim Tarvin, supt. Fax 347-3586
www.shelbyk12.org
Shelby HS 600/9-12
1 Whippet Way 44875 419-342-5065
John Gies, prin. Fax 342-5095
Shelby MS 300/7-8
109 W Smiley Ave 44875 419-347-5451
Jeff Eichorn, prin. Fax 347-2095

Sherrodsville, Carroll, Pop. 303
Conotton Valley Union Local SD 400/K-12
PO Box 187 44675 740-269-2000
Adam Pittis, supt. Fax 269-7901
www.conottonvalley.k12.oh.us
Other Schools – See Bowerston

Sherwood, Defiance, Pop. 819
Central Local SD 1,100/K-12
6289 US Highway 127 43556 419-658-2808
Vicki L. Brunn, supt. Fax 658-4010
www.centrallocal.org
Fairview HS 300/9-12
6289 US Highway 127 43556 419-658-2378
Troy Merillat, prin. Fax 658-4011
Fairview MS 300/6-8
6289 US Highway 127 43556 419-658-2331
Robert Lloyd, prin. Fax 658-4010

Sidney, Shelby, Pop. 20,551
Fairlawn Local SD 500/K-12
18800 Johnston Rd 45365 937-492-1974
Steve Mascho, supt. Fax 492-8613
www.fairlawn.k12.oh.us
Fairlawn MSHS 200/7-12
18800 Johnston Rd 45365 937-492-5930
Jo DeMotte, prin. Fax 492-5225

Sidney CSD 3,500/K-12
750 S 4th Ave 45365 937-497-2200
John Scheu, supt. Fax 497-2211
www.sidney.k12.oh.us
Sidney HS 1,000/9-12
1215 Campbell Rd 45365 937-497-2238
Jon Geuy, prin. Fax 497-2216
Sidney MS 800/6-8
980 Fair Rd 45365 937-497-2225
Diane Voress, prin. Fax 497-2204

Christian Academy S 200/K-12
2151 W Russell Rd 45365 937-492-7556
Mary Smith, supt. Fax 492-5399
Lehman HS 200/9-12
2400 Saint Marys Rd 45365 937-498-1161
Denise Stauffer, prin. Fax 492-9877

Smithville, Wayne, Pop. 1,248
Green Local SD 1,200/K-12
PO Box 438 44677 330-669-3921
Judith Robinson, supt. Fax 669-2121
www.green-local.k12.oh.us/
Greene MS 400/5-8
PO Box 367 44677 330-669-2751
Jason DeMassimo, prin. Fax 669-2069
Smithville HS 300/9-12
PO Box 156 44677 330-669-3165
Tim Keib, prin. Fax 669-2999

Wayne County JVSD 330-669-7000
518 W Prospect St 44677 Fax 669-7001
Kip Crain, supt.
www.wcscc.org
Wayne County Schools Career Center Vo/Tech
518 W Prospect St 44677 330-669-7000
Matt Brown, prin. Fax 669-7001

Wooster CSD
Supt. — See Wooster
Boys Village S 100/Alt
PO Box 518 44677 330-262-3442
Joseph Kacsandi, prin. Fax 202-3890

Solon, Cuyahoga, Pop. 23,009
Solon CSD 5,200/PK-12
33800 Inwood Dr 44139 440-248-1600
Joseph Regano, supt. Fax 248-7665
www.solonschools.org
Solon HS 1,800/9-12
33600 Inwood Dr 44139 440-349-6230
Erin Short, prin. Fax 349-8041
Solon MS 800/7-8
6835 Som Center Rd 44139 440-349-3848
Eugenia Robinson-Green, prin. Fax 349-8034

South Amherst, Lorain, Pop. 1,662
Firelands Local SD 1,800/K-12
112 N Lake St 44001 440-965-5821
Dr. Robert Hill, supt. Fax 986-5990
www.firelandsschools.org/
South Amherst MS 500/6-8
152 W Main St 44001 440-986-7021
Leo Spagnola, prin. Fax 986-7022
Other Schools – See Oberlin

South Charleston, Clark, Pop. 1,672
Southeastern Local SD 700/K-12
226 Clifton Rd 45368 888-627-6745
David Shea, supt. Fax 650-9129
www.sels.us
Southeastern HS 200/9-12
PO Box Z 45368 937-462-8308
P.J. Bertemes, prin. Fax 462-8394
Southeastern JHS 7-8
PO Box Z 45368 937-462-8308
P.J. Bertemes, prin. Fax 462-8394

Southington, Trumbull
Southington Local SD 600/K-12
2482 State Route 534 44470 330-898-7480
John McMahan, supt. Fax 898-4828
www.southington.k12.oh.us/
Chalker HS 100/9-12
2482 State Route 534 44470 330-898-1781
Amy Burzanko, prin. Fax 898-4828
Southington MS 200/5-8
2482 State Route 534 44470 330-898-1781
Amy Burzanko, prin. Fax 898-4828

South Point, Lawrence, Pop. 3,885
South Point Local SD 1,800/K-12
302 High St 45680 740-377-4315
Ken Cook, supt. Fax 377-9735
www.southpoint.k12.oh.us
South Point HS 400/9-12
983 County Road 60 45680 740-377-4323
Jayshree Shah, prin. Fax 377-4326
South Point MS 400/6-8
983 County Road 60 45680 740-377-4343
T.J. Howard, prin. Fax 377-3228

Tri-State Bible College Post-Sec.
506 Margaret St 45680 740-377-2520

South Vienna, Clark, Pop. 375
Northeastern Local SD
Supt. — See Springfield
South Vienna MS 400/6-8
140 W Main St 45369 937-568-4765
Ted Williams, prin. Fax 568-4988

South Webster, Scioto, Pop. 856
Bloom-Vernon Local SD 900/K-12
PO Box 237 45682 740-778-2281
Rick Carrington, supt. Fax 778-2526
www.bv.k12.oh.us/
South Webster JSHS 400/7-12
PO Box 100 45682 740-778-2320
Robert Johnson, prin. Fax 778-3227

Spencerville, Allen, Pop. 2,168
Spencerville Local SD 900/K-12
600 School St 45887 419-647-4111
Joel Hatfield, supt. Fax 647-6498
www.spencervillebearcats.com

Spencerville HS 200/9-12
2500 Wisher Dr 45887 419-647-4111
Scott Gephart, prin. Fax 647-5124
Spencerville MS 300/5-8
2500 Wisher Dr 45887 419-647-4112
Dennis Fuge, prin. Fax 647-5124

Springboro, Warren, Pop. 17,124
Springboro Community CSD 5,600/K-12
1685 S Main St 45066 937-748-3960
Todd Petrey, supt. Fax 748-3956
www.springboro.org
Springboro HS 1,500/9-12
1675 S Main St 45066 937-748-3950
Dr. Ron Malone, prin. Fax 748-3983
Springboro JHS 900/7-8
1605 S Main St 45066 937-748-3953
Andrea Cook, prin. Fax 748-3964

Miami-Jacobs Career College Post-Sec.
875 W Central Ave 45066 937-806-1000

Springfield, Clark, Pop. 58,259
Clark-Shawnee Local SD 2,000/K-12
3680 Selma Rd 45502 937-328-5378
Gregg Morris, supt. Fax 328-5379
www.clark-shawnee.k12.oh.us/
Shawnee HS 600/9-12
1675 E Possum Rd 45502 937-325-9296
Nathan Dockter, prin. Fax 328-5389

Greenon Local SD
Supt. — See Enon
Greenon HS 600/9-12
3950 S Tecumseh Rd 45502 937-340-6372
Rick Newsock, prin. Fax 340-6371

Northeastern Local SD 3,600/K-12
1414 Bowman Rd 45502 937-325-7615
Louis Kramer, supt. Fax 328-6592
www.nelsd.org/
Kenton Ridge HS 700/9-12
4444 Middle Urbana Rd 45503 937-390-1274
John Hill, prin. Fax 390-0013
Northeastern HS 500/9-12
1480 Bowman Rd 45502 937-328-6575
Chris James, prin. Fax 328-6581
Northridge MS 500/6-8
4445 Ridgewood Rd E 45503 937-399-2852
Gregory Stickel, prin. Fax 342-4631
Other Schools – See South Vienna

Northwestern Local SD 1,800/PK-12
5610 Troy Rd 45502 937-964-1318
Anthony Orr, supt. Fax 964-6019
www.northwestern.k12.oh.us
Northwestern HS 500/9-12
5650 Troy Rd 45502 937-964-1324
Lori Swafford, prin. Fax 964-6006
Northwestern MS 600/5-8
5610 Troy Rd 45502 937-964-1391
J.M. Gerberick, prin. Fax 964-6003

Springfield CSD 7,400/PK-12
1500 W Jefferson St 45506 937-505-2800
David Estrop Ph.D., supt. Fax 328-6855
www.spr.k12.oh.us
Hayward MS 400/7-8
1700 Clifton Ave 45505 937-505-4190
Susie Samuels, prin. Fax 323-9812
Keifer Alternative Center 200/Alt
601 Selma Rd 45505 937-505-4120
Gary Cross, prin. Fax 323-8785
Roosevelt MS 400/7-8
721 E Home Rd 45503 937-505-4370
Monte Brigham, prin. Fax 342-0280
Schaefer MS 300/7-8
147 S Fostoria Ave 45505 937-505-4390
Dean Lynch, prin. Fax 325-8974
Springfield HS 1,800/9-12
701 E Home Rd 45503 937-342-4320
Jonathan Kuehnle, prin. Fax 342-4110

Springfield-Clark Career Technology Ctr
1901 Selma Rd 45505 937-325-7368
Rick Smith, supt. Fax 325-7452
www.scctc.org
Springfield-Clark Career Technology Ctr Vo/Tech
1901 Selma Rd 45505 937-325-7368
Rick Smith, supt. Fax 325-7452

Carousel Beauty College Post-Sec.
1475 Upper Valley Pike #956 45504 937-323-0277
Catholic Central JSHS 400/7-12
1200 E High St 45505 937-325-9204
Patrick Finneran, prin. Fax 328-7426
Clark State Community College Post-Sec.
570 E Leffel Ln 45505 937-325-0691
Emmanuel Christian Academy 400/PK-12
2177 Emmanuel Way 45502 937-390-3777
Dr. G.B. Simon, supt. Fax 390-0966
Nightingale Montessori S 100/PK-12
1106 E High St 45505 937-324-0336
Nancy Schwab, prin. Fax 398-0086
Wittenberg University Post-Sec.
PO Box 720 45501 937-327-6231

Steubenville, Jefferson, Pop. 18,007
Steubenville CSD 2,400/PK-12
PO Box 189 43952 740-283-3767
Mike McVey, supt. Fax 283-8930
scs.steubenville.k12.oh.us
Harding MS 700/5-8
2002 Sunset Blvd 43952 740-282-3481
Joe Yanok, prin. Fax 283-8949
Steubenville HS 600/9-12
420 N 4th St 43952 740-282-9741
Shawn Crosier, prin. Fax 283-8943

Bishop John King Mussio Central JHS 7-8
320 Westview Ave Ste 2 43952 740-346-0028
Theresa Danaher, prin. Fax 346-0070
Catholic Central HS 300/9-12
320 Westview Ave Ste 1 43952 740-264-5538
Richard Wilinski, prin. Fax 264-5443
Eastern Gateway Community College Post-Sec.
4000 Sunset Blvd 43952 740-264-5591
Franciscan University of Steubenville Post-Sec.
1235 University Blvd 43952 800-783-6220
Ohio Valley Hospital Post-Sec.
1 Ross Park Blvd 43952 740-283-7273
Trinity Medical Center East Post-Sec.
380 Summit Ave 43952 740-283-7213

Stewart, Athens, Pop. 244
Federal Hocking Local SD 1,000/PK-12
PO Box 117 45778 740-662-6691
Dr. George Wood, supt. Fax 662-5065
www.fedhock.com
Federal Hocking HS 300/9-12
8461 State Route 144 45778 740-662-6691
Dr. George Wood, prin. Fax 662-3805
Federal Hocking MS 200/7-8
8461 State Route 144 45778 740-662-6691
Dr. George Wood, prin. Fax 662-5065

Stow, Summit, Pop. 34,347
Stow-Munroe Falls CSD 5,600/PK-12
4350 Allen Rd 44224 330-689-5445
Dr. Russell Jones, supt. Fax 688-1629
www.smfcsd.org
Stow-Munroe Falls HS 1,900/9-12
3227 Graham Rd 44224 330-689-5300
Chris DiMauro, prin. Fax 678-3899
Other Schools – See Munroe Falls

National College Post-Sec.
3855 Fishcreek Rd 44224 330-676-1351

Strasburg, Tuscarawas, Pop. 2,588
Strasburg-Franklin Local SD 600/K-12
140 N Bodmer Ave 44680 330-878-5571
Curtis Clough, supt. Fax 878-7900
www.strasburg.k12.oh.us/
Strasburg-Franklin HS 300/6-12
140 N Bodmer Ave 44680 330-878-5571
Robert Hartline, prin. Fax 878-7900

Streetsboro, Portage, Pop. 15,768
Streetsboro CSD 2,100/PK-12
9000 Kirby Ln 44241 330-626-4900
Lisa Shannon, dir. Fax 626-8102
www.streetsboroschools.com
Streetsboro HS 600/9-12
1900 Annalane Dr 44241 330-626-4902
Eric Rauschkolb, prin. Fax 626-8103
Streetsboro MS 300/7-8
1951 Annalane Dr 44241 330-626-4905
Steve Hatch, prin. Fax 626-8104

Strongsville, Cuyahoga, Pop. 44,134
Strongsville CSD 6,800/PK-12
13200 Pearl Rd 44136 440-572-7000
John Krupinski, supt. Fax 572-7041
strongnet.org
Albion MS 500/7-8
11109 Webster Rd 44136 440-572-7070
David Riley, prin. Fax 572-7079
Center MS 600/7-8
13200 Pearl Rd 44136 440-572-7090
Jennifer Pelko, prin. Fax 572-7094
Strongsville HS 2,500/9-12
20025 Lunn Rd 44149 440-572-7100
William Steffen, prin. Fax 572-7107

ITT Technical Institute Post-Sec.
14955 W Sprague Rd 44136 440-234-9091

Struthers, Mahoning, Pop. 10,554
Struthers CSD 1,900/K-12
99 Euclid Ave 44471 330-750-1061
Robert Rostan, supt. Fax 750-5516
www.strutherscityschools.org
Struthers HS 600/9-12
111 Euclid Ave 44471 330-750-1062
Joseph Fuline, prin. Fax 755-4525
Struthers MS 600/5-8
800 5th St 44471 330-750-1064
Peter Pirone, prin. Fax 755-4749

Stryker, Williams, Pop. 1,320
Stryker Local SD 400/K-12
400 S Defiance St 43557 419-682-6961
Nathaniel Johnson, supt. Fax 682-2646
www.stryker.k12.oh.us
Stryker JSHS 200/7-12
400 S Defiance St 43557 419-682-4591
Denise Meyer, prin. Fax 682-3508

Sugarcreek, Tuscarawas, Pop. 2,197
Garaway Local SD 1,200/K-12
146 Dover Rd NW 44681 330-852-2421
Teresa Alberts, supt. Fax 852-2991
www.garaway.org
Garaway HS 300/9-12
146 Dover Rd NW 44681 330-852-4292
Jason Phillips, prin. Fax 852-4382
Garaway MS 200/7-8
146 Dover Rd NW 44681 330-852-3418
Jason Phillips, prin. Fax 852-3213

Sugar Grove, Fairfield, Pop. 424
Berne Union Local SD 600/K-12
PO Box 187 43155 740-746-8341
Dale Dickson, supt. Fax 746-9824
www.buschools.com/
Berne Union HS 300/7-12
PO Box 187 43155 740-746-9956
Steve House, prin. Fax 746-9824

Sullivan, Ashland
Black River Local SD 1,500/PK-12
257A County Road 40 44880 419-736-3300
Janice Wyckoff, supt. Fax 736-3308
www.blackriver.k12.oh.us/
Black River HS 400/9-12
233 County Road 40 44880 419-736-3303
Martin Yoder, prin. Fax 736-3302
Black River MS 300/6-8
257 County Road 40 44880 419-736-3304
Cathy Aviles, prin. Fax 736-3309

Sunbury, Delaware, Pop. 4,313
Big Walnut Local SD 2,500/PK-12
105 Baughman St Ste A 43074 740-965-3010
Steve Mazzi, supt. Fax 965-4688
www.bigwalnut.k12.oh.us/
Big Walnut HS 900/9-12
555 S Old 3C Rd 43074 740-965-3766
Steve Fujii, prin. Fax 965-1954
Big Walnut MS 400/7-8
777 Cheshire Rd 43074 740-965-3006
Penny Sturtevant, prin. Fax 965-6471

Swanton, Fulton, Pop. 3,658
Swanton Local SD 1,300/K-12
108 N Main St 43558 419-826-7085
Lester Schultz, supt. Fax 825-1197
www.swanton.k12.oh.us
Swanton HS 400/9-12
601 N Main St 43558 419-826-3045
Steve Gfell, prin. Fax 826-1611
Swanton MS 300/6-8
206 Cherry St 43558 419-826-4016
Ted Haselman, prin. Fax 826-5176

Sycamore, Wyandot, Pop. 857
Mohawk Local SD 900/K-12
605 State Highway 231 44882 419-927-2414
Ken Ratliff, supt. Fax 927-2393
www.mohawklocal.org
Mohawk HS 400/7-12
605 State Highway 231 44882 419-927-6292
Brett Graham, prin. Fax 927-6297

Sylvania, Lucas, Pop. 18,670
Sylvania CSD 7,500/K-12
4747 N Holland Sylvania Rd 43560 419-824-8500
Bradley Rieger Ph.D., supt. Fax 824-8503
www.sylvaniaschools.org
Arbor Hills JHS 600/6-8
5334 Whiteford Rd 43560 419-824-8640
Rose Gaiffe, prin. Fax 824-8659
McCord JHS 600/6-8
4304 N McCord Rd 43560 419-824-8650
Keith Limes, prin. Fax 824-8619
Northview HS 1,200/9-12
5403 Silica Dr 43560 419-824-8570
Steve Swaggerty, prin. Fax 824-8698
Southview HS 1,300/9-12
7225 Sylvania Ave 43560 419-824-8580
Dave McMurray, prin. Fax 824-8678
Timberstone JHS 600/6-8
9000 Sylvania Ave 43560 419-824-8680
Mike Bader, prin. Fax 824-8690

Lourdes University Post-Sec.
6832 Convent Blvd 43560 419-885-3211
Toledo Islamic Academy 200/PK-12
5225 Alexis Rd 43560 419-882-3339
Fax 882-3334

Tallmadge, Summit, Pop. 17,273
Tallmadge CSD 2,100/K-12
486 East Ave 44278 330-633-3291
Jeffrey Ferguson, supt. Fax 633-5331
www.tallmadgeschools.org
Tallmadge HS 900/9-12
140 N Munroe Rd 44278 330-633-5505
Rebecca Decapua, prin. Fax 475-0567
Tallmadge MS 600/6-8
484 East Ave 44278 330-633-4994
Rob Kearns, prin. Fax 630-5984

The Plains, Athens, Pop. 2,987
Athens CSD 2,500/K-12
25 S Plains Rd 45780 740-797-4544
Carl Martin, supt. Fax 797-2486
athenscity.k12.oh.us/
Athens HS 700/9-12
1 High School Rd 45780 740-797-4521
Mike Meek, prin. Fax 797-1421
Other Schools – See Athens

Thompson, Geauga
Ledgemont Local SD 500/K-12
16200 Burrows Rd 44086 440-298-3341
Julie Ramos, supt. Fax 298-3342
www.ledgemontschools.org
Ledgemont JSHS 200/7-12
16700 Thompson Rd 44086 440-298-3343
Jennifer Catanese, prin. Fax 298-1481

Thornville, Perry, Pop. 982
Northern Local SD 2,300/K-12
8700 Sheridan Dr 43076 740-743-1303
Thomas Perkins, supt. Fax 743-3301
nlsd.k12.oh.us
Sheridan HS 700/9-12
8725 Sheridan Dr 43076 740-743-1335
Chris King, prin. Fax 743-3311
Sheridan MS 500/6-8
8660 Sheridan Dr 43076 740-743-1315
Jay Hickman, prin. Fax 743-3319

Tiffin, Seneca, Pop. 17,722
Tiffin CSD 1,800/K-12
244 S Monroe St 44883 419-447-2515
Donald Coletta, supt. Fax 448-5202
www.tiffin.k12.oh.us
Columbian HS 800/9-12
300 S Monroe St 44883 419-447-6331
Mark Verroco, prin. Fax 448-5252
Tiffin MS 600/6-8
103 Shepherd Dr 44883 419-447-3358
Robert Boes, prin. Fax 448-5250

Vanguard-Sentinel JVSD
Supt. — See Fremont
Sentinel Career Center Vo/Tech
793 E Township Road 201 44883 419-448-1212
Elissa Heal, prin. Fax 447-2544

Calvert HS 200/9-12
152 Madison St 44883 419-447-3844
Dominic Helmstetter, prin. Fax 447-2922
Heidelberg University Post-Sec.
310 E Market St 44883 419-448-2000
Tiffin Academy of Hair Design Post-Sec.
104 E Market St 44883 419-447-3117
Tiffin University Post-Sec.
155 Miami St 44883 800-968-6446

Tipp City, Miami, Pop. 9,564
Bethel Local SD 900/K-12
7490 State Route 201 45371 937-845-9414
Larry Smith, supt. Fax 845-5007
www.bethel.k12.oh.us
Bethel HS 300/9-12
7490 State Route 201 45371 937-845-9487
John Zigler, prin. Fax 845-5007
Bethel JHS 200/7-8
7490 State Route 201 45371 937-845-9430
Fax 845-5007

Tipp City EVD 2,200/K-12
90 S Tippecanoe Dr 45371 937-667-8444
John Kronour Ph.D., supt. Fax 667-6886
www.tippcityschools.com/
Tippecanoe HS 800/9-12
615 E Kessler Cowlesville 45371 937-667-8448
Belinda Banks, prin. Fax 667-0912
Tippecanoe MS 600/6-8
555 N Hyatt St 45371 937-667-8454
Greg Southers, prin. Fax 667-0874

Toledo, Lucas, Pop. 278,478
ESC of Lake Erie West 100/
2275 Collingwood Blvd 43620 419-245-4150
Sandra C. Frisch, supt. Fax 245-4186
www.esclakeeriewest.org
Alternate Learning Center Alt
3939 Wrenwood Rd 43623 419-473-3442
Mike Smurr, prin. Fax 473-3445
Other Schools – See Oregon

Toledo CSD 22,700/PK-12
420 E Manhattan Blvd 43608 419-671-8200
Dr. Jerry Pecko, supt. Fax 671-8425
www.tps.org
Bowsher HS 1,400/9-12
2200 Arlington Ave 43614 419-671-2000
Linda Meyers, prin. Fax 671-2060
Natural Science Technology Center Vo/Tech
5561 Elmer Dr 43615 419-537-1198
Fax 534-5819
Rogers HS 900/9-12
222 McTigue Dr 43615 419-671-1000
Jack Renz, prin. Fax 671-1060
Scott HS 300/9-12
2400 Collingwood Blvd 43620 419-671-4000
Treva Jeffries, admin. Fax 671-4052
Start HS 1,400/9-12
2010 Tremainsville Rd 43613 419-671-3000
Edward Perozek, prin. Fax 671-3060
Toledo Early College HS 200/9-12
2225 Nebraska Ave 43607 419-530-3003
Dr. Robin Wheatley, prin. Fax 530-3040
Toledo Technology Academy Vo/Tech
3301 Upton Ave 43613 419-671-3900
Gary Thompson, dir. Fax 479-3192
Waite HS 1,200/9-12
301 Morrison Dr 43605 419-671-7000
David Yenrick, prin. Fax 671-7060
Woodward HS 800/9-12
701 E Central Ave 43608 419-671-6000
Emilio Ramirez, prin. Fax 671-6050
Adult Education Center Adult
3281 Upton Ave 43613 419-671-8700
Fax 671-8704

Washington Local SD 5,600/PK-12
3505 W Lincolnshire Blvd 43606 419-473-8220
Patrick Hickey, supt. Fax 473-8200
www.wls4kids.org
Career & Tech Center Vo/Tech
5719 Clegg Dr 43613 419-473-8339
Debra Heban, dir. Fax 473-8309
Jefferson JHS 50/8-8
5530 Whitmer Dr 43613 419-473-8482
Scott Scharf, prin. Fax 473-8393
Whitmer HS 2,100/9-12
5601 Clegg Dr 43613 419-473-8490
Kristine Martin, prin. Fax 473-8461

Central Catholic HS 1,100/9-12
2550 Cherry St 43608 419-255-2280
Michael Kaucher, prin. Fax 259-2848
Davis College Post-Sec.
4747 Monroe St 43623 419-473-2700
Emmanuel Christian S 400/K-12
4607 W Laskey Rd 43623 419-885-3558
Robert Flamm, admin. Fax 885-0139
Lincoln College of Technology Post-Sec.
5203 Airport Hwy 43615 419-389-4725
Maumee Valley Country Day S 500/PK-12
1715 S Reynolds Rd 43614 419-381-1313
Gary Boehm, hdmstr. Fax 381-8341
Mercy College of Ohio Post-Sec.
2221 Madison Ave 43604 419-251-1313
Notre Dame Academy 600/7-12
3535 W Sylvania Ave 43623 419-475-9359
Kim Grilliot, prin. Fax 725-1262
Owens Community College Post-Sec.
PO Box 10000 43699 567-661-7000
Professional Skills Institute Post-Sec.
5115 Glendale Ave 43614 419-720-6670
Riverside Hospital Post-Sec.
3404 W Sylvania Ave 43623 419-729-6059
St. Francis De Sales HS 600/9-12
2323 W Bancroft St 43607 419-531-1618
Eric Smola, prin. Fax 531-9740
St. John's Jesuit Academy 100/7-8
5901 Airport Hwy 43615 419-865-5743
Dr. Bryon Borgelt, prin. Fax 861-5002
St. John's Jesuit HS 800/9-12
5901 Airport Hwy 43615 419-865-5743
Brad Bonham, prin. Fax 861-5002
St. Ursula Academy 500/6-12
4025 Indian Rd 43606 419-531-1693
Nichole Flores, prin. Fax 534-5777
Toledo Christian S 600/PK-12
2303 Brookford Dr 43614 419-389-8700
Jeff Gagle, admin. Fax 389-8704
University of Toledo Post-Sec.
2801 W Bancroft St 43606 419-530-4636

Tontogany, Wood, Pop. 367
Otsego Local SD 800/PK-12
PO Box 290 43565 419-823-4381
Adam Koch, supt. Fax 823-3035
www.otsegoknights.org
Otsego HS 500/9-12
PO Box 290 43565 419-823-4381
Kevin O'Shea, prin. Fax 823-1397
Otsego JHS 400/6-8
PO Box 290 43565 419-823-4381
Mike Wiley, prin. Fax 832-2803

Toronto, Jefferson, Pop. 5,027
Toronto CSD 500/PK-12
1307 Dennis Way 43964 740-537-2456
Fred Burns, supt. Fax 537-1102
www.torontocityschools.k12.oh.us
Toronto HS 300/6-12
300 Myers St 43964 740-537-2442
Maureen Taggart, prin. Fax 537-1102

Trenton, Butler, Pop. 11,671
Edgewood CSD 2,700/PK-12
3440 Busenbark Rd 45067 513-863-4692
Doug Lantz, supt. Fax 867-7421
www.edgewoodschools.com
Edgewood HS 900/9-12
3445 Busenbark Rd 45067 513-867-6300
Russ Fussnecker, prin. Fax 867-6341
Edgewood MS 900/6-8
3045 Busenbark Rd 45067 513-867-7425
Bob Buchheim, prin. Fax 867-7428

Trotwood, Montgomery, Pop. 23,764
Trotwood-Madison CSD 1,400/PK-12
3594 N Snyder Rd 45426 937-854-3050
Kevin Bell, supt. Fax 854-3057
www.trotwood.k12.oh.us/
Trotwood-Madison HS 900/7-12
4440 N Union Rd 45426 937-854-4908
Terry Logan, prin. Fax 854-0594

Troy, Miami, Pop. 24,463
Troy CSD 4,400/K-12
500 N Market St 45373 937-332-6700
Eric Herman, admin. Fax 332-6771
www.troy.k12.oh.us
Troy HS 1,200/9-12
151 Staunton Rd 45373 937-332-6710
William Overla, admin. Fax 332-6738
Troy JHS 700/7-8
556 Adams St 45373 937-332-6720
Dave Dilbone, admin. Fax 332-3812

Hobart Institute of Welding Technology Post-Sec.
400 Trade Sq E 45373 800-332-9448
Miami-Jacobs Career College Post-Sec.
865 W Market St 45373 888-657-9551
Troy Christian HS 300/7-12
700 S Dorset Rd 45373 937-339-5692
Dr. Gary Wilber, supt. Fax 335-6258

Tuscarawas, Tuscarawas, Pop. 1,051
Indian Valley Local SD
Supt. — See Gnadenhutten
Indian Valley MS 400/6-8
PO Box 356 44682 740-922-4226
Brent Carter, prin. Fax 922-2493

Twinsburg, Summit, Pop. 18,443
Twinsburg CSD 4,300/PK-12
11136 Ravenna Rd 44087 330-486-2000
Kathryn Powers, supt. Fax 425-7216
www.twinsburg.k12.oh.us
Chamberlin MS 700/7-8
10270 Ravenna Rd 44087 330-486-2281
Belinda Scott, prin. Fax 963-8313
Twinsburg HS 1,400/9-12
10084 Ravenna Rd 44087 330-486-2400
Louise Teringo, prin. Fax 405-7406

The Ohio Academy Post-Sec.
10735 Ravenna Rd Ste 3 44087 330-282-3312

Uhrichsville, Tuscarawas, Pop. 5,330
Claymont CSD
Supt. — See Dennison
Claymont HS 600/9-12
4205 Indian Hill Rd SE 44683 740-922-3471
Scott Golec, prin. Fax 922-1031
Claymont JHS 300/7-8
215 E 6th St 44683 740-922-5241
Brian Watkins, prin. Fax 922-7330

Union City, Darke, Pop. 1,628
Mississinawa Valley Local SD 700/K-12
1469 State Road 47 E 45390 937-968-5656
Lisa Wendel, supt. Fax 968-6731
www.mississinawa.k12.oh.us
Mississinawa Valley JSHS 300/7-12
10480 Staudt Rd 45390 937-968-4464
Jeffrey Winchester, prin. Fax 968-3434

Uniontown, Stark, Pop. 3,274
Green Local SD 3,700/PK-12
1755 Town Park Blvd 44685 330-896-7500
Michael Nutter, supt. Fax 896-7580
www.greenlocalschools.org
Green HS 1,300/9-12
1474 Boettler Rd 44685 330-896-7575
Cindy Brown, prin. Fax 896-7550
Green MS 700/7-8
1711 Steese Rd 44685 330-896-7710
Jeffrey Miller, prin. Fax 896-7760

Lake Local SD 3,600/K-12
11936 King Church Ave NW 44685 330-877-9383
Jeff Wendorf, supt. Fax 877-4754
www.lakelocal.org
Lake HS 1,200/9-12
1025 Lake Center St NW 44685 330-877-4282
Kevin Tobin, prin. Fax 877-0853
Other Schools – See Hartville

Portage Lakes JVSD
4401 Shriver Rd 44685 330-896-8200
Benjamin Moore, supt. Fax 896-8297
www.plcc.edu/
Portage Lakes Career Center Vo/Tech
4401 Shriver Rd 44685 330-896-8200
Michael Kaschak, prin. Fax 896-8297

Hondros College Post-Sec.
1505 Crprt Woods Pky #100 44685 330-896-9666

University Heights, Cuyahoga, Pop. 13,323
Cleveland Hts - University Hts CSD 6,000/PK-12
2155 Miramar Blvd 44118 216-371-7171
Douglas Heuer, supt. Fax 397-3880
www.chuh.org
Wiley MS 400/6-8
2181 Miramar Blvd 44118 216-371-7270
Dr. Octavia Reid, prin. Fax 397-5968
Other Schools – See Cleveland Heights

Upper Arlington, Franklin, Pop. 33,225
Upper Arlington CSD 5,600/K-12
1950 N Mallway Dr 43221 614-487-5000
Paul Imhoff, supt. Fax 487-5012
www.uaschools.org
Hastings MS 600/6-8
1850 Hastings Ln 43220 614-487-5100
Robb Gonda, prin. Fax 487-5116
Jones MS 600/6-8
2100 Arlington Ave 43221 614-487-5080
Shelly Hughes, prin. Fax 487-5307
Upper Arlington HS 1,800/9-12
1650 Ridgeview Rd 43221 614-487-5200
Ryan McClure, prin. Fax 487-5238

Upper Sandusky, Wyandot, Pop. 6,540
Upper Sandusky EVD 1,700/K-12
800 N Sandusky Ave Ste A 43351 419-294-2307
Michael Eaglowski, supt. Fax 294-6891
www.uppersandusky.k12.oh.us
Union MS 600/4-8
390 W Walker St 43351 419-294-5721
James Wheeler, prin. Fax 294-2586
Upper Sandusky HS 600/9-12
800 N Sandusky Ave 43351 419-294-2308
James Clifford, prin. Fax 294-6889

Urbana, Champaign, Pop. 11,459
Urbana CSD 2,100/K-12
711 Wood St 43078 937-653-1402
Charles Thiel, supt. Fax 652-3845
www.urbana.k12.oh.us
Urbana HS 600/9-12
500 Washington Ave 43078 937-653-1412
Kristin Mays, prin. Fax 653-1487
Urbana JHS 300/7-8
500 Washington Ave 43078 937-653-1439
Greg Stickel, prin. Fax 658-1487

Urbana University Post-Sec.
579 College Way 43078 937-484-1400

Utica, Licking, Pop. 2,106
North Fork Local SD 1,700/K-12
PO Box 497 43080 740-892-3666
Scott Hartley, supt. Fax 892-2937
www.northfork.k12.oh.us
Utica HS 500/9-12
PO Box 677 43080 740-892-2855
Mark Bowman, prin. Fax 892-2090
Utica JHS 300/7-8
PO Box 647 43080 740-892-2691
Ryan McLane, prin. Fax 892-2203

Van Buren, Hancock, Pop. 327
Van Buren Local SD 1,000/PK-12
217 S Main St 45889 419-299-3578
Timothy Myers, supt. Fax 299-3668
www.vbschools.net

Van Buren HS 300/9-12
217 S Main St 45889 419-299-3384
Michael Brand, prin. Fax 299-3340
Van Buren MS 200/6-8
217 S Main St 45889 419-299-3385
Jason Clark, prin. Fax 299-3340

Vandalia, Montgomery, Pop. 14,921
Vandalia-Butler CSD 3,200/PK-12
306 S Dixie Dr 45377 937-415-6400
Bradley Neavin, supt. Fax 415-6429
www.vbcsd.com
Butler HS 1,000/9-12
600 S Dixie Dr 45377 937-415-6300
Chad Hill, prin. Fax 415-6457
Morton MS 500/6-8
8555 Peters Pike 45377 937-415-6600
Shannon White, prin. Fax 415-6648

Vanlue, Hancock, Pop. 358
Vanlue Local SD 200/K-12
PO Box 250 45890 419-387-7724
Rodney Russell, supt. Fax 387-7722
vanlueschool.org
Vanlue JSHS 100/6-12
PO Box 250 45890 419-387-7724
Traci Conley, prin. Fax 387-7722

Van Wert, Van Wert, Pop. 10,671
Lincolnview Local SD 800/K-12
15945 Middle Point Rd 45891 419-968-2226
Jeffrey Synder, supt. Fax 968-2227
www.lincolnview.k12.oh.us
Lincolnview JSHS 400/7-12
15945 Middle Point Rd 45891 419-968-2214
Kelly Dye, prin. Fax 968-2227
Lincolnview Marsh S 50/Alt
PO Box 150 45891 419-238-1695
Roger Salisbury, prin. Fax 238-3986

Van Wert CSD 1,200/PK-12
205 W Crawford St 45891 419-238-0648
Ken Amstutz, supt. Fax 238-3974
www.vanwertcougars.net
Van Wert HS 600/9-12
10708 State Route 118 45891 419-238-3350
William Clifton, prin. Fax 238-0526
Van Wert MS 400/6-8
10694 State Route 118 45891 419-238-0727
Mark Bagley, prin. Fax 238-7166

Vantage JVSD
818 N Franklin St 45891 419-238-5411
Staci Kaufman, supt. Fax 238-4058
www.vantagecareercenter.com
Vantage Career Center Vo/Tech
818 N Franklin St 45891 419-238-5411
Ben Winans, dir. Fax 238-4058

Vermilion, Erie, Pop. 10,413
Vermilion Local SD 1,400/K-12
1230 Beechview Dr 44089 440-204-1700
Philip Pempin, supt. Fax 204-1771
vermilionschools.org
Vermilion HS 900/8-12
1250 Sanford St 44089 440-204-1700
Heidi Riddle, prin. Fax 204-1781

Versailles, Darke, Pop. 2,673
Versailles EVD 1,400/K-12
PO Box 313 45380 937-526-4773
Dr. David Vail, supt. Fax 526-5745
www.versailles.k12.oh.us
Versailles HS 400/9-12
PO Box 313 45380 937-526-4427
Roger McEldowney, prin. Fax 526-4356
Versailles MS 400/5-8
PO Box 313 45380 937-526-4426
Jeanne Osterfeld, prin. Fax 526-3085

Vienna, Trumbull, Pop. 1,067
Mathews Local SD 600/K-12
4434 Warren Sharon Rd Ste B 44473 330-394-1800
Lew Lowery, supt. Fax 394-1930
www.mathews.k12.oh.us
Mathews JSHS 200/7-12
4429 Warren Sharon Rd 44473 330-394-1138
Robert Cameron, prin.

Pittsburgh Institute of Aeronautics Post-Sec.
1453 Youngstown Kingsville 44473 330-399-9992

Vincent, Washington, Pop. 337
Warren Local SD 2,400/K-12
220 Sweetapple Rd 45784 740-678-2366
Thomas Gibbs, supt. Fax 678-8275
www.warrenlocal.org
Warren HS 800/9-12
130 Warrior Dr 45784 740-678-2393
Dan Leffingwell, prin. Fax 678-2783

Wadsworth, Medina, Pop. 21,350
Wadsworth CSD 4,800/PK-12
150 Silvercreek Rd 44281 330-336-3571
Dale Fortner, supt. Fax 335-1313
www.wadsworthschools.org
Wadsworth HS 1,600/9-12
625 Broad St 44281 330-335-1400
Jerry Parsons, prin. Fax 335-1376
Wadsworth MS 800/7-8
150 Silvercreek Rd 44281 330-335-1410
Roger Wright, prin. Fax 336-3820

Wapakoneta, Auglaize, Pop. 9,743
Wapakoneta CSD 2,700/K-12
1102 Gardenia Dr 45895 419-739-2900
Keith Horner, supt. Fax 739-2918
www.wapak.org/
Wapakoneta HS 800/8-12
1 Redskin Trl 45895 419-739-5200
Scott Minnig, prin. Fax 739-5305

Warren, Trumbull, Pop. 40,148
Champion Local SD 1,500/K-12
5759 Mahoning Ave NW 44483 330-847-2330
Pamela Hood, supt. Fax 847-2336
www.championschools.org
Champion HS 500/9-12
5976 Mahoning Ave NW 44483 330-847-2305
John Grabowski, prin. Fax 847-2353
Champion MS 500/5-8
5435 Kuszmaul Ave NW 44483 330-847-2340
Heather Campbell, prin. Fax 847-2355

Howland Local SD 3,000/K-12
8200 South St SE 44484 330-856-8200
John Sheets, supt. Fax 856-8214
www.howlandschools.com
Howland HS 1,000/9-12
200 Shaffer Dr NE 44484 330-856-8220
Frank Thomas, prin. Fax 856-7827
Howland MS 700/6-8
8100 South St SE 44484 330-856-8250
Kevin Spicher, prin. Fax 856-2157

Lordstown Local SD 600/K-12
1824 Salt Springs Rd W 44481 330-824-2534
William Pfahler, supt. Fax 824-2847
www.lordstown.k12.oh.us/
Lordstown JSHS 300/7-12
1824 Salt Springs Rd W 44481 330-824-2581
James Rasile, prin. Fax 824-2586

Trumbull Career & Technical Center
528 Educational Hwy NW 44483 330-847-0503
Wayne McClain, supt. Fax 847-6817
www.tctchome.com
Trumbull Career & Technical Center Vo/Tech
528 Educational Hwy NW 44483 330-847-0503
David Phillips, admin. Fax 847-0339

Warren CSD 5,300/PK-12
105 High St NE 44481 330-841-2321
Michael Notar, supt. Fax 841-2434
www.warrenschools.k12.oh.us
Harding HS 1,500/9-12
860 Elm Rd NE 44483 330-841-2316
Dante Capers, prin. Fax 841-2289

Kennedy HS 300/7-12
2550 Central Parkway Ave SE 44484 330-369-1804
Staci Raab, prin. Fax 369-1125
Kent State University-Trumbull Campus Post-Sec.
4314 Mahoning Ave NW 44483 330-847-0571
Trumbull Business College Post-Sec.
3200 Ridge Ave SE 44484 330-369-3200

Warrensville Heights, Cuyahoga, Pop. 13,282
Warrensville Heights CSD 2,100/PK-12
4500 Warrensville Center Rd 44128 216-295-7710
Marva Kay Jones, supt. Fax 921-5902
www.warrensville.k12.oh.us
Warrensville Heights HS 700/9-12
4270 Northfield Rd 44128 216-752-8585
Lori Crum-Glenn, prin. Fax 752-8116
Warrensville Heights MS 500/5-8
4285 Warrensville Center Rd 44128 216-752-4050
Constance Rudolph, prin. Fax 752-5813

ITT Technical Institute Post-Sec.
4700 Richmond Rd 44128 216-896-6500

Warsaw, Coshocton, Pop. 679
River View Local SD 2,000/K-12
26496 State Route 60 43844 740-824-3521
Dalton Summers, supt. Fax 824-3760
www.river-view.k12.oh.us
River View HS 600/9-12
26496 State Route 60 43844 740-824-3522
Chuck Rinkes, prin. Fax 824-4746
River View MS 300/7-8
26546 State Route 60 43844 740-824-3523
Sharon Tatro, prin. Fax 824-5241

Washington Court House, Fayette, Pop. 13,899
Miami Trace Local SD 2,400/K-12
3818 State Route 41 NW 43160 740-335-3010
Daniel Roberts, supt. Fax 335-1959
miamitrace.k12.oh.us
Miami Trace HS 800/9-12
3722 State Route 41 NW 43160 740-333-4700
Jeff Spears, prin. Fax 636-2010
Miami Trace MS 600/6-8
3800 State Route 41 NW 43160 740-333-4900
Jeff Conroy, prin. Fax 333-4901

Washington Court House CSD 2,300/K-12
306 Highland Ave 43160 740-335-6620
Keith Brown, supt. Fax 335-1245
www.washingtonch.k12.oh.us
Washington HS 600/9-12
400 S Elm St 43160 740-636-4221
Jeff Hodson, prin. Fax 636-4261
Washington MS 600/6-8
500 S Elm St 43160 740-335-0291
Eric Wayne, prin. Fax 333-3606

Waterford, Washington, Pop. 445
Wolf Creek Local SD 600/K-12
PO Box 67 45786 740-984-2373
Robert Caldwell, supt. Fax 984-4420
www.wolfcreek.k12.oh.us
Waterford HS 200/9-12
PO Box 67 45786 740-984-2373
Randy Shrider, prin. Fax 984-4420

Wauseon, Fulton, Pop. 7,227
Wauseon EVD 1,900/K-12
126 S Fulton St 43567 419-335-6616
Larry Brown, supt. Fax 335-3978
www.wauseon.k12.oh.us
Wauseon HS 600/9-12
840 Parkview St 43567 419-335-5756
William Hanak, prin. Fax 335-4228
Wauseon MS 400/6-8
940 E Oak St 43567 419-335-2701
Joe Friess, prin. Fax 335-0089

Waverly, Pike, Pop. 5,086
Waverly CSD 1,900/PK-12
1 Tiger Dr 45690 740-947-4770
Cheryl Francis, supt. Fax 947-4483
www.waverly.k12.oh.us
Waverly HS 500/9-12
1 Tiger Dr 45690 740-947-7701
Bill Hoover, prin. Fax 947-8877
Waverly JHS 400/6-8
3 Tiger Dr 45690 740-947-4527
Melissa Marquez, prin. Fax 947-8047

Pike Christian Academy 200/PK-12
400 Clough St 45690 740-947-5700
Dr. Euggie Robertson, prin. Fax 947-9500

Waynesfield, Auglaize, Pop. 843
Waynesfield-Goshen Local SD 500/K-12
500 N Westminster St 45896 419-568-9100
J. Chris Pfister, supt. Fax 568-8024
www.wgschools.org
Waynesfield-Goshen Local HS 300/6-12
500 N Westminster St 45896 419-568-9100
Thomas Winkler, prin. Fax 568-6282

Waynesville, Warren, Pop. 2,780
Wayne Local SD 1,400/K-12
659 Dayton Rd 45068 513-897-6971
Patrick Dubbs, supt. Fax 897-9605
www.wayne-local.com
Waynesville HS 400/9-12
735 Dayton Rd 45068 513-897-2776
Randy Gebhardt, prin. Fax 897-2713
Waynesville MS 400/6-8
723 Dayton Rd 45068 513-897-4706
Randy Gebhardt, prin. Fax 897-2083

Wellington, Lorain, Pop. 4,725
Wellington EVD 1,300/K-12
201 S Main St 44090 440-647-4286
John Nolan, supt. Fax 647-4806
www.wellington.k12.oh.us
McCormick MS 500/4-8
201 S Main St 44090 440-647-2342
Tim Simpson, prin. Fax 647-7310
Wellington HS 400/9-12
629 N Main St 44090 440-647-3734
Christopher Wert, prin. Fax 647-7318

Wellston, Jackson, Pop. 5,598
Wellston CSD 1,500/PK-12
1 E Broadway St 45692 740-384-2152
Karen Boch, supt. Fax 384-3948
www.wcs.k12.oh.us
Wellston HS 400/9-12
200 Golden Rocket Dr 45692 740-384-2162
Megan Aubrey, prin. Fax 384-9581
Wellston MS 300/6-8
227 Golden Rocket Dr 45692 740-384-2251
Fax 384-9801

Wellsville, Columbiana, Pop. 3,433
Wellsville Local SD 900/PK-12
929 Center St 43968 330-532-2643
Richard Bereschik, supt. Fax 532-6204
www.wellsville.k12.oh.us
Daw MS, 929 Center St 43968 300/4-8
David Buzzard, prin. 330-532-1372
Wellsville HS 300/9-12
1 Bengal Blvd 43968 330-532-1188
Linda Rolley, prin. Fax 532-9004

West Alexandria, Preble, Pop. 1,321
Twin Valley Community Local SD 800/K-12
100 Education Dr 45381 937-839-4688
Clinton Moore Ed.D., supt. Fax 839-4898
www.tvs.k12.oh.us
Twin Valley South HS 300/9-12
100 Education Dr 45381 937-839-4693
Scott Cottingim, prin. Fax 839-4898
Twin Valley South MS 200/7-8
100 Education Dr 45381 937-839-4165
Scott Cottingim, prin. Fax 839-4898

West Carrollton, Montgomery, Pop. 12,886
West Carrollton CSD 3,700/PK-12
430 E Pease Ave 45449 937-859-5121
Rusty Clifford, supt. Fax 859-2766
www.westcarrolltonschools.com
West Carrollton HS 1,000/9-12
5833 Student St 45449 937-859-5121
Fred Gehron, prin. Fax 435-2315
West Carrollton MS 900/6-8
424 E Main St 45449 937-859-5121
Doug Mescher, prin. Fax 859-2780

West Chester, Butler
Lakota Local SD
Supt. — See Liberty Twp
Hopewell JHS 600/7-8
8200 Cox Rd 45069 513-777-2258
Jeff Rouff, prin. Fax 777-1908
Lakota Ridge JHS 600/7-8
6199 Beckett Ridge Blvd 45069 513-777-0552
Andre Gendreau, prin. Fax 777-0919
Lakota West Freshman HS 700/9-9
5050 Tylersville Rd 45069 513-874-8390
Jason Jackson, prin. Fax 682-4230
Lakota West SHS 2,000/10-12
8940 Union Centre Blvd 45069 513-874-5699
Gary Card, prin. Fax 682-4133

Antonelli College Post-Sec.
9100 W Chester Towne Fl 3 45069 513-330-6807
Hondros College Post-Sec.
7600 Tylers Place Blvd 45069 888-466-3767

Westerville, Franklin, Pop. 35,380
Westerville CSD 14,200/PK-12
936 Eastwind Dr 43081 614-797-5700
Dr. John R. Kellogg, supt. Fax 797-5701
www.wcsoh.org
Blendon MS 600/6-8
223 S Otterbein Ave 43081 614-797-6400
Kendall Harris, prin. Fax 797-6401
Genoa MS 1,000/6-8
5948 S Old 3C Hwy 43082 614-797-6500
Carrie Trusley, prin. Fax 797-6501
Heritage MS 800/6-8
390 N Spring Rd 43082 614-797-6600
Joseph Kacsandi, prin. Fax 797-6601
Walnut Springs MS 900/6-8
888 E Walnut St 43081 614-797-6700
Leslie Kelly, prin. Fax 797-6701
Westerville Central HS 1,600/9-12
7118 Mount Royal Ave 43082 614-797-6800
Todd Spinner, prin. Fax 797-6801
Westerville-North HS 1,500/9-12
950 County Line Rd 43081 614-797-6200
Kurt Yancey, prin. Fax 797-6201
Westerville-South HS 1,500/9-12
303 S Otterbein Ave 43081 614-797-6000
Steven Andersson, prin. Fax 797-6001

Fortis College Post-Sec.
4151 Executive Pkwy Ste 120 43081 614-882-2551
Genoa Christian Academy 300/PK-12
7562 Lewis Center Rd 43082 740-965-5433
Terri Foltz, supt. Fax 965-8214
Hondros College Post-Sec.
4140 Executive Pkwy 43081 614-508-7277
Ohio State Cosmetology School Post-Sec.
5970 Westerville Rd 43081 614-890-3535
Otterbein University Post-Sec.
1 S Grove St 43081 614-890-3000
Worthington Christian MS 200/6-8
8225 Worthington Galena Rd 43081 614-431-8230
Lori Thayer, prin. Fax 431-8216

West Jefferson, Madison, Pop. 4,287
Jefferson Local SD 1,200/PK-12
906 W Main St 43162 614-879-7654
William Mullett, supt. Fax 879-5376
www.west-jefferson.k12.oh.us
West Jefferson HS 400/9-12
1 Roughrider Dr 43162 614-879-7681
Dave Metz, prin. Fax 879-5381
West Jefferson MS 300/6-8
2 Roughrider Dr 43162 614-879-8345
Debbie Omen, prin. Fax 879-5399

West Lafayette, Coshocton, Pop. 2,307
Ridgewood Local SD 1,300/PK-12
301 S Oak St 43845 740-545-6354
Deborah Kapp-Salupo, supt. Fax 545-6336
www.ridgewood.k12.oh.us
Ridgewood HS 400/8-12
602 Johnson St 43845 740-545-6345
Todd Stoffer, prin. Fax 545-5311

Westlake, Cuyahoga, Pop. 32,199
Westlake CSD 4,000/PK-12
27200 Hilliard Blvd 44145 440-871-7300
Dr. Daniel Keenan, supt. Fax 871-6034
www.wlake.org/
Burneson MS 700/7-8
2240 Dover Center Rd 44145 440-835-6340
Paul Wilson, prin. Fax 835-5987
Westlake HS 1,400/9-12
27830 Hilliard Blvd 44145 440-250-1002
Tim Freeman, prin. Fax 835-5572

West Liberty, Champaign, Pop. 1,773
West Liberty-Salem Local SD 1,200/K-12
7208 US Highway 68 N 43357 937-465-1075
Kraig Hissong, supt. Fax 465-1095
www.wlstigers.org/
West Liberty-Salem MSHS 700/6-12
7208 US Highway 68 N 43357 937-465-1060
Greg Johnson, prin. Fax 465-1095

West Milton, Miami, Pop. 4,568
Milton-Union EVD 1,400/PK-12
7610 Milton Potsdam Rd 45383 937-884-7910
Dr. Virginia Rammel, supt. Fax 884-7911
www.milton-union.k12.oh.us
Milton-Union HS 500/9-12
7640 Milton Potsdam Rd 45383 937-884-7940
Brian Powderly, prin. Fax 884-7941
Milton-Union MS 400/5-8
7630 Milton Potsdam Rd 45383 937-884-7930
Laurie Grube, prin. Fax 884-7931

West Portsmouth, Scioto, Pop. 3,091
Washington-Nile Local SD 1,400/K-12
15332 US Highway 52 45663 740-858-1111
Jeff Stricklett, supt. Fax 858-1110
www.west.k12.oh.us
Portsmouth West MS 300/6-8
15332 US Highway 52 Unit B 45663 740-858-6668
Christopher Jordan, prin. Fax 858-4101
Other Schools – See Portsmouth

West Salem, Wayne, Pop. 1,452
Northwestern Local SD 1,400/K-12
7571 N Elyria Rd 44287 419-846-3151
Jeffrey Layton, supt. Fax 846-3361
www.northwestern-wayne.k12.oh.us
Northwestern HS 400/9-12
7473 N Elyria Rd 44287 419-846-3833
Michael Burkholder, prin. Fax 846-3163
Northwestern MS 300/6-8
7569 N Elyria Rd 44287 419-846-3974
Scott Smith, prin. Fax 846-3750

West Union, Adams, Pop. 3,193
Adams County/Ohio Valley Local SD 4,000/K-12
141 Lloyd Rd 45693 937-544-5586
Rodney Wallace, supt. Fax 544-3720
www.ovsd.us/
Ohio Valley Career & Technical Center Vo/Tech
175 Lloyd Rd 45693 937-544-2336
Tad Mitchell, prin. Fax 544-5176
West Union HS 600/7-12
97 Dragon Lair Dr 45693 937-544-5553
Timothy Davis, prin. Fax 544-5361
Other Schools – See Peebles, Seaman

Adams County Christian S 100/K-12
187 Willow Dr 45693 937-544-5502
Kenneth Jones, admin. Fax 544-5503

West Unity, Williams, Pop. 1,653
Millcreek-West Unity Local SD 600/K-12
1401 W Jackson St 43570 419-924-2365
Larry Long, supt. Fax 924-2367
www.hilltop.k12.oh.us
Hilltop HS 300/7-12
1401 W Jackson St 43570 419-924-2365
Steven Riley, prin. Fax 924-2367

Wheelersburg, Scioto, Pop. 6,353
Wheelersburg Local SD 1,600/PK-12
PO Box 340 45694 740-574-8484
Mark Knapp, supt. Fax 574-6134
www.burg.k12.oh.us
Wheelersburg HS 400/9-12
800 Pirate Dr 45694 740-574-2527
Matthew McCorkle, prin. Fax 574-6178
Wheelersburg MS 600/4-8
800 Pirate Dr 45694 740-574-2515
David Rucker, prin. Fax 574-9201

Whitehall, Franklin, Pop. 17,402
Whitehall CSD 2,800/K-12
625 S Yearling Rd 43213 614-417-5000
Judyth Dobbert-Meloy, supt. Fax 417-5001
www.whitehallcityschools.org
Whitehall-Yearling HS 800/9-12
675 S Yearling Rd 43213 614-417-5100
Carl Svagerko, prin. Fax 417-5101
Other Schools – See Columbus

Whitehouse, Lucas, Pop. 4,098
Anthony Wayne Local SD 4,300/K-12
PO Box 2487 43571 419-877-5377
Jim Fritz, supt. Fax 877-9352
www.anthonywayneschools.org
Wayne HS 1,300/9-12
5967 Finzel Rd 43571 419-877-0466
Jeri Hoellrich, prin. Fax 877-5020
Wayne JHS 700/7-8
6035 Finzel Rd 43571 419-877-5342
Kevin Pfefferle, prin. Fax 877-4908

Wickliffe, Lake, Pop. 12,545
Wickliffe CSD 1,500/K-12
2221 Rockefeller Rd 44092 440-943-6900
Rosemary Gornik, supt. Fax 943-7738
www.wickliffeschools.org
Wickliffe HS 500/9-12
2255 Rockefeller Rd 44092 440-944-0800
Cynthia Anderson, prin. Fax 943-7738
Wickliffe MS 500/5-8
29240 Euclid Ave 44092 440-943-3220
William Basel, prin. Fax 943-7755

Rabbinical College of Telshe Post-Sec.
28400 Euclid Ave 44092 440-943-5300
St. Mary Seminary/Graduate Sch. Theology Post-Sec.
28700 Euclid Ave 44092 440-943-7600
Telshe HS 100/9-12
28400 Euclid Ave 44092 440-944-0299

Wilberforce, Greene, Pop. 2,180

Central State University Post-Sec.
PO Box 1004 45384 937-376-6011
Payne Theological Seminary Post-Sec.
PO Box 474 45384 937-376-2946
Wilberforce University Post-Sec.
PO Box 1001 45384 937-376-2911

Willard, Huron, Pop. 6,140
Willard CSD 1,800/PK-12
110 S Myrtle Ave 44890 419-935-1541
Jeffrey Ritz, supt. Fax 935-8491
www.willardschools.org/
Willard HS 500/9-12
110 S Myrtle Ave 44890 419-935-0181
Chris Schaaf, prin. Fax 933-6701
Willard MS, 949 S Main St 44890 500/5-8
Mike Eicher, prin. 419-933-8312

Williamsburg, Clermont, Pop. 2,468
Clermont County ESC
Supt. — See Batavia
Genesis Alternative S Alt
549 W Main St Ste B 45176 513-724-8555
Travis Etling, prin. Fax 724-0708

Williamsburg Local SD 1,000/PK-12
549 W Main St Ste A 45176 513-724-3077
Matthew Earley, supt. Fax 724-1504
www.burgschools.org
Williamsburg MSHS 500/6-12
500 S 5th St 45176 513-724-2211
Heather Powell, prin. Fax 724-6577

Williamsport, Pickaway, Pop. 1,007
Westfall Local SD 1,600/PK-12
19463 Pherson Pike 43164 740-986-3671
Cara Riddel, supt. Fax 986-8375
www.westfall.k12.oh.us
Westfall HS 500/9-12
19463 Pherson Pike 43164 740-986-2911
Billy Dennis, prin. Fax 986-8897
Westfall MS 400/6-8
19545 Pherson Pike 43164 740-986-2941
Kathy Payne, prin. Fax 986-8882

Willoughby, Lake, Pop. 21,949
Lake County ESC
Supt. — See Painesville
Lake Academy Alt
25 Public Sq 44094 440-942-7401
John Weiss, dir. Fax 942-1790

Willoughby-Eastlake CSD 8,200/K-12
37047 Ridge Rd 44094 440-946-5000
Stephen Thompson, supt. Fax 946-4671
www.weschools.org
South HS 1,400/9-12
5000 Shankland Rd 44094 440-975-3647
Lee Walker, prin. Fax 975-3645
Willoughby-Eastlake Tech Ctr Vo/Tech
25 Public Sq 44094 440-946-7085
Susan Vargo Roseum, prin. Fax 975-3741
Willoughby MS 900/6-8
36901 Ridge Rd 44094 440-975-3600
Lawrence Keller, prin. Fax 975-3618
Other Schools – See Eastlake, Willowick

Andrews Osborne Academy 400/PK-12
38588 Mentor Ave 44094 440-942-3600
Charles Roman, hdmstr. Fax 942-3660
Hondros College Post-Sec.
35103 Maplegrove Rd 44094 888-466-3767

Willoughby Hills, Lake, Pop. 9,326

Cornerstone Christian Academy 400/PK-12
2846 SOM Center Rd, 440-943-9260
Daniel Buell Ph.D., hdmstr. Fax 943-9262
National College Post-Sec.
27557 Chardon Rd 44092 440-944-0825

Willowick, Lake, Pop. 14,003
Willoughby-Eastlake CSD
Supt. — See Willoughby
Willowick MS 600/6-8
31500 Royalview Dr 44095 440-943-2950
Loretta Rodman, prin. Fax 943-9964

Willow Wood, Lawrence
Symmes Valley Local SD 800/K-12
14778 State Route 141 45696 740-643-2451
Jeff Saunders, supt. Fax 643-1219
www.symmesvalley.k12.oh.us
Symmes Valley HS 200/9-12
14778 State Route 141 45696 740-643-2371
Darrell Humphreys, prin. Fax 643-1606

Wilmington, Clinton, Pop. 12,076
Great Oaks Institute of Technology
Supt. — See Cincinnati
Laurel Oaks CDC Vo/Tech
300 Oak Dr 45177 937-382-1411
Mike Thomas, prin. Fax 383-2095

Wilmington CSD 3,200/K-12
341 S Nelson Ave 45177 937-382-1641
Ronald Sexton, supt. Fax 382-1645
www.wilmingtoncityschools.com
Borror MS 700/6-8
275 Thorne Ave 45177 937-382-7556
Matthew Freeman, prin. Fax 382-3295
Wilmington HS 800/9-12
300 Richardson Pl 45177 937-382-7716
Brent Carey, prin. Fax 382-1139

Wilmington Christian Academy 50/K-12
909 W Locust St 45177 937-383-1319
Tari Heath, admin. Fax 366-6188
Wilmington College Post-Sec.
1870 Quaker Way 45177 937-382-6661

Winchester, Adams, Pop. 1,044
Eastern Local SD 1,300/K-12
11479 US Highway 62 45697 937-378-3981
Michele Filon, supt. Fax 695-9046
www.eb.k12.oh.us
Eastern HS 300/9-12
11557 US Highway 62 45697 937-378-6016
Jennifer Grimes, prin. Fax 695-0303
Eastern MS 300/6-8
11479 US Highway 62 45697 937-378-6720
Rob Beucler, prin. Fax 695-1299

Windham, Portage, Pop. 2,132
Windham EVD 700/PK-12
9530 Bauer Ave 44288 330-326-2711
Gregory Isler, supt. Fax 326-2134
www.windham-schools.org
Windham HS 200/9-12
9530 Bauer Ave 44288 330-326-3916
Michael Chaffee, prin. Fax 326-2052
Windham JHS 100/6-8
9530 Bauer Ave 44288 330-326-3490
Michael Chaffee, prin. Fax 326-3713

Wintersville, Jefferson, Pop. 3,879
Indian Creek Local SD 1,900/PK-12
587 Bantam Ridge Rd 43953 740-264-3502
John Rocchi, supt. Fax 266-2915
www.indian-creek.k12.oh.us
Indian Creek HS 600/9-12
200 Park Dr 43953 740-264-1163
Steve Cowser, prin. Fax 266-2929

Other Schools – See Mingo Junction

Jefferson County Christian S 200/K-12
125 Fernwood Rd Ste 1 43953 740-275-4326
Diane Hutchison, prin. Fax 275-4296

Woodsfield, Monroe, Pop. 2,354
Switzerland of Ohio Local SD 2,500/PK-12
304 Mill St 43793 740-472-5801
Larry Elliott, supt. Fax 472-5806
www.swissohio.k12.oh.us
Monroe Central HS 300/9-12
469 Lewisville Rd 43793 740-472-0414
Jerry Calder, prin. Fax 472-2055
Swiss Hills Career Center Vo/Tech
46601 State Route 78 43793 740-472-0722
Darren Cook, prin. Fax 472-0367
Other Schools – See Beallsville, Hannibal

Wooster, Wayne, Pop. 25,513
Triway Local SD 1,800/K-12
3205 Shreve Rd 44691 330-264-9491
David Rice, supt. Fax 262-3955
www.tccsa.net/dp/trwy
Triway HS 500/9-12
3205 Shreve Rd 44691 330-264-8685
Scott Wharton, prin. Fax 262-3955
Triway JHS 300/7-8
3145 Shreve Rd 44691 330-264-2114
Mitchell Caraway, prin. Fax 264-6025

Wooster CSD 2,400/K-12
144 N Market St 44691 330-988-1111
Dr. Michael Tefs, supt. Fax 262-3407
www.woostercityschools.org
Wooster HS 1,000/8-12
515 Oldman Rd 44691 330-345-4000
Anita Jorney-Gifford, prin. Fax 345-3501
Other Schools – See Smithville

College of Wooster Post-Sec.
1189 Beall Ave 44691 330-263-2000
Ohio State University-A & T Institute Post-Sec.
1328 Dover Rd 44691 330-287-1331

Worthington, Franklin, Pop. 13,300
Worthington CSD 9,400/PK-12
200 E Wilson Bridge Rd 43085 614-450-6000
Thomas Tucker Ph.D., supt. Fax 883-3010
www.worthington.k12.oh.us
Kilbourne MS 300/7-8
50 E Dublin Granville Rd 43085 614-450-4200
Pete Scully, prin. Fax 883-3510
Linworth Campus Alternative Program Alt
2075 W Dublin Granville Rd 43085 614-450-6900
Wayne Harvey, dir. Fax 883-3710
Phoenix MS 200/Alt
2341 Snouffer Rd 43085 614-450-4100
Paul Roman, prin. Fax 883-3610
Worthington HS 1,500/9-12
300 W Dublin Granville Rd 43085 614-450-6200
James Gaskill, prin. Fax 450-6390
Worthingway MS 400/7-8
6625 Guyer St 43085 614-450-4300
Nathan Kellenberger, prin. Fax 883-3660
Other Schools – See Columbus

Worthington Christian HS 300/9-12
6670 Worthington Galena Rd 43085 614-431-8210
Dr. Scott Inboden, prin. Fax 431-8213

Wyoming, Hamilton, Pop. 8,224
Wyoming CSD 2,000/K-12
420 Springfield Pike 45215 513-206-7000
Susan Lang, supt. Fax 672-3355
www.wyomingcityschools.org
Wyoming HS 700/9-12
106 Pendery Ave 45215 513-206-7050
Aaron Marshall, prin. Fax 206-7132
Wyoming MS 700/5-8
17 Wyoming Ave 45215 513-206-7170
Mike Overbey, prin. Fax 206-7245

Xenia, Greene, Pop. 24,906
Greene County JVSD
2960 W Enon Rd 45385 937-372-6941
Daniel Schroer, supt. Fax 372-8283
www.greeneccc.com
Greene County Career Center Vo/Tech
2960 W Enon Rd 45385 937-426-6636
Matthew Lindley, dir. Fax 372-8283

Xenia Community CSD 3,400/K-12
578 E Market St 45385 937-376-2961
Dr. Deborah Piotrowski, supt. Fax 372-4701
www.xenia.k12.oh.us
Warner MS 300/7-8
600 Buckskin Trl 45385 937-376-9488
Michael Earley, prin. Fax 374-4228
Xenia HS 1,300/9-12
303 Kinsey Rd 45385 937-372-6983
Ted Holop, prin. Fax 374-4390

Xenia Christian S 400/PK-12
1101 Wesley Ave 45385 937-352-1640
Robert Elliott, pres. Fax 352-1641

Yellow Springs, Greene, Pop. 3,226
Yellow Springs EVD 700/K-12
201 S Walnut St 45387 937-767-7381
Mario Basora, supt. Fax 767-6604
www.yellow-springs.k12.oh.us/
Yellow Springs HS / McKinney MS 300/7-12
420 E Enon Rd 45387 937-767-7224
Tim Krier, prin. Fax 767-6154

Antioch University Midwest Post-Sec.
900 Dayton St 45387 937-769-1800

Youngstown, Mahoning, Pop. 65,039
Austintown Local SD 2,800/K-12
700 S Raccoon Rd 44515 330-797-3900
Vincent Colauca, supt. Fax 792-8625
www.austintown.k12.oh.us
Austintown MS 1,200/6-8
800 S Raccoon Rd 44515 330-797-3900
James Penk, prin. Fax 797-3965
Fitch HS 1,500/9-12
4560 Falcon Dr 44515 330-797-3900
Christopher Berni, prin. Fax 797-3944

Boardman Local SD 4,600/K-12
7410 Market St 44512 330-726-3404
Frank Lazzeri, supt. Fax 726-3432
www.boardmanschools.org
Boardman HS 1,500/9-12
7777 Glenwood Ave 44512 330-758-7511
Tim Saxton, prin. Fax 758-7515
Center MS 700/5-8
7410 Market St 44512 330-726-3400
Randall Ebie, prin. Fax 726-3431
Glenwood MS 700/5-8
7635 Glenwood Ave 44512 330-726-3414
Anthony Alvino, prin. Fax 758-8067

Liberty Local SD 1,200/K-12
4115 Shady Rd 44505 330-759-0807
Stan Watson, supt. Fax 759-1209
www.liberty.k12.oh.us
Guy MS 300/5-8
4115 Shady Rd 44505 330-759-1733
Judd Rubin, prin. Fax 759-4507
Liberty HS 500/9-12
1 Leopard Way 44505 330-759-2301
Michele Stewart, prin. Fax 759-4506

Youngstown CSD 4,700/PK-12
PO Box 550 44501 330-744-6900
Connie Hathorn Ph.D., supt. Fax 743-1157
www.youngstown.k12.oh.us
Chaney VPA/STEM Campus 800/6-12
731 S Hazelwood Ave 44509 330-744-8822
Sharon Butler, prin. Fax 480-1909
Choffin Career & Technical Center Vo/Tech
200 E Wood St 44503 330-744-8700
Joseph Meranto, admin. Fax 744-8705
East HS 700/9-11
474 Bennington Ave 44505 330-744-4005
Holly Seimetz, prin. Fax 742-6464
Rayen Early College MS 200/6-8
731 S Hazelwood Ave 44509 330-744-7602
Deborah DiFrancesco, prin. Fax 793-9675
Wilson S of Promise Alt
2725 Gibson St 44502 330-744-7535
Tod Morris, prin. Fax 788-1326
Youngstown Early College HS 200/9-12
Fedor Hall Elm St 44555 330-744-7923
Michele Dotson, prin. Fax 480-5875

Cardinal Mooney HS 600/9-12
2545 Erie St 44507 330-788-5007
John Young, prin. Fax 788-4511

ITT Technical Institute Post-Sec.
1030 N Meridian Rd 44509 330-270-1600
National College Post-Sec.
3487 Belmont Ave 44505 330-759-0205
St. Elizabeth Hospital Post-Sec.
PO Box 1790 44501 330-746-7211
Ursuline HS 400/9-12
750 Wick Ave 44505 330-744-4563
Patricia Fleming, prin. Fax 744-3358
Western Reserve Care System Post-Sec.
345 Oak Hill Ave 44502 330-747-0777
Youngstown Christian S 500/PK-12
4401 Southern Blvd 44512 330-788-8088
Michael Pecchia, pres. Fax 788-2875
Youngstown State University Post-Sec.
1 University Plz 44555 330-941-3000

Zanesville, Muskingum, Pop. 24,279
Maysville Local SD 2,100/K-12
3715 Panther Dr 43701 740-453-0754
Monte Bainter, supt. Fax 455-4081
maysvillelsd.schoolwires.com/
Maysville HS 600/9-12
3725 Panther Dr 43701 740-454-7999
James Retton, prin. Fax 452-9921
Maysville MS 500/6-8
3725 Panther Dr 43701 740-454-7982
Joseph Daniels, prin. Fax 452-9921

Mid-East Career & Technology Centers
400 Richards Rd 43701 740-454-0105
William Bussey, supt. Fax 454-0731
www.mideastctc.org
Mid-East Career & Tech Ctr - Zanesville Vo/Tech
400 Richards Rd 43701 740-454-0101
Mike Hawley, dir. Fax 454-0723
Adult Center for Education Adult
400 Richards Rd 43701 740-455-3111
Doug Spade, dir. Fax 455-2043
Other Schools – See Senecaville

West Muskingum Local SD 1,300/PK-12
4880 West Pike 43701 740-455-4052
Dr. William Harbron, supt. Fax 455-4063
www.westm.k12.oh.us
West Muskingum HS 400/9-12
150 Kimes Rd 43701 740-455-4050
Ray Peyton, prin. Fax 452-7648
West Muskingum MS 400/5-8
100 Kimes Rd 43701 740-455-4055
Jacob Wiese, prin. Fax 455-9717

Zanesville CSD 3,200/K-12
160 N 4th St 43701 740-454-9751
Terry Martin, supt. Fax 455-4325
www.zanesville.k12.oh.us
Zanesville HS 1,000/9-12
1701 Blue Ave 43701 740-453-0335
Mark Ulbrich, prin. Fax 455-4329
Zanesville MS 500/6-8
1429 Blue Ave 43701 740-453-0711
Ronald Denton, prin. Fax 454-7005

Bishop Fenwick MS 100/4-8
1030 E Main St 43701 740-453-2637
Kelly Sagan, prin. Fax 454-0653
Bishop Rosecrans HS 100/9-12
1040 E Main St 43701 740-452-7504
Jennifer Mallett, prin. Fax 455-5080
Ohio University Post-Sec.
1425 Newark Rd 43701 740-453-0762
Valley Beauty School Post-Sec.
627 Main St 43701 740-452-6821
Zane State College Post-Sec.
1555 Newark Rd 43701 740-454-2501

Zoarville, Tuscarawas
Tuscarawas Valley Local SD 1,500/PK-12
2637 Tusky Valley Rd NE 44656 330-859-2213
Mark Murphy, supt. Fax 859-2706
www.tvtrojans.org/
Tuscarawas Valley HS 400/9-12
2637 Tusky Valley Rd NE 44656 330-859-2421
Susan Huth, prin. Fax 859-8805
Tuscarawas Valley MS 500/5-8
2633 Tusky Valley Rd NE 44656 330-859-2427
Scott Young, prin. Fax 859-8845

OKLAHOMA

OKLAHOMA DEPARTMENT OF EDUCATION
2500 N Lincoln Blvd Rm 112, Oklahoma City 73105-4503
Telephone 405-521-3301
Fax 405-521-6205
Website http://www.sde.state.ok.us

Superintendent of Public Instruction Janet Barresi

OKLAHOMA BOARD OF EDUCATION
2500 N Lincoln Blvd Rm 112, Oklahoma City 73105-4596

Chairperson Janet Baressi

INTERLOCAL COOPERATIVES (IC)

Atoka-Coal Counties IC
Kris Hall, dir. 580-889-2664
PO Box 1231, Atoka 74525 Fax 889-6302
Cherokee County IC
Sheryl Lynn Rountree, dir. 918-456-1064
15481 N Jarvis Rd Fax 456-1041
Tahlequah 74464
Choctaw Nation IC
Shari Williams, dir. 580-931-0691
PO Box 602, Durant 74702 Fax 931-0120
choctawinterlocal.org

Five Star IC
Nancy Anderson, dir. 918-225-5600
1405 E Moses St, Cushing 74023 Fax 225-3026
www.fsilc.k12.ok.us
Garfield County IC
Joel Quinn, dir., 200 E Broadway St 580-532-4242
Pond Creek 73766 Fax 532-4965
Osage County IC
Jacque Canady, dir. 918-885-2667
207 E Main St, Hominy 74035 Fax 885-6742
www.ocic.k12.ok.us/

Pooled Investment IC
Steven Crawford, pres. 405-524-1191
2801 N Lincoln Blvd Fax 528-5695
Oklahoma City 73105
Seminole County IC
Dr. Audie Woodard, dir. 405-382-6121
630 Golf Rd, Seminole 74868 Fax 382-5254
Southeastern Oklahoma IC
Tracy Mussett, dir. 580-286-3344
103 NE Ave A, Idabel 74745 Fax 286-5598
Tri-County IC
Ty Harman, dir. 580-673-2310
PO Box 217, Fox 73435 Fax 673-2309

PUBLIC, PRIVATE AND CATHOLIC SECONDARY SCHOOLS

Achille, Bryan, Pop. 443
Achille ISD 400/PK-12
PO Box 280 74720 580-283-3775
Rick Beene, supt. Fax 283-3787
achilleisd.org
Achille HS 100/9-12
PO Box 280 74720 580-283-3775
Dana Beene, prin. Fax 283-3524

Ada, Pontotoc, Pop. 15,623
Ada ISD 2,700/PK-12
PO Box 1359 74821 580-310-7200
Pat Harrison, supt. Fax 310-7206
www.adapss.com/
Ada JHS 500/7-9
223 W 18th St 74820 580-310-7260
Bryan Harwell, prin. Fax 310-7261
Ada SHS 500/10-12
1400 Stadium Dr 74820 580-310-7220
Charlie Golightly, prin. Fax 310-7221

Byng ISD 1,800/PK-12
500 S New Bethel Blvd 74820 580-436-3020
Vickie Erichsen, supt. Fax 436-3052
www.byngschools.com
Byng Alternative S Alt
500 S New Bethel Blvd 74820 580-436-3020
Todd Crabtree, admin. Fax 436-3052
Byng JHS 300/7-9
500 S New Bethel Blvd 74820 580-310-6743
Kevin Wilson, prin. Fax 310-6741
Byng SHS 300/10-12
500 S New Bethel Blvd 74820 580-310-6732
Scott Lowrance, prin. Fax 310-6730

Latta ISD 600/PK-12
13925 County Road 1560 74820 580-332-2092
Cliff Johnson, supt. Fax 332-3116
www.latta.k12.ok.us/
Latta HS 100/9-12
13925 County Road 1560 74820 580-332-3300
Stan Cochran, prin.
Latta MS 100/6-8
13925 County Road 1560 74820 580-332-8180
Terry Painter, prin.

OK Dept. of Voc. & Tech. Education
Supt. — None
Phil Berkenbile Ed.D., dir.
Pontotoc Technology Center Vo/Tech
601 W 33rd St 74820 580-310-2200
Greg Pierce, supt. Fax 436-0236

Vanoss ISD 500/PK-12
4665 County Road 1555 74820 580-759-2251
Janet Blocker, supt. Fax 759-3080
www.vanoss.k12.ok.us/
Vanoss HS 200/9-12
4665 County Road 1555 74820 580-759-2503
Gary Stidham, prin. Fax 759-3080
Vanoss MS 200/4-8
4665 County Road 1555 74820 580-759-2623
Marjana Tharp, prin. Fax 759-3080

East Central University Post-Sec.
1100 E 14th St 74820 580-332-8000

Valley View Regional Hospital Post-Sec.
430 N Monte Vista St 74820 580-332-2323

Adair, Mayes, Pop. 736
Adair ISD 1,000/PK-12
PO Box 197 74330 918-785-2424
Tom Linihan, supt. Fax 785-2491
adairschools.org
Adair HS 300/9-12
PO Box 197 74330 918-785-2424
Clifton Collins, prin. Fax 785-2491
Adair MS 300/6-8
PO Box 197 74330 918-785-2425
Brad Rogers, prin. Fax 785-2491

Afton, Ottawa, Pop. 950
Afton ISD 500/PK-12
PO Box 100 74331 918-257-8303
Randy Gardner, supt. Fax 257-4846
www.aftonschools.net/
Afton HS 100/9-12
PO Box 100 74331 918-257-8305
Owen Bowen, prin. Fax 257-5406

OK Dept. of Voc. & Tech. Education
Supt. — None
Phil Berkenbile Ed.D., dir.
Northeast Tech Center Afton Campus Vo/Tech
PO Box 219 74331 918-257-8324
Patricia Tipton, admin. Fax 257-4342

Agra, Lincoln, Pop. 313
Agra ISD 400/PK-12
PO Box 279 74824 918-375-2261
Jay Thomas, supt. Fax 375-2263
www.agra.k12.ok.us/
Agra HS 100/9-12
PO Box 279 74824 918-375-2261
Joe McElroy, prin. Fax 375-2260

Alex, Grady, Pop. 528
Alex ISD 300/PK-12
PO Box 188 73002 405-785-2605
Jim Washburn, supt. Fax 785-2914
www.alex.k12.ok.us
Alex JSHS 100/7-12
PO Box 188 73002 405-785-2264
Doug Tolson, prin. Fax 785-9976

Aline, Alfalfa, Pop. 202
Aline-Cleo ISD 200/PK-12
PO Box 49 73716 580-463-2255
Barry Nault, supt. Fax 463-2256
www.alinecleo.k12.ok.us
Aline-Cleo Springs HS 50/9-12
PO Box 49 73716 580-463-2256
Barry Nault, prin. Fax 463-2256

Allen, Pontotoc, Pop. 878
Allen ISD 400/PK-12
PO Box 430 74825 580-857-2417
Ty Harman, supt. Fax 857-2636
www.allen.k12.ok.us/
Allen HS 100/9-12
PO Box 430 74825 580-857-2416
Rip Garcia, prin. Fax 857-2636

Altus, Jackson, Pop. 19,118
Altus ISD 3,900/PK-12
PO Box 558 73522 580-481-2100
Bob Drury, supt. Fax 481-2129
www.altusschools.k12.ok.us
Altus JHS 600/7-8
PO Box 558 73522 580-481-2173
Roe Worbes, prin. Fax 481-2547
Altus SHS 1,000/9-12
PO Box 558 73522 580-481-2167
Mark Haught, prin. Fax 481-2545

Navajo ISD 400/PK-12
15695 S County Road 210 73521 580-482-7742
Vicki Nance, supt. Fax 482-7749
www.navajo.k12.ok.us
Navajo JSHS 100/7-12
15695 S County Road 210 73521 580-482-7742
Floyd Roach, prin. Fax 482-7749

OK Dept. of Voc. & Tech. Education
Supt. — None
Phil Berkenbile Ed.D., dir.
Southwest Technology Center Vo/Tech
711 W Tamarack Rd 73521 580-477-2250
Dale Latham, supt. Fax 477-0138

Western Oklahoma State College Post-Sec.
2801 N Main St 73521 580-477-2000

Alva, Woods, Pop. 4,829
Alva ISD 800/PK-12
418 Flynn St 73717 580-327-4823
J. Stephen Parkhurst, supt. Fax 327-2965
www.alvaschools.com
Alva HS 200/9-12
501 14th St 73717 580-327-3682
Randy Atkins, prin. Fax 327-4240
Alva MS 200/6-8
800 Flynn St 73717 580-327-0608
Ron Sunderland, prin. Fax 327-4255

OK Dept. of Voc. & Tech. Education
Supt. — None
Phil Berkenbile Ed.D., dir.
Northwest Technology Center Vo/Tech
1801 11th St 73717 580-327-0344
Daren Slater, dir. Fax 327-5467

Northwestern Oklahoma State University Post-Sec.
709 Oklahoma Blvd 73717 580-327-1700

Amber, Grady, Pop. 416
Amber-Pocasset ISD 500/PK-12
PO Box 38 73004 405-224-5768
Chad Hance, supt. Fax 224-5115
www.ampo.k12.ok.us/
Amber-Pocasset HS 100/10-12
PO Box 38 73004 405-224-4017
Rob Friesen, prin. Fax 224-5115
Amber-Pocasset JHS 100/7-9
PO Box 38 73004 405-224-4017
Rob Friesen, prin. Fax 224-5115

Anadarko, Caddo, Pop. 6,230
Anadarko ISD 2,000/PK-12
1400 S Mission St 73005 405-247-6605
Cindy Hackney, supt. Fax 247-6819
www.apswarriors.com
Anadarko HS 500/9-12
1400 Warrior Dr 73005 405-247-2486
Mike Sparks, prin. Fax 247-7066
Anadarko MS 400/6-8
900 W College St 73005 405-247-6671
Doug Hall, prin. Fax 247-3666

Antlers, Pushmataha, Pop. 2,335
Antlers ISD 1,000/K-12
219 NE A St 74523 580-298-5504
Cary Ammons, supt. Fax 298-4006
www.antlers.k12.ok.us
Antlers HS 300/9-12
219 NE A St 74523 580-298-2141
Bryan McNutt, prin. Fax 298-4019
Obuch MS 200/6-8
219 NE A St 74523 580-298-3308
Pam Matthews, prin. Fax 298-4012

Apache, Caddo, Pop. 1,370
Boone-Apache ISD 600/PK-12
PO Box 354 73006 580-588-3369
Wade Stafford, supt. Fax 588-3400
www.apache.k12.ok.us/
Apache HS 200/9-12
PO Box 354 73006 580-588-3358
Jennie Nunn, prin. Fax 588-2079
Apache MS, PO Box 354 73006 100/7-8
Jennie Nunn, prin. 580-588-2122

Arapaho, Custer, Pop. 774
Arapaho-Butler ISD 300/PK-12
PO Box 160 73620 580-323-3261
Bob Haggard, supt. Fax 323-5886
www.arapaho.k12.ok.us/
Arapaho-Butler HS 100/9-12
PO Box 160 73620 580-323-3261
Ken Downs, prin. Fax 323-5886

Ardmore, Carter, Pop. 22,734
Ardmore ISD 3,100/PK-12
PO Box 1709 73402 580-223-2483
Sonny Bates, supt. Fax 226-2472
www.ardmoreschools.org
Ardmore HS 800/9-12
PO Box 1709 73402 580-226-7680
Kim Holland, prin. Fax 221-3012
Ardmore MS 600/6-8
PO Box 1709 73402 580-223-2475
Jill Day, prin. Fax 221-3060

Dickson ISD 1,300/PK-12
4762 State Highway 199 73401 580-223-9557
Sherry Howe, supt. Fax 223-3624
www.dickson.k12.ok.us
Dickson HS 400/9-12
4762 State Highway 199 73401 580-226-0633
Rex Trent, prin. Fax 226-3974
Dickson MS 300/6-8
4762 State Highway 199 73401 580-223-2700
Toby Ringwald, prin. Fax 223-3972

Lone Grove ISD
Supt. — See Lone Grove
Lone Grove HS 400/9-12
6286 Meridian Rd 73401 580-657-3133
Chris Sudderth, prin. Fax 657-6624
Lone Grove MS 400/6-8
6362 Meridian Rd 73401 580-657-3132
Michael Tamez, prin. Fax 657-2691

OK Dept. of Voc. & Tech. Education
Supt. — None
Phil Berkenbile Ed.D., dir.
Southern Oklahoma Technology Center Vo/Tech
2610 Sam Noble Pkwy 73401 580-223-2070
Dr. David Powell, supt. Fax 223-2120

Plainview ISD 1,400/PK-12
1140 S Plainview Rd 73401 580-223-6319
Karl Stricker, supt. Fax 490-3190
www.plainview.k12.ok.us/
Plainview HS 400/9-12
1140 S Plainview Rd 73401 580-223-5877
Brian Nickel, prin. Fax 490-3191
Plainview MS 300/6-8
1140 S Plainview Rd 73401 580-223-6502
Tim Parham, prin. Fax 490-3192

Oklahoma State Horseshoeing School Post-Sec.
4802 Dogwood Rd 73401 580-223-0064

Arkoma, LeFlore, Pop. 1,878
Arkoma ISD 400/PK-12
PO Box 349 74901 918-875-3351
John Turner Ed.D., supt. Fax 875-3780
Arkoma HS 100/9-12
PO Box 349 74901 918-875-3353
Cyal Walden, prin. Fax 875-3780

Arnett, Ellis, Pop. 514
Arnett ISD 200/PK-12
PO Box 317 73832 580-885-7811
Doug Spillman, supt. Fax 885-7307
www.arnett.k12.ok.us/
Arnett HS 100/9-12
PO Box 317 73832 580-885-7285
Bob Dobrinski, prin. Fax 885-7922

Asher, Pottawatomie, Pop. 357
Asher ISD 200/PK-12
PO Box 168 74826 405-784-2332
Terry Grissom, supt. Fax 784-2306
www.asher.k12.ok.us
Asher HS 100/9-12
PO Box 168 74826 405-784-2331
Jami Chambers, prin. Fax 784-2306

Atoka, Atoka, Pop. 2,819
Atoka ISD 900/PK-12
PO Box 720 74525 580-889-6611
Dwayne Noble, supt. Fax 889-2513
atoka.org
Atoka HS 300/9-12
PO Box 720 74525 580-889-3361
Steve Osborn, prin. Fax 889-6453
McCall MS 200/6-8
PO Box 720 74525 580-889-5640
Robert Prentice, prin. Fax 889-4064

OK Dept. of Voc. & Tech. Education
Supt. — None
Phil Berkenbile Ed.D., dir.
Kiamichi Technology Center Vo/Tech
PO Box 240 74525 580-889-7321
Elaine Gee, dir. Fax 889-5642

Tushka ISD 500/PK-12
204 S Pecan St 74525 580-889-7355
Bill Pingleton, supt. Fax 889-6144
www.tushka.k12.ok.us
Tushka HS 200/9-12
204 S Pecan St 74525 580-889-7355
Matt Simpson, prin. Fax 889-6144

Balko, Beaver
Balko ISD, RR 1 Box 37 73931 200/PK-12
Larry Mills, supt. 580-646-3385
www.balko.k12.ok.us/
Balko HS, RR 1 Box 37 73931 50/9-12
Braden Naylor, prin. 580-646-3385

Barnsdall, Osage, Pop. 1,134
Barnsdall ISD 400/PK-12
PO Box 629 74002 918-847-2271
Rick Loggins, supt. Fax 847-3029
www.barnsdall.k12.ok.us/
Barnsdall HS, PO Box 629 74002 100/10-12
Russell McCauley, prin. 918-847-2721
Barnsdall JHS, PO Box 629 74002 100/7-9
Russell McCauley, prin. 918-847-2721

Bartlesville, Washington, Pop. 33,922
Bartlesville ISD 5,700/PK-12
PO Box 1357 74005 918-336-8600
Dr. Gary Quinn, supt. Fax 337-3643
www.bartlesville.k12.ok.us
Alternative HS Alt
1700 Hillcrest Dr 74003 918-336-3311
LaDonna Chancellor, prin. Fax 337-6226
Bartlesville Mid HS 900/9-10
5900 Baylor Dr 74006 918-333-4444
Jason Langham, prin. Fax 335-6311
Bartlesville SHS 800/11-12
1700 Hillcrest Dr 74003 918-336-3311
LaDonna Chancellor, prin. Fax 337-6226
Central MS 600/6-8
408 E 9th St 74003 918-336-9302
Ryan Huff, prin. Fax 337-6270
Madison MS 600/6-8
500 S Madison Blvd 74006 918-333-3176
Joey Eidson, prin. Fax 335-6377

OK Dept. of Voc. & Tech. Education
Supt. — None
Phil Berkenbile Ed.D., dir.
Tri-County Technology Center Vo/Tech
6101 Nowata Rd 74006 918-333-2422
Lindel Fields, supt. Fax 331-3274

Oklahoma Wesleyan University Post-Sec.
2201 Silver Lake Rd 74006 918-333-6151
Wesleyan Christian S 300/PK-12
1780 Silver Lake Rd 74006 918-333-8631
Rev. Mark Listen, admin. Fax 333-8632

Battiest, McCurtain
Battiest ISD 300/PK-12
PO Box 199 74722 580-241-7810
Lendall Martin, supt. Fax 241-7847
www.battiest.k12.ok.us/
Battiest HS 100/9-12
PO Box 199 74722 580-241-5550
Stacey Ebert, prin. Fax 241-7847

Beaver, Beaver, Pop. 1,494
Beaver ISD 400/PK-12
PO Box 580 73932 580-625-3444
Scott Kinsey, supt. Fax 625-3690
www.beaver.k12.ok.us
Beaver HS 100/9-12
PO Box 580 73932 580-625-3444
Michael McVay, prin. Fax 625-3690

Beggs, Okmulgee, Pop. 1,177
Beggs ISD 1,100/PK-12
1201 W 9th St 74421 918-267-3628
Cindy Swearingen, supt. Fax 267-3635
www.beggs.k12.ok.us
Beggs HS 300/9-12
1201 W 9th St 74421 918-267-3625
Gary McElroy, prin. Fax 267-3624
Beggs MS 200/5-8
1201 W 9th St 74421 918-267-4916
Doug Price, prin. Fax 267-4779

Bennington, Bryan, Pop. 304
Bennington ISD 200/K-12
729 N Perry St 74723 580-847-2737
Donna Anderson, supt. Fax 847-2787
www.benningtonisd.org/
Bennington HS 100/9-12
729 N Perry St 74723 580-847-2310
Jeremy Atwood, prin. Fax 847-2790

Bethany, Oklahoma, Pop. 18,252
Bethany ISD 1,600/PK-12
6721 NW 42nd St 73008 405-789-3801
Dr. Kent Shellenberger, supt. Fax 499-4606
www.bethanyschools.com/
Bethany HS 500/9-12
6721 NW 42nd St 73008 405-789-6370
Dr. Don Wentroth, prin. Fax 499-4634
Bethany MS 400/6-8
6721 NW 42nd St 73008 405-787-3240
Matthew Flinton, prin. Fax 499-4606

Putnam City ISD
Supt. — See Oklahoma City
Western Oaks MS 600/6-8
7200 NW 23rd St 73008 405-789-4434
Patricia Balenseifen, prin. Fax 491-7616

Southern Nazarene University Post-Sec.
6729 NW 39th Expy 73008 405-789-6400
Southwestern Christian University Post-Sec.
PO Box 340 73008 405-789-7661

Billings, Noble, Pop. 499
Billings ISD 100/PK-12
PO Box 39 74630 580-725-3271
Rodney Vollmer, supt. Fax 725-3278
www.billings.k12.ok.us
Billings HS 50/9-12
PO Box 39 74630 580-725-3271
Rodney Vollmer, prin. Fax 725-3278

Binger, Caddo, Pop. 635
Binger-Oney ISD 300/K-12
PO Box 280 73009 405-656-2304
Kirk Wilson, supt. Fax 656-2267
www.binger-oney.k12.ok.us/
Binger-Oney HS 100/9-12
PO Box 280 73009 405-656-2304
Doyle Bates, prin. Fax 656-2267

Bixby, Tulsa, Pop. 19,948
Bixby ISD 4,800/PK-12
109 N Armstrong St 74008 918-366-2200
Dr. Kyle Wood, supt. Fax 366-4241
www.bixbyps.org
Bixby HS 1,300/9-12
109 N Armstrong St 74008 918-366-2234
Terry Adams, prin. Fax 366-2350
Bixby MS 700/7-8
109 N Armstrong St 74008 918-366-2201
Mike Lemon, prin. Fax 366-2337

Blackwell, Kay, Pop. 6,745
Blackwell ISD 1,500/PK-12
201 E Blackwell Ave 74631 580-363-2570
Monte Sill, supt. Fax 363-5513
www.blackwell.k12.ok.us/
Blackwell HS 400/9-12
303 E Coolidge Ave 74631 580-363-3553
Harold LeValley, prin. Fax 363-2133
Blackwell MS 400/6-8
1041 S 1st St 74631 580-363-2100
Jaylene Soulek, prin. Fax 363-7010

Blair, Jackson, Pop. 786
Blair ISD 300/PK-12
PO Box 428 73526 580-563-2632
Jimmy Smith, supt. Fax 563-9166
www.blairschool.org
Blair HS 100/9-12
PO Box 428 73526 580-563-2486
Ronnie McKee, prin. Fax 563-9166

Blanchard, McClain, Pop. 7,360
Blanchard ISD 1,600/PK-12
400 N Harrison Ave 73010 405-485-3391
Dr. Jim Beckham, supt. Fax 485-2985
www.blanchard.k12.ok.us/
Blanchard HS 500/9-12
400 N Harrison Ave 73010 405-485-3392
Glen Castle, prin. Fax 485-9549
Blanchard MS 300/6-8
400 N Harrison Ave 73010 405-485-3393
Larry McVay, prin. Fax 485-9103

Bridge Creek ISD 1,400/PK-12
2209 E Sooner Rd 73010 405-387-4880
David Morrow, supt. Fax 387-4882
www.bridgecreek.k12.ok.us/
Bridge Creek HS 400/9-12
2209 E Sooner Rd 73010 405-387-3981
K.B. Wedel, prin. Fax 387-2554
Bridge Creek MS 300/6-8
2209 E Sooner Rd 73010 405-387-9681
Dena Rogers, prin. Fax 387-2552

Bluejacket, Craig, Pop. 318
Bluejacket ISD 200/PK-12
PO Box 29 74333 918-784-2365
Almeda Carroll, supt. Fax 784-2130
www.bluejacket.k12.ok.us
Bluejacket HS 100/9-12
PO Box 29 74333 918-784-2133
Shellie Baker, prin. Fax 784-2130
Bluejacket MS, PO Box 29 74333 100/6-8
Shellie Baker, prin. 918-784-2133

Boise City, Cimarron, Pop. 1,253
Boise City ISD 300/PK-12
PO Box 1116 73933 580-544-3110
Dr. Ira Harris, supt. Fax 544-2972
www.boisecity.k12.ok.us/
Boise City HS, PO Box 1115 73933 100/9-12
Mark Hayes, prin. 580-544-3111

Bokchito, Bryan, Pop. 591
Rock Creek ISD 400/PK-12
200 E Steakley St 74726 580-295-3137
Preston Burns, supt. Fax 295-3762
www.rockcreekisd.net

Rock Creek HS 100/9-12
200 E Steakley St 74726 580-295-3761
John Cartwright, prin. Fax 295-3854

Bokoshe, LeFlore, Pop. 466
Bokoshe ISD 200/PK-12
PO Box 158 74930 918-969-2491
Dennis Shoup, supt. Fax 969-2493
www.bokoshe.k12.ok.us
Bokoshe HS, PO Box 158 74930 50/10-12
Jeremy Dyer, prin. 918-969-2341
Bokoshe JHS, PO Box 158 74930 50/7-9
Jeremy Dyer, prin. 918-969-2341

Boswell, Choctaw, Pop. 659
Boswell ISD 400/PK-12
PO Box 839 74727 580-566-2558
Gerald Stegall, supt. Fax 566-2265
www.boswellschools.org/
Boswell HS 100/9-12
PO Box 839 74727 580-566-2735
Keith Edge, prin. Fax 566-2265
Boswell MS 50/7-8
PO Box 839 74727 580-566-2735
Keith Edge, prin. Fax 566-2265

Bowlegs, Seminole, Pop. 377
Bowlegs ISD 300/PK-12
PO Box 88 74830 405-398-4172
Tommy Eaton, supt. Fax 398-4175
www.bowlegs.k12.ok.us
Bowlegs HS 100/9-12
PO Box 88 74830 405-398-4321
Tommy Eaton, prin. Fax 398-4327

Braggs, Muskogee, Pop. 242
Braggs ISD 200/PK-12
PO Box 59 74423 918-487-5265
Michael Broyles, supt. Fax 487-7171
www.braggs.k12.ok.us
Braggs HS 100/9-12
PO Box 59 74423 918-487-5265
Bill Rogers, prin. Fax 487-7171

Bristow, Creek, Pop. 3,811
Bristow ISD 1,700/PK-12
420 N Main St 74010 918-367-5555
Dr. Jeanene Barnett, supt. Fax 367-5848
www.bristow.k12.ok.us
Bristow HS 500/9-12
420 N Main St 74010 918-367-2241
Mike Wayland, prin. Fax 367-5849
Bristow MS 400/6-8
420 N Main St 74010 918-367-3551
Brian Burden, prin. Fax 367-1362

Broken Arrow, Tulsa, Pop. 94,005
Broken Arrow ISD 15,500/PK-12
701 S Main St 74012 918-259-5700
Jarod Mendenhall Ed.D., supt. Fax 258-0399
www.baschools.org/
Broken Arrow Academy Alt
637 E College St 74012 918-259-4600
Jack Pugh, prin. Fax 258-7531
Broken Arrow North Intermediate HS 1,300/9-10
808 E College St 74012 918-259-4320
Kenneth Kinzer, prin. Fax 258-0796
Broken Arrow SHS 2,200/11-12
1901 E Albany St 74012 918-259-4310
Derek Blackburn, prin. Fax 355-3676
Broken Arrow South Intermediate HS 1,100/9-10
301 W New Orleans St 74011 918-259-4330
Dr. Richard Dale, prin. Fax 451-1964
Centennial MS 900/6-8
225 E Omaha St 74012 918-259-4340
Margaret Coates, prin. Fax 251-8347
Childers MS 600/6-8
301 E Tucson St 74011 918-259-4350
Elizabeth Burns, prin. Fax 451-5465
Haskell MS 900/6-8
412 S 9th St 74012 918-259-4360
Mickey Replogle, prin. Fax 251-8685
Oliver MS 700/6-8
3100 W New Orleans St 74011 918-259-4590
Mark Officer, prin. Fax 250-8185
Sequoyah MS 600/6-8
2701 S Elm Pl 74012 918-259-4370
Cindy Williamson, prin. Fax 451-2167

OK Dept. of Voc. & Tech. Education
Supt. — None
Phil Berkenbile Ed.D., dir.
Tulsa Tech Center Broken Arrow Campus Vo/Tech
4000 W Florence St 74011 918-828-3000
Brad Wayman, dir. Fax 828-3009

Union ISD
Supt. — See Tulsa
Union 9th Grade Center 1,100/9-9
7616 S Garnett Rd 74012 918-357-4324
John Federline, prin. Fax 357-7696
Union Eighth Grade Center 1,100/8-8
6501 S Garnett Rd 74012 918-357-4325
Marla Robinson, prin. Fax 357-7899

Broken Arrow Beauty College Post-Sec.
400 S Elm Pl 74012 918-251-9660
Immanuel Lutheran Christian Academy 100/K-12
400 N Aspen Ave 74012 918-251-5422
Katherine McGrew, hdmstr. Fax 251-8365
Summit Christian Academy 500/K-12
200 E Broadway St 74012 918-251-1997
Dan Giddens, supt. Fax 251-2831

Broken Bow, McCurtain, Pop. 3,865
Broken Bow ISD 1,700/PK-12
108 W 5th St 74728 580-584-3306
Carla Ellisor, supt. Fax 584-9482
www.bbisd.org
Broken Bow HS 600/9-12
108 W 5th St 74728 580-584-3365
Daryl Williams, prin. Fax 584-2064
Rector Johnson MS 300/6-8
108 W 5th St 74728 580-584-9603
David Williams, prin. Fax 584-2549

Buffalo, Harper, Pop. 1,288
Buffalo ISD 100/K-12
PO Box 130 73834 580-735-2448
Martin Adams, supt. Fax 735-2619
www.buffalo.k12.ok.us
Buffalo S 100/K-12
PO Box 130 73834 580-735-2448
Martin Adams, prin. Fax 735-2619

Bunch, Adair
Cave Springs ISD 200/PK-12
PO Box 200 74931 918-775-2364
Terry Mays, supt. Fax 776-2052
www.cavesprings.k12.ok.us
Cave Springs HS, PO Box 200 74931 100/9-12
Gerald Fishinghawk, prin. 918-776-2050

Burlington, Alfalfa, Pop. 145
Burlington ISD 200/PK-12
PO Box 17 73722 580-431-2501
Glen Elliott, supt. Fax 431-2237
www.burlingtonschool.com/
Burlington HS 100/9-12
PO Box 17 73722 580-431-2222
Shane Feely, prin. Fax 431-2237

Burneyville, Love
Turner ISD 300/PK-12
PO Box 159 73430 580-276-1307
Leslie Christian, supt. Fax 276-2006
www.turnerisd.org
Turner HS 100/9-12
PO Box 159 73430 580-276-3873
Leslie Christian, prin. Fax 276-2493

Burns Flat, Washita, Pop. 1,998
Burns Flat-Dill City ISD 600/PK-12
PO Box 129 73624 580-562-4844
Ron Hughes, supt. Fax 562-4847
www.bfdc.k12.ok.us
Burns Flat-Dill City HS 100/9-12
PO Box 129 73624 580-562-4846
Cliff McCown, prin.

OK Dept. of Voc. & Tech. Education
Supt. — None
Phil Berkenbile Ed.D., dir.
Western Technology Center Vo/Tech
PO Box 1469 73624 580-562-3181
Hoyt Lewis, supt. Fax 562-4476

Cache, Comanche, Pop. 2,626
Cache ISD 1,500/PK-12
100 Buffalo Cir 73527 580-429-3266
Randy Batt, supt. Fax 429-3271
www.cache.k12.ok.us
Cache HS, 100 Buffalo Cir 73527 500/9-12
Randy Harris, prin. 580-429-3214
Cache MS, 100 Buffalo Cir 73527 400/5-8
Debbie Hoffman, prin. 580-429-8489

Caddo, Bryan, Pop. 914
Caddo ISD 500/PK-12
PO Box 128 74729 580-367-2208
Richard Thomas, supt. Fax 367-2837
www.caddoisd.org
Caddo HS 100/9-12
PO Box 128 74729 580-367-2208
J.T. Busby, prin. Fax 367-2837

Calera, Bryan, Pop. 1,972
Calera ISD 600/PK-12
PO Box 386 74730 580-434-5700
Gerald Parks, supt. Fax 434-5800
www.caleraisd.k12.ok.us
Calera HS 200/9-12
PO Box 386 74730 580-434-5158
Kevin Robinson, prin. Fax 434-7842

Calumet, Canadian, Pop. 484
Calumet ISD 300/PK-12
PO Box 10 73014 405-893-2222
Keith Weldon, supt. Fax 893-8019
www.chs.k12.ok.us
Calumet HS 100/9-12
PO Box 10 73014 405-893-2222
Michael Higgins, prin. Fax 893-8019
Calumet JHS 50/7-8
PO Box 10 73014 405-893-2222
Michael Higgins, prin. Fax 893-8019

Calvin, Hughes, Pop. 277
Calvin ISD 200/PK-12
PO Box 127 74531 405-645-2411
Chris Karch, supt. Fax 645-2384
www.calvin.k12.ok.us
Calvin HS 50/9-12
PO Box 127 74531 405-645-2411
Larry Marlow, prin. Fax 645-2384

Cameron, LeFlore, Pop. 274
Cameron ISD 400/PK-12
PO Box 190 74932 918-654-3225
Jim Caughern, supt. Fax 654-7387
www.cameron.k12.ok.us
Cameron HS 100/9-12
PO Box 190 74932 918-654-3224
Jeremy Williams, prin. Fax 654-3826

Canadian, Pittsburg, Pop. 206
Canadian ISD 400/PK-12
PO Box 168 74425 918-339-7251
Rodney Karch, supt. Fax 339-2393
Canadian HS 100/9-12
PO Box 168 74425 918-339-2705
Bud Rattan, prin. Fax 339-2393

Caney, Atoka, Pop. 176
Caney ISD 200/PK-12
PO Box 60 74533 580-889-1996
Lori Boehme, supt. Fax 889-5033
www.caneyisd.org
Caney HS 100/9-12
PO Box 60 74533 580-889-6607
Matt Brister, prin. Fax 889-7922

Canton, Blaine, Pop. 594
Canton ISD 400/PK-12
PO Box 639 73724 580-886-3516
Carl Baker, supt. Fax 886-3501
www.canton.k12.ok.us
Canton HS, PO Box 639 73724 100/9-12
Marcus Chapman, prin. 580-886-2256

Canute, Washita, Pop. 537
Canute ISD 300/PK-12
PO Box 490 73626 580-472-3295
Mike Maddox, supt. Fax 472-3187
Canute HS 100/9-12
PO Box 490 73626 580-472-3782
Kevin Merz, prin. Fax 472-3187

Carnegie, Caddo, Pop. 1,645
Carnegie ISD 600/PK-12
315 S Carnegie St 73015 580-654-1470
Dr. Kathy Carroll, supt. Fax 654-1644
www.carnegie.k12.ok.us
Carnegie HS 200/9-12
315 S Carnegie St 73015 580-654-1266
Jerry Hulme, prin. Fax 654-2772
Carnegie MS 100/6-8
315 S Carnegie St 73015 580-654-1766
Jane Nix, prin. Fax 654-2281

Carney, Lincoln, Pop. 589
Carney ISD 200/PK-12
PO Box 240 74832 405-865-2344
Dewayne Osborn, supt. Fax 865-2345
www.carney.k12.ok.us/
Carney HS, PO Box 240 74832 50/9-12
Sandra Butler, prin. 405-865-2344

Cashion, Logan, Pop. 779
Cashion ISD 500/PK-12
101 N Euclid Ave 73016 405-433-2741
Marva Oard, supt. Fax 433-2646
www.cashion.k12.ok.us/
Cashion HS 100/9-12
101 N Euclid Ave 73016 405-433-2575
Kyle Vandruff, prin. Fax 433-2646

Catoosa, Rogers, Pop. 6,601
Catoosa SD 2,100/PK-12
2000 S Cherokee St 74015 918-266-8603
Rick Kibbe, supt. Fax 266-8647
www.catoosaps.net/
Catoosa HS 600/9-12
2000 S Cherokee St 74015 918-266-8619
Connie Cypert, prin. Fax 266-1486
Wells MS 500/6-8
2000 S Cherokee St 74015 918-266-8623
Della Parrish, prin. Fax 266-1282

Cement, Caddo, Pop. 491
Cement ISD 300/PK-12
PO Box 60 73017 405-489-3216
Bill Pascoe, supt. Fax 489-3219
www.cement.k12.ok.us
Cement HS 100/9-12
PO Box 60 73017 405-489-3216
Brad McNeil, prin. Fax 489-3219

Chandler, Lincoln, Pop. 2,922
Chandler ISD 1,200/PK-12
901 S CHS 74834 405-258-1450
Wayland Kimble, supt. Fax 258-2657
www.chandler.k12.ok.us
Chandler HS 300/9-12
901 S CHS 74834 405-258-1269
Randy Hedge, prin. Fax 258-0071
Chandler JHS 200/7-8
901 S CHS 74834 405-258-0183
Kent Barton, prin. Fax 258-1850

Chattanooga, Comanche, Pop. 452
Chattanooga ISD 300/PK-12
PO Box 129 73528 580-597-3347
Jerry Brown, supt. Fax 597-3344
www.chatty.k12.ok.us/
Chattanooga HS 100/9-12
PO Box 129 73528 580-597-3347
James Higdon, prin. Fax 597-3344

Checotah, McIntosh, Pop. 3,060
Checotah ISD 1,500/PK-12
PO Box 289 74426 918-473-5610
Mark Calavan, supt. Fax 473-1020
www.checotah.k12.ok.us/
Checotah HS 400/9-12
PO Box 289 74426 918-473-2239
Brian Terry, prin. Fax 473-2532
Checotah MS 300/6-8
PO Box 289 74426 918-473-5912
Jason Donathan, prin. Fax 473-1020

Chelsea, Rogers, Pop. 1,729
Chelsea ISD 700/PK-12
401 Redbud Ln 74016 918-789-2528
Rich McSpadden, supt. Fax 789-3271
www.chelseadragons.net
Chelsea HS, 401 Redbud Ln 74016 300/9-12
Howard Hill, prin. 918-789-2533
Chelsea MS, 401 Redbud Ln 74016 200/6-8
Debbie Hoskins, prin. 918-789-2521

Cherokee, Alfalfa, Pop. 1,474
Cherokee ISD 300/PK-12
PO Box 325 73728 580-596-3391
Cory Ellis, supt. Fax 596-2319
www.cherokee.k12.ok.us
Cherokee HS, PO Box 325 73728 100/9-12
Jeremy Hickman, prin. 580-596-3391

Cheyenne, Roger Mills, Pop. 783
Cheyenne ISD 300/PK-12
PO Box 650 73628 580-497-3371
Rick Garrison, supt. Fax 497-3373
www.cheyenne.k12.ok.us
Cheyenne HS 100/9-12
PO Box 650 73628 580-497-3371
Phillip Butler, prin. Fax 497-3373

Chickasha, Grady, Pop. 15,287
Chickasha ISD 2,100/PK-12
900 W Choctaw Ave 73018 405-222-6500
Jim Glaze, supt. Fax 222-6590
www.chickasha.k12.ok.us/
Caraway Christian S K-12
730 County Road 1330 73018 405-224-1998
Tracy Caraway, supt.
Chickasha HS 700/9-12
900 W Choctaw Ave 73018 405-222-6550
Beth Reigh-Edwards, prin. Fax 222-6558
Chickasha MS 300/6-8
900 W Choctaw Ave 73018 405-222-6530
Dan Turner, prin. Fax 222-6594

OK Dept. of Voc. & Tech. Education
Supt. — None
Phil Berkenbile Ed.D., dir.
Canadian Valley Technology Center Vo/Tech
1401 W Michigan Ave 73018 405-224-7220
George Tiner, admin. Fax 222-3839

Academy of Cosmetology Post-Sec.
607 W Grand Ave 73018 405-222-2323
University of Sciences & Arts of OK Post-Sec.
1727 W Alabama Ave 73018 405-224-3140

Choctaw, Oklahoma, Pop. 10,497
Choctaw-Nicoma Park ISD 5,100/PK-12
12880 NE 10th St 73020 405-769-4859
Dr. Jim McCharen, supt. Fax 769-9821
www.cnpschools.org
Choctaw HS 1,500/9-12
14300 NE 10th St 73020 405-390-8899
David Reid, prin. Fax 390-2275
Choctaw MS 600/6-8
14667 NE 3rd St 73020 405-390-2207
JeanAnn Gaona, prin. Fax 390-4439
Nicoma Park MS 600/6-8
1321 Hickman Ave 73020 405-769-3106
Brent Ingraham, prin. Fax 769-9355

OK Dept. of Voc. & Tech. Education
Supt. — None
Phil Berkenbile Ed.D., dir.
Eastern Oklahoma County Technology Ctr Vo/Tech
4601 N Choctaw Rd 73020 405-390-9591
Dr. Terry Underwood, supt. Fax 390-9598

Chouteau, Mayes, Pop. 1,930
Chouteau-Mazie ISD 900/PK-12
PO Box 969 74337 918-476-8376
Kenny Mason, supt. Fax 476-8538
www.chouteauwildcats.com
Chouteau-Mazie HS 200/9-12
PO Box 969 74337 918-476-8337
Glen Bibelheimer, prin. Fax 476-8372
Chouteau-Mazie MS 200/6-8
PO Box 969 74337 918-476-8337
Michelle Middleton, prin. Fax 476-8306

Claremore, Rogers, Pop. 17,084
Claremore ISD 3,800/PK-12
102 W 10th St 74017 918-923-4200
Mike McClaren, supt. Fax 341-8447
www.claremore.k12.ok.us
Alternative Learning Center Alt
101 W 11th St Ste D 74017 918-341-8292
John Killebrew, dir. Fax 342-3022
Claremore HS 1,300/9-12
1910 N Florence Ave 74017 918-923-4211
Todd Steidley, prin. Fax 343-6331
Rogers JHS 900/6-8
1915 N Florence Ave 74017 918-923-4205
Lindsey Schnoebelen, prin. Fax 343-6332

Justus-Tiawah SD 600/PK-8
14902 E School Rd, 918-341-3626
David Garroutte, supt. Fax 341-4920
www.justustiawah.com
Justus-Tiawah MS North Campus 100/7-8
14902 E School Rd, 918-341-1252
David Garroutte, prin. Fax 341-4920

OK Dept. of Voc. & Tech. Education
Supt. — None
Phil Berkenbile Ed.D., dir.
Northeast Technology Center - Claremore Vo/Tech
1901 N Highway 88 74017 918-342-8066
Rick Reimer, supt. Fax 342-9066

Sequoyah ISD 1,200/PK-12
16441 S 4180 Rd 74017 918-341-5472
Terry Saul, supt. Fax 341-5764
www.sequoyaheagles.net
Sequoyah HS 200/11-12
16401 S 4180 Rd 74017 918-341-0642
Steve Johnson, prin. Fax 343-8105
Sequoyah MS 300/6-8
16403 S 4180 Rd 74017 918-343-5105
Troy Steidley, prin. Fax 343-8109
Sequoyah Mid HS 100/9-10
16405 S 4180 Rd 74017 918-341-5537
Kevin White, prin. Fax 343-8102

Verdigris ISD 1,100/PK-12
26501 S 4110 Rd, 918-266-7227
Michael Payne, supt. Fax 266-3910
vps.k12.ok.us
Verdigris HS 300/10-12
8204 E 540 Rd, 918-266-2336
Randall Risenhoover, prin. Fax 266-0546
Verdigris JHS 200/7-9
8207 E 540 Rd, 918-266-6343
Denton Holland, prin. Fax 266-1554

Claremore Beauty College Post-Sec.
200 N Cherokee Ave 74017 918-341-4370
Claremore Christian S 100/PK-12
1055 W Blue Starr Dr 74017 918-341-1765
Ryan Mullins, prin. Fax 341-1011
Rogers State University Post-Sec.
1701 W Will Rogers Blvd 74017 918-343-7777

Clayton, Pushmataha, Pop. 740
Clayton ISD 300/PK-12
PO Box 190 74536 918-569-4492
Randall Erwin, supt. Fax 569-7757
www.clayton.k12.ok.us/
Clayton HS 100/9-12
PO Box 190 74536 918-569-4156
Keith Milligan, prin. Fax 569-4680

Cleveland, Pawnee, Pop. 3,054
Cleveland ISD 1,700/PK-12
600 N Gilbert Ave 74020 918-358-2210
John Weaver, supt. Fax 358-3071
www.clevelandtigers.com/
Cleveland HS 500/9-12
323 N Gilbert Ave 74020 918-358-2210
Alan Baker, prin. Fax 358-2141
Cleveland MS 400/6-8
322 N Gilbert Ave 74020 918-358-2210
Noel Nation, prin. Fax 358-2534

Clinton, Custer, Pop. 8,804
Clinton ISD 2,100/PK-12
PO Box 729 73601 580-323-1800
Kevin Hime, supt. Fax 323-1804
www.clintonokschools.org/
Clinton HS 500/9-12
PO Box 729 73601 580-323-1230
Kenny Stringer, prin. Fax 323-1236
Clinton MS 300/7-8
PO Box 729 73601 580-323-4228
Janelle Shepherd, prin. Fax 323-3896

Coalgate, Coal, Pop. 1,800
Coalgate ISD 700/PK-12
PO Box 368 74538 580-927-2351
Jim Girten, supt. Fax 927-2694
www.coalgateschools.org
Byrd MS 100/7-8
PO Box 368 74538 580-927-3560
Phillip Wilkinson, prin. Fax 927-4031
Coalgate HS 300/9-12
PO Box 368 74538 580-927-2592
John Plunkett, prin. Fax 927-4020

Colbert, Bryan, Pop. 1,037
Colbert ISD 900/PK-12
PO Box 310 74733 580-296-2624
Jarvis Dobbs, supt. Fax 296-2088
www.colbert.k12.ok.us/
Colbert HS, PO Box 310 74733 200/9-12
Gary Walton, prin. 580-296-2590
Colbert MS, PO Box 310 74733 100/7-8
Gary Walton, prin. 580-296-2590

Colcord, Delaware, Pop. 719
Colcord ISD 600/PK-12
433 S Larmon 74338 918-326-4116
J.D. Parkerson, supt. Fax 326-4471
www.colcordschools.com
Colcord HS 200/9-12
433 S Larmon 74338 918-326-4107
Jerry Swank, prin. Fax 326-4493
Colcord MS 100/6-8
433 S Larmon 74338 918-326-4852
Robert Hampton, prin. Fax 326-4468

Coleman, Johnston
Coleman ISD 200/PK-12
PO Box 188 73432 580-937-4418
Steve Evans, supt. Fax 937-4866
www.colemanisd.org/
Coleman HS 100/9-12
PO Box 188 73432 580-937-4418
Steve Evans, prin. Fax 937-4866

Collinsville, Tulsa, Pop. 5,212
Collinsville ISD 2,600/PK-12
1119 W Broadway St 74021 918-371-2386
Terry Due, supt. Fax 371-4285
www.collinsville.k12.ok.us/
Collinsville HS 700/9-12
2400 W Broadway St 74021 918-371-3382
Jon Coleman, prin. Fax 371-6904
Collinsville MS 600/6-8
1415 W Center St 74021 918-371-2541
Kelly Hamlin, prin. Fax 371-1302

Comanche, Stephens, Pop. 1,590
Comanche ISD 1,000/K-12
1030 Ash Ave 73529 580-439-2900
Terry Davidson, supt. Fax 439-2907
www.comanche.k12.ok.us
Comanche HS 300/9-12
1030 Ash Ave 73529 580-439-2933
Steven Dunham, prin. Fax 439-2950
Comanche MS 200/6-8
1030 Ash Ave 73529 580-439-2922
Brent Crow, prin. Fax 439-2979

Commerce, Ottawa, Pop. 2,364
Commerce ISD 900/PK-12
217 Commerce St 74339 918-675-4316
Jim Haynes, supt. Fax 675-4464
www.commercetigers.net
Commerce HS 200/9-12
420 D St 74339 918-675-4343
Jim Buttram, prin. Fax 675-4682
Commerce MS 200/6-8
500 Commerce St 74339 918-675-4101
Jack Kelley, prin. Fax 675-5353

Copan, Washington, Pop. 683
Copan ISD 300/PK-12
PO Box 429 74022 918-532-4344
Rick Ruckman, supt. Fax 532-4649
www.copan.k12.ok.us/
Copan HS 100/9-12
PO Box 429 74022 918-532-4344
Chris Tanner, prin. Fax 532-4649

Cordell, Washita, Pop. 2,865
Cordell ISD 800/PK-12
PO Box 290 73632 580-832-3420
Brad Overton, supt. Fax 832-1090
www.cordell.k12.ok.us
Cordell JHS 200/7-9
PO Box 290 73632 580-832-3420
Larry Johnson, prin. Fax 832-1091
Cordell SHS 100/10-12
PO Box 290 73632 580-832-3420
Larry Johnson, prin. Fax 832-1091

Corn, Washita, Pop. 497

Corn Bible Academy 100/7-12
PO Box 38 73024 580-343-2262
Curt Cloud, supt. Fax 343-2261

Council Hill, Muskogee, Pop. 140
Midway ISD 200/PK-12
PO Box 127 74428 918-474-3434
John Truesdell, supt. Fax 474-3636
www.midway.k12.ok.us
Midway HS 100/9-12
PO Box 127 74428 918-474-3434
Randy Shaw, prin. Fax 474-3636

Covington, Garfield, Pop. 512
Covington-Douglas ISD 300/PK-12
400 E Main St 73730 580-864-7481
Darren Sharp, supt. Fax 864-7644
www.c-d.k12.ok.us
Covington-Douglas HS 100/9-12
400 E Main St 73730 580-864-7482
Brian Smith, prin. Fax 864-7644

Coweta, Wagoner, Pop. 9,182
Coweta ISD 3,200/PK-12
PO Box 550 74429 918-486-6506
Jeff Holmes, supt. Fax 486-4167
www.cowetaps.com/
Coweta Intermediate HS 200/9-9
PO Box 550 74429 918-486-6103
Leslie Frazier, prin.
Coweta JHS 500/7-8
PO Box 550 74429 918-486-2127
Scott Kempenich, prin. Fax 486-7307
Coweta SHS 700/10-12
PO Box 550 74429 918-486-4474
Doyle Burress, prin. Fax 486-1062

Coyle, Logan, Pop. 317
Coyle ISD 300/PK-12
PO Box 287 73027 405-466-2242
Josh Sumrall M.Ed., supt. Fax 466-2448
www.coyle.k12.ok.us
Coyle HS 100/9-12
PO Box 287 73027 405-466-2242
Patrick Smith, prin. Fax 466-2448

Crescent, Logan, Pop. 1,340
Crescent ISD 600/PK-12
PO Box 719 73028 405-969-3738
H.T. Gee, supt. Fax 969-2003
www.crescentok.com/
Crescent HS 200/9-12
PO Box 719 73028 405-969-2545
Bart Watkins, prin. Fax 969-2003
Crescent MS 100/6-8
PO Box 719 73028 405-969-2227
Michael Wininger, prin. Fax 969-2003

Cromwell, Seminole, Pop. 270
Butner ISD 200/PK-12
PO Box 157 74837 405-944-5545
Bobbette Hamilton, supt. Fax 944-5746
Butner HS 100/9-12
PO Box 157 74837 405-944-5526
Bobbette Hamilton, prin. Fax 944-5746

Crowder, Pittsburg, Pop. 420
Crowder ISD 500/PK-12
PO Box B 74430 918-334-3203
Keith Kincade, supt. Fax 334-3295
www.crowder.k12.ok.us/
Crowder HS, PO Box B 74430 200/9-12
Robert Florenzano, prin. 918-334-3204

Cushing, Payne, Pop. 7,369
Cushing ISD 1,800/PK-12
PO Box 1609 74023 918-225-3425
Koln Knight, supt. Fax 225-5256
cushing.k12.ok.us
Cushing HS 500/9-12
1700 E Walnut St 74023 918-225-6622
James Lauerman, prin. Fax 225-0933
Cushing MS, 316 N Steele Ave 74023 400/6-8
Pat Elder, prin. 918-225-1311

Cyril, Caddo, Pop. 1,013
Cyril ISD 300/PK-12
PO Box 449 73029 580-464-2272
Jamie Mitchell, supt. Fax 464-2445
www.cyril.k12.ok.us
Cyril HS 100/9-12
PO Box 449 73029 580-464-2272
Tim Persinger, prin. Fax 464-2445

Dale, Pottawatomie, Pop. 176
Dale ISD 700/PK-12
300 Smith Ave 74851 405-964-5558
Charles Dickinson, supt. Fax 964-5559
www.dale.k12.ok.us
Dale HS 200/9-12
300 Smith Ave 74851 405-964-5555
Ky Wilkins, prin. Fax 964-5539
Dale MS, 300 Smith Ave 74851 200/6-8
Ky Wilkins, prin. 405-964-2799

Davenport, Lincoln, Pop. 781
Davenport ISD 400/PK-12
PO Box 849 74026 918-377-2277
Daniel Acord, supt. Fax 377-2553
www.davenport.k12.ok.us/
Davenport HS 100/9-12
PO Box 849 74026 918-377-2278
Daniel Acord, prin. Fax 377-4001

Davidson, Tillman, Pop. 307
Davidson ISD 100/PK-12
PO Box 338 73530 580-568-2423
Phillip Ratcliff, supt. Fax 568-2219
www.davidson.k12.ok.us/
Davidson HS 50/9-12
PO Box 338 73530 580-568-2261
Phillip Ratcliff, prin. Fax 568-2219

Davis, Murray, Pop. 2,557
Davis ISD 1,000/PK-12
400 E Atlanta Ave 73030 580-369-2386
Mike Martin, supt. Fax 369-3507
www.davis.k12.ok.us/
Davis HS 300/9-12
400 E Atlanta Ave 73030 580-369-5541
Rod Maynard, prin. Fax 369-3071
Davis MS 300/5-8
400 E Atlanta Ave 73030 580-369-5565
Jeff Jennings, prin. Fax 369-3289

Del City, Oklahoma, Pop. 19,870
Midwest City-Del City ISD
Supt. — See Midwest City
Del City SHS 1,300/9-12
1900 S Sunnylane Rd 73115 405-677-5777
Gina Hill, prin. Fax 671-8675
Del Crest MS 600/6-8
4731 Judy Dr 73115 405-671-8615
Scott Perry, prin. Fax 671-8618
Kerr MS 700/6-8
2300 Linda Ln 73115 405-671-8625
Rob Cherry, prin. Fax 671-8626

Christian Heritage Academy 600/PK-12
4400 SE 27th St 73115 405-672-1787
Josh Bullard, hdmstr. Fax 672-1839
Destiny Christian S 500/PK-12
3801 SE 29th St 73115 405-677-6000
Jim Howard, admin. Fax 677-6066

Depew, Creek, Pop. 440
Depew ISD 400/PK-12
PO Box 257 74028 918-324-5466
Leon Hiett, supt. Fax 324-5336
depew.k12.ok.us
Depew HS 200/9-12
PO Box 257 74028 918-324-5543
Greg Benson, prin. Fax 324-5336

Dewar, Okmulgee, Pop. 790
Dewar ISD 500/PK-12
PO Box 790 74431 918-652-9625
Todd Been, supt. Fax 652-3096
www.dewar.k12.ok.us/
Dewar HS 100/9-12
PO Box 790 74431 918-652-9625
Josh Kilhoffer, prin. Fax 652-3096
Dewar MS 100/6-8
PO Box 790 74431 918-652-9625
Josh Kilhoffer, prin. Fax 652-3096

Dewey, Washington, Pop. 3,212
Dewey ISD 1,200/PK-12
1 Bulldogger Rd 74029 918-534-2241
Dr. David Wilkins, supt. Fax 534-0149
www.dewey.k12.ok.us
Dewey HS, 1 Bulldogger Rd 74029 400/9-12
Vince Vincent, prin. 918-534-0933
Dewey MS, 1 Bulldogger Rd 74029 300/6-8
Leta Moreland, prin. 918-534-0111

Dibble, McClain, Pop. 838
Dibble ISD 700/PK-12
PO Box 9 73031 405-344-6375
Chad Clanton, supt. Fax 344-6977
dibble.k12.ok.us
Dibble HS, PO Box 9 73031 200/9-12
Jerime Parker, prin. 405-344-6380
Dibble MS 200/6-8
PO Box 9 73031 405-344-6380
Darlene Hayhurst, prin. Fax 344-7275

Dover, Kingfisher, Pop. 461
Dover ISD 200/PK-12
PO Box 195 73734 405-828-4206
Floyd Kirk, supt. Fax 828-7150
www.dover.k12.ok.us
Dover HS 100/9-12
PO Box 195 73734 405-828-4204
Darci Lingle, prin. Fax 828-8019

Drummond, Garfield, Pop. 444
Drummond ISD 300/PK-12
PO Box 240 73735 580-493-2216
Mike Woods, supt. Fax 493-2273
www.drummond.k12.ok.us/
Drummond HS, PO Box 240 73735 100/9-12
Greg Kokojan, prin. 580-493-2271

Drumright, Creek, Pop. 2,673
Drumright ISD 600/PK-12
505 W 2nd St 74030 918-352-2492
Robbie Dorsey, supt. Fax 352-4430
www.drumright.k12.ok.us/
Cooper MS 100/6-8
505 W 2nd St 74030 918-352-2318
Kevin Bilyeu, prin. Fax 352-4033
Drumright HS 200/9-12
505 W 2nd St 74030 918-352-2152
Judd Matthes, prin. Fax 352-9845

OK Dept. of Voc. & Tech. Education
Supt. — None
Phil Berkenbile Ed.D., dir.
Central Tech Vo/Tech
3 Central Tech Cir 74030 918-352-2551
Phil Waul, dir. Fax 352-4117

Olive ISD 400/PK-12
9352 S 436th West Ave 74030 918-352-9567
Loren Tackett, supt. Fax 352-4379
www.olive.k12.ok.us/
Olive HS 100/9-12
9352 S 436th West Ave 74030 918-352-9568
Aaron Espolt, prin. Fax 352-4379

Duke, Jackson, Pop. 417
Duke ISD 200/PK-12
PO Box 160 73532 580-679-3014
Kevin Cansler, supt. Fax 679-3017
www.dukeschools.com/
Duke HS, PO Box 160 73532 50/9-12
Darrel Humphries, prin. 580-679-3311

Duncan, Stephens, Pop. 22,474
Duncan ISD 3,900/PK-12
PO Box 1548 73534 580-255-0686
Dr. Sherry Labyer, supt. Fax 252-2453
www.duncanps.org
Duncan HS 1,000/9-12
PO Box 1548 73534 580-255-0700
Gary Reed, prin. Fax 252-2445
Duncan MS 900/6-8
PO Box 1548 73534 580-470-8106
Mike Toone, prin. Fax 470-8743
Edge Academy Alt
PO Box 1548 73534 580-252-2403
Gary Reed, prin. Fax 252-3515

Empire SD 500/PK-12
9450 W Cherokee Rd 73533 580-252-5392
Vicki Davison, supt. Fax 252-4231
www.empireschools.org
Empire JSHS 100/7-12
9450 W Cherokee Rd 73533 580-255-7515
Jodie Roberts, prin. Fax 255-2971

OK Dept. of Voc. & Tech. Education
Supt. — None
Phil Berkenbile Ed.D., dir.
Red River Technology Center Vo/Tech
PO Box 1807 73534 580-255-2903
Ken Layn, supt. Fax 255-5652

Eve's College of Hairstyling Post-Sec.
PO Box 1545 73534 580-355-6620

Durant, Bryan, Pop. 14,924
Durant ISD 3,400/PK-12
1323 Waco St 74701 580-924-1276
Jason Simeroth Ph.D., supt. Fax 924-6019
www.durantisd.org
Durant HS 800/9-12
950 Gerlach Dr 74701 580-924-4424
Cheryl Conditt, prin. Fax 924-3642
Durant MS 500/7-8
802 W Walnut St 74701 580-924-1321
Kenny Chaffin, prin. Fax 924-8278

OK Dept. of Voc. & Tech. Education
Supt. — None
Phil Berkenbile Ed.D., dir.
Kiamichi Technology Center Vo/Tech
810 Waldron Dr 74701 580-924-7081
Roy Davis, dir. Fax 924-2790

Silo ISD 800/PK-12
122 W Bourne St 74701 580-924-7000
Bill Caruthers, supt. Fax 920-7988
www.siloisd.org
Silo HS 200/9-12
122 W Bourne St 74701 580-924-7000
Mike Palmer, prin. Fax 924-7045
Silo JHS 100/7-8
122 W Bourne St 74701 580-924-7000
Mike Palmer, prin. Fax 924-7045

Southeastern Oklahoma State University Post-Sec.
1405 N 4th Ave 74701 580-745-2000
Southern School of Beauty Post-Sec.
140 W Main St 74701 580-924-1049
Victory Life Academy 200/K-12
3412 W University Blvd 74701 580-920-0850
Misti Mosley, admin. Fax 920-9923

Dustin, Hughes, Pop. 344
Dustin ISD 100/PK-12
PO Box 390660 74839 918-656-3230
Joe Cummings, supt. Fax 656-3242
www.dustin.k12.ok.us
Dustin HS 50/9-12
PO Box 390660 74839 918-656-3230
Joe Cummings, prin. Fax 656-3242

Eagletown, McCurtain, Pop. 515
Eagletown ISD 200/PK-12
PO Box 38 74734 580-835-2242
Kent Hendon, supt. Fax 835-7420
www.eagletownisd.org
Eagletown S 200/PK-12
PO Box 38 74734 580-835-2241
Brian Armstrong, prin. Fax 835-7420

Earlsboro, Pottawatomie, Pop. 569
Earlsboro ISD 300/PK-12
PO Box 10 74840 405-997-5616
Mark Maloy, supt. Fax 997-3181
Earlsboro HS 100/9-12
PO Box 10 74840 405-997-5252
Mark Maloy, prin. Fax 997-3181

Edmond, Oklahoma, Pop. 78,271
Deer Creek ISD 3,100/PK-12
20701 N MacArthur Blvd, 405-348-6100
Sean McDaniel, supt. Fax 348-3049
www.deercreekschools.org/
Deer Creek Freshman Academy 300/9-9
6101 NW 206th St, 405-348-5720
Melissa Jordan, prin. Fax 359-3179
Deer Creek HS 700/10-12
6101 NW 206th St, 405-348-5720
Tracy Skinner, prin. Fax 359-3155
Deer Creek MS 600/7-8
21175 N MacArthur Blvd, 405-348-4830
Reuben Bellows, prin. Fax 359-3163

Edmond ISD 21,100/PK-12
1001 W Danforth Rd 73003 405-340-2800
Dr. David Goin, supt. Fax 340-2835
www.edmondschools.net/
Boulevard Academy Alt
1000 E 15th St 73013 405-340-2865
Mark Andrus, dir. Fax 330-6057
Central MS 800/6-8
500 E 9th St 73034 405-340-2890
Brandon Kysar, prin. Fax 340-3961
Cheyenne MS 900/6-8
1271 W Covell Rd 73003 405-340-2940
Susie Schinnerer, prin. Fax 330-7397
Cimarron MS 800/6-8
3701 S Bryant Ave 73013 405-340-2935
Cordell Ehrich, prin. Fax 330-3398
Edmond Memorial HS 2,000/9-12
1000 E 15th St 73013 405-340-2850
Debbie Bendick Ed.D., prin. Fax 340-2856
Edmond North HS 2,400/9-12
215 W Danforth Rd 73003 405-340-2875
Jason Pittenger, prin. Fax 330-7349
Edmond Santa Fe HS 1,900/9-12
1901 W 15th St 73013 405-340-2230
Jason Hayes, prin. Fax 340-2240
Sequoyah MS 1,100/6-8
1125 E Danforth Rd 73034 405-340-2900
Jason Galloway, prin. Fax 340-2909
Summit MS 1,000/6-8
1703 NW 150th St 73013 405-340-2920
Desarae Witmer, prin. Fax 340-2933

Oklahoma Christian Academy PK-12
1101 E 9th St 73034 405-348-3108
Gabe Schmidt, prin. Fax 844-6884
Oklahoma Christian S 800/PK-12
PO Box 509 73083 405-341-2265
Al King, hdmstr. Fax 341-4710
University of Central Oklahoma Post-Sec.
100 N University Dr 73034 405-974-2000

Eldorado, Jackson, Pop. 420
Eldorado SD I025 100/PK-12
PO Box J 73537 580-633-2219
Dr. Harold Hayes, supt. Fax 633-2316
www.eldorado.k12.ok.us/
Eldorado HS 50/9-12
PO Box J 73537 580-633-2219
Chrystal Bryant, prin. Fax 633-2316

Elgin, Comanche, Pop. 2,058
Elgin ISD 1,800/PK-12
PO Box 369 73538 580-492-3663
Tom Crimmins, supt. Fax 492-4084
www.elginps.org
Elgin HS 500/9-12
PO Box 369 73538 580-492-3670
Curtis Lorah, prin. Fax 492-3697
Elgin MS 600/5-8
PO Box 369 73538 580-492-3655
Chris Garner, prin. Fax 492-3658

Elk City, Beckham, Pop. 11,396
Elk City ISD 2,300/PK-12
222 W Broadway Ave 73644 580-225-0175
Buddy Wood, supt. Fax 225-8644
www.elkcityschools.com/
EC Alternative Education Alt
222 W Broadway Ave 73644 580-225-4135
Jamey Cook, prin. Fax 225-4135
Elk City HS 400/10-12
222 W Broadway Ave 73644 580-225-0105
Jeff Lewallen, prin. Fax 225-1359
Elk City JHS 300/8-9
222 W Broadway Ave 73644 580-225-0476
Tammy Russell, prin. Fax 225-0208
Adult Education Adult
222 W Broadway Ave 73644 580-225-4135
DeRoy Elledge, admin.

Merritt ISD 600/PK-12
19693 E 1130 Rd 73644 580-225-5460
Jeff Daugherty, supt. Fax 225-5469
www.merritt.k12.ok.us
Merritt HS 100/9-12
19693 E 1130 Rd 73644 580-225-5460
Don Bradshaw, prin. Fax 225-5469

Elmore City, Garvin, Pop. 671
Elmore City-Pernell ISD 500/PK-12
100 N Muse Ave 73433 580-788-2565
Donny Darrow, supt. Fax 788-4665
www.ecphs.k12.ok.us
Elmore City-Pernell HS 100/9-12
100 N Muse Ave 73433 580-788-2565
Jackie Sadler, prin. Fax 788-4665

El Reno, Canadian, Pop. 16,130
El Reno ISD 2,300/PK-12
PO Box 580 73036 405-262-1703
Ranet Tippens, supt. Fax 262-8620
www.elreno.ps.org
Dale JHS 200/8-9
PO Box 580 73036 405-262-3253
Pat Liticker, prin. Fax 262-8650
El Reno Alternative Academy Alt
PO Box 580 73036 405-262-3374
Garland Delk, dir. Fax 262-8650
El Reno HS 600/10-12
PO Box 580 73036 405-262-3254
Matt Goucher, prin. Fax 262-8629

OK Dept. of Voc. & Tech. Education
Supt. — None
Phil Berkenbile Ed.D., dir.
Canadian Valley Technology Center Vo/Tech
6505 E US Highway 66 73036 405-422-2200
Dr. Greg Winters, supt. Fax 422-2292

Canadian Valley Area Voc-Tech School Post-Sec.
6505 E US Highway 66 73036 405-262-2629
Redlands Community College Post-Sec.
1300 S Country Club Rd 73036 405-262-2552

Enid, Garfield, Pop. 46,752
Chisholm ISD 900/PK-12
300 Colorado Ave 73701 580-237-5512
Roydon Tilley, supt. Fax 234-5334
www.chisholm.k12.ok.us
Chisholm HS 200/9-12
4018 W Carrier Rd 73703 580-233-2852
Jaymie Morley, prin. Fax 233-9325
Chisholm MS 200/6-8
4202 W Carrier Rd 73703 580-234-0234
Shane Dent, prin. Fax 234-0343

Enid ISD 7,000/PK-12
500 S Independence St 73701 580-366-7000
Shawn Hime, supt. Fax 249-3565
www.enidk12.org/
Emerson MS 500/6-8
700 W Elm Ave 73701 580-366-7250
Doug Stafford, prin. Fax 249-3587
Enid HS 1,700/9-12
611 W Wabash Ave 73701 580-366-8300
Jim Beierschmitt, prin. Fax 249-3576
Longfellow MS 400/6-8
900 E Broadway Ave 73701 580-366-8200
Scott Fitzgerald, prin. Fax 249-3586
Waller MS 600/6-8
2604 W Randolph Ave 73703 580-366-7900
Charles Carpenter, prin. Fax 249-3585

OK Dept. of Voc. & Tech. Education
Supt. — None
Phil Berkenbile Ed.D., dir.
Autry Technology Center Vo/Tech
1201 W Willow Rd 73703 580-242-2750
Dr. Jim Strate, supt. Fax 233-8262

Enid Beauty College Post-Sec.
3905 S La Mesa Dr 73703 580-237-6677
Northern Oklahoma College Post-Sec.
PO Box 2300 73702 580-242-6300
Oklahoma Bible Academy 300/6-12
5913 W Chestnut Ave 73703 580-242-4104
Dallas Caldwell, hdmstr. Fax 242-4106
O T Autry Area Vocational Tech Center Post-Sec.
1201 W Willow Rd 73703 580-242-2750
St. Mary's Hospital Post-Sec.
305 S 5th St 73701 580-233-6100

Erick, Beckham, Pop. 1,034
Erick ISD 200/PK-12
PO Box 9 73645 580-526-3476
Jeff Kelly, supt. Fax 526-3308
www.erickps.k12.ok.us/
Erick HS 100/9-12
PO Box 9 73645 580-526-3351
Lantze Blevins, prin. Fax 526-3351

Eufaula, McIntosh, Pop. 2,615
Eufaula ISD 1,300/PK-12
215 N 6th St 74432 918-689-2152
Rita Ford, supt. Fax 689-1080
www.eufaula.k12.ok.us/
Eufaula HS 400/9-12
1 Bell Anderson 74432 918-689-2556
Garrett Davis, prin. Fax 689-1099
Eufaula MS 300/6-8
1711 W J M Bailey Hwy 74432 918-689-2711
Chris Whelan, prin. Fax 689-2874

Fairfax, Osage, Pop. 1,241
Woodland SD 400/PK-12
100 N 6th St 74637 918-642-3297
Todd Kimrey, supt. Fax 642-5754
www.woodland.k12.ok.us/
Woodland HS 100/9-12
100 N 6th St 74637 918-642-3295
Rick Rogers, prin. Fax 642-5754
Other Schools – See Ralston

Fairland, Ottawa, Pop. 935
Fairland ISD 600/PK-12
202 W Washington Ave 74343 918-676-3811
Mark Alexander, supt. Fax 676-3594
www.fairlandowls.com
Fairland HS 200/9-12
202 W Washington Ave 74343 918-676-3246
Jerry Johnson, prin.

Fairview, Major, Pop. 2,532
Fairview ISD 600/PK-12
408 E Broadway 73737 580-227-2531
Rocky Burchfield, supt. Fax 227-2642
www.fairviewhigh.com
Chamberlain MS 100/6-8
1000 E Elm St 73737 580-227-2555
Cheryl Hasty, prin. Fax 227-2642
Fairview HS 200/9-12
316 N 8th Ave 73737 580-227-4446
Brian Hamar, prin. Fax 227-1004

OK Dept. of Voc. & Tech. Education
Supt. — None
Phil Berkenbile Ed.D., dir.
Northwest Technology Center Vo/Tech
801 S Vo Tech Dr 73737 580-227-3708
Colt Shaw, dir. Fax 227-2651

Fargo, Ellis, Pop. 359
Fargo ISD 200/PK-12
PO Box 200 73840 580-698-2298
Terry Stevens, supt. Fax 698-8019
www.fargo.k12.ok.us
Fargo HS 100/9-12
PO Box 200 73840 580-698-2298
Sherri Tune, prin. Fax 698-8019

Felt, Cimarron, Pop. 89
Felt ISD 100/PK-12
PO Box 47 73937 580-426-2220
Lewetta Hefley, supt. Fax 426-2799
www.felt.k12.ok.us
Felt HS 50/9-12
PO Box 47 73937 580-426-2220
Lewetta Hefley, prin. Fax 426-2799

Fletcher, Comanche, Pop. 1,123
Fletcher ISD 400/PK-12
PO Box 489 73541 580-549-6027
Randy Harris, supt. Fax 549-6016
www.fletcherschools.org/
Fletcher HS, PO Box 489 73541 100/10-12
Amanda Grimes, prin. 580-549-6015
Fletcher JHS 100/7-9
PO Box 489 73541 580-549-3031
Amanda Grimes, prin. Fax 549-6016

Forgan, Beaver, Pop. 539
Forgan ISD 200/PK-12
PO Box 406 73938 580-487-3366
Travis Smalts, supt. Fax 487-3368
www.forgan.k12.ok.us
Forgan HS 100/9-12
PO Box 406 73938 580-487-3366
Todd Kerr, prin. Fax 487-3368

Fort Cobb, Caddo, Pop. 599
Fort Cobb-Broxton ISD 300/PK-12
PO Box 130 73038 405-643-2336
Kyle Lierle, supt. Fax 643-2547
Fort Cobb-Broxton HS 100/9-12
PO Box 130 73038 405-643-2820
Kyle Lierle, prin. Fax 643-3115
Fort Cobb-Broxton MS 100/6-8
PO Box 130 73038 405-643-2820
James Biddy, prin.

OK Dept. of Voc. & Tech. Education
Supt. — None
Phil Berkenbile Ed.D., dir.
Caddo-Kiowa Technology Center Vo/Tech
PO Box 190 73038 405-643-5511
Dennis Ruttman, supt. Fax 643-3014

Fort Gibson, Muskogee, Pop. 3,804
Fort Gibson ISD 1,800/PK-12
500 Ross Ave 74434 918-478-2474
Derald Glover, supt. Fax 478-8533
www.ftgibson.k12.ok.us
Fort Gibson HS 600/9-12
500 Ross Ave 74434 918-478-2452
Gary Sparks, prin. Fax 478-6244
Fort Gibson MS 400/6-8
500 Ross Ave 74434 918-478-2471
Gregory Phares, prin. Fax 478-6412

Fort Supply, Woodward, Pop. 320
Fort Supply ISD 100/PK-12
PO Box 160 73841 580-766-2611
Pat Howell, supt. Fax 766-8019
www.fortsupply.k12.ok.us/
Fort Supply HS 50/9-12
PO Box 160 73841 580-766-2611
Melva Little, prin. Fax 766-8019

Fort Towson, Choctaw, Pop. 508
Fort Towson ISD 400/PK-12
PO Box 39 74735 580-873-2712
Jason Price, supt. Fax 873-1053
www.forttowson.k12.ok.us/
Fort Towson HS 100/9-12
PO Box 39 74735 580-873-2325
Tammy Neese, prin. Fax 873-2712

Fox, Carter
Fox ISD 300/PK-12
PO Box 248 73435 580-673-2081
Brent Phelps, supt. Fax 673-2389
www.foxps.k12.ok.us
Fox HS 100/8-12
PO Box 248 73435 580-673-2082
Brent Phelps, prin. Fax 673-2389

Foyil, Rogers, Pop. 287
Foyil ISD 500/PK-12
PO Box 49 74031 918-341-1113
Rod Carter, supt. Fax 341-1223
www.foyil.k12.ok.us
Foyil JSHS 100/7-12
PO Box 49 74031 918-342-1782
Benny Ballard, prin. Fax 341-1223

Frederick, Tillman, Pop. 3,832
Frederick ISD 600/PK-12
PO Box 370 73542 580-335-5516
Shannon Vanderburg, supt. Fax 335-2324
www.frederickbombers.net
Frederick HS 300/9-12
PO Box 610 73542 580-335-5521
Randy Biggs, prin. Fax 335-2634
Frederick MS 200/6-8
PO Box 490 73542 580-335-2014
Jeremy Newton, prin. Fax 335-2763

OK Dept. of Voc. & Tech. Education
Supt. — None
Phil Berkenbile Ed.D., dir.
Great Plains Technology Center Vo/Tech
2001 E Gladstone Ave 73542 580-335-5525
Gary Tyler, admin. Fax 335-2209

Freedom, Woods, Pop. 280
Freedom ISD 100/PK-12
PO Box 5 73842 580-621-3271
Danny McCuiston, supt. Fax 621-3699
www.freedom.k12.ok.us
Freedom HS 50/9-12
PO Box 5 73842 580-621-3272
Brett Hill, prin. Fax 621-3699

Gage, Ellis, Pop. 437
Gage ISD 100/PK-12
PO Box 60 73843 580-923-7666
Greg Gregory, supt. Fax 923-7907
www.gage.k12.ok.us/
Gage HS 50/9-12
PO Box 60 73843 580-923-7909
Greg Gregory, admin. Fax 923-7907

Gans, Sequoyah, Pop. 289
Gans ISD 400/PK-12
PO Box 70 74936 918-775-2236
Brenda Taylor, supt. Fax 775-5145
www.gans.k12.ok.us
Gans HS 100/9-12
PO Box 70 74936 918-775-2236
Larry Calloway, prin. Fax 775-5145

Garber, Garfield, Pop. 806
Garber ISD 300/PK-12
PO Box 539 73738 580-863-2220
Jim Lamer, supt. Fax 863-2259
www.garber.k12.ok.us/
Garber HS, PO Box 539 73738 100/9-12
Phil Hoopes, prin. 580-863-2231

Geary, Blaine, Pop. 1,213
Geary ISD 400/PK-12
110 SW Embree Dr 73040 405-884-2989
Todd Glasgow, supt. Fax 884-2099
www.gearyschools.org
Bison Alternative Academy Alt
110 SW Embree Dr 73040 405-884-2989
Jim Shelton, dir.
Geary JHS 50/7-9
110 SW Embree Dr 73040 405-884-2362
Jim Shelton, prin. Fax 884-5487
Geary SHS 100/10-12
110 SW Embree Dr 73040 405-884-2362
Jim Shelton, prin. Fax 884-5487

Geronimo, Comanche, Pop. 1,179
Geronimo ISD 300/PK-12
800 W Main St 73543 580-355-3160
Chuck Karpe, supt. Fax 357-8307
www.geronimo.k12.ok.us
Geronimo HS 100/7-12
800 W Main St 73543 580-355-3160
Trae Koch, prin. Fax 357-8307

Glencoe, Payne, Pop. 577
Glencoe ISD 300/PK-12
201 E Lone Chimney Rd 74032 580-669-2261
John Lazenby, supt. Fax 669-2961
www.glencoe.k12.ok.us
Glencoe HS 100/9-12
201 E Lone Chimney Rd 74032 580-669-2261
Trevor Maxwell, prin. Fax 669-2961

Glenpool, Tulsa, Pop. 9,951
Glenpool ISD 2,400/PK-12
PO Box 1149 74033 918-322-9500
Kathy Coley, supt. Fax 322-1529
www.glenpool.k12.ok.us
Glenpool HS 600/9-12
PO Box 1149 74033 918-322-9500
Jerry Olansen, prin. Fax 322-6410
Glenpool MS 500/6-8
PO Box 1149 74033 918-322-9500
Kim Coody, prin. Fax 322-6411

Goodwell, Texas, Pop. 1,268
Goodwell ISD 200/PK-12
PO Box 580 73939 580-349-2271
Freida Burgess, supt. Fax 349-2531

Goodwell HS 50/9-12
PO Box 580 73939 580-349-2271
Steve Moore, prin. Fax 349-2531

Yarbrough ISD 100/PK-12
RR 1 Box 31 73939 580-545-3327
Jim Wiggin, supt. Fax 545-3392
www.yarbrough.k12.ok.us/
Yarbrough HS 50/9-12
RR 1 Box 31 73939 580-545-3328
Cliff Benson, prin. Fax 545-3392

Oklahoma Panhandle State University Post-Sec.
PO Box 430 73939 580-349-2611

Gore, Sequoyah, Pop. 891
Gore ISD 500/PK-12
1200 N Highway 10 74435 918-489-5587
Lucky McCrary, supt. Fax 489-5664
www.gore.k12.ok.us/
Gore HS 200/9-12
1200 N Highway 10 74435 918-489-5587
Beverly Robison, prin. Fax 489-5664
Gore MS 100/6-8
1200 N Highway 10 74435 918-487-5587
Beverly Robison, prin. Fax 489-5664

Gracemont, Caddo, Pop. 298
Gracemont ISD 200/PK-12
PO Box 5 73042 405-966-2236
Mike Jones, supt. Fax 966-2395
www.gracemont.k12.ok.us
Gracemont HS 50/9-12
PO Box 5 73042 405-966-2233
Mike Jones, prin. Fax 966-2395

Grandfield, Tillman, Pop. 1,001
Grandfield ISD 300/PK-12
PO Box 639 73546 580-479-5237
Eva Spaulding, supt. Fax 479-3381
www.grandfield.k12.ok.us/
Grandfield HS 100/9-12
PO Box 639 73546 580-479-3140
James Vines, prin. Fax 479-5563

Granite, Greer, Pop. 2,034
Granite ISD 200/PK-12
PO Box 98 73547 580-535-2104
Rickey Webb, supt. Fax 535-2106
www.granite.k12.ok.us
Granite HS 100/9-12
PO Box 98 73547 580-535-2104
Rickey Webb, prin. Fax 535-2106

Grove, Delaware, Pop. 6,167
Grove ISD 2,400/PK-12
PO Box 450789 74345 918-786-3003
Sandy Coaly, supt. Fax 786-9365
www.ridgerunners.net
Grove HS 700/9-12
PO Box 450789 74345 918-786-2208
Renae Dozier, prin. Fax 787-5238
Grove MS 400/7-8
PO Box 450789 74345 918-786-2209
Pat Dodson, prin. Fax 786-6454

Guthrie, Logan, Pop. 9,702
Guthrie ISD 3,300/PK-12
802 E Vilas Ave 73044 405-282-8900
Dr. Mike Simpson, supt. Fax 282-5904
www.guthrie.k12.ok.us
Faver Alternative S Alt
1021 E Perkins Ave 73044 405-282-5941
Pat Hughes, dir. Fax 282-5931
Guthrie HS 900/9-12
200 N Crooks Dr 73044 405-282-5906
Chris LeGrande, prin. Fax 282-5909
Guthrie JHS 500/7-8
705 E Oklahoma Ave 73044 405-282-5936
Tim Rawls, prin. Fax 282-3598

Guymon, Texas, Pop. 11,299
Guymon ISD 2,900/PK-12
PO Box 1307 73942 580-338-4340
Doug Melton, supt. Fax 338-3812
www.guymontigers.com
Central JHS 400/7-8
PO Box 1307 73942 580-338-4360
Claudia Winters, prin. Fax 338-0212
Guymon HS 700/9-12
PO Box 1307 73942 580-338-4350
Randy Williams, prin. Fax 338-0994

Haileyville, Pittsburg, Pop. 762
Haileyville ISD 400/PK-12
PO Box 29 74546 918-297-2626
Roger Hemphill, supt. Fax 297-7136
www.haileyville.k12.ok.us
Haileyville HS 100/9-12
PO Box 29 74546 918-297-2627
Fax 297-3215

Hammon, Roger Mills, Pop. 547
Hammon ISD 200/PK-12
PO Box 279 73650 580-473-2221
Randy Ann Stickney, supt. Fax 473-2464
www.hammon.k12.ok.us/
Hammon HS 100/9-12
PO Box 279 73650 580-473-2737
Richard Megli, prin. Fax 473-2464

Hanna, McIntosh, Pop. 131
Hanna ISD 400/PK-12
PO Box 10 74845 918-657-2523
Patricia Berry, supt. Fax 657-2424
Hanna HS, PO Box 10 74845 400/9-12
David Dewalt, prin. 918-657-2527

Hardesty, Texas, Pop. 209
Hardesty ISD 100/PK-12
PO Box 129 73944 580-888-4258
Stephen Carroll, supt. Fax 888-4560
www.hardesty.k12.ok.us
Hardesty HS 50/9-12
PO Box 129 73944 580-888-4258
Aaron Dewlen, prin. Fax 888-4560

Harrah, Oklahoma, Pop. 4,831
Harrah ISD 2,200/PK-12
20670 Walker St 73045 405-454-6244
Dr. Dean Hughes, supt. Fax 454-0022
www.harrahschools.com
Harrah HS 500/10-12
20370 Elm St 73045 405-454-2416
Kenneth Riddle, prin. Fax 454-6842
Harrah JHS 300/8-9
1480 N Dobbs Rd 73045 405-347-2900
John Hunt, prin. Fax 454-6361

Hartshorne, Pittsburg, Pop. 1,925
Hartshorne ISD 800/PK-12
520 S 5th St 74547 918-297-2534
Mark Ichord, supt. Fax 297-2698
www.hartshorne.k12.ok.us
Hartshorne JHS 200/7-9
520 S 5th St 74547 918-297-2433
John Bernardi, prin. Fax 297-2698
Hartshorne SHS 200/10-12
520 S 5th St 74547 918-297-2536
Mike Reddick, prin. Fax 297-2025

Haskell, Muskogee, Pop. 1,802
Haskell ISD 900/PK-12
PO Box 278 74436 918-482-5221
Sharon Herrington, supt. Fax 482-3346
www.haskell.k12.ok.us
Beavers MS 200/6-8
PO Box 278 74436 918-482-5221
Erin Jones, prin. Fax 482-3346
Haskell HS 300/9-12
PO Box 278 74436 918-482-5223
Erin Jones, prin. Fax 482-3346

Haworth, McCurtain, Pop. 273
Haworth ISD 600/PK-12
HC 73 Box 1 74740 580-245-1406
Ted Brewer, supt. Fax 245-2265
www.haworth.k12.ok.us
Haworth JHS 100/7-9
HC 73 Box 1 74740 580-245-1461
Brandy Wall, prin. Fax 245-4911
Haworth SHS 200/10-12
HC 73 Box 1 74740 580-245-1440
Johnny Crabtree, prin. Fax 245-4913

Healdton, Carter, Pop. 2,670
Healdton ISD 500/PK-12
PO Box 490 73438 580-229-0566
Terry Shaw, supt. Fax 229-1522
www.healdtonschools.org/
Healdton HS 100/9-12
PO Box 490 73438 580-229-0540
Terry Shaw, prin. Fax 229-0557
Healdton MS 100/6-8
PO Box 490 73438 580-229-0303
Greg Munholland, prin. Fax 229-1475

Heavener, LeFlore, Pop. 3,279
Heavener ISD 1,100/PK-12
PO Box 698 74937 918-653-7223
Edward Wilson, supt. Fax 653-7843
www.heavenerschools.org
Heavener HS, PO Box 698 74937 300/9-12
Michael Culwell, prin. 918-653-4307

Helena, Alfalfa, Pop. 1,366
Timberlake ISD 200/PK-12
PO Box 287 73741 580-852-3307
Brent Rousey, supt. Fax 852-8019
www.tlake.k12.ok.us
Timberlake HS 100/9-12
PO Box 287 73741 580-852-3281
Charlie Berg, prin. Fax 852-3280

Hennessey, Kingfisher, Pop. 2,093
Hennessey ISD 800/PK-12
604 E Oklahoma St 73742 405-853-4321
Joe McCulley, supt. Fax 853-4439
www.hps.k12.ok.us
Hennessey HS 200/9-12
707 E Oklahoma St 73742 405-853-4394
Brady Barnes, prin. Fax 853-4644
Hennessey MS 200/5-8
120 N Mitchell Rd 73742 405-853-4303
David Garner, prin. Fax 853-4848

Henryetta, Okmulgee, Pop. 5,595
Henryetta ISD 1,300/PK-12
1801 W Troy Aikman Dr 74437 918-652-6523
John Walker, supt. Fax 652-6510
www.henryetta.k12.ok.us
Henryetta HS 300/9-12
1801 W Troy Aikman Dr 74437 918-652-6571
Kolby Johnson, prin. Fax 652-6572
Henryetta MS 300/6-8
1801 W Troy Aikman Dr 74437 918-652-6578
Brad Wion, prin. Fax 652-6506

Wilson ISD 300/PK-12
8867 Chestnut Rd 74437 918-652-3374
Andrea James, supt. Fax 652-8140
www.wpstigers.k12.ok.us
Wilson HS 100/9-12
8867 Chestnut Rd 74437 918-652-3384
Vernie Thomas, prin. Fax 650-9725

Hinton, Caddo, Pop. 3,079
Hinton ISD 700/PK-12
PO Box 1036 73047 405-542-3257
Richard Brownen, supt. Fax 542-3286
www.hintonschools.org
Hinton HS 200/9-12
PO Box 1036 73047 405-542-3235
Chad Broughton, prin. Fax 542-3286
Hinton MS 100/6-8
PO Box 1036 73047 405-542-3235
Chad Broughton, prin. Fax 542-3286

Hobart, Kiowa, Pop. 3,599
Hobart ISD 800/PK-12
PO Box 899 73651 580-726-5691
Roger Hill, supt. Fax 726-2855
www.hobart.k12.ok.us
Hobart HS, PO Box 899 73651 200/9-12
Cathy Hunt, prin. 580-726-5611
Hobart MS, PO Box 899 73651 200/6-8
Misty Reents, prin. 580-726-5615

Holdenville, Hughes, Pop. 5,493
Holdenville ISD 1,100/PK-12
210 Grimes Ave 74848 405-379-5483
Don Ford, supt. Fax 379-5874
www.holdenville.k12.ok.us
Holdenville HS 300/9-12
210 Grimes Ave 74848 405-379-3387
Travis Graham, prin. Fax 379-2012
Thomas MS 300/5-8
210 Grimes Ave 74848 405-379-6661
Mark Turner, prin. Fax 379-8118

Moss ISD 300/PK-12
8087 E 134 Rd 74848 405-379-2273
John Long, supt. Fax 379-2333
www.mossps.k12.ok.us/
Moss HS 100/9-12
8087 E 134 Rd 74848 405-379-7251
Bob Sifers, prin. Fax 379-2333

Hollis, Harmon, Pop. 1,997
Hollis ISD 500/PK-12
PO Box 193 73550 580-688-3450
Jennifer McQueen, supt. Fax 688-2532
www.hollis.k12.ok.us
Hollis HS, PO Box 193 73550 100/9-12
Marty Webb, prin. 580-688-2707
Hollis MS, PO Box 193 73550 100/6-8
Marty Webb, prin. 580-688-2707

Hominy, Osage, Pop. 3,347
Hominy ISD 600/PK-12
200 S Pettit Ave 74035 918-885-6511
Russell Hull, supt. Fax 885-2538
www.hominy.k12.ok.us/
Hominy HS, 200 S Pettit Ave 74035 200/9-12
Doyle Edwards, prin. 918-885-2141
Hominy MS, 200 S Pettit Ave 74035 100/7-8
Pat Drummond, prin. 918-885-6253

Hooker, Texas, Pop. 1,875
Hooker ISD 600/PK-12
PO Box 247 73945 580-652-2162
Dan Faulkner, supt. Fax 652-3118
hookerpublicschools.org
Hooker HS, PO Box 247 73945 100/9-12
Brian Stalder, prin. 580-652-2516

Howe, LeFlore, Pop. 762
Howe ISD 500/PK-12
PO Box 259 74940 918-658-3666
Scott Parks, supt. Fax 658-2233
www.howeschools.org
Howe HS 100/9-12
PO Box 259 74940 918-658-3368
Scott Parks, prin. Fax 658-2233

Hugo, Choctaw, Pop. 4,926
Hugo ISD 1,000/PK-12
208 N 2nd St 74743 580-326-6483
Karen Lyles, supt. Fax 326-2480
www.hugoschools.com
Hugo HS 300/9-12
208 N 2nd St 74743 580-326-9648
Debbie Golden, prin. Fax 326-4811
Hugo MS 300/6-8
208 N 2nd St 74743 580-326-3365
Glen Martin, prin. Fax 326-7352

OK Dept. of Voc. & Tech. Education
Supt. — None
Phil Berkenbile Ed.D., dir.
Kiamichi Technology Center Vo/Tech
PO Box 699 74743 580-326-6491
Debbie Golden, dir. Fax 326-5696

Hulbert, Cherokee, Pop. 518
Hulbert ISD 500/PK-12
PO Box 188 74441 918-772-2501
Dr. Marilyn Dewoody, supt. Fax 772-2766
www.hulbertriders.com
Hulbert JSHS 200/7-12
PO Box 188 74441 918-772-2501
Brad Ferguson, prin. Fax 772-1275

Hydro, Caddo, Pop. 947
Hydro-Eakly ISD 500/PK-12
435 E 7th St 73048 405-663-2774
Bill Derryberry, supt. Fax 663-2139
www.hydroeakly.k12.ok.us/
Hydro-Eakly HS 100/9-12
435 E 7th St 73048 405-663-2246
Jeremy Bussey, prin. Fax 663-2139
Hydro-Eakly MS 100/6-8
435 E 7th St 73048 405-663-2246
Jeremy Bussey, prin. Fax 663-2139

Idabel, McCurtain, Pop. 6,641
Idabel ISD 1,100/PK-12
200 NE Ave C 74745 580-286-7639
James Sharpe, supt. Fax 286-5585
www.idabelps.org
Idabel HS 400/9-12
901 E Lincoln Rd 74745 580-286-7693
Alan Bryant, prin. Fax 286-6755
Idabel MS 200/6-8
100 NE Ave D 74745 580-286-6558
Laura Bullock, prin. Fax 286-8272

OK Dept. of Voc. & Tech. Education
Supt. — None
Phil Berkenbile Ed.D., dir.
Kiamichi Technology Center Vo/Tech
3205 NE Lincoln Rd 74745 580-286-7555
Johnnie Meredith, dir. Fax 286-3753

Indiahoma, Comanche, Pop. 331
Indiahoma ISD 200/PK-12
PO Box 8 73552 580-246-3448
Barbalee Blair, supt. Fax 246-3372
www.indiahoma.k12.ok.us
Indiahoma HS 100/9-12
PO Box 8 73552 580-246-3333
Greg Ellis, prin. Fax 246-3372

Indianola, Pittsburg, Pop. 149
Indianola ISD 300/PK-12
PO Box 119 74442 918-823-4231
Mark Baumann, supt. Fax 823-4234
Indianola HS, PO Box 119 74442 100/9-12
Gina Hernandez, prin. 918-823-4231

Inola, Rogers, Pop. 1,643
Inola ISD 1,300/PK-12
PO Box 1149 74036 918-543-3100
Dr. Kent Holbrook, supt. Fax 543-8754
www.inola.k12.ok.us
Inola HS 400/9-12
PO Box 789 74036 918-543-2404
Paul Gruenberg, prin. Fax 543-2345
Inola MS 400/5-8
PO Box 819 74036 918-543-2434
Jeff Unrau, prin. Fax 543-6268

Jay, Delaware, Pop. 2,212
Jay ISD 1,800/PK-12
PO Box 630 74346 918-253-4293
Charles Thomas, supt. Fax 253-8970
www.jay.k12.ok.us
Jay HS 500/9-12
PO Box 630 74346 918-253-4466
James Bryant, prin. Fax 253-6249
Jay MS 200/7-8
PO Box 630 74346 918-253-8510
Shane Carroll, prin. Fax 253-3342

Jenks, Tulsa, Pop. 16,162
Jenks ISD 10,400/PK-12
205 E B St 74037 918-299-4411
Stacey Butterfield, supt. Fax 299-9197
jenksps.org
Jenks Alternative Center Alt
205 E B St 74037 918-299-4411
Amie Hardy, prin. Fax 298-6640
Jenks Freshman Academy 800/9-9
205 E B St 74037 918-299-4411
Mark Cyrus, prin. Fax 298-0807
Jenks HS 2,200/10-12
205 E B St 74037 918-299-4411
Mike Means, prin. Fax 298-0336
Other Schools – See Tulsa

Jenks Beauty College Post-Sec.
535 W Main St 74037 918-299-0901

Jones, Oklahoma, Pop. 2,585
Jones ISD 1,200/PK-12
412 SW 3rd St 73049 405-399-9215
Mike Steele, supt. Fax 399-9212
www.joneshs.k12.ok.us
Jones HS 300/9-12
304 Dr Lee Simmons 73049 405-399-9122
Carl Johnson, prin. Fax 399-9212
Jones MS 300/6-8
16011 E Wilshire Blvd 73049 405-399-9114
Pam Lucas, prin. Fax 399-6101

Kansas, Delaware, Pop. 726
Kansas ISD 1,000/PK-12
PO Box 196 74347 918-868-2562
Leann Barnwell, supt. Fax 868-3103
www.kansasps.com/
Kansas HS 300/9-12
PO Box 196 74347 918-868-3308
Phil Isom, prin. Fax 868-3103
Kansas JHS 200/6-8
PO Box 196 74347 918-868-5308
Bryon Arnold, prin. Fax 868-5582

OK Dept. of Voc. & Tech. Education
Supt. — None
Phil Berkenbile Ed.D., dir.
Northeast Tech Center Kansas Campus Vo/Tech
PO Box 30 74347 918-868-3535
Greg Mitchell, supt. Fax 868-3530

Kaw City, Kay, Pop. 358
Shidler ISD
Supt. — See Shidler
Shidler MS, PO Box 150 74641 100/5-8
Janice Finton, prin. 580-269-2911

Kellyville, Creek, Pop. 1,083
Kellyville ISD 1,200/PK-12
PO Box 99 74039 918-247-6133
Joe Pierce, supt. Fax 247-6120
www.kellyvilleschools.org/
Kellyville HS, PO Box 99 74039 400/9-12
Danny Woods, prin. 918-247-6333
Kellyville MS, PO Box 99 74039 200/7-8
John Castillo, prin. 918-247-6134

Keota, Haskell, Pop. 531
Keota ISD 400/PK-12
110 NE 6th St 74941 918-966-3950
Rita Echelle, supt. Fax 966-3247
www.keota.k12.ok.us
Keota HS 100/9-12
110 NE 6th St 74941 918-966-3950
Richard Reed, prin. Fax 966-3247

Ketchum, Mayes, Pop. 396
Ketchum ISD 600/PK-12
PO Box 720 74349 918-782-5091
Rick Pool, supt. Fax 782-9018
www.ketchumwarriors.com
Ketchum HS 200/9-12
PO Box 720 74349 918-782-4481
Joe Gramlich, prin. Fax 782-4848
Ketchum MS 100/6-8
PO Box 720 74349 918-782-3242
Leslie Janis, prin. Fax 782-3016

Keyes, Cimarron, Pop. 321
Keyes ISD 100/PK-12
PO Box 47 73947 580-546-7231
Jim Washburn, supt. Fax 546-7338
www.keyes.k12.ok.us
Keyes HS 50/9-12
PO Box 47 73947 580-546-7231
Jim Washburn, prin. Fax 546-7338

Kiefer, Creek, Pop. 1,550
Kiefer ISD 500/PK-12
4600 W 151st St S 74041 918-321-3421
Mary Murrell, supt. Fax 321-5216
www.kiefer.k12.ok.us/
Kiefer HS 200/9-12
4600 W 151st St S 74041 918-321-3533
Sabrina Shaw, prin. Fax 321-4443
Rongey MS 100/7-8
4600 W 151st St S 74041 918-321-3533
Sabrina Shaw, prin. Fax 321-4443

Kingfisher, Kingfisher, Pop. 4,523
Kingfisher SD 1,300/PK-12
602 W Chisholm Dr 73750 405-375-4194
Jason Sternberger, supt. Fax 375-5565
www.kingfisher.k12.ok.us
Kingfisher HS 400/9-12
1500 S 13th St 73750 405-375-4191
Sammy Jackson, prin. Fax 375-4456
Kingfisher MS 400/5-8
601 S 13th St 73750 405-375-6607
Keith Campbell, prin. Fax 375-6410

Kingston, Marshall, Pop. 1,514
Kingston ISD 1,200/PK-12
PO Box 370 73439 580-564-9033
Jay McAdams, supt. Fax 564-9516
www.kingston.k12.ok.us
Kingston HS 300/9-12
PO Box 370 73439 580-564-2384
Brenda Foster, prin. Fax 564-0901
Kingston MS 300/6-8
PO Box 370 73439 580-564-2996
Brian Brister, prin. Fax 564-0902

Kinta, Haskell, Pop. 279
Kinta ISD 200/PK-12
PO Box 219 74552 918-768-3338
Patricia Deville, supt. Fax 768-3221
Kinta HS, PO Box 219 74552 100/9-12
Patricia Deville, prin. 918-768-3338

Kiowa, Pittsburg, Pop. 681
Kiowa ISD 300/PK-12
PO Box 6 74553 918-432-5631
Michael Kellogg, supt. Fax 432-5683
www.kiowa.k12.ok.us
Kiowa HS, PO Box 6 74553 100/9-12
Ron Slawson, prin. 918-432-5641

Konawa, Seminole, Pop. 1,168
Konawa ISD 700/PK-12
701 W South St 74849 580-925-3244
Joe Sharber, supt. Fax 925-2146
konawa.k12.ok.us
Konawa JHS 200/6-8
701 W South St 74849 580-925-3221
Sean Walker, prin. Fax 925-2146
Konawa SHS 200/9-12
701 W South St 74849 580-925-3221
Torrey Gaines, prin. Fax 925-2146

Kremlin, Garfield, Pop. 247
Kremlin-Hillsdale ISD 300/PK-12
PO Box 198 73753 580-874-2284
Jim Patton, supt. Fax 874-4488
www.kremlin.k12.ok.us/
Kremlin-Hillsdale HS 100/9-12
PO Box 198 73753 580-874-2281
Jeremy Brashears, prin. Fax 874-4488

Lahoma, Garfield, Pop. 597
Cimarron ISD 300/PK-12
PO Box 8 73754 580-796-2204
Steve Walker, supt. Fax 796-2350
www.cimarron.k12.ok.us
Cimarron HS 100/9-12
PO Box 8 73754 580-796-2204
Gene Novosad, prin. Fax 796-2350

Lamont, Grant, Pop. 412
Deer Creek-Lamont ISD 200/PK-12
PO Box 10 74643 580-388-4335
David Zachary, supt. Fax 388-4341
www.dcla.k12.ok.us/
Deer Creek-Lamont HS 100/9-12
PO Box 10 74643 580-388-4333
Micheal Thompson, prin.

Langston, Logan, Pop. 1,691

Langston University Post-Sec.
PO Box 907 73050 405-466-2231

Laverne, Harper, Pop. 1,316
Laverne ISD 500/PK-12
PO Box 40 73848 580-921-3362
Ed Thomas, supt. Fax 921-3636
www.laverne.k12.ok.us
Laverne HS 100/9-12
PO Box 40 73848 580-921-3361
Todd Overstreet, prin. Fax 921-3936

Lawton, Comanche, Pop. 91,002
Lawton ISD 15,600/PK-12
PO Box 1009 73502 580-357-6900
Barry Beauchamp, supt. Fax 585-6319
www.lawtonps.org
Central MS 800/6-8
1201 NW Fort Sill Blvd 73507 580-355-8544
Regina Lambert, prin. Fax 585-6452
Eisenhower HS 1,400/9-12
5202 W Gore Blvd 73505 580-355-9144
Rod Elam, prin. Fax 585-6329
Eisenhower MS 1,000/6-8
5702 W Gore Blvd 73505 580-353-1040
Beverly Mattingly, prin. Fax 585-6436
Gateway Success Center Alt
1701 NW Taft Ave 73507 580-353-4903
Brett Barrett, prin. Fax 585-6479
Lawton HS 1,900/9-12
601 NW Fort Sill Blvd 73507 580-355-5170
Jerri Manning, prin. Fax 585-6433
MacArthur HS 1,100/9-12
4402 E Gore Blvd 73501 580-355-5230
Rick Owens, prin. Fax 585-6434
MacArthur MS 800/6-8
510 NE 45th St 73507 580-353-5111
Mark Mattingly, prin. Fax 585-6435
Tomlinson MS 800/6-8
702 NW Homestead Dr 73505 580-585-6416
Eddie Williams, prin. Fax 585-6451

OK Dept. of Voc. & Tech. Education
Supt. — None
Phil Berkenbile Ed.D., dir.
Great Plains Technology Center Vo/Tech
4500 SW Lee Blvd 73505 580-355-6371
Dr. Tom Thomas, supt. Fax 250-5677

Cameron University Post-Sec.
2800 W Gore Blvd 73505 580-581-2200
Comanche Co. Memorial Hospital Post-Sec.
PO Box 129 73502 580-355-8620
Great Plains Area Voc. Tech. School Post-Sec.
4500 SW Lee Blvd 73505 580-355-6371
Lawton Christian S 400/PK-12
1 NW Crusader Dr 73505 580-536-6885
Platt College Post-Sec.
112 SW 11th St 73501 580-355-4416
St. Mary S 200/PK-12
611 SW A Ave 73501 580-355-5288
Paolo Dulcamara, prin. Fax 355-4336

Leedey, Dewey, Pop. 416
Leedey ISD 200/PK-12
PO Box 67 73654 580-488-3424
Rusty Puffinbarger, supt. Fax 488-3428
www.leedey.k12.ok.us
Leedey HS, PO Box 67 73654 100/9-12
Darren Danielson, prin. 580-488-3377

LeFlore, LeFlore, Pop. 182
LeFlore ISD 200/PK-12
PO Box 147 74942 918-753-2345
Tina Judkins, supt. Fax 753-2604
www.lefloreps.k12.ok.us
LeFlore HS 100/9-12
PO Box 147 74942 918-753-2345
Tina Judkins, prin. Fax 753-2604

Lexington, Cleveland, Pop. 2,050
Lexington ISD 1,100/PK-12
420 NE 4th St 73051 405-527-7236
Denny Prince, supt. Fax 527-9517
www.lexington.k12.ok.us/
Lexington HS 200/10-12
801 E Broadway St 73051 405-527-3810
Randall Fuller, prin. Fax 527-3814
Lexington JHS 200/7-9
420 NE 4th St 73051 405-527-7236
Terri Helvey, prin. Fax 527-9517

Lindsay, Garvin, Pop. 2,771
Lindsay ISD 1,200/PK-12
800 W Creek St 73052 405-756-3131
Dan Chapman, supt. Fax 756-8819
www.lindsay.k12.ok.us
Lindsay HS 300/9-12
800 W Creek St 73052 405-756-3132
Tom Inman, prin. Fax 756-8554
Lindsay MS, 800 W Creek St 73052 300/6-8
Tom Inman, prin. 405-756-3133

Locust Grove, Mayes, Pop. 1,264
Locust Grove ISD 1,600/PK-12
PO Box 399 74352 918-479-5243
David Cash, supt. Fax 479-6468
www.lg.k12.ok.us
Locust Grove HS 500/9-12
PO Box 399 74352 918-479-5247
Joel Green, prin. Fax 479-2743
Locust Grove MS 300/6-8
PO Box 399 74352 918-479-5244
Clint Hall, prin. Fax 479-2930

Lone Grove, Carter, Pop. 4,751
Lone Grove ISD 1,600/PK-12
PO Box 1330 73443 580-657-3131
Todd Garrison, supt. Fax 657-4355
www.lonegrove.k12.ok.us/
Other Schools – See Ardmore

Lone Wolf, Kiowa, Pop. 435
Lone Wolf ISD 100/PK-12
PO Box 158 73655 580-846-9091
James Sutherland, supt. Fax 846-5266
Lone Wolf HS 50/9-12
PO Box 158 73655 580-846-9091
James Sutherland, prin. Fax 846-5266

Lookeba, Caddo, Pop. 163
Lookeba-Sickles ISD 300/PK-12
10108 County Road 1150 73053 405-457-6623
Chuck Hood, supt. Fax 457-6619
Lookeba-Sickles HS 100/9-12
10108 County Road 1150 73053 405-457-6621
Brian Hunt, prin.

Luther, Oklahoma, Pop. 1,168
Luther ISD 900/PK-12
PO Box 430 73054 405-277-3233
Paul Blessington, supt. Fax 277-3498
www.lutherlions.org
Luther HS 200/9-12
PO Box 430 73054 405-277-3263
Jan Scheffler, prin. Fax 277-3630
Luther MS 300/5-8
PO Box 430 73054 405-277-3264
Barry Gunn, prin. Fax 277-3877

McAlester, Pittsburg, Pop. 17,248
McAlester ISD 3,000/PK-12
PO Box 1027 74502 918-423-4771
Marsha Gore, supt. Fax 423-8166
www.mcalester.k12.ok.us
McAlester HS 900/9-12
PO Box 1027 74502 918-423-4776
Paula Meadows, prin. Fax 423-8689
Puterbaugh MS 400/7-8
PO Box 1027 74502 918-423-5445
Skip Gore, prin. Fax 423-7021

OK Dept. of Voc. & Tech. Education
Supt. — None
Phil Berkenbile Ed.D., dir.
Kiamichi Technology Center Vo/Tech
301 Kiamichi Dr 74501 918-426-0940
April Murray, dir. Fax 426-1626

Mc Curtain, Haskell, Pop. 484
McCurtain ISD 300/PK-12
PO Box 189 74944 918-945-7237
Darl Drummonds, supt. Fax 945-7064
www.mccurtain.k12.ok.us/
McCurtain HS 100/9-12
PO Box 109 74944 918-945-7236
Perry Arnwine, prin. Fax 945-7064

Mc Loud, Pottawatomie, Pop. 3,818
McLoud ISD 1,800/PK-12
PO Box 240, 405-964-3314
Doran Smith, supt. Fax 964-2801
www.mcloudschools.us/
McLoud HS 600/9-12
PO Box 60, 405-964-3311
Leigh Todd, prin. Fax 964-3498
McLoud JHS 300/7-8
PO Box 730, 405-964-3312
Angie Drew, prin. Fax 964-7530

Macomb, Pottawatomie, Pop. 32
Macomb ISD 400/PK-12
36591 Highway 59B 74852 405-598-3892
Brett Byrum, supt. Fax 598-8041
www.macomb.k12.ok.us/
Macomb HS 100/9-12
36591 Highway 59B 74852 405-598-5420
Brett Byrum, prin. Fax 598-3295

Madill, Marshall, Pop. 3,605
Madill ISD 1,700/K-12
601 W McArthur St 73446 580-795-3303
Jon Tuck, supt. Fax 795-3210
www.madillok.com
Madill HS 500/9-12
700 S 5th Ave 73446 580-795-3339
Andy Gower, prin. Fax 795-2657
Madill MS 400/6-8
601 W McArthur St 73446 580-795-7373
Tena Houser, prin. Fax 795-6930

Mangum, Greer, Pop. 2,935
Mangum ISD 700/PK-12
400 N Pennsylvania Ave 73554 580-782-3371
Micky Lively, supt. Fax 782-2313
www.mangum.k12.ok.us/
Mangum HS 200/9-12
301 N Oklahoma Ave 73554 580-782-3343
Travis Reese, prin. Fax 782-3265
Mangum JHS 100/7-8
400 N Oklahoma Ave 73554 580-782-2702
Barbara Gahagan, prin. Fax 782-5911

Mannford, Creek, Pop. 2,901
Mannford ISD 1,400/PK-12
136 Evans Ave 74044 918-865-4062
Dr. Steve Waldvogel, supt. Fax 865-3405
www.mannford.k12.ok.us
Mannford HS 500/9-12
220 Evans Ave 74044 918-865-3841
Tim Wright, prin. Fax 865-2813
Mannford MS 300/6-8
100 Green Valley Rd 74044 918-865-4680
Kelly Spradlin, prin. Fax 865-2862

Marietta, Love, Pop. 2,521
Marietta ISD 1,000/PK-12
PO Box 289 73448 580-276-9444
Joe Neely, supt. Fax 276-4037
www.mariettaisd.org/
Marietta HS 300/9-12
PO Box 289 73448 580-276-3204
Jack Kapella, prin. Fax 276-1208
Marietta MS 200/6-8
PO Box 289 73448 580-276-3886
Rodd Davis, prin. Fax 276-1203

Marlow, Stephens, Pop. 4,444
Bray-Doyle ISD 400/PK-12
1205 S Brooks Rd 73055 580-658-5076
David Eads, supt. Fax 658-5888
www.braydoyle.k12.ok.us
Bray-Doyle HS 100/9-12
1205 S Brooks Rd 73055 580-658-5071
Brandon Voss, prin. Fax 658-5888

Central High ISD 300/PK-12
7202 W Bronco Rd 73055 580-658-6858
Bennie Newton, supt. Fax 658-8006
www.central.k12.ok.us
Central JSHS 100/7-12
7202 W Bronco Rd 73055 580-658-2929
Mark Perry M.Ed., prin. Fax 658-8010

Marlow ISD 1,400/PK-12
PO Box 73 73055 580-658-2719
George Coffman, supt. Fax 658-6455
www.marlow.k12.ok.us
Marlow HS 400/9-12
PO Box 73 73055 580-658-1516
Bryan Brantley, prin. Fax 658-2718
Marlow MS 300/6-8
PO Box 73 73055 580-658-2619
Kirk Harris, prin. Fax 658-1169

Mason, Okfuskee
Mason ISD 200/PK-12
374006 E 1000 Rd 74859 918-623-0231
Jerry Bogle, supt. Fax 623-0884
www.mason.k12.ok.us/
Mason HS 100/9-12
374006 E 1000 Rd 74859 918-623-0107
Eddie Weaver, prin. Fax 623-0147

Maud, Pottawatomie, Pop. 993
Maud ISD 300/PK-12
PO Box 130 74854 405-374-2416
J.E. Pryor, supt. Fax 374-2628
www.maud.k12.ok.us
Maud HS 100/9-12
PO Box 130 74854 405-374-2425
Wayde Coleman, prin. Fax 374-2895

Maysville, Garvin, Pop. 1,159
Maysville ISD 400/PK-12
600 1st St 73057 888-806-5220
William Martin, supt. Fax 867-4864
Maysville HS 100/9-12
600 1st St 73057 888-806-5330
Dr. Shelly Hildebrand, prin. Fax 867-4864

Medford, Grant, Pop. 970
Medford ISD 200/PK-12
301 N Main St 73759 580-395-2392
Mickey Geurkink, supt. Fax 395-2391
www.medford.k12.ok.us/
Medford HS 100/9-12
301 N Main St 73759 580-395-2392
Tyler Locke, prin. Fax 395-2391

Meeker, Lincoln, Pop. 1,096
Meeker ISD 900/PK-12
214 E Carl Hubbell Blvd 74855 405-279-3511
Rita Palmer, supt. Fax 279-2765
www.meeker.k12.ok.us/
Meeker HS 300/9-12
214 E Carl Hubbell Blvd 74855 405-279-2113
Mike Hedge, prin.
Meeker MS 200/6-8
214 E Carl Hubbell Blvd 74855 405-279-2414
Virgil Fowler, dean

Miami, Ottawa, Pop. 12,277
Miami ISD 2,500/PK-12
26 N Main St 74354 918-542-8455
Loretta Robinson, supt. Fax 542-1236
www.miami.k12.ok.us
Miami HS 700/9-12
2000 E Central Ave 74354 918-542-4421
Lisa Munson, prin. Fax 542-7421
Rogers MS 600/6-8
504 Goodrich Blvd 74354 918-542-5588
Justin Chase, prin. Fax 542-4400

Northeastern Oklahoma A&M College Post-Sec.
200 I St NE 74354 918-542-8441

Midwest City, Oklahoma, Pop. 51,213
Midwest City-Del City ISD 14,700/PK-12
7217 SE 15th St 73110 405-737-4461
Dr. Pam Deering, supt. Fax 739-1615
www.mid-del.net
Albert MS 800/6-8
2515 S Post Rd 73130 405-739-1761
Joyce Honey, prin. Fax 739-1780
Albert SHS 1,100/9-12
2009 S Post Rd 73130 405-739-1726
Kristin Goggans, prin. Fax 739-1685
Jarman MS 500/6-8
5 W McArthur Dr 73110 405-739-1771
Danette Hall, prin. Fax 739-1773
Mid-Del Academy Alt
213 Elm St 73110 405-739-1741
Dale Didlot, prin. Fax 739-1675
Midwest City SHS 1,600/9-12
213 Elm St 73110 405-739-1741
Chris Reynolds, prin. Fax 739-1675
Monroney MS 600/6-8
7400 E Reno Ave 73110 405-739-1786
Mark Flies, prin. Fax 739-1789
Other Schools – See Del City

OK Dept. of Voc. & Tech. Education
Supt. — None
Phil Berkenbile Ed.D., dir.
Mid-Del Technology Center Vo/Tech
1621 Maple Dr 73110 405-739-1707
Debbie Neugent, prin. Fax 739-1716

Rose State College Post-Sec.
6420 SE 15th St 73110 405-733-7673

Milburn, Johnston, Pop. 295
Milburn ISD 200/PK-12
PO Box 429 73450 580-443-5522
Bobby Waitman, supt. Fax 443-5303
www.milburnps.org
Milburn HS 100/9-12
PO Box 429 73450 580-443-5522
Joey McBride, prin. Fax 443-5303

Mill Creek, Johnston, Pop. 283
Mill Creek ISD 200/PK-12
PO Box 118 74856 580-384-5514
Lorinda Chancellor, supt. Fax 384-3920
www.millcreek.k12.ok.us
Mill Creek HS 100/9-12
PO Box 118 74856 580-384-5447
Chris Grimm, prin. Fax 384-3920

Minco, Grady, Pop. 1,580
Minco ISD 600/PK-12
PO Box 428 73059 405-352-4867
Kevin Sims, supt. Fax 352-4006
www.minco.k12.ok.us
Minco HS 100/9-12
PO Box 428 73059 405-352-4377
Jon Mages, prin. Fax 352-4006
Minco MS 100/6-8
PO Box 428 73059 405-352-4377
Troy Wittrock, prin. Fax 352-4006

Moore, Cleveland, Pop. 51,925
Moore ISD 21,300/PK-12
1500 SE 4th St 73160 405-735-4200
Susan Pierce, supt. Fax 735-4392
www.mooreschools.com/
Central JHS 600/7-8
400 N Broadway St 73160 405-735-4560
David Peak, prin. Fax 895-7398
Highland East JHS 700/7-8
1200 SE 4th St 73160 405-735-4580
Kathy Knowles, prin. Fax 703-3198
Highland West JHS 600/7-8
901 N Santa Fe Ave 73160 405-735-4600
Peggy Pate, prin. Fax 703-3218
Moore HS 2,200/9-12
300 N Eastern Ave 73160 405-735-4700
Mike Coyle, prin. Fax 793-3140
Southmoore HS 2,000/9-12
2901 S Santa Fe Ave 73160 405-735-4900
Roy Smith, prin. Fax 735-4992
Vista Academy Alt
224 SE 4th St 73160 405-735-4640
Dr. Sandra Ludwig, prin. Fax 793-3062
Vista Academy HS Alt
224 SE 4th St 73160 405-735-4640
Dr. Sandra Ludwig, prin. Fax 793-3062
Vista MAST Academy Alt
624 NW 5th St 73160 405-799-3379
Fax 799-0912

Other Schools – See Oklahoma City

Hillsdale Free Will Baptist College Post-Sec.
PO Box 7208 73153 405-912-9000
Platt College Post-Sec.
201 N Eastern Ave 73160 405-912-3260
Southwest Christian Academy 200/PK-12
1005 SW 4th St Ste A 73160 405-794-9000
Glen Sims, pres. Fax 794-7558

Mooreland, Woodward, Pop. 1,172
Mooreland ISD 500/PK-12
PO Box 75 73852 580-994-5388
Terry Kellner, supt. Fax 994-5900
www.mooreland.k12.ok.us
Mooreland HS 200/9-12
PO Box 75 73852 580-994-5426
Ron Wilson, prin. Fax 994-2344

Morris, Okmulgee, Pop. 1,388
Morris ISD 1,000/PK-12
PO Box 80 74445 918-733-9072
James Lyons, supt. Fax 733-4205
www.morris.k12.ok.us/
Morris HS 300/9-12
PO Box 80 74445 918-733-4198
Andrew Ewton, prin. Fax 733-2857
Morris MS 200/6-8
PO Box 80 74445 918-733-4551
Greg Large, prin. Fax 733-4618

Morrison, Noble, Pop. 700
Morrison ISD 400/PK-12
PO Box 176 73061 580-724-3341
Jay Vernon, supt. Fax 724-3004
www.morrisonps.com
Morrison HS, PO Box 176 73061 100/9-12
Shalon Reynolds, prin. 580-724-3307

Mounds, Creek, Pop. 1,107
Liberty ISD 600/PK-12
2727 E 201st St S 74047 918-366-8496
Donna Campo, supt. Fax 366-8497
www.liberty.k12.ok.us
Liberty HS, 2727 E 201st St S 74047 200/9-12
Patty Medill, prin. 918-366-8784

Mounds ISD 600/PK-12
PO Box 189 74047 918-827-6100
Alfred Gaches, supt. Fax 827-3704
www.mounds.k12.ok.us/
Mounds HS 200/6-12
PO Box 189 74047 918-827-6100
Stephen Sturgeon, prin. Fax 827-3705

Mountain View, Kiowa, Pop. 770
Mountain View-Gotebo ISD 200/PK-12
RR 2 Box 88 73062 580-347-2211
Andy Evans, supt. Fax 347-2869
www.mvgschools.com
Mountain View-Gotebo HS 100/9-12
150 S 1st St 73062 580-347-2211
Andy Evans, prin.

Moyers, Pushmataha
Moyers ISD 200/K-12
PO Box 88 74557 580-298-5549
Donna Dudley, supt. Fax 298-2022
www.moyers.k12.ok.us/
Moyers HS 100/9-12
PO Box 88 74557 580-298-5547
LaWanda Vaughn, prin. Fax 298-2022

Muldrow, Sequoyah, Pop. 3,165
Muldrow ISD 1,700/PK-12
PO Box 660 74948 918-427-7406
Roger Sharp, supt. Fax 427-6088
www.muldrowps.org
Muldrow HS 600/9-12
PO Box 660 74948 918-427-3274
David Rhodes, prin. Fax 427-1035
Muldrow MS 500/5-8
PO Box 660 74948 918-427-5421
Montea Wight, prin. Fax 427-1034

Muskogee, Muskogee, Pop. 36,324
Hilldale ISD 1,800/PK-12
500 E Smith Ferry Rd 74403 918-683-0273
Kaylin Coody, supt. Fax 683-8725
www.hilldale.k12.ok.us
Hilldale HS 500/9-12
300 E Smith Ferry Rd 74403 918-683-3253
Deborah Tennison, prin. Fax 683-0622
Hilldale MS 400/6-8
400 E Smith Ferry Rd 74403 918-683-0763
Darren Riddle, prin. Fax 683-0766

Muskogee ISD 6,400/PK-12
202 W Broadway St 74401 918-684-3700
Michael Garde, supt. Fax 684-3827
www.mpsi20.org
Muskogee 7th & 8th Grade Center 700/7-8
402 N S St 74403 918-684-3775
Dr. Edwin Strickland, prin. Fax 684-3776
Muskogee HS 1,600/9-12
3200 E Shawnee Rd 74403 918-684-3750
Dewayne Pemberton, prin. Fax 684-3751

OK Dept. of Voc. & Tech. Education
Supt. — None
Phil Berkenbile Ed.D., dir.
Indian Capital Technology Center Vo/Tech
2403 N 41st St E 74403 918-687-6383
Thomas Stiles, dir. Fax 687-6624

Bacone College Post-Sec.
2299 Old Bacone Rd 74403 918-683-4581
Muskogee General Hospital Post-Sec.
300 Rockefeller Dr 74401 918-682-5501
Parkview School OK School for the Blind Post-Sec.
3300 Gibson St 74403 918-682-6641
Virgil's Beauty College Post-Sec.
111 S 9th St 74401 918-682-9429

Mustang, Canadian, Pop. 16,780
Mustang ISD 8,800/PK-12
906 S Heights Dr 73064 405-376-2461
Sean McDaniel, supt. Fax 376-7333
www.mustangps.org
Mustang HS 1,800/10-12
906 S Heights Dr 73064 405-376-2404
Angela Hunt, prin. Fax 376-7347
Mustang MS 1,000/6-8
906 S Heights Dr 73064 405-376-2448
Linda Wilkes, prin. Fax 376-7373
Mustang Mid HS 700/9-9
906 S Heights Dr 73064 405-376-7855
Kenny Nelson, prin. Fax 376-7852
Mustang North MS 1,000/6-8
906 S Heights Dr 73064 405-324-2236
Dan Allen, prin. Fax 324-2258

Mutual, Woodward, Pop. 59
Sharon-Mutual ISD 300/PK-12
210 S Maple St 73853 580-989-3210
Jeff Thompson, supt. Fax 989-3241
www.smps.k12.ok.us
Sharon-Mutual HS 100/9-12
210 S Maple St 73853 580-989-3231
Chris Syms, prin. Fax 989-8019

Newcastle, McClain, Pop. 7,304
Newcastle ISD 1,700/PK-12
101 N Main St 73065 405-387-2890
Robert Everett, supt. Fax 387-3482
www.newcastle.k12.ok.us
Newcastle HS 500/9-12
101 N Main St 73065 405-387-4304
Jason Brunk, prin. Fax 387-3461
Newcastle MS 400/6-8
611 E Fox Ln 73065 405-387-3139
Joey Billington, prin. Fax 387-5563

Newkirk, Kay, Pop. 2,182
Newkirk ISD 800/PK-12
PO Box 91 74647 580-362-2388
Steve Stanley, supt. Fax 362-3413
www.newkirk.k12.ok.us
Newkirk HS 300/9-12
PO Box 91 74647 580-362-6241
Patty Stanley, prin. Fax 362-6242
Newkirk MS 200/5-8
PO Box 91 74647 580-362-2516
Jeff Wilson, prin. Fax 362-1150

Ninnekah, Grady, Pop. 970
Ninnekah ISD 500/PK-12
PO Box 275 73067 405-224-4092
Todd Bunch, supt. Fax 224-4096
www.ninnekah.ok.nph.schoolinsites.com/
Ninnekah HS 100/9-12
PO Box 275 73067 405-224-4299
David Pitts, prin. Fax 224-4665
Ninnekah JHS 100/7-8
PO Box 275 73067 405-224-4299
David Pitts, prin. Fax 224-4665

Noble, Cleveland, Pop. 6,155
Noble ISD 3,000/PK-12
PO Box 499 73068 405-872-3452
Ronda Bass, supt. Fax 872-3271
www.nobleps.com
Inge MS 700/6-8
1201 N 8th St 73068 405-872-3495
Ronald Fulks, prin. Fax 872-8670
Noble HS 800/9-12
4601 E Etowah Rd 73068 405-872-3441
Frank Solomon, prin. Fax 872-9824

Norman, Cleveland, Pop. 105,378
Little Axe ISD 1,200/PK-12
2000 168th Ave NE 73026 405-329-7691
Tony Smith, supt. Fax 579-2929
littleaxeps.org/
Little Axe HS 400/9-12
2000 168th Ave NE 73026 405-329-1612
Steven Edwards, prin. Fax 329-2914
Little Axe MS 200/6-8
2000 168th Ave NE 73026 405-329-2156
Dalton Griffin, prin. Fax 579-2937

Norman ISD 14,200/PK-12
131 S Flood Ave 73069 405-364-1339
Dr. Joseph Siano, supt. Fax 366-5851
www.norman.k12.ok.us
Alcott MS 600/6-8
1919 W Boyd St 73069 405-366-5845
Dr. Dana Morris, prin. Fax 447-6572
Alternative Support Education Alt
1101 E Main St 73071 405-579-1880
Gayla Mears, prin. Fax 579-1881
Irving MS 800/6-8
125 Vicksburg Ave 73071 405-366-5941
Linda Baxter, prin. Fax 366-5944
Longfellow MS 600/6-8
215 N Ponca Ave 73071 405-366-5948
Peter Liesenfeld, prin. Fax 366-5952
Norman HS 1,700/9-12
911 W Main St 73069 405-366-5812
Scott Beck, prin. Fax 366-5945
Norman North HS 2,100/9-12
1809 Stubbeman Ave 73069 405-366-5954
Bryan Young, prin. Fax 573-3590
Whittier MS 1,100/6-8
2000 W Brooks St 73069 405-366-5956
Fax 447-6562

OK Dept. of Voc. & Tech. Education
Supt. — None
Phil Berkenbile Ed.D., dir.
Moore Norman Technology Center Vo/Tech
PO Box 4701 73070 405-364-5763
Dr. Jane Bowen, supt. Fax 217-8277

Community Christian S 700/PK-12
3002 Broce Dr 73072 405-329-2500
Barbara Ohsfeldt, admin. Fax 329-3510
University of Oklahoma Post-Sec.
660 Parrington Oval 73019 405-325-0311

Nowata, Nowata, Pop. 3,335
Nowata ISD 1,000/PK-12
707 W Osage Ave 74048 918-273-3425
Kathy Berry, supt. Fax 273-2105
www.nowataps.k12.ok.us
Nowata HS 300/9-12
707 W Osage Ave 74048 918-273-2221
Bron Williams, prin. Fax 273-2105
Nowata MS 200/6-8
707 W Osage Ave 74048 918-273-1346
Shawn Imhoff, prin. Fax 273-2105

Oaks, Delaware, Pop. 277
Oaks-Mission ISD 300/PK-12
PO Box 160 74359 918-868-2183
Wyman Thompson, supt. Fax 868-2707
Oaks-Mission HS 100/9-12
PO Box 160 74359 918-868-2499
Shawn Gillespie, prin. Fax 868-5012

Oilton, Creek, Pop. 965
Oilton ISD 300/PK-12
PO Box 130 74052 918-862-3954
Matt Posey, supt. Fax 862-3955
www.oilton.k12.ok.us
Oilton HS 100/9-12
PO Box 130 74052 918-862-3272
Matt Posey, prin. Fax 862-3763

Okarche, Kingfisher, Pop. 1,196
Okarche ISD 300/PK-12
PO Box 276 73762 405-263-7300
Robert Barnett, supt. Fax 263-7515
www.okarche.k12.ok.us/
Okarche HS 100/10-12
PO Box 276 73762 405-263-7212
Robert Barnett, prin. Fax 263-7515
Okarche JHS 100/7-9
PO Box 276 73762 405-263-7212
Robert Barnett, prin. Fax 263-7515

Okay, Wagoner, Pop. 586
Okay ISD 400/PK-12
PO Box 830 74446 918-682-2548
Mickey Igert, supt. Fax 683-8331
Okay HS 100/9-12
PO Box 830 74446 918-682-0371
Charles McMahan, prin. Fax 682-7653

Okeene, Blaine, Pop. 1,187
Okeene ISD 300/K-12
PO Box 409 73763 580-822-3268
Ron Pittman, supt. Fax 822-4123
www.okeene.k12.ok.us
Okeene JSHS 100/7-12
PO Box 409 73763 580-822-3219
Jeremy Osmus, prin. Fax 822-4123

Okemah, Okfuskee, Pop. 3,000
Okemah ISD 800/PK-12
107 W Date St 74859 918-623-1874
Tony Dean, supt. Fax 623-1203
www.okemah.k12.ok.us
Okemah HS 300/9-12
704 E Date St 74859 918-623-1274
Beverly Robison, prin. Fax 623-1884
Okemah MS 200/4-8
107 W Date St 74859 918-623-0212
Sandra Lambert, prin. Fax 623-9151

Oklahoma City, Oklahoma, Pop. 555,623
Crooked Oak ISD 1,100/PK-12
1901 SE 15th St 73129 405-677-5252
Brad Richards, supt. Fax 670-8070
www.crookedoak.org/
Crooked Oak HS 300/9-12
1901 SE 15th St 73129 405-677-3452
Patsy Orth, prin. Fax 670-8072
Crooked Oak MS 200/6-8
1901 SE 15th St 73129 405-677-5133
Travis Gates, prin. Fax 670-2256

Millwood ISD 1,100/PK-12
6724 N Martin Luther King 73111 405-478-1336
Dr. Gloria Griffin, supt. Fax 478-4698
www.millwood.k12.ok.us
Millwood Arts Academy 4-8
6700 N Martin Luther King 73111 405-478-0630
Christine Harrison, prin. Fax 478-7134
Millwood HS 300/9-12
6718 N Martin Luther King 73111 405-475-1015
C Kay Cudjoe, prin. Fax 478-4194

Moore ISD
Supt. — See Moore
Brink JHS 900/7-8
11420 S Western Ave 73170 405-735-4540
Janet Southard, prin. Fax 692-5634
Moore West JHS 700/7-8
9400 S Pennsylvania Ave 73159 405-735-4620
Dr. Michaele Benn, prin. Fax 692-5660
Westmoore HS 2,000/9-12
12613 S Western Ave 73170 405-735-4800
Mark Hunt, prin. Fax 692-5711

OK Dept. of Voc. & Tech. Education
Supt. — None

Metro Tech-Adult & Continuing Ed Vo/Tech
201 NE 48th St 73105 405-424-8324
Barbara Loudermilk, dir. Fax 528-1512
Metro Tech-Aviation Career Center Vo/Tech
5600 S MacArthur Blvd 73179 405-685-0008
Peter Lee, dir. Fax 681-5644
Metro Tech South Bryant Campus Vo/Tech
4901 S Bryant Ave 73129 405-424-8324
Ed Melott, dir. Fax 670-6895
Metro Tech-Springlake Campus Vo/Tech
1900 Springlake Dr 73111 405-424-8324
Dr. James Branscum, supt. Fax 424-8589
Tuttle-Portland Campus Vo/Tech
3500 NW 150th St 73134 405-717-7799
Danny King, dir. Fax 755-0028
Tuttle-Reno Campus Vo/Tech
7301 W Reno Ave 73127 405-717-4646
Marie Howard, dir.
Tuttle-Rockwell Campus Vo/Tech
12777 N Rockwell Ave 73142 405-717-7799
Richard Dimit, dir. Fax 717-4112

Oklahoma City ISD 40,400/PK-12
900 N Klein Ave 73106 405-587-0000
Karl Springer, supt. Fax 587-0443
www.okcps.org/
Belle Isle Enterprise MS 500/6-8
5904 N Villa Ave 73112 405-587-6600
Lynn Kellert, prin. Fax 841-3127
Capitol Hill HS 1,000/9-12
500 SW Grand Blvd 73109 405-587-9000
Alex Souza, prin.
Classen S of Advanced Studies 500/6-12
1901 N Ellison Ave 73106 405-587-5400
Valerie Harris, prin.
Douglass MSHS 500/7-12
900 N Martin Luther King Av 73117 405-587-4200
Dr. Barbara Davis, prin. Fax 587-4205
Emerson Center 400/Alt
715 N Walker Ave 73102 405-232-5273
Sheryl Kishore, prin. Fax 231-2014

Extended Educational Services Alt
900 N Klein Ave 73106 405-587-0402
Dr. Debra Thomas, prin. Fax 297-6806
Grant HS 1,600/9-12
5016 S Pennsylvania Ave 73119 405-587-2200
Tamie Sanders, prin. Fax 587-2205
Jackson MS 500/6-8
2601 S Villa Ave 73108 405-634-6357
Marcus Macias, prin. Fax 636-5078
Jefferson MS 1,000/6-8
6800 S Blackwelder Ave 73159 405-632-2341
Adya Altstatt, prin. Fax 636-5084
Marshall MSHS 400/6-12
12201 N Portland Ave 73120 405-587-7200
Aspasia Carlson, prin. Fax 587-7205
Northeast Academy for Health Sci./Eng. 200/6-12
3100 N Kelley Ave 73111 405-587-3300
Mylissa Hall, prin. Fax 587-3305
Northwest Classen HS 1,100/9-12
2801 NW 27th St 73107 405-587-6300
Brad Herzer, prin. Fax 587-6305
Oklahoma Centennial HS 400/6-12
1301 NE 101st St 73131 405-587-5200
Helen Johnson, prin. Fax 587-5205
Pathways Middle College HS Alt
7777 S May Ave 73159 405-682-7840
Carol Brogan, admin. Fax 685-7883
Roosevelt MS 900/6-8
3233 SW 44th St 73119 405-685-7795
Michelle Pontikos, prin. Fax 686-4059
Southeast HS 700/9-12
5401 S Shields Blvd 73129 405-587-9600
Pat Borelli, prin. Fax 587-9605
Taft MS 800/6-8
2901 NW 23rd St 73107 405-946-1431
Eric Schellenger, prin. Fax 945-1126
Webster MS 700/6-8
6708 S Santa Fe Ave 73139 405-632-6653
Tracy Sowinski, prin. Fax 636-5096
Other Schools – See Spencer

Oklahoma School of Science & Math 11-12
1141 N Lincoln Blvd 73104 405-521-6436
Dr. Frank Wang, pres. Fax 521-6442
www.ossm.edu/
Oklahoma S of Science & Math 11-12
1141 N Lincoln Blvd 73104 405-521-6436
Dr. Frank Wang, pres. Fax 521-6442

Putnam City ISD 18,600/PK-12
5401 NW 40th St 73122 405-495-5200
Paul Hurst, supt. Fax 495-8648
www.putnamcityschools.org
Cooper MS 800/6-8
8001 River Bend Blvd 73132 405-720-9887
Mark Lebsack, prin. Fax 728-5632
Hefner MS 1,100/6-8
8400 N MacArthur Blvd 73132 405-721-2411
Dena Rogers, prin. Fax 728-5645
Mayfield MS 700/6-8
1600 N Purdue Ave 73127 405-947-8693
John Murphey, prin. Fax 948-9000
Putnam City North HS 2,000/9-12
11800 N Rockwell Ave 73162 405-722-4220
Dr. Brian Chastain, prin. Fax 721-4946
Putnam City West HS 1,600/9-12
8500 NW 23rd St 73127 405-787-1140
Buster Meeks, prin. Fax 491-7602
Other Schools – See Bethany, Warr Acres

Western Heights ISD 3,600/PK-12
8401 SW 44th St 73179 405-350-3410
Joe Kitchens, supt. Fax 745-6322
www.westernheights.k12.ok.us
Jets Academy Alt
8005 SW 44th St 73179 405-350-3485
Khristi Barkett, prin. Fax 789-2909
Western Heights 9th Grade Center 200/9-9
8401 SW 44th St 73179 405-350-3415
Alan Dale, prin. Fax 261-0280
Western Heights HS 600/10-12
8201 SW 44th St 73179 405-350-3435
John Erickson, prin. Fax 745-6315
Western Heights MS 500/7-8
8435 SW 44th St 73179 405-350-3455
Randy Atkins, prin. Fax 745-6341

ATI Career Training Center Post-Sec.
2401 NW 23rd St Ste 14 73107 405-445-5760
Bishop McGuinness HS 700/9-12
801 NW 50th St 73118 405-842-6638
David Morton, prin. Fax 858-9550
Brookline College Post-Sec.
9801 Broadway Ext 73114 405-842-9400
Brown Mackie College Post-Sec.
7101 NW Expressway Ste 800 73132 405-621-8000
Casady S 900/PK-12
9500 N Pennsylvania Ave 73120 405-749-3100
Christopher Bright, hdmstr. Fax 749-3214
CC's Cosmetology College Post-Sec.
4439 NW 50th St 73112 405-943-2300
Central State Beauty Academy Post-Sec.
8494 NW Expressway 73162 405-722-4499
Crossings Christian S 600/PK-12
14400 N Portland Ave 73134 405-842-8495
Paul MacDonald, hdmstr. Fax 767-1520
DeVry University Post-Sec.
4013 NW Expressway Ste 100 73116 405-767-9516
Heritage College Post-Sec.
7100 S I 35 Service Rd 7118 73149 405-631-3399
Heritage Hall S 900/PK-12
1800 NW 122nd St 73120 405-749-3001
Guy Bramble, hdmstr. Fax 751-7372
Hollywood Cosmetology Center Post-Sec.
PO Box 890488 73189 405-364-3375
ITT Technical Institute Post-Sec.
1900 NW Expressway Ste 305R 73118 405-810-4100

Life Christian Academy 200/PK-12
6801 S Anderson Rd 73150 405-737-4902
Rodney Burchett, admin. Fax 869-9151
Metro Area Vocational Technical School Post-Sec.
1900 Springlake Dr 73111 405-424-8324
Mid-America Christian University Post-Sec.
3500 SW 119th St 73170 405-691-3800
Mt. St. Mary's HS 300/9-12
2801 S Shartel Ave 73109 405-631-8865
Talita DeNegri, prin. Fax 631-9209
Oklahoma Christian University Post-Sec.
PO Box 11000 73136 405-425-5000
Oklahoma City Community College Post-Sec.
7777 S May Ave 73159 405-682-1611
Oklahoma City University Post-Sec.
2501 N Blackwelder Ave 73106 405-208-5000
Oklahoma State University-Oklahoma City Post-Sec.
900 N Portland Ave 73107 405-947-4421
Parkview Adventist Academy 100/PK-12
4201 N Martin Luther King 73111 405-427-6525
Fax 427-1154
Platt College Post-Sec.
309 S Ann Arbor Ave 73128 405-946-7799
Platt College Post-Sec.
2727 W Memorial Rd 73134 405-749-2433
Tuttle Vocational Technical Center Post-Sec.
12777 N Rockwell Ave 73142 405-722-7799
University Hospital of Oklahoma City Post-Sec.
PO Box 26307 73126 405-271-4000
University of Oklahoma Health Sciences Post-Sec.
1100 N Lindsay Ave 73104 405-271-4000
Wright Career College Post-Sec.
2219 W I 240 Service Rd 73159 405-681-2300

Okmulgee, Okmulgee, Pop. 11,317
OK Dept. of Voc. & Tech. Education
Supt. — None
Phil Berkenbile Ed.D., dir.
Green Country Technology Center Vo/Tech
PO Box 1217 74447 918-758-0840
Brady McCullough, supt. Fax 758-0422

Okmulgee ISD 1,700/PK-12
PO Box 1346 74447 918-758-2000
Tod Williams, supt. Fax 758-2088
www.okmulgeeps.com
Okmulgee HS 400/9-12
415 W 3rd St 74447 918-758-2075
Jeremy Ramsey, prin. Fax 758-2096
Okmulgee MS 300/6-8
1421 Martin Luther King Dr 74447 918-758-2050
John Whitfield, prin. Fax 758-2095

Oklahoma State Univ Institute of Tech Post-Sec.
1801 E 4th St 74447 800-722-4471

Oktaha, Muskogee, Pop. 343
Oktaha ISD 700/PK-12
PO Box 9 74450 918-687-7556
Jerry Needham M.Ed., supt. Fax 687-0074
www.oktahaschool.com/
Oktaha HS 200/9-12
PO Box 9 74450 918-687-3672
Chris Burt M.Ed., prin. Fax 687-8551

Olustee, Jackson, Pop. 583
Olustee ISD 200/PK-12
PO Box 70 73560 580-648-2243
Gaylene Freeman, supt. Fax 648-2501
www.olustee.k12.ok.us
Olustee HS 100/9-12
PO Box 70 73560 580-648-2243
Brent Drury, prin. Fax 648-2501

Omega, Kingfisher
Lomega ISD 200/PK-12
18319 N 2700 Rd 73764 405-729-4215
Steve Mendell, supt. Fax 729-4666
www.lomega.k12.ok.us
Lomega HS 50/9-12
18319 N 2700 Rd 73764 405-729-4281
Karen Castonguay, prin. Fax 729-4666

OK Dept. of Voc. & Tech. Education
Supt. — None
Phil Berkenbile Ed.D., dir.
Chisholm Trail Technology Center Vo/Tech
283 State Highway 33 73764 405-729-8324
Max Thomas, supt. Fax 729-8335

Oologah, Rogers, Pop. 1,080
Oologah-Talala ISD 1,700/K-12
PO Box 189 74053 918-443-6000
Rob Armstrong, supt. Fax 443-9088
www.oologah.k12.ok.us
Oologah HS 600/9-12
PO Box 189 74053 918-443-6211
Robert Schornick, prin. Fax 443-2418
Oologah MS 400/6-8
PO Box 189 74053 918-443-6161
Kelli Dixon, prin. Fax 443-2875

Orlando, Logan, Pop. 142
Mulhall-Orlando ISD 200/PK-12
PO Box 8 73073 405-649-2000
Michael Parsons, supt. Fax 649-2020
m-oschools.org
Mulhall-Orlando HS 100/9-12
PO Box 8 73073 580-455-2211
Pat Smith, prin. Fax 455-8019

Owasso, Tulsa, Pop. 27,251
Owasso ISD 8,800/PK-12
1501 N Ash St 74055 918-272-5367
Dr. Clark Ogilvie, supt. Fax 272-8111
www.owasso.k12.ok.us
Owasso Eighth Grade Center 700/8-8
1501 N Ash St 74055 918-272-6274
Deirdre Hodge, prin. Fax 272-5562

Owasso HS 1,300/11-12
1501 N Ash St 74055 918-272-5334
Matt Roberts, prin. Fax 272-8108
Owasso Mid HS 1,400/9-10
1501 N Ash St 74055 918-274-3000
Don Huggins, prin. Fax 274-3006
Owasso Ram Academy Alt
1501 N Ash St 74055 918-272-8040
Johanna Woodard, coord. Fax 272-0712

Rejoice Christian S 700/PK 12
12200 E 86th St N 74055 918-516-0050
Dr. Craig Shaw, supt. Fax 516-0299

Paden, Okfuskee, Pop. 430
Paden ISD 300/PK-12
PO Box 370 74860 405-932-5053
Lee Northcutt, supt. Fax 932-4132
www.paden.k12.ok.us
Paden HS, PO Box 370 74860 100/9-12
Chris Howk, prin. 405-932-4465

Panama, LeFlore, Pop. 1,335
Panama ISD 600/PK-12
PO Box 1680 74951 918-963-2217
Grant Ralls, supt. Fax 963-4860
www.panama.k12.ok.us
Panama HS 200/9-12
PO Box 1680 74951 918-963-2215
Richard Haynes, prin. Fax 963-2638
Panama MS 100/6-8
PO Box 1680 74951 918-963-4479
James Hoffman, prin. Fax 963-4493

Panola, Latimer
Panola ISD 200/PK-12
PO Box 6 74559 918-465-3298
Alan Lumpkins, supt. Fax 465-3656
www.panola.k12.ok.us/
Panola HS 100/9-12
PO Box 6 74559 918-465-3813
Linda Albright, prin. Fax 465-2996

Paoli, Garvin, Pop. 587
Paoli ISD 300/PK-12
PO Box 278 73074 405-484-7336
Rick Worden, supt. Fax 484-7268
www.paoli.k12.ok.us/
Paoli HS 100/9-12
PO Box 278 73074 405-484-7336
David Morris, prin. Fax 484-7268

Park Hill, Cherokee, Pop. 3,515
Keys ISD 900/PK-12
26622 S 520 Rd 74451 918-458-1835
Billie Jordan, supt. Fax 456-1656
www.keys.k12.ok.us
Keys HS 400/9-12
26622 S 520 Rd 74451 918-458-1835
Leon Ashlock, prin. Fax 456-7502

Pauls Valley, Garvin, Pop. 5,834
Pauls Valley ISD 1,300/PK-12
PO Box 780 73075 405-238-6453
Darsha Huckabaa, supt. Fax 238-9178
www.paulsvalleyschools.com/
Pauls Valley JHS 300/7-9
PO Box 780 73075 405-238-1239
Martha Graham, prin. Fax 238-1410
Pauls Valley SHS 300/10-12
PO Box 780 73075 405-238-6497
Chris Caldwell, prin. Fax 238-1236

Pawhuska, Osage, Pop. 3,306
Pawhuska ISD 900/PK-12
1801 McKenzie Rd 74056 918-287-1281
Dr. Landon Berry, supt. Fax 287-4461
www.pawhuskadistrict.org/
Pawhuska HS 300/9-12
621 E 15th St 74056 918-287-1266
Rod Pitts, prin. Fax 287-1236
Pawhuska JHS 100/7-8
615 E 15th St 74056 918-287-1264
Jon Culver, prin. Fax 287-2062

Pawnee, Pawnee, Pop. 2,051
Pawnee ISD 700/PK-12
615 Denver St 74058 918-762-3676
Ned Williams, supt. Fax 762-2704
www.pawnee.k12.ok.us
Pawnee HS 200/9-12
615 Denver St 74058 918-762-3676
Bob Miller, prin. Fax 762-2704
Pawnee MS 200/6-8
605 Denver St 74058 918-762-3055
Stacy Womack, prin. Fax 762-3585

Perkins, Payne, Pop. 2,678
Perkins-Tryon ISD 1,400/PK-12
PO Box 549 74059 405-547-5703
James Ramsey, supt. Fax 547-2020
www.p-t.k12.ok.us
Perkins-Tryon HS 300/10-12
PO Box 549 74059 405-547-5724
Jeff Colclasure, prin. Fax 547-5760
Perkins-Tryon JHS 300/7-9
PO Box 549 74059 405-547-5715
Ken Latham, prin. Fax 547-5761

Perry, Noble, Pop. 4,921
Perry ISD 1,200/PK-12
900 Fir St 73077 580-336-4511
Scott Chenoweth, supt. Fax 336-5185
www.perry.k12.ok.us/
Perry HS, 900 Fir St 73077 300/9-12
Les Justus, prin. 580-336-4415
Perry JHS, 901 Elm St 73077 200/7-8
Ranay Roth, prin. 580-336-2265

Piedmont, Canadian, Pop. 5,527
Piedmont ISD 2,500/PK-12
713 Piedmont Rd N 73078 405-373-2311
James White, supt. Fax 373-0912
www.piedmontschools.org
Piedmont HS 700/9-12
1055 Edmond Rd NW 73078 405-373-5011
Todd Glasgow, prin. Fax 373-3055
Piedmont MS 400/7-8
823 2nd St NW 73078 405-373-1315
Terri Merveldt, prin. Fax 373-5006

Pittsburg, Pittsburg, Pop. 206
Pittsburg ISD 300/PK-12
PO Box 200 74560 918-432-5062
Jimmy Harwood, supt. Fax 432-5312
Pittsburg HS, PO Box 200 74560 200/9-12
Ernie Michaelis, prin. 918-432-5513

Pocola, LeFlore, Pop. 3,869
Pocola ISD 900/PK-12
PO Box 640 74902 918-436-2424
Monty Guthrie, supt. Fax 436-2437
www.pocola.k12.ok.us
Pocola HS 200/9-12
PO Box 640 74902 918-436-2042
Randy Ragland, prin. Fax 436-2920
Pocola MS 200/6-8
PO Box 640 74902 918-436-2091
Mark McKenzie, prin. Fax 436-9880

Ponca City, Kay, Pop. 24,217
OK Dept. of Voc. & Tech. Education
Supt. — None
Phil Berkenbile Ed.D., dir.
Pioneer Technology Center Vo/Tech
2101 N Ash St 74601 580-762-8336
Bruce DeMuth, supt. Fax 762-3107

Ponca City ISD 5,100/PK-12
111 W Grand Ave 74601 580-767-8000
Dr. David Pennington, supt. Fax 767-8007
www.pcps.us
East MS 300/8-8
612 E Grand Ave 74601 580-767-8010
Barbara Davis, prin. Fax 762-5301
Ponca City HS 1,600/9-12
927 N 5th St 74601 580-767-9500
Kent Marshall, prin. Fax 767-9515

Ponca City Beauty College Post-Sec.
122 N 1st St 74601 888-557-6709

Pond Creek, Grant, Pop. 839
Pond Creek-Hunter ISD 200/PK-12
200 E Broadway St 73766 580-532-4242
Joel Quinn, supt. Fax 532-4965
www.pondcreek-hunter.k12.ok.us
Pond Creek-Hunter HS 100/7-12
200 E Broadway St 73766 580-532-4241
Kelly Childress, prin. Fax 532-4965

Porter, Wagoner, Pop. 534
Porter Consolidated ISD 600/PK-12
PO Box 120 74454 918-483-2401
Mark Fenton, supt. Fax 483-2310
www.porter.k12.ok.us
Porter Consolidated HS 100/9-12
PO Box 120 74454 918-483-7011
Larry Shackelford, prin. Fax 483-2310

Porum, Muskogee, Pop. 622
Porum ISD 500/PK-12
PO Box 189 74455 918-484-5121
Curtis Curry, supt. Fax 484-2310
www.porum.k12.ok.us/
Porum HS 100/9-12
PO Box 189 74455 918-484-5122
Brent Pearce, prin. Fax 484-5121

Poteau, LeFlore, Pop. 8,045
OK Dept. of Voc. & Tech. Education
Supt. — None
Phil Berkenbile Ed.D., dir.
Kiamichi Technology Center Vo/Tech
PO Box 825 74953 918-647-4525
Doug Hall, dir. Fax 647-4527

Poteau ISD 2,300/PK-12
100 Mockingbird Ln 74953 918-647-7700
Dr. Don Sjoberg, supt. Fax 647-9357
www.poteau.k12.ok.us
Kidd MS 500/6-8
100 Mockingbird Ln 74953 918-647-7741
Lorraine Caldwell, prin. Fax 647-4286
Poteau HS 600/9-12
100 Mockingbird Ln 74953 918-647-7716
Cory Wood, prin. Fax 647-4383

Carl Albert State College Post-Sec.
1507 S McKenna St 74953 918-647-1200

Prague, Lincoln, Pop. 2,232
Prague ISD 1,000/K-12
3504 NBU 74864 405-567-4455
Rick Martin, supt. Fax 567-3095
www.prague.k12.ok.us/
Prague HS 300/9-12
3504 NBU 74864 405-567-2281
David Smith, prin. Fax 567-4982
Prague MS 200/6-8
3504 NBU 74864 405-567-2281
Jerry Martin, prin. Fax 567-3095

Preston, Okmulgee
Preston ISD 600/PK-12
PO Box 40 74456 918-756-3388
Mark Hudson, supt. Fax 756-2122
www.preston.k12.ok.us/
Preston HS 200/9-12
PO Box 40 74456 918-756-8636
Pam Snowden, prin. Fax 756-2122

Prue, Osage, Pop. 443
Prue ISD 300/PK-12
PO Box 130 74060 918-242-3351
Tom Scully, supt. Fax 242-3392
www.prue.k12.ok.us/
Prue HS 100/9-12
PO Box 130 74060 918-242-3384
Tom Scully, prin. Fax 242-3888

Pryor, Mayes, Pop. 8,842
OK Dept. of Voc. & Tech. Education
Supt. — None
Phil Berkenbile Ed.D., dir.
Northeast Tech Center Pryor Campus Vo/Tech
PO Box 825 74362 918-825-5555
Debby Peaster, dir. Fax 825-6281

Pryor ISD 2,400/PK-12
PO Box 548 74362 918-825-1255
Don Raleigh, supt. Fax 825-3938
www.pryorok.org
Pryor JHS 600/7-9
PO Box 548 74362 918-825-2371
Terry Gwartney, prin. Fax 825-3950
Pryor SHS 600/10-12
PO Box 548 74362 918-825-2340
Brad Bates, prin. Fax 825-3914

Bradford Christian S 50/K-12
2320 NE 1st St 74361 918-825-7038
Amanda Rutherford, admin. Fax 825-7037
Pryor Beauty College Post-Sec.
330 W Graham Ave 74361 918-825-2795

Purcell, McClain, Pop. 5,558
Purcell ISD 1,600/PK-12
919 N 9th Ave Ste 1 73080 405-527-2146
Kathy Draper, supt. Fax 527-6366
www.purcellps.org/
Purcell HS 400/9-12
2020 N Green Ave 73080 405-527-4400
Don Schneberger, prin. Fax 527-4410
Purcell JHS 200/7-8
201 Lester Ln 73080 405-527-6591
Bret Petty, prin. Fax 527-6593

Quapaw, Ottawa, Pop. 859
Quapaw ISD 700/PK-12
305 W 1st St 74363 918-674-2501
Dennis Earp, supt. Fax 674-2721
www.quapaw.k12.ok.us
Quapaw HS 200/9-12
305 W 1st St 74363 918-674-2474
Terry Tyree, prin. Fax 674-2721
Quapaw MS 200/6-8
305 W 1st St 74363 918-674-2496
Larry Radford, prin. Fax 674-2721

Quinton, Pittsburg, Pop. 953
Quinton ISD 600/PK-12
PO Box 670 74561 918-469-3100
Don Cox, supt. Fax 469-3308
quintonschools.com
Quinton HS 200/9-12
PO Box 670 74561 918-469-3309
Paul Ogden, prin. Fax 469-2310

Ralston, Pawnee, Pop. 314
Woodland SD
Supt. — See Fairfax
Woodland MS 100/5-8
6th & McKinley 74650 918-738-4286
Joe Sindelar, prin. Fax 738-4287

Ramona, Washington, Pop. 498
Caney Valley ISD 800/PK-12
PO Box 410 74061 918-536-2500
Rick Peters, supt. Fax 536-2600
www.caneyvalleyschool.org/
Caney Valley HS 300/9-12
PO Box 410 74061 918-536-3425
Debra Keil, prin. Fax 536-7105
Caney Valley MS, PO Box 410 74061 100/6-8
James Farrell, prin. 918-536-2705

Randlett, Cotton, Pop. 435
Big Pasture ISD 200/PK-12
PO Box 167 73562 580-281-3831
Ernest Copus, supt. Fax 281-3299
www.bigpastureps.k12.ok.us/
Big Pasture HS 100/9-12
PO Box 167 73562 580-281-3276
Nat Lunn, prin. Fax 281-3299

Rattan, Pushmataha, Pop. 299
Rattan ISD 500/PK-12
PO Box 44 74562 580-587-2546
Shari Pillow, supt. Fax 587-4000
www.rattan.k12.ok.us
Rattan JHS 100/7-8
PO Box 44 74562 580-587-2715
Neil Birchfield, prin. Fax 587-2476
Rattan SHS 200/9-12
PO Box 44 74562 580-587-2715
Neil Birchfield, prin. Fax 587-2476

Red Oak, Latimer, Pop. 508
Red Oak ISD 200/PK-12
PO Box 310 74563 918-754-2426
Bryan Deatherage, supt. Fax 754-2898
Red Oak HS 100/9-12
PO Box 310 74563 918-754-2283
Terry Shaw, prin. Fax 754-2898

Red Rock, Noble, Pop. 265
Frontier ISD 400/PK-12
PO Box 130 74651 580-723-4361
Terri Taflinger, supt. Fax 723-4516
www.frontierok.com
Frontier HS 100/9-12
PO Box 130 74651 580-723-4360
Randy Robinson, prin. Fax 723-4516

Reydon, Roger Mills, Pop. 205
Reydon ISD 100/PK-12
PO Box 10 73660 580-655-4375
Phil Drouhard, supt. Fax 655-4622
www.reydonps.k12.ok.us
Reydon HS, PO Box 10 73660 50/9-12
Jeff Kelly, prin. 580-655-4375

Ringling, Jefferson, Pop. 968
Ringling ISD 500/PK-12
PO Box 1010 73456 580-662-2385
Rick Hatfield, supt. Fax 662-2683
Ringling HS 100/10-12
PO Box 1010 73456 580-662-2386
Tracy Gandy, prin. Fax 662-3323
Ringling JHS 100/7-9
PO Box 1010 73456 580-662-2386
Tracy Gandy, prin. Fax 662-3323

Ringwood, Major, Pop. 490
Ringwood ISD 400/PK-12
101 W 5th St 73768 580-883-2201
Wade Detrick, supt. Fax 883-2220
www.ringwood.k12.ok.us
Ringwood HS 100/9-12
101 W 5th St 73768 580-883-2201
Wade Detrick, prin. Fax 883-2220

Ripley, Payne, Pop. 385
Ripley ISD 500/PK-12
PO Box 97 74062 918-372-4567
Dr. Kenny Beams, supt. Fax 372-4608
www.ripley.k12.ok.us/
Ripley HS 100/9-12
PO Box 97 74062 918-372-4245
Les Tilley, prin. Fax 372-4608

Roff, Pontotoc, Pop. 687
Roff ISD 300/PK-12
PO Box 157 74865 580-456-7663
Craig McVay, supt. Fax 456-7245
www.roff.k12.ok.us
Roff HS 100/9-12
PO Box 157 74865 580-456-7252
Mike Stewart, prin. Fax 456-7499
Roff MS, PO Box 157 74865 100/6-8
Ead Simon, prin. 580-456-7663

Roland, Sequoyah, Pop. 2,907
Roland ISD 1,200/PK-12
300 Ranger Blvd 74954 918-427-4601
Paul Wood, supt. Fax 427-1785
www.rolandschools.org
Roland JHS 300/7-9
300 Ranger Blvd 74954 918-427-4631
Charles Morton, prin. Fax 427-0093
Roland SHS 300/10-12
300 Ranger Blvd 74954 918-427-7419
Gary Lattimore, prin. Fax 427-6993

Rush Springs, Grady, Pop. 1,191
Rush Springs ISD 600/PK-12
PO Box 308 73082 580-476-3929
Mike Zurline, supt. Fax 476-2018
www.rushsprings.k12.ok.us
Rush Springs HS 200/9-12
PO Box 308 73082 580-476-3596
Shawn Haskins, prin. Fax 476-2018
Rush Springs MS 100/6-8
PO Box 308 73082 580-476-3447
Shawn Haskins, prin. Fax 476-2148

Ryan, Jefferson, Pop. 785
Ryan ISD 200/PK-12
PO Box 369 73565 580-757-2308
Larry Ninman, supt. Fax 757-2609
Ryan HS, PO Box 369 73565 100/9-12
Pete Maples, prin. 580-757-2296

Salina, Mayes, Pop. 1,257
Salina ISD 900/PK-12
PO Box 98 74365 918-434-5091
Tony Thomas, supt. Fax 434-5346
www.salina.k12.ok.us
Salina HS 300/9-12
PO Box 98 74365 918-434-5347
Honesti Williams, prin. Fax 434-5537
Salina MS 200/6-8
PO Box 98 74365 918-434-5311
Debbie Cox, prin. Fax 434-5173

Sallisaw, Sequoyah, Pop. 7,974
Central ISD 500/PK-12
108089 S 4670 Rd 74955 918-775-5525
Max Tanner, supt. Fax 775-8557
www.centralps.k12.ok.us
Central HS 200/9-12
108089 S 4670 Rd 74955 918-775-5525
Brooks Cawhorn, prin. Fax 775-8557

OK Dept. of Voc. & Tech. Education
Supt. — None
Phil Berkenbile Ed.D., dir.
Indian Capital Technology Center Vo/Tech
401 E Houser Blvd 74955 918-775-9119
Curtis Shumaker, dir. Fax 775-7305

Sallisaw ISD — 2,100/PK-12
701 S J T Stites St 74955 — 918-775-5544
Scott Farmer, supt. — Fax 775-1257
sallisawps.org
Sallisaw HS — 700/9-12
2301 W Ruth Ave 74955 — 918-775-7761
Ernie Martens, prin. — Fax 775-1275
Spear MS — 400/6-8
211 S Main St 74955 — 918-775-6561
Greg Cast, prin. — Fax 775-1276

Sand Springs, Tulsa, Pop. 17,953
Sand Springs ISD — 5,100/PK-12
PO Box 970 74063 — 918-246-1400
Lloyd Snow, supt. — Fax 246-1401
www.sandites.org/
Boyd MS — 1,200/6-8
PO Box 970 74063 — 918-246-1535
Nancy Ogle, prin. — Fax 246-1544
Central 9th Grade Center — 400/9-9
PO Box 970 74063 — 918-246-1440
Ernie Kothe, prin. — Fax 246-1446
Page HS — 1,200/10-12
PO Box 970 74063 — 918-246-1470
Stan Trout, prin. — Fax 246-1480

Moriah Christian Academy — 100/PK-12
680 E 41st St 74063 — 918-241-8410
Leslie Rea, prin. — Fax 246-1109
Sand Springs Beauty College — Post-Sec.
28 E 2nd St 74063 — 918-245-6627

Sapulpa, Creek, Pop. 19,322
Lone Star SD — 900/PK-8
PO Box 1170 74067 — 918-224-0201
Tracie Hale, supt. — Fax 224-3927
www.lonestar.k12.ok.us/
Lone Star JHS — 300/5-8
PO Box 1170 74067 — 918-224-0201
Dusty Kragel, prin. — Fax 224-3927

OK Dept. of Voc. & Tech. Education
Supt. — None
Phil Berkenbile Ed.D., dir.
Central Tech — Vo/Tech
1720 S Main St 74066 — 918-224-9300
Kim Howard, dir. — Fax 224-3190

Sapulpa ISD — 3,400/PK-12
511 E Lee Ave 74066 — 918-224-3400
Kevin Burr, supt. — Fax 227-8347
sapulpaps.org/
Bartlett Academy — Alt
603 S Park St 74066 — 918-224-7958
Rhonda Thompson, prin. — Fax 224-0049
Sapulpa JHS — 600/8-9
7 S Mission St 74066 — 918-224-6710
Johnny Bilby, prin. — Fax 227-0473
Sapulpa SHS — 1,000/10-12
3 S Mission St 74066 — 918-224-6560
Dr. Jenyfer Glisson, prin. — Fax 224-0174

Eagle Point Christian Academy — 100/PK-12
602 S Mounds St 74066 — 918-227-2441
Jim Pryor, admin. — Fax 248-3117

Sasakwa, Seminole, Pop. 141
Sasakwa ISD — 300/PK-12
PO Box 323 74867 — 405-941-3213
Kyle Wilson, supt. — Fax 941-3561
www.sasakwaschools.org
Sasakwa HS — 100/9-12
PO Box 323 74867 — 405-941-3250
Brent Griffin, prin. — Fax 941-3561

Savanna, Pittsburg, Pop. 629
Savanna ISD — 400/PK-12
PO Box 266 74565 — 918-548-3777
Gary Reeder, supt. — Fax 548-3836
www.savanna.k12.ok.us/
Savanna HS — 200/9-12
PO Box 266 74565 — 918-548-3887
Chad Graham, prin. — Fax 548-3836

Sayre, Beckham, Pop. 4,304
OK Dept. of Voc. & Tech. Education
Supt. — None
Phil Berkenbile Ed.D., dir.
Western Technology Center — Vo/Tech
2002 NE Highway 66 73662 — 580-928-2097
Chris Stickney, dir. — Fax 928-9827

Sayre ISD — 700/PK-12
716 NE Highway 66 73662 — 580-928-5531
Todd Winn, supt. — Fax 928-5538
www.sayre.k12.ok.us
Sayre HS — 200/9-12
716 NE Highway 66 73662 — 580-928-5576
Danny Crabb, prin. — Fax 928-3045
Sayre MS — 100/6-8
716 NE Highway 66 73662 — 580-928-5578
Monica Brower, prin. — Fax 928-3045

Southwestern Oklahoma State University — Post-Sec.
409 E Mississippi Ave 73662 — 580-928-5533

Schulter, Okmulgee, Pop. 449
Schulter ISD — 200/PK-12
PO Box 203 74460 — 918-652-8219
Allen Callahan, supt. — Fax 652-8474
www.schulter.k12.ok.us/
Schulter HS — 100/9-12
PO Box 203 74460 — 918-652-8200
Allen Callahan, prin. — Fax 652-8474

Seiling, Dewey, Pop. 824
Seiling ISD — 300/PK-12
PO Box 780 73663 — 580-922-7383
Bob Bush, supt. — Fax 922-8019
www.seiling.k12.ok.us
Seiling JSHS — 100/7-12
PO Box 780 73663 — 580-922-7382
Gary Baker, prin. — Fax 922-8019

Seminole, Seminole, Pop. 6,934
Seminole ISD — 1,500/PK-12
PO Box 1031 74818 — 405-382-5085
Jeff Pritchard, supt. — Fax 382-8281
www.sps.k12.ok.us
Seminole HS — 500/9-12
PO Box 1031 74818 — 405-382-1415
Michael Crawford, prin. — Fax 382-1062
Seminole MS — 200/7-8
PO Box 1031 74818 — 405-382-5065
David Dean, prin. — Fax 382-8653

Strother ISD — 400/PK-12
36085 EW 1140 74868 — 405-382-4014
Dr. Bob Gragg, supt. — Fax 382-3339
www.strother.k12.ok.us/
Strother HS — 100/9-12
36085 EW 1140 74868 — 405-382-0982
Vernie Thomas, prin. — Fax 382-9430

Varnum ISD — 300/PK-12
11929 NS 3550 74868 — 405-382-1448
Jon Dotson, supt. — Fax 382-8618
www.varnum.k12.ok.us
Varnum HS — 100/9-12
11929 NS 3550 74868 — 405-382-1408
Kevin Romine, prin. — Fax 382-8618

Seminole State College — Post-Sec.
PO Box 351 74818 — 405-382-9950

Sentinel, Washita, Pop. 867
Sentinel ISD — 300/PK-12
PO Box 640 73664 — 580-393-2101
Hal Holt, supt. — Fax 393-2101
www.sentinel.k12.ok.us/
Thomas HS — 100/9-12
PO Box 640 73664 — 580-393-2112
Benny Barnett, prin. — Fax 393-4334

Shattuck, Ellis, Pop. 1,338
Shattuck ISD — 300/PK-12
PO Box 159 73858 — 580-938-2586
Randy Holley, supt. — Fax 938-8019
www.shattuck.k12.ok.us/
Shattuck HS — 100/9-12
PO Box 159 73858 — 580-938-2586
Terry Conder, prin. — Fax 938-8019

Shawnee, Pottawatomie, Pop. 28,106
Bethel ISD — 1,300/PK-12
36000 Clearpond Rd 74801 — 405-273-0385
Jerry Johnson, supt. — Fax 273-5056
www.bethel.k12.ok.us
Bethel HS — 400/9-12
36000 Clearpond Rd 74801 — 405-273-3633
Jeff Pruitt, prin. — Fax 878-5571
Bethel MS — 300/6-8
36000 Clearpond Rd 74801 — 405-273-5944
Tina Moon, prin. — Fax 273-6025

OK Dept. of Voc. & Tech. Education
Supt. — None
Phil Berkenbile Ed.D., dir.
Cooper Technology Center — Vo/Tech
1 John C Bruton Blvd 74804 — 405-273-7493
Marty Lewis, supt. — Fax 273-4704

Shawnee ISD — 4,000/PK-12
326 N Union Ave 74801 — 405-273-0653
Marc Moore, supt. — Fax 273-6818
www.shawnee.k12.ok.us
Shawnee HS — 1,200/9-12
1001 N Kennedy Ave 74801 — 405-275-3084
Lee Hamilton, prin. — Fax 275-9501
Shawnee MS — 800/6-8
4300 N Union Ave 74804 — 405-273-0403
Brent Houston, prin. — Fax 275-9651
Thorpe Academy — Alt
1111 N Kennedy Ave 74801 — 405-273-3525
Debra Watson, dir. — Fax 878-1046

Family of Faith Christian S — 100/K-12
PO Box 1442 74802 — 405-273-5331
Christopher Belyeu, admin. — Fax 273-8535
Family of Faith College — Post-Sec.
PO Box 1805 74802 — 405-273-5331
Liberty Academy — 300/PK-12
PO Box 1176 74802 — 405-273-3022
Susan Harmon, admin. — Fax 273-3029
Oklahoma Baptist University — Post-Sec.
500 W University St 74804 — 405-275-2850
St. Gregory's University — Post-Sec.
1900 W MacArthur St 74804 — 888-784-7347
Shawnee Beauty College — Post-Sec.
410 E Main St 74801 — 405-275-3182

Shidler, Osage, Pop. 394
Shidler ISD — 300/PK-12
PO Box 85 74652 — 918-793-2021
John Herzig, supt. — Fax 793-2061
www.shidler.k12.ok.us
Shidler HS — 100/9-12
PO Box 85 74652 — 918-793-2461
Janice Finton, prin. — Fax 793-2062
Other Schools – See Kaw City

Skiatook, Tulsa, Pop. 6,871
Skiatook ISD — 2,600/PK-12
355 S Osage St 74070 — 918-396-1792
Rick Thomas, supt. — Fax 396-1799
www.skiatookschools.org
Newman MS — 600/6-8
355 S Osage St 74070 — 918-396-2307
Steve Cantrell, prin. — Fax 396-1799
Skiatook HS — 700/9-12
355 S Osage St 74070 — 918-396-1790
Donna Brogan, prin. — Fax 396-1799

Smithville, McCurtain, Pop. 106
Smithville ISD — 300/PK-12
PO Box 8 74957 — 580-244-3333
Delbert McBroom, supt. — Fax 244-7214
www.smithville.k12.ok.us
Smithville HS — 100/9-12
PO Box 8 74957 — 580-244-3281
Curtis McDaniel, prin. — Fax 244-7277
Smithville MS — 100/6-8
PO Box 8 74957 — 580-244-7212
Stacy Nichols, prin. — Fax 244-3651

Snyder, Kiowa, Pop. 1,354
Snyder ISD — 500/PK-12
PO Box 368 73566 — 580-569-2773
Robert Trammell, supt. — Fax 569-4205
www.snyder.k12.ok.us
Snyder HS, PO Box 368 73566 — 200/9-12
Mark Batt, prin. — 580-569-2730
Snyder MS, PO Box 368 73566 — 200/4-8
Carol McPhail, prin. — 580-569-2691

Soper, Choctaw, Pop. 237
Soper ISD — 400/PK-12
PO Box 149 74759 — 580-345-2757
Scotty Van Worth, supt. — Fax 345-2222
soperisd.com
Soper HS — 100/9-12
PO Box 149 74759 — 580-345-2212
James Eberts M.A., prin. — Fax 345-2896

South Coffeyville, Nowata, Pop. 715
Oklahoma Union ISD — 700/PK-12
RR 1 Box 377-7 74072 — 918-255-6550
Dr. Robert Jobe, supt. — Fax 255-6817
www.okunion.k12.ok.us/
Oklahoma Union HS — 200/9-12
RR 1 Box 377-7 74072 — 918-255-6550
David Lovelace, prin. — Fax 255-6817
Oklahoma Union MS — 200/6-8
RR 1 Box 377-7 74072 — 918-255-6550
Lance Williams, prin. — Fax 255-6817

South Coffeyville ISD — 300/PK-12
PO Box 190 74072 — 918-255-6202
Clem Haddox, supt. — Fax 255-6230
South Coffeyville HS — 100/9-12
PO Box 190 74072 — 918-255-6087
Michael Wilson, prin. — Fax 255-6115

Spencer, Oklahoma, Pop. 3,660
Oklahoma City ISD
Supt. — See Oklahoma City
Rogers MS — 400/6-8
4000 Spencer Rd 73084 — 405-771-3205
Michael Adams, prin. — Fax 771-2114
Star Spencer HS — 400/9-12
3001 Spencer Rd 73084 — 405-587-8800
Chris Gardner, prin. — Fax 587-8875

Sperry, Tulsa, Pop. 1,118
Sperry ISD — 1,200/PK-12
PO Box 610 74073 — 918-288-6258
Brian Beagles Ed.D., supt. — Fax 288-7067
www.sperry.k12.ok.us
Sperry HS — 400/9-12
PO Box 610 74073 — 918-288-7213
Mike Haney, prin. — Fax 288-7230
Sperry MS — 300/6-8
PO Box 610 74073 — 918-288-7213
Tim Weaver, prin. — Fax 288-7231

Oklahoma Farriers College — Post-Sec.
PO Box 788 74073 — 918-288-7221

Spiro, LeFlore, Pop. 2,077
OK Dept. of Voc. & Tech. Education
Supt. — None
Phil Berkenbile Ed.D., dir.
Kiamichi Technology Center — Vo/Tech
610 SW 3rd St 74959 — 918-962-3722
Fax 962-4627

Spiro ISD — 1,100/K-12
600 W Broadway St 74959 — 918-962-2463
Don Atkinson, supt. — Fax 962-2757
www.spiro.k12.ok.us/
Spiro HS, 600 W Broadway St 74959 — 400/9-12
Tracy Saling, prin. — 918-962-2493
Spiro MS, 600 W Broadway St 74959 — 200/6-8
Nick Carter, prin. — 918-962-2488

Springer, Carter, Pop. 636
Springer ISD — 200/PK-12
PO Box 249 73458 — 580-653-2656
Matt Holder, supt. — Fax 653-2666
www.springerschools.com
Springer HS, PO Box 249 73458 — 100/9-12
John Mann, prin. — 580-653-2471

Sterling, Comanche, Pop. 758
Sterling ISD — 400/PK-12
PO Box 158 73567 — 580-365-4307
Julie Poteete, supt. — Fax 365-4705
www.sterling.k12.ok.us/
Sterling HS — 100/9-12
PO Box 158 73567 — 580-365-4303
Marty Curry, prin. — Fax 365-4705

Stigler, Haskell, Pop. 2,525
OK Dept. of Voc. & Tech. Education
Supt. — None
Phil Berkenbile Ed.D., dir.
Kiamichi Technology Center — Vo/Tech
1410 Old Military Rd 74462 — 918-967-2801
Joe Carrick, dir. — Fax 967-2803

Stigler ISD 1,300/PK-12
309 NW E St 74462 918-967-2805
Clayton Edwards, supt. Fax 967-4550
www.stigler.k12.ok.us
Stigler HS 400/9-12
309 NW E St 74462 918-967-8834
David Morgan, prin. Fax 967-8974
Stigler MS 300/5-8
309 NW E St 74462 918-967-2521
Tony Gilmore, prin. Fax 967-5125

Stillwater, Payne, Pop. 43,498
OK Dept. of Voc. & Tech. Education
Supt. — None
Phil Berkenbile Ed.D., dir.
Meridian Technology Center Vo/Tech
1312 S Sangre Rd 74074 405-377-3333
Dr. Douglas Major, supt. Fax 372-3466
Other Schools – See Ada OK, Afton OK, Altus OK, Alva OK, Ardmore OK, Atoka OK, Bartlesville OK, Broken Arrow OK, Burns Flat OK, Chickasha OK, Choctaw OK, Claremore OK, Drumright OK, Duncan OK, Durant OK, El Reno OK, Enid OK, Fairview OK, Fort Cobb OK, Frederick OK, Hugo OK, Idabel OK, Kansas OK, Lawton OK, McAlester OK, Midwest City OK, Muskogee OK, Norman OK, Oklahoma City OK, Okmulgee OK, Omega OK, Ponca City OK, Poteau OK, Pryor OK, Sallisaw OK, Sapulpa OK, Sayre OK, Shawnee OK, Spiro OK, Stigler OK, Stilwell OK, Tahlequah OK, Talihina OK, Tinker AFB OK, Tulsa OK, Wayne OK, Wetumka OK, Woodward OK, Yukon OK

Stillwater ISD 5,700/PK-12
314 S Lewis St 74074 405-533-6300
Dr. Ann Caine, supt. Fax 743-6311
www.stillwaterschools.com
Lincoln Alternative Academy Alt
215 E 12th Ave 74074 405-533-6331
Caryl Talley, prin. Fax 743-7725
Stillwater HS 1,100/10-12
1224 N Husband St 74075 405-533-6450
Uwe Gordon, prin. Fax 743-6488
Stillwater JHS 700/8-9
1900 N Skyline St 74075 405-533-6420
Trent Swanson, prin. Fax 743-6444

Meridian Technology Center Post-Sec.
1312 S Sangre Rd 74074 405-377-3333
Northern Oklahoma College Post-Sec.
PO Box 1869 74076 405-744-2246
Oklahoma State University 74078 Post-Sec.
405-744-5000
Stillwater Beauty Academy Post-Sec.
1684 Cimarron Plz 74075 405-377-4100

Stilwell, Adair, Pop. 3,604
OK Dept. of Voc. & Tech. Education
Supt. — None
Phil Berkenbile Ed.D., dir.
Indian Capital Technology Center Vo/Tech
RR 6 Box 3320 74960 918-696-3111
Dan Collins, dir. Fax 696-3031

Stilwell ISD 1,400/PK-12
1801 W Locust St 74960 918-696-7001
Geri Gilstrap, supt. Fax 696-2193
stilwellk12.org
Stilwell HS 600/9-12
1801 W Locust St 74960 918-696-7276
Ramona Ketcher, prin. Fax 696-4695
Stilwell MS 300/5-8
12 N 7th St 74960 918-696-2685
Dale Girdner, prin. Fax 696-7761

Stonewall, Pontotoc, Pop. 416
Stonewall ISD 400/PK-12
600 Highschool 74871 580-265-4241
Kevin Flowers, supt. Fax 265-4536
www.stonewall.k12.ok.us
McLish MS 100/5-8
600 Highschool 74871 580-777-2221
Jack Wofford, prin. Fax 777-2222
Stonewall HS 100/9-12
600 Highschool 74871 580-265-4242
Tamara Newberry, prin. Fax 265-4231

Stratford, Garvin, Pop. 1,461
Stratford ISD 600/PK-12
PO Box 589 74872 580-759-3615
Michael Blackburn, supt. Fax 759-2669
Stratford HS 200/9-12
PO Box 589 74872 580-759-2381
Paul Savage, prin. Fax 759-8913
Stratford MS 200/6-8
PO Box 589 74872 580-759-3615
Tracy Felan, prin. Fax 759-2513

Stringtown, Atoka, Pop. 364
Stringtown ISD 200/PK-12
PO Box 130 74569 580-346-7423
Tony Potts, supt. Fax 346-7726
Stringtown HS 100/9-12
PO Box 130 74569 580-346-7423
Tony Potts, prin. Fax 346-7726

Stroud, Lincoln, Pop. 2,575
Stroud ISD 900/PK-12
212 W 7th St 74079 918-968-2541
Joe Van Tuyl, supt. Fax 968-2582
www.stroud.k12.ok.us
Stroud HS 300/9-12
212 W 7th St 74079 918-968-2542
Scott Baade, prin. Fax 968-3656
Stroud MS 200/6-8
212 W 7th St 74079 918-968-2200
Betty Wages, prin. Fax 968-2391

Stuart, Hughes, Pop. 165
Stuart ISD 200/PK-12
8837 4th St 74570 918-546-2476
Bill San Millan, supt. Fax 546-2329
www.stuart.k12.ok.us/
Stuart HS 100/9-12
8837 4th St 74570 918-546-2474
Tracy Blasengame, prin. Fax 546-2329

Sulphur, Murray, Pop. 4,613
Sulphur ISD 1,400/PK-12
1021 W 9th St 73086 580-622-2061
Gary Jones, supt. Fax 622-6789
www.sulphur.k12.ok.us
Sulphur HS 300/9-12
1021 W 9th St 73086 580-622-3174
Gary Jones, prin. Fax 622-5735
Sulphur JHS 300/6-8
1021 W 9th St 73086 580-622-4010
Tony Duck, prin. Fax 622-3900

Oklahoma School for the Deaf Post-Sec.
1100 E Oklahoma Ave 73086 580-622-4900

Sweetwater, Roger Mills, Pop. 86
Sweetwater ISD 100/PK-12
11107 N Highway 30 73666 580-534-2272
Casey Reed, supt. Fax 534-2273
www.sweetwater.k12.ok.us/
Sweetwater HS 50/9-12
11107 N Highway 30 73666 580-534-2272
Casey Reed, prin. Fax 534-2273

Tahlequah, Cherokee, Pop. 14,483
OK Dept. of Voc. & Tech. Education
Supt. — None
Phil Berkenbile Ed.D., dir.
Indian Capital Technology Center Vo/Tech
240 Vo Tech Dr 74464 918-456-2594
Robin Roberts, dir. Fax 456-0140

Tahlequah ISD 3,200/PK-12
PO Box 517 74465 918-458-4100
Lisa Presley, supt. Fax 458-4103
www.tahlequahschools.org
Tahlequah HS 1,200/9-12
591 Pendleton St 74464 918-458-4150
Jeff Thorne, prin. Fax 458-4152
Tahlequah MS 900/5-8
871 Pendleton St 74464 918-458-4140
Jaycie Smith, prin. Fax 458-4142

Beauty Technical College Post-Sec.
PO Box 1506 74465 918-456-6360
Northeastern State University Post-Sec.
600 N Grand Ave 74464 918-456-5511

Talihina, Latimer, Pop. 1,013
Buffalo Valley ISD 200/K-12
4384 SE Highway 63 74571 918-522-4426
Charles Caughern, supt. Fax 522-4287
www.buffalovalley.k12.ok.us
Buffalo Valley HS 100/9-12
4384 SE Highway 63 74571 918-522-4803
Charles Caughern, prin. Fax 522-4287

OK Dept. of Voc. & Tech. Education
Supt. — None
Phil Berkenbile Ed.D., dir.
Kiamichi Technology Center Vo/Tech
13739 SE 202nd Rd 74571 918-567-2264
Larry Brooks, dir. Fax 567-3359

Talihina ISD 600/PK-12
PO Box 38 74571 918-567-2259
Jason Lockhart, supt. Fax 567-3507
www.talihina.k12.ok.us/
Talihina HS 100/9-12
PO Box 38 74571 918-567-2266
Maria Carden, prin. Fax 567-3507
Talihina JHS, PO Box 38 74571 100/7-8
Maria Carden, prin. 918-567-2266

Taloga, Dewey, Pop. 290
Taloga ISD 100/PK-12
PO Box 158 73667 580-328-5577
George Kellner, supt. Fax 328-5237
www.taloga.k12.ok.us
Taloga HS 50/9-12
PO Box 158 73667 580-328-5586
Carl Baker, prin. Fax 328-5237

Tecumseh, Pottawatomie, Pop. 6,036
Tecumseh ISD 2,000/K-12
1301 E Highland St 74873 405-598-3739
Tom Wilsie, supt. Fax 598-2861
www.tecumseh.k12.ok.us
Tecumseh HS 600/9-12
901 N 13th St 74873 405-598-2113
Danny Sterling, prin. Fax 598-2432
Tecumseh MS 500/6-8
315 W Park St 74873 405-598-3744
Robert Kinsey, prin. Fax 598-1948

Temple, Cotton, Pop. 952
Temple ISD 200/PK-12
PO Box 400 73568 580-342-6230
David Brewer, supt. Fax 342-6463
www.temple.k12.ok.us/
Temple HS 100/9-12
PO Box 400 73568 580-342-6221
Darrell Lamar, prin. Fax 342-6463

Texhoma, Texas, Pop. 917
Texhoma ISD 200/5-12
PO Box 648 73949 580-423-7433
Eric Smith, supt. Fax 423-7096
www.texhoma61.net/
Texhoma HS 100/9-12
PO Box 648 73949 580-423-7371
Johnny James, prin. Fax 423-7096
Texhoma S 100/5-8
PO Box 648 73949 580-423-7371
Johnny James, prin. Fax 423-7096

Thackerville, Love, Pop. 429
Thackerville ISD 300/PK-12
18943 US Highway 77 73459 580-276-2630
Greg Raper, supt. Fax 276-2638
www.thackervilleschools.org
Thackerville HS 100/9-12
18943 US Highway 77 73459 580-276-3610
Matt Means, prin. Fax 276-8314

Thomas, Custer, Pop. 1,152
Thomas-Fay-Custer Unified ISD 300/PK-12
PO Box 190 73669 580-661-3522
Rob Royalty, supt. Fax 661-3589
thomas.k12.ok.us/
Thomas JSHS 100/7-12
PO Box 190 73669 580-661-3522
Ray Oakes, prin. Fax 661-3589

Tinker AFB, See Oklahoma City
OK Dept. of Voc. & Tech. Education
Supt. — None
Phil Berkenbile Ed.D., dir.
Mid-Del-Tinker Career Tech Vo/Tech
Building 1 D Ave 73145 405-734-7266
Jefferson Tarver, dir. Fax 737-2330

Tipton, Tillman, Pop. 830
Tipton ISD 200/K-12
PO Box 340 73570 580-667-5268
Shane Boothe, supt. Fax 667-5267
www.tiptontigers.net
Tipton HS 100/9-12
PO Box 340 73570 580-667-5268
Steve Glenn, prin. Fax 667-5478

Tishomingo, Johnston, Pop. 2,754
Tishomingo ISD 900/PK-12
1300 E Main St 73460 580-371-9190
Kevin Duncan, supt. Fax 371-3765
www.tishomingo.k12.ok.us/
Tishomingo HS, 1300 E Main St 73460 300/9-12
Kevin Duncan, prin. 580-371-2322
Tishomingo MS, 1300 E Main St 73460 200/6-8
Larry Davis, prin. 580-371-3602

Murray State College Post-Sec.
1 Murray Campus St 73460 580-371-2371

Tonkawa, Kay, Pop. 3,131
Tonkawa ISD 600/PK-12
500 E North Ave 74653 580-628-3597
Rod Reese, supt. Fax 628-5132
www.tonkawa.k12.ok.us/
Tonkawa JSHS 200/6-12
500 E North Ave 74653 580-628-2566
Kyle Simpson, prin. Fax 628-3646

Northern Oklahoma College Post-Sec.
PO Box 310 74653 580-628-6200

Tulsa, Tulsa, Pop. 371,916
Berryhill ISD 1,200/PK-12
3128 S 63rd West Ave 74107 918-446-1966
Mike Campbell, supt. Fax 446-6370
www.berryhillschools.org/
Berryhill HS 400/9-12
3128 S 63rd West Ave 74107 918-445-6035
Donnie Bridgeman, prin. Fax 445-6015
Berryhill MS 200/7-8
3128 S 63rd West Ave 74107 918-445-6039
Ronna Taylor, prin. Fax 445-6018

Jenks ISD
Supt. — See Jenks
Jenks MS 1,600/7-8
3019 E 101st St 74137 918-299-4411
Rob Miller, prin. Fax 298-0652

OK Dept. of Voc. & Tech. Education
Supt. — None
Phil Berkenbile Ed.D., dir.
Tulsa Tech Center Lemley Vo/Tech
3420 S Memorial Dr 74145 918-828-1000
Randy Dean, dir. Fax 828-1009
Tulsa Tech Center Peoria Vo/Tech
3850 N Peoria Ave 74106 918-828-2000
John Robinson, dir. Fax 828-2009
Tulsa Tech Center Riverside Campus Vo/Tech
801 E 91st St 74132 918-828-4000
Joyce McClellan, dir. Fax 828-4009

Tulsa ISD 35,900/PK-12
PO Box 470208 74147 918-746-6800
Keith Ballard Ed.D., supt. Fax 746-6850
www.tulsaschools.org
Carver MS 600/6-8
624 E Oklahoma Pl 74106 918-925-1420
Melissa Woolridge, prin. Fax 925-1450
Central JSHS Fine & Performing Arts 700/7-12
3101 W Edison St 74127 918-833-8400
Jacqueline Tolbert, prin. Fax 833-8417
Clinton MS 500/6-8
2224 W 41st St 74107 918-746-8640
Shelly Holman, prin. Fax 746-8691
Continuation S Alt
1205 W Newton St 74127 918-833-8650
Mary McNamara, dir.
Early College HS 9-12
3727 E Apache St 74115 918-595-7466
Dr. Rodney Clark, prin.
East Central HS 1,100/9-12
12150 E 11th St 74128 918-746-9700
Sean Brannon, prin. Fax 746-9760
East Central JHS 700/6-8
12121 E 21st St 74129 918-746-9500
Darin Schmidt, prin. Fax 746-9519

Edison Preparatory MSHS 1,200/6-12
2906 E 41st St 74105 918-746-8500
Derrick Schmidt, prin. Fax 746-8511
Hale HS 1,000/9-12
6960 E 21st St 74129 918-925-1200
Caleb Starr, prin. Fax 925-1262
Hale JHS 700/6-8
2177 S 67th East Ave 74129 918-746-9260
Melissa Venable, prin. Fax 746-9291
McLain MSHS for Science & Technology 400/6-12
4929 N Peoria Ave 74126 918-833-8500
Darius Kirk, prin. Fax 833-8559
Memorial HS 1,200/9-12
5840 S Hudson Ave 74135 918-833-9600
Fax 833-9659
Memorial JHS 600/6-8
7502 E 57th St 74145 918-833-9520
Ginger Bunnell, prin. Fax 833-9551
Monroe Demonstration S 400/6-8
2010 E 48th St N 74130 918-833-8900
Fax 833-8918
Rogers JSHS 1,000/7-12
3909 E 5th Pl 74112 918-833-9000
Stacey Vernon, prin. Fax 833-9065
Street S Alt
1135 S Yale Ave 74112 918-833-9800
Lori McGinnis-Madland Ed.D., dir. Fax 833-9858
Thoreau Demonstration Academy 600/6-8
7370 E 71st St 74133 918-833-9700
Thomas Padalino, prin. Fax 833-9720
TRAICE MSHS Academy 50/Alt
2740 E 41st St N 74110 918-925-1360
Cheryl Carter, prin.
Tulsa Met HS, 6201 E Virgin St 74115 600/Alt
Michelle Butler, prin. 918-746-9300
Tulsa Met JHS 200/Alt
6201 E Virgin St 74115 918-746-9300
Michelle Butler, prin. Fax 833-9875
Washington HS 1,300/9-12
1514 E Zion St 74106 918-925-1000
James Furch, prin. Fax 928-1001
Webster HS 600/9-12
1919 W 40th St 74107 918-746-8000
Jim Rector, prin. Fax 746-8056

Union ISD 13,800/PK-12
8506 E 61st St 74133 918-357-4321
Dr. Kirt Hartzler, supt. Fax 357-6019
www.unionps.org
Union Alternative S Alt
8506 E 61st St 74133 918-357-7085
Richard Storm, prin. Fax 357-7094
Union SHS 2,100/10-12
6636 S Mingo Rd 74133 918-357-4323
John Chargois, prin. Fax 357-7210
Other Schools – See Broken Arrow

Bishop Kelley HS 800/9-12
3905 S Hudson Ave 74135 918-627-3390
Fr. Brian O'Brien, pres. Fax 664-2134
Brown Mackie College Post-Sec.
4608 S Garnett Rd Ste 110 74146 918-628-3700
Career Point Institute Post-Sec.
3138 S Garnett Rd 74146 918-627-8074
Cascia Hall Preparatory S 600/6-12
2520 S Yorktown Ave 74114 918-746-2600
Roger Carter, hdmstr. Fax 746-2636
CC's Cosmetology College Post-Sec.
11630 E 21st St 74129 918-234-9444
Clary Sage College Post-Sec.
3131 S Sheridan Rd 74145 918-298-8200
Community Care College Post-Sec.
4242 S Sheridan Rd 74145 918-610-0027
Holland Hall 1,000/PK-12
5666 E 81st St 74137 918-481-1111
Fax 481-1145
ITT Technical Institute Post-Sec.
4500 S 129th East Ave # 152 74134 918-615-3900
Lincoln Christian S 800/PK-12
1003 N 129th East Ave 74116 918-234-8150
Darren Melton, prin. Fax 234-8152
Metro Christian Academy 900/K-12
6363 S Trenton Ave 74136 918-745-9868
Mingo Valley Christian S 300/PK-12
8720 E 61st St 74133 918-294-0404
Joel Staggers, admin. Fax 294-0555
Oklahoma Health Academy Post-Sec.
2865 E Skelly Dr Ste 224 74105 918-748-9900
Oklahoma State University Post-Sec.
700 N Greenwood Ave 74106 918-594-8000
Oklahoma Technical College Post-Sec.
4444 S Sheridan Rd 74145 918-895-7500
Oral Roberts University Post-Sec.
7777 S Lewis Ave 74171 918-495-6161
OSU Center for Health Sciences Post-Sec.
1111 W 17th St 74107 918-582-1972
Phillips Theological Seminary Post-Sec.
901 N Mingo Rd 74116 918-610-8303
Platt College Post-Sec.
3801 S Sheridan Rd 74145 918-663-9000
Roberts University eAcademy 100/3-12
7777 S Lewis Ave 74171 800-678-5899
Nancy Herrera, admin. Fax 493-8996
St. Francis Hospital Post-Sec.
6161 S Yale Ave 74136 918-494-1370
San Miguel MS 6-8
2444 E Admiral Blvd 74110 918-728-7337
Cathy Moore, prin. Fax 660-2040
Spartan Coll of Aeronautics & Technology Post-Sec.
8820 E Pine St 74115 800-331-1204
Technical Institute of Cosmetology Arts Post-Sec.
822 E 6th St 74120 918-660-8828
Tulsa Adventist Academy 100/PK-10
900 S New Haven Ave 74112 918-834-1107
Fax 834-2151
Tulsa Community College Post-Sec.
3727 E Apache St 74115 918-595-7000
Tulsa Community College Metro Campus Post-Sec.
909 S Boston Ave 74119 918-595-7000
Tulsa Community College Southeast Campus Post-Sec.
10300 E 81st St 74133 918-595-7000
Tulsa Community College West Campus Post-Sec.
7505 W 41st St 74107 918-595-7000
Tulsa Welding School Post-Sec.
2545 E 11th St 74104 918-587-6789
University of Oklahoma Tulsa Post-Sec.
4502 E 41st St 74135 918-660-3000
University of Tulsa Post-Sec.
800 Tucker Dr 74104 918-631-2000
Vatterott College Post-Sec.
4343 S 118th East Ave Ste A 74146 918-835-8288
Victory Christian S 1,200/K-12
7700 S Lewis Ave 74136 918-491-7720
Dr. Dennis Demuth, supt. Fax 491-7727
Virginia College Post-Sec.
5124 S Peoria Ave 74105 918-960-5400
Wichita Technical Institute - Tulsa Post-Sec.
8421 E 61st St Ste U 74133 888-859-4564
Wright Career College Post-Sec.
4908 S Sheridan Rd 74145 918-628-7700
Wright Christian Academy 300/PK-12
11391 E Admiral Pl 74116 918-438-0922
Jeffrey L. Brown, supt. Fax 438-0700

Tupelo, Coal, Pop. 308
Tupelo ISD 300/PK-12
PO Box 239 74572 580-845-2460
Tony Stevens, supt. Fax 845-2565
www.tupelo.k12.ok.us
Tupelo HS 100/9-12
PO Box 239 74572 580-845-2381
Jerry Romines, prin. Fax 845-2565

Turpin, Beaver, Pop. 457
Turpin ISD 300/PK-12
PO Box 187 73950 580-778-3333
Bret Rider, supt. Fax 778-3179
www.turpinps.org
Turpin HS 100/7-12
PO Box 187 73950 580-778-3333
Gary Wallace, prin. Fax 778-3179

Tuttle, Grady, Pop. 5,837
Tuttle ISD 1,700/PK-12
PO Box 780 73089 405-381-2605
Lee Coker, supt. Fax 381-4008
www.tuttleschools.info/
Tuttle HS 500/9-12
PO Box 780 73089 405-381-2396
Pat Ragsdale, prin. Fax 381-4637
Tuttle MS 400/6-8
PO Box 780 73089 405-381-2062
Scott Moore, prin. Fax 381-4630

Tyrone, Texas, Pop. 753
Tyrone ISD 300/PK-12
PO Box 168 73951 580-854-6298
Josh Bell, supt. Fax 854-6474
www.tyrone.k12.ok.us/
Tyrone HS 100/9-12
PO Box 168 73951 580-854-6298
Donovan Smith, prin. Fax 854-6474

Union City, Canadian, Pop. 1,578
Union City ISD 300/PK-12
PO Box 279 73090 405-483-3531
Todd Carel, supt. Fax 483-5599
www.unioncity.k12.ok.us/
Union City HS 100/9-12
PO Box 279 73090 405-483-3531
Todd Carel, admin. Fax 483-5599

Valliant, McCurtain, Pop. 701
Valliant ISD 1,000/PK-12
604 E Lucas St 74764 580-933-7232
Craig Wall, supt. Fax 933-7289
www.vpsd.org
Valliant HS 300/9-12
604 E Lucas St 74764 580-933-7292
Glenn Williamson, prin. Fax 933-7278
Valliant MS 200/6-8
604 E Lucas St 74764 580-933-4253
Dennis Robberson, prin. Fax 933-4254

Velma, Stephens, Pop. 608
Velma-Alma ISD 400/PK-12
PO Box 8 73491 580-444-3355
Jerry Garrett, supt. Fax 444-2554
www.velma-alma.k12.ok.us
Velma-Alma HS 100/9-12
PO Box 8 73491 580-444-3356
Mike Thompson, prin. Fax 444-2554

Verden, Grady, Pop. 510
Verden ISD 200/PK-12
PO Box 99 73092 405-453-7247
David Davidson, supt. Fax 453-7246
www.verdenschools.org
Verden HS 100/7-12
PO Box 99 73092 405-453-7836
David Davidson, prin. Fax 453-7246

Vian, Sequoyah, Pop. 1,346
Vian ISD 1,000/PK-12
PO Box 434 74962 918-773-5798
Lawrence Barnes, supt. Fax 773-3051
www.vian.k12.ok.us/
Vian HS 300/9-12
PO Box 434 74962 918-773-5475
David Vinson, prin. Fax 773-3051
Vian MS 200/6-8
PO Box 434 74962 918-773-8631
Dr. Carla Wortman, prin. Fax 773-3051

Vici, Dewey, Pop. 673
Vici ISD 300/PK-12
PO Box 60 73859 580-995-4744
Coby Nelson, supt. Fax 995-3101
www.vicischools.k12.ok.us
Vici HS 100/9-12
PO Box 60 73859 580-995-4251
Sheldon Halderman, prin. Fax 995-3101

Vinita, Craig, Pop. 5,215
Vinita ISD 1,700/PK-12
114 S Scraper St 74301 918-256-6778
Kelly Grimmett, supt. Fax 256-5617
www.vinitahornets.com
Vinita HS 600/9-12
801 N Adair St 74301 918-256-6777
Rusty Rankin, prin. Fax 256-5300
Vinita MS 400/6-8
226 N Miller St 74301 918-256-2402
Eddie Sturgeon, prin. Fax 256-5401

Ketchum Adventist Academy 50/PK-10
35369 S Highway 82 74301 918-782-2986
Wes McWilliams, prin. Fax 782-1567

Wagoner, Wagoner, Pop. 7,460
Wagoner ISD 2,500/K-12
PO Box 508 74477 918-485-4046
Monte Thompson, supt. Fax 485-8710
www.wagonerps.org
Wagoner HS 700/9-12
300 Bulldog Cir 74467 918-485-5553
Mike Christy, prin. Fax 485-8886
Wagoner MS 500/6-8
500 Bulldog Cir 74467 918-485-9541
Dawn Henley, prin. Fax 485-4149

Walters, Cotton, Pop. 2,379
Walters ISD 700/PK-12
418 S Broadway St 73572 580-875-2568
Jimmie Dedmon, supt. Fax 875-2831
blued.org
Walters HS 200/9-12
418 S Broadway St 73572 580-875-3257
Fax 875-6097
Walters MS 200/6-8
418 S Broadway St 73572 580-875-3214
Laurie Graham, prin. Fax 875-3401

Wanette, Pottawatomie, Pop. 331
Wanette ISD 200/PK-12
PO Box 161 74878 405-383-2656
Rick Riggs, supt. Fax 383-2449
www.wanette.k12.ok.us/
Wanette HS 100/9-12
PO Box 161 74878 405-383-2254
Gary Stidham, prin. Fax 383-2180

Wapanucka, Johnston, Pop. 399
Wapanucka ISD 300/PK-12
PO Box 188 73461 580-937-4466
Stanley Williams, supt. Fax 937-4804
www.wpss.k12.ok.us
Wapanucka HS, PO Box 188 73461 100/9-12
Max Rowland, prin. 580-937-4288

Warner, Muskogee, Pop. 1,489
Warner ISD 700/PK-12
RR 1 Box 1240 74469 918-463-5171
David Vinson, supt. Fax 463-2542
www.warner.k12.ok.us
Warner HS 200/9-12
RR 1 Box 1240 74469 918-463-5172
Jeremy Jackson, prin. Fax 463-2378

Connors State College Post-Sec.
RR 1 Box 1000 74469 918-463-2931

Warr Acres, Oklahoma, Pop. 9,574
Putnam City ISD
Supt. — See Oklahoma City
Capps MS 800/6-8
4020 N Grove Ave 73122 405-787-3660
Keely Frayser, prin. Fax 491-7536
Putnam City Academy Alt
5604 NW 41st St Ste 300 73122 405-495-8838
Shelly Roper, prin. Fax 491-7529
Putnam City HS 1,800/9-12
5300 NW 50th St 73122 405-789-4350
Diana Lebsack, prin. Fax 789-1662

Vatterott College - Oklahoma City Post-Sec.
5537 NW Expressway 73132 405-234-3600

Washington, McClain, Pop. 585
Washington ISD 900/PK-12
PO Box 98 73093 405-288-6190
A.J. Brewer, supt. Fax 288-6214
www.washington.k12.ok.us/
Washington HS 300/9-12
PO Box 98 73093 405-288-2354
David Crabbe, prin. Fax 288-6214
Washington MS 200/6-8
PO Box 98 73093 405-288-2428
Stuart McPherson, prin. Fax 288-6214

Watonga, Blaine, Pop. 4,947
Watonga ISD 800/PK-12
PO Box 310 73772 580-623-7364
Bill Seitter, supt. Fax 623-7370
www.watonga.k12.ok.us
Eagle Academy Alt
PO Box 310 73772 580-623-7362
Shannon Grimes, dir. Fax 623-8019
Watonga HS 200/9-12
PO Box 310 73772 580-623-7362
Shannon Grimes, prin. Fax 623-8019

Watonga MS 200/6-8
PO Box 310 73772 580-623-7361
Robin Roof, prin. Fax 623-7371

Watts, Adair, Pop. 292
Watts ISD 400/PK-12
RR 2 Box 1 74964 918-422-5311
J. David Smith, supt. Fax 422-5556
www.wattsschool.com
Watts HS 100/9-12
RR 2 Box 1 74964 918-422-5132
Twylah Morris, prin. Fax 422-5556

Waukomis, Garfield, Pop. 1,254
Pioneer-Pleasant Vale ISD 600/PK-12
6520 E Wood Rd 73773 580-758-3282
Brent Koontz, supt. Fax 758-3504
www.ppv.k12.ok.us/
Pioneer-Pleasant Vale HS 200/9-12
6520 E Wood Rd 73773 580-758-3282
Tom Betchan, prin. Fax 758-1541
Pioneer-Pleasant Vale JHS 100/7-8
6520 E Wood Rd 73773 580-758-3282
Tom Betchan, prin. Fax 758-1541

Waukomis ISD 300/PK-12
PO Box 729 73773 580-758-3247
Dale Bledsoe, supt. Fax 758-3834
www.waukomis.k12.ok.us
Waukomis HS 100/6-12
PO Box 729 73773 580-758-3245
Matt Cue, prin. Fax 758-3256

Waurika, Jefferson, Pop. 1,993
Waurika ISD 300/PK-12
600 E Florida Ave 73573 580-228-3373
Roxie Terry, supt. Fax 228-3428
www.waurikaschools.org
Waurika MSHS 100/6-12
600 E Florida Ave 73573 580-228-2341
Dale Spradlin, prin. Fax 228-3428

Wayne, McClain, Pop. 635
OK Dept. of Voc. & Tech. Education
Supt. — None
Phil Berkenbile Ed.D., dir.
Mid-America Technology Center Vo/Tech
PO Box H 73095 405-449-3391
Dusty Ricks, supt. Fax 449-7321

Wayne ISD 500/PK-12
212 S Seifried St 73095 405-449-3646
David Powell, supt. Fax 449-7095
www.wayne.k12.ok.us
Wayne HS 200/9-12
212 S Seifried St 73095 405-449-3317
James Lewis, prin. Fax 449-7095
Wayne MS 100/6-8
212 S Seifried St 73095 405-449-7047
Billy Lucas, prin. Fax 449-7095

Waynoka, Woods, Pop. 895
Waynoka ISD 200/PK-12
2134 Lincoln St 73860 580-824-6561
Peggy Constien, supt. Fax 824-0656
www.waynoka.k12.ok.us/
Waynoka HS, 2134 Lincoln St 73860 100/9-12
Michael Meriwether, prin. 580-824-4341

Weatherford, Custer, Pop. 10,475
Weatherford ISD 1,900/PK-12
516 N Broadway St 73096 580-772-3327
Matt Holder, supt. Fax 774-0821
www.wpsok.org
Weatherford HS 500/9-12
1500 N Washington St 73096 580-772-3385
Mark Shadid, prin. Fax 774-1939
Weatherford MS 400/6-8
509 N Custer St 73096 580-772-2270
Eddie Bennett, prin. Fax 774-1981

Southwestern Oklahoma State University Post-Sec.
100 Campus Dr 73096 580-772-6611

Webbers Falls, Muskogee, Pop. 572
Webbers Falls ISD 300/PK-12
PO Box 300 74470 918-464-2334
Dudley Hume, supt. Fax 464-2313
www.webbersfalls.k12.ok.us/
Webbers Falls HS 100/9-12
PO Box 300 74470 918-464-2334
Judy Morton, prin. Fax 464-2313

Welch, Craig, Pop. 576
Welch ISD 300/PK-12
PO Box 189 74369 918-788-3129
Dr. Clark McKeon, supt. Fax 788-3734
welchwildcats.net
Welch JSHS 100/7-12
PO Box 189 74369 918-788-3222
Bruce Chrz, prin. Fax 788-3734

Weleetka, Okfuskee, Pop. 906
Graham ISD 200/PK-12
391125 E 1165 Rd 74880 918-652-8935
Dusty Chancey, supt. Fax 652-2422
www.graham.k12.ok.us
Graham HS 200/9-12
391125 E 1165 Rd 74880 918-652-8935
Peggy Reynolds, prin. Fax 652-2422

Weleetka ISD 500/PK-12
PO Box 278 74880 405-786-2442
Dan Parrish, supt. Fax 786-2625
www.weleetka.k12.ok.us
Weleetka HS 100/10-12
PO Box 278 74880 405-786-2203
Chris Carter, prin. Fax 786-2625
Weleetka JHS, PO Box 278 74880 100/7-9
Chris Carter, prin. 405-786-2204

Wellston, Lincoln, Pop. 751
Wellston ISD 700/PK-12
PO Box 60 74881 405-356-2534
Dwayne Danker, supt. Fax 356-2838
Wellston HS 200/9-12
PO Box 60 74881 405-356-2533
Ethel Grubbs, prin. Fax 356-2838
Wellston MS 100/6-8
PO Box 60 74881 405-356-2533
Mark Grubbs, prin. Fax 356-2838

Westville, Adair, Pop. 1,479
Westville ISD 1,100/PK-12
PO Box 410 74965 918-723-3181
Terry Heustis, supt. Fax 723-3042
www.westville.k12.ok.us
Westville JHS 200/7-9
PO Box 410 74965 918-723-3432
Shelly Cooper, prin. Fax 723-3042
Westville SHS 200/10-12
PO Box 410 74965 918-723-5644
Renae Price, prin. Fax 723-3042

Wetumka, Hughes, Pop. 1,171
OK Dept. of Voc. & Tech. Education
Supt. — None
Phil Berkenbile Ed.D., dir.
Watkins Technology Center Vo/Tech
7892 Highway 9 74883 405-452-5500
Wade Walling, supt. Fax 452-5706

Wetumka ISD 500/PK-12
416 S Tiger St 74883 405-452-5150
Michael Jaggars, supt. Fax 452-3052
www.wetumka.k12.ok.us/
Wetumka HS 100/9-12
416 S Tiger St 74883 405-452-3291
Robin Gann, prin. Fax 452-5836

Wewoka, Seminole, Pop. 3,192
New Lima ISD 300/PK-12
116 Gross St 74884 405-257-5771
Gil Turpin, supt. Fax 257-3127
www.newlima.k12.ok.us
New Lima HS 100/9-12
116 Gross St 74884 405-257-5771
Rhonda Barkhimer, prin. Fax 257-2587

Wewoka ISD 700/PK-12
PO Box 870 74884 405-257-5475
Sam McElvany, supt. Fax 257-2303
www.wps.k12.ok.us/
Wewoka HS 200/9-12
PO Box 870 74884 405-257-5473
Steve Couch, prin. Fax 257-2303
Wewoka MS 100/6-8
PO Box 870 74884 405-257-5340
Darrell Brown, prin. Fax 257-2303

Whitesboro, LeFlore, Pop. 244
Whitesboro ISD 200/PK-12
PO Box 150 74577 918-567-2556
Katie Blagg, supt. Fax 567-2842
www.whitesborops.k12.ok.us/
Whitesboro HS, PO Box 150 74577 100/9-12
Katie Blagg, prin. 918-567-2624

Wilburton, Latimer, Pop. 2,654
Wilburton ISD 1,000/PK-12
1201 W Blair Ave 74578 918-465-2100
Charles Enis, supt. Fax 465-3086
www.wilburton.k12.ok.us/
Wilburton MS 200/6-8
1201 W Blair Ave 74578 918-465-2281
Dr. Beatrice Butler, prin. Fax 465-3094
Wilburton SHS 300/9-12
1201 W Blair Ave 74578 918-465-3125
Gary Lay, prin. Fax 465-1141

Eastern Oklahoma State College Post-Sec.
1301 W Main St 74578 918-465-2361

Wilson, Carter, Pop. 1,643
Wilson ISD 500/PK-12
1860 Hewitt Rd 73463 580-668-2306
Kevin Stinson, supt. Fax 668-2170
www.wilson.k12.ok.us/
Wilson HS 100/9-12
1860 Hewitt Rd 73463 580-668-2317
Gary Labeth, prin. Fax 668-2412

Wister, LeFlore, Pop. 1,038
Wister ISD 600/PK-12
201 Logan St 74966 918-655-7381
Jerry Carpenter, supt. Fax 655-7402
www.wister.k12.ok.us
Wister HS 200/9-12
201 Logan St 74966 918-655-7276
Albert Cole, prin. Fax 655-7402

Woodward, Woodward, Pop. 11,818
OK Dept. of Voc. & Tech. Education
Supt. — None
Phil Berkenbile Ed.D., dir.
High Plains Technology Center Vo/Tech
3921 34th St 73801 580-256-6618
Dwight Hughes, supt. Fax 571-6190

Woodward ISD 2,600/PK-12
PO Box 668 73802 580-256-6063
Tim Merchant, supt. Fax 256-4391
www.woodwardps.net
Woodward HS 600/9-12
PO Box 668 73802 580-256-5329
Kirk Warnick, prin. Fax 256-8716
Woodward MS 500/6-8
PO Box 668 73802 580-256-7901
Frank Harrington, prin. Fax 256-8014

Woodward Beauty College Post-Sec.
502 Texas St 73801 580-256-7520

Wright City, McCurtain, Pop. 687
Wright City ISD 400/PK-12
PO Box 329 74766 580-981-2824
David Hawkins, supt. Fax 981-2115
www.wcisd.org/
Wright City HS 100/9-12
PO Box 329 74766 580-981-2558
Mike Converse, prin. Fax 981-2329
Wright City JHS 100/7-8
PO Box 329 74766 580-981-2558
Mike Converse, prin. Fax 981-2329

Wyandotte, Ottawa, Pop. 310
Wyandotte ISD 800/PK-12
PO Box 360 74370 918-678-2255
Troy Gray M.A., supt. Fax 678-2304
www.wyandotte.k12.ok.us
Wyandotte HS 200/9-12
PO Box 360 74370 918-678-2222
Steve Buckingham, prin. Fax 678-3906
Wyandotte MS 200/6-8
PO Box 360 74370 918-678-2222
Stacy Sloan, prin. Fax 678-3906

Wynnewood, Garvin, Pop. 2,125
Wynnewood ISD 700/PK-12
702 E Robert S Kerr Blvd 73098 405-665-2004
Raymond Cole, supt. Fax 665-5425
www.wynnewood.k12.ok.us/
Wynnewood HS 200/9-12
702 E Robert S Kerr Blvd 73098 405-665-2045
Steve Musgrove, prin.
Wynnewood MS 200/5-8
702 E Robert S Kerr Blvd 73098 405-665-4105
Billy Carter, prin.

Wynona, Osage, Pop. 396
Wynona ISD 200/PK-12
PO Box 700 74084 918-846-2467
Dixie Hurd, supt. Fax 846-2883
www.wynona.k12.ok.us
Wynona HS 200/9-12
PO Box 700 74084 918-846-2467
Dixie Hurd, prin. Fax 846-2883

Yale, Payne, Pop. 1,132
Yale ISD 500/PK-12
315 E Chicago Ave 74085 918-387-2434
Steve Shanks, supt. Fax 387-2503
www.yale.k12.ok.us/
Yale HS 200/9-12
315 E Chicago Ave 74085 918-387-2282
Bobby Rose, prin. Fax 387-2503
Yale JHS 100/7-8
315 E Chicago Ave 74085 918-387-2118
Marla Hewitt, prin. Fax 387-2503

Yukon, Canadian, Pop. 21,966
OK Dept. of Voc. & Tech. Education
Supt. — None
Phil Berkenbile Ed.D., dir.
Canadian Valley Technology Center Vo/Tech
1701 S Czech Hall Rd 73099 405-345-3333
Donna Alloway, dir.

Yukon ISD 8,300/PK-12
600 Maple St 73099 405-354-2587
Bill Denton, supt. Fax 354-4208
www.yukonps.com
Yukon HS 2,100/9-12
1777 S Yukon Pkwy 73099 405-354-6692
Joe Meziere, prin. Fax 354-8411
Yukon MS 2,000/6-8
801 Garth Brooks Blvd 73099 405-354-5274
Tresa Smith, prin. Fax 354-6640

Southwest Covenant S 300/PK-12
2300 S Yukon Pkwy 73099 405-354-0772
Steve Lessman, hdmstr. Fax 350-2670
Yukon Beauty College Post-Sec.
221 W Main St 73099 405-354-3172

OREGON

OREGON DEPARTMENT OF EDUCATION
255 Capitol St NE, Salem 97310-0406
Telephone 503-947-5600
Fax 503-378-5156
Website http://www.ode.state.or.us

Superintendent of Public Instruction Vacant

OREGON BOARD OF EDUCATION
255 Capitol St NE, Salem 97310-0406

Chairperson Artemio Paz

EDUCATION SERVICE DISTRICTS (ESD)

Clackamas ESD
Milt Dennison, supt. 503-675-4000
13455 SE 97th Ave Fax 675-4200
Clackamas 97015
www.clackesd.k12.or.us

Columbia Gorge ESD
Gary Peterson, supt. 541-298-5155
400 E Scenic Dr Ste 207 Fax 296-2965
The Dalles 97058
www.cgesd.k12.or.us/

Douglas ESD
George Murdock, supt. 541-440-4777
1871 NE Stephens St Fax 440-4771
Roseburg 97470
www.douglasesd.k12.or.us

Grant ESD
Robert Waltenburg, supt. 541-575-1349
835 S Canyon Blvd Ste A Fax 575-3601
John Day 97845
www.grantesd.k12.or.us

Harney ESD
Dennis Mills, supt. 541-573-2426
PO Box 460, Burns 97720 Fax 573-1002
www.harneyesd.k12.or.us

High Desert ESD
Dennis Dempsey, supt. 541-693-5600
145 SE Salmon Ave Ste A Fax 693-5601
Redmond 97756
www.hdesd.org

InterMountain ESD
Mark Mulvihill Ed.D., supt. 541-276-6616
2001 SW Nye Ave Fax 276-4252
Pendleton 97801
www.imesd.k12.or.us

Jefferson ESD
Richard Molitor, supt. 541-475-2804
295 SE Buff St, Madras 97741 Fax 475-2827
www.jcesd.k12.or.us

Lake ESD
Alice Hunsaker, supt. 541-947-3371
357 N L St, Lakeview 97630 Fax 947-3373
www.lakeesd.k12.or.us/

Lane ESD
Debbie Egan, supt. 541-461-8200
1200 Highway 99 N, Eugene 97402 Fax 461-8298
www.lesd.k12.or.us/

Linn-Benton-Lincoln ESD
Susan Waddell, supt. 541-812-2600
905 4th Ave SE, Albany 97321 Fax 926-6047
www.lblesd.k12.or.us

Malheur ESD
Steven Phillips, supt. 541-473-3138
363 A St W, Vale 97918 Fax 473-3915
www.malesd.k12.or.us

Multnomah ESD
Barbara Jorgensen, supt. 503-255-1841
PO Box 301039, Portland 97294 Fax 257-1519
www.mesd.k12.or.us

North Central ESD
Mike Carroll, supt. 541-384-2732
PO Box 637, Condon 97823 Fax 384-2752
www.ncesd.k12.or.us

Northwest Regional ESD
James Sager, supt. 503-614-1428
5825 NE Ray Cir, Hillsboro 97124 Fax 614-1440
www.nwresd.k12.or.us

Region 18 ESD
Edward Jensen, supt. 541-426-4997
107 SW 1st St Ste 105 Fax 426-3732
Enterprise 97828
www.r18esd.org/

South Coast ESD
Tenneal Wetherell, supt. 541-269-1611
1350 Teakwood Ave Fax 266-4040
Coos Bay 97420
www.scesd.k12.or.us

Southern Oregon ESD
Scott Perry, supt. 541-776-8590
101 N Grape St, Medford 97501 Fax 779-2018
www.soesd.k12.or.us

Willamette ESD
Pat Evenson-Brady, supt. 503-588-5330
2611 Pringle Rd SE, Salem 97302 Fax 363-5787
www.wesd.org

PUBLIC, PRIVATE AND CATHOLIC SECONDARY SCHOOLS

Adel, Lake
Adel SD 21
Supt. — See Lakeview
Adel S, PO Box 117 97620 50/4-8
Larry Ferguson, prin. 541-947-3371

Adrian, Malheur, Pop. 173
Adrian SD 61 200/K-12
PO Box 108 97901 541-372-2335
Gene Mills, supt. Fax 372-5380
www.adriansd.com
Adrian HS 100/9-12
PO Box 108 97901 541-372-2335
Kevin Purnell, prin. Fax 372-5380

Albany, Linn, Pop. 48,696
Greater Albany SD 8J 8,900/K-12
718 7th Ave SW 97321 541-967-4501
Maria Delapoer, supt. Fax 967-4587
albany.k12.or.us
Albany Options S 100/Alt
701 19th Ave SE, 541-967-4563
Dan Knight, prin. Fax 924-3780
Calapooia MS 700/6-8
830 24th Ave SE, 541-967-4555
Pat Weidmann, prin. Fax 924-3702
Memorial MS 700/6-8
1050 Queen Ave SW 97321 541-967-4537
Ken Gilbert, prin. Fax 924-3703
North Albany MS 600/6-8
1205 NW North Albany Rd 97321 541-967-4541
Jane Evans, prin. Fax 924-3704
South Albany HS 1,300/9-12
3705 Columbus St SE, 541-967-4522
Brent Belveal, prin. Fax 924-3700
Timber Ridge S 600/3-8
373 Timber Ridge St NE, 541-704-1095
Jason Hoffert-Hay, prin. Fax 704-1099
West Albany HS 1,400/9-12
1130 Queen Ave SW 97321 541-967-4545
Susie Orsborn, prin. Fax 924-3701

Linn-Benton Community College Post-Sec.
6500 Pacific Blvd SW 97321 541-917-4999

Aloha, Washington, Pop. 47,267

Life Christian S 300/PK-12
5585 SW 209th Ave 97007 503-259-1329
Dr. Werner Rienas, supt. Fax 649-5484

Alsea, Benton, Pop. 157
Alsea SD 7J 100/K-12
PO Box B 97324 541-487-4305
Marc Thielman, supt. Fax 487-4089
www.alsea.k12.or.us/
Alsea HS 100/7-12
PO Box B 97324 541-487-4305
Marc Thielman, prin. Fax 487-4089

Amity, Yamhill, Pop. 1,569
Amity SD 4J 800/K-12
807 S Trade St 97101 503-835-2171
Reg McShane, supt. Fax 835-5050
www.amity.k12.or.us
Amity HS 200/9-12
807 S Trade St 97101 503-835-2181
Chris Daniels, prin. Fax 835-6113
Amity MS 200/6-8
807 S Trade St 97101 503-835-0518
Dave Lund, prin. Fax 835-0418

Perrydale SD 21 300/K-12
7445 Perrydale Rd 97101 503-835-3184
Robin Stoutt, supt. Fax 835-0631
www.perrydale.k12.or.us
Perrydale S 300/K-12
7445 Perrydale Rd 97101 503-835-3184
Robin Stoutt, prin. Fax 835-0631

Ashland, Jackson, Pop. 19,339
Ashland SD 5 2,600/K-12
885 Siskiyou Blvd 97520 541-482-2811
Juli DiChiro, supt. Fax 482-2185
www.ashland.k12.or.us/
Ashland HS 1,100/9-12
201 S Mountain Ave 97520 541-482-8771
Michelle Zundel, prin. Fax 482-2172
Ashland MS 500/6-8
100 Walker Ave 97520 541-482-1611
Steve Retzlaff, prin. Fax 482-8112

Southern Oregon University Post-Sec.
1250 Siskiyou Blvd 97520 541-552-7672

Astoria, Clatsop, Pop. 9,193
Astoria SD 1 1,900/K-12
785 Alameda Ave 97103 503-325-6441
Craig Hoppes, supt. Fax 325-6524
www.astoria.k12.or.us/
Astoria HS 700/9-12
1001 W Marine Dr 97103 503-325-3911
Lynn Jackson, prin. Fax 325-2891
Astoria MS 500/6-8
1100 Klaskanine Ave 97103 503-325-4331
Ron Alley, prin. Fax 325-3040

Knappa SD 4 500/K-12
41535 Old Highway 30 97103 503-458-5993
Jeff Leo, supt. Fax 458-6979
www.knappa.k12.or.us
Knappa HS 100/9-12
41535 Old Highway 30 97103 503-458-6166
Jeff Leo, prin. Fax 458-5466

Clatsop Community College Post-Sec.
1651 Lexington Ave 97103 503-325-0910

Athena, Umatilla, Pop. 1,106
Athena-Weston SD 29RJ 500/K-12
375 S 5th St 97813 541-566-3551
Jerry Copeland, supt. Fax 566-9454
www.athwest.k12.or.us/
Weston-McEwen HS 200/9-12
540 E Main St 97813 541-566-3555
Rollie Marshall, prin. Fax 566-2751
Other Schools – See Weston

Aumsville, Marion, Pop. 3,437
Cascade SD 5
Supt. — See Turner
West Stayton Alternative S Alt
11463 W Stayton Rd SE 97325 503-749-8406
Matt Thatcher, prin. Fax 749-2607

Aurora, Marion, Pop. 900
North Marion SD 15 1,900/PK-12
20256 Grim Rd NE 97002 503-678-7100
Boyd Keyser, supt. Fax 678-1473
www.nmarion.k12.or.us
North Marion HS 600/9-12
20167 Grim Rd NE 97002 503-678-7123
DeAnn Jenness, prin. Fax 678-7186
North Marion MS 500/6-8
20246 Grim Rd NE 97002 503-678-7118
Laurie Cooper, prin. Fax 678-7185

Baker City, Baker, Pop. 9,619
Baker SD 5J 1,800/K-12
2090 4th St 97814 541-524-2260
Walt Wegener, supt. Fax 524-2564
www.baker.k12.or.us
Baker HS 600/9-12
2500 E St 97814 541-524-2600
Jerry Peacock, prin. Fax 524-2699

Baker MS 300/7-8
2320 Washington Ave 97814 541-524-2500
Mindi Vaughan, prin. Fax 524-2563
EAGLE CAP Innovative HS Alt
2725 7th St 97814 541-524-2285
Barry Nemec, prin. Fax 359-2564

Bandon, Coos, Pop. 2,978
Bandon SD 54 700/K-12
455 9th St SW 97411 541-347-4411
Diane Buche, supt. Fax 347-3974
www.bandon.k12.or.us/
Bandon HS 300/9-12
550 9th St SW 97411 541-347-4413
Gaye Knapp, prin. Fax 347-3714
Harbor Lights MS 200/5-8
390 9th St SW 97411 541-347-4415
Deborah Greenfield, prin. Fax 347-1280

Bandon Pacific Christian S 50/PK-12
PO Box 949 97411 541-290-7322
Janice Fox, admin. Fax 347-3922

Banks, Washington, Pop. 1,714
Banks SD 13 1,100/K-12
12950 NW Main St 97106 503-324-8591
Bob Huston, supt. Fax 324-6969
www.banks.k12.or.us
Banks HS 400/9-12
13050 NW Main St 97106 503-324-2281
Mark Everett, prin. Fax 324-8221
Banks JHS 200/7-8
12850 NW Main St 97106 503-324-3111
Shelley Mitchell, prin. Fax 324-7441

Beaverton, Washington, Pop. 86,161
Beaverton SD 48J 38,300/K-12
16550 SW Merlo Rd 97006 503-591-8000
Jeff Rose, supt. Fax 591-4175
www.beaverton.k12.or.us
Aloha HS 1,900/9-12
18550 SW Kinnaman Rd 97007 503-259-4700
Ken Yarnell, prin. Fax 259-4713
Arts & Communication Magnet Academy 300/6-12
11375 SW Center St 97005 503-672-3700
Michael Johnson, prin. Fax 672-3706
Beaverton HS 1,700/9-12
13000 SW 2nd St 97005 503-259-5000
Anne Erwin, prin. Fax 259-4990
Carson MS 200/6-8
1600 NW 173rd Ave 97006 503-533-1890
Shirley Brock, prin. Fax 533-1898
Community S 200/Alt
1841 SW Merlo Dr 97006 503-259-5575
MaryJean Katz, prin. Fax 259-4220
Conestoga MS 1,000/6-8
12250 SW Conestoga Dr 97008 503-524-1345
Zan Hess, prin. Fax 524-1349
Deer Park Academy Alt
16550 SW Merlo Rd 97006 503-591-4131
Ruth White, prin. Fax 591-4132
Five Oaks MS 1,100/6-8
1600 NW 173rd Ave 97006 503-533-1890
Shirley Brock, prin. Fax 533-1898
Health & Science HS 600/6-12
18640 NW Walker Rd 97006 503-533-1853
Steve Day, prin. Fax 533-1856
Highland Park MS 800/6-8
7000 SW Wilson Ave 97008 503-672-3640
Ronda Haun, prin. Fax 672-3644
International S of Beaverton 700/6-12
17770 SW Blanton St 97007 503-259-3800
Jill O'Neill, prin. Fax 259-3803
Meadow Park MS 900/6-8
14100 SW Downing St 97006 503-672-3660
Toshiko Maurizio, prin. Fax 672-3664
Mountain View MS 900/6-8
17500 SW Farmington Rd 97007 503-259-3890
Claudia Ruf, prin. Fax 259-3894
School of Science & Technology 200/9-12
1841 SW Merlo Dr 97006 503-259-5575
MaryJean Katz, prin. Fax 259-4220
Southridge HS 1,900/9-12
9625 SW 125th Ave 97008 503-259-5400
Todd Corsetti, prin. Fax 259-5425
Whitford MS 700/6-8
7935 SW Scholls Ferry Rd 97008 503-672-3680
Aaron Persons, prin. Fax 672-3684
Merlo Station Night S Adult
1841 SW Merlo Dr 97006 503-259-5575
MaryJean Katz, prin. Fax 259-4220
Other Schools – See Portland

Anthem College Post-Sec.
4145 SW Watson Ave Ste 300 97005 503-646-6000
St. Stephen's Academy 200/K-12
7275 SW Hall Blvd 97008 503-646-4617
John Breckenridge, hdmstr. Fax 459-7715
Valley Catholic HS 500/7-12
4275 SW 148th Ave 97007 503-644-3745
Ross Thomas, prin. Fax 646-4054
Valley Catholic MS 6-8
4450 SW Saint Marys Dr 97007 503-718-6500
Jen Gfroerer, prin. Fax 718-6520

Bend, Deschutes, Pop. 74,904
Bend-LaPine Administrative SD 1 15,800/K-12
520 NW Wall St 97701 541-355-1000
Ron Wilkinson, supt. Fax 355-1009
www.bend.k12.or.us
Bend HS 1,500/9-12
230 NE 6th St 97701 541-355-3700
H.D. Weddel, prin. Fax 355-3710
Cascade MS 900/6-8
19619 Mountaineer Way 97702 541-355-7000
Stephanie Bennett, prin. Fax 355-7010
High Desert MS 800/6-8
61111 SE 27th St 97702 541-355-7200
Gary DeFrang, prin. Fax 355-7210
Marshall HS 100/Alt
1291 NE 5th St 97701 541-355-3500
Julie Linhares, prin. Fax 355-3510
Mountain View HS 1,400/9-12
2755 NE 27th St 97701 541-355-4400
Kathryn Legace, prin. Fax 355-4410
Pilot Butte MS 600/6-8
1501 NE Neff Rd 97701 541-355-7400
Michael Hecker, prin. Fax 355-7410
Sky View MS 700/6-8
63555 18th St 97701 541-355-7600
D. Scott Edmondson, prin. Fax 355-7610
Summit HS 1,300/9-12
2855 NW Clearwater Dr 97701 541-322-3300
Alice Dewittie, prin. Fax 322-3310
Other Schools – See La Pine

Central Oregon Community College Post-Sec.
2600 NW College Way 97701 541-383-7700
Phagans' Central Oregon Beauty College Post-Sec.
1310 NE Cushing Dr 97701 541-382-6171
Trinity Lutheran S 300/PK-12
2550 NE Butler Market Rd 97701 541-382-1850
HanneKrause, prin. Fax 382-1850

Boardman, Morrow, Pop. 3,160
Morrow SD 1
Supt. — See Lexington
Riverside JSHS 400/7-12
210 NE Boardman Ave 97818 541-481-2525
Robert Elizondo, prin. Fax 481-2047

Bonanza, Klamath, Pop. 407
Klamath County SD
Supt. — See Klamath Falls
Bonanza S 200/K-12
PO Box 128 97623 541-545-6581
Art Ochoa, prin. Fax 545-1719

Boring, Clackamas
Oregon Trail SD 46
Supt. — See Sandy
Boring MS 400/6-8
27801 SE Dee St 97009 503-668-9393
Courtney Murphy, prin. Fax 668-5291

Brookings, Curry, Pop. 6,146
Brookings-Harbor SD 17C 1,600/K-12
629 Easy St 97415 541-469-7443
Brian Hodge, supt. Fax 463-6599
www.brookings.k12.or.us
Azalea MS 400/6-8
629 Easy St 97415 541-469-7427
Sheryl Lipski, prin. Fax 469-7080
Brookings-Harbor HS 600/9-12
629 Easy St 97415 541-469-2108
Larry Martindale, prin. Fax 469-0176

Brookings Harbor Christian S 100/PK-12
PO Box 5809 97415 541-469-6478
Kari Schultz, admin. Fax 412-7242

Brooks, Marion, Pop. 395

Willamette Valley Christian S 100/PK-12
9075 Pueblo Ave NE 97305 503-393-5236
Debbie Tipton, admin. Fax 485-8203

Brownsville, Linn, Pop. 1,618
Central Linn SD 552 700/K-12
331 E Blakely Ave 97327 541-369-2813
Brian Gardner, supt. Fax 466-3180
www.centrallinn.k12.or.us
Other Schools – See Halsey

Burns, Harney, Pop. 2,728
Harney County SD 3 900/K-12
550 N Court Ave 97720 541-573-6811
Dr. Marilyn McBride, supt. Fax 573-7557
www.burnsschools.k12.or.us
Burns Alternative S Alt
550 N Court Ave 97720 541-573-8198
Ronald Wassom, prin. Fax 573-7557
Burns HS 200/9-12
1100 Oregon Ave 97720 541-573-2044
Ron Wassom, prin. Fax 573-5456
Other Schools – See Hines

Canby, Clackamas, Pop. 15,520
Canby SD 86 4,400/K-12
1130 S Ivy St 97013 503-266-7861
John Steach Ed.D., supt. Fax 266-0022
www.canby.k12.or.us
Baker Prairie MS 500/6-8
1859 S Township Rd 97013 503-263-7170
Jennifer Turner, prin. Fax 263-7189
Canby HS 1,600/9-12
721 SW 4th Ave 97013 503-263-7200
Pat Johnson, prin. Fax 263-7211

Canyon City, Grant, Pop. 694
Grant SD 3 500/K-12
401 N Canyon City Blvd 97820 541-575-1280
Mark Witty, supt. Fax 575-3614
www.grantesd.k12.or.us
Other Schools – See John Day

Canyonville, Douglas, Pop. 1,804

Canyonville Christian Academy 100/9-12
PO Box 1100 97417 541-839-4401
Cathy Lovato, hdmstr. Fax 839-6228

Cave Junction, Josephine, Pop. 1,818
Three Rivers SD
Supt. — See Grants Pass
Byrne MS 300/6-8
101 S Junction Ave 97523 541-592-2163
Rachael Huish, prin. Fax 592-4851
Illinois Valley HS 400/9-12
625 E River St 97523 541-592-2116
JoAnn Bethany, prin. Fax 592-4853

Central Point, Jackson, Pop. 16,683
Central Point SD 6 4,000/K-12
300 Ash St 97502 541-494-6200
Randal Gravon, supt. Fax 664-1637
www.district6.org
Crater Academy of Health Public Services 400/9-12
655 N 3rd St 97502 541-494-6300
Julie Howland, prin. Fax 664-7589
Crater Renaissance Academy 400/9-12
655 N 3rd St 97502 541-494-6300
Bob King, prin. Fax 664-7589
Crater S of Business Innovation Science 300/9-12
655 N 3rd St 97502 541-494-6300
Todd Bennett, prin. Fax 664-7589
Scenic MS 800/6-8
1955 Scenic Ave 97502 541-494-6400
David Heard, prin. Fax 664-8534
Other Schools – See Gold Hill

Chiloquin, Klamath, Pop. 678
Klamath County SD
Supt. — See Klamath Falls
Chiloquin JSHS 200/7-12
PO Box 397 97624 541-783-2321
Doug Wilson, prin. Fax 783-2792

Christmas Valley, Lake

Solid Rock Christian S 50/K-12
PO Box 745 97641 541-576-2895
Dell Renee Wilson, prin. Fax 576-3554

Clackamas, Clackamas, Pop. 2,578
North Clackamas SD 12
Supt. — See Milwaukie
Clackamas HS 2,300/9-12
14486 SE 122nd Ave 97015 503-353-5800
Matt Utterback, prin. Fax 353-5815
Rock Creek MS 600/6-8
14897 SE Parklane Dr 97015 503-353-5680
Tom Higginbotham, prin. Fax 353-5695

Northwest College of Hair Design Post-Sec.
8307 SE Monterey Ave 97086 503-659-2834
Pioneer Pacific College Post-Sec.
8800 SE Sunnyside Rd 97015 503-654-8000

Clatskanie, Columbia, Pop. 1,681
Clatskanie SD 6J 800/K-12
PO Box 678 97016 503-728-0587
Mary Mitchell, supt. Fax 728-0608
www.csd.k12.or.us/
Clatskanie MSHS 400/7-12
PO Box 68 97016 503-728-2146
Jeff Baughman, prin. Fax 728-4632

Cloverdale, Tillamook, Pop. 245
Nestucca Valley SD 101 500/K-12
PO Box 99 97112 503-392-4892
Dr. Kathryn Hedrick, supt. Fax 392-9061
www.nestucca.k12.or.us
Nestucca HS 300/7-12
PO Box 38 97112 503-392-3194
Dr. Randy Wharton, prin. Fax 392-3724

Colton, Clackamas
Colton SD 53 600/K-12
30429 S Grays Hill Rd 97017 503-824-3535
Linda Johnson, supt. Fax 824-3530
www.colton.k12.or.us
Colton HS 300/9-12
30205 S Wall St 97017 503-824-2311
Tom Crane, prin. Fax 824-2312
Colton MS 200/6-8
21580 S Schieffer Rd 97017 503-824-2319
Beth Lund, prin. Fax 824-2309

Condon, Gilliam, Pop. 677
Condon SD 25J 100/K-12
210 E Bayard St 97823 541-384-2581
Jan Zarate, supt. Fax 384-2585
www.condon.k12.or.us
Condon HS 100/7-12
210 E Bayard St 97823 541-384-2441
Jan Zarate, prin. Fax 384-2504

Coos Bay, Coos, Pop. 15,210
Coos Bay SD 9 2,500/K-12
1255 Hemlock Ave 97420 541-267-3104
Dawn Granger, supt. Fax 269-5366
www.cbd9.net
Destinations S 100/Alt
1255 Hemlock Ave 97420 541-267-1485
Shelly McKnight, prin. Fax 266-7314
Harding Learning Center Alt
1255 Hemlock Ave 97420 541-267-1485
Shelly McKnight, prin. Fax 266-7314
Marshfield HS 900/8-12
1255 Hemlock Ave 97420 541-267-1405
Doug Holland, prin. Fax 269-0161

Southwestern Oregon Community College Post-Sec.
1988 Newmark Ave 97420 541-888-2525

Coquille, Coos, Pop. 3,760
Coquille SD 8 700/K-12
1366 N Gould St 97423 541-396-2181
Tim Sweeney, supt. Fax 396-5015
www.coquille.k12.or.us/
Coquille HS 300/9-12
499 W Central Blvd 97423 541-396-2163
Jeff Philley, prin. Fax 396-4635
Coquille Valley IS 200/3-8
1115 N Baxter St 97423 541-396-2914
Geoff Wetherell, prin. Fax 396-4543
Winter Lakes HS Alt
1366 N Gould St 97423 541-824-0115
Tony Jones, prin. Fax 824-0116

Corbett, Multnomah
Corbett SD 39 — 1,100/K-12
35800 E Historic Colmb Riv 97019 — 503-261-4200
Dr. Randy Trani, supt. — Fax 695-3641
www.corbett.k12.or.us
Corbett HS — 200/9-12
35800 E Historic Colmb Riv 97019 — 503-261-4226
Phillip Pearson, prin. — Fax 261-4285
Corbett MS — 100/6-8
35800 E Historic Colmb Riv 97019 — 503-261-4226
Phillip Pearson, prin. — Fax 261-4285

Corvallis, Benton, Pop. 52,340
Corvallis SD 509J — 6,500/K-12
PO Box 3509J 97339 — 541-757-5811
Dr. Erin Prince, supt. — Fax 757-5703
www.corvallis.k12.or.us
Cheldelin MS — 600/6-8
987 NE Conifer Blvd 97330 — 541-757-5971
Jeff Brew, prin. — Fax 757-4596
Corvallis HS — 1,200/9-12
1400 NW Buchanan Ave 97330 — 541-757-5871
Matt Boring, prin. — Fax 757-5875
Crescent Valley HS — 1,100/9-12
4444 NW Highland Dr 97330 — 541-757-5801
Cherie Stroud, prin. — Fax 757-4522
Pauling MS — 700/6-8
1111 NW Cleveland Ave 97330 — 541-757-5961
Eric Beasley, prin. — Fax 757-4598

Oregon State University 97333 — Post-Sec.
541-737-1000
Phagans' Beauty College — Post-Sec.
1565 SW 53rd St 97333 — 541-753-6466
Santiam Christian S — 700/PK-12
7220 NE Arnold Ave 97330 — 541-745-5524
Lance Villers, supt. — Fax 745-6338

Cottage Grove, Lane, Pop. 9,371
South Lane SD 45J3 — 2,700/K-12
PO Box 218 97424 — 541-942-3381
Krista Parent, supt. — Fax 942-8098
www.slane.k12.or.us/dsc
Cottage Grove HS — 800/9-12
PO Box 160 97424 — 541-942-3391
Kay Graham, prin. — Fax 942-7492
Kennedy Alternative HS — 100/Alt
1310 S 8th St 97424 — 541-942-1962
Tom Horn, prin. — Fax 942-3672
Lincoln MS — 600/6-8
1565 S 4th St 97424 — 541-942-3316
Brian McCasline, prin. — Fax 942-9801

Crane, Harney, Pop. 128
Harney County UNHSD 1J — 100/9-12
PO Box 828 97732 — 541-493-2641
Gail Buermann, supt. — Fax 493-2051
www.harneyesd.k12.or.us/
Crane Union HS — 100/9-12
PO Box 828 97732 — 541-493-2641
Gail Buermann, supt. — Fax 493-2051

Creswell, Lane, Pop. 4,867
Creswell SD 40 — 1,300/K-12
998 A St 97426 — 541-895-6000
Todd Hamilton, supt. — Fax 895-6019
www.creswell.k12.or.us
Creswell HS — 400/9-12
33390 Nieblock Ln 97426 — 541-895-6020
Gary Mounce, prin. — Fax 895-6089
Creswell MS — 300/6-8
655 W Oregon Ave 97426 — 541-895-6090
Shirley Burrus, prin. — Fax 895-6139

Culver, Jefferson, Pop. 1,338
Culver SD 4 — 600/K-12
4229 SW Iris Ln 97734 — 541-546-2541
Stefanie Garber, supt. — Fax 546-7517
www.culver.k12.or.us/
Culver HS — 200/9-12
4229 SW Iris Ln 97734 — 541-546-2251
Tim Fields, prin. — Fax 546-2201
Culver MS — 200/6-8
4229 SW Iris Ln 97734 — 541-546-3090
Brad Kudlac, prin. — Fax 546-2137

Dallas, Polk, Pop. 14,264
Dallas SD 2 — 3,200/K-12
111 SW Ash St 97338 — 503-623-5594
Christy Perry, supt. — Fax 623-5597
www.dallas.k12.or.us
Dallas HS — 1,000/9-12
1250 SE Holman Ave 97338 — 503-623-8336
Steve Spencer, prin. — Fax 623-4669
LaCreole MS — 800/6-8
701 SE Lacreole Dr 97338 — 503-623-6662
Jamie Richardson, prin. — Fax 623-8477

Damascus, Clackamas, Pop. 10,286
Gresham-Barlow SD 10J
Supt. — See Gresham
Damascus MS — 200/6-8
14151 SE 242nd Ave, — 503-658-3171
Lori Walter, prin. — Fax 658-6275

Damascus Christian S — 200/K-12
14251 SE Rust Way, — 503-658-4100
Dave Wakefield, prin. — Fax 658-5827

Days Creek, Douglas, Pop. 264

Milo Adventist Academy — 100/9-12
PO Box 278 97429 — 541-825-3200
Randy Thornton, prin. — Fax 825-3723

Dayton, Yamhill, Pop. 2,476
Dayton SD 8 — 900/K-12
PO Box 219 97114 — 503-864-2215
Janelle Beers, supt. — Fax 864-3927
www.dayton.k12.or.us
Dayton HS — 300/9-12
801 Ferry St 97114 — 503-864-2273
Jami Fluke, prin. — Fax 864-2932
Dayton JHS — 200/6-8
801 Ferry St 97114 — 503-864-2246
Jami Fluke, prin. — Fax 864-3697

Dayville, Grant, Pop. 148
Dayville SD 16J — 100/K-12
PO Box C 97825 — 541-987-2412
Debbie Gillespie, supt. — Fax 987-2155
www.grantesd.k12.or.us/dayville
Dayville S — 100/K-12
PO Box C 97825 — 541-987-2412
Debbie Gillespie, prin. — Fax 987-2155

Drain, Douglas, Pop. 1,120
North Douglas SD 22 — 400/K-12
PO Box 428 97435 — 541-836-2223
John Lahley, supt. — Fax 836-7558
www.northdouglas.k12.or.us
North Douglas HS — 100/9-12
PO Box 488 97435 — 541-836-2222
Scott Yakovich, prin. — Fax 836-2387

Dufur, Wasco, Pop. 590
Dufur SD 29 — 300/K-12
802 NE 5th St 97021 — 541-467-2509
Jack Henderson, supt. — Fax 467-2589
www.dufur.k12.or.us
Dufur S — 300/K-12
802 NE 5th St 97021 — 541-467-2509
Bert Wyatt, prin. — Fax 467-2589

Eagle Point, Jackson, Pop. 8,245
Jackson County SD 9 — 4,100/K-12
PO Box 548 97524 — 541-830-6551
Cynda Rickert, supt. — Fax 830-6550
www.eaglepnt.k12.or.us
Eagle Point HS — 1,300/9-12
PO Box 198 97524 — 541-830-1300
Paul Cataldo, prin. — Fax 830-6682
Eagle Point MS — 500/6-8
PO Box 218 97524 — 541-830-1250
Joni Parsons, prin. — Fax 830-6086
Other Schools – See White City

Echo, Umatilla, Pop. 686
Echo SD 5 — 300/K-12
600 E Gerone St 97826 — 541-376-8436
Raymon Smith, supt. — Fax 376-8473
www.echo.k12.or.us/
Echo S — 300/K-12
600 E Gerone St 97826 — 541-376-8436
Norm Stewart, prin. — Fax 376-8473

Elgin, Union, Pop. 1,678
Elgin SD 23 — 400/K-12
PO Box 68 97827 — 541-437-1211
Larry Christman, supt. — Fax 437-1231
www.elgin.k12.or.us
Elgin HS — 100/9-12
PO Box 68 97827 — 541-437-2021
Wayne Herron, prin. — Fax 437-1705

Elkton, Douglas, Pop. 193
Elkton SD 34 — 200/K-12
PO Box 390 97436 — 541-584-2228
Mike Hughes, supt. — Fax 584-2227
www.elkton.k12.or.us/
Elkton HS — 100/9-12
PO Box 390 97436 — 541-584-2228
Mike Hughes, prin. — Fax 584-2227

Elmira, Lane
Fern Ridge SD 28J — 1,500/K-12
88834 Territorial Rd 97437 — 541-935-2253
Dennis Friedrich Ed.D., supt. — Fax 935-8222
www.fernridge.k12.or.us
Elmira HS — 500/9-12
24936 Fir Grove Ln 97437 — 541-935-8200
Gary Carpenter, prin. — Fax 935-8205
Fern Ridge MS — 400/6-8
88831 Territorial Rd 97437 — 541-935-8230
Karen McKenzie, prin. — Fax 935-8234

Enterprise, Wallowa, Pop. 1,904
Enterprise SD 21 — 400/K-12
201 SE 4th St 97828 — 541-426-3193
Brad Royse, supt. — Fax 426-3504
www.enterprise.k12.or.us/
Enterprise HS — 200/7-12
201 SE 4th St 97828 — 541-426-3193
Blake Carlsen, prin. — Fax 426-3504

Estacada, Clackamas, Pop. 2,646
Estacada SD 108 — 2,400/K-12
255 NE 6th Ave 97023 — 503-630-6871
Howard Fetz, supt. — Fax 630-8513
www.esd108.org/
Estacada Alternative HS — 100/Alt
255 NE 6th Ave 97023 — 503-630-6871
Gary Hatcher, prin. — Fax 630-8513
Estacada HS — 700/9-12
355 NE 6th Ave 97023 — 503-630-8515
Scott Sullivan, prin. — Fax 630-8699
Estacada JHS — 300/7-8
500 NE Main St 97023 — 503-630-8516
Dan Draper, prin. — Fax 630-8693

Eugene, Lane, Pop. 149,658
Bethel SD 52 — 5,700/K-12
4640 Barger Dr 97402 — 541-689-3280
Colt Gill, supt. — Fax 689-0719
www.bethel.k12.or.us
Cascade MS — 400/6-8
1525 Echo Hollow Rd 97402 — 541-689-0641
Dana Miller, prin. — Fax 689-9622
Kalapuya HS — 200/9-12
1200 N Terry St 97402 — 541-607-9853
Stefan Aumack, prin. — Fax 607-9857
Shasta MS — 500/6-8
4656 Barger Dr 97402 — 541-688-9611
Greg James, prin. — Fax 689-9382
Willamette HS — 1,500/9-12
1801 Echo Hollow Rd 97402 — 541-689-0731
Peter Burrows, prin. — Fax 689-7119
Crow-Applegate-Lorane SD 66 — 200/K-12
85955 Territorial Hwy 97402 — 541-935-2100
Susan Nakaba, supt. — Fax 935-6107
www.cal.k12.or.us
Crow MSHS — 100/7-12
25863 Crow Rd 97402 — 541-935-2227
Ron Osibov, prin. — Fax 935-6829
Eugene SD 4J — 16,000/K-12
200 N Monroe St 97402 — 541-790-7700
Sheldon Berman, supt. — Fax 790-7711
www.4j.lane.edu
Churchill HS — 1,100/9-12
1850 Bailey Hill Rd 97405 — 541-790-5100
Kim Finch, prin. — Fax 790-5110
Eugene College and Career Options — Alt
4000 E 30th Ave 97405 — 541-463-3930
Brad New, prin. — Fax 463-3937
Family S — 6-8
500 E 43rd Ave 97405 — 541-790-8300
B.J. Blake, prin. — Fax 790-8305
French Immersion MS — 6-8
680 E 24th Ave 97405 — 541-790-8500
Chris Mitchell, prin. — Fax 790-8505
International HS Churchill Campus — 9-12
1850 Bailey Hill Rd 97405 — 541-790-5225
Kim Finch, prin. — Fax 790-5110
International HS Sheldon Campus — 9-12
2455 Willakenzie Rd 97401 — 541-790-6636
Dr. Bob Bolden, prin. — Fax 790-6605
International HS South Eugene Campus — 9-12
400 E 19th Ave 97401 — 541-790-8030
Randy Bernstein, prin. — Fax 790-8005
Kelly MS — 500/6-8
850 Howard Ave 97404 — 541-790-4740
Wes Flinn, prin. — Fax 790-4746
Kennedy MS — 500/6-8
2200 Bailey Hill Rd 97405 — 541-790-5500
Charlie Smith, prin. — Fax 790-5505
Madison MS — 400/6-8
875 Wilkes Dr 97404 — 541-790-4300
Scott Marsh, prin. — Fax 790-4320
Monroe MS — 500/6-8
2800 Bailey Ln 97401 — 541-790-6300
Mike Johnson, prin. — Fax 790-6305
North Eugene HS — 1,000/9-12
200 Silver Ln 97404 — 541-790-4500
Eric Anderson, prin. — Fax 790-4440
Roosevelt MS — 600/6-8
680 E 24th Ave 97405 — 541-790-8500
Chris Mitchell, prin. — Fax 790-8505
Sheldon HS — 1,500/9-12
2455 Willakenzie Rd 97401 — 541-790-6600
Bob Bolden, prin. — Fax 790-6605
South Eugene HS — 1,500/9-12
400 E 19th Ave 97401 — 541-790-8000
Randy Bernstein, prin. — Fax 790-8005
Spanish Immersion MS — 6-8
2000 Bailey Ln 97401 — 541-790-6300
Mike Johnson, prin. — Fax 790-6305
Spencer Butte MS — 400/6-8
500 E 43rd Ave 97405 — 541-790-8300
B.J. Blake, prin. — Fax 790-8305
Young MS — 600/6-8
2555 Gilham Rd 97408 — 541-790-6400
Kim Watry, prin. — Fax 790-6456
Yujin Gakuen Japanese MS — 6-8
850 Howard Ave 97404 — 541-790-4740
Wes Flinn, prin. — Fax 790-4746

Gutenberg College — Post-Sec.
1883 University St 97403 — 541-683-5141
Lane Community College — Post-Sec.
4000 E 30th Ave 97405 — 541-463-3000
Lifegate Christian S — 50/6-12
1052 Fairfield Ave 97402 — 541-689-5847
Angie Taylor, prin. — Fax 689-6028
Marist HS — 500/9-12
1900 Kingsley Rd 97401 — 541-686-2234
Jay Conroy, prin. — Fax 342-6451
New Hope Christian College — Post-Sec.
2155 Bailey Hill Rd 97405 — 541-485-1780
Northwest Christian University — Post-Sec.
828 E 11th Ave 97401 — 541-343-1641
Oak Hill S — 200/K-12
86397 Eldon Schafer Dr 97405 — 541-744-0954
Robert Sarkisian, admin. — Fax 741-6968
University of Oregon — Post-Sec.
1217 University of Oregon 97403 — 541-346-1000
Wellsprings Friends S — 100/9-12
3590 W 18th Ave 97402 — 541-686-1223
Dennis Hoerner, hdmstr. — Fax 687-1493

Fairview, Multnomah, Pop. 8,478
Reynolds SD 7 — 11,000/K-12
1204 NE 201st Ave 97024 — 503-661-7200
Linda Florence, supt. — Fax 667-6932
www.reynolds.k12.or.us
Reynolds MS — 1,000/6-8
1200 NE 201st Ave 97024 — 503-665-8166
Stacy Talus, prin. — Fax 667-6751
Reynolds Learning Academy — Adult
20234 NE Halsey St 97024 — 503-667-4678
Justin McCauley, prin. — Fax 667-0530
Other Schools – See Portland, Troutdale

Falls City, Polk, Pop. 925
Falls City SD 57 — 200/K-12
111 N Main St 97344 — 503-787-3521
Pat Evenson-Brady Ph.D., supt. — Fax 787-5805
www.fallscityschools.org/
Falls City HS — 100/9-12
111 N Main St 97344 — 503-787-3521
Shari Blackburn, prin. — Fax 787-1507

Finn Rock, Lane
McKenzie SD 68 — 200/K-12
51187 Blue River Dr, Vida OR 97488 — 541-822-3338
Dr. Sally Storm, supt. — Fax 822-8014
www.mckenzie.k12.or.us

McKenzie HS 100/9-12
51187 Blue River Dr, Vida OR 97488 541-822-3313
Dr. Sally Storm, prin. Fax 822-8014
McKenzie MS 50/6-8
51187 Blue River Dr, Vida OR 97488 541-822-3313
Dr. Sally Storm, prin. Fax 822-8014

Florence, Lane, Pop. 8,201
Siuslaw SD 97J 1,300/K-12
2111 Oak St 97439 541-997-2651
Jeff Davis, supt. Fax 997-6748
www.siuslaw.k12.or.us
Siuslaw HS 400/9-12
2975 Oak St 97439 541-997-3448
Matt Henry, prin. Fax 997-4160
Siuslaw MS 300/6-8
2525 Oak St 97439 541-997-8241
Lisa Petersen, prin. Fax 997-4161

Forest Grove, Washington, Pop. 20,448
Forest Grove SD 15 6,200/K-12
1728 Main St 97116 503-357-6171
Yvonne Curtis, supt. Fax 359-2520
www.fgsd.k12.or.us
Armstrong MS 900/7-8
1777 Mountain View Ln 97116 503-359-2465
Brandon Hundley, prin. Fax 359-2560
Forest Grove HS 2,000/9-12
1401 Nichols Ln 97116 503-359-2432
Karen Robinson, prin. Fax 359-2521

Pacific University Post-Sec.
2043 College Way 97116 800-677-6712

Gaston, Washington, Pop. 631
Gaston SD 511J 500/K-12
PO Box 68 97119 503-985-0210
David Beasley, supt. Fax 985-3366
www.gaston.k12.or.us
Gaston JSHS 200/7-12
PO Box 68 97119 503-985-7516
Susy McKinzie, prin. Fax 985-3279

Gervais, Marion, Pop. 2,415
Gervais SD 1 1,000/K-12
PO Box 100 97026 503-792-3803
Rick Hensel, supt. Fax 792-3809
www.gervais.k12.or.us
Douglas Avenue Alternative S 50/Alt
PO Box 195 97026 503-792-3656
Sylvia Valentine-Garcia, prin. Fax 792-3770
Gervais HS 300/9-12
PO Box 195 97026 503-792-3656
Mike Solem, prin. Fax 792-3770
Gervais MS 300/6-8
PO Box 176 97026 503-792-3624
Mike Solem, prin. Fax 792-3626

Gilchrist, Klamath
Klamath County SD
Supt. — See Klamath Falls
Gilchrist S 100/K-12
PO Box 668 97737 541-433-2295
Kevin McDaniel, prin. Fax 433-2688

Gladstone, Clackamas, Pop. 11,109
Gladstone SD 115 1,900/PK-12
17789 Webster Rd 97027 503-655-2777
Bob Stewart, supt. Fax 655-5201
www.gladstone.k12.or.us
Gladstone HS 700/9-12
18800 Portland Ave 97027 503-655-2544
Natalie Osburn, prin. Fax 655-0320
Kraxberger MS 500/6-8
17777 Webster Rd 97027 503-655-3636
Nancy Bailey, prin. Fax 650-2596

Grace Christian S 100/PK-12
6460 Glen Echo Ave 97027 503-655-3074
Twila Denham, prin. Fax 655-1702

Glendale, Douglas, Pop. 847
Glendale SD 77 400/K-12
PO Box E 97442 541-832-1761
Lloyd Hartley, supt. Fax 832-3183
www.glendale.k12.or.us
Glendale JSHS 200/7-12
PO Box E 97442 541-832-1801
Patty Fleming, prin. Fax 832-2486

Glide, Douglas, Pop. 1,756
Glide SD 12 700/K-12
301 Glide Loop Dr 97443 541-496-3521
Mike Narkiewicz, supt. Fax 496-4300
www.glide.k12.or.us
Glide HS 200/9-12
18990 N Umpqua Hwy 97443 541-496-3554
Pam Maurice, prin. Fax 496-4304
Glide MS 100/7-8
301 Glide Loop Dr 97443 541-496-3516
Joanne Callaway, prin. Fax 496-4302

Gold Beach, Curry, Pop. 2,158
Central Curry SD 1 600/K-12
29516 Ellensburg Ave 97444 541-247-2003
Jeff Davis, supt. Fax 247-9717
www.ccsd.k12.or.us
Gold Beach HS 200/9-12
29516 Ellensburg Ave 97444 541-247-6647
Jeff Davis, prin. Fax 247-4557

Gold Hill, Jackson, Pop. 1,181
Central Point SD 6
Supt. — See Central Point
Hanby MS 200/6-8
806 6th Ave 97525 541-494-6800
Scott Dippel, prin. Fax 855-1120

Grants Pass, Josephine, Pop. 33,499
Grants Pass SD 7 5,800/K-12
725 NE Dean Dr 97526 541-474-5700
John Higgins, supt. Fax 474-5705
www.grantspass.k12.or.us
Grants Pass HS 1,900/9-12
830 NE 9th St 97526 541-474-5710
Ernie Baldwin, prin. Fax 474-5717
Grants Pass HS - Gladiola Campus Alt
1137 SE Gladiola Dr 97526 541-474-5790
Jeff Weiss, admin. Fax 474-0098
North MS 700/6-8
1725 NW Highland Ave 97526 541-474-5740
Greg Tardieu, prin. Fax 474-5739
South MS 600/6-8
350 W Harbeck Rd 97527 541-474-5750
Rene Cardiff, prin. Fax 474-9742

Three Rivers SD 4,900/K-12
8550 New Hope Rd 97527 541-862-3111
Patricia Adams, supt. Fax 862-3119
www.threerivers.k12.or.us
Fleming MS 400/6-8
6001 Monument Dr 97526 541-476-8284
John George, prin. Fax 471-2458
Hidden Valley HS 800/9-12
651 Murphy Creek Rd 97527 541-862-2124
Dennis Misner, prin. Fax 862-2872
Lincoln Savage MS 500/6-8
8551 New Hope Rd 97527 541-862-2171
Damian Crowson, prin. Fax 862-2713
North Valley HS 600/9-12
6741 Monument Dr 97526 541-479-3388
Dennis Misner, prin. Fax 471-2462
Other Schools – See Cave Junction

New Hope Christian S 200/PK-12
5961 New Hope Rd 97527 541-476-4588
Ernest Stone, admin. Fax 474-7626
Phagans' Grants Pass College of Beauty Post-Sec.
304 NE Agness Ave Ste F 97526 541-479-6678
Rogue Community College Post-Sec.
3345 Redwood Hwy 97527 541-956-7500
Vineyard Christian S 100/PK-12
275 Potts Way 97526 541-479-9649
Doug Thomas, prin. Fax 479-3506

Grass Valley, Sherman, Pop. 160
Sherman County SD 200/K-12
PO Box 68 97029 541-333-2250
Ivan Ritchie, supt. Fax 333-2388
www.sherman.k12.or.us/District/
Other Schools – See Moro

Gresham, Multnomah, Pop. 101,317
Centennial SD 28J
Supt. — See Portland
Centennial HS 1,900/9-12
3505 SE 182nd Ave 97030 503-762-6180
Kevin Ricker, prin. Fax 661-5296

Gresham-Barlow SD 10J 11,900/PK-12
1331 NW Eastman Pkwy 97030 503-261-4550
Jim Schlachter, supt. Fax 261-4552
www.gresham.k12.or.us
Barlow HS 1,800/9-12
5105 SE 302nd Ave 97080 503-258-4850
Dave Lovelin, prin. Fax 258-4840
Clear Creek MS 700/6-8
219 NE 219th Ave 97030 503-492-6700
David Atherton, prin. Fax 492-6707
Gresham HS 1,800/9-12
1200 N Main Ave 97030 503-674-5500
John Koch, prin. Fax 674-5549
McCarty MS 700/6-8
1400 SE 5th St 97080 503-665-0148
Derek Garrison, prin. Fax 669-1892
Russell MS 800/6-8
3625 SE Powell Valley Rd 97080 503-667-6900
Bruce Schmidt, prin. Fax 492-6708
Springwater Trail HS 200/9-12
1440 SE Fleming Ave 97080 503-261-4600
Terrence Smyth, prin. Fax 261-4630
West Orient MS 500/6-8
29805 SE Orient Dr 97080 503-663-3323
Elise Cantanese, prin. Fax 663-2504
Other Schools – See Damascus

Multnomah ESD
Supt. — See Portland
Alpha HS 100/Alt
876 NE 8th St 97030 503-262-4050
Peter Kane, prin. Fax 262-4065

Mayer Christian S 300/PK-10
PO Box 2128 97030 503-661-5632
Brian Mayer, admin. Fax 907-5827
Mt. Hood Community College Post-Sec.
26000 SE Stark St 97030 503-491-6422

Halsey, Linn, Pop. 874
Central Linn SD 552
Supt. — See Brownsville
Central Linn HS 300/7-12
32433 Highway 228 97348 541-369-2811
Jon Zwemke, prin. Fax 369-3455

Happy Valley, Clackamas, Pop. 13,434
North Clackamas SD 12
Supt. — See Milwaukie
Happy Valley MS 700/6-8
13865 SE King Rd Ste B, 503-353-1920
Chris Boyd, prin. Fax 353-1935

Phagans' School of Hair Design Post-Sec.
11860 SE 82nd Ave # K-217, 503-652-2668

Harrisburg, Linn, Pop. 3,472
Harrisburg SD 7 900/K-12
PO Box 208 97446 541-995-6626
Brian Wolf, supt. Fax 995-3453
www.harrisburg.k12.or.us
Harrisburg HS 300/9-12
PO Box 209 97446 541-995-6626
Larry Cote, prin. Fax 995-6697
Harrisburg MS 200/6-8
PO Box 317 97446 541-995-6551
Darci Stuller, prin. Fax 995-5120

Helix, Umatilla, Pop. 175
Helix SD 1 200/K-12
PO Box 398 97835 541-457-2175
Darrick Cope, supt. Fax 457-2481
www.helix.k12.or.us/
Helix S 200/K-12
PO Box 398 97835 541-457-2175
Darrick Cope, prin. Fax 457-2481

Heppner, Morrow, Pop. 1,251
Morrow SD 1
Supt. — See Lexington
Heppner JSHS 200/7-12
PO Box 67 97836 541-676-9138
Matt Combe, prin. Fax 676-5836

Hermiston, Umatilla, Pop. 16,457
Hermiston SD 8 5,200/K-12
502 W Standard Ave 97838 541-667-6000
Dr. Fred Maiocco, supt. Fax 667-6050
www.hermiston.k12.or.us
Hermiston HS 1,500/9-12
600 S 1st St 97838 541-667-6100
Jocelyn Jones, prin. Fax 667-6150
Innovative Learning Center 50/Alt
581 S 1st St 97838 541-667-6100
Ryan Keefauver, prin. Fax 667-6153
Larive MS 500/6-8
1497 SW 9th St 97838 541-667-6200
Tom Spoo, prin. Fax 667-6250
Sandstone MS 700/6-8
400 NE 10th St 97838 541-667-6300
Neely Kirwan, prin. Fax 667-6350

Hillsboro, Washington, Pop. 88,100
Hillsboro SD 1J 20,600/K-12
3083 NE 49th Pl 97124 503-844-1500
Mike Scott, supt. Fax 844-1540
www.hsd.k12.or.us
Brown MS 800/7-8
1505 SW Cornelius Pass Rd 97123 503-844-1070
Don Brown, prin. Fax 844-1071
Century HS 1,700/9-12
2000 SE Century Blvd 97123 503-844-1800
Ted Zehr, prin. Fax 844-1825
Evergreen MS 800/7-8
29850 NW Evergreen Rd 97124 503-844-1400
Rian Petrick, prin. Fax 844-1402
Glencoe HS 1,600/9-12
2700 NW Glencoe Rd 97124 503-844-1900
Bob Macauley, prin. Fax 844-1949
Hillsboro HS 1,500/9-12
3285 SE Rood Bridge Rd 97123 503-844-1980
Arturo Lomeli, prin. Fax 844-1999
Liberty HS 1,300/9-12
21945 NW Wagon Way 97124 503-844-1250
Gregg O'Mara, prin. Fax 844-1299
Miller Education Center 50/Alt
440 SE Oak St 97123 503-844-1680
Stan Esselstrom, prin. Fax 844-1684
Miller Education Center 100/Alt
215 SE 6th Ave 97123 503-844-1000
Stan Esselstrom, prin. Fax 844-1019
Poynter MS 700/7-8
1535 NE Grant St 97124 503-844-1580
Greg Timmons, prin. Fax 844-1583
South Meadows MS 800/7-8
4690 SE Davis Rd 97123 503-844-1220
Carlos Perez, prin. Fax 844-1221

Airman Proficiency Center Post-Sec.
3565 NE Cornell Rd 97124 503-648-2831
Faith Bible Christian HS 100/9-12
2299 SE 45th Ave 97123 503-681-8254
Jim Cochran, supt. Fax 681-9274
Tualatin Valley Academy 200/PK-10
21975 SW Baseline Rd 97123 503-649-5518

Hines, Harney, Pop. 1,525
Harney County SD 3
Supt. — See Burns
Hines MS 200/6-8
PO Box 38 97738 541-573-6436
Eric Nichols, prin. Fax 573-7255

Hood River, Hood River, Pop. 7,008
Hood River County SD 3,600/K-12
1011 Eugene St 97031 541-386-2511
Charlie Beck, supt. Fax 387-5099
www.hoodriver.k12.or.us
Hood River MS 500/6-8
1602 May St 97031 541-386-2114
Brent Emmons, prin. Fax 386-5070
Hood River Valley HS 1,200/9-12
1220 Indian Creek Rd 97031 541-386-4500
Karen Neitzel, prin. Fax 386-2400
Wy'East MS 400/6-8
3000 Wyeast Rd 97031 541-354-1548
Catherine Dalbey, prin. Fax 354-5120

Horizon Christian S 200/PK-12
700 Pacific Ave 97031 541-387-3200
Ken Block, supt. Fax 387-3651
Mid-Columbia Adventist Academy 50/K-10
1100 22nd St 97031 541-386-3187
Peter Hardy, prin. Fax 386-5702

Huntington, Baker, Pop. 429
Huntington SD 16J 100/K-12
520 3rd St E 97907 541-869-2204
Scott Bullock, supt. Fax 869-2444
www.huntington.k12.or.us/
Huntington S 100/K-12
520 3rd St E 97907 541-869-2204
Scott Bullock, admin. Fax 869-2444

Imbler, Union, Pop. 298
Imbler SD 11 300/K-12
PO Box 164 97841 541-534-5331
Doug Hislop, supt. Fax 534-9650
www.imbler.k12.or.us
Imbler JSHS 200/7-12
PO Box 164 97841 541-534-5331
Mike Mills, prin. Fax 534-9650

Independence, Polk, Pop. 8,352
Central SD 13J 2,900/K-12
1610 Monmouth St 97351 503-838-0030
Buzz Brazeau, supt. Fax 838-0033
www.central.k12.or.us
Central HS 900/9-12
1530 Monmouth St 97351 503-838-0480
Sylvia Warren, prin. Fax 838-0483
Talmadge MS 700/6-8
51 S 16th St 97351 503-606-2252
Perry LaBounty, prin. Fax 606-2436

Irrigon, Morrow, Pop. 1,788
Morrow SD 1
Supt. — See Lexington
Irrigon JSHS 300/7-12
315 E Wyoming Ave 97844 541-922-5551
Craig Bensen, prin. Fax 922-5558
Morrow Education Center 100/Alt
240 W Columbia Ln 97844 541-922-4004
Mark Jones, dir. Fax 922-4004

Jefferson, Marion, Pop. 3,013
Jefferson SD 14J 900/K-12
1328 N 2nd St 97352 541-327-3337
Kent Klewitz, supt. Fax 327-2960
www.jefferson.k12.or.us
Jefferson HS 300/9-12
2200 Talbot Rd SE 97352 541-327-3337
Cathy Emmert, prin. Fax 327-1867
Jefferson MS 200/6-8
1344 N 2nd St 97352 541-327-3337
Scott Linenberger, prin. Fax 327-7762

John Day, Grant, Pop. 1,713
Grant SD 3
Supt. — See Canyon City
Grant Union JSHS 200/7-12
911 S Canyon Blvd 97845 541-575-1799
Curt Shelley, prin. Fax 575-2754

Jordan Valley, Malheur, Pop. 179
Jordan Valley SD 3 100/K-12
PO Box 99 97910 541-586-2213
Andree Scown, supt. Fax 586-2568
www.jordanvalley.k12.or.us/
Jordan Valley HS 50/7-12
PO Box 99 97910 541-586-2213
Andree Scown, prin. Fax 586-2568

Junction City, Lane, Pop. 5,249
Junction City SD 69 1,700/K-12
325 Maple St 97448 541-998-6311
Dr. Kathleen Rodden-Nord, supt. Fax 998-3926
www.junctioncity.k12.or.us
Junction City HS 500/9-12
1135 W 6th Ave 97448 541-998-2343
Malcolm McRae, prin. Fax 998-6303
Oaklea MS 500/5-8
1515 Rose St 97448 541-998-3381
Brian Young, prin. Fax 998-3383

Keizer, Marion, Pop. 35,273
Salem-Keizer SD 24J
Supt. — See Salem
Claggett Creek MS 900/6-8
1810 Alder Dr NE 97303 503-399-3701
Colleen Johnson, prin. Fax 399-3708
McNary HS 2,100/9-12
595 Chemawa Rd N 97303 503-399-3233
John Honey, prin. Fax 391-4025
Whiteaker MS 900/6-8
1605 Lockhaven Dr NE 97303 503-399-3224
Laura Perez, prin. Fax 375-7872

Klamath Falls, Klamath, Pop. 20,019
Klamath County SD 6,000/K-12
10501 Washburn Way 97603 541-883-5000
Greg Thede, supt. Fax 883-6677
www.kcsd.k12.or.us
Brixner JHS 300/7-8
4727 Homedale Rd 97603 541-883-5025
Leslie Garrett, prin. Fax 883-5019
Falcon Heights Academy 100/Alt
5825 Climax Ave 97603 541-883-6699
Laura Blair, prin. Fax 273-8763
Henley HS 700/9-12
8245 Highway 39 97603 541-883-5040
Mark Risen, prin. Fax 883-6663
Henley MS 400/7-8
7925 Highway 39 97603 541-883-5050
Kristine Creed, prin. Fax 883-5012
Mazama HS 800/9-12
3009 Summers Ln 97603 541-883-5024
Terry Bennett, prin. Fax 883-5044
Other Schools – See Bonanza, Chiloquin, Gilchrist, Merrill

Klamath Falls CSD 2,900/K-12
1336 Avalon St 97603 541-883-4700
Dr. Paul Hillyer, supt. Fax 850-2766
www.kfalls.k12.or.us
Klamath Union HS 800/9-12
1300 Monclaire St 97601 541-883-4710
Jeff Bullock, prin. Fax 885-4276
Link River HS 100/Alt
2858 Eberlein Ave 97603 541-850-7653
Scott Mason, admin.
Ponderosa JHS 500/6-8
2554 Main St 97601 541-883-4740
Daymond Monteith, prin. Fax 885-4286

College of Cosmetology Post-Sec.
357 E Main St 97601 541-882-6644
Hosanna Christian S 300/PK-12
5000 Hosanna Way 97603 541-882-7732
Sara Irvine, admin. Fax 882-6940
Klamath Community College Post-Sec.
7390 S 6th St 97603 541-882-3521
Oregon Institute of Technology Post-Sec.
3201 Campus Dr 97601 541-885-1000
Triad S 200/PK-12
2450 Summers Ln 97603 541-885-7940
Fax 884-7945

La Grande, Union, Pop. 12,606
La Grande SD 1 2,200/K-12
1305 N Willow St 97850 541-663-3202
Larry Glaze, supt. Fax 663-3233
www.lagrande.k12.or.us
La Grande HS 600/9-12
708 K Ave 97850 541-663-3301
Andrea Waldrop, prin. Fax 663-3313
La Grande MS 500/6-8
1108 4th St 97850 541-663-3421
Kyle McKinney, prin. Fax 663-3422

Eastern Oregon University Post-Sec.
1 University Blvd 97850 541-962-3672

Lake Oswego, Clackamas, Pop. 35,589
Lake Oswego SD 7J 5,900/K-12
PO Box 70 97034 503-534-2000
William Korach, supt. Fax 534-2030
www.loswego.k12.or.us
Lake Oswego HS 1,300/9-12
PO Box 310 97034 503-534-2313
Cindy Schubert, prin. Fax 534-2327
Lake Oswego JHS 600/6-8
2500 Country Club Rd 97034 503-534-2335
Robert Caplinger, prin. Fax 534-2341
Lakeridge HS 1,100/9-12
PO Box 739 97034 503-534-2319
Jennifer Schiele, prin. Fax 534-2392
Lakeridge JHS 500/6-8
4700 Jean Rd 97035 503-534-2343
Kurt Schultz, prin. Fax 534-2276

McAuliffe Academy S of Arts & Sci 200/K-12
5200 Meadows Rd Ste 150 97035 503-226-7374
Christopher Geis, dir. Fax 920-1619
Westside Christian HS 200/9-12
4565 Carman Dr 97035 503-697-4711
Steve Pringle, prin. Fax 697-4605

Lakeview, Lake, Pop. 2,216
Adel SD 21 50/4-8
357 N L St 97630 541-947-5418
Alice Hunsaker, supt. Fax 947-3373
Other Schools – See Adel

Lake County SD 7 600/K-12
1341 S 1st St 97630 541-947-3347
Sean Gallagher, supt. Fax 947-3386
www.lakeview.k12.or.us/
Daly/Lakeview MSHS 200/7-12
906 S 3rd St 97630 541-947-2287
Robert Nash, prin. Fax 947-3601

La Pine, Deschutes, Pop. 1,617
Bend-LaPine Administrative SD 1
Supt. — See Bend
La Pine HS 500/9-12
PO Box 306 97739 541-355-8400
Matt Montgomery, prin. Fax 355-8410
La Pine MS 300/6-8
PO Box 305 97739 541-355-8200
Jim Boen, prin. Fax 355-8210

Lebanon, Linn, Pop. 15,042
Lebanon Community SD 9 4,300/K-12
485 S 5th St 97355 541-451-8511
Rob Hess, supt. Fax 451-8519
www.lebanon.k12.or.us
Lebanon HS 1,400/9-12
1700 S 5th St 97355 541-451-8555
Bo Yates, prin. Fax 451-8550
Seven Oak MS 600/6-8
550 Cascade Dr 97355 541-451-8416
Jennifer Meckley, prin. Fax 451-8431

East Linn Christian Academy 300/PK-12
36883 Victory Dr 97355 541-259-2324
Janelle Detweiler, admin. Fax 451-3800

Lexington, Morrow, Pop. 223
Morrow SD 1 2,200/K-12
PO Box 368 97839 541-989-8202
Dirk Dirksen, supt. Fax 989-8470
www.morrow.k12.or.us
Other Schools – See Boardman, Heppner, Irrigon

Lincoln City, Lincoln, Pop. 7,723
Lincoln County SD
Supt. — See Newport
Taft HS 700/7-12
3780 SE Spy Glass Ridge Dr 97367 541-996-2115
Scott Reed, prin. Fax 996-4335

Lincoln City SDA Junior Academy 100/1-12
2126 NE Surf Ave 97367 541-994-5181
Ed Hollister, prin. Fax 994-5181

Long Creek, Grant, Pop. 191
Long Creek SD 17 50/PK-12
PO Box 429 97856 541-421-3896
Roy Durfee, supt. Fax 421-3012
www.grantesd.k12.or.us/LongCreek/Templates/index.htm
Long Creek S 50/PK-12
PO Box 429 97856 541-421-3896
Roy Durfee, prin. Fax 421-3012

Lowell, Lane, Pop. 983
Lowell SD 71 300/K-12
65 S Pioneer St 97452 541-937-8405
Aaron Brown, supt. Fax 937-2112
www.lowell.k12.or.us
Lowell JSHS 100/7-12
65 S Pioneer St 97452 541-937-2124
Aaron Brown, prin. Fax 937-2112

Mc Minnville, Yamhill, Pop. 31,337
McMinnville SD 40 6,200/K-12
1500 NE Baker St 97128 503-565-4000
Maryalice Russell, supt. Fax 565-4043
www.msd.k12.or.us
Duniway MS 700/6-8
575 NW Michelbook Ln 97128 503-565-4400
Cathy Carnahan, prin. Fax 565-4414
McMinnville HS 1,800/9-12
615 NE 15th St 97128 503-565-4200
Kris Olsen, prin. Fax 565-4244
Patton MS 800/6-8
1175 NE 19th St 97128 503-565-4500
Marty Palacios, prin. Fax 565-4515

Bethel Christian S 200/PK-12
325 NW Baker Creek Rd 97128 503-472-6076
Danielle Boldt, admin. Fax 434-5543
Linfield College Post-Sec.
900 SE Baker St 97128 503-883-2200

Madras, Jefferson, Pop. 5,846
Jefferson County SD 509J 2,800/K-12
445 SE Buff St 97741 541-475-6192
Rick Molitor, supt. Fax 475-6856
www.jcsd.k12.or.us
Jefferson County MS 700/6-8
1180 SE City View St 97741 541-475-7253
Craig Morgan, prin. Fax 475-4825
Madras HS 800/9-12
390 SE 10th St 97741 541-475-7265
Sarah Braman-Smith, prin. Fax 475-7744

Mapleton, Lane
Mapleton SD 32 200/K-12
10868 E Mapleton Rd 97453 541-268-4312
Kyle Tucker, supt. Fax 268-4632
www.mapleton.k12.or.us
Mapleton MSHS 100/7-12
10868 E Mapleton Rd 97453 541-268-4322
Kyle Tucker, prin. Fax 268-4632

Marcola, Lane
Marcola SD 79J 200/K-12
PO Box 820 97454 541-933-2512
Joel Bradford, supt. Fax 933-2338
www.marcola.k12.or.us
Mohawk HS 100/7-12
PO Box 820 97454 541-933-2512
Joel Bradford, prin. Fax 933-2338

Marylhurst, Clackamas

Marylhurst University Post-Sec.
PO Box 261 97036 503-636-8141

Maupin, Wasco, Pop. 405
South Wasco County SD 1 200/K-12
PO Box 346 97037 541-395-2645
Ryan Wraught, supt. Fax 395-2679
www.swasco.net
South Wasco County HS 100/7-12
PO Box 347 97037 541-395-2225
Ryan Wraught, prin. Fax 395-2223

Medford, Jackson, Pop. 72,448
Medford SD 549C 12,000/K-12
815 S Oakdale Ave 97501 541-842-3636
Dr. Philip Long, supt. Fax 842-1087
www.medford.k12.or.us
Central Medford HS Alt
815 S Oakdale Ave 97501 541-842-3669
Amy Herbst, prin. Fax 842-1990
Hedrick MS 900/7-8
1501 E Jackson St 97504 541-842-3700
Dan Smith, prin. Fax 842-1548
McLoughlin MS 800/7-8
320 W 2nd St 97501 541-842-3720
Amy Tiger, prin. Fax 842-1652
Medford Opportunity S Alt
609 W 10th St 97501 541-774-4860
Fax 774-4889
North Medford HS 1,800/9-12
1900 N Keene Way Dr 97504 541-842-3670
Ron Beick, prin. Fax 842-5206
South Medford HS 1,800/9-12
1551 Cunningham Ave 97501 541-842-3680
Kevin Campbell, prin. Fax 842-1513

Abdill Career College Post-Sec.
843 E Main St Ste 203 97504 541-779-8384
Cascade Christian HS 400/9-12
855 Chevy Way 97504 541-772-0606
Devon Rickabaugh, supt. Fax 608-1369
Harvest Baptist Christian S 100/PK-12
2001 S Columbus Ave 97501 541-773-6974
Brian Harrington, admin. Fax 773-4331
Phagans' Medford Beauty School Post-Sec.
2320 Poplar Dr 97504 541-772-6155
Rogue Valley Adventist Academy 100/K-12
3675 S Stage Rd 97501 541-773-2988
Fax 779-7575
St. Mary's HS 400/6-12
816 Black Oak Dr 97504 541-773-7877
Frank Phillips, prin. Fax 772-8973

Merrill, Klamath, Pop. 817
Klamath County SD
Supt. — See Klamath Falls
Lost River JSHS 200/7-12
23330 Highway 50 97633 541-798-5666
Steve Johnson, prin. Fax 798-5072

Mill City, Linn, Pop. 1,789
Santiam Canyon SD 129J 300/K-12
PO Box 197 97360 503-897-2321
Todd Miller, supt. Fax 897-2034
www.santiam.k12.or.us
Santiam JSHS 200/7-12
PO Box 199 97360 503-897-2311
David Plotts, prin. Fax 897-2034

Milton Freewater, Umatilla, Pop. 6,982
Milton-Freewater USD 7 2,000/K-12
1020 S Mill St 97862 541-938-3551
Dr. Robert Clark, supt. Fax 938-6704
www.miltfree.k12.or.us
Central MS 400/6-8
306 SW 2nd Ave 97862 541-938-5504
Tim Sprenger, prin. Fax 938-6615
McLoughlin HS 500/9-12
120 S Main St 97862 541-938-5591
Ralph Brown, prin. Fax 938-5593
Pleasant View S 100/Alt
52274 Pleasant Vw 97862 541-938-8297
Suzy Mayes, prin. Fax 938-5138

Milwaukie, Clackamas, Pop. 19,622
North Clackamas SD 12 15,300/K-12
4444 SE Lake Rd 97222 503-353-6000
Tim Mills, supt. Fax 353-6007
www.nclack.k12.or.us
Alder Creek MS 700/6-8
13801 SE Webster Rd 97267 503-353-5700
Alyson Brant, prin. Fax 353-5715
Milwaukie HS 1,200/9-12
11300 SE 23rd Ave 97222 503-353-5830
Mark Pinder, prin. Fax 353-5845
New Urban HS 200/Alt
1905 SE Oak Grove Blvd 97267 503-353-5925
Michael Englen, dir. Fax 353-5928
Putnam HS 1,300/9-12
4950 SE Roethe Rd 97267 503-353-5860
Kathleen Walsh, prin. Fax 353-5875
Rowe MS 700/6-8
3606 SE Lake Rd 97222 503-353-5725
Courtney Ross, prin. Fax 353-5740
Other Schools – See Clackamas, Happy Valley, Portland

LaSalle College Prep HS 600/9-12
11999 SE Fuller Rd 97222 503-659-4155
Andrew Kuffner, prin. Fax 659-2535
Portland Waldorf S 300/PK-12
2300 SE Harrison St 97222 503-654-2200
Jeff Smith, admin. Fax 652-5162

Mitchell, Wheeler, Pop. 123
Mitchell SD 55 100/K-12
PO Box 247 97750 541-462-3311
Tim Wilson, supt. Fax 462-3849
www.mitchell.k12.or.us
Mitchell S 100/K-12
PO Box 247 97750 541-462-3311
Tim Wilson, prin. Fax 462-3849

Molalla, Clackamas, Pop. 7,927
Molalla River SD 35 2,800/K-12
PO Box 188 97038 503-829-2359
Tony Mann, supt. Fax 829-8428
www.molallariv.k12.or.us
Molalla HS 800/9-12
PO Box 309 97038 503-829-2355
Randy Dalton, prin. Fax 829-6382
Molalla River MS 600/6-8
PO Box 225 97038 503-829-6133
Mike Nelson, prin. Fax 829-5680

Monmouth, Polk, Pop. 9,171

Mid Valley Christian Academy 100/PK-12
1483 N 16th St 97361 503-838-2818
Gaye Stewart, admin.
Western Oregon University Post-Sec.
345 Monmouth Ave N 97361 503-838-8000

Monroe, Benton, Pop. 601
Monroe SD 1J 500/K-12
365 N 5th St 97456 541-847-6292
Randall Crowson, supt. Fax 847-6290
www.monroe.k12.or.us
Monroe HS 200/9-12
365 N 5th St 97456 541-847-5161
Bill Crowson, prin. Fax 847-6161

Monument, Grant, Pop. 127
Monument SD 8 50/K-12
PO Box 127 97864 541-934-2646
Earl Pettit, supt. Fax 934-2005
www.grantesd.k12.or.us/Monument/
Monument S 50/K-12
PO Box 127 97864 541-934-2646
Earl Pettit, prin. Fax 934-2005

Moro, Sherman, Pop. 321
Sherman County SD
Supt. — See Grass Valley
Sherman JSHS 100/7-12
65912 High School Loop 97039 541-565-3500
Wes Owens, prin. Fax 565-3319

Mount Angel, Marion, Pop. 3,231
Mt. Angel SD 91 700/K-12
PO Box 1129 97362 503-845-2345
Troy Stoops, supt. Fax 845-2789
www.mtangel.k12.or.us
Kennedy HS 200/9-12
890 E Marquam St 97362 503-845-6128
Debi Brazelton, prin. Fax 845-2789
Mount Angel MS 200/6-8
460 E Marquam St 97362 503-845-6137
Jennifer McCallum, prin. Fax 845-2856

Myrtle Creek, Douglas, Pop. 3,296
South Umpqua SD 19 1,500/K-12
558 Chadwick Ln 97457 541-863-3115
Steve Kelley, supt. Fax 863-5212
www.susd.k12.or.us
Coffenberry MS 300/6-8
591 Rice St 97457 541-863-3104
Doug Park, prin. Fax 863-5187
South Umpqua HS 500/9-12
501 Chadwick Ln 97457 541-863-3118
Kristi McGree, prin. Fax 863-5486

Myrtle Point, Coos, Pop. 2,411
Myrtle Point SD 41 700/K-12
413 C St 97458 541-572-1220
Bruce Shull, supt. Fax 572-5401
www.mpsd.k12.or.us/
Myrtle Point JSHS 300/7-12
717 4th St 97458 541-572-1270
Jennifer Sweeney, prin. Fax 572-5221

Newberg, Yamhill, Pop. 21,511
Newberg SD 29J 5,200/K-12
714 E 6th St 97132 503-554-5000
Dr. Kym LeBlanc-Esparza, supt. Fax 538-4374
www.newberg.k12.or.us
Chehalem Valley MS 600/6-8
403 W Foothills Dr 97132 503-554-4600
John Franco, prin. Fax 537-3239
Mountain View MS 600/6-8
2015 N Emery Dr 97132 503-554-4500
Wayne Strong, prin. Fax 537-3337
Newberg HS Blue 1,600/9-12
2400 Douglas Ave 97132 503-554-4403
Dan Malone, prin. Fax 538-6560
Newberg HS Green 9-12
2400 Douglas Ave 97132 503-584-4444
Karen Pugsley, prin. Fax 538-6560
Newberg HS Silver 9-12
2400 Douglas Ave 97132 503-554-4412
Eric Bergmann, prin. Fax 538-6560
Newberg HS Yellow 9-12
2400 Douglas Ave 97132 503-554-4428
Stafford Boyd, prin. Fax 538-6560

George Fox University Post-Sec.
414 N Meridian St 97132 503-538-8383
Lewis Academy 200/PK-12
PO Box 3250 97132 503-538-0114
Mike McConaughey, prin. Fax 538-4113

Newport, Lincoln, Pop. 9,688
Lincoln County SD 5,000/K-12
PO Box 1110 97365 541-265-9211
Tom Rinearson, supt. Fax 265-3231
www.lincoln.k12.or.us
Newport HS 600/9-12
322 NE Eads St 97365 541-265-9281
Jon Zagel, prin. Fax 574-2228
Newport Prep Academy 200/7-8
322 NE Eads St 97365 541-265-9281
Jon Zagel, prin. Fax 574-2228
Newton Magnet S 100/6-8
825 NE 7th St 97365 541-265-6601
Majalise Tolan, prin. Fax 265-6493
Other Schools – See Lincoln City, Toledo, Waldport

Phagans' Newport Academy of Cosmetology Post-Sec.
158 E Olive St 97365 541-265-3083

North Bend, Coos, Pop. 9,275
North Bend SD 13 2,700/K-12
1913 Meade St 97459 541-756-2521
Dr. B.J. Hollensteiner, supt. Fax 756-1313
www.nbend.k12.or.us
North Bend HS 400/9-12
2323 Pacific St 97459 541-756-8328
Bill Lucero, prin. Fax 756-6945
North Bend MS 400/5-8
1500 16th St 97459 541-756-8341
Ralph Brooks, prin. Fax 756-6460

Nyssa, Malheur, Pop. 3,244
Nyssa SD 26 1,100/K-12
804 Adrian Blvd 97913 541-372-2275
Janine Weeks, supt. Fax 372-2204
www.nyssa.k12.or.us
Nyssa HS 300/9-12
824 Adrian Blvd 97913 541-372-2287
Larry Ramirez, prin. Fax 372-5634
Nyssa MS 300/6-8
101 S 11th St 97913 541-372-3891
Geno Bates, prin. Fax 372-3260

Oakland, Douglas, Pop. 890
Oakland SD 1 500/K-12
PO Box 390 97462 541-459-4341
Nanette Hagen, supt. Fax 459-4120
www.oakland.k12.or.us
Lincoln MS 200/5-8
PO Box 420 97462 541-459-3407
Diana Sweeden, prin. Fax 459-9167
Oakland HS 200/9-12
PO Box 479 97462 541-459-2597
Jeff Clark, prin. Fax 459-4765

Oakridge, Lane, Pop. 3,091
Oakridge SD 76 600/K-12
76499 Rose St 97463 541-782-2813
Dr. Donald Kordosky, supt. Fax 782-2982
www.oakridge.k12.or.us/
Oakridge HS 200/9-12
47997 W 1st St 97463 541-782-2231
Dr. Donald Kordosky, prin. Fax 782-4692
Oakridge JHS 100/7-8
76486 Rose St 97463 541-782-2731
Dr. Donald Kordosky, prin. Fax 782-4647

Ontario, Malheur, Pop. 11,152
Ontario SD 8C 2,300/K-12
195 SW 3rd Ave 97914 541-889-5374
Linda Florence, supt. Fax 889-8553
www.ontario.k12.or.us
Ontario HS 800/9-12
1115 W Idaho Ave 97914 541-889-5309
Joe LaFountaine, prin. Fax 889-8117
Ontario MS 400/7-8
573 SW 2nd Ave 97914 541-889-5377
Brett Clevenger, prin. Fax 881-0060

Treasure Valley Christian S 100/PK-12
386 N Verde Dr 97914 541-889-4662
Fran Renk, prin. Fax 889-9199
Treasure Valley Community College Post-Sec.
650 College Blvd 97914 541-881-8822

Oregon City, Clackamas, Pop. 30,976
Oregon City SD 62 6,300/K-12
PO Box 2110 97045 503-785-8000
Larry Didway, supt. Fax 657-2492
www.orecity.k12.or.us
Gardiner MS 600/6-8
180 Ethel St 97045 503-785-8200
Kelly Schmidt, prin. Fax 650-5482
Ogden MS 600/6-8
14133 Donovan Rd 97045 503-785-8300
Libby Miller, prin. Fax 657-2508
Oregon City HS 2,200/9-12
19761 Beavercreek Rd 97045 503-785-8900
Nancy Bush-Lange, prin. Fax 785-8578

Clackamas Community College Post-Sec.
19600 Molalla Ave 97045 503-594-6000
North Clackamas Christian S 200/PK-12
19575 Sebastian Way 97045 503-655-5961
Julie Phipps, admin. Fax 655-4875

Paulina, Crook
Crook County SD
Supt. — See Prineville
Paulina S 50/K-12
70050 SE Paulina City Rd 97751 541-477-3182
Kurt Sloper, prin. Fax 477-3512

Pendleton, Umatilla, Pop. 16,180
Pendleton SD 16 3,200/K-12
1207 SW Frazer Ave 97801 541-276-6711
Jon Peterson, supt. Fax 278-3208
www.pendleton.k12.or.us
Hawthorne Alternative Education S Alt
1308 SW Emigrant Ave 97801 541-966-3378
Tom Lovell, prin. Fax 966-3291
Pendleton HS 900/9-12
1800 NW Carden Ave 97801 541-966-3804
Tom Lovell, prin. Fax 966-3813
Sunridge MS 700/6-8
700 SW Runnion Ave 97801 541-276-4560
Matt Yoshioka, prin. Fax 276-4724

Blue Mountain Community College Post-Sec.
PO Box 100 97801 541-276-1260
Harris Junior Academy 100/K-10
3121 SW Hailey Ave 97801 541-276-0615

Philomath, Benton, Pop. 4,445
Philomath SD 17J 1,400/K-12
535 S 19th St 97370 541-929-3169
Dan Forbess, supt. Fax 929-3991
www.philomath.k12.or.us
Philomath HS 500/9-12
2054 Applegate St 97370 541-929-3211
Ken Ball, prin. Fax 929-3244
Philomath MS 400/6-8
2021 Chapel Dr 97370 541-929-3167
Steve Bell, prin. Fax 929-3180

Phoenix, Jackson, Pop. 4,376
Phoenix-Talent SD 4 2,700/K-12
PO Box 698 97535 541-535-1517
Teresa Sayre, supt. Fax 535-3928
www.phoenix.k12.or.us
Phoenix HS 800/9-12
PO Box 697 97535 541-535-1526
Jani Hale, prin. Fax 535-7511
Other Schools – See Talent

Pilot Rock, Umatilla, Pop. 1,457
Pilot Rock SD 2 400/K-12
PO Box BB 97868 541-443-8291
Gordon Munck, supt. Fax 443-8000
www.pilotrock.k12.or.us
Pilot Rock JSHS 200/7-12
PO Box BB 97868 541-443-2671
Ed Sherman, prin. Fax 443-2120

Pleasant Hill, Lane
Pleasant Hill SD 1 800/K-12
36386 Highway 58 97455 541-746-9646
Tony Scurto, supt. Fax 746-2537
www.pleasanthill.k12.or.us
Pleasant Hill HS 400/7-12
36386 Highway 58 97455 541-747-4541
Randy Fisher, prin. Fax 744-3351

Emerald Christian Academy 100/K-12
35582 Zephyr Way 97455 541-746-1708
Christopher Tait, prin. Fax 746-8353

Portland, Multnomah, Pop. 557,791
Beaverton SD 48J
Supt. — See Beaverton
Cedar Park MS 900/6-8
11100 SW Park Way 97225 503-672-3620
Ken Struckmeier, prin. Fax 672-3626
Early College HS 11-12
17705 NW Springville Rd 97229 503-614-7473
Linda West, prin. Fax 614-7553
Stoller MS 1,100/6-8
14141 NW Laidlaw Rd 97229 503-533-1910
Florence Richey, prin. Fax 533-1914
Sunset HS 2,000/9-12
13840 NW Cornell Rd 97229 503-259-5050
John Huelskamp, prin. Fax 259-5066

Westview HS 2,600/9-12
4200 NW 185th Ave 97229 503-259-5218
Mike Chamberlain, prin. Fax 259-5230

Centennial SD 28J 6,400/K-12
18135 SE Brooklyn St 97236 503-760-7990
Sam Breyer, supt. Fax 762-3689
www.centennial.k12.or.us
Centennial MS 1,000/7-8
17650 SE Brooklyn St 97236 503-762-3206
Rise' Hawley, prin. Fax 762-3236
Centennial Park S 100/Alt
17630 SE Main St 97233 503-762-3202
Ajai Huja, prin. Fax 760-1651
Other Schools – See Gresham

David Douglas SD 40 10,500/K-12
1500 SE 130th Ave 97233 503-252-2900
Don Grotting, supt. Fax 261-8208
www.ddouglas.k12.or.us
Douglas HS 3,300/9-12
1001 SE 135th Ave 97233 503-261-8300
John Bier, prin. Fax 261-8399
Light MS 800/6-8
10800 SE Washington St 97216 503-256-6511
Mark Gaulke, prin. Fax 261-8423
Ott MS 800/6-8
12500 SE Ramona St 97236 503-256-6510
James Johnston, prin. Fax 261-8403
Russell MS 900/6-8
3955 SE 112th Ave 97266 503-256-6519
Andy Long, prin. Fax 761-7246

Multnomah ESD 200/
PO Box 301039 97294 503-255-1841
Barbara Jorgensen, supt. Fax 257-1519
www.mesd.k12.or.us
Helensview HS 100/Alt
8678 NE Sumner St 97220 503-262-4150
Kris Persson, prin. Fax 255-1767
Other Schools – See Gresham

North Clackamas SD 12
Supt. — See Milwaukie
Sabin-Schellenberg Professional-Tech Ctr Vo/Tech
14450 SE Johnson Rd 97267 503-353-5900
Karen Phillips, prin. Fax 353-5915

Parkrose SD 3 3,400/K-12
10636 NE Prescott St 97220 503-408-2100
Dr. Karen Fischer Gray, supt. Fax 408-2140
www.parkrose.k12.or.us
Parkrose HS 1,000/9-12
12003 NE Shaver St 97220 503-408-2600
Jared Freeman, prin. Fax 408-2739
Parkrose MS 800/6-8
11800 NE Shaver St 97220 503-408-2700
Molly Ouche, prin. Fax 408-2998

Portland SD 1J 41,800/PK-12
PO Box 3107 97208 503-916-2000
Carole Smith, supt. Fax 916-3110
www.pps.k12.or.us/
Alliance HS @ Benson 11-12
546 NE 12th Ave 97232 503-916-6486
A.J. Morrison, prin. Fax 916-2696
Alliance HS @ Madison 10-12
2735 NE 82nd Ave 97220 503-916-5747
A.J. Morrison, prin. Fax 916-2680
Alliance HS @ Meek ProTech 10-12
4039 NE Alberta Ct 97211 503-916-5747
A.J. Morrison, prin. Fax 916-2680
Beaumont MS 500/6-8
4043 NE Fremont St 97212 503-916-5610
Elizabeth Casson-Taylor, prin. Fax 916-2609
Benson Polytechnic HS Vo/Tech
546 NE 12th Ave 97232 503-916-5100
Carol Campbell, prin. Fax 916-2690
Cleveland HS 1,600/9-12
3400 SE 26th Ave 97202 503-916-5120
Paul Cook, prin. Fax 916-2692
Da Vinci Arts MS 500/6-8
2508 NE Everett St 97232 503-916-5356
Fred Locke, prin. Fax 916-2721
Franklin HS 1,000/9-12
5405 SE Woodward St 97206 503-916-5140
Shay James, prin. Fax 916-2694
George MS 400/6-8
10000 N Burr Ave 97203 503-916-6262
Ben Keefer, prin. Fax 916-2627
Grant HS 1,600/9-12
2245 NE 36th Ave 97212 503-916-5160
Vivian Orlen, prin. Fax 916-2695
Gray MS 400/6-8
5505 SW 23rd Ave, 503-916-5676
Beth Madison, prin. Fax 916-2629
Hosford International MS 500/6-8
2303 SE 28th Pl 97214 503-916-5640
Kevin Bacon, prin. Fax 916-2637
Jackson MS 600/6-8
10625 SW 35th Ave 97219 503-916-5680
John Ferraro, prin. Fax 916-2640
Jefferson HS 600/6-12
5210 N Kerby Ave 97217 503-916-5180
Margaret Calvert, prin. Fax 916-2698
Lane MS 400/6-8
7200 SE 60th Ave 97206 503-916-6355
Pam Joyner, prin. Fax 916-2648
Lincoln HS 1,400/9-12
1600 SW Salmon St 97205 503-916-5200
Peyton Chapman, prin. Fax 916-2700
Madison HS 900/8-12
2735 NE 82nd Ave 97220 503-916-5220
Petra Callin, prin. Fax 916-2702
Metropolitan Learning Center S 400/Alt
2033 NW Glisan St 97209 503-916-5737
Macarre Traynham, prin. Fax 916-2658
Mt. Tabor MS 600/6-8
5800 SE Ash St 97215 503-916-5646
Robi Osborne, prin. Fax 916-2659
Roosevelt - ACT HS 300/9-12
6941 N Central St 97203 503-916-5260
Charlene Williams, prin. Fax 916-2704

Sellwood MS 500/6-8
8300 SE 15th Ave 97202 503-916-5656
Charlene Russell, prin. Fax 916-2672
West Sylvan MS 600/7-8
8111 SW West Slope Dr 97225 503-916-5690
Cate Boyce, prin. Fax 916-2681
Wilson HS 1,400/9-12
1151 SW Vermont St 97219 503-916-5280
Brian Chatard, prin. Fax 916-2705

Reynolds SD 7
Supt. — See Fairview
Lee MS 800/6-8
1121 NE 172nd Ave 97230 503-255-5686
Mario Alba, prin. Fax 252-0522

Riverdale SD 51J 600/K-12
11733 SW Breyman Ave 97219 503-262-4840
Michael Taylor, supt. Fax 262-4841
www.riverdale.k12.or.us
Riverdale HS 200/9-12
9727 SW Terwilliger Blvd 97219 503-262-4844
Paula Robinson, prin. Fax 262-4845

American College of Healthcare Sciences Post-Sec.
5940 SW Hood Ave, 800-487-8839
Art Institute of Portland Post-Sec.
1122 NW Davis St 97209 503-228-6528
Beau Monde College Acad of Cosmetology Post-Sec.
525 SW 12th Ave 97205 503-252-7444
Beau Monde College of Hair Design Post-Sec.
1221 SW 12th Ave 97205 503-226-7355
Birthingway College of Midwifery Post-Sec.
12113 SE Foster Rd 97266 503-760-3131
Carrington College Post-Sec.
2004 Lloyd Ctr Fl 3 97232 503-761-6100
Catlin Gabel S 700/PK-12
8825 SW Barnes Rd 97225 503-297-1894
Dr. Lark Palma, prin. Fax 297-0139
Central Catholic HS 800/9-12
2401 SE Stark St 97214 503-235-3138
John Garrow, prin. Fax 233-0073
City Christian S 300/PK-12
9200 NE Fremont St 97220 503-252-5207
Columbia Christian S 200/PK-12
413 NE 91st Ave 97220 503-252-8577
Ami Vensel, prin. Fax 252-2108
Concorde Career Institute Post-Sec.
1425 NE Irving St Ste 300 97232 503-281-4181
Concordia University Post-Sec.
2811 NE Holman St 97211 503-288-9371
De La Salle North HS 300/9-12
7528 N Fenwick Ave 97217 503-285-9385
Matt Powell, prin. Fax 285-9546
DeVry University Post-Sec.
9755 SW Barnes Rd Ste 150 97225 503-296-7468
Edison HS 100/9-12
9020 SW Bvrtn Hillsdale Hwy 97225 503-297-2336
Patrick Maguire, dir. Fax 297-2527
Everest College Post-Sec.
425 SW Washington St 97204 503-222-3225
George Fox University Post-Sec.
12753 SW 68th Ave 97223 503-554-6100
Heald College Post-Sec.
6035 NE 78th Ct 97218 503-229-0492
ITT Technical Institute Post-Sec.
9500 NE Cascades Pkwy 97220 503-255-6500
Jesuit HS 1,200/9-12
9000 SW Beaverton Hillsdale 97225 503-292-2663
Paul Hogan, prin. Fax 291-5464
Le Cordon Bleu College of Culinary Arts Post-Sec.
600 SW 10th Ave Ste 500 97205 503-223-2245
Lewis & Clark College Post-Sec.
0615 SW Palatine Hill Rd 97219 503-768-7000
Linfield College Post-Sec.
2255 NW Northrup St 97210 503-413-8481
Multnomah University Post-Sec.
8435 NE Glisan St 97220 503-255-0332
National College of Natural Medicine Post-Sec.
049 SW Porter St 97201 503-552-1555
Open Meadow Alternative S 100/9-12
7654 N Crawford St 97203 503-285-0508
Andrew Mason, dir. Fax 285-0798
Oregon College of Art and Craft Post-Sec.
8245 SW Barnes Rd 97225 503-297-5544
Oregon College of Oriental Medicine Post-Sec.
10525 SE Cherry Blossom Dr 97216 503-253-3443
Oregon Culinary Institute Post-Sec.
1701 SW Jefferson St 97201 503-961-6200
Oregon Episcopal S 900/PK-12
6300 SW Nicol Rd 97223 503-246-7771
Mo Copeland, head sch Fax 293-1105
Oregon Health & Science University Post-Sec.
3181 SW Sam Jackson Park Rd, 503-494-8311
Pacific Northwest College of Art Post-Sec.
1241 NW Johnson St 97209 503-226-4391
Phagans' School of Hair Design Post-Sec.
1542 NE Weidler St 97232 503-239-0838
Portland Adventist Academy 200/9-12
1500 SE 96th Ave 97216 503-255-8372
Gale Crosby, prin. Fax 255-5132
Portland Christian JSHS 300/6-12
12425 NE San Rafael St 97230 503-256-3960
Jim Hill, prin. Fax 256-2773
Portland Community College Post-Sec.
PO Box 19000 97280 971-722-6111
Portland Lutheran S 200/PK-12
740 SE 182nd Ave 97233 503-667-3199
Donn Maier, dir. Fax 667-4520
Portland State University Post-Sec.
PO Box 751 97207 503-725-3000
Reed College Post-Sec.
3203 SE Woodstock Blvd 97202 503-771-1112
St. Andrew Nativity S 100/6-8
4925 NE 9th Ave 97211 503-335-9600
Michael Chambers, prin. Fax 335-9494
St. Mary Academy 600/9-12
1615 SW 5th Ave 97201 503-228-8306
Kelli Clark, prin. Fax 223-0995
St. Vincent Hospital & Medical Center Post-Sec.
9205 SW Barnes Rd 97225 503-216-3031

Serendipity Center 100/K-12
PO Box 33350 97292 503-761-7139
Sumner College Post-Sec.
8909 SW Barbur Blvd 97219 503-928-3431
University of Portland Post-Sec.
5000 N Willamette Blvd 97203 503-943-8000
University of Western States Post-Sec.
2900 NE 132nd Ave 97230 503-256-3180
Veterans Administration Medical Center Post-Sec.
PO Box 1034 97207 503-220-8262
Walla Walla University School of Nursing Post-Sec.
10345 SE Market St 97216 503-251-6115
Warner Pacific College Post-Sec.
2219 SE 68th Ave 97215 503-517-1000
Western Seminary Post-Sec.
5511 SE Hawthorne Blvd 97215 503-517-1800

Port Orford, Curry, Pop. 1,095
Port Orford-Langlois SD 2CJ 300/K-12
PO Box 8 97465 541-366-2111
Christine Nichols, supt. Fax 332-0190
www.2cj.com
Other Schools – See Sixes

Powers, Coos, Pop. 625
Powers SD 31 100/K-12
PO Box 479 97466 541-439-2291
Matt Shorb, supt. Fax 439-2875
www.powers.k12.or.us
Powers HS 100/7-12
PO Box 479 97466 541-439-2291
Matt Shorb, prin. Fax 439-2875

Prairie City, Grant, Pop. 882
Prairie City SD 4 200/K-12
740 Overholt St 97869 541-820-3314
Ryan Gerry, supt. Fax 820-4352
www.grantesd.k12.or.us
Prairie City S 200/K-12
740 Overholt St 97869 541-820-3314
Ryan Gerry, prin. Fax 820-4352

Prineville, Crook, Pop. 9,076
Crook County SD 2,700/K-12
471 NE Ochoco Plaza Dr 97754 541-447-5664
Dr. Duane Yecha, supt. Fax 447-3645
www.crookcounty.k12.or.us
Crook County HS 800/9-12
1100 SE Lynn Blvd 97754 541-416-6900
Rocky Miner, prin. Fax 416-6907
Crook County MS 700/6-8
100 NE Knowledge St 97754 541-447-6283
Stacy Smith, prin. Fax 447-3293
Pioneer HS Alt
297 NE Holly St 97754 541-447-1268
Rocky Miner, prin. Fax 447-1862
Other Schools – See Paulina

Rainier, Columbia, Pop. 1,842
Rainier SD 13 1,100/K-12
28168 Old Rainier Rd 97048 503-556-0777
R. Michael Carter, supt. Fax 556-3778
www.rainier.k12.or.us
Rainier JSHS 500/7-12
28170 Old Rainier Rd 97048 503-556-4215
Dr. Michael Carter, prin. Fax 556-1120

Redmond, Deschutes, Pop. 25,592
Redmond SD 2J 7,000/K-12
145 SE Salmon Ave 97756 541-923-5437
Shay Mikalson, supt. Fax 923-5142
www.redmond.k12.or.us
Brown Education Center 100/Alt
850 SW Antler Ave 97756 541-923-4868
Deborah Newport, prin. Fax 923-4867
Gregory MS 700/6-8
1220 NW Upas Ave 97756 541-526-6440
John Hartford, prin. Fax 526-6441
Obsidian MS 700/6-8
1335 SW Obsidian Ave 97756 541-923-4900
Sandra Harris, prin. Fax 923-6509
Redmond HS 1,900/9-12
675 SW Rimrock Way 97756 541-923-4800
Lee Loving, prin. Fax 548-0809
Ridgeview HS 9-12
4555 SW Elkhorn Ave 97756 541-504-3600
Lee Loving, prin. Fax 504-3601

Central Christian S 200/PK-12
PO Box 639 97756 541-548-7803
Elisa Carlson, hdmstr. Fax 548-2801

Riddle, Douglas, Pop. 1,134
Riddle SD 70 400/K-12
PO Box 45 97469 541-874-3131
Dave Gianotti, supt. Fax 874-2345
www.riddle.k12.or.us
Riddle JSHS, PO Box 45 97469 200/7-12
Terry Prestianni, prin. 541-874-2251

Rockaway, Tillamook, Pop. 1,282
Neah-Kah-Nie SD 56 700/K-12
PO Box 28 97136 503-355-2222
Jay Kosik, supt. Fax 355-3434
www.neahkahnie.k12.or.us
Neah-Kah-Nie HS 200/9-12
24705 Highway 101 N 97136 503-355-2272
Heidi Buckmaster, prin. Fax 355-8200
Neah-Kah-Nie MS 200/6-8
25111 Highway 101 N 97136 503-355-2990
Jim Severson, prin. Fax 355-8514

Rogue River, Jackson, Pop. 2,091
Rogue River SD 35 600/K-12
PO Box 1045 97537 541-582-3235
Paul Young, supt. Fax 582-1600
www.rogueriver.k12.or.us
Rogue River JSHS 300/7-12
PO Box 1045 97537 541-582-3297
Jesse Pershin, prin. Fax 582-6005

Roseburg, Douglas, Pop. 20,494
Douglas County SD 4 6,200/K-12
1419 NW Valley View Dr, 541-440-4015
Larry Parsons, supt. Fax 440-4003
www.roseburg.k12.or.us
Fremont MS 700/6-8
850 W Keady Ct, 541-440-4055
Keith Kronser, prin. Fax 440-4060
Lane MS 800/6-8
2153 NE Vine St 97470 541-440-4104
Bill Bartlett, prin. Fax 440-4100
Roseburg HS 1,800/9-12
400 W Harvard Ave 97470 541-440-4142
Karen Goirigolzarri, prin. Fax 440-8296

Roseburg Beauty College Post-Sec.
700 SE Stephens St 97470 541-673-5533
Umpqua Community College Post-Sec.
PO Box 967 97470 541-440-4600
Umpqua Valley Christian HS 100/7-12
359 Roberts Creek Rd, 541-679-8827
Doug Tharp, admin. Fax 679-1881

Saint Benedict, Marion, Pop. 55

Mt. Angel Seminary Post-Sec.
1 Abbey Dr 97373 503-845-3951

Saint Helens, Columbia, Pop. 12,364
Saint Helens SD 502 3,200/K-12
474 N 16th St 97051 503-397-3085
Mark Davalos, supt. Fax 397-1907
www.sthelens.k12.or.us
Saint Helens HS 1,000/9-12
2375 Gable Rd 97051 503-397-1900
Andy Croley, prin. Fax 397-1828
Saint Helens MS 500/7-8
354 N 15th St 97051 503-366-7300
Joanna Tobin, prin. Fax 366-7306

Saint Paul, Marion, Pop. 420
St. Paul SD 45 300/PK-12
20449 Main St NE 97137 503-633-2541
Sid Hobgood, supt. Fax 633-2540
www.stpaul.k12.or.us
Saint Paul HS 100/7-12
20449 Main St NE 97137 503-633-2541
Sid Hobgood, prin. Fax 633-2540

Salem, Marion, Pop. 148,676
Salem-Keizer SD 24J 39,500/K-12
PO Box 12024 97309 503-399-3000
Sandy Husk, supt. Fax 399-5579
www.salkeiz.k12.or.us
Crossler MS 800/6-8
1155 Davis Rd S 97306 503-399-3444
Kristine Walton, prin. Fax 391-4005
Early College HS 200/Alt
4071 Winema Pl NE Ste 50 97305 503-365-4801
Ken Phillips, prin. Fax 365-4703
Houck MS 900/6-8
1155 Connecticut St SE, 503-399-3446
Greg Cole, prin. Fax 391-4167
Judson MS 1,000/6-8
4512 Jones Rd SE 97302 503-399-3201
Lara Tiffin, prin. Fax 391-4041
Leslie MS 900/6-8
3850 Pringle Rd SE 97302 503-399-3206
Steve Nelson, prin. Fax 399-3479
McKay HS 1,800/9-12
2440 Lancaster Dr NE 97305 503-399-3080
Ken Parshall, prin. Fax 375-7807
North Salem HS 2,000/9-12
765 14th St NE 97301 503-399-3241
Cynthia Richardson, prin. Fax 375-7808
Parrish MS 700/6-8
802 Capitol St NE 97301 503-399-3210
Rob Schoepper, prin. Fax 391-4004
Roberts HS 500/Alt
3620 State St 97301 503-399-5550
Ken Phillips, prin. Fax 391-4075
South Salem HS 2,000/9-12
1910 Church St SE 97302 503-399-3252
David Phelps, prin. Fax 375-7805
Sprague HS 1,700/9-12
2373 Kuebler Rd S 97302 503-399-3261
Curtiss Scholl, prin. Fax 391-4046
Stephens MS 1,000/6-8
4962 Hayesville Dr NE 97305 503-399-3442
Matt Biondi, prin. Fax 391-4079
Straub MS 6-8
1920 Wilmington Ave NW 97304 503-399-2030
Neil Anderson, prin. Fax 399-2032
Waldo MS 800/6-8
2805 Lansing Ave NE 97301 503-399-3215
Tricia Nelson, prin. Fax 391-4070
Walker MS 1,100/6-8
1075 8th St NW 97304 503-399-3220
Peter Danner, prin. Fax 399-5540
West Salem HS 1,700/9-12
1776 Titan Dr NW 97304 503-399-5533
Ed John, prin. Fax 584-5004
Other Schools – See Keizer

Academy of Hair Design Post-Sec.
305 Court St NE 97301 503-585-8122
Blanchet S 400/6-12
4373 Market St NE 97301 503-391-2639
Anthony Guevara, prin. Fax 399-1259
Chemeketa Community College Post-Sec.
PO Box 14007 97309 503-399-5000
College of Hair Design Careers Post-Sec.
1684 Clay St NE 97301 503-588-5888
Corban University Post-Sec.
5000 Deer Park Dr SE, 503-581-8600
George Fox University Post-Sec.
4910 Brooklake Rd NE 97305 971-239-4930
Institute of Technology Post-Sec.
4700 Silverton Rd NE 97305 877-887-8007
Livingstone Adventist Academy 200/PK-12
5771 Fruitland Rd NE, 503-363-9408
Trevor Kendall, admin. Fax 363-5721
Oregon State School for the Deaf Post-Sec.
999 Locust St NE 97301
Phagans' School of Beauty Post-Sec.
622 Lancaster Dr NE 97301 503-363-6800
Salem Academy 300/6-12
942 Lancaster Dr NE 97301 503-378-1219
Stan Baker, supt. Fax 375-3522
Western Mennonite S 300/6-12
9045 Wallace Rd NW 97304 503-363-2000
Paul Schultz, prin. Fax 370-9455
Willamette University Post-Sec.
900 State St 97301 503-370-6300

Sandy, Clackamas, Pop. 9,279
Oregon Trail SD 46 3,800/K-12
PO Box 547 97055 503-668-5541
Aaron Bayer, supt. Fax 668-7906
www.oregontrailschools.com
Cedar Ridge MS 400/6-8
17225 Smith Ave 97055 503-668-8067
Matt Newell, prin. Fax 668-3977
Sandy HS 1,300/9-12
17100 SE Bluff Rd 97055 503-668-8011
Tim Werner, prin. Fax 668-7646
Other Schools – See Boring, Welches

Scappoose, Columbia, Pop. 6,380
Scappoose SD 1J 2,300/K-12
33589 High School Way 97056 503-543-6374
Stephen Jupe, supt. Fax 543-7011
www.scappoose.k12.or.us
Scappoose HS 700/9-12
33700 High School Way 97056 503-543-6376
Eric Clendenin, prin. Fax 543-3796
Scappoose MS 400/7-8
52265 Columbia River Hwy 97056 503-543-7163
Pam Reynolds, prin. Fax 543-7917

Scio, Linn, Pop. 809
Scio SD 95 3,300/K-12
38875 NW 1st Ave 97374 503-394-3261
Gary Tempel, supt. Fax 394-3920
www.scio.k12.or.us/
Scio HS 200/9-12
38875 NW 1st Ave 97374 503-394-3276
Bryan Starr, prin. Fax 394-3236
Scio MS 200/6-8
38875 NW 1st Ave 97374 503-394-3271
Sean Aker, prin. Fax 394-4042

Seaside, Clatsop, Pop. 6,285
Jewell SD 8 200/K-12
83874 Highway 103 97138 503-755-2451
Jim Carlile, supt. Fax 755-0616
www.jewell.k12.or.us
Jewell S 200/K-12
83874 Highway 103 97138 503-755-2451
Jim Carlile, prin. Fax 755-0616

Seaside SD 10 1,400/K-12
1801 S Franklin St 97138 503-738-5591
Doug Dougherty, supt. Fax 738-3471
www.seaside.k12.or.us/
Broadway MS 300/6-8
1120 Broadway St 97138 503-738-6892
Doug Pease, prin. Fax 738-3900
Seaside HS 400/9-12
1901 N Holladay Dr 97138 503-738-5586
Sheila Roley, prin. Fax 738-5589

Sheridan, Yamhill, Pop. 5,880
Sheridan SD 48J 1,000/K-12
435 S Bridge St 97378 503-843-2433
Steven Sugg, supt. Fax 843-3505
www.sheridan.k12.or.us
Opportunity House Alternative S 50/Alt
433 S Bridge St 97378 503-843-2162
Dean Rech, prin. Fax 843-3466
Sheridan Spartan Academy 200/6-12
433 S Bridge St 97378 503-843-2162
Dean Rech, prin. Fax 843-3466

Delphian S 200/PK-12
20950 SW Rock Creek Rd 97378 503-843-3521
Rosemary Didear, head sch Fax 843-4158

Sherwood, Washington, Pop. 17,504
Sherwood SD 88J 4,900/K-12
23295 SW Main St 97140 503-825-5000
Heather Cordie, supt. Fax 825-5001
www.sherwood.k12.or.us
Laurel Ridge MS 500/6-8
21416 SW Copper Ter 97140 503-825-5800
Steve Emmert, prin. Fax 825-5801
Sherwood HS 1,400/9-12
16956 SW Meinecke Rd 97140 503-825-5500
Michelle DeBoard, prin. Fax 825-5501
Sherwood MS 600/6-8
21970 SW Sherwood Blvd 97140 503-825-5400
Gary Bennett, prin. Fax 825-5401

Silver Lake, Lake, Pop. 147
North Lake SD 14 200/K-12
57566 Fort Rock Rd 97638 541-576-2121
Steve Staniak, supt. Fax 576-2705
www.nlake.k12.or.us/
North Lake S 200/K-12
57566 Fort Rock Rd 97638 541-576-2121
Steve Staniak, prin. Fax 576-2705

Silverton, Marion, Pop. 9,064
Silver Falls SD 4J 3,600/K-12
802 Schlador St 97381 503-873-5303
Andy Bellando, supt. Fax 873-2936
silverfalls.orvsd.org
Silverton HS 1,200/9-12
1456 Pine St 97381 503-873-6331
Mark Hannan, prin. Fax 873-8606
Twain MS 300/7-8
425 N Church St 97381 503-873-5317
Dandy Stevens, prin. Fax 873-7108

Sisters, Deschutes, Pop. 2,007
Sisters SD 6 1,300/K-12
525 E Cascade Ave 97759 541-549-8521
Jim Golden, supt. Fax 549-8951
www.sisters.k12.or.us
Sisters HS 500/9-12
1700 W McKinney Butte Rd 97759 541-549-4045
Joe Hosang, prin. Fax 549-4051
Sisters MS 400/5-8
15200 McKenzie Rd 97759 541-549-2099
Mark Stewart, prin. Fax 549-2098

Sixes, Curry
Port Orford-Langlois SD 2CJ
Supt. — See Port Orford
Pacific HS 100/9-12
45525 Highway 101 97476 541-348-2293
Krista Nieraeth, prin. Fax 348-2389

Spray, Wheeler, Pop. 157
Spray SD 1 50/K-12
PO Box 230 97874 541-468-2226
Phil Starkey, supt. Fax 468-2630
www.spray.k12.or.us
Spray S 50/K-12
PO Box 230 97874 541-468-2226
Mary Doherty, prin. Fax 468-2630

Springfield, Lane, Pop. 57,056
Springfield SD 19 9,600/K-12
525 Mill St 97477 541-747-3331
Dr. Nancy Golden, supt. Fax 726-9555
www.springfield.k12.or.us
Briggs MS 400/6-8
2355 Yolanda Ave 97477 541-744-6350
Jeff Mather, prin. Fax 744-6354
Gateways HS 100/9-12
665 Main St 97477 541-744-8862
Paul Weill, prin. Fax 744-8863
Hamlin MS 400/6-8
326 Centennial Blvd 97477 541-744-6356
Dennis Gray, prin. Fax 744-6360
Springfield HS 1,400/9-12
875 7th St 97477 541-744-4700
Carmen Gelman, prin. Fax 744-4875
Stewart MS 600/6-8
900 S 32nd St 97478 541-988-2520
Jeff Fuller, prin. Fax 988-2530
Thurston HS 1,500/9-12
333 58th St 97478 541-744-5000
Ed Mendelssohn, prin. Fax 744-5029
Thurston MS 600/6-8
6300 Thurston Rd 97478 541-744-6368
Carl Swan, prin. Fax 744-6372

Pioneer Pacific College Post-Sec.
3800 Sports Way 97477 541-684-4644
Springfield College of Beauty Post-Sec.
307 Q St 97477 541-746-4473

Stanfield, Umatilla, Pop. 1,997
Stanfield SD 61 500/K-12
1120 N Main St 97875 541-449-8766
Wayne Kostur, supt. Fax 449-8768
www.stanfield.k12.or.us
Stanfield Secondary S 300/7-12
1120 N Main St 97875 541-449-3851
Bryan Johnson, prin. Fax 449-8751

Stayton, Marion, Pop. 7,435
North Santiam SD 29J 2,400/K-12
1155 N 3rd Ave 97383 503-769-6924
Andrew Gardner, supt. Fax 769-3578
www.nsantiam.k12.or.us
Stayton HS 800/9-12
757 W Locust St 97383 503-769-2171
Graham Hughes, prin. Fax 769-6050
Stayton Intermediate / MS 600/4-8
1021 Shaff Rd 97383 503-769-2198
Jamie McCarty, prin. Fax 769-9524

Regis HS 100/9-12
550 W Regis St 97383 503-769-2159
Joni Gilles, prin. Fax 769-1706

Sutherlin, Douglas, Pop. 7,596
Sutherlin SD 130 1,400/K-12
531 E Central Ave 97479 541-459-2228
Steve Perkins, supt. Fax 459-2484
www.sutherlin.k12.or.us
Sutherlin HS 400/9-12
500 E Fourth Ave 97479 541-459-9551
Justin Huntley, prin. Fax 459-4887
Sutherlin MS 200/7-8
649 E Fourth Ave 97479 541-459-2668
Terry Prestianni, prin. Fax 459-2047

Sweet Home, Linn, Pop. 8,693
Sweet Home SD 55 2,300/K-12
1920 Long St 97386 541-367-7126
Don Schrader, supt. Fax 367-7105
www.sweethome.k12.or.us
Sweet Home HS 700/9-12
1641 Long St 97386 541-367-7142
Keith Winslow, prin. Fax 367-7196
Sweet Home JHS 400/7-8
880 22nd Ave 97386 541-367-7187
Colleen Henry, prin. Fax 367-7107

Talent, Jackson, Pop. 5,873
Phoenix-Talent SD 4
Supt. — See Phoenix
Talent MS 600/6-8
PO Box 359 97540 541-535-1552
Aaron Santi, prin. Fax 535-7532

The Dalles, Wasco, Pop. 13,258
North Wasco County SD 21 3,000/K-12
3632 W 10th St 97058 541-506-3420
Candy Armstrong, supt. Fax 298-6018
www.nwasco.k12.or.us

The Dalles MS 600/6-8
1100 E 12th St 97058 541-506-3380
Pat Consoliver, prin. Fax 298-1942
The Dalles - Wahtonka HS 1,000/9-12
220 E 10th St 97058 541-506-3400
Nick Nelson, prin. Fax 298-4964

Columbia Gorge Community College Post-Sec.
400 E Scenic Dr 97058 541-506-6000

Tigard, Washington, Pop. 46,005
Tigard-Tualatin SD 23J 12,600/K-12
6960 SW Sandburg St 97223 503-431-4000
Ernest Brown, supt. Fax 431-4047
www.ttsd.k12.or.us
Durham Center 100/Alt
8040 SW Durham Rd 97224 503-431-4580
Karen Twain, prin. Fax 431-4590
Fowler MS 800/6-8
10865 SW Walnut St 97223 503-431-5000
Dan Busch, prin. Fax 431-5010
Tigard HS 2,000/9-12
9000 SW Durham Rd 97224 503-431-5400
Mark Neffendorf, prin. Fax 431-5410
Twality MS 1,000/6-8
14650 SW 97th Ave 97224 503-431-5200
Carol Kinch, prin. Fax 431-5210
Other Schools – See Tualatin

Everest Institute Post-Sec.
9600 SW Oak St Fl 4 97223 503-892-8100
Phagans' Tigard Beauty School Post-Sec.
8820 SW Center St 97223 503-639-6107

Tillamook, Tillamook, Pop. 4,782
Tillamook SD 9 2,000/K-12
2510 1st St 97141 503-842-4414
Randy Schild, supt. Fax 842-6854
www.tillamook.k12.or.us
Tillamook HS 700/9-12
2605 12th St 97141 503-842-2566
Kevin Barnes, prin. Fax 842-1340
Tillamook JHS 300/7-8
3906 Alder Ln 97141 503-842-7531
J.P. Richards, prin. Fax 842-1349
Tillamook Options Program Alt
2510 1st St 97141 503-842-7538
Rachel Sip, dir. Fax 842-1378
Trask River HS 100/Alt
6700 Officers Row 97141 503-842-2565
Jerry Dorland, prin. Fax 842-4918

Tillamook Bay Community College Post-Sec.
4301 3rd St 97141 503-842-8222

Toledo, Lincoln, Pop. 3,349
Lincoln County SD
Supt. — See Newport
Toledo JSHS 400/7-12
1800 NE Sturdevant Rd 97391 541-336-5104
Clint Raever, prin. Fax 336-2970

Mid Coast Christian S 50/K-12
1811 NE Arcadia Dr Ste C 97391 541-336-2234
Greg Wood, prin. Fax 336-2702

Troutdale, Multnomah, Pop. 15,404
Reynolds SD 7
Supt. — See Fairview
Morey MS 700/6-8
2801 SW Lucas Ave 97060 503-491-1935
Damian Reardon, prin. Fax 491-0245
Reynolds HS 2,600/9-12
1698 SW Cherry Park Rd 97060 503-667-3186
Susan McKinney, prin. Fax 669-0776

Tualatin, Washington, Pop. 25,026
Tigard-Tualatin SD 23J
Supt. — See Tigard
Hazelbrook MS 1,000/6-8
11300 SW Hazelbrook Rd 97062 503-431-5100
Eric Nesse, prin. Fax 431-5110
Tualatin HS 1,900/9-12
22300 SW Boones Ferry Rd 97062 503-431-5600
Darin Barnard, prin. Fax 431-5610

West Linn-Wilsonville SD 3J 8,300/PK-12
22210 SW Stafford Rd 97062 503-673-7000
Dr. William Rhoads, supt. Fax 673-7001
www.wlwv.k12.or.us
Athey Creek MS 600/6-8
2900 SW Borland Rd 97062 503-673-7400
Joel Sebastian, prin. Fax 638-8302
Other Schools – See West Linn, Wilsonville

Horizon Christian S 500/PK-12
PO Box 4190 97062 503-692-9312
Jay Anderson, supt. Fax 691-9677
Northwest College of Hair Design Post-Sec.
8345 SW Nyberg St 97062 503-218-2265

Turner, Marion, Pop. 1,825
Cascade SD 5 2,200/K-12
10226 Marion Rd SE 97392 503-749-8488
Darin Drill, supt. Fax 749-8321
www.cascade.k12.or.us
Cascade HS 700/9-12
10226 Marion Rd SE 97392 503-749-8490
Matt Thatcher, prin. Fax 749-8324
Cascade JHS 500/6-8
10226 Marion Rd SE 97392 503-749-8489
Peter Rasmussen, prin. Fax 749-8323
Other Schools – See Aumsville

Crosshill Christian S 300/PK-12
2707 Maranatha Ct SE 97392 503-391-9082
Adam Kronberger, prin. Fax 378-0507

Ukiah, Umatilla, Pop. 181
Ukiah SD 80R 50/PK-12
PO Box 218 97880 541-427-3731
Dan Korber, supt. Fax 427-3730
www.ukiah.k12.or.us
Ukiah S 50/PK-12
PO Box 218 97880 541-427-3731
Dan Korber, admin. Fax 427-3730

Umatilla, Umatilla, Pop. 6,845
Umatilla SD 6R 1,300/K-12
1001 6th St 97882 541-922-6500
Heidi Sipe, supt. Fax 922-6507
www.umatilla.k12.or.us
Brownell MS 300/6-8
1300 7th St 97882 541-922-6625
Dianna Veleke, prin. Fax 922-6649
Umatilla HS 400/9-12
1400 7th St 97882 541-922-6525
Scott Depew, prin. Fax 922-6599

Union, Union, Pop. 2,065
Union SD 5 400/K-12
PO Box K 97883 541-562-6115
Jon St. Germaine, supt. Fax 562-8116
www.union.k12.or.us
Union JSHS 200/7-12
PO Box 908 97883 541-562-5166
Carter Wells, prin. Fax 562-8116

Vale, Malheur, Pop. 1,833
Vale SD 84 900/K-12
403 E St W 97918 541-473-0201
Matthew Hawley, supt. Fax 473-3294
www.vale.k12.or.us
Vale HS 300/9-12
505 Viking Dr 97918 541-473-3181
Mary Jo Sharp, prin. Fax 473-2364
Vale MS 100/7-8
403 E St W 97918 541-473-0241
Matt Cobb, prin. Fax 473-3293

Vernonia, Columbia, Pop. 2,091
Vernonia SD 47J 600/K-12
1201 Texas Ave 97064 503-429-5891
Kenneth Cox, supt. Fax 429-7742
www.vernonia.k12.or.us/
Vernonia HS 200/9-12
1000 Missouri Ave 97064 503-429-1333
Nate Underwood, prin. Fax 429-4539
Vernonia MS 100/6-8
1000 Missouri Ave 97064 503-429-1333
Nate Underwood, prin. Fax 429-4539

Waldport, Lincoln, Pop. 1,936
Lincoln County SD
Supt. — See Newport
Waldport HS 200/9-12
PO Box 370 97394 541-563-3243
Tyler Stiner, prin. Fax 563-4145

Wallowa, Wallowa, Pop. 785
Wallowa SD 12 300/K-12
PO Box 425 97885 541-886-2061
Bret Uptmor, supt. Fax 886-7355
www.wallowa.k12.or.us/
Wallowa JSHS 100/7-12
PO Box 425 97885 541-886-2951
Bret Uptmor, admin. Fax 886-7355

Warren, Columbia, Pop. 1,740

Columbia County Christian S 50/K-10
56523 Columbia River Hwy 97053 503-366-9209
Beth Winegar, admin. Fax 717-5568

Warrenton, Clatsop, Pop. 4,827
Warrenton-Hammond SD 30 900/K-12
820 SW Cedar Ave 97146 503-861-2281
Mark Jeffery, supt. Fax 861-2911
www.gowarrenton.com/
Warrenton HS 300/9-12
1700 S Main Ave 97146 503-861-3317
Rod Heyen, prin. Fax 861-2997

Welches, Clackamas
Oregon Trail SD 46
Supt. — See Sandy
Welches MS 200/6-8
24903 E Salmon River Rd 97067 503-622-3166
Michael McKinney, prin. Fax 622-3398

West Linn, Clackamas, Pop. 24,356
West Linn-Wilsonville SD 3J
Supt. — See Tualatin
Rosemont Ridge MS 700/6-8
20001 Salamo Rd 97068 503-673-7550
Debi Briggs-Crispin, prin. Fax 657-8720
West Linn HS 1,500/9-12
5464 W A St 97068 503-673-7800
Lou Bailey, prin. Fax 657-8710

Weston, Umatilla, Pop. 646
Athena-Weston SD 29RJ
Supt. — See Athena
Weston MS 200/4-8
PO Box 158 97886 541-566-3548
Lori Mills, prin. Fax 566-2326

White City, Jackson, Pop. 7,814
Jackson County SD 9
Supt. — See Eagle Point
White Mountain MS 400/6-8
550 Wilson Way 97503 541-830-6315
Tim Rupp, prin. Fax 830-6751

Willamina, Yamhill, Pop. 1,910
Willamina SD 30J 800/K-12
PO Box 1000 97396 503-876-1501
Gus Forster, supt. Fax 876-3610
www.willamina.k12.or.us
Willamina HS 300/9-12
PO Box 1000 97396 503-876-2545
Tim France, prin. Fax 876-2511
Willamina MS 100/7-8
PO Box 1000 97396 503-876-2545
Tim France, prin. Fax 876-2511

Wilsonville, Clackamas, Pop. 18,997
West Linn-Wilsonville SD 3J
Supt. — See Tualatin
Arts and Technology HS PK-PK, 9-
29796 SW Town Center Loop E 97070 503-673-7375
Saskia Dresler, prin. Fax 570-8720
Wilsonville HS 1,000/9-12
6800 SW Wilsonville Rd 97070 503-673-7600
Aaron Downs, prin. Fax 682-0917
Wood MS 700/6-8
11055 SW Wilsonville Rd 97070 503-673-7500
Barbara Soisson, prin. Fax 682-9109

Pioneer Pacific College Post-Sec.
27501 SW Parkway Ave 97070 503-682-3903
Pioneer Pacific College Post-Sec.
27375 SW Parkway Ave 97070 503-682-1862

Winston, Douglas, Pop. 5,205
Winston-Dillard SD 116 1,500/K-12
620 NW Elwood St 97496 541-679-3000
Kevin Miller, supt. Fax 679-4819
www.wdsd.org
Douglas HS 500/9-12
1381 NW Douglas Blvd 97496 541-679-3001
Rob Boye, prin. Fax 679-7284
Winston MS 200/7-8
330 SE Thompson Ave 97496 541-679-3002
David Welker, prin. Fax 679-3026

Woodburn, Marion, Pop. 23,765
Woodburn SD 103 5,400/PK-12
965 N Boones Ferry Rd 97071 503-981-9555
Charles Ransom, supt. Fax 981-8018
www.woodburn.k12.or.us
Academy of International Studies 300/9-12
1785 N Front St 97071 503-980-6100
Victor Vergara, prin. Fax 981-2629
French Prairie MS 600/6-8
1025 N Boones Ferry Rd 97071 971-983-3550
Ricardo Marquez, prin. Fax 981-2724
Valor MS 600/6-8
450 Parr Rd 97071 503-981-2750
Danny Nanez, prin. Fax 981-2790
Wellness Business and Sports S 300/9-12
1785 N Front St 97071 503-980-6150
Casey Woolley, prin. Fax 981-2621
Woodburn Academy of Art/Science & Tech 400/9-12
1785 N Front St 97071 503-980-6200
Geri Federico, prin. Fax 980-6209
Woodburn Arts and Communication Academy 300/9-12
1785 N Front St 97071 503-980-6250
Greg Baisch, prin. Fax 980-6255
Woodburn Success HS 200/Alt
PO Box 583 97071 503-980-6185
Jennifer Dixon, prin. Fax 982-8372

Yamhill, Yamhill, Pop. 999
Yamhill-Carlton SD 1 1,100/K-12
120 N Larch 97148 503-852-6980
Steve Chiovaro, supt. Fax 662-4931
www.ycsd.k12.or.us
Yamhill-Carlton HS 400/9-12
275 N Maple St 97148 503-852-7600
James Orth, prin. Fax 662-3220
Yamhill-Carlton IS 400/5-8
310 E Main St 97148 503-852-7680
Gretchen Brunner, prin. Fax 662-4079

Yoncalla, Douglas, Pop. 1,008
Yoncalla SD 32 300/K-12
PO Box 568 97499 541-849-2782
George Murdock, supt. Fax 849-2190
www.yoncalla.k12.or.us
Yoncalla HS 100/9-12
PO Box 568 97499 541-849-2175
Brian Berry, prin. Fax 849-2669

PENNSYLVANIA

PENNSYLVANIA DEPARTMENT OF EDUCATION
333 Market St Fl 9, Harrisburg 17101-2215
Telephone 717-783-6788
Fax 717-787-7222
Website http://www.education.state.pa.us

Secretary of Education Carolyn Dumaresq

PENNSYLVANIA BOARD OF EDUCATION
333 Market St Fl 10, Harrisburg 17101-2215

Chairperson James Barker

INTERMEDIATE UNITS (IU)

Allegheny IU 3
Dr. Linda Hippert, dir. 412-394-5700
475 Waterfront Dr E Fax 394-5706
Homestead 15120
www.aiu3.net/

Appalachia IU 8
Dr. Joseph Macharola, dir. 814-940-0223
4500 6th Ave, Altoona 16602 Fax 472-5033
www.iu08.org/

ARIN IU 28
Dr. Robert Coad, dir. 724-463-5300
2895 W Pike Rd, Indiana 15701 Fax 463-5315
www.iu28.org

Beaver Valley IU 27
Thomas Zelesnik, dir. 724-774-7800
147 Poplar Ave, Monaca 15061 Fax 774-4751
www.bviu.org/

Berks County IU 14
Dr. John George, dir. 610-987-2248
PO Box 16050, Reading 19612 Fax 987-8400
www.berksiu.org

BLaST IU 17
William Martens, dir. 570-323-8561
PO Box 3609, Williamsport 17701
www.iu17.org

Bucks County IU 22
Barry Galasso Ed.D., dir. 215-348-2940
705 N Shady Retreat Rd Fax 489-7874
Doylestown 18901
www.bciu.k12.pa.us

Capital Area IU 15
Dr. Mary Jane Gales, dir. 717-732-8400
55 Miller St, Summerdale 17093 Fax 732-8421
www.caiu.org

Carbon-Lehigh IU 21
Elaine Eib Ed.D., dir. 610-769-4111
4210 Independence Dr Fax 769-1290
Schnecksville 18078
www.cliu.org

Central IU 10
Dr. Hugh Dwyer, dir. 814-342-0884
345 Link Rd, West Decatur 16878 Fax 342-5137
www.ciu10.com

Central Susquehanna IU 16
Dr. Kevin Singer, dir. 570-523-1155
90 Lawton Ln, Milton 17847 Fax 524-7104
www.csiu.org/

Chester County IU 24
Dr. Joseph O'Brien, dir. 484-237-5000
455 Boot Rd, Downingtown 19335 Fax 237-5154
www.cciu.org/

IU 1
Charles Mahoney, dir. 724-938-3241
1 Intermediate Unit Dr Fax 938-8722
Coal Center 15423
www.iu1.k12.pa.us/

Colonial IU 20
Dr. Charlene Brennan, dir. 610-252-5550
6 Danforth Rd, Easton 18045 Fax 252-5740
www.ciu20.org

Delaware County IU 25
Dr. Lawrence O'Shea, dir. 610-938-9000
200 Yale Ave, Morton 19070 Fax 565-1315
www.dciu.org/

Lancaster-Lebanon IU 13
Dr. Cynthia Burkhart, dir. 717-606-1600
1020 New Holland Ave
Lancaster 17601
www.iu13.org

Lincoln IU 12
Dr. Michael Thew, dir. 717-624-4616
PO Box 70, New Oxford 17350 Fax 624-6519
www.iu12.org

Luzerne IU 18
Dr. Anthony Grieco, dir. 570-287-9681
368 Tioga Ave, Kingston 18704
www.liu18.org/

Midwestern IU 4
Cecilia Yauger, dir. 724-458-6700
453 Maple St, Grove City 16127 Fax 458-5083
www.miu4.k12.pa.us/

Montgomery County IU 23
Dr. Jerry Shiveley, dir. 610-539-8550
1605 W Main St Ste B Fax 539-5973
Norristown 19403
www.mciu.org

Northeastern Educational IU 19
Dr. Clarence Lamanna, dir. 570-876-9200
1200 Line St, Archbald 18403 Fax 876-8660
www.iu19.org

Northwest Tri-County IU 5
Dr. Marjorie Wallace, dir. 814-734-5610
252 Waterford St, Edinboro 16412 Fax 734-5806
www.iu5.org/

Philadelphia IU 26
Thomas Knudsen, dir. 215-400-4000
440 N Broad St, Philadelphia 19130
www.phila.k12.pa.us/

Pittsburgh/Mt. Oliver IU 2
Dr. Linda Lane, dir. 412-224-4580
3816 S Water St Bldg 5
Pittsburgh 15203
www.pmoiu2.k12.pa.us/

Riverview IU 6
Dr. John Cornish, dir. 814-226-7103
270 Mayfield Rd, Clarion 16214 Fax 226-4850
www.riu6.org/

Schuylkill IU 29
Dr. Diane Niederriter, dir. 570-544-9131
PO Box 130, Mar Lin 17951 Fax 544-6412
www.iu29.org/

Seneca Highlands IU 9
Mary Colf, dir. 814-887-5512
PO Box 1566, Smethport 16749 Fax 887-2157
www.iu9.org

Tuscarora IU 11
Richard Daubert, dir. 717-899-7143
2527 US Highway 522 S
Mc Veytown 17051
www.tiu11.org

Westmoreland IU 7
Dr. Luanne Matta, dir. 724-836-2460
102 Equity Dr, Greensburg 15601 Fax 836-1747
wiu.k12.pa.us/

PUBLIC, PRIVATE AND CATHOLIC SECONDARY SCHOOLS

Abington, Montgomery, Pop. 56,600

Abington SD 7,300/K-12
970 Highland Ave 19001 215-884-4700
Amy Sichel Ph.D., supt. Fax 881-2545
www.abington.k12.pa.us

Abington JHS 1,700/7-9
2056 Susquehanna Rd 19001 215-884-4700
Dr. Mark Pellico, prin. Fax 885-0293

Abington SHS 1,900/10-12
900 Highland Ave 19001 215-884-4700
Angelo Berrios, prin. Fax 886-1871

Abington Memorial Hospital Post-Sec.
1200 Old York Rd 19001 215-576-2000

Penn State Abington Post-Sec.
1600 Woodland Rd 19001 215-881-7300

Albion, Erie, Pop. 1,497

Northwestern SD 1,600/K-12
100 Harthan Way 16401 814-756-9400
Dr. Karen Downie, supt. Fax 756-9414
www.nwsd.org

Northwestern HS 600/9-12
200 Harthan Way 16401 814-756-9400
Daniel Shreve, prin. Fax 756-9411

Northwestern MS 400/6-8
150 Harthan Way 16401 814-756-9400
Sandi Shaner, prin. Fax 756-9415

Alexandria, Huntingdon, Pop. 344

Juniata Valley SD 800/K-12
PO Box 318 16611 814-669-9150
David Christopher, supt. Fax 669-4492
www.jvsd.org

Juniata Valley JSHS 400/7-12
PO Box 318 16611 814-669-4401
Michael Estep, prin. Fax 669-4421

Aliquippa, Beaver, Pop. 9,176

Aliquippa SD 1,200/K-12
800 21st St 15001 724-857-7500
David Wytiaz, supt. Fax 857-3404
www.quipsd.org

Aliquippa JSHS 500/7-12
100 Harding Ave 15001 724-857-7500
Alvin Gipson, prin. Fax 857-7560

Hopewell Area SD 2,500/K-12
2354 Brodhead Rd 15001 724-375-6691
Dr. Charles Reina, supt. Fax 375-0942
www.hopewell.k12.pa.us

Hopewell HS 900/9-12
1215 Longvue Ave 15001 724-378-8565
Michael Allison, prin. Fax 378-4952

Hopewell JHS 700/5-8
2354 Brodhead Rd 15001 724-375-7765
Edward Katkich, prin. Fax 378-2594

Allentown, Lehigh, Pop. 115,413

Allentown CSD 16,600/PK-12
PO Box 328 18105 484-765-4000
C. Russ Mayo, supt. Fax 765-4239
www.allentownsd.org/

Allen HS 2,900/9-12
126 N 17th St 18104 484-765-5000
Shannon Mayfield, prin. Fax 765-5010

Dieruff HS 1,800/9-12
815 N Irving St 18109 484-765-5500
Susan Bocian, prin. Fax 765-5512

Harrison-Morton MS 900/6-8
137 N 2nd St 18101 484-765-5700
Daria Custer, prin. Fax 765-5715

Raub MS 900/6-8
102 S Saint Cloud St 18104 484-765-5300
Susan Elliott, prin. Fax 765-5310

South Mountain MS 1,100/6-8
709 W Emaus Ave 18103 484-765-4300
Frank Derrick, prin. Fax 765-4310

Trexler MS 900/6-8
851 N 15th St 18102 484-765-4600
Steve Serensits, prin. Fax 765-4610

Parkland SD 9,300/K-12
1210 Springhouse Rd 18104 610-351-5503
Richard Sniscak, supt. Fax 351-5509
www.parklandsd.org

Parkland HS 3,200/9-12
2700 N Cedar Crest Blvd 18104 610-351-5600
James Moniz, prin. Fax 351-5656

Springhouse MS 1,100/6-8
1200 Springhouse Rd 18104 610-351-5700
Robert Holmes, prin. Fax 351-5748

Other Schools – See Orefield

Salisbury Township SD 1,500/K-12
1140 Salisbury Rd 18103 610-797-2062
Dr. Louise Beauchemin, supt. Fax 791-9983
www.stsd.org/

Salisbury HS 400/9-12
500 E Montgomery St 18103 610-797-4107
Heather Morningstar, prin. Fax 797-1972

Salisbury MS 400/6-8
3301 Devonshire Rd 18103 610-791-0830
Robert Cassidy, prin. Fax 797-9648

Allentown Central Catholic HS 900/9-12
301 N 4th St 18102 610-437-4601
Dennis Nemes, prin. Fax 437-6760
Allentown School of Cosmetology Post-Sec.
1921 Union Blvd 18109 610-437-4626
Blackstone Career Institute Post-Sec.
PO Box 3717 18106 610-871-0031
Cedar Crest College Post-Sec.
100 College Dr 18104 610-437-4471
Lehigh Valley Hospital & Health Network Post-Sec.
PO Box 7017 18105 610-402-2556
Lincoln Technical Institute Post-Sec.
5151 W Tilghman St 18104 610-398-5300
McCann School of Business & Technology Post-Sec.
2200 N Irving St 18109 484-223-4600
Muhlenberg College Post-Sec.
2400 Chew St 18104 484-664-3100
Pennsylvania School of Business Post-Sec.
406 Hamilton St 18101 610-841-3333
Sacred Heart Hospital Post-Sec.
421 Chew St 18102 610-776-4745
Welder Training & Testing Institute Post-Sec.
729 E Highland St 18109 610-437-9720

Allison Park, Allegheny, Pop. 21,377
Area Vocational Technical School
Supt. — None
Beattie Career Center Vo/Tech
9600 Babcock Blvd 15101 412-366-2800
Eric Heasley, prin. Fax 366-9600

Hampton Township SD 3,100/K-12
4591 School Dr 15101 412-486-6000
Dr. John Hoover, supt.
www.ht-sd.org/
Hampton HS 1,100/9-12
2929 McCully Rd 15101 412-492-6376
Jeffrey Finch, prin. Fax 486-7050
Hampton MS 800/6-8
4589 School Dr 15101 412-492-6356
Dr. Eric Stennett, prin. Fax 487-7544

Altoona, Blair, Pop. 45,425
Altoona Area SD 8,000/K-12
1415 6th Ave 16602 814-946-8211
Dennis Murray M.Ed., supt. Fax 946-8226
www.aasdcat.com/aasd/
Altoona Area JHS 1,800/7-9
1400 7th Ave 16602 814-381-7500
Lori Mangan, prin. Fax 381-7501
Altoona Area SHS 1,700/10-12
1415 6th Ave 16602 814-946-8273
Patricia Burlingame, prin. Fax 946-8272
Kimmel Alternative S 50/Alt
900 S Jaggard St 16602 814-946-8246
Paul Hasson, prin. Fax 946-8402

Area Vocational Technical School
Supt. — None
Greater Altoona CTC Vo/Tech
1500 4th Ave 16602 814-946-8450
Dr. Lanny Ross, prin. Fax 946-8351

Altoona Beauty School Post-Sec.
1528 Valley View Blvd 16602 814-942-3141
Altoona Hospital Post-Sec.
620 Howard Ave 16601 814-946-2223
Bishop Guilfoyle Catholic HS 300/9-12
2400 Pleasant Valley Blvd 16602 814-944-4014
Joan Donnelly, prin. Fax 944-8695
Great Commission S 200/PK-12
1100 6th Ave 16602 814-942-9710
Kimberly Salyards, supt. Fax 942-7147
Penn State Altoona Post-Sec.
3000 Ivyside Park 16601 814-949-5000
Pruonto's Hair Design Institute Post-Sec.
705 12th St 16602 814-944-4494
South Hills School of Business & Tech. Post-Sec.
541 58th St 16602 814-944-6134
YTI Career Institute Post-Sec.
2900 Fairway Dr 16602 814-944-5643

Alverton, Westmoreland
Southmoreland SD
Supt. — See Scottdale
Southmoreland HS 600/9-12
PO Box A 15612 724-887-2010
Dan Krofcheck, prin. Fax 887-2980

Ambler, Montgomery, Pop. 6,216
Wissahickon SD 4,500/K-12
601 Knight Rd 19002 215-619-8000
Judith Clark, supt. Fax 619-8002
wsdweb.org
Wissahickon HS 1,500/9-12
521 Houston Rd 19002 215-619-8112
Lyn Fields, prin. Fax 619-8113
Wissahickon MS 1,100/6-8
500 Houston Rd 19002 215-619-8110
Dr. Kevin McAneny, prin. Fax 619-8111

Ambler Beauty Academy Post-Sec.
50 E Butler Ave 19002 215-643-5994

Ambridge, Beaver, Pop. 6,737
Ambridge Area SD 2,800/K-12
901 Duss Ave 15003 724-266-2833
Dr. Erwin Weischedel, supt. Fax 266-3981
www.ambridge.k12.pa.us
Ambridge Area HS 800/9-12
909 Duss Ave 15003 724-266-2833
Alan Fritz, prin. Fax 266-5056
Other Schools – See Freedom

Trinity School for Ministry Post-Sec.
311 11th St 15003 724-266-3838

Annville, Lebanon, Pop. 4,714
Annville-Cleona SD 1,600/K-12
520 S White Oak St 17003 717-867-7600
Dr. Steven E. Houser, supt. Fax 867-7610
www.acschools.org
Annville-Cleona JSHS 800/7-12
500 S White Oak St 17003 717-867-7700
David Wright, prin. Fax 867-7712

Lebanon Valley College Post-Sec.
101 N College Ave 17003 717-867-6100

Apollo, Armstrong, Pop. 1,610
Apollo-Ridge SD 1,400/K-12
1825 State Route 56 15613 724-478-6000
Dr. Matthew E. Curci, supt. Fax 478-1149
www.apolloridge.com/
Other Schools – See Spring Church

Orchard Hills Christian Academy 50/K-12
385 Kings Rd 15613 724-478-3455
Sandra Cornell, prin. Fax 478-1174

Archbald, Lackawanna, Pop. 6,931
Valley View SD 2,600/K-12
1 Columbus Dr 18403 570-876-5080
Donald Kanavy, supt. Fax 876-6365
www.valleyviewsd.org/
Valley View HS 800/9-12
1 Columbus Dr 18403 570-876-4110
Peter Chapla, prin. Fax 803-0217
Valley View MS 600/6-8
1 Columbus Dr 18403 570-876-6461
Craig Sweeney, prin. Fax 803-0276

Ardmore, Montgomery, Pop. 12,170
Lower Merion SD 7,100/K-12
301 E Montgomery Ave 19003 610-645-1800
Dr. Christopher McGinley, supt. Fax 645-9772
www.lmsd.org
Lower Merion HS 1,300/9-12
315 E Montgomery Ave 19003 610-645-1810
Sean Hughes, prin. Fax 645-9657
Other Schools – See Bala Cynwyd, Narberth, Rosemont

Armagh, Indiana, Pop. 121
United SD 1,300/PK-12
10780 Route 56 Hwy E 15920 814-446-5618
Dr. Barbara Parkins, supt. Fax 446-6615
www.unitedsd.net/
United JSHS 600/7-12
10780 Route 56 Hwy E 15920 814-446-5615
Michael Worthington, prin. Fax 446-6615

Armbrust, Westmoreland

Armbrust Christian Academy 100/PK-12
PO Box 115 15616 724-925-3830
Jonathan Priest, prin. Fax 925-2523

Arnold, Westmoreland, Pop. 4,917
New Kensington Arnold SD
Supt. — See New Kensington
Valley MS 500/6-8
1701 Alcoa Dr 15068 724-335-2511
Patrick Nee, prin. Fax 339-5532

Ashland, Schuylkill, Pop. 2,790
North Schuylkill SD 1,900/K-12
15 Academy Ln 17921 570-874-0466
Dr. Andrew Smarkanic, supt. Fax 874-3334
www.northschuylkill.net
North Schuylkill JSHS 900/7-12
15 Academy Ln 17921 570-874-0495
Christian Temchatin, prin. Fax 874-1531

Aston, Delaware
Area Vocational Technical School
Supt. — None
Delaware County Technical HS Aston Vo/Tech
100 Crozerville Rd 19014 610-459-3050
Christopher Moritzen, prin.

Chichester SD 3,400/K-12
401 Cherry Tree Rd 19014 610-485-6881
Barbara DiMarino, supt. Fax 485-3086
www.chichestersd.org
Other Schools – See Boothwyn

Penn-Delco SD 3,400/K-12
2821 Concord Rd 19014 610-497-6300
Dr. George Steinhoff, supt. Fax 497-1798
www.pdsd.org
Northley MS 800/6-8
2801 Concord Rd 19014 610-497-6300
Lanny Blair, prin. Fax 497-5737
Sun Valley HS 1,100/9-12
2881 Pancoast Ave 19014 610-497-6300
Pete Donaghy, prin. Fax 497-2863

Neumann University Post-Sec.
1 Neumann Dr 19014 610-459-0905

Atglen, Chester, Pop. 1,387
Octorara Area SD 2,200/K-12
228 Highland Rd Ste 1 19310 610-593-8238
Dr. Thomas Newcome, supt. Fax 593-6425
www.octorara.k12.pa.us
Octorara Area JSHS 900/7-12
226 Highland Rd 19310 610-593-8238
Scott Rohrer, prin. Fax 593-4945

Athens, Bradford, Pop. 3,332
Athens Area SD 1,700/K-12
204 Willow St 18810 570-888-7766
Diane Place, supt. Fax 882-6250
www.athensasd.org
Athens Area HS 500/9-12
401 W Frederick St 18810 570-888-7766
Beth Schulze, prin. Fax 888-4038

Rowe MS 200/6-8
116 W Pine St Ste 1 18810 570-888-7766
Scott Webster, prin. Fax 888-9536

Austin, Potter, Pop. 562
Austin Area SD 200/PK-12
138 Costello Ave 16720 814-647-8603
Jerome Sasala, supt. Fax 647-8869
www.austinsd.net
Austin Area HS 100/7-12
138 Costello Ave 16720 814-647-8603
Jerome Sasala, prin. Fax 647-8869

Avella, Washington, Pop. 795
Avella Area SD 600/K-12
1000 Avella Rd 15312 724-356-2218
Dr. Janell Logue-Belden, supt. Fax 356-2207
www.avella.k12.pa.us
Avella Area JSHS 300/7-12
1000 Avella Rd 15312 724-356-2216
Thomas Graham, prin. Fax 356-7905

Avis, Clinton, Pop. 1,476

Walnut Street Christian S 100/PK-12
PO Box 616 17721 570-753-3400
Kathy Gottschall, prin. Fax 753-5728

Baden, Beaver, Pop. 4,097

Quigley HS 200/9-12
200 Quigley Dr 15005 724-869-2188
Rita McCormick, prin. Fax 869-3091

Bala Cynwyd, Montgomery, Pop. 8,000
Lower Merion SD
Supt. — See Ardmore
Bala Cynwyd MS 800/6-8
510 Bryn Mawr Ave 19004 610-645-1480
Jason Potten, prin. Fax 664-2798

Bangor, Northampton, Pop. 5,192
Bangor Area SD 3,300/K-12
123 Five Points Richmond Rd 18013 610-588-2163
Dr. Frank J. DeFelice, supt. Fax 599-7040
www.bangor.k12.pa.us
Bangor Area HS 1,100/9-12
187 Five Points Richmond Rd 18013 610-599-7011
Tami Gary, prin. Fax 599-7043
Bangor Area MS 500/7-8
401 Five Points Richmond Rd 18013 610-599-7012
Allison Tucker, prin. Fax 599-7045

Pius X HS 300/7-12
580 3rd Ave 18013 610-588-3291
Anthony Ingenito Ed.D., prin. Fax 599-3048

Bartonsville, Monroe
Area Vocational Technical School
Supt. — None
Monroe Career & Tech Institute Vo/Tech
194 Laurel Lake Rd 18321 570-629-2001
Dr. Thomas Rushton, dir. Fax 629-9698

Beaver, Beaver, Pop. 4,471
Beaver Area SD 2,000/K-12
855 2nd St 15009 724-774-4010
Dr. John Hansen, supt. Fax 774-8770
www.basd.k12.pa.us/
Beaver Area HS 700/9-12
Gypsy Glen Rd 15009 724-774-0251
David Zupsic, prin. Fax 774-3926
Beaver Area MS 300/7-8
Gypsy Glen Rd 15009 724-774-0253
Jeff Beltz, prin. Fax 774-3926

Medical Center of Beaver County Post-Sec.
1000 Dutch Ridge Rd 15009 724-728-7000

Beaver Falls, Beaver, Pop. 8,590
Big Beaver Falls Area SD 1,700/K-12
1503 8th Ave 15010 724-843-3470
Dr. Donna Nugent, supt. Fax 843-2360
www.tigerweb.org
Beaver Falls Area HS 600/9-12
1701 8th Ave 15010 724-843-7470
Mary Beth Leeman, prin. Fax 843-0892
Beaver Falls MS 300/6-8
1601 8th Ave 15010 724-846-5470
Thomas House, prin. Fax 846-2579

Blackhawk SD 2,500/K-12
500 Blackhawk Rd 15010 724-846-6600
Dr. Michelle Miller, supt. Fax 846-2021
www.bsd.k12.pa.us
Blackhawk JSHS 1,000/8-12
500 Blackhawk Rd 15010 724-846-9600
Scott Nelson, prin. Fax 891-7113

Beaver County Christian HS 100/9-12
510 37th St 15010 724-843-3002
Mary Lou Capan, prin. Fax 843-5224
Beaver Falls Beauty Academy Post-Sec.
720 13th St 15010 724-843-7700
Geneva College Post-Sec.
3200 College Ave 15010 724-846-5100

Bedford, Bedford, Pop. 2,806
Bedford Area SD 1,800/K-12
330 E John St 15522 814-623-4290
Dr. Allen Sell, supt. Fax 623-4299
www.bedford.k12.pa.us
Bedford HS 600/9-12
330 E John St 15522 814-623-4250
Kyle Kane, prin. Fax 623-4265
Bedford MS 400/6-8
440 E Watson St 15522 814-623-4200
Kevin Windows, prin. Fax 623-4214

Bellefonte, Centre, Pop. 6,107
Bellefonte Area SD 2,900/K-12
318 N Allegheny St 16823 814-355-4814
Dr. Cheryl Potteiger, supt. Fax 353-5342
www.basd.net
Bellefonte Area HS 1,000/9-12
830 E Bishop St 16823 814-355-4833
Jennifer Brown, prin. Fax 353-5320
Bellefonte Area MS 600/6-8
100 N School St 16823 814-355-5466
Sommer Garman, prin. Fax 353-5350

Belle Vernon, Fayette, Pop. 1,081
Belle Vernon Area SD 2,700/K-12
270 Crest Ave 15012 724-808-2500
Dr. John Wilkinson, supt. Fax 929-5598
www.bellevernonarea.net/bvasd/site/default.asp
Belle Vernon Area HS 900/9-12
425 Crest Ave 15012 724-808-2500
Gregory Zborovancik, prin.
Bellmar MS, 500 Perry Ave 15012 300/6-8
John Grice, prin. 724-808-2500
Rostraver MS, 250 Crest Ave 15012 300/6-8
Dr. John Folmar, prin. 724-808-2500

Belleville, Mifflin, Pop. 1,819

Belleville Mennonite S 200/PK-12
4105 Front Mountain Rd 17004 717-935-2184
Starla Fogleman, supt. Fax 935-5641

Bellwood, Blair, Pop. 1,814
Bellwood-Antis SD 1,300/K-12
300 Martin St 16617 814-742-2271
Dr. G. Brian Toth, supt. Fax 742-9049
moss.blwd.k12.pa.us
Bellwood-Antis HS 400/9-12
400 Martin St 16617 814-742-2274
Lisa Hartsock, prin. Fax 742-9817
Bellwood-Antis MS 400/5-8
400 Martin St 16617 814-742-2273
Donald Wagner, prin. Fax 742-9817

Bensalem, Bucks, Pop. 59,700
Bensalem Township SD 6,100/K-12
3000 Donallen Dr 19020 215-750-2800
Dr. David Baugh, supt. Fax 359-0181
www.bensalemsd.org/
Bensalem HS 1,900/9-12
4319 Hulmeville Rd 19020 215-750-2800
Stephen Brandt, prin. Fax 244-2970
Shafer MS 600/7-8
3333 Hulmeville Rd 19020 215-750-2800
William Incollingo, prin. Fax 244-2964
Snyder MS 400/7-8
3330 Hulmeville Rd 19020 215-750-2800
Thomas Evert, prin. Fax 244-2851

Everest Institute Post-Sec.
3050 Tillman Dr 19020 267-233-2900
Holy Family University Post-Sec.
1311 Bristol Pike 19020 215-637-7700
Holy Ghost Prep S 500/9-12
2429 Bristol Pike 19020 215-639-2102
Fr. Jeffrey Duaime, pres. Fax 639-4225

Bentleyville, Washington, Pop. 2,539
Bentworth SD 1,200/K-12
150 Bearcat Dr 15314 724-239-2861
Charles Baker, supt. Fax 239-2865
bentworth.org
Bentworth HS 400/9-12
75 Bearcat Dr 15314 724-239-5911
George Lammay, prin. Fax 239-4010
Bentworth MS 400/5-8
563 Lincoln Ave 15314 724-239-4431
David Schreiber, prin. Fax 239-5889

Benton, Columbia, Pop. 821
Benton Area SD 700/K-12
600 Green Acres Rd 17814 570-925-6651
Penny Lenig-Zerby, supt. Fax 925-6973
www.bentonsd.k12.pa.us/
Benton Area MSHS 300/7-12
400 Park St 17814 570-925-2651
Fax 925-0956

Berlin, Somerset, Pop. 2,084
Berlin Brothersvalley SD 900/K-12
1025 Main St 15530 814-267-4621
Dwayne Northcraft, supt. Fax 267-6060
www.bbsd.com/
Berlin Brothersvalley HS 300/9-12
1025 Main St 15530 814-267-4622
William Deal, prin. Fax 267-6060
Berlin Brothersvalley MS 300/5-8
1025 Main St 15530 814-267-6931
Martin Mudry, prin. Fax 267-6060

Bernville, Berks, Pop. 942
Tulpehocken Area SD
Supt. — See Bethel
Tulpehocken Area JSHS 800/7-12
430 New Schaefferstown Rd 19506 610-488-6286
Don Jones, prin. Fax 488-7976

Berwick, Columbia, Pop. 10,321
Berwick Area SD 3,000/K-12
500 Line St 18603 570-759-6400
Wayne Brookhart, supt. Fax 759-6439
www.berwicksd.org
Berwick Area HS 900/9-12
1100 Fowler Ave 18603 570-759-6400
Robert Croop, prin. Fax 759-6466
Berwick Area MS 800/6-8
1100 Evergreen Dr 18603 570-759-6400
Christopher Rivera, prin. Fax 759-7978

Berwyn, Chester, Pop. 3,583
Tredyffrin-Easttown SD
Supt. — See Wayne
Conestoga HS 2,000/9-12
200 Irish Rd 19312 610-240-1000
Dr. Amy Meisinger, prin. Fax 240-1055
Tredyffrin-Easttown MS 1,000/5-8
801 Conestoga Rd 19312 610-240-1200
Mark Cataldi, prin. Fax 240-1225

Bessemer, Lawrence, Pop. 1,097
Mohawk Area SD 1,500/K-12
PO Box 25 16112 724-667-7723
Kathleen Kwolek, supt. Fax 667-0602
www.mohawk.k12.pa.us
Mohawk JSHS 800/7-12
PO Box 25 16112 724-667-7782
Raymond Omer, prin. Fax 667-0602

Bethel, Berks, Pop. 495
Tulpehocken Area SD 1,500/K-12
27 Rehrersburg Rd 19507 717-933-4611
Edward Albert Ed.D., supt. Fax 933-9724
www.tulpehocken.org
Other Schools – See Bernville

Bethel Park, Allegheny, Pop. 32,036
Bethel Park SD 4,700/K-12
301 Church Rd 15102 412-854-8402
Nancy Rose, supt. Fax 854-8430
www.bpsd.org
Bethel Park HS 1,700/9-12
309 Church Rd 15102 412-854-8581
Zeb Jansante, prin. Fax 854-8552
Independence MS 700/7-8
2807 Bethel Church Rd 15102 412-854-8677
David Muench, prin. Fax 854-8732

Hillcrest Christian Academy 300/PK-11
2500 Bethel Church Rd 15102 412-854-4040
Colleen Kelly, prin. Fax 854-4051

Bethlehem, Northampton, Pop. 73,573
Area Vocational Technical School
Supt. — None
Bethlehem AVTS Vo/Tech
3300 Chester Ave 18020 610-866-8013
Brian Williams, dir. Fax 866-6124

Bethlehem Area SD 14,700/K-12
1516 Sycamore St 18017 610-861-0500
Dr. Joseph J. Roy, supt. Fax 807-5599
www.beth.k12.pa.us
Broughal MS 600/6-8
114 W Morton St 18015 610-866-5041
Edward Docalovich, prin. Fax 807-5909
East Hills MS 1,100/6-8
2005 Chester Rd 18017 610-867-0541
David Horvath, prin. Fax 807-5941
Freedom HS 2,000/9-12
3149 Chester Ave 18020 610-867-5843
Michael LaPorta, prin. Fax 867-7360
Liberty HS 2,900/9-12
1115 Linden St 18018 610-691-7200
Harrison Bailey, prin. Fax 691-0741
Nitschmann MS 900/6-8
909 W Union Blvd 18018 610-866-5781
Jacqueline Santanasto, prin. Fax 866-1435
Northeast MS 900/6-8
1170 Fernwood St 18018 610-868-8581
Joseph Rahs, prin. Fax 807-5997

Bethlehem Catholic HS 800/9-12
2133 Madison Ave 18017 610-866-0791
John Petruzzelli M.Ed., prin. Fax 866-4429
International Inst Restorative Practices Post-Sec.
PO Box 229 18016 610-807-9221
Lehigh University Post-Sec.
27 Memorial Dr W 18015 610-758-3000
Moravian Academy MS 200/6-8
11 W Market St 18018 610-866-6677
George King, hdmstr. Fax 866-6337
Moravian Academy - Upper S Campus 300/9-12
4313 Green Pond Rd 18020 610-691-1600
George King, hdmstr. Fax 691-3354
Moravian College Post-Sec.
1200 Main St 18018 610-861-1300
Moravian Theological Seminary Post-Sec.
60 W Locust St 18018 610-861-1516
Northampton Community College Post-Sec.
3835 Green Pond Rd 18020 610-861-5300
St. Luke's Hospital Post-Sec.
801 Ostrum St 18015 610-954-3400
Triangle Tech Post-Sec.
3184 Airport Rd 18017 610-266-2910

Biglerville, Adams, Pop. 1,195
Upper Adams SD 1,700/K-12
PO Box 847 17307 717-677-7191
Dr. Wesley Doll, supt. Fax 677-9807
www.uasd.k12.pa.us
Biglerville HS 500/9-12
161 N Main St 17307 717-677-7191
Richard Sterner, prin. Fax 677-0142
Upper Adams MS 300/7-8
161 N Main St 17307 717-677-7191
David Zinn, prin. Fax 677-0219

Birdsboro, Berks, Pop. 5,083
Daniel Boone Area SD 3,900/K-12
PO Box 490 19508 610-582-6140
Dr. Gary Otto, supt. Fax 582-0059
www.dboone.org
Boone Area HS 1,200/9-12
PO Box 450 19508 610-582-6100
Thomas Hankel, prin. Fax 582-5400
Other Schools – See Douglassville

Berks Christian S 100/PK-12
926 Philadelphia Ter 19508 610-582-1000
Philip Warner, admin. Fax 404-0126

Blairsville, Indiana, Pop. 3,366
Blairsville-Saltsburg SD 1,700/K-12
102 School Ln 15717 724-459-5500
Tammy Whitfield Ed.D., supt. Fax 459-9209
www.b-ssd.org
Blairsville HS 400/9-12
100 School Ln 15717 724-459-8882
Joseph Baker, prin. Fax 459-3392
Blairsville MS 300/6-8
104 School Ln 15717 724-459-8880
Jeffrey Soles, prin. Fax 459-0213
Other Schools – See Saltsburg

WyoTech - Blairsville Post-Sec.
500 Innovation Dr 15717 724-459-9500

Bloomsburg, Columbia, Pop. 14,675
Area Vocational Technical School
Supt. — None
Columbia-Montour AVTS Vo/Tech
5050 Sweppenheiser Dr 17815 570-784-8040
William Forsythe, supt. Fax 784-3565

Bloomsburg Area SD 1,400/K-12
728 E 5th St 17815 570-784-5000
Dr. Cosmas Curry, supt. Fax 387-8832
bloomsburgasd.schoolwires.com
Bloomsburg Area HS 400/9-12
1200 Railroad St 17815 570-784-6100
Daniel Bonomo M.Ed., prin. Fax 387-3492
Bloomsburg Area MS 200/6-8
1100 Railroad St 17815 570-784-9100
Marc Freeman, prin. Fax 387-3491

Central Columbia SD 2,000/K-12
4777 Old Berwick Rd 17815 570-784-2850
Harry Mathias, supt. Fax 387-0192
www.ccsd.cc
Central Columbia HS 600/9-12
4777 Old Berwick Rd 17815 570-784-2850
Jeffrey Groshek, prin. Fax 784-0863
Central Columbia MS 600/5-8
4777 Old Berwick Rd 17815 570-784-2850
Chad Heintzelman, prin. Fax 784-4935

Bloomsburg University of Pennsylvania Post-Sec.
400 E 2nd St 17815 570-389-4000
Columbia County Christian S 200/PK-12
123 Schoolhouse Rd 17815 570-784-2977
Gary Heinke, hdmstr. Fax 784-1755

Blossburg, Tioga, Pop. 1,532
Southern Tioga SD 2,000/K-12
241 Main St 16912 570-638-2183
Keith Yarger, supt. Fax 638-3512
www.southerntioga.org
North Penn JSHS 300/7-12
300 Morris St 16912 570-638-2158
Dr. Albert Lindner, prin. Fax 638-2150
Other Schools – See Liberty, Mansfield

Blue Bell, Montgomery, Pop. 6,001

Montgomery County Community College Post-Sec.
340 Dekalb Pike 19422 215-641-6300
Reformed Episcopal Seminary Post-Sec.
826 2nd Ave 19422 610-292-9852

Boalsburg, Centre, Pop. 3,655

St. Joseph's Catholic Academy 9-12
901 Boalsburg Pike 16827 814-808-6118
Douglas Bleggi, prin. Fax 808-6170

Boiling Springs, Cumberland, Pop. 3,185
South Middleton SD 2,200/K-12
4 Forge Rd 17007 717-258-6484
Patricia Sanker Ed.D., supt. Fax 258-1214
www.bubblers.k12.pa.us
Boiling Springs HS 700/9-12
4 Forge Rd 17007 717-258-6484
Joseph Mancuso, prin. Fax 258-5014
Yellow Breeches MS 500/6-8
4 Forge Rd 17007 717-258-6484
Jesse R. White, prin. Fax 258-0301

Boothwyn, Delaware, Pop. 4,830
Chichester SD
Supt. — See Aston
Chichester HS 1,100/9-12
3333 Chichester Ave 19061 610-485-6881
Nancy Alexander, prin. Fax 485-6510
Chichester MS 1,000/5-8
925 Meetinghouse Rd 19061 610-485-6881
Ken Salamone, prin. Fax 494-3064

Boswell, Somerset, Pop. 1,262
North Star SD 1,200/K-12
1200 Morris Ave 15531 814-629-5631
Shawn Kovac, supt. Fax 629-6181
district.nscougars.com/
North Star HS 400/9-12
400 Ohio St 15531 814-629-6651
Louis Lepley, prin. Fax 629-9346
Other Schools – See Stoystown

Boyertown, Berks, Pop. 4,017
Boyertown Area SD 7,100/K-12
911 Montgomery Ave 19512 610-367-6031
Dion Betts Ed.D., supt. Fax 369-7620
www.boyertownasd.org
Boyertown Area JHS West 800/7-9
380 S Madison St 19512 610-369-7471
Gregory Galtere, prin. Fax 369-7476

Boyertown Area SHS 1,700/10-12
120 N Monroe St 19512 610-369-7435
Brett Cooper, prin. Fax 369-7359
Other Schools – See Gilbertsville

Bradford, McKean, Pop. 8,658
Bradford Area SD 2,700/PK-12
PO Box 375 16701 814-362-3841
Katharine Pude, supt. Fax 362-2552
www.bradfordareaschools.org
Bradford Area HS 900/9-12
81 Interstate Pkwy 16701 814-362-3845
David Ray, prin. Fax 362-1765
Fretz MS 600/6-8
140 Lorana Ave 16701 814-362-3500
Tina Slaven, prin. Fax 362-1812

Bradford Regional Medical Center Post-Sec.
116 Interstate Pkwy 16701 814-362-8292
University of Pittsburgh at Bradford Post-Sec.
300 Campus Dr 16701 814-362-7500

Bridgeville, Allegheny, Pop. 5,046
Chartiers Valley SD
Supt. — See Pittsburgh
Chartiers Valley HS 1,100/9-12
50 Thoms Run Rd 15017 412-429-2273
Dr. Amy Wodnicki, prin. Fax 276-5808
Chartiers Valley MS 800/6-8
50 Thoms Run Rd 15017 412-429-2223
John Ackermann, prin. Fax 429-2226

Bristol, Bucks, Pop. 9,494
Bristol Borough SD 1,000/PK-12
1776 Farragut Ave 19007 215-781-1000
Gregory Wright, supt. Fax 781-1012
www.bbsd.org/
Bristol HS, 1801 Wilson Ave 19007 400/9-12
Dr. Thomas Shaffer, prin. 215-781-1000

Bristol Township SD
Supt. — See Levittown
Roosevelt MS 500/7-8
1001 New Rodgers Rd 19007 215-788-0436
Ruth Geisel, prin. Fax 788-2629

Pennco Tech Post-Sec.
3815 Otter St 19007 215-785-0111

Brockway, Jefferson, Pop. 2,057
Brockway Area SD 1,000/K-12
40 North St 15824 814-265-8411
Daniel Hawkins, supt. Fax 265-8498
www.brockway.k12.pa.us/
Brockway Area JSHS 500/7-12
100 Alexander St 15824 814-265-8414
Denise Carlini, prin. Fax 265-8413

Brodheadsville, Monroe, Pop. 1,770
Pleasant Valley SD 4,300/K-12
2233 Route 115 Ste 100 18322 570-402-1000
Carole Geary, supt. Fax 992-7275
www.pvbears.org
Pleasant Valley HS 1,600/9-12
1671 Route 209 18322 570-402-1000
John Gress, prin. Fax 992-7733
Pleasant Valley MS 500/7-8
2233 Route 115 18322 570-402-1000
Howard Drake, prin. Fax 992-6968

Brookhaven, Delaware, Pop. 7,890

Christian Academy 400/K-12
4301 Chandler Dr 19015 610-872-7600
Dr. Timothy Sierer, hdmstr. Fax 876-2173

Brookville, Jefferson, Pop. 3,884
Brookville Area SD 1,600/K-12
PO Box 479 15825 814-849-1100
Sandra Craft, supt. Fax 849-6842
www.basd.us
Brookville Area JSHS 700/7-12
PO Box 479 15825 814-849-1106
Robert Rocco, prin. Fax 849-1117

Broomall, Delaware, Pop. 10,688
Area Vocational Technical School
Supt. — None
Delaware County Technical HS - Marple Vo/Tech
85 N Malin Rd 19008 610-423-7000
Dr. Philip Lachimia, dir.

Marple Newtown SD
Supt. — See Newtown Square
Paxon Hollow MS 900/6-8
815 Paxon Hollow Rd 19008 610-359-4320
Stephen Subers Ed.D., prin. Fax 353-4061

Kaplan Career Institute Post-Sec.
1991 Sproul Rd Ste 42 19008 610-353-7630

Brownstown, Lancaster, Pop. 741
Area Vocational Technical School
Supt. — None
Lancaster County CTC-Brownstown Vo/Tech
PO Box 519 17508 717-859-5100
Margaret Roth, prin. Fax 859-4529

Brownsville, Fayette, Pop. 2,220
Brownsville Area SD 1,500/K-12
5 Falcon Dr 15417 724-785-2021
Dr. Philip Savini, supt. Fax 785-6988
www.basd.org
Brownsville Area HS 600/9-12
1 Falcon Dr 15417 724-785-8200
Justin Dellarose, prin. Fax 785-8930
Brownsville MS 300/7-8
3 Falcon Dr 15417 724-785-2155
Vincent Nesser, prin. Fax 785-2502

Bryn Athyn, Montgomery, Pop. 1,347

Academy of the New Church-Boys 100/9-12
PO Box 707 19009 267-502-2500
Jeremy Irwin, prin. Fax 502-2617
Academy of the New Church Girls S 100/9-12
PO Box 707 19009 267-502-4200
Susan Odhner, prin. Fax 502-2617
Bryn Athyn College Post-Sec.
PO Box 717 19009 267-502-6000

Bryn Mawr, Montgomery, Pop. 3,847

American College Post-Sec.
270 S Bryn Mawr Ave 19010 610-526-1000
Baldwin S 600/PK-12
701 Montgomery Ave 19010 610-525-2700
Sally Powell, hdmstr. Fax 525-7534
Barrack Hebrew Academy 300/6-12
272 S Bryn Mawr Ave 19010 610-922-2300
Sharon Levin, head sch Fax 922-2301
Bryn Mawr College Post-Sec.
101 N Merion Ave 19010 610-526-5000
Country Day S of the Sacred Heart 300/PK-12
480 S Bryn Mawr Ave 19010 610-527-3915
Sr. Anita MacDonald Ph.D., hdmstr. Fax 527-0942
Harcum College Post-Sec.
750 Montgomery Ave 19010 610-525-4100
Shipley S 800/PK-12
814 Yarrow St 19010 610-525-4300
Dr. Steven Piltch, hdmstr. Fax 525-5082

Burgettstown, Washington, Pop. 1,365
Burgettstown Area SD 1,400/K-12
100 Bavington Rd 15021 724-947-8136
David Palmer, supt. Fax 947-8143
www.burgettstown.k12.pa.us
Burgettstown MSHS 800/6-12
104 Bavington Rd 15021 724-947-8100
Michael Wright, prin. Fax 947-3325

Tri State Christian Academy 100/PK-12
750 Steubenville Pike 15021 724-947-8722
Jarrett Gum, prin. Fax 947-0821

Butler, Butler, Pop. 13,451
Area Vocational Technical School
Supt. — None
Butler County AVTS Vo/Tech
210 Campus Ln 16001 724-282-0735
Dr. Joseph Cunningham, prin. Fax 282-7448

Butler Area SD 7,600/K-12
110 Campus Ln 16001 724-287-8721
Dr. Michael Strutt, supt. Fax 287-1802
www.butlerk12.com/
Butler Area Intermediate HS 1,300/9-10
551 Fairground Hill Rd 16001 724-287-8721
John Wyllie, prin. Fax 287-5457
Butler Area JHS 1,200/7-8
225 E North St 16001 724-287-8721
Alicia Beighley, prin. Fax 287-7847
Butler Area SHS 1,300/11-12
120 Campus Ln 16001 724-287-8721
Brian Slamecka, prin. Fax 287-1596

Butler Beauty School Post-Sec.
233 S Main St 16001 724-287-0708
Butler County Community College Post-Sec.
107 College Dr 16002 724-287-8711
First Baptist Christian S 100/PK-12
221 New Castle St 16001 724-287-1188
Fax 287-6934

Cairnbrook, Somerset, Pop. 520
Shade-Central CSD 600/K-12
203 McGreagor Ave 15924 814-754-4648
John Krupper, supt. Fax 754-5848
www.shade.k12.pa.us
Shade JSHS 300/7-12
203 McGreagor Ave 15924 814-754-4648
Sean Wechtenhiser, prin.

California, Washington, Pop. 6,712

California University of Pennsylvania Post-Sec.
250 University Ave 15419 724-938-4000

Cambridge Springs, Crawford, Pop. 2,577
Penncrest SD
Supt. — See Saegertown
Cambridge Springs JSHS 600/7-12
641 Venango Ave 16403 814-398-4631
David Nuhfer, prin. Fax 398-8343

Camp Hill, Cumberland, Pop. 7,766
Camp Hill SD 1,200/K-12
2627 Chestnut St 17011 717-901-2401
Dr. David Reeder, supt. Fax 901-2421
www.camphillsd.k12.pa.us
Camp Hill HS 400/9-12
100 S 24th St 17011 717-901-2500
Scott Shelley, prin. Fax 901-2614
Camp Hill MS 300/6-8
2401 Chestnut St 17011 717-901-2450
Dr. Daniel Roesch, prin. Fax 901-2573

West Shore SD
Supt. — See Lewisberry
Allen MS 500/6-8
4225 Gettysburg Rd 17011 717-901-9552
Timothy Dorsey, prin. Fax 901-8201
Cedar Cliff HS 1,300/9-12
1301 Carlisle Rd 17011 717-737-8654
Kevin Fillgrove, prin. Fax 737-0874

Holy Spirit Hospital Post-Sec.
505 N 21st St 17011 717-763-2106

Trinity HS 700/9-12
3601 Simpson Ferry Rd 17011 717-761-1116
Dr. David Bouton, admin. Fax 761-7309

Canonsburg, Washington, Pop. 8,707
Area Vocational Technical School
Supt. — None
Western Area CTC Vo/Tech
688 Western Ave 15317 724-746-2890
Dr. Joseph Iannetti, prin. Fax 746-0817

Canon-McMillan SD 5,000/K-12
1 N Jefferson Ave 15317 724-746-2940
Michael Daniels, supt. Fax 746-9184
www.cmsd.k12.pa.us
Canon-McMillan HS 1,500/9-12
314 Elm Street Ext 15317 724-745-1400
Dave Helinski, prin. Fax 745-2258
Canonsburg MS 700/7-8
25 E College St 15317 724-745-9030
Greg Taranto, prin. Fax 873-5230

Canton, Bradford, Pop. 1,948
Canton Area SD 1,000/K-12
509 E Main St 17724 570-673-3191
Mathew Gordon, supt. Fax 673-3680
www.canton.k12.pa.us
Canton JSHS 500/7-12
509 E Main St 17724 570-673-5134
Craig Coleman, prin. Fax 673-3680

Carbondale, Lackawanna, Pop. 8,778
Carbondale Area SD 1,600/PK-12
101 Brooklyn St 18407 570-282-2507
Joseph M. Gorham, supt. Fax 282-6988
gateway.ca.k12.pa.us
Carbondale Area JSHS 600/7-12
101 Brooklyn St 18407 570-282-4500
Joseph Farrell, prin. Fax 282-3394

Carlisle, Cumberland, Pop. 18,109
Carlisle Area SD 4,800/K-12
623 W Penn St 17013 717-240-6800
Dr. John W. Friend, supt. Fax 240-6898
www.carlisleschools.org
Carlisle HS 1,500/9-12
623 W Penn St 17013 717-240-6800
Jay Rauscher, prin. Fax 240-7145
Lamberton MS 500/6-8
623 W Penn St 17013 717-240-6800
Keith Colestock, prin. Fax 240-2066
Wilson MS 500/6-8
623 W Penn St 17013 717-240-6800
Colleen Friend, prin. Fax 240-2050

Carlisle Christian Academy 100/K-12
1412 Holly Pike, 717-249-3692
Jane Kitchen, prin. Fax 240-0644
Dickinson College Post-Sec.
PO Box 1773 17013 717-243-5121
McCann School of Business & Technology Post-Sec.
346 York Rd 17013 714 218 3400

Carmichaels, Greene, Pop. 473
Carmichaels Area SD 1,100/K-12
300 W Greene St 15320 724-966-5045
Craig Baily, supt. Fax 966-8793
www.carmarea.org/Carm_Web/MainIndex.htm
Carmichaels Area JSHS 500/7-12
300 W Greene St 15320 724-966-5045
John Menhart, prin. Fax 966-5556

Carnegie, Allegheny, Pop. 7,765
Carlynton SD 1,400/K-12
435 Kings Hwy 15106 412-429-8400
Gary D. Peiffer, supt. Fax 429-2502
www.carlynton.k12.pa.us
Carlynton JSHS 600/7-12
435 Kings Hwy 15106 412-429-2500
Fax 429-2508

Catasauqua, Lehigh, Pop. 6,277
Catasauqua Area SD 1,600/K-12
201 N 14th St 18032 610-264-5571
Robert Spengler, supt. Fax 264-5618
www.cattysd.org
Catasauqua MS 500/5-8
850 Pine St 18032 610-264-4341
Melissa Inselmann, prin. Fax 264-5458
Other Schools – See Northampton

Lehigh Valley Christian HS 100/9-12
330 Howertown Rd 18032 610-403-1000
Robert Brennan, head sch Fax 403-1004

Catawissa, Columbia, Pop. 1,525
Southern Columbia Area SD 1,400/K-12
800 Southern Dr 17820 570-356-2331
Charles Reh, supt. Fax 356-2892
www.scasd.us/
Southern Columbia HS 400/9-12
812 Southern Dr 17820 570-356-3450
James Becker, prin. Fax 356-2835
Southern Columbia MS 500/5-8
810 Southern Dr 17820 570-356-3400
Angela Farronato, prin. Fax 356-2835

Center Valley, Lehigh
Southern Lehigh SD 3,100/K-12
5775 Main St 18034 610-282-3121
Leah M. Christman, supt. Fax 282-0193
www.slsd.org
Southern Lehigh HS 1,000/9-12
5800 Main St Unit 1 18034 610-282-1421
Christine Siegfried, prin. Fax 282-2965
Southern Lehigh MS 500/7-8
3715 Preston Ln 18034 610-282-3700
Dr. Edward Donahue, prin. Fax 282-2963

Achieve Test Prep — Post-Sec.
3477 Corporate Pkwy 18034 — 610-628-0912
DeSales University — Post-Sec.
2755 Station Ave 18034 — 610-282-1100
Penn State Lehigh Valley — Post-Sec.
2809 Saucon Valley Rd 18034 — 610-285-5000

Chalfont, Bucks, Pop. 3,976
Central Bucks SD
Supt. — See Doylestown
Unami MS — 900/7-9
160 Moyer Rd 18914 — 267-893-3400
David Bolton Ed.D., prin. — Fax 893-5820

Chambersburg, Franklin, Pop. 19,639
Area Vocational Technical School
Supt. — None
Franklin County CTC — Vo/Tech
2463 Loop Rd, — 717-263-9033
Keith Yohn, dir. — Fax 263-6568

Chambersburg Area SD — 7,800/PK-12
435 Stanley Ave 17201 — 717-263-9281
Dr. Joseph Padasak, supt. — Fax 261-3321
casdonline.org
Chambersburg Area MS North — 600/6-8
1957 Scotland Ave 17201 — 717-261-3369
Kurt Widmann, prin. — Fax 261-3379
Chambersburg Area MS South — 1,400/6-8
1151 E McKinley St 17201 — 717-261-3385
Melissa Cashdollar, prin. — Fax 261-3401
Chambersburg Area SHS — 1,700/9-12
511 S 6th St 17201 — 717-261-3328
Burdette Chapel, prin. — Fax 261-3490

Cumberland Valley Christian S — 400/PK-12
600 Miller St 17201 — 717-264-3266
Dr. Wilford Rathel, admin. — Fax 264-0416
Shalom Christian Academy — 400/PK-12
126 Social Island Rd, — 717-375-2223
Angie Petersheim, admin. — Fax 375-2224
Wilson College — Post-Sec.
1015 Philadelphia Ave 17201 — 717-264-4141

Charleroi, Washington, Pop. 4,003
Area Vocational Technical School
Supt. — None
Mon Valley CTC — Vo/Tech
5 Guttman Blvd 15022 — 724-489-9581
Bradley Dei Cas, dir. — Fax 489-0711

Charleroi Area SD — 1,700/K-12
125 Fecsen Dr 15022 — 724-483-3509
Dr. Brad Ferko, supt. — Fax 483-3776
www.charleroisd.org
Charleroi Area HS — 600/9-12
100 Fecsen Dr 15022 — 724-483-3575
Patricia Mason, prin. — Fax 483-2294
Charleroi Area MS — 400/6-8
100 Fecsen Dr 15022 — 724-483-3600
Mary Tickner, prin. — Fax 489-9128

Chester, Delaware, Pop. 33,256
Chester-Upland SD — 2,400/PK-12
232 W 9th St 19013 — 610-447-3600
Dr. Thomas Persing, supt. — Fax 447-3616
www.chesteruplandsd.org/
Chester HS — 1,100/9-12
232 W 9th St 19013 — 610-447-3700
Dr. Will Towson, prin. — Fax 447-3682
Smedley STEM HS — 300/9-12
232 W 9th St 19013 — 610-447-3660
Dr. Robin Smith, prin.

Widener University — Post-Sec.
1 University Pl 19013 — 610-499-4000

Cheswick, Allegheny, Pop. 1,738
Allegheny Valley SD — 1,100/K-12
300 Pearl Ave 15024 — 724-274-5300
Cheryl Griffith Ed.D., supt. — Fax 274-8040
www.avsd.k12.pa.us
Other Schools – See Springdale

Deer Lakes SD — 1,900/K-12
19 E Union Rd 15024 — 724-265-5300
Dr. Janet Ciramella, supt. — Fax 265-5025
www.deerlakes.net
Deer Lakes HS — 600/9-12
163 E Union Rd 15024 — 724-265-5320
Joe Orr, prin. — Fax 265-3970
Deer Lakes MS — 500/6-8
17 E Union Rd 15024 — 724-265-5310
Thomas Lesniewski Ed.D., prin. — Fax 265-3711

Cheswick Christian Academy — 200/K-12
1407 Pittsburgh St 15024 — 724-274-4846
Todd Rosio, prin. — Fax 274-8300

Cheyney, Delaware

Cheyney University of Pennsylvania — Post-Sec.
PO Box 200 19319 — 610-399-2275

Clairton, Allegheny, Pop. 6,590
Clairton CSD — 700/PK-12
501 Waddell Ave 15025 — 412-233-9200
Dr. Wayde Killmeyer, supt. — Fax 233-4755
www.clairton.k12.pa.us/
Clairton MSHS — 300/6-12
501 Waddell Ave 15025 — 412-233-9200
Thomas McCloskey, prin. — Fax 233-3243

Clarion, Clarion, Pop. 5,178
Clarion Area SD — 800/K-12
221 Liberty St 16214 — 814-226-6110
Michael Stahlman, supt. — Fax 226-9292
www.clarion-schools.com
Clarion Area JSHS — 400/7-12
219 Liberty St 16214 — 814-226-8112
Dr. Randy Cathcart, prin. — Fax 226-9004

Clarion University of Pennsylvania — Post-Sec.
840 Wood St 16214 — 814-393-2000

Clarks Summit, Lackawanna, Pop. 5,073
Abington Heights SD — 3,500/K-12
200 E Grove St 18411 — 570-586-2511
Michael Mahon, supt. — Fax 586-1756
www.ahsd.org
Abington Heights HS — 1,200/9-12
222 Noble Rd 18411 — 570-585-5300
Pamela Murray, prin. — Fax 586-9093
Abington Heights MS — 1,000/5-8
1555 Newton Ransom Blvd 18411 — 570-586-1281
Michael Elia, prin. — Fax 586-6361

Baptist Bible College and Seminary — Post-Sec.
538 Venard Rd 18411 — 570-586-2400

Claysburg, Blair, Pop. 1,606
Claysburg-Kimmel SD — 900/K-12
531 Bedford St 16625 — 814-239-5141
Royce Boyd, supt. — Fax 239-5896
www.cksdbulldogs.com
Claysburg-Kimmel JSHS — 400/7-12
531 Bedford St 16625 — 814-239-5141
Mark Mitchell, prin. — Fax 239-8949

Claysville, Washington, Pop. 815
McGuffey SD — 2,000/K-12
90 McGuffey Dr 15323 — 724-948-3731
Beverly Arbore, supt. — Fax 948-3769
www.mcguffey.k12.pa.us
McGuffey HS — 700/9-12
86 McGuffey Dr 15323 — 724-948-3328
Mark Bonus, prin. — Fax 948-3344
McGuffey MS — 500/6-8
86 McGuffey Dr 15323 — 724-948-3323
Michael Wilson, prin. — Fax 948-2413

Clearfield, Clearfield, Pop. 6,141
Area Vocational Technical School
Supt. — None
Clearfield County CTC — Vo/Tech
1620 River Rd 16830 — 814-765-5308
Lois Richards, prin. — Fax 765-5474

Clearfield Area SD — 2,300/K-12
PO Box 710 16830 — 814-765-5511
Dr. Thomas Otto, supt. — Fax 765-5515
www.clearfield.org
Clearfield Area HS — 900/9-12
PO Box 910 16830 — 814-765-2401
Tim Janocko, prin. — Fax 765-2405
Clearfield Area MS — 700/5-8
PO Box 710 16830 — 814-765-5302
Fred Redden, prin. — Fax 765-4604

Clearfield Beauty Academy — Post-Sec.
22 N 3rd St 16830 — 814-765-2022
Clearfield Hospital — Post-Sec.
PO Box 992 16830 — 814-768-2496
Lock Haven University-Clearfield Campus — Post-Sec.
201 University Dr 16830 — 814-768-3405

Clymer, Indiana, Pop. 1,351
Penns Manor Area SD — 1,000/PK-12
6003 Route 553 Hwy 15728 — 724-254-2666
Thomas Kakabar, supt. — Fax 254-3418
www.pennsmanor.org/
Penns Manor Area JSHS — 400/7-12
6003 Route 553 Hwy 15728 — 724-254-2666
Daren Johnston, prin. — Fax 254-3417

Coal Center, Washington, Pop. 134
California Area SD — 800/K-12
11 Trojan Way Ste 100 15423 — 724-785-5800
Brian R. Jackson, supt. — Fax 785-4866
www.calsd.org/
California Area HS — 300/9-12
11 Trojan Way 15423 — 724-785-5800
Leigh Ann Folmar, prin. — Fax 785-8860
California Area MS — 100/5-8
40 Trojan Way 15423 — 724-785-5800
Raymond Huffman, prin. — Fax 785-5458

Coal Township, Northumberland, Pop. 9,922
Area Vocational Technical School
Supt. — None
Northumberland County AVTS — Vo/Tech
1700 W Montgomery St 17866 — 570-644-0304
James Monaghan, admin.

Shamokin Area SD — 2,700/PK-12
2000 W State St 17866 — 570-648-5752
James Zack, supt. — Fax 648-2592
www.indians.k12.pa.us/
Shamokin Area JSHS — 1,300/7-12
2000 W State St 17866 — 570-648-5731
Chris Venna, prin.

Our Lady of Lourdes Regional S — 400/K-12
2108 N Jackson St 17866 — 570-644-0375
Sr. Margaret Quinn, prin. — Fax 644-7655

Coatesville, Chester, Pop. 12,560
Coatesville Area SD — 6,900/K-12
545 E Lincoln Hwy 19320 — 610-466-2400
Richard Como, supt. — Fax 383-1426
www.coatesville.k12.pa.us/
Coatesville Area 9-10 Center — 1,200/9-10
1425 E Lincoln Hwy 19320 — 610-383-3735
Brian Chenger, prin. — Fax 383-3723
Coatesville Area SHS — 1,000/11-12
1445 E Lincoln Hwy 19320 — 610-383-3730
Robert Fisher, prin. — Fax 383-3725
North Brandywine MS — 500/6-8
256 Reeceville Rd 19320 — 610-383-3745
Chamise Taylor, prin. — Fax 383-3749
Scott MS — 400/6-8
800 Olive St 19320 — 610-383-6946
Dr. Denise Ray, prin. — Fax 383-7110
South Brandywine MS — 600/6-8
600 Doe Run Rd 19320 — 610-383-3750
Anthony Mallozzi, prin. — Fax 383-3754

Brandywine Hospital — Post-Sec.
201 Reeceville Rd 19320 — 610-383-9000

Cochranton, Crawford, Pop. 1,126
Crawford Central SD
Supt. — See Meadville
Cochranton JSHS — 400/7-12
PO Box 127 16314 — 814-425-7421
Donald Wigton, prin. — Fax 425-2071

Collegeville, Montgomery, Pop. 4,996
Perkiomen Valley SD — 5,900/K-12
3 Iron Bridge Dr 19426 — 610-489-8506
Dr. Clifford Rogers, supt. — Fax 489-2974
www.pvsd.org
Perkiomen Valley East MS — 800/6-8
100 Kagey Rd 19426 — 610-409-8580
Seamus Clune, prin. — Fax 489-8851
Perkiomen Valley HS — 1,700/9-12
509 Gravel Pike 19426 — 610-489-1230
Cyndi Lewis, prin. — Fax 489-1921
Other Schools – See Zieglerville

Ursinus College — Post-Sec.
PO Box 1000 19426 — 610-409-3000
Valley Forge Baptist Academy — 200/K-12
616 S Trappe Rd 19426 — 610-792-1884
Lois Rall, admin. — Fax 948-6423

Columbia, Lancaster, Pop. 10,150
Columbia Borough SD — 1,400/K-12
200 N 5th St 17512 — 717-684-2283
Dr. Barry Clippinger, supt. — Fax 681-2220
www.columbia.k12.pa.us
Columbia JSHS — 600/7-12
901 Ironville Pike 17512 — 717-684-7500
Virginia Babic, prin. — Fax 681-2219

NAWCC School of Horology — Post-Sec.
454 Poplar St 17512 — 717-684-8261

Commodore, Indiana, Pop. 325
Purchase Line SD — 900/K-12
PO Box 374 15729 — 724-254-4312
Tina Hazelet, supt. — Fax 254-1621
www.plsd.k12.pa.us/
Purchase Line JSHS — 500/7-12
16559 Route 286 Hwy E 15729 — 724-254-4312
James Price, prin. — Fax 254-2306

Confluence, Somerset, Pop. 758
Turkeyfoot Valley Area SD — 400/K-12
172 Turkeyfoot Rd 15424 — 814-395-3621
Darlene Pritt, supt. — Fax 395-3366
www.turkeyfoot.k12.pa.us
Turkeyfoot Valley Area JSHS — 200/7-12
172 Turkeyfoot Rd 15424 — 814-395-3622
Jeffrey Malaspino, prin. — Fax 395-3366

Conneaut Lake, Crawford, Pop. 646
Conneaut SD
Supt. — See Linesville
Conneaut Lake MS — 100/5-8
10331 US Highway 6 16316 — 814-382-5315
Joel Wentling, prin. — Fax 382-0165

Conneautville, Crawford, Pop. 765
Conneaut SD
Supt. — See Linesville
Conneaut Valley MS — 100/5-8
22154 State Highway 18 16406 — 814-587-2091
Kevin Burns, prin. — Fax 587-2094

Connellsville, Fayette, Pop. 7,510
Area Vocational Technical School
Supt. — None
Connellsville Area CTC — Vo/Tech
720 Locust St 15425 — 724-626-0236
Linda Murphy, dir.

Connellsville Area SD — 4,100/K-12
732 Rockridge Rd 15425 — 724-628-3300
Dr. Daniel Lujetic, supt. — Fax 628-9002
www.casdfalcons.org
Connellsville Area HS — 1,000/9-12
201 Falcon Dr 15425 — 724-628-1350
Nicholas Bosnic, prin. — Fax 628-0280
Connellsville JHS — 400/7-8
710 Locust St 15425 — 724-628-8910
Richard Evans, prin. — Fax 628-9293

Geibel Catholic JSHS — 200/7-12
611 E Crawford Ave 15425 — 724-628-5600
Donald Favero, prin. — Fax 626-5700

Coraopolis, Allegheny, Pop. 5,475
Cornell SD — 700/K-12
1099 Maple Street Ext 15108 — 412-264-5010
Aaron Thomas, supt. — Fax 264-1445
www.cornell.k12.pa.us
Cornell JSHS — 300/7-12
1099 Maple Street Ext 15108 — 412-264-5010
Robert Motte, prin. — Fax 264-1445

Montour SD
Supt. — See Mc Kees Rocks
Williams MS — 500/5-8
Porters Hollow Rd 15108 — 412-771-8802
Dominic Salpeck, prin. — Fax 771-3772

Our Lady of Sacred Heart HS 400/9-12
1504 Woodcrest Ave 15108 412-264-5140
Tim Plocinik, prin. Fax 264-4143

Corry, Erie, Pop. 6,515
Corry Area SD 2,300/PK-12
540 E Pleasant St 16407 814-664-4677
William A. Nichols, supt. Fax 664-9645
www.corrysd.net
Career & Technical Center Vo/Tech
534 E Pleasant St 16407 814-664-4677
Anthony Miller, prin. Fax 663-0722
Corry Area HS 800/9-12
534 E Pleasant St 16407 814-665-8297
Kelly Cragg, prin. Fax 664-3650
Corry MS 400/7-8
534 E Pleasant St 16407 814-665-8297
Gail Swank, prin. Fax 664-3650

Coudersport, Potter, Pop. 2,519
Coudersport Area SD 900/K-12
698 Dwight St 16915 814-274-9480
Alanna Huck, supt. Fax 274-7551
coudersport.schoolwires.com/
Coudersport Area JSHS 400/7-12
698 Dwight St 16915 814-274-8500
Steve Mongillo, prin. Fax 274-8053

Cresson, Cambria, Pop. 1,702
Penn Cambria SD 1,800/PK-12
201 6th St 16630 814-886-8121
Mary Beth Whited, supt. Fax 886-4809
www.pcam.org
Penn Cambria HS 600/9-12
401 Linden Ave 16630 814-886-8188
William Marshall, prin. Fax 884-3977
Other Schools – See Gallitzin

Mount Aloysius College Post-Sec.
7373 Admiral Peary Hwy 16630 814-886-4131

Curwensville, Clearfield, Pop. 2,529
Curwensville Area SD 1,200/K-12
650 Beech St 16833 814-236-1101
Dr. Norman Hatten, supt. Fax 236-1103
www.curwensville.org/
Curwensville Area JSHS 600/7-12
650 Beech St 16833 814-236-1100
William Hayward, prin. Fax 236-2392

Dallas, Luzerne, Pop. 2,782
Dallas SD 2,700/K-12
PO Box 2000 18612 570-674-7221
Frank Galicki, supt. Fax 674-7295
www.dallassd.com/
Dallas HS 900/9-12
PO Box 2000 18612 570-674-7230
Jeffrey Shaffer, prin. Fax 674-6843
Dallas MS 700/6-8
PO Box 2000 18612 570-674-7245
Dr. Thomas Duffy, prin. Fax 674-7219

Lake-Lehman SD 2,100/K-12
1237 Market St 18612 570-675-2165
James McGovern, supt. Fax 675-7657
www.lake-lehman.k12.pa.us/
Other Schools – See Lehman

Misericordia University Post-Sec.
301 Lake St 18612 570-674-6400

Dallastown, York, Pop. 3,985
Dallastown Area SD 5,900/K-12
700 New School Ln 17313 717-244-4021
Ronald Dyer Ed.D., supt. Fax 894-0583
www.dallastown.net
Dallastown Area HS 1,900/9-12
700 New School Ln 17313 717-244-4021
Kevin Duckworth, prin. Fax 223-7505
Dallastown Area MS 900/7-8
700 New School Ln 17313 717-244-4021
Dr. Sue Cathcart, prin. Fax 233-9796

Danville, Montour, Pop. 4,646
Danville Area SD 2,000/K-12
600 Walnut St 17821 570-271-3268
Cheryl Latorre, supt. Fax 275-7712
www.danville.k12.pa.us
Danville Area HS 700/9-12
600 Walnut St 17821 570-271-3268
Lee Gump, prin. Fax 275-5463
Danville Area MS 500/6-8
401 E Front St 17821 570-271-3268
Charles Smargiassi, prin. Fax 275-1281

Geisinger Medical Center Post-Sec.
100 N Academy Ave 17822 570-271-5200

Darby, Delaware, Pop. 10,364
William Penn SD
Supt. — See Lansdowne
Penn Wood MS 800/7-8
121 Summit St 19023 610-586-1804
Brian Wilson, prin. Fax 586-7372

Davidsville, Somerset, Pop. 1,129
Conemaugh Township Area SD 800/K-12
PO Box 407 15928 814-479-7575
Gary Buchsen, supt. Fax 479-2620
www.ctasd.org
Conemaugh Township Area MSHS 500/6-12
PO Box 407 15928 814-479-4014
David Koba, prin. Fax 479-2038

Denver, Lancaster, Pop. 3,812
Cocalico SD 3,200/PK-12
PO Box 800 17517 717-336-1413
Dr. Bruce Sensenig, supt. Fax 336-1415
www.cocalico.org/
Cocalico HS 1,000/9-12
PO Box 800 17517 717-336-1421
Christopher Irvine, prin. Fax 336-1486
Cocalico MS 800/6-8
PO Box 800 17517 717-336-1471
Dr. Stephen Melnyk, prin. Fax 336-1482

Gehmans Mennonite S 100/K-12
650 Gehman School Rd 17517 717-484-4222
Michael Burkholder, prin. Fax 484-4222

Derry, Westmoreland, Pop. 2,670
Derry Area SD 1,900/K-12
982 N Chestnut Street Ext 15627 724-694-1401
David Welling, supt. Fax 694-1429
derryasd.schoolwires.com/derryasd/
Derry Area HS 800/9-12
988 N Chestnut Street Ext 15627 724-694-2780
Kathy Perry, prin. Fax 694-1482
Derry Area MS 600/6-8
994 N Chestnut Street Ext 15627 724-694-8231
Jeff Metzger, prin. Fax 694-0288

Devon, Chester, Pop. 1,486

Devon Preparatory S 300/6-12
363 N Valley Forge Rd 19333 610-688-7337
James Shea, hdmstr. Fax 688-2409

Dickson City, Lackawanna, Pop. 5,996

McCann School of Business & Technology Post-Sec.
2227 Scranton Carbondale 18519 570-307-2000

Dillsburg, York, Pop. 2,514
Northern York County SD 3,200/K-12
149 S Baltimore St 17019 717-432-8691
Dr. Eric Eshbach, supt. Fax 432-1421
www.northernpolarbears.com
Northern HS 1,000/9-12
653 S Baltimore St 17019 717-432-8691
Matthew LaBuda, prin. Fax 432-0375
Northern MS 700/6-8
655 S Baltimore St 17019 717-432-8691
Sylvia Murray, prin. Fax 432-5889

Dimock, Susquehanna
Area Vocational Technical School
Supt. — None
Susquehanna County Career & Tech. Center Vo/Tech
PO Box 100 18816 570-278-9229
Dr. Alice Davis, dir. Fax 278-3913

Dingmans Ferry, Pike
Delaware Valley SD
Supt. — See Milford
Dingman-Delaware MS 600/6-8
1365 Route 739 18328 570-296-3140
James Mitchell, prin. Fax 296-3170

East Stroudsburg Area SD
Supt. — See East Stroudsburg
East Stroudsburg HS North 1,300/9-12
279 Timberwolf Dr 18328 570-588-4420
Stephen Zall, prin. Fax 588-4421
Lehman IS 800/6-8
257 Timberwolf Dr 18328 570-588-4410
Robert Dilliplane, prin. Fax 588-4411

Donegal, Westmoreland, Pop. 120

Champion Christian S 100/PK-PK, 5-
1076 Kings Way 15628 724-593-9200
D. Merle Skinner, dir. Fax 593-9210

Douglassville, Berks, Pop. 444
Daniel Boone Area SD
Supt. — See Birdsboro
Boone Area MS 900/6-8
1845 Weavertown Rd 19518 610-689-6300
Robert Hurley, prin. Fax 689-6306

Dover, York, Pop. 1,967
Dover Area SD 3,500/K-12
101 Edgeway Rd 17315 717-292-3671
Dr. Robert Krantz, supt. Fax 292-9659
www.doversd.org/
Dover Area HS 1,000/9-12
46 W Canal St 17315 717-292-8066
William Rickard, prin. Fax 292-7303
Dover Area IS 600/7-8
4500 Intermediate Ave 17315 717-292-8067
Dr. Philip Livelsberger, prin. Fax 292-9849

Downingtown, Chester, Pop. 7,678
Area Vocational Technical School
Supt. — None
Technical College HS - Brandywine Campus Vo/Tech
443 Boot Rd 19335 484-593-5100
Seth Schram, prin.

Downingtown Area SD 11,800/K-12
540 Trestle Pl 19335 610-269-8460
Lawrence Mussoline Ph.D., supt. Fax 873-1404
www.dasd.org
Downingtown HS - West Campus 1,700/9-12
445 Manor Ave 19335 610-269-4400
Thomas Mulvey, prin. Fax 269-1801
Downingtown MS 1,300/6-8
115 Rock Raymond Rd 19335 610-518-0685
Nick Indeglio, prin. Fax 518-0685
Downingtown STEM Academy 9-12
335 Manor Ave 19335 610-269-8460
Arthur Campbell, prin.
Other Schools – See Exton

Bishop Shanahan HS 1,300/9-12
220 Woodbine Rd 19335 610-518-1300
Sr. Maureen McDermott, prin. Fax 343-6220

Doylestown, Bucks, Pop. 8,255
Central Bucks SD 20,400/K-12
20 Weldon Dr 18901 267-893-2000
Dr. Rodney Green, supt. Fax 893-5800
www.cbsd.org
Central Bucks SHS - East 1,600/10-12
2804 Holicong Rd, 267-893-2300
Abram Lucabaugh, prin. Fax 794-5446
Central Bucks SHS - West 1,500/10-12
375 W Court St 18901 267-893-2500
J. Kevin Munnelly, prin. Fax 348-9832
Holicong MS 1,200/7-9
2900 Holicong Rd, 267-893-2700
Jason Bucher, prin. Fax 893-5816
Lenape MS 900/7-9
313 W State St 18901 267-893-2800
H. Nicholas Chubb Ed.D., prin. Fax 345-4699
Tohickon MS 1,100/7-9
5051 Old Easton Rd, 267-893-3300
Karen Wychock Ed.D., prin. Fax 893-5819
Other Schools – See Chalfont, Warrington

Delaware Valley College Post-Sec.
700 E Butler Ave 18901 215-345-1500

Dresher, Montgomery
Upper Dublin SD
Supt. — See Maple Glen
Sandy Run MS 1,000/6-8
520 Twining Rd 19025 215-576-3280
Denise Falconi Ed.D., prin. Fax 572-3886

Drexel Hill, Delaware, Pop. 27,609
Upper Darby SD 12,000/K-12
4611 Bond Ave 19026 610-789-7200
Louis DeVlieger, supt. Fax 789-8671
www.upperdarbysd.org
Drexel Hill MS, 3001 State Rd 19026 1,200/6-8
Gregory Manfre, prin. 610-853-4580
Upper Darby HS 3,800/9-12
601 N Lansdowne Ave 19026 610-622-7000
Christopher Dormer, prin. Fax 622-7844
Other Schools – See Upper Darby

Bonner/Prendergast HS 1,300/9-12
403 N Lansdowne Ave 19026 610-259-0280
William Brannick, prin. Fax 259-1630

Du Bois, Clearfield, Pop. 7,711
Du Bois Area SD 4,100/K-12
500 Liberty Blvd 15801 814-371-2700
Timothy Deluccia, supt. Fax 371-2544
www.dasd.k12.pa.us
Du Bois Area HS 1,200/9-12
425 Orient Ave 15801 814-371-8111
Roger Collins, prin. Fax 371-3928
Du Bois Area MS 1,000/6-8
404 Liberty Blvd 15801 814-375-8770
Dr. Marianne Konior, prin. Fax 375-8775

Du Bois Area Catholic HS 200/9-12
PO Box 567 15801 814-371-3060
Dawn Bressler, prin. Fax 371-3215
DuBois Business College Post-Sec.
1 Beaver Dr 15801 814-371-6920
Du Bois Central Catholic MS 100/6-8
PO Box 567 15801 814-371-3060
Dawn Bressler, prin. Fax 371-3215
DuBois Christian S 100/K-12
197 Eastern Ave 15801 814-371-7395
Mark Montgomery, admin. Fax 371-7399
Penn State Du Bois Post-Sec.
1 College Place 15801 814-375-4700
PA Academy of Cosmetic Arts & Sciences Post-Sec.
19 N Brady St 15801 814-371-4151
Triangle Tech Post-Sec.
PO Box 551 15801 814-371-2090

Duke Center, McKean
Otto-Eldred SD 700/PK-12
143 Sweitzer Dr 16729 814-817-1380
Matthew D. Splain, supt. Fax 966-3911
www.ottoeldred.org
Otto-Eldred JSHS 300/7-12
143 Sweitzer Dr 16729 814-817-1380
Harley D. Ramsey, prin. Fax 966-3911

Duncannon, Perry, Pop. 1,503
Susquenita SD 1,900/K-12
1725 Schoolhouse Rd 17020 717-957-6000
Kent R. Smith, supt. Fax 957-2463
www.susq.k12.pa.us/
Susquenita HS 600/9-12
309 Schoolhouse Rd 17020 717-957-6000
Craig Funk, prin. Fax 957-1792
Susquenita MS 600/5-8
200 Susquenita Dr 17020 717-957-6000
William Quigley, prin. Fax 957-6022

Duncansville, Blair, Pop. 1,222

Blair County Christian S 100/PK-12
PO Box 840 16635 814-696-3702
Duey Whitefield, admin. Fax 696-2783

Dunmore, Lackawanna, Pop. 13,930
Dunmore SD 1,300/K-12
300 W Warren St 18512 570-343-2110
Richard McDonald, supt. Fax 343-1458
www.dunmoreschooldistrict.net/
Dunmore HS 400/9-12
300 W Warren St 18512 570-346-2043
Robert Galella, prin. Fax 343-1458
Dunmore MS 100/7-8
300 W Warren St 18512 570-346-2043
Robert Gallela, prin. Fax 343-1458

Holy Cross HS 300/9-12
501 E Drinker St 18512 570-346-7541
Ben Tolerico, prin. Fax 348-1070
ITT Technical Institute Post-Sec.
1000 Meade St 18512 570-330-0600
Penn State Worthington Scranton Post-Sec.
120 Ridgeview Dr 18512 570-963-2500

Eagleville, Montgomery, Pop. 4,719
Methacton SD 4,600/K-12
1001 Kriebel Mill Rd 19403 610-489-5000
Dr. Jeffrey A. Miller, supt. Fax 489-5019
www.methacton.org
Arcola IS 900/7-8
4001 Eagleville Rd Ste A 19403 610-489-5000
Lucretia Page, prin. Fax 831-5317
Methacton HS 1,800/9-12
1005 Kriebel Mill Rd 19403 610-489-5000
Judith Landis, prin. Fax 489-8165

East Greenville, Montgomery, Pop. 2,902
Upper Perkiomen SD
Supt. — See Pennsburg
Upper Perkiomen MS 700/6-8
510 Jefferson St 18041 215-679-6288
Duane Wickard, prin. Fax 679-3091

Easton, Northampton, Pop. 25,861
Area Vocational Technical School
Supt. — None
Career Institute of Technology Vo/Tech
5335 Kesslersville Rd 18040 610-258-2857
Priscilla Riskin, dir.

Easton Area SD 9,000/K-12
1801 Bushkill Dr 18040 610-250-2400
Susan McGinley, supt. Fax 923-8954
www.eastonsd.org
Eastern Area Academy Alt
2035 Edgewood Ave 18045 610-829-5700
Kyle Yanders, admin. Fax 829-5708
Easton Area HS 2,800/9-12
2601 William Penn Hwy 18045 610-250-2481
Michael Koch, prin. Fax 250-2483
Easton Area MS 1,300/7-8
1010 Echo Trl 18040 610-250-2460
Angela DeVietro, prin. Fax 250-2613

Wilson Area SD 2,100/K-12
2040 Washington Blvd 18042 484-373-6000
Douglas Wagner, supt. Fax 258-6421
www.wilsonareasd.org
Wilson Area HS 700/9-12
424 Warrior Ln 18042 484-373-6030
John Martuscelli, prin. Fax 258-8831
Wilson Area IS 500/5-8
2400 Firmstone St 18042 484-373-6110
Anthony Tarsi, prin. Fax 258-4014

Bethlehem Christian S Calvary Campus 100/5-8
5300 Green Pond Rd 18045 610-365-8176
Carol Aversa, prin. Fax 365-8407
Lafayette College Post-Sec.
High St 18042 610-330-5000
Notre Dame HS 600/9-12
3417 Church Rd 18045 610-868-1431
Joseph Kramer, prin. Fax 868-6710
Rock Christian Academy 50/PK-12
PO Box 636 18044 610-253-8161
Rev. Arlene Santos, admin. Fax 250-8794

East Stroudsburg, Monroe, Pop. 9,606
East Stroudsburg Area SD 7,800/K-12
PO Box 298 18301 570-424-8500
Sharon Laverdure, supt. Fax 424-5646
www.esasd.net
East Stroudsburg HS South 1,500/9-12
279 N Courtland St 18301 570-424-8471
Michael Catrillo, prin. Fax 420-8338
Lambert IS 1,000/6-8
2000 Milford Rd 18301 570-424-8430
John Burrus, prin. Fax 476-0464
Other Schools – See Dingmans Ferry

East Stroudsburg University of PA Post-Sec.
200 Prospect St 18301 570-422-3211
Notre Dame HS 300/7-12
60 Spangenburg Ave 18301 570-421-0466
Jeffrey Lyons, prin. Fax 476-0629

Ebensburg, Cambria, Pop. 3,337
Area Vocational Technical School
Supt. — None
Admiral Peary AVTS Vo/Tech
948 Ben Franklin Hwy 15931 814-472-6490
Ken Jubas, dir. Fax 472-6494

Central Cambria SD 1,800/K-12
208 Schoolhouse Rd 15931 814-472-8870
Vincent DiLeo Ed.D., supt. Fax 472-9695
www.cchs.k12.pa.us/
Central Cambria HS 600/9-12
204 Schoolhouse Rd 15931 814-472-8860
Kimberly McDermott, prin. Fax 472-8886
Central Cambria MS 400/6-8
206 Schoolhouse Rd 15931 814-472-6505
Christopher Santini, prin. Fax 472-4187

Bishop Carroll Catholic HS 200/9-12
728 Ben Franklin Hwy 15931 814-472-7500
Lorie Ratchford, prin. Fax 472-8020
Pennsylvania Institute of Taxidermy Post-Sec.
118 Industrial Park Rd 15931 814-472-4510

Edinboro, Erie, Pop. 6,330
General McLane SD 2,100/K-12
11771 Edinboro Rd 16412 814-273-1033
Richard Scaletta, supt. Fax 273-1030
www.generalmclane.org
McLane HS 700/9-12
11761 Edinboro Rd 16412 814-273-1033
Daniel Mennow, prin. Fax 273-1035
Parker MS 700/5-8
11781 Edinboro Rd 16412 814-273-1033
John Hansen, prin. Fax 273-1038

Edinboro University of Pennsylvania Post-Sec.
219 Meadville St 16444 814-732-2000

Elizabeth, Allegheny, Pop. 1,455
Elizabeth Forward SD 2,500/K-12
401 Rock Run Rd 15037 412-896-2312
Dr. Bart Rocco, supt. Fax 751-9483
www.efsd.net
Elizabeth Forward HS 900/9-12
1000 Weigles Hill Rd 15037 412-896-2349
Michael Routh, prin. Fax 384-2030
Elizabeth Forward MS 600/6-8
401 Rock Run Rd 15037 412-896-2335
Michael Routh, prin. Fax 751-6669

Elizabethtown, Lancaster, Pop. 11,397
Elizabethtown Area SD 3,000/K-12
600 E High St 17022 717-367-1521
Michele Balliet, supt. Fax 367-1920
www.etownschools.org
Elizabethtown Area HS 1,300/9-12
600 E High St 17022 717-367-1533
Timothy Re, prin. Fax 367-4149
Elizabethtown Area MS 600/7-8
600 E High St 17022 717-361-7525
Brad Sterner, prin. Fax 361-2597

Elizabethtown College Post-Sec.
1 Alpha Dr 17022 717-361-1000
Mt. Calvary Christian S 300/PK-12
629 Holly St 17022 717-367-1649
Dr. Daniel Sheard, hdmstr. Fax 367-5672

Elizabethville, Dauphin, Pop. 1,493
Upper Dauphin Area SD
Supt. — See Lykens
Upper Dauphin Area HS 400/9-12
220 N Church St 17023 717-362-8181
David Geanette, prin. Fax 362-8088

Elkins Park, Montgomery, Pop. 4,700
Cheltenham Township SD 4,400/K-12
2000 Ashbourne Rd 19027 215-886-9500
Dr. Darlene Davis, supt. Fax 884-3029
www.cheltenham.org
Other Schools – See Wyncote

Medical College Hospitals Post-Sec.
60 Township Line Rd 19027 215-663-6150
Salus University Post-Sec.
8360 Old York Rd 19027 215-780-1400

Elkland, Tioga, Pop. 1,798
Northern Tioga SD 1,900/K-12
110 Ellison Rd 16920 814-258-5642
Diane Barnes, supt. Fax 258-7083
www.ntiogasd.org
Other Schools – See Tioga, Westfield

Elliottsburg, Perry
West Perry SD 2,700/K-12
2606 Shermans Valley Rd 17024 717-789-3934
Dr. Rhonda Brunner, supt. Fax 789-4997
www.westperry.org
West Perry HS 900/9-12
2608 Shermans Valley Rd 17024 717-789-3931
Christopher Rahn, prin. Fax 789-2110
West Perry MS 600/6-8
2620 Shermans Valley Rd 17024 717-789-3012
Bernard Danko, prin. Fax 789-3393

Ellwood City, Lawrence, Pop. 7,833
Ellwood City Area SD 1,200/K-12
501 Crescent Ave 16117 724-752-1591
Frank Aloi, supt. Fax 752-8556
www.ellwood.k12.pa.us
Lincoln JSHS 900/7-12
501 Crescent Ave 16117 724-752-1591
Kirk Lape, prin. Fax 752-8556

Riverside Beaver County SD 1,200/PK-12
318 Country Club Dr 16117 724-758-7512
David Anney, supt. Fax 758-2070
www.riverside.k12.pa.us
Riverside HS 600/9-12
300 Country Club Dr 16117 724-758-7512
Michael Brooks, prin. Fax 758-7519
Riverside MS 200/6-8
302 Country Club Dr 16117 724-758-7512
Alicia Dwyer, prin. Fax 758-0919

Elverson, Chester, Pop. 1,218
Twin Valley SD 3,400/K-12
4851 N Twin Valley Rd 19520 610-286-8611
Dr. Robert Pleis, supt. Fax 286-8608
www.tvsd.org
Twin Valley HS 1,000/9-12
4897 N Twin Valley Rd 19520 610-286-8614
Fax 286-8604
Twin Valley MS 1,000/5-8
770 Clymer Hill Rd 19520 610-286-8660
Dr. Gerald Catagnus, prin. Fax 286-8662

Emmaus, Lehigh, Pop. 11,070
East Penn SD 7,400/K-12
800 Pine St 18049 610-966-8300
Dr. Thomas Seidenberger, supt. Fax 966-8339
www.eastpenn.k12.pa.us/
Emmaus HS 2,600/9-12
500 N Macungie St 18049 610-966-1651
David Piperato, prin.
Other Schools – See Macungie

Emporium, Cameron, Pop. 2,061
Cameron County SD 700/K-12
601 Woodland Ave 15834 814-486-4000
Christine Holjencin, supt. Fax 486-4006
www.cameroncountyschools.org/
Cameron County JSHS 400/7-12
601 Woodland Ave 15834 814-486-4000
Lynn Newcomer, prin. Fax 486-4003

Enola, Cumberland, Pop. 5,946
East Pennsboro Area SD 2,800/K-12
890 Valley St 17025 717-732-3601
Bruce Deveney, supt. Fax 732-8927
www.epasd.k12.pa.us
East Pennsboro Area HS 800/9-12
425 W Shady Ln 17025 717-732-0723
Craig Robbins, prin. Fax 732-8932
East Pennsboro Area MS 900/5-8
529 N Enola Dr 17025 717-732-0771
Dr. Stephen Andrejack, prin. Fax 732-8948

Ephrata, Lancaster, Pop. 13,209
Ephrata Area SD 4,100/K-12
803 Oak Blvd 17522 717-721-1400
Dr. Brian Troop, supt. Fax 721-1514
www.easdpa.org
Ephrata HS 1,300/9-12
803 Oak Blvd 17522 717-721-1478
Joane Eby, prin. Fax 721-1129
Ephrata MS 600/7-8
957 Hammon Ave 17522 717-721-1468
Gangi Cucciuffo, prin. Fax 721-1469

Ephrata Mennonite S 200/K-10
598 Stevens Rd 17522 717-738-4266
Glendon Strickler, prin. Fax 738-1644
Pleasant Valley Mennonite S 100/K-12
144 Pleasant Valley Rd 17522 717-738-1833
Larry Weaver, prin. Fax 738-3941

Erdenheim, Montgomery
Springfield Township SD
Supt. — See Oreland
Springfield Township HS 600/9-12
1801 Paper Mill Rd 19038 215-233-6030
Greg Puckett, prin. Fax 233-0691

Antonelli Institute Post-Sec.
300 Montgomery Ave 19038 215-836-2222
Philadelphia-Montgomery Christian Acad 400/PK-12
35 Hillcrest Rd 19038 215-233-0782
Donald Beebe, hdmstr. Fax 233-0829

Erie, Erie, Pop. 98,321
Area Vocational Technical School
Supt. — None
Erie County Technical S Vo/Tech
8500 Oliver Rd 16509 814-464-8600
Joseph Tarasovich, prin. Fax 464-8625

Erie CSD 10,500/K-12
148 W 21st St 16502 814-874-6000
Dr. Jay Badams, supt. Fax 874-6010
eriesd.org
Central Career and Technical S Vo/Tech
3325 Cherry St 16508 814-874-6200
Mathew Pundt, prin. Fax 874-6207
East HS 1,000/9-12
1001 Atkins St 16503 814-874-6400
James Smith, prin. Fax 874-6407
Northwest Pennsylvania Collegiate Acad 900/9-12
2825 State St 16508 814-874-6300
Tammie Smith, dean Fax 874-6307
Roosevelt MS 300/6-8
3325 Cherry St 16508 814-874-6800
Teresa Szumigala, prin. Fax 874-6807
Vincent HS 900/9-12
1330 W 8th St 16502 814-874-6500
Scherry Prater, prin. Fax 874-6507
Wilson MS 500/6-8
718 E 28th St 16504 814-874-6600
Donald Orlando, prin. Fax 874-6607

Iroquois SD, 800 Tyndall Ave 16511 1,300/K-12
Dr. Sam Signorino, supt. 814-899-7643
www.iroquoissd.org
Iroquois JSHS 600/7-12
4301 Main St 16511 814-899-7643
Kenneth Berlin, prin. Fax 898-4105

Millcreek Township SD 7,200/K-12
3740 W 26th St 16506 814-835-5300
Michael Golde, supt. Fax 835-5307
www.mtsd.org
McDowell Intermediate HS 1,200/9-10
3320 Caughey Rd 16506 814-835-5487
Stephanie Williams, prin. Fax 835-5417
McDowell SHS 1,200/11-12
3580 W 38th St 16506 814-835-5403
Timothy Rankin, prin. Fax 836-6810
Millcreek Learning Center 50/Alt
3814 Asbury Rd 16506 814-836-6888
Timothy Stoops, prin. Fax 836-6871
Westlake MS 600/6-8
4330 W Lake Rd 16505 814-835-5750
Marty Kaverman, prin. Fax 835-5770
Wilson MS 600/6-8
901 W 54th St 16509 814-835-5500
John Cavanagh, prin. Fax 835-5542
Other Schools – See Fairview

Wattsburg Area SD 1,600/K-12
10782 Wattsburg Rd 16509 814-824-3400
Alan Karns, supt. Fax 824-5200
www.wattsburg.org/
Seneca HS 500/9-12
10770 Wattsburg Rd 16509 814-824-3400
Keith Miller, prin. Fax 825-2262

Wattsburg Area MS 500/5-8
10774 Wattsburg Rd 16509 814-824-3400
Christopher Paris, prin. Fax 825-6337

Bethel Christian S of Erie 100/K-12
1781 W 38th St 16508 814-868-2365
David Miles, admin. Fax 864-7674
Cathedral Preparatory HS 600/9-12
225 W 9th St 16501 814-453-7737
Rev. Scott Jabo, pres. Fax 459-6188
Erie Business Center Post-Sec.
246 W 9th St 16501 814-456-7504
Erie First Christian Academy 200/PK-12
8150 Oliver Rd 16509 814-866-6979
John Richardson, supt. Fax 866-5829
Erie Institute of Technology Post-Sec.
940 Millcreek Mall 16565 814-868-9900
Gannon University Post-Sec.
109 University Sq 16541 814-871-7000
Great Lakes Institute of Technology Post-Sec.
5100 Peach St 16509 814-864-6666
Lake Erie College\Osteopathic Medicine Post-Sec.
1858 W Grandview Blvd 16509 814-866-6641
Mercyhurst Prep S 600/9-12
538 E Grandview Blvd 16504 814-824-2210
Deborah Laughlin, prin. Fax 824-3638
Mercyhurst University Post-Sec.
501 E 38th St 16546 814-824-2000
Northwest Regional Technology Institute Post-Sec.
3104 State St 16508 814-455-4446
Penn State Erie The Behrend College Post-Sec.
4701 College Dr 16563 814-898-6000
Toni & Guy Hairdressing Academy Post-Sec.
930 Peach St 16501 800-775-4187
Triangle Tech Post-Sec.
2000 Liberty St 16502 814-453-6016
Tri-State Business Institute Post-Sec.
5757 W 26th St 16506 814-838-7673
Villa Maria Academy 300/9-12
2403 W 8th St 16505 814-838-2061
Sr. Mary Drexler, prin. Fax 836-0881

Essington, Delaware

All-State Career School Post-Sec.
50 W Powhattan Ave 19029 610-362-1124

Everett, Bedford, Pop. 1,810
Area Vocational Technical School
Supt. — None
Bedford County Technical Center Vo/Tech
195 Pennknoll Rd 15537 814-623-2760
David DiPasquale, prin. Fax 623-7234

Everett Area SD 1,200/K-12
427 E South St 15537 814-652-9114
Dr. Danny Webb, supt. Fax 652-6191
www.everett.k12.pa.us
Everett Area HS 500/9-12
1 Renaissance Cir 15537 814-652-9114
Christina Ramsey, prin. Fax 652-0107
Everett Area MS 200/6-8
1 Renaissance Cir 15537 814-652-9114
Rebecca Pupo, prin. Fax 652-0107

Snake Spring Valley Christian Academy 50/PK-12
377 Upper Snake Spring Rd 15537 814-623-2840
Stephanie Holliday, admin. Fax 623-4864

Exeter, Luzerne, Pop. 5,622
Wyoming Area SD 2,500/K-12
20 Memorial St 18643 570-655-2836
Raymond Bernardi, supt. Fax 883-1280
www.wyomingarea.org
Wyoming Area JSHS 1,200/7-12
20 Memorial St 18643 570-655-2836
Vito Quaglia, prin. Fax 883-1280

Exton, Chester, Pop. 4,742
Downingtown Area SD
Supt. — See Downingtown
Downingtown HS - East Campus 2,000/9-12
50 Devon Dr 19341 610-363-6400
Paul Hurley, prin. Fax 903-1047
Lionville MS 1,500/6-8
550 W Uwchlan Ave 19341 610-524-6300
Jonathan Ross, prin. Fax 524-0152

Automotive Training Center Post-Sec.
114 Pickering Way 19341 610-363-6716
CFS The School at Church Farm 200/7-12
1001 E Lincoln Hwy 19341 610-363-7500
Rev. Edmund Sherrill, hdmstr. Fax 363-5367
Universal Technical Institute Post-Sec.
750 Pennsylvania Dr 19341 877-884-3986

Factoryville, Wyoming, Pop. 1,146
Lackawanna Trail SD 1,200/K-12
PO Box 85 18419 570-945-5184
Matthew Rakauskas, supt. Fax 945-3154
www.ltsd.org
Lackawanna Trail JSHS 600/7-12
PO Box 85 18419 570-945-5181
John Rushefski, prin. Fax 945-3832

Fairfield, Adams, Pop. 504
Fairfield Area SD 1,200/K-12
4840 Fairfield Rd 17320 717-642-8228
William Chain, supt. Fax 642-2036
www.fairfieldpaschools.org/
Fairfield Area HS 400/9-12
4840 Fairfield Rd 17320 717-642-2004
Brian McDowell, prin. Fax 642-2029
Fairfield Area MS 400/5-8
4840 Fairfield Rd 17320 717-642-2005
Patricia Weber, prin. Fax 642-2030

Fairless Hills, Bucks, Pop. 8,316
Area Vocational Technical School
Supt. — None
Bucks County Technical HS Vo/Tech
610 Wistar Rd 19030 215-949-1700
Dr. Leon Poeske, prin.

Bristol Township SD
Supt. — See Levittown
Armstrong MS 500/7-8
475 Wistar Rd 19030 215-945-4940
Edward Dayton, prin. Fax 945-1664

Pennsbury SD
Supt. — See Fallsington
Pennsbury HS East 3,300/9-12
705 Hood Blvd 19030 215-949-6700
Shawn Neely, prin. Fax 949-3896
Pennsbury HS West 9-12
608 S Olds Blvd 19030 215-949-6780
Lisa Becker, prin. Fax 949-6857

Conwell-Egan HS 800/9-12
611 Wistar Rd 19030 215-945-6200
Dr. Marion Mann, prin. Fax 945-6206

Fairview, Erie, Pop. 2,337
Fairview SD 1,600/K-12
7460 McCray Rd 16415 814-474-2600
Erik Kincade, supt. Fax 474-5497
www.fairviewschools.org/
Fairview HS 600/9-12
7460 McCray Rd 16415 814-474-2600
David Park, prin. Fax 474-1367
Fairview MS 500/5-8
4967 Avonia Rd 16415 814-474-2600
Steve Ferringer, prin. Fax 474-1640

Millcreek Township SD
Supt. — See Erie
Walnut Creek MS 600/6-8
5901 Sterrettania Rd 16415 814-835-5700
Darcie Moseley, prin. Fax 835-5720

Fallsington, Bucks
Pennsbury SD 10,900/K-12
134 Yardley Ave 19054 215-428-4100
Dr. Kevin McHugh, supt. Fax 295-8912
www.pennsbury.k12.pa.us
Other Schools – See Fairless Hills, Yardley

Farrell, Mercer, Pop. 4,855
Farrell Area SD 800/PK-12
1600 Roemer Blvd 16121 724-346-6585
Rev. Lora Adams-King, supt. Fax 346-0223
www.farrellareaschools.com
Farrell Area MSHS 400/7-12
1700 Roemer Blvd 16121 724-346-6585
Tracy Hood, prin. Fax 346-2381

Fawn Grove, York, Pop. 449
South Eastern SD 2,900/K-12
377 Main St 17321 717-382-4843
Dr. Rona Kaufmann, supt. Fax 382-4769
www.sesdweb.net/
Kennard-Dale HS 900/9-12
393 Main St 17321 717-382-4871
Heather Venne, prin. Fax 382-4869
South Eastern MS - East 500/7-8
375 Main St 17321 717-382-4851
Joseph Terch, prin. Fax 382-9033

Feasterville, Bucks, Pop. 3,026
Neshaminy SD
Supt. — See Langhorne
Poquessing MS 600/6-8
300 Heights Ln 19053 215-809-6210
Joann Holland, prin.

Bucks County School of Beauty Culture Post-Sec.
1761 Bustleton Pike 19053 215-322-0666

Finleyville, Washington, Pop. 453
Ringgold SD
Supt. — See New Eagle
Ringgold MS 700/6-8
6023 State Route 88 15332 724-348-7154
Mark Alberta, prin. Fax 348-8839

Fishertown, Bedford
Chestnut Ridge SD 1,600/K-12
3281 Valley Rd 15539 814-839-4195
Mark Kudlawiec, supt. Fax 839-2088
www.crsd.k12.pa.us/
Chestnut Ridge MS 500/5-8
3281 Valley Rd 15539 814-839-4195
Max Shoemaker, prin. Fax 839-2088
Other Schools – See New Paris

Fleetwood, Berks, Pop. 4,046
Fleetwood Area SD 2,700/K-12
801 N Richmond St 19522 610-944-9598
Dr. Paul Eaken, supt. Fax 944-9408
www.fleetwoodasd.k12.pa.us
Fleetwood Area HS 800/9-12
803 N Richmond St 19522 610-944-7656
Thomas Salpino, prin. Fax 944-6952
Fleetwood Area MS 800/5-8
407 N Richmond St 19522 610-944-7634
Christopher Redding, prin. Fax 944-5307

Flinton, Cambria
Glendale SD 800/K-12
1466 Beaver Valley Rd 16640 814-687-3402
Arnold Nadonley, supt. Fax 687-3341
www.gsd1.org
Glendale JSHS 400/7-12
1466 Beaver Valley Rd 16640 814-687-4261
Gary Walstrom, prin. Fax 687-4718

Flourtown, Montgomery, Pop. 4,474

Mount St. Joseph Academy 600/9-12
120 W Wissahickon Ave 19031 215-233-3177
Dr. Judith Caviston, prin. Fax 233-4734

Folcroft, Delaware, Pop. 6,473
Area Vocational Technical School
Supt. — None
Delaware County Technical HS - Folcroft Vo/Tech
701 Henderson Blvd 19032 610-583-7620
Ryan Coughlin, prin. Fax 583-6537

Southeast Delco SD 4,000/K-12
1560 Delmar Dr 19032 610-522-4300
Dr. Stephen D. Butz, supt. Fax 461-4874
www.sedelco.org
Other Schools – See Sharon Hill

Folsom, Delaware, Pop. 8,224
Ridley SD 5,800/K-12
901 Morton Ave 19033 610-534-1900
Lee Ann Wentzel, supt. Fax 534-2335
www.ridleysd.org/
Ridley HS 2,100/9-12
901 Morton Ave 19033 610-237-8034
William Mills, prin. Fax 237-9641
Other Schools – See Ridley Park

Ford City, Armstrong, Pop. 2,961
Area Vocational Technical School
Supt. — None
Lenape Tech Vo/Tech
2215 Chaplin Ave 16226 724-763-7116
Dawn Kocher-Taylor, prin.

Armstrong SD 5,100/K-12
410 Main St 16226 724-763-5200
Dr. Stan Chapp, supt. Fax 763-7295
www.asd.k12.pa.us
Ford City JSHS 700/7-12
1100 4th Ave 16226 724-763-5289
Michael Cominos, prin. Fax 763-7813
Other Schools – See Kittanning, Rural Valley

Forest City, Susquehanna, Pop. 1,887
Forest City Regional SD 900/PK-12
100 Susquehanna St 18421 570-785-2400
John Kopicki, supt. Fax 785-9557
www.fcrsd.org
Forest City Regional JSHS 400/7-12
100 Susquehanna St 18421 570-785-2400
Christine Acevedo, prin. Fax 785-3785

Fort Washington, Montgomery, Pop. 5,372
Upper Dublin SD
Supt. — See Maple Glen
Upper Dublin HS 1,500/9-12
800 Loch Alsh Ave 19034 215-643-8900
Robert Schultz M.Ed., prin. Fax 643-8898

DeVry University Post-Sec.
1140 Virginia Dr 19034 215-591-5700
Germantown Academy 1,100/PK-12
340 Morris Rd 19034 215-646-3300
James Connor, hdmstr. Fax 646-1216

Forty Fort, Luzerne, Pop. 4,182

Fortis Institute Post-Sec.
166 Slocum St 18704 570-288-8400

Foxburg, Clarion, Pop. 183
Allegheny-Clarion Valley SD 800/K-12
PO Box 100 16036 724-659-5820
David McDeavitt, supt. Fax 659-2963
www.acvsd.org/
Allegheny-Clarion Valley JSHS 400/7-12
PO Box 345 16036 724-659-4661
William Jordan, prin. Fax 659-4774

Frackville, Schuylkill, Pop. 3,786
Area Vocational Technical School
Supt. — None
Schuylkill Technology Center - North Vo/Tech
101 Technology Dr 17931 570-874-1034
Cynthia Stasulli, prin. Fax 874-4028

Franklin, Venango, Pop. 6,385
Franklin Area SD 1,800/K-12
702 Liberty St 16323 814-432-8917
Dr. Pamela Dye, supt. Fax 437-5754
www.fasd.k12.pa.us/
Franklin Area HS 700/9-12
246 Pone Ln 16323 814-432-2121
George Forster, prin. Fax 432-5031
Franklin Area MS 300/7-8
246 Pone Ln 16323 814-432-2224
Christina Cohlhepp, prin. Fax 437-1491

Valley Grove SD 1,000/K-12
429 Wiley Ave 16323 814-432-4919
Jeffrey Clark, supt. Fax 437-1243
www.vgsd.org/
Rocky Grove JSHS 400/7-12
403 Rocky Grove Ave 16323 814-437-3759
Matthew LaVerde, prin. Fax 437-1062

Fredericksburg, Lebanon, Pop. 1,345
Northern Lebanon SD 2,400/K-12
PO Box 100 17026 717-865-2117
Dr. Don Bell, supt. Fax 865-0606
www.norleb.k12.pa.us
Northern Lebanon HS 800/9-12
PO Box 100 17026 717-865-2117
Richard Hornberger, prin. Fax 865-7818
Northern Lebanon MS 400/7-8
PO Box 100 17026 717-865-2117
David Yavoich, prin. Fax 865-5835

Fredericktown, Washington, Pop. 397
Bethlehem-Center SD 1,300/K-12
194 Crawford Rd 15333 724-267-4910
Joseph Nepa, supt. Fax 267-4904
www.bc.k12.pa.us
Bethlehem-Center HS 400/9-12
179 Crawford Rd 15333 724-267-4944
Aaron Cornella, prin. Fax 267-4907
Bethlehem-Center MS 300/6-8
136 Crawford Rd 15333 724-267-4935
Amanda Kinneer, prin. Fax 267-4937

Freedom, Beaver, Pop. 1,529
Ambridge Area SD
Supt. — See Ambridge
Ambridge Area JHS 400/7-8
401 1st St 15042 724-266-2833
Megan Mealie, prin. Fax 869-5321

Freedom Area SD 1,300/K-12
1701 8th Ave 15042 724-775-5464
Dr. Jeffrey Fuller, supt. Fax 775-7434
www.freedomareaschools.org
Freedom Area HS 600/9-12
1190 Bulldog Dr 15042 724-775-7400
Timothy Dadich, prin. Fax 775-7753
Freedom Area MS 200/5-8
1701 8th Ave 15042 724-775-7641
Darlene Corris, prin. Fax 775-7748

Freeland, Luzerne, Pop. 3,500

MMI Prep S 300/6-12
154 Centre St 18224 570-636-1108
Thomas G. Hood, head sch Fax 636-0742

Freeport, Armstrong, Pop. 1,775
Freeport Area SD
Supt. — See Sarver
Freeport Area JHS 300/7-8
325 4th St 16229 724-295-9020
Donald Dell, prin. Fax 295-4630

Friedens, Somerset, Pop. 1,520
Shanksville-Stonycreek SD 300/PK-12
1325 Corner Stone Rd 15541 814-267-6499
Thomas McInroy, supt. Fax 267-4372
www.sssd.com
Other Schools – See Shanksville

Galeton, Potter, Pop. 1,134
Galeton Area SD 400/PK-12
27 Bridge St 16922 814-435-6571
David Wishard, supt. Fax 435-6981
gasd.net
Galeton Area S 400/PK-12
25 Bridge St 16922 814-435-6571
Larry Smith, prin. Fax 435-6981

Gallitzin, Cambria, Pop. 1,656
Penn Cambria SD
Supt. — See Cresson
Penn Cambria MS 500/5-8
401 Division St 16641 814-886-4181
Jeff Baird, prin. Fax 886-9308

Geigertown, Berks

High Point Baptist Academy 300/K-12
PO Box 188 19523 610-286-5942
Brad Feldmeier, admin. Fax 286-7525

Gettysburg, Adams, Pop. 7,466
Gettysburg Area SD 2,900/K-12
900 Biglerville Rd 17325 717-334-6254
Dr. Larry Redding, supt. Fax 334-5220
www.gettysburg.k12.pa.us
Gettysburg Area HS 1,200/9-12
1130 Old Harrisburg Rd 17325 717-334-6254
Mark Blanchard, prin. Fax 337-4439
Gettysburg Area MS 700/6-8
37 Lefever St 17325 717-334-6254
Dr. James O'Connor, prin. Fax 334-6999

Adams County Christian Academy 100/PK-12
1865 Biglerville Rd 17325 717-334-9177
Rhonda Fertich, prin. Fax 334-7691
Freedom Christian S 100/PK-12
3185 York Rd 17325 717-624-3884
Karen Trout, prin. Fax 624-1562
Gettysburg College Post-Sec.
300 N Washington St 17325 717-337-6300
Gettysburg SDA S 50/PK-11
1493 Biglerville Rd 17325 717-338-0131
Lutheran Theological Seminary Post-Sec.
61 Seminary Rdg 17325 717-334-6286

Gibsonia, Allegheny, Pop. 2,710
Pine-Richland SD 4,600/K-12
702 Warrendale Rd 15044 724-625-7773
Dr. Mary Bucci, supt. Fax 625-1490
www.pinerichland.org
Pine-Richland HS 1,500/9-12
700 Warrendale Rd 15044 724-625-4444
John Pietrusinski, prin. Fax 625-4640
Pine-Richland MS 800/7-8
100 Logan Rd 15044 724-625-3111
David Kristofic, prin. Fax 625-3144

Aquinas Academy 300/K-12
2308 W Hardies Rd 15044 724-444-0722
Leslie Mitros, hdmstr. Fax 444-0750

Gilbertsville, Montgomery, Pop. 4,774
Boyertown Area SD
Supt. — See Boyertown
Boyertown Area JHS East 900/7-9
2020 Big Rd 19525 610-754-9550
Andrew Ruppert, prin. Fax 754-9567

Girard, Erie, Pop. 3,073
Girard SD 2,000/PK-12
1203 Lake St 16417 814-774-5666
Dr. James Tracy, supt. Fax 774-4220
www.girardsd.org
Girard HS 600/9-12
1135 Lake St 16417 814-774-5607
Gregg McClelland, prin. Fax 774-2239
Rice Avenue MS 600/5-8
1100 Rice Ave 16417 814-774-5604
David Koma, prin. Fax 774-5259

Glen Mills, Delaware
Garnet Valley SD, 80 Station Rd 19342 4,800/K-12
Dr. Marc Bertrando, supt. 610-579-7300
www.garnetvalleyschools.com/
Garnet Valley HS 1,500/9-12
552 Smithbridge Rd 19342 610-579-7745
Dr. Joseph Hook, prin.
Garnet Valley MS 1,200/6-8
601 Smithbridge Rd 19342 610-579-5100
M. Christopher Marchese, prin.

Glen Rock, York, Pop. 1,997
Southern York County SD 3,200/K-12
PO Box 128 17327 717-235-4811
Dr. Thomas Hensley, supt. Fax 235-0863
www.syc.k12.pa.us
Southern MS 500/7-8
PO Box 128 17327 717-235-4811
Dr. Len Reppert, prin. Fax 227-9681
Susquehannock HS 1,000/9-12
PO Box 128 17327 717-235-4811
Dr. Robert Bryson, prin. Fax 227-1951

Glenshaw, Allegheny, Pop. 8,914
Shaler Area SD 4,900/K-12
1800 Mount Royal Blvd 15116 412-492-1200
Dr. Wesley Shipley, supt. Fax 492-1293
www.sasd.k12.pa.us
Shaler Area MS 800/7-8
1810 Mount Royal Blvd 15116 412-492-1200
Martin Martynuska, prin. Fax 492-1237
Other Schools – See Pittsburgh

Glenside, Montgomery, Pop. 8,249

Arcadia University Post-Sec.
450 S Easton Rd 19038 215-572-2900
LaSalle College HS 1,100/9-12
8605 Cheltenham Ave 19038 215-233-2911
Joseph Marchese, prin. Fax 233-1418
Princeton Information Technology Center Post-Sec.
140 S Easton Rd 19038 215-576-5650
Won Institute of Graduate Studies Post-Sec.
137 S Easton Rd 19038 215-884-8942

Greencastle, Franklin, Pop. 3,946
Greencastle-Antrim SD 3,000/K-12
500 Leitersburg St 17225 717-597-3226
C. Gregory Hoover Ed.D., supt. Fax 597-2180
www.greencastle.k12.pa.us
Greencastle-Antrim HS 1,000/9-12
300 S Ridge Ave 17225 717-597-3226
Edward Rife, prin. Fax 597-2912
Greencastle-Antrim MS 700/6-8
370 S Ridge Ave 17225 717-597-3226
Mark Herman, prin. Fax 597-6468

Shady Grove Mennonite S 200/1-10
1442 Buchanan Trl E 17225 717-597-0843

Greensboro, Greene, Pop. 254
Southeastern Greene SD 600/K-12
1000 Mapletown Rd 15338 724-943-3630
William Henderson, supt. Fax 943-3052
www.segsd.org
Mapletown JSHS 300/7-12
1000 Mapletown Rd 15338 724-943-3401
Jason Pappas, prin. Fax 943-4769

Greensburg, Westmoreland, Pop. 14,523
Greensburg Salem SD 2,900/K-12
1 Academy Hill Pl 15601 724-832-2901
Dr. Eileen Amato, supt. Fax 832-2968
www.greensburgsalem.org
Greensburg Salem HS 1,000/9-12
65 Mennel Dr 15601 724-832-2960
David Zilli, prin. Fax 832-2922
Greensburg Salem MS 600/6-8
301 N Main St 15601 724-832-2930
Todd McMillen, prin. Fax 832-2937

Hempfield Area SD 6,200/K-12
4347 State Route 136 15601 724-834-2590
Andrew Leopold, supt. Fax 850-2298
www.hasdpa.net
Harrold MS 500/6-8
1368 Middletown Rd 15601 724-850-2301
Jason Lochner, prin. Fax 850-2302
Hempfield Area HS 2,000/9-12
4345 State Route 136 15601 724-834-9000
Kathy Charlton, prin. Fax 850-2090
Wendover MS 500/6-8
425 Wendover Jr High Rd 15601 724-838-4070
Deanna Mikesic, prin. Fax 838-4071
Other Schools – See Irwin

Education and Technology Institute Post-Sec.
219 Donohoe Rd 15601 724-836-2395
Greensburg Central Catholic JSHS 500/7-12
911 Armory Dr 15601 724-834-0310
Denise Myers, prin. Fax 834-2472
K.A.R.A.T. S of Learning 50/6-12
701 Sheridan Ave 15601 724-420-5316
Susan McDonald, head sch Fax 216-5160
Lake Erie College/Osteopathic Medicine Post-Sec.
20 Seton Hill Dr 15601 724-552-2880
Seton Hill University Post-Sec.
Seton Hill Dr 15601 724-834-2200
Triangle Tech Post-Sec.
222 E Pittsburgh St # A 15601 724-832-1050
University of Pittsburgh Post-Sec.
150 Finoli Dr 15601 724-837-7040
Westmoreland Christian Academy 100/PK-12
538 Rugh St 15601 724-853-8308
Jordan Tomson, prin. Fax 836-7472

Greenville, Mercer, Pop. 5,850
Greenville Area SD 1,400/K-12
9 Donation Rd 16125 724-588-2502
Dr. Patrick Hefflin, supt. Fax 588-5024
www.greenville.k12.pa.us
Greenville JSHS 700/7-12
9 Donation Rd 16125 724-588-2500
Joseph Tucci, prin. Fax 588-4397

Reynolds SD 1,300/PK-12
531 Reynolds Rd 16125 724-646-5501
Joseph Neuch, supt. Fax 646-5505
www.reynolds.k12.pa.us
Reynolds JSHS 600/7-12
531 Reynolds Rd 16125 724-646-5701
Scott Shearer, prin Fax 646-5705

Living Word Christian S 50/1-12
21 S Maysville Rd 16125 724-588-2140
Jan Chapin, admin. Fax 588-8742
Thiel College Post-Sec.
75 College Ave 16125 724-589-2000

Grove City, Mercer, Pop. 8,236
Grove City Area SD 1,800/K-12
511 Highland Ave 16127 724-458-6733
Dr. Richard Mextorf, supt. Fax 458-5868
www.grovecity.k12.pa.us
Grove City Area HS 800/9-12
511 Highland Ave 16127 724-458-5456
Dr. RaeLin Howard, prin. Fax 450-0678
Grove City Area MS 300/6-8
100 Middle School Dr 16127 724-458-8040
Larry Connelly, prin. Fax 450-0780

Grove City College Post-Sec.
100 Campus Dr 16127 724-458-2000

Guys Mills, Crawford, Pop. 121
Penncrest SD
Supt. — See Saegertown
Maplewood JSHS 600/7-12
30383 Guys Mills Rd 16327 814-789-3666
Michael Costa, prin. Fax 789-2409

Faith Builders Christian S 100/1-12
28500 Guys Mills Rd 16327 814-789-2303
Gerald Miller, prin. Fax 789-3396

Gwynedd Valley, Montgomery

Gwynedd-Mercy Academy 400/9-12
PO Box 902 19437 215-646-8815
Sr. Patricia Flynn, prin. Fax 646-4361
Gwynedd-Mercy College Post-Sec.
PO Box 901 19437 215-646-7300

Hadley, Mercer
Commodore Perry SD 500/K-12
3002 Perry Hwy 16130 724-253-3255
Richard Rossi, supt. Fax 253-3467
www.cppanthers.org/CPWeb.htm
Perry JSHS 300/7-12
3002 Perry Hwy 16130 724-253-2232
Doug Mays, prin. Fax 253-3467

Halifax, Dauphin, Pop. 814
Halifax Area SD 1,100/PK-12
3940 Peters Mountain Rd 17032 717-896-3416
Robert Hassinger, supt. Fax 896-3976
www.hasd.us
Halifax Area HS 400/9-12
3940 Peters Mountain Rd 17032 717-896-3416
David Hatfield, prin. Fax 896-3976
Halifax Area MS 200/6-8
3940 Peters Mountain Rd 17032 717-896-3416
Gregory Milbrand, prin. Fax 896-3976

Hamburg, Berks, Pop. 4,259
Hamburg Area SD 2,400/K-12
Windsor St 19526 610-562-2241
Steven Keifer, supt. Fax 562-2634
www.hasdhawks.org
Hamburg Area HS 800/9-12
701 Windsor St 19526 610-562-3861
Christopher Spohn, prin. Fax 561-3394
Hamburg Area MS 600/6-8
Windsor St 19526 610-562-3990
Kenneth Buck, prin. Fax 562-1425

Blue Mountain Academy 200/9-12
2363 Mountain Rd 19526 484-662-7000

Hanover, York, Pop. 15,077
Hanover Public SD 1,600/K-12
403 Moul Ave 17331 717-637-9000
Dr. Alan Moyer, supt. Fax 630-4617
www.hpsd.k12.pa.us
Hanover HS 500/9-12
401 Moul Ave 17331 717-637-9000
Joel Hain, prin. Fax 630-4634
Hanover MS 500/5-8
300 Keagy Ave 17331 717-637-9000
Mark Hershner, prin. Fax 630-4632

South Western SD 4,100/K-12
225 Bowman Rd Ste 2 17331 717-632-2500
Dr. Barbara Rupp, supt. Fax 632-7993
www.swsd.k12.pa.us/
Markle IS 900/6-8
225 Bowman Rd Ste 1 17331 717-633-4840
Kevin Duckworth, prin. Fax 633-7073
South Western HS 1,300/9-12
200 Bowman Rd 17331 717-632-2500
Walt Graves, prin. Fax 633-4819

Empire Beauty School Post-Sec.
1000 Carlisle St 17331 717-633-6201
St. Joseph MS 100/6-8
5125 Grandview Rd 17331 717-632-0118
Susan Mummert, prin. Fax 632-0030

Hanover Twp, Lehigh
Hanover Area SD 1,600/K-12
1600 Sans Souci Pkwy 18706 570-831-2300
Anthony Podczasy, supt. Fax 831-2322
www.hanoverarea.org
Hanover Area JSHS 900/7-12
1600 Sans Souci Pkwy 18706 570-831-2300
David Fisher, prin. Fax 831-2316

Harborcreek, Erie
Harbor Creek SD 2,000/K-12
6375 Buffalo Rd 16421 814-897-2100
Dr. Patricia Hawley-Horner, supt. Fax 897-2142
www.hcsd.iu5.org
Harbor Creek HS 700/9-12
6375 Buffalo Rd 16421 814-897-2100
Andrew Krahe, prin. Fax 897-2136
Harbor Creek JHS 300/7-8
6375 Buffalo Rd 16421 814-897-2100
Pamela Chodubski, prin. Fax 897-2121

Harleysville, Montgomery, Pop. 9,178
Souderton Area SD
Supt. — See Souderton
Indian Valley MS 800/6-8
130 Maple Ave 19438 215-256-8896
Dr. Dale Burkhard, prin. Fax 256-1288

Harmony, Butler, Pop. 882
Seneca Valley SD 7,300/K-12
124 Seneca School Rd 16037 724-452-6040
Dr. Tracy Vitale, supt. Fax 452-6105
www.svsd.net/
Seneca Valley Intermediate HS 1,100/9-10
126 Seneca School Rd 16037 724-452-6040
Alan Cumo, prin. Fax 452-3718
Seneca Valley MS 1,100/7-8
122 Seneca School Rd 16037 724-452-6040
Andrea Peck, prin. Fax 452-0331
Seneca Valley SHS 1,100/11-12
128 Seneca School Rd 16037 724-452-6040
Mark Korcinsky, prin. Fax 452-8357

Harrisburg, Dauphin, Pop. 47,794
Area Vocational Technical School
Supt. — None
Dauphin County Technical S Vo/Tech
6001 Locust Ln 17109 717-652-3170
Dr. Kevin Lacey, prin. Fax 652-9326

Central Dauphin SD 10,700/K-12
600 Rutherford Rd 17109 717-545-4703
Dr. Carol Johnson, supt. Fax 545-5624
www.cdschools.org
Central Dauphin East HS 1,400/9-12
626 Rutherford Rd 17109 717-541-1662
Dr. Jesse Rawls, prin. Fax 545-7139
Central Dauphin East MS 600/6-8
628 Rutherford Rd 17109 717-545-4703
Christine Miller, prin. Fax 657-4987
Central Dauphin HS 1,800/9-12
437 Piketown Rd 17112 717-703-5360
Ken Miller, prin. Fax 703-5730
Central Dauphin MS 700/6-8
4600 Locust Ln 17109 717-540-4606
Jeffrey Matzner, prin. Fax 214-5055
Linglestown MS 700/6-8
1200 N Mountain Rd 17112 717-657-3060
David Wright, prin. Fax 657-0537
Other Schools – See Steelton

Harrisburg City SD 5,300/PK-12
2101 N Front St Bldg 2 17110 717-703-4000
Dr. Sybil Knight-Burney, supt. Fax 703-4115
www.hbgsd.k12.pa.us
Camp Curtin S 300/5-8
2900 N 6th St 17110 717-703-4200
Portia Slaughter, prin. Fax 703-4225
Harrisburg HS 1,800/9-12
2451 Market St 17103 717-703-4300
Eugene Spells, prin. Fax 703-4333
Marshall S 200/5-8
301 Hale Ave 17104 717-703-1400
Marisol Craig, prin. Fax 703-1420
Math Science Academy @ Marshall S 200/Alt
301 Hale Ave 17104 717-703-1200
Marisol Craig, prin. Fax 703-1215
Rowland S 600/5-8
1842 Derry St 17104 717-703-4500
Roma Benjamin, prin. Fax 703-4520
Sci-Tech HS 400/9-12
215 Market St 17101 717-703-1900
Sieta Achampong, dir. Fax 703-1915

Susquehanna Township SD 3,000/K-12
2579 Interstate Dr 17110 717-657-5100
Dr. Susan Kegerise, supt. Fax 724-1851
www.hannasd.org
Susquehanna Township HS 1,000/9-12
3500 Elmerton Ave 17109 717-657-5117
Ralph Lovelidge, prin. Fax 657-2919
Susquehanna Township MS 700/6-8
801 Wood St 17109 717-657-5125
Harold Wilson, prin. Fax 657-2919

Bishop McDevitt HS 700/9-12
1 Crusader Way 17111 717-236-7973
Sr. Mary Anne Bednar, prin. Fax 234-1270
Covenant Christian Academy 200/PK-12
1982 Locust Ln 17109 717-540-9885
Joseph Sanelli, hdmstr. Fax 540-7176
Empire Beauty School Post-Sec.
3941 Jonestown Rd 17109 717-652-8500
Harrisburg Area Community College Post-Sec.
1 Hacc Dr 17110 717-780-2300
Harrisburg Christian S 300/K-12
2000 Blue Mountain Pkwy 17112 717-545-3728
Phillip Puleo, hdmstr. Fax 545-9370
Harrisburg University of Science & Tech Post-Sec.
326 Market St 17101 717-901-5100
ITT Technical Institute Post-Sec.
449 Eisenhower Blvd Ste 100 17111 717-565-1700
Kaplan Career Institute Post-Sec.
5650 Derry St 17111 717-564-4112
Keystone Technical Institute Post-Sec.
2301 Academy Dr 17112 717-545-4747
Widener University School of Law Post-Sec.
PO Box 69380 17106 717-541-3900

Harrison City, Westmoreland, Pop. 134
Penn-Trafford SD 4,200/K-12
PO Box 530 15636 724-744-4496
Dr. Thomas Butler, supt. Fax 744-4016
www.penntrafford.org
Penn-Trafford HS 1,500/9-12
3381 Route 130 15636 724-744-4471
Scott Inglese, prin. Fax 744-1214
Other Schools – See Jeannette, Trafford

Hatboro, Montgomery, Pop. 7,268
Upper Moreland Township SD
Supt. — See Willow Grove
Upper Moreland MS 700/6-8
4000 Orangemans Rd 19040 215-674-4185
Charles Hafele, prin. Fax 956-1906

Hatfield, Montgomery, Pop. 3,211
North Penn SD
Supt. — See Lansdale
Northbridge S Alt
2374 N Penn Rd 19440 215-412-4009
Debra Harper, prin. Fax 853-1627
Pennfield MS 800/7-9
726 Forty Foot Rd 19440 215-368-9600
Dr. Barbara Galloway, prin. Fax 368-9791

Biblical Theological Seminary Post-Sec.
200 N Main St 19440 800-235-4021

Haverford, Montgomery, Pop. 6,000

Haverford College Post-Sec.
370 Lancaster Ave 19041 610-896-1000
Haverford S 1,000/PK-12
450 Lancaster Ave 19041 610-642-3020
Joseph Cox Ph.D., hdmstr. Fax 649-4898

Havertown, Delaware, Pop. 30,000
Haverford Township SD 5,600/K-12
50 E Eagle Rd 19083 610-853-5900
William Keilbaugh Ed.D., supt. Fax 853-5942
www.haverford.k12.pa.us
Haverford HS 1,800/9-12
200 Mill Rd 19083 610-853-5900
Jeffrey Nesbitt Ed.D., prin. Fax 853-5952
Haverford MS 1,300/6-8
1701 Darby Rd 19083 610-853-5900
Daniel Horan, prin. Fax 853-5937

Hawley, Pike, Pop. 1,191
Wallenpaupack Area SD 3,500/K-12
2552 Route 6 18428 570-226-4557
Michael Silsby, supt. Fax 226-0638
www.wallenpaupack.org/
Wallenpaupack Area HS 1,300/9-12
2552 Route 6 18428 570-226-4557
Jay Starnes, prin. Fax 251-3153
Wallenpaupack Area MS 900/6-8
139 Atlantic Ave 18428 570-226-4557
Keith Gunuskey, prin. Fax 251-3165

Hazleton, Luzerne, Pop. 25,114
Hazleton Area SD
Supt. — See Hazle Township
Hazleton S 1,100/3-8
700 N Wyoming St 18201 570-459-3221
Maureen DeRose, prin. Fax 501-8433

Academy of Hair Design Post-Sec.
1057 N Church St # A 18202 570-784-1020
Immanuel Christian S 100/K-12
725 N Locust St 18201 570-459-1111
Kelly Knowlden, prin. Fax 459-6920
McCann School of Business & Technology Post-Sec.
370 Maplewood Dr 18202 570-454-6172
Penn State Hazleton Post-Sec.
76 University Dr 18202 570-450-3000

Hazle Township, Luzerne
Area Vocational Technical School
Supt. — None
Hazleton Area Career Center Vo/Tech
1451 W 23rd St, 570-459-3221
Lori Herman, prin. Fax 459-3181

Hazleton Area SD 10,200/K-12
1515 W 23rd St 18202 570-459-3111
Dr. Frank Antonelli, supt. Fax 459-3118
www.hasdk12.org
Hazle Building 9th Grade Center 800/9-9
1400 W 23rd St, 570-459-3221
Rocco Petrone, prin. Fax 450-6547
Hazleton Area HS 2,600/10-12
1601 W 23rd St, 570-459-3221
Rocco Petrone, prin. Fax 459-3242
Other Schools – See Hazleton

Hegins, Schuylkill, Pop. 805
Tri-Valley SD
Supt. — See Valley View
Tri-Valley JSHS 400/7-12
155 E Main St 17938 570-682-3125
Charles Hall, prin. Fax 682-9873

Hellertown, Northampton, Pop. 5,840
Saucon Valley SD 2,400/K-12
2097 Polk Valley Rd 18055 610-838-7026
Sandra Fellin, supt. Fax 838-6419
www.svpanthers.org
Saucon Valley HS 800/9-12
2100 Polk Valley Rd 18055 610-838-7001
Eric Kahler, prin. Fax 838-2365
Saucon Valley MS 600/6-8
2095 Polk Valley Rd 18055 610-838-7071
Pamela Bernardo, prin. Fax 838-7473

Herminie, Westmoreland, Pop. 785
Yough SD 2,300/K-12
915 Lowber Rd 15637 724-446-7272
Dr. Janet Sardon, supt. Fax 446-5017
www.yough.net
Yough HS 800/9-12
919 Lowber Rd 15637 724-446-5520
Earl Thompson, prin. Fax 446-6008
Other Schools – See Ruffs Dale

Hermitage, Mercer, Pop. 16,014
Hermitage SD 1,900/K-12
411 N Hermitage Rd 16148 724-981-8750
Dr. Daniel Bell, supt. Fax 981-5080
www.hermitage.k12.pa.us
Hickory HS 700/8-12
640 N Hermitage Rd 16148 724-981-8750
Chris Gill, prin. Fax 347-4558

Kennedy Catholic HS 200/9-12
2120 Shenango Valley Fwy 16148 724-346-5531
Heidi Patterson, prin. Fax 346-3011
Kennedy Catholic MS 100/6-8
2120 Shenango Valley Fwy 16148 724-346-5531
Victoria Wagner, prin. Fax 346-3011

Herndon, Northumberland, Pop. 322
Line Mountain SD 1,200/K-12
185 Line Mountain Rd 17830 570-758-2640
David Campbell, supt. Fax 758-2842
www.linemountain.com
Line Mountain JSHS 600/7-12
187 Line Mountain Rd 17830 570-758-2011
Jeffrey Roadcap, prin. Fax 758-1514

Hershey, Dauphin, Pop. 13,934
Derry Township SD 3,600/K-12
PO Box 898 17033 717-534-2501
Joseph McFarland, supt. Fax 533-4357
www.hershey.k12.pa.us
Hershey HS 1,100/9-12
PO Box 898 17033 717-531-2244
Dale Reimann, prin. Fax 534-2684
Hershey MS 900/6-8
PO Box 898 17033 717-531-2222
Stacey Winslow, prin. Fax 531-2245

Hershey S 1,800/PK-12
PO Box 830 17033 717-520-2000
Dr. Anthony Colistra, pres. Fax 520-2002
M. Hershey Medical Center Coll of Med. Post-Sec.
500 University Dr 17033 717-531-8521

Hilltown, Bucks

St. Agnes-Sacred Heart MS 100/5-8
PO Box 31 18927 215-822-9174
Margaret Graham, prin. Fax 822-7942

Holland, Bucks, Pop. 5,300
Council Rock SD
Supt. — See Newtown
Council Rock HS South 2,100/9-12
2002 Rock Way 18966 215-944-1100
Al Funk, prin. Fax 944-1145
Holland MS 700/7-8
400 E Holland Rd 18966 215-944-2700
Daniel Greenland, prin. Fax 944-2789

Villa Joseph Marie HS 400/9-12
1180 Holland Rd 18966 215-357-8810
Diana Koopman, prin. Fax 357-2477

Hollidaysburg, Blair, Pop. 5,745
Hollidaysburg Area SD 3,200/K-12
201 Jackson St 16648 814-695-8702
Dr. Paul Gallagher, supt. Fax 695-2315
www.tigerwires.com
Hollidaysburg Area JHS 900/7-9
1000 Hewit St 16648 814-695-4426
Edward Barton, prin. Fax 696-2959
Hollidaysburg Area SHS 800/10-12
1500 N Montgomery St 16648 814-695-4416
Linda McCall, prin. Fax 696-2958

Hollsopple, Somerset

Johnstown Christian S 200/PK-12
125 Christian School Rd 15935 814-288-2588
Dr. Kathy Keafer, admin. Fax 288-1447

Homer City, Indiana, Pop. 1,691
Homer-Center SD 900/K-12
65 Wildcat Ln 15748 724-479-8080
Dr. Charles Koren, supt. Fax 479-3967
homercenter.org/
Homer-Center JSHS 400/7-12
70 Wildcat Ln 15748 724-479-8026
Jody Rainey, prin. Fax 479-4236

Honesdale, Wayne, Pop. 4,431
Wayne Highlands SD 3,000/K-12
474 Grove St 18431 570-253-4661
Gregory Frigoletto, supt. Fax 253-9409
www.waynehighlands.org
Honesdale HS 1,000/9-12
459 Terrace St 18431 570-253-2046
Diane Scarfalloto, prin. Fax 253-1502
Wayne Highlands MS 500/6-8
482 Grove St 18431 570-253-5900
Chris Pietraszewski, prin. Fax 253-5259

Hookstown, Beaver, Pop. 144
South Side Area SD 1,200/PK-12
4949 Route 151 15050 724-573-9581
Michael Bjalobok Ed.D., supt. Fax 573-0414
www.sssd.k12.pa.us/
South Side IS 200/8-9
4949 Route 151 15050 724-573-9581
Samuel Adams, prin. Fax 573-0449
South Side SHS 300/10-12
4949 Route 151 15050 724-573-9581
Anthony Paull, prin. Fax 573-0449

Horsham, Montgomery, Pop. 14,608
Hatboro-Horsham SD 5,000/K-12
229 Meetinghouse Rd 19044 215-420-5000
Dr. Curtis Griffin, supt. Fax 420-5262
www.hatboro-horsham.org
Hatboro-Horsham HS 1,700/9-12
899 Horsham Rd 19044 215-420-5500
Dennis Williams, prin. Fax 420-5613
Keith Valley MS 1,200/6-8
227 Meetinghouse Rd 19044 215-420-5050
Jonathan Kircher, prin. Fax 420-5291

Houston, Washington, Pop. 1,253
Chartiers-Houston SD 1,100/K-12
2020 W Pike St 15342 724-746-1400
John George, supt. Fax 746-3971
www.chbucs.k12.pa.us/
Chartiers-Houston JSHS 500/7-12
2050 W Pike St 15342 724-745-3350
Philip Mary, prin. Fax 745-3495

Houtzdale, Clearfield, Pop. 791
Moshannon Valley SD 900/K-12
4934 Green Acre Rd 16651 814-378-7609
Tonya C. DeVecchis-Kerr, supt. Fax 378-7100
www.movalley.org
Moshannon Valley JSHS 400/7-12
4934 Green Acre Rd 16651 814-378-7616
John Dibert, prin. Fax 378-5205

Hughesville, Lycoming, Pop. 2,101
Area Vocational Technical School
Supt. — None
Lycoming CTC Vo/Tech
293 Cemetery St 17737 570-584-2300
Eric Butler, prin.

East Lycoming SD 1,600/K-12
349 Cemetery St 17737 570-584-2131
Michael Pawlik, supt. Fax 584-5701
www.eastlycoming.net
Hughesville JSHS 800/7-12
349 Cemetery St 17737 570-584-5111
Ron Lorson, prin. Fax 584-5378

Hummelstown, Dauphin, Pop. 4,481
Lower Dauphin SD 3,800/K-12
291 E Main St 17036 717-566-5300
Dr. Sherri Smith, supt. Fax 566-3670
www.ldsd.org
Lower Dauphin HS 1,200/9-12
201 S Hanover St 17036 717-566-5330
Todd Neuhard, prin. Fax 566-3970
Lower Dauphin MS 900/6-8
251 Quarry Rd 17036 717-566-5310
Daniel Berra, prin. Fax 566-5383

Hershey Christian S 300/K-12
1525 Sand Hill Rd 17036 717-533-4900
Al Roth, hdmstr. Fax 835-0256

Huntingdon, Huntingdon, Pop. 6,994
Huntingdon Area SD 1,900/K-12
2400 Cassady Ave Ste 2 16652 814-643-4140
Fred Foster, supt. Fax 643-6244
www.hasd.tiu.k12.pa.us/
Huntingdon Area HS 700/9-12
2400 Cassady Ave 16652 814-643-1080
Brian Pelka, prin. Fax 643-3800
Huntingdon Area MS 500/6-8
2500 Cassady Ave 16652 814-643-2900
Patricia Wargo, prin. Fax 643-6513

DuBois Business College Post-Sec.
1001 Moore St 16652 814-641-0440
Juniata College Post-Sec.
1700 Moore St 16652 814-641-3000

Huntingdon Valley, Montgomery, Pop. 10,000
Lower Moreland Township SD 2,100/K-12
2551 Murray Ave 19006 215-938-0270
Dr. Marykay Feeley, supt. Fax 947-6933
www.lmtsd.org
Lower Moreland HS 700/9-12
555 Red Lion Rd 19006 215-938-0220
Julien Drennan, prin. Fax 947-0333
Murray Avenue MS 500/6-8
2551 Murray Ave 19006 215-938-0230
Jennifer Dilks, prin. Fax 947-3697

Huntingdon Valley Christian Academy 100/PK-10
1845 Byberry Rd 19006 215-947-6595
Richard Bianco, prin. Fax 947-4277

Immaculata, Chester

Immaculata University Post-Sec.
1145 King Rd 19345 610-647-4400

Imperial, Allegheny, Pop. 2,507
West Allegheny SD
Supt. — See Oakdale
West Allegheny HS 1,000/9-12
205 W Allegheny Rd 15126 724-695-5245
Daniel Smith, prin. Fax 695-8690
West Allegheny MS 800/6-8
207 W Allegheny Rd 15126 724-695-8979
Rick Smith, prin. Fax 695-8211

Indiana, Indiana, Pop. 13,787
Area Vocational Technical School
Supt. — None
Indiana County Technology Center Vo/Tech
441 Hamill Rd 15701 724-349-6700
Carol Fry, dir.

Indiana Area SD 2,300/K-12
501 E Pike Rd 15701 724-463-8713
Dale Kirsch, supt. Fax 463-0868
www.iasd.cc
Indiana Area JHS 400/6-8
245 N 5th St 15701 724-463-8568
Michael Minnick, prin. Fax 463-2133
Indiana Area SHS 700/9-12
450 N 5th St 15701 724-463-8562
Wade McElheny, prin. Fax 463-9709

Cambria-Rowe Business College Post-Sec.
422 S 13th St 15701 724-463-0222
Indiana University of Pennsylvania Post-Sec.
15705 724-357-2100
Seeds of Faith Christian Academy 100/PK-12
640 Church St 15701 724-463-7719
Dr. Stan Kesler, prin. Fax 463-8097

Industry, Beaver, Pop. 1,815
Western Beaver County SD
Supt. — See Midland
Western Beaver County JSHS 500/6-12
216 Engle Rd 15052 724-643-8500
Steve Wellendorf, prin. Fax 643-8504

Irwin, Westmoreland, Pop. 3,935
Hempfield Area SD
Supt. — See Greensburg
West Hempfield MS 500/6-8
156 Northumberland Dr 15642 724-850-2140
Aaron Steinly, prin. Fax 850-2141

Jamestown, Mercer, Pop. 614
Jamestown Area SD 600/K-12
PO Box 217 16134 724-932-5557
Shane Murray, supt. Fax 932-5632
www.jamestown.k12.pa.us
Jamestown Area JSHS 300/7-12
PO Box 217 16134 724-932-3186
Brian Keyser, prin.

Jamison, Bucks
Area Vocational Technical School
Supt. — None
Middle Bucks Institute of Tech Vo/Tech
2740 York Rd 18929 215-343-2480
Kathryn Strouse, hdmstr. Fax 343-8626

Jeannette, Westmoreland, Pop. 9,284
Jeannette CSD 1,200/K-12
198 Park St 15644 724-523-5497
Matthew Hutcheson, supt. Fax 523-3289
www.jeannette.k12.pa.us/
Jeannette HS 400/9-12
800 Florida Ave 15644 724-523-5591
Patricia Rozycki, prin. Fax 523-2313
Jeannette McKee MS 300/6-8
1000 Lowry Ave 15644 724-527-1591
Matthew Jones, prin. Fax 523-6792

Penn-Trafford SD
Supt. — See Harrison City
Penn MS 600/6-8
11 Penn Middle Way 15644 724-744-4431
James Simpson, prin. Fax 744-1215

Christian Fellowship Academy 200/PK-12
2005 Ridge Rd 15644 724-523-2358
Kathy Gustovich, prin. Fax 523-5439

Jefferson, Greene, Pop. 979
Jefferson-Morgan SD 700/K-12
PO Box 158 15344 724-883-2310
Donna Furnier, supt. Fax 883-4942
www.jmsd.org/
Jefferson-Morgan HS 300/9-12
PO Box 158 15344 724-883-2310
Bartolomew Donley, prin. Fax 883-3786
Jefferson-Morgan MS 7-8
PO Box 158 15344 724-883-2310
Carol Korber, prin. Fax 883-3786

Jefferson Hills, Allegheny, Pop. 9,642
Area Vocational Technical School
Supt. — None
Steel Center AVTS Vo/Tech
565 N Lewis Run Rd 15025 412-469-3200
Kevin Rice, prin. Fax 469-2196

West Jefferson Hills SD 2,800/K-12
835 Old Clairton Rd 15025 412-655-8450
Dr. Michael A. Panza, supt. Fax 655-9544
www.wjhsd.net
Jefferson HS 900/9-12
310 Old Clairton Rd 15025 412-655-8610
Timothy Haselhoff, prin. Fax 655-8618
Other Schools – See Pittsburgh

Jenkintown, Montgomery, Pop. 4,346
Jenkintown SD 600/K-12
325 Highland Ave 19046 215-885-3722
Dr. Timothy Wade, supt. Fax 885-2090
www.jenkintown.org/
Jenkintown JSHS 300/7-12
325 Highland Ave 19046 215-884-1801
Thomas Roller, prin. Fax 885-2090

Abington Friends S 700/PK-12
575 Washington Ln 19046 215-886-4350
Richard Nourie, hdmstr. Fax 886-9143
Manor College Post-Sec.
700 Fox Chase Rd 19046 215-885-2360
St. Basil Academy 400/9-12
711 Fox Chase Rd 19046 215-885-3771
Sr. Carla Hernandez, prin. Fax 885-4025

Jersey Shore, Lycoming, Pop. 4,319
Jersey Shore Area SD 2,700/K-12
175 A and P Dr 17740 570-398-1561
Richard Emery, supt. Fax 398-5089
www.jsasd.k12.pa.us
Jersey Shore Area HS 900/9-12
701 Cemetery St 17740 570-398-7170
Reed Mellinger, prin. Fax 398-5612
Jersey Shore Area MS 600/6-8
601 Thompson St 17740 570-398-7400
Laura Milarch, prin. Fax 398-5618

Jessup, Lackawanna, Pop. 4,627

LaSalle Academy 200/4-8
309 1st Ave 18434 570-489-2010
Ellen Murphy, prin. Fax 489-3887

Jim Thorpe, Carbon, Pop. 4,724
Area Vocational Technical School
Supt. — None
Carbon Career & Technical Institute Vo/Tech
150 W 13th St 18229 570-325-3682
David Reinbold, prin.

Jim Thorpe Area SD 2,200/K-12
410 Center Ave 18229 570-325-3691
Dr. Barbara Conway, supt. Fax 325-3699
www.jtasd.org
Jim Thorpe Area HS 600/9-12
1 Olympian Way 18229 570-325-3663
Thomas Lesisko, prin. Fax 325-8973

Johnsonburg, Elk, Pop. 2,464
Johnsonburg Area SD 600/PK-12
315 High School Rd 15845 814-965-2536
Dennis Crotzer, supt. Fax 965-5809
www.johnsonburgareaschooldistrict.net
Johnsonburg Area JSHS 300/7-12
315 High School Rd 15845 814-965-2556
Brock Benson, prin. Fax 965-5809

Johnstown, Cambria, Pop. 20,140
Area Vocational Technical School
Supt. — None
Greater Johnstown AVTS Vo/Tech
445 Schoolhouse Rd 15904 814-266-6073
John Augustine, prin. Fax 269-4394

Conemaugh Valley SD 800/K-12
1451 Frankstown Rd 15902 814-535-3957
David Lehman, supt. Fax 536-8902
www.cvk12.org/
Conemaugh Valley JSHS 400/7-12
1342 William Penn Ave 15906 814-535-5523
Shane Hazenstab, prin. Fax 536-4025

Ferndale Area SD 800/K-12
100 Dartmouth Ave 15905 814-535-1507
Carole Kakabar, supt. Fax 535-8527
www.fasdk12.org
Ferndale Area JSHS 400/7-12
600 Harlan Ave 15905 814-288-5757
Br. Brian McDermott, prin. Fax 288-5224

Greater Johnstown SD 3,200/PK-12
1091 Broad St 15906 814-533-5651
Dr. Gerald Zahorchak, supt. Fax 533-5655
www.gjsd.net
Greater Johnstown HS 900/9-12
222 Central Ave 15902 814-533-5601
Michael Vuckovich, prin. Fax 533-5698
Greater Johnstown MS 600/6-8
280 Decker Ave 15906 814-533-5570
Douglas Henry, prin. Fax 533-5564

Richland SD 1,600/K-12
319 Schoolhouse Rd 15904 814-266-6063
Thomas Fleming, supt. Fax 266-7349
www.richlandsd.com/
Richland HS 800/7-12
1 Academic Ave 15904 814-266-6081
Brandon Bailey, prin. Fax 269-9506

Westmont Hilltop SD 1,700/K-12
827 Diamond Blvd 15905 814-255-6751
Dr. Susan Anderson, supt. Fax 255-7735
www.whsd.org
Westmont Hilltop HS 600/9-12
200 Fair Oaks Dr 15905 814-255-8726
Matthew Thomas, prin. Fax 255-2704
Westmont Hilltop MS 500/5-8
827 Diamond Blvd 15905 814-255-8704
Nicole Kuzmiak, prin. Fax 255-8783

Bishop McCort Catholic HS 400/9-12
25 Osborne St 15905 814-536-8991
Kenneth Salem, prin. Fax 535-4118
Cambria County Christian S 100/K-12
561 Pike Rd 15909 814-749-7406
Bonnie Berkebile, admin. Fax 749-7028
Cambria-Rowe Business College Post-Sec.
221 Central Ave 15902 814-536-5168
Commonwealth Technical Institute Post-Sec.
727 Goucher St 15905 814-255-8200
Conemaugh Valley Memorial Hospital Post-Sec.
1086 Franklin St 15905 814-534-9118
Greater Johnstown Area Voc Tech School Post-Sec.
445 Schoolhouse Rd 15904 814-266-6073
PA Academy of Cosmetic Arts & Sciences Post-Sec.
2445 Bedford St 15904 814-269-3444
Pennsylvania Highlands Community College Post-Sec.
101 Community College Way 15904 814-262-6400
University of Pittsburgh at Johnstown Post-Sec.
450 Schoolhouse Rd 15904 814-269-7000

Jonestown, Lebanon, Pop. 1,873

Blue Mountain Christian S 100/PK-12
14 Silvertown Rd 17038 717-865-9650
Greg Firestone, admin. Fax 865-4732

Kane, McKean, Pop. 3,695
Kane Area SD 1,200/K-12
400 W Hemlock Ave 16735 814-837-9570
Dr. Maryann Anderson, supt. Fax 837-7450
www.kasd.net
Kane Area HS 400/9-12
6965 Route 321 16735 814-837-6821
Jeff Kepler, prin. Fax 837-6158
Kane Area MS 300/6-8
400 W Hemlock Ave 16735 814-837-6030
James Fryzlewicz, prin. Fax 837-9133

Karns City, Butler, Pop. 209
Karns City Area SD 1,400/K-12
1446 Kittanning Pike 16041 724-756-2030
Eric Ritzert, supt. Fax 756-2121
www.karnscity.k12.pa.us
Karns City JSHS 800/7-12
1446 Kittanning Pike 16041 724-756-2030
Dave Beck, prin. Fax 756-2121

Kennett Square, Chester, Pop. 6,014
Kennett Consolidated SD 4,200/K-12
300 E South St 19348 610-444-6600
Dr. Barry Tomasetti, supt. Fax 444-6614
kcsd.org
Kennett HS 1,300/9-12
100 E South St 19348 610-444-6620
Dr. Michael Barber, prin. Fax 444-7013
Other Schools – See Landenberg

Unionville-Chadds Ford SD 4,100/K-12
740 Unionville Rd 19348 610-347-0970
Dr. John Sanville, supt. Fax 347-0976
www.ucfsd.org
Patton MS 1,000/6-8
760 Unionville Rd 19348 610-347-2000
Timothy V. Hoffman, prin. Fax 347-0421
Unionville HS 1,400/9-12
750 Unionville Rd 19348 610-347-1600
Paula Massanari, prin. Fax 347-1890

Kimberton, Chester

Kimberton Waldorf S 300/PK-12
PO Box 350 19442 610-933-3635
Allyn Weiser, hdmstr. Fax 935-6985

King of Prussia, Montgomery, Pop. 19,511
Upper Merion Area SD 3,800/K-12
435 Crossfield Rd 19406 610-205-6401
Dr. Jane Callaghan, supt. Fax 205-6433
www.umasd.org
Upper Merion HS 1,100/9-12
440 Crossfield Rd 19406 610-205-3801
Jonathan Bauer, prin. Fax 205-3993
Upper Merion MS 1,100/5-8
450 Keebler Rd 19406 610-205-8801
Dr. Karen Geller, prin. Fax 205-8999

Achieve Test Prep Post-Sec.
1150 1st Ave 19406 267-687-0333
Cortiva Institute - King of Prussia Post-Sec.
211 S Gulph Rd 19406 484-690-1400
DeVry University Post-Sec.
150 Allendale Rd Ste 3250 19406 610-205-3130
ITT Technical Institute Post-Sec.
760 Moore Rd 19406 610-491-8004

Kingsley, Susquehanna
Mountain View SD 1,200/K-12
11748 State Route 106 18826 570-434-2180
Francine R. Shea, supt. Fax 434-2404
www.mvsd.net
Mountain View JSHS 600/7-12
11748 State Route 106 18826 570-434-2501
Andrew Doster, prin. Fax 434-9582

Kingston, Luzerne, Pop. 12,983
Area Vocational Technical School
Supt. — None

West Side CTC, 75 Evans St 18704 Vo/Tech
Nancy Tkatch, prin. 570-288-8493

Wyoming Valley West SD 4,300/K-12
450 N Maple Ave 18704 570-288-6551
Charles R. Suppon, supt. Fax 714-6948
www.wvwsd.org/
Wyoming Valley West MS 1,200/6-8
201 Chester St 18704 570-287-2131
Deborah Troy, prin. Fax 287-6343
Other Schools – See Plymouth

Wyoming Seminary Upper S 400/9-12
201 N Sprague Ave 18704 570-270-2100
Kip Nygren Ph.D., pres. Fax 270-2199

Kintnersville, Bucks
Palisades SD 1,900/K-12
39 Thomas Free Dr 18930 610-847-5131
Dr. Bridget O'Connell, supt. Fax 847-8116
www.palisadessd.org
Palisades HS 700/9-12
35 Church Hill Rd 18930 610-847-5131
Richard Heffernan, prin. Fax 847-2562
Palisades MS 400/6-8
4710 Durham Rd 18930 610-847-5131
Edward Baumgartner, prin. Fax 847-2691

Kinzers, Lancaster
Pequea Valley SD 1,700/K-12
PO Box 130 17535 717-768-5530
Erik Orndorff, supt. Fax 768-7176
www.pequeavalley.org
Pequea Valley HS 600/9-12
PO Box 287 17535 717-768-5500
Arlen Mummau, prin. Fax 768-5523
Pequea Valley IS 400/6-8
PO Box 257 17535 717-768-5535
Taylor Croft, prin. Fax 768-5656

Kittanning, Armstrong, Pop. 3,989
Armstrong SD
Supt. — See Ford City
Kittanning HS 700/9-12
1200 Orr Ave 16201 724-543-1591
James Rummel, prin. Fax 543-1712
Kittanning JHS 400/6-8
210 N Mckean St 16201 724-543-1295
Kirk Lorigan, prin. Fax 543-1155

Armstrong County Memorial Hospital Post-Sec.
1 Nolte Dr 16201 724-543-8404
Grace Christian S 50/PK-12
215 Arthur St 16201 724-543-4019
Sandy Hankinson, admin. Fax 545-6738
Kittanning Beauty School Post-Sec.
120 Market St 16201 800-833-4247

Knox, Clarion, Pop. 1,139
Keystone SD 1,100/K-12
451 Huston Ave 16232 814-797-5921
Richard Bonnar, supt. Fax 797-2382
www.keyknox.com
Keystone JSHS 500/7-12
700 Beatty Ave 16232 814-797-1261
Vicky Walters, prin. Fax 797-2868

Kutztown, Berks, Pop. 4,969
Kutztown Area SD 1,500/K-12
251 Long Lane Rd 19530 610-683-7361
Katherine Metrick, supt. Fax 683-7230
www.kasd.org
Kutztown Area HS 600/9-12
50 Trexler Ave 19530 610-683-7346
Fax 894-4801
Kutztown Area MS 300/6-8
10 Deisher Ln 19530 610-683-3575
James Brown, prin. Fax 683-5460

Kutztown University of Pennsylvania Post-Sec.
15200 Kutztown Rd 19530 610-683-4000

Lake Ariel, Wayne
Western Wayne SD 1,600/PK-12
1970 Easton Tpke Bldg C 18436 800-321-9973
Clayton S. LaCoe Ph.D., supt. Fax 341-1221
www.westernwayne.org
Western Wayne HS 700/9-12
1970 Easton Tpke Bldg A 18436 800-321-9973
Patrick Sheehan, prin.
Western Wayne MS 500/6-8
1970 Easton Tpke Bldg B 18436 570-937-3010
Kristin Donohue, prin. Fax 937-3440

Canaan Christian Academy 200/PK-12
30 Hemlock Rd 18436 570-937-4848
David Marquette, admin. Fax 937-4800

Lancaster, Lancaster, Pop. 57,600
Conestoga Valley SD 4,000/K-12
2110 Horseshoe Rd 17601 717-397-2421
Dr. Gerald Huesken, supt. Fax 397-0442
www.cvsd.k12.pa.us
Conestoga Valley HS 1,200/9-12
2110 Horseshoe Rd 17601 717-397-5231
Perry Pritchard, prin. Fax 397-8841
Conestoga Valley MS 600/7-8
500 Mount Sidney Rd 17602 717-397-1294
Robert Houghton, prin. Fax 397-4404

Hempfield SD
Supt. — See Landisville
Centerville MS 600/7-8
865 Centerville Rd 17601 717-898-5580
James Dague, prin. Fax 618-0999
Rohrerstown Education Center Alt
1 Mayer Ave 17603 717-406-3400
Brendan Cregan, prin. Fax 618-1992

Lampeter-Strasburg SD 2,900/K-12
1600 Book Rd 17602 717-464-3311
Kevin Peart Ed.D., supt. Fax 464-4699
www.l-spioneers.org
Lampeter-Strasburg HS 1,100/9-12
1600 Book Rd 17602 717-464-3311
Eric Spencer, prin. Fax 509-0485
Meylin MS 700/6-8
1600 Book Rd 17602 717-464-3311
Jamie Raum, prin. Fax 509-0289

Lancaster SD 10,400/K-12
251 S Prince St 17603 717-291-6121
Pedro Rivera, supt. Fax 339-6844
www.lancaster.k12.pa.us
Hand MS 500/6-8
431 S Ann St 17602 717-291-6161
Mark Simms, prin. Fax 391-8600
Lincoln MS 600/6-8
1001 Lehigh Ave 17602 717-291-6187
Josh Keene, prin. Fax 399-6408
McCaskey East HS 9-12
1051 Lehigh Ave 17602 717-291-6172
Bill Jimenez, prin. Fax 391-8601
McCaskey HS 2,800/9-12
445 N Reservoir St 17602 717-291-6211
Dwight Nolt, prin. Fax 390-2567
Reynolds MS 500/6-8
605 W Walnut St 17603 717-291-6257
Stephen Sohonyay, prin. Fax 396-6823
Wheatland MS 600/6-8
919 Hamilton Park Dr 17603 717-291-6285
Dr. Jay Butterfield, prin. Fax 399-6411

Manheim Township SD 5,400/K-12
PO Box 5134 17606 717-569-8231
Gene Freeman, supt. Fax 569-3729
www.mtwp.net/
Manheim Township HS 1,800/9-12
PO Box 5134 17606 717-560-3097
Deborah Mitchell, prin. Fax 569-2806
Manheim Township MS 900/7-8
PO Box 5134 17606 717-560-3111
Jason Reifsnyder, prin. Fax 569-1670

Penn Manor SD 5,200/K-12
2950 Charlestown Rd 17603 717-872-9500
Dr. Michael Leichliter, supt. Fax 872-9505
www.pennmanor.net
Manor MS 500/7-8
2950 Charlestown Rd 17603 717-872-9510
Dana Edwards, prin. Fax 872-9505
Other Schools – See Millersville, Pequea

Consolidated School of Business Post-Sec.
2124 Ambassador Cir 17603 717-394-6211
Empire Beauty School Post-Sec.
1801 Columbia Ave 17603 717-394-8561
Franklin & Marshall College Post-Sec.
PO Box 3003 17604 717-291-3911
Lancaster Bible College Post-Sec.
901 Eden Rd 17601 717-569-7071
Lancaster Christian S - Leola Campus 300/PK-12
2390 New Holland Pike 17601 717-556-0711
Sharon Brobst, prin. Fax 656-4868
Lancaster Country Day S 500/PK-12
725 Hamilton Rd 17603 717-392-2916
Stephen Lisk, hdmstr. Fax 392-0425
Lancaster General College of Nursing Post-Sec.
410 N Lime St 17602 800-622-5443
Lancaster HS 800/9-12
650 Juliette Ave 17601 717-509-0315
Thomas Fertal, prin. Fax 509-0312
Lancaster Mennonite HS 800/6-12
2176 Lincoln Hwy E 17602 717-299-0436
J. Richard Thomas, supt. Fax 299-0823
Lancaster School of Cosmetology Post-Sec.
50 Ranck Ave 17602 717-299-0200
Lancaster Theological Seminary Post-Sec.
555 W James St 17603 717-393-0654
Pennsylvania College of Art and Design Post-Sec.
PO Box 59 17608 717-396-7833
Resurrection MS 100/4-8
521 E Orange St 17602 717-392-3083
Brenda Weaver, prin. Fax 735-7793
Thaddeus Stevens College of Technology Post-Sec.
750 E King St 17602 717-299-7730
YTI Career Institute Post-Sec.
3050 Hempland Rd 17601 717-295-1100

Landenberg, Chester
Kennett Consolidated SD
Supt. — See Kennett Square
Kennett MS, 195 Sunny Dell Rd 19350 900/6-8
John Carr, prin. 610-268-5800

Landisville, Lancaster, Pop. 1,881
Hempfield SD 7,000/K-12
200 Church St 17538 717-898-5564
Dr. Brenda Becker, supt. Fax 898-5628
www.hempfieldsd.org
Hempfield HS 2,300/9-12
200 Stanley Ave 17538 717-898-5510
Dr. Wilbur Stout, prin. Fax 618-1210
Landisville MS 500/7-8
340 Mumma Dr 17538 717-898-5607
Tab Musser, prin. Fax 618-0871
Other Schools – See Lancaster

Langhorne, Bucks, Pop. 1,596
Neshaminy SD 8,600/K-12
2001 Old Lincoln Hwy 19047 215-809-6500
Robert Copeland, supt. Fax 809-6502
www.neshaminy.k12.pa.us
Maple Point MS 1,000/6-8
2250 Langhorne Yardley Rd 19047 215-809-6230
Ronald Sayre, prin.

Neshaminy HS 2,800/9-12
2001 Old Lincoln Hwy 19047 215-809-6102
Dr. Rob McGee, prin.
Other Schools – See Feasterville, Levittown

Philadelphia Biblical University Post-Sec.
200 Manor Ave 19047 215-752-5800
Woods Services Post-Sec.
PO Box 36 19047 800-782-3646

Lansdale, Montgomery, Pop. 15,885
Area Vocational Technical School
Supt. — None
North Montco Tech Career Center Vo/Tech
1265 Sumneytown Pike 19446 215-368-1177
Michael Lucas, dir.

North Penn SD 12,700/K-12
401 E Hancock St 19446 215-368-0400
Dr. Curtis Dietrich, supt. Fax 368-3161
www.npenn.org
North Penn SHS 3,100/10-12
1340 S Valley Forge Rd 19446 215-368-9800
Burton Hynes, prin. Fax 855-0632
Penndale MS 1,400/7-9
400 Penn St 19446 215-368-2700
Dr. Sean O'Sullivan, prin. Fax 368-6817
Other Schools – See Hatfield, North Wales

Calvary Baptist Christian S 400/PK-12
1380 S Valley Forge Rd 19446 215-368-1100
Randall Thaxton, admin. Fax 368-1003
Calvary Baptist Theological Seminary Post-Sec.
1380 S Valley Forge Rd 19446 215-368-7538
Dock Mennonite HS 300/9-12
1000 Forty Foot Rd 19446 215-362-2675
Dr. Conrad Swartzentruber, prin. Fax 362-2943
Lansdale Catholic HS 800/9-12
700 Lansdale Ave 19446 215-362-6160
Fax 362-5746
Lansdale School of Cosmetology Post-Sec.
215 W Main St 19446 215-362-2322

Lansdowne, Delaware, Pop. 10,265
William Penn SD 5,300/K-12
100 Green Ave 19050 610-284-8000
Joseph Bruni, supt. Fax 284-8053
www.wpsd.k12.pa.us
Penn Wood HS Green Ave Campus 800/11-12
100 Green Ave 19050 610-284-8080
D. Brandon Cooley, prin. Fax 284-2141
Other Schools – See Darby, Yeadon

Lansford, Carbon, Pop. 3,876
Panther Valley SD 1,700/K-12
1 Panther Way 18232 570-645-4248
Rosemary Porembo, supt. Fax 645-6232
www.panthervalley.org/
Panther Valley HS 500/9-12
912 Coal Region Way 18232 570-645-2171
Joseph Gunnels, prin. Fax 645-2507
Panther Valley MS 400/6-8
678 Panther Pride Way 18232 570-645-2175
Lisa Mace, prin. Fax 645-9723

La Plume, Lackawanna

Keystone College Post-Sec.
PO Box 50 18440 570-945-8000

Laporte, Sullivan, Pop. 316
Sullivan County SD 500/K-12
PO Box 240 18626 570-946-8200
Craig R. Skaluba, supt. Fax 946-8210
www.sulcosd.k12.pa.us
Sullivan County JSHS 300/7-12
PO Box 98 18626 570-946-7001
Edward J. Pietroski, prin. Fax 946-5070

Latrobe, Westmoreland, Pop. 8,261
Area Vocational Technical School
Supt. — None
Eastern Westmoreland CTC Vo/Tech
4904 State Route 982 15650 724-539-9788
Marie Bowers, dir. Fax 539-1907

Greater Latrobe SD 4,200/K-12
1816 Lincoln Ave 15650 724-539-4200
Judith Swigart, supt. Fax 539-4202
www.glsd.k12.pa.us
Greater Latrobe JHS 1,000/7-9
130 High School Rd 15650 724-539-4265
Jeff Ingel, prin. Fax 539-4223
Greater Latrobe SHS 1,100/10-12
131 High School Rd 15650 724-539-4225
Steven LoCascio, prin. Fax 539-4295

Latrobe Area Hospital Post-Sec.
101 W 2nd Ave 15650 724-537-1001
St. Vincent College Post-Sec.
300 Fraser Purchase Rd 15650 724-532-6600
St. Vincent Seminary Post-Sec.
300 Fraser Purchase Rd 15650 724-805-2592

Laureldale, Berks, Pop. 3,857
Muhlenberg SD 3,500/K-12
801 E Bellevue Ave 19605 610-921-8000
Dr. Theresa Haught, supt. Fax 921-8076
www.muhlsdk12.org
Muhlenberg HS 900/10-12
400 Sharp Ave 19605 610-921-8078
Michael Mish, prin. Fax 921-7925
Muhlenberg MS 900/7-9
801 E Bellevue Ave 19605 610-921-8034
Donna Albright, prin. Fax 921-8038

Lebanon, Lebanon, Pop. 25,113
Area Vocational Technical School
Supt. — None
Lebanon County CTC Vo/Tech
833 Metro Dr 17042 717-273-8551
George Custer, dir. Fax 273-0534

Cornwall-Lebanon SD 4,700/K-12
105 E Evergreen Rd 17042 717-272-2031
Joseph Kristobak, supt. Fax 274-2786
www.clsd.k12.pa.us
Cedar Crest HS 1,500/9-12
115 E Evergreen Rd 17042 717-272-2033
David Helsel, prin. Fax 389-1823
Cedar Crest MS 1,100/6-8
101 E Evergreen Rd 17042 717-272-2032
Mariah Rackley, prin. Fax 389-1856

Lebanon SD 4,600/PK-12
1000 S 8th St 17042 717-273-9391
Dr. Marianne Bartley, supt. Fax 270-6778
www.lebanon.k12.pa.us
Lebanon HS 1,200/9-12
1000 S 8th St 17042 717-273-9391
William Giovino, prin. Fax 270-6778
Lebanon MS 1,000/6-8
350 N 8th St 17046 717-273-9391
Mary Garrett-Giovino, prin. Fax 270-6859

Empire Beauty School Post-Sec.
1776 Quentin Rd 17042 717-272-3323
Lebanon Catholic S 300/K-12
1400 Chestnut St 17042 717-273-3731
Rose Kury, prin. Fax 274-5167
Lebanon County Career School Post-Sec.
18 E Weidman St 17046 717-274-8804
New Covenant Christian S 200/PK-12
452 Ebenezer Rd 17046 717-274-2423
James Hubbard, prin. Fax 274-9830

Leechburg, Armstrong, Pop. 2,128
Kiski Area SD 3,900/K-12
250 Hyde Park Rd 15656 724-845-2022
Dr. John Meighan, supt. Fax 842-0444
www.kiskiarea.com
Kiski Area HS 1,300/9-12
250 Hyde Park Rd 15656 724-845-8181
Chad Roland, prin. Fax 842-0403
Kiski Area IS 600/7-8
260 Hyde Park Rd 15656 724-845-2219
Jason Lohr, prin. Fax 845-3208

Leechburg Area SD 800/K-12
210 Penn Ave 15656 724-842-9681
Frank C. Prazenica Ph.D., supt. Fax 845-2241
www.leechburg.k12.pa.us
Leechburg Area HS 200/9-12
215 1st St 15656 724-842-0571
Matthew Kruluts B.S., prin. Fax 845-4761
Leechburg Area JHS 200/7-8
215 1st St 15656 724-842-0571
Matthew Kruluts B.S., prin. Fax 845-4761

Leesport, Berks, Pop. 1,904
Area Vocational Technical School
Supt. — None
Berks CTC - West Vo/Tech
1057 County Road 19533 610-374-4073
Lisa Greenawalt, prin. Fax 987-6106

Schuylkill Valley SD 1,900/K-12
929 Lakeshore Dr 19533 610-916-0957
Dr. Warren Mata, supt. Fax 926-3960
www.schuylkillvalley.org/
Schuylkill Valley HS 700/9-12
929 Lakeshore Dr 19533 610-926-1706
David Haughney, prin. Fax 926-8341
Schuylkill Valley MS 600/5-8
114 Ontelaunee Dr 19533 610-926-7111
Michael Mitchell, prin. Fax 926-3321

Leetsdale, Allegheny, Pop. 1,172
Quaker Valley SD 2,000/K-12
100 Leetsdale Industrial Dr 15056 412-749-3600
Dr. Joseph Clapper, supt. Fax 749-3601
www.qvsd.org
Quaker Valley HS 600/9-12
625 Beaver St 15056 412-749-6020
Andrew Surloff, prin. Fax 749-1226
Other Schools – See Sewickley

Lehighton, Carbon, Pop. 5,438
Lehighton Area SD 2,400/K-12
1000 Union St 18235 610-377-4490
Jonathan J. Cleaver, supt. Fax 577-0035
www.lehighton.org/
Lehighton Area HS 700/9-12
1 Indian Ln 18235 610-377-6180
Craig Reichl, prin. Fax 377-1852
Lehighton Area MS 700/5-8
301 Beaver Run Rd 18235 610-377-6535
Mark McGalla Ph.D., prin. Fax 377-6503

Lehman, Luzerne
Lake-Lehman SD
Supt. — See Dallas
Lake-Lehman JSHS 1,000/7-12
PO Box 38 18627 570-675-7458
Douglas Klopp, prin. Fax 675-2951

Penn State Wilkes-Barre Post-Sec.
PO Box PSU 18627 570-675-2171

Lemont Furnace, Fayette, Pop. 807

Penn State Fayette Eberly Campus Post-Sec.
2201 University Dr 15456 724-430-4100

Lemoyne, Cumberland, Pop. 4,428
West Shore SD
Supt. — See Lewisberry
Lemoyne MS 400/6-8
701 Market St 17043 717-761-6345
Brian Kocsi, prin. Fax 901-9529

Leola, Lancaster, Pop. 7,126

Veritas Academy 200/K-12
26 Hillcrest Ave 17540 717-556-0690
G. Tyler Fischer, hdmstr. Fax 556-0736

Lester, Delaware

All-State Career School Post-Sec.
501 Seminole St 19029 610-521-1818

Levittown, Bucks, Pop. 52,008
Bristol Township SD 5,900/K-12
6401 Mill Creek Rd 19057 215-943-3200
Samuel Lee Ed.D., supt. Fax 949-2210
www.btsd.us/
Franklin Freshman Academy 100/9-9
6403 Mill Creek Rd 19057 215-949-8903
James Moore, prin. Fax 547-8415
Truman HS 1,200/10-12
3001 Green Ln 19057 215-547-3000
James Moore, prin Fax 547-4802
Other Schools – See Bristol, Fairless Hills

Neshaminy SD
Supt. — See Langhorne
Sandburg MS 600/6-8
30 Harmony Rd 19056 215-809-6220
Dawn Kelly, prin. Fax 809-6701

ITT Technical Institute Post-Sec.
311 Veterans Hwy Ste 100E 19056 215-702-3600
Levittown Beauty Academy Post-Sec.
8919 New Falls Rd 19054 215-943-0298

Lewisberry, York, Pop. 357
West Shore SD 7,700/K-12
507 Fishing Creek Rd 17339 717-938-9577
Jemry Small, supt. Fax 938-2779
www.wssd.k12.pa.us
Crossroads MS 600/6-8
535 Fishing Creek Rd 17339 717-932-1295
Ken Edwards, prin. Fax 938-3599
Red Land HS 1,200/9-12
560 Fishing Creek Rd 17339 717-938-6561
Holly Sayre, prin. Fax 938-0886
Other Schools – See Camp Hill, Lemoyne, New Cumberland

Lewisburg, Union, Pop. 5,667
Lewisburg Area SD 1,900/K-12
PO Box 351 17837 570-523-3220
Dr. Mark DiRocco, supt. Fax 522-3278
www.dragon.k12.pa.us
Eichhorn MS 400/6-8
2057 Washington Ave 17837 570-523-3220
George Drogin, prin. Fax 522-3331
Lewisburg Area HS 600/9-12
815 Market St 17837 570-523-3220
David Himes, prin. Fax 524-9484

Bucknell University Post-Sec.
1 Dent Dr 17837 570-577-2000

Lewistown, Mifflin, Pop. 8,199
Area Vocational Technical School
Supt. — None
Mifflin-Juniata CTC Vo/Tech
700 Pitt St 17044 717-248-3933
Daniel Potutschnig, dir. Fax 248-5148

Mifflin County SD 2,700/K-12
201 8th St 17044 717-248-0148
James Estep, supt. Fax 248-5345
www.mcsdk12.org
Mifflin County HS 500/10-12
501 6th St 17044 717-242-0240
Mark Crosson, prin. Fax 447-2600
Mifflin County JHS 200/8-9
700 Cedar St 17044 717-248-5441
Mike Zinobile, prin. Fax 242-5806

Mifflin-Juniata Career & Technology Ctr Post-Sec.
700 Pitt St 17044 717-248-3933
South Hills School of Business & Tech. Post-Sec.
124 E Market St 17044 717-248-8140

Liberty, Tioga, Pop. 247
Southern Tioga SD
Supt. — See Blossburg
Liberty JSHS 300/7-12
8675 Route 414 16930 570-324-2071
William Swingle, prin. Fax 324-2313

Ligonier, Westmoreland, Pop. 1,565
Ligonier Valley SD 1,700/K-12
339 W Main St 15658 724-238-5696
Christine Oldham Ed.D., supt. Fax 238-7877
lvsd.k12.pa.us/
Ligonier Valley HS 600/9-12
40 Springer Rd 15658 724-238-9531
Timothy Kantor, prin. Fax 238-2675
Ligonier Valley MS 400/6-8
536 Bell Street Ext 15658 724-238-6412
David Steimer, prin. Fax 238-2358

Limerick, Montgomery
Area Vocational Technical School
Supt. — None
Western Montgomery Career/Technology Ctr Vo/Tech
77 Gratersford Rd 19468 610-489-7272
Joseph Greb, dir.

Lincoln University, Chester, Pop. 1,678

Lincoln University — Post-Sec.
PO Box 179 19352 — 484-365-8000

Linesville, Crawford, Pop. 1,024
Conneaut SD — 1,100/K-12
219 W School Dr 16424 — 814-683-5900
Jarrin Sperry, supt. — Fax 683-4127
www.conneautsd.org
Conneaut Area SHS — 300/9-12
302 W School Dr 16424 — 814-683-5551
Sharon Sielski, prin. — Fax 683-5221
Other Schools – See Conneaut Lake, Conneautville

Lititz, Lancaster, Pop. 9,235
Warwick SD — 4,500/K-12
301 W Orange St 17543 — 717-626-3734
Dr. April Hershey, supt. — Fax 626-3850
www.warwicksd.org/
Warwick HS — 1,500/9-12
301 W Orange St 17543 — 717-626-3700
Troy Price, prin. — Fax 626-6199
Warwick MS — 700/7-8
401 Maple St 17543 — 717-626-3701
Dr. Michael Smith, prin. — Fax 627-6089

Linden Hall — 100/6-12
212 E Main St 17543 — 717-626-8512
Dr. Vincent Stumpo, hdmstr. — Fax 627-1384
Lititz Christian S — 300/PK-12
501 W Lincoln Ave 17543 — 717-626-9518
Rick Bernhardt, admin. — Fax 626-9028
New Haven Mennonite S — 100/1-12
225 Crest Rd 17543 — 717-626-1603

Littlestown, Adams, Pop. 4,373
Littlestown Area SD — 2,100/K-12
162 Newark St 17340 — 717-359-4146
Dr. Donald Wills, supt. — Fax 359-9617
www.lasd.k12.pa.us
Littlestown HS — 700/9-12
200 E Myrtle St 17340 — 717-359-4146
Matthew Meakin, prin. — Fax 359-9461
Maple Avenue MS — 500/6-8
75 Maple Ave 17340 — 717-359-4146
Eric Naylor, prin. — Fax 359-9617

Lock Haven, Clinton, Pop. 9,648

Lock Haven University — Post-Sec.
401 N Fairview St 17745 — 570-484-2011

Loretto, Cambria, Pop. 1,282

St. Francis University — Post-Sec.
PO Box 600 15940 — 814-472-3000

Lower Burrell, Westmoreland, Pop. 11,648
Burrell SD — 1,500/K-12
1021 Puckety Church Rd 15068 — 724-334-1406
Shannon Wagner, supt. — Fax 334-1429
www.burrell.k12.pa.us
Burrell HS — 600/9-12
1021 Puckety Church Rd 15068 — 724-334-1403
John Boylan, prin. — Fax 334-1420
Huston MS — 500/6-8
1020 Puckety Church Rd 15068 — 724-334-1443
Brian Ferra, prin. — Fax 334-1434

Newport Business Institute — Post-Sec.
945 Greensburg Rd 15068 — 724-339-7542
Oakbridge Academy of Arts — Post-Sec.
1250 Greensburg Rd 15068 — 724-335-5336

Loysburg, Bedford
Northern Bedford County SD — 1,100/PK-12
152 NBC Dr 16659 — 814-766-2221
Scott King, supt. — Fax 766-3772
www.nbcsd.org/
Northern Bedford County HS — 400/9-12
152 NBC Dr 16659 — 814-766-2221
David Burkett, prin. — Fax 766-3772
Northern Bedford County MS — 200/6-8
152 NBC Dr 16659 — 814-766-2221
Wayne Sherlock, prin. — Fax 766-3772

Lykens, Dauphin, Pop. 1,762
Upper Dauphin Area SD — 1,300/K-12
5668 State Route 209 17048 — 717-362-8134
Paul Caputo, supt. — Fax 362-3050
www.udasd.org/
Upper Dauphin Area MS — 400/5-8
5668 State Route 209 17048 — 717-362-8177
Abbey Walshaw-Wertz, prin. — Fax 362-6567
Other Schools – See Elizabethville

Mc Alisterville, Juniata, Pop. 971
Juniata County SD
Supt. — See Mifflintown
East Juniata JSHS — 500/7-12
32944 Route 35 N 17049 — 717-463-2111
Benjamin Fausey, prin. — Fax 463-3268

Juniata Mennonite S — 200/K-12
PO Box 278 17049 — 717-463-2898
Tom Getz, admin. — Fax 463-0134

Mc Clellandtown, Fayette
Albert Gallatin Area SD
Supt. — See Uniontown
Gallatin North MS — 500/6-8
113 College Ave 15458 — 724-737-5423
Randy Wilson, prin. — Fax 737-5312

Mc Clure, Fayette

Mifflin County Christian Academy — 100/PK-12
5113 Back Maitland Rd 17841 — 717-543-2200
Craig Todd, admin. — Fax 543-2206

Mc Connellsburg, Fulton, Pop. 1,183
Area Vocational Technical School
Supt. — None
Fulton County AVTS — Vo/Tech
145 E Cherry St 17233 — 717-485-5813
Donald Burd, prin.

Central Fulton SD — 1,000/PK-12
151 E Cherry St 17233 — 717-485-3183
Dr. Dwayne Northcraft, supt. — Fax 485-5984
www.cfsd.info
Mc Connellsburg HS — 200/9-12
151 E Cherry St 17233 — 717-485-3195
Todd Beatty, prin. — Fax 485-0175
Mc Connellsburg MS — 200/6-8
151 E Cherry St 17233 — 717-485-3195
Todd Beatty, prin. — Fax 485-0175

Mc Donald, Washington, Pop. 2,125
Fort Cherry SD — 1,100/K-12
110 Fort Cherry Rd 15057 — 724-796-1551
Robert Dinnen Ph.D., supt. — Fax 796-0065
www.fortcherry.org
Fort Cherry JSHS — 500/7-12
110 Fort Cherry Rd 15057 — 724-796-1551
Robert Frioni, prin. — Fax 356-2769

South Fayette Township SD — 2,600/K-12
3680 Old Oakdale Rd 15057 — 412-221-4542
Dr. Bille Rondinelli, supt. — Fax 693-2883
www.southfayette.org
South Fayette Township HS — 700/9-12
3640 Old Oakdale Rd 15057 — 412-221-4542
Scott Milburn, prin. — Fax 693-9843
South Fayette Township MS — 600/6-8
3700 Old Oakdale Rd 15057 — 412-221-4542
David Deramo, prin. — Fax 693-0860

Mc Keesport, Allegheny, Pop. 18,886
Area Vocational Technical School
Supt. — None
McKeesport Area Tech Center — Vo/Tech
1960 Eden Park Blvd, — 412-664-3664
Patricia Scales, dir. — Fax 664-3784

McKeesport Area SD — 3,700/K-12
3590 Oneil Blvd, — 412-664-3610
Dr. Timothy Gabauer, supt. — Fax 664-3638
www.mckasd.net
Founders Hall MS — 600/7-8
3600 Oneil Blvd, — 412-664-3690
Dr. Karen Chapman, prin. — Fax 664-3768
McKeesport Area HS — 1,300/9-12
1960 Eden Park Blvd, — 412-664-3650
Mark Holtzman, prin. — Fax 664-3787

South Allegheny SD — 1,600/K-12
2743 Washington Blvd, — 412-675-3070
Wayne Gdovic, supt. — Fax 672-2836
www.southallegheny.org
South Allegheny HS — 500/9-12
2743 Washington Blvd, — 412-675-3070
Jeff Solomon, prin. — Fax 673-4903
South Allegheny MS — 300/7-8
2743 Washington Blvd, — 412-675-3070
Lisa Duval, prin. — Fax 673-4905

Penn State Greater Allegheny — Post-Sec.
4000 University Dr 15131 — 412-675-9000
Serra Catholic HS — 300/9-12
200 Hershey Dr, — 412-751-2020
Timothy Chirdon, prin. — Fax 751-3488

Mc Kees Rocks, Allegheny, Pop. 5,853
Montour SD — 2,300/K-12
225 Clever Rd 15136 — 412-490-6500
Dr. Donald Boyer, supt. — Fax 490-0828
www.montourschools.com
Montour HS — 1,000/9-12
223 Clever Rd 15136 — 412-490-6500
Todd Price, prin. — Fax 494-9747
Other Schools – See Coraopolis

Sto-Rox SD — 1,400/K-12
600 Russellwood Ave 15136 — 412-778-8871
Frank Dalmas, supt. — Fax 771-5205
www.srsd.k12.pa.us
Sto-Rox HS — 400/9-12
1105 Valley St 15136 — 412-771-3213
Heath Bailey, prin. — Fax 771-8395
Sto-Rox MS — 300/6-8
298 Ewing Rd 15136 — 412-331-2170
Dr. Melanie Kerber, prin. — Fax 771-3848

Ohio Valley General Hospital — Post-Sec.
25 Heckel Rd 15136 — 412-777-6207
Robinson Township Christian S — 100/PK-12
77 Phillips Ln 15136 — 412-787-5919
Arthur Broadwick, prin. — Fax 787-1558

Mc Murray, Washington, Pop. 4,622
Peters Township SD — 4,500/K-12
631 E McMurray Rd 15317 — 724-941-6251
Dr. Joseph Dimperio, supt. — Fax 941-6565
www.ptsd.k12.pa.us
Peters Township HS — 1,500/9-12
264 E McMurray Rd 15317 — 724-941-6250
Lori Pavlik, prin. — Fax 942-0915
Peters Township MS — 700/7-8
625 E McMurray Rd 15317 — 724-941-2688
Dr. Robert Freado, prin. — Fax 941-1426

Mc Sherrystown, Adams, Pop. 3,006

Delone Catholic HS — 600/9-12
140 S Oxford Ave 17344 — 717-637-5969
Dr. Maureen Thiec, prin. — Fax 637-0442

Macungie, Lehigh, Pop. 3,024
East Penn SD
Supt. — See Emmaus
Eyer MS, 5616 Buckeye Rd 18062 — 800/6-8
Dr. Douglas Wells, prin. — 610-965-1600
Lower Macungie MS — 1,100/6-8
6299 Lower Macungie Rd 18062 — 610-395-8593
Suzanne Vincent, prin. — Fax 398-4385

Salem Christian S — 200/PK-12
8031 Salem Bible Church Rd 18062 — 610-966-5823
Mark Stanton, admin. — Fax 965-8368

Mahanoy City, Schuylkill, Pop. 4,109
Mahanoy Area SD — 1,100/K-12
1 Golden Bear Dr 17948 — 570-773-3443
Dr. Joie Green, supt. — Fax 773-2913
www.mabears.net
Mahanoy Area HS — 300/9-12
1 Golden Bear Dr 17948 — 570-773-3443
Thomas Smith, prin. — Fax 773-4020
Mahanoy Area MS — 400/5-8
1 Golden Bear Dr 17948 — 570-773-3443
Michael Heater, prin. — Fax 773-4034

Malvern, Chester, Pop. 2,955
Great Valley SD — 4,100/K-12
47 Church Rd 19355 — 610-889-2100
Dr. Alan Lonoconus, supt. — Fax 889-2120
www.gvsd.org
Great Valley HS — 1,200/9-12
225 Phoenixville Pike 19355 — 610-889-1900
Michael Flick, prin. — Fax 695-8901
Great Valley MS — 1,000/6-8
255 Phoenixville Pike 19355 — 610-644-6440
Dr. Edward Souders, prin. — Fax 889-1166

Malvern Prep S — 600/6-12
418 S Warren Ave 19355 — 484-595-1100
Rev. James Flynn, hdmstr. — Fax 595-1124
Penn State Great Valley Grad Prof Stds — Post-Sec.
30 E Swedesford Rd 19355 — 610-648-3200
Phelps S — 100/7-12
583 Sugartown Rd 19355 — 610-644-1754
Daniel Knopp, head sch — Fax 644-6679
Villa Maria Academy — 400/9-12
370 Old Lincoln Hwy 19355 — 610-644-2551
Sr. Marita Carmel, prin. — Fax 644-2866

Manchester, York, Pop. 2,703
Northeastern York SD — 3,700/K-12
41 Harding St 17345 — 717-266-3667
Dr. Shawn Minnich, supt. — Fax 266-5792
www.nesd.k12.pa.us
Northeastern HS — 1,000/9-12
300 High St 17345 — 717-266-3644
Mathew Gay, prin. — Fax 266-0616
Northeastern MS — 600/7-8
4855 Board Rd 17345 — 717-266-3676
Michael Alessandroni, prin. — Fax 266-9735

Manheim, Lancaster, Pop. 4,777
Manheim Central SD — 2,500/K-12
71 N Hazel St 17545 — 717-664-8540
Fred Cummins, supt. — Fax 664-8539
www.manheimcentral.org
Manheim Central HS — 1,000/9-12
400 Adele Ave 17545 — 717-664-8400
Jeffrey Hughes, prin. — Fax 664-8420
Manheim Central MS — 500/7-8
261 White Oak Rd 17545 — 717-664-1700
Scott Richardson, prin. — Fax 664-1859

Mansfield, Tioga, Pop. 3,545
Southern Tioga SD
Supt. — See Blossburg
Mansfield JSHS — 400/7-12
73 W Wellsboro St 16933 — 570-662-2674
Bill David, prin. — Fax 662-2808

Mansfield University of Pennsylvania — Post-Sec.
71 S Academy St 16933 — 570-662-4000
New Covenant Academy — 200/PK-12
310 Extension St 16933 — 570-662-2996

Maple Glen, Montgomery, Pop. 6,682
Upper Dublin SD — 4,200/K-12
1580 Fort Washington Ave 19002 — 215-643-8800
Michael Pladus Ed.D., supt. — Fax 643-8808
www.udsd.org
Other Schools – See Dresher, Fort Washington

Marienville, Forest, Pop. 3,126
Forest Area SD
Supt. — See Tionesta
East Forest JSHS — 100/7-12
120 W Birch St 16239 — 814-927-6688
William Jordan, prin. — Fax 927-8452

Marion Center, Indiana, Pop. 450
Marion Center Area SD — 1,500/PK-12
PO Box 156 15759 — 724-397-5551
Frank Garritano Ed.D., supt. — Fax 397-9144
www.mcasd.net/
Marion Center Area JSHS — 700/7-12
PO Box 209 15759 — 724-397-5551
Matt Jioio, prin. — Fax 397-9162

Markleysburg, Fayette, Pop. 283
Uniontown Area SD
Supt. — See Uniontown

McMullen MS 200/6-8
4773 National Pike 15459 724-329-8811
Joseph Galie, prin. Fax 329-4696

Mar Lin, Schuylkill, Pop. 649
Area Vocational Technical School
Supt. — None
Schuylkill Technology Center - South Vo/Tech
PO Box 110 17951 570-544-4748
Kurt Lynch, prin. Fax 544-3895

Mars, Butler, Pop. 1,685
Mars Area SD 3,200/K-12
545 Route 228 16046 724-625-1518
Dr. William Pettigrew, supt. Fax 625-1060
www.marsk12.org
Mars Area HS 1,000/9-12
520 Route 228 16046 724-625-1581
Todd Kolson, prin. Fax 625-4541
Mars Area MS 500/7-8
1775 Three Degree Rd 16046 724-625-3145
Richard Cornell, prin. Fax 625-2147

Martinsburg, Blair, Pop. 1,949
Spring Cove SD
Supt. — See Roaring Spring
Central HS 600/9-12
718 Central High Rd 16662 814-793-2111
David Crumrine, prin. Fax 793-4942

Meadville, Crawford, Pop. 13,058
Area Vocational Technical School
Supt. — None
Crawford County CTC Vo/Tech
860 Thurston Rd 16335 814-724-6024
Neil Donovan, prin. Fax 337-0602

Crawford Central SD 3,200/K-12
11280 Mercer Pike 16335 814-724-3960
Charles Heller, supt. Fax 333-8731
www.craw.org
Meadville Area HS 900/9-12
930 North St 16335 814-336-1121
John Higgins, prin. Fax 337-1486
Meadville Area MS 400/7-8
974 North St 16335 814-333-1188
Scott Lynch, prin. Fax 333-2799
Other Schools – See Cochranton

Allegheny College Post-Sec.
520 N Main St 16335 814-332-3100
Calvary Baptist Christian Academy 200/PK-12
543 Randolph St 16335 814-724-6606
Daryl Van Norman, admin. Fax 337-4357
Laurel Technical Institute Post-Sec.
847 N Main St Ste 204 16335 814-724-0700
Precision Manufacturing Institute Post-Sec.
764 Bessemer St 16335 814-333-2415

Mechanicsburg, Cumberland, Pop. 8,802
Area Vocational Technical School
Supt. — None
Cumberland-Perry AVTS Vo/Tech
110 Old Willow Mill Rd 17050 717-697-0354
Justin Bruhn, prin. Fax 697-0592

Cumberland Valley SD 7,700/K-12
6746 Carlisle Pike 17050 717-697-8261
William Harner, supt. Fax 506-3302
www.cvschools.org
Cumberland Valley HS 2,500/9-12
6746 Carlisle Pike 17050 717-766-0217
Judy Baumgardner, prin. Fax 506-3777
Eagle View MS 900/6-8
6746 Carlisle Pike 17050 717-766-0217
John Gallagher, prin. Fax 506-3806
Good Hope MS 900/6-8
451 Skyport Rd 17050 717-761-1865
Doris Baboian, prin. Fax 761-5910

Mechanicsburg Area SD 3,700/K-12
100 E Elmwood Ave 17055 717-691-4500
Mark K. Leidy Ed.D., supt. Fax 691-3438
www.mbgsd.org
Mechanicsburg Area HS 1,200/9-12
500 S Broad St 17055 717-691-4530
David R. Harris, prin. Fax 691-7632
Mechanicsburg MS 900/6-8
1750 S Market St 17055 717-691-4560
Joel A. Yohn, prin. Fax 791-7977

Faith Tabernacle S 200/1-12
1410 Good Hope Rd 17050 717-975-0641
Lori Feaser, prin. Fax 975-9920
Messiah College Post-Sec.
1 College Ave 17055 717-766-2511
YTI Career Institute Post-Sec.
401 E Winding Hill Rd # 101 17055 717-761-1481

Media, Delaware, Pop. 5,231
Rose Tree Media SD 3,700/K-12
308 N Olive St 19063 610-627-6000
James Wigo, supt. Fax 891-0959
www.rtmsd.org
Penncrest HS 1,300/9-12
134 Barren Rd 19063 610-627-6200
Richard Gregg, prin. Fax 891-0898
Simon Youth Academy Alt
1067 W Baltimore Pike 19063 610-627-6461
Joseph Fuhr, prin.
Springton Lake MS 900/6-8
1900 N Providence Rd 19063 610-627-6500
Fax 566-8665

Delaware County Community College Post-Sec.
901 Media Line Rd 19063 610-359-5000
Penn State Brandywine Post-Sec.
25 Yearsley Mill Rd 19063 610-892-1200

Pennsylvania Institute of Technology Post-Sec.
800 Manchester Ave 19063 610-892-1500
Williamson Free School of Mech. Trades Post-Sec.
106 S New Middletown Rd 19063 610-566-1776

Melrose Park, Montgomery, Pop. 6,500

Gratz College Post-Sec.
7605 Old York Rd 19027 215-635-7300
Saligman MS of Perelman Jewish Day S 100/6-8
7613 Old York Rd 19027 215-635-3303

Mercer, Mercer, Pop. 1,978
Area Vocational Technical School
Supt. — None
Mercer County Career Center Vo/Tech
776 Greenville Rd 16137 724-662-3000
Rachel Martin, prin. Fax 662-1025

Mercer Area SD 1,300/K-12
545 W Butler St 16137 724-662-5100
Dr. William Gathers, supt. Fax 662-5109
www.mercer.k12.pa.us
Mercer Area HS 500/9-12
545 W Butler St 16137 724-662-5104
Michael Piddington, prin. Fax 662-2993
Mercer Area MS 200/7-8
545 W Butler St 16137 724-662-5104
Michael Piddington, prin. Fax 662-2993

Mercersburg, Franklin, Pop. 1,540
Tuscarora SD 2,600/K-12
100 W Seminary St 17236 717-328-3127
Dr. Rebecca Erb, supt. Fax 328-9316
www.tus.k12.pa.us/
Buchanan HS 800/9-12
4773 Fort Loudon Rd 17236 717-328-2146
Rodney Benedick, prin. Fax 328-5428
Buchanan MS 700/6-8
5191 Fort Loudon Rd 17236 717-328-5221
James Carbaugh, prin. Fax 328-9081

Mercersburg Academy 400/9-12
300 E Seminary St 17236 717-328-6113
Douglas Hale, head sch Fax 328-6319

Merion Station, Montgomery, Pop. 700

Merion Mercy Academy 500/9-12
511 Montgomery Ave 19066 610-664-6655
Sr. Barbara Buckley, prin. Fax 664-6322

Mertztown, Berks, Pop. 656
Brandywine Heights Area SD
Supt. — See Topton
Brandywine Heights Area HS 600/9-12
103 Old Topton Rd 19539 610-682-5102
Heather Piperato, prin. Fax 682-5139

Gateway Christian S 50/PK-12
245 Fredericksville Rd 19539 610-682-2748
Mary Kamp, prin. Fax 682-9670

Meyersdale, Somerset, Pop. 2,169
Meyersdale Area SD 900/K-12
309 Industrial Park Rd 15552 814-634-5123
Dr. Tracey Karlie, supt. Fax 634-0832
www.masd.net
Meyersdale Area HS 300/9-12
1349 Shaw Mines Rd 15552 814-634-5123
John Wiltrout, prin. Fax 634-0832
Meyersdale Area MS 200/6-8
1353 Shaw Mines Rd 15552 814-634-5123
Tim Kretchman, prin. Fax 634-0832

Middleburg, Snyder, Pop. 1,296
Midd-West SD 1,500/K-12
568 E Main St 17842 570-837-0046
Dr. Wesley L. Knapp, supt. Fax 837-3018
www.mwsd.cc
Midd-West HS 700/8-12
540 E Main St 17842 570-837-0046
Cynthia L. Hutchinson, prin. Fax 837-5267

Middletown, Dauphin, Pop. 8,620
Middletown Area SD 2,300/K-12
55 W Water St Ste 2 17057 717-948-3300
Lori Suski Ed.D., supt. Fax 948-3329
www.raiderweb.org
Middletown Area HS 700/9-12
1155 N Union St 17057 717-948-3333
Patrick Hruz, prin. Fax 948-3359
Middletown Area MS 500/6-8
215 Oberlin Rd 17057 717-930-0739
Kevin Cook, prin. Fax 944-0951

Penn State Harrisburg Post-Sec.
777 W Harrisburg Pike 17057 717-948-6250

Midland, Beaver, Pop. 2,534
Western Beaver County SD 800/K-12
343 Ridgemont Dr 15059 724-643-9310
Dr. Robert Postupac, supt. Fax 643-8048
www.westernbeaver.org
Other Schools – See Industry

Mifflinburg, Union, Pop. 3,516
Mifflinburg Area SD 2,100/K-12
PO Box 285 17844 570-966-8200
Daniel Lichtel, supt. Fax 966-8210
www.mifflinburg.org
Mifflinburg Area HS 700/9-12
75 Market St 17844 570-966-8230
Michelle Shearer, prin. Fax 966-8260
Mifflinburg Area MS 500/6-8
100 Mabel St 17844 570-966-8290
Marion Lynn, prin. Fax 966-8304

Mifflintown, Juniata, Pop. 920
Juniata County SD 3,000/K-12
75 S 7th St 17059 717-436-2111
Richard Musselman, supt. Fax 436-2777
www.jcsdk12.org
Juniata HS 600/9-12
3931 William Penn Hwy 17059 717-436-2193
Edward Apple, prin. Fax 436-2858
Tuscarora JHS 400/6-8
3873 William Penn Hwy 17059 717-436-2165
Aaron Bennett, prin. Fax 436-5999
Other Schools – See Mc Alisterville

Milford, Pike, Pop. 1,003
Delaware Valley SD 4,100/K-12
236 Route 6 and 209 18337 570-296-1800
John Bell, supt. Fax 296-3172
www.dvsd.org
Delaware Valley HS 9-10 9-10
256 Route 6 and 209 18337 570-409-2001
Ronald Collins, prin. Fax 409-2002
Delaware Valley HS 11-12 900/11-12
252 Route 6 and 209 18337 570-296-1850
Ronald Collins, prin. Fax 296-3160
Delaware Valley MS 400/6-8
258 Route 6 and 209 18337 570-296-1830
Peter Ioppolo, prin. Fax 296-3162
Other Schools – See Dingmans Ferry

Mill Creek, Huntingdon, Pop. 326
Area Vocational Technical School
Supt. — None
Huntingdon County CTC Vo/Tech
PO Box E 17060 814-643-0951
Mary Lou Lebo, prin.

Millersburg, Dauphin, Pop. 2,536
Millersburg Area SD 800/K-12
799 Center St 17061 717-692-2108
Sheree-Lee Knorr, supt. Fax 692-2895
www.mlbgsd.k12.pa.us/
Millersburg Area HS 300/9-12
799 Center St 17061 717-692-2108
Stephen Herman, prin. Fax 692-2895
Millersburg Area MS 200/6-8
799 Center St 17061 717-692-2108
Jennifer Wicht, prin. Fax 692-2895

Millerstown, Perry, Pop. 664
Greenwood SD 800/K-12
405 E Sunbury St 17062 717-589-3117
Ed Burns, supt. Fax 589-1017
www.greenwoodsd.org
Greenwood HS 200/9-12
405 E Sunbury St 17062 717-589-3116
Nicholas Guarente, prin. Fax 589-1016
Greenwood MS 100/7-8
405 E Sunbury St 17062 717-589-3116
Nicholas Guarente, prin. Fax 589-1016

Millersville, Lancaster, Pop. 8,074
Penn Manor SD
Supt. — See Lancaster
Penn Manor HS 1,700/9-12
PO Box 1001 17551 717-872-9520
Dr. Philip Gale, prin. Fax 872-0934

Millersville University of Pennsylvania Post-Sec.
PO Box 1002 17551 717-872-3024

Mill Hall, Clinton, Pop. 1,602
Area Vocational Technical School
Supt. — None
Keystone Central CTC Vo/Tech
64 Keystone Central Dr 17751 570-748-6584
Scott Owens, prin. Fax 748-5467

Keystone Central SD 4,100/K-12
86 Administration Dr 17751 570-893-4900
Kelly Hastings, supt. Fax 893-4923
www.kcsd.k12.pa.us
Central Mountain HS 1,300/9-12
64 Keystone Central Dr 17751 570-893-4646
Karen Probst, prin. Fax 893-4946
Central Mountain MS 900/6-8
200 Ben Ave 17751 570-726-3141
Norman Palovcsik, prin. Fax 726-7227
Other Schools – See Renovo

Millville, Columbia, Pop. 940
Millville Area SD 700/K-12
PO Box 260 17846 570-458-5538
Kathleen Stark Ed.D., supt. Fax 458-5584
www.millville.k12.pa.us
Millville Area JSHS 300/7-12
PO Box 260 17846 570-458-5538
Eric Stair, prin. Fax 458-5583

Milton, Northumberland, Pop. 6,900
Milton Area SD 2,200/K-12
700 Mahoning St 17847 570-742-7614
Cathy Groller, supt. Fax 742-4523
www.miltonsd.org/
Milton Area HS 700/9-12
700 Mahoning St 17847 570-742-7611
Bryan Noaker, prin. Fax 742-4928
Milton Area MS 500/6-8
700 Mahoning St 17847 570-742-7685
Gregory Scoggins, prin. Fax 742-4857

Meadowbrook Christian S 300/PK-12
363 Stamm Rd 17847 570-742-2638
Rodney Baughman, admin. Fax 742-4710

Minersville, Schuylkill, Pop. 4,345
Minersville Area SD 1,200/PK-12
PO Box 787 17954 570-544-1400
M. Joseph Brady, supt. Fax 544-6162
www.battlinminers.com

Minersville Area JSHS 500/7-12
PO Box 787 17954 570-544-1400
Carl McBreen, prin. Fax 544-5866

Mohrsville, Berks, Pop. 375

King's Academy 200/PK-12
1562 Main St 19541 610-926-9639
Daniel Tubbs, hdmstr. Fax 926-8089

Monaca, Beaver, Pop. 5,641
Area Vocational Technical School
Supt. — None
Beaver County CTC Vo/Tech
145 Poplar Dr 15061 724-728-5800
Denise Kempa, dir. Fax 775-2299

Central Valley SD 2,400/K-12
160 Baker Road Ext 15061 724-775-5600
Nicholas Perry, supt. Fax 775-4302
www.centralvalleysd.org/District
Central Valley HS 800/9-12
160 Baker Road Ext 15061 724-775-5600
Anthony Mendicino, prin. Fax 775-6560
Central Valley MS 600/6-8
1500 Allen Ave 15061 724-775-5600
Michael McCullough, prin. Fax 775-4302

Community College of Beaver County Post-Sec.
1 Campus Dr 15061 724-480-2222
Penn State Beaver Post-Sec.
100 University Dr 15061 724-773-3800

Monessen, Westmoreland, Pop. 7,447
Monessen CSD 900/K-12
1275 Rostraver St 15062 724-684-3600
Linda Marcolini, supt. Fax 684-6782
monessenschooldistrict.com
Monessen HS 300/9-12
1245 State Rd 15062 724-684-7100
Brian Sutherland, prin. Fax 684-7925
Monessen MS 200/6-8
1245 State Rd 15062 724-684-6282
Sherry Castaneda-Black, prin. Fax 684-7931

Douglas Education Center Post-Sec.
130 7th St 15062 724-684-3684

Monongahela, Washington, Pop. 4,226
Ringgold SD
Supt. — See New Eagle
Ringgold HS 1,000/9-12
1 Ram Dr 15063 724-258-2200
Dwayne Homa, prin. Fax 258-7360

Monroeville, Allegheny, Pop. 28,591
Area Vocational Technical School
Supt. — None
Forbes Road CTC Vo/Tech
607 Beatty Rd 15146 412-373-8100
Paul Balint, prin. Fax 373-8106

Gateway SD 3,600/K-12
9000 Gateway Campus Blvd 15146 412-372-5300
Dr. Nina Zetty, supt. Fax 373-5731
www.gatewayk12.org
Gateway HS 1,400/9-12
3000 Gateway Campus Blvd 15146 412-373-5744
William Short, prin. Fax 373-5872
Gateway MS 600/7-8
4450 Old William Penn Hwy 15146 412-373-5780
Anthony Aquilio, prin. Fax 373-5794

Career Training Academy Post-Sec.
4314 Old William Penn # 103 15146 412-372-3900
Community College of Allegheny County Post-Sec.
595 Beatty Rd 15146 724-325-1327
Empire Beauty School Post-Sec.
320 Mall Blvd 15146 412-373-7727

Mont Alto, Franklin, Pop. 1,684

Penn State Mont Alto Post-Sec.
1 Campus Dr 17237 717-749-6000

Montgomery, Lycoming, Pop. 1,554
Montgomery Area SD 900/K-12
120 Penn St 17752 570-547-1608
Daphne Ross, supt. Fax 547-6271
www.montasd.org
Montgomery HS 300/9-12
120 Penn St 17752 570-547-1608
Michael Prowant, prin. Fax 547-6755
Montgomery MS 200/6-8
120 Penn St 17752 570-547-1608
Michael Prowant, prin. Fax 547-6755

Montoursville, Lycoming, Pop. 4,566
Loyalsock Township SD 1,400/K-12
1720 Sycamore Rd 17754 570-326-6508
Robert Grantier, supt. Fax 326-0770
www.loyalsocklancers.org/
Other Schools – See Williamsport

Montoursville Area SD 2,000/K-12
50 N Arch St 17754 570-368-2491
Dr. Timothy Bowers, supt. Fax 368-3501
www.montoursville.k12.pa.us/
McCall MS 600/5-8
600 Willow St 17754 570-368-2441
Jeffrey Moore, prin. Fax 368-3521
Montoursville Area HS 600/9-12
100 N Arch St 17754 570-368-2611
Daniel Taormina, prin. Fax 368-2768

Montrose, Susquehanna, Pop. 1,608
Montrose Area SD 1,500/K-12
273 Meteor Way 18801 570-278-6221
Michael Ognosky, supt. Fax 278-4798
www.masd.info/
Montrose JSHS 700/7-12
75 Meteor Way 18801 570-278-3731
James Tallarico, prin. Fax 278-9143

Moon Township, Allegheny, Pop. 10,187
Moon Area SD 3,700/K-12
8353 University Blvd 15108 412-264-9440
Donna Milanovich, supt. Fax 264-3268
www.moonarea.net
Moon Area MS 900/6-8
904 Beaver Grade Rd 15108 412-264-9440
Melissa Heasley, prin. Fax 264-3013
Moon HS 1,100/9-12
8353 University Blvd 15108 412-264-9440
Barry Balaski, prin. Fax 264-1271

Robert Morris University Post-Sec.
6001 University Blvd 15108 412-397-3000

Moosic, Lackawanna, Pop. 5,672

Empire Beauty School Post-Sec.
3370 Birney Ave 18507 570-823-5987

Morgantown, Lancaster, Pop. 817

Conestoga Christian S 200/PK-12
2760 Main St 19543 610-286-0353
Kenneth Parris, admin. Fax 286-0350

Morrisdale, Clearfield, Pop. 747
West Branch Area SD 1,200/K-12
516 Allport Cutoff 16858 814-345-5615
Michelle Dutrow, supt. Fax 345-5220
www.westbranch.org
West Branch Area JSHS 600/7-12
444 Allport Cutoff 16858 814-345-5615
Joseph Holenchik, prin. Fax 345-6116

Morrisville, Bucks, Pop. 8,532
Morrisville Borough SD 800/PK-12
550 W Palmer St 19067 215-736-2681
William Ferrara, supt. Fax 736-2413
mv.org
Morrisville HS 200/9-12
550 W Palmer St 19067 215-736-5260
William Ferrara, prin. Fax 736-3958
Morrisville IS, 550 W Palmer St 19067 300/3-8
William Ferrara, prin. 215-736-5270

Moscow, Lackawanna, Pop. 2,016
North Pocono SD 3,200/K-12
701 Church St 18444 570-842-7659
Bryan McGraw, supt. Fax 842-0886
www.npsd.org/
North Pocono HS 1,100/9-12
97 Bochicchio Blvd 18444 570-842-7606
John Marichak, prin. Fax 842-2163
North Pocono MS 800/6-8
701 Church St 18444 570-842-4588
Edward Bugno, prin. Fax 842-1783

Mountain Top, Luzerne, Pop. 10,876
Crestwood SD 3,000/K-12
281 S Mountain Blvd 18707 570-474-6782
Dave McLaughlin-Smith, supt. Fax 474-2254
www.csdcomets.org/
Crestwood HS 1,000/9-12
281 S Mountain Blvd 18707 570-474-6782
Christopher Gegaris, prin. Fax 474-1175
Crestwood MS 500/7-8
281 S Mountain Blvd 18707 570-474-6782
Bonnie Gregory, prin. Fax 474-2254

Mount Braddock, Fayette

Pennsylvania Institute of Health & Tech Post-Sec.
PO Box 278 15465 724-437-4600

Mount Carmel, Northumberland, Pop. 5,840
Mt. Carmel Area SD 1,400/PK-12
600 W 5th St 17851 570-339-1500
Bernard Stellar, supt. Fax 339-0487
www.mca.k12.pa.us
Mt. Carmel Area JSHS 500/7-12
600 W 5th St 17851 570-339-1500
Lisa Varano, prin. Fax 339-0487

Mount Joy, Lancaster, Pop. 7,283
Area Vocational Technical School
Supt. — None
Lancaster County CTC-Mt. Joy Vo/Tech
PO Box 537 17552 717-653-3000
James Catino, prin. Fax 653-0901

Donegal SD 1,700/K-12
1051 Koser Rd 17552 717-653-1447
Susan Ursprung Ed.D., supt. Fax 492-1350
www.donegal.k12.pa.us
Donegal HS 800/9-12
1025 Koser Rd 17552 717-653-1871
John Felix, prin. Fax 492-1241
Donegal JHS 400/7-8
915 Anderson Ferry Rd 17552 717-928-2900
Judy Haugh, prin. Fax 426-2417

Mount Pleasant, Westmoreland, Pop. 4,419
Mt. Pleasant Area SD 1,800/K-12
271 State St 15666 724-547-4100
Terry Struble, supt. Fax 547-0629
www.mpasd.net
Mount Pleasant Area JSHS 700/7-12
265 State St 15666 724-547-4100
Kenneth Williams, prin. Fax 547-0526

Mount Union, Huntingdon, Pop. 2,343
Mt. Union Area SD 1,500/K-12
603 N Industrial Dr 17066 814-542-8631
Dr. Brett Gilliland, supt. Fax 542-8633
www.muasd.org/
Mount Union Area HS 500/9-12
706 N Shaver St 17066 814-542-2518
Curt Whitsel, prin. Fax 542-5451
Mount Union JHS 200/7-8
706 N Shaver St 17066 814-542-9311
Amy Smith, prin.

Mountville, Lancaster, Pop. 2,760

Dayspring Christian Academy 300/PK-12
120 College Ave 17554 717-285-2000
Dr. Michael Myers, hdmstr.

Muncy, Lycoming, Pop. 2,457
Muncy SD 1,000/K-12
206 Sherman St 17756 570-546-3125
Dr. Portia Brandt, supt. Fax 546-6676
www.muncysd.org
Muncy JSHS 500/7-12
200 W Penn St 17756 570-546-3127
Timothy Welliver, prin. Fax 546-7688

Munhall, Allegheny, Pop. 11,221
Steel Valley SD 1,800/K-12
220 E Oliver Rd 15120 412-464-3600
Edward Wehrer, supt. Fax 464-3626
www.svsd.k12.pa.us
Steel Valley HS 600/9-12
3113 Main St 15120 412-464-3600
Bryan Macuga, prin. Fax 464-3609
Steel Valley MS 400/6-8
3114 Main St 15120 412-464-3600
Kevin Walsh, prin. Fax 464-3642

Murrysville, Westmoreland, Pop. 19,098
Franklin Regional SD 3,700/K-12
3210 School Rd 15668 724-327-5456
Gennaro R. Piraino Ed.D., supt. Fax 327-6149
www.franklinregional.k12.pa.us
Franklin Regional HS 1,300/9-12
3200 School Rd 15668 724-327-5456
Ron Suvak, prin. Fax 327-2782
Franklin Regional MS 900/6-8
4660 Old William Penn Hwy 15668 724-327-5456
Shelley Shaneyfelt, prin. Fax 733-0949

Myerstown, Lebanon, Pop. 3,030
Eastern Lebanon County SD 2,500/K-12
180 Elco Dr 17067 717-866-7117
Dr. David Zuilkoski, supt. Fax 866-7084
www.elcosd.org/
Eastern Lebanon County HS 800/9-12
180 Elco Dr 17067 717-866-7447
Jennifer Haas, prin. Fax 866-7287
Eastern Lebanon County MS 500/6-8
60 Evergreen Dr 17067 717-866-6591
Michael Gerhart, prin. Fax 866-5837

Evangelical Theological Seminary Post-Sec.
121 S College St 17067 717-866-5775
Lebanon Valley Christian S 100/1-12
7821 Lancaster Ave 17067 717-933-5171
Myerstown Mennonite S 200/1-12
739 E Lincoln Ave 17067 717-866-5667
Fax 866-8652

Nanticoke, Luzerne, Pop. 10,349
Greater Nanticoke Area SD 2,200/K-12
427 Kosciuszko St 18634 570-735-1270
Anthony Perrone, supt. Fax 735-1350
www.gnasd.com
Greater Nanticoke Area HS 900/8-12
425 Kosciuszko St 18634 570-735-7781
John Gorham, prin. Fax 733-1002

Luzerne County Community College Post-Sec.
1333 S Prospect St 18634 570-740-0200

Nanty Glo, Cambria, Pop. 2,702
Blacklick Valley SD 700/K-12
555 Birch St 15943 814-749-9211
John Mastillo, supt. Fax 749-8627
www.bvsd.k12.pa.us
Blacklick Valley JSHS 300/7-12
555 Birch St 15943 814-749-9211
Michael McDermott, prin.

Narberth, Montgomery, Pop. 4,161
Lower Merion SD
Supt. — See Ardmore
Welsh Valley MS 800/6-8
325 Tower Ln 19072 610-658-3920
Dr. Orathia Bradley, prin. Fax 667-4749

Natrona Heights, Allegheny, Pop. 11,400
Highlands SD 1,900/K-12
PO Box 288 15065 724-226-2400
Patrick Graczyk, supt. Fax 226-8437
www.goldenrams.com
Highlands HS 800/9-12
1500 Pacific Ave 15065 724-226-1000
Catherine Russo, prin. Fax 226-9611
Highlands MS 600/6-8
1350 Broadview Blvd 15065 724-226-0600
Charles Mort, prin. Fax 226-3287

Allegheny Valley Hospital Post-Sec.
1301 Carlisle St 15065 724-226-7000
St. Joseph HS 200/9-12
800 Montana Ave 15065 724-224-5552
Beverly Kaniecki, prin. Fax 224-3205

Nazareth, Northampton, Pop. 5,699
Nazareth Area SD 4,700/K-12
1 Education Plz 18064 610-759-1170
Dr. Dennis L. Riker, supt. Fax 759-9637
www.nazarethasd.k12.pa.us

Nazareth Area HS 1,600/9-12
501 E Center St 18064 610-759-1730
Alan Davis, prin. Fax 746-2599
Nazareth Area MS 800/7-8
94 Friedensthal Ave 18064 610-759-3350
Robert Kern, prin. Fax 759-3725

Needmore, Fulton, Pop. 168

Fulton County Community Christian S 50/PK-12
PO Box 235 17238 717-573-4400
Dr. Louise Hine, admin. Fax 573-2731

New Berlin, Union, Pop. 870
Area Vocational Technical School
Supt. — None
SUN Area Technology Institute Vo/Tech
815 Market St 17855 570-966-1031
Dennis Hain, dir. Fax 966-9492

New Bethlehem, Clarion, Pop. 986
Redbank Valley SD 800/K-12
920 Broad St 16242 814-275-2426
Michael Drzewiecki, supt. Fax 275-2428
www.redbankvalley.net/
Redbank Valley JSHS 600/7-12
910 Broad St 16242 814-275-2424
Jeffrey Long, prin. Fax 275-2428

New Bloomfield, Perry, Pop. 1,237

Carson Long Military Academy 100/6-12
200 N Carlisle St 17068 717-582-2121
Col. Matthew Brown, pres. Fax 582-8763

New Brighton, Beaver, Pop. 5,744
New Brighton Area SD 1,700/K-12
3225 43rd St 15066 724-843-1795
David Pietro Ed.D., supt. Fax 843-6144
www.nbasd.org
New Brighton Area HS 600/9-12
3202 43rd St 15066 724-846-1050
Edward Kasparek, prin. Fax 846-2204
New Brighton Area MS 400/6-8
901 Penn Ave 15066 724-846-8100
Julian Underwood, prin. Fax 846-2337

New Castle, Lawrence, Pop. 22,422
Area Vocational Technical School
Supt. — None
Lawrence County CTC Vo/Tech
750 Phelps Way 16101 724-658-3583
Brad Ovial, prin. Fax 658-8530

Laurel SD 1,400/K-12
2497 Harlansburg Rd 16101 724-658-8940
Sandra Hennon Ph.D., supt. Fax 658-2992
www.laurel.k12.pa.us
Laurel JSHS 700/7-12
2497 Harlansburg Rd 16101 724-658-9056
Fax 658-2992

Neshannock Township SD 1,300/K-12
3834 Mitchell Rd 16105 724-658-4793
Dr. Mary Todora, supt. Fax 658-1828
www.neshannock.k12.pa.us
Neshannock JSHS 600/7-12
3834 Mitchell Rd 16105 724-658-5513
Dr. Tracy McCalla, prin. Fax 657-8169

New Castle Area SD 3,300/PK-12
420 Fern St 16101 724-656-4756
George Gabriel, supt. Fax 656-4767
www.ncasd.com
New Castle JSHS 1,400/7-12
300 E Lincoln Ave 16101 724-656-4700
Richard Litrenta, prin. Fax 658-3916

Shenango Area SD 1,300/K-12
2501 Old Pittsburgh Rd 16101 724-658-7287
Dr. Michael Schreck, supt. Fax 658-5370
www.shenango.k12.pa.us
Shenango HS 600/7-12
2550 Ellwood Rd 16101 724-658-5537
Joseph McCormick, prin. Fax 658-7584

Union Area SD 600/K-12
2106 Camden Ave 16101 724-658-4775
Dr. Alfonso Angelucci, supt. Fax 658-5151
www.union.k12.pa.us/
Union Area MSHS 300/5-12
2106 Camden Ave 16101 724-658-4501
Mike Ross, prin. Fax 658-8617

Erie Business Center South Post-Sec.
170 Cascade Galleria 16101 724-658-9066
Jameson Memorial Hosp School of Nursing Post-Sec.
1211 Wilmington Ave 16105 724-656-4240
New Castle School of Beauty Culture Post-Sec.
314 E Washington St 16101 724-654-6611
New Castle School of Trades Post-Sec.
4117 Pulaski Rd 16101 800-837-8299

New Cumberland, Cumberland, Pop. 7,166
West Shore SD
Supt. — See Lewisberry
New Cumberland MS 400/6-8
331 8th St 17070 717-774-0162
Karen Hertzler, prin. Fax 901-9474

New Eagle, Washington, Pop. 2,165
Ringgold SD 2,700/K-12
400 Main St 15067 724-258-9329
Dr. Karen Polkabla, supt. Fax 258-5363
www.ringgold.org
Other Schools – See Finleyville, Monongahela

New Holland, Lancaster, Pop. 5,286
Eastern Lancaster County SD 3,100/K-12
PO Box 609 17557 717-354-1500
Dr. Robert Hollister, supt. Fax 354-1512
www.elanco.org
Garden Spot HS 1,000/9-12
PO Box 609 17557 717-354-1550
Matthew Sanger, prin. Fax 354-1128
Garden Spot MS 500/7-8
PO Box 609 17557 717-354-1560
Jeffrey Starr, prin. Fax 354-1129

New Hope, Bucks, Pop. 2,495
New Hope-Solebury SD 1,600/K-12
180 W Bridge St 18938 215-862-2552
Dr. Raymond Boccuti, supt. Fax 744-6012
www.nhsd.org
New Hope-Solebury HS 500/9-12
182 W Bridge St 18938 215-862-2028
Christina Lang, prin. Fax 862-3198
New Hope-Solebury MS 400/6-8
184 W Bridge St 18938 215-862-0608
Charles Malone, prin. Fax 862-2862

Solebury S 200/7-12
6832 Phillips Mill Rd 18938 215-862-5261
Tom Wilschutz, head sch Fax 862-3366

New Kensington, Westmoreland, Pop. 12,575
Area Vocational Technical School
Supt. — None
Northern Westmoreland CTC Vo/Tech
705 Stevenson Blvd 15068 724-335-9389
Kurt Kiefer, dir. Fax 337-9010

New Kensington-Arnold SD 2,100/PK-12
707 Stevenson Blvd 15068 724-335-4401
John Pallone J.D., supt. Fax 994-1213
nkasd.com
Valley HS 700/9-12
703 Stevenson Blvd 15068 724-337-4536
Jon Banko, prin. Fax 337-8054
Other Schools – See Arnold

Career Training Academy Post-Sec.
950 5th Ave 15068 724-337-1000
Citizens General Hospital Post-Sec.
651 4th Ave 15068 724-337-5090
Mary Queen of Apostles IS 100/4-8
1129 Leishman Ave 15068 724-339-4411
Catherine Collett, prin. Fax 337-6457
Penn State New Kensington Post-Sec.
3550 7th Street Rd 15068 724-334-5466

New Milford, Susquehanna, Pop. 860
Blue Ridge SD 1,100/PK-12
5058 School Rd 18834 570-465-3141
Robert McTiernan, supt. Fax 465-3148
www.brsd.org
Blue Ridge HS 400/9-12
5058 School Rd 18834 570-465-3144
Matthew Nebzydoski, prin. Fax 465-3148
Blue Ridge MS 300/6-8
5058 School Rd 18834 570-465-3177
Matthew Nebzydoski, prin. Fax 465-3148

Faith Mountain Christian Academy 50/K-12
19 Ward St 18834 570-465-2220
Lois Frantz, prin. Fax 465-2220

New Oxford, Adams, Pop. 1,767
Conewago Valley SD 3,900/K-12
130 Berlin Rd 17350 717-624-2157
Dr. Rebecca Harbaugh, supt. Fax 624-5020
www.conewago.k12.pa.us
New Oxford HS 1,300/9-12
130 Berlin Rd 17350 717-624-2157
Kevin Thomas, prin. Fax 624-5021
New Oxford MS 600/7-8
130 Berlin Rd 17350 717-624-2157
Gretchen Gates, prin. Fax 624-6560

New Paris, Bedford, Pop. 183
Chestnut Ridge SD
Supt. — See Fishertown
Chestnut Ridge HS 500/9-12
2588 Quaker Valley Rd 15554 814-839-4195
George Knisely, prin. Fax 839-0018

Newport, Perry, Pop. 1,551
Newport SD 1,200/K-12
PO Box 9 17074 717-567-3806
Norman Shea, supt. Fax 567-6468
www.newportsd.org
Newport HS 400/9-12
PO Box 9 17074 717-567-3806
Ryan Neuhard, prin. Fax 567-2619
Newport MS 200/6-8
PO Box 9 17074 717-567-3806
Joseph Stroup, prin. Fax 567-2619

New Stanton, Westmoreland, Pop. 2,152
Area Vocational Technical School
Supt. — None
Central Westmoreland CTC Vo/Tech
240 Arona Rd 15672 724-925-3532
Brad Elwood, dir. Fax 925-1423

Newtown, Bucks, Pop. 2,215
Council Rock SD 11,900/K-12
30 N Chancellor St 18940 215-944-1000
Mark Klein, supt. Fax 944-1031
www.crsd.org
Council Rock HS North 2,100/9-12
62 Swamp Rd 18940 215-944-1300
Susan McCarthy, prin. Fax 944-1387
Newtown MS 800/7-8
116 Richboro Newtown Rd 18940 215-944-2600
Timothy Long, prin. Fax 944-2698
Other Schools – See Holland, Richboro

Bucks County Community College Post-Sec.
275 Swamp Rd 18940 215-968-8000
George S 500/9-12
PO Box 4460 18940 215-579-6547
Nancy Starmer, hdmstr. Fax 579-6549
Holy Family University Post-Sec.
1 Campus Dr 18940 215-637-7700

Newtown Square, Delaware, Pop. 11,300
Marple Newtown SD 3,500/K-12
40 Media Line Rd 19073 610-359-4200
Merle Horowitz Ed.D., supt. Fax 723-3340
www.mnsd.net
Marple Newtown HS 1,200/9-12
120 Media Line Rd 19073 610-359-4218
Greg Puckett, prin. Fax 356-2194
Other Schools – See Broomall

Delaware County Christian HS 500/6-12
462 Malin Rd 19073 610-353-6522
Dr. Timothy Wiens, hdmstr. Fax 356-9684
Episcopal Academy 1,200/PK-12
1785 Bishop White Dr 19073 484-424-1400
Dr. T.J. Locke, hdmstr. Fax 424-1600

New Tripoli, Lehigh, Pop. 887
Northwestern Lehigh SD 2,300/K-12
6493 Route 309 18066 610-298-8661
Mary Anne Wright Ph.D., supt. Fax 298-8002
www.nwlehighsd.org
Northwestern Lehigh HS 800/9-12
6493 Route 309 18066 610-298-8661
Aileen Yadush, prin. Fax 298-4645
Northwestern Lehigh MS 500/6-8
6636 Northwest Rd 18066 610-298-8661
Laurie Hoppes, prin. Fax 298-8178

Newville, Cumberland, Pop. 1,313
Big Spring SD 2,700/K-12
45 Mount Rock Rd 17241 717-776-2000
Richard Fry, supt. Fax 776-4428
www.bigspring.k12.pa.us
Big Spring HS 1,000/9-12
100 Mount Rock Rd 17241 717-776-2000
Steven Smith, prin. Fax 776-2433
Big Spring MS 700/6-8
47 Mount Rock Rd 17241 717-776-2000
Dr. Linda Wilson, prin. Fax 776-2468

New Wilmington, Lawrence, Pop. 2,444
Wilmington Area SD 1,300/K-12
300 Wood St 16142 724-656-8866
Dr. Catherine Nicksick, supt. Fax 946-8982
www.wilmington.k12.pa.us/
Wilmington Area HS 500/9-12
350 Wood St 16142 724-656-8866
Benjamin Fennick, prin.
Wilmington Area MS 500/5-8
400 Wood St 16142 724-656-8866
George Endrizzi, prin.

Westminster College Post-Sec.
319 S Market St 16172 724-946-7100

Norristown, Montgomery, Pop. 33,250
Norristown Area SD 6,800/K-12
401 N Whitehall Rd 19403 610-630-5000
Janet Samuels Ph.D., supt. Fax 630-5013
www.nasd.k12.pa.us
East Norriton MS 900/5-8
330 Roland Dr 19401 610-275-6520
Dr. Christina Spink, prin. Fax 272-0531
Eisenhower MS 500/5-8
1601 Markley St 19401 610-277-8720
Christina Taylor, prin. Fax 270-2901
Norristown Area HS 1,900/9-12
1900 Eagle Dr 19403 610-630-5090
Jeffrey Smith, prin. Fax 630-5115
Roosevelt Alternative S 100/Alt
1161 Markley St 19401 610-275-9720
Janet Simpkins, prin. Fax 272-0552
Stewart MS 500/5-8
1315 W Marshall St 19401 610-275-6870
Martina Walls, prin. Fax 272-0560

Star Career Academy Post-Sec.
2501 Monroe Blvd 19403 610-783-7827
The Pathway School Post-Sec.
162 Egypt Rd 19403 610-277-0660

Northampton, Northampton, Pop. 9,830
Catasauqua Area SD
Supt. — See Catasauqua
Catasauqua HS 500/9-12
2500 W Bullshead Rd 18067 610-697-0111
David Ascani, prin. Fax 697-0116

Northampton Area SD 5,600/K-12
2014 Laubach Ave 18067 610-262-7811
Joseph Kovalchik, supt. Fax 262-1150
www.nasdschools.org/
Northampton Area HS 1,900/9-12
1619 Laubach Ave 18067 610-262-7812
Stephen Seier, prin. Fax 262-3024
Northampton Area MS 800/7-8
1617 Laubach Ave 18067 610-262-7817
Patrice Turner, prin. Fax 262-6583

North East, Erie, Pop. 4,255
North East SD 1,700/K-12
50 E Division St 16428 814-725-8671
James Brotz, supt. Fax 725-9380
www.nesd1.org/
North East HS 600/9-12
1901 Freeport Rd 16428 814-725-8671
Regan Tanner, prin. Fax 725-3357

North East MS 400/6-8
1903 Freeport Rd 16428 814-725-8671
Gregory Beardsley, prin. Fax 725-1086

Northern Cambria, Cambria, Pop. 4,022
Northern Cambria SD 1,100/K-12
601 Joseph St 15714 814-948-5481
Dr. John Jubas, supt. Fax 948-6058
www.ncsd.k12.pa.us/
Northern Cambria HS 400/9-12
813 35th St 15714 814-948-6800
Joy Tibbott, prin. Fax 948-9810
Northern Cambria MS 300/6-8
601 Joseph St 15714 814-948-5880
Marilyn Wargo, prin. Fax 948-5561

North Huntingdon, Westmoreland, Pop. 28,158
Norwin SD 5,200/K-12
281 McMahon Dr 15642 724-861-3000
Dr. William Kerr, supt. Fax 863-9467
www.norwinsd.org
Norwin HS 1,700/9-12
251 McMahon Dr 15642 724-861-3005
Dr. Edward Federinko, prin. Fax 861-0581
Norwin MS 800/7-8
10870 Mockingbird Dr 15642 724-863-5707
Robert Suman, prin. Fax 863-5408

Northumberland, Northumberland, Pop. 3,769

Northumberland Christian S 200/K-12
351 5th St 17857 570-473-9786
John Rees, prin. Fax 473-8405
Sunbury Christian Academy 200/PK-12
135 Spruce Hollow Rd 17857 570-473-7592
Nancy Gross, admin. Fax 473-7531

North Versailles, Allegheny, Pop. 12,302
East Allegheny SD 1,700/PK-12
1150 Jacks Run Rd 15137 412-824-8012
Roger D'Emidio, supt. Fax 824-1062
www.eawildcats.net
East Allegheny HS 700/9-12
1150 Jacks Run Rd 15137 412-824-9700
Don MacFann, prin. Fax 825-4570
Logan MS 400/4-8
1154 Jacks Run Rd 15137 412-824-6053
M. Draskovich, prin. Fax 824-6095

North Wales, Montgomery, Pop. 3,136
North Penn SD
Supt. — See Lansdale
Pennbrook MS 800/7-9
1201 N Wales Rd 19454 215-699-9287
Jim Galante, prin. Fax 699-0151

Lansdale School of Business Post-Sec.
290 Wissahickon Ave 19454 215-699-5700

North Warren, Warren, Pop. 1,910
Warren County SD 4,900/K-12
589 Hospital Dr Ste A 16365 814-723-6900
Brandon Hufnagel, supt. Fax 723 4244
www.wcsdpa.org
Other Schools – See Russell, Sheffield, Warren, Youngsville

Oakdale, Allegheny, Pop. 1,442
Area Vocational Technical School
Supt. — None
Parkway West CTC Vo/Tech
7101 Steubenville Pike 15071 412-923-1772
Dr. Darby Copeland, prin. Fax 787-7257

West Allegheny SD 3,300/K-12
600 Donaldson Rd 15071 724-695-3422
John DiSanti Ph.D., supt. Fax 695-3788
www.westasd.org
Other Schools – See Imperial

Pittsburgh Technical Institute Post-Sec.
1111 McKee Rd 15071 800-784-9675

Oakmont, Allegheny, Pop. 6,258
Riverview SD 1,100/K-12
701 10th St 15139 412-828-1800
Margaret DiNinno, supt. Fax 828-9346
www.rsd.k12.pa.us
Riverview HS 600/7-12
100 Hulton Rd 15139 412-828-1800
Jay Moser, prin. Fax 828-6296

Oil City, Venango, Pop. 10,397
Area Vocational Technical School
Supt. — None
Venango Technology Center Vo/Tech
1 Vo Tech Dr 16301 814-677-3097
Mario Fontanazza, dir. Fax 676-0075

Oil City Area SD 1,900/K-12
825 Grandview Rd 16301 814-676-1867
Dr. Joseph Carrico, supt. Fax 676-2211
www.ocasd.org
Oil City Area MS 500/5-8
8 Lynch Blvd 16301 814-676-5702
Sue Ann Boyles, prin. Fax 676-2306
Oil City HS 700/9-12
10 Lynch Blvd 16301 814-676-2771
Scott Stahl, prin. Fax 677-7256

Clarion University - Venango Campus Post-Sec.
1801 W 1st St 16301 814-676-6591
DuBois Business College Post-Sec.
701 E 3rd St 16301 814-677-1322
Venango Catholic HS 100/9-12
1505 W 1st St 16301 814-677-3098
Shane Matthew, hdmstr. Fax 676-4453

Old Forge, Lackawanna, Pop. 8,255
Old Forge SD 1,000/K-12
300 Marion St 18518 570-457-6721
Al Semenza, supt. Fax 457-8389
www.ofsd.cc
Old Forge JSHS 400/7-12
300 Marion St 18518 570-457-6721
Christopher Thomas, prin. Fax 414-0997

Oley, Berks, Pop. 1,277
Area Vocational Technical School
Supt. — None
Berks CTC - East Vo/Tech
3307 Friedensburg Rd 19547 610-987-6201
Dr. James Kraft, prin. Fax 987-6106

Oley Valley SD 1,900/K-12
17 Jefferson St 19547 610-987-4100
Tracy Shank Ed.D., supt. Fax 987-4138
www.oleyvalleysd.org
Oley Valley HS 600/9-12
17 Jefferson St 19547 610-987-4100
Darrell Markley Ed.D., prin. Fax 987-4138
Oley Valley MS 400/6-8
3247 Friedensburg Rd 19547 610-987-4100
Dan Marks, prin. Fax 987-4240

Orefield, Lehigh
Parkland SD
Supt. — See Allentown
Orefield MS 1,100/6-8
2675 PA Route 309 18069 610-351-5750
Todd Gombos, prin. Fax 351-5799

Oreland, Montgomery, Pop. 5,575
Springfield Township SD 2,100/K-12
1901 Paper Mill Rd 19075 215-233-6000
Dr. Nancy Hacker, supt. Fax 233-5815
www.sdst.org
Springfield Township MS 500/6-8
1901 Paper Mill Rd 19075 215-233-6070
Lauren Davis, prin. Fax 233-6091
Other Schools – See Erdenheim

Orwigsburg, Schuylkill, Pop. 3,077
Blue Mountain SD 2,600/K-12
PO Box 188 17961 570-366-0515
Dr. Robert Urzillo, supt. Fax 366-0838
www.bmsd.org
Blue Mountain MS 600/6-8
PO Box 279 17961 570-366-0546
James McGonigle, prin. Fax 366-2513
Other Schools – See Schuylkill Haven

Oxford, Chester, Pop. 4,949
Oxford Area SD 3,900/K-12
125 Bell Tower Ln 19363 610-932-6600
David Woods, supt. Fax 932-6614
www.oxford.k12.pa.us
Oxford Area HS 1,200/9-12
705 Waterway Rd 19363 610-932-6640
Christopher Dormer, prin. Fax 932-6649
Penn's Grove S 600/7-8
301 S 5th St 19363 610-932-6615
Lisa Stenz, prin. Fax 932-6619

Palmerton, Carbon, Pop. 5,366
Palmerton Area SD 1,900/K-12
680 4th St 18071 610-826-7101
Carol Boyce, supt. Fax 826-4958
www.palmerton.org/
Palmerton Area HS 600/9-12
3525 Fireline Rd 18071 610-826-3155
Kathleen Egan, prin. Fax 826-4929
Palmerton Area JHS 300/7-8
3529 Fireline Rd 18071 610-826-2492
Paula Husak, prin. Fax 826-2366

Palmyra, Lebanon, Pop. 7,238
Palmyra Area SD 3,000/K-12
1125 Park Dr 17078 717-838-3144
Dr. Collene Van Noord, supt. Fax 838-5105
www.pasd.us
Palmyra Area HS 900/9-12
1125 Park Dr 17078 717-838-1331
Dr. Benjamin Ruby, prin. Fax 838-7915
Palmyra Area MS 800/6-8
50 W Cherry St 17078 717-838-1331
Anne Hoover, prin. Fax 838-4402

Paoli, Chester, Pop. 5,479

Delaware Valley Friends S 200/6-12
19 E Central Ave 19301 610-640-4150
Pritchard Garrett, head sch Fax 296-9970
Royer-Greaves School for Blind Post-Sec.
118 S Valley Rd 19301

Patton, Cambria, Pop. 1,764
Cambria Heights SD 1,500/K-12
PO Box 66 16668 814-674-6072
Michael Strasser, supt. Fax 674-5411
www.chsd1.org/
Cambria Heights HS 500/9-12
PO Box 6 16668 814-674-3601
Timothy Laurito, prin. Fax 674-5605
Cambria Heights MS 300/6-8
PO Box 216 16668 814-674-6290
David Caldwell, prin. Fax 674-5054

Pen Argyl, Northampton, Pop. 3,551
Pen Argyl Area SD 1,800/K-12
1620 Teels Rd 18072 610-863-3191
William Haberl Ed.D., supt. Fax 863-7040
www.penargyl.k12.pa.us
Pen Argyl Area HS 600/9-12
501 W Laurel Ave 18072 610-863-1293
John Smith, prin. Fax 863-7660
Wind Gap MS 700/4-8
1620 Teels Rd 18072 610-863-9093
Dr. Terry Barry, prin. Fax 863-3817

Pennsburg, Montgomery, Pop. 3,798
Upper Perkiomen SD 3,200/K-12
2229 E Buck Rd 18073 215-679-7961
Dr. Elizabeth Yonson, supt. Fax 679-6214
www.upsd.org/
Upper Perkiomen HS 1,000/9-12
2 Walt Rd 18073 215-679-5935
Dr. William Shirk, prin. Fax 679-0911
Other Schools – See East Greenville

Perkiomen S 300/6-12
200 Seminary St 18073 215-679-9511
Christopher Tompkins, hdmstr. Fax 679-5202

Penns Creek, Snyder, Pop. 711

Penn View Christian Academy 100/PK-12
PO Box 970 17862 570-837-1855
Brent Lenhart, prin. Fax 837-1865

Pequea, Lancaster
Penn Manor SD
Supt. — See Lancaster
Marticville MS 300/7-8
356 Frogtown Rd 17565 717-284-4135
Christine Santaniello, prin. Fax 284-5954

Perkasie, Bucks, Pop. 8,390
Area Vocational Technical School
Supt. — None
Upper Bucks County AVTS Vo/Tech
3115 Ridge Rd 18944 215-795-2911
Bernard Wagenseller, dir. Fax 795-0530

Pennridge SD 7,300/K-12
1200 N 5th St 18944 215-257-5011
Dr. Robert Kish, supt. Fax 453-8699
www.pennridge.org
Pennridge Central MS 600/6-8
144 N Walnut St 18944 215-258-0939
Dr. Thomas Rutter, prin. Fax 258-0938
Pennridge HS 2,300/9-12
1228 N 5th St 18944 215-453-6944
Dr. Thomas Creeden, prin. Fax 257-4986
Pennridge North MS 700/6-8
1500 N 5th St 18944 215-453-6932
Gina DeBona, prin. Fax 453-7867
Pennridge South MS 400/6-8
610 S 5th St 18944 215-257-0467
Dr. Felicia McAllister, prin. Fax 257-3094

Perryopolis, Fayette, Pop. 1,762
Frazier SD 1,100/K-12
142 Constitution St 15473 724-736-4432
Dr. David Blozowich, supt. Fax 736-0688
www.frazierschooldistrict.org
Frazier HS 400/9-12
142 Constitution St 15473 724-736-4426
Chris Sefcheck, prin. Fax 736-0688
Frazier MS 300/6-8
142 Constitution St 15473 724-736-4428
Michael Turek, prin. Fax 736-0688

Philadelphia, Philadelphia, Pop. 1,493,502
Area Vocational Technical School
Supt. — None
Bok Technical HS Vo/Tech
1901 S 9th St 19148 215-952-6200
Barbara McCreery, prin. Fax 952-6410
Communications Technology HS Vo/Tech
8110 Lyons Ave 19153 215-492-6958
Colette Langston, prin. Fax 492-6074
Dobbins AVTS Vo/Tech
2150 W Lehigh Ave 19132 215-227-4421
Dr. Toni Damon, prin. Fax 227-4944
Edison HS Vo/Tech
151 W Luzerne St 19140 215-324-9599
Charles Baltimore, prin. Fax 329-5824
Kensington Culinary Arts S Vo/Tech
2463 Emerald St 19125 215-291-5185
James Williams, prin. Fax 291-6320
Mastbaum AVTS Vo/Tech
3116 Frankford Ave 19134 215-291-4703
Loise Mondesire, prin. Fax 291-5657
Randolph AVTS Vo/Tech
3101 Henry Ave 19129 215-227-4407
Darryl Overton, prin. Fax 227-8655
Saul Agricultural S Vo/Tech
7100 Henry Ave 19128 215-487-4467
Tamera Conaway, prin. Fax 487-4844
School for Exceptional Adults AVTS Vo/Tech
1400 W Olney Ave 19141 215-299-3699
Swenson Arts & Technology HS Vo/Tech
2750 Red Lion Rd 19114 215-961-2009
Linda Graham, prin. Fax 961-2081

Philadelphia CSD 177,300/PK-12
440 N Broad St 19130 215-400-4000
William Hite Ed.D., supt.
www.philasd.org/
Academy at Palumbo 600/9-12
1100 Catharine St 19147 215-351-7618
Dr. Adrienne Chew, prin. Fax 351-7685
Alternative Ed Reg Ctr at Hunting Park Alt
4224 N Front St 19140 267-336-6000
Alternative Ed Regional Center West 700/Alt
4300 Westminster Ave 19104 267-292-6600
Alternative Ed Regional Ctr at 440 Alt
440 N Broad St 19130 215-271-0791
Arts Academy at Benjamin Rush 400/9-12
11081 Knights Rd 19154 215-281-2603
Jessica Brown, prin. Fax 281-2674
Baldi MS 1,300/6-8
8801 Verree Rd 19115 215-961-2003
Eugene McLaughlin, prin. Fax 961-2116
Bartram HS 1,100/9-12
2401 S 67th St 19142 215-492-6450
Constance McAlister, prin. Fax 492-6117

Beeber MS 500/6-8
5925 Malvern Ave 19131 215-581-5513
Joseph Starinieri, prin. Fax 581-5694
Bodine HS for International Affairs 500/9-12
1101 N 4th St 19123 215-351-7332
Deborah Jumpp, prin. Fax 351-7370
Carroll HS 400/9-12
2700 E Auburn St 19134 215-291-4707
Joyce Hoog, prin. Fax 291-5174
Carver HS for Engineering & Science 700/9-12
1600 W Norris St 19121 215-684-5079
Linda Ahmed, prin. Fax 684-5151
Central HS 2,400/9-12
1700 W Olney Ave 19141 215-276-5262
Tim McKenna, prin. Fax 276-4721
Clemente MS 700/5-8
122 W Erie Ave 19140 215-291-5400
Edward Penn, prin. Fax 291-5421
Constitution HS 400/9-12
18 S 7th St 19106 215-351-7310
Dr. Tom Davidson, prin. Fax 351-7694
Conwell MS 800/5-8
1849 E Clearfield St 19134 215-291-4722
Tamara Thomas-Smith, prin. Fax 291-5019
Creative & Performing Arts HS 700/9-12
901 S Broad St 19147 215-952-2462
Johnny Whaley, prin. Fax 952-6472
Fels HS 1,600/9-12
5500 Langdon St 19124 215-537-2516
Shawn McGuigan, prin. Fax 537-2556
Feltonville Arts & Sciences MS 700/6-8
210 E Courtland St 19120 215-456-5603
Michael Reid, prin. Fax 456-5614
Frankford HS 1,800/9-12
5000 Oxford Ave 19124 215-537-2519
Reginald Fisher, prin. Fax 537-2598
Franklin HS 700/9-12
550 N Broad St 19130 215-299-4662
Greg Haley, prin. Fax 299-7285
Furness HS 600/9-12
1900 S 3rd St 19148 215-952-6226
Daniel Peou, prin. Fax 952-8635
Germantown HS 900/9-12
40 E High St 19144 215-951-4004
Margret Bavwidinsi, prin. Fax 843-8946
Girard Academic Music Program 500/5-12
2201 W Ritner St 19145 215-952-8589
John Carr, prin. Fax 952-6544
Harding MS 800/6-8
2000 Wakeling St 19124 215-537-2528
Michael Calderone, prin. Fax 537-2850
Hill/Freedman MS 200/6-8
6200 Crittenden St 19138 215-276-5260
Anthony Majewski, prin. Fax 276-5873
Kensington Business & Finance HS 500/9-12
2501 Coral St 19125 215-291-5168
Eileen Maicon-Weissman, prin. Fax 291-5708
Kensington CAPA HS 500/9-12
1901 N Front St 19122 215-291-5010
Debora Carrera, prin. Fax 291-6334
Kensington Urban Education 100/Alt
2051 E Cumberland St 19125 215-291-5420
Michelle Burns, prin. Fax 291-5427
King HS 1,100/9-12
6100 Stenton Ave 19138 215-276-5253
William Wade, prin. Fax 276-5844
LaBrum MS 200/6-8
10800 Hawley Rd 19154 215-281-2607
William Griffin, prin. Fax 281-5800
Lamberton HS 300/9-12
7501 Woodbine Ave 19151 215-581-5647
Marla Travis-Jones, prin. Fax 581-3403
Lankenau HS 300/9-12
201 Spring Ln 19128 215-487-4465
Karen Dean, prin. Fax 487-4879
Leeds MS 300/7-8
1100 E Mount Pleasant Ave 19150 215-248-6602
Dontae Wilson, prin. Fax 248-6623
Lincoln HS 1,800/9-12
3201 Ryan Ave 19136 215-335-5653
Dr. Donald Anticoli, prin. Fax 335-5997
Masterman MSHS 1,200/5-12
1699 Spring Garden St 19130 215-299-4661
Marjorie Neff, prin. Fax 299-3425
Meehan MS 600/7-8
3001 Ryan Ave 19152 215-335-5654
Mary Jackson, prin. Fax 335-5992
Middle Years Alternative-MYA 200/Alt
4725 Fairmount Ave 19139 215-581-5633
Kathleen Fitzpatrick, prin. Fax 581-5668
Motivation HS 200/9-12
2555 S 78th St 19153 215-492-6451
Yvonne Jones, prin. Fax 492-6924
Northeast HS 3,300/9-12
1601 Cottman Ave 19111 215-728-5018
Linda Carroll, prin. Fax 728-5004
Overbrook HS 1,500/9-12
5898 Lancaster Ave 19131 215-581-5507
Ethelyn Young, prin. Fax 581-3406
Parkway Center City HS 400/9-12
540 N 13th St 19123 215-351-7095
Catherine Blunt, prin. Fax 351-7097
Parkway Northwest HS 300/9-12
7500 Germantown Ave 19119 215-248-6220
Ethel McGee, prin. Fax 248-6015
Parkway West HS 300/9-12
4725 Fairmount Ave 19139 215-581-5510
Dr. Kathleen McCladdie, prin. Fax 581-5600
Penn Treaty MS 400/6-8
600 E Thompson St 19125 215-291-4715
Sam Howell, prin. Fax 291-5172
Pepper MS 600/5-8
2901 S 84th St 19153 215-492-6457
Yolanda Armstrong, prin. Fax 492-1844
Philadelphia HS for Girls 1,100/9-12
1400 W Olney Ave 19141 215-276-5258
Parthenia Moore, prin. Fax 276-5738
HS of the Future 400/9-12
4021 Parkside Ave 19104 215-823-5502
Rosalind Chivis, prin. Fax 823-5504
Philadelphia Military Academy 200/9-12
2118 N 13th St 19122 215-684-5091
Dr. Robert Manning, prin. Fax 684-5507
Philadelphia Military Academy at Leeds 300/9-12
1100 E Mount Pleasant Ave 19150 215-248-6650
Patricia Randzo, prin. Fax 248-6654
Rhodes MS 100/7-8
2900 W Clearfield St 19132 215-227-4402
Ivy Lewis, prin. Fax 227-4926
Robeson HS for Human Services 300/9-12
4125 Ludlow St 19104 215-823-8207
Hiromi Hernandez, prin. Fax 823-8252
Roosevelt MS 400/7-8
430 E Washington Ln 19144 215-951-4170
Cassandra Houston, prin. Fax 951-7762
Roxborough HS 700/9-12
6498 Ridge Ave 19128 215-487-4464
Stephen Brandt, prin. Fax 487-4843
Sayre HS 600/9-12
5800 Walnut St 19139 215-471-2904
Charles Ireland, prin. Fax 471-3486
Science Leadership Academy 500/9-12
55 N 22nd St 19103 215-979-5620
Christopher Lehmann, prin. Fax 567-2809
Shaw MS 200/7-8
5400 Warrington Ave 19143 215-727-2161
Kwand Lang, prin. Fax 727-2248
Sheridan West Academy 200/7-8
3701 Frankford Ave 19124 215-537-2920
Lisa Mesi, prin. Fax 537-2962
South Philadelphia HS 900/9-12
2101 S Broad St 19148 215-952-6220
Otis Hackney, prin. Fax 551-2275
Strawberry Mansion HS 400/9-12
3133 Ridge Ave 19121 215-684-5089
Linda Cliatt-Wayman, prin. Fax 684-5380
Tilden MS 400/6-8
6601 Elmwood Ave 19142 215-492-6454
Jonas Crenshaw, prin. Fax 492-6128
University City HS 700/9-12
3601 Filbert St 19104 215-387-5100
Timothy Stults, prin. Fax 387-6362
Vaux HS 300/9-12
2300 W Master St 19121 215-684-5068
Richard Gordon, prin. Fax 684-2106
Wagner MS 600/6-8
1701 W Chelten Ave 19126 215-276-5252
Maya Johnstone, prin. Fax 276-5849
Washington HS 2,000/9-12
10175 Bustleton Ave 19116 215-961-2001
Kathy Murphy, prin. Fax 961-2545
Washington Jr. MS 800/5-8
201 E Olney Ave 19120 215-456-0422
Terry Pearsall-Hargett, prin. Fax 456-2181
West Philadelphia HS 800/9-12
4901 Chestnut St 19139 215-471-2902
Mary Dean, prin. Fax 471-6402
Wilson MS 1,200/6-8
1800 Cottman Ave 19111 215-728-5015
Stefanie Ressler, prin. Fax 728-5051

Achieve Test Prep Post-Sec.
1015 Chestnut St Ste 515 19107 610-400-1641
Al-Aqsa Islamic Academy 300/PK-12
1501 Germantown Ave 19122 215-765-6660
Claude Crumpton, prin. Fax 765-6640
Albert Einstein Medical Center Post-Sec.
5501 Old York Rd 19141 215-456-7010
American Beauty Academy Post-Sec.
6912 Frankford Ave 19135 215-331-1515
ARAMARK Healthcare Support Services Post-Sec.
1101 Market St Fl 12 19107 610-687-8600
Archbishop Ryan HS 1,800/9-12
11201 Academy Rd 19154 215-637-1800
Helen Chaykowsky, prin. Fax 637-8833
Aria Health School of Nursing Post-Sec.
4918 Penn St 19124 215-831-6740
Aviation Institute of Maintenance Post-Sec.
3001 Grant Ave 19114 215-676-7700
Calvary Christian Academy 1,000/PK-12
13500 Philmont Ave 19116 215-969-1579
Dr. Samuel Pennington, hdmstr. Fax 969-9732
Chestnut Hill College Post-Sec.
9601 Germantown Ave 19118 215-248-7001
City Center Academy 100/9-12
315 S 17th St 19103 215-731-1930
Owen Davis, prin. Fax 731-0515
Community College of Philadelphia Post-Sec.
1700 Spring Garden St 19130 215-751-8000
Crefeld S 100/7-12
8836 Crefeld St 19118 215-242-5545
George Zeleznik, head sch Fax 242-8869
Crooked Places Made Straight Chr Academy 300/K-12
PO Box 19179 19143 215-726-4151
Winona Stewart Ph.D., admin. Fax 726-5241
Curtis Institute of Music Post-Sec.
1726 Locust St 19103 215-893-5252
DeVry University Post-Sec.
1800 JFK Blvd Ste 200 19103 215-568-2911
Drexel University Post-Sec.
3141 Chestnut St 19104 215-895-2000
Empire Beauty School Post-Sec.
4026 Woodhaven Rd 19154 215-637-3700
Empire Beauty School Post-Sec.
1522 Chestnut St 19102 215-568-3980
Faith Tabernacle S 200/1-12
3611 N Randolph St Ste 15 19140 215-221-0909
Father Judge HS 1,100/9-12
3301 Solly Ave 19136 215-338-9494
Rev. James Dalton, prin. Fax 338-0250
Finshing Trades Institute Post-Sec.
2190 Hornig Rd 19116 215-501-0130
First Century Gospel S 100/1-10
6807 Rising Sun Ave 19111 215-742-6615
Friends Select S 500/PK-12
1651 Benjamin Franklin Pkwy 19103 215-561-5900
Rose Hagan, hdmstr. Fax 864-2979
Germantown Friends S 900/K-12
31 W Coulter St 19144 215-951-2300
Richard Wade, hdmstr. Fax 951-2312
Girard College S 400/1-12
2101 S College Ave 19121 215-787-2600
Clarence Armbrister, pres. Fax 787-2725
Hallahan HS 600/9-12
311 N 19th St 19103 215-563-8930
Michelle Beachy, prin. Fax 563-3809
Holy Family University Post-Sec.
9801 Frankford Ave 19114 215-637-7700
Hope Church S 200/PK-12
6707 Old York Rd 19126 215-927-7770
Dr. Suzette Ajedho, prin. Fax 927-8070
Hussian School of Art Post-Sec.
111 S Indpndnce Mall E #300 19106 215-574-9600
International Christian HS 100/8-12
413 E Tabor Rd 19120 215-455-9334
Ben Brittin, admin. Fax 455-7198
ITT Technical Institute Post-Sec.
105 S 7th St Ste 100 19106 215-413-4300
Jean Madeline Educ. Ctr. for Cosmetology Post-Sec.
315A Bainbridge St 19147 215-238-9998
JNA Institute of Culinary Arts Post-Sec.
1212 S Broad St 19146 215-468-8800
Kaplan Career Institute Post-Sec.
3010 Market St 19104 215-594-4000
Kaplan Career Institute Post-Sec.
177 Franklin Mills Blvd 19154 215-612-6600
La Salle Academy 100/3-8
1434 N 2nd St 19122 215-739-5804
Teresa Diamond, prin. Fax 739-1664
La Salle University Post-Sec.
1900 W Olney Ave 19141 215-951-1000
Lincoln Technical Institute Post-Sec.
9191 Torresdale Ave 19136 215-335-0800
Lincoln Technical Institute Post-Sec.
3600 Market St 19104 215-382-1553
Lincoln Technical Institute Post-Sec.
2180 Hornig Rd 19116 215-969-0869
Little Flower HS 700/9-12
1000 W Lycoming St 19140 215-455-6900
Sr. Kathleen Klarich, prin. Fax 329-0478
L.T. International Beauty School Post-Sec.
830 N Broad St 19130 215-922-4478
Lutheran Theological Seminary Post-Sec.
7301 Germantown Ave 19119 215-248-4616
Mercy Vocational HS Vo/Tech
2900 W Hunting Park Ave 19129 215-226-1225
Sr. Rosemary Herron, prin. Fax 228-6337
Messiah College Post-Sec.
2026 N Broad St 19121 215-769-2526
Methodist Hospital Post-Sec.
2301 S Broad St 19148 215-952-9402
Metropolitan Career Center Post-Sec.
100 S Broad St Ste 830 19110 215-568-9215
Moore College of Art and Design Post-Sec.
20th St and The Parkway 19103 215-965-4000
Nazareth Academy HS 500/9-12
4001 Grant Ave 19114 215-637-7676
Sr. Mary Joan Jacobs, prin. Fax 637-8523
Nazareth Hospital Post-Sec.
2601 Holme Ave 19152 215-335-6000
Northeastern Hospital School of Nursing Post-Sec.
2301 E Allegheny Ave 19134 215-291-3145
Northeast Prep S 100/7-12
1309 Cottman Ave 19111 215-342-5500
Howard Schwartz, dir. Fax 342-8866
Orleans Technical Institute Post-Sec.
2770 Red Lion Rd 19114 215-728-4700
Our Mother of Sorrows S 200/4-8
1008 N 48th St 19131 215-473-5828
Sr. Patricia Bonner, prin. Fax 473-3096
Overbrook School for the Blind Post-Sec.
6333 Malvern Ave 19151 215-877-0313
Peirce College Post-Sec.
1420 Pine St 19102 215-545-6400
Penn Charter S 1,000/PK-12
3000 W School House Ln 19144 215-844-3460
Dr. Darryl Ford, head sch Fax 843-3939
Pennsylvania Academy of the Fine Arts Post-Sec.
128 N Broad St 19102 215-972-7600
Pennsylvania Hospital Post-Sec.
800 Spruce St 19107 215-829-3312
Pennsylvania School for the Deaf Post-Sec.
100 W School House Ln 19144
Philadelphia Coll. Osteopathic Medicine Post-Sec.
4170 City Ave 19131 215-871-6100
Philadelphia Mennonite HS 100/9-12
860 N 24th St 19130 215-769-5363
Dr. Barbara Moses, prin. Fax 769-4063
Philadelphia University Post-Sec.
4201 Henry Ave 19144 215-951-2700
Restaurant School at Walnut Hill College Post-Sec.
4207 Walnut St 19104 215-222-4200
Roman Catholic HS 1,000/9-12
301 N Broad St 19107 215-627-1270
Robert O'Neill, prin. Fax 627-4979
Roxborough Memorial Hospital Post-Sec.
5800 Ridge Ave 19128 215-487-4459
St. Hubert HS 800/9-12
7320 Torresdale Ave 19136 215-624-6840
Regina Craig, prin. Fax 624-5940
St. Joseph's Prep S 1,000/9-12
1733 W Girard Ave 19130 215-978-1950
Fr. George Bur, pres. Fax 765-1710
St. Joseph's University Post-Sec.
5600 City Ave 19131 610-660-1000
St. Monica S - Senior Campus 200/4-8
2500 S 16th St 19145 215-467-5338
Sr. Patricia McKee, prin. Fax 467-4599
Settlement Music School Post-Sec.
416 Queen St 19147 215-336-0400

Springside Chestnut Hill Academy 1,100/PK-12
500 W Willow Grove Ave 19118 215-247-4700
Dr. Priscilla Sands, pres. Fax 247-8516
SS. John Neumann/Maria Goretti HS 1,100/9-12
1736 S 10th St 19148 215-465-8437
Robert Selg, prin. Fax 462-2410
Star Career Academy Post-Sec.
2371 Welsh Rd 19114 215-969-5877
Talmudical Yeshiva of Philadelphia Post-Sec.
6063 Drexel Rd 19131 215-473-1212
Talmudical Yeshiva of Philadelphia 100/9-12
6063 Drexel Rd 19131 215-477-1000
Rabbi Pinchas Lando, admin. Fax 477-5065
Temple University Post-Sec.
1801 N Broad St 19122 215-204-7000
The Art Institute of Philadelphia Post-Sec.
1622 Chestnut St 19103 215-567-7080
Thomas Jefferson University Post-Sec.
1020 Walnut St 19107 215-955-6000
University of Pennsylvania Post-Sec.
3451 Walnut St 19104 215-898-5000
University of the Arts Post-Sec.
320 S Broad St 19102 215-717-6000
University of the Sciences Philadelphia Post-Sec.
600 S 43rd St 19104 215-596-8800
Westminster Theological Seminary Post-Sec.
PO Box 27009 19118 215-887-5511
West Philadelphia Catholic HS 500/9-12
4501 Chestnut St 19139 215-386-2244
Sr. Mary Bur, prin. Fax 222-1651

Philipsburg, Centre, Pop. 2,742
Philipsburg-Osceola Area SD 1,200/K-12
200 Short St 16866 814-342-1050
Dr. Gregg Paladina, supt. Fax 342-7208
www.pomounties.org
Philipsburg-Osceola Area HS 600/9-12
502 Philips St 16866 814-342-1521
Robin Stewart, prin. Fax 342-7521
Philipsburg-Osceola Area MS 100/5-8
200 Short St 16866 814-342-4906
Linda Kline, prin. Fax 342-7532

Phoenixville, Chester, Pop. 15,988
Area Vocational Technical School
Supt. — None
Technical College HS - Pickering Campus Vo/Tech
1580 Charlestown Rd 19460 610-933-8877
Brian Hughes, prin. Fax 983-0680

Phoenixville Area SD 3,300/K-12
386 City Line Ave 19460 484-927-5000
Dr. Alan Fegley, supt. Fax 983-3729
www.pasd.com
Phoenixville Area HS 900/9-12
1200 Gay St 19460 484-927-5100
Dr. Craig Parkinson, prin. Fax 933-6009
Phoenixville Area MS 800/6-8
1000 Purple Pride Pkwy 19460 484-927-5200
Dr. Frank Garritano, prin. Fax 933-6121

Valley Forge Christian College Post-Sec.
1401 Charlestown Rd 19460 610-935-0450

Pine Forge, Berks

Pine Forge Academy 100/9-12
PO Box 338 19548 610-326-5800
Delmas Campbell, prin. Fax 326-4260

Pine Grove, Schuylkill, Pop. 2,160
Pine Grove Area SD 1,700/K-12
103 School St 17963 570-345-2731
Brian Uplinger, supt. Fax 345-2790
www.pgasd.com
Pine Grove Area HS 600/9-12
101 School St 17963 570-345-2731
Michael Janicelli, prin. Fax 345-2793
Pine Grove Area MS 500/5-8
105 School St 17963 570-345-2731
Steve Brill, prin. Fax 345-2791

Pittsburgh, Allegheny, Pop. 297,895
Avonworth SD 1,400/K-12
258 Josephs Ln 15237 412-369-8738
Thomas W. Ralston, supt. Fax 369-8746
www.avonworth.k12.pa.us
Avonworth HS 400/9-12
304 Josephs Ln 15237 412-366-6360
Kenneth Lockette, prin. Fax 366-7603
Avonworth MS 300/6-8
256 Josephs Ln 15237 412-366-9650
Michael Hall, prin. Fax 358-9621

Baldwin-Whitehall SD 4,200/K-12
4900 Curry Rd 15236 412-885-7810
Dr. Randal A. Lutz, supt. Fax 885-7802
www.bwschools.net/
Baldwin HS 1,500/9-12
4653 Clairton Blvd 15236 412-885-7500
Kevin O'Toole, prin. Fax 885-6652
Harrison MS 900/6-8
129 Windvale Dr 15236 412-885-7530
Michael Wetmiller, prin. Fax 885-6766

Brentwood Borough SD 1,300/K-12
3601 Brownsville Rd 15227 412-881-2227
Ronald Dufalla Ph.D., supt. Fax 881-1640
www.brentwoodpgh.k12.pa.us
Brentwood HS 400/9-12
3601 Brownsville Rd 15227 412-881-4940
Jason Olexa, prin. Fax 881-4170
Brentwood MS 300/6-8
3601 Brownsville Rd 15227 412-881-4940
David Radcliffe Ph.D., prin. Fax 881-4170

Chartiers Valley SD 3,400/K-12
2030 Swallow Hill Rd 15220 412-429-2201
Dr. Brian White, supt. Fax 429-2237
www.cvsd.net
Other Schools – See Bridgeville

Fox Chapel Area SD 4,300/K-12
611 Field Club Rd 15238 412-963-9600
Anne Stephens Ph.D., supt. Fax 967-0697
www.fcasd.edu
Dorseyville MS 1,000/6-8
3732 Saxonburg Blvd 15238 412-967-2520
Matthew Harris, prin. Fax 967-2531
Fox Chapel Area HS 1,400/9-12
611 Field Club Rd 15238 412-967-2433
Michael Hower, prin. Fax 967-0697

Keystone Oaks SD 2,100/K-12
1000 Kelton Ave 15216 412-571-6000
Dr. William Stropkaj, supt. Fax 571-6006
www.kosd.org
Keystone Oaks HS 700/9-12
1000 Kelton Ave 15216 412-571-6040
Scott Hagy, prin. Fax 571-6043
Keystone Oaks MS 500/6-8
1002 Kelton Ave 15216 412-571-6146
Keith Konyk, prin. Fax 571-6092

Mt. Lebanon SD 5,300/K-12
7 Horsman Dr 15228 412-344-2077
Dr. Timothy Steinhauer, supt. Fax 344-2047
www.mtlsd.org
Jefferson MS 600/6-8
21 Moffett St 15243 412-344-2123
Dr. James Walsh, prin. Fax 344-1252
Mellon MS 600/6-8
11 Castle Shannon Blvd 15228 412-344-2122
Christopher Wolfson, prin. Fax 344-0590
Mt. Lebanon HS 1,800/9-12
155 Cochran Rd 15228 412-344-2003
Brian McFeeley, prin. Fax 344-2021

North Allegheny SD 8,100/K-12
200 Hillvue Ln 15237 412-366-2100
Raymond Gualtieri Ed.D., supt. Fax 369-5513
www.northallegheny.org
Carson MS, 200 Hillvue Ln 15237 700/6-8
Katherine Jenkins, prin. 412-369-5520
Ingomar MS 600/6-8
1521 Ingomar Heights Rd 15237 412-348-1470
Heidi Stark, prin. Fax 366-4487
North Allegheny Intermediate HS 1,300/9-10
350 Cumberland Rd 15237 412-369-5530
Brendan Hyland, prin. Fax 369-4825
Other Schools – See Wexford

North Hills SD 3,600/K-12
135 6th Ave 15229 412-318-1000
Dr. Patrick Mannarino, supt. Fax 318-1084
www.nhsd.net
North Hills HS 1,100/9-12
53 Rochester Rd 15229 412-318-1400
John Kreider, prin. Fax 318-1403
North Hills JHS 700/7-8
55 Rochester Rd 15229 412-318-1450
Beth Williams, prin. Fax 318-1453

Northgate SD 1,200/K-12
591 Union Ave 15202 412-732-3300
Dr. Joseph Pasquerilla, supt. Fax 734-8008
www.northgate.k12.pa.us
Northgate MSHS 600/7-12
589 Union Ave 15202 412-732-3300
Bryan Kyle, prin. Fax 734-8086

Penn Hills SD 4,300/PK-12
260 Aster St 15235 412-793-7000
Thomas Washington, supt. Fax 793-6402
www.phsd.k12.pa.us
Linton MS 1,300/5-8
250 Aster St 15235 412-795-3000
Devaun Barnett, prin. Fax 795-6087
Penn Hills HS 1,500/9-12
309 Collins Dr 15235 412-793-7000
Eric Kostic, prin. Fax 712-1047

Pittsburgh SD 22,600/PK-12
341 S Bellefield Ave 15213 412-622-3600
Dr. Linda Lane, supt. Fax 622-3604
www.pps.k12.pa.us
Pittsburgh Allderdice HS 1,400/9-12
2409 Shady Ave 15217 412-422-4800
Melissa Friez, prin. Fax 422-4803
Pittsburgh Allegheny 6-8 400/6-8
810 Arch St 15212 412-323-4115
Toni Kendrick, prin. Fax 323-4114
Pittsburgh Arlington Prek-8 300/3-8
2500 Jonquil St 15210 412-488-3641
Kevin McGuire, prin. Fax 488-3760
Pittsburgh Arsenal 6-8 300/6-8
110 40th St 15201 412-622-5740
Patti Camper, prin. Fax 622-5743
Pittsburgh Brashear HS 1,300/9-12
590 Crane Ave 15216 412-571-7300
John Vater, prin. Fax 571-7305
Pittsburgh CAPA 6-12 900/6-12
111 9th St 15222 412-338-6100
Melissa Pearlman, prin. Fax 338-6143
Pittsburgh Carrick HS 800/9-12
125 Parkfield St 15210 412-885-7700
Dennis Chakey, prin. Fax 885-7708
Pittsburgh Classical 6-8 300/6-8
1463 Chartiers Ave 15220 412-928-3110
Valerie Merlo, prin. Fax 928-3106
Pittsburgh Milliones 6-12 500/6-12
3117 Centre Ave 15219 412-622-5900
Derrick Hardy, prin. Fax 622-5925
Pittsburgh Obama 6-12 700/6-12
515 N Highland Ave 15206 412-622-5980
Dr. Wayne Walters, prin. Fax 622-5983

Pittsburgh Perry HS 700/9-12
3875 Perrysville Ave 15214 412-323-3400
Nina Sacco, prin. Fax 323-3404
Pittsburgh Schiller 6-8 300/6-8
1018 Peralta St 15212 412-323-4190
Paula Heinzman, prin. Fax 323-4192
Pittsburgh Science\Technology Acad 6-112 300/6-12
107 Thackeray St 15213 412-325-7620
Dr. Robert Scherrer, prin. Fax 622-5991
Pittsburgh South Brook 6-8 500/6-8
779 Dunster St 15226 412-572-8170
Gina Reichert, prin. Fax 572-8177
Pittsburgh South Hills 6-8 500/6-8
595 Crane Ave 15216 412-572-8130
Dr. Deborah Ann Cox, prin. Fax 572-8148
Pittsburgh Sterrett 6-8 400/6-8
7100 Reynolds St 15208 412-247-7870
Dr. MiChele Holly, prin. Fax 247-7877
Pittsburgh Student Achievement Center 50/Alt
925 Brushton Ave 15208 412-247-7860
Dalhart Dobbs, prin. Fax 247-7926
Pittsburgh Westinghouse Academy 6-12 300/6-12
1101 N Murtland St 15208 412-665-3940
Dr. Shemeca Crenshaw, prin. Fax 665-4977

Plum Borough SD 4,100/K-12
900 Elicker Rd 15239 412-795-0100
Dr. Timothy Glasspool, supt. Fax 795-9115
www.pbsd.k12.pa.us
O'Block JHS 600/7-8
440 Presque Isle Dr 15239 724-733-2400
Joseph Fishell, prin. Fax 327-6880
Plum HS 1,400/9-12
900 Elicker Rd 15239 412-795-4880
Ryan Kociela, prin. Fax 795-6823

Shaler Area SD
Supt. — See Glenshaw
Shaler Area HS 1,700/9-12
381 Wible Run Rd 15209 412-492-1200
Timothy Royall, prin. Fax 684-1076

Upper St. Clair SD
Supt. — See Upper Saint Clair
Ft. Couch MS 600/7-8
515 Fort Couch Rd 15241 412-833-1600
Joseph DeMar, prin. Fax 854-3095
Upper Saint Clair HS 1,400/9-12
1825 Mclaughlin Run Rd 15241 412-833-1600
Dr. Michael Ghilani, prin. Fax 833-4889

West Jefferson Hills SD
Supt. — See Jefferson Hills
Pleasant Hills MS 600/6-8
404 Old Clairton Rd 15236 412-655-8680
Daniel Como, prin. Fax 655-5691

Woodland Hills SD 3,900/K-12
2430 Greensburg Pike 15221 412-731-1300
Walter Calinger Ph.D., supt. Fax 731-1562
www.whsd.k12.pa.us
Woodland Hills HS 1,400/9-12
2550 Greensburg Pike 15221 412-244-1100
Daniel Stephens, prin. Fax 242-2344
Woodland Hills JHS 500/7-8
7600 Evans St 15218 412-351-0698
Dawn Golden, prin. Fax 351-5841

Academy of Court Reporting & Technology Post-Sec.
717 Liberty Ave Fl 13 15222 216-834-1400
Bidwell Training Center Post-Sec.
1815 Metropolitan St 15233 412-323-4000
Bishop Canevin Catholic HS 500/9-12
2700 Morange Rd 15205 412-922-7400
Karen Walker, prin. Fax 922-7403
Bradford School Post-Sec.
125 W Station Square # 129 15219 412-391-6710
Byzantine Catholic Seminary Post-Sec.
3605 Perrysville Ave 15214 412-321-8383
Career Training Academy Post-Sec.
1500 Shoppes Northway Mall 15237 412-367-4000
Carlow University Post-Sec.
3333 5th Ave 15213 412-578-6000
Carnegie Mellon University Post-Sec.
5000 Forbes Ave 15213 412-268-2000
Center for Emergency Medicine/Western PA Post-Sec.
230 McKee Pl # 500 15213 412-647-4665
Central Catholic HS 900/9-12
4720 5th Ave 15213 412-621-8189
Br. Robert Schaefer, prin. Fax 208-0555
Chatham University Post-Sec.
Woodland Rd 15232 412-365-1100
Community College of Allegheny County Post-Sec.
808 Ridge Ave 15212 412-237-2525
Community College of Allegheny County Post-Sec.
8701 Perry Hwy 15237 412-366-7000
Dean Institute of Technology Post-Sec.
1501 W Liberty Ave 15226 412-531-4433
DeVry University Post-Sec.
210 6th Ave Ste 200 15222 412-642-9072
Duquesne University Post-Sec.
600 Forbes Ave 15282 412-396-6000
Ellis S 500/PK-12
6425 5th Ave 15206 412-661-5992
Randie Benedict M.Ed., head sch Fax 661-3979
Empire Beauty School Post-Sec.
1000 McKnight Park Dr #1006 15237 800-575-5983
Everest Institute Post-Sec.
100 Forbes Ave # 1200 15222 412-261-4520
Hillel Academy of Pittsburgh 200/K-12
5685 Beacon St 15217 412-521-8131
Rabbi Sam Weinberg, prin. Fax 521-5150
Home for Crippled Children Post-Sec.
1426 Denniston St 15217
Imani Christian Academy 300/K-12
2150 E Hills Dr 15221 412-731-7982
Marilyn Barnett Waters Ph.D., prin. Fax 731-7343
ITT Technical Institute Post-Sec.
10 Parkway Ctr 15220 412-937-9150

Kaplan Career Institute Post-Sec.
10 Wood St 15222 412-261-2647
La Roche College Post-Sec.
9000 Babcock Blvd 15237 412-367-9300
Mercy Hospital School of Nursing Post-Sec.
1401 Blvd of the Allies 15219 412-232-7940
North Catholic HS 200/9-12
1400 Troy Hill Rd 15212 412-321-4823
Dr. Michael Pendred, prin. Fax 321-0599
North Hills Beauty Academy Post-Sec.
813 W View Park Dr 15229 412-931-8563
Oakland Catholic HS 600/9-12
144 N Craig St 15213 412-682-6633
Dr. Maureen Marsteller, prin. Fax 682-2496
Pennsylvania Gunsmith School Post-Sec.
812 Ohio River Blvd 15202 412-766-1812
Pittsburgh Institute of Aeronautics Post-Sec.
PO Box 10897 15236 412-346-2100
Pittsburgh Institute of Mortuary Science Post-Sec.
5808 Baum Blvd 15206 412-362-8500
Pittsburgh Theological Seminary Post-Sec.
616 N Highland Ave 15206 412-362-5610
Point Park University Post-Sec.
201 Wood St 15222 412-391-4100
Point Park Univ.-St. Francis Med. Ctr. Post-Sec.
201 Wood St 15222 412-392-3879
Pressley Ridge School Post-Sec.
530 Marshall Ave 15214 412-442-4468
Reformed Presbyterian Theological Sem. Post-Sec.
7418 Penn Ave 15208 412-731-8690
Rosedale Technical Institute Post-Sec.
215 Beecham Dr Ste 2 15205 412-521-6200
St. Margaret Schools of Nursing Post-Sec.
221 7th St Ste 100 15238 412-784-4980
Sanford-Brown Institute Post-Sec.
421 7th Ave 15219 412-281-2600
Seton-LaSalle HS 500/9-12
1000 McNeilly Rd 15226 412-561-3583
Lauren Martin, prin. Fax 561-9097
Shady Side Academy MS 200/6-8
500 Squaw Run Rd E 15238 412-968-3100
Amy Nixon, head sch Fax 968-3008
Shady Side Academy Senior S 500/9-12
423 Fox Chapel Rd 15238 412-968-3000
Katharine Vavpetic, head sch Fax 968-3002
Shadyside Hospital Post-Sec.
5230 Centre Ave 15232 412-622-2010
South Hills Beauty Academy Post-Sec.
3269 W Liberty Ave 15216 412-561-3381
The Art Institute of Pittsburgh Post-Sec.
420 Blvd of the Allies 15219 412-263-6600
Triangle Tech Post-Sec.
1940 Perrysville Ave 15214 412-359-1000
Trinity Christian S 300/K-12
299 Ridge Ave 15221 412-242-8886
Dale McLane, hdmstr. Fax 242-8859
University Health Center Post-Sec.
300 Halket St 15213 412-641-4664
University of Pittsburgh Post-Sec.
4200 5th Ave 15213 412-624-4141
UPMC School of Medical Imaging Post-Sec.
3434 Forbes Ave 15213 412-647-3528
Vet Tech Institute Post-Sec.
125 7th St 15222 412-391-7021
Vincentian Academy 200/9-12
8100 McKnight Rd 15237 412-364-1616
Richard Behun, prin. Fax 367-5722
Western Pennsylvania Hospital Post-Sec.
4900 Friendship Ave 15224 412-578-5538
Western Pennsylvania School for Blind Post-Sec.
Bayard at Bellefield 15213
Western Pennsylvania School for the Deaf Post-Sec.
300 E Swissvale Ave 15218 412-371-7000
Winchester Thurston S 600/PK-12
555 Morewood Ave 15213 412-578-7500
Gary Niels, hdmstr. Fax 578-7504
Yeshiva S 100/PK-12
2100 Wightman St 15217 412-422-7300
Rabbi Yisroel Rosenfeld, dean Fax 422-5930

Pittston, Luzerne, Pop. 7,622
Pittston Area SD 3,400/K-12
5 Stout St 18640 570-654-2271
Dr. Michael Garzella, supt. Fax 654-5548
www.pittstonarea.com
Pittston Area HS 1,100/9-12
5 Stout St 18640 570-654-3541
John Haas, prin. Fax 602-0823
Pittston Area MS 800/6-8
120 New St 18640 570-655-2927
Patrick Bilbow, prin. Fax 654-0862

Plains, Luzerne, Pop. 4,288
Wilkes-Barre Area SD
Supt. — See Wilkes Barre
Solomon/Plains JHS 500/7-8
43 Abbott St 18705 570-826-7224
John Woloski, prin. Fax 820-3715

Pleasant Gap, Centre, Pop. 2,844
Area Vocational Technical School
Supt. — None
Central PA Institute of Science & Tech Vo/Tech
540 N Harrison Rd 16823 814-359-2793
Dr. Richard Makin, dir. Fax 359-2599

Plumsteadville, Bucks, Pop. 2,600

Plumstead Christian HS 300/6-12
PO Box 216 18949 215-766-8073
Patrick Fitzpatrick, hdmstr. Fax 766-2033

Plymouth, Luzerne, Pop. 5,852
Wyoming Valley West SD
Supt. — See Kingston
Wyoming Valley West HS 1,300/9-12
150 Wadham St 18651 570-779-5361
Erin Keating, prin. Fax 779-9510

Plymouth Meeting, Montgomery, Pop. 6,092
Area Vocational Technical School
Supt. — None
Central Montco Technical HS Vo/Tech
821 Plymouth Rd 19462 610-277-2301
Walter Slauch, prin.

Colonial SD 4,700/K-12
230 Flourtown Rd 19462 610-834-1670
Dr. Mary Ellen Gorodetzer, supt. Fax 834-7535
www.colonialsd.org
Colonial MS 1,000/6-8
716 Belvoir Rd 19462 610-275-5100
Robert Fahler, prin. Fax 278-2447
Plymouth-Whitemarsh HS 1,600/9-12
201 E Germantown Pike 19462 610-825-1500
Jason Bacani, prin. Fax 832-0766

ITT Technical Institute Post-Sec.
220 W Germantown Pike # 100 19462 610-832-3400
La Salle University Post-Sec.
4000 Chemical Rd Ste 110 19462 610-834-1258

Pocono Summit, Monroe
Pocono Mountain SD
Supt. — See Swiftwater
Pocono Mountain West HS 1,700/9-12
180 Panther Ln 18346 570-839-7121
Thomas Barbush, prin. Fax 839-5968
Pocono Mountain West JHS 1,600/7-8
181 Panther Ln 18346 570-839-7121
Dr. Eric Vogt, prin. Fax 839-7397

Point Marion, Fayette, Pop. 1,152
Albert Gallatin Area SD
Supt. — See Uniontown
Gallatin South MS 400/6-8
224 New Geneva Rd 15474 724-725-5241
Joetta Britvich, prin. Fax 725-5424

Portage, Cambria, Pop. 2,610
Portage Area SD 900/PK-12
84 Mountain Ave 15946 814-736-9636
Richard Bernazzoli, supt. Fax 736-9634
www.portageareasd.org
Portage Area JSHS 400/7-12
85 Mountain Ave 15946 814-736-9636
Ralph Cecere, prin. Fax 736-9597

Port Allegany, McKean, Pop. 2,134
Area Vocational Technical School
Supt. — None
Seneca Highlands Career & Technical Ctr Vo/Tech
PO Box 219 16743 814-642-2573
James Young, dir.

Port Allegany SD 900/K-12
20 Oak St 16743 814-642-2596
Martin Flint, supt. Fax 642-9574
www.pahs.net
Port Allegany JSHS 500/7-12
20 Oak St 16743 814-642-2544
Marc Budd, prin. Fax 642-5082

Portersville, Butler, Pop. 235

Portersville Christian S 200/PK-12
343 E Portersville Rd 16051 724-368-8787
Lee Saunders, admin. Fax 368-3100

Pottstown, Montgomery, Pop. 21,544
Owen J. Roberts SD 5,000/K-12
901 Ridge Rd 19465 610-469-5100
Dr. Michael Christian, supt. Fax 469-0403
www.ojrsd.com
Roberts HS 1,500/9-12
981 Ridge Rd 19465 610-469-5101
Dr. Richard Marchini, prin. Fax 469-5898
Roberts MS 800/7-8
881 Ridge Rd 19465 610-469-5102
Sean Burns, prin. Fax 469-5832

Pottsgrove SD 3,300/K-12
1301 Kauffman Rd 19464 610-327-2277
Dr. Shellie Feola, supt. Fax 327-2530
www.pgsd.org
Pottsgrove HS 1,100/9-12
1345 Kauffman Rd 19464 610-326-5105
Yolanda Williams, prin. Fax 970-6191
Pottsgrove MS 800/6-8
1351 N Hanover St 19464 610-326-8243
Dr. William Ziegler, prin. Fax 718-0581

Pottstown SD 3,100/PK-12
230 Beech St 19464 610-323-8200
Reed Lindley, supt. Fax 326-6540
www.pottstownschools.com
Pottstown HS 800/9-12
750 N Washington St 19464 610-970-6700
Stephen Rodriguez, prin. Fax 970-1363
Pottstown MS 600/6-8
600 N Franklin St 19464 610-970-6665
Gail Cooper, prin. Fax 970-8738

Antonelli Medical & Professional Inst Post-Sec.
1700 Industrial Hwy 19464 610-323-7270
Coventry Christian S 300/PK-12
699 N Pleasantview Rd 19464 610-326-3320
Paul Q. Fisher M.Ed., hdmstr. Fax 326-0085
Empire Beauty School Post-Sec.
141 E High St 19464 610-327-1313
Hill S 500/9-12
717 E High St 19464 610-326-1000
Zachary Lehman, hdmstr. Fax 705-1753
West-Mont Christian Academy 300/K-12
873 S Hanover St 19465 610-326-7690
Dr. James Smock, admin. Fax 326-7126

Pottsville, Schuylkill, Pop. 14,045
Area Vocational Technical School
Supt. — None
Schuylkill Technology Center - Airport Vo/Tech
240 Airport Rd 17901 570-544-4904
Albert Gurka, prin.

Pottsville Area SD 3,000/K-12
1501 Laurel Blvd 17901 570-621-2900
Dr. Jeffrey Zweibel, supt. Fax 621-2025
www.pottsville.k12.pa.us/
Lengel MS 900/5-8
1541 Laurel Blvd 17901 570-621-2920
Raymond Yost, prin. Fax 621-2999
Pottsville Area HS 1,100/9-12
16th St and Elk Ave 17901 570-621-2960
Tiffany Reedy, prin. Fax 621-2036

McCann School of Business & Technology Post-Sec.
2650 Woodglen Rd 17901 570-622-7622
Nativity BVM HS 200/9-12
1 Lawtons Hl 17901 570-622-8110
Lynn Sabol, prin. Fax 622-0454
Schuylkill Health School of Nursing Post-Sec.
420 S Jackson St 17901 570-621-5027

Prospect Park, Delaware, Pop. 6,344
Interboro SD 3,600/K-12
900 Washington Ave 19076 610-461-6700
John Cleghorn, supt. Fax 583-1678
www.interborosd.org
Interboro HS 1,300/9-12
500 16th Ave 19076 610-237-6410
Paul Gibson, prin. Fax 237-8103

Prospectville, Montgomery

Lakeside S 100/6-12
111 S Chestnut Ln 19002 215-542-7737
Peter Dillard, dir. Fax 542-8904

Punxsutawney, Jefferson, Pop. 5,912
Punxsutawney Area SD 2,400/K-12
475 Beyer Ave 15767 814-938-5151
Dr. Keith Wolfe, supt. Fax 938-6677
www.punxsy.k12.pa.us/
Punxsutawney Area HS 1,000/8-12
500 N Findley St 15767 814-938-5151
David London, prin. Fax 938-5101

Punxsutawney Christian S 200/PK-12
216 N Jefferson St 15767 814-938-2295
Lori Galbraith, admin. Fax 938-2251

Quakertown, Bucks, Pop. 8,835
Quakertown Community SD 5,200/K-12
100 Commerce Dr 18951 215-529-2000
Lisa Andrejko Ed.D., supt. Fax 529-2042
www.qcsd.org/
Freshman Center 400/9-9
349 S 9th St 18951 267-371-1200
Karen Shanton, prin. Fax 371-1201
Milford MS 400/6-8
2255 Allentown Rd 18951 215-529-2210
Derek Peiffer, prin. Fax 529-2211
Quakertown Community HS 1,200/10-12
600 Park Ave 18951 215-529-2060
Rod Stone, prin. Fax 529-2061
Strayer MS 800/6-8
1200 Ronald Reagan Dr 18951 215-529-2290
Cynthia Lapinski, prin. Fax 529-2291

Quarryville, Lancaster, Pop. 2,535
Solanco SD 3,700/K-12
121 S Hess St 17566 717-786-8401
Dr. Martin Hudacs, supt. Fax 786-8245
www.solanco.k12.pa.us
Smith MS 400/6-8
645 Kirkwood Pike 17566 717-786-2244
Paul Gladfelter, prin. Fax 786-8796
Solanco HS 1,200/9-12
585 Solanco Rd 17566 717-786-2151
Brian Gallagher, prin. Fax 786-1808
Swift MS 400/6-8
1866 Robert Fulton Hwy 17566 717-548-2187
Paul Gladfelter, prin. Fax 548-3350

Radnor, Delaware, Pop. 31,300
Radnor Township SD
Supt. — See Wayne
Radnor HS 1,200/9-12
130 King of Prussia Rd 19087 610-293-0855
Mark Schellenger, prin. Fax 989-9146

Archbishop Carroll HS 1,000/9-12
211 Matsonford Rd 19087 610-688-7610
Joseph Denelsbeck, prin. Fax 688-8326
Cabrini College Post-Sec.
610 King of Prussia Rd 19087 610-902-8100

Reading, Berks, Pop. 86,403
Antietam SD 1,000/K-12
100 Antietam Rd 19606 610-779-0554
Dr. Lawrence Mayes, supt. Fax 779-4424
www.antietamsd.org
Antietam MSHS 500/7-12
100 Antietam Rd 19606 610-779-3545
Dr. Melissa Brewer, prin. Fax 779-0378

Area Vocational Technical School
Supt. — None
Reading-Muhlenberg CTC Vo/Tech
2615 Warren Rd 19604 610-921-7300
Gerald Witmer, admin. Fax 921-7367

Exeter Township SD 3,900/K-12
200 Elm St 19606 610-779-0700
Dr. Beverly Martin, supt. Fax 779-7104
www.exeter.k12.pa.us
Exeter Township HS 1,400/9-12
201 E 37th St 19606 610-779-3060
William Cain, prin. Fax 370-0518
Exeter Township JHS 700/7-8
151 E 39th St 19606 610-779-3320
Eric Flamm, prin. Fax 370-0678

Reading SD 12,900/PK-12
800 Washington St 19601 610-371-5611
Dr. Carlinda Purcell, supt. Fax 371-5971
www.readingsd.org
Reading HS 2,800/10-12
801 N 13th St 19604 610-371-5710
Eric Turman, prin. Fax 371-8723
Reading Intermediate HS 8-9
215 N 12th St 19604 484-258-7365
Dennis Campbell, prin. Fax 258-7333

Albright College Post-Sec.
PO Box 15234 19612 610-921-2381
Alvernia University Post-Sec.
400 Saint Bernardine St 19607 610-796-8200
Berks Catholic HS 500/9-12
955 E Wyomissing Blvd 19611 610-374-8361
Tony Balistiere, prin. Fax 374-4309
Empire Beauty School Post-Sec.
2302 N 5th Street Hwy 19605 610-372-2777
Fairview Christian S 200/K-12
410 S 14th St 19602 610-372-8826
Jay Fox, prin. Fax 478-0896
Pace Institute Post-Sec.
606 Court St 19601 610-375-1212
Penn State Berks Post-Sec.
PO Box 7009 19610 610-396-6000
Reading Area Community College Post-Sec.
PO Box 1706 19603 610-372-4721
Reading Hospital & Medical Center Post-Sec.
PO Box 16052 19612 610-378-6664
Reading Junior Academy 100/PK-10
309 N Kenhorst Blvd 19607 610-777-8424
Fax 603-0129
St. Joseph's Hospital Post-Sec.
PO Box 316 19603 610-378-2000

Red Lion, York, Pop. 6,289
Red Lion Area SD 5,500/K-12
696 Delta Rd 17356 717-244-4518
Dr. Scott Deisley, supt. Fax 244-2196
www.rlasd.net
Red Lion Area JHS 900/7-8
200 Country Club Rd 17356 717-244-1448
Kevin Peters, prin. Fax 244-6160
Red Lion Area SHS 1,700/9-12
200 Horace Mann Ave 17356 717-246-1611
Mark Shue, prin. Fax 246-9181

Red Lion Christian S 300/PK-12
105 Springvale Rd 17356 717-244-3905
Steven Schmuck, prin. Fax 246-3738

Renovo, Clinton, Pop. 1,205
Keystone Central SD
Supt. — See Mill Hall
Bucktail Area JSHS 100/7-12
1300 Bucktail Ave 17764 570-923-1166
Kurt Smith, prin. Fax 923-2233

Reynoldsville, Jefferson, Pop. 2,735
Area Vocational Technical School
Supt. — None
Jefferson County-Dubois AVTS Vo/Tech
576 Vo Tech Rd 15851 814-653-8265
Marsha Welsh, prin. Fax 653-8425

Richboro, Bucks, Pop. 6,518
Council Rock SD
Supt. — See Newtown
Richboro MS 400/7-8
98 Upper Holland Rd 18954 215-944-2500
Richard Hollahan, prin. Fax 944-2598

Ridgway, Elk, Pop. 4,043
Ridgway Area SD 1,000/K-12
PO Box 447 15853 814-773-3146
Dr. Michael O'Brien, supt. Fax 776-4299
www.ridgwayareaschooldistrict.com/
Ridgway Area HS 300/9-12
PO Box 447 15853 814-773-3164
Heather McMahon-Vargas, prin. Fax 776-4247
Ridgway Area MS 200/6-8
PO Box 447 15853 814-773-3156
Heather McMahon-Vargas, prin. Fax 776-4239

North Central Industrial Tech. Ed. Ctr. Post-Sec.
651 Montmorenci Rd 15853 814-772-1012

Ridley Park, Delaware, Pop. 6,923
Ridley SD
Supt. — See Folsom
Ridley MS 1,300/6-8
400 Free St 19078 610-237-8034
Adam Staples, prin. Fax 237-8032

Rimersburg, Clarion, Pop. 942
Union SD 600/K-12
354 Baker St Ste 2 16248 814-473-6311
Jean McCleary, supt. Fax 473-8201
www.unionsd.net/
Union JSHS 300/7-12
354 Baker St Ste 1 16248 814-473-3121
Michael Moore, prin. Fax 473-8201

Roaring Spring, Blair, Pop. 2,566
Spring Cove SD 1,800/K-12
1100 E Main St 16673 814-224-5124
Robert Vadella, supt. Fax 224-5516
scsd.schoolwires.net
Spring Cove MS 400/6-8
185 Spring Cove Dr 16673 814-224-2106
Carol Louden, prin. Fax 224-2842
Other Schools – See Martinsburg

Robesonia, Berks, Pop. 2,034
Conrad Weiser Area SD 2,800/K-12
44 Big Spring Rd 19551 610-693-8545
Dr. Randall Grove, supt. Fax 693-8586
www.conradweiser.org
Weiser HS 1,000/9-12
44 Big Spring Rd 19551 610-693-8528
Dr. Betsy Adams, prin. Fax 693-8511
Weiser MS 900/5-8
347 E Penn Ave 19551 610-693-8514
Dr. Peter Aiken, prin. Fax 693-8543

Rochester, Beaver, Pop. 3,481
Rochester Area SD 900/K-12
540 Reno St 15074 724-775-7500
Dr. Jane Bovalino, supt. Fax 775-4077
rasd.org
Rochester Area JSHS 400/7-12
540 Reno St 15074 724-775-7500
Michael Damon, prin. Fax 775-9268

Rockwood, Somerset, Pop. 885
Rockwood Area SD 800/K-12
439 Somerset Ave 15557 814-926-4688
Mark Bower, supt. Fax 926-2880
www.rockwoodschools.org
Rockwood Area JSHS 400/7-12
437 Somerset Ave 15557 814-926-4631
Mark Bower, prin. Fax 926-2631

Rome, Bradford, Pop. 437
Northeast Bradford SD 800/K-12
526 Panther Ln 18837 570-744-2521
Heather McPherson, supt. Fax 744-2933
www.neb.k12.pa.us
Northeast Bradford JSHS 400/7-12
526 Panther Ln 18837 570-744-2521
Gary Martell, prin. Fax 744-1445

North Rome Christian S 200/K-12
3376 N Rome Rd 18837 570-247-2800
Lee Ann Carmichael, admin. Fax 247-7288

Rosemont, Montgomery
Lower Merion SD
Supt. — See Ardmore
Harriton HS 1,000/9-12
600 N Ithan Ave 19010 610-658-3950
Scott Eveslage, prin. Fax 525-6771

Hill Top Preparatory S 100/5-12
737 S Ithan Ave 19010 610-527-3230
Tom Needham, hdmstr. Fax 527-7683
Irwin S 700/PK-12
275 S Ithan Ave 19010 610-525-8400
Dr. Mary Seppala, head sch Fax 525-8908
Rosemont College Post-Sec.
1400 Montgomery Ave 19010 610-527-0200

Roseto, Northampton, Pop. 1,552

Faith Christian S 200/K-12
122 Dante St 18013 610-588-3414
LuAnn Berger, admin. Fax 588-8103

Royersford, Montgomery, Pop. 4,653
Spring-Ford Area SD 7,700/K-12
857 S Lewis Rd 19468 610-705-6000
Dr. David Goodin, supt. Fax 705-6245
www.spring-ford.net
Spring-Ford 9th Grade Center 600/9-9
400 S Lewis Rd 19468 610-705-6011
Dr. Theresa Weidenbaugh, prin. Fax 705-6233
Spring-Ford HS 1,700/10-12
350 S Lewis Rd 19468 610-705-6001
Patrick Nugent, prin. Fax 705-6258
Spring-Ford MS 8th Grade Center 600/8-8
700 Washington St 19468 610-705-6002
Michael Siggins, prin. Fax 705-6255

Pope John Paul II HS 9-12
181 Rittenhouse Rd 19468 484-975-6500
Sr. Janet Purcell, prin. Fax 792-3082

Ruffs Dale, Westmoreland
Yough SD
Supt. — See Herminie
Yough MS 700/5-8
171 State Route 31 15679 724-872-5164
Anthony DeMaro, prin. Fax 872-5319

Rural Valley, Armstrong, Pop. 873
Armstrong SD
Supt. — See Ford City
West Shamokin JSHS 600/7-12
178 Wolf Dr 16249 724-783-7040
Stephen Shutters, prin. Fax 783-6747

Russell, Warren, Pop. 1,393
Warren County SD
Supt. — See North Warren
Eisenhower MSHS 500/7-12
3700 Route 957 16345 814-757-8878
Erik Leamon, prin. Fax 757-8516

Calvary Chapel Christian S 50/PK-12
PO Box 579 16345 814-757-8744
James Hunt, admin. Fax 757-8745

Saegertown, Crawford, Pop. 988
Penncrest SD 3,400/K-12
PO Box 808 16433 814-763-2323
Constance Youngblood, supt. Fax 763-5129
www.penncrest.org
Saegertown JSHS 600/7-12
18079 Mook Rd 16433 814-763-2615
Douglas Wilson, prin. Fax 763-6702
Other Schools – See Cambridge Springs, Guys Mills

French Creek Valley Christian S 50/PK-12
420 North St 16433 814-763-3282
Patrick Lashrook, prin. Fax 763-3283

Saint Davids, Delaware

Eastern University Post-Sec.
1300 Eagle Rd 19087 610-341-5800

Saint Marys, Elk, Pop. 12,994
Saint Marys Area SD 2,300/K-12
977 S Saint Marys St 15857 814-834-7831
Anna Kearney, supt. Fax 781-2190
smasd.org
Saint Marys Area HS 800/9-12
977 S Saint Marys St 15857 814-834-7831
Dr. Joshua Williams, prin. Fax 781-2190
Saint Marys Area MS 500/6-8
979 S Saint Marys St 15857 814-834-7831
James Wortman, prin. Fax 781-2191

Elk County Catholic HS 300/9-12
600 Maurus St 15857 814-834-7800
Sandra Florig, prin. Fax 781-3441
St. Marys Catholic MS 200/6-8
325 Church St 15857 814-834-2665
John Schneider, prin. Fax 834-5339

Salisbury, Somerset, Pop. 724
Salisbury-Elk Lick SD 300/PK-12
PO Box 68 15558 814-662-2733
Joseph Renzi, supt. Fax 662-2544
selsd.com
Salisbury-Elk Lick JSHS 100/7-12
PO Box 68 15558 814-662-2741
Kenneth Fusina, prin. Fax 662-2091

Saltsburg, Indiana, Pop. 862
Blairsville-Saltsburg SD
Supt. — See Blairsville
Saltsburg MSHS 400/6-12
84 Trojan Ln 15681 724-639-3547
Allan Berkhimer, prin. Fax 639-0071

Kiski S 200/9-12
1888 Brett Ln 15681 724-639-3586
Christopher Brueningsen, hdmstr. Fax 639-8596

Sarver, Butler
Freeport Area SD 2,000/K-12
621 S Pike Rd 16055 724-295-5141
Chris DeVivo, supt. Fax 295-3001
www.freeport.k12.pa.us
Freeport Area HS 600/9-12
625 S Pike Rd 16055 724-295-5143
Jeffrey Lesko, prin. Fax 295-2390
Other Schools – See Freeport

Evangel Heights Christian Academy 200/PK-12
120 Beale Rd 16055 724-295-9199
Rev. John Kuert, prin. Fax 295-9009

Saxonburg, Butler, Pop. 1,517
South Butler County SD 2,700/K-12
328 Knoch Rd 16056 724-352-1700
Dr. Dale Lumley, supt. Fax 352-3622
southbutler.org
Knoch HS 1,000/9-12
345 Knoch Rd 16056 724-352-1700
Todd Trofimuk, prin. Fax 352-0160
Knoch MS 700/6-8
754 Dinnerbell Rd 16056 724-352-1700
Frank Moxie, prin. Fax 352-0170

Saxton, Bedford, Pop. 730
Tussey Mountain SD 900/K-12
199 Front St 16678 814-635-3670
Mark Bollman, supt. Fax 635-3928
www.tmsd.net
Tussey Mountain JSHS 400/7-12
199 Front St 16678 814-635-2975
Melinda Damiano, prin.

Sayre, Bradford, Pop. 5,530
Sayre Area SD 1,000/PK-12
333 W Lockhart St 18840 570-888-7615
Dean Hosterman, supt. Fax 888-8248
www.sayresd.org
Sayre Area JSHS 500/7-12
331 W Lockhart St 18840 570-888-6622
Dayton Handrick, prin. Fax 882-9385

Robert Packer Hospital Post-Sec.
1 Guthrie Sq 18840 570-888-6666

Schnecksville, Lehigh, Pop. 2,900
Area Vocational Technical School
Supt. — None
Lehigh Career & Technical Institute Vo/Tech
4500 Education Park Dr 18078 610-799-1323
Sandra Himes, prin.

Lehigh Carbon Community College Post-Sec.
4525 Education Park Dr 18078 610-799-2121

Schuylkill Haven, Schuylkill, Pop. 5,373
Blue Mountain SD
Supt. — See Orwigsburg

Blue Mountain HS 1,000/9-12
1076 W Market St 17972 570-366-0511
Kevin Berger, prin. Fax 366-1965

Schuylkill Haven Area SD 1,300/K-12
501 E Main St 17972 570-385-6705
Lorraine Felker, supt. Fax 385-6736
www.haven.k12.pa.us/
Schuylkill Haven Area HS 500/8-12
501 E Main St 17972 570-385-6717
Andrew Netznik, prin. Fax 385-6745

Penn State Schuylkill Post-Sec.
200 University Dr 17972 570-385-6000

Scottdale, Westmoreland, Pop. 4,332
Southmoreland SD 2,000/K-12
200 Scottie Way 15683 724-887-2005
Dr. John Molnar, supt. Fax 887-2055
www.southmoreland.net
Southmoreland MS 500/6-8
200 Scottie Way 15683 724-887-2029
Vince Mascia, prin. Fax 887-2032
Other Schools – See Alverton

Scott Township, Allegheny, Pop. 17,118
Lakeland SD 1,600/K-12
1355 Lakeland Dr, 570-254-9485
Dr. Margaret Billings-Jones, supt. Fax 254-9224
www.lakelandsd.org
Lakeland JSHS 800/7-12
1355 Lakeland Dr, 570-254-9485
Thomas Kameroski, prin. Fax 254-6730

Scranton, Lackawanna, Pop. 74,482
Area Vocational Technical School
Supt. — None
CTC of Lackawanna County Vo/Tech
3201 Rockwell Ave 18508 570-346-8471
Vincent Nallo, dir. Fax 342-4251

Scranton SD 8,500/PK-12
425 N Washington Ave 18503 570-348-3400
Bill King, admin. Fax 348-3563
www.scrsd.org/
Northeast IS, 721 Adams Ave 18510 800/6-8
Robert Butka, prin. 570-348-3651
Scranton HS 1,800/9-12
63 Munchak Way 18508 570-348-3481
John Coyle, prin. Fax 348-3561
South Scranton IS 500/6-8
355 Maple St 18505 570-348-3631
Melissa McTiernan, prin.
West Scranton HS 1,100/9-12
1201 Luzerne St 18504 570-348-3616
Robert Gentilezza, prin. Fax 348-3594
West Scranton IS 800/6-8
1401 Fellows St 18504 570-348-3475
Paul Dougherty, prin.

Bais Yaakov of Scranton 50/9-12
1025 Vine St 18510 570-347-5003
Bnos Yisroel of Scranton 100/9-12
620 Monroe Ave 18510 570-558-1370
Fortis Institute Post-Sec.
517 Ash St 18509 570-558-1818
Johnson College Post-Sec.
3427 N Main Ave 18508 570-342-6404
Lackawanna College Post-Sec.
501 Vine St 18509 570-961-7810
Marywood University Post-Sec.
2300 Adams Ave 18509 570-348-6211
Penn Foster Career School Post-Sec.
925 Oak St 18515 570-342-7701
St. Clare/St. Paul S-Main Campus 200/3-8
1527 Penn Ave 18509 570-343-7880
Elizabeth Murray, prin. Fax 343-0069
Scranton Prep S 800/9-12
1000 Wyoming Ave 18509 570-941-7737
Matthew Bernard, prin. Fax 941-6118
Scranton State School for the Deaf Post-Sec.
1800 N Washington Ave 18509
The Commonwealth Medical College Post-Sec.
525 Pine St 18509 570-504-7000
University of Scranton 18510 Post-Sec.
570-941-7400
Yeshiva Beth Moshe Post-Sec.
930 Hickory St 18505 570-346-1747
Yeshiva Beth Moshe 100/9-12
930 Hickory St 18505 570-346-1747

Selinsgrove, Snyder, Pop. 5,582
Selinsgrove Area SD 2,700/K-12
401 18th St 17870 570-374-1144
Chad Cohrs, supt. Fax 372-2222
www.seal-pa.org/
Selinsgrove Area HS 900/9-12
500 N Broad St 17870 570-372-2230
Lorinda Krause, prin. Fax 372-2240
Selinsgrove Area MS 600/6-8
401 18th St 17870 570-372-2250
John Bohle, prin. Fax 372-2251

Susquehanna University Post-Sec.
514 University Ave 17870 570-374-0101

Sellersville, Bucks, Pop. 4,161

Faith Christian Academy 300/K-12
700 N Main St 18960 215-257-4577
Ryan Clymer, head sch
Upper Bucks Christian S 200/PK-12
754 E Rockhill Rd 18960 215-536-9200
Ruud Stolvoort, admin. Fax 536-2229

Seneca, Venango, Pop. 1,053
Cranberry Area SD 1,000/K-12
3 Education Dr 16346 814-676-5628
Maria Pappas, supt. Fax 677-5728
www.edline.net/pages/cranberry_area_school_district
Cranberry Area JSHS 600/7-12
1 Education Dr 16346 814-676-8504
Bill Vonada, prin. Fax 676-5156

Christian Life Academy 100/PK-12
3973 State Route 257 Ste 1 16346 814-676-9360
Michael Lloyd, admin. Fax 676-2908
Northwest Medical Center Post-Sec.
100 Fairfield Dr 16346 814-677-1711

Sewickley, Allegheny, Pop. 3,749
Quaker Valley SD
Supt. — See Leetsdale
Quaker Valley MS 500/6-8
618 Harbaugh St 15143 412-749-5079
Sean Aiken, prin. Fax 749-9844

Eden Christian Academy - Mt. Nebo Campus 200/7-12
318 Nicholson Rd 15143 412-741-2825
Todd Aiken, hdmstr. Fax 324-1101
Sewickley Academy 700/PK-12
315 Academy Ave 15143 412-741-2230
Kolia John O'Connor, head sch Fax 741-9234
Sewickley Valley Hospital Post-Sec.
700 Blackburn Rd 15143 412-741-6600
The Education Center at Watson Inst. Post-Sec.
301 Campmeeting Rd 15143 412-741-1800

Shamokin Dam, Snyder, Pop. 1,672

Empire Beauty School Post-Sec.
PO Box 397 17876 570-743-1410

Shanksville, Somerset, Pop. 229
Shanksville-Stonycreek SD
Supt. — See Friedens
Shanksville-Stonycreek MSHS 100/6-12
PO Box 128 15560 814-267-4649
Samuel Romesberg, prin. Fax 267-4372

Sharon, Mercer, Pop. 13,523
Sharon CSD 2,100/K-12
215 Forker Blvd 16146 724-983-4000
John Sarandrea, supt. Fax 981-0844
sharoncitysd.schoolwires.com
Sharon HS 600/9-12
1129 E State St 16146 724-983-4030
Leonard Rich, prin. Fax 981-0840
Sharon MS 300/7-8
1129 E State St 16146 724-983-4032
Terry Karsonovich, prin. Fax 983-4050

Laurel Technical Institute Post-Sec.
200 Sterling Ave 16146 724-983-0700
Penn State Shenango Post-Sec.
147 Shenango Ave 16146 724-983-2803
Sharon Regional Health System Post-Sec.
740 E State St 16146 724-983-5603

Sharon Hill, Delaware, Pop. 5,504
Southeast Delco SD
Supt. — See Folcroft
Academy Park HS 1,200/9-12
300 Calcon Hook Rd 19079 610-522-4330
Dr. Edward Small, prin. Fax 522-4335

Venus Beauty Academy Post-Sec.
1033 Chester Pike 19079 610-586-2500

Sharpsville, Mercer, Pop. 4,343
Sharpsville Area SD 1,300/K-12
701 Pierce Ave 16150 724-962-7874
Mark Ferrara, supt. Fax 962-7873
www.sharpsville.k12.pa.us/
Sharpsville Area HS 400/9-12
301 Blue Devil Way 16150 724-962-7861
Kirk Scurpa, prin. Fax 962-7730
Sharpsville Area MS 300/6-8
303 Blue Devil Way 16150 724-962-7863
John Vannoy, prin. Fax 962-7891

Sheffield, Warren, Pop. 1,128
Warren County SD
Supt. — See North Warren
Sheffield Area MSHS 300/6-12
6760 Route 6 16347 814-968-3720
Amy Beers, prin. Fax 968-4233

Shenandoah, Schuylkill, Pop. 5,009
Shenandoah Valley SD 1,100/PK-12
805 W Centre St 17976 570-462-1936
Dr. Stanley Rakowsky, supt. Fax 462-4611
www.svbluedevils.org
Shenandoah Valley JSHS 500/7-12
805 W Centre St 17976 570-462-1957
Phillip Andras, prin. Fax 462-2982

Shickshinny, Luzerne, Pop. 832
Northwest Area SD 1,200/K-12
243 Thorne Hill Rd 18655 570-542-4126
Dr. Ronald Grevera, supt. Fax 542-0187
www.northwest.k12.pa.us/
Northwest Area JSHS 600/7-12
243 Thorne Hill Rd 18655 570-542-4126
Ryan Miner, prin. Fax 542-7538

Shillington, Berks, Pop. 5,201
Governor Mifflin SD 4,200/K-12
10 S Waverly St 19607 610-775-1461
Dr. Daniel Bulinski, supt. Fax 775-6586
www.governormifflinsd.org
Mifflin HS 1,400/9-12
10 S Waverly St 19607 610-775-5089
John Althouse, prin. Fax 796-7471
Mifflin MS 600/7-8
10 S Waverly St 19607 610-775-1465
Kevin Hohl, prin. Fax 685-3760

Shinglehouse, Potter, Pop. 1,122
Oswayo Valley SD 400/PK-12
PO Box 610 16748 814-697-7175
Frank McClard, supt. Fax 697-7439
www.oswayo.com/
Oswayo Valley MSHS 200/6-12
PO Box 610 16748 814-697-6132
Carolyn Fugate, prin. Fax 697-6375

Shippensburg, Cumberland, Pop. 5,366
Shippensburg Area SD 3,400/K-12
317 N Morris St 17257 717-530-2700
Kristin Carroll, supt. Fax 530-2724
www.ship.k12.pa.us
Shippensburg Area HS 1,100/9-12
201 Eberly Dr 17257 717-530-2730
Bruce Levy, prin. Fax 530-2835
Shippensburg Area MS 800/6-8
101 Park Pl W 17257 717-530-2750
Teri Mowery, prin. Fax 530-2757

Shippensburg University Post-Sec.
1871 Old Main Dr 17257 717-477-7447

Shippenville, Clarion, Pop. 476
Area Vocational Technical School
Supt. — None
Clarion County Career Center Vo/Tech
447 Career Ln 16254 814-226-4391
William Powell, dir. Fax 226-7350

Shiremanstown, Cumberland, Pop. 1,540

Bible Baptist S 300/PK-12
201 W Main St 17011 717-737-3550
Roy Oakes, admin. Fax 761-3977

Sidman, Cambria, Pop. 430
Forest Hills SD 2,000/PK-12
PO Box 158 15955 814-487-7613
Edwin Bowser, supt. Fax 487-7775
www.fhsd.k12.pa.us/
Forest Hills HS 500/10-12
PO Box 325 15955 814-487-7613
Curt Vasas, prin. Fax 487-2371
Forest Hills MS 500/7-9
1427 Frankstown Rd 15955 814-487-7613
Fax 495-7367

Sinking Spring, Berks, Pop. 3,938
Wilson SD
Supt. — See West Lawn
Wilson Southern MS 400/7-9
3100 Iroquois Ave 19608 610-670-0180
Dr. Stephen Burnham, prin. Fax 334-6445
Wilson West MS 500/7-9
450 Faust Rd 19608 610-670-0180
Kyle Wetherhold, prin. Fax 334-6440

Slatington, Lehigh, Pop. 4,171
Northern Lehigh SD 1,800/K-12
1201 Shadow Oaks Ln 18080 610-767-9800
Michael Michaels, supt. Fax 767-9809
www.nlsd.org
Northern Lehigh HS 700/9-12
1 Bulldog Ln 18080 610-767-9832
Robert Vlasaty, prin. Fax 767-9848
Northern Lehigh MS 300/7-8
600 Diamond St 18080 610-767-9812
Jill Chamberlain, prin. Fax 767-9850

Slippery Rock, Butler, Pop. 3,557
Slippery Rock Area SD 2,100/K-12
201 Kiester Rd 16057 724-794-2960
Dr. Kathleen Nogay, supt. Fax 794-2001
www.slipperyrock.k12.pa.us
Slippery Rock Area HS 700/9-12
201 Kiester Rd 16057 724-794-2960
Kristie Shulsky, prin. Fax 794-1952
Slippery Rock Area MS 500/6-8
201 Kiester Rd 16057 724-794-2960
Cory Hake, prin. Fax 794-6265

Slippery Rock University Post-Sec.
1 Morrow Way 16057 724-738-9000

Smethport, McKean, Pop. 1,646
Smethport Area SD 900/PK-12
414 S Mechanic St 16749 814-887-5543
Charles Leasure, supt. Fax 887-5544
www.smethportschools.com/
Smethport Area JSHS 500/7-12
412 S Mechanic St 16749 814-887-5545
Robert Miller, prin. Fax 887-5546

Somerset, Somerset, Pop. 6,210
Area Vocational Technical School
Supt. — None
Somerset County Technology Center Vo/Tech
281 Technology Dr 15501 814-443-3651
Georgia Yeager, prin. Fax 445-6716

Somerset Area SD 1,700/K-12
645 S Columbia Ave Ste 110 15501 814-443-2831
Krista Mathias, supt. Fax 443-1964
sasd.us
Somerset Area HS 600/9-12
645 S Columbia Ave Ste 130 15501 814-443-2831
Scott Shirley, prin. Fax 444-3202
Somerset Area MS 400/6-8
645 S Columbia Ave Ste 120 15501 814-443-2831
Jeff Boyer, prin. Fax 444-3301

Somerset Christian S 100/PK-10
708 Stoystown Rd Ste 2 15501 814-443-1960
Susie Harshbarger, prin. Fax 443-9830

Somerset Community Hospital Post-Sec.
225 S Center Ave 15501 814-443-5221

Souderton, Montgomery, Pop. 6,521
Souderton Area SD 6,700/K-12
760 Lower Rd 18964 215-723-6061
Frank Gallagher, supt. Fax 723-8897
www.soudertonsd.org
Indian Crest MS 800/6-8
139 Harleysville Pike 18964 215-723-9193
Jeff Pammer, prin. Fax 723-8897
Souderton Area HS 2,100/9-12
625 Lower Rd 18964 215-723-2808
Dr. Sam Varano, prin. Fax 723-6352
Other Schools – See Harleysville

South Abington, Lackawanna

Summit Christian Academy 100/PK-12
660 Griffin Pond Rd, 570-587-1545
Matt Allan, head sch Fax 309-0038

Southampton, Bucks, Pop. 11,500
Centennial SD
Supt. — See Warminster
Klinger MS 600/6-8
1415 2nd Street Pike 18966 215-364-5950
Michael Johnson, prin. Fax 364-5955

South Canaan, Wayne

St. Tikhon's Orthodox Theological Sem. Post-Sec.
PO Box 130 18459 570-561-1818

South Park, Allegheny
South Park SD 2,100/K-12
2005 Eagle Ridge Dr 15129 412-655-3111
Jeanine Gregory, supt. Fax 655-2952
www.sparksd.org
South Park HS 800/9-12
2005 Eagle Ridge Dr 15129 412-655-4900
Dr. Patricia Smith, prin. Fax 655-1463
South Park MS 700/5-8
2500 Stewart Rd 15129 412-831-7200
Kevin Monaghan, prin. Fax 831-7204

Cornerstone Christian Prep Academy 50/8-12
3701 Brownsville Rd 15129 724-835-1100
Cindi McCall, dir. Fax 835-1106

South Williamsport, Lycoming, Pop. 6,306
South Williamsport Area SD 1,300/K-12
515 W Central Ave 17702 570-327-1581
Dr. Mark Stamm, supt. Fax 326-0641
www.mounties.k12.pa.us
South Williamsport Area JSHS 600/7-12
700 Percy St 17702 570-326-2684
Jesse Smith, prin. Fax 326-2687

Spring Church, Armstrong
Apollo Ridge SD
Supt. — See Apollo
Apollo-Ridge HS 400/9-12
1825 State Route 56 15686 724-478-6000
Clint Weimer, prin. Fax 478-9775
Apollo-Ridge MS 400/6-8
1829 State Route 56 15686 724-478-6000
Travis Barta, prin. Fax 478-3730

Springdale, Allegheny, Pop. 3,373
Allegheny Valley SD
Supt. — See Cheswick
Springdale JSHS 500/7-12
501 Butler Rd 15144 724-274-8100
Andrew Leviski, prin. Fax 274-2106

Springfield, Delaware, Pop. 24,160
Springfield SD 3,100/K-12
111 W Leamy Ave 19064 610-938-6000
Dr. James Capolupo, supt. Fax 938-6005
www.ssdcougars.org
Richardson MS 800/6-8
20 W Woodland Ave 19064 610-938-6300
Daniel Tracy, prin. Fax 938-6305
Springfield HS 1,200/9-12
49 W Leamy Ave 19064 610-938-6100
Joseph Hepp, prin. Fax 938-6105

Anthem Institute Post-Sec.
400 S State Rd 19064 877-600-8860
Cardinal O'Hara HS 1,500/9-12
1701 S Sproul Rd 19064 610-544-3800
Marie Rogai, prin. Fax 544-1189

Spring Grove, York, Pop. 2,145
Spring Grove Area SD 3,800/K-12
100 E College Ave 17362 717-225-4731
Dr. Robert Lombardo, supt. Fax 225-6028
www.sgasd.org
Spring Grove Area HS 1,200/9-12
1490 Roth Church Rd 17362 717-225-4731
Dr. Rosemary Cugliari, prin. Fax 225-0736
Spring Grove Area MS 600/7-8
244 Old Hanover Rd 17362 717-225-4731
Steve Guadagnino, prin. Fax 225-0146

Spring Mills, Centre, Pop. 267
Penns Valley Area SD 1,500/K-12
4528 Penns Valley Rd 16875 814-422-2000
Brian Griffith, supt. Fax 422-8020
www.pennsvalley.org
Penns Valley Area JSHS 700/7-12
4545 Penns Valley Rd 16875 814-422-8854
Randy Seely, prin. Fax 422-8280

Springville, Susquehanna
Elk Lake SD 1,400/K-12
2380 Elk Lake School Rd 18844 570-278-1106
William Bush, supt. Fax 278-4838
www.elklakeschool.org
Elk Lake JSHS 600/7-12
2210 Elk Lake School Rd 18844 570-278-1106
Kenneth Cuomo, prin. Fax 278-4838

State College, Centre, Pop. 41,187
State College Area SD 6,900/K-12
131 W Nittany Ave 16801 814-231-1011
Dr. Robert O'Donnell, supt. Fax 231-4130
www.scasd.org
Mount Nittany MS 700/6-8
656 Brandywine Dr 16801 814-272-4050
Brian Ishler, prin. Fax 272-4055
Park Forest MS 800/6-8
2180 School Dr 16803 814-237-5301
Dr. Karen Wiser, prin. Fax 272-0196
State College Area HS 2,400/9-12
653 Westerly Pkwy 16801 814-231-1111
Scott DeShong, prin. Fax 231-5024

Empire Beauty School Post-Sec.
206 W Hamilton Ave 16801 814-238-1961
Grace Prep HS 100/9-12
3006 Research Dr Ste D1 16801 814-867-1177
Pat Sullivan, prin. Fax 240-3977
South Hills School of Business & Tech. Post-Sec.
480 Waupelani Dr 16801 814-234-7755

Steelton, Dauphin, Pop. 5,688
Central Dauphin SD
Supt. — See Harrisburg
Swatara MS 500/6-8
1101 Highland St 17113 717-939-9363
Erick Valentin, prin. Fax 939-2156

Steelton-Highspire SD 1,200/K-12
250 Reynders St 17113 717-704-3800
Dr. Audrey Utley, supt. Fax 704-3808
www.shsd.k12.pa.us
Steelton-Highspire JSHS 500/7-12
250 Reynders St 17113 717-704-3800
Willie Slade, prin. Fax 704-3808

Stoneboro, Mercer, Pop. 1,041
Lakeview SD 1,300/K-12
2482 Mercer St 16153 724-376-7911
Douglas J. Mays, supt. Fax 376-7910
www.lakeview.k12.pa.us
Lakeview HS 400/9-12
2482 Mercer St 16153 724-376-7911
Carol O. Lilly, prin. Fax 376-7910
Lakeview MS 400/5-8
2482 Mercer St 16153 724-376-7911
David Blakley, prin. Fax 376-7910

Stoystown, Somerset, Pop. 354
North Star SD
Supt. — See Boswell
North Star MS 300/5-8
3598 Whistler Rd 15563 814-893-5616
Thaddeus Kiesnowski, prin. Fax 893-5922

Strafford, Chester, Pop. 4,500

Woodlynde S 300/K-12
445 Upper Gulph Rd 19087 610-687-9660
Christopher Fulco Ed.D., head sch Fax 687-4752

Strattanville, Clarion, Pop. 547
Clarion-Limestone Area SD 1,000/K-12
4091 C L School Rd 16258 814-764-5111
John Johnson, supt. Fax 764-5729
www.clasd.net/
Clarion-Limestone JSHS 500/7-12
4091 C L School Rd 16258 814-764-5111
Wendy Benton, prin. Fax 764-5274

Stroudsburg, Monroe, Pop. 5,412
Stroudsburg Area SD 5,600/K-12
123 Linden St 18360 570-421-1990
Dr. John Toleno, supt. Fax 424-5986
www.sburg.org
Stroudsburg HS 1,500/10-12
1100 W Main St 18360 570-421-1991
Jeff Sodl, prin. Fax 424-1383
Stroudsburg JHS 900/8-9
1901 Chipperfield Dr 18360 570-424-4848
Dr. Maryellen Mross, prin. Fax 424-4839

Stroudsburg School of Cosmetology Post-Sec.
100 N 8th St 18360 570-421-3387

Summerdale, Cumberland

Central Penn College Post-Sec.
PO Box 309 17093 800-759-2727

Sunbury, Northumberland, Pop. 9,716
Shikellamy SD 2,500/K-12
200 Island Blvd 17801 570-286-3720
Patrick Kelley, supt. Fax 286-3776
www.shikbraves.org
Shikellamy HS 900/9-12
600 Walnut St 17801 570-286-3700
Michael Hubicki, prin. Fax 286-3775
Shikellamy MS 200/7-8
520 Walnut St 17801 570-286-3736
Frank Boyer, prin. Fax 286-3780

McCann School of Business & Technology Post-Sec.
1147 N 4th St 17801 570-286-3058
Triangle Tech Post-Sec.
191 Performance Rd 17801 570-988-0700

Susquehanna, Susquehanna, Pop. 1,631
Susquehanna Community SD 900/K-12
3192 Turnpike St 18847 570-853-4921
Bronson Stone, supt. Fax 853-3768
www.scschools.org/
Susquehanna Community JSHS 400/7-12
3192 Turnpike St 18847 570-853-4921
Mark Gerchman, prin. Fax 853-3918

Swarthmore, Delaware, Pop. 5,977

Swarthmore College Post-Sec.
500 College Ave 19081 610-328-8000

Swiftwater, Monroe
Pocono Mountain SD 8,500/K-12
PO Box 200 18370 570-839-7121
Dr. Elizabeth Robison, supt. Fax 895-4768
www.pmsd.org
Pocono Mountain East HS 1,300/9-12
PO Box 200 18370 570-839-7121
Todd Burns, prin. Fax 839-5934
Pocono Mountain East JHS 400/7-8
PO Box 200 18370 570-839-7121
Dr. Kathy Fanelli, prin. Fax 839-3242
Swiftwater IS 1,000/7-8
PO Box 200 18370 570-839-7121
Kristine Kunsman, prin. Fax 839-7820
Other Schools – See Pocono Summit

Swissvale, Allegheny, Pop. 8,692

Grace Academy 50/7-12
2121 Noble St 15218 412-871-5455
Ronald Malamisuro, admin. Fax 243-1465

Tamaqua, Schuylkill, Pop. 7,032
Tamaqua Area SD 2,100/K-12
138 W Broad St 18252 570-668-2570
Carol Makuta, supt. Fax 668-6850
www.tamaqua.k12.pa.us
Tamaqua Area HS 700/9-12
500 Penn St 18252 570-668-1901
Stephen Toth, prin. Fax 668-2970
Tamaqua Area MS 500/6-8
502 Penn St 18252 570-668-1210
Christopher Czapla, prin. Fax 668-5027

Marian HS 300/9-12
166 Marian Ave 18252 570-467-3335
Sr. Bernard Agnes Smith, prin. Fax 467-0186

Tarentum, Allegheny, Pop. 4,449

ITT Technical Institute Post-Sec.
100 Pittsburgh Mills Cir 15084 724-274-1400

Taylor, Lackawanna, Pop. 6,195
Riverside SD 1,500/K-12
300 Davis St 18517 570-562-2121
David Woods, supt. Fax 562-3205
www.riversidesd.com/
Riverside JSHS 700/7-12
310 Davis St 18517 570-562-2121
Joseph Moceyunas, prin. Fax 562-7551

Three Springs, Huntingdon, Pop. 439
Southern Huntingdon County SD 1,200/K-12
10339 Pogue Rd 17264 814-447-5529
Dr. Tod Kline, supt. Fax 447-3967
www.shcsd.k12.pa.us
Southern Huntingdon County MSHS 700/6-12
10339 Pogue Rd 17264 814-447-5529
Michael Adamek, prin. Fax 447-3750

Throop, Lackawanna, Pop. 4,041
Mid Valley SD 1,600/K-12
52 Underwood Rd 18512 570-307-1108
Randy Parry, supt. Fax 307-1107
www.mvsd.us
Mid Valley HS 600/9-12
52 Underwood Rd 18512 570-307-2180
Chad Vinansky, prin. Fax 307-1912
Mid Valley MS 300/7-8
54 Underwood Rd 18512 570-307-2130
Chad Vinansky, prin. Fax 307-2193

Tioga, Tioga, Pop. 659
Northern Tioga SD
Supt. — See Elkland
Williamson JSHS 400/7-12
33 Jct Cross Rd 16946 570-827-2191
Kris Kaufman, prin. Fax 827-3557

Tionesta, Forest, Pop. 478
Forest Area SD 500/K-12
22318 Route 62 Unit 16 16353 814-755-4491
Amanda Hetrick, supt. Fax 755-2426
www.forestareaschools.org/
West Forest JSHS 200/7-12
22318 Route 62 Unit 15 16353 814-755-3611
Richard Smith, prin. Fax 755-2427
Other Schools – See Marienville

North Clarion County SD 600/K-12
10439 Route 36 16353 814-744-8536
Steven Young, supt. Fax 744-9378
www.northclarion.org
North Clarion County JSHS 300/7-12
10439 Route 36 16353 814-744-8544
Steven Young, prin. Fax 744-8762

Titusville, Crawford, Pop. 5,544
Titusville Area SD 2,100/PK-12
221 N Washington St 16354 814-827-2715
Karen Jez, supt. Fax 827-7761
www.gorockets.org/
Titusville HS 600/9-12
302 E Walnut St 16354 814-827-2715
Stephanie Keebler, prin. Fax 827-0551
Titusville MS 500/6-8
415 Water St 16354 814-827-2715
Michael McGaughey, prin. Fax 827-0552

University of Pittsburgh at Titusville Post-Sec.
504 E Main St # 287 16354 814-827-4400

Topton, Berks, Pop. 2,055
Brandywine Heights Area SD 1,400/K-12
200 W Weis St 19562 610-682-5100
Dr. Martin Handler, supt. Fax 682-5136
www.bhasd.org
Brandywine Heights Area MS 400/6-8
200 W Weis St 19562 610-682-5131
Dr. Kathy Johnson, prin. Fax 682-5105
Other Schools – See Mertztown

Towanda, Bradford, Pop. 2,864
Area Vocational Technical School
Supt. — None
Northern Tier Career Center Vo/Tech
120 Career Center Ln 18848 570-265-8111
Elizabeth Frankhouser, dir. Fax 265-3002

Towanda Area SD 1,600/K-12
410 State St 18848 570-265-9154
Steve Gobble, supt. Fax 265-4881
www.tsd.k12.pa.us
Towanda Area JSHS 800/7-12
1 High School Dr 18848 570-265-2101
Dennis Peachey, prin. Fax 268-2069

Tower City, Schuylkill, Pop. 1,337
Williams Valley SD 1,000/K-12
10330 Route 209 Rd 17980 717-647-2167
Dr. Donald Burkhardt, supt. Fax 647-2055
www.wvschools.net
Williams Valley JSHS 500/7-12
10330 Route 209 Rd 17980 717-647-2167
Tracey Weller, prin. Fax 647-2055

Trafford, Westmoreland, Pop. 3,138
Penn-Trafford SD
Supt. — See Harrison City
Trafford MS 400/6-8
100 Brinton Ave 15085 412-372-6600
Karen Garner, prin. Fax 372-1554

Trevose, Bucks, Pop. 3,515

Strayer University Post-Sec.
3600 Horizon Blvd Ste 100 19053 215-354-2700

Troy, Bradford, Pop. 1,340
Troy Area SD 900/K-12
30 Taylor St 16947 570-297-2750
Charles Young, supt. Fax 297-1600
www.troyareasd.org/
Troy Area JSHS 500/7-12
150 High St 16947 570-297-2176
Susan Shipman, prin. Fax 297-2058

Martha Lloyd School Post-Sec.
66 Lloyd Ln 16947 570-297-2185

Tunkhannock, Wyoming, Pop. 1,809
Tunkhannock Area SD 2,800/K-12
41 Philadelphia Ave 18657 570-836-3111
Michael Healey, supt. Fax 836-2942
www.tasd.net/
Tunkhannock HS 1,000/9-12
135 Tiger Dr 18657 570-836-8223
Gregory Ellsworth, prin. Fax 836-4719
Tunkhannock MS 900/5-8
200 Franklin Ave 18657 570-836-8235
Cynthia Basila, prin. Fax 836-5796

Turbotville, Northumberland, Pop. 705
Warrior Run SD 1,600/K-12
4800 Susquehanna Trl 17772 570-649-5138
Dr. John Kurelja, supt. Fax 649-5475
www.wrsd.org
Warrior Run HS 500/9-12
4800 Susquehanna Trl 17772 570-649-5166
Patricia Cross, prin. Fax 649-5591
Warrior Run MS 500/5-8
4800 Susquehanna Trl 17772 570-649-5135
Susan Mabus, prin. Fax 649-6173

Tyrone, Blair, Pop. 5,415
Tyrone Area SD 1,900/PK-12
701 Clay Ave 16686 814-684-0710
Dr. William Miller, supt. Fax 684-2678
www.tyrone.k12.pa.us/
Tyrone Area HS 600/9-12
1001 Clay Ave 16686 814-684-4240
Thomas Yoder, prin. Fax 684-4245
Tyrone Area MS 500/5-8
1001 Clay Ave 16686 814-684-4240
Kristen N. Pinter, prin. Fax 682-1013

Grier S 200/7-12
PO Box 308 16686 814-684-3000
Andrew Wilson, hdmstr. Fax 684-2177

Ulysses, Potter, Pop. 619
Northern Potter SD 600/PK-12
745 Northern Potter Rd 16948 814-848-7506
Scott Graham, supt. Fax 848-7431
www.northernpottersd.org
Northern Potter JSHS 300/7-12
763 Northern Potter Rd 16948 814-848-7534
Susan Valentine, prin. Fax 848-9671

Union City, Erie, Pop. 3,286
Union City Area SD 1,300/PK-12
107 Concord St 16438 814-438-3804
Sandra Myers, supt. Fax 438-2030
www.ucasd.org
Union City HS 400/9-12
105 Concord St 16438 814-438-7673
Joan Quickle, prin. Fax 438-8079
Union City MS 300/6-8
105 Concord St 16438 814-438-7673
Joan Quickle, prin. Fax 438-8079

Uniontown, Fayette, Pop. 10,023
Albert Gallatin Area SD 3,600/K-12
2625 Morgantown Rd 15401 724-564-7190
Carl Bezjak, supt. Fax 564-7195
www.albertgallatin.k12.pa.us/
Gallatin Area HS 1,100/9-12
1119 Township Dr 15401 724-564-2024
Jason Hutchinson, prin. Fax 564-4525
Other Schools – See Mc Clellandtown, Point Marion

Area Vocational Technical School
Supt. — None
Fayette County Career & Technical Inst Vo/Tech
175 Georges Fairchance Rd 15401 724-437-2721
Dr. Edward Jeffreys, prin.

Laurel Highlands SD 3,300/K-12
304 Bailey Ave 15401 724-437-2821
Jesse Wallace, supt. Fax 437-8929
www.lhsd.org
Laurel Highlands HS 1,100/9-12
300 Bailey Ave 15401 724-437-4741
John Diamond, prin. Fax 437-5653
Laurel Highlands MS 800/6-8
18 Hookton Ave 15401 724-437-2865
Mary Macar, prin. Fax 437-8518

Uniontown Area SD 3,000/K-12
205 Wilson Ave 15401 724-438-4501
Charles Machesky, supt. Fax 437-7007
www.uniontown.k12.pa.us
Lafayette MS 200/6-8
303 Connellsville St 15401 724-438-3581
Renee Pramuk, prin. Fax 439-5023
Uniontown Area HS 1,000/9-12
146 E Fayette St 15401 724-439-5000
Robert Manges, prin. Fax 439-5004
Other Schools – See Markleysburg

Chestnut Ridge Christian Academy 100/PK-12
115 Downer Ave 15401 724-439-1090
Patricia Cowsert, admin. Fax 439-4540
Laurel Business Institute Post-Sec.
PO Box 877 15401 724-439-4900

University Park, See State College

Penn State The Dickinson School of Law Post-Sec.
Lewis Katz Building 16802 814-865-8900
Penn State University Post-Sec.
201 Old Main 16802 814-865-4700

Upper Darby, See Darby
Upper Darby SD
Supt. — See Drexel Hill
Beverly Hills MS 1,500/6-8
1400 Garrett Rd 19082 610-626-9317
Dr. William Bailey, prin.

Harris School of Business Post-Sec.
20 S 69th St 19082 484-463-3800
Prism Career Institute Post-Sec.
6800 Market St 19082 610-789-6700

Upper Saint Clair, Allegheny, Pop. 19,692
Upper St. Clair SD 4,100/K-12
1820 McLaughlin Run Rd 15241 412-833-1600
Dr. Patrick O'Toole, supt. Fax 833-5535
www.uscsd.k12.pa.us
Other Schools – See Pittsburgh

Valley View, Schuylkill, Pop. 1,675
Tri-Valley SD 900/K-12
110 W Main St 17983 570-682-9013
Mark Snyder, supt. Fax 682-9544
www.tri-valley.k12.pa.us
Other Schools – See Hegins

Verona, Allegheny, Pop. 2,433

Redeemer Lutheran S 200/PK-10
700 Idaho Ave 15147 412-793-5884
Gail Holzer, prin. Fax 793-1890

Villanova, Delaware

Academy of Notre Dame De Namur 500/6-12
560 Sproul Rd 19085 610-687-0650
Veronica Harrington, pres. Fax 687-1912
Devereux Foundation in Pennsylvania Post-Sec.
444 Devereux Dr 19085 610-542-3030
Villanova University Post-Sec.
800 E Lancaster Ave 19085 610-519-4500

Wallingford, Delaware
Wallingford-Swarthmore SD 3,400/K-12
200 S Providence Rd 19086 610-892-3470
Dr. Rich Noonan, supt. Fax 892-3493
www.wssd.org
Strath Haven HS 1,200/9-12
205 S Providence Rd 19086 610-892-3470
Dr. Mary Jo Yannacone, prin. Fax 892-3494
Strath Haven MS 800/6-8
200 S Providence Rd 19086 610-892-3470
George King, prin. Fax 892-3492

Warfordsburg, Fulton
Southern Fulton SD 900/K-12
3072 Great Cove Rd Ste 100 17267 717-294-2203
Hervey P. Hann, supt. Fax 294-2207
sfsd.k12.pa.us
Southern Fulton JSHS 400/7-12
13083 Buck Valley Rd 17267 717-294-3251
Meredith Hendershot, prin. Fax 294-6248

Warminster, Bucks, Pop. 32,400
Centennial SD 4,600/K-12
433 Centennial Rd 18974 215-441-6000
Joyce Mundy, supt. Fax 441-6101
www.centennialsd.org
Log College MS 700/6-8
730 Norristown Rd 18974 215-441-6075
Dr. Harry Clark, prin. Fax 441-6073
Tennent HS 1,900/9-12
333 Centennial Rd 18974 215-441-6181
Dennis Best, prin. Fax 441-6175
Other Schools – See Southampton

Archbishop Wood HS 1,100/9-12
655 York Rd 18974 215-672-5050
Mary Harkins, prin. Fax 672-9572
Automotive Training Center Post-Sec.
900 Johnsville Blvd 18974 888-233-0476
Empire Beauty School Post-Sec.
435 York Rd 18974 215-443-8446

Warren, Warren, Pop. 9,619
Area Vocational Technical School
Supt. — None
Warren County AVTS Vo/Tech
347 E 5th Ave 16365 814-726-1260
James Miller, prin. Fax 726-9673

Warren County SD
Supt. — See North Warren
Beaty-Warren MS 500/6-8
2 E 3rd Ave 16365 814-723-5200
Rhonda Decker, prin. Fax 723-9503
Warren Area HS 800/9-12
345 E 5th Ave 16365 814-723-3370
Jeffrey Flickner, prin. Fax 726-3126

Warrington, Bucks, Pop. 7,000
Central Bucks SD
Supt. — See Doylestown
Central Bucks SHS - South 1,800/10-12
1100 Folly Rd 18976 267-893-3000
Scott Davidheiser, prin. Fax 893-5824
Tamanend MS 1,000/7-9
1492 Stuckert Rd 18976 267-893-2900
Cheryl Leatherbarrow, prin. Fax 893-5818

Washington, Washington, Pop. 13,036
Trinity Area SD 3,400/K-12
231 Park Ave 15301 724-223-2000
Dr. Paul Kasunich, supt. Fax 228-2640
www.trinitypride.org
Trinity HS 1,100/9-12
231 Park Ave 15301 724-225-5380
Donald Snoke, prin. Fax 228-9057
Trinity MS 800/6-8
50 Scenic Dr 15301 724-228-2112
Peter Keruskin, prin. Fax 228-1196

Washington SD 1,600/K-12
311 Allison Ave 15301 724-223-5112
Dr. Roberta DiLorenzo, supt. Fax 223-5024
www.washington.k12.pa.us
Washington HS 500/9-12
201 Allison Ave 15301 724-223-5080
Frank Rotunda, prin. Fax 223-5046
Washington JHS 200/7-8
201 Allison Ave 15301 724-223-5060
Kenneth Patterson, prin. Fax 223-5123

Faith Christian S 100/PK-12
524 E Beau St 15301 724-222-5440
First Love Christian Academy 50/9-12
1530 Hillcrest St 15301 724-228-3547
Zonie Jackson, dean Fax 228-3547
Penn Commercial Business/Technical Sch. Post-Sec.
242 Oak Spring Rd 15301 724-222-5330
Washington & Jefferson College Post-Sec.
60 S Lincoln St 15301 724-222-4400
Washington Hospital Post-Sec.
155 Wilson Ave 15301 724-223-3167

Waterfall, Fulton
Forbes Road SD 500/K-12
159 Red Bird Dr 16689 814-685-3866
Mark Loucks, supt. Fax 685-3159
www.frsd.k12.pa.us
Forbes Road JSHS 200/7-12
159 Red Bird Dr 16689 814-685-3866
Christina Ramsey, prin. Fax 685-3159

Waterford, Erie, Pop. 1,509
Fort LeBoeuf SD 2,200/K-12
PO Box 810 16441 814-796-2638
Dr. Debra Spaulding, supt. Fax 796-6459
flb.fortleboeuf.net
Fort LeBoeuf HS 800/9-12
931 N High St 16441 814-796-2616
Martin Rimpa, prin. Fax 796-2141
Fort LeBoeuf MS 500/6-8
PO Box 516 16441 814-796-2681
Matthew Bennett, prin. Fax 796-4712

Watsontown, Northumberland, Pop. 2,340

Watsontown Christian Academy 50/PK-12
1225 8th Street Dr 17777 570-538-9276
H. W. Wilhelm, admin. Fax 538-9148

Wayne, Delaware
Radnor Township SD 3,600/K-12
135 S Wayne Ave 19087 610-688-8100
Dr. Linda Grobman, supt. Fax 687-3318
www.rtsd.org/
Radnor MS 800/6-8
150 Louella Ave 19087 610-386-6300
Anthony Stevenson, prin. Fax 688-2491
Other Schools – See Radnor

Tredyffrin-Easttown SD 6,300/K-12
940 W Valley Rd Ste 1700 19087 610-240-1900
Dr. Daniel Waters, supt. Fax 240-1965
www.tesd.net/
Valley Forge MS 1,000/5-8
105 W Walker Rd 19087 610-240-1300
Matthew Gibson, prin. Fax 240-1325
Other Schools – See Berwyn

Valley Forge Military Academy 200/7-12
1001 Eagle Rd 19087 610-989-1300
Jeffrey Brown Ed.D., hdmstr. Fax 989-1545
Valley Forge Military Academy & College Post-Sec.
1001 Eagle Rd 19087 610-989-1200

Waynesboro, Franklin, Pop. 10,360
Waynesboro Area SD 4,200/K-12
210 Clayton Ave 17268 717-762-1191
Sherran Diller, supt. Fax 762-0028
www.wasd.k12.pa.us
Waynesboro Area HS 1,200/9-12
550 E 2nd St 17268 717-762-1191
Steve Pappas, prin. Fax 762-3787
Waynesboro Area MS 700/7-8
702 E 2nd St 17268 717-762-1191
Aaron Taylor, prin. Fax 762-6566

Waynesburg, Greene, Pop. 4,116
Area Vocational Technical School
Supt. — None
Greene County CTC Vo/Tech
60 Zimmerman Dr 15370 724-627-3106
Karen Pflugh, dir.

Central Greene SD 1,900/K-12
PO Box 472 15370 724-627-8151
Matthew Blair, supt. Fax 627-9591
www.cgsd.org
Bell MS 500/6-8
126 E Lincoln St 15370 724-852-2722
John Lipscomb, prin. Fax 627-0637
Waynesburg Central HS 600/9-12
30 Zimmerman Dr 15370 724-852-1050
Dave Mason, prin. Fax 852-2109

West Greene SD 500/K-12
1367 Hargus Creek Rd 15370 724-499-5183
Thelma Szarell, supt. Fax 499-5623
www.edline.net/pages/West_Greene_SD
West Greene MSHS 200/6-12
1352 Hargus Creek Rd 15370 724-499-5051
Scott Sakai, prin. Fax 499-5492

Waynesburg University Post-Sec.
51 W College St 15370 724-627-8191

Weatherly, Carbon, Pop. 2,496
Weatherly Area SD 700/K-12
602 6th St 18255 570-427-8681
Thomas McLaughlin, supt. Fax 427-8918
www.weatherlysd.org
Weatherly Area HS 200/9-12
601 6th St 18255 570-427-8521
Stuart Tripler, prin. Fax 427-4642
Weatherly Area MS 200/6-8
602 6th St 18255 570-427-8689
Sandra Slavick, prin. Fax 427-8918

Wellsboro, Tioga, Pop. 3,220
Wellsboro Area SD 1,500/K-12
227 Nichols St 16901 570-724-4424
Christopher Morral, supt. Fax 724-5103
www.wellsborosd.org
Butler MS 500/5-8
9 Nichols St 16901 570-724-2306
Michael Pietropola, prin. Fax 724-4143
Wellsboro Area HS 500/9-12
225 Nichols St 16901 570-724-3547
David Krick, prin. Fax 724-3027

West Chester, Chester, Pop. 18,141
West Chester Area SD 11,800/K-12
829 Paoli Pike 19380 484-266-1000
Dr. James R. Scanlon, supt. Fax 266-1175
www.wcasd.net
Fugett MS 1,000/6-8
500 Ellis Ln 19380 484-266-2900
Le Roy G. Whitehead, prin. Fax 266-2999
Peirce MS 900/6-8
1314 Burke Rd 19380 484-266-2500
Geoffrey Mills, prin. Fax 266-2599
Stetson MS 900/6-8
1060 Wilmington Pike 19382 484-266-2700
Dr. Charles A. Cognato, prin. Fax 266-2799
West Chester Bayard Rustin HS 1,300/9-12
1100 Shiloh Rd 19382 484-266-4300
Dr. Phyllis R. Simmons, prin. Fax 266-4399
West Chester East HS 1,400/9-12
450 Ellis Ln 19380 484-266-3800
Fax 266-3899
West Chester Henderson HS 1,300/9-12
400 Montgomery Ave 19380 484-266-3300
Dr. Jason P. Sherlock, prin. Fax 266-3399

Devereux Kanner Center Post-Sec.
390 E Boot Rd 19380 866-532-2212
West Chester Christian S 100/K-12
1237 Paoli Pike 19380 610-692-3700
Dave Douglass, admin. Fax 631-0132
West Chester University of Pennsylvania Post-Sec.
S High St 19383 610-436-1000
Westtown S 800/PK-12
975 Westtown Rd 19382 610-399-0123
John Baird, hdmstr. Fax 399-3760

West Easton, Northampton, Pop. 1,236

Intl Academy of Medical Reflexology Post-Sec.
304 9th St 18042 267-424-4549

Westfield, Tioga, Pop. 1,060
Northern Tioga SD
Supt. — See Elkland
Cowanesque Valley JSHS 400/7-12
51 N Fork Rd 16950 814-367-2233
Matthew Sottolano, prin. Fax 367-5874

West Grove, Chester, Pop. 2,811
Area Vocational Technical School
Supt. — None
Technical College HS - Pennocks Bridge Vo/Tech
280 Pennocks Bridge Rd 19390 610-345-1800
Michael Katch, prin. Fax 345-1803

Avon Grove SD 5,400/K-12
375 S Jennersville Rd 19390 610-869-2441
Dr. Augustus Massaro, supt. Fax 869-8651
www.avongrove.org/
Avon Grove HS 1,800/9-12
257 State Rd 19390 610-869-2446
Thomas Alexander, prin. Fax 869-4511
Engle MS 900/7-8
107 Schoolhouse Rd 19390 610-869-3022
Dr. Michael Snopkowski, prin. Fax 869-0827

West Lawn, Berks, Pop. 1,678
Wilson SD 4,600/K-12
2601 Grandview Blvd 19609 610-670-0180
Dr. Thomas Ruth, supt. Fax 334-6430
www.wilsonsd.org/
Wilson SHS 1,400/10-12
2601 Grandview Blvd 19609 610-670-0180
E. Wayne Foley, prin. Fax 670-9101
Other Schools – See Sinking Spring

West Middlesex, Mercer, Pop. 850
West Middlesex Area SD 1,100/K-12
3591 Sharon Rd 16159 724-634-3030
Alan Baldarelli, supt. Fax 528-0380
www.wmasd.k12.pa.us
West Middlesex JSHS 500/7-12
3591 Sharon Rd 16159 724-634-3030
Kevin Briggs, prin. Fax 528-0380

West Mifflin, Allegheny, Pop. 19,950
West Mifflin Area SD 2,700/PK-12
3000 Lebanon Church Rd 15122 412-466-9131
Dr. Daniel Castagna, supt. Fax 466-9260
www.wmasd.org
West Mifflin Area HS 1,200/9-12
91 Commonwealth Ave 15122 412-466-9131
Phillip Woods, prin. Fax 466-4595
West Mifflin Area MS 600/4-8
81 Commonwealth Ave 15122 412-466-9131
Brian Plichta, prin. Fax 466-0836

All-State Career School Post-Sec.
1200 Lebanon Rd 15122 412-823-1818
Community College of Allegheny County Post-Sec.
1750 Clairton Rd 15122 412-469-1100
Empire Beauty School Post-Sec.
2393 Mountain View Dr 15122 800-575-5983
Wilson Christian Academy 300/PK-12
1900 Clairton Rd 15122 412-466-1919
Chadd Schafer, head sch Fax 466-0303

Westover, Clearfield, Pop. 390
Harmony Area SD 400/PK-12
5239 Ridge Rd 16692 814-845-7918
Dr. Jill M. Dillon, supt. Fax 845-2305
www.harmonyowls.com/
Harmony Area MS 100/7-9
5239 Ridge Rd 16692 814-845-7655
Terry Young, prin. Fax 845-7811
Harmony Area SHS 100/10-12
5239 Ridge Rd 16692 814-845-7918
Terry Young, prin. Fax 845-2305

West Sunbury, Butler, Pop. 190
Moniteau SD 1,500/K-12
1810 W Sunbury Rd 16061 724-637-2117
George Svolos, supt. Fax 637-3862
www.moniteau.k12.pa.us
Moniteau JSHS 700/7-12
1810 W Sunbury Rd 16061 724-637-2091
Maynard Harvey, prin. Fax 637-3878

Wexford, Allegheny
North Allegheny SD
Supt. — See Pittsburgh
Marshall MS 600/6-8
5145 Wexford Run Rd 15090 724-934-6060
Dr. Cynthia Kainaroi, prin. Fax 935-2474
North Allegheny SHS 1,300/11-12
10375 Perry Hwy 15090 724-934-7200
Walter Sieminski, prin. Fax 935-5846

Whitehall, Lehigh, Pop. 13,797
Whitehall-Coplay SD 4,200/K-12
2940 MacArthur Rd 18052 610-439-1431
John Corby, supt. Fax 435-0124
www.whitehallcoplay.org/districtsite/
Whitehall-Coplay MS 1,000/6-8
2930 Zephyr Blvd 18052 610-439-1439
Peter Bugbee, prin. Fax 740-9308
Whitehall HS 1,400/9-12
3800 Mechanicsville Rd 18052 610-437-5081
Christopher Schiffert, prin. Fax 820-7520

Empire Beauty School Post-Sec.
1634 MacArthur Rd 18052 610-776-8908

Wilkes Barre, Luzerne, Pop. 40,594
Area Vocational Technical School
Supt. — None
Wilkes-Barre CTC Vo/Tech
PO Box 1699 18705 570-822-4131
Peter Halesey, prin.

Wilkes-Barre Area SD 7,000/K-12
730 S Main St 18702 570-826-7131
Jeffrey Namey Ed.D., supt. Fax 829-5031
www.wbasd.k12.pa.us
Coughlin HS 1,100/9-12
80 N Washington St 18701 570-826-7201
Patrick Patte, prin. Fax 826-7252
G.A.R. Memorial JSHS 900/7-12
250 S Grant St 18702 570-826-7165
Colleen Robatin, prin. Fax 826-7164
Meyers JSHS 900/7-12
341 Carey Ave 18702 570-826-7145
Michael Elias, prin. Fax 820-3770
Other Schools – See Plains

Academy of Creative Hair Design Post-Sec.
125 N Wilkes Barre Blvd 18702 570-825-8363
CDE Career Institute Post-Sec.
100 N Wilkes Barre Ste 100 18702 570-823-3891
Holy Redeemer HS 700/9-12
159 S Pennsylvania Ave 18701 570-829-2424
Anita Sirak, prin. Fax 829-4412
King's College Post-Sec.
133 N River St 18711 570-208-5900
McCann School of Business & Technology Post-Sec.
264 Highland Park Blvd 18702 570-235-2200
Wilkes Barre General Hospital Post-Sec.
575 N River St 18764 570-829-8111
Wilkes University Post-Sec.
84 W South St 18766 570-408-5000

Wilkinsburg, Allegheny, Pop. 15,450
Wilkinsburg Borough SD 1,000/PK-12
718 Wallace Ave 15221 412-371-9667
Archie Perrin J.D., supt. Fax 371-4058
www.wilkinsburgschools.org/
Wilkinsburg HS 300/9-12
747 Wallace Ave 15221 412-371-9500
Stephen Puskar, prin. Fax 371-3981
Wilkinsburg MS 200/7-8
747 Wallace Ave 15221 412-244-9303
Christine French, prin. Fax 871-2277

Williamsburg, Blair, Pop. 1,244
Williamsburg Community SD 500/K-12
515 W 3rd St 16693 814-832-2125
Linda K. Smith M.Ed., supt. Fax 832-3657
www.williamsburg.k12.pa.us/
Williamsburg Community JSHS 200/7-12
515 W 3rd St 16693 814-832-2125
Travis Lee M.Ed., prin. Fax 832-0115

Williamsport, Lycoming, Pop. 28,270
Loyalsock Township SD
Supt. — See Montoursville
Loyalsock Township HS 400/9-12
1801 Loyalsock Dr 17701 570-326-3581
Dr. Matthew Reitz, prin. Fax 322-3952
Loyalsock Township MS 300/6-8
2101 Loyalsock Dr 17701 570-323-9439
Robert Gaetano, prin. Fax 323-5303

Williamsport Area SD 3,500/K-12
2780 W 4th St 17701 570-327-5500
Don Adams, supt. Fax 327-8122
www.wasd.org
Williamsport Area Alternative S 50/Alt
2990 W 4th St 17701 570-323-4623
Jeff Robbins, coord. Fax 329-0222
Williamsport Area HS 1,700/9-12
2990 W 4th St 17701 570-323-8411
Michael Reed, prin. Fax 322-4150
Williamsport Area MS 7-8
2800 W 4th St 17701 570-323-6177
Brandon Pardoe, prin. Fax 326-6851

Divine Providence Hospital Post-Sec.
1100 Grampian Blvd 17701 570-326-8101
Empire Beauty School Post-Sec.
1808 E 3rd St 17701 570-322-8243
Lycoming College Post-Sec.
700 College Pl 17701 570-321-4000
Newport Business Institute Post-Sec.
941 W 3rd St 17701 570-326-2869
Pennsylvania College of Technology Post-Sec.
1 College Ave 17701 570-326-3761
St. John Neumann Regional Academy 200/7-12
901 Penn St 17701 570-323-9953
Denise Tobin, prin. Fax 321-7146
Williamsport Hospital Post-Sec.
777 Rural Ave 17701 570-326-8101

Willow Grove, Montgomery, Pop. 15,410
Area Vocational Technical School
Supt. — None
Eastern Center for Arts & Technology Vo/Tech
3075 Terwood Rd 19090 215-784-4800
Thomas Allen, dir. Fax 784-4801

Upper Moreland Township SD 3,000/K-12
2900 Terwood Rd 19090 215-830-1511
Robert Milrod Ph.D., supt. Fax 659-3421
www.umtsd.org/
Upper Moreland HS 1,000/9-12
3000 Terwood Rd 19090 215-830-1500
Joy Perisho, prin. Fax 830-1581
Other Schools – See Hatboro

Willow Hill, Franklin
Fannett-Metal SD 400/K-12
PO Box 91 17271 717-349-7172
James Duffey, supt. Fax 349-2748
fmsd.schoolwires.net
Fannett-Metal MSHS 200/6-12
PO Box 91 17271 717-349-2363
Adam Whitsel, prin. Fax 349-2173

Willow Street, Lancaster, Pop. 7,536

Area Vocational Technical School
Supt. — None
Lancaster County CTC-Willow Street — Vo/Tech
PO Box 527 17584 — 717-464-7050
Matthew Mann, prin. — Fax 464-9518

Lancaster County Career & Technology Ctr — Post-Sec.
1730 Hans Herr Dr 17584 — 717-464-7050

Windber, Somerset, Pop. 4,117

Windber Area SD — 1,300/PK-12
2301 Graham Ave 15963 — 814-467-5551
Rick Huffman, supt. — Fax 467-4208
www.windberschools.org
Windber Area HS — 400/9-12
2301 Graham Ave 15963 — 814-467-4567
Ralph DeMarco, prin. — Fax 467-0677
Windber Area MS — 200/6-8
2301 Graham Ave 15963 — 814-467-4620
Lisa James, prin. — Fax 467-6218

Wingate, Centre

Bald Eagle Area SD — 1,900/K-12
751 S Eagle Valley Rd 16823 — 814-355-4860
Jeffrey Miles, supt. — Fax 355-1028
www.beasd.org
Bald Eagle Area MSHS — 900/6-12
751 S Eagle Valley Rd 16823 — 814-355-4868
David Reichelderfer, prin. — Fax 355-2146

Wormleysburg, Cumberland, Pop. 3,002

Harrisburg Academy — 400/PK-12
10 Erford Rd 17043 — 717-763-7811
Dr. James Newman, head sch — Fax 975-0894

Wrightsville, York, Pop. 2,269

Eastern York SD — 2,600/K-12
PO Box 150 17368 — 717-252-1555
Dr. Darla Pianowski, supt. — Fax 478-6000
www.eyork.k12.pa.us/
Eastern York HS — 800/9-12
PO Box 2002 17368 — 717-252-1551
Dr. Timothy Mitzel, prin. — Fax 252-4808
Eastern York MS — 600/6-8
PO Box 2003 17368 — 717-252-3400
Dr. Paula Westerman, prin. — Fax 252-4891

Wyalusing, Bradford, Pop. 591

Wyalusing Area SD — 1,000/K-12
PO Box 157 18853 — 570-746-1600
Dr. Chester Mummau, supt. — Fax 746-0281
www.wyalusingrams.com/
Wyalusing Valley JSHS — 700/7-12
11364 Wyalusing New Albany 18853 — 570-746-1218
Gary Otis, prin. — Fax 746-2053

Wyncote, Montgomery, Pop. 2,980

Cheltenham Township SD
Supt. — See Elkins Park
Cedarbrook MS — 700/7-8
300 Longfellow Rd 19095 — 215-881-6423
Iris Parker, prin. — Fax 576-5610
Cheltenham HS — 1,500/9-12
500 Rices Mill Rd 19095 — 215-517-3700
Andrew Kuhn, prin. — Fax 517-3771

Bishop McDevitt HS — 700/9-12
125 Royal Ave 19095 — 215-887-5575
Mary Kirby, prin. — Fax 887-1371
Reconstructionist Rabbinical College — Post-Sec.
1299 Church Rd 19095 — 215-576-0800

Wynnewood, Montgomery, Pop. 7,800

Friends' Central S — 700/5-12
1101 City Ave 19096 — 610-649-7440
Craig Sellers, hdmstr. — Fax 649-5669
Lankenau Hospital — Post-Sec.
100 E Lancaster Ave 19096 — 610-526-3019
Palmer Theological Seminary — Post-Sec.
6 E Lancaster Ave 19096 — 610-896-5000
St. Charles Borromeo Seminary — Post-Sec.
100 E Wynnewood Rd 19096 — 610-667-3394
Torah Academy of Greater Philadelphia — 300/K-12
742 Argyle Rd 19096 — 610-642-7870
Rabbi Shmuel Jablon, prin. — Fax 642-2265

Wyomissing, Berks, Pop. 10,332

Wyomissing Area SD — 1,900/K-12
630 Evans Ave 19610 — 610-374-0739
Julia Vicente, supt. — Fax 374-0948
www.wyoarea.org/
Wyomissing Area JSHS — 900/7-12
630 Evans Ave 19610 — 610-374-0739
Dr. Corey Jones, prin. — Fax 374-6012

Berks Technical Institute — Post-Sec.
2205 Ridgewood Rd 19610 — 610-372-1722

Yardley, Bucks, Pop. 2,392

Pennsbury SD
Supt. — See Fallsington
Boehm MS — 800/6-8
866 Big Oak Rd 19067 — 215-428-4220
Theresa Ricci, prin. — Fax 428-9605
Penn MS — 1,000/6-8
1524 Derbyshire Rd 19067 — 215-428-4280
Paul Meehan, prin. — Fax 428-1549
Pennwood MS — 1,000/6-8
1523 Makefield Rd 19067 — 215-428-4237
Patricia Steckroat, prin. — Fax 428-4265

Yeadon, Delaware, Pop. 11,214

William Penn SD
Supt. — See Lansdowne
Penn Wood HS Cypress Street Campus — 800/9-10
600 Cypress St 19050 — 610-626-3223
D. Brandon Cooley, prin. — Fax 284-8061

York, York, Pop. 41,931

Area Vocational Technical School
Supt. — None
York County School of Technology — Vo/Tech
2179 S Queen St 17402 — 717-741-0820
Dr. David Thomas, dir. — Fax 741-0694

Central York SD — 5,700/K-12
775 Marion Rd 17406 — 717-846-6789
Dr. Michael Snell, supt. — Fax 840-0451
www.cysd.k12.pa.us
Central York HS — 1,700/9-12
601 Mundis Mill Rd 17406 — 717-846-6789
Ryan Caufman, prin. — Fax 848-4684
Central York MS — 900/7-8
1950 N Hills Rd 17406 — 717-846-6789
Edmund McManama, prin.

West York Area SD — 3,100/K-12
2605 W Market St 17404 — 717-792-2796
Dr. Emilie Lonardi, supt. — Fax 792-5114
www.wyasd.k12.pa.us
West York Area HS — 1,000/9-12
1800 Bannister St 17404 — 717-845-6634
Janet May, prin. — Fax 846-9691
West York Area MS — 800/6-8
1700 Bannister St 17404 — 717-845-1671
Chad Bumsted, prin. — Fax 845-9083

York CSD — 4,000/K-12
31 N Pershing Ave 17401 — 717-845-3571
Dr. Deborah Wortham, supt. — Fax 849-1394
www.ycs.k12.pa.us
Lindbergh Education Center — 100/Alt
329 Lindberg Ave 17401 — 717-849-1388
Darlene Freeman, prin.
Penn HS — 1,300/9-12
101 W College Ave 17401 — 717-849-1218
Randy James, prin. — Fax 848-1143

York Suburban SD — 3,000/K-12
1800 Hollywood Dr 17403 — 717-885-1210
Dr. Kathryn Orban, supt. — Fax 885-1211
www.yssd.org/
York Suburban HS — 900/9-12
1800 Hollywood Dr 17403 — 717-885-1270
Brian Ellis, prin. — Fax 885-1271
York Suburban MS — 700/6-8
455 Sundale Dr 17402 — 717-885-1260
Victoria Gross, prin. — Fax 885-1261

Art Institute of York - Pennsylvania — Post-Sec.
1409 Williams Rd 17402 — 717-755-2300
Baltimore School of Massage-York Campus — Post-Sec.
170 Red Rock Rd 17406 — 717-268-1881
Bible Baptist Christian Academy — 100/K-12
4190 N Susquehanna Trl 17404 — 717-266-2544
David Dukes, prin.
Christian S of York — 300/PK-12
907 Greenbriar Rd 17404 — 717-767-6842
Kevin Hofer, admin. — Fax 767-4904
Consolidated School of Business — Post-Sec.
1605 Clugston Rd 17404 — 717-764-9550
Empire Beauty School — Post-Sec.
2592 Eastern Blvd 17402 — 717-600-8111
Motorcycle Technology Center — Post-Sec.
52 Grumbacher Rd 17406 — 717-767-4300
Penn State York — Post-Sec.
1031 Edgecomb Ave 17403 — 717-771-4000
York Catholic HS — 700/7-12
601 E Springettsbury Ave 17403 — 717-846-8871
Katie Seufert, prin. — Fax 843-4588
York College of Pennsylvania — Post-Sec.
441 Country Club Rd 17403 — 717-846-7788
York Country Day S — 200/PK-12
1071 Regents Glen Blvd 17403 — 717-843-9805
Dr. Nathaniel Coffman, head sch — Fax 815-6769
York Hospital — Post-Sec.
1001 S George St 17403 — 717-851-2942
Yorktowne Business Institute — Post-Sec.
W 7th Ave 17404 — 717-846-5000
YTI Career Institute — Post-Sec.
1405 Williams Rd 17402 — 717-757-1100

York Springs, Adams, Pop. 827

Bermudian Springs SD — 2,100/K-12
7335 Carlisle Pike 17372 — 717-528-4113
Dr. Shane Hotchkiss, supt. — Fax 528-7981
www.bermudian.org
Bermudian Springs HS — 600/9-12
7335 Carlisle Pike 17372 — 717-528-5127
Steven Brown, prin. — Fax 528-4149
Bermudian Springs MS — 600/5-8
7335 Carlisle Pike 17372 — 717-528-5137
Wade Hunt, prin. — Fax 528-0034

Youngsville, Warren, Pop. 1,716

Warren County SD
Supt. — See North Warren
Youngsville HS — 300/8-12
227 College St 16371 — 814-563-7573
Darrell Jaskolka, prin. — Fax 563-4459

Warren County Christian S — 100/K-12
165 Mead Run Rd 16371 — 814-563-4457
Richard Kolcharno, prin. — Fax 563-7647

Youngwood, Westmoreland, Pop. 3,014

Westmoreland County Community College — Post-Sec.
145 Pavilion Ln 15697 — 724-925-4000

Zieglerville, Montgomery

Perkiomen Valley SD
Supt. — See Collegeville
Perkiomen Valley West MS — 600/6-8
220 Big Rd 19492 — 484-977-7210
Ryan Stanson-Marsh, prin. — Fax 977-7212

RHODE ISLAND

RHODE ISLAND DEPARTMENT OF EDUCATION
255 Westminster St, Providence 02903-3400
Telephone 401-222-4600
Fax 401-277-6178
Website http://www.ride.ri.gov

Commissioner of Education Deborah Gist

RHODE ISLAND BOARD OF REGENTS
255 Westminster St, Providence 02903-3414

Chairperson George Caruolo

PUBLIC, PRIVATE AND CATHOLIC SECONDARY SCHOOLS

Barrington, Bristol, Pop. 15,849
Barrington SD 3,500/PK-12
PO Box 95 02806 401-245-5000
Michael Messore, supt. Fax 245-5003
barringtonschools.org
Barrington HS 1,200/9-12
220 Lincoln Ave 02806 401-247-3150
Joseph Hurley, prin. Fax 245-6170
Barrington MS 800/6-8
261 Middle Hwy 02806 401-247-3160
Dr. Andrew Anderson, prin. Fax 247-3164

Barrington Christian Academy 200/K-12
9 Old County Rd 02806 401-246-0113
Elsie R. Wright, head sch Fax 246-2540
St. Andrew's S 200/3-12
63 Federal Rd 02806 401-246-1230
John Martin, hdmstr. Fax 246-0510

Block Island, Washington
New Shoreham SD 100/K-12
PO Box 1890 02807 401-466-7732
Dr. Robert Hicks, supt. Fax 466-3249
blockislandschool.net/
Block Island S 100/K-12
PO Box 1890 02807 401-466-5600
John Canole, prin. Fax 466-5610

Bristol, Bristol, Pop. 21,625
Bristol Warren Regional SD 3,400/PK-12
151 State St 02809 401-253-4000
Melinda Thies Ed.D., supt. Fax 253-1740
www2.bw.k12.ri.us/
Mt. Hope HS 1,100/9-12
199 Chestnut St 02809 401-254-5980
Don Rebello, prin. Fax 254-5925
Other Schools – See Warren

Roger Williams University Post-Sec.
1 Old Ferry Rd 02809 401-253-1040

Central Falls, Providence, Pop. 18,222
Central Falls SD 2,700/PK-12
949 Dexter St 02863 401-727-7700
Frances Gallo, supt. Fax 727-7722
www.cfschools.net/
Calcutt MS 600/5-8
112 Washington St 02863 401-727-7726
David Alba, prin. Fax 724-0870
Central Falls HS 800/9-12
24 Summer St 02863 401-727-7710
Joshua Laplante, prin. Fax 727-6157

Coventry, Kent, Pop. 31,083
Coventry SD 5,300/PK-12
1675 Flat River Rd 02816 401-822-9400
Michael Almeida, supt. Fax 822-9464
www.coventryschools.net
Career & Technical Center Vo/Tech
40 Reservoir Rd 02816 401-822-9499
Fax 822-9492
Coventry HS 1,800/9-12
40 Reservoir Rd 02816 401-822-9499
Michael Hobin, prin. Fax 822-9492
Feinstein MS of Coventry 1,200/6-8
15 Foster Dr 02816 401-822-9426
Fax 822-9469

Cranston, Providence, Pop. 78,728
Cranston SD 10,400/PK-12
845 Park Ave 02910 401-270-8000
Dr. Judith Lundsten, supt. Fax 270-8703
www.cpsed.net
Bain MS 400/7-8
135 Gansett Ave 02910 401-270-8010
Jenny Remka, prin. Fax 270-8567
Cranston Area Career & Technical Center Vo/Tech
100 Metropolitan Ave 02920 401-270-8070
Fax 270-8611
Cranston HS East 1,600/9-12
899 Park Ave 02910 401-270-8126
Sean Kelly, prin. Fax 270-8509
Cranston HS West 1,600/9-12
80 Metropolitan Ave 02920 401-270-8049
Thomas Barbieri, prin. Fax 270-8526
Park View MS 500/7-8
25 Park View Blvd 02910 401-270-8090
Joseph Rotz, prin. Fax 270-8527
Western Hills MS 700/7-8
400 Phenix Ave 02920 401-270-8030
Anthony Corrente, prin. Fax 270-8635

Cumberland, Providence
Cumberland SD 4,800/PK-12
2602 Mendon Rd 02864 401-658-1600
Philip Thornton Ed.D., supt. Fax 658-4620
www.cumberlandschools.org/
Cumberland HS 1,500/9-12
2600 Mendon Rd 02864 401-658-2600
Alan Tenreiro, prin. Fax 658-3124
McCourt MS 500/6-8
45 Highland Ave 02864 401-725-2092
Jason Masterson Ed.D., prin. Fax 723-1188
North Cumberland MS 600/6-8
400 Nate Whipple Hwy 02864 401-333-6306
Richard Drolet Ed.D., prin. Fax 333-1926

East Greenwich, Kent, Pop. 11,865
East Greenwich SD 2,100/PK-12
111 Peirce St 02818 401-398-1201
Victor Mercurio, supt. Fax 886-3203
www.egsd.net
Cole MS 400/6-8
100 Cedar Ave 02818 401-398-1213
Alexis Meyer, prin. Fax 886-3283
East Greenwich HS 800/9-12
300 Avenger Dr 02818 401-398-1574
Michael Podraza, prin. Fax 885-1336

New England Institute of Technology Post-Sec.
One New England Tech Blvd 02818 401-467-7744
Rocky Hill S 300/PK-12
530 Ives Rd 02818 401-884-9070
Jonathan Schoenwald Ph.D., hdmstr. Fax 885-4985

East Providence, Providence, Pop. 44,064
East Providence SD 5,500/PK-12
145 Taunton Ave 02914 401-431-4640
Kim Mercer, supt. Fax 435-7507
www.epschoolsri.com/
East Providence Career & Technical Ctr Vo/Tech
1998 Pawtucket Ave 02914 401-435-7815
Karen Mellen, dir. Fax 435-7854
East Providence HS 1,700/9-12
2000 Pawtucket Ave 02914 401-435-7806
Janet Sheehan, prin. Fax 435-7864
Martin MS 600/6-8
111 Brown St 02914 401-435-7819
Frank Devall, prin. Fax 435-7851
Other Schools – See Riverside

Providence Country Day S 200/6-12
660 Waterman Ave 02914 401-438-5170
Vince Watchorn, head sch Fax 435-4514
St. Mary Academy-Bay View 900/PK-12
3070 Pawtucket Ave 02915 401-434-0113
Colleen Gribbin, prin. Fax 438-5936

Greenville, Providence, Pop. 8,588

Mater Ecclesiae College Post-Sec.
60 Austin Ave 02828 401-949-2820

Harrisville, Providence, Pop. 1,581
Burrillville SD 2,400/PK-12
2300 Broncos Hwy 02830 401-568-1301
Dr. Frank Pallotta, supt. Fax 568-4111
www.bsd-ri.net/
Burrillville HS 700/9-12
425 East Ave 02830 401-568-1310
Michael Whaley, prin. Fax 568-1363
Burrillville MS 500/6-8
2220 Broncos Hwy 02830 401-568-1320
Dennis Kafalas, prin. Fax 568-1317

Jamestown, Newport, Pop. 4,999
Jamestown SD 500/PK-8
76 Melrose Ave 02835 401-423-7020
Dr. Marcia Lukon, supt. Fax 423-7022
www.jamestownri.com/school
Lawn Avenue S 200/5-8
55 Lawn Ave 02835 401-423-7010
Deborah DiBiase, prin. Fax 423-7012

Johnston, Providence, Pop. 26,542
Johnston SD 3,000/PK-12
10 Memorial Ave 02919 401-233-1900
Dr. Bernard DiLullo, supt. Fax 233-1907
www.johnstonschools.org
Ferri MS 700/6-8
10 Memorial Ave 02919 401-233-1930
Dennis Morrell, prin. Fax 233-1943
Johnston SHS 900/9-12
345 Cherry Hill Rd 02919 401-233-1920
Gerald Foley, prin. Fax 233-0031

Kingston, Washington, Pop. 6,817

University of Rhode Island 02881 Post-Sec.
401-874-1000

Lincoln, Providence, Pop. 18,045
Lincoln SD 3,300/PK-12
1624 Lonsdale Ave 02865 401-721-3300
Georgia Fortunato, supt. Fax 728-5482
www.lincolnps.org/
Lincoln HS 1,000/9-12
135 Old River Rd 02865 401-334-7500
Kevin McNamara, prin. Fax 334-8753
Lincoln MS 800/6-8
152 Jenckes Hill Rd 02865 401-721-3400
Mark Thompson, prin. Fax 721-3428

Rhode Island Technical Schools
Supt. — None
Davies Career-Technical HS Vo/Tech
50 Jenckes Hill Rd 02865 401-728-1500
Victoria Garrick, prin. Fax 728-8910

Community College of Rhode Island Post-Sec.
1762 Louisquisset Pike 02865 401-333-7000
Lincoln Technical Institute Post-Sec.
622 George Washington Hwy 02865 401-334-2430

Middletown, Newport, Pop. 3,400
Middletown SD 2,200/PK-12
26 Oliphant Ln 02842 401-849-2122
Rosemarie Kraeger, supt. Fax 849-0202
www.mpsri.net/
Gaudet MS 700/4-8
1113 Aquidneck Ave 02842 401-846-6395
Michael Mancieri, prin. Fax 847-7580
Middletown HS 700/9-12
130 Valley Rd 02842 401-846-7250
Gail Abromitis, prin. Fax 849-7170

St. George's S 400/9-12
372 Purgatory Rd 02842 401-847-7565
Eric Peterson, head sch Fax 842-6677

Narragansett, Washington, Pop. 3,721
Narragansett SD 1,500/PK-12
25 5th Ave 02882 401-792-9450
Katherine Sipala, supt. Fax 792-9439
www.narragansett.k12.ri.us/
Narragansett HS 500/9-12
245 S Pier Rd 02882 401-792-9400
Daniel Warner, prin. Fax 792-9410
Narragansett Pier MS 400/5-8
235 S Pier Rd 02882 401-792-9430
Dr. Marie Ahern, prin. Fax 792-9436

Newport, Newport, Pop. 23,495
Newport SD 1,800/PK-12
15 Wickham Rd 02840 401-847-2100
John Ambrogi Ed.D., supt. Fax 849-0170
www.newportrischools.org/

Newport Area Career & Technical Center Vo/Tech
15 Wickham Rd 02840 401-847-6235
James Nelson, dir. Fax 849-3295
Rogers HS 600/9-12
15 Wickham Rd 02840 401-847-6235
James Nelson, prin. Fax 849-3295
Thompson MS 400/6-8
55 Broadway 02840 401-847-1493
Jaime Crowley, prin. Fax 849-3426

Rhode Island Technical Schools
Supt. — None
MET East Bay Campus Vo/Tech
1 York St 02840 401-849-7711
Mary Vieira, prin. Fax 846-5703

Community College of Rhode Island Post-Sec.
1 John H Chafee Blvd 02840 401-851-1600
International Yacht Restoration School Post-Sec.
449 Thames St 02840 401-848-5777
Salve Regina University Post-Sec.
100 Ochre Point Ave 02840 401-847-6650

North Kingstown, Washington, Pop. 2,800
North Kingstown SD 4,400/PK-12
100 Fairway Dr 02852 401-268-6200
Philip Auger, supt. Fax 268-6405
www.nksd.net
Davisville MS 500/6-8
200 School St 02852 401-541-6300
Ruthanne Logan, prin. Fax 541-6310
North Kingstown HS 1,600/9-12
150 Fairway Dr 02852 401-268-6236
Thomas Kenworthy, prin. Fax 268-6210
Wickford MS 400/6-8
250 Tower Hill Rd 02852 401-268-6470
Terry Merkel, prin. Fax 268-6480

North Providence, Providence, Pop. 32,500
North Providence SD 3,300/PK-12
2240 Mineral Spring Ave 02911 401-233-1100
Timothy P. Ryan Ph.D., supt. Fax 233-1106
www.northprovschools.org/
Birchwood MS 400/6-8
10 Birchwood Dr 02904 401-233-1120
David Flaherty, prin. Fax 353-6903
North Providence HS 1,100/9-12
1828 Mineral Spring Ave 02904 401-233-1150
Joseph Goho, prin. Fax 233-1166
Ricci MS 400/6-8
51 Intervale Ave 02911 401-233-1170
Lucille Delasanta, prin. Fax 232-5421

St. Joseph's Hospital Post-Sec.
200 High Service Ave 02904 401-456-3050

North Scituate, Providence
Foster-Glocester Regional SD 1,300/6-12
91 Anan Wade Rd 02857 401-710-7500
Michael Barnes Ph.D., supt. Fax 713-3676
www.fg.k12.ri.us/
Ponaganset HS 800/9-12
137 Anan Wade Rd 02857 401-710-7500
Sandy Nolan, prin. Fax 647-5743
Ponaganset MS 500/6-8
7 Rustic Hill Rd 02857 401-647-3361
Patricia Marcotte, prin. Fax 647-9080

Scituate SD 1,600/PK-12
PO Box 188 02857 401-647-4100
Dr. Paul Lescault, supt. Fax 647-4102
www.scituateri.net
Scituate HS 500/9-12
94 Trimtown Rd 02857 401-647-4120
Michael Sollitto, prin. Fax 647-4126
Scituate MS 400/6-8
94 Trimtown Rd 02857 401-647-4123
Michael Zajac, prin. Fax 647-4104

North Smithfield, Providence, Pop. 10,497
North Smithfield SD
Supt. — See Slatersville
North Smithfield HS 500/9-12
412 Greenville Rd 02896 401-766-2500
Robert Mezzanotte, prin. Fax 765-8629
North Smithfield MS 300/6-8
1850 Providence Pike 02896 401-597-6100
John Lahar, prin. Fax 597-6121

Pawtucket, Providence, Pop. 64,391
Pawtucket SD 8,800/PK-12
PO Box 388 02862 401-729-6300
Deborah Cylke, supt. Fax 727-1641
www.psdri.net
Alternative Learning Program Alt
286 Main St 02860 401-721-2127
Joseph McNamara, prin. Fax 729-6351
Goff JHS 500/7-8
974 Newport Ave 02861 401-729-6500
Lisa Benedetti Ramzi, prin. Fax 721-2105
Jenks JHS 300/7-8
350 Division St 02860 401-729-6520
John Haidemenos, prin. Fax 729-6523
Shea HS 1,000/9-12
485 East Ave 02860 401-729-6445
Pamela Bernardi, prin. Fax 729-6454
Slater JHS 600/7-8
281 Mineral Spring Ave 02860 401-729-6480
Dr. Jacqueline Ash, prin. Fax 729-6490
Tolman HS 1,300/9-12
150 Exchange St 02860 401-729-6400
Christopher Savastano, prin. Fax 729-6407
Walsh S for Performing & Visual Arts 100/9-12
350 Division St 02860 401-721-2148
John Haidemenos, prin. Fax 721-2147

Bishop Keough Regional HS 100/9-12
145 Power Rd 02860 401-726-0335
Jeanne Leclerc, prin. Fax 726-0336
New England Tractor Trailer Training Post-Sec.
600 Mshssuck Valley Ind Hwy 02860 401-725-1220
Newport School of Hairdressing Post-Sec.
226 Main St 02860 401-725-6882
St. Raphael Academy 500/9-12
123 Walcott St 02860 401-723-8100
Daniel Richard, prin. Fax 723-8740
Sawyer School Post-Sec.
101 Main St 02860 401-272-8400

Portsmouth, Newport, Pop. 3,600
Portsmouth SD 2,800/PK-12
29 Middle Rd 02871 401-683-1039
Dr. Lynn Krizic, supt. Fax 683-5204
portsmouthschoolsri.net
Portsmouth HS 1,000/9-12
120 Education Ln 02871 401-683-2124
Robert Littlefield, prin. Fax 683-6404
Portsmouth MS 1,000/4-8
125 Jepson Ln 02871 401-849-3700
Joseph Amaral, prin. Fax 841-8420

Aquidneck Island Christian Academy 50/K-12
321 E Main Rd 02871 401-849-5550
Stephen Bailey, hdmstr. Fax 849-6108
Portsmouth Abbey S 400/9-12
285 Corys Ln 02871 401-683-2000
Dr. James De Vecchi, hdmstr. Fax 683-5888

Providence, Providence, Pop. 170,517
Providence SD 20,600/PK-12
797 Westminster St 02903 401-456-9100
Susan Lusi, supt. Fax 456-9252
www.providenceschools.org
Alvarez HS 600/9-12
375 Adelaide Ave 02907 401-456-0676
Jesse Rivers, prin. Fax 456-0679
Bishop MS 500/6-8
101 Sessions St 02906 401-456-9344
Michael Lazzareschi, prin. Fax 456-9110
Central HS 1,200/9-12
70 Fricker St 02903 401-456-9111
John Hunt, prin. Fax 456-9113
Classical HS 1,000/9-12
770 Westminster St 02903 401-456-9145
Scott Barr, prin. Fax 456-9155
Cooley Health & Science Technology HS 400/9-12
182 Thurbers Ave 02905 401-456-1781
Janelle Clarke, prin. Fax 456-1782
DelSesto MS 500/6-8
152 Springfield St 02909 401-278-0557
Dr. Dinah Larbi, prin. Fax 278-0564
E-Cubed Academy 400/9-12
812 Branch Ave 02904 401-456-0694
Regina Winkfield, prin. Fax 456-0696
Greene MS 800/6-8
721 Chalkstone Ave 02908 401-456-9347
Dr. Nicole Mathis, prin. Fax 453-8630
Hope Arts HS 600/9-12
324 Hope St 02906 401-456-9161
Tamara Sterling, prin. Fax 456-1747
Hope Information Technology HS 600/9-12
324 Hope St 02906 401-456-9161
Tamara Sterling, prin. Fax 456-1747
Hopkins MS 500/6-8
480 Charles St 02904 401-456-9203
Gloria Jackson, prin. Fax 456-9226
Mt. Pleasant HS 1,100/9-12
434 Mount Pleasant Ave 02908 401-456-9181
Scott Sutherland, prin. Fax 453-8655
Providence Academy/International Studies 400/9-12
182 Thurbers Ave 02905 401-456-1781
Janelle Clarke, dir. Fax 456-1782
Providence Career And Technical S Vo/Tech
41 Fricker St 02903 401-456-9136
Ramon Torres, dir. Fax 456-9172
Stuart MS 800/6-8
188 Princeton Ave 02907 401-456-9340
Jeffrey Goss, prin. Fax 453-8659
Williams MS 700/6-8
278 Thurbers Ave 02905 401-456-9355
Brearn Wright, prin. Fax 453-8631

Rhode Island Technical Schools
Supt. — None
MET Equality S Vo/Tech
325 Public St 02905 401-752-2610
Steven Bartholomew, prin. Fax 752-2612
MET Justice Campus Vo/Tech
325 Public St 02905 401-752-2630
Janet Vilanueva-Williams, prin. Fax 752-2612
MET Liberty S Vo/Tech
325 Public St 02905 401-752-2680
Arthur Baraf, prin. Fax 752-2612
MET Peace Street Campus Vo/Tech
362 Dexter St 02907 401-752-3400
Brandee Lapisky, prin. Fax 752-3425
MET Unity S Vo/Tech
325 Public St 02905 401-752-2650
Chantel Wyllie, prin. Fax 752-2612
Other Schools – See Lincoln RI, Newport RI

Brown S 800/PK-12
250 Lloyd Ave 02906 401-831-7350
Matt Glendinning, hdmstr. Fax 455-0084
Brown University Post-Sec.
1 Prospect St 02912 401-863-1000
Community College of Rhode Island Post-Sec.
1 Hilton St 02905 401-455-6000
Community Preparatory S 200/3-8
126 Somerset St 02907 401-521-9696
Dan Corley, hdmstr. Fax 521-9715
Empire Beauty School Post-Sec.
151 Broadway 02903 401-272-4300
Johnson & Wales University Post-Sec.
8 Abbott Park Pl 02903 401-598-1000
LaSalle Academy 1,500/7-12
612 Academy Ave 02908 401-351-7750
Donald Kavanagh, prin. Fax 444-1782
Lincoln S 400/PK-12
301 Butler Ave 02906 401-331-9696
Julia Eells, head sch Fax 751-6670
Providence College Post-Sec.
1 Cunningham Sq 02918 401-865-1000
Providence Hebrew Day S 200/PK-12
450 Elmgrove Ave 02906 401-331-5327
Rabbi Peretz Scheinerman, dean Fax 331-0030
Rhode Island College Post-Sec.
600 Mount Pleasant Ave 02908 401-456-8000
Rhode Island Hospital Post-Sec.
593 Eddy St 02903 401-444-5123
Rhode Island School of Design Post-Sec.
2 College St 02903 401-454-6100
St. Patrick S 50/8-10
244 Smith St 02908 401-421-9300
Bruce Daigle, prin. Fax 421-0810
Sawyer School Post-Sec.
550 Hartford Ave 02909 401-272-3280
School One 100/9-12
220 University Ave 02906 401-331-2497
Jennifer Borman, head sch Fax 421-8869
Wheeler S 700/PK-12
216 Hope St 02906 401-421-8100
Dan Miller, hdmstr. Fax 751-7674
Women & Infants Hospital Post-Sec.
101 Dudley St 02905 401-274-1100

Riverside, See East Providence
East Providence SD
Supt. — See East Providence
Riverside MS 600/6-8
179 Forbes St 02915 401-433-6230
Stephen Prew M.Ed., prin. Fax 433-6261

Slatersville, Providence
North Smithfield SD 1,600/PK-12
PO Box 72 02876 401-769-5492
Stephen Lindberg, supt. Fax 769-5493
www.northsmithfieldschools.com/
Other Schools – See North Smithfield

Smithfield, Providence, Pop. 19,163
Smithfield SD 2,500/PK-12
49 Farnum Pike 02917 401-231-6606
Robert O'Brien, supt. Fax 232-0870
www.smithfield-ps.org
Gallagher MS 600/6-8
10 Indian Run Trl 02917 401-949-2056
Laurie Beauvais, prin. Fax 949-5697
Smithfield HS 800/9-12
90 Pleasant View Ave 02917 401-949-2050
Daniel Kelley, prin. Fax 949-2052

Bryant University Post-Sec.
1150 Douglas Pike 02917 401-232-6000
Masters Regional Academy 200/7-12
915 Douglas Pike 02917 401-232-7061
Michael Dube, prin. Fax 233-9267

Tiverton, Newport, Pop. 7,434
Tiverton SD 1,900/PK-12
100 N Brayton Rd 02878 401-624-8475
William Rearick, supt. Fax 624-4086
www.tivertonschools.org/
Tiverton HS 600/9-12
100 N Brayton Rd 02878 401-624-8494
Steven Fezette, prin. Fax 624-8495
Tiverton MS 600/5-8
10 Quintal Dr 02878 401-624-6668
Laurie Dias-Mitchell, prin. Fax 624-6669

Wakefield, Washington, Pop. 8,226
South Kingstown SD 3,700/PK-12
307 Curtis Corner Rd 02879 401-360-1300
Dr. Kristen Stringfellow, supt. Fax 360-1330
www.skschools.net/
Curtis Corner MS 600/7-8
301 Curtis Corner Rd 02879 401-360-1333
Patricia Aull, prin. Fax 360-1334
South Kingstown HS 1,100/9-12
215 Columbia St 02879 401-360-1000
Robert McCarthy, prin. Fax 360-1464

Prout HS 600/9-12
4640 Tower Hill Rd 02879 401-789-9262
David Carradini, prin. Fax 782-2262

Warren, Bristol, Pop. 11,385
Bristol Warren Regional SD
Supt. — See Bristol
Kickemuit MS 800/6-8
525 Child St 02885 401-245-2010
Beth Hayes, prin. Fax 254-5960

Our Lady of Fatima HS 100/7-12
360 Market St 02885 401-245-4449
Sr. Mary Margaret Souza, prin. Fax 245-1380

Warwick, Kent, Pop. 81,173
Warwick SD 10,200/PK-12
34 Warwick Lake Ave 02889 401-734-3100
Dr. Richard D'Agostino, supt. Fax 734-3105
www.warwickschools.org
Aldrich JHS 600/7-8
789 Post Rd 02888 401-734-3500
William Sangster, prin. Fax 734-3508
Gorton JHS 500/7-8
69 Draper Ave 02889 401-734-3350
Jeffrey Taylor, prin. Fax 734-3359

Pilgrim HS 1,200/9-12
111 Pilgrim Pkwy 02888 401-734-3250
Marie Cote, prin. Fax 734-3264
Toll Gate HS 1,000/9-12
575 Centerville Rd Ste 1 02886 401-734-3300
Stephen Chrabaszcz, prin. Fax 734-3314
Warwick Area Career & Technical Center Vo/Tech
575 Centerville Rd 02886 401-734-3150
William McCaffrey, dir. Fax 734-3160
Warwick Veterans Memorial HS 1,100/9-12
2401 W Shore Rd 02889 401-734-3200
Gerry Habershaw, prin. Fax 734-3214
Winman JHS 600/7-8
575 Centerville Rd 02886 401-734-3375
Joanne Pelletier, prin. Fax 734-3385

Bishop Hendricken HS 1,000/9-12
2615 Warwick Ave 02889 401-739-3450
Joseph Brennan, prin. Fax 732-8261
Community College of Rhode Island Post-Sec.
400 East Ave 02886 401-825-1000
Overbrook Academy 100/6-9
836 Warwick Neck Ave 02889 401-737-2850
Valerie McGovern, dir. Fax 737-2884
Warwick Academy of Beauty Culture Post-Sec.
1276 Bald Hill Rd Unit 100 02886 401-737-4946

Westerly, Washington, Pop. 17,600
Westerly SD 3,100/PK-12
15 Highland Ave 02891 401-348-2700
Roy Seitsinger Ph.D., supt. Fax 348-2707
www.westerly.k12.ri.us

Westerly HS 1,000/9-12
23 Ward Ave 02891 401-596-2109
Steven Ruscito, prin. Fax 596-5098
Westerly MS 1,000/5-8
10 Sandy Hill Rd 02891 401-348-2750
Paula Fusco, prin. Fax 348-2752

West Greenwich, Kent, Pop. 3,492
Exeter-West Greenwich Regional SD 1,700/PK-12
940 Nooseneck Hill Rd 02817 401-397-5125
James Erinakes M.Ed., supt. Fax 397-2407
www.ewg.k12.ri.us
Exeter-West Greenwich Regional HS 600/9-12
930 Nooseneck Hill Rd 02817 401-397-6893
Brian Butler, admin. Fax 392-0134
Exeter-West Greenwich Regional JHS 300/7-8
930 Nooseneck Hill Rd 02817 401-397-6897
Mary Smith, admin. Fax 392-0109

West Warwick, Kent, Pop. 29,600
West Warwick SD 3,500/PK-12
10 Harris Ave 02893 401-821-1180
Kenneth Sheehan, supt. Fax 822-8463
www.westwarwickpublicschools.com/
Deering MS 1,000/5-8
2 Webster Knight Dr 02893 401-822-8445
Brian Dillon, prin. Fax 822-8474
West Warwick HS 1,000/9-12
Webster Knight Dr 02893 401-821-6596
Karen Tarasevich, prin. Fax 822-8473

Wood River Junction, Washington
Chariho Regional SD 3,500/PK-12
455A Switch Rd 02894 401-364-7575
Barry Ricci, supt. Fax 364-1176
www.chariho.k12.ri.us/
Chariho Area Career & Technical Center Vo/Tech
459 Switch Rd 02894 401-364-6869
Marilyn Massey, dir. Fax 364-1191
Chariho Regional HS 1,200/9-12
453 Switch Rd 02894 401-364-7778
Robert Mitchell, prin. Fax 364-1190
Chariho Regional MS 1,000/5-8
455b Switch Rd 02894 401-364-0651
Gregory Zenion, prin. Fax 364-1189
RYSE 50/Alt
459 Switch Rd 02894 401-364-1160
Carolyn Garlick, dir. Fax 364-1161

Woonsocket, Providence, Pop. 39,726
Woonsocket SD 4,600/PK-12
108 High St 02895 401-767-4600
Giovanna Donoyan Ph.D., supt. Fax 767-4607
www.woonsocketschools.com/
Woonsocket Area Career & Tech. Center Vo/Tech
400 Aylsworth Ave 02895 401-767-4662
Claire Dumas, dir. Fax 767-4665
Woonsocket HS 1,800/9-12
777 Cass Ave 02895 401-767-4700
Dr. Lynne Bedard, prin. Fax 767-4748
Woonsocket MS at Hamlet 6-8
60 Florence Dr 02895 401-235-6110
Dr. Patrick McGee, prin.
Woonsocket MS at Villenova 6-8
240 Florence Dr 02895 401-235-6125
Dr. Patrick McGee, prin.

Good Shepherd Regional S 200/3-8
1210 Mendon Rd 02895 401-767-5906
Lawrence Poitras, prin. Fax 767-5905
Mt. St. Charles Academy 900/7-12
800 Logee St 02895 401-769-0310
Edwin Burke, prin. Fax 762-2327

SOUTH CAROLINA

SOUTH CAROLINA DEPARTMENT OF EDUCATION
1429 Senate St Ste 100, Columbia 29201-3799
Telephone 803-734-8500
Fax 803-734-3389
Website ed.sc.gov/

Superintendent of Education Mick Zais

SOUTH CAROLINA BOARD OF EDUCATION
1429 Senate St Ste 100, Columbia 29201-3730

Chairperson Dennis Thompson

PUBLIC, PRIVATE AND CATHOLIC SECONDARY SCHOOLS

Abbeville, Abbeville, Pop. 5,157
Abbeville County SD 3,000/PK-12
400 Greenville St 29620 864-366-5427
Dr. Ivan Randolph, supt. Fax 366-8531
www.acsd.k12.sc.us/
Abbeville County Career Center Vo/Tech
100 Old Calhoun Falls Rd 29620 864-366-9069
Nick Hyduke, prin. Fax 366-4774
Abbeville HS 500/9-12
701 Washington St 29620 864-366-5916
Steve Garrett, prin. Fax 366-4939
Wright MS 400/6-8
111 Highway 71 29620 864-366-5998
Dick Williams, prin. Fax 366-4282
Other Schools – See Due West

Aiken, Aiken, Pop. 29,094
Aiken County SD 23,800/PK-12
1000 Brookhaven Dr 29803 803-641-2428
Elizabeth Everitt Ph.D., supt. Fax 642-8903
www.aiken.k12.sc.us
Aiken HS 1,500/9-12
449 Rutland Dr NW 29801 803-641-2500
Garen Cofer, prin. Fax 641-2501
Aiken MS 600/6-8
101 Gator Ln 29801 803-641-2570
John Bradley, prin. Fax 641-2578
Kennedy MS 900/6-8
274 E Pine Log Rd 29803 803-641-2470
Kyle Smith, prin. Fax 641-2405
Pinecrest Center Alt
1050 Pinecrest Ave 29801 803-641-2680
Ben Osborne, prin. Fax 641-2681
Schofield MS 600/6-8
224 Kershaw St NE 29801 803-641-2770
Jacquelyn Barnwell, prin. Fax 641-2529
Silver Bluff HS 700/9-12
64 Desoto Dr 29803 803-652-8100
Collette Johnson, prin. Fax 652-8104
South Aiken HS 1,500/9-12
232 E Pine Log Rd 29803 803-641-2600
Bryan Skipper, prin. Fax 641-2607
Aiken County Adult Education Adult
1000 Brookhaven Dr 29803 803-641-2476
Dr. Rosa Ishmal, dir. Fax 641-2492
Other Schools – See Graniteville, Jackson, Monetta, New Ellenton, North Augusta, Wagener, Warrenville

---

Aiken Preparatory S 200/PK-12
129 Pendleton St SW 29801 803-648-3223
Deborah Boehner, hdmstr. Fax 648-6482
Aiken School of Cosmetology Post-Sec.
225 Richland Ave E 29801 803-644-7133
Aiken Technical College Post-Sec.
PO Box 696 29802 803-593-9231
Lacy Cosmetology School Post-Sec.
3084 Whiskey Rd 29803 803-648-6181
South Aiken Baptist Christian S 300/PK-12
980 Dougherty Rd 29803 803-648-7871
Randy Martin, prin. Fax 643-9533
University of South Carolina Post-Sec.
471 University Pkwy 29801 803-648-6851

Allendale, Allendale, Pop. 3,449

University of South Carolina Post-Sec.
PO Box 617 29810 803-584-3446

Anderson, Anderson, Pop. 26,180
Anderson SD 3
Supt. — See Iva
Anderson County Alternative S Alt
805 E Whitner St 29624 864-260-4888
Randolph Dillingham, dir. Fax 260-4004

Anderson SD 4
Supt. — See Pendleton
Pendleton HS 800/9-12
7324 Highway 187 29625 864-403-2100
Brian Couch, prin. Fax 646-8066

Anderson SD 5 12,600/PK-12
PO Box 439 29622 864-260-5000
Betty Bagley, supt. Fax 260-5074
www.anderson5.net
Anderson MS of Choice 6-8
2302 Dobbins Bridge Rd 29626 864-716-3890
Evelyn Murphy, prin. Fax 716-4070
Anderson V Career Campus Vo/Tech
1225 S McDuffie St 29624 864-260-5160
Cathy Shaw, prin. Fax 260-5685
Glenview MS of Choice 6-8
2725 Old Williamston Rd 29621 864-716-4060
Walter Mayfield, prin. Fax 716-3883
Hanna HS IB World S 1,800/9-12
2600 N Highway 81 29621 864-260-5110
Sheila Hilton, prin. Fax 260-5213
Lakeside MS of Inquiry & Innovation 1,000/6-8
315 Pearman Dairy Rd 29625 864-260-5135
Martha Hanwell, prin. Fax 260-5885
McCants MS IB World S 1,300/6-8
2123 Marchbanks Ave 29621 864-260-5145
Jacky Stamps, prin. Fax 260-5846
Southwood Academy of the Arts 500/6-8
1110 Southwood St 29624 864-260-5205
Gary Bruhjell, prin. Fax 964-2607
Westside HS Early College Academy 1,700/9-12
806 Pearman Dairy Rd 29625 864-260-5230
Henry Adair, prin. Fax 260-5007

Anderson Memorial Hospital Post-Sec.
800 N Fant St 29621 864-261-1109
Anderson University Post-Sec.
316 Boulevard 29621 864-231-2000
Forrest College Post-Sec.
601 E River St 29624 864-225-7653
Montessori S of Anderson 200/PK-12
280 Sam McGee Rd 29621 864-226-5344
Craig Drennon Ph.D., admin. Fax 231-6562

Andrews, Georgetown, Pop. 2,842
Georgetown County SD
Supt. — See Georgetown
Andrews HS 600/9-12
12890 County Line Rd 29510 843-264-3414
Dr. Michelle Greene, prin. Fax 264-3326
Rosemary MS 400/6-8
12804 County Line Rd 29510 843-264-9780
Michael Caviris, prin. Fax 264-9787

Aynor, Horry, Pop. 554
Horry County SD
Supt. — See Conway
Aynor HS 700/9-12
201 Jordanville Rd 29511 843-488-7100
Janet Lawrence, prin. Fax 488-7101

Bamberg, Bamberg, Pop. 3,560
Bamberg SD 1 900/PK-12
3830 Faust St 29003 803-245-3053
Phyllis Schwarting, supt. Fax 245-3056
www.bamberg1.com
Bamberg-Ehrhardt HS 500/9-12
267 Red Raider Dr 29003 803-245-3030
Randall Maxwell, prin. Fax 245-6502
Bamberg-Ehrhardt MS 200/7-8
897 North St 29003 803-245-3058
Troy Phillips, prin. Fax 245-6501

Barnwell, Barnwell, Pop. 4,670
Barnwell SD 45 2,400/K-12
770 Hagood Ave 29812 803-541-1300
Roy Sapough, supt. Fax 541-1348
www.barnwell45.org
Barnwell HS 700/9-12
474 Jackson St 29812 803-541-1390
Jon Burdge, prin. Fax 541-0726
Guinyard-Butler MS 400/7-8
779 Allen St 29812 803-541-1370
Senaca Baines, prin. Fax 541-1306

Batesburg, Lexington, Pop. 5,296
Lexington County SD 3 2,000/PK-12
338 W Columbia Ave 29006 803-532-4423
Dr. Chester Floyd, supt. Fax 532-8000
www.lex3.k12.sc.us
Batesburg-Leesville HS 600/9-12
600 Summerland Ave 29006 803-532-9251
Pat Padgett, prin. Fax 532-3232
Batesburg-Leesville MS 400/6-8
425 Shealy Rd 29006 803-532-3831
Randall Price, prin. Fax 532-8021

King Academy 200/K-12
1046 Sardis Rd 29006 803-532-6682
Dennis Gibson, hdmstr. Fax 604-0409

Beaufort, Beaufort, Pop. 12,089
Beaufort County SD 19,200/PK-12
PO Box 309 29901 843-322-2300
Dr. Valerie Page Truesdale, supt. Fax 322-2330
www.beaufort.k12.sc.us/
Battery Creek HS 900/9-12
1 Blue Dolphin Dr 29906 843-322-5500
Edmond Burnes, prin. Fax 322-5608
Beaufort HS 1,600/9-12
84 Sea Island Pkwy, 843-322-2000
Corey Murphy, prin. Fax 322-2158
Beaufort MS 700/6-8
2501 Mossy Oaks Rd 29902 843-322-5700
Carole Ingram, prin. Fax 322-5723
Ladys Island MS 700/5-8
30 Cougar Dr, 843-322-3100
Mona Lise Dickson, prin. Fax 322-3179
Smalls MS 500/6-8
43 W K Alston Dr 29906 843-322-2500
Denise Smith, prin. Fax 322-2564
Adult Education S Adult
2900 Mink Point Blvd 29902 843-322-2300
Dr. Juanita Murrell, prin. Fax 322-2371
Other Schools – See Bluffton, Hilton Head Island, Seabrook

Beaufort Academy 300/PK-12
240 Sams Point Rd, 843-524-3393
Julie Corner, hdmstr. Fax 524-1171
Beaufort Christian S 100/PK-12
378 Parris Island Gtwy 29906 843-525-0635
Rev. Douglas Wadsworth, hdmstr. Fax 525-0635
Technical College of the Lowcountry Post-Sec.
921 Ribaut Rd 29902 843-525-8211

Belton, Anderson, Pop. 4,063
Anderson SD 2
Supt. — See Honea Path
Belton MS 500/6-8
102 Cherokee Rd 29627 864-338-6595
Dr. Adrienne Davenport, prin. Fax 338-3301

Bennettsville, Marlboro, Pop. 8,964
Marlboro County SD 4,100/PK-12
PO Box 947 29512 843-479-4016
Dr. Helena Tillar, supt. Fax 479-5944
www.marlboro.k12.sc.us
Marlboro County HS 1,300/9-12
951 Fayetteville Avenue Ext 29512 843-479-5900
Walter Baker, prin. Fax 479-5916
Other Schools – See Clio

Bishopville, Lee, Pop. 3,442
Lee County SD 2,200/PK-12
PO Box 507 29010 803-484-5327
Cleo Richardson Ed.D., supt. Fax 484-9107
www.leeschoolsk12.org/home.asp
Lee Central HS 600/9-12
1800 Wisacky Hwy 29010 803-428-4010
Ron Webb, prin. Fax 428-4062
Lee Central MS 500/5-8
41 Charlenes Ln 29010 803-428-2100
Deitra Johnson, prin. Fax 428-2174
Lee County Academic Learning Center 100/Alt
123 E College St 29010 803-483-0111
May Caesar, prin. Fax 483-0113
Lee County Career & Technology Center Vo/Tech
521 Park St 29010 803-484-5327
Betty Lowery, coord. Fax 484-4171

Lee Academy 500/K-12
630 Cousar St 29010 803-484-5532

Blacksburg, Cherokee, Pop. 1,800
Cherokee County SD
Supt. — See Gaffney
Blacksburg HS 600/9-12
201 W Ramseur Dr 29702 864-839-6371
Craig Bramlett, prin. Fax 839-2960
Blacksburg MS 400/6-8
101 London St 29702 864-839-6476
Virgil Hampton, prin. Fax 839-2390

Blackville, Barnwell, Pop. 2,378
Area Vocational Schools
Supt. — None
Barnwell County Career Center Vo/Tech
5214 Reynolds Rd 29817 803-259-5512
H. Samuel McKay, dir. Fax 541-4701

Barnwell SD 19 900/PK-12
297 Pascallas St 29817 803-284-5605
Teresa Pope Ph.D., supt. Fax 284-4417
www.barnwell19.k12.sc.us
Blackville-Hilda HS 200/9-12
PO Box 245 29817 803-284-5700
David Norman, prin. Fax 284-3766
Blackville-Hilda JHS 100/7-8
PO Box 186 29817 803-284-5900
Ernest Dotson, prin. Fax 284-0961

Barnwell Christian S 100/1-12
5675 SC Highway 70 29817 803-259-2100
Andrew Korver, prin. Fax 259-2100
Davis Academy 200/K-12
5061 Hilda Rd 29817 803-284-2476

Bluffton, Beaufort, Pop. 12,248
Beaufort County SD
Supt. — See Beaufort
Bluffton HS 1,000/10-12
12 H E McCraken Cir 29910 843-706-8800
Mark Dievendorf, prin. Fax 706-8819
McCracken MS 800/8-9
250 HE McCraken Cir 29910 843-706-8700
Phillip Shaw, prin. Fax 706-8778

Professional Golfers Career College Post-Sec.
4454 Bluffton Park Cres 200 29910 843-757-9611
University of South Carolina Post-Sec.
1 University Blvd, 843-208-8000

Blythewood, Richland, Pop. 2,008
Richland SD 2
Supt. — See Columbia
Blythewood Academy Alt
501 Main St 29016 803-691-6890
Perry Mills, prin. Fax 691-4396
Blythewood HS 2,100/9-12
10901 Wilson Blvd 29016 803-691-4090
Keith Price, prin. Fax 691-4097
Blythewood MS 1,100/6-8
2351 Longtown Rd E 29016 803-691-6850
Brenda Hafner, prin. Fax 691-6860
Kelly Mill MS 1,000/6-8
1141 Kelly Mill Rd 29016 803-691-7210
Katie Wall, prin. Fax 691-7212
Muller Road MS 6-8
1031 Muller Rd 29016 803-691-6851
Lori Marrero, prin. Fax 738-7531
Westwood HS 9-12
180 Turkey Farm Rd 29016 803-691-4049
Ralph Schmidt, prin. Fax 738-7520

Boiling Springs, Spartanburg, Pop. 8,098
Spartanburg SD 2
Supt. — See Chesnee
Boiling Springs HS 9th Grade Campus 600/9-9
3655 Boiling Springs Rd 29316 864-578-2610
Eddie Cole, prin. Fax 578-2620
Boiling Springs HS 1,600/10-12
2251 Old Furnace Rd 29316 864-578-8465
Chuck Gordon, prin. Fax 578-6825

Branchville, Orangeburg, Pop. 1,014
Orangeburg County Consolidated SD 4
Supt. — See Cope
Branchville HS 300/7-12
PO Box 188 29432 803-274-8875
David Hess, prin. Fax 274-8645

Camden, Kershaw, Pop. 6,772
Kershaw County SD 10,300/PK-12
2029 W Dekalb St 29020 803-432-8416
Dr. Frank Morgan, supt. Fax 425-8918
www.kershaw.k12.sc.us
Applied Technical Education Campus Vo/Tech
874 Vocational Ln 29020 803-425-8982
Chet Horton, dir. Fax 425-8983
Camden HS 1,000/9-12
1022 Ehrenclou Dr 29020 803-425-8930
Dave Matthews, prin. Fax 424-2861
Camden MS 800/6-8
902 McRae Rd 29020 803-425-8975
Byron Johnson, prin. Fax 425-8954
Continuous Learning Center Alt
1109 Campbell St 29020 803-425-7712
John Thompson, dir. Fax 425-7713
Kershaw County Adult Education Adult
874 Vocational Ln 29020 803-425-8980
Weyland Burns, dir. Fax 425-8988
Other Schools – See Elgin, Kershaw, Lugoff

Camden Military Academy 300/7-12
520 Highway 1 N 29020 803-432-6001
Fax 425-1020

Campobello, Spartanburg, Pop. 498
Spartanburg SD 1 5,100/PK-12
PO Box 218 29322 864-472-2846
Ron Garner Ed.D., supt. Fax 472-4118
www.spart1.org/do/
Landrum HS 600/9-12
18818 Asheville Hwy 29322 864-457-2606
Brian Sherman, prin. Fax 457-3148
Other Schools – See Inman, Landrum

Cayce, Lexington, Pop. 12,278
Lexington County SD 2
Supt. — See West Columbia
Brookland-Cayce HS 1,100/9-12
1300 State St 29033 803-791-5000
Gregg Morton, prin. Fax 739-4970
Busbee Creative Arts Academy 300/6-8
501 Bulldog Blvd 29033 803-739-4070
C.R. Hall, prin. Fax 739-4133

Central, Pickens, Pop. 5,067
Pickens County SD
Supt. — See Easley
Daniel HS 1,000/9-12
140 Blue and Gold Blvd 29630 864-624-4430
Dr. Danny Merk, prin. Fax 624-4428
Edwards MS 800/6-8
1157 Madden Bridge Rd 29630 864-397-4200
Gary Culler, prin. Fax 624-4426

Southern Wesleyan University Post-Sec.
PO Box 1020 29630 864-644-5000

Chapin, Lexington, Pop. 1,420
SD Five of Lexington & Richland Counties
Supt. — See Irmo
Alternative Academy for Success Alt
107 Columbia Ave 29036 803-575-5300
Donald Hardie, prin. Fax 575-5320
Center for Advanced Technical Studies 9-12
916 Mount Vernon Church Rd 29036
Bob Couch, prin. 803-476-8000
Chapin HS 1,300/9-12
300 Columbia Ave 29036 803-575-5400
Akil Ross, prin. Fax 575-5420
Chapin MS 1,000/6-8
1130 Old Lexington Hwy 29036 803-575-5700
Anna Miller, prin. Fax 575-5720

Charleston, Charleston, Pop. 118,351
Charleston County SD 43,500/PK-12
75 Calhoun St Fl 2 29401 843-937-6300
Dr. Nancy McGinley, supt. Fax 937-6307
www.charleston.k12.sc.us
Academic Magnet HS 600/9-12
5109 W Enterprise St Ste A 29405 843-746-1300
Judith Peterson, prin. Fax 746-1310
Burke MSHS 600/7-12
244 President St 29403 843-579-4815
Maurice Cannon, prin. Fax 722-3651
Clark Corporate Academy 100/Alt
1929 N Grimball Rd 29412 843-762-2774
Andrew Halevi, dir. Fax 762-6218
Ft. Johnson MS 500/6-8
1825 Camp Rd 29412 843-762-2740
David Parler, prin. Fax 762-6212
James Island MS 400/6-8
1484 Camp Rd 29412 843-762-2784
Murton Hudson, prin. Fax 762-6209
St. Andrews MS 500/6-8
721 Wappoo Rd 29407 843-763-1533
Michael Ryan, prin. Fax 763-1596
West Ashley HS 1,900/9-12
4060 Wildcat Blvd 29414 843-573-1201
Mary Runyon, prin. Fax 573-1223
West Ashley MS 400/6-8
1776 William Kennerty Dr 29407 843-763-1546
LaCarma Brown-McMillan, prin. Fax 852-6557
Williams MS 600/6-8
640 Butte St 29414 843-763-1529
Kevin Smith, prin. Fax 763-5955
Zucker Science MS 500/6-8
6401 Dorchester Rd 29418 843-767-8383
Jacob Perlmutter, prin. Fax 207-3073
Other Schools – See Hollywood, Johns Island, Mc Clellanville, Mount Pleasant, North Charleston

---

Academy of Cosmetology Post-Sec.
5117 Dorchester Rd 29418 843-552-3241
Ashley Hall 700/PK-12
172 Rutledge Ave 29403 843-722-4088
Jill Muti, admin. Fax 720-2868
Bishop England HS 800/9-12
363 Seven Farms Dr 29492 843-849-9599
Michael Bolchoz, prin. Fax 849-9221
Charleston Cosmetology Institute Post-Sec.
8484 Dorchester Rd 29420 843-552-3670
Charleston School of Law Post-Sec.
PO Box 535 29402 843-329-1000
Charleston Southern University Post-Sec.
9200 University Blvd 29406 843-863-7000
College of Charleston Post-Sec.
66 George St 29424 843-805-5507
First Baptist S 500/PK-12
48 Meeting St 29401 843-722-6646
Thomas Mullins, head sch Fax 720-2521
James Island Christian S 200/PK-12
15 Crosscreek Dr 29412 843-795-1762
Jeremy Schwartz, admin. Fax 762-1619
Medical University of South Carolina Post-Sec.
171 Ashley Ave 29425 843-792-1414
Porter-Gaud S 900/1-12
300 Albemarle Rd 29407 843-556-3620
D. DuBose Egleston B.S., head sch Fax 769-9926
The Art Institute of Charleston Post-Sec.
24 N Market St 29401 866-211-0107
The Citadel Post-Sec.
171 Moultrie St 29409 843-225-3294
Trident Technical College Post-Sec.
PO Box 118067 29423 843-574-6111

Cheraw, Chesterfield, Pop. 5,741
Chesterfield County SD
Supt. — See Chesterfield
Cheraw HS 800/9-12
649 Chesterfield Hwy 29520 843-921-1000
Jason Bryant, prin. Fax 921-1006
Long MS 500/6-8
1010 W Greene St 29520 843-921-1010
Matt Brantley, prin. Fax 921-1017

Northeastern Technical College Post-Sec.
1201 Chesterfield Hwy 29520 843-921-6900

Chesnee, Spartanburg, Pop. 845
Spartanburg SD 2 8,200/K-12
3231 Old Furnace Rd 29323 864-578-0128
Scott Mercer, supt. Fax 578-8924
www.spartanburg2.k12.sc.us
Chesnee HS 600/9-12
795 S Alabama Ave 29323 864-461-7318
Thomas Ezell, prin. Fax 461-4137
Chesnee MS 500/6-8
805 S Alabama Ave 29323 864-461-3900
Dale Campbell, prin. Fax 461-3950
Rainbow Lake MS 6-8
1951 Riveroak Rd 29323 864-253-5700
Donald Barnette, prin. Fax 253-5701
Other Schools – See Boiling Springs, Inman

Chester, Chester, Pop. 5,520
Chester County SD 5,300/PK-12
509 District Office Dr 29706 803-385-6122
Agnes Slayman Ph.D., supt. Fax 581-6965
www.chester.k12.sc.us/
Chester County Career Center Vo/Tech
1324 J A Cochran Byp 29706 803-377-1991
Lee Green, dir. Fax 581-0912
Chester HS 900/9-12
1330 J A Cochran Byp 29706 803-377-3161
Martin Tiller, prin. Fax 581-2363
Chester MS 600/6-8
1014 McCandless Rd 29706 803-377-8192
Cedrick Tidwell, prin. Fax 581-1875
Other Schools – See Great Falls, Richburg

Chesterfield, Chesterfield, Pop. 1,462
Chesterfield County SD 7,700/PK-12
401 West Blvd 29709 843-623-2175
Dr. Harrison Goodwin, supt. Fax 623-3434
www.chesterfield.k12.sc.us
Chesterfield HS 600/9-12
401 N Page St 29709 843-623-2161
Scott Radkin, prin. Fax 623-2050
Chesterfield-Ruby MS 400/6-8
14445 Highway 9 29709 843-623-9401
Dr. Andrea Hampton, prin. Fax 623-9429
Palmetto Learning Center Alt
116 Edwards Rd 29709 843-623-5101
Ryan Young, coord. Fax 623-5105
Other Schools – See Cheraw, Jefferson, Mc Bee, Pageland

Clemson, Pickens, Pop. 13,699

Clemson University Post-Sec.
105 Sikes Hall 29634 864-656-3311

Clinton, Laurens, Pop. 8,368
Laurens County SD 56 3,100/PK-12
211 N Broad St Ste B 29325 864-833-0800
Dr. David O'Shields, supt. Fax 833-0804
www.laurens56.k12.sc.us
Bell Street MS 700/6-8
600 Peachtree St 29325 864-833-0807
Brenda Romines, prin. Fax 833-0810
Clinton HS 900/9-12
18132 Highway 72 E 29325 864-833-0817
Maureen Tiller, prin. Fax 833-0825

Presbyterian College Post-Sec.
503 S Broad St 29325 864-833-2820

Clio, Marlboro, Pop. 720
Marlboro County SD
Supt. — See Bennettsville
Marlboro School of Discovery 100/Alt
PO Box 517 29525 843-586-8376
Jack Swann, prin. Fax 586-9078

Clover, York, Pop. 5,008
Clover SD 2 6,500/PK-12
604 Bethel St 29710 803-810-8005
Dr. Marc Sosne, supt. Fax 222-8010
www.clover2.k12.sc.us
Blue Eagle Academy Alt
300 Clinton Ave 29710 803-810-8420
Hezekiah Massey, dir. Fax 222-8042
Clover HS 1,900/9-12
1625 Highway 55 E 29710 803-810-8200
Mark Hopkins, prin. Fax 222-8021
Clover MS 700/6-8
1555 Highway 55 E 29710 803-810-8300
Melanie Wall, prin. Fax 222-8034
Oakridge MS 800/6-8
5650 Highway 557 29710 803-631-8000
William Largen, prin. Fax 631-8102

Columbia, Richland, Pop. 126,841
Richland SD 1 24,000/PK-12
1616 Richland St 29201 803-231-7000
Dr. Percy Mack, supt. Fax 231-7502
www.richlandone.org/
Alcorn MS 400/6-8
5125 Fairfield Rd 29203 803-735-3439
Dr. Baron Davis, prin. Fax 735-3487
Columbia HS 700/9-12
1701 Westchester Dr 29210 803-731-8950
Shenequa Coles, prin. Fax 731-8953
Crayton MS 1,000/6-8
5000 Clemson Ave 29206 803-738-7224
Susan Childs, prin. Fax 738-7901
Dreher HS 1,200/9-12
3319 Millwood Ave 29205 803-253-7000
Jeanne Stiglbauer, prin. Fax 253-7007
Eau Claire HS 800/9-12
4800 Monticello Rd 29203 803-735-7600
June Page, prin. Fax 735-7629

Flora HS 1,300/9-12
1 Falcon Dr 29204 803-738-7300
Richard McClure, prin. Fax 738-7307
Gibbes MS 300/6-8
500 Summerlea Dr 29203 803-343-2942
Kwamine Simpson, prin. Fax 733-3040
Hand MS 900/6-8
2600 Wheat St 29205 803-343-2947
Marisa Vickers, prin. Fax 733-6173
Heyward Career & Technology Center Vo/Tech
3560 Lynhaven Dr 29204 803-735-3343
Sherry Rivers, prin. Fax 691-4253
Johnson HS 400/9-12
2219 Barhamville Rd 29204 803-253-7092
Nathan White, prin. Fax 253-5713
Keenan HS 800/9-12
361 Pisgah Church Rd 29203 803-714-2500
Alvin Pressley, prin. Fax 714-2593
Olympia Learning Center Alt
621 Bluff Rd 29201 803-400-1650
Russell Perkins, admin. Fax 400-1700
Perry MS 300/6-8
2600 Barhamville Rd 29204 803-256-6347
Quantina Haggwood, prin. Fax 255-2262
St. Andrews MS 600/6-8
1231 Bluefield Dr 29210 803-731-8910
Ken Richardson, prin. Fax 731-8913
Sanders MS, 3455 Pine Belt Rd 29204 400/6-8
Andrenna Smith, prin. 803-738-7575
Adult & Community Education Adult
2612 Covenant Rd 29204 803-343-2935
Marva Coates, dir. Fax 212-1453
Other Schools – See Hopkins

Richland SD 2 25,200/PK-12
6831 Brookfield Rd 29206 803-787-1910
Katie Brochu Ed.D., supt. Fax 738-7393
www.richland2.org
Center for Accelerated Preparation 6-8
7502 Brookfield Rd 29223 803-738-8433
Theresa Counts-Davis, prin. Fax 738-8434
Dent MS 1,300/6-8
2721 Decker Blvd 29206 803-699-2750
Randall Gary, prin. Fax 699-2754
Longleaf MS 600/6-8
1160 Longreen Pkwy 29229 803-691-4870
Dan Reyes, prin. Fax 691-4043
Richland Northeast HS 1,500/9-12
7500 Brookfield Rd 29223 803-699-2800
Sabrina Suber, prin. Fax 699-3679
Ridge View HS 2,000/9-12
4801 Hard Scrabble Rd 29229 803-699-2999
Dr. Marty Martin, prin. Fax 699-2888
Spring Valley HS 2,100/9-12
120 Sparkleberry Ln 29229 803-699-3500
Baron Davis, prin. Fax 699-3541
Summit Parkway MS 900/6-8
200 Summit Pkwy 29229 803-699-3580
Andrew Barbone, prin. Fax 699-3682
Wright MS 1,000/6-8
2740 Alpine Rd 29223 803-736-8740
Mary Paige Wylie, prin. Fax 736-8798
Rogers Adult Continuing Center Adult
750 Old Clemson Rd 29229 803-736-8787
Bobbie Cunningham, prin. Fax 736-8785
Other Schools – See Blythewood

SD Five of Lexington & Richland Counties
Supt. — See Irmo
Irmo HS 1,900/9-12
6671 Saint Andrews Rd 29212 803-476-3000
Rob Weinkle, prin. Fax 476-3020
Irmo MS 900/7-8
6051 Wescott Rd 29212 803-476-3600
Robert Jackson, prin. Fax 476-3620

Allen University Post-Sec.
1530 Harden St 29204 803-376-5700
Baptist Medical Center Post-Sec.
1519 Marion St 29201 803-771-5042
Benedict College Post-Sec.
1600 Harden St 29204 803-253-5000
Cardinal Newman HS 400/7-12
4701 Forest Dr 29206 803-782-2814
Jacquie Kasprowski, prin. Fax 782-9314
Centura College Post-Sec.
7500 Two Notch Rd 29223 803-754-7544
Columbia Biblical Seminary Post-Sec.
7435 Monticello Rd 29203 800-777-2227
Columbia College Post-Sec.
1301 Columbia College Dr 29203 800-277-1301
Columbia International University Post-Sec.
7435 Monticello Rd 29203 803-754-4100
Covenant Classical Christian S 100/K-12
3120 Covenant Rd 29204 803-787-0225
William N. Pevey, admin. Fax 782-7309
ECPI University Post-Sec.
250 Berryhill Rd Ste 300 29210 803-772-3333
Fortis College Post-Sec.
246 Stoneridge Dr Ste 101 29210 803-678-4800
Hammond S 900/PK-12
854 Galway Ln 29209 803-776-0295
Christopher Angel, prin. Fax 776-0122
Heathwood Hall Episcopal S 800/PK-12
3000 S Beltline Blvd 29201 803-765-2309
Dr. Michael Heath, hdmstr. Fax 748-4755
ITT Technical Institute Post-Sec.
1628 Browning Rd Ste 180 29210 803-216-6000
Kenneth Shuler's School of Cosmetology Post-Sec.
449 Saint Andrews Rd 29210 803-772-6042
Lippen MSHS 500/6-12
7401 Monticello Rd 29230 803-807-4100
Gerald Porter, prin. Fax 744-1387
Lutheran Theological Southern Seminary Post-Sec.
4201 N Main St 29203 803-786-5150
Midlands Technical College Post-Sec.
PO Box 2408 29202 803-738-8324
National Ctr for Credibility Assessment Post-Sec.
7540 Pickens Ave 29207 803-751-9100
Remington College Columbia Post-Sec.
607 Bush River Rd 29210 803-214-9000
Sandhills S 50/1-12
1500 Hallbrook Dr 29209 803-695-1400
Anne Vickers, head sch Fax 695-1214
Southeastern Institute Post-Sec.
1420 Colonial Life Blvd #80 29210 803-798-8800
South University Post-Sec.
9 Science Ct 29203 803-799-9082
Strayer University Post-Sec.
200 Center Point Cir # 300 29210 803-750-2500
University of South Carolina 29208 Post-Sec.
803-777-7700
Virginia College Post-Sec.
7201 Two Notch Rd 29223 803-509-7100
W.L. Bonner College Post-Sec.
4430 Argent Ct 29203 803-754-3950

Conway, Horry, Pop. 16,872
Horry County SD 38,800/PK-12
PO Box 260005 29528 843-488-6700
Cindy Elsberry, supt. Fax 488-6722
www.horrycountyschools.net
Academy for Technology and Academics Vo/Tech
5639 Highway 701 N 29526 843-488-6600
David Stoudenmire, prin. Fax 488-6601
Black Water MS 700/6-8
900 E Cox Ferry Rd 29526 843-903-8440
Cindy Thibodeau, prin. Fax 903-8441
Conway HS 1,600/9-12
2301 Church St 29526 843-488-0662
Steven Fitch, prin. Fax 488-0686
Conway MS 700/6-8
1104 Elm St 29526 843-488-6040
Margaret Sordian, prin. Fax 488-0611
Early College HS 200/9-12
2050 E Highway 501 29526 843-349-7102
Joan Grimmett, dir. Fax 349-7895
Horry County Education Center Alt
2694 Highway 905 29526 843-488-7500
Lisa Day, prin. Fax 488-7501
Scholars Academy 9-12
215 University Hall 29526 843-349-4117
Renn Dominguez, prin. Fax 349-6144
Whittemore Park MS 600/6-8
1808 Rhue St 29527 843-488-0669
Judy Beard, prin. Fax 488-0669
Other Schools – See Aynor, Galivants Ferry, Green Sea, Little River, Loris, Murrells Inlet, Myrtle Beach

---

Coastal Carolina University Post-Sec.
PO Box 261954 29528 843-347-3161
Conway Christian S 200/K-12
PO Box 1245 29528 843-365-2005
Connie Smith, prin. Fax 365-2021
Horry-Georgetown Technical College Post-Sec.
PO Box 261966 29528 843-347-3186
Miller-Motte Technical College Post-Sec.
2451 E Highway 501 29526 843-591-1100

Cope, Orangeburg, Pop. 75
Orangeburg County Consolidated SD 4 4,100/PK-12
PO Box 68 29038 803-534-8081
Brenda Turner, supt. Fax 531-5614
www.orangeburg4.com
Cope Area Career Center Vo/Tech
PO Box 128 29038 803-534-7661
Sandra Jameson, prin. Fax 535-4301
STAR Center for Learning 100/Alt
6064 Slab Landing Rd 29038 803-533-1783
Belinda Johnson, prin. Fax 533-1785
Other Schools – See Branchville, Cordova, Neeses

Cordova, Orangeburg, Pop. 167
Orangeburg County Consolidated SD 4
Supt. — See Cope
Carver-Edisto MS 600/6-8
PO Box 65 29039 803-534-3554
Jeannie Monson, prin. Fax 535-0937
Edisto HS 800/9-12
PO Box 101 29039 803-536-1553
David Damm, prin. Fax 531-5615

Cowpens, Spartanburg, Pop. 2,133
Spartanburg SD 3
Supt. — See Glendale
Cowpens MS 500/6-8
150 Foster St 29330 864-279-6400
Cynthia James, prin. Fax 279-6410

Cross, Berkeley
Berkeley County SD
Supt. — See Moncks Corner
Cross JSHS 300/7-12
1293 Old Highway 6 29436 843-899-8900
Adrian Busch, prin. Fax 899-8910

Dalzell, Sumter, Pop. 2,975
Sumter SD
Supt. — See Sumter
Hillcrest MS 400/6-8
PO Box 151 29040 803-499-3341
Tarsha Staggers, prin. Fax 499-3353

Darlington, Darlington, Pop. 6,253
Darlington County SD 10,700/PK-12
PO Box 1117 29540 843-398-5100
Dr. Rainey Knight, supt. Fax 398-5198
www.darlington.k12.sc.us
Darlington Co. Institute of Technology Vo/Tech
160 Pinedale Dr 29532 843-398-4796
Bert Guerry, dir. Fax 395-1044
Darlington County Intervention S Alt
100 Magnolia St 29532 843-393-5617
Stephanie Bridges, dir. Fax 398-2640
Darlington HS 1,200/9-12
525 Spring St 29532 843-398-5140
Dr. Greg Harrison, prin. Fax 398-2739
Darlington MS 1,100/6-8
150 Pinedale Dr 29532 843-398-5088
Carlita Davis, prin. Fax 398-3390
Mayo HS for Math Science & Technology 400/9-12
405 Chestnut St 29532 843-398-5050
Arlene Johnson, prin. Fax 398-2647
Other Schools – See Hartsville, Lamar

Trinity-Byrnes Collegiate S 200/6-12
5001 Hoffmeyer Rd 29532 843-395-9124
Ed Hoffman, hdmstr. Fax 395-6495

Denmark, Bamberg, Pop. 3,519
Bamberg SD 2 900/PK-12
62 Holly Ave 29042 803-793-3346
Dr. Thelma Sojourner, supt. Fax 793-2006
www.denmarkolarschooldistrict2.org
Denmark-Olar HS 300/9-12
197 Viking Cir 29042 803-793-3307
Mickey Pringle, prin. Fax 793-2004
Denmark-Olar MS 200/6-8
45 Green St 29042 803-793-3383
Daryl Brockington, prin. Fax 793-2038

Denmark Technical College Post-Sec.
PO Box 327 29042 803-793-5176
Voorhees College Post-Sec.
PO Box 678 29042 803-780-1234

Dillon, Dillon, Pop. 6,694
Area Vocational Schools
Supt. — None
Dillon County Technology Center Vo/Tech
PO Box 1130 29536 843-774-5143
Jerry Strickland, prin. Fax 774-7711

Dillon SD Four 4,000/PK-12
405 W Washington St 29536 843-774-1200
D. Ray Rogers, supt. Fax 774-1203
www.dillon.k12.sc.us
Dillon HS 900/9-12
1730 Highway 301 N 29536 843-774-1230
Shawn Johnson, prin. Fax 774-1234
Dillon MS 500/6-8
1803 Joan Dr 29536 843-774-1212
Rodney Cook, prin. Fax 841-3616
Other Schools – See Lake View

Dillon Christian S 300/K-12
PO Box 151 29536 843-841-1000
Amanda Mussman, head sch Fax 841-0810

Dorchester, Dorchester
Area Vocational Schools
Supt. — None
Dorchester Co. Career & Technology Ctr Vo/Tech
507 Schoolhouse Rd 29437 843-563-2361
James Villeponteaux, prin. Fax 563-9038
Other Schools – See Blackville SC, Dillon SC, Manning SC, Ridgeland SC, Williamston SC

Dorchester SD 4
Supt. — See Saint George
Harleyville-Ridgeville MS 200/6-8
1650 E Main St 29437 843-462-2470
LaShawna Rivers, admin. Fax 462-2479
Woodland HS 700/9-12
4128 Highway 78 29437 843-563-5956
Bernard Utsey, prin. Fax 563-5997

Due West, Abbeville, Pop. 1,226
Abbeville County SD
Supt. — See Abbeville
Dixie HS 400/8-12
1 Haynes St 29639 864-379-2186
Lori Brownlee-Brewton, prin. Fax 379-8187

Erskine College Post-Sec.
PO Box 338 29639 864-379-2131

Duncan, Spartanburg, Pop. 3,086
Spartanburg SD 5 7,300/K-12
PO Box 307 29334 864-949-2350
Dr. Scott Turner, supt. Fax 439-0051
www.spart5.net
Byrnes Freshman Academy 600/9-9
PO Box 277 29334 864-949-2320
Pat Monteith, prin. Fax 949-2328
Byrnes HS 1,600/10-12
PO Box 187 29334 864-949-2355
Jeff Rogers, prin. Fax 949-2362
Florence Chapel MS 600/7-8
290 Shoals Rd 29334 864-949-2310
Tammy White, prin. Fax 949-2315
Other Schools – See Lyman

Easley, Pickens, Pop. 19,670
Pickens County SD 15,800/K-12
1348 Griffin Mill Rd 29640 864-397-1000
Dr. Kelly Pew, supt. Fax 855-8159
www.pickens.k12.sc.us
Dacusville MS 300/6-8
899 Thomas Mill Rd 29640 864-397-3525
Andy Hooker, prin. Fax 850-2094
Easley HS 1,600/9-12
154 Green Wave Blvd 29642 864-397-3100
Dr. Tim Mullis, prin. Fax 855-8194
Gettys MS 1,300/6-8
105 Stewart Dr 29640 864-397-3900
Michael Cory, prin. Fax 855-6413
Simpson Alternative Education Center Alt
200 W D Ave 29640 864-397-4700
Reggia Stapleton, admin. Fax 850-2093
Adult Learning Center Adult
106 Glazner St 29640 864-397-3825
Dr. Mary Gaston, dir. Fax 850-8116
Other Schools – See Central, Liberty, Pickens

Elgin, Kershaw, Pop. 1,286
Kershaw County SD
Supt. — See Camden
Stover MS 600/6-8
1649 Smyrna Rd 29045 803-438-7414
Mike Garity, prin. Fax 438-7014

Elloree, Orangeburg, Pop. 678
Orangeburg County Consolidated SD 3
Supt. — See Holly Hill

Elloree MS 100/6-8
PO Box 810 29047 803-897-2233
Trina Gordon, dir. Fax 897-2034

Estill, Hampton, Pop. 2,023
Hampton SD 2 1,000/PK-12
PO Box 1028 29918 803-625-5000
Dr. Beverly Gurley, supt. Fax 625-2573
hampton2.org/home/
Estill HS 300/9-12
PO Box 757 29918 803-625-5100
Dr. Raedell Brown, prin. Fax 625-4695
Estill MS 200/6-8
PO Box 817 29918 803-625-5200
Synetria Hawkins, prin. Fax 625-3588

Henry Academy 300/PK-12
8766 Savannah Hwy 29918 803-625-2440

Fairfax, Allendale, Pop. 2,023
Allendale County SD 1,500/PK-12
3249 Allendale Fairfax Hwy 29827 803-584-4603
Walter L. Tobin Ph.D., supt. Fax 584-5303
www.acs.k12.sc.us
Allendale-Fairfax HS 400/9-12
3581 Allendale Fairfax Hwy 29827 803-584-2311
Ron Youmans, prin. Fax 584-1787
Allendale-Fairfax MS 300/6-8
3305 Allendale Fairfax Hwy 29827 803-584-3489
Robert Hemby, prin. Fax 584-5331

Fair Play, Oconee, Pop. 674

Foothills Christian S 50/1-12
104 Feltman Rd 29643 864-972-9962
Joe Mullet, prin.

Florence, Florence, Pop. 36,588
Florence County SD One 17,700/PK-12
319 S Dargan St 29506 843-669-4141
Dr. Allie Brooks, supt. Fax 673-1108
www.fsd1.org
Beck Learning Center Alt
1001 W Sumter St 29501 843-679-6768
Gerard Edwards, prin.
Florence Career Ctr Vo/Tech
126 E Howe Springs Rd 29505 843-664-8465
Alphonso Bradley, dir. Fax 413-4688
Sneed MS 900/7-8
1102 S Ebenezer Rd 29501 843-673-1199
Tony Lunsford, prin. Fax 679-6890
South Florence HS 1,600/9-12
3200 S Irby St 29505 843-664-8190
Theodore Greene, prin. Fax 664-8184
Southside MS 800/7-8
200 E Howe Springs Rd 29505 843-664-8467
Craig Washington, prin. Fax 673-5766
West Florence HS 1,700/9-12
221 N Beltline Dr 29501 843-664-8472
Pamela Quick, prin. Fax 664-8475
Williams MS 600/7-8
1119 N Irby St 29501 843-664-8162
Leon McCray, prin. Fax 664-8178
Wilson HS 1,300/9-12
1411 E Old Marion Hwy 29506 843-664-8440
Eric Robinson, prin. Fax 664-8176
Poynor Adult and Community Education Ctr Adult
301 S Dargan St 29506 843-664-8152
Til Morisey, dir. Fax 664-8155

Byrnes Schools 200/PK-12
1201 E Ashby Rd 29506 843-662-0131
Florence Christian S 700/PK-12
PO Box 12809 29504 843-662-0454
Jim Berry, prin. Fax 661-4301
Florence-Darlington Technical College Post-Sec.
PO Box 100548 29502 843-661-8324
Francis Marion University Post-Sec.
PO Box 100547 29502 843-661-1362
King's Academy 300/PK-12
1015 S Ebenezer Rd 29501 843-661-7464
Mike Hiltibidal, head sch Fax 661-7647
Maranatha Christian S 300/PK-12
2624 W Palmetto St 29501 843-665-6395
Chad Reel, prin. Fax 629-0510
McLeod Regional Medical Center Post-Sec.
555 E Cheves St 29506 843-667-2297

Fort Mill, York, Pop. 10,605
Fort Mill SD 10,200/K-12
2233 Deerfield Dr 29715 803-548-2527
James Epps Ph.D., supt. Fax 547-4696
www.fort-mill.k12.sc.us
Fort Mill HS 1,500/9-12
225 Munn Rd E 29715 803-548-1900
Dee Christopher, prin. Fax 548-1911
Fort Mill MS 800/6-8
200 Springfield Pkwy 29715 803-547-5553
Greg Norton, prin. Fax 548-2911
Nation Ford HS 1,500/9-12
1400 A O Jones Blvd 29715 803-835-0000
Beverley Bowman, prin. Fax 835-0010
Springfield MS 800/6-8
1711 Springfield Pkwy 29715 803-548-8199
Keith Griffin, prin. Fax 547-1013
Other Schools – See Tega Cay

Walnut Grove Christian S 100/K-12
1036 Maxwell Mill Rd 29708 803-835-2000
Kyle Boyd, prin.

Gaffney, Cherokee, Pop. 12,231
Cherokee County SD 9,000/PK-12
PO Box 460 29342 864-206-2201
Dr. Quincie Moore, supt. Fax 902-3541
www.cherokee1.k12.sc.us
Cherokee Technology Center Vo/Tech
3206 Cherokee Ave 29340 864-206-2576
Dr. Harold Talley, prin. Fax 487-1287
Copeland Community Learning Center Alt
243 Allison Dr 29341 864-206-6992
LaTunya Means, prin. Fax 487-1238
Ewing MS 400/6-8
171 E Junior High Rd 29340 864-489-3176
Dr. Denise Wooten, prin. Fax 489-8534
Gaffney HS 2,100/9-12
149 Twin Lake Rd 29341 864-902-3600
Marlene Davis, prin. Fax 902-3628
Gaffney MS 600/6-8
805 E Frederick St 29340 864-902-3630
Dr. Shirley Sealy, prin. Fax 902-3637
Granard MS 500/6-8
815 W Rutledge Ave 29341 864-489-6833
Dr. Mark Bunch, prin. Fax 488-1553
Adult & Community Education Adult
243 Allison Dr 29341 864-487-7152
Lisa Hannon, prin. Fax 487-1260
Other Schools – See Blacksburg

Limestone College Post-Sec.
1115 College Dr 29340 864-489-7151

Galivants Ferry, Horry
Horry County SD
Supt. — See Conway
Aynor MS 600/6-8
400 Frye Rd 29544 843-358-6000
Robbie Watkins, prin. Fax 358-5065

Gaston, Lexington, Pop. 1,599
Lexington County SD 4
Supt. — See Swansea
Sandhills MS 500/7-8
582 Meadowfield Rd 29053 803-926-1890
Justin Nutter, prin. Fax 926-1910

Georgetown, Georgetown, Pop. 9,055
Georgetown County SD 9,800/PK-12
2018 Church St 29440 843-436-7000
Dr. Randy Dozier, supt. Fax 436-7171
www.gcsd.k12.sc.us
Georgetown HS 1,000/9-12
2500 Anthuan Maybank St 29440 843-546-8516
Craig Evans, prin. Fax 546-8521
Georgetown MS 800/6-8
2400 Anthuan Maybank St 29440 843-527-4495
Rosemary Gray, prin. Fax 527-2290
Howard Adult Center & Optional S Adult
500 S Kaminski St 29440 843-546-0219
James Ferdon, dir.
Other Schools – See Andrews, Hemingway, Pawleys Island

Horry-Georgetown Technical College Post-Sec.
4003 S Fraser St 29440 843-546-8406

Gilbert, Lexington, Pop. 564
Lexington County SD 1
Supt. — See Lexington
Gilbert HS 900/9-12
840 Main St 29054 803-821-1900
Ann O'Cain, prin. Fax 821-1903
Gilbert MS 700/6-8
120 Rikard Cir 29054 803-821-1700
Benji Ricard, prin. Fax 821-1703

Glendale, Spartanburg, Pop. 305
Spartanburg SD 3 3,000/PK-12
PO Box 267 29346 864-279-6000
Dr. James Mack, supt. Fax 279-6010
www.spartanburg3.org/
Other Schools – See Cowpens, Pacolet, Spartanburg

Goose Creek, Berkeley, Pop. 34,642
Berkeley County SD
Supt. — See Moncks Corner
Goose Creek HS 1,600/9-12
1137 Red Bank Rd 29445 843-553-5300
Jimmy Huskey, prin. Fax 553-8034
Marrington MS 300/6-8
109 Gearing St 29445 843-572-0313
Jim Spencer, prin. Fax 820-4063
Sedgefield MS 900/6-8
131 Charles B Gibson Blvd 29445 843-797-2620
Shameka Washington, prin. Fax 820-5401
Stratford HS 1,900/9-12
951 Crowfield Blvd 29445 843-820-4000
Conrad Lopes, prin. Fax 820-4042
Westview MS 900/6-8
101 Westview Dr 29445 843-572-1700
Robert Bowes, prin. Fax 820-3728

Graniteville, Aiken, Pop. 2,553
Aiken County SD
Supt. — See Aiken
Leavelle-McCampbell MS 500/6-8
82 Canal St 29829 803-663-4300
Dr. Lloydette Young, prin. Fax 663-4302
Midland Valley HS 1,200/9-12
227 Mustang Dr 29829 803-593-7100
Carl White, prin. Fax 593-7106

Gray Court, Laurens, Pop. 784
Laurens SD 55
Supt. — See Laurens
Gray Court-Owings MS 200/6-8
PO Box 187 29645 864-876-2171
Marilyn Ramsey, prin. Fax 876-2965
Hickory Tavern MS 300/6-8
163 Neely Ferry Rd 29645 864-575-4301
Russell Scott, prin. Fax 575-4305

Great Falls, Chester, Pop. 1,942
Chester County SD
Supt. — See Chester
Great Falls HS 300/9-12
411 Sunset Ave 29055 803-482-2210
Brenda Fort, prin. Fax 482-4896
Great Falls MS 200/5-8
409 Sunset Ave 29055 803-482-2220
Brenda Fort, prin. Fax 482-6025

Greeleyville, Williamsburg, Pop. 428
Williamsburg County SD
Supt. — See Kingstree
Murray JSHS 500/7-12
PO Box 188 29056 843-426-2121
Dr. Janice Gamble, prin. Fax 426-2151

Green Sea, Horry
Horry County SD
Supt. — See Conway
Green Sea-Floyds JSHS 600/6-12
4990 Tulip Grove Rd 29545 843-392-3131
Andrea Parsons, prin. Fax 392-9805

Greenville, Greenville, Pop. 57,469
Anderson SD 1
Supt. — See Williamston
Powdersville HS 9-12
145 Hood Rd 29611 864-312-5641
Dr. Chris Ferguson, prin. Fax 312-5640
Powdersville MS 600/6-8
135 Hood Rd 29611 864-269-1821
Todd Binnicker, prin. Fax 269-0795

Greenville County SD 73,500/PK-12
PO Box 2848 29602 864-355-3100
W. Burke Royster, supt. Fax 241-4195
www.greenville.k12.sc.us/
Beck Academy 1,100/6-8
901 Woodruff Rd 29607 864-355-1400
Jason Warren, prin. Fax 355-1490
Berea HS 1,100/9-12
201 Burdine Dr 29617 864-355-1600
Mike Noel, prin. Fax 355-1625
Berea MS 800/6-8
151 Berea Middle School Rd 29617 864-355-1700
Robin Mill, prin. Fax 355-1777
Carolina Academy 700/9-12
2725 Anderson Rd 29611 864-355-2300
Michael Delaney, prin. Fax 355-2375
Donaldson Career Center Vo/Tech
100 Vocational Dr 29605 864-355-4650
Cassina Allen, prin. Fax 355-4683
Enoree Career Center Vo/Tech
108 Scalybark Rd 29617 864-355-7400
Mike Parris, prin. Fax 355-7407
Fine Arts Center 400/11-12
102 Pine Knoll Dr 29609 864-355-2550
Dr. Roy Fluhrer, prin. Fax 355-2579
Golden Strip Career Ctr Vo/Tech
1120 E Butler Rd 29607 864-355-1050
Leroy Elrod, prin. Fax 355-1058
Greenville High Academy 1,400/9-12
1 Vardry St 29601 864-355-5500
Dalton Lucas, prin. Fax 355-5492
Greenville Middle Academy 800/6-8
339 Lowndes Ave 29607 864-355-5600
Dr. Robert Palmer, prin. Fax 355-5682
Hampton HS 1,600/9-12
100 Pine Knoll Dr 29609 864-355-0100
Lance Radford, prin. Fax 355-0194
Hughes Academy 900/6-8
122 Deoyley Ave 29605 864-355-6200
Dr. Patrick Mark, prin. Fax 355-6275
Lakeview MS 500/6-8
3801 Old Buncombe Rd 29617 864-355-6400
Dr. Tracy Hall, prin. Fax 355-6416
League Academy 800/6-8
125 Twin Lake Rd 29609 864-355-8100
Merry Cox, prin. Fax 355-8160
Mann Academy 1,600/9-12
160 Fairforest Way 29607 864-355-6300
Charles Mayfield, prin. Fax 355-6329
Sevier MS 600/6-8
1000 Piedmont Park Rd 29609 864-355-8200
Karen Kapp, prin. Fax 355-8255
Southside HS 900/9-12
6630 Frontage Rd 29605 864-355-8700
Carlos Brooks, prin. Fax 355-8798
Star Academy - Donaldson Alt
100 Vocational Dr 29605 864-355-4669
Robert Lancaster, admin. Fax 355-4683
Star Academy - Enoree Vo/Tech
108 Scalybark Rd 29617 864-355-7401
Terry Manigault, dir. Fax 355-7407
Tanglewood MS 600/6-8
44 Merriwoods Dr 29611 864-355-4500
William Price, prin. Fax 355-4512
Adult Education/Lifelong Learning Adult
206 Wilkins St 29605 864-355-6088
Dr. Chuck Welch, prin. Fax 355-6077
Other Schools – See Greer, Mauldin, Piedmont, Simpsonville, Taylors, Travelers Rest

Academy of Hair Technology Post-Sec.
3715 E North St Ste F 29615 864-322-0300
Bob Jones University Post-Sec.
1700 Wade Hampton Blvd 29614 864-242-5100
Brown Mackie College Post-Sec.
75 Beattie Pl Ste 100 29601 864-239-5300
Christ Church Episcopal S 1,000/K-12
245 Cavalier Dr 29607 864-299-1522
Dr. Leonard Kupersmith, hdmstr. Fax 299-4285
ECPI University Post-Sec.
1001 Keys Dr # 100 29615 864-288-2828
Furman University Post-Sec.
3300 Poinsett Hwy 29613 864-294-2000
Greenville Technical College Post-Sec.
PO Box 5616 29606 864-250-8000
Hampton Park Christian S 500/PK-12
875 State Park Rd 29609 864-233-0556
Dr. Bruce Mizell, admin. Fax 235-5621
ITT Technical Institute Post-Sec.
6 Independence Pt 29615 864-288-0777
Jones Academy 1,200/PK-12
1700 Wade Hampton Blvd 29614 864-770-1395
Dan Nelson, admin. Fax 271-7278
St. Joseph's HS 300/9-12
100 Saint Josephs Dr 29607 864-234-9009
Keith Kiser, hdmstr. Fax 234-5516

Shannon Forest Christian S 500/PK-12
829 Garlington Rd 29615 864-678-5107
Bob Collins, pres. Fax 281-9372
Strayer University Post-Sec.
555 N Pleasantburg Dr # 300 29607 864-250-7000
University of SC School of Medicine Post-Sec.
701 Grove Rd 29605 864-455-7992
Virginia College Post-Sec.
78 Global Dr Ste 200 29607 864-679-4900

Greenwood, Greenwood, Pop. 22,959
Greenwood SD 50 9,200/PK-12
PO Box 248 29648 864-941-5400
Dr. Darrell Johnson, supt. Fax 941-5427
www.gwd50.org
Brewer MS 700/6-8
1000 Emerald Rd 29646 864-941-5500
Chad Evans, prin. Fax 941-5527
Emerald HS 900/9-12
150 Bypass 225 29646 864-941-5730
Brad Nickles, prin. Fax 941-3487
Genesis Education Center Alt
400 Glenwood St 29649 864-941-5460
Damian Coleman, prin.
Greenwood HS 1,600/9-12
1816 Cokesbury Rd 29649 864-941-5600
Dr. Beth Taylor, prin. Fax 941-5498
Northside MS 700/6-8
431 Deadfall Rd W 29649 864-941-5780
Cyndi Storer, prin. Fax 941-3434
Russell Career Center Vo/Tech
601 Northside Dr E 29649 864-941-5750
Dr. Steve Glenn, prin. Fax 941-5375
Westview MS 700/6-8
1410 W Alexander Rd 29646 864-229-4301
Bonnie Corbitt, prin. Fax 229-4827

Charzanne Beauty College Post-Sec.
1549 Highway 72 E 29649 864-223-7321
Greenwood Christian S 300/PK-12
2026 Woodlawn Rd 29649 864-229-2427
Susie Benjamin, hdmstr. Fax 852-5278
Lander University Post-Sec.
320 Stanley Ave 29649 864-388-8000
Palmetto Christian Academy of Greenwood 100/PK-12
308 Deadfall Rd W 29649 864-223-0391
Joan Gore, prin. Fax 223-1692
Piedmont Technical College Post-Sec.
PO Box 1467 29648 864-941-8324

Greer, Greenville, Pop. 25,060
Greenville County SD
Supt. — See Greenville
Blue Ridge HS 1,100/8-12
2151 Fews Chapel Rd 29651 864-355-1800
Reena Watson, prin. Fax 355-1821
Blue Ridge MS 1,000/6-8
2423 E Tyger Bridge Rd 29651 864-355-1900
Rebecca Greene, prin. Fax 355-1966
Bonds Resource Center Vo/Tech
505 N Main St 29650 864-355-8080
Wayne Rhodes, prin. Fax 355-8264
Greer HS 1,100/9-12
3000 E Gap Creek Rd 29651 864-355-5700
Marion Waters, prin. Fax 355-5725
Greer MS 900/6-8
3032 E Gap Creek Rd 29651 864-355-5800
Scott Rhymer, prin. Fax 355-5880
Riverside HS 1,600/9-12
794 Hammett Bridge Rd 29650 864-355-7800
Andy Crowley, prin. Fax 355-7898
Riverside MS 1,000/6-8
615 Hammett Bridge Rd 29650 864-355-7900
Eric Williams, prin. Fax 355-7918

Hanahan, Berkeley, Pop. 17,513
Berkeley County SD
Supt. — See Moncks Corner
Hanahan HS 900/9-12
6015 Murray Dr 29410 843-820-3710
Ric Raycroft, prin. Fax 820-3716
Hanahan MS 800/5-8
5815 Murray Dr 29410 843-820-3800
Robin Rogers, prin. Fax 820-3804

Hardeeville, Jasper, Pop. 2,902
Jasper County SD
Supt. — See Ridgeland
Hardeeville-Ridgeland MS 200/6-8
150 Hurricane Alley 29927 843-784-8600
Jeannie Jefferson, prin. Fax 784-8609

Harleyville, Dorchester, Pop. 670
Dorchester SD 4
Supt. — See Saint George
Odyssey Educational Center Alt
145 Hill St 29448 843-462-2270
Dr. Catherine Yates, prin. Fax 462-2275

Hartsville, Darlington, Pop. 7,682
Darlington County SD
Supt. — See Darlington
Hartsville HS 1,300/9-12
701 Lewellyn Ave 29550 843-383-3130
Dr. Charlie Burry, prin. Fax 857-3715
Hartsville MS 1,100/6-8
1427 14th St 29550 843-383-3121
Meredith Taylor, prin. Fax 857-4510

State Supported Schools
Supt. — None
Governers S of Science/Math 11-12
401 Railroad Ave 29550 843-383-3900
Dr. Murray Brockman, pres. Fax 383-3903

Coker College Post-Sec.
300 E College Ave 29550 843-383-8000
Emmanuel Christian S 400/PK-12
1001 N Marquis Hwy 29550 843-332-0164

Hemingway, Williamsburg, Pop. 449
Georgetown County SD
Supt. — See Georgetown
Carvers Bay HS 400/9-12
13002 Choppee Rd 29554 843-545-5837
Rich Neal, prin. Fax 558-6927
Carvers Bay MS 300/6-8
13000 Choppee Rd 29554 843-545-0918
Comeletia Pyatt, prin. Fax 558-6937

Williamsburg County SD
Supt. — See Kingstree
Hemingway Career and Technology Center Vo/Tech
1593 Hemingway Hwy 29554 843-558-5813
Torrance Wilson, admin. Fax 558-5991
Hemingway HS 400/9-12
PO Box 1509 29554 843-558-9413
Levi Keith, prin. Fax 558-9335
Hemingway M.B. Lee MS 6-8
PO Box 1509 29554 843-558-2721
Erica Barcus, prin. Fax 558-0792

Hilton Head Island, Beaufort, Pop. 36,811
Beaufort County SD
Supt. — See Beaufort
Hilton Head Island HS 1,200/9-12
70 Wilborn Rd 29926 843-689-4800
Elizabeth O'Nan, prin. Fax 689-4947
Hilton Head Island MS 900/6-8
55 Wilborn Rd 29926 843-689-4500
Jim Shirley, prin. Fax 689-4600

Hilton Head Christian Academy 400/K-12
55 Gardner Dr 29926 843-681-2878
Matt Skinner, hdmstr. Fax 681-9758
Hilton Head Preparatory S 400/PK-12
8 Foxgrape Rd 29928 843-671-2286
Dr. Anthony Kandel, hdmstr. Fax 671-7624

Holly Hill, Orangeburg, Pop. 1,261
Orangeburg County Consolidated SD 3 3,100/PK-12
PO Box 98 29059 803-496-3288
Dr. Cynthia Cash-Greene, supt. Fax 496-5850
www.obg3.k12.sc.us
Holly Hill-Roberts MS 400/6-8
PO Box 879 29059 803-496-3818
Loretta G. Washington, prin. Fax 496-7584
STEM Magnet S 100/6-8
PO Box 249 29059 803-496-1566
Loretta G. Washington, dir. Fax 496-7132
Other Schools – See Elloree, Santee

Holly Hill Academy 300/K-12
PO Box 757 29059 803-496-3243
Garland Crump, hdmstr. Fax 496-9778

Hollywood, Charleston, Pop. 4,680
Charleston County SD
Supt. — See Charleston
Baptist Hill HS 400/7-12
5117 Baptist Hill Rd 29449 843-889-2276
Kala Goodwine, prin. Fax 889-2101

Honea Path, Anderson, Pop. 3,518
Anderson SD 2 3,700/PK-12
10990 Belton Honea Path Hwy 29654 864-369-7364
Thomas Chapman, supt. Fax 369-4006
www.anderson2.k12.sc.us
Belton-Honea Path HS 1,100/9-12
11000 Belton Honea Path Hwy 29654 864-369-7382
Lester McCall, prin. Fax 369-4011
Honea Path MS 500/5-8
107 Brock Ave 29654 864-369-7641
Dr. John Snead, prin. Fax 369-4034
Other Schools – See Belton

Hopkins, Richland, Pop. 2,838
Richland SD 1
Supt. — See Columbia
Hopkins MS 500/6-8
1601 Clarkson Rd 29061 803-695-3331
Goler Collins, prin. Fax 695-3320
Lower Richland HS 1,400/9-12
2615 Lower Richland Blvd 29061 803-695-3000
Kelvin Wymbs, prin. Fax 695-3062
Southeast MS 600/6-8
731 Horrell Hill Rd 29061 803-695-5700
Stacey Whitaker, prin. Fax 695-5703

Indian Land, Lancaster
Lancaster County SD
Supt. — See Lancaster
Indian Land HS 700/9-12
8063 River Rd, 803-547-7571
David Shamble, prin. Fax 547-7366
Indian Land MS 500/6-8
8361 Charlotte Hwy, 803-578-2500
Chris Thorpe, prin. Fax 578-2549

Inman, Spartanburg, Pop. 2,273
Spartanburg SD 1
Supt. — See Campobello
Chapman HS 1,000/9-12
1420 Compton Bridge Rd 29349 864-472-2836
Stephanie Mathis, prin. Fax 472-0914
Mabry MS 400/7-8
35 Oakland Ave 29349 864-472-8402
Marsha Clark, prin. Fax 472-7438
Swofford Career Center Vo/Tech
5620 Highway 11 29349 864-592-2790
Scott Simpkins, dir. Fax 592-1469

Spartanburg SD 2
Supt. — See Chesnee
Boiling Springs MS 700/6-8
4801 Highway 9 29349 864-578-5954
Penny Atkinson, prin. Fax 599-5489

Irmo, Richland, Pop. 10,848
SD Five of Lexington & Richland Counties 16,600/PK-12
1020 Dutch Fork Rd 29063 803-476-8000
Dr. Stephen Hefner, supt. Fax 476-8017
www.lexrich5.org/
Dutch Fork HS 2,000/9-12
1400 Old Tamah Rd 29063 803-476-3300
Greg Owings, prin. Fax 476-3320
Dutch Fork MS 1,100/7-8
1528 Old Tamah Rd 29063 803-476-4800
Roderic Taylor, prin. Fax 476-4820
Other Schools – See Chapin, Columbia

Islandton, Colleton, Pop. 70

New Hope Christian S of Islandton 50/PK-12
PO Box 55 29929 843-866-2608
Mark Givens, prin.

Iva, Anderson, Pop. 1,209
Anderson SD 3 2,600/PK-12
PO Box 118 29655 864-348-6196
Dr. Mason Gary, supt. Fax 348-6198
www.anderson3.k12.sc.us
Crescent HS 700/9-12
9104 Highway 81 S 29655 864-352-6175
Devon Smith, prin. Fax 352-2308
Other Schools – See Anderson, Starr

Jackson, Aiken, Pop. 1,680
Aiken County SD
Supt. — See Aiken
Jackson MS 300/6-8
8217 Atomic Rd 29831 803-279-3525
Earl Ishmal, prin. Fax 471-2202

Jefferson, Chesterfield, Pop. 722
Chesterfield County SD
Supt. — See Chesterfield
New Heights MS 600/6-8
5738 Highway 151 29718 843-658-6830
Matthew Scandrol, prin. Fax 658-6812

Johns Island, Charleston
Charleston County SD
Supt. — See Charleston
Haut Gap MS 400/5-8
1861 Bohicket Rd 29455 843-559-6418
Travis Benintendo, prin. Fax 559-6439
St. Johns HS 300/9-12
1518 Main Rd 29455 843-559-6400
William Runyon, prin. Fax 559-6409

Charleston Collegiate S 200/PK-12
2024 Academy Rd 29455 843-559-5506
Hacker Burr, prin. Fax 559-6172

Johnsonville, Florence, Pop. 1,455
Florence County SD Five 1,500/PK-12
PO Box 98 29555 843-386-2358
Robert Smiley, supt. Fax 386-3139
www.flo5.k12.sc.us
Johnsonville HS 400/9-12
237 S Georgetown Hwy 29555 843-386-2707
Sam Tuten, prin. Fax 386-9058
Johnsonville MS 400/5-8
PO Box 67 29555 843-386-2066
Randy Willis, prin. Fax 386-3786

Johnston, Edgefield, Pop. 2,346
Edgefield County SD 4,000/PK-12
3 Par Dr 29832 803-275-4601
Greg Anderson, supt. Fax 275-4426
www.edgefield.k12.sc.us
JET MS 500/6-8
1095 Columbia Rd 29832 803-275-1997
Stephen Hampton, prin. Fax 275-1783
Thurmond Career Center Vo/Tech
17 Par Dr 29832 803-275-1767
Willie Green, dir. Fax 275-1766
Thurmond HS 900/9-12
1131 Columbia Rd 29832 803-275-1768
Jill Jett, prin. Fax 275-1764
Other Schools – See North Augusta

Wardlaw Academy 200/PK-12
1296 Columbia Rd 29832 803-275-4794

Kershaw, Lancaster, Pop. 1,779
Kershaw County SD
Supt. — See Camden
North Central HS 500/9-12
3000 Lockhart Rd 29067 803-432-9858
Worth Thomasson, prin. Fax 425-8992
North Central MS 400/6-8
805 Keys Ln 29067 803-424-2740
Burchell Richardson Ed.D., prin. Fax 424-2742

Lancaster County SD
Supt. — See Lancaster
Jackson HS 600/9-12
6925 Kershaw Camden Hwy 29067 803-475-2381
Alex Dabney, prin. Fax 475-7317
Jackson MS 500/6-8
6865 Kershaw Camden Hwy 29067 803-475-6021
Daryl Hinson, prin. Fax 475-8256

Kingstree, Williamsburg, Pop. 3,310
Williamsburg County SD 4,200/PK-12
PO Box 1067 29556 843-355-5571
Dr. Yvonne Jefferson-Barnes, supt. Fax 355-3213
wcsd.k12.sc.us/
Kingstree HS 800/9-12
616 Martin Luther King Ave 29556 843-355-6525
Willie Frazier, prin. Fax 355-7019
Kingstree MS 500/6-8
616 Martin Luther King Ave 29556 843-355-6823
Valeria Brown, prin. Fax 355-9207
Other Schools – See Greeleyville, Hemingway

Williamsburg Academy 400/K-12
PO Box 770 29556 843-355-9400
Evan Powell, hdmstr. Fax 355-7734
Williamsburg Technical College Post-Sec.
601 Martin Luther King Ave 29556 843-355-4110

Ladson, Berkeley, Pop. 13,352
Berkeley County SD
Supt. — See Moncks Corner
College Park MS 700/6-8
713 College Park Rd 29456 843-553-8300
Ingrid Dukes, prin. Fax 820-4026
Sangaree MS 700/6-8
1050 Discovery Dr 29456 843-821-4028
Margaret Day, prin. Fax 871-8974

Dorchester SD 2
Supt. — See Summerville
Oakbrook MS 900/6-8
286 Old Fort Dr 29456 843-873-9750
Brion Rutherford, prin. Fax 821-3931

Lake City, Florence, Pop. 6,625
Florence County SD Three 3,400/K-12
PO Box 1389 29560 843-374-8652
Dr. V. Keith Callicutt, supt. Fax 374-2946
www.florence3.k12.sc.us/
Lake City HS 900/9-12
PO Box 1569 29560 843-374-3321
Kasey Feagin, prin. Fax 374-3138
McNair MS 400/6-8
PO Box 1209 29560 843-374-8651
Margie Myers, prin. Fax 374-8504
Truluck MS 300/6-8
PO Box 1239 29560 843-374-8685
Ned Blake, prin. Fax 374-7341

Carolina Academy 200/PK-12
351 N Country Club Rd 29560 843-374-5485
Stevie Phillips, head sch Fax 374-0164

Lake View, Dillon, Pop. 805
Dillon SD Four
Supt. — See Dillon
Lake View JSHS 300/6-12
PO Box 624 29563 843-759-3009
Edison Arnette, prin. Fax 759-3015

Lamar, Darlington, Pop. 980
Darlington County SD
Supt. — See Darlington
Lamar HS 300/9-12
216 N Darlington Ave 29069 843-326-5543
Kathy Gainey, prin. Fax 326-7507
Spaulding MS 300/6-8
400 Cartersville Hwy 29069 843-326-7625
Derrick Glover, prin. Fax 326-7656

Lancaster, Lancaster, Pop. 8,450
Lancaster County SD 11,700/PK-12
300 S Catawba St 29720 803-286-6972
Dr. Gene Moore, supt. Fax 416-8860
www.lancasterscschools.org/
Buford HS 600/9-12
4290 Tabernacle Rd 29720 803-286-7068
Butch Dutton, prin. Fax 286-8147
Buford MS 500/6-8
1890 N Rocky River Rd 29720 803-285-8473
Sheri Wells, prin. Fax 283-2023
Lancaster High Career Center Vo/Tech
625 Normandy Rd 29720 803-285-7404
Dr. Joe Keenan, prin. Fax 285-2720
Lancaster HS 1,500/9-12
617 Normandy Rd 29720 803-283-2001
Dr. Joseph Keenan, prin. Fax 286-6962
Rucker MS 500/6-8
422 Old Dixie Rd 29720 803-416-8555
Phillip Mickles, prin. Fax 285-1534
South MS 600/6-8
1551 Billings Dr 29720 803-283-8416
Joyce Crimminger, prin. Fax 283-8417
Adult Education Adult
610 E Meeting St 29720 803-285-7660
Dr. Kim Linton, dir. Fax 285-9281
Other Schools – See Indian Land, Kershaw

University of South Carolina Post-Sec.
PO Box 889 29721 803-313-7000

Landrum, Spartanburg, Pop. 2,337
Spartanburg SD 1
Supt. — See Campobello
Landrum MS 300/6-8
104 Redland Rd 29356 864-457-2629
Crystal McSwain, prin. Fax 457-5372

Blue Ridge Christian Academy 200/PK-12
424 Highway 101 29356 864-895-9008
Jill Bird, admin. Fax 895-8797

Latta, Dillon, Pop. 1,366
Latta SD 1,600/K-12
205 King St 29565 843-752-7101
Dr. John Kirby, supt. Fax 752-2081
www.dillon3.k12.sc.us
Latta HS 400/9-12
618 N Richardson St 29565 843-752-5751
George Liebenrood, prin. Fax 752-2707
Latta MS 400/6-8
612 N Richardson St 29565 843-752-7117
George Liebenrood, prin. Fax 752-2722

Laurens, Laurens, Pop. 9,035
Laurens SD 55 5,900/PK-12
1029 W Main St 29360 864-984-3568
Billy Strickland, supt. Fax 984-8100
www.laurens55.k12.sc.us/
Laurens District 55 HS 1,500/9-12
5058 Highway 76 W 29360 864-682-3151
Sonya Bryant, prin. Fax 682-7426
Laurens MS 400/6-8
1035 W Main St 29360 864-984-2400
Dr. Rhett Harris, prin. Fax 984-6013
Sanders MS 400/6-8
609 Green St 29360 864-984-0354
George Ward, prin. Fax 984-2452
Other Schools – See Gray Court

Lexington, Lexington, Pop. 17,606
Lexington County SD 1 21,600/K-12
PO Box 1869 29071 803-821-1000
Karen Woodward Ed.D., supt. Fax 821-1010
www.lexington1.net
Carolina Springs MS 800/6-8
6180 Platt Springs Rd 29073 803-821-4900
Alan Zwart, prin. Fax 821-4903
Focus Program Alternative Learning Ctr Alt
420 Hendrix St 29072 803-821-1300
Jim Harpe, coord. Fax 821-1303
Lexington HS 2,900/9-12
2463 Augusta Hwy 29072 803-821-3400
Melissa Rawl, prin. Fax 821-3403
Lexington MS 1,400/6-8
702 N Lake Dr 29072 803-821-3700
Ryan Pool, prin. Fax 821-3703
Lexington Technology Center Vo/Tech
2421 Augusta Hwy 29072 803-821-3000
Kenneth Lake, dir. Fax 821-3003
Meadow Glen MS 6-8
440 Ginny Ln 29072 803-821-0600
Bill Coon, prin. Fax 821-0603
Pleasant Hill MS 1,100/6-8
660 Rawl Rd 29072 803-821-2700
Thomas Rivers, prin. Fax 821-2703
River Bluff HS 9-12
320 Corley Mill Rd 29072 803-821-0702
Luke Clamp, prin. Fax 821-1156
White Knoll HS 1,900/9-12
5643 Platt Springs Rd 29073 803-821-5200
Ryan Player, prin. Fax 821-5203
Other Schools – See Gilbert, Pelion, West Columbia

Liberty, Pickens, Pop. 3,217
Pickens County SD
Supt. — See Easley
Liberty HS 700/9-12
124 Red Devil Dr 29657 864-397-2600
Lori Gwinn, prin. Fax 843-5828
Liberty MS 600/6-8
125 Falcon Ln 29657 864-397-3400
Donivan Edwards, prin. Fax 843-5857
Pickens County Career & Technology Ctr Vo/Tech
990 Chastain Rd 29657 864-397-4500
Leonard Williams, dir. Fax 843-9064

Little River, Horry, Pop. 8,858
Horry County SD
Supt. — See Conway
North Myrtle Beach HS 1,300/9-12
3750 Sea Mountain Hwy 29566 843-399-6171
Trevor Strawderman, prin. Fax 399-6509
North Myrtle Beach MS 1,000/6-8
11240 Highway 90 29566 843-399-6136
Virginia Horton, prin. Fax 399-2233

Longs, Horry

North Myrtle Beach Christian S 100/PK-12
9535 Highway 90 29568 843-399-7181
Linda Adams, prin. Fax 399-7183

Loris, Horry, Pop. 2,350
Horry County SD
Supt. — See Conway
Loris HS 800/9-12
301 Loris Lions Rd 29569 843-390-6800
Dirk Gurley, prin. Fax 390-6801
Loris MS 600/6-8
5209 Highway 66 29569 843-756-2181
Ann Hall, prin. Fax 756-0522

Lugoff, Kershaw, Pop. 7,335
Kershaw County SD
Supt. — See Camden
Lugoff-Elgin HS 1,600/9-12
1284 Highway 1 S 29078 803-438-3481
Thomas Gladden, prin. Fax 438-8005
Lugoff-Elgin MS 600/6-8
1244 Highway 1 S 29078 803-438-3591
Dave Matthews, prin. Fax 438-8027

Lyman, Spartanburg, Pop. 3,187
Spartanburg SD 5
Supt. — See Duncan
Hill MS 600/7-8
PO Box 1329 29365 864-949-2370
Terry Glasgow, prin. Fax 949-2369

Mc Bee, Chesterfield, Pop. 855
Chesterfield County SD
Supt. — See Chesterfield
Mc Bee HS 500/7-12
PO Box 218 29101 843-335-8251
Dennis McDaniel, prin. Fax 335-6515

Mc Clellanville, Charleston, Pop. 499
Charleston County SD
Supt. — See Charleston
Lincoln MSHS 200/7-12
714 Lincoln Rd 29458 843-577-0970
Dr. Yvonne Commodore, prin. Fax 887-3116

Mc Cormick, McCormick, Pop. 2,752
McCormick County SD 900/PK-12
821 N Mine St 29835 864-852-2435
Dr. William Wright, supt. Fax 852-2883
www.mccormick.k12.sc.us
McCormick HS 300/9-12
6981 SC Highway 28 S 29835 864-443-0040
Dr. Mark Dean, prin. Fax 443-0049
McCormick MS 200/6-8
6979 SC Highway 28 S 29835 864-443-2243
David Schoolfield, prin. Fax 443-3298

Manning, Clarendon, Pop. 4,077
Area Vocational Schools
Supt. — None
Dubose Career Center Vo/Tech
PO Box 1249 29102 803-473-2531
Susan Anderson, prin. Fax 473-4320

Clarendon SD 2 3,000/PK-12
PO Box 1252 29102 803-435-4435
John Tindal, supt. Fax 435-8172
www.clarendon2.k12.sc.us
Manning HS 900/9-12
2155 Paxville Hwy 29102 803-435-4417
Neshunda Walters, prin. Fax 435-4404
Manning JHS 500/7-8
1101 W L Hamilton Rd 29102 803-435-8195
Jerry Coker, prin. Fax 435-6848

Marion, Marion, Pop. 6,862
Marion County SD 5,300/PK-12
719 N Main St 29571 843-423-1811
Dan Strickland, supt. Fax 423-8328
www.marion.k12.sc.us
Academy of Careers and Technology Vo/Tech
PO Box 890 29571 843-423-1941
Paul Crandall, dir. Fax 423-1943
Creek Bridge HS 400/6-12
6641 S Highway 41 29571 843-362-3500
Robert Smalls, prin. Fax 362-3506
Johnakin MS 600/6-8
601 Gurley St 29571 843-423-8360
Shalah Sweeney, prin. Fax 423-8383
Marion HS 800/9-12
1205 S Main St 29571 843-423-2571
Alfred McFadden, prin. Fax 423-8330
Other Schools – See Mullins

Mauldin, Greenville, Pop. 22,445
Greenville County SD
Supt. — See Greenville
Mauldin HS 2,100/9-12
701 E Butler Rd 29662 864-355-6500
Ann Miller, prin. Fax 355-6657

Moncks Corner, Berkeley, Pop. 7,746
Berkeley County SD 28,200/PK-12
PO Box 608 29461 843-899-8600
Dr. Rodney Thompson, supt. Fax 899-8791
www.bcsdschools.net
Berkeley Alternative S Alt
106 S Live Oak Dr 29461 843-899-8830
Don Brown, dir. Fax 899-8817
Berkeley County Middle College HS 9-12
1001 S Live Oak Dr 29461 843-899-8110
Claire Freeman, prin. Fax 899-8113
Berkeley HS 1,300/9-12
406 W Main St 29461 843-899-8800
Steven Steele, prin. Fax 899-8810
Berkeley MS 1,100/6-8
320 N Live Oak Dr 29461 843-899-8840
Mike Wilkerson, prin. Fax 899-8846
Macedonia MS 400/5-8
200 Macedonia Foxes Cir 29461 843-899-8940
Janie Langley, prin. Fax 899-8929
Other Schools – See Cross, Goose Creek, Hanahan, Ladson, Saint Stephen, Summerville

---

St. John Christian Academy 400/PK-12
204 W Main St 29461 843-761-8539
Eric Denton, hdmstr. Fax 899-5514
Trident Technical College Post-Sec.
1001 S Live Oak Dr 29461 843-899-8033

Monetta, Aiken, Pop. 227
Aiken County SD
Supt. — See Aiken
Ridge Spring-Monetta HS 300/9-12
10 J P Kneece Dr 29105 803-685-2100
Warren Wintrode, prin. Fax 685-2108

Moore, Spartanburg
Spartanburg County SD 6
Supt. — See Roebuck
Anderson Applied Technology Center Vo/Tech
PO Box 248 29369 864-576-5020
Sherri Yarborough, prin. Fax 576-8642
Dawkins MS 800/6-8
1300 E Blackstock Rd 29369 864-576-8088
Jay Seegars, prin. Fax 595-2418

Mount Pleasant, Charleston, Pop. 67,140
Charleston County SD
Supt. — See Charleston
Cario MS 1,300/6-8
3500 Thomas Cario Blvd 29466 843-856-4595
Benjamin Bragg, prin. Fax 856-4599
Laing MS 500/6-8
1560 Mathis Ferry Rd 29464 843-849-2809
Deborah Price, prin. Fax 849-2895
Moultrie MS 900/6-8
645 Coleman Blvd 29464 843-849-2819
Anna Dassing, prin. Fax 849-2899
Wando HS 3,400/9-12
1000 Warrior Way 29466 843-849-2830
Lucy Beckham, prin. Fax 849-2890

Coastal Christian Preparatory S 300/PK-12
681 McCants Dr 29464 843-884-3663
Joe Hulsey, hdmstr. Fax 884-9608
Palmetto Christian Academy 500/PK-12
361 Egypt Rd 29464 843-881-9967
Mike Lindsey, hdmstr. Fax 881-4662
Trident Academy 100/K-12
1455 Wakendaw Rd 29464 843-884-7046
Joe Ferber, head sch Fax 881-8320

Mullins, Marion, Pop. 4,600
Marion County SD
Supt. — See Marion
Mullins HS 600/9-12
747 Millers Rd 29574 843-464-3710
Beck Ford, prin. Fax 464-3717
Palmetto MS 400/6-8
305 ONeal St 29574 843-464-3730
Coleman Barbour, prin. Fax 464-3736

Pee Dee Academy 400/PK-12
PO Box 449 29574 843-423-1771
Hal Townsend, hdmstr. Fax 423-0301

Murrells Inlet, Horry, Pop. 7,501
Horry County SD
Supt. — See Conway
St. James HS 1,400/9-12
10800 Highway 707 29576 843-650-5600
Vann Pennell, prin. Fax 650-1004

Myrtle Beach, Horry, Pop. 26,336
Horry County SD
Supt. — See Conway
Academy for Arts Science & Technology Vo/Tech
895 International Dr 29579 843-903-8460
Robin Jones, prin. Fax 903-8461
Carolina Forest HS 1,900/9-12
700 Gardner Lacy Rd 29579 843-236-7997
Gaye Driggers, prin. Fax 236-7504
Forestbrook MS 1,100/6-8
4430 Gator Ln 29588 843-236-7300
April Scott, prin. Fax 236-8065
Myrtle Beach HS 1,200/9-12
3302 Robert M Grissom Pkwy 29577 843-448-7149
Nona Kerr, prin. Fax 445-2036
Myrtle Beach MS 800/6-8
950 Seahawk Way 29577 843-448-3932
Roger Gray, prin. Fax 448-1182
Ocean Bay MS 1,000/6-8
905 International Dr 29579 843-903-8420
Connie Huddle, prin. Fax 903-8421
St. James MS 1,100/6-8
9775 Saint James Rd 29588 843-650-5543
Dr. Dwight Boykin, prin. Fax 650-5610
Socastee HS 1,500/9-12
4900 Socastee Blvd 29588 843-293-2513
Dr. Paul Browning, prin. Fax 293-3393

Calvary Christian S 200/PK-12
4511 Dick Pond Rd 29588 843-650-2829
Mark Roland, prin. Fax 215-4125
Christian Academy of Myrtle Beach 300/K-12
PO Box 2250 29578 843-236-6222
Nancy Henry, admin. Fax 236-2262
Golf Academy of America Post-Sec.
3268 Waccamaw Blvd 29579 800-342-7342
Horry-Georgetown Technical College Post-Sec.
743 Hemlock Ave 29577 843-477-0808
ITT Technical Institute Post-Sec.
9654 N Kings Hwy Ste 101 29572 843-497-7820
Pittsburgh Institute of Aeronautics Post-Sec.
1038 Shine Ave 29577 800-444-1440
Risen Christ Lutheran S 100/PK-12
10595 Highway 17 N 29572 843-272-8163
Sean E. O'Connor, prin. Fax 272-4039
Strand College of Hair Design Post-Sec.
423 79th Ave N 29572 843-449-1017

Neeses, Orangeburg, Pop. 371
Orangeburg County Consolidated SD 4
Supt. — See Cope
Hunter-Kinard-Tyler HS 300/7-12
7066 Norway Rd 29107 803-263-4832
Ernest Holiday, prin. Fax 263-4467

Newberry, Newberry, Pop. 10,123
Newberry County SD 5,600/PK-12
PO Box 718 29108 803-321-2600
Bennie Bennett, supt. Fax 321-2604
www.newberry.k12.sc.us/
Newberry County Career Ctr Vo/Tech
3413 Main St 29108 803-321-2674
Buddy Livingston, prin. Fax 321-2676
Newberry HS 700/9-12
3113 Main St 29108 803-321-2621
Katrina Singletary, prin. Fax 321-2633
Newberry MS 700/6-8
125 ONeal St 29108 803-321-2640
Kelli Farmer, prin. Fax 321-2647
Other Schools – See Prosperity, Whitmire

Newberry Academy 200/PK-12
2055 Smith Rd 29108 803-276-2760
Brian Fitzgerald, head sch Fax 276-2401
Newberry College Post-Sec.
2100 College St 29108 800-845-4955

New Ellenton, Aiken, Pop. 1,998
Aiken County SD
Supt. — See Aiken
New Ellenton MS 200/6-8
814 Main St S 29809 803-652-8200
Elisa Sanders-Pee, prin. Fax 652-8203

Ninety Six, Greenwood, Pop. 1,979
Greenwood SD 52 1,600/PK-12
605 Johnston Rd 29666 864-543-3100
Dr. Mark Petersen, supt. Fax 543-3704
www.greenwood52.org
Edgewood MS 400/6-8
644 S Cambridge St 29666 864-543-3511
Kelly Fisher, prin. Fax 543-4994
Ninety Six HS 500/9-12
640 S Cambridge St 29666 864-543-2911
Rex Ward, prin. Fax 543-3132

North, Orangeburg, Pop. 730
Orangeburg Consolidated SD 5
Supt. — See Orangeburg
North MSHS 300/6-12
692 Cromer Ave 29112 803-247-2541
Charles Gregory, prin. Fax 247-5090

North Augusta, Aiken, Pop. 20,954
Aiken County SD
Supt. — See Aiken
Knox MS 600/6-8
1804 Wells Rd 29841 803-442-6300
John Murphy, prin. Fax 442-6302
North Augusta HS 1,600/9-12
2000 Knobcone Ave 29841 803-442-6100
Todd Bornscheuer, prin. Fax 442-6127
North Augusta MS 600/6-8
725 Old Edgefield Rd 29841 803-442-6200
Wendy Jacobs, prin. Fax 442-6202

Edgefield County SD
Supt. — See Johnston
Merriwether MS 400/6-8
430 Murrah Rd 29860 803-279-2511
Kevin Butler, prin. Fax 279-1710

Kenneth Shuler's School of Cosmetology Post-Sec.
736 Martintown Rd 29841 803-278-1200
Victory Christian S 100/K-12
620 W Martintown Rd 29841 803-278-0125
Dr. Ed Martin, prin. Fax 278-7310

North Charleston, Charleston, Pop. 95,273
Charleston County SD
Supt. — See Charleston
ARMS Academy at Morningside 6-8
1999 Singley St 29405 843-745-2030
Dr. Joseph Williams, prin. Fax 745-2029
Charleston County S of the Arts 1,100/6-12
5109 W Enterprise St 29405 843-529-4990
Dr. Shannon Cook, prin. Fax 529-4991
Excel Academy at Morningside 500/6-8
1999 Singley St 29405 843-745-2000
Dr. Joseph Williams, prin. Fax 745-7191
Garrett Academy of Technology Vo/Tech
2731 Gordon St 29405 843-745-7126
Charity Summers, prin. Fax 529-3914
Jenkins Creative Learning Center 200/Alt
2670 Bonds Ave 29405 843-747-6609
Jennifer Coker, prin. Fax 746-7438
Liberty Hill Academy 100/Alt
5025 W Enterprise St 29405 843-566-8892
Sarah Jamme, prin. Fax 566-8897
Military Magnet Academy 500/6-12
2950 Carner Ave 29405 843-745-7102
Anderson Townsend, prin. Fax 566-7791
North Charleston HS 600/9-12
1087 E Montague Ave 29405 843-745-7140
Robert Grimm, prin. Fax 566-1954
Northwoods MS 700/6-8
7763 Northside Dr 29420 843-764-2212
Daniel Conner, prin. Fax 569-5466
Stall HS 1,000/9-12
3625 Ashley Phosphate Rd 29418 843-764-2200
Kim Wilson, prin. Fax 764-2240

Dorchester SD 2
Supt. — See Summerville
Fort Dorchester HS 2,300/9-12
8500 Patriot Blvd 29420 843-760-4450
Bert Postell, prin. Fax 760-4852
River Oaks MS 900/6-8
8642 River Oaks Dr 29420 843-695-2470
Scott Matthews, prin. Fax 695-2475

Cathedral Academy 300/K-12
PO Box 41129, 843-760-1192
Donna Lewis, head sch Fax 760-1197
Centura College Post-Sec.
8088 Rivers Ave 29406 843-569-0889
ECPI University Post-Sec.
7410 Northside Dr Ste G101 29420 843-414-0350
ITT Technical Institute Post-Sec.
2431 W Aviation Ave 29406 843-745-5700
Miller-Motte Technical College Post-Sec.
8085 Rivers Ave Ste E 29406 843-574-0101
Northside Christian S 400/PK-12
7800 Northside Dr 29420 843-797-2690
Dr. Cecil Beach, admin. Fax 797-7402
Northwood Academy 400/6-12
2263 Otranto Rd 29406 843-764-2273
Larry Evanoff, dir. Fax 764-3713
Southeastern Institute Post-Sec.
4600 Goer Dr Ste 105 29406 843-747-1279
Virginia College Post-Sec.
6185 Rivers Ave 29406 843-614-4300

Orangeburg, Orangeburg, Pop. 13,823
Orangeburg Consolidated SD 5 6,500/PK-12
578 Ellis Ave 29115 803-534-5454
Cynthia Wilson, supt. Fax 533-7953
www.ocsd5schools.org
Clark MS 700/6-8
919 Bennett St 29115 803-531-2200
Dr. Lana Williams, prin. Fax 533-6503
Howard MS 400/6-8
1255 Belleville Rd 29115 803-534-5470
Rena Bowman, prin. Fax 535-1606
Orangeburg-Wilkinson HS 1,400/9-12
601 Bruin Pkwy 29118 803-534-6180
Goler Collins, prin. Fax 533-6310
Technology Center Vo/Tech
3720 Magnolia St 29118 803-536-4473
Cleve Pilot, prin. Fax 533-6365
Other Schools – See North, Rowesville

Claflin University Post-Sec.
400 Magnolia St 29115 803-535-5000
Orangeburg-Calhoun Technical College Post-Sec.
3250 Saint Matthews Rd 29118 803-536-0311
Orangeburg Preparatory S 800/K-12
2651 North Rd 29118 803-534-7970
Kelley Mims, head sch Fax 535-2190
South Carolina State University Post-Sec.
300 College Ave 29115 803-536-7000
Southern Methodist College Post-Sec.
541 Broughton St 29115 803-534-7826

Pacolet, Spartanburg, Pop. 2,212
Spartanburg SD 3
Supt. — See Glendale
Middle School of Pacolet 200/6-8
850 Sunny Acres Rd 29372 864-279-6600
Max Deaton, prin. Fax 279-6610

Pageland, Chesterfield, Pop. 2,713
Chesterfield County SD
Supt. — See Chesterfield
Central HS 700/9-12
200 Zion Church Rd 29728 843-672-6115
Dr. Juddson Starling, prin. Fax 672-2694

South Pointe Christian S 200/PK-12
PO Box 188 29728 843-672-2760
Larry Stinson, prin. Fax 672-3913

Pamplico, Florence, Pop. 1,212
Florence County SD 2 1,200/PK-12
2121 S Pamplico Hwy 29583 843-493-2502
Robert Sullivan, supt. Fax 493-1912
www.flo2.k12.sc.us/
Hannah-Pamplico HS 300/9-12
2055 S Pamplico Hwy 29583 843-493-5781
Timothy Gibbs, prin. Fax 493-5424

New Prospect Christian S 100/K-12
4221 Sheminally Rd 29583 843-493-2189
Lula Mims, prin. Fax 493-0899

Pawleys Island, Georgetown, Pop. 101
Georgetown County SD
Supt. — See Georgetown
Waccamaw HS 800/9-12
2412 Kings River Rd 29585 843-237-9899
David Hammel, prin. Fax 237-9883
Waccamaw MS 400/7-8
247 Wildcat Way 29585 843-237-0106
Jamie Curry, prin. Fax 237-0237

Pelion, Lexington, Pop. 671
Lexington County SD 1
Supt. — See Lexington
Pelion HS 700/9-12
600 Lydia Dr 29123 803-821-2200
Clark Cooper, prin. Fax 821-2203
Pelion MS 600/6-8
758 Magnolia St 29123 803-821-2300
Dr. Sandra Jowers, prin. Fax 821-2303

Pendleton, Anderson, Pop. 2,884
Anderson SD 4 2,800/K-12
PO Box 545 29670 864-403-2000
Lee D'Andrea Ph.D., supt. Fax 403-2029
www.anderson4.k12.sc.us
Riverside MS 400/7-8
458 Riverside St 29670 864-403-2200
Dr. Kevin Black, prin. Fax 646-8025
Other Schools – See Anderson

Tri-County Technical College Post-Sec.
PO Box 587 29670 864-646-8361

Pickens, Pickens, Pop. 3,062
Pickens County SD
Supt. — See Easley
Pickens HS 1,500/9-12
150 Blue Flame Dr 29671 864-397-3600
Marion Lawson, prin. Fax 898-5611
Pickens MS 800/6-8
467 Sparks Ln 29671 864-397-4100
Dr. Libba Floyd, prin. Fax 878-8734

Lakeview Christian S 200/PK-12
107 Mauldin Lake Rd 29671 864-878-6959
Rev. Mike Belcher, admin. Fax 878-6927

Piedmont, Greenville, Pop. 5,025
Anderson SD 1
Supt. — See Williamston
Wren HS 1,700/9-12
905 Wren School Rd 29673 864-850-5900
Robbie Binnicker, prin. Fax 850-5929
Wren MS 800/6-8
1010 Wren School Rd 29673 864-850-5930
Robin Fulbright, prin. Fax 850-5941

Greenville County SD
Supt. — See Greenville
Woodmont HS 1,700/9-12
2831 W Georgia Rd 29673 864-355-8600
Darryl Imperati, prin. Fax 355-8695
Woodmont MS 700/6-8
325 N Flat Rock Rd 29673 864-355-8500
Greg Scott, prin. Fax 355-8587

Prosperity, Newberry, Pop. 1,173
Newberry County SD
Supt. — See Newberry
Mid-Carolina HS 700/9-12
377 Cy Schumpert Rd 29127 803-364-2134
Ray Cooper, prin. Fax 364-4395
Mid-Carolina MS 600/6-8
6794 US Highway 76 29127 803-364-3634
Deedee Westwood, prin. Fax 364-4877

Rembert, Sumter, Pop. 296

Sumter Academy 500/PK-12
5265 Camden Hwy 29128 803-499-3378
Debbie Nix, hdmstr. Fax 499-3391

Richburg, Chester, Pop. 273
Chester County SD
Supt. — See Chester
Lewisville HS 400/9-12
3971 Lewisville High School 29729 803-789-5131
James Knox, prin. Fax 789-3188
Lewisville MS 300/6-8
PO Box 280 29729 803-789-5858
H.L. Erwin, prin. Fax 789-6159

Ridgeland, Jasper, Pop. 4,009
Area Vocational Schools
Supt. — None
Beaufort-Jasper Acad Career Excellence Vo/Tech
80 Lowcountry Dr 29936 843-987-8107
Dr. Deon Simmons, dir. Fax 987-4136

Jasper County SD 2,600/PK-12
10942 N Jacob Smart Blvd 29936 843-717-1100
Dr. Vashti Washington, supt. Fax 717-1199
www.jcsd.net
Ridgeland-Hardeeville HS 600/9-12
250 Jaguar Trl 29936 843-717-1500
Cassandra Jennings, prin. Fax 717-1596
Other Schools – See Hardeeville

Heyward Academy 400/PK-12
1727 Malphrus Rd 29936 843-726-3673
Marilyn Davis, head sch Fax 726-5773

Ridgeville, Dorchester, Pop. 1,972
Dorchester SD 2
Supt. — See Summerville
Givhans Community S Adult
273 Highway 61 29472 843-832-5559
Joyce Dearing, prin. Fax 821-3944

Rock Hill, York, Pop. 64,898
Rock Hill SD 3 17,400/PK-12
PO Box 10072 29731 803-981-1000
Lynn Moody Ed.D., supt. Fax 981-1094
www.rock-hill.k12.sc.us/
Castle Heights MS 800/6-8
2382 Fire Tower Rd 29730 803-981-1400
Kelly Kane, prin. Fax 981-1430
Dutchman Creek MS 900/6-8
4757 Mount Gallant Rd 29732 803-985-1700
Norris Williams, prin. Fax 985-1740
Northwestern HS 1,700/9-12
2503 W Main St 29732 803-981-1200
James Blake, prin. Fax 981-1250
Phoenix Academy Alt
1234 Flint Street Ext 29730 803-981-1975
Dr. Walter Wolff, dir. Fax 981-1396
Rawlinson Road MS 700/6-8
2631 W Main St 29732 803-981-1500
Dr. Jean Dickson, prin. Fax 981-1532
Rebound Alternative S Alt
1234 Flint Street Ext 29730 803-981-1087
Hank Hammond, dir. Fax 981-1259
Renaissance Academy Alt
1234 Flint Street Ext 29730 803-985-3737
James Quinn, dir. Fax 981-1396
Rock Hill Applied Technology Center Vo/Tech
2399 W Main St 29732 803-981-1100
Don Gillman, dir. Fax 981-1125
Rock Hill HS 2,000/9-12
320 W Springdale Rd 29730 803-981-1300
Ozzie Ahl, prin. Fax 981-1343
Saluda Trail MS 800/6-8
2300 Saluda Rd 29730 803-981-1800
Brenda Campbell, prin. Fax 981-1888
South Pointe HS 1,500/9-12
801 Neely Rd 29730 803-980-2100
Dr. Al Leonard, prin. Fax 980-2105
Sullivan MS 800/6-8
1825 Eden Ter 29730 803-981-1450
Michael Waiksnis, prin. Fax 981-1456
Adult & Community Education Adult
1234 Flint Street Ext 29730 803-981-1375
Sandy Andrews, dir. Fax 981-1397

Clinton Junior College Post-Sec.
1029 Crawford Rd 29730 803-327-7402
Westminster Catawba Christian S 600/PK-12
2650 India Hook Rd 29732 803-366-4119
Ray Casey, hdmstr. Fax 328-5465
Winthrop University Post-Sec.
701 W Oakland Ave 29733 803-323-2211
York Technical College Post-Sec.
452 Anderson Rd S 29730 803-327-8000

Roebuck, Spartanburg, Pop. 2,173
Spartanburg County SD 6 11,400/PK-12
1390 Cavalier Way 29376 864-576-4212
Dr. Darryl Owings, supt. Fax 574-6265
www.spart6.org
Dorman HS 2,400/10-12
1050 Cavalier Way 29376 864-582-4347
Ken Kiser, prin. Fax 587-8738
Dorman HS - Freshman Campus 800/9-9
1225 Cavalier Way 29376 864-582-3479
Mark Smith, prin. Fax 342-8997
Gable MS 700/6-8
198 Otts Shoals Rd 29376 864-576-3500
Karen Bush, prin. Fax 595-2428
Other Schools – See Moore, Spartanburg

Rowesville, Orangeburg, Pop. 302
Orangeburg Consolidated SD 5
Supt. — See Orangeburg
Bethune-Bowman MSHS 400/6-12
4857 Charleston Hwy 29133 803-516-6011
Marvin Foster, prin. Fax 516-6013

Saint George, Dorchester, Pop. 2,077
Dorchester SD 4 2,400/PK-12
500 Ridge St 29477 843-563-4535
Jerry Montjoy, supt. Fax 563-9269
www.dorchester4.k12.sc.us
Saint George MS 300/6-8
600 Minus St 29477 843-563-3171
Jeffery Thompson, prin. Fax 563-5936
Other Schools – See Dorchester, Harleyville

Dorchester Academy 300/K-12
234 Academy Rd 29477 843-563-9511
Karen Neil, hdmstr. Fax 563-4764

Saint Matthews, Calhoun, Pop. 2,002
Calhoun County SD 1,700/PK-12
PO Box 215 29135 803-655-7310
Dr. Steve Wilson, supt. Fax 655-7393
www.ccpsonline.net/
Calhoun County HS 500/9-12
150 Saints Ave 29135 803-874-3071
Cynthia Johnson, prin. Fax 655-5948

Calhoun Academy 500/PK-12
PO Box 526 29135 803-874-2734

Saint Stephen, Berkeley, Pop. 1,670
Berkeley County SD
Supt. — See Moncks Corner
Saint Stephen MS 200/6-8
225 Carolina Dr 29479 843-567-3128
Brenda Fleming, prin. Fax 567-8162
Timberland HS 800/9-12
1418 Gravel Hill Rd 29479 843-567-8110
Kerry Daugherty, prin. Fax 567-8116

Salem, Oconee, Pop. 134
Oconee County SD
Supt. — See Walhalla
Tamassee-Salem MSHS 300/6-12
4 Eagle Ln 29676 864-886-4545
Steve Moore, prin. Fax 886-4541

Saluda, Saluda, Pop. 3,519
Saluda SD 2,100/PK-12
404 N Wise Rd 29138 864-445-8441
David Mathis Ed.D., supt. Fax 445-9598
www.saludaschools.org
Saluda HS 600/9-12
160 Ivory Key Rd 29138 864-445-3011
Dr. Harvey Livingston, prin. Fax 445-3542
Saluda MS 500/6-8
140 Ivory Key Rd 29138 864-445-3767
Lori Corley, prin. Fax 445-3980

Santee, Orangeburg, Pop. 941
Orangeburg County Consolidated SD 3
Supt. — See Holly Hill
Lake Marion HS 900/9-12
PO Box 650 29142 803-854-9213
Rodney Zimmerman, prin. Fax 854-5202

Seabrook, Beaufort
Beaufort County SD
Supt. — See Beaufort
Whale Branch Early College HS 400/9-12
169 Detour Rd 29940 843-466-2700
Priscilla Drake, prin. Fax 846-6827
Whale Branch MS 300/5-8
2009 Trask Pkwy 29940 843-466-3000
Matthew Hunt, prin. Fax 466-3087

Seneca, Oconee, Pop. 7,931
Oconee County SD
Supt. — See Walhalla
Hamilton Career Center Vo/Tech
100 Vocational Dr 29672 864-886-4425
Michael Pearson, prin. Fax 886-4426
Seneca HS 1,000/9-12
100 Bobcat Rdg 29678 864-886-4460
Cliff Roberts, prin. Fax 886-4457
Seneca MS 700/6-8
810 W South 4th St 29678 864-886-4455
Al LeRoy, prin. Fax 886-4452

Oconee Christian Academy 200/PK-12
150 His Way Cir 29672 864-882-6925
Thad Cloer, admin. Fax 882-7217

Simpsonville, Greenville, Pop. 17,848
Greenville County SD
Supt. — See Greenville
Bryson MS 1,100/6-8
3657 S Industrial Dr 29681 864-355-2100
Phillip Davie, prin. Fax 355-2194
Chandler MS 700/6-8
4231 Fork Shoals Rd 29680 864-452-0300
Rita Mantooth, prin. Fax 452-0365
Hillcrest HS 2,100/9-12
3665 S Industrial Dr 29681 864-355-3500
Steve Chamness, prin. Fax 355-3382
Hillcrest MS 1,000/6-8
510 Garrison Rd 29681 864-355-6100
Keith Russell, prin. Fax 355-6120
Mauldin MS 1,200/6-8
1190 Holland Rd 29681 864-355-6770
Rosia Gardner, prin. Fax 355-6988

Greenville Classical Academy 100/K-12
2519 Woodruff Rd 29681 864-329-9884
Tim Cockrell, prin.
Southside Christian S 1,000/PK-12
2211 Woodruff Rd 29681 864-234-7595
Stephen Reel Ph.D., supt. Fax 234-7048

Spartanburg, Spartanburg, Pop. 36,415
Spartanburg County SD 6
Supt. — See Roebuck
Fairforest MS 800/6-8
4120 N Blackstock Rd 29301 864-576-1270
Ty Dawkins, prin. Fax 576-2600

Spartanburg SD 3
Supt. — See Glendale
Broome HS 900/9-12
381 Cherry Hill Rd 29307 864-279-6700
Todd Hardy, prin. Fax 279-6710

Spartanburg SD 7 6,900/PK-12
PO Box 970 29304 864-594-4400
Dr. Russell Booker, supt. Fax 594-4406
www.spart7.org
Carver MS 400/6-8
467 S Church St 29306 864-594-4435
RaaShad Fitzpatrick, prin. Fax 594-6144
McCracken MS 500/6-8
300 Webber Rd 29307 864-594-4457
Margaret Peach, prin. Fax 596-8418
Morgan Technology Center Vo/Tech
201 Zion Hill Rd 29307 864-579-2810
Wayne Chapman, prin. Fax 579-7392
Spartanburg County Alternative S Alt
364 Successful Way 29303 864-594-4482
Paul Hughes, prin. Fax 594-6154
Spartanburg HS Freshman Academy 500/9-9
50 Emory Rd 29307 864-594-4513
Dr. Shawn Foster, prin. Fax 594-4518
Spartanburg SHS 1,500/10-12
500 Dupre Dr 29307 864-594-4410
Jeff Stevens, prin. Fax 594-6142

Converse College Post-Sec.
580 E Main St 29302 864-596-9000
Sherman College of Chiropractic Post-Sec.
PO Box 1452 29304 864-578-8770
South Carolina School for Deaf and Blind Post-Sec.
355 Cedar Springs Rd 29302 864-577-7557
Spartanburg Christian Academy 500/PK-12
8740 Asheville Hwy 29316 864-578-4238
Robert McDonald, hdmstr. Fax 542-1846
Spartanburg Community College Post-Sec.
PO Box 4386 29305 864-592-4800
Spartanburg Day S 500/PK-12
1701 Skylyn Dr 29307 864-582-7539
Rachel Deems, hdmstr. Fax 582-7530
Spartanburg Methodist College Post-Sec.
1000 Powell Mill Rd 29301 864-587-4000
University of South Carolina Post-Sec.
800 University Way 29303 864-503-5000
Virginia College Post-Sec.
8150 Warren H Abernathy Hwy 29301 864-504-3200
Westgate Christian S 200/K-12
1990 Old Reidville Rd 29301 864-576-4953
Rev. Tony Seiber, admin. Fax 576-7581
Wofford College Post-Sec.
429 N Church St 29303 864-597-4000

Starr, Anderson, Pop. 170
Anderson SD 3
Supt. — See Iva
Starr-Iva MS 700/6-8
1034 Rainey Rd 29684 864-352-6146
Barry Jacks, prin. Fax 352-2095

Summerton, Clarendon, Pop. 994
Clarendon SD 1 900/PK-12
PO Box 38 29148 803-485-2325
Dr. Rose Wilder, supt. Fax 485-3308
www.clarendon1.k12.sc.us
Scott's Branch HS 300/9-12
9253 Alex Harvin Hwy 29148 803-478-7818
Dr. Gwendolyn Harris, prin. Fax 478-7659
Scott's Branch MS 100/7-8
1154 4th St 29148 803-485-2043
Dr. Gwendolyn Harris, prin. Fax 485-7012

Clarendon Hall S 200/K-12
PO Box 609 29148 803-485-3550
Lindy Brunson, hdmstr. Fax 485-3205

Summerville, Dorchester, Pop. 42,232
Berkeley County SD
Supt. — See Moncks Corner
Cane Bay HS 1,500/9-12
1624 State Rd 29483 843-899-8786
Dr. Lee Westberry, prin. Fax 899-8789
Cane Bay MS 6-8
1175 Cane Bay Blvd 29483 843-899-1857
Deon Jackson, prin.

Dorchester SD 2 21,900/K-12
102 Greenwave Blvd 29483 843-873-2901
Joseph Pye, supt. Fax 821-3959
www.dorchester2.k12.sc.us
Alston MS 900/6-8
500 Bryan St 29483 843-873-3890
Thad Schmenk, prin. Fax 821-3978
Ashley Ridge HS 1,200/9-12
9800 Delemar Hwy 29485 843-695-4900
Karen Radcliffe, prin. Fax 695-4905
DuBose MS 1,000/6-8
1005 DuBose School Rd 29483 843-875-7012
Christie O'Rear, prin. Fax 821-3995
Gregg MS 900/6-8
500 Greenwave Blvd 29483 843-871-3150
Lori Estep, prin. Fax 821-3992
Rollings MS of the Arts 600/6-8
815 S Main St 29483 843-873-3610
Kathy Sobolewski, prin. Fax 821-3985
Summerville HS 2,800/9-12
1101 Boone Hill Rd 29483 843-873-6460
Kenny Farrell, prin. Fax 821-3989
Other Schools – See Ladson, North Charleston, Ridgeville

Faith Christian S 300/PK-12
337 Farmington Rd 29483 843-873-8464
John Davis, hdmstr. Fax 923-6806
Pinewood Preparatory S 700/PK-12
1114 Orangeburg Rd 29483 843-873-1643
Stephen Mandell, hdmstr. Fax 821-4257

Sumter, Sumter, Pop. 39,747
Sumter SD 17,100/PK-12
1345 Wilson Hall Rd 29150 803-469-6900
Randolph Bynum, supt. Fax 469-3769
district.sumterschools.net/
Academic Learning Center Alt
220 Hasel St 29150 803-773-6362
Samuel Myers, admin. Fax 773-7137
Alice Drive MS 700/6-8
40 Miller Rd 29150 803-775-0821
Jeannie Pressley, prin. Fax 778-2929
Bates MS 700/6-8
715 Estate St 29150 803-775-0711
Dr. Ayesha Hunter, prin. Fax 775-0715
Brewington Academy Alt
4300 E Brewington Rd 29153 803-495-8069
Dana Fall, prin. Fax 495-8068
Chestnut Oaks MS 500/6-8
1200 Oswego Hwy 29153 803-775-7272
David Laws, prin. Fax 775-7601
Crestwood HS 1,200/9-12
2000 Oswego Hwy 29153 803-469-6200
John Huggins, prin. Fax 469-7678

Ebenezer MS 400/6-8
3440 Ebenezer Rd 29153 803-469-8571
Marlene DeWit, prin. Fax 469-8575
Furman MS 900/6-8
3400 Bethel Church Rd 29154 803-481-8519
Maria Newton Ta'Bon, prin. Fax 481-8923
Lakewood HS 1,200/9-12
350 Old Manning Rd 29150 803-506-2700
Sherril Ray, prin. Fax 506-2712
Mayewood MS 200/6-8
4300 E Brewington Rd 29153 803-495-8014
John Koumas, prin. Fax 495-8016
Sumter County Career Center Vo/Tech
2612 McCrays Mill Rd 29154 803-481-8575
John Michalik, dir. Fax 481-4232
Sumter HS 2,300/9-12
2580 McCrays Mill Rd 29154 803-481-4480
Sterling Harris, prin. Fax 481-4021
Other Schools – See Dalzell

Central Carolina Technical College Post-Sec.
506 N Guignard Dr 29150 803-778-1961
Morris College Post-Sec.
100 W College St 29150 803-934-3200
St. Francis Xavier HS 50/9-12
15 School St 29150 803-773-0210
Sue Lavergne, prin. Fax 775-0119
Sumter Beauty College Post-Sec.
921 Carolina Ave 29150 803-773-7311
Sumter Christian S 200/PK-12
420 S Pike W 29150 803-773-1902
Ron Davis, admin. Fax 775-1676
University of South Carolina Post-Sec.
200 Miller Rd 29150 803-775-8727
Wilson Hall S 800/PK-12
520 Wilson Hall Rd 29150 803-469-3475

Swansea, Lexington, Pop. 808
Lexington County SD 4 2,800/PK-12
607 E 5th St 29160 803-568-1000
Dr. Linda Lavender, supt. Fax 568-1020
www.lexington4.net
Swansea HS Freshman Academy 100/9-9
1195 I W Hutto Rd 29160 803-568-1050
Bryan Evans, prin. Fax 568-1052
Swansea SHS 600/10-12
500 E 1st St 29160 803-568-1100
Leslie Hightower, prin. Fax 568-1117
Other Schools – See Gaston

Foundation Christian S 50/2-12
2153 Old State Rd 29160 803-603-8064
Margaret Nelson M.Ed., admin.

Taylors, Greenville, Pop. 21,240
Greenville County SD
Supt. — See Greenville
Eastside HS 1,300/9-12
1300 Brushy Creek Rd 29687 864-355-2800
Mike Thorne, prin. Fax 355-2992
Northwood MS 900/6-8
710 Ikes Rd 29687 864-355-7000
Richard Griffin, prin. Fax 355-7077

Tega Cay, York, Pop. 7,516
Fort Mill SD
Supt. — See Fort Mill
Gold Hill MS 800/6-8
1025 Dave Gibson Blvd 29708 803-548-8300
Tommy Johnston, prin. Fax 548-8322

Tigerville, Greenville, Pop. 1,267

North Greenville University Post-Sec.
PO Box 1892 29688 864-977-7000

Timmonsville, Florence, Pop. 2,312
Florence County SD Four 800/PK-12
304 Kemper St 29161 843-346-3956
Matrell Sturkey, supt. Fax 346-5159
www.florence4.k12.sc.us
Johnson MS 200/6-8
304 Kemper St 29161 843-346-4685
Dr. William McCall, prin. Fax 346-5199
Timmonsville HS 300/9-12
304 Kemper St 29161 843-346-4586
Dr. William McCall, prin. Fax 346-5416

Travelers Rest, Greenville, Pop. 4,504
Greenville County SD
Supt. — See Greenville
Northwest MS 900/6-8
1606 Geer Hwy 29690 864-355-6900
Lee Givins, prin. Fax 355-6920
Travelers Rest HS 1,300/9-12
301 N Main St 29690 864-355-0000
Louis Lavely, prin. Fax 355-0088

Turbeville, Clarendon, Pop. 765
Clarendon SD 3 1,300/PK-12
PO Box 270 29162 843-659-2188
Connie Dennis Ph.D., supt. Fax 659-3204
www.clarendon3.org/
East Clarendon MSHS 600/6-12
PO Box 67 29162 843-659-2185
Kelvin Lemon, prin. Fax 659-2192

Union, Union, Pop. 8,281
Union County SD 4,100/K-12
PO Box 907 29379 864-429-1740
Dr. Kristi Woodall, supt. Fax 429-1745
www.union.k12.sc.us

Sims MS 800/6-8
2200 Whitmire Hwy 29379 864-429-1755
Mickey Connolly, prin. Fax 429-2811
Union County HS 1,300/9-12
1163 Lakeside Dr 29379 864-429-1750
Floyd Lyles, prin. Fax 429-5401
Adult Education / Lifelong Learning Adult
517 E Main St 29379 864-429-1770
Eric Childers, dir. Fax 429-1771

University of South Carolina Post-Sec.
PO Box 729 29379 864-429-8728

Varnville, Hampton, Pop. 2,133
Hampton SD 1 2,600/PK-12
372 Pine St E 29944 803-943-4576
Doug McTeer, supt. Fax 943-5943
www.hampton1.k12.sc.us
Hampton HS 700/9-12
115 Airport Rd 29944 803-943-3568
Barry Rosenburg, prin. Fax 943-5036
North District MS 400/7-8
PO Box 368 29944 803-943-3507
Patricia Brantley, prin. Fax 943-4074

Wagener, Aiken, Pop. 778
Aiken County SD
Supt. — See Aiken
Corbett MS 200/6-8
10 Corbett Cir 29164 803-564-1050
Laura Bacon, prin. Fax 564-1058
Wagener-Salley HS 300/9-12
272 Main St S 29164 803-564-1100
Pat Keating, prin. Fax 564-1109

Walhalla, Oconee, Pop. 4,200
Oconee County SD 11,400/PK-12
414 S Pine St 29691 864-886-4400
Dr. Mike Lucas, supt. Fax 886-4408
www.oconee.k12.sc.us
Walhalla HS 1,000/9-12
151 Razorback Ln 29691 864-886-4490
Josh Young, prin. Fax 886-4488
Walhalla MS 700/6-8
177 Razorback Ln 29691 864-886-4485
Scott Dixon, prin. Fax 886-4483
Other Schools – See Salem, Seneca, Westminster

Walterboro, Colleton, Pop. 5,325
Colleton County SD 5,200/PK-12
213 N Jefferies Blvd 29488 843-782-4510
Leila Williams, supt. Fax 549-2606
colletonsd.org
Colleton County HS 1,700/9-12
150 Cougar Nation Dr 29488 843-782-0031
Cliff Warren, prin. Fax 782-0042
Colleton MS 400/6-8
1379 Tuskegee Airmen Dr 29488 843-782-0040
Dr. Kenneth Jenkins, prin. Fax 782-0041
Thunderbolt Career & Technology Center Vo/Tech
1069 Thunderbolt Dr 29488 843-782-4514
Michael Thomas, dir. Fax 538-3009
Adult Education Adult
609 Colleton Loop 29488 843-782-0018
Lynn Jones, dir. Fax 549-6285

Colleton Prep Academy 300/K-12
PO Box 1426 29488 843-538-8959
Jennifer Bratsafolis, head sch Fax 538-8260
Cosmetic Arts Institute Post-Sec.
1789 Hampton St 29488 843-549-8587

Ware Shoals, Greenwood, Pop. 2,149
Greenwood SD 51 1,000/PK-12
25 E Main St 29692 864-456-7496
Dr. Fay Sprouse, supt. Fax 456-3578
www.gwd51.k12.sc.us
Ware Shoals JSHS 500/7-12
56 S Greenwood Ave 29692 864-456-7923
Fr. Paul Anderson, prin. Fax 456-2959

Warrenville, Aiken, Pop. 1,205
Aiken County SD
Supt. — See Aiken
Aiken County Career & Technical Center Vo/Tech
2455 Jefferson Davis Hwy 29851 803-593-7300
Brooks Smith, dir. Fax 593-7115
Langley-Bath-Clearwater MS 500/6-8
29 Lions Trl 29851 803-593-7260
Brenda DeLoache, prin. Fax 593-7119

West Columbia, Lexington, Pop. 14,742
Lexington County SD 1
Supt. — See Lexington
White Knoll MS 800/6-8
116 White Knoll Way 29170 803-821-4300
Guy Smith, prin. Fax 821-4303

Lexington County SD 2 8,100/PK-12
715 9th St 29169 803-796-4708
Dr. Venus Holland, supt. Fax 739-4063
www.lex2.org/
Airport HS 1,400/9-12
1315 Boston Ave 29170 803-822-5600
Dr. Dixon Brooks, prin. Fax 822-5665
Fulmer MS 600/6-8
1614 Walterboro St 29170 803-822-5660
Megan Carrero, prin. Fax 822-5664
Northside MS 600/6-8
157 Cougar Dr 29169 803-739-4190
Dr. Julia Kaczor, prin. Fax 739-3188
Pair Education Center Alt
2325 Platt Springs Rd 29169 803-739-4085
Leonard Frierson, prin. Fax 739-3195

Pine Ridge MS 500/6-8
735 Pine Ridge Dr 29172 803-755-7400
Brad Coleman, prin. Fax 755-7449
Other Schools – See Cayce

State Supported Schools
Supt. — None
Gray Opportunity S 9-12
3300 W Campus Rd 29170 803-896-6480
Pat Smith, dir. Fax 896-6463

Westminster, Oconee, Pop. 2,380
Oconee County SD
Supt. — See Walhalla
West-Oak HS 1,000/9-12
130 Warrior Ln 29693 864-886-4530
Kurt Kreuzberger, prin. Fax 886-4527
West Oak MS 800/6-8
501 Westminster Hwy 29693 864-886-4525
Jami Verderosa, prin. Fax 886-4524

Whitmire, Newberry, Pop. 1,424
Newberry County SD
Supt. — See Newberry
Whitmire Community S 300/K-12
2597 Hwy 66 29178 803-694-2320
Joey Haney, prin. Fax 694-3835

Williamston, Anderson, Pop. 3,887
Anderson SD 1 9,200/PK-12
PO Box 99 29697 864-847-7344
Dr. Wayne Fowler, supt. Fax 847-3543
www.anderson1.k12.sc.us
Palmetto HS 900/9-12
804 N Hamilton St 29697 864-847-7311
Ray Callaham, prin. Fax 847-3532
Palmetto MS 800/6-8
803 N Hamilton St 29697 864-847-4333
Barry Knight, prin. Fax 847-3529
Other Schools – See Greenville, Piedmont

Area Vocational Schools
Supt. — None
Career & Technology Center Vo/Tech
702 Belton Hwy 29697 864-847-4121
Dr. Jere Kirkley, dir. Fax 847-3539

Williston, Barnwell, Pop. 3,095
Williston SD 29 1,000/PK-12
12255 Main St 29853 803-266-7878
Dr. Tom Siler, supt. Fax 266-3879
www.williston.k12.sc.us
Williston-Elko HS 300/9-12
12233 Main St 29853 803-266-3110
Dr. Brian Newsome, prin. Fax 266-5489
Williston-Elko MS 200/6-8
12333 Main St 29853 803-266-3430
Greg Sweet, prin. Fax 266-7623

Winnsboro, Fairfield, Pop. 3,508
Fairfield County SD 3,300/PK-12
PO Box 622 29180 803-635-4607
J.R. Green, supt. Fax 635-6578
www.fairfield.k12.sc.us/
Fairfield Career & Technology Center Vo/Tech
1451 US Highway 321 N 29180 803-635-5506
Christopher Dinkins, prin. Fax 635-9958
Fairfield Central HS 900/9-12
836 US Highway 321 Byp S 29180 803-635-1441
David Corley, prin. Fax 635-3997
Fairfield MS 400/7-8
728 US Highway 321 Byp S 29180 803-635-4270
Leevette Malloy, prin. Fax 635-9108
Gordon Odyssey Academy 200/Alt
560 Fairfield St 29180 803-635-4859
Dr. Nathaniel Bryan, dir. Fax 635-5835

Winn Academy 300/K-12
PO Box 390 29180 803-635-5494

Woodruff, Spartanburg, Pop. 3,990
Spartanburg SD 4 3,100/PK-12
118 McEdco Rd 29388 864-476-3186
Dr. W. Rallie Liston, supt. Fax 476-8616
www.spartanburg4.org
Woodruff HS 900/9-12
710 Cross Anchor Rd 29388 864-476-7045
Aaron Fulmer, prin. Fax 476-7224
Woodruff MS 700/6-8
205 SJ Workman Hwy 29388 864-476-3150
Denise Brown, prin. Fax 476-6036

York, York, Pop. 7,594
York SD 1 5,700/PK-12
PO Box 770 29745 803-684-9916
Dr. Vernon Prosser, supt. Fax 684-1903
www.york.k12.sc.us
Johnson Technical Center Vo/Tech
275 E Alexander Love Hwy 29745 803-684-1910
Ron Roveri, prin. Fax 684-1913
York Comprehensive HS 1,500/9-12
275 E Alexander Love Hwy 29745 803-684-2336
Chris Black, prin. Fax 684-1932
York MS 800/7-8
1010 Devinney Rd 29745 803-684-5008
Howard Snelling, prin. Fax 684-1916
York One Academy Alt
37 Pinckney St 29745 803-684-2381
Shelton Clinton, prin. Fax 684-1932

Blessed Hope Baptist S 200/K-12
410 Blessed Hope Rd 29745 803-684-9819
Fax 684-9849

SOUTH DAKOTA

SOUTH DAKOTA DEPARTMENT OF EDUCATION
800 Governors Dr, Pierre 57501-2235
Telephone 605-773-3134
Fax 605-773-6139
Website doe.sd.gov/

Secretary of Education — Dr. Melody Schopp

SOUTH DAKOTA BOARD OF EDUCATION
700 Governors Dr, Pierre 57501-2291

President — Donald Kirkegaard

PUBLIC, PRIVATE AND CATHOLIC SECONDARY SCHOOLS

Aberdeen, Brown, Pop. 25,591
Aberdeen SD 6-1 — 3,900/K-12
1224 S 3rd St 57401 — 605-725-7100
Dr. Gary Harms, supt. — Fax 725-7199
www.aberdeen.k12.sd.us
Central HS — 1,200/9-12
2200 S Roosevelt St 57401 — 605-725-8100
Jason Uttermark, prin. — Fax 725-8199
Holgate MS — 400/6-8
2200 N Dakota St 57401 — 605-725-7700
Dr. Greg Aas, prin. — Fax 725-7799
Simmons MS — 400/6-8
1300 S 3rd St 57401 — 605-725-7900
Kelly Northrup, prin. — Fax 725-7999

Hub Area Multi-District
640 9th Ave SW 57401 — 605-725-7800
Scott Pudwill, supt. — Fax 725-7899
www.hubarea.com
Hub Area Technical S — Vo/Tech
640 9th Ave SW 57401 — 605-725-7800
Scott Pudwill, prin. — Fax 725-7899

Aberdeen Christian S — 100/PK-12
1500 E Melgaard Rd 57401 — 605-225-2053
Shawn W. Yates, admin. — Fax 226-2106
Northern State University — Post-Sec.
1200 S Jay St 57401 — 605-626-3011
Presentation College — Post-Sec.
1500 N Main St 57401 — 800-437-6060
Roncalli HS — 300/7-12
1400 N Dakota St 57401 — 605-226-2100
Peggy Cox, prin. — Fax 226-0616
St. Luke's Midland Regional Medical Ctr. — Post-Sec.
305 S State St 57401 — 605-622-5230
South Dakota School Visually Handicapped — Post-Sec.
423 17th Ave SE 57401 — 605-626-2580

Alcester, Union, Pop. 801
Alcester-Hudson SD 61-1 — 300/PK-12
PO Box 198 57001 — 605-934-1890
Tim Rhead, supt. — Fax 934-1936
www.alcester-hudson.k12.sd.us
Alcester-Hudson HS — 100/9-12
PO Box 198 57001 — 605-934-1890
LeeAnn Haisch, prin. — Fax 934-1936
Alcester-Hudson JHS — 50/7-8
PO Box 198 57001 — 605-934-1890
LeeAnn Haisch, prin. — Fax 934-1936

Alexandria, Hanson, Pop. 613
Hanson SD 30-1 — 400/PK-12
PO Box 490 57311 — 605-239-4387
James Bridge, supt. — Fax 239-4293
www.hanson.k12.sd.us/
Hanson HS — 100/9-12
PO Box 490 57311 — 605-239-4387
Ray Slaba, prin. — Fax 239-4293
Hanson MS — 100/6-8
PO Box 490 57311 — 605-239-4387
Ray Slaba, prin. — Fax 239-4293
Other Schools – See Mitchell

Arlington, Kingsbury, Pop. 909
Arlington SD 38-1 — 300/PK-12
PO Box 359 57212 — 605-983-5597
Chris Lund, supt. — Fax 983-2820
www.arlington.k12.sd.us
Arlington HS — 100/9-12
PO Box 359 57212 — 605-983-5598
Rhonda Gross, prin. — Fax 983-4652
Arlington JHS — 100/7-8
PO Box 359 57212 — 605-983-5598
Rhonda Gross, prin. — Fax 983-4652

Armour, Douglas, Pop. 693
Armour SD 21-1 — 200/K-12
PO Box 640 57313 — 605-724-2153
Burnell Glanzer, supt. — Fax 724-2977
www.armour.k12.sd.us/
Armour HS — 100/9-12
PO Box 640 57313 — 605-724-2153
Brad Preheim, prin. — Fax 724-2799
Armour MS — 100/5-8
PO Box 640 57313 — 605-724-2698
Burnell Glanzer, prin. — Fax 724-2799

Avon, Bon Homme, Pop. 586
Avon SD 4-1 — 200/PK-12
PO Box 407 57315 — 605-286-3291
Tom Culver, supt. — Fax 286-3712
www.avon.k12.sd.us/
Avon HS — 100/9-12
PO Box 407 57315 — 605-286-3291
Matt Yost, prin. — Fax 286-3510
Avon JHS — 50/7-8
PO Box 407 57315 — 605-286-3291
Matt Yost, prin. — Fax 286-3510

Baltic, Minnehaha, Pop. 1,070
Baltic SD 49-1 — 400/PK-12
PO Box 309 57003 — 605-529-5464
Robert Sittig, supt. — Fax 529-5443
www.baltic.k12.sd.us/
Baltic HS — 100/9-12
PO Box 309 57003 — 605-529-5461
James Aisenbery, prin. — Fax 529-5467
Baltic MS — 100/6-8
PO Box 309 57003 — 605-529-5461
James Aisenbery, prin. — Fax 529-5467

Batesland, Shannon, Pop. 108
Shannon County SD 65-1 — 1,600/PK-8
PO Box 109 57716 — 605-288-1921
Richard Zephier Ph.D., supt. — Fax 288-1814
www.shannon.ws
Other Schools – See Pine Ridge, Porcupine

Belle Fourche, Butte, Pop. 5,472
Belle Fourche SD 9-1 — 1,300/K-12
2305 13th Ave 57717 — 605-723-3355
Dr. Steve Willard, supt. — Fax 723-3366
www.bellefourche.k12.sd.us
Belle Fourche Education Connection — 50/Alt
2305 13th Ave 57717 — 605-723-0955
Mathew Raba, prin. — Fax 723-0941
Belle Fourche HS — 400/9-12
2305 13th Ave 57717 — 605-723-3350
Mathew Raba, prin. — Fax 723-3357
Belle Fourche MS — 400/5-8
2305 13th Ave 57717 — 605-723-3367
Kevin Smidt, prin. — Fax 723-3374

Beresford, Union, Pop. 1,991
Beresford SD 61-2 — 600/PK-12
301 W Maple St 57004 — 605-763-4293
Brian Field, supt. — Fax 763-5305
www.beresford.k12.sd.us/
Beresford HS — 200/9-12
301 W Maple St 57004 — 605-763-2145
Dustin Degen, prin. — Fax 763-5305
Beresford MS — 100/6-8
205 W Maple St 57004 — 605-763-2139
Dustin Degen, prin. — Fax 763-5305

Big Stone City, Grant, Pop. 465
Big Stone CSD 25-1 — 100/PK-8
655 Walnut St 57216 — 605-862-8108
James Gagner, supt. — Fax 862-8640
www.bigstonecity.k12.sd.us
Big Stone City JHS — 50/6-8
655 Walnut St 57216 — 605-862-8108
James Gagner, prin. — Fax 862-8640

Bison, Perkins, Pop. 326
Bison SD 52-1 — 100/K-12
PO Box 9 57620 — 605-244-5271
Don Kraemer, admin. — Fax 244-5276
www.bison.k12.sd.us/
Bison HS — 50/9-12
PO Box 9 57620 — 605-244-5271
Don Kraemer, prin. — Fax 244-5276
Bison JHS — 50/7-8
PO Box 9 57620 — 605-244-5271
Don Kraemer, prin. — Fax 244-5276

Bonesteel, Gregory, Pop. 272
South Central SD 26-5 — 100/PK-12
401 Birdsell St 57317 — 605-654-2314
Dr. Cheryl Thaler, supt.
www.southcentral.k12.sd.us/
South Central HS — 50/9-12
401 Birdsell St 57317 — 605-654-2314
Dr. Cheryl Thaler, supt.
South Central MS — 50/6-8
401 Birdsell St 57317 — 605-654-2314
Dr. Cheryl Thaler, supt.

Bowdle, Edmunds, Pop. 501
Bowdle SD 22-1 — 100/K-12
PO Box 563 57428 — 605-285-6272
Dan Trefz, supt. — Fax 285-6830
www.bowdle.k12.sd.us
Bowdle HS — 50/9-12
PO Box 563 57428 — 605-285-6590
Dan Trefz, prin. — Fax 285-6830
Bowdle JHS — 50/7-8
PO Box 563 57428 — 605-285-6590
Dan Trefz, prin. — Fax 285-6830

Box Elder, Pennington, Pop. 7,381
Douglas SD 51-1 — 2,500/PK-12
400 Patriot Dr 57719 — 605-923-0000
Dr. Loren Scheer, supt. — Fax 923-0018
www.dsdk12.net
Douglas HS — 700/9-12
420 Patriot Dr 57719 — 605-923-0030
Bud Gusso, prin. — Fax 923-0031
Douglas MS — 600/6-8
401 Tower Rd 57719 — 605-923-0050
Dan Baldwin, prin. — Fax 923-0051

Brandon, Minnehaha, Pop. 8,690
Brandon Valley SD 49-2 — 3,300/PK-12
300 S Splitrock Blvd 57005 — 605-582-2049
David Pappone, supt. — Fax 582-7456
www.brandonvalleyschools.com
Brandon Valley HS — 1,000/9-12
301 S Splitrock Blvd 57005 — 605-582-3211
Dr. Gregg Talcott, prin. — Fax 582-2652
Brandon Valley MS — 800/6-8
700 E Holly Blvd 57005 — 605-582-3214
Dan Pansch, prin. — Fax 582-7206

Bridgewater, McCook, Pop. 491
Bridgewater-Emery SD 30-3 — 200/PK-12
PO Box 350 57319 — 605-729-2541
Jason Bailey, supt. — Fax 449-4270
www.bridgewater-emery.k12.sd.us/
Bridgewater-Emery MS — 50/6-8
PO Box 350 57319 — 605-449-4271
Christena Schultz, prin. — Fax 449-4270
Other Schools – See Emery

Britton, Marshall, Pop. 1,232
Britton-Hecla SD 45-4 — 500/PK-12
PO Box 190 57430 — 605-448-2234
Kevin Coles, supt. — Fax 448-5994
www.britton.k12.sd.us/
Britton-Hecla HS — 200/9-12
PO Box 190 57430 — 605-448-2234
Shad Storley, prin. — Fax 448-5994
Britton-Hecla JHS — 100/7-8
PO Box 190 57430 — 605-448-2234
Shad Storley, prin. — Fax 448-5994

Brookings, Brookings, Pop. 21,716
Brookings SD 5-1 — 2,900/K-12
2130 8th St S 57006 — 605-696-4700
Dr. Roger DeGroot, supt. — Fax 696-4704
www.brookings.k12.sd.us/
Brookings HS — 800/9-12
530 Elm Ave 57006 — 605-696-4100
Paul vonFischer, prin. — Fax 696-4128
Mickelson MS — 600/6-8
1801 12th St S 57006 — 605-696-4500
Melinda Jensen, prin. — Fax 696-4506

South Dakota State University 57007 — Post-Sec.
605-688-4151

Buffalo, Harding, Pop. 328
Harding County SD 31-1 — 200/K-12
PO Box 367 57720 — 605-375-3241
Ruth Krogh, supt. — Fax 375-3246
www.hardingcounty.k12.sd.us/
Harding County HS — 100/9-12
PO Box 367 57720 — 605-375-3241
Josh Page, prin. — Fax 375-3246
Harding County MS — 50/6-8
PO Box 367 57720 — 605-375-3241
Josh Page, prin. — Fax 375-3246

Burke, Gregory, Pop. 594
Burke SD 26-2 200/PK-12
PO Box 382 57523 605-775-2644
Erik Person, supt. Fax 775-2468
www.burke.k12.sd.us
Burke HS 100/9-12
PO Box 382 57523 605-775-2645
Mark Otten, prin. Fax 775-2468
Burke MS 50/6-8
PO Box 382 57523 605-775-2645
Mark Otten, prin. Fax 775-2468

Canistota, McCook, Pop. 646
Canistota SD 43-1 200/K-12
PO Box 8 57012 605-296-3458
Dean Jones, supt. Fax 296-3158
www.canistota.k12.sd.us
Canistota HS 100/9-12
PO Box 8 57012 605-296-3458
Larry Nebelsick, prin. Fax 296-3158
Canistota JHS 50/6-8
PO Box 8 57012 605-296-3458
Larry Nebelsick, prin. Fax 296-3158

Canton, Lincoln, Pop. 3,010
Canton SD 41-1 900/PK-12
800 N Main St 57013 605-764-2706
Terry Gerber, supt. Fax 764-2700
www.canton.k12.sd.us
Canton HS 300/9-12
800 N Main St 57013 605-764-2706
Russell Townsend, prin. Fax 764-2700
Canton MS 200/6-8
800 N Main St 57013 605-764-2706
Russell Townsend, prin. Fax 764-2700

Carpenter, Clark
Willow Lake SD 12-3
Supt. — See Willow Lake
Shamrock Colony Alternative HS 50/Alt
19087 413th Ave 57322 605-625-5945
Terry Winegar, supt. Fax 625-3101

Castlewood, Hamlin, Pop. 623
Castlewood SD 28-1 300/PK-12
310 E Harry St 57223 605-793-2497
Keith Fodness, supt. Fax 793-2679
www.castlewood.k12.sd.us/
Castlewood HS 100/9-12
310 E Harry St 57223 605-793-2497
Keith Fodness, prin. Fax 793-2679
Castlewood JHS 50/7-8
310 E Harry St 57223 605-793-2497
Keith Fodness, prin. Fax 793-2679

Centerville, Turner, Pop. 877
Centerville SD 60-1 200/PK-12
PO Box 100 57014 605-563-2291
Doug Voss, supt. Fax 563-2615
www.centerville.k12.sd.us
Centerville HS 100/9-12
PO Box 100 57014 605-563-2291
Chad Conaway, prin. Fax 563-2615
Centerville JHS 50/5-8
PO Box 100 57014 605-563-2291
Chad Conaway, prin. Fax 563-2615

Chamberlain, Brule, Pop. 2,326
Chamberlain SD 7-1 900/PK-12
PO Box 119 57325 605-234-4477
Debra Johnson, supt. Fax 234-4479
www.chamberlain.k12.sd.us
Chamberlain HS 300/9-12
PO Box 119 57325 605-234-4467
Allan Bertram, prin. Fax 234-4479
Chamberlain MS 100/7-8
PO Box 119 57325 605-234-4467
Allan Bertram, prin. Fax 234-4479

Chester, Lake, Pop. 257
Chester Area SD 39-1 600/PK-12
PO Box 159 57016 605-489-2416
Mark Greguson, supt. Fax 489-2413
www.chester.k12.sd.us
Chester HS 100/9-12
PO Box 159 57016 605-489-2411
Michael Reinhiller, prin. Fax 489-2413
Chester JHS 50/7-8
PO Box 159 57016 605-489-2411
Michael Reinhiller, prin. Fax 489-2413
High Plains Alternative S 50/Alt
PO Box 159 57016 605-489-2411
Mark Greguson, prin. Fax 489-2413

Clark, Clark, Pop. 1,130
Clark SD 12-2 300/PK-12
220 N Clinton St 57225 605-532-3603
Brian Heupel, supt. Fax 532-3600
clark.k12.sd.us/
Clark HS 100/9-12
220 N Clinton St 57225 605-532-3605
Jerry Hartley, prin. Fax 532-3600
Clark MS 100/7-8
220 N Clinton St 57225 605-532-3603
Brian Heupel, prin. Fax 532-3600

Clear Lake, Deuel, Pop. 1,256
Deuel SD 19-4 600/PK-12
PO Box 770 57226 605-874-2163
Dean Christensen, supt. Fax 874-8585
www.deuel.k12.sd.us/
Clear Lake MS 100/6-8
PO Box 770 57226 605-874-2163
Steve Benson, prin. Fax 874-8585
Deuel HS 200/9-12
PO Box 770 57226 605-874-2163
Steve Benson, prin. Fax 874-8585

Colman, Moody, Pop. 586
Colman-Egan SD 50-5 300/K-12
PO Box 1 57017 605-534-3534
Darold Rounds, supt. Fax 534-3670
www.colman-egan.k12.sd.us
Colman-Egan HS 100/9-12
PO Box 1 57017 605-534-3534
Terrance Stulken, prin. Fax 534-3670
Colman-Egan JHS 50/7-8
PO Box 1 57017 605-534-3534
Terrance Stulken, prin. Fax 534-3670

Colome, Tripp, Pop. 291
Colome SD 59-3 300/PK-12
PO Box 367 57528 605-842-1624
Alan Armstrong, supt. Fax 842-0783
www.colome.k12.sd.us/
Colome HS 100/9-12
PO Box 367 57528 605-842-1624
Scott Kortan, prin. Fax 842-0783
Colome JHS 50/7-8
PO Box 367 57528 605-842-1624
Scott Kortan, prin. Fax 842-0783

Colton, Minnehaha, Pop. 682
Tri-Valley SD 49-6 800/PK-12
46450 252nd St 57018 605-446-3538
Mike Lodmel, supt. Fax 446-3520
www.tri-valley.k12.sd.us/
Tri-Valley HS 300/9-12
46450 252nd St 57018 605-446-3538
Tim Pflanz, prin. Fax 446-3520
Tri-Valley MS 100/7-8
46450 252nd St 57018 605-446-3538
Tim Pflanz, prin. Fax 446-3520

Corsica, Douglas, Pop. 584
Corsica SD 21-2 200/PK-12
120 S Napoleon Ave 57328 605-946-5475
Vern DeGeest, supt. Fax 946-5607
www.corsica.k12.sd.us
Corsica HS 100/9-12
120 S Napoleon Ave 57328 605-946-5475
Scott Muckey, prin. Fax 946-5607
Corsica MS 50/6-8
120 S Napoleon Ave 57328 605-946-5475
Brittney Eide, prin. Fax 946-5607

Dakota Christian S 100/PK-12
37614 SD Highway 44 57328 605-243-2211
Gary Cookson, admin. Fax 243-2379

Custer, Custer, Pop. 2,043
Custer SD 16-1 900/PK-12
527 Montgomery St 57730 605-673-3154
Scott Lepke, supt. Fax 673-5607
www.csd.k12.sd.us
Custer HS 300/9-12
1645 Wild Cat Ln 57730 605-673-4473
Dr. Paul Anderson, prin. Fax 673-4710
Custer MS 200/6-8
527 Montgomery St 57730 605-673-4540
Dr. Paul Anderson, prin. Fax 673-3079

Dell Rapids, Minnehaha, Pop. 3,605
Dell Rapids SD 49-3 900/PK-12
1216 N Garfield Ave 57022 605-428-5473
Summer Schultz, supt. Fax 428-5609
dr-k12.org
Dell Rapids HS 300/9-12
1216 N Garfield Ave 57022 605-428-5473
Kimberly Kludt, prin. Fax 428-5609
Dell Rapids MS 300/5-8
1216 N Garfield Ave 57022 605-428-5473
Fran Ruesink, prin. Fax 428-5609

St. Mary HS 100/7-12
812 N State Ave 57022 605-428-5591
Brad Peters, prin. Fax 428-5377

De Smet, Kingsbury, Pop. 1,084
De Smet SD 38-2 300/K-12
PO Box 157 57231 605-854-3423
Jim Altenburg, admin. Fax 854-9138
www.desmet.k12.sd.us
De Smet HS 100/9-12
PO Box 157 57231 605-854-3423
Jim Altenburg, prin. Fax 854-9138
De Smet MS 100/6-8
PO Box 157 57231 605-854-3423
Jim Altenburg, prin. Fax 854-9138

Dewey, Custer
Elk Mountain SD 16-2 50/K-12
10222 Valley Rd 57735 605-749-2248
Susan Ostenson M.Ed., admin. Fax 749-2258
Elk Mountain S 50/K-12
10222 Valley Rd 57735 605-673-2683
Susan Ostenson M.Ed., admin. Fax 749-2258

Doland, Spink, Pop. 180
Doland SD 56-2 200/K-12
PO Box 385 57436 605-635-6302
Jim Hulscher, supt. Fax 635-6504
www.doland.k12.sd.us/
Doland HS 50/9-12
PO Box 385 57436 605-635-6241
Jim Hulscher, prin. Fax 635-6504
Doland JHS 50/7-8
PO Box 385 57436 605-635-6241
Jim Hulscher, prin. Fax 635-6504

Dupree, Ziebach, Pop. 511
Dupree SD 64-2 300/PK-12
PO Box 10 57623 605-365-5140
Quinn Lenk, supt. Fax 365-5514
www.dupree.k12.sd.us/
Dupree HS 100/9-12
PO Box 10 57623 605-365-5140
Patrick Frederick, prin. Fax 365-5514
Dupree JHS 50/7-8
PO Box 10 57623 605-365-5140
Patrick Frederick, prin. Fax 365-5514

Eagle Butte, Dewey, Pop. 1,279
Eagle Butte SD 20-1 300/K-12
PO Box 260 57625 605-964-4911
Carol Veit, supt. Fax 964-4912
www.c-eb.com/
Eagle Butte HS 50/9-12
PO Box 672 57625 605-964-8744
Dr. James Nelson, prin. Fax 964-8700
Eagle Butte JHS 50/7-8
PO Box 672 57625 605-964-7841
Kathie Bowker, prin. Fax 964-1224
E.A.G.L.E. Center 50/Alt
PO Box 672 57625 605-964-8773
Dr. Vicki Birkeland, prin. Fax 964-1218

Windswept Academy 50/K-12
PO Box 1576 57625 605-200-0757
Clint Holley, admin.

Edgemont, Fall River, Pop. 746
Edgemont SD 23-1 200/K-12
PO Box 29 57735 605-662-7294
David Cortney, supt. Fax 662-7721
edgemont.k12.sd.us
Edgemont HS 50/9-12
PO Box 29 57735 605-662-7254
David Cortney, admin. Fax 662-7721

Elk Point, Union, Pop. 1,939
Elk Point-Jefferson SD 61-7 700/PK-12
PO Box 578 57025 605-356-5950
Brian Shanks, supt. Fax 356-5953
www.epj.k12.sd.us/
Elk Point-Jefferson HS 200/9-12
PO Box 578 57025 605-356-5900
Travis Aslesen, prin. Fax 356-5999
Elk Point-Jefferson MS 100/7-8
PO Box 578 57025 605-356-5900
Janet Ries, prin. Fax 356-5999

Elkton, Brookings, Pop. 721
Elkton SD 5-3 300/K-12
PO Box 190 57026 605-542-5361
Brian Jandahl, supt. Fax 542-4441
elkton.k12.sd.us
Elkton HS 100/9-12
PO Box 190 57026 605-542-2541
Kelly Neill, prin. Fax 542-4441
Elkton JHS 100/7-8
PO Box 190 57026 605-542-2541
Kelly Neill, prin. Fax 542-4441

Ellsworth AFB, Meade, Pop. 7,017

National American University Post-Sec.
1000 Ellsworth St Ste 2400B 57706 605-718-6550

Emery, Hanson, Pop. 443
Bridgewater-Emery SD 30-3
Supt. — See Bridgewater
Bridgewater-Emery HS 100/9-12
130 N 6th St 57332 605-449-4271
Christena Schultz, prin. Fax 449-4270

Estelline, Hamlin, Pop. 763
Estelline SD 28-2 200/K-12
PO Box 306 57234 605-873-2201
Patrick Kraning, supt. Fax 873-2102
www.estelline.k12.sd.us
Estelline HS 100/7-12
PO Box 306 57234 605-873-2201
Rob Sylliaasen, prin. Fax 873-2102

Ethan, Davison, Pop. 328
Ethan SD 17-1 200/PK-12
PO Box 169 57334 605-227-4211
Terry Eckstaine, supt. Fax 227-4236
www.ethan.k12.sd.us/
Ethan HS 100/9-12
PO Box 169 57334 605-227-4211
Tim Hawkins, prin. Fax 227-4236
Ethan MS 100/6-8
PO Box 169 57334 605-227-4211
Tim Hawkins, prin. Fax 227-4236

Eureka, McPherson, Pop. 856
Eureka SD 44-1 200/K-12
PO Box 10 57437 605-284-2875
Bo Beck, supt. Fax 284-2810
www.eureka.k12.sd.us/
Eureka HS 100/9-12
PO Box 10 57437 605-284-2521
Bo Beck, prin. Fax 284-2810
Eureka JHS 50/7-8
PO Box 10 57437 605-284-2521
Bo Beck, prin. Fax 284-2810

Faith, Meade, Pop. 405
Faith SD 46-2 200/K-12
PO Box 619 57626 605-967-2152
Elsie Baye, supt. Fax 967-2153
www.faith.k12.sd.us/
Faith HS 100/9-12
PO Box 619 57626 605-967-2152
Elsie Baye, supt. Fax 967-2153
Faith JHS 50/7-8
PO Box 619 57626 605-967-2152
Elsie Baye, supt. Fax 967-2153

Faulkton, Faulk, Pop. 724
Faulkton Area SD 24-4 300/K-12
PO Box 308 57438 605-598-6266
Joel Price, supt. Fax 598-6666
www.faulkton.k12.sd.us
Faulkton HS 100/9-12
PO Box 308 57438 605-598-6266
Craig Cassens, prin. Fax 598-6666
Faulkton JHS 50/7-8
PO Box 308 57438 605-598-6266
Craig Cassens, prin. Fax 598-6666

Flandreau, Moody, Pop. 2,264
Flandreau SD 50-3 600/K-12
600 W Community Dr 57028 605-997-3263
Rick Weber, supt. Fax 997-2457
www.flandreau.k12.sd.us
Flandreau HS 200/9-12
600 W Community Dr 57028 605-997-2455
Todd Foster, prin. Fax 997-2457

Flandreau MS 100/6-8
700 W Community Dr 57028 605-997-2705
Brian Relf, prin. Fax 997-2457

Florence, Codington, Pop. 370
Florence SD 14-1 200/PK-12
PO Box 66 57235 605-758-2412
Gary Leighton, supt. Fax 758-2433
www.florence.k12.sd.us/
Florence HS 100/9-12
PO Box 66 57235 605-758-2412
Gary Leighton, prin. Fax 758-2433
Florence JHS 50/7-8
PO Box 66 57235 605-758-2412
Gary Leighton, prin. Fax 758-2433

Forestburg, Sanborn, Pop. 70
Sanborn Central SD 55-5 200/PK-12
40405 SD Highway 34 57314 605-495-4183
Linda Whitney, supt. Fax 495-4185
www.sanborncentral.com/
Sanborn Central HS 100/9-12
40405 SD Highway 34 57314 605-495-4183
Linda Whitney, prin. Fax 495-4185
Sanborn Central MS 50/6-8
40405 SD Highway 34 57314 605-495-4183
Connie Vermeulen, prin. Fax 495-4185

Fort Pierre, Stanley, Pop. 2,009
Stanley County SD 57-1 400/K-12
PO Box 370 57532 605-223-7741
Don Hotalling Ed.D., supt. Fax 223-7750
www.stanleycounty.k12.sd.us
Stanley County HS 100/9-12
PO Box 370 57532 605-223-7743
Timothy Hollar M.S., prin. Fax 223-7751
Stanley County MS 100/6-8
PO Box 370 57532 605-223-7743
Timothy Hollar M.S., prin. Fax 223-7751

Frederick, Brown, Pop. 197
Frederick Area SD 6-2 200/PK-12
PO Box 486 57441 605-329-2145
Beverly Myer, supt. Fax 329-2722
www.frederickarea.k12.sd.us/
Frederick HS 100/9-12
PO Box 486 57441 605-329-2145
Justin Downes, prin. Fax 329-2722
Frederick JHS 50/7-8
PO Box 486 57441 605-329-2145
Justin Downes, prin. Fax 329-2722

Freeman, Hutchinson, Pop. 1,290
Freeman SD 33-1 400/PK-12
PO Box 220 57029 605-925-4214
Don Hotchkiss, supt. Fax 925-4814
www.freeman.k12.sd.us/
Freeman HS 100/9-12
PO Box 220 57029 605-925-4214
Kim Krull, prin. Fax 925-4814
Freeman JHS 100/7-8
PO Box 220 57029 605-925-4214
Kim Krull, prin. Fax 925-4814

Garretson, Minnehaha, Pop. 1,155
Garretson SD 49-4 500/PK-12
PO Box C 57030 605-594-3451
Robert Arend, supt. Fax 594-3443
www.garretson.k12.sd.us/
Garretson HS 200/9-12
PO Box C 57030 605-594-3452
Chris Long, prin. Fax 594-3443
Garretson MS 100/6-8
PO Box C 57030 605-594-3452
Chris Long, prin. Fax 594-3443

Gayville, Yankton, Pop. 403
Gayville-Volin SD 63-1 200/K-12
PO Box 158 57031 605-267-4476
Jason Selchert, supt. Fax 267-4294
www.gayvillevolin.k12.sd.us/
Gayville-Volin HS 100/9-12
PO Box 158 57031 605-267-4476
Tom Rice, prin. Fax 267-4294
Gayville-Volin MS 50/7-8
PO Box 158 57031 605-267-4476
Tom Rice, prin. Fax 267-4294

Gettysburg, Potter, Pop. 1,150
Gettysburg SD 53-1 200/K-12
100 E King Ave 57442 605-765-2436
Tim Hagedorn, supt. Fax 765-2249
www.gettysburg.k12.sd.us/
Gettysburg HS 100/9-12
100 E King Ave 57442 605-765-2436
Wendy Smith, prin. Fax 765-2249
Gettysburg JHS 50/6-8
100 E King Ave 57442 605-765-2436
Wendy Smith, prin. Fax 765-2249

Gregory, Gregory, Pop. 1,270
Gregory SD 26-4 300/K-12
PO Box 438 57533 605-835-9651
Sara Klein, supt. Fax 835-8146
www.gregory.k12.sd.us/
Gregory HS 100/9-12
PO Box 438 57533 605-835-9672
Jeff Determan, prin. Fax 835-8146
Gregory MS 100/6-8
PO Box 438 57533 605-835-8771
Jeff Determan, prin. Fax 835-8146

Groton, Brown, Pop. 1,444
Groton Area SD 6-6 600/PK-12
PO Box 410 57445 605-397-2351
Laura Schuster, supt. Fax 397-8453
www.grotonarea.com/
Groton HS 200/9-12
PO Box 410 57445 605-397-8381
Joe Schwan, prin. Fax 397-8453
Groton MS 100/6-8
PO Box 410 57445 605-397-8381
Joe Schwan, prin. Fax 397-8453

Harrisburg, Lincoln, Pop. 4,018
Harrisburg SD 41-2 2,400/PK-12
PO Box 187 57032 605-743-2567
James Holbeck, supt. Fax 743-2569
www.harrisburg.k12.sd.us
Harrisburg HS 400/9-12
PO Box 339 57032 605-743-2567
Kevin Lein, prin. Fax 743-9040
Harrisburg MS 500/6-8
PO Box 309 57032 605-743-2567
Tim Koehler, prin. Fax 743-5630

Hartford, Minnehaha, Pop. 2,498
West Central SD 49-7 1,300/PK-12
PO Box 730 57033 605-528-3217
Dr. Jeff Danielsen, supt. Fax 528-3219
www.westcentral.k12.sd.us/
West Central HS 400/9-12
PO Box 730 57033 605-528-6236
Mark Rockafellow, prin. Fax 528-6217
West Central MS 300/6-8
PO Box 730 57033 605-528-3799
Guy Johnson, prin. Fax 528-3702

Hayti, Hamlin, Pop. 381
Hamlin SD 28-3 700/PK-12
44577 188th St 57241 605-783-3631
Joel Jorgenson, supt. Fax 783-3632
www.hamlin.k12.sd.us/
Hamlin HS 200/9-12
44577 188th St 57241 605-783-3644
Jeff Sheehan, prin. Fax 783-3360
Hamlin MS 100/7-8
44577 188th St 57241 605-783-3631
Jeff Sheehan, prin. Fax 783-3632

Henry, Codington, Pop. 264
Henry SD 14-2 200/K-12
PO Box 8 57243 605-532-5364
Steve Zirbel, supt. Fax 532-3795
www.henry.k12.sd.us/
Henry HS 100/9-12
PO Box 8 57243 605-532-5364
Steve Zirbel, prin. Fax 532-3795
Henry MS 50/6-8
PO Box 8 57243 605-532-5364
Steve Zirbel, prin. Fax 532-3795

Herreid, Campbell, Pop. 436
Herreid SD 10-1 100/K-12
PO Box 276 57632 605-437-2263
Ron Jacobson, supt. Fax 437-2264
herreid.k12.sd.us
Herreid HS 50/9-12
PO Box 276 57632 605-437-2263
Ron Jacobson, prin. Fax 437-2264
Herreid MS 50/6-8
PO Box 276 57632 605-437-2263
Ron Jacobson, prin. Fax 437-2264

Highmore, Hyde, Pop. 788
Highmore-Harrold SD 34-2 300/PK-12
PO Box 416 57345 605-852-2275
Dr. Frank Palleria, supt. Fax 852-2295
www.highmore.k12.sd.us/
Highmore HS 100/9-12
PO Box 416 57345 605-852-2275
Kevin Segrud, prin. Fax 852-2295
Highmore JHS 50/7-8
PO Box 416 57345 605-852-2275
Kevin Segrud, prin. Fax 852-2295

Hill City, Pennington, Pop. 926
Hill City SD 51-2 500/PK-12
PO Box 659 57745 605-574-3030
Mike Hanson, supt. Fax 574-3031
hillcity.k12.sd.us
Hill City HS 200/9-12
PO Box 659 57745 605-574-3000
Todd Satter, prin. Fax 574-3046
Hill City MS 100/6-8
PO Box 659 57745 605-574-3032
Blake Gardner, prin. Fax 574-3040

Hot Springs, Fall River, Pop. 3,587
Hot Springs SD 23-2 800/PK-12
1609 University Ave 57747 605-745-4145
Dr. Donald Marchant, supt. Fax 745-4178
www.hssd.k12.sd.us
Hot Springs HS 300/9-12
1609 University Ave 57747 605-745-4147
Mary Weiss, prin. Fax 745-4061
Hot Springs MS 200/6-8
1609 University Ave 57747 605-745-4146
John Fitzgerald, prin. Fax 745-6387

Hoven, Potter, Pop. 401
Hoven SD 53-2 100/PK-12
PO Box 128 57450 605-948-2252
Peggy Petersen, supt. Fax 948-2477
www.hoven.k12.sd.us/
Hoven HS 50/9-12
PO Box 128 57450 605-948-2252
Peggy Petersen, prin. Fax 948-2477
Hoven JHS 50/7-8
PO Box 128 57450 605-948-2252
Peggy Petersen, prin. Fax 948-2477

Howard, Miner, Pop. 846
Howard SD 48-3 400/PK-12
500 N Section Line St 57349 605-772-5515
Mike Cullen, supt. Fax 772-5516
www.howard.k12.sd.us/
Howard HS 100/9-12
500 N Section Line St 57349 605-772-5515
Mike Cullen, prin. Fax 772-5516
Howard JHS 50/7-8
500 N Section Line St 57349 605-772-5515
Mike Cullen, prin. Fax 772-5516

Hurley, Turner, Pop. 413
Viborg-Hurley SD 60-6
Supt. — See Viborg
Viborg-Hurley MS 50/5-8
PO Box 278 57036 605-238-5221
Barb Hansen, prin. Fax 238-5223

Huron, Beadle, Pop. 12,413
Huron SD 2-2 1,500/K-12
PO Box 949 57350 605-353-6990
Terry Nebelsick Ed.D., supt. Fax 353-6994
www.huron.k12.sd.us
Huron HS 700/9-12
PO Box 949 57350 605-353-7800
Demetria Moon, prin. Fax 353-7807
Huron MS 500/5-8
1045 18th St SW 57350 605-353-6900
Michael Taplett, prin. Fax 353-6913

James Valley Christian S 200/PK-12
1550 Dakota Ave N 57350 605-352-7737
Brian Held, admin. Fax 352-9893

Ipswich, Edmunds, Pop. 945
Ipswich SD 22-6 400/PK-12
PO Box 306 57451 605-426-6571
Trent Osborne, supt. Fax 426-6029
www.ipswich.k12.sd.us
Ipswich HS 100/9-12
PO Box 306 57451 605-426-6571
Trent Osborne, prin. Fax 426-6029
Ipswich MS 100/6-8
PO Box 306 57451 605-426-6571
Mathew Pollock, prin. Fax 426-6029

Irene, Yankton, Pop. 419
Irene-Wakonda SD 13-3 300/PK-12
PO Box 5 57037 605-263-3311
Larry Johnke, supt. Fax 263-3316
www.irene-wakonda.k12.sd.us/
Irene-Wakonda JSHS 100/7-12
PO Box 5 57037 605-263-3313
David Hutchison, prin. Fax 263-3316

Iroquois, Kingsbury, Pop. 263
Iroquois SD 2-3 200/PK-12
PO Box 98 57353 605-546-2210
Mark Sampson, supt. Fax 546-8540
www.iroquois.k12.sd.us/
Iroquois HS 50/9-12
PO Box 98 57353 605-546-2426
Rick Soma, prin. Fax 546-8540
Iroquois MS 50/6-8
PO Box 98 57353 605-546-2426
Rick Soma, prin. Fax 546-8540

Kadoka, Jackson, Pop. 622
Kadoka Area SD 35-2 300/PK-12
PO Box 99 57543 605-837-2175
Jamie Hermann, supt. Fax 837-2176
kadoka.k12.sd.us/
Kadoka HS 100/9-12
PO Box 99 57543 605-837-2172
George Seiler, prin. Fax 837-2176

Kennebec, Lyman, Pop. 232
Lyman SD 42-1
Supt. — See Presho
Lyman MS 100/6-8
PO Box 188 57544 605-869-2213
Julie Eppard, prin. Fax 869-2283

Kimball, Brule, Pop. 698
Kimball SD 7-2 200/K-12
PO Box 479 57355 605-778-6232
Sheri Hardman, supt. Fax 778-6393
www.kimball.k12.sd.us
Kimball HS 100/9-12
PO Box 479 57355 605-778-6232
Collin Knudson, prin. Fax 778-6393
Kimball JHS 50/7-8
PO Box 479 57355 605-778-6231
Collin Knudson, prin. Fax 778-6393

Kyle, Shannon, Pop. 840

Oglala Lakota College Post-Sec.
PO Box 490 57752 605-455-6000

Lake Andes, Charles Mix, Pop. 832
Andes Central SD 11-1 400/PK-12
PO Box 40 57356 605-487-7671
Darrell Mueller, supt. Fax 487-7051
www.andescentral.k12.sd.us/
Andes Central HS 100/9-12
PO Box 40 57356 605-487-5207
Rocky Brinkman, prin. Fax 487-7051
Andes Central JHS 100/7-8
PO Box 40 57356 605-487-5207
Rocky Brinkman, prin. Fax 487-7051

Lake Preston, Kingsbury, Pop. 595
Lake Preston SD 38-3 200/K-12
300 1st St NE 57249 605-847-4455
Tim Casper, supt. Fax 847-4311
www.lakepreston.k12.sd.us
Lake Preston HS 100/9-12
300 1st St NE 57249 605-847-4455
Tim Casper, prin. Fax 847-4311
Lake Preston JHS 50/7-8
300 1st St NE 57249 605-847-4455
Tim Casper, prin. Fax 847-4311

Langford, Marshall, Pop. 312
Langford SD 45-5 200/PK-12
PO Box 127 57454 605-493-6454
Monte Nipp, supt. Fax 493-6447
www.langford.k12.sd.us/
Langford HS 100/9-12
PO Box 127 57454 605-493-6454
Toni Brown, prin. Fax 493-6447
Langford MS 50/7-8
PO Box 127 57454 605-493-6454
Toni Brown, prin. Fax 493-6447

Lead, Lawrence, Pop. 3,058
Lead-Deadwood SD 40-1 900/PK-12
320 S Main St 57754 605-717-3890
Dr. Dan Leikvold, supt. Fax 717-2813
www.lead-deadwood.k12.sd.us/
Lead-Deadwood HS 200/9-12
320 S Main St 57754 605-717-3899
Nick Gottlob, prin. Fax 717-2815
Lead-Deadwood MS 200/6-8
234 S Main St 57754 605-717-3898
Nick Gottlob, prin. Fax 717-2821
Other Schools – See Nemo

Lemmon, Perkins, Pop. 1,211
Lemmon SD 52-4 300/PK-12
209 3rd St W 57638 605-374-3762
Rick Herbel, supt. Fax 374-3562
www.lemmon.k12.sd.us
Lemmon HS 100/9-12
209 3rd St W 57638 605-374-3762
Rick Herbel, prin. Fax 374-3562
Lemmon JHS 50/7-8
209 3rd St W 57638 605-374-3762
Cynthia Schneider, prin. Fax 374-3562

Lennox, Lincoln, Pop. 2,100
Lennox SD 41-4 1,000/PK-12
PO Box 38 57039 605-647-2202
Dr. Robert Mayer, supt. Fax 647-2201
www.lennox.k12.sd.us
Lennox HS 300/9-12
PO Box 38 57039 605-647-2203
Tim Raabe, prin. Fax 647-6045
Lennox MS 200/6-8
PO Box 38 57039 605-647-2204
Darren Ellwein, prin. Fax 647-6043

Leola, McPherson, Pop. 451
Leola SD 44-2 200/PK-12
PO Box 350 57456 605-439-3477
Julie Nikolas, supt. Fax 439-3206
www.leola.k12.sd.us/
Leola HS 50/9-12
PO Box 350 57456 605-439-3477
Cynthia Rall, prin. Fax 439-3206
Leola JHS 50/7-8
PO Box 350 57456 605-439-3477
Cynthia Rall, prin. Fax 439-3206

Mc Intosh, Corson, Pop. 167
Mc Intosh SD 15-1 200/PK-12
PO Box 80 57641 605-273-4298
Dick Schaffan, supt. Fax 273-4531
www.mcintosh.k12.sd.us/
Mc Intosh HS 100/9-12
PO Box 80 57641 605-273-4298
Dick Schaffan, prin. Fax 273-4531
Mc Intosh JHS 50/7-8
PO Box 80 57641 605-273-4298
Dick Schaffan, prin. Fax 273-4531

Mc Laughlin, Corson, Pop. 634
Mc Laughlin SD 15-2 500/PK-12
PO Box 880 57642 605-823-4484
Patricia Stone, supt. Fax 823-4886
www.mclaughlin.k12.sd.us
McLaughlin HS 100/9-12
PO Box 880 57642 605-823-4484
Tim Thompson, prin. Fax 823-4481
McLaughlin MS 100/6-8
PO Box 880 57642 605-823-4484
Tim Thompson, prin. Fax 823-4481

Madison, Lake, Pop. 6,389
Madison Central SD 39-2 1,100/K-12
800 NE 9th St 57042 605-256-7700
Vincent Schaefer, supt. Fax 256-7711
www.madison.k12.sd.us
Madison HS 300/9-12
800 NE 9th St 57042 605-256-7706
Sharon Knowlton, prin. Fax 256-7711
Madison MS 300/6-8
830 NE 9th St 57042 605-256-7717
Cotton Koch, prin. Fax 256-7728

Dakota State University Post-Sec.
820 N Washington Ave 57042 605-256-5111

Marion, Turner, Pop. 780
Marion SD 60-3 200/PK-12
PO Box 207 57043 605-648-3615
Adam Shaw, supt. Fax 648-3652
www.marion.k12.sd.us
Marion HS 100/9-12
PO Box 207 57043 605-648-3615
Chad Allison, prin. Fax 648-3617
Marion MS 50/6-8
PO Box 207 57043 605-648-3615
Chad Allison, prin. Fax 648-3617

Martin, Bennett, Pop. 986
Bennett County SD 3-1 500/PK-12
PO Box 580 57551 605-685-6697
Wayne Semmler, supt. Fax 685-6694
www.bennettco.k12.sd.us/
Bennett County HS 200/9-12
PO Box 580 57551 605-685-6330
Duane Sundberg, prin. Fax 685-6935
Bennett County JHS 100/7-8
PO Box 580 57551 605-685-6343
Belinda Ready, prin. Fax 685-6935

Mellette, Spink, Pop. 205
Northwestern Area SD 56-7 300/PK-12
PO Box 45 57461 605-887-3467
Ray Sauerwein, supt. Fax 887-3101
www.northwestern.k12.sd.us
Northwestern HS 100/9-12
PO Box 45 57461 605-887-3467
Richard Osborn, prin. Fax 887-3101
Northwestern MS 100/6-8
PO Box 45 57461 605-887-3467
Richard Osborn, prin. Fax 887-3101

Menno, Hutchinson, Pop. 603
Menno SD 33-2 300/PK-12
PO Box 346 57045 605-387-5161
Dr. Chris Christensen, supt. Fax 387-5171
www.menno.k12.sd.us/
Menno HS 100/9-12
PO Box 346 57045 605-387-5161
Dr. Chris Christensen, prin. Fax 387-5171
Menno MS 50/6-8
PO Box 346 57045 605-387-5161
Terry Quam, prin. Fax 387-5171

Milbank, Grant, Pop. 3,335
Milbank SD 25-4 900/K-12
1001 E Park Ave 57252 605-432-5579
Tim Graf, supt. Fax 432-4137
www.milbankschooldistrict.com
Milbank HS 300/9-12
1001 E Park Ave 57252 605-432-5546
Dan Snaza, prin. Fax 432-5514
Milbank MS 200/6-8
1001 E Park Ave 57252 605-432-5519
Dan Snaza, prin. Fax 432-6610

Miller, Hand, Pop. 1,475
Miller SD 29-4 400/PK-12
PO Box 257 57362 605-853-2614
Michael Ruth, supt. Fax 853-3041
www.miller.k12.sd.us/
Miller HS 100/9-12
PO Box 257 57362 605-853-2455
Steve Schumacher, prin. Fax 853-3041
Miller JHS 100/7-8
PO Box 257 57362 605-853-2455
Steve Schumacher, prin. Fax 853-3041

Sunshine Bible Academy 100/K-12
400 Sunshine Dr 57362 605-853-3071
Jason Watson, supt. Fax 853-3072

Mission, Todd, Pop. 1,157
Todd County SD 66-1 2,000/PK-12
PO Box 87 57555 605-856-3501
Roger Bordeaux, supt. Fax 856-2449
www.tcsdk12.org/
Todd County HS 400/9-12
PO Box 726 57555 605-856-3503
Steven Swartout, prin. Fax 856-4723
Todd County MS 400/6-8
PO Box 248 57555 605-856-3504
Cheryl Whirlwind Soldier, prin. Fax 856-2032

Sinte Gleska University Post-Sec.
PO Box 105 57555 605-856-5880

Mitchell, Davison, Pop. 15,009
Hanson SD 30-1
Supt. — See Alexandria
Hanson Colony Alternative HS Alt
41659 256th St 57301 605-239-4387
Ray Slaba, prin. Fax 239-4293

Mitchell SD 17-2 2,500/K-12
800 W 10th Ave 57301 605-995-3010
Joseph Graves, supt. Fax 995-3089
www.mitchell.k12.sd.us
Mitchell HS 800/9-12
920 N Capital St 57301 605-995-3034
Yvonne Palli, prin. Fax 995-3047
Mitchell MS 500/6-8
800 W 10th Ave 57301 605-995-3051
Brad Berens, prin. Fax 995-3037
Second Chance Alternative S 100/Alt
821 N Capital St 57301 605-995-7509
Shane Thill, dir. Fax 995-8099

Dakota Wesleyan University Post-Sec.
1200 W University Ave 57301 605-995-2600
Mitchell Christian S 200/PK-12
805 W 18th Ave 57301 605-996-8861
Rev. Joseph Fox, admin. Fax 996-3642
Mitchell Technical Institute Post-Sec.
1800 E Spruce St 57301 800-684-1969
Queen of Peace Hospital Post-Sec.
5th & Foster 57301 605-995-2250

Mobridge, Walworth, Pop. 3,357
Mobridge-Pollock SD 62-6 600/PK-12
1107 1st Ave E 57601 605-845-9200
Tim Frederick, supt. Fax 845-3455
www.mobridge-pollock.k12.sd.us/
Mobridge HS 200/9-12
1107 1st Ave E 57601 605-845-9200
Andrew Overland, prin. Fax 845-3455
Mobridge MS 100/6-8
1107 1st Ave E 57601 605-845-9200
Joe Lenz, prin. Fax 845-3455

Montrose, McCook, Pop. 466
Montrose SD 43-2 200/K-12
309 S Church Ave 57048 605-363-5025
Dean Kueter, supt. Fax 363-3513
www.montroseschool.k12.sd.us/
Montrose HS 50/9-12
309 S Church Ave 57048 605-363-5025
Lonny Johnson, prin. Fax 363-3513
Montrose JHS 50/7-8
309 S Church Ave 57048 605-363-5025
Lonny Johnson, prin. Fax 363-3513

Mount Vernon, Davison, Pop. 457
Mount Vernon SD 17-3 200/PK-12
PO Box 46 57363 605-236-5237
Patrick Mikkonen, supt. Fax 236-5604
www.mtvernon.k12.sd.us
Mount Vernon HS 100/9-12
PO Box 46 57363 605-236-5237
Patrick Mikkonen, prin. Fax 236-5604
Mount Vernon MS 100/6-8
PO Box 46 57363 605-236-5237
Margaret Freidal, prin. Fax 236-5604

Murdo, Jones, Pop. 476
Jones County SD 37-3 200/PK-12
PO Box 109 57559 605-669-2297
Grant Vander Vorst, supt. Fax 669-3248
www.jonesco.k12.sd.us/
Jones County HS 100/9-12
PO Box 109 57559 605-669-2258
Grant Vander Vorst, supt. Fax 669-2904
Jones County MS 50/7-8
PO Box 109 57559 605-669-2258
Larry Ball, prin. Fax 669-2904

Nemo, Lawrence
Lead-Deadwood SD 40-1
Supt. — See Lead
Career & Technical Education Campus Vo/Tech
PO Box 110 57759 605-578-2371
Bonnie Fuller, dir. Fax 578-1157

Newell, Butte, Pop. 575
Newell SD 9-2 300/K-12
PO Box 99 57760 605-456-2393
Blake Dahlberg, supt. Fax 456-2395
www.newell.k12.sd.us
Newell HS 100/9-12
PO Box 99 57760 605-456-2393
Blake Dahlberg, prin. Fax 456-2395
Newell MS 100/6-8
PO Box 99 57760 605-456-0102
Blake Dahlberg, prin. Fax 456-2395

New Underwood, Pennington, Pop. 640
New Underwood SD 51-3 300/K-12
PO Box 128 57761 605-754-6485
Jeff Marlette, supt. Fax 754-6492
www.newunderwood.k12.sd.us
New Underwood HS 100/9-12
PO Box 128 57761 605-754-6485
Joel Hovland, prin. Fax 754-6492
New Underwood JHS 50/7-8
PO Box 128 57761 605-754-6485
Joel Hovland, prin. Fax 754-6492

North Sioux City, Union, Pop. 2,476
Dakota Valley SD 61-8 900/K-12
1150 Northshore Dr 57049 605-422-3800
Al Leber, supt. Fax 422-3807
www.dakotavalley.k12.sd.us/
Dakota Valley HS 300/9-12
1150 Northshore Dr 57049 605-422-3820
Jerry Rasmussen, prin. Fax 422-3827
Dakota Valley MS 200/5-8
1150 Northshore Dr 57049 605-422-3830
Harlan Halverson, prin. Fax 422-3837

Oelrichs, Fall River, Pop. 123
Oelrichs SD 23-3 100/K-12
PO Box 65 57763 605-535-2631
Rob Davis, supt. Fax 535-2046
www.oelrichs.k12.sd.us/
Oelrichs HS 100/9-12
PO Box 65 57763 605-535-2631
Charles Frederickson, prin. Fax 535-2046
Oelrichs JHS 50/7-8
PO Box 65 57763 605-535-2631
Charles Frederickson, prin. Fax 535-2046

Onida, Sully, Pop. 643
Agar-Blunt-Onida SD 58-3 300/K-12
PO Box 205 57564 605-258-2619
Kevin Pickner, supt. Fax 258-2361
www.abo.k12.sd.us
Sully Buttes HS 100/9-12
PO Box 205 57564 605-258-2618
Jeremy Chicoine, prin. Fax 258-2361
Sully Buttes JHS 50/7-8
PO Box 205 57564 605-258-2618
Jeremy Chicoine, prin. Fax 258-2361

Parker, Turner, Pop. 1,005
Parker SD 60-4 400/K-12
PO Box 517 57053 605-297-3456
Keith Buckridge, supt. Fax 297-4381
parker.k12.sd.us
Parker HS 100/9-12
PO Box 517 57053 605-297-3456
Chris McGregor, prin. Fax 297-4381
Parker JHS 50/7-8
PO Box 517 57053 605-297-3456
Chris McGregor, prin. Fax 297-4381

Parkston, Hutchinson, Pop. 1,496
Parkston SD 33-3 500/PK-12
102C S Chapman Dr 57366 605-928-3368
Shayne McIntosh, supt. Fax 928-7284
sp.parkston.k12.sd.us/
Parkston HS 200/9-12
102A S Chapman Dr 57366 605-928-3368
Joseph Kollmann, prin. Fax 928-4032
Parkston JHS 100/7-8
102A S Chapman Dr 57366 605-928-3368
Joseph Kollmann, prin. Fax 928-4032

Philip, Haakon, Pop. 760
Haakon SD 27-1 300/PK-12
PO Box 730 57567 605-859-2679
Keven Morehart, supt. Fax 859-3005
www.philip.k12.sd.us
Philip HS 100/9-12
PO Box 730 57567 605-859-2680
Cory Lambley, prin. Fax 859-3550
Philip MS 50/7-8
PO Box 730 57567 605-859-2680
Cory Lambley, prin. Fax 859-3550

Pierre, Hughes, Pop. 13,369
Pierre SD 32-2 2,600/PK-12
211 S Poplar Ave 57501 605-773-7300
Dr. Kelly Glodt, supt. Fax 773-7304
www.pierre.k12.sd.us
Morse MS 600/6-8
309 E Capitol Ave 57501 605-773-7330
Troy Wiebe, prin. Fax 773-7338

Riggs HS 800/9-12
1010 E Broadway Ave 57501 605-773-7350
Kevin Mutchelknaus, prin. Fax 773-7360

Pine Ridge, Shannon, Pop. 3,284
Shannon County SD 65-1
Supt. — See Batesland
Wolf Creek MS 300/5-8
PO Box 469 57770 605-867-5174
Theresa Mendoza, prin. Fax 867-5067

Red Cloud Indian S 200/PK-12
100 Mission Dr 57770 605-867-5888
Bob Brave Heart, supt. Fax 867-2528

Plankinton, Aurora, Pop. 706
Plankinton SD 1-1 200/PK-12
PO Box 190 57368 605-942-7743
James Jones, supt. Fax 942-7453
www.plankinton.k12.sd.us
Plankinton HS 100/9-12
PO Box 190 57368 605-942-7743
James Jones, admin. Fax 942-7453
Plankinton JHS 50/7-8
PO Box 190 57368 605-942-7743
James Jones, admin. Fax 942-7453

Platte, Charles Mix, Pop. 1,219
Platte-Geddes SD 11-5 400/PK-12
PO Box 140 57369 605-337-3391
Dennis Goodwin, supt. Fax 337-2549
www.platte-geddes.k12.sd.us/
Platte HS 100/9-12
PO Box 140 57369 605-337-3391
Steve Randall, prin. Fax 337-2549
Platte JHS 100/7-8
PO Box 140 57369 605-337-3391
Steve Randall, prin. Fax 337-2549

Porcupine, Shannon, Pop. 1,058
Shannon County SD 65-1
Supt. — See Batesland
Rockyford MS 200/5-8
HC 49 Box 175 57772 605-455-6300
Monica Horse, prin. Fax 455-2091

Presho, Lyman, Pop. 489
Lyman SD 42-1 400/K-12
PO Box 1000 57568 605-895-2579
Douglas Eppard, supt. Fax 895-2216
www.lyman.k12.sd.us/
Lyman HS 100/9-12
PO Box 1000 57568 605-895-2579
Cooper Garnos, prin. Fax 895-2216
Other Schools – See Kennebec

Ramona, Lake, Pop. 174
Oldham-Ramona SD 39-5 100/PK-12
PO Box 8 57054 605-482-8244
Tom Ludens, supt. Fax 482-8282
www.oldhamramona.k12.sd.us
Oldham-Ramona HS 50/9-12
PO Box 8 57054 605-482-8244
Tom Ludens, prin. Fax 482-8282
Oldham-Ramona JHS 50/7-8
PO Box 8 57054 605-482-8244
Tom Ludens, prin. Fax 482-8282

Rapid City, Pennington, Pop. 65,557
Rapid City Area SD 51-4 12,900/K-12
300 6th St Ste 2 57701 605-394-4031
Dr. Timothy Mitchell, supt. Fax 394-2514
www.rcas.org
Central HS 1,900/9-12
433 N Mount Rushmore Rd 57701 605-394-4023
Mike Talley, prin. Fax 394-2537
East MS 700/6-8
4860 Homestead St 57703 605-394-4092
Stan Evans, prin. Fax 394-6935
North MS 500/6-8
1501 N Maple Ave 57701 605-394-4042
Danny Janklow, prin. Fax 394-6120
Rapid City Academy 100/Alt
21 Saint Joseph St 57701 605-394-4048
Deb Steele, prin. Fax 394-6941
South MS 700/6-8
2 Indiana St 57701 605-394-4024
Larry Stevens, prin. Fax 394-5834
Southwest MS 500/6-8
4501 Park Dr 57702 605-394-6792
Jackie Talley, prin. Fax 355-3095
Stevens HS 1,600/9-12
1200 44th St 57702 605-394-4051
John Julius, prin. Fax 394-1820
Western Dakota Technical Institute Vo/Tech
800 Mickelson Dr 57703 605-718-2400
Mark Wilson, prin. Fax 394-1789
West MS 600/6-8
1003 Soo San Dr 57702 605-394-4033
Doug Foley, prin. Fax 394-1889

Black Hills Beauty College Post-Sec.
623 Saint Joseph St 57701 605-342-0697
National American University Post-Sec.
5301 S Highway 16 57701 605-394-4800
Rapid City Christian HS 100/6-12
23757 Arena Dr 57702 605-341-3377
Roy Roberts, admin. Fax 341-2248
Rapid City Regional Hospital Post-Sec.
353 Fairmont Blvd 57701 605-341-8100
St. Thomas More HS 300/9-12
300 Fairmont Blvd 57701 605-343-8484
Wayne Sullivan, prin. Fax 343-1315
St. Thomas More MS 200/6-8
431 Oakland St 57701 605-348-1477
Keiz Shultz, prin. Fax 342-4367
South Dakota School Mines and Technology Post-Sec.
501 E Saint Joseph St 57701 605-394-2511
Western Dakota Technical Institute Post-Sec.
800 Mickelson Dr 57703 605-394-4034

Redfield, Spink, Pop. 2,312
Redfield SD 56-4 700/PK-12
PO Box 560 57469 605-472-4520
Randy Joyce, supt. Fax 472-4525
www.redfield.k12.sd.us
Mickelson Alternative Program 50/Alt
PO Box 560 57469 605-472-4520
Rob Lewis, prin. Fax 472-4525
Redfield HS 200/9-12
PO Box 560 57469 605-472-4520
Rob Lewis, prin. Fax 472-4525
Redfield JHS 100/7-8
PO Box 560 57469 605-472-4520
Rob Lewis, prin. Fax 472-4525

Revillo, Grant, Pop. 117
Grant-Deuel SD 25-3 200/PK-12
16370 482nd Ave 57259 605-623-4241
Grant VanderVorst, supt. Fax 623-4215
www.grant-deuel.k12.sd.us/
Grant-Deuel HS 100/9-12
16370 482nd Ave 57259 605-623-4241
Paulette Grube, prin. Fax 623-4215
Grant-Deuel JHS 50/7-8
16370 482nd Ave 57259 605-623-4241
Paulette Grube, prin. Fax 623-4215

Roscoe, Edmunds, Pop. 323
Edmunds Central SD 22-5 100/PK-12
PO Box 317 57471 605-287-4251
Lew Paulson, supt. Fax 287-4813
www.echs.k12.sd.us/
Edmunds Central HS 100/9-12
PO Box 317 57471 605-287-4251
Lew Paulson, prin. Fax 287-4813
Edmunds Central MS 50/6-8
PO Box 317 57471 605-287-4251
Lew Paulson, prin. Fax 287-4813

Rosholt, Roberts, Pop. 406
Rosholt SD 54-4 200/PK-12
PO Box 106 57260 605-537-4283
Teresa Appel, supt. Fax 537-4285
www.rosholt.k12.sd.us/
Rosholt HS 100/9-12
PO Box 106 57260 605-537-4278
Scott Klicker, prin. Fax 537-4285
Rosholt JHS 50/7-8
PO Box 106 57260 605-537-4278
Scott Klicker, prin. Fax 537-4285

Rutland, Lake
Rutland SD 39-4 100/K-12
102 School St 57057 605-586-4352
Dr. Carl Fahrenwald, supt. Fax 586-4343
www.rutland.k12.sd.us
Rutland HS 50/9-12
102 School St 57057 605-586-4352
Carl Fahrenwald, supt. Fax 586-4343
Rutland JHS 50/7-8
102 School St 57057 605-586-4352
Sara Holmberg, admin. Fax 586-4343

Salem, McCook, Pop. 1,343
McCook Central SD 43-7 400/PK-12
PO Box 310 57058 605-425-2264
Dr. Dan Swartos, supt. Fax 425-2079
www.mccookcentral.k12.sd.us/
McCook Central HS 100/9-12
PO Box 310 57058 605-425-2264
Brad Seamer, prin. Fax 425-2079
McCook Central MS 100/5-8
PO Box 310 57058 605-425-2264
Brad Seamer, prin. Fax 425-2079

Scotland, Bon Homme, Pop. 830
Scotland SD 4-3 300/PK-12
711 4th St 57059 605-583-2237
Damon Alvey, supt. Fax 583-2239
www.scotland.k12.sd.us
Scotland HS 100/9-12
711 4th St 57059 605-583-2237
Ryan Bruns, prin. Fax 583-2239
Scotland MS 100/6-8
711 4th St 57059 605-583-2237
Ryan Bruns, prin. Fax 583-2239

Selby, Walworth, Pop. 634
Selby Area SD 62-5 200/PK-12
PO Box 324 57472 605-649-7818
Darrel McFarland, supt. Fax 649-7282
www.selby.k12.sd.us/
Selby Area HS 100/9-12
PO Box 324 57472 605-649-7818
Darrel McFarland, prin. Fax 649-7282
Selby Area JHS 50/7-8
PO Box 324 57472 605-649-7818
Darrel McFarland, prin. Fax 649-7282

Sioux Falls, Minnehaha, Pop. 150,371
Sioux Falls SD 49-5 21,100/PK-12
201 E 38th St 57105 605-367-7900
Dr. Pam Homan, supt. Fax 367-4637
www.sf.k12.sd.us
Axtell Park MS 600/6-8
201 N West Ave 57104 605-367-7647
LaVonna Emanuel, prin. Fax 367-8326
Career and Technical Education Academy Vo/Tech
4700 W Career Cir 57107 605-367-5504
Jim Kayl, prin. Fax 367-5508
Edison MS 800/6-8
2101 S West Ave 57105 605-367-7643
Steve Griffith, prin. Fax 367-8457
Foss Alternative S 400/Alt
1200 E 3rd St 57103 605-367-4285
Gary Evjen, prin. Fax 367-4335
Henry MS 1,100/6-8
2200 S 5th Ave 57105 605-367-7639
Darryl Walker, prin. Fax 367-7693
Lincoln HS 1,900/9-12
2900 S Cliff Ave 57105 605-367-7990
Val Fox, prin. Fax 367-8492
Memorial MS 1,000/6-8
1401 S Sertoma Ave 57106 605-362-2785
Carrie Aaron, prin. Fax 362-2790
Roosevelt HS 2,000/9-12
6600 W 41st St 57106 605-362-2860
Tim Hazlett, prin. Fax 362-2883
MS Immersion Center 50/Alt
201 N West Ave 57104 605-367-7647
Joshua Hall, prin. Fax 367-8326
Sioux Falls New Technology HS 100/9-12
2205 N Career Ave 57107 605-367-5850
Dolly Ellwein, prin. Fax 367-5852
Washington HS 2,100/9-12
501 N Sycamore Ave 57110 605-367-7970
James Nold, prin. Fax 367-8494
Whittier MS 900/6-8
930 E 6th St 57103 605-367-7620
Dr. JoJean Callison, prin. Fax 367-8357

Augustana College Post-Sec.
2001 S Summit Ave 57197 605-274-0770
Globe University Post-Sec.
5101 S Broadband Ln 57108 605-977-0705
Kilian Community College Post-Sec.
300 E 6th St 57103 605-221-3100
McKennan Hospital Post-Sec.
800 E 21st St 57105 605-339-8113
National American University Post-Sec.
5801 S Corporate Pl 57108 605-336-4600
O'Gorman HS 800/9-12
3201 S Kiwanis Ave 57105 605-336-3644
Kyle Groos, prin. Fax 336-9272
O'Gorman JHS 400/7-8
3100 W 41st St 57105 605-988-0546
Wade Charron, prin. Fax 336-9839
Sioux Falls Christian S 400/6-12
6120 S Charger Cir 57108 605-334-1422
Jay Woudstra, supt. Fax 334-6928
Sioux Falls Seminary Post-Sec.
2100 S Summit Ave 57105 605-336-6588
Sioux Valley Hospital Post-Sec.
PO Box 5039 57117 605-333-6424
South Dakota School for the Deaf Post-Sec.
2001 E 8th St 57103 605-367-5200
Southeast Technical Institute Post-Sec.
2320 N Career Ave 57107 605-367-7624
Stewart School Post-Sec.
604 N West Ave 57104 605-336-2775
University of Sioux Falls Post-Sec.
1101 W 22nd St 57105 605-331-5000

Sisseton, Roberts, Pop. 2,369
Sisseton SD 54-2 900/K-12
516 8th Ave W 57262 605-698-7613
Dr. Stephen Schulte, supt. Fax 698-3032
www.sisseton.k12.sd.us/
Sisseton HS 300/9-12
516 8th Ave W 57262 605-698-7613
Jim Frederick, prin. Fax 698-7353
Sisseton MS 200/6-8
516 8th Ave W 57262 605-698-7613
Karen Whitney, prin. Fax 698-7487

Sisseton-Wahpeton College Post-Sec.
PO Box 689 57262 605-698-3966

Spearfish, Lawrence, Pop. 10,283
Spearfish SD 40-2 2,000/PK-12
525 E Illinois St 57783 605-717-1201
Dave Peters, supt. Fax 717-1200
www.spearfish.k12.sd.us
Spearfish HS 600/9-12
1725 N Main St 57783 605-717-1212
Steve Morford, prin. Fax 717-1211
Spearfish MS 400/6-8
1600 N Canyon St 57783 605-717-1215
Shane Baier, prin. Fax 717-1252

Black Hills Christian Academy 100/PK-12
630 S 32nd St 57783 605-722-1276
Jullie Totino, admin. Fax 722-1217
Black Hills State University Post-Sec.
1200 University St 57799 605-642-6011

Stickney, Aurora, Pop. 284
Stickney SD 1-2 100/K-12
PO Box 67 57375 605-732-4221
Robert Krietlow, supt. Fax 732-4281
www.stickney.k12.sd.us/
Stickney HS 50/9-12
PO Box 67 57375 605-732-4221
Robert Krietlow, prin. Fax 732-4281
Stickney JHS 50/8-8
PO Box 67 57375 605-732-4221
Robert Krietlow, prin. Fax 732-4281

Sturgis, Meade, Pop. 6,462
Meade SD 46-1 2,400/K-12
1230 Douglas St 57785 605-347-2523
Don Kirkegaard, supt. Fax 347-0005
meade.k12.sd.us
Sturgis Brown HS 700/9-12
12930 SD Highway 34 57785 605-347-2686
Jeff Simmons, prin. Fax 347-0225
Sturgis Williams MS 500/6-8
1425 Cedar St 57785 605-347-5232
Lonny Harter, prin. Fax 720-0190
Other Schools – See Union Center

Summit, Roberts, Pop. 270
Summit SD 54-6 200/PK-12
PO Box 791 57266 605-398-6211
Loren Lutz, supt. Fax 398-6311
www.summit.k12.sd.us
Summit HS 50/9-12
PO Box 791 57266 605-398-6211
Loren Lutz, prin. Fax 398-6311

Tabor, Bon Homme, Pop. 415
Bon Homme SD 4-2
Supt. — See Tyndall

Hutterische Colony Alternative HS — Alt
31232 Colony Rd 57063 — 605-589-3387
Ed Mitzel, prin. — Fax 589-3468

Tea, Lincoln, Pop. 3,745
Tea Area SD 41-5 — 1,300/K-12
PO Box 488 57064 — 605-498-2700
Jennifer Lowery, supt. — Fax 498-2702
www.teaschools.k12.sd.us/
Tea HS — 300/9-12
PO Box 488 57064 — 605-498-2700
Al Laboranti, prin. — Fax 498-0280
Tea MS — 200/7-8
PO Box 488 57064 — 605-498-2700
Chris Fechner, prin. — Fax 498-0280

Timber Lake, Dewey, Pop. 419
Timber Lake SD 20-3 — 300/K-12
PO Box 1000 57656 — 605-865-3654
Jarod Larson, supt. — Fax 865-3294
www.tls.new.rschooltoday.com
Timber Lake HS — 100/9-12
PO Box 1000 57656 — 605-865-3654
Julie Marshall, prin. — Fax 865-3294
Timber Lake MS — 100/6-8
PO Box 1000 57656 — 605-865-3654
Julie Marshall, prin. — Fax 865-3294

Tripp, Hutchinson, Pop. 645
Tripp-Delmont SD 33-5 — 200/PK-12
PO Box 430 57376 — 605-935-6766
Lynn Vlasman, supt. — Fax 935-6507
www.tridel.k12.sd.us/
Tripp-Delmont HS — 100/9-12
PO Box 430 57376 — 605-935-6766
Lynn Vlasman, prin. — Fax 935-6507

Tulare, Spink, Pop. 205
Hitchcock-Tulare SD 56-6 — 200/PK-12
PO Box 108 57476 — 605-596-4171
Jeff Clark, supt. — Fax 596-4172
www.hitchcock-tulare.k12.sd.us/
Hitchcock-Tulare HS — 100/9-12
PO Box 108 57476 — 605-596-4171
Jeff Clark, prin. — Fax 596-4172
Hitchcock-Tulare JHS — 50/7-8
PO Box 108 57476 — 605-596-4171
Bill Barrie, prin. — Fax 596-4172

Tyndall, Bon Homme, Pop. 1,060
Bon Homme SD 4-2 — 600/PK-12
PO Box 28 57066 — 605-589-3388
Dr. Bryce Knudson, supt. — Fax 589-3468
www.bonhomme.k12.sd.us/
Bon Homme HS — 200/9-12
PO Box 28 57066 — 605-589-3387
Ed Mitzel, prin. — Fax 589-3468
Bon Homme MS — 100/6-8
PO Box 28 57066 — 605-589-3387
Ed Mitzel, prin. — Fax 589-3468
Other Schools – See Tabor

Union Center, Meade
Meade SD 46-1
Supt. — See Sturgis
Union Center S — 50/5-8
1700 SD Highway 34 57787 — 605-269-2264
Bev Rosenboom, prin. — Fax 269-2099

Vermillion, Clay, Pop. 10,331
Vermillion SD 13-1 — 1,300/PK-12
17 Prospect St 57069 — 605-677-7000
Dr. Mark Froke, supt. — Fax 677-7002
www.vermillion.k12.sd.us
Vermillion Area Alternative Education — Alt
840 E Cherry St 57069 — 605-677-5404
Vermillion HS — 400/9-12
1001 E Main St 57069 — 605-677-7035
Curt Cameron, prin. — Fax 677-7042
Vermillion MS — 300/6-8
422 Princeton St 57069 — 605-677-7025
Pat Anderson, prin. — Fax 677-7028

University of South Dakota — Post-Sec.
414 E Clark St 57069 — 605-677-5011

Viborg, Turner, Pop. 777
Viborg-Hurley SD 60-6 — 200/PK-12
PO Box 397 57070 — 605-766-5418
Jerry Joachim, supt. — Fax 766-5635
www.viborg.k12.sd.us/
Viborg-Hurley HS — 100/9-12
PO Box 397 57070 — 605-766-5418
Barbara Hansen, prin. — Fax 766-5635
Other Schools – See Hurley

Volga, Brookings, Pop. 1,762
Sioux Valley SD 5-5 — 600/PK-12
PO Box 278 57071 — 605-627-5657
Thomas Oster, supt. — Fax 627-5291
www.svs.k12.sd.us/
Sioux Valley HS — 200/9-12
PO Box 278 57071 — 605-627-5657
Belinda Miller, prin. — Fax 627-5291
Sioux Valley MS — 100/6-8
PO Box 278 57071 — 605-627-5657
Belinda Miller, prin. — Fax 627-5291

Wagner, Charles Mix, Pop. 1,520
Wagner Community SD 11-4 — 800/PK-12
101 Walnut Ave SW 57380 — 605-384-3677
Susan Smit, supt. — Fax 384-3678
www.wagner.k12.sd.us/
Wagner HS — 200/9-12
101 Walnut Ave SW 57380 — 605-384-5426
Neil Goter, prin. — Fax 384-3200
Wagner JHS — 200/5-8
101 Walnut Ave SW 57380 — 605-384-3913
Steve Petry, prin. — Fax 384-3678

Wakpala, Corson
Smee SD 15-3 — 200/PK-12
PO Box B 57658 — 605-845-3040
Chris Fried, supt. — Fax 845-7244
www.smee.k12.sd.us
Wakpala HS — 100/9-12
PO Box B 57658 — 605-845-3040
Todd Dillon, prin. — Fax 845-7244
Wakpala MS — 50/6-8
PO Box B 57658 — 605-845-3040
Todd Dillon, admin. — Fax 845-7244

Wall, Pennington, Pop. 739
Wall SD 51-5 — 200/K-12
PO Box 414 57790 — 605-279-2156
Dennis Rieckman, supt. — Fax 279-2613
www.wall.k12.sd.us
Wall HS — 100/7-12
PO Box 414 57790 — 605-279-2156
Dennis Rieckman, prin. — Fax 279-2613

Warner, Brown, Pop. 453
Warner SD 6-5 — 300/PK-12
PO Box 20 57479 — 605-225-6397
Kirk Easton, supt. — Fax 225-0007
www.warner.k12.sd.us/
Warner HS — 100/9-12
PO Box 20 57479 — 605-225-6194
Kirk Easton, prin. — Fax 225-0007
Warner MS — 100/6-8
PO Box 20 57479 — 605-225-6194
Donneley Kay, prin. — Fax 225-0007

Watertown, Codington, Pop. 21,216
Lake Area Multi-District
1311 3rd Ave NE 57201 — 605-882-6380
Bert Falak, dir. — Fax 882-6381
www.lakeareamulti.k12.sd.us/
Lake Area Vocational S — Vo/Tech
1311 3rd Ave NE 57201 — 605-882-6380
Bert Falak, dir. — Fax 882-6381

Watertown SD 14-4 — 3,700/PK-12
PO Box 730 57201 — 605-882-6312
Dr. Lesli Jutting, supt. — Fax 882-6327
www.watertown.k12.sd.us/
Watertown HS — 1,200/9-12
200 9th St NE 57201 — 605-882-6316
Dr. Michael Butts, prin. — Fax 882-6327
Watertown MS — 600/7-8
601 11th St NE 57201 — 605-882-6370
Todd Brist, prin. — Fax 886-6372

Great Plains Lutheran HS — 100/9-12
1200 Luther Ln NE 57201 — 605-886-0672
Bert Falak, prin. — Fax 882-9089
Lake Area Technical Institute — Post-Sec.
PO Box 730 57201 — 605-882-5284

Waubay, Day, Pop. 561
Waubay SD 18-3 — 200/PK-12
202 W School Rd 57273 — 605-947-4529
Al Stewart M.A., supt. — Fax 947-4243
www.waubay.k12.sd.us/
Waubay HS — 50/10-12
202 W School Rd 57273 — 605-947-4529
Doug Riter M.A., prin. — Fax 947-4243
Waubay JHS — 50/7-9
202 W School Rd 57273 — 605-947-4529
Thomas Lee, prin. — Fax 947-4243

Waverly, Codington, Pop. 37
Waverly SD 14-5 — 200/PK-12
319 Mary Pl, — 605-886-9174
John Bjorkman, supt. — Fax 886-6630
www.waverly.k12.sd.us
Waverly HS — 100/9-12
319 Mary Pl, — 605-886-9174
John Bjorkman, prin. — Fax 886-6630
Waverly JHS — 50/7-8
319 Mary Pl, — 605-886-9174
John Bjorkman, prin. — Fax 886-6630

Webster, Day, Pop. 1,853
Webster SD 18-4 — 500/PK-12
102 E 9th Ave 57274 — 605-345-3548
James Block, supt. — Fax 345-4421
www.webster.k12.sd.us/
Webster HS — 200/9-12
102 E 9th Ave 57274 — 605-345-4653
James Block, prin. — Fax 345-4421
Webster MS — 100/6-8
102 E 9th Ave 57274 — 605-345-4653
Craig Case, prin. — Fax 345-4421

Wessington Springs, Jerauld, Pop. 954
Wessington Springs SD 36-2 — 300/PK-12
PO Box 449 57382 — 605-539-9391
Lance Witte, supt. — Fax 539-1029
www.wessingtonsprings.k12.sd.us
Spring Valley HS — 50/9-12
32064 365th Avenue 57382 — 605-539-9687
Jason Kolousek, prin. — Fax 539-1029
Wessington Springs HS — 100/9-12
PO Box 449 57382 — 605-539-9391
Jason Kolousek, prin. — Fax 539-1029
Wessington Springs MS — 50/5-8
PO Box 449 57382 — 605-539-9311
Jason Kolousek, prin. — Fax 539-1029

White, Brookings, Pop. 482
Deubrook Area SD 5-6 — 300/K-12
PO Box 346 57276 — 605-629-1100
Kevin Keenaghan, supt. — Fax 629-3701
www.deubrook.com
Deubrook JSHS — 100/7-12
PO Box 346 57276 — 605-629-1101
Paul Nepodal, prin. — Fax 629-3701
Norfeld Colony S — 50/K-12
PO Box 346 57276 — 605-629-1114
Kristy Olson, prin. — Fax 629-3701

White Lake, Aurora, Pop. 368
White Lake SD 1-3 — 100/PK-12
PO Box 246 57383 — 605-249-2251
Robert Schroeder, supt. — Fax 249-2725
www.whitelake.k12.sd.us/
White Lake HS — 100/9-12
PO Box 246 57383 — 605-249-2251
Robert Schroeder, prin. — Fax 249-2725
White Lake JHS — 50/7-8
PO Box 246 57383 — 605-249-2251
Robert Schroeder, prin. — Fax 249-2725

White River, Mellette, Pop. 529
White River SD 47-1 — 400/PK-12
PO Box 273 57579 — 605-259-3311
Thomas Cameron, supt. — Fax 259-3133
www.whiteriver.k12.sd.us/
White River HS — 100/9-12
PO Box 273 57579 — 605-259-3135
David Colberg, prin. — Fax 259-3133
White River MS — 100/6-8
PO Box 273 57579 — 605-259-3135
Kendra Becker, prin. — Fax 259-3133

Willow Lake, Clark, Pop. 262
Willow Lake SD 12-3 — 200/PK-12
PO Box 170 57278 — 605-625-5945
Terry Winegar, supt. — Fax 625-3103
www.willowlake.k12.sd.us/
Mayfield Alternative HS — 50/Alt
PO Box 170 57278 — 605-625-5945
Terry Winegar, supt. — Fax 625-3103
Willow Lake HS — 100/9-12
PO Box 170 57278 — 605-625-5924
Hector Serna, prin. — Fax 625-3103
Willow Lake JHS — 50/6-8
PO Box 170 57278 — 605-625-5924
Hector Serna, prin. — Fax 625-3103
Other Schools – See Carpenter

Wilmot, Roberts, Pop. 481
Wilmot SD 54-7 — 200/PK-12
PO Box 100 57279 — 605-938-4647
Larry Hulscher, supt. — Fax 938-4185
www.wilmot.k12.sd.us
Wilmot HS — 100/9-12
PO Box 100 57279 — 605-938-4647
Larry Hulscher, prin. — Fax 938-4185
Wilmot MS — 50/6-8
PO Box 100 57279 — 605-938-4647
Mike Schmidt, prin. — Fax 938-4185

Winner, Tripp, Pop. 2,819
Winner SD 59-2 — 500/K-12
PO Box 231 57580 — 605-842-8101
Bruce Carrier, supt. — Fax 842-8120
www.winner.k12.sd.us
Winner MSHS — 200/6-12
PO Box 231 57580 — 605-842-8125
Gerald Witte, prin. — Fax 842-8121

Wolsey, Beadle, Pop. 376
Wolsey Wessington SD 2-6 — 300/K-12
375 Ash St SE 57384 — 605-883-4221
James Cutshaw, supt. — Fax 883-4720
Wolsey Wessington HS — 100/9-12
375 Ash St SE 57384 — 605-883-4221
James Cutshaw, prin. — Fax 883-4720
Wolsey Wessington MS — 100/6-8
375 Ash St SE 57384 — 605-883-4221
Carol Rowen, prin. — Fax 883-4720

Woonsocket, Sanborn, Pop. 652
Woonsocket SD 55-4 — 200/PK-12
PO Box 428 57385 — 605-796-4431
Dr. Rodrick Weber, supt. — Fax 796-4352
www.woonsocket.k12.sd.us/
Woonsocket HS — 50/9-12
PO Box 428 57385 — 605-796-4431
Dr. Rodrick Weber, prin. — Fax 796-4352

Yankton, Yankton, Pop. 14,259
Yankton SD 63-3 — 2,700/PK-12
PO Box 738 57078 — 605-665-3998
Dr. Wayne Kindle, supt. — Fax 665-1422
www.ysd.k12.sd.us
Alternative Learning Center — Alt
PO Box 738 57078 — 605-665-2073
Dr. Jennifer Johnke, prin. — Fax 655-5948
Yankton HS — 900/9-12
PO Box 738 57078 — 605-665-2073
Dr. Jennifer Johnke, prin. — Fax 655-5948
Yankton MS — 600/6-8
PO Box 738 57078 — 605-665-2419
Todd Dvoracek, prin. — Fax 665-6239

Mt. Marty College — Post-Sec.
1105 W 8th St 57078 — 605-668-1545
Sacred Heart Hospital — Post-Sec.
501 Summit St 57078 — 605-655-9371
Sacred Heart MS — 100/5-8
504 Capitol St 57078 — 605-665-1808
Regan Manning, prin. — Fax 260-9787

TENNESSEE

TENNESSEE DEPARTMENT OF EDUCATION
710 James Robertson Pkwy, Nashville 37243-1219
Telephone 615-741-2731
Fax 615-532-4791
Website http://www.state.tn.us/education

Commissioner of Education Kevin Huffman

TENNESSEE BOARD OF EDUCATION
710 James Robertson Pkwy, Nashville 37243-1219

Executive Director Dr. Gary Nixon

PUBLIC, PRIVATE AND CATHOLIC SECONDARY SCHOOLS

Adamsville, McNairy, Pop. 2,170
McNairy County SD
Supt. — See Selmer
Adamsville JSHS 700/7-12
PO Box 407 38310 731-632-3273
Greg Martin, prin. Fax 632-3080

Afton, Greene
Greene County SD
Supt. — See Greeneville
Chuckey-Doak HS 700/9-12
365 Ripley Island Rd 37616 423-798-2636
Mike Garland, prin. Fax 639-5761
Chuckey Doak MS 500/6-8
120 Chuckey Doak Rd 37616 423-787-2038
Amy Brooks, prin. Fax 787-2096

Alamo, Crockett, Pop. 2,420
Crockett County SD 1,900/PK-12
102 N Cavalier Dr 38001 731-696-2604
Robert Mullins, supt. Fax 696-4734
www.ccschools.net
Crockett County HS 800/9-12
2014 Highway 88 38001 731-696-4525
Steve Ramsey, prin. Fax 696-3124
Crockett County MS 600/6-8
497 N Cavalier Dr 38001 731-696-5583
Bobby McLaughlin, prin. Fax 696-2034

Alcoa, Blount, Pop. 8,239
Alcoa CSD 1,800/PK-12
524 Faraday St 37701 865-984-0531
Dr. Brian Bell, supt. Fax 984-5832
www.alcoaschools.net/
Alcoa HS 500/9-12
532 Faraday St 37701 865-982-4631
Dr. Scott Porter, prin. Fax 380-2240
Alcoa MS 500/5-8
1325 Springbrook Rd 37701 865-982-5211
James Kirk, prin. Fax 380-2533

Algood, Putnam, Pop. 3,428
Putnam County SD
Supt. — See Cookeville
Algood MS 800/PK-PK, 5-
540 Dry Valley Rd, Cookeville TN 38506
931-537-6141
Tim Martin, prin. Fax 537-3700

Altamont, Grundy, Pop. 1,042
Grundy County SD 2,400/PK-12
PO Box 97 37301 931-692-3467
Joel Hargis, dir. Fax 692-2188
Other Schools – See Coalmont

Antioch, Davidson
Metropolitan Nashville SD
Supt. — See Nashville
Antioch HS 1,400/9-12
1900 Hobson Pike 37013 615-641-5400
Dr. Adrienne Battle-Koger, prin. Fax 641-5422
Antioch MS 400/5-8
5050 Blue Hole Rd 37013 615-333-5642
Dr. Canidra Henderson, prin. Fax 333-5053
Apollo MS 500/5-8
631 Richards Rd 37013 615-333-5025
Jon Hubble, prin. Fax 333-5029
Cane Ridge HS 1,800/9-12
12848 Old Hickory Blvd 37013 615-687-4000
Michel Sanchez-Wall, prin. Fax 641-5007
Kennedy MS 900/5-8
2087 Hobson Pike 37013 615-501-7900
Dr. Sam Braden, prin.
Marshall MS, 5832 Pettus Rd 37013 1,100/5-8
Roderick Webb, prin. 615-941-7515
Academy at Hickory Hollow Adult
5248 Hickory Hollow Pkwy 37013 615-687-4028
Billy Fellman, prin.

Ezell-Harding Christian S 700/PK-12
574 Bell Rd 37013 615-367-0532
Beecher Frasier, pres. Fax 399-8747
Jon Nave University of Cosmetology Post-Sec.
5510 Crossings Cir 37013 - -
Lighthouse Christian S 600/PK-12
5100 Blue Hole Rd 37013 615-331-6286
Brian Sweatt, admin. Fax 331-2491

Arlington, Shelby, Pop. 11,290
Shelby County SD
Supt. — See Memphis
Arlington HS 2,400/9-12
5475 Airline Rd 38002 901-867-1541
Tammy Mason, prin. Fax 867-1546
Arlington MS 1,100/6-8
5470 Lamb Rd 38002 901-867-6015
Dr. Allison Clark, prin. Fax 867-7080
Bolton HS 2,000/9-12
7323 Brunswick Rd 38002 901-873-8150
Dan Haddow, prin. Fax 829-2435
Shadowlawn MS 900/6-8
4734 Shadowlawn Rd 38002 901-373-2654
John McDonald, prin. Fax 373-1363

Macon Road Baptist S - East 300/K-12
11017 Highway 64 38002 901-867-8161
Jeremy Errett, prin. Fax 766-1610

Ashland City, Cheatham, Pop. 4,449
Cheatham County SD 6,800/PK-12
102 Elizabeth St 37015 615-792-5664
Dr. Stan Curtis, dir. Fax 792-2551
www.cheathamcountyschools.net
Cheatham County Central HS 700/9-12
1 Cub Cir 37015 615-792-5641
Glenna Barrow, prin. Fax 792-2090
Cheatham MS 600/5-8
700 Scoutview Rd 37015 615-792-2334
Dr. Beth Batson, prin. Fax 792-2337
Cheatham County Adult HS Adult
102 Elizabeth St 37015 615-792-9287
Jo Jones, prin.
Other Schools – See Kingston Springs, Pleasant View

Athens, McMinn, Pop. 13,106
Athens CSD 1,200/PK-8
943 Crestway Dr 37303 423-745-2863
Robert Greene, dir. Fax 745-9041
www.athenscityschools.net
Athens City MS 300/6-8
200 Keith Ln 37303 423-745-1177
Michael Simmons, prin. Fax 745-9679

McMinn County SD 6,100/PK-12
3 S Hill St 37303 423-745-1612
Mickey Blevins Ed.D., supt. Fax 744-1641
www.mcminn.k12.tn.us
McMinn Career & Technical Center Vo/Tech
2103 Congress Pkwy S 37303 423-745-8633
Ed McCleary, prin. Fax 746-4293
McMinn County HS 1,400/9-12
2215 Congress Pkwy S 37303 423-745-4142
John Burroughs, prin. Fax 745-0584
Other Schools – See Englewood

Fairview Christian Academy 100/PK-12
261 County Road 439 37303 423-745-6781
Greg Ranck, admin.
Tennessee Technology Center at Athens Post-Sec.
PO Box 848 37371 423-744-2814
Tennessee Wesleyan College Post-Sec.
204 E College St 37303 423-745-7504

Atwood, Carroll, Pop. 925
West Carroll Special SD 1,000/PK-12
1415 State Route 77 38220 731-662-4200
Eric Williams, dir. Fax 662-4250
www.wcssd.org
West Carroll JSHS 500/7-12
760 State Route 77 38220 731-662-7116
Lex Suite, prin. Fax 662-4198

Bartlett, Shelby, Pop. 53,815
Shelby County SD
Supt. — See Memphis
Appling MS 700/6-8
3700 Appling Rd 38133 901-373-1410
Dr. Keshia Newborn, prin. Fax 373-1360
Bartlett HS 1,500/9-12
5688 Woodlawn St 38134 901-373-2620
Ken Demetriou, prin. Fax 373-2624
Bon Lin MS 700/6-8
3862 N Germantown Rd 38133 901-347-1520
Cody Duncan, prin. Fax 347-1491
Elmore Park MS 700/6-8
6330 Althorne Rd 38134 901-373-2642
Marjorie Lowe, prin. Fax 373-1361

National College of Business & Tech Post-Sec.
5760 Stage Rd 38134 901-213-1681

Baxter, Putnam, Pop. 1,354
Putnam County SD
Supt. — See Cookeville
Cornerstone MS 700/5-8
371 1st Ave S 38544 931-858-6601
Billy Stepp, prin. Fax 858-6637
Upperman HS 700/PK-PK, 9
6950 Nashville Hwy 38544 931-858-3112
Penny Nash, prin. Fax 858-4641

Bell Buckle, Bedford, Pop. 495

Webb S 300/6-12
PO Box 488 37020 888-733-9322
Raymond Broadhead, admin. Fax 389-6657

Benton, Polk, Pop. 1,374
Polk County SD 2,800/PK-12
PO Box 665 37307 423-299-0471
James Jones, supt. Fax 338-2691
www.polk-schools.com
Chilhowee MS 500/6-8
PO Box 977 37307 423-338-3102
Connie Dunn, prin. Fax 338-3158
Polk County HS 600/9-12
PO Box 188 37307 423-299-0078
Jason Bell, prin. Fax 338-4521
Other Schools – See Copperhill

Big Sandy, Benton, Pop. 553
Benton County SD
Supt. — See Camden
Big Sandy S 300/K-12
13305 Highway 69A 38221 731-593-3221
Marty Caruthers, prin. Fax 593-3245

Blountville, Sullivan, Pop. 3,052
Sullivan County SD 10,200/PK-12
PO Box 306 37617 423-354-1000
Dr. Jubal Yennie, supt. Fax 354-1004
www.sullivank12.net
Blountville MS 300/6-8
1651 Blountville Blvd 37617 423-354-1600
Michael Wilson, prin. Fax 354-1606
Holston MS 400/6-8
2348 Highway 75 37617 423-354-1500
Bill Miller, prin. Fax 354-1505
Sullivan Central HS 1,100/9-12
131 Shipley Ferry Rd 37617 423-354-1200
Dee Musser, prin. Fax 354-1206
Other Schools – See Bluff City, Bristol, Kingsport

Northeast State Community College Post-Sec.
PO Box 246 37617 423-323-3191
Tri-Cities Christian S 400/PK-12
1500 Highway 75 37617 423-323-7128
Melody Archer, admin. Fax 323-8298

Bluff City, Sullivan, Pop. 1,717
Sullivan County SD
Supt. — See Blountville
Bluff City MS 400/6-8
337 Carter St 37618 423-354-1801
Greg Stallcup, prin. Fax 354-1818
Sullivan East HS 1,000/9-12
4180 Weaver Pike 37618 423-354-1900
Angie Buckles, prin. Fax 354-1906

Bolivar, Hardeman, Pop. 5,360
Hardeman County SD 4,200/PK-12
10815 Old Highway 64 38008 731-658-2510
Warner Ross, dir. Fax 658-2061
www.hardemancountyschools.org
Bolivar MS 400/6-8
915 Pruitt St 38008 731-658-3656
Mary Ann Polk, prin. Fax 658-6625
Central HS 800/9-12
313 Harris St 38008 731-658-3151
Fred Kessler, prin. Fax 658-6697
Other Schools – See Middleton

Bradford, Gibson, Pop. 1,036
Bradford Special SD 600/PK-12
PO Box 220 38316 731-742-3180
Dan Black, supt. Fax 742-3994
www.bradfordssd.schoolinsites.com
Bradford JSHS 300/7-12
136 Highway 45 S 38316 731-742-3729
Shane Paschall, prin. Fax 742-3088

Brentwood, Williamson, Pop. 36,506
Williamson County SD
Supt. — See Franklin
Brentwood HS 1,500/9-12
5304 Murray Ln 37027 615-472-4220
Kevin Keidel, prin. Fax 472-4241
Brentwood MS 1,000/6-8
5324 Murray Ln 37027 615-472-4250
Bill Harlin, prin. Fax 472-4263
Ravenwood HS 1,900/9-12
1724 Wilson Pike 37027 615-472-4800
Dr. Pam Vaden, prin. Fax 472-4821
Sunset MS 800/6-8
200 Sunset Trl 37027 615-472-5040
Dr. Tim Brown, prin. Fax 472-5050
Woodland MS 800/6-8
1500 Volunteer Pkwy 37027 615-472-4930
Priscilla Fizer, prin. Fax 472-4941

Brentwood Academy 700/6-12
219 Granny White Pike 37027 615-523-0611
Curt Masters, hdmstr. Fax 377-3709
Currey Ingram Academy 300/K-12
6544 Murray Ln 37027 615-507-3242
Kathleen Rayburn, head sch Fax 507-3170

Brighton, Tipton, Pop. 2,690
Tipton County SD
Supt. — See Covington
Brighton HS 1,500/9-12
8045 Highway 51 S 38011 901-837-5800
Christie Huffman, prin. Fax 837-5829
Brighton MS 1,100/6-8
7785 Highway 51 S 38011 901-837-5600
Sabrina Sneed-Mathews, prin. Fax 837-5625

Bristol, Sullivan, Pop. 26,322
Bristol CSD 4,000/PK-12
615 Martin Luther King Blvd 37620 423-652-9451
Dr. Gary Lilly, dir. Fax 652-9238
www.btcs.org
Tennessee HS 1,200/9-12
1112 Edgemont Ave 37620 423-652-9494
Mary Rouse, prin. Fax 652-9327
Vance MS 600/7-8
815 Edgemont Ave 37620 423-652-9449
Dr. Amy Scott, prin. Fax 652-9297

Sullivan County SD
Supt. — See Blountville
Holston Valley MS 200/6-8
1717 Bristol Caverns Hwy 37620 423-354-1880
Jess Lockhart, prin. Fax 354-1891

King College Post-Sec.
1350 King College Rd 37620 423-968-1187
National College of Business & Tech Post-Sec.
1328 Highway 11 W 37620 423-878-4440

Brownsville, Haywood, Pop. 10,196
Haywood County SD 2,700/PK-12
900 E Main St 38012 731-772-9613
Teresa Russell, dir. Fax 772-3275
www.haywoodschools.com
Haywood HS 900/9-12
1175 E College St 38012 731-772-1845
Dr. Jerry Pyron, prin. Fax 772-6079
Haywood JHS 500/6-8
1201 Haralson St 38012 731-772-3265
Yvette Blue, prin. Fax 772-3352

Bruceton, Carroll, Pop. 1,455
Hollow Rock-Bruceton Special SD 700/PK-12
PO Box 135 38317 731-418-4180
Rod Sturdivant, supt. Fax 418-4188
www.hrbedu.org
Central HS, PO Box 135 38317 200/9-12
Tim Gilmer, prin. 731-418-4189
Central MS 200/6-8
PO Box 135 38317 731-418-4167
Joe Norval, prin. Fax 418-4188

Buchanan, Henry
Henry County SD
Supt. — See Paris
Lakewood MS 300/6-8
6745 Highway 79 N Ste B 38222 731-644-1600
Mike Bell, prin. Fax 644-0680

Byrdstown, Pickett, Pop. 803
Pickett County SD 700/PK-12
141 Skyline Dr 38549 931-864-3123
Diane Elder, supt. Fax 864-7185
pickett.k12tn.net/
Pickett County HS 200/9-12
130 Skyline Dr 38549 931-864-3422
Rebecca Wallin, prin. Fax 864-6297

Camden, Benton, Pop. 3,542
Benton County SD 2,300/PK-12
197 Briarwood St 38320 731-584-6111
Mark Florence, supt. Fax 584-8142
www.bentoncountyschools.org
Benton County Career/Technical Center Vo/Tech
155 Schools Dr 38320 731-584-4492
Dr. Randy Shannon, prin. Fax 584-4493
Camden Central HS 600/9-12
115 Schools Dr 38320 731-584-7254
Linda Phelps, prin. Fax 584-4221
Camden JHS 400/6-8
75 Schools Dr 38320 731-584-4518
Michelle Leonard, prin. Fax 584-4493
Other Schools – See Big Sandy

Carthage, Smith, Pop. 2,267
Smith County SD 3,400/PK-12
126 Smith Co Middle Schl Ln 37030 615-735-9625
Roger Lewis, supt. Fax 735-8271
boe.smithcounty.com/
Smith County HS 600/9-12
312 Fite Ave E 37030 615-735-9219
Stephen Robbins, prin. Fax 735-9049
Smith County MS 400/5-8
134 Smith Co Mid School Ln 37030 615-735-8277
Jamie Kelley, prin. Fax 735-8255
Other Schools – See Gordonsville

Cedar Hill, Robertson, Pop. 308
Robertson County SD
Supt. — See Springfield
Byrns HS 500/6-12
7025 Highway 41 N 37032 615-696-2251
Doug Haskins, prin. Fax 696-0526

Celina, Clay, Pop. 1,478
Clay County SD 1,100/PK-12
PO Box 469 38551 931-243-3310
Jerry Strong, dir. Fax 243-3706
www.clayedu.com
Clay County HS 300/9-12
PO Box 40 38551 931-243-2340
Melissa White, prin. Fax 243-2376
Clay County Adult HS Adult
PO Box 469 38551 931-243-3310
Jayne Donaldson, prin. Fax 243-3706

Centerville, Hickman, Pop. 3,602
Hickman County SD 3,900/PK-12
115 Murphree Ave 37033 931-729-3391
Dr. Jerry Nash, dir. Fax 729-3834
www.hickmank12.org
Hickman County HS 600/9-12
1645 Bulldog Blvd 37033 931-729-2616
Philip Jacobs, prin. Fax 729-2925
Hickman County MS 400/6-8
1639 Bulldog Blvd 37033 931-729-4234
Jeremy Qualls, prin. Fax 729-5688
Other Schools – See Lyles

Chapel Hill, Marshall, Pop. 1,427
Marshall County SD
Supt. — See Lewisburg
Forrest MSHS 800/6-12
310 N Horton Pkwy 37034 931-364-7260
Danny Morgan, prin. Fax 364-2928

Charlotte, Dickson, Pop. 1,221
Dickson County SD
Supt. — See Dickson
Charlotte MS 400/6-8
250 Humphries St 37036 615-740-6060
Ray Lecomte, prin. Fax 789-7033
Creek Wood HS 900/9-12
3499 Highway 47 N 37036 615-740-6000
Corey Duke, prin. Fax 441-2868
New Directions Academy 100/Alt
4000 Highway 48 N 37036 615-740-6070
Karen Willey, prin. Fax 789-7032

Chattanooga, Hamilton, Pop. 164,861
Hamilton County SD 41,500/PK-12
3074 Hickory Valley Rd 37421 423-209-8400
Rick Smith, supt. Fax 209-8601
www.hcde.org
Brainerd HS 700/9-12
1020 N Moore Rd 37411 423-855-2615
Uras Agee, prin. Fax 855-2651
Chattanooga HS Center for Creative Arts 500/6-12
1301 Dallas Rd 37405 423-209-5929
Deborah Smith, prin. Fax 209-5930
Chattanooga S for Arts & Sciences 400/K-12
865 E 3rd St 37403 423-209-5816
Kelly Coffelt, prin. Fax 209-5831
Dalewood MS 300/6-8
1300 Shallowford Rd 37411 423-493-0323
Christian Earl, prin. Fax 493-0327
East Lake Academy of Fine Arts 400/6-8
2700 E 34th St 37407 423-493-0334
Lakesha Carson, prin. Fax 493-0343
East Ridge HS 800/9-12
4320 Bennett Rd 37412 423-867-6200
Zac Brown, prin. Fax 867-6220
East Ridge MS 600/6-8
4400 Bennett Rd 37412 423-867-6214
Steven Robinson, prin. Fax 867-6226
Hamilton County Middle College HS 100/10-12
4501 Amnicola Hwy 37406 423-697-4492
Sonja Rich, coord. Fax 697-2676
Hamilton County STEM HS 9-12
4501 Amnicola Hwy 37406 423-531-6270
Dr. Tony Donen, prin. Fax 531-6268
Howard HS of Academics & Technology Vo/Tech
2500 S Market St 37408 423-209-5868
Dr. Paul Smith, prin. Fax 209-5869
Lookout Valley MSHS 300/6-12
350 Lookout High St 37419 423-825-7352
Derrick Rushworth, prin. Fax 821-7951
Normal Park Museum Magnet Upper S 200/6-8
1219 W Mississippi Ave 37405 423-209-5914
Jill Levine, prin. Fax 209-5920
Orchard Knob MS 400/6-8
500 N Highland Park Ave 37404 423-493-7793
Crystal Sorrells, prin. Fax 493-7795
Red Bank HS 800/9-12
640 Morrison Springs Rd 37415 423-874-1900
Justin Robertson, prin. Fax 874-1924
Red Bank MS 600/6-8
3715 Dayton Blvd 37415 423-874-1908
John Pierce, prin. Fax 874-1938
Tyner Academy 600/9-12
6836 Tyner Rd 37421 423-855-2635
Carol Goss, prin. Fax 855-9417
Tyner Middle Academy 500/6-8
6837 Tyner Rd 37421 423-855-2648
Wendy Jung, prin. Fax 855-2699
Washington Alternative JSHS 50/Alt
7821 Hancock Rd 37416 423-893-3520
Tina Aslinger, coord. Fax 893-3521
Other Schools – See Harrison, Hixson, Ooltewah, Sale Creek, Signal Mountain, Soddy Daisy

---

Baylor S 1,000/6-12
171 Baylor School Rd 37405 423-267-8505
Scott Wilson, hdmstr. Fax 265-4276
Boyd-Buchanan S 900/PK-12
4650 Buccaneer Trl 37411 423-622-6177
Jill C. Hartness, pres. Fax 508-2218
Calvary Christian S 200/PK-12
4601 North Ter 37411 423-622-2181
Les Wallace, prin.
Chattanooga Christian S 1,100/K-12
3354 Charger Dr 37409 423-265-6411
Chad Dirkse, pres. Fax 756-4044
Chattanooga College Post-Sec.
3805 Brainerd Rd 37411 423-624-0077
Chattanooga State Community College Post-Sec.
4501 Amnicola Hwy 37406 423-697-4400
Girls Preparatory S 600/6-12
PO Box 4736 37405 423-634-7600
Stanley Tucker, head sch Fax 634-7643
Grace Baptist Academy 800/PK-12
7815 Shallowford Rd 37421 423-892-8224
Matt Pollock, hdmstr. Fax 892-1194
Hamilton Heights Christian Academy 100/9-12
2201 Hickory Valley Rd 37421 423-894-0597
Rev. Duke Stone, admin. Fax 894-4259
ITT Technical Institute Post-Sec.
5600 Brainerd Rd Ste G1 37411 423-510-6800
McCallie S 900/6-12
500 Dodds Ave 37404 423-624-8300
R. Kirk Walker Ph.D., hdmstr. Fax 493-5690
Miller-Motte Technical College Post-Sec.
6020 Shallowford Rd Ste 100 37421 423-510-9675
Notre Dame HS 500/9-12
2701 Vermont Ave 37404 423-624-4618
George Valadie, pres. Fax 624-4621
Silverdale Baptist Academy 800/PK-12
7236 Bonny Oaks Dr 37421 423-892-2319
Rebecca Hansard, hdmstr. Fax 648-7600
Tennessee Temple University Post-Sec.
1815 Union Ave 37404 800-553-4050
University of Tennessee Post-Sec.
615 McCallie Ave 37403 423-425-4111
Virginia College Post-Sec.
721 Eastgate Loop 37411 423-893-2000

Christiana, Rutherford
Rutherford County SD
Supt. — See Murfreesboro
Christiana MS 800/6-8
4675 Shelbyville Pike 37037 615-904-3885
Bob Horne, prin. Fax 904-3886

Church Hill, Hawkins, Pop. 6,688
Hawkins County SD
Supt. — See Rogersville
Church Hill MS 500/7-8
PO Box 38 37642 423-357-3051
Scott Jones, prin. Fax 357-9873
Volunteer HS 1,200/9-12
1050 Volunteer St 37642 423-357-3641
James Dykes, prin. Fax 357-6694

Clarkrange, Fentress, Pop. 575
Fentress County SD
Supt. — See Jamestown
Clarkrange HS 300/9-12
5801 S York Hwy 38553 931-863-3143
Marty Walker, prin. Fax 863-3981

Clarksville, Montgomery, Pop. 126,966
Clarksville-Montgomery County SD 29,300/PK-12
621 Gracey Ave 37040 931-920-7808
Dr. B.J. Worthington, supt. Fax 648-5612
www.cmcss.net
Alternative S Alt
430 Greenwood Ave 37040 931-542-5057
Kim Sigears, prin. Fax 553-2057
Clarksville HS 1,300/9-12
151 Richview Rd 37043 931-648-5690
Jean Luna, prin. Fax 648-5624
Kenwood HS 1,100/9-12
251 E Pine Mountain Rd 37042 931-905-7900
Hal Bedell, prin. Fax 905-7906
Kenwood MS 900/6-8
241 E Pine Mountain Rd 37042 931-553-2080
Evelyn Martinez, prin. Fax 552-3080
Middle College HS at APSU 100/9-12
PO Box 4654 37044 931-221-1350
Melissa Champion, prin. Fax 221-1360
New Providence MS 900/6-8
146 Cunningham Ln 37042 931-648-5655
Laura Barnett, prin. Fax 503-3409

Northeast HS 900/9-12
3701 Trenton Rd 37040 931-648-5640
Galea Jefferies, prin. Fax 503-3413
Northeast MS 800/6-8
3703 Trenton Rd 37040 931-648-5665
Tracy Hollinger, prin. Fax 503-3410
Northwest HS 1,200/9-12
800 Lafayette Rd 37042 931-648-5675
Dr. Bryan Johnson, prin. Fax 648-0094
Richview MS 1,100/6-8
2350 Memorial Drive Ext 37043 931-648-5620
Lisa Clark, prin. Fax 551-8111
Rossview HS 1,500/9-12
1237 Rossview Rd 37043 931-553-2070
Frank Myers, prin. Fax 503-3419
Rossview MS 1,100/6-8
2265 Cardinal Ln 37043 931-920-6150
Christina Harris, prin. Fax 920-6147
STEM Academy 9-12
251 E Pine Mountain Rd 37042 931-905-7900
Christi Fordham, prin. Fax 905-7906
West Creek HS 1,200/9-12
1210 W Creek Coyote Trl 37042 931-503-1788
Dr. Tosha Diggs, prin. Fax 503-1802
West Creek MS 1,000/6-8
1200 W Creek Coyote Trl 37042 931-503-3288
Bryan Feldman, prin. Fax 503-3296
Adult Ed-Greenwood Complex Adult
430 Greenwood Ave 37040 931-542-5040
Betty Cook, prin. Fax 920-9260
Other Schools – See Cunningham

Academy for Keener Minds 100/K-12
420 Madison St Ste D 37040 931-809-8776
Austin Peay State University Post-Sec.
601 College St 37044 931-221-7011
Clarksville Academy 500/PK-12
710 N 2nd St 37040 931-647-6311
Kay Drew, head sch Fax 906-0610
Clarksville Christian S 200/K-12
505 Highway 76 37043 931-647-8180
Amanda Binkley, prin. Fax 741-0953
Draughons Junior College Post-Sec.
1860 Wilma Rudolph Blvd 37040 931-552-7600
Miller-Motte Technical College Post-Sec.
1820 Business Park Dr 37040 931-553-0071
North Central Institute Post-Sec.
168 Jack Miller Blvd 37042 931-431-9700
Queen City College Post-Sec.
1594 Fort Campbell Blvd 37042 931-645-2361

Cleveland, Bradley, Pop. 40,418
Bradley County SD 9,900/PK-12
800 S Lee Hwy 37311 423-476-0620
Johnny McDaniel, dir. Fax 476-0485
www.bradleyschools.org
Bradley Central HS 1,700/9-12
1000 S Lee Hwy 37311 423-476-0650
Todd Shoemaker, prin. Fax 476-0613
Goal Academy 50/Alt
209 Sunset Dr NW 37312 423-476-0699
Kyle Page, prin. Fax 478-8829
Lake Forest MS 1,100/6-8
610 Kile Lake Rd SE 37323 423-478-8821
Ritchie Stevenson, prin. Fax 478-8832
Ocoee MS 1,200/6-8
2250 N Ocoee St 37311 423-476-0630
Ron Spangler, prin. Fax 476-0588
Walker Valley HS 1,500/9-12
750 Lauderdale Mem Hwy NW 37312 423-336-1383
Danny Coggin, prin. Fax 336-1578
REACH Adult HS Adult
1450 Strawberry Ln NE 37311 423-473-8473
Zoe Renfro, prin. Fax 473-8483

Cleveland CSD 5,000/K-12
4300 Mouse Creek Rd NW 37312 423-472-9571
Dr. Martin Ringstaff, dir. Fax 472-3390
www.clevelandschools.org
Cleveland HS 1,300/9-12
850 Raider Dr NW 37312 423-478-1113
Autumn O'Bryan, prin. Fax 559-1560
Cleveland MS 1,100/6-8
3635 Georgetown Rd NW 37312 423-479-9641
Michael Collier, prin. Fax 479-9553
Teen Learning Center Alt
350 Central Ave NW 37311 423-339-0902
Barbara Ector, prin. Fax 559-9477

Cleveland State Community College Post-Sec.
PO Box 3570 37320 423-472-7141
Franklin Academy Post-Sec.
1605 Professional Park Dr N 37312 423-476-3742
Lee University Post-Sec.
1120 N Ocoee St 37311 800-533-9930
Pentecostal Theological Seminary Post-Sec.
900 Walker St NE 37311 423-478-1131
Tennessee Christian Preparatory S 300/PK-12
4995 N Lee Hwy 37312 423-559-8939
Dr. Bill Balzano, pres. Fax 476-4974

Clifton, Wayne, Pop. 2,664
Wayne County SD
Supt. — See Waynesboro
Hughes S 300/PK-12
PO Box A 38425 931-676-3325
Tracy Love, prin. Fax 676-3903

Clinton, Anderson, Pop. 9,667
Anderson County SD 7,900/PK-12
101 S Main St 37716 865-463-2800
Larry Foster, supt. Fax 457-9157
www.acs.ac
Anderson County Career & Technical Ctr Vo/Tech
140 Maverick Cir 37716 865-457-4205
Kelly Myers, prin. Fax 457-1715
Anderson County HS 1,000/9-12
130 Maverick Cir 37716 865-457-4716
Andrea Russell, prin. Fax 457-3398
Clinch River Community S 100/Alt
160 Maverick Cir 37716 865-457-7462
Gary Houck, prin. Fax 457-6546
Clinton HS 1,200/9-12
425 Dragon Dr 37716 865-457-2611
Eric Snider, prin. Fax 457-8805
Clinton MS 700/6-8
110 N Hicks St 37716 865-457-3451
Doug Jacobs, prin. Fax 457-9486
Other Schools – See Lake City, Norris, Oliver Springs

Coalfield, Morgan, Pop. 2,425
Morgan County SD
Supt. — See Wartburg
Coalfield S 500/K-12
PO Box 98 37719 865-435-7332
David Treece, prin. Fax 435-2646

Coalmont, Grundy, Pop. 825
Grundy County SD
Supt. — See Altamont
Grundy County HS 700/9-12
24970 SR 108 37313 931-692-5400
James Rust, prin. Fax 692-5403

Collegedale, Hamilton, Pop. 8,113

Collegedale Academy 300/9-12
PO Box 628 37315 423-396-2124
Brent Baldwin M.Ed., prin. Fax 396-3363
Collegedale Adventist MS 200/6-8
4856 College Dr E 37315 423-396-3020
Larry Robbins, prin. Fax 396-3043
Southern Adventist University Post-Sec.
PO Box 370 37315 423-236-2000

Collierville, Shelby, Pop. 43,413
Shelby County SD
Supt. — See Memphis
Collierville HS 1,900/9-12
1101 New Byhalia Rd 38017 901-853-3310
Dr. Russell Dyer, prin. Fax 853-3313
Collierville MS 900/6-8
580 Quinn Rd 38017 901-853-3320
Ingrid Warren, prin. Fax 853-3327
Schilling Farms MS 1,100/6-8
935 Colbert St S 38017 901-854-2345
Jeff Jones, prin. Fax 854-8200

St. George's Independent S Collierville 700/6-12
1880 Wolf River Blvd 38017 901-457-2000
William Taylor, pres. Fax 457-2111

Collinwood, Wayne, Pop. 979
Wayne County SD
Supt. — See Waynesboro
Collinwood HS 300/9-12
401 N Trojan Blvd 38450 931-724-4316
Herbert Luker, prin. Fax 724-4488
Collinwood MS 300/5-8
300 4th Ave N 38450 931-724-9510
Walter Butler, prin. Fax 924-2519

Columbia, Maury, Pop. 33,976
Maury County SD 11,700/PK-12
501 W 8th St 38401 931-388-8403
Edward Hickman, dir. Fax 840-4410
www.mauryk12.org/
Columbia Central HS 1,300/9-12
921 Lion Pkwy 38401 931-381-2222
Vince Springer, prin. Fax 381-6434
Cox MS 600/5-8
633 Bear Creek Pike 38401 931-840-3902
Dr. Debbie Steen, prin. Fax 840-3903
Spring Hill HS 800/9-12
1 Raider Ln 38401 931-486-2207
Richard Callahan, prin. Fax 486-3113
Whitthorne MS 1,200/5-8
915 Lion Pkwy 38401 931-388-2558
Linda Lester, prin. Fax 380-4684
Other Schools – See Culleoka, Hampshire, Mount Pleasant, Santa Fe, Spring Hill

Columbia Academy 600/PK-12
1101 W 7th St 38401 931-388-5363
Dr. James Thomas, pres. Fax 380-8506
Columbia State Community College Post-Sec.
1665 Hampshire Pike 38401 931-540-2722
Zion Christian Academy 400/PK-12
6901 Old Zion Rd 38401 931-388-5731
Don Wahlman, hdmstr. Fax 388-5842

Cookeville, Putnam, Pop. 29,908
Putnam County SD 10,800/PK-12
1400 E Spring St 38506 931-526-9777
Dr. Kathleen Airhart, dir. Fax 528-6942
www.putnamcountyschools.com
Cookeville HS 2,100/9-12
1 Cavalier Dr 38501 931-520-2287
Edward L. Ward, prin. Fax 520-2268
Prescott South MS 800/5-8
1859 S Jefferson Ave 38506 931-528-3647
Cindy Taylor, prin. Fax 520-2019
Trace MS 800/5-8
230 Raider Dr 38501 931-520-2200
Michael Miehls, prin. Fax 520-2204
White Plains Academy 100/Alt
288 E Main St 38506 931-537-3862
Joe Matheney, prin. Fax 537-3062
Adult Learning Center Adult
288 E Main St 38506 931-528-8685
Jimmie Webber, prin. Fax 537-2516
Other Schools – See Algood, Baxter, Monterey

Fortis Institute Post-Sec.
1025 Highway 111 38501 931-526-3660
Genesis Career College Post-Sec.
880 E 10th St Ste A 38501 931-526-8735
Highland Rim Academy 100/K-10
PO Box 3022 38502 931-526-4472
Dan Bailey, hdmstr.
Mister Wayne's Sch of Unisex Hair Design Post-Sec.
170 S Willow Ave 38501 931-526-1478
Tennessee Technological University Post-Sec.
1 William L Jones Dr 38505 931-372-3101

Copperhill, Polk, Pop. 348
Polk County SD
Supt. — See Benton
Copper Basin HS 300/7-12
300 Cougar Dr 37317 423-496-3291
Jared Bigham, prin. Fax 496-5308

Cordova, Shelby
Memphis CSD
Supt. — See Memphis
Cordova HS 1,900/9-12
1800 Berryhill Rd 38016 901-416-4540
Felicia Everson, prin. Fax 416-4545
Cordova MS 1,000/5-8
900 N Sanga Rd 38018 901-416-2189
Joy Whitehead, prin. Fax 416-2191

Shelby County SD
Supt. — See Memphis
Dexter MS 600/5-8
6998 Raleigh LaGrange Rd 38018 901-373-3134
Phyllis Jones, prin. Fax 373-3378
Mt. Pisgah MS 1,100/5-8
1444 Pisgah Rd 38016 901-756-2386
John Gilmer, prin. Fax 756-2306

Evangelical Christian S 700/6-12
PO Box 1030 38088 901-754-7217
Barrett Luketic, prin. Fax 754-8123
First Assembly Christian S 800/PK-12
8650 Walnut Grove Rd 38018 901-458-5543
Wendell Meadows, supt. Fax 324-3558
ITT Technical Institute Post-Sec.
7260 Goodlett Farms Pkwy 38016 901-381-0200
L'Ecole Culinaire Post-Sec.
1245 N Germantown Pkwy 38016 901-754-7115
Mid-America Baptist Theological Seminary Post-Sec.
2095 Appling Rd 38016 901-751-8453
St. Benedict HS 800/9-12
8250 Varnavas Dr 38016 901-260-2840
George Valadie, prin. Fax 260-2850

Cornersville, Marshall, Pop. 1,184
Marshall County SD
Supt. — See Lewisburg
Cornersville JSHS 400/7-12
323 S Main St 37047 931-246-4170
Bob Edens, prin. Fax 293-6567

Corryton, Knox, Pop. 100
Knox County SD
Supt. — See Knoxville
Gibbs HS 1,000/9-12
7628 Tazewell Pike 37721 865-689-9130
Lynn Hill, prin. Fax 689-9128

Cosby, Cocke
Cocke County SD
Supt. — See Newport
Cosby HS 500/9-12
3320 Cosby Hwy 37722 423-487-5602
Brad Flatford, prin. Fax 487-5502

Covington, Tipton, Pop. 8,910
Tipton County SD 11,900/PK-12
1580 Highway 51 S 38019 901-476-7148
Dr. William Bibb, dir. Fax 476-4870
www.tipton-county.com
Covington HS 800/9-12
803 S College St 38019 901-475-5850
Marcus Heaston, prin. Fax 476-5778
Crestview MS 600/6-8
201 Mark Walker Dr 38019 901-475-5900
Steve Maclin, prin. Fax 475-2607
Tipton Co. Alternative Learning Center 100/Alt
800 Bert Johnston Ave 38019 901-837-5755
Steve Zurhellen, prin. Fax 476-4612
Other Schools – See Brighton, Munford

Tennessee Technology Center at Covington Post-Sec.
1600 Highway 51 S 38019 901-475-2526

Cowan, Franklin, Pop. 1,690
Franklin County SD
Supt. — See Winchester
South MS 400/6-8
601 Cumberland St W 37318 931-967-7355
Sandra Stewart, prin. Fax 967-1413

Cross Plains, Robertson, Pop. 1,691
Robertson County SD
Supt. — See Springfield
East Robertson HS 800/6-12
158 Kilgore Trce 37049 615-654-2191
Mary Cook, prin. Fax 654-4563

Crossville, Cumberland, Pop. 10,670
Cumberland County SD 7,600/PK-12
368 Fourth St 38555 931-484-6135
Donald E. Andrews, supt. Fax 484-6491
ccschools.k12tn.net/
Cumberland County HS 1,100/9-12
660 Stanley St 38555 931-484-6194
Janet Graham, prin. Fax 456-6872
Stone Memorial HS 1,100/9-12
2800 Cook Rd 38571 931-484-5767
Scott Maddox, prin. Fax 484-4801

Christian Academy of the Cumberlands 100/PK-12
325 Braun St 38555 931-707-9540
Douglas Reid, admin. Fax 707-9545
Tennessee Technology Center Crossville Post-Sec.
910 Miller Ave 38555 931-484-7502

Crump, Hardin, Pop. 1,405

Tennessee Technology Center at Crump Post-Sec.
PO Box 89 38327 731-632-3393

Culleoka, Maury
Maury County SD
Supt. — See Columbia
Culleoka S 1,000/K-12
1921 Warrior Way 38451 931-987-2511
Jeff Quirk, prin. Fax 987-2594

Hopewell Church Covenant Family S 50/1-12
3886 Hopewell Rd 38451 931-381-2605
Charles Mangum, admin. Fax 406-4971

Cumberland Gap, Claiborne, Pop. 477
Claiborne County SD
Supt. — See Tazewell
Cumberland Gap HS 600/9-12
661 Old Jacksboro Pike 37724 423-869-9964
Linda Keck, prin. Fax 869-4352

Cunningham, Montgomery
Clarksville-Montgomery County SD
Supt. — See Clarksville
Montgomery Central HS 900/9-12
3955 Highway 48 37052 931-387-3201
Christy Houston, prin. Fax 387-4578
Montgomery Central MS 800/6-8
3941 Highway 48 37052 931-387-2575
Dee-Etta Whitlock, prin. Fax 387-3391

Dandridge, Jefferson, Pop. 2,785
Jefferson County SD 8,200/PK-12
PO Box 190 37725 865-397-3194
Dr. Charles Edmonds, dir. Fax 397-3301
jc-schools.net/
Jefferson County HS 2,200/9-12
115 W Dumplin Valley Rd 37725 865-397-3182
Dr. Scott Walker, prin. Fax 397-4121
Maury MS 600/6-8
965 Maury Cir 37725 865-397-3424
Michelle Walker, prin. Fax 397-4253
Other Schools – See Jefferson City

Dayton, Rhea, Pop. 7,052
Rhea County SD 4,300/PK-12
305 California Ave 37321 423-775-7812
Jerry Levengood, dir. Fax 775-7831
www.rheacounty.org
Other Schools – See Evensville, Spring City

Bryan College Post-Sec.
PO Box 7000 37321 423-775-2041
Laurelbrook Academy 50/K-12
114 Campus Dr 37321 423-775-3339
Fax 775-6052
Oxford Graduate School Post-Sec.
500 Oxford Dr 37321 423-775-6596

Decatur, Meigs, Pop. 1,593
Meigs County SD 1,800/PK-12
345 N Main St 37322 423-334-5793
Donald Roberts, supt. Fax 334-1462
www.meigscounty.net
Meigs County HS 500/9-12
PO Box 1182 37322 423-334-5797
Clint Baker, prin. Fax 334-5732
Meigs MS 400/6-8
564 N Main St 37322 423-334-9187
Ronald Woods, prin. Fax 334-1353

Decaturville, Decatur, Pop. 853
Decatur County SD 1,600/PK-12
PO Box 369 38329 731-852-2391
Dr. Michael Price, supt. Fax 852-2960
www.decaturcountytn.org/decatur_county_schools.asp
Riverside HS 500/9-12
4250 Highway 641 S 38329 731-852-3941
Robert Myracle, prin. Fax 852-3955
Other Schools – See Parsons

Denmark, Madison
Jackson-Madison County SD
Supt. — See Jackson
West MS 500/6-8
317 Denmark Rd 38391 731-988-3810
John Burks, prin. Fax 988-3814

Dickson, Dickson, Pop. 14,179
Dickson County SD 8,400/PK-12
817 N Charlotte St 37055 615-446-7571
Dr. Danny Weeks, dir. Fax 441-1375
www.dicksoncountyschools.org
Dickson County HS 1,500/9-12
509 Henslee Dr 37055 615-446-9003
Doug Phillips, prin. Fax 441-4135
Dickson MS 1,200/6-8
401 E College St 37055 615-446-2273
Dr. Robbie Faulkner, prin. Fax 441-4139
Other Schools – See Charlotte, White Bluff

Tennessee Technology Center at Dickson Post-Sec.
740 Highway 46 S 37055 615-441-6220

Dover, Stewart, Pop. 1,392
Stewart County SD 2,100/PK-12
PO Box 433 37058 931-232-5176
Dr. Phillip Wallace, dir. Fax 232-5390
www.stewartcountyschools.net
Stewart County HS 700/9-12
120 Robertson Hill Rd 37058 931-232-5179
Michael Craig, prin. Fax 232-3119
Stewart County MS 500/6-8
PO Box 1001 37058 931-232-9112
Steve Nolen, prin. Fax 232-4608

Dresden, Weakley, Pop. 2,945
Weakley County SD 4,600/PK-12
8319 Highway 22 Ste A 38225 731-364-2247
Randy Frazier, supt. Fax 364-2662
www.weakleycountyschools.com
Dresden HS 400/9-12
7150 Highway 22 38225 731-364-2949
Charles West, prin. Fax 364-5328
Dresden MS 400/5-8
759 Linden St Ste A 38225 731-364-2407
Pam Harris, prin. Fax 364-5840
Weakley County Adult Learning Center Adult
8250 Highway 22 38225 731-364-5481
Mitchell Parham, prin. Fax 364-3580
Other Schools – See Gleason, Greenfield, Martin

Dunlap, Sequatchie, Pop. 4,760
Bledsoe County SD
Supt. — See Pikeville
Bledsoe County Vocational Center Vo/Tech
26297 US 127 37327 423-554-3293
Steve Reel, dir. Fax 554-3142

Sequatchie County SD 2,400/PK-12
PO Box 488 37327 423-949-3617
Johnny Cordell, supt. Fax 949-5257
sequatchieschools.net
Sequatchie County HS 700/9-12
PO Box 759 37327 423-949-2154
Tommy Layne, prin. Fax 949-4696
Sequatchie County MS 700/5-8
PO Box 789 37327 423-949-4149
Sandra Nash, prin. Fax 949-4140

Sequatchie Valley Preparatory Academy 50/K-12
1050 Ray Hixson Rd 37327 423-554-4677
Robert Young, admin. Fax 554-4398

Dyer, Gibson, Pop. 2,288
Gibson County Special SD 3,800/PK-12
PO Box 60 38330 731-692-3803
Eddie Pruett, dir. Fax 692-4375
www.gcssd.org
Gibson County HS 600/9-12
PO Box 190 38330 731-692-3616
Jim Hughes, prin. Fax 692-2123
Other Schools – See Medina

Dyersburg, Dyer, Pop. 16,802
Dyer County SD 3,700/PK-12
159 Everett Ave 38024 731-285-6712
Dr. Dwight Hedge, dir. Fax 286-6721
www.dyercs.net
Three Oaks MS 400/6-8
3200 Upper Finley Rd 38024 731-285-3100
Laura Brimm, prin. Fax 285-3360
Other Schools – See Newbern

Dyersburg CSD 3,200/PK-12
307 College St 38024 731-286-3600
Neel Durbin, dir. Fax 286-2754
www.dyersburgcityschools.org/
Dyersburg HS 1,000/9-12
125 US Highway 51 Byp W 38024 731-286-3630
Jon Frye, prin. Fax 286-2209
Dyersburg MS 700/6-8
400 Frank Maynard Dr 38024 731-286-3625
Cal Johnson, prin. Fax 286-3624

Dyersburg State Community College Post-Sec.
1510 Lake Rd 38024 731-286-3200
Emmanuel Christian S 50/PK-12
92 Kendall Ln 38024 731-676-8708
Thomas Kendall, supt.

Eads, Shelby

Briarcrest Christian HS 600/9-12
76 S Houston Levee Rd 38028 901-751-6400
Eric Sullivan, prin. Fax 751-6402
Briarcrest Christian MS 300/6-8
76 S Houston Levee Rd 38028 901-765-4628
Sharon Watson, prin. Fax 765-4667

Eagleville, Rutherford, Pop. 600
Rutherford County SD
Supt. — See Murfreesboro
Eagleville S 800/PK-12
500 Old Highway 99 37060 615-904-6710
Bill Tollett, prin. Fax 274-6859

Elizabethton, Carter, Pop. 13,969
Carter County SD 5,700/PK-12
305 Academy St 37643 423-547-4000
Dr. Kevin Ward, dir. Fax 547-8338
carter.k12.tn.us
Happy Valley HS 600/9-12
121 Warpath Ln 37643 423-547-4094
Terry Hubbard, prin. Fax 547-4083
Happy Valley MS 500/5-8
163 Warpath Ln 37643 423-547-4070
Carter Blevins, prin. Fax 547-8352
Siam Learning Center 50/Alt
2453 Siam Rd 37643 423-547-4050
C.B. Hardin, prin. Fax 547-4061
Unaka HS 300/9-12
119 Robinson Ln 37643 423-474-4100
Richard Thomas, prin. Fax 474-4108
Carter County Adult HS Adult
386 Highway 91 37643 423-547-8348
Sonya Miller, admin. Fax 547-8913
Other Schools – See Hampton, Roan Mountain

Elizabethton CSD 2,300/PK-12
804 S Watauga Ave 37643 423-547-8000
Edwin Alexander, supt. Fax 547-8929
www.ecschools.net
Dugger JHS 500/6-8
306 W E St 37643 423-547-8025
Randy Little, prin. Fax 547-8021
Elizabethton HS 800/9-12
907 Jason Witten Way 37643 423-547-8015
David Wright, prin. Fax 547-8016

Tennessee Technology Center Elizabethton Post-Sec.
426 Highway 91 37643 423-543-0070

Englewood, McMinn, Pop. 1,491
McMinn County SD
Supt. — See Athens
Central HS 800/9-12
145 County Road 461 37329 423-263-5541
Roger Freeman, prin. Fax 263-0399

Erin, Houston, Pop. 1,288
Houston County SD 1,500/PK-12
PO Box 209 37061 931-289-4148
Cathy Harvey, dir. Fax 289-5543
www.houston.k12.tn.us
Houston County HS 400/9-12
2500 Highway 149 37061 931-289-4447
Linda Jolly, prin. Fax 289-4924
Houston County MS 300/6-8
3460 W Main St 37061 931-289-5591
Ray Busey, prin. Fax 289-5599
Houston County Adult S Adult
2500 Highway 149 37061 931-289-5525
Linda McDonough, prin.

Erwin, Unicoi, Pop. 6,036
Unicoi County SD 2,600/PK-12
100 Nolichucky Ave 37650 423-743-1600
Denise Brown, dir. Fax 743-1615
www.unicoischools.com/
Unicoi County Career & Technical S Vo/Tech
100 Okolona Dr 37650 423-743-1639
Kevin Lingerfelt, prin. Fax 743-1671
Unicoi County HS 700/9-12
700 S Mohawk Dr 37650 423-743-1632
Becky Love, prin. Fax 743-1636
Unicoi County MS 600/6-8
599 S Mohawk Dr 37650 423-735-0236
John English, prin. Fax 735-0728

Evensville, Rhea
Rhea County SD
Supt. — See Dayton
Rhea County HS 1,300/9-12
405 Pierce Rd 37332 423-775-7821
Jesse Messimer, prin. Fax 775-7889

Fairview, Williamson, Pop. 7,635
Williamson County SD
Supt. — See Franklin
Fairview HS 600/9-12
2595 Fairview Blvd 37062 615-472-4400
Dr. Juli Dyer, prin. Fax 472-4421
Fairview MS 500/6-8
7200 Cumberland Dr 37062 615-472-4430
Gary Shrader, prin. Fax 472-4441

Fayetteville, Lincoln, Pop. 6,705
Fayetteville CSD 1,200/PK-12
110 Elk Ave S Ste A 37334 931-433-5542
Janine Wilson, supt. Fax 433-7499
www.fcsboe.org
Fayetteville HS 200/8-12
1800 Wilson Pkwy Ste A 37334 931-433-3158
Eric Jones, prin. Fax 433-4611

Lincoln County SD 4,000/PK-12
206 Davidson St E 37334 931-433-3565
Wanda Shelton Ed.D., dir. Fax 433-7397
www.lcdoe.org
Lincoln County SHS 1,100/10-12
1233 Huntsville Hwy 37334 931-433-6505
Jacob Sorrells, prin. Fax 438-1490
Ninth Grade Academy 300/9-9
900 Main Ave S 37334 931-433-6156
Sarah Wallace, prin. Fax 438-2465

Fayetteville College of Cosmetology Post-Sec.
201 College St W 37334 931-433-1305
Riverside Christian Academy 300/PK-12
PO Box 617 37334 931-438-4722
Paul Fisher, head sch

Franklin, Williamson, Pop. 61,495
Franklin Special SD 3,900/PK-8
507 New Highway 96 W 37064 615-794-6624
David Snowden Ph.D., supt. Fax 790-4716
www.fssd.org
Freedom MS 600/7-8
750 New Highway 96 W 37064 615-794-0987
Kristi Jefferson Ed.D., prin. Fax 790-4742
Poplar Grove MS 400/5-8
2959 Del Rio Pike 37069 615-790-4721
Dr. Anthony Johnson, prin. Fax 790-4730

Williamson County SD 31,200/PK-12
1320 W Main St Ste 202 37064 615-472-4000
Dr. Michael Looney, supt. Fax 472-4190
www.wcs.edu
Centennial HS 1,400/9-12
5050 Mallory Ln 37067 615-472-4270
Sandra Joyner, prin. Fax 472-4291
Franklin HS 1,800/9-12
810 Hillsboro Rd 37064 615-472-4450
Willie Dickerson, prin. Fax 472-4478
Grassland MS 1,000/6-8
2390 Hillsboro Rd 37069 615-472-4500
Dr. Lily Leffler, prin. Fax 472-4511

Middle College HS 200/9-12
108 Everbright St 37064 615-472-4670
Dr. Brian Bass, prin. Fax 472-4675
Page HS 900/9-12
6281 Arno Rd 37064 615-472-4730
Dr. Andrea Anthony, prin. Fax 472-4751
Page MS 1,000/6-8
6262 Arno Rd 37064 615-472-4760
Dr. Eric Lifsey, prin. Fax 472-4771
Other Schools – See Brentwood, Fairview, Spring Hill, Thompsons Station

---

Battle Ground Academy 900/K-12
PO Box 1889 37065 615-794-3501
Dr. John Griffith, hdmstr. Fax 567-8360
Classical Academy of Franklin 100/PK-12
810 Del Rio Pike 37064 615-790-8556
Carson Sensing, admin. Fax 790-8617
Franklin Christian Academy 100/5-12
PO Box 157 37065 615-599-9229
Hugh Harris, hdmstr. Fax 599-9441
Franklin Classical S 100/K-12
PO Box 1601 37065 615-595-5337
Melinda Mahand, dean Fax 595-5339
O'More College of Design Post-Sec.
423 S Margin St 37064 615-794-4254
Williamson Christian College Post-Sec.
200 Seaboard Ln 37067 615-771-7821

Friendsville, Blount, Pop. 902
Blount County SD
Supt. — See Maryville
Union Grove MS 800/6-8
334 S Old Grey Ridge Rd 37737 865-980-1320
Alicia Lail, prin. Fax 980-1323

Gainesboro, Jackson, Pop. 959
Jackson County SD 1,600/PK-12
711 School Dr 38562 931-268-0268
Joe Barlow, supt. Fax 268-3647
volweb.utk.edu/school/jackson/
Jackson County HS 500/9-12
190 Blue Devil Ln 38562 931-268-9771
Charles Breidert, prin. Fax 268-9433
Jackson County MS 500/PK-PK, 4-
170 Blue Devil Ln 38562 931-268-9779
Gail Myers, prin. Fax 268-9413

Gallatin, Sumner, Pop. 29,705
Sumner County SD 27,400/PK-12
695 E Main St 37066 615-451-5200
Dr. Del Phillips, dir. Fax 451-5216
www.sumnerschools.org
Fisher Alternative S 100/Alt
455 N Boyers Ave 37066 615-451-6558
Bob Gideon, prin. Fax 451-5290
Gallatin HS 1,400/9-12
700 Dan P Herron Dr 37066 615-452-2621
Dr. Ron Becker, prin. Fax 451-5426
Rucker-Stewart MS 700/6-8
350 Hancock St 37066 615-452-1734
Andrew Turner, prin. Fax 451-5297
Shafer MS 600/6-8
240 Albert Gallatin Ave 37066 615-452-9100
David Hallman, prin. Fax 451-6545
Station Camp HS 1,300/9-12
1040 Bison Trl 37066 615-451-6551
Art Crook, prin. Fax 451-6556
Station Camp MS 600/6-8
281 Big Station Camp Blvd 37066 615-206-0116
Mike Brown, prin. Fax 206-0165
Other Schools – See Hendersonville, Portland, Westmoreland, White House

---

Volunteer State Community College Post-Sec.
1480 Nashville Pike 37066 615-452-8600

Gatlinburg, Sevier, Pop. 3,902
Sevier County SD
Supt. — See Sevierville
Gatlinburg-Pittman HS 600/9-12
150 Proffitt Rd 37738 865-436-5637
Tony Ogle, prin. Fax 436-2567

Germantown, Shelby, Pop. 38,412
Shelby County SD
Supt. — See Memphis
Germantown HS 2,000/9-12
7653 Poplar Pike 38138 901-756-2350
Dr. Ted Horrell, prin. Fax 756-2356
Germantown MS 700/6-8
7925 CD Smith Rd 38138 901-756-2338
Russell Joy, prin. Fax 759-4521
Houston HS 1,700/9-12
9755 Wolf River Blvd 38139 901-756-2370
Dr. Leisa Justus, prin. Fax 756-2377
Houston MS 900/6-8
9400 Wolf River Blvd 38139 901-756-2366
Jason Manuel, prin. Fax 756-2346

Gleason, Weakley, Pop. 1,427
Weakley County SD
Supt. — See Dresden
Gleason S 500/PK-12
9299 State Championship Dr 38229 731-648-5351
Trish Price, prin. Fax 648-9199

Goodlettsville, Davidson, Pop. 15,590
Metropolitan Nashville SD
Supt. — See Nashville
Goodlettsville MS 500/5-8
300 S Main St 37072 615-859-8956
Dr. Sarah Moore, prin. Fax 859-8965

Metro Christian Academy 200/PK-12
322 E Cedar St 37072 615-859-1184
Cyndi Augustin, prin. Fax 859-5562

Gordonsville, Smith, Pop. 1,200
Smith County SD
Supt. — See Carthage
Gordonsville HS 500/7-12
110 Main St E 38563 615-683-8245
Ronnie Scudder, prin. Fax 683-5193

Gray, Washington, Pop. 1,206
Washington County SD
Supt. — See Jonesborough
Boone HS 1,400/9-12
1440 Suncrest Dr 37615 423-477-1600
Roger Jackson, prin. Fax 477-1625

Greenback, Loudon, Pop. 1,059
Loudon County SD
Supt. — See Loudon
Greenback S 600/PK-12
400 Chilhowee Ave 37742 865-856-3028
Barbara Bradley, prin. Fax 856-8379

Greenbrier, Robertson, Pop. 6,354
Robertson County SD
Supt. — See Springfield
Greenbrier HS 800/9-12
126 Cuniff Dr 37073 615-643-4526
Dr. Katie Osborne, prin. Fax 643-8873
Greenbrier MS 600/6-8
2450 Highway 41 S 37073 615-643-7823
Chris Causey, prin. Fax 643-4580

Greeneville, Greene, Pop. 14,821
Greene County SD 7,400/PK-12
910 W Summer St 37743 423-639-4194
Dr. Vicki Kirk, dir. Fax 639-1615
www2.greenek12.org
North Greene HS 400/9-12
4675 Old Baileyton Rd 37745 423-234-1752
David McLain, prin. Fax 234-3103
South Greene HS 500/9-12
7469 Asheville Hwy 37743 423-639-3790
Cindy Bowman, prin. Fax 636-3791
Other Schools – See Afton, Mosheim

Greeneville CSD 2,800/PK-12
PO Box 1420 37744 423-787-8000
Dr. Linda Stroud, dir. Fax 638-2540
www.gcschools.net
Greeneville HS 900/9-12
210 Tusculum Blvd 37745 423-787-8030
Dr. Linda Stroud, prin. Fax 787-8028
Greeneville MS 600/6-8
433 E Vann Rd 37743 423-639-7841
Heather Boegemann, prin. Fax 639-4112
Greenville/Greene Co. Ctr for Technology Vo/Tech
1121 Hal Henard Rd 37743 423-639-0171
Jerry Ayers, prin. Fax 639-0176

Greeneville Adventist Academy 100/K-12
305 Takoma Ave 37743 423-639-2011
R. Nomura, prin. Fax 639-5002
Tusculum College Post-Sec.
60 Shiloh Rd 37745 423-636-7300

Greenfield, Weakley, Pop. 2,162
Weakley County SD
Supt. — See Dresden
Greenfield S 600/PK-12
101 N Faxon St 38230 731-235-3424
Mike Riggs, prin. Fax 235-3480

Gruetli Laager, Grundy, Pop. 1,795

Faith Missionary Academy 100/K-12
495 Red Barn Rd 37339 931-779-3338
Stacey Smith, prin. Fax 779-4338

Halls, Lauderdale, Pop. 2,218
Lauderdale County SD
Supt. — See Ripley
Halls HS 400/9-12
800 W Tigrett St 38040 731-836-9642
Andy Pugh, prin. Fax 836-1072
Halls JHS 200/7-8
800 W Tigrett St 38040 731-836-5579
Michael Blackwood, prin. Fax 836-5555

Hampshire, Maury
Maury County SD
Supt. — See Columbia
Hampshire S 400/K-12
4235 Old State Rd 38461 931-285-2300
Leigh Ann Willey, prin. Fax 285-2612

Hampton, Carter
Carter County SD
Supt. — See Elizabethton
Hampton HS 400/9-12
766 First Ave 37658 423-725-5200
Dale Campbell, prin. Fax 725-5204

Harriman, Roane, Pop. 6,223
Roane County SD
Supt. — See Kingston
Harriman HS 300/9-12
920 N Roane St 37748 865-882-1821
Scott Calahan, prin. Fax 882-6479
Harriman MS 300/6-8
1025 Cumberland St 37748 865-882-1727
David Stevens, prin. Fax 882-6285
Midtown Educational Center 100/Alt
3096 Roane State Hwy 37748 865-882-0242
Chris Johnson, prin. Fax 882-7734

Roane State Community College Post-Sec.
276 Patton Ln 37748 865-354-3000
Tennessee Technology Center at Harriman Post-Sec.
PO Box 1109 37748 865-882-6703

Harrison, Hamilton, Pop. 7,602
Hamilton County SD
Supt. — See Chattanooga
Brown MS 500/6-8
5716 Highway 58 37341 423-344-1439
Jane Reynolds, prin. Fax 344-1471
Central HS 1,000/9-12
5728 Highway 58 37341 423-344-1447
Ronald King, prin. Fax 344-1470

Harrogate, Claiborne, Pop. 4,333
Claiborne County SD
Supt. — See Tazewell
Livesay MS 300/5-8
PO Box 460 37752 423-869-4663
Karyn Clark, prin. Fax 869-8389

Lincoln Memorial University Post-Sec.
6965 Cumberland Gap Pkwy 37752 423-869-3611
White Academy 100/5-12
6965 Cumberland Gap Pkwy 37752 423-869-6404

Hartsville, Trousdale, Pop. 2,373
Trousdale County SD 1,300/K-12
103 Lock Six Rd 37074 615-374-2193
Clint Satterfield, dir. Fax 374-1108
www.tcschools.org
Satterfield MS 300/6-8
210 Damascus St 37074 615-374-2748
Amanda Gregory, prin. Fax 374-2602
Trousdale County HS 400/9-12
262 McMurry Blvd W 37074 615-374-2201
Teresa Dickerson, prin. Fax 374-1120

Tennessee Technology Center Hartsville Post-Sec.
716 McMurry Blvd E 37074 615-374-2147

Henderson, Chester, Pop. 6,177
Chester County SD 2,800/PK-12
PO Box 327 38340 731-989-5134
Cherrie Pipkin, supt. Fax 989-4755
www.chestercountyschools.org
Chester County HS 800/9-12
552 E Main St 38340 731-989-8125
Troy Kilzer, prin. Fax 989-8131
Chester County JHS 400/7-8
930 E Main St 38340 731-989-8135
Britt Eads, prin. Fax 989-8137

Freed-Hardeman University Post-Sec.
158 E Main St 38340 731-989-6000

Hendersonville, Sumner, Pop. 50,488
Sumner County SD
Supt. — See Gallatin
Beech HS 1,300/9-12
3126 Long Hollow Pike 37075 615-824-6200
Frank Cardwell, prin. Fax 264-6553
Ellis MS 600/6-8
100 Indian Lake Rd 37075 615-264-6093
Darren Frank, prin. Fax 264-5800
Hawkins MS 500/6-8
487A Walton Ferry Rd 37075 615-824-3456
Bob Cotter, prin. Fax 264-6003
Hendersonville HS 1,500/9-12
123 Cherokee Rd 37075 615-824-6162
Joni Worsham, prin. Fax 264-6027
Hunter MS 700/6-8
2101 New Hope Rd 37075 615-822-4720
Ahmed White, prin. Fax 264-6036
Hyde Magnet S 600/K-12
128 Township Dr 37075 615-264-6543
Brad Schreiner, prin. Fax 264-6546
Knox Doss MS 600/6-8
1338 Drakes Creek Rd 37075 615-824-8383
Kenny Powell, prin. Fax 824-8448

Hendersonville Christian Academy 300/PK-12
355 Old Shackle Island Rd 37075 615-824-1550
William Slater, prin. Fax 590-3025
Pope John Paul II HS 600/9-12
117 Caldwell Dr 37075 615-822-2375
Faustin Weber, hdmstr. Fax 822-6226

Hermitage, See Nashville
Metropolitan Nashville SD
Supt. — See Nashville
DuPont-Tyler MS 700/5-8
431 Tyler Dr 37076 615-885-8827
Jamila Martin, prin. Fax 847-7322

Hixson, See Chattanooga
Hamilton County SD
Supt. — See Chattanooga
Hixson HS 700/9-12
5705 Middle Valley Rd 37343 423-847-4800
Lee Sims, prin. Fax 847-4801
Hixson MS 600/6-8
5681 Old Hixson Pike 37343 423-847-4810
Leangela Rogers, prin. Fax 847-4811
Loftis MS 700/6-8
8611 Columbus Rd 37343 423-843-4749
Brentley Eller, prin. Fax 843-4758

Berean Academy 200/PK-12
441 Berean Ln 37343 423-877-1288
Joey Harmon, prin. Fax 875-5965

Hohenwald, Lewis, Pop. 3,706
Lewis County SD 2,000/PK-12
206 S Court St 38462 931-796-3264
Benny Pace, supt. Fax 796-5127
www.lewis.k12.tn.us
Lewis County HS 600/9-12
818 W Main St 38462 931-796-4085
Allen Trull, prin. Fax 796-1172

Lewis County MS 400/6-8
207 S Court St 38462 931-796-4586
Clayton Callicott, prin. Fax 796-7601

Tennessee Technology Center at Hohenwald Post-Sec.
813 W Main St 38462 931-796-5351

Humboldt, Gibson, Pop. 8,376

Humboldt CSD 1,300/PK-12
2602 Viking Dr 38343 731-784-2652
Steve Bayko, dir. Fax 784-2480
www.humboldtschools.com
Humboldt HS 400/9-12
2600 Viking Dr 38343 731-784-2781
Arthur Moss, prin. Fax 784-8536
Humboldt MS 300/6-8
1811 Ferrell St 38343 731-784-9514
Lillian Shelton, prin. Fax 784-6832

Huntingdon, Carroll, Pop. 3,896

Carroll County SD
PO Box 799 38344 731-986-4482
Johnny McAdams, supt. Fax 986-0198
www.carrollschools.com
Carroll County Technical Center Vo/Tech
1235 Buena Vista Rd 38344 731-986-8908
John McAdams, prin. Fax 986-3200
Adult Education Center Adult
13345 Paris St 38344 731-986-4841
Brenda Parish, prin. Fax 986-4841

Huntingdon Special SD 1,200/PK-12
585 High St 38344 731-986-2222
Pat Dillahunty, supt. Fax 986-4365
www.huntingdonschools.org/
Huntingdon HS 400/9-12
475 Mustang Dr 38344 731-986-8223
Mike Henson, prin. Fax 986-4031
Huntingdon MS 400/4-8
199 Browning Ave 38344 731-986-4544
Dr. Jonathan Kee, prin. Fax 986-8689

South Carroll County Special SD 400/PK-12
145 Clarksburg Rd 38344 731-986-4534
Dr. Tony Tucker, supt. Fax 986-4562
www.rocketsonline.org/
Clarksburg S 400/PK-12
145 Clarksburg Rd 38344 731-986-3165
Teresa Davis, prin. Fax 986-4562

Huntland, Franklin, Pop. 866

Franklin County SD
Supt. — See Winchester
Huntland S 700/PK-12
400 Gore St 37345 931-469-7506
Ken Bishop, prin. Fax 469-0590

Huntsville, Scott, Pop. 1,235

Scott County SD 3,000/PK-12
PO Box 37 37756 423-663-2159
Bill Hall, supt. Fax 663-9682
www.scottcounty.net
Huntsville MS 300/5-8
3101 Baker Hwy 37756 423-663-2192
Lamance Bryant, prin. Fax 663-2967
Scott HS 800/9-12
400 Scott High Dr 37756 423-663-2801
Melissa Rector, prin. Fax 663-2368

Tennessee Technology Center Oneida/Hunts Post-Sec.
355 Scott High Dr 37756 423-663-4900

Jacksboro, Campbell, Pop. 2,000

Campbell County SD 6,200/PK-12
PO Box 445 37757 423-562-8377
Donnie Poston, dir. Fax 566-7562
www.campbell.k12.tn.us
Campbell County Comprehensive HS 1,400/9-12
150 Cougar Ln 37757 423-562-8308
Jamie Wheeler, prin. Fax 566-2019
Jacksboro MS 500/6-8
150 Eagle Cir 37757 423-562-3773
Dixie Crouch, prin. Fax 562-8994
Other Schools – See Jellico, La Follette

Tennessee Technology Center at Jacksboro Post-Sec.
PO Box 419 37757 423-566-9629

Jackson, Madison, Pop. 64,311

Jackson-Madison County SD 12,700/PK-12
310 N Parkway 38305 731-664-2592
Thomas White, supt. Fax 664-2502
www.jmcss.org
Jackson Central-Merry HS 600/9-12
332 Lane Ave 38301 731-424-2200
Eric Jones, prin. Fax 423-6158
Liberty Technology Magnet HS Vo/Tech
3470 Ridgecrest Road Ext 38305 731-423-9086
Dr. June Murry, prin. Fax 424-3445
Madison Academic Magnet S 500/9-12
179 Allen Ave 38301 731-427-3501
Janice Epperson, prin. Fax 427-3587
Northeast MS 600/6-8
2665 Christmasville Rd 38305 731-422-6687
James Bailey, prin. Fax 423-1805
North Parkway MS 600/6-8
1341 N Parkway 38305 731-427-3384
Tracey Vowell, prin. Fax 427-2591
North Side HS 1,200/9-12
3066 N Highland Ave 38305 731-668-3171
Ricky Catlett, prin. Fax 661-9756
Parkview Learning Center 100/Alt
905 E Chester St 38301 731-427-2841
Paul Thacker, prin. Fax 427-2529
Rose Hill MS 600/6-8
2233 Beech Bluff Rd 38301 731-423-6170
Ned Lewis, prin. Fax 423-6171
South Side HS 800/9-12
84 Harts Bridge Rd 38301 731-422-9923
Anita Tucker, prin. Fax 423-3411
Tigrett MS 500/6-8
716 Westwood Ave 38301 731-988-3840
Dexter Williams, prin. Fax 988-3838
Other Schools – See Denmark

Augustine S 100/PK-12
1171 Old Humboldt Rd 38305 731-660-6822
Donna Nelson, admin. Fax 660-6833
Jackson Christian S 1,000/PK-12
832 Country Club Ln 38305 731-668-8055
Dr. Rick Brooks, pres. Fax 664-5763
Jackson Preparatory S 200/PK-12
130 Old Denmark Rd 38301 731-554-9647
Sidney Mayo, prin.
Jackson State Community College Post-Sec.
2046 N Parkway 38301 731-424-3520
Lane College Post-Sec.
545 Lane Ave 38301 731-426-7500
Sacred Heart of Jesus & Mary HS 9-12
185 Greenfield Dr 38305 731-660-4774
Robin Perry, prin. Fax 984-7200
Tennessee Technology Center at Jackson Post-Sec.
2468 Technology Center Dr 38301 731-424-0691
Trinity Christian Academy 800/PK-12
10 Windy City Rd 38305 731-668-8500
Nelson Piercey, hdmstr. Fax 668-3232
Union University Post-Sec.
1050 Union University Dr 38305 731-668-1818
University S of Jackson 1,200/PK-12
232 McClellan Rd 38305 731-664-0812
Clay Lilienstern, hdmstr. Fax 664-5046
West Tennessee Business College Post-Sec.
1186 Highway 45 Byp 38301 800-737-9822

Jamestown, Fentress, Pop. 1,935

Fentress County SD 2,500/PK-12
1011 Old Highway 127 S 38556 931-879-9218
Mike Jones, dir. Fax 879-4050
www.fentress.k12tn.net
Fentress County Adult HS Adult
209 S Main St 38556 931-879-3802
Gertie Campbell, prin. Fax 879-1802
Other Schools – See Clarkrange

Jasper, Marion, Pop. 3,248

Marion County SD 4,300/PK-12
204 Betsy Pack Dr 37347 423-942-3434
Mark Griffith, supt. Fax 942-4210
www.marionschools.org/
Jasper MS 500/5-8
601 Elm Ave 37347 423-942-6251
Ramona McEntyre, prin. Fax 942-0141
Marion County HS 500/9-12
160 Ridley Ave 37347 423-942-5120
Larry Ziegler, prin. Fax 942-5544
Other Schools – See South Pittsburg, Whitwell

Jefferson City, Jefferson, Pop. 7,885

Jefferson County SD
Supt. — See Dandridge
Jefferson MS 600/6-8
361 W Broadway Blvd 37760 865-475-6133
Joel Sanford, prin. Fax 471-6878

Carson-Newman College Post-Sec.
1646 Russell Ave 37760 865-471-2000

Jellico, Campbell, Pop. 2,326

Campbell County SD
Supt. — See Jacksboro
Jellico HS 400/9-12
141 High School Ln 37762 423-784-9455
Harry Chitwood, prin. Fax 784-9456

Joelton, See Nashville

Metropolitan Nashville SD
Supt. — See Nashville
Joelton MS 400/5-8
3500 Old Clarksville Pike 37080 615-876-5100
William Moody, prin. Fax 876-1469

Johnson City, Washington, Pop. 61,881

Johnson City CSD 5,800/PK-12
PO Box 1517 37605 423-434-5200
Dr. Richard Bales, dir. Fax 434-5237
www.jcschools.org
Liberty Bell MS 7-8
806 Morningside Dr 37604 423-232-2192
Tammy Pearce, prin.
Science Hill HS 2,200/9-12
1509 John Exum Pkwy 37604 423-232-2190
Melanie Riden-Bacon, prin. Fax 434-5570
Science Hill Technology Center Vo/Tech
251 Cotty Jones Dr 37604 423-232-2200
Kenneth Ralston, dir. Fax 461-1695

Washington County SD
Supt. — See Jonesborough
Asbury Optional HS Alt
2002 Indian Ridge Rd 37604 423-434-4900
Kari Arnold, prin. Fax 434-4902
Boones Creek MS 400/5-8
4352 N Roan St 37615 423-283-3520
Mike Edmonds, prin. Fax 283-3524

East Tennessee State University Post-Sec.
807 University Pkwy 37614 423-439-1000
Emmanuel School of Religion Post-Sec.
1 Walker Dr 37601 423-926-1186
ITT Technical Institute Post-Sec.
4721 Lake Park Dr Ste 100 37615 423-952-4400
Providence Academy 500/K-12
2788 Carroll Creek Rd 37615 423-854-9819
Jerry Williams, admin. Fax 854-8958

Jonesborough, Washington, Pop. 4,977

Washington County SD 9,100/PK-12
405 W College St 37659 423-753-1100
Ronald Dykes, dir. Fax 753-1114
www.wcde.org
Crockett HS 1,300/9-12
684 Old State Route 34 37659 423-753-1150
Andy Hare, prin. Fax 753-1167
Jonesborough MS 400/5-8
308 Forrest Dr 37659 423-753-1190
Terry Crowe, prin. Fax 753-1570
Other Schools – See Gray, Johnson City

Kingsport, Sullivan, Pop. 47,353

Kingsport CSD 6,700/PK-12
400 Clinchfield St Ste 200 37660 423-378-2100
Dr. Lyle Ailshie, supt. Fax 378-2120
www.k12k.com/
Cox Academy Alt
520 Myrtle St 37660 423-378-2185
Dr. Stephanie Tweed, prin. Fax 378-2187
Dobyns-Bennett HS 1,900/9-12
1800 Legion Dr 37664 423-378-8400
Dr. Chris Hampton, prin. Fax 378-8535
Robinson MS 800/6-8
1517 Jessee St 37664 423-378-2200
Jim Nash, prin. Fax 378-2220
Sevier MS 700/6-8
1200 Wateree St 37660 423-378-2450
Kim Harvey, prin. Fax 378-2430

Sullivan County SD
Supt. — See Blountville
Colonial Heights MS 500/6-8
415 Lebanon Rd 37663 423-354-1360
Randall Gilmore, prin. Fax 354-1365
Sullivan MS 200/6-8
4154 Sullivan Gardens Dr 37660 423-354-1780
Zada Church, prin. Fax 354-1796
Sullivan North HS 600/9-12
2533 N John B Dennis Hwy 37660 423-354-1400
Richard Carroll, prin. Fax 354-1406
Sullivan North MS 6-8
2533 N John B Dennis Hwy 37660 423-354-1750
Thomas Bowers, admin. Fax 354-1459
Sullivan South HS 1,000/9-12
1236 Moreland Dr 37664 423-354-1300
Greg Harvey, prin. Fax 354-1306

Cedar View Christian School 200/PK-12
PO Box 143 37662 423-245-6341
Dr. Jim Fields, admin.

Kingston, Roane, Pop. 5,854

Roane County SD 6,800/PK-12
105 Bluff Rd 37763 865-376-5592
Gary Aytes, dir. Fax 376-1284
www.roaneschools.com
Cherokee MS 600/6-8
200 Paint Rock Ferry Rd 37763 865-376-9281
Elizabeth Rose, prin. Fax 376-8525
Midway HS 300/9-12
530 Loudon Hwy 37763 865-376-5645
Scott Mason, prin. Fax 376-8516
Roane County HS 800/9-12
540 W Cumberland St 37763 865-376-6534
Lance Duff, prin. Fax 376-8530
Other Schools – See Harriman, Oliver Springs, Rockwood, Ten Mile

Kingston Springs, Cheatham, Pop. 2,732

Cheatham County SD
Supt. — See Ashland City
Harpeth HS 600/9-12
170 E Kingston Springs Rd 37082 615-952-2811
Allen Collins, prin. Fax 952-5013
Harpeth MS 600/5-8
170 Harpeth View Trl 37082 615-952-2293
Lucas Winstead, prin. Fax 952-4527

Knoxville, Knox, Pop. 174,475

Knox County SD 56,800/PK-12
PO Box 2188 37901 865-594-1800
Dr. James McIntyre, supt. Fax 594-1627
knoxschools.org/
Austin-East HS 600/9-12
2800 Martin Luther King Jr 37914 865-594-3792
Benny Perry, prin. Fax 594-1165
Bearden HS 2,000/9-12
8352 Kingston Pike 37919 865-539-7800
Dr. John Bartlett, prin. Fax 539-7805
Bearden MS 1,000/6-8
1000 Francis Rd 37909 865-539-7839
Sonya Winstead, prin. Fax 539-7851
Byington-Solway Technology Center Vo/Tech
2700 Byington Solway Rd 37931 865-693-3511
David Bell, admin. Fax 694-7094
Cedar Bluff MS 600/6-8
707 N Cedar Bluff Rd 37923 865-539-7891
Christine Oehler, prin. Fax 539-7792
Central HS 1,100/9-12
5321 Jacksboro Pike 37918 865-689-1400
Danny Trent, prin. Fax 689-1403
Farragut HS 1,800/9-12
11237 Kingston Pike, 865-966-9775
Mike Reynolds, prin. Fax 671-7120
Farragut MS 1,300/6-8
200 W End Ave, 865-966-9756
Heather Karnes, prin. Fax 671-7048
Fulton HS 1,000/9-12
2509 N Broadway St 37917 865-594-1240
Rob Speas, prin. Fax 594-1228
Gresham MS 800/6-8
500 Gresham Rd 37918 865-689-1430
Donna Parker, prin. Fax 689-7437
Halls HS 1,300/9-12
4321 E Emory Rd 37938 865-922-7757
Mark Duff, prin. Fax 925-7700

Halls MS 1,100/6-8
4317 E Emory Rd 37938 865-922-7494
Tim Wiegenstein, prin. Fax 925-7439
Hardin Valley Academy 1,900/9-12
11345 Hardin Valley Rd 37932 865-690-9690
Sallee Reynolds, prin.
Holston MS 900/6-8
600 N Chilhowee Dr 37924 865-594-1300
Tom Brown, prin. Fax 594-4429
Karns HS 1,300/9-12
2710 Byington Solway Rd 37931 865-539-8670
Tracy Sands, prin. Fax 539-8679
Karns MS 1,200/6-8
2925 Gray Hendrix Rd 37931 865-539-7732
Cynthia White, prin. Fax 539-7745
Kelley Volunteer Academy Alt
3001 Knoxville Center Dr 37924 865-525-0069
Kim Towe, prin. Fax 525-2666
L & N STEM Academy 10-12
401 Henley St 37902 865-329-8440
Becky Ashe, prin.
Lincoln Park Tech/Trade Center Vo/Tech
535 Chickamauga Ave 37917 865-689-1454
Rick Bise, admin. Fax 689-1456
North Knox Vocational Center Vo/Tech
7411 Ledgerwood Rd 37938 865-922-7576
Fax 925-7551
Northwest MS 800/6-8
5301 Pleasant Ridge Rd 37912 865-594-1345
Dr. Karen Loy, prin. Fax 594-1339
South-Doyle HS 1,200/9-12
2020 Tipton Station Rd 37920 865-577-4475
Tim Berry, prin. Fax 577-4540
South-Doyle MS 1,100/6-8
3900 Decatur Dr 37920 865-579-2133
Beth Blevins, prin. Fax 579-2128
Vine MS 300/6-8
1807 Martin Luther King Jr 37915 865-594-4461
Becky Ervin, prin. Fax 594-1702
West HS 1,300/9-12
3300 Sutherland Ave 37919 865-594-4477
Katherine Banner, prin. Fax 594-4486
West Valley MS 1,200/6-8
9118 George Williams Rd 37922 865-539-5145
Renee Kelly, prin. Fax 539-5155
Whittle Springs MS 500/6-8
2700 White Oak Ln 37917 865-594-4474
Nadriene Jackson, prin. Fax 594-1132
Yoakley S 100/Alt
4415 Washington Pike 37917 865-594-3790
Tom Watson, prin. Fax 594-3770
Historic Knoxville HS Adult
101 E 5th Ave 37917 865-594-3713
Carol Russell, prin. Fax 594-3711
Other Schools – See Corryton, Powell, Strawberry Plains

Apostolic Christian S 100/K-12
5020 Pleasant Ridge Rd 37912 865-523-5262
Carolyn Daniel, prin. Fax 523-8576
Berean Christian S 400/K-12
2329 Prosser Rd 37914 865-521-6054
George Waller, hdmstr. Fax 522-5063
Christian Academy of Knoxville 1,200/PK-12
529 Academy Way 37923 865-690-4721
Scott Sandie, supt. Fax 690-4752
Concord Christian S 400/K-12
11704 Kingston Pike, 865-966-8858
Dr. Daniel Patton, hdmstr. Fax 288-1617
Fort Sanders School of Nursing Post-Sec.
9821 Cogdill Rd Ste 2 37932
Fountainhead College of Technology Post-Sec.
10208 Technology Dr 37932 865-688-9422
Grace Christian Academy 800/K-12
5914 Beaver Ridge Rd 37931 865-691-3427
Donald Criss, admin. Fax 342-3827
Huntington College of Health Sciences Post-Sec.
1204 Kenesaw Ave Ste D 37919 800-290-4226
ITT Technical Institute Post-Sec.
9123 Executive Park Dr 37923 865-342-2300
Johnson University Post-Sec.
7900 Johnson Dr 37998 865-573-4517
Knoxville Baptist Christian S 100/PK-12
2434 E 5th Ave 37917 865-524-3211
Fax 523-4814
Knoxville Catholic HS 700/9-12
9245 Fox Lonas Rd 37923 865-560-0313
Richard Sompayrac Ed.D., prin. Fax 560-0314
Knoxville Christian S 200/PK-12
11549 Snyder Rd 37932 865-966-7060
Jarra Snyder, prin. Fax 671-2148
National College of Business & Tech Post-Sec.
8415 Kingston Pike 37919 865-539-2011
Paideia Academy 100/K-10
10825 Yarnell Rd 37932 865-670-0440
James Cowart, hdmstr. Fax 670-0440
Pellissippi State Community College Post-Sec.
PO Box 22990 37933 865-694-6400
Reuben Allen College Post-Sec.
120 Center Park Dr 37922 865-966-0400
River's Edge Christian Academy 300/PK-11
PO Box 31733 37930 865-693-6779
Maynard Nordmoe, admin. Fax 693-2434
South College Post-Sec.
3904 Lonas Dr 37909 865-251-1800
Tennessee School for the Deaf Post-Sec.
2725 Island Home Blvd 37920 865-594-6022
Tennessee School of Beauty Post-Sec.
4704 Western Ave 37921 865-588-7878
Tennessee Technology Center at Knoxville Post-Sec.
1100 Liberty St 37919 865-546-5567
University of Tennessee Knoxville Post-Sec.
320 Student Services Bldg 37996 865-974-1000
University of Tennessee Medical Center Post-Sec.
1924 Alcoa Hwy 37920 865-546-5567
Webb S of Knoxville 1,000/K-12
9800 Webb School Ln 37923 865-693-0011
Scott Hutchinson, pres. Fax 691-8057

Kodak, Sevier
Sevier County SD
Supt. — See Sevierville
Northview MS 500/5-8
3295 Douglas Dam Rd 37764 865-933-7985
Rene Walker, prin. Fax 933-7387

Lafayette, Macon, Pop. 4,440
Macon County SD 3,700/K-12
501 College St 37083 615-666-2125
Margaret Oldham, dir. Fax 666-7878
www.maconcountyschools.com/
Macon County HS 1,000/9-12
2550 Days Rd 37083 615-666-4320
Stephanie Meador, prin. Fax 666-4757
Macon County JHS 700/6-8
1003 Highway 52 Byp E 37083 615-666-7545
Vent West, prin. Fax 666-9264
Other Schools – See Red Boiling Springs

Lighthouse Academy 300/PK-12
5576 Highway 52 W 37083 615-666-7151
Rev. Leon Keith, prin. Fax 666-7151

La Follette, Campbell, Pop. 7,339
Campbell County SD
Supt. — See Jacksboro
La Follette MS 500/6-8
1309 E Central Ave 37766 423-562-8448
Robbie Heatherly, prin. Fax 562-2107
Campbell County Adult HS Adult
318 W Beech St 37766 423-566-5436
Dr. Rita Goins, prin. Fax 562-5219

Lake City, Anderson, Pop. 1,756
Anderson County SD
Supt. — See Clinton
Lake City MS 300/6-8
1132 S Main St 37769 865-426-2609
Kelvin McCullom, prin. Fax 426-9319

La Vergne, Rutherford, Pop. 31,758
Rutherford County SD
Supt. — See Murfreesboro
La Vergne HS 2,100/9-12
250 Wolverine Trl 37086 615-904-3870
Dirk Ash, prin. Fax 904-3871
La Vergne MS 1,000/6-8
382 Stones River Rd 37086 615-904-3877
Cary Holman, prin. Fax 904-3878

Lawrenceburg, Lawrence, Pop. 10,194
Lawrence County SD 6,900/PK-12
700 Mahr Ave 38464 931-762-3581
Dr. Bill Heath, supt. Fax 762-7299
www.lcss.us/
Coffman MS 400/7-8
111 Lafayette Ave 38464 931-762-6395
Robin Thompson, prin. Fax 762-7176
Lawrence County HS 1,100/9-12
1800 Springer Rd 38464 931-762-9412
Michael Adkins, prin. Fax 766-0761
Lawrence County Vo Ctr Vo/Tech
1906 Springer Rd 38464 931-762-6472
Michael Adkins, prin. Fax 766-1551
Other Schools – See Loretto, Summertown

Lebanon, Wilson, Pop. 25,677
Lebanon Special SD 3,100/PK-8
701 Coles Ferry Pike 37087 615-449-6060
Scott Benson, dir. Fax 449-5673
www.lssd.org
Baird MS 600/6-8
131 WJB Pride Ln 37087 615-444-2190
Pam Sampson, prin. Fax 453-2690
Winfree Bryant MS 6-8
1213 Leeville Pike 37090 615-449-4560
Becky Kegley, prin. Fax 449-4590

Wilson County SD 15,300/PK-12
351 Stumpy Ln 37090 615-444-3282
Mike Davis, dir. Fax 449-3858
www.wcschools.com
Lebanon HS 1,500/9-12
500 Blue Devil Blvd 37087 615-444-9610
Myra Sloan, prin. Fax 443-1373
MAP Academy Alt
205 Stumpy Ln 37090 615-453-3400
Rick Miller, prin. Fax 453-3401
Wilson Central HS 1,700/9-12
419 Wildcat Way 37090 615-453-4600
Pat Suddarth, prin. Fax 453-4610
Adult Basic Education Adult
351 Stumpy Ln 37090 615-443-8731
Betty Byrd, dir. Fax 453-2529
Wilson County Adult HS Adult
207 J Branham Dr 37087 615-443-7199
Mary Ashby, prin. Fax 443-2690
Other Schools – See Mount Juliet, Watertown

Cumberland University Post-Sec.
1 Cumberland Sq 37087 615-444-2562
Friendship Christian S 500/PK-12
5400 Coles Ferry Pike 37087 615-449-1573
Jon Shoulders, pres. Fax 449-2769
McClain Christian Academy 100/PK-12
528 Vance Ln 37087 615-444-2678
Charles Poston, head sch

Lenoir City, Loudon, Pop. 8,520
Lenoir CSD 2,100/PK-12
2145 Harrison Ave 37771 865-986-8058
Wayne Miller, supt. Fax 988-6732
www.lenoircityschools.com/
Lenoir City HS 1,300/9-12
1485 Old Highway 95 37771 865-986-2072
Steve Millsaps, prin. Fax 988-2054
Lenoir City Intermediate MS 400/4-8
2141 Harrison Ave 37771 865-986-2038
Chip Orr, prin. Fax 988-1964

Loudon County SD
Supt. — See Loudon
North MS 900/5-8
421 Hickory Creek Rd 37771 865-986-9944
Mike Casteel, prin. Fax 988-9089

Crossroads Christian Academy 100/PK-12
1963 Martel Rd 37772 865-986-9823
Shannon Klenkel, prin.

Lewisburg, Marshall, Pop. 10,852
Marshall County SD 4,300/PK-12
700 Jones Cir 37091 931-359-1581
Jackie Abernathy, dir. Fax 270-8816
www.k12marshall.net
Lewisburg MS 400/7-8
500 Tiger Blvd 37091 931-359-1265
Randy Hubbell, prin. Fax 359-4030
Marshall County HS 800/9-12
597 W Ellington Pkwy 37091 931-359-1549
John Bush, prin. Fax 359-4784
Spot Lowe Vocational S Vo/Tech
1771 Jason Maxwell Blvd 37091 931-359-4911
Lyn Stacey, dir. Fax 359-3041
Other Schools – See Chapel Hill, Cornersville

Lexington, Henderson, Pop. 7,427
Henderson County SD 3,900/PK-12
35 E Wilson St 38351 731-968-3661
Steve Wilkinson, dir. Fax 968-9457
hcschoolstn.org
Lexington HS 900/9-12
284 White St 38351 731-968-2961
Steve Lindsey, prin. Fax 968-9399
Other Schools – See Reagan

Lexington CSD 1,000/PK-8
99 Monroe Ave 38351 731-967-5591
Susan Bunch, dir. Fax 967-0794
www.caywood.org
Lexington MS 300/6-8
112 Airways Dr 38351 731-968-8457
Beth Deere, prin. Fax 967-7130

Linden, Perry, Pop. 889
Perry County SD 1,200/PK-12
857 Squirrel Hollow Dr 37096 931-589-2102
Eric Lomax, dir. Fax 589-5110
www.perrycountyschools.us
Linden MS 300/5-8
130 College Ave 37096 931-589-5000
Brent Cunningham, prin. Fax 589-3685
Perry County HS 300/9-12
1056 Squirrel Hollow Dr 37096 931-589-2831
Mike Rhodes, prin. Fax 589-5063

Livingston, Overton, Pop. 4,018
Overton County SD 3,500/K-12
302 Zachary St 38570 931-823-1287
Matt Eldridge, supt. Fax 823-4673
www.overtoncountyschools.net
Livingston Academy HS 1,000/9-12
120 Melvin Johnson Dr 38570 931-823-5911
Lesley Riddle, prin. Fax 823-8626
Livingston MS 400/5-8
216 Bilbrey St 38570 931-823-5917
Doug Smith, prin. Fax 823-7549
Reach Academy 50/Alt
312 W Broad St 38570 931-823-9388
Terry Melton, prin. Fax 823-4673

Tennessee Technology Center Livingston Post-Sec.
740 HI Tech Dr 38570 931-823-5525

Loretto, Lawrence, Pop. 1,696
Lawrence County SD
Supt. — See Lawrenceburg
Loretto HS 600/9-12
525 2nd Ave S 38469 931-853-4324
Dr. Jennifer Littleton, prin. Fax 853-4340

Loudon, Loudon, Pop. 5,315
Loudon County SD 5,200/PK-12
100 River Rd 37774 865-458-5411
Jason Vance, dir. Fax 458-6138
www.loudoncounty.org/
Ft. Loudoun MS 400/6-8
1703 Roberts Rd 37774 865-458-2026
Tiffany Ratledge, prin. Fax 458-6611
Loudon HS 800/9-12
1039 Mulberry St 37774 865-458-4326
Cheri Parrish, prin. Fax 458-0717
Other Schools – See Greenback, Lenoir City

Lyles, Hickman, Pop. 722
Hickman County SD
Supt. — See Centerville
East Hickman HS 600/9-12
7700 Highway 7 37098 931-670-1366
Bruce Jackson, prin. Fax 670-1039
East Hickman MS 500/6-8
9414 E Eagle Dr 37098 931-670-4237
Julia Thomasson, prin. Fax 670-4239

Lynchburg, Moore, Pop. 5,241
Moore County SD 1,000/K-12
PO Box 219 37352 931-759-7303
Chad Moorehead, supt. Fax 759-6386
www.moorecountyschools.net
Moore County JSHS 500/7-12
1502 Lynchburg Hwy 37352 931-759-4231
Brantley Smith, prin. Fax 759-6390

Motlow State Community College Post-Sec.
PO Box 8500 37352 931-393-1500

Lynnville, Giles, Pop. 286
Giles County SD
Supt. — See Pulaski
Richland MSHS 700/5-12
10610 Columbia Hwy 38472 931-527-3577
Barry Laxson, prin. Fax 527-3720

Mc Ewen, Humphreys, Pop. 1,735
Humphreys County SD
Supt. — See Waverly
Mc Ewen HS 300/9-12
335 Melrose St 37101 931-582-6950
Jerry Honea, prin. Fax 582-6952
McEwen JHS 200/6-8
365 Melrose St 37101 931-582-8417
T. Coleman, prin. Fax 582-8418

Mc Kenzie, Carroll, Pop. 5,208
Mc Kenzie Special SD 1,400/PK-12
114 Bell Ave 38201 731-352-2246
Lynn Watkins, dir. Fax 352-7550
www.mckenzieschools.org
Mc Kenzie HS 400/9-12
23292 Highway 22 38201 731-352-2133
Tim Watkins, prin. Fax 352-1424
Mc Kenzie MS 400/5-8
80 Woodrow Ave 38201 731-352-2792
David Duncan, prin. Fax 352-4709

Bethel University Post-Sec.
325 Cherry Ave 38201 731-352-4000
Tennessee Technology Center at Mc Kenzie Post-Sec.
16940 Highland Dr 38201 731-352-5364

Mc Minnville, Warren, Pop. 13,384
Warren County SD 6,600/PK-12
2548 Morrison St 37110 931-668-4022
John R. Cox, dir. Fax 815-2685
www.warrenschools.com
Warren Academy 50/Alt
421 N Spring St 37110 931-473-8723
Frank Fisher, prin. Fax 473-6094
Warren County HS 1,800/9-12
199 Pioneer Ln 37110 931-668-5858
Tony Cassel, prin. Fax 668-5801
Warren County MS 900/6-8
200 Caldwell St 37110 931-473-6557
Gerald Tidwell, prin. Fax 473-2432

Boyd Christian S 200/PK-12
806 Morrison St 37110 931-473-9631
Weldon Parkinson, prin. Fax 473-9632
Tennessee Technology Center Mc Minnville Post-Sec.
241 Vo Tech Dr 37110 931-473-5587

Madison, See Nashville
Metropolitan Nashville SD
Supt. — See Nashville
Madison MS 400/5-8
300 W Old Hickory Blvd 37115 615-684-4018
Dr. Nancy Meador, prin. Fax 612-3664
Neelys Bend MS 600/5-8
1251 Neelys Bend Rd 37115 615-860-1477
Philip Hammonds, prin. Fax 612-3669

Goodpasture Christian S 900/PK-12
619 W Due West Ave 37115 615-868-2600
Rick Perry, pres. Fax 865-1766
Madison Academy 100/9-12
100 Academy Rd 37115 615-865-4055
Dan Johnson, prin. Fax 865-4117
Middle Tennessee School of Anesthesia Post-Sec.
PO Box 417 37116 615-732-7662
Miller-Motte Technical College Post-Sec.
1515 Gallatin Pike N 37115 615-859-8090
Nashville College Post-Sec.
1556 Crestview Dr 37115 615-868-2963
National College of Business & Tech Post-Sec.
900 Madison Sq 37115 615-612-3015
Nossi College of Art Post-Sec.
590 Cheron Rd 37115 615-514-2787
Volunteer Beauty Academy Post-Sec.
1793 Gallatin Pike N 37115 615-860-4200

Madisonville, Monroe, Pop. 4,500
Monroe County SD 5,500/PK-12
205 Oak Grove Rd 37354 423-442-2373
Michael Lowry, dir. Fax 442-1389
www.monroe.k12.tn.us/
Madisonville MS 500/6-8
175 Oak Grove Rd 37354 423-442-4137
Kristi Windsor, prin. Fax 442-9338
Monroe Academy HS 50/9-12
205 Oak Grove Rd 37354 423-442-2373
Rick Saunders, prin. Fax 442-7101
Sequoyah HS 1,000/9-12
3128 Highway 411 37354 423-442-9230
Maurice Moser, prin. Fax 442-5520
Other Schools – See Sweetwater, Tellico Plains, Vonore

Achievement Academy of Monroe County 50/K-12
380 Oak Grove Rd 37354 423-420-1821
Julia Atchley-Pace, prin. Fax 420-1821
Hiwassee College Post-Sec.
225 Hiwassee College Dr 37354 423-442-2001

Manchester, Coffee, Pop. 9,924
Coffee County SD 4,600/PK-12
1343 McArthur St 37355 931-723-5150
Dr. LaDonna McFall, dir. Fax 723-5153
www.coffeecountyschools.com/
Coffee County Central HS 1,700/9-12
100 Red Raider Dr 37355 931-723-5159
John Bush, prin. Fax 723-5161
Coffee County Koss Center 50/Alt
1756 McMinnville Hwy 37355 931-723-5189
Major Shelton, prin. Fax 723-5172
Coffee County MS 900/6-8
865 McMinnville Hwy 37355 931-723-5177
Kimberly Aaron, prin. Fax 723-5180

Manchester CSD 1,200/PK-8
215 E Fort St 37355 931-728-2316
Dr. Prater Powell, supt. Fax 728-7075
www.manchestercitysch.org/
Westwood MS 200/6-8
505 E Taylor St 37355 931-728-2071
Dana Morris, prin. Fax 728-0962

Martin, Weakley, Pop. 11,280
Weakley County SD
Supt. — See Dresden
Martin MS 500/6-8
700 Fowler Rd 38237 731-587-2346
Nate Holmes, prin. Fax 588-0529
Westview HS 700/9-12
8161 Highway 45 S 38237 731-587-4202
David Byars, prin. Fax 588-0806

University of Tennessee Post-Sec.
554 University Ct 38237 731-881-7000

Maryville, Blount, Pop. 26,990
Blount County SD 11,800/PK-12
831 Grandview Dr 37803 865-984-1212
Rob Britt, dir. Fax 980-1002
www.blountk12.org
Blount 9th Grade Academy 500/9-9
1126 William Blount Dr 37801 865-984-5500
Cassandra Dowd, prin. Fax 980-1183
Blount HS 1,300/10-12
219 County Farm Rd 37801 865-984-5500
Rob Clark, prin. Fax 977-0153
Carpenters MS 700/6-8
920 Huffstetler Rd 37803 865-980-1414
Mike Crabtree, prin. Fax 980-1404
Eagleton MS 400/6-8
2610 Cinema Dr 37804 865-982-3211
Becky Stone, prin. Fax 982-4203
Everett Learning Opportunity Center 100/Alt
1500 Jett Rd 37804 865-984-9420
Danny Galyon, prin. Fax 984-7189
Heritage HS 1,600/9-12
3741 E Lamar Alexander Pkwy 37804 865-984-8110
Earl McMahan, prin. Fax 984-0147
Heritage MS 800/6-8
3737 E Lamar Alexander Pkwy 37804 865-980-1300
Dr. Steve Moser, prin. Fax 980-1281
Other Schools – See Friendsville

Maryville CSD 3,600/PK-12
833 Lawrence Ave 37803 865-982-7121
Stephanie Thompson, supt. Fax 977-5055
www.maryville-schools.org
Maryville HS 1,100/10-12
825 Lawrence Ave 37803 865-982-1132
Greg Roach, prin. Fax 983-1440
Maryville JHS 400/8-9
805 Montvale Station Rd 37803 865-983-2070
Lisa McGinley, prin. Fax 977-9413

Adventist Christian S of Maryville 50/1-10
PO Box 4128 37802 865-982-7584
Kathy Mather, prin.
Maryville Christian S 400/PK-12
2525 Morganton Rd 37801 865-681-3205
Dr. Glenn Slater, admin. Fax 681-4086
Maryville College Post-Sec.
502 E Lamar Alexander Pkwy 37804 865-981-8000

Maynardville, Union, Pop. 2,385
Union County SD 3,400/PK-12
PO Box 10 37807 865-992-5466
Dr. James Carter, dir. Fax 992-0126
www.ucps.org/
Maynard MS 700/6-8
PO Box 669 37807 865-992-1030
Melanie Maples, prin. Fax 992-1060
Union County HS 800/9-12
150 Main St 37807 865-992-5232
Linda Harrell, prin. Fax 992-5724
Union County Alternative Learning Center Adult
PO Box 609 37807 865-992-7747
Chris Price, prin. Fax 992-9076

Medina, Gibson, Pop. 3,452
Gibson County Special SD
Supt. — See Dyer
Medina MS 800/3-8
PO Box 369 38355 731-783-1962
Steve Maloan, prin. Fax 783-1964
South Gibson County HS 400/9-12
PO Box 249 38355 731-783-0999
Phil Rogers, prin. Fax 783-0011

Memphis, Shelby, Pop. 639,057
Achievement SD
Supt. — See Nashville
Westside Achievement MS 500/6-8
3389 Dawn Dr 38127 901-416-3700
Fax 416-3701

Memphis CSD 104,800/PK-12
2597 Avery Ave 38112 901-416-5300
Dr. Kriner Cash, supt. Fax 416-5578
www.mcsk12.net
Airways MS 300/6-8
2601 Ketchum Rd 38114 901-416-5006
Dr. LeCharle Harris, prin. Fax 416-5009
American Way MS 900/6-8
3805 American Way 38118 901-416-1250
Lisa Maclin-Love, prin. Fax 416-1251
Bellevue MS 600/6-8
575 S Bellevue Blvd 38104 901-416-4488
Kevin Malone, prin. Fax 416-4490
Bond MS 6-8
2737 Kate Bond Rd 38133 901-416-0640
Angela Brown, prin. Fax 416-0634
Carver HS 600/9-12
1591 Pennsylvania St 38109 901-416-7594
Monifa Johnson, prin. Fax 416-2235
Central HS 1,800/9-12
306 S Bellevue Blvd 38104 901-416-4500
Gregory McCullough, prin. Fax 416-4506
Chickasaw MS 400/7-8
4060 Westmont Rd 38109 901-416-8134
Phillip Nelson, prin. Fax 416-8139
Colonial MS 1,200/6-8
1370 Colonial Rd 38117 901-416-8980
Marty Pettigrew, prin. Fax 416-8996
Corry MS 300/6-8
2230 Corry Rd 38106 901-416-7804
William Taylor, prin. Fax 416-7863
Craigmont HS 1,200/9-12
3333 Covington Pike 38128 901-416-4312
Sherilyn Brown, prin. Fax 416-7675
Craigmont MS 900/6-8
3455 Covington Pike 38128 901-416-7780
Reggie Jackson, prin. Fax 416-1454
Cypress MS 400/6-8
2109 Howell Ave 38108 901-416-4524
Gina Nicholson, prin. Fax 416-4528
Douglass HS 700/9-12
3200 Mount Olive Rd 38108 901-416-0990
Janet Thompson, prin. Fax 416-9887
East HS Career Technology Center 1,000/7-12
3206 Poplar Ave 38111 901-416-6160
Eric Harris, prin. Fax 416-6161
Fairley HS 800/9-12
4950 Fairley Rd 38109 901-416-8060
Fax 416-8064
Fairview MS 300/6-8
750 E Parkway S 38104 901-416-4536
Selina Sparkman, prin. Fax 416-4539
Frayser MSHS 700/7-12
1530 Dellwood Ave 38127 901-416-3880
Yolanda Lunford, prin. Fax 416-3894
Geeter MS 500/6-8
4649 Horn Lake Rd 38109 901-416-8157
Kenneth Pickney, prin. Fax 416-8160
Georgian Hills JHS 400/7-9
3925 Denver St 38127 901-416-3740
Rosalind Martin, prin. Fax 416-6500
Hamilton HS 1,100/9-12
1363 E Person Ave 38106 901-416-7838
Michael Bates, prin. Fax 416-7829
Hamilton MS 400/6-8
1478 Wilson St 38106 901-416-7832
Kelly Henderson, prin. Fax 416-3314
Hamilton Success Academy Alt
1478 Wilson St 38106 901-416-7949
Dr. James Suggs, prin. Fax 416-7948
Havenview MS 800/6-8
1481 Hester Rd 38116 901-416-3092
Corey Kelly, prin. Fax 416-3093
Hickory Ridge MS 900/6-8
3920 Ridgeway Rd 38115 901-416-9337
Cedric Smith, prin. Fax 416-9210
Hillcrest HS 800/9-12
4184 Graceland Dr 38116 901-416-3104
Eric Moore, prin. Fax 416-9432
Humes Academy Alt
659 N Manassas St 38107 901-416-2820
Deartis Barber, prin. Fax 416-2815
Humes MS 300/6-8
659 N Manassas St 38107 901-416-3226
Deartis Barber, prin. Fax 416-2815
Kingsbury Career Technology Center Vo/Tech
1328 N Graham St 38122 901-416-6000
Timothy Batts, prin. Fax 416-6003
Kingsbury HS 1,100/9-12
1270 N Graham St 38122 901-416-6060
Carlos Fuller, prin. Fax 416-6061
Kingsbury MS 500/7-8
1276 N Graham St 38122 901-416-6040
Melvin Harris, prin. Fax 416-6058
Kirby HS 1,500/9-12
4080 Kirby Pkwy 38115 901-416-1960
Dr. Reginald Williams, prin. Fax 416-1968
Kirby MS 700/6-8
6670 E Raines Rd 38115 901-416-1980
Pamela Yancy-Taylor, prin. Fax 416-0974
Lanier MS 400/6-8
817 Brownlee Rd 38116 901-416-3128
Dalton Blackwell, prin. Fax 416-9875
Lester S 400/4-8
320 Carpenter St 38112 901-416-5969
Elaine Stewart-Price, prin. Fax 416-5971
Manassas HS 600/9-12
1111 N Manassas St 38107 901-416-3244
James Griffin, prin. Fax 416-3248
MCS Prep Northeast 300/Alt
968 N Mendenhall Rd 38122 901-416-2132
Melita Jordan-Thomas, prin. Fax 416-2157
MCS Prep Northwest 500/Alt
1266 Poplar Ave 38104 901-416-4400
Chemella Branch, prin. Fax 416-4683
MCS Prep Southeast 300/Alt
5396 Mendenhall Mall 38115 901-416-1430
Roger Jones, prin. Fax 416-1422
MCS Prep Southwest 300/Alt
1237 College St 38106 901-416-7884
Dr. Billy Walker, prin. Fax 416-7886
Melrose HS 1,000/9-12
2870 Deadrick Ave 38114 901-416-5974
Leviticus Pointer, prin. Fax 416-5984
Memphis Health Careers Academy 100/Alt
80 W Olive Ave 38106 901-416-1950
Brenda Diaz Williams, prin. Fax 416-1951
Messick Career & Technology Center Vo/Tech
703 S Greer St 38111 901-416-4840
Carol Miller, prin. Fax 416-4842

Middle College SHS 200/10-12
750 E Parkway S 38104 901-416-4550
Docia Generette, prin. Fax 416-4555
Mitchell HS 600/9-12
658 W Mitchell Rd 38109 901-416-8174
Kelvin Meeks, prin. Fax 416-8176
Northside HS 400/9-12
1212 Vollintine Ave 38107 901-416-4582
Dr. Lowell Winston, prin. Fax 416-9813
Northside Innovative Academy Alt
1212 Vollintine Ave 38107 901-416-9838
Robert Washington, prin. Fax 416-1737
Oakhaven HS 500/9-12
3125 Ladbrook Rd 38118 901-416-2300
Dr. Tisha Durrah, prin. Fax 416-2301
Oakhaven MS 200/7-8
3125 Ladbrook Rd 38118 901-416-2380
Shari Jones, prin. Fax 416-9780
Overton HS 1,400/9-12
1770 Lanier Ln 38117 901-416-2136
Brett Lawson, prin. Fax 416-2135
Price Middle College HS 100/9-12
807 Walker Ave 38126 901-435-1765
Daphne Beasley, prin. Fax 435-1779
Raleigh-Egypt HS 1,000/9-12
3970 Voltaire Ave 38128 901-416-4108
Michael Bailey, prin. Fax 416-4143
Raleigh-Egypt MS 700/6-8
4215 Alice Ann Dr 38128 901-416-4141
Rommie Vasser, prin. Fax 416-4110
Reconation Academy Alt
868 N Manassas St 38107 901-577-2500
Michael Smith, prin. Fax 578-3435
Ridgeway HS 1,200/9-12
2009 Ridgeway Rd 38119 901-416-8820
James Long, prin. Fax 416-2199
Ridgeway MS 900/6-8
6333 Quince Rd 38119 901-416-1588
Corey Williams, prin. Fax 416-1477
Riverview MS 300/6-8
241 Majuba Ave 38109 901-416-7340
Betty Parks, prin. Fax 416-7343
Sheffield Career & Tech Center Vo/Tech
4350 Chuck Ave 38118 901-416-2340
Charles Grove, prin. Fax 416-2394
Sheffield HS 1,000/9-12
4315 Sheffield Ave 38118 901-416-2370
Kymberli Chandler, prin. Fax 416-2407
Sherwood MS 600/6-8
3480 Rhodes Ave 38111 901-416-4870
Frederick White, prin. Fax 416-4881
South Side MS 400/6-8
1880 Prospect St 38106 901-416-7420
Kobie Sweeten, prin. Fax 416-7301
Southwest Career & Technology Center Vo/Tech
3746 Horn Lake Rd 38109 901-416-8186
Leroy McClain, prin. Fax 416-8188
Treadwell MS 300/6-8
920 N Highland St 38122 901-416-6100
Suzanne Brown, prin. Fax 416-6133
Trezevant Career & Tech Center Vo/Tech
3224 Range Line Rd 38127 901-416-3800
Milton Burchfield, prin. Fax 416-3839
Trezevant HS 800/9-12
3350 N Trezevant St 38127 901-416-3760
Dr. Joe Canada, prin. Fax 416-3761
Vance MS 300/6-8
673 Vance Ave 38126 901-416-3256
Taurin Hardy, prin. Fax 416-3257
Walker MS 700/6-8
1900 E Raines Rd 38116 901-416-1030
Tonya McBride, prin. Fax 416-1075
Washington HS 500/9-12
715 S Lauderdale St 38126 901-416-7240
Alisha Kiner, prin. Fax 416-7228
Wells Academy 100/7-8
995 S Lauderdale St 38126 901-416-3210
Sandra Johnson, prin. Fax 416-3205
Westhaven Success Academy Alt
4585 Hodge Rd 38109 901-416-7122
Valerie Matthews, prin. Fax 416-7171
Westwood HS 600/9-12
4480 Westmont Rd 38109 901-416-8000
Isaac White, prin. Fax 416-8027
Whitehaven HS 2,200/9-12
4851 Elvis Presley Blvd 38116 901-416-3000
Dr. Vincent Hunter, prin. Fax 416-3058
White Station HS 2,200/9-12
514 S Perkins Rd 38117 901-416-8880
David Mansfield, prin. Fax 416-8910
White Station MS 800/7-8
5465 Mason Rd 38120 901-416-2184
Shawn Page, prin. Fax 416-2187
Wooddale HS 1,500/9-12
5151 Scottsdale Ave 38118 901-416-2440
Michael Kyle, prin. Fax 416-2476
Wooddale MS 800/6-8
3467 Castleman St 38118 901-416-2420
Dr. Robert Gordon, prin. Fax 416-2426
Other Schools – See Cordova

Shelby County SD 47,000/K-12
160 S Hollywood St 38112 901-321-2500
John Aitken, supt. Fax 321-2501
www.scsk12.org/
Highland Oaks MS 900/6-8
5600 Meadowbriar Trl 38125 901-432-4114
Monica Bates, prin. Fax 432-4122
Southwind HS 1,900/9-12
7900 E Shelby Dr 38125 901-752-2881
Susan Vaughn, prin. Fax 752-2898
Other Schools – See Arlington, Bartlett, Collierville, Cordova, Germantown, Millington

---

All Saints Bible College Post-Sec.
938 Mason St 38126 901-322-0120
Anthem College Post-Sec.
5865 Shelby Oaks Cir #100 38134 901-432-3800
Baptist Memorial Coll. of Health Science Post-Sec.
1003 Monroe Ave 38104 901-575-2247
Baptist Memorial Hospital Post-Sec.
350 N Humphreys Blvd #EagB2 38103 901-227-5121
Central Baptist S 200/PK-12
5470 Raleigh LaGrange Rd 38134 901-386-8161
Greg Reese, prin. Fax 386-9165
Christian Brothers HS 800/9-12
5900 Walnut Grove Rd 38120 901-261-4900
Chris Fay, prin. Fax 261-4909
Christian Brothers University Post-Sec.
650 E Parkway S 38104 901-321-3000
Concorde Career College Post-Sec.
5100 Poplar Ave Ste 132 38137 901-761-9494
Creative Life Preparatory S 100/PK-12
1222 Riverside Blvd 38106 901-775-0304
Dr. Carolyn Bibbs, pres. Fax 946-5433
DeVry University Post-Sec.
6401 Poplar Ave Ste 600 38119 901-537-2560
Gateway Christian S 1,300/1-12
4070 Macon Rd 38122 901-458-4276
Donna Bumgardner, prin. Fax 323-0914
Harding Academy of Memphis 500/7-12
1100 Cherry Rd 38117 901-767-4494
Harding School of Theology Post-Sec.
1000 Cherry Rd 38117 901-761-1350
Holy Names of Jesus and Mary ES 100/3-8
709 Keel Ave 38107 901-507-1503
Lytia Reese, prin. Fax 507-1507
Hutchison S 900/PK-12
1740 Ridgeway Rd 38119 901-761-2220
Annette Smith Ed.D., hdmstr. Fax 432-6655
Immaculate Conception Cathedral S 200/PK-12
1695 Central Ave 38104 901-725-2705
Sally Hermsdorfer, prin. Fax 725-2709
Lausanne Collegiate S 800/PK-12
1381 W Massey Rd 38120 901-474-1000
Stuart McCathie, hdmstr. Fax 474-1010
Le Moyne-Owen College Post-Sec.
807 Walker Ave 38126 901-435-1000
Macon Road Baptist S - Berclair 200/PK-12
1082 Berclair Rd 38122 901-683-6363
Trent Thorell, prin.
Margolin Hebrew Academy 200/PK-12
390 S White Station Rd 38117 901-682-2400
Gil Perl, dean Fax 767-1871
Memphis Catholic MSHS 200/7-12
61 N McLean Blvd 38104 901-276-1221
Nicholas Green, prin. Fax 725-1447
Memphis College of Art Post-Sec.
1930 Poplar Ave 38104 901-272-5100
Memphis Junior Academy 100/PK-10
50 N Mendenhall Rd 38117 901-683-1061
CHris Wilhelm, prin. Fax 683-1012
Memphis Theological Seminary Post-Sec.
168 E Parkway S 38104 901-458-8232
Memphis University S 700/7-12
6191 Park Ave 38119 901-260-1300
Ellis Haguewood, hdmstr. Fax 260-1301
Methodist Hospital Post-Sec.
1265 Union Ave 38104 901-726-8274
Mid-South Christian College Post-Sec.
3097 Knight Rd 38118 901-375-4400
National College of Business & Tech Post-Sec.
2576 Thousand Oaks Blvd 38118 901-363-9046
New Wave Hair Academy Post-Sec.
3250 Coleman Rd 38128 901-323-6100
New Wave Hair Academy Post-Sec.
804 S Highland St 38111 901-320-9283
NHLA Inspector Training School Post-Sec.
6830 Raleigh LaGrange Rd 38134 901-377-1818
Plaza Beauty School Post-Sec.
4682 Spottswood Ave 38117 901-761-4445
Remington College Post-Sec.
2710 Nonconnah Blvd # 160 38132 901-345-1000
Rhodes College Post-Sec.
2000 N Parkway 38112 901-843-3000
St. Agnes Academy 400/PK-12
4830 Walnut Grove Rd 38117 901-767-1377
Barbara Daush, pres. Fax 435-5866
St. Mary's Episcopal S 800/PK-12
60 Perkins Ext 38117 901-537-1472
Albert L. Throckmorton, hdmstr. Fax 682-0119
Southern College of Optometry Post-Sec.
1245 Madison Ave 38104 901-722-3200
Southern Institute of Cosmetology Post-Sec.
4030 Muirfield Dr 38125 - -
Southern Institute of Cosmetology Post-Sec.
3099 S Perkins Rd 38118 901-363-3553
Southwest Tennessee Community College Post-Sec.
PO Box 780 38101 901-333-5000
Strayer University Post-Sec.
2620 Thousand Oaks Ste 1100 38118 901-369-0835
Strayer University Post-Sec.
7275 Appling Farms Pkwy 38133 901-251-7100
Tennessee Academy of Cosmetology Post-Sec.
7041 Stage Rd Ste 101 38133 901-382-9085
Tennessee Academy of Cosmetology Post-Sec.
7020 E Shelby Dr Ste 104 38125 901-757-4166
Tennessee Technology Center at Memphis Post-Sec.
550 Alabama Ave 38105 901-543-6100
The Beauty Institute Post-Sec.
568 Colonial Rd 38117 901-761-1888
University of Memphis 38152 Post-Sec. 901-678-2000
Univ. of Tennessee Health Science Center Post-Sec.
800 Madison Ave 38163 901-448-5500
Vatterott Career College Post-Sec.
6991 Appling Farms Pkwy 38133 901-372-2399
Vatterott College Post-Sec.
2655 Dividend Dr 38132 901-761-5730
Victory University Post-Sec.
255 N Highland St 38111 800-960-9777
Visible Music College Post-Sec.
200 Madison Ave 38103 901-381-3939
Westminster Academy 300/K-12
2500 Ridgeway Rd 38119 901-380-9192
Peter Baur, hdmstr. Fax 405-2019
William Moore College of Technology Post-Sec.
1200 Poplar Ave 38104 901-726-1977

Middleton, Hardeman, Pop. 695
Hardeman County SD
Supt. — See Bolivar
Middleton HS 600/7-12
PO Box 477 38052 731-376-8391
Darlene Cardwell, prin. Fax 376-8157

Milan, Gibson, Pop. 7,701
Milan Special SD 2,300/PK-12
1165 S Main St 38358 731-686-0844
Mary Reel Ed.D., dir. Fax 686-8781
www.milanssd.org
Milan HS 600/9-12
7060 E Van Hook St 38358 731-686-0841
Kris Todd, prin. Fax 686-9829
Milan MS 700/5-8
4040 Middle Rd 38358 731-686-7232
Sam Rhodes, prin. Fax 723-8872

Arnold's Beauty School Post-Sec.
1179 S 2nd St 38358 731-686-7351

Milligan College, Carter

Milligan College Post-Sec.
1 Milligan College 37682 423-461-8700

Millington, Shelby, Pop. 9,878
Shelby County SD
Supt. — See Memphis
Millington Central HS 1,400/9-12
8050 West St 38053 901-873-8100
Mark Neal, prin. Fax 873-8105
Millington MS 400/6-8
4964 Cuba Millington Rd 38053 901-873-8130
Amie Mansh, prin. Fax 873-8136
Woodstock MS 500/6-8
5885 Woodstock Cuba Rd 38053 901-353-8590
Eric Linsy, prin. Fax 353-8599

Faith Heritage Christian Academy 200/K-12
4274 Duncan Rd 38053 901-872-0828
M.O. Eckel, hdmstr. Fax 872-0803
Lighthouse Christian Academy 100/PK-12
3660 Shelby Rd 38053 901-873-3353
Brett Frans, hdmstr. Fax 873-3394
Tipton Rosemark Academy 600/PK-12
8696 Rosemark Rd 38053 901-829-4221
John Scott, head sch Fax 829-4477

Monterey, Putnam, Pop. 2,832
Putnam County SD
Supt. — See Cookeville
Monterey HS 300/9-12
112 N Elm St 38574 931-839-2970
Sonja Farley, prin. Fax 839-6070

Morristown, Hamblen, Pop. 28,494
Hamblen County SD 9,800/K-12
210 E Morris Blvd 37813 423-586-7700
Dale Lynch, supt. Fax 586-7747
www.hcboe.net
Lincoln Heights MS 500/6-8
219 Lincoln Ave 37813 423-581-3200
Joe Ely, prin. Fax 585-3763
Meadowview MS 500/6-8
1623 Meadowview Ln 37814 423-581-6360
Dominique Salaciak, prin. Fax 585-3771
Miller Boyd Alternative S 50/Alt
376 Snyder Rd 37813 423-585-3785
Calvin Decker, prin. Fax 585-3786
Morristown-Hamblen HS East 1,400/9-12
1 Hurricane Ln 37813 423-586-2543
Gary Johnson, prin. Fax 585-3779
Morristown-Hamblen HS West 1,400/9-12
1 Trojan Trl 37813 423-581-1600
Jeff Moorhouse, prin. Fax 585-3791
West View MS 700/6-8
1 Indian Path 37813 423-581-2407
Rebekah Patrick, prin. Fax 585-3807
Hamblen County Adult HS Adult
376 Snyder Rd 37813 423-585-3785
Anna James, coord. Fax 585-3786
Other Schools – See Whitesburg

Cornerstone Academy 200/K-12
260 Jacobs Rd 37813 423-307-1189
Dr. Byron Greene, hdmstr.
Tennessee Technology Center Morristown Post-Sec.
821 W Louise Ave 37813 423-586-5771
Walters State Community College Post-Sec.
500 S Davy Crockett Pkwy 37813 423-585-2600

Mosheim, Greene, Pop. 2,337
Greene County SD
Supt. — See Greeneville
West Greene HS 700/9-12
275 W Greene Dr 37818 423-422-4061
Julia Lamons, prin. Fax 638-3180

Mountain City, Johnson, Pop. 2,508
Johnson County SD 2,300/PK-12
211 N Church St 37683 423-727-2640
Morris Woodring, dir. Fax 727-2663
www.jocoed.k12tn.net
Johnson County HS 600/9-12
510 Fairground Ln 37683 423-727-2620
Lisa Arnold, prin. Fax 727-2677
Johnson County MS 300/7-8
500 Fairground Ln 37683 423-727-2600
Stephen Long, prin. Fax 727-2608

Johnson County Vocational S Vo/Tech
520 Fairground Ln 37683 423-727-1860
Jim Crowder, prin. Fax 727-2693

Mount Juliet, Wilson, Pop. 23,208
Wilson County SD
Supt. — See Lebanon
Mount Juliet HS 1,900/9-12
1800 Curd Rd 37122 615-758-5606
Mel Brown, prin. Fax 758-5645
Mount Juliet MS 1,400/6-8
3565 N Mount Juliet Rd 37122 615-754-6688
Tim Bell, prin. Fax 754-7566
West Wilson MS 1,000/6-8
935 N Mount Juliet Rd 37122 615-758-5152
Wendell Marlowe, prin. Fax 758-5283

Heritage Christian Academy - Mt. Juliet 300/K-12
PO Box 1135 37121 615-754-7946
Katrina Hagerty, prin.
Mt. Juliet Christian Academy 500/PK-12
735 N Mount Juliet Rd 37122 615-758-2427
Dr. Mike Lee, head sch Fax 758-3662

Mount Pleasant, Maury, Pop. 4,471
Maury County SD
Supt. — See Columbia
Mount Pleasant JSHS 400/6-12
600 Greenwood St 38474 931-379-5583
Beverly Miller, prin. Fax 379-2093
Mt. Pleasant MS of Visual/Performing Art 500/5-8
410 Gray Ln 38474 931-379-1100
Kevin Eady, prin. Fax 379-1108

Munford, Tipton, Pop. 5,823
Tipton County SD
Supt. — See Covington
Munford HS 1,300/9-12
1080 McLaughlin Dr 38058 901-837-5701
Courtney Fee, prin. Fax 837-5729
Munford MS 1,000/6-8
100 Education Ave 38058 901-837-1700
Vicki Shipley, prin. Fax 837-5749

Murfreesboro, Rutherford, Pop. 106,177
Rutherford County SD 38,800/PK-12
2240 Southpark Dr 37128 615-893-5812
Harry Gill, supt. Fax 898-7940
www.rcs.k12.tn.us
Blackman HS 2,200/9-12
3956 Blaze Dr 37128 615-904-3850
Gail Vick, prin. Fax 904-3851
Blackman MS 1,000/6-8
3945 Blaze Dr 37128 615-904-3860
Will Shelton, prin. Fax 904-3861
Central Magnet S 700/6-12
701 E Main St 37130 615-904-6789
Dr. John Ash, prin. Fax 904-6788
Holloway HS 200/9-12
619 S Highland Ave 37130 615-890-6004
Sumatra Drayton, prin. Fax 904-7508
McKee Alternative S 50/Alt
2623 Halls Hill Pike 37130 615-890-2282
Mary Jo Yeager, prin. Fax 898-7726
Oakland HS 1,800/9-12
2225 Patriot Dr 37130 615-904-3780
Bill Spurlock, prin. Fax 904-3781
Oakland MS 1,000/6-8
853 Dejarnette Ln 37130 615-904-6760
Sandra Eaton, prin. Fax 904-6761
Riverdale HS 2,100/9-12
802 Warrior Dr 37128 615-890-6450
Tom Nolan, prin. Fax 890-9790
Siegel HS 2,000/9-12
3300 Siegel Rd 37129 615-904-3800
Jason Bridgeman, prin. Fax 904-3801
Siegel MS 1,000/6-8
355 W Thompson Ln 37129 615-904-3830
Tom Delbridge, prin. Fax 904-3831
Whitworth-Buchanan MS 700/6-8
5555 Manchester Pike 37127 615-904-6765
Avy Seymore, prin. Fax 904-6766
Other Schools – See Christiana, Eagleville, La Vergne, Rockvale, Smyrna

---

Daymar Institute Post-Sec.
415 Golden Bear Ct 37128 615-217-9347
Franklin Road Christian S 300/PK-12
3124 Franklin Rd 37128 615-890-0894
Kenton Kramer, admin. Fax 893-2837
Middle Tennessee Christian S 800/PK-12
100 E MTCS Rd 37129 615-893-0601
Dr. Lynn Watson, admin. Fax 895-8815
Middle Tennessee State University Post-Sec.
1301 E Main St 37132 615-898-2300
Providence Christian Academy 400/PK-12
410 Dejarnette Ln 37130 615-904-0902
Butch Vaughn, hdmstr. Fax 904-0859
Tennessee Technology Center Murfreesboro Post-Sec.
1303 Old Fort Pkwy 37129 615-898-8010

Nashville, Davidson, Pop. 588,359
Achievement SD 1,300/PK-8
710 James Robertson 37243 615-532-4710
Chris Barbic, supt.
www.achievementschooldistrict.org/
Other Schools – See Memphis

Metropolitan Nashville SD 77,000/PK-12
2601 Bransford Ave 37204 615-259-4636
Dr. Jesse Register, dir. Fax 259-8492
www.mnps.org
Allen MS 500/5-8
500 Spence Ln 37210 615-291-6385
Dr. Dorothy Gunn, prin. Fax 291-6066
Bailey MS 500/5-8
2000 Greenwood Ave 37206 615-262-6670
Dr. Christian Sawyer, prin. Fax 262-6979
Bass Learning Center Alt
5200 Delaware Ave 37209 615-298-3278
Henry Johnson, prin.
Baxter Alternative Center 100/Alt
3515 Gallatin Pike 37216 615-650-5381
Karl Lang, coord. Fax 650-5384
Baxter MS 500/5-8
350 Hart Ln 37207 615-262-6710
Dr. Corey Walker, prin. Fax 262-6743
Bellevue MS 700/5-8
655 Colice Jeanne Rd 37221 615-662-3000
Dr. Barbara Springer, prin. Fax 662-5728
Brick Church MS 300/6-8
2835 Brick Church Pike 37207 615-262-6665
Chirelle Jefferson, prin. Fax 262-6966
Cameron MS 300/7-8
1034 1st Ave S 37210 615-291-6365
Chris Hames, prin. Fax 291-6072
Cohn Adult HS 100/Alt
4805 Park Ave 37209 615-298-6617
Debbie Booker, prin. Fax 298-8052
Creswell Magnet MS 600/5-8
3500 John Mallette Dr 37218 615-291-6515
Dr. Ted Murcray, prin. Fax 291-5326
Croft Design Center MS 700/5-8
482 Elysian Fields Rd 37211 615-332-0217
Juana Grandberry, prin. Fax 333-5650
Donelson MS 800/5-8
110 Stewarts Ferry Pike 37214 615-884-4080
Jennifer Rheinecker, prin. Fax 885-8970
Early Museum Magnet MS 300/5-8
1000 Cass St 37208 615-291-6369
Rise Pope, prin. Fax 298-8497
East Nashville Magnet S 1,300/5-12
110 Gallatin Ave 37206 615-262-6947
Stephen Ball, prin. Fax 262-3972
Glencliff Comprehensive HS 1,400/9-12
160 Antioch Pike 37211 615-333-5070
Clint Wilson, prin. Fax 333-5003
Gra-Mar MS 500/5-8
575 Joyce Ln 37216 615-262-6685
Dr. Antoinette Williams, prin. Fax 262-6901
Haynes Health/Medical Science Design Ctr 300/5-8
510 W Trinity Ln 37207 615-262-6688
Dr. Tonya Dennis, prin. Fax 298-8084
Head Magnet S 600/5-8
1830 Jo Johnston Ave 37203 615-329-8160
Dr. Angela Carr, prin. Fax 321-8389
Hill MS 500/5-8
150 Davidson Rd 37205 615-353-2020
Connie Gwinn, prin. Fax 884-4028
Hillsboro Comprehensive HS 1,300/9-12
3812 Hillsboro Pike 37215 615-298-8400
Terry Shrader, prin. Fax 353-1159
Hillwood Comprehensive HS 1,200/9-12
400 Davidson Rd 37205 615-353-2025
Dr. Steve Chauncy, prin. Fax 298-8402
Hume-Fogg Magnet HS 900/9-12
700 Broadway 37203 615-291-6300
Dr. Kellie Hargis, prin. Fax 291-6065
Hunters Lane Comprehensive HS 1,800/9-12
1150 Hunters Ln 37207 615-860-1401
Dr. Susan Kessler, prin. Fax 291-6304
King Magnet JSHS 1,200/7-12
613 17th Ave N 37203 615-329-8400
Dr. Schunn Turner, prin. Fax 501-7907
Litton MS 300/5-8
4601 Hedgewood Dr 37216 615-262-6700
Tracy Bruno, prin. Fax 262-6995
Maplewood Comprehensive HS 1,100/9-12
401 Walton Ln 37216 615-262-6770
Ron Woodard, prin. Fax 262-6772
McGavock Comprehensive HS 2,600/9-12
3150 Mcgavock Pike 37214 615-885-8850
Robbin Wall, prin. Fax 885-8900
McKissack MS 100/5-8
915 38th Ave N 37209 615-329-8170
Janet Murphy, prin. Fax 329-8183
McMurray MS 800/5-8
520 McMurray Dr 37211 615-333-5126
T'Shaka Coverson, prin. Fax 333-5125
Meigs Magnet MS 700/5-8
713 Ramsey St 37206 615-271-3222
Dr. Scott Underwood, prin. Fax 271-3223
Middle College HS 100/10-12
120 White Bridge Pike 37209 615-353-3742
Roderick Manuel, prin.
Moore MS 700/5-8
4425 Granny White Pike 37204 615-298-8095
Dr. Gary Hughes, prin. Fax 298-8452
Nashville Big Picture HS 200/9-12
160 Rural Ave 37209 615-353-2081
Chaerea Denning, prin.
Nashville S of the Arts 700/9-12
1250 Foster Ave 37210 615-291-6600
Dr. Gregory Stewart, prin. Fax 271-1767
Oliver MS 800/5-8
6211 Nolensville Pike 37211 615-332-3011
Jeanna Collins, prin. Fax 332-3019
Overton Comprehensive HS 1,800/9-12
4820 Franklin Pike 37220 615-333-5135
Dr. Andrew Shuler-Pelham, prin. Fax 333-5141
Pearl-Cohn Entertainment Industry HS 800/9-12
904 26th Ave N 37208 615-329-8150
Sonia Stewart, prin. Fax 329-8192
Rose Park Math/Science MS 400/5-8
1025 9th Ave S 37203 615-291-6405
Robert Blankenship, prin. Fax 262-6717
Stratford STEM HS 800/9-12
1800 Stratford Ave 37216 615-242-6730
Michael Steele, prin. Fax 885-8929
Two Rivers MS 600/5-8
2991 Mcgavock Pike 37214 615-885-8931
Dr. Shelly Dunaway, prin. Fax 333-5641
West End MS, 3529 W End Ave 37205 400/5-8
Jeff Keith, prin. 615-298-8425
Wright MS 900/5-8
180 McCall St 37211 615-333-5189
Jud Haynie, prin. Fax 333-5635
Academy at Old Cockrill HS Adult
610 49th Ave N 37209 615-298-2294
Elaine Fahrner, prin.
Academy at Opry Mills HS Adult
433 Opry Mills Dr 37214 615-810-8306
Carmon Brown, prin.
Other Schools – See Antioch, Goodlettsville, Hermitage, Joelton, Madison, Old Hickory, Whites Creek

---

American Baptist College Post-Sec.
1800 Baptist World Ctr Dr 37207 615-256-1463
Anthem Career College Post-Sec.
560 Royal Pkwy 37214 615-232-3700
Aquinas College Post-Sec.
4210 Harding Pike 37205 615-297-7545
Argosy University / Nashville Post-Sec.
100 Centerview Dr Ste 225 37214 615-525-2800
Art Institute of Tennessee - Nashville Post-Sec.
100 Centerview Dr Ste 250 37214 866-747-5770
Belmont University Post-Sec.
1900 Belmont Blvd 37212 615-460-6000
Cedarcreek Schoolhouse Academy 400/K-12
2803 Foster Ave Ste 109 37210 615-333-0405
Beth Buchanan, dir.
Christ Presbyterian Academy 900/K-12
2323A Old Hickory Blvd 37215 615-373-9550
Richard Anderson, hdmstr. Fax 370-0884
Davidson Academy 700/PK-12
1414 Old Hickory Blvd 37207 615-860-5300
Bill Chaney Ed.D., hdmstr. Fax 868-7918
Daymar Institute Post-Sec.
340 Plus Park Blvd 37217 615-361-7555
DeVry University Post-Sec.
3343 Perimeter Hill Dr #200 37211 615-445-3456
Diamond Council of America Post-Sec.
3212 W End Ave Ste 202 37203 615-385-5301
Donelson Christian Academy 800/PK-12
300 Danyacrest Dr 37214 615-883-2926
Keith Singer, hdmstr. Fax 883-2998
Emmaus Christian S 50/1-12
PO Box 111954 37222 615-499-0540
Teresa Cayeros, hdmstr.
Ensworth S 1,100/K-12
211 Ensworth Pl 37205 615-383-0661
David Braemer, lead tchr. Fax 269-4840
Father Ryan HS 900/9-12
700 Norwood Dr 37204 615-383-4200
Paul Davis, prin. Fax 383-9056
Fisk University Post-Sec.
1000 17th Ave N 37208 615-329-8500
Franklin Road Academy 900/PK-12
4700 Franklin Pike 37220 615-832-8845
Dr. Margaret Wade, head sch Fax 834-4137
Harpeth Hall S 700/5-12
3801 Hobbs Rd 37215 615-297-9543
Ann Teaff, head sch Fax 297-0480
International Academy of Design & Tech Post-Sec.
1 Bridgestone Park 37214 615-232-7384
ITT Technical Institute Post-Sec.
2845 Elm Hill Pike 37214 615-889-8700
John A. Gupton College Post-Sec.
1616 Church St 37203 615-327-3927
Kaplan Career Institute Post-Sec.
750 Envious Ln 37217 615-279-8300
Lipscomb Academy 1,300/PK-12
3901 Granny White Pike 37204 615-966-6409
Dr. Michael Hammond, hdmstr. Fax 966-7639
Lipscomb University Post-Sec.
1 University Park Dr 37204 800-333-4358
Meharry Medical College Post-Sec.
1005 Dr DB Todd Jr Blvd 37208 615-327-6111
Montgomery Bell Academy 700/7-12
4001 Harding Pike 37205 615-298-5514
Bradford Gioia, hdmstr. Fax 297-0271
Nashville Auto-Diesel College Post-Sec.
1524 Gallatin Ave 37206 615-226-3990
Nashville Christian S 400/PK-12
7555 Sawyer Brown Rd 37221 615-356-5600
Connie Jo Shelton, pres. Fax 352-1324
Nashville State Community College Post-Sec.
120 White Bridge Pike 37209 615-353-3333
National College of Business & Tech. Post-Sec.
1638 Bell Rd 37211 615-333-3344
Remington College Post-Sec.
441 Donelson Pike Ste 150 37214 615-889-5520
SAE Institute Nashville Post-Sec.
7 Music Cir N 37203 615-244-5848
St. Cecilia Academy 300/9-12
4210 Harding Pike Ste 2 37205 615-298-4525
Sr. Anne Catherine, prin. Fax 783-0561
St. Thomas Hospital Post-Sec.
PO Box 380 37202 615-222-2111
Seminary Ext. Independent Study Inst. Post-Sec.
901 Commerce St Ste 500 37203 800-229-4612
Southeastern Institute Post-Sec.
3055 Lebanon Pike Ste 300 37214 615-889-9388
Strayer University Post-Sec.
1809 Dabbs Ave 37210 615-871-2260
Tennessee School for the Blind Post-Sec.
115 Stewarts Ferry Pike 37214 615-231-7300
Tennessee State University Post-Sec.
3500 John A Merritt Blvd 37209 615-963-5000
Tennessee Technology Center at Nashville Post-Sec.
100 White Bridge Pike 37209 615-425-5500
Trevecca Nazarene University Post-Sec.
333 Murfreesboro Pike 37210 615-248-1200
University S of Nashville 1,000/K-12
2000 Edgehill Ave 37212 615-321-8000
Vincent Durnan, dir. Fax 321-0889
Vanderbilt University Post-Sec.
2301 Vanderbilt Pl 37235 615-322-7311
Watkins College of Art Design and Film Post-Sec.
2298 Rosa L Parks Blvd 37228 615-383-4848

Welch College Post-Sec.
3606 W End Ave 37205 615-844-5000

Newbern, Dyer, Pop. 3,269
Dyer County SD
Supt. — See Dyersburg
Dyer County HS 1,100/9-12
1000 W Main St 38059 731-627-2229
Peggy Dodds, prin. Fax 627-2152
Northview MS 400/6-8
820 Williams St 38059 731-627-3713
Anthony Jones, prin. Fax 627-4823

Tennessee Technology Center at Newbern Post-Sec.
340 Washington St 38059 731-627-2511

Newport, Cocke, Pop. 6,817
Cocke County SD 4,800/K-12
305 Hedrick Dr 37821 423-623-7821
Manney Moore, dir. Fax 625-3947
www.cocke-lea.cocke.k12.tn.us
Cocke County Alternative S Alt
345 Hedrick Dr 37821 423-625-9768
Bryan Douglas, coord. Fax 625-1807
Cocke County HS 1,200/9-12
216 Hedrick Dr 37821 423-623-8718
Dr. Marvin Stewart, prin. Fax 623-1213
Cocke County Vocational HS Vo/Tech
210 Hedrick Dr 37821 423-623-6072
Gail Burchette, prin. Fax 623-6070
Other Schools – See Cosby

New Tazewell, Claiborne, Pop. 2,986
Claiborne County SD
Supt. — See Tazewell
Claiborne HS 800/9-12
815 Davis Dr 37825 423-626-3532
Susan Essary, prin. Fax 626-3555

Norris, Anderson, Pop. 1,472
Anderson County SD
Supt. — See Clinton
Norris MS 500/6-8
PO Box 980 37828 865-494-7171
Jeff Harshbarger, prin. Fax 494-6693

Oakdale, Morgan, Pop. 205
Morgan County SD
Supt. — See Wartburg
Oakdale S 600/K-12
225 Clifty Creek Rd 37829 423-369-3885
Mike Barber, prin. Fax 369-2821

Oakland, Fayette, Pop. 6,569
Fayette County SD
Supt. — See Somerville
West JHS 400/6-8
13100 Highway 194 38060 901-465-9213
Stephanie Neal, prin. Fax 465-1599

Oak Ridge, Anderson, Pop. 28,500
Oak Ridge CSD 4,800/PK-12
PO Box 6588 37831 865-425-9001
Dr. Bob Smallridge, supt. Fax 425-9070
www.ortn.edu
Jefferson MS 600/5-8
200 Fairbanks Rd 37830 865-425-9301
Bruce Lay, prin. Fax 425-9339
Oak Ridge HS 1,500/9-12
1450 Oak Ridge Tpke 37830 865-425-9601
Jody Goins, prin. Fax 425-9678
Robertsville MS 700/5-8
245 Robertsville Rd 37830 865-425-9201
Laurie Campbell, prin. Fax 425-9236

Christian Academy of Oak Ridge 100/K-12
535 Oak Ridge Tpke 37830 865-481-2519
Connie Lisenbea, prin.

Old Hickory, See Nashville
Metropolitan Nashville SD
Supt. — See Nashville
DuPont-Hadley MS 600/5-8
1901 Old Hickory Blvd 37138 615-847-7300
Kevin Armstrong, prin. Fax 847-7311

Oliver Springs, Morgan, Pop. 3,166
Anderson County SD
Supt. — See Clinton
Norwood MS 200/6-8
803 E Tri County Blvd 37840 865-435-7749
Rae Ann Owens, prin. Fax 435-5426

Roane County SD
Supt. — See Kingston
Oliver Springs HS 400/9-12
419 Kingston Ave 37840 865-435-7216
Jeffrey Woods, prin. Fax 435-6774
Oliver Springs MS 300/5-8
317 Roane St 37840 865-435-0011
Nancy Wilson, prin. Fax 435-1621

Faith Christian Academy 100/PK-12
864 Poplar Creek Rd 37840 828-435-0670
Dr. Paul Cates, prin. Fax 435-0670

Oneida, Scott, Pop. 3,699
Oneida Special SD 1,300/PK-12
PO Box 4819 37841 423-569-8912
Ann Sexton, dir. Fax 569-2201
www.oneidaschools.org/
Oneida HS 400/9-12
372 N Main St 37841 423-569-8818
Kevin Byrd, prin. Fax 569-1681
Oneida MS 300/6-8
376 N Main St 37841 423-569-2468
Cheryl Butler, prin. Fax 569-5977

Ooltewah, Hamilton, Pop. 676
Hamilton County SD
Supt. — See Chattanooga
East Hamilton MSHS 1,900/6-12
2015 Ooltewah Ringgold Rd 37363 423-893-3535
Brenda Chuy, prin. Fax 893-3536
Hamilton County HS 200/Alt
9050 Career Ln 37363 423-344-1433
Gary Kuehn, prin. Fax 344-1434
Hunter MS 700/6-8
6810 Teal Ln 37363 423-344-1474
Robert Alford, prin. Fax 344-1485
Ooltewah HS 1,300/9-12
6123 Mountain View Rd 37363 423-238-5221
Mark Bean, prin. Fax 238-5871
Ooltewah MS 600/6-8
5100 Ooltewah Ringgold Rd 37363 423-238-5732
Chrissy Easterly, prin. Fax 238-5735

Paris, Henry, Pop. 9,926
Henry County SD 3,200/PK-12
217 Grove Blvd 38242 731-642-9733
Sam Miles, dir. Fax 642-8073
www.henryk12.net/
Grove S 400/9-9
215 Grove Blvd 38242 731-642-4586
Samuel Tharpe, prin. Fax 642-4577
Henry County HS 1,100/10-12
315 S Wilson St 38242 731-642-5232
Lennies McFerren, prin. Fax 642-5240
Other Schools – See Buchanan

Paris Special SD 1,700/K-8
1219 Highway 641 S 38242 731-642-9322
Mike Brown, supt. Fax 642-9327
www.parisssd.org/
Inman MS 500/6-8
400 Harrison St 38242 731-642-8131
Jason Scarbrough, prin. Fax 642-8209

Tennessee Technology Center at Paris Post-Sec.
312 S Wilson St 38242 731-644-7365

Parsons, Decatur, Pop. 2,355
Decatur County SD
Supt. — See Decaturville
Decatur County MS 400/5-8
2740 Highway 641 S 38363 731-847-6510
Chris Villaflor, prin. Fax 847-6572

Pigeon Forge, Sevier, Pop. 5,787
Sevier County SD
Supt. — See Sevierville
Pigeon Forge HS 700/9-12
414 Tiger Dr 37863 865-774-5790
Ben Clabo, prin. Fax 774-5798
Pigeon Forge MS 600/5-8
300 Wears Valley Rd 37863 865-453-2401
Scott Hensley, prin. Fax 453-0799

Pikeville, Bledsoe, Pop. 1,590
Bledsoe County SD 2,000/PK-12
PO Box 369 37367 423-447-2914
Jennifer Terry, dir. Fax 447-7135
bledsoecounty.schoolinsites.com/
Bledsoe County HS 500/9-12
877 Main St 37367 423-447-6851
Linda Pickett, prin. Fax 447-6286
Bledsoe County MS 400/6-8
PO Box 147 37367 423-447-3212
Debbie Thompson, prin. Fax 447-3085
Other Schools – See Dunlap

Pleasant View, Cheatham, Pop. 4,108
Cheatham County SD
Supt. — See Ashland City
Sycamore HS 800/9-12
1021 Old Clarksville Pike 37146 615-746-5013
Jenny Simpkins, prin. Fax 746-3653
Sycamore MS 800/5-8
1025 Old Clarksville Pike 37146 615-746-8852
Lisa Young, prin. Fax 746-5770

Pleasant View Christian S 300/PK-12
160 Hicks Edgen Rd 37146 615-746-8555
Dr. Seldon Buck, admin. Fax 746-2646

Portland, Sumner, Pop. 11,308
Sumner County SD
Supt. — See Gallatin
Portland East MS 400/6-8
604 S Broadway St 37148 615-325-4146
Jackson Howell, prin. Fax 325-5320
Portland HS 1,100/9-12
600 College St 37148 615-325-9201
David Woods, prin. Fax 325-5302
Portland West MS 500/6-8
110 Nolan Private Dr 37148 615-325-8066
Cam MacLean, prin. Fax 325-4073

Highland Academy 100/9-12
211 Highland Circle Dr 37148 615-325-2036
Jere Clayburn, prin. Fax 325-4824

Powell, Knox, Pop. 7,534
Knox County SD
Supt. — See Knoxville
Powell HS 1,400/9-12
2136 W Emory Rd 37849 865-938-2171
Ken Dunlap, prin. Fax 947-2805
Powell MS 900/6-8
3329 W Emory Rd 37849 865-938-9008
Gary Critselous, prin. Fax 947-4357

First Baptist Academy 200/K-12
7706 Ewing Rd 37849 865-947-8503
Darrell Vandergriff, admin. Fax 961-6525

Temple Baptist Academy 300/K-12
PO Box 159 37849 865-938-8180
David Whitaker, prin. Fax 938-8147

Pulaski, Giles, Pop. 7,654
Giles County SD 4,200/PK-12
270 Richland Dr 38478 931-363-4558
Debbie Braden, dir. Fax 363-8975
www.giles-lea.giles.k12.tn.us
Bridgeforth MS 400/6-8
1051 Bridgeforth Cir 38478 931-363-7526
J.B. Smith, prin. Fax 424-7021
Giles County HS 900/9-12
200 Sheila Frost Dr 38478 931-363-6532
Mark Cardin, prin. Fax 424-7010
Other Schools – See Lynnville

Martin Methodist College Post-Sec.
433 W Madison St 38478 931-363-9804
Tennessee Technology Center at Pulaski Post-Sec.
PO Box 614 38478 931-424-4014

Reagan, Henderson
Henderson County SD
Supt. — See Lexington
Scotts Hill HS 500/9-12
7871 Highway 100 38368 731-602-6112
Brian Norton, prin. Fax 602-6118

Red Boiling Springs, Macon, Pop. 1,106
Macon County SD
Supt. — See Lafayette
Red Boiling Springs JSHS 300/6-12
415 Hillcrest Dr 37150 615-699-3125
Don Jones, prin. Fax 699-3371

Ripley, Lauderdale, Pop. 8,322
Lauderdale County SD 4,700/PK-12
PO Box 350 38063 731-635-2941
Joey Hassell, supt. Fax 635-7985
www.lced.net
Lauderdale MS 800/6-8
309 Charles Griggs St 38063 731-635-1391
Latonya Jackson, prin. Fax 635-0028
Optional HS Alt
192 Viar Ave 38063 731-635-4856
Shirley Robinson, prin. Fax 635-4821
Ripley HS 900/9-12
254 S Jefferson St 38063 731-635-2642
Joe Bridges, prin. Fax 635-7151
Other Schools – See Halls

Tennessee Technology Center at Ripley Post-Sec.
127 Industrial Dr 38063 731-635-3368

Roan Mountain, Carter, Pop. 1,355
Carter County SD
Supt. — See Elizabethton
Cloudland JSHS 300/7-12
476 Cloudland Dr 37687 423-772-5300
Randy Birchfield, prin. Fax 772-5309

Rockvale, Rutherford
Rutherford County SD
Supt. — See Murfreesboro
Rockvale MS 800/6-8
6543 Highway 99 37153 615-904-6745
Fred Barlow, prin. Fax 904-6746

Rockwood, Roane, Pop. 5,395
Roane County SD
Supt. — See Kingston
Rockwood HS 400/9-12
512 W Rockwood St 37854 865-354-0882
Alan Reed, prin. Fax 354-5170
Rockwood MS 400/6-8
434 W Rockwood St 37854 865-354-0931
Amanda Evans, prin. Fax 354-5160

Rogersville, Hawkins, Pop. 4,364
Hawkins County SD 7,600/PK-12
200 N Depot St 37857 423-272-7629
Charlotte Britton, dir. Fax 272-2207
www.hck12.net
Cherokee HS 1,200/9-12
2927 Highway 66 S 37857 423-272-6507
Gloria Silvers, prin. Fax 272-3556
Rogersville MS 500/6-8
958 E Mckinney Ave 37857 423-272-7603
Jim Ailshie, prin. Fax 272-0185
Other Schools – See Church Hill, Sneedville, Surgoinsville

Rossville, Fayette, Pop. 656

Rossville Christian Academy 300/K-12
PO Box 369 38066 901-853-0200
Mike Coggins, head sch

Rutledge, Grainger, Pop. 1,113
Grainger County SD 3,600/PK-12
PO Box 38 37861 865-828-3611
Edwin Jarnagin, dir. Fax 828-4357
www.grainger.k12.tn.us/
Grainger Academy 50/Alt
232 Pioneer Dr 37861 865-828-6330
Kip Combs, prin.
Grainger HS 900/9-12
2201 Highway 11W S 37861 865-828-5291
Mark Briscoe, prin. Fax 828-4828
Rutledge MS 500/7-8
140 Pioneer Dr 37861 865-828-3366
Roger Blanken, prin. Fax 828-3364
Grainger County Adult S Adult
PO Box 38 37861 865-828-3611
Dr. James Atkins, prin. Fax 828-4357
Other Schools – See Washburn

New System S 400/K-12
250 Tampico Church Rd 37861 865-828-4488
Brenda Young, prin.

Sale Creek, Hamilton, Pop. 2,811
Hamilton County SD
Supt. — See Chattanooga
Sale Creek MSHS 500/6-12
211 Patterson Rd 37373 423-332-8819
Charles Davidson, prin. Fax 332-8847

Santa Fe, Maury
Maury County SD
Supt. — See Columbia
Santa Fe S 700/PK-12
2629 Santa Fe Pike 38482 931-682-2172
Cathy Cook, prin. Fax 682-2606

Savannah, Hardin, Pop. 6,820
Hardin County SD 3,700/PK-12
155 Guinn St 38372 731-925-3943
John Thomas, dir. Fax 925-7313
www.hardincountyschools.net
Hardin County HS 1,100/9-12
1170 Pickwick St 38372 731-925-3976
William McAdams, prin. Fax 925-7407
Hardin County MS 800/6-8
299 Lacefield Dr 38372 731-925-9037
Steve Haffly, prin. Fax 925-0253

Selmer, McNairy, Pop. 4,308
McNairy County SD 4,300/K-12
170 W Court Ave 38375 731-645-3267
Charles Miskelly, supt. Fax 645-8085
www.mcnairy.org
McNairy Central HS 800/9-12
493 High School Rd 38375 731-645-3226
Cecil Stroup, prin. Fax 645-8014
Selmer MS 400/5-8
635 E Poplar Ave 38375 731-645-7977
Dr. Brenda Armstrong, prin. Fax 645-6377
Other Schools – See Adamsville

Styles & Profiles Beauty College Post-Sec.
119 S 2nd St 38375 731-645-9728

Sevierville, Sevier, Pop. 14,595
Sevier County SD 14,500/PK-12
226 Cedar St 37862 865-453-4671
Dr. Jack Parton, supt. Fax 522-1497
www.sevier.org
Alternative Learning Center 50/Alt
2540 Boyds Creek Hwy 37876 865-453-8338
Scott Sutton, prin. Fax 453-7875
Sevier County HS 1,800/9-12
1200 Dolly Parton Pkwy 37862 865-453-5525
Toby Ward, prin. Fax 428-5867
Sevierville MS 600/6-8
520 High St 37862 865-453-0311
Donna Rolen, prin. Fax 428-2316
Whites Adult HS Adult
226 Cedar St 37862 865-429-1492
Curtis Clabo, prin. Fax 774-4564
Other Schools – See Gatlinburg, Kodak, Pigeon Forge, Seymour

Smokey Mountain Trucking Institute Post-Sec.
3173 Newport Hwy 37876 800-495-4056

Sewanee, Franklin, Pop. 2,295

St. Andrew's-Sewanee S 200/6-12
290 Quintard Rd 37375 931-598-5651
Rev. John Thomas, hdmstr. Fax 598-0039
Sewanee The University of the South Post-Sec.
735 University Ave 37383 931-598-1000

Seymour, Sevier, Pop. 10,811
Sevier County SD
Supt. — See Sevierville
Seymour HS 1,300/9-12
732 Boyds Creek Hwy 37865 865-577-7040
Kristy Wallen, prin. Fax 579-1492
Seymour MS 700/6-8
737 Boyds Creek Hwy 37865 865-579-0730
Faye Nelson, prin. Fax 579-0905

King's Academy 500/PK-12
202 Smothers Rd 37865 865-573-8321
Walter Grubb, hdmstr. Fax 573-8323

Shelbyville, Bedford, Pop. 19,855
Bedford County SD 7,900/PK-12
500 Madison St 37160 931-684-3284
Dr. Ray Butrum, supt. Fax 684-1133
www.bedfordk12tn.com/
Harris MS 800/6-8
570 Eagle Blvd 37160 931-684-5195
James Sullivan, prin. Fax 685-9455
Shelbyville Central HS 1,200/9-12
401 Eagle Blvd 37160 931-684-5672
Don Embry, prin. Fax 684-9359
Other Schools – See Unionville, Wartrace

Tennessee Technology Center Shelbyville Post-Sec.
1405 Madison St 37160 931-685-5013

Signal Mountain, Hamilton, Pop. 7,474
Hamilton County SD
Supt. — See Chattanooga
Signal Mountain MSHS 1,200/6-12
2650 Sam Powell Trl 37377 423-886-0880
Thomas McCullough, prin. Fax 886-0881

Smithville, DeKalb, Pop. 4,481
DeKalb County SD 3,000/PK-12
110 S Public Sq 37166 615-597-4084
Mark Willoughby, supt. Fax 597-6326
web.dekalb.k12tn.net/
DeKalb County HS 800/9-12
1130 W Broad St 37166 615-597-4094
Patrick Cripps, prin. Fax 597-8104
DeKalb MS 500/6-8
1132 W Broad St 37166 615-597-7987
Randy Jennings, prin. Fax 597-2640

Smyrna, Rutherford, Pop. 39,070
Rutherford County SD
Supt. — See Murfreesboro
Rock Springs MS 900/6-8
3301 Rock Springs Rd 37167 615-904-3825
Chris Treadway, prin. Fax 904-3826
Smyrna HS 2,000/9-12
100 Bulldog Dr 37167 615-904-3865
Rick Powell, prin. Fax 904-3866
Smyrna MS 900/6-8
712 Hazelwood Dr 37167 615-904-3845
Jeannie Nicholson, prin. Fax 904-3846
Smyrna West Alternative S 100/Alt
12619 Old Nashville Hwy 37167 615-904-3856
Kay Davenport, prin. Fax 904-3857
Stewarts Creek MS 900/6-8
400 Red Hawk Blvd 37167 615-904-6700
Larry Creasy, prin. Fax 904-6701

Lancaster Christian Academy 500/PK-12
150 Soccer Way 37167 615-223-0451
Kevin O'Dea, prin. Fax 223-6946

Sneedville, Hancock, Pop. 1,364
Hancock County SD 1,000/K-12
PO Box 629 37869 423-733-2591
Mike Antrican, dir. Fax 733-8757
www.hancockcountyschools.com/
Hancock County MSHS 600/6-12
2700 Main St 37869 423-733-4611
Dr. Michael Belcher, prin. Fax 733-1427

Hawkins County SD
Supt. — See Rogersville
Clinch S 100/K-12
1540 Clinch Valley Rd 37869 423-272-3202
George Barton, prin. Fax 272-3206

Soddy Daisy, Hamilton, Pop. 12,577
Hamilton County SD
Supt. — See Chattanooga
Sequoya HS Vo/Tech
9517 W Ridge Trail Rd 37379 423-843-4707
Todd Jackson, prin. Fax 843-4719
Soddy Daisy HS 1,500/9-12
618 Sequoyah Access Rd 37379 423-332-8828
John Maynard, prin. Fax 332-8831
Soddy Daisy MS 600/6-8
200 Turner Rd 37379 423-332-8800
Blake Freeman, prin. Fax 332-8810

Somerville, Fayette, Pop. 3,069
Fayette County SD 3,800/PK-12
PO Box 9 38068 901-465-5260
James Teague, supt. Fax 466-3725
East JHS 400/6-8
400 Leach Dr 38068 901-465-3151
Diane Hicks, prin. Fax 465-5084
Fayette-Ware HS 900/9-12
PO Box 849 38068 901-465-9838
Dr. Walter Owens, prin. Fax 465-1377
Other Schools – See Oakland

Fayette Academy 700/PK-12
PO Box 130 38068 901-465-3241
Ron Canada, hdmstr. Fax 465-2141

South Fulton, Obion, Pop. 2,320
Obion County SD
Supt. — See Union City
South Fulton MSHS 500/6-12
1302 John C Jones Pkwy 38257 731-479-1441
Keith Frazier, prin. Fax 479-0586

South Pittsburg, Marion, Pop. 2,934
Marion County SD
Supt. — See Jasper
South Pittsburg JSHS 400/7-12
717 Elm Ave 37380 423-837-7561
Vic Grider, prin. Fax 837-4532

Richard CSD 300/PK-12
1620 Hamilton Ave 37380 423-837-7282
Cindy Blevins, dir. Fax 837-0641
www.richardhardy.org
Hardy Memorial S 300/PK-12
1620 Hamilton Ave 37380 423-837-7282
Beth Webb, prin. Fax 837-0641

Sparta, White, Pop. 4,841
White County SD 4,100/PK-12
136 Baker St 38583 931-836-2229
Sandra Crouch, dir. Fax 836-8128
www.whitecountyschools.org
White County HS 1,200/9-12
267 Allen Dr 38583 931-836-3214
Grant Swallows, prin. Fax 836-6295
White County MS 1,000/6-8
300 Turn Table Rd 38583 931-738-9238
Craig Lynn, prin. Fax 738-9271

Spencer, Van Buren, Pop. 1,580
Van Buren County SD 800/PK-12
PO Box 98 38585 931-946-2242
Michael Martin, dir. Fax 946-2858
www.vanburenschools.org
Van Buren County JSHS 400/6-12
337 Sparta St 38585 931-946-2442
Chris Binkley, prin. Fax 946-2265

Spring City, Rhea, Pop. 1,936
Rhea County SD
Supt. — See Dayton
Spring City MS 300/6-8
751 Wassom Memorial Hwy 37381 423-365-9105
Buddy Jackson, prin. Fax 365-9102

Springfield, Robertson, Pop. 16,188
Robertson County SD 11,000/PK-12
PO Box 130 37172 615-384-5588
Daniel Whitlow, dir. Fax 384-9749
www.rcstn.net/
Coopertown MS 600/4-8
3820 Highway 49 W 37172 615-382-4166
Lewis Walling, prin. Fax 382-4171
Robertson County Alternative Program Alt
104 7th Ave W 37172 615-382-2328
Nancy Williams, prin. Fax 382-2328
Springfield HS 1,100/9-12
5240 Highway 76 E 37172 615-384-3516
Dr. Justin Grimes, prin. Fax 384-5484
Springfield MS 600/6-8
715 5th Ave W 37172 615-384-4821
Grant Bell, prin. Fax 382-7890
Other Schools – See Cedar Hill, Cross Plains, Greenbrier, White House

South Haven Christian S 400/PK-12
112 Academy Dr 37172 615-384-5073
Dr. Steve Blaser, prin. Fax 425-2403

Spring Hill, Maury, Pop. 28,520
Maury County SD
Supt. — See Columbia
Spring Hill MS 700/5-8
3501 Cleburne Rd 37174 931-451-1531
Phillip Wright, prin. Fax 486-3954

Williamson County SD
Supt. — See Franklin
Spring Station MS 700/6-8
1000 Spring Station Dr 37174 615-472-5080
Paula Pulliam, prin. Fax 472-5091
Summit HS 9-12
2830 Twin Lakes Dr 37174 615-472-5100
Dr. Charles Farmer, prin. Fax 472-5121

Strawberry Plains, Jefferson
Knox County SD
Supt. — See Knoxville
Carter HS 900/9-12
210 N Carter School Rd 37871 865-933-3434
Cheryl Hickman, prin. Fax 932-8180
Carter MS 800/6-8
204 N Carter School Rd 37871 865-933-3426
Michael Derrick, prin. Fax 932-8170

Blue Springs Christian Academy 50/K-10
3265 Blue Springs Rd 37871 865-932-7603
June Ingram, prin.

Summertown, Lawrence, Pop. 852
Lawrence County SD
Supt. — See Lawrenceburg
Summertown JSHS 600/7-12
411 W College St 38483 931-964-3539
Brent Long, prin. Fax 964-3302

Sunbright, Morgan, Pop. 550
Morgan County SD
Supt. — See Wartburg
Sunbright S 600/K-12
PO Box 129 37872 423-628-2244
Bill Hunter, prin. Fax 628-2120

Surgoinsville, Hawkins, Pop. 1,786
Hawkins County SD
Supt. — See Rogersville
Surgoinsville MS 300/5-8
1044 Main St 37873 423-345-2252
Shane Bailey, prin. Fax 345-3598

Sweetwater, Monroe, Pop. 5,664
Monroe County SD
Supt. — See Madisonville
Sweetwater HS 600/9-12
414 S High St 37874 423-337-7881
David Watts, prin. Fax 337-0685

Sweetwater CSD 1,600/PK-8
PO Box 231 37874 423-337-7051
Dr. Melanie Miller, supt. Fax 337-6773
www.compurdy.com/scs2/
Sweetwater JHS 300/7-8
1013 Cannon Ave 37874 423-337-7336
Rodney Boruff, prin. Fax 337-7360

Cross Creek Christian S 100/PK-12
501 E North St 37874 423-337-9330
Timothy Womac, prin. Fax 337-9335

Tazewell, Claiborne, Pop. 2,172
Claiborne County SD 4,900/PK-12
PO Box 179 37879 423-626-3543
Connie Holdway, supt. Fax 626-5945
www.claibornecountyschools.com
Soldiers Memorial MS 500/5-8
1510 Legion St 37879 423-626-3531
Jim Shipley, prin. Fax 626-2151
Claiborne Adult HS Adult
PO Box 600 37879 423-626-8222
Sandra Williams, prin. Fax 626-5945
Other Schools – See Cumberland Gap, Harrogate, New Tazewell

Tellico Plains, Monroe, Pop. 866
Monroe County SD
Supt. — See Madisonville
Tellico Plains HS 500/9-12
9180 Highway 68 37385 423-253-2530
Russell Harris, prin. Fax 253-2541
Tellico Plains JHS 300/5-8
120 Old High School Rd 37385 423-253-2250
Missy Carter, prin. Fax 253-7824

Ten Mile, Roane
Roane County SD
Supt. — See Kingston
Midway MS 300/6-8
104 Dogtown Rd 37880 865-717-5464
Nadine Jackson, prin. Fax 376-0948

Thompsons Station, Williamson, Pop. 2,172
Williamson County SD
Supt. — See Franklin
Heritage MS 700/6-8
4803 Columbia Pike 37179 615-472-4540
Marlena Gross-Taylor, prin. Fax 472-4553
Independence HS 1,900/9-12
1776 Declaration Way 37179 615-472-4600
Dr. Todd Campbell, prin. Fax 472-4621

Tiptonville, Lake, Pop. 4,409
Lake County SD 1,000/PK-12
PO Box 397 38079 731-253-6601
Corwin Robinson, dir. Fax 253-7111
Lake County HS 200/9-12
300 Cochran St 38079 731-253-7733
Suzanne Keefe, prin. Fax 253-7766

Trenton, Gibson, Pop. 4,197
Trenton Special SD 1,400/PK-12
201 W 10th St 38382 731-855-1191
Sandra Harper, supt. Fax 855-1414
www.trentonssd.org
Peabody HS 400/9-12
2069 US Highway 45 Byp N 38382 731-855-2601
Tim Haney, prin. Fax 855-1217
Trenton Rosenwald MS 400/5-8
2065 US Highway 45 Byp S 38382 731-855-2422
John Prince, prin. Fax 855-1826

Troy, Obion, Pop. 1,363
Obion County SD
Supt. — See Union City
Career Technology Center Vo/Tech
528 N US Highway 51 38260 731-536-4688
Russ Davis, prin. Fax 536-0469
Obion County Central HS 900/9-12
528 N US Highway 51 38260 731-536-4688
Linda Crigger, prin. Fax 536-0469

Tullahoma, Coffee, Pop. 18,247
Tullahoma CSD 3,300/PK-12
510 S Jackson St 37388 931-454-2600
Dr. Dan Lawson, dir. Fax 454-2642
www.tullahomacityschools.net/
East MS 400/6-8
908 Country Club Dr 37388 931-454-2632
Debbie Edens, prin. Fax 454-2660
Tullahoma HS 1,100/9-12
1001 N Jackson St 37388 931-454-2620
Mike Landis, prin. Fax 454-2662
West MS 400/6-8
90 Hermitage Dr 37388 931-454-2605
Dr. Mickey Shuran, prin. Fax 454-2661

Union City, Obion, Pop. 10,735
Obion County SD 4,100/PK-12
316 S 3rd St 38261 731-885-9743
Dr. David W. Huss, dir. Fax 885-4902
www.obioncountyschools.com
Other Schools – See South Fulton, Troy

Union CSD 1,500/PK-12
PO Box 749 38281 731-885-3922
Gary Houston, dir. Fax 885-6033
www.tornadotouch.net
Union City HS 300/9-12
1305 High School Dr 38261 731-885-2373
Wesley Kennedy, prin. Fax 885-5011
Union City MS 300/6-8
1111 High School Dr 38261 731-885-2901
Michael Miller, prin. Fax 885-3677

Unionville, Bedford, Pop. 1,363
Bedford County SD
Supt. — See Shelbyville
Community HS 500/9-12
100 Community Xing 37180 931-685-1418
Robert Ralston, prin. Fax 294-2107
Community MS 400/6-8
3470 Highway 41A N 37180 931-685-1426
Michael Wright, prin. Fax 294-5126

Vonore, Monroe, Pop. 1,458
Monroe County SD
Supt. — See Madisonville
Vonore MS 300/5-8
414 Hall St 37885 423-884-2730
Debra Tipton, prin. Fax 884-2731

Wartburg, Morgan, Pop. 898
Morgan County SD 3,200/K-12
136 Flat Fork Rd 37887 423-346-6214
Dr. Edward Diden, supt. Fax 346-6043
mcsed.net/
Central HS 400/9-12
1119 Knoxville Hwy 37887 423-346-6616
Dallas Davis, prin. Fax 346-5665
Central MS 300/6-8
146 Liberty Rd 37887 423-346-2800
Dr. Myrna Sumner, prin. Fax 346-2805
Morgan County Career & Technical Center Vo/Tech
132 Flat Fork Rd 37887 423-346-6285
Dr. Joseph Miller, prin. Fax 346-5857
Other Schools – See Coalfield, Oakdale, Sunbright

Wartrace, Bedford, Pop. 637
Bedford County SD
Supt. — See Shelbyville
Cascade HS 500/9-12
1165 Bell Buckle Wartrace 37183 931-389-9389
Sharon Edwards, prin. Fax 389-6223
Cascade MS 400/6-8
1165 Bell Buckle Wartrace 37183 931-389-9389
David Parker, prin. Fax 389-6223

Washburn, Grainger
Grainger County SD
Supt. — See Rutledge
Washburn S 600/PK-12
7925 Highway 131 37888 865-497-2557
Ginny McElhaney, prin. Fax 497-2934

Watertown, Wilson, Pop. 1,450
Wilson County SD
Supt. — See Lebanon
Watertown HS 400/7-12
515 W Main St 37184 615-237-3434
Jeff Luttrell, prin. Fax 237-3030

Waverly, Humphreys, Pop. 4,056
Humphreys County SD 3,100/PK-12
2443 Highway 70 E 37185 931-296-2568
James Long, supt. Fax 296-6501
www.hcss.org
Humphreys County Vocational Center Vo/Tech
1327 Highway 70 W 37185 931-296-7867
Lori Dell, dir. Fax 296-7252
Waverly Central HS 600/9-12
1325 Highway 70 W 37185 931-296-3911
Robert Martin, prin. Fax 296-2575
Waverly JHS 600/4-8
520 E Main St 37185 931-296-4514
Andy Daniels, prin. Fax 296-6507
Other Schools – See Mc Ewen

Waynesboro, Wayne, Pop. 2,423
Wayne County SD 2,600/PK-12
PO Box 658 38485 931-722-3548
Gailand Grinder, supt. Fax 722-7579
www.waynetn.net/
Wayne County HS 300/9-12
707 S Main St 38485 931-722-3238
David Byrd, prin. Fax 722-7641
Wayne County Technology Center Vo/Tech
703 S Main St 38485 931-722-5495
Beverly Hall, prin. Fax 722-5496
Waynesboro MS 300/5-8
PO Box 657 38485 931-722-5545
Talitha Willard, prin. Fax 722-3953
Other Schools – See Clifton, Collinwood

Westmoreland, Sumner, Pop. 2,182
Sumner County SD
Supt. — See Gallatin
Westmoreland HS 500/9-12
4300 Hawkins Dr 37186 615-644-2280
Rick Duffer, prin. Fax 644-3395
Westmoreland MS 400/6-8
4128 Hawkins Dr 37186 615-644-3003
Danny Robinson, prin. Fax 644-5584

White Bluff, Dickson, Pop. 3,171
Dickson County SD
Supt. — See Dickson
James MS 300/6-8
3030 Trace Creek Rd 37187 615-740-5770
Jan Ford, prin. Fax 797-6401

White House, Sumner, Pop. 10,123
Robertson County SD
Supt. — See Springfield
White House-Heritage HS 800/7-12
7744 Highway 76 E 37188 615-672-0311
Mary Jo Holmes, prin. Fax 672-7178

Sumner County SD
Supt. — See Gallatin
White House HS 900/9-12
508 Tyree Springs Rd 37188 615-672-3761
Jeff Cordell, prin. Fax 672-6404
White House MS 700/6-8
2020 Highway 31 W 37188 615-672-4379
Jerry Apple, prin. Fax 672-6409

Whitesburg, Hamblen
Hamblen County SD
Supt. — See Morristown
East Ridge MS 600/6-8
6595 Saint Clair Rd 37891 423-581-3041
James Templin, prin. Fax 585-3765

Whites Creek, See Nashville
Metropolitan Nashville SD
Supt. — See Nashville
Whites Creek Comprehensive HS 1,000/9-12
7277 Old Hickory Blvd 37189 615-876-5132
Dr. James Bailey, prin. Fax 321-8720

Whiteville, Hardeman, Pop. 4,622

Tennessee Technology Center Whiteville Post-Sec.
1685 US Highway 64 38075 731-254-8521

Whitwell, Marion, Pop. 1,684
Marion County SD
Supt. — See Jasper
Whitwell HS 400/9-12
200 Tiger Trl 37397 423-658-5141
Josh Holtcamp, prin. Fax 658-0313
Whitwell MS 400/5-8
1 Butterfly Ln 37397 423-658-5635
Kim Headrick, prin. Fax 658-6949

Winchester, Franklin, Pop. 8,370
Franklin County SD 6,100/PK-12
215 S College St 37398 931-967-0626
Dr. Rebecca Sharber, supt. Fax 967-7832
www.fcstn.net
Franklin County HS 1,400/9-12
833 Bypass Rd 37398 931-967-2821
Greg Mantooth, prin. Fax 967-6945
North MS 700/6-8
2990 Decherd Blvd 37398 931-967-5323
Stanley Bean, prin. Fax 967-1413
Other Schools – See Cowan, Huntland

Woodbury, Cannon, Pop. 2,647
Cannon County SD 2,200/PK-12
301 W Main St Ste 100 37190 615-563-5752
Barbara Parker, supt. Fax 563-2716
www.ccstn.com/
Cannon County HS 700/9-12
1 Lion Dr 37190 615-563-2144
Tim Knox, prin. Fax 563-8068

TEXAS

TEXAS EDUCATION AGENCY
1701 Congress Ave, Austin 78701-1494
Telephone 512-463-9734
Fax 512-463-9838
Website http://www.tea.state.tx.us

Commissioner of Education Michael Williams

TEXAS BOARD OF EDUCATION
1701 Congress Ave, Austin 78701-1402

Chairperson Barbara Cargill

REGIONAL EDUCATION SERVICE CENTERS (RESC)

Region 1 ESC
Jack Damron, dir. 956-984-6000
1900 W Schunior St, Edinburg Fax 984-6009
www.esc1.net/

Region 2 ESC
Dr. Linda Villarreal, dir. 361-561-8400
209 N Water St Fax 883-3442
Corpus Christi 78401
www.esc2.net

Region 3 ESC
Dr. Julius Cano, dir. 361-573-0731
1905 Leary Ln, Victoria 77901 Fax 576-4804
www.esc3.net/

Region 4 ESC
Rudy Okruhlik, dir. 713-462-7708
7145 W Tidwell Rd, Houston 77092 Fax 744-6514
www.esc4.net/

Region 5 ESC
Dr. Danny Lovett, dir. 409-951-1700
350 Pine St Ste 500
Beaumont 77701
www.esc5.net

Region 6 ESC
Thomas Poe, dir. 936-435-8400
3332 Montgomery Rd Fax 295-1447
Huntsville 77340
www.esc6.net/

Region 7 ESC
Elizabeth Abernethy, dir. 903-988-6700
1909 N Longview St, Kilgore 75662 Fax 988-6708
www.esc7.net/

Region 8 ESC
Dr. Ray Glynn, dir., PO Box 1894 903-572-8551
Mount Pleasant 75456 Fax 575-2611
www.reg8.net/

Region 9 ESC
Anne Poplin, dir. 940-322-6928
301 Loop 11, Wichita Falls 76306 Fax 767-3836
www.esc9.net

Region 10 ESC
Terry Smith, dir. 972-348-1700
400 E Spring Valley Rd Fax 231-3642
Richardson 75081
www.region10.org/

Region 11 ESC
Dr. Clyde Steelman, dir. 817-740-3600
3001 North Fwy, Fort Worth 76106 Fax 740-7600
www.esc11.net

Region 12 ESC
Dr. Jerry Maze, dir. 254-297-1212
PO Box 23409, Waco 76702 Fax 666-0625
www.esc12.net

Region 13 ESC
Terry Smith, dir. 512-919-5313
5701 Springdale Rd, Austin 78723 Fax 919-5374
www5.esc13.net/

Region 14 ESC
Ronnie Kincaid, dir. 325-675-8600
1850 State Highway 351 Fax 675-8659
Abilene 79601
www.esc14.net/

Region 15 ESC
Scot Goen, dir. 325-658-6571
PO Box 5199, San Angelo 76902 Fax 658-6571
www.netxv.net/

Region 16 ESC
John Bass, dir. 806-677-5000
5800 Bell St, Amarillo 79109 Fax 677-5001
www.esc16.net/

Region 17 ESC
Dr. Kyle Wargo, dir. 806-792-4000
1111 W Loop 289, Lubbock 79416 Fax 792-1523
www.esc17.net/

Region 18 ESC
John Thomas, dir. 432-563-2380
PO Box 60580, Midland 79711 Fax 567-3290
www.esc18.net

Region 19 ESC
Dr. James Vasquez, dir. 915-780-1919
PO Box 971127, El Paso 79997 Fax 780-6537
www.esc19.net/

Region 20 ESC
Dr. Ronald Beard, dir. 210-370-5200
1314 Hines, San Antonio 78208 Fax 370-5750
www.esc20.net

PUBLIC, PRIVATE AND CATHOLIC SECONDARY SCHOOLS

Abbott, Hill, Pop. 355

Abbott ISD 300/PK-12
PO Box 226 76621 254-582-3011
Richard Edison, supt. Fax 582-5430
www.abbottisd.org

Abbott S 300/PK-12
PO Box 226 76621 254-582-3011
Travis Walker, prin. Fax 582-5430

Abernathy, Hale, Pop. 2,787

Abernathy ISD 800/PK-12
505 7th St 79311 806-298-2563
Herb Youngblood, supt. Fax 298-2400
www.abernathyisd.com

Abernathy HS 200/9-12
505 7th St 79311 806-298-2563
Gary Pugh, prin. Fax 298-4653

Abernathy JHS 200/6-8
505 7th St 79311 806-298-2563
Bill Black, prin. Fax 298-4775

Abilene, Taylor, Pop. 114,633

Abilene ISD 16,200/PK-12
PO Box 981 79604 325-677-1444
Dr. Heath Burns, supt. Fax 794-1325
www.abileneisd.org/

Abilene HS 2,000/9-12
2800 N 6th St 79603 325-677-1731
Jennifer Raney, prin. Fax 794-1387

Academy for Tech/Eng/Math/Science 200/9-12
650 US Highway 80 E 79601 325-794-4140
John Martinez, dir. Fax 794-1341

Clack MS 700/6-8
1610 Corsicana Ave 79605 325-692-1961
Rodney Brown, prin. Fax 794-1371

Cooper HS 1,900/9-12
3639 Sayles Blvd 79605 325-691-1000
Karen Munoz, prin. Fax 794-1375

Craig MS 900/6-8
702 S Judge Ely Blvd 79602 325-794-4100
Daniel Dukes, prin. Fax 794-1385

Holland Medical HS 9-12
2442 Cedar St 79601 325-794-4120
Gail Gregg, prin. Fax 794-1377

Jefferson Center 50/Alt
1741 S 14th St 79602 325-794-4150
Jane Allred-May, admin.

Madison MS 900/6-8
3145 Barrow St 79605 325-692-5661
George McFarland, prin. Fax 794-1313

Mann MS 800/6-8
2545 Mimosa Dr 79603 325-672-8493
Kim Farmer, prin. Fax 794-1374

Woodson Center for Excellence 200/Alt
342 Cockerell Dr 79601 325-671-4736
Kathryn Walker, prin. Fax 794-1377

Adult Learning Center Adult
1929 S 11th St 79602 325-671-4419
Mignon Lawson, dir. Fax 794-1327

Wylie ISD 3,100/PK-12
6249 Buffalo Gap Rd 79606 325-692-4353
Joey Light, supt. Fax 695-3438
www.wylie.esc14.net

Wylie HS 900/9-12
4502 Antilley Rd 79606 325-690-1181
Mitch Davis, prin. Fax 690-0320

Wylie JHS 800/6-8
4010 Beltway S 79606 325-695-1910
Tommy Vaughn, prin. Fax 692-5786

Abilene Christian S 300/PK-12
2550 N Judge Ely Blvd 79601 325-672-9200
Dr. John Tyson, pres. Fax 672-1262

Abilene Christian University Post-Sec.
ACU Box 29000 79699 325-674-2000

American Commercial College Post-Sec.
402 Butternut St 79602 325-672-8495

Hardin-Simmons University Post-Sec.
2200 Hickory St 79698 325-670-1000

Hendrick Medical Center Post-Sec.
1900 Pine St 79601 325-670-2201

McMurry University Post-Sec.
1 McMurry Sta 79697 325-793-3800

Texas College of Cosmetology Post-Sec.
117 Sayles Blvd 79605 325-677-0532

Ackerly, Dawson, Pop. 220

Sands Consolidated ISD 200/PK-12
PO Box 218 79713 432-353-4888
Wayne Blount, supt. Fax 353-4650
sands.esc17.net

Sands S 200/PK-12
PO Box 218 79713 432-353-4888
Zelda Bilbo, prin. Fax 353-4650

Addison, Dallas, Pop. 12,782

Greenhill S 1,300/PK-12
4141 Spring Valley Rd 75001 972-628-5400
Scott Griggs, head sch Fax 404-8217

Trinity Christian Academy 1,500/K-12
17001 Addison Rd 75001 972-931-8325
David Delph, hdmstr. Fax 931-8923

Adrian, Oldham, Pop. 165

Adrian ISD 100/K-12
PO Box 189 79001 806-538-6203
Mike Norrell, supt. Fax 538-6291
www.adrianisd.net

Adrian S 100/K-12
PO Box 189 79001 806-538-6203
Mike Winter, prin. Fax 538-6291

Afton, Dickens

Patton Springs ISD 100/PK-12
PO Box 32 79220 806-689-2220
Larry McClenny, supt. Fax 689-2253
pattonsprings.net

Patton Springs S 100/PK-12
PO Box 32 79220 806-689-2220
Bryan White, prin. Fax 689-2253

Agua Dulce, Nueces, Pop. 795

Agua Dulce ISD 300/PK-12
PO Box 250 78330 361-998-2542
Dr. Russ Perry, supt. Fax 998-2816
www.adisd.esc2.net

Agua Dulce JSHS 200/6-12
PO Box 250 78330 361-998-2214
Guadalupe Martinez, prin. Fax 998-2994

Alamo, Hidalgo, Pop. 18,315

Pharr-San Juan-Alamo ISD
Supt. — See Pharr

Alamo MS 1,000/6-8
1819 W US Highway 83 78516 956-354-2550
Juan Garza, prin. Fax 702-5893

Murphy MS 200/6-8
924 Sioux Rd 78516 956-354-2530
Lizette Longoria, prin. Fax 783-4846

Phar-San Juan-Alamo Memorial HS 2,200/9-12
800 S Alamo Rd 78516 956-354-2420
Judith Solis, prin. Fax 783-3636

Valley Christian Heritage S 100/PK-12
932 N Alamo Rd 78516 956-787-9743
Fax 787-1977

Alba, Wood, Pop. 497
Alba-Golden ISD 900/PK-12
1373 County Road 2377 75410 903-768-2472
Dwayne Ellis, supt. Fax 768-2130
www.agisd.com
Alba-Golden JSHS 500/6-12
1373 County Road 2377 75410 903-768-2472
Michael Mize, prin. Fax 768-2303

Albany, Shackelford, Pop. 1,992
Albany ISD 500/PK-12
PO Box 2050 76430 325-762-2823
Shane Fields, supt. Fax 762-3876
www.albany.esc14.net
Albany JSHS 200/7-12
PO Box 2050 76430 325-762-3974
Kevin Hill, prin. Fax 762-3850

Aledo, Parker, Pop. 2,690
Aledo ISD 4,700/PK-12
1008 Bailey Ranch Rd 76008 817-441-8327
Dr. Derek Citty, supt. Fax 441-5144
www.aledo.k12.tx.us
Aledo 9th Grade Campus 400/9-9
990 Bailey Ranch Rd 76008 817-441-4504
Angela Tims, prin. Fax 441-2146
Aledo HS 1,100/10-12
1000 Bailey Ranch Rd 76008 817-441-8711
Dan Peterson, prin. Fax 441-5136
Aledo Learning Center 50/Alt
1016 Bailey Ranch Rd 76008 817-441-5176
Ron Miller, prin. Fax 441-9488
Aledo MS 800/7-8
416 S FM 1187 76008 817-441-5198
Cheryl Jones, prin. Fax 441-5133

Aledo Christian S 100/PK-12
PO Box 117 76008 817-441-7357
Kay Ross, prin. Fax 441-2713

Alice, Jim Wells, Pop. 19,053
Alice ISD 5,100/PK-12
2 Coyote Trl 78332 361-664-0981
Dr. Grace Everett, supt. Fax 660-2113
www.aliceisd.net
Adams MS 800/7-8
901 E 3rd St 78332 361-660-2055
Dr. Ruben Pena, prin. Fax 660-2094
Alice HS 1,500/9-12
1 Coyote Trl 78332 361-664-0126
Debra Garcia, prin. Fax 660-2128

Alice Christian S 50/PK-12
1200 N Stadium Rd 78332 361-668-6636
Robert Garcia, prin. Fax 668-0840

Allen, Collin, Pop. 82,168
Allen ISD 18,600/PK-12
PO Box 13 75013 972-727-0511
Dr. Ken Helvey, supt. Fax 727-0518
www.allenisd.org
Allen SHS 3,800/10-12
300 Rivercrest Blvd 75002 972-727-0400
Steve Payne, prin. Fax 727-0515
Curtis MS 800/7-8
1530 Rivercrest Blvd 75002 972-727-0340
Becky Kennedy, prin. Fax 727-0345
Dillard Center Alt
610 E Bethany Dr 75002 972-727-7163
David Greer, prin. Fax 727-7162
Ereckson MS 1,100/7-8
450 Tatum Dr 75013 972-747-3308
Phyllis Spain, prin. Fax 747-3311
Ford MS 900/7-8
630 Park Place Dr 75002 972-727-0590
Susan Horowitz, prin. Fax 727-0596
Lowery Freshman Center 1,400/9-9
601 E Main St 75002 972-396-6975
Jill Stafford, prin. Fax 396-6981

Lovejoy ISD 3,400/K-12
259 Country Club Rd 75002 469-742-8000
Ted Moore, supt. Fax 742-8001
www.lovejoyisd.net/
Other Schools – See Fairview, Lucas

Alpine, Brewster, Pop. 5,819
Alpine ISD 1,100/PK-12
704 W Sul Ross Ave 79830 432-837-7700
Steve White, supt. Fax 837-7740
www.alpine.esc18.net
Alpine HS 300/9-12
300 E Hendryx Ave 79830 432-837-7710
Verl O'Bryant, prin. Fax 837-9813
Alpine MS 300/5-8
801 Middle School Dr 79830 432-837-7720
Miriam Scown, prin. Fax 837-9814

Sul Ross State University Post-Sec.
E Highway 90 79832 432-837-8032

Altair, Colorado
Rice Consolidated ISD 1,300/PK-12
PO Box 338 77412 979-234-3531
Bill Hefner, supt. Fax 234-3409
www.ricecisd.org
Rice HS 300/9-12
PO Box 338 77412 979-234-3531
Eric Grogan, prin. Fax 234-5901
Rice JHS 200/7-8
PO Box 338 77412 979-234-3531
John Post, prin. Fax 234-3191

Alto, Cherokee, Pop. 1,204
Alto ISD 700/PK-12
244 County Road 2429 75925 936-858-7101
Kerry Birdwell, supt. Fax 858-2101
www.alto.esc7.net/
Alto HS 200/9-12
244 County Road 2429 75925 936-858-7110
Ronald Musgrove, prin. Fax 858-4387
Alto MS 200/5-8
244 County Road 2429 75925 936-858-7140
Kelly West, prin. Fax 858-4579

Alton, Hidalgo, Pop. 12,339
Mission Consolidated ISD
Supt. — See Mission
Alton Memorial JHS 800/6-8
521 S Los Ebanos Blvd, 956-323-5000
Sylvia Garcia, prin. Fax 323-5045

Alvarado, Johnson, Pop. 3,699
Alvarado ISD 3,500/PK-12
PO Box 387 76009 817-783-6800
Dr. Chester Juroska, supt. Fax 783-3844
www.alvaradoisd.net/
Alvarado HS 1,000/9-12
PO Box 387 76009 817-783-6940
Chris Magee, prin. Fax 783-6944
Alvarado JHS 600/7-8
PO Box 387 76009 817-783-6840
Melodye Broods, prin. Fax 783-6844

Alvin, Brazoria, Pop. 23,976
Alvin ISD 17,300/PK-12
301 E House St 77511 281-388-1130
Dr. Fred Brent, supt. Fax 388-2719
www.alvinisd.net/
Alvin HS 2,400/9-12
802 S Johnson St 77511 281-245-3000
Dr. Johnny Briseno, prin. Fax 331-3053
Alvin JHS 800/6-8
2300 W South St 77511 281-245-2770
Trent Thrasher, prin. Fax 331-5926
ASSETS Learning Center 200/Alt
605 W House St 77511 281-331-1690
Tracy Hummel, dir. Fax 331-1667
Fairview JHS 700/6-8
2600 County Road 190 77511 281-245-3100
Kelly Jackson, prin. Fax 245-3213
Harby JHS 700/6-8
1500 Heights Rd 77511 281-585-6626
Lisa Burns, prin. Fax 388-2247
Other Schools – See Manvel, Pearland

Alvin Community College Post-Sec.
3110 Mustang Rd 77511 281-756-3500
Living Stones Christian S 200/PK-12
1407 Victory Ln 77511 281-331-0086
Jessica Sanders, admin. Fax 331-6747

Alvord, Wise, Pop. 1,324
Alvord ISD 700/PK-12
PO Box 70 76225 940-427-5975
William Branum, supt. Fax 427-2313
www.alvordisd.net/
Alvord HS 200/9-12
PO Box 70 76225 940-427-9643
Dr. Rhett King, prin. Fax 427-9648
Alvord MS 200/6-8
PO Box 70 76225 940-427-5511
Janis Branum, prin. Fax 427-2461

Amarillo, Potter, Pop. 187,598
Amarillo ISD 32,400/PK-12
7200 W Interstate 40 79106 806-326-1000
Rod Schroder, supt. Fax 354-4378
www.amaisd.org
Amarillo Area Ctr for Advanced Learning 50/Alt
1100 N Forest St 79106 806-326-2800
Jay Barrett, prin. Fax 371-6100
Amarillo HS 2,100/9-12
4225 Danbury Dr 79109 806-326-2000
Mark Webster, prin. Fax 354-5092
Austin MS 700/6-8
1808 Wimberly Rd 79109 806-326-3000
Alan Nickson, prin. Fax 356-4802
Bonham MS 800/6-8
5600 SW 49th Ave 79109 806-326-3100
David Vincent, prin. Fax 356-4865
Bowie MS 1,000/6-8
3001 E 12th Ave 79104 806-326-3200
John Smith, prin. Fax 371-6016
Caprock HS 1,900/9-12
3001 E 34th Ave 79103 806-326-2200
David Bishop, prin. Fax 371-6042
Crockett MS 800/6-8
4720 Floyd Ave 79106 806-326-3300
Lisa Loan, prin. Fax 356-4873
de Zavala MS 400/5-8
2801 N Coulter St 79124 806-326-3400
Angie Noel, prin. Fax 354-4286
Fannin MS 600/6-8
4627 S Rusk St 79110 806-326-3500
Nathan Culwell, prin. Fax 354-4588
Houston MS 800/6-8
815 S Independence St 79106 806-326-3600
Tammie Villarreal, prin. Fax 371-5577
Mann MS 500/7-8
610 N Buchanan St 79107 806-326-3700
Renee Mott, prin. Fax 371-5617
North Heights Alternative S 200/Alt
607 N Hughes St 79107 806-326-2850
Mark Leach, prin. Fax 371-5715
Palo Duro HS 1,900/9-12
1400 N Grant St 79107 806-326-2400
Sandy Whitlow, prin. Fax 381-7166
Tascosa HS 2,200/9-12
3921 Westlawn St 79102 806-326-2600
Dr. Lynn Pulliam, prin. Fax 356-4805
Travis MS 900/6-8
2815 Martin Rd 79107 806-326-3800
David Manchee, prin. Fax 381-7207

Canyon ISD
Supt. — See Canyon
Midway Alternative HS 50/Alt
13501 Bell St 79118 806-677-2455
Shawn Neeley, prin. Fax 677-2459
Randall HS 1,400/9-12
5800 Attebury Dr 79118 806-677-2333
Steve Williams, prin. Fax 677-2329
Westover Park JHS 800/7-8
7200 Pinnacle Dr 79119 806-677-2420
Doug Voran, prin. Fax 677-2439
Youth Center S 50/Alt
9300 S Georgia St 79118 806-677-2450
Shawn Neeley, prin. Fax 468-5714

Highland Park ISD 1,000/PK-12
PO Box 30430 79120 806-335-2823
Mike Brown, supt. Fax 335-3547
www.hpisd.net
Highland Park HS 200/9-12
PO Box 30430 79120 806-335-2821
Shelley Collins, prin. Fax 335-3215
Highland Park MS 200/6-8
PO Box 30430 79120 806-335-2821
Neila Malcom, prin. Fax 335-3215

River Road ISD 1,500/PK-12
9500 N US Highway 287 79108 806-381-7800
Randy Owen, supt. Fax 381-1357
www.rrisd.net
River Road HS 400/9-12
101 W Mobley St 79108 806-383-8867
Steve Scott, prin. Fax 381-7818
River Road MS 200/7-8
9500 N US Highway 287 79108 806-383-8721
Marvin Elam, prin. Fax 381-7815

Amarillo College Post-Sec.
PO Box 447 79178 806-371-5000
Ascension Academy 200/6-12
PO Box 50729 79159 806-342-0515
Rev. William Summerhill Ph.D., hdmstr. Fax 342-0535
Exposito School of Hair Design Post-Sec.
3710 Mockingbird Ln 79109 806-355-9111
Holy Cross Catholic Academy 100/6-12
4110 S Bonham St 79110 806-355-9637
Fr. Robert Busch, head sch Fax 353-9520
Milan Institute Post-Sec.
7001 W Interstate 40 79106 806-353-3500
Milan Institute of Cosmetology Post-Sec.
2400 SE 27th Ave 79103 806-371-7600
San Jacinto Christian Academy 500/PK-12
PO Box 3428 79116 806-372-2285
Mark McKnight, supt. Fax 376-6712
Vista College Post-Sec.
3440 Bell St Unit 100 79109 866-442-4197

Amherst, Lamb, Pop. 712
Amherst ISD 200/PK-12
PO Box 248 79312 806-246-3221
Joel Rodgers, supt. Fax 246-3494
www.amherstisd.com/
Amherst S 200/PK-12
PO Box 248 79312 806-246-3221
Fax 246-3649

Anahuac, Chambers, Pop. 2,205
Anahuac ISD 1,200/PK-12
PO Box 369 77514 409-267-3600
James Hopper, supt. Fax 267-3855
www.anahuacisd.net
Anahuac HS 400/9-12
PO Box 1560 77514 409-267-3600
Eric Humphrey, prin. Fax 267-5192
Anahuac MS 300/6-8
PO Box 849 77514 409-267-2040
Patti Nauman, prin. Fax 267-2046

Anderson, Grimes, Pop. 220
Anderson - Shiro Consolidated ISD 700/PK-12
458 FM 149 Rd W 77830 936-873-4500
Brandon Core, supt. Fax 873-4515
www.ascisd.net
Anderson - Shiro JSHS 400/6-12
458 FM 149 Rd W 77830 936-873-4550
Sara Goolsby, prin. Fax 873-4575

Andrews, Andrews, Pop. 10,989
Andrews ISD 3,300/PK-12
405 NW 3rd St 79714 432-523-3640
Bobby Azam, supt. Fax 523-3343
www.andrews.esc18.net
Andrews Alternative S 50/Alt
405 NW 3rd St 79714 432-523-3640
Charlie Falcon, prin. Fax 524-1986
Andrews HS 800/9-12
405 NW 3rd St 79714 432-523-3640
Doug Bawcom, prin. Fax 523-6807
Andrews MS 700/6-8
405 NW 3rd St 79714 432-523-3640
Benny Granger, prin. Fax 524-1904

Angleton, Brazoria, Pop. 18,559
Angleton ISD 6,400/PK-12
1900 N Downing Rd 77515 979-864-8000
Patricia Montgomery Ed.D., supt. Fax 864-8070
www.angletonisd.net/
Angleton HS 1,800/9-12
1 Campus Dr 77515 979-864-8001
Jerry Crowell, prin. Fax 864-8090
Angleton HS - ACE 100/Alt
1201 W Henderson Rd 77515 979-864-8003
Colleen Tribble, prin.
Angleton JHS 1,400/6-8
1201 W Henderson Rd 77515 979-849-8206
Roy Gardner, prin. Fax 864-8675

Angleton Christian S — 50/PK-12
3133 N Valderas St 77515 — 979-864-3842
Gordon Smith, admin. — Fax 864-3843

Anna, Collin, Pop. 8,055
Anna ISD — 2,300/PK-12
501 S Sherley Ave 75409 — 972-924-1000
Larry Johnson, supt. — Fax 924-1001
www.annaisd.org
Anna HS — 600/9-12
501 S Sherley Ave 75409 — 972-924-1100
Andy Cellars, prin. — Fax 924-1101
Anna MS — 500/6-8
501 S Sherley Ave 75409 — 972-924-1200
Todd Southard, prin. — Fax 924-1201

Anson, Jones, Pop. 2,396
Anson ISD — 700/PK-12
1431 Commercial Ave 79501 — 325-823-3671
Jay Baccus, supt. — Fax 823-4444
www.ansontigers.com
Anson HS — 200/9-12
1509 Commercial Ave 79501 — 325-823-2404
Troy Hinds, prin. — Fax 823-2514
Anson MS — 100/6-8
1120 Avenue M 79501 — 325-823-2771
David Hagler, prin. — Fax 823-3667

Anthony, El Paso, Pop. 4,964
Anthony ISD — 800/PK-12
840 6th St 79821 — 915-886-6500
Ronald Haugen, supt. — Fax 886-2420
www.anthonyisd.net
Anthony HS — 200/9-12
825 Wildcat Dr 79821 — 915-886-6550
Oscar Troncoso, prin. — Fax 886-3875
Anthony MS — 200/6-8
813 6th St 79821 — 915-886-6530
Oscar Troncoso, prin. — Fax 886-3875

Anton, Hockley, Pop. 1,117
Anton ISD — 100/PK-12
PO Box 309 79313 — 806-997-2301
Jim Knight, supt. — Fax 997-2062
www.antonisd.org
Anton S — 100/PK-12
PO Box 309 79313 — 806-997-5211
Brian Bailey, prin. — Fax 997-2196

Apple Springs, Trinity
Apple Springs ISD — 200/PK-12
PO Box 125 75926 — 936-831-3344
Gregg Spivey, supt. — Fax 831-2824
www.asisd.com/
Apple Springs JSHS — 100/7-12
PO Box 125 75926 — 936-831-2241
Cody Moree, prin. — Fax 831-2824

Aquilla, Hill, Pop. 108
Aquilla ISD — 300/PK-12
404 N Richards 76622 — 254-694-3770
David Edison, supt. — Fax 694-6237
www.aquillaisd.net
Aquilla S — 300/PK-12
404 N Richards 76622 — 254-694-3770
Karry Ward, prin. — Fax 694-6237

Aransas Pass, San Patricio, Pop. 8,090
Aransas Pass ISD — 1,800/PK-12
2300 McMullen Ln 78336 — 361-758-3466
Dr. Royce Avery, supt. — Fax 758-2962
www.apisd.org
Aransas Pass HS — 500/9-12
450 S Avenue A 78336 — 361-758-3248
Wayne Bennett, prin. — Fax 758-3251
Blunt MS — 300/6-8
2103 Demory Ln 78336 — 361-758-2711
Mark Kemp, prin. — Fax 758-4690

Archer City, Archer, Pop. 1,806
Archer City ISD — 500/PK-12
PO Box 926 76351 — 940-574-4536
C.D. Knobloch, supt. — Fax 574-4051
www.archercityisd.net
Archer City JSHS — 200/7-12
PO Box 926 76351 — 940-574-4713
Vance Morris, prin. — Fax 574-4051

Argyle, Denton, Pop. 3,241
Argyle ISD — 1,700/PK-12
800 Eagle Dr 76226 — 940-464-7241
Dr. Telena Wright, supt. — Fax 464-7297
www.argyleisd.com
Argyle HS — 600/9-12
800 Eagle Dr 76226 — 940-262-7777
Jeff Butts, prin. — Fax 262-7783
Argyle MS — 300/7-8
800 Eagle Dr 76226 — 940-246-2126
Scott Gibson, prin. — Fax 246-2128

Denton ISD
Supt. — See Denton
Harpool MS — 900/6-8
9601 Stacee St 76226 — 940-369-1700
Mike Vance, prin. — Fax 241-1342

Liberty Christian S — 1,300/PK-12
1301 S US Highway 377 76226 — 940-294-2000
Rodney Haire, pres. — Fax 294-2045

Arlington, Tarrant, Pop. 357,280
Arlington ISD — 63,500/PK-12
1203 W Pioneer Pkwy 76013 — 682-867-4611
Dr. Marcelo Cavazos, supt. — Fax 459-7299
www.aisd.net
Arlington HS — 2,900/9-12
818 W Park Row Dr 76013 — 682-867-8100
Jennifer Young, prin. — Fax 801-6105
Bailey JHS — 800/7-8
2411 Winewood Ln 76013 — 682-867-0700
Tiffany Benavides, prin. — Fax 801-0705
Barnett JHS — 1,000/7-8
2101 E Sublett Rd 76018 — 682-867-5000
Stephanie Hawthorne, prin. — Fax 419-5005
Boles JHS — 800/7-8
3900 SW Green Oaks Blvd 76017 — 682-867-8000
Jeff Provence, prin. — Fax 561-8005
Bowie HS — 3,200/9-12
2101 Highbank Dr 76018 — 682-867-4400
Bill Manley, prin. — Fax 472-4444
Carter JHS — 900/7-8
701 Tharp St 76010 — 682-867-1700
Rachael Brown, prin. — Fax 801-1705
Ferguson JHS — 500/7-8
600 SE Green Oaks Blvd 76018 — 682-867-1600
Ben Bholan, prin. — Fax 472-1605
Gunn JHS — 600/7-8
3000 S Fielder Rd 76015 — 682-867-5400
Shahveer Dhalla, prin. — Fax 419-5405
Houston HS — 2,900/9-12
2000 Sam Houston Dr 76014 — 682-867-8200
Fernando Benavides, prin. — Fax 801-4505
Hutcheson JHS — 800/7-8
2101 Browning Dr 76010 — 682-867-2400
David Tapia, prin. — Fax 801-2415
Lamar HS — 2,900/9-12
1400 W Lamar Blvd 76012 — 682-867-8300
Dr. Larry Harmon, prin. — Fax 801-6255
Martin HS — 3,400/9-12
4501 W Pleasant Ridge Rd 76016 — 682-867-8600
Marlene Roddy, prin. — Fax 561-8705
Newcomer Center — 200/Alt
701 E Arbrook Blvd 76014 — 682-867-7100
Mark Strand, prin. — Fax 419-1221
Nichols JHS — 800/7-8
2201 Ascension Blvd 76006 — 682-867-2600
Julie Harcrow, prin. — Fax 801-2605
Ousley JHS — 600/7-8
950 Southeast Pkwy 76018 — 682-867-5700
Lora Thurston, prin. — Fax 419-5705
Seguin HS — 1,800/9-12
7001 Silo Rd 76002 — 682-867-6700
Sam Nix, prin. — Fax 375-6705
Shackelford JHS — 700/7-8
2000 N Fielder Rd 76012 — 682-867-3600
Andrew Hagman, prin. — Fax 801-3605
Turning Point Alternative HS — 100/Alt
5618 W Arkansas Ln 76016 — 682-867-3000
Juan Villarreal, prin. — Fax 492-3005
Turning Point Alternative JHS — 50/Alt
2209 N Davis Dr 76012 — 682-867-3050
Linda Williams, prin. — Fax 459-7331
Venture Alternative HS — 400/Alt
4900 W Arkansas Ln 76016 — 682-867-6400
Beverley McReynolds, prin. — Fax 492-6405
Workman JHS — 500/7-8
701 E Arbrook Blvd 76014 — 682-867-1200
Kelvin Stroy, prin. — Fax 419-1205
Young JHS — 800/7-8
3200 Woodside Dr 76016 — 682-867-3400
Kelly Hastings, prin. — Fax 492-3405

Mansfield ISD
Supt. — See Mansfield
Coble MS — 700/7-8
1200 Ballweg Rd 76002 — 817-299-6400
Dr. Charlotte Ford, prin. — Fax 453-7331
Howard MS — 1,000/7-8
7501 Calendar Rd 76001 — 817-299-3500
Donna O'Brian, prin. — Fax 561-3840
Summit HS — 2,000/9-12
1071 Turner Warnell Rd 76001 — 817-299-7400
Jimmy Neal, prin. — Fax 473-5732
Timberview HS — 2,400/9-12
7700 S Watson Rd 76002 — 817-299-2600
Derrell Douglas, prin. — Fax 472-2978

Arlington Baptist College — Post-Sec.
3001 W Division St 76012 — 817-461-8741
Arlington Medical Institute — Post-Sec.
1001 NE Green Oaks Ste 190 76006 — 817-265-0706
B.H. Carroll Theological Institute — Post-Sec.
301 S Center St Ste 100 76010 — 817-274-4284
Burton Adventist Academy — 300/PK-12
4611 Kelly Elliott Rd 76017 — 817-572-0081
Concorde Career Institute — Post-Sec.
600 E Lamar Blvd Ste 200 76011 — 817-261-1594
Everest College — Post-Sec.
300 Six Flags Dr Ste 100 76011 — 817-652-7790
High Point Preparatory Academy — 300/PK-12
2500 E Arbrook Blvd 76014 — 817-394-3100
Stephen Collins, hdmstr. — Fax 394-3101
ITT Technical Institute — Post-Sec.
551 Ryan Plaza Dr 76011 — 817-794-5100
Oakridge S — 900/PK-12
5900 W Pioneer Pkwy 76013 — 817-451-4994
Jonathan Kellam, hdmstr. — Fax 457-6681
Ogle School of Hair Design — Post-Sec.
2200 W Park Row Dr Ste 106 76013 — 888-820-4224
Pantego Christian Academy — 900/PK-12
2201 W Park Row Dr 76013 — 817-460-3315
Jay Pritcher, hdmstr. — Fax 459-4687
St. Paul's Preparatory Academy — 300/PK-12
6900 US 287 Hwy 76001 — 817-561-3500
Gayla Rockwell M.Ed., prin. — Fax 561-3408
Tarrant County College — Post-Sec.
2100 Southeast Pkwy 76018 — 817-515-8223
University of Texas — Post-Sec.
701 S Nedderman Dr 76019 — 817-272-2011

Arp, Smith, Pop. 957
Arp ISD — 900/PK-12
PO Box 70 75750 — 903-859-8482
Toney Lowery, supt. — Fax 859-2621
www.arpisd.org/
Arp HS — 300/9-12
PO Box 70 75750 — 903-859-4917
Randy Copeland, prin. — Fax 859-1541
Arp JHS — 200/6-8
PO Box 70 75750 — 903-859-4936
Dwight Thomas, prin. — Fax 859-3980

Aspermont, Stonewall, Pop. 909
Aspermont ISD — 200/PK-12
PO Box 549 79502 — 940-989-3355
Cliff Gilmore, supt. — Fax 989-3353
www.aspermont.esc14.net
Aspermont JSHS — 100/6-12
PO Box 549 79502 — 940-989-2707
Zach Morris, prin. — Fax 989-3486

Atascosa, Bexar
Southwest ISD
Supt. — See San Antonio
McNair MS — 900/6-8
11553 Old Pearsall Rd 78002 — 210-622-4480
Jason Migura, prin. — Fax 622-4481

Athens, Henderson, Pop. 12,562
Athens ISD — 3,400/PK-12
104 Hawn St 75751 — 903-677-6900
Blake Stiles, supt. — Fax 677-6908
www.athensisd.net
Athens HS — 900/9-12
708 E College St 75751 — 903-677-6920
Jami Ivey, prin. — Fax 677-6925
Athens MS — 800/6-8
6800 State Highway 19 S 75751 — 903-677-3030
Vicki Weatherford, prin. — Fax 677-2111

Athens Christian Preparatory Academy — 100/7-12
PO Box 2157 75751 — 903-386-0400
Teresa DeMay, admin.
Trinity Valley Community College — Post-Sec.
100 Cardinal St 75751 — 903-677-8822

Atlanta, Cass, Pop. 5,585
Atlanta ISD — 1,600/PK-12
106 W Main St 75551 — 903-796-4194
Roger Hailey, supt. — Fax 799-1004
www.atlisd.net/
Atlanta HS — 500/9-12
705 Rabbit Blvd 75551 — 903-796-4411
Tim Lambert, prin. — Fax 799-1033
Atlanta MS — 400/5-8
600 High School Ln 75551 — 903-796-7928
Rex Stone, prin. — Fax 799-1021

Champions Christian Academy — 50/PK-12
PO Box 777 75551 — 903-796-1805
Dr. Beth Hill, supt. — Fax 796-4350

Aubrey, Denton, Pop. 2,543
Aubrey ISD — 1,900/PK-12
415 Tisdell Ln 76227 — 940-668-0060
Debby Sanders, supt. — Fax 365-2627
www.aubreyisd.net/
Aubrey HS — 500/9-12
510 Spring Hill Rd 76227 — 940-668-3900
Jeff Mulkey, prin. — Fax 668-3903
Aubrey MS — 400/6-8
815 W Sherman Dr 76227 — 940-668-0200
Delore Jones, prin. — Fax 365-3135

Denton ISD
Supt. — See Denton
Navo MS — 1,000/6-8
1701 Navo Rd 76227 — 972-347-7500
Shaun Perry, prin. — Fax 346-2562

Austin, Travis, Pop. 774,864
Austin ISD — 87,700/PK-12
1111 W 6th St 78703 — 512-414-1700
Meria Carstarphen Ph.D., supt. — Fax 414-1707
www.austinisd.org
Akins HS — 2,700/9-12
10701 S 1st St 78748 — 512-841-9900
Daniel Girard, prin. — Fax 841-9903
Alternative Learning Center — 200/Alt
901 Neal St 78702 — 512-414-2554
Jeffrey Black, prin. — Fax 476-2809
Anderson HS — 2,100/9-12
8403 Mesa Dr 78759 — 512-414-2538
Donna Houser, prin. — Fax 338-1293
Austin HS — 2,300/9-12
1715 W Cesar Chavez St 78703 — 512-414-2505
Sandy Compian, prin. — Fax 414-7373
Bailey MS — 1,000/6-8
4020 Lost Oasis Holw 78739 — 512-414-4990
Julia Fletcher, prin. — Fax 292-0898
Bedichek MS — 1,100/6-8
6800 Bill Hughes Rd 78745 — 512-414-3265
Dan Diehl, prin. — Fax 444-4382
Bowie HS — 2,900/9-12
4103 W Slaughter Ln 78749 — 512-414-5247
Stephen Kane, prin. — Fax 292-0527
Burnet MS — 1,000/6-8
8401 Hathaway Dr 78757 — 512-414-3225
Cesar Martinez, prin. — Fax 452-0695
Covington MS — 800/6-8
3700 Convict Hill Rd 78749 — 512-414-3276
Candace Hughs, prin. — Fax 892-4547
Crockett HS — 1,600/9-12
5601 Manchaca Rd 78745 — 512-414-2532
Craig Shapiro, prin. — Fax 447-0489
Dobie MS — 600/6-8
1200 E Rundberg Ln 78753 — 512-414-3270
Carol Chapman, prin. — Fax 836-8411
Eastside Memorial Global Tech HS — 400/9-12
1012 Arthur Stiles Rd 78721 — 512-414-5810
Bryan Miller, prin. — Fax 841-5935
Fulmore Magnet S — 100/6-8
201 E Mary St 78704 — 512-841-4916
Debra Price, dir. — Fax 841-4915

Fulmore MS 1,000/6-8
201 E Mary St 78704 512-414-3207
Lisa Bush, prin. Fax 441-3129
Garcia MS 700/6-8
7414 Johnny Morris Rd 78724 512-841-9400
Manuel Ornelas, prin. Fax 841-9401
Garza Independence HS 300/11-12
1600 Chicon St 78702 512-414-8600
Dr. Linda Webb, prin. Fax 414-8610
Gorzycki MS 1,000/6-8
7412 W Slaughter Ln 78749 512-841-8600
Vicki Bauerle, prin. Fax 841-8601
Henry MS 1,000/6-8
2610 W 10th St 78703 512-414-3229
Peter Price, prin. Fax 477-7428
International HS 200/9-10
1012 Arthur Stiles Rd 78721 512-414-6817
Susan Galvan, prin. Fax 841-5621
Johnson Early College HS 1,000/9-12
7309 Lazy Creek Dr 78724 512-414-2543
Sheila Henry, prin. Fax 929-3955
Kealing Magnet Program 100/6-8
1607 Pennsylvania Ave 78702 512-414-3180
Beth Cooper, dir. Fax 414-6704
Kealing MS 1,200/6-8
1607 Pennsylvania Ave 78702 512-414-3214
Robin Lowe, prin. Fax 478-9133
Lamar MS 600/6-8
6201 Wynona Ave 78757 512-414-3217
George Llewellyn, prin. Fax 467-6862
Lanier Health Sciences Inst of Austin 1,600/9-12
1201 Payton Gin Rd 78758 512-414-2514
Katherine Ryan, prin. Fax 832-1203
Lanier HS 1,500/9-12
1201 Payton Gin Rd 78758 512-414-2514
Katherine Ryan, prin. Fax 832-1203
Liberal Arts & Science Academy 900/9-12
7309 Lazy Creek Dr 78724 512-414-5272
Stacia Crescenzi, dir. Fax 414-6050
Martin MS 600/6-8
1601 Haskell St 78702 512-414-3243
Leticia Vega, prin. Fax 320-0125
McCallum Fine Arts Academy 1,700/9-12
5600 Sunshine Dr 78756 512-414-7506
Lanier Bayliss, prin. Fax 841-7319
McCallum HS 1,800/9-12
5600 Sunshine Dr 78756 512-414-2519
Michael Garrison, prin. Fax 453-2599
Mendez MS 900/6-8
5106 Village Square Dr 78744 512-414-3284
Ron Gonzales, prin. Fax 442-5738
Murchison MS 1,300/6-8
3700 N Hills Dr 78731 512-414-3254
Sammilu Harrison, prin. Fax 343-1710
Paredes MS 900/6-8
10100 S Mary Moore Searight 78748 512-841-6800
Karla Wright, prin. Fax 841-7036
Pearce MS 300/6-8
6401 N Hampton Dr 78723 512-414-3234
Texanna Turner, prin. Fax 926-6146
Reagan HS 800/9-12
7104 Berkman Dr 78752 512-414-2523
Anabel Garza, prin. Fax 452-7089
Richards S for Young Women Leaders 500/6-12
2206 Prather Ln 78704 512-414-3236
Jeanne Goka, prin. Fax 441-5208
Small MS 1,000/6-8
4801 Monterey Oaks Blvd 78749 512-841-6700
Amy Taylor, prin. Fax 841-6703
Travis HS 1,400/9-12
1211 E Oltorf St 78704 512-414-2527
Ty Davidson, prin. Fax 707-0050
Webb MS 600/6-8
601 E Saint Johns Ave 78752 512-414-3258
Reynaldo Garcia, prin. Fax 452-9683

Del Valle ISD
Supt. — See Del Valle
Dailey MS 6-8
14000 Westall 78725 512-386-3600
Dr. T.J. Dilworth, prin. Fax 386-3605
Ojeda MS 800/6-8
4900 McKinney Falls Pkwy 78744 512-386-3500
David Williams, prin. Fax 386-3505

Eanes ISD 7,700/PK-12
601 Camp Craft Rd 78746 512-732-9001
Dr. Nola Wellman, supt. Fax 732-9005
www.eanesisd.net/
Hill Country MS 900/6-8
1300 Walsh Tarlton Ln 78746 512-732-9220
Kathleen Sullivan, prin. Fax 732-9229
Westlake HS 2,600/9-12
4100 Westbank Dr 78746 512-732-9280
Dr. John Carter, prin. Fax 732-9289
West Ridge MS 900/6-8
9201 Scenic Bluff Dr 78733 512-732-9240
Steve Ramsey, prin. Fax 732-9249
Other Schools – See West Lake Hills

Lake Travis ISD 6,900/PK-12
3322 Ranch Road 620 S 78738 512-533-6000
Brad Lancaster, supt. Fax 533-6001
www.ltisdschools.org/
Hudson Bend MS 800/6-8
15600 Lariat Trl 78734 512-533-6400
Mark Robinson, prin. Fax 533-6401
Lake Travis HS 2,100/9-12
3324 Ranch Road 620 S 78738 512-533-6100
Kim Brents, prin. Fax 533-6102
Lake Travis MS 800/6-8
3328 Ranch Road 620 S 78738 512-533-6200
Russell Maedgen, prin. Fax 533-6201

Leander ISD
Supt. — See Leander
Canyon Ridge MS 900/6-8
12601 Country Trl 78732 512-570-3500
Susan Sullivan, prin. Fax 570-3505

Four Points MS 6-8
9700 McNeil Dr 78750 512-570-3700
Dr. Joe Ciccarelli, prin. Fax 570-3705
Vandegrift HS 1,000/9-12
9500 McNeil Dr 78750 512-570-2300
Charlie Little, prin. Fax 570-2306

Manor ISD
Supt. — See Manor
Decker MS 600/6-8
8104 Decker Ln 78724 512-278-4630
Fax 278-4654

Pflugerville ISD
Supt. — See Pflugerville
Connally HS 2,100/9-12
13212 N Lamar Blvd 78753 512-594-0800
Daniel Garcia, prin. Fax 594-0805
Dessau MS 1,000/6-8
12900 Dessau Rd 78754 512-594-2600
Orlando Vargas, prin. Fax 594-2605
Westview MS 1,000/6-8
1805 Scofield Ln 78727 512-594-2200
Kermit Ward, prin. Fax 594-2205

Round Rock ISD
Supt. — See Round Rock
Canyon Vista MS 1,200/6-8
8455 Spicewood Springs Rd 78759 512-464-8100
Barbara Paris, prin. Fax 464-8210
Cedar Valley MS 1,200/6-8
8139 Racine Trl 78717 512-428-2300
Matt Groff, prin. Fax 428-2420
Deerpark MS 1,000/6-8
8849 Anderson Mill Rd 78729 512-464-6600
Sonya Hayes, prin. Fax 464-6740
Grisham MS 700/6-8
10805 School House Ln 78750 512-428-2650
Georgia Johnson, prin. Fax 428-2790
McNeil HS 2,600/9-12
5720 McNeil Dr 78729 512-464-6300
John Yonker, prin. Fax 464-6550
Success - West Campus 200/Alt
12515 Mellow Meadow Dr 78750 512-428-2935
Mark Gesch, dir. Fax 428-2944
Westwood HS 2,400/9-12
12400 Mellow Meadow Dr 78750 512-464-4000
Laurelyn Arterbury, prin. Fax 464-4020

A New Beginning School of Massage Post-Sec.
2525 Wallingwood Dr # 1501 78746 512-306-0975
AOMA Graduate School of Integrative Med Post-Sec.
4701 W Gate Blvd 78745 512-454-1188
Austin Community College Post-Sec.
5930 Middle Fiskville Rd 78752 512-223-7000
Austin Graduate School of Theology Post-Sec.
7640 Guadalupe St 78752 512-476-2772
Austin Montessori S - Gaines Creek Cmps 7-9
5006 Sunset Trl 78745 512-892-0826
Austin Presbyterian Theological Seminary Post-Sec.
100 E 27th St 78705 512-404-4800
Austin Waldorf S 400/K-12
8700 S View Rd 78737 512-288-5942
Susan Darcy, admin. Fax 301-8997
Baldwin Beauty School - North Post-Sec.
8440 Burnet Rd 78757 512-458-4127
Baldwin Beauty School - South Post-Sec.
3005 S Lamar Blvd Ste 103 78704 512-441-6898
Brentwood Christian S 700/PK-12
11908 N Lamar Blvd 78753 512-835-5983
Marquita Moss, pres. Fax 835-2184
Capitol City Careers Post-Sec.
5424 W Highway 290 Ste 200 78735 512-892-2640
Capitol City Trade and Technical School Post-Sec.
205 E Riverside Dr 78704 512-444-3257
Concordia University Texas Post-Sec.
11400 Concordia Univ Dr 78726 512-313-3000
DeVry University Post-Sec.
11044 Research Blvd # B100 78759 512-231-2500
Escoffier School of Culinary Arts Post-Sec.
6020 Dillard Cir Ste B 78752 512-451-5743
Everest Institute Post-Sec.
9100 E Highway 290 # 100 78724 512-928-1933
Hill Country Christian S of Austin 500/PK-12
12124 Ranch Road 620 N 78750 512-331-7036
Bill McGee, hdmstr. Fax 257-4190
Huston-Tillotson University Post-Sec.
900 Chicon St 78702 512-505-3000
Hyde Park HS - Quarries Campus 300/9-12
PO Box 4486 78765 512-465-8333
ITT Technical Institute Post-Sec.
6330 E Highway 290 Ste 150 78723 512-467-6800
Kussad Institute of Court Reporting Post-Sec.
2800 S Interstate 35 # 110 78704 512-443-7286
Le Cordon Bleu College of Culinary Arts Post-Sec.
3110 Esperanza Xing Ste 100 78758 512-837-2665
Mediatech Institute Post-Sec.
4719 S Congress Ave 78745 512-447-2002
Regents S of Austin 1,000/K-12
3230 Travis Country Cir 78735 512-899-8095
Rod Gilbert, hdmstr. Fax 899-8623
St. Andrew's Episcopal S 300/9-12
5901 Southwest Pkwy 78735 512-299-9700
Sean Murphy, head sch Fax 299-9660
St. Domic Savio Catholic HS 9-12
9300 Neenah Ave 78717 512-388-8846
Dr. John Cummings, prin. Fax 388-1335
St. Edward's University Post-Sec.
3001 S Congress Ave 78704 512-448-8400
St. Michael's Catholic Academy 500/9-12
3000 Barton Creek Blvd 78735 512-328-2323
Sharon Scamardo, prin. Fax 328-2327
St. Stephen's Episcopal S 700/6-12
6500 Saint Stephens Dr 78746 512-327-1213
Robert Kirkpatrick, hdmstr. Fax 327-6771
San Juan Diego Catholic HS 200/9-12
800 Herndon Ln 78704 512-804-1935
Pamela Jupe, prin. Fax 804-1937

Seminary of the Southwest Post-Sec.
PO Box 2247 78768 512-472-4133
Southern Careers Institute Post-Sec.
2301 S Congress Ave Ste 27 78704 512-448-4795
Southwest Institute of Technology Post-Sec.
5424 W Highway 290 Ste 200 78735 512-892-2640
Texas College of Traditional Chinese Med Post-Sec.
4005 Manchaca Rd 78704 512-444-8082
The College of Health Care Professions Post-Sec.
6505 Airport Blvd Ste 102 78752 512-892-2835
University of Texas at Austin Post-Sec.
1 University Sta 78712 512-471-3434
Virginia College at Austin Post-Sec.
6301 E Highway 290 78723 512-371-3500

Avalon, Ellis
Avalon ISD 300/PK-12
PO Box 455 76623 972-627-3251
Dr. David Del Bosque, supt. Fax 627-3220
avalon.tx.schoolwebpages.com/education/
Avalon S 300/PK-12
PO Box 455 76623 972-627-3251
Dr. David Del Bosque, supt. Fax 627-3220

Avery, Red River, Pop. 482
Avery ISD 400/PK-12
150 San Antonio St 75554 903-684-3460
Kelly Burns, supt. Fax 684-3294
www.averyisd.net/
Avery HS 100/9-12
150 San Antonio St 75554 903-684-3431
Daniel Pritchett, prin. Fax 684-3294
Avery MS 100/5-8
150 San Antonio St 75554 903-684-3079
Rhonda Jeans, prin. Fax 684-3294

Avinger, Cass, Pop. 437
Avinger ISD 100/K-12
245 Conner 75630 903-562-1271
Jacquelyn Smith, supt. Fax 562-1271
www.avingerisd.net/
Avinger S 100/K-12
245 Conner 75630 903-562-1355
Lori Rich, prin. Fax 562-1271

Avoca, Jones
Lueders-Avoca ISD
Supt. — See Lueders
Lueders-Avoca HS 50/9-12
8762 County Road 604 79503 325-773-2785
Rebecca Russell, supt. Fax 773-3072

Axtell, McLennan
Axtell ISD 700/PK-12
308 Ottawa 76624 254-863-5301
Stanley Harris, supt. Fax 863-5651
www.axtellisd.net/
Axtell HS 200/9-12
308 Ottawa 76624 254-863-5301
Dale Monsey, prin. Fax 863-5651
Axtell MS 200/6-8
308 Ottawa 76624 254-863-5301
Dale Monsey, prin. Fax 863-5651

Azle, Tarrant, Pop. 10,777
Azle ISD 5,800/PK-12
300 Roe St 76020 817-444-3235
Ray Lea, supt. Fax 444-6866
www.azleisd.net
Azle HS 1,700/9-12
1200 Boyd Rd 76020 817-444-5555
Sam Robinson, prin. Fax 444-8884
Azle JHS 500/7-8
201 School St 76020 817-444-2564
Scott McPherson, prin. Fax 270-0880
Forte JHS 400/7-8
479 Sandy Beach Rd 76020 817-270-1133
Kim Bates, prin. Fax 270-1157

Azle Christian S 100/PK-12
1801 S Stewart St 76020 817-444-9964
Sheryl Rushing, admin. Fax 444-9914

Baird, Callahan, Pop. 1,483
Baird ISD 200/PK-12
PO Box 1147 79504 325-854-1400
Jarod Bellar, supt. Fax 854-2058
www.bairdisd.net
Baird HS 100/9-12
PO Box 1147 79504 325-854-1400
Cynthia Bessent, prin. Fax 854-2808

Balch Springs, Dallas, Pop. 23,383
Dallas ISD
Supt. — See Dallas
Balch Springs MS 6-8
710 Cheyenne Rd 75180 972-892-5800
Clarita Rivera, prin.

Ballinger, Runnels, Pop. 3,731
Ballinger ISD 1,000/PK-12
PO Box 231 76821 325-365-3588
Will Brewer, supt. Fax 365-5920
www.ballingerisd.net
Ballinger HS 300/9-12
PO Box 231 76821 325-365-3547
Mike Carter, prin. Fax 365-5422
Ballinger JHS 200/6-8
PO Box 231 76821 325-365-3537
Gordon Gloria, prin. Fax 365-5420

Balmorhea, Reeves, Pop. 479
Balmorhea ISD 200/PK-12
PO Box 368 79718 432-375-2223
Mary Lou Carrasco, supt. Fax 375-2511
www.bisdbears.esc18.net
Balmorhea S 200/PK-12
PO Box 368 79718 432-375-2223
Teri Barragan, prin. Fax 375-2511

Bandera, Bandera, Pop. 852
Bandera ISD 2,500/PK-12
PO Box 727 78003 830-796-3313
Regina Howell, supt. Fax 796-6238
www.banderaisd.net
Bandera HS 800/9-12
PO Box 727 78003 830-796-6254
Gary Bitzkie, prin. Fax 796-6251
Bandera MS 600/6-8
PO Box 727 78003 830-796-6270
Donald Tosh, prin. Fax 796-6277

Bangs, Brown, Pop. 1,570
Bangs ISD 1,100/PK-12
PO Box 969 76823 325-752-6612
Bill Foster, supt. Fax 752-6253
www.bangsisd.net
Bangs HS 300/9-12
PO Box 969 76823 325-752-6822
Vick Orlando, prin. Fax 752-7028
Bangs MS 300/5-8
PO Box 969 76823 325-752-6088
Tony Truelove, prin. Fax 752-6253

Banquete, Nueces, Pop. 721
Banquete ISD 800/PK-12
PO Box 369 78339 361-387-2551
Jim Rumage, supt. Fax 387-7188
www.banqueteisd.esc2.net/
Banquete HS 200/9-12
PO Box 369 78339 361-387-8588
Nancy Mooney, prin. Fax 767-6504
Banquete JHS 200/6-8
PO Box 369 78339 361-387-6504
Ramiro Pena, prin. Fax 387-7051

Barksdale, Edwards
Nueces Canyon Consolidated ISD 300/K-12
PO Box 118 78828 830-234-3514
Rick Howard, supt. Fax 234-3435
www.nccisd.net/
Nueces Canyon JSHS 100/7-12
PO Box 118 78828 830-234-3524
Kristi Powers, prin. Fax 234-4129

Bartlett, Bell, Pop. 1,605
Bartlett ISD 400/PK-12
PO Box 170 76511 254-527-4247
Brett Springston, supt. Fax 527-3340
www.bartlett.txed.net
Bartlett HS 200/7-12
PO Box 170 76511 254-527-3351
Allen Reese, prin. Fax 527-3513

Bastrop, Bastrop, Pop. 7,084
Bastrop ISD 9,000/PK-12
906 Farm St 78602 512-321-2292
Steve Murray, supt. Fax 321-7469
www.bisdtx.org/
Bastrop HS 1,800/9-12
1614 Chambers St 78602 512-772-7200
Dr. Celina Estrada-Thomas, prin. Fax 321-7502
Bastrop MS 700/7-8
709 Old Austin Hwy 78602 512-321-3911
Sami Kinsey, prin. Fax 321-1557
Gateway Alternative S 50/Alt
1019 Lovers Ln 78602 512-321-2339
Patricia Alford, prin. Fax 332-0498
Genesis HS 100/Alt
1200 Cedar St 78602 512-772-7230
Martin Conrardy, prin. Fax 321-3212
Other Schools – See Cedar Creek

Bay City, Matagorda, Pop. 17,441
Bay City ISD 3,200/PK-12
520 7th St 77414 979-245-5766
Keith Brown, supt. Fax 245-3175
www.bcblackcats.net
Bay City HS 1,100/9-12
400 7th St 77414 979-245-5771
Heath Koenig, prin. Fax 245-1220
Bay City JHS 800/6-8
1507 Sycamore Ave 77414 979-245-6345
Glenn Ging, prin. Fax 245-1419

Baytown, Harris, Pop. 70,920
Goose Creek Consolidated ISD 20,900/PK-12
PO Box 30 77522 281-420-4800
Dr. Salvador Cavazos, supt. Fax 420-4815
www.gccisd.net/
Baytown JHS 700/6-8
7707 Bayway Dr 77520 281-420-4560
Juan Castillo, prin. Fax 420-4908
Cedar Bayou JHS 1,000/6-8
2610 Elvinta St 77520 281-420-4570
Greg Lynd, prin. Fax 420-4909
Gentry JHS 1,000/6-8
1919 E Archer Rd 77521 281-420-4590
Dave Gillings, prin. Fax 420-4909
Goose Creek Memorial HS 1,700/9-12
6001 E Wallisville Rd 77521 281-421-4400
Michael Wahl, prin. Fax 421-4444
Hyland Center Alt
4026 Decker Dr 77520 281-420-4555
Michelle Verdun, prin. Fax 420-4558
Impact Early College HS 9-12
200 Lee Dr 77520 281-420-4802
Karen Smithson, prin. Fax 556-5781
Lee HS 1,700/9-12
1809 Market St 77520 281-420-4535
Bruce Davis, prin. Fax 420-4548
Mann JHS 700/6-8
310 S Highway 146 77520 281-420-4585
Dr. Michael Coopersmith, prin. Fax 420-4664
Sterling HS 2,300/9-12
300 W Baker Rd 77521 281-420-4500
Dr. Don Beck, prin. Fax 420-4974
Stuart Career Center Vo/Tech
300 W Wye Dr 77521 281-420-4550
Renea Dillon, dir. Fax 420-4553
Other Schools – See Highlands

Baytown Christian Academy 300/PK-12
5555 N Main St 77521 281-421-4150
M. Wade Ortego, hdmstr. Fax 421-4038
Lee College Post-Sec.
PO Box 818 77522 281-427-5611

Beaumont, Jefferson, Pop. 116,638
Beaumont ISD 18,100/PK-12
3395 Harrison Ave 77706 409-617-5000
Dr. Timothy Chargois, supt. Fax 617-5184
www.bmtisd.com
Austin MS 400/6-8
3410 Austin St 77706 409-617-5800
Dr. Aaron Covington, prin. Fax 617-5823
Brown Center 100/Alt
1900 Pope St 77703 409-617-5720
Elvena Colbert, prin. Fax 617-5738
Central HS 1,700/9-12
88 Jaguar Dr 77702 409-617-5300
O. Lorenzo Carr, prin. Fax 617-5396
King MS 400/6-8
1400 Avenue A 77701 409-617-5850
Michael Shelton, prin. Fax 617-5873
Marshall MS 800/6-8
6455 Gladys Ave 77706 409-617-5900
Shannon Allen, prin. Fax 617-5924
Odom Academy 900/6-8
2550 W Virginia St 77705 409-617-5925
Tillie Hickman, prin. Fax 617-5949
Ozen HS 1,200/9-12
3443 Fannett Rd 77705 409-617-5400
James Broussard, prin. Fax 617-5496
Pathways Learning Center 100/Alt
1800 Tulane St 77703 409-617-5700
Jessie Kibbles, prin. Fax 617-5718
Smith MS 500/6-8
4415 Concord Rd 77703 409-617-5825
Wilbert Andrews, prin. Fax 617-5848
South Park MS 300/6-8
4500 Highland Ave 77705 409-617-5875
Odis Norris, prin. Fax 617-5899
Taylor Career Center Vo/Tech
2330 North St 77702 409-617-5740
Thom Campbell-Amons, prin. Fax 617-5759
Vincent MS 800/6-8
350 Eldridge Dr 77707 409-617-5950
Dr. Brian Abel, prin. Fax 617-5974
West Brook HS 2,400/9-12
8750 Phelan Blvd 77706 409-617-5500
Randall Maxwell, prin. Fax 617-5582

Hamshire-Fannett ISD
Supt. — See Hamshire
Hamshire-Fannett MS 300/7-8
11375 Dugat Rd 77705 409-794-2361
Mark Martin, prin. Fax 794-3042

Baptist Hospital of Southeast Texas Post-Sec.
PO Box 1591 77704 409-654-5351
Kaplan College Post-Sec.
6115 Eastex Fwy 77706 409-347-5900
Lamar Institute of Technology Post-Sec.
PO Box 10043 77710 409-880-8321
Lamar University Post-Sec.
PO Box 10009 77710 409-880-7011
Legacy Christian Academy 400/PK-12
8200 Highway 105 77713 409-924-0500
Roger Pricer Ph.D., dir. Fax 924-0953
Monsignor Kelly Catholic HS 400/9-12
5950 Kelly Dr 77707 409-866-2351
Roger Bemis, prin. Fax 866-0917
St. Elizabeth Hospital Post-Sec.
2830 Calder St 77702 409-892-7171
Vista College Post-Sec.
3871 Stagg Dr Ste 194 77701 409-291-4900

Beckville, Panola, Pop. 830
Beckville ISD 700/PK-12
PO Box 37 75631 903-678-3311
Devin Tate, supt. Fax 678-2157
www.beckvilleisd.net/
Beckville HS 200/9-12
PO Box 37 75631 903-678-3591
Phillip Works, prin. Fax 678-3645
Beckville JHS 200/6-8
PO Box 37 75631 903-678-3851
Loretta Blair, prin. Fax 678-3827

Bedford, Tarrant, Pop. 45,838
Hurst-Euless-Bedford ISD 21,000/PK-12
1849 Central Dr Ste A 76022 817-283-4461
Gene Buinger Ed.D., supt. Fax 354-3311
www.hebisd.edu
Bedford JHS 800/7-9
325 Carolyn Dr 76021 817-788-3101
Scott Hurbough, prin. Fax 788-3105
Harwood JHS 1,000/7-9
3000 Martin Dr 76021 817-354-3360
Leslie Guajardo, prin. Fax 354-3369
Technical Education Center Vo/Tech
1849 Central Dr 76022 817-354-3542
Lisa Karr, prin. Fax 354-3546
Other Schools – See Euless, Hurst

Beeville, Bee, Pop. 12,739
Beeville ISD 3,500/PK-12
201 N Saint Marys St 78102 361-358-7111
Dr. Sue Thomas, supt. Fax 358-7837
www.beevilleisd.net
Jones HS 1,100/9-12
1902 N Adams St 78102 361-362-6000
Jaime Rodriguez, prin. Fax 362-6016
Moreno MS 800/6-8
301 N Minnesota St 78102 361-358-6262
Joni Barber, prin. Fax 362-6092

Coastal Bend College Post-Sec.
3800 Charco Rd 78102 361-358-2838

Bellaire, Harris, Pop. 16,508
Houston ISD
Supt. — See Houston
Bellaire HS 3,500/9-12
5100 Maple St 77401 713-295-3704
Michael McDonough, prin. Fax 295-3763
Pin Oak MS 1,200/6-8
4601 Glenmont St 77401 713-295-6500
Susan Monaghan, prin. Fax 295-6511

Episcopal HS 700/9-12
4650 Bissonnet St 77401 713-512-3400
Ned Smith, hdmstr. Fax 512-3603
Post Oak S 400/PK-12
4600 Bissonnet St 77401 713-661-6688
John Long, head sch Fax 661-4959

Bellevue, Clay, Pop. 360
Bellevue ISD 200/K-12
PO Box 38 76228 940-928-2104
Dean Gilstrap, supt. Fax 928-2583
www.bellevueisd.org/
Bellevue S 200/K-12
PO Box 38 76228 940-928-2104
Aaron Tefertiller, prin. Fax 928-2583

Bells, Grayson, Pop. 1,356
Bells ISD 800/PK-12
PO Box 7 75414 903-965-7721
Joe Moore, supt. Fax 965-7036
bellsisd.net/
Bells HS 200/9-12
PO Box 7 75414 903-965-7315
Dan Crawford, prin. Fax 965-5205
Prichard JHS 100/6-8
PO Box 7 75414 903-965-4835
Paula Mortensen, prin. Fax 965-7428

Bellville, Austin, Pop. 4,068
Bellville ISD 2,200/PK-12
518 S Mathews St 77418 979-865-3133
Mike Coker, supt. Fax 865-8591
www.bellvilleisd.org
Bellville HS 700/9-12
518 S Mathews St 77418 979-865-3681
Dr. Michael Coopersmith, prin. Fax 865-7080
Bellville JHS 500/6-8
518 S Mathews St 77418 979-865-5966
Natalie Jones, prin. Fax 865-7060
Spicer Alternative Education Center Alt
518 S Mathews St 77418 979-865-7095
Laura Bailey, prin. Fax 865-7094

Faith Academy 200/PK-12
12177 Highway 36 77418 979-865-1811
Merlene Byler, admin. Fax 865-2454

Belton, Bell, Pop. 17,870
Belton ISD 9,200/PK-12
PO Box 269 76513 254-215-2000
Dr. Susan Kincannon, supt. Fax 215-2001
www.bisd.net
Belton Alternative Center Alt
540 E 3rd Ave 76513 254-215-2550
Ted Smith, coord. Fax 215-2551
Belton HS 2,400/9-12
600 Lake Rd 76513 254-215-2200
Chris DuBois, prin. Fax 215-2201
Belton MS 1,000/6-8
1704 Sparta Rd 76513 254-215-2800
Joe Brown, prin. Fax 215-2801
Belton New Tech HS 9-11
320 N Blair St 76513 254-215-2500
Dr. Deanna Lovesmith, prin. Fax 215-2501
Career Studies Center Vo/Tech
600 Lake Rd 76513 254-215-2260
Lori Rockwood, dir. Fax 215-2261
South Belton MS 6-8
805 Sage Brush 76513 254-215-3000
Tammy Becker, prin. Fax 215-3001
Other Schools – See Temple

University of Mary Hardin-Baylor Post-Sec.
900 College St 76513 254-295-8642

Benavides, Duval, Pop. 1,353
Benavides ISD 400/PK-12
PO Box P 78341 361-256-3003
Daniel Ceballos, supt. Fax 256-3002
www.benavidesisd.net
Benavides HS 200/7-12
PO Box P 78341 361-256-3040
Adell Cueva, prin. Fax 256-3043

Ben Bolt, Jim Wells
Ben Bolt-Palito Blanco ISD 600/PK-12
PO Box 547 78342 361-664-9904
Dr. Scott Norris, supt. Fax 668-0446
www.bbpbisd.org/
Ben Bolt MS 200/4-8
PO Box 547 78342 361-664-9568
Fernando Galvan, prin. Fax 664-5235
Ben Bolt-Palito Blanco HS 200/9-12
PO Box 547 78342 361-664-9822
Dr. Arnoldo Barrera, prin. Fax 664-5481

Benbrook, Tarrant, Pop. 20,889
Fort Worth ISD
Supt. — See Fort Worth
Benbrook MS 6-8
201 Overcrest Dr 76126 817-815-7100
Sarah Weeks, prin. Fax 815-7150
Leonard MS 800/6-8
8900 Chapin Rd 76116 817-815-6200
Richard Pritchett, prin. Fax 815-6250

Western Hills HS 1,500/9-12
3600 Boston Ave 76116 817-815-6000
James Wellman, prin. Fax 815-6050

Benjamin, Knox, Pop. 256
Benjamin ISD 100/K-12
PO Box 166 79505 940-459-2231
Olivia Gloria, supt. Fax 459-2007
www.benjaminisd.net/
Benjamin S 100/K-12
PO Box 166 79505 940-459-2231
Olivia Gloria, prin. Fax 459-2007

Ben Wheeler, Van Zandt
Martins Mill ISD 500/PK-12
301 FM 1861 75754 903-479-3872
Todd Schneider, supt. Fax 479-3711
www.martinsmillisd.net
Martins Mill HS 200/7-12
301 FM 1861 75754 903-479-3234
Cory Hines, prin. Fax 479-3486

Big Lake, Reagan, Pop. 2,917
Reagan County ISD 800/PK-12
1111 E 12th St 76932 325-884-3705
Steve Long, supt. Fax 884-3021
www.reagancountyisd.net/
Reagan County HS 200/9-12
1111 E 12th St 76932 325-884-3714
Kara Garlitz, prin. Fax 884-5759
Reagan County MS 200/6-8
500 N Pennsylvania Ave 76932 325-884-3728
David Kohutek, prin. Fax 884-2327

Big Sandy, Upshur, Pop. 1,325
Big Sandy ISD 700/PK-12
PO Box 598 75755 903-636-5287
Scott Beene, supt. Fax 636-5117
www.bigsandyisd.org
Big Sandy HS 200/9-12
PO Box 598 75755 903-636-5287
Kim Stradley, prin. Fax 636-5111
Big Sandy JHS 200/6-8
PO Box 598 75755 903-636-5287
Lance Morrow, prin. Fax 636-5111

Harmony ISD 1,100/PK-12
9788 State Highway 154 W 75755 903-725-5492
Jed Whitaker, supt. Fax 725-6737
www.harmonyisd.net
Harmony HS 300/9-12
9788 State Highway 154 W 75755 903-725-5495
Dennis Glenn, prin. Fax 725-7079
Harmony JHS 200/6-8
9788 State Highway 154 W 75755 903-725-5485
Perry Cowan, prin. Fax 725-7270

Big Spring, Howard, Pop. 26,933
Big Spring ISD 3,400/PK-12
700 E 11th Pl 79720 432-264-3600
Steven Saldivar, supt. Fax 264-3646
bsisd.esc18.net/
Big Spring HS 1,000/9-12
708 E 11th Pl 79720 432-264-3641
Mike Ritchey, prin. Fax 264-4133
Big Spring JHS 500/7-8
708 E 11th Pl 79720 432-264-4135
Dalia Benavides, prin. Fax 264-4146
D.A.E.P. Alt
708 E 11th Pl 79720 432-264-3641
Charles Thomas, dir. Fax 264-3646

Howard College Post-Sec.
1001 N Birdwell Ln 79720 432-264-5000
Scenic Mountain Medical Center Post-Sec.
1601 W 11th Pl 79720 432-263-1211

Bishop, Nueces, Pop. 3,126
Bishop Consolidated ISD 1,200/PK-12
719 E 6th St 78343 361-584-3591
Christina Gutierrez, supt. Fax 584-3593
www.bishopcisd.esc2.net/
Bishop HS 400/9-12
100 Badger Ln 78343 361-584-2547
Ray Garza, prin. Fax 584-2549
Luehrs JHS 200/7-8
717 E 6th St 78343 361-584-3576
Andrea Kuyatt, prin. Fax 584-3577

Blackwell, Nolan, Pop. 309
Blackwell Consolidated ISD 200/PK-12
PO Box 505 79506 325-282-2311
Abe Gott, supt. Fax 282-2027
www.blackwellhornets.org
Blackwell S 200/PK-12
PO Box 505 79506 325-282-2311
Bryan Shipman, prin. Fax 282-2027

Blanco, Blanco, Pop. 1,722
Blanco ISD 1,000/PK-12
814 11th St 78606 830-833-4414
Dr. Jon Ford, supt. Fax 833-2019
www.blancoisd.com/
Blanco HS 300/9-12
814 11th St 78606 830-833-4337
Dustin Barton, prin. Fax 833-5028
Blanco MS 200/6-8
814 11th St 78606 830-833-5570
Bill Luna, prin. Fax 833-2507

Blanket, Brown, Pop. 382
Blanket ISD 200/K-12
901 Avenue H 76432 325-748-5311
Kevy Allred, supt. Fax 748-3391
www.blanketisd.net/
Blanket HS 100/7-12
901 Avenue H 76432 325-748-3341
Damon Wilson, prin. Fax 748-2110

Bloomburg, Cass, Pop. 398
Bloomburg ISD 300/PK-12
307 W Cypress St 75556 903-728-5216
Michael White, supt. Fax 728-5399
www.bloomburgisd.net
Bloomburg HS 100/6-12
307 W Cypress St 75556 903-728-5216
Lorinda Clark, prin. Fax 728-5399

Blooming Grove, Navarro, Pop. 812
Blooming Grove ISD 800/PK-12
PO Box 258 76626 903-695-2541
Jimmie Malone, supt. Fax 695-2594
www.bgisd.org
Blooming Grove HS 300/9-12
PO Box 258 76626 903-695-2541
Karen Lane, prin. Fax 695-2594
Blooming Grove JHS 200/6-8
PO Box 258 76626 903-695-4201
Doyle Bell, prin. Fax 695-4601

Bloomington, Victoria, Pop. 2,445
Bloomington ISD
Supt. — See Victoria
Bloomington HS 200/9-12
PO Box 158 77951 361-897-1551
James Pieper, prin. Fax 897-1888
Bloomington MS 200/6-8
PO Box 158 77951 361-897-2260
Michael Hannum, prin. Fax 897-3822

Blue Ridge, Collin, Pop. 807
Blue Ridge ISD 600/PK-12
10688 County Road 504 75424 972-752-5554
Todd Lintzen, supt. Fax 752-9084
brisd.net
Blue Ridge HS 200/9-12
11020 County Road 504 75424 972-752-5707
Danny Henderson, prin. Fax 752-5361
Blue Ridge MS 100/6-8
710 Tiger Pride Cir 75424 972-752-4243
Danny Henderson, prin. Fax 752-5363

Blum, Hill, Pop. 439
Blum ISD 400/PK-12
PO Box 520 76627 254-874-5231
Elsa Scott, supt. Fax 874-5233
www.blumisd.net
Blum JSHS 200/6-12
PO Box 520 76627 254-874-5231
Jeff Sanders, prin. Fax 874-5233

Boerne, Kendall, Pop. 10,349
Boerne ISD 6,600/PK-12
123 Johns Rd 78006 830-357-2000
David Stelmazewski, supt. Fax 357-2009
www.boerne-isd.net
Boerne Academy Alt
210 Live Oak St 78006 830-357-2925
Tom Brown, admin. Fax 357-2919
Boerne HS 900/9-12
1 Greyhound Ln 78006 830-357-2200
Natalie Farber, prin. Fax 357-2299
Boerne MS - North 500/7-8
240 Johns Rd 78006 830-357-3100
Tommy Hungate, prin. Fax 357-3199
Boerne MS - South 600/7-8
10 Cascade Caverns Rd 78015 830-357-3300
Susan Cleveland, prin. Fax 357-3399
Boerne-Samuel V. Champion HS 1,300/9-12
201 Charger Blvd 78006 830-357-2600
Dr. Jodi Spoor, prin. Fax 357-2699

Geneva S 400/K-10
113 Cascade Caverns Rd 78015 830-775-6101
Brad Ryden, hdmstr. Fax 755-6102
Vanguard Christian Institute 100/PK-12
43360 Interstate 10 W 78006 830-537-5244
Dr. Walter Tracy, supt. Fax 537-5785

Bogata, Red River, Pop. 1,141
Rivercrest ISD 700/PK-12
4100 US Highway 271 S 75417 903-632-5205
Charlie Martin, supt. Fax 632-4691
www.rivercrestisd.net
Rivercrest HS 200/9-12
4126 US Highway 271 S 75417 903-632-5204
James Littlejohn, prin. Fax 632-5231
Rivercrest JHS 200/6-8
4100 US Highway 271 S 75417 903-632-0878
Stanley Jessee, prin. Fax 632-4691

Boling, Wharton, Pop. 1,118
Boling ISD 1,000/PK-12
PO Box 160 77420 979-657-2770
Wade Stidevent, supt. Fax 657-3265
www.bolingisd.net
Boling HS 300/9-12
PO Box 119 77420 979-657-2816
Keith Jedlicka, prin. Fax 657-2026
Iago JHS 200/6-8
PO Box 89 77420 979-657-2826
Brett Pohler, prin. Fax 657-2828

Bonham, Fannin, Pop. 9,979
Bonham ISD 1,800/K-12
1005 Chestnut St 75418 903-583-5526
Sonny Cruse, supt. Fax 583-8463
www.bonhamisd.org/
Bonham HS 500/9-12
1002 War Path St 75418 903-583-5567
Steve Hill, prin. Fax 583-5560
Rather JHS 300/7-8
1201 N Main St 75418 903-583-7474
Karol Alexander, prin. Fax 583-3713

Booker, Lipscomb, Pop. 1,488
Booker ISD 400/PK-12
PO Box 288 79005 806-658-4501
Terri Zink, supt. Fax 658-4503
www.bookerisd.net/
Booker JSHS 200/6-12
PO Box 288 79005 806-658-4521
Kelly Lampe, prin. Fax 658-4503

Borger, Hutchinson, Pop. 13,012
Borger ISD 2,800/PK-12
200 E 9th St 79007 806-273-1000
Chance Welch, supt. Fax 273-1066
www.borgerisd.net
Borger HS 700/9-12
600 W 1st St 79007 806-273-1029
Matt Ammerman, prin. Fax 273-1036
Borger MS 600/6-8
1321 S Florida St 79007 806-273-1037
Michael Cano, prin. Fax 273-1069

Frank Phillips College Post-Sec.
PO Box 5118 79008 806-457-4200

Bovina, Parmer, Pop. 1,863
Bovina ISD 500/PK-12
PO Box 70 79009 806-251-1336
Dale Fullerton, supt. Fax 251-1578
www.esc16.net/bovinaisd/
Bovina HS 100/9-12
PO Box 70 79009 806-251-1317
Denise Anderson, prin. Fax 251-1002
Bovina MS 100/6-8
PO Box 70 79009 806-251-1377
Steve Arias, prin. Fax 251-1578

Bowie, Montague, Pop. 5,161
Bowie ISD 1,500/PK-12
PO Box 1168 76230 940-872-1151
Steven Monkres, supt. Fax 872-5979
www.bowieisd.net/
Bowie HS 400/9-12
341 US Highway 287 N Access 76230 940-872-1154
Kelly Shackelford, prin. Fax 872-1299
Bowie JHS 300/6-8
501 E Tarrant St 76230 940-872-1152
Sean McBeath, prin. Fax 872-8921

Gold-Burg ISD 100/K-12
468 Prater Rd 76230 940-872-3562
Kenny Miller, supt. Fax 872-5933
www.esc9.net/gold-burg/
Gold-Burg S 100/K-12
468 Prater Rd 76230 940-872-3562
Jeff Jackson, prin. Fax 872-5933

Boyd, Wise, Pop. 1,184
Boyd ISD 1,100/PK-12
PO Box 92308 76023 940-433-2327
Ted West, supt. Fax 433-9569
www.boydisd.net
Boyd HS 400/9-12
PO Box 92308 76023 940-433-2327
Ted West, prin. Fax 433-9593
Boyd MS 200/7-8
PO Box 92308 76023 940-433-9560
James McDonald, prin. Fax 433-9568

Boys Ranch, Oldham, Pop. 281
Boys Ranch ISD 300/K-12
PO Box 219 79010 806-534-2221
Vita Sotelo, supt. Fax 534-2384
www.boysranchisd.org/
Blakemore MS 100/6-8
PO Box 219 79010 806-534-2361
Michelle Ellis, prin. Fax 534-0041
Boys Ranch HS 200/9-12
PO Box 219 79010 806-534-0032
Derek Davis, prin. Fax 534-0033
STARR Academy 50/Alt
PO Box 219 79010 806-533-1413
Shelly Allen, prin. Fax 533-2220

Brackettville, Kinney, Pop. 1,675
Brackett ISD 600/PK-12
PO Box 586 78832 830-563-2491
Taylor Stephenson, supt. Fax 563-9264
www.brackettisd.net/
Brackett HS 200/9-12
PO Box 586 78832 830-563-2480
Kevin Newsom, prin. Fax 563-3213
Brackett JHS 100/6-8
PO Box 586 78832 830-563-2480
George Burks, prin. Fax 563-9559

Brady, McCulloch, Pop. 5,490
Brady ISD 1,100/PK-12
1003 11th St 76825 325-597-2301
Johnny Clawson, supt. Fax 597-3984
www.bradyisd.org
Brady HS 300/9-12
100 W Main St 76825 325-597-2491
Eric Bierman, prin. Fax 597-2147
Brady MS 300/6-8
100 W Main St 76825 325-597-8110
Shona Moore, prin. Fax 597-4166

Brazoria, Brazoria, Pop. 2,978
Columbia-Brazoria ISD
Supt. — See West Columbia
West Brazos JHS 400/7-8
111 Roustabout Dr 77422 979-799-1730
Joe Longoria, prin. Fax 798-8000

Breckenridge, Stephens, Pop. 5,738
Breckenridge ISD 1,600/PK-12
PO Box 1738 76424 254-559-2278
Jennings Teel, supt. Fax 559-2353
www.breckenridgeisd.org

Breckenridge HS 400/9-12
500 W Lindsey St 76424 254-559-2231
Bryan Dieterich, prin. Fax 559-7485
Breckenridge JHS 200/7-8
502 W Lindsey St 76424 254-559-6581
Jessica Stapp, prin. Fax 559-1082

Bremond, Robertson, Pop. 926
Bremond ISD 500/PK-12
601 W Collins St 76629 254-746-7145
Daryl Stuard, supt. Fax 746-7726
www.bremondisd.net
Bremond HS 100/9-12
601 W Collins St 76629 254-746-7145
Harold Schroeder, prin. Fax 746-7726
Bremond MS 100/6-8
601 W Collins St 76629 254-746-7145
John Burnett, prin. Fax 746-7726

Brenham, Washington, Pop. 15,543
Brenham ISD 4,900/PK-12
PO Box 1147 77834 979-277-3700
Sam Bell, supt. Fax 277-3701
www.brenhamisd.net
Brenham Alternative S 50/Alt
1301 S Market St 77833 979-277-6537
Kay Schulze, prin. Fax 277-6532
Brenham HS 1,400/9-12
525 A H Ehrig Dr 77833 979-277-3800
Steve Skrla, prin. Fax 277-3801
Brenham JHS 700/7-8
1200 Carlee Dr 77833 979-277-3830
Paul Aschenbeck, prin. Fax 277-3831

Blinn College Post-Sec.
902 College Ave 77833 979-830-4000
Brenham Christian Academy 100/PK-12
2111 S Blue Bell Rd 77833 979-830-8480
Dr. Charles Loyd, head sch Fax 830-1687

Bridge City, Orange, Pop. 7,734
Bridge City ISD 2,200/PK-12
1031 W Round Bunch Rd 77611 409-735-1500
Mike King, supt. Fax 735-1512
www.bridgecityisd.net/
Bridge City HS 700/9-12
2690 Texas Ave 77611 409-735-1501
Richard Briggs, prin. Fax 735-1519
Bridge City MS 600/6-8
300 Bower Dr 77611 409-735-1513
Lance Groppel, prin. Fax 735-1517

Bridgeport, Wise, Pop. 5,936
Bridgeport ISD 2,300/PK-12
2107 15th St 76426 940-683-5124
Eddie Bland, supt. Fax 683-4268
www.bridgeportisd.net
Alternative Learning Center Alt
1101 17th St 76426 940-683-1830
Jennifer Miller, prin. Fax 683-3582
Bridgeport HS 600/9-12
1 Maroon Dr 76426 940-683-4064
Jaime Sturdivant, prin. Fax 683-4014
Bridgeport MS 500/6-8
702 17th St 76426 940-683-2273
Travis Whisenant, prin. Fax 683-5812

Briscoe, Wheeler
Fort Elliott Consolidated ISD 200/PK-12
PO Box 138 79011 806-375-2454
Roy Baker, supt. Fax 375-2327
Ft. Elliott JSHS 100/6-12
PO Box 138 79011 806-375-2454
Brad Slatton, prin. Fax 375-2327

Broaddus, San Augustine, Pop. 202
Broaddus ISD 500/PK-12
PO Box 58 75929 936-872-3041
Shane McGown, supt. Fax 872-3699
www.broaddus.esc7.net
Broaddus JSHS 200/7-12
PO Box 58 75929 936-872-3610
Clark Bynum, prin. Fax 872-9020

Brock, Parker
Brock ISD 900/K-12
410 Eagle Spirit Ln 76087 817-594-7642
Richard Tedder, supt. Fax 599-3246
www.brockisd.net
Brock HS 300/9-12
400 Eagle Spirit Ln 76087 817-596-7425
Jamie Payne, prin. Fax 594-2509
Brock MS 200/6-8
300 Grindstone Rd 76087 817-594-3195
Chad Massey, prin. Fax 594-3191

Bronte, Coke, Pop. 986
Bronte ISD 300/PK-12
PO Box 670 76933 325-473-2511
Alan Richey, supt. Fax 473-2313
www.bronteisd.net/
Bronte JSHS 100/7-12
PO Box 670 76933 325-473-2521
David Bedford, prin. Fax 473-2022

Brookeland, Sabine
Brookeland ISD 400/PK-12
187 Wildcat Walk 75931 409-698-2677
Kevin McCugh, supt. Fax 698-2533
www.brookelandisd.net
Brookeland JSHS 200/6-12
187 Wildcat Walk 75931 409-698-2413
Brad Hranicky, prin. Fax 698-2891

Brookesmith, Brown
Brookesmith ISD 200/PK-12
PO Box 706 76827 325-643-3023
Dr. Jay Smith, supt. Fax 643-3378
www.brookesmithisd.net/
Brookesmith S 200/PK-12
PO Box 706 76827 325-646-3791
Dr. Jay Smith, prin. Fax 646-3378

Brookshire, Waller, Pop. 4,653
Royal ISD
Supt. — See Pattison
Royal HS 500/9-12
34499 Royal Rd 77423 281-934-2215
Dr. Jimmy Golden, prin. Fax 934-2866
Royal JHS 400/6-8
2520 Durkin Rd 77423 281-934-2241
Dr. Gary Bates, prin. Fax 934-2329

Brownfield, Terry, Pop. 9,594
Brownfield ISD 1,600/PK-12
601 E Tahoka Rd 79316 806-637-2591
Jerry Jones, supt. Fax 637-9208
www.brownfieldisd.net/
Brownfield HS 400/9-12
701 Cub Dr 79316 806-637-4523
Jerry Lawrence, prin. Fax 637-3801
Brownfield MS 400/6-8
1001 E Broadway St 79316 806-637-7521
Michelle Cooper, prin. Fax 637-2919

Brownsboro, Henderson, Pop. 1,031
Brownsboro ISD 2,900/PK-12
PO Box 465 75756 903-852-3701
Dr. Christopher Moran, supt. Fax 852-3957
www.gobearsgo.net
Brownsboro HS 900/9-12
PO Box 465 75756 903-852-2321
Brandon Jones, prin. Fax 852-5195
Brownsboro JHS 400/7-8
PO Box 465 75756 903-852-6931
Bradley Robertson, prin. Fax 852-5238

Brownsville, Cameron, Pop. 174,679
Brownsville ISD 48,700/PK-12
1900 Price Rd 78521 956-548-8000
Dr. Carl Montoya, supt. Fax 548-8010
www.bisd.us/
Besteiro MS 900/6-8
6280 Southmost Rd 78521 956-544-3900
Irene Hernandez, prin. Fax 544-3946
Brownsville Academic Center Alt
3308 Robindale Rd 78526 956-504-6305
Carlos Guerra, prin. Fax 831-8267
Brownsville Early College HS 300/9-12
733 Palm Blvd 78520 956-698-1476
Dawn Hall, prin. Fax 548-8842
Brownsville Learning Academy Alt
1351 Polk St 78520 956-982-2860
Aimee Garza, prin. Fax 982-3028
Cummings MS 800/6-8
1800 Cummings Pl 78520 956-548-8630
Dr. Edward Ude, prin. Fax 548-8218
Faulk MS 900/6-8
2000 Roosevelt St 78521 956-548-8500
Carla Pereira, prin. Fax 548-8507
Garcia MS 1,200/6-8
5701 FM 802 78526 956-832-6300
Teresa Nunez, prin. Fax 832-6304
Hanna HS 3,100/9-12
2615 E Price Rd 78521 956-548-7600
Terri Alarcon, prin. Fax 548-7603
Lopez HS 2,300/9-12
3205 S Dakota Ave 78521 956-982-7400
Dahlia Aguilar, prin. Fax 982-7499
Lucio MS 1,100/6-8
300 N Vermillion Ave 78521 956-831-4550
Dr. Linda Gallegos, prin. Fax 838-2298
Manzano MS 600/6-8
2580 W Alton Gloor Blvd 78520 956-548-9800
Norma Torres, prin. Fax 548-6772
Oliveira MS 1,200/6-8
444 Land O Lakes Dr 78521 956-548-8530
Jennifer Gonzales, prin. Fax 544-3968
Pace HS 2,100/9-12
314 W Los Ebanos Blvd 78520 956-548-7700
Rose Longoria, prin. Fax 548-7710
Perkins MS 800/6-8
4750 Austin Rd 78521 956-831-8770
Dr. Jose Puga, prin. Fax 831-8789
Porter HS 2,200/9-12
3500 International Blvd 78521 956-548-7800
Liz Valdez, prin. Fax 982-2892
Rivera HS 2,100/9-12
6955 FM 802 78526 956-831-8700
Hector Hernandez, prin. Fax 831-8705
Stell MS 1,100/6-8
1105 E Los Ebanos Blvd 78520 956-548-8560
Luis Segura, prin. Fax 548-8666
Stillman MS 1,000/6-8
2977 W Tandy Rd 78520 956-698-1000
Eduardo Martinez, prin. Fax 350-3231
Vela MS 1,100/6-8
4905 Paredes Line Rd 78526 956-548-7770
Rosie Ara, prin. Fax 548-7780
Veterans Memorial HS 9-12
4550 US Highway 281 78520 956-574-5600
Maria Solis, prin. Fax 452-1341

First Baptist S 300/PK-12
1600 Boca Chica Blvd 78520 956-542-4854
Terry Roberts, supt. Fax 542-6188
Guadalupe Regional MS 100/6-8
1214 Lincoln St 78521 956-504-5568
Kathy Stapleton, pres. Fax 504-9393
Kaplan College Post-Sec.
1900 N Expressway 78521 956-547-8200
St. Joseph Academy 800/7-12
101 Saint Joseph Dr 78520 956-542-3581
Lucy Williams, prin. Fax 542-4748
University of Texas at Brownsville Post-Sec.
80 Fort Brown St 78520 956-882-8200
Valley Christian HS 100/9-12
PO Box 4220 78523 956-542-5222
Gail Hanson, prin. Fax 542-0038

Brownwood, Brown, Pop. 19,003
Brownwood ISD 3,600/PK-12
PO Box 730 76804 325-643-5644
Reece Blincoe, supt. Fax 643-5640
www.brownwoodisd.org
Brownwood HS 900/9-12
2100 Slayden St 76801 325-646-9549
Bill Faircloth, prin. Fax 643-1965
Brownwood MS 500/7-8
PO Box 1286 76804 325-646-9545
Bryan Allen, prin. Fax 646-3785

Howard Payne University Post-Sec.
1000 Fisk Ave 76801 325-646-2502
Victory Life Academy 100/PK-12
PO Box 940 76804 325-641-2223
Cathy Roberts, supt. Fax 643-9772

Bruni, Webb, Pop. 377
Webb Consolidated ISD 400/PK-12
PO Box 206 78344 361-747-5415
Dr. Severita Sanchez, supt. Fax 747-5202
webbcisd.org
Bruni HS 100/9-12
PO Box 206 78344 361-747-5415
Humberto Soliz, prin. Fax 747-5301
Bruni MS 100/6-8
PO Box 206 78344 361-747-5415
Josie Castillo, prin. Fax 747-5298

Bryan, Brazos, Pop. 75,248
Bryan ISD 15,700/PK-12
101 N Texas Ave 77803 979-209-1000
Thomas Wallis, supt. Fax 209-1004
www.bryanisd.org
Austin MS 900/6-8
801 S Ennis St 77803 979-209-6700
Patti Moore, prin. Fax 209-6741
Bryan Collegiate HS 300/9-12
1901 E Villa Maria Rd 77802 979-209-2790
Christina Richardson, prin. Fax 209-2791
Bryan HS 2,300/9-12
3450 Campus Dr 77802 979-209-2400
Lamond Dean, prin. Fax 209-2402
Davila MS 600/6-8
2751 N Earl Rudder Fwy 77803 979-209-7150
Scott Martindale, prin. Fax 209-7151
Harris S 200/Alt
1307 Memorial Dr 77802 979-209-2700
Rebecca Stringer, prin. Fax 209-2704
Long MS 900/6-8
1106 N Harvey Mitchell Pkwy 77803 979-209-6500
Lindsay Harris, prin. Fax 209-6566
Oliver HS for Human Sciences 9-12
1305 Memorial Dr 77802 979-209-2800
Judy Hughson, dean Fax 209-2809
Rayburn MS 900/6-8
1048 N Earl Rudder Fwy 77802 979-209-6600
Lane Buban, prin. Fax 209-6611
Rudder HS 1,200/9-12
3251 Austins Colony Pkwy 77808 979-209-7900
Hugh Piatt, prin. Fax 209-7901
Adult Learning Center Adult
1700 Palasota Dr 77803 979-209-7040
Becky Collet, dir. Fax 209-7041

Allen Academy 300/PK-12
3201 Boonville Rd 77802 979-776-0731
John Rouse, hdmstr. Fax 774-7769
Blinn College Post-Sec.
PO Box 6030 77805 979-209-7200
Brazos Christian S 400/PK-12
3000 W Villa Maria Rd 77807 979-823-1000
Keith Currivean, hdmstr. Fax 823-1774
Charlie & Sue's School of Hair Design Post-Sec.
1711 Briarcrest Dr 77802 979-776-4375
St. Joseph Catholic HS 200/6-12
600 S Coulter Dr 77803 979-822-6641
Bea Janssen, admin. Fax 779-2810
St. Michael's Episcopal S 100/PK-12
2500 S College Ave 77801 979-822-2715
Jenny Morris, head sch Fax 823-4971
Texas A&M University Health Science Ctr Post-Sec.
8441 State Highway 47 #3100 77807 979-436-9100

Bryson, Jack, Pop. 518
Bryson ISD 200/PK-12
PO Box 309 76427 940-392-3281
David Stout, supt. Fax 392-2086
www.brysonisd.net
Bryson S 200/PK-12
PO Box 309 76427 940-392-2601
Eric Wilson, prin. Fax 392-2086

Buckholts, Milam, Pop. 513
Buckholts ISD 200/PK-12
PO Box 248 76518 254-593-2744
Dirk Dykstra, supt. Fax 593-2270
www.buckholtsisd.net
Buckholts S 200/PK-12
PO Box 248 76518 254-593-2744
Julie House, prin. Fax 593-2270

Buda, Hays, Pop. 7,167
Hays Consolidated ISD
Supt. — See Kyle
Barton MS 800/6-8
4950 Jack C Hays Trl 78610 512-268-1472
Teri Eubank, prin. Fax 268-1610
Dahlstrom MS 700/6-8
3600 FM 967 78610 512-268-8441
Rod Trevino, prin. Fax 295-5346
Hays HS 2,000/9-12
4800 Jack C Hays Trl 78610 512-268-2911
David Pierce, prin. Fax 268-1394

Impact Center — 100/Alt
4125 FM 967 78610 — 512-268-8473
Sylvia Villejo, prin. — Fax 295-5006
Live Oak Academy — 100/Alt
4820 Jack C Hays Trl 78610 — 512-268-8462
Julie Ruisinger, prin. — Fax 268-4142

Buffalo, Leon, Pop. 1,845
Buffalo ISD — 900/PK-12
708 Cedar Creek Rd 75831 — 903-322-3765
Lacy Freeman, supt. — Fax 322-3091
www.buffaloisd.net
Buffalo HS — 300/9-12
1724 N Buffalo Ave 75831 — 903-322-4243
Tracy Gleghorn, prin. — Fax 322-5806
Buffalo JHS — 300/4-8
335 Bison Trl 75831 — 903-322-4340
Amanda Davis, prin. — Fax 322-4803

Bullard, Smith, Pop. 2,447
Bullard ISD — 2,100/PK-12
PO Box 250 75757 — 903-894-6639
Keith Bryant, supt. — Fax 894-9291
www.bullardisd.net
Bullard HS — 600/9-12
PO Box 250 75757 — 903-894-3272
Scott Franks, prin. — Fax 894-3051
Bullard MS — 300/7-8
PO Box 250 75757 — 903-894-6533
Cheryl Hendrix, prin. — Fax 894-7592

Brook Hill S — 500/PK-12
1051 N Houston St 75757 — 903-894-5000
Rod Fletcher, hdmstr. — Fax 894-6332

Bulverde, Comal, Pop. 4,570

Bracken Christian S — 400/PK-12
670 Old Boerne Rd 78163 — 830-438-3211
Jason Detty, admin. — Fax 980-2327

Buna, Jasper, Pop. 2,103
Buna ISD — 1,600/PK-12
PO Box 1087 77612 — 409-994-5101
Robin Porez Ed.D., supt. — Fax 994-4808
www.bunaisd.net
Buna HS — 400/9-12
PO Box 1087 77612 — 409-994-4811
Nathan Ross, prin. — Fax 994-4818
Buna JHS — 400/6-8
PO Box 1087 77612 — 409-994-4860
Kelley Peck, prin. — Fax 994-4808

Burkburnett, Wichita, Pop. 10,638
Burkburnett ISD — 3,400/PK-12
416 Glendale St 76354 — 940-569-3326
Danny Taylor, supt. — Fax 569-4776
www.burkburnettisd.org
Burkburnett HS — 800/9-12
109 W Kramer Rd 76354 — 940-569-1411
Brad Owen, prin. — Fax 569-1512
Burkburnett MS — 700/6-8
108 S Avenue D 76354 — 940-569-3381
Scott Slater, prin. — Fax 569-7116

Burkeville, Newton
Burkeville ISD — 300/PK-12
PO Box 218 75932 — 409-565-2201
Paula Quick, supt. — Fax 565-2012
www.burkeville.org/
Burkeville JSHS — 100/7-12
PO Box 218 75932 — 409-565-4338
Terry Young, prin. — Fax 565-2461

Burleson, Johnson, Pop. 36,116
Burleson ISD — 10,000/PK-12
1160 SW Wilshire Blvd 76028 — 817-245-1000
Richard Crummel, supt. — Fax 447-5737
www.burlesonisd.net
Burleson HS — 1,900/9-12
100 Elk Dr 76028 — 817-245-0000
Aaron McWilliams, prin. — Fax 447-5796
Centennial HS — 800/9-12
201 S Hurst Rd 76028 — 817-245-0250
Lance Campbell, prin. — Fax 447-2152
Crossroads HS — 100/Alt
505 Pleasant Manor Ave 76028 — 817-447-0500
Janna McCollough, prin. — Fax 447-5889
Hughes MS — 1,100/6-8
316 SW Thomas St 76028 — 817-245-0600
Mekasha Brown, prin. — Fax 447-5748
Kerr MS — 1,200/6-8
517 SW Johnson Ave 76028 — 817-245-0750
Dr. Miller Beaird, prin. — Fax 447-5742

Burnet, Burnet, Pop. 5,927
Burnet Consolidated ISD — 3,400/PK-12
208 E Brier Ln 78611 — 512-756-2124
Keith McBurnett, supt. — Fax 756-7498
www.burnet.txed.net
Burnet HS — 1,000/9-12
1000 The Green Mile Rd 78611 — 512-756-6193
Mark Kincaid, prin. — Fax 756-4553
Burnet MS — 800/6-8
1401 N Main St 78611 — 512-756-6182
Kevin Jones, prin. — Fax 756-7955
Highland Lakes Achievement Ctr.\Quest HS — 50/Alt
303 N Pierce St 78611 — 512-756-6747
Jeff Conovan, prin. — Fax 756-6289

Burton, Washington, Pop. 298
Burton ISD — 400/PK-12
PO Box 37 77835 — 979-289-3131
James Palmer, supt. — Fax 289-3076
www.burtonisd.net
Burton JSHS — 200/7-12
PO Box 499 77835 — 979-289-3830
Karen Steenken, prin. — Fax 289-4609

Bushland, Potter
Bushland ISD — 1,300/PK-12
PO Box 60 79012 — 806-359-6683
Don Wood, supt. — Fax 359-6769
bushlandisd.org/
Bushland HS — 400/9-12
PO Box 60 79012 — 806-359-6683
Rick Davis, prin. — Fax 322-1180
Bushland MS — 400/5-8
PO Box 60 79012 — 806-359-5418
Mark Reasor, prin. — Fax 355-2841

Bynum, Hill, Pop. 197
Bynum ISD — 200/PK-12
PO Box 68 76631 — 254-623-4251
Brenda Speer, supt. — Fax 623-4290
www.bynumisd.net/
Bynum S — 200/PK-12
PO Box 68 76631 — 254-623-4251
Amy Feller, prin. — Fax 623-4290

Caddo Mills, Hunt, Pop. 1,323
Caddo Mills ISD — 1,500/PK-12
PO Box 160 75135 — 903-527-6056
Vicki Payne, supt. — Fax 527-4883
www.caddomillsisd.org/caddomillsisd/site/default.asp
Caddo Mills HS — 500/9-12
PO Box 160 75135 — 903-527-3164
Brian McKamy, prin. — Fax 527-4772
Caddo Mills MS — 300/6-8
PO Box 160 75135 — 903-527-3161
Michael Powell, prin. — Fax 527-2379

Caldwell, Burleson, Pop. 4,063
Caldwell ISD — 1,900/PK-12
203 N Gray St 77836 — 979-567-9000
Dr. Janet Cummings, supt. — Fax 567-9876
www.caldwell.k12.tx.us/
Caldwell HS — 500/9-12
203 N Gray St 77836 — 979-567-9030
Dr. Brad Vestal, prin. — Fax 567-9032
Caldwell MS — 400/6-8
203 N Gray St 77836 — 979-567-6270
Gary Stout, prin. — Fax 567-7433

Callisburg, Cooke, Pop. 352
Callisburg ISD — 1,200/PK-12
148 Dozier St, — 940-665-0540
Steve Clugston, supt. — Fax 668-2706
www.cisdtx.net
Callisburg HS — 400/9-12
148 Dozier St, — 940-665-0961
Tommy Cummings, prin. — Fax 665-2849
Callisburg MS — 200/6-8
148 Dozier St, — 940-665-0961
Bronwyn Werts, prin. — Fax 665-2849

Calvert, Robertson, Pop. 1,179
Calvert ISD — 200/PK-12
PO Box 7 77837 — 979-364-2824
Maxie Morgan, supt. — Fax 364-2468
www.calvertisd.com/
Calvert S — 200/PK-12
PO Box 7 77837 — 979-364-2845
James Ponder, prin. — Fax 364-2043

Cameron, Milam, Pop. 5,512
Cameron ISD — 1,600/PK-12
PO Box 712 76520 — 254-697-3512
Collin Clark, supt. — Fax 697-2448
www.cameronisd.net
Cameron JHS — 300/6-8
PO Box 712 76520 — 254-697-2131
Missi Giesenschlag, prin. — Fax 605-0379
Yoe HS — 400/9-12
PO Box 712 76520 — 254-697-3902
Kenneth Driska, prin. — Fax 605-0413

Campbell, Hunt, Pop. 622
Campbell ISD — 400/PK-12
480 N Patterson St 75422 — 903-862-3259
Earnie Phelps, supt. — Fax 862-2222
www.campbellisd.org
Campbell JSHS — 200/6-12
480 N Patterson St 75422 — 903-862-3257
James Daugherty, admin. — Fax 862-3547

Canadian, Hemphill, Pop. 2,631
Canadian ISD — 800/PK-12
800 Hillside Ave 79014 — 806-323-5393
Kyle Lynch, supt. — Fax 323-8143
www.canadianisd.net
Canadian HS — 200/9-12
800 Hillside Ave 79014 — 806-323-5373
Rick Berry, prin. — Fax 323-9345
Canadian MS — 200/6-8
800 Hillside Ave 79014 — 806-323-5351
Bruce Bryant, prin. — Fax 323-8791

Canton, Van Zandt, Pop. 3,519
Canton ISD — 2,000/PK-12
225 W Elm St 75103 — 903-567-4179
Jay Tullos, supt. — Fax 567-2370
www.cantonisd.net
Canton HS — 600/9-12
1110 W Highway 243 75103 — 903-567-6561
Joe Nicks, prin. — Fax 567-6562
Canton JHS — 500/6-8
1115 S Buffalo St 75103 — 903-567-4329
Amy Autry, prin. — Fax 567-1298

Canutillo, El Paso, Pop. 6,297
Canutillo ISD
Supt. — See El Paso
Alderete MS — 700/6-8
PO Box 100 79835 — 915-877-6600
Marina Rocha, prin. — Fax 877-6607
Canutillo MS — 700/6-8
PO Box 100 79835 — 915-877-7900
Dr. Monica Reyes-Garcia, prin. — Fax 877-7907

Canyon, Randall, Pop. 13,164
Canyon ISD — 8,800/PK-12
PO Box 899 79015 — 806-677-2600
Mike Wartes, supt. — Fax 677-2659
www.canyonisd.net
Canyon HS — 1,100/9-12
1701 23rd St 79015 — 806-677-2740
Tim Gilliland, prin. — Fax 677-2779
Canyon JHS — 600/7-8
910 9th Ave 79015 — 806-677-2700
Kirk Kear, prin. — Fax 677-2739
Other Schools – See Amarillo

West Texas A&M University — Post-Sec.
2501 4th Ave 79016 — 806-651-0000

Carmine, Fayette, Pop. 250
Round Top - Carmine ISD — 200/PK-12
PO Box 385 78932 — 979-249-3200
Ronald Goehring, supt. — Fax 249-4084
www.rtcisd.net/
Round Top - Carmine HS — 100/7-12
PO Box 385 78932 — 979-278-3252
Mark Conley, prin. — Fax 278-3063

Carrizo Springs, Dimmit, Pop. 5,350
Carrizo Springs Consolidated ISD — 2,400/PK-12
300 N 7th St 78834 — 830-876-2473
Dr. Deborah Dobie, supt. — Fax 876-9700
www.cscisd.net
Carrizo Springs HS — 600/9-12
300 N 7th St 78834 — 830-876-5237
Jesse Salazar, prin. — Fax 876-3052
Carrizo Springs JHS — 500/6-8
300 N 7th St 78834 — 830-876-2496
David Davis, prin. — Fax 876-3655

Carrollton, Denton, Pop. 116,719
Carrollton-Farmers Branch ISD — 25,600/PK-12
PO Box 115186 75011 — 972-968-6100
Dr. Bobby Burns, supt. — Fax 968-6210
www.cfbisd.edu
Blalack MS — 1,000/6-8
1706 E Peters Colony Rd 75007 — 972-968-3500
Lance Hamlin, prin. — Fax 968-3510
Creekview HS — 2,100/9-12
3201 Old Denton Rd 75007 — 972-968-4800
Joe LaPuma, prin. — Fax 968-4810
Grimes Education Center — 300/Alt
1745 Hutton Dr 75006 — 972-968-5600
Bob Tipton, prin. — Fax 968-5610
Perry MS — 900/6-8
1709 E Belt Line Rd 75006 — 972-968-4400
Asheley Brown, prin. — Fax 968-4410
Polk MS — 1,000/6-8
2001 Kelly Blvd 75006 — 972-968-4600
Melanie Magee, prin. — Fax 968-4610
Salazar S — 100/Alt
2416 Keller Springs Rd 75006 — 972-968-5600
Melissa Wesley, prin. — Fax 968-5610
Smith HS — 2,000/9-12
2335 N Josey Ln 75006 — 972-968-5200
Joe Pouncey, prin. — Fax 968-5210
Turner HS — 2,000/9-12
1600 S Josey Ln Bldg 1 75006 — 972-968-5400
Brooke Puricelli, prin. — Fax 968-5410
Other Schools – See Dallas, Farmers Branch, Irving

Lewisville ISD
Supt. — See Flower Mound
Arbor Creek MS — 900/6-8
2109 Arbor Creek Dr 75010 — 469-713-5971
Joanie Finch, prin. — Fax 350-9163
Creek Valley MS — 600/6-8
4109 Creek Valley Blvd 75010 — 469-713-5184
Nicole Jund, prin. — Fax 350-9172
Hebron HS — 2,000/10-12
4207 Plano Pkwy 75010 — 469-713-5183
Scot Finch, prin. — Fax 350-9255
Hebron Ninth Grade Center — 100/9-9
4211 Plano Pkwy 75010 — 469-713-5996
Mark Dalton, prin. — Fax 626-1630

Carrollton Christian Academy — 300/PK-12
2205 E Hebron Pkwy 75010 — 972-242-6688
Rev. David Culpepper, head sch — Fax 245-0321
Prince of Peace Christian S — 900/PK-12
4000 Midway Rd 75007 — 972-447-9887
Chris Hahn, hdmstr. — Fax 447-0877
Toni & Guy Hairdressing Academy — Post-Sec.
2810 E Trinity Mills Rd 75006 — 972-416-8396

Carthage, Panola, Pop. 6,679
Carthage ISD — 2,900/PK-12
1 Bulldog Dr 75633 — 903-693-3806
J. Glenn Hambrick, supt. — Fax 693-3650
www.carthageisd.org
Carthage HS — 700/9-12
1 Bulldog Dr 75633 — 903-693-2552
Otis Amy, prin. — Fax 693-9752
Carthage JHS — 400/7-8
1 Bulldog Dr 75633 — 903-693-2751
Mike Baysinger, prin. — Fax 693-9582

Panola College — Post-Sec.
1109 W Panola St 75633 — 903-693-2000

Castroville, Medina, Pop. 2,662
Medina Valley ISD — 3,500/PK-12
8449 FM 471 S 78009 — 830-931-2243
James Stansberry, supt. — Fax 931-4050
www.mvisd.com
Medina Valley HS — 1,000/9-12
8365 FM 471 S 78009 — 830-931-2243
Toby Tyler, prin. — Fax 931-0371
Medina Valley MS — 800/6-8
8395 FM 471 S 78009 — 830-931-2243
Michael Homann, prin. — Fax 931-3258

Cayuga, Anderson
Cayuga ISD — 600/PK-12
PO Box 427 75832 — 903-928-2102
Dr. Rick Webb, supt. — Fax 928-2646
www.cayuga.esc7.net
Cayuga HS — 200/9-12
PO Box 427 75832 — 903-928-2294
Gregory Branch, prin. — Fax 928-2646
Cayuga MS — 200/6-8
PO Box 427 75832 — 903-928-2699
Sherri McInnis, prin. — Fax 928-2646

Cedar Creek, Bastrop
Bastrop ISD
Supt. — See Bastrop
Cedar Creek HS — 600/9-12
793 Union Chapel Rd 78612 — 512-772-7300
Adelaida Olivares, prin. — Fax 772-7930
Cedar Creek MS — 700/7-8
125 Voss Pkwy 78612 — 512-332-2626
Jim Hallamek, prin. — Fax 332-2631

Cedar Hill, Dallas, Pop. 44,182
Cedar Hill ISD — 7,800/PK-12
PO Box 248 75106 — 972-291-1581
Horace Williams, supt. — Fax 291-5231
www.ohiod.not
Cedar Hill SHS — 1,700/10-12
PO Box 248 75106 — 469-272-2000
Tammy Mariani, prin. — Fax 293-7125
Coleman MS — 500/7-8
PO Box 248 75106 — 972-293-4505
Constance Jawaid, prin. — Fax 272-9445
Ninth Grade Center — 600/9-9
PO Box 248 75106 — 469-272-2050
Dr. Rickie Harris, prin. — Fax 272-3443
Permenter MS — 800/7-8
PO Box 248 75106 — 972-291-5270
Dr. Shauntee Mayfield, prin. — Fax 291-5296

Northwood University — Post-Sec.
1114 W FM 1382 75104 — 800-622-9000
Trinity Christian S — 600/PK-12
1231 E Pleasant Run Rd 75104 — 972-291-2505
Dr. Kathleen Watts, supt. — Fax 291-4739

Cedar Park, Williamson, Pop. 47,764
Leander ISD
Supt. — See Leander
Cedar Park HS — 2,000/9-12
2150 Cypress Creek Rd 78613 — 512-570-1200
Barb Spelman, prin. — Fax 570-1205
Cedar Park MS — 1,300/6-8
2100 Sun Chase Blvd 78613 — 512-570-3100
Sandra Stewart, prin. — Fax 570-3105
Henry MS — 1,400/6-8
100 N Vista Ridge Pkwy 78613 — 512-570-3400
Dr. David Ellis, prin. — Fax 570-3405
Running Brushy MS — 1,100/6-8
2303 N Lakeline Blvd 78613 — 512-570-3300
Karin Johnson, prin. — Fax 570-3305
Vista Ridge HS — 1,900/9-12
200 S Vista Ridge Pkwy 78613 — 512-570-1800
Paul Johnson, prin. — Fax 570-1805

Summit Christian Academy of Cedar Park — 300/PK-12
2121 Cypress Creek Rd 78613 — 512-250-1369
Shannon Dare, hdmstr. — Fax 257-1851

Celeste, Hunt, Pop. 800
Celeste ISD — 500/PK-12
PO Box 67 75423 — 903-568-4825
Ricky Beadles, supt. — Fax 568-4495
www.celesteisd.org/
Celeste HS — 200/9-12
PO Box 67 75423 — 903-568-4721
Jerry Card, prin. — Fax 568-4115
Celeste JHS — 100/6-8
PO Box 67 75423 — 903-568-4721
Staci Beadles, prin. — Fax 568-4277

Celina, Collin, Pop. 5,948
Celina ISD — 2,000/PK-12
205 S Colorado St 75009 — 469-742-9100
Donny O'Dell, supt. — Fax 382-3607
www.celinaisd.com/
Celina HS — 600/9-12
3455 N Preston Rd 75009 — 469-742-9102
Bill Hemby, prin. — Fax 382-4830
Celina MS — 500/6-8
710 E Pecan St 75009 — 469-742-9101
John Mathews, prin. — Fax 382-4258

Center, Shelby, Pop. 5,149
Center ISD — 2,700/PK-12
PO Box 1689 75935 — 936-598-5642
James Hockenberry, supt. — Fax 598-1515
www.centerisd.org/
Center HS — 600/9-12
658 Rough Rider Dr 75935 — 936-598-6173
Tim Norman, prin. — Fax 598-1557
Center MS — 500/6-8
302 Kennedy St 75935 — 936-598-5619
Patricia Tiller, prin. — Fax 598-1534

Center Point, Kerr
Center Point ISD — 600/PK-12
PO Box 377 78010 — 830-634-2171
Cody Newcomb, supt. — Fax 634-2254
www.cpisd.net
Center Point HS — 200/9-12
PO Box 377 78010 — 830-634-2244
Keith Mills, prin. — Fax 634-7430
Center Point MS — 100/6-8
PO Box 377 78010 — 830-634-2533
Keith Mills, prin. — Fax 634-7825

Centerville, Leon, Pop. 862
Centerville ISD — 700/PK-12
813 S Commerce St 75833 — 903-536-7812
Cathy Nichols, supt. — Fax 536-7148
www.centerville.k12.tx.us
Centerville JSHS — 400/7-12
813 S Commerce St 75833 — 903-536-2935
Dan Parker, prin. — Fax 536-3133

Channelview, Harris, Pop. 37,941
Channelview ISD — 8,300/PK-12
828 Sheldon Rd 77530 — 281-452-8002
Greg Ollis, supt. — Fax 457-9073
www.cvisd.org/
Channelview HS — 1,600/10-12
1100 Sheldon Rd 77530 — 281-452-1450
Cindi Ollis, prin. — Fax 457-7346
Endeavor S — 100/Alt
915 Sheldon Rd 77530 — 281-457-0086
Mark Sims, prin. — Fax 860-3801
Johnson JHS — 1,200/7-8
15500 Proctor St 77530 — 281-452-8030
Jules Pichon, prin. — Fax 452-1022
Kolarik 9th Grade Center — 800/9-9
1120 Sheldon Rd 77530 — 713-378-3400
Cindi Ollis, prin. — Fax 378-3498
Other Schools – See Houston

Channing, Hartley, Pop. 363
Channing ISD — 200/PK-12
PO Box A 79018 — 806-235-3719
Robert McLain, supt. — Fax 235-2609
www.channingisd.net/
Channing S — 200/PK-12
PO Box A 79018 — 806-235-3719
Forrest Herbert, prin. — Fax 235-2609

Charlotte, Atascosa, Pop. 1,708
Charlotte ISD — 500/PK-12
PO Box 489 78011 — 830-277-1431
Brett Starkweather, supt. — Fax 277-1551
www.charlotteisd.net
Charlotte HS — 100/9-12
PO Box 489 78011 — 830-277-1432
Bryan Borth, prin. — Fax 277-1605
Charlotte MS — 200/5-8
PO Box 489 78011 — 830-277-1646
Denise Cruz, prin. — Fax 277-1654

Cherokee, San Saba
Cherokee ISD — 100/K-12
PO Box 100 76832 — 325-622-4298
Chris Perry, supt. — Fax 622-4430
www.cherokeeisd.net
Cherokee S — 100/K-12
PO Box 100 76832 — 325-622-4298
Barbara Irick, prin. — Fax 622-4430

Chester, Tyler, Pop. 312
Chester ISD — 200/K-12
273 Yellow Jacket Dr 75936 — 936-969-2371
Wayne Ivey, supt. — Fax 969-2080
www.chesterisd.com
Chester JSHS — 100/6-12
273 Yellow Jacket Dr 75936 — 936-969-2353
Wayne Ivey, prin.

Chico, Wise, Pop. 994
Chico ISD — 600/PK-12
PO Box 95 76431 — 940-644-2228
Mike Jones, supt. — Fax 644-5642
www.chico.k12.tx.us
Chico HS — 200/9-12
PO Box 95 76431 — 940-644-5783
Gerald Rosebure, prin. — Fax 644-5876
Chico MS — 100/6-8
PO Box 95 76431 — 940-644-5550
Maury Martin, prin. — Fax 644-5642

Childress, Childress, Pop. 6,037
Childress ISD — 1,100/PK-12
PO Box 179 79201 — 940-937-2501
Rick Teran, supt. — Fax 937-2938
www.childressisd.net/
Childress HS — 300/9-12
800 Avenue J NW 79201 — 940-937-6131
Eric Kirkpatrick, prin. — Fax 937-2039
Childress JHS — 300/6-8
700 Commerce St 79201 — 940-937-3641
Marsha Meacham, prin. — Fax 937-8427

Chillicothe, Hardeman, Pop. 698
Chillicothe ISD — 200/PK-12
PO Box 418 79225 — 940-852-5391
Coby Norman, supt. — Fax 852-5269
cisd-tx.net
Chillicothe JSHS — 100/7-12
PO Box 550 79225 — 940-852-5391
Tony Martinez, prin. — Fax 852-5465

Chilton, Falls, Pop. 896
Chilton ISD — 500/PK-12
PO Box 488 76632 — 254-546-1200
Benny Bobo, supt. — Fax 546-1201
www.chiltonisd.org
Chilton JSHS — 200/6-12
PO Box 488 76632 — 254-546-1200
Ray Rabroker, prin. — Fax 546-1201

China Spring, McLennan, Pop. 1,276
China Spring ISD
Supt. — See Waco
China Spring HS — 700/9-12
7301 N River Xing 76633 — 254-836-1771
Dr. Brian Holt, prin. — Fax 836-1418
China Spring MS — 300/7-8
7201 N River Xing 76633 — 254-836-4611
Heather Jenkins, prin. — Fax 836-4777

Chireno, Nacogdoches, Pop. 378
Chireno ISD — 300/K-12
PO Box 85 75937 — 936-362-2132
Roger Dees, supt. — Fax 362-2490
www.chirenoisd.org/
Chireno JSHS — 100/7-12
PO Box 85 75937 — 936-362-2132
Daniel Johnson, prin. — Fax 362-9331

Christoval, Tom Green, Pop. 503
Christoval ISD — 400/K-12
PO Box 162 76935 — 325-896-2520
David Walker, supt. — Fax 896-7405
www.christovalisd.org
Christoval JSHS — 300/6-12
PO Box 162 76935 — 325-896-2355
John Choate, prin. — Fax 896-2671

Cibolo, Guadalupe, Pop. 14,799
Schertz-Cibolo-Universal City ISD
Supt. — See Schertz
Dobie JHS — 1,000/7-8
395 W Borgfeld Rd 78108 — 210-619-4100
Vernon Simmons, prin. — Fax 619-4142
Steele HS — 100/9-12
1300 FM 1103 78108 — 210-619-4000
Mike Wohlfarth, prin — Fax 619-4057

Cisco, Eastland, Pop. 3,863
Cisco ISD — 800/PK-12
PO Box 1645 76437 — 254-442-3056
Kelly West, supt. — Fax 442-1412
www.ciscoisd.net/
Cisco HS — 200/9-12
PO Box 1645 76437 — 254-442-3051
Craig Kent, prin. — Fax 442-2516
Cisco JHS — 200/6-8
PO Box 1645 76437 — 254-442-3004
Mark Lewis, prin. — Fax 442-1832
Cisco Learning Center — 50/Alt
PO Box 1645 76437 — 254-442-4852
Julie Patterson, prin. — Fax 442-1917

Cisco College — Post-Sec.
101 College Hts 76437 — 254-442-5000

Clarendon, Donley, Pop. 1,994
Clarendon ISD — 500/PK-12
PO Box 610 79226 — 806-874-2062
Monty Hysinger, supt. — Fax 874-2579
www.clarendonisd.net
Clarendon HS — 200/9-12
PO Box 610 79226 — 806-874-2181
Larry Jeffers, prin. — Fax 874-3428
Clarendon JHS — 100/6-8
PO Box 610 79226 — 806-874-3232
John Taylor, prin. — Fax 874-9748

Clarendon College — Post-Sec.
PO Box 968 79226 — 806-874-3571

Clarksville, Red River, Pop. 3,231
Clarksville ISD — 700/PK-12
1500 W Main St 75426 — 903-427-3891
Pam Bryant, supt. — Fax 427-5071
www.clarksvilleisd.net/
Clarksville HS — 200/9-12
1500 W Main St 75426 — 903-427-3891
Chris Vaughn, prin. — Fax 427-1344
Clarksville MS — 200/6-8
1500 W Main St 75426 — 903-427-3891
Tonya Nelson, prin. — Fax 427-4118

Claude, Armstrong, Pop. 1,174
Claude ISD — 300/PK-12
PO Box 209 79019 — 806-226-7331
Dr. Jadie Matthew, supt. — Fax 226-2244
www.claudeisd.net/
Claude JSHS — 200/6-12
PO Box 209 79019 — 806-226-2191
Scott Wilkerson, prin. — Fax 226-2244

Cleburne, Johnson, Pop. 28,861
Cleburne ISD — 6,900/PK-12
505 N Ridgeway Dr Ste 100 76033 — 817-202-1100
Dr. Tim Miller, supt. — Fax 202-1460
www.cleburne.k12.tx.us/
Cleburne HS — 1,700/9-12
1501 Harlin Dr 76033 — 817-202-1200
Jennifer Baadsgaard, prin. — Fax 202-1470
Smith MS — 800/6-8
1710 Country Club Rd 76033 — 817-202-1500
William Allen, prin. — Fax 202-1475
TEAM — 100/Alt
505 N Ridgeway Dr Ste 100 76033 — 817-202-2160
Georganne Storm, prin. — Fax 202-1489
Wheat MS — 700/6-8
810 N Colonial Dr 76033 — 817-202-1300
Suzanne Keesee, prin. — Fax 202-1479

Hill College - Cleburne Campus — Post-Sec.
2112 Mayfield Pkwy 76033 — 817-760-5500

Cleveland, Liberty, Pop. 7,571
Cleveland ISD — 2,900/PK-12
316 E Dallas St 77327 — 281-592-8717
Kerry Cowart, supt. — Fax 592-8283
www.clevelandisd.org
Cleveland HS — 800/9-12
1600 E Houston St 77327 — 281-592-8752
Stephen McCanless, prin. — Fax 592-7485
Cleveland MS — 500/7-8
2000 E Houston St 77327 — 281-593-1148
Glenn Barnes, prin. — Fax 593-3400
Douglass Learning Academy — 100/Alt
900 Sam Wiley Dr 77327 — 281-592-7595
Therese Harris, prin. — Fax 432-2754

Tarkington ISD — 1,900/PK-12
2770 FM 163 Rd 77327 — 281-592-8781
Kevin Weldon, supt. — Fax 592-3969
www.tarkingtonisd.net/
Tarkington HS — 600/9-12
2770 FM 163 Rd 77327 — 281-592-7739
Jim Hair, prin. — Fax 592-0693
Tarkington MS — 500/6-8
2770 FM 163 Rd 77327 — 281-592-7737
Peter Pitts, prin. — Fax 592-5241

Clifton, Bosque, Pop. 3,399
Clifton ISD — 1,100/PK-12
1102 Key St 76634 — 254-675-2827
Rhoda White, supt. — Fax 675-4351
cubs.clifton.k12.tx.us
Clifton HS — 300/9-12
1101 N Avenue Q 76634 — 254-675-2827
Sharon Bergman, prin. — Fax 675-8002
Clifton MS — 300/6-8
1102 Key St 76634 — 254-675-2827
Andy Ball, prin. — Fax 675-2005

Clint, El Paso, Pop. 926
Clint ISD
Supt. — See El Paso
Clint HS — 600/9-12
13890 Alameda Ave 79836 — 915-926-8300
Daniel Gurany, prin. — Fax 851-5375
Clint ISD Early College Academy — 100/9-12
13100 Alameda Ave 79836 — 915-926-8100
David Medlin, prin. — Fax 851-3459
Clint JHS — 500/6-8
12625 Alameda Ave 79836 — 915-926-8000
Josephine A. Guzman, prin. — Fax 851-3895

Clute, Brazoria, Pop. 11,087
Brazosport ISD — 12,600/PK-12
301 W Brazoswood Dr 77531 — 979-730-7000
Dr. Karin Holacka, supt. — Fax 266-2409
www.brazosportisd.net
Brazoswood HS — 2,500/9-12
302 W Brazoswood Dr 77531 — 979-730-7300
Ron Redden, prin. — Fax 266-2447
Clute IS — 900/5-8
421 E Main St 77531 — 979-730-7230
John Galaviz, prin. — Fax 730-7363
Lighthouse Learning Center — 100/Alt
1035 Dixie Dr 77531 — 979-730-7340
Robert Rasberry, prin. — Fax 730-7369
Other Schools – See Freeport, Lake Jackson

Clyde, Callahan, Pop. 3,655
Clyde Consolidated ISD — 1,500/PK-12
PO Box 479 79510 — 325-893-4222
Keith Scharnhorst, supt. — Fax 893-4024
www.clyde.esc14.net
Clyde HS — 400/9-12
500 N Hays Rd 79510 — 325-893-2161
Terry Phillips, prin. — Fax 893-2993
Clyde JHS — 300/6-8
211 S 3rd St W 79510 — 325-893-5788
Greg Edwards, prin. — Fax 893-5019

Eula ISD — 300/PK-12
6040 FM 603 79510 — 325-529-3186
Tim Kelley, supt. — Fax 529-4461
www.eulaisd.us
Eula JSHS — 100/7-12
6040 FM 603 79510 — 325-529-3605
Candilyn Smith, prin. — Fax 529-5534

Coahoma, Howard, Pop. 815
Coahoma ISD — 700/PK-12
PO Box 110 79511 — 432-394-5000
Amy Jacobs, supt. — Fax 394-4302
www.coahomaisd.com/
Coahoma HS — 200/9-12
PO Box 110 79511 — 432-394-5000
Carrie Conley, prin. — Fax 394-4301
Coahoma JHS — 100/6-8
PO Box 110 79511 — 432-394-5000
Brett Ramsey, prin. — Fax 394-4419

Coldspring, San Jacinto, Pop. 837
Coldspring-Oakhurst Consolidated ISD — 1,700/PK-12
PO Box 39 77331 — 936-653-1115
Dr. LaTonya Goffney, supt. — Fax 653-2197
www.cocisd.org
Coldspring-Oakhurst HS — 500/9-12
PO Box 39 77331 — 936-653-1140
Dr. Elizabeth Jarvis, prin. — Fax 653-3687
Lincoln JHS — 400/6-8
PO Box 39 77331 — 936-653-1166
Penny Spivey, prin. — Fax 653-3688

Coleman, Coleman, Pop. 4,660
Coleman ISD — 900/PK-12
PO Box 900 76834 — 325-625-3575
Royce Young, supt. — Fax 625-4751
www.colemanisd.net/
Coleman HS — 200/9-12
201 15th St 76834 — 325-625-2156
Richard Holloway, prin. — Fax 625-4557
Coleman JHS — 200/6-8
301 15th St 76834 — 325-625-3593
Paula Ringo, prin. — Fax 625-3358

College Station, Brazos, Pop. 92,151
College Station ISD — 10,500/PK-12
1812 Welsh Ave 77840 — 979-764-5400
Dr. Eddie Coulson, supt. — Fax 764-5535
www.csisd.org
A & M Consolidated HS — 2,800/9-12
1801 Harvey Mitchell Pkwy S 77840 — 979-764-5500
Gwen Elder, prin. — Fax 693-0212
A & M Consolidated MS — 700/7-8
105 Holik St 77840 — 979-764-5575
Nkrumah Dixon, prin. — Fax 764-4294
Alternative Education Programs — 100/Alt
105 Timber St 77840 — 979-764-5540
Margie Martinez, prin. — Fax 764-7009
College Station MS — 800/7-8
900 Rock Prairie Rd 77845 — 979-764-5545
Oliver Hadnot, prin. — Fax 764-4015

Brazos Valley Cornerstone Christian Acad — 100/K-10
2475 Earl Rudder Fwy S 77845 — 979-694-8200
Rebecca Curry, prin.
Texas A&M University 77843 — Post-Sec.
979-845-3211

Colleyville, Tarrant, Pop. 22,415
Grapevine-Colleyville ISD
Supt. — See Grapevine
BRIDGES S — 100/Alt
5800 Colleyville Blvd 76034 — 817-251-5474
Dr. Lynda Burr, prin. — Fax 251-5477
Colleyville Heritage HS — 2,300/9-12
5401 Heritage Ave 76034 — 817-358-4700
Dr. Joe Harrington, prin. — Fax 358-4765
Colleyville MS — 700/6-8
1100 Bogart Dr 76034 — 817-788-4400
David Denning, prin. — Fax 498-9764
Heritage MS — 900/6-8
5300 Heritage Ave 76034 — 817-358-4790
Pete Valamides, prin. — Fax 267-9929
VISTA S — Alt
5800 Colleyville Blvd 76034 — 817-251-5466
Dr. Lynda Burr, prin. — Fax 251-5464

Covenant Christian Academy — 700/PK-12
901 Cheek Sparger Rd 76034 — 817-281-4333
Keith Castello, admin. — Fax 334-0367

Collinsville, Grayson, Pop. 1,601
Collinsville ISD — 500/PK-12
PO Box 49 76233 — 903-429-6272
Dwain Milam, supt. — Fax 429-6665
www.collinsvilleisd.org
Collinsville JSHS — 200/7-12
PO Box 49 76233 — 903-429-6164
Mark Dykes, prin. — Fax 429-6493

Colmesneil, Tyler, Pop. 588
Colmesneil ISD — 500/K-12
PO Box 37 75938 — 409-837-5757
Yvette Carlton, supt. — Fax 837-9107
www.colmesneilisd.net
Colmesneil JSHS — 300/7-12
PO Box 37 75938 — 409-837-2225
Walter McAlpin, prin. — Fax 837-9107

Colorado City, Mitchell, Pop. 4,115
Colorado ISD — 1,100/PK-12
PO Box 1268 79512 — 325-728-3721
Reggy Spencer, supt. — Fax 728-8471
www.ccity.esc14.net
Colorado HS — 300/9-12
1500 Lone Wolf Blvd 79512 — 325-728-3424
Dalton West, prin. — Fax 728-1083
Colorado MS — 200/6-8
312 E 12th St 79512 — 325-728-2673
Mark Merrell, prin. — Fax 728-1051

Columbus, Colorado, Pop. 3,623
Columbus ISD — 1,600/PK-12
105 Cardinal Ln 78934 — 979-732-5704
Dr. Robert O'Connor, supt. — Fax 732-5960
www.columbusisd.org/
Columbus HS — 500/9-12
103 Cardinal Ln 78934 — 979-732-5746
Jerry Brem, prin. — Fax 732-8862
Columbus JHS — 300/6-8
702 Rampart St 78934 — 979-732-2891
Gary leopold, prin. — Fax 732-9081

Comanche, Comanche, Pop. 4,301
Comanche ISD — 1,100/PK-12
1414 N Austin St 76442 — 325-356-2727
Marshall Harrison, supt. — Fax 356-2312
www.comancheisd.net
Comanche HS — 300/9-12
1600 N Austin St 76442 — 325-356-2581
Scott Carlisle, prin. — Fax 356-2658
Jeffries JHS — 200/7-8
1 Valley Forge Dr 76442 — 325-356-5220
Joseph Simmons, prin. — Fax 356-1949

Comfort, Kendall, Pop. 2,348
Comfort ISD — 1,200/PK-12
PO Box 398 78013 — 830-995-6400
John Chapman, supt. — Fax 995-2236
www.comfort.txed.net
Comfort HS — 300/9-12
PO Box 280 78013 — 830-995-6430
Katherine Kuenstler, prin. — Fax 995-2261
Comfort MS — 300/6-8
PO Box 187 78013 — 830-995-6420
Christopher Yeschke, prin. — Fax 995-2248

Commerce, Hunt, Pop. 7,851
Commerce ISD — 1,600/PK-12
3315 Washington St 75428 — 903-886-3755
Blake Cooper, supt. — Fax 886-6025
www.commerceisd.org
Commerce HS — 500/9-12
3315 Washington St 75428 — 903-886-3756
Adam Rupert, prin. — Fax 886-6209
Commerce MS — 300/6-8
3315 Washington St 75428 — 903-886-3795
Patrick Just, prin. — Fax 886-6102

Texas A&M University Commerce — Post-Sec.
PO Box 3011 75429 — 903-886-5102

Como, Hopkins, Pop. 696
Como-Pickton Consolidated ISD — 800/PK-12
PO Box 18 75431 — 903-488-3671
Dr. Kay Handlin, supt. — Fax 488-3133
www.cpcisd.net
Como-Pickton HS — 200/9-12
PO Box 18 75431 — 903-488-3671
Dustin Carr, prin. — Fax 488-3133
Como-Pickton JHS — 200/6-8
PO Box 18 75431 — 903-488-3671
Randy Stuard, prin. — Fax 488-3133

Comstock, Val Verde
Comstock ISD — 200/K-12
PO Box 905 78837 — 432-292-4444
Orlie Wolfenbarger, supt. — Fax 292-4436
www.comstockisd.net/
Comstock S — 200/K-12
PO Box 905 78837 — 432-292-4444
Ebby Loeffler, prin. — Fax 292-4436

Conroe, Montgomery, Pop. 55,526
Conroe ISD — 50,800/PK-12
3205 W Davis St 77304 — 936-709-7751
Dr. Don Stockton, supt. — Fax 709-9701
www.conroeisd.net/
Academy for Science & Health Professions — 9-12
3200 W Davis St 77304 — 936-709-5731
Dr. Mike Papadimitriou, hdmstr. — Fax 709-5842
Caney Creek HS — 1,700/9-12
13470 FM 1485 Rd 77306 — 936-709-2000
Trish McClure, prin. — Fax 709-2099
Conroe HS — 3,100/9-12
3200 W Davis St 77304 — 936-709-5700
Dr. Curtis Null, prin. — Fax 709-5655
Hauke Alternative Education — 100/Alt
701 N 3rd St 77301 — 936-709-3420
Dr. Jo Ann Beken, prin. — Fax 709-3499
Irons JHS — 7-8
16780 Needham Rd 77385 — 936-709-8500
Jeff Fuller, prin. — Fax 709-8599
Moorehead JHS — 1,000/7-8
13475 FM 1485 Rd 77306 — 936-709-2400
Allan Sapp, prin. — Fax 709-2499
Oak Ridge 9th Grade Campus — 800/9-9
27310 Oak Ridge School Rd 77385 — 281-465-5000
Julie Miller, prin. — Fax 465-5099
Oak Ridge SHS — 2,000/10-12
27330 Oak Ridge School Rd 77385 — 832-592-5300
Tommy Johnson, prin. — Fax 592-5544
Peet JHS — 1,000/7-8
400 Sgt Ed Holcomb Blvd N 77304 — 936-709-3700
Dr. Mark Weatherly, prin. — Fax 709-3828
Washington JHS — 600/7-8
507 Dr Martin Luther King 77301 — 936-709-7400
Hartwell Brown, prin. — Fax 709-7492
Other Schools – See Spring, The Woodlands

Adventist Christian Academy of Texas — 100/PK-12
3601 S Loop 336 E 77301 — 936-756-5078
Russell Shafer, prin. — Fax 365-1764
Calvary Baptist S — 200/PK-12
3401 N Frazier St 77303 — 936-756-0743
Mark Parker, admin. — Fax 756-0764
Covenant Christian S — 300/PK-12
4503 Interstate 45 N 77304 — 936-890-8080
John Weaver, admin. — Fax 890-5343
Lifestyle Christian S — 200/K-12
3993 Interstate 45 N 77304 — 936-756-9383
Pat Maddoux, prin. — Fax 760-3003
Lone Star College - Montgomery — Post-Sec.
3200 College Park Dr 77384 — 936-273-7000
PCAL Christian S — 50/K-12
9268 Highway 242 77385 — 936-273-3239
Karen Parish, admin.

Converse, Bexar, Pop. 17,584
Judson ISD
Supt. — See Live Oak
Judson Alternative S — 100/Alt
102 School St 78109 — 210-945-6730
Joe Gonzalez, prin. — Fax 658-2206
Judson HS — 3,300/9-12
9142 FM 78 78109 — 210-945-1100
Jesus Hernandez, prin. — Fax 659-4359
Judson MS — 3,000/6-8
9695 Schaefer Rd 78109 — 210-357-0801
Ted Haynes, prin. — Fax 659-8769
Thompson Learning Center — 50/Alt
PO Box 369 78109 — 210-945-5053
Joe Gonzalez, prin. — Fax 659-6257
Judson Evening HS — Adult
102 School St 78109 — 210-945-6753
Joe Gonzalez, dir. — Fax 945-6747

Coolidge, Limestone, Pop. 937
Coolidge ISD — 300/PK-12
PO Box 70 76635 — 254-786-2206
Chris Hulen Ph.D., supt. — Fax 786-4835
www.coolidge.k12.tx.us/
Coolidge HS — 100/6-12
PO Box 70 76635 — 254-786-4822
Robert Lowry, prin. — Fax 786-4835

Cooper, Delta, Pop. 1,923
Cooper ISD — 800/PK-12
PO Box 478 75432 — 903-395-2111
Denicia Hohenberger, supt. — Fax 395-2117
www.cooperisd.net/
Cooper HS — 200/9-12
PO Box 429 75432 — 903-395-2111
Chris Kiser, prin. — Fax 395-2382
Cooper JHS — 200/6-8
PO Box 429 75432 — 903-395-2111
Richard Roan, prin. — Fax 395-2382

Coppell, Dallas, Pop. 37,827
Coppell ISD 10,200/PK-12
200 S Denton Tap Rd 75019 214-496-6000
Dr. Jeff Turner, supt. Fax 496-6036
www.coppellisd.com
Coppell HS 2,700/9-12
185 W Parkway Blvd 75019 214-496-6100
Mike Jasso, prin. Fax 496-6166
Coppell MS East 800/6-8
400 Mockingbird Ln 75019 214-496-6600
Laura Springer, prin. Fax 496-6603
Coppell MS North 900/6-8
120 Natches Trce 75019 214-496-7100
Dr. Leanne Dorhout, prin. Fax 496-7103
Coppell MS West 800/6-8
1301 Wrangler Cir 75019 214-496-8600
Vernon Edin, prin. Fax 496-8606
New Tech HS @ Coppell 500/9-12
113 Samuel Blvd 75019 214-496-5900
Deana Harrell, prin. Fax 496-5906

Copperas Cove, Coryell, Pop. 30,055
Copperas Cove ISD 8,300/PK-12
703 W Avenue D 76522 254-547-1227
Dr. Joe Burns, supt. Fax 547-7060
www.ccisd.com
Avenue E Alternative Learning Center 100/Alt
306 E Avenue E 76522 254-547-9164
Colby Blackwell, prin. Fax 547-4039
Copperas Cove HS 2,100/9-12
400 S 25th St 76522 254-547-2534
Earl Parcell, prin. Fax 547-9870
Copperas Cove JHS 800/6-8
702 Sunny Ave 76522 254-547-6959
Randy Troub, prin. Fax 518-2620
Lee JHS 900/6-8
1205 Courtney Ln 76522 254-542-7877
Kayleen Love, prin. Fax 542-8103

Corinth, Denton, Pop. 19,502
Denton ISD
Supt. — See Denton
Crownover MS 900/6-8
1901 Creekside Dr 76210 940-369-4700
Gwen Perkins, prin. Fax 321-0502

Lake Dallas ISD
Supt. — See Lake Dallas
Lake Dallas HS 1,200/9-12
3016 Parkridge Dr 76210 940-497-4031
Kristi Strickland, prin. Fax 497-1524

Corpus Christi, Nueces, Pop. 301,876
Calallen ISD 3,800/PK-12
4205 Wildcat Dr 78410 361-242-5600
Arturo Almendarez, supt. Fax 242-5620
www.calallen.org
Calallen HS 1,200/9-12
4001 Wildcat Dr 78410 361-242-5626
Yvonne Marquez-Neth, prin. Fax 242-5632
Calallen MS 900/6-8
4602 Cornett Dr 78410 361-242-5672
Marcos Flores, prin. Fax 242-0628

Corpus Christi ISD 36,700/PK-12
PO Box 110 78403 361-695-7200
Doyne Elliff, supt. Fax 886-9109
www.ccisd.us
Baker MS 900/6-8
3445 Pecan St 78411 361-878-4600
Darla Reid, prin. Fax 878-1834
Browne MS 800/6-8
4301 Schanen Blvd 78413 361-878-4270
John Trevino, prin. Fax 878-1836
Carroll HS 2,200/9-12
5301 Weber Rd 78411 361-878-5140
Charles Chachere, prin. Fax 857-2548
Coles HS & Education Ctr 300/Alt
924 Winnebago St 78401 361-844-0432
Monica Bayarena, prin. Fax 844-0436
Cullen Place MS 500/6-8
5225 Greely Dr 78412 361-878-2960
Dr. Jennitta Rupp, prin. Fax 994-3624
Cunningham MS 600/6-8
4321 Prescott St 78416 361-878-4630
Elizabeth Perez, prin. Fax 878-1838
Driscoll MS 600/6-8
3501 Kenwood Dr 78408 361-878-4660
Elodia Gutierrez, prin. Fax 886-9890
Grant MS 1,000/6-8
4350 Aaron Dr 78413 361-878-3740
Carla Rosa-Villarreal, prin. Fax 878-1871
Haas MS 600/6-8
6630 McArdle Rd 78412 361-878-4240
Dr. Lynda DeLeon, prin. Fax 994-3626
Hamlin MS 700/6-8
3900 Hamlin Dr 78411 361-878-4210
Delma Yzaguirre, prin. Fax 878-1839
Kaffie MS 1,000/6-8
5922 Brockhampton St 78414 361-878-3700
Kelly Manlove, prin. Fax 994-3604
King HS 2,400/9-12
5225 Gollihar Rd 78412 361-906-3400
Minerva Abrego, prin. Fax 994-6918
Martin Special Emphasis S 500/6-8
3502 Greenwood Dr 78416 361-878-4690
Dr. Rafael Silva, prin. Fax 878-1841
Miller HS 1,000/9-12
1 Battlin Buc Blvd 78408 361-878-5100
Stella Torres, prin. Fax 883-1928
Moody HS 1,800/9-12
1818 Trojan Dr 78416 361-878-7340
Dr. Sandra Clement, prin. Fax 857-8253
Ray HS 1,900/9-12
1002 Texan Trl 78411 361-878-7300
Cissy Perez, prin. Fax 852-6528
Seale Academy of Fine Arts 600/6-8
1707 Ayers St 78404 361-878-4750
Angela Portis-Woodson, prin. Fax 886-9892
South Park MS 500/6-8
3001 McArdle Rd 78415 361-878-4720
Steve Barrera, prin. Fax 878-1844
Student Learning & Guidance Center 100/Alt
2944 Cactus Dr 78415 361-878-2840
Douglas Cross, prin. Fax 878-1437
Adult Learning Center Adult
2212 Morris St 78405 361-878-2560
Fax 886-9219

Flour Bluff ISD 5,500/PK-12
2505 Waldron Rd 78418 361-694-9200
Dr. Julie Carbajal, supt. Fax 694-9809
www.flourbluffschools.net
Flour Bluff HS 1,800/9-12
2505 Waldron Rd 78418 361-694-9100
James Crenshaw, prin. Fax 694-9802
Flour Bluff JHS 900/7-8
2505 Waldron Rd 78418 361-694-9300
Cindy Holder, prin. Fax 694-9803

London ISD 400/PK-12
1306 FM 43 78415 361-855-0092
Hal Roberts, supt. Fax 855-0198
www.londonisd.net
London S 400/PK-12
1306 FM 43 78415 361-855-0092
Brandon Stiewig, prin. Fax 855-0198

Tuloso-Midway ISD 3,600/PK-12
PO Box 10900 78460 361-903-6400
Sue Nelson, supt. Fax 241-1554
www.tmisd.esc2.net
Tuloso-Midway HS 1,000/9-12
PO Box 10900 78460 361-903-6700
Ann Bartosh, prin. Fax 241-4258
Tuloso-Midway MS 800/6-8
PO Box 10900 78460 361-903-6600
Thomas Walker, prin. Fax 241-9829

West Oso ISD 2,000/PK-12
5050 Rockford Dr 78416 361-806-5900
Elizabeth Saenz, supt. Fax 225-8308
www.westosoisd.net
West Oso HS 500/9-12
754 Flato Rd 78405 361-806-5960
Dr. Luz Martinez, prin. Fax 299-3111
West Oso JHS 500/6-8
5202 Bear Ln 78405 361-806-5950
Terry Avery, prin. Fax 299-3111

Annapolis Christian Academy 200/PK-12
3875 S Staples St 78411 361-991-6004
Bishop Garriga MS 100/6-8
3114 Saratoga Blvd 78415 361-851-0853
Mario Vasquez, prin. Fax 853-5145
Del Mar College Post-Sec.
101 Baldwin Blvd 78404 361-698-1200
Incarnate Word Academy 300/6-8
2917 Austin St 78404 361-883-0857
Adolfo Garza, prin. Fax 882-9193
Incarnate Word Academy 300/9-12
2910 S Alameda St 78404 361-883-0857
Jose Torres, prin. Fax 881-8742
Institute of Cosmetic Arts and Science Post-Sec.
1105 Airline Rd 78412 361-991-8868
John Paul II HS 400/9-12
3036 Saratoga Blvd 78415 361-855-5744
Perry LeGrange M.Ed., prin. Fax 855-1343
Kaplan College Post-Sec.
1620 S Padre Island Dr #600 78416 361-852-2900
Southern Careers Institute Post-Sec.
2422 Airline Rd 78414 361-857-5700
South Texas Barber College Post-Sec.
3917 Ayers St 78415 361-855-0262
Texas A&M University Corpus Christi Post-Sec.
6300 Ocean Dr 78412 361-825-5700
Yorktown Christian Academy 200/PK-12
5025 Yorktown Blvd Ste A 78413 361-985-9960
John Gilbert, admin. Fax 985-9821

Corrigan, Polk, Pop. 1,578
Corrigan-Camden ISD 1,000/PK-12
504 S Home St 75939 936-398-4040
Tom Bowman, supt. Fax 398-4616
www.corrigan-camdenisd.net
Corrigan-Camden HS 300/9-12
504 S Home St 75939 936-398-2543
Jason Purke, prin. Fax 398-2685
Corrigan-Camden JHS 200/7-8
504 S Home St 75939 936-398-2962
Robert Elliott, prin. Fax 398-4608

Corsicana, Navarro, Pop. 23,195
Corsicana ISD 5,700/PK-12
601 N 13th St 75110 903-874-7441
Dr. Diane Frost, supt. Fax 872-2100
www.cisd.org
Collins MS 800/7-8
1500 Dobbins Rd 75110 903-872-3979
Jose Antunez, prin. Fax 874-1423
Corsicana HS 1,500/9-12
3701 W State Highway 22 75110 903-874-8211
Herbert O'Neil, prin. Fax 874-7403

Mildred ISD 700/K-12
5475 S US Highway 287 75109 903-872-6505
Becky Burns, supt. Fax 872-1341
www.mildredisd.org/
Mildred JSHS 400/6-12
5475 S US Highway 287 75109 903-872-0392
Monte Thacker, prin. Fax 641-0356

Navarro College Post-Sec.
3200 W 7th Ave 75110 903-874-6501

Cotton Center, Hale
Cotton Center ISD 100/PK-12
PO Box 350 79021 806-879-2160
Rocky J. Stone, supt. Fax 879-2175
www.cottoncenterisd.org
Cotton Center S 100/PK-12
PO Box 350 79021 806-879-2176
Clay Williams, prin. Fax 879-2175

Cotulla, LaSalle, Pop. 3,594
Cotulla ISD 1,200/PK-12
310 N Main St 78014 830-879-3073
Dr. Jack Seals, supt. Fax 879-3609
www.cotullaisd.org
Cotulla HS 300/9-12
310 N Main St 78014 830-879-2374
Joe Reyes, prin. Fax 879-4302
Newman MS 300/6-8
310 N Main St 78014 830-879-2224
Lila West, prin. Fax 879-4357

Covington, Hill, Pop. 269
Covington ISD 300/PK-12
501 N Main 76636 254-854-2215
Diane Innis, supt. Fax 854-2272
www.covingtonisd.org/
Covington S 300/PK-12
501 N Main 76636 254-854-2215
Hugh Ellison, prin. Fax 854-2272

Crandall, Kaufman, Pop. 2,834
Crandall ISD 2,600/PK-12
PO Box 128 75114 972-427-6000
Dr. Robert Jolly, supt. Fax 427-6036
www.crandall-isd.net
Crandall Alternative Center 50/Alt
PO Box 400 75114 972-472-6100
Gail Barnes, prin.
Crandall HS 800/9-12
PO Box 520 75114 972-427-8030
David Williams, prin. Fax 427-8234
Crandall MS 400/6-8
PO Box 490 75114 972-427-6080
Amy Teague, prin. Fax 427-8031

Crane, Crane, Pop. 3,329
Crane ISD 1,000/PK-12
511 W 8th St 79731 432-558-1022
Larry Lee, supt. Fax 558-1025
www.craneisd.com/css/home.htm
Crane HS 300/9-12
511 W 8th St 79731 432-558-1030
Carlin Grammer, prin. Fax 558-1056
Crane MS 200/6-8
511 W 8th St 79731 432-558-1040
Tony Priest, prin. Fax 558-1046

Cranfills Gap, Bosque, Pop. 280
Cranfills Gap ISD 100/PK-12
PO Box 67 76637 254-597-2505
Vincent Gilbert, supt. Fax 597-0001
www.cranfillsgapisd.net
Cranfills Gap S 100/PK-12
PO Box 67 76637 254-597-2505
Randal Edwards, prin. Fax 597-0001

Crawford, McLennan, Pop. 703
Crawford ISD 600/K-12
200 Pirate Dr 76638 254-486-2381
Kenneth Hall, supt. Fax 486-2198
www.crawfordisd.net/
Crawford HS 300/7-12
200 Pirate Dr 76638 254-486-2381
Don Harris, prin. Fax 486-2198

Crockett, Houston, Pop. 6,873
Crockett ISD 1,400/PK-12
1400 W Austin St 75835 936-544-2125
Dr. Douglas Moore, supt. Fax 544-5727
www.crockettisd.net
Crockett Alternative Campus 50/Alt
1400 W Austin St 75835 936-546-5972
Debra Lamb, prin. Fax 546-0721
Crockett HS 300/9-12
1400 W Austin St 75835 936-544-2193
Deborah Revels, prin. Fax 546-0104
Crockett JHS 300/6-8
1400 W Austin St 75835 936-544-2125
Judy Leediker, prin. Fax 544-4164

Crosby, Harris, Pop. 2,268
Crosby ISD 5,100/PK-12
PO Box 2009 77532 281-328-9200
Keith Moore Ed.D., supt. Fax 328-9208
www.crosbyisd.org
Crosby HS 1,500/9-12
PO Box 2009 77532 281-328-9237
Greg Bower, prin. Fax 328-9219
Crosby MS 800/7-8
PO Box 2009 77532 281-328-9264
Karen Grey, prin. Fax 328-9356

Crosbyton, Crosby, Pop. 1,731
Crosbyton Consolidated ISD 400/PK-12
204 S Harrison St 79322 806-675-7331
Gary Harrell, supt. Fax 675-2409
www.crosbyton.k12.tx.us
Crosbyton HS 100/9-12
204 S Harrison St 79322 806-675-7331
Joe Jones, prin. Fax 675-1049
Crosbyton MS 100/6-8
204 S Harrison St 79322 806-675-7331
Dennis Verkamp, prin. Fax 675-2409

Cross Plains, Callahan, Pop. 974
Cross Plains ISD 400/PK-12
700 N Main St 76443 254-725-6121
Phil Mitchell, supt. Fax 725-6559
www.crossplains.esc14.net/

Cross Plains JSHS 200/7-12
700 N Main St 76443 254-725-6121
Diana Dobbins, prin. Fax 725-6559

Crowell, Foard, Pop. 945
Crowell ISD 200/PK-12
PO Box 239 79227 940-684-1403
Steven Pyburn, supt. Fax 684-1616
www.crowellisd.net/
Crowell JSHS 100/7-12
PO Box 239 79227 940-684-1331
Amie Bell, prin. Fax 684-1978

Crowley, Tarrant, Pop. 12,575
Crowley ISD 15,400/PK-12
PO Box 688 76036 817-297-5800
Dr. Dan Powell, supt. Fax 297-5805
www.crowleyisdtx.org/
Crowley 9th Grade Campus 500/9-9
1016 FM 1187 W 76036 817-297-5845
Jim Phillips, prin. Fax 297-5847
Crowley HS 1,400/10-12
1005 W Main St 76036 817-297-5810
Lyndsae Benton, prin. Fax 297-5854
Crowley Learning Center Alt
PO Box 688 76036 817-297-6992
Leo Gardiner, prin. Fax 297-4087
Johnson Career & Tech Center Vo/Tech
1033 McCart Ave 76036 817-297-3018
Annette Duvall, dir. Fax 297-1839
Stevens MS 900/7-8
940 N Crowley Rd 76036 817-297-5840
Renee Treat, prin. Fax 297-5850
Summer Creek MS 800/7-8
10236 Summercreek Dr 76036 817-297-5090
Pam Berry, prin. Fax 297-5094
Other Schools – See Fort Worth

Nazarene Christian Academy 400/K-12
2001 E Main St 76036 817-297-7003
Kathie Starks, prin. Fax 297-1509

Crystal City, Zavala, Pop. 7,131
Crystal City ISD 2,000/PK-12
805 E Crockett St 78839 830-374-2367
Imelda Allen, supt. Fax 374-8004
www.crystalcityisd.org
Alternative S Alt
805 E Crockett St 78839 830-374-9840
Crystal City HS 500/9-12
805 E Crockett St 78839 830-374-2341
Russell Baldwin, prin. Fax 374-8012
Fly JHS 300/7-8
805 E Crockett St 78839 830-374-2371
Laura Barajas, prin. Fax 374-8060

Cuero, DeWitt, Pop. 6,679
Cuero ISD 1,900/PK-12
405 Park Heights Dr 77954 361-275-1914
Pam Longbotham, supt. Fax 275-2981
www.cueroisd.org
Cuero HS 600/9-12
920 E Broadway St 77954 361-275-1900
Michael Cavanaugh, prin. Fax 275-2430
Cuero JHS 300/7-8
608 Jr High Dr 77954 361-275-1900
Donald Garrison, prin. Fax 275-6912
GOALS Alternative Campus 50/Alt
301 Daule St 77954 361-275-1900
Brenda Billstein, prin. Fax 277-9288
Learning Connections 50/Alt
303 Daule St 77954 361-275-9408
Helen Reese, dir. Fax 275-9599

Cumby, Hopkins, Pop. 769
Cumby ISD 400/PK-12
303 Sayle St 75433 903-994-2260
Lance Campbell, supt. Fax 994-2399
www.cumbyisd.net
Cumby HS 200/7-12
303 Sayle St 75433 903-994-2260
Shelly Slaughter, prin. Fax 994-2510

Miller Grove ISD 300/PK-12
7819 Farm Road 275 S 75433 903-459-3288
Steve Johnson, supt. Fax 459-3744
www.mgisd.net
Miller Grove HS 100/6-12
7819 Farm Road 275 S 75433 903-459-3288
Kim Irby, prin. Fax 459-3744

Cushing, Nacogdoches, Pop. 594
Cushing ISD 500/PK-12
PO Box 337 75760 936-326-4890
Michael Davis, supt. Fax 326-4115
www.cushingisd.org
Cushing HS 200/9-12
PO Box 337 75760 936-326-4890
James Moore, prin. Fax 326-4131
Cushing JHS 100/6-8
PO Box 337 75760 936-326-4890
Martha Lee, prin. Fax 326-4131

Cypress, Harris
Cypress-Fairbanks ISD
Supt. — See Houston
Arnold MS 1,500/6-8
11111 Telge Rd 77429 281-897-4700
Vicki Snokhous, prin. Fax 807-8610
Carlton Vocational Center Vo/Tech
13550 Woods Spillane Blvd 77429 281-213-1950
Rhonda Turns, dir. Fax 213-1951
Cy-Fair HS 3,300/9-12
22602 Hempstead Hwy 77429 281-897-4600
Mike Smith, prin. Fax 517-6530
Cypress Ranch HS 2,300/9-12
10700 Fry Rd 77433 281-373-2300
Robert Hull, prin. Fax 213-1979
Cypress Springs HS 2,500/9-12
7909 Fry Rd 77433 281-345-3000
Travis Fanning, prin. Fax 345-3010
Cypress Woods HS 2,700/9-12
13550 Woods Spillane Blvd 77429 281-213-1800
Gary Kinninger, prin. Fax 213-1827
Goodson MS 1,800/6-8
17333 Huffmeister Rd 77429 281-373-2350
Sheri McCaig, prin. Fax 373-2355
Hamilton MS 1,600/6-8
12330 Kluge Rd 77429 281-320-7000
Kim Sempe, prin. Fax 320-7021
Hopper MS 1,400/6-8
7811 Fry Rd 77433 281-463-5353
Wendi Whitthaus, prin. Fax 463-5354
Salyards MS 6-8
21757 Fairfield Place Dr 77433 281-373-2400
Jill Smith, prin. Fax 373-2425
Smith MS 1,400/6-8
10300 Warner Smith Blvd 77433 281-213-1010
Susan Higgins, prin. Fax 213-1020
Spillane MS 1,700/6-8
13403 Woods Spillane Blvd 77429 281-213-1645
Michael Manes, prin. Fax 213-1799

Lone Star College Cyfair Post-Sec.
9191 Barker Cypress Rd 77433 281-290-3200
Oaks Adventist Christian S 100/PK-12
11735 Grant Rd 77429 713-896-0071
Fax 896-0721

Daingerfield, Morris, Pop. 2,512
Daingerfield-Lone Star ISD 1,300/PK-12
200 Tiger Dr 75638 903-645-2239
Sandra Quarles, supt. Fax 645-2137
www.dlsisd.org
Daingerfield HS 400/9-12
202 Tiger Dr 75638 903-645-3968
Dr. Larry Miears, prin. Fax 645-7662
Daingerfield JHS 300/6-8
200 Texas St 75638 903-645-2261
Linda Rhymes, prin. Fax 645-4010

Daisetta, Liberty, Pop. 957
Hull-Daisetta ISD 500/PK-12
PO Box 477 77533 936-536-6321
Mary Huckabay, supt. Fax 536-6251
www.hdisd.net/
Hull-Daisetta HS 200/9-12
PO Box 477 77533 936-536-6321
Quinn Godwin, prin. Fax 536-3839
Hull-Daisetta JHS 100/7-8
PO Box 477 77533 936-536-6321
Quinn Godwin, prin. Fax 536-3839

Dalhart, Dallam, Pop. 7,836
Dalhart ISD 1,700/PK-12
701 E 10th St 79022 806-244-7810
David Foote, supt. Fax 244-7822
www.dalhart.k12.tx.us
Dalhart HS 500/9-12
701 E 10th St 79022 806-244-7300
David Steele, prin. Fax 244-7307
Dalhart JHS 400/6-8
701 E 10th St 79022 806-244-7825
John Machel, prin. Fax 244-7835
XIT Secondary S 50/Alt
701 E 10th St 79022 806-244-7340
Kevin Douglas, prin. Fax 244-7345

Dallardsville, Polk
Big Sandy ISD 500/PK-12
PO Box 188 77332 936-563-1000
Dianne Holbrook, supt. Fax 563-1010
www.bigsandyisd.net/
Other Schools – See Livingston

Dallas, Dallas, Pop. 1,183,449
Carrollton-Farmers Branch ISD
Supt. — See Carrollton
Long MS 800/6-8
2525 Frankford Rd 75287 972-968-4100
Joe Copeland, prin. Fax 968-4110

Dallas ISD 153,400/PK-12
3700 Ross Ave 75204 972-925-3700
Mike Miles, supt. Fax 925-3201
www.dallasisd.org
Adams HS 1,900/9-12
2101 Millmar Dr 75228 972-502-4900
Stan VanHoozer, prin. Fax 502-4901
Adamson HS 1,300/9-12
309 E 9th St 75203 972-749-1400
Evangelina Kircher, prin. Fax 749-1401
Anderson Learning Center 500/6-8
3400 Garden Ln 75215 972-925-7900
Benita Noiel-Ashford, prin. Fax 925-7901
Angelou HS 50/Alt
4528 Rusk Ave 75204 972-749-2200
Cheryl Humphrey, prin. Fax 749-2264
Atwell Law Academy 900/6-8
1303 Reynoldston Ln 75232 972-794-6400
Selena Deboskie, prin. Fax 794-6401
Browne MS 800/7-8
3333 Sprague Dr 75233 972-502-2500
Mary Fitzgibbon, prin. Fax 502-2501
Carter HS 1,200/9-12
1819 W Wheatland Rd 75232 214-932-5700
Fred Davis, prin. Fax 932-5701
Cary MS 500/6-8
3978 Killion Dr 75229 972-502-7600
Belinda Rosas-Delgado, prin. Fax 502-7601
Collins-Sorrells S of Educ & Social Srvc 300/9-12
1201 E 8th St 75203 972-925-5940
Fax 925-5901
Comstock MS 1,100/7-8
7044 Hodde St 75217 972-794-1300
Willie Johnson, prin. Fax 794-1301
Conrad HS 1,600/9-12
7502 Fair Oaks Ave 75231 972-502-2300
Lucy Hakemack, prin. Fax 502-2301
Dade Learning Center 400/6-8
2801 Park Row Ave 75215 972-749-3800
David Welch, prin. Fax 749-3801
Dallas Environmental Science Academy 200/6-8
3635 Greenleaf St 75212 972-794-3950
Angela West, prin. Fax 794-3951
Edison MS 800/6-8
2940 Singleton Blvd 75212 972-794-4100
Derrick Spurlock, prin. Fax 794-4101
Florence MS 1,000/6-8
1625 N Masters Dr 75217 972-749-6000
Chanel Howard-Veazy, prin. Fax 749-6001
Franklin MS 1,100/6-8
6920 Meadow Rd 75230 972-502-7100
Jonathan Parker, prin. Fax 502-7101
Garcia MS, 700 E 8th St 75203 1,000/6-8
Gary Auld, prin. 972-502-5500
Garza Early College HS 400/9-12
4849 W Illinois Ave Rm W53A 75211 214-860-3680
Janice Lombardi, prin. Fax 860-3639
Gaston MS 1,100/6-8
9565 Mercer Dr 75228 972-502-5400
Susie Stauss, prin. Fax 502-5401
Gilliam Collegiate Academy 300/9-12
1700 E Camp Wisdom Rd 75241 214-925-1400
Gayle Smith, prin. Fax 925-1401
Greiner Exploratory Arts Academy 1,700/6-8
501 S Edgefield Ave 75208 972-925-7100
Stephanie Taylor, prin. Fax 925-7101
Hillcrest HS 1,200/9-12
9924 Hillcrest Rd 75230 972-502-6800
Ronald Jones, prin. Fax 502-6801
Hill MS 800/6-8
505 Easton Rd 75218 972-502-5700
Irene Aguilar, prin. Fax 502-5701
Holmes MS 6-8
2939 Saint Rita Dr 75233 214-932-7800
Barbara Moham, prin. Fax 932-7801
Holmes MS & Classical Academy 1,000/6-8
2001 E Kiest Blvd 75216 972-925-8500
Keith Baker, prin. Fax 925-8501
Hood MS 1,400/6-8
7625 Hume Dr 75227 972-749-4100
C.A. Williams, prin. Fax 749-4101
Jefferson HS 1,400/9-12
4001 Walnut Hill Ln 75229 972-502-7300
Fax 502-7301
Kennedy-Curry MS 600/6-8
6605 Sebring Dr 75241 972-925-1600
Regina Rice, prin.
Kimball HS 1,300/9-12
3606 S Westmoreland Rd 75233 972-502-2100
Earl Jones, prin. Fax 502-2101
Lang MS, 1678 Chenault St 75228 1,300/6-8
Johanna Weaver, prin 972-925-2400
Learning Alt Ctr for Empowering Youth 200/Alt
4949 Village Fair Dr 75224 972-925-7060
Gail Dupree, prin. Fax 925-7061
Lincoln Humanities/Communications HS 900/9-12
2826 Hatcher St 75215 972-925-7600
Leslie Swann, prin. Fax 925-7601
Longfellow Career Academy 400/6-8
5314 Boaz St 75209 972-749-5400
Cheryl Breedlove-Wright, prin. Fax 749-5401
Long MS 1,200/6-8
6116 Reiger Ave 75214 972-502-4700
Danielle Petters, prin. Fax 502-4701
Madison HS 600/9-12
3000 Mrtn Lthr King Jr Blvd 75215 972-925-2800
Marian Willard, prin. Fax 925-2801
Manns HS, 3313 S Beckley Ave 75224 Alt
Carlos Lee, prin. 972-932-7300
Marsh MS 1,200/6-8
3838 Crown Shore Dr 75244 972-502-6600
Raymundo Gonzalez, prin. Fax 502-6601
Medrano MS 800/6-8
9815 Brockbank Dr 75220 972-925-1300
Theresa Sigurdson, prin. Fax 925-1301
Middle College HS 200/9-12
801 Main St 75202 214-860-2356
Eric Markinson, prin. Fax 860-2359
Molina HS 1,900/9-12
2355 Duncanville Rd 75211 972-502-1000
Mark Ramirez, prin. Fax 502-1001
Multiple Careers Magnet HS Vo/Tech
4528 Rusk Ave 75204 972-925-2200
Cheryl Humphrey, prin. Fax 925-2201
North Dallas HS 1,500/9-12
3120 N Haskell Ave 75204 972-925-1500
Dinnah Escanilla, prin. Fax 925-1501
Obama Male Leadership Academy 6-8
4730 S Lancaster Rd 75216 972-749-2100
Nakia Douglas, prin.
Patton Academic Center Alt
3313 S Beckley Ave 75224 214-932-5160
Sylvia Fuentes, prin. Fax 932-5149
Pinkston HS 1,000/9-12
2200 Dennison St 75212 972-502-2700
Norma Villegas, prin. Fax 502-2701
Quintanilla MS 800/7-8
2700 Remond Dr 75211 972-502-3200
Luis Valdez, prin. Fax 502-3201
Rangel Young Women's Leadership S 200/6-12
1718 Robert B Cullum Blvd 75210 972-749-5200
Vivian Taylor, prin. Fax 749-5201
Richards MS 6-8
3831 N Prairie Creek Rd 75217 972-892-5400
Timothy Hise, prin.
Roosevelt HS 700/9-12
525 Bonnie View Rd 75203 972-925-6800
Leicha Shaver, prin. Fax 925-6801
Rusk MS 800/6-8
2929 Inwood Rd 75235 972-925-2000
James Roe, prin. Fax 925-2001

Samuell HS 2,100/9-12
8928 Palisade Dr 75217 972-892-5100
Juan Vega, prin. Fax 892-5101

Sanders Magnet Center for Law 400/9-12
1201 E 8th St Ste 203 75203 972-925-5950
Anthony Palagonia, prin. Fax 925-6010

School for the Talented & Gifted 200/9-12
1201 E 8th St Ste 216 75203 972-925-5970
Michael Satarino, prin. Fax 925-6018

School of Business & Management 500/9-12
1201 E 8th St Ste 241 75203 972-925-5920
Edith Krutilek, prin. Fax 925-5901

School of Health Professions 500/9-12
1201 E 8th St Ste 281 75203 972-925-5930
Myrtle Walker, prin. Fax 925-6007

School of Science & Engineering HS 400/9-12
1201 E 8th St 75203 972-925-5960
Fax 925-6016

Seagoville HS 1,000/9-12
15920 Seagoville Rd 75253 972-892-5900
Delinda Castro, prin. Fax 892-5901

Seagoville MS 1,000/6-8
950 N Woody Rd 75253 972-892-7100
Kathryn Kreger, prin. Fax 892-7101

Skyline HS 4,500/9-12
7777 Forney Rd 75227 972-502-3400
Harold Wright, prin. Fax 502-3401

Smith HS 800/9-12
3030 Stag Rd 75241 214-932-7600
Lisa DeVeaux, prin. Fax 932-7601

South Oak Cliff HS 1,200/9-12
3601 S Marsalis Ave 75216 214-932-7000
Rodney Cooksy, prin. Fax 932-7001

Spence Talented/Gifted Academy 1,100/6-8
4001 Capitol Ave 75204 972-925-2300
Roberto Basurto, prin. Fax 925-2301

Spruce HS 1,000/9-12
9733 Old Seagoville Rd 75217 972-892-5500
Rawly Sanchez, prin. Fax 892-5501

Stockard MS 900/7-8
2300 S Ravinia Dr 75211 972-794-5700
Ahna Gomez, prin. Fax 794-5701

Storey MS 700/6-8
3000 Maryland Ave 75216 972-925-8700
Ronald Morris, prin. Fax 925-8701

Sunset HS 2,300/9-12
2120 W Jefferson Blvd 75208 972-502-1500
Tony Tovar, prin. Fax 502-1501

Tasby MS 900/6-8
7001 Fair Oaks Ave 75231 972-502-1900
Jose Cardenas, prin. Fax 502-1901

Travis Academy 100/4-8
3001 Mckinney Ave 75204 972-794-7500
Mari Smith, prin. Fax 794-7501

Walker MS 700/6-8
12532 Nuestra Dr 75230 972-502-6100
Grace Casey, prin. Fax 502-6101

Washington Performing & Visual Arts HS 800/9-12
2501 Flora St 75201 972-925-1200
Tracie Fraley, prin. Fax 925-1201

White HS 2,300/9-12
4505 Ridgeside Dr 75244 972-502-6200
Michelle Thompson, prin. Fax 502-6201

Wilmer-Hutchins HS 700/9-12
5520 Langdon Rd 75241 972-925-2900
Marlon Brooks, prin.

Wilson HS 1,500/9-12
100 S Glasgow Dr 75214 972-502-4400
Russell Richardson, prin. Fax 502-4401

Zumwalt MS 500/6-8
2445 E Ledbetter Dr 75216 972-749-3600
Verna Farmer, prin. Fax 749-3601

Evening Academy Adult
7777 Forney Rd 75227 972-502-3458
Fax 502-3633

Other Schools – See Balch Springs

Duncanville ISD
Supt. — See Duncanville

Kennemer MS 700/7-8
7101 W Wheatland Rd 75249 972-708-3600
Brandee King, prin. Fax 708-3636

Highland Park ISD 6,600/PK-12
7015 Westchester Dr 75205 214-780-3000
Dr. Dawson Orr, supt. Fax 780-3099
www.hpisd.org

Highland Park Alternative Education Ctr Alt
4220 Emerson Ave 75205 214-780-3700
Walter Kelly, prin. Fax 780-3799

Highland Park HS 2,000/9-12
4220 Emerson Ave 75205 214-780-3700
Walter Kelly, prin. Fax 780-3799

Highland Park MS 1,000/7-8
3555 Granada Ave 75205 214-780-3600
Dr. Laurie Hitzelberger, prin. Fax 780-3699

Plano ISD
Supt. — See Plano

Frankford MS 1,200/6-8
7706 Osage Plaza Pkwy 75252 469-752-5200
Shurandia Holden, prin. Fax 752-5201

Richardson ISD
Supt. — See Richardson

Forest Meadow JHS 700/7-8
9373 Whitehurst Dr 75243 469-593-1500
Charles Bruner, prin. Fax 593-1461

Lake Highlands Freshman Center 600/9-9
10200 White Rock Trl 75238 469-593-1300
Bill Gallo, prin. Fax 593-1327

Lake Highlands HS 1,600/10-12
9449 Church Rd 75238 469-593-1000
Peggy Dillon, prin. Fax 593-1030

Lake Highlands JHS 600/7-8
10301 Walnut Hill Ln 75238 469-593-1600
Veronica Escalante, prin. Fax 593-1606

Liberty JHS 600/7-9
10330 Lawler Rd 75243 469-593-7888
Stephen Quisenberry, prin. Fax 593-7764

Parkhill JHS 600/7-9
16500 Shadybank Dr 75248 469-593-5600
Judy Marcum, prin. Fax 593-5500

Westwood Magnet JHS 600/7-9
7630 Arapaho Rd 75248 469-593-3600
Tony Gray, prin. Fax 593-3508

Alameda Heights Elite Academy of Dallas 50/9-12
2721 Lyola St 75241 214-372-4620
Elzada Mays, hdmstr. Fax 372-6020

Argosy University/Dallas Post-Sec.
5001 Lyndon B Johnson # 176 75244 214-890-9900

Art Institute of Dallas Post-Sec.
8080 Park Ln Ste 100 75231 214-692-8080

ATI Career Training Center Post-Sec.
10003 Technology Blvd W 75220 214-902-8191

Baylor University Medical Center Post-Sec.
3700 Worth St 75246 214-820-3361

Bishop Dunne HS 600/6-12
3900 Rugged Dr 75224 214-339-6561
Kate Dailey, pres. Fax 339-1438

Bishop Lynch HS 1,100/9-12
9750 Ferguson Rd 75228 214-324-3607
Evelyn Grubbs, prin. Fax 324-3600

Cambridge S of Dallas 6-12
3877 Walnut Hill Ln 75229 214-357-2995
Paul Wolfe, hdmstr. Fax 357-0880

Cannon Institute of Higher Learning Post-Sec.
8500 N Stemmons Fwy 75247 214-630-6768

Concorde Career College Post-Sec.
12606 Greenville Ave # 130 75243 469-221-3400

Court Reporting Institute of Dallas Post-Sec.
1341 W Mockingbird Ln #200E 75247 214-350-9722

Covenant S 300/K-12
7300 Valley View Ln 75240 214-358-5818
Kyle Queal, hdmstr. Fax 358-5809

Criswell College Post-Sec.
4010 Gaston Ave 75246 214-821-5433

Dallas Academy 200/K-12
950 Tiffany Way 75218 214-324-1481
James Richardson, hdmstr. Fax 327-8537

Dallas Baptist University Post-Sec.
3000 Mountain Creek Pkwy 75211 214-333-7100

Dallas Barber and Stylist College Post-Sec.
9357 Forest Ln 75243 214-575-2168

Dallas Christian Academy 100/PK-12
4025 N Central Expy 75204 214-528-6327
Allison Tucker, prin. Fax 528-6450

Dallas Christian College Post-Sec.
2700 Christian Pkwy 75234 972-241-3371

Dallas Institute of Funeral Service Post-Sec.
3909 S Buckner Blvd 75227 214-388-5466

Dallas Lutheran HS 200/7-12
8494 Stults Rd 75243 214-349-8912
David Bangert, dir. Fax 340-3095

Dallas Nursing Institute Post-Sec.
12170 Abrams Rd Ste 200 75243 214-351-0223

Dallas Theological Seminary Post-Sec.
3909 Swiss Ave 75204 214-824-3094

El Centro College Post-Sec.
801 Main St 75202 214-860-2000

Episcopal S of Dallas 700/5-12
4100 Merrell Rd 75229 214-358-4368
Kim MaGee, head sch Fax 357-1232

Everest College Post-Sec.
6080 N Central Expy 75206 214-234-4850

First Baptist Academy 400/K-12
1606 Patterson St 75201 214-969-7861
Brian Littlefield, hdmstr. Fax 969-7797

Golf Academy of America Post-Sec.
1861 Valley View Ln Ste 100 75234 972-763-8100

Graduate Institute of Applied Linguistic Post-Sec.
7500 W Camp Wisdom Rd 75236 972-708-7340

Hockaday S 1,100/PK-12
11600 Welch Rd 75229 214-363-6311
Kim Wargo, head sch Fax 360-6563

Jesuit College Preparatory S 1,000/9-12
12345 Inwood Rd 75244 972-387-8700
Thomas Garrison, prin. Fax 661-9349

Kaplan College Post-Sec.
12005 Ford Rd Ste 100 75234 972-385-1446

KD Studio - Actors Conservatory Post-Sec.
2600 N Stemmons Fwy Ste 117 75207 214-638-0484

Lakehill Prep S 400/K-12
2720 Hillside Dr 75214 214-826-2931
Roger Perry, hdmstr. Fax 826-4623

Lawyer's Assistant School of Dallas Post-Sec.
8150 N Central Expy # M2240 75206 214-777-6433

Le Cordon Bleu Inst of Culinary Arts Post-Sec.
11830 Webb Chapel Rd # 1200 75234 214-647-8500

Lighthouse College Post-Sec.
9400 N Central Expy Ste 200 75231 214-368-3680

Mesorah HS for Girls 50/9-12
12712 Park Central Dr #B190 75251 214-420-1990
Rabbi Avraham Kosowsky, hdmstr. Fax 420-1993

MJ's Beauty Academy Post-Sec.
3939 S Polk St Ste 505 75224 214-374-7500

Mountain View College Post-Sec.
4849 W Illinois Ave 75211 214-860-8680

Neilson Beauty College Post-Sec.
416 W Jefferson Blvd 75208 214-941-8756

New Beginnings Preparatory S 100/9-12
5787 S Hampton Rd Ste 430 75232 214-375-8000
Reginner Randle, dir. Fax 375-8005

Ogle School of Hair Design Post-Sec.
6333 E Mockingbird Ln #201 75214 214-821-0819

Parish Episcopal S 1,200/PK-12
4101 Sigma Rd 75244 972-239-8011
David Monaco, hdmstr. Fax 991-1237

Parker University Post-Sec.
2540 Walnut Hill Ln 75229 972-438-6932

Paul Quinn College Post-Sec.
3837 Simpson Stuart Rd 75241 214-376-1000

PCI Health Training Center Post-Sec.
8101 John W Carpenter Fwy 75247 214-630-0568

Platt College Post-Sec.
2974 Lyndon B Johnson Fwy 75234 972-243-0900

Presbyterian Hospital Post-Sec.
8200 Walnut Hill Ln 75231 214-345-7558

Redeemer Seminary Post-Sec.
6060 N Central Expy Ste 700 75206 214-528-8600

Richland College Post-Sec.
12800 Abrams Rd 75243 972-238-6100

St. Marks S of Texas 800/1-12
10600 Preston Rd 75230 214-346-8000
Arnold Holtberg, hdmstr. Fax 346-8002

Sanford-Brown College Post-Sec.
1250 W Mockingbird Ln # 150 75247 214-459-8490

Shelton S 900/PK-12
15720 Hillcrest Rd 75248 972-774-1772

Southern Methodist University Post-Sec.
PO Box 750100 75275 214-768-2000

Sterling Health Center Post-Sec.
17084 Dallas Pkwy 75248 972-991-9293

Texas A&M Univ.-Baylor Coll. Dentistry Post-Sec.
3302 Gaston Ave 75246 214-828-8100

Texas Barber Colleges & Hairstyling Sch Post-Sec.
5148 S Lancaster Rd 75241 214-943-7255

Texas Women's Univ Pickens Inst Health Post-Sec.
5500 Southwestern Medical 75235 214-689-6500

Tint School of Makeup & Cosmetology Post-Sec.
10909 Webb Chapel Rd # 129 75229 214-956-0088

Tyler Street Christian Academy 200/PK-12
915 W 9th St 75208 214-941-9717
Dr. Karen Egger, supt. Fax 941-0324

University of Texas S.W. Medical Center Post-Sec.
5323 Harry Hines Blvd 75390 214-648-3111

Ursuline Academy 800/9-12
4900 Walnut Hill Ln 75229 469-232-1800
Elizabeth Bourgeois, prin. Fax 232-1836

Vatterott Education Center Post-Sec.
9713 Harry Hines Blvd # 100 75220 214-352-8288

Velma B's Beauty Academy Post-Sec.
1511 S Ewing Ave 75216 214-942-1541

Wade College Dallas Market Center Post-Sec.
1950 N Stemmons Ste 4080 75207 800-624-4850

West Coast University Post-Sec.
8435 N Stemmons Fwy 75247 866-489-5275

Westwood College Post-Sec.
8390 Lyndon B Johnson # 100 75243 214-570-0100

Winston S 200/1-12
5707 Royal Ln 75229 214-691-6950
Dr. Polly Peterson, hdmstr. Fax 691-1509

Yavneh Academy of Dallas 100/9-12
12324 Merit Dr 75251 214-295-3500
Dr. David Portnoy, head sch Fax 295-3505

Danbury, Brazoria, Pop. 1,690

Danbury ISD 800/PK-12
PO Box 378 77534 979-922-1218
Greg Anderson, supt. Fax 922-8246
www.danburyisd.org/

Danbury HS 200/9-12
PO Box 377 77534 979-922-1226
Jon Hill, prin. Fax 922-1051

Danbury MS 100/7-8
PO Box 586 77534 979-922-1226
Jon Hill, prin. Fax 922-1051

Darrouzett, Lipscomb, Pop. 347

Darrouzett ISD 200/PK-12
PO Box 98 79024 806-624-3001
Dwight Rice, supt. Fax 624-4361
www.darrouzettisd.net

Darrouzett S 200/PK-12
PO Box 98 79024 806-624-2221
Danny Cochran, prin. Fax 624-4361

Dawson, Navarro, Pop. 793

Dawson ISD 400/PK-12
199 N School Ave 76639 254-578-1031
Stacy Henderson, supt. Fax 578-1721
www.dawsonisd.net/

Dawson HS 200/7-12
199 N School Ave 76639 254-578-1031
Amy Callarman, prin. Fax 578-1721

Dayton, Liberty, Pop. 7,114

Dayton ISD 4,900/PK-12
PO Box 248 77535 936-258-2667
Michael Kuhrt, supt. Fax 258-5616
www.daytonisd.net/

Dayton HS 1,400/9-12
PO Box 248 77535 936-258-2510
Travis Young, prin. Fax 257-4047

Wilson JHS 700/7-8
PO Box 248 77535 936-258-2309
Rita Gilmore, prin. Fax 257-4109

Decatur, Wise, Pop. 6,000

Decatur ISD 3,000/PK-12
501 E Collins St 76234 940-393-7100
Rod Townsend, supt. Fax 627-3141
www.decaturisd.us/

Decatur HS 900/9-12
750 E Eagle Smt 76234 940-393-7200
Jason Cochran, prin. Fax 627-3669

McCarroll MS 700/6-8
1201 W Thompson St 76234 940-393-7300
Dewayne Tamplen, prin. Fax 627-2497

Deer Park, Harris, Pop. 31,669

Deer Park ISD, 2800 Texas Ave 77536 15,000/PK-12
Arnold Adair, supt. 832-668-7000
www.dpisd.org

Bonnette JHS 800/6-8
5010 W Pasadena Blvd 77536 832-668-7700
Stephen Harrell, prin. Fax 930-4756

Deer Park HS - North Campus 3,800/9-9
402 Ivy Ave 77536 832-668-7300
Ernie Salazar, prin. Fax 930-4840

Deer Park HS - South Campus 2,800/10-12
710 W San Augustine St 77536 832-668-7200
Ronda Kouba, prin. Fax 930-4894
Deer Park JHS 800/6-8
410 E 9th St 77536 832-668-7500
Tiffany Regan, prin. Fax 930-4726
Wolters Accelerated HS Alt
400 Ivy Ave 77536 832-668-7400
Clyde Skarke, prin. Fax 930-0525
Other Schools – See Pasadena

De Kalb, Bowie, Pop. 1,672
De Kalb ISD 800/PK-12
101 Maple St 75559 903-667-2566
Dr. John Booth, supt. Fax 667-3791
www.dekalbisd.net
De Kalb HS 300/9-12
152 Maple St 75559 903-667-2422
Richard Coleman, prin. Fax 667-4086
De Kalb MS 200/5-8
929 W Grizzley St 75559 903-667-2834
Neilan Hensley, prin. Fax 667-5509

De Leon, Comanche, Pop. 2,226
De Leon ISD 600/PK-12
425 S Texas St 76444 254-893-8210
Dana Marable Ph.D., supt. Fax 893-8214
www.deleon.esc14.net
De Leon HS 200/9-12
425 S Texas St 76444 254-893-8240
Liesa Nowlin, prin. Fax 893-4985
Perkins MS 100/6-8
425 S Texas St 76444 254-893-8230
Liesa Nowlin, prin. Fax 893-8234

Dell City, Hudspeth, Pop. 357
Dell City ISD 100/K-12
PO Box 37 79837 915-964-2663
Tanya Lewis, supt. Fax 964-2473
dellcity.schoolwires.com/
Dell City S 100/K-12
PO Box 37 79837 915-964-2663
Juanita Snyder, prin. Fax 964-2473

Del Rio, Val Verde, Pop. 35,427
San Felipe-Del Rio Consolidated ISD 10,000/PK-12
PO Box 428002 78842 830-778-4000
JoAnne Ruark-Ackermann Ed.D., supt. Fax 774-9892
www.sfdr-cisd.org
Del Rio Freshman S 800/9-9
PO Box 428002 78842 830-778-4400
Aidee Garcia, prin. Fax 774-9873
Del Rio HS 2,000/10-12
PO Box 428002 78842 830-778-4329
Jorge Garza, prin. Fax 774-9320
Del Rio MS 1,500/7-8
PO Box 428002 78842 830-778-4530
Aida Gomez, prin. Fax 778-4912

Del Valle, Travis
Del Valle ISD 10,700/PK-12
5301 Ross Rd 78617 512-386-3000
Kelly Crook Ph.D., supt. Fax 386-3015
delvalle.tx.schoolwebpages.com/
Del Valle HS 2,300/9-12
5201 Ross Rd 78617 512-386-3200
Scott Lipton, prin. Fax 386-3205
Del Valle MS 800/6-8
5500 Ross Rd 78617 512-386-3400
Ruth Vail, prin. Fax 386-3405
Del Valle Opportunity Center 300/Alt
5301 Ross Rd Ste B 78617 512-386-3300
Ray Macias, prin. Fax 386-3305
Other Schools – See Austin

Denison, Grayson, Pop. 22,067
Denison ISD 4,300/PK-12
1201 S Rusk Ave 75020 903-462-7000
Dr. Henry Scott, supt. Fax 462-7002
www.denisonisd.net
Denison HS 1,300/9-12
1901 S Mirick Ave 75020 903-462-7125
Dr. Cavin Boettger, prin. Fax 462-7217
McDaniel MS 1,000/6-8
400 S Lillis Ln 75020 903-462-7200
Alvis Dunlap, prin. Fax 462-7328
Pathways HS 100/Alt
318 W Morgan St 75020 903-462-7150
Lance SanMillan, prin. Fax 462-7220

Sherman ISD
Supt. — See Sherman
Perrin Learning Center 100/Alt
81 Vandenburg Dr 75020 903-891-6680
Ryan Harper, prin. Fax 786-4766

Grayson County College Post-Sec.
6101 FM 691 75020 903-465-6030

Denton, Denton, Pop. 110,797
Denton ISD 23,100/PK-12
1307 N Locust St 76201 940-369-0000
Dr. Jamie Wilson, supt. Fax 369-4982
www.dentonisd.org
Calhoun MS 600/6-8
709 W Congress St 76201 940-369-2400
Carlos Ramirez, prin. Fax 369-4939
Davis S 50/Alt
1125 Davis St 76209 940-369-4050
Jeff Tinch, prin. Fax 369-4966
Denton HS 1,700/9-12
1007 Fulton St 76201 940-369-2000
Dan Ford, prin. Fax 369-4953
Guyer HS 2,200/9-12
7501 Teasley Ln 76210 940-369-1000
Barbara Fischer, prin. Fax 369-4965
LaGrone Advanced Technology Complex Vo/Tech
1504 Long Rd 76207 940-369-4850
Carla Ruge, dir. Fax 369-4971
McMath MS 800/6-8
1900 Jason Dr 76205 940-369-3300
Dr. Debra Nobles, prin. Fax 369-4946
Moore HS 50/Alt
815 Cross Timber St 76205 940-369-4000
Beth Kelly, prin. Fax 369-4957
Ryan HS 2,000/9-12
5101 E McKinney St 76208 940-369-3000
Vernon Reeves, prin. Fax 369-4960
Strickland MS 800/6-8
324 E Windsor Dr 76209 940-369-4200
Kathleen Carmona, prin. Fax 369-4950
Other Schools – See Argyle, Aubrey, Corinth

Denton Calvary Academy 200/K-12
PO Box 2414 76202 940-320-1944
Stacey Baxter, prin. Fax 591-9311
Selwyn S 200/PK-12
3333 W University Dr 76207 940-382-6771
Karen Morris, hdmstr. Fax 383-0704
Texas Woman's University Post-Sec.
PO Box 425589 76204 940-898-2000
University of North Texas Post-Sec.
1155 Union Cir # 311277 76203 940-565-2000

Denver City, Yoakum, Pop. 4,445
Denver City ISD 1,500/PK-12
501 Mustang Dr 79323 806-592-5900
Dagobert Azam, supt. Fax 592-5909
www.dcisd.org
Denver City HS 400/9-12
601 Mustang Dr 79323 806-592-5950
Bruce Patterson, prin. Fax 592-5959
Gravitt JHS 300/6-8
419 Mustang Dr 79323 806-592-5940
Howard Wright, prin. Fax 592-5949

DeSoto, Dallas, Pop. 48,350
De Soto ISD 9,200/PK-12
200 E Belt Line Rd 75115 972-223-6666
Dr. David Harris, supt. Fax 274-8209
www.desotoisd.org
De Soto East MS 600/6-8
601 E Belt Line Rd 75115 972-223-0690
Donna Blackburn, prin. Fax 274-8156
De Soto HS Freshman Campus 800/9-9
620 S Westmoreland Rd 75115 972-274-1818
Carlos Meekins, prin. Fax 274-2501
De Soto SHS 2,000/10-12
600 Eagle Dr 75115 972-230-0726
Dr. Thurston Lamb, prin. Fax 274-8115
De Soto West MS 800/6-8
800 N Westmoreland Rd 75115 972-230-1820
Wanda Randall, prin. Fax 274-8183
PASS Learning Center 50/Alt
200 E Belt Line Rd 75115 972-223-6666
Homer Webb, admin. Fax 274-8011
Other Schools – See Glenn Heights

Canterbury Episcopal S 300/K-12
1708 N Westmoreland Rd 75115 972-572-7200
Sandy Doerge, admin. Fax 572-7400
ITT Technical Institute Post-Sec.
921 W Belt Line Rd Ste 181 75115 972-274-8600
PC Center Post-Sec.
1229 E Pleasant Run Rd 75115 972-224-9800

Detroit, Red River, Pop. 712
Detroit ISD 500/PK-12
110 E Garner St 75436 903-674-6131
Mark Keahey, supt. Fax 674-2478
www.detroiteagles.net
Detroit HS 100/9-12
110 E Garner St 75436 903-674-2646
Brian Howie, prin. Fax 674-2206
Detroit JHS 100/6-8
110 E Garner St 75436 903-674-2646
Brian Howie, prin. Fax 674-2206

Devers, Liberty, Pop. 439
Devers ISD 200/PK-8
PO Box 488 77538 936-549-7135
Elizabeth A. Harris, supt. Fax 549-7595
www.deversisd.net
Devers JHS 100/6-8
PO Box 488 77538 936-549-7591
Elizabeth A. Harris, prin. Fax 549-7595

Devine, Medina, Pop. 4,321
Devine ISD 2,000/PK-12
205 W College Ave 78016 830-851-0795
Linda McAnelly, supt. Fax 663-6706
www.devineisd.org
Devine HS 600/9-12
1225 W Hondo Ave 78016 830-851-0895
Derrick Byrd, prin. Fax 663-6792
Devine MS 400/6-8
400 Cardinal Dr 78016 830-851-0695
Michael Murphy, prin. Fax 663-6769

Faith Christian Academy 50/PK-12
PO Box 172 78016 830-663-4718
Karen Bishop, dir. Fax 665-3332

Deweyville, Newton, Pop. 997
Deweyville ISD 500/PK-12
PO Box 408 77614 409-746-2731
Joseph Mathis, supt. Fax 746-3360
www.deweyvilleisd.com
Other Schools – See Orange

D Hanis, Medina, Pop. 845
D'Hanis ISD 300/PK-12
PO Box 307 78850 830-363-7216
Pam Seipp, supt. Fax 363-7390
www.dhanisisd.net/
D'Hanis MSHS 300/PK-12
PO Box 307 78850 830-363-7216
Kurt Schumacher, prin. Fax 363-7390

Diana, Upshur
New Diana ISD 900/PK-12
1373 US Highway 259 S 75640 903-663-8000
Carl Key, supt. Fax 241-7393
www.ndisd.org
New Diana HS 300/9-12
11826 State Highway 154 E 75640 903-663-8001
Jenifer Politi, prin. Fax 663-2200
New Diana MS 200/6-8
11854 State Highway 154 E 75640 903-663-8002
Greg Pope, prin. Fax 663-1812

Diboll, Angelina, Pop. 4,716
Diboll ISD 1,700/PK-12
PO Box 550 75941 936-829-4718
Gary Martel, supt. Fax 829-5558
www.dibollisd.com
Diboll HS 500/9-12
1000 Lumberjack Dr 75941 936-829-5626
Andy Trekell, prin. Fax 829-5708
Diboll JHS 300/7-8
403 Dennis St 75941 936-829-5225
Mark Kettering, prin. Fax 829-5848

Dickinson, Galveston, Pop. 18,370
Dickinson ISD 8,300/PK-12
PO Box Z 77539 281-229-6000
Vicki Mims, supt. Fax 229-6023
www.dickinsonisd.org
Dickinson HS 2,200/9-12
3800 Baker Dr 77539 281-229-6400
Dr. Billye Smith, prin. Fax 229-6401
McAdams JHS 1,300/7-8
11415 Hughes Rd 77539 281-229-7100
Dr. Jeff Pack, prin. Fax 229-7101

Pine Drive Christian S 200/PK-12
705 FM 517 Rd E 77539 281-534-4881
Frances Templeton, dir. Fax 534-4318

Dilley, Frio, Pop. 3,879
Dilley ISD 900/PK-12
245 W FM 117 78017 830-965-1912
Clint McLain, supt. Fax 965-4069
dilleyisd.net
Dilley HS 300/9-12
245 W FM 117 78017 830-965-1814
Tammie Duff, prin. Fax 965-1276
Harper MS 200/6-8
245 W FM 117 78017 830-965-2195
JoEllen Fisk, prin. Fax 965-2171

Dime Box, Lee
Dime Box ISD 200/PK-12
PO Box 157 77853 979-884-2324
Dr. Jeroladette Centllll, supt. Fax 884-0106
dimebox.groupfusion.net
Dime Box S 200/PK-12
PO Box 157 77853 979-884-3366
Dr. Jeroladette Centilli, prin. Fax 884-0106

Dimmitt, Castro, Pop. 4,377
Dimmitt ISD 1,200/PK-12
608 W Halsell St 79027 806-647-3101
Charles Miller, supt. Fax 647-5433
www.dimmittisd.net
Dimmitt HS 300/9-12
1405 Western Cir 79027 806-647-3105
Jimmy Burns, prin. Fax 647-5795
Dimmitt MS 400/5-8
1505 Western Cir 79027 806-647-3108
Max Newman, prin. Fax 647-2996

Dodd City, Fannin, Pop. 356
Dodd City ISD 300/PK-12
602 N Main St 75438 903-583-7585
Craig Reed, supt. Fax 583-9545
www.doddcityisd.org
Dodd City S 300/PK-12
602 N Main St 75438 903-583-7585
Lesia Bridges, prin. Fax 583-9545

Donna, Hidalgo, Pop. 15,775
Donna ISD 15,000/PK-12
116 N 10th St 78537 956-464-1600
Roberto Loredo, supt. Fax 464-1752
www.donnaisd.net/
Alternative Education Program Alt
116 N 10th St 78537 956-464-1954
John Mendoza, prin. Fax 464-1951
Donna HS 2,200/10-12
116 N 10th St 78537 956-464-1700
Nancy Castillo, prin. Fax 464-1629
Sauceda MS 1,000/6-8
116 N 10th St 78537 956-464-1360
Angie Gonzalez, prin. Fax 464-1349
Solis MS 1,000/6-8
116 N 10th St 78537 956-464-1650
Mary Lou Rodriguez, prin. Fax 464-1786
3D Academy 100/Alt
116 N 10th St 78537 956-464-7493
Lydia Gonzalez, prin. Fax 464-2375
Todd 9th Grade Campus 1,000/9-9
116 N 10th St 78537 956-464-1800
David Moreno, prin. Fax 464-1824
Veterans MS 1,100/6-8
116 N 10th St 78537 956-464-1350
Claudia Guerrero, prin. Fax 464-1356

Douglass, Nacogdoches
Douglass ISD 400/K-12
PO Box 38 75943 936-569-9804
Eric Samford, supt. Fax 569-9446
www.douglass.schoolfusion.us/
Douglass S 400/K-12
PO Box 38 75943 936-569-9804
Jeffrey Roquemore, prin. Fax 569-9446

Dripping Springs, Hays, Pop. 1,763
Dripping Springs ISD 4,500/PK-12
PO Box 479 78620 512-858-3002
Bruce Gearing Ed.D., supt. Fax 858-3099
www.dsisd.txed.net
Dripping Springs HS 1,300/9-12
PO Box 479 78620 512-858-3100
Joe Burns, prin. Fax 858-3199
Dripping Springs MS 1,000/6-8
PO Box 479 78620 512-858-3400
Blake Hays, prin. Fax 858-3499

Driscoll, Nueces, Pop. 733
Driscoll ISD 300/PK-8
PO Box 238 78351 361-387-7349
Cynthia Garcia, supt. Fax 387-6088
www.driscollisd.net
Driscoll MS 100/6-8
PO Box 238 78351 361-387-7349
Lynn Landenberger, prin. Fax 387-6088

Dublin, Erath, Pop. 3,617
Dublin ISD 1,100/PK-12
PO Box 169 76446 254-445-3341
Rodney Schneider, supt. Fax 445-3345
www.dublinisd.us
Dublin HS 300/9-12
PO Box 169 76446 254-445-0362
Keith Owen, prin. Fax 445-1706
Dublin JHS 200/7-8
PO Box 169 76446 254-445-2555
Terry Johnson M.Ed., prin. Fax 445-2607

Dumas, Moore, Pop. 14,542
Dumas ISD 4,400/PK-12
PO Box 615 79029 806-935-6461
Mark Stroebel, supt. Fax 935-6275
www.dumas-k12.net/
Dumas HS 1,100/9-12
PO Box 695 79029 806-935-4151
Bob Callahan, prin. Fax 934-1433
Dumas JHS 600/7-8
PO Box 697 79029 806-935-4155
Kurt Baxter, prin. Fax 934-1434

Duncanville, Dallas, Pop. 38,022
Duncanville ISD 12,900/PK-12
710 S Cedar Ridge Dr 75137 972-708-2000
Dr. Alfred Ray, supt. Fax 708-2020
www.duncanvilleisd.org
Byrd MS 800/7-8
1040 W Wheatland Rd 75116 972-708-3400
Michael McDonald, prin. Fax 708-3434
Duncanville HS 3,800/9-12
900 W Camp Wisdom Rd 75116 972-708-3700
Andre Smith, prin. Fax 708-3737
Pace HS 100/Alt
502 E Freeman St 75116 972-708-2470
Keith Butcher, prin. Fax 708-2474
Reed MS 500/7-8
530 E Freeman St 75116 972-708-3500
Dr. Kathy Culbertson, prin. Fax 708-3535
Summit Center Alt
900 S Cedar Ridge Dr #300A 75137 972-708-2570
Dwight Weaver, prin. Fax 708-2585
Other Schools – See Dallas

Masters Academy 50/4-12
PO Box 381174 75138 972-780-2616
Lynn Watson, admin. Fax 283-0296
State Beauty Academy Post-Sec.
663 Oriole Blvd 75116 972-298-0100

Eagle Pass, Maverick, Pop. 26,203
Eagle Pass ISD 14,700/PK-12
1420 Eidson Rd 78852 830-773-5181
Gilberto Gonzalez, supt. Fax 773-7252
www.eaglepassisd.net
Eagle Pass HS 2,200/9-12
2020 2nd St 78852 830-773-2381
Valeriano Moreno, prin. Fax 758-1795
Eagle Pass JHS 1,100/7-8
1750 N Bibb Ave 78852 830-758-7037
Mario Escobar, prin. Fax 757-1278
Memorial JHS 1,000/7-8
1800 Lewis St 78852 830-758-7053
Maria Sumpter, prin. Fax 773-8900
Winn HS 2,100/9-12
265 Foster Maldonado Blvd 78852 830-757-0828
Jesus Diaz-Wever, prin. Fax 757-3268

Southwest School Post-Sec.
272 Commercial St 78852 830-773-1373

Early, Brown, Pop. 2,720
Early ISD 1,300/PK-12
PO Box 3315, Brownwood TX 76803 325-646-7934
Brett Koch, supt. Fax 646-9238
www.earlyisd.net
Early HS 300/9-12
PO Box 3315, Brownwood TX 76803 325-643-4593
Jennifer Kent, prin. Fax 646-4061
Early MS 300/6-8
PO Box 3315, Brownwood TX 76803 325-643-5665
Randy Lancaster, prin. Fax 646-9972

Earth, Lamb, Pop. 1,057
Springlake-Earth ISD 400/PK-12
PO Box 130 79031 806-257-3310
Denver Crum, supt. Fax 257-3927
www.springlake-earth.org
Springlake-Earth HS 100/9-12
PO Box 130 79031 806-257-3819
Liz Anthony, prin. Fax 257-3370

East Bernard, Wharton, Pop. 2,255
East Bernard ISD 1,000/PK-12
723 College St 77435 979-335-7519
Ross Aschenbeck, supt. Fax 335-6561
www.ebisd.org/
East Bernard HS 300/9-12
723 College St 77435 979-335-7519
Buck Wenglar, prin. Fax 335-6085
East Bernard JHS 300/5-8
723 College St 77435 979-335-7519
Emmett Tugwell, prin. Fax 335-6415

Eastland, Eastland, Pop. 3,922
Eastland ISD 1,100/PK-12
PO Box 31 76448 254-631-5120
Donald W. Hughes, supt. Fax 631-5126
www.eastland.esc14.net/
Eastland HS 300/9-12
PO Box 31 76448 254-631-5000
Joel Lawson, prin. Fax 631-5025
Eastland MS 200/6-8
PO Box 31 76448 254-631-5040
Mark Decker, prin. Fax 631-5049

Ector, Fannin, Pop. 677
Ector ISD 300/PK-12
PO Box 128 75439 903-961-2355
Gary Bohannon, supt. Fax 961-2110
ector.ednet10.net
Ector HS 100/7-12
PO Box 128 75439 903-961-2076
Jason Jones, prin. Fax 961-2356

Edcouch, Hidalgo, Pop. 3,161
Edcouch-Elsa ISD 5,400/PK-12
PO Box 127 78538 956-262-6000
Jose Perez, supt. Fax 262-6032
www.eeisd.org
Other Schools – See Elsa

Eddy, McLennan, Pop. 1,113
Bruceville-Eddy ISD 800/PK-12
1 Eagle Dr 76524 254-859-5832
Richard Kilgore, supt. Fax 859-4023
www.beisd.net
Bruceville-Eddy HS 200/9-12
1 Eagle Dr 76524 254-859-5848
Grady Fulbright, prin. Fax 859-5001
Bruceville-Eddy MS 100/7-8
1 Eagle Dr 76524 254-859-5525
Mike Hawkins, prin. Fax 859-3207
Other Schools – See Waco

Eden, Concho, Pop. 2,753
Eden Consolidated ISD 300/K-12
PO Box 988 76837 325-869-4121
John Massey, supt. Fax 869-5210
www.edencisd.net
Eden JSHS 100/7-12
PO Box 988 76837 325-869-5180
Misty Kinnibrugh, prin. Fax 869-5023

Edgewood, Van Zandt, Pop. 1,419
Edgewood ISD 900/PK-12
804 E Pine St 75117 903-896-4332
Emmett Baker, supt. Fax 896-7056
www.edgewood-isd.net
Edgewood HS 300/9-12
804 E Pine St 75117 903-896-4856
Kristin Prater, prin. Fax 896-1050
Edgewood MS 200/6-8
804 E Pine St 75117 903-896-1530
Brenda Sanford, prin. Fax 896-7056

Edinburg, Hidalgo, Pop. 76,876
Edinburg Consolidated ISD 34,100/PK-12
PO Box 990 78540 956-289-2300
Dr. Rene Gutierrez, supt. Fax 383-3576
www.ecisd.us/
Barrientes MS 1,100/6-8
PO Box 990 78540 956-289-2430
Christina Esparza, prin. Fax 316-7749
Economedes HS 2,800/9-12
PO Box 990 78540 956-289-2450
Anthony Garza, prin. Fax 385-3050
Edinburg Alternative Education Academy Alt
PO Box 990 78540 956-289-2598
Susana Aguilar, prin. Fax 316-7391
Edinburg HS 3,100/9-12
PO Box 990 78540 956-289-2400
Daniel Roma, prin. Fax 386-1225
Edinburg North HS 2,800/9-12
PO Box 990 78540 956-289-2500
Ramiro Guerra, prin. Fax 316-7712
Edinburg South MS 1,500/6-8
PO Box 990 78540 956-289-2415
Sylvia Ledesma, prin. Fax 316-8817
Garza MS 1,400/6-8
PO Box 990 78540 956-289-2480
Anibal Gorena, prin. Fax 316-3109
Harwell MS 1,700/6-8
PO Box 990 78540 956-289-2440
Gilda Sanchez, prin. Fax 316-7303
Longoria MS 900/6-8
PO Box 990 78540 956-289-2486
Jorge Botello, prin. Fax 381-6442
Memorial MS 1,200/6-8
PO Box 990 78540 956-289-2470
Carlos Guzman, prin. Fax 316-7581
Vela HS 9-12
PO Box 990 78540 956-289-2650
Eva Torres, prin. Fax 383-3576
Vision Academy of Excellence Alt
PO Box 990 78540 956-289-2584
Ernestina Cano, prin. Fax 287-0812

South Texas ISD
Supt. — See Mercedes
South Texas Business Educ &Tech Academy 600/9-12
510 S Sugar Rd 78539 956-383-1684
Magdalena Gutierrez, prin. Fax 383-8544
South Texas Preparatory Academy 500/7-8
724 S Sugar Rd 78539 956-381-5522
Ana Castro, prin. Fax 381-1177

Rio Grande Bible Institute Post-Sec.
4300 S US Highway 281 78539 956-380-8100
University of Texas Pan American Post-Sec.
1201 W University Dr 78539 866-441-8812

Edna, Jackson, Pop. 5,438
Edna ISD 1,400/PK-12
1307 W Gayle St 77957 361-782-3573
Robert Wells, supt. Fax 781-1002
www.ednaisd.org
Edna HS 400/9-12
1303 W Gayle St 77957 361-782-5255
Demetric Wells, prin. Fax 781-1014
Edna JHS 300/6-8
PO Box 919 77957 361-782-2351
Paul Fleener, prin. Fax 781-1025

El Campo, Wharton, Pop. 11,547
El Campo ISD 3,500/PK-12
700 W Norris St 77437 979-543-6771
Robert Pool, supt. Fax 543-1670
www.ecisd.org/
El Campo HS 1,000/9-12
600 W Norris St 77437 979-543-6341
Rich DuBroc, prin. Fax 543-2528
El Campo MS 700/6-8
4010 FM 2765 Rd 77437 979-543-6362
Mark Freeman, prin. Fax 541-5210

Eldorado, Schleicher, Pop. 1,941
Schleicher ISD 600/PK-12
PO Box W 76936 325-853-2514
Billy Collins, supt. Fax 853-2695
www.scisd.net
Eldorado HS 200/9-12
PO Box W 76936 325-853-2514
Robert Gibson, prin. Fax 853-2710
Eldorado MS 200/5-8
PO Box W 76936 325-853-2514
Dr. Richard Evans, prin. Fax 853-2895

Electra, Wichita, Pop. 2,739
Electra ISD 500/PK-12
PO Box 231 76360 940-495-3683
Gary Nightingale, supt. Fax 495-3945
www.electraisd.net
Electra HS 100/9-12
400 E Roosevelt Ave 76360 940-495-2218
Ben Frieling, prin. Fax 495-3303
Electra JHS 100/5-8
621 S Bailey St 76360 940-495-2533
Gene Jarvis, prin. Fax 495-3627

Elgin, Bastrop, Pop. 7,996
Elgin ISD 3,700/PK-12
PO Box 351 78621 512-281-9731
Dr. Jodi Duron, supt. Fax 285-9935
www.elginisd.net
Elgin HS 1,100/9-12
PO Box 311 78621 512-281-3438
Janis Linder, prin. Fax 281-9804
Elgin MS 900/6-8
1351 N Avenue C 78621 512-281-3382
Riza Cooper, prin. Fax 281-9781
Phoenix HS 50/Alt
902 W 2nd St 78621 512-281-9774
Larry Thomas, prin. Fax 281-9862

Elkhart, Anderson, Pop. 1,338
Elkhart ISD 1,300/PK-12
301 E Parker St 75839 903-764-2952
Dr. Ray DeSpain, supt. Fax 764-2466
www.elkhartisd.org/
Elkhart HS 400/9-12
301 E Parker St 75839 903-764-5161
Kevin Clark, prin. Fax 764-8288
Elkhart MS 300/6-8
301 E Parker St 75839 903-764-2459
Ron Mays, prin. Fax 764-8287

Slocum ISD 400/PK-12
5765 E State Highway 294 75839 903-478-3624
Cliff Lasiter, supt. Fax 478-3030
www.slocumisd.org
Slocum JSHS 200/6-12
5765 E State Highway 294 75839 903-478-3624
Errin Deer, prin. Fax 478-3030

Elmaton, Matagorda
Tidehaven ISD 800/PK-12
PO Box 129 77440 361-588-6321
Andrew Seigrist, supt. Fax 588-7109
www.tidehavenisd.com
Tidehaven HS 200/9-12
PO Box 159 77440 361-588-6810
Jim Sides, prin. Fax 588-6966
Tidehaven IS 200/6-8
PO Box 130 77440 361-588-6600
Gerry Talley, prin. Fax 588-6368

Elm Mott, McLennan
Connally ISD
Supt. — See Waco
Connally JHS 400/6-8
100 Hancock Dr 76640 254-296-7700
Vicki Dean, prin. Fax 829-2354

El Paso, El Paso, Pop. 643,027
Canutillo ISD 6,000/PK-12
7965 Artcraft Rd 79932 915-877-7400
Dr. Pedro Galaviz, supt. Fax 877-7414
www.canutillo-isd.org

Canutillo HS 1,500/9-12
6675 S Desert Blvd 79932 915-877-7800
Dino Coronado, prin. Fax 877-7807
Learning Center Alt
6675 S Desert Blvd 79932 915-877-7885
Cary Flores, lead tchr. Fax 877-7881
Other Schools – See Canutillo

Clint ISD 10,900/PK-12
14521 Horizon Blvd 79928 915-926-4000
Juan Martinez, supt. Fax 926-4009
www.clintweb.net
East Montana MS 700/6-8
3490 Ascension Rd 79938 915-926-5200
David Morales, prin. Fax 855-0821
Estrada JHS 8-9
851 Darrington Rd 79928 915-926-4800
Robert Mendoza, prin. Fax 852-2455
Horizon HS 1,100/10-12
14651 Horizon Blvd 79928 915-926-4200
Ramon Lozano, prin. Fax 852-0357
Mountain View HS 1,000/9-12
14964 Greg Dr 79938 915-926-5000
Edmond Martinez, prin. Fax 855-2503
Other Schools – See Clint

El Paso ISD 64,000/PK-12
PO Box 20100 79998 915-230-2000
Vernon Butler, supt. Fax 887-5484
www.episd.org
Andress HS 1,900/9-12
5400 Sun Valley Dr 79924 915-832-8600
Samuel Hogue, prin. Fax 757-6443
Armendariz MS 800/6-8
2231 Arizona Ave 79930 915-546-9012
Lorenzo Munoz, prin. Fax 577-0848
Austin HS 1,600/9-12
3500 Memphis Ave 79930 915-587-2500
John Tanner, prin. Fax 566-7360
Bassett MS 900/6-8
4400 Elm St 79930 915-231-2260
Lesa Provenghi, prin. Fax 565-1562
Bowie HS 1,200/9-12
801 S San Marcial St 79905 915-496-8200
Nicasio Cobos, prin. Fax 532-1918
Brown MS 1,000/6-8
7820 Helen Of Troy Dr 79912 915-774-4080
Victoria York, prin. Fax 581-6424
Burges HS 1,600/9-12
7800 Edgemere Blvd 79925 915-780-1100
Randall Woods, prin. Fax 771-6914
Canyon Hills MS 900/6-8
8930 Eclipse St 79904 915-231-2240
Deborah Lunow, prin. Fax 757-8067
Center for Career & Technology Education Vo/Tech
1170 N Walnut St 79930 915-545-5900
Eric Winkleman, prin. Fax 544-5976
Chapin HS 1,900/9-12
7000 Dyer St 79904 915-832-6730
Dr. Carla Gonzales, prin. Fax 565-9716
Charles MS 600/6-8
4909 Trojan Dr 79924 915-849-3940
Michael Mendoza, prin. Fax 821-0505
Coronado HS 2,700/9-12
100 Champions Pl 79912 915-834-2460
Maria Morales, prin. Fax 587-6458
Delta Academy 100/Alt
6400 Delta Dr 79905 915-774-0447
Alicia Loya, admin. Fax 775-0433
El Paso HS 1,300/9-12
800 E Schuster Ave 79902 915-496-8300
Kristine Ferret, prin. Fax 532-2008
Franklin HS 3,000/9-12
900 N Resler Dr 79912 915-832-6600
Carla Gasway, prin. Fax 587-4094
Guillen MS 900/6-8
900 S Cotton St 79901 915-496-4620
Cesar Uribe, prin. Fax 532-1143
Henderson MS 900/6-8
5505 Robert Alva Ave 79905 915-887-3080
Elizabeth Maldonado, prin. Fax 772-3425
Hornedo MS 1,100/6-8
6101 High Ridge Dr 79912 915-881-2900
Angela Henderson, prin. Fax 581-7371
Irvin HS 1,700/9-12
9465 Roanoke Dr 79924 915-587-3500
Luis Loya, prin. Fax 757-6450
Jefferson HS 1,100/9-12
4700 Alameda Ave 79905 915-496-8010
Federico Rojas, prin. Fax 532-2033
Lafarelle Alternative S 50/Alt
5209 Hercules Ave 79904 915-751-7186
Teresa Clapsaddle-Ramos, prin. Fax 751-1316
Lincoln MS 1,000/6-8
500 Mulberry Ave 79932 915-231-2180
Sandy Whitney, prin. Fax 581-1371
Magoffin MS 900/6-8
4931 Hercules Ave 79904 915-774-4040
Raul Ruiz, prin. Fax 757-7675
Morehead MS 900/6-8
5625 Confetti Dr 79912 915-231-2140
John McAlpine, prin. Fax 587-5355
Occupational Center Vo/Tech
5300 Warriors Dr 79932 915-587-9680
Toni Bowermaster, prin. Fax 584-2940
Richardson MS 900/6-8
11350 Loma Franklin Dr 79934 915-822-8829
Joseph Manago, prin. Fax 822-8812
Ross MS 900/6-8
6101 Hughey Cir 79925 915-887-3060
Jason Yturralde, prin. Fax 771-6792
Silva Health Magnet HS 600/9-12
121 Val Verde St 79905 915-496-8100
Federico Rojas, prin. Fax 533-3695
Sunset HS 200/Alt
2851 Grant Ave 79930 915-587-2630
Maria Ponce-Kreye, prin. Fax 587-2630

Telles Academy 50/Alt
320 S Campbell St 79901 915-496-4600
Ernie Watts, prin. Fax 532-0540
Terrace Hills MS 600/6-8
4835 Blossom Ave 79924 915-231-2120
Wayne Jones, prin. Fax 759-0615
Transmountain Early College HS 300/9-12
9570 Gateway Blvd N 79924 915-832-4270
Dianne Jones, prin. Fax 751-2011
Wiggs MS 900/6-8
1300 Circle Dr 79902 915-231-2100
Jesus Teran, prin. Fax 533-2902
San Jacinto Adult Learning Center Adult
1216 Olive Ave 79901 915-230-3200
Fax 544-7163

Socorro ISD 40,200/PK-12
12440 Rojas Dr 79928 915-937-0000
Patrick O'Neil, supt. Fax 851-7572
www.sisd.net
Americas HS 2,700/9-12
12101 Pellicano Dr 79936 915-937-2800
Lucia Borrego, prin. Fax 855-6898
Clarke MS 1,100/6-8
1515 Bob Hope Dr 79936 915-937-5600
Chelaine Marion, prin. Fax 857-3765
El Dorado 9th Grade Academy 100/9-9
14400 Pebble Hills Blvd 79938 915-937-3200
Troy Byrne, prin. Fax 851-7820
El Dorado HS 2,500/9-12
12401 Edgemere Blvd 79938 915-937-3200
Nora Paugh, prin. Fax 851-7820
Hernando MS 1,000/6-8
3451 Rich Beem 79938 915-937-9800
Cynthia Retana, prin. Fax 937-9898
K.E.Y.S. Academy 100/Alt
12380 Pine Springs Dr 79928 915-937-4000
Ellen Brewer, prin. Fax 937-4006
Mission Early College HS 500/9-12
10700 Gateway Blvd E 79927 915-937-1200
Jason Long, prin. Fax 860-2935
Montwood HS 2,800/9-12
12000 Montwood Dr 79936 915-937-2400
Rosa Mireles-Menchaca, prin. Fax 937-2438
Montwood MS 800/6-8
11710 Pebble Hills Blvd 79936 915-937-5800
Libby Tidwell, prin. Fax 856-9909
Options HS 200/Alt
12380 Pine Springs Dr 79928 915-937-1300
Ray Aguilar, prin. Fax 859-2603
Sanchez MS 800/6-8
321 N Rio Vista Rd 79927 915-937-5200
Clarice Jones, prin. Fax 859-6636
Slider MS 900/6-8
11700 School Ln 79936 915-937-5400
Steve Troxel, prin. Fax 857-5804
Socorro HS 2,700/9-12
10150 Alameda Ave 79927 915-937-2000
Miguel Serrano, prin. Fax 859-0206
Socorro MS 700/6-8
321 Bovee Rd 79927 915-937-5000
Lori Diaz, prin. Fax 859-6955
Sun Ridge MS 800/6-8
2210 Sun Country Dr 79938 915-937-6600
Dr. Kim Baxter, prin. Fax 851-7730
Other Schools – See Horizon City

Ysleta ISD 44,600/PK-12
9600 Sims Dr 79925 915-434-0000
Dr. Michael Zolkoski, supt. Fax 591-4144
www.yisd.net
Bel Air HS 2,200/9-12
731 N Yarbrough Dr 79915 915-434-2000
Louis Martinez, prin. Fax 593-6110
Camino Real MS 700/6-8
9393 Alameda Ave 79907 915-434-8300
Dolores Chaparro, prin. Fax 858-3743
Chavez Academy 100/Alt
7814 Alameda Ave 79915 915-434-9600
Graciela Martinez, prin. Fax 779-2068
Del Valle HS 1,900/9-12
950 Bordeaux Dr 79907 915-434-3000
Carmen Crosse, prin. Fax 858-1427
Desert View MS 600/7-8
1641 Billie Marie Dr 79936 915-434-5300
Michelle Kehrwald, prin. Fax 591-9327
Eastwood HS 2,200/9-12
2430 Mcrae Blvd 79925 915-434-4000
Armenia Smith, prin. Fax 594-8014
Eastwood MS 900/7-8
2612 Chaswood St 79935 915-434-4300
Malinda Carri-Villalobos, prin. Fax 591-9426
Hanks HS 2,100/9-12
2001 N Lee Trevino Dr 79936 915-434-5000
Gloria Spencer, prin. Fax 598-4621
Hillcrest MS 600/7-8
8040 Yermoland Dr 79907 915-434-2200
Dr. Lucy Lozano, prin. Fax 591-9439
Indian Ridge MS 700/6-8
11201 Pebble Hills Blvd 79936 915-434-5400
Pauline Muela, prin. Fax 591-9447
Parkland HS 1,300/9-12
5932 Quail Ave 79924 915-434-6000
Miles Hume, prin. Fax 434-6291
Parkland MS 700/7-8
6045 Nova Way 79924 915-434-6300
Javier Selgado, prin. Fax 757-6608
Plato Academy 200/Alt
8441 Alameda Ave 79907 915-434-9000
Juan Contreras, prin. Fax 434-9080
Ranchland Hills MS 400/7-8
7615 Yuma Dr 79915 915-434-2300
Carmen Crawford, prin. Fax 592-0036
Rio Bravo MS 400/6-8
525 Greggerson Dr 79907 915-434-8400
Antonio Acuna, prin. Fax 872-0269

Riverside HS 1,400/9-12
301 Midway Dr 79915 915-434-7000
Michael Martinez, prin. Fax 779-6983
Riverside MS 600/7-8
7615 Mimosa Ave 79915 915-434-7300
Marie Anaya, prin. Fax 772-7549
Tejas School of Choice 200/Alt
7500 Alpha Ave 79915 915-434-9900
Juan Contreras, prin. Fax 434-9997
Valle Verde Early College HS 400/9-12
919 Hunter Dr 79915 915-434-1500
Paul Covey, prin. Fax 594-7112
Valley View MS 700/7-8
8660 N Loop Dr 79907 915-434-3300
Catherine Kennedy, prin. Fax 858-3615
Ysleta HS 1,700/9-12
8600 Alameda Ave 79907 915-434-8000
Silvia Rendon, prin. Fax 858-3299
Ysleta MS 400/7-8
8691 Independence Dr 79907 915-434-8200
Irene Medina, prin. Fax 858-0261
Ysleta Community Learning Center Adult
121 Padres Dr 79907 915-434-9400
Fred Anaya, prin. Fax 858-6307

Anamarc College Post-Sec.
3210 Dyer St 79930 915-351-8100
Anamarc College Post-Sec.
8720 Gateway Blvd E Ste D 79907 915-351-8100
Cathedral HS 500/9-12
1309 N Stanton St 79902 915-532-3238
Br. Nick Gonzalez, prin. Fax 533-8248
El Paso Community College Post-Sec.
PO Box 20500 79998 915-831-2000
Faith Christian Academy 600/PK-12
8960 Escobar Dr 79907 915-594-3305
Cesar Ramirez, prin. Fax 593-5474
Father Yermo HS 200/9-12
250 Washington St 79905 915-533-3185
Karina Tapia, prin. Fax 544-0738
Immanuel Christian S 600/PK-12
1201 Hawkins Blvd 79925 915-778-6160
J.D. Zubia, head sch Fax 772-8207
International Business College Post-Sec.
5700 Cromo Dr 79912 915-842-0422
International Business College Post-Sec.
1155 N Zaragoza Rd Ste 100 79907 915-859-0422
Jesus Chapel S 200/PK-12
10200 Album Ave 79925 915-593-1153
Alba Wilcox, prin. Fax 593-1113
Kaplan College Post-Sec.
8360 Burnham Rd Ste 100 79907 915-595-1935
Loretto Academy 500/6-12
1300 Hardaway St 79903 915-566-8400
Abe Ramirez, prin. Fax 564-0563
Patterson Institute 300/9-12
517 S Florence St 79901 915-533-8286
Hector Lachica, prin. Fax 533-5236
Pipo Academy of Hair Design Post-Sec.
3000 Pershing Dr 79903 915-565-3491
Radford S 200/PK-12
2001 Radford St 79903 915-565-2737
Fax 565-2700
Southwest University Post-Sec.
1414 Geronimo Dr 79925 915-778-4001
Tri-State Cosmetology Institute Post-Sec.
601 N Cotton St Ste 5 79902 915-585-8777
Tri-State Cosmetology Institute Post-Sec.
6800 Gateway Blvd E Ste 4A 79915 915-778-1741
University of Texas at El Paso Post-Sec.
500 W University Ave 79968 915-747-5000
Vista College Post-Sec.
6101 Montana Ave 79925 866-442-4197
Western Technical College Post-Sec.
9624 Plaza Cir 79927 915-532-3737
Western Technical College Post-Sec.
9451 Diana Dr 79924 915-566-9621

Elsa, Hidalgo, Pop. 5,655
Edcouch-Elsa ISD
Supt. — See Edcouch
Edcouch-Elsa HS 1,500/9-12
401 N Yellowjacket Dr 78543 956-262-6944
Rene Ramos, prin. Fax 262-9018
Truan JHS 800/7-8
E 9th St 78543 956-262-6082
Nehemias Cantu, prin. Fax 262-6079

Elysian Fields, Harrison
Elysian Fields ISD 1,000/PK-12
PO Box 120 75642 903-633-2420
Maynard Chapman, supt. Fax 633-2498
www.efisd.net
Elysian Fields HS 300/9-12
PO Box 120 75642 903-633-2420
Gary Holt, prin. Fax 633-2498
Elysian Fields MS 300/6-8
PO Box 120 75642 903-633-2420
Brandon Goswick, prin. Fax 633-2326

Emory, Rains, Pop. 1,215
Rains ISD 1,500/PK-12
PO Box 247 75440 903-473-2222
John Rouse, supt. Fax 473-3053
www.rains.k12.tx.us/
Rains HS 500/9-12
PO Box 247 75440 903-473-2222
Randell Wellman, prin. Fax 473-5584
Rains JHS 400/6-8
PO Box 247 75440 903-473-2222
Denise Flagg, prin. Fax 473-5162

Ennis, Ellis, Pop. 18,329
Ennis ISD 5,800/PK-12
PO Box 1420 75120 972-872-7000
Barbara Qualls Ph.D., supt. Fax 875-8667
www.ennis.k12.tx.us

Ennis HS 1,500/9-12
2301 Ensign Rd 75119 972-872-3500
David Averett, prin. Fax 875-6337
Ennis JHS 800/7-8
3101 Ensign Rd 75119 972-872-3850
Kristin Cantrell, prin. Fax 875-1433

Era, Cooke
Era ISD 400/K-12
PO Box 98 76238 940-665-5961
Jeremy Thompson, supt. Fax 665-5311
www.eraisd.net
Era JSHS 200/6-12
PO Box 98 76238 940-665-5961
Jereme Dietz, prin. Fax 665-5311

Euless, Tarrant, Pop. 48,852
Hurst-Euless-Bedford ISD
Supt. — See Bedford
Alternative Education Program 50/Alt
1100 Raider Dr Ste 100 76040 817-354-3398
Dr. June Jacoby, prin. Fax 358-5001
Central JHS 900/7-9
3191 W Pipeline Rd 76040 817-354-3350
Jonathan James, prin. Fax 354-3357
Euless JHS 900/7-9
306 Airport Fwy 76039 817-354-3340
Rita Wiles, prin. Fax 354-3345
Keys Learning Center 100/Alt
1100 Raider Dr Ste 100 76040 817-354-3580
Dr. June Jacoby, prin. Fax 354-3586
Trinity SHS 2,300/10-12
500 N Industrial Blvd 76039 817-571-0271
Micheal Harris, prin. Fax 354-3322

Eustace, Henderson, Pop. 976
Eustace ISD 1,500/PK-12
PO Box 188 75124 903-425-5151
Dr. Coy Holcombe, supt. Fax 425-5147
www.eustaceisd.net
Eustace HS 400/9-12
PO Box 188 75124 903-425-5161
Stan Sowers, prin. Fax 425-5227
Eustace MS 300/6-8
PO Box 188 75124 903-425-5171
Truman Oakley, prin. Fax 425-5146

Evadale, Jasper, Pop. 1,471
Evadale ISD 400/PK-12
PO Box 497 77615 409-276-1337
Gary Fairchild, supt. Fax 276-1908
www.evadalek12.net
Evadale HS 100/9-12
PO Box 497 77615 409-276-1337
Rusty Minyard, prin. Fax 276-1050
Evadale JHS 100/6-8
PO Box 497 77615 409-276-1337
Cheryl Jones, prin. Fax 276-1588

Evant, Coryell, Pop. 421
Evant ISD 200/PK-12
PO Box 339 76525 254-471-5536
James Slone, supt. Fax 471-5629
www.evantisd.org/
Evant HS 100/7-12
PO Box 339 76525 254-471-5536
Rick Panter, prin. Fax 471-5629

Everman, Tarrant, Pop. 6,051
Everman ISD 5,100/PK-12
608 Townley Dr 76140 817-568-3500
Dr. Jeri Pfeifer, supt. Fax 568-3508
www.eisd.org
Baxter JHS 800/7-8
3038 Shelby Rd 76140 817-568-3530
Felicia Donaldson, prin. Fax 568-3594
Everman Academy HS 1,200/9-12
1 Bulldog Rd 76140 817-568-3520
Mario Layne, prin. Fax 568-3516
Shelby Learning Center Alt
300 Shelby Rd 76140 817-568-3592
Nita Page, prin. Fax 568-3520

Fabens, El Paso, Pop. 8,249
Fabens ISD 2,400/PK-12
PO Box 697 79838 915-765-2600
Poncho Garcia, supt. Fax 764-2968
www.fabensisd.net/
Fabens HS 700/9-12
PO Box 697 79838 915-765-2620
Robert Sepulveda, prin. Fax 764-4953
Fabens MS 600/6-8
PO Box 697 79838 915-765-2630
Dr. Joe Keith, prin. Fax 764-7263

Fairfield, Freestone, Pop. 2,920
Fairfield ISD 1,800/PK-12
615 Post Oak Rd 75840 903-389-2532
Katie Ryan Ed.D., supt. Fax 389-7050
www.fairfield.k12.tx.us
Fairfield HS 500/9-12
615 Post Oak Rd 75840 903-389-4177
Von Wade M.Ed., prin. Fax 389-5453
Fairfield JHS 400/6-8
615 Post Oak Rd 75840 903-389-4210
Bryan Gawryszewski M.Ed., prin. Fax 389-5454

Fairview, Collin, Pop. 7,141
Lovejoy ISD
Supt. — See Allen
Sloan Creek MS 800/6-8
440 Country Club Rd 75069 469-742-8400
Kent Messer, prin. Fax 742-8401

Falfurrias, Brooks, Pop. 4,970
Brooks County ISD 1,500/PK-12
PO Box 589 78355 361-325-8000
David Perry, supt. Fax 325-1913
www.bcisdistrict.net
Falfurrias HS 400/9-12
PO Box 589 78355 361-325-8091
Lucilia Munoz, prin. Fax 325-8158
Falfurrias JHS 300/6-8
PO Box 589 78355 361-325-8071
Dr. Cynthia Perez, prin. Fax 325-2220

Falls City, Karnes, Pop. 604
Falls City ISD 300/K-12
PO Box 399 78113 830-254-3551
Linda Bettin, supt. Fax 254-3354
www.fcisd.net/
Falls City JSHS 200/7-12
PO Box 399 78113 830-254-3551
Christy Blocker, prin. Fax 254-3354

Farmers Branch, Dallas, Pop. 28,241
Carrollton-Farmers Branch ISD
Supt. — See Carrollton
Field MS 900/6-8
13551 Dennis Ln 75234 972-968-3900
Stephanie Cherney, prin. Fax 968-3910

Brookhaven College Post-Sec.
3939 Valley View Ln 75244 972-860-4700

Farmersville, Collin, Pop. 3,235
Farmersville ISD 1,400/PK-12
501A State Highway 78 N 75442 972-782-6601
Jeff Adams, supt. Fax 784-7293
www.farmersvilleisd.net/
Farmersville HS 400/9-12
499 State Highway 78 N 75442 972-548-0576
Wayne Callaway, prin. Fax 529-3750
Farmersville JHS 300/6-8
501 State Highway 78 N 75442 972-782-6202
Dr. Josh Martin, prin. Fax 782-7029

Farwell, Parmer, Pop. 1,360
Farwell ISD 600/PK-12
PO Box F 79325 806-481-3371
Mike Read, supt. Fax 481-9275
www.farwellschools.org
Farwell HS 200/9-12
PO Box F 79325 806-481-3351
Brian Patterson, prin. Fax 481-3531
Farwell JHS 100/6-8
PO Box F 79325 806-481-9260
Jimmie Mace, prin. Fax 481-9258

Fayetteville, Fayette, Pop. 257
Fayetteville ISD 200/K-12
PO Box 129 78940 979-378-4242
Rich Elsasser, supt. Fax 378-4246
www.fayettevilleisd.net
Fayetteville JSHS 100/6-12
PO Box 129 78940 979-378-4242
Janice Motal, prin. Fax 378-4246

Ferris, Ellis, Pop. 2,412
Ferris ISD 2,400/PK-12
PO Box 459 75125 972-544-3858
Michael Bodine, supt. Fax 544-2784
www.ferrisisd.org
Ferris HS 700/9-12
PO Box 461 75125 972-544-3737
Kevin Dixon, prin. Fax 544-2029
Ferris JHS 400/7-8
PO Box 459 75125 972-544-2279
Rhonda Renner, prin. Fax 544-2281

Fischer, Comal
Comal ISD
Supt. — See New Braunfels
Canyon Lake HS 900/9-12
8555 FM 32 78623 830-885-1700
Cheryl Koury, prin. Fax 885-1701

Flatonia, Fayette, Pop. 1,376
Flatonia ISD 600/PK-12
PO Box 189 78941 361-865-2941
Dr. Donald Egg, supt. Fax 865-2940
www.esc13.net/flatonia/
Flatonia HS 300/7-12
PO Box 189 78941 361-865-2941
Robin Branecky, prin. Fax 865-2944

Florence, Williamson, Pop. 1,128
Florence ISD 1,000/PK-12
PO Box 489 76527 254-793-2850
Sam Atwood, supt. Fax 793-3055
florenceisd.net
Florence HS 300/9-12
PO Box 489 76527 254-793-2495
Harold Steele, prin. Fax 793-3784
Florence MS 200/6-8
PO Box 489 76527 254-793-2504
Steve Ham, prin. Fax 793-3054

Floresville, Wilson, Pop. 6,407
Floresville ISD 3,600/PK-12
1200 5th St 78114 830-393-5300
Jerry Lee Hunkapiller Ed.D., supt. Fax 393-5399
www.fisd.us
Floresville Alternative S 50/Alt
335 Alternative Ln 78114 830-393-5368
Bud Box, prin. Fax 393-5706
Floresville HS 1,100/9-12
1813 Tiger Ln 78114 830-393-5370
Sandra Galinzoga, prin. Fax 393-5719
Floresville MS 800/6-8
2601 B St 78114 830-393-5350
Sara Mann, prin. Fax 393-5339

Flower Mound, Denton, Pop. 63,499
Lewisville ISD 49,800/PK-12
1800 Timber Creek Rd 75028 972-713-5200
Dr. Stephen Waddell, supt. Fax 350-9500
www.lisd.net
Downing MS 700/6-8
5555 Bridlewood Blvd 75028 469-713-5962
Lisa Lingren, prin. Fax 350-9176
Flower Mound HS 3,200/9-12
3411 Peters Colony Rd 75022 469-713-5192
Sonya Lail, prin. Fax 350-9244
Forestwood MS 600/6-8
2810 Morriss Rd 75028 469-713-5972
Dave Tickner, prin. Fax 350-9184
Lamar MS 800/6-8
4000 Timber Creek Rd 75028 469-713-5966
Leigh Lewis, prin. Fax 350-9204
Marcus HS 3,200/9-12
5707 Morriss Rd 75028 469-713-5196
Gary Shafferman, prin. Fax 350-9313
McKamy MS 1,100/6-8
2401 Old Settlers Rd 75022 469-713-5991
Peter Taggart, prin. Fax 350-9477
Shadow Ridge MS 800/6-8
2050 Aberdeen Dr 75028 469-713-5984
Gary Gibson, prin. Fax 350-9215
Other Schools – See Carrollton, Highland Village, Lewisville, The Colony

---

Temple Christian Academy 200/K-12
2501 Northshore Blvd 75028 972-874-8700
Dr. Richard Wallace, admin. Fax 539-4649

Floydada, Floyd, Pop. 3,029
Floydada ISD 600/PK-12
226 W California St 79235 806-983-3498
Gilbert Trevino, supt. Fax 983-5739
www.floydadaisd.esc17.net
Floydada HS 200/9-12
618 Whirlwind Aly 79235 806-983-4970
Wayne Morren, prin. Fax 983-5739
Floydada JHS 200/6-8
910 S 5th St 79235 806-983-2161
Wayne Morren, prin. Fax 983-5739

Follett, Lipscomb, Pop. 459
Follett ISD 200/PK-12
PO Box 28 79034 806-653-2301
George Auld, supt. Fax 653-2036
www.follettisd.net
Follett S 200/PK-12
PO Box 28 79034 806-653-2301
Brianna Ethridge, prin. Fax 653-2036

Forestburg, Montague
Forestburg ISD 200/PK-12
PO Box 415 76239 940-964-2323
John Metzler, supt. Fax 964-2531
www.esc9.net/forestburgisd/
Forestburg S 200/PK-12
PO Box 415 76239 940-964-2323
Jennifer Steadham, prin. Fax 964-2531

Forney, Kaufman, Pop. 14,459
Forney ISD 8,100/PK-12
600 S Bois d Arc St 75126 972-564-4055
Michael Holland, supt. Fax 552-3038
www.forneyisd.net
Brown MS 600/7-8
1050 Windmill Farms Blvd 75126 972-564-3967
Jody Fadely, prin. Fax 564-7022
Forney HS 1,400/9-12
800 FM 741 75126 972-564-3890
Stephen Whiffen, prin. Fax 564-5616
North Forney HS 800/9-12
6170 N Mason Blvd 75126 972-762-4159
Dr. Joe Kucera, prin. Fax 762-4159
Warren MS 700/7-8
811 S Bois D Arc St 75126 469-762-4156
Kenneth Pearce, prin. Fax 552-1693

Forsan, Howard, Pop. 209
Forsan ISD 700/K-12
PO Box A 79733 432-457-2223
Randy Johnson, supt. Fax 457-2225
forsan.esc18.net
Forsan JSHS 400/6-12
PO Box A 79733 432-457-2223
Keith Stone, prin. Fax 457-2225

Fort Davis, Jeff Davis, Pop. 1,186
Fort Davis ISD 300/PK-12
PO Box 1339 79734 432-426-4440
Dr. Judy Whitis, supt. Fax 426-3841
www.fdisd.com
Fort Davis Alternative Education Campus 100/Alt
PO Box 1339 79734 432-364-2450
Becky Farrer, prin. Fax 364-2315
Fort Davis JSHS 100/7-12
PO Box 1339 79734 432-426-4444
Graydon Hicks, prin. Fax 426-4449

Fort Hancock, Hudspeth, Pop. 1,741
Fort Hancock ISD 500/K-12
PO Box 98 79839 915-769-3811
Jose Franco, supt. Fax 769-3940
www.forthancockisd.net/
Fort Hancock HS 200/9-12
PO Box 98 79839 915-769-3811
Dino Coronado, prin. Fax 769-0044
Fort Hancock MS 100/6-8
PO Box 98 79839 915-769-3811
Jess Schultz, prin. Fax 769-0045

Fort Hood, Bell, Pop. 27,754
Killeen ISD
Supt. — See Killeen
Murphy MS 500/6-8
53393 Sun Dance Dr 76544 254-336-6530
Mike Quinn, prin. Fax 336-6579
Smith MS 700/6-8
51000 Tank Destroyer Blvd 76544 254-336-1050
Chad Wolf, prin. Fax 532-1247

Fort Stockton, Pecos, Pop. 8,231
Fort Stockton ISD 2,400/PK-12
101 W Division St 79735 432-336-4000
Ralph Traynham, supt. Fax 336-4008
www.fsisd.net/
Fort Stockton HS 600/9-12
101 W Division St 79735 432-336-4101
Gil-Ray Madrid, prin. Fax 336-4113
Fort Stockton MS 500/6-8
101 W Division St 79735 432-336-4131
Betty McCallister, prin. Fax 336-4136

Fort Worth, Tarrant, Pop. 728,297
Castleberry ISD 3,600/PK-12
315 Churchill Rd 76114 817-252-2000
Gary Jones, supt. Fax 738-1062
www.castleberryisd.net
Castleberry HS 800/9-12
215 Churchill Rd 76114 817-252-2100
Dr. Julie Davis, prin. Fax 252-2575
Marsh MS 800/6-8
415 Hagg Dr 76114 817-252-2200
Hope Conner, prin. Fax 738-3454
Other Schools – See River Oaks

Crowley ISD
Supt. — See Crowley
Crowley MS 700/7-8
3800 W Risinger Rd 76123 817-370-5650
Jaretha Jordan, prin. Fax 370-5656
North Crowley 9th Grade Campus 600/9-9
4630 McPherson Blvd 76123 817-297-5896
Lucretia Newton, prin. Fax 297-5878
North Crowley HS 1,700/10-12
9100 S Hulen St 76123 817-263-1250
Stefani Allen, prin. Fax 263-1282

Eagle Mtn.-Saginaw ISD 16,800/PK-12
1200 Old Decatur Rd 76179 817-232-0880
Jim Chadwell Ed.D., supt. Fax 847-6124
www.emsisd.com
Boswell HS 2,100/9-12
5805 W Bailey Boswell Rd 76179 817-237-3314
Ross Roberts, prin. Fax 238-8706
Chisholm Trail HS 900/9-12
4800 Education Dr 76179 817-232-7112
Dr. Michael Schwei, prin. Fax 306-1327
Creekview MS 700/6-8
6716 Bob Hanger St 76179 817-237-4261
Anthe Anagnostis, prin. Fax 237-2387
Highland MS 800/6-8
1001 E Bailey Boswell Rd 76131 817-847-5143
Karen Pressley, prin. Fax 847-1922
Hollenstein Career and Technology Center Vo/Tech
5501 Marine Creek Pkwy 76179 817-306-1925
Fredelyn Christian, prin. Fax 306-1327
Prairie Vista MS 800/6-8
8000 Comanche Springs Dr 76131 817-847-9210
Karen Norris, prin Fax 847-4255
Watson Learning Center 100/Alt
5901 Hereford Dr 76179 817-238-7925
Jack Kemppainen, prin Fax 237-0753
Wayside MS 800/6-8
1300 Old Decatur Rd 76179 817-232-0541
Dana Barnes, prin. Fax 232-2391
Willkie MS 800/6-8
6129 Texas Shiner Dr 76179 817-237-9631
Melanie Caldwell, prin. Fax 237-9643
Other Schools – See Saginaw

Fort Worth ISD 79,700/PK-12
100 N University Dr 76107 817-871-2000
Walter Dansby, supt. Fax 871-2112
www.fwisd.org/
Applied Learning Academy 300/Alt
7060 Camp Bowie Blvd 76116 817-815-5500
Randall Scott, prin. Fax 815-5550
Arlington Heights HS 1,800/9-12
4501 West Fwy 76107 817-815-1000
Jason Oliver, prin. Fax 815-1050
Carter-Riverside HS 1,100/9-12
3301 Yucca Ave 76111 817-814-9000
Greg Ruthart, prin. Fax 814-9050
Daggett MS 400/6-8
1108 Carlock St 76110 817-814-5200
Erin Deel, prin. Fax 814-5250
Diamond Hill-Jarvis HS 900/9-12
1411 Maydell St 76106 817-815-0000
Yassmin Lee, prin. Fax 815-0050
Dunbar HS 800/9-12
5700 Ramey Ave 76112 817-815-3000
Carlos Walker, prin. Fax 815-3050
Dunbar MS 500/7-8
2501 Stalcup Rd 76119 817-815-3500
Howard Robinson, prin. Fax 815-3550
Eastern Hills HS 1,300/9-12
5701 Shelton St 76112 817-815-4000
Cherie Washington, prin. Fax 815-4050
Elder MS 1,100/6-8
709 NW 21st St 76164 817-814-4100
James Garcia, prin. Fax 814-4150
Forest Oak MS 800/6-8
3221 Pecos St 76119 817-815-8200
Paula Woods, prin. Fax 815-8250
Handley MS 700/6-8
2801 Patino Rd 76112 817-815-4200
Cheryl Johnson, prin. Fax 815-4250
International Newcomer Academy 400/Alt
7060 Camp Bowie Blvd 76116 817-815-5600
Joshua Garcia, prin. Fax 815-5650
James MS 1,200/6-8
1101 Nashville Ave 76105 817-814-0200
Joycelyn Barnett, prin. Fax 814-0250
Kirkpatrick MS 500/6-8
3201 Refugio Ave 76106 817-814-4200
Xavier Sanchez, prin. Fax 814-4250
McClung MS 6-8
3000 Forest Ave 76112 817-815-5300
David Marion, prin. Fax 815-5350
McLean MS 800/7-8
3816 Stadium Dr 76109 817-814-5300
John Engel, prin. Fax 814-8350
Meacham MS 700/6-8
3600 Weber St 76106 817-815-0200
Elodia Escamilla, prin. Fax 815-0250
Meadowbrook MS 900/6-8
2001 Ederville Rd S 76103 817-815-4300
Rodrigo Durbin, prin. Fax 815-4350
Metro Opportunity S Vo/Tech
2720 Cullen St 76107 817-814-6700
Richard Brown, prin. Fax 814-6750
Monnig MS 600/6-8
3136 Bigham Blvd 76116 817-815-1200
Jennifer Orona, prin. Fax 815-1250
Morningside MS 700/6-8
2751 Mississippi Ave 76104 817-815-8300
Angele Hodges, prin. Fax 815-8350
New Lives S 100/Alt
4713 E Lancaster Ave 76103 817-814-6900
Maria Bishop, prin. Fax 814-6950
North Side HS 1,500/9-12
2211 Mckinley Ave 76164 817-814-4000
Antonio Martinez, prin. Fax 814-4050
Paschal HS 2,500/9-12
3001 Forest Park Blvd 76110 817-814-5000
Terri Mossige, prin. Fax 814-5050
Polytechnic HS Vo/Tech
1300 Conner Ave 76105 817-814-0000
Daniel Scroggins, prin. Fax 814-0050
Riverside MS 1,000/6-8
1600 Bolton St 76111 817-814-9200
Joshua Delich, prin. Fax 814-9250
Rosemont MS 900/7-8
1501 W Seminary Dr 76115 817-814-7200
Benjamin Leos, prin. Fax 814-7250
South Hills HS 1,400/9-12
6101 Mccart Ave 76133 817-814-7000
Dorothy Gomez, prin. Fax 814-7050
Southwest HS 1,500/9-12
4100 Altamesa Blvd 76133 817-814-8000
Gayla Dawson, prin. Fax 814-8050
Stripling MS 500/6-8
2100 Clover Ln 76107 817-815-1300
Keri Flores, prin. Fax 815-1350
Success HS 200/Alt
1003 W Cannon St 76104 817-815-2700
Ingrid Williams, prin. Fax 815-2750
Texas Academy of Biomedical Sciences 9-12
3813 Valentine St 76107 817-815-2300
Troy Langston, prin. Fax 815-2350
Trimble Technical HS Vo/Tech
1003 W Cannon St 76104 817-815-2500
Joe Dugan, prin. Fax 815-2550
Wedgwood MS 800/7-8
3909 Wilkie Way 76133 817-814-8200
Theodore Jarchow, prin. Fax 814-8250
Wyatt HS 1,100/9-12
2400 E Seminary Dr 76119 817-815-8000
Lewis Washington, prin. Fax 815-8050
Young Men's Leadership Academy 300/6-8
5100 Willie St 76105 817-815-3400
Rodney White, prin. Fax 815-3450
Other Schools – See Benbrook

Keller ISD
Supt. — See Keller
Central HS 2,600/9-12
9450 Ray White Rd, 817-744-2000
David Hinson, prin. Fax 744-2038
Fossil Hill MS 900/7-8
3821 Staghorn Cir S 76137 817-744-3050
Todd Lacey, prin. Fax 744-3438
Fossil Ridge HS 2,300/9-12
4101 Thompson Rd, 817-744-1700
David Hadley, prin. Fax 744-1738
Hillwood MS 1,200/7-8
8250 Parkwood Hill Blvd 76137 817-744-3350
Mark Smith, prin. Fax 744-3438
Timber Creek HS 1,600/9-12
12350 Timberland Blvd, 817-744-2300
Todd Tunnell, prin. Fax 744-2338
Timberview MS 1,000/5-8
10300 Old Denton Rd, 817-744-2600
Carrie Jackson, prin. Fax 744-2638
Trinity Springs MS 900/7-8
3550 Keller Hicks Rd, 817-744-3500
Lindsay Anderson, prin. Fax 744-3538

Lake Worth ISD
Supt. — See Lake Worth
Collins MS 400/7-8
3651 Santos Dr 76106 817-306-4250
Kathy Harmon, prin. Fax 624-7058

White Settlement ISD 6,300/PK-12
401 S Cherry Ln 76108 817-367-1300
Frank Molinar, supt. Fax 367-1351
www.wsisd.com/
Brewer HS 1,600/9-12
1025 W Loop 820 N 76108 817-367-1200
Pam Turner, prin. Fax 367-1242
DAEP/Mesa HS 50/Alt
1000 S Cherry Ln Ste A 76108 817-367-1364
Lorimer Arendse, prin. Fax 367-1366
Other Schools – See White Settlement

All Saints' Episcopal S 800/K-12
9700 Saints Cir 76108 817-560-5700
Dr. Thaddeus Bird, head sch Fax 560-5722
Bethesda Christian S 400/K-12
4700 N Beach St 76137 817-281-6446
Vicki Vaughn, admin. Fax 581-5123
Brite Divinity School Post-Sec.
2925 Princeton St 76109 817-257-7575
Calvary Christian Academy 400/PK-12
1401 Oakhurst Scenic Dr 76111 817-332-3351
Sue Tidwell, admin. Fax 332-4621
Cassata HS 200/9-12
1400 Hemphill St 76104 817-926-1745
Nancy Martin, prin. Fax 926-3132
Christian Life Preparatory S 200/K-12
6250 South Fwy 76134 817-293-1500
Deborah Henry, admin. Fax 293-1500
College of Sts John Fisher & Thomas More Post-Sec.
801 W Shaw St 76110 817-923-8459
DeVry University Post-Sec.
301 Commerce St Ste 2000 76102 817-810-9114
Everest College Post-Sec.
5237 N Riverside Dr Ste 100 76137 817-838-3000
Everest College Post-Sec.
4200 South Fwy Ste 1940 76115 817-566-7700
Fort Worth Beauty School Post-Sec.
6785 Camp Bowie Blvd # 100 76116 817-924-4289
Fort Worth Country Day S 1,100/K-12
4200 Country Day Ln 76109 817-732-7718
Evan Peterson, hdmstr. Fax 377-3425
Harris Hospital Post-Sec.
1301 Pennsylvania Ave 76104 817-878-2106
Harvest Christian Academy 300/K-12
7200 Denton Hwy 76148 817-485-1660
Terry Caywood, hdmstr. Fax 514-6279
Hill S 200/1-12
4817 Odessa Ave 76133 817-923-9482
Roxann Breyer, prin. Fax 923-4894
JPS Inst. for Health Career Development Post-Sec.
2400 Circle Dr 76119 817-920-7380
Kaplan College Post-Sec.
2001 Beach St Ste 201 76103 817-413-2000
Lake Country Christian S 400/PK-12
7050 Lake Country Dr 76179 817-236-8703
Nancy Purtell, admin. Fax 236-1103
Nolan HS 1,000/9-12
4501 Bridge St 76103 817-457-2920
Cathy Buckingham, prin. Fax 496-9775
Ogle School of Hair Design Post-Sec.
6125 Interstate 20 Ste 128 76132 817-294-2950
Remington College Post-Sec.
300 E Loop 820 76112 817-451-0017
Southwest Christian Prep S 400/7-12
7001 Benbrook Lake Dr 76123 817-294-9596
Dr. Penny Armstrong, pres. Fax 292-3644
Southwestern Baptist Theological Sem. Post-Sec.
PO Box 22000 76122 817-923-1921
Tarrant County College Post-Sec.
5301 Campus Dr 76119 817-515-8223
Tarrant County College Post-Sec.
4801 Marine Creek Pkwy 76179 817-515-8223
Temple Christian S 800/PK-12
6824 Randol Mill Rd 76120 817-457-0770
Dorothy Stringer, supt. Fax 457-0777
Texas Christian University Post-Sec.
2800 S University Dr 76129 817-257-7000
Texas Wesleyan University Post-Sec.
1201 Wesleyan St 76105 817-531-4444
Trinity Valley S 1,000/K-12
7500 Dutch Branch Rd 76132 817-321-0100
Gary Krahn Ph.D., head sch Fax 321-0105
University of N Texas Health Science Ctr Post-Sec.
3500 Camp Bowie Blvd 76107 817-735-2000
Westwood College Post-Sec.
4232 North Fwy 76137 817-547-9600

Franklin, Robertson, Pop. 1,547
Franklin ISD 1,100/PK-12
PO Box 909 77856 979-828-7000
Timothy Bret Lowry, supt. Fax 828-1910
www.franklinisd.net/
Franklin HS 300/9-12
PO Box 909 77856 979-828-7100
Timothy Luza, prin. Fax 828-3364
Franklin MS 200/6-8
PO Box 909 77856 979-828-7200
Susan Nelson, prin. Fax 828-7202

Frankston, Anderson, Pop. 1,210
Frankston ISD 800/PK-12
PO Box 428 75763 903-876-2556
Keith Murphy, supt. Fax 876-4558
www.frankstonisd.net
Frankston HS 200/9-12
PO Box 428 75763 903-876-3219
John Clements, prin. Fax 876-4558
Frankston MS 200/6-8
PO Box 428 75763 903-876-2215
Chris White, prin. Fax 876-4558

Fredericksburg, Gillespie, Pop. 10,449
Fredericksburg ISD 3,000/PK-12
234 Friendship Ln 78624 830-997-9551
Dr. Marc Williamson, supt. Fax 997-6164
www.fisd.org/
Fredericksburg HS 1,000/9-12
1107 S State Highway 16 78624 830-997-7551
Ralf Halderman, prin. Fax 997-8583
Fredericksburg MS 700/6-8
110 W Travis St 78624 830-997-7657
Missy Stevens, prin. Fax 997-1927
G.C.L.C. 50/Alt
1110 S Adams St 78624 830-997-9788
Blaine Hahn, prin. Fax 997-9788

Heritage S 200/K-12
PO Box 1217 78624 830-997-6597
Steve Marshall, hdmstr. Fax 997-4900

Freeport, Brazoria, Pop. 11,851
Brazosport ISD
Supt. — See Clute
Brazosport HS 1,100/9-12
PO Box Z 77542 979-730-7260
Ronnie Barnes, prin. Fax 730-7366
Freeport IS 500/7-8
PO Box Z 77542 979-730-7240
Kristine Traylor, prin. Fax 237-6329

Freer, Duval, Pop. 2,808
Freer ISD 800/PK-12
PO Box 240 78357 361-394-6025
Dr. George Padilla, supt. Fax 394-5005
www.freerisd.org/
Freer HS 200/9-12
PO Box 240 78357 361-394-6717
Cynthia Ries, prin. Fax 394-5012
Freer JHS 200/6-8
PO Box 240 78357 361-394-7102
Jim Sadler, prin. Fax 394-5016

Friendswood, Galveston, Pop. 35,202
Clear Creek ISD
Supt. — See League City
Brookside IS 800/6-8
3535 E FM 528 Rd 77546 281-284-3600
Deanna Daws, prin. Fax 284-3605
Clear Brook HS 2,600/9-12
4607 FM 2351 Rd 77546 281-284-2100
Michele Staley, prin. Fax 284-2105
Westbrook IS 1,300/6-8
302 W El Dorado Blvd 77546 281-284-3800
Dr. Lori Broughton, prin. Fax 284-3805

Friendswood ISD 5,600/PK-12
302 Laurel Dr 77546 281-482-1267
Trish Hanks, supt. Fax 996-2513
www.fisdk12.net
Friendswood HS 2,000/9-12
702 Greenbriar Ave 77546 281-482-3413
Mark Griffon, prin. Fax 996-2523
Friendswood JHS 1,500/6-8
1000 Manison Pkwy 77546 281-996-6200
Dana Drew, prin. Fax 996-6262

Texas School of Business Post-Sec.
3208 E FM 528 Rd 77546 281-648-0880

Friona, Parmer, Pop. 4,104
Friona ISD 1,200/PK-12
909 E 11th St 79035 806-250-2747
Kenny Austin, supt. Fax 250-3805
www.frionaisd.com
Friona HS 300/9-12
909 E 11th St 79035 806-250-3951
Pam Ray, prin. Fax 259-2281
Friona JHS 300/6-8
909 E 11th St 79035 806-250-2788
Mark Sundre, prin. Fax 250-8155

Frisco, Collin, Pop. 113,923
Frisco ISD 33,200/PK-12
5515 Ohio Dr 75035 469-633-6000
Jeremy Lyon, supt. Fax 633-6050
www.friscoisd.org
Career Technology Education Center Vo/Tech
9889 Wade Blvd 75035 469-633-6780
Dianna Manvel, prin. Fax 633-6790
Clark MS 800/6-8
4600 Colby Dr 75035 469-633-4600
Joel Partin, prin. Fax 633-4650
Cobb MS 6-8
9400 Teel Pkwy, 469-633-4300
Phil Evans, prin. Fax 633-4310
Frisco Centennial HS 1,800/9-12
6901 Coit Rd 75035 469-633-5600
Randy Spain, prin. Fax 633-5650
Frisco HS 1,600/9-12
6401 Parkwood Blvd 75034 469-633-5500
Sylvia Palacios, prin. Fax 633-5550
Griffin MS 500/6-8
3703 Eldorado Pkwy, 469-633-4900
Elizabeth Holcomb, prin. Fax 633-4950
Heritage HS 1,000/9-12
14040 Eldorado Pkwy 75035 469-633-5900
Mark Mimms, prin. Fax 633-5950
Hunt MS 6-8
4900 Legendary Dr 75034 469-633-5200
Gary Nye, prin. Fax 633-5210
Liberty HS 1,700/9-12
15250 Rolater Rd 75035 469-633-5800
Scott Warstler, prin. Fax 633-5850
Lone Star HS 9-12
2606 Panther Creek Pkwy, 469-633-5300
Karen Kraft, prin. Fax 633-5350
Maus MS 6-8
12175 Coit Rd 75035 469-633-5250
Cory McClendon, prin. Fax 633-5260
Pioneer Heritage MS 600/6-8
1649 High Shoals Dr 75034 469-633-4700
Rocky Agan, prin. Fax 633-4750
Roach MS 600/6-8
12499 Independence Pkwy 75035 469-633-5000
Terri Gladden, prin. Fax 633-5010
Stafford MS 700/6-8
2288 Little River Rd, 469-633-5100
Robin Scott, prin. Fax 633-5110
Staley MS 600/6-8
6927 Stadium Ln, 469-633-4500
Dennis McDonald, prin. Fax 633-4550
Student Opportunity Center Alt
6928 Maple St, 469-633-6700
Sue Kirk, prin. Fax 633-6750
Vandeventer MS 6-8
6075 Independence Pkwy 75035 469-633-4350
Kristin Hebert, prin. Fax 633-4360
Wakeland HS 1,700/9-12
10700 Legacy Dr, 469-633-5700
Clarence Williams, prin. Fax 633-5750
Wester MS 800/6-8
12293 Shepherds Hill Ln 75035 469-633-4800
Angela Romney, prin. Fax 633-4850
Other Schools – See Mc Kinney, Plano

Collin College Post-Sec.
9700 Wade Blvd 75035 972-377-1790

Grace Covenant Academy 100/K-12
10633 John W Elliott Dr, 972-836-9422
Brian Smith, hdmstr.
Legacy Christian Academy 700/PK-12
5000 Academy Dr 75034 469-633-1330
Chris Harmon, hdmstr. Fax 633-1348

Fritch, Hutchinson, Pop. 2,086
Sanford-Fritch ISD 900/PK-12
PO Box 1290 79036 806-857-3122
Jim McClellan, supt. Fax 857-3795
www.sfisd.net
CHAMPS Alternative Campus 50/Alt
PO Box 1290 79036 806-857-3438
Fax 857-3427
Sanford-Fritch HS 200/9-12
PO Box 1290 79036 806-857-3121
Jason Garrison, prin. Fax 857-9147
Sanford-Fritch JHS 200/6-8
PO Box 1290 79036 806-857-9268
Edith Allen, prin. Fax 857-9431

Frost, Navarro, Pop. 641
Frost ISD 400/PK-12
PO Box K 76641 903-682-2711
Jim Revill, supt. Fax 682-2107
www.frostisd.org
Frost JSHS 200/6-12
PO Box K 76641 903-682-2541
Becky Melton, prin. Fax 682-2107

Fruitvale, Van Zandt, Pop. 408
Fruitvale ISD 400/PK-12
PO Box 77 75127 903-896-1191
Dr. Jennifer Jones, supt. Fax 896-1011
www.fruitvaleisd.com
Fruitvale HS 100/9-12
PO Box 77 75127 903-896-4363
Charles Harford, prin. Fax 896-1011
Fruitvale MS 100/6-8
PO Box 77 75127 903-896-4363
Charles Harford, prin. Fax 896-1011

Gail, Borden, Pop. 230
Borden County ISD 200/K-12
PO Box 95 79738 806-756-4313
Jimmy Thomas, supt. Fax 756-4310
www.bcisd.net/
Borden S 200/K-12
PO Box 95 79738 806-756-4314
Bart McMeans, prin. Fax 756-4310

Gainesville, Cooke, Pop. 15,668
Gainesville ISD 2,700/PK-12
800 S Morris St 76240 940-665-4362
Jeffrey L. Brasher, supt. Fax 665-4473
www.gainesvilleisd.org
Gainesville HS 600/9-12
2201 S Interstate 35 76240 940-665-5528
David Glancy, prin. Fax 612-2795
Gainesville MS 600/6-8
1201 S Lindsay St 76240 940-665-4062
Terry Ashby, prin. Fax 665-1432

North Central Texas College Post-Sec.
1525 W California St 76240 940-668-7731

Galena Park, Harris, Pop. 10,842
Galena Park ISD
Supt. — See Houston
Galena Park HS 1,900/9-12
1000 Keene St 77547 832-386-2800
Tony Gardea, prin. Fax 386-2802
Galena Park MS 1,000/6-8
400 Keene St 77547 832-386-1700
Chris Blake, prin. Fax 386-1738

Galveston, Galveston, Pop. 47,004
Galveston ISD 4,900/PK-12
PO Box 660 77553 409-766-5100
Larry Nichols, supt. Fax 762-8391
www.gisd.org/
Austin Magnet MS 500/5-8
1514 Avenue N 1/2 77550 409-761-3500
Cathy Vanness, prin. Fax 765-5946
Ball HS 1,900/9-12
4115 Avenue O 77550 409-766-5700
Joe Pillar, prin. Fax 766-5738
Ball Preparatory Academy 9-12
4115 Avenue O 77550 409-766-5768
Dr. Marsha Ricks, prin.
Central MS 400/5-8
3014 Sealy St 77550 409-761-6200
Annette Dailey, prin. Fax 770-0649

Galveston College Post-Sec.
4015 Avenue Q 77550 409-944-4242
O'Connell College Preparatory HS 100/9-12
1320 Tremont St 77550 409-765-5534
Patti Abbott, prin. Fax 765-5536
Texas A&M University Galveston Post-Sec.
PO Box 1675 77553 409-740-4400
University of Texas Medical Branch Post-Sec.
301 University Blvd 77555 409-772-1011

Ganado, Jackson, Pop. 1,997
Ganado ISD 500/PK-12
PO Box 1200 77962 361-771-4200
Jeff Black, supt. Fax 771-2280
www.ganadoisd.org/
Ganado JSHS 200/6-12
PO Box 1200 77962 361-771-4300
Andy Bridges, prin. Fax 771-2280

Garden City, Glasscock, Pop. 334
Glasscock County ISD 300/PK-12
PO Box 9 79739 432-354-2230
Johnny Tubb, supt. Fax 354-2503
www.gckats.net/
Glasscock County JSHS 100/7-12
PO Box 9 79739 432-354-2244
Gary Jones, prin. Fax 354-2503

Garland, Dallas, Pop. 223,158
Garland ISD 57,200/PK-12
PO Box 469026 75046 972-494-8201
Dr. Bob Morrison, supt. Fax 485-4928
www.garlandisd.net
Austin Academy for Excellence MS 900/6-8
1125 Beverly Dr 75040 972-926-2620
Holly Muzzicato, prin. Fax 926-2633
Bussey MS 900/6-8
1204 Travis St 75040 972-494-8391
Mary Garcia, prin. Fax 494-8971
Classical Center at Brandenburg MS 1,100/6-8
626 Nickens Rd 75043 972-926-2630
Elise Mosty, prin. Fax 926-2633
Garland Alternative Education Center 100/Alt
2015 S Country Club Rd 75041 972-926-2691
Robert Weyman, prin. Fax 926-2692
Garland HS 2,700/9-12
310 S Garland Ave 75040 972-494-8492
Atticus Wisener, prin. Fax 494-8415
Houston MS 900/6-8
2232 Sussex Dr 75041 972-926-2640
Don Hernandez, prin. Fax 926-2647
Jackson Tech Center for Math & Science 1,200/6-8
1310 Bobbie Ln 75042 972-494-8362
David Dunphy, prin. Fax 494-8802
Lakeview Centennial HS 2,300/9-12
3505 Hayman Dr 75043 972-240-3740
Angel Rivera, prin. Fax 240-3750
Lyles MS 1,000/6-8
4655 S Country Club Rd 75043 972-240-3720
Darrin Hemphill, prin. Fax 240-3723
Memorial Pathway Academy 100/Alt
2825 S 1st St 75041 972-926-2650
Dr. Kim Lozada, prin. Fax 926-2651
Naaman Forest HS 2,400/9-12
4843 Naaman Forest Blvd 75040 972-675-3091
Erika Crump, prin. Fax 675-3100
North Garland HS 2,200/9-12
2109 W Buckingham Rd 75042 972-675-3120
Dan Cummings, prin. Fax 675-3145
O'Banion MS 1,100/6-8
700 Birchwood Dr 75043 972-279-6103
John Tucci, prin. Fax 613-9532
Sellers MS 800/6-8
1009 Mars Dr 75040 972-494-8337
Vikki Mahagan, prin. Fax 494-8607
South Garland HS 2,000/9-12
600 Colonel Dr 75043 972-926-2700
Tracy Curtis, prin. Fax 926-2727
Webb MS 1,200/6-8
1610 Spring Creek Dr 75040 972-675-3080
Jim Lewis, prin. Fax 675-3089
Other Schools – See Rowlett, Sachse

Amberton University Post-Sec.
1700 Eastgate Dr 75041 972-279-6511
Garland Christian Academy 300/PK-12
1516 Lavon Dr 75040 972-487-0043
Brian Keith, admin. Fax 276-4079
International Beauty College #3 Post-Sec.
1225 Belt Line Rd Ste 7 75040 972-530-1103
National Beauty College Post-Sec.
354 E Interstate 30 Ste A 75043 972-226-6900
Remington College Post-Sec.
1800 Eastgate Dr 75041 972-686-7878

Garrison, Nacogdoches, Pop. 884
Garrison ISD 700/PK-12
459 N US Highway 59 75946 936-347-7000
Darren Webb, supt. Fax 347-2529
www.garrisonisd.com
Garrison HS 200/9-12
459 N US Highway 59 75946 936-347-7030
Lance Bernard, prin. Fax 347-7059
Garrison MS 200/6-8
459 N US Highway 59 75946 936-347-7020
Allan Metcalf, prin. Fax 347-7004

Gary, Panola
Gary ISD 400/PK-12
132 Bobcat Trl 75643 903-685-2291
Todd Greer, supt. Fax 685-2639
www.garyisd.org
Gary S 400/PK-12
132 Bobcat Trl 75643 903-685-2291
Tony Wood, prin. Fax 685-2639

Gatesville, Coryell, Pop. 15,526
Gatesville ISD 2,900/PK-12
311 S Lovers Ln 76528 254-865-7251
Stewart Speer, supt. Fax 865-2279
www.gatesvilleisd.org/
Gatesville HS 800/9-12
311 S Lovers Ln 76528 254-865-8281
John Westbrook, prin. Fax 865-2293
Gatesville JHS 400/7-8
311 S Lovers Ln 76528 254-865-8271
Cindy Venable, prin. Fax 865-2252

Georgetown, Williamson, Pop. 46,741
Georgetown ISD 9,700/PK-12
603 Lakeway Dr 78628 512-943-5000
Joe Dan Lee, supt. Fax 943-5004
www.georgetownisd.org
Benold MS 900/6-8
3407 Northwest Blvd 78628 512-943-5090
Leslie Michalik, prin. Fax 943-5099
Forbes MS 700/6-8
1911 NE Inner Loop 78626 512-943-5150
Leonard Rhoads, prin. Fax 943-5159
Georgetown Alternative Program 50/Alt
502 Patriot Way 78626 512-943-5196
Louis Garza, prin. Fax 943-5197

Georgetown East View HS 800/9-12
4490 E University Ave 78626 512-943-1800
Dr. Dave Denny, prin. Fax 943-1819
Georgetown HS 2,100/9-12
2211 N Austin Ave 78626 512-943-5100
Cade Smith, prin. Fax 943-5109
Richarte HS 100/Alt
2201 Old Airport Rd 78626 512-943-5120
Marsha Winship, prin. Fax 943-5121
Tippit MS 800/6-8
1601 Leander Rd 78628 512-943-5040
Brian Dawson, prin. Fax 943-5049
Williamson County Academy 50/Alt
200 Wilco Way 78626 512-943-3260
Robert Fischer, prin. Fax 943-3288

Grace Academy 100/K-12
PO Box 5005 78627 512-864-9500
Fax 868-5429
Southwestern University Post-Sec.
1001 E University Ave 78626 512-863-6511

George West, Live Oak, Pop. 2,431
George West ISD 1,100/PK-12
913 Houston St 78022 361-449-1914
Ty Sparks, supt. Fax 449-1426
www.gwisd.esc2.net/
George West HS 300/9-12
1013 Houston St 78022 361-449-1914
Jay Newberry, prin. Fax 449-3128
George West JHS 200/7-8
900 Houston St 78022 361-449-1914
Heather Lee, prin. Fax 449-3909

Giddings, Lee, Pop. 4,822
Giddings ISD 1,900/PK-12
PO Box 389 78942 979-542-2854
Allen Law, supt. Fax 542-9264
www.giddings.txed.net
Giddings HS 600/9-12
PO Box 389 78942 979-542-3351
Chad Rood, prin. Fax 542-5312
Giddings MS 400/6-8
PO Box 389 78942 979-542-2057
R. Glenn Buscha, prin. Fax 542-3941

Gilmer, Upshur, Pop. 4,805
Gilmer ISD 2,400/PK-12
500 S Trinity St 75644 903-841-7400
Rick Albritton, supt. Fax 843-5279
www.gilmerisd.org
Bruce JHS 300/7-8
111 Bruce St 75645 903-841-7600
Dawn Harris, prin. Fax 843-6108
Gilmer HS 600/9-12
850 Buffalo St 75644 903-843-7500
Greg Watson, prin. Fax 843-2171

Union Hill ISD 300/PK-12
2197 FM 2088 75644 903-762-2140
Sharon Richardson, supt. Fax 762-6845
www.uhisd.com
Union Hill HS 100/7-12
2197 FM 2088 75644 903-762-2138
Karen Saunders, prin. Fax 762-6845

Gladewater, Gregg, Pop. 6,285
Gladewater ISD 2,000/PK-12
500 W Quitman Ave 75647 903-845-6991
Dr. Jerry Richardson, supt. Fax 845-6994
www.gladewaterisd.com
Gladewater HS 600/9-12
2201 W Gay Ave 75647 903-845-5591
Cathy Bedair, prin. Fax 845-3694
Gladewater MS 500/6-8
700 Melba Ave 75647 903-845-2243
James Griffin, prin. Fax 844-1738

Sabine ISD 1,300/PK-12
5424 FM 1252 W 75647 903-984-8564
Stacey Bryce, supt. Fax 984-6108
www.sabine.esc7.net
Sabine HS 400/9-12
5424 FM 1252 W 75647 903-984-8587
Eddie Shawn, prin. Fax 986-1103
Sabine MS 300/6-8
5424 FM 1252 W 75647 903-984-4767
Bill Middendorf, prin. Fax 984-8823

Union Grove ISD 600/PK-12
PO Box 1447 75647 903-845-5509
Brian Gray, supt. Fax 845-6178
uniongroveisd.org
Union Grove JSHS 200/7-12
PO Box 1447 75647 903-845-5506
Chris Wayt, prin. Fax 845-3003

Glenn Heights, Dallas, Pop. 11,061
De Soto ISD
Supt. — See DeSoto
McCowan MS 800/6-8
1500 Majestic Meadows Dr 75154 972-274-8090
Sissy Lowe, prin. Fax 274-8099

Community Christian Academy 50/1-12
1810 S Hampton Rd 75154 972-274-0015
Dr. Nancie Rowe, admin. Fax 274-0078

Glen Rose, Somervell, Pop. 2,402
Glen Rose ISD 1,600/PK-12
PO Box 2129 76043 254-898-3900
Wayne Rotan, supt. Fax 897-3651
www.grisd.net
Glen Rose HS 500/9-12
PO Box 2129 76043 254-898-3800
Tommy Corcoran, prin. Fax 897-9871
Glen Rose JHS 400/6-8
PO Box 2129 76043 254-898-3700
Susan Wright, prin. Fax 897-4059

Godley, Johnson, Pop. 999
Godley ISD 1,400/PK-12
313 N Pearson St 76044 817-389-2536
Rich Dear, supt. Fax 389-2543
www.godleyisd.net/
Godley HS 500/9-12
9401 N Highway 171 76044 817-389-2265
Leigh Brown, prin. Fax 389-4455
Godley MS 300/7-8
409 N Pearson St 76044 817-389-2121
David Williams, prin. Fax 389-4357

Goldthwaite, Mills, Pop. 1,857
Goldthwaite ISD 600/PK-12
PO Box 608 76844 325-648-3531
Ronny Wright, supt. Fax 648-2456
www.goldisd.net/
Goldthwaite HS 200/9-12
PO Box 608 76844 325-648-3081
Gary Speegle, prin. Fax 648-2325
Goldthwaite MS 100/6-8
PO Box 608 76844 325-648-3630
Brad Jones, prin. Fax 648-3571

Goliad, Goliad, Pop. 1,901
Goliad ISD 1,400/PK-12
PO Box 830 77963 361-645-3259
Christy Paulsgrove, supt. Fax 645-3614
www.goliadisd.org
Goliad DAEP 50/Alt
PO Box 830 77963 361-645-3257
Emilio Vargas, prin. Fax 645-8039
Goliad HS 400/9-12
PO Box 830 77963 361-645-3257
Emilio Vargas, prin. Fax 645-8039
Goliad MS 200/7-8
PO Box 830 77963 361-645-3146
Mary Tippin, prin. Fax 645-8040

Gonzales, Gonzales, Pop. 7,175
Gonzales ISD 2,600/PK-12
PO Box 157 78629 830-672-9551
Kimberly Strozier Ed.D., supt. Fax 672-7159
www.gonzales.txed.net
Gonzales HS 700/9-12
1801 N Sarah DeWitt Dr 78629 830-672-7535
Dwight MacAllister, prin. Fax 672-8273
Gonzales JHS 400/7-8
426 N College St 78629 830-672-8641
Wanda Fryer, prin. Fax 672-6466

Goodrich, Polk, Pop. 267
Goodrich ISD 200/PK-12
PO Box 789 77335 936-365-1100
Guylene Robertson, supt. Fax 365-3518
www.goodrichisd.net
Goodrich HS 100/9-12
PO Box 789 77335 936-365-1100
James Snead, prin. Fax 365-2370
Goodrich MS 100/6-8
PO Box 789 77335 936-365-1100
James Snead, prin. Fax 365-2370

Gordon, Palo Pinto, Pop. 475
Gordon ISD 200/K-12
PO Box 47 76453 254-693-5582
Eric Hough, supt. Fax 693-5503
gordonisd.net
Gordon S 200/K-12
PO Box 47 76453 254-693-5342
David Low, prin. Fax 693-5503

Gorman, Eastland, Pop. 1,079
Gorman ISD 300/PK-12
PO Box 8 76454 254-734-3171
Ray Crass, supt. Fax 734-3393
www.gorman.esc14.net/
Gorman HS 100/9-12
PO Box 8 76454 254-734-3171
Nick Heupel, prin. Fax 734-3425
Gorman MS 100/6-8
PO Box 8 76454 254-734-3171
Nick Heupel, prin. Fax 734-4729

Graford, Palo Pinto, Pop. 570
Graford ISD 300/PK-12
400 W Division Ave 76449 940-664-3101
Dennis Holt, supt. Fax 664-2123
www.grafordisd.net
Graford JSHS 100/7-12
400 W Division Ave 76449 940-664-3101
Lori Henderson, prin. Fax 664-2026

Graham, Young, Pop. 8,817
Graham ISD 2,500/PK-12
400 3rd St 76450 940-549-0595
Dr. Lane Ledbetter, supt. Fax 549-8656
www.grahamisd.com
Graham HS 700/9-12
1000 Brazos St 76450 940-549-1504
Robert Loomis, prin. Fax 549-4031
Graham JHS 500/6-8
1000 2nd St 76450 940-549-2002
Joe Gordy, prin. Fax 549-6991
Graham Learning Center 50/Alt
701 Tennessee St 76450 940-549-1546
Gary Browning, prin. Fax 549-4561

Granbury, Hood, Pop. 7,903
Granbury ISD 6,500/PK-12
600 W Pearl St 76048 817-408-4000
James Largent Ed.D., supt. Fax 408-4014
www.granburyisd.org
Acton MS 800/6-8
1300 James Rd 76049 817-408-4800
Jimmy Dawson, prin. Fax 408-4849
Crossland 9th Grade Ctr. 400/9-9
217 N Jones St 76048 817-408-4700
Diane Fullerton, prin. Fax 408-4749
Granbury HS 1,300/10-12
2000 W Pearl St 76048 817-408-4600
Jeremy Ross, prin. Fax 408-4699
Granbury MS 800/6-8
2000 Crossland Rd 76048 817-408-4850
Pat Yelverton, prin. Fax 408-4899
STARS Academy 100/Alt
3000 Acton School Rd 76049 817-408-4450
Edwin Young, prin. Fax 408-4474

Cornerstone Christian Academy 100/PK-12
603 Meander Rd 76049 817-573-6485
Marci Martinez, admin. Fax 573-7604
North Central Texas Academy 200/PK-12
3846 N Highway 144 76048 254-897-4822
Jennifer Smith M.Ed., prin. Fax 897-7650

Grandfalls, Ward, Pop. 353
Grandfalls-Royalty ISD 100/PK-12
PO Box 10 79742 432-547-2266
J.D. Stocks, supt. Fax 547-2960
www.grisd.com
Grandfalls-Royalty JSHS 50/7-12
PO Box 10 79742 – Joe Helms, prin. 432-547-2266

Grand Prairie, Dallas, Pop. 172,425
Grand Prairie ISD 25,300/PK-12
PO Box 531170 75053 972-264-6141
Dr. Susan Simpson-Hull, supt. Fax 237-5440
www.gpisd.org
Adams MS 800/6-8
833 W Tarrant Rd 75050 972-262-1934
Nneka Bernard, prin. Fax 522-3099
Crosswinds HS 400/Alt
1100 N Carrier Pkwy 75050 972-522-2950
Craig Spears, prin. Fax 522-2999
Dubiski Career HS Vo/Tech
2990 S State Highway 161 75052 972-343-7800
Vicki Villarreal, prin. Fax 343-7899
Fannin MS 400/6-8
301 NE 28th St 75050 972-262-8668
Michelle Brinkman, prin. Fax 343-4799
Grand Prairie HS 9th Grade Center 700/9-9
102 High School Dr 75050 972-237-5603
Veronica Kunschik, prin. Fax 343-6399
Grand Prairie SHS 2,000/10-12
101 High School Dr 75050 972-809-5711
Demetrus Liggins, prin. Fax 809-5775
Jackson MS 1,100/6-8
3504 Corn Valley Rd 75052 972-264-2704
Laura Stout, prin. Fax 343-7599
Lamar Alternative Education 100/Alt
2099 Walnut St 75050 972-262-7244
Kerry Rapier, prin. Fax 264-9479
Reagan MS 700/6-8
4616 Bardin Rd 75052 972-522-7300
Chris Bayer, prin. Fax 522-7399
South Grand Prairie HS 9th Grade Campus 900/9-9
305 W Warrior Trl 75052 972-264-1769
Apryl Baylor, prin. Fax 343-7698
South Grand Prairie SHS 2,300/10-12
301 W Warrior Trl 75052 972-343-1500
Donna Grant, prin. Fax 642-7902
Truman MS 600/6-8
1501 Coffeyville Trl 75052 972-641-7676
Ruben Molinar, prin. Fax 522-3999
Young Mens Leadership Academy 1,000/6-8
2205 SE 4th St 75051 972-264-8651
Sterlin McGruder, prin. Fax 522-3699
Young Womens Leadership Academy 1,000/6-8
1204 E Marshall Dr 75051 972-343-7400
Jennifer Oliver, prin. Fax 343-7499

Arlington Career Institute Post-Sec.
901 E Avenue K 75050 972-647-1607
Jones Beauty College #2 Post-Sec.
311 W Pioneer Pkwy 75051 972-237-1988
Lincoln College of Technology Post-Sec.
2915 Alouette Dr 75052 972-660-5701
Mid Cities Barber College Post-Sec.
2345 SW 3rd St Ste 101 75051 972-642-1892

Grand Saline, Van Zandt, Pop. 3,102
Grand Saline ISD 1,100/PK-12
400 Stadium Dr 75140 903-962-7546
Trish Elliott, supt. Fax 962-7464
www.grandsalineisd.net
Grand Saline HS 300/9-12
500 Stadium Dr 75140 903-962-7533
Ricky LaPrade, prin. Fax 962-7482
Grand Saline MS 200/6-8
400 Stadium Dr 75140 903-962-7537
Brad Swain, prin. Fax 962-7474

Grandview, Johnson, Pop. 1,542
Grandview ISD 800/PK-12
PO Box 310 76050 817-866-2450
Joe Perrin, supt. Fax 866-3351
www.gvisd.org
Grandview HS 300/9-12
PO Box 310 76050 817-866-3320
Kirby Basham, prin. Fax 866-2645
Grandview JHS 300/6-8
PO Box 310 76050 817-866-2492
Jeff Hudson, prin. Fax 866-3912

Granger, Williamson, Pop. 1,404
Granger ISD 400/PK-12
PO Box 578 76530 512-859-2613
Randy Willis, supt. Fax 859-2446
www.grangerisd.net
Granger S 400/PK-12
PO Box 578 76530 512-859-2173
Todd Granjean, prin. Fax 859-2446

Grapeland, Houston, Pop. 1,478
Grapeland ISD 500/PK-12
PO Box 249 75844 936-687-4619
K.L. Groholski, supt. Fax 687-4624
www.grapelandisd.net/
Grapeland HS 200/9-12
PO Box 249 75844 936-687-4661
Rick Frauenberger, prin. Fax 687-9739
Grapeland JHS 100/6-8
PO Box 249 75844 936-687-2351
Jim Dillard, admin. Fax 687-9739

Grapevine, Tarrant, Pop. 45,499
Grapevine-Colleyville ISD 13,600/PK-12
3051 Ira E Woods Ave 76051 817-251-5501
Dr. Robin Ryan, supt. Fax 481-2907
www.gcisd-k12.org
Cross Timbers MS 900/6-8
2301 Pool Rd 76051 817-251-5320
Lisa Dunn, prin. Fax 424-4296
Grapevine HS 2,100/9-12
3223 Mustang Dr 76051 817-251-5210
Shannon Tovar, prin. Fax 481-5957
Grapevine MS 800/6-8
301 Pony Pkwy 76051 817-251-5660
Linda Young, prin. Fax 424 1626
Other Schools – See Colleyville

Grapevine Faith Christian S 700/PK-12
730 E Worth St 76051 817-442-9144
Ed C. Smith Ed.D., pres. Fax 601-0815

Greenville, Hunt, Pop. 25,073
Greenville ISD 4,800/PK-12
4004 Moulton St 75401 903-457-2500
Donald Jefferies, supt. Fax 457-2504
www.greenvilleisd.com
Greenville HS 1,000/9-12
3515 Lions Lair Rd 75402 903-457-2550
Heath Jarvis, prin. Fax 455-5158
Greenville MS 600/7-8
3611 Texas St 75401 903-457-2620
David Gish, prin. Fax 457-2628
Houston Education Center 100/Alt
3923 Henry St 75401 903-457-2688
Chip Gregory, prin. Fax 457-2689

Greenville Christian S 200/PK-12
8420 Jack Finney Blvd 75402 903-454-1111
Steven Bowers, hdmstr. Fax 455-8470

Groesbeck, Limestone, Pop. 4,255
Groesbeck ISD 1,500/PK-12
PO Box 559 76642 254-729-4100
Dr. Harold Ramm, supt. Fax 729-5167
www.groesbeckisd.net
Alternative Learning Center 50/Alt
PO Box 559 76642 254-729-4105
Fax 729-3965
Groesbeck HS 500/9-12
1202 N Ellis St 76642 254-729-4101
Luke Allison, prin. Fax 729-5458
Groesbeck MS 200/7-8
410 Elwood Enge Dr 76642 254-729-4102
Ladena King, prin. Fax 729-8763

Groom, Carson, Pop. 567
Groom ISD 100/K-12
PO Box 598 79039 806-248-7557
Jay Lamb, supt. Fax 248-7949
www.groomisd.net
Groom S 100/K-12
PO Box 598 79039 806-248-7474
Matt Johnson, prin. Fax 248-7949

Groves, Jefferson, Pop. 15,978
Port Neches-Groves ISD
Supt. — See Port Neches
Groves MS 500/6-8
5201 Wilson St 77619 409-962-0225
James Arnett, prin. Fax 963-1898

Groveton, Trinity, Pop. 1,043
Centerville ISD 200/PK-12
10327 N State Highway 94 75845 936-642-1597
Michael Ford, supt. Fax 642-2810
www.centervilleisd.net
Centerville JSHS 100/7-12
10327 N State Highway 94 75845 936-642-1597
Robert Welsh, prin. Fax 642-2810

Groveton ISD 700/PK-12
PO Box 728 75845 936-642-1473
Joe Driskell, supt. Fax 642-1628
www.grovetonisd.net
Groveton JSHS 400/6-12
PO Box 700 75845 936-642-1128
Todd Moore, prin. Fax 642-1616

Grulla, Starr, Pop. 1,621
Rio Grande City ISD
Supt. — See Rio Grande City
Grulla MS 700/6-8
PO Box 338 78548 956-487-5558
Serapio Trillayes, prin. Fax 487-5633

Gruver, Hansford, Pop. 1,190
Gruver ISD 400/PK-12
PO Box 650 79040 806-733-2001
David Teal, admin. Fax 733-5416
www.gruverisd.net
Gruver HS 100/9-12
PO Box 747 79040 806-733-2477
Troy Seagler, prin. Fax 733-2596
Gruver JHS 100/5-8
PO Box 709 79040 806-733-2081
Wade Callaway, prin. Fax 733-5523

Gunter, Grayson, Pop. 1,485
Gunter ISD 800/PK-12
PO Box 109 75058 903-433-4750
Dr. Jill Siler, supt. Fax 433-1053
www.gunterisd.org
Gunter HS 300/9-12
PO Box 109 75058 903-433-1542
Kelly Teems, prin. Fax 433-1492
Gunter MS 300/5-8
PO Box 109 75058 903-433-1545
Pat Autry, prin. Fax 433-9306

Gustine, Comanche, Pop. 473
Gustine ISD 200/PK-12
503 W Main St 76455 325-667-7303
Ken Baugh, supt. Fax 667-7281
www.gustine.esc14.net/
Gustine S 200/PK-12
503 W Main St 76455 325-667-7303
Alan Luker, prin. Fax 667-0203

Guthrie, King, Pop. 160
Guthrie Common SD 100/PK-12
PO Box 70 79236 806-596-4466
Dr. Nelson Coulter, supt. Fax 596-4519
www.guthriejags.com/
Guthrie S 100/PK-12
PO Box 70 79236 806-596-4466
Kevin Chisum, prin. Fax 596-4519

Hale Center, Hale, Pop. 2,231
Hale Center ISD 700/PK-12
PO Box 1210 79041 806-839-2451
Carl Krug, supt. Fax 839-2195
www.hcisdowls.net
Carr MS 200/5-8
PO Box 1210 79041 806-839-2141
Mike Wiley, prin. Fax 839-4417
Hale Center HS 200/9-12
PO Box 1210 79041 806-839-2452
Alan Berry, prin. Fax 839-2059

Hallettsville, Lavaca, Pop. 2,529
Hallettsville ISD 900/PK-12
PO Box 368 77964 361-798-2242
Dr. JoAnn Bludau, supt. Fax 798-5902
www.hisdbrahmas.org
Hallettsville HS 300/9-12
PO Box 368 77964 361-798-2242
Russell Kowalik, prin. Fax 798-9297
Hallettsville JHS 200/5-8
PO Box 368 77964 361-798-2242
Sophie Teltschik, prin. Fax 798-3573

Sacred Heart S 300/PK-12
313 S Texana St 77964 361-798-4251
David Smolik, prin. Fax 798-4970

Hallsville, Harrison, Pop. 3,526
Hallsville ISD 3,300/PK-12
PO Box 810 75650 903-668-5990
Jim Dunlap, supt. Fax 668-5990
www.hisd.com
Hallsville DAEP Alt
PO Box 810 75650 903-668-5990
Jesse Casey, prin. Fax 668-5990
Hallsville HS 1,200/9-12
PO Box 810 75650 903-668-5990
John Martin, prin. Fax 668-5990
Hallsville JHS 700/6-8
PO Box 810 75650 903-668-5990
Brandon Jones, prin. Fax 668-5990

Haltom City, Tarrant, Pop. 41,719
Birdville ISD 23,600/PK-12
6125 E Belknap St 76117 817-847-5700
Darrell Brown Ph.D., supt. Fax 838-7261
www.birdvilleschools.net
Haltom HS 2,600/9-12
5501 Haltom Rd 76137 817-547-6000
Clarence Simmons, prin. Fax 547-6352
Haltom MS 800/6-8
5000 Hires Ln 76117 817-547-4000
Jeff Russell, prin. Fax 831-5778
North Oaks MS 600/6-8
4800 Jordan Park Dr 76117 817-547-4600
Bob Koerner, prin. Fax 581-5352
Shannon Education Center 50/Alt
6010 Walker St 76117 817-547-5400
Greg Farr, prin. Fax 831-5847
Other Schools – See North Richland Hills, Richland Hills, Watauga

Hamilton, Hamilton, Pop. 3,076
Hamilton ISD 800/PK-12
400 S College St 76531 254-386-3149
Clay Tarpley, supt. Fax 386-8885
hamiltonisd.org
Hamilton HS 200/9-12
611 S College St 76531 254-386-8167
Louis Lowe, prin. Fax 386-4677
Hamilton MS 200/6-8
400 S College St 76531 254-386-8168
Mona Gloff, prin. Fax 386-8885

Hamlin, Jones, Pop. 2,109
Hamlin ISD 500/PK-12
PO Box 338 79520 325-576-2722
Jim Fuller, supt. Fax 576-2152
www.hamlin.esc14.net
Hamlin HS 100/9-12
450 SW Avenue F 79520 325-576-3624
Tim Siler, prin. Fax 576-3926
Hamlin MS 100/6-8
250 SW Avenue F 79520 325-576-2933
Laura O'Rear, prin. Fax 576-2317

Hamshire, Jefferson
Hamshire-Fannett ISD 1,700/PK-12
PO Box 223 77622 409-243-2517
Pamela Morris, supt. Fax 243-3437
www.hfisd.net/
Hamshire-Fannett HS 500/9-12
PO Box 223 77622 409-243-2512
Jon Burris, prin. Fax 243-2518
Other Schools – See Beaumont

Happy, Swisher, Pop. 670
Happy ISD 300/K-12
PO Box 458 79042 806-558-5331
Bill Mayfield, supt. Fax 558-2070
www.happyisd.net
Happy HS 100/7-12
PO Box 458 79042 806-558-5311
Jody Johnson, prin. Fax 558-4301

Hardin, Liberty, Pop. 804
Hardin ISD 1,200/PK-12
PO Box 330 77561 936-298-2112
Bob Parker, supt. Fax 298-9161
www.hardinisd.net/
Hardin HS 300/9-12
PO Box 330 77561 936-298-2118
Richard Rossler, prin. Fax 298-3612
Hardin MS 200/7-8
PO Box 330 77561 936-298-2054
Alan Tidwell, prin. Fax 298-3264

Harker Heights, Bell, Pop. 25,289
Killeen ISD
Supt. — See Killeen
Eastern Hills MS 700/6-8
300 Indian Trl 76548 254-336-1100
Jamie Blassingame, prin. Fax 680-6606
Harker Heights HS 2,400/9-12
1001 E FM 2410 Rd 76548 254-336-0800
David Manley, prin. Fax 698-5267
Union Grove MS 50/6-8
101 E Iowa Dr 76548 254-336-6580
Dagmar Harris, prin. Fax 336-6593

Harleton, Harrison
Harleton ISD 700/PK-12
PO Box 510 75651 903-777-2372
Dr. Craig Coleman, supt. Fax 777-2406
www.harletonisd.net/
Harleton HS 200/9-12
PO Box 710 75651 903-777-2711
Tonya Knowlton, prin. Fax 777-2547
Harleton JHS 200/6-8
PO Box 610 75651 903-777-3010
Paul Davis, prin. Fax 777-3009

Harlingen, Cameron, Pop. 64,588
Harlingen Consolidated ISD 18,200/PK-12
407 N 77 Sunshine Strip 78550 956-430-9503
Dr. Steve Flores, supt. Fax 430-9514
www.hcisd.org
Coakley MS 800/6-8
1402 S 6th St 78550 956-427-3000
Pedro Sanchez, prin. Fax 427-3006
Early College HS 300/9-12
2510 Pecan St Bldg R 78550 956-430-9690
Angel Paxton, prin. Fax 430-9693
Gutierrez MS 700/6-8
3205 Wilson Rd 78552 956-430-4400
Dr. Marsha Gramley, prin. Fax 430-4480
Harlingen HS 2,500/9-12
1201 Marshall St 78550 956-427-3600
Imelda Munivez, prin. Fax 427-3792
Harlingen HS South 2,000/9-12
1701 Dixieland Rd 78552 956-427-3800
Dr. Joe Rodriguez, prin. Fax 427-3995
Keys Academy 100/Alt
2809 N 7th St 78550 956-427-3220
Jesse Gallegos, prin. Fax 427-3223
Memorial MS 800/6-8
1901 Rio Hondo Rd 78550 956-427-3020
Alex Gonzalez, prin. Fax 427-3024
Secondary Education Alternative Center 50/Alt
1310 Sam Houston Dr 78550 956-427-3210
Daniel Araiza, prin. Fax 430-4487
Vela MS 800/6-8
801 S Palm Blvd 78552 956-427-3479
Dr. Alicia Noyola, prin. Fax 427-3549
Vernon MS 700/6-8
125 S 13th St 78550 956-427-3040
Gracie Gutierrez, prin. Fax 427-3046

Marine Military Academy 300/8-12
320 Iwo Jima Blvd 78550 956-423-6006
Col R. Glenn Hill, supt. Fax 421-9273
Texas State Technical College Post-Sec.
1902 Loop 499 N 78550 956-364-4000
University of Cosmetology Arts & Science Post-Sec.
913 N 13th St 78550 956-412-1212

Harper, Gillespie, Pop. 1,183
Harper ISD 600/PK-12
PO Box 68 78631 830-864-4044
Pari Whitten, supt. Fax 864-4060
www.harper.txed.net/
Harper HS 200/9-12
PO Box 68 78631 830-864-4044
Chris Stevenson, prin. Fax 864-4748
Harper MS 200/6-8
PO Box 68 78631 830-864-4044
Chris Stevenson, prin. Fax 864-4748

Harrold, Wilbarger
Harrold ISD 100/K-12
PO Box 400 76364 940-886-2213
David Thweatt, supt. Fax 886-2215
www.harroldisd.net/
Harrold S 100/K-12
PO Box 400 76364 940-886-2213
Craig Templeton, prin. Fax 886-2215

Hart, Castro, Pop. 1,112
Hart ISD 300/PK-12
PO Box 490 79043 806-938-2143
Alex Salazar, supt. Fax 938-2610
www.hartisd.net
Hart JSHS 100/7-12
PO Box 490 79043 806-938-2141
Ramona Neudorf, prin. Fax 938-2610

Hartley, Hartley, Pop. 536
Hartley ISD 200/PK-12
PO Box 408 79044 806-365-4458
Scott Vincent, supt. Fax 365-4459
www.hartleyisd.net
Hartley S 200/PK-12
PO Box 408 79044 806-365-4458
Scott Vincent, supt. Fax 365-4459

Haskell, Haskell, Pop. 3,278
Haskell Consolidated ISD 700/PK-12
PO Box 937 79521 940-864-2602
Bill Alcorn, supt. Fax 864-8096
www.haskell.esc14.net/
Haskell HS 200/9-12
PO Box 937 79521 940-864-8535
Jeff York, prin. Fax 864-3977
Rochester JHS 100/6-8
PO Box 937 79521 940-864-5981
Kent Colley, prin. Fax 864-5982

Paint Creek ISD 200/PK-12
4485 FM 600 79521 940-864-2471
Donald L. Ballard, supt. Fax 864-8038
www.paintcreek.esc14.net
Paint Creek S 200/PK-12
4485 FM 600 79521 940-864-2471
Richard Cumby, prin. Fax 864-8038

Haslet, Tarrant, Pop. 1,481
Northwest ISD
Supt. — See Justin
Wilson MS 6-8
14250 Sendera Ranch Blvd 76052 817-698-7900
Mike Blankenship, prin. Fax 698-7970

Hawkins, Wood, Pop. 1,237
Hawkins ISD 700/PK-12
PO Box 1430 75765 903-769-2181
Dan Rose, supt. Fax 769-0505
www.hawkinsisd.org
Hawkins HS 200/9-12
PO Box 1430 75765 903-769-0571
Kevin White, prin. Fax 769-0573
Hawkins MS 200/6-8
PO Box 1430 75765 903-769-0552
David Ledkins, prin. Fax 769-0583

Jarvis Christian College Post-Sec.
Highway 80 E PR 7631 75765 903-730-4890

Hawley, Jones, Pop. 626
Hawley ISD 700/PK-12
PO Box 440 79525 325-537-2214
Glenn Coles, supt. Fax 537-2265
www.hawley.esc14.net
Hawley HS 200/9-12
PO Box 440 79525 325-537-2722
Tim Smith, prin. Fax 537-2265
Hawley MS 200/6-8
PO Box 440 79525 325-537-2070
Nikki Grisham, prin. Fax 537-2265

Hearne, Robertson, Pop. 4,418
Hearne ISD 1,100/PK-12
900 Wheelock St 77859 979-279-3200
Norris McDaniel, supt. Fax 279-3631
www.hearne.k12.tx.us/
Hearne HS 300/9-12
1201 W Brown St 77859 979-279-2332
Jonathan Wells, prin. Fax 279-8006
Hearne JHS 100/7-8
1201B W Brown St 77859 979-279-2449
Caronda Williams, prin. Fax 279-8033

Heath, Rockwall, Pop. 6,837
Rockwall ISD
Supt. — See Rockwall
Rockwall-Heath HS 2,000/9-12
801 Laurence Dr 75032 972-772-2474
Tom Maglisceau, prin. Fax 698-2608

Hebbronville, Jim Hogg, Pop. 4,553
Jim Hogg County ISD 1,200/PK-12
PO Box 880 78361 361-527-3203
Pedro Lopez, supt. Fax 527-4823
www.jhcisd.net/
Hebbronville HS 300/9-12
PO Box 880 78361 361-527-3203
Fantina Garcia, prin. Fax 527-5989
Hebbronville JHS 200/6-8
PO Box 880 78361 361-527-3203
Patricia Gonzalez, prin. Fax 527-5986

Hedley, Donley, Pop. 328
Hedley ISD 100/PK-12
PO Box 69 79237 806-856-5323
Bill Sanders, supt. Fax 856-5372
www.hedleyisd.net
Hedley S 100/PK-12
PO Box 69 79237 806-856-5323
David O'Dell, prin. Fax 856-5372

Helotes, Bexar, Pop. 7,218
Northside ISD
Supt. — See San Antonio
O'Connor HS 2,900/9-12
12221 Leslie Rd 78023 210-397-4800
Jacqueline Horras, prin. Fax 695-4804

Hemphill, Sabine, Pop. 1,176
Hemphill ISD 900/PK-12
PO Box 1950 75948 409-787-3371
Glenn Pearson, supt. Fax 787-4005
www.hemphill.esc7.net
Hemphill HS 300/9-12
PO Box 1950 75948 409-787-3371
Marc Griffin, prin. Fax 787-1259
Hemphill MS 300/5-8
PO Box 1950 75948 409-787-3371
Paula Pruitt, prin. Fax 787-4005

Hempstead, Waller, Pop. 5,718
Hempstead ISD 1,500/PK-12
PO Box 1007 77445 979-826-3304
Fax 826-5510
www.hempsteadisd.org
Hempstead HS 400/9-12
PO Box 1007 77445 979-826-3331
Joy Toney, prin. Fax 826-4779
Hempstead MS 300/6-8
PO Box 1007 77445 979-826-2530
Rose Uherek, prin. Fax 826-5583

Henderson, Rusk, Pop. 13,557
Carlisle ISD 700/PK-12
8960 FM 13 W 75654 903-861-3801
Michael Payne, supt. Fax 861-3932
www.carl.sprnet.org/cisd2.htm
Carlisle HS 200/9-12
8960 FM 13 W 75654 903-861-3811
Sarah Baker, prin. Fax 861-0100
Carlisle JHS 200/6-8
8960 FM 13 W 75654 903-861-3811
Rex Thompson, prin. Fax 861-0100

Henderson ISD 3,300/PK-12
PO Box 728 75653 903-655-5000
Keith Boles, supt. Fax 657-9271
www.hendersonisd.org/
Henderson HS 900/9-12
PO Box 728 75653 903-655-5500
Terry Everitt, prin. Fax 657-7604
Henderson MS 700/6-8
PO Box 728 75653 903-655-5400
Hardy Dotson, prin. Fax 657-6499

Full Armor Christian Academy 100/K-12
PO Box 2035 75653 903-655-8489
Jaynellen Wylie, admin. Fax 657-8267

Henrietta, Clay, Pop. 3,103
Henrietta ISD 900/PK-12
1801 E Crafton St 76365 940-720-7900
Jeff McClure, supt. Fax 538-7505
www.henrietta-isd.net
Henrietta HS 300/9-12
1700 E Crafton St 76365 940-720-7930
Gary Parrish, prin. Fax 538-7535
Henrietta JHS 200/6-8
308 E Gilbert St 76365 940-720-7920
Quana West, prin. Fax 538-7525

Midway ISD 100/PK-12
12142 State Highway 148 S 76365 940-476-2215
Hollis Adams, supt. Fax 476-2226
www2.esc9.net/midway
Midway S 100/PK-12
12142 State Highway 148 S 76365 940-476-2222
Cherry Johnston, prin. Fax 476-2226

Hereford, Deaf Smith, Pop. 15,284
Hereford ISD 4,000/K-12
601 N 25 Mile Ave 79045 806-363-7600
Kelli Moulton, supt. Fax 363-7647
www.herefordisd.net
Hereford HS 1,200/9-12
200 Avenue F 79045 806-363-7620
Richard Sauceda, prin. Fax 363-7688
Hereford Preparatory Academy 300/8-8
704 La Plata St 79045 806-363-7740
Rene Cano, prin. Fax 363-7699

Hermleigh, Scurry, Pop. 343
Hermleigh ISD 200/PK-12
8010 Business 84 H 79526 325-863-2772
Gary Rotan, supt. Fax 863-2713
www.hermleigh.esc14.net/
Hermleigh S 200/PK-12
8010 Business 84 H 79526 325-863-2482
Ronnie Roemisch, prin. Fax 863-2713

Hewitt, McLennan, Pop. 13,309
Midway ISD
Supt. — See Woodway
Midway MS 1,100/7-8
800 N Hewitt Dr 76643 254-761-5680
Dr. Herbert Cox, prin. Fax 761-5775

Hico, Hamilton, Pop. 1,369
Hico ISD 600/PK-12
PO Box 218 76457 254-796-2181
Jon Hartgraves, supt. Fax 796-2446
www.hico-isd.net
Hico HS 200/9-12
PO Box 218 76457 254-796-2184
Shelli Stegall, prin. Fax 796-2446
Hico JHS 100/6-8
PO Box 218 76457 254-796-2182
Gary Brister, prin. Fax 796-9830

Hidalgo, Hidalgo, Pop. 11,192
Hidalgo ISD 3,400/PK-12
PO Box 8220 78557 956-843-4404
Librado De Hoyos, supt. Fax 843-3343
www.hidalgo-isd.com
Diaz JHS 700/6-8
PO Box 8220 78557 956-843-4350
Brenda De Hoyos, prin. Fax 843-3198
Hidalgo Academy 50/Alt
PO Box 8220 78557 956-843-4390
Gregorio Solano, prin. Fax 843-3339
Hidalgo HS 1,000/9-12
PO Box 8220 78557 956-843-4300
Domingo Villarreal, prin. Fax 843-3322

Higgins, Lipscomb, Pop. 392
Higgins ISD 100/PK-12
PO Box 218 79046 806-852-2171
Steve James, supt. Fax 852-3502
www.region16.net/higginsisd/
Higgins S 100/PK-12
PO Box 218 79046 806-852-2631
Steve James, admin. Fax 852-3502

High Island, Galveston
High Island ISD 200/PK-12
PO Box 246 77623 409-286-5317
D'Ann Cathriner-Vonderau Ed.D., supt. Fax 286-5351
www.highislandisd.com
High Island HS 100/9-12
PO Box 246 77623 409-286-5314
Kathy Smith, prin. Fax 286-2120
High Island MS 50/6-8
PO Box 246 77623 409-286-5314
Kathy Smith, prin. Fax 286-2120

Highlands, Harris, Pop. 7,443
Goose Creek Consolidated ISD
Supt. — See Baytown
Highlands JHS 1,100/6-8
1212 E Wallisville Rd 77562 281-420-4695
Kevin Foxworth, prin. Fax 426-4301

Chinquapin S 100/6-12
2615 E Wallisville Rd 77562 281-426-5551
Bill Heinzerling, prin. Fax 426-5553

Highland Village, Denton, Pop. 14,764
Lewisville ISD
Supt. — See Flower Mound
Briarhill MS 1,000/6-8
2100 Briarhill Blvd 75077 469-713-5975
Chris Mattingly, prin. Fax 350-9167

Hillsboro, Hill, Pop. 8,341
Hillsboro ISD 1,900/PK-12
121 E Franklin St 76645 254-582-8585
Dr. Buck Gilcrease, supt. Fax 582-4165
www.hillsboroisd.org
Hillsboro HS 400/9-12
1600 Abbott Ave 76645 254-582-4100
Tommy McEwen, prin. Fax 582-4108
Hillsboro JHS 200/7-8
210 E Walnut St 76645 254-582-4120
Cathryn Patterson, prin. Fax 582-4122

Hill College Post-Sec.
112 Lamar Dr 76645 254-659-7500

Hitchcock, Galveston, Pop. 6,879
Hitchcock ISD 800/PK-12
8117 Highway 6 77563 409-316-6545
Barbara Derrick Ed.D., supt. Fax 986-5141
www.hitchcockisd.org
Crosby MS 200/5-8
7801 Neville Ave 77563 409-316-6542
Larry Allen, prin. Fax 986-9254
Hitchcock HS 300/9-12
6625 FM 2004 Rd 77563 409-316-6544
Evangelina Guerra, prin. Fax 986-9339

Holland, Bell, Pop. 1,111
Holland ISD 600/PK-12
PO Box 217 76534 254-657-0175
Cindy Gunn, supt. Fax 657-0172
www.hollandisd.org
Holland HS 100/9-12
PO Box 217 76534 254-657-2523
Britt Gordon, prin. Fax 657-2250
Holland MS 200/6-8
PO Box 217 76534 254-657-2224
Janet Frazier, prin. Fax 657-2872

Holliday, Archer, Pop. 1,747
Holliday ISD 900/PK-12
PO Box 689 76366 940-586-1281
Dr. Kevin Dyes, supt. Fax 586-1492
www.hollidayisd.net
Holliday HS 300/9-12
PO Box 947 76366 940-586-1624
Shannon Owen, prin. Fax 586-9501
Holliday MS 200/6-8
PO Box 977 76366 940-586-1314
Kelly Carver, prin. Fax 583-4480

Hondo, Medina, Pop. 8,749
Hondo ISD 2,200/PK-12
PO Box 308 78861 830-426-3027
Clay Rosenbaum, supt. Fax 426-7683
www.hondoisd.net
Hondo HS 600/9-12
2603 Avenue H 78861 830-426-3341
James Angst, prin. Fax 426-7690
McDowell MS 500/6-8
1602 27th St S 78861 830-426-2261
Georgia Neuman, prin. Fax 426-7624

Honey Grove, Fannin, Pop. 1,640
Honey Grove ISD 600/PK-12
1206 17th St 75446 903-378-2264
Todd Morrison, supt. Fax 378-2991
www.honeygroveisd.net/
Honey Grove HS 200/9-12
1206 17th St 75446 903-378-2264
Kevin Weaver, prin. Fax 378-3050
Honey Grove MS 100/6-8
1206 17th St 75446 903-378-2264
Kyle Hutchings, prin. Fax 378-2095

Hooks, Bowie, Pop. 2,693
Hooks ISD 1,000/PK-12
100 E 5th St 75561 903-547-6077
Ronnie Thompson, supt. Fax 547-2943
www.hooksisd.net/
Hooks HS 400/9-12
401 E Avenue A 75561 903-547-2215
Shane Krueger, prin. Fax 547-6514
Hooks JHS 200/5-8
3921 FM 560 75561 903-547-2568
Noreen Freeman, prin. Fax 547-2595

Horizon City, El Paso, Pop. 16,659
Socorro ISD
Supt. — See El Paso
Eastlake HS 100/9-12
13000 Emerald Pass Ave 79928 915-937-3600
Fax 851-7121
Ensor MS 800/6-8
13600 Ryderwood Dr 79928 915-937-6000
Naomie Byrne, prin. Fax 851-7590

Houston, Harris, Pop. 2,071,912
Aldine ISD 62,800/PK-12
14910 Aldine Westfield Rd 77032 281-449-1011
Dr. Wanda Bamberg, supt. Fax 449-4911
www.aldine.k12.tx.us
Aldine MS 800/7-8
14908 Aldine Westfield Rd 77032 281-985-6580
Marcus Pruitt, prin. Fax 985-6480
Aldine Ninth Grade S 900/9-9
10650 North Fwy 77037 281-878-6800
Walter Stewart, prin. Fax 878-6824
Aldine SHS 2,200/10-12
11101 Airline Dr 77037 281-448-5231
Herminia Mancha, prin. Fax 878-0641
Carver HS for Applied Tech/Eng & Arts 900/9-12
2100 S Victory Dr 77088 281-878-0310
Rosalyn Sweat, prin. Fax 591-8579
COMPASS 200/Alt
1617 Lauder Rd 77039 281-985-6264
James Metcalf, prin. Fax 985-7129
Davis HS 9-12
12525 Ella Blvd 77067 281-539-4070
Thomas Colwell, prin. Fax 539-4075
Drew Academy 700/7-8
1910 W Little York Rd 77091 281-878-0360
Earnest Washington, prin. Fax 447-4694
Eisenhower Ninth Grade S 900/9-9
3550 W Gulf Bank Rd 77088 281-878-7700
Laura Hunter, prin. Fax 878-7736
Eisenhower SHS 2,200/10-12
7922 Antoine Dr 77088 281-878-0900
Benjamin Ibarra, prin. Fax 448-2936
Grantham Academy 1,000/7-8
13300 Chrisman Rd 77039 281-985-6590
Rebecca Brown, prin. Fax 985-6595
Hall Education Center 300/Alt
15014 Aldine Westfield Rd 77032 281-985-7446
Heather Kirk, prin. Fax 985-7453
Hambrick MS 900/7-8
4600 Aldine Mail Rd 77039 281-985-6570
Rebecca Hoyt, prin. Fax 442-9036
Hoffman MS 800/7-8
6101 W Little York Rd 77091 713-613-7670
Cheryl Matthews, prin. Fax 613-7675
Lewis MS 800/7-8
21255 W Hardy Rd 77073 281-209-8257
Cassandra Bell, prin. Fax 985-7139
MacArthur Ninth Grade S 900/9-9
12111 Gloger St 77039 281-985-7400
Craig Mullenix, prin. Fax 985-7423
MacArthur SHS 2,400/10-12
4400 Aldine Mail Rd 77039 281-985-6330
Nancy Blackwell, prin. Fax 985-6294
Nimitz 9th Grade S 900/9-9
2425 WW Thorne Blvd 77073 281-209-8200
Crystal Watson-Barrow, prin. Fax 209-8220
Nimitz SHS 2,500/10-12
2005 WW Thorne Blvd 77073 281-443-7480
Alex Jordan, prin. Fax 233-4331
Plummer MS 900/7-8
11429 Spears Rd 77067 281-539-4000
John Picklesimer, prin. Fax 539-4017
Shotwell MS 1,000/7-8
6515 Trail Valley Way 77086 281-878-0960
Mable Holt, prin. Fax 591-8564
Stovall MS 1,000/7-8
11201 Airline Dr 77037 281-878-0670
Elsa Wright, prin. Fax 448-0636
Victory Early College HS 300/9-12
2330 S Victory Dr 77088 281-878-7885
Phyllis Cormier, prin. Fax 618-5803
Other Schools – See Humble

Alief ISD 45,700/PK-12
4250 Cook Rd 77072 281-498-8110
H.D. Chambers, supt. Fax 498-8730
www.aliefisd.net/
Albright MS 1,200/7-8
6315 Winkleman Rd 77083 281-983-8411
Lori Wyatt, prin. Fax 983-8443
Alief Early College HS 200/9-12
2811 Hayes Rd Ste A 77082 281-988-3010
Beth Smith, prin. Fax 988-3066
Alief Learning Center Alt
4427 Belle Park Dr 77072 281-983-8000
Mary Wilson, prin. Fax 983-7701
Alief MS 1,000/6-8
4415 Cook Rd 77072 281-983-8422
Nancy Trent, prin. Fax 983-8053
Alief Taylor HS 2,900/9-12
7555 Howell Sugar Land Rd 77083 281-988-3500
Mary Williams, prin. Fax 561-7214
Crossroads Alternative Technology S Alt
12360 Bear Ram Rd 77072 281-988-3266
Tremayne Wickliffe, prin. Fax 988-3277
Elsik HS 2,900/10-12
12601 High Star Dr 77072 281-988-3150
Hilda Rodriguez, prin. Fax 530-7058
Elsik Ninth Grade Center 1,300/9-9
6767 S Dairy Ashford Rd 77072 281-988-3029
Vinson Lewis, prin. Fax 988-3319
Hastings HS 2,900/10-12
4410 Cook Rd 77072 281-498-8110
Patrick Cherry, prin. Fax 561-5763
Hastings Ninth Grade Center 1,300/9-9
6750 Cook Rd 77072 281-988-3139
Dr. Jackie Armwood, prin. Fax 988-3419
Holub MS 900/7-8
9515 S Dairy Ashford Rd 77099 281-983-8433
Pauline Beckley, prin. Fax 983-8398
Kerr HS 800/9-12
8150 Howell Sugar Land Rd 77083 281-983-8484
Greg Freeman, prin. Fax 983-8014
Killough MS 1,000/7-8
7600 Synott Rd 77083 281-983-8444
Bryan Brown, prin. Fax 983-8067
O'Donnell MS 1,300/6-8
14041 Alief Clodine Rd 77082 281-495-6000
Janie Saxton, prin. Fax 568-5029
Olle MS 1,000/7-8
9200 Boone Rd 77099 281-983-8455
Nelda Billescas, prin. Fax 983-8077
S.O.A.R. Adult
12501 High Star Dr 77072 281-988-3499
Kathleen Jameson, prin. Fax 988-3097

Channelview ISD
Supt. — See Channelview
Aguirre JHS 7-8
15726 Wallisville Rd 77049 281-860-3300
Steve McCanless, prin. Fax 860-3720

Clear Creek ISD
Supt. — See League City
Clear Lake HS 2,900/9-12
2929 Bay Area Blvd 77058 281-284-1900
Debra Dixon, prin. Fax 284-1905
Clear Lake IS 1,100/6-8
15545 El Camino Real 77062 281-284-3200
Brett Lemley, prin. Fax 284-3205
Space Center IS 1,200/6-8
17400 Saturn Ln 77058 281-284-3300
Susan Carpenter, prin. Fax 284-3305

Cypress-Fairbanks ISD 103,900/PK-12
PO Box 692003 77269 281-897-4000
Dr. Mark Henry, supt. Fax 897-4125
www.cfisd.net
Adaptive Behavior Center Alt
12508 Windfern Rd 77064 281-897-4174
Maybelline Carpenter, dir. Fax 517-2884
Alternative Learning Center - E Alt
12508 Windfern Rd 77064 281-897-4171
Laurie Snyder, prin. Fax 897-4170
Aragon MS 1,700/6-8
16823 West Rd 77095 281-856-5100
Maria Mamaux, prin. Fax 856-5105
Bleyl MS 1,600/6-8
10800 Mills Rd 77070 281-897-4340
Stacia Carew, prin. Fax 897-4353
Campbell MS 1,200/6-8
11415 Bobcat Rd 77064 281-897-4300
Dr. Cheryl Henry, prin. Fax 807-8634
Cook MS 1,600/6-8
9111 Wheatland Dr 77064 281-897-4400
Sherma Duck, prin. Fax 897-3850
Cypress Creek HS 3,300/9-12
9815 Grant Rd 77070 281-897-4200
Sandy Trujillo, prin. Fax 807-8925
Cypress Falls HS 3,400/9-12
9811 Huffmeister Rd 77095 281-856-1000
Becky Denton, prin. Fax 856-1445
Cypress Ridge HS 3,000/9-12
7900 N Eldridge Pkwy 77041 713-807-8000
Claudio Garcia, prin. Fax 807-8045
Dean MS 1,500/6-8
14104 Reo St 77040 713-460-6153
Chris Hecker, prin. Fax 460-6197
Jersey Village HS 3,100/9-12
7600 Solomon St 77040 713-896-3400
Ralph Funk, prin. Fax 896-3438
Kahla MS 1,400/6-8
16212 W Little York Rd 77084 281-345-3260
Ana Martin, prin. Fax 345-5275
Labay MS 1,600/6-8
15435 Willow River Dr 77095 281-463-5800
Patty Mooney, prin. Fax 463-5804
Langham Creek HS 2,900/9-12
17610 FM 529 Rd 77095 281-463-5400
David Hughes, prin. Fax 345-3153
Truitt MS 1,400/6-8
6600 Addicks Satsuma Rd 77084 281-856-1100
Teresa Baranowski, prin. Fax 856-1104
Watkins MS 1,300/6-8
4800 Cairnvillage St 77084 281-463-5850
Dr. Jose Martinez, prin. Fax 856-1565
Windfern HS 300/Alt
12630 Windfern Rd 77064 281-807-8684
Martha Strother, prin. Fax 807-8693
Other Schools – See Cypress, Katy

Fort Bend ISD
Supt. — See Sugar Land
Hodges Bend MS 1,300/6-8
16510 Bissonnet St 77083 281-634-3000
Deidra Lyons-Lewis, prin. Fax 634-3028
McAuliffe MS 500/7-8
16650 S Post Oak Rd 77053 281-634-3360
Vonda Washington, prin. Fax 634-3393
Willowridge HS 1,400/9-12
16301 Chimney Rock Rd 77053 281-634-2450
Lee Crews, prin. Fax 634-2513

Galena Park ISD 22,600/PK-12
14705 Woodforest Blvd 77015 832-386-1000
Dr. Angi Williams, supt. Fax 386-1298
www.galenaparkisd.com
Accelerated Center for Education Alt
13801 Hollypark Dr 77015 832-386-3670
Sherrhonda Johnson, prin. Fax 386-3671
Center for Success Alt
13801 Hollypark Dr 77015 832-386-3630
Sherrhonda Johnson, prin. Fax 386-3631
Cunningham MS 900/7-8
14110 Wallisville Rd 77049 832-386-4470
Justin May, prin. Fax 386-4471
North Shore 9th Grade Center 1,200/9-9
13501 Hollypark Dr 77015 832-386-3400
Jason Bollich, prin. Fax 386-3401
North Shore MS 1,300/7-8
120 Castlegory Rd 77015 832-386-2600
Paul Drexler, prin. Fax 386-2643
North Shore SHS 4,200/10-12
353 N Castlegory Rd 77049 832-386-4100
Dr. Joe Coleman, prin. Fax 386-4101
Woodland Acres MS 500/6-8
12947 Myrtle Ln 77015 832-386-4700
Lee Ramirez, prin. Fax 386-4701
Other Schools – See Galena Park

Houston ISD 193,000/PK-12
4400 W 18th St 77092 713-556-6300
Terry Grier Ed.D., supt. Fax 556-6323
www.houstonisd.org/
Attucks MS 500/6-8
4330 Bellfort St 77051 713-732-3670
Diedre Sharkey, prin. Fax 732-3677
Austin HS 1,900/9-12
1700 Dumble St 77023 713-924-1600
Jorge Arredondo, prin. Fax 923-3157
Black MS 500/6-8
1575 Chantilly Ln 77018 713-613-2505
Meilin Jao, prin. Fax 613-2533
Burbank MS 1,300/6-8
315 Berry Rd 77022 713-696-2720
Rosa Hernandez, prin. Fax 696-2723
Carnegie-Vanguard HS 500/9-12
1501 Taft St 77019 713-732-3690
Ramon Moss, prin. Fax 732-3694
Chavez HS 2,800/9-12
8501 Howard Dr 77017 713-495-6950
Dan DeLeon, prin. Fax 495-6986
Clifton MS 1,000/6-8
6001 Golden Forest Dr 77092 713-613-2516
Rosa Cruz-Gaona, prin. Fax 613-2523
Community Services Alt
8110 Bertwood St 77016 713-636-6488
Rhonda Cotton, prin. Fax 556-7589
Crossroads Alternative S Alt
4425 N Shepherd Dr 77018 713-802-4760
Raymond Glass, prin. Fax 636-6484
Cullen MS 600/6-8
6900 Scott St 77021 713-746-8180
Clayton Crook, prin. Fax 746-8181
Davis HS 1,700/9-12
1101 Quitman St 77009 713-226-4900
Jaime Castaneda, prin. Fax 226-4999
Deady MS 900/6-8
2500 Broadway St 77012 713-845-7411
Ivonne Rodriguez, prin. Fax 845-5645
DeBakey Health Professions HS 900/9-12
3100 Shenandoah St 77021 713-741-2410
Agnes Perry, prin. Fax 746-5211
Dowling MS 1,300/6-8
14000 Stancliff St 77045 713-434-5600
Kenneth Davis, prin. Fax 434-5608
Edison MS 800/6-8
6901 Avenue I 77011 713-924-1800
Javier Villarreal, prin. Fax 924-1316
Fleming MS 500/6-8
4910 Collingsworth St 77026 713-671-4170
Sabrina Cuby-King, prin. Fax 671-4176
Fondren MS 600/6-8
6333 S Braeswood Blvd 77096 713-778-3360
Charles Foust, prin. Fax 778-3362
Fonville MS 1,100/6-8
725 E Little York Rd 77076 713-696-2825
Roger Ibarra, prin. Fax 696-2829
Furr HS 800/9-12
520 Mercury Dr 77013 713-675-1118
Dr. Bertie Simmons, prin. Fax 671-3612
Grady MS 500/6-8
5215 San Felipe St 77056 713-625-1411
Gretchen Kasper-Hoffman, prin. Fax 625-1415
Hamilton MS 1,400/6-8
139 E 20th St 77008 713-802-4725
Roger Bunnell, prin. Fax 802-4731
Harper Alternative S 100/Alt
4425 N Shepherd Dr 77018 713-802-4760
Raymond Glass, prin. Fax 802-4768
Hartman MS 1,500/6-8
7111 Westover St 77087 713-845-7435
Geovanny Ponce, prin. Fax 847-4706
HCC Life Skills 50/Alt
1301 Alabama St 77004 713-718-6882
Holly Ortega, prin. Fax 718-6815
Henry MS 1,000/6-8
10702 E Hardy Rd 77093 713-696-2650
Diana De La Rosa, prin. Fax 696-2657
High School Ahead Academy 400/6-8
5320 Yale St 77091 713-696-2643
Tynette Guinn, prin. Fax 696-2999
Hogg MS 700/6-8
1100 Merrill St 77009 713-802-4700
Mina Schnitta, prin. Fax 802-4708
Holland MS 700/6-8
1600 Gellhorn Dr 77029 713-671-3860
Tarrynce Robinson, prin. Fax 671-3874
HS for Law Enforcement/Criminal Justice 600/9-12
4701 Dickson St 77007 713-867-5100
Carol Mosteit, prin. Fax 802-4600

HS for Performing & Visual Arts 700/9-12
4001 Stanford St 77006 713-942-1960
Robert Allen, prin. Fax 942-1968
Houston Math Science Tech Ctr 1,900/10-12
9400 Irvington Blvd 77076 713-696-0200
Jane Crump, prin. Fax 696-8984
Jackson MS 900/6-8
5100 Polk St 77023 713-924-1760
Kelly Vaughn, prin. Fax 924-1768
Johnston MS 1,500/6-8
10410 Manhattan Dr 77096 713-726-3616
Wenden Sanders, prin. Fax 726-3622
Jones HS 600/9-12
7414 St Lo Rd 77033 713-733-1111
Elaine Lewis, prin. Fax 732-3450
Jordan HS for Careers Vo/Tech
5800 Eastex Fwy 77026 713-636-6900
Andria Schur, prin. Fax 636-6917
Kashmere HS 600/9-12
6900 Wileyvale Rd 77028 713-631-2185
Amber Wilson, prin. Fax 636-6433
Key MS 500/6-8
4000 Kelley St 77026 713-636-6000
Nicole Moore, prin. Fax 636-6008
Lamar HS 3,300/9-12
3325 Westheimer Rd 77098 713-522-5960
James McSwain, prin. Fax 535-3769
Las Americas MS 100/6-8
6501 Bellaire Blvd 77074 713-773-5300
Maria Moreno, prin. Fax 773-5303
Lee HS 1,700/9-12
6529 Beverlyhill St 77057 713-787-1700
Monica Quintero, prin. Fax 787-1723
Long MS 700/6-8
6501 Bellaire Blvd 77074 713-778-3380
Marcela Baez, prin. Fax 778-3387
Madison HS 2,200/9-12
13719 White Heather Dr 77045 713-433-9801
Sonja Williams, prin. Fax 434-5242
Marshall MS 1,000/6-8
1115 Noble St 77009 713-226-2600
Michael Harrison, prin. Fax 226-2605
McReynolds MS 600/6-8
5910 Market St 77020 713-671-3650
Siro Gutierrez, prin. Fax 671-3657
Milby HS 2,200/9-12
1601 Broadway St 77012 713-928-7401
Roy de la Garza, prin. Fax 928-7474
North Houston Early College HS 300/9-12
99 Lyerly St 77022 713-696-6168
Angela Lundy-Jackson, prin. Fax 696-6172
Ortiz MS 1,000/6-8
6767 Telephone Rd 77061 713-845-5650
Noelia Longoria, prin. Fax 845-5646
Pershing MS 1,800/6-8
3838 Blue Bonnet Blvd 77025 713-295-5240
Kim Heckman, prin. Fax 295-5252
Reagan HS 2,000/9-12
413 E 13th St 77008 713-865-4400
Connie Berger, prin. Fax 802-4749
Revere MS 900/6-8
10502 Briar Forest Dr 77042 713-917-3500
Hafedh Azeiz, prin. Fax 917-3505
Ryan MS 300/6-8
2610 Elgin St 77004 713-942-1932
Jeannine Porter, prin. Fax 942-1943
Scarborough HS 800/9-12
4141 Costa Rica Rd 77092 713-613-2200
Jason Catchings, prin. Fax 613-2205
Sharpstown HS 1,300/9-12
7504 Bissonnet St 77074 713-771-7215
Rob Gasparello, prin. Fax 773-6103
Sharpstown International S 600/6-12
8330 Triola Ln 77036 713-778-3440
Chang Yu, prin. Fax 778-3444
Soar Center 100/Alt
4400 W 18th St 77092 713-556-7025
Ardalia Idlebird, prin. Fax 892-7945
Sterling HS 1,100/9-12
11625 Martindale Rd 77048 713-991-0510
Edward Mitchell, prin. Fax 991-8111
Stevenson MS 1,400/6-8
9595 Winkler Dr 77017 713-943-5700
Alisa Zapata, prin. Fax 943-5711
Sugar Grove MS 400/6-8
8405 Bonhomme Rd 77074 713-271-0214
Terra Smith, prin. Fax 771-9342
Thomas MS 500/6-8
5655 Selinsky Rd 77048 713-732-3500
Khalilah Campbell-Rhone, prin. Fax 732-3511
Waltrip HS 1,800/9-12
1900 W 34th St 77018 713-688-1361
Steven Siebenalar, prin. Fax 957-7743
Washington HS 900/9-12
119 E 39th St 77018 713-692-5947
LaShonda Bilbo-Ervin, prin. Fax 696-6657
Welch MS 1,100/6-8
11544 S Gessner Rd 77071 713-778-3300
Cynthia Iyamu, prin. Fax 995-6067
West Briar MS 1,300/6-8
13733 Brimhurst Dr 77077 281-368-2140
Cynthia Henry, prin. Fax 368-2194
Westbury HS 2,200/9-12
11911 Chimney Rock Rd 77035 713-723-6015
Andrew Wainright, prin. Fax 726-2165
Westside HS 3,100/9-12
14201 Briar Forest Dr 77077 281-920-8000
Fax 920-8059
Wheatley HS 1,100/9-12
4801 Providence St 77020 713-671-3900
David Edgerson, prin. Fax 671-3951
Worthing HS 900/9-12
9215 Scott St 77051 713-733-3433
Gregory Nix, prin. Fax 731-5537
Yates HS 1,200/9-12
3703 Sampson St 77004 713-748-5400
Marla McNeal-Sheppard, prin. Fax 746-8206

Young Mens College Preparatory Academy 6-12
1701 Bringhurst St 77020 713-226-2668
Dameion Crook, prin. Fax 226-2680
Young Womens College Preparatory Academy 6-12
1906 Cleburne St 77004 713-942-1441
Delesa O'Dell-Thomas, prin. Fax 942-1448
Other Schools – See Bellaire

Humble ISD
Supt. — See Humble
Quest Early College HS 200/9-12
15903 W Lake Houston Pkwy 77044 281-641-7300
Kim Klepcyk, prin. Fax 641-7317
Summer Creek HS 1,400/9-12
14000 Weckford Blvd 77044 281-641-5400
Trey Kraemer, prin. Fax 641-5417
Woodcreek MS 1,000/6-8
14600 Woodson Park Dr 77044 281-641-5200
Thyrun Hurst, prin. Fax 641-5217

Katy ISD
Supt. — See Katy
Mayde Creek HS 2,700/9-12
19202 Groschke Rd 77084 281-237-3000
Dr. Cazilda Steele, prin. Fax 644-1715
Mayde Creek JHS 1,200/6-8
2700 Greenhouse Rd 77084 281-237-3900
Tory Hill, prin. Fax 644-1650

Klein ISD
Supt. — See Klein
Klein Forest HS 3,500/9-12
11400 Misty Valley Dr 77066 832-484-4500
Patricia Crittendon, prin. Fax 484-7801
Klein IS 1,200/6-8
4710 W Mount Houston Rd 77088 832-249-4900
Bob Anderson, prin. Fax 249-4046
Ulrich IS 800/6-8
10103 Spring Cypress Rd 77070 832-375-7500
Dr. Jeff Bailey, prin. Fax 375-7599
Vistas HS Program Alt
12550 Bammel North Houston 77066 832-484-7650
Peggy Ekster, dir. Fax 484-7697
Wunderlich IS 1,400/6-8
11800 Misty Valley Dr 77066 832-249-5200
Dr. Chris Ruggerio, prin. Fax 249-4050

North Forest ISD 7,300/PK-12
6010 Little York Rd 77016 713-633-1600
Edna Forte, supt. Fax 636-7946
www.nfisd.org
Elmore MS 500/6-8
8200 Tate St 77028 713-672-7466
Steven Hemderson, prin. Fax 671-3570
Forest Brook MS 800/6-8
7525 Tidwell Rd 77016 713-633-0670
Wiley Johnson, prin. Fax 636-4114
Learning Academy Alt
11433 Suburban Rd 77016 281-986-6466
Victor Nash, prin. Fax 986-6470
North Forest HS 1,400/9-12
10725 Mesa Dr 77078 713-636-4300
Angelanet Allen, prin. Fax 636-8116

Pasadena ISD
Supt. — See Pasadena
Beverly Hills IS 1,000/6-8
11111 Beamer Rd 77089 713-740-0420
Alyta Harrell, prin. Fax 740-4051
Dobie HS 3,500/9-12
10220 Blackhawk Blvd 77089 713-740-0370
Franklin Moses, prin. Fax 740-4158
Thompson IS 900/6-8
11309 Sagedowne Ln 77089 713-740-0510
Toni Lopez, prin. Fax 740-4083

Sheldon ISD 7,300/PK-12
11411 C E King Pkwy 77044 281-727-2000
Dr. Vickey Giles, supt. Fax 727-2085
www.sheldonisd.com/
King HS 1,700/9-12
8540 C E King Pkwy 77044 281-727-3500
John Kirchner, prin. Fax 459-7346
King MS 800/6-8
8530 C E King Pkwy 77044 281-727-4300
Roberto Hernandez, prin. Fax 459-7452
Null MS 700/6-8
12117 Garrett Rd 77044 281-436-2800
Becky Zalesnik, prin. Fax 436-2875

Spring Branch ISD 31,700/PK-12
955 Campbell Rd 77024 713-464-1511
Duncan Klussmann Ed.D., supt. Fax 365-4071
www.springbranchisd.com/
Academy of Choice 100/Alt
9016 Westview Dr 77055 713-251-1500
Michele Hilbreth, dir. Fax 365-4226
Guthrie Center for Excellence Vo/Tech
10660 Hammerly Blvd 77043 713-251-1300
Joe Kolenda, prin. Fax 365-4621
Landrum MS 700/6-8
2200 Ridgecrest Dr 77055 713-251-3700
Luis Pratts, prin. Fax 365-4040
Memorial HS 2,400/9-12
935 Echo Ln 77024 713-251-2500
William Lakin, prin. Fax 365-5138
Memorial MS 1,200/6-8
12550 Vindon Dr 77024 713-251-3900
Lisa Weir, prin. Fax 365-5411
Northbrook HS 2,000/9-12
1 Raider Cir 77080 713-251-2800
Randolph Adami, prin. Fax 365-4412
Northbrook MS 600/6-8
3030 Rosefield Dr 77080 713-251-4100
Valerie Johnson, prin. Fax 329-6523
Spring Branch MS 1,100/6-8
1000 Piney Point Rd 77024 713-251-4400
Bryan Williams, prin. Fax 365-5515

Spring Forest MS 900/6-8
14240 Memorial Dr 77079 713-251-4600
Kaye Williams, prin. Fax 560-7509
Spring Oaks MS 800/6-8
2150 Shadowdale Dr 77043 713-251-4800
David Sablatura, prin. Fax 365-4522
Spring Woods HS 2,000/9-12
2045 Gessner Rd 77080 713-251-3100
Lance Stallworth, prin. Fax 365-4474
Spring Woods MS 900/6-8
9810 Neuens Rd 77080 713-251-5000
Karen Liska, prin. Fax 365-4115
Stratford HS 1,900/9-12
14555 Fern Dr 77079 713-251-3400
Christopher Juntti, prin. Fax 560-7588

Spring ISD 37,200/PK-12
16717 Ella Blvd 77090 281-891-6000
Ralph Draper Ed.D., supt. Fax 891-6006
www.springisd.org
Bammel MS 1,300/6-8
16711 Ella Blvd 77090 281-891-7900
Cleotis Wadley, prin. Fax 891-7901
Claughton MS 1,400/6-8
3000 Spears Rd 77067 281-891-7950
Becky Hernandez, prin. Fax 891-7951
DeKaney HS 2,800/9-12
22351 Imperial Valley Dr 77073 281-891-7260
Delic Loyde, prin. Fax 891-7621
Early College Academy 100/9-12
1001 S Ridge Rd 77090 281-891-6880
Dr. Rene Garganta, prin. Fax 891-6891
Roberson MS 1,200/6-8
1500 S Ridge Rd 77090 281-891-7702
Thad Gittens, prin. Fax 891-7701
Wells MS 1,200/6-8
4033 Gladeridge Dr 77068 281-891-7750
Lenny Hardoin, prin. Fax 891-7751
Westfield HS 3,200/9-12
16713 Ella Blvd 77090 281-891-7132
Steve Kinney, prin. Fax 891-7131
Other Schools – See Spring

Aerosim Flight Academy Post-Sec.
12711 Blume Ave 77034 281-481-4700
Alexander-Smith Academy 50/9-12
10255 Richmond Ave Ste 100 77042 713-266-0920
J. David Arnold, pres. Fax 266-8857
Alfred G. Glassell School of Art Post-Sec.
PO Box 6826 77265 713-639-7500
American College of Acupuncture Post-Sec.
9100 Park West Dr 77063 713-780-9777
American InterContinental University Post-Sec.
9999 Richmond Ave 77042 832-201-3600
Art Institute of Houston Post-Sec.
4140 Southwest Fwy 77027 713-623-2040
Astrodome Career Center Post-Sec.
2656 S Loop W Ste 380 77054 713-664-5300
Aviation Institute of Maintenance Post-Sec.
7651 Airport Blvd 77061 713-644-7777
Awty International S 1,200/PK-12
7455 Awty School Ln 77055 713-686-4850
Dr. Stephen Codrington, hdmstr. Fax 686-4956
Banff S 100/PK-12
13726 Cutten Rd 77069 281-444-9326
Deborah Wasser, prin. Fax 444-3632
Baylor College of Medicine Post-Sec.
1 Baylor Plz 77030 713-798-4951
Behold! Beauty Academy Post-Sec.
3823 Charleston St 77021 713-635-5252
Ben Taub Hospital Post-Sec.
2525 Holly Hall St 77054 713-746-6400
Beren Academy 300/PK-12
11333 Cliffwood Dr 77035 713-723-7170
Rabbi Harry Sinoff, head sch Fax 723-8343
Bridge S, 3333 Bering Dr 77057 300/7-12
Dr. Spyros Catechis, head sch 713-234-6117
Center for Advanced Legal Studies Post-Sec.
3910 Kirby Dr Ste 200 77098 713-529-2778
Central Christian Academy 100/PK-12
2217 Bingle Rd 77055 713-468-3248
Scott Jacobs, admin. Fax 468-7322
Chamberlain College of Nursing Post-Sec.
11025 Equity Dr 77041 713-277-9800
Champion Beauty College Post-Sec.
3920 FM 1960 Ste 210 77068 281-583-9117
Clear Lake Christian S 400/K-12
14325 Crescent Landing Dr 77062 281-488-4883
Rev. Bruce Guillot, prin. Fax 480-3287
College of Biblical Studies Post-Sec.
7000 Regency Square Blvd 77036 713-785-5995
Commonwealth Institute / Funeral Service Post-Sec.
415 Barren Springs Dr 77090 281-873-0262
Cornerstone Christian Academy 100/PK-12
14314 Walters Rd 77014 281-580-1671
John Brassel, dir. Fax 580-2316
Cristo Rey Jesuit HS 9-12
6700 Mount Carmel St 77087 281-501-1298
Katherine Cater, prin. Fax 501-3485
Culinary Institute LeNotre Post-Sec.
7070 Allensby St 77022 713-692-0077
Cypress Christian S 500/K-12
11123 Cypress N Houston Rd 77065 281-469-8829
Stephen Novotny, hdmstr. Fax 469-6040
DeVry University Post-Sec.
5051 Westheimer Rd Ste 500 77056 713-850-0888
DeVry University Post-Sec.
11125 Equity Dr 77041 713-973-3100
Duchesne Academy HS 300/9-12
10202 Memorial Dr 77024 713-468-8211
Dr. Rae Flory, prin. Fax 465-9809
Duchesne Academy MS 200/5-8
10202 Memorial Dr 77024 713-468-8211
Tony Houle, hdmstr. Fax 465-9809
Emery/Weiner S 400/6-12
9825 Stella Link Rd 77025 832-204-5900
Stuart Dow, hdmstr. Fax 204-5910

Everest Institute Post-Sec.
255 Northpoint Dr Ste 100 77060 281-447-7037
Everest Institute Post-Sec.
9700 Bissonnet St Ste 1400 77036 713-772-4200
Everest Institute Post-Sec.
7151 Office City Dr Ste 100 77087 713-645-7404
Family Christian Academy 200/PK-12
14718 Woodford Dr 77015 713-455-4483
Robert Anderson, admin. Fax 450-3730
Fortis College Post-Sec.
6220 Westpark Dr Ste 180 77057 713-266-6594
Fortis College Post-Sec.
450 N Sam Houston Pkwy #200 77060 713-332-0062
Franklin Beauty School #2 Post-Sec.
4965 Martin Luther King 77021 713-645-9060
Gulf Coast Regional Blood Center Post-Sec.
1400 La Concha Ln 77054 713-790-1200
Holy Trinity Episcopal S 200/PK-12
11810 Lockwood Rd 77044 281-459-4323
Dr. Nici Esch, hdmstr. Fax 459-4302
Houston Baptist University Post-Sec.
7502 Fondren Rd 77074 281-649-3000
Houston Christian HS 500/9-12
2700 W Sam Houston Pkwy N 77043 713-580-6000
Dr. Steve Livingston, hdmstr. Fax 580-6001
Houston Community College Post-Sec.
3100 Main St 77002 713-718-2000
Houston Graduate School of Theology Post-Sec.
2501 Central Pkwy Ste A19 77092 713-942-9505
Houston Learning Academy - North 50/9-12
13029 Champions Dr Ste B-1 77069 281-537-5668
Lesley Boyer, prin. Fax 537-2361
Houston Training School Post-Sec.
6630 Gulf Fwy 77087 713-649-5050
ICC Technical Institute Post-Sec.
3333 Fannin St Ste 203 77004 713-522-7799
Incarnate Word Academy 300/9-12
609 Crawford St 77002 713-227-3637
Dr. Mary Aamodt, prin. Fax 227-1014
Institute of Cosmetology Post-Sec.
7011 Harwin Dr Ste 100 77036 713-783-9988
ITT Technical Institute Post-Sec.
2950 S Gessner Rd Ste 100 77063 713-952-2294
ITT Technical Institute Post-Sec.
15651 North Fwy 77090 281-873-0512
Jay's Technical Institute Post-Sec.
11910 Fondren Meadow Dr 77071 713-772-2410
Kinkaid S 1,400/PK-12
201 Kinkaid School Dr 77024 713-782-1640
Donald North, hdmstr. Fax 243-5055
Lone Star College - North Harris Post-Sec.
2700 WW Thorne Blvd 77073 281-618-5400
Lone Star College - University Park Post-Sec.
20515 State Highway 249 77070 281-290-2600
Lutheran HS North 300/9-12
1130 W 34th St 77018 713-880-3131
Dr. Wayne Kramer, head sch Fax 880-5447
Lutheran South Academy 800/PK-12
12555 Ryewater Dr 77089 281-464-8299
Sheila Psencik, hdmstr. Fax 464-6119
Mediatech Institute Post-Sec.
3324 Walnut Bend Ln 77042 832-242-3426
Memorial Hall S 100/4-12
5400 Mitchelldale St Ste A1 77092 713-688-5566
Rev. George Aurich, hdmstr. Fax 956-9751
Memorial Hospital System Post-Sec.
7737 Southwest Fwy 77074 713-776-5100
Methodist Hospital Post-Sec.
6565 Fannin St 77030 713-441-2599
Michigan Institute of Aviation & Tech Post-Sec.
533 Northpark Central Dr 77073 713-401-3399
North American College Post-Sec.
3203 N Sam Houston Pkwy W 77038 832-230-5555
Northland Christian S 600/PK-12
4363 Sylvanfield Dr 77014 281-440-1060
Northwest Educational Center Post-Sec.
2910 Antoine Dr Ste B100 77092 713-680-2929
Our Redeemer Lutheran North S 50/2-12
215 Rittenhouse St 77076 713-694-0332
Fax 699-1032
Page Parkes Center of Modeling & Acting Post-Sec.
1535 West Loop S Ste 100 77027 713-807-8200
Prairie View A&M University Post-Sec.
6436 Fannin St 77030 713-797-7000
Professional Career Training Institute Post-Sec.
227 Airtex Dr 77090 832-484-9100
Remington College - Houston Post-Sec.
3110 Hayes Rd Ste 380 77082 281-899-1240
Remington College North Houston Post-Sec.
11310 Greens Crossing # 300 77067 281-885-4450
Rice University Post-Sec.
PO Box 1892 77251 713-348-0000
Royal Beauty Careers Post-Sec.
5020 FM 1960 Rd W Ste A12 77069 281-580-2554
St. Agnes Academy 900/9-12
9000 Bellaire Blvd 77036 713-219-5400
Sr. Jane Meyer, hdmstr. Fax 219-5499
St. John's S 1,200/K-12
2401 Claremont Ln 77019 713-850-0222
Mark Desjardins, hdmstr. Fax 622-2309
St. Pius X HS 700/9-12
811 W Donovan St 77091 713-692-3581
Sr. Donna Pollard, hdmstr. Fax 692-5725
St. Stephen's Episcopal School Houston 200/PK-12
1800 Sul Ross St 77098 713-821-9100
David Coe, hdmstr. Fax 821-9156
St. Thomas' Episcopal S 600/K-12
4900 Jackwood St 77096 713-666-3111
Michael Cusack, hdmstr. Fax 668-3887
St. Thomas HS 700/9-12
4500 Memorial Dr 77007 713-864-6348
Rev. Patrick Fulton, prin. Fax 864-5750
Sanford-Brown College Post-Sec.
9999 Richmond Ave 77042 713-779-1110
Sanford-Brown College Post-Sec.
2627 North Loop W Ste 100 77008 713-863-0429
San Jacinto College Post-Sec.
5800 Uvalde Rd 77049 281-458-4050
San Jacinto College Post-Sec.
13735 Beamer Rd 77089 281-484-1900
School of Automotive Machinists Post-Sec.
1911 Antoine Dr 77055 713-683-3817
School of the Woods 400/PK-12
1321 Wirt Rd 77055 713-686-8811
Second Baptist S 1,100/PK-12
6410 Woodway Dr 77057 713-365-2310
Dr. Jeff Williams, head sch Fax 365-2355
Shady Acres Christian S 50/1-12
7330 Vogel Rd 77088 281-999-2040
Danny Farley, admin. Fax 999-2040
South Texas College of Law Post-Sec.
1303 San Jacinto St 77002 713-659-8040
Southwest Christian Academy 200/K-12
7400 Eldridge Pkwy 77083 281-561-7400
Paula Thurmond, prin. Fax 561-9823
Strake Jesuit College Prep S 900/9-12
8900 Bellaire Blvd 77036 713-774-7651
Ken Lojo, prin. Fax 774-6427
Texas Barber Colleges & Hairstyling Sch Post-Sec.
9275 Richmond Ave Ste 184 77063 713-953-0262
Texas Christian S 200/PK-12
17810 Kieth Harrow Blvd 77084 281-550-6060
Herc Palmquist, pres. Fax 550-2400
Texas Health School Post-Sec.
11211 Katy Fwy Ste 170 77079 713-932-9333
Texas Heart Institute Post-Sec.
PO Box 20345 77225 713-791-4026
Texas School of Business Post-Sec.
711 E Airtex Dr 77073 281-443-8900
Texas Southern University Post-Sec.
3100 Cleburne St 77004 713-313-7011
Texas Woman's University Post-Sec.
6700 Fannin St 77030 713-794-2000
The College of Health Care Professions Post-Sec.
240 Northwest Mall 77092 713-425-3100
The Ocean Corporation Post-Sec.
10840 Rockley Rd 77099 281-530-0202
Torah Girls Academy 50/9-12
10101 Fondren Rd Ste 136 77096 713-936-0644
Rabbi Yehoshua Wender, dean
Trend Barber College Post-Sec.
7725 W Bellfort St 77071 713-721-0000
Universal Technical Institute Post-Sec.
721 Lockhaven Dr 77073 281-443-6262
University of Houston Post-Sec.
4800 Calhoun Rd 77204 713-743-1000
University of Houston-Clear Lake Post-Sec.
2700 Bay Area Blvd 77058 281-283-7600
University of Houston-Downtown Post-Sec.
1 Main St 77002 713-221-8000
University of St. Thomas Post-Sec.
3800 Montrose Blvd 77006 713-522-7911
University of Texas Anderson Cancer Ctr. Post-Sec.
1515 Holcombe Blvd Unit 2 77030 713-792-6161
University of TX Health Science Center Post-Sec.
PO Box 20036 77225 713-500-4472
Veterans Affairs Medical Center Post-Sec.
2002 Holcombe Blvd 77030 713-794-7100
Vet Tech Institute Post-Sec.
4669 Southwest Fwy 77027 800-275-2736
Village S 800/PK-12
13077 Westella Dr 77077 281-496-7900
Westbury Christian S 600/PK-12
10420 Hillcroft St 77096 713-551-8100
Greg Glenn, head sch Fax 551-8117
Westwood College Post-Sec.
7322 Southwest Fwy Ste 110 77074 713-777-4433

Howe, Grayson, Pop. 2,551
Howe ISD 1,000/PK-12
105 W Tutt St 75459 903-532-3228
Kevin Wilson, supt. Fax 532-3205
www.howeisd.net
Howe HS 300/9-12
200 Ponderosa Rd 75459 903-532-3236
Michael Smiley, prin. Fax 532-3237
Howe MS 300/5-8
300 Beatrice St 75459 903-532-3286
Ritchie Bowling, prin. Fax 532-3287

Hubbard, Hill, Pop. 1,406
Hubbard ISD 400/PK-12
PO Box 218 76648 254-576-2564
Randy O'Brien, supt. Fax 576-5019
www.hubbardisd.com/
Hubbard HS 100/9-12
PO Box 218 76648 254-576-2549
David Sustala, prin. Fax 576-2477
Hubbard MS 100/6-8
PO Box 218 76648 254-576-2758
Sunny Beseda, prin. Fax 576-5017

Huffman, Harris
Huffman ISD 3,200/PK-12
PO Box 2390 77336 281-324-1871
Dr. Christopher Soileau, supt. Fax 324-4319
www.huffmanisd.net
Hargrave HS 900/9-12
PO Box 2390 77336 281-324-1845
Shirley Hitt, prin. Fax 324-3368
Huffman MS 800/6-8
PO Box 2390 77336 281-324-2598
Chris Flowers, prin. Fax 324-2710

Hughes Springs, Cass, Pop. 1,726
Hughes Springs ISD 1,100/PK-12
871 Taylor St 75656 903-639-3800
Rick Ogden, supt. Fax 639-2624
www.hsisd.net
Hughes Springs HS 300/9-12
701 Russell 75656 903-639-3841
Michael Walker, prin. Fax 639-3928
Hughes Springs JHS 200/6-8
609 Russell 75656 903-639-3812
Brian Nation, prin. Fax 639-3929

Humble, Harris, Pop. 14,835
Aldine ISD
Supt. — See Houston
Teague MS 800/7-8
21700 Rayford Rd 77338 281-233-4310
Sonya Hicks, prin. Fax 233-4318

Humble ISD 36,000/PK-12
PO Box 2000 77347 281-641-1000
Dr. Guy Sconzo, supt. Fax 641-1050
www.humble.k12.tx.us/
Atascocita HS 3,100/9-12
13300 Will Clayton Pkwy 77346 281-641-7500
Dania Rovegno, prin. Fax 641-7713
Atascocita MS 1,100/6-8
18810 W Lake Houston Pkwy 77346 281-641-4600
Karl Koehler, prin. Fax 641-4617
Cambridge S Alt
18901 Timber Forest Dr 77346 281-641-7445
Tammey Harlan, prin. Fax 641-7417
Career & Technology Education Center Vo/Tech
9155 Will Clayton Pkwy 77338 281-641-7950
Thomas Wagener, prin. Fax 641-7967
Community Learning Center 100/Alt
18901 Timber Forest Dr 77346 281-641-7400
Marlon Farr, prin. Fax 641-7417
Humble HS 1,700/9-12
1700 Wilson Rd 77338 281-641-6300
Charles Ned, prin. Fax 641-6517
Humble MS 1,100/6-8
11207 Will Clayton Pkwy 77346 281-641-4170
Henry Phipps, prin. Fax 641-4117
Sterling MS 800/6-8
1131 Wilson Rd 77338 281-641-6000
Brandon Garza, prin. Fax 641-6017
Timberwood MS 1,200/6-8
18450 Timber Forest Dr 77346 281-641-3800
Kenneth Buck, prin. Fax 641-3817
Other Schools – See Houston, Kingwood

Christian Life Center Academy 200/PK-12
6650 Rankin Rd 77396 281-319-0077
Rev. Richard Rodriguez, admin. Fax 319-4523
Humble Christian S 300/PK-12
16202 Old Humble Rd 77396 281-441-1313
Ted Howell, admin. Fax 441-1329

Huntington, Angelina, Pop. 2,087
Huntington ISD 1,700/PK-12
PO Box 328 75949 936-876-4287
Dr. Eric Wright, supt. Fax 876-3212
www.huntingtonisd.com/
Huntington HS 500/9-12
PO Box 328 75949 936-876-4150
Jason Adams, prin. Fax 876-4009
Huntington MS 400/6-8
PO Box 328 75949 936-876-4722
Shane Stover, prin. Fax 876-4009
Pride Alternative S 100/Alt
PO Box 328 75949 936-876-4287
Harold Hill, dir. Fax 422-4352

Huntsville, Walker, Pop. 38,042
Huntsville ISD 6,200/PK-12
441 FM 2821 Rd E 77320 936-435-6300
Steve Johnson Ed.D., supt. Fax 291-3444
www.huntsville-isd.org
Huntsville HS 1,600/9-12
441 FM 2821 Rd E 77320 936-435-6100
Beth Burt, prin. Fax 293-2609
Mance Park MS 900/7-8
441 FM 2821 Rd E 77320 936-293-2755
Ingrid Purvis, prin. Fax 293-2759

Alpha Omega Academy 400/K-12
PO Box 8419 77340 936-438-8833
Paul Davidhizar, hdmstr. Fax 438-8844
Sam Houston State University Post-Sec.
1806 Avenue J 77340 936-294-1111
Summit Christian Academy 100/PK-10
PO Box 1590 77342 936-295-9601
Joyce Kumba, prin. Fax 295-9236

Hurst, Tarrant, Pop. 36,447
Hurst-Euless-Bedford ISD
Supt. — See Bedford
Bell SHS 2,100/10-12
1601 Brown Trl 76054 817-282-2551
Jim Bannister, prin. Fax 285-3200
Hurst JHS 1,000/7-9
500 Harmon Rd 76053 817-285-3220
Dr. Toby Givens, prin. Fax 285-3225

Ogle School of Hair Design Post-Sec.
720 Arcadia St Apt B 76053 817-284-9231
Tarrant County College Post-Sec.
828 W Harwood Rd 76054 817-515-8223

Hutto, Williamson, Pop. 14,315
Hutto ISD 4,500/PK-12
200 College St 78634 512-759-3771
Dr. Douglas Killian, supt. Fax 759-4796
www.hutto.txed.net
Farley MS 600/5-8
303 County Road 137 78634 512-759-2050
Roy Christian, prin. Fax 759-2033
Hutto HS 1,300/9-12
101 FM 685 78634 512-759-4700
Brandy Baker, prin. Fax 759-4757
Hutto MS 600/5-8
1005 Exchange Blvd 78634 512-759-4541
Liz Comeaux, prin. Fax 759-4753

Idalou, Lubbock, Pop. 2,236
Idalou ISD 1,000/PK-12
PO Box 1338 79329 806-892-1900
Jim Waller, supt. Fax 892-3204
www.idalouisd.net/

Idalou HS 300/9-12
PO Box 1558 79329 806-892-1900
Janet Thornton, prin. Fax 892-2690
Idalou MS 300/5-8
PO Box 1353 79329 806-892-1900
Steve Gunter, prin. Fax 892-2388

Imperial, Pecos, Pop. 277
Buena Vista ISD 100/PK-12
PO Box 310 79743 432-536-2336
Mark Dominguez, supt. Fax 536-2469
www.buenavistaisd.net/
Buena Vista S 100/PK-12
PO Box 310 79743 432-536-2336
Mark Dominguez, prin. Fax 536-2469

Ingleside, San Patricio, Pop. 9,243
Ingleside ISD 2,200/PK-12
PO Box 1320 78362 361-776-7631
Troy Mircovich, supt. Fax 776-0267
www.inglesideisd.org
Ingleside HS 600/9-12
2807 Mustang Dr 78362 361-776-2712
Danny Glover, prin. Fax 776-5200
Taylor JHS 300/7-8
2739 Mustang Dr 78362 361-776-2232
Heather Waugh-Freeze, prin. Fax 776-2192

Ingram, Kerr, Pop. 1,786
Ingram ISD 900/PK-12
510 College St 78025 830-367-5517
Dr. Robert Templeton, supt. Fax 367-5631
www.ingramisd.net
Ingram-Tom Moore HS 300/7-12
510 College St 78025 830-367-4111
Sarah McCrae, prin. Fax 367-7332

Iola, Grimes, Pop. 393
Iola ISD 500/PK-12
PO Box 159 77861 936-394-2361
Douglas Devine, supt. Fax 394-2132
www.iolaisd.net
Iola JSHS 200/7-12
PO Box 159 77861 936-394-2361
Jeff Dyer, prin. Fax 394-4700

Iowa Park, Wichita, Pop. 6,289
Iowa Park Consolidated ISD 1,800/PK-12
PO Box 898 76367 940-592-4193
Jerry Baird, supt. Fax 592-2136
www.ipcisd.net/
George MS 400/6-8
412 E Cash St 76367 940-592-2196
Darla Biddy, prin. Fax 592-2801
Iowa Park HS 500/9-12
1 Bob Dawson Dr 76367 940-592-2144
Tim Hartram, prin. Fax 592-2583

Ira, Scurry
Ira ISD 300/K-12
6143 W FM 1606 79527 325-573-2629
Jay Waller, supt. Fax 573-5825
www.ira.esc14.net/
Ira S 300/K-12
6123 W FM 1606 79527 325-573-2628
Dale Jones, prin. Fax 573-5825

Iraan, Pecos, Pop. 1,225
Iraan-Sheffield ISD 500/PK-12
PO Box 486 79744 432-639-2512
Kevin Allen, supt. Fax 639-2501
isisd.net
Iraan HS 100/9-12
PO Box 486 79744 432-639-2512
Randy Doege, prin. Fax 639-2501
Iraan JHS 100/6-8
PO Box 486 79744 432-639-2512
Melissa Hanna, prin. Fax 639-2501
Other Schools – See Sheffield

Iredell, Bosque, Pop. 338
Iredell ISD 100/PK-12
PO Box 39 76649 254-364-2411
Bryan Lee, supt. Fax 364-2206
www.iredell-isd.com
Iredell S 100/PK-12
PO Box 39 76649 254-364-2411
Patrick Murphy, prin. Fax 364-2206

Irving, Dallas, Pop. 212,044
Carrollton-Farmers Branch ISD
Supt. — See Carrollton
Bush MS 800/6-8
515 Cowboys Pkwy 75063 972-968-3700
Matt Warnock, prin. Fax 968-3710
Ranchview HS 800/9-12
8401 Valley Ranch Pkwy E 75063 972-968-5000
Sherie Skruch, prin. Fax 968-5010

Irving ISD 34,200/PK-12
PO Box 152637 75015 972-600-5000
Dana Bedden Ed.D., supt. Fax 215-5201
www.irvingisd.net
Austin MS 900/6-8
825 E Union Bower Rd 75061 972-600-3100
Julie Miller, prin. Fax 721-3105
Bowie MS 1,000/6-8
600 E 6th St 75060 972-600-3000
Rocci Malone, prin. Fax 721-3044
Cardwell Career Preparatory Center 300/Alt
101 E Union Bower Rd 75061 972-600-6140
Curtis Mauricio, prin. Fax 273-6188
Crockett MS 1,000/6-8
2431 Hancock St 75061 972-600-4700
Raymond Edwards, prin. Fax 313-4770
de Zavala MS 1,000/6-8
707 W Pioneer Dr 75061 972-600-6000
John Rose, prin. Fax 273-8924
Houston MS 1,000/6-8
3033 Country Club Dr W 75038 972-600-7500
Dionn Dahl, prin. Fax 261-2399
Irving HS 2,300/9-12
900 N O Connor Rd 75061 972-600-6300
Linda Kimm, prin. Fax 273-8319
Johnson MS 6-8
3601 W Pioneer Dr 75061 972-600-0500
Angie Gaylord, prin. Fax 215-5003
Lamar MS 1,200/6-8
219 Crandall Rd 75060 972-600-4400
Joe Moreno, prin. Fax 313-4499
MacArthur HS 2,600/9-12
3700 N MacArthur Blvd 75062 972-600-7200
Robert Abel, prin. Fax 261-2298
Nimitz HS 2,400/9-12
100 W Oakdale Rd 75060 972-600-5700
Randy Cobb, prin. Fax 273-8610
Singley Academy 1,600/9-12
4601 N MacArthur Blvd 75038 972-600-5300
David Saenz, prin. Fax 258-5301
Travis MS 1,000/6-8
1600 Finley Rd 75062 972-600-0100
Cindy Bean, prin. Fax 261-2450
Wheeler Transitional Center 50/Alt
1600 E Shady Grove Rd 75060 972-600-3750
Sam Bean, prin. Fax 554-3769

Anthem College Post-Sec.
4250 N Belt Line Rd 75038 469-499-5100
Aviation Institute of Maintenance Post-Sec.
400 E Airport Fwy 75062 214-333-9711
Cistercian Preparatory S 400/5-12
3660 Cistercian Rd 75039 469-499-5400
Fr. Paul McCormick, hdmstr. Fax 499-5440
DeVry University Post-Sec.
4800 Regent Blvd 75063 972-929-6777
Highlands S 500/PK-12
1451 E Northgate Dr 75062 972-554-1980
Gerard Doyle, prin. Fax 721-1691
Mediatech Institute Post-Sec.
400 E Royal Ln Ste 100 75039 866-498-1122
North Lake College Post-Sec.
5001 N MacArthur Blvd 75038 972-273-3000
StoneGate Christian Academy 100/PK-12
2833 W Shady Grove Rd 75060 972-790-0070
Virginia Wirth, prin. Fax 790-6560
Tint School of Makeup & Cosmetology Post-Sec.
2716 W Irving Blvd 75061 972-513-1176
Universal Technical Institute Post-Sec.
5151 Regent Blvd 75063 800-873-1083
University of Dallas Post-Sec.
1845 E Northgate Dr 75062 972-721-5000

Italy, Ellis, Pop. 1,835
Italy ISD 600/PK-12
300 College 76651 972-483-1815
Barry Bassett, supt. Fax 483-6152
www.italyisd.org
Italy JSHS 300/7-12
300 College 76651 972-483-7411
Lee Joffre, prin. Fax 483-1500

Itasca, Hill, Pop. 1,623
Itasca ISD 700/PK-12
123 N College St 76055 254-687-2922
Glenn Pittman, supt. Fax 687-2637
www.itascaisd.org
Itasca HS 200/9-12
123 N College St 76055 254-687-2922
Derek Driver, prin. Fax 687-2637
Itasca MS 200/5-8
208 N Files St 76055 254-687-2922
Kristi Sargent, prin. Fax 687-2637

Ivanhoe, Fannin, Pop. 869
Sam Rayburn ISD 400/PK-12
9363 E FM 273 75447 903-664-2255
Jeff Irvin, supt. Fax 664-2406
www.samrayburnisd.com
Rayburn JSHS 200/7-12
9363 E FM 273 75447 903-664-2165
Wendy Keeton, prin. Fax 664-2406

Jacksboro, Jack, Pop. 4,489
Jacksboro ISD 900/PK-12
750 W Belknap St 76458 940-567-7203
Dennis Bennett, supt. Fax 567-2214
www.jacksboroisd.net/
Jacksboro HS 300/9-12
1400 N Main St 76458 940-567-7204
Brad Burnett, prin. Fax 567-6028
Jacksboro Learning Center 50/Alt
815 W Belknap St 76458 940-567-7207
Brad Burnett, prin. Fax 567-2754
Jacksboro MS 200/6-8
812 W Belknap St 76458 940-567-7205
Sara Mathis, prin. Fax 567-2681

Jacksonville, Cherokee, Pop. 14,356
Jacksonville ISD 5,000/PK-12
PO Box 631 75766 903-586-6511
Dr. Joe Wardell, supt. Fax 586-3133
www.jacksonvilleisd.org
Compass Center 50/Alt
PO Box 631 75766 903-589-3926
Kimberly Wilson, prin. Fax 586-7158
Jacksonville HS 1,100/9-12
PO Box 631 75766 903-586-3661
Tammy Jones, prin. Fax 586-8229
Jacksonville MS 700/7-8
PO Box 631 75766 903-586-3686
Lisa Cox, prin. Fax 586-8071

Baptist Missionary Theological Seminary Post-Sec.
PO Box 670 75766 903-586-2501
Jacksonville College Post-Sec.
105 B J Albritton Dr 75766 903-586-2518

Jarrell, Williamson, Pop. 971
Jarrell ISD 1,000/PK-12
PO Box 9 76537 512-746-2124
Dr. Bill Chapman, supt. Fax 746-2518
www.jarrellisd.org
Jarrell HS 300/9-12
PO Box 9 76537 512-746-2188
Robert Reyes, prin. Fax 746-2183
Jarrell MS 300/5-8
PO Box 9 76537 512-746-4180
Abbe Lester, prin. Fax 746-4280

Jasper, Jasper, Pop. 7,490
Jasper ISD 2,800/PK-12
128 Park Ln 75951 409-384-2401
Dr. Richard Skuza, supt. Fax 382-1084
www.jasperisd.net
Jasper HS 700/9-12
400 Bulldog Ave 75951 409-384-3242
Victor Williams, prin. Fax 382-1310
Jasper JHS 400/7-8
211 2nd St 75951 409-384-3585
John Seybold, prin. Fax 382-1160

Jayton, Kent, Pop. 530
Jayton-Girard ISD 200/PK-12
PO Box 168 79528 806-237-2991
Tim Seymore, supt. Fax 237-2670
www.jaytonjaybirds.com
Jayton S 200/PK-12
PO Box 168 79528 806-237-2991
Jodie Reel, prin. Fax 237-2670

Jefferson, Marion, Pop. 2,067
Jefferson ISD 1,200/PK-12
1600 Martin Luther King Dr 75657 903-665-2461
Dr. Sharon Ross, supt. Fax 665-7367
jeffersonisd.org/
Jefferson HS 400/9-12
1 Bulldog Dr 75657 903-665-2461
Anthony Evers, prin. Fax 665-2146
Jefferson JHS 400/5-8
804 N Alley St 75657 903-665-2461
Paul Peteet, prin. Fax 665-7149

Jefferson Christian Academy 50/9-12
3060 FM 728 75657 903-665-3973
Dr. Sunith Das, prin. Fax 665-5987

Jewett, Leon, Pop. 1,158
Leon ISD 800/PK-12
12168 US Highway 79 75846 903-626-1400
Mike Baldree, supt. Fax 626-1420
www.leonisd.net/
Leon HS 200/9-12
12168 US Highway 79 75846 903-626-1475
Jay Winn, prin. Fax 626-1490
Leon JHS 200/6-8
12168 US Highway 79 75846 903-626-1450
J.D. Foley, prin. Fax 626-1455

Joaquin, Shelby, Pop. 818
Joaquin ISD 800/PK-12
11109 US Highway 84 E 75954 936-269-3128
Phil Worsham, supt. Fax 269-3615
www.joaquinisd.net/
Joaquin HS 200/9-12
11109 US Highway 84 E 75954 936-269-3128
James Jackson, prin. Fax 269-9123
Joaquin JHS 200/6-8
11109 US Highway 84 E 75954 936-269-3128
Terri Gray, prin. Fax 269-9123

Johnson City, Blanco, Pop. 1,640
Johnson City ISD 700/K-12
PO Box 498 78636 830-868-7410
David Shanley, supt. Fax 868-7375
johnsoncity.tx.schoolwebpages.com/
Johnson HS 200/9-12
PO Box 498 78636 830-868-4025
Julie Storer, prin. Fax 868-9244
Johnson MS 200/5-8
PO Box 498 78636 830-868-9025
Cammie Ockman, prin. Fax 868-7375

Jonesboro, Coryell
Jonesboro ISD 100/PK-12
PO Box 125 76538 254-463-2111
Matt Dossey, supt. Fax 463-4457
jonesboroisd.net
Jonesboro S 100/PK-12
PO Box 125 76538 254-463-2111
Matt Dossey, admin. Fax 463-4457

Joshua, Johnson, Pop. 5,826
Joshua ISD 5,400/PK-12
PO Box 40 76058 817-202-2500
Fran Marek, supt. Fax 641-2738
www.joshuaisd.org
Joshua HS Ninth Grade Campus 900/9-9
1035 S Broadway St 76058 817-202-2500
Ken Bodine, prin. Fax 556-4640
Joshua SHS 900/10-12
909 S Broadway St 76058 817-202-2500
Mick Cochran, prin. Fax 556-3404
Loflin MS 700/7-8
6801 FM 1902 76058 817-202-2500
Damon Patterson, prin. Fax 202-9140
New Horizon HS 100/Alt
603 Plum St 76058 817-202-2500
Ken Bodine, prin. Fax 202-8948

Joshua Christian Academy 100/PK-12
PO Box 1379 76058 817-295-7377
Mary Zornes, admin. Fax 484-2415

Jourdanton, Atascosa, Pop. 3,848
Jourdanton ISD 1,300/PK-12
200 Zanderson Ave 78026 830-769-3548
Dr. Lana Collavo, supt. Fax 769-3272
www.jourdantonisd.net/
Jourdanton HS 300/9-12
200 Zanderson Ave 78026 830-769-2350
Keith Chapman, prin. Fax 769-3065
Jourdanton JHS 300/6-8
200 Zanderson Ave 78026 830-769-2234
Robert Rutkowski, prin. Fax 769-2998

Junction, Kimble, Pop. 2,554
Junction ISD 700/PK-12
1700 College St 76849 325-446-3510
Renee Schulze, supt. Fax 446-4413
www.junctionisd.net
Junction HS 200/9-12
1700 College St 76849 325-446-3326
Melissa Hogett, prin. Fax 446-8206
Junction MS 100/6-8
1700 College St 76849 325-446-2464
Josh Limmer, prin. Fax 446-2255

Justin, Denton, Pop. 3,207
Northwest ISD 14,500/PK-12
2001 Texan Dr 76247 817-215-0000
Dr. Karen Rue, supt. Fax 215-0170
www.nisdtx.org
Northwest HS 2,500/9-12
2301 Texan Dr 76247 817-215-0200
Rose Brenner, prin. Fax 215-0262
Pike MS 1,000/6-8
2200 Texan Dr 76247 817-215-0400
Conrad Streeter, prin. Fax 215-0425
Other Schools – See Haslet, Rhome, Roanoke, Trophy Club

Karnack, Harrison
Karnack ISD 200/PK-12
PO Box 259 75661 903-679-3117
Cozzetta Robinson, supt. Fax 679-4252
karnackisd.org/
Karnack JSHS 100/7-12
PO Box 259 75661 903-679-3113
Tony Thomas, prin. Fax 679-4264

Karnes City, Karnes, Pop. 3,027
Karnes City ISD 1,000/PK-12
314 N Highway 123 78118 830-780-2321
Jeanette Winn, supt. Fax 780-3823
www.kcisd.net
Karnes City HS 300/9-12
400 N Highway 123 78118 830-780-2321
Tom Warlick, prin. Fax 780-4352
Karnes City JHS 200/6-8
410 N Highway 123 78118 830-780-2321
Vanessa Pawelek, prin. Fax 780-4382

Katy, Harris, Pop. 13,902
Cypress-Fairbanks ISD
Supt. — See Houston
Alternative Learning Center - W Alt
19350 Rebel Yell Dr 77449 281-855-4310
Stacie Wicke, prin. Fax 855-4307
Cypress Lakes HS 3,200/9-12
5750 Greenhouse Rd 77449 281-856-3800
Sarah Harty, prin. Fax 856-3808
Thornton MS 1,300/6-8
19802 Kieth Harrow Blvd 77449 281-856-1500
Laura Perry, prin. Fax 856-1548

Katy ISD 59,700/PK-12
PO Box 159 77492 281-396-6000
Alton Frailey, supt. Fax 644-1800
www.katyisd.org/
Beckendorff JHS 1,500/6-8
8200 S Fry Rd 77494 281-237-8800
Mindy Dickerson, prin. Fax 644-1635
Beck JHS 1,200/6-8
5200 S Fry Rd 77450 281-237-3300
Jeffrey Stocks, prin. Fax 644-1630
Cardiff JHS 1,100/6-8
3900 Dayflower Dr 77449 281-234-0600
Richard Hull, prin. Fax 644-1855
Cinco Ranch HS 3,000/9-12
23440 Cinco Ranch Blvd 77494 281-237-7000
James Cross, prin. Fax 644-1734
Cinco Ranch JHS 1,100/6-8
23420 Cinco Ranch Blvd 77494 281-237-7300
Elizabeth Kuylen, prin. Fax 644-1640
Katy HS 2,700/9-12
6331 Highway Blvd 77494 281-237-6700
Dr. Steve Robertson, prin. Fax 644-1700
Katy JHS 1,200/6-8
5350 Franz Rd 77493 281-237-6800
Dr. Jake Leblanc, prin. Fax 644-1645
McDonald JHS 900/6-8
3635 Lakes of Bridgewater 77449 281-237-5300
Kenneth Cummings, prin. Fax 644-1655
McMeans JHS 1,200/6-8
21000 Westheimer Pkwy 77450 281-237-8000
Dr. Susan Rice, prin. Fax 644-1660
Memorial Parkway JHS 900/6-8
21203 Highland Knolls Dr 77450 281-237-5800
Dr. Joe Graham, prin. Fax 644-1665
Miller Career and Technology Ctr Vo/Tech
1734 Katyland Dr 77493 281-237-6300
Dr. Anna Webb-Storey, prin. Fax 644-1775
Morton Ranch HS 3,100/9-12
21000 Franz Rd 77449 281-237-7800
Mark Grisdale, prin. Fax 644-1746
Morton Ranch JHS 1,300/6-8
2498 N Mason Rd 77449 281-237-7400
Mark McCord, prin. Fax 644-1670
Raines HS 50/Alt
1732 Katyland Dr 77493 281-237-1500
Becky Bracewell-Tucker, prin. Fax 644-1781
Seven Lakes HS 3,400/9-12
9251 S Fry Rd 77494 281-237-2800
Ted Vierling, prin. Fax 644-1785
Taylor HS 2,700/9-12
20700 Kingsland Blvd 77450 281-237-3100
David Kendler, prin. Fax 644-1760
West Memorial JHS 800/6-8
22311 Provincial Blvd 77450 281-237-6400
Marcus Forney, prin. Fax 644-1675
WoodCreek JHS 1,500/6-8
1801 WoodCreek Bend Ln 77494 281-234-0800
Kerri Finnesand, prin. Fax 644-1860
Other Schools – See Houston

Faith West Academy 600/PK-12
2225 Porter Rd 77493 281-391-5683
Rev. Kirk Rightmire, dir. Fax 391-2606
Pope John XXIII HS 300/9-12
1800 W Grand Pkwy 77449 281-693-1000
Tim Peterson, prin. Fax 693-1001

Kaufman, Kaufman, Pop. 6,619
Kaufman ISD 3,800/PK-12
1000 S Houston St 75142 972-932-2622
Todd Williams, supt. Fax 932-3325
www.kaufmanisd.net
Alternative Learning Center 100/Alt
4814 County Road 151 75142 972-932-8789
Gary Campbell, prin. Fax 932-2278
Kaufman HS 1,000/9-12
3205 S Houston St 75142 972-932-2811
Kenny Campbell, prin. Fax 932-1948
Norman JHS 600/7-8
3701 S Houston St 75142 972-932-2410
Jeri Ann Campbell, prin. Fax 932-7771

Trinity Valley Community College Post-Sec.
800 Ed Hall Dr 75142 972-932-4309

Keene, Johnson, Pop. 5,659
Keene ISD 800/PK-12
PO Box 656 76059 817-774-5200
Wanda Smith, supt. Fax 774-5400
www.keeneisd.org/
Keene Alternative Learning Center 50/Alt
PO Box 656 76059 817-774-5370
Stan Rhone, prin. Fax 774-5405
Keene JHS 200/6-8
PO Box 656 76059 817-774-5270
Billie Hopps, prin. Fax 774-5402
Keene-Smith HS 200/9-12
PO Box 656 76059 817-774-5220
Sandra Denning, prin. Fax 774-5401

Chisholm Trail Academy 200/9-12
PO Box 717 76059 817-641-6626
Tommy Simons M.Ed., prin. Fax 556-2009
Southwestern Adventist University Post-Sec.
PO Box 567 76059 817-645-3921

Keller, Tarrant, Pop. 38,916
Keller ISD 32,700/PK-12
350 Keller Pkwy 76248 817-744-1000
Randy Reid, supt. Fax 744-1263
www.kellerisd.net
Indian Springs MS 900/7-8
305 Bursey Rd 76248 817-744-3200
Sandy Troudt, prin. Fax 744-3238
Keller HS 2,800/9-12
601 Pate Orr Rd N 76248 817-744-1400
Jeff Bradley, prin. Fax 337-1438
Keller Learning Center 100/Alt
250 College Ave 76248 817-744-4465
Kenneth Anderson, prin. Fax 744-4464
Keller MS 800/7-8
300 College Ave 76248 817-744-2900
Sandra Chapa, prin. Fax 744-2938
Other Schools – See Fort Worth

Toni & Guy Hairdressing Academy Post-Sec.
1185 S Main St 76248 817-697-3037

Kemp, Kaufman, Pop. 1,139
Kemp ISD 1,300/PK-12
905 S Main St 75143 903-498-1314
Dr. Peter Running, supt. Fax 498-1315
kemp.ednet10.net
Kemp HS 500/9-12
220 State Highway 274 75143 903-498-9222
Marietta Maxwell, prin. Fax 498-9275
Kemp JHS 200/6-8
1000 Tolosa Rd 75143 903-498-1343
Michael Taylor, prin. Fax 498-1359

Kenedy, Karnes, Pop. 3,282
Kenedy ISD 700/PK-12
401 FM 719 78119 830-583-4100
Brad Lane, supt. Fax 583-9950
www.kenedy.isd.tenet.edu
Karnes County Academy 50/Alt
401 FM 719 78119 830-583-4100
Randy Tiemann, prin. Fax 583-9126
Kenedy HS 200/9-12
401 FM 719 78119 830-583-4100
Randy Tiemann, prin. Fax 583-9126
Kenedy MS 100/6-8
401 FM 719 78119 830-583-4100
Timothy Richter, prin. Fax 583-9519

Kennard, Houston, Pop. 331
Kennard ISD 300/PK-12
304 State Highway 7 E 75847 936-655-2121
David Baxter, supt. Fax 655-2327
www.kennardisd.net/
Kennard JSHS 100/7-12
304 State Highway 7 E 75847 936-655-2121
Jason Crow, prin. Fax 655-2327

Kennedale, Tarrant, Pop. 6,631
Kennedale ISD 3,200/PK-12
PO Box 467 76060 817-563-8000
Gary Dugger, supt. Fax 483-3610
www.kennedale.net
Kennedale HS 1,000/9-12
PO Box 1208 76060 817-563-8100
Rita Whatley, prin. Fax 563-3718
Kennedale JHS 500/7-8
PO Box 489 76060 817-563-8200
Sherri Kottwitz, prin. Fax 483-3655

Fellowship Academy 300/PK-12
PO Box 738 76060 817-483-2400
Monica Collier, admin. Fax 483-2404

Kerens, Navarro, Pop. 1,548
Kerens ISD 600/PK-12
PO Box 310 75144 903-396-2924
Kevin Stanford, supt. Fax 396-2334
www.kerens.k12.tx.us/
Kerens S 600/PK-12
PO Box 310 75144 903-396-2931
Monte Thacker, admin. Fax 396-2334

Kermit, Winkler, Pop. 5,630
Kermit ISD 1,200/PK-12
601 S Poplar St 79745 432-586-1000
Bill Boyd, supt. Fax 586-1016
www.kisd.esc18.net/
Kermit HS 300/9-12
601 S Poplar St 79745 432-586-1050
Jim Fish, prin. Fax 586-1055
Kermit JHS 300/6-8
601 S Poplar St 79745 432-586-1040
Rocky Ford, prin. Fax 586-1045

Kerrville, Kerr, Pop. 22,087
Kerrville ISD 4,600/PK-12
1009 Barnett St 78028 830-257-2200
Dan Troxell Ph.D., supt. Fax 257-2249
www.kerrvilleisd.net
Hill Country HS 50/Alt
1200 Sidney Baker St 78028 830-257-2232
Steve Schwartz, prin. Fax 792-5020
Peterson MS 700/7-8
1607 Sidney Baker St 78028 830-257-2204
Donna Jenschke, prin. Fax 257-1300
Tivy HS 1,300/9-12
3250 Loop 534 78028 830-257-2212
Robert Templeton, prin. Fax 895-3575

Conlee's College of Cosmetology Post-Sec.
320 W Water St Ste E 78028 830-896-2380
Our Lady of the Hills Catholic HS 100/9-12
235 Peterson Farm Rd 78028 830-895-0501
Therese Schwarz, prin. Fax 895-3470
Schreiner University Post-Sec.
2100 Memorial Blvd 78028 830-896-5411

Kilgore, Gregg, Pop. 12,762
Kilgore ISD 3,900/PK-12
301 N Kilgore St 75662 903-988-3900
Dennis Williams, supt. Fax 983-3212
www.kisd.org/
Elder Cooperative Alternative S 50/Alt
301 N Kilgore St 75662 903-903-3901
Karla Hicks, coord.
Kilgore HS 1,000/9-12
301 N Kilgore St 75662 903-988-3901
Greg Brown, prin. Fax 984-0571
Laird MS, 301 N Kilgore St 75662 800/6-8
April Cox, prin. 903-988-3902

Kilgore College Post-Sec.
1100 Broadway Blvd 75662 903-984-8531

Killeen, Bell, Pop. 120,349
Killeen ISD 38,800/PK-12
PO Box 967 76540 254-336-0006
Dr. Robert Muller, supt. Fax 526-3103
www.killeenisd.org
Ellison HS 2,400/9-12
909 E Elms Rd 76542 254-336-0600
David Dominguez, prin. Fax 520-1919
Gateway Complex 100/Alt
4100 Zephyr Rd 76543 254-336-1700
Christopher Halpayne, prin. Fax 336-1711
Killeen HS 1,900/9-12
500 N 38th St 76543 254-336-7204
Michael Sibberson, prin. Fax 680-2424
KISD Career Center Vo/Tech
1320 Stagecoach Rd 76542 254-336-0563
Marvin Rainwater, dir. Fax 519-7737
Liberty Hill MS 900/6-8
4500 Kit Carson Trl 76542 254-336-1370
Kurt Hulett, prin. Fax 953-4367
Live Oak Ridge MS 800/6-8
2600 Robinett Rd 76549 254-336-2490
Brenda Adams, prin. Fax 554-2170
Manor MS 700/6-8
1700 S W S Young Dr 76543 254-336-1310
Joseph Welch, prin. Fax 680-7029
Nolan MS 700/6-8
505 E Jasper Dr 76541 254-336-1150
Lolly Garcia, prin. Fax 519-5598
Palo Alto MS 900/6-8
2301 W Elms Rd 76549 254-336-1200
Matt Widacki, prin. Fax 519-5577
Patterson MS 700/6-8
8383 W Trimmier Rd 76542 254-336-7100
Jill Balzer, prin. Fax 526-3364
Rancier MS 700/6-8
3301 Hilliard Ave 76543 254-336-1250
Amanda Silkett, prin. Fax 680-6601
Shoemaker HS 2,200/9-12
3302 S Clear Creek Rd 76549 254-336-0900
Ron Gray, prin. Fax 336-2416

Other Schools – See Fort Hood, Harker Heights

Central Texas College Post-Sec.
PO Box 1800 76540 254-526-7161
Memorial Christian Academy 300/PK-12
PO Box 11269 76547 254-526-5403
Doyle Banks, admin. Fax 634-2030
Texas A&M University Central Texas Post-Sec.
1001 Leadership Pl 76549 254-519-5400

Kingsville, Kleberg, Pop. 25,996
Kingsville ISD 3,900/PK-12
PO Box 871 78364 361-592-3387
Edward Blaha, supt. Fax 595-7805
www.kingsvilleisd.com
King HS 1,000/9-12
PO Box 871 78364 361-592-6401
Juan Sandoval Ed.D., prin. Fax 595-9170
Memorial MS 500/7-8
PO Box 871 78364 361-595-5771
Delores Hernandez, prin. Fax 592-4198
Pogue Options Alternative Academy 9-12
PO Box 871 78364 361-595-9137
Ismael Maldonado, prin.

Ricardo ISD 700/PK-8
138 W County Road 2160 78363 361-592-6465
Dr. Maria Canales, supt. Fax 592-3101
www.ricardoisd.us
Ricardo MS 300/5-8
138 W County Road 2160 78363 361-592-6465
Cynthia Flores, prin. Fax 593-0707

Santa Gertrudis ISD 400/PK-12
PO Box 592 78364 361-592-3937
Mary Springs, supt. Fax 592-3128
www.sgisd.net
Santa Gertrudis Academy 200/9-12
PO Box 592 78364 361-592-0058
Les Dragon, prin. Fax 592-5335

Presbyterian Pan American S 200/9-12
PO Box 1578 78364 361-592-4307
Ellie Perez, prin. Fax 592-6126
Texas A&M University Kingsville Post-Sec.
700 University Blvd 78363 361-593-2111

Kingwood, Harris, Pop. 37,397
Humble ISD
Supt. — See Humble
Creekwood MS 900/6-8
3603 W Lake Houston Pkwy 77339 281-641-4400
Walt Winicki, prin. Fax 641-4417
Kingwood HS 2,700/9-12
2701 Kingwood Dr 77339 281-641-6900
Melissa Hayhurst, prin. Fax 641-7217
Kingwood MS 1,000/6-8
2407 Pine Terrace Dr 77339 281-641-4200
Bob Atteberry, prin. Fax 641-4217
Kingwood Park HS 1,600/9-12
4015 Woodland Hills Dr 77339 281-641-6600
Lisa Drabing, prin. Fax 641-6617
Riverwood MS 1,100/6-8
2910 High Valley Dr 77345 281-641-4800
Greg Joseph, prin. Fax 641-4817

Lone Star College - Kingwood Post-Sec.
20000 Kingwood Dr 77339 281-312-1600
Northeast Christian Academy 300/PK-12
1711 Hamblen Rd 77339 281-359-1090
Brad Baggett, head sch Fax 359-5560

Kirbyville, Jasper, Pop. 2,112
Kirbyville Consolidated ISD 1,500/PK-12
206 E Main St 75956 409-423-2284
Richard Hazlewood, supt. Fax 423-2367
www.kirbyvillecisd.org/
Kirbyville HS 400/9-12
100 E Wildcat Dr 75956 409-423-7500
Mike Brewster, prin. Fax 423-5313
Kirbyville JHS 200/7-8
2200 S Margaret Ave 75956 409-420-0692
Thomas Adams, prin. Fax 423-6654

Klein, Harris, Pop. 12,000
Klein ISD 45,100/PK-12
7200 Spring Cypress Rd 77379 832-249-4000
Dr. Jim Cain, supt. Fax 249-4015
www.kleinisd.net
Doerre IS 1,200/6-8
18218 Theiss Mail Route Rd 77379 832-249-5700
Cecilia Saccomanno, prin. Fax 249-4054
Kleb IS 1,300/6-8
7425 Louetta Rd 77379 832-249-5500
Pam Bourgeois, prin. Fax 249-4053
Klein Annex - Alternative Education Alt
7302 Kleingreen Ln 77379 832-249-4800
Kim Kaufman, dir. Fax 249-4045
Klein HS 3,000/9-12
16715 Stuebner Airline Rd 77379 832-484-4000
Larry Whitehead, prin. Fax 484-7821
Krimmel IS 1,000/6-8
7070 FM 2920 Rd 77379 832-375-7200
Scott Crowe, prin. Fax 375-7150
Strack IS 1,100/6-8
18027 Kuykendahl Rd Ste S 77379 832-249-5400
Steve Owen, prin. Fax 249-4051
Other Schools – See Houston, Spring

Knippa, Uvalde, Pop. 688
Knippa ISD 300/PK-12
PO Box 99 78870 830-934-2176
Jeff Cottrill, supt. Fax 934-2490
www.knippaisd.net
Knippa S 300/PK-12
PO Box 99 78870 830-934-2177
Jeff Cottrill, prin. Fax 934-2490

Knox City, Knox, Pop. 1,121
Knox City-O'Brien Consolidated ISD 300/PK-12
606 E Main St 79529 940-657-3521
Louis Baty, supt. Fax 657-3379
www.esc9.net/knoxcity/
Knox City HS 100/9-12
606 E Main St 79529 940-657-3565
Rick Moeller, prin. Fax 657-3379
Other Schools – See O Brien

Kopperl, Bosque
Kopperl ISD 300/PK-12
PO Box 67 76652 254-889-3502
Kenneth Bateman, supt. Fax 889-3443
www.kopperlisd.org
Kopperl S 300/PK-12
PO Box 67 76652 254-889-3502
Katrina Adcock, prin. Fax 889-3443

Kountze, Hardin, Pop. 2,103
Kountze ISD 1,400/PK-12
PO Box 460 77625 409-246-3352
Reese Briggs, supt. Fax 246-3217
kountzeisd.org
Kountze HS 400/9-12
PO Box 460 77625 409-246-3474
Craig Ruby, prin. Fax 246-8180
Kountze MS 200/7-8
PO Box 460 77625 409-246-3551
John Ferguson, prin. Fax 246-8907

Kress, Swisher, Pop. 707
Kress ISD 200/PK-12
200 E 5th St 79052 806-684-2652
Doug Setliff, supt. Fax 684-2687
www.kressonline.net
Kress JSHS 100/7-12
200 E 5th St 79052 806-684-2651
Leah Zeigler, prin. Fax 684-2687

Krum, Denton, Pop. 4,096
Krum ISD 1,700/PK-12
1200 Bobcat Blvd 76249 940-482-6000
Mike Davis, supt. Fax 482-3929
www.krumisd.net
Krum HS 400/9-12
1200 Bobcat Blvd 76249 940-482-2601
Jeremy Harpole, prin. Fax 482-2997
Krum MS 400/6-8
1200 Bobcat Blvd 76249 940-482-2602
Michelle Pieniazek, prin. Fax 482-6299

Kyle, Hays, Pop. 27,512
Hays Consolidated ISD 14,700/PK-12
21003 Interstate 35 78640 512-268-2141
Dr. Jeremy Lyon, supt. Fax 268-2147
www.hayscisd.net
Chapa MS 600/6-8
3311 Dacy Ln 78640 512-268-8500
Lisa Walls, prin. Fax 295-7824
Lehman HS 1,900/9-12
1700 Lehman Rd 78640 512-268-8454
Michelle Chae, prin. Fax 268-2146
Simon MS 500/6-8
3839 E FM 150 78640 512-268-8507
Matthew Pope, prin. Fax 268-4146
Wallace MS 800/6-8
1500 W Center St 78640 512-268-2891
Brenda Agnew, prin. Fax 268-1853
Other Schools – See Buda

Ladonia, Fannin, Pop. 606
Fannindel ISD 200/PK-12
601 W Main St 75449 903-367-7251
H.L. Milton, supt. Fax 367-7252
fannindel.esc8.net/
Fannindel HS 100/6-12
601 W Main St 75449 903-367-7251
Robert Milton, prin. Fax 367-7252

La Feria, Cameron, Pop. 7,287
La Feria ISD 3,600/PK-12
PO Box 1159 78559 956-797-8300
Nabor Cortez, supt. Fax 797-3737
www.laferiaisd.org/
Green JHS 500/7-8
PO Box 1159 78559 956-797-8400
Michael Torres, prin. Fax 797-2157
La Feria Academy 100/Alt
PO Box 1159 78559 956-797-8360
Carlos Verduzco, prin. Fax 797-1583
La Feria HS 900/9-12
PO Box 1159 78559 956-797-8370
Robert Munoz, prin. Fax 797-9374

Lago Vista, Travis, Pop. 5,961
Lago Vista ISD 1,300/PK-12
PO Box 4929 78645 512-267-8300
Matt Underwood, supt. Fax 267-8304
www.lagovistaisd.net
Lago Vista HS 400/9-12
PO Box 4929 78645 512-267-8300
Donna Larkin, prin. Fax 267-8330
Lago Vista MS 300/6-8
PO Box 4929 78645 512-267-8300
Paul Thailing, prin. Fax 267-8329

La Grange, Fayette, Pop. 4,573
La Grange ISD 1,900/PK-12
PO Box 100 78945 979-968-7000
Dr. Randy Albers, supt. Fax 968-8155
www.lgisd.net/
La Grange HS 600/9-12
PO Box 100 78945 979-968-4800
William Wagner, prin. Fax 968-6744
La Grange MS 300/7-8
PO Box 100 78945 979-968-4747
Cliff Kinder, prin. Fax 968-6419

La Joya, Hidalgo, Pop. 3,984
La Joya ISD 28,800/PK-12
201 E Expressway 83 78560 956-580-5000
Dr. Alda Benavides, supt. Fax 580-5444
www.lajoyaisd.net/
Carter Early College HS 9-12
603 N Coyote Dr 78560 956-584-4842
Sylvia Sepulveda, prin. Fax 584-4843
De Zavala MS 700/6-8
603 Tabasco Rd 78560 956-580-5472
Magda Villarreal, prin. Fax 580-5494
HOPE Academy 100/Alt
221 N Stadium Dr 78560 956-580-5962
Lindolfo Zamora, prin. Fax 580-5968
La Joya HS 2,500/9-12
604 N Coyote Dr 78560 956-580-5100
Rolando Rios, prin. Fax 580-5103
LaJoya ISD West Academy 200/Alt
101 E Expressway 83 78560 956-580-6120
Antonio Cano, prin. Fax 580-6126
Other Schools – See Mission, Palmview, Penitas

Lake Dallas, Denton, Pop. 6,973
Lake Dallas ISD 4,100/PK-12
PO Box 548 75065 940-497-4039
Gayle Stinson, supt. Fax 497-3737
www.ldisd.net
Lake Dallas MS 1,000/6-8
PO Box 548 75065 940-497-4037
Jim Parker, prin. Fax 497-8431
Other Schools – See Corinth

Lake Jackson, Brazoria, Pop. 26,471
Brazosport ISD
Supt. — See Clute
Lake Jackson IS 900/7-8
100 Oyster Creek Dr 77566 979-730-7250
Brent Jaco, prin. Fax 292-2804

Brazosport Christian S 300/PK-12
200 Willow Dr Ste B 77566 979-297-0563
Stephen Meier, hdmstr. Fax 297-8455
Brazosport College Post-Sec.
500 College Dr 77566 979-230-3000

Lake Worth, Tarrant, Pop. 4,497
Lake Worth ISD 3,200/PK-12
6805 Telephone Rd 76135 817-306-4200
Dr. Janice Cooper, supt. Fax 237-5284
www.lwisd.org/
Lake Worth HS 700/9-12
4210 Boat Club Rd 76135 817-306-4200
Mike Ellis, prin. Fax 237-0697
Other Schools – See Fort Worth

La Marque, Galveston, Pop. 14,302
La Marque ISD 2,700/PK-12
PO Box 7 77568 409-938-4251
Ecomet Burley, supt. Fax 908-5012
www.lmisd.net
La Marque HS 700/9-12
PO Box 7 77568 409-938-4261
Morris Gurnell, prin. Fax 908-5036
La Marque MS 400/7-8
PO Box 7 77568 409-938-4286
Kellie Edmundson, prin. Fax 908-5071

Lamesa, Dawson, Pop. 9,364
Klondike ISD 200/PK-12
2911 County Road H 79331 806-462-7334
Steve McLaren, supt. Fax 462-7333
klondike.esc17.net
Klondike S 200/PK-12
2911 County Road H 79331 806-462-7332
Tony Bushong, prin. Fax 462-7333

Lamesa ISD 1,900/PK-12
PO Box 261 79331 806-872-5461
John Ramos, supt. Fax 872-6220
www.lamesa.esc17.net
Lamesa HS 400/9-12
PO Box 261 79331 806-872-8385
David Vasquez, prin. Fax 872-6608
Lamesa MS 400/6-8
PO Box 261 79331 806-872-8301
David Rodriguez, prin. Fax 872-2949
Lamesa Success Academy 50/Alt
PO Box 261 79331 806-872-5410
Rod Mayberry, admin. Fax 872-6220

Howard College Post-Sec.
1810 Lubbock Hwy 79331 806-872-2223

Lampasas, Lampasas, Pop. 6,551
Lampasas ISD 3,400/PK-12
207 W 8th St 76550 512-556-6224
Randall Hoyer Ed.D., supt. Fax 556-8711
www.lampasas.k12.tx.us
Lampasas HS 1,000/9-12
207 W 8th St 76550 512-564-2310
Mark Kehoe, prin. Fax 564-2406
Lampasas MS 800/6-8
207 W 8th St 76550 512-556-3101
Dana Holcomb, prin. Fax 556-0245

Lancaster, Dallas, Pop. 35,843
Lancaster ISD 6,300/PK-12
PO Box 400 75146 972-218-1400
Dr. Michael McFarland, supt. Fax 218-1401
www.lancasterisd.org
Alternative Educational Program Alt
602 E 2nd St 75146 972-218-1441
Stephaney Johnson, prin. Fax 218-1442
Lancaster HS 1,800/9-12
200 E Wintergreen Rd 75134 972-218-1800
Joseph Showell, prin. Fax 218-5797
Lancaster MS 800/7-8
822 W Pleasant Run Rd 75146 972-218-1660
Elijah Granger, prin. Fax 218-3080

Berne Academy 100/K-12
1311 Johns Ave 75134 972-218-7373
Theresa Smith, admin. Fax 218-7372
Cedar Valley College Post-Sec.
3030 N Dallas Ave 75134 972-860-8201

Laneville, Rusk
Laneville ISD 200/PK-12
7415 FM 1798 W 75667 903-863-5353
Dr. Brian Nichols, supt. Fax 863-2736
www.lanevilleisd.org/
Laneville S 200/PK-12
7415 FM 1798 W 75667 903-863-5353
Dr. Major Templeton, prin. Fax 863-2376

La Porte, Harris, Pop. 33,263
La Porte ISD 7,800/PK-12
1002 San Jacinto St 77571 281-604-7000
Lloyd Graham, supt. Fax 604-7010
www.lpisd.org
Dewalt Alternative S 100/Alt
1002 San Jacinto St 77571 281-604-6900
Debbie Stewart, prin. Fax 604-6904
La Porte HS 2,200/9-12
1002 San Jacinto St 77571 281-604-7500
Todd Schoppe, prin. Fax 604-7516
La Porte JHS 600/7-8
1002 San Jacinto St 77571 281-604-6600
Cynthia Anderson, prin. Fax 604-6605
Lomax JHS 600/7-8
1002 San Jacinto St 77571 281-604-6700
Danette Tilley, prin. Fax 604-6730

La Pryor, Zavala, Pop. 1,634
La Pryor ISD 500/PK-12
PO Box 519 78872 830-365-4000
Benny P. Hernandez, supt. Fax 365-4006
www.lapryor.net
La Pryor HS 200/7-12
PO Box 519 78872 830-365-4007
David Rivera, prin. Fax 365-4026

Laredo, Webb, Pop. 235,714
Laredo ISD 24,700/PK-12
1604 Houston St 78040 956-273-1400
Dr. A. Marcus Nelson, supt. Fax 795-3405
www.laredoisd.org/
Cantu Health Science Magnet S 9-12
2002 San Bernardo Ave 78040 956-273-7100
Geraldina Arredondo, dir. Fax 795-3875
Christen MS 1,400/6-8
2001 Santa Maria Ave 78040 956-273-6400
Carlos Cruz, prin. Fax 795-3732
Cigarroa HS 1,500/9-12
2600 Zacatecas St 78046 956-273-6800
Laura Flores, prin. Fax 795-3814
Cigarroa MS 1,200/6-8
2600 Palo Blanco St 78046 956-273-6100
Alberto Ibarra, prin. Fax 718-2208
Lamar MS 1,300/6-8
1818 N Arkansas Ave 78043 956-273-6200
Margarita Taboada, prin. Fax 795-3766
Lara Academy 100/Alt
2901 E Travis St 78043 956-273-7900
Robert Chaney, prin. Fax 726-0350
Magnet S for Engineering & Technology 9-12
2600 Zacatecas St 78046 956-273-6800
Alfredo Perez, prin. Fax 795-3814
Martin HS 1,800/9-12
2002 San Bernardo Ave 78040 956-273-7100
Guillermo Pro, prin. Fax 795-3860
Memorial MS 700/6-8
2002 Marcella Ave 78040 956-273-6600
Lizzy Newsome, prin. Fax 795-3780
Nixon HS 2,000/9-12
2000 E Plum St 78043 956-273-7400
Dr. Gerardo Cruz, prin. Fax 795-3844
Trevino S of Communications & Fine Arts 9-12
820 Main Ave 78040 956-273-7800
Dr. Martha Villarreal, prin. Fax 795-3330

United ISD 40,300/PK-12
201 Lindenwood Dr 78045 956-473-6201
Roberto Santos, supt. Fax 728-8691
www.uisd.net
Alexander HS 2,700/9-12
3600 E Del Mar Blvd 78041 956-473-5800
Dolores Barrera, prin. Fax 473-5999
Alexander Magnet HS 9-12
3600 E Del Mar Blvd 78041 956-473-5866
Elvira Gaona, dean Fax 473-5998
Bruni-Vergar MS 800/6-8
5910 Saint Luke 78046 956-473-6600
Annabel Castillo-Gomez, prin. Fax 473-6699
Clark MS 800/6-8
500 W Hillside Rd 78041 956-473-7500
Rene Rodriguez, prin. Fax 473-7599
Garcia MS 500/6-8
499 Pena Dr 78046 956-473-5000
Cleotilde Gamez, prin. Fax 473-5099
Gonzalez MS 1,000/6-8
5208 Santa Claudia 78043 956-473-7000
Adriana Ramirez, prin. Fax 473-7099
Johnson HS 2,400/9-12
5626 Cielito Lindo 78046 956-473-5100
Margarita Martinez, prin. Fax 473-5281
LBJ Magnet Career Academy 9-12
5626 Cielito Lindo 78046 956-473-5350
Yesenia Sandoval, dean Fax 473-5281
Los Obispos MS 900/6-8
4801 S Ejido Ave 78046 956-473-7800
Armando Salazar, prin. Fax 473-1899
Trautmann MS 1,000/7-8
8501 Curly Ln 78045 956-473-7400
Leticia Turner, prin. Fax 473-7499
United 9th Grade Campus 9-9
8800 McPherson Rd 78045 956-473-2400
Arlene Trevino, dean Fax 473-2499
United HS 2,700/10-12
2811 United Ave 78045 956-473-5600
Alberto Aleman, prin. Fax 473-1980
United Magnet HS 9-12
2811 United Ave 78045 956-473-5627
Angelica Sanchez, dean Fax 473-1981
United MS 1,000/6-8
700 E Del Mar Blvd 78041 956-473-7300
Roberta Ramirez, prin. Fax 473-7399
United S.T.E.P. Academy 100/Alt
5201 Bob Bullock Loop 78041 956-473-6500
Eduardo Garza, dean Fax 473-6599
United South HS 2,700/9-12
4001 Los Presidentes Ave 78046 956-473-5400
David Canales, prin. Fax 473-5599
United South Magnet HS 9-12
4001 Los Presidentes Ave 78046 956-473-5440
Priscilla Munoz, dean Fax 473-5598
United South MS 1,300/6-8
3707 Los Presidentes Ave 78046 956-473-7700
Beth Porter, prin. Fax 473-7799
Washington MS 1,300/6-8
10306 Riverbank Dr 78045 956-473-7600
David Gonzalez, prin. Fax 473-7699

Kaplan College Post-Sec.
6410 McPherson Rd 78041 956-717-5909
Laredo Community College Post-Sec.
1 W End Washington St 78040 956-722-0521
St. Augustine HS 400/9-12
1300 Galveston St 78040 956-724-8131
Olga Gentry, prin. Fax 725-9241
Texas A&M International University Post-Sec.
5201 University Blvd 78041 956-326-2000

LaRue, Henderson
La Poynor ISD 500/PK-12
13155 US Highway 175 E 75770 903-876-4057
Sherry Douglas, supt. Fax 876-4541
www.lapoynorisd.net/
La Poynor HS 100/9-12
13155 US Highway 175 E 75770 903-876-2373
Ken Barrow, prin. Fax 876-2374
La Poynor JHS 100/6-8
13155 US Highway 175 E 75770 903-876-2373
Ken Barrow, prin. Fax 876-2374

Lasara, Willacy, Pop. 1,039
Lasara ISD 500/PK-12
PO Box 57 78561 956-642-3598
Sara Alvarado, supt. Fax 642-3546
www.lasaraisd.net/
Lasara HS 100/9-12
PO Box 57 78561 956-642-3271
Sulema Davila, prin. Fax 642-3546

Latexo, Houston, Pop. 319
Latexo ISD 500/PK-12
PO Box 975 75849 936-544-5664
Don Elsom, supt. Fax 544-5332
www.latexoisd.net
Latexo JSHS 200/7-12
PO Box 975 75849 936-544-5638
Dr. Stacy Easterly, prin. Fax 544-8456

La Vernia, Wilson, Pop. 1,011
La Vernia ISD 3,000/PK-12
13600 US Highway 87 W 78121 830-779-6600
Dr. Tom Harvey, supt. Fax 779-2304
www.lvisd.org
La Vernia HS 900/9-12
225 Bluebonnet Rd 78121 830-779-6630
Cheryl Barron, prin. Fax 779-3218
La Vernia JHS 700/6-8
195 Bluebonnet Rd 78121 830-779-6650
Bill Mikeska, prin. Fax 779-6651

La Villa, Hidalgo, Pop. 1,955
La Villa ISD 600/PK-12
PO Box 9 78562 956-262-4755
Narciso Garcia, supt. Fax 262-7323
www.lavillaisd.org
La Villa Early College HS 200/9-12
PO Box 9 78562 956-262-4715
Maria Farias, prin. Fax 262-9798
La Villa MS 100/6-8
PO Box 9 78562 956-262-4760
Vilma Gomez, prin. Fax 262-5243

Lazbuddie, Parmer
Lazbuddie ISD 100/PK-12
PO Box 9 79053 806-965-2156
Joanna Martinez, supt. Fax 965-2892
www.lazbuddieisd.org
Lazbuddie S 100/PK-12
PO Box 9 79053 806-965-2152
Joanna Martinez, supt. Fax 965-2892

League City, Galveston, Pop. 81,913
Clear Creek ISD 36,600/PK-12
PO Box 799 77574 281-284-0000
Dr. Greg Smith, supt. Fax 284-0005
www.ccisd.net
Bayside IS 6-8
4430 Village Way 77573 281-284-3000
Jamey Majewski, prin. Fax 284-3005
Clear Creek HS 2,100/9-12
2305 E Main St 77573 281-284-1700
Scott Bockart, prin. Fax 284-1705
Clear Creek IS 800/6-8
2451 E Main St 77573 281-284-2300
Jerry Herd, prin. Fax 284-2305
Clear Falls HS 9-12
4380 Village Way 77573 281-284-1100
Karen Engle, prin. Fax 284-1106
Clear Path Alternative S 200/Alt
400 S Kansas Ave 77573 281-284-1600
Sandra Davenport, prin. Fax 284-1605
Clear Springs HS 2,400/9-12
501 Palomino St 77573 281-284-1300
Gail Love, prin. Fax 284-1305
Creekside IS 900/6-8
4320 W Main St 77573 281-284-3500
Pete Caterina, prin. Fax 284-3505
League City IS 500/6-8
2588 Webster St 77573 281-284-3400
Kimberly Brouillard, prin. Fax 284-3405
Victory Lakes IS 800/6-8
2880 W Walker St 77573 281-284-3700
Paul House, prin. Fax 284-3705
Other Schools – See Friendswood, Houston, Seabrook, Webster

Bay Area Christian S 700/K-12
4800 W Main St 77573 281-332-4814
Jason Nave, head sch Fax 554-5495
Devereux-Texas Treatment Network Post-Sec.
1150 Devereux Dr 77573 800-373-0011

Leakey, Real, Pop. 417
Leakey ISD 300/PK-12
PO Box 1129 78873 830-232-5595
Dr. Barbara Skipper, supt. Fax 232-5535
www.leakeyisd.net
Leakey S 300/PK-12
PO Box 1129 78873 830-232-5595
Kay Keen, prin. Fax 232-5535

Leander, Williamson, Pop. 25,831
Leander ISD 31,500/PK-12
PO Box 218 78646 512-570-0000
Bret Champion Ed.D., supt. Fax 570-0048
www.leanderisd.org
Leander Extended Opportunity Center Alt
300 S West Dr 78641 512-570-2230
Teresa Hatcher, prin. Fax 570-2234
Leander HS 2,200/9-12
3301 S Bagdad Rd 78641 512-570-1000
Brad Mansfield, prin. Fax 570-1005
Leander MS 800/6-8
410 S West Dr 78641 512-570-3200
Christine Simpson, prin. Fax 570-3205
New Hope HS 50/Alt
401 S West Dr 78641 512-570-2200
Harold Seifert, prin. Fax 570-2204
Rouse HS 1,300/9-12
1501 County Road 271 78641 512-570-2000
John Graham, prin. Fax 570-2005
Stiles MS 6-8
3250 Barley Rd 78641 512-570-3800
Susan Cole, prin. Fax 570-3805
Wiley MS 1,200/6-8
1701 County Road 271 78641 512-570-3600
Sylvia Flannery, prin. Fax 570-3605
Other Schools – See Austin, Cedar Park

Fortis Academy K-12
2220 Downing Ln 78641 512-528-5323
Pamela Helgerson, hdmstr.

Lefors, Gray, Pop. 490
Lefors ISD 200/PK-12
PO Box 390 79054 806-835-2533
Bill Morgan, supt. Fax 835-2238
www.region16.net/leforsisd/
Lefors S 200/PK-12
PO Box 390 79054 806-835-2533
Kelley Porter, prin. Fax 835-2238

Leggett, Polk
Leggett ISD 200/PK-12
PO Box 68 77350 936-398-2804
Vicki Jones, supt. Fax 398-2078
www.leggettisd.net/
Leggett JSHS 100/7-12
PO Box 68 77350 936-398-2412
Jana Lowe, prin. Fax 398-0889

Lenorah, Martin
Grady ISD 200/K-12
3500 FM 829 79749 432-459-2444
Leandro Gonzales, supt. Fax 459-2729
grady.tx.schoolwebpages.com
Grady S 200/K-12
3500 FM 829 79749 432-459-2445
Brad Cox, prin. Fax 459-2729

Leonard, Fannin, Pop. 1,933
Leonard ISD 900/PK-12
1 Tiger Aly 75452 903-587-2318
Larry LaFavers, supt. Fax 587-2845
www.leonardisd.net
Leonard HS 300/9-12
1 Tiger Aly 75452 903-587-3556
Brad Connelly, prin. Fax 587-8011
Leonard JHS 200/6-8
1 Tiger Aly 75452 903-587-2315
Brandi Savage, prin. Fax 587-2228

Levelland, Hockley, Pop. 13,427
Levelland ISD 2,000/PK-12
704 11th St 79336 806-894-9628
Kelly Baggett, supt. Fax 894-2583
www.levellandisd.net
Cactus Academic Center Alt
704 11th St 79336 806-894-3323
Primo Lara, prin. Fax 894-2234
Levelland HS 700/9-12
704 11th St 79336 806-894-8515
Gary Bridges, prin. Fax 894-6029
Levelland MS 50/6-8
704 11th St 79336 806-894-6355
John Clanton, prin. Fax 894-8935

South Plains College Post-Sec.
1401 College Ave 79336 806-894-9611

Lewisville, Denton, Pop. 93,105
Lewisville ISD
Supt. — See Flower Mound
Career Center East Vo/Tech
2553 FM 544 75056 469-713-5211
Jeff Wagley, prin. Fax 626-1640
Delay MS 800/6-8
2103 Savage Ln 75057 469-713-5191
Jim Baker, prin. Fax 350-9174
Durham MS 800/6-8
2075 S Edmonds Ln 75067 469-713-5963
Brian McCoo, prin. Fax 350-9182
Hedrick MS 600/6-8
1526 Bellaire Blvd 75067 469-713-5188
Barbara Hamric, prin. Fax 350-9196
Huffines MS 900/6-8
1440 N Valley Pkwy 75077 469-713-5990
Tim Baxter, prin. Fax 350-9199
Jackson Career Center Vo/Tech
1597 S Edmonds Ln 75067 469-713-5186
Randall Holder, prin. Fax 350-9342
Killian MS 700/6-8
2561 FM 544 75056 469-713-5977
Alan Cassel, prin. Fax 350-9200
Lewisville HS 1,500/11-12
1098 W Main St 75067 469-713-5190
Jeffrey Kajs, prin. Fax 350-9291
Lewisville HS Harmon Campus 500/9-10
1250 W Round Grove Rd 75067 469-713-5201
Andy Plunkett, prin. Fax 626-1680
Lewisville HS Killough Campus 900/9-9
1301 Summit Ave 75077 469-713-5987
Pam Flores, prin. Fax 350-9304
Lewisville Learning Center 200/Alt
1601 S Edmonds Ln 75067 469-713-5185
Chantell Upshaw, prin. Fax 350-9350
Night HS Adult
1601 S Edmonds Ln 75067 469-948-7665
Bronson Lewis, admin. Fax 350-9588

Lakeland Christian Academy 500/PK-12
397 S Stemmons Fwy 75067 972-219-3939
Tena Mitchell, dir. Fax 219-9601

Lexington, Lee, Pop. 1,158
Lexington ISD 900/PK-12
8731 N Highway 77 78947 979-773-2254
Dr. Frances McArthur, supt. Fax 773-4455
www.lexington.isd.tenet.edu
Lexington HS 300/9-12
8731 N Highway 77 78947 979-773-2255
Rebecca Otte French, prin. Fax 773-4455
Lexington MS 200/6-8
8731 N Highway 77 78947 979-773-2255
Sarah Garrison, prin. Fax 773-4455

Liberty, Liberty, Pop. 8,274
Liberty ISD 2,100/PK-12
1600 Grand Ave 77575 936-336-7213
Dr. Cody Abshier, supt. Fax 336-2283
www.libertyisd.net
Liberty HS 600/9-12
2615 Jefferson Dr 77575 936-336-6483
Bruce Lacefield, prin. Fax 336-3931
Liberty MS 500/6-8
2515 Jefferson Dr 77575 936-336-3582
Rhonda Smith, prin. Fax 336-1021

Liberty Hill, Williamson, Pop. 951
Liberty Hill ISD 2,700/PK-12
14001 W State Highway 29 78642 512-260-5580
Dr. Rob Hart, supt. Fax 260-5581
www.libertyhill.txed.net
Liberty Hill HS 800/9-12
13125 W State Highway 29 78642 512-260-5500
Bobby Mabry, prin. Fax 260-5510
Liberty Hill JHS 500/7-8
101 Loop 332 78642 512-515-5636
Chad Pirtle, prin. Fax 778-5937

Lindale, Smith, Pop. 4,737
Lindale ISD 3,700/PK-12
PO Box 370 75771 903-881-4000
Stan Surratt, supt. Fax 881-4004
www.lindaleeagles.org
Lindale HS 1,100/9-12
PO Box 370 75771 903-881-4050
Casey Neal, prin. Fax 882-2813
Lindale JHS 500/7-8
PO Box 370 75771 903-881-4150
Vicki Thrasher, prin. Fax 881-4049

Linden, Cass, Pop. 1,960
Linden-Kildare Consolidated ISD 800/PK-12
205 Kildare Rd 75563 903-756-5027
Dr. James B. Cowley, supt. Fax 756-7242
www.lkcisd.net
Linden-Kildare HS 300/9-12
205 Kildare Rd 75563 903-756-7026
Keri Winters, prin. Fax 756-8512
Linden-Kildare JHS 200/6-8
205 Kildare Rd 75563 903-756-5381
Kelly Kinney, prin. Fax 756-8832

Lindsay, Cooke, Pop. 1,000
Lindsay ISD 500/K-12
PO Box 145 76250 940-668-8923
Dennis Holt, supt. Fax 668-2662
www.lindsayisd.org/
Lindsay HS 300/7-12
PO Box 145 76250 940-668-8474
Robert Haynes, prin. Fax 665-1637

Lingleville, Erath
Lingleville ISD 200/PK-12
PO Box 134 76461 254-968-2596
Dennis Hughes, supt. Fax 965-5821
www.lingleville.us
Lingleville S 200/PK-12
PO Box 134 76461 254-968-2596
Curt Haley, prin. Fax 965-5821

Lipan, Hood, Pop. 426
Lipan ISD 200/PK-8
211 N Kickapoo St 76462 254-646-2266
Cindy Edwards, supt. Fax 646-3499
www.lipanindians.net/
Lipan JHS 50/6-8
211 N Kickapoo St 76462 254-646-2266
Mike Permenter, prin. Fax 646-3499

Little Elm, Denton, Pop. 25,208
Little Elm ISD 5,600/PK-12
PO Box 6000 75068 972-292-1847
Lynne Leuthard, supt. Fax 294-1107
www.leisd.ws/
King Learning Academy 400/Alt
101 Main St 75068 972-292-1908
Kristi Hargrove, prin. Fax 292-3368
Lakeside MS 800/6-8
400 Lobo Ln 75068 972-292-3200
Ray Winkler, prin. Fax 292-3009
Little Elm HS 1,600/9-12
1900 Walker Ln 75068 972-292-1840
Shon Joseph, prin. Fax 292-3505

Littlefield, Lamb, Pop. 6,333
Littlefield ISD 1,500/PK-12
1207 E 14th St 79339 806-385-4150
Jerry Blakely, supt. Fax 385-6297
www.littlefield.k12.tx.us
Littlefield HS 400/9-12
1207 E 14th St 79339 806-385-5683
Ricky Hobbs, prin. Fax 385-3603
Littlefield JHS 300/6-8
1207 E 14th St 79339 806-385-3922
Trevor Edgemon, prin. Fax 385-5603

Little River, Bell, Pop. 1,936
Academy ISD 1,100/PK-12
704 E Main St 76554 254-982-4304
Kevin Sprinkles, supt. Fax 982-0023
www.academyisd.net
Academy HS 300/9-12
602 E Main St 76554 254-982-4201
Alex Remschel, prin. Fax 982-4420
Academy JHS 400/5-8
501 E Main St 76554 254-982-4620
Stephen Ash, prin. Fax 982-4776
Bell County Alternative S Alt
706 E Rio Poco 76554 254-982-3505
Terry Day, prin. Fax 982-3506

Live Oak, Bexar, Pop. 12,703
Judson ISD 23,200/PK-12
8012 Shin Oak Dr 78233 210-945-5100
Dr. Willis Mackey, supt. Fax 945-6900
www.judsonisd.org
Judson Early College Academy 9-12
8230 Palisades Dr 78148 210-619-0200
Yvonne Anglada, prin. Fax 659-1990
Other Schools – See Converse, San Antonio, Universal City

Livingston, Polk, Pop. 5,275
Big Sandy ISD
Supt. — See Dallardsville
Big Sandy S 500/PK-12
FM 1276 77351 936-563-1017
Kevin Foster, prin. Fax 563-1010

Livingston ISD 4,000/PK-12
PO Box 1297 77351 936-328-2100
Dr. Darrell Myers, supt. Fax 328-2109
www.livingstonisd.com
Alternative Education Program Alt
300 E Milam St 77351 936-328-2353
Karen Maxey, prin. Fax 328-2352
Livingston HS 1,100/9-12
1 Lions Ave 77351 936-328-2240
Bakewell Barron, prin. Fax 328-2231
Livingston JHS 900/6-8
1801 Highway 59 Loop N 77351 936-328-2120
Michael Woodard, prin. Fax 328-2139

Llano, Llano, Pop. 3,210
Llano ISD 1,900/PK-12
1400 Oatman St 78643 325-247-4747
Dennis Hill, supt. Fax 247-5623
www.llanoisd.org
Llano HS 500/9-12
2509 S State Highway 16 78643 325-248-2200
James Scott, prin. Fax 247-2122
Llano JHS 400/6-8
400 E State Highway 71 E 78643 325-247-4659
Todd Keele, prin. Fax 247-5821

Lockhart, Caldwell, Pop. 12,574
Lockhart ISD 4,700/PK-12
PO Box 120 78644 512-398-0000
Dr. Jose Parra, supt. Fax 398-0025
www.lockhartisd.org
Lockhart HS 900/10-12
1 Lion Country Dr 78644 512-398-0300
Monica Guillory, prin. Fax 398-0302
Lockhart HS Freshman Campus 400/9-9
419 Bois DArc St 78644 512-398-0170
Heather Stull, prin. Fax 398-0226
Lockhart JHS 1,100/6-8
500 City Line Rd 78644 512-398-0770
Laura Gilcrease, prin. Fax 398-0772
Pride HS 50/Alt
1503 N Colorado St 78644 512-398-0130
Sam Lockhart, prin. Fax 398-0132

Lockney, Floyd, Pop. 1,837
Lockney ISD 600/PK-12
PO Box 428 79241 806-652-2115
Phil Cotham, supt. Fax 652-2729
www.lockneyisd.net
Lockney HS 200/9-12
PO Box 1058 79241 806-652-3325
Todd Hallmark, prin. Fax 652-4945
Lockney JHS 100/6-8
PO Box 550 79241 806-652-2236
Craig Setliff, prin. Fax 652-4920

Lohn, McCulloch
Lohn ISD 100/PK-12
PO Box 277 76852 325-344-5749
Leon Freeman, supt. Fax 344-5789
www.lohnisd.net
Lohn S 100/PK-12
PO Box 277 76852 325-344-5749
David Dillard, prin. Fax 344-5790

Lometa, Lampasas, Pop. 834
Lometa ISD 300/PK-12
PO Box 250 76853 512-752-3384
David Rice, supt. Fax 752-8531
www.lometaisd.net
Lometa S 300/PK-12
PO Box 250 76853 512-752-3384
Robby Moore, prin. Fax 752-3424

Lone Oak, Hunt, Pop. 584
Lone Oak ISD 900/PK-12
8162 US Highway 69 S 75453 903-662-5427
Eddie White, supt. Fax 662-5290
www.loisd.net
Lone Oak HS 300/9-12
8204 US Highway 69 S 75453 903-662-0981
Jeff Hicks, prin. Fax 662-0984
Lone Oak MS 200/6-8
8160 US Highway 69 S 75453 903-662-5121
Kim White, prin. Fax 662-5017

Longview, Gregg, Pop. 79,235
Longview ISD 7,700/PK-12
PO Box 3268 75606 903-381-2200
Dr. James Wilcox, supt. Fax 753-5389
www.lisd.org
Forest Park MS 500/6-8
PO Box 3268 75606 903-446-2510
Bill Bradshaw, prin. Fax 446-2501
Foster MS 700/6-8
PO Box 3268 75606 903-446-2710
John York, prin. Fax 758-2052
Judson MS 500/6-8
PO Box 3268 75606 903-446-2610
Brian Kasper, prin. Fax 663-0275
Longview HS 1,900/9-12
PO Box 3268 75606 903-663-1301
James Brewer, prin. Fax 663-7180

Pine Tree ISD 5,000/PK-12
PO Box 5878 75608 903-295-5000
Dr. Teresa Farler, supt. Fax 295-5004
www.ptisd.org
PACE Alternative Discipline Center 300/Alt
PO Box 5878 75608 903-295-5130
Jerrett Turner, prin. Fax 295-5145
Pine Tree JHS 700/7-8
PO Box 5878 75608 903-295-5081
Clay Gillentine, prin. Fax 295-5082
Pine Tree SHS 1,200/9-12
PO Box 5878 75608 903-295-5031
Cindy Gabehart, prin. Fax 295-5029

Spring Hill ISD 1,600/PK-12
3101 Spring Hill Rd 75605 903-759-4404
Wes Jones, supt. Fax 297-0141
www.shisd.net
Spring Hill HS 500/9-12
3101 Spring Hill Rd 75605 903-446-3300
Denny Lind, prin. Fax 323-7766
Spring Hill JHS 300/6-8
3101 Spring Hill Rd 75605 903-323-7718
David Reed, prin. Fax 323-7765

Christian Heritage S 200/K-12
2715 FM 1844 75605 903-663-4151
Jim McCormick, prin. Fax 663-4587
East Texas Christian S 200/PK-12
PO Box 8053 75607 903-757-7891
Chandra Watson, admin. Fax 619-0349
Le Tourneau University Post-Sec.
PO Box 7001 75607 903-233-3000
Longview Christian S 100/K-12
1236 Pegues Pl 75601 903-297-3501
Karen Williams, prin. Fax 759-4415
St. Mary's Catholic S 200/PK-12
405 Hollybrook Dr 75605 903-753-1657
Amy Allen, prin. Fax 758-7347
Trinity S of Texas 300/PK-12
215 N Teague St 75601 903-753-0612
Gary Whitwell, head sch Fax 753-4812
Vista College Post-Sec.
1905 W Loop 281 Ste 21 75604 866-442-4197

Loop, Gaines, Pop. 223
Loop ISD 100/PK-12
PO Box 917 79342 806-487-6412
Brock Cartwright, supt. Fax 487-6420
www.loopisd.net/
Loop S 100/PK-12
PO Box 917 79342 806-487-6411
Bryan Ritchey, prin. Fax 487-6416

Loraine, Mitchell, Pop. 595
Loraine ISD 200/PK-12
PO Box 457 79532 325-737-2235
Travis Edwards, supt. Fax 737-2019
www.loraine.esc14.net

Loraine S 200/PK-12
PO Box 457 79532 325-737-2225
Reida Penman, prin. Fax 737-2019

Lorena, McLennan, Pop. 1,682
Lorena ISD 1,600/PK-12
PO Box 97 76655 254-857-3239
Dr. Sandra Talbert, supt. Fax 857-4533
www.lorenaisd.net
Lorena HS 500/9-12
PO Box 97 76655 254-857-4604
Rusty Grimm, prin. Fax 857-3883
Lorena MS 500/5-8
PO Box 97 76655 254-857-4621
Dr. Celia Drews, prin. Fax 857-3419

Lorenzo, Crosby, Pop. 1,134
Lorenzo ISD 300/PK-12
PO Box 520 79343 806-634-5591
Dr. Jerrod Pickering, supt. Fax 634-5928
www.lorenzoisd.net/
Lorenzo JSHS 100/7-12
PO Box 520 79343 806-634-5592
Derek Hollingsworth, prin. Fax 634-5788

Los Fresnos, Cameron, Pop. 5,528
Los Fresnos Consolidated ISD 9,800/PK-12
PO Box 309 78566 956-254-5010
Gonzalo Salazar, supt. Fax 233-4031
www.lfcisd.net
Liberty Memorial MS 700/6-8
PO Box 309 78566 956-233-3900
Glafira Braga, prin. Fax 233-1074
Los Cuates MS 600/6-8
PO Box 309 78566 956-254-5182
Alma Atkinson, prin. Fax 233-6265
Los Fresnos HS 1,800/10-12
PO Box 309 78566 956-254-5300
Ronnie Rodriguez, prin. Fax 233-3570
Reseca MS 900/6-8
PO Box 309 78566 956-254-5159
Asael Ruvalcaba, prin. Fax 233-6209
Other Schools – See San Benito

Lott, Falls, Pop. 750
Rosebud-Lott ISD 800/PK-12
1789 US Highway 77 76656 254-583-4510
Anthony Price, supt. Fax 583-4469
www.rlisd.org/
Rosebud-Lott HS 200/9-12
1789 US Highway 77 76656 254-583-7967
Steve Coston, prin. Fax 583-1130
Rosebud-Lott MS 200/6-8
1789 US Highway 77 76656 254-583-7692
Todd Williams, prin. Fax 583-2904
Other Schools – See Rosebud

Louise, Wharton, Pop. 991
Louise ISD 500/PK-12
PO Box 97 77455 979-648-2982
Dr. Michael Seabolt, supt. Fax 648-2520
www.louiseisd.org
Louise HS 200/9-12
PO Box 97 77455 979-648-2202
Donna Kutac, prin. Fax 648-2142
Louise JHS 100/6-8
PO Box 97 77455 979-648-2262
Donna Kutac, prin. Fax 648-2520

Lovelady, Houston, Pop. 635
Lovelady ISD 500/PK-12
PO Box 99 75851 936-636-7616
Dr. Micah Dyer, supt. Fax 636-2212
www.loveladyisd.net
Lovelady JSHS 200/7-12
PO Box 280 75851 936-636-7636
Richard Cooper, prin. Fax 636-2305

Lubbock, Lubbock, Pop. 226,600
Frenship ISD
Supt. — See Wolfforth
Heritage MS 700/6-8
6110 73rd St 79424 806-794-9400
Greg Hernandez, prin. Fax 793-8956
Reese Education Center 100/Alt
9421 4th St 79416 806-885-4910
Farley Reeves, prin. Fax 885-2442
Terra Vista MS 800/6-8
1111 Upland Ave 79416 806-796-0076
Brent Lowrey, prin. Fax 796-1540

Lubbock ISD 26,600/K-12
1628 19th St 79401 806-766-1000
Dr. Karen Garza, supt. Fax 766-1210
www.lubbockisd.org
Atkins MS 500/6-8
5401 Avenue U 79412 806-766-1522
Chris Huber, prin. Fax 766-2226
Cavazos MS 600/6-8
210 N University Ave 79415 806-766-6600
Mike Worth, prin. Fax 766-6627
Coronado HS 2,200/9-12
3307 Vicksburg Ave 79410 806-766-0600
Lynn Akin, prin. Fax 766-0560
Dunbar College Preparatory Academy 400/6-8
2010 E 26th St 79404 806-766-1300
Brian Yearwood, prin. Fax 766-1320
Estacado HS 800/9-12
1504 E Itasca St 79403 806-766-1400
Dr. Sam Ayers, prin. Fax 766-1952
Evans MS 800/6-8
4211 58th St 79413 806-766-0722
Flo Touchstone, prin. Fax 766-0570
Hutchinson MS 900/6-8
3102 Canton Ave 79410 806-766-0755
Heidi Dye, prin. Fax 766-0538
Irons MS 700/6-8
5214 79th St 79424 806-766-2044
Ken Casarez, prin. Fax 766-2070
Lubbock HS 2,100/9-12
2004 19th St 79401 806-766-1444
Doug Young, prin. Fax 766-1469
MacKenzie MS 600/6-8
5402 12th St 79416 806-766-0777
Karen Bayer, prin. Fax 766-0510
Martin ATC Vo/Tech
3201 Avenue Q 79411 806-766-6651
Jill Berset, dir. Fax 766-6675
Matthews Alternative HS 100/Alt
417 N Akron Ave 79415 806-766-1533
Carolyn Conwright, prin. Fax 766-1532
Monterey HS 2,100/9-12
3211 47th St 79413 806-766-0700
Les Purkeypile, prin. Fax 766-0509
Slaton MS 700/6-8
1602 32nd St 79411 806-766-1555
Glen Teal, prin. Fax 766-1571
Talkington S for Young Women Leaders 200/6-10
415 N Ivory Ave 79403 806-766-1744
Berta Fogerson, prin. Fax 766-1738
Wilson MS 500/6-8
4402 31st St 79410 806-766-0799
Cindy Wallace, prin. Fax 766-0814

Lubbock-Cooper ISD 4,000/PK-12
16302 Loop 493 79423 806-863-7100
Pat Henderson, supt. Fax 863-3130
www.lcisd.net
Lubbock-Cooper HS 900/9-12
16302 Loop 493 79423 806-863-7105
Angie Inklebarger, prin. Fax 863-2877
Lubbock-Cooper MS 900/6-8
16302 Loop 493 79423 806-863-3140
Dave Paschall, prin. Fax 863-2654

Roosevelt ISD 1,100/PK-12
1406 County Road 3300 79403 806-842-3282
Jimmy Parker, supt. Fax 842-3266
www.roosevelt.k12.tx.us/
Roosevelt HS 300/9-12
1406 County Road 3300 79403 806-842-3283
Michael Brooks, prin. Fax 842-3931
Roosevelt JHS 300/6-8
1406 County Road 3300 79403 806-842-3218
Damon McCall, prin. Fax 842-3337

All Saints Episcopal S 400/PK-12
3222 103rd St 79423 806-745-7701
Dr. Mike Bennett, hdmstr. Fax 748-0454
American Commercial College Post-Sec.
2007 34th St 79411 806-747-4339
Christ the King S 300/PK-12
4011 54th St 79413 806-795-8283
Christine Wanjura, prin. Fax 795-9715
Covenant Sch. of Nursing & Allied Health Post-Sec.
2002 W Loop 289 Ste 120 79407 806-797-0955
Kaplan College Post-Sec.
1421 9th St 79401 806-765-7051
Lubbock Christian S 300/PK-12
2604 Dover Ave 79407 806-796-8700
Peter Dahlstrom, supt. Fax 791-3569
Lubbock Christian University Post-Sec.
5601 19th St 79407 806-796-8800
Lubbock Hair Academy Post-Sec.
2844 34th St 79410 806-795-0806
Methodist Hospital Post-Sec.
3615 19th St 79410 806-792-1011
Southcrest Christian S 300/PK-12
3801 S Loop 289 79423 806-797-7400
Linda Merriott M.Ed., supt. Fax 776-0546
South Plains College Post-Sec.
819 S Gilbert Dr 79416 806-885-3048
Texas Tech University Post-Sec.
PO Box 45005 79409 806-742-2011
Texas Tech University Health Science Ctr Post-Sec.
3601 4th St 79430 806-743-1000
Trinity Christian HS 300/7-12
6701 University Ave 79413 806-791-6583
Moira Jacobson, prin. Fax 745-8461
Vista College Post-Sec.
4620 50th St 79414 866-442-4197

Lucas, Collin, Pop. 5,074
Lovejoy ISD
Supt. — See Allen
Lovejoy HS 1,100/9-12
2350 Estates Pkwy, 469-742-8700
Gavan Goodrich, prin. Fax 742-8701

Lucas Christian Academy 300/K-12
415 W Lucas Rd, 972-429-4362
Julie Montgomery, admin. Fax 429-5141

Lueders, Jones, Pop. 342
Lueders-Avoca ISD 100/PK-12
334 Vandeventer St 79533 325-228-4211
Rebecca Russell, supt. Fax 228-4513
laisd.com
Other Schools – See Avoca

Lufkin, Angelina, Pop. 34,621
Hudson ISD 2,600/PK-12
6735 Ted Trout Dr 75904 936-875-3351
Mary Ann Whiteker, supt. Fax 875-9209
www.hudsonisd.org
Hudson HS 700/9-12
6735 Ted Trout Dr 75904 936-875-9232
John Courtney, prin. Fax 875-9307
Hudson MS 600/6-8
6735 Ted Trout Dr 75904 936-875-9292
Richard Crenshaw, prin. Fax 875-9317

Lufkin ISD 8,600/PK-12
PO Box 1407 75902 936-634-6696
Roy Knight, supt. Fax 634-8864
www.lufkinisd.org
Alternative S Alt
PO Box 1407 75902 936-632-7203
Drew Huffty, prin. Fax 632-7209
Lufkin HS 2,200/9-12
309 S Medford Dr 75901 936-632-7721
Mark Smith, prin. Fax 632-8132
Lufkin MS 1,800/6-8
900 E Denman Ave 75901 936-630-4444
Jesus Gomez, prin. Fax 632-4444

Zavalla ISD
Supt. — See Zavalla
Stubblefield Learning Center 50/Alt
208 N John Redditt Dr 75904 936-897-2271

Academy of Hair Design Post-Sec.
512 S Chestnut St 75901 936-634-8440
Angelina College Post-Sec.
PO Box 1768 75902 936-639-1301

Luling, Caldwell, Pop. 5,365
Luling ISD 1,500/PK-12
212 E Bowie St 78648 830-875-3191
Tim Glover, supt. Fax 875-3193
www.luling.txed.net
Luling HS 400/9-12
218 E Travis St 78648 830-875-2458
Joe Timms, prin. Fax 875-2751
Luling JHS 300/6-8
214 E Bowie St 78648 830-875-2121
Duane Limbaugh, prin. Fax 875-5482

Lumberton, Hardin, Pop. 11,830
Lumberton ISD 3,600/PK-12
121 S Main St 77657 409-923-7580
John Valastro, supt. Fax 755-7848
www.lumberton.k12.tx.us
Lumberton HS 1,100/9-12
103 S LHS Dr 77657 409-923-7890
Gretchen Scoggins, prin. Fax 755-6576
Lumberton MS 600/7-8
123 S Main St 77657 409-923-7581
Leanna Stringer, prin. Fax 751-0641

Lyford, Willacy, Pop. 2,606
Lyford Consolidated ISD 1,500/PK-12
PO Box 220 78569 956-347-3900
Eduardo Infante, supt. Fax 347-5588
www.lyfordcisd.net
Lyford HS 400/9-12
PO Box 220 78569 956-347-3909
Kristin Brown, prin. Fax 347-5034
Lyford MS 300/6-8
PO Box 220 78569 956-347-3910
Jose Escamilla, prin. Fax 347-2351

Lytle, Atascosa, Pop. 2,470
Lytle ISD 1,700/PK-12
PO Box 745 78052 830-709-5100
Michelle Carroll Smith, supt. Fax 709-5104
lytleisd.squarespace.com
Lytle HS 500/9-12
PO Box 190 78052 830-709-5105
Jesse Vela, prin. Fax 709-5107
Lytle JHS 400/6-8
PO Box 825 78052 830-709-5115
Amy Bibler, prin. Fax 709-5119

Mabank, Kaufman, Pop. 2,981
Mabank ISD 3,300/PK-12
310 E Market St 75147 903-880-1300
Dr. Russell Marshall, supt. Fax 880-1303
www.mabankisd.net
Mabank Academy Alt
310 E Market St 75147 903-880-1600
Brad Koskelin, prin. Fax 880-1603
Mabank DAEP Alt
310 E Market St 75147 903-880-1600
Brad Koskelin, prin. Fax 880-1603
Mabank HS 1,000/9-12
310 E Market St 75147 903-880-1600
Brad Koskelin, prin. Fax 880-1603
Mabank JHS 500/7-8
310 E Market St 75147 903-880-1670
Dr. Darin Jolly, prin. Fax 880-1673

Mc Allen, Hidalgo, Pop. 129,344
McAllen ISD 25,200/PK-12
2000 N 23rd St 78501 956-618-6000
James Ponce, supt. Fax 686-8362
www.mcallenisd.org/
Achieve Early College HS 300/9-12
3201 Pecan Blvd 78501 956-872-1653
Rosalva DeHoyos, prin. Fax 872-1650
Brown MS 900/6-8
2700 S Ware Rd 78503 956-632-8700
Carlos Hernandez, prin. Fax 632-8709
Cathey MS 1,000/6-8
1800 N Cynthia St 78501 956-971-4300
Fax 632-2811
De Leon MS 800/6-8
4201 N 29th Ln 78504 956-632-8800
Philip Grossweiler, prin. Fax 632-8805
Fossum MS 800/6-8
7800 N Ware Rd 78504 956-971-1105
Alberto Canales, prin. Fax 618-9718
Instruction & Guidance Center 50/Alt
2604 Galveston Ave 78501 956-971-4393
Lisette Hinojosa, prin. Fax 971-4294
Lamar Academy 100/Alt
1009 N 10th St 78501 956-632-3222
Cindy Pena, prin. Fax 632-3662
Lincoln MS 700/6-8
1601 N 27th St 78501 956-971-4200
Pedro Alvarez, prin. Fax 971-4273

McAllen HS 2,200/9-12
2021 La Vista Ave 78501 956-632-3100
Chris Beck, prin. Fax 632-3114
Memorial HS 2,100/9-12
101 E Hackberry Ave 78501 956-632-5201
Rosa Larson, prin. Fax 632-5226
Morris MS 700/6-8
1400 Trenton Rd 78504 956-618-7300
Brian McClenny, prin. Fax 632-3666
Rowe HS 2,000/9-12
2101 N Ware Rd 78501 956-632-5100
Bridgette Vieh, prin. Fax 632-8850
Travis MS 800/6-8
600 Houston Ave 78501 956-971-4242
Sonia Casas, prin. Fax 632-8454

Sharyland ISD
Supt. — See Mission
Sharyland North JHS 800/7-8
5100 W Dove Ave 78504 956-686-1415
Leticia Leal, prin. Fax 668-0425

Kaplan College Post-Sec.
1500 S Jackson Rd 78503 956-630-1499
South Texas Christian Academy 300/PK-12
7001 N Ware Rd 78504 956-682-1117
Jim Donlon, prin. Fax 682-7398
South Texas College Post-Sec.
3201 Pecan Blvd 78501 956-872-8311
South Texas Vocational-Technical Inst. Post-Sec.
2400 Daffodil Ave 78501 956-631-1107
Taylor Christian S 50/PK-12
2021 W Jackson Ave 78501 956-686-7574
Laura Vaca M.Ed., dir. Fax 682-4945
University of Cosmetology Arts & Science Post-Sec.
8401 N 10th St 78504 956-687-9444

Mc Camey, Upton, Pop. 1,870
Mc Camey ISD 500/PK-12
PO Box 1069 79752 432-652-3666
Janet Hunt, supt. Fax 652-4219
www.mcisd.esc18.net
Mc Camey HS 100/9-12
PO Box 1069 79752 432-652-3666
Jay McWilliams, prin. Fax 652-4245
Mc Camey MS 100/5-8
PO Box 1069 79752 432-652-3666
Randy Hutchins, prin. Fax 652-4246

Mc Gregor, McLennan, Pop. 4,934
Mc Gregor ISD 1,300/PK-12
PO Box 356 76657 254-840-2828
Kevin Houchin, supt. Fax 840-4077
www.mcgregor-isd.org
Isbill JHS 400/5-8
PO Box 356 76657 254-840-3251
Paul Miller, prin. Fax 840-3572
Mc Gregor HS 300/9-12
PO Box 356 76657 254-840-2853
Robert White, prin. Fax 840-2489

Mc Kinney, Collin, Pop. 128,217
Frisco ISD
Supt. — See Frisco
Scoggins MS 800/6-8
7070 Stacy Rd 75070 469-633-5150
Barbara Warner, prin. Fax 633-5160

Mc Kinney ISD 24,300/PK-12
1 Duvall St 75069 469-302-4000
J.D. Kennedy, supt. Fax 302-4071
www.mckinneyisd.net
Cockrill MS 1,100/6-8
1351 Hardin Rd 75071 469-302-7900
Dr. Melinda DeFelice, prin. Fax 302-7901
Dowell MS 1,200/6-8
301 Ridge Rd 75070 469-302-6700
Alan Arbabi, prin. Fax 302-6701
Evans MS 1,400/6-8
6998 Eldorado Pkwy 75070 469-302-7100
Todd Young, prin. Fax 302-7101
Faubion MS 1,000/6-8
2000 Rollins St 75069 469-302-6900
Patsy Turner, prin. Fax 302-6901
Johnson MS 800/6-8
3400 Community Ave 75071 469-302-4900
Mitch Curry, prin. Fax 302-4901
Mc Kinney Boyd HS 2,900/9-12
600 N Lake Forest Dr 75071 469-302-5400
Rick McDaniel, prin. Fax 302-5401
Mc Kinney HS 2,000/9-12
1400 Wilson Creek Pkwy 75069 469-302-5700
Dr. Logan Faris, prin. Fax 302-5701
Mc Kinney North HS 1,600/9-12
2550 Wilmeth Rd 75071 469-302-4300
Jimmy Spann, prin. Fax 302-4301
Serenity HS 50/Alt
2100 W White Ave 75069 469-302-7830
Juli Ferraro, prin. Fax 302-7831

Collin College Post-Sec.
2200 W University Dr 75071 972-548-6790
Cornerstone Christian Academy 200/K-12
PO Box 3143 75070 972-562-8200
Jeff Guleserian, hdmstr.
Mc Kinney Christian Academy 500/PK-12
3601 Bois D Arc Rd 75071 214-544-2658
Bob Lovelady, head sch Fax 542-5056

Mc Lean, Gray, Pop. 771
McLean ISD 200/PK-12
PO Box 90 79057 806-779-2571
Pam Mitchell, supt. Fax 779-2248
mcleanisd.org/
McLean HS 100/7-12
PO Box 90 79057 806-779-2571
Raymond Glass, prin. Fax 779-2315

Mc Leod, Cass
Mc Leod ISD 400/K-12
PO Box 350 75565 903-796-7181
Cathy May, supt. Fax 796-8443
www.mcleodisd.net
Mc Leod HS 100/9-12
PO Box 350 75565 903-796-7181
Beth Prince, prin. Fax 796-8443
Mc Leod MS 100/6-8
PO Box 350 75565 903-796-7181
Beth Prince, prin. Fax 796-8443

Madisonville, Madison, Pop. 4,327
Madisonville Consolidated ISD 2,300/PK-12
PO Box 879 77864 936-348-2797
Keith Smith, supt. Fax 348-2751
www.madisonvillecisd.org
Madisonville HS 600/9-12
PO Box 879 77864 936-348-2721
Shaye Murphy, prin. Fax 348-5753
Madisonville JHS 500/6-8
PO Box 819 77864 936-348-3587
C. Keith Smith, prin. Fax 348-5603

Magnolia, Montgomery, Pop. 1,381
Magnolia ISD 11,800/PK-12
PO Box 88 77353 281-356-3571
Todd Stephens Ph.D., supt. Fax 356-1328
www.magnoliaisd.org
Alpha Academy 100/Alt
PO Box 329 77353 281-252-2265
Keith Doerhmann, prin. Fax 252-2268
Bear Branch JHS 900/7-8
PO Box 606 77353 281-356-6088
Gerald Evans, prin. Fax 252-2060
Magnolia HS 1,600/9-12
PO Box 428 77353 281-356-3572
Jeff Springer, prin. Fax 252-2092
Magnolia JHS 900/7-8
PO Box 476 77353 281-356-1327
Fax 252-2125
Magnolia West HS 1,800/9-12
PO Box 426 77353 281-356-3571
Brad Schnautz, prin. Fax 252-2560

Legacy Preparatory Christian Academy 300/PK-12
5150 FM 1488 Rd 77354 936-337-2000
Audra May, admin. Fax 273-0641

Malakoff, Henderson, Pop. 2,275
Cross Roads ISD 600/PK-12
14434 FM 59 75148 903-489-2001
Clay Tompkins, supt. Fax 489-2527
www.crossroadsisd.org/
Cross Roads HS 200/9-12
14434 FM 59 75148 903-489-1275
Dr. Regina Davis, prin. Fax 489-0054
Cross Roads JHS 100/6-8
14434 FM 59 75148 903-489-2667
Julie West, prin. Fax 489-3840

Malakoff ISD 1,300/PK-12
1308 FM 3062 75148 903-489-1152
Randy Perry, supt. Fax 489-2566
www.malakoffisd.org/
Malakoff Alternative Program 50/Alt
1209 W Royall Blvd 75148 903-489-4132
Gary Lucius, prin. Fax 489-3239
Malakoff HS 300/9-12
15201 FM 3062 75148 903-489-1527
Daniel Barton, prin. Fax 489-0971
Malakoff MS 300/6-8
106 N Cedar St 75148 903-489-0264
Quinton Watkins, prin. Fax 489-1812

Manor, Travis, Pop. 4,931
Manor ISD 7,200/PK-12
10335 US Highway 290 E 78653 512-278-4000
Kevin Brackmeyer, supt. Fax 278-4017
www.manorisd.net
Manor Excel Academy 100/Alt
600 E Parsons St 78653 512-278-4075
Fax 278-4859
Manor HS 1,200/9-12
12700 Gregg Manor Rd 78653 512-278-4800
Jennifer Mann, prin. Fax 278-4803
Manor MS 700/6-8
12900 Gregg Manor Rd 78653 512-278-4600
Davin Vogler, prin. Fax 278-4285
Manor New Tech HS 300/9-12
10323 US Highway 290 E 78653 512-278-4875
Steven Zipkes, prin. Fax 278-4880
Other Schools – See Austin

Mansfield, Tarrant, Pop. 55,102
Mansfield ISD 32,100/PK-12
605 E Broad St 76063 817-299-6300
Dr. Jim Vaszauskas, supt. Fax 473-5465
www.mansfieldisd.org
Anderson Education Complex 100/Alt
902 E Broad St 76063 817-299-5800
Jerry Gray, prin. Fax 473-5477
Barber Career Tech Academy Vo/Tech
1120 W Debbie Ln 76063 817-299-1900
Catherine Hudgins, prin. Fax 453-6840
Jobe MS 700/7-8
2491 Gertie Barrett Rd 76063 817-299-7040
Elizabeth Hostin, prin. Fax 561-3899
Jones MS 800/7-8
4500 E Broad St 76063 817-276-6200
Travis Moore, prin. Fax 453-7380
Lake Ridge HS 9-12
101 N Day Miar Rd 76063 817-299-7920
Dr. Vonda Nunley, prin. Fax 548-2110
Legacy HS 2,300/9-12
1263 N Main St 76063 817-299-1100
Dr. Shelly Butler, prin. Fax 453-7650

Mansfield Frontier HS 100/9-12
1120 W Debbie Ln 76063 817-299-1900
Catherine Hudgins, prin. Fax 453-6840
Mansfield HS 2,400/9-12
3001 E Broad St 76063 817-299-7500
Cynthia McCallum, prin. Fax 473-5424
Wester MS 900/7-8
1520 N Walnut Creek Dr 76063 817-299-7000
Andrea Hensley, prin. Fax 453-7213
Worley MS 900/7-8
500 Pleasant Ridge Dr 76063 817-299-5900
Julia McMains, prin. Fax 473-5623
Other Schools – See Arlington

Manvel, Brazoria, Pop. 5,107
Alvin ISD
Supt. — See Alvin
Manvel HS 2,000/9-12
19601 Highway 6 77578 281-245-2232
Darrell Alexander, prin. Fax 245-2268
Manvel JHS 500/6-8
101 Palm Desert Dr 77578 281-245-2078
Shawn Williams, prin. Fax 489-8169

Marathon, Brewster, Pop. 427
Marathon ISD 100/PK-12
PO Box 416 79842 432-386-4431
Ebby Loeffler, supt. Fax 386-4395
www.marathonisd.com/
Marathon S 100/PK-12
PO Box 416 79842 432-386-4431
Ebby Loeffler, supt. Fax 386-4395

Marble Falls, Burnet, Pop. 5,987
Marble Falls ISD 4,100/PK-12
1800 Colt Cir 78654 830-693-4357
Rob O'Connor, supt. Fax 693-5685
www.mfisd.txed.net
Falls Career HS Vo/Tech
1800 Colt Cir 78654 830-798-3621
Peggy Little, admin. Fax 798-3636
Marble Falls HS 1,100/9-12
2101 Mustang Dr 78654 830-693-4375
Manuel Lunoff, prin. Fax 693-6079
Marble Falls MS 900/6-8
1511 Pony Dr 78654 830-693-4439
John Schumacher, prin. Fax 798-3632

Faith Academy of Marble Falls 200/K-12
PO Box 1240 78654 830-798-1333
Mark Earwood, admin. Fax 798-1332
Living Word Academy 50/1-12
918 2nd St 78654 – Robert Hill, prin. 830-693-3339

Marfa, Presidio, Pop. 1,967
Marfa ISD 400/PK-12
PO Box T 79843 432-729-4252
Andrew Peters, supt. Fax 729-4310
www.marfaisd.com
Marfa JSHS 200/7-12
PO Box T 79843 432-729-4252
Graydon Hicks, prin. Fax 729-4053

Marion, Guadalupe, Pop. 1,060
Marion ISD 1,400/PK-12
PO Box 189 78124 830-914-2803
Kelly Walters, supt. Fax 420-2300
www.marion.txed.net
Marion HS 400/9-12
PO Box 189 78124 830-914-2803
Johanna Lopez, prin. Fax 420-3639
Marion MS 400/6-8
PO Box 189 78124 830-914-2803
Kelly Walters, prin. Fax 420-3206

Marlin, Falls, Pop. 5,913
Marlin ISD 1,100/PK-12
130 Coleman St 76661 254-883-3585
Michael Steck, supt. Fax 883-6612
www.marlinisd.org
Learning Center 50/Alt
207 Kendrick St 76661 254-883-3964
Daniel Falls, prin. Fax 883-6956
Marlin HS 300/9-12
1400 Capps St 76661 254-883-2394
Dr. Howard Hughes, prin. Fax 883-3470
Marlin MS 200/6-8
678 Success Dr 76661 254-883-9241
Sue Willert, prin. Fax 883-2839

Marshall, Harrison, Pop. 23,237
Marshall ISD 5,800/PK-12
1305 E Pinecrest Dr 75670 903-927-8701
Dr. Marcell Smith, supt. Fax 935-0203
www.marshallisd.com
Marshall HS 1,500/9-12
1900 Maverick Dr 75670 903-927-8800
Ted Huffhines, prin. Fax 938-7052
Marshall JHS 800/7-8
700 W Houston St 75670 903-927-8830
David Segers, prin. Fax 927-8837

East Texas Baptist University Post-Sec.
1 Tiger Dr 75670 903-935-7963
Texas State Technical College Post-Sec.
2650 E End Blvd S 75672 903-935-1010
Wiley College Post-Sec.
711 Wiley Ave 75670 903-927-3300

Mart, McLennan, Pop. 2,183
Mart ISD 600/PK-12
PO Box 120 76664 254-876-2523
Todd Gooden, supt. Fax 876-3028
www.martisd.org/
Mart HS 200/9-12
PO Box 120 76664 254-876-2574
Lou Ann Wolf, prin. Fax 876-2575

Mart MS 200/5-8
PO Box 120 76664 254-876-2762
Dr. Tawnya Nail, prin. Fax 876-2792

Mason, Mason, Pop. 2,094
Mason ISD 700/PK-12
PO Box 410 76856 325-347-1144
Pam Kruse, supt. Fax 347-5877
www.masonisd.net/
Mason HS 200/9-12
PO Box 410 76856 325-347-1122
Chris Habecker, prin. Fax 347-8247
Mason JHS 200/5-8
PO Box 410 76856 325-347-1122
Clint Askins, prin. Fax 347-5461

Matador, Motley, Pop. 605
Motley County ISD 200/PK-12
PO Box 310 79244 806-347-2676
William Cochran, supt. Fax 347-2871
www.motleyco.org
Motley County S 200/PK-12
PO Box 310 79244 806-347-2676
Tim Hill, prin. Fax 347-2871

Mathis, San Patricio, Pop. 4,929
Mathis ISD 1,600/PK-12
PO Box 1179 78368 361-547-3378
Dr. Maria Rodriguez-Casas, supt. Fax 547-4198
www.mathisisd.org
Mathis HS 400/9-12
PO Box 1179 78368 361-547-3322
Valerie Robertson, prin. Fax 547-4139
Mathis MS 300/6-8
PO Box 1179 78368 361-547-2381
Leo Cano, prin. Fax 547-4156

Maud, Bowie, Pop. 1,042
Maud ISD 500/PK-12
PO Box 1028 75567 903-585-2219
Brandon Peavy, supt. Fax 585-5451
www.maud.esc8.net
Maud S 500/PK-12
PO Box 1028 75567 903-585-2219
Karen Townsend, prin. Fax 585-5451

May, Brown
May ISD 300/PK-12
3400 E County Road 411 76857 254-259-2091
Donald Rhodes, supt. Fax 259-3514
www.mayisd.com
May JSHS 100/7-12
3400 E County Road 411 76857 254-259-2131
Steven Howard, prin. Fax 259-2706

Maypearl, Ellis, Pop. 920
Maypearl ISD 1,100/PK-12
PO Box 40 76064 972-435-1000
Ronnie Neill, supt. Fax 435-1001
www.maypearlisd.org
Maypearl HS 300/9-12
PO Box 40 76064 972-435-1020
Debbie Griffin, prin. Fax 435-1021
Maypearl MS 300/6-8
PO Box 40 76064 972-435-1015
Ernie Amaton, prin. Fax 435-1016

Meadow, Terry, Pop. 593
Meadow ISD 300/PK-12
604 4th St 79345 806-539-2246
Darrian Dover, supt. Fax 539-2529
www.meadowisd.net
Meadow HS 100/6-12
604 4th St 79345 806-539-2222
David Cox, prin. Fax 539-2334

Medina, Bandera, Pop. 3,931
Medina ISD 300/K-12
PO Box 1470 78055 830-589-2855
Ross Hord, supt. Fax 589-7150
www.medinaisd.org
Medina HS 200/7-12
PO Box 1470 78055 830-589-2851
John McNamara, prin. Fax 589-7150

Melissa, Collin, Pop. 4,615
Melissa ISD 1,300/PK-12
1904 Cooper St 75454 972-837-2411
Loyd Jason Smith Ed.D., supt. Fax 837-4233
www.melissaisd.org
Melissa HS 400/9-12
3150 Cardinal Dr 75454 972-837-4216
Lance Rainey, prin. Fax 837-4381
Melissa MS 200/7-8
2950 Cardinal Dr 75454 972-837-4355
Christy Fiori, prin. Fax 837-4497

Memphis, Hall, Pop. 2,281
Memphis ISD 600/PK-12
PO Box 460 79245 806-259-5900
Tanya Monroe, supt. Fax 259-2515
www.memphisisd.net
Memphis HS 100/9-12
PO Box 460 79245 806-259-5910
Dick Hutcherson, prin. Fax 259-3026
Memphis MS 100/6-8
PO Box 460 79245 806-259-5920
Ed Bailey, prin. Fax 259-2051

Menard, Menard, Pop. 1,468
Menard ISD 300/PK-12
PO Box 729 76859 325-396-2404
amy bannowsky, supt. Fax 396-2143
www.menardisd.net
Menard HS 100/9-12
PO Box 729 76859 325-396-2513
Amy Bannowsky, supt. Fax 396-2053
Menard JHS 100/6-8
PO Box 729 76859 325-396-2348
Cordelia Kothmann, admin. Fax 396-2761

Mercedes, Hidalgo, Pop. 15,537
Mercedes ISD 5,400/PK-12
PO Box 419 78570 956-514-2000
Dr. Daniel Trevino, supt. Fax 514-2033
www.misdtx.net
Mercedes Academic Academy 100/Alt
PO Box 419 78570 956-825-5076
Sylvia Carlin, dir. Fax 514-2171
Mercedes Early College HS 9-12
PO Box 419 78570 956-825-5180
Jeanne Venecia, prin. Fax 514-2175
Mercedes HS 1,100/9-12
PO Box 419 78570 956-514-2100
Patricia Masso, prin. Fax 514-2111
Mercedes JHS 800/7-8
PO Box 419 78570 956-514-2200
Orlando Rodriguez, prin. Fax 514-2212

South Texas ISD 3,200/7-12
100 Med High Dr 78570 956-565-2454
Marla Guerra Ed.D., supt. Fax 565-9129
www.stisd.net
Science Academy of South Texas 700/9-12
900 Med High Dr 78570 956-565-4620
Michael Aranda, prin. Fax 565-9112
South Texas HS for Health Professions 800/9-12
700 Med High Dr 78570 956-565-2237
Barbara Heater, prin. Fax 565-4039
Other Schools – See Edinburg, San Benito

Meridian, Bosque, Pop. 1,479
Meridian ISD 500/PK-12
PO Box 349 76665 254-435-2081
Scott Hogue, supt. Fax 435-2025
www.meridianisd.org
Meridian JSHS 200/7-12
PO Box 349 76665 254-435-2723
Larry Mynarcik, prin. Fax 435-2199

Merit, Hunt
Bland ISD 600/PK-12
PO Box 216 75458 903-776-2239
Bryan Clark, supt. Fax 776-2240
www.blandisd.net
Bland HS 200/9-12
PO Box 216 75458 903-776-2161
Brian Garner, prin. Fax 776-2426
Bland MS 100/6-8
PO Box 216 75458 903-527-5490
Kevin Hamilton, prin. Fax 527-5491

Merkel, Taylor, Pop. 2,564
Merkel ISD 800/PK-12
PO Box 430 79536 325-928-5813
William Hood, supt. Fax 928-3910
www.merkel.esc14.net
Merkel HS 300/9-12
PO Box 430 79536 325-928-4667
Bryan Allen, prin. Fax 928-4684
Merkel JHS 200/7-8
PO Box 430 79536 325-928-5511
David Acevedo, prin. Fax 928-3138

Mertzon, Irion, Pop. 768
Irion County ISD 300/PK-12
PO Box 469 76941 325-835-6111
Billy Barnett, supt. Fax 835-2017
irioncounty.netxv.net
Irion County MSHS 200/7-12
PO Box 469 76941 325-835-2881
Alan Gillespie, prin. Fax 835-2298

Mesquite, Dallas, Pop. 137,317
Mesquite ISD 37,700/PK-12
405 E Davis St 75149 972-288-6411
Dr. Linda Henrie, supt. Fax 882-7787
www.mesquiteisd.org
Agnew MS 800/7-8
729 Wilkinson Dr 75149 972-882-5750
Donna Gallegos, prin. Fax 882-5760
Berry MS 800/6-8
2675 Bear Dr 75181 972-882-5850
Sandra Bibb, prin. Fax 882-5888
Horn HS 2,300/9-12
3300 E Cartwright Rd 75181 972-882-5200
Bruce Perkins, prin. Fax 882-5291
Kimbrough MS 800/7-8
3900 N Galloway Ave 75150 972-882-5900
Dr. Alane Malone, prin. Fax 882-5942
McDonald MS 1,000/7-8
2930 N Town East Blvd 75150 972-882-5700
Cathy Swann, prin. Fax 882-5710
Mesquite Academy 200/Alt
2704 Motley Dr 75150 972-882-7570
Connie Boone, prin. Fax 882-7579
Mesquite HS 2,700/9-12
300 E Davis St 75149 972-882-7800
Christy Starrett, prin. Fax 882-7876
New MS 1,000/6-8
3700 S Belt Line Rd 75181 972-882-5600
Marvin Daniel, prin. Fax 882-5620
North Mesquite HS 2,400/9-12
18201 Lyndon B Johnson Fwy 75150 972-882-7900
Douglas Barber, prin. Fax 882-7908
Poteet HS 1,600/9-12
3300 Poteet Dr 75150 972-882-5300
Karyn Cummings, prin. Fax 882-5353
Terry MS 1,000/6-8
2351 Edwards Church Rd 75181 972-882-5650
Danny Taylor, prin. Fax 882-5660
Vanston MS 700/7-8
3230 Karla Dr 75150 972-882-5801
Emilio Duran, prin. Fax 882-5848
West Mesquite HS 1,700/9-12
2500 Memorial Blvd 75149 972-882-7600
Alisia Coday, prin. Fax 882-7611
Wilkinson MS 900/6-8
2100 Crest Park Dr 75149 972-882-5950
Leslie Feinglas, prin. Fax 882-5988

Carrington College Post-Sec.
3733 W Emporium Cir 75150 972-682-2800
Dallas Christian S 700/PK-12
1515 Republic Pkwy 75150 972-270-5495
Eastfield College Post-Sec.
3737 Motley Dr 75150 214-860-7100
Hands On Therapy School Post-Sec.
1804 N Galloway Ave 75149 972-285-6133
Metroplex Beauty School Post-Sec.
519 N Galloway Ave 75149 972-288-5485

Mexia, Limestone, Pop. 7,378
Mexia ISD 1,900/PK-12
PO Box 2000 76667 254-562-4000
John Turpin, supt. Fax 562-4007
www.mexia.k12.tx.us
Mexia HS 500/9-12
PO Box 2000 76667 254-562-4010
Russ Meggs, prin. Fax 562-2142
Mexia JHS 400/6-8
PO Box 2000 76667 254-562-4020
Larry Adair, prin. Fax 562-5053
Mexia S of Choice 50/Alt
PO Box 2000 76667 254-562-4000
Greg Goodrum, prin. Fax 562-4007

Miami, Roberts, Pop. 592
Miami ISD 200/PK-12
PO Box 368 79059 806-868-3971
Donna Gill, supt. Fax 868-3171
www.miamiisd.net
Miami S 200/PK-12
PO Box 368 79059 806-868-3971
Kelly Carrell, prin. Fax 868-3171

Midland, Midland, Pop. 109,776
Greenwood ISD 1,300/PK-12
2700 FM 1379 79706 432-685-7800
Doug Young, supt. Fax 685-7804
www.greenwood.esc18.net/
Brooks MS 200/7-8
2700 FM 1379 79706 432-685-7837
Sam Magallan, prin. Fax 685-7838
Greenwood HS 500/9-12
2700 FM 1379 79706 432-685-7805
Ariel Elliott, prin. Fax 685-7814

Midland ISD 20,700/PK-12
615 W Missouri Ave 79701 432-689-1000
Dr. Ryder Warren, supt. Fax 689-1976
www.midlandisd.net/
Abell JHS 800/7-8
3201 Heritage Blvd 79707 432-689-6200
Melissa Horner, prin. Fax 689-6217
Alamo JHS 800/7-8
3800 Storey Ave 79703 432-689-1700
Leann Dumas, prin. Fax 689-1712
Coleman HS 100/9-12
1600 E Golf Course Rd 79701 432-689-5000
Mike Seerey, prin. Fax 689-5016
Early College at Midland College 9-12
3600 N Garfield St 79705 432-685-4641
Jeanette McNeely, prin.
Goddard JHS 900/7-8
2500 Haynes Dr 79705 432-689-1300
Rick Wood, prin. Fax 689-1321
Lee Freshman HS 800/9-9
1400 E Oak Ave 79705 432-689-1250
Bobby Stults, prin. Fax 689-1253
Lee SHS 2,100/10-12
3500 Neely Ave 79707 432-689-1600
Stephanie Howard, prin. Fax 689-1647
Midland Freshman HS 700/9-9
100 E Gist Ave 79701 432-689-1200
Jill Rivera, prin. Fax 689-1209
Midland SHS 2,100/10-12
906 W Illinois Ave 79701 432-689-1100
Jeff Horner, prin. Fax 689-1144
San Jacinto JHS 700/7-8
1400 N N St 79701 432-689-1350
Deborah Kendricks, prin. Fax 689-1385

Midland Christian S 1,000/PK-12
2001 Culver Dr 79705 432-694-1661
Midland College Post-Sec.
3600 N Garfield St 79705 432-685-4500
Trinity S of Midland 600/PK-12
3500 W Wadley Ave 79707 432-697-3281
Rev. Walter Prehn Ph.D., head sch Fax 697-7403

Midlothian, Ellis, Pop. 17,760
Midlothian ISD 7,500/PK-12
100 Walter Stephenson Rd 76065 972-775-8296
Dr. Jerome Stewart, supt. Fax 775-1757
www.midlothian-isd.net
Midlothian HS 2,300/9-12
923 S 9th St 76065 972-775-8237
Dr. Al Hemmle, prin. Fax 775-3178
Seale MS 900/6-8
700 George Hopper Rd 76065 972-775-6145
Coy Tipton, prin. Fax 775-1502
Walnut Grove MS 900/6-8
990 N Walnut Grove Rd 76065 972-775-5355
Brian Blackwell, prin. Fax 775-8127

Milano, Milam, Pop. 425
Milano ISD 400/PK-12
PO Box 145 76556 512-455-2533
Robert Westbrook, supt. Fax 455-9311
www.milanoisd.net
Milano HS 100/9-12
PO Box 145 76556 512-455-9333
Brad Jones, prin. Fax 455-9336
Milano JHS 100/6-8
PO Box 145 76556 512-455-6701
Brad Jones, prin. Fax 455-9186

Miles, Runnels, Pop. 823
Miles ISD 400/PK-12
PO Box 308 76861 325-468-2861
Robert Gibson, supt. Fax 468-2179
miles.netxv.net
Miles JSHS 200/7-12
PO Box 308 76861 325-468-2861
Robin Graves, prin. Fax 468-2179

Milford, Ellis, Pop. 717
Milford ISD 200/K-12
PO Box 545 76670 972-493-2911
Don Clingenpeel, supt. Fax 493-2429
www.milfordisd.org
Milford S 200/K-12
PO Box 545 76670 972-493-2921
Marilee Byrne, prin. Fax 493-4600

Millsap, Parker, Pop. 400
Millsap ISD 800/PK-12
201 E Brazos St 76066 940-682-3101
Dr. David Belding, supt. Fax 682-4476
www.millsapisd.net
Millsap HS 300/9-12
600 Bulldog Dr 76066 940-682-3194
Kayce Haenisch, prin. Fax 682-4035
Millsap MS 200/6-8
301 E Brazos St 76066 940-682-4994
Jeff Clark, prin. Fax 682-4476

Mineola, Wood, Pop. 4,457
Mineola ISD 1,600/PK-12
1000 W Loop 564 75773 903-569-2448
Dr. John Fuller, supt. Fax 569-5155
www.mineolaisd.net
Mineola HS 400/9-12
1000 W Loop 564 75773 903-569-3000
Ricky Stephens, prin. Fax 569-1930
Mineola MS 400/6-8
1000 W Loop 564 75773 903-569-5338
Bob Simmons, prin. Fax 569-5339

Mineral Wells, Palo Pinto, Pop. 16,580
Mineral Wells ISD 3,600/PK-12
906 SW 5th Ave 76067 940-325-6404
Dr. Gail G. Haterius, supt. Fax 325-6378
www.mwisd.net/
Mineral Wells Academy 50/Alt
3810 Ram Blvd 76067 940-325-3033
Jim Yancey, admin. Fax 325-6044
Mineral Wells HS 1,000/9-12
3801 Ram Blvd 76067 940-325-4408
Jon Almeida, prin. Fax 325-7623
Mineral Wells JHS 500/7-8
1301 SE 14th Ave 76067 940-325-0711
Kelly Wilkerson, prin. Fax 328-0450

Community Christian S 100/PK-12
2501 Garrett Morris Pkwy 76067 940-328-1333
Doug Jefferson, admin. Fax 328-1277

Mission, Hidalgo, Pop. 76,804
La Joya ISD
Supt. — See La Joya
Chavez MS 800/6-8
78 Showers Rd 78572 956-580-6182
Daniel Villarreal, prin. Fax 580-6169
Garcia MS 800/6-8
933 Paula St, 956-584-0800
Santana Galven, prin. Fax 584-0817
Juarez-Lincoln HS 2,100/9-12
7801 W Mile 7 Rd, 956-519-4150
Clemencia Garza, prin. Fax 519-4160
LaJoya ISD East Academy Alt
2919 W Mile 3 Rd, 956-519-5746
Lionel Perez, prin. Fax 519-5752
Memorial MS 600/6-8
2610 N Moorefield Rd, 956-580-6087
Maria Rodriguez, prin. Fax 580-6084
Salinas MS 800/6-8
6101 N Bentsen Palm Dr, 956-584-6355
Leticia Martinez, prin. Fax 584-6363
Trevino MS 600/6-8
301 S Inspiration Rd 78572 956-581-3050
Jose Garcia, prin. Fax 581-3099

Mission Consolidated ISD 15,900/PK-12
1201 Bryce Dr 78572 956-323-5505
Dr. Cornelio Gonzalez, supt. Fax 323-5634
www.mcisd.net/
Mission Collegiate HS 100/9-12
1201 Bryce Dr 78572 956-323-6120
Orlando Farias, prin.
Mission HS 2,200/9-12
1201 Bryce Dr 78572 956-323-5700
Jose Lopez, prin. Fax 323-5890
Mission JHS 900/6-8
1201 Bryce Dr 78572 956-323-3300
Raul Sanchez, prin. Fax 323-3338
Mission Options S Alt
1201 Bryce Dr 78572 956-323-3960
Juan Jimenez, prin. Fax 323-8223
Roosevelt Alternative S Alt
1201 Bryce Dr 78572 956-323-3900
Eduardo Alaniz, prin. Fax 323-3925
Veterans Memorial HS 1,900/9-12
1201 Bryce Dr 78572 956-323-3000
Leticia Pena, prin. Fax 323-3280
White JHS 900/6-8
1201 Bryce Dr 78572 956-323-3600
Fax 323-3632

Other Schools – See Alton, Palmhurst

Sharyland ISD 9,900/PK-12
1106 N Shary Rd 78572 956-580-5200
Dr. Virginia Richter, supt. Fax 585-2972
www.sharylandisd.org/
Gray JHS 800/7-8
1106 N Shary Rd 78572 956-580-5333
James Heath, prin. Fax 580-5346
Sharyland HS 3,000/9-12
1106 N Shary Rd 78572 956-580-5300
Cynthia Wilson, prin. Fax 580-5311
Other Schools – See Mc Allen

Juan Diego Academy 9-12
PO Box 3888 78573 956-583-2752
Bob Schmidt, prin. Fax 583-3782

Missouri City, Fort Bend, Pop. 65,862
Fort Bend ISD
Supt. — See Sugar Land
Baines MS 1,500/6-8
9000 Sienna Ranch Rd 77459 281-634-6870
David Yaffie, prin. Fax 634-6880
Elkins HS 2,000/9-12
7007 Knights Ct 77459 281-634-2600
Barbara Whitaker, prin. Fax 634-2674
Hightower HS 2,400/9-12
3333 Hurricane Ln 77459 281-634-5240
Viretta West, prin. Fax 634-5333
Lake Olympia MS 1,300/6-8
3100 Lake Olympia Pkwy 77459 281-634-3520
Kimberly Carroll, prin. Fax 634-3549
Marshall HS 1,400/9-12
1220 Buffalo Run 77489 281-634-6630
Shirley Rose-Gilliam, prin. Fax 634-6650
Missouri City MS 800/7-8
202 Martin Ln 77489 281-634-3440
Dr. Jesus Acosta, prin. Fax 634-3473
Progressive HS Alt
1555 Independence Blvd 77489 281-634-2900
Trevor Lemon, prin. Fax 634-2913
Quail Valley MS 900/6-8
3019 FM 1092 Rd 77459 281-634-3600
Thomas Heinly, prin. Fax 634-3632
Ridge Point HS 600/9-12
500 Waters Lake Blvd 77459 281-327-5200
Tammy Edwards, prin. Fax 327-5201

Monahans, Ward, Pop. 6,896
Monahans-Wickett-Pyote ISD 2,000/PK-12
606 S Betty Ave 79756 432-943-6711
Keith Richardson, supt. Fax 943-2307
www.mwpisd.esc18.net
Monahans Education Center 50/Alt
813 S Alice Ave 79756 432-943-2019
Doug Doege, prin. Fax 943-2593
Monahans HS 500/9-12
809 S Betty Ave 79756 432-943-2519
Jeff Jones, prin. Fax 943-3327
Walker JHS 300/7-8
800 S Faye Ave 79756 432-943-4622
Roy Rutledge, prin. Fax 943-3723

Mont Belvieu, Chambers, Pop. 3,784
Barbers Hill ISD 4,200/PK-12
PO Box 1108 77580 281-576-2221
Greg Poole, supt. Fax 576-3410
www.bhisd.net/
Barbers Hill HS 1,200/9-12
PO Box 1108 77580 281-576-2221
Rick Kana, prin. Fax 576-3356
Barbers Hill MS 700/7-8
PO Box 1108 77580 281-576-2221
Lance Murphy, prin. Fax 576-3353

Monte Alto, Hidalgo, Pop. 1,914
Monte Alto ISD 1,100/PK-12
25149 1st St 78538 956-262-1381
Olivia Almanza, supt. Fax 262-5535
www.montealtoisd.org
Monte Alto HS 300/9-12
25149 1st St 78538 956-262-1381
Sabrina Franco, admin. Fax 262-5535
Monte Alto MS 200/6-8
25149 1st St 78538 956-262-1374
Jimmy Padilla, prin. Fax 262-1377

Montgomery, Montgomery, Pop. 621
Montgomery ISD 6,900/PK-12
PO Box 1475 77356 936-582-1333
Dr. Beau Rees, supt. Fax 582-6447
www.misd.org
Montgomery HS 2,000/9-12
22825 Highway 105 W 77356 936-597-6401
Phil Eaton, prin. Fax 597-6415
Montgomery JHS 1,100/7-8
19000 Stewart Creek Rd 77356 936-582-6400
Duane McFadden, prin. Fax 582-6329

Moody, McLennan, Pop. 1,359
Moody ISD 700/PK-12
107 Coralee Ln 76557 254-853-2172
Chane Rascoe, supt. Fax 853-2886
www.moodyisd.org
Moody HS 200/9-12
107 Coralee Ln 76557 254-853-3622
Joe Satterwhite, prin. Fax 853-3822
Moody MS 200/5-8
107 Coralee Ln 76557 254-853-2182
Andrew Miller, prin. Fax 853-2886

Moran, Shackelford, Pop. 270
Moran ISD 100/K-12
PO Box 98 76464 325-945-3101
Scott Higgins, supt. Fax 945-2741
www.moran.esc14.net/
Moran S 100/K-12
PO Box 98 76464 325-945-3101
Kim Holland, prin. Fax 945-2741

Morgan, Bosque, Pop. 480
Morgan ISD 100/PK-12
PO Box 300 76671 254-635-2311
John Bryant, supt. Fax 635-2224
www.morganisd.org
Morgan S 100/PK-12
PO Box 300 76671 254-635-2311
John Bryant, prin. Fax 635-2224

Morton, Cochran, Pop. 1,996
Morton ISD 500/PK-12
500 Champion Dr 79346 806-266-5505
Vicki Rice, supt. Fax 266-5449
www.mortonisd.net/
Morton HS 100/9-12
500 Champion Dr 79346 806-266-5505
John Albin, prin. Fax 266-5780
Morton JHS 100/6-8
500 Champion Dr 79346 806-266-5505
Hulon Kirkland, prin. Fax 266-5739

Moulton, Lavaca, Pop. 877
Moulton ISD 300/K-12
PO Box C 77975 361-596-4609
Chad Rothbauer, supt. Fax 596-7578
www.moultonisd.net
Moulton JSHS 100/7-12
PO Box C 77975 361-596-4691
Jamie Dornak, prin. Fax 596-7119

Mount Calm, Hill, Pop. 312
Mount Calm ISD 100/PK-12
PO Box 105 76673 254-993-2611
Barbara Lane, supt. Fax 993-1022
Mount Calm S 100/PK-12
PO Box 105 76673 254-993-2611
Angela Nors, prin. Fax 993-1022

Mount Enterprise, Rusk, Pop. 445
Mount Enterprise ISD 400/PK-12
301 NW 3rd St 75681 903-822-3721
Byron Jordan, supt. Fax 822-3633
www.meisd.esc7.net
Mount Enterprise JSHS 200/6-12
301 NW 3rd St 75681 903-822-3721
Riley Armstrong, prin. Fax 822-3633

Mount Pleasant, Titus, Pop. 15,466
Chapel Hill ISD 900/PK-12
1069 County Road 4660 75455 903-572-8096
Marc Levesque, supt. Fax 572-1086
www.chisddevils.com
Chapel Hill HS 300/9-12
1069 County Road 4660 75455 903-572-1086
Brandon Dennard, prin. Fax 572-3850
Chapel Hill JHS 200/6-8
1069 County Road 4660 75455 903-572-1086
Mike Clifton, prin. Fax 572-9747

Mount Pleasant ISD 5,300/PK-12
PO Box 1117 75456 903-575-2000
Lynn Dehart Ph.D., supt. Fax 575-2014
www.mpisd.net
Mount Pleasant HS 1,400/9-12
PO Box 1117 75456 903-575-2020
Judd Marshall, prin. Fax 575-2036
Mount Pleasant JHS 700/7-8
PO Box 1117 75456 903-575-2110
Dustin Cook, prin. Fax 575-2117

Northeast Texas Community College Post-Sec.
PO Box 1307 75456 903-434-8100

Mount Vernon, Franklin, Pop. 2,608
Mount Vernon ISD 1,600/PK-12
PO Box 98 75457 903-537-2546
John Kaufman, supt. Fax 537-4784
www.mtvernonisd.com/
Mount Vernon HS 400/9-12
PO Box 1139 75457 903-537-3700
Kelly Baird, prin. Fax 537-2536
Mount Vernon JHS 200/7-8
PO Box 1139 75457 903-537-2267
Ronny Alsup, prin. Fax 537-3601

Muenster, Cooke, Pop. 1,534
Muenster ISD 500/PK-12
PO Box 608 76252 940-759-2281
Clay Richerson, supt. Fax 759-5200
www.muensterisd.net
Muenster HS 200/7-12
PO Box 608 76252 940-759-2282
Sharon Browning, prin. Fax 759-4614

Sacred Heart S 200/PK-12
PO Box 588 76252 940-759-2511
Dr. Rafael Rondon, prin. Fax 759-4422

Muleshoe, Bailey, Pop. 5,137
Muleshoe ISD 1,500/PK-12
514 W Avenue G 79347 806-272-7400
Dr. Gene Sheets, supt. Fax 272-4120
www.muleshoeisd.net
Muleshoe HS 300/9-12
514 W Avenue G 79347 806-272-7303
Steve Myatt, prin. Fax 272-7574
Watson JHS 300/6-8
514 W Avenue G 79347 806-272-7349
Cindy Bessire, prin. Fax 272-4983

Mullin, Mills, Pop. 179
Mullin ISD 200/PK-12
PO Box 128 76864 325-985-3374
Steven Mickelson, supt. Fax 985-3915
www.mullinisd.net
Mullin HS 100/7-12
PO Box 128 76864 325-985-3374
Steven Mickelson, admin. Fax 985-3372

Mumford, Robertson
Mumford ISD 500/PK-12
PO Box 268 77867 979-279-3678
Pete Bienski, supt. Fax 279-5044
www.mumford.k12.tx.us
Mumford JSHS 200/7-12
PO Box 268 77867 979-279-3678
Pete Bienski, prin. Fax 279-5044

Munday, Knox, Pop. 1,285
Munday Consolidated ISD 400/PK-12
PO Box 300 76371 940-422-4241
Robert Dillard, supt. Fax 422-5331
www.esc9.net/munday
Munday Secondary S 200/7-12
PO Box 300 76371 940-422-4321
Tra Hall, prin. Fax 422-5331

Murphy, Collin, Pop. 17,219
Plano ISD
Supt. — See Plano
Murphy MS 1,000/6-8
620 N Murphy Rd 75094 469-752-7000
Brant Perry, prin. Fax 752-7001

Nacogdoches, Nacogdoches, Pop. 32,466
Central Heights ISD 1,000/PK-12
10317 US Highway 259 75965 936-564-2681
Dr. Jeremy Glenn, supt. Fax 569-6889
www.centralhts.org
Central Heights HS 200/9-12
10317 US Highway 259 75965 936-552-3408
David Russell, prin. Fax 560-2016
Central Heights MS 300/6-8
10317 US Highway 259 75965 936-552-3441
Andrew Binford, prin. Fax 564-0177

Martinsville ISD 300/PK-12
12952 E State Highway 7 75961 936-564-3455
Kevin Burton, supt. Fax 569-0498
www.martinsville.esc7.net
Martinsville S 300/PK-12
12952 E State Highway 7 75961 936-564-3455
Monty Pepper, prin. Fax 569-0498

Nacogdoches ISD 6,500/PK-12
PO Box 631521 75963 936-569-5000
Dr. Fred Hayes, supt. Fax 569-5797
www.nacisd.org
Martin S of Choice 100/Alt
PO Box 631521 75963 936-569-3175
Gerrie Lockett, prin. Fax 569-5775
McMichael MS 700/6-8
PO Box 631521 75963 936-552-0519
Kristi Shofner, prin. Fax 552-0523
Moses MS 700/6-8
PO Box 631521 75963 936-569-5001
Tammy Pankratz, prin. Fax 569-5031
Nacogdoches HS 1,700/9-12
PO Box 631521 75963 936-564-2466
Nathan Chaddick, prin. Fax 560-8162

Woden ISD
Supt. — See Woden
Nacogdoches Boys Ranch 50/Alt
7245 FM 1275 75961 936-560-1310
Bambi Spurgeon, prin. Fax 462-1101

Stephen F. Austin State University Post-Sec.
1936 North St 75965 936-468-3401

Natalia, Medina, Pop. 1,422
Natalia ISD 1,100/PK-12
PO Box 548 78059 830-663-4416
Guillermo Mancha Ed.D., supt. Fax 663-4186
www.nataliaisd.net/
Natalia HS 300/9-12
PO Box 548 78059 830-663-4417
Donald Mathis, prin. Fax 663-6410
Natalia JHS 200/6-8
PO Box 548 78059 830-663-4027
Joseph Justice, prin. Fax 663-2347

Navasota, Grimes, Pop. 6,996
Navasota ISD 2,900/PK-12
PO Box 511 77868 936-825-4200
Rory Gesch, supt. Fax 825-4297
www.navasotaisd.org
Bizzell Academy, PO Box 511 77868 Alt
Kristi Jones, prin. 936-825-4296
Navasota HS 800/9-12
PO Box 511 77868 936-825-4250
Deanna Beauchamp, prin. Fax 825-4293
Navasota JHS 600/6-8
PO Box 511 77868 936-825-4225
Charles Lester, prin. Fax 825-4260

Nazareth, Castro, Pop. 311
Nazareth ISD 200/K-12
PO Box 189 79063 806-945-2231
James Oliver, supt. Fax 945-2431
www.nazarethisd.net/
Nazareth S 200/K-12
PO Box 189 79063 806-945-2231
Deborah Clinton, prin. Fax 945-2431

Neches, Anderson
Neches ISD 400/PK-12
PO Box 310 75779 903-584-3311
Randy Snider, supt. Fax 584-3686
www.nechesisd.com
Other Schools – See Palestine

Nederland, Jefferson, Pop. 17,344
Nederland ISD 5,000/PK-12
220 N 17th St 77627 409-724-2391
Robert Madding, supt. Fax 724-4280
www.nederland.k12.tx.us
Alternative S Alt
220 N 17th St 77627 409-727-5241
Karen Bussell, prin. Fax 724-4236
Central MS 800/5-8
220 N 17th St 77627 409-727-5765
Charles Jehlen, prin. Fax 724-4275
Nederland HS 1,400/9-12
220 N 17th St 77627 409-727-2741
Dr. Steven Beagle, prin. Fax 726-2679
Wilson MS 800/5-8
220 N 17th St 77627 409-727-6224
Scott Clemmons, prin. Fax 726-2699

Faris Computer School Post-Sec.
1119 Kent Ave 77627 409-722-4072

Needville, Fort Bend, Pop. 2,792
Needville ISD 2,600/PK-12
PO Box 412 77461 979-793-4308
Curtis Rhodes, supt. Fax 793-3823
www.needvilleisd.com
Needville HS 800/9-12
PO Box 412 77461 979-793-4158
Richard Janacek, prin. Fax 793-5590
Needville JHS 400/7-8
PO Box 412 77461 979-793-4250
Karen Smart, prin. Fax 793-4575

Nevada, Collin, Pop. 815
Community ISD 1,200/PK-12
PO Box 400 75173 972-843-8400
Dr. Cole McClendon, supt. Fax 843-8401
www.communityisd.org
Community HS 500/9-12
PO Box 400 75173 972-843-8414
Dr. Erika Crump, prin. Fax 843-8415
Community MS 400/6-8
PO Box 400 75173 972-843-8411
Travis Taylor, prin. Fax 843-8412

New Boston, Bowie, Pop. 4,450
New Boston ISD 1,400/PK-12
600 N McCoy Blvd 75570 903-628-2521
Gary Van Deaver Ed.D., supt. Fax 628-2235
www.nbschools.net
New Boston HS 400/9-12
1 W Lion Dr 75570 903-628-6551
Brian Bobbitt, prin. Fax 628-3695
New Boston MS 300/6-8
1215 N State Highway 8 75570 903-628-6588
Glenn Barfield, prin. Fax 628-5132

New Braunfels, Comal, Pop. 57,097
Comal ISD 17,000/PK-12
1404 N Interstate 35 78130 830-221-2000
Andrew Kim, supt. Fax 221-2001
www.comalisd.org
Canyon HS 1,900/9-12
1510 N Interstate 35 78130 830-221-2400
Brad Brown, prin. Fax 221-2401
Canyon MS 900/6-8
2014 FM 1101 78130 830-221-2300
Patti Vlieger, prin. Fax 221-2301
Church Hill MS 700/6-8
1275 N Business IH 35 78130 830-221-2800
Scott Hammond, prin. Fax 221-2801
Memorial Early College HS 100/9-12
1419 N Business 35 78130 830-221-2900
Dr. Dolly Adams, prin. Fax 221-2901
Mountain Valley MS 600/6-8
1165 Sattler Rd 78132 830-885-1300
Dr. Sean Maika, prin. Fax 885-1301
Other Schools – See Fischer, Spring Branch

New Braunfels ISD 7,600/PK-12
PO Box 311688 78131 830-643-5700
Randy Moczygemba, supt. Fax 643-5701
www.nbisd.org/
New Braunfels 9th Grade Center 600/9-9
659 S Guenther Ave 78130 830-643-5700
Christie Lawson, prin.
New Braunfels HS 1,600/10-12
2551 Loop 337 78130 830-627-6000
John Burks, prin. Fax 627-6001
New Braunfels MS 600/7-8
656 S Guenther Ave 78130 830-627-6270
Jana Cervantes, prin. Fax 627-6271
Oakrun MS 900/6-8
415 Oak Run Pt 78132 830-627-6400
Dr. David Simmons, prin. Fax 627-6401
The Learning Center 100/Alt
902 W San Antonio St 78130 830-627-6960
Greg Hughes, admin. Fax 627-6961

John Paul II HS 100/9-12
6720 FM 482 78132 830-643-0802
Nolite Timere, prin. Fax 643-0806
New Braunfels Christian Academy 400/PK-12
220 FM 1863 78132 830-629-1821
Eric Pipkin, hdmstr. Fax 629-1880

New Caney, Montgomery, Pop. 3,000
New Caney ISD 10,100/PK-12
21580 Loop 494 77357 281-577-8600
Kenn Franklin, supt. Fax 354-2639
www.newcaneyisd.org
Keefer Crossing MS 700/7-8
20350 FM 1485 Rd 77357 281-577-8840
Andy Pearson, prin. Fax 399-9859
Learning Center 50/Alt
20419 FM 1485 Rd 77357 281-577-2850
Jeremy Harris, prin. Fax 399-4005
New Caney HS 1,500/9-12
21650 Loop 494 77357 281-577-2800
David Loyacano, prin. Fax 354-0186
Other Schools – See Porter

Newcastle, Young, Pop. 582
Newcastle ISD 200/PK-12
PO Box 129 76372 940-846-3551
Ty Spitzer, supt. Fax 846-3452
esc9.net/newcastle
Newcastle S 200/PK-12
PO Box 129 76372 940-846-3531
Ty Spitzer, supt. Fax 846-3452

New Deal, Lubbock, Pop. 782
New Deal ISD 700/PK-12
PO Box 280 79350 806-746-5833
Steven McCray, supt. Fax 746-5707
www.ndisd.net
New Deal HS 200/9-12
PO Box 250 79350 806-746-5933
Dr. Jerry Adams, prin. Fax 746-5544
New Deal MS 200/5-8
PO Box 308 79350 806-746-6633
Matt Reed, prin. Fax 746-5244

New Home, Lynn, Pop. 334
New Home ISD 200/PK-12
225 N Main St, 806-924-7542
Leland Zant, supt. Fax 924-7520
www.newhomeisd.org/
New Home S 200/PK-12
225 N Main St, 806-924-7543
Shane Fiedler, prin. Fax 924-7520

New London, Rusk, Pop. 978
West Rusk ISD 1,000/PK-12
PO Box 168 75682 903-895-6000
Tommy Alexander, supt. Fax 895-2267
www.westrusk.esc7.net
West Rusk HS 200/9-12
PO Box 168 75682 903-895-6000
Jake Jackson, prin. Fax 895-4317
West Rusk JHS 200/6-8
PO Box 168 75682 903-895-6000
Leah Bobbitt, prin. Fax 895-6085

New Summerfield, Cherokee, Pop. 1,102
New Summerfield ISD 500/PK-12
PO Box 6 75780 903-726-3306
Gregg Weiss, supt. Fax 726-3405
www.nsisd.sprnet.org/
New Summerfield S 500/PK-12
PO Box 6 75780 903-726-3306
Gregg Weiss, supt. Fax 726-3405

Newton, Newton, Pop. 2,458
Newton ISD 1,100/PK-12
414 Main St 75966 409-379-8137
Mike Terry, supt. Fax 379-2189
www.newtonisd.net
Newton HS 300/9-12
414 Main St 75966 409-379-4731
Johnny Metz, prin. Fax 379-3321
Newton MS 300/6-8
414 Main St 75966 409-379-8324
Judy Holleman, prin. Fax 379-5082

New Waverly, Walker, Pop. 1,019
New Waverly ISD 900/PK-12
355 Front St 77358 936-344-6751
Dr. Darol Hail, supt. Fax 344-2438
www.new-waverly.k12.tx.us
New Waverly HS 300/9-12
355 Front St 77358 936-344-6451
Kris Drane, prin. Fax 344-6113
New Waverly JHS 200/6-8
355 Front St 77358 936-344-2246
Dudley Hawkes, prin. Fax 344-8313

Nixon, Gonzales, Pop. 2,375
Nixon-Smiley Consolidated ISD 1,100/PK-12
PO Box 400 78140 830-582-1536
Cathy Booth Ph.D., supt. Fax 582-1920
www.nixonsmiley.net
Nixon-Smiley HS 300/9-12
PO Box 400 78140 830-582-1536
Gary Tausch, prin. Fax 582-2168
Nixon-Smiley MS 400/4-8
PO Box 400 78140 830-582-1536
Sarah Loer, prin. Fax 582-2258

Nocona, Montague, Pop. 3,004
Nocona ISD 800/PK-12
220 Clay St 76255 940-825-3267
Vickie Gearheart, supt. Fax 825-4945
www.noconaisd.net/
Nocona HS 200/9-12
220 Clay St 76255 940-825-3264
Lynn Lierly, prin. Fax 825-7270
Nocona MS 200/6-8
220 Clay St 76255 940-825-3121
Laura Ice, prin. Fax 825-6151

Prairie Valley ISD 100/PK-12
12920 FM 103 76255 940-825-4425
W. Tucker, supt. Fax 825-4650
www.prairievalleyisd.net/
Prairie Valley JSHS 100/6-12
12920 FM 103 76255 940-825-4425
Tim West, prin. Fax 825-4650

Nordheim, DeWitt, Pop. 305
Nordheim ISD 100/PK-12
500 Broadway 78141 361-938-5211
Kevin Wilson, supt. Fax 938-5266
www.nordheimisd.org
Nordheim S 100/PK-12
500 Broadway 78141 361-938-5211
Kevin Wilson, prin. Fax 938-5266

Normangee, Leon, Pop. 671
Normangee ISD 500/PK-12
PO Box 219 77871 936-396-3111
Jerry Burger, supt. Fax 396-3112
www.normangeeisd.org
Normangee HS 100/9-12
PO Box 219 77871 936-396-6111
Kristi Lee, prin. Fax 396-6879
Normangee MS 100/6-8
PO Box 219 77871 936-396-4621
Wendee Binford, prin. Fax 396-1690

North Richland Hills, Tarrant, Pop. 62,179
Birdville ISD
Supt. — See Haltom City
Birdville Center of Tech & Advanced Lrng Vo/Tech
7020 Mid Cities Blvd 76180 817-547-3800
Dr. Linda Anderson, dir. Fax 503-8965
Birdville HS 1,900/9-12
9100 Mid Cities Blvd 76180 817-547-8000
Jason Wells, prin. Fax 547-8009
North Richland MS 900/6-8
4800 Rufe Snow Dr 76180 817-547-4200
Ernie Valamides, prin. Fax 581-5372
North Ridge MS 800/6-8
7332 Douglas Ln 76182 817-547-5200
Steve Ellis, prin. Fax 581-5460
Richland HS 2,200/9-12
5201 Holiday Ln 76180 817-547-7000
Carla Rix, prin. Fax 581-5454
Smithfield MS 700/6-8
8400 Main St 76182 817-547-5000
Kyle Pekurney, prin. Fax 581-5480

ATI Distant Education Post-Sec.
8053 Boulevard 26 Ste CD 76180 817-591-1762
Fort Worth Christian S 900/PK-12
6200 Holiday Ln 76180 817-281-6504

North Zulch, Madison
North Zulch ISD 300/PK-12
PO Box 158 77872 936-399-1000
Morris Lyon, supt. Fax 399-2025
www.nzisd.org
North Zulch JSHS 100/7-12
PO Box 158 77872 936-399-1030
Chris Bradshaw, prin. Fax 399-2038

Oak Ridge North, Montgomery, Pop. 3,010

Oak Ridge Christian Academy 100/PK-12
27420 Robinson Rd, 281-298-5800
Jess Larson, hdmstr. Fax 292-2818

Oakwood, Leon, Pop. 506
Oakwood ISD 200/PK-12
631 N Holly St 75855 903-545-2600
Stu Musick, supt. Fax 545-2666
www.oakwoodisd.net
Oakwood JSHS 100/7-12
631 N Holly St 75855 903-545-2106
Judy Thomason, prin. Fax 545-1820

O Brien, Haskell, Pop. 105
Knox City-O'Brien Consolidated ISD
Supt. — See Knox City
O'Brien MS 100/5-8
711 9th St 79539 940-657-3731
Mark Tucker, prin. Fax 657-3379

Odem, San Patricio, Pop. 2,386
Odem-Edroy ISD 1,100/PK-12
1 Owl Sq 78370 361-368-2561
Lisa Gonzales, supt. Fax 368-2879
www.oeisd.org/
Odem HS 300/9-12
1 Owl Sq 78370 361-368-3401
Thomas White, prin. Fax 368-3781
Odem JHS 200/6-8
1 Owl Sq 78370 361-368-8661
James Brannigan, prin. Fax 368-2033

Odessa, Ector, Pop. 98,924
Ector County ISD 28,100/PK-12
PO Box 3912 79760 432-456-0000
Hector Mendez, supt. Fax 456-9878
www.ectorcountyisd.org
Advanced Technical Center Vo/Tech
PO Box 3912 79760 432-456-6999
Alternative Education Center 50/Alt
PO Box 3912 79760 432-456-0049
Charles Quintela, prin. Fax 456-0048
Bonham JHS 1,000/7-9
PO Box 3912 79760 432-456-0429
James Ramage, prin. Fax 456-0428
Bowie JHS 1,100/7-9
PO Box 3912 79760 432-456-0439
Shelia Stevenson, prin. Fax 456-0438
Crockett JHS 700/7-9
PO Box 3912 79760 432-456-0449
Mauricio Marquez, prin. Fax 456-0448
Ector JHS 1,500/7-9
PO Box 3912 79760 432-456-0479
Val Hernandez, prin. Fax 456-0478
Hood JHS 600/7-9
PO Box 3912 79760 432-456-0459
Wayne Squiers, prin. Fax 456-0458
New Tech Odessa HS 9-12
PO Box 3912 79760 432-456-6989
Adrian Vega, prin. Fax 456-6988
Nimitz JHS 900/7-9
PO Box 3912 79760 432-456-0469
Robin Fawcett, prin. Fax 456-0468
Odessa SHS 2,800/10-12
PO Box 3912 79760 432-456-0029
Gregory Nelson, prin. Fax 456-0028
Permian SHS 2,400/10-12
PO Box 3912 79760 432-456-0039
Roy Garcia, prin. Fax 456-0038

American Commercial College Post-Sec.
5119 Twin Towers Blvd 79762 432-362-6768
Odessa College Post-Sec.
201 W University Blvd 79764 432-335-6400
University of Texas of the Permian Basin Post-Sec.
4901 E University Blvd 79762 432-552-2020

O Donnell, Lynn, Pop. 817
O'Donnell ISD 300/PK-12
PO Box 487 79351 806-428-3241
Dr. Cathy Amonett, supt. Fax 428-3395
odonnell.esc17.net
O'Donnell HS 100/6-12
PO Box 487 79351 806-428-3247
Dusty Palmer, prin. Fax 428-3759

Oglesby, Coryell, Pop. 480
Oglesby ISD 200/PK-12
PO Box 158 76561 254-456-2271
Edna Kennedy, supt. Fax 456-2522
www.oglesbyisd.net
Oglesby S 200/PK-12
PO Box 158 76561 254-456-2271
Kendall Smith, prin. Fax 456-2916

Olney, Young, Pop. 3,242
Olney ISD 700/PK-12
809 W Hamilton St 76374 940-564-3519
Tom Bailey, supt. Fax 564-5205
www.olneyisd.net
Olney HS 200/9-12
704 W Grove St 76374 940-564-5637
Steve Fleming, prin. Fax 564-5733
Olney JHS 200/6-8
300 S Avenue H 76374 940-564-3517
Terry Dunlap, prin. Fax 564-8824

Olton, Lamb, Pop. 2,197
Olton ISD 700/PK-12
PO Box 388 79064 806-285-2641
Charles McIver, supt. Fax 285-2724
www.oltonisd-esc17.net/
Olton HS 200/9-12
PO Box 667 79064 806-285-2691
Briant Hunt, prin. Fax 285-3316
Olton JHS 100/6-8
PO Box 509 79064 806-285-2681
Mike Wiley, prin. Fax 285-3348

Omaha, Morris, Pop. 1,001
Pewitt Consolidated ISD 1,000/PK-12
PO Box 1106 75571 903-884-2804
Jackie Dammann, supt. Fax 884-2866
www.pewittcisd.net
Pewitt HS 300/9-12
PO Box 1106 75571 903-884-2293
Michael Rutherford, prin. Fax 884-3111
Pewitt JHS 200/6-8
PO Box 1106 75571 903-884-2505
Ronnie Herron, prin. Fax 884-2142

Onalaska, Polk, Pop. 1,736
Onalaska ISD 1,000/PK-12
PO Box 2289 77360 936-646-1000
Lynn Redden, supt. Fax 646-2605
www.onalaskaisd.net
Onalaska JSHS 400/7-12
PO Box 2289 77360 936-646-1020
Charles Boyce, prin. Fax 646-1022

Orange, Orange, Pop. 18,289
Deweyville ISD
Supt. — See Deweyville
Deweyville JSHS 200/7-12
615 State Hwy 12 W 77632 409-746-2685
Darryl Dans, prin. Fax 746-9343

Little Cypress-Mauriceville Cons ISD 3,600/PK-12
6586 FM 1130 77632 409-883-2232
Pauline Hargrove, supt. Fax 883-3509
www.lcmcisd.org/
Little Cypress JHS 500/6-8
6765 FM 1130 77632 409-883-2317
Mitzi Conn, prin. Fax 883-5044
Little Cypress-Mauriceville HS 1,100/9-12
7327 Highway 87 N 77632 409-886-5821
Terri Estes, prin. Fax 886-5762
Mauriceville MS 300/6-8
19952 FM 1130 77632 409-745-3970
Todd Loupe, prin. Fax 745-3383

West Orange-Cove Consolidated ISD 2,500/PK-12
PO Box 1107 77631 409-882-5500
James Colbert, supt. Fax 882-5467
www.woccisd.net
West Orange-Stark HS 700/9-12
PO Box 1107 77631 409-882-5570
Hutcherson Hill, prin. Fax 882-5573
West Orange-Stark MS 500/6-8
PO Box 1107 77631 409-882-5520
Anthony Moten, prin. Fax 882-5545

Baptist Hospital Post-Sec.
608 Strickland Dr 77630 409-883-9361
Community Christian S 300/PK-12
3400 Martin Luther King Jr 77632 409-883-4531
Daniel Rose, admin. Fax 883-8855
Lamar State College Orange Post-Sec.
410 W Front St 77630 409-883-7750

Orangefield, Orange
Orangefield ISD 1,700/PK-12
PO Box 228 77639 409-735-5337
Dr. Stephen D. Patterson, supt. Fax 735-2080
www.orangefieldisd.com/
Orangefield HS 500/9-12
PO Box 228 77639 409-735-3851
Dr. Benjamin Petty, prin. Fax 697-2301
Orangefield JHS 500/5-8
PO Box 228 77639 409-735-6737
Preston Clark, prin. Fax 792-9605

Orange Grove, Jim Wells, Pop. 1,306
Orange Grove ISD 1,800/PK-12
PO Box 534 78372 361-384-2495
Lynn Burton, supt. Fax 384-2148
ogisd.net
Orange Grove HS 500/9-12
PO Box 534 78372 361-384-2330
Arnold Diaz, prin. Fax 384-0206
Orange Grove JHS 400/6-8
PO Box 534 78372 361-384-2323
Gildardo Salazar, prin. Fax 384-9579

Ore City, Upshur, Pop. 1,130
Ore City ISD 900/PK-12
100 Rebel Rd N 75683 903-968-3300
Lynn Heflin, supt. Fax 968-3797
www.ocisd.net
Ore City HS 200/9-12
100 Rebel Rd N 75683 903-968-3300
Scot Wright, prin. Fax 968-8726
Ore City JHS 200/6-8
100 Rebel Rd N 75683 903-968-3300
Selenia Cato, prin. Fax 968-4913

Overton, Rusk, Pop. 2,503
Leveretts Chapel ISD 200/PK-12
8956 State Highway 42/135 N 75684 903-834-6675
Donna Johnson, supt. Fax 834-6602
www.leverettschapelisd.net
Leveretts Chapel HS 100/9-12
8956 State Highway 42/135 N 75684 903-834-3181
Mark Perry, prin. Fax 834-6602
Leveretts Chapel JHS 50/6-8
8956 State Highway 42/135 N 75684 903-834-3181
Joshua Johnson, prin. Fax 834-6602

Overton ISD 500/PK-12
PO Box 130 75684 903-834-6145
Alan Umholtz, supt. Fax 834-6755
www.overtonisd.net/
Overton HS 200/9-12
PO Box 130 75684 903-834-6143
Stephen DuBose, prin. Fax 834-3246
Overton MS 100/6-8
PO Box 130 75684 903-834-6146
Stephen DuBose, prin. Fax 834-3256

Ovilla, Ellis, Pop. 3,449

Ovilla Christian S 400/PK-12
3251 Ovilla Rd 75154 972-617-1177
Julie Weyand, admin. Fax 218-0135

Ozona, Crockett, Pop. 3,206
Crockett County Consolidated SD 800/PK-12
PO Box 400 76943 325-392-5501
Chris duBois, supt. Fax 392-5177
www.ozonaschools.net
Ozona HS 200/9-12
PO Box 400 76943 325-392-5501
Josh Carty, prin. Fax 392-5177
Ozona MS 200/6-8
PO Box 400 76943 325-392-5501
Tamara McWilliams, prin. Fax 392-5177

Paducah, Cottle, Pop. 1,174
Paducah ISD 200/PK-12
PO Box P 79248 806-492-3524
Troy Parton, supt. Fax 492-2432
www.paducahisd.org
Paducah S 200/PK-12
810 Goodwin Ave 79248 806-492-2009
Jay Cantrell, prin. Fax 492-2193

Paint Rock, Concho, Pop. 270
Paint Rock ISD 200/PK-12
PO Box 277 76866 325-732-4314
Ron Cline, supt. Fax 732-4384
paintrock.netxv.net/
Paint Rock S 100/PK-12
PO Box 277 76866 325-732-4314
Ron Cline, prin. Fax 732-4384

Palacios, Matagorda, Pop. 4,670
Palacios ISD 1,500/PK-12
1209 12th St 77465 361-972-5491
Vicki Adams, supt. Fax 972-3567
www.palaciosisd.org/
Palacios HS 500/9-12
100 Shark Dr 77465 361-972-2571
Sherri Seaman, prin. Fax 972-6287
Palacios JHS 200/7-8
200 Shark Dr 77465 361-972-2417
Joe Adams, prin. Fax 972-6372

Palestine, Anderson, Pop. 18,404
Neches ISD
Supt. — See Neches
Neches HS 100/9-12
1509 County Road 346 75803 903-584-3443
Trent Cook, prin. Fax 584-3686

Palestine ISD 2,400/PK-12
1007 E Park Ave 75801 903-731-8000
Jason Marshall, supt. Fax 729-5588
www.palestineschools.org/
Palestine HS 800/9-12
1600 S Loop 256 75801 903-731-8005
William Stewart, prin. Fax 839-6489
Palestine MS 400/7-8
233 Ben Milam Dr 75801 903-731-8008
Larissa Loveless, prin. Fax 655-0731

Westwood ISD 1,700/PK-12
PO Box 260 75802 903-729-1776
Dr. Ed Lyman, supt. Fax 729-3696
www.westwoodisd.net
Westwood HS 500/9-12
PO Box 260 75802 903-729-1773
Dr. Clint McLain, prin. Fax 729-8695
Westwood JHS 300/7-8
PO Box 260 75802 903-723-0423
Rusty Ressler, prin. Fax 723-6765

Palmer, Ellis, Pop. 1,973
Palmer ISD 1,100/PK-12
PO Box 790 75152 972-449-3389
Kevin Noack, supt. Fax 845-2112
www.palmer-isd.org
Palmer HS 300/9-12
PO Box 790 75152 972-449-3487
Brian Warner, prin. Fax 845-3517
Palmer MS 400/4-8
PO Box 790 75152 972-449-3319
Jacob Perry, prin. Fax 845-3380

Palmhurst, Hidalgo, Pop. 2,600
Mission Consolidated ISD
Supt. — See Mission
Cantu JHS 700/6-8
5101 N Stewart Rd 78572 956-323-7800
Jose Rios, prin. Fax 323-7880

Faith Christian Academy 100/PK-12
4301 N Shary Rd, 956-581-7777
Robert Munne, admin. Fax 581-7786

Palmview, Hidalgo, Pop. 5,455
La Joya ISD
Supt. — See La Joya
Palmview HS 2,400/9-12
3901 N La Homa Rd, 956-519-5779
Norma Garcia, prin. Fax 323-2775
Richards MS 900/6-8
7005 Ann Richards Rd 78572 956-519-5710
Thomas Ocana, prin. Fax 519-5726

Pampa, Gray, Pop. 17,739
Pampa ISD 3,500/PK-12
321 W Albert St 79065 806-669-4700
Dr. David Young, supt. Fax 665-0506
www.pampaisd.net
Pampa HS 900/9-12
111 E Harvester Ave 79065 806-669-4800
Tanya Larkin, prin. Fax 669-4826
Pampa JHS 700/6-8
4000 Bad Cattle Company Rd 79065 806-669-4901
Janet Hancock, prin. Fax 669-4742
Pampa Learning Center 50/Alt
400 N Faulkner St 79065 806-669-4750
Richard Steele, prin. Fax 669-4734

Panhandle, Carson, Pop. 2,431
Panhandle ISD 700/PK-12
PO Box 1030 79068 806-537-3568
Blair Brown, supt. Fax 537-5553
www.panhandleisd.net
Panhandle HS 200/9-12
PO Box 1030 79068 806-537-3897
Jerry Schaeffer, prin. Fax 537-3476
Panhandle JHS 200/6-8
PO Box 1030 79068 806-537-3541
Gary Cates, prin. Fax 537-5725

Paradise, Wise, Pop. 438
Paradise ISD 1,100/PK-12
338 School House Rd 76073 940-969-5000
Monty Chapman, supt. Fax 969-5008
www.pisd.net
Paradise HS 300/9-12
338 School House Rd 76073 940-969-5010
Mac Edwards, prin. Fax 969-5009
Paradise MS 300/6-8
338 School House Rd 76073 940-969-5034
Mark Mathis, prin. Fax 969-5025

Paris, Lamar, Pop. 24,458
Chisum ISD 800/PK-12
3250 S Church St 75462 903-737-2830
Tommy Chalaire, supt. Fax 737-2831
www.chisumisd.org
Chisum HS 300/9-12
3250 S Church St 75462 903-737-2800
Clint Miller, prin. Fax 737-2801
Chisum MS 200/6-8
3250 S Church St 75462 903-737-2806
Cliff Chadwick, prin. Fax 737-2805

North Lamar ISD 2,900/PK-12
3201 Lewis Ln 75460 903-737-2000
James Dawson, supt. Fax 669-0129
www.northlamar.net
North Lamar HS 800/9-12
3201 Lewis Ln 75460 903-737-2011
Paul Allen, prin. Fax 669-0119
Stone MS 700/6-8
3201 Lewis Ln 75460 903-737-2041
Kelli Stewart, prin. Fax 669-0149

Paris ISD 3,300/PK-12
1920 Clarksville St 75460 903-737-7473
Paul Trull, supt. Fax 737-7484
www.parisisd.net
Paris Alternative S for Success 50/Alt
3270 Graham St 75460 903-737-7560
Joan Moore, prin. Fax 737-7574
Paris HS 1,000/9-12
2255 S Collegiate Dr 75460 903-737-7400
Gary Preston, prin. Fax 737-7515
Paris JHS 500/7-8
2400 Jefferson Rd 75460 903-737-7434
Althea Dixon, prin. Fax 737-7534

Paris Junior College Post-Sec.
2400 Clarksville St 75460 903-785-7661
Trinity Christian Academy 100/PK-12
2060 Farm Road 79 75460 903-789-9557
Gary W. Ballard Ed.D., dir. Fax 785-7372

Pasadena, Harris, Pop. 147,777
Deer Park ISD
Supt. — See Deer Park
Deepwater JHS 600/6-8
501 Glenmore Dr 77503 832-668-7600
Scott Davis, prin. Fax 475-6138
Fairmont JHS 800/6-8
4911 Holly Bay Ct 77505 832-668-7800
Neil Munro, prin. Fax 998-4456

Pasadena ISD 49,400/PK-12
1515 Cherrybrook Ln 77502 713-740-0000
Kirk Lewis, supt. Fax 740-4042
www.pasadenaisd.org
Bondy IS 900/6-8
5101 Keith Ave 77505 713-740-0430
Dan Connolly, prin. Fax 740-4152
Card Career & Technical Center Vo/Tech
4320 Crenshaw Rd 77504 713-740-0802
Sarah Wrobleski, dir. Fax 740-4081
Guidance Center Alt
3010 Bayshore Blvd 77502 713-740-0792
Keith Moore, prin. Fax 740-4108
Jackson IS 700/6-8
1020 Thomas Ave 77506 713-740-0440
Paula Sword, prin. Fax 740-4109
Miller IS 800/6-8
1002 Fairmont Pkwy 77504 713-740-0450
Kimberly Kelley, prin. Fax 740-4106
Park View IS 900/6-8
3003 Dabney Dr 77502 713-740-0460
Rob Hasson, prin. Fax 740-4115
Pasadena HS 2,300/9-12
206 Shaver St 77506 713-740-0310
Joe Saavedra, prin. Fax 740-4085
Pasadena Memorial HS 2,800/9-12
4410 Crenshaw Rd 77504 713-740-0390
Angela Stallings, prin. Fax 740-4156
Queens IS 700/6-8
1112 Queens Rd 77502 713-740-0470
Troy Jones, prin. Fax 740-4102
Rayburn HS 2,700/9-12
2121 Cherrybrook Ln 77502 713-740-0330
Robert Stock, prin. Fax 740-4157
San Jacinto IS 600/6-8
3600 Red Bluff Rd 77503 713-740-0480
Dianna Walker, prin. Fax 740-4153
Southmore IS 800/6-8
2000 Patricia Ln 77502 713-740-0500
Lana Stahl, prin. Fax 740-4154
Summit S 100/Alt
1838 E Sam Houston Pkwy S 77503 713-740-0290
Robert DeWolfe, prin. Fax 740-4049
Tegeler Career Center Vo/Tech
4949 Burke Rd 77504 713-740-0410
Jean Cain, prin. Fax 740-4077
Community S Adult
1838A E Sam Houston Pkwy S 77503 713-740-0298
Tom Swan, admin. Fax 740-4048
Other Schools – See Houston, South Houston

First Baptist Christian Academy 400/PK-12
7500 Fairmont Pkwy 77505 281-991-9191
Toni Shuman, admin. Fax 991-7092
Interactive Learning Systems Post-Sec.
213 W Southmore Ave 77502 713-920-1120
San Jacinto College Post-Sec.
8060 Spencer Hwy 77505 281-476-1501
Texas Chiropractic College Post-Sec.
5912 Spencer Hwy 77505 281-487-1170

Pattison, Waller, Pop. 462
Royal ISD 2,000/PK-12
PO Box 489 77466 281-934-2248
Stacy Ackley, supt. Fax 934-2846
www.royal-isd.com
Other Schools – See Brookshire

Pattonville, Lamar
Prairiland ISD 1,100/PK-12
466 Farm Road 196 75468 903-652-6476
Jeff Ballard, supt. Fax 652-3738
www.prairiland.net
Prairiland HS 300/9-12
466 Farm Road 196 75468 903-652-5681
Jason Hostetler, prin. Fax 652-6400
Prairiland JHS 300/6-8
466 Farm Road 196 75468 903-652-5681
Leslie Watson, prin. Fax 652-3232

Pearland, Brazoria, Pop. 89,386
Alvin ISD
Supt. — See Alvin
Ryan JHS 1,200/6-8
11500 Shadow Creek Pkwy 77584 281-245-3210
Christina Lovette, prin. Fax 245-3221

Pearland ISD, PO Box 7 77588 18,800/PK-12
John Kelly Ph.D., supt. 281-485-3203
www.pearlandisd.org
Dawson HS, 2050 Cullen Blvd 77581 2,000/9-12
David Moody, prin. 281-412-8800
Miller JHS, 3301 Manvel Rd 77584 800/7-8
Kim Brooks, prin. 281-997-3900
PACE Center 100/Alt
2314 Old Alvin Rd 77581 281-412-1599
Julia Hall, prin.
Pearland HS, 3775 S Main St 77581 2,300/10-12
Larry Berger, prin. 281-997-7445
Pearland JHS East 700/7-8
2315 Old Alvin Rd 77581 281-485-2481
Annette Chambliss, prin.
Pearland JHS South 700/7-8
4719 Bailey Rd 77584 281-727-1500
Mollye Dahlstrom, prin.
Pearland JHS West 600/7-8
2337 Galveston Ave 77581 281-412-1222
Pam Wilson, prin.
Searcy Ninth Grade Center 900/9-9
3775 S Main St 77581 281-412-1600
Andrea Wenke, prin.

Eagle Heights Christian Academy 300/PK-12
3005 Pearland Pkwy 77581 281-485-6330
John Stahl, prin. Fax 485-8682

Pearsall, Frio, Pop. 9,098
Pearsall ISD 2,300/PK-12
318 Berry Ranch Rd 78061 830-334-8001
Dr. Esthela Allison, supt. Fax 334-8007
www.pearsall.k12.tx.us
Pearsall HS 600/9-12
1990 Maverick Dr 78061 830-334-8011
Julian Hernandez, prin. Fax 334-5018
Pearsall JHS 500/6-8
607 E Alabama St 78061 830-334-8021
L. Derrick Byrd, prin. Fax 334-8025

Pecos, Reeves, Pop. 8,754
Pecos-Barstow-Toyah ISD 2,200/PK-12
PO Box 869 79772 432-447-7201
Clarke Boyd, supt. Fax 447-3076
pbtisd.esc18.net
Crockett MS 500/6-8
PO Box 869 79772 432-447-7461
Sam Martinez, prin. Fax 447-4853
Pecos HS 600/9-12
PO Box 869 79772 432-447-7400
Perry Putman, prin. Fax 447-9055

Penelope, Hill, Pop. 198
Penelope ISD 200/PK-12
PO Box 68 76676 254-533-2215
Scot Kelley, supt. Fax 533-2262
www.penelopeisd.org/
Penelope S 200/PK-12
PO Box 68 76676 254-533-2215
Gordon Vogel, prin. Fax 533-2262

Penitas, Hidalgo, Pop. 4,401
La Joya ISD
Supt. — See La Joya
Saenz MS 600/6-8
39200 Mile 7 Rd 78576 956-519-4007
Paz Elizondo, prin. Fax 519-4016

Pep, Hockley, Pop. 85
Whiteface Consolidated ISD
Supt. — See Whiteface
P E P Alternative Co-op S 50/Alt
PO Box 394 79353 806-933-4499
Jeff Hill, prin. Fax 933-4699

Perrin, Jack, Pop. 396
Perrin-Whitt Consolidated ISD 400/PK-12
216 N Benson St 76486 940-798-3718
John Kuhn, supt. Fax 798-3071
www.pwcisd.net
Perrin JSHS 200/7-12
216 N Benson St 76486 940-798-3845
Diane Edge, prin. Fax 798-3071

Perryton, Ochiltree, Pop. 8,746
Perryton ISD 2,300/PK-12
PO Box 1048 79070 806-435-5478
Robert Hall, supt. Fax 435-4689
www.perrytonisd.com
Perryton HS 600/9-12
PO Box 1048 79070 806-435-3633
Allan Herbert, prin. Fax 435-2602
Perryton JHS 500/6-8
PO Box 1048 79070 806-435-3601
Janet Slaughter, prin. Fax 435-3624
Top-of-Texas Accelerated Education Ctr 50/Alt
PO Box 1048 79070 806-434-0389
Ludi Martin, prin. Fax 434-0402

Petersburg, Hale, Pop. 1,201
Petersburg ISD 300/PK-12
PO Box 160 79250 806-667-3585
Joey Nichols, supt. Fax 667-3463
www.petersburgisd.net
Petersburg JSHS 100/7-12
PO Box 160 79250 806-667-3574
Joseph O'Malley, prin. Fax 667-3463

Petrolia, Clay, Pop. 676
Petrolia ISD 400/PK-12
PO Box 176 76377 940-524-3555
Derrith Welch, supt. Fax 524-3370
www.petroliaisd.org/
Petrolia JSHS 100/7-12
PO Box 176 76377 940-524-3264
Wade Wesley, prin. Fax 524-3215

Pettus, Bee, Pop. 551
Pettus ISD 400/PK-12
PO Box D 78146 361-375-2296
Brian Thompson, supt. Fax 375-2295
www.pettusisd.esc2.net
Pettus HS 200/6-12
PO Box D 78146 361-375-2296
Brent Niemeier, prin. Fax 375-2565

Pflugerville, Travis, Pop. 45,841
Pflugerville ISD 22,500/PK-12
1401 Pecan St W 78660 512-594-0000
Charles Dupre, supt. Fax 594-0005
cms.pflugervilleisd.net
Hendrickson HS 2,200/9-12
2905 FM 685 78660 512-594-1100
Devin Padavil, prin. Fax 594-1105
Kelly Lane MS 1,100/6-8
18900 Falcon Pointe Blvd 78660 512-594-2800
Brian Ernest, prin. Fax 594-2805
Park Crest MS 900/6-8
1500 N Railroad Ave 78660 512-594-2400
Tiffany Commerford, prin. Fax 594-2405
Pflugerville HS 2,300/9-12
1301 Pecan St W 78660 512-594-0500
Kirk Wrinkle, prin. Fax 594-0505

Pflugerville MS 1,000/6-8
1600 Settlers Valley Dr 78660 512-594-2000
Mary Kimmins, prin. Fax 594-2005
Provan Opportunity Center 200/Alt
1401 Pecan St W Ste A 78660 512-594-3600
Billy Harden, prin. Fax 594-3605
Other Schools – See Austin

Century Christian Academy 50/3-12
14400 Immanuel Rd 78660 512-989-3698
William Wright, dir.

Pharr, Hidalgo, Pop. 70,290
Pharr-San Juan-Alamo ISD 32,100/PK-12
PO Box 1150 78577 956-354-2000
Dr. Daniel King, supt. Fax 702-5648
www.psjaisd.us/
Ballew HS 200/Alt
1100 E US Highway 83 78577 956-354-2520
Larissa Saenz-Mancha, prin. Fax 354-2525
Buell Academy 200/Alt
218 E Juarez Ave 78577 956-354-2500
Ruben Borrego, prin. Fax 354-3110
College Career & Technology Academy 200/Alt
1100 E US Highway 83 78577 956-784-8515
Irma Linda Carillo, prin. Fax 783-2870
Escalante MS 600/6-8
6123 S Cage Blvd 78577 956-354-2670
Janie Gomez, prin. Fax 354-3200
Johnson MS 900/6-8
500 E Sioux Rd 78577 956-354-2590
Linda Soto, prin. Fax 702-5661
Kennedy MS 700/6-8
600 W Hall Acres Rd 78577 956-354-2650
Norma Garza, prin. Fax 354-2667
Liberty MS 900/6-8
1212 Fir Rdg 78577 956-354-2610
Mario Bracamontes, prin. Fax 783-2820
Pharr-San Juan-Alamo North HS 2,300/9-12
500 E Nolana Loop 78577 956-354-2360
Dalila Garcia, prin. Fax 783-3307
Pharr-San Juan-Alamo SW HS 800/9-12
300 E Rancho Blanco Rd 78577 956-354-2480
Melba Lozano, prin. Fax 283-0543
T-Stem Early College HS 300/9-12
300 E Rancho Blanco Rd 78577 956-784-8525
Marisela Zepeda, prin. Fax 702-5820
Other Schools – See Alamo, San Juan

Valley View ISD 3,800/PK-12
9701 S Jackson Rd 78577 956-340-1000
Leonel Galaviz, supt. Fax 843-8688
www.vviewisd.net
Valley View Early College Campus 50/8-9
9701 S Jackson Rd 78577 956-340-1200
Miguel Castillo, prin. Fax 213-8438
Valley View HS 1,000/9-12
9701 S Jackson Rd 78577 956-340-1500
Monica Luna, prin. Fax 843-8195
Valley View Phoenix Academy 50/Alt
9701 S Jackson Rd 78577 956-340-1500
Jorge Flores, prin. Fax 843-8195

Oratory Academy 500/PK-12
1407 W Moore Rd 78577 956-781-3056
Fr. Mario Aviles, prin. Fax 787-1516
Southern Careers Institute Post-Sec.
1500 N Jackson Rd 78577 956-687-1415

Pilot Point, Denton, Pop. 3,793
Pilot Point ISD 1,600/PK-12
829 S Harrison St 76258 940-686-8700
Glenn Barber, supt. Fax 686-8705
www.pilotpointisd.com
Pilot Point HS 400/9-12
1300 N Washington St 76258 940-686-8740
Lori Sitzes, prin. Fax 686-8745
Pilot Point MS - J. Earl Selz Campus 200/7-8
828 S Harrison St 76258 940-686-8730
Larry Shuman, prin. Fax 686-8735

Pineland, Sabine, Pop. 835
West Sabine ISD 600/PK-12
PO Box 869 75968 409-584-2655
Mike Pate, supt. Fax 584-2139
www.westsabine.esc7.net
West Sabine JSHS 300/6-12
PO Box 869 75968 409-584-2525
Mike Ogden, prin. Fax 584-2695

Pittsburg, Camp, Pop. 4,399
Pittsburg ISD 2,500/PK-12
PO Box 1189 75686 903-856-3628
Judy Pollan, supt. Fax 856-0269
pittsburgisd.net
Pittsburg HS 700/9-12
300 N Texas St 75686 903-856-3646
Jonathan Hill, prin. Fax 855-3325
Pittsburg MS 400/7-8
313 Broach St 75686 903-856-6432
Terri Brown, prin. Fax 855-3357

Plains, Yoakum, Pop. 1,468
Plains ISD 500/PK-12
PO Box 479 79355 806-456-7401
Michael Michaelson, supt. Fax 456-4325
plainsisd.net/
Plains HS 100/9-12
PO Box 479 79355 806-456-7498
Jim Baum, prin. Fax 456-4325
Plains MS 100/5-8
PO Box 479 79355 806-456-7490
Jim Baum, prin. Fax 456-4325

Plainview, Hale, Pop. 21,983
Plainview ISD 5,800/PK-12
PO Box 1540 79073 806-296-6392
Dr. Ron Miller, supt. Fax 296-4014
www.plainview.k12.tx.us
Estacado JHS 400/8-8
2500 W 20th St 79072 806-296-4165
Ritchie Thornton, prin. Fax 296-4169
Houston S 100/Alt
2417 Yonkers St 79072 806-296-4184
Dana Broyles, prin. Fax 296-4183
Plainview HS 1,400/9-12
1501 Quincy St 79072 806-296-4051
Tye Rogers, prin. Fax 296-4069

Plainview Christian Academy 200/PK-12
310 S Ennis St 79072 806-296-6034
Karen Earhart, admin. Fax 296-0074
Wayland Baptist University Post-Sec.
1900 W 7th St 79072 806-291-1000

Plano, Collin, Pop. 253,492
Frisco ISD
Supt. — See Frisco
Fowler MS 1,100/6-8
3801 McDermott Rd 75025 469-633-5050
Donnie Wiseman, prin. Fax 633-5060

Plano ISD 54,600/PK-12
2700 W 15th St 75075 469-752-8100
Richard Matkin, supt. Fax 752-8096
www.pisd.edu
Armstrong MS 800/6-8
3805 Timberline Dr 75074 469-752-4600
Steven Ewing, prin. Fax 752-4601
Bowman MS 800/6-8
2501 Jupiter Rd 75074 469-752-4800
Gloria Martinez, prin. Fax 752-4801
Carpenter MS 900/6-8
3905 Rainier Rd 75023 469-752-5000
Courtney Washington, prin. Fax 752-5001
Clark HS 1,300/9-10
523 W Spring Creek Pkwy 75023 469-752-7200
Janis Williams, prin. Fax 752-7201
Guinn Special Programs Center Alt
2221 Legacy Dr 75023 469-752-6900
Sharon Bradley, prin. Fax 752-6901
Haggard MS 900/6-8
2832 Parkhaven Dr 75075 469-752-5400
Julie-Anne Dean, prin. Fax 752-5401
Hendrick MS 900/6-8
7400 Red River Dr 75025 469-752-5600
Lisa Long, prin. Fax 752-5601
Jasper HS 2,100/9-10
6800 Archgate Dr 75024 469-752-7400
Dr. Kary Cooper, prin. Fax 752-7401
Otto MS 6-8
504 N Star Rd 75074 469-752-8500
Antoine Spencer, prin. Fax 752-8501
Plano East SHS 2,900/11-12
3000 Los Rios Blvd 75074 469-752-9000
Karen McDonald, prin. Fax 752-9001
Plano SHS 2,700/11-12
2200 Independence Pkwy 75075 469-752-9300
Sarah Watkins, prin. Fax 752-9301
Plano West SHS 2,000/11-12
5601 W Parker Rd 75093 469-752-9600
Kathy King, prin. Fax 752-9601
Renner MS 1,300/6-8
5701 W Parker Rd 75093 469-752-5800
Bill McLaughlin, prin. Fax 752-5801
Rice MS 1,200/6-8
8500 Gifford Dr 75025 469-752-6000
Chris Glasscock, prin. Fax 752-6001
Robinson MS 1,000/6-8
6701 Preston Meadow Dr 75024 469-752-6200
Billie Jean Lee, prin. Fax 752-6201
Schimelpfenig MS 1,000/6-8
2400 Maumelle Dr 75023 469-752-6400
Jason Myatt, prin. Fax 752-6401
Shepton HS 1,600/9-10
5505 W Plano Pkwy 75093 469-752-7600
Courtney Gober, prin. Fax 752-7601
Vines HS 1,300/9-10
1401 Highedge Dr 75075 469-752-7800
Shauna Koehne, prin. Fax 752-7801
Williams HS 2,100/9-10
1717 17th St 75074 469-752-8300
Lynn Ojeda, prin. Fax 752-8301
Wilson MS 1,000/6-8
1001 Custer Rd 75075 469-752-6700
Selenda Sager, prin. Fax 752-6701
Other Schools – See Dallas, Murphy

Collin College Post-Sec.
2800 E Spring Creek Pkwy 75074 972-881-5790
Faith Lutheran S 100/PK-12
1701 E Park Blvd 75074 972-423-7448
Timothy Merritt, hdmstr. Fax 423-9618
John Paul II HS 600/9-12
900 Coit Rd 75075 972-867-0005
Steven Mininger, pres. Fax 867-7555
Prestonwood Christian Academy 1,500/PK-12
6801 W Park Blvd 75093 972-820-5300
Dr. Larry Taylor, hdmstr. Fax 820-5068
St. Timothy Christian Academy 50/K-10
1501 H Ave 75074 972-509-7822
Margaret Whitaker, head sch Fax 509-7829

Pleasanton, Atascosa, Pop. 8,878
Pleasanton ISD 3,200/PK-12
831 Stadium Dr 78064 830-569-1200
Cynthia Clinesmith, supt. Fax 569-2171
www.pisd.us
Pleasanton HS 900/9-12
831 Stadium Dr 78064 830-569-1250
Dr. Matthew Mann, prin. Fax 569-4747
Pleasanton JHS 500/7-8
831 Stadium Dr 78064 830-569-1280
Helen Osterman, prin. Fax 569-1290

Pollok, Angelina
Central ISD 1,400/PK-12
7622 N US Highway 69 75969 936-853-2216
Allen Garner, supt. Fax 853-2215
www.centralisd.com
Central HS 400/9-12
7622 N US Highway 69 75969 936-853-2167
Richard Nash, prin. Fax 853-2208
Central JHS 400/5-8
7622 N US Highway 69 75969 936-853-2115
Kris Whisenant, prin. Fax 853-2348

Ponder, Denton, Pop. 1,372
Ponder ISD 1,200/PK-12
400 W Bailey St 76259 940-479-8200
Bruce Yeager, supt. Fax 479-8209
www.ponderisd.net
Ponder HS 300/9-12
400 W Bailey St 76259 940-479-8210
Shawn Simmons, prin. Fax 479-8219
Ponder JHS 300/6-8
400 W Bailey St 76259 940-479-8220
Ted Heers, prin. Fax 479-8229

Poolville, Parker
Poolville ISD 500/PK-12
PO Box 96 76487 817-594-4452
Jimmie Dobbs, supt. Fax 594-2651
www.poolville.net
Poolville HS 100/9-12
1001 Lone Star Rd 76487 817-599-5134
Kurt Kronenberger, prin. Fax 599-5171
Poolville JHS 100/6-8
PO Box 96 76487 817-594-4539
Matt Scott, prin. Fax 594-0081

Port Aransas, Nueces, Pop. 3,435
Port Aransas ISD 600/PK-12
100 S Station St 78373 361-749-1205
Dr. Sharon Doughty, supt. Fax 749-1215
www.paisd.net
Brundrett MS 100/6-8
100 S Station St 78373 361-749-1209
Gina McKeever, prin. Fax 749-1218
Port Aransas HS 200/9-12
100 S Station St 78373 361-749-1206
Sharon McKinney, prin. Fax 749-1219

Port Arthur, Jefferson, Pop. 53,210
Port Arthur ISD 9,200/PK-12
PO Box 1388 77641 409-989-6100
Mark Porterie, supt. Fax 989-6229
www.paisd.org
Career and Technical Education Vo/Tech
3501 Sgt Lucien Adams Blvd 77642 409-989-4750
Calvin Rice, dir. Fax 983-2204
Jefferson MS 800/6-8
2200 Jefferson Dr 77642 409-984-4860
Dr. Barbara Polk, prin. Fax 960-6057
Lincoln MS 500/6-8
1023 Abe Lincoln Ave 77640 409-984-8700
LaSonya Baptiste, prin. Fax 982-2847
Memorial 9th Grade Academy 600/9-9
2441 61st St 77640 409-736-1521
Dr. Lisa Chambers, prin. Fax 736-0267
Memorial HS 1,700/10-12
3501 Sgt Lucien Adams Blvd 77642 409-984-4000
Dr. Glenn Mitchell, prin. Fax 985-3376
Port Arthur Alternative Center Alt
PO Box 1388 77641 409-984-8650
Sharon Dozier-Davis, prin. Fax 962-6013

Lamar State College Port Arthur Post-Sec.
1500 Procter St 77640 409-983-4921
Ridgewood Christian S PK-12
2920 Lake Arthur Dr 77642 409-729-6000
Dwayne Oxner, hdmstr. Fax 724-2469

Porter, Montgomery, Pop. 7,000
New Caney ISD
Supt. — See New Caney
Porter HS 1,000/9-12
22625 Sandy Ln 77365 281-577-5900
Ken Hodgkinson Ed.D., prin. Fax 354-2493
White Oak MS 800/7-8
24161 Briar Berry Ln 77365 281-577-8800
Roger McAdoo, prin. Fax 354-5186

Port Isabel, Cameron, Pop. 4,982
Point Isabel ISD 2,500/PK-12
101 Port Rd 78578 956-943-0000
Lisa Garcia, supt. Fax 943-0014
www.pi-isd.net/
Port Isabel HS 600/9-12
101 Port Rd 78578 956-943-0030
Dr. William Roach, prin. Fax 943-0648
Port Isabel JHS 500/6-8
101 Port Rd 78578 956-943-0060
Nancy Gonzalez, prin. Fax 943-0055

Portland, San Patricio, Pop. 14,859
Gregory-Portland ISD 4,300/PK-12
608 College St 78374 361-777-1091
Dr. Paul Clore, supt. Fax 777-1093
www.g-pisd.org
Gregory-Portland HS 1,300/9-12
4601 Wildcat Dr 78374 361-777-4251
Barbara Cade, prin. Fax 777-4272
Gregory-Portland JHS 600/7-8
4600 Wildcat Dr 78374 361-777-4042
Xavier Barrera, prin. Fax 643-3187

Port Lavaca, Calhoun, Pop. 12,146
Calhoun County ISD 4,100/PK-12
525 N Commerce St 77979 361-552-9728
Billy Wiggins, supt. Fax 551-2648
www.calcoisd.org
Calhoun HS 1,200/9-12
201 Sandcrab Blvd 77979 361-552-3775
Brandon Stiewig, prin. Fax 551-2620

Hope HS 50/Alt
300 Alcoa Dr 77979 361-552-7084
Casey Crowder, prin. Fax 551-2677
Travis MS 800/6-8
705 N Nueces St 77979 361-552-3784
Lina Moore, prin. Fax 551-2692

Port Neches, Jefferson, Pop. 12,912
Port Neches-Groves ISD 4,500/PK-12
620 Avenue C 77651 409-722-4244
Dr. Rodney Cavness, supt. Fax 724-7864
www.pngisd.org
Port Neches-Groves HS 1,400/9-12
1401 Merriman St 77651 409-729-7644
Marc Keith Ed.D., prin. Fax 722-7371
Port Neches MS 500/6-8
749 Central Dr 77651 409-722-8115
Kyle Hooper, prin. Fax 727-8342
Other Schools – See Groves

Post, Garza, Pop. 5,351
Post ISD 800/PK-12
501 S Avenue K 79356 806-495-3343
Mike Comeaux, supt. Fax 495-2945
www.postisd.net
Post HS 200/9-12
200 W 6th St 79356 806-495-2770
John Berry, prin. Fax 495-2792
Post MS 200/6-8
405 W 8th St 79356 806-495-2874
Marvin Self, prin. Fax 495-2426

Poteet, Atascosa, Pop. 3,241
Poteet ISD 1,800/PK-12
PO Box 138 78065 830-742-3567
Andres Castillo, supt. Fax 742-8038
www.poteet.k12.tx.us
Poteet HS 500/9-12
PO Box 138 78065 830-742-3522
Van Johnson, prin. Fax 742-8497
Poteet JHS 400/6-8
PO Box 138 78065 830-742-3571
Manuel Aragon, prin. Fax 742-8495

Poth, Wilson, Pop. 1,900
Poth ISD 800/PK-12
PO Box 250 78147 830-484-3330
Scott Caloss, supt. Fax 484-2961
www.pothisd.us
Poth HS 300/9-12
PO Box 250 78147 830-484-3322
Frank Hosek, prin. Fax 484-3304
Poth JHS 200/6-8
PO Box 250 78147 830-484-3323
Todd Pawelek, prin. Fax 484-3682

Pottsboro, Grayson, Pop. 2,115
Pottsboro ISD 1,300/PK-12
PO Box 555 75076 903-771-0083
Dr. Kevin Matthews, supt. Fax 786-9085
www.pottsboroisd.org/
Pottsboro HS 300/9-12
PO Box 555 75076 903-771-0085
Josh Recer, prin. Fax 786-6349
Pottsboro MS 300/6-8
PO Box 555 75076 903-771-2982
John Reves, prin. Fax 786-4902

Prairie Lea, Caldwell
Prairie Lea ISD 200/PK-12
PO Box 9 78661 512-488-2328
Jesus Lopez, supt. Fax 488-9006
www.prairielea.txed.net/
Prairie Lea S 200/PK-12
PO Box 9 78661 512-488-2328
Darren Kesselus, prin. Fax 488-2425

Prairie View, Waller, Pop. 5,483

Prairie View A&M University Post-Sec.
PO Box 519 77446 936-261-3311

Premont, Jim Wells, Pop. 2,649
Premont ISD 500/PK-12
PO Box 530 78375 361-348-3915
Ernest Singleton, supt. Fax 348-2882
www.premontisd.net
Premont HS 200/7-12
PO Box B 78375 361-348-3915
Enrique Ruiz, prin. Fax 348-2914

Presidio, Presidio, Pop. 4,416
Presidio ISD 1,500/PK-12
PO Box 1401 79845 432-229-3275
Dennis McEntire, supt. Fax 229-4228
www.presidio-isd.net
Franco MS 300/7-9
PO Box 1401 79845 432-229-3113
Dr. Edgar Tibayan, prin. Fax 229-4087
Presidio HS 300/10-12
PO Box 1401 79845 432-229-3365
Dr. Dale Morris, prin. Fax 229-4625

Priddy, Mills
Priddy ISD 100/K-12
PO Box 40 76870 325-966-3323
Adrianne Burden, supt. Fax 966-3380
www.priddyisd.net
Priddy S 100/K-12
PO Box 40 76870 325-966-3323
Adrianne Klein, prin. Fax 966-3380

Princeton, Collin, Pop. 6,693
Princeton ISD 3,200/PK-12
321 Panther Pkwy 75407 469-952-5400
Philip Anthony, supt. Fax 736-3505
www.princetonisd.net
Clark JHS 500/7-8
301 Panther Pkwy 75407 469-952-5400
Greg Tabor, prin. Fax 736-5903
Princeton HS 900/9-12
1000 E Princeton Dr 75407 469-952-5400
Rene Mullins, prin. Fax 736-5902

Progreso, Hidalgo, Pop. 5,505
Progreso ISD 1,600/PK-12
PO Box 610 78579 956-565-3002
Dr. Fernando Castillo, supt. Fax 565-2128
www.progresoedu.net
Progreso HS 500/9-12
PO Box 610 78579 956-565-4142
Adela Troncoso, prin. Fax 565-6029
Thompson MS 300/7-8
PO Box 610 78579 956-565-6539
Joan Alvarez, prin. Fax 565-2128

Prosper, Collin, Pop. 9,238
Prosper ISD 4,500/PK-12
605 E 7th St 75078 469-219-2000
Drew Watkins Ed.D., supt. Fax 346-9247
www.prosper-isd.net
Prosper HS 1,100/9-12
301 Eagle Dr 75078 469-219-2180
Greg Wright, prin. Fax 346-9246
Reynolds MS 7-8
700 N Coleman St 75078 469-219-2165
Greg Bradley, prin. Fax 346-2455

Quanah, Hardeman, Pop. 2,586
Quanah ISD 500/PK-12
PO Box 150 79252 940-663-2281
Buddy Freeman, supt. Fax 663-2875
www.qisd.net
Quanah HS 200/9-12
PO Box 150 79252 940-663-2791
Rusty Brawley, prin. Fax 663-6447
Travis MS 100/6-8
PO Box 150 79252 940-663-2226
Gayle McKinley, prin. Fax 663-6361

Queen City, Cass, Pop. 1,456
Queen City ISD 1,100/PK-12
PO Box 128 75572 903-796-8256
Rob Barnwell, supt. Fax 796-0248
www.qcisd.net
Queen City HS 300/9-12
PO Box 128 75572 903-796-8259
Charlotte Williams, prin. Fax 796-8258
Upchurch MS 300/5-8
PO Box 128 75572 903-796-6412
Steve Holmes, prin. Fax 796-0834

Quinlan, Hunt, Pop. 1,373
Boles ISD 500/PK-12
9777 FM 2101 75474 903-883-4464
Dr. Graham Sweeney, supt. Fax 883-4531
boles.ednet10.net
Boles HS 200/9-12
9777 FM 2101 75474 903-883-2918
Carol Brown, prin. Fax 883-5109
Boles MS 200/5-8
9777 FM 2101 75474 903-883-4464
Mikayle Moreland, prin. Fax 883-3097

Quinlan ISD 2,000/PK-12
401 E Richmond 75474 903-356-1200
Micheal French, supt. Fax 356-1201
www.quinlanisd.net
Ford HS 700/9-12
10064 Business Highway 34 S 75474 903-356-1600
Kell Clopton, prin. Fax 356-1699
Thompson MS 600/6-8
423 Panther Path 75474 903-356-1500
Christopher Taylor, prin. Fax 356-2414

Quitman, Wood, Pop. 1,780
Quitman ISD 1,100/PK-12
1201 E Goode St 75783 903-763-5000
Rick Flanagan, supt. Fax 763-2710
www.quitmanisd.net/
Quitman HS 300/9-12
1101 E Goode St 75783 903-763-5000
James Young, prin. Fax 763-2589
Quitman JHS 200/6-8
1101 E Goode St 75783 903-763-5000
Garland Willis, prin. Fax 763-2589

Ralls, Crosby, Pop. 1,930
Ralls ISD 600/PK-12
810 Avenue I 79357 806-253-2509
Chris Wade, supt. Fax 253-2508
rallsisd.org
Ralls HS 100/9-12
1106 10th St 79357 806-253-2571
Migueal Salazar, prin. Fax 253-2609
Ralls MS 100/6-8
810 Avenue I 79357 806-253-2549
Jeremy Griffith, prin. Fax 253-4031
Recovery Educational Campus 50/Alt
1106 10th St 79357 806-253-2571
Miguel Salazar, prin. Fax 253-2609

Randolph AFB, Bexar, Pop. 1,177
Randolph Field ISD 1,200/PK-12
Building 1225 78148 210-357-2300
Lance Johnson, supt. Fax 357-2469
www.rfisd.net
Randolph HS 300/9-12
Building 1225 78148 210-357-2400
Mark Malone Ed.D., prin. Fax 357-2475
Randolph MS 300/6-8
Building 1225 78148 210-357-2400
Mark Malone Ed.D., prin. Fax 357-2475

Ranger, Eastland, Pop. 2,441
Ranger ISD 400/PK-12
1842 E Loop 254 76470 254-647-1187
Mike Thompson, supt. Fax 647-5215
www.ranger.esc14.net
Ranger JSHS 100/6-12
1842 E Loop 254 76470 254-647-3216
Leanne Ingram, prin. Fax 647-1895

Ranger College Post-Sec.
1100 College Cir 76470 254-647-3234

Rankin, Upton, Pop. 776
Rankin ISD 200/PK-12
PO Box 90 79778 432-693-2461
Danny Davis, supt. Fax 693-2353
www.rankin.k12.tx.us
Rankin JSHS 100/7-12
PO Box 90 79778 432-693-1161
Samuel Wyatt, prin. Fax 693-2453

Raymondville, Willacy, Pop. 11,257
Raymondville ISD 2,200/PK-12
419 FM 3168 78580 956-689-8176
Johnny Pineda, supt. Fax 689-0201
www.raymondvilleisd.org/
Green MS 500/6-8
419 FM 3168 78580 956-689-8171
Dora Hernandez, prin. Fax 689-2302
Raymondville HS 600/9-12
419 FM 3168 78580 956-689-8170
Dr. John Jauregui, prin. Fax 689-8152

Red Oak, Ellis, Pop. 10,592
Red Oak ISD 5,500/PK-12
PO Box 9000 75154 972-617-2941
Dr. J. Scott Niven, supt. Fax 617-4333
www.redoakisd.org
Red Oak HS 1,900/9-12
PO Box 9000 75154 972-617-3535
Kevin Freels, prin. Fax 617-4796
Red Oak JHS 900/7-8
PO Box 9000 75154 972-617-0066
Cristi Watts, prin. Fax 617-4786

Redwater, Bowie, Pop. 1,037
Redwater ISD 1,100/PK-12
PO Box 347 75573 903-671-3481
Bobby Wheeley, supt. Fax 671-2019
www.redwaterisd.org/
Redwater HS 400/9-12
PO Box 347 75573 903-671-3421
Kelly Lusk, prin. Fax 671-3259
Redwater JHS 200/7-8
PO Box 347 75573 903-671-3227
Kelly Lusk, prin. Fax 671-9921

Refugio, Refugio, Pop. 2,860
Refugio ISD 700/PK-12
212 W Vance St 78377 361-526-2325
Jack Gaskins, supt. Fax 526-2326
www.refugioisd.net/
Refugio JSHS 300/7-12
212 W Vance St 78377 361-526-2344
Todd Deaver, prin. Fax 526-1075

Rhome, Wise, Pop. 1,498
Northwest ISD
Supt. — See Justin
Chisholm Trail MS 1,000/6-8
583 FM 3433 76078 817-215-0600
Dr. Todd Rogers, prin. Fax 215-0648

Rice, Ellis, Pop. 908
Rice ISD 800/PK-12
1302 SW McKinney St 75155 903-326-4287
Judith Pritchett, supt. Fax 326-4164
Rice HS 200/9-12
1400 SW McKinney St 75155 903-326-4502
Dan Taylor, prin. Fax 326-5042
Rice IS 400/3-8
1402 SW McKinney St 75155 903-326-4190
Amy Harvell, prin. Fax 326-4620

Richards, Grimes
Richards ISD 200/PK-12
PO Box 308 77873 936-851-2364
Martey Ainsworth, supt. Fax 851-2210
www.richardsisd.net
Richards JSHS 100/7-12
PO Box 308 77873 936-851-2364
William Boyce, prin. Fax 851-2210

Richardson, Dallas, Pop. 96,979
Richardson ISD 33,800/PK-12
400 S Greenville Ave 75081 469-593-0000
Dr. Kay Waggoner, supt. Fax 593-0402
www.risd.org
Apollo JHS 700/7-9
1600 Apollo Rd 75081 469-593-7900
Jack Noleware, prin. Fax 593-7911
Berkner HS 1,900/10-12
1600 E Spring Valley Rd 75081 469-593-7000
Ron Griffen, prin. Fax 593-7211
McAuliffe Learning Center 100/Alt
900 S Greenville Ave 75081 469-593-5800
Lorine Burrell, prin. Fax 593-5805
Pearce HS 1,500/10-12
1600 N Coit Rd 75080 469-593-5000
Beverly Vance, prin. Fax 593-5169
Richardson Arts Law & Science Magnet HS 10-12
1250 W Belt Line Rd 75080 469-593-3038
Josh Eason, admin. Fax 593-3082
Richardson HS 1,800/10-12
1250 W Belt Line Rd 75080 469-593-3000
Charles Pickitt, prin. Fax 593-3010
Richardson-North JHS 500/7-9
1820 N Floyd Rd 75080 469-593-5400
Philip Bates, prin. Fax 593-5434
Richardson-West JHS Tech Magnet 700/7-9
1309 Holly Dr 75080 469-593-3700
Henry Hall, prin. Fax 593-3666
STEM Academy 9-12
1600 E Spring Valley Rd 75081 469-593-7006
Elizabeth Swaner, prin. Fax 593-7211

Other Schools – See Dallas

Alexander S — 50/7-12
409 International Pkwy 75081 — 972-690-9210
Andrew Cody, prin. — Fax 690-9284
ATI Career Training Center — Post-Sec.
1111 Digital Dr Ste 101 75081 — 214-646-8460
Canyon Creek Christian Academy — 500/PK-12
2800 Custer Pkwy 75080 — 972-231-4890
Andy Wright, hdmstr. — Fax 234-8414
DeVry University — Post-Sec.
2201 N Central Expy Ste 200 75080 — 972-792-7450
ITT Technical Institute — Post-Sec.
2101 Waterview Pkwy 75080 — 972-690-9100
North Dallas Adventist Academy — 200/PK-12
302 Centennial Blvd 75081 — 972-234-6322
PCI Health Training Center — Post-Sec.
1300 International Pkwy 75081 — 214-630-0568
University of Texas at Dallas — Post-Sec.
800 W Campbell Rd 75080 — 972-883-2111

Richland Hills, Tarrant, Pop. 7,627
Birdville ISD
Supt. — See Haltom City
Richland MS — 600/6-8
7400 Hovenkamp Ave 76118 — 817-547-4400
Leeann Bartee Ph.D., prin. — Fax 595-5139

Richland Springs, San Saba, Pop. 332
Richland Springs ISD — 100/PK-12
700 W Coyote Trl 76871 — 325-452-3524
Don Fowler, supt. — Fax 452-3230
www.rscoyotes.net
Richland Springs S — 100/PK-12
700 W Coyote Trl 76871 — 325-452-3427
Don Fowler, prin. — Fax 452-3580

Richmond, Fort Bend, Pop. 11,601
Fort Bend ISD
Supt. — See Sugar Land
Bowie MS — 6-8
700 Plantation Dr 77406 — 281-327-6200
Chris Morgan, prin. — Fax 327-6201
Bush HS — 2,000/9-12
6707 FM 1464 Rd, — 281-634-6060
Cecilia Crear, prin. — Fax 634-6066
Crockett MS — 1,400/6-8
19001 Beechnut St, — 281-634-6380
Thomas Graham, prin. — Fax 327-6380
Travis HS — 2,200/9-12
11111 Harlem Rd 77406 — 281-634-7000
J.J. Kyle, prin. — Fax 634-7010

Lamar Consolidated ISD
Supt. — See Rosenberg
Briscoe JHS — 900/7-8
4300 FM 723 Rd 77406 — 832-223-4000
Mike Semmler, prin. — Fax 223-4001
Foster HS — 2,000/9-12
4400 FM 723 Rd 77406 — 832-223-3800
Gene Tomas, prin. — Fax 223-3801
George Ranch HS — 1,300/9-12
8181 FM 762 Rd 77469 — 832-223-4200
Leslie Haack, prin. — Fax 223-4201
Heading JHS — 1,500/6-8
8101 FM 762 Rd 77469 — 832-223-4400
Juan Nava, prin. — Fax 223-4401

Calvary Episcopal S — 300/PK-12
1201 Austin St 77469 — 281-342-3161
Malcolm Smith, hdmstr. — Fax 232-9449

Riesel, McLennan, Pop. 994
Riesel ISD — 600/PK-12
600 E Frederick St 76682 — 254-896-6411
Brian Garner, supt. — Fax 896-2981
www.rieselisd.org
Riesel JSHS — 300/7-12
600 E Frederick St 76682 — 254-896-3171
Stephen English, prin. — Fax 896-2981

Rio Grande City, Starr, Pop. 13,814
Rio Grande City ISD — 10,800/PK-12
1 S Fort Ringgold St 78582 — 956-716-6700
Roel Gonzalez, supt. — Fax 487-8506
www.rgccisd.org/
Grulla HS — 1,000/9-12
6884 E Highway 83 78582 — 956-487-7278
Joel Trigo, prin. — Fax 487-4312
Ringgold MS — 800/6-8
1 S Fort Ringgold St 78582 — 956-716-6849
Olga Smedley, prin. — Fax 716-6807
Rio Grande City HS — 1,900/9-12
144 N FM 3167 78582 — 956-488-6000
Adolfo Pena, prin. — Fax 488-6050
Veterans MS — 900/6-8
2700 W Eisenhower St 78582 — 956-488-0252
Maricela Garcia, prin. — Fax 488-0261
Other Schools – See Grulla

Roma ISD
Supt. — See Roma
Barrera MS — 700/6-8
258 N FM 649 78582 — 956-486-2670
Carlos Gonzalez, prin. — Fax 486-2607

Rio Hondo, Cameron, Pop. 2,354
Rio Hondo ISD — 2,300/PK-12
215 W Colorado St 78583 — 956-748-1000
Anneliese McMinn, supt. — Fax 748-1038
www.riohondoisd.net
Rio Hondo HS — 600/9-12
215 W Colorado St 78583 — 956-748-1200
Veronica Puente, prin. — Fax 748-1204
Rio Hondo JHS — 500/6-8
215 W Colorado St 78583 — 956-748-1150
Fidel Garza, prin. — Fax 748-1154

Rio Vista, Johnson, Pop. 866
Rio Vista ISD — 900/PK-12
PO Box 369 76093 — 817-373-2009
Tim Wright, supt. — Fax 373-2076
www.rvisd.net
Rio Vista HS — 200/9-12
PO Box 369 76093 — 817-373-2669
Tony Martin, prin. — Fax 373-3047
Rio Vista MS — 300/5-8
PO Box 369 76093 — 817-373-2009
Kathleen Kemphaus, prin. — Fax 373-3046

Rising Star, Eastland, Pop. 829
Rising Star ISD — 200/PK-12
PO Box 37 76471 — 254-643-2717
Dr. Max Thompson, supt. — Fax 643-1922
www.risingstarisd.org
Rising Star JSHS — 100/7-12
PO Box 37 76471 — 254-643-3521
Dr. Max Thompson, prin. — Fax 643-5408

River Oaks, Tarrant, Pop. 7,362
Castleberry ISD
Supt. — See Fort Worth
REACH HS, 1101 Merritt St 76114 — 50/Alt
Wanda Mitchell, prin. — 817-252-2390

Riviera, Kleberg, Pop. 688
Riviera ISD — 500/PK-12
203 Seahawk Dr 78379 — 361-296-3101
Karen Unterbrink, supt. — Fax 296-3108
www.rivieraisd.esc2.net
De La Paz MS — 100/6-8
203 Seahawk Dr 78379 — 361-296-3610
Linda Morales, prin. — Fax 296-3890
Kaufer HS — 200/9-12
203 Seahawk Dr 78379 — 361-296-3607
Linda Morales, prin. — Fax 296-3845

Roanoke, Denton, Pop. 5,845
Northwest ISD
Supt. — See Justin
Steele Accelerated HS — 100/10-12
606 N Walnut St 76262 — 817-698-5800
Robin Ellis, prin. — Fax 698-5840
Tidwell MS — 800/6-8
3937 Haslet Roanoke Rd 76262 — 817-698-5900
Shane Conklin, prin. — Fax 698-5870

Robert Lee, Coke, Pop. 1,034
Robert Lee ISD — 200/PK-12
1323 W Hamilton St 76945 — 325-453-4555
Aaron Hood, supt. — Fax 453-2326
www.rlisd.net
Robert Lee HS — 100/7-12
1323 W Hamilton St 76945 — 325-453-4557
David O'Dell, prin. — Fax 453-2326

Robinson, McLennan, Pop. 10,380
Robinson ISD — 2,100/PK-12
500 W Lyndale Ave 76706 — 254-662-0194
Michael Hope, supt. — Fax 662-0215
www.robinson.k12.tx.us
Robinson HS — 700/9-12
500 W Lyndale Ave 76706 — 254-662-3840
Russ Meggs, prin. — Fax 662-4007
Robinson JHS — 500/6-8
500 W Lyndale Ave 76706 — 254-662-3843
David Wrzesinski, prin. — Fax 662-1845

Robstown, Nueces, Pop. 11,474
Robstown ISD — 2,500/PK-12
801 N 1st St 78380 — 361-767-6600
Dr. Leobardo Cano, supt. — Fax 387-6311
www.robstownisd.org/
Alternative Learning Center — 100/Alt
408 W Main Ave 78380 — 361-387-5999
Esme Limon, prin. — Fax 387-3849
Robstown HS — 800/9-12
609 Highway 44 78380 — 361-387-5999
Richard Waterhouse, prin. — Fax 767-6629
Seale JHS — 500/7-8
401 E Avenue G 78380 — 361-767-6631
Cristina De Alejandro, prin. — Fax 387-6202

Roby, Fisher, Pop. 640
Roby Consolidated ISD — 300/PK-12
PO Box 519 79543 — 325-776-2222
Heath Dickson, supt. — Fax 776-2823
www.roby.esc14.net
Roby HS — 100/9-12
PO Box 519 79543 — 325-776-2223
Jason Carter, prin. — Fax 776-2823

Rochelle, McCulloch
Rochelle ISD — 200/PK-12
PO Box 167 76872 — 325-243-5224
Steve Butler, supt. — Fax 243-5283
www.rochelleisd.net
Rochelle S — 200/PK-12
PO Box 167 76872 — 325-243-5224
Jym Dennis, prin. — Fax 243-5283

Rockdale, Milam, Pop. 5,537
Rockdale ISD — 1,700/PK-12
PO Box 632 76567 — 512-430-6000
Don Denbow, supt. — Fax 446-3460
www.rockdaleisd.net
Rockdale HS — 500/9-12
PO Box 632 76567 — 512-430-6140
Joseph Geletka, prin. — Fax 446-3512
Rockdale JHS — 400/6-8
PO Box 632 76567 — 512-430-6100
April Eschberger, prin. — Fax 446-2597

Rockport, Aransas, Pop. 8,668
Aransas County ISD — 3,100/PK-12
PO Box 907 78381 — 361-790-2212
Joseph Patek, supt. — Fax 790-2299
www.acisd.org
Rockport-Fulton HS — 900/9-12
PO Box 907 78381 — 361-790-2220
Kim James, prin. — Fax 790-2206
Rockport-Fulton MS — 700/6-8
PO Box 907 78381 — 361-790-2230
Michael Hannum, prin. — Fax 790-2030

New Beginnings Christian S — 50/1-12
922 Highway 35 S 78382 — 361-729-5887
Laura Baylor, admin. — Fax 729-5861

Rocksprings, Edwards, Pop. 1,182
Rocksprings ISD — 300/PK-12
PO Box 157 78880 — 830-683-4137
David Velky, supt. — Fax 683-4141
www.rockspringsisd.net
Rocksprings HS — 100/9-12
PO Box 157 78880 — 830-683-4136
John Clark, prin. — Fax 683-4141

Rockwall, Rockwall, Pop. 36,881
Rockwall ISD — 13,900/PK-12
1050 Williams St 75087 — 972-771-0605
Jeff Bailey, supt. — Fax 771-2637
www.rockwallisd.com
Cain MS — 900/7-8
6620 FM 3097 75032 — 972-772-1170
Jason Johnston, prin. — Fax 772-2414
Rockwall HS — 2,100/9-12
901 W Yellowjacket Ln 75087 — 972-771-7339
Dr. Mark LeMaster, prin. — Fax 772-2099
Rockwall Quest Academy — 50/Alt
1050 Williams St 75087 — 972-772-2077
Todd Bradford, prin. — Fax 772-1055
Utley MS — 600/7-8
1201 T L Townsend Dr 75087 — 972-771-5281
Carri Eddy, prin. — Fax 772-1164
Williams MS — 700/7-8
625 E FM 552 75087 — 972-771-8313
Billy Pringle, prin. — Fax 772-2033
Other Schools – See Heath

Heritage Christian Academy — 300/PK-12
1408 S Goliad St 75087 — 972-772-3003
Dr. Ron Taylor, hdmstr. — Fax 772-3770

Rogers, Bell, Pop. 1,192
Rogers ISD — 900/PK-12
1 Eagle Dr 76569 — 254-642-3802
Bob Callaghan, supt. — Fax 642-3851
www.rogersisd.org
Rogers HS — 300/9-12
1 Eagle Dr 76569 — 254-642-3224
Lee Vi Moses, prin. — Fax 642-3037
Rogers MS — 200/6-8
1 Eagle Dr 76569 — 254-642-3011
Lucinda Smith, prin. — Fax 642-0033

Roma, Starr, Pop. 9,764
Roma ISD — 6,600/PK-12
PO Box 187 78584 — 956-849-1377
Jesus O. Guerra, supt. — Fax 849-3118
www.romaisd.com/
ALAS/I & G Center — 50/Alt
PO Box 187 78584 — 956-849-2803
Jose Maria Saenz, prin. — Fax 849-4421
Roma HS — 1,800/9-12
PO Box 187 78584 — 956-849-1333
Noe Muniz, prin. — Fax 849-2655
Roma MS — 700/6-8
PO Box 187 78584 — 956-849-1434
Abraham Gonzalez, prin. — Fax 849-1895
Other Schools – See Rio Grande City

Ropesville, Hockley, Pop. 433
Ropes ISD — 300/PK-12
304 Ranch Rd 79358 — 806-562-4031
Gary Lehnen, supt. — Fax 562-4059
www.ropesisd.us
Choices Alternative S — 50/Alt
304 Ranch Rd 79358 — 806-562-2160
Joel Willmon, prin. — Fax 562-4059
Ropes JSHS — 200/6-12
304 Ranch Rd 79358 — 806-562-4031
Joel Willmon, prin. — Fax 562-4059

Smyer ISD
Supt. — See Smyer
Choices Alternative S — 50/Alt
304 Ranch Rd 79358 — 806-539-4031
Fax 539-2502

Roscoe, Nolan, Pop. 1,308
Highland ISD — 200/PK-12
6625 FM 608 79545 — 325-766-3652
Duane Hyde, supt. — Fax 766-2281
www.highland.esc14.net/
Highland S — 200/PK-12
6625 FM 608 79545 — 325-766-3652
Duane Hyde, prin. — Fax 766-3869

Roscoe ISD — 300/PK-12
PO Box 579 79545 — 325-766-3629
Dr. Kim Alexander, supt. — Fax 766-3138
www.roscoe.esc14.net
Roscoe JSHS — 100/7-12
PO Box 10 79545 — 325-766-3327
Edward Morales, prin. — Fax 766-3419

Rosebud, Falls, Pop. 1,384
Rosebud-Lott ISD
Supt. — See Lott
Rosebud-Lott Learning Center — 50/Alt
PO Box 638 76570 — 254-883-2724
Steve Coston, prin.

Rosenberg, Fort Bend, Pop. 30,297
Lamar Consolidated ISD 24,900/PK-12
3911 Avenue I 77471 832-223-0000
Dr. Thomas Randle, supt. Fax 223-0002
www.lcisd.org
Alternative Learning Center 100/Alt
1708 Avenue M 77471 832-223-0900
Randal Donnell, admin. Fax 223-0901
Fort Bend Alternative S 50/Alt
3409 Avenue F 77471 281-239-3431
Randall Donnell, admin. Fax 341-5293
George JHS 900/7-8
4601 Airport Ave 77471 832-223-3600
Kelly Waters, prin. Fax 223-3601
Lamar Consolidated HS 1,800/9-12
4606 Mustang Ave 77471 832-223-3000
Michael Milstead, prin. Fax 223-3001
Lamar JHS 800/7-8
4814 Mustang Ave 77471 832-223-3200
Jerry Kipping, prin. Fax 223-3201
Terry HS 1,700/9-12
5500 Avenue N 77471 832-223-3400
Vera Wehring, prin. Fax 223-3401
Other Schools – See Richmond

Rosharon, Brazoria, Pop. 1,128
Fort Bend ISD
Supt. — See Sugar Land
Ferndell Henry Center for Learning 50/Alt
7447 FM 521 Rd 77583 281-327-6000
Michael Bolton, prin. Fax 327-6001

Rotan, Fisher, Pop. 1,488
Rotan ISD 300/PK-12
102 N McKinley Ave 79546 325-735-2332
Lindy Robinson, supt. Fax 735-2686
www.rotan.org
Rotan HS 100/9-12
102 N McKinley Ave 79546 325-735-3041
Gary Nelson, prin. Fax 735-2520
Rotan JHS 100/6-8
102 N McKinley Ave 79546 325-735-3162
Katy Cade, prin. Fax 735-2686

Round Rock, Williamson, Pop. 97,480
Round Rock ISD 42,200/PK-12
1311 Round Rock Ave 78681 512-464-5000
Jesus Chavez Ph.D., supt. Fax 464-5090
www.roundrockisd.org
Cedar Ridge HS 9-12
2801 Gattis School Rd 78664 512-704-0100
Dr. Daniel Presley, prin. Fax 704-0280
Chisholm Trail MS 1,100/6-8
500 Oakridge Dr 78681 512-428-2500
Robert Sormani, prin. Fax 428-2629
Fulkes MS 700/6-8
300 W Anderson Ave 78664 512-428-3100
Nancy Guererro, prin. Fax 428-3240
Hernandez MS 800/6-8
1901 Sunrise Rd 78664 512-424-8800
Dr. Deborah Brennan, prin. Fax 424-8940
Hopewell MS 800/6-8
1535 Gulf Way, 512-464-5200
Anthony Watson, prin. Fax 464-5349
Ridgeview MS 1,400/6-8
2000 Via Sonoma Dr, 512-424-8400
Dr. Holly Galloway, prin. Fax 424-8540
Round Rock HS 2,600/9-12
300 N Lake Creek Dr 78681 512-464-6000
Natalie Nichols, prin. Fax 464-6190
Stony Point HS 2,800/9-12
1801 Tiger Trl 78664 512-428-7000
Albert Hernandez, prin. Fax 428-7280
Success - East Campus 50/Alt
1801 Tiger Trl 78664 512-428-7196
Mark Gesch, dir. Fax 428-7284
Walsh MS 1,100/6-8
3850 Walsh Ranch Blvd 78681 512-704-0800
Toni Hicks, prin. Fax 704-0940
Other Schools – See Austin

Concordia HS 100/9-12
1500 Royston Ln Ste A 78664 512-248-2547
Patrick Maynard, prin. Fax 252-3839
Round Rock Christian Academy 500/PK-12
301 N Lake Creek Dr Ste A 78681 512-255-4491
Rebecca Blauser, hdmstr. Fax 255-6043

Rowlett, Dallas, Pop. 55,115
Garland ISD
Supt. — See Garland
Coyle MS 1,200/6-8
4500 Skyline Dr 75088 972-475-3711
Doug Miller, prin. Fax 412-7222
Rowlett HS 2,600/9-12
4700 Kirby Rd 75088 972-463-1712
Michelle Bounds, prin. Fax 412-2951
Schrade MS 1,300/6-8
6201 Danridge Rd 75089 972-463-8790
Jim Thomas, prin. Fax 463-8793

Rockwall Christian Academy 200/PK-12
6005 Dalrock Rd 75088 972-412-8266
Jeanne Zakem, admin. Fax 463-3746

Roxton, Lamar, Pop. 632
Roxton ISD 200/PK-12
PO Box 307 75477 903-346-3213
Trevor Rogers, supt. Fax 346-3356
www.roxtonisd.org/
Roxton S 200/PK-12
PO Box 307 75477 903-346-3213
Greg Carpenter, prin. Fax 346-3356

Royse City, Rockwall, Pop. 9,169
Royse City ISD 4,500/PK-12
PO Box 479 75189 972-636-2413
Kevin Worthy, supt. Fax 635-7037
www.rcisd.org
Brownling Alternative Learning Ctr Alt
PO Box 479 75189 972-635-5077
Lloyd Blaine, prin. Fax 635-2504
Royse City HS 1,200/9-12
PO Box 479 75189 972-636-9991
Dr. Brent Ringo, prin. Fax 635-2906
Royse City MS 700/7-8
PO Box 479 75189 972-636-9544
Jere Craighead, prin. Fax 635-5093

Rule, Haskell, Pop. 627
Rule ISD 100/PK-12
1100 Union Ave 79547 940-997-2521
Bryan Davis, supt. Fax 997-2446
www.rule.esc14.net/
Rule S 100/PK-12
1100 Union Ave 79547 940-997-2246
Barry McBroom, prin. Fax 997-2446

Runge, Karnes, Pop. 1,025
Runge ISD 300/PK-12
PO Box 158 78151 830-239-4315
Janice Sykora, supt. Fax 239-4816
www.rungeisd.org
Runge JSHS 100/7-12
PO Box 158 78151 830-239-4315
Chad Fox, prin. Fax 239-4816

Rusk, Cherokee, Pop. 5,468
Rusk ISD 2,100/PK-12
203 E 7th St 75785 903-683-5592
Scott Davis, supt. Fax 683-2104
www.ruskisd.net
Rusk HS 500/9-12
203 E 7th St 75785 903-683-5401
Scott Schwartz, prin. Fax 683-6090
Rusk JHS 500/6-8
203 E 7th St 75785 903-683-2502
John Burkhalter, prin. Fax 683-4363

Sabinal, Uvalde, Pop. 1,672
Sabinal ISD 500/PK-12
PO Box 338 78881 830-988-2472
Richard Grill, supt. Fax 988-7151
www.sabinalisd.net
Sabinal HS 100/9-12
PO Box 338 78881 830-988-2475
Luciano Castro, prin. Fax 988-7170
Sabinal JHS 100/6-8
PO Box 338 78881 830-988-2475
Luciano Castro, prin. Fax 988-7170

Sabine Pass, Jefferson
Sabine Pass ISD 300/PK-12
PO Box 1148 77655 409-971-2321
Kristi Heid, supt. Fax 971-2120
www.sabinepass.net
Sabine Pass S 300/PK-12
PO Box 1148 77655 409-971-2321
Patricia Heid, prin. Fax 971-2120

Sachse, Dallas, Pop. 19,902
Garland ISD
Supt. — See Garland
Hudson MS 1,300/6-8
4405 Hudson Park 75048 972-675-3070
Bob Clare, prin. Fax 675-3077
Sachse HS 2,600/9-12
3901 Miles Rd 75048 972-414-7450
Ray Merrill, prin. Fax 414-7458

Sadler, Grayson, Pop. 336
S & S Consolidated ISD 800/PK-12
PO Box 837 76264 903-564-6051
Tommy Hunter, supt. Fax 564-3492
www.sscisd.net/
S & S Consolidated HS 300/9-12
PO Box 837 76264 903-564-3768
Roger Reed, prin. Fax 564-7308
S & S Consolidated MS 200/6-8
PO Box 837 76264 903-564-7626
Kimberly Patterson, prin. Fax 564-7857

Saginaw, Tarrant, Pop. 19,433
Eagle Mtn.-Saginaw ISD
Supt. — See Fort Worth
Saginaw HS 2,200/9-12
800 N Blue Mound Rd 76131 817-306-0914
David Priddy, prin. Fax 306-1344

Trinity Baptist Temple Academy 100/PK-12
6045 WJ Boaz Rd 76179 817-237-4255
Michael Crain, prin. Fax 237-5233

Saint Jo, Montague, Pop. 1,027
Saint Jo ISD 300/PK-12
PO Box L 76265 940-995-2668
Larry Smith, supt. Fax 995-2026
www.saintjoisd.net
Saint Jo JSHS 100/7-12
PO Box L 76265 940-995-2532
Curtis Eldridge, prin. Fax 995-2087

Salado, Bell, Pop. 2,113
Salado ISD 1,400/PK-12
PO Box 98 76571 254-947-5479
Dr. Michael Novotny, supt. Fax 947-5605
www.saladoisd.org
Salado HS 500/9-12
PO Box 98 76571 254-947-5429
Burt Smith, prin. Fax 947-6984
Salado JHS 200/7-8
PO Box 98 76571 254-947-6935
Chris Diem, prin. Fax 947-6934

Saltillo, Hopkins
Saltillo ISD 300/PK-12
PO Box 269 75478 903-537-2386
Paul Jones, supt. Fax 537-2191
www.saltilloisd.net/
Saltillo S 300/PK-12
PO Box 269 75478 903-537-2386
Kevin Woolley, prin. Fax 537-2191

San Angelo, Tom Green, Pop. 91,751
Grape Creek ISD 1,100/PK-12
8207 US Highway 87 N 76901 325-658-7823
David Hale, supt. Fax 658-8719
www.grapecreekisd.net/
Grape Creek HS 300/9-12
8207 US Highway 87 N 76901 325-653-1852
Roger Henderson, prin. Fax 653-3568
Grape Creek MS 200/6-8
8207 US Highway 87 N 76901 325-655-1735
Greg Baucom, prin. Fax 657-2997

San Angelo ISD 14,200/PK-12
1621 University Ave 76904 325-947-3700
Dr. Carol Bonds, supt. Fax 947-3771
www.saisd.org
Carver Learning Center 100/Alt
301 W 9th St 76903 325-659-3648
Noe Acosta, prin. Fax 657-4087
Central Freshman Campus 600/9-9
218 N Oakes St 76903 325-659-3576
Tim Reid, prin. Fax 659-3583
Central HS 2,100/10-12
655 Caddo St 76901 325-659-3400
Bill Waters, prin. Fax 659-3413
Glenn MS 1,200/6-8
2201 University Ave 76904 325-947-3841
Mary Stinnett, prin. Fax 947-3847
Lake View HS 1,200/9-12
900 E 43rd St 76903 325-659-3500
Monte Althaus, prin. Fax 653-8661
Lee MS 900/6-8
2500 Sherwood Way 76901 325-947-3871
Farrah Gomez, prin. Fax 947-3890
Lincoln MS 900/6-8
255 Lake View Heroes Dr 76903 325-659-3550
Merl Brandon, prin. Fax 659-3559

Wall ISD
Supt. — See Wall
Fairview Alternative Educational Coop 50/Alt
2405 Fairview School Rd 76904 325-651-7656
Albert Johnson, prin. Fax 651-8504

American Commercial College Post-Sec.
3177 Executive Dr 76904 325-942-6797
Angelo State University Post-Sec.
2601 W Avenue N 76909 800-946-8627
Cornerstone Christian S 200/PK-12
1502 N Jefferson St 76901 325-655-3439
Mike Dixon, prin. Fax 658-8998
Howard College Post-Sec.
3501 N US Highway 67 76905 325-481-8300
San Angelo Christian Academy 100/PK-10
518 Country Club Rd 76904 325-651-8363
Jennifer Rackley, admin. Fax 651-1682
Shannon West Texas Memorial Hospital Post-Sec.
120 E Harris Ave 76903 325-653-6741

San Antonio, Bexar, Pop. 1,308,790
Alamo Heights ISD 4,700/PK-12
7101 Broadway St 78209 210-824-2483
Dr. Kevin Brown, supt. Fax 822-2221
www.ahisd.net
Alamo Heights HS 1,500/9-12
6900 Broadway St 78209 210-820-8850
Dr. Linda Foster, prin. Fax 832-5777
Alamo Heights JHS 1,100/6-8
7607 N New Braunfels Ave 78209 210-824-3231
Dr. Cordell Jones, prin. Fax 832-5825

East Central ISD 9,600/PK-12
6634 New Sulphur Springs Rd 78263 210-648-7861
Gary Patterson, supt. Fax 648-0931
www.ecisd.net
Bexar County Learning Center 100/Alt
3621 Farm Rd 78223 210-335-1745
Patricia White, prin. Fax 335-1746
East Central Heritage MS 1,000/6-8
8004 New Sulphur Springs Rd 78263 210-648-4546
Matt Morgan, prin. Fax 648-3501
East Central HS 2,700/9-12
7173 FM 1628 78263 210-649-2951
Roland Toscano, prin. Fax 649-2752
Legacy MS 1,200/6-8
5903 SE Loop 410 78222 210-648-3118
Damon Trainer, prin. Fax 648-1068

Edgewood ISD 10,800/PK-12
5358 W Commerce St 78237 210-444-4500
Dr. Jose Cervantes, supt. Fax 444-4602
www.eisd.net/
Brentwood MS 700/6-8
1626 Thompson Pl 78226 210-444-7675
Gustavo Cordova, prin. Fax 444-7698
Edgewood Fine Arts Academy 100/9-12
402 Lance St 78237 210-444-7925
Reynaldo Juarez, prin. Fax 444-7973
Frey Alternative Education Complex 50/Alt
900 S San Eduardo Ave 78237 210-444-8230
Emilia Lira, admin. Fax 444-8233
Garcia MS 700/6-8
3306 Ruiz St 78228 210-444-8075
Cristina Solis, prin. Fax 444-8098
Kennedy HS 1,500/9-12
1922 S General McMullen Dr 78226 210-444-8040
Karen Hartmann, prin. Fax 444-8020
Memorial HS 1,100/9-12
1227 Memorial St 78228 210-444-8300
Dr. William Telford, prin. Fax 444-8336
Wrenn MS 700/6-8
627 S Acme Rd 78237 210-444-8475
Michael Rodriguez, prin. Fax 444-8498

Fort Sam Houston ISD 1,400/PK-12
4005 Winans Rd 78234 210-368-8701
Dr. Gail Siller, supt. Fax 368-8741
www.fshisd.net
Cole MSHS 700/6-12
4001 Winans Rd 78234 210-368-8730
Isabell Clayton, prin. Fax 368-8731

Harlandale ISD 14,800/PK-12
102 Genevieve Dr 78214 210-989-4355
Reynaldo Madrigal, supt. Fax 921-4356
www.harlandale.net
Film School of San Antonio @ Harlandale 9-12
114 E Gerald Ave 78214 210-989-1092
Melissa Casey, prin. Fax 924-2335
Harlandale HS 1,900/9-12
114 E Gerald Ave 78214 210-989-1000
Melissa Casey, prin. Fax 924-2335
Harlandale MS 900/6-8
300 W Huff Ave 78214 210-989-2000
Katherine Pena, prin. Fax 977-8764
Kingsborough MS 700/6-8
422 E Ashley Rd 78221 210-989-2200
William Hall, prin. Fax 977-9463
Leal MS 800/6-8
743 W Southcross Blvd 78211 210-989-2400
Marianela Gonzalez, prin. Fax 977-1459
McCollum HS 1,700/9-12
500 W Formosa Blvd 78221 210-989-1500
Aracelie Bunsen, prin. Fax 989-1580
School for Leadership & Public Service 9-12
500 W Formosa Blvd 78221 210-989-1539
Aracelie Bunsen, prin. Fax 989-1580
Tejeda Academy 200/Alt
12121 SE Loop 410 78221 210-989-4900
Jerry Soto, prin. Fax 977-1628
Wells MS 700/6-8
422 W Hutchins Pl 78221 210-989-2600
Fred Anthony, prin. Fax 923-5126
Extended Learning Center Adult
12121 SE Loop 410 78221 210-989-4921
Jim Bernal, prin. Fax 977-1372

Judson ISD
Supt. — See Live Oak
Judson Learning Academy 100/Alt
6909 N Loop 1604 E Ste 2010 78247 210-651-4080
Brandon VanVleck, prin. Fax 651-6834
Kirby MS 1,000/6-8
5441 Seguin Rd 78219 210-661-1140
Melinda Salinas, prin. Fax 662-9275
Metzger MS 900/6-8
7475 Binz Engleman Rd 78244 210-662-2210
Caroline Ross, prin. Fax 662-8390
Wagner HS 2,400/9-12
3000 N Foster Rd 78244 210-662-5000
Milton Fields, prin. Fax 662-5010
Woodlake Hills MS 900/6-8
6625 Woodlake Pkwy 78244 210-661-1110
Don Pittman, prin. Fax 666-0169

Lackland ISD 1,000/PK-12
2460 Kenly Ave Bldg 8265 78236 210-357-5000
Dr. Burnie L. Roper, supt. Fax 357-5050
www.lacklandisd.net/
Stacey JSHS 300/7-12
2460 Kenly Ave Bldg 8265 78236 210-357-5100
Gail Horn, prin. Fax 357-5109

North East ISD 66,100/PK-12
8961 Tesoro Dr 78217 210-407-0000
Dr. Brian Gottardy, supt. Fax 804-7017
www.neisd.net
Academy of Creative Education 100/Alt
3736 Perrin Central Bldg 2 78217 210-407-0740
Dr. Mary Jo McLaughlin, prin. Fax 657-8976
Automotive Technology Academy Vo/Tech
3736 Perrin Central Blvd 78217 210-407-0742
David Bailey, dir. Fax 637-4992
Bradley MS 1,200/6-8
14819 Heimer Rd 78232 210-356-2600
Justin Oxley, prin. Fax 491-8314
Bulverde Ranch MS 6-8
21314 Bulverde Rd 78259
Bush MS 1,400/6-8
1500 Evans Rd 78258 210-356-2900
Gary Comalander, prin. Fax 491-8471
Center S 50/Alt
3736 Perrin Central Blvd 78217 210-407-0739
Nancy Neugebauer, prin. Fax 637-4956
Churchill HS 2,900/9-12
12049 Blanco Rd 78216 210-356-0000
Jeffrey Vaughan, prin. Fax 442-0879
Design and Technology Academy 9-12
5110 Walzem Rd 78218 210-356-2200
Stacia FitzSimon, dir. Fax 650-1285
Driscoll MS 1,100/6-8
17150 Jones Maltsberger Rd 78247 210-356-3200
Debra Aceves, prin. Fax 491-6467
Eisenhower MS 1,100/6-8
8231 Blanco Rd 78216 210-356-3500
Rudy Jimenez, prin. Fax 442-0537
Electrical Systems Technology S Vo/Tech
2923 MacArthur Vw 78217 210-650-1100
Stephen Albert, prin.
Engineering & Technologies Academy 9-12
5110 Walzem Rd 78218 210-650-1200
Bill Sturgis, dir. Fax 650-1227
Garner MS 900/6-8
4302 Harry Wurzbach Rd 78209 210-805-5100
David Crowe, prin. Fax 805-5138
Harris MS 1,400/6-8
5300 Knollcreek 78247 210-356-4100
Stephen Watson, prin. Fax 657-8892
International HS of America 500/9-12
1400 Jackson Keller Rd 78213 210-356-0900
Emily Bieser, dir. Fax 442-0409

Jackson MS 900/6-8
4538 Vance Jackson Rd 78230 210-442-0550
Brian Hurley, prin. Fax 442-0580
Johnson HS 2,400/9-12
23203 Bulverde Rd 78259 210-356-0400
John Mehlbrech, prin. Fax 356-0430
Krueger MS 1,200/6-8
438 Lanark Dr 78218 210-650-1350
John Smith, prin. Fax 650-1374
Lee HS 2,300/9-12
1400 Jackson Keller Rd 78213 210-356-0800
Richard Canales, prin. Fax 442-0325
Lopez MS 1,200/6-8
23103 Hardy Oak Blvd 78258 210-356-5000
Barry Lanford, prin. Fax 481-4072
MacArthur HS 2,600/9-12
2923 MacArthur Vw 78217 210-650-1100
Peter Martinez, prin. Fax 650-1195
Madison HS 3,400/9-12
5005 Stahl Rd 78247 210-356-1400
Chris Thompson, prin. Fax 637-4435
Nimitz MS 1,100/6-8
5426 Blanco Rd 78216 210-442-0450
Dana Stolhandske, prin. Fax 442-0489
North East Alternative Center 100/Alt
103 W Rampart Dr 78216 210-442-0609
Bill Fish, dir. Fax 442-0623
North East S of the Arts 9-12
1400 Jackson Keller Rd 78213 210-442-2505
Dena Mabry, dir. Fax 442-2507
Reagan HS 2,700/9-12
19000 Ronald Reagan 78258 210-482-2200
Bill Boyd, prin. Fax 482-2222
Roosevelt HS 2,900/9-12
5110 Walzem Rd 78218 210-356-2200
Melvin Echard, prin. Fax 650-1291
STEM Academy 6-8
5426 Blanco Rd 78216 210-442-0477
Cynthia Rinehart, dir. Fax 442-0476
STEM RAM Academy 6-9
1400 Jackson Keller Rd 78213 210-356-1001
Cynthia Rinehart, dir. Fax 442-0327
Tejeda MS 1,500/6-8
2909 E Evans Rd 78259 210-356-5600
Brenda Shelton, prin. Fax 482-2277
White MS 1,000/6-8
7800 Midcrown Dr 78218 210-650-1400
Philip Carney, prin. Fax 650-1443
Wood MS 1,000/6-8
14800 Judson Rd 78233 210-650-1300
Christine Lowak, prin. Fax 650-1309
Evening HS Adult
3736 Perrin Central Blvd #4 78217 210-637-4970
David Bailey, prin.

Northside ISD 90,400/PK-12
5900 Evers Rd 78238 210-397-8600
Dr. Brian Woods, supt. Fax 706-8772
www.nisd.net
Brandeis HS 2,400/9-12
13011 Kyle Seale Pkwy 78249 210-397-8200
Dr. Geri Berger, prin. Fax 561-2000
Brennan HS 9-12
2400 Cottonwood Way 78253 210-398-1250
Gerardo Marquez, prin. Fax 645-3311
Briscoe MS 6-8
4265 Lone Star Pkwy 78253 210-398-1100
Javier Martinez, prin. Fax 674-0220
Business Careers HS 9-12
6500 Ingram Rd 78238 210-397-7070
Linda Burk, prin. Fax 706-7076
Clark HS 2,600/9-12
5150 De Zavala Rd 78249 210-397-5150
Dr. Jerry Woods, prin. Fax 561-5250
Communications Arts HS 9-12
11600 W FM 471 78253 210-397-6043
Windy Barker, prin. Fax 688-6092
Connally MS 1,000/6-8
8661 Silent Sunrise 78250 210-397-1000
Cornelius Phelps, prin. Fax 257-1004
Construction Careers Academy Vo/Tech
9411 W Military Dr 78251 210-397-4294
Guillermo Vasquez, lead tchr.
Garcia MS 1,300/6-8
14900 Kyle Seale Pkwy 78255 210-397-8400
Eric Tobias, prin. Fax 695-3830
Health Careers HS 800/9-12
4646 Hamilton Wolfe Rd 78229 210-397-5400
Dorothy Hall, prin. Fax 617-5423
Hobby MS 1,100/6-8
11843 Vance Jackson Rd 78230 210-397-6300
Tracy Tietze, prin. Fax 690-6332
Holmes HS 2,600/9-12
6500 Ingram Rd 78238 210-397-7000
Ada Bohlken, prin. Fax 706-7030
Holmgreen Center 100/Alt
8580 Ewing Halsell Dr 78229 210-397-5460
Krista Garcia, prin. Fax 617-5476
Jay HS 2,900/9-12
7611 Marbach Rd 78227 210-397-2700
Robert Harris, prin. Fax 678-2753
Jay Science and Engineering Academy 9-12
7611 Marbach Rd 78227 210-397-2700
Jay Sumpter, lead tchr. Fax 678-2753
Jefferson MS 1,500/6-8
10900 Shaenfield Rd 78254 210-397-3700
Kevin Kearns, prin. Fax 257-4988
Jones MS 1,100/6-8
1256 Pinn Rd 78227 210-397-2100
Wendy Reyes, prin. Fax 678-2113
Jordan MS 1,200/6-8
1725 Richland Hills Dr 78251 210-397-6150
Jennifer Alvarez, prin. Fax 523-4876
Luna MS 1,000/6-8
200 Grosenbacher Rd N 78253 210-397-5300
Lynn Pierson, prin. Fax 645-5246

Marshall HS 2,500/9-12
8000 Lobo Ln 78240 210-397-7100
Anthony Jarrett, prin. Fax 706-7175
Neff MS 1,300/6-8
5227 Evers Rd 78238 210-397-4100
Yvonne Correa, prin. Fax 523-4566
Northside Alternative HS 200/Alt
144 Hunt Ln 78245 210-397-7080
John Dubose, prin. Fax 706-7086
Northside Alternative MS South 50/Alt
5223 Blessing St 78228 210-397-6900
Dr. Karen Petersen, prin. Fax 431-6901
Northside Excel Academy 100/Alt
6500 Ingram Rd 78238 210-397-8120
Irene Chavez, prin. Fax 522-8953
Pease MS 1,100/6-8
201 Hunt Ln 78245 210-397-2950
Barry Perez, prin. Fax 678-2974
Rawlinson MS 1,000/6-8
14100 Vance Jackson Rd 78249 210-397-4900
Nancy Pena, prin. Fax 767-4055
Rayburn MS 900/6-8
1400 Cedarhurst Dr 78227 210-397-2150
Scott McKenzie, prin. Fax 678-2181
Ross MS 1,000/6-8
3630 Callaghan Rd 78228 210-397-6350
Lisa McConoghy, prin. Fax 431-6383
Rudder MS 1,200/6-8
6558 Horn Blvd 78240 210-397-5000
Mary Jewell, prin. Fax 561-5022
Stevens HS 2,700/9-12
600 N Ellison Dr 78251 210-397-6450
Harold Maldonado, prin. Fax 257-4304
Stevenson MS 1,400/6-8
8403 Tezel Rd 78254 210-397-7300
Glenda Munson, prin. Fax 706-7336
Stinson MS 1,200/6-8
13200 Skyhawk Dr 78249 210-397-3600
Willie Frantzen, prin. Fax 561-3609
Taft HS 2,600/9-12
11600 W FM 471 78253 210-397-6000
Tommy Garcia, prin. Fax 688-6072
Vale MS 1,400/6-8
2120 N Ellison Dr 78251 210-397-5700
Erika Foerster, prin. Fax 257-1000
Warren HS 2,800/9-12
9411 W Military Dr 78251 210-397-4200
David Empson, prin. Fax 257-4246
Zachry MS 1,100/6-8
9410 Timber Path 78250 210-397-7400
Susan Allain, prin. Fax 706-7432
Northside Evening HS Adult
6500 Ingram Rd 78238 210-397-7060
George McKnight, prin. Fax 706-7060
Other Schools – See Helotes

San Antonio ISD 54,700/PK-12
141 Lavaca St 78210 210-554-2200
Dr. Sylvester Perez, supt.
www.saisd.net
Brackenridge HS 1,900/9-12
400 Eagleland Dr 78210 210-533-8144
Moises Ortiz, prin. Fax 534-9770
Burbank HS 1,400/9-12
1002 Edwards 78204 210-532-4241
Maria Cordova, prin. Fax 533-4394
Connell MS 600/6-8
400 Hot Wells Blvd 78223 210-438-6835
Travis McKelvain, prin. Fax 534-6589
Cooper Academy 400/Alt
1700 Tampico St 78207 210-226-3042
Joseph Zatarain, prin. Fax 223-9031
Davis MS 700/6-8
4702 E Houston St 78220 210-978-7920
Anita O'Neal, prin. Fax 662-8189
Edison HS 1,700/9-12
701 Santa Monica 78212 210-733-9147
Charles Munoz, prin. Fax 738-2408
Estrada Achievement Center 100/Alt
1112 S Zarzamora St 78207 210-438-6820
Gary Pollock, prin. Fax 227-8656
Fox Tech HS Vo/Tech
637 N Main Ave 78205 210-226-5103
Dawn Parker, prin. Fax 224-8792
Highlands HS 2,000/9-12
3118 Elgin Ave 78210 210-333-0421
Lorna Klokkenga, prin. Fax 337-2567
Houston HS 800/9-12
4635 E Houston St 78220 210-661-4134
Darnell White, prin. Fax 666-2915
Jefferson HS 1,900/9-12
723 Donaldson Ave 78201 210-736-1981
Joanne Cockrell, prin. Fax 738-2406
Lanier HS 1,500/9-12
1514 W Cesar E Chavez Blvd 78207 210-223-2926
Miguel Elizondo, prin. Fax 224-9516
Longfellow MS 900/6-8
1130 E Sunshine Dr 78228 210-438-6520
Liz Solis, prin. Fax 433-0375
Navarro Academy 200/Alt
623 S Pecos La Trinidad 78207 210-438-6810
Joseph Zatarain, prin. Fax 226-5426
Page MS 500/6-8
401 Berkshire Ave 78210 210-228-1230
Lemelle Taylor, prin. Fax 533-7369
Pickett Academy 50/Alt
1931 E Houston St 78202 210-212-4684
Mary Alvarez-Garcia, prin. Fax 212-3997
Poe MS 800/6-8
814 Aransas Ave 78210 210-228-1235
Lewis Barr, prin. Fax 534-7299
Rogers MS 600/6-8
314 Galway St 78223 210-438-6840
Kristin Willmann, prin. Fax 333-7954
Tafolla MS 900/6-8
1303 W Cesar E Chavez Blvd 78207 210-978-7930
Carolina Elizondo, prin. Fax 227-7044

Twain MS 600/6-8
2411 San Pedro Ave 78212 210-738-9745
Christopher Castro, prin. Fax 738-0518
Wheatley MS 400/6-8
415 Gabriel 78202 210-738-9750
Mary Olison, prin. Fax 227-9972

South San Antonio ISD 9,800/PK-12
5622 Ray Ellison Blvd 78242 210-977-7000
Mourette Hodge, supt. Fax 977-7021
www.southsanisd.net
Alternative S, 324 Fenfield Ave 78211 100/Alt
Max Rodriguez, prin. 210-977-7508
Career Education Center Vo/Tech
2615 Navajo St 78224 210-977-7350
Charles Ervin, prin. Fax 977-7356
Dwight MS 500/6-8
2454 W Southcross Blvd 78211 210-977-7300
David Abundis, prin. Fax 977-7316
Kazen MS 500/6-8
1520 Gillette Blvd 78224 210-977-7150
Arla Maldonado-Chapa, prin. Fax 977-7155
Shepard MS 500/6-8
5558 Ray Ellison Blvd 78242 210-623-1875
Eusebio Vega, prin. Fax 623-1894
South San Antonio HS 2,200/9-12
2515 Bobcat Ln 78224 210-977-7400
Henry Yzaguirre, prin. Fax 977-7430
Zamora MS 500/6-8
8638 Larkia St 78224 210-977-7278
Patti Annunzio, prin. Fax 977-7285

Southside ISD 5,300/PK-12
1460 Martinez Losoya Rd 78221 210-882-1600
Dr. Juan Jasso, supt. Fax 626-0101
www.southsideisd.org/
Matthey MS 700/7-8
1460 Martinez Losoya Rd 78221 210-882-1601
Michelle Hickman, prin. Fax 626-0113
Southside HS 1,400/9-12
1460 Martinez Losoya Rd 78221 210-882-1606
Benjamin Johnson, prin. Fax 626-0119

Southwest ISD 11,600/PK-12
11914 Dragon Ln 78252 210-622-4300
Dr. Lloyd Verstuyft, supt. Fax 622-4301
www.swisd.net/
McAuliffe MS 900/6-8
11914 Dragon Ln 78252 210-623-6260
Mark Figueroa, prin. Fax 623-6261
Scobee MS 800/6-8
11914 Dragon Ln 78252 210-645-7500
Darin Kasper, prin. Fax 645-7501
Southwest Academy 9-12
11914 Dragon Ln 78252 210-622-4750
Rosie Hidalgo, prin. Fax 622-9502
Southwest HS 3,100/9-12
11914 Dragon Ln 78252 210-622-4500
Paul Black, prin. Fax 622-4501
Other Schools – See Atascosa

Achievers' Center for Education 50/5-12
5084 De Zavala Rd 78249 210-690-7359
Anne Zuber, admin. Fax 690-7307
Antonian College Preparatory HS 700/9-12
6425 West Ave 78213 210-344-9265
Gilbert Saenz, prin. Fax 344-9267
Atonement Academy 500/PK-12
15415 Red Robin Rd 78255 210-695-2240
Fr. Christopher Phillips, hdmstr. Fax 695-9679
Baptist Health System-Sch of Health Prof Post-Sec.
8400 Datapoint Dr 78229 210-297-9636
Baptist University of the Americas Post-Sec.
8019 S Panam Expy 78224 210-924-4338
Blessed Hope Academy 200/9-12
4930 Research Dr 78240 210-697-9191
Alice Ashcraft, dir. Fax 690-9299
Brown Mackie College Post-Sec.
4715 Fredericksburg Rd #100 78229 210-425-2210
Cancer Therapy & Research Center Post-Sec.
7979 Wurzbach Rd 78229 210-450-5664
Career Point College Post-Sec.
4522 Fredericksburg Rd #A22 78201 210-732-3000
Castle Hills First Baptist S 300/PK-12
2220 NW Military Hwy 78213 210-377-8485
Michael Pinkston, supt. Fax 377-8473
Central Catholic HS 500/9-12
1403 N Saint Marys St 78215 210-225-6794
Edward Ybarra, prin. Fax 227-9353
Christian Academy of San Antonio 500/PK-12
325 Castroville Rd 78207 210-436-2277
Yolanda Molina, supt. Fax 436-2210
Concorde Career College Post-Sec.
4803 NW Loop 410 Ste 200 78229 210-428-2000
Cornerstone Christian S 900/PK-12
4802 Vance Jackson Rd 78230 210-979-9203
Jerry Eshleman Ph.D., supt. Fax 979-0310
Culinary Institute of America Post-Sec.
312 Pearl Pkwy Bldg 2 #2102 78215 210-554-6400
Everest Institute Post-Sec.
6550 1st Park Ten Blvd 78213 210-732-7800
Hallmark College of Aeronautics Post-Sec.
8901 Wetmore Rd 78216 210-826-1000
Hallmark College of Tehnology Post-Sec.
10401 W Interstate 10 78230 210-690-9000
Healy-Murphy Center HS 200/9-12
618 Live Oak 78202 210-223-2944
Janie Whiteley, prin. Fax 224-1033
Holy Cross of San Antonio 400/6-12
426 N San Felipe Ave 78228 210-433-9395
Henry Galindo, prin. Fax 433-2117
Incarnate Word HS 600/9-12
727 E Hildebrand Ave 78212 210-829-3100
B.J. Nelsen, prin. Fax 829-3120
International Academy of Design & Tech Post-Sec.
4511 Horizon Hill Blvd 78229 210-530-9449
ITT Technical Institute Post-Sec.
5700 Northwest Pkwy 78249 210-694-4612
ITT Technical Institute Post-Sec.
2895 NE Loop 410 78218 210-651-8500
Kaplan College Post-Sec.
7142 San Pedro Ave Ste 100 78216 210-733-0777
Kaplan College Post-Sec.
6441 NW Loop 410 78238 210-308-8584
Keystone S 400/K-12
119 E Craig Pl 78212 210-735-4022
Brian Yager, head sch Fax 732-4905
Lamson Institute Post-Sec.
5819 NW Loop 410 Ste 160 78238 210-520-1800
Lutheran HS of San Antonio 100/9-12
18104 Babcock Rd 78255 210-694-4962
Stephen Eggold, prin. Fax 694-9150
Milan Institute Post-Sec.
6804 Ingram Rd 78238 210-647-5100
Milan Institute of Cosmetology Post-Sec.
605 SW Military Dr 78221 210-922-5900
Mims Classic Beauty College Post-Sec.
5121 Blanco Rd 78216 210-344-2041
New Life Christian Academy 200/PK-12
6622 W US Highway 90 78227 210-679-6001
Anthony Jackson, prin. Fax 679-6080
Northwest Vista College Post-Sec.
3535 N Ellison Dr 78251 210-486-4000
Oblate School of Theology Post-Sec.
285 Oblate Dr 78216 210-341-1366
Our Lady of the Lake University Post-Sec.
411 SW 24th St 78207 210-434-6711
Palo Alto College Post-Sec.
1400 W Villaret Blvd 78224 210-486-3000
Providence Catholic S 300/6-12
1215 N Saint Marys St 78215 210-224-6651
Alicia Garcia, prin. Fax 224-6214
Quest College Post-Sec.
5430 Frdrcksburg Rd #310 78229 210-366-2701
Rainbow Hills Baptist S 200/PK-12
2255 Horal St 78227 210-674-0490
Rev. Dennis Wall, chnclr. Fax 674-3615
River City Believers Academy 100/PK-12
16765 Lookout Rd 78233 210-656-2999
Shane Land, prin. Fax 496-2888
St. Anthony HS 400/9-12
3200 McCullough Ave 78212 210-832-5600
Rene Escobedo, prin. Fax 832-5615
St. Gerard HS 100/9-12
521 S New Braunfels Ave 78203 210-533-8061
Peter Rivera, prin. Fax 533-3697
St. Mary's Hall 500/PK-12
9401 Starcrest Dr 78217 210-483-9100
Jonathan Eades, hdmstr. Fax 483-9299
St. Mary's University Post-Sec.
1 Camino Santa Maria St 78228 210-436-3011
St. Phillip's College Post-Sec.
1801 Martin Luther King Dr 78203 210-486-2000
San Antonio Beauty College #3 Post-Sec.
4130 Naco Perrin Blvd 78217 210-654-9734
San Antonio Beauty College #4 Post-Sec.
2423 Jamar St # 2 78226 210-433-7222
San Antonio Christian HS 400/9-12
19202 Redland Rd 78259 210-340-1864
Robert Armstrong, prin. Fax 530-9624
San Antonio Christian MS 300/6-8
19202 Redland Rd 78259 210-340-1864
Dr. Thomas Erbaugh, prin. Fax 348-6030
San Antonio College Post-Sec.
1300 San Pedro Ave 78212 210-486-0000
Sanford-Brown College Post-Sec.
4511 Horizon Hill Blvd 78229 210-246-7700
Southern Careers Institute Post-Sec.
238 SW Military Dr Ste 101 78221 210-271-0096
South Texas Vocational Technical Inst Post-Sec.
734 SE Military Dr 78214 210-807-7400
Southwest School Post-Sec.
602 W Southcross Blvd 78221 210-921-0951
Southwest School Post-Sec.
2402 San Pedro Ave 78212 210-225-7287
Texas A&M University San Antonio Post-Sec.
1 University Way 78224 210-784-1000
TMI - The Episcopal S of Texas 400/6-12
20955 W Tejas Trl 78257 210-698-7171
John Cooper, hdmstr. Fax 698-0715
Trinity Christian Academy 200/K-12
5401 N Loop 1604 E 78247 210-653-2800
Susan Oldfield, prin. Fax 653-0303
Trinity University Post-Sec.
1 Trinity Pl 78212 210-999-7011
University Hospital Post-Sec.
4502 Medical Dr 78229 210-616-2000
University of Texas at San Antonio Post-Sec.
1 UTSA Cir 78249 210-458-4011
University of Texas Health Science Ctr. Post-Sec.
7703 Floyd Curl Dr 78229 210-567-7000
University of the Incarnate Word Post-Sec.
4301 Broadway St 78209 210-829-6000
Winston S San Antonio 200/K-12
8565 Ewing Halsell Dr 78229 210-615-6544
Dr. Charles Karulak, hdmstr. Fax 615-6627

San Augustine, San Augustine, Pop. 2,090
San Augustine ISD 900/PK-12
100 High School Dr 75972 936-275-2306
Walter Key, supt. Fax 275-9776
www.saisd.us/
San Augustine HS 200/9-12
702 High School Dr 75972 936-275-9603
Fleashia Ford, prin. Fax 275-9829
San Augustine MS 200/6-8
1002 Barrett St 75972 936-275-2318
Timothy Little, prin. Fax 275-2962

San Benito, Cameron, Pop. 24,199
Los Fresnos Consolidated ISD
Supt. — See Los Fresnos
Los Fresnos United HS 800/9-9
33790 FM 803 78586 956-254-5250
Joseph Villarreal, prin. Fax 399-2047

San Benito Consolidated ISD 11,300/PK-12
240 N Crockett St 78586 956-361-6100
Antonio Limon, supt. Fax 361-6115
www.sbcisd.net
Cabaza MS 800/6-8
2901 Shafer Rd 78586 956-361-6600
William Snavely, prin. Fax 361-6608
Callandret Positive Redirection Center 50/Alt
305 Doherty St 78586 956-361-6275
Rolando Guerra, prin. Fax 361-6278
Gateway Academy 100/Alt
600 N Austin St 78586 956-361-6446
Rolando Guerra, prin. Fax 399-7985
Jordan MS 900/6-8
700 N McCullough St 78586 956-361-6650
Rigo Rodriguez, prin. Fax 361-6658
San Benito HS 2,000/10-12
450 S Williams Rd 78586 956-361-6500
Delia Weaver, prin. Fax 361-6579
San Benito Riverside MS 700/6-8
35428 Padilla St 78586 956-361-6940
Joel Wood, prin. Fax 361-6948
San Benito Veterans Memorial Academy 800/9-9
2115 N Williams Rd 78586 956-276-6000
Teresa Servellon, prin. Fax 276-6008

South Texas ISD
Supt. — See Mercedes
South Texas Acad for Medical Professions 500/9-12
151 S Helen Moore Rd 78586 956-399-4331
Harry Goette, prin. Fax 399-3570

South Texas Training Center Post-Sec.
1901 W US Highway 77 78586 956-399-9698

Sanderson, Terrell, Pop. 834
Terrell County ISD 100/PK-12
PO Box 747 79848 432-345-2515
Gary Hamilton, supt. Fax 345-2670
www.terrell.esc18.net
Sanderson HS 50/9-12
PO Box 747 79848 432-345-2282
Jerry Garza, prin. Fax 345-2670
Sanderson JHS 50/6-8
PO Box 747 79848 432-345-2601
Jerry Garza, prin. Fax 345-2404

San Diego, Duval, Pop. 4,473
San Diego ISD 1,400/PK-12
609 W Labbe St 78384 361-279-3382
Dr. Ignacio Salinas, supt. Fax 279-3388
www.sdisd.esc2.net
Jaime JHS 300/6-8
609 W Labbe St 78384 361-279-3382
Sam Bueno, prin. Fax 279-3139
San Diego HS 400/9-12
609 W Labbe St 78384 361-279-3382
Michael Gonzalez, prin. Fax 279-5098

San Elizario, El Paso, Pop. 13,596
San Elizario ISD 3,800/PK-12
PO Box 920 79849 915-872-3900
Sylvia Hopp, supt. Fax 872-3903
www.seisd.net
Garcia-Enriquez MS 600/7-8
PO Box 920 79849 915-872-3960
April Marioni, prin. Fax 872-3961
San Elizario HS 1,100/9-12
PO Box 920 79849 915-872-3970
Maribel Guillen, prin. Fax 872-3971

Sanger, Denton, Pop. 6,799
Sanger ISD 2,600/PK-12
601 Elm St 76266 940-458-7438
Kent Crutsinger, supt. Fax 458-5140
www.sangerisd.net/
Sanger HS 700/9-12
100 Indian Ln 76266 940-458-7497
Shannon Saylor, prin. Fax 458-4637
Sanger MS 400/7-8
105 Berry St 76266 940-458-7916
Luci Schulz, prin. Fax 458-5111
Tutt HS 50/Alt
404 Hughes St 76266 940-458-5701
Dr. Ann Hughes, prin. Fax 458-5759

San Isidro, Starr, Pop. 240
San Isidro ISD 300/PK-12
PO Box 10 78588 956-481-3110
Miguel Garcia, supt. Fax 481-3930
www.sanisidroisd.org/
San Isidro HS 100/9-12
PO Box 10 78588 956-481-3110
Mario Alvarado, prin. Fax 481-3950

San Juan, Hidalgo, Pop. 33,835
Pharr-San Juan-Alamo ISD
Supt. — See Pharr
Austin MS 900/6-8
804 S Stewart Rd 78589 956-354-2570
Liza Navarro, prin. Fax 702-5858
Pharr-San Juan-Alamo HS 2,200/9-12
805 Ridge Rd 78589 956-354-2300
Nora Rivas-Garza, prin. Fax 783-2293
San Juan MS 900/6-8
1229 S Veterans Blvd 78589 956-354-2630
Rebecca Luna, prin. Fax 783-3811
Sotomayor HS 200/Alt
1229 S Veterans Blvd 78589 956-354-2510
Rosie Rakay, prin. Fax 354-3120

San Marcos, Hays, Pop. 44,109
San Marcos Consolidated ISD 7,400/PK-12
PO Box 1087 78667 512-393-6700
Mark E. Eads, supt. Fax 393-6709
www.smcisd.net/
Goodnight MS 900/6-8
1301 N State Highway 123 78666 512-393-6550
Steve Dow, prin. Fax 393-6560

Miller MS 700/6-8
301 Foxtail Run 78666 512-393-6660
Ricardo Soliz, prin. Fax 393-6602
Phoenix Learning Center Alt
500 W Hutchison St 78666 512-393-6932
Judy Mitchell, prin. Fax 393-6999
San Marcos HS 2,100/9-12
2601 Rattler Rd 78666 512-393-6300
Michelle Darling, prin. Fax 393-6893

Gary Job Corps Center Post-Sec.
PO Box 967 78667 512-396-6561
San Marcos Academy 200/7-12
2801 Ranch Road 12 78666 512-353-2400
Robert Bryant, prin. Fax 753-8031
San Marcos Adventist Academy 50/PK-12
PO Box 801 78667 512-392-9475
Texas State University San Marcos Post-Sec.
601 University Dr 78666 512-245-2111

San Perlita, Willacy, Pop. 573
San Perlita ISD 300/PK-12
PO Box 37 78590 956-248-5563
Albert Pena, supt. Fax 248-5561
www.spisd.org
San Perlita HS 100/9-12
PO Box 37 78590 956-248-5250
Ramiro Moreno, prin. Fax 248-5103
San Perlita MS 100/6-8
PO Box 37 78590 956-248-5250
Ramiro Moreno, prin. Fax 248-5103

San Saba, San Saba, Pop. 3,082
San Saba ISD 700/PK-12
808 W Wallace St 76877 325-372-3771
Leigh Ann Glaze, supt. Fax 372-5977
www.san-saba.net
San Saba HS 200/9-12
808 W Wallace St 76877 325-372-3786
Brian Williams, prin. Fax 372-3478
San Saba MS 200/5-8
808 W Wallace St 76877 325-372-3200
Vicki Key, prin. Fax 372-5228

Santa Anna, Coleman, Pop. 1,086
Santa Anna ISD 300/PK-12
701 Bowie St 76878 325-348-3136
James Bible, supt. Fax 348-3141
santaanna.netxv.net/
Santa Anna HS 100/7-12
701 Bowie St 76878 325-348-3137
David Robinett, prin. Fax 348-3149

Santa Fe, Galveston, Pop. 12,112
Santa Fe ISD 3,200/PK-12
PO Box 370 77510 409-925-9001
Dr. Leigh Wall, supt. Fax 925-4002
www.sfisd.org/
Santa Fe HS 1,400/9-12
PO Box 370 77510 409-925-2700
Mandy Scott, prin. Fax 925-2773
Santa Fe JHS 700/6-8
PO Box 370 77510 409-925-9300
Rachel Blundell, prin. Fax 927-4106

Santa Maria, Cameron, Pop. 732
Santa Maria ISD 700/PK-12
PO Box 448 78592 956-565-6308
Maria Chavez, supt. Fax 565-0598
www.smisd.net
Santa Maria HS 200/9-12
PO Box 448 78592 956-565-9144
James Jauregui, prin. Fax 514-1968
Santa Maria MS 200/6-8
PO Box 448 78592 956-565-6309
Cindy Taylor, prin. Fax 565-6720

Santa Rosa, Cameron, Pop. 2,866
Santa Rosa ISD 1,200/PK-12
PO Box 368 78593 956-636-9800
Heriberto Villarreal, supt. Fax 636-1439
www.srtx.org
Nelson MS 300/6-8
PO Box 368 78593 956-636-9850
Sylvia Cranfill, prin. Fax 636-9869
Santa Rosa HS 400/9-12
PO Box 368 78593 956-636-9830
Ruben Arguelles, prin. Fax 636-9846

Santo, Palo Pinto
Santo ISD 500/PK-12
PO Box 67 76472 940-769-2835
Greg Gilbert, supt. Fax 769-3116
www.santoisd.net/
Santo JSHS 300/6-12
PO Box 67 76472 940-769-3847
Mike Scott, prin. Fax 769-2796

Saratoga, Hardin
West Hardin County Consolidated ISD 600/PK-12
39227 Highway 105 77585 936-274-5061
Chad Jones, supt. Fax 274-4321
westhardin.org
West Hardin HS 200/9-12
39227 Highway 105 77585 936-274-5061
Dr. Ralph Carter, prin. Fax 274-5671
West Hardin MS 100/6-8
39227 Highway 105 77585 936-274-5061
Dr. Ralph Carter, prin. Fax 274-5671

Savoy, Fannin, Pop. 820
Savoy ISD 300/PK-12
302 W Hayes St 75479 903-965-5262
Brian Neal, supt. Fax 965-7282
www.savoyisd.org
Savoy JSHS 200/7-12
302 W Hayes St 75479 903-965-4024
Mike Smith, prin. Fax 965-5608

Schertz, Guadalupe, Pop. 30,563
Schertz-Cibolo-Universal City ISD 12,400/PK-12
1060 Elbel Rd 78154 210-945-6200
Greg Gibson Ed.D., supt. Fax 945-6252
www.scuc.txed.net
Clemens HS 1,600/9-12
1001 Elbel Rd 78154 210-945-6501
Melissa Sosa, prin. Fax 945-6590
Corbett JHS 900/7-8
12000 Ray Corbett Dr 78154 210-619-4150
David Knox, prin. Fax 619-4190
Steele Enhanced Learning Center 2,100/Alt
204 Wright Ave 78154 210-945-6401
David Berry, prin. Fax 945-6410
Other Schools – See Cibolo

Schulenburg, Fayette, Pop. 2,828
Schulenburg ISD 700/PK-12
521 North St 78956 979-743-3448
Walter Padgett, supt. Fax 743-4721
www.schulenburg.txed.net
Schulenburg HS 300/7-12
150 College St 78956 979-743-3605
Michelle Michaelsen, prin. Fax 743-4721

Blinn College Post-Sec.
100 Ranger Dr 78956 979-743-5200

Scurry, Kaufman, Pop. 668
Scurry-Rosser ISD 800/PK-12
10705 S State Highway 34 75158 972-452-8823
Rhonda Porter, supt. Fax 452-8586
www.scurry-rosser.com/
Scurry-Rosser HS 200/9-12
8321 S State Highway 34 75158 972-452-8823
J.R. Proctor, prin. Fax 452-3694
Scurry-Rosser MS 300/4-8
10729 S State Highway 34 75158 972-452-8823
Chad Collins, prin. Fax 452-8902

Seabrook, Harris, Pop. 11,727
Clear Creek ISD
Supt. — See League City
Seabrook IS 1,000/6-8
2401 Meyer Rd 77586 281-284-3100
David Williams, prin. Fax 284-3105

Seagraves, Gaines, Pop. 2,405
Seagraves ISD 600/PK-12
PO Box 577 79359 806-387-2035
Dr. Kevin Spiller, supt. Fax 387-2944
www.seagravesisd.net/
Seagraves HS 200/9-12
PO Box 1505 79359 806-387-2520
Artemio Ontiveros, prin. Fax 387-2944
Seagraves JHS 100/6-8
PO Box 938 79359 806-387-2646
Josh Goen, prin. Fax 387-2451

Sealy, Austin, Pop. 5,953
Sealy ISD 2,600/PK-12
939 Tiger Ln 77474 979-885-3516
Scott Kana, supt. Fax 885-6457
www.sealyisd.com
Sealy HS 800/9-12
2372 Championship Dr 77474 979-885-3515
Megan Oliver, prin. Fax 987-3398
Sealy JHS 600/6-8
939 Tiger Ln 77474 979-885-3292
Terri Kendrick, prin. Fax 877-0743

Blinn College Post-Sec.
3701 Outlet Center Dr 77474 979-627-7997

Seguin, Guadalupe, Pop. 24,967
Navarro ISD 1,600/PK-12
6450 N State Highway 123 78155 830-372-1930
Dee Carter, supt. Fax 372-1853
www.nisd.us
Navarro HS 500/9-12
6350 N State Highway 123 78155 830-372-1931
Gary Haass, prin. Fax 401-5570
Navarro JHS 300/7-8
6450 N State Highway 123 78155 830-401-5550
Luke Morales, prin. Fax 379-3135

Seguin ISD 7,300/PK-12
1221 E Kingsbury St 78155 830-372-5771
Dr. Irene Garza, supt. Fax 379-0392
www.seguin.k12.tx.us
Barnes MS 500/7-8
1539 Joe Carrillo Blvd 78155 830-379-4717
Jesus Uranga, prin. Fax 379-4239
Briesemeister MS 600/7-8
1616 W Court St 78155 830-379-0600
Elisa Carter, prin. Fax 379-0615
Mercer-Blumberg Learning Center 100/Alt
1205 E Kingsbury St 78155 830-401-8690
Marcus Jones, prin. Fax 379-1362
Seguin HS 2,000/9-12
815 Lamar 78155 830-372-5770
Yomcido Guerra, prin. Fax 372-9851

Lifegate Christian S 200/K-12
395 Lifegate Ln 78155 830-372-0850
Gerard Lopez, prin. Fax 372-0895
Seguin Beauty College Post-Sec.
102 E Court St 78155 830-372-0935
Texas Lutheran University Post-Sec.
1000 W Court St 78155 830-372-8000

Seminole, Gaines, Pop. 6,373
Seminole ISD 2,400/PK-12
207 SW 6th St 79360 432-758-3662
Doug Harriman, supt. Fax 758-9833
www.seminoleisd.net/
Seminole HS 600/9-12
2100 NW Avenue D 79360 432-758-5873
Robert Chappell, prin. Fax 758-8146

Seminole JHS 500/6-8
600 NW Avenue J 79360 432-758-9431
Daylan Sellers, prin. Fax 758-5795
Seminole Success Center 50/Alt
206 SW 3rd St 79360 432-758-2772
Seth Davis, prin. Fax 758-3625

Seymour, Baylor, Pop. 2,715
Seymour ISD 600/PK-12
409 W Idaho St 76380 940-889-3525
Dr. John Baker, supt. Fax 889-5340
www.seymour-isd.net
Seymour HS 100/9-12
409 W Idaho St 76380 940-888-2947
Dr. Greg Roach, prin. Fax 889-1045
Seymour MS 200/5-8
409 W Idaho St 76380 940-889-4548
Morris Davis, prin. Fax 889-4962

Shallowater, Lubbock, Pop. 2,469
Shallowater ISD 1,500/PK-12
1100 Avenue K 79363 806-832-4531
Phil Warren, supt. Fax 832-4350
www.shallowaterisd.net
Shallowater HS 400/9-12
1100 Avenue K 79363 806-832-4531
Tom Johnson, prin. Fax 832-4523
Shallowater MS 400/5-8
1100 Avenue K 79363 806-832-4531
Dr. Kenny Border, prin. Fax 832-5543
Woodward Academy 50/Alt
1100 Avenue K 79363 806-832-4531
Carol Johnson, prin. Fax 832-4350

Shamrock, Wheeler, Pop. 1,874
Shamrock ISD 200/K-12
100 S Illinois St 79079 806-256-3492
Wes Beck, supt. Fax 256-3628
www.shamrockisd.net
Shamrock HS 100/9-12
100 S Illinois St 79079 806-256-2241
Kenneth Shields, prin. Fax 256-3628

Sheffield, Pecos
Iraan-Sheffield ISD
Supt. — See Iraan
Challenge HS 100/Alt
1 Schoolhouse Rd 79781 432-836-4572
Candra Cade, prin. Fax 836-4691

Shelbyville, Shelby
Shelbyville ISD 800/PK-12
PO Box 325 75973 936-598-2641
Dr. Ray West, supt. Fax 598-6842
www.shelbyville.k12.tx.us
Shelbyville S 800/PK-12
PO Box 325 75973 936-598-7323
Mario Osby, prin. Fax 598-6842

Shenandoah, Montgomery, Pop. 2,111

Aveda Institute Post-Sec.
10241 David Memorial Dr 77385 936-539-6770

Shepherd, San Jacinto, Pop. 2,281
Shepherd ISD 1,900/PK-12
1401 S Byrd Ave 77371 936-628-3396
Jody Cronin, supt. Fax 628-3841
www.shepherdisd.net/
Shepherd HS 500/9-12
1401 S Byrd Ave 77371 936-628-3371
Jimmy Meekins, prin. Fax 628-6986
Shepherd MS 400/6-8
1401 S Byrd Ave 77371 936-628-3377
Brenda Cronin, prin. Fax 628-6749

Sherman, Grayson, Pop. 37,575
Sherman ISD 6,600/PK-12
2701 N Loy Lake Rd 75090 903-891-6400
Dr. Al Hambrick, supt. Fax 891-6407
www.shermanisd.net
Piner MS 1,000/7-8
402 W Pecan St 75090 903-891-6470
Clinton Petty, prin. Fax 891-6475
Sherman HS 1,600/9-12
2201 E Lamar St 75090 903-891-6440
Peggy VanMarter, prin. Fax 891-6446
Other Schools – See Denison

Austin College Post-Sec.
900 N Grand Ave 75090 903-813-2000
Diamonds Cosmetology College Post-Sec.
1950 N Grand Ave 75090 903-891-0758
Texoma Christian S 400/PK-12
3500 W Houston St 75092 903-893-7076
Beckie Soliz, dir. Fax 891-8486

Shiner, Lavaca, Pop. 2,046
Shiner ISD 600/PK-12
PO Box 804 77984 361-594-3121
Trey Lawrence, supt. Fax 594-3925
www.shinerisd.net
Shiner JSHS 300/7-12
PO Box 804 77984 361-594-3131
Brad Oden, prin. Fax 594-4295

Shiner Catholic S 300/PK-12
PO Box 725 77984 361-594-2313
Neely Yackel, prin. Fax 594-8599

Sidney, Comanche
Sidney ISD 100/PK-12
PO Box 190 76474 254-842-5500
Doug Bowden, supt. Fax 842-5731
www.sidney.esc14.net/
Sidney S 100/PK-12
PO Box 190 76474 254-842-5500
Ben Carroll, prin. Fax 842-5731

Sierra Blanca, Hudspeth, Pop. 550
Sierra Blanca ISD 200/K-12
PO Box 308 79851 915-369-3741
Denise Mendoza, supt. Fax 369-2605
www.sierrablancaisd.net
Sierra Blanca S 200/K-12
PO Box 308 79851 915-369-2781
Michelle Melendez, prin. Fax 369-2605

Silsbee, Hardin, Pop. 6,524
Silsbee ISD 2,800/K-12
415 Highway 327 W 77656 409-980-7800
Richard Bain, supt. Fax 980-7897
www.silsbeeisd.org
Edwards-Johnson Memorial Silsbee MS 700/6-8
1140 Highway 327 E 77656 409-980-7800
Murrell Stewart, prin. Fax 980-7875
Silsbee HS 800/9-12
1575 US Highway 96 N 77656 409-980-7800
Eldon Franco, prin. Fax 980-7881

Southeast Texas Career Institute Post-Sec.
975 Highway 327 E Ste 150 77656 409-386-2020

Silverton, Briscoe, Pop. 724
Silverton ISD 200/PK-12
PO Box 608 79257 806-823-2476
Bill Wood, supt. Fax 823-2276
www.silvertonisd.net
Silverton S 200/PK-12
PO Box 608 79257 806-823-2476
Michelle Francis, prin. Fax 823-2276

Simms, Bowie
Simms ISD 500/PK-12
PO Box 9 75574 903-543-2219
Rex Burks, supt. Fax 543-2512
www.simmsisd.net/
Bowie HS 200/9-12
PO Box 9 75574 903-543-2275
Lisa Hudgeons, prin. Fax 543-2512
Bowie JHS 100/6-8
PO Box 9 75574 903-543-2275
Lisa Hudgeons, prin. Fax 543-2512

Sinton, San Patricio, Pop. 5,646
Sinton ISD 2,100/PK-12
PO Box 1337 78387 361-364-6800
Steve VanMatre, supt. Fax 364-6905
www.sintonisd.net/
Sinton HS 600/9-12
400 N Pirate Blvd 78387 361-364-6650
Daniel Smith, prin. Fax 364-6668
Smith MS 500/6-8
900 S San Patricio St 78387 361-364-6840
Jennifer Davis, prin. Fax 364-6856

Skidmore, Bee, Pop. 917
Skidmore-Tynan ISD 800/K-12
224 W Main St 78389 361-287-3426
Dr. Brett Belmarez, supt. Fax 287-3442
www.stisd.esc2.net
Skidmore-Tynan HS 200/9-12
224 W Main St 78389 361-287-3426
Justin Crittenden, prin. Fax 287-0146
Skidmore-Tynan JHS 200/6-8
224 W Main St 78389 361-287-3426
John Matus, prin. Fax 287-0714

Slaton, Lubbock, Pop. 6,048
Slaton ISD 1,100/PK-12
140 E Panhandle St 79364 806-828-6591
Julee Becker, supt. Fax 828-5506
www.slatonisd.net/
Slaton HS 300/9-12
105 N 20th St 79364 806-828-5833
Chris Kennedy, prin. Fax 828-1229
Slaton JHS 300/6-8
300 W Jean St 79364 806-828-6583
Jim Andrus, prin. Fax 828-2080

Slidell, Wise
Slidell ISD 300/PK-12
PO Box 69 76267 940-466-3118
Greg Enis, supt. Fax 466-3062
www.slidellisd.net/
Slidell JSHS 100/6-12
PO Box 69 76267 940-466-3118
Marty Hair, prin. Fax 466-3607

Smithville, Bastrop, Pop. 3,753
Smithville ISD 1,700/PK-12
PO Box 479 78957 512-237-2487
Dr. Rock McNulty, supt. Fax 237-2775
www.smithvilleisd.org
Smithville HS 500/9-12
PO Box 479 78957 512-237-2451
David Edwards, prin. Fax 237-5643
Smithville JHS 400/6-8
PO Box 479 78957 512-237-2407
Andra Sparks, prin. Fax 237-5624

Smyer, Hockley, Pop. 469
Smyer ISD 400/PK-12
PO Box 206 79367 806-234-2935
Dane Kerns, supt. Fax 234-2411
www.smyer-isd.org
Smyer JSHS 100/7-12
PO Box 206 79367 806-234-3871
Bruce Cunningham, prin. Fax 234-2411
Other Schools – See Ropesville

Snook, Burleson, Pop. 502
Snook ISD 500/PK-12
PO Box 87 77878 979-272-8307
Larry Williams, supt. Fax 272-5041
www.snookisd.com
Snook HS 100/9-12
PO Box 87 77878 979-272-8307
Robert Hudson, prin. Fax 272-5041
Snook MS 100/6-8
PO Box 87 77878 979-272-8307
Jonathan Pozzi, prin. Fax 272-5041

Snyder, Scurry, Pop. 11,101
Snyder ISD 2,800/PK-12
2901 37th St 79549 325-574-8900
Dr. Randy Brown, supt. Fax 573-9025
www.snyderisd.net
Snyder HS 700/9-12
2901 37th St 79549 325-574-8800
Tryg Overbo, prin. Fax 573-9500
Snyder JHS 500/6-8
2901 37th St 79549 325-574-8700
Robert Webb, prin. Fax 574-6024

Western Texas College Post-Sec.
6200 College Ave 79549 325-573-8511

Somerset, Bexar, Pop. 1,624
Somerset ISD 3,800/PK-12
PO Box 279 78069 866-852-9858
Saul Hinojosa, supt. Fax 852-9860
www.sisdk12.net
Somerset HS 1,000/9-12
PO Box 279 78069 866-852-9861
Angela Dominguez, prin. Fax 667-2608
Other Schools – See Von Ormy

Somerville, Burleson, Pop. 1,362
Somerville ISD 400/PK-12
PO Box 997 77879 979-596-2153
Charles Camarillo, supt. Fax 596-1778
www.somervilleisd.org
Somerville Secondary S 100/7-12
PO Box 997 77879 979-596-1534
Karla Sparks, prin. Fax 596-1778

Sonora, Sutton, Pop. 3,018
Sonora ISD 1,000/PK-12
807 S Concho Ave 76950 325-387-6940
James Hartman, supt. Fax 387-5090
www.sonoraisd.net/
Sonora HS 300/9-12
807 S Concho Ave 76950 325-387-6940
Raul Chavarria, prin. Fax 387-5348
Sonora JHS 200/6-8
807 S Concho Ave 76950 325-387-6940
Brandon Duncan, prin. Fax 387-2007

Sour Lake, Hardin, Pop. 1,788
Hardin-Jefferson ISD 2,000/PK-12
PO Box 490 77659 409-981-6400
Shannon Holmes, supt. Fax 287-2283
www.hjisd.net/
Hardin-Jefferson HS 600/9-12
PO Box 639 77659 409-981-6430
Diana Valdez, prin.
Henderson MS, PO Box 649 77659 500/6-8
Melanie Nunez, prin. 409-981-6420

South Houston, Harris, Pop. 16,918
Pasadena ISD
Supt. — See Pasadena
South Houston HS 2,400/9-12
3820 S Shaver St 77587 713-740-0350
Steve Fullen, prin. Fax 740-4155
South Houston IS 900/6-8
900 College Ave 77587 713-740-0490
Laura Gomez, prin. Fax 740-4097

Southlake, Tarrant, Pop. 26,042
Carroll ISD 7,700/PK-12
2400 N Carroll Ave 76092 817-949-8282
Dr. David Faltys, supt. Fax 949-8228
www.southlakecarroll.edu
Carroll HS 1,200/9-10
800 N White Chapel Blvd 76092 817-949-5600
Paul Giamanco, prin. Fax 949-5656
Carroll MS 600/7-8
1800 Kirkwood Blvd 76092 817-949-5400
Matt Miller, prin. Fax 949-5454
Carroll SHS 1,300/11-12
1501 W Southlake Blvd 76092 817-949-5800
M. Shawn Duhon, prin. Fax 949-5858
Dawson MS 700/7-8
400 S Kimball Ave 76092 817-949-5500
Ryan Wilson, prin. Fax 949-5555

Clariden S 200/PK-12
100 Clariden Ranch Rd 76092 682-237-0400

Southland, Garza
Southland ISD 200/PK-12
190 Eighth St 79364 806-996-5599
Toby Miller, supt. Fax 996-5342
www.southlandisd.net
Southland S 200/PK-12
190 Eighth St 79364 806-996-5339
Craig Hamilton, prin. Fax 996-5595

Spearman, Hansford, Pop. 3,341
Spearman ISD 800/PK-12
403 E 11th Ave 79081 806-659-3233
Wm. Clay Montgomery, supt. Fax 659-2079
www.spearmanisd.com
Spearman HS 200/9-12
403 E 11th Ave 79081 806-659-2584
Bill Belger, prin. Fax 659-3824
Spearman JHS 100/6-8
313 W 5th Ave 79081 806-659-2563
Shane Whiteley, prin. Fax 659-3933

Splendora, Montgomery, Pop. 1,597
Splendora ISD 3,500/PK-12
23419 FM 2090 Rd 77372 281-689-3129
Dr. Genese Bell, supt. Fax 689-7509
www.splendoraisd.org/
Splendora HS 1,000/9-12
23747 FM 2090 Rd 77372 281-689-8008
Rick Kershner, prin. Fax 689-8675
Splendora JHS 500/7-8
23411 FM 2090 Rd 77372 281-689-6343
Brandon Perry, prin. Fax 689-8702

Spring, Harris, Pop. 53,043
Conroe ISD
Supt. — See Conroe
York JHS 1,700/7-8
3515 Waterbend Cv 77386 832-592-8600
Amy Porter, prin. Fax 592-8684

Klein ISD
Supt. — See Klein
Hildebrandt IS 900/6-8
22800 Hildebrandt Rd 77389 832-249-5100
Joffrey Jones, prin. Fax 249-4068
Klein Collins HS 3,300/9-12
20811 Ella Blvd 77388 832-484-5500
Randy Kirk, prin. Fax 484-7811
Klein Oak HS 3,900/9-12
22603 Northcrest Dr 77389 832-484-5000
Dr. Brian Greeney, prin. Fax 484-7831
Schindewolf IS 1,300/6-8
20903 Ella Blvd 77388 832-249-5900
Debbie Hamilton, prin. Fax 249-4072

Spring ISD
Supt. — See Houston
Bailey MS 1,200/6-8
3377 James Leo Dr 77373 281-891-8000
Veronica Vijil, prin. Fax 891-8001
Dueitt MS 1,000/6-8
1 Eagle Xing 77373 281-891-7800
Paul LeBlanc, prin. Fax 891-7801
Spring HS 3,600/9-12
19428 Interstate 45 77373 281-891-7000
Donna Ullrich, prin. Fax 891-7001
Twin Creeks MS 800/6-8
27100 Cypresswood Dr 77373 281-891-7850
Charlie Rooke, prin. Fax 891-7851
Wunsche SHS Vo/Tech
900 Wunsche Loop 77373 281-891-7650
Bob Thompson, prin. Fax 891-7651

Spring Branch, Comal
Comal ISD
Supt. — See New Braunfels
Smithson Valley HS 2,100/9-12
14001 State Highway 46 W 78070 830-885-1000
John Montelongo, prin. Fax 885-1001
Smithson Valley MS 900/6-8
6101 FM 311 78070 830-885-1200
Michael Keranen, prin. Fax 885-1201
Spring Branch MS 800/6-8
21053 State Highway 46 W 78070 830-885-8800
Chris Smith, prin. Fax 885-8801

Springtown, Parker, Pop. 2,624
Springtown ISD 3,000/PK-12
301 E 5th St 76082 817-220-1700
Mike Kelley, supt. Fax 523-5766
www.springtownisd.net
Springtown HS 1,000/9-12
915 W Highway 199 76082 817-220-3888
Chris Pennington, prin. Fax 523-5290
Springtown MS 500/7-8
500 Pojo Dr 76082 817-220-7455
Mark Wilson, prin. Fax 220-2395

Spur, Dickens, Pop. 1,312
Spur ISD 300/PK-12
PO Box 250 79370 806-271-3272
Earl Jarrett, supt. Fax 271-4575
www.spurbulldogs.com/
Spur MSHS 100/6-12
PO Box 250 79370 806-271-3385
Loretta Velez, prin. Fax 271-4575

Spurger, Tyler
Spurger ISD 400/PK-12
PO Box 38 77660 409-429-3464
Joseph Fisher, supt. Fax 429-3770
www.spurgerisd.org/
Spurger HS 200/7-12
PO Box 38 77660 409-429-3464
Brandon Shumake, prin. Fax 429-3770

Stafford, Fort Bend, Pop. 17,344
Stafford Municipal SD 3,200/PK-12
1625 Staffordshire Rd 77477 281-261-9200
Lance Hindt Ed.D., supt. Fax 261-9249
www.staffordmsd.org
Stafford Alternative Education Center Alt
1625 Staffordshire Rd 77477 281-261-9280
Dr. Jon Gray, prin. Fax 208-6118
Stafford HS 900/9-12
1625 Staffordshire Rd 77477 281-261-9239
Debbie Nordt, prin. Fax 261-9347
Stafford MS 500/7-8
1625 Staffordshire Rd 77477 281-261-9215
Debbie Nordt, prin. Fax 261-9349

Houston Learning Academy 50/9-12
3964 Bluebonnet Dr 77477 281-240-6060
Diana Monn, prin. Fax 240-0022

Stamford, Jones, Pop. 3,075
Stamford ISD 700/PK-12
507 S Orient St 79553 325-773-2705
Shaun Barnett, supt. Fax 773-5684
www.stamford.esc14.net
Stamford HS 200/9-12
507 S Orient St 79553 325-773-2701
Jim Raughton, prin. Fax 773-4015
Stamford MS 100/6-8
507 S Orient St 79553 325-773-2651
Kevin White, prin. Fax 773-4052

Stanton, Martin, Pop. 2,466
Stanton ISD 800/PK-12
PO Box 730 79782 432-756-2244
David Carr, supt. Fax 756-2052
www.stanton.esc18.net/
Stanton HS 200/9-12
PO Box 730 79782 432-756-3326
Mark Cotton, prin. Fax 756-2248
Stanton MS 200/6-8
PO Box 730 79782 432-756-2544
Albert Chavez, prin. Fax 756-2702

Star, Mills
Star ISD 100/K-12
PO Box 838 76880 325-948-3661
Barbara Marchbanks, supt. Fax 948-3398
Star S 100/K-12
PO Box 838 76880 325-948-3661
Barbara Marchbanks, supt. Fax 948-3398

Stephenville, Erath, Pop. 16,950
Huckabay ISD 200/K-12
200 County Road 421 76401 254-968-8476
Cheryl Floyd, supt. Fax 965-3740
www.hisd.us
Huckabay S 200/K-12
200 County Road 421 76401 254-968-5274
Tylor Chaplin, prin. Fax 965-3740

Stephenville ISD 3,600/PK-12
2655 W Overhill Dr 76401 254-968-7990
Dr. Darrell Floyd, supt. Fax 968-5942
www.sville.us
Henderson JHS 500/7-8
2798 W Frey St 76401 254-968-6967
Rene Goodwin, prin. Fax 965-7018
Stephenville HS 1,100/9-12
2650 W Overhill Dr 76401 254-968-4141
Travis Stilwell, prin. Fax 968-4897

Stephenville Beauty College Post-Sec.
951 S Lillian St 76401 254-968-2111
Tarleton State University Post-Sec.
PO Box T0001 76402 254-968-9000

Sterling City, Sterling, Pop. 875
Sterling City ISD 200/K-12
PO Box 786 76951 325-378-4781
Bob Rauch, supt. Fax 378-2283
sterlingcity.netxv.net
Sterling City HS 100/6-12
PO Box 786 76951 325-378-5821
Ty Stevens, prin. Fax 378-2087

Stinnett, Hutchinson, Pop. 1,860
Plemons-Stinnett-Phillips Cons ISD 600/PK-12
PO Box 3440 79083 806-878-2858
Bill Wiggins, supt. Fax 878-3585
www.pspcisd.net
West Texas HS 200/9-12
PO Box 3440 79083 806-878-2456
Larry Green, prin. Fax 878-3585
West Texas MS 100/6-8
PO Box 3440 79083 806-878-2247
Kevin Freriks, prin. Fax 878-3585

Stockdale, Wilson, Pop. 1,428
Stockdale ISD 700/K-12
PO Box 7 78160 830-996-3551
Paul Darilek, supt. Fax 996-1071
www.stockdaleisd.net
Stockdale HS 200/9-12
PO Box 7 78160 830-996-3103
Sandy Lynn, prin. Fax 996-1071
Stockdale JHS 200/6-8
PO Box 7 78160 830-996-3153
Sharon Dunn, prin. Fax 996-1071

Stratford, Sherman, Pop. 2,009
Stratford ISD 600/PK-12
PO Box 108 79084 806-366-3300
Jerry Birdsong, supt. Fax 366-3304
www.stratfordisd.net
Stratford HS 200/9-12
PO Box 108 79084 806-366-3330
Paul Uttley, prin. Fax 366-3304
Stratford JHS 200/5-8
PO Box 108 79084 806-366-3320
Clint Seward, prin. Fax 366-3304

Strawn, Palo Pinto, Pop. 647
Strawn ISD 200/PK-12
PO Box 428 76475 254-672-5313
Lane Jackson, supt. Fax 672-5662
www.strawnschool.net/
Strawn S 200/PK-12
PO Box 428 76475 254-672-5776
Brent Dawson, prin. Fax 672-5662

Sudan, Lamb, Pop. 949
Sudan ISD 400/PK-12
PO Box 249 79371 806-227-2431
Lyndell Lance, supt. Fax 227-2146
www.sudanisd.net
Sudan JSHS 200/8-12
PO Box 249 79371 806-227-2431
Scott Harrell, prin. Fax 227-2146

Sugar Land, Fort Bend, Pop. 76,889
Fort Bend ISD 68,500/PK-12
16431 Lexington Blvd 77479 281-634-1000
Michael McKie, supt. Fax 634-1700
www.fortbendisd.com
Austin HS 2,400/9-12
3434 Pheasant Creek Dr, 281-634-2000
Mary Ellen Edge, prin. Fax 634-2074
Clements HS 2,900/9-12
4200 Elkins Rd 77479 281-634-2150
Ken Gregorski, prin. Fax 634-2168
Dulles HS 2,100/9-12
550 Dulles Ave 77478 281-634-5600
Mark Foust, prin. Fax 634-5681
Dulles MS 1,300/6-8
500 Dulles Ave 77478 281-634-5750
Michael Heinzen, prin. Fax 634-5781
First Colony MS 1,000/6-8
3225 Austin Pkwy 77479 281-634-3240
Jerrie Kammerman, prin. Fax 634-3267
Fort Settlement MS 1,100/6-8
5440 Elkins Rd 77479 281-634-6440
Julie Diaz, prin. Fax 634-6456
Garcia MS 1,400/6-8
18550 Old Richmond Rd, 281-634-3160
Joseph Chandler, prin. Fax 634-3166
Kempner HS 2,500/9-12
14777 Voss Rd, 281-634-2300
Dr. Anthony Indelicato, prin. Fax 634-2378
Sartartia MS 1,200/6-8
8125 Homeward Way 77479 281-634-6310
Ginger Carrabine, prin. Fax 634-6373
Sugar Land MS 1,400/6-8
321 7th St, 281-634-3080
Lillie Vega, prin. Fax 634-3108
Technical Education Center Vo/Tech
540 Dulles Ave 77478 281-634-5671
Kennith Kendziora, admin. Fax 634-5700
Wood Alternative Ctr for Learning 50/Alt
138 Avenue F, 281-634-3320
Justo Robinson, admin. Fax 634-3331
Other Schools – See Houston, Missouri City, Richmond, Rosharon

---

Ft. Bend Christian Academy 900/PK-12
1250 7th St 77478 281-263-9175
Dr. Norm Slosted, head sch Fax 263-9147

Sulphur Bluff, Hopkins
Sulphur Bluff ISD 200/PK-12
PO Box 30 75481 903-945-2460
John McCullough, supt. Fax 945-2459
www.sulphurbluffisd.net/
Sulphur Bluff S 200/PK-12
PO Box 30 75481 903-945-2460
Amy Northcutt, prin. Fax 945-2459

Sulphur Springs, Hopkins, Pop. 15,115
North Hopkins ISD 500/PK-12
1994 Farm Road 71 W 75482 903-945-2192
Donna George, supt. Fax 945-2531
www.northhopkins.net/
North Hopkins JSHS 200/7-12
1994 Farm Road 71 W 75482 903-945-2192
Rob Stanley, prin. Fax 945-2531

Sulphur Springs ISD 3,400/PK-12
631 Connally St 75482 903-885-2153
Michael Lamb, supt. Fax 439-6162
www.ssisd.net/
Sulphur Springs HS 1,100/9-12
1200 Connally St 75482 903-885-2158
Charles Alderman, prin. Fax 439-6116
Sulphur Springs MS 900/6-8
832 Wildcat Way 75482 903-885-7741
Rusty Harden, prin. Fax 439-6126

Sundown, Hockley, Pop. 1,386
Sundown ISD 700/PK-12
PO Box 1110 79372 806-229-3021
Scott Marshall, supt. Fax 229-2004
www.sundownisd.com
Sundown HS 200/9-12
PO Box 1110 79372 806-229-2511
Brent Evans, prin. Fax 229-2004
Sundown JHS 100/6-8
PO Box 1110 79372 806-229-4691
Eddie Carter, prin. Fax 229-2004

Sunnyvale, Dallas, Pop. 5,012
Sunnyvale ISD 1,200/PK-12
417 E Tripp Rd 75182 972-226-7601
Doug Williams, supt. Fax 226-6882
www.sunnyvaleisd.com
Sunnyvale HS 300/9-12
222 N Collins Rd 75182 972-203-4600
Zach Hobbs, prin. Fax 226-2854
Sunnyvale MS 400/5-8
216 N Collins Rd 75182 972-226-2922
Carmen Ayo, prin. Fax 226-0982

Sunray, Moore, Pop. 1,899
Sunray ISD 500/PK-12
PO Box 240 79086 806-948-4411
Glen Waldo, supt. Fax 948-5274
www.sunrayisd.net
Sunray HS 200/9-12
PO Box 240 79086 806-948-5515
Colynn Harrison, prin. Fax 948-5399
Sunray MS 200/5-8
PO Box 240 79086 806-948-4444
Terry Mulbery, prin. Fax 948-4208

Sweeny, Brazoria, Pop. 3,645
Sweeny ISD 2,000/PK-12
1310 N Elm St 77480 979-491-8000
Randy Miksch, supt. Fax 491-8030
www.sweenyisd.org
Sweeny HS 600/9-12
1310 N Elm St 77480 979-491-8100
Brian Brooks, prin. Fax 491-8171
Sweeny JHS 400/6-8
1310 N Elm St 77480 979-491-8200
Michael Saul, prin. Fax 491-8274

Sweetwater, Nolan, Pop. 10,784
Sweetwater ISD 1,900/PK-12
207 Musgrove St 79556 325-235-8601
Terry Pittman, supt. Fax 235-5561
www.sweetwaterisd.net/
Sweetwater HS 500/9-12
1205 Ragland St 79556 325-235-4371
Stacy Jones, prin. Fax 235-4861
Sweetwater MS 500/6-8
305 Lamar St 79556 325-236-6303
Jeff Withrow, prin. Fax 236-6941

Texas State Technical College Post-Sec.
300 Homer K Taylor Dr 79556 325-235-7300

Taft, San Patricio, Pop. 3,018
Taft ISD 1,100/PK-12
400 College St 78390 361-528-2636
Dr. Chad Kelly, supt. Fax 528-2223
www.taftisd.net
Taft HS 300/9-12
502 Rincon Rd 78390 361-528-2636
Angel Lopez, prin. Fax 528-3918
Taft JHS 200/6-8
727 McIntyre Ave 78390 361-528-2636
Jill Blankenship, prin. Fax 528-5477

Tahoka, Lynn, Pop. 2,660
Tahoka ISD 600/PK-12
PO Box 1230 79373 806-561-4105
Steve Burleson, supt. Fax 561-4160
www.tahokaisd.us
Tahoka HS 200/9-12
PO Box 1500 79373 806-561-4538
Jeffrey Perez, prin. Fax 561-6082
Tahoka MS 100/6-8
PO Box 1500 79373 806-561-4538
Jeffrey Fleenor, prin. Fax 561-6082

Tatum, Rusk, Pop. 1,369
Tatum ISD 1,500/PK-12
PO Box 808 75691 903-947-6482
Dee Hartt Ed.D., supt. Fax 947-3295
www.tatumisd.org
Tatum HS 400/9-12
PO Box 808 75691 903-947-6482
Bob Garcia, prin. Fax 947-6206
Tatum MS 200/6-8
PO Box 808 75691 903-947-6482
Brandon Milam, prin. Fax 947-3295

Taylor, Williamson, Pop. 14,982
Taylor ISD 2,800/PK-12
602 W 12th St 76574 512-365-1391
Jerry Vaughn, supt. Fax 365-3800
www.taylorisd.org
Taylor HS 900/9-12
355 FM 973 76574 512-365-1291
Danny Ward, prin. Fax 365-9334
Taylor MS 600/6-8
304 Carlos Parker Blvd NW 76574 512-365-8591
Hector Martinez, prin. Fax 365-8589

Teague, Freestone, Pop. 3,527
Teague ISD 1,300/PK-12
420 N 10th Ave 75860 254-739-3071
Ned Burns, supt. Fax 739-5223
www.teagueisd.org/
Teague HS 300/9-12
420 N 10th Ave 75860 254-739-1500
Darrell Evans, prin. Fax 739-2724
Teague JHS 300/6-8
420 N 10th Ave 75860 254-739-1450
Donnie Osborn, prin. Fax 739-5896

Temple, Bell, Pop. 64,746
Belton ISD
Supt. — See Belton
Lake Belton MS 1,100/6-8
8818 Tarver Dr 76502 254-215-2900
Suzy McKinney, prin. Fax 215-2901

Temple ISD 9,000/PK-12
PO Box 788 76503 254-215-8473
Dr. Robin Battershell, supt. Fax 215-6783
www.tisd.org
Bonham MS 600/6-8
4600 Midway Dr 76502 254-215-6600
Jason Mayo, prin. Fax 215-6634
Edwards Academy 100/Alt
1414 W Barton Ave 76504 254-215-6944
Sharon Holleman, prin. Fax 215-6946
Lamar MS 600/6-8
2120 N 1st St 76501 254-215-6444
Dean Frederick, prin. Fax 215-6483
Temple HS 2,100/9-12
415 N 31st St 76504 254-215-7000
Bob James, prin. Fax 899-6926
Travis MS 500/6-8
1551 S 25th St 76504 254-215-6300
Glenda Williams, prin. Fax 215-6352
Wheatley Alternative Education Center 100/Alt
515 E Avenue D 76501 254-215-5665
Carl Pleasant, prin. Fax 215-5673

Central Texas Beauty College Post-Sec.
2010 S 57th St 76504 254-773-9911
Central Texas Christian S 600/PK-12
4141 W FM 93 76502 254-939-5700
Ed Thomas, supt. Fax 939-5769
Holy Trinity Catholic HS 100/9-12
6608 W Adams Ave 76502 254-771-0787
Dr. Veronica Alonzo, prin. Fax 771-2285
Scott & White Memorial Hospital & Clinic Post-Sec.
2401 S 31st St 76508 254-724-5177
Temple College Post-Sec.
2600 S 1st St 76504 254-298-8282

Tenaha, Shelby, Pop. 1,146
Tenaha ISD 500/PK-12
PO Box 318 75974 936-248-5000
Scott Tyner, supt. Fax 248-3902
www.tenahaisd.com/

Tenaha HS 200/7-12
PO Box 318 75974 936-248-5000
Judy Monroe, prin. Fax 248-3626

Terlingua, Brewster, Pop. 54
Terlingua Common SD 100/K-12
PO Box 256 79852 432-371-2281
Kathy Killingsworth, supt. Fax 371-2245
www.terlinguacsd.com
Big Bend HS 50/9-12
PO Box 256 79852 432-371-2281
Bobbie Jones, prin. Fax 371-2245

Terrell, Kaufman, Pop. 15,583
Terrell ISD 4,100/PK-12
700 N Catherine St 75160 972-563-7504
Kelly Rodgers, supt. Fax 551-2842
www.terrellisd.com/
Furlough MS 600/7-8
1351 Colquitt Rd 75160 972-563-7501
Danielle Whiffen, prin. Fax 563-5721
Phoenix Center Alt
305 W College St 75160 972-563-6319
Dexter Dumas, prin. Fax 563-4786
Terrell HS 1,000/9-12
400 Poetry Rd 75160 972-563-7525
Eduardo Hernandez, prin. Fax 563-6318

Poetry Community Christian S 200/K-12
18688 FM 986 75160 972-563-7227
Dr. Anne Horan, admin. Fax 563-0025
Southwestern Christian College Post-Sec.
PO Box 10 75160 972-524-3341

Texarkana, Bowie, Pop. 35,750
Liberty-Eylau ISD 2,800/PK-12
2901 Leopard Dr 75501 903-832-1535
Nick Blain, supt. Fax 838-9444
www.leisd.net
Liberty-Eylau HS 700/9-12
2905 Leopard Dr 75501 903-832-1535
Rick Fowler, prin. Fax 831-6113
Liberty-Eylau MS 800/5-8
5555 Leopard Dr 75501 903-838-5555
William Houff, prin. Fax 832-6700
Liberty-Eylau S of Success 50/Alt
766 Macedonia Rd 75501 903-831-5657
Donald Patton, prin. Fax 838-0493

Pleasant Grove ISD 1,800/PK-12
8500 N Kings Hwy 75503 903-831-4086
Margaret Davis, supt. Fax 831-4435
www.pgisd.net
Pleasant Grove HS 600/9-12
5406 McKnight Rd 75503 903-832-8005
William Harp, prin. Fax 832-5381
Pleasant Grove MS 400/6-8
5605 Cooks Ln 75503 903-831-4295
Linda Erie, prin. Fax 831-5501

Red Lick ISD 500/K-8
3511 N FM 2148 75503 903-838-8230
Rose Mary Neshyba, supt. Fax 831-6134
www.redlickisd.com
Red Lick MS 200/5-8
3511 N FM 2148 75503 903-838-6006
Steve White, prin. Fax 831-6134

Texarkana ISD 6,800/PK-12
4241 Summerhill Rd 75503 903-794-3651
Paul Norton, supt. Fax 792-2632
www.txkisd.net
Options S 100/Alt
3201 Lincoln Ave 75503 903-793-5632
Marsha Burris, prin. Fax 792-2632
Texas HS 1,900/9-12
4001 Summerhill Rd 75503 903-794-3891
Brad Bailey, prin. Fax 792-8971
Texas MS 1,500/6-8
2100 College Dr 75503 903-793-5631
Donna McDaniel, prin. Fax 792-2935

Texarkana College Post-Sec.
2500 N Robison Rd 75501 903-823-3456
Texas A&M University Texarkana Post-Sec.
7101 University Ave 75503 903-223-3000
Wadley Regional Medical Center Post-Sec.
1000 Pine St 75501 903-798-8000

Texas City, Galveston, Pop. 44,454
Texas City ISD 5,900/PK-12
PO Box 1150 77592 409-916-0100
Cynthia Lusignolo Ed.D., supt. Fax 942-2655
www.tcisd.org/
Blocker MS 900/7-8
500 14th Ave N 77590 409-916-0700
Julie Southworth, prin. Fax 942-2755
Texas City HS 1,600/9-12
1431 9th Ave N 77590 409-916-0800
Mark Chatham, prin. Fax 942-2672
Wilson Alternative S 50/Alt
300 14th Ave N 77590 409-916-0280
Caye Powada, prin. Fax 942-2462

College of the Mainland Post-Sec.
1200 N Amburn Rd 77591 409-938-1211

Texline, Dallam, Pop. 485
Texline ISD 200/K-12
PO Box 60 79087 806-362-4667
Gary Laramore, supt. Fax 362-4538
www.texlineisd.net
Texline S 200/K-12
PO Box 60 79087 806-362-4284
Russell Schaub, prin. Fax 362-4938

The Colony, Denton, Pop. 35,324
Lewisville ISD
Supt. — See Flower Mound
Griffin MS 700/6-8
5105 N Colony Blvd 75056 469-713-5973
Michele Sandefur, prin. Fax 350-9187
Lakeview MS 800/6-8
4300 Keys Dr 75056 469-713-5974
Jeremy Turner, prin. Fax 350-9202
The Colony HS 1,900/9-12
4301 Blair Oaks Dr 75056 469-713-5178
James Hill, prin. Fax 350-9336

The Woodlands, Montgomery, Pop. 92,202
Conroe ISD
Supt. — See Conroe
Academy of Science & Technology 9-12
3701 College Park Dr 77384 936-709-3250
Dr. Susan Caffery, hdmstr. Fax 709-3299
Knox JHS 1,100/7-8
12104 Sawmill Rd 77380 832-592-8400
Joe Daw, prin. Fax 592-8410
McCullough JHS 2,100/7-8
3800 S Panther Creek Dr 77381 832-592-5100
Chris McCord, prin. Fax 592-5116
The Woodlands College Park SHS 2,600/9-12
3701 College Park Dr 77384 936-709-3000
Dr. Mark Murrell, prin. Fax 709-3019
The Woodlands HS Ninth Grade Campus 1,100/9-9
10010 Branch Crossing Dr 77382 832-592-8200
Dr. Chris Povich, prin. Fax 592-8299
The Woodlands SHS 2,900/10-12
6101 Research Forest Dr 77381 936-709-1200
Dr. Gregg Colschen, prin. Fax 709-1299

Cooper S 1,000/PK-12
1 John Cooper Dr 77381 281-367-0900
Michael Maher, hdmstr. Fax 292-9201
Esprit International S 100/PK-10
4890 W Panther Creek Dr 77381 281-298-9200
Fax 415-0486
Grace School of Theology Post-Sec.
PO Box 7477 77387 877-476-8674
Woodlands Christian Academy 400/PK-12
5800 Academy Way 77384 936-273-2555
Julie Ambler, hdmstr. Fax 271-3115

Thorndale, Milam, Pop. 1,329
Thorndale ISD 500/PK-12
PO Box 870 76577 512-898-2538
Dr. Craig Spinn, supt. Fax 898-5356
www.thorndale.txed.net/
Thorndale HS 200/9-12
PO Box 870 76577 512-898-2321
Hank Laywell, prin. Fax 898-5558
Thorndale MS 100/6-8
PO Box 870 76577 512-898-2670
Dr. John Rueter, prin. Fax 898-5505

Thrall, Williamson, Pop. 832
Thrall ISD 500/K-12
201 S Bounds St 76578 512-898-0062
Tommy Hooker, supt. Fax 898-5349
www.thrallisd.com
Thrall MSHS 200/6-12
201 S Bounds St 76578 512-898-5193
Travis Dube, prin. Fax 898-2132

Three Rivers, Live Oak, Pop. 1,845
Three Rivers ISD 500/PK-12
351 S School Rd 78071 361-786-3626
Kenneth Rohrbach, supt. Fax 786-2555
www.trisd.org
Three Rivers Alternative S Alt
351-A S School Rd 78071 361-786-3626
Charles Odom, prin. Fax 786-2555
Three Rivers JSHS 200/7-12
351-A S School Rd 78071 361-786-3531
Charles Odom, prin. Fax 786-3533

Throckmorton, Throckmorton, Pop. 823
Throckmorton ISD 200/PK-12
210 College St 76483 940-849-2411
Clay Tarpley, supt. Fax 849-3345
www.throck.org/
Throckmorton HS 100/9-12
210 College St 76483 940-849-2421
Troy Batts, prin. Fax 849-3345

Tilden, McMullen, Pop. 261
McMullen County ISD 200/PK-12
PO Box 359 78072 361-274-2000
Dave Underwood, supt. Fax 274-3665
www.mcisd.us
McMullen County S 200/PK-12
PO Box 359 78072 361-274-3371
Rosie Cavazos, prin. Fax 274-3580

Timpson, Shelby, Pop. 1,144
Timpson ISD 700/PK-12
PO Box 370 75975 936-254-2463
Mid Johnson, supt. Fax 254-3878
www.timpsonisd.com
Timpson HS 200/9-12
PO Box 370 75975 936-254-3125
Ronald Lindgren, prin. Fax 254-3263
Timpson MS 100/6-8
PO Box 370 75975 936-254-2078
Calvin Smith, prin. Fax 254-2355

Tivoli, Refugio, Pop. 475
Austwell-Tivoli ISD 200/K-12
207 Redfish St 77990 361-286-3212
Dr. Antonio Aguirre, supt. Fax 286-3637
www.atisd.net
Austwell-Tivoli JSHS 100/7-12
207 Redfish St 77990 361-286-3582
Stephen Maldonado, prin. Fax 286-3637

Tolar, Hood, Pop. 677
Tolar ISD 600/PK-12
PO Box 368 76476 254-835-4718
Bruce Gibbs, supt. Fax 835-4704
www.tolarisd.org
Tolar HS 200/9-12
PO Box 368 76476 254-835-4316
Brandon Wood, prin. Fax 835-4237
Tolar JHS 100/6-8
PO Box 368 76476 254-835-5207
Brad Morgan, prin. Fax 835-5208

Tomball, Harris, Pop. 10,569
Tomball ISD 11,000/PK-12
310 S Cherry St 77375 281-357-3100
John Neubauer, supt. Fax 357-3128
www.tomballisd.net
Tomball Alternative Education Center Alt
1302 Keefer Rd 77375 281-357-3281
Becky Dale, prin. Fax 357-3291
Tomball HS 3,000/9-12
30330 Quinn Rd 77375 281-357-3220
Greg Quinn, prin. Fax 357-3248
Tomball JHS 700/7-8
30403 Quinn Rd 77375 281-357-3000
Dr. Amy Schindewolf, prin. Fax 357-3027
Tomball Memorial HS 9-12
19100 Northpointe Ridge Ln 77377 281-357-3230
Carol Houston, prin. Fax 357-3240
Willow Wood JHS 900/7-8
11770 Gregson Rd 77377 281-357-3030
Dr. Kate Lacy, prin. Fax 357-3044

Concordia Lutheran HS 500/9-12
700 E Main St 77375 281-351-2547
Joel Bode, head sch Fax 255-8806
Lone Star College - Tomball Post-Sec.
30555 State Highway 249 77375 281-351-3300
Rosehill Christian S 400/PK-12
19830 FM 2920 Rd 77377 281-351-8114
Dean Unsicker, head sch Fax 516-3418
Woodlands Preparatory S 300/K-12
27440 Kuykendahl Rd 77375 281-516-0600
Ken West, dir. Fax 516-1155

Tom Bean, Grayson, Pop. 1,019
Tom Bean ISD 800/K-12
PO Box 128 75489 903-546-6076
Kathy Garrison, supt. Fax 546-6104
www.tombean-isd.org
Tom Bean HS 300/9-12
PO Box 128 75489 903-546-6319
Roger Ellis, prin. Fax 546-6319
Tom Bean MS 200/6-8
PO Box 128 75489 903-546-6161
Dewitt Smith, prin. Fax 546-6798

Tornillo, El Paso, Pop. 1,568
Tornillo ISD 1,400/PK-12
PO Box 170 79853 915-765-3000
Paul Vranish, supt. Fax 765-3099
www.tisd.us/
Tornillo HS 400/9-12
PO Box 170 79853 915-765-3500
Margaret Ruybe, prin. Fax 765-3599
Tornillo JHS 200/7-8
PO Box 170 79853 915-765-3400
Lisa Estrada, prin. Fax 765-3499

Trent, Taylor, Pop. 330
Trent ISD 200/PK-12
PO Box 105 79561 325-862-6125
Greg Priddy, supt. Fax 862-6448
www.trent.esc14.net
Trent S 200/PK-12
PO Box 105 79561 325-862-6125
Leanna West, prin. Fax 862-6448

Trenton, Fannin, Pop. 627
Trenton ISD 500/PK-12
PO Box 5 75490 903-989-2245
Jerry Don Cook, supt. Fax 989-2767
www.trentonisd.com
Trenton HS 200/9-12
PO Box 5 75490 903-989-2242
Rick Foreman, prin. Fax 989-2767
Trenton MS 100/6-8
PO Box 5 75490 903-989-2243
Rick Largent, prin. Fax 989-5173

Trinidad, Henderson, Pop. 863
Trinidad ISD 200/PK-12
105 W Eaton St 75163 903-778-2673
Corey Jenkins, supt. Fax 778-4120
www.trinidadisd.com
Trinidad S 200/PK-12
105 W Eaton St 75163 903-778-2415
Corey Jenkins, admin. Fax 778-4120

Trinity, Trinity, Pop. 2,644
Trinity ISD 1,100/PK-12
PO Box 752 75862 936-594-3569
Dave Plymale, supt. Fax 594-8425
www.trinityisd.net/
Trinity HS 300/9-12
PO Box 752 75862 936-594-3560
Craig Ruby, prin. Fax 594-2162
Trinity JHS 200/7-8
PO Box 752 75862 936-594-2321
Natalie Barrett, prin. Fax 594-3041

Trophy Club, Denton, Pop. 7,926
Northwest ISD
Supt. — See Justin
Medlin MS 700/6-8
601 Parkview Dr 76262 817-215-0500
Eric Drewery, prin. Fax 215-0548
Nelson HS 1,400/9-12
2775 Bobcat Blvd 76262 817-698-5600
Linda Parker, prin. Fax 698-5670

Troup, Smith, Pop. 1,837
Troup ISD 1,100/PK-12
PO Box 578 75789 903-842-3067
Stuart Bird, supt. Fax 842-4563
www.troupisd.org
Troup HS 300/9-12
PO Box 578 75789 903-842-3065
David Smith, prin. Fax 842-4563
Troup MS 300/6-8
PO Box 578 75789 903-842-3081
Ava Johnson, prin. Fax 842-4563

Troy, Bell, Pop. 1,625
Troy ISD 1,300/PK-12
PO Box 409 76579 254-938-2595
Neil Jeter, supt. Fax 938-7323
www.troyisd.org
Mays MS 300/6-8
PO Box 409 76579 254-938-2543
Michelle Jolliff, prin. Fax 938-2880
Troy HS 400/9-12
PO Box 409 76579 254-938-2561
Randy Hicks, prin. Fax 938-2328

Tulia, Swisher, Pop. 4,912
Tulia ISD 1,100/PK-12
702 NW 8th St 79088 806-995-4591
Steve Post, supt. Fax 995-3169
www.tuliaisd.net
Tulia HS 300/9-12
501 Hornet Pl 79088 806-995-2759
Mike Allison, prin. Fax 995-4413
Tulia JHS 200/6-8
421 NE 3rd St 79088 806-995-4842
Johnny Lara, prin. Fax 995-4498

Turkey, Hall, Pop. 416
Turkey-Quitaque ISD 200/PK-12
PO Box 397 79261 806-455-1411
Jon Davidson, supt. Fax 455-1718
www.valleypatriots.com/
Valley S 200/PK-12
PO Box 397 79261 806-455-1411
Jackie Jenkins, prin. Fax 455-1718

Tuscola, Taylor, Pop. 734
Jim Ned Consolidated ISD 1,000/PK-12
PO Box 9 79562 325-554-7500
Bobby Easterling, supt. Fax 554-7740
www.jimned.esc14.net/
Jim Ned HS 300/9-12
PO Box 9 79562 325-554-7755
David Hogan, prin. Fax 554-7550
Jim Ned MS 200/6-8
PO Box 9 79562 325-554-7870
Jay Wise, prin. Fax 554-7750

Tyler, Smith, Pop. 95,596
Chapel Hill ISD 3,300/PK-12
11134 County Road 2249 75707 903-566-2441
Donni Cook Ed.D., supt. Fax 566-8469
www.chapelhillisd.org
Chapel Hill HS 900/9-12
13172 State Highway 64 E 75707 903-566-2311
Andy Owens, prin. Fax 566-5343
Chapel Hill MS 700/6-8
13174 State Highway 64 E 75707 903-566-1491
Debbie Black, prin. Fax 566-6441
STEPS Alternative S 50/Alt
13172 State Highway 64 E 75707 903-565-0718
Richard Palmer, prin. Fax 565-0486

Tyler ISD 18,500/PK-12
PO Box 2035 75710 903-262-1000
Gary Mooring, supt. Fax 262-1178
www.tylerisd.org
Anderson Educational Complex/PACE 100/Alt
1818 N Confederate Ave 75702 903-262-3040
Jack Antilley, dir. Fax 262-3041
Boulter Creative Arts Magnet S 500/6-8
2926 Garden Valley Rd 75702 903-262-1390
Misti Rasure, prin. Fax 262-1392
Dogan MS 400/6-8
2621 N Border Ave 75702 903-262-1450
Masud Shamsid-Deen, prin. Fax 262-1451
Hogg MS 700/6-8
920 S Broadway Ave 75701 903-262-1500
Jo Ann Simmons, prin. Fax 262-1501
Hubbard MS 1,000/6-8
1300 Hubbard Dr 75703 903-262-1560
Scott Farler, prin. Fax 262-1566
Lee HS 2,800/9-12
411 E Southeast Loop 323 75701 903-262-2625
Gary Brown, prin. Fax 262-2630
Moore MST Magnet MS 900/6-8
1200 S Tipton Ave 75701 903-262-1640
Claude Lane, prin. Fax 262-1641
Plyler Instructional Complex 100/Alt
807 W Glenwood Blvd 75701 903-262-3070
Vanessa Choice, dir. Fax 262-3138
Stewart MS 400/6-8
2800 W Shaw St 75701 903-262-1710
Debra Robertson, prin. Fax 262-1711
Tyler HS 1,900/9-12
1120 N Northwest Loop 323 75702 903-262-2850
Michael Timms, prin. Fax 262-2852

All Saints Episcopal S 700/PK-12
2695 S Southwest Loop 323 75701 903-579-6000
Randal Brown, hdmstr. Fax 579-6002
Bishop Gorman Regional Catholic MSHS 400/6-12
1405 E Southeast Loop 323 75701 903-561-2424
Jim Franz, prin. Fax 561-2645
Christian Heritage S 100/K-12
961 County Road 1143 75704 903-593-2702
Calvin Todd, admin. Fax 531-2226
East Texas Christian Academy 200/PK-12
2448 Roy Rd 75707 903-561-8642
Wayne Boshears, pres. Fax 561-9620
Good Shepherd S 100/PK-12
2525 Old Jacksonville Rd 75701 903-592-4045
Fr. Walter Banek, hdmstr. Fax 596-7149
Grace Community S 500/6-12
3001 University Blvd 75701 903-566-5661
Wanda Shaeffer, prin. Fax 566-5639
King's Academy Christian S 100/K-12
604 W 4th St 75701 903-534-9992
Kenny Cargill, admin. Fax 534-9555
Star College of Cosmetology Post-Sec.
520 E Front St 75702 903-596-7860
Texas College Post-Sec.
2404 N Grand Ave 75702 903-593-8311
Tyler Junior College Post-Sec.
PO Box 9020 75711 903-510-2200
University of Texas at Tyler Post-Sec.
3900 University Blvd 75701 903-566-7203

Universal City, Bexar, Pop. 18,038
Judson ISD
Supt. — See Live Oak
Kitty Hawk MS 1,200/6-8
840 Old Cimarron Trl 78148 210-945-1220
Michael McFalls, prin. Fax 659-0687

First Baptist Academy 400/PK-12
1401 Pat Booker Rd 78148 210-658-5331
Teri Flynn, admin. Fax 658-7024

Utopia, Uvalde, Pop. 224
Utopia ISD 200/K-12
PO Box 880 78884 830-966-1928
John Walts, supt. Fax 966-6162
www.utopiaisd.net
Utopia S 200/K-12
PO Box 880 78884 830-966-3339
Ken Mueller, prin. Fax 966-6162

Uvalde, Uvalde, Pop. 15,676
Uvalde Consolidated ISD 5,100/PK-12
PO Box 1909 78802 830-278-6655
John Harrell, supt. Fax 591-4909
www.ucisd.net
Excel Academy 100/Alt
PO Box 1909 78802 830-591-4973
John Gatica, prin. Fax 591-4978
Uvalde HS 1,200/9-12
PO Box 1909 78802 830-591-2950
Victor Baron, prin. Fax 591-2960
Uvalde JHS 700/7-8
PO Box 1909 78802 830-591-2980
Leo Villarreal, prin. Fax 591-2975

Southwest School Post-Sec.
122 W North St 78801 830-278-4103
Southwest Texas Junior College Post-Sec.
2401 Garner Field Rd 78801 830-278-4401

Valentine, Jeff Davis, Pop. 134
Valentine ISD 50/PK-12
PO Box 188 79854 432-467-2671
William Cook, supt. Fax 467-2004
www.valentineisd.com
Valentine S 50/PK-12
PO Box 188 79854 432-467-2671
William Cook, supt. Fax 467-2004

Valera, Coleman
Panther Creek Consolidated ISD 100/PK-12
129 Private Road 3421 76884 325-357-4506
Dwin Nanny, supt. Fax 357-4470
www.pcreek.net
Panther Creek S 100/PK-12
129 Private Road 3421 76884 325-357-4449
Dwin Nanny, prin. Fax 357-4470

Valley Mills, Bosque, Pop. 1,193
Valley Mills ISD 600/PK-12
PO Box 518 76689 254-932-5210
Larry Robinson, supt. Fax 932-6601
www.vmisd.net
Valley Mills HS 200/9-12
PO Box 518 76689 254-932-5251
Joe Crownover, prin. Fax 932-6601
Valley Mills JHS 100/7-8
PO Box 518 76689 254-932-5251
Joe Crownover, prin. Fax 932-6601

Valley View, Cooke, Pop. 748
Valley View ISD 600/K-12
106 Newton St 76272 940-726-3659
William Stokes, supt. Fax 726-3614
www.vvisd.net
Valley View HS 200/9-12
106 Newton St 76272 940-726-3522
Chris Heskett, prin. Fax 726-3862
Valley View MS 200/5-8
106 Newton St 76272 940-726-3244
Matthew Chalmers, prin. Fax 726-3786

Van, Van Zandt, Pop. 2,615
Van ISD 2,100/PK-12
PO Box 697 75790 903-963-8328
Don Dunn, supt. Fax 963-3904
www.vanschools.org
Van HS 700/9-12
PO Box 697 75790 903-963-8623
Jeff Hutchins, prin. Fax 963-5591
Van JHS 300/7-8
PO Box 697 75790 903-963-8321
Jason Johnson, prin. Fax 963-3277

Van Alstyne, Grayson, Pop. 2,993
Van Alstyne ISD 1,400/PK-12
549 Miller Ln 75495 903-482-8802
Dr. John Spies, supt. Fax 482-6086
www.vanalstyneisd.org
Van Alstyne HS 400/9-12
1722 N Waco St 75495 903-482-8803
Dr. David Brown, prin. Fax 482-8887
Van Alstyne MS 400/5-8
1314 N Waco St 75495 903-482-8804
Ryan Coleman, prin. Fax 482-8890

Vanderbilt, Jackson, Pop. 392
Industrial ISD 1,100/PK-12
PO Box 369 77991 361-284-3226
Anthony Williams, supt. Fax 284-3349
www.iisd1.org
Industrial HS 300/9-12
PO Box 399 77991 361-284-3226
Jim Green, prin. Fax 284-3328
Industrial JHS 300/6-8
PO Box 367 77991 361-284-3226
Caleb McCain, prin. Fax 284-3049

Van Horn, Culberson, Pop. 2,041
Culberson County-Allamore ISD 500/PK-12
PO Box 899 79855 432-283-2245
Marc A. Puig, supt. Fax 283-9062
www.ccaisd.net/
Van Horn HS 100/9-12
PO Box 899 79855 432-283-2245
Debbie Engle, prin. Fax 283-9062
Van Horn JHS 100/6-8
PO Box 899 79855 432-283-2245
Kittie Gibson, prin. Fax 283-9062

Van Vleck, Matagorda, Pop. 1,828
Van Vleck ISD 900/PK-12
142 4th St S 77482 979-245-8518
John O'Brien, supt. Fax 245-1214
www.vvisd.org
Herman MS 200/6-8
719 1st St 77482 979-245-6401
Joe Ros, prin. Fax 245-8538
Van Vleck HS 300/9-12
133 S 4th St 77482 979-245-4664
Brandon Hood, prin. Fax 244-3485

Vega, Oldham, Pop. 874
Vega ISD 300/K-12
PO Box 190 79092 806-267-2123
Margo Knox, supt. Fax 267-2146
www.region16.net/vegaisd
Vega HS 200/7-12
PO Box 190 79092 806-267-2126
Micah Timmons, prin. Fax 267-2146

Venus, Johnson, Pop. 2,914
Venus ISD 1,800/PK-12
100 Student Dr 76084 972-366-3448
Robert Matthews, supt. Fax 366-8742
www.venusisd.net
Venus HS 500/9-12
12 Bulldog Dr 76084 972-366-8815
Juan Castaneda, prin. Fax 366-8919
Venus MS 400/6-8
1 Bulldog Dr 76084 972-366-3350
Randall Buck, prin. Fax 366-1740

Veribest, Tom Green
Veribest ISD 300/PK-12
PO Box 490 76886 325-655-4912
Bobby Fryar, supt. Fax 655-3355
www.veribestisd.net
Veribest HS 100/7-12
PO Box 490 76886 325-655-2851
Ken Newman, prin. Fax 655-3355

Vernon, Wilbarger, Pop. 10,848
Northside ISD 200/K-12
18040 US Highway 283 76384 940-552-2551
James Rice, supt. Fax 553-4919
www.northsideisd.us/
Northside S 200/K-12
18040 US Highway 283 76384 940-552-2551
Cindy Riggins, prin. Fax 553-4913

Vernon ISD 2,200/PK-12
1713 Wilbarger St 76384 940-553-1900
Tom Woody, supt. Fax 553-3802
www.vernonisd.org
Vernon HS 600/9-12
2102 Yucca Ln 76384 940-553-3377
Denise Cato, prin. Fax 553-4531
Vernon MS 400/6-8
2200 Yamparika St 76384 940-552-6231
Kenneth Kenner, prin. Fax 552-0504

Vernon College Post-Sec.
4400 College Dr 76384 940-552-6291

Victoria, Victoria, Pop. 61,923
Bloomington ISD 700/PK-12
2875 FM 616 77905 361-897-1652
Delores Warnell, supt. Fax 897-1214
www.bisd-tx.org/
Other Schools – See Bloomington

Victoria ISD 10,000/PK-12
PO Box 1759 77902 361-576-3131
Robert Jaklich, supt. Fax 788-9643
www.visd.net/
Cade MS 6-8
PO Box 1759 77902 361-788-2840
Lisa Blundell, prin. Fax 788-2886
Career and Technology Institute Vo/Tech
PO Box 1759 77902 361-788-9288
David Lynn, prin. Fax 788-9656
Howell MS 700/6-8
PO Box 1759 77902 361-578-1561
Clark Motley, prin. Fax 788-9547
Liberty Academy 200/9-12
PO Box 1759 77902 361-788-9650
Sherri Hathaway, prin. Fax 788-9649
Mitchell Guidance Center 100/Alt
PO Box 1759 77902 361-788-9658
Trey Edwards, prin. Fax 788-9665

Stroman MS 800/6-8
PO Box 1759 77902 361-578-2711
Lisa Cortez, prin. Fax 788-9800
Victoria Area Ctr for Advanced Learning 9-12
PO Box 1759 77902 361-788-2880
Sherri Hathaway, prin. Fax 788-9649
Victoria East HS 9-12
PO Box 1759 77902 361-788-2820
Greg Crockett, prin. Fax 788-2826
Victoria West HS 9-12
PO Box 1759 77902 361-788-2830
Debbie Crick, prin. Fax 788-2836
Welder Magnet MS 700/6-8
PO Box 1759 77902 361-575-4553
Richard Wright, prin. Fax 788-9629

Citizens Medical Center Post-Sec.
2701 Hospital Dr 77901 361-573-9181
Devereux-Texas Treatment Network Post-Sec.
120 David Wade Dr 77902 800-383-5000
Faith Academy 300/PK-12
PO Box 4824 77903 361-572-4568
Dr. Chris Royael, supt. Fax 573-5058
St. Joseph HS 400/9-12
110 E Red River St 77901 361-573-2446
Bill McArdle, prin. Fax 573-4221
Texas Vocational School Post-Sec.
1921 E Red River St 77901 361-575-4768
University of Houston-Victoria Post-Sec.
3007 N Ben Wilson St 77901 361-570-4848
Victoria Beauty College Post-Sec.
1508 N Laurent St 77901 361-575-4526
Victoria College Post-Sec.
2200 E Red River St 77901 361-573-3291

Vidor, Orange, Pop. 10,443
Vidor ISD 5,000/PK-12
120 E Bolivar St 77662 409-951-8714
Dr. Jay Killgo, supt. Fax 769-0093
www.vidorisd.org/
AIM Center HS 100/Alt
500 Stadium St 77662 409-951-8780
Johnny Ross, prin. Fax 769-0443
Vidor HS 1,400/9-12
500 Orange St 77662 409-951-8902
Travis Maines, prin. Fax 769-6767
Vidor JHS 700/7-8
945 N Tram Rd 77662 409-951-8970
Debra Jordan, prin. Fax 769-6754

Von Ormy, Bexar, Pop. 1,084
Somerset ISD
Supt. — See Somerset
Somerset JHS 500/7-8
4730 W Loop 1604 78073 866-852-9862
Rose Chapa, prin. Fax 448-2738

Waco, McLennan, Pop. 122,806
Bosqueville ISD 600/PK-12
7636 Rock Creek Rd 76708 254-757-3113
James Hopper, supt. Fax 752-4909
www.bosqueville.k12.tx.us
Bosqueville JSHS 300/6-12
7636 Rock Creek Rd 76708 254-752-8513
Sara Mynarcik, prin. Fax 752-0326

Bruceville-Eddy ISD
Supt. — See Eddy
Axtell/Bruceville-Eddy Learning Center 50/Alt
2601 Franklin Ave 76710 254-753-3422
Clyde Fluitt, prin. Fax 753-3602

China Spring ISD 2,300/PK-12
6301 Sylvia St 76708 254-836-1115
Marc Faulkner, supt. Fax 836-0559
www.chinaspringisd.net
Other Schools – See China Spring

Connally ISD 2,100/PK-12
200 Cadet Way 76705 254-296-6460
Frances Penland, supt. Fax 412-5530
www.connally.org/
Connally HS 600/9-12
900 N Lacy Dr 76705 254-296-6700
Jill Talamantez, prin. Fax 412-5549
Other Schools – See Elm Mott

Gholson ISD 100/PK-12
137 Hamilton Dr 76705 254-829-1528
Pamela Brown, supt. Fax 829-0054
www.gholsonisd.org/
Gholson S 100/PK-12
137 Hamilton Dr 76705 254-829-1528
Pamela Brown, prin. Fax 829-0054

La Vega ISD 2,900/PK-12
400 E Loop 340 76705 254-799-4963
Dr. Sharon Shields, supt. Fax 799-8642
www.lavegaisd.org
La Vega HS 700/9-12
555 N Loop 340 76705 254-799-4951
Sam Sexton, prin. Fax 799-0720
La Vega JHS George Dixon Campus 400/7-8
4401 Orchard Ln 76705 254-799-2428
Elicia Krumnow, prin. Fax 799-8943

Midway ISD
Supt. — See Woodway
Midway HS 2,100/9-12
8200 Mars Dr 76712 254-761-5650
Jeff Gasaway, prin. Fax 761-5770

Waco ISD 11,800/PK-12
PO Box 27 76703 254-755-9473
Bonny Cain Ed.D., supt. Fax 755-9690
www.wacoisd.org
ATLAS Academy 6-8
6100 Tennyson Dr 76710 254-754-5491
Sandra Gibson, dean Fax 750-3576
Carver MS 500/6-8
1601 J J Flewellen Rd 76704 254-757-0787
Ed Love, prin. Fax 750-3442
Chavez MS 500/6-8
700 S 15th St 76706 254-750-3736
Beau Sanchez, prin. Fax 750-3739
Greater Waco Advanced Manufacturing Acad Vo/Tech
2401 J J Flewellen Rd 76704 254-412-7900
Marcus Walker, prin. Fax 755-9620
STARS Credit Recovery 100/Alt
200 W Waco Dr 76701 254-754-6283
Robin Wilson, prin. Fax 753-2975
Tennyson MS 600/6-8
6100 Tennyson Dr 76710 254-772-1440
Keith Hannah, prin. Fax 741-4970
University HS 1,300/9-12
3201 S New Rd 76706 254-756-1843
Dr. Bill Shepard, prin. Fax 750-3709
Waco HS 1,600/9-12
2020 N 42nd St 76710 254-776-1150
Sam Sexton, prin. Fax 741-4815
Wiley Opportunity Center 100/Alt
1030 E Live Oak St 76704 254-757-3829
Dr. Richard Fletcher, prin. Fax 750-3772

ATI Career Training Center Post-Sec.
1417 S Valley Mills Dr 76711 254-230-4950
Baylor University Post-Sec.
1 Bear Pl Unit 97056 76798 254-710-1011
ITT Technical Institute Post-Sec.
3700 S Jack Kultgen Ste 100 76706 254-523-3940
Live Oak Classical S 200/PK-12
PO Box 647 76703 254-714-1007
Alison Moffatt, hdmstr. Fax 714-1150
McLennan Community College Post-Sec.
1400 College Dr 76708 254-299-8000
New Creation Adventist S 50/K-10
800 W State Highway 6 76712 254-772-8775
Wanda Wilson, prin. Fax 829-3175
Reicher Catholic HS 200/9-12
2102 N 23rd St 76708 254-752-8349
Jeff Heiple, admin. Fax 752-8408
Texas Christian Academy 200/K-12
1100 E Lake Shore Dr 76708 254-753-0159
Gary Bender, head sch Fax 753-0271
Texas State Technical College Post-Sec.
3801 Campus Dr 76705 254-799-3611
Vanguard College Preparatory S 100/7-12
2517 Mount Carmel Dr 76710 254-772-8111
Bill Borg, hdmstr. Fax 772-8263

Waelder, Gonzales, Pop. 1,062
Waelder ISD 200/K-12
PO Box 247 78959 830-788-7161
Mark Weisner, supt. Fax 788-7429
www.waelderisd.org
Waelder S 200/K-12
PO Box 247 78959 830-788-7151
Mark Cantu, prin. Fax 788-7323

Wall, Tom Green
Wall ISD 1,000/K-12
PO Box 259 76957 325-651-7790
Walter Holik, supt. Fax 651-5081
www.wallisd.net
Miles Vocational Training Vo/Tech
PO Box 259 76957 325-651-7521
Russell Dacy, prin. Fax 651-9419
Wall HS 300/9-12
PO Box 259 76957 325-651-7521
Russell Dacy, prin. Fax 651-9419
Wall MS 300/6-8
PO Box 259 76957 325-651-7648
Ryan Snowden, prin. Fax 651-9664
Other Schools – See San Angelo

Waller, Waller, Pop. 2,288
Waller ISD 5,400/PK-12
2214 Waller St 77484 936-931-3685
Danny Twardowski, supt. Fax 372-5576
www.wallerisd.net
Schultz JHS 700/6-8
19010 Stokes Rd 77484 936-931-9103
Bennie Mayes, prin. Fax 372-9302
Waller HS 1,500/9-12
20950 Fields Store Rd 77484 936-372-3654
Dr. Brian Merrell, prin. Fax 372-4114
Waller JHS 600/6-8
2402 Waller St 77484 936-931-1353
Eric Meldahl, prin. Fax 931-4044

Wallis, Austin, Pop. 1,240
Brazos ISD 800/PK-12
PO Box 819 77485 979-478-6551
Jack Ellis, supt. Fax 478-6413
www.brazosisd.net/
Brazos HS 200/9-12
PO Box 458 77485 979-478-6000
Lyle Ebner, prin. Fax 478-6002
Brazos MS 200/6-8
PO Box 879 77485 979-478-6411
Clay Hudgins, prin. Fax 478-6042

Walnut Springs, Bosque, Pop. 805
Walnut Springs ISD 200/PK-12
PO Box 63 76690 254-797-2133
Pat Garrett, supt. Fax 797-2191
www.walnutspringsisd.net
Walnut Springs S 200/PK-12
PO Box 63 76690 254-797-2133
Craig Taylor, prin. Fax 797-2191

Warren, Tyler, Pop. 751
Warren ISD 1,200/PK-12
PO Box 69 77664 409-547-2241
Lance Johnson, supt. Fax 547-3405
www.warrenisd.net
Warren HS 300/9-12
PO Box 190 77664 409-547-2243
James Swinney, prin. Fax 547-0214
Warren JHS 300/6-8
PO Box 205 77664 409-547-2241
Bradley McEachern, prin. Fax 547-2740

Waskom, Harrison, Pop. 2,131
Waskom ISD 800/PK-12
PO Box 748 75692 903-687-3361
Jimmy Cox, supt. Fax 687-3253
www.waskomisd.net
Waskom HS 200/9-12
PO Box 748 75692 903-687-3361
Jay Ratcliff, prin. Fax 687-2897
Waskom MS 200/5-8
PO Box 748 75692 903-687-3361
Rachel Hawkins, prin. Fax 687-3372

Watauga, Tarrant, Pop. 22,948
Birdville ISD
Supt. — See Haltom City
Watauga MS 700/6-8
6300 Maurie Dr 76148 817-547-4800
Shannon Houston, prin. Fax 581-5369

Water Valley, Tom Green
Water Valley ISD 300/PK-12
PO Box 250 76958 325-484-2478
Jimmy Hannon, supt. Fax 484-3359
www.wvisd.net/
Water Valley JSHS 200/7-12
PO Box 250 76958 325-484-2424
Brent Kirkland, prin. Fax 484-3359

Waxahachie, Ellis, Pop. 29,212
Waxahachie ISD 6,900/PK-12
411 N Gibson St 75165 972-923-4631
Thomas Collins, supt. Fax 923-4759
www.wisd.org
Finley JHS 500/6-8
2401 Brown St 75165 972-923-4680
Ruth Sutton, prin. Fax 923-4687
Howard JHS 500/6-8
265 Broadhead Rd 75165 972-923-4771
Robert Woodhouse, prin. Fax 923-3817
Waxahachie 9th Grade Academy 500/9-9
275 Indian Dr 75165 972-923-4780
Brad Burns, prin. Fax 923-4782
Waxahachie Challenge Academy Alt
614 N Getzendaner St 75165 972-923-4695
David Nix, prin. Fax 923-4717
Waxahachie Global HS 300/9-12
600 W 2nd St 75165 972-923-4761
Donald Snook, prin. Fax 923-4738
Waxahachie HS 1,400/10-12
1000 N Highway 77 75165 972-923-4600
Brad Burns, prin. Fax 923-4617
Waxahachie HS of Choice 50/Alt
614 N Getzendaner St 75165 972-923-4758
David Nix, prin. Fax 923-4717

Southwestern Assemblies of God Univ. Post-Sec.
1200 Sycamore St 75165 972-937-4010
Waxahachie Preparatory Academy 100/K-12
PO Box P 75168 972-937-0440
Scott Marks, admin. Fax 937-5033

Weatherford, Parker, Pop. 24,879
Peaster ISD 1,100/PK-12
3602 Harwell Lake Rd 76088 817-341-5000
Matt Adams, supt. Fax 341-5003
www.peaster.net
Peaster HS 300/9-12
3600 Harwell Lake Rd 76088 817-341-5000
Darla Henry, prin. Fax 341-5027
Peaster MS 200/6-8
8512 FM Road 920 76088 817-341-5000
Darren Grudt, prin. Fax 341-5052

Weatherford ISD 7,600/PK-12
1100 Longhorn Dr 76086 817-598-2800
Dr. Jeffrey Hanks, supt. Fax 598-2955
www.weatherfordisd.com
Hall MS 600/7-8
902 Charles St 76086 817-598-2822
Debbie Braudaway, prin. Fax 598-2854
Tison MS 600/7-8
102 Meadowview Rd 76087 817-598-2960
Elizabeth Ward, prin. Fax 598-2963
Weatherford HS 1,600/10-12
2121 Bethel Rd 76087 817-598-2858
Lynn Pool, prin. Fax 598-2881
Weatherford Ninth Grade Center 600/9-9
1007 S Main St 76086 817-598-2847
Kristy Dowd, prin. Fax 598-2928

Weatherford Christian S 200/PK-12
111 E Columbia St 76086 817-596-7807
Jared Roan, hdmstr. Fax 596-0529
Weatherford College Post-Sec.
225 College Park Dr 76086 817-594-5471

Webster, Harris, Pop. 10,170
Clear Creek ISD
Supt. — See League City
Clear View Education Center 200/Alt
400 S Walnut St 77598 281-284-1500
Dr. Robert Branch, prin. Fax 284-1505
Clear Stars Evening S Adult
400 S Walnut St 77598 281-284-1550
Gail Love, prin.

ITT Technical Institute Post-Sec.
1001 Magnolia St 77598 281-316-4700
Remington College Houston Southeast Post-Sec.
20985 Interstate 45 S 77598 800-560-6192

Weimar, Colorado, Pop. 2,127
Weimar ISD 600/PK-12
506 W Main St 78962 979-725-9504
Jon Wunderlich, supt. Fax 725-8737
www.weimarisd.org/
Weimar HS 200/9-12
506 W Main St 78962 979-725-9504
Darrin Bickham, prin. Fax 725-8737
Weimar JHS 100/6-8
101 N West St 78962 979-725-9515
Stacy Heger, prin. Fax 725-8383

Welch, Dawson, Pop. 221
Dawson ISD 200/PK-12
PO Box 180 79377 806-489-7568
Lindsey Wallace, supt. Fax 489-7463
www.dawson.esc17.net/
Dawson S 200/PK-12
PO Box 180 79377 806-489-7461
Krista Scott, prin. Fax 489-7463

Wellington, Collingsworth, Pop. 2,160
Wellington ISD 600/PK-12
609 15th St 79095 806-447-3102
Carl Taylor, supt. Fax 447-5124
www.wellingtonisd.net
Wellington HS 200/9-12
811 15th St 79095 806-447-2527
Kurt Ashmore, prin. Fax 447-9012
Wellington JHS 100/6-8
1504 Amarillo St 79095 806-447-5726
Tim Webb, prin. Fax 447-5089

Wellman, Terry, Pop. 202
Wellman-Union Consolidated ISD 200/PK-12
PO Box 69 79378 806-637-4910
Dwayne Chenault, supt. Fax 637-2585
wellman.esc17.net
Wellman-Union HS 100/6-12
PO Box 129 79378 806-637-4619
Michael Norman, prin. Fax 637-2585

Wells, Cherokee, Pop. 772
Wells ISD 300/PK-12
PO Box 469 75976 936-867-4466
Dale Morton, supt. Fax 867-4466
www.wells.esc7.net
Wells HS 100/9-12
PO Box 469 75976 936-867-4400
James Moore, prin. Fax 867-4466

Weslaco, Hidalgo, Pop. 35,580
Weslaco ISD 17,900/PK-12
PO Box 266 78599 956-969-6500
Ruben Alejandro Ph.D., supt. Fax 969-2664
www.wisd.us
Central MS 1,000/6-8
503 E 6th St 78596 956-969-6710
Patricia Munoz, prin. Fax 969-0779
Cuellar MS 800/6-8
1201 S Bridge Ave 78596 956-969-6720
Mario Hernandez, prin. Fax 973-9797
Garza MS 1,100/6-8
1111 W Sugar Cane Dr 78599 956-969-6774
John Garlic, prin. Fax 447-0484
Hoge MS 1,000/6-8
2302 N International Blvd 78596 956-969-6730
Pablo Vallejo, prin. Fax 514-0903
Horton Alternative Education Program Alt
103 S Iowa Ave 78596 956-969-6916
Jose Garcia, prin. Fax 969-6782
South Palms Garden HS 100/Alt
2607 Camino Real Viejo Rd 78596 956-565-0404
Fax 565-5994
Weslaco East HS 2,100/9-12
810 S Pleasantview Dr 78596 956-969-6950
Sue Peterson, prin. Fax 968-8693
Weslaco HS 2,600/9-12
1005 W Pike Blvd 78596 956-969-6700
Isidoro Nieto, prin. Fax 968-8008

Advanced Barber College and Hair Design Post-Sec.
2818 S International Blvd 78596 956-969-0341
South Texas Vocational-Technical Inst. Post-Sec.
2419 Haggar St 78599 956-969-1564
Valley Grande Adventist Academy 200/PK-12
1000 S Bridge Ave 78596 956-968-0573
Trinidad Torres, prin. Fax 968-9814

West, McLennan, Pop. 2,777
West ISD 1,400/PK-12
801 N Reagan St 76691 254-826-7500
Dr. Marty Crawford, supt. Fax 826-7503
www.westisd.net/
West HS 500/9-12
801 N Reagan St 76691 254-826-7510
Wayne Leek, prin. Fax 826-7514
West MS 300/6-8
801 N Reagan St 76691 254-826-7520
Amanda Adams, prin. Fax 826-7524

Westbrook, Mitchell, Pop. 253
Westbrook ISD 200/PK-12
PO Box 99 79565 325-644-2311
Todd Burleson, supt. Fax 644-5101
www.westbrookisd.com
Colorado City Alternative S Alt
PO Box 99 79565 325-644-2311
Cassie Petty, prin.
Westbrook S 200/PK-12
PO Box 99 79565 325-644-2311
Cassie Petty, prin. Fax 644-5101

West Columbia, Brazoria, Pop. 3,841
Columbia-Brazoria ISD 3,100/PK-12
PO Box 158 77486 979-345-5147
Steven Galloway, supt. Fax 345-4890
www.cbisd.com
Columbia HS 800/9-12
PO Box 158 77486 979-799-1720
Chris Miller, prin. Fax 345-6785
Other Schools – See Brazoria

West Lake Hills, Travis, Pop. 3,003
Eanes ISD
Supt. — See Austin
Westlake Alternative S Alt
601 Camp Craft Rd 78746 512-327-2203
Dr. John Carter, prin.

Wharton, Wharton, Pop. 8,727
Wharton ISD 2,000/PK-12
2100 N Fulton St 77488 979-532-6201
King Davis, supt. Fax 532-6228
www.whartonisd.net
Wharton HS 600/9-12
1 Tiger Ave 77488 979-532-6800
Steve May, prin. Fax 532-6807
Wharton JHS 300/6-8
1120 N Rusk St 77488 979-532-6840
Mark Anglin, prin. Fax 532-6849

Wharton County Junior College Post-Sec.
911 E Boling Hwy 77488 979-532-4560

Wheeler, Wheeler, Pop. 1,576
Kelton ISD 200/PK-12
16703 FM 2697 79096 806-826-5795
Jay Watson, supt. Fax 826-3601
keltonisd.com
Kelton S 200/PK-12
16703 FM 2697 79096 806-826-5708
Heather Hardcastle, prin. Fax 826-3601

Wheeler ISD 400/PK-12
PO Box 1010 79096 806-826-5241
Frank Belcher, supt. Fax 826-3118
www.wheelerschools.net
Wheeler S 400/PK-12
PO Box 1010 79096 806-826-5534
Bryan Markham, prin. Fax 826-3118

White Deer, Carson, Pop. 983
White Deer ISD 400/PK-12
PO Box 517 79097 806-883-2311
Karl Vaughn, supt. Fax 883-2321
www.whitedeerisd.net/
White Deer HS 100/9-12
PO Box 248 79097 806-883-2311
Darla Forney, prin. Fax 883-5029

Whiteface, Cochran, Pop. 442
Whiteface Consolidated ISD 300/PK-12
PO Box 7 79379 806-287-1154
Elbert Wuthrich, supt. Fax 287-1131
www.whitefaceschool.net
Whiteface JSHS 200/6-12
PO Box 67 79379 806-287-1104
James German, prin. Fax 287-1131
Other Schools – See Pep

Whitehouse, Smith, Pop. 7,533
Whitehouse ISD 4,600/PK-12
106 Wildcat Dr 75791 903-839-5500
Daniel DuPree, supt. Fax 839-5515
www.whitehouseisd.org
Whitehouse HS 1,300/9-12
901 E Main St 75791 903-839-5551
Duane Barber, prin. Fax 839-5530
Whitehouse JHS 800/7-8
108 Wildcat Dr 75791 903-839-5590
Jarrod Bitter, prin. Fax 839-5518

White Oak, Gregg, Pop. 6,394
White Oak ISD 1,400/PK-12
200 S White Oak Rd 75693 903-291-2000
Michael Gilbert, supt. Fax 291-2222
www.woisd.net
White Oak HS 400/9-12
200 S White Oak Rd 75693 903-291-2000
Don Noll, prin. Fax 291-2034
White Oak MS 300/6-8
200 S White Oak Rd 75693 903-291-2050
Ronnie Hinkle, prin. Fax 291-2035

Whitesboro, Grayson, Pop. 3,755
Whitesboro ISD 1,500/PK-12
115 4th St 76273 903-564-4200
Pete Slaughter, supt. Fax 564-9303
www.whitesboroisd.org
Whitesboro HS 400/9-12
1 Bearcat Dr 76273 903-564-4208
Rendell Cole, prin. Fax 564-4288
Whitesboro MS 300/6-8
600 4th St 76273 903-564-4240
Patty Mitchell, prin. Fax 564-5939

White Settlement, Tarrant, Pop. 15,816
White Settlement ISD
Supt. — See Fort Worth
Brewer MS 900/7-8
1000 S Cherry Ln 76108 817-367-1267
Brian Bowman, prin. Fax 367-1268

Whitewright, Grayson, Pop. 1,571
Whitewright ISD 800/PK-12
PO Box 888 75491 903-364-2155
Steve Arthur, supt. Fax 364-2839
www.wwisd.com/
Whitewright HS 200/9-12
PO Box 888 75491 903-364-2535
Kelly Hayes, prin. Fax 364-2579
Whitewright MS 200/6-8
PO Box 888 75491 903-364-2151
Bobby Worthy, prin. Fax 364-5263

Whitharral, Hockley
Whitharral ISD 200/K-12
PO Box 225 79380 806-299-1184
Ed Sharp, supt. Fax 299-1257
www.whitharralisd.org/
Whitharral S 200/K-12
PO Box 225 79380 806-299-1135
Carla Kristinek, prin. Fax 299-1257

Whitney, Hill, Pop. 2,048
Whitney ISD 1,500/PK-12
PO Box 518 76692 254-694-2254
Gene Solis, supt. Fax 694-4001
www.whitney.k12.tx.us
Whitney HS 400/9-12
PO Box 518 76692 254-694-3457
Chris Hestilow, prin. Fax 694-4206
Whitney MS 400/6-8
PO Box 518 76692 254-694-3446
Wayne Redding, prin. Fax 694-2064

Wichita Falls, Wichita, Pop. 102,278
City View ISD 900/PK-12
1025 City View Dr 76306 940-855-4042
Steve Harris, supt. Fax 851-8889
www.cityview-isd.net/
City View JSHS 400/7-12
1600 City View Dr 76306 940-855-7511
Raymond Weathersbee, prin. Fax 851-5027

Wichita Falls ISD 13,700/PK-12
PO Box 97533 76307 940-235-1000
Dr. John Frossard, supt.
www.wfisd.net
Barwise JHS 600/7-8
3807 Kemp Blvd 76308 940-235-1108
Linda Muehlberger, prin. Fax 235-1109
Carrigan Vocational Center Vo/Tech
1609 Blonde St 76301 940-235-1091
Steve Wolf, prin. Fax 720-3368
Denver Alternative Center Alt
1823 5th St 76301 940-235-1101
Linda Nichols, prin. Fax 720-3382
Harrell Accelerated Learning Center 100/Alt
3115 5th St 76301 940-235-1096
Gena Woodard, prin. Fax 235-1097
Hirschi HS 700/9-12
3106 Borton St 76306 940-235-1070
Wanda Jackson, prin. Fax 235-1300
Kirby JHS 400/7-8
1715 Loop 11 76306 940-235-1113
Larry Menefee, prin. Fax 235-1114
McNiel JHS 600/7-8
4712 Barnett Rd 76310 940-235-1118
Carol English, prin. Fax 235-1119
Rider HS 1,700/9-12
4611 Cypress Ave 76310 940-235-1077
Judy McDonald, prin. Fax 235-1301
Wichita Falls HS 1,500/9-12
2149 Avenue H 76309 940-235-1084
Debbie Dipprey, prin. Fax 235-1302
Zundy JHS 500/7-8
1706 Polk St 76309 940-235-1123
Omar Montemayor, prin. Fax 720-3172

American Commercial College Post-Sec.
4317 Barnett Rd 76310 940-691-0454
Christ Academy 300/PK-12
5105 Stone Lake Dr 76310 940-692-2853
Dr. Jerry Meadows, hdmstr. Fax 692-2657
Midwestern State University Post-Sec.
3410 Taft Blvd 76308 940-397-4000
Notre Dame S 200/PK-12
2821 Lansing Blvd 76309 940-692-6041
Doug Jones, prin. Fax 692-2811
United Regional Health Care System Post-Sec.
1600 11th St 76301 940-764-3187
Wichita Christian S 300/PK-12
1615 Midwestern Pkwy 76302 940-763-1347
Karla Wallace, supt. Fax 264-1643

Willis, Montgomery, Pop. 5,574
Willis ISD 6,500/PK-12
204 W Rogers St 77378 936-856-1200
Dr. Bret Jimerson, supt. Fax 856-5182
www.willisisd.org/
Brabham MS 700/6-8
10000 FM 830 Rd 77318 936-890-2312
Kimmie Devillier, prin. Fax 856-2910
Lucas MS 700/6-8
1304 N Campbell St 77378 936-856-1274
Rebecca Godsey, prin. Fax 856-1065
Stubblefield Academy 50/Alt
207 Philpot St 77378 936-856-1288
Lee Sloan, prin. Fax 890-0312
Willis HS 1,700/9-12
1201 FM 830 Rd 77378 936-856-1250
Tim Harkrider, prin. Fax 856-3391

Willow Park, Parker, Pop. 3,938

Trinity Christian Academy 500/PK-12
4954 E IH-20 Service Rd S 76087 817-441-7901
Michael Skaggs, head sch Fax 441-7912

Wills Point, Van Zandt, Pop. 3,473
Wills Point ISD 2,600/PK-12
338 W North Commerce St 75169 903-873-3161
Suzanne Blasingame, supt. Fax 873-2462
www.wpisd.com/
Wills Point HS 800/9-12
1800 W South Commerce St 75169 903-873-2371
Jim Lamb, prin. Fax 873-6008
Wills Point JHS 400/7-8
200 Tiger Dr 75169 903-873-4924
Larry Lewis, prin. Fax 873-4873

New Frontiers Lighthouse Christian Acad 50/K-12
24385 Interstate 20 75169 903-873-2440
Wendy Strickland, admin. Fax 873-2440

Wilson, Lynn, Pop. 487
Wilson ISD 100/PK-12
PO Box 9 79381 806-628-6271
John Horak, supt. Fax 628-6441
wilson.esc17.net
Wilson S 100/PK-12
PO Box 9 79381 806-628-6261
Brenda Prather, prin. Fax 628-6441

Wimberley, Hays, Pop. 2,602
Wimberley ISD 2,000/PK-12
14401 Ranch Road 12 78676 512-847-2414
Dwain York, supt. Fax 847-2142
www.wimberley.txed.net/
Danforth JHS 500/6-8
200 Texan Blvd 78676 512-847-2181
Jason Valentine, prin. Fax 847-7897
Wimberley HS 700/9-12
100 Carney Ln 78676 512-847-5729
Greg Bonewald, prin. Fax 847-7269

Windcrest, Bexar, Pop. 5,256

Milan Institute of Cosmetology Post-Sec.
5403 Walzem Rd 78218 210-656-1991

Windthorst, Archer, Pop. 398
Windthorst ISD 500/PK-12
PO Box 190 76389 940-423-6688
Don Windham, supt. Fax 423-6505
www.windthorstisd.net
Windhorst JHS 100/6-8
PO Box 190 76389 940-423-6605
Darla Tackett, prin. Fax 423-6505
Windthorst HS 200/9-12
PO Box 190 76389 940-423-6680
Lonnie Hise, prin. Fax 423-6505

Wink, Winkler, Pop. 931
Wink-Loving ISD 400/PK-12
PO Box 637 79789 432-527-3880
John Benham, supt. Fax 527-3505
www.wlisd.net
Wink JSHS 200/7-12
PO Box 637 79789 432-527-3880
Daron Worrell, prin. Fax 527-3505

Winnie, Chambers, Pop. 3,222
East Chambers ISD 1,300/PK-12
1955 State Highway 124 77665 409-296-6100
Scott Campbell, supt. Fax 296-3528
www.eastchambers.net
East Chambers HS 400/9-12
234 E Buccaneer Dr 77665 409-296-6100
Steve Franzen, prin. Fax 296-9596
East Chambers JHS 200/7-8
1931 State Highway 124 77665 409-296-6100
Lou Ann Rainey, prin. Fax 296-2724

Winnsboro, Wood, Pop. 3,395
Winnsboro ISD 1,500/PK-12
207 E Pine St 75494 903-342-3737
Dr. Mark Bosold, supt. Fax 342-3380
www.winnsboroisd.org
Memorial MS 400/5-8
505 S Chestnut St 75494 903-342-5711
Jeff Akin, prin. Fax 342-6689
Winnsboro HS 400/9-12
409 Newsome St 75494 903-342-3641
Susan Morton, prin. Fax 342-3645

Winona, Smith, Pop. 574
Winona ISD 1,000/PK-12
611 Wildcat Dr 75792 903-939-4001
Denise Shetter, supt. Fax 877-9387
www.winonaisd.org
Winona HS 300/9-12
611 Wildcat Dr 75792 903-939-4100
Leland Hand, prin. Fax 939-4199
Winona MS 200/6-8
611 Wildcat Dr 75792 903-939-4040
Oscar Rendon, prin. Fax 877-2451

Winters, Runnels, Pop. 2,547
Winters ISD 600/PK-12
603 N Heights St 79567 325-754-5574
Don Kuempel, supt. Fax 754-5374
www.wintersisd.org
Winters HS 200/9-12
603 N Heights St 79567 325-754-5516
Casey Stone, prin. Fax 754-5085
Winters JHS 100/6-8
603 N Heights St 79567 325-754-5518
Jeff Henry, prin. Fax 754-5085

Woden, Nacogdoches
Woden ISD 800/PK-12
PO Box 100 75978 936-564-2073
Brady Taylor, supt. Fax 564-1250
www.wodenisd.org/
Woden HS 300/9-12
PO Box 100 75978 936-564-7903
Dr. Jerry Meador, prin. Fax 462-4962
Woden JHS 200/6-8
PO Box 100 75978 936-564-2481
Dr. Jerry Meador, prin. Fax 462-4982
Other Schools – See Nacogdoches

Wolfe City, Hunt, Pop. 1,375
Wolfe City ISD 600/PK-12
505 W Dallas St 75496 903-496-7333
Vernon Richardson, supt. Fax 496-7905
www.a2zfast.com/wcisd/
Wolfe City HS 200/9-12
8353 State Highway 34 N 75496 903-496-2891
Sean Martin, prin. Fax 496-7124
Wolfe City MS 100/6-8
505 W Dallas St 75496 903-496-7333
Sean Martin, prin. Fax 496-2112

Wolfforth, Lubbock, Pop. 3,636
Frenship ISD 8,200/PK-12
PO Box 100 79382 806-866-9541
Dr. David Vroonland, supt. Fax 866-4135
www.frenship.us
Frenship HS 1,800/9-12
PO Box 100 79382 806-866-4440
Kim Spicer, prin. Fax 866-9370
Frenship MS 900/6-8
PO Box 100 79382 806-866-4464
Jerry Jerabek, prin. Fax 866-2181
Other Schools – See Lubbock

Woodsboro, Refugio, Pop. 1,498
Woodsboro ISD 500/PK-12
PO Box 770 78393 361-543-4518
Steven Self, supt. Fax 543-4856
www.wisd.net
Woodsboro Secondary S 200/7-12
PO Box 770 78393 361-543-4521
Linda Garza, prin. Fax 543-5140

Woodson, Throckmorton, Pop. 262
Woodson ISD 100/PK-12
PO Box 287 76491 940-345-6528
Gordon Thomas, supt. Fax 345-6549
www.woodsonisd.net
Woodson S 100/PK-12
PO Box 287 76491 940-345-6521
Gordon Thomas, prin. Fax 345-6549

Woodville, Tyler, Pop. 2,545
Woodville ISD 1,300/PK-12
505 N Charlton St 75979 409-283-3752
Glen Conner, supt. Fax 283-7962
www.woodvilleeagles.org
Woodville HS 300/9-12
505 N Charlton St 75979 409-283-3714
Neil Hennigan, prin. Fax 331-3427
Woodville MS 300/6-8
505 N Charlton St 75979 409-283-7109
Morgan Wright, prin. Fax 331-3418

Woodway, McLennan, Pop. 8,360
Midway ISD 7,200/PK-12
13885 Woodway Dr 76712 254-761-5610
George Kazanas Ed.D., supt. Fax 761-5789
www.midwayisd.org/
Other Schools – See Hewitt, Waco

Wortham, Freestone, Pop. 1,060
Wortham ISD 500/PK-12
PO Box 247 76693 254-765-3095
Dr. Bruce Tabor, supt. Fax 765-3473
www.worthamisd.org
Wortham HS 200/9-12
PO Box 247 76693 254-765-3094
Sandi King, prin. Fax 765-3473
Wortham MS 100/6-8
PO Box 247 76693 254-765-3523
Candace Kennemer, prin. Fax 765-3473

Wylie, Dallas, Pop. 40,460
Wylie ISD 12,500/PK-12
PO Box 490 75098 972-429-3000
Dr. David Vinson, supt. Fax 442-5368
www.wylieisd.net
Burnett JHS 700/7-8
PO Box 490 75098 972-429-3200
Mike Evans, prin. Fax 442-1447
Cooper JHS 600/7-8
PO Box 490 75098 972-429-3250
Tami Nauyokas, prin. Fax 941-9175
McMillan JHS 600/7-8
PO Box 490 75098 972-429-3225
Jon Peters, prin. Fax 941-6372
Wylie East HS 1,200/9-12
PO Box 490 75098 972-429-3150
Mike Williams, prin. Fax 442-2874
Wylie HS 2,000/9-12
PO Box 490 75098 972-429-3100
Virdie Montgomery, prin. Fax 442-1879

Wylie Preparatory Academy 200/K-12
4110 Skyview Ct 75098 972-442-1388
Julie Calhoun, admin. Fax 429-3568

Yantis, Wood, Pop. 386
Yantis ISD 400/PK-12
105 W Oak St 75497 903-383-2463
Penny Armstrong, supt. Fax 383-7620
www.yantisisd.net
Yantis HS 100/6-12
105 W Oak St 75497 903-383-2463
Michael Alphin, prin. Fax 383-3075

Yoakum, Lavaca, Pop. 5,752
Yoakum ISD 1,600/PK-12
PO Box 737 77995 361-293-3162
Tom Kelley, supt. Fax 293-6678
www.yoakumisd.net/
Yoakum HS 500/9-12
PO Box 737 77995 361-293-3442
Chris Wegener, prin. Fax 293-2145
Yoakum JHS 300/6-8
PO Box 737 77995 361-293-3111
Patrick Frank, prin. Fax 293-5787

Yorktown, DeWitt, Pop. 2,079
Yorktown ISD 500/PK-12
PO Box 487 78164 361-564-2252
Deborah Kneese, supt. Fax 564-2254
www.yisd.org
Yorktown HS 200/9-12
PO Box 487 78164 361-564-2252
Nolan Alexander, prin. Fax 564-2274
Yorktown JHS 100/6-8
PO Box 487 78164 361-564-2252
Sylvia Hernandez, prin. Fax 564-2289

Zapata, Zapata, Pop. 5,080
Zapata County ISD 3,000/PK-12
PO Box 158 78076 956-765-6546
Norma Garcia Ph.D., supt. Fax 765-8350
www.zcisd.org
Zapata HS 1,000/9-12
PO Box 3750 78076 956-765-0280
Pedro Morales, prin. Fax 765-0274
Zapata MS 800/6-8
PO Box 3636 78076 956-765-6542
Norma Arellano, prin. Fax 765-9204

Zavalla, Angelina, Pop. 708
Zavalla ISD 500/PK-12
431 E Main St 75980 936-897-2271
David Flowers, supt. Fax 897-2674
www.zavallaisd.org
Zavalla JSHS 200/6-12
431 E Main St 75980 936-897-2301
Ricky Oliver, prin. Fax 897-2674
Other Schools – See Lufkin

Zephyr, Brown
Zephyr ISD 100/K-12
11625 County Road 281 76890 325-739-5331
David Whisenhunt, supt. Fax 739-2126
zephyr.netxv.net/
Zephyr S 100/K-12
11625 County Road 281 76890 325-739-5331
Stanton Marwitz, prin. Fax 739-2126

UTAH

UTAH OFFICE OF EDUCATION
PO Box 144200, Salt Lake City 84114-4200
Telephone 801-538-7500
Fax 801-538-7768
Website http://www.schools.utah.gov/main/

Superintendent of Public Instruction   Martell Menlove

UTAH BOARD OF EDUCATION
250 E 500 S, Salt Lake City 84111-3284

Chairperson   Debra Roberts

REGIONAL SERVICE CENTERS (RSC)

Central Utah Educational Services
Glen Taylor, dir.   435-896-4469
195 E 500 N, Richfield 84701   Fax 896-4767
www.cues.k12.ut.us

Northeastern Utah Educational Services
Duke Mossman, dir.   435-654-1921
3111 College Way   Fax 654-2403
Heber City 84032
www.nucenter.org

Southeast Educational Service Center
J.J. Grant, dir.   435-637-1173
685 E 200 S, Price 84501   Fax 637-1178
seschools.org

Southwest Educational Development Ctr
Randy Johnson, dir.   435-586-2865
520 W 800 S, Cedar City 84720   Fax 586-2868
www.sedc.k12.ut.us

PUBLIC, PRIVATE AND CATHOLIC SECONDARY SCHOOLS

Alpine, Utah, Pop. 9,390
Alpine SD
Supt. — See American Fork
Timberline MS   1,300/7-9
500 W Canyon Crest Rd 84004   801-610-8765
Terry Hill, prin.   Fax 763-7045

Altamont, Duchesne, Pop. 222
Duchesne SD
Supt. — See Duchesne
Altamont JSHS   200/7-12
PO Box 130 84001   435-738-1345
John Huitt, prin.   Fax 738-1370

American Fork, Utah, Pop. 25,678
Alpine SD   62,900/K-12
575 N 100 E 84003   801-610-8400
Dr. Vernon Henshaw, supt.   Fax 610-8516
alpineschools.org/
American Fork JHS   1,700/7-9
20 W 1120 N 84003   801-610-8750
Shane Farnsworth, prin.   Fax 756-8407
American Fork SHS   2,000/10-12
510 N 600 E 84003   801-756-8547
Doug Finch, prin.   Fax 756-8575
Other Schools – See Alpine, Highland, Lehi, Lindon, Orem, Pleasant Grove, Saratoga Sprngs

---

American Heritage S   500/K-12
736 N 1100 E 84003   801-642-0055

Beaver, Beaver, Pop. 3,076
Beaver SD   1,500/K-12
PO Box 31 84713   435-438-2291
Ray Terry, supt.   Fax 438-5898
www.beaver.k12.ut.us
Beaver JSHS   500/7-12
PO Box 71 84713   435-438-2301
David Green, prin.   Fax 438-1519
Other Schools – See Milford

Bicknell, Wayne, Pop. 324
Wayne SD   600/K-12
PO Box 127 84715   435-425-3813
Burke Torgerson, supt.   Fax 425-3806
www.wayne.k12.ut.us
Wayne HS   200/9-12
PO Box 217 84715   435-425-3411
Mark Elmer, prin.   Fax 425-3480
Wayne MS   100/6-8
PO Box 128 84715   435-425-3421
Mary Bray, prin.   Fax 425-3130

Big Water, Kane, Pop. 468
Kane SD
Supt. — See Kanab
Big Water HS   50/7-12
PO Box 410126 84741   435-675-5821
Gerry Rankin, prin.   Fax 675-5821

Blanding, San Juan, Pop. 3,283
San Juan SD   2,700/K-12
200 N Main St 84511   435-678-1211
Dr. Douglas Wright, supt.   Fax 678-1272
www.sjsd.org
Lyman MS   300/6-8
535 N 100 E 84511   435-678-1398
Kim Bailey, prin.   Fax 678-1399
San Juan HS   400/9-12
180 N Bronco Way 84511   435-678-1301
Bob Peterson, prin.   Fax 678-1396
Other Schools – See Montezuma Creek, Monticello, Monument Valley

Bountiful, Davis, Pop. 41,539
Davis SD
Supt. — See Farmington
Bountiful JHS   600/7-9
30 W 400 N 84010   801-402-6000
Vickie Ingram, prin.   Fax 402-6001
Bountiful SHS   1,400/10-12
695 Orchard Dr 84010   801-402-3900
Gregory Wilkey, prin.   Fax 402-3901
Millcreek JHS   800/7-9
245 E 1000 S 84010   801-402-6200
Karyn Bertelson, prin.   Fax 402-6201
Mueller Park JHS   600/7-9
955 Mueller Park Rd 84010   801-402-6300
Joyce Jones, prin.   Fax 402-6301
South Davis JHS   900/7-9
298 W 2600 S 84010   801-402-6400
Jeff Jorgensen, prin.   Fax 402-6401
Viewmont SHS   1,600/10-12
120 W 1000 N 84010   801-402-4200
Dan Linford, prin.   Fax 402-4201

Brigham City, Box Elder, Pop. 17,553
Box Elder SD   10,900/K-12
960 S Main St 84302   435-734-4800
Ronald Wolff, supt.   Fax 734-4833
www.besd.net
Box Elder MS   1,000/8-9
18 S 500 E 84302   435-734-4880
Jason Sparks, prin.   Fax 734-4885
Box Elder SHS   1,400/10-12
380 S 600 W 84302   435-734-4840
Darrell Eddington, prin.   Fax 734-4846
Young Community HS   Adult
230 W 200 S 84302   435-734-4834
Matt Webb, prin.   Fax 734-4860
Other Schools – See Garland, Grouse Creek, Park Valley

Northridge Learning Center   100/K-12
44 S Main St 84302   435-734-2550
Dixie Evans, dir.   Fax 723-3903

Castle Dale, Emery, Pop. 1,623
Emery County SD
Supt. — See Huntington
Emery SHS   400/10-12
PO Box 499 84513   435-381-2689
Larry Davis, prin.   Fax 381-5370

Castle Valley, Grand, Pop. 315

Daystar Adventist Academy   50/9-12
HC 64 Box 2201 84532   435-259-7719
Alexa Hernandez, prin.   Fax 259-5209

Cedar City, Iron, Pop. 28,202
Iron SD   7,300/K-12
2077 W Royal Hunte Dr 84720   435-586-2804
Dr. Shannon Dulaney, supt.   Fax 586-2815
irondistrict.org
Canyon View HS   1,000/9-12
166 W 1925 N 84721   435-586-2813
Rich Nielsen, prin.   Fax 586-2849
Canyon View MS   800/6-8
1865 N Main St 84721   435-586-2830
Conrad Aitken, prin.   Fax 586-2837
Cedar HS   1,100/9-12
703 W 600 S 84720   435-586-2820
John Dodds, prin.   Fax 586-2826
Cedar MS   900/6-8
2215 W Royal Hunte Dr 84720   435-586-2810
Kendall Benson, prin.   Fax 586-2829
Foothill HS   50/Alt
270 E 1600 N 84721   435-867-2513
Steve Schofield, prin.   Fax 586-2815
Adult HS/Southwest Education Academy   Adult
510 W 800 S 84720   435-586-2870
Steve Schofield, prin.   Fax 586-2815
Other Schools – See Parowan

Southern Utah University   Post-Sec.
351 W Center St 84720   435-586-7700
Southwest Applied Technology College   Post-Sec.
510 W 800 S 84720   435-586-2899

Centerville, Davis, Pop. 15,086
Davis SD
Supt. — See Farmington
Centerville JHS   1,000/7-9
625 S Main St 84014   801-402-6100
Spencer Hansen, prin.   Fax 402-6101

Clearfield, Davis, Pop. 28,950
Davis SD
Supt. — See Farmington
Clearfield SHS   1,500/10-12
931 S 1000 E 84015   801-402-8200
Suzi Jensen, prin.   Fax 402-8336
North Davis JHS   1,000/7-9
835 S State St 84015   801-402-6500
Ryan Hansen, prin.   Fax 402-6501

Vista College   Post-Sec.
1785 E 1450 S Ste 300 84015   888-410-4297

Coalville, Summit, Pop. 1,348
North Summit SD   1,000/PK-12
PO Box 497 84017   435-336-5654
Jerre Holmes, supt.   Fax 336-2401
www.nsummit.org
North Summit HS   300/9-12
PO Box 497 84017   435-336-5656
Russell Hendry, prin.   Fax 336-0309
North Summit MS   300/5-8
PO Box 497 84017   435-336-5678
Brett Richins, prin.   Fax 336-4474

Cottonwood Heights, Salt Lake, Pop. 32,636
Canyons SD
Supt. — See Sandy
Brighton SHS   2,000/10-12
2220 E Bengal Blvd,   801-826-5800
Charisse Hilton, prin.   Fax 826-5809
Butler MS   900/7-9
7530 S 2700 E,   801-826-6800
Marsha Morgan, prin.   Fax 826-6809

Delta, Millard, Pop. 3,399
Millard SD   3,000/PK-12
285 E 450 N 84624   435-864-1000
David Styler, supt.   Fax 864-5684
www.millardk12.org/
Delta HS   600/9-12
50 W 300 N 84624   435-864-5610
Dean Fowles, prin.   Fax 864-5619
Delta MS   600/5-8
251 E 300 N 84624   435-864-5660
Rebecca Callister, prin.   Fax 864-5669
Delta Tech Ctr   Vo/Tech
305 E 200 N 84624   435-864-5710
Teresa Thompson, prin.   Fax 864-5719
Other Schools – See Fillmore, Garrison

Draper, Salt Lake, Pop. 41,208

Ameritech College Post-Sec.
12257 Business Park Dr #108 84020 801-816-1444
Argosy University / Salt Lake City Post-Sec.
121 W Election Rd Ste 300 84020 801-601-5000
Art Institute of Salt Lake City Post-Sec.
121 W Election Rd 84020 801-601-4700
Juan Diego Catholic HS 800/9-12
300 E 11800 S 84020 801-984-7602
Galey Colosimo, prin. Fax 984-7601
Oxford Academy 50/PK-12
1259 E Draper Pkwy 84020 801-501-0228
Millicent Jacobson, dir. Fax 501-0269
St. John the Baptist MS 400/6-8
300 E 11800 S 84020 801-984-7613
Jim Markosian, prin. Fax 984-7649

Duchesne, Duchesne, Pop. 1,664
Duchesne SD 4,100/K-12
PO Box 446 84021 435-738-1240
David Brotherson, supt. Fax 738-1254
www.dcsd.org
Duchesne JSHS 300/7-12
PO Box 330 84021 435-738-1260
Stan Young, prin. Fax 738-1261
Other Schools – See Altamont, Roosevelt, Tabiona

Dugway, Tooele, Pop. 749
Tooele County SD
Supt. — See Tooele
Dugway JSHS 100/7-12
5020 5th St 84022 435-831-4566
Robin Nielson, prin. Fax 831-4951

Eden, Weber, Pop. 593
Weber SD
Supt. — See Ogden
Snowcrest JHS 400/7-9
2755 N Highway 162 84310 801-476-5360
Scott Elliott, prin. Fax 476-5399

Enterprise, Washington, Pop. 1,701
Washington County SD
Supt. — See Saint George
Enterprise JSHS 400/7-12
PO Box 460 84725 435-878-2248
Russell Holmes, prin. Fax 878-2479

Ephraim, Sanpete, Pop. 5,963
South Sanpete SD
Supt. — See Manti
Ephraim MS 500/6-8
555 S 100 E 84627 435-283-4037
Timothy Miller, prin. Fax 283-4885

Snow College Post-Sec.
150 College Ave 84627 435-283-7000

Escalante, Garfield, Pop. 794
Garfield SD
Supt. — See Panguitch
Escalante HS 100/7-12
PO Box 228 84726 435-826-4205
Eugene King, prin. Fax 826-4231

Eureka, Juab, Pop. 666
Tintic SD 200/PK-12
PO Box 210 84628 435-433-6363
Kodey Hughes, supt. Fax 433-6643
www.tintic.k12.ut.us
Tintic JSHS 100/7-12
PO Box 230 84628 435-433-6939
Fax 433-6845
Other Schools – See Trout Creek

Farmington, Davis, Pop. 17,985
Davis SD 65,500/PK-12
PO Box 588 84025 801-402-5261
Dr. W. Bryan Bowles, supt. Fax 402-5249
www.davis.k12.ut.us
Farmington JHS 1,100/7-9
150 S 200 W 84025 801-402-6900
Brent Stephens, prin. Fax 402-6901
Other Schools – See Bountiful, Centerville, Clearfield, Kaysville, Layton, Sunset, Syracuse, West Point, Woods Cross

Ferron, Emery, Pop. 1,614
Emery County SD
Supt. — See Huntington
San Rafael JHS 300/7-9
PO Box 790 84523 435-384-2335
Doug Mecham, prin. Fax 384-3354

Fillmore, Millard, Pop. 2,397
Millard SD
Supt. — See Delta
Fillmore MS 300/5-8
435 S 500 W 84631 435-743-5660
George Richardson, prin. Fax 743-5669
Millard HS 300/9-12
200 W Eagle Ave 84631 435-743-5610
Dennis Alldredge, prin. Fax 743-5619

Garland, Box Elder, Pop. 2,370
Box Elder SD
Supt. — See Brigham City
Bear River MS 600/8-9
300 E 1500 S 84312 435-257-2540
Eldon Petersen, prin. Fax 257-3945
Bear River SHS 900/10-12
1450 S Main St 84312 435-257-2500
Gary Allen, prin. Fax 257-3899

Garrison, Millard
Millard SD
Supt. — See Delta
EskDale HS 50/9-12
1000 Circle Dr 84728 435-855-2148
Greg Faber, lead tchr. Fax 855-2148
Garrison JHS 50/7-8
1000 Circle Dr 84728 435-855-2148
Greg Faber, lead tchr. Fax 855-2148

Grantsville, Tooele, Pop. 8,741
Tooele County SD
Supt. — See Tooele
Grantsville HS 700/9-12
155 Cowboy Dr 84029 435-884-4500
Travis McCluskey, prin. Fax 884-4519
Grantsville JHS 400/7-8
318 S Hale St 84029 435-884-4510
Charles Mohler, prin. Fax 884-4513

Green River, Emery, Pop. 946
Emery County SD
Supt. — See Huntington
Green River JSHS 100/7-12
PO Box 450 84525 435-564-3461
Nolan Johnson, prin. Fax 564-3508

Grouse Creek, Box Elder
Box Elder SD
Supt. — See Brigham City
Grouse Creek S 50/K-10
PO Box 16 84313 435-747-7321
Duane Runyan, prin. Fax 747-7182

Gunnison, Sanpete, Pop. 3,235
South Sanpete SD
Supt. — See Manti
Gunnison Valley HS 300/9-12
PO Box 460 84634 435-528-7256
Trevor Powell, prin. Fax 528-3556
Gunnison Valley MS 300/6-8
PO Box 1090 84634 435-528-5337
Alan Peterson, prin. Fax 528-5397

Harrisville, Weber, Pop. 5,477
Weber SD
Supt. — See Ogden
Orion JHS 900/7-9
370 W 2000 N, 801-452-4700
Nick Harris, prin. Fax 452-4777

Heber City, Wasatch, Pop. 11,241
Wasatch SD 5,100/K-12
101 E 200 N 84032 435-654-0280
Terry Shoemaker, supt. Fax 654-4714
www.wasatch.edu/
Rocky Mountain MS 800/7-8
800 School House Way 84032 435-654-9350
Justin Kelly, prin. Fax 654-9343
Wasatch Alternative S 50/Alt
180 E 600 S 84032 435-654-4231
Adam Hagen, prin.
Wasatch HS 1,400/9-12
930 S 500 E 84032 435-654-0640
Shawn Kelly, prin. Fax 654-3011

Helper, Carbon, Pop. 2,166
Carbon SD
Supt. — See Price
Helper JHS 200/7-9
151 Uintah St 84526 435-472-5441
Mika Salas, prin. Fax 472-3502

Herriman, Salt Lake, Pop. 21,297
Jordan SD
Supt. — See West Jordan
Copper Mountain MS 7-9
10106 S Anthem Park Blvd, 801-412-1200
Kim Baker, prin. Fax 412-1230
Fort Herriman MS 1,500/7-9
14058 S Mirabella Dr, 801-412-2450
Rodney Shaw, prin. Fax 412-2460
Herriman SHS 10-12
11917 S 6000 W, 801-567-8530
James Birch, prin. Fax 567-8545

Highland, Utah, Pop. 15,197
Alpine SD
Supt. — See American Fork
Lone Peak SHS 2,200/10-12
10189 N 4800 W 84003 801-717-4568
Kenneth Koop, prin. Fax 763-7064
Mountain Ridge JHS 1,300/7-9
5525 W 10400 N 84003 801-610-8758
Mark Whitaker, prin. Fax 763-7018

Huntington, Emery, Pop. 2,105
Emery County SD 2,400/PK-12
PO Box 120 84528 435-687-9846
Kirk Sitterud, supt. Fax 687-9849
emerycsd.org
Canyon View JHS 200/7-9
PO Box 250 84528 435-687-2265
James Jones, prin. Fax 687-9546
Other Schools – See Castle Dale, Ferron, Green River

Hurricane, Washington, Pop. 13,404
Washington County SD
Supt. — See Saint George
Hurricane HS 800/10-12
345 W Tiger Blvd 84737 435-635-3280
Jody Rich, prin. Fax 635-3719
Hurricane MS 600/8-9
395 N 200 W 84737 435-635-4634
Roy Hoyt, prin. Fax 635-4663

Hyrum, Cache, Pop. 7,476
Cache County SD
Supt. — See Logan
Mountain Crest SHS 1,600/10-12
255 S 800 E 84319 435-245-6093
Bob Henke, prin. Fax 245-3818
South Cache JHS 1,200/8-9
10 S 480 W 84319 435-245-6433
Lynn Archibald, prin. Fax 245-6662

Junction, Piute, Pop. 190
Piute SD 300/PK-12
PO Box 69 84740 435-577-2912
Shane Erickson, supt. Fax 577-2561
www.piutek12.org
Piute JSHS 200/7-12
550 N 100 W 84740 435-577-2912
Kennedy Sylvester, prin. Fax 577-2512

Kamas, Summit, Pop. 1,803
South Summit SD 1,400/PK-12
375 E 300 S 84036 435-783-4301
Barry Walker, supt. Fax 783-4501
www.ssummit.org
South Summit HS 400/9-12
45 S 300 E 84036 435-783-4313
Gary Twitchell, prin. Fax 783-4765
South Summit MS 500/5-8
355 E 300 S 84036 435-783-4341
Wade Woolstenhulme, prin. Fax 783-2787

Kanab, Kane, Pop. 4,263
Kane SD 1,200/K-12
746 S 175 E 84741 435-644-2555
Robert Johnson, supt. Fax 644-2509
www.kane.k12.ut.us
Kanab HS 300/9-12
59 Cowboy Dr 84741 435-644-5821
Doug Jacobs, prin. Fax 644-5242
Kanab MS 100/7-8
690 Cowboy Way 84741 435-644-5800
Doug Jacobs, prin. Fax 644-5121
Other Schools – See Big Water, Lake Powell, Orderville

Kaysville, Davis, Pop. 26,897
Davis SD
Supt. — See Farmington
Canyon Heights S 100/Alt
525 DATC Dr 84037 801-402-0720
Peggy Hill, prin. Fax 402-0721
Centennial JHS 7-9
740 Sunset Dr 84037 801-402-0100
Aaron Hogge, prin. Fax 402-0101
Davis Applied Technology College Vo/Tech
550 E 300 S 84037 801-593-2500
Mike Bouwhuis, dir. Fax 593-2400
Davis SHS 2,300/10-12
325 S Main St 84037 801-402-8800
Dee Burton, prin. Fax 402-8801
Fairfield JHS 1,200/7-9
951 N Fairfield Rd 84037 801-402-7000
Bryon Nielsen, prin. Fax 402-7001
Kaysville JHS 1,300/7-9
100 E 350 S 84037 801-402-7200
Curtis Stromberg, prin. Fax 402-7201
Mountain HS 200/Alt
490 S 500 E 84037 801-402-0450
Kathleen Chronister, prin. Fax 402-0451

Davis Applied Technology College Post-Sec.
550 E 300 S 84037 801-593-2500

Kearns, Salt Lake, Pop. 34,126
Granite SD
Supt. — See Salt Lake City
Jefferson JHS 1,100/7-9
5850 S 5600 W 84118 385-646-5194
Jared Reynolds, prin. Fax 646-5195
Kearns JHS 800/7-9
4040 W Sams Blvd 84118 385-646-5204
Kandace Barber, prin. Fax 646-5206
Kearns SHS 1,700/10-12
5525 S Cougar Ln 84118 385-646-5380
Maile Loo, prin. Fax 646-5382

Koosharem, Sevier, Pop. 311

Sorenson's Ranch S 100/6-12
PO Box 440219 84744 435-638-7318
Ron Cazier, prin. Fax 638-7582

Lake Powell, San Juan, Pop. 15
Kane SD
Supt. — See Kanab
Lake Powell HS 50/7-12
1000 Ferry Rd 84533 435-684-2268
Gordon Miller, prin. Fax 684-3821

Laketown, Rich, Pop. 240
Rich SD
Supt. — See Randolph
Rich MS 100/6-8
PO Box 129 84038 435-946-3359
Kip Motta, prin. Fax 946-3366

La Verkin, Washington, Pop. 3,978

Cross Creek Academy 100/7-12
150 N State St 84745 435-635-6016
Karr Farnsworth, admin. Fax 635-1099

Layton, Davis, Pop. 65,397
Davis SD
Supt. — See Farmington
Central Davis JHS 900/7-9
663 Church St 84041 801-402-7100
Dave Tanner, prin. Fax 402-7101
Layton SHS 1,700/10-12
440 Wasatch Dr 84041 801-402-4800
Ryck Astle, prin. Fax 402-4801
Legacy JHS 700/7-8
411 N 3200 W 84041 801-402-4700
Dr. Kenneth Hadlock, prin. Fax 402-4701
North Layton JHS 1,000/7-9
1100 W Antelope Dr 84041 801-402-6600
Kathy Ashton, prin. Fax 402-6601
Northridge SHS 1,800/10-12
2430 N Hill Field Rd 84041 801-402-8500
Luke Rasmussen, prin. Fax 402-8501

Broadview University Post-Sec.
869 W Hill Field Rd 84041 801-660-6000
Eagle Gate College Post-Sec.
915 N 400 W 84041 801-546-7500
Faith Baptist Academy K-12
2430 N Fairfield Rd 84041 801-771-0308
Fran Brown College of Beauty Post-Sec.
587 N Main St 84041 801-546-6166
Layton Christian Academy 700/PK-12
2352 E Highway 193 84040 801-771-7141
Greg Miller, admin. Fax 771-0921

Northridge Learning Center 200/K-12
2405 N Hill Field Rd 84041 801-776-4532
Dixie Evans, dir. Fax 776-0638

Lehi, Utah, Pop. 46,111
Alpine SD
Supt. — See American Fork
Lehi JHS 1,300/7-9
700 Cedar Hollow Rd 84043 801-768-7010
Joel Perkins, prin. Fax 768-7016
Lehi SHS 1,700/10-12
180 N 500 E 84043 801-610-8805
David Mower, prin. Fax 768-7040
Willowcreek MS 1,000/7-9
2275 W 300 N 84043 801-766-5273
Kestin Mattinson, prin. Fax 766-5168

Mountainland Applied Technology College Post-Sec.
2301 N Ashton Blvd 84043 801-753-6282

Lindon, Utah, Pop. 9,825
Alpine SD
Supt. — See American Fork
Oak Canyon JHS 1,100/7-9
111 S 725 E 84042 801-610-8138
Doug Webb, prin. Fax 785-8768

Evan's Hairstyling College Post-Sec.
284 W 200 N 84042 801-224-6034

Logan, Cache, Pop. 47,175
Cache County SD 14,600/K-12
2063 N 1200 E 84341 435-752-3925
Dr. Steven Norton, supt. Fax 753-2168
www.ccsdut.org
Cache HS 100/Alt
265 W 1400 N 84341 435-755-0716
Sheri Hansen, prin. Fax 755-0721
Other Schools – See Hyrum, Richmond, Smithfield

Logan CSD 6,200/PK-12
101 W Center St 84321 435-755-2300
Marshal Garrett, supt. Fax 755-2311
www.loganschools.org
Logan HS 1,700/9-12
162 W 100 S 84321 435-755-2380
Shane Ogden, prin. Fax 755-2387
Logan North Campus Alt
83 S 100 W 84321 435-755-2393
Shane Ogden, dir.
Logan South Campus 100/Alt
325 W 400 S 84321 435-755-2395
Shane Ogden, prin. Fax 755-2396
Mt. Logan MS 1,300/6-8
875 N 200 E 84321 435-755-2370
Mike Monson, prin. Fax 755-2370

Bridgerland Applied Technology Center Post-Sec.
1301 N 600 W 84321 435-753-6780
New Horizons Beauty College Post-Sec.
550 N Main St Ste 115 84321 435-753-9779
Stevens Henager College Post-Sec.
755 S Main St 84321 435-752-0903
Utah State University Post-Sec.
1400 Old Main Hl 84322 435-797-1000

Magna, Salt Lake, Pop. 25,413
Granite SD
Supt. — See Salt Lake City
Brockbank JHS 900/7-9
2935 S 8560 W 84044 385-646-5134
Terri VanWinkle, prin. Fax 646-5135
Cyprus SHS 1,600/10-12
8623 W 3000 S 84044 385-646-5300
Stephen Hess, prin. Fax 646-5303
Matheson JHS 1,200/7-9
3650 S Montclair St 84044 385-646-5290
Marijean Woolf, prin. Fax 646-5299

Vista S 100/7-12
PO Box 69 84044 801-250-9762

Manila, Daggett, Pop. 308
Daggett SD 200/K-12
PO Box 249 84046 435-784-3174
Bruce Northcott, supt. Fax 784-3549
www.dsdf.org
Manila JSHS 100/7-12
PO Box 249 84046 435-784-3174
Guy Gonder, prin. Fax 784-3271

Manti, Sanpete, Pop. 3,220
South Sanpete SD 3,100/PK-12
39 S Main St 84642 435-835-2261
Kent Larsen, supt. Fax 835-2265
www.ssanpete.org/
Manti HS 500/9-12
100 W 500 N 84642 435-835-2281
George Henrie, prin. Fax 835-2285
Other Schools – See Ephraim, Gunnison

Mapleton, Utah, Pop. 7,784
Nebo SD
Supt. — See Spanish Fork
Mapleton JHS 1,200/7-9
362 E 1200 N 84664 801-489-2892
RaShel Anderson, prin. Fax 489-2899

Midvale, Salt Lake, Pop. 27,166
Canyons SD
Supt. — See Sandy
Hillcrest SHS 1,600/10-12
7350 S 900 E 84047 801-826-6000
Sue Malone, prin. Fax 826-6009
Midvale MS 700/7-9
7852 S Pioneer St 84047 801-826-7300
Paula Logan, prin. Fax 826-7301

Kendall's Academy of Beauty Arts/Science Post-Sec.
7353 S 900 E 84047 801-561-5610

Milford, Beaver, Pop. 1,385
Beaver SD
Supt. — See Beaver
Milford JSHS 200/7-12
PO Box 159 84751 435-387-2751
Greg Dettinger, prin. Fax 387-2494

Moab, Grand, Pop. 4,967
Grand SD 1,500/PK-12
264 S 400 E 84532 435-259-5317
Dr. Scott Crane, supt. Fax 259-6212
www.grandschools.org
Grand County HS 500/9-12
608 S 400 E 84532 435-259-8931
Stephen Hren, prin. Fax 259-4191
Grand County MS 200/7-8
439 S 100 E 84532 435-259-7158
Melinda Snow, prin. Fax 259-6221
Arches Education Center Adult
125 W 200 S 84532 435-260-8764
Trish Hedin, dir.

Monroe, Sevier, Pop. 2,221
Sevier SD
Supt. — See Richfield
South Sevier HS 400/9-12
430 W 100 S 84754 435-527-4651
Randy Madsen, prin. Fax 527-4653
South Sevier MS 300/6-8
300 E Center St 84754 435-527-4607
Michael Willes, prin. Fax 527-4636

Montezuma Creek, San Juan, Pop. 332
San Juan SD
Supt. — See Blanding, UT
Whitehorse HS, PO Box 660 84534 300/7-12
John Fahey, prin. 435-678-1854

Monticello, San Juan, Pop. 1,935
San Juan SD
Supt. — See Blanding, UT
Monticello JSHS, PO Box 69 84535 300/7-12
Scott Shakespeare, prin. 435-587-2465

Monument Valley, San Juan
San Juan SD
Supt. — See Blanding, UT
Monument Valley JSHS 300/7-12
PO Box 360008 84536 435-678-1208
Sylvia McMillan, prin. Fax 678-1258

Morgan, Morgan, Pop. 3,652
Morgan SD 2,400/PK-12
PO Box 530 84050 801-829-3411
Kenneth Adams, supt. Fax 829-3531
www.morgansd.org
Morgan HS 700/9-12
PO Box 917 84050 801-829-3418
Wade Murdock, prin. Fax 829-6553
Morgan MS 600/6-8
PO Box 470 84050 801-829-3467
Terry Allen, prin. Fax 829-0645

Moroni, Sanpete, Pop. 1,398
North Sanpete SD
Supt. — See Mount Pleasant
North Sanpete MS 400/7-8
PO Box 307 84646 435-436-8206
Jason Strate, prin. Fax 436-8208

Mount Pleasant, Sanpete, Pop. 3,193
North Sanpete SD 2,400/PK-12
220 E 700 S 84647 435-462-2485
Leslie Keisel, supt. Fax 462-2480
www.nsanpete.k12.ut.us
North Sanpete HS 700/9-12
390 E 700 S 84647 435-462-2452
Nan Ault, prin. Fax 462-3112
Other Schools – See Moroni

Wasatch Academy 300/8-12
120 S 100 W 84647 435-462-1400
Joseph Loftin, hdmstr. Fax 462-1450

Murray, Salt Lake, Pop. 45,548
Murray CSD 6,500/K-12
147 E 5065 S 84107 801-264-7400
Dr. Steven Hirase, supt. Fax 264-7456
www.murrayschools.org/
Hillcrest JHS 800/7-9
126 E 5300 S 84107 801-264-7442
Jennifer Covington, prin. Fax 264-4820
Murray SHS 1,500/10-12
5440 S State St 84107 801-264-7460
Dr. David Dunn, prin. Fax 264-7461
Riverview JHS 700/7-9
751 W Tripp Ln 84123 801-264-7446
Jim Bouwman, prin. Fax 264-7458

Cameo College of Essential Beauty Post-Sec.
124 E 5770 S 84107 801-484-6173
Eagle Gate College Post-Sec.
5588 S Green St 84123 801-333-8100
ITT Technical Institute Post-Sec.
920 W Levoy Dr 84123 801-263-3313
Mt. Vernon Academy 100/K-12
184 E Vine St 84107 801-266-5521
Michael Lambson, prin. Fax 269-8080
Realms of Inquiry S 100/6-12
120 W Vine St Ste 200 84107 801-467-5911
Ross Jones, head sch Fax 590-7701

Nephi, Juab, Pop. 5,328
Juab SD 2,300/K-12
346 E 600 N 84648 435-623-1940
Jim Shank, supt. Fax 623-1941
www.juab.k12.ut.us
Juab HS 700/9-12
802 N 650 E 84648 435-623-1764
Rick Robins, prin. Fax 623-1772
Juab JHS 300/7-8
555 E 800 N 84648 435-623-1541
Ken Rowley, prin. Fax 623-4995

Oakley, Summit, Pop. 1,459

Oakley S 100/9-12
PO Box 357 84055 435-783-5001
James Meyer, head sch Fax 783-5010

Ogden, Weber, Pop. 80,717
Ogden CSD 12,200/K-12
1950 Monroe Blvd 84401 801-737-7300
Brad Smith, supt. Fax 627-7654
www.ogdensd.org
Highland JHS 900/7-9
325 Gramercy Ave 84404 801-737-7700
Ed Morris, prin. Fax 625-8860
Lomond HS 1,000/10-12
1080 9th St 84404 801-737-7976
Ben Smith, prin. Fax 737-8510
Mill Creek Youth Center 100/Alt
790 W 12th St 84404 801-625-8775
Eulogio Alejandre, coord. Fax 625-1104
Mound Fort JHS 800/7-9
1396 Liberty Ave 84404 801-737-7800
Peggy Dooling-Baker, prin. Fax 625-8993
Mt. Ogden JHS 900/7-9
3260 Harrison Blvd 84403 801-737-8600
Clyde Moore, prin. Fax 627-7641
Ogden HS 1,100/10-12
2828 Harrison Blvd 84403 801-737-8673
Stacey Briggs, prin. Fax 392-7338
Washington Alternative HS 300/Alt
455 28th St 84401 801-737-7400
Sarah Roberts, prin. Fax 625-1171
Adult Education S Adult
455 28th St 84401 801-737-8281
Eulogio Alejandre, prin. Fax 737-8299

Weber SD 30,100/K-12
5320 Adams Ave Pkwy 84405 801-476-7800
Jeff Stephens, supt. Fax 476-7893
www.wsd.net
Bonneville SHS 1,300/10-12
251 E 4800 S 84405 801-452-4050
Ray Long, prin. Fax 476-1837
North Ogden JHS 700/7-9
575 E 2900 N 84414 801-452-4800
Jay Anderson, prin. Fax 452-4839
South Ogden JHS 900/7-9
650 E 5700 S 84405 801-452-4460
Don Tanner, prin. Fax 452-4499
Two Rivers HS 200/Alt
955 W 12th St 84404 801-476-3920
Jeff Marchant, prin. Fax 476-3940
Wahlquist JHS 1,000/7-9
1033 N 1200 W 84404 801-452-4640
Sue Sweet, prin. Fax 452-4679
Weber SHS 1,800/10-12
430 W Weber High Dr 84414 801-476-3700
Velden Wardle, prin. Fax 476-3799
Other Schools – See Eden, Harrisville, Plain City, Roy, Washington Tr, West Haven

Evergreen Montessori Academy PK-10
5875 S Adams Ave 84405 801-479-7799
Amy Van Vliet, dir. Fax 479-7797
Marinello School of Beauty Post-Sec.
3721 S 250 W 84405 801-394-5718
Ogden-Weber Applied Technology College Post-Sec.
200 N Washington Blvd 84404 801-627-8300
St. Joseph's HS 200/9-12
1790 Lake St 84401 801-394-1515
Patrick Lambert, prin. Fax 394-6428
Stevens Henager College Post-Sec.
PO Box 9428 84409 801-392-1471
Utah Schools for the Deaf and the Blind Post-Sec.
742 Harrison Blvd 84404 801-629-4700
Weber State University Post-Sec.
1001 University Cir 84408 801-626-6000

Orderville, Kane, Pop. 575
Kane SD
Supt. — See Kanab
Valley HS 100/7-12
PO Box 128 84758 435-648-2278
Jim Wood, prin. Fax 648-2366

Orem, Utah, Pop. 85,397
Alpine SD
Supt. — See American Fork
Alpine Summit 50/Alt
1581 W 1000 S 84058 801-610-8183
Lynn Gerratt, dir. Fax 227-7831
Canyon View JHS 1,200/7-9
655 E 950 N 84097 801-610-8130
Wade Lott, prin. Fax 227-8706
Lakeridge JHS 1,100/7-9
951 S 400 W 84058 801-610-8134
Dr. Garrick Peterson, prin. Fax 227-2490
Mountain View SHS 1,400/10-12
665 W Center St 84057 801-227-2400
Blaine Edman, prin. Fax 227-2460
Orem JHS 800/7-9
765 N 600 W 84057 801-610-8142
Joe Jensen, prin. Fax 227-8796
Orem SHS 1,100/10-12
175 S 400 E 84097 801-610-8165
Mike Browning, prin. Fax 227-8774
Timpanogos SHS 1,400/10-12
1450 N 200 E 84057 801-610-8175
Theron Murphy, prin. Fax 223-3134

Broadview University Post-Sec.
898 N 1200 W 84057 801-822-5800
Meridian S 200/PK-12
280 S 400 E 84097 801-374-5480
Tasi Young, hdmstr. Fax 374-5491
Stevens Henager College Post-Sec.
1476 Sandhill Rd 84058 801-373-0285
Utah College of Dental Hygiene Post-Sec.
1176 S 1480 W 84058 801-426-8234
Utah Valley University Post-Sec.
800 W University Pkwy 84058 801-863-8000

Panguitch, Garfield, Pop. 1,509
Garfield SD 900/K-12
PO Box 398 84759 435-676-8821
Ben Dalton, supt. Fax 676-8266
www.garfk12.org
Panguitch HS 100/9-12
PO Box 393 84759 435-676-8805
Rod Quarnberg, prin. Fax 676-8521
Panguitch MS 100/7-8
PO Box 393 84759 435-676-8225
Nick Reynolds, prin. Fax 676-2518
Other Schools – See Escalante, Tropic

Park City, Summit, Pop. 7,439
Park City SD 4,300/K-12
2700 Kearns Blvd 84060 435-645-5600
Tom Van Gorder, supt. Fax 645-5609
www.pcschools.us
Park City SHS 1,000/10-12
1750 Kearns Blvd 84060 435-645-5650
Bob O'Connor, prin. Fax 645-5659
Treasure Mountain International S 700/8-9
2530 Kearns Blvd 84060 435-645-5640
Dave McNaughtan, prin. Fax 645-5649
Park City Learning Center Adult
2400 Kearns Blvd 84060 435-645-5626
Nicole Stewart, prin. Fax 645-5627

Park Valley, Box Elder
Box Elder SD
Supt. — See Brigham City
Park Valley S 50/K-10
788 Education Dr 84329 435-871-4411
Brian Anderson, lead tchr. Fax 871-4444

Parowan, Iron, Pop. 2,772
Iron SD
Supt. — See Cedar City
Parowan HS 400/7-12
PO Box 337 84761 435-477-3366
Roy Mathews, prin. Fax 477-3743

Payson, Utah, Pop. 18,014
Nebo SD
Supt. — See Spanish Fork
Mt. Nebo JHS 900/7-9
851 W 450 S 84651 801-465-6040
Kaye Isakson, prin. Fax 465-6045
Payson JHS 1,100/7-9
1025 S Highway 91 84651 801-465-6015
Carl Swenson, prin. Fax 465-6023
Payson SHS 1,000/10-12
1050 S Main St 84651 801-465-6025
Ben Ford, prin. Fax 465-6067

Plain City, Weber, Pop. 5,416
Weber SD
Supt. — See Ogden
Fremont SHS 1,700/10-12
1900 N 4700 W 84404 801-452-4000
Rod Belnap, prin. Fax 452-4049

Pleasant Grove, Utah, Pop. 32,692
Alpine SD
Supt. — See American Fork
Pleasant Grove JHS 1,400/7-9
810 N 100 E 84062 801-785-8707
Brian Jolley, prin. Fax 785-8743
Pleasant Grove SHS 1,900/10-12
700 E 200 S 84062 801-610-8170
Tim Brantley, prin. Fax 785-8744

Llahona Preparatory Academy 100/5-12
2464 W 450 S 84062 801-785-7850
Kolleen DeGraff, admin. Fax 785-4723

Price, Carbon, Pop. 8,585
Carbon SD 3,500/K-12
251 W 400 N 84501 435-637-1732
Steve Carlsen, supt. Fax 637-9417
www.carbonschools.org
Carbon SHS 600/10-12
750 E 400 N 84501 435-637-2463
Bruce Bean, prin. Fax 637-4127
Lighthouse HS 100/Alt
251 W 400 N 84501 435-637-7540
Karlene Bianco, prin. Fax 637-4019
Mont Harmon JHS 500/7-9
60 W 400 N 84501 435-637-0510
Carol Wells, prin. Fax 637-6074
Other Schools – See Helper

UT State Univ-College of Eastern Utah Post-Sec.
451 E 400 N 84501 435-613-5000

Provo, Utah, Pop. 108,411
Provo CSD 12,900/PK-12
280 W 940 N 84604 801-374-4800
Keith C. Rittel, supt. Fax 374-4808
www.provo.edu
Centennial MS 1,000/7-8
305 E 2320 N 84604 801-374-4621
Mitch Swenson, prin. Fax 374-4626
Dixon MS 900/7-8
750 W 200 N 84601 801-374-4980
Jarod Sites, prin. Fax 374-4884
Independence HS 300/Alt
636 Independence Ave 84601 801-374-4920
Rosanna Ungerman, prin. Fax 370-4614
Oak Springs S Alt
1300 E Center St 84606 801-374-4858
Dennis Meyers, prin. Fax 374-4999
Provo HS 1,700/9-12
1125 N University Ave 84604 801-373-6550
Jeff Schoonover, prin. Fax 374-4880
Timpview HS 1,900/9-12
3570 Timpview Dr 84604 801-221-9720
Dr. Todd McKee, prin. Fax 224-4210
East Bay Post HS Adult
1170 S 350 E 84606 801-375-0414
Bret MacCabe, admin. Fax 374-8066

Provo Adult Education Adult
243 E 2320 N 84604 801-374-4840
Anita Craven, coord. Fax 374-4816

AmeriTech College Post-Sec.
2035 N 550 W 84604 801-377-2900
Brigham Young University 84602 Post-Sec.
801-422-4636
Dallas Roberts Academy of Hair Design Post-Sec.
1700 N State St Ste 18 84604 801-375-1501
Discovery Academy 50/7-12
105 N 500 W 84601 801-374-2121
Lanny Adamson, hdmstr. Fax 373-4451
Heritage S 200/7-12
5600 Heritage School Dr 84604 801-226-4600
Benjamin Parker, prin. Fax 226-4696
Provo College Post-Sec.
1450 W 820 N 84601 801-818-8900
Rocky Mountain Univ of Health Profession Post-Sec.
561 E 1860 S 84606 801-375-5125
Utah Valley Regional Medical Center Post-Sec.
1034 N 500 W 84604 801-373-7850
Von Curtis Academy of Hair Design Post-Sec.
480 N 900 E 84606 801-374-5111

Randolph, Rich, Pop. 458
Rich SD 500/K-12
PO Box 67 84064 435-793-2135
Dale Lamborn, supt. Fax 793-2136
www.richschool.org
Rich HS 100/9-12
PO Box 278 84064 435-793-2365
Rick Larsen, prin. Fax 793-2375
Other Schools – See Laketown

Richfield, Sevier, Pop. 7,458
Sevier SD 4,700/PK-12
180 E 600 N 84701 435-896-8214
Cade Douglas, supt. Fax 896-8804
www.sevier.k12.ut.us
Cedar Ridge HS 100/Alt
555 W 100 N 84701 435-896-9464
George Chappell, prin. Fax 896-9475
Red Hills MS 500/6-8
400 S 600 W 84701 435-896-6421
Selena Terry, prin. Fax 896-6423
Richfield HS 600/9-12
510 W 100 S 84701 435-896-8247
Brent Gubler, prin. Fax 896-8246
Other Schools – See Monroe, Salina

Richmond, Cache, Pop. 2,447
Cache County SD
Supt. — See Logan
North Cache JHS 1,100/8-9
157 W 600 S 84333 435-258-2452
Mike Thompson, prin. Fax 258-5437

Riverton, Salt Lake, Pop. 37,974
Jordan SD
Supt. — See West Jordan
Oquirrh Hills MS 1,200/7-9
12949 S 2700 W 84065 801-412-2350
Michael Glenn, prin. Fax 412-2370
Riverton SHS 2,000/10-12
12476 S 2700 W 84065 801-256-5800
Carolyn Gough, prin. Fax 256-5880
South Hills MS 1,100/7-9
13508 S 4000 W 84065 801-412-2400
Ben Jameson, prin. Fax 412-2430

Concordia HS 100/9-12
12723 S Park Ave 84065 801-266-6676
Fax 266-1953

Roosevelt, Duchesne, Pop. 5,853
Duchesne SD
Supt. — See Duchesne
Roosevelt JHS 400/6-8
350 W 200 S 84066 435-725-4585
Dean Wilson, prin. Fax 725-4622
Thompsen S 50/Alt
3087 S 7000 W 84066 435-725-4770
Fred Arko, prin. Fax 725-4776
Union HS 800/9-12
135 N Union St Ste 124-3 84066 435-725-4525
Rick Nielsen, prin. Fax 725-4576

Uintah Basin Applied Technology College Post-Sec.
1100 E Lagoon St 84066 435-722-6900

Roy, Weber, Pop. 35,969
Weber SD
Supt. — See Ogden
Roy JHS 900/7-9
5400 S 2100 W 84067 801-476-5260
Kirt Swalberg, prin. Fax 476-5299
Roy SHS 1,500/10-12
2150 W 4800 S 84067 801-476-3600
Gina Butters, prin. Fax 476-3699
Sand Ridge JHS 800/7-9
2075 W 4600 S 84067 801-476-5320
Larry Hadley, prin. Fax 476-5359

Saint George, Washington, Pop. 70,848
Washington County SD 24,100/K-12
121 W Tabernacle St 84770 435-673-3553
Max Rose Ph.D., supt. Fax 673-3216
www.washk12.org
Desert Hills HS 900/10-12
828 Desert Hills Dr 84790 435-674-0885
Rusty Taylor, prin. Fax 674-2606
Desert Hills MS 300/6-8
936 Desert Hills Dr 84790 435-628-0001
Brian Stevenson, prin. Fax 674-6477
Dixie HS 1,000/10-12
350 E 700 S 84770 435-673-4682
Larry Bergeson, prin. Fax 673-2384
Dixie MS 700/7-9
825 S 100 E 84770 435-628-0441
Tim Lowe, prin. Fax 674-6467
Millcreek HS 200/10-12
2410 E Riverside Dr 84790 435-628-2462
Terry Ogborn, prin. Fax 628-8206
Pine View HS 900/10-12
2850 E 750 N 84790 435-628-5255
Mike Mees, prin. Fax 628-0327
Pine View MS 700/8-9
2145 E 130 N 84790 435-628-7915
Mike Stephenson, prin. Fax 634-0470
Snow Canyon HS 1,000/10-12
1385 Lava Flow Dr 84770 435-634-1967
Warren Brooks, prin. Fax 634-1130
Snow Canyon MS 900/8-9
1215 Lava Flow Dr 84770 435-674-6474
Cheri Stevenson, prin. Fax 628-3289
Other Schools – See Enterprise, Hurricane

Dixie Applied Technology College Post-Sec.
1506 S Silicon Way 84770 435-674-8400
Dixie State College of Utah Post-Sec.
225 S 700 E 84770 435-652-7500
Evan's Hairstyling College Post-Sec.
955 E Tabernacle St 84770 435-673-6128
Hairitage Hair Academy Post-Sec.
900 S Bluff St Ste 9 84770 435-673-5233
Stevens-Henager College Post-Sec.
720 S River Rd Ste C130 84790 435-628-9150

Salem, Utah, Pop. 6,343
Nebo SD
Supt. — See Spanish Fork
Salem Hills SHS 1,100/10-12
150 Skyhawk Blvd 84653 801-423-3200
Bart Peery, prin. Fax 423-3206
Salem JHS 7-9
140 W 100 S 84653 801-423-6550
Suzanne Kimball, prin. Fax 423-6569

Salina, Sevier, Pop. 2,467
Sevier SD
Supt. — See Richfield
North Sevier HS 300/9-12
350 W 400 N 84654 435-529-3717
Jill Porter, prin. Fax 529-7910
North Sevier MS 300/6-8
135 N 100 W 84654 435-529-3841
Rod Hinck, prin. Fax 529-7377

Salt Lake City, Salt Lake, Pop. 178,350
Granite SD 67,400/PK-12
2500 S State St 84115 385-646-5000
Dr. Martin Bates, supt. Fax 646-4128
www.graniteschools.org
Bennion JHS 1,000/7-9
6055 S 2700 W, 385-646-5114
Rod Horton, prin. Fax 646-5115
Bonneville JHS 800/7-9
5330 S 1660 E 84117 385-646-5124
Karl Moody, prin. Fax 646-5127
Churchill JHS 600/7-9
3450 E Oakview Dr 84124 385-646-5144
Steve Hogan, prin. Fax 646-5147
Cottonwood SHS 1,600/10-12
5715 S 1300 E 84121 385-646-5264
Alan Parrish, prin. Fax 646-5266
Evergreen JHS 900/7-9
3401 S 2000 E 84109 385-646-5164
Mark Grant, prin. Fax 646-5165
Granite Park JHS 700/7-9
3031 S 200 E 84115 385-646-5174
Dr. Taran Chun, prin. Fax 646-5175
Granite Peaks Alternative HS 300/Alt
501 E 3900 S 84107 385-646-5435
Michele Callahan, prin. Fax 646-5440
Granite Technical Institute Vo/Tech
2500 S State St 84115 385-646-4350
Devon Hartley, prin. Fax 646-4347
Hartvigsen S 200/Alt
350 E Baird Cir 84115 385-646-4585
Janice Wayman, prin. Fax 646-4256
Olympus JHS 800/7-9
2217 E Murray Holladay Rd 84117 385-646-5224
Carole Harris, prin. Fax 646-5227
Olympus SHS 1,500/10-12
4055 S 2300 E 84124 385-646-5400
Mark Manning, prin. Fax 646-5403
Skyline SHS 1,500/10-12
3251 E 3760 S 84109 385-646-5420
Doug Bingham, prin. Fax 646-5422
Taylorsville SHS 1,900/10-12
5225 S Redwood Rd 84123 385-646-5455
Dr. Garett Muse, prin. Fax 646-5457
Wasatch JHS 900/7-9
3750 S 3100 E 84109 385-646-5244
Christine Rydalch, prin. Fax 646-5246
Other Schools – See Kearns, Magna, Taylorsville, West Valley

Salt Lake City SD 25,100/PK-12
440 E 100 S 84111 801-578-8599
Dr. McKell Withers, supt. Fax 578-8248
www.slcschools.org
Bryant MS 500/7-8
40 S 800 E 84102 801-578-8118
Francis Battle, prin. Fax 578-8125
Clayton MS 600/7-8
1470 S 1900 E 84108 801-481-4810
Linda Richins, prin. Fax 481-4884
Columbus Community Center 50/Alt
3495 S West Temple 84115 801-262-1552
Dean Hoffman, dir. Fax 262-2066
East HS 2,100/9-12
840 S 1300 E 84102 801-583-1661
Paul Sagers, prin. Fax 584-2927
Glendale MS 800/6-8
1430 W Andrew Ave 84104 801-974-8319
Chris Gesteland, prin. Fax 974-8356
Highland HS 1,500/9-12
2166 S 1700 E 84106 801-484-4343
Paul Schulte, prin. Fax 481-4893

Hillside MS 500/7-8
1825 S Nevada St 84108 801-481-4828
Jane Bernston, prin. Fax 481-4831
Horizonte Instruction & Training Center 600/Alt
1234 S Main St 84101 801-578-8574
Mindi Holmdahl, prin. Fax 578-8577
Northwest MS 800/7-8
1730 W 1700 N 84116 801-578-8547
Brian Conley, prin. Fax 578-8558
West HS 2,400/9-12
241 N 300 W 84103 801-578-8500
Parley Jacobs, prin. Fax 578-8516

Broadview University Post-Sec.
240 Morris Ave 84115 801-300-4300
Fortis College Post-Sec.
3949 S 700 E Ste 150 84107 801-713-0915
Independence University Post-Sec.
4021 S 700 E Ste 400 84107 800-972-5149
Intermountain Christian S 300/PK-12
6515 S Lion Ln 84121 801-942-8811
James Kerr, dean Fax 942-8813
Judge Memorial Catholic HS 700/9-12
650 S 1100 E 84102 801-363-8895
Richard Bartman, prin. Fax 521-3920
Kendall's Academy of Beauty Arts/Science Post-Sec.
2230 S 700 E 84106 801-486-0101
Latter Day Saints Business College Post-Sec.
95 N 300 W Fl 8th 84101 801-524-8100
Midwives College of Utah Post-Sec.
1174 E Graystone Way Ste 2 84106 801-649-5230
Myotherapy College of Utah Post-Sec.
336 Bugatti Dr 84115 801-484-7624
Rowland Hall HS 300/9-12
843 S Lincoln St 84102 801-355-7494
Lee Thomsen, prin. Fax 355-0474
Rowland Hall MS 200/6-8
970 E 800 S 84102 801-355-0272
Tyler Fonarow, prin. Fax 359-8318
Salt Lake Community College Post-Sec.
4600 S Redwood Rd 84123 801-957-4111
Skin Works School of Advanced Skin Care Post-Sec.
2121 Nowell Cir 84115 801-530-0001
Stevens Henager College Post-Sec.
383 W Vine St 84123 801-531-1180
University of Utah Post-Sec.
201 S 1460 E 84112 801-581-7200
Upper Limit Aviation Post-Sec.
619 N 2360 W 84116 801-596-7722
Veterans Affairs Medical Center Post-Sec.
500 Foothill Dr 84148 801-582-1565
Western Governors University Post-Sec.
4001 S 700 E Ste 700 84107 801-274-3280
Westminster College Post-Sec.
1840 S 1300 E 84105 801-484-7651

Sandy, Salt Lake, Pop. 85,199
Canyons SD 32,100/K-12
9150 S 500 W 84070 801-826-5000
Dr. David Doty, supt. Fax 826-5053
www.canyonsdistrict.org/
Albion MS 1,000/7-9
2755 E Newcastle Dr 84093 801-826-6700
Joanne Ackerman, prin. Fax 826-6709
Alta SHS 2,600/10-12
11055 S 1000 E 84094 801-826-5600
Fidel Montero, prin. Fax 826-5609
Crescent View MS 1,400/7-9
11150 S 300 E 84070 801-826-6900
Gregory Leavitt, prin. Fax 826-6909
CTEC Vo/Tech
825 E 9085 S 84094 801-826-6600
Ken Spurlock, prin. Fax 826-6609
Eastmont MS 900/7-9
10100 S 1300 E 84094 801-826-7000
Janice Sterzer, prin. Fax 826-7009
Indian Hills MS 1,100/7-9
1180 E Sanders Rd 84094 801-826-7100
Floyd Stensrud, prin. Fax 826-7109
Jordan SHS 1,700/10-12
95 E Beetdigger Blvd 84070 801-826-6200
Tom Sherwood, prin. Fax 826-6209
Entrada HS Adult
825 E 9085 S 84094 801-826-6670
Amy Boettger, coord. Fax 826-6679
Other Schools – See Cottonwood Heights, Midvale

DeVry University Post-Sec.
9350 S 150 E Ste 420 84070 801-565-5110
Francois D. Hair Design Academy Post-Sec.
11339 S 700 E 84070 801-561-2244
Waterford S 1,000/PK-12
1480 E 9400 S 84093 801-572-1780
Nancy Heuston, admin. Fax 572-1787

Saratoga Sprngs, Utah, Pop. 17,223
Alpine SD
Supt. — See American Fork
Vista Heights MS 7-9
484 W Pony Express Pkwy, 801-610-8770
Dr. Steve Stewart, prin. Fax 768-4226
Westlake HS 2,000/9-12
99 N 200 W, 801-610-8815
Fred Openshaw, prin. Fax 768-1068

Smithfield, Cache, Pop. 9,375
Cache County SD
Supt. — See Logan
Sky View SHS 1,500/10-12
520 S 250 E 84335 435-563-6273
Dave Swenson, prin. Fax 563-9534

South Jordan, Salt Lake, Pop. 49,075
Jordan SD
Supt. — See West Jordan
Bingham SHS 2,300/10-12
2160 W South Jordan Pkwy 84095 801-256-5100
Christen Richards-Khong, prin. Fax 256-5151
Elk Ridge MS 1,500/7-9
3659 W 9800 S 84095 801-412-2800
Larry Urry, prin. Fax 412-2830
South Jordan MS 1,600/7-9
10245 S 2700 W 84095 801-412-2900
Shawn McLeod, prin. Fax 412-2930
Valley SHS 500/Alt
325 W 11000 S 84095 801-572-7035
Sharon Jensen, prin. Fax 572-7038

Neumont University Post-Sec.
10701 River Front Pkwy #300 84095 801-302-2800

Spanish Fork, Utah, Pop. 33,849
Nebo SD 29,200/PK-12
350 S Main St 84660 801-354-7400
Rick Nielsen, supt. Fax 798-4010
www.nebo.edu
Cornerstone S 50/Alt
99 N 300 W 84660 801-798-0652
Joe Kelly, coord. Fax 798-1183
Diamond Fork JHS 1,300/7-9
50 N 900 E 84660 801-798-4052
Troy Peterson, prin. Fax 798-4098
Landmark HS 200/Alt
320 S Main St 84660 801-798-4030
Joe Kelly, prin. Fax 798-4044
Maple Mountain SHS 1,200/10-12
51 N 2550 E 84660 801-794-6740
John Penrod, prin. Fax 794-6744
Spanish Fork JHS 1,200/7-9
600 S 820 E 84660 801-798-4075
Robert Fleming, prin. Fax 798-4097
Spanish Fork SHS 1,000/10-12
99 N 300 W 84660 801-798-4060
Dave McKee, prin. Fax 798-0483
Other Schools – See Mapleton, Payson, Salem, Springville

New Haven S 100/7-12
2172 E 7200 S 84660 801-794-1218
Laurie Laird, admin. Fax 794-9558

Springville, Utah, Pop. 28,786
Nebo SD
Supt. — See Spanish Fork
Springville JHS 900/7-9
165 S 700 E 84663 801-489-2880
Ken VanAusdal, prin. Fax 489-2838
Springville SHS 1,100/10-12
1205 E 900 S 84663 801-489-2870
Mike Brown, prin. Fax 489-2806

Stansbury Park, Tooele, Pop. 5,041
Tooele County SD
Supt. — See Tooele
Stansbury HS 50/9-12
5300 Aberdeen Ln 84074 435-882-2479
Kendall Topham, prin. Fax 882-4049

Sunset, Davis, Pop. 4,981
Davis SD
Supt. — See Farmington
Sunset JHS 900/7-9
1610 N 250 W 84015 801-402-6700
Rich Swanson, prin. Fax 402-6701

Syracuse, Davis, Pop. 23,777
Davis SD
Supt. — See Farmington
Syracuse JHS 1,100/7-9
1450 S 2000 W 84075 801-402-6800
Chris Keime, prin. Fax 402-6801
Syracuse SHS 1,900/10-12
665 S 2000 W 84075 801-402-7900
Wendy Nelson, prin. Fax 402-7901

Island View S 100/8-12
2650 W 2700 S 84075 801-773-0200
David Hans, dir. Fax 773-0208

Tabiona, Duchesne, Pop. 166
Duchesne SD
Supt. — See Duchesne
Tabiona HS 100/7-12
PO Box 470 84072 435-738-1320
Robert Park, prin. Fax 738-1332

Taylorsville, Salt Lake, Pop. 56,089
Granite SD
Supt. — See Salt Lake City
Eisenhower JHS 1,000/7-9
4351 S Redwood Rd 84123 385-646-5154
Dr. Mary Rhodes, prin. Fax 646-5158

Tooele, Tooele, Pop. 30,935
Tooele County SD 11,100/K-12
92 Lodestone Way 84074 435-833-1900
Terry Linares, supt. Fax 833-1912
tooeleschools.org
Blue Peak HS Alt
211 Tooele Blvd 84074 435-833-8700
Mark Ernst, prin. Fax 833-8785
Community Learning Center Vo/Tech
211 Toele Blvd 84074 435-833-8700
Mark Ernest, prin. Fax 833-8785
Johnsen JHS 800/7-8
2152 N 400 W 84074 435-833-1939
Jared Small, prin. Fax 843-3816
Tooele JHS 700/7-8
411 W Vine St 84074 435-833-1921
Larry Abraham, prin. Fax 833-1923
Other Schools – See Dugway, Grantsville, Stansbury Park, Wendover

---

Tooele Applied Technology College Post-Sec.
66 W Vine St 84074 435-248-1800

Tropic, Garfield, Pop. 524
Garfield SD
Supt. — See Panguitch
Bryce Valley HS 100/7-12
PO Box 70 84776 435-679-8835
Jeff Brinkerhoff, prin. Fax 679-8539

Trout Creek, Tooele
Tintic SD
Supt. — See Eureka
West Desert JSHS 50/7-12
440 Pony Express Rd 84083 435-693-3112
Tony White, head sch Fax 693-3109

Vernal, Uintah, Pop. 8,901
Uintah SD 6,700/PK-12
635 W 200 S 84078 435-781-3100
Mark Dockins Ed.D., supt. Fax 781-3107
www.uintah.net/
Uintah SHS 1,100/10-12
1880 W 500 N 84078 435-781-3110
Julie Wilde, prin. Fax 781-3117
Vernal JHS 800/8-9
161 N 1000 W 84078 435-781-3130
Kathleen Hawkins, prin. Fax 781-3134
Ashley Valley Adult Education Adult
559 N 1700 W 84078 435-781-4675
Andrea McKea, admin. Fax 781-4679

Washington Tr, Weber, Pop. 8,858
Weber SD
Supt. — See Ogden
Bell JHS 600/7-9
165 W 5100 S 84405 801-452-4600
Curtis Vanden Bosch, prin. Fax 452-4639

Wendover, Tooele, Pop. 1,381
Tooele County SD
Supt. — See Tooele
Wendover JSHS 200/7-12
PO Box 610 84083 435-665-2343
Jason Saari, prin. Fax 665-7706

West Haven, Weber, Pop. 10,042
Weber SD
Supt. — See Ogden
Rocky Mountain JHS 1,000/7-9
4350 W 4800 S 84401 801-476-5220
Nicole Meibos, prin. Fax 476-5259

West Jordan, Salt Lake, Pop. 99,828
Jordan SD 48,200/K-12
7387 S Campus View Dr 84084 801-567-8100
Dr. Patrice Johnson, supt. Fax 567-8064
www.jordandistrict.org
Copper Hills SHS 2,400/10-12
5445 W New Bingham Hwy, 801-256-5300
Todd Quarnberg, prin. Fax 256-5393
Jensen MS 800/7-9
8105 S 3200 W 84088 801-412-2850
Bryan Leggat, prin. Fax 412-2875
Jordan Applied Technology Center Vo/Tech
9301 S Wights Fort Rd 84088 801-256-5900
Chris Titus, prin. Fax 256-5930
Sunset Ridge MS 1,300/7-9
8292 S Skyline Arch Dr, 801-412-2475
Travis Hamblin, prin. Fax 412-2490
West Hills MS 1,100/7-9
8270 S Grizzly Way, 801-412-2300
Stacy Evans, prin. Fax 412-2327
West Jordan MS 1,000/7-9
7550 S Redwood Rd 84084 801-412-2100
Dixie Crowther, prin. Fax 412-2140
West Jordan SHS 1,800/10-12
8136 S 2700 W 84088 801-256-5600
Michael Kochevar, prin. Fax 256-5670
Southpointe Adult HS Adult
9301 S Wights Fort Rd 84088 801-256-5954
Renee Hyer, coord. Fax 256-5955
Other Schools – See Herriman, Riverton, South Jordan

Broadview University Post-Sec.
1902 W 7800 S 84088 801-304-4224
West Ridge Academy 100/4-12
5500 W Bagley Park Rd, 801-282-1000
Ken Allen, dir. Fax 282-1198

West Point, Davis, Pop. 9,305
Davis SD
Supt. — See Farmington
West Point JHS 1,200/7-9
2775 W 550 N 84015 801-402-8100
Jed Johansen, prin. Fax 402-8101

West Valley, Salt Lake, Pop. 122,084
Granite SD
Supt. — See Salt Lake City
Granger SHS 1,700/10-12
3690 S 3600 W 84119 385-646-5320
Jerry Haslam, prin. Fax 646-5322
Hunter JHS 1,200/7-9
6131 W Wending Ln 84128 385-646-5184
Doug Wagstaff, prin. Fax 646-5185
Hunter SHS 2,200/10-12
4200 S 5600 W 84120 385-646-5360
John Welburn, prin. Fax 646-5374
Kennedy JHS 1,100/7-9
4495 S 4800 W 84120 385-646-5214
Mary Anne Stevens, prin. Fax 646-5215
Valley JHS 900/7-9
4195 S 3200 W 84119 385-646-5234
David Holt, prin. Fax 646-5235
West Lake JHS 1,200/7-9
3400 S 3450 W 84119 385-646-5254
Ike Spencer, prin. Fax 646-5259

Everest College Post-Sec.
3280 W 3500 S 84119 801-840-4800
Premier Hair Academy Post-Sec.
4062 S 4000 W 84120 801-966-8414

Woods Cross, Davis, Pop. 9,426
Davis SD
Supt. — See Farmington
Woods Cross SHS 1,300/10-12
600 W 2200 S 84010 801-402-4500
John Haning, prin. Fax 402-4501

Benchmark S 100/8-12
592 W 1350 S 84010 801-299-5300

VERMONT

VERMONT DEPARTMENT OF EDUCATION
120 State St, Montpelier 05620-0002
Telephone 802-828-3135
Fax 802-828-3140
Website http://www.state.vt.us/educ/

Commissioner of Education Armando Vilaseca

VERMONT BOARD OF EDUCATION
120 State St, Montpelier 05620-0002

Chairperson Stephan Morse

PUBLIC, PRIVATE AND CATHOLIC SECONDARY SCHOOLS

Arlington, Bennington, Pop. 1,195
Battenkill Valley Supervisory Union 300/K-12
529 E Arlington Rd 05250 802-375-9744
Karen Gallese, supt. Fax 375-2368
www.bvsu.org
Arlington Memorial HS 200/6-12
529 E Arlington Rd 05250 802-375-2589
Christopher Barnes, prin. Fax 375-1547

Barre, Washington, Pop. 8,882
Barre Supervisory Union 2,500/PK-12
120 Ayers St 05641 802-476-5011
John Bacon Ed.D., supt. Fax 476-4944
www.bsuvt.org/
Spaulding HS / Barre Technical Center 800/9-12
155 Ayers St 05641 802-476-4811
Tom Sedore, prin. Fax 479-4535

VT Technical Centers
Supt. — None
Barre Technical Center Vo/Tech
155 Ayers St 05641 802-476-4811
Penny Chamberlin, prin. Fax 476-4045

Central Vermont Academy 50/K-12
317 Vine St 05641 802-479-0868
Kevin Wall, prin. Fax 479-4311

Barton, Orleans, Pop. 727
Orleans Central Supervisory Union 1,100/PK-12
130 Kinsey Rd 05822 802-525-1204
Stephen Urgenson Ed.D., supt. Fax 525-1276
www.ocsu.org
Other Schools – See Orleans

Bellows Falls, Windham, Pop. 3,056
Windham Northeast Supervisory Union 1,200/K-12
25 Cherry St 05101 802-463-9958
Christopher Kibbe, supt. Fax 463-9705
www.wnesu.org
Bellows Falls MS 200/5-8
15 School St 05101 802-463-4366
Heidi Lucas-Moccia, prin. Fax 463-9738
Bellows Falls Union HS 300/9-12
PO Box 429 05101 802-463-3944
Christopher Hodsden, prin. Fax 463-9322

Bennington, Bennington, Pop. 8,960
Southwest Vermont Supervisory Union 3,100/K-12
246 S Stream Rd 05201 802-447-7501
Catherine McClure, supt. Fax 447-0475
www.svsu.org
Mt. Anthony Union HS 1,000/9-12
301 Park St 05201 802-447-7511
Suzanne Maguire, prin. Fax 442-1260
Mt. Anthony Union MS 600/6-8
747 East Rd 05201 802-447-7541
Tim Payne, prin. Fax 442-1262

VT Technical Centers
Supt. — None
SW VT Career Development Center Vo/Tech
321 Park St 05201 802-447-0220
James Culkeen, prin. Fax 442-1745

Bennington College Post-Sec.
1 College Dr 05201 802-442-5401
Grace Christian S 200/PK-12
104 Kocher Dr 05201 802-447-2233
Joyce Lloyd, admin. Fax 442-8403
Southern Vermont College Post-Sec.
982 Mansion Dr 05201 802-447-4000

Bethel, Windsor, Pop. 558
Windsor Northwest Supervisory Union 500/PK-12
PO Box 395 05032 802-234-0264
John Poljacik, supt. Fax 234-0261
www.wnwsu.org/
Whitcomb JSHS 100/7-12
273 Pleasant St 05032 802-234-9966
Dr. Kevin Dirth, prin. Fax 234-5779
Other Schools – See Rochester

Bradford, Orange, Pop. 774
Orange East Supervisory Union 1,200/K-12
PO Box 396 05033 802-222-5216
Beth Cobb, supt. Fax 222-4451
www.oesu.org
Oxbow HS 400/7-12
36 Oxbow Dr 05033 802-222-5214
Larry Walsh, prin. Fax 222-5847

VT Technical Centers
Supt. — None
River Bend Career & Tech Center Vo/Tech
PO Box 618 05033 802-222-5212
Dean Stearns, admin. Fax 222-4621

Brandon, Rutland, Pop. 1,631
Rutland Northeast Supervisory Union 1,600/PK-12
49 Court Dr 05733 802-247-5757
John Castle, supt. Fax 247-5548
www.rnesu.org
Otter Valley Union JSHS 600/7-12
2997 Franklin St 05733 802-247-6833
James Avery, prin. Fax 247-4627

Brattleboro, Windham, Pop. 7,206
VT Technical Centers
Supt. — None
Windham Regional Career Center Vo/Tech
45 Career Cir 05301 802-257-7335
David Coughlin, prin. Fax 451-3933

Windham Southeast Supervisory Union 2,600/K-12
53 Green St 05301 802-254-3730
Ron Stahley, supt. Fax 254-3733
www.wssu.k12.vt.us
Brattleboro Area MS 300/7-8
109 Sunny Acres St 05301 802-451-3500
Ingrid Chrisco, prin. Fax 451-3502
Brattleboro Union HS 900/9-12
131 Fairground Rd 05301 802-451-3400
Steve Perrin, prin. Fax 451-3935

Austine School for the Deaf Post-Sec.
60 Austine Dr 05301 802-258-9522
SIT Post-Sec.
PO Box 676 05302 802-257-7751
The William Center Post-Sec.
209 Austine Dr 05301 802-258-9537
Union Institute & University Post-Sec.
3 University Way Ste 3 05301 800-871-8165

Bristol, Addison, Pop. 1,992
Addison Northeast Supervisory Union 1,600/PK-12
72 Munsill Ave Ste 601 05443 802-453-3657
David Adams, supt. Fax 453-2029
www.anesu.org
Mt. Abraham Union MSHS 28 800/7-12
220 Airport Dr 05443 802-453-2333
Andrew Kepes, prin. Fax 453-4359

Brookfield, Orange

Fieldbrook Christian S 50/4-10
108 E Hill Rd 05036 802-276-3323
Patricia Hood, admin.

Burlington, Chittenden, Pop. 41,355
Burlington SD 3,700/PK-12
150 Colchester Ave 05401 802-865-5332
Jeanne Collins, supt. Fax 864-8501
www.bsdvt.org/
Burlington HS 1,100/9-12
52 Institute Rd, 802-864-8411
Amy Mellencamp, prin. Fax 864-8408
Edmunds MS 400/6-8
275 Main St 05401 802-864-8486
Bonnie Johnson-Aten, prin. Fax 864-2218
Horizon S Alt
14 S Williams St 05401 802-864-8496
Lynn Kennedy, dir. Fax 864-2213
Hunt MS 400/6-8
1364 North Ave, 802-864-8469
Rich Amato, prin. Fax 864-8467

VT Technical Centers
Supt. — None
Burlington Technical Center Vo/Tech
52 Institute Rd, 802-864-8426
Mark Aliquo, dir. Fax 864-8521

Burlington College Post-Sec.
351 North Ave 05401 802-862-9616
Champlain College Post-Sec.
PO Box 670 05402 802-860-2700
Fletcher Allen Health Care Post-Sec.
111 Colchester Ave 05401 802-847-5133
Rock Point S 50/9-12
1 Rock Point Rd, 802-863-1104
Hillary Kramer, admin. Fax 863-6628
University of Vermont Post-Sec.
194 S Prospect St 05401 802-656-3131

Cabot, Washington, Pop. 226
Washington NE Supervisory Union
Supt. — See Plainfield
Cabot S 200/PK-12
PO Box 98 05647 802-563-2289
Karen Stewart, prin. Fax 563-2022

Canaan, Essex, Pop. 390
Essex North Supervisory Union 200/PK-12
PO Box 100 05903 802-266-3330
Christopher Masson, supt. Fax 266-7085
www.essexnorth.org
Canaan S 200/PK-12
99 School St 05903 802-266-8910
Deborah Lynch, prin. Fax 266-7068

Castleton, Rutland, Pop. 1,470
Addison-Rutland Supervisory Union
Supt. — See Fair Haven
Castleton Village S 100/6-8
PO Box 68 05735 802-468-2203
Linda Peltier, prin. Fax 468-5131

Castleton State College Post-Sec.
86 Seminary St 05735 802-468-5611

Charlotte, Chittenden

Lake Champlain Waldorf HS 50/9-12
735 Ferry Rd 05445 802-425-6195

Chelsea, Orange
Orange-Windsor Supervisory Union
Supt. — See South Royalton
Chelsea S 200/K-12
6 School St 05038 802-685-4551
Mark Blount, prin. Fax 685-3310

Chester, Windsor, Pop. 997
Two Rivers Supervisory Union
Supt. — See Ludlow
Green Mountain Union MSHS 400/7-12
716 VT Route 103 S 05143 802-875-2146
Tom Ferenc, prin. Fax 875-3183

Colchester, Chittenden
Colchester SD 2,200/K-12
PO Box 27 05446 802-264-5999
Larry Waters, supt. Fax 863-4774
www.csdvt.org
Colchester HS 700/9-12
PO Box 900 05446 802-264-5700
Amy Minor, prin. Fax 264-5757
Colchester MS 500/6-8
PO Box 30 05446 802-264-5800
Dawn Gruss, prin. Fax 264-5858

St. Michael's College Post-Sec.
1 Winooski Park 05439 802-654-2000

Concord, Essex, Pop. 268
Essex-Caledonia Supervisory Union 500/PK-12
PO Box 255 05824 802-695-3373
Brian Rayburn, supt. Fax 695-1334
ecsuvt.org
Concord S 200/PK-12
173 School St 05824 802-695-2550
Patty Lyons, prin. Fax 695-3311
Other Schools – See Gilman

Craftsbury Common, Orleans
Orleans Southwest Supervisory Union
Supt. — See Hardwick
Craftsbury Academy 100/7-12
PO Box 73 05827 802-586-2541
Merri Greenia, prin. Fax 586-7524

Sterling College — Post-Sec.
PO Box 72 05827 — 800-648-3591

Danville, Caledonia, Pop. 378
Caledonia Central Supervisory Union — 700/PK-12
PO Box 216 05828 — 802-684-3801
Martha Tucker, supt. — Fax 684-1190
www.ccsuonline.org
Danville S — 400/PK-12
148 Peacham Rd 05828 — 802-684-3651
Noah Noyes, prin. — Fax 684-1192

Derby, Orleans, Pop. 595
North Country Supervisory Union
Supt. — See Newport
North Country Union JHS — 300/7-8
57 Jr High Dr 05829 — 802-766-2276
Nicole Corbett, prin. — Fax 766-2287

Dorset, Bennington, Pop. 249

Long Trail S — 200/6-12
1045 Kirby Hollow Rd 05251 — 802-867-5717
Fax 867-4525

Duxbury, See Waterbury
Washington West Supervisory Union
Supt. — See Waitsfield
Crossett Brook MS — 300/5-8
5672 VT Route 100 05676 — 802-244-6100
Tom Drake, prin. — Fax 244-6899

East Burke, Caledonia, Pop. 132

Burke Mountain Academy — 50/8-12
PO Box 78 05832 — 802-626-5607
Kirk Dwyer, hdmstr. — Fax 626-3784

Enosburg Falls, Franklin, Pop. 1,309
Franklin Northeast Supervisory Union
Supt. — See Richford
Enosburg Falls HS — 300/9-12
PO Box 417 05450 — 802-933-7777
Erik Remmers, prin. — Fax 933-5375
Enosburg Falls MS — 100/6-8
PO Box 417 05450 — 802-933-7777
Michael McRaith, prin. — Fax 933-5013

VT Technical Centers
Supt. — None
Cold Hollow Career Center — Vo/Tech
PO Box 530 05450 — 802-933-4003
Nathan Demar, dir. — Fax 933-2431

Essex Junction, Chittenden, Pop. 9,092
Chittenden Central Supervisory Union — 2,600/PK-12
51 Park St 05452 — 802-879-5579
Michael Deweese, supt. — Fax 878-1370
www.ccsuvt.org
Essex HS — 1,300/9-12
2 Educational Dr 05452 — 802-879-7121
Robert Reardon, prin. — Fax 879-5503
Lawton MS — 300/6-8
104 Maple St 05452 — 802-878-1388
Laurie Singer, prin. — Fax 879-8175

Essex Town SD — 1,200/PK-8
58 Founders Rd 05452 — 802-878-8168
Mark Andrews, supt. — Fax 878-5190
www.etsdvt.org
Essex MS — 400/6-8
60 Founders Rd 05452 — 802-879-7173
Kevin Briggs, prin. — Fax 879-1363

VT Technical Centers
Supt. — None
Essex Technical Center — Vo/Tech
3 Educational Dr 05452 — 802-879-5558
Robert Travers, dir. — Fax 879-5593

Fairfax, Franklin
Franklin West Supervisory Union — 1,300/PK-12
4497 Highbridge Rd 05454 — 802-370-3113
Ned Kirsch, supt. — Fax 370-3115
www.fwsu.org
Bellows Free Academy — 600/PK-12
75 Hunt St 05454 — 802-849-6711
Michael Clark, prin. — Fax 849-2611

Fair Haven, Rutland, Pop. 2,236
Addison-Rutland Supervisory Union — 1,500/PK-12
49 Main St 05743 — 802-265-4905
Ronald Ryan, supt. — Fax 265-2158
www.arsu.org
Fair Haven Union HS — 500/9-12
33 Mechanic St 05743 — 802-265-4966
Brett Blanchard, prin. — Fax 265-3602
Other Schools – See Castleton

Gilman, Essex
Essex-Caledonia Supervisory Union
Supt. — See Concord
Gilman MS — 100/5-8
PO Box 97 05904 — 802-892-5969
Nancy Croteau, prin. — Fax 892-9045

Hardwick, Caledonia, Pop. 1,309
Orleans Southwest Supervisory Union — 1,000/K-12
PO Box 338 05843 — 802-472-6531
JoAn Canning, supt. — Fax 472-6250
www.ossu.org/
Hazen Union JSHS — 400/7-12
PO Box 368 05843 — 802-472-6511
Cynthia Donlon, prin. — Fax 472-3327
Other Schools – See Craftsbury Common

Hinesburg, Chittenden, Pop. 642
Chittendon South Supervisory Union
Supt. — See Shelburne
Champlain Valley Union HS 15 — 1,300/9-12
369 CVU Rd 05461 — 802-482-7100
Sean McMannon, prin. — Fax 482-7108

Hyde Park, Lamoille, Pop. 449
Lamoille North Supervisory Union — 1,900/PK-12
95 Cricket Hill Rd 05655 — 802-888-3142
Joseph Ciccolo, supt. — Fax 888-7908
www.lnsu.org
Lamoille Union HS — 600/9-12
736 VT 15 W 05655 — 802-888-4261
Brian Schaffer, prin. — Fax 888-2997
Lamoille Union MS — 300/7-8
736 VT 15 W 05655 — 802-851-1300
Chris Hindes, prin. — Fax 851-1397

VT Technical Centers
Supt. — None
Green Mountain Technology & Career Ctr — Vo/Tech
PO Box 600 05655 — 802-888-4447
Joe Teagarden, prin. — Fax 888-7838

Jericho, Chittenden, Pop. 1,303
Chittenden East Supervisory Union
Supt. — See Richmond
Browns River MS — 400/5-8
20 River Rd 05465 — 802-899-3711
Kevin Hamilton, prin. — Fax 899-4281
Mt. Mansfield Union HS — 1,000/9-12
211 Browns Trace Rd 05465 — 802-899-4690
Michael Weston, prin. — Fax 899-2904

Johnson, Lamoille, Pop. 1,395

Johnson State College — Post-Sec.
337 College Hl 05656 — 802-635-2356

Ludlow, Windsor, Pop. 795
Two Rivers Supervisory Union — 1,100/PK-12
609 VT Route 103 S 05149 — 802-875-3365
Bruce Williams, supt. — Fax 875-6439
www.wswsu.org
Black River MSHS — 200/7-12
43 Main St 05149 — 802-228-4721
James Frail, prin. — Fax 228-7233
Other Schools – See Chester

Lyndon Center, Caledonia
VT Technical Centers
Supt. — None
Lyndon Institute Technical Center — Vo/Tech
PO Box 127 05850 — 802-626-3357
Twila Perry, dir. — Fax 626-9345

Lyndonville, Caledonia, Pop. 1,188

Lyndon State College — Post-Sec.
PO Box 919 05851 — 802-626-6200

Manchester, Bennington, Pop. 746

Burr and Burton Academy — 700/9-12
PO Box 498 05254 — 802-362-1775
Mark Tashjian, hdmstr — Fax 362 0574

Marlboro, Windham

Marlboro College — Post-Sec.
PO Box A 05344 — 802-257-4333

Middlebury, Addison, Pop. 6,363
Addison Central Supervisory Union — 1,800/PK-12
49 Charles Ave 05753 — 802-382-1274
Dr. Gail Conley, supt. — Fax 388-0024
www.addisoncentralsu.org
Middlebury Union HS — 600/9-12
73 Charles Ave 05753 — 802-382-1500
William Lawson, prin. — Fax 382-1101
Middlebury Union MS — 300/7-8
48 Deerfield Ln 05753 — 802-382-1600
Patrick Reen, prin. — Fax 382-1215

VT Technical Centers
Supt. — None
Hannaford Career Center — Vo/Tech
51 Charles Ave 05753 — 802-382-1012
D. Lynn Coale, prin. — Fax 388-2591

Middlebury College 05753 — Post-Sec.
802-443-5000

Milton, Chittenden, Pop. 1,843
Milton Town SD — 1,600/PK-12
42 Herrick Ave 05468 — 802-893-3210
Dr. John Barone, supt. — Fax 893-3213
www.mtsd-vt.org
Milton HS — 500/9-12
17 Rebecca Lander Dr 05468 — 802-893-3230
Anne Blake, prin. — Fax 893-3247
Milton JHS — 300/6-8
17 Rebecca Lander Dr 05468 — 802-893-3230
Barbara Burrington, prin. — Fax 893-3247

Montpelier, Washington, Pop. 7,675
Montpelier SD — 900/K-12
5 High School Dr Unit 1 05602 — 802-223-9796
Dr. Brian Ricca, supt. — Fax 223-9795
www.mpsvt.org/
Main Street MS — 200/6-8
170 Main St 05602 — 802-223-3404
Pamela Arnold, prin. — Fax 223-9225
Montpelier HS — 300/9-12
5 High School Dr 05602 — 802-225-8000
Adam Bunting, prin. — Fax 223-9227

Washington Central Supervisory Union — 1,700/PK-12
1130 Gallison Hill Rd 05602 — 802-229-0553
William Kimball, supt. — Fax 229-2761
www.wcsuonline.org
Union 32 JSHS — 800/7-12
930 Gallison Hill Rd 05602 — 802-229-0321
Keith Gerritt, prin. — Fax 223-7411

Community College of Vermont — Post-Sec.
PO Box 489 05601 — 802-828-2800

New England Culinary Institute — Post-Sec.
56 College St 05602 — 877-223-6324
Union Institute & University — Post-Sec.
62 Ridge St Ste 2 05602 — 802-828-8500
Vermont College of Fine Arts — Post-Sec.
36 College St 05602 — 802-828-8600

Morrisville, Lamoille, Pop. 1,933
Lamoille South Supervisory Union — 1,600/K-12
46 Copley Ave 05661 — 802-888-4541
Tracy Wrend, supt. — Fax 888-6710
www.lamoillesouthsu.org/
Peoples Academy — 300/9-12
202 Copley Ave 05661 — 802-888-4600
Phil Grant, prin. — Fax 888-6726
Peoples Academy MS — 200/5-8
202 Copley Ave 05661 — 802-888-1402
Wendy Baker, prin. — Fax 888-6488
Other Schools – See Stowe

Newport, Orleans, Pop. 4,495
North Country Supervisory Union — 2,600/K-12
338 Highland Ave Ste 4 05855 — 802-334-5847
Robert Kern, supt. — Fax 334-6528
www.ncsuvt.org
North Country Union HS — 900/9-12
209 Veterans Ave 05855 — 802-334-7921
William Rivard, prin. — Fax 334-1618
Other Schools – See Derby

VT Technical Centers
Supt. — None
North Country Career Center — Vo/Tech
PO Box 725 05855 — 802-334-5469
Eileen Illuzzi, prin. — Fax 334-3492

United Christian Academy — 100/K-12
65 School St 05855 — 802-334-3112
Dr. Richard O'Hara, head sch — Fax 334-2305

North Clarendon, Rutland
Rutland South Supervisory Union — 1,000/PK-12
PO Box 87 05759 — 802-775-3264
Dana Cole-Levesque, supt. — Fax 775-8063
www.rssu.org/
Mill River Union JSHS — 600/7-12
PO Box 6 05759 — 802-775-1925
Andy Pomeroy, prin. — Fax 775-6447

Northfield, Washington, Pop. 2,049
Washington South Supervisory Union — 700/PK-12
37 Cross St Ste 1 05663 — 802-485-7755
Laurie Gossens, supt. — Fax 485-3348
www.wssu.org
Northfield MSHS — 300/6-12
37 Cross St Ste 1 05663 — 802-485-4500
Ryan Parkman, prin. — Fax 485-4440

Norwich University — Post-Sec.
158 Harmon Dr 05663 — 802-485-2000

Orleans, Orleans, Pop. 796
Orleans Central Supervisory Union
Supt. — See Barton
Lake Region Union HS 24 — 400/9-12
317 Lake Region Rd 05860 — 802-754-6521
Andre Messier, prin. — Fax 754-2780

Plainfield, Washington, Pop. 393
Washington NE Supervisory Union — 700/PK-12
PO Box 470 05667 — 802-454-9924
Nancy Thomas, supt. — Fax 454-9934
Twinfield Union S — 400/PK-12
106 Nasmith Brook Rd 05667 — 802-426-3213
Mark Mooney, prin. — Fax 426-4085
Other Schools – See Cabot

Goddard College — Post-Sec.
123 Pitkin Rd 05667 — 802-454-8311

Poultney, Rutland, Pop. 1,589
Rutland Southwest Supervisory Union — 600/PK-12
168 York St 05764 — 802-287-5286
Joan Paustian Ed.D., supt. — Fax 287-2284
www.rswsu.org
Poultney HS — 200/7-12
154 E Main St 05764 — 802-287-5861
Fax 287-2304

Green Mountain College — Post-Sec.
1 Brennan Cir 05764 — 802-287-8000

Proctor, Rutland
Rutland Central Supervisory Union
Supt. — See Rutland
Proctor JSHS — 200/7-12
4 Park St 05765 — 802-459-3353
Adam Rosenberg, prin. — Fax 459-6323

Putney, Windham, Pop. 508

Landmark College — Post-Sec.
1 River Rd S 05346 — 802-387-4767
Putney S — 200/9-12
418 Houghton Brook Rd 05346 — 802-387-5566
Br. Emily Jones, dir. — Fax 387-6278

Randolph, Orange, Pop. 1,947
Orange Southwest Supervisory Union — 900/K-12
24 Central St 05060 — 802-728-5052
Brent Kay, supt. — Fax 728-4844
www.orangesouthwest.org
Randolph Union JSHS — 500/7-12
15 Forest St 05060 — 802-728-3397
David Barnett, prin. — Fax 728-6703

VT Technical Centers
Supt. — None
Randolph Technical Center — Vo/Tech
17 Forest St 05060 — 802-728-9595
Bill Sugarman, prin. — Fax 728-9596

Randolph Center, Orange

Vermont Technical College — Post-Sec.
PO Box 500 05061 — 802-728-1000

Richford, Franklin, Pop. 1,314
Franklin Northeast Supervisory Union — 1,700/PK-12
PO Box 130 05476 — 802-848-7661
Jay Nichols, supt. — Fax 848-3531
fnesu.net
Richford JSHS — 200/7-12
1 Corliss Hts 05476 — 802-848-7416
David Perrigo, prin. — Fax 848-3210
Other Schools – See Enosburg Falls

Richmond, Chittenden, Pop. 707
Chittenden East Supervisory Union — 2,800/PK-12
PO Box 282 05477 — 802-434-2128
John Alberghini, supt. — Fax 434-2196
www.cesu.k12.vt.us
Camels Hump MS — 400/5-8
173 School St 05477 — 802-434-2188
Mark Carbone, prin. — Fax 434-2192
Other Schools – See Jericho

Rochester, Windsor, Pop. 297
Windsor Northwest Supervisory Union
Supt. — See Bethel
Rochester S — 200/K-12
222 S Main St 05767 — 802-767-3161
Catherine Knight, prin. — Fax 767-1130

Rutland, Rutland, Pop. 16,220
Rutland Central Supervisory Union — 1,000/PK-12
16 Evelyn St 05701 — 802-775-4342
Dr. Debra Taylor, supt. — Fax 775-7319
www.rcsu.org
Other Schools – See Proctor, West Rutland

Rutland City SD — 2,400/K-12
6 Church St 05701 — 802-773-1900
Mary Moran, supt. — Fax 773-1927
rutlandcitypublicschools.org/
Rutland HS — 1,000/9-12
22 Stratton Rd 05701 — 802-773-1955
William Olsen, prin. — Fax 770-1020
Rutland MS — 300/7-8
65 Library Ave 05701 — 802-773-1960
Wilfred Cunningham, prin. — Fax 773-1914

VT Technical Centers
Supt. — None
Stafford Technical Center — Vo/Tech
8 Stratton Rd 05701 — 802-770-1033
Lyle Jepson, dir. — Fax 770-1066

College of Saint Joseph — Post-Sec.
71 Clement Rd 05701 — 802-773-5900
Mt. St. Joseph Academy — 100/9-12
127 Convent Ave 05701 — 802-775-0151
Sandra Wilkes, prin. — Fax 775-0424
Rutland Area Christian S — 100/PK-12
112 Lincoln Ave 05701 — 802-775-0709
Dawn Doherty, prin. — Fax 786-0111
Rutland Regional Medical Center — Post-Sec.
160 Allen St 05701 — 802-775-7111

Saint Albans, Franklin, Pop. 6,736
Franklin Central Supervisory Union — 2,700/PK-12
28 Catherine St 05478 — 802-524-2600
Julie Regimbal, supt. — Fax 524-1540
www.fcsuvt.org
Bellows Free Academy — 1,100/9-12
71 S Main St 05478 — 802-527-6555
Chris Mosca, prin. — Fax 527-6402

VT Technical Centers
Supt. — None
Northwest Technical Center — Vo/Tech
71 S Main St 05478 — 802-527-6517
Leann Wright, dir. — Fax 527-6469

Direct Learning International — Post-Sec.
PO Box 846 05478 — 800-489-4114

Saint Johnsbury, Caledonia, Pop. 6,424
VT Technical Centers
Supt. — None
St. Johnsbury Academy — Vo/Tech
PO Box 906 05819 — 802-748-8171
Howard Crawford, dir. — Fax 748-2358

Caledonia Christian S — 50/K-10
1274 Main St 05819 — 802-748-9528
David Knott, prin. — Fax 748-9528

Saxtons River, Windham, Pop. 550

Vermont Academy — 200/9-12
PO Box 500 05154 — 802-869-6200
Sean Brennan, head sch — Fax 869-6242

Sharon, Windsor

Sharon Academy — 200/6-12
PO Box 207 05065 — 802-763-2500

Shelburne, Chittenden, Pop. 581
Chittendon South Supervisory Union — 4,100/PK-12
5420 Shelburne Rd Ste 300 05482 — 802-383-1234
Elaine Pinckney, admin. — Fax 383-1242
www.cssu.org/
Other Schools – See Hinesburg, Williston

South Burlington, Chittenden, Pop. 17,544
South Burlington SD — 2,400/K-12
550 Dorset St 05403 — 802-652-7250
David Young, supt. — Fax 652-7257
www.sbschools.net
South Burlington HS — 900/9-12
550 Dorset St 05403 — 802-652-7001
Patrick Burke, prin. — Fax 652-7006
Tuttle MS — 500/6-8
500 Dorset St 05403 — 802-652-7100
Karsten Schlenter, prin. — Fax 652-7152

Advanced Welding Institute — Post-Sec.
2 Green Tree Dr Ste 3 05403 — 802-660-0600
O'Briens Training Center — Post-Sec.
1233 Shelburne Rd Ste 200 05403 — 802-658-9591
Rice Memorial HS — 400/9-12
99 Proctor Ave 05403 — 802-862-6521
Msgr. Bernard Bourgeois, prin. — Fax 864-9931

South Duxbury, Washington
Washington West Supervisory Union
Supt. — See Waitsfield
Harwood Union HS — 600/7-12
458 VT Route 100 05660 — 802-244-5186
Lisa Atwood, prin. — Fax 882-1199

South Royalton, Windsor, Pop. 674
Orange-Windsor Supervisory Union — 900/PK-12
3590 VT Route 14 05068 — 802-763-8840
David Bickford Ed.D., supt. — Fax 763-3235
www.owsu.org/
South Royalton S — 400/PK-12
223 S Windsor St 05068 — 802-763-8844
Gail Trotin, prin. — Fax 763-3233
Other Schools – See Chelsea

Vermont Law School — Post-Sec.
PO Box 96 05068 — 802-831-1000

Springfield, Windsor, Pop. 3,895
Springfield SD — 1,400/K-12
60 Park St 05156 — 802-885-5141
Dr. Frank S. Perotti, supt. — Fax 885-8169
www.ssdvt.org
Gateway S — Alt
38 Pleasant St 05156 — 802-885-3477
Nancy Wiese, coord. — Fax 885-3473
Riverside MS — 300/6-8
13 Fairground Rd 05156 — 802-885-8490
Becky Read, prin. — Fax 885-8442
Springfield HS — 500/9-12
303 South St 05156 — 802-885-7900
Bob Thibault, prin. — Fax 885-4459

VT Technical Centers
Supt. — None
River Valley Technical Center — Vo/Tech
307 South St 05156 — 802-885-8300
Judith Pallinen, dir. — Fax 885-8454

Stowe, Lamoille, Pop. 492
Lamoille South Supervisory Union
Supt. — See Morrisville
Stowe HS — 200/9-12
413 Barrows Rd 05672 — 802-253-7229
Jeff Maher, prin. — Fax 253-6911
Stowe MS — 200/6-8
413 Barrows Rd 05672 — 802-253-6913
Melanie Carpenter, prin. — Fax 253-5314

Stratton Mountain, Windham, Pop. 50

Stratton Mountain S — 100/7-12
7 World Cup Cir 05155 — 802-297-1886
Christopher Kaltsas, hdmstr. — Fax 297-0020

Swanton, Franklin, Pop. 2,303
Franklin Northwest Supervisory Union — 2,200/PK-12
100 Robin Hood Dr 05488 — 802-868-4967
Dr. John McCarthy, supt. — Fax 868-4265
www.fnwsu.org
Missisquoi Valley Union MSHS — 900/7-12
100 Thunderbird Dr 05488 — 802-868-7311
Robert Pequignot, prin. — Fax 868-3129

Thetford, Orange

Thetford Academy — 400/7-12
PO Box 190 05074 — 802-785-4805
Bill Bugg, head sch — Fax 785-4805

Townshend, Windham
Windham Central Supervisory Union — 900/PK-12
1219 VT Route 30 05353 — 802-365-9510
Dr. Steven John, supt. — Fax 365-7934
www.windhamcentral.org
Leland & Gray Union HS — 400/7-12
PO Box 128 05353 — 802-365-7355
Dorinne Dorfman, prin. — Fax 365-4126

Vergennes, Addison, Pop. 2,536
Addison Northwest Supervisory Union — 1,100/K-12
48 Green St Ste 1 05491 — 802-877-3332
Thomas O'Brien, supt. — Fax 877-3628
www.anwsu.org
Vergennes Union HS — 600/7-12
50 Monkton Rd 05491 — 802-877-2938
Edwin Webbley, prin. — Fax 877-2558

Waitsfield, Washington, Pop. 162
Washington West Supervisory Union — 1,900/PK-12
340 Mad River Park Ste 7 05673 — 802-496-2272
Brigid Scheffert, supt. — Fax 496-6515
www.wwsu.org/
Other Schools – See Duxbury, South Duxbury

Green Mountain Valley S — 100/8-12
271 Moulton Rd 05673 — 802-496-2150
David Gavett, prin. — Fax 496-6819

Websterville, Washington, Pop. 545

Websterville Baptist Christian S — 100/PK-12
PO Box 1 05678 — 802-479-0141

Wells River, Orange, Pop. 387
Blue Mountain SD — 400/PK-12
2420 Route 302 05081 — 802-757-2766
Richard Pike, supt. — Fax 757-2790
www.bmuschool.org
Blue Mountain Union S 21 — 400/PK-12
2420 Route 302 05081 — 802-757-2711
Emilie Knisley, prin. — Fax 757-3894

West Rutland, Rutland, Pop. 2,007
Rutland Central Supervisory Union
Supt. — See Rutland
West Rutland S — 400/PK-12
713 Main St 05777 — 802-438-2288
Joseph Fleming, prin. — Fax 438-5708

White River Junction, Windsor, Pop. 2,238
Hartford SD — 1,600/PK-12
73 Highland Ave 05001 — 802-295-8600
Tom DeBalsi, supt. — Fax 295-8602
www.hartfordschools.net/
Hartford HS — 600/9-12
37 Highland Ave 05001 — 802-295-8610
Joseph Collea, prin. — Fax 295-8611
Hartford Memorial MS — 300/6-8
245 Highland Ave 05001 — 802-295-8640
John Grant, prin. — Fax 295-8641

VT Technical Centers
Supt. — None
Hartford Area Career & Technology Center — Vo/Tech
1 Gifford Rd 05001 — 802-295-8630
Doug Heavisides, prin. — Fax 295-8631

Mid Vermont Christian S — 100/PK-12
399 W Gilson Ave 05001 — 802-295-6800
Robert Bracy M.Ed., hdmstr. — Fax 295-3748

Whitingham, Windham
Windham Southwest Supervisory Union
Supt. — See Wilmington
Twin Valley MSHS — 200/6-12
4299 VT Route 100 05361 — 802-464-5255
Robert Morse, prin. — Fax 464-5903

Williamstown, Orange
Orange North Supervisory Union — 700/PK-12
111B Brush Hill Rd 05679 — 802-433-5818
Susette Bollard, supt. — Fax 433-5825
www.onsu.org/
Williamstown MSHS — 300/6-12
120 Hebert Rd 05679 — 802-433-5350
Scott Lang, prin. — Fax 433-1037

Williston, Chittenden
Chittendon South Supervisory Union
Supt. — See Shelburne
Williston Central S — 700/3-8
195 Central School Dr 05495 — 802-878-2762
Jackie Parks, prin. — Fax 879-5830

Northern Vermont Regional Day Program — Post-Sec.
195 Central School Dr 05495 — 802-879-4787
Trinity Baptist S — 100/K-12
280 Trinity Dr 05495 — 802-878-8118
Randy Krystowiak, admin. — Fax 879-5272
Vermont College of Cosmetology — Post-Sec.
400 Cornerstone Dr Ste 220 05495 — 802-863-4666

Wilmington, Windham, Pop. 457
Windham Southwest Supervisory Union — 500/PK-12
211 Route 9 W 05363 — 802-464-1300
Nancy Talbott, supt. — Fax 464-1303
www.windhamsw.k12.vt.us/
Other Schools – See Whitingham

Windsor, Windsor, Pop. 2,011
Windsor Southeast Supervisory Union — 1,200/K-12
105 Main St Ste 200 05089 — 802-674-2144
David Baker, supt. — Fax 674-6357
wsesu.net
Windsor HS — 300/7-12
19 Ascutney St 05089 — 802-674-6344
Michael Kell, prin. — Fax 674-9802

Winooski, Chittenden, Pop. 7,032
Winooski SD — 800/PK-12
60 Normand St 05404 — 802-655-0485
Sean McMannon, supt. — Fax 655-7602
www.wsdschools.org
Winooski HS — 300/9-12
80 Normand St 05404 — 802-655-3530
Leon Wheeler, prin. — Fax 655-6538
Winooski MS — 100/6-8
80 Normand St 05404 — 802-655-3530
Leon Wheeler, prin. — Fax 655-6538

Woodstock, Windsor, Pop. 897
Windsor Central Supervisory Union — 1,100/PK-12
70 Amsden Way 05091 — 802-457-1213
Alice Worth, supt. — Fax 457-2989
www.wcsu.net/
Woodstock Union HS — 400/9-12
100 Amsden Way 05091 — 802-457-1317
Greg Schillinger, prin. — Fax 457-1850
Woodstock Union MS — 200/7-8
100 Amsden Way 05091 — 802-457-1330
Dana Peterson, prin. — Fax 457-5048

VIRGINIA

VIRGINIA DEPARTMENT OF EDUCATION
PO Box 2120, Richmond 23218-2120
Telephone 804-225-2020
Fax 804-371-2099
Website http://www.pen.k12.va.us

Superintendent of Public Instruction Dr. Patricia Wright

VIRGINIA BOARD OF EDUCATION
PO Box 2120, Richmond 23218-2120

President David Foster

PUBLIC, PRIVATE AND CATHOLIC SECONDARY SCHOOLS

Abingdon, Washington, Pop. 8,107
Regional Academic Governors SD
Supt. — See Richmond
Holton Governor's S 10-12
PO Box 1987 24212 276-619-4326
Danny Dixon, dir. Fax 619-4328

Washington County SD 7,400/PK-12
812 Thompson Dr 24210 276-739-3003
Dr. Brian Ratliff, supt. Fax 623-4137
www.wcs.k12.va.us
Abingdon HS 900/9-12
705 Thompson Dr 24210 276-739-3200
Fax 628-1897
Neff Center for Science & Tech Vo/Tech
255 Stanley St 24210 276-739-3100
Brian Johnson, prin. Fax 623-4126
Stanley MS 700/6-8
297 Stanley St 24210 276-739-3300
Scott Allen, prin. Fax 676-1945
Washington County Technical S Vo/Tech
850 Thompson Dr 24210 276-739-3140
Brian Johnson, prin. Fax 623-4197
Other Schools – See Bristol, Damascus, Glade Spring

Cornerstone Christian Academy 100/K-11
PO Box 2228 24212 276-623-7164
Dr. Clay Brinson, hdmstr.
Virginia Highlands Community College Post-Sec.
PO Box 828 24212 276-739-2400
Washington County Adult Skill Center Post-Sec.
848 Thompson Dr 24210 276-676-1948

Accomac, Accomack, Pop. 513
Accomack County SD 5,100/PK-12
PO Box 330 23301 757-787-5754
Dr. W. Bruce Benson, supt. Fax 787-2951
www.sbo.accomack.k12.va.us
Other Schools – See Chincoteague, Oak Hall, Onley, Tangier

Afton, Nelson

Afton Christian S 50/PK-12
9357 Critzers Shop Rd 22920 540-456-6853
Lori Knight, head sch Fax 456-6236

Alberta, Brunswick, Pop. 294

Southside Virginia Community College Post-Sec.
109 Campus Dr 23821 434-949-1000

Aldie, Loudoun
Loudoun County SD
Supt. — See Ashburn
Champe HS 9-12
41535 Sacred Mountain St 20105 703-722-2680
John Gabriel, prin.
Mercer MS 1,300/6-8
42149 Greenstone Dr 20105 703-957-4340
John Duellman, prin. Fax 444-8068

Alexandria, Alexandria, Pop. 135,858
Alexandria CSD 12,000/PK-12
2000 N Beauregard St 22311 703-824-6600
Dr. Morton Sherman, supt. Fax 824-6699
www.acps.k12.va.us
Hammond MS 1 400/6-8
4646 Seminary Rd 22304 703-461-4100
Blanche Maness, prin. Fax 461-4111
Hammond MS 2 400/6-8
4646 Seminary Rd 22304 703-461-4100
Jason Sutton, prin. Fax 461-4111
Hammond MS 3 400/6-8
4646 Seminary Rd 22304 703-461-4100
Andrea Sparks-Brown, prin. Fax 461-4111
Washington MS 1 500/6-8
1005 Mount Vernon Ave 22301 703-706-4500
Gerald Mann, prin. Fax 706-4507
Washington MS 2 500/6-8
1005 Mount Vernon Ave 22301 703-706-4500
Linda Whitfield, prin. Fax 706-4507
Williams HS 2,300/10-12
3330 King St 22302 703-824-6800
Suzanne Maxey, prin. Fax 824-6826
Williams HS - Howard Campus 9th Grade 800/9-9
3801 W Braddock Rd 22302 703-824-6750
Suzanne Maxey, prin. Fax 824-6781

Fairfax County SD
Supt. — See Falls Church
Bryant Alternative HS 300/Alt
2709 Popkins Ln 22306 703-660-2100
William Hunt, admin. Fax 660-2097
Edison HS 1,700/9-12
5801 Franconia Rd 22310 703-924-8000
Pamela Brumfield, prin. Fax 924-8097
Glasgow MS 1,200/6-8
4101 Fairfax Pkwy 22312 703-813-8700
Deirdre Lavery, prin. Fax 813-8797
Hayfield JSHS 3,000/7-12
7630 Telegraph Rd 22315 703-924-7400
David Tremaine, prin. Fax 924-7497
Holmes MS 700/6-8
6525 Montrose St 22312 703-658-5900
Roberto Pamas, prin. Fax 658-5997
Jefferson HS 9-12
6560 Braddock Rd 22312 703-750-8300
Dr. Evan Glazer, prin. Fax 750-5010
Landmark Career Academy Vo/Tech
5801 Duke St Ste D216 22304 703-658-6451
Larry Jones, prin. Fax 658-6497
Montrose Alternative Learning Center Alt
6525 Montrose St 22312 703-658-5800
Zora Marschall, prin.
Mt. Vernon HS 1,800/9-12
8515 Old Mount Vernon Rd 22309 703-619-3100
Nardos King, prin. Fax 619-3197
Sandburg MS 1,200/7-8
8428 Fort Hunt Rd 22308 703-799-6100
Terrence Yarborough, prin. Fax 799-6197
Twain MS 800/7-8
4700 Franconia Rd 22310 703-313-3700
Aimee Holleb, prin. Fax 313-3797
West Potomac HS 2,300/9-12
6500 Quander Rd 22307 703-718-2500
Cliff Hardison, prin. Fax 718-2597
Whitman MS 1,000/7-8
2500 Parkers Ln 22306 703-660-2400
Jean Bell, prin. Fax 660-2497

Regional Academic Governors SD
Supt. — See Richmond
Jefferson Science & Tech HS 1,800/9-12
6560 Braddock Rd 22312 703-750-8306
Dr. Evan Glazer, prin. Fax 750-5036

Bishop Ireton HS 800/9-12
201 Cambridge Rd 22314 703-751-7606
Timothy Hamer, prin. Fax 212-8173
Centura College Post-Sec.
6295 Edsall Rd Ste 250 22312 703-778-4444
Commonwealth Academy 100/3-12
1321 Leslie Ave 22301 703-548-6912
Dr. Susan Johnson, hdmstr. Fax 548-6914
Episcopal HS 400/9-12
1200 N Quaker Ln 22302 703-933-3000
F. Robertson Hershey, hdmstr. Fax 933-3017
Global Health College Post-Sec.
25 S Quaker Ln 22314 703-212-7410
Islamic Saudi Academy 700/PK-12
8333 Richmond Hwy 22309 703-780-0606
Northern Virginia Community College Post-Sec.
3001 N Beauregard St 22311 703-323-3000
Protestant Episcopal Theologcl. Seminary Post-Sec.
3737 Seminary Rd 22304 703-370-6600
St. Stephen's and St. Agnes MS 300/6-8
4401 W Braddock Rd 22304 703-212-2741
Joan Holden, head sch Fax 751-7142
St. Stephen's & St. Agnes S 500/9-12
1000 Saint Stephens Rd 22304 703-751-2700
Joan Holden, head sch Fax 751-7142

Altavista, Campbell, Pop. 3,366
Campbell County SD
Supt. — See Rustburg
Altavista JSHS 800/6-12
904 Bedford Ave 24517 434-369-4768
Ty Gafford, prin. Fax 369-5191

Amelia Court House, Amelia, Pop. 1,087
Amelia County SD 1,800/PK-12
8701 Otterburn Rd Ste 101 23002 804-561-2621
Dr. B.J. Brewer, supt. Fax 561-3057
www.amelia.k12.va.us
Amelia County HS 500/9-12
8500 Otterburn Rd 23002 804-561-2101
Tommy Moon, prin. Fax 561-4567
Amelia County MS 600/5-8
8740 Otterburn Rd 23002 804-561-4422
Shirley Booker, prin. Fax 561-6525

Amelia Academy 200/PK-12
PO Box 106 23002 804-561-2270
Diane Grondin, head sch Fax 561-4934

Amherst, Amherst, Pop. 2,173
Amherst County SD 4,600/PK-12
PO Box 1257 24521 434-946-9387
Brian Ratliff Ed.D., supt. Fax 946-9346
www.amherst.k12.va.us
Amherst County HS 1,500/9-12
139 Lancer Ln 24521 434-946-2898
Haywood Hand, prin. Fax 946-2263
Amherst MS 400/6-8
165 Gordons Fairgrounds Rd 24521 434-946-0691
Christie Cundiff, prin. Fax 946-0258
Other Schools – See Madison Heights

Annandale, Fairfax, Pop. 39,850
Fairfax County SD
Supt. — See Falls Church
Annandale HS 2,700/9-12
4700 Medford Dr 22003 703-642-4100
Vincent Randazzo, prin. Fax 642-4197
Poe MS 1,200/6-8
7000 Cindy Ln 22003 703-813-3800
Sonya Swansbrough, prin. Fax 813-3897

iGlobal University Post-Sec.
7700 Little River Tpke #600 22003 703-941-2020
Northern Virginia Community College Post-Sec.
8333 Little River Tpke 22003 703-323-3000
Springfield Beauty Academy Post-Sec.
4223 Annandale Rd 22003 703-256-5662
University of Northern Virginia Post-Sec.
7601 Little River Tpke 22003 703-941-0949
Washington Baptist University Post-Sec.
4300 Evergreen Ln 22003 703-333-5904
Westwood College - Annandale Post-Sec.
7619 Little River Tpke #500 22003 703-642-3770

Appomattox, Appomattox, Pop. 1,694
Appomattox County SD 2,300/PK-12
PO Box 548 24522 434-352-8251
Dorinda Grasty Ed.D., supt. Fax 352-0883
www.appomattox.schoolfusion.us
Appomattox HS 700/9-12
198 Evergreen Ave 24522 434-352-7146
Martha Eagle, prin. Fax 352-0822
Appomattox MS 500/6-8
2020 Church St 24522 434-352-8257
Todd Reichert, prin. Fax 352-5621

Cornerstone Christian Academy 100/PK-12
PO Box 897 24522 434-352-2345
Marcie Jones, hdmstr. Fax 352-2345

Arlington, Arlington, Pop. 201,587
Arlington County SD 22,100/PK-12
1426 N Quincy St 22207 703-228-6000
Dr. Patrick Murphy, supt. Fax 228-6188
www.apsva.us
Arlington Career Center Vo/Tech
816 S Walter Reed Dr 22204 703-228-5800
Nancy Opsut, prin. Fax 228-5815
Arlington Mill HS Alt
4600 Fairfax Dr 22203 703-228-5350
Dr. Barbara Thompson, prin. Fax 522-2437
Gunston MS 800/6-8
2700 S Lang St 22206 703-228-6900
Lori Wiggins, prin. Fax 519-9183
Jefferson MS 600/6-8
125 S Old Glebe Rd 22204 703-228-5900
Keisha Boggan, prin. Fax 979-3744

Kenmore MS 700/6-8
200 S Carlin Springs Rd 22204 703-228-6800
Dr. John Word, prin. Fax 998-3069
Langston HS Continuation Alt
2121 N Culpeper St 22207 703-228-5295
Cleveland James, prin. Fax 807-0614
Swanson MS 1,000/6-8
5800 Washington Blvd 22205 703-228-5500
Bridget Loft, prin. Fax 536-2775
Wakefield HS 1,700/9-12
4901 S Chesterfield Rd 22206 703-228-6700
Dr. Christian Willmore, prin. Fax 575-8832
Washington-Lee HS 2,200/9-12
1301 N Stafford St 22201 703-228-6200
Gregg Robertson, prin. Fax 524-9814
Williamsburg MS 1,000/6-8
3600 N Harrison St 22207 703-228-5450
Dr. Ann McCarty, prin. Fax 536-2870
Woodland Program 600/Alt
4100 Vacation Ln 22207 703-228-6363
Frank Haltiwanger, prin. Fax 558-0317
Yorktown HS 2,000/9-12
5200 Yorktown Blvd 22207 703-228-5400
Dr. Raymond Pasi, prin. Fax 228-5409

Argosy University/Washington DC Post-Sec.
1550 Wilson Blvd Ste 600 22209 703-526-5800
Art Institute of Washington Post-Sec.
1820 Fort Myer Dr 22209 703-358-9550
Bishop Denis J. O'Connell HS 1,300/9-12
6600 Little Falls Rd 22213 703-237-1400
Joseph Vorbach, prin. Fax 237-1412
Chamberlain College of Nursing Post-Sec.
2450 Crystal Dr 22202 703-416-7300
Court Reporting Institute of Arlington Post-Sec.
4300 Wilson Blvd Ste 140 22203 703-875-1200
DeVry University Post-Sec.
2450 Crystal Dr 22202 703-414-4000
Graham Webb Intl. Academy of Hair Post-Sec.
1621 N Kent St # 1617LL 22209 703-243-9322
Institute for the Psychological Sciences Post-Sec.
2001 Jefferson Davis # 511 22202 703-416-1441
Keller Graduate School Post-Sec.
2450 Crystal Dr 22202 703-414-4000
Marymount University Post-Sec.
2807 N Glebe Rd 22207 703-522-5600
University of Management and Technology Post-Sec.
1901 Fort Myer Dr Ste 700 22209 703-516-0035
Westwood College - Ballston Post-Sec.
4420 Fairfax Dr 22203 703-243-3900

Ashburn, Loudoun, Pop. 41,992
Loudoun County SD 59,800/PK-12
21000 Education Ct 20148 571-252-1000
Dr. Edgar Hatrick, supt. Fax 252-1669
www.lcps.org/
Briar Woods HS 1,600/9-12
22525 Belmont Ridge Rd 20148 703-957-4400
Edward Starzenski, prin. Fax 542-5923
Broad Run HS 1,700/9-12
21670 Ashburn Rd 20147 571-252-2300
Douglas Anderson, prin. Fax 252-2301
Eagle Ridge MS 1,100/6-8
42901 Waxpool Rd 20148 571-252-2140
Bridget Beichler, prin. Fax 779-8977
Farmwell Station MS 1,200/6-8
44281 Gloucester Pkwy 20147 571-252-2320
Sherryl Loya, prin. Fax 771-6495
Stone Bridge HS 1,900/9-12
43100 Hay Rd 20147 571-252-2200
James Person, prin. Fax 252-2201
Stone Hill MS 1,300/6-8
23415 Evergreen Ridge Dr 20148 703-957-4420
Rodney Moore, prin. Fax 223-0585
Other Schools – See Aldie, Chantilly, Hamilton, Leesburg, Potomac Falls, Purcellville, South Riding, Sterling

---

Strayer University Post-Sec.
45150 Russell Branch Pkwy 20147 703-729-8800

Ashland, Hanover, Pop. 7,029
Hanover County SD 18,300/K-12
200 Berkley St 23005 804-365-4500
Dr. Jamelle Wilson, supt. Fax 365-4680
www.hcps.us
Henry HS 1,600/9-12
12449 W Patrick Henry Rd 23005 804-365-8000
Dr. Wanda Bibb, prin. Fax 365-8027
Liberty MS 1,100/6-8
13496 Liberty School Rd 23005 804-365-8060
Donald Latham, prin. Fax 365-8061
Other Schools – See Mechanicsville

Randolph-Macon College Post-Sec.
PO Box 5005 23005 804-752-7200

Axton, Henry

Carlisle S 500/PK-12
300 Carlisle Rd 24054 276-632-7288
Simon Owen-Williams, hdmstr. Fax 632-9545

Bassett, Henry, Pop. 1,078
Henry County SD
Supt. — See Collinsville
Bassett HS 1,200/9-12
85 Riverside Dr 24055 276-629-1731
Garrett Dillard, prin. Fax 629-9329

Bastian, Bland
Bland County SD 900/K-12
361 Bears Trl 24314 276-688-3361
Kyle Rhodes, supt. Fax 688-4659
www.bland.k12.va.us
Other Schools – See Bland, Rocky Gap

Bealeton, Fauquier, Pop. 4,295
Fauquier County SD
Supt. — See Warrenton

Cedar-Lee MS 700/6-8
11138 Marsh Rd 22712 540-422-7430
Steven Parker, prin. Fax 422-7449
Liberty HS 1,300/9-12
6300 Independence Ave 22712 540-422-7630
Roger Lee, prin. Fax 422-7389

Bedford, Bedford, Pop. 6,098
Bedford County SD 10,100/PK-12
PO Box 748 24523 540-586-1045
Dr. Douglas Schuch, supt. Fax 586-7747
www.bedford.k12.va.us
Alternative Education Center Alt
600 Edmund St 24523 540-586-3517
Gus Exstrom, prin.
Bedford MS 500/6-8
503 Longwood Ave 24523 540-586-7735
Rhetta Watkins, prin. Fax 586-4957
Bedford Science and Technology Center Vo/Tech
600 Edmund St 24523 540-586-3933
Barbara Rezzonico, prin. Fax 586-7711
Liberty HS 900/9-12
100 Minute Man Dr 24523 540-586-2541
Tim Overstreet, prin. Fax 586-7720
Other Schools – See Forest, Moneta

Ben Hur, Lee
Lee County SD
Supt. — See Jonesville
Lee County Career & Technical Center Vo/Tech
PO Box 100 24218 276-346-1960
James Graham, prin. Fax 346-2831

Bent Mountain, Roanoke

Bent Mountain Christian Academy 50/K-10
PO Box 66 24059 540-494-8356
Karen Scott, admin. Fax 929-9028

Berryville, Clarke, Pop. 4,082
Clarke County SD 2,100/PK-12
309 W Main St 22611 540-955-6100
Dr. Michael Murphy, supt. Fax 955-6109
www.clarke.k12.va.us
Clarke County HS 700/9-12
627 Mosby Blvd 22611 540-955-6130
Dr. Jeff Jackson, prin. Fax 955-6139
Johnson-Williams MS 500/6-8
200 Swan Ave 22611 540-955-6160
Evan Robb, prin. Fax 955-6169

Big Stone Gap, Wise, Pop. 5,523
Wise County SD
Supt. — See Wise
Powell Valley MS 500/5-8
3137 2nd Ave E 24219 276-523-0195
Paul Clendenon, prin. Fax 523-4762
Union HS 500/9-12
2 Avenue of Champions 24219 276-523-1290
William Austin, prin. Fax 523-6804

Mountain Empire Community College Post-Sec.
3441 Mountain Empire Rd 24219 276-523-2400

Blacksburg, Montgomery, Pop. 41,455
Montgomery County SD
Supt. — See Christiansburg
Blacksburg HS 1,100/9-12
3109 Prices Fork Rd 24060 540-951-5706
Brian Kitts, prin. Fax 951-5714

Dayspring Christian Academy 200/K-12
PO Box 909 24063 540-552-7777
William Hampton, admin. Fax 552-7778
Edward Via College of Osteopathic Med. Post-Sec.
2265 Kraft Dr 24060 540-231-4000
Virginia Polytechnic Inst. & State Univ. Post-Sec.
24061 540-231-6000

Blackstone, Nottoway, Pop. 3,575

Kenston Forest S 400/PK-12
75 Ridge Rd 23824 434-292-7218
John Colby, hdmstr. Fax 292-7455

Bland, Bland, Pop. 406
Bland County SD
Supt. — See Bastian
Bland HS 200/8-12
31 Rocket Dr 24315 276-688-3621
Temple Musser, prin. Fax 688-4451

Bluefield, Tazewell, Pop. 5,359
Tazewell County SD
Supt. — See Tazewell
Graham HS 500/9-12
210 Valleydale St 24605 276-326-1235
John O'Neal, prin. Fax 326-1128
Graham MS 400/6-8
1 Academic Cir 24605 276-326-1101
Lee Salyers, prin. Fax 322-1409

Bluefield College Post-Sec.
3000 College Dr 24605 276-326-3682

Bowling Green, Caroline, Pop. 1,090
Caroline County SD 4,300/PK-12
16221 Richmond Tpke 22427 804-633-5088
Dr. Gregory Killough, supt. Fax 633-5563
www.ccps.us
Other Schools – See Milford, Ruther Glen

Boydton, Mecklenburg, Pop. 430
Mecklenburg County SD 4,600/PK-12
PO Box 190 23917 434-738-6111
Dr. James Thornton, supt. Fax 738-6679
www.mcpsweb.org
Other Schools – See Skipwith, South Hill

Bridgewater, Rockingham, Pop. 5,553
Rockingham County SD
Supt. — See Harrisonburg
Ashby HS 1,100/9-12
800 N Main St 22812 540-828-2008
Steve Walk, prin. Fax 828-4764

Bridgewater College Post-Sec.
402 E College St 22812 540-828-8000

Bristol, Bristol, Pop. 17,490
Bristol CSD 2,400/PK-12
220 Lee St 24201 276-821-5600
Dr. Mark Lineburg, supt. Fax 821-5601
www.bvps.org/
Virginia HS 700/9-12
1200 Long Crescent Dr 24201 276-821-5858
Ronnie Collins, prin. Fax 821-5851
Virginia MS 600/6-8
501 Piedmont Ave 24201 276-821-5660
Gary Ritchie, prin. Fax 821-5661

Washington County SD
Supt. — See Abingdon
Battle HS 600/9-12
21264 Battle Hill Dr 24202 276-642-5300
Jeff Hawkins, prin. Fax 645-2386
Wallace MS 400/6-8
13077 Wallace Pike 24202 276-642-5400
David Lambert, prin. Fax 645-2365

Graham Bible College Post-Sec.
PO Box 1630 24203 423-968-4201
Southeast Culinary & Hospitality College Post-Sec.
100 Piedmont Ave 24201 276-591-5699
Virginia Intermont College Post-Sec.
1013 Moore St 24201 276-466-7867

Bristow, Prince William
Prince William County SD
Supt. — See Manassas
Marsteller MS 1,500/6-8
14000 Sudley Manor Dr 20136 703-393-7608
Roberta Knetter, prin. Fax 530-6327

Broadway, Rockingham, Pop. 3,640
Rockingham County SD
Supt. — See Harrisonburg
Broadway HS 1,000/9-12
269 Gobbler Dr 22815 540-896-7081
Dr. Seth Muraskin, prin. Fax 896-2640
Hillyard MS 800/6-8
226 Hawks Hill Dr 22815 540-896-8961
Dave Baker, prin. Fax 896-6641

Buchanan, Botetourt, Pop. 1,142
Botetourt County SD
Supt. — See Fincastle
James River HS 500/9-12
9906 Springwood Rd 24066 540-254-1121
James Talbott, prin. Fax 254-2765

Buckingham, Buckingham, Pop. 370
Buckingham County SD 1,700/K-12
15595 W James Anderson Hwy 23921 434-969-6100
Dr. Cecil Snead, supt. Fax 969-1176
www.bcpschools.org
Buckingham County HS 600/9-12
78 Knights Rd 23921 434-969-6160
Roger Coleman, prin. Fax 969-3209
Buckingham County MS 400/6-8
1184 High School Rd 23921 434-969-1044
J.B. Heslip, prin. Fax 969-4290

Buena Vista, Buena Vista, Pop. 6,530
Buena Vista CSD 800/K-12
2329 Chestnut Ave Ste A 24416 540-261-2129
Dr. Mary Holm, supt. Fax 261-2967
www.bvcps.net
McCluer HS 300/8-12
100 Bradford Dr 24416 540-261-2127
Anna Graham, prin. Fax 261-1828

Southern Virginia University Post-Sec.
1 University Hill Dr 24416 540-261-8400

Bumpass, Louisa

Piedmont Christian S 100/PK-12
2382 Bethany Church Rd 23024 540-872-3543
Marsha Badertscher, hdmstr. Fax 872-3873

Burke, Fairfax, Pop. 39,726
Fairfax County SD
Supt. — See Falls Church
Lake Braddock JSHS 4,000/7-12
9200 Burke Lake Rd 22015 703-426-1000
David Thomas, prin. Fax 426-1093

Carson, Prince George
Jointly Operated Vo Tech SD
Supt. — None – Lolita Hall, dir.
Rowanty Vocational Tech Center Vo/Tech
20000 Rowanty Rd 23830 434-246-5741
Tom Cope, prin. Fax 246-5721

Castlewood, Russell, Pop. 2,028
Russell County SD
Supt. — See Lebanon
Castlewood HS 300/8-12
304 Blue Devil Cir 24224 276-762-9449
Thomas Graves, prin. Fax 762-9418

Centreville, Fairfax, Pop. 68,513
Fairfax County SD
Supt. — See Falls Church
Mountain View Alternative HS 300/Alt
5775 Spindle Ct 20121 703-227-2316
David Jagels, prin. Fax 222-6927
Stone MS 900/7-8
5500 Sully Park Dr 20120 703-631-5500
Scott Phillips, prin. Fax 631-5598

Ad Fontes Academy 200/K-12
PO Box 916 20122 703-673-1145
Dean Luckenbaugh, pres. Fax 440-1686
Columbia College Post-Sec.
5940 Centreville Crest Ln 20121 703-266-0508

Chantilly, Fairfax, Pop. 22,194
Fairfax County SD
Supt. — See Falls Church
Chantilly HS 2,700/9-12
4201 Stringfellow Rd 20151 703-222-8100
Teresa Johnson, prin. Fax 222-8197
Franklin MS 900/7-8
3300 Lees Corner Rd 20151 703-904-5100
Sharon Eisenberg, prin. Fax 904-5197
Rocky Run MS 1,000/7-8
4400 Stringfellow Rd 20151 703-802-7700
Matthew Eline, prin. Fax 802-7797
Westfield HS 2,900/9-12
4700 Stonecroft Blvd 20151 703-488-6300
Tim Thomas, prin. Fax 488-6397

Loudoun County SD
Supt. — See Ashburn
Lunsford MS 6-8
26020 Ticonderoga Rd 20152 703-722-2660
Neil Slevin, prin. Fax 327-2420

ITT Technical Institute Post-Sec.
14420 Albemarle Point # 100 20151 703-263-2541

Charles City, Charles City, Pop. 131
Charles City County SD 800/PK-12
10910 Courthouse Rd 23030 804-652-4612
Dr. Janet Crawley, supt. Fax 829-6723
www.ccps.net
Charles City County HS 300/9-12
10039 Courthouse Rd 23030 804-829-9249
Stephannie Crutchfield, prin. Fax 829-2644
Charles City County MS 200/6-8
10035 Courthouse Rd 23030 804-829-9252
Dr. Brenda Petteway, prin. Fax 829-2363

Charlotte Court House, Charlotte, Pop. 538
Charlotte County SD 2,000/PK-12
PO Box 790 23923 434-542-5151
Dr. Melody Hackney, supt. Fax 542-4261
www.ccpsk12.org
Central MS 500/6-8
PO Box 748 23923 434-542-4536
Shep Critzer, prin. Fax 542-4630
Randolph-Henry HS 700/9-12
PO Box 668 23923 434-542-4111
Charlene Bowman, prin. Fax 542-4114

Charlottesville, Charlottesville, Pop. 42,217
Albemarle County SD 13,300/PK-12
401 McIntire Rd 22902 434-296-5826
Dr. Pamela Moran, supt. Fax 296-5869
www.k12albemarle.org/
Albemarle HS 1,700/9-12
2775 Hydraulic Rd 22901 434-975-9300
Jay Thomas, prin. Fax 974-4335
Burley MS 500/6-8
901 Rose Hill Dr 22903 434-295-5101
James Asher, prin. Fax 984-4975
Health and Medical Sciences Academy 9-12
1400 Independence Way 22902 434-244-3100
Kitina Dudley, dir.
Jouett MS 600/6-8
210 Lambs Ln 22901 434-975-9320
Kathryn Baylor, prin. Fax 975-9325
Math Engineering and Science Academy 9-12
2775 Hydraulic Rd 22901 434-975-9300
Jeff Prillaman, dir.
Monticello HS 1,200/9-12
1400 Independence Way 22902 434-244-3100
Dr. Jesse Turner, prin. Fax 244-3104
Murray HS 100/Alt
1200 Forest St 22903 434-296-3090
Ashby Kindler, prin. Fax 979-6479
Sutherland MS 600/6-8
2801 Powell Creek Dr 22911 434-975-0599
David Rogers, prin. Fax 975-0852
Walton MS 400/6-8
4217 Red Hill Rd 22903 434-977-5615
Alison Dwier-Selden, prin. Fax 296-6648
Other Schools – See Crozet

Charlottesville CSD 4,000/PK-12
1562 Dairy Rd 22903 434-245-2400
Dr. Rosa Atkins, supt. Fax 245-2603
www.ccs.k12.va.us
Buford MS 500/7-8
1000 Cherry Ave 22903 434-245-2411
Eric Johnson, prin. Fax 245-2611
Charlottesville HS 1,200/9-12
1400 Melbourne Rd 22901 434-245-2410
Dr. Thomas Taylor, prin. Fax 245-2610
Henry Avenue Learning Center Alt
715 Henry Ave 22903 434-245-2406
Kenneth Leatherwood, prin.

Jointly Operated Vo Tech SD
Supt. — None – Lolita Hall, dir.
Charlottesville-Albemarle Tech Center Vo/Tech
1000 Rio Rd E 22901 434-973-4461
Dr. Adam Hastings, dir. Fax 973-4876

Covenant S 500/PK-12
175 Hickory St 22902 434-220-7329
George Sanker, hdmstr. Fax 979-3204
Miller S of Albemarle 200/8-12
1000 Samuel Miller Loop 22903 434-823-4805
Sam Hale, dir. Fax 823-6617
National College Post-Sec.
3926 Seminole Trl 22911 434-220-7960
Piedmont Virginia Community College Post-Sec.
501 College Dr 22902 434-977-3900
St. Anne's Belfield S 900/PK-12
2132 Ivy Rd 22903 434-296-5106
David Lourie, hdmstr. Fax 979-1486
Tandem Friends S 200/5-12
279 Tandem Ln 22902 434-296-1303
Andy Jones-Wilkins, hdmstr. Fax 296-1886
University of Virginia Post-Sec.
PO Box 400160 22904 434-924-0311
Virginia School of Massage Post-Sec.
153 Zan Rd 22901 434-293-4031

Chatham, Pittsylvania, Pop. 1,254
Pittsylvania County SD 9,200/PK-12
PO Box 232 24531 434-432-2761
James McDaniel, supt. Fax 432-9560
www.pcs.k12.va.us
Chatham HS 700/9-12
100 Chatham Cavalier Cir 24531 434-432-8305
Randy Foster, prin. Fax 432-8351
Chatham MS 500/6-8
11650 US Highway 29 24531 434-432-2169
Cedric Hairston, prin. Fax 432-2842
Pittsylvania Career Tech Vo/Tech
11700 US Highway 29 24531 434-432-9416
Jimmie Tickle, prin. Fax 432-0516
Other Schools – See Dry Fork, Gretna, Ringgold

Chatham Hall S 100/9-12
800 Chatham Hall Cir 24531 434-432-2941
Dr. Gary Fountain, prin. Fax 432-1002
Hargrave Military Academy 300/7-12
200 Military Dr 24531 434-432-2481
Don Broome, pres. Fax 432-3129

Chesapeake, Chesapeake, Pop. 216,170
Chesapeake CSD 39,000/K-12
PO Box 16496 23328 757-547-0165
Dr. James Roberts, supt. Fax 547-0196
www.cpschools.com/
Chesapeake Alternative S Alt
605 Providence Rd 23325 757-578-7046
Melvina Herbert, prin. Fax 578-7068
Chesapeake Center Science & Tech Vo/Tech
1617 Cedar Rd 23322 757-547-0134
William Joe, prin. Fax 547-2391
Crestwood MS 600/6-8
1420 Great Bridge Blvd 23320 757-494-7560
Michael Ward, prin. Fax 494-7599
Deep Creek HS 1,300/9-12
2900 Margaret Booker Dr 23323 757-558-5302
Page Bagley, prin. Fax 558-5305
Deep Creek MS 500/6-8
1955 Deal Dr 23323 757-558-5321
Dr. Muriel Barefield, prin. Fax 558-5320
Grassfield HS 2,100/9-12
2007 Grizzly Trl 23323 757-558-4749
Carolyn Bernard, prin. Fax 558-9240
Great Bridge HS 1,700/9-12
301 Hanbury Rd W 23322 757-482-5191
Michelle Porter, prin. Fax 482-5559
Great Bridge MS 1,200/6-8
441 Battlefield Blvd S 23322 757-482-5128
Craig Mills, prin. Fax 482-0210
Greenbrier MS 900/6-8
1016 Greenbrier Pkwy 23320 757-548-5309
Dr. Michael Mustain, prin. Fax 548-8921
Hickory HS 1,900/9-12
1996 Hawk Blvd 23322 757-421-4295
Alfredia Turner, prin. Fax 421-2190
Hickory MS 1,700/6-8
1997 Hawk Blvd 23322 757-421-0468
Dr. Deborah Hutchens, prin. Fax 421-0475
Indian River HS 1,700/9-12
1969 Braves Trl 23325 757-578-7000
James Frye, prin. Fax 578-7004
Indian River MS 800/6-8
2300 Old Greenbrier Rd 23325 757-578-7030
Naomi Dunbar, prin. Fax 578-7036
Jolliff MS 700/6-8
1021 Jolliff Rd 23321 757-465-5246
Quentin Hicks, prin. Fax 465-1646
Owens MS 1,100/6-8
1997 Horseback Run 23323 757-558-5382
Michael Perez, prin. Fax 558-5386
Smith HS 2,200/9-12
1994 Tiger Dr 23320 757-548-0696
Paul Joseph, prin. Fax 548-0531
Smith MS 1,000/6-8
2500 Rodgers St 23324 757-494-7590
Judith Thurston, prin. Fax 494-7680
Western Branch HS 2,200/9-12
1968 Bruin Pl 23321 757-638-7900
John Sykes, prin. Fax 638-7904
Western Branch MS 900/6-8
4201 Hawksley Dr 23321 757-638-7920
Craig Jones, prin. Fax 638-7926

Atlantic Shores Christian S 300/7-12
1217 Centerville Tpke N 23320 757-479-9598
Gary Carlson, admin. Fax 479-5311
Aviation Institute of Maintenance Post-Sec.
2211 S Military Hwy 23320 757-363-2121
Centura College Post-Sec.
932 Ventures Way 23320 757-549-2121
DeVry University Post-Sec.
1317 Executive Blvd Ste 100 23320 757-382-5680
Everest College Post-Sec.
825 Greenbrier Cir Ste 100 23320 757-361-3900
Greenbrier Christian Academy 600/PK-12
311 Kempsville Rd 23320 757-547-9595
Dr. Ron White, supt. Fax 547-9569
Sentara College of Health Sciences Post-Sec.
1441 Crossways Blvd Ste 105 23320 757-388-2900
StoneBridge S 300/PK-12
PO Box 9247 23321 757-488-2214
Jeff Carlucci, hdmstr. Fax 465-7637
Strayer University Post-Sec.
676 Independence Pkwy # 300 23320 757-382-9900
Tidewater Community College Post-Sec.
1428 Cedar Rd 23322 757-822-5100

Chester, Chesterfield, Pop. 20,491
Chesterfield County SD
Supt. — See Chesterfield
Carver MS 1,100/6-8
3800 Cougar Trl 23831 804-524-3620
Donald Ashburn, prin. Fax 520-0189
Chesterfield Community HS 400/Alt
12400 Branders Bridge Rd 23831 804-768-6156
Jamie Accashian, prin. Fax 768-6171
Dale HS 2,400/9-12
3626 W Hundred Rd 23831 804-768-6245
Pamela Lunsden, prin. Fax 768-6256
Davis MS 1,200/6-8
601 Corvus Ct 23836 804-541-4700
Dr. Tameshia Grimes, prin. Fax 530-2717

Evangel Christian S 100/PK-12
16801 Harrowgate Rd 23831 804-526-5941
John Tyler Community College Post-Sec.
13101 Jefferson Davis Hwy 23831 804-796-4000

Chesterfield, Chesterfield
Chesterfield County SD 59,000/PK-12
PO Box 10 23832 804-748-1405
Dr. Marcus Newsome, supt. Fax 796-7178
mychesterfieldschools.com/
Bird HS 1,800/9-12
10301 Courthouse Rd 23832 804-768-6110
Dr. Laura Hebert, prin. Fax 768-6117
Chesterfield Technical Center Vo/Tech
10101 Courthouse Rd 23832 804-768-6160
Dr. Michael Gill, prin. Fax 768-6164
Matoaca HS 1,800/9-12
17700 Longhouse Ln 23838 804-590-3108
Stephen Cunningham, prin. Fax 590-3022
Other Schools – See Chester, Matoaca, Midlothian, N Chesterfield

Richmond Christian S 500/PK-12
6511 Belmont Rd 23832 804-276-3193
Trevor Collazo, prin. Fax 276-9106

Chilhowie, Smyth, Pop. 1,774
Smyth County SD
Supt. — See Marion
Chilhowie HS 400/9-12
PO Box 2280 24319 276-646-8966
Mike Sturgill, prin. Fax 646-5951
Chilhowie MS 300/6-8
PO Box 5018 24319 276-646-3942
Sam Blevins, prin. Fax 646-0210

Chincoteague, Accomack, Pop. 2,859
Accomack County SD
Supt. — See Accomac
Chincoteague HS 300/6-12
4586 Main St 23336 757-336-6166
Warren Holland, prin. Fax 336-1902

Christchurch, Middlesex

Christchurch S 200/9-12
49 Seahorse Ln 23031 804-758-2306
John Byers, hdmstr. Fax 758-0721

Christiansburg, Montgomery, Pop. 20,645
Montgomery County SD 9,500/PK-12
750 Imperial St 24073 540-382-5100
Brenda Blackburn, supt. Fax 381-6127
www.mcps.org
Blacksburg MS 800/6-8
208 College St 24073 540-951-5800
John Wheeler, prin. Fax 951-5808
Christiansburg HS 1,100/9-12
100 Independence Blvd 24073 540-382-5178
Dr. Kevin Siers, prin. Fax 381-6525
Christiansburg MS 800/6-8
1205 Buffalo Dr 24073 540-394-2180
Mark Baetz, prin. Fax 394-2197
Independence Secondary S Alt
412 Roanoke St 24073 540-381-6100
Larry Lowe, prin. Fax 381-6185
Other Schools – See Blacksburg, Elliston, Riner, Shawsville

Pathway Christian Academy 100/PK-12
1550 Roanoke St Ste B 24073 540-394-7300

Clifton, Fairfax, Pop. 280
Fairfax County SD
Supt. — See Falls Church
Centreville HS 2,300/9-12
6001 Union Mill Rd 20124 703-802-5400
Martin Grimm, prin. Fax 802-5497
Liberty MS 1,100/7-8
6801 Union Mill Rd 20124 703-988-8100
Catherine Cipperly, prin. Fax 988-8197

Clifton Forge, Alleghany, Pop. 3,785
Regional Academic Governors SD
Supt. — See Richmond
Jackson River Governor's HS 11-12
PO Box 1000 24422 540-863-2872
Eddie Graham, dir. Fax 863-2915

Dabney S. Lancaster Community College Post-Sec.
PO Box 1000 24422 540-863-2800

Clinchco, Dickenson, Pop. 335
Dickenson County SD
Supt. — See Clintwood
Dickenson County Career Center Vo/Tech
335 Vocational Dr 24226 276-835-8049
Brian Baker, prin. Fax 835-8058

Clintwood, Dickenson, Pop. 1,403
Dickenson County SD 1,700/PK-12
PO Box 1127 24228 276-926-4643
Haydee Robinson, supt. Fax 926-6374
www.dickenson.k12.va.us
Clintwood HS 300/9-12
PO Box 577 24228 276-926-8400
Rodney Compton, prin. Fax 926-8696
Longs Fork MS 100/5-8
1280 Browning Holw 24228 276-926-6339
Jettie Mullins, prin. Fax 926-6651
Other Schools – See Clinchco, Haysi

Cloverdale, Botetourt, Pop. 3,095
Botetourt County SD
Supt. — See Fincastle
Read Mountain MS 700/6-8
182 Orchard Hill Dr 24077 540-966-8655
Michael Tetreault, prin. Fax 966-8656

Coeburn, Wise, Pop. 2,115
Wise County SD
Supt. — See Wise
Coeburn MS 400/5-8
PO Box 670 24230 276-395-2135
Scott Keith, prin. Fax 395-5453
Eastside HS 400/9-12
PO Box 2036 24230 276-395-3389
Dante Lee, prin. Fax 395-5167

Collinsville, Henry, Pop. 7,233
Henry County SD 7,300/PK-12
PO Box 8958 24078 276-634-4700
Dr. Jared Cotton, supt. Fax 638-2925
www.henry.k12.va.us
Fieldale-Collinsville MS 900/6-8
645 Miles Rd 24078 276-647-3841
Elizabeth Minter, prin. Fax 647-4090
Other Schools – See Bassett, Martinsville, Ridgeway

Colonial Beach, Westmoreland, Pop. 3,440
Colonial Beach SD 600/K-12
16 Irving Ave N 22443 804-224-0906
Dr. Donna Power, supt. Fax 224-8357
www.cbschools.net
Colonial Beach HS 200/8-12
100 1st St 22443 804-224-7166
Clint Runyan, prin. Fax 224-7465

Colonial Heights, Colonial Heights, Pop. 17,059
Colonial Heights CSD 2,900/K-12
512 Boulevard, 804-524-3400
Dr. Joseph Cox, supt. Fax 526-4524
www.colonialhts.net
Colonial Heights HS 900/9-12
3600 Conduit Rd, 804-524-3405
Kristin Janssen, prin. Fax 520-7222
Colonial Heights MS 700/6-8
500 Conduit Rd, 804-524-3420
William Hortz, prin. Fax 526-9288

Courtland, Southampton, Pop. 1,266
Southhampton County SD 2,900/PK-12
PO Box 96 23837 757-653-2692
Dr. Alvera Parrish, supt. Fax 653-9422
www.southampton.k12.va.us/
Southampton HS 900/9-12
23350 Southampton Pkwy 23837 757-653-2751
Allene Atkinson, prin. Fax 653-0414
Southampton MS 600/6-8
23450 Southampton Pkwy 23837 757-653-9250
Michael Booth, prin. Fax 653-7251
Southampton Technical Career Center Vo/Tech
23350 Southampton Pkwy 23837 757-653-9170
Linda Adams, admin. Fax 653-9404

Southampton Academy 200/PK-12
26495 Old Plank Rd 23837 757-653-2512
Dr. Mercer Neale, hdmstr. Fax 653-0011

Covington, Covington, Pop. 5,839
Alleghany County SD
Supt. — See Low Moor
Alleghany HS 900/9-12
210 Mountaineer Dr 24426 540-863-1700
Fred Vaughan, prin. Fax 863-1705
Clifton MS 700/6-8
1000 Riverview Farm Rd 24426 540-863-1726
Brenda Siple, prin. Fax 863-1731

Covington CSD 1,000/PK-12
340 E Walnut St 24426 540-965-1400
Thomas Long, supt. Fax 965-1404
www.covington.k12.va.us/
Covington JSHS 300/8-12
606 S Lexington Ave 24426 540-965-1410
Robert McClintic, prin.

Jointly Operated Vo Tech SD
Supt. — None – Lolita Hall, dir.
Jackson River Tech Center Vo/Tech
105 E Country Club Ln 24426 540-862-1308
Glenn Spangler, prin. Fax 862-3592

Crewe, Nottoway, Pop. 2,296
Nottoway County SD
Supt. — See Nottoway
Nottoway HS 600/9-12
5267 Old Nottoway Rd 23930 434-292-5373
Anne Stinson, prin. Fax 292-3021
Nottoway MS 300/7-8
5279 Old Nottoway Rd 23930 434-292-5375
George Smith, prin. Fax 292-7479

Crozet, Albemarle, Pop. 5,475
Albemarle County SD
Supt. — See Charlottesville
Henley MS 800/6-8
5880 Rockfish Gap Tpke 22932 434-823-4393
Dr. Patrick McLaughlin, prin. Fax 823-2711
Western Albemarle HS 1,100/9-12
5941 Rockfish Gap Tpke 22932 434-823-8700
David Francis, prin. Fax 823-8711

Crozier, Goochland

Salem Christian S 100/PK-12
1700 Cardwell Rd 23039 804-784-4174
Todd Brooking, admin.

Culpeper, Culpeper, Pop. 15,837
Culpeper County SD 7,500/K-12
450 Radio Ln 22701 540-825-3677
Dr. Bobbi Johnson, supt. Fax 829-2111
www.culpeperschools.org
Binns MS 700/6-8
205 E Grandview Ave 22701 540-825-6894
Sherri Harkness, prin. Fax 829-9926
Culpeper County HS 1,000/9-12
14240 Achievement Dr 22701 540-825-8310
Jeff Dietz, prin. Fax 829-6615
Culpeper County MS 1,000/6-8
14300 Achievement Dr 22701 540-825-4140
Margery Southard, prin. Fax 825-7543
Eastern View HS 1,200/9-12
16332 Cyclone Way 22701 540-825-0621
E.G. Bradshaw, prin. Fax 825-9802

Cumberland, Cumberland, Pop. 383
Cumberland County SD 1,500/PK-12
PO Box 170 23040 804-492-4212
Amy Griffin Ed.D., supt. Fax 492-9869
www.cucps.k12.va.us
Cumberland HS 500/9-12
PO Box 140 23040 804-492-4212
Jeff Scales, prin. Fax 492-9871
Cumberland MS 300/5-8
PO Box 184 23040 804-492-4212
Jeff Dingeldein, prin. Fax 492-9868

Daleville, Botetourt, Pop. 2,539
Botetourt County SD
Supt. — See Fincastle
Lord Botetourt HS 1,100/9-12
1435 Roanoke Rd 24083 540-992-1261
Janet Womack, prin. Fax 992-8381

Damascus, Washington, Pop. 807
Washington County SD
Supt. — See Abingdon
Damascus MS 200/6-8
32101 Government Rd 24236 276-739-4100
Dixie Hunter, prin. Fax 475-4032
Holston HS 300/9-12
21308 Monroe Rd 24236 276-739-4000
Jimmy King, prin. Fax 475-4024

Danville, Danville, Pop. 42,537
Danville CSD 6,100/PK-12
PO Box 9600 24543 434-799-6400
Sue Davis Ed.D., supt. Fax 799-5008
web.dps.k12.va.us
Bonner MS 600/6-8
300 Apollo Ave 24540 434-799-6446
Larry Bailey, prin. Fax 797-8867
Galileo Magnet HS 300/9-12
230 S Ridge St 24541 434-773-8186
Jay Lancaster, prin. Fax 773-8188
Gibson MS 400/6-8
1215 Industrial Ave 24541 434-799-6426
Kenny Lewis, prin. Fax 797-8857
Langston Focus S 100/Alt
228 Cleveland St 24541 434-799-5249
Kevin Whitlock, prin. Fax 797-8925
Washington HS 1,500/9-12
701 Broad St 24541 434-799-6410
Chris Carter, prin. Fax 799-5251
Westwood MS 400/6-8
500 Apollo Ave 24540 434-797-8860
Christie Dawson, prin. Fax 797-8874
Adult & Continuing Education Center Adult
141 Goode St 24541 434-799-6471
Jackie Rochford, coord.

Averett University Post-Sec.
420 W Main St 24541 434-791-5600
Danville Community College Post-Sec.
1008 S Main St 24541 434-797-2222
Danville Regional Medical Center Post-Sec.
142 S Main St 24541 434-799-4510
National College Post-Sec.
336 Old Riverside Dr 24541 434-793-6822
Westover Christian Academy 400/PK-12
5665 Riverside Dr 24541 434-822-0800
Shawn Weeks, admin. Fax 822-0441

Dayton, Rockingham, Pop. 1,520
Rockingham County SD
Supt. — See Harrisonburg
Dayton Learning Center Alt
290 Mill St 22821 540-879-2831
Mary Bert Hawkins, prin. Fax 879-2578
Pence MS 700/6-8
375 Bowman Rd 22821 540-879-2535
Mary Shifflett, prin. Fax 879-2179

Dendron, Surry, Pop. 267
Surry County SD
Supt. — See Surry
Jackson MS 300/5-8
4255 New Design Rd 23839 757-267-2810
Dr. Charlome Pierce, prin. Fax 267-0809
Surry County HS 300/9-12
1675 Hollybush Rd 23839 757-267-2211
Rita Holmes, prin. Fax 267-2978

Dinwiddie, Dinwiddie
Dinwiddie County SD 3,800/K-12
PO Box 7 23841 804-469-4190
William Clark, supt. Fax 469-4197
www.dinwiddie.k12.va.us
Dinwiddie County HS 1,100/9-12
PO Box 299 23841 804-469-4280
Randall Johnson, prin. Fax 469-4293
Dinwiddie County MS 700/6-8
PO Box 340 23841 804-469-5430
Alfred Cappellanti, prin. Fax 469-3389

Disputanta, Prince George
Prince George County SD
Supt. — See Prince George
Prince George Education Center Alt
11455 Prince George Dr 23842 804-733-2748
Mattie Thweatt, prin. Fax 733-2749

Dry Fork, Pittsylvania
Pittsylvania County SD
Supt. — See Chatham
Regional Alternative Center Alt
1461 Dry Fork Rd 24549 434-432-8185
Deborah Powell, prin. Fax 432-8186
Tunstall HS 900/9-12
100 Trojan Cir 24549 434-724-7111
Barbara Brown, prin. Fax 724-4588
Tunstall MS 700/6-8
1160 Tunstall High Rd 24549 434-724-7086
Deborah Stowe, prin. Fax 724-7907

Dublin, Pulaski, Pop. 2,500
Pulaski County SD
Supt. — See Pulaski
Dublin MS 600/6-8
650 Giles Ave 24084 540-643-0367
Robin Keener, prin. Fax 674-0813
Pulaski County HS 1,500/9-12
5414 Cougar Trail Rd 24084 540-643-0747
Michael Myers, prin. Fax 674-4722

New River Community College Post-Sec.
PO Box 1127 24084 540-674-3600

Duffield, Scott, Pop. 90
Scott County SD
Supt. — See Gate City
Rye Cove HS 300/8-12
164 Eagles Nest Ln 24244 276-940-2701
Reagan Mullins, prin. Fax 940-2277

Dumfries, Prince William, Pop. 4,762
Prince William County SD
Supt. — See Manassas
Potomac HS 1,700/9-12
3401 Panther Pride Dr 22026 703-441-4200
Michael Wright, prin. Fax 441-4497
Potomac MS 1,100/6-8
3130 Panther Pride Dr 22026 703-221-4996
Alfie Turner, prin. Fax 221-4998

Pope John Paul the Great HS 9-12
17700 Dominican Dr 22026 703-445-0300
Sr. Mary Jordan Hoover, prin. Fax 445-0301

Eastville, Northampton, Pop. 300
Northampton County SD
Supt. — See Machipongo
Northampton HS 600/7-12
PO Box 38 23347 757-678-5151
Alvin Coleman, prin. Fax 678-5244

Elkton, Rockingham, Pop. 2,698
Rockingham County SD
Supt. — See Harrisonburg
East Rockingham HS 9-12
250 Eagle Rock Rd 22827 540-298-7450
Eric Baylor, prin. Fax 298-7462
Elkton MS 500/6-8
21063 Blue and Gold Dr 22827 540-298-1228
Ramona Pence, prin. Fax 298-0029

Elliston, Montgomery, Pop. 900
Montgomery County SD
Supt. — See Christiansburg
Eastern Montgomery HS 300/9-12
4695 Crozier Rd 24087 540-268-3010
Daniel Knott, prin. Fax 268-3012

Emory, Washington, Pop. 1,238

Emory & Henry College Post-Sec.
PO Box 947 24327 276-944-4121

Emporia, Emporia, Pop. 5,846
Greensville County SD 2,700/PK-12
105 Ruffin St 23847 434-634-3748
Dr. Philip Worrell, supt. Fax 634-3495
www.greensville.k12.va.us/
Greensville County HS 800/9-12
403 Harding St 23847 434-634-2195
Dr. Wayne Scott, prin.
Wyatt MS 600/6-8
206 Slagles Lake Rd 23847 434-634-5159
Dr. Jason Sears, prin. Fax 634-0442

Ewing, Lee, Pop. 438
Lee County SD
Supt. — See Jonesville
Walker HS 300/8-12
PO Box 39 24248 276-445-4111
Ron Earley, prin. Fax 445-3046

Exmore, Northampton, Pop. 1,433

Broadwater Academy 400/PK-12
PO Box 546 23350 757-442-9041
Jeremy McLean, admin. Fax 442-9615

Fairfax, Fairfax, Pop. 21,900
Fairfax County SD
Supt. — See Falls Church
Fairfax HS 2,500/9-12
3501 Rebel Run 22030 703-219-2200
David Goldfarb, prin. Fax 219-2297

Frost MS 1,000/7-8
4101 Pickett Rd 22032 703-426-5700
Marti Jackson, prin. Fax 426-5797
Lanier MS 1,300/7-8
3801 Jermantown Rd 22030 703-934-2400
Scott Poole, prin. Fax 934-2497
Robinson JSHS 3,900/7-12
5035 Sideburn Rd 22032 703-426-2100
Dan Meier, prin. Fax 426-2197
Woodson HS 2,100/9-12
9525 Main St 22031 703-503-4600
Jeff Yost, prin. Fax 503-4697
Fairfax County Adult HS Adult
4105 Whitacre Rd 22032 703-503-6407
Jane Cruz, prin.

Columbia College Post-Sec.
8300 Merrifield Ave 22031 703-206-0508
George Mason University Post-Sec.
4400 University Dr 22030 703-993-1000
New S of Northern VA 100/4-12
9431 Silver King Ct 22031 703-691-3040
John Potter, hdmstr.
Paul VI HS 1,000/9-12
10675 Fairfax Blvd 22030 703-352-0925
Ginny Colwell, prin. Fax 273-9845
Trinity Christian S 700/K-12
11204 Braddock Rd 22030 703-273-0966
David Vanderpoel Ph.D., hdmstr. Fax 501-6744
Virginia International University Post-Sec.
11200 Waples Mill Rd # 360 22030 703-591-7042

Falls Church, Falls Church, Pop. 11,898
Fairfax County SD 169,500/PK-12
8115 Gatehouse Rd 22042 703-423-1000
Dr. Jack Dale, supt. Fax 423-1007
www.fcps.edu
Falls Church HS 1,600/9-12
7521 Jaguar Trl 22042 703-207-4000
Cathy Benner, prin. Fax 207-4097
Jackson MS 1,200/7-8
3020 Gallows Rd 22042 703-204-8100
Louise Porter, prin. Fax 204-8197
Longfellow MS 1,300/7-8
2000 Westmoreland St 22043 703-533-2600
Carole Kihm, prin. Fax 533-2697
Marshall HS 1,600/9-12
7731 Leesburg Pike 22043 703-714-5400
Jay Pearson, prin. Fax 714-5497
Stuart HS 1,800/9-12
3301 Peace Valley Ln 22044 703-824-3900
Prosperanta Calhoun, prin. Fax 824-3997
Fairfax County Adult HS Adult
7510 Lisle Ave 22043 703-506-2251
Robert Landon, admin.
Other Schools – See Alexandria, Annandale, Burke, Centreville, Chantilly, Clifton, Fairfax, Herndon, Lorton, Mc Lean, Reston, Springfield, Vienna

Falls Church CSD 2,100/K-12
800 W Broad St Ste 203 22046 703-248-5600
Dr. Toni Jones, supt. Fax 248-5613
www.fccps.org/
Mason HS 800/8-12
7124 Leesburg Pike 22043 703-248-5500
Tyrone Byrd, prin. Fax 248-5533

California University of Management/Sci Post-Sec.
400 N Washington St 22046 703-663-8088
Child Development Ctr. of Northern VA Post-Sec.
111 N Cherry St 22046
Fairfax Hospital Post-Sec.
3300 Gallows Rd 22042 703-698-3371
J Leland Center for Theological Studies Post-Sec.
405 N Washington St Ste 200 22046 703-812-4757
MedTech College Post-Sec.
6565 Arlington Blvd Ste 100 22042 703-237-6200
Stratford University Post-Sec.
7777 Leesburg Pike Ste 100S 22043 703-821-8570
Trinity S at Meadow View 200/7-12
2849 Meadow View Rd 22042 703-876-1920
Andrew Zwerneman, hdmstr. Fax 641-9220

Falmouth, Stafford, Pop. 4,116
Stafford County SD
Supt. — See Stafford
Drew MS 500/6-8
501 Cambridge St 22405 540-371-1415
Catherine Williams, prin. Fax 371-1447

Farmville, Prince Edward, Pop. 8,093
Prince Edward County SD 2,400/K-12
35 Eagle Dr 23901 434-315-2100
Dr. K. David Smith, supt. Fax 392-1911
www.pecps.k12.va.us
Prince Edward County HS 800/9-12
35 Eagle Dr 23901 434-315-2130
Craig Reed, prin. Fax 392-1901
Prince Edward MS 800/5-8
35 Eagle Dr 23901 434-315-2120
Lucy Carson, prin. Fax 392-4286

Fuqua S 500/PK-12
PO Box 328 23901 434-392-4131
Longwood University Post-Sec.
201 High St 23909 434-395-2000
New Life Christian Academy 100/PK-12
9 Mahan Rd 23901 434-392-6236
Dr. Betty Weaver, admin. Fax 392-4462

Ferrum, Franklin, Pop. 1,932

Ferrum College Post-Sec.
PO Box 1000 24088 540-365-2121

Fincastle, Botetourt, Pop. 352
Botetourt County SD 5,600/PK-12
143 Poor Farm Rd 24090 540-473-8263
Dr. Anthony Brads, supt. Fax 473-8298
www.bcps.k12.va.us
Botetourt Technical Education Center Vo/Tech
253 Poor Farm Rd 24090 540-473-8216
Joe Harden, prin. Fax 473-8376
Central Academy MS 500/6-8
367 Poor Farm Rd 24090 540-473-8333
Tim McClung, prin. Fax 473-8398
Other Schools – See Buchanan, Cloverdale, Daleville

Fishersville, Augusta, Pop. 7,346
Augusta County SD 10,600/K-12
6 John Lewis Rd 22939 540-245-5100
Chuck Bishop, supt. Fax 245-5115
www.augusta.k12.va.us
Wilson Memorial HS 700/9-12
189 Hornet Rd 22939 540-886-4286
Doug Shifflett, prin. Fax 886-4611
Wilson MS 600/6-8
232 Hornet Rd 22939 540-245-5185
Donald Curtis, prin. Fax 245-5189
Other Schools – See Fort Defiance, Staunton, Stuarts Draft, Swoope

Jointly Operated Vo Tech SD
Supt. — None – Lolita Hall, dir.
Valley Vocational Tech Center Vo/Tech
49 Hornet Rd 22939 540-245-5002
Darla Miller, prin. Fax 885-0407

Regional Academic Governors SD
Supt. — See Richmond
Shenandoah Valley Governor's S 11-12
49 Hornet Rd 22939 540-245-5088
Lee Ann Whitesell, dir. Fax 886-6476

Augusta Health Post-Sec.
PO Box 1000 22939 540-332-4539

Flint Hill, Rappahannock, Pop. 207

Wakefield Country Day S 300/PK-12
PO Box 739 22627 540-635-8555
Jessica Lindstrom, hdmstr. Fax 636-1501

Floyd, Floyd, Pop. 419
Floyd County SD 2,100/PK-12
140 Harris Hart Rd NE 24091 540-745-9400
Kevin W. Harris Ed.D., supt. Fax 745-9496
www.floyd.k12.va.us
Floyd County HS 800/8-12
721 Baker St SE 24091 540-745-9450
Tony Deibler, prin. Fax 745-9481

Forest, Bedford, Pop. 9,010
Bedford County SD
Supt. — See Bedford
Forest MS 1,000/6-8
100 Ashwood Dr 24551 434-525-6630
Scott Simmons, prin. Fax 525-1284
Jefferson Forest HS 1,300/9-12
1 Cavalier Cir 24551 434-525-2074
Anthony Francis, prin. Fax 525-0106

Timberlake Christian S 400/PK-12
202 Horizon Dr 24551 434-237-5943
Charlie Williams, admin. Fax 239-3319

Fork Union, Fluvanna

Fork Union Military Academy 400/6-12
PO Box 278 23055 434-842-3212
J. Scott Burhoe, pres. Fax 842-4300

Fort Defiance, Augusta
Augusta County SD
Supt. — See Fishersville
Fort Defiance HS 900/9-12
195 Fort Defiance Rd 24437 540-245-5050
Larry Landes, prin. Fax 245-5054
Stewart MS 600/6-8
118 Fort Defiance Rd 24437 540-245-5046
Brenda Walton, prin. Fax 245-5049

Franklin, Southampton, Pop. 8,431
Franklin CSD 1,300/PK-12
207 W 2nd Ave 23851 757-569-8111
Dr. Michelle Belle, supt. Fax 516-1015
www.franklincity.k12.va.us
Franklin HS 400/9-12
310 Crescent Dr 23851 757-562-5187
Travis Felts, prin. Fax 562-3656
King MS 200/6-8
501 Charles St 23851 757-562-4631
Lisa B. Francis, prin. Fax 562-0231

Paul D. Camp Community College Post-Sec.
100 N College Dr 23851 757-569-6700

Fredericksburg, Fredericksburg, Pop. 23,462
Fredericksburg CSD 3,200/PK-12
817 Princess Anne St 22401 540-372-1130
Dr. David Melton, supt. Fax 372-1111
www.cityschools.com
Monroe HS 900/9-12
2300 Washington Ave 22401 540-372-1100
Dr. John Gordon, prin. Fax 373-8643
Walker-Grant MS 600/6-8
1 Learning Ln 22401 540-372-1145
Melanie Kay-Wyatt, prin. Fax 891-5449

Regional Academic Governors SD
Supt. — See Richmond
Commonwealth Governor's HS 9-12
12301 Spotswood Furnace Rd 22407 540-548-1278
Merri Kae Vanderploeg, dir. Fax 548-1736

Spotsylvania County SD 23,500/PK-12
8020 River Stone Dr 22407 540-834-2500
Scott Baker Ed.D., supt. Fax 834-2550
www.spotsylvania.k12.va.us
Battlefield MS 800/6-8
11120 Leavells Rd 22407 540-786-4400
Sheila Smith, prin. Fax 786-7109
Chancellor HS 1,400/9-12
6300 Harrison Rd 22407 540-786-2606
Jacqueline Bass-Fortune, prin. Fax 786-1176
Chancellor MS 800/6-8
6320 Harrison Rd 22407 540-786-8099
Keith Wolfe, prin. Fax 785-9392
Freedom MS 900/6-8
7315 Smith Station Rd 22407 540-548-1030
Alan Jacobs, prin. Fax 786-0782
Massaponax HS 1,900/9-12
8201 Jefferson Davis Hwy 22407 540-710-0419
Dr. Joe Pisani, prin. Fax 710-1596
Riverbend HS 2,000/9-12
12301 Spotswood Furnace Rd 22407 540-548-4051
Dr. Troy Wright, prin. Fax 548-2964
Other Schools – See Spotsylvania

Stafford County SD
Supt. — See Stafford
Dixon-Smith MS 900/6-8
503 Deacon Rd 22405 540-899-0860
Lisa Besceglia, prin. Fax 899-0881
Gayle MS 900/6-8
100 Panther Dr 22406 540-373-0383
Fax 373-8856
Stafford HS 1,900/9-12
33 Stafford Indians Ln 22405 540-371-7200
Joe Lewis, prin. Fax 371-2389

Career Training Solutions Post-Sec.
10304 Spotsylvania Ave #400 22408 540-373-2200
Faith Baptist S 300/PK-12
4105 Plank Rd 22407 540-786-4953
Kenneth Biggs, admin. Fax 786-3380
Fredericksburg Academy 400/PK-12
10800 Academy Dr 22408 540-898-0020
Karen Moschetto, hdmstr. Fax 898-8951
Fredericksburg Christian Upper S 600/6-12
9400 Thornton Rolling Rd 22408 540-371-3852
Cliff Williams, prin. Fax 371-4121
Mary Washington Hospital Post-Sec.
1001 Sam Perry Blvd 22401 540-899-1565
Massaponax Christian Academy 50/PK-12
5101 Massaponax Church Rd 22407
Edward Haynes, admin. 724-804-8003
Odyssey Montessori S 100/PK-12
125 Olde Greenwich Dr #100 22408 540-891-9080
Wendy LaRue Ph.D., head sch Fax 891-9877
University of Mary Washington Post-Sec.
1301 College Ave 22401 540-654-1000
Virginia Baptist College Post-Sec.
4105 Plank Rd 22407 540-785-5440

Front Royal, Warren, Pop. 14,067
Warren County SD 5,300/K-12
210 N Commerce Ave 22630 540-635-2171
Pamela McInnis, supt. Fax 636-4195
www.wcps.k12.va.us
Skyline HS 1,200/8-12
151 Skyline Vista Dr 22630 540-631-0366
Andrew Keller, prin. Fax 635-4026
Warren County HS 900/8-12
155 Westminster Dr 22630 540-635-4144
Ernestine Jordan, prin. Fax 636-3244

Christendom College Post-Sec.
134 Christendom Dr 22630 540-636-2900
Front Royal Christian S 100/PK-12
80 N Lake Ave 22630 540-635-6799
Lorraine Hewitt, dir. Fax 635-6152
Randolph-Macon Academy 300/6-12
200 Academy Dr 22630 540-636-5200
Henry Hobgood, pres. Fax 636-5344
Riverfront Christian S 100/PK-12
55 E Strasburg Rd 22630 540-635-8202
Cindy Martin, admin. Fax 636-4418

Gainesville, Prince William, Pop. 11,049
Prince William County SD
Supt. — See Manassas
Bull Run MS 1,600/6-8
6308 Catharpin Rd 20155 703-753-9969
Matthew Phythian, prin. Fax 753-9610
Gainesville MS 1,400/6-8
8001 Limestone Dr 20155 703-753-2997
Dr. Sally MacLean, prin. Fax 753-4331

Galax, Galax, Pop. 6,941
Galax CSD 1,300/K-12
223 Long St 24333 276-236-2911
Bill Sturgill, supt. Fax 236-5776
www.gcps.k12.va.us/
Galax JSHS 500/8-12
200 Maroon Tide Dr 24333 276-236-2991
Jody Ray, prin. Fax 236-8011

Gate City, Scott, Pop. 2,016
Scott County SD 3,700/K-12
340 E Jackson St 24251 276-386-6118
John Ferguson, supt. Fax 386-2684
scott.k12.va.us/
Gate City HS 500/10-12
178 Harry Fry Dr 24251 276-386-7522
Greg Ervin, prin. Fax 386-2695
Gate City MS 500/7-9
170 Harry Fry Dr 24251 276-386-6065
Cindy Dorton, prin. Fax 386-2556
Scott County Career & Technical Center Vo/Tech
150 Broadwater Ave 24251 276-386-6515
Ralph Quesinberry, prin. Fax 386-2852
Other Schools – See Duffield, Nickelsville

Glade Spring, Washington, Pop. 1,443
Washington County SD
Supt. — See Abingdon
Glade Spring MS 300/6-8
33474 Stagecoach Rd 24340 276-739-3800
Kelly Holmes, prin. Fax 429-4211
Henry HS 400/9-12
31437 Hillman Hwy 24340 276-739-3700
Keith Perrigan, prin. Fax 944-2125

Glen Allen, Henrico, Pop. 14,427
Henrico County SD
Supt. — See Richmond
Academy at Virginia Randolph 300/Alt
2204 Mountain Rd 23060 804-261-5085
Tamika Lawson, prin. Fax 261-5087
Center for Education & Human Development 9-12
10700 Staples Mill Rd 23060 804-360-0731
Tracie Weston, prin.
Center for Information Technology 9-12
4801 Twin Hickory Rd 23059 804-364-8000
Leonard Pritchard, prin.
Deep Run HS 1,900/9-12
4801 Twin Hickory Rd 23059 804-364-8000
Leonard Pritchard, prin. Fax 364-0887
Glen Allen HS 9-12
10700 Staples Mill Rd 23060 804-501-3300
Tracie Weston, prin. Fax 501-3309
Holman MS 6-8
600 Concourse Blvd 23059 804-346-1300
Brian Fellows Ph.D., prin.
Hungary Creek MS 900/6-8
4909 Francistown Rd 23060 804-527-2640
Robert Moose, prin. Fax 527-2642
Short Pump MS 800/6-8
4701 Pouncey Tract Rd 23059 804-360-0800
Dr. Mark Chamberlain, prin. Fax 360-0808

ECPI University Post-Sec.
4305 Cox Rd 23060 804-934-0100
Stratford University Post-Sec.
11104 W Broad St 23060 804-290-4231

Glenns, Middlesex

Rappahannock Community College Post-Sec.
12745 College Dr 23149 804-758-6700

Gloucester, Gloucester
Gloucester County SD 5,000/PK-12
6489 Main St 23061 804-693-5300
Dr. Howard B. Kiser, supt. Fax 693-1426
gets.gc.k12.va.us/
Gloucester HS 2,000/9-12
6680 Short Ln 23061 804-693-2526
Dr. Layton Beverage, prin. Fax 693-7685
Page MS 200/8-8
6636 Short Ln 23061 804-693-2540
Dr. Travis Burns, prin. Fax 693-2111

Gloucester Point, Gloucester, Pop. 9,193

College of William and Mary Post-Sec.
PO Box 1346 23062 804-684-7000

Goochland, Goochland, Pop. 840
Goochland County SD 2,500/PK-12
PO Box 169 23063 804-556-5630
James Lane, supt. Fax 556-3847
www.glnd.k12.va.us
Goochland HS 800/9-12
3250 River Rd W Ste A 23063 804-556-5322
Mike Newman, prin. Fax 556-6485
Goochland MS 600/6-8
3250 River Rd W Ste B 23063 804-556-5320
Johnette Burdette, prin. Fax 556-6223

Great Falls, Fairfax, Pop. 14,902

AVI Career Training Post-Sec.
10130 Colvin Run Rd Ste A 22066 703-759-2200

Gretna, Pittsylvania, Pop. 1,254
Pittsylvania County SD
Supt. — See Chatham
Gretna HS 600/9-12
PO Box 398 24557 434-656-2246
Kenyon Scott, prin. Fax 656-3045
Gretna MS 500/6-8
201 Coffey St 24557 434-656-2217
Vera Glass, prin. Fax 656-6122

Grundy, Buchanan, Pop. 1,011
Buchanan County SD 3,300/PK-12
PO Box 833 24614 276-935-4551
Larry Ashby, supt. Fax 935-7150
www.buc.k12.va.us
Buchanan County Tech & Career Center Vo/Tech
1124 Almarine Dr 24614 276-935-4541
Sue Cook, prin. Fax 935-4682
Grundy HS 500/9-12
1300 Golden Wave Dr 24614 276-935-2106
Leslie Horne, prin. Fax 935-8602
Other Schools – See Honaker, Hurley, Pilgrims Knob

Appalachian School of Law Post-Sec.
PO Box 2825 24614 800-895-7411

Halifax, Halifax, Pop. 1,298
Halifax County SD 5,600/K-12
PO Box 1849 24558 434-476-2171
Dr. Merle Herndon, supt. Fax 476-1858
www.halifax.k12.va.us
Halifax County Career Center Vo/Tech
PO Box 1849 24558 434-476-5515
David Riddle, lead tchr. Fax 476-5527
Other Schools – See South Boston

Hamilton, Loudoun, Pop. 498
Loudoun County SD
Supt. — See Ashburn
Harmony MS 600/6-8
38174 W Colonial Hwy 20158 540-751-2500
Sherron Gladden, prin. Fax 751-2501

The Catholic Distance University Post-Sec.
120 E Colonial Hwy 20158 888-254-4238

Hampden Sydney, Prince Edward, Pop. 1,436

Hampden-Sydney College Post-Sec.
1 College Rd 23943 434-223-6000

Hampton, Hampton, Pop. 132,850
Hampton CSD 21,600/PK-12
1 Franklin St 23669 757-727-2000
Dr. Linda Shifflette, supt. Fax 727-2002
www.hampton.k12.va.us
Bethel HS 1,900/9-12
1067 Big Bethel Rd 23666 757-825-4400
Ralph Saunders, prin. Fax 825-4465
Campus at Lee Alt
1646 Briarfield Rd 23669 757-727-1327
Myra Chambers, dir.
Davis MS 600/6-8
1435 Todds Ln 23666 757-825-4520
Elizabeth Winebarger, prin Fax 825-4533
Eaton MS 700/6-8
2108 Cunningham Dr 23666 757-825-4540
Mark Hudson, prin. Fax 825-4551
Hampton HS 1,700/9-12
1491 W Queen St 23669 757-825-4430
Dr. Sharmaine Grove, prin. Fax 825-4711
Jones Magnet MS 700/6-8
1819 Nickerson Blvd 23663 757-850-7900
Dr. Daniel Bowling, prin. Fax 850-5395
Kecoughtan HS 1,900/9-12
522 Woodland Rd 23669 757-850-5000
Raymond Haynes, prin. Fax 850-5153
Lindsay MS 600/6-8
1636 Briarfield Rd 23661 757-825-4560
Angela Byrd-Wright, prin. Fax 825-4839
Phoebus HS 1,300/9-12
100 Ireland St 23663 757-727-1000
William Beverley, prin. Fax 727-0981
Spratley Gifted Center 600/3-8
339 Woodland Rd 23669 757-850-5032
Dr. Kenneth Crum, prin. Fax 850-5186
Syms MS 1,200/6-8
170 Fox Hill Rd 23669 757-850-5050
Sharon Slater, prin. Fax 850-5413

Jointly Operated Vo Tech SD
Supt. — None - Lolita Hall, dir.
New Horizons Career & Tech-Butler Farm Vo/Tech
520 Butler Farm Rd 23666 757-766-1100
David Creamer, prin. Fax 766-3591

Newport News CSD
Supt. — See Newport News
New Horizons Alt
520 Butler Farm Rd 23666 757-766-1100
David Creamer, prin. Fax 766-3591

Regional Academic Governors SD
Supt. — See Richmond
New Horizons Governor's S Science/Tech. 11-12
520 Butler Farm Rd 23666 757-766-1100
Vikki Wismer, dir. Fax 766-3591

Bethel College Post-Sec.
1705 Todds Ln 23666 757-826-1883
Bryant & Stratton College Post-Sec.
4410 Claiborne Sq E Ste 233 23666 757-896-6001
Faith Outreach Education Center 100/PK-12
3105 W Mercury Blvd 23666 757-838-8949
Bobby Hartman, prin. Fax 838-4434
Hampton Christian MSHS 300/6-12
2419 N Armistead Ave 23666 757-838-7427
Frank Carvell, supt. Fax 827-8067
Hampton University 23669 Post-Sec.
757-727-5000
Riverside Academy Post-Sec.
2244 Executive Dr 23666 757-315-3683
Thomas Nelson Community College Post-Sec.
99 Thomas Nelson Dr 23666 757-825-2700
Virginia School of Hair Design Post-Sec.
101 W Queens Way 23669 757-722-0211

Harrisonburg, Harrisonburg, Pop. 47,739
Harrisonburg CSD 4,600/K-12
1 Court Sq 22802 540-434-9916
Scott Kizner, supt. Fax 434-5196
www.harrisonburg.k12.va.us
Harrisonburg HS 1,300/9-12
1001 Garbers Church Rd 22801 540-433-2651
Tracy Shaver, prin. Fax 433-3595
Harrison MS 800/5-8
1311 W Market St 22801 540-434-1949
Don Vale, prin. Fax 434-4052
Skyline MS 500/5-8
470 Linda Ln 22802 540-434-6862
Joe Glick, prin. Fax 434-6453

Jointly Operated Vo Tech SD
Supt. — None - Lolita Hall, dir.
Massanutten Tech Center Vo/Tech
325 Pleasant Valley Rd 22801 540-434-5961
Fax 434-1402

Rockingham County SD 11,300/PK-12
100 Mount Clinton Pike 22802 540-564-3200
Dr. Carol Fenn, supt. Fax 564-3241
www.rockingham.k12.va.us/
Other Schools – See Bridgewater, Broadway, Dayton, Elkton, Penn Laird

---

Eastern Mennonite S 400/K-12
801 Parkwood Dr 22802 540-236-6000
Paul Leaman, head sch Fax 236-6028
Eastern Mennonite University Post-Sec.
1200 Park Rd 22802 540-432-4000
James Madison University Post-Sec.
800 S Main St 22807 540-568-6211
National College Post-Sec.
1515 Country Club Rd 22802 540-432-0943
Rockingham Memorial Hospital Post-Sec.
235 Cantrell Ave 22801 540-564-5407

Haymarket, Prince William, Pop. 1,713
Prince William County SD
Supt. — See Manassas
Battlefield HS 3,000/9-12
15000 Graduation Dr 20169 571-261-4400
Amy Ethridge-Conti, prin. Fax 261-4411
Reagan MS 6-8
15801 Tanning House Pl 20169 571-402-3500
Ed Stephenson Ed.D., prin.

Haysi, Dickenson, Pop. 495
Dickenson County SD
Supt. — See Clintwood
Haysi HS 300/9-12
PO Box G 24256 276-865-5126
John Whitner, prin. Fax 865-5240

Heathsville, Northumberland, Pop. 142
Northumberland County SD
Supt. — See Lottsburg
Northumberland HS 400/9-12
201 Academic Ln 22473 804-580-5192
David Dixon, prin.
Northumberland MS 300/6-8
175 Academic Ln 22473 804-580-5753
Robert Bailey, prin.

Herndon, Fairfax, Pop. 22,605
Fairfax County SD
Supt. — See Falls Church
Carson MS 1,300/7-8
13618 McLearen Rd 20171 703-925-3600
August Frattali, prin. Fax 925-3697
Herndon HS 2,300/9-12
700 Bennett St 20170 703-810-2200
William Bates, prin. Fax 810-2262
Herndon MS 1,000/7-8
901 Locust St 20170 703-904-4800
Justine Klena, prin. Fax 904-4897

Auburn S 50/K-10
13525 Dulles Tech Dr # 101 20171 703-793-9353
Liz Caffrey, dir. Fax 793-9355
Temple Baptist S 300/PK-12
1545 Dranesville Rd 20170 703-437-7400
Dr. Samuel Dalton, admin. Fax 437-7430

Highland Springs, Henrico, Pop. 15,359
Henrico County SD
Supt. — See Richmond
Center for Engineering 9-12
15 S Oak Ave 23075 804-328-4000
Dr. Dana Bost, prin.
Highland Springs HS 1,800/9-12
15 S Oak Ave 23075 804-328-4000
Dr. Dana Bost, prin. Fax 328-4013
Highland Springs Technical Center Vo/Tech
100 Tech Dr 23075 804-328-4075
Johnnie Collie, prin. Fax 328-4074
Highland Springs Adult Ed Center Adult
201 E Nine Mile Rd 23075 804-328-4095
Beverly Godwin, prin.

Hillsville, Carroll, Pop. 2,663
Carroll County SD 3,800/K-12
605 Pine St Ste 9 24343 276-728-3191
Dr. Strader Blankenship, supt. Fax 728-3195
www.ccpsd.k12.va.us
Carroll County HS 900/9-12
100 Cavs Ln 24343 276-728-2125
Charles Thompson, prin. Fax 728-9067
Carroll County MS 700/6-8
1036 N Main St 24343 276-728-2382
Marc Quesenberry, prin. Fax 728-4089

Honaker, Russell, Pop. 1,440
Buchanan County SD
Supt. — See Grundy
Council HS 100/8-12
7802 Helen Henderson Hwy 24260 276-859-2627
Karen Taylor, prin. Fax 859-6227

Russell County SD
Supt. — See Lebanon
Honaker HS 500/8-12
PO Box 764 24260 276-873-6363
Tony Bush, prin. Fax 873-7252

Hopewell, Hopewell, Pop. 21,953
Hopewell CSD 4,200/K-12
103 N 12th Ave 23860 804-541-6400
Dr. John Fahey, supt. Fax 541-6401
www.hopewell.k12.va.us
Hopewell HS 1,100/9-12
400 S Mesa Dr 23860 804-541-6402
Dr. Rodney Berry, prin. Fax 541-6403
Woodlawn Learning Center 300/Alt
1100 Dinwiddie Ave 23860 804-541-6414
Belinda Piercy, prin. Fax 458-2064
Woodson MS 900/6-8
1000 Winston Churchill Dr 23860 804-541-6404
Shannon Royster, prin. Fax 541-6405

West End Christian S 200/PK-12
1600 Atlantic St 23860 804-458-6142
Kim Ange, prin. Fax 458-7183

Hot Springs, Bath, Pop. 727
Bath County SD
Supt. — See Warm Springs
Bath County HS 300/8-12
464 Charger Ln 24445 540-839-2431
Sarah Rowe, prin. Fax 839-3290

Hurley, Buchanan
Buchanan County SD
Supt. — See Grundy
Hurley HS 200/8-12
6339 Hurley Rd 24620 276-566-7642
Pam Dotson, prin. Fax 566-7127

Hurt, Pittsylvania, Pop. 1,295

Faith Christian Academy 200/PK-12
PO Box 670 24563 434-324-8276
Lisa Moore, admin. Fax 324-8279

Independence, Grayson, Pop. 933
Grayson County SD 1,800/PK-12
PO Box 888 24348 276-773-2832
Kevin Chalfant, supt. Fax 773-2939
www.grayson.k12.va.us
Grayson County Career & Technical Center Vo/Tech
PO Box 707 24348 276-773-2951
Karen Blevins, prin. Fax 773-2396
Grayson County HS 800/8-12
PO Box 828 24348 276-773-2131
Brandi Ray, prin. Fax 773-2682

Isle of Wight, Isle of Wight

Isle of Wight Academy 700/PK-12
PO Box 105 23397 757-357-3866
Benjamin Vaughan, hdmstr. Fax 357-6886

Jetersville, Nottoway
Jointly Operated Vo Tech SD
Supt. — None – Lolita Hall, dir.
Amelia-Nottoway Vo Tech Ctr Vo/Tech
148 Votech Rd 23083 434-645-7854
Fax 645-1044

Nottoway County SD
Supt. — See Nottoway
Piedmont Alternative S Alt
128 Votech Rd 23083 434-645-7854
Parcilla Salley, dir. Fax 645-1044

Jonesville, Lee, Pop. 1,025
Lee County SD 3,200/PK-12
153 School Board Pl 24263 276-346-2107
Mark Carter, supt. Fax 346-0307
www.leectysch.com/
Jonesville MS 300/6-8
160 Bulldog Cir 24263 276-346-1011
Lisa Brewer, prin. Fax 346-1411
Lee HS 700/9-12
200 General Ln 24263 276-346-0173
Connie Daugherty, prin. Fax 346-4032
Other Schools – See Ben Hur, Ewing, Pennington Gap

Kenbridge, Lunenburg, Pop. 1,244
Lunenburg County SD 1,600/PK-12
PO Box 710 23944 434-676-2467
Dora Wynn, supt. Fax 676-1000
www.lun.k12.va.us
Other Schools – See Victoria

Keysville, Charlotte, Pop. 820
Regional Academic Governors SD
Supt. — See Richmond
Governor's S of Southside VA 11-12
200 Daniel Rd 23947 434-736-2086
Patrizia Humphrey, dir. Fax 736-2082

Southside Virginia Community College Post-Sec.
200 Daniel Rd 23947 434-736-2018

Kilmarnock, Lancaster, Pop. 1,466
Lancaster County SD
Supt. — See Weems
Lancaster MS 500/4-8
191 School St 22482 804-435-1681
Kimberly Hammond, prin. Fax 435-0589

King and Queen Court House, King and Queen, Pop. 84
King & Queen County SD 800/PK-12
PO Box 97 23085 804-785-5981
Charles Clare, supt. Fax 785-5686
www.kqps.net
Central HS 300/8-12
17024 The Trl 23085 804-785-6102
Bernard Davis, prin. Fax 785-5129

King George, King George, Pop. 4,296
King George County SD 4,100/K-12
PO Box 1239 22485 540-775-5833
Robert B. Benson, supt. Fax 775-2165
www.kgcs.k12.va.us
King George HS 1,300/9-12
10100 Foxes Way 22485 540-775-3535
Clifton Conway, prin. Fax 775-8426
King George MS 700/7-8
8246 Dahlgren Rd 22485 540-775-2331
Kevin Newman, prin. Fax 775-0263

King William, King William, Pop. 228
King William County SD 2,200/PK-12
PO Box 185 23086 804-769-3434
Dr. Mark Jones, supt. Fax 769-3312
www.kwcps.k12.va.us
Hamilton-Holmes MS 500/6-8
18444 King William Rd 23086 804-769-3434
Beverly Young, prin.
King William HS, 80 Cavalier Dr 23086 600/9-12
Dr. Stanley Waskiewicz, prin. 804-769-3434

Lancaster, Lancaster
Lancaster County SD
Supt. — See Weems
Lancaster HS 400/9-12
PO Box 790 22503 804-462-5177
Dr. Lorena Watrous, prin. Fax 462-5174

Lawrenceville, Brunswick, Pop. 1,414
Brunswick County SD 2,100/PK-12
1718 Farmers Field Rd 23868 434-848-3138
Dr. Oliver Spencer, supt. Fax 848-4001
www.brun.k12.va.us
Brunswick HS 600/9-12
2171 Lawrenceville Plank Rd 23868 434-848-2716
Dr. Mark Harrison, prin. Fax 848-6303
Russell MS 500/6-8
19400 Christanna Hwy 23868 434-848-2132
Jerome Williams, prin. Fax 848-6201

Brunswick Academy 400/PK-12
2100 Planters Rd 23868 434-848-2220
Brad Farmer, head sch Fax 848-4729
St. Paul's College Post-Sec.
115 College Dr 23868 434-848-3111

Lebanon, Russell, Pop. 3,395
Russell County SD 4,200/PK-12
PO Box 8 24266 276-889-6500
Dr. Brenda Hess, supt. Fax 889-6508
www.russell.k12.va.us
Lebanon HS 700/8-12
PO Box 217 24266 276-889-6539
Brian Hooker, prin. Fax 889-0622
Russell County Alternative Center Alt
PO Box 8 24266 276-889-6521
Michael Roberson, prin. Fax 889-6527
Russell County Career & Technology Ctr Vo/Tech
PO Box 849 24266 276-889-6550
Brenda Campbell, prin. Fax 889-4470
Other Schools – See Castlewood, Honaker

Leesburg, Loudoun, Pop. 41,241
Loudoun County SD
Supt. — See Ashburn
Belmont Ridge MS 1,300/6-8
19045 Upper Belmont Pl 20176 571-252-2220
Michael Surma, prin. Fax 669-1455
Douglass S Alt
407 E Market St 20176 571-252-2060
Dr. John Robinson, prin. Fax 771-6555
Harper Park MS 1,000/6-8
701 Potomac Station Dr NE 20176 571-252-2820
Elizabeth Robinson, prin. Fax 779-8867
Heritage HS 1,300/9-12
520 Evergreen Mill Rd SE 20175 571-252-2800
Jeffrey Adam, prin. Fax 252-2801
Loudoun County HS 1,400/9-12
415 Dry Mill Rd SW 20175 571-252-2000
William Oblas, prin. Fax 252-2001
Monroe Technology Center Vo/Tech
715 Childrens Center Rd SW 20175 571-252-2080
Wagner Grier, prin. Fax 771-6563
Simpson MS 1,000/6-8
490 Evergreen Mill Rd SE 20175 571-252-2840
Chad Runfola, prin. Fax 771-6643
Smart's Mill MS 1,000/6-8
850 N King St 20176 571-252-2030
William Waldman, prin. Fax 252-2043
Tuscarora HS 9-12
801 N King St 20176 571-252-1900
Pamela Paul-Jacobs, prin. Fax 252-1901

Lexington, Lexington, Pop. 6,907
Lexington CSD 500/K-8
300 Diamond St 24450 540-463-7146
Dr. Daniel Lyons, supt. Fax 464-5230
www.lexedu.org/
Lylburn-Downing MS 200/6-8
302 Diamond St 24450 540-463-3532
Richard Dowd, prin.

Rockbridge County SD 2,800/PK-12
1972 Big Spring Dr 24450 540-463-7386
John Reynolds, supt. Fax 463-7823
www.rockbridge.k12.va.us/
Maury River MS 400/6-8
600 Waddell St 24450 540-463-3129
Phillip Thompson, prin. Fax 464-4838
Rockbridge County HS 1,000/9-12
143 Greenhouse Rd 24450 540-463-5555
Scott Jefferies, prin. Fax 463-6152

Rockbridge Christian Academy 100/PK-12
PO Box 570 24450 540-463-5456
Mary Phillips, admin. Fax 463-3485
Virginia Military Institute Post-Sec.
319 Letcher Ave 24450 540-464-7230
Washington and Lee University Post-Sec.
204 W Washington St 24450 540-458-8400

Locust Grove, Orange
Orange County SD
Supt. — See Orange
Locust Grove MS 700/6-8
6368 Flat Run Rd 22508 540-661-4480
Kimberly Crandall, prin. Fax 854-6430

Germanna Community College Post-Sec.
2130 Germanna Hwy 22508 540-423-9030

Locust Hill, Middlesex
Middlesex County SD
Supt. — See Saluda
St. Clare Walker MS 300/6-8
PO Box 9 23092 804-758-2561
Tracy Seitz, prin. Fax 758-0834

Lorton, Fairfax, Pop. 17,779
Fairfax County SD
Supt. — See Falls Church
South County HS 2,000/9-12
8501 Silverbrook Rd 22079 703-446-1600
Jane Lipp, prin. Fax 446-1697
South County MS 6-8
8700 Laurel Crest Dr 22079 703-690-5500
Marsha Manning, prin. Fax 690-5597

Lottsburg, Northumberland
Northumberland County SD 1,500/PK-12
2172 Northumberland Hwy 22511 804-529-6134
Dr. Rebecca Gates, supt. Fax 529-6449
www.nucps.net
Other Schools – See Heathsville

Lovingston, Nelson, Pop. 495
Nelson County SD 2,000/PK-12
PO Box 276 22949 434-263-7100
Roger Dale Collins Ed.D., supt. Fax 263-7115
www.nelson.k12.va.us
Nelson County HS 600/9-12
6919 Thomas Nelson Hwy 22949 434-263-8317
Todd Weidow, prin. Fax 263-5987
Nelson MS 400/6-8
6925 Thomas Nelson Hwy 22949 434-263-4801
Matt Schoener, prin. Fax 263-4483

Low Moor, Alleghany, Pop. 252
Alleghany County SD 2,700/K-12
PO Box 140 24457 540-863-1800
Dr. Sarah Campbell, supt. Fax 863-1804
www.alleghany.k12.va.us/
Other Schools – See Covington

Luray, Page, Pop. 4,837
Page County SD 3,700/PK-12
735 W Main St 22835 540-743-6533
Fax 743-7784
www.pagecounty.k12.va.us
Luray HS 500/9-12
243 Bulldog Dr 22835 540-743-3800
Dr. Randall Thomas, prin. Fax 743-5524
Luray MS 400/6-8
14 Luray Ave 22835 540-843-2660
Kelly Lawton, prin. Fax 743-1709
Page County Technical Ctr Vo/Tech
525 Middleburg Rd 22835 540-778-2878
Todd Lynn, prin. Fax 778-4272
Other Schools – See Shenandoah

Lynchburg, Lynchburg, Pop. 73,910
Campbell County SD
Supt. — See Rustburg
Brookville HS 1,000/9-12
100 Laxton Rd 24502 434-239-2636
Tom Cole, prin. Fax 239-6706
Brookville MS 700/6-8
320 Bee Dr 24502 434-239-9267
Edwin Martin, prin. Fax 237-8974

Lynchburg CSD 8,600/PK-12
PO Box 2497 24505 434-515-5000
Dr. Scott Brabrand, supt. Fax 846-1500
www.lcsedu.net
Amelia Pride Center Alt
1200 Polk St Ste1208 24504 434-522-3742
Gloria C. Preston, prin. Fax 522-2308
Dunbar MS for Innovation 600/6-8
1200 Polk St 24504 434-522-3740
Brian Wray, prin. Fax 522-3727
Glass HS 1,400/9-12
2111 Memorial Ave 24501 434-522-3712
Dr. Tracy Richardson, prin. Fax 522-3741
Heritage HS 1,100/9-12
3020 Wards Ferry Rd 24502 434-582-1147
Timothy Beatty, prin. Fax 582-1137
Linkhorne MS 600/6-8
2525 Linkhorne Dr 24503 434-384-5150
Robert Kerns, prin. Fax 384-2810
PHOENIX Alternative S Alt
PO Box 4726 24502 434-832-8130
Anne Bond-Gentry, prin. Fax 832-3132
Sandusky MS 600/6-8
805 Chinook Pl 24502 434-477-5959
Maria Jaeger, prin. Fax 582-1183
Adult Learning Center Adult
1015 Miller Park Sq 24501 434-515-5000
Gloria C. Preston, prin. Fax 522-2320

Regional Academic Governors SD
Supt. — See Richmond
Central VA Governor's S Science & Tech 11-12
3020 Wards Ferry Rd 24502 434-582-1104
Dr. Steve Smith, dir. Fax 239-4140

Centra Health Post-Sec.
1920 Atherholt Rd 24501 434-947-4705
Central Virginia Community College Post-Sec.
3506 Wards Rd 24502 434-832-7600
Doss Junior Academy 100/K-10
19 George St 24502 434-237-1899
Holy Cross Regional S 200/PK-12
2125 Langhorne Rd 24501 434-847-5436
Patricia Culbreth, prin. Fax 847-4156
Liberty Christian Academy 1,900/PK-12
100 Mountain View Rd 24502 434-832-2000
John Patterson, supt. Fax 832-2027
Liberty University Post-Sec.
1971 University Blvd 24502 434-582-2000
Lynchburg College Post-Sec.
1501 Lakeside Dr 24501 434-544-8100
Lynchburg General Hosp School of Nursing Post-Sec.
1901 Tate Springs Rd 24501 434-947-3070
Miller-Motte Technical College Post-Sec.
1011 Creekside Ln 24502 434-239-5222
National College Post-Sec.
104 Candlewood Ct 24502 434-239-3500
New Covenant S 300/K-12
122 Fleetwood Dr 24501 434-847-8313
Rev. John Heaton, hdmstr.
Randolph College Post-Sec.
2500 Rivermont Ave 24503 434-947-8000
Virginia Episcopal S 200/9-12
400 V E S RD 24503 434-385-3600
Thomas Battle, hdmstr. Fax 385-3603
Virginia University of Lynchburg Post-Sec.
2058 Garfield Ave 24501 434-528-5276

Machipongo, Northampton
Northampton County SD 1,700/PK-12
7207 Young St 23405 757-678-5151
Dr. Walter Clemons, supt. Fax 678-7267
www.ncpsk12.com
TECH Center Alt
7207 Young St 23405 757-678-5151
Melinda Phillips, prin. Fax 678-7267
Other Schools – See Eastville

Mc Lean, Fairfax, Pop. 46,663
Fairfax County SD
Supt. — See Falls Church
Cooper MS 800/7-8
977 Balls Hill Rd 22101 703-442-5800
Arlene Randall, prin. Fax 442-5897
Langley HS 2,000/9-12
6520 Georgetown Pike 22101 703-287-2700
Matt Ragone, prin. Fax 287-2797
Mc Lean HS 2,000/9-12
1633 Davidson Rd 22101 703-714-5700
Ellen Reilly, prin. Fax 714-5797

Madeira S 300/9-12
8328 Georgetown Pike 22067 703-556-8200
Pilar Cabeza de Vaca, hdmstr. Fax 803 3289
Oakcrest HS 200/6-12
850 Balls Hill Rd 22101 703-790-5450
Ellen Cavanagh, prin. Fax 790-5380
Potomac S 1,000/K-12
1301 Potomac School Rd 22101 703-356-4100
Fax 883-9031
Reformed Theological Seminary Post-Sec.
1651 Old Meadow Rd Ste 300 22102 703-448-3393

Madison, Madison, Pop. 214
Madison County SD 1,800/PK-12
60 School Board Ct 22727 540-948-3780
Dr. Matthew Eberhardt, supt. Fax 948-6988
www.madisonschools.k12.va.us
Madison County HS 600/9-12
68 Mountaineer Ln 22727 540-948-3785
Mike Sisler, prin. Fax 948-4425
Wetsel MS 400/6-8
186 Mountaineer Ln 22727 540-948-3783
Timothy Taylor, prin. Fax 948-4809

Madison Heights, Amherst, Pop. 11,015
Amherst County SD
Supt. — See Amherst
Monelison MS 600/6-8
257 Trojan Rd 24572 434-846-1307
William Wells, prin. Fax 846-5318

Temple Christian S 300/PK-12
PO Box 970 24572 434-846-0024
Stephanie Sweat, prin. Fax 846-1807

Manassas, Manassas, Pop. 36,735
Manassas CSD 6,800/K-12
8700 Centreville Rd Ste 400 20110 571-377-6000
Dr. Catherine Magouyrk, supt. Fax 257-8801
www.manassas.k12.va.us
Johnson Learning Center Alt
9051 Tudor Ln 20110 571-377-7250
Dr. Lukisa Barrera-Gibbs, prin. Fax 257-8844
Metz JHS 1,000/7-8
9700 Fairview Ave 20110 571-377-6800
Angela Burnett, prin. Fax 257-8615
Osbourn HS 2,000/9-12
9005 Tudor Ln 20110 571-377-7000
Cathy Benner, prin. Fax 530-0937

Prince William County SD 79,900/PK-12
PO Box 389 20108 703-791-7200
Steven Walts Ed.D., supt. Fax 791-8033
www.pwcs.edu
Benton MS 1,300/6-8
7411 Hoadly Rd 20112 703-791-0727
Kevin Smith, prin. Fax 791-0977
Jackson HS 2,500/9-12
8820 Rixlew Ln 20109 703-365-2900
Richard Nichols, prin. Fax 365-6984
New Directions Alt
8886 Rixlew Ln 20109 703-393-7261
Robert Eichorn, prin. Fax 393-3083
Osbourn Park HS 2,800/9-12
8909 Euclid Ave 20111 703-365-6500
Neil Beech, prin. Fax 365-6798
Parkside MS 1,100/6-8
8602 Mathis Ave 20110 703-361-3106
Mary Jane Boynton, prin. Fax 361-8993
Saunders MS 1,100/6-8
13557 Spriggs Rd 20112 703-670-9188
Myca Gray, prin. Fax 670-3078
Stonewall MS 1,100/6-8
10100 Lomond Dr 20109 703-361-3185
John Miller, prin. Fax 368-1266
Other Schools – See Bristow, Dumfries, Gainesville, Haymarket, Manassas Park, Nokesville, Triangle, Woodbridge

Regional Academic Governors SD
Supt. — See Richmond
Governor's S @ Innovation Park 11-12
10900 University Blvd 20110 703-993-7027
Karen Dalfrey Ph.D., dir. Fax 993-7025

American Military University Post-Sec.
10110 Battleview Pkwy # 114 20109 703-330-5398
Aviation Institute of Maintenance Post-Sec.
10640 Davidson Pl 20109 703-257-5515
DeVry University Post-Sec.
10432 Balls Ford Rd Ste 130 20109 866-613-8662
ECPI University Post-Sec.
10021 Balls Ford Rd # 100 20109 703-330-5300
Emmanuel Christian S 200/PK-12
8302 Spruce St 20111 703-369-3950
Allan Edgar, head sch Fax 330-9285
Northern Virginia Community College Post-Sec.
6901 Sudley Rd 20109 703-323-3000
Seton S 400/7-12
9314 Maple St 20110 703-368-3220
Anne Carroll, prin. Fax 393-1199
Strayer University Post-Sec.
9990 Battleview Pkwy 20109 703-330-8400

Manassas Park, Manassas Park, Pop. 13,791
Manassas Park CSD 3,000/PK-12
1 Park Center Ct Ste A 20111 703-335-8850
Dr. C. Bruce McDade, supt. Fax 361-4583
www.mpark.net
Manassas Park HS 800/9-12
8200 Euclid Ave 20111 703-361-9131
Eric Doyle, prin. Fax 330-1218
Manassas Park MS 700/6-8
8202 Euclid Ave 20111 703-361-1510
Eric Neff, prin. Fax 331-3538

Prince William County SD
Supt. — See Manassas
New Dominion Alternative S Alt
8220 Conner Dr 20111 703-361-9808
Michael Lint, prin. Fax 361-2864

Marion, Smyth, Pop. 5,878
Smyth County SD 4,900/PK-12
121 Bagley Cir Ste 300 24354 276-783-3791
Dr. Michael Robinson, supt. Fax 783-3291
www.scsb.org
Marion MS 500/6-8
134 Wilden St 24354 276-783-4466
Tim Duncan, prin. Fax 783-4952
Marion SHS 700/9-12
848 Stage St 24354 276-783-4731
Mike Davidson, prin. Fax 783-4117
Smyth Career & Technology Center Vo/Tech
147 Fox Valley Rd 24354 276-646-8117
Songia Widener, prin. Fax 646-4009
Other Schools – See Chilhowie, Saltville

Marshall, Fauquier, Pop. 1,447

Fresta Valley Christian S 200/PK-12
6428 Wilson Rd 20115 540-364-1929
Kevin Worsham, admin. Fax 364-4603

Martinsville, Martinsville, Pop. 13,595
Henry County SD
Supt. — See Collinsville
Laurel Park MS 700/6-8
280 Laurel Park Ave 24112 276-632-7216
Ben Gravely, prin. Fax 632-4865
Center for Community Learning Adult
340 Ridgedale Dr 24112 276-638-1668
Lynn Fitzgibbons, coord. Fax 638-3942

Martinsville CSD 2,400/PK-12
PO Box 5548 24115 276-403-5820
Pamela Heath, supt. Fax 403-5825
www.martinsville.k12.va.us
Martinsville HS 700/9-12
351 Commonwealth Blvd E 24112 276-403-5870
Ajamu Dixon, prin. Fax 632-1516
Martinsville MS 500/6-8
201 Brown St 24112 276-403-5886
Cynthia Tarpley, prin. Fax 638-4140

Regional Academic Governors SD
Supt. — See Richmond
Piedmont Governor's S for Math/Sci/Tech 11-12
PO Box 984 24114 276-403-5624
Brian Pace, prin. Fax 403-5638

National College Post-Sec.
905 Memorial Blvd N 24112 276-632-5621
Patrick Henry Community College Post-Sec.
645 Patriot Ave 24112 276-638-8777

Mathews, Mathews, Pop. 530
Mathews County SD 1,200/K-12
PO Box 369 23109 804-725-3909
David Holleran Ed.D., supt. Fax 725-3951
www.mathews.k12.va.us
Hunter MS 400/5-8
PO Box 339 23109 804-725-2434
Mike Comer, prin. Fax 725-2337
Mathews HS 400/9-12
PO Box 38 23109 804-725-3702
Albert Green, prin. Fax 725-5778

Matoaca, Chesterfield, Pop. 2,359
Chesterfield County SD
Supt. — See Chesterfield
Matoaca MS 1,100/6-8
6001 Hickory Rd 23803 804-590-3110
Wayne Carter, prin. Fax 590-9378

Max Meadows, Wythe, Pop. 559
Wythe County SD
Supt. — See Wytheville
Ft. Chiswell HS 500/9-12
1 Pioneer Trl 24360 276-637-3437
David Booher, prin. Fax 637-6316
Ft. Chiswell MS 400/6-8
101 Pioneer Trl 24360 276-637-4400
Rebecca James, prin. Fax 637-4452

Covenant Christian Academy 50/K-12
122 Apache Run 24360 276-637-4522
Cristy Munro, admin. Fax 637-0035

Mechanicsville, Hanover, Pop. 35,793
Hanover County SD
Supt. — See Ashland
Atlee HS 1,600/9-12
9414 Atlee Station Rd 23116 804-723-2100
Jennifer Cohodas, prin. Fax 723-2131
Chickahominy MS 1,200/6-8
9450 Atlee Station Rd 23116 804-723-2160
Mark Beckett, prin. Fax 723-2191
Georgetown S Alt
10000 Learning Ln 23116 804-723-3460
Fax 723-3470
Hanover Center for Trades and Technology Vo/Tech
10002 Learning Ln 23116 804-723-2020
Justin Roerink, prin. Fax 723-2039
Hanover HS 1,300/9-12
10307 Chamberlayne Rd 23116 804-723-3700
Dr. Dana Gresham, prin. Fax 723-3759
Jackson MS 1,100/6-8
8021 Lee Davis Rd 23111 804-723-2260
Nancy Disharoon, prin. Fax 723-2261
Lee-Davis HS 1,600/9-12
7052 Mechanicsville Tpke 23111 804-723-2200
Carol Moore, prin. Fax 723-2202
Oak Knoll MS 800/6-8
10295 Chamberlayne Rd 23116 804-365-4740
Caroline Harris, prin. Fax 365-4741

Melfa, Accomack, Pop. 396

Eastern Shore Community College Post-Sec.
29300 Lankford Hwy 23410 757-789-1789

Middleburg, Loudoun, Pop. 655

Foxcroft S 200/9-12
PO Box 5555 20118 540-687-5555
Mary Leipheimer, head sch Fax 687-8061
Middleburg Academy 200/9-12
35321 Notre Dame Ln 20117 540-687-5581
Dr. Ronald Sykes, hdmstr. Fax 687-3103

Middletown, Frederick, Pop. 1,237

Lord Fairfax Community College Post-Sec.
173 Skirmisher Ln 22645 540-868-7000

Midland, Fauquier, Pop. 218
Fauquier County SD
Supt. — See Warrenton
Southeastern Alternative S Alt
4484 Catlett Rd 22728 540-422-7390
Dr. Shelly Neibauer, prin. Fax 422-7409

Midlothian, Chesterfield
Chesterfield County SD
Supt. — See Chesterfield
Bailey Bridge MS 1,400/6-8
12501 Bailey Bridge Rd 23112 804-739-6200
Kume Goranson, prin. Fax 739-6211
Clover Hill HS 1,800/9-12
13301 Kelly Green Ln 23112 804-639-4940
Deborah Marks, prin. Fax 739-5000
Cosby HS 2,100/9-12
14300 Fox Club Pkwy 23112 804-639-8340
Dr. Brenda Mayo, prin. Fax 639-8357
James River HS 2,100/9-12
3700 James River Rd 23113 804-378-2420
Jeff Ellick, prin. Fax 379-2695
Manchester HS 1,900/9-12
12601 Bailey Bridge Rd 23112 804-739-6275
Pete Koste, prin. Fax 739-6340
Midlothian HS 1,500/9-12
401 Charter Colony Pkwy 23114 804-378-2440
Shawn Abel, prin. Fax 378-2450
Midlothian MS 1,200/6-8
13501 Midlothian Tpke 23113 804-378-2460
Patrick Stanfield, prin. Fax 378-7556
Robious MS 1,300/6-8
2701 Robious Crossing Dr 23113 804-378-2510
Juliette Myers, prin. Fax 378-2519
Swift Creek MS 1,000/6-8
3700 Old Hundred Rd S 23112 804-739-6315
James Frye, prin. Fax 739-6322
Tomahawk Creek MS 1,200/6-8
1600 Learning Place Loop 23114 804-378-7120
David Ellena, prin. Fax 794-2672

Empire Beauty School Post-Sec.
10807 Hull Street Rd 23112 800-575-5983

Milford, Caroline
Caroline County SD
Supt. — See Bowling Green
Caroline HS 1,200/9-12
19155 Rogers Clark Blvd 22514 804-633-9886
Charles Stevens, prin. Fax 633-2435
Caroline MS 900/6-8
13325 Devils Three Jump Rd 22514 804-633-6561
Angela Wright, prin. Fax 633-9014

Mineral, Louisa, Pop. 464
Louisa County SD 4,200/PK-12
953 Davis Hwy 23117 540-894-5115
Dr. Deborah Pettit, supt. Fax 894-0252
www.lcps.k12.va.us
Louisa HS 1,400/9-12
757 Davis Hwy 23117 540-894-5436
Tom Smith, prin. Fax 894-0534
Louisa MS 1,000/6-8
1009 Davis Hwy 23117 540-894-5457
Lee Downey, prin. Fax 894-5096

Moneta, Bedford
Bedford County SD
Supt. — See Bedford
Staunton River HS 1,100/9-12
1095 Golden Eagle Dr 24121 540-297-7151
Michelle Morgan, prin. Fax 297-4514
Staunton River MS 800/6-8
1293 Golden Eagle Dr 24121 540-297-4152
Karen Woodford, prin. Fax 297-4076

Monterey, Highland, Pop. 147
Highland County SD 200/PK-12
PO Box 250 24465 540-468-6300
Dr. William Crawford, supt. Fax 468-6306
www.highland.k12.va.us

Highland JSHS 100/6-12
PO Box 430 24465 540-468-6320
April Goff, prin. Fax 468-6332

Montross, Westmoreland, Pop. 382
Westmoreland County SD 1,700/PK-12
141 Opal Ln 22520 804-493-8018
Rebecca Lowry, supt. Fax 493-9323
division.wmlcps.org
Montross MS 400/6-8
8884 Menokin Rd 22520 804-493-9818
Jane Geyer, prin. Fax 493-0918
Washington & Lee HS 500/9-12
16380 Kings Hwy 22520 804-493-8015
Andrea Roane, prin. Fax 493-0243

Mount Jackson, Shenandoah, Pop. 1,975
Regional Academic Governors SD
Supt. — See Richmond
Massanutten Governor's S 11-12
6375 Main St 22842 540-477-3226
Susan Fream, prin. Fax 477-3523

Shenandoah County SD
Supt. — See Woodstock
Triplett Tech Vo/Tech
6375 Main St 22842 540-477-3161
Barry Arey, prin. Fax 477-2402

Mouth of Wilson, Grayson

Oak Hill Academy 100/8-12
2635 Oak Hill Rd 24363 276-579-2619
Dr. Michael Groves, pres. Fax 579-4722

Narrows, Giles, Pop. 2,019
Giles County SD
Supt. — See Pearisburg
Narrows HS 300/8-12
1 Green Wave Ln 24124 540-726-2384
Dr. Jill Hopkins, prin. Fax 726-2775

Naruna, Campbell
Campbell County SD
Supt. — See Rustburg
Campbell JSHS 600/6-12
PO Box 7 24576 434-376-2015
James Rinella, prin. Fax 376-5859

New Castle, Craig, Pop. 151
Craig County SD 700/PK-12
PO Box 245 24127 540-864-5191
Kelly Wilmore, supt. Fax 864-6885
www.craig.k12.va.us/
Craig County MSHS 400/6-12
25239 Craigs Creek Rd 24127 540-864-5185
Daniel Bowman, prin. Fax 864-5636

New Kent, New Kent, Pop. 227
Jointly Operated Vo Tech SD
Supt. — None - Lolita Hall, dir.
Bridging Comm Reg Career & Technical Ctr Vo/Tech
7930 New Chipping Ln 23124 804-966-8575

New Kent County SD 2,900/PK-12
PO Box 110 23124 804-966-9650
Dr. Robert Richardson, supt. Fax 966-9879
www.newkentschools.org/
New Kent County HS 900/9-12
7365 Egypt Rd 23124 804-966-9671
Yvonne Jones, prin. Fax 966-2773
New Kent County MS 700/6-8
7501 Egypt Rd 23124 804-966-9655
Sammy Fudge, prin. Fax 966-2703

New Market, Shenandoah, Pop. 2,116

Shenandoah Valley Academy 200/9-12
234 W Lee Hwy 22844 540-740-3161
Travis Johnson, prin. Fax 740-3336

Newport News, Newport News, Pop. 174,010
Jointly Operated Vo Tech SD
Supt. — None - Lolita Hall, dir.
New Horizons Career & Tech-Woodside Vo/Tech
13400 Woodside Ln 23608 757-874-4444
Bruce Schaffer, prin. Fax 872-8951

Newport News CSD 29,900/PK-12
12465 Warwick Blvd 23606 757-591-4500
Dr. Ashby Kilgore, supt. Fax 599-8270
www.sbo.nn.k12.va.us
Achievable Dream MSHS 400/6-12
5720 Marshall Ave 23605 757-283-7820
Marylin Sinclair-White, prin. Fax 283-7844
Aviation Academy Vo/Tech
902B Bland Blvd 23602 757-886-2745
Dr. Aaron Smith, dir. Fax 877-5647
Crittenden MS 800/6-8
6158 Jefferson Ave 23605 757-591-4900
Felicia Barnett, prin. Fax 838-8261
Denbigh HS 1,500/9-12
259 Denbigh Blvd 23608 757-886-7700
Anthony Vladu, prin. Fax 872-6542
Dozier MS 1,100/6-8
432 Industrial Park Dr 23608 757-888-3300
Lisa Gatz, prin. Fax 887-3662
Enterprise Academy Alt
813 Diligence Dr Ste 110 23606 757-591-4971
Dr. Willie Carrington, prin. Fax 873-3507
Gildersleeve MS 1,000/6-8
1 Minton Dr 23606 757-591-4862
Courtney Mompoint, prin. Fax 596-2059
Heritage HS 1,400/9-12
5800 Marshall Ave 23605 757-928-6100
Michael Nichols, prin. Fax 247-9058
Hines MS 900/6-8
561 McLawhorne Dr 23601 757-591-4878
Dr. Amanda Corbin-Staton, prin. Fax 591-0119
Huntington MS 600/6-8
3401 Orcutt Ave 23607 757-928-6846
Cleo Holloway, prin. Fax 245-8451

Menchville HS 1,900/9-12
275 Menchville Rd 23602 757-886-7722
Robert Surry, prin. Fax 875-0648
New Horizons Alt
13400 Woodside Ln 23608 757-874-4444
Roger Tomlinson, prin. Fax 872-8951
Passage MS 1,000/6-8
400 Atkinson Way 23608 757-886-7600
Janelle Spitz, prin. Fax 886-7661
Point Option Alternative S Alt
606 Denbigh Blvd Ste 200 23608 757-591-7408
Michael Bonfiglio, dir. Fax 865-4508
Telecommunications Program Vo/Tech
4 Minton Dr 23606 757-591-4687
Ray Price, dir. Fax 599-7925
Warwick HS 1,700/9-12
51 Copeland Ln 23601 757-591-4700
Dr. Rory Stapleton, prin. Fax 596-7415
Washington MS 400/6-8
3700 Chestnut Ave 23607 757-928-6860
Deborah Fields, prin. Fax 247-1119
Woodside HS 2,100/9-12
13450 Woodside Ln 23608 757-886-7530
Sean Callender, prin. Fax 877-0480
Other Schools – See Hampton

Apprentice School Post-Sec.
4101 Washington Ave 23607 757-380-3809
Centura College Post-Sec.
616 Denbigh Blvd 23608 757-874-2121
Christopher Newport University Post-Sec.
1 Avenue of the Arts 23606 757-594-7000
Denbigh Baptist Christian S 400/K-12
13010 Mitchell Point Rd 23602 757-249-2654
Robert Law, admin. Fax 249-9480
ECPI University Post-Sec.
1001 Omni Blvd Ste 305 23606 757-838-9191
Everest College Post-Sec.
803 Diligence Dr 23606 757-873-1111
Hampton Roads Academy 600/PK-12
739 Academy Ln 23602 757-884-9100
Peter Mertz, hdmstr. Fax 884-9137
Peninsula Catholic HS 300/8-12
600 Harpersville Rd 23601 757-596-7247
Jennie Franklin, prin. Fax 591-9718
Riverside School of Health Careers Post-Sec.
316 Main St 23601 757-240-2200

Nickelsville, Scott, Pop. 382
Scott County SD
Supt. — See Gate City
Twin Springs HS 300/8-12
273 Titan Ln 24271 276-479-2185
Sammy Parks, prin. Fax 479-3103

Nokesville, Prince William, Pop. 1,327
Fauquier County SD
Supt. — See Warrenton
Kettle Run HS 1,000/9-12
7403 Academic Ave 20181 540-422-7330
Major Warner, prin. Fax 422-7359

Prince William County SD
Supt. — See Manassas
Brentsville District HS 1,700/9-12
12109 Aden Rd 20181 703-594-2161
Katherine Meints, prin. Fax 594-2365
Patriot HS 100/9-12
10504 Kettle Run Rd 20181 703-594-3020
Michael Bishop Ed.D., prin. Fax 594-3022

Norfolk, Norfolk, Pop. 234,855
Norfolk CSD 32,800/PK-12
PO Box 1357 23501 757-628-3830
Dr. Samuel King, supt. Fax 628-3820
www.nps.k12.va.us/
Academy of Intl Studies at Rosemont 100/6-8
1330 Branch Rd 23513 757-852-4610
Adrian Day, prin. Fax 852-4615
Azalea Gardens MS 900/6-8
7721 Azalea Garden Rd 23518 757-531-3000
Dr. Reuthenia Clark, prin. Fax 531-3013
Blair MS 1,100/6-8
730 Spotswood Ave 23517 757-628-2400
Jeanne Kruger, prin. Fax 628-2422
Granby HS 2,200/9-12
7101 Granby St 23505 757-451-4110
Ted Daughtrey, prin. Fax 451-4118
Lafayette-Winona MS 700/6-8
1701 Alsace Ave 23509 757-628-2477
Margarietta Stallings, prin. Fax 628-2486
Lake Taylor HS 1,400/9-12
1384 Kempsville Rd 23502 757-892-3200
Reba Miller, prin. Fax 892-3210
Lake Taylor MS 900/6-8
1380 Kempsville Rd 23502 757-892-3230
Dr. Lynnell Gibson, prin. Fax 892-3240
Madison Career Alternative S Alt
3700 Bowdens Ferry Rd 23508 757-628-3417
Leesa Mundell, coord. Fax 628-3406
Maury HS 1,800/9-12
322 Shirley Ave 23517 757-628-3344
Karen Berg, prin. Fax 628-3359
Norfolk Technical Center Vo/Tech
1330 N Military Hwy 23502 757-892-3300
Fax 892-3305
Northside MS 800/6-8
8720 Granby St 23503 757-531-3150
Dr. Mark Makovec, prin. Fax 531-3144
Norview HS 1,900/9-12
6501 Chesapeake Blvd 23513 757-852-4500
Dr. Marjorie Stealey, prin. Fax 852-4511
Norview MS 1,100/6-8
6325 Sewells Point Rd 23513 757-852-4600
Dennis Fifer, prin. Fax 852-4590
Ruffner Academy 900/6-8
610 May Ave 23504 757-628-2466
Richard Fraley, prin. Fax 628-2465

Washington HS 1,500/9-12
1111 Park Ave 23504 757-628-3575
Kevin Monroe, prin. Fax 628-3566
Granby Evening School Adult
7101 Granby St 23505 757-451-4050
Terry Holmes, prin. Fax 451-4049

Regional Academic Governors SD
Supt. — See Richmond
Governor's S for the Arts 400/9-12
1542 W 49th St 23508 757-451-4711
Dr. Andrea Warren, dir. Fax 451-4715

Advanced Technology Institute Post-Sec.
994 Scott St 23502 800-468-1093
Binah HS 50/9-12
425 Washington Park 23517 757-627-2462
Centura College Post-Sec.
7020 N Military Hwy 23518 757-853-2121
De Paul Medical Center Post-Sec.
150 Kingsley Ln 23505 757-489-5120
Eastern Virginia Medical School Post-Sec.
PO Box 1980 23501 757-446-5600
Fortis College Post-Sec.
6300 Center Dr Ste 100 23502 757-499-5447
ITT Technical Institute Post-Sec.
863 Glenrock Rd Ste 100 23502 757-466-1260
Norfolk Academy 1,200/1-12
1585 Wesleyan Dr 23502 757-461-6236
Dennis Manning, hdmstr. Fax 455-3181
Norfolk Christian S 400/6-12
255 Thole St 23505 757-423-5770
Norfolk Collegiate S 500/6-12
7336 Granby St 23505 757-480-2885
Scott Kennedy, hdmstr. Fax 588-8655
Norfolk State University Post-Sec.
700 Park Ave 23504 757-823-8600
Old Dominion University Post-Sec.
5115 Hampton Blvd 23529 757-683-3000
Tidewater Community College Post-Sec.
121 College Pl 23510 757-822-1122
Tidewater Tech Post-Sec.
5301 E Princess Anne Rd 23502 757-858-8324
Virginia Wesleyan College Post-Sec.
1584 Wesleyan Dr 23502 757-455-3200
Wards Corner Beauty Academy Post-Sec.
7525 Tidewater Dr Ste 200 23505 757-583-3300
Yeshiva Aish Kodesh 50/9-12
612 Colonial Ave 23507 757-623-6070
Ramona Drury, prin. Fax 623-6074

N Chesterfield, Chesterfield
Chesterfield County SD
Supt. — See Chesterfield
Falling Creek MS 1,200/6-8
4724 Hopkins Rd, 804-743-3640
Melanie Knowles, prin. Fax 743-3644
Manchester MS 1,400/6-8
7401 Hull Street Rd, 804-674-1385
Sarah Fraher, prin. Fax 674-1394
Meadowbrook HS 1,800/9-12
4901 Cogbill Rd, 804-743-3675
Dr. Thomas Ferrell, prin. Fax 743-3686
Monacan HS 1,400/9-12
11501 Smoketree Dr, 804-378-2480
William Broyles, prin. Fax 378-2489
Providence MS 900/6-8
900 Starlight Ln, 804-674-1355
Dr. Derek Wasnock, prin. Fax 674-1361
Salem Church MS 900/6-8
9700 Salem Church Rd, 804-768-6225
Kenneth Butta, prin. Fax 768-6230

Bryant & Stratton College Post-Sec.
8141 Hull Street Rd, 804-745-2444
Centura College Post-Sec.
7914 Midlothian Tpke, 804-330-0111
Virginia College Post-Sec.
7200 Midlothian Tpke, 804-977-5100

Norton, Norton, Pop. 3,857
Norton CSD 900/PK-12
PO Box 498 24273 276-679-2330
Dr. Jeff Comer, supt. Fax 679-4315
www.nortoncityschools.org/
Burton HS 300/8-12
109 11th St SW 24273 276-679-2554
Aaron Williams, prin. Fax 679-2664

Nottoway, Nottoway
Nottoway County SD 2,300/PK-12
10321 E Colonial Trail Hwy 23955 434-645-9596
Dr. Daniel Grounard, supt. Fax 645-1266
www.nottowayschools.org/
Other Schools – See Crewe, Jetersville

Oak Hall, Accomack, Pop. 245
Accomack County SD
Supt. — See Accomac
Arcadia HS 600/9-12
PO Box 69 23416 757-824-5613
Rose Taylor, prin. Fax 824-0767
Arcadia MS 500/6-8
PO Box 220 23416 757-824-4862
Brian Tupper, prin. Fax 824-6618
Badger Vocational Education Center North Vo/Tech
PO Box 69 23416 757-824-6386
Rose Taylor, dir. Fax 824-0767

Oakton, Fairfax, Pop. 32,914

Dominion Christian S 200/K-12
10922 Vale Rd 22124 703-758-1055
Chuck Evans, head sch
Flint Hill S 1,100/PK-12
3320 Jermantown Rd 22124 703-584-2300
John Thomas, hdmstr. Fax 584-2369

Oakwood, Buchanan

Appalachian College of Pharmacy | Post-Sec.
1060 Dragon Rd 24631 | 276-498-4190

Onley, Accomack, Pop. 509
Accomack County SD
Supt. — See Accomac
Badger Vocational Education Center South | Vo/Tech
PO Box 302 23418 | 757-787-4522
Brian Patterson, dir. | Fax 787-2194
Nandua HS | 600/9-12
26350 Lankford Hwy 23418 | 757-787-4514
Brian Patterson, prin. | Fax 787-2194
Nandua MS | 500/6-8
20330 Warrior Dr 23418 | 757-787-7037
John Killmon, prin. | Fax 787-8807

Orange, Orange, Pop. 4,610
Orange County SD | 5,100/PK-12
200 Dailey Dr 22960 | 540-661-4550
Dr. Robert Grimesey, supt. | Fax 661-4599
www.ocss-va.org
Orange County HS | 1,600/9-12
201 Selma Rd 22960 | 540-661-4300
Doug Duncan, prin | Fax 661-4299
Prospect Heights MS | 500/6-8
202 Dailey Dr 22960 | 540-661-4400
Renee Bourke, prin. | Fax 661-4399
Other Schools – See Locust Grove

Palmyra, Fluvanna, Pop. 102
Fluvanna County SD | 2,600/K-12
14455 James Madison Hwy 22963 | 434-589-8208
Gena Keller, supt. | Fax 589-2248
www.fluco.org
Fluvanna County HS | 1,100/8-12
1918 Thomas Jefferson Pkwy 22963 | 434-589-3666
James Barlow, prin. | Fax 591-2075

Regional Academic Governors SD
Supt. — See Richmond
Blue Ridge Governor's HS | 9-12
PO Box 419 22963 | 434-589-8208
Marc Carraway, dir. | Fax 589-2248

Pearisburg, Giles, Pop. 2,771
Giles County SD | 2,500/PK-12
151 School Rd 24134 | 540-921-1421
Dr. Terry Arbogast, supt. | Fax 921-1424
sbo.gilesk12.org/
Giles County Technology Center | Vo/Tech
1827 Wenonah Ave 24134 | 540-921-1166
Forest Fowler, prin. | Fax 921-3906
Giles HS | 700/8-12
1825 Wenonah Ave 24134 | 540-921-1711
Jason Mills, prin. | Fax 921-3861
Other Schools – See Narrows

Pennington Gap, Lee, Pop. 1,760
Lee County SD
Supt. — See Jonesville
Pennington MS | 300/6-8
201 Middle School Dr 24277 | 276-546-1453
Michelle Warner, prin. | Fax 546-3515

Penn Laird, Rockingham
Rockingham County SD
Supt. — See Harrisonburg
Montevideo MS | 600/6-8
7648 McGaheysville Rd 22846 | 540-289-3401
Drew Miller, prin. | Fax 289-3601
Spotswood HS | 800/9-12
368 Blazer Dr 22846 | 540-289-3100
Dr. Steve Leaman, prin. | Fax 289-3301

Petersburg, Petersburg, Pop. 31,887
Petersburg CSD | 4,900/PK-12
255 E South Blvd 23805 | 804-732-0510
Stanley Jones, supt. | Fax 732-0514
www.petersburg.k12.va.us
Blandford Academy | 300/Alt
816 E Bank St 23803 | 804-862-7078
Pam Branch, coord. | Fax 862-7198
Johns JHS | 700/8-9
3101 Homestead Dr 23805 | 804-862-7020
Dr. Ronnie Watson, prin. | Fax 862-5434
Petersburg HS | 800/10-12
3101 Johnson Rd 23805 | 804-861-4884
Alicia Fields, prin. | Fax 862-7188

Regional Academic Governors SD
Supt. — See Richmond
Appomattox Reg. Governor's S Arts/Tech | 400/9-12
512 W Washington St 23803 | 804-722-0200
Dr. James Victory, dir. | Fax 722-0201

Richard Bland College | Post-Sec.
11301 Johnson Rd 23805 | 804-862-6100
Rock Church Academy | 50/PK-12
2301 County Dr 23803 | 804-733-3973
Kristen Davis, prin. | Fax 733-3093
Southside Regional Medical Center | Post-Sec.
737 S Sycamore St 23803 | 804-765-5800
Virginia State University | Post-Sec.
1 Hayden Dr 23806 | 804-524-5000

Pilgrims Knob, Buchanan
Buchanan County SD
Supt. — See Grundy
Twin Valley HS | 300/8-12
PO Box 190 24634 | 276-259-7818
Russell Street, prin. | Fax 259-6147

Poquoson, Poquoson, Pop. 11,990
Poquoson CSD | 2,300/PK-12
500 City Hall Ave 23662 | 757-868-3055
Dr. Jennifer Parish, supt. | Fax 868-3107
www.sbo.poquoson.k12.va.us
Poquoson HS | 800/9-12
51 Odd Rd 23662 | 757-868-7123
Bernard Wright, prin. | Fax 868-3141
Poquoson MS | 600/6-8
985 Poquoson Ave 23662 | 757-868-6031
Todd Perelli, prin. | Fax 868-4220

Portsmouth, Portsmouth, Pop. 93,145
Portsmouth CSD | 14,100/PK-12
PO Box 998 23705 | 757-393-8742
Dr. David Stuckwisch, supt. | Fax 393-5236
www.pps.k12.va.us
Churchland HS | 1,500/9-12
4301 Cedar Ln 23703 | 757-686-2500
Dr. Susan Bechtol, prin. | Fax 686-2504
Churchland MS | 900/7-8
4051 River Shore Rd 23703 | 757-686-2512
Dr. Kurt Kreassig, prin. | Fax 686-2515
Cradock MS | 600/7-8
21 Alden Ave 23702 | 757-393-8788
Elizabeth Horne, prin. | Fax 393-5020
New Directions Center | Alt
401 West Rd 23707 | 757-393-8728
Dr. Robert Sheppard, prin. | Fax 393-5351
Norcom HS | 1,300/9-12
1801 London Blvd 23704 | 757-393-5442
Dr. Rosalynn Sanderlin, prin. | Fax 393-5449
Waters MS | 500/7-8
600 Roosevelt Blvd 23701 | 757-558-2813
Dr. Eric Fischer, prin. | Fax 485-2829
Wilson HS | 1,300/9-12
1401 Elmhurst Ln 23701 | 757-465-2907
Timothy Johnson, prin. | Fax 405-1335
Adult Education | Adult
2801 Turnpike Rd 23707 | 757-393-8822
Judith Eure, prin. | Fax 393-5246
EXCEL Campus | Adult
1401 Elmhurst Ln 23701 | 757-465-2958
Timothy Johnson, prin. | Fax 465-2913

Alliance Christian Academy | 300/PK-12
5809 Portsmouth Blvd 23701 | 757-488-5552
Kim Johnson, admin. | Fax 488-3192
Hicks Academy of Beauty Culture | Post-Sec.
904 Loudoun Ave 23707 | 757-399-2400
Portsmouth Christian S | 700/PK-12
3214 Elliott Ave 23702 | 757-393-0725
Nancy Stafford, admin. | Fax 397-7487
Tidewater Community College | Post-Sec.
120 Campus Dr 23701 | 757-822-2124

Potomac Falls, Loudoun
Loudoun County SD
Supt. — See Ashburn
Potomac Falls HS | 1,500/9-12
46400 Algonkian Pkwy 20165 | 571-434-3200
Janice Koslowski, prin. | Fax 434-3201

Powhatan, Powhatan
Powhatan County SD | 3,800/PK-12
2320 Skaggs Rd 23139 | 804-598-5700
Dr. Margaret Meara, supt. | Fax 598-5705
www.powhatan.k12.va.us
Powhatan HS | 1,400/9-12
1800 Judes Ferry Rd 23139 | 804-598-5710
Kris Gwaltney, prin. | Fax 598-0036
Powhatan JHS | 700/7-8
4135 Old Buckingham Rd 23139 | 804-598-5782
Richard Stewart, prin. | Fax 403-3065
Powhatan Vo-Tech | Vo/Tech
1800 Judes Ferry Rd 23139 | 804-598-5700
Kathryn Garrett, prin.

Blessed Sacrament S | 400/PK-12
2501 Academy Rd 23139 | 804-598-4211
Dr. Tracy Bonday-deLeon, pres. | Fax 598-1053

Prince George, Prince George, Pop. 2,019
Prince George County SD | 6,400/PK-12
PO Box 400 23875 | 804-733-2700
Dr. Bobby Browder, supt. | Fax 733-2737
pgs.k12.va.us
Clements JHS | 1,000/8-9
7800 Laurel Spring Rd 23875 | 804-733-2730
Peter Fisher, prin. | Fax 733-3783
Prince George SHS | 1,300/10-12
7801 Laurel Spring Rd 23875 | 804-733-2720
Tracey Smallwood, prin. | Fax 861-4530
Other Schools – See Disputanta

Pulaski, Pulaski, Pop. 8,916
Pulaski County SD | 4,700/PK-12
202 N Washington Ave 24301 | 540-994-2550
Dr. Thomas Brewster, supt. | Fax 994-2552
www.pcva.us
Pulaski MS | 500/6-8
500 Pico Ter 24301 | 540-643-0767
Theresa Reed, prin. | Fax 980-8571
Other Schools – See Dublin

Regional Academic Governors SD
Supt. — See Richmond
SW VA Governor's S Science Math & Tech | 11-12
100 Northwood Dr 24301 | 540-440-5502
Rebecca Phillips, dir. | Fax 994-5841

Purcellville, Loudoun, Pop. 7,498
Loudoun County SD
Supt. — See Ashburn
Blue Ridge MS | 900/6-8
551 E A St 20132 | 540-751-2520
Brion Bell, prin. | Fax 338-6823
Loudoun Valley HS | 1,300/9-12
340 N Maple Ave 20132 | 540-751-2400
Susan Ross, prin. | Fax 751-2401
Woodgrove HS | 9-12
36811 Allder School Rd 20132 | 540-751-2600
William Shipp, prin. | Fax 751-2601

Patrick Henry College | Post-Sec.
10 Patrick Henry Cir 20132 | 540-338-1776

Quicksburg, Shenandoah
Shenandoah County SD
Supt. — See Woodstock
Jackson HS | 500/9-12
150 Stonewall Ln 22847 | 540-477-2732
Michael Dorman, prin. | Fax 477-2098
North Fork MS | 300/6-8
1018 Caverns Rd 22847 | 540-477-2953
Shelby Kline, prin. | Fax 477-2562

Radford, Radford, Pop. 16,003
Radford CSD | 1,600/PK-12
1612 Wadsworth St 24141 | 540-731-3647
Dr. Becky Greer, supt. | Fax 731-4419
www.rcps.org/
Dalton IS | 200/7-8
60 Dalton Dr 24141 | 540-731-3651
Greg Payne, prin. | Fax 731-5033
Radford HS | 500/9-12
50 Dalton Dr 24141 | 540-731-3649
W. Jeff Smith, prin. | Fax 731-4427

Radford University | Post-Sec.
801 E Main St 24142 | 540-831-5000

Reston, Fairfax, Pop. 56,325
Fairfax County SD
Supt. — See Falls Church
Hughes MS | 900/7-8
11401 Ridge Heights Rd 20191 | 703-715-3600
Aimee Monticchio, prin. | Fax 715-3697
South Lakes HS | 2,200/9-12
11400 S Lakes Dr 20191 | 703-715-4500
Kimberly Retzer, prin. | Fax 715-4597

AKS Massage School | Post-Sec.
11793 Indian Ridge Rd 20191 | 703-304-1146

Richlands, Tazewell, Pop. 5,766
Tazewell County SD
Supt. — See Tazewell
Richlands HS | 700/9-12
138 Tornado Aly 24641 | 276-964-4602
Kimberly Ringstaff, prin. | Fax 963-1049
Richlands MS | 600/6-8
185 Learning Ln 24641 | 276-963-5370
Glayde Brown, prin. | Fax 963-0210

Southwest Virginia Community College | Post-Sec.
PO Box SVCC 24641 | 276-964-2555

Richmond, Richmond, Pop. 200,073
Henrico County SD | 47,400/PK-12
PO Box 23120 23223 | 804-652-3600
Dr. Pat Russo, supt. | Fax 652-3856
www.henrico.k12.va.us
Advance College Academy | 9-12
2910 N Parham Rd 23294 | 804-527-4600
Robert Lowerre, prin.
Brookland MS | 1,000/6-8
9200 Lydell Dr 23228 | 804-261-5000
Derrick Deloatch, prin. | Fax 261-5003
Byrd MS | 1,000/6-8
9400 Quioccasin Rd 23238 | 804-750-2630
Dr. Gwen Miller, prin. | Fax 750-2629
Center for Communications | 9-12
7053 Messer Rd 23231 | 804-226-8700
Tracie Omohundro, prin.
Center for Science Mathematics & Tech | 9-12
2101 Pump Rd 23238 | 804-750-2600
Elizabeth Armbruster, prin.
Center for the Arts | 9-12
302 Azalea Ave 23227 | 804-228-2718
Ronald Rodriguez, prin.
Center for the Humanities | 9-12
8301 Hungary Spring Rd 23228 | 804-756-3000
Omega Wilson, prin.
Center for World Languages | 9-12
2910 N Parham Rd 23294 | 804-527-4600
Dr. Robert Lowerre, prin.
Ctr for Leadrshp Govt & Global Economics | 9-12
8701 Three Chopt Rd 23229 | 804-673-3700
Anne Poates, prin.
Fairfield MS | 800/6-8
5121 Nine Mile Rd 23223 | 804-328-4020
Art Raymond, prin. | Fax 328-4031
Freeman HS | 1,800/9-12
8701 Three Chopt Rd 23229 | 804-673-3700
Anne Poates, prin. | Fax 673-3713
Godwin HS | 1,900/9-12
2101 Pump Rd 23238 | 804-750-2600
Elizabeth Armbruster, prin. | Fax 750-2611
Henrico HS | 1,800/9-12
302 Azalea Ave 23227 | 804-228-2700
Ronald Rodriguez, prin. | Fax 228-2715
Hermitage HS | 1,900/9-12
8301 Hungary Spring Rd 23228 | 804-756-3000
Omega Wilson, prin. | Fax 672-1501
Hermitage Technical Center | Vo/Tech
8301 Hungary Spring Rd 23228 | 804-756-3020
Terrie Allsbrooks, prin. | Fax 756-3025
Moody MS | 1,000/6-8
7800 Woodman Rd 23228 | 804-261-5015
Paul Llewellyn, prin. | Fax 261-5024
Pocahontas MS | 900/6-8
12000 Three Chopt Rd 23233 | 804-364-0830
Kimberly Sigler, prin. | Fax 364-0847
Rolfe MS | 1,000/6-8
6901 Messer Rd 23231 | 804-226-8730
Andrew Armstrong, prin. | Fax 226-8739
Tuckahoe MS | 1,000/6-8
9000 Three Chopt Rd 23229 | 804-673-3720
Marilyn Royal, prin. | Fax 673-3731
Tucker HS | 1,600/9-12
2910 N Parham Rd 23294 | 804-527-4600
Dr. Robert Lowerre, prin. | Fax 527-4618
Varina HS | 2,000/9-12
7053 Messer Rd 23231 | 804-226-8700
Tracie Omohundro, prin. | Fax 226-8706

Wilder MS 900/6-8
6900 Wilkinson Rd 23227 804-515-1100
Sharon Pope, prin. Fax 515-1110
Mt. Vernon Adult Ed Complex Adult
7850 Carousel Ln 23294 804-527-4660
Beverly Godwin, admin.
Other Schools – See Glen Allen, Highland Springs, Sandston

Regional Academic Governors SD 2,500/9-12
PO Box 2120 23218 804-225-2884
Donna Poland Ph.D., admin. Fax 786-5466
www.doe.virginia.gov/instruction/governors_school_programs
Walker Governor's S for Gov & Int Study 9-12
1000 N Lombardy St 23220 804-354-6800
Jeff McGee, dir. Fax 354-6939
Other Schools – See Abingdon, Alexandria, Clifton Forge, Fishersville, Fredericksburg, Hampton, Keysville, Lynchburg, Manassas, Martinsville, Mount Jackson, Norfolk, Palmyra, Petersburg, Pulaski, Roanoke, Tappahannock, Warrenton

Richmond CSD 23,100/PK-12
301 N 9th St 23219 804-780-7700
Dr. Yvonne Brandon, supt. Fax 780-4122
www.richmond.k12.va.us
Armstrong HS 1,100/9-12
2300 Cool Ln 23223 804-780-4449
April Hawkins, prin. Fax 780-4485
Binford MS 400/6-8
1701 Floyd Ave 23220 804-780-6231
Tyrus Lyles, prin. Fax 780-6057
Boushall MS 400/6-8
3400 Hopkins Rd 23234 804-780-5016
Widad Abed, prin. Fax 780-5396
Brown MS 700/6-8
6300 Jahnke Rd 23225 804-319-3013
Denise Lewis, prin. Fax 319-3009
Elkhardt MS 400/6-8
6300 Hull Street Rd 23224 804-745-3600
Eric Jones, prin. Fax 674-5518
Franklin Military Academy 400/6-12
701 N 37th St 23223 804-780-8526
Sheron Carter-Gunter, prin. Fax 780-8054
Henderson MS 600/6-8
4319 Old Brook Rd 23227 804-780-8288
Jeanine Turner, prin. Fax 228-5357
Hill MS 500/6-8
3400 Patterson Ave 23221 804-780-6107
Racquel Jones, prin. Fax 780-8754
Huguenot HS 1,200/9-12
7945 Forest Hill Ave 23225 804-320-7967
Jafar Barakat, prin. Fax 560-9103
Jefferson HS 800/9-12
4100 W Grace St 23230 804-780-6028
Candance Veney-Chaplin, prin. Fax 780-6295
King MS 700/6-8
1000 Mosby St 23223 804-780-8011
Dr. Valerie Harris, prin. Fax 780-5590
Marshall HS 1,000/9-12
4225 Old Brook Rd 23227 804-780-6052
Beverly Britt, prin. Fax 780-4991
MathScience Innovation Center K-12
2401 Hartman St 23223 804-343-6525
Julia Cothran Ed.D., prin. Fax 780-4454
Open HS 200/9-12
600 S Pine St 23220 804-780-4661
Pete Glessman, prin. Fax 780-4865
Richmond Community HS 300/9-12
201 E Brookland Park Blvd 23222 804-285-1015
J. Austin Brown, prin. Fax 282-1303
Richmond Technical Center North Vo/Tech
2015 Seddon Way 23230 804-780-6272
Nancy Holmes, prin. Fax 780-6040
Richmond Technical Center South Vo/Tech
2020 Westwood Ave 23230 804-780-6237
Nancy Holmes, prin. Fax 780-6061
Thompson MS 600/6-8
7824 Forest Hill Ave 23225 804-272-7554
Rickie Hopkins, prin. Fax 560-5115
Wythe HS 1,000/9-12
4314 Crutchfield St 23225 804-780-5037
Reva Green, prin. Fax 780-5043
Adult Career Development Center Adult
119 W Leigh St 23220 804-780-4388
Dr. Clara Scott, prin. Fax 780-8184

Banner Christian S 200/K-12
1501 S Providence Rd 23236 804-276-5200
Dr. Thomas Burkett, hdmstr. Fax 276-7620
Baptist Theological Seminary Post-Sec.
3400 Brook Rd 23227 804-355-8135
Benedictine HS 300/9-12
304 N Sheppard St 23221 804-342-1300
Jesse Grapes, hdmstr. Fax 355-2407
Bon Secours Memorial College of Nursing Post-Sec.
8550 Magellan Pkwy Ste 1100 23227 804-627-5300
Centura College Post-Sec.
7001 W Broad St 23294 804-672-2300
Collegiate S 1,600/K-12
103 N Mooreland Rd 23229 804-741-9700
Keith Evans, hdmstr. Fax 741-9797
Cooper Episcopal S 100/6-8
2124 N 29th St 23223 804-822-6610
Mike Maruca, head sch
East End Christian Academy 50/PK-12
3294 Britton Rd 23231 804-795-9266
Suzanne Helland, dir. Fax 795-2222
ECPI University Post-Sec.
800 Moorefield Park Dr 23236 804-330-5533
ECPI University Post-Sec.
2809 Emerywood Pkwy 23294 866-708-6177
Elijah House Academy 200/PK-12
6627 Jahnke Rd 23225 804-755-7051
Jesse Kell, dir. Fax 377-6800
Fortis College Post-Sec.
2000 Westmoreland St Ste A 23230 804-323-1020
Grove Christian S 200/PK-12
8701 Ridge Rd 23229 804-741-2860
Heidi Smith, admin. Fax 754-8534
ITT Technical Institute Post-Sec.
300 Gateway Centre Pkwy 23235 804-330-4992
J. Sargeant Reynolds Community College Post-Sec.
PO Box 85622 23285 804-371-3000
Orchard House S 100/5-8
500 N Allen Ave 23220 804-228-2436
Nancy Davies, dir. Fax 228-1069
Richmond Academy of SDA 100/PK-12
3809 Patterson Ave 23221 804-353-0036
Dr. Malcolm Hutchinson, prin. Fax 358-8797
St. Catherine's S 1,000/PK-12
6001 Grove Ave 23226 804-288-2804
Terrie Scheckelhoff Ph.D., head sch Fax 285-8169
St. Christopher's S 1,000/PK-12
711 Saint Christophers Rd 23226 804-282-3185
Charles Stillwell, hdmstr. Fax 285-3914
St. Gertrude HS 300/9-12
3215 Stuart Ave 23221 804-358-9114
Judith Lynch, prin. Fax 355-5682
St. Mary's Hospital Post-Sec.
5801 Bremo Rd 23226 804-285-2011
Southside Baptist Christian S 200/PK-12
5515 Bryce Ln 23224 804-745-8699
Dr. Lonnie Stinson, head sch Fax 591-2833
Steward S 600/K-12
11600 Gayton Rd 23238 804-740-3394
Kenneth Seward, hdmstr. Fax 740-1464
Trinity Episcopal S 400/8-12
3850 Pittaway Dr 23235 804-272-5864
Dr. Thomas Aycock, hdmstr. Fax 272-4652
Union Presbyterian Seminary Post-Sec.
3401 Brook Rd 23227 804-355-0671
University of Richmond Post-Sec.
28 Westhampton Way 23173 804-289-8000
Veritas S 300/K-12
6627 Jahnke Rd Ste B 23225 804-272-9517
Keith Nix, head sch Fax 272-9518
Victory Christian Academy 200/PK-12
8491 Chamberlayne Rd 23227 804-262-8256
Andrea Cassidy M.Ed., prin. Fax 553-1905
Virginia Commonwealth University Post-Sec.
901 W Franklin St 23284 804-828-0100
Virginia Home for Boys & Girls Post-Sec.
8716 W Broad St 23294 804-270-6566
Virginia School for the Deaf and Blind Post-Sec.
PO Box 2120 23218 757-247-2058
Virginia Union University Post-Sec.
1500 N Lombardy St 23220 804-257-5600
Yeshiva of Virginia 50/9-12
6801 Patterson Ave 23226 804-288-7610
Rabbi Hal Klestzick, prin. Fax 784-9005

Ridgeway, Henry, Pop. 734

Henry County SD
Supt. — See Collinsville
Magna Vista HS 1,000/9-12
701 Magna Vista School Rd 24148 276-956-3147
Gracie Agnew, prin. Fax 956-1401

Riner, Montgomery, Pop. 845

Montgomery County SD
Supt. — See Christiansburg
Auburn HS 400/9-12
4163 Riner Rd 24149 540-382-5160
Carl Pauli, prin. Fax 381-6110
Auburn MS 300/6-8
4069 Riner Rd 24149 540-382-5165
Guylene Wood-Setzer, prin. Fax 381-6562

Ringgold, Pittsylvania

Pittsylvania County SD
Supt. — See Chatham
Dan River HS 600/9-12
100 Wildcat Circle 24586 434-822-7081
Steven D. Mayhew, prin. Fax 822-7347
Dan River MS 500/6-8
5875 Kentuck Rd 24586 434-822-6027
Emily Reynolds, prin. Fax 822-6548

Roanoke, Roanoke, Pop. 94,517

Regional Academic Governors SD
Supt. — See Richmond
Roanoke Valley Governor's S Science/Tech 9-12
2104 Grandin Rd SW 24015 540-853-2116
Dr. John Kowalski, dir. Fax 853-1056

Roanoke CSD 12,800/PK-12
PO Box 13145 24031 540-853-2502
Dr. Rita Bishop, supt. Fax 853-2951
www.rcps.info
Addison Aerospace Magnet MS 500/6-8
1220 5th St NW 24016 540-853-2681
Robert Johnson, prin. Fax 853-2842
Breckinridge MS 600/6-8
3901 Williamson Rd NW 24012 540-853-2251
Tracey Anderson, prin. Fax 853-6505
Fleming HS 1,600/9-12
3649 Ferncliff Ave NW 24017 540-853-2781
Archie Freeman, admin. Fax 563-1984
Henry HS 2,000/9-12
2102 Grandin Rd SW 24015 540-853-2255
Connie Ratcliffe, prin. Fax 853-1575
Jackson MS 500/6-8
1004 Montrose Ave SE 24013 540-853-6040
Ed Shepherd, prin. Fax 853-6027
Madison MS 600/6-8
1160 Overland Rd SW 24015 540-853-2351
Stephanie Hogan, prin. Fax 853-1050
Taylor Learning Academy Alt
3229 Williamson Rd NW 24012 540-853-1461
Elizabeth Williams, prin. Fax 853-1216
Wilson MS 500/6-8
1813 Carter Rd SW 24015 540-853-2358
Rosalind Henderson, prin. Fax 853-2004

Roanoke County SD 14,400/K-12
5937 Cove Rd 24019 540-562-3700
Dr. Lorraine Lange, supt. Fax 562-3993
www.rcs.k12.va.us
Cave Spring HS 800/9-12
3712 Chaparral Dr 24018 540-772-7550
Steve Spangler, prin. Fax 772-2107
Cave Spring MS 600/6-8
4880 Brambleton Ave 24018 540-772-7560
Steven Boyer, prin. Fax 772-2195
Hidden Valley HS 1,100/9-12
5000 Titan Trl 24018 540-776-7320
Rhonda Stegall, prin. Fax 776-7322
Hidden Valley MS 800/6-8
4902 Hidden Valley School 24018 540-772-7570
Ken Nicely, prin. Fax 772-7519
Northside HS 1,000/9-12
6758 Northside High School 24019 540-561-8155
Frank Dent, prin. Fax 561-8160
Northside MS 700/6-8
6810 Northside High School 24019 540-561-8145
Lori Wimbush, prin. Fax 561-8152
Other Schools – See Salem, Vinton

BarPalma Beauty Careers Academy Post-Sec.
3535 Franklin Rd SW Ste D 24014 540-343-0153
Community HS 50/9-12
302 Campbell Ave SE 24013 540-345-1688
Josh Chapman, dir. Fax 400-0335
Faith Christian S 300/K-12
3585 Buck Mountain Rd 24018 540-769-5200
Samuel Cox M.A., hdmstr. Fax 769-6030
Hollins University Post-Sec.
PO Box 9707 24020 540-362-6000
Jefferson College of Health Sciences Post-Sec.
101 Elm Ave SE 24013 540-985-8483
Life Academy 100/PK-12
7422 Deer Branch Rd 24019 540-563-5140
Sally Truslow, supt. Fax 563-2557
Miller-Motte Technical College Post-Sec.
4444 Electric Rd Ste A 24018 540-597-1010
North Cross S 500/PK-12
4254 Colonial Ave 24018 540-989-6641
Dr. Christian Proctor, hdmstr. Fax 989-7299
Parkway Christian Academy 300/PK-12
3230 King St NE 24012 540-982-2400
Erica Dixon, admin. Fax 982-2005
Roanoke Catholic S 500/PK-12
621 N Jefferson St 24016 540-982-3532
Patrick Patterson, prin. Fax 345-0785
Roanoke Valley Christian S 300/PK-12
PO Box 7010 24019 540-366-2432
Rick Brown, admin. Fax 366-9719
Skyline College Post-Sec.
5234 Airport Rd NW 24012 540-563-8080
Virginia Western Community College Post-Sec.
PO Box 14007 24038 540-857-8922

Rocky Gap, Bland

Bland County SD
Supt. — See Bastian
Rocky Gap HS 200/8-12
PO Box 9 24366 276-928-1100
Joe Makolandra, prin. Fax 928-1988

Rocky Mount, Franklin, Pop. 4,700

Franklin County SD 7,400/PK-12
25 Bernard Rd 24151 540-483-5138
W. Mark Church Ph.D., supt. Fax 483-5806
www.frco.k12.va.us
Franklin County HS 2,200/9-12
700 Tanyard Rd 24151 540-483-0221
Debora Decker, prin. Fax 483-5149
Franklin MS West 800/7-8
225 Middle School Rd 24151 540-483-5105
Brenda Muse, prin. Fax 483-5585
Gereau CATCE Vo/Tech
150 Technology Dr 24151 540-483-5446
Dr. Kevin Bezy, prin. Fax 483-5788
Adult Education Center Adult
50 Claiborne Ave 24151 540-483-0179
Debbie Hamrick, coord. Fax 483-1279

Christian Heritage Academy 100/PK-12
625 Glennwood Dr 24151 540-483-5855
Deke Andrews, hdmstr. Fax 483-9355

Rural Retreat, Wythe, Pop. 1,472

Wythe County SD
Supt. — See Wytheville
Rural Retreat HS 400/9-12
321 E Buck Ave 24368 276-686-4143
Michael Neal, prin. Fax 686-4601
Rural Retreat MS 200/6-8
325 E Buck Ave 24368 276-686-5200
Shannon Phillips, prin. Fax 686-4944

Rustburg, Campbell, Pop. 1,389

Campbell County SD 8,300/PK-12
PO Box 99 24588 434-332-3458
Dr. Robert Johnson, supt. Fax 528-1655
www.campbell.k12.va.us
Campbell Technical Center Vo/Tech
194 Dennis Riddle Dr 24588 434-821-6213
Jon Hardie, prin. Fax 821-2808
Rustburg HS 900/9-12
PO Box 830 24588 434-332-5171
Clayton Stanley, prin. Fax 332-1187
Rustburg MS 600/6-8
PO Box 130 24588 434-332-5141
Katherine Bowles, prin. Fax 332-2058
Other Schools – See Altavista, Lynchburg, Naruna

Ruther Glen, Caroline

Caroline County SD
Supt. — See Bowling Green
Caroline Diversified Learning Center Alt
7278 Ladysmith Rd 22546 804-448-3211
Derrick Scarborough, admin.

Carmel S 100/PK-12
PO Box 605 22546 804-448-3288
Brent Miller, hdmstr. Fax 448-3146

Saint George, Greene

Blue Ridge S 200/9-12
273 Mayo Dr, 434-985-2811
William Darrin, hdmstr. Fax 985-7215

Salem, Salem, Pop. 24,439
Roanoke County SD
Supt. — See Roanoke
Burton Center for Arts and Technology Vo/Tech
1760 Roanoke Blvd 24153 540-857-5000
Jason Suhr, prin. Fax 857-5061
Glenvar HS 600/9-12
4549 Malus Dr 24153 540-387-6536
Joseph Hafey, prin. Fax 387-6347
Glenvar MS 400/6-8
4555 Malus Dr 24153 540-387-6322
Jamie Soltis, prin. Fax 387-6283

Salem CSD 3,900/PK-12
510 S College Ave 24153 540-389-0130
Dr. H. Alan Seibert, supt. Fax 389-4135
www.salem.k12.va.us
Lewis MS 900/6-8
616 S College Ave 24153 540-387-2513
Dr. Forest Jones, prin. Fax 389-8914
Salem HS 1,300/9-12
400 Spartan Dr 24153 540-387-2437
Scott Habeeb, prin. Fax 387-2543

ITT Technical Institute Post-Sec.
2159 Apperson Dr 24153 540-989-2500
National College Post-Sec.
1813 E Main St 24153 540-986-1800
Roanoke College Post-Sec.
221 College Ln 24153 540-375-2500

Saltville, Smyth, Pop. 2,062
Smyth County SD
Supt. — See Marion
Northwood HS 300/9-12
PO Box Y 24370 276-496-7751
Stan Dunham, prin. Fax 496-3216
Northwood MS 200/6-8
156 Long Hollow Rd 24370 276-624-3341
Damon Mazoff, prin. Fax 624-3535

Saluda, Middlesex, Pop. 753
Middlesex County SD 1,200/PK-12
PO Box 205 23149 804-758-2277
Dr. James Lane, supt. Fax 758-3727
www.mcps.k12.va.us/
Middlesex HS 400/9-12
PO Box 206 23149 804-758-2132
Jeannie Duke, prin. Fax 758-2786
Other Schools – See Locust Hill

Sandston, Henrico, Pop. 7,426
Henrico County SD
Supt. — See Richmond
Elko MS, 5901 Elko Rd 23150 900/6-8
Cheri Guempel, prin. 804-328-4110

New Bridge Academy 100/K-12
5701 Elko Rd 23150 804-737-7833
J.D. Sluss, admin. Fax 737-1181

Shawsville, Montgomery, Pop. 1,291
Montgomery County SD
Supt. — See Christiansburg
Shawsville MS 200/6-8
4179 Oldtown Rd 24162 540-268-2262
David Dickinson, prin. Fax 268-1868

Shenandoah, Page, Pop. 2,351
Page County SD
Supt. — See Luray
Page County HS 600/9-12
184 Panther Dr 22849 540-652-8712
Eric Benson, prin. Fax 652-8308
Page County MS 400/6-8
198 Panther Dr 22849 540-652-3400
Dr. Teresa Wiita, prin. Fax 652-8308

Skipwith, Mecklenburg
Mecklenburg County SD
Supt. — See Boydton
Bluestone HS 700/9-12
6825 Skipwith Rd 23968 434-372-5177
Kristy Somerville, prin. Fax 372-5217
Bluestone MS 500/6-8
250 Middle School Rd 23968 434-372-3266
Mary Shores, prin. Fax 372-3362

Smithfield, Isle of Wight, Pop. 7,922
Isle of Wight County SD 5,500/PK-12
820 W Main St 23430 757-357-4393
A. Katrise Perera M.Ed., supt. Fax 357-0849
www.iwcs.k12.va.us
Smithfield HS 1,300/9-12
14171 Turner Dr 23430 757-357-3108
Dr. Stenette Byrd, prin. Fax 357-7253
Smithfield MS 600/7-8
14175 Turner Dr 23430 757-365-4100
Jeff Mordica, prin. Fax 365-4222
Other Schools – See Windsor

South Boston, Halifax, Pop. 8,032
Halifax County SD
Supt. — See Halifax
Halifax HS 1,800/9-12
PO Box 310 24592 434-572-4977
Albert Randolph, prin. Fax 572-2675
Halifax MS 1,300/6-8
1011 Middle School Cir 24592 434-572-4100
Faye Bruce, prin. Fax 572-4106

Carlbrook S 100/9-12
3046 Carlbrook Rd 24592 434-476-2406
Timothy Brace, hdmstr. Fax 832-7089

South Hill, Mecklenburg, Pop. 4,561
Mecklenburg County SD
Supt. — See Boydton
Park View HS 800/9-12
205 Park View Cir 23970 434-447-3435
Jeff Davis, prin. Fax 447-7876
Park View MS 600/6-8
365 Dockery Rd 23970 434-447-3761
Randall Spain, prin. Fax 447-4920

South Riding, Loudoun, Pop. 23,365
Loudoun County SD
Supt. — See Ashburn
Freedom HS 1,800/9-12
25450 Riding Center Dr 20152 703-957-4300
Douglas Fulton, prin. Fax 542-2086

Spotsylvania, Spotsylvania
Spotsylvania County SD
Supt. — See Fredericksburg
Courtland HS 1,200/9-12
6701 Smith Station Rd 22553 540-898-4445
Larry Marks, prin. Fax 898-4458
Ni River MS 700/6-8
11632 Catharpin Rd 22553 540-785-3990
Veronne Davis, prin. Fax 785-0658
Post Oak MS 700/6-8
6959 Courthouse Rd, 540-582-7517
Karen Foster, prin. Fax 582-7510
Spotsylvania Career & Technical Center Vo/Tech
6713 Smith Station Rd 22553 540-898-2655
Lee Browning, prin. Fax 891-1784
Spotsylvania HS 1,100/9-12
6975 Courthouse Rd, 540-582-3882
Rusty Davis, prin. Fax 582-3890
Spotsylvania MS 800/6-8
8801 Courthouse Rd 22553 540-582-6341
Lane Byrd, prin. Fax 582-3207
Thornburg MS 600/6-8
6929 N Roxbury Mill Rd, 540-582-7600
Kirk Tower, prin. Fax 582-7606

Springfield, Fairfax, Pop. 29,504
Fairfax County SD
Supt. — See Falls Church
Irving MS 1,100/7-8
8100 Old Keene Mill Rd 22152 703-912-4500
Danny Little, prin. Fax 912-4597
Key MS 800/7-8
6402 Franconia Rd 22150 703-313-3900
Christopher Larrick, prin. Fax 313-3997
Lee HS 1,800/9-12
6540 Franconia Rd 22150 703-924-8300
Abe Jeffers, prin. Fax 924-8397
West Springfield HS 2,300/9-12
6100 Rolling Rd 22152 703-913-3800
Mark Greenfelder, prin. Fax 913-3897

Accotink Academy Post-Sec.
8519 Tuttle Rd 22152
ITT Technical Institute Post-Sec.
7300 Boston Blvd 22153 703-440-9535
Word of Life Christian Academy 300/PK-12
5225 Backlick Rd 22151 703-354-4222
Bonnie Johnson, admin. Fax 750-1306

Stafford, Stafford
Stafford County SD 26,900/PK-12
31 Stafford Ave 22554 540-658-6000
Dr. Randy Bridges, supt. Fax 658-5963
stafford.schoolfusion.us/
Brooke Point HS 1,700/9-12
1700 Courthouse Rd 22554 540-658-6080
Scott McClellan, prin. Fax 658-6072
Colonial Forge HS 2,100/9-12
550 Courthouse Rd 22554 540-658-6115
Michael Byers, prin. Fax 658-6120
Heim MS 800/6-8
320 Telegraph Rd 22554 540-658-5910
Mary McGraw, prin. Fax 658-0329
Mountain View HS 1,800/9-12
2135 Mountain View Rd, 540-658-6840
James Stemple, prin. Fax 658-6855
North Stafford HS 1,700/9-12
839 Garrisonville Rd 22554 540-658-6150
Thomas Nichols, prin. Fax 658-6158
Poole MS 900/6-8
800 Eustace Rd 22554 540-658-6190
Greg Daniel, prin. Fax 658-6176
Stafford MS 500/6-8
101 Spartan Dr 22554 540-658-6210
Mark Smith, prin. Fax 658-6204
Thompson MS 1,200/6-8
75 Walpole St 22554 540-658-6420
Andrew Grider, prin. Fax 658-6430
Wright MS 800/6-8
100 Wood Dr, 540-658-6240
William Boatwright, prin. Fax 658-6238
Other Schools – See Falmouth, Fredericksburg

Grace Preparatory S 100/K-12
2202 Jefferson Davis Hwy 22554 540-657-4500
Ken Gross, admin. Fax 657-4000

Stanardsville, Greene, Pop. 363
Greene County SD 2,900/PK-12
PO Box 1140 22973 434-985-5254
David Jeck, supt. Fax 985-4686
www.greenecountyschools.com
Greene County Technical Education Center Vo/Tech
10415 Spotswood Trl 22973 434-985-5239
Harry Daniel, prin. Fax 985-2071
Monroe HS 800/9-12
254 Monroe Dr 22973 434-985-5273
Mike Jamerson, prin. Fax 985-1461
Monroe MS 700/6-8
148 Monroe Dr 22973 434-985-5240
Kyle Pursel, prin. Fax 985-1359

Staunton, Staunton, Pop. 23,179
Augusta County SD
Supt. — See Fishersville
Beverley Manor MS 800/6-8
58 Cedar Green Rd 24401 540-886-5806
Nancy Miller, prin. Fax 886-4019
Riverheads HS 500/9-12
19 Howardsville Rd 24401 540-337-1921
P. Steve Barnett, prin. Fax 337-0258

Staunton CSD 2,600/K-12
116 W Beverley St 24401 540-332-3920
Dr. Linda Reviea, supt. Fax 332-3924
www.staunton.k12.va.us
Genesis Alternative S Alt
1751 Shutterlee Mill Rd 24401 540-213-6507
Gregory Ciszek, prin. Fax 213-8870
Lee HS 800/9-12
1200 N Coalter St 24401 540-332-3926
Dr. Mark Rowicki, prin. Fax 332-3994
Shelburne MS 600/6-8
300 Grubert Ave 24401 540-332-3930
Robert Craft, prin. Fax 332-3933

Grace Christian HS 100/9-12
19 S Market St 24401 540-886-9109
Jason Bailey, prin. Fax 886-5958
Mary Baldwin College Post-Sec.
PO Box 1500 24402 540-887-7019
Richards Jr Academy 100/K-10
414 Sterling St 24401 540-886-4984
Grant Wolters, prin. Fax 886-7087
Staunton School of Cosmetology Post-Sec.
PO Box 2385 24402 540-885-0808
Stuart Hall S 300/PK-12
PO Box 210 24402 540-885-0356
Mark Eastham, hdmstr. Fax 886-2275
Virginia School for the Deaf and Blind Post-Sec.
PO Box 2069 24402 540-332-9000

Stephens City, Frederick, Pop. 1,772
Frederick County SD
Supt. — See Winchester
Aylor MS 600/6-8
901 Aylor Rd 22655 540-869-3736
David Rudy, prin. Fax 867-2756
Sherando HS 1,500/9-12
185 S Warrior Dr 22655 540-869-0060
John Nelson, prin. Fax 869-5183

Shenandoah Valley Christian Academy 300/PK-12
PO Box 1360 22655 540-869-4600
Dr. Robert Quinn, supt. Fax 869-4662

Sterling, Loudoun, Pop. 26,953
Loudoun County SD
Supt. — See Ashburn
Dominion HS 1,300/9-12
21326 Augusta Dr 20164 571-434-4400
Dr. W. John Brewer, prin. Fax 434-4401
Loudoun Academy of Science 9-12
21326 Augusta Dr 20164 571-434-4470
George Wolfe, dir. Fax 434-4471
Park View HS 1,300/9-12
400 W Laurel Ave 20164 571-434-4500
Dr. Virginia Minshew, prin. Fax 434-4501
River Bend MS 1,100/6-8
46240 Algonkian Pkwy 20165 571-434-3220
Bennett Lacy, prin. Fax 444-7578
Seneca Ridge MS 1,000/6-8
98 Seneca Ridge Dr 20164 571-434-4420
Mark McDermott, prin. Fax 444-7567
Sterling MS 900/6-8
201 W Holly Ave 20164 571-434-4520
Nereida Gonzalez-Sales, prin. Fax 444-7492

Northern Virginia Community College Post-Sec.
1000 Harry Flood Byrd Hwy 20164 703-323-3000

Strasburg, Shenandoah, Pop. 6,272
Shenandoah County SD
Supt. — See Woodstock
Signal Knob MS 500/6-8
687 Sandy Hook Rd 22657 540-465-3422
Christopher Cook, prin. Fax 465-5412
Strasburg HS 700/9-12
250 Ram Dr 22657 540-465-5195
Kenneth Knesh, prin. Fax 465-5461

Stuart, Patrick, Pop. 1,391
Patrick County SD 2,500/PK-12
PO Box 346 24171 276-694-3163
Dr. Roger Morris, supt. Fax 694-3170
www.patrick.k12.va.us
Patrick County HS 1,000/8-12
215 Cougar Ln 24171 276-694-7137
Tammy Waldron, prin. Fax 694-6997

Stuarts Draft, Augusta, Pop. 9,108
Augusta County SD
Supt. — See Fishersville
Stuarts Draft HS 800/9-12
1028 Augusta Farms Rd 24477 540-946-7600
Donna Abernathy, prin. Fax 946-7605
Stuarts Draft MS 500/6-8
1088 Augusta Farms Rd 24477 540-946-7611
Scott Musick, prin. Fax 946-7613

Ridgeview Christian S 100/PK-12
PO Box 477 24477 540-337-1025
Br. Danny Thomas, prin. Fax 337-3718

Suffolk, Suffolk, Pop. 82,776
Jointly Operated Vo Tech SD
Supt. — None – Lolita Hall, dir.

Pruden Center for Industry/Technology Vo/Tech
4169 Pruden Blvd 23434 757-539-7407

Suffolk CSD 14,100/PK-12
100 N Main St 23434 757-925-6750
Dr. Deran Whitney, supt. Fax 925-6751
www.spsk12.net/
Forest Glen MS 400/6-8
200 Forest Glen Dr 23434 757-925-5780
Melvin Bradshaw, prin. Fax 925-5557
Kennedy MS 600/6-8
2325 E Washington St 23434 757-934-6212
Vivian Covington, prin. Fax 925-5594
King's Fork HS 1,500/9-12
351 Kings Fork Rd 23434 757-923-5240
Dr. Suzanne Rice, prin. Fax 923-5242
King's Fork MS 1,100/6-8
350 Kings Fork Rd 23434 757-923-5246
Jennifer Presson, prin. Fax 925-5754
Lakeland HS 1,300/9-12
214 Kenyon Rd 23434 757-925-5790
Dr. Thomas Whitley, prin. Fax 925-5599
Nansemond River HS 1,400/9-12
3301 Nansemond Pkwy 23434 757-923-4101
Thomas McLemore, prin. Fax 538-5430
Turlington Woods S Alt
629 Turlington Rd 23434 757-934-6215
Pamela Brandon-Lipscomb, prin. Fax 925-5583
Yeates MS 1,100/6-8
4901 Bennetts Pasture Rd 23435 757-923-4105
Daniel O'Leary, prin. Fax 538-5416

Nansemond-Suffolk Academy 900/PK-12
3373 Pruden Blvd 23434 757-539-8789
Colley W. Bell, hdmstr. Fax 934-8363
Suffolk Beauty Academy Post-Sec.
860 Portsmouth Blvd 23434 757-934-0656
Suffolk Christian Academy 200/PK-12
237 N Main St 23434 757-539-3163
Tamra VanDorn, prin. Fax 539-2575

Surry, Surry, Pop. 239
Surry County SD 1,000/PK-12
PO Box 317 23883 757-294-5229
Lloyd Hamlin, supt. Fax 294-5263
www.surryschools.net/
Other Schools – See Dendron

Sussex, Sussex, Pop. 256
Sussex County SD 600/K-12
PO Box 1368 23884 434-246-1099
Arthur Jarrett Ed.D., supt. Fax 246-8214
www.sussex.k12.va.us
Sussex Central HS 400/9-12
PO Box 1307 23884 434-246-6051
Julius Hamlin, prin. Fax 246-5503
Sussex Central MS 200/6-8
PO Box 1387 23884 434-246-2251
Morris Taylor, prin. Fax 246-8912

Sweet Briar, Amherst

Sweet Briar College Post-Sec.
134 Chapel Rd 24595 434-381-6100

Swoope, Augusta
Augusta County SD
Supt. — See Fishersville
Buffalo Gap HS 600/9-12
1800 Buffalo Gap Hwy 24479 540-337-6021
William Deardorff, prin. Fax 337-6236

Tangier, Accomack, Pop. 722
Accomack County SD
Supt. — See Accomac
Tangier S 100/K-12
PO Box 245 23440 757-891-2234
Dr. Nina Pruitt, prin. Fax 891-2572

Tappahannock, Essex, Pop. 2,335
Essex County SD 1,600/PK-12
PO Box 756 22560 804-443-4366
Dr. Scott Burckbuchler, supt. Fax 443-4498
www.essex.k12.va.us
Essex HS 500/9-12
PO Box 1006 22560 804-443-4301
Darnell Carter, prin. Fax 443-4272
Essex IS 500/5-8
PO Box 609 22560 804-443-3040
Angela Gross, prin. Fax 445-1079

Regional Academic Governors SD
Supt. — See Richmond
Chesapeake Bay Governor's S 10-12
PO Box 1410 22560 804-443-0267
Dianne Pollard, dir. Fax 443-4039

St. Margaret's S 100/8-12
PO Box 158 22560 804-443-3357
Lindy Williams, head sch Fax 443-1832
Tappahannock Junior Academy 100/PK-10
PO Box 790 22560 804-443-5076

Tazewell, Tazewell, Pop. 4,565
Tazewell County SD 6,600/PK-12
PO Box 927 24651 276-988-5511
Dr. Brenda Lawson, supt. Fax 988-6765
tazewell.k12.va.us
Tazewell County Career Technical Center Vo/Tech
100 Advantage Dr 24651 276-988-2529
Chris Stacy, prin. Fax 988-5494
Tazewell HS 700/9-12
627 E Fincastle Tpke 24651 276-988-6502
Rodney Reid, prin. Fax 988-3263
Tazewell MS 500/6-8
100 Bull Dog Ave 24651 276-988-6513
Sarah Reid, prin. Fax 988-6514
Other Schools – See Bluefield, Richlands

The Plains, Fauquier, Pop. 213
Fauquier County SD
Supt. — See Warrenton
Marshall MS 500/6-8
4048 Zulla Rd 20198 540-422-7450
Christine Moschetti, prin. Fax 422-7469

Wakefield S 400/PK-12
PO Box 107 20198 540-253-7600
Peter Quinn, hdmstr. Fax 253-5492

Toano, James City
Williamsburg-James City County SD
Supt. — See Williamsburg
Toano MS 700/6-8
7817 Richmond Rd 23168 757-566-4251
Sammy Fudge, prin. Fax 566-3006

Triangle, Prince William, Pop. 7,762
Prince William County SD
Supt. — See Manassas
Graham Park MS 800/6-8
3613 Graham Park Rd 22172 703-221-2118
Gary Anderson, prin. Fax 221-1079

Calvary Christian S 200/PK-12
4345 Inn St 22172 703-221-2016
John Wallace, admin. Fax 221-7698

Victoria, Lunenburg, Pop. 1,693
Lunenburg County SD
Supt. — See Kenbridge
Central HS 500/9-12
131 K V Rd 23974 434-696-2137
Frances Ball, prin. Fax 696-1322
Lunenburg MS 400/6-8
583 Tomlinson Rd 23974 434-696-2161
Kathleen Rainey, prin. Fax 696-2162

Vienna, Fairfax, Pop. 15,197
Fairfax County SD
Supt. — See Falls Church
Kilmer MS 1,000/7-8
8100 Wolftrap Rd 22182 703-846-8800
Douglas Tyson, prin. Fax 846-8897
Madison HS 2,000/9-12
2500 James Madison Dr 22181 703-319-2300
Mark Merrell, prin. Fax 319-2397
Oakton HS 2,300/9-12
2900 Sutton Rd 22181 703-319-2700
John Banbury, prin. Fax 319-2797
Thoreau MS 800/7-8
2505 Cedar Ln 22180 703-846-8000
Greg Hood, prin. Fax 846-8097

Everest College Post-Sec.
8620 Westwood Center Dr 22182 703-288-3131
Fairfax Christian S 200/PK-12
1624 Hunter Mill Rd 22182 703-759-5100
Jo Thoburn, dir. Fax 759-2143
Potomac College Post-Sec.
2070 Chain Bridge Rd # G100 22182 703-709-5875
University of Fairfax Post-Sec.
2070 Chain Bridge Rd # G100 22182 703-790-3200

Vinton, Roanoke, Pop. 7,942
Roanoke County SD
Supt. — See Roanoke
Byrd HS 1,200/9-12
2902 E Washington Ave 24179 540-890-3090
Richard Turner, prin. Fax 890-7568
Byrd MS 900/6-8
2910 E Washington Ave 24179 540-890-1035
Tammy Newcomb, prin. Fax 890-0703

Virginia Beach, Virginia Beach, Pop. 422,328
Virginia Beach CSD 70,900/PK-12
PO Box 6038 23456 757-263-1000
Dr. James Merrill, supt. Fax 263-1397
www.vbschools.com/
Advanced Technology Center Vo/Tech
1800 College Cres, 757-648-5800
Michael Taylor, dir. Fax 468-4235
Bayside HS 2,000/9-12
4960 Haygood Rd 23455 757-648-5200
James Miller, prin. Fax 473-5123
Bayside MS 1,000/6-8
965 Newtown Rd 23462 757-648-4400
Stacy Bland, prin. Fax 473-5185
Brandon MS 1,300/6-8
1700 Pope St 23464 757-648-4450
Dr. Christy McQueeney, prin. Fax 366-4550
Corporate Landing MS 1,400/6-8
1597 Corporate Landing Pkwy 23454 757-648-4500
Dr. Daniel Smith, prin. Fax 437-6487
Cox HS 2,000/9-12
2425 Shorehaven Dr 23454 757-648-5250
Dr. Randi Riesbeck, prin. Fax 496-6731
First Colonial HS 2,100/9-12
1272 Mill Dam Rd 23454 757-648-5300
Dr. Nancy Farrell, prin. Fax 496-6719
Great Neck MS 1,100/6-8
1848 N Great Neck Rd 23454 757-648-4550
Dr. Eugene Soltner, prin. Fax 496-6774
Green Run HS 1,800/9-12
1700 Dahlia Dr, 757-648-5350
Dr. George Parker, prin. Fax 431-4153
Independence MS 1,300/6-8
1370 Dunstan Ln 23455 757-648-4600
Carey Manugo, prin. Fax 460-0508
Kellam HS 1,900/9-12
2323 Holland Rd, 757-648-5400
Bruce Biehl, prin. Fax 427-6265
Kemps Landing Magnet MS 600/6-8
4722 Jericho Rd 23462 757-648-4650
Charles Foster, prin. Fax 473-5106
Kempsville HS 1,800/9-12
5194 Chief Trl 23464 757-648-5450
Evangeline Petrich, prin. Fax 474-7919
Kempsville MS 900/6-8
860 Churchill Dr 23464 757-648-4700
Dr. James Smith, prin. Fax 474-8449
Landstown HS 2,400/9-12
2001 Concert Dr 23456 757-648-5500
Dr. Brian Matney, prin. Fax 468-1860
Landstown MS 1,500/6-8
2204 Recreation Dr 23456 757-648-4750
John Parkman, prin. Fax 430-3247
Larkspur MS 1,600/6-8
4696 Princess Anne Rd 23462 757-648-4800
Matthew Delaney, prin. Fax 474-8598
Lynnhaven MS 1,200/6-8
1250 Bayne Dr 23454 757-648-4850
Dr. Patti Jenkins, prin. Fax 496-6793
Ocean Lakes HS 2,400/9-12
885 Schumann Dr 23454 757-648-5550
Cheryl Askew, prin. Fax 721-4309
Plaza MS 1,100/6-8
3080 S Lynnhaven Rd 23452 757-648-4900
Dr. Violet Hoyle, prin. Fax 431-5331
Princess Anne HS 2,000/9-12
4400 Virginia Beach Blvd 23462 757-648-5600
James Pohl, prin. Fax 473-5004
Princess Anne MS 1,400/6-8
2509 Seaboard Rd 23456 757-648-4950
Alex Bergren, prin. Fax 430-0972
Renaissance Academy Alt
5100 Cleveland St 23462 757-648-6000
Kay Thomas, prin. Fax 473-5111
Salem HS 1,900/9-12
1993 Sundevil Dr 23464 757-648-5650
Daniel Keever, prin. Fax 474-0100
Salem MS 1,100/6-8
2380 Lynnhaven Pkwy 23464 757-648-5000
James Avila, prin. Fax 474-8467
Tallwood HS 2,200/9-12
1668 Kempsville Rd 23464 757-648-5700
Cheryl Woodhouse, prin. Fax 479-5534
Technical & Career Education Center Vo/Tech
2925 N Landing Rd 23456 757-648-5850
David Swanger, dir. Fax 427-5558
Virginia Beach MS 800/6-8
600 25th St 23451 757-648-5050
Dr. Sandra Brown, prin. Fax 437-4708
Adult Learning Center Adult
4160 Virginia Beach Blvd 23452 757-648-6050
Paul Palonbo, dir. Fax 306-0999

Advanced Technology Institute Post-Sec.
5700 Southern Blvd # 100 23462 757-490-1241
Advanced Technology Institute Post-Sec.
1429 Miller Store Rd 23455 800-468-1093
Atlantic University Post-Sec.
215 67th St 23451 757-631-8101
Bishop Sullivan Catholic HS 500/9-12
4552 Princess Anne Rd 23462 757-467-2881
Dennis Price, prin. Fax 467-0284
Bryant & Stratton College Post-Sec.
301 Centre Pointe Dr 23462 757-499-7900
Cape Henry Collegiate S 900/PK-12
1320 Mill Dam Rd 23454 757-481-2446
Dr. John Lewis, hdmstr. Fax 481-9194
Centura College Post-Sec.
2697 Dean Dr Ste 100 23452 757-340-2121
Coastal Christian Academy 50/K-12
640 Kempsville Rd 23464 757-217-2151
Rev. Mary Strickland, admin. Fax 467-5298
ECPI University Post-Sec.
5555 Greenwich Rd Ste 300 23462 757-671-7171
Oaktree Academy 200/K-12
817 Kempsville Rd 23464 757-248-9560
Terri Turley, admin. Fax 248-9594
Regent University Post-Sec.
1000 Regent University Dr 23464 757-352-4127
Rudy & Kelly Academy of Hair & Nails Post-Sec.
1920 Centerville Tpke # 114 23464 757-473-0994
Tidewater Community College Post-Sec.
1700 College Cres, 757-822-7100
Virginia Beach Friends S 200/PK-12
1537 Laskin Rd 23451 757-428-7534
Linda Serrette, hdmstr. Fax 428-7511
Virginia Beach Theological Seminary Post-Sec.
2221 Centerville Tpke 23464 757-479-3706
World College Post-Sec.
5193 Shore Dr Ste 105 23455 757-464-4600

Wakefield, Sussex, Pop. 921

Tidewater Academy 200/PK-12
PO Box 1000 23888 757-899-5401
Rodney Taylor, hdmstr. Fax 899-2521

Warm Springs, Bath, Pop. 122
Bath County SD 600/K-12
PO Box 67 24484 540-839-2722
Sue Hirsh, supt. Fax 839-3040
www.bath.k12.va.us
Other Schools – See Hot Springs

Warrenton, Fauquier, Pop. 9,361
Fauquier County SD 11,300/PK-12
320 Hospital Dr Ste 40 20186 540-422-7000
Dr. Jonathan Lewis, supt. Fax 422-7057
www.fcps1.org
Auburn MS 600/6-8
7270 Riley Rd 20187 540-422-7410
Steve Kadilak, prin. Fax 422-7429
Fauquier HS 1,200/9-12
705 Waterloo Rd 20186 540-347-6100
Roger Sites, prin. Fax 347-0089
Taylor MS 400/6-8
350 E Shirley Ave 20186 540-347-6140
Ruth Nelson, prin. Fax 347-6145
Warrenton MS 500/6-8
244 Waterloo St 20186 540-347-6160
Barbara Bannister, prin. Fax 347-6169
Other Schools – See Bealeton, Midland, Nokesville, The Plains

Regional Academic Governors SD
Supt. — See Richmond
Mountain Vista Governor's S 11-12
6480 College St 20187 540-347-6237
Dr. Rosanne Williamson, prin. Fax 347-6215

Highland S 500/PK-12
597 Broadview Ave 20186 540-878-2700
Hank Berg, prin. Fax 878-2731
Providence Christian Academy 100/PK-12
6872 Watson Ct 20187 540-349-4989
Young Shin, hdmstr. Fax 349-3915

Warsaw, Richmond, Pop. 1,495
Jointly Operated Vo Tech SD
Supt. — None - Lolita Hall, dir.
Northern Neck Technical Center Vo/Tech
13946 History Land Hwy 22572 804-333-4940
Fax 333-0538

Richmond County SD 1,200/K-12
PO Box 1507 22572 804-333-3681
James Smith Ed.D., supt. Fax 333-5586
www.richmond-county.k12.va.us
Rappahannock HS 400/9-12
6914 Richmond Rd 22572 804-333-3551
Jesse Boyd, prin. Fax 333-5186
Richmond County IS 300/6-8
13207 History Land Hwy 22572 804-333-3560
Patricia Means, prin. Fax 333-5387

Rappahannock Community College Post-Sec.
52 Campus Dr 22572 804-333-6700

Washington, Rappahannock, Pop. 133
Rappahannock County SD 900/K-12
6 School House Rd 22747 540-227-0023
Dr. Aldridge Boone, supt. Fax 987-8896
www.rappahannockschools.us/
Rappahannock County HS 400/8-12
12576 Lee Hwy 22747 540-227-0745
Michael Tupper, prin. Fax 987-9331

Waynesboro, Waynesboro, Pop. 20,421
Waynesboro CSD 3,200/PK-12
301 Pine Ave 22980 540-946-4600
Dr. Robin Crowder, supt. Fax 946-4608
www.waynesboro.k12.va.us
Collins MS 700/6-8
1625 Ivy St 22980 540-946-4635
Janet Buchheit, prin. Fax 946-4642
Waynesboro HS 900/9-12
1200 W Main St 22980 540-946-4616
Tim Teachey, prin. Fax 946-4621

Fishburne Military S 100/7-12
PO Box 988 22980 540-946-7700

Weems, Lancaster
Lancaster County SD 1,300/PK-12
2330 Irvington Rd 22576 804-435-3183
Dr. Daniel Lukich, supt. Fax 435-3309
www.lcs.k12.va.us
Other Schools – See Kilmarnock, Lancaster

West Point, King William, Pop. 3,232
West Point SD 800/PK-12
PO Box T 23181 804-843-4368
Dr. Jeffery Smith, supt. Fax 843-4421
www.wpps.k12.va.us
West Point HS 300/9-12
2700 Mattaponi Ave 23181 804-843-3630
Mark Dorsey, prin. Fax 843-3406
West Point MS 200/6-8
1040 Thompson Ave 23181 804-843-9810
David Daniel, prin. Fax 843-9812

Weyers Cave, Augusta, Pop. 2,429

Blue Ridge Community College Post-Sec.
PO Box 80 24486 540-234-9261

Williamsburg, Williamsburg, Pop. 13,648
Williamsburg-James City County SD 10,600/K-12
PO Box 8783 23187 757-253-6777
Steven Constantino Ed.D., supt. Fax 565-9383
www.edline.net/pages/WJCC
Berkeley MS 900/6-8
1118 Ironbound Rd 23188 757-229-8051
Karen Swann, prin. Fax 229-6133
Hornsby MS 900/6-8
850 Jolly Pond Rd 23188 757-565-9400
Dr. Byron Bishop, prin. Fax 565-9401
Jamestown HS 1,200/9-12
3751 John Tyler Hwy 23185 757-259-3600
Dr. Cathy Worley, prin. Fax 259-3759
Lafayette HS 1,100/9-12
4460 Longhill Rd 23188 757-565-0373
Anita Swinton, prin. Fax 565-4268
Warhill HS 1,100/9-12
4615 Opportunity Way 23188 757-565-4615
Dan Fields, prin. Fax 565-9101
Other Schools – See Toano

York County SD
Supt. — See Yorktown
Bruton HS 600/9-12
185 E Rochambeau Dr 23188 757-220-4050
Vicky Corlett, prin. Fax 220-4090
Queens Lake MS 500/6-8
124 W Queens Dr 23185 757-220-4080
Kendra Crump Ed.D., prin. Fax 220-4074

School of the Arts 9-12
185 E Rochambeau Dr 23188 757-220-4050
Vicky Corlett, prin. Fax 220-2611

College of William and Mary Post-Sec.
PO Box 8795 23187 757-221-4000
Providence Classical S 200/K-12
6000 Easter Cir 23188 757-565-2900
Susan Oweis, admin. Fax 565-3720
Walsingham Academy Upper S 300/8-12
PO Box 8702 23187 757-229-6026
Katherine Johnson, prin. Fax 259-1401
Williamsburg Christian Academy 300/PK-12
101 School House Ln 23188 757-220-1978
Gwendolyn Martin, head sch Fax 741-4009

Winchester, Winchester, Pop. 25,545
Frederick County SD 13,100/K-12
PO Box 3508 22604 540-662-3888
Dr. David Sovine, supt. Fax 722-2788
www.frederick.k12.va.us
Byrd MS 900/6-8
134 Rosa Ln 22602 540-662-0500
Teresa Ritenour, prin. Fax 662-7790
Frederick County MS 700/6-8
441 Linden Dr 22601 540-667-4233
Susan Brinkmeier, prin. Fax 667-2392
Howard Center Vo/Tech
156 Dowell J Cir 22602 540-662-8997
Janelle Ball-Brooks, dir. Fax 662-9112
Millbrook HS 1,300/9-12
251 First Woods Dr 22603 540-545-2800
Carolyn Butler, prin. Fax 545-7962
Wood HS 1,300/9-12
161 Apple Pie Ridge Rd 22603 540-667-5226
Joseph Salyer, prin. Fax 667-3154
Wood MS 800/6-8
1313 Amherst St 22601 540-667-7500
Grant Javersak, prin. Fax 667-7500
Other Schools – See Stephens City

Winchester CSD 4,000/PK-12
PO Box 551 22604 540-667-4253
Dr. Ricky Leonard, supt. Fax 722-6198
www.wps.k12.va.us
Handley HS 1,100/9-12
PO Box 910 22604 540-662-3471
Dr. Jesse Dingle, prin. Fax 722-6722
Morgan MS 1,100/5-8
48 S Purcell Ave 22601 540-667-7171
Sarah Kish, prin. Fax 723-8897

Grafton School Post-Sec.
PO Box 2500 22604 540-542-0200
Mountain View Christian Academy 100/K-12
153 Narrow Ln 22602 540-868-1231
Minta Hardman, admin. Fax 869-8976
Shenandoah University Post-Sec.
1460 University Dr 22601 540-665-4500
Winchester Academy 200/PK-12
2400 Roosevelt Blvd 22601 540-542-1100
Cherie Cintron, head sch Fax 542-6101
Winchester Memorial Hospital Post-Sec.
PO Box 3340 22604 540-722-8000

Windsor, Isle of Wight, Pop. 2,598
Isle of Wight County SD
Supt. — See Smithfield
Windsor HS 500/9-12
24 Church St 23487 757-242-6172
Daniel Soderholm, prin. Fax 242-4948
Windsor MS 300/6-8
23320 N Court St 23487 757-242-3229
Susan Goetz, prin. Fax 242-3405

Wirtz, Franklin

Smith Mountain Lake Christian Academy 100/PK-10
2485 Lost Mountain Rd # B 24184 540-719-1192
Christina Perdue, admin. Fax 721-4627

Wise, Wise, Pop. 3,248
Wise County SD 6,000/PK-12
PO Box 1217 24293 276-328-8017
Dr. Jeff Perry, supt. Fax 328-3350
www.wise.k12.va.us
Addington MS 500/5-8
PO Box 977 24293 276-328-8821
Greg Jessee, prin. Fax 328-2044
Central HS 500/9-12
PO Box 796 24293 276-328-8015
Charles Collins, prin. Fax 328-8316
Wise County Career-Technical Center Vo/Tech
PO Box 1218 24293 276-328-6113
Larry Hamilton, prin. Fax 328-4443
Other Schools – See Big Stone Gap, Coeburn

University of Virginia College at Wise Post-Sec.
1 College Ave 24293 276-328-0100
Wise County Christian S 100/PK-12
PO Box 3297 24293 276-328-3297
Carson Slone, prin. Fax 328-3248

Woodberry Forest, Madison

Woodberry Forest S 400/9-12
898 Woodberry Forest Rd 22989 540-672-3900
Dennis Campbell, hdmstr. Fax 672-0928

Woodbridge, Prince William, Pop. 3,887
Prince William County SD
Supt. — See Manassas
Beville MS 1,200/6-8
4901 Dale Blvd 22193 703-878-2593
Timothy Keenan, prin. Fax 730-1274
Forest Park HS 2,400/9-12
15721 Forest Park Dr 22193 703-583-3200
Eric Brent, prin. Fax 583-6867
Freedom HS 1,900/9-12
15201 Neabsco Mills Rd 22191 703-583-1405
Inez Bryant, prin. Fax 583-8705
Gar-Field HS 2,600/9-12
14000 Smoketown Rd 22192 703-730-7000
William Bixby, prin. Fax 730-7197
Godwin MS 1,000/6-8
14800 Darbydale Ave 22193 703-670-6166
Jehovanni Mitchell, prin. Fax 670-9888
Hylton HS 2,300/9-12
14051 Spriggs Rd 22193 703-580-4000
David Cassady, prin. Fax 580-4299
Lake Ridge MS 1,300/6-8
12350 Mohican Rd 22192 703-494-5154
Jo Fitzgerald, prin. Fax 494-8246
Lynn MS 900/6-8
1650 Prince William Pkwy 22191 703-494-5157
Cherif Sadki Ph.D., prin. Fax 491-5141
Rippon MS 1,000/6-8
15101 Blackburn Rd 22191 703-491-2171
Gail Stone, prin. Fax 491-2487
Woodbridge HS 2,600/9-12
3001 Old Bridge Rd 22192 703-497-8000
David Huckestein, prin. Fax 497-8117
Woodbridge MS 1,000/6-8
2201 York Dr 22191 703-494-3181
Skyles Calhoun, prin. Fax 491-1441

Christ Chapel Academy 600/PK-12
13909 Smoketown Rd 22192 703-670-3822
Rev. Paul Miklich, admin. Fax 897-7905
Everest College Post-Sec.
14555 Potomac Mills Rd 22192 571-408-2100
Northern Virginia Community College Post-Sec.
15200 Neabsco Mills Rd 22191 703-323-3000
Stratford University Post-Sec.
14349 Gideon Dr 22192 703-897-1982

Woodstock, Shenandoah, Pop. 5,017
Shenandoah County SD 6,200/PK-12
600 N Main St Ste 200 22664 540-459-6222
Dr. B. Keith Rowland, supt. Fax 459-6707
www.shenandoah.k12.va.us
Central HS 800/9-12
1147 Susan Ave 22664 540-459-2161
Melissa Hensley, prin. Fax 459-5932
Muhlenberg MS 600/6-8
1251 Susan Ave 22664 540-459-2941
Gina Stetter, prin. Fax 459-5965
Other Schools – See Mount Jackson, Quicksburg, Strasburg

Massanutten Military Academy 100/7-12
614 S Main St 22664 540-459-2167
Craig Jones, head sch Fax 459-5421

Wytheville, Wythe, Pop. 8,065
Wythe County SD 4,400/PK-12
1570 W Reservoir St 24382 276-228-5411
Dr. W. Lee Brannon, supt. Fax 228-9192
wcps.wythe.k12.va.us
Scott Memorial MS 400/6-8
950 S 7th St 24382 276-228-2851
Robbie Patton, prin. Fax 228-8261
Wythe Co. Technical Center Vo/Tech
1505 W Spiller St 24382 276-228-5481
Anthony Sykes, prin. Fax 228-8254
Wythe HS 400/9-12
1 Maroon Way 24382 276-228-3157
Ricky Skeens, prin. Fax 228-4124
Other Schools – See Max Meadows, Rural Retreat

Wytheville Community College Post-Sec.
1000 E Main St 24382 276-223-4700

Yorktown, York, Pop. 195
York County SD 12,500/PK-12
302 Dare Rd 23692 757-898-0300
Dr. Eric Williams, supt. Fax 890-0771
www.yorkcountyschools.org
Grafton HS 1,300/9-12
403 Grafton Dr 23692 757-898-0530
Royce Hart, prin. Fax 898-0533
Grafton MS 900/6-8
405 Grafton Dr 23692 757-898-0525
Karen Cagle, prin. Fax 898-0534
Tabb HS 1,200/9-12
4431 Big Bethel Rd 23693 757-867-7400
Angela Seiders, prin. Fax 867-7414
Tabb MS 800/6-8
300 Yorktown Rd 23693 757-898-0320
Antonia Fox, prin. Fax 867-7425
York HS 1,100/9-12
9300 George Washington Mem 23692 757-898-0354
Margaret Constantino, prin. Fax 898-8235
Yorktown MS 700/6-8
11201 George Washington Mem 23690
757-898-0360
Susan Hutton, prin. Fax 898-0412
Other Schools – See Williamsburg

Summit Christian Academy 100/7-12
4209 Big Bethel Rd 23693 757-867-7005
Marilyn Lane, prin.

WASHINGTON

WASHINGTON DEPARTMENT OF EDUCATION
PO Box 47200, Olympia 98504-7200
Telephone 360-725-6000
Fax 360-753-6712
Website http://www.k12.wa.us

Superintendent of Public Instruction Randy Dorn

WASHINGTON BOARD OF EDUCATION
PO Box 47206, Olympia 98504-7206

Executive Director

EDUCATIONAL SERVICE DISTRICTS (ESD)

North Central ESD 171
Dr. Richard McBride, supt. 509-665-2610
PO Box 1847, Wenatchee 98807 Fax 662-9027
www.ncesd.org
Northeast Washington ESD 101
Dr. Michael Dunn, supt. 509-789-3800
4202 S Regal St, Spokane 99223 Fax 789-3780
www.esd101.net
Northwest ESD 189
Dr. Gerald Jenkins, supt. 360-299-4000
1601 R Ave, Anacortes 98221 Fax 299-4070
www.nwesd.org/

Olympic ESD 114
Dr. Walt Bigby, supt. 360-479-0993
105 National Ave N Fax 478-6869
Bremerton 98312
www.oesd.wednet.edu
ESD 123
Bruce Hawkins, supt. 509-547-8441
3918 W Court St, Pasco 99301 Fax 544-5795
www.esd123.org
Puget Sound ESD
Dr. Monte Bridges, supt. 800-917-7600
800 Oakesdale Ave SW Fax 917-7777
Renton 98057
www.psesd.org

ESD 113
Dr. Bill Keim, supt. 360-464-6700
6005 Tyee Dr SW, Tumwater 98512 Fax 464-6900
www.esd113.org
ESD 112
Dr. Twyla Barnes, supt. 360-750-7500
2500 NE 65th Ave Fax 750-9706
Vancouver 98661
www.esd112.org
ESD 105
Steve Myers, supt. 509-575-2885
33 S 2nd Ave, Yakima 98902 Fax 575-2918
www.esd105.org/

PUBLIC, PRIVATE AND CATHOLIC SECONDARY SCHOOLS

Aberdeen, Grays Harbor, Pop. 16,223
Aberdeen SD 5 3,300/PK-12
216 N G St 98520 360-538-2000
Thomas Opstad, supt. Fax 538-2014
www.asd5.org
Aberdeen HS 900/9-12
410 N G St 98520 360-538-2040
Rocky Rocquin, prin. Fax 538-2046
Harbor HS 100/Alt
300 N Williams St 98520 360-538-2180
Sherri Northington, prin. Fax 538-2183
Miller JHS 500/7-8
100 E Lindstrom St 98520 360-538-2100
Mark Decker, prin. Fax 538-2106

Wishkah Valley SD 117 100/K-12
4640 Wishkah Rd 98520 360-532-3128
Ray Yoder, supt. Fax 533-4638
www.wishkah.org
Wishkah Valley S 100/K-12
4640 Wishkah Rd 98520 360-532-3128
Ray Yoder, prin. Fax 533-4638

Grays Harbor College Post-Sec.
1620 Edward P Smith Dr 98520 360-532-9020

Amanda Park, Grays Harbor, Pop. 240
Lake Quinault SD 97 200/K-12
PO Box 38 98526 360-288-2260
Rich DuBois, supt. Fax 288-2732
www.quinault.k12.wa.us/
Lake Quinault MSHS 100/6-12
PO Box 38 98526 360-288-2414
Keith Samplawski, prin. Fax 288-2209

Amboy, Clark, Pop. 1,593
Battle Ground SD 119
Supt. — See Brush Prairie
Amboy MS 600/5-8
22115 NE Chelatchie Rd 98601 360-885-6050
Michael Maloney, prin. Fax 885-6055

Anacortes, Skagit, Pop. 15,315
Anacortes SD 103 2,700/PK-12
2200 M Ave 98221 360-293-1212
Chris Borgen, supt. Fax 293-1222
www.asd103.org/
Anacortes HS 800/9-12
1600 20th St 98221 360-293-2166
Jon Ronngren, prin. Fax 293-0744
Anacortes MS 400/7-8
2202 M Ave 98221 360-293-9545
Patrick Harrington, prin. Fax 293-1231
Cap Sante HS 50/Alt
1717 J Ave 98221 360-293-1225
Jon Ronngren, admin. Fax 293-0744

Arlington, Snohomish, Pop. 17,235
Arlington SD 16 5,500/PK-12
315 N French Ave 98223 360-618-6200
Kristine McDuffy Ed.D., supt. Fax 618-6221
www.asd.wednet.edu
Arlington HS 1,600/9-12
18821 Crown Ridge Blvd 98223 360-618-6300
Brian Beckley, prin. Fax 618-6310

Haller MS 600/6-8
600 E 1st St 98223 360-618-6400
Eric DeJong, prin. Fax 618-6411
Post MS 600/6-8
1220 E 5th St 98223 360-618-6450
Yvonne Walker, prin. Fax 618-6455
Weston HS 100/Alt
4407 172nd St NE 98223 360-618-6340
Amie Verellen Grubbs, prin. Fax 618-6341

Academy Northwest / Family Academy 300/K-12
23420 Jordan Rd 98223 206-246-9227
Candice Childs, admin. Fax 246-5618
Highland Christian S 100/K-12
135 S French Ave 98223 360-403-8351
Tana Litwin, admin. Fax 403-4821

Asotin, Asotin, Pop. 1,220
Asotin-Anatone SD 420 600/K-12
PO Box 489 99402 509-243-1100
Dale Bonfield, supt. Fax 243-4251
www.aasd.wednet.edu
Asotin JSHS 300/7-12
PO Box 489 99402 509-243-4151
Jerry Uhling, prin. Fax 243-4090

Auburn, King, Pop. 65,915
Auburn SD 408 14,500/K-12
915 4th St NE 98002 253-931-4900
Dr. Kip Herren, supt. Fax 931-8006
www.auburn.wednet.edu
Auburn HS 1,700/9-12
800 4th St NE 98002 253-931-4880
Richard Zimmerman, prin. Fax 931-4701
Auburn Mountainview HS 1,400/9-12
28900 124th Ave SE 98092 253-804-4539
Terri Herren, prin. Fax 876-2507
Auburn Riverside HS 1,700/9-12
501 Oravetz Rd SE 98092 253-804-5154
Dave Halford, prin. Fax 804-5168
Cascade MS 700/6-8
1015 24th St NE 98002 253-931-4995
Isaiah Johnson, prin. Fax 833-7580
Mt. Baker MS 900/6-8
620 37th St SE 98002 253-804-4555
Greg Brown, prin. Fax 931-0661
Olympic MS 700/6-8
1825 K St SE 98002 253-931-4966
Jason Hill, prin. Fax 939-2753
Rainier MS 900/6-8
30620 116th Ave SE 98092 253-931-4843
Ben Talbert, prin. Fax 939-4318
West Auburn HS 200/Alt
401 W Main St 98001 253-931-4990
Lenny Holloman, prin. Fax 931-4707

Federal Way SD 210
Supt. — See Federal Way
Jefferson HS 1,900/9-12
4248 S 288th St 98001 253-945-5600
Liz Drake, prin. Fax 945-5656
Kilo MS 600/6-8
4400 S 308th St 98001 253-945-4700
Margaret Peterson, prin. Fax 945-4747

Sequoyah MS 600/6-8
3425 S 360th St 98001 253-945-3670
Springy Yamasaki, prin. Fax 945-3699

Auburn Adventist Academy 300/9-12
5000 Auburn Way S 98092 253-939-5000
Samir Berbawy, prin. Fax 351-9806
Green River Community College Post-Sec.
12401 SE 320th St 98092 253-833-9111
Ranier Christian HS 200/9-12
19830 SE 328th Pl 98092 253-735-1413
Justin Evans, admin. Fax 887-8234

Bainbridge Island, Kitsap, Pop. 22,174
Bainbridge Island SD 303 3,900/PK-12
8489 Madison Ave NE 98110 206-842-4714
Faith Chapel, supt. Fax 842-2928
www.bisd303.org
Bainbridge HS 1,400/9-12
9330 NE High School Rd 98110 206-842-2634
Brent Peterson, prin. Fax 780-1260
Eagle Harbor HS 100/9-12
9530 NE High School Rd 98110 206-780-1646
Catherine Camp, prin. Fax 855-0511
Woodward MS 500/7-8
9125 Sportsman Club Rd NE 98110 206-842-4787
Mike Florian, prin. Fax 780-4525

Battle Ground, Clark, Pop. 16,976
Battle Ground SD 119
Supt. — See Brush Prairie
Agriculture Science & Environmental Ed Alt
PO Box 200 98604 360-885-5361
Richard Hogg, lead tchr. Fax 885-5365
Battle Ground HS 2,100/9-12
PO Box 200 98604 360-885-6500
Tim Lexow, prin. Fax 687-6590
CAM Academy 500/Alt
PO Box 200 98604 360-885-6825
Colleen O'Neal, prin. Fax 885-6808
Chief Umtuch MS 600/5-8
PO Box 200 98604 360-885-6350
David Cresap, prin. Fax 885-6355
Daybreak MS 500/5-8
PO Box 200 98604 360-885-6900
Shelly Whitten, prin. Fax 885-6948
Tukes Valley MS 400/5-8
PO Box 200 98604 360-885-6250
Diana Harris, prin. Fax 885-6297

Columbia Adventist Academy 100/9-12
11100 NE 189th St 98604 360-687-3161
Matthew Butte, prin. Fax 687-9856
Firm Foundation Christian S 400/PK-12
1919 SW 25th Ave 98604 360-687-8382
Scott Grove, admin. Fax 687-8799

Belfair, Mason, Pop. 3,769
North Mason SD 403 2,100/PK-12
71 E Campus Dr 98528 360-277-2300
David Peterson, supt. Fax 277-2320
www.northmasonschools.org
Hawkins MS 500/6-8
300 E Campus Dr 98528 360-277-2302
Thomas Worlund, prin. Fax 277-2324

North Mason HS 700/9-12
200 E Campus Dr 98528 360-277-2303
Chad Collins, prin. Fax 277-2323
PACE Academy Alt
71 E Campus Dr 98528 360-277-2210
Anne Crosby, admin. Fax 277-2320

Bellevue, King, Pop. 117,650
Bellevue SD 405 17,900/PK-12
PO Box 90010 98009 425-456-4000
J. Tim Mills Ed.D., supt. Fax 456-4176
www.bsd405.org
Bellevue Big Picture S 200/Alt
14844 SE 22nd St 98007 425-456-7800
Bethany Spinler, prin. Fax 456-7811
Bellevue HS 1,400/9-12
10416 Wolverine Way 98004 425-456-7000
Scott Powers, prin. Fax 456-7005
Chinook MS 1,000/6-8
11650 SE 60th St 98006 425-456-6300
Dr. Vic Anderson, prin. Fax 456-6304
Highland MS 500/6-8
15027 Bel Red Rd 98007 425-456-6400
Anissa Bereano, prin. Fax 456-6499
Interlake HS 1,500/9-12
16245 NE 24th St 98008 425-456-7200
Maria Frieboes-Gee, prin. Fax 456-7215
International S 500/6-12
445 128th Ave SE 98005 425-456-6500
Jennifer Rose, prin. Fax 456-6565
Newport HS 1,700/9-12
4333 Factoria Blvd SE 98006 425-456-7400
Heidi Fedore, prin. Fax 456-7530
Odle MS 700/6-8
14401 NE 8th St 98007 425-456-6600
Eric McDowell, prin. Fax 456-6616
Sammamish HS 1,100/9-12
100 140th Ave SE 98005 425-456-7600
Tom Duenwald, prin. Fax 456-7630
Tillicum MS 700/6-8
16020 SE 16th St 98008 425-456-6700
Dion Yahoudy, prin. Fax 456-6770
Tyee MS 800/6-8
13630 SE Allen Rd 98006 425-456-6800
Aaron Miller, prin. Fax 456-6859

Bellevue College Post-Sec.
3000 Landerholm Cir SE 98007 425-564-1000
DeVry University Post-Sec.
600 108th Ave NE Ste 230 98004 425-455-2242
Evergreen Beauty School Post-Sec.
14045 NE 20th St Ste B 98007 425-643-0270
Forest Ridge School of the Sacred Heart 400/5-12
4800 139th Ave SE 98006 425-641-0700
Mark Pierotti, hdmstr. Fax 643-3881

Bellingham, Whatcom, Pop. 77,637
Bellingham SD 501 11,100/K-12
1306 Dupont St 98225 360-676-6400
Dr. Greg Baker, supt. Fax 676-2793
bellinghamschools.org
Bellingham HS 1,100/9-12
2020 Cornwall Ave 98225 360-676-6575
Jeff Vaughn, prin. Fax 647-6803
Fairhaven MS 700/6-8
110 Parkridge Rd 98225 360-676-6450
Robert Kalahan, prin. Fax 647-6887
Kulshan MS 700/6-8
1250 Kenoyer Dr, 360-676-4886
Jeannie Hayden, prin. Fax 647-6892
Options HS 100/Alt
2015 Franklin St 98225 360-647-6871
Byron Gerard, prin. Fax 647-6872
Sehome HS 1,100/9-12
2700 Bill McDonald Pkwy 98225 360-676-6481
Phyllis Textor, prin. Fax 647-6863
Shuksan MS 800/6-8
2717 Alderwood Ave 98225 360-676-6454
Jay Jordan, prin. Fax 647-6879
Squalicum HS 1,400/9-12
3773 E McLeod Rd 98226 360-676-6471
Keith Schacht, prin. Fax 676-6561
Whatcom MS 600/6-8
810 Halleck St 98225 360-676-6460
Jeffrey Coulter, prin. Fax 647-6899

Meridian SD 505 1,400/PK-12
214 W Laurel Rd 98226 360-398-7111
Tom Churchill, supt. Fax 398-8966
www.meridian.wednet.edu
Meridian HS 500/9-12
194 W Laurel Rd 98226 360-398-8111
James Everett, prin. Fax 398-7720
Other Schools – See Lynden

Bellingham Beauty School Post-Sec.
4192 Meridian St 98226 360-734-1090
Bellingham Technical College Post-Sec.
3028 Lindbergh Ave 98225 360-752-7000
Charter College Bellingham Post-Sec.
410 W Bakerview Rd 98226 360-647-5000
Northwest Indian College Post-Sec.
2522 Kwina Rd 98226 360-676-2772
St. Paul's Academy 400/PK-12
1509 E Victor St 98225 360-733-1750
Dr. Lily Driskill, head sch Fax 734-1882
Toni & Guy Hairdressing Academy Post-Sec.
1411 Railroad Ave 98225 360-676-8444
Western Washington University Post-Sec.
516 High St 98225 360-650-3000
Whatcom Community College Post-Sec.
237 W Kellogg Rd 98226 360-383-3000

Benton City, Benton, Pop. 2,971
Kiona-Benton City SD 52 1,300/PK-12
1107 Grace 99320 509-588-2000
Rom Castilleja, supt. Fax 588-5580
www.kibesd.org
Kiona-Benton City HS 500/9-12
1107 Grace 99320 509-588-2140
Wayne Barrett, prin. Fax 588-2651
Kiona-Benton City MS 400/6-8
1107 Grace 99320 509-588-2040
Chuck Feth, prin. Fax 588-2905

Bickleton, Klickitat, Pop. 87
Bickleton SD 203 100/K-12
PO Box 10 99322 509-896-5473
Ric Palmer, supt. Fax 896-2071
www.bickletonschools.org
Bickleton S 100/K-12
PO Box 10 99322 509-896-5473
Ric Palmer, prin. Fax 896-2071

Blaine, Whatcom, Pop. 4,469
Blaine SD 503 2,100/PK-12
765 H St 98230 360-332-5881
Ron Spanjer, supt. Fax 332-7568
www.blaine.k12.wa.us
Blaine HS 600/9-12
1055 H St 98230 360-332-6045
Scott Ellis, prin. Fax 332-7568
Blaine MS 500/6-8
975 H St 98230 360-332-8226
Darren Benson, prin. Fax 332-7568

Bonney Lake, Pierce, Pop. 16,669
Sumner SD 320
Supt. — See Sumner
Bonney Lake HS 1,400/9-12
10920 199th Avenue Ct E, 253-891-5725
Linda Masteller, prin. Fax 891-5797
Lakeridge MS 600/6-8
5909 Myers Rd E, 253-891-5100
Steve Fulkerson, prin. Fax 891-5145
Mountain View MS 600/6-8
10921 199th Avenue Ct E, 253-891-5200
Curtis Hurst, prin. Fax 891-5245

Bothell, King, Pop. 32,149
Edmonds SD 15
Supt. — See Lynnwood
Lynnwood HS 1,600/9-12
18218 North Rd 98012 425-431-7520
David Golden, prin. Fax 431-7527

Northshore SD 417 19,200/PK-12
3330 Monte Villa Pkwy 98021 425-408-7701
Larry Francois, supt. Fax 408-7702
www.nsd.org
Bothell SHS 1,600/10-12
9130 NE 180th St 98011 425-408-7000
Bob Stewart, prin. Fax 408-7002
Canyon Park JHS 800/7-9
23723 23rd Ave SE 98021 425-408-6300
Sebastian Ziz, prin. Fax 408-6302
Northshore JHS 700/7-9
12101 NE 160th St 98011 425-408-6700
Josh Sanchez, prin. Fax 408-6702
Secondary Academy for Success 200/Alt
22107 23rd Dr SE 98021 425-408-6600
Donna Tyo, prin. Fax 408-6602
Skyview JHS 800/7-9
21404 35th Ave SE 98021 425-408-6800
Dawn Mark, prin. Fax 408-6802
Other Schools – See Kenmore, Woodinville

Bastyr University Post-Sec.
14500 Juanita Dr NE 98028 425-602-3000
Cascadia Community College Post-Sec.
18345 Campus Way NE 98011 425-352-8000
Cedar Park Christian S 1,700/PK-12
16300 112th Ave NE 98011 425-488-9778
Clint Behrends, supt. Fax 483-5765

Bremerton, Kitsap, Pop. 34,864
Bremerton SD 100-C 4,900/PK-12
134 Marion Ave N 98312 360-473-1000
Flip Herndon Ed.D., supt. Fax 473-1040
www.bremertonschools.org
Bremerton HS 1,300/9-12
1500 13th St 98337 360-473-0800
John Polm, prin. Fax 473-0820
Mountain View MS 1,000/6-8
2400 Perry Ave 98310 360-473-0600
Michaeleen Gelhaus, prin. Fax 473-0640
Renaissance HS / Phoenix Academy 100/Alt
3400 1st St 98312 360-473-4700
Kristen Morga, prin. Fax 792-1350
West Sound Technical Skills Center Vo/Tech
101 National Ave N 98312 360-473-0550
Lillian Hunter, dir. Fax 478-5090

Central Kitsap SD 401
Supt. — See Silverdale
Eastside Alternative HS 100/Alt
7070 Tibardis Rd NW 98311 360-662-2870
Richard Arena, prin. Fax 662-2871
Fairview JHS 700/7-9
8107 Central Valley Rd NW 98311 360-662-2600
Kathy Wales, prin. Fax 662-2601
Olympic HS 900/10-12
7070 Stampede Blvd NW 98311 360-662-2700
Robert Barnes, prin. Fax 662-2701

Everest College Post-Sec.
155 Washington Ave Ste 200 98337 360-473-1120
Gateway Christian S 200/K-12
4012 Chico Way NW 98312 360-377-7700
Nick Sweeney, admin. Fax 377-7795
Olympic College Post-Sec.
1600 Chester Ave 98337 360-792-6050

Brewster, Okanogan, Pop. 2,353
Brewster SD 111 800/PK-12
PO Box 97 98812 509-689-3418
Eric Driessen, supt. Fax 689-0749
brewsterbears.org/
Brewster JSHS 300/7-12
PO Box 97 98812 509-689-3449
Linda Dezellem, prin. Fax 689-0675

Bridgeport, Douglas, Pop. 2,379
Bridgeport SD 75 800/PK-12
PO Box 1060 98813 509-686-5656
Scott Sattler, supt. Fax 686-2221
www.bridgeport.wednet.edu
Aurora HS 50/Alt
PO Box 1060 98813 509-686-8770
Tamra Jackson, prin. Fax 686-9622
Bridgeport HS 200/9-12
PO Box 1060 98813 509-686-8770
Tamra Jackson, prin. Fax 686-9622
Bridgeport MS 200/6-8
PO Box 1060 98813 509-686-9501
Brian Ellis, admin. Fax 686-4052

Brier, Snohomish, Pop. 5,840
Edmonds SD 15
Supt. — See Lynnwood
Brier Terrace MS 700/7-8
22200 Brier Rd 98036 425-431-7834
Donna Alexander, prin. Fax 431-7836

Brush Prairie, Clark, Pop. 2,603
Battle Ground SD 119 11,900/K-12
11104 NE 149th St 98606 360-885-5300
Duane Rose, supt. Fax 885-5310
www.battlegroundps.org
Summit View HS 400/Alt
11104 NE 149th St 98606 360-885-5331
Bill Penrose, prin. Fax 885-5402
Other Schools – See Amboy, Battle Ground, Vancouver

Hockinson SD 98 2,000/K-12
17912 NE 159th St 98606 360-448-6400
Sandra Yager, supt. Fax 448-6409
www.hock.k12.wa.us/
Hockinson HS 700/9-12
16819 NE 159th St 98606 360-448-6450
Brian Lehner, prin. Fax 448-6459
Hockinson MS 500/6-8
15916 NE 182nd Ave 98606 360-448-6440
Slade McSheehy, prin. Fax 448-6449

Buckley, Pierce, Pop. 4,221
White River SD 416 3,600/K-12
PO Box 2050 98321 360-829-0600
Janel Keating, supt. Fax 829-3843
www.whiteriver.wednet.edu
Glacier MS 800/6-8
PO Box 1976 98321 360-829-3395
Dr. Greg Borgerding, prin. Fax 829-3391
White River HS 1,200/9-12
PO Box 1683 98321 360-829-3352
Elaine Mathews, prin. Fax 829-3351

Rainier School, PO Box 600 98321 Post-Sec.

Burbank, Walla Walla, Pop. 3,235
Columbia SD 400 900/PK-12
755 Maple St 99323 509-547-2136
Dr. Lou Gates, supt. Fax 546-0603
www.csd400.org/
Columbia HS 300/9-12
787 Maple St 99323 509-545-8573
Kyle Miller, prin. Fax 545-6553
Columbia MS 200/6-8
835 Maple St 99323 509-545-8571
Mike Taylor, prin. Fax 547-4277

Burien, King, Pop. 31,292
Highline SD 401 18,700/PK-12
15675 Ambaum Blvd SW 98166 206-433-0111
Dr. Susan Enfield, supt. Fax 433-2351
www.highlineschools.org
Big Picture MSHS 100/7-12
440 S 186th St 98148 206-631-7700
Jeff Petty, prin. Fax 631-7749
CHOICE Academy 50/7-12
18367 8th Ave S 98148 206-631-7630
Michael Sita, prin. Fax 631-7648
Highline HS 1,400/9-12
225 S 152nd St 98148 206-631-6700
Damon Hunter, prin. Fax 631-6758
Puget Sound Skills Center Vo/Tech
18010 8th Ave S 98148 206-631-7300
Dr. Sue Shields, prin. Fax 433-2405
Sylvester MS 700/7-8
16222 Sylvester Rd SW 98166 206-433-2401
Vicki Fisher, prin. Fax 433-2530
Other Schools – See Des Moines, SeaTac, Seattle

Kennedy HS 1,000/9-12
140 S 140th St 98168 206-246-0500
Michael Prato, prin. Fax 242-0831

Burlington, Skagit, Pop. 8,211
Burlington-Edison SD 100 3,800/K-12
927 E Fairhaven Ave 98233 360-757-3311
Laurel Browning, supt. Fax 755-9198
www.be.wednet.edu/
Burlington-Edison HS 1,100/9-12
301 N Burlington Blvd 98233 360-757-4074
Beth VanderVeen, prin. Fax 757-3350
Burlington North Alternative HS 100/Alt
301 N Burlington Blvd 98233 360-757-4074
Linda Larabee, lead tchr.

Skagit Adventist Academy 200/PK-12
530 N Section St 98233 360-755-9261

Camas, Clark, Pop. 18,670
Camas SD 117 — 5,900/K-12
841 NE 22nd Ave 98607 — 360-335-3000
Dr. Mike Nerland, supt. — Fax 335-3001
www.camas.wednet.edu/
Camas HS — 1,800/9-12
26900 SE 15th St 98607 — 360-833-5750
Steve Marshall, prin. — Fax 833-5751
Hayes Freedom HS — 100/9-12
1919 NE Ione St 98607 — 360-833-5600
Amy Holmes, prin. — Fax 833-5601
Liberty MS — 700/6-8
1612 NE Garfield St 98607 — 360-833-5850
Marilyn Boerke, prin. — Fax 833-5851
Skyridge MS — 800/6-8
5220 NW Parker St 98607 — 360-833-5800
Aaron Smith, prin. — Fax 833-5801

Evergreen SD 114
Supt. — See Vancouver
Union HS — 2,000/9-12
6201 NW Friberg Strunk St 98607 — 360-604-6250
Brian Grimsted, prin. — Fax 604-6202

Carnation, King, Pop. 1,754
Riverview SD 407
Supt. — See Duvall
Riverview Learning Center — 200/Alt
32302 NE 50th St 98014 — 425-844-4960
Janet Gavigan, prin. — Fax 844-4962
Tolt MS — 700/6-8
3740 Tolt Ave 98014 — 425-844-4600
Christopher Lupo, prin. — Fax 844-4602

Cashmere, Chelan, Pop. 3,023
Cashmere SD 222 — 1,400/PK-12
210 S Division St 98815 — 509-782-3355
Glenn Johnson, supt. — Fax 782-4747
www.cashmere.wednet.edu
Cashmere HS — 400/9-12
329 Tigner Rd 98815 — 509-782-2914
Tony Boyle, prin. — Fax 782-2891
Cashmere MS — 400/5-8
300 Tigner Rd 98815 — 509-782-2001
Rob Cline, prin. — Fax 782-2547

Castle Rock, Cowlitz, Pop. 1,912
Castle Rock SD 401 — 1,400/PK-12
600 Huntington Ave S 98611 — 360-501-2940
Susan Barker, supt. — Fax 501-3140
www.castlerock.wednet.edu
Castle Rock HS — 400/9-12
5180 Westside Hwy 98611 — 360-501-2930
Jenny Risner, prin. — Fax 501-2999
Castle Rock MS — 200/7-8
615 Front Ave SW 98611 — 360-501-2920
Tiffany Golden, prin. — Fax 501-3125

Cathlamet, Wahkiakum, Pop. 521
Wahkiakum SD 200 — 500/K-12
PO Box 398 98612 — 360-795-3971
Bob Garrett, supt. — Fax 795-0545
www.wahksd.k12.wa.us
Thomas MS — 100/6-8
PO Box 398 98612 — 360-795-3261
Theresa Libby, prin. — Fax 795-3205
Wahkiakum HS — 200/9-12
PO Box 398 98612 — 360-795-3271
Stephanie Leitz, prin. — Fax 795-0545

Centralia, Lewis, Pop. 15,816
Centralia SD 401 — 3,500/K-12
PO Box 610 98531 — 360-330-7600
Dr. Steven Bodnar, supt. — Fax 330-7604
www.centralia.k12.wa.us
Centralia HS — 1,100/9-12
813 Eshom Rd 98531 — 360-330-7605
Tom Boehme, prin. — Fax 330-7616
Centralia MS — 500/7-8
901 Johnson Rd 98531 — 360-330-7619
Greg Domingos, prin. — Fax 330-7622
Other Schools – See Chehalis

Centralia College — Post-Sec.
600 Centralia College Blvd 98531 — 360-736-9391

Chattaroy, Spokane
Riverside SD 416 — 1,500/PK-12
34515 N Newport Hwy 99003 — 509-464-8201
Roberta Kramer, supt. — Fax 464-8206
www.riversidesd.org
Riverside Achievement/Opportunity Center — 50/Alt
34515 N Newport Hwy 99003 — 509-464-8204
Janet Kemp, prin.
Riverside HS — 500/9-12
4120 E Deer Park Milan Rd 99003 — 509-464-8550
John McCoy, prin. — Fax 464-8556
Riverside MS — 400/6-8
3814 E Deer Park Milan Rd 99003 — 509-464-8450
Lynn Rowse, prin. — Fax 464-8447

Chehalis, Lewis, Pop. 7,074
Adna SD 226 — 600/PK-12
179 Dieckman Rd 98532 — 360-748-0362
Jim Forrest, supt. — Fax 748-9217
www.adnaschools.org
Adna JSHS — 300/6-12
121 Adna School Rd 98532 — 360-748-0315
Kevin Ryan, prin. — Fax 748-1625

Centralia SD 401
Supt. — See Centralia
Centralia Alternative Program — 50/Alt
2100 N National Ave 98532 — 360-748-2163
Faye Olason, lead tchr. — Fax 748-2164

Chehalis SD 302 — 2,700/PK-12
310 SW 16th St 98532 — 360-807-7200
Ed Rothlin, supt. — Fax 748-8899
www.chehalis.k12.wa.us
Chehalis MS — 600/6-8
1060 SW 20th St 98532 — 360-807-7230
Chris Simpson, prin. — Fax 740-1849
West HS — 1,000/9-12
342 SW 16th St 98532 — 360-807-7235
Bob Walters, prin. — Fax 748-3664

Lewis County Adventist S — 50/PK-10
PO Box 1203 98532 — 360-748-3213
Karen Carlton, prin. — Fax 748-6399

Chelan, Chelan, Pop. 3,828
Lake Chelan SD 129 — 1,400/K-12
PO Box 369 98816 — 509-682-3515
Robert Manahan, supt. — Fax 682-5842
www.chelanschools.org/
Chelan HS — 400/9-12
PO Box 369 98816 — 509-682-4061
Barry DePaoli, prin. — Fax 682-5001
Chelan MS — 300/6-8
PO Box 369 98816 — 509-682-4073
Chris Anderson, prin. — Fax 682-5001
Chelan Preparatory Night S — 50/Alt
PO Box 369 98816 — 509-682-2537
Kari Lewinsohn, prin. — Fax 682-8291
Glacier Valley HS — 50/Alt
PO Box 369 98816 — 509-682-2537
Kari Lewinsohn, prin. — Fax 682-8291
Holden Village Community S — 50/K-12
PO Box 369 98816 — 509-682-4061
Kelly Kronbauer, prin. — Fax 682-5842

Cheney, Spokane, Pop. 10,120
Cheney SD 360 — 4,800/PK-12
520 4th St 99004 — 509-559-4599
Dr. Debra Clemens, supt. — Fax 559-4508
www.cheneysd.org
Cheney HS — 1,200/9-12
460 N 6th St 99004 — 509-559-4000
Troy Heuett, prin. — Fax 559-4005
Cheney MS — 900/6-8
740 W Betz Rd 99004 — 509-559-4400
Mike Stark, prin. — Fax 559-4479
Three Springs HS — 100/Alt
460 N 6th St 99004 — 509-559-4521
Troy Heuett, prin. — Fax 559-4582
Other Schools – See Spokane

Eastern Washington University — Post-Sec.
526 5th St 99004 — 509-359-6200

Chewelah, Stevens, Pop. 2,514
Chewelah SD 36 — 800/PK-12
PO Box 47 99109 — 509-685-6800
Richard Linehan, supt. — Fax 935-8605
chewelah.schoolwires.net
Jenkins HS — 300/9-12
PO Box 138 99109 — 509-685-6800
Kim Hogan, prin. — Fax 935-9206
Jenkins MS — 100/7-8
PO Box 1099 99109 — 509-685-6800
Jon Symonds, prin. — Fax 935-4404

Chimacum, Jefferson
Chimacum SD 49 — 1,000/K-12
PO Box 278 98325 — 360-732-4090
Rich Stewart, supt. — Fax 732-4336
www.csd49.org
Chimacum HS — 300/9-12
PO Box 278 98325 — 360-732-4090
Whitney Meissner, prin. — Fax 732-7359
Chimacum MS — 300/6-8
PO Box 278 98325 — 360-732-4090
Whitney Meissner, prin. — Fax 732-6859

Clallam Bay, Clallam, Pop. 345
Cape Flattery SD 401
Supt. — See Sekiu
Clallam Bay S — 100/K-12
PO Box 337 98326 — 360-963-2324
Stephanie Teel, prin. — Fax 963-2228

Clarkston, Asotin, Pop. 7,028
Clarkston SD J 250-185 — 2,700/K-12
PO Box 70 99403 — 509-758-2531
Darcy Weisner, supt. — Fax 758-3326
www.csdk12.org
Adams HS — 700/9-12
PO Box 370 99403 — 509-758-5591
Eric Anderson, prin. — Fax 758-2831
Educational Opportunity Center — 200/Alt
1284 Chestnut St 99403 — 509-758-4508
Elece Lockridge, prin. — Fax 758-4509
Lincoln MS — 400/7-8
1945 4th Ave 99403 — 509-758-5506
Mike Sperry, prin. — Fax 758-7838

Cle Elum, Kittitas, Pop. 1,804
Cle Elum-Roslyn SD 404 — 900/K-12
2690 State Route 903 98922 — 509-649-4850
Mark Flatau, supt. — Fax 649-2404
www.cleelum.wednet.edu
Cle Elum-Roslyn HS — 300/9-12
2692 State Route 903 98922 — 509-649-4900
Brett Simpson, prin. — Fax 649-3563
Strom MS — 200/6-8
2694 State Route 903 98922 — 509-649-4800
Kim Headrick, prin. — Fax 649-3634
Other Schools – See Roslyn

Clyde Hill, King, Pop. 2,918

Bellevue Christian JSHS — 500/7-12
1601 98th Ave NE 98004 — 425-454-4028
Sue Tameling, prin. — Fax 454-4418

Colbert, Spokane
Mead SD 354
Supt. — See Mead
Mountainside MS — 800/7-8
4717 E Day Mount Spokane Rd 99005 — 509-465-7400
Craig Busch, prin. — Fax 465-7420

Northwest Christian HS — 300/9-12
5104 E Bernhill Rd 99005 — 509-238-4005
Jack Hancock, hdmstr. — Fax 238-2242

Colfax, Whitman, Pop. 2,773
Colfax SD 300 — 500/K-12
1110 N Morton St 99111 — 509-397-3042
Michael Morgan, supt. — Fax 397-5835
www.colfax.k12.wa.us
Colfax JSHS — 200/7-12
1110 N Morton St 99111 — 509-397-4368
Buck Marsh, prin. — Fax 397-2414

College Place, Walla Walla, Pop. 8,557
College Place SD 250 — 500/K-8
1755 S College Ave 99324 — 509-525-4827
Timothy Payne, supt. — Fax 525-3741
www.cpps.org
Sager MS — 100/5-8
1755 S College Ave 99324 — 509-525-5300
Linda Byerley, prin. — Fax 525-6005

Walla Walla University — Post-Sec.
204 S College Ave 99324 — 509-527-2615
Walla Walla Valley Academy — 200/9-12
300 SW Academy Way 99324 — 509-525-1050
Brian Harris, prin. — Fax 525-1056

Colton, Whitman, Pop. 412
Colton SD 306 — 200/K-12
706 Union St 99113 — 509-229-3385
Nathan Smith, supt. — Fax 229-3374
www.colton.k12.wa.us
Colton S — 200/K-12
706 Union St 99113 — 509-229-3386
Nathan Smith, prin. — Fax 229-3374

Colville, Stevens, Pop. 4,534
Colville SD 115 — 2,600/K-12
217 S Hofstetter St 99114 — 509-684-7850
Michael Cashion, supt. — Fax 684-7855
www.colsd.org
Colville HS — 600/9-12
154 Highway 20 E 99114 — 509-684-7800
Kevin Knight, prin. — Fax 684-7809
Colville JHS — 300/6-8
990 S Cedar St 99114 — 509-684-7820
Paul Dumas, prin. — Fax 684-7825
Panorama S — 100/Alt
225 S Hofstetter St 99114 — 509-684-7840
Ann McKern, prin. — Fax 684-2819

Concrete, Skagit, Pop. 682
Concrete SD 11 — 600/K-12
45389 Airport Way Rm 103 98237 — 360-853-8141
Barbara Hawkings, supt. — Fax 853-7521
www.concrete.k12.wa.us
Concrete HS — 200/9-12
7830 S Superior Ave 98237 — 360-853-8143
Mike Holbrook, prin. — Fax 853-7709
Twin Cedars HS — 50/Alt
45389 Airport Way Rm 110 98237 — 360-853-8071
Mike Holbrook, dir. — Fax 853-7521

Connell, Franklin, Pop. 4,122
North Franklin SD J 51-162 — 2,000/K-12
PO Box 829 99326 — 509-234-2021
Gregg Taylor, supt. — Fax 234-9200
www.nfsd.org
Connell HS — 500/9-12
PO Box 829 99326 — 509-234-2911
Tim Peterson, prin. — Fax 234-9226
Olds JHS — 300/7-8
PO Box 829 99326 — 509-234-3931
Jim Jacobs, prin. — Fax 234-8171
Palouse Junction Alternative S — 50/Alt
PO Box 829 99326 — 509-234-1055
George Farrah, prin. — Fax 234-9200

Cosmopolis, Grays Harbor, Pop. 1,610
North River SD 200 — 50/PK-12
2867 N River Rd 98537 — 360-532-3079
David Pickering, supt. — Fax 532-1738
www.nr.k12.wa.us/
North River S — 50/PK-12
2867 N River Rd 98537 — 360-532-3079
David Pickering, prin. — Fax 532-1738

Coulee City, Grant, Pop. 541
Coulee-Hartline SD 151 — 200/K-12
PO Box 428 99115 — 509-632-5231
Dr. James Evans, supt. — Fax 632-5166
www.achsd.org
Almira-Coulee-Hartline HS — 100/9-12
413 N 4th St 99115 — 509-632-5231
Dr. James Evans, prin. — Fax 632-5166

Coulee Dam, Okanogan, Pop. 1,042
Grand Coulee Dam SD 301J — 700/PK-12
110 Stevens Ave 99116 — 509-633-2143
Dr. Dennis Carlson, supt. — Fax 633-2530
www.gcdsd.org
Lake Roosevelt HS — 200/9-12
500 Civic Way 99116 — 509-633-1442
Brandon Byers, prin. — Fax 633-0356
Other Schools – See Grand Coulee

Coupeville, Island, Pop. 1,760
Coupeville SD 204 — 1,000/K-12
501 S Main St 98239 — 360-678-4522
James Shank, supt. — Fax 678-4834
www.coupeville.k12.wa.us

Coupeville HS 300/9-12
501 S Main St 98239 360-678-4409
Sheldon Rosenkrance, prin. Fax 678-0540
Coupeville MS 200/6-8
501 S Main St 98239 360-678-4409
Sheldon Rosenkrance, prin. Fax 678-0540

Covington, King, Pop. 16,615
Kent SD 415
Supt. — See Kent
Cedar Heights MS 700/7-8
19640 SE 272nd St 98042 253-373-7620
Heidi Maurer, prin. Fax 373-7628
Kentwood HS 2,100/9-12
25800 164th Ave SE 98042 253-373-7680
Doug Hostetter, prin. Fax 373-7326
Mattson MS 600/7-8
16400 SE 251st St 98042 253-373-7670
Tammy Unruh, prin. Fax 373-7673

Tahoma SD 409
Supt. — See Maple Valley
Tahoma SHS 1,800/10-12
18200 SE 240th St 98042 425-413-6200
Terry Duty, prin. Fax 413-6333

Rainier Christian MS 100/7-8
26201 180th Ave SE 98042 253-639-7715
Glenn Olson, prin. Fax 639-3184

Cowiche, Yakima, Pop. 418
Highland SD 203 1,100/K-12
PO Box 38 98923 509-678-4173
Mark Anderson, supt. Fax 678-4177
www.highland.wednet.edu/
Highland HS 300/10-12
PO Box 38 98923 509-678-7268
Kelly Thorson, prin. Fax 678-4140
Highland JHS 200/7-9
PO Box 38 98923 509-678-7200
Mindy Schultz, prin. Fax 678-4006

Creston, Lincoln, Pop. 228
Creston SD 73 100/K-12
PO Box 17 99117 509-636-2721
William Wadlington, supt. Fax 636-2910
www.creston.wednet.edu
Creston JSHS 50/7-12
PO Box 17 99117 509-636-2721
William Wadlington, prin. Fax 636-2910

Curlew, Ferry, Pop. 114
Curlew SD 50 200/K-12
PO Box 370 99118 509-779-4931
Steve McCullough, supt. Fax 779-4938
www.curlew.wednet.edu
Curlew S 200/K-12
PO Box 370 99118 509-779-4931
Steve McCullough, supt. Fax 779-4938

Cusick, Pend Oreille, Pop. 205
Cusick SD 59 300/K-12
305 Monumental Rd 99119 509-445-1125
Dan Read, supt. Fax 445-1598
www.cusick.wednet.edu/
Cusick JSHS 100/7-12
305 Monumental Rd 99119 509-445-1125
Kathy Christiansen, prin. Fax 445-1598

Darrington, Snohomish, Pop. 1,303
Darrington SD 330 400/K-12
PO Box 27 98241 360-436-1323
Dave Holmer, supt. Fax 436-2045
www.dsd.k12.wa.us
Darrington MSHS 200/7-12
PO Box 27 98241 360-436-1140
Dave Holmer, prin. Fax 436-1089

Davenport, Lincoln, Pop. 1,697
Davenport SD 207 600/PK-12
801 7th St 99122 509-725-1481
Jim Kowalkowski, supt. Fax 725-2260
www.davenport.wednet.edu/
Davenport ALC Alt
801 7th St 99122 509-725-4021
Fax 725-2260
Davenport JSHS 300/7-12
801 7th St 99122 509-725-4021
Chad Prewitt, prin. Fax 725-2260

Dayton, Columbia, Pop. 2,459
Dayton SD 2 500/PK-12
609 S 2nd St 99328 509-382-2543
Doug Johnson, supt. Fax 382-2081
www.dayton.wednet.edu
Dayton HS 200/9-12
614 S 3rd St 99328 509-382-4775
Andy Maheras, prin. Fax 382-2081
Dayton MS 100/6-8
614 S 3rd St 99328 509-382-4775
Andy Maheras, prin. Fax 382-2081

Deer Park, Spokane, Pop. 3,505
Deer Park SD 414 2,000/K-12
PO Box 490 99006 509-464-5500
Travis Hanson, supt. Fax 464-5510
www.dpsd.org
Alternative S Alt
PO Box 550 99006 509-468-3500
Joe Feist, prin. Fax 468-3510
Deer Park HS 700/9-12
PO Box 550 99006 509-468-3500
Joe Feist, prin. Fax 468-3510
Deer Park MS 500/6-8
PO Box 882 99006 509-464-5800
Tim Olietti, prin. Fax 464-5810

Deming, Whatcom, Pop. 349
Mt. Baker SD 507 1,700/K-12
PO Box 95 98244 360-383-2000
Charles Burleigh, supt. Fax 383-2009
www.mtbaker.wednet.edu
Mt. Baker JSHS 700/7-12
PO Box 95 98244 360-383-2015
Steve King, prin. Fax 383-2029

Des Moines, King, Pop. 27,680
Highline SD 401
Supt. — See Burien
Aviation HS 400/9-12
615 S 200th St 98198 206-716-0006
Reba Gilman, prin. Fax 716-0020
Mount Rainier HS 1,700/9-12
22450 19th Ave S 98198 206-631-7000
Julie Hunter, prin. Fax 631-7099
Pacific MS 700/7-8
22705 24th Ave S 98198 206-631-5800
Cecilia Beaman, prin. Fax 631-5860

Kent SD 415
Supt. — See Kent
Kent Mountain View Academy 300/Alt
22420 Military Rd S 98198 253-373-7488
Debbie Dempsey, prin. Fax 373-7490

Evergreen Lutheran HS 100/9-12
2021 S 260th St 98198 253-946-4488
Rev. Nathan Seiltz, prin. Fax 529-9475
Highline Community College Post-Sec.
PO Box 98000 98198 206-878-3710

DuPont, Pierce, Pop. 7,501
Steilacoom Historical SD 1
Supt. — See Steilacoom
Pioneer MS 700/6-8
1750 Bobs Hollow Ln 98327 253-583-7200
Andre Stout, prin. Fax 583-7292

Duvall, King, Pop. 6,458
Riverview SD 407 3,200/K-12
PO Box 519 98019 425-844-4500
Dr. Anthony L. Smith, supt. Fax 844-4502
www.riverview.wednet.edu
Cedarcrest HS 900/9-12
29000 NE 150th St 98019 425-844-4800
Clarence Lavarias, prin. Fax 844-4802
Other Schools – See Carnation

Easton, Kittitas, Pop. 472
Easton SD 28 100/PK-12
PO Box 8 98925 509-656-2317
Patrick Dehuff, supt. Fax 656-2585
www.easton.wednet.edu/
Easton S 100/PK-12
PO Box 8 98925 509-656-2317
Patrick Dehuff, supt. Fax 656-2585

Eastsound, San Juan
Orcas Island SD 137 400/K-12
557 School Rd 98245 360-376-2284
Barbara Kline, supt. Fax 376-2283
www.orcasislandschools.org/
Orcas Island HS 100/9-12
715 School Rd 98245 360-376-2287
Barbara Kline, prin. Fax 376-6078
Orcas Island MS 100/7-8
611 School Rd 98245 360-376-2286
Kyle Freeman, prin. Fax 376-5410

Orcas Christian Day S 100/K-12
PO Box 669 98245 360-376-6683
Tom Roosma, prin. Fax 376-7642

East Wenatchee, Douglas, Pop. 12,915
Eastmont SD 206 4,900/K-12
460 9th St NE 98802 509-884-7169
Dr. Garn Christensen, supt. Fax 884-4210
www.eastmont206.org
Eastmont JHS 800/8-9
905 8th St NE 98802 509-884-2407
David Woods, prin. Fax 884-1988
Eastmont SHS 1,400/10-12
955 3rd St NE 98802 509-884-6665
Lance Noell, prin. Fax 884-8805

Eatonville, Pierce, Pop. 2,651
Eatonville SD 404 2,000/K-12
PO Box 698 98328 360-879-1000
Rich Stewart, supt. Fax 879-1086
www.eatonville.wednet.edu/
Eatonville HS 700/9-12
PO Box 699 98328 360-879-1200
Garth Steedman, prin. Fax 879-1284
Eatonville MS 500/6-8
PO Box 910 98328 360-879-1400
Ken Andersen, prin. Fax 879-1480

Edgewood, Pierce, Pop. 9,076
Puyallup SD 3
Supt. — See Puyallup
Edgemont JHS 400/7-9
2300 110th Ave E 98372 253-841-8727
Eric Hogan, prin. Fax 840-8883

Slavic Christian Academy - Edgewood 100/K-12
10622 8th St E 98372 253-952-7163
Vadim Hetman, admin. Fax 952-7164

Edmonds, Snohomish, Pop. 38,105
Edmonds SD 15
Supt. — See Lynnwood
Edmonds-Woodway HS 1,700/9-12
7600 212th St SW 98026 425-431-7900
Miriam Mickelson, prin. Fax 431-7929
Scriber Lake HS 200/Alt
23200 100th Ave W 98020 425-431-7270
Kathy Clift, prin. Fax 431-7272

Solomon Christian S 50/7-12
8021 230th St SW 98026 425-640-9000
Richard Lee, prin. Fax 458-9327

Edwall, Lincoln

Christian Heritage S 100/K-12
PO Box 118 99008 509-236-2224
Marty Klein, admin. Fax 236-2412

Ellensburg, Kittitas, Pop. 17,598
Ellensburg SD 401 3,000/K-12
1300 E 3rd Ave 98926 509-925-8000
Paul Farris, supt. Fax 925-8025
ellensburg.schoolfusion.us/
Ellensburg HS 900/9-12
1203 E Capitol Ave 98926 509-925-8300
Jeff Ellersick, prin. Fax 925-8305
Excel HS Alt
Michaelson Hall # 108 CWU 98926 509-963-3585
Neil Musser, prin.
Morgan MS 700/6-8
400 E 1st Ave 98926 509-925-8200
Michelle Bibich, prin. Fax 925-8202

Central Washington University Post-Sec.
400 E University Way 98926 509-963-1111

Elma, Grays Harbor, Pop. 2,963
Elma SD 68 1,600/K-12
1235 Monte Elma Rd 98541 360-482-2822
Howard King, supt. Fax 482-2092
www.elma.wednet.edu
East Grays Harbor HS 50/Alt
1235 Monte Elma Rd 98541 360-482-5086
Linda Meister, admin. Fax 482-2109
Elma HS 600/9-12
1235 Monte Elma Rd 98541 360-482-3121
Kevin Acuff, prin. Fax 482-1200
Elma MS 400/6-8
1235 Monte Elma Rd 98541 360-482-2237
Gina Franchini, prin. Fax 482-4872

Mary M. Knight SD 311 200/PK-12
2987 W Matlock Brady Rd 98541 360-426-6767
Beth Daneker, supt. Fax 427-5516
maryknightschooldistrict.yolasite.com/
Knight JSHS 100/7-12
2987 W Matlock Brady Rd 98541 360-426-6767
John Schultz, prin. Fax 427-5516

Endicott, Whitman, Pop. 289
Endicott SD 308 100/PK-8
308 School Dr 99125 509-657-3523
Gary Wargo, supt. Fax 657-3521
www.endicott.wednet.edu
Endicott-St. John MS 100/6-8
308 School Dr 99125 509-657-3523
Michael Olsen, prin. Fax 657-3521

Entiat, Chelan, Pop. 1,090
Entiat SD 127 300/PK-12
2650 Entiat Way 98822 509-784-1800
Michael Wyant, supt. Fax 784-2986
www.entiatschools.org
Entiat MSHS 200/6-12
2650 Entiat Way 98822 509-784-1911
Miles Caples, prin. Fax 784-2986

Enumclaw, King, Pop. 10,407
Enumclaw SD 216 4,200/K-12
2929 McDougall Ave 98022 360-802-7100
Michael Nelson, supt. Fax 802-7140
www.enumclaw.wednet.edu/
Enumclaw HS 1,500/9-12
226 Semanski St 98022 360-802-7669
Jill Burnes, prin. Fax 802-7676
Enumclaw MS 500/6-8
550 Semanski St 98022 360-802-7150
Steve Rabb, prin. Fax 802-7224
Thunder Mountain MS 500/6-8
42018 264th Ave SE 98022 360-802-7492
Virginia Callison, prin. Fax 802-7500

Ephrata, Grant, Pop. 7,502
Ephrata SD 165 2,300/K-12
499 C St NW 98823 509-754-2474
Dr. Jerry Simon, supt. Fax 754-4712
www.ephrataschools.org
Ephrata HS 700/9-12
333 4th Ave NW 98823 509-754-5285
Dan Martell, prin. Fax 754-4993
Ephrata MS 400/7-8
384 A St SE 98823 509-754-4659
Ken Murray, prin. Fax 754-5625
Sage Hills Alternative S 100/Alt
35 K St SE 98823 509-754-7547
Charlotte Throgmorton, prin. Fax 754-7227

New Life Christian S 100/PK-12
911 E Division Ave 98823 509-754-5558
Matthew Tucker, admin. Fax 754-3540

Everett, Snohomish, Pop. 98,083
Everett SD 2 18,700/PK-12
PO Box 2098, 425-385-4000
Dr. Gary Cohn, supt. Fax 385-4012
www.everett.k12.wa.us
Cascade HS 1,900/9-12
801 E Casino Rd 98203 425-385-6000
Cathy Woods, prin. Fax 385-6002
Eisenhower MS 900/6-8
10200 25th Ave SE 98208 425-385-7500
Karen Koester, prin. Fax 385-7502
Everett HS 1,500/9-12
2416 Colby Ave 98201 425-385-4400
Sally Lancaster, prin. Fax 385-4402

Evergreen MS 1,100/6-8
7621 Beverly Ln 98203 425-385-5700
Larry Fleckenstein, prin. Fax 385-5702
Gateway MS 700/6-8
15404 Silver Firs Dr 98208 425-385-6600
Shelley Petillo, prin. Fax 385-6602
North MS 700/6-8
2514 Rainier Ave 98201 425-385-4800
Mary O'Brien, prin. Fax 385-4802
Sequoia Alternative HS 300/Alt
3516 Rucker Ave 98201 425-385-5100
Kelly Shepherd, prin. Fax 385-5102
Other Schools – See Mill Creek

Mukilteo SD 6 14,500/K-12
9401 Sharon Dr 98204 425-356-1274
Marci Larsen, supt. Fax 356-1310
www.mukilteo.wednet.edu
ACES Alternative HS 200/Alt
9700 Holly Dr 98204 425-366-3900
Marcie Polin, prin. Fax 366-3902
Explorer MS 900/6-8
9600 Sharon Dr 98204 425-366-5000
Ali Williams, prin. Fax 366-5002
Mariner HS 2,100/9-12
200 120th St SW 98204 425-366-5700
Brent Kline, prin. Fax 366-5702
Sno-Isle Vo Skills Ctr Vo/Tech
9001 Airport Rd 98204 425-348-2220
Dave Rudy, prin. Fax 356-2201
Voyager MS 800/6-8
11711 4th Ave W 98204 425-366-5300
Wes Bailey, prin. Fax 366-5302
Other Schools – See Mukilteo

Archbishop Thomas Murphy HS 600/9-12
12911 39th Ave SE 98208 425-379-6363
Steve Schmutz, prin. Fax 385-2875
Everest College Post-Sec.
906 SE Evertt Mall Way #600 98208 425-789-7960
Everett Community College Post-Sec.
2000 Tower St 98201 425-388-9100
ITT Technical Institute Post-Sec.
1615 75th St SW Ste 220 98203 425-583-0200
Milan Institute of Cosmotology Post-Sec.
607 SE Everett Mall Way #5 98208 425-353-8193
Montessori S of Snohomish County 200/PK-12
1804 Puget Dr 98203 425-355-1311
Kathleen Gunnell, admin. Fax 347-1000
Trinity Lutheran College Post-Sec.
2802 Wetmore Ave 98201 425-249-4800

Everson, Whatcom, Pop. 2,414
Nooksack Valley SD 506 1,600/PK-12
3326 E Badger Rd 98247 360-988-4754
Dr. Mark Johnson, supt. Fax 988-8983
www.nv.k12.wa.us/
Nooksack Valley HS 500/9-12
3326 E Badger Rd 98247 360-988-2641
Matt Galley, prin. Fax 988-7058
Other Schools – See Nooksack

Fall City, King, Pop. 1,940
Snoqualmie Valley SD 410
Supt. — See Snoqualmie
Chief Kanim MS 400/6-8
PO Box 639 98024 425-831-8225
Kirk Dunckel, prin. Fax 831-8290

Federal Way, King, Pop. 82,130
Federal Way SD 210 21,900/PK-12
33330 8th Ave S 98003 253-945-2000
Rob Neu, supt. Fax 945-2001
www.fwps.org
Beamer HS 1,800/9-12
35999 16th Ave S 98003 253-945-2570
Randy Kaczor, prin. Fax 945-2599
Career Academy Vo/Tech
31455 28th Ave S 98003 253-945-5800
Patricia Larson, prin. Fax 945-5858
Decatur HS 1,500/9-12
2800 SW 320th St 98023 253-945-5200
David Brower, prin. Fax 945-5252
Federal Way HS 1,500/9-12
30611 16th Ave S 98003 253-945-5400
Lisa Griebel, prin. Fax 945-5454
Federal Way Public Academy 300/Alt
34620 9th Ave S 98003 253-945-3270
Kurt Lauer, prin. Fax 945-3399
Illahee MS 800/6-8
36001 1st Ave S 98003 253-945-4600
Jerry Warren, prin. Fax 945-4646
International Academy Alt
31455 28th Ave S 98003 253-945-5800
Regina Hauptman, prin. Fax 945-5858
Lakota MS 800/6-8
1415 SW 314th St 98023 253-945-4800
Pam Tuggle, prin. Fax 945-4848
Sacajawea MS 700/6-8
1101 S Dash Point Rd 98003 253-945-4900
JoAnne Landis, prin. Fax 945-4949
Saghalie MS 500/6-8
33914 19th Ave SW 98023 253-945-5000
Laura Davis-Brown, prin. Fax 945-5050
Other Schools – See Auburn, Kent

Christian Faith S 300/PK-12
33645 20th Ave S 98003 253-943-2500
Tom Puddy, prin. Fax 200-1335
Cortiva Institute - Federal Way Post-Sec.
2030 S 314th St 98003 253-237-5300
DeVry University Post-Sec.
3600 S 344th Way 98001 253-943-2800
Gene Juarez Academy of Beauty Post-Sec.
2222 S 314th St 98003 253-839-6483
Life Academy of Puget Sound 50/PK-12
414 SW 312th St 98023 253-839-7378
Rev. Sue Austin, admin. Fax 839-1031

Ferndale, Whatcom, Pop. 10,997
Ferndale SD 502 3,900/PK-12
PO Box 698 98248 360-383-9200
Linda Quinn Ed.D., supt. Fax 383-9201
www.ferndale.wednet.edu
Ferndale HS 1,600/9-12
PO Box 428 98248 360-383-9240
Aaron Kombol, prin. Fax 383-9242
Horizon MS 400/6-8
PO Box 1769 98248 360-383-9850
David Hutchinson, prin. Fax 383-9852
Vista MS 400/6-8
PO Box 1328 98248 360-383-9370
Kim Hawes, prin. Fax 383-9372
Windward HS 100/9-12
PO Box 428 98248 360-383-9289
Tim Keigley, prin. Fax 383-9152

Fife, Pierce, Pop. 8,348
Fife SD 417
Supt. — See Tacoma
Columbia JHS 500/8-9
2901 54th Ave E 98424 253-517-1600
Jeff Nelson, prin. Fax 517-1605

Forks, Clallam, Pop. 3,383
Quillayute Valley SD 402 4,100/PK-12
411 S Spartan Ave 98331 360-374-6262
Diana Reaume, supt. Fax 374-6990
www.forks.wednet.edu
Forks Alternative S 50/Alt
411 S Spartan Ave 98331 360-374-6262
Cindy Feasel, prin. Fax 374-2360
Forks HS 300/9-12
261 S Spartan Ave 98331 360-374-6262
Cindy Feasel, prin. Fax 374-9657
Forks MS 300/6-8
121 S Spartan Ave 98331 360-374-6262
Patti Fouts, prin. Fax 374-2362

Freeland, Island, Pop. 1,970

Northwest Institute of Literary Arts Post-Sec.
PO Box 639 98249 360-331-0307

Friday Harbor, San Juan, Pop. 2,106
San Juan Island SD 149 800/K-12
PO Box 458 98250 360-378-4133
Rick Thompson, supt. Fax 378-6276
www.sjisd.wednet.edu
Friday Harbor HS 300/9-12
PO Box 458 98250 360-378-5215
Fred Woods, prin. Fax 378-2647
Friday Harbor MS 100/7-8
PO Box 458 98250 360-378-5214
Fred Woods, prin. Fax 378-9750
Griffin Bay Alternative HS 50/Alt
PO Box 458 98250 360-378-3292
Suzanne Cowden, lead tchr. Fax 378-2211

Garfield, Whitman, Pop. 585
Garfield SD 302 100/PK-8
PO Box 398 99130 509-635-1331
Zane Wells, supt. Fax 635-1332
www.garpal.wednet.edu
Garfield-Palouse MS 50/6-8
PO Box 398 99130 509-635-1331
Zane Wells, prin. Fax 635-1332

Gig Harbor, Pierce, Pop. 6,870
Peninsula SD 401 9,300/PK-12
14015 62nd Ave NW 98332 253-530-1000
Charles Cuzzetto, supt. Fax 530-1010
www.psd401.net/
Gig Harbor HS 1,600/9-12
5101 Rosedale St NW 98335 253-530-1400
Tom Leacy, prin. Fax 530-1420
Goodman MS 600/6-8
3701 38th Ave NW 98335 253-530-1600
Scott McDaniel, prin. Fax 530-1620
Harbor Ridge MS 600/6-8
9010 Prentice Ave 98332 253-530-1900
Mike Benoit, prin. Fax 530-1920
Henderson Bay HS 200/Alt
8402 Skansie Ave 98332 253-530-1700
Dave Goodwin, prin. Fax 530-1720
Kopachuck MS 700/6-8
10414 56th St NW 98335 253-530-4100
Iva Scott, prin. Fax 530-4120
Peninsula HS 1,400/9-12
14105 Purdy Ln NW 98332 253-530-4400
Tim Winter, prin. Fax 530-4420
Other Schools – See Lakebay

Glenwood, Klickitat
Glenwood SD 401 50/K-12
PO Box 12 98619 509-364-3438
Dr. Shane Couch, supt. Fax 364-3689
www.glenwood.k12.wa.us/
Glenwood S 50/K-12
PO Box 12 98619 509-364-3438
Dr. Shane Couch, prin. Fax 364-3689

Goldendale, Klickitat, Pop. 3,344
Goldendale SD 404 1,000/K-12
604 E Brooks St 98620 509-773-5177
Mark Heid, supt. Fax 773-6028
goldendaleschools.org
Goldendale HS 400/9-12
525 E Simcoe Dr 98620 509-773-5846
Clay Henry, prin. Fax 773-6900
Goldendale MS 300/5-8
520 E Collins St 98620 509-773-4323
Dave Barta, prin. Fax 773-4579

Graham, Pierce, Pop. 21,945
Bethel SD 403
Supt. — See Spanaway
Cougar Mountain MS 500/7-8
5108 260th St E 98338 253-683-8000
Sara Stewart, prin. Fax 683-8098
Frontier MS 500/7-8
22110 108th Ave E 98338 253-683-8300
Mark Barnes, prin. Fax 683-8398
Graham-Kapowsin HS 1,400/9-12
22100 108th Ave E 98338 253-683-6100
Lynn Gill, prin. Fax 683-6198

Grand Coulee, Grant, Pop. 957
Grand Coulee Dam SD 301J
Supt. — See Coulee Dam
Grand Coulee Dam MS 200/5-8
PO Box J 99133 509-633-1520
Ronanda Liberty, prin. Fax 633-2257

Grandview, Yakima, Pop. 10,766
Grandview SD 200 3,500/K-12
913 W 2nd St 98930 509-882-8500
Kevin Chase, supt. Fax 882-2029
www.gsd200.org
Compass HS 100/Alt
913 W 2nd St 98930 509-882-8540
Brian Anderson, prin. Fax 882-8739
Grandview HS 800/9-12
1601 W 5th St 98930 509-882-8750
Mike Closner, prin. Fax 882-8739
Grandview MS 800/6-8
1401 W 2nd St 98930 509-882-8600
Paul Voorhees, prin. Fax 882-3538

Granger, Yakima, Pop. 3,222
Granger SD 204 1,500/PK-12
701 E Ave 98932 509-854-1515
Margarita C. Lopez, supt. Fax 854-1126
www.gsd.wednet.edu
Granger HS 400/9-12
701 E Ave 98932 509-854-1115
Tricia Anderson, prin. Fax 854-2757
Granger MS 500/5-8
701 E Ave 98932 509-854-1003
Stephanie Funk, prin. Fax 854-1083

Granite Falls, Snohomish, Pop. 3,190
Granite Falls SD 332 2,200/K-12
205 N Alder St 98252 360-691-7717
Linda Hall, supt. Fax 691-4459
www.gfalls.wednet.edu
Crossroads HS 100/Alt
205 N Alder Ave 98252 360-283-4407
Bridgette Perrigoue, prin. Fax 283-4307
Granite Falls HS 700/9-12
1401 100th St NE 98252 360-691-7713
Michele Wadeikis, prin. Fax 283-4414
Granite Falls MS 600/6-8
405 N Alder Ave 98252 360-691-7710
Dave Bianchini, prin. Fax 283-4415

Harrington, Lincoln, Pop. 416
Harrington SD 204 100/PK-12
PO Box 204 99134 509-253-4331
Dr. Mike Perry, supt. Fax 456-6306
www.harrsd.k12.wa.us
Harrington HS 100/7-12
PO Box 204 99134 509-253-4331
Jacob Bang, prin. Fax 456-6306

Hoquiam, Grays Harbor, Pop. 8,401
Hoquiam SD 28 1,800/PK-12
305 Simpson Ave 98550 360-538-8200
Mike Parker, supt. Fax 538-8202
hoquiam.schoolwires.net
Hoquiam HS 600/9-12
501 W Emerson Ave 98550 360-538-8210
Brock Maxfield, prin. Fax 538-8212
Hoquiam MS 400/6-8
200 Spencer St 98550 360-538-8220
Dale Stopperan, prin. Fax 538-8222

Hunters, Stevens
Columbia SD 206 200/PK-12
PO Box 7 99137 509-722-3311
Chuck Wyborney, supt. Fax 722-3310
www.columbia206.com
Columbia S 200/PK-12
PO Box 7 99137 509-722-3311
Chuck Wyborney, prin. Fax 722-3310

Ilwaco, Pacific, Pop. 906
Ocean Beach SD 101
Supt. — See Long Beach
Ilwaco MSHS 400/7-12
PO Box F 98624 360-642-3731
Dave Tobin, prin. Fax 642-1224

Inchelium, Ferry, Pop. 393
Inchelium SD 70 50/K-12
PO Box 285 99138 509-722-6181
Ron Washington, supt. Fax 722-6192
www.Inchelium.wednet.edu
Inchelium S 50/K-12
PO Box 285 99138 509-722-6181
John Moddrell, prin. Fax 722-6192

Ione, Pend Oreille, Pop. 442
Selkirk SD 70
Supt. — See Metaline Falls
Selkirk MSHS 100/6-12
10372 Highway 31 99139 509-446-3505
Larry Reed, prin. Fax 446-2408

Issaquah, King, Pop. 29,272
Issaquah SD 411 17,300/PK-12
565 NW Holly St 98027 425-837-7000
Steve Rasmussen, supt. Fax 837-7005
www.issaquah.wednet.edu
Beaver Lake MS 800/6-8
25025 SE 32nd St 98029 425-837-4150
Stacy Cho, prin. Fax 837-4195

Issaquah HS 1,800/9-12
700 2nd Ave SE 98027 425-837-6000
Paula Phelps, prin. Fax 837-6078
Issaquah MS 700/6-8
400 1st Ave SE 98027 425-837-6800
Corrine DeRosa, prin. Fax 837-6855
Pacific Cascade MS 900/6-8
24635 SE Issaquah Fall City 98029 425-837-5900
Dana Bailey, prin. Fax 837-5910
Pine Lake MS 700/6-8
3200 228th Ave SE 98075 425-837-5700
Michelle Caponigro, prin. Fax 837-5762
Skyline HS 1,900/9-12
1122 228th Ave SE 98075 425-837-7700
Lisa Hechtman, prin. Fax 837-7705
Tiger Mountain Community HS 100/Alt
355 SE Evans St 98027 425-837-6200
Michael Schiehser, prin. Fax 837-6225
Other Schools – See Renton

Joyce, Clallam
Crescent SD 313 200/K-12
PO Box 20 98343 360-928-3311
Clayton Mork, supt. Fax 928-3066
www.crescentschooldistrict.org
Crescent JSHS 100/7-12
PO Box 20 98343 360-928-3311
Clayton Mork, prin. Fax 928-3066

Kahlotus, Franklin, Pop. 189
Kahlotus SD 56 100/PK-12
PO Box 69 99335 509-282-3338
Sergio Hernandez, supt. Fax 282-3339
www.kahlotussd.org
Kahlotus S 100/PK-12
PO Box 69 99335 509-282-3338
Ron Hopkins, prin. Fax 282-3339

Kalama, Cowlitz, Pop. 2,270
Kalama SD 402 1,000/K-12
548 China Garden Rd 98625 360-673-5282
James Sutton, supt. Fax 673-5228
www.kalama.k12.wa.us
Kalama JSHS 600/6-12
548 China Garden Rd 98625 360-673-5212
Mike Hamilton, prin. Fax 673-1280

Kelso, Cowlitz, Pop. 11,473
Kelso SD 458 5,000/PK-12
601 Crawford St 98626 360-501-1900
Robert MacGregor, supt. Fax 501-1944
www.kelso.wednet.edu
Coweeman MS 500/6-8
2000 Allen St 98626 360-501-1750
Chris Rugg, prin. Fax 501-1782
Huntington MS 500/6-8
500 Redpath St 98626 360-501-1700
Chris Clark, prin. Fax 501-1723
Kelso HS 1,700/9-12
1904 Allen St 98626 360-501-1800
John Gummel, prin. Fax 501-1843
Loowit HS 50/Alt
2001 Allen St 98626 360-501-1951
Kay Fine, lead tchr. Fax 501-1954

Three Rivers Christian S 100/7-12
1209 Minor Rd 98626 360-636-1600
Randy Lemiere, prin. Fax 577-5955

Kenmore, King, Pop. 19,563
Northshore SD 417
Supt. — See Bothell
Inglemoor SHS 1,800/10-12
15500 Simonds Rd NE 98028 425-408-7200
Vicki Sherwood, prin. Fax 408-7202
Kenmore JHS 700/7-9
20323 66th Ave NE 98028 425-408-6400
Tim Gordon, prin. Fax 408-6402

Kennewick, Benton, Pop. 72,070
Finley SD 53 1,000/PK-12
224606 E Game Farm Rd 99337 509-586-3217
Lance Hahn, supt. Fax 586-4408
www.finleysd.org
Finley MS 200/6-8
37208 S Finley Rd 99337 509-586-7561
Michael Harrington, prin. Fax 582-8452
River View HS 300/9-12
36509 S Lemon Dr 99337 509-582-2158
Lance Hahn, prin. Fax 586-9297

Kennewick SD 17 15,800/K-12
1000 W 4th Ave 99336 509-222-5000
Dave Bond, supt. Fax 222-5050
www.ksd.org
Desert Hills MS 900/6-8
6011 W 10th Pl 99338 509-222-6600
Steve Jones, prin. Fax 222-6601
Highlands MS 900/6-8
425 S Tweedt St 99336 509-222-6700
Alyssa St. Hillaire, prin. Fax 222-6701
Horse Heaven Hills MS 900/6-8
3500 S Vancouver St 99337 509-222-6800
Diana Burns, prin. Fax 222-6801
Kamiakin HS 1,600/9-12
600 N Arthur St 99336 509-222-7000
Chris Chelin, prin. Fax 222-7001
Kennewick HS 1,500/9-12
500 S Dayton St 99336 509-222-7100
Van Cummings, prin. Fax 222-7101
Legacy HS Alt
202 S Dayton St 99336 509-222-5029
Dennis Boatman, prin. Fax 222-5059
Park MS 800/6-8
1011 W 10th Ave 99336 509-222-6900
Kevin Pierce, prin. Fax 222-6901
Phoenix HS 100/9-12
418 S Vancouver St 99336 509-222-7400
Jill Mulhousen, prin. Fax 222-5153

Southridge HS 1,500/9-12
3520 Southridge Blvd 99338 509-222-7200
Steve Biehn, prin. Fax 222-7201
Tri-Tech Vocational Skills Center Vo/Tech
5929 W Metaline Ave 99336 509-222-7300
Paul Randall, prin. Fax 222-7301

Kent, King, Pop. 85,961
Federal Way SD 210
Supt. — See Federal Way
TAF Academy 200/Alt
26630 40th Ave S 98032 253-945-5187
Paul Tyler, prin. Fax 945-5191
Totem MS 600/6-8
26630 40th Ave S 98032 253-945-5100
Christine Baker, prin. Fax 945-5151

Kent SD 415 26,900/PK-12
12033 SE 256th St 98030 253-373-7000
Dr. Edward Vargas, supt. Fax 373-7231
www.kent.k12.wa.us
iGrad Alt
25668 104th Ave SE, 253-373-4723
Carol Cleveland, prin. Fax 373-7989
Kentlake HS 1,800/9-12
21401 SE Falcon Way 98042 253-373-4900
Dr. Joe Potts, prin. Fax 373-4908
Kent-Meridian HS 2,000/9-12
10020 SE 256th St, 253-373-7405
Dr. Wade Barringer, prin. Fax 373-7411
Kent Phoenix Academy 300/9-12
11000 SE 264th St, 253-373-7542
Merrilee Lyle, prin. Fax 373-7554
Kentridge HS 2,300/9-12
12430 SE 208th St 98031 253-373-7345
Mike Albrecht, prin. Fax 373-7363
Meridian MS 700/7-8
23480 120th Ave SE 98031 253-373-7383
James Schiechl, prin. Fax 373-7395
Mill Creek MS 900/7-8
620 Central Ave N 98032 253-373-7446
Sherilyn Ulland, prin. Fax 373-7478
Other Schools – See Covington, Des Moines, Renton

Kettle Falls, Stevens, Pop. 1,505
Kettle Falls SD 212 800/K-12
PO Box 458 99141 509-738-6625
Fax 738-6375
www.kfsd.org
Kettle Falls HS 300/9-12
PO Box 458 99141 509-738-6388
James Hill, prin. Fax 738-2670
Kettle Falls MS 200/5-8
PO Box 458 99141 509-738-6014
Tracy Vining, prin. Fax 738-2401

Kingston, Kitsap, Pop. 2,022
North Kitsap SD 400
Supt. — See Poulsbo
Kingston HS 900/9-12
26201 Siyaya Ave NE 98346 360-394-1200
Christy Cole, prin. Fax 394-1212
Kingston MS 700/6-8
9000 NE West Kingston Rd 98346 360-394-4900
Susan Wistrand, prin. Fax 394-4901
Spectrum Community S 100/Alt
25800 Siyaya Ave NE 98346 360-394-2860
Christy Cole, prin. Fax 394-7861

Kirkland, King, Pop. 46,527
Lake Washington SD 414
Supt. — See Redmond
Emerson HS 100/9-12
10903 NE 53rd St 98033 425-936-2300
Nell Ballard-Jones, prin. Fax 936-2305
Environmental & Adventure S 100/6-8
8040 NE 132nd St 98034 425-936-2355
Victor Scarpelli, prin. Fax 825-0921
Finn Hill MS 300/6-8
8040 NE 132nd St 98034 425-936-2340
Victor Scarpelli, prin. Fax 814-2955
International Community S 400/7-12
11133 NE 65th St 98033 425-936-2380
Matthew Livingston, prin. Fax 889-6881
Juanita HS 1,000/9-12
10601 NE 132nd St 98034 425-936-1600
Gary Moed, prin. Fax 936-1637
Kamiakin MS 300/6-8
14111 132nd Ave NE 98034 425-936-2400
Joe Joss, prin. Fax 823-2921
Kirkland MS 400/6-8
430 18th Ave 98033 425-936-2420
Deborah McCarson, prin. Fax 889-1589
Lake Washington HS 1,000/9-12
12033 NE 80th St 98033 425-936-1700
Christina Thomas, prin. Fax 936-1751
Northstar MS 100/6-8
11822 NE 75th St 98033 425-936-1760
Nell Ballard-Jones, prin. Fax 828-3364

Eastside Preparatory S 300/5-12
10613 NE 38th Pl 98033 425-822-5668
Dr. Terry Macaluso, admin. Fax 822-5648
Lake Washington Institute of Technology Post-Sec.
11605 132nd Ave NE 98034 425-739-8100
Northwest University Post-Sec.
PO Box 579 98083 425-822-8266
Puget Sound Adventist Academy 100/9-12
5320 108th Ave NE 98033 425-822-7554
Linda Taber, prin. Fax 828-0856

Kittitas, Kittitas, Pop. 1,352
Kittitas SD 403 700/K-12
PO Box 599 98934 509-968-3115
Monty Sabin, supt. Fax 968-4730
www.ksd403.org/
Kittitas HS 400/6-12
PO Box 599 98934 509-968-3902
Christopher Brauer, prin. Fax 968-3370

Klickitat, Klickitat, Pop. 348
Klickitat SD 402 100/K-12
PO Box 37 98628 509-369-4145
Jerry Lynch, supt. Fax 369-3422
www.klickitat.wednet.edu/
Klickitat S 100/K-12
PO Box 37 98628 509-369-4145
Kevin Davis, prin. Fax 369-3422

La Center, Clark, Pop. 2,714
La Center SD 101 1,600/K-12
PO Box 1840 98629 360-263-2131
Dr. Mark Mansell, supt. Fax 263-1140
www.lacenterschools.org/
La Center HS 500/9-12
PO Box 1780 98629 360-263-1700
Carol Patton, prin. Fax 263-1705
La Center MS 400/6-8
PO Box 1750 98629 360-263-2136
David Cooke, prin. Fax 263-5936

Lacey, Thurston, Pop. 39,269
North Thurston SD 3 14,000/PK-12
305 College St NE 98516 360-412-4400
Raj Manhas, supt. Fax 412-4410
www.nthurston.k12.wa.us
Aspire MS 300/6-8
5900 54th Ave SE 98513 360-412-4730
Monica Sweet, prin. Fax 412-4739
Chinook MS 600/6-8
4301 6th Ave NE 98516 360-412-4760
Kirsten Rae, prin. Fax 412-4769
Komachin MS 700/7-8
3650 College St SE 98503 360-412-4740
Joyce Ott, prin. Fax 412-4749
Nisqually MS 600/7-8
8100 Steilacoom Rd SE 98503 360-412-4770
Karen Owen, prin. Fax 493-2756
North Thurston HS 1,400/9-12
600 Sleater Kinney Rd NE 98506 360-412-4800
Steve Rood, prin. Fax 412-4819
River Ridge HS 1,200/9-12
350 River Ridge Dr SE 98513 360-412-4820
Karen Remy-Anderson, prin. Fax 412-4839
South Sound HS 200/Alt
411 College St NE 98516 360-412-4880
Rich Yelenich, prin. Fax 412-4889
Timberline HS 1,600/9-12
6120 Mullen Rd SE 98503 360-412-4860
Dave Lehnis, prin. Fax 412-4879

Northwest Christian HS 200/9-12
4710 Park Center Ave NE 98516 360-491-2966
Dr. Terry Ketchum, prin. Fax 491-3086
Pope John Paul II HS 100/9-12
5608 Pacific Ave SE 98503 360-438-7600
Ronald Edwards, prin. Fax 438-7607
St. Martin's University Post-Sec.
5000 Abbey Way SE 98503 360-491-4700

La Conner, Skagit, Pop. 873
La Conner SD 311 600/K-12
PO Box 2103 98257 360-466-3171
Dr. Tim Bruce, supt. Fax 466-3523
www.lcsd.wednet.edu
La Conner HS 200/9-12
PO Box 2103 98257 360-466-3173
Marsha Hanson, prin. Fax 466-1062
La Conner MS 100/6-8
PO Box 2103 98257 360-466-4113
Marsha Hanson, prin. Fax 466-0153

LaCrosse, Whitman, Pop. 304
LaCrosse SD 126 100/K-12
111 Hill Ave 99143 509-549-3591
Gary Wargo, supt. Fax 549-3529
www.lacrossesd.k12.wa.us
LaCrosse JSHS 50/6-12
111 Hill Ave 99143 509-549-3592
Doug Curtis, prin. Fax 549-3529

Lakebay, Pierce
Peninsula SD 401
Supt. — See Gig Harbor
Key Penninsula MS 500/6-8
5510 Key Peninsula Hwy N 98349 253-530-4200
Jeri Goebel, prin. Fax 530-4220

Lake Tapps, Pierce, Pop. 11,482
Dieringer SD 343 1,300/K-8
1320 178th Ave E, 253-862-2537
Dr. Judy Neumeier-Martinson, supt. Fax 862-8472
www.dieringer.wednet.edu
North Tapps MS 400/6-8
20029 12th St E, 253-862-2776
Nate Salisbury, prin. Fax 862-2587

Lake Stevens, Snohomish, Pop. 26,753
Lake Stevens SD 4 7,900/PK-12
12309 22nd St NE 98258 425-335-1500
Dr. Amy Beth Cook, supt. Fax 335-1549
www.lkstevens.wednet.edu
Cavelero Mid HS 1,200/8-9
8220 24th St SE 98258 425-335-1630
Mike Snow, prin. Fax 397-9413
Lake Stevens HS 1,700/10-12
2908 113th Ave NE 98258 425-335-1515
Eric Cahan, prin. Fax 335-1524

Lakewood, Pierce, Pop. 52,506
Clover Park SD 400 11,400/PK-12
10903 Gravelly Lake Dr SW 98499 253-583-5000
Debbie LeBeau, supt. Fax 583-5198
www.cloverpark.k12.wa.us/
Clover Park HS 1,200/9-12
11023 Gravelly Lake Dr SW 98499 253-583-5500
John Seaton, prin. Fax 583-5508
Harrison Preparatory S 6-12
8800 121st St SW 98498 253-583-5418
Lisa Boyd, prin. Fax 583-5417

Hudtloff MS 600/6-8
8102 Phillips Rd SW 98498 253-583-5400
Moureen David, prin. Fax 583-5408
Lakes HS 1,300/9-12
10320 Farwest Dr SW 98498 253-583-5550
Karen Mauer-Smith, prin. Fax 583-5558
Lakewood Career Academy 50/Alt
4500 Steilacoom Blvd SW 98499 253-583-5390
Kevin Rupprecht, prin. Fax 583-5398
Lochburn MS 600/6-8
5431 Steilacoom Blvd SW 98499 253-583-5420
Helen Wilson, prin. Fax 583-5428
Mann MS 400/6-8
11509 Holden Rd SW 98498 253-583-5440
Ron Banner, prin. Fax 583-5448
Woodbrook MS 500/6-8
14920 Spring St SW 98439 253-583-5460
Nancy LaChapelle, prin. Fax 583-5468

Clover Park Technical College Post-Sec.
4500 Steilacoom Blvd SW 98499 253-589-5800
Pierce College Post-Sec.
9401 Farwest Dr SW 98498 253-964-6500

Lamont, Whitman, Pop. 66
Lamont SD 264 50/5-8
602 Main St 99017 509-257-2463
Joseph Whipple, supt. Fax 257-2316
Lamont MS 50/5-8
602 Main St 99017 509-257-2463
Joseph Whipple, prin. Fax 257-2316

Langley, Island, Pop. 1,005
South Whidbey SD 206 1,600/K-12
5520 Maxwelton Rd 98260 360-221-6100
Dr. Josephine Moccia, supt. Fax 221-3835
www.sw.wednet.edu
Langley MS 400/6-8
723 Camano Ave 98260 360-221-5100
Eric Nerison, prin. Fax 221-8545
South Whidbey Academy 100/Alt
5476 Maxwelton Rd 98260 360-221-7879
David Pfeiffer, dir.
South Whidbey HS 600/9-12
5675 Maxwelton Rd 98260 360-221-4300
John Paton, prin. Fax 221-5797

Leavenworth, Chelan, Pop. 1,933
Cascade SD 228 1,300/PK-12
330 Evans St 98826 509-548-5885
Steve McKenna, supt. Fax 548-6149
cascadesd.org
Cascade HS 400/9-12
10190 Chumstick Hwy 98826 509-548-5277
Mike Hill, prin. Fax 548-7458
Icicle River MS 300/6-8
10195 Titus Rd 98826 509-548-4042
Kelli Doherty, prin. Fax 548-6646

Lind, Adams, Pop. 553
Lind SD 158 200/PK-8
PO Box 340 99341 509-677-3481
Robert Roettger, supt. Fax 677-3463
www.lind.k12.wa.us
Lind/Ritzville MS 100/6-8
PO Box 340 99341 509-677-3408
Brian Ellis, prin. Fax 677-3420

Long Beach, Pacific, Pop. 1,362
Ocean Beach SD 101 900/K-12
PO Box 778 98631 360-642-3739
Mark Hottowe, supt. Fax 642-1298
www.ocean.k12.wa.us
Other Schools – See Ilwaco

Longview, Cowlitz, Pop. 35,373
Longview SD 122 7,000/PK-12
2715 Lilac St 98632 360-575-7000
Dr. Suzanne Cusick, supt. Fax 575-7022
www.longview.k12.wa.us
Cascade MS 500/6-8
2821 Parkview Dr 98632 360-577-2703
Kenneth Hermanson, prin. Fax 577-2790
Long HS 1,000/9-12
2903 Nichols Blvd 98632 360-575-7225
Rich Reeves, prin. Fax 575-7112
Monticello MS 500/6-8
1225 28th Ave 98632 360-575-7050
Angela Allen, prin. Fax 575-7220
Morris HS 1,200/9-12
1602 Mark Morris Ct 98632 360-575-7770
Philip Suek, prin. Fax 575-7699
Mt. Solo MS 500/6-8
5300 Mt Solo Rd 98632 360-577-2800
Lori Cournyer, prin. Fax 577-2888

Lower Columbia College Post-Sec.
PO Box 3010 98632 360-442-2311
Stylemasters College of Hair Design Post-Sec.
1224 Commerce Ave 98632 360-636-2720

Lopez Island, San Juan
Lopez Island SD 144 200/K-12
86 School Rd 98261 360-468-2202
Bill Evans, supt. Fax 468-2212
www.lopezislandschool.org/
Lopez Island MSHS 100/6-12
86 School Rd 98261 360-468-2202
Lisa Shelby, prin. Fax 468-2212

Lyle, Klickitat, Pop. 484
Lyle SD 406 300/K-12
PO Box 368 98635 509-365-2191
Dr. Glenys Hill, supt. Fax 365-5000
www.lyleschools.org/
Lyle HS 100/9-12
PO Box 368 98635 509-365-2211
Phil Williams, prin. Fax 365-2665
Lyle MS 100/7-8
PO Box 368 98635 509-365-2211
Phil Williams, prin. Fax 365-2665

Lynden, Whatcom, Pop. 11,746
Lynden SD 504 2,600/K-12
1203 Bradley Rd 98264 360-354-4443
Jim Frey, supt. Fax 354-7662
www.lynden.wednet.edu
Lynden HS 900/9-12
1201 Bradley Rd 98264 360-354-4401
Todd Apple, prin. Fax 354-0991
Lynden MS 600/6-8
516 Main St 98264 360-354-2952
Tim Metz, prin. Fax 354-6631

Meridian SD 505
Supt. — See Bellingham
Meridian MS 300/6-8
861 Ten Mile Rd 98264 360-398-2291
Gerald Sanderson, prin. Fax 398-8131

Cornerstone Christian S 100/1-12
8872 Northwood Rd 98264 360-318-0663
Otto Bouwman, prin. Fax 318-8175
Lynden Christian HS 400/9-12
515 Drayton St 98264 360-354-3221
Kevin Kaemingk, prin. Fax 354-1047
Lynden Christian MS 300/5-8
503 Lyncs Dr 98264 360-354-3358
Aaron Bishop, prin. Fax 354-6690

Lynnwood, Snohomish, Pop. 34,119
Edmonds SD 15 19,300/PK-12
20420 68th Ave W 98036 425-431-7000
Nick Brossoit Ed.D., supt. Fax 431-7006
www.edmonds.wednet.edu
Alderwood MS 900/7-8
20000 28th Ave W 98036 425-431-7579
Erin Murphy, prin. Fax 431-7580
College Place MS 600/7-8
7501 208th St SW 98036 425-431-7451
Thea Gardner, prin. Fax 431-7449
Meadowdale HS 1,500/9-12
6002 168th St SW 98037 425-431-7650
Kevin Allen, prin. Fax 431-7655
Meadowdale MS 600/7-8
6500 168th St SW 98037 425-431-7707
Christine Avery, prin. Fax 431-7714
Other Schools – See Bothell, Brier, Edmonds, Mountlake Terrace

---

Edmonds Community College Post-Sec.
20000 68th Ave W 98036 425-640-1459
Providence Classical Christian S 200/PK-12
21500 Cypress Way Ste B 98036 425-774-6622
Ryan Evans, hdmstr. Fax 672-5796

Mabton, Yakima, Pop. 2,272
Mabton SD 120 800/K-12
PO Box 37 98935 509-894-4852
Minerva Morales, supt. Fax 894-4769
www.mabton.wednet.edu
Mabton JSHS 300/7-12
PO Box 38 98935 509-894-4951
Jose Elizondo, prin. Fax 894-4761

Mansfield, Douglas, Pop. 319
Mansfield SD 207 100/PK-12
PO Box 188 98830 509-683-1012
Eugene Nelson, supt. Fax 683-1281
www.mansfield.wednet.edu/
Mansfield S 100/PK-12
PO Box 188 98830 509-683-1012
Lawrence Keller, prin. Fax 683-1281

Manson, Chelan, Pop. 1,456
Manson SD 19 600/PK-12
PO Box A 98831 509-687-3140
Matt Charlton, supt. Fax 687-9877
www.manson.org
Manson JSHS 300/7-12
PO Box A 98831 509-687-9585
Don Vanderholm, prin. Fax 687-6109

Maple Valley, King, Pop. 21,591
Tahoma SD 409 7,500/PK-12
25720 Maple Valley Black Di 98038 425-413-3400
Mike Maryanski, supt. Fax 413-3455
www.tahomasd.us
Russell Ridge Center 100/Alt
22615 Sweeney Rd SE 98038 425-413-5490
Fax 413-5495
Other Schools – See Covington, Ravensdale

Marysville, Snohomish, Pop. 56,950
Lakewood SD 306 2,400/PK-12
17110 16th Dr NE 98271 360-652-4500
Dr. Dennis Haddock, supt. Fax 652-4502
www.lwsd.wednet.edu
Lakewood HS 800/9-12
17023 11th Ave NE 98271 360-652-4505
Dale Leach, prin. Fax 652-4507
Lakewood MS 600/6-8
16800 16th Dr NE 98271 360-652-4510
Crystal Knight, prin. Fax 652-4512

Marysville SD 25 9,500/PK-12
4220 80th St NE 98270 360-653-7058
Dr. Larry Nyland, supt. Fax 629-1993
www.msvl.k12.wa.us
Academy of Construction & Engineering 9-12
8301 84th St NE 98270 360-657-6374
Shawn Stevenson, prin. Fax 657-6288
Arts & Technology HS 400/9-12
7204 27th Ave NE 98271 360-653-0664
Terri Kaltenbach, prin. Fax 629-1940
Bio Med Academy 9-12
8301 84th St NE 98270 360-629-1891
Angela Delgado, prin. Fax 629-1887
Cedarcrest MS 900/6-8
6400 88th St NE 98270 360-653-0850
Sheila Gerrish, prin. Fax 657-6470
Heritage HS 100/9-12
7204 27th Ave NE 98271 360-653-0690
Shelly Lacy, prin. Fax 629-1960
International S of Communication 9-12
8301 84th St NE 98270 360-653-0695
Angela Hansen, prin. Fax 653-0655
Marysville MS 800/6-8
4923 67th St NE 98270 360-653-0615
Susan Hegeberg, prin. Fax 657-6396
Marysville Mountain View HS 300/9-12
4317 76th St NE 98270 360-653-0628
Dawn Bechtholdt, prin. Fax 629-1989
Pathways of Choice S 1,200/9-12
5611 108th St NE 98271 360-653-0600
Andrew Frost, prin. Fax 657-6184
School for the Entrepreneur 9-12
8301 84th St NE 98270 360-651-5702
David Rose, prin. Fax 657-5773
Tenth Street MS 200/6-8
7204 27th Ave NE 98271 360-653-0665
Rob Lowry, prin. Fax 629-1950
Totem MS 700/6-8
1605 7th St 98270 360-653-0610
Robert Kalahan, prin. Fax 657-6297

Grace Academy 300/PK-12
8521 67th Ave NE 98270 360-659-8517
Timothy Lugg, prin. Fax 653-5899

Mattawa, Grant, Pop. 4,417
Wahluke SD 73 1,800/K-12
PO Box 907 99349 509-932-4565
Aaron Chavez, supt. Fax 932-4571
www.wsd73.wednet.edu
Sentinel Technical Alternative HS 50/Alt
PO Box 907 99349 509-932-3133
Mia Benjamin, prin. Fax 932-3320
Wahluke HS 500/9-12
PO Box 907 99349 509-932-4477
Jeffery Pietila, prin. Fax 932-4241
Wahluke JHS 200/6-8
PO Box 907 99349 509-932-4455
Dale Hedman, prin. Fax 932-4282

Mead, Spokane, Pop. 7,091
Mead SD 354 9,300/K-12
2323 E Farwell Rd 99021 509-465-6000
Thomas Rockefeller, supt. Fax 465-6020
www.mead354.org
Mount Spokane HS 1,500/9-12
6015 E Mt Spokane Park Dr 99021 509-465-7200
Darren Nelson, prin. Fax 465-7220
Other Schools – See Colbert, Spokane

Medical Lake, Spokane, Pop. 4,877
Medical Lake SD 326 1,600/PK-12
PO Box 128 99022 509-565-3100
Dr. Pam Veltri, supt. Fax 565-3102
www.mlsd.org/
Medical Lake Alternative HS 50/Alt
PO Box 128 99022 509-565-3141
Tricia Hensel-Smith, prin. Fax 565-3149
Medical Lake HS 600/9-12
PO Box 128 99022 509-565-3200
John McSmith, prin. Fax 565-3201
Medical Lake MS 300/6-8
PO Box 128 99022 509-565-3300
Sylvia Campbell, prin. Fax 565-3301

Lakeland Village School Post-Sec.
PO Box 200 99022

Mercer Island, King, Pop. 21,809
Mercer Island SD 400 4,300/K-12
4160 86th Ave SE 98040 206-236-3300
Dr. Gary Plano, supt. Fax 236-3333
www.misd.k12.wa.us
Crest Learning Center 100/Alt
4150 86th Ave SE 98040 206-236-3390
Vicki Puckett, admin. Fax 236-3394
Islander MS 900/6-8
8225 SE 72nd St 98040 206-236-3400
MaryJo Budzius, prin. Fax 236-3408
Mercer Island HS 1,400/9-12
9100 SE 42nd St 98040 206-236-3345
Vicki Puckett, prin. Fax 236-3358

Northwest Yeshiva HS 100/9-12
5017 90th Ave SE 98040 206-232-5272
Rabbi Bernie Fox, head sch Fax 232-2711
Privett Academy, PO Box 42 98040 100/6-12
Carol Meyer, dir. 206-232-0059

Metaline Falls, Pend Oreille, Pop. 233
Selkirk SD 70 300/PK-12
PO Box 129 99153 509-446-2951
Nancy Lotze, supt. Fax 446-2929
www.selkirk.k12.wa.us
Other Schools – See Ione

Mill Creek, Snohomish, Pop. 17,443
Everett SD 2
Supt. — See Everett
Heatherwood MS 900/6-8
1419 Trillium Blvd SE 98012 425-385-6300
Janet Gillingham, prin. Fax 385-6302
Jackson HS 1,900/9-12
1508 136th St SE 98012 425-385-7000
Terry Cheshire, prin. Fax 385-7002

Monroe, Snohomish, Pop. 16,699
Monroe SD 103 7,100/K-12
200 E Fremont St 98272 360-804-2500
Dr. Ken Hoover, supt. Fax 804-2529
www.monroe.wednet.edu

Leaders in Learning HS 400/Alt
200 E Fremont St 98272 360-804-2800
Karen Rosencrans, prin.
Monroe HS 1,700/9-12
17001 Tester Rd 98272 360-804-4500
John Lombardi, prin. Fax 804-4699
Park Place MS 500/6-8
1408 W Main St 98272 360-804-4300
JoAnn Carbonetti, prin. Fax 804-4399
Sky Valley Education Center 900/Alt
200 E Fremont St 98272 360-804-2700
Karen Rosencrans, dir. Fax 804-2759
Other Schools – See Snohomish

Montesano, Grays Harbor, Pop. 3,841
Montesano SD 66 1,300/PK-12
302 N Church St 98563 360-249-3942
Dan Winter, supt. Fax 249-3391
www.monteschools.org
Montesano JSHS 600/7-12
303 N Church St 98563 360-249-4041
Robert Corley, prin. Fax 249-4459

Morton, Lewis, Pop. 1,107
Morton SD 214 300/PK-12
PO Box 1219 98356 360-496-5300
Tom Manke, supt. Fax 586-3208
www.morton.wednet.edu
Morton JSHS 100/7-12
PO Box 1169 98356 360-496-5137
Josh Brooks, prin. Fax 496-6035

Moses Lake, Grant, Pop. 19,890
Moses Lake SD 161 7,900/PK-12
920 W Ivy Ave 98837 509-766-2650
Dr. Michelle Price, supt. Fax 766-2678
www.moseslakeschools.org
Chief Moses MS 1,000/6-8
1111 E Nelson Rd 98837 509-766-2661
Kristi Hofheins, prin. Fax 766-2680
Columbia Basin Secondary S 200/7-12
6527 Patton Blvd NE 98837 509-766-2667
James Yonko, prin. Fax 766-2690
Frontier MS 800/6-8
517 W 3rd Ave 98837 509-766-2662
Frank Atkinson, prin. Fax 766-2663
Moses Lake HS 2,000/9-12
803 Sharon Ave E 98837 509-766-2666
Josh Meek, prin. Fax 766-2682

Wellpinit SD 49
Supt. — See Wellpinit
Columbia Basin Job Corps 100/Alt
6739 24th Ave NE 98837 509-874-8900
Shelley Sonnabend, dir. Fax 793-1754

Big Bend Community College Post-Sec.
7662 Chanute St NE 98837 509-793-2222
Moses Lake Christian Academy 200/PK-12
1475 Nelson Rd NE Ste A 98837 509-765-9704
Jeni Chandler, coord. Fax 765-3698

Mossyrock, Lewis, Pop. 745
Mossyrock SD 206 500/K-12
PO Box 478 98564 360-983-3181
Dr. Karen Ernest, supt. Fax 983-8111
mossyrock.k12.wa.us
Mossyrock HS 200/9-12
PO Box 454 98564 360-983-3183
Kevin Wilson, prin. Fax 983-3188
Mossyrock JHS 100/7-8
PO Box 454 98564 360-983-3183
Kevin Wilson, prin. Fax 983-3188

Mountlake Terrace, Snohomish, Pop. 18,701
Edmonds SD 15
Supt. — See Lynnwood
Mountlake Terrace HS 1,400/9-12
21801 44th Ave W 98043 425-431-7776
Greg Schwab, prin. Fax 431-7771

Cedar Park Christian JSHS - Mountlake 100/7-12
23607 54th Ave W 98043 425-774-7773
Rev. Patrick Russell, prin. Fax 774-3218

Mount Vernon, Skagit, Pop. 30,973
Mount Vernon SD 320 6,000/K-12
124 E Lawrence St 98273 360-428-6110
Carl Bruner, supt. Fax 428-6172
www.mountvernonschools.org/
LaVenture MS 400/7-8
1200 N Laventure Rd 98273 360-428-6116
Dan Berard, prin. Fax 428-6189
Mount Baker MS 500/7-8
2310 E Section St 98274 360-428-6127
Tim Newall, prin. Fax 428-6155
Mount Vernon HS 1,800/9-12
314 N 9th St 98273 360-428-6100
Rod Merrell, prin. Fax 428-6152

Mt. Vernon Christian S 300/PK-12
820 W Blackburn Rd 98273 360-424-9157
Jeffrey Droog, supt. Fax 424-9256
Northwest Hair Academy Post-Sec.
615 S 1st St 98273 360-336-6553
Skagit Valley College Post-Sec.
2405 E College Way 98273 360-416-7600

Mukilteo, Snohomish, Pop. 19,401
Mukilteo SD 6
Supt. — See Everett
Harbour Pointe MS 800/6-8
5000 Harbour Pointe Blvd 98275 425-366-5100
Nikki Cannon, prin. Fax 366-5102
Kamiak HS 2,200/9-12
10801 Harbour Pointe Blvd 98275 425-366-5400
Mike Gallagher, prin. Fax 366-5402
Olympic View MS 800/6-8
2602 Mukilteo Speedway 98275 425-366-5200
Devin McLane, prin. Fax 366-5202

Naches, Yakima, Pop. 787
Naches Valley SD JT3 1,500/K-12
PO Box 99 98937 509-653-2220
Duane Lyons, supt. Fax 653-1211
www.nvsd.org
Naches Valley HS 500/9-12
PO Box 159 98937 509-653-2342
Rich Rouleau, prin. Fax 653-2921
Naches Valley MS 400/5-8
PO Box 39 98937 509-653-2725
Todd Hilmes, prin. Fax 653-2729

Nile Christian S / Hope Academy 50/K-12
370 Flying H Loop 98937 509-658-2990
Bruce Gillespie, prin. Fax 658-2009

Napavine, Lewis, Pop. 1,693
Napavine SD 14 800/PK-12
PO Box 840 98565 360-262-3303
Dr. Richard Jones, supt. Fax 262-9737
www.napa.k12.wa.us
Napavine JSHS 300/7-12
PO Box 357 98565 360-262-3301
Jason Prather, prin. Fax 262-9541

Naselle, Pacific, Pop. 396
Naselle-Grays River Valley SD 155 200/K-12
793 State Route 4 98638 360-484-7121
Dr. Rick Pass, supt. Fax 484-3191
www.naselle.wednet.edu
Naselle-Grays River Valley S 100/K-12
793 State Route 4 98638 360-484-7121
Karen Wirkkala, prin. Fax 484-3191
Naselle Youth Camp HS 100/Alt
11S Youth Camp Ln 98638 360-484-3269
Lisa Nelson, prin. Fax 484-7109

Neah Bay, Clallam, Pop. 795
Cape Flattery SD 401
Supt. — See Sekiu
Neah Bay S 200/K-12
PO Box 86 98357 360-645-2221
Ann Renker, prin. Fax 645-2574

Newport, Pend Oreille, Pop. 2,055
Newport SD 56-415 1,100/PK-12
PO Box 70 99156 509-447-3167
Dave Smith, supt. Fax 447-2553
www.newport.wednet.edu
Halstead MS 300/5-8
PO Box 70 99156 509-447-2426
Janet Burcham, prin. Fax 447-4914
Newport HS 400/9-12
PO Box 70 99156 509-447-2481
Dennis Matson, prin. Fax 447-4354

Nine Mile Falls, Spokane
Nine Mile Falls SD 325 1,600/PK-12
10110 W Charles Rd 99026 509-340-4300
Brian Talbott, supt. Fax 340-4301
www.9mile.org
Lakeside HS 500/9-12
5909 Highway 291 99026 509-340-4200
Brent Osborn, prin. Fax 340-4201
Lakeside MS 400/6-8
6169 Highway 291 99026 509-340-4100
Jeff Baerwald, prin. Fax 340-4101

Nooksack, Whatcom, Pop. 1,290
Nooksack Valley SD 506
Supt. — See Everson
Nooksack Valley MS 300/6-8
404 W Columbia St 98276 360-966-7561
Joel VanderYacht, prin. Fax 966-7805

North Bend, King, Pop. 5,558
Snoqualmie Valley SD 410
Supt. — See Snoqualmie
Twin Falls MS 600/6-8
46910 SE Middle Fork Rd 98045 425-831-4150
Ruth Moen, prin. Fax 831-4140
Two Rivers S 100/Alt
330 Ballarat Ave N 98045 425-831-4200
Amy Montanye-Johnson, prin. Fax 831-4210

Northport, Stevens, Pop. 287
Northport SD 211 300/K-12
PO Box 1280 99157 509-732-4441
Wes Harris, supt. Fax 732-6606
www.northportschools.org
Northport HS 100/9-12
PO Box 1280 99157 509-732-4430
Don Baribault, prin. Fax 732-6606

Oakesdale, Whitman, Pop. 413
Oakesdale SD 324 100/PK-12
PO Box 228 99158 509-285-5296
Dr. Jake Dingman, supt. Fax 285-5121
www.gonighthawks.net
Oakesdale HS 50/7-12
PO Box 228 99158 509-285-5296
Jason Reed, prin. Fax 285-5121

Oak Harbor, Island, Pop. 20,413
Oak Harbor SD 201 5,400/PK-12
350 S Oak Harbor St 98277 360-279-5000
Dr. Lance Gibbon, supt. Fax 279-5070
www.ohsd.net
Midway HS Alt
350 S Oak Harbor St 98277 360-279-5575
Ray Cone, prin. Fax 279-5565
North Whidbey MS 600/6-8
67 NE Izett St 98277 360-279-5500
William Weinsheimer, prin. Fax 279-5516
Oak Harbor HS 1,600/9-12
1 Wildcat Way 98277 360-279-5800
Dwight Lundstrom, prin. Fax 279-5794
Oak Harbor MS 600/6-8
150 SW 6th Ave 98277 360-279-5300
Shane Evans, prin. Fax 279-5399

North Whidbey Christian HS 9-12
675 E Whidbey Ave 98277 360-675-5352
Doug Fakkema, prin.

Oakville, Grays Harbor, Pop. 661
Oakville SD 400 300/K-12
PO Box H 98568 360-273-0171
Kathy Lorton, supt. Fax 273-6724
oakvilleschools.org/
Oakville JSHS 100/7-12
PO Box H 98568 360-273-5947
Rich Rasanen, prin. Fax 273-8229

Ocean Shores, Grays Harbor, Pop. 5,358
North Beach SD 64 600/PK-12
PO Box 159 98569 360-289-2447
Stanley Pinnick, supt. Fax 289-2492
www.northbeach.k12.wa.us
North Beach HS 200/9-12
PO Box 969 98569 360-289-3888
Brett Mackey, prin. Fax 289-0996
North Beach JHS 100/7-8
PO Box 969 98569 360-289-3888
Brett Mackey, prin. Fax 289-0996

Odessa, Lincoln, Pop. 895
Odessa SD 105-157-166 J 200/PK-12
PO Box 248 99159 509-982-2668
Suellen White, supt. Fax 982-0163
www.odessa.wednet.edu
Odessa JSHS 100/7-12
PO Box 248 99159 509-982-2111
Ken Schutz, prin. Fax 982-0163

Okanogan, Okanogan, Pop. 2,464
Okanogan SD 105 1,000/K-12
PO Box 592 98840 509-422-3629
Dr. Richard Johnson, supt. Fax 422-1525
www.oksd.wednet.edu
Okanogan HS 300/9-12
PO Box 592 98840 509-422-3770
Bob Shacklett, prin. Fax 422-3656
Okanogan MS 200/6-8
PO Box 592 98840 509-422-2680
Brett Baum, prin. Fax 422-0068

Olympia, Thurston, Pop. 44,308
Olympia SD 111 9,200/PK-12
1113 Legion Way SE 98501 360-596-6100
Dick Cvitanich, supt. Fax 596-6111
osd.wednet.edu
Avanti HS 100/9-12
1113 Legion Way SE 98501 360-596-7900
Michael Velasquez, prin. Fax 596-7901
Capital HS 1,300/9-12
2707 Conger Ave NW 98502 360-596-8000
Chris Woods, prin. Fax 596-8001
Jefferson MS 300/6-8
2200 Conger Ave NW 98502 360-596-3200
Michael Cimino, prin. Fax 596-3201
Marshall MS 400/6-8
3939 20th Ave NW 98502 360-596-7600
John Hitchman, prin. Fax 596-7601
Olympia HS 1,700/9-12
1302 North St SE 98501 360-596-7000
Matt Grant, prin. Fax 596-7001
Reeves MS 400/6-8
2200 Quince St NE 98506 360-596-3400
Aaron Davis, prin. Fax 596-3401
Washington MS 800/6-8
3100 Cain Rd SE 98501 360-596-3000
Paul Anders, prin. Fax 596-3001

Tumwater SD 33
Supt. — See Tumwater
Secondary Options HS 100/Alt
7741 Littlerock Rd SW 98512 360-709-7760
Jeanette Holocher, lead tchr. Fax 709-7762
West Black Hills HS 900/9-12
7741 Littlerock Rd SW 98512 360-709-7800
Dr. Kerry Mance, prin. Fax 709-7802

Evergreen State College Post-Sec.
2700 Evergreen Pkwy NW 98505 360-867-6000
Gospel Outreach Christian S 50/1-12
1925 S Bay Rd NE 98506 360-786-0070
David Hill, prin. Fax 357-1417
Nova S 100/6-8
2020 22nd Ave SE 98501 360-491-7097
Jack Fallat, dir. Fax 491-0775
South Puget Sound Community College Post-Sec.
2011 Mottman Rd SW 98512 360-754-7711

Omak, Okanogan, Pop. 4,701
Omak SD 19 1,500/PK-12
PO Box 833 98841 509-826-0320
Dr. Erik Swanson, supt. Fax 826-7689
www.omaksd.wednet.edu
Omak Alternative HS 50/Alt
PO Box 833 98841 509-826-8504
Joanne Warren, prin. Fax 826-8532
Omak HS 400/9-12
PO Box 833 98841 509-826-5150
David Kirk, prin. Fax 826-8515
Omak MS 300/6-8
PO Box 833 98841 509-826-2320
Kathy Miller, prin. Fax 826-7696

Wenatchee Valley College Post-Sec.
116 W Apple Ave 98841 509-422-7800

Onalaska, Lewis, Pop. 606
Onalaska SD 300 1,000/PK-12
540 Carlisle Ave 98570 360-978-4111
Scott Fenter, supt. Fax 978-4185
www.onysd.wednet.edu
Onalaska HS 300/9-12
540 Carlisle Ave 98570 360-978-4111
Dan Greenough, prin. Fax 978-5040
Onalaska MS 300/6-8
540 Carlisle Ave 98570 360-978-4111
C.J. Gray, prin. Fax 978-6142

Oroville, Okanogan, Pop. 1,653
Oroville SD 410 600/PK-12
816 Juniper St 98844 509-476-2281
Steve Quick, supt. Fax 476-2190
www.oroville.wednet.edu/
Oroville JSHS 300/7-12
816 Juniper St 98844 509-476-3612
Kristin Sarmiento, prin. Fax 476-3224

Orting, Pierce, Pop. 6,443
Orting SD 344 2,300/K-12
121 Whitesell St NE 98360 360-893-6500
Michelle Curry, supt. Fax 893-2300
www.orting.wednet.edu
Orting HS 700/9-12
320 Washington Ave N 98360 360-893-2246
Ed Hatzenbeler, prin. Fax 893-5701
Orting MS 500/6-8
111 Whitehawk Blvd NW 98360 360-893-3565
Jack Widmann, prin. Fax 893-2919

Othello, Adams, Pop. 7,325
Othello SD 147-163-55 3,800/K-12
1025 S 1st Ave 99344 509-488-2659
George Juarez, supt. Fax 488-5876
www.othello.wednet.edu
Desert Oasis HS, 825 E Ash St 99344 Alt
Russell Kovalenko, prin. 509-488-4534
McFarland MS 900/6-8
790 S 10th Ave 99344 509-488-3326
Dennis Adams, prin. Fax 488-6788
Othello HS 1,000/9-12
340 S 7th Ave 99344 509-488-3351
Carlos Gonzalez, prin. Fax 488-6779

Palouse, Whitman, Pop. 974
Palouse SD 301 200/PK-12
600 E Alder St 99161 509-878-1921
Jake Dingman, supt. Fax 878-1948
www.garpal.net
Garfield-Palouse HS 100/9-12
600 E Alder St 99161 509-878-1921
Darcy Eliason, prin. Fax 878-1675

Pasco, Franklin, Pop. 58,798
Pasco SD 1 15,100/PK-12
1215 W Lewis St 99301 509-543-6700
Saundra Hill, supt. Fax 546-2685
www.psd1.org
Chiawana HS 2,000/9-12
8125 W Argent Rd 99301 509-543-6786
Teri Kessle, prin. Fax 543-6730
McLoughlin MS 1,500/6-8
2803 N Road 88 99301 509-547-4542
John Wallwork, prin. Fax 543-6797
New Horizons/Discovery HS 200/Alt
3110 W Argent Rd 99301 509-543-6796
Christy Rasmussen, prin. Fax 546-2864
Ochoa MS 1,000/6-8
1801 E Sheppard St 99301 509-543-6742
Jackie Ramirez, prin. Fax 543-6744
Pasco HS 1,800/9-12
1108 N 10th Ave 99301 509-547-5581
Raul Sital, prin. Fax 546-2684
Stevens MS 900/6-8
1120 N 22nd Ave 99301 509-543-6798
Carla Lobos, prin. Fax 546-2854
Other Schools – See Richland

Charter College Pasco Post-Sec.
5278 Outlet Dr 99301 509-546-3900
Columbia Basin College Post-Sec.
2600 N 20th Ave 99301 509-547-0511
Kingspoint Christian S 200/PK-12
7900 W Court St 99301 509-547-6498
DeAnna Henning, admin. Fax 547-6788
Tri Cities Preparatory S 100/9-12
9612 Saint Thomas Dr 99301 509-546-2465
Arlene Jones, prin. Fax 546-2490
Tri-City Junior Academy 100/PK-10
4115 W Henry St 99301 509-547-8092

Pateros, Okanogan, Pop. 658
Pateros SD 122 200/K-12
PO Box 98 98846 509-923-2751
Lois Davies, supt. Fax 923-2283
www.pateros.org
Pateros S 200/K-12
PO Box 98 98846 509-923-2343
Michael Hull, prin. Fax 923-1931

Pe Ell, Lewis, Pop. 610
Pe Ell SD 301 300/PK-12
PO Box 368 98572 360-291-3244
Kyle MacDonald, supt. Fax 291-3823
www.peell.k12.wa.us/
Pe Ell S 300/PK-12
PO Box 368 98572 360-291-3244
Kyle MacDonald, admin. Fax 291-3823

Pomeroy, Garfield, Pop. 1,407
Pomeroy SD 110 300/K-12
PO Box 950 99347 509-843-3393
Kim Spacek, supt. Fax 843-3046
www.psd.wednet.edu
Pomeroy JSHS 200/7-12
PO Box 950 99347 509-843-1331
Doug LaMunyan, prin. Fax 843-8245

Port Angeles, Clallam, Pop. 18,283
Port Angeles SD 121 3,800/PK-12
216 E 4th St 98362 360-457-8575
Jane Pryne Ed.D., supt. Fax 457-4649
www.portangelesschools.org/
Lincoln HS 100/Alt
924 W 9th St 98363 360-452-9502
Cindy Crumb, prin. Fax 417-1993
North Olympic Peninsula Skills Center Vo/Tech
905 W 9th St 98363 360-565-1533
Ronald Craig, dir. Fax 565-1998
Port Angeles HS 1,200/9-12
304 E Park Ave 98362 360-452-7602
Dr. Garry Cameron, prin. Fax 452-0256
Stevens MS 600/7-8
1139 W 14th St 98363 360-452-5590
Charles Lisk, prin. Fax 457-5709

Peninsula College Post-Sec.
1502 E Lauridsen Blvd 98362 360-452-9277

Port Hadlock, Jefferson, Pop. 2,742

Northwest School of Wooden Boatbuilding Post-Sec.
42 N Water St 98339 360-385-4948

Port Orchard, Kitsap, Pop. 10,384
South Kitsap SD 402 9,800/K-12
2689 Hoover Ave SE 98366 360-874-7000
Bev Cheney, supt. Fax 874-7068
www.skitsap.wednet.edu
Cedar Heights JHS 700/7-9
2220 Pottery Ave 98366 360-874-6020
Andrew Cain, prin. Fax 874-6420
Explorer Academy 100/Alt
425 Mitchell Ave 98366 360-443-3605
Pat Oster, prin. Fax 443-3624
Sedgewick JHS 800/7-9
8995 SE Sedgwick Rd 98366 360-874-6090
Jay Villars, prin. Fax 874-6430
South Kitsap Discovery/Alternative HS 200/Alt
2150 Fircrest Dr SE 98366 360-443-3680
Pat Oster, prin. Fax 443-3704
South Kitsap SHS 2,200/10-12
425 Mitchell Ave 98366 360-874-5600
Jerry Holsten, prin. Fax 874-5892
Whitman JHS 800/7-9
1887 Madrona Dr SE 98366 360-874-6160
Brian Carlson, prin. Fax 874-6440

Burley Christian S 100/PK-12
14687 Olympic Dr SE 98367 253-851-8619
Dennis Myers, admin.

Port Townsend, Jefferson, Pop. 8,812
Port Townsend SD 50 1,300/PK-12
1610 Blaine St 98368 360-379-4501
David Engle, supt. Fax 385-3617
www.ptschools.org/
Blue Heron MS 400/4-8
3939 San Juan Ave 98368 360-379-4540
Diane Lashinsky, prin. Fax 379-4548
Port Townsend HS 500/9-12
1500 Van Ness St 98368 360-379-4520
Carrie Ehrhardt, prin. Fax 379-4505

Poulsbo, Kitsap, Pop. 8,738
North Kitsap SD 400 6,600/PK-12
18360 Caldart Ave NE 98370 360-779-8700
Dr. Patrice Page, supt. Fax 697-3175
www.nkschools.org
North Kitsap HS 1,300/9-12
1780 NE Hostmark St 98370 360-779-4408
Judson Miller, prin. Fax 598-8406
Poulsbo MS 800/6-8
2003 NE Hostmark St 98370 360-779-4453
Matt Vandeleur, prin. Fax 598-1041
Other Schools – See Kingston

Northwest College of Art and Design Post-Sec.
16301 Creative Dr NE 98370 360-779-9993

Prescott, Walla Walla, Pop. 314
Prescott SD 402-37 200/K-12
PO Box 65 99348 509-849-2215
Dr. Bill Jordan, supt. Fax 849-2800
www.prescott.k12.wa.us/
Prescott JSHS, PO Box 65 99348 100/7-12
Dr. Jodi Thew, prin. 509-849-2215

Prosser, Benton, Pop. 5,618
Prosser SD 116 2,900/K-12
1126 Meade Ave Ste A 99350 509-786-3323
Dr. Ray Tolcacher, supt. Fax 786-2062
www.prosserschools.org/
Housel MS 700/6-8
2001 Highland Dr 99350 509-786-1732
Deanna Flores, prin. Fax 786-2814
Prosser Falls HS 50/Alt
1500 Grant Ave 99350 509-786-2527
Syndi Duehn, dean Fax 786-3427
Prosser HS 900/9-12
1203 Prosser Ave 99350 509-786-1224
Kevin Lusk, prin. Fax 786-4227

Pullman, Whitman, Pop. 28,533
Pullman SD 267 2,400/PK-12
240 SE Dexter St 99163 509-332-3581
Dr. Paul Sturm, supt. Fax 334-0375
www.psd267.org
Lincoln MS 500/6-8
315 SE Crestview St 99163 509-334-3411
Cameron Grow, prin. Fax 334-9678
Pullman HS 700/9-12
510 NW Greyhound Way 99163 509-332-1551
Joseph Thornton, prin. Fax 332-6868

Pullman Christian S 50/K-12
345 SW Kimball Dr 99163 509-332-3545
Sherri Goetze, prin. Fax 332-5433
Washington State University Post-Sec.
PO Box 641067 99164 509-335-3564

Puyallup, Pierce, Pop. 35,083
Bethel SD 403
Supt. — See Spanaway
Pierce County Skills Center Vo/Tech
16117 Canyon Rd E 98375 253-683-5950
Michelle Ledbetter, dir. Fax 683-6079

Puyallup SD 3 20,800/PK-12
PO Box 370 98371 253-841-1301
Dr. Timothy Yeomans, supt. Fax 840-8959
www.puyallup.k12.wa.us
Aylen JHS 700/7-9
101 15th St SW 98371 253-841-8723
Janet Wojtala, prin. Fax 840-8856
Ballou JHS 700/7-9
9916 136th St E 98373 253-841-8725
Krista Bates, prin. Fax 840-8819
Emerald Ridge SHS 1,600/10-12
12405 184th St E 98374 253-435-6300
Brian Lowney, prin. Fax 435-6310
Ferrucci JHS 700/7-9
3213 Wildwood Park Dr 98374 253-841-8756
Ailene Baxter, prin. Fax 840-8855
Glacier View JHS 900/7-9
12807 184th St E 98374 253-840-8922
Mark Vetter, prin. Fax 435-6570
Kalles JHS 700/7-9
501 7th Ave SE 98372 253-841-8729
Mario Casello, prin. Fax 840-8984
Puyallup SHS 1,600/10-12
105 7th St SW 98371 253-841-8711
Jason Smith, prin. Fax 841-8624
Rogers SHS 1,800/10-12
12801 86th Ave E 98373 253-841-8717
John Bustad, prin. Fax 840-8802
Stahl JHS 800/7-9
9610 168th Street Ct E 98375 253-840-8881
Troy Hodge, prin. Fax 840-8992
Walker HS 100/Alt
5715 Milwaukee Ave E 98372 253-841-8781
Alicia Nosworthy, prin. Fax 840-8981
Other Schools – See Edgewood

BJ's Beauty & Barber College Post-Sec.
12020 Meridian E Ste G 98373 253-848-1595
Cascade Christian JSHS 500/7-12
811 21st St SE 98372 253-445-9706
Joyce Blum, admin. Fax 445-0859
Pierce College Post-Sec.
1601 39th Ave SE 98374 253-840-8470

Quilcene, Jefferson, Pop. 571
Quilcene SD 48 200/K-12
PO Box 40 98376 360-765-3363
Wally Lis, supt. Fax 765-3015
www.quilcene.wednet.edu
Crossroads Community S 50/Alt
PO Box 40 98376 360-765-3363
Phil Davis, dir. Fax 765-4183
P.E.A.R.L. 500/Alt
PO Box 40 98376 360-765-3363
Dr. Gary Stebbins, prin. Fax 765-3015
Quilcene S 200/K-12
PO Box 40 98376 360-765-3363
Dr. Gary Stebbins, prin. Fax 765-4183

Quincy, Grant, Pop. 6,701
Quincy SD 144-101 2,600/K-12
119 J St SW 98848 509-787-4571
Dr. Burton Dickerson, supt. Fax 787-4336
www.qsd.wednet.edu
Quincy HS 600/9-12
16 6th Ave SE 98848 509-787-3501
David Talley, prin. Fax 787-8989
Quincy High Tech HS Vo/Tech
404 1st Ave SW 98848 509-787-1678
Garry Stidman, prin. Fax 787-1680
Quincy JHS 500/7-8
417 C St SE 98848 509-787-4435
Scott Ramsey, prin. Fax 787-8949

Rainier, Thurston, Pop. 1,719
Rainier SD 307 900/K-12
PO Box 98 98576 360-446-2207
Tim Garchow, supt. Fax 446-2918
www.rainier.wednet.edu
Rainier HS 300/9-12
PO Box 98 98576 360-446-2205
Bryon Bahr, prin. Fax 446-2208
Rainier MS 200/6-8
PO Box 98 98576 360-446-2206
Bryon Bahr, prin. Fax 446-7414

Randle, Lewis
White Pass SD 303 400/PK-12
PO Box 188 98377 360-497-3791
Rebecca Miner, supt. Fax 497-2560
www.whitepass.k12.wa.us
White Pass JSHS 200/7-12
516 Silverbrook Rd 98377 360-497-5816
Gary Stamper, prin. Fax 497-7773

Ravensdale, King, Pop. 1,086
Tahoma SD 409
Supt. — See Maple Valley
Tahoma JHS 1,200/8-9
25600 SE Summit Landsburg 98051 425-413-5600
Rob Morrow, prin. Fax 413-5500

Raymond, Pacific, Pop. 2,787
Raymond SD 116 900/PK-12
1016 Commercial St 98577 360-942-3415
Dr. Stephen Holland, supt. Fax 942-3416
www.raymondschooldistrict.org
Raymond JSHS 300/7-12
1016 Commercial St 98577 360-942-3415
Dale Bowen, prin. Fax 942-2504

Willapa Valley SD 160 300/K-12
22 Viking Way 98577 360-942-5855
Rob Friese, supt. Fax 942-3216
www.willapa.wednet.edu
Willapa Valley HS 100/9-12
22 Viking Way 98577 360-942-2006
Rob Friese, prin. Fax 942-3216
Willapa Valley MS 100/6-8
22 Viking Way 98577 360-942-2006
Rob Friese, prin. Fax 942-3216

Reardan, Lincoln, Pop. 562
Reardan-Edwall SD 9 600/PK-12
PO Box 225 99029 509-796-2701
Marcus Morgan, supt. Fax 796-4954
www.reardan.net
Reardan JSHS 300/7-12
PO Box 225 99029 509-796-2701
Courtney Strozyk, prin. Fax 796-4954
Reardan Online Academy 50/Alt
PO Box 225 99029 509-796-2701
Jeff Roberts, admin. Fax 796-4954

Redmond, King, Pop. 51,981
Lake Washington SD 414 20,800/K-12
PO Box 97039 98073 425-936-1200
Dr. Traci Pierce, supt. Fax 936-1213
www.lwsd.org
Evergreen MS 500/6-8
6900 208th Ave NE 98053 425-936-2320
Sean Cassidy, prin. Fax 868-0105
Redmond HS 1,500/9-12
17272 NE 104th St 98052 425-936-1800
Jane Todd, prin. Fax 936-1839
Redmond MS 600/6-8
10055 166th Ave NE 98052 425-936-2440
Kelly Clapp, prin. Fax 556-9806
Rose Hill MS 300/6-8
13505 NE 75th St 98052 425-936-2460
Erin Bowser, prin. Fax 556-0629
Stella Schola MS 100/6-8
13505 NE 75th St 98052 425-936-2475
Erin Bowser, prin. Fax 936-2476
Other Schools – See Kirkland, Sammamish

Bear Creek S 700/PK-12
8905 208th Ave NE 98053 425-898-1720
Patrick Carruth, hdmstr. Fax 898-1430
Dartmoor S 100/1-12
7735 178th Pl NE Ste A 98052 425-885-6296
Jeffrey Woolley M.A., admin. Fax 885-1137
DigiPen Institute of Technology Post-Sec.
9931 Willows Rd NE 98052 425-558-0299
Overlake S 500/5-12
20301 NE 108th St 98053 425-868-1000
Dr. Francisco Grijalva, hdmstr. Fax 868-5771

Renton, King, Pop. 85,890
Issaquah SD 411
Supt. — See Issaquah
Liberty HS 1,200/9-12
16655 SE 136th St 98059 425-837-4800
Josh Almy, prin. Fax 837-4905
Maywood MS 900/6-8
14490 168th Ave SE 98059 425-837-6900
Jason Morse, prin. Fax 837-6910

Kent SD 415
Supt. — See Kent
Meeker MS 600/7-8
12600 SE 192nd St 98058 253-373-7284
Jeff Pelzel, prin. Fax 373-7560
Northwood MS 700/7-8
17007 SE 184th St 98058 253-373-7780
Colleen Nelson, prin. Fax 373-7788

Renton SD 403 14,500/K-12
300 SW 7th St 98057 425-204-2300
Merri Rieger Ed.D., supt. Fax 204-2456
www.rentonschools.us
Hazen HS 1,500/9-12
1101 Hoquiam Ave NE 98059 425-204-4200
Randy Taylor, prin. Fax 204-4220
Lindbergh HS 1,300/9-12
16426 128th Ave SE 98058 425-204-3200
Tres Genger, prin. Fax 204-3220
McKnight MS 1,200/6-8
1200 Edmonds Ave NE 98056 425-204-3600
Craig Cooper, prin. Fax 204-3680
Nelsen MS 1,000/6-8
2403 Jones Ave S 98055 425-204-3000
Colin Falk, prin. Fax 204-3079
Renton HS 1,300/9-12
400 S 2nd St 98057 425-204-3400
Giovanna San Martin, prin. Fax 204-3412
Other Schools – See Seattle

Everest College Post-Sec.
981 Powell Ave SW Ste 200 98057 425-255-3281
Pima Medical Institute Post-Sec.
555 S Renton Village Pl 110 98057 425-228-9600
Renton Technical College Post-Sec.
3000 NE 4th St 98056 425-235-2352

Republic, Ferry, Pop. 1,028
Republic SD 309 300/K-12
30306 E Highway 20 99166 509-775-3173
Kyle Rydell, supt. Fax 775-3712
www.republic.wednet.edu
Republic HS 100/9-12
30306 E Highway 20 99166 509-775-3171
Shawn Anderson, prin. Fax 775-1098
Republic JHS 100/7-8
30306 E Highway 20 99166 509-775-3171
Shawn Anderson, prin. Fax 775-1098

Richland, Benton, Pop. 46,846
Pasco SD 1
Supt. — See Pasco
Delta HS 9-12
901 Northgate Dr 99352 509-544-8355
Deidre Holmberg, prin. Fax 544-8367

Richland SD 400 11,200/K-12
615 Snow Ave 99352 509-967-6000
Rick Schulte, supt. Fax 942-2401
www.rsd.edu
Carmichael MS 900/6-8
620 Thayer Dr 99352 509-967-6425
Brian Stadelman, prin. Fax 942-2471
Chief Joseph MS 700/6-8
504 Wilson St, 509-967-6400
Jon Lobdell, prin. Fax 942-2492
Hanford HS 1,500/9-12
450 Hanford St, 509-967-6500
Ken Gosney, prin. Fax 371-2001
Richland HS 1,900/9-12
930 Long Ave 99352 509-967-6535
Tim Praino, prin. Fax 942-2512
River's Edge HS 200/Alt
975 Gillespie St 99352 509-967-6450
Dan Chubb, prin. Fax 942-2598
Other Schools – See West Richland

Liberty Christian S of the Tri-Cities 500/PK-12
2200 Williams Blvd, 509-946-0602
Joe Morgan, supt. Fax 943-5623
Lucas Marc Academy Post-Sec.
71 Gage Blvd 99352 509-591-4979

Ridgefield, Clark, Pop. 4,650
Ridgefield SD 122 2,100/K-12
2724 S Hillhurst Rd 98642 360-619-1300
Art Edgerly, supt. Fax 619-1397
www.ridge.k12.wa.us
Ridgefield HS 700/9-12
2630 S Hillhurst Rd 98642 360-619-1320
Tony VanderMaas, prin. Fax 619-1395
View Ridge MS 300/7-8
510 Pioneer St 98642 360-619-1400
Chris Griffith, prin. Fax 619-1459

Cedar Tree Classical Christian S 200/K-12
20601 NE 29th Ave 98642 360-887-0190
Tom Bradshaw, hdmstr.

Ritzville, Adams, Pop. 1,650
Ritzville SD 160-67 300/PK-12
209 E Wellsandt Rd 99169 509-659-1660
Robert Roettger, supt. Fax 659-0927
www.ritzville.wednet.edu
Ritzville HS 100/9-12
209 E Wellsandt Rd 99169 509-659-1720
Cheryl Henjum, prin. Fax 659-5140

Rochester, Thurston, Pop. 2,337
Rochester SD 401 2,200/K-12
10140 Highway 12 SW 98579 360-273-5536
Kimberly Fry, supt. Fax 273-5547
www.rochester.wednet.edu
HEART Alternative HS 50/Alt
10140 Highway 12 SW 98579 360-273-5017
Matt Ishler, prin. Fax 273-5017
Rochester HS 600/9-12
19800 Carper Rd SW 98579 360-273-5534
Matt Ishler, prin. Fax 273-2570
Rochester MS 500/6-8
PO Box 398 98579 360-273-5958
Will Maus, prin. Fax 273-2045

Rockford, Spokane, Pop. 465
Freeman SD 358 900/K-12
15001 S Jackson Rd 99030 509-291-3695
Randy Russell, supt. Fax 291-3636
www.freemansd.org
Freeman HS 300/9-12
14626 S Jackson Rd 99030 509-291-3721
Dave Smith, prin. Fax 291-7337
Freeman MS 200/6-8
14917 S Jackson Rd 99030 509-291-7301
Jim Straw, prin. Fax 291-7339

Rosalia, Whitman, Pop. 547
Rosalia SD 320 200/K-12
916 S Josephine Ave 99170 509-523-3061
Dr. Bill Thurston, supt. Fax 523-3861
www.rosalia.wednet.edu
Rosalia S 200/K-12
916 S Josephine Ave 99170 509-523-3061
Darrell Kuhn, prin. Fax 523-3861

Roslyn, Kittitas, Pop. 872
Cle Elum-Roslyn SD 404
Supt. — See Cle Elum
Swiftwater Alternative S 50/Alt
205 W Idaho St 98941 509-649-4990
Mel Blair, prin. Fax 649-2270

Royal City, Grant, Pop. 2,135
Royal SD 160 1,500/PK-12
PO Box 486 99357 509-346-2222
Rosemarie Search, supt. Fax 346-8746
www.royal.wednet.edu/
Royal HS 400/9-12
PO Box 486 99357 509-346-2256
Jack Hill, prin. Fax 346-9739
Royal MS 400/6-8
PO Box 486 99357 509-346-2268
David Jaderlund, prin. Fax 346-2269

Saint John, Whitman, Pop. 519
St. John SD 322 200/PK-12
301 W Nob Hill Rd 99171 509-648-3336
Gary Wargo, supt. Fax 648-3451
www.sje.wednet.edu/
St. John-Endicott HS 100/9-12
301 W Nob Hill Rd 99171 509-648-3336
Michael Olsen, prin. Fax 648-3451

Sammamish, King, Pop. 44,087
Lake Washington SD 414
Supt. — See Redmond
Eastlake HS 1,300/9-12
400 228th Ave NE 98074 425-936-1500
Brad Malloy, prin. Fax 836-6609
Inglewood MS 700/6-8
24120 NE 8th St 98074 425-936-2360
Tim Patterson, prin. Fax 868-0628
Renaissance S of Art & Reasoning 100/6-8
400 228th Ave NE 98074 425-936-1544
Brad Malloy, prin. Fax 836-6609
STEM, 400 228th Ave SE 98074 9-12
Cindy Dueanas, prin. 425-936-2770

Eastside Catholic HS 900/6-12
232 228th Ave SE 98074 425-295-3000
Polly Skinner, prin. Fax 392-5160

SeaTac, King, Pop. 24,721
Highline SD 401
Supt. — See Burien
Academy of Citizenship & Empowerment HS 1,100/9-12
4424 S 188th St 98188 206-433-2342
Janae Landis, prin. Fax 998-7238
Chinook MS 500/7-8
18650 42nd Ave S 98188 206-631-5700
Mark Demick, prin. Fax 631-5770
Global Connections HS 300/9-12
4424 S 188th St Ste 300 98188 206-433-2343
Rick Harwood, prin. Fax 433-2227
Odyssey HS 200/9-12
4424 S 188th St Ste 800 98188 206-433-2344
Joan Ferrigno, prin. Fax 988-7239

Seattle Christian S 600/K-12
18301 Military Rd S 98188 206-246-8241
Gloria Hunter, supt. Fax 246-9066

Seattle, King, Pop. 578,438
Highline SD 401
Supt. — See Burien
Arts and Academics Academy 300/9-12
830 SW 116th St 98146 206-631-6250
Norma Barrinieau, prin. Fax 631-6162
Cascade MS 500/7-8
11212 10th Ave SW 98146 206-631-5500
Diana Garcia, prin. Fax 631-5568
Health Sciences & Human Services HS 400/9-12
830 SW 116th St 98146 206-631-6200
Jenni MacDonald, prin. Fax 631-6160
New Start HS 100/Alt
814 SW 120th St 98146 206-433-8760
Michael Sita, prin. Fax 433-2293
Technology Engineering Communications HS 300/9-12
830 SW 116th St 98146 206-631-6300
Kelly Raymond, prin. Fax 631-6164

Renton SD 403
Supt. — See Renton
Dimmitt MS 900/6-8
12320 80th Ave S 98178 425-204-2800
Anna Horton, prin. Fax 204-2812
Secondary Learning Center 300/Alt
7800 S 132nd St 98178 425-204-2100
Ronald Mahan, prin. Fax 204-2111

Seattle SD 1 47,000/PK-12
PO Box 34165 98124 206-252-0000
Jose Banda, supt. Fax 252-0102
www.seattleschools.org
Ballard HS 1,600/9-12
1418 NW 65th St 98117 206-252-1000
Keven Wynkoop, prin. Fax 252-1001
Center S 300/9-12
305 Harrison St 98109 206-252-9850
Oksana Britsova, prin. Fax 252-9851
Cleveland STEM HS 700/9-12
5511 15th Ave S 98108 206-252-7800
Princess Shareef, prin. Fax 252-7801
Denny International MS 800/6-8
2601 SW Kenyon St 98126 206-252-9000
Jeff Clarke, prin. Fax 252-9001
Eckstein MS 1,200/6-8
3003 NE 75th St 98115 206-252-5010
Sherri Kokx, prin. Fax 252-5011
Franklin HS 1,300/9-12
3013 S Mount Baker Blvd 98144 206-252-6150
Jennifer Wiley, prin. Fax 252-6151
Garfield HS 1,800/9-12
400 23rd Ave 98122 206-252-2270
Ted Howard, prin. Fax 252-2271
Hale HS 1,100/9-12
10750 30th Ave NE 98125 206-252-3680
Jill Hudson, prin. Fax 262-3681
Hamilton International MS 900/6-8
1610 N 41st St 98103 206-252-5810
Cindy Watters, prin. Fax 252-5811
Ingraham HS 1,000/9-12
1819 N 135th St 98133 206-252-3880
Martin Floe, prin. Fax 252-3881
Interagency Academy 400/Alt
3100 S Alaska St 98108 206-252-6816
Kaaren Andrews, prin. Fax 252-6811
Kurose MS 600/6-8
3928 S Graham St 98118 206-252-7700
Mia Williams, prin. Fax 252-7701

Madison MS 800/6-8
3429 45th Ave SW 98116 206-252-9200
Henterson Carlisle, prin. Fax 252-9201
McClure MS 500/6-8
1915 1st Ave W 98119 206-252-1900
Sarah Pritchett, prin. Fax 252-1901
Mercer MS 800/6-8
1600 S Columbian Way 98108 206-252-8000
Chris Carter, prin. Fax 252-8001
Middle College HS at High Point Center 9-12
6400 Sylvan Way SW 98126 206-252-4785
Cindy Nash, prin. Fax 252-4787
Middle College HS at Seattle University 9-12
1330 N 90th St 98103 206-252-4785
Cindy Nash, prin. Fax 252-4787
Middle College HS at Univ of WA 9-12
PO Box 355845 98195 206-685-3476
Cindy Nash, prin. Fax 616-3664
Middle College HS Northgate Mall Academy 200/9-12
401 NE Northgate Way 98125 206-366-7940
Cindy Nash, prin. Fax 366-7941
Middle Coll HS @ Amer Indian Heritage 9-12
1330 N 90th St Bldg 100 98103 206-252-4785
Cindy Nash, prin. Fax 252-4787
NOVA HS 300/9-12
300 20th Ave 98122 206-252-3500
Mark Perry, prin. Fax 252-3501
Rainier Beach HS 400/9-12
8815 Seward Park Ave S 98118 206-252-6350
Dwane Chappelle, prin. Fax 252-6351
Roosevelt HS 1,700/9-12
1410 NE 66th St 98115 206-252-4810
Brian Vance, prin. Fax 252-4811
Sealth International HS 1,100/9-12
2600 SW Thistle St 98126 206-252-8550
Chris Kinsey, prin. Fax 252-8551
Seattle World S 200/Alt
301 21st Ave E 98112 206-252-2200
Martin O'Callaghan, prin. Fax 252-2201
South Lake Alternative HS 200/Alt
8601 Rainier Ave S 98118 206-252-6600
Barbara Moore, prin. Fax 252-6601
Washington MS 1,100/6-8
2101 S Jackson St 98144 206-252-2600
Jon Halfaker, prin. Fax 252-2601
West Seattle HS 1,000/9-12
3000 California Ave SW 98116 206-252-8800
Ruth Medsker, prin. Fax 252-8801
Whitman MS 1,000/6-8
9201 15th Ave NW 98117 206-252-1200
Susan Kleitsch, prin. Fax 252-1201

Antioch University Post-Sec.
2326 6th Ave 98121 206-441-5352
Argosy University/Seattle Post-Sec.
2601A Elliott Ave 98121 206-283-4500
Art Institute of Seattle Post-Sec.
2323 Elliott Ave 98121 206-448-0900
Bainbridge Graduate Institute Post-Sec.
220 2nd Ave S Ste 400 98104 206-855-9559
Bakke Graduate University Post-Sec.
1013 8th Ave Ste 401 98104 206-264-9100
Billings MS 100/6-8
7217 Woodlawn Ave NE 98115 206-547-4614
Ted Kalmus, hdmstr. Fax 545-8505
Bishop Blanchet HS 1,000/9-12
8200 Wallingford Ave N 98103 206-527-7700
Sheila Kries, prin. Fax 527-7712
Bush S 600/K-12
3400 E Harrison St 98112 206-322-7978
Frank Magusin, hdmstr. Fax 860-3876
City University of Seattle Post-Sec.
521 Wall St Ste 100 98121 206-239-4500
Cornish College of the Arts Post-Sec.
1000 Lenora St 98121 800-726-ARTS
Cortiva Institute - Seattle Post-Sec.
425 Pontius Ave N Ste 100 98109 206-282-1233
Divers Institute of Technology Post-Sec.
1341 N Northlake Way 98103 800-634-8377
Everest College Post-Sec.
2111 N Northgate Way 98133 206-440-3090
Explorer West MS 100/6-8
10015 28th Ave SW 98146 206-935-0495
Evan Hundley, head sch Fax 932-7113
Gene Juarez Academy of Beauty Post-Sec.
10715 8th Ave NE 98125 206-365-6900
Holy Names Academy 700/9-12
728 21st Ave E 98112 206-323-4272
Elizabeth Swift, prin. Fax 323-5254
International Academy of Design & Tech Post-Sec.
645 Andover Park W 98188 206-575-1865
ITT Technical Institute Post-Sec.
12720 Gateway Dr S Ste 100 98168 206-244-3300
King's HS 500/9-12
19303 Fremont Ave N 98133 206-546-7241
Bob Ruhlman, prin. Fax 546-7214
Lakeside MS 300/5-8
13510 1st Ave NE 98125 206-368-3630
Bernie Noe, hdmstr. Fax 368-3638
Lakeside Upper S 500/9-12
14050 1st Ave NE 98125 206-368-3600
Bernie Noe, hdmstr. Fax 368-3638
Menachem Mendel Seattle Cheder 100/PK-12
8511 15th Ave NE 98115 206-523-9766
North Seattle Community College Post-Sec.
9600 College Way N 98103 206-934-3600
Northwest S 500/6-12
1415 Summit Ave 98122 206-682-7309
Mike McGill, head sch Fax 467-7353
O'Dea HS 500/9-12
802 Terry Ave 98104 206-622-6596
James Walker, prin. Fax 340-4110
Photographic Center Northwest Post-Sec.
900 12th Ave 98122 206-720-7222
Pima Medical Institute Post-Sec.
9709 3rd Ave NE Ste 400 98115 206-322-6100
Seattle Academy of Arts & Sciences 300/6-8
1432 15th Ave 98122 206-676-6880
Joe Puggelli, hdmstr. Fax 676-6880
Seattle Academy of Arts & Sciences 400/9-12
1201 E Union St 98122 206-323-6600
Joe Puggelli, hdmstr. Fax 323-6618
Seattle Central Community College Post-Sec.
1701 Broadway 98122 206-587-3800
Seattle Girls' S 100/5-8
2706 S Jackson St 98144 206-709-2228
Rafael del Castillo, hdmstr. Fax 329-1580
Seattle Institute of Oriental Medicine Post-Sec.
444 NE Ravenna Blvd Ste 101 98115 206-517-4541
Seattle Lutheran HS 200/9-12
4100 SW Genesee St 98116 206-937-7722
Mark Henderson, prin. Fax 937-6781
Seattle Pacific University Post-Sec.
3307 3rd Ave W 98119 206-281-2000
Seattle Preparatory S 700/9-12
2400 11th Ave E 98102 206-324-0400
Maureen Reid, prin. Fax 323-6509
Seattle School of Theology & Psychology Post-Sec.
2501 Elliott Ave 98121 206-876-6100
Seattle University Post-Sec.
901 12th Ave 98122 206-296-6000
Seattle Waldorf HS 100/9-12
160 John St 98109 206-522-2644
Tracy Bennett, dir. Fax 522-2631
Shorewood Christian S 200/PK-12
10300 28th Ave SW 98146 206-933-1056
Tim Lorenz, prin. Fax 932-9002
South Seattle Community College Post-Sec.
6000 16th Ave SW 98106 206-934-5300
University of Washington 98195 Post-Sec.
206-543-2100
University Preparatory Academy 500/6-12
8000 25th Ave NE 98115 206-525-2714
Erica Hamlin, head sch Fax 525-9659

Sedro Woolley, Skagit, Pop. 10,288
Sedro-Woolley SD 101 4,200/K-12
801 Trail Rd 98284 360-855-3500
Mark Venn, supt. Fax 855-3574
www.swsd.k12.wa.us
Cascade MS 600/7-8
201 N Township St 98284 360-855-3520
Scott McPhee, prin. Fax 855-3521
Sedro-Woolley HS 1,200/9-12
1235 3rd St 98284 360-855-3510
Mike Schweigert, prin. Fax 855-3517
State Street HS 300/Alt
800 State St 98284 360-855-3550
Doug Walker, prin. Fax 855-3551

Alger Learning Center & Independence HS 1,300/K-12
121 Alder Dr 98284 360-595-2630
John Lackey, dir. Fax 595-1141

Sekiu, Clallam, Pop. 27
Cape Flattery SD 401 300/K-12
PO Box 109 98381 360-963-2329
Kandy Ritter, supt. Fax 963-2373
www.capeflattery.wednet.edu
Other Schools – See Clallam Bay, Neah Bay

Selah, Yakima, Pop. 6,994
Selah SD 119 3,400/K-12
105 W Bartlett Ave 98942 509-697-0706
Shane Backlund, supt. Fax 697-0823
www.selah.k12.wa.us
Selah Academy 100/Alt
801 N 1st St 98942 509-697-0815
Joe Coscarart, prin. Fax 697-0814
Selah HS 700/10-12
801 N 1st St 98942 509-697-0800
Rich Rees, prin. Fax 697-0811
Selah JHS 500/8-9
411 N 1st St 98942 509-697-0500
Marc Gallaway, prin. Fax 697-0696

Sequim, Clallam, Pop. 6,414
Sequim SD 323 2,900/K-12
503 N Sequim Ave 98382 360-582-3260
Kelly Shea, supt. Fax 683-6303
www.sequim.k12.wa.us/
Sequim Community S 100/Alt
221 W Fir St 98382 360-582-3400
Randy Hill, admin. Fax 582-9229
Sequim HS 1,000/9-12
601 N Sequim Ave 98382 360-582-3600
Shawn Langston, prin. Fax 681-8688
Sequim MS 700/6-8
301 W Hendrickson Rd 98382 360-582-3500
Brian Jones, prin. Fax 582-9486

Shelton, Mason, Pop. 9,392
Pioneer SD 402 800/PK-8
611 E Agate Rd 98584 360-426-9115
Martin Brewer, supt. Fax 426-1036
www.psd402.org
Pioneer MS 400/4-8
611 E Agate Rd 98584 360-426-8291
Joe Riley, prin. Fax 426-1036

Shelton SD 309 4,200/PK-12
700 S 1st St 98584 360-426-1687
Wayne Massie, supt. Fax 427-8610
www.sheltonschools.org
Choice HS 200/Alt
807 W Pine St 98584 360-426-7664
Stacey Anderson, prin. Fax 462-1203
Oakland Bay JHS 700/8-9
3301 N Shelton Springs Rd 98584 360-426-7991
Bracken Budge, prin. Fax 427-2940
Shelton SHS 1,100/10-12
3737 N Shelton Springs Rd 98584 360-426-4471
Wanda Berndtson, prin. Fax 427-6141

Shoreline, King, Pop. 50,457
Shoreline SD 412 8,700/PK-12
18560 1st Ave NE 98155 206-393-4203
Sue Walker, supt. Fax 393-4204
www.shorelineschools.org
Einstein MS 700/7-8
19343 3rd Ave NW 98177 206-393-4730
Stephanie Clark-Lander, prin. Fax 393-4735
Kellogg MS 600/7-8
16045 25th Ave NE 98155 206-393-4783
Lisa Gonzalez Scott, prin. Fax 393-4780
Shorecrest HS 1,400/9-12
15343 25th Ave NE 98155 206-393-4286
Pat Hegarty, prin. Fax 393-4284
Shorewood HS 1,600/9-12
17300 Fremont Ave N 98133 206-393-4372
Bill Dunbar, prin. Fax 393-4711

Greenwood Academy of Hair Design Post-Sec.
18336 Aurora Ave N Ste 103 98133 206-542-1111
King's JHS 200/7-8
19345 Crista Ln N 98133 206-546-7243
Jordana Halkett, prin. Fax 546-7250
Shoreline Christian S 200/PK-12
2400 NE 147th St 98155 206-364-7777
Timothy Visser, admin. Fax 364-0349
Shoreline Community College Post-Sec.
16101 Greenwood Ave N 98133 206-546-4101

Silverdale, Kitsap, Pop. 17,925
Central Kitsap SD 401 11,200/K-12
PO Box 8 98383 360-662-1610
Gregory Lynch, supt. Fax 662-1611
www.cksd.wednet.edu
Career & Technical Education Vo/Tech
PO Box 8 98383 360-662-1605
John Cervinsky, dir. Fax 662-1601
Central Kitsap HS 1,300/10-12
PO Box 8 98383 360-662-2400
Steve Coons, prin. Fax 662-2401
Central Kitsap JHS 800/7-9
PO Box 8 98383 360-662-2300
Jeremy Monroe, prin. Fax 662-2301
Klahowya Secondary S 1,000/7-12
PO Box 8 98383 360-662-4000
Ryan Stevens, prin. Fax 662-4001
New Frontiers Alternative S 50/Alt
PO Box 8 98383 360-662-1570
Richard Arena, prin. Fax 662-1571
Ridgetop JHS 700/7-9
PO Box 8 98383 360-662-2900
Stuart Crisman, prin. Fax 662-2901
Westside Alternative HS 100/Alt
PO Box 8 98383 360-662-2570
Richard Arena, prin. Fax 662-2571
Other Schools – See Bremerton

Skykomish, King, Pop. 197
Skykomish SD 404 50/K-12
PO Box 325 98288 360-677-2623
Edwina Hargrave, supt. Fax 677-2418
www.skykomishschool.com
Skykomish JSHS 50/7-12
PO Box 325 98288 360-677-2623
Edwina Hargrave, admin. Fax 677-2418

Snohomish, Snohomish, Pop. 8,810
Monroe SD 103
Supt. — See Monroe
Hidden River MS 400/6-8
9224 Paradise Lake Rd 98296 360-804-4100
Linda Boyle, prin. Fax 804-4199

Snohomish SD 201 9,800/PK-12
1601 Avenue D 98290 360-563-7300
William Mester Ph.D., supt. Fax 563-7279
www.sno.wednet.edu
AIM HS 200/Alt
525 13th St 98290 360-563-3400
June Shirey, admin. Fax 862-9433
Centennial MS 900/7-8
3000 S Machias Rd 98290 360-563-4525
Dave Sage, prin. Fax 563-4585
Glacier Peak HS 1,500/9-12
7401 144th Pl SE 98296 360-563-7500
Jim Dean, prin. Fax 563-7631
Snohomish HS 1,700/9-12
1316 5th St 98290 360-563-4000
Beth Porter, prin. Fax 563-4183
Valley View MS 700/7-8
14308 Broadway Ave 98296 360-563-4225
Nancy Rhoades, prin. Fax 563-4236

Snoqualmie, King, Pop. 10,237
Snoqualmie Valley SD 410 6,100/PK-12
PO Box 400 98065 425-831-8000
Joel Aune, supt. Fax 831-8040
www.svsd410.org/
Mount Si HS 1,500/9-12
8651 Meadowbrook Way SE 98065 425-831-8100
John Belcher, prin. Fax 831-8222
Snoqualmie MS 400/6-8
9200 Railroad Ave SE 98065 425-831-8450
Vernie Newell, prin. Fax 831-8440
Other Schools – See Fall City, North Bend

Soap Lake, Grant, Pop. 1,484
Soap Lake SD 156 400/K-12
PO Box 158 98851 509-246-1822
Dan McDonald, supt. Fax 246-0669
www.slschools.org
Smokiam Alternative HS 100/Alt
PO Box 1269 98851 509-246-0572
Loris Blair, prin. Fax 246-0669
Soap Lake MSHS 200/6-12
PO Box 878 98851 509-246-1201
Kevin Kemp, prin. Fax 246-0669

South Bend, Pacific, Pop. 1,566
South Bend SD 118 600/PK-12
PO Box 437 98586 360-875-6041
Mike Morris, supt. Fax 875-6062
www.southbend.wednet.edu
South Bend JSHS 200/7-12
PO Box 437 98586 360-875-5707
Jason Nelson, prin. Fax 875-6036

Spanaway, Pierce, Pop. 24,048
Bethel SD 403 15,500/PK-12
516 176th St E 98387 253-683-6000
Tom Seigel, supt. Fax 683-6059
www.bethelsd.org
Bethel HS 1,100/9-12
22215 38th Ave E 98387 253-683-7000
Cliff Anderson, prin. Fax 683-7098
Bethel MS 400/7-8
22001 38th Ave E 98387 253-683-7200
Jeff Gutfeld, prin. Fax 683-7298
Cedarcrest MS 400/7-8
19120 13th Avenue Ct E 98387 253-683-7500
Cheryl Barnett, prin. Fax 683-7598
Challenger HS 300/Alt
18020 B St E 98387 253-683-6800
Dave LaBounty, prin. Fax 847-2530
Liberty MS 7-8
7319 Eustis Hunt Rd 98387 253-683-6500
Tom Mitchell, prin. Fax 683-6598
Spanaway Lake HS 1,200/9-12
1305 168th St E 98387 253-683-5600
Julie Baublits, prin. Fax 683-5698
Other Schools – See Graham, Puyallup, Tacoma

Spangle, Spokane, Pop. 277
Liberty SD 362 500/PK-12
29818 S North Pine Creek Rd 99031 509-624-4415
Bill Motsenbocker, supt. Fax 245-3288
www.libertysd.us
Liberty HS 200/9-12
6404 E Spangle Waverly Rd 99031 509-245-3229
Aaron Fletcher, prin. Fax 245-3205

Upper Columbia Academy 300/9-12
3025 E Spangle Waverly Rd 99031 509-245-3600

Spokane, Spokane, Pop. 199,521
Cheney SD 360
Supt. — See Cheney
Westwood MS 500/6-8
6120 S Abbott Rd 99224 509-559-4150
Dr. Erika Burden, prin.

Mead SD 354
Supt. — See Mead
Five Mile Prairie S Alt
8621 N Five Mile Rd 99208 509-465-7700
Bruce Olgard, prin. Fax 465-7720
M.E.A.D Alternative HS 100/Alt
529 W Hastings Rd 99218 509-465-6900
Bruce Olgard, prin. Fax 465-6920
Mead HS 1,600/9-12
302 W Hastings Rd 99218 509-465-7000
Ken Russell, prin. Fax 465-7020
Northwood MS 800/7-8
13120 N Pittsburg St 99208 509-465-7500
Dave Stenersen, prin. Fax 465-7520

Spokane SD 81 30,300/PK-12
200 N Bernard St 99201 509-354-5900
Shelley Redinger Ph.D., supt. Fax 354-5965
www.spokaneschools.org
ACE Alt
3754 W Indian Trail Rd 99208 509-328-7041
Sandi Skok, prin. Fax 328-7582
Bancroft Alternative S 100/Alt
1025 W Spofford Ave 99205 509-354-7100
Melinda Keberle, prin. Fax 354-7070
Chase MS 800/7-8
4747 E 37th Ave 99223 509-354-5000
John Andes, prin. Fax 354-5100
Crosswalk S 100/Alt
525 W 2nd Ave 99201 509-353-4368
Fred Schrumpf, prin. Fax 624-2275
Daybreak S 50/Alt
628 S Cowley St 99202 509-624-3227
Richard Miles, prin. Fax 835-4272
Ferris HS 1,600/9-12
3020 E 37th Ave 99223 509-354-6000
Kevin Foster, prin. Fax 354-6161
Garry MS 600/7-8
725 E Joseph Ave 99208 509-354-5200
Brenda McDonald, prin. Fax 354-5212
Glover MS 700/7-8
2404 W Longfellow Ave 99205 509-354-5400
Travis Schulhauser, prin. Fax 354-5399
Havermale HS 600/Alt
1300 W Knox Ave 99205 509-354-6409
Fred Schrumpf, prin. Fax 354-6400
Lewis & Clark HS 2,000/9-12
521 W 4th Ave 99204 509-354-7000
Shawn Jordan, prin. Fax 354-6969
Medicine Wheel Academy Alt
1300 W Knox Ave 99205 509-354-6477
Fred Schrumpf, prin. Fax 354-6400
North Central HS 1,400/9-12
1600 N Howard St 99205 509-354-6300
Christine Lynch, prin. Fax 354-6303
Northeast Washington Tech Ed Center Vo/Tech
4141 N Regal St 99207 509-354-7470
Dennis Conger, prin. Fax 354-7474
Rogers HS 1,700/9-12
1622 E Wellesley Ave 99207 509-354-6600
Lori Wyborney, prin. Fax 354-6665
Sacajawea MS 700/7-8
401 E 33rd Ave 99203 509-354-5500
Jeremy Ochse, prin. Fax 354-5505
Salk MS 700/7-8
6411 N Alberta St 99208 509-354-5600
Carole Meyer, prin. Fax 354-5542
Shadle Park HS 1,500/9-12
4327 N Ash St 99205 509-354-6700
Eric Sylling, prin. Fax 354-6710
Shaw MS 600/7-8
4106 N Cook St 99207 509-354-5800
Pete Hall, prin. Fax 354-5899
TEC at Bryant Alternative S 300/Alt
910 N Ash St 99201 509-354-7810
Gwen Harris, prin. Fax 354-7816

West Valley SD 363
Supt. — See Spokane Valley
West Valley HS 900/9-12
8301 E Buckeye Ave 99212 509-922-5488
Gary Neal, prin. Fax 928-3676

All Saints MS 200/PK-PK, 5-
1428 E 33rd Ave 99203 509-624-5712
Katherine Hicks, prin. Fax 624-7752
Carrington College Post-Sec.
10102 E Knox Ave Ste 200 99206 509-532-8888
Glen Dow Academy of Hair Design Post-Sec.
309 W Riverside Ave 99201 509-624-3244
Gonzaga Preparatory S 1,000/9-12
1224 E Euclid Ave 99207 509-483-8511
Cindy Reopelle, prin. Fax 483-3124
Gonzaga University Post-Sec.
502 E Boone Ave 99258 800-986-9585
Holy Family Hospital Post-Sec.
5633 N Lidgerwood St 99208 509-482-2450
Interface College Post-Sec.
178 S Stevens St 99201 509-467-1727
Northwest HVAC Training Center Post-Sec.
204 E Nora Ave 99207 509-747-8810
Palisades Christian Academy 100/PK-10
1115 N Government Way 99224 509-325-1985
Dr. Marvin Mitchell, prin. Fax 324-8904
Sacred Heart Medical Center Post-Sec.
101 W 8th Ave 99204 509-455-3040
St. George's S 400/K-12
2929 W Waikiki Rd 99208 509-466-1636
Joe Kennedy, hdmstr. Fax 467-3258
St. Patrick S 100/PK-PK, 6-
2706 E Queen Ave 99217 509-487-2830
Fax 484-3101
Slavic Christian Academy - Spokane 100/K-12
8913 N Nettleton Ln 99208 509-924-4618
Elena Solodyankin M.Ed., admin. Fax 467-4942
Spokane Community College Post-Sec.
1810 N Greene St 99217 509-533-7000
Spokane Falls Community College Post-Sec.
3410 W Fort George Wright 99224 509-533-3500
Whitworth University Post-Sec.
300 W Hawthorne Rd 99251 509-777-1000

Spokane Valley, Spokane, Pop. 87,059
Central Valley SD 356 12,400/PK-12
19307 E Cataldo Ave, 509-228-5400
Ben Small, supt. Fax 228-5409
www.cvsd.org
Barker HS and Learning Center 100/Alt
13313 E Broadway Ave, 509-228-4050
Keri Ames, prin. Fax 228-4059
Bowdish MS 500/6-8
2109 S Skipworth Rd, 509-228-4700
Dave Bouge, prin. Fax 228-4714
Central Valley HS 1,900/9-12
821 S Sullivan Rd, 509-228-5100
Mike Hittle, prin. Fax 228-5109
Evergreen MS 600/6-8
14221 E 16th Ave, 509-228-4780
John Parker, prin. Fax 228-4789
Greenacres MS 700/6-8
17409 E Sprague Ave, 509-228-4860
Vern DiGiovanni, prin. Fax 228-4869
Horizon MS 400/6-8
3915 S Pines Rd, 509-228-4940
Jesse Hardt, prin. Fax 228-4983
North Pines MS 500/6-8
701 N Pines Rd, 509-228-5020
Gordon Grassi, prin. Fax 228-5029
University HS 1,700/9-12
12420 E 32nd Ave, 509-228-5240
Alan Robbins, prin. Fax 228-5249

East Valley SD 361 3,600/K-12
12325 E Grace Ave, 509-924-1830
Dr. John Glenewinkel, supt. Fax 927-9500
www.evsd.org
East Valley HS 1,100/9-12
15711 E Wellesley Ave, 509-927-3200
Jim McAdam, prin. Fax 921-6830
Washington Academy of Arts & Technology 600/Alt
4920 N Progress Rd, 509-241-5001
Barbara Cruse, prin. Fax 921-5687

West Valley SD 363 3,600/PK-12
PO Box 11739 99211 509-924-2150
Dr. Gene Sementi, supt. Fax 922-5295
www.wvsd.com
Centennial MS 600/6-8
915 N Ella Rd, 509-922-5482
Karen Bromps, prin. Fax 891-9520
Dishman Hills HS 400/Alt
115 S University Rd Ste A, 509-927-1100
Julie Poage, prin. Fax 891-5052
Spokane Valley HS 100/9-12
2011 N Hutchinson Rd, 509-922-5475
Larry Bush, prin. Fax 922-5477
West Valley City MS 200/5-8
8920 E Valleyway Ave, 509-921-2836
Dusty Andres, prin. Fax 921-2849
Other Schools – See Spokane

ITT Technical Institute Post-Sec.
13518 E Indiana Ave, 509-926-2900
Valley Christian S 200/K-12
10212 E 9th Ave, 509-924-9131
Nathan Williams, admin. Fax 924-2971

Sprague, Lincoln, Pop. 438
Sprague SD 8 100/K-12
PO Box 305 99032 509-257-2591
Patrick Whipple, supt. Fax 257-2539
www.spraguelamont.com/
Sprague HS 50/9-12
PO Box 305 99032 509-257-2511
Patrick Whipple, prin. Fax 257-2539

Springdale, Stevens, Pop. 275
Mary Walker SD 207 400/PK-12
PO Box 159 99173 509-258-4534
Kevin Jacka, supt. Fax 258-4707
www.marywalker.org/
Springdale MS 100/6-8
PO Box 159 99173 509-258-7357
Matthew Cobb, prin. Fax 258-7756
Walker Alternative HS 50/Alt
PO Box 159 99173 509-258-4533
Matthew Cobb, prin. Fax 258-4555
Walker HS 200/9-12
PO Box 159 99173 509-258-4533
Matthew Cobb, prin. Fax 258-4555
Other Schools – See Valley

Stanwood, Snohomish, Pop. 6,009
Stanwood-Camano SD 401 5,000/K-12
26920 Pioneer Hwy 98292 360-629-1200
Dr. Jean Shumate, supt. Fax 629-1242
www.stanwood.wednet.edu
Lincoln Hill Academy 50/Alt
7600 272nd St NW 98292 360-629-1340
Maurene Stanton, prin. Fax 629-1341
Lincoln Hill HS 200/Alt
7400 272nd St NW 98292 360-629-1340
Maurene Stanton, prin. Fax 629-1341
Port Susan MS 500/6-8
7506 267th St NW 98292 360-629-1360
Dan Johnston, prin. Fax 629-1365
Saratoga S 100/Alt
9307 271st St NW 98292 360-629-1372
Curt Chester, lead tchr. Fax 629-1256
Stanwood HS 1,600/9-12
7400 272nd St NW 98292 360-629-1300
Christine Gruver, prin. Fax 629-1310
Stanwood MS 600/6-8
9405 271st St NW 98292 360-629-1350
Barbara Marsh, prin. Fax 629-1354

Steilacoom, Pierce, Pop. 5,521
Steilacoom Historical SD 1 2,900/PK-12
510 Chambers St 98388 253-983-2200
Kathi Weight, supt. Fax 584-7198
www.steilacoom.k12.wa.us
Steilacoom HS 800/9-12
54 Sentinel Dr 98388 253-983-2300
Debra Hay, prin. Fax 983-2393
Other Schools – See DuPont

Stevenson, Skamania, Pop. 1,431
Stevenson-Carson SD 303 1,400/K-12
PO Box 850 98648 509-427-5674
Dan Read, supt. Fax 427-4028
www.scsd.k12.wa.us
Stevenson HS 300/9-12
PO Box 850 98648 509-427-5631
Kim Meche, prin. Fax 427-5639
Wind River MS 100/7-8
PO Box 850 98648 509-427-5631
Kim Meche, prin. Fax 427-5639

Sultan, Snohomish, Pop. 4,514
Sultan SD 311 1,900/K-12
514 4th St 98294 360-793-9800
Dan Chaplik, supt. Fax 793-9890
www.sultan.k12.wa.us
Sky Valley Options Alternative HS 50/Alt
211 6th St 98294 360-793-9810
Sarita Whitmire-Skeith, prin. Fax 799-0486
Sultan HS 600/9-12
13715 310th Ave SE 98294 360-793-9860
Cal Johnson, prin. Fax 793-9864
Sultan MS 500/6-8
301 High Ave 98294 360-793-9850
Robin Briganti, prin. Fax 793-9859

Sumner, Pierce, Pop. 9,086
Sumner SD 320 8,100/K-12
1202 Wood Ave 98390 253-891-6000
Craig Spencer, supt. Fax 891-6097
www.sumner.wednet.edu
Sumner HS 1,300/9-12
1707 Main St 98390 253-891-5500
Bill Gaines, prin. Fax 891-5585
Sumner MS 700/6-8
1508 Willow St 98390 253-891-5000
Steve Sjolund, prin. Fax 891-5045
Other Schools – See Bonney Lake

Sunnyside, Yakima, Pop. 15,748
Sunnyside SD 201 6,200/K-12
1110 S 6th St 98944 509-837-5851
Dr. Richard Cole, supt. Fax 837-0535
www.sunnysideschools.org
Harrison MS 700/6-8
810 S 16th St 98944 509-837-3601
Robert Bowman, prin. Fax 837-0450
Sierra Vista MS 700/6-8
916 N 16th St 98944 509-836-8500
Doug Rogers, prin. Fax 836-8515
Sunnyside HS 1,700/9-12
1801 E Edison Ave 98944 509-837-2601
Ryan Maxwell, prin. Fax 837-0494

Sunnyside Christian HS 100/9-12
1820 Sheller Rd 98944 509-837-8995
Dean Wagenaar, prin. Fax 837-8895

Tacoma, Pierce, Pop. 182,594
Bethel SD 403
Supt. — See Spanaway
Spanaway MS 500/7-8
15701 B St E 98445 253-683-5400
Tami Nelson, prin. Fax 683-5498

Fife SD 417 3,500/PK-12
5802 20th St E 98424 253-517-1000
John McCrossin, supt. Fax 517-1055
district.fifeschools.com
Fife HS 800/10-12
5616 20th St E 98424 253-517-1100
Amanda Fox, prin. Fax 517-1105
Learning Opportunity Center 50/Alt
5802 20th St E 98424 253-517-1130
Chris Carnrite, coord.
Other Schools – See Fife

Franklin Pierce SD 402 7,400/PK-12
315 129th St S 98444 253-298-3000
Dr. Frank Hewins, supt. Fax 298-3015
www.fpschools.org
Ford MS 900/6-8
1602 104th St E 98445 253-298-3600
Heather Renner, prin. Fax 298-3615
Gates HS 200/Alt
813 132nd St S 98444 253-298-4000
Val Jones, prin. Fax 298-4015
Keithley MS 800/6-8
12324 12th Ave S 98444 253-298-4300
Tom Edwards, prin. Fax 298-4315
New Pathways/iSchool Alt
9516 Waller Rd E 98446 253-298-4080
Val Jones, prin. Fax 298-4083
Pierce HS 1,200/9-12
11002 18th Ave E 98445 253-298-3800
Jennifer Shaw, prin. Fax 298-3814
Washington HS 1,000/9-12
12420 Ainsworth Ave S 98444 253-298-4700
James Hester, prin. Fax 298-4715

Tacoma SD 10 26,400/PK-12
PO Box 1357 98401 253-571-1000
Dr. Arthur Jarvis, supt. Fax 571-1440
www.tacoma.k12.wa.us
Baker MS 600/6-8
8001 S J St 98408 253-571-5000
Steve Holmes, prin. Fax 571-5090
First Creek MS 800/6-8
1801 E 56th St 98404 253-571-2700
Brad Brown, prin. Fax 571-2717
Foss HS 1,100/9-12
2112 S Tyler St 98405 253-571-7300
Bonnie McGuire, prin. Fax 571-7460
Giaudrone MS 500/6-8
4902 S Alaska St 98408 253-571-5811
Zeek Edmond, prin. Fax 571-5812
Gray MS 600/6-8
6229 S Tyler St 98409 253-571-5200
Brenda McBrayer, prin. Fax 571-5201
Lee MS 400/6-8
602 N Sprague Ave 98403 253-571-7700
Jon Kellett, prin. Fax 571-7710
Lincoln HS 1,400/9-12
701 S 37th St 98418 253-571-6700
Patrick Erwin, prin. Fax 571-6789
Mason MS 800/6-8
3901 N 28th St 98407 253-571-7000
Patrice Sulkosky, prin. Fax 571-7091
Meeker MS 700/6-8
4402 Nassau Ave NE 98422 253-571-6500
Christine Brandt, prin. Fax 571-6503
Mount Tahoma HS 1,500/9-12
4634 S 74th St 98409 253-571-3800
Kevin Kannier, prin. Fax 571-3801
Oakland Alternative HS 200/Alt
3319 S Adams St 98409 253-571-5100
Thu Ament, prin. Fax 571-5101
Science and Math Institute 200/9-12
5501 N Pearl St 98407 253-571-2300
Jon Ketler, prin. Fax 571-2310
Stadium HS 1,600/9-12
111 N E St 98403 253-571-3100
Kevin Ikeda, prin. Fax 571-3101
Stewart MS 500/6-8
5010 Pacific Ave 98408 253-571-4200
Janet Gates-Cortez, prin. Fax 571-4244
Tacoma Business Academy 50/Alt
1101 Yakima Ave 98405 253-680-7000
Rue Palmer, admin. Fax 680-7239
Tacoma School of the Arts 500/9-12
1102 A St 98402 253-571-7900
Jon Ketler, dir. Fax 571-7901
Truman MS 700/6-8
5801 N 35th St 98407 253-571-5600
Justina Johnson, prin. Fax 571-5680
Wilson HS 1,400/9-12
1202 N Orchard St 98406 253-571-6000
Dan Besett, prin. Fax 571-6162

Bates Technical College Post-Sec.
1101 Yakima Ave 98405 253-680-7000
Bellarmine Prep S 1,000/9-12
2300 S Washington St 98405 253-752-7701
Chris Gavin, prin. Fax 756-3887
BJ's Beauty & Barber College Post-Sec.
5239 S Tacoma Way 98409 253-473-4320
Corban University School of Ministry Post-Sec.
4301 N Stevens St 98407 253-759-6104
Covenant HS 100/9-12
620 S Shirley St 98465 253-759-9570
Richard Hannula, prin. Fax 759-1377
Everest College Post-Sec.
2156 Pacific Ave 98402 253-207-4000
Faith Evangelical College & Seminary Post-Sec.
3504 N Pearl St 98407 253-752-2020
Life Christian Academy 800/PK-12
1717 S Union Ave 98405 253-756-5300
Mount Rainier Lutheran HS 100/9-12
7306 Waller Rd E 98443 253-284-4433
Sarah Elliott, prin. Fax 284-4435
Pacific Lutheran University Post-Sec.
12180 Park Ave S 98447 253-531-6900
Slavic Christian Academy - Tacoma 100/PK-10
2014 S 15th St 98405 253-359-0608
Alex Slobodyanik, prin.
Tacoma Baptist S 400/PK-12
2052 S 64th St 98409 253-475-7226
Debbie Schindler, supt. Fax 471-9949
Tacoma Community College Post-Sec.
6501 S 19th St 98466 253-566-5000
University of Puget Sound Post-Sec.
1500 N Warner St 98416 253-879-3100
Wright S 400/PK-12
827 N Tacoma Ave 98403 253-272-2216
Christian Sullivan, head sch Fax 572-3616

Taholah, Grays Harbor, Pop. 818
Taholah SD 77 100/PK-12
PO Box 249 98587 360-276-4780
Lyn Roberts, supt. Fax 276-4370
www.taholah.org
Taholah S 100/PK-12
PO Box 249 98587 360-276-4729
Scott Stockslager, prin. Fax 276-4370

Tekoa, Whitman, Pop. 764
Tekoa SD 265 200/PK-12
PO Box 869 99033 509-284-3281
Dr. Connie Kliewer, supt. Fax 284-2045
www.tekoa.wednet.edu
Tekoa JSHS 100/7-12
PO Box 869 99033 509-284-3401
Daniel Hutton, prin. Fax 284-5802

Tenino, Thurston, Pop. 1,631
Tenino SD 402 1,300/PK-12
PO Box 4024 98589 360-264-3400
Russ Pickett, supt. Fax 264-3438
www.teninoschools.org/
Tenino HS 400/9-12
PO Box 4024 98589 360-264-3500
David Chappell, prin. Fax 264-3538
Tenino MS 300/6-8
PO Box 4024 98589 360-264-3600
Sharon Connally, prin. Fax 264-3638

Thorp, Kittitas, Pop. 235
Thorp SD 400 200/PK-12
PO Box 150 98946 509-964-2107
Dr. Linda Martin, supt. Fax 964-2313
www.thorpschools.org/
Thorp S 200/PK-12
PO Box 150 98946 509-964-2107
Dr. Linda Martin, prin. Fax 964-2313

Toledo, Lewis, Pop. 712
Toledo SD 237 800/PK-12
PO Box 469 98591 360-864-6325
Sharon Bower, supt. Fax 864-6326
www.toledo.k12.wa.us
Toledo HS 300/9-12
PO Box 820 98591 360-864-2391
Martin Huffman, prin. Fax 864-2396
Toledo MS 200/6-8
PO Box 668 98591 360-864-2395
Bill Waag, prin. Fax 864-8147

Tonasket, Okanogan, Pop. 1,010
Tonasket SD 404 1,200/PK-12
35 Highway 20 98855 509-486-2126
Paul Turner, supt. Fax 486-1263
www.tonasket.wednet.edu
Tonasket Alternative HS 100/Alt
35 Highway 20 98855 509-486-1428
Chelsea Freeman, lead tchr.
Tonasket HS 400/9-12
35 Highway 20 98855 509-486-2161
Jeff Hardesty, prin. Fax 486-4382
Tonasket MS 200/6-8
35 Highway 20 98855 509-486-2147
Jay Tyus, prin. Fax 486-1576

Toppenish, Yakima, Pop. 8,831
Toppenish SD 202 3,500/PK-12
306 Bolin Dr 98948 509-865-4455
John M. Cerna, supt. Fax 865-2067
www.toppenish.wednet.edu/
EAGLE Alternative HS 300/Alt
143 Ward Rd 98948 509-865-3377
Deborah Crinzi, prin. Fax 865-7327
Toppenish HS 700/9-12
141 Ward Rd 98948 509-865-3370
Trevor Greene, prin. Fax 865-3244
Toppenish MS 700/6-8
104 Goldendale Ave 98948 509-865-2730
Dawn Weddle, prin. Fax 865-7503

Heritage University Post-Sec.
3240 Fort Rd 98948 509-865-8500

Touchet, Walla Walla, Pop. 415
Touchet SD 300 300/K-12
PO Box 135 99360 509-394-2352
Susan Bell, supt. Fax 394-2952
www.touchet.k12.wa.us
Touchet JSHS 200/5-12
PO Box 135 99360 509-394-2352
Elissa Tinder, prin. Fax 394-2952

Toutle, Cowlitz
Toutle Lake SD 130 600/K-12
5050 Spirit Lake Hwy 98649 360-274-6182
Scott Grabenhorst, supt. Fax 274-7608
www.toutlesd.k12.wa.us
Toutle Lake JSHS 300/7-12
5050 Spirit Lake Hwy 98649 360-274-6132
Greg McDaniel, prin. Fax 274-7608

Trout Lake, Klickitat, Pop. 545
Trout Lake SD R-400 100/K-12
PO Box 488 98650 509-395-2571
Doug Dearden, supt. Fax 395-2399
www.troutlake.k12.wa.us/
Trout Lake JSHS 100/5-12
PO Box 488 98650 509-395-2571
Doug Dearden, prin. Fax 395-2399

Tukwila, King, Pop. 17,643
Tukwila SD 406 2,900/K-12
4640 S 144th St 98168 206-901-8000
Dr. Mellody Matthes, supt. Fax 901-8016
www.tukwila.wednet.edu
Foster HS 900/9-12
4242 S 144th St 98168 206-901-7900
Dr. Forrest Griek, prin. Fax 901-7907
Showalter MS 700/6-8
4628 S 144th St 98168 206-901-7800
Brett Christopher, prin. Fax 901-7807

Le Cordon Bleu College of Culinary Arts Post-Sec.
360 Corporate Dr N 98188 407-888-4000

Tumwater, Thurston, Pop. 16,544
Tumwater SD 33 6,100/K-12
621 Linwood Ave SW 98512 360-709-7000
Mike Kirby, supt. Fax 709-7002
www.tumwater.k12.wa.us
Bush MS 500/7-8
2120 83rd Ave SW 98512 360-709-7400
Linda O'Shaughnessy, prin. Fax 709-7402
New Market Skills Center Vo/Tech
7299 New Market St SW 98501 360-570-4500
Kris Blum, prin. Fax 570-4502
Tumwater HS 1,100/9-12
700 Israel Rd SW 98501 360-709-7600
Jeff Broome, prin. Fax 709-7602
Tumwater MS 500/7-8
6335 Littlerock Rd SW 98512 360-709-7500
Jon Wilcox, prin. Fax 709-7502
Other Schools – See Olympia

Twisp, Okanogan, Pop. 890
Methow Valley SD 350
Supt. — See Winthrop
Methow Valley Independent Learning Ctr 50/Alt
220 Highway 20 98856 509-997-8006
Deborah Dekalb, prin. Fax 997-5980

Union Gap, Yakima, Pop. 5,960

La Salle HS 200/9-12
3000 Lightning Way 98903 509-225-2900
Ted Kanelopoulos, prin. Fax 225-2950

University Place, Pierce, Pop. 28,698
University Place SD 83 5,500/K-12
3717 Grandview Dr W 98466 253-566-5600
Patricia Banks, supt. Fax 566-5607
www.upsd.wednet.edu
Curtis JHS 1,000/8-9
3725 Grandview Dr W 98466 253-566-5670
Jeff Chamberlin, prin. Fax 566-5644
Curtis SHS 1,400/10-12
8425 40th St W 98466 253-566-5710
David Hammond, prin. Fax 566-5626

Wright Academy 700/PK-12
7723 Chambers Creek Rd W 98467 253-620-8300
Robert Camner, hdmstr. Fax 620-8431

Valley, Stevens, Pop. 135
Mary Walker SD 207
Supt. — See Springdale
Springdale Academy Alt
PO Box 158 99181 509-937-2224
John Axtell, coord.

Valley SD 070 1,100/K-12
3030 Huffman Rd 99181 509-937-2791
Dr. Mark Selle, supt. Fax 937-2691
www.valleysd.org/
Paideia HS 50/9-12
3043 Huffman Rd 99181 509-937-2655
Matthew Cox, prin. Fax 937-2656

Vancouver, Clark, Pop. 153,919
Battle Ground SD 119
Supt. — See Brush Prairie
Laurin MS 700/5-8
13601 NE 97th Ave 98662 360-885-5200
Nick Krause, prin. Fax 885-5205
Pleasant Valley MS 400/5-8
14320 NE 50th Ave 98686 360-885-5500
Travis Drake, prin. Fax 885-5510
Prairie HS 1,400/9-12
11500 NE 117th Ave 98662 360-885-5000
Jason Perrins, prin. Fax 885-5050

Evergreen SD 114 25,500/K-12
PO Box 8910 98668 360-604-4000
John Deeder, supt. Fax 892-5307
www.evergreenps.org/
Cascade MS 900/6-8
PO Box 8910 98668 360-604-3600
Lisa Wagner, prin. Fax 604-3602
Clark County Skills Center Vo/Tech
PO Box 8910 98668 360-604-1050
Dennis Kampe, dir. Fax 604-1052

Covington MS 1,100/6-8
PO Box 8910 98668 360-604-6300
Byron Molle, prin. Fax 604-6302
Evergreen HS 1,800/9-12
PO Box 8910 98668 360-604-3700
Lisa Emmerich, prin. Fax 604-3702
Frontier MS 1,000/6-8
PO Box 8910 98668 360-604-3200
Maria Stevens, prin. Fax 604-3202
Heritage HS 2,000/9-12
PO Box 8910 98668 360-604-3400
Mark Ross, prin. Fax 604-3402
Legacy HS 200/Alt
PO Box 8910 98668 360-604-3900
Michele DeShaw, coord. Fax 604-3902
Mountain View HS 1,700/9-12
PO Box 8910 98668 360-604-6100
Mike Meloy, prin. Fax 604-6102
Pacific MS 1,100/6-8
PO Box 8910 98668 360-604-6500
Kathy Stellfox, prin. Fax 604-6502
Shahala MS 1,100/6-8
PO Box 8910 98668 360-604-3800
Renee Bernazzani, prin. Fax 604-3802
Wy' East MS 900/6-8
PO Box 8910 98668 360-604-6400
Caroline Garrett, prin. Fax 604-6402
Other Schools – See Camas

Vancouver SD 37 22,000/K-12
PO Box 8937 98668 360-313-1000
Dr. Steven Webb, supt. Fax 313-1001
www.vansd.org
Alki MS 700/6-8
1800 NW Bliss Rd 98685 360-313-3200
Curtis Smith, prin. Fax 313-3201
Columbia River HS 1,300/9-12
800 NW 99th St 98665 360-313-3900
Alex Otoupal, prin. Fax 313-3901
Discovery MS 800/6-8
800 E 40th St 98663 360-313-3300
Chris Olsen, prin. Fax 313-3301
Fir Grove Childrens Center 100/Alt
2920 Falk Rd 98661 360-313-1800
Daniel Bettis, prin. Fax 313-1801
Ft. Vancouver HS 1,400/9-12
5700 E 18th St 98661 360-313-4000
Scott Parker, prin. Fax 313-4001
Gaiser MS 900/6-8
3000 NE 99th St 98665 360-313-3400
Mike Lane, prin. Fax 313-3401
Hudson's Bay HS 1,500/9-12
1601 E McLoughlin Blvd 98663 360-313-4400
Bill Oman, prin. Fax 313-4401
Jefferson MS 800/6-8
3000 NW 119th St 98685 360-313-3700
Tom Adams, prin. Fax 313-3701
Lee MS 600/6-8
8500 NW 9th Ave 98665 360-313-3500
Curt Scheidel, prin. Fax 313-3501
Lewis and Clark HS 300/Alt
2901 General Anderson Rd 98661 360-313-4350
Rob Duncan, prin. Fax 313-4351
McLoughlin MS 800/6-8
5802 MacArthur Blvd 98661 360-313-3600
Jody ViDelco, prin. Fax 313-3601
School of Arts & Academics 600/6-12
3101 Main St 98663 360-313-4600
James O'Banion, prin. Fax 313-4601
Skyview HS 2,000/9-12
1300 NW 139th St 98685 360-313-4200
Kym Tyelyn-Carlson, prin. Fax 313-4201

Charter College Vancouver Post-Sec.
17200 SE Mill Plain Ste 100 98683 360-448-2000
Clark College Post-Sec.
1933 Fort Vancouver Way 98663 360-992-2000
Everest College Post-Sec.
120 NE 136th Ave Ste 130 98684 360-254-3282
International Air & Hospitality Academy Post-Sec.
2901 E Mill Plain Blvd 98661 360-695-2500
King's Way Christian S 800/PK-12
3300 NE 78th St 98665 360-574-1613
Mike Brown, supt. Fax 573-5895
School of Piano Technology for the Blind Post-Sec.
2510 E Evergreen Blvd 98661 360-693-1511
Seton Catholic HS 9-12
811 NE 112th Ave 98684 360-258-1932
Ed Little, prin. Fax 258-1936
Washington State School for the Blind Post-Sec.
2214 E 13th St 98661
Washington State School for the Deaf Post-Sec.
611 Grand Blvd 98661

Vashon, King, Pop. 10,291
Vashon Island SD 402 1,500/PK-12
PO Box 547 98070 206-463-2121
Michael Soltman, supt. Fax 463-6262
www.vashonsd.org
McMurray MS 400/6-8
9329 SW Cemetery Rd 98070 206-463-9168
Greg Allison, prin. Fax 463-9707
Vashon Island HS 500/9-12
20120 Vashon Hwy SW 98070 206-463-9171
Susan Hanson, prin. Fax 463-1944

Waitsburg, Walla Walla, Pop. 1,189
Waitsburg SD 401-100 300/K-12
PO Box 217 99361 509-337-6301
Dr. Carol Clarke, supt. Fax 337-6042
www.waitsburgsd.org/
Preston Hall MS 100/7-8
PO Box 217 99361 509-337-9474
Stephanie Wooderchak, prin. Fax 337-6170
Waitsburg HS 100/9-12
PO Box 217 99361 509-337-6351
Stephanie Wooderchak, prin. Fax 337-6551

Walla Walla, Walla Walla, Pop. 30,829
Walla Walla SD 140 6,000/PK-12
364 S Park St 99362 509-527-3000
Mick Miller, supt. Fax 529-7713
www.wwps.org
Garrison MS 600/6-8
906 Chase Ave 99362 509-527-3040
Gina Yonts, prin. Fax 527-3048
Lincoln Alternative HS Alt
421 S 4th Ave 99362 509-527-3083
Jim Sporleder, prin. Fax 527-3011
Pioneer MS 600/6-8
450 Bridge St 99362 509-527-3050
Mira Gobel, prin. Fax 526-5212
Walla Walla HS 2,000/9-12
800 Abbott Rd 99362 509-527-3020
Pete Peterson, prin. Fax 527-3034

DeSales HS 100/8-12
919 E Sumach St 99362 509-525-3030
John Lesko, prin. Fax 527-0361
Walla Walla Community College Post-Sec.
500 Tausick Way 99362 509-522-2500
Whitman College Post-Sec.
345 Boyer Ave 99362 509-527-5111

Wapato, Yakima, Pop. 4,948
Wapato SD 207 3,400/K-12
PO Box 38 98951 509-877-4181
Becky Imler, supt. Fax 877-6077
www.wapatosd.org
Pace Alternative HS 100/Alt
310 S Wasco Ave 98951 509-877-6138
Gary Babcock, prin. Fax 877-6164
Wapato HS 900/9-12
1103 S Wasco Ave 98951 509-877-3138
Eric Diener, prin. Fax 877-4334
Wapato MS 800/6-8
1309 Kateri Ln 98951 509-877-2173
Karen Harrington, prin. Fax 877-6232

Warden, Grant, Pop. 2,646
Warden SD 146-161 1,000/K-12
101 W Beck Way 98857 509-349-2366
Dr. David LaBounty, supt. Fax 349-2367
www.warden.wednet.edu
Warden HS 300/9-12
101 W Beck Way 98857 509-349-2581
Chris Rust, prin. Fax 349-2531
Warden MS 200/6-8
101 W Beck Way 98857 509-349-2902
Chris McKnight, prin. Fax 349-2531

Washougal, Clark, Pop. 13,617
Washougal SD 112-6 3,000/K-12
4855 Evergreen Way 98671 360-954-3000
Dawn Tarzian, supt. Fax 835-7776
www.washougal.k12.wa.us
Canyon Creek MS 300/6-8
9731 Washougal River Rd 98671 360-954-3500
Sandi Christensen, prin. Fax 837-1500
Excelsior HS 100/Alt
1401 39th St 98671 360-954-3300
Aaron Hansen, prin. Fax 835-1182
Jemtegaard MS 400/6-8
35300 SE Evergreen Hwy 98671 360-954-3400
David Cooke, prin. Fax 835-9145
Washougal HS 900/9-12
1201 39th St 98671 360-954-3100
Aaron Hansen, prin. Fax 835-3968

Washtucna, Adams, Pop. 206
Washtucna SD 109-43 100/K-12
PO Box 688 99371 509-646-3237
Robert Allen, supt. Fax 646-3249
www.tucna.wednet.edu
Washtucna S 100/K-12
PO Box 688 99371 509-646-3237
Glenn Martin, prin. Fax 646-3249

Waterville, Douglas, Pop. 1,124
Waterville SD 209 300/K-12
PO Box 490 98858 509-745-8584
Cathi Nelson, supt. Fax 745-9073
www.waterville.wednet.edu/
Waterville JSHS 200/7-12
PO Box 490 98858 509-745-8583
Tabatha Mires, dean Fax 745-9073

Wellpinit, Stevens
Wellpinit SD 49 500/K-12
PO Box 390 99040 509-258-4535
Tim Ames, supt. Fax 258-4065
www.wellpinit.org
Wellpinit Alliance HS 50/Alt
PO Box 390 99040 509-258-4535
Shelley Sonnabend, dir. Fax 258-8959
Wellpinit HS 100/9-12
PO Box 390 99040 509-258-4535
Terry Bartolino, prin. Fax 258-7378
Wellpinit MS 100/6-8
PO Box 390 99040 509-258-4535
Terry Bartolino, prin. Fax 258-7378
Other Schools – See Moses Lake, White Swan

Wenatchee, Chelan, Pop. 31,295
Wenatchee SD 246 7,300/K-12
PO Box 1767 98807 509-663-8161
Brian Flones, supt. Fax 663-3082
home.wsd.wednet.edu
Foothills MS 600/6-8
1410 Maple St 98801 509-664-8961
Mark Goveia, prin. Fax 663-6610
Orchard MS 500/6-8
1024 Orchard Ave 98801 509-662-7745
Mike Hopkins, prin. Fax 663-8042
Pioneer MS 600/6-8
1620 Russell St 98801 509-663-7171
Mark Helm, prin. Fax 663-0453
Wenatchee HS 2,100/9-12
1101 Millerdale Ave 98801 509-663-8117
Mike Franza, prin. Fax 663-2573
Wenatchee Valley Technical Skills Center Vo/Tech
327 E Penny Rd Ste D 98801 509-662-8827
Jon Torrence, dir. Fax 662-5993
Westside HS 200/Alt
PO Box 1767 98807 509-663-7947
Kory Kalahar, prin. Fax 664-3005

Academy of Hair Design Post-Sec.
208 S Wenatchee Ave 98801 509-662-9082
Cascade Christian Academy 100/PK-12
600 N Western Ave 98801 509-662-2723
Stephanie Gates, prin. Fax 662-5892
River Academy 200/PK-12
PO Box 4485 98807 509-665-2415
Eric DeVries, hdmstr. Fax 662-9235
Wenatchee Valley College Post-Sec.
1300 5th St 98801 509-682-6800

Westport, Grays Harbor, Pop. 2,036
Ocosta SD 172 700/PK-12
2580 S Montesano St 98595 360-268-9125
Dr. Paula Akerlund, supt. Fax 268-2540
Ocosta JSHS 300/7-12
2580 S Montesano St 98595 360-268-9125
Brian Hunter, prin. Fax 268-0908

West Richland, Benton, Pop. 11,498
Richland SD 400
Supt. — See Richland
Enterprise MS 900/6-8
5200 Paradise Dr 99353 509-967-6200
Jennifer Klauss, prin. Fax 967-5685

White Salmon, Klickitat, Pop. 2,180
White Salmon Valley SD 405-17 1,200/K-12
PO Box 157 98672 509-493-1500
Dr. Jerry Lewis, supt. Fax 493-2275
www.whitesalmonschools.org/
Columbia HS 400/9-12
PO Box 1339 98672 509-493-1970
Troy Whittle, prin. Fax 493-4182
Henkle MS 300/5-8
PO Box 1309 98672 509-493-1502
Rick George, prin. Fax 493-3385
White Salmon Valley Academy 50/Alt
PO Box 157 98672 509-493-1500
Troy Whittle, prin.

White Swan, Yakima, Pop. 779
Mount Adams SD 209 1,000/PK-12
PO Box 578 98952 509-874-2611
Henry Strom, supt. Fax 874-2960
www.mtadams.wednet.edu
Mount Adams MS 200/7-8
PO Box 578 98952 509-874-8626
Dana Jarnecke, prin. Fax 874-2646
White Swan HS 300/9-12
PO Box 578 98952 509-874-2324
Dana Jarnecke, prin. Fax 874-2646

Wellpinit SD 49
Supt. — See Wellpinit
Fort Simcoe S 100/Alt
40 Abella Ln 98952 509-874-8900
Shelley Sonnabend, dir. Fax 874-2004

Wilbur, Lincoln, Pop. 857
Wilbur SD 200 300/K-12
PO Box 1090 99185 509-647-2221
Steve Gaub, supt. Fax 647-2509
www.wilbur.wednet.edu
Wilbur JSHS 100/7-12
PO Box 1090 99185 509-647-5602
Thomas Johnson, prin. Fax 647-2509

Wilson Creek, Grant, Pop. 198
Wilson Creek SD 167-202 100/K-12
PO Box 46 98860 509-345-2541
Brad Smedley, supt. Fax 345-2288
www.wilsoncreek.org
Wilson Creek JSHS 100/7-12
PO Box 46 98860 509-345-2541
Brad Smedley, prin. Fax 345-2288

Winlock, Lewis, Pop. 1,291
Winlock SD 232 800/PK-12
311 NW Fir St 98596 360-785-3582
Shannon Criss, supt. Fax 785-3583
www.winlock.wednet.edu
APOLO Alternative S 100/Alt
311 NW Fir St 98596 360-785-3582
Brian Maley, prin. Fax 785-3583
Winlock HS 200/9-12
241 N Military Rd 98596 360-785-3537
Brian Maley, prin. Fax 785-3538
Winlock MS 200/6-8
241 N Military Rd 98596 360-785-3046
Brian Maley, prin. Fax 785-3047

Winthrop, Okanogan, Pop. 390
Methow Valley SD 350 500/PK-12
18 Twin Lakes Rd 98862 509-996-9205
Tom Venable, supt. Fax 996-9208
www.methow.org
Liberty Bell JSHS 200/7-12
18 Twin Lakes Rd 98862 509-996-2215
Deborah Dekalb, prin. Fax 996-3609
Other Schools – See Twisp

Wishram, Klickitat, Pop. 339
Wishram SD 94 100/PK-12
PO Box 8 98673 509-748-2551
Duane Grams, supt. Fax 748-2127
www.wishramschool.org
Wishram S 100/PK-12
PO Box 8 98673 509-748-2551
Duane Grams, prin. Fax 748-2127

Woodinville, King, Pop. 10,516

Northshore SD 417
Supt. — See Bothell

Leota JHS 700/7-9
19301 168th Ave NE 98072 425-408-6500
Obadiah Dunham, prin. Fax 408-6502

Timbercrest JHS 800/7-9
19115 215th Way NE, 425-408-6900
Heather Miller, prin. Fax 408-6902

Woodinville SHS 1,300/10-12
19819 136th Ave NE 98072 425-408-7400
Kurt Criscione, prin. Fax 408-7402

Chrysalis S 200/K-12
14241 NE Woodinville Duvall 98072 425-481-2228
Karen Fogle, dir. Fax 486-8107

Woodland, Cowlitz, Pop. 5,391

Woodland SD 404 2,200/PK-12
800 3rd St 98674 360-841-2700
Michael Green, supt. Fax 841-2701
www.woodlandschools.org/

Woodland HS 600/9-12
757 Park St 98674 360-841-2800
John Shoup, prin. Fax 841-2801

Woodland MS 300/7-8
755 Park St 98674 360-841-2850
Cari Thomson Ph.D., prin. Fax 841-2851

Woodland TEAM HS 100/Alt
800 3rd St 98674 360-841-2800
Dan Uhlenkott, dir. Fax 841-2801

West Coast Training Post-Sec.
PO Box 970 98674 360-225-6787

Yakima, Yakima, Pop. 89,018

East Valley SD 90 2,900/K-12
2002 Beaudry Rd 98901 509-573-7300
John Schieche, supt. Fax 573-7340
www.evsd90.org

East Valley Central MS 700/6-8
2010 Beaudry Rd 98901 509-573-7500
Jeri Young, prin. Fax 573-7540

East Valley HS 900/9-12
1900 Beaudry Rd 98901 509-573-7400
Dorthea Say, prin. Fax 573-7440

West Valley SD 208 4,900/K-12
8902 Zier Rd 98908 509-972-6000
Dr. Michael Brophy, supt. Fax 972-6001
www.wvsd208.org

West Valley Freshman Campus 400/9-9
9206 Zier Rd 98908 509-972-5600
Bill Oppliger, prin. Fax 972-5601

West Valley HS 1,100/10-12
9800 Zier Rd 98908 509-972-5900
Bill Oppliger, prin. Fax 972-5901

West Valley JHS 800/7-8
7505 Zier Rd 98908 509-966-5800
Jim Fannin, prin. Fax 972-5801

Yakima SD 7 15,100/PK-12
104 N 4th Ave 98902 509-573-7000
Dr. Elaine Beraza, supt. Fax 573-7181
www.yakimaschools.org/

Davis HS 2,100/9-12
212 S 6th Ave 98902 509-573-2500
Ben Ramirez, prin. Fax 573-2525

Eisenhower HS 2,100/9-12
702 S 40th Ave 98908 509-573-2600
Stacey Locke, prin. Fax 573-2626

Franklin MS 800/6-8
410 S 19th Ave 98902 509-573-2100
Bill Hilton, prin. Fax 573-2121

Lewis & Clark MS 700/6-8
1114 W Pierce St 98902 509-573-2200
Victor Nourani, prin. Fax 573-2222

Stanton Academy 300/Alt
802 River Rd 98902 509-573-1200
Clinton Endicott, prin. Fax 573-1212

Washington MS 700/6-8
510 S 9th St 98901 509-573-2300
Dave Chaplin, prin. Fax 573-2323

Wilson MS 800/6-8
902 S 44th Ave 98908 509-573-2400
Ernesto Araiza, prin. Fax 573-2424

Yakima Valley Technical Skills Center Vo/Tech
1120 S 18th St 98901 509-573-5500
Craig Dwight, prin. Fax 834-2041

Pacific Northwest Univ of Health Science Post-Sec.
111 University Pkwy Ste 202 98901 509-452-5100

Perry Technical Institute Post-Sec.
2011 W Washington Ave 98903 509-453-0374

Professional Beauty School Post-Sec.
PO Box 9243 98909 509-877-6443

Riverside Christian S 500/PK-12
721 Keys Rd 98901 509-965-2602
Rick Van Beek, admin. Fax 966-7031

Westpark Christian Academy 100/PK-12
3902 Summitview Ave 98902 509-966-1632
Rev. Colleen Sheahan, admin. Fax 966-6282

Yakima Adventist Christian S 100/K-10
1200 City Reservoir Rd 98908 509-966-1933

Yakima Valley Community College Post-Sec.
PO Box 22520 98907 509-574-4600

Yelm, Thurston, Pop. 6,363

Yelm Community SD 2 5,500/PK-12
PO Box 476 98597 360-458-1900
Andy Wolf, supt. Fax 458-6178
www.ycs.wednet.edu

Ridgeline MS 600/7-9
PO Box 476 98597 360-458-1100
John Johnson, prin. Fax 400-1256

Yelm Extension S 200/Alt
PO Box 476 98597 360-458-2002
Brian Wharton, admin. Fax 458-6146

Yelm HS 1,200/10-12
PO Box 476 98597 360-458-7777
Brian Wharton, prin. Fax 458-6198

Yelm MS 700/7-9
PO Box 476 98597 360-458-3600
Heidi Bunker, prin. Fax 458-6122

Eagle View Christian S 100/PK-12
13036 Morris Rd SE 98597 360-458-3090
Barbara Ballou, prin. Fax 458-4990

Zillah, Yakima, Pop. 2,907

Zillah SD 205 1,400/PK-12
213 4th Ave 98953 509-829-5911
Kevin McKay, supt. Fax 829-6290
www.zillahschools.org/

Zillah HS 400/9-12
1602 2nd Ave 98953 509-829-5565
Mike Torres, prin. Fax 829-5285

Zillah MS 200/7-8
1301 Cutler Way 98953 509-829-5511
Justin Irion, prin. Fax 829-0754

WEST VIRGINIA

WEST VIRGINIA DEPARTMENT OF EDUCATION
1900 Kanawha Blvd E Rm 358, Charleston 25305-0330
Telephone 304-558-2681
Fax 304-558-0048
Website wvde.state.wv.us

State Superintendent of Schools James Phares

WEST VIRGINIA BOARD OF EDUCATION
1900 Kanawha Blvd E Rm 358, Charleston 25305-0330

President L. Wade Linger

REGIONAL EDUCATION SERVICE AGENCIES (RESA)

RESA I
Keith Butcher, dir. 304-256-4712
400 Neville St, Beckley 25801 Fax 256-4683
resa1.k12.wv.us/

RESA II
Dr. Dee Cockrille, dir. 304-529-6205
2001 McCoy Rd, Huntington 25701 Fax 529-6209
resa2.k12.wv.us/

RESA III
Kelly Watts, dir. 304-766-7655
501 22nd St, Dunbar 25064 Fax 766-7915
resa3.k12.wv.us

RESA IV
Dr. Gus Penix, dir., 404 Old Main Dr 304-872-6440
Summersville 26651 Fax 872-6442
resa4.k12.wv.us/

RESA V
Ralph Board, dir. 304-485-6513
2507 9th Ave, Parkersburg 26101 Fax 485-6515
sites.google.com/site/yourresa5/

RESA VII
Gabriel Devono, dir. 304-624-6554
1201 N 15th St, Clarksburg 26301 Fax 624-5223
resa7.k12.wv.us

RESA VIII
Jane Lynch, dir., 109 S College St 304-267-3595
Martinsburg 25401 Fax 367-3728
www.resa8.org/resa8/site/default.asp

RESA VI
Nick Zervos, dir. 304-243-0440
30 G C and P Rd, Wheeling 26003 Fax 243-0443
resa6.k12.wv.us/

PUBLIC, PRIVATE AND CATHOLIC SECONDARY SCHOOLS

Ansted, Fayette, Pop. 1,400
Fayette County SD
Supt. — See Fayetteville
Ansted MS 100/6-8
PO Box 766 25812 304-658-5170
Victor Whitt, prin. Fax 658-3059

Ashton, Mason
Mason County SD
Supt. — See Point Pleasant
Hannan JSHS 200/7-12
15638 Ashton Upland Rd 25503 304-743-2571
Karen Bare-Oldham, prin. Fax 743-4513

Athens, Mercer, Pop. 1,039

Concord University Post-Sec.
PO Box 1000 24712 800-344-6679

Avondale, McDowell
McDowell County SD
Supt. — See Welch
Sandy River MS 300/6-8
PO Box 419 24811 304-938-2407
Stacy Lusk, prin. Fax 938-2418

Baker, Hardy
Hardy County SD
Supt. — See Moorefield
East Hardy HS 200/9-12
PO Box 120 26801 304-897-5948
Brad Simmons, prin. Fax 897-6261

Barboursville, Cabell, Pop. 3,916
Cabell County SD
Supt. — See Huntington
Barboursville MS 800/6-8
1400 Central Ave 25504 304-733-3003
Brent Jarrell, prin. Fax 733-3009

Beaver, Raleigh, Pop. 1,300

Victory Baptist Academy 100/K-12
PO Box 549 25813 304-255-4535

Beckley, Raleigh, Pop. 17,086
Raleigh County SD 12,000/PK-12
105 Adair St 25801 304-256-4500
James Brown, supt. Fax 256-4739
boe.rale.k12.wv.us
Academy of Careers and Technology Vo/Tech
390 Stanaford Rd 25801 304-256-4615
Charles Pack, prin. Fax 256-4674
Beckley-Stratton MS 600/6-8
401 Grey Flats Rd 25801 304-256-4616
Rachel Pauley, prin. Fax 256-4616
Park MS 400/6-8
212 Park Ave 25801 304-256-4586
Jacquelin McPeake, prin. Fax 256-4709
Wilson HS 1,400/9-12
400 Stanaford Rd 25801 304-256-4646
Marsha Smith, prin. Fax 256-4642
Other Schools – See Coal City, Glen Daniel, Shady Spring, Sophia

Mountain State University Post-Sec.
410 Neville St 25801 866-367-6781
New River Community & Technical College Post-Sec.
221 George St Ste 2 25801 304-929-5445
Valley College Post-Sec.
713 S Oakwood Ave 25801 304-252-9547
Veterans Administration Hospital Post-Sec.
200 Veterans Ave 25801 304-255-2121

Belington, Barbour, Pop. 1,905
Barbour County SD
Supt. — See Philippi
Belington MS 200/6-8
RR 2 Box 343 26250 304-823-1281
H. Moke Post, prin. Fax 823-2403

Belle, Kanawha, Pop. 1,248
Kanawha County SD
Supt. — See Charleston
DuPont MS 400/6-8
1 Panther Dr 25015 304-348-1978
Tommy Canterbury, prin. Fax 949-1793
Riverside HS 1,200/9-12
1 Warrior Way 25015 304-348-1996
Valery Harper, prin. Fax 348-1921

Belmont, Pleasants, Pop. 892
Pleasants County SD
Supt. — See Saint Marys
Pleasants County MS 400/5-8
510 Riverview Dr 26134 304-299-5275
Lori Barnhart, prin. Fax 665-2451

Berkeley Springs, Morgan, Pop. 614
Morgan County SD 2,600/PK-12
247 Harrison Ave 25411 304-258-2430
David Banks, supt. Fax 258-9146
www.morganschools.net
Berkeley Springs HS 700/9-12
149 Concord Ave 25411 304-258-2871
Dan Fox, prin. Fax 258-5058
Warm Springs MS 500/6-8
271 Warm Springs Way 25411 304-258-1500
Gene Brock, prin. Fax 258-4600
Other Schools – See Paw Paw

Bethany, Brooke, Pop. 1,014

Bethany College 26032 Post-Sec.
304-829-7000

Blacksville, Monongalia, Pop. 166
Monongalia County SD
Supt. — See Morgantown
Clay-Battelle MSHS 500/6-12
PO Box A 26521 304-432-8208
David Cottrell, prin. Fax 432-8189

Bluefield, Mercer, Pop. 10,213
Mercer County SD
Supt. — See Princeton
Bluefield HS 700/9-12
535 W Cumberland Rd 24701 304-325-9116
Fax 325-0529
Bluefield MS 600/6-8
2002 Stadium Dr 24701 304-325-2481
Jeff Matthews, prin. Fax 325-2156

Bluefield Regional Medical Center Post-Sec.
500 Cherry St 24701 304-327-1701
Bluefield State College Post-Sec.
219 Rock St 24701 304-327-4000
Valley View SDA S 50/K-12
PO Box 6312 24701 304-325-8679
Fax 325-8679

Bradshaw, McDowell, Pop. 335
McDowell County SD
Supt. — See Welch
Riverview HS 600/9-12
512 Mountaineer Hwy 24817 304-967-7480
Michael Tye, prin. Fax 967-2502

Branchland, Lincoln
Lincoln County SD
Supt. — See Hamlin
Guyan Valley MS 300/6-8
5312 McLellan Hwy 25506 304-824-3235
Jonah Adkins, prin. Fax 824-3459

Bridgeport, Harrison, Pop. 8,059
Harrison County SD
Supt. — See Clarksburg
Bridgeport HS 800/9-12
515 Johnson Ave 26330 304-326-7137
Mark DeFazio, prin. Fax 842-6288
Bridgeport MS 500/6-8
413 Johnson Ave 26330 304-326-7142
Carole Crawford, prin. Fax 842-6275

Heritage Christian S 100/PK-12
225 Newton Ave 26330 304-842-1740
Linda Simms, admin. Fax 842-1750
West Virginia Junior College Post-Sec.
176 Thompson Dr 26330 304-842-4007

Buckeye, Pocahontas
Pocahontas County SD
Supt. — See Marlinton
Marlinton MS 200/5-8
1 Copperhead Way 24924 304-799-6773
Joseph Riley, prin. Fax 799-7278

Buckhannon, Upshur, Pop. 5,544
Upshur County SD 3,900/PK-12
102 Smithfield St 26201 304-472-5480
Scott Lampinen, supt. Fax 472-0258
boe.wvlink.com/upshurschools
Buckhannon-Upshur HS 1,100/9-12
50 BU Dr 26201 304-472-3720
Robert Wilmoth, prin. Fax 472-0772
Buckhannon-Upshur MS 800/6-8
RR 6 Box 303 26201 304-472-1520
Renee Warner, prin. Fax 472-6864
Eberle Tech Ctr Vo/Tech
RR 5 Box 2 26201 304-472-1259
Mike Cutright Ed.D., dir. Fax 472-3418

West Virginia Wesleyan College Post-Sec.
59 College Ave 26201 304-473-8000

Buffalo, Putnam, Pop. 1,223
Putnam County SD
Supt. — See Winfield
Buffalo HS 300/9-12
3317 Buffalo Rd 25033 304-937-2661
Richard Grim, prin. Fax 937-3470

Bunker Hill, Berkeley
Berkeley County SD
Supt. — See Martinsburg
Musselman MS 1,200/6-8
105 Pride Ave 25413 304-229-1965
James Holland, prin. Fax 229-1967

Cameron, Marshall, Pop. 941
Marshall County SD
Supt. — See Moundsville
Cameron JSHS 300/7-12
2012 Blue and Gold Rd 26033 304-686-3336
Jack Cain, prin. Fax 686-3510

Capon Bridge, Hampshire, Pop. 353
Hampshire County SD
Supt. — See Romney
Capon Bridge MS 300/6-8
PO Box 147 26711 304-856-2534
Ann Downs, prin. Fax 856-3192

Cedar Grove, Kanawha, Pop. 982
Kanawha County SD
Supt. — See Charleston
Cedar Grove MS 6-8
200 John St 25039 304-949-1642
Melissa Lawrence, prin. Fax 949-3418

Ceredo, Wayne, Pop. 1,432
Wayne County SD
Supt. — See Wayne
Ceredo-Kenova MS 200/6-8
PO Box 705 25507 304-453-3588
Tonji Bowen, prin. Fax 453-4420

Chapmanville, Logan, Pop. 1,250
Logan County SD
Supt. — See Logan
Chapmanville HS 700/9-12
200 Vance St 25508 304-855-4522
Katherine Moore, prin. Fax 855-1911
Chapmanville MS 600/5-8
300 Vance St 25508 304-855-8378
Jason Browning, prin. Fax 855-1307

Charleston, Kanawha, Pop. 49,755
Kanawha County SD 27,500/PK-12
200 Elizabeth St 25311 304-348-7731
Ronald Duerring Ed.D., supt. Fax 348-7735
kcs.kana.k12.wv.us/
Adams MS 700/6-8
2002 Presidential Dr 25314 304-348-6652
John Moyers, prin. Fax 348-6592
Capital HS 1,200/9-12
1500 Greenbrier St 25311 304-348-6500
Clinton Giles, prin. Fax 348-6509
Carver Career Center Vo/Tech
4799 Midland Dr 25306 304-348-1965
James Casdorph, prin. Fax 348-1938
Chandler Academy Alt
1900 School St 25387 304-348-6133
Roy Jones, prin.
Garnet Career Center Vo/Tech
422 Dickinson St 25301 304-348-6195
Dawn Mahon, prin. Fax 348-6198
Jackson MS 500/6-8
812 Park Ave 25302 304-348-6123
Donnell Gilliam, prin. Fax 348-1999
Mann MS 500/6-8
4300 MacCorkle Ave SE 25304 304-348-1971
Jon Anderson, prin. Fax 348-6591
Sissonville HS 600/9-12
6100 Sissonville Dr 25312 304-348-1954
Ron Reedy, prin. Fax 348-6565
Sissonville MS 500/6-8
100 Middle School Ln 25312 304-348-1993
Brian Eddy, prin. Fax 348-6594
Washington HS 1,100/9-12
1522 Tennis Club Rd 25314 304-348-7729
George Aulenbacher, prin. Fax 344-4947
Other Schools – See Belle, Cedar Grove, Clendenin, Cross Lanes, Dunbar, East Bank, Elkview, Nitro, Saint Albans, South Charleston

---

Carver Career and Tech Education Center Post-Sec.
4799 Midland Dr 25306 304-348-1965
Charleston Catholic HS 500/6-12
1033 Virginia St E 25301 304-342-8415
Debra Sullivan, prin. Fax 342-1259
Charleston School of Beauty Culture Post-Sec.
210 Capitol St 25301 304-346-9603
Cross Lanes Christian S 300/K-12
5330 Floradale Dr 25313 304-776-5020
Dr. Gordon Fenlason, admin. Fax 776-5074
Garnet Career Center Post-Sec.
422 Dickinson St 25301 304-348-6195
Kanawha Vlly Community Technical College Post-Sec.
2001 Union Carbide Dr 25303 304-205-6700
University of Charleston Post-Sec.
2300 MacCorkle Ave SE 25304 304-357-4800
West Virginia Junior College Post-Sec.
1000 Virginia St E 25301 304-345-2820

Charles Town, Jefferson, Pop. 5,074
Jefferson County SD 8,700/PK-12
110 Mordington Ave 25414 304-725-9741
Susan Wall, supt. Fax 725-6487
boe.jeff.k12.wv.us
Charles Town MS 600/6-8
193 High St 25414 304-725-7821
Charles Hampton, prin. Fax 725-7526
Washington HS 1,100/9-12
300 Washington Patriots Dr 25414 304-885-5110
Judy Marcus, prin. Fax 885-5108
Other Schools – See Harpers Ferry, Shenandoah Junction, Shepherdstown

---

American Public University Post-Sec.
111 W Congress St 25414 877-755-2787

Charmco, Greenbrier
Greenbrier County SD
Supt. — See Lewisburg
Greenbrier West HS 400/9-12
PO Box 325 25958 304-438-6191
Randy Auvil, prin. Fax 438-9189

Clarksburg, Harrison, Pop. 16,197
Harrison County SD 11,100/PK-12
PO Box 1370 26302 304-624-3325
Susan Collins, supt. Fax 624-3361
www.harcoboe.com
Byrd HS 800/9-12
1 Eagle Way 26301 304-326-7200
Martin Pigg, prin. Fax 624-3211
Harrison County Alternative S Alt
RR 3 Box 43B 26301 304-326-7560
Ed Propst, prin. Fax 624-3245
Irving MS 600/6-8
443 Lee Ave 26301 304-326-7420
William Tucker, prin. Fax 624-3388
Liberty HS 600/9-12
1 Mountaineer Dr 26301 304-326-7470
Pamela Knight, prin. Fax 623-3159
Mountaineer MS 500/6-8
2 Mountaineer Dr 26301 304-326-7620
John Rogers, prin. Fax 326-7632
United Technical Ctr Vo/Tech
RR 3 Box 43C 26301 304-326-7580
Joan Smith, dir. Fax 622-6138
Other Schools – See Bridgeport, Lost Creek, Lumberport, Shinnston

---

Clarksburg Beauty Academy Post-Sec.
120 S 3rd St 26301 304-624-6475
Emmanuel Christian S 100/PK-12
1318 N 16th St 26301 304-624-6125
Fax 624-5349
Notre Dame HS 100/7-12
127 E Pike St 26301 304-623-1026
Dr. Carroll Morrison, prin. Fax 623-1026

Clay, Clay, Pop. 483
Clay County SD 2,100/PK-12
PO Box 120 25043 304-587-4266
Kenneth Tanner, supt. Fax 587-4181
www.claycountyschools.org
Clay County HS 600/9-12
PO Box 729 25043 304-587-4226
Melinda Isaacs, prin. Fax 587-2723
Clay County MS 400/6-8
PO Box 489 25043 304-587-2343
Joe Paxton, prin. Fax 587-2759

Clear Fork, Wyoming
Wyoming County SD
Supt. — See Pineville
Westside HS 600/9-12
HC 65 Box 275 24822 304-682-8965
Robin Hall, prin. Fax 682-6273

Clendenin, Kanawha, Pop. 1,218
Kanawha County SD
Supt. — See Charleston
Hoover HS 700/9-12
5856 Elk River Rd N 25045 304-965-3394
Michael Kelley, prin. Fax 965-1871

Coal City, Raleigh, Pop. 1,761
Raleigh County SD
Supt. — See Beckley
Independence HS 700/9-12
PO Box 1595 25823 304-683-3228
Chris Perkins, prin. Fax 683-4393

Cowen, Webster, Pop. 533
Webster County SD
Supt. — See Webster Springs
Glade MS 200/5-8
25 Mill St 26206 304-226-5353
Stephen White, prin. Fax 226-3666

Craigsville, Nicholas, Pop. 2,184
Nicholas County SD
Supt. — See Summersville
Nicholas County Career and Technical Ctr Vo/Tech
215 Milam Addition Rd 26205 304-742-5416
Thomas Bayless, prin. Fax 742-3953

Crawley, Greenbrier
Greenbrier County SD
Supt. — See Lewisburg
Western Greenbrier MS 300/6-8
315 Timberwolf Dr 24931 304-392-6446
Amy Robertson, prin. Fax 392-6785

Cross Lanes, Kanawha, Pop. 9,816
Kanawha County SD
Supt. — See Charleston
Jackson MS 700/6-8
5445 Big Tyler Rd 25313 304-776-3310
Rhonda Donohoe, prin. Fax 776-3305

Everest Institute Post-Sec.
5514 Big Tyler Rd 25313 304-776-6290

Crum, Wayne, Pop. 179
Wayne County SD
Supt. — See Wayne
Crum MS 100/6-8
PO Box 9 25669 304-393-3200
Sherri Brewer, prin. Fax 393-4429

Delbarton, Mingo, Pop. 564
Mingo County SD
Supt. — See Williamson
Burch MS 100/5-8
RR 2 Box 52A1 25670 304-475-2700
Jada Hunter, prin. Fax 475-5106

Dunbar, Kanawha, Pop. 7,684
Kanawha County SD
Supt. — See Charleston
Dunbar MS 400/6-8
325 27th St 25064 304-766-0363
Lynda Gilkeson, prin. Fax 766-0365
Franklin Career & Tech Ed Vo/Tech
500 28th St 25064 304-766-0369
Dr. Paula Potter, prin. Fax 766-0371

Dunmore, Pocahontas
Pocahontas County SD
Supt. — See Marlinton
Pocahontas County HS 400/9-12
271 Warrior Way 24934 304-799-6565
Thomas Sanders, prin. Fax 799-6893

East Bank, Kanawha, Pop. 953
Kanawha County SD
Supt. — See Charleston
East Bank MS 400/6-8
PO Box 897 25067 304-595-2311
Michael Wilkinson, prin. Fax 595-4676

Eleanor, Putnam, Pop. 1,501
Putnam County SD
Supt. — See Winfield
Putnam County Technical Center Vo/Tech
PO Box 640 25070 304-586-3494
Michael Erwin, prin. Fax 586-4467
Washington MS 300/6-8
PO Box 660 25070 304-586-2875
Valerie Stewart, prin. Fax 586-3037

Elizabeth, Wirt, Pop. 816
Wirt County SD 1,000/PK-12
PO Box 189 26143 304-275-4279
Dan Metz, supt. Fax 275-4581
www.edline.net/pages/wirtboe
Wirt County HS 300/9-12
PO Box 219 26143 304-275-4241
Kenneth Heiney, prin. Fax 275-3271
Wirt County MS 300/5-8
PO Box 699 26143 304-275-3977
John McKown, prin. Fax 275-4257

Elkins, Randolph, Pop. 7,020
Randolph County SD 4,200/PK-12
40 11th St 26241 304-636-9150
Dr. Jim Phares, supt. Fax 636-9157
boe.rand.k12.wv.us
Elkins HS 900/9-12
100 Kennedy Dr 26241 304-636-9170
David Fincham, prin. Fax 636-9168
Elkins MS 700/6-8
308 Robert E Lee Ave 26241 304-636-9176
Rich Carr, prin. Fax 636-9178
Randolph Co. Alternative Learning Center 50/Alt
1425 S Davis Ave 26241 304-636-9150
Angela Wilson, prin. Fax 636-9157
Randolph County Technical Center Vo/Tech
200 Kennedy Dr 26241 304-636-9195
Fax 636-9169
Other Schools – See Harman, Mill Creek, Pickens

Davis & Elkins College Post-Sec.
100 Campus Dr 26241 304-637-1900
Highland Adventist S 50/K-12
1 Old Leadsville Rd 26241 304-636-4274
Cheryl Jacko, prin. Fax 636-4274

Elkview, Kanawha, Pop. 1,216
Kanawha County SD
Supt. — See Charleston
Elkview MS 700/6-8
5090 Elk River Rd N 25071 304-348-1947
Rick Messinger, prin. Fax 348-6590

Elk Valley Christian S 200/PK-12
58 Mount Pleasant Dr 25071 304-965-7063
Scott Lilly, prin. Fax 965-7064

Ellenboro, Ritchie, Pop. 363
Ritchie County SD
Supt. — See Harrisville
Ritchie County HS 400/9-12
107 Ritchie Co School Rd 26346 304-869-3526
Kelly Waggoner, prin. Fax 869-3031
Ritchie County MS 300/6-8
105 Ritchie Co School Rd 26346 304-869-3512
Michael Dotson, prin. Fax 869-3519

Fairmont, Marion, Pop. 18,276
Marion County SD 8,000/PK-12
200 Gaston Ave 26554 304-367-2100
Gary Price, supt. Fax 367-2111
www.marionboe.com/
East Fairmont HS 800/9-12
1993 Airport Rd 26554 304-367-2140
David Nuzum, prin. Fax 367-2180
East Fairmont MS 400/5-8
1 Orion Ln 26554 304-367-2123
Christine Miller, prin. Fax 367-2179
Fairmont HS 700/9-12
1 Loop Park Dr 26554 304-367-2150
Chad Norman, prin. Fax 366-5988
West Fairmont MS 600/5-8
110 10th St 26554 304-366-5631
Lisa Lister, prin. Fax 366-5636
Marion County Adult & Community Educ. Adult
601 Locust Ave 26554 304-363-7323
Donna Metz, prin. Fax 366-2483
Other Schools – See Fairview, Farmington, Mannington, Monongah

---

Fairmont State University Post-Sec.
1201 Locust Ave 26554 304-367-4892
Pierpont Community & Technical College Post-Sec.
1201 Locust Ave 26554 304-367-4692

Fairview, Marion, Pop. 404
Marion County SD
Supt. — See Fairmont
Fairview MS 100/5-8
PO Box 300 26570 304-449-1312
Steve Rodriguez, prin. Fax 449-1305

Farmington, Marion, Pop. 368
Marion County SD
Supt. — See Fairmont
Marion County Technical Center Vo/Tech
2 N Marion Dr 26571 304-986-3590
Matt Call, prin. Fax 986-3440
North Marion HS 800/9-12
1 N Marion Dr 26571 304-986-3063
Russelle DeVito, prin. Fax 986-3086

Fayetteville, Fayette, Pop. 2,872
Fayette County SD 6,100/PK-12
111 Fayette Ave 25840 304-574-1176
Keith Butcher, supt. Fax 574-3643
fayettecntywv.web1.schoolpointe.com
Fayetteville HS 500/7-12
515 W Maple Ave 25840 304-574-0560
Bryan Parsons, prin. Fax 574-0118
Other Schools – See Ansted, Hico, Meadow Bridge, Oak Hill, Smithers

Follansbee, Brooke, Pop. 2,935
Brooke County SD
Supt. — See Wellsburg
Follansbee MS 500/5-8
1400 Main St 26037 304-527-1942
Kim Johnson, prin. Fax 527-1954

Fort Gay, Wayne, Pop. 690
Wayne County SD
Supt. — See Wayne
Fort Gay MS 200/6-8
675 Court St 25514 304-648-5404
Donita Webb, prin. Fax 648-7082
Tolsia HS 500/9-12
1 Rebel Dr 25514 304-648-5566
L. Matthew Stanley, prin. Fax 648-5447

Foster, Boone
Boone County SD
Supt. — See Madison
Boone County Career & Tech Ctr Vo/Tech
3505 Daniel Boone Pkwy # B 25081 304-369-4585
Jeffrey Nelson, prin. Fax 369-3692

Boone County Career Center Post-Sec.
3505 Daniel Boone Pkwy # B 25081 304-369-4585
Southern WV Community & Technical Coll. Post-Sec.
3505 Daniel Boone Pkwy # A 25081 304-369-2952

Franklin, Pendleton, Pop. 713
Pendleton County SD 1,100/PK-12
PO Box 888 26807 304-358-2207
Doug Lambert, supt. Fax 358-2936
pendletoncountyschools.com/
Pendleton County MSHS 500/7-12
PO Box 40 26807 304-358-2573
Timothy Woodward, prin. Fax 358-7701

Future Generations Graduate School Post-Sec.
400 Road Less Traveled Rd 26807 304-358-2000

Gilbert, Mingo, Pop. 447
Mingo County SD
Supt. — See Williamson
Gilbert HS 100/5-8
100 Lion Dr 25621 304-664-8197
Daniel Dean, prin. Fax 664-8249

Glen Dale, Marshall, Pop. 1,510
Marshall County SD
Supt. — See Moundsville
Marshall HS 1,200/9-12
1300 Wheeling Ave 26038 304-843-4444
Rick Jones, prin. Fax 843-4419

Glen Daniel, Raleigh
Raleigh County SD
Supt. — See Beckley
Liberty HS 500/9-12
PO Box 265 25844 304-934-5307
Clyde Stepp, prin. Fax 934-5307
Trap Hill MS 400/6-8
665 Coal River Rd 25844 304-934-5392
Jerry Bawgus, prin. Fax 934-5393

Glenville, Gilmer, Pop. 1,501
Gilmer County SD 900/PK-12
201 N Court St 26351 304-462-7386
Ronald Blankenship, supt. Fax 462-5103
www.edline.net/pages/Gilmer_County_SD
Gilmer County JSHS 400/7-12
300 Pine St 26351 304-462-7960
Athanasia Butcher, prin. Fax 462-7059

Glenville State College Post-Sec.
200 High St 26351 304-462-7361

Grafton, Taylor, Pop. 5,091
Taylor County SD 2,400/PK-12
RR 2 Box 157 26354 304-265-2497
Charles Maynard, supt. Fax 265-2508
www.edline.net/pages/Taylor_CBOE
Grafton HS 700/9-12
400 Riverside Dr 26354 304-265-3046
Joseph Findley, prin. Fax 265-2156
Taylor County MS 700/5-8
670 Spring Hills Rd 26354 304-265-0722
Pam Gallaher, prin. Fax 265-4623
Taylor County Vocational Center Vo/Tech
115 Luby St 26354 304-265-1050
Fax 265-1058

Grantsville, Calhoun, Pop. 561
Calhoun County SD
Supt. — See Mount Zion
Calhoun Gilmer Career Center Vo/Tech
5260 E Little Kanawha Hwy 26147 304-354-6151
Bryan Sterns, dir. Fax 354-6154

Hambleton, Tucker, Pop. 231
Tucker County SD
Supt. — See Parsons
Tucker County HS 300/9-12
RR 1 Box 153 26269 304-478-2651
Jay Hamric, prin. Fax 478-4357

Hamlin, Lincoln, Pop. 1,134
Lincoln County SD 3,400/PK-12
10 Marland Ave 25523 304-824-3033
Patricia Lucas, supt. Fax 824-7947
boe.linc.k12.wv.us
Lincoln HS 900/9-12
81 Lincoln Panther Way 25523 304-824-6000
Dana Snyder, prin. Fax 824-6063
Other Schools – See Branchland

Harman, Randolph, Pop. 143
Randolph County SD
Supt. — See Elkins
Harman S 200/PK-12
PO Box 130 26270 304-227-4114
Tammie Daniels, prin. Fax 227-3610

Harpers Ferry, Jefferson, Pop. 283
Jefferson County SD
Supt. — See Charles Town
Harpers Ferry MS 400/6-8
1710 W Washington St 25425 304-535-6357
Joseph Spurgas, prin. Fax 535-6986

Harrisville, Ritchie, Pop. 1,865
Ritchie County SD 1,600/PK-12
134 S Penn Ave 26362 304-643-2991
Edward Toman, supt. Fax 643-2994
ritchieschools.com
Other Schools – See Ellenboro

Hedgesville, Berkeley, Pop. 311
Berkeley County SD
Supt. — See Martinsburg
Hedgesville HS 1,700/9-12
109 Ridge Rd N 25427 304-754-3354
Ron Lyons, prin. Fax 754-7445
Hedgesville MS 700/6-8
334 School House Dr 25427 304-754-3313
Elizabeth Adams, prin. Fax 754-6613

Hico, Fayette, Pop. 272
Fayette County SD
Supt. — See Fayetteville
Midland Trail HS 300/9-12
PO Box 89 25854 304-658-5184
Diane Blume, prin. Fax 658-5185

Hilltop, Fayette, Pop. 613

Mountainview Christian S 200/PK-12
2 Mountain View Rd 25855 304-465-0502
Rev. Rudell Bloomfield, hdmstr. Fax 465-5484

Hinton, Summers, Pop. 2,623
Summers County SD 1,500/PK-12
116 Main St 25951 304-466-6000
Vicki Hinerman, supt. Fax 466-6008
www.edline.net/pages/summerscountyschools
Summers County HS 400/9-12
1 Bobcat Dr 25951 304-466-6040
Josh Houchins, prin. Fax 466-6044
Summers MS 300/5-8
400 Temple St 25951 304-466-6030
Kitrick Durnan, prin. Fax 466-2271

Hundred, Wetzel, Pop. 296
Wetzel County SD
Supt. — See New Martinsville
Hundred HS 100/9-12
PO Box 830 26575 304-775-5221
Jessica Stine, prin. Fax 775-2922

Huntington, Cabell, Pop. 47,796
Cabell County SD 12,700/PK-12
2850 5th Ave 25702 304-528-5000
William Smith, supt. Fax 528-5080
boe.cabe.k12.wv.us
Beverly Hills MS 500/6-8
2901 Saltwell Rd 25705 304-528-5102
Frank Barnett, prin. Fax 528-5197
Cabell County Alternative S 50/Alt
2850 5th Ave 25702 304-528-5060
Brenda Scott, prin. Fax 528-5134
Cabell County Career Technology Center Vo/Tech
1035 Norway Ave 25705 304-528-5106
Brenda Tanner, prin. Fax 528-5110
Enslow MS 300/6-8
2613 Collis Ave 25702 304-528-5121
Ryan McKenzie, prin. Fax 528-5097
Huntington HS 1,600/9-12
1 Highlander Way 25701 304-528-6400
Greg Webb, prin. Fax 528-6422
Huntington MS 600/6-8
925 3rd St 25701 304-528-5180
Joe Brison, prin. Fax 528-5215
Other Schools – See Barboursville, Milton, Ona

Wayne County SD
Supt. — See Wayne
Spring Valley HS 1,000/9-12
1 Timberwolf Ln 25704 304-429-1699
Steve Morris, prin. Fax 429-7315
Vinson MS 300/6-8
3851 Piedmont Rd 25704 304-429-1641
Tammy Forbush, prin. Fax 429-6162

Cabell Huntington Hospital Post-Sec.
1340 Hal Greer Blvd 25701 304-526-2111
Covenant S 200/K-12
2400 Johnstown Rd 25701 304-781-6741
Tom Bowen, hdmstr. Fax 781-6742
Grace Christian S 300/PK-12
1111 Adams Ave 25704 304-522-8635
Dr. Dan Brokke, admin. Fax 522-3240
Huntington Junior College Post-Sec.
900 5th Ave 25701 304-697-7550
Huntington School of Beauty Culture Post-Sec.
5636 US Route 60 Ste 14 25705 304-736-6289
ITT Technical Institute Post-Sec.
5183 US Route 60 Bldg 1 25705 304-733-8700
Marshall University Post-Sec.
1 John Marshall Dr 25755 304-696-3170
Mountwest Community & Technical College Post-Sec.
1 Mountwest Way 25701 866-676-5533
St. Joseph Central HS 100/9-12
600 13th St 25701 304-525-5096
William Archer, prin. Fax 525-0781
St. Mary's Medical Center Post-Sec.
2900 1st Ave 25702 304-526-1270

Hurricane, Putnam, Pop. 6,205
Putnam County SD
Supt. — See Winfield
Hurricane HS 1,100/9-12
3350 Teays Valley Rd 25526 304-562-3991
Richard Campbell, prin. Fax 562-5460
Hurricane MS 900/6-8
518 Midland Trl 25526 304-562-9271
Doug Cross, prin. Fax 562-7163

Calvary Baptist Academy 200/K-12
3655 Teays Valley Rd 25526 304-757-6768
Milton Thompson, prin. Fax 757-6777

Institute, Kanawha

West Virginia State University Post-Sec.
PO Box 1000 25112 304-766-3000

Inwood, Berkeley, Pop. 2,871
Berkeley County SD
Supt. — See Martinsburg
Musselman HS 1,600/9-12
126 Excellence Way 25428 304-229-1950
Holly Kleppner, prin. Fax 229-1959

Kenova, Wayne, Pop. 3,199
Wayne County SD
Supt. — See Wayne
Buffalo MS 300/6-8
298 Buffalo Creek Rd 25530 304-429-6062
Elizabeth Ryder, prin. Fax 429-7245

Keyser, Mineral, Pop. 5,316
Mineral County SD 4,400/PK-12
1 Baker Pl 26726 304-788-4200
Robert Woy, supt. Fax 788-4204
boe.mine.k12.wv.us/
Keyser HS 700/9-12
1 Tornado Way 26726 304-788-4230
Charles Wimer, prin. Fax 788-4234
Mineral County Alternative S 50/Alt
50 Clary St 26726 304-788-4213
Jenni Woy, prin. Fax 788-4623
Mineral County Technical Center Vo/Tech
600 Harley O Staggers Sr Dr 26726 304-788-4240
Scott Staley, dir. Fax 788-4243
Other Schools – See Ridgeley

Potomac State College of West Virginia U Post-Sec.
101 Fort Ave 26726 304-788-6820

Kingwood, Preston, Pop. 2,912
Preston County SD 4,600/PK-12
731 Preston Dr 26537 304-329-0580
Dr. Larry Parsons, supt. Fax 329-0720
www.prestonboe.com
Central Preston MS 300/6-8
500 Knight Dr 26537 304-329-0033
Karen Ovesney, prin. Fax 329-2389
Preston HS 1,300/9-12
400 Knight Dr 26537 304-329-0400
Dr. David Pastrick, prin. Fax 329-3899
Other Schools – See Masontown, Tunnelton

Le Roy, Jackson
Jackson County SD
Supt. — See Ripley
Roane-Jackson Tech Ctr Vo/Tech
9450 Spencer Rd 25252 304-372-7335
Ben Cummings, dir. Fax 372-7336

Lewisburg, Greenbrier, Pop. 3,773
Greenbrier County SD 5,200/PK-12
PO Box 987 24901 304-647-6470
Sallie Dalton, supt. Fax 647-6490
www.edline.net/pages/Greenbrier_County_Schools
Greenbrier East HS 1,100/9-12
1 Spartan Ln 24901 304-647-6464
Jeff Bryant, prin. Fax 645-2698
Other Schools – See Charmco, Crawley, Ronceverte

West Virginia Sch./Osteopathic Medicine Post-Sec.
400 N Lee St 24901 304-645-6270

Lindside, Monroe
Monroe County SD
Supt. — See Union
Monroe County Technical Center Vo/Tech
RR 1 Box 97 24951 304-753-9971
Fax 753-9792
Monroe HS 600/9-12
RR 1 Box 97-1A 24951 304-753-5182
Lisa Mustain, prin. Fax 753-5184

Logan, Logan, Pop. 1,749
Logan County SD 6,400/PK-12
PO Box 477 25601 304-792-2060
Wilma Zigmond, supt. Fax 752-3711
lc2.boe.loga.k12.wv.us
Logan HS 800/9-12
1 Wildcat Way 25601 304-752-6606
Robert Lucas, prin. Fax 752-6614
Logan MS 800/5-8
14 Wildcat Way 25601 304-752-1804
Ernestine Sutherland, prin. Fax 752-0207
Willis Vo-Tech Center Vo/Tech
PO Box 1747 25601 304-752-4687
David Adkins, prin. Fax 752-2943
Other Schools – See Chapmanville, Mallory, Man

Lost Creek, Harrison, Pop. 482
Harrison County SD
Supt. — See Clarksburg
South Harrison HS 400/9-12
RR 1 Box 58 26385 304-326-7440
James Lopez, prin. Fax 745-4292
South Harrison MS 300/6-8
RR 1 Box 58B 26385 304-326-7460
Katrina Hill, prin. Fax 745-5587

Lumberport, Harrison, Pop. 868
Harrison County SD
Supt. — See Clarksburg
Lumberport MS 400/6-8
314 Main St 26386 304-326-7540
Lori Scott, prin. Fax 584-4602

Mc Mechen, Marshall, Pop. 1,914

Bishop Donahue Memorial HS 100/9-12
325 Logan St, 304-233-3850
Thomas Wise, prin. Fax 233-8677

Madison, Boone, Pop. 3,064
Boone County SD 4,500/PK-12
69 Avenue B 25130 304-369-3131
John Hudson, supt. Fax 369-0855
www.boonecountyboe.org
Madison MS 600/6-8
404 Riverside Dr W 25130 304-369-4464
Shann Elkins, prin. Fax 369-5800
Scott HS 600/9-12
1 Skyhawk Pl 25130 304-369-3011
Allen Halley, prin. Fax 369-6564
Other Schools – See Foster, Seth, Van

Mallory, Logan, Pop. 1,628
Logan County SD
Supt. — See Logan
Man MS 500/5-8
PO Box 390 25634 304-583-8037
Cynthia Caldwell, prin. Fax 583-8253

Man, Logan, Pop. 759
Logan County SD
Supt. — See Logan
Man HS 400/9-12
800 E McDonald Ave 25635 304-583-6521
Sandy Manning, prin. Fax 583-6566

Mannington, Marion, Pop. 2,054
Marion County SD
Supt. — See Fairmont
Mannington MS 300/5-8
113 Clarksburg St 26582 304-986-1050
Richard Ott, prin. Fax 986-1747

Marlinton, Pocahontas, Pop. 1,050
Pocahontas County SD 1,200/PK-12
926 5th Ave 24954 304-799-4505
C. C. Lester, supt. Fax 799-4499
sites.google.com/site/pocahontasboe
Other Schools – See Buckeye, Dunmore

Martinsburg, Berkeley, Pop. 16,642
Berkeley County SD 17,000/PK-12
401 S Queen St 25401 304-267-3500
Manny Arvon, supt. Fax 267-3524
berkeleycountyschools.org/
Martinsburg HS 1,700/9-12
701 S Queen St 25401 304-267-3530
Trent Sherman, prin. Fax 267-3536
Martinsburg North MS 500/6-8
250 East Rd, 304-267-3540
Rebekah Eyler, prin. Fax 264-5066
Martinsburg South MS 900/6-8
150 Bulldog Blvd 25401 304-267-3545
David Rogers, prin. Fax 264-5062
Rumsey Technical Institute Vo/Tech
3274 Hedgesville Rd, 304-754-7925
Vicki Jenkins, dir. Fax 754-7933
Spring Mills MS 700/6-8
255 Campus Dr, 304-274-5030
Nancy White, prin. Fax 274-3598
Other Schools – See Bunker Hill, Hedgesville, Inwood

Blue Ridge Community & Technical College Post-Sec.
400 W Stephen St 25401 304-260-4380
Faith Christian Academy 300/PK-12
138 Greensburg Rd, 304-263-0011
Eric Kerns, admin. Fax 267-0638
International Beauty School Post-Sec.
201 W King St 25401 304-263-4929
Martinsburg Institute Post-Sec.
341 Aikens Ctr, 304-263-6262
Valley College Post-Sec.
287 Aikens Ctr, 304-263-0979

Mason, Mason, Pop. 951
Mason County SD
Supt. — See Point Pleasant
Wahama JSHS 400/7-12
PO Box 348 25260 304-773-5539
Kenny Bond, prin. Fax 773-5216

Masontown, Preston, Pop. 539
Preston County SD
Supt. — See Kingwood
West Preston MS 200/6-8
167 S Main St 26542 304-864-5221
James Hoit, prin. Fax 864-5298

Matewan, Mingo, Pop. 490
Mingo County SD
Supt. — See Williamson
Matewan MS 200/5-8
200 Tiger Ln 25678 304-426-8569
Shannon Blackburn, prin. Fax 426-4480

Meadow Bridge, Fayette, Pop. 378
Fayette County SD
Supt. — See Fayetteville
Meadow Bridge JSHS 200/7-12
870 Main St 25976 304-484-7917
Al Martine, prin. Fax 484-7921

Middlebourne, Tyler, Pop. 809
Tyler County SD 1,400/PK-12
PO Box 25 26149 304-758-2145
Robin Daquilante, supt. Fax 758-4566
www.tylercountypublicschools.com
Other Schools – See Sistersville

Mill Creek, Randolph, Pop. 718
Randolph County SD
Supt. — See Elkins
Tygarts Valley MSHS 400/7-12
RR 1 Box 290 26280 304-335-4575
Steve Wamsley, prin. Fax 335-6963

Milton, Cabell, Pop. 2,401
Cabell County SD
Supt. — See Huntington
Milton MS 600/6-8
1 Panther Trl 25541 304-743-7308
Dan Gleason, prin. Fax 743-7324

Monongah, Marion, Pop. 1,032
Marion County SD
Supt. — See Fairmont
Monongah MS 200/5-8
550 Camden Ave 26554 304-367-2164
Steve Malnick, prin. Fax 367-2190

Montcalm, Mercer, Pop. 722
Mercer County SD
Supt. — See Princeton
Montcalm HS 300/7-12
PO Box 330 24737 304-589-3719
Mark Page, prin. Fax 589-7140

Montgomery, Fayette, Pop. 1,593

Bridgemont Community & Technical College Post-Sec.
619 2nd Ave 25136 304-734-6600
West Virginia University Inst of Tech. Post-Sec.
405 Fayette Pike 25136 888-554-8324

Moorefield, Hardy, Pop. 2,511
Hardy County SD 2,200/PK-12
510 Ashby St 26836 304-530-2348
Barbara Whitecotton, supt. Fax 530-2340
www.hardycountyschools.com/
Moorefield HS 400/9-12
401 N Main St 26836 304-530-6034
Avery Anderson, prin. Fax 530-7569
Moorefield MS 300/6-8
303 Caledonia Heights Rd 26836 304-434-3000
Patrick McGregor, prin. Fax 434-3003
Other Schools – See Baker

Eastern WV Community & Technical College Post-Sec.
316 Eastern Dr 26836 304-434-8000

Morgantown, Monongalia, Pop. 29,068
Monongalia County SD 10,000/PK-12
13 S High St 26501 304-291-9210
Dr. Frank Devono, supt. Fax 291-3015
boe.mono.k12.wv.us
Alternative Learning Center Alt
550 Mylan Park Ln 26501 304-983-8972
Kim Greene, prin. Fax 983-8972
Monongalia County Tech Education Center Vo/Tech
1000 Mississippi St 26501 304-291-9240
Nancy Napolillo, prin. Fax 291-9247
Morgantown HS 1,600/9-12
109 Wilson Ave 26501 304-291-9260
Robert DeSantis, prin. Fax 291-9263
Mountaineer MS 500/6-8
991 Price St 26505 304-594-1165
Crystal Nantz, prin. Fax 594-1677
South MS 700/6-8
500 E Parkway Dr 26501 304-291-9340
Charlene Brown, prin. Fax 291-9306
Suncrest MS 500/6-8
360 Baldwin St 26505 304-291-9335
James Napolillo, prin. Fax 284-9362
University HS 1,300/9-12
131 Bakers Ridge Rd 26508 304-291-9270
Shari Burgess, prin. Fax 291-9248
Westwood MS 400/6-8
670 River Rd 26501 304-291-9300
Leonard Haney, prin. Fax 284-9368
Adult Basic Education Adult
1000 Mississippi St 26501 304-291-9243
Johnnie Hamilton, prin. Fax 291-9247
Other Schools – See Blacksville

Lighthouse Christian Academy 50/K-12
980 Stewartstown Rd 26505 304-276-1482
Judith Sloane, admin. Fax 599-6163
Monongalia County Tech Education Center Post-Sec.
1000 Mississippi St 26501 304-291-9240
Morgantown Beauty College Post-Sec.
276 Walnut St 26505 304-292-8475

Trinity Christian S 300/PK-12
200 Trinity Way 26505 304-291-4659
Ken Howard, supt. Fax 291-4660
West Virginia Junior College Post-Sec.
148 Willey St 26505 304-296-8282
West Virginia University Post-Sec.
PO Box 6201 26506 304-293-0111
West Virginia University Hospital Post-Sec.
PO Box 8150 26506 304-598-4000

Moundsville, Marshall, Pop. 9,248
Marshall County SD 4,600/PK-12
PO Box 578 26041 304-843-4400
Michael Hince, supt. Fax 843-4409
boe.mars.k12.wv.us
Moundsville MS 500/6-8
223 Tomlinson Ave 26041 304-843-4440
M. Jan Madden, prin. Fax 843-4446
Other Schools – See Cameron, Glen Dale, Wheeling

Mount Gay Shamrock, Logan, Pop. 1,768

Southern WV Community & Technical Coll. Post-Sec.
2900 Dempsey Branch Rd 25637 304-792-7098

Mount Hope, Fayette, Pop. 1,370

Appalachian Bible College Post-Sec.
161 College Dr 25880 304-877-6428

Mount Zion, Calhoun
Calhoun County SD 1,100/PK-12
540 Alan B Mollohan Dr 26151 304-354-7011
Roger Propst, supt. Fax 354-7420
www.edline.net/pages/Calhoun_CSD
Calhoun County MSHS 600/5-12
50 Underwood Cir 26151 304-354-6148
Karen Kirby, prin. Fax 354-7382
Other Schools – See Grantsville

Mullens, Wyoming, Pop. 1,540
Wyoming County SD
Supt. — See Pineville
Mullens MS 200/5-8
801 Moran Ave 25882 304-294-5757
Terri Lea Smith, prin. Fax 294-5762

New Cumberland, Hancock, Pop. 1,085
Hancock County SD 4,200/PK-12
PO Box 1300 26047 304-564-3411
Suzan Smith, supt. Fax 564-3990
www.hancockschools.org
Oak Glen HS 600/9-12
195 Golden Bear Dr 26047 304-564-3500
Barb Logue, prin. Fax 387-2079
Oak Glen MS 600/5-8
39 Golden Bear Dr 26047 304-387-2363
Virginia Greene, prin Fax 387-4624
Rockefeller Career Center Vo/Tech
95 Rockyside Rd 26047 304-564-3337
Martin Hudek, dir Fax 564-4058
Other Schools – See Weirton

New Martinsville, Wetzel, Pop. 5,337
Wetzel County SD 2,800/PK-12
333 Foundry St 26155 304-455-2441
Diane Watt, supt. Fax 455-3446
www.wetzelcountyschools.com
Magnolia HS 400/9-12
601 Maple Ave 26155 304-455-1990
Kathi Schmalz, prin. Fax 455-5536
Other Schools – See Hundred, Paden City, Pine Grove

New Richmond, Wyoming, Pop. 235
Wyoming County SD
Supt. — See Pineville
Wyoming County East HS 500/9-12
PO Box 390 24867 304-294-5200
Barry Smith, prin. Fax 294-5400

Nitro, Kanawha, Pop. 7,083
Kanawha County SD
Supt. — See Charleston
Nitro HS 800/9-12
1300 Park Ave 25143 304-755-4321
Dianne Smith, prin. Fax 755-4345

Nutter Fort Stonewood, Harrison, Pop. 1,562

West Virginia Business College Post-Sec.
116 Pennsylvania Ave 26301 304-624-7695

Oak Hill, Fayette, Pop. 7,618
Fayette County SD
Supt. — See Fayetteville
Collins MS 700/5-8
601 Jones Ave 25901 304-469-3711
Joel Harris, prin. Fax 465-1352
Fayette Institute of Technology Vo/Tech
300 W Oyler Ave 25901 304-469-2911
Barry Crist, prin. Fax 469-6963
Oak Hill HS 800/9-12
350 W Oyler Ave 25901 304-469-3551
Tim Payton, prin. Fax 465-1769

Oceana, Wyoming, Pop. 1,373
Wyoming County SD
Supt. — See Pineville
Oceana MS 300/5-8
HC 65 Box 403 24870 304-682-6296
Timmy Spolarich, prin. Fax 682-6330

Omar, Logan, Pop. 551

Beth Haven Christian S 100/PK-12
PO Box 620 25638 304-946-4447

Ona, Cabell
Cabell County SD
Supt. — See Huntington

Cabell Midland HS 1,800/9-12
2300 US Route 60 25545 304-743-7400
David Tackett, prin. Fax 743-7577

Paden City, Wetzel, Pop. 2,615
Wetzel County SD
Supt. — See New Martinsville
Paden City HS 200/7-12
201 N 4th Ave 26159 304-337-2266
Jason Salva, prin. Fax 337-2290

Parkersburg, Wood, Pop. 30,848
Wood County SD 13,400/PK-12
1210 13th St 26101 304-420-9663
Patrick Law, supt. Fax 420-9513
www.edline.net/pages/WCS
Blennerhassett MS 500/6-8
444 Jewell Rd 26101 304-863-3356
Jim Hostottle, prin. Fax 863-3357
Caperton Center for Applied Tech Vo/Tech
300 Campus Dr 26104 304-424-8365
Fax 424-8366
Edison MS 700/6-8
1201 Hillcrest St 26101 304-420-9525
Jean Mewshaw, prin. Fax 420-9527
Hamilton MS 600/6-8
3501 Cadillac Dr 26104 304-420-9547
Kevin Campbell, prin. Fax 420-9567
Parkersburg HS 1,800/9-12
2101 Dudley Ave 26101 304-420-9595
Pam Goots, prin. Fax 420-9604
Parkersburg South HS 1,600/9-12
1511 Blizzard Dr 26101 304-420-9610
Tom Eschbacher, prin. Fax 420-9607
Van Devender MS 400/6-8
918 31st St 26104 304-420-9645
Steve Taylor, prin. Fax 420-9647
Wood County Technical Center Vo/Tech
1515 Blizzard Dr 26101 304-420-9501
Doug Kiger, prin. Fax 485-1048
Other Schools – See Vienna, Williamstown

Camden Clark Memorial Hospital Post-Sec.
800 Garfield Ave 26101 304-424-2204
Mountain State College Post-Sec.
1508 Spring St 26101 304-485-5487
National College Post-Sec.
110 Park Shopping Center Dr 26101 304-699-3005
Parkersburg Catholic HS 200/7-12
3201 Fairview Ave 26104 304-485-6341
Karen Robinson, prin. Fax 485-4697
Parkersburg Christian S 100/K-12
1093 Core Rd 26104 304-485-6654
Fax 428-4444
West Virginia University at Parkersburg Post-Sec.
300 Campus Dr 26104 304-424-8000

Parsons, Tucker, Pop. 1,472
Tucker County SD 1,100/PK-12
501 Chestnut St 26287 304-478-2771
Eddie Campbell Ed.D., supt. Fax 478-3422
www.tuckercountyschools.com
Other Schools – See Hambleton

Paw Paw, Morgan, Pop. 498
Morgan County SD
Supt. — See Berkeley Springs
Paw Paw JSHS 100/7-12
60 Pirate Cir 25434 304-947-7425
Melinda Kasekamp, prin. Fax 947-5513

Petersburg, Grant, Pop. 2,438
Grant County SD 1,900/PK-12
204 Jefferson Ave 26847 304-257-1011
Dr. DeEdra Bolton, supt. Fax 257-2453
www.grantcountyschools.com
Petersburg JSHS 700/7-12
207 Viking Dr 26847 304-257-1444
Randolph West, prin. Fax 257-2453
South Branch Career & Technical Center Vo/Tech
401 Pierpont St 26847 304-257-1331
Shawn Dilly, dir. Fax 257-2270

Peterstown, Monroe, Pop. 646
Monroe County SD
Supt. — See Union
Peterstown MS 300/5-8
36 College Dr 24963 304-753-4322
Steven Ballengee, prin. Fax 753-5376

Philippi, Barbour, Pop. 2,882
Barbour County SD 2,500/PK-12
105 S Railroad St 26416 304-457-3030
Dr. F. Joseph Super, supt. Fax 457-3559
www.wvschools.com/barbourcountyschools/
Barbour County Vocational Center Vo/Tech
25 Horseshoe Dr 26416 304-457-4807
Rebecca Nesbitt, dir. Fax 457-3009
Barbour HS 800/9-12
99 Horseshoe Dr 26416 304-457-1360
Lisa Heinbaugh, prin. Fax 457-2658
Philippi MS 300/6-8
RR 3 Box 40 26416 304-457-2999
David Neff, prin. Fax 457-2561
Other Schools – See Belington

Alderson-Broaddus College Post-Sec.
101 College Hill Dr 26416 304-457-1700

Pickens, Randolph, Pop. 66
Randolph County SD
Supt. — See Elkins
Pickens S 50/K-12
PO Box 146 26230 304-924-5525
Diane Betler, prin. Fax 924-6460

Pine Grove, Wetzel, Pop. 551
Wetzel County SD
Supt. — See New Martinsville

Valley HS 200/9-12
1 Lumberjack Ln 26419 304-889-3151
Jackie Shepard, prin. Fax 889-2534

Pineville, Wyoming, Pop. 659
Wyoming County SD 4,200/PK-12
PO Box 69 24874 304-732-6262
Frank Blackwell, supt. Fax 732-7226
boe.wyom.k12.wv.us/
Pineville MS 300/5-8
PO Box 470 24874 304-732-6442
Terry Shumate, prin. Fax 732-6737
Wyoming County Career & Technical Center Vo/Tech
HC 72 Box 200 24874 304-732-8050
Sheila D. Mann, dir. Fax 732-8332
Other Schools – See Clear Fork, Mullens, New Richmond, Oceana

Poca, Putnam, Pop. 970
Putnam County SD
Supt. — See Winfield
Poca HS 500/9-12
RR 2 Box 5B 25159 304-755-5001
Victor Donalson, prin. Fax 755-5009
Poca MS 300/6-8
PO Box 647 25159 304-755-7343
Carl Caldwell, prin. Fax 755-8930

Point Pleasant, Mason, Pop. 4,266
Mason County SD 4,400/PK-12
1200 Main St 25550 304-675-4540
Suzanne Dickens, supt. Fax 675-7226
www.edline.net/pages/mcboewv
Mason County Career Center Vo/Tech
281 Scenic Dr 25550 304-675-3039
Stephen Kingery, dir. Fax 675-3413
Point Pleasant MSHS 1,200/7-12
280 Scenic Dr 25550 304-675-1350
William Cottrill, prin. Fax 675-7480
Other Schools – See Ashton, Mason

Princeton, Mercer, Pop. 6,324
Mercer County SD 9,200/PK-12
1403 Honaker Ave 24740 304-487-1551
Deborah Akers Ed.D., supt. Fax 425-5844
boe.merc.k12.wv.us/
Mercer County Technical Education Ctr Vo/Tech
1397 Stafford Dr, 304-425-9551
Linda Cox, prin. Fax 425-0833
Pikeview HS 700/9-12
3566 Eads Mill Rd, 304-384-7586
Ben Disibbio, prin. Fax 384-7901
Pike View MS 6-8
3550 Eads Mill Rd, 304-384-3600
J. Bryan Staten, prin. Fax 384-3605
Princeton HS 1,100/9-12
1321 Stafford Dr 24740 304-425-8101
Jack Parker, prin. Fax 425-2823
Princeton MS 600/6-8
300 N Johnston St 24740 304-425-7517
Danny Buckner, prin. Fax 487-2250
Other Schools – See Bluefield, Montcalm

Mercer Christian Academy 200/PK-12
314 Oakvale Rd Ste A 24740 304-425-5671
Robert Brooks, admin. Fax 431-2514
National College Post-Sec.
421 Hilltop Dr, 304-431-1600
Valley College Post-Sec.
616 Harrison St 24740 304-425-2323

Prosperity, Raleigh, Pop. 1,474

Greater Beckley Christian S 200/PK-12
PO Box 670 25909 304-255-1571
Dr. James Fritz, admin. Fax 582-0341

Ravenswood, Jackson, Pop. 3,825
Jackson County SD
Supt. — See Ripley
Ravenswood HS 500/9-12
100 Plaza Dr 26164 304-273-9301
Jaquetta Hendricks, prin. Fax 273-9556
Ravenswood MS 300/6-8
409 Sycamore St 26164 304-273-5480
Gary Higginbotham, prin. Fax 273-5746

Richwood, Nicholas, Pop. 2,006
Nicholas County SD
Supt. — See Summersville
Richwood HS 400/9-12
1 Valley Ave 26261 304-846-2591
James Weber, prin. Fax 846-2684
Richwood MS 300/6-8
2 Valley Ave 26261 304-846-2638
Gene Collins, prin. Fax 846-9632

Ridgeley, Mineral, Pop. 658
Mineral County SD
Supt. — See Keyser
Frankfort HS 500/9-12
393 Falcon Way 26753 304-726-4767
Joseph Riley, prin. Fax 726-8597
Frankfort MS 600/5-8
356 Golden Rd 26753 304-726-4339
Patricia Twigg, prin. Fax 726-4626

Ripley, Jackson, Pop. 3,223
Jackson County SD 5,000/PK-12
PO Box 770 25271 304-372-7300
Blaine Hess, supt. Fax 372-7312
jackson.wv.schoolwebpages.com
Ripley HS 1,000/9-12
2 School St 25271 304-372-7355
William Hosaflook, prin. Fax 372-7334
Ripley MS 800/6-8
1 W School St 25271 304-372-7350
Tim Brown, prin. Fax 372-7332
Other Schools – See Le Roy, Ravenswood

Romney, Hampshire, Pop. 1,832
Hampshire County SD 3,600/PK-12
111 School St 26757 304-822-3528
Robin Lewis, supt. Fax 822-5382
boe.hamp.k12.wv.us/
Hampshire HS 1,100/9-12
157 Trojan Way 26757 304-822-5016
Candy Canan, prin. Fax 822-5760
Romney MS 400/6-8
296 Calvert Dr 26757 304-822-5014
John Watson, prin. Fax 822-5744
Other Schools – See Capon Bridge

West Virginia Schools/Deaf and Blind Post-Sec.
26757

Ronceverte, Greenbrier, Pop. 1,742
Greenbrier County SD
Supt. — See Lewisburg
Eastern Greenbrier MS 900/6-8
RR 1 Box 150 24970 304-647-6498
Nancy Hanna, prin. Fax 647-3087

Saint Albans, Kanawha, Pop. 10,870
Kanawha County SD
Supt. — See Charleston
Hayes MS 500/6-8
830 Strawberry Rd 25177 304-722-0222
Scott Monty, prin. Fax 722-0247
McKinley MS 400/6-8
3000 Kanawha Ter 25177 304-722-0218
Amy Scott, prin. Fax 722-0246
Saint Albans HS 1,100/9-12
2100 Kanawha Ter 25177 304-722-0212
Jeff Kelley, prin. Fax 722-0211

Mountaineer Beauty College Post-Sec.
PO Box 547 25177 304-727-9999

Saint Marys, Pleasants, Pop. 1,851
Pleasants County SD 1,300/PK-12
202 Fairview Ave 26170 304-684-2215
George Wells, supt. Fax 684-3569
www.edline.net/pages/pleasantscountyschools
Mid-Ohio Valley Technical Institute Vo/Tech
2134 N Pleasants Hwy 26170 304-684-2464
Ryan Haught, prin. Fax 684-2544
Saint Marys HS 400/9-12
1002 2nd St 26170 304-684-2421
Jayne Tebay, prin. Fax 684-3859
Other Schools – See Belmont

Salem, Harrison, Pop. 1,554

Miracle Meadows S 50/K-12
99 Miracle Meadows Dr 26426 304-782-3628
Gayle Clark, dir. Fax 782-3660
Salem International University Post-Sec.
PO Box 500 26426 888-235-5024

Scott Depot, Putnam

Teays Valley Christian S 300/K-12
4373 Teays Valley Rd 25560 304-757-9550
Jack Davis, prin. Fax 757-2560

Seth, Boone
Boone County SD
Supt. — See Madison
Sherman HS 400/9-12
PO Box AB 25181 304-837-3301
Todd Barnette, prin. Fax 837-7529
Sherman JHS 200/7-8
PO Box AA 25181 304-837-3694
Fax 837-7603

Shady Spring, Raleigh, Pop. 2,968
Raleigh County SD
Supt. — See Beckley
Shady Spring HS 800/9-12
PO Box 2001 25918 304-256-4647
Danny Moye, prin. Fax 256-4711
Shady Spring MS 700/6-8
500 Flat Top Rd 25918 304-256-4570
Gary Nichols, prin. Fax 256-4612

Shenandoah Junction, Jefferson, Pop. 673
Jefferson County SD
Supt. — See Charles Town
Jefferson HS 1,400/9-12
4141 Flowing Springs Rd 25442 304-725-8491
Howard Guth, prin. Fax 728-6590
Wildwood MS 600/6-8
1209 Shenandoah Junction Rd 25442 304-728-4518
Patricia Votel, prin. Fax 728-9521

Shepherdstown, Jefferson, Pop. 1,690
Jefferson County SD
Supt. — See Charles Town
Shepherdstown MS 300/6-8
54 Minden St 25443 304-876-6120
Betsey Best, prin. Fax 876-6428

Shepherd University Post-Sec.
PO Box 5000 25443 304-876-5000

Shinnston, Harrison, Pop. 2,173
Harrison County SD
Supt. — See Clarksburg
Lincoln HS 600/9-12
100 Jerry Toth Dr 26431 304-326-7400
Brad Underwood, prin. Fax 592-3415

Sistersville, Tyler, Pop. 1,391
Tyler County SD
Supt. — See Middlebourne
Tyler Consolidated HS 400/9-12
1993 Silver Knight Dr 26175 304-758-9000
Kent Yoho, prin. Fax 758-9006

Tyler Consolidated MS 300/6-8
1993 Silver Knight Dr 26175 304-758-9000
Tab Mathis, prin. Fax 758-9006

Smithers, Fayette, Pop. 800
Fayette County SD
Supt. — See Fayetteville
Valley MSHS 500/6-12
PO Box 459 25186 304-442-8284
Lee Loy, prin. Fax 442-5865

Sophia, Raleigh, Pop. 1,330
Raleigh County SD
Supt. — See Beckley
Independence MS 500/6-8
PO Box 1171 25921 304-683-4542
Randy Adkins, prin. Fax 683-4552

South Charleston, Kanawha, Pop. 13,050
Kanawha County SD
Supt. — See Charleston
South Charleston HS 1,000/9-12
1 Eagle Way 25309 304-766-0352
Michael Arbogast, prin. Fax 768-4663
South Charleston MS 400/6-8
400 3rd Ave 25303 304-348-1918
Henry Graves, prin. Fax 744-4869

Spencer, Roane, Pop. 2,289
Roane County SD 2,500/PK-12
PO Box 609 25276 304-927-6400
Mickey Blackwell, supt. Fax 927-6402
www.roanecountyschools.com/
Roane County HS 700/9-12
1 Raider Way 25276 304-927-6420
Mitchell Nida, prin. Fax 927-6404
Spencer MS 500/5-8
102 Chapman Ave 25276 304-927-6415
Jacqueline Durst, prin. Fax 927-6416

Summersville, Nicholas, Pop. 3,550
Nicholas County SD 4,000/PK-12
400 Old Main Dr 26651 304-872-3611
Beverly Kingery, supt. Fax 872-4626
boe.nich.k12.wv.us
Nicholas County HS 800/9-12
30 Grizzley Ln 26651 304-872-2141
Kendra Rapp, prin. Fax 872-3026
Summersville MS 600/6-8
40 Grizzley Ln 26651 304-872-5092
Bethany King, prin. Fax 872-6314
Other Schools – See Craigsville, Richwood

New Life Christian Academy 100/PK-12
899 Broad St 26651 304-872-1148
Dennis Chasteen, admin. Fax 872-7477

Sutton, Braxton, Pop. 987
Braxton County SD 2,200/PK-12
98 Carter Braxton Dr 26601 304-765-7101
Dennis Albright, supt. Fax 765-7148
boe.brax.k12.wv.us/
Braxton County HS 700/9-12
200 Jerry Burton Dr 26601 304-765-7331
Dawn Dooley, prin. Fax 765-7976
Braxton County MS 600/5-8
100 Carter Braxton Dr 26601 304-765-2644
Denver Drake, prin. Fax 765-2696

Tunnelton, Preston, Pop. 293
Preston County SD
Supt. — See Kingwood
South Preston MS 100/6-8
48 Middle School Dr 26444 304-568-2331
Steve Plum, prin. Fax 568-2759

Union, Monroe, Pop. 551
Monroe County SD 1,900/PK-12
PO Box 330 24983 304-772-3094
Joetta Basile, supt. Fax 772-5020
boe.monr.k12.wv.us
Other Schools – See Lindside, Peterstown

Upperglade, Webster
Webster County SD
Supt. — See Webster Springs
Webster County HS 500/9-12
1 Highlander Dr 26266 304-226-5772
Stacey Cutlip, prin. Fax 226-5792

Van, Boone, Pop. 209
Boone County SD
Supt. — See Madison
Van JSHS 200/6-12
PO Box 100 25206 304-245-8237
Matthew Riggs, prin. Fax 245-8695

Christian Faith Academy 50/K-12
PO Box 210 25206 304-245-5711
Melanie Harvey, prin. Fax 823-0573

Vienna, Wood, Pop. 10,628
Wood County SD
Supt. — See Parkersburg
Jackson MS 600/6-8
1601 34th St 26105 304-420-9551
Richard Summers, prin. Fax 295-9954

Ohio Valley University Post-Sec.
1 Campus View Dr 26105 304-865-6000

Wayne, Wayne, Pop. 1,402
Wayne County SD 7,400/PK-12
212 N Court St 25570 304-272-5116
Gary Adkins, supt. Fax 272-6500
boe.wayn.k12.wv.us
Wayne HS 600/9-12
100 Pioneer Rd 25570 304-272-5639
Sara Stapleton, prin. Fax 272-6439
Wayne MS 600/6-8
200 Pioneer Rd 25570 304-272-3227
Beth Webb, prin. Fax 272-5811
Other Schools – See Ceredo, Crum, Fort Gay, Huntington, Kenova

Webster Springs, Webster, Pop. 772
Webster County SD 1,500/PK-12
315 S Main St 26288 304-847-5638
Dr. Martha Dean, supt. Fax 847-2538
boe.webs.k12.wv.us/
Other Schools – See Cowen, Upperglade

Weirton, Hancock, Pop. 19,434
Hancock County SD
Supt. — See New Cumberland
Weir HS 600/9-12
100 Red Rider Rd 26062 304-748-7600
Dan Enich, prin. Fax 748-7602
Weir MS 600/5-8
125 Sinclair Ave 26062 304-748-6080
Terry McAtee, prin. Fax 748-0847

Madonna HS 200/9-12
150 Michael Way 26062 304-723-0545
Steve Grasser, prin. Fax 723-0564
West Virginia Northern Community College Post-Sec.
150 Park Ave 26062 304-723-2210

Welch, McDowell, Pop. 2,358
McDowell County SD 3,500/PK-12
30 Central Ave 24801 304-436-8441
Nelson Spencer, supt. Fax 436-4008
boe.mcdo.k12.wv.us
McDowell County Vocational Tech Ctr Vo/Tech
PO Box V 24001 304-436-3488
Dennis Jarvis, prin. Fax 436-8063
Mount View HS 400/9-12
950 Mount View Rd 24801 304-436-2939
Jonathan Henry, prin. Fax 436-4714
Mount View MS 400/6-8
960 Mount View Rd 24801 304-436-4657
Leon Gravely, prin. Fax 436-3472
Other Schools – See Avondale, Bradshaw

Wellsburg, Brooke, Pop. 2,772
Brooke County SD 3,300/PK-12
1201 Pleasant Ave 26070 304-737-3481
Dr. Kathy Kidder-Wilkerson, supt. Fax 737-3480
www.edline.net/pages/brookecountyschools
Brooke County Alternative Learning Ctr Alt
29 Bruin Dr 26070 304-527-1410
Melissa Figlioli, admin. Fax 527-3604
Brooke HS 1,100/9-12
29 Bruin Dr 26070 304-527-1410
Toni Ann Shute, prin. Fax 527-3604
Wellsburg MS 500/5-8
1447 Main St 26070 304-737-2922
Jennifer Schiffbauer, prin. Fax 737-2976
Other Schools – See Follansbee

West Liberty, Ohio, Pop. 1,514

West Liberty University Post-Sec.
208 University Dr 26074 304-336-5000

Weston, Lewis, Pop. 4,051
Lewis County SD 2,600/PK-12
239 Court Ave 26452 304-269-8300
Dr. Joseph Mace, supt. Fax 269-8305
www.edline.net/pages/Lewis_County_School_District
Bland MS 700/5-8
358 Court Ave 26452 304-269-8325
Rhonda Judy, prin. Fax 269-8310
Lewis County HS 800/9-12
205 Minuteman Dr 26452 304-269-8315
Timothy Derico, prin. Fax 269-8319

West Union, Doddridge, Pop. 823
Doddridge County SD 1,200/PK-12
103 Sistersville Pike 26456 304-873-2300
Rick Coffman, supt. Fax 873-2210
boe.dodd.k12.wv.us
Doddridge County HS 400/9-12
79 Bulldog Dr 26456 304-873-2521
Gregory Kuhns, prin. Fax 873-1873
Doddridge County MS 300/5-8
65 Doddridge County School 26456 304-873-2332
Dr. Deborah Kuhns, prin. Fax 873-2541

Wheeling, Ohio, Pop. 27,794
Marshall County SD
Supt. — See Moundsville
Sherrard MS 400/6-8
1000 Fairmont Pike 26003 304-233-3331
Cassie Porter, prin. Fax 233-6418

Ohio County SD 5,300/PK-12
2203 National Rd 26003 304-243-0300
Dianna Vargo, supt. Fax 243-0328
wphs.ohio.k12.wv.us/ocbe/
Bridge Street MS 300/6-8
19 Junior Ave 26003 304-243-0381
Raquel Welch, prin. Fax 243-0385
Triadelphia MS 400/6-8
1636 National Rd 26003 304-243-0387
Walter Saunders, prin. Fax 243-0392
Wheeling MS 200/6-8
3500 Chapline St 26003 304-243-0425
Richard Jones, prin. Fax 243-0426
Wheeling Park HS 1,700/9-12
1976 Park View Rd 26003 304-243-0400
Amy Minch, prin. Fax 243-0449

Central Catholic HS 300/9-12
75 14th St 26003 304-233-1660
Julie Shively, prin. Fax 233-3187
Linsly S 500/5-12
60 Knox Ln 26003 304-233-3260
Chad Barnett, hdmstr. Fax 232-1975
Ohio Valley Medical Center Post-Sec.
2000 Eoff St 26003 304-234-8294
Scott College of Cosmetology Post-Sec.
1502 Market St 26003 304-232-7798
West Virginia Business College Post-Sec.
1052 Main St 26003 304-232-0361
West Virginia Northern Community College Post-Sec.
1704 Market St 26003 304-233-5900
Wheeling Hospital Post-Sec.
1 Medical Park 26003 304-243-3000
Wheeling Jesuit University Post-Sec.
316 Washington Ave 26003 304-243-2000

Williamson, Mingo, Pop. 3,116
Mingo County SD 3,700/PK-12
RR 2 Box 310 25661 304-235-3333
Randy Keathley, supt. Fax 235-3410
mingoboe.us/
Tug Valley HS 400/9-12
555 Panther Ave 25661 304-235-2266
Johnny Branch, prin. Fax 235-2636
Williamson MS 200/5-8
701 Alderson St 25661 304-235-3430
Helen Curry, prin. Fax 235-5567
Other Schools – See Delbarton, Gilbert, Matewan

Southern WV Community & Technical Coll. Post-Sec.
1601 Armory Dr 25661 304-235-6046

Williamstown, Wood, Pop. 2,880
Wood County SD
Supt. — See Parkersburg
Williamstown HS 600/7-12
219 W 5th St 26187 304-375-6151
Pat Peters, prin. Fax 375-6194

Winfield, Putnam, Pop. 2,257
Putnam County SD 9,600/PK-12
9 Courthouse Dr 25213 304-586-0500
Harold Hatfield, supt. Fax 586-0553
www.putnamschools.com
Winfield HS 800/9-12
3022 Winfield Rd 25213 304-586-3279
Bruce McGrew, prin. Fax 586-3601
Winfield MS 600/6-8
3280 Winfield Rd 25213 304-586-3072
Gary Cook, prin. Fax 586-0920
Other Schools – See Buffalo, Eleanor, Hurricane, Poca

WISCONSIN

WISCONSIN DEPARTMENT PUBLIC INSTRUCTION
PO Box 7841, Madison 53707-7841
Telephone 608-266-3390
Fax 608-267-1052
Website dpi.wi.gov

Superintendent of Public Instruction Tony Evers PhD

COOPERATIVE EDUCATIONAL SERVICE AGENCIES (CESA)

CESA 1
Jim Rickabaugh, admin. 262-787-9500
N25W23131 Paul Rd Ste 100 Fax 787-9501
Pewaukee 53072
www.cesa1.k12.wi.us

CESA 2
Gary Albrecht, admin. 262-473-1473
1221 Innovation Dr Fax 472-2269
Whitewater 53190
www.cesa2.k12.wi.us

CESA 3
Joe Price, admin., 1300 Industrial Dr 608-822-3276
Fennimore 53809 Fax 822-3860
www.cesa3.k12.wi.us

CESA 4
Guy Leavitt, admin. 800-514-3075
923 Garland St E Fax 786-4801
West Salem 54669
www.cesa4.k12.wi.us

CESA 5
Jeremy Biehl, admin. 608-742-8811
PO Box 564, Portage 53901 Fax 742-2384
www.cesa5.org/

CESA 6
Joan Wade, admin. 920-233-2372
2935 Universal Ct, Oshkosh 54904 Fax 236-0580
www.cesa6.k12.wi.us

CESA 7
Jeffery Dickert, admin. 920-492-5960
595 Baeten Rd, Green Bay 54304 Fax 492-5965
www.cesa7.k12.wi.us

CESA 8
Donald Viegut, admin. 920-855-2114
PO Box 320, Gillett 54124 Fax 855-2299
www.cesa8.k12.wi.us

CESA 9
Karen Wendorf-Heldt, admin. 715-453-2141
PO Box 449, Tomahawk 54487 Fax 453-7519
www.cesa9.k12.wi.us

CESA 10
Mike Haynes, admin. 715-723-0341
725 W Park Ave Fax 720-2070
Chippewa Falls 54729
www.cesa10.k12.wi.us

CESA 11
Jerry Walters, admin. 715-986-2020
225 Ostermann Dr Fax 986-2040
Turtle Lake 54889
www.cesa11.k12.wi.us

CESA 12
Kenneth Kasinski, admin. 715-682-2363
618 Beaser Ave, Ashland 54806 Fax 682-7244
www.cesa12.k12.wi.us

PUBLIC, PRIVATE AND CATHOLIC SECONDARY SCHOOLS

Abbotsford, Clark, Pop. 2,301
Abbotsford SD 700/PK-12
PO Box A 54405 715-223-6715
Reed Welsh, supt. Fax 223-4239
www.abbotsford.k12.wi.us
Abbotsford JSHS 300/6-12
PO Box 70 54405 715-223-2386
Lucas Barth, prin. Fax 223-4239
Falcon Enterprise Alternative HS Alt
PO Box A 54405 715-223-0118
Kate Hallstrand, prin. Fax 223-0119

Adams, Adams, Pop. 1,940
Adams-Friendship Area SD
Supt. — See Friendship
Adams-Friendship HS 600/9-12
1109 E North St 53910 608-339-3921
Tanya Kotlowski, prin. Fax 339-2569
Adams-Friendship MS 400/6-8
420 N Main St 53910 608-339-4064
Jeffrey Krull, prin. Fax 339-2434

Mid-State Technical College Post-Sec.
401 N Main St 53910 608-339-3379

Albany, Green, Pop. 1,005
Albany SD 400/PK-12
PO Box 349 53502 608-862-3225
Stephen Guenther, supt. Fax 862-3230
www.albany.k12.wi.us
Albany HS 100/9-12
PO Box 349 53502 608-862-3135
Traci Davis, prin. Fax 862-3230
Albany MS 100/5-8
PO Box 349 53502 608-862-3135
Traci Davis, prin. Fax 862-3230

Algoma, Kewaunee, Pop. 3,136
Algoma SD 600/PK-12
1715 Division St 54201 920-487-7001
Ronald Welch, supt. Fax 487-7016
www.alghs.k12.wi.us
Algoma MSHS 300/7-12
1715 Division St 54201 920-487-7001
Nicholas Cochart, prin. Fax 487-7005

Alma, Buffalo, Pop. 776
Alma SD 300/PK-12
S1618 State Road 35 54610 608-685-4416
Steven Sedlmayr, supt. Fax 685-4446
www.alma.k12.wi.us
Alma HS 100/9-12
S1618 State Road 35 54610 608-685-4416
Steven Sedlmayr, prin. Fax 685-4446

Alma Center, Jackson, Pop. 492
Alma Center-Humbird-Merrillan SD 600/PK-12
PO Box 308 54611 715-964-8271
Robert Fasbender, supt. Fax 964-1005
www.achm.k12.wi.us
Lincoln HS 200/9-12
PO Box 308 54611 715-964-5311
Paul Janson, prin. Fax 964-1005
Lincoln JHS 100/7-8
PO Box 308 54611 715-964-5311
Paul Janson, prin. Fax 964-1005

Almond, Portage, Pop. 447
Almond-Bancroft SD 200/PK-12
1336 Elm St 54909 715-366-2941
Dann Boxx, admin. Fax 366-2940
www.abschools.k12.wi.us
Almond-Bancroft S 200/PK-12
1336 Elm St 54909 715-366-2941
Jeff Rykal, prin. Fax 366-2943

Altoona, Eau Claire, Pop. 6,546
Altoona SD 1,500/PK-12
1903 Bartlett Ave 54720 715-839-6032
Connie Biedron, supt. Fax 839-6066
www.altoona.k12.wi.us
Altoona HS 500/9-12
711 7th St W 54720 715-839-6031
Jeff Pepowski, prin. Fax 839-6028
Altoona MS 400/5-8
1903 Bartlett Ave 54720 715-839-6030
Gary Pszeniczny, prin. Fax 839-6099

Amery, Polk, Pop. 2,886
Amery SD 1,700/PK-12
543 Minneapolis Ave S 54001 715-268-9771
Stephen Schiell, supt. Fax 268-7300
www.amerysd.k12.wi.us
Amery HS 500/9-12
555 Minneapolis Ave S 54001 715-268-9771
Shawn Doerfler, prin. Fax 268-7792
Amery MS 400/6-8
501 Minneapolis Ave S 54001 715-268-9771
Thomas Bensen, prin. Fax 268-4967

Amherst, Portage, Pop. 1,031
Tomorrow River SD 1,000/PK-12
357 N Main St 54406 715-824-5521
LeAnn Chase, supt. Fax 824-7177
www.amherst.k12.wi.us
Amherst HS 300/9-12
357 N Main St 54406 715-824-5522
Mark Luetschwager, prin. Fax 824-5454
Amherst MS 200/6-8
357 N Main St 54406 715-824-5524
Phillip Tubbs, prin. Fax 824-5454

Antigo, Langlade, Pop. 8,127
Antigo SD 2,600/PK-12
120 S Dorr St 54409 715-627-4355
Steven Smolek, supt. Fax 623-3279
www.antigo.k12.wi.us/
Antigo HS 900/9-12
1900 10th Ave 54409 715-623-7611
Thomas Zamzow, prin. Fax 623-7624
Antigo MS 500/6-8
815 7th Ave 54409 715-623-4173
Douglas Knol, prin. Fax 627-4982

Appleton, Outagamie, Pop. 71,375
Appleton Area SD 15,200/PK-12
PO Box 2019 54912 920-832-6161
Lee Allinger, supt. Fax 832-1725
www.aasd.k12.wi.us
Appleton East HS 1,400/9-12
2121 E Emmers Dr 54915 920-832-6212
Matt Mineau, prin. Fax 832-4880
Appleton North HS 1,500/9-12
5000 N Ballard Rd 54913 920-832-4300
James Huggins, prin. Fax 832-4301
Appleton West HS 1,300/9-12
610 N Badger Ave 54914 920-832-6219
Greg Hartjes, prin. Fax 832-4198
Einstein MS 400/7-8
324 E Florida Ave 54911 920-832-6240
Dave Mueller, prin. Fax 832-6164
Madison MS 600/7-8
2020 S Carpenter St 54915 920-832-6276
David Torrey, prin. Fax 832-6337
Roosevelt MS 300/7-8
318 E Brewster St 54911 920-832-6294
Al Brant, prin. Fax 832-4605
Wilson MS 400/7-8
225 N Badger Ave 54914 920-832-6226
John Magas, prin. Fax 832-4857

Fox Valley Lutheran HS 600/9-12
5300 N Meade St 54913 920-739-4441
Paul Hartwig, prin. Fax 739-4418
Fox Valley Technical College Post-Sec.
PO Box 2277 54912 920-735-5600
Gill-Tech Academy of Hair Design Post-Sec.
230 S McCarthy Rd 54914 920-739-8684
Globe University Post-Sec.
5045 W Grande Market Dr 54913 920-364-1100
Lawrence University Post-Sec.
711 E Boldt Way 54911 920-832-7000
Rasmussen College Post-Sec.
3500 E Destination Dr # 100 54915 920-750-5900
St. Elizabeth Hospital Post-Sec.
1506 S Oneida St 54915 920-738-2015
St. Joseph MS 300/6-8
2626 N Oneida St 54911 920-730-8849
Joseph Linsmeier, prin. Fax 730-4147
Xavier HS 500/9-12
1600 W Prospect Ave 54914 920-733-6632
Matt Reynebeau, prin. Fax 733-5513

Arcadia, Trempealeau, Pop. 2,912
Arcadia SD 1,100/PK-12
756 Raider Dr 54612 608-323-3315
Louie Ferguson, supt. Fax 323-2256
www.arcadia.k12.wi.us/
Arcadia HS 300/9-12
756 Raider Dr 54612 608-323-3334
Michele Butler, prin. Fax 323-2256
Arcadia MS 200/6-8
358 E River St 54612 608-323-7500
Sam Ruud, prin. Fax 323-7015

Argyle, Lafayette, Pop. 857
Argyle SD 300/PK-12
PO Box 256 53504 608-543-3318
Dr. Robert Gilpatrick, supt. Fax 543-3868
www.argyle.k12.wi.us
Argyle MSHS 200/6-12
PO Box 256 53504 608-543-3318
Phillip Updike, prin. Fax 543-3868

Ashland, Ashland, Pop. 7,896
Ashland SD 2,200/PK-12
2000 Beaser Ave 54806 715-682-7080
Keith Hilts, supt. Fax 682-7097
www.ashland.k12.wi.us
Ashland HS 700/9-12
1900 Beaser Ave 54806 715-682-7089
Barry Wolff, prin. Fax 682-2075

Ashland MS 500/6-8
203 11th St E 54806 715-682-7087
Paul Gilbertson, prin. Fax 682-7944

Northland College Post-Sec.
1411 Ellis Ave 54806 715-682-1699
Wisconsin Indianhead Technical College Post-Sec.
2100 Beaser Ave 54806 715-682-4591

Athens, Marathon, Pop. 1,096
Athens SD 500/PK-12
PO Box F 54411 715-257-7511
Timothy Micke, supt. Fax 257-7502
www.athens1.org
Athens HS 200/9-12
PO Box F 54411 715-257-7511
Timothy Micke, prin. Fax 257-7651
Athens MS 100/6-8
PO Box F 54411 715-257-7511
Timothy Micke, prin. Fax 257-7651

Auburndale, Wood, Pop. 703
Auburndale SD 900/PK-12
PO Box 139 54412 715-652-2117
Gerald Eichman, supt. Fax 652-2836
www.aubschools.com
Auburndale MSHS 500/6-12
PO Box 190 54412 715-652-2115
Aaron Engel, prin. Fax 652-6322

Augusta, Eau Claire, Pop. 1,531
Augusta SD 600/PK-12
E19320 Bartig Rd 54722 715-286-3300
William Perry, supt. Fax 286-3336
www.augusta.k12.wi.us
Augusta MSHS 200/6-12
E19320 Bartig Rd 54722 715-286-2291
Jason Kestner, prin. Fax 286-3393

Baldwin, Saint Croix, Pop. 3,900
Baldwin-Woodville Area SD 1,600/PK-12
550 US Highway 12 54002 715-684-3411
Russell Helland, supt. Fax 684-3168
www.bwsd.k12.wi.us/
Baldwin-Woodville HS 500/9-12
1000 13th Ave 54002 715-684-3321
Eric Russell, prin. Fax 684-5160
Other Schools – See Woodville

Balsam Lake, Polk, Pop. 991
Unity SD 1,100/PK-12
1908 150th St 54810 715-825-3515
Brandon Robinson, supt. Fax 825-3517
www.unity.k12.wi.us/
Unity HS 400/9-12
1908 150th St 54810 715-825-2131
Jason Cress, prin. Fax 825-4430
Unity MS 300/5-8
1908 150th St 54810 715-825-2101
Elizabeth Jorgensen, prin. Fax 825-4410

Bangor, LaCrosse, Pop. 1,446
Bangor SD 600/PK-12
PO Box 99 54614 608-486-2331
David Laehn, supt. Fax 486-4587
www.bangor.k12.wi.us
Bangor MSHS 300/6-12
PO Box 99 54614 608-486-2331
Don Addington, prin. Fax 486-4587

Baraboo, Sauk, Pop. 11,882
Baraboo SD 3,000/PK-12
101 2nd Ave 53913 608-355-4698
Crystal Ritzenthaler Ed.D., supt. Fax 355-3960
www.baraboo.k12.wi.us
Baraboo HS 1,000/9-12
1201 Draper St 53913 608-355-3940
William Loss, prin. Fax 355-3962
Young MS 700/6-8
1531 Draper St 53913 608-355-3930
John Gunnell, prin. Fax 355-3998

University of Wisconsin Baraboo/Sauk Co. Post-Sec.
1006 Connie Rd 53913 608-355-5230

Barneveld, Iowa, Pop. 1,221
Barneveld SD 400/K-12
PO Box 98 53507 608-924-4711
Joe Bertone, supt. Fax 924-1646
www.barneveld.k12.wi.us
Barneveld MSHS 200/6-12
PO Box 98 53507 608-924-4711
Kevin Knudson, prin. Fax 924-1646

Barron, Barron, Pop. 3,378
Barron Area SD 1,300/PK-12
100 W River Ave 54812 715-537-5612
Craig Broeren, supt. Fax 637-5161
www.barron.k12.wi.us
Barron HS 400/9-12
1050 E Woodland Ave 54812 715-537-5627
Kirk Haugestuen, prin. Fax 637-1603
Riverview MS 300/5-8
135 W River Ave 54812 715-537-5641
John Gevens, prin. Fax 637-5373

Bayfield, Bayfield, Pop. 459
Bayfield SD 400/PK-12
300 N 4th St 54814 715-779-3201
Dr. David Aslyn, supt. Fax 779-5268
www.bayfield.k12.wi.us
Bayfield HS 100/9-12
300 N 4th St 54814 715-779-3201
Scott Stralka, prin. Fax 779-5226
Bayfield MS 100/6-8
300 N 4th St 54814 715-779-3201
Scott Stralka, prin. Fax 779-5226

Bayside, Milwaukee, Pop. 4,320
Fox Point Bayside SD
Supt. — See Fox Point
Bayside MS 400/5-8
601 E Ellsworth Ln 53217 414-247-4167
Don Galster, prin. Fax 351-7164

Beaver Dam, Dodge, Pop. 16,040
Beaver Dam SD 3,400/PK-12
705 McKinley St 53916 920-885-7300
Steven Vessey, supt. Fax 885-7305
www.beaverdam.k12.wi.us
Beaver Dam HS 1,000/9-12
500 Gould St 53916 920-885-7313
Mark DiStefano, prin. Fax 885-7317
Beaver Dam MS 700/6-8
108 4th St 53916 920-885-7365
Tonya Broyles-Brouillard, prin. Fax 885-7415
Smith Learning Academy 100/Alt
400 E Burnett St 53916 920-885-7423
Debra Lins, prin. Fax 885-7429

Moraine Park Technical College Post-Sec.
700 Gould St 53916 920-887-1101
Wayland Academy 200/9-12
101 N University Ave 53916 920-885-3373
Joseph Lennertz, head sch Fax 887-3373

Belleville, Dane, Pop. 2,367
Belleville SD 1,000/PK-12
625 W Church St 53508 608-424-3315
Dr. Randy Freese, supt. Fax 424-3486
www.belleville.k12.wi.us/
Belleville HS 300/9-12
635 W Church St 53508 608-424-1902
Rick Conroy, prin. Fax 424-3692
Belleville MS 100/7-8
625 W Church St 53508 608-424-1902
Rick Conroy, prin. Fax 424-3692

Belmont, Lafayette, Pop. 980
Belmont Community SD 300/K-12
PO Box 348 53510 608-762-5131
Jim Siedenburg, supt. Fax 762-5129
www.belmont.k12.wi.us
Belmont JSHS 100/7-12
PO Box 348 53510 608-762-5131
Christy Larson, prin. Fax 762-5129

Beloit, Rock, Pop. 35,780
Beloit SD 5,000/K-12
1633 Keeler Ave 53511 608-361-4000
Steve McNeal, supt. Fax 361-4122
www.sdb.k12.wi.us
Aldrich MS 600/6-8
1859 Northgate Dr 53511 608-361-3600
Mark Smullen, prin. Fax 361-3620
McNeel MS 800/6-8
1524 Frederick St 53511 608-361-3800
Anthony Bosco, prin. Fax 361-3820
Memorial HS 1,800/9-12
1225 4th St 53511 608-361-3000
Tom Johnson, prin. Fax 361-3080
Wright S 300/Alt
1033 Woodward Ave 53511 608-361-4300
Brice Gustafson, prin. Fax 361-4320

School District of Beloit Turner 1,400/PK-12
1237 E Inman Pkwy 53511 608-364-6372
Dr. Dennis McCarthy, supt. Fax 364-6373
www.turnerschools.org/
Turner HS 400/9-12
1231 E Inman Pkwy 53511 608-364-6370
Ryan Bertelsen, prin. Fax 365-4768
Turner MS 400/6-8
1237 E Inman Pkwy 53511 608-364-6367
Cory Everson, prin. Fax 364-6369

Beloit College Post-Sec.
700 College St 53511 608-363-2000
Rock County Christian HS 100/6-12
916 Bushnell St 53511 608-365-7378
Bob Cerniglia, admin. Fax 365-7382

Benton, Lafayette, Pop. 970
Benton SD 200/PK-12
PO Box 7 53803 608-759-4002
Kyle Luedtke, admin. Fax 759-3805
www.benton.k12.wi.us
Benton HS 100/7-12
PO Box 7 53803 608-759-4002
Kyle Luedtke, prin. Fax 759-3805

Berlin, Green Lake, Pop. 5,480
Berlin Area SD 1,600/PK-12
295 E Marquette St 54923 920-361-2004
Robert Eidahl, supt. Fax 361-2170
www.berlin.k12.wi.us
Berlin HS 600/9-12
222 Memorial Dr 54923 920-361-2000
Lynn Mork, prin. Fax 361-2005
Berlin MS 400/6-8
289 E Huron St 54923 920-361-2441
Rick Hammes, prin. Fax 361-3379

Birchwood, Washburn, Pop. 440
Birchwood SD 200/PK-12
300 S Wilson St 54817 715-354-3471
Frank Helquist, supt. Fax 354-3469
www.birchwood.k12.wi.us/
Birchwood HS 100/9-12
300 S Wilson St 54817 715-354-3471
Jeff Stanley, prin. Fax 354-3469

Black River Falls, Jackson, Pop. 3,539
Black River Falls SD 1,800/PK-12
301 N 4th St 54615 715-284-4357
Shelly Severson, supt. Fax 284-7064
www.brf.org
Black River Falls HS 500/9-12
1200 Pierce St 54615 715-284-4324
Thomas Chambers, prin. Fax 284-7626
Black River Falls MS 400/6-8
1202 Pierce St 54615 715-284-5315
David Roou, prin. Fax 284-0364

Blair, Trempealeau, Pop. 1,358
Blair-Taylor SD 600/PK-12
PO Box 125 54616 608-989-2881
Dennis Dervetski, supt. Fax 989-2451
btsd.k12.wi.us
Blair-Taylor MSHS 300/7-12
PO Box 107 54616 608-989-2525
Jeff Eide, prin. Fax 989-9161

Blanchardville, Lafayette, Pop. 822
Pecatonica Area SD 400/PK-12
PO Box 117 53516 608-523-4248
Nancy Hendrickson, supt. Fax 523-4286
www.pecatonica.k12.wi.us
Pecatonica JSHS 200/6-12
PO Box 117 53516 608-523-4285
Aaron Lancaster, prin. Fax 523-4286

Bloomer, Chippewa, Pop. 3,508
Bloomer SD 1,100/PK-12
1310 17th Ave 54724 715-568-2800
Dr. Mary Randall, supt. Fax 568-5315
www.bloomer.k12.wi.us
Bloomer HS 400/9-12
1310 17th Ave 54724 715-568-5300
Chad Steinmetz, prin. Fax 568-5304
Bloomer MS 300/5-8
600 Jackson St 54724 715-568-1025
Dr. Barry Kamrath, prin. Fax 568-3687

Bloomington, Grant, Pop. 728
River Ridge SD
Supt. — See Patch Grove
River Ridge MS 100/5-8
PO Box 97 53804 608-994-2711
Rodney Lewis, prin. Fax 994-2714

Bonduel, Shawano, Pop. 1,465
Bonduel SD 800/PK-12
PO Box 310 54107 715-758-4860
Peter Behnke, supt. Fax 758-4869
www.bonduel.k12.wi.us
Bonduel HS 300/9-12
PO Box 310 54107 715-758-4850
Patrick Rau, prin. Fax 758-4859
Bonduel MS 200/6-8
PO Box 310 54107 715-758-4840
Mark Margelofsky, prin. Fax 758-4849

Boscobel, Grant, Pop. 3,210
Boscobel Area SD 900/PK-12
1110 Park St 53805 608-375-4164
Dr. Stephen Smith, supt. Fax 375-2378
www.boscobel.k12.wi.us
Boscobel HS 300/9-12
300 Brindley St 53805 608-375-4161
Greg Bell, prin. Fax 375-2640
Boscobel MS 100/7-8
300 Brindley St 53805 608-375-4161
Greg Bell, prin. Fax 375-2640

Bowler, Shawano, Pop. 282
Bowler SD 400/PK-12
PO Box 8 54416 715-793-4101
Faith Gagnon, supt. Fax 793-1302
www.bowler.k12.wi.us
Bowler JSHS 200/7-12
PO Box 8 54416 715-793-4101
Kim Ninabuck, prin. Fax 793-1302

Boyceville, Dunn, Pop. 1,080
Boyceville Community SD 800/PK-12
1003 Tiffany St 54725 715-643-3647
Kevin Sipple, supt. Fax 643-3127
www.boyceville.k12.wi.us
Boyceville MSHS 300/7-12
1003 Tiffany St 54725 715-643-3647
Steven Glocke, prin. Fax 643-2209

Brillion, Calumet, Pop. 3,113
Brillion SD 900/PK-12
315 S Main St 54110 920-756-2368
Dominick Madison Ph.D., supt. Fax 756-3705
www.brillion.k12.wi.us
Brillion HS 300/9-12
W1101 County Road HR 54110 920-756-9238
Paul Nistler, prin. Fax 756-9427
Brillion MS 200/6-8
315 S Main St 54110 920-756-2166
Ann Hatch, prin. Fax 756-3705

Brodhead, Green, Pop. 3,270
Brodhead SD 1,100/PK-12
2501 W 5th Ave 53520 608-897-2141
Leonard Lueck, supt. Fax 897-2770
www.brodhead.k12.wi.us
Brodhead HS 400/9-12
2501 W 5th Ave 53520 608-897-2155
James Matthys, prin. Fax 897-3026
Brodhead MS 200/6-8
2100 W 9th Ave 53520 608-897-2184
Dr. Lisa Semrow, prin. Fax 897-2789

Brookfield, Waukesha, Pop. 37,413
Elmbrook SD 6,900/PK-12
PO Box 1830 53008 262-781-3030
Mark Hansen, supt. Fax 790-4095
www.elmbrookschools.org
Central HS 1,300/9-12
16900 Gebhardt Rd 53005 262-785-3910
Don La Bonte, prin. Fax 785-3993
East HS 1,300/9-12
3305 Lilly Rd 53005 262-781-3500
Dan Pavletich, prin. Fax 790-5445
Wisconsin Hills MS 900/6-8
18700 W Wisconsin Ave 53045 262-785-3960
Robyn Martino, prin. Fax 785-3967

Other Schools – See Elm Grove

Anthem College — Post-Sec.
440 S Executive Dr Ste 200 53005 — 888-852-7272
Brookfield Academy — 700/PK-12
3460 N Brookfield Rd 53045 — 262-783-3200
Heritage Christian Schools — 600/PK-12
175 S Barker Rd 53045 — 262-432-0333
Mark MacKay, prin. — Fax 432-0542
Ottawa University — Post-Sec.
245 S Executive Dr Ste 110 53005 — 262-879-0200

Brown Deer, Milwaukee, Pop. 11,652
Brown Deer SD — 1,700/PK-12
8200 N 60th St 53223 — 414-371-6750
Dr. Deb Kerr, admin. — Fax 371-6751
browndeer.schoolfusion.us
Brown Deer HS — 700/9-12
8060 N 60th St 53223 — 414-371-7000
James Piatt, prin. — Fax 371-7001
Brown Deer MS — 500/5-8
5757 W Dean Rd 53223 — 414-371-6900
Dr. Marirose Lucey, prin. — Fax 371-6901

Bruce, Rusk, Pop. 772
Bruce SD — 500/PK-12
104 W Washington Ave 54819 — 715-868-2533
Joni Weinert, supt. — Fax 868-2534
www.bruce.k12.wi.us
Bruce HS — 200/9-12
104 W Washington Ave 54819 — 715-868-2585
Larry Villiard, prin. — Fax 868-2534
Bruce MS — 100/6-8
104 W Washington Ave 54819 — 715-868-2585
Larry Villiard, prin. — Fax 868-2534

Brussels, Door
Southern Door SD — 1,200/PK-12
2073 County Road DK 54204 — 920-825-7311
Patricia Vickman, supt. — Fax 825-7311
www.southerndoor.k12.wi.us
Southern Door HS — 400/9-12
2073 County Road DK 54204 — 920-825-7333
Steve Bousley, prin. — Fax 825-7081
Southern Door MS — 300/6-8
2073 County Road DK 54204 — 920-825-7321
Gary Langenberg, prin. — Fax 825-7692

Burlington, Racine, Pop. 10,361
Burlington Area SD — 3,400/K-12
100 N Kane St 53105 — 262-763-0210
Peter Smet, supt. — Fax 763-0215
www.basd.k12.wi.us
Burlington HS — 1,300/9-12
400 Mc Canna Pkwy 53105 — 262-763-0200
Eric Burling, prin. — Fax 763-0216
Karcher MS — 500/7-8
225 Robert St 53105 — 262-763-0190
Marty McGinley, prin. — Fax 767-5580

Catholic Central HS — 100/9-12
148 McHenry St 53105 — 262-763-1510
Eric Henderson, prin. — Fax 763-1509

Butternut, Ashland, Pop. 367
Butternut SD — 100/PK-12
PO Box 247 54514 — 715-769-3434
Fax 769-3712
Butternut S — 100/PK-12
PO Box 247 54514 — 715-769-3434
Fax 769-3712

Cadott, Chippewa, Pop. 1,424
Cadott Community SD — 900/PK-12
PO Box 310 54727 — 715-289-3795
Joe Zydowsky, supt. — Fax 289-3748
www.cadott.k12.wi.us
Cadott HS — 300/9-12
PO Box 310 54727 — 715-289-3795
Matthew McDonough, prin. — Fax 289-3085
Cadott JHS — 100/7-8
PO Box 310 54727 — 715-289-3795
Matthew McDonough, prin. — Fax 289-3085

Cambria, Columbia, Pop. 765
Cambria-Friesland SD — 400/PK-12
410 E Edgewater St 53923 — 920-348-5548
John Litscher, supt. — Fax 348-5119
www.cf.k12.wi.us
Cambria-Friesland MSHS — 200/6-12
410 E Edgewater St 53923 — 920-348-5135
Rebecca Eberhardt, prin. — Fax 348-5119

Cambridge, Dane, Pop. 1,441
Cambridge SD — 900/PK-12
403 Blue Jay Way 53523 — 608-423-4345
Bernard Nikolay, supt. — Fax 423-9869
www.cambridge.k12.wi.us
Cambridge HS — 300/9-12
403 Blue Jay Way 53523 — 608-423-3261
Robert Rosen, prin. — Fax 423-9598
Nikolay MS — 200/6-8
211 South St 53523 — 608-423-7335
Krista Jones, prin. — Fax 423-4499

Cameron, Barron, Pop. 1,761
Cameron SD — 1,000/PK-12
PO Box 378 54822 — 715-458-4560
Randal Braun, supt. — Fax 458-4822
www.cameron.k12.wi.us
Cameron HS — 300/9-12
PO Box 378 54822 — 715-458-4560
Joseph Leschisin, prin. — Fax 458-4236
Cameron MS — 300/5-8
PO Box 378 54822 — 715-458-4560
Thomas Spanel, prin. — Fax 458-3436

Campbellsport, Fond du Lac, Pop. 1,998
Campbellsport SD — 1,400/PK-12
114 W Sheboygan St 53010 — 920-533-8381
Fax 533-5726
www.csd.k12.wi.us
Campbellsport HS — 500/9-12
114 W Sheboygan St 53010 — 920-533-4811
Kristen Langer, prin. — Fax 533-3521
Campbellsport MS — 200/6-8
114 W Sheboygan St 53010 — 920-533-4811
Kristen Langer, prin. — Fax 533-3521

Casco, Kewaunee, Pop. 569
Luxemburg-Casco SD
Supt. — See Luxemburg
Luxemburg-Casco MS — 300/7-8
619 Church Ave 54205 — 920-837-2205
Mike Snowberry, prin. — Fax 837-7517

Cashton, Monroe, Pop. 1,094
Cashton SD — 600/PK-12
PO Box 129 54619 — 608-654-5131
Bradford Saron, supt. — Fax 654-5136
www.cashton.k12.wi.us
Cashton JSHS — 300/6-12
PO Box 129 54619 — 608-654-5131
David Bell, prin. — Fax 654-5136

Cassville, Grant, Pop. 939
Cassville SD — 200/PK-12
715 E Amelia St 53806 — 608-725-5116
Leland Kulland, supt. — Fax 725-2353
www.cassvillesd.k12.wi.us
Cassville JSHS — 100/7-12
715 E Amelia St 53806 — 608-725-5116
John Luster, prin. — Fax 725-2353

Cazenovia, Sauk, Pop. 314
Weston SD — 300/PK-12
E2511A County Rd S 53924 — 608-986-2151
Tom Andres, supt. — Fax 986-2205
www.weston.k12.wi.us
Weston HS — 100/9-12
E2511A County Rd S 53924 — 608-986-2151
Melissa Wiegel, prin. — Fax 986-2205
Weston MS — 100/6-8
E2511A County Rd S 53924 — 608-986-2151
Melissa Wiegel, prin. — Fax 986-2205

Cedarburg, Ozaukee, Pop. 11,308
Cedarburg SD — 3,000/K-12
W68N611 Evergreen Blvd 53012 — 262-376-6100
Dr. Daryl Herrick, supt. — Fax 376-6110
www.cedarburg.k12.wi.us
Cedarburg HS — 1,100/9-12
W68N611 Evergreen Blvd 53012 — 262-376-6200
Jeffrey Nelson, prin. — Fax 376-6210
Webster MS — 700/6-8
W75N624 Wauwatosa Rd 53012 — 262-376-6500
Tony DeRosa, prin. — Fax 376-6510

Cedar Grove, Sheboygan, Pop. 2,097
Cedar Grove-Belgium Area SD — 1,100/PK-12
321 N 2nd St 53013 — 920-668-8686
Steven Shaw, supt. — Fax 668-8605
www.cedargrovebelgium.k12.wi.us/
Cedar Grove-Belgium HS — 300/9-12
321 N 2nd St 53013 — 920-668-8686
Lawrence Theiss, prin. — Fax 668-8605
Cedar Grove-Belgium MS — 300/5-8
321 N 2nd St 53013 — 920-668-8518
Dr. Jeanne Courneene, prin. — Fax 668-8566

Chetek, Barron, Pop. 2,205
Chetek-Weyerhaeuser Area SD — 800/PK-12
PO Box 6 54728 — 715-924-2226
Al Brown, supt. — Fax 924-2376
www.cwasd.k12.wi.us
Chetek-Weyerhaeuser Area HS — 300/9-12
PO Box 6 54728 — 715-924-3137
Larry Zeman, prin. — Fax 924-2921
Chetek-Weyerhaeuser Area MS — 200/6-8
PO Box 6 54728 — 715-924-3136
Bryan Yenter, prin. — Fax 924-1794

Chilton, Calumet, Pop. 3,890
Chilton SD — 1,200/PK-12
530 W Main St 53014 — 920-849-8109
Claire Martin, supt. — Fax 849-4539
www.chilton.k12.wi.us
Chilton HS — 400/9-12
530 W Main St 53014 — 920-849-2358
Ty Breitlow, prin. — Fax 849-3998
Chilton MS — 300/5-8
530 W Main St 53014 — 920-849-9152
Richard Appel, prin. — Fax 849-7210

Chippewa Falls, Chippewa, Pop. 13,496
Chippewa Falls Area USD — 4,600/PK-12
1130 Miles St 54729 — 715-726-2417
Brad Saron, supt. — Fax 726-2781
cfsd.chipfalls.k12.wi.us
Chippewa Falls HS — 1,500/9-12
735 Terrill St 54729 — 715-726-2406
Becky Davis, prin. — Fax 726-2792
Chippewa Falls MS — 1,000/6-8
750 Tropicana Blvd 54729 — 715-726-2400
Heidi Taylor-Eliopoulos, prin. — Fax 726-2789

McDonell Central HS — 200/7-12
1316 Bel Air Blvd 54729 — 715-723-9126
Br. Roger Betzold, prin. — Fax 723-1501
Notre Dame MS — 100/6-8
1316 Bel Air Blvd 54729 — 715-723-4777
Br. Roger Betzold, prin. — Fax 723-3353

Clayton, Polk, Pop. 562
Clayton SD — 400/PK-12
PO Box 130 54004 — 715-948-2163
Cathleen Shimon, supt. — Fax 948-2362
www.claytonsd.k12.wi.us
Clayton HS — 100/9-12
PO Box 130 54004 — 715-948-2163
Edward Cerney, prin. — Fax 948-2362
Clayton MS — 100/6-8
PO Box 130 54004 — 715-948-2163
Edward Cerney, prin. — Fax 948-2362

Clear Lake, Polk, Pop. 1,055
Clear Lake SD — 600/PK-12
1101 3rd St SW 54005 — 715-263-2114
Brad Ayer, supt. — Fax 263-2933
www.clearlake.k12.wi.us
Clear Lake HS — 200/9-12
1101 3rd St SW 54005 — 715-263-2113
George Smith, prin. — Fax 263-3550
Clear Lake JHS — 100/7-8
1101 3rd St SW 54005 — 715-263-2113
George Smith, prin. — Fax 263-3550

Cleveland, Manitowoc, Pop. 1,481

Lakeshore Technical College — Post-Sec.
1290 North Ave 53015 — 920-693-1000

Clinton, Rock, Pop. 2,131
Clinton Community SD — 1,200/PK-12
PO Box 566 53525 — 608-676-5482
Dr. Donald Childs, supt. — Fax 676-4444
www.clinton.k12.wi.us
Clinton HS — 400/9-12
PO Box 566 53525 — 608-676-2223
Nichole Erickson, prin. — Fax 676-4444
Clinton MS — 400/5-8
PO Box 559 53525 — 608-676-2275
Robert Parker, prin. — Fax 676-5176

Clintonville, Waupaca, Pop. 4,497
Clintonville SD — 1,400/PK-12
45 W Green Tree Rd 54929 — 715-823-7215
Tom O'Toole, supt. — Fax 823-1315
www.clintonville.k12.wi.us
Clintonville HS — 500/9-12
64 W Green Tree Rd 54929 — 715-823-7215
Lance Bagstad, prin. — Fax 823-1481
Clintonville MS — 400/5-8
255 N Main St 54929 — 715-823-7215
Tom Dechant, prin. — Fax 823-1443

Colby, Clark, Pop. 1,841
Colby SD — 1,000/PK-12
PO Box 139 54421 — 715-223-2301
Steven Kolden, supt. — Fax 223-4539
www.colby.k12.wi.us
Colby HS — 300/9-12
PO Box 110 54421 — 715-223-2338
Marcia Diedrich, prin. — Fax 223-4388
Colby MS — 300/5-8
PO Box 110 54421 — 715-223-8869
James Hagen, prin. — Fax 223-6754

Coleman, Marinette, Pop. 713
Coleman SD — 600/PK-12
343 Business 141 N 54112 — 920-897-4011
Dr. Brian Walters, supt. — Fax 897-2015
www.coleman.k12.wi.us
Coleman MSHS — 200/6-12
343 Business 141 N 54112 — 920-897-3822
Kelly Casper, prin. — Fax 897-2015

Colfax, Dunn, Pop. 1,143
Colfax SD — 700/PK-12
601 University Ave 54730 — 715-962-3773
William Yingst, supt. — Fax 962-4024
www.colfax.k12.wi.us/
Colfax MSHS — 200/7-12
601 University Ave 54730 — 715-962-3155
John Dachel, prin. — Fax 962-4024

Columbus, Columbia, Pop. 4,934
Columbus SD — 1,200/PK-12
200 W School St 53925 — 920-623-5950
Dr. Bryan Davis, supt. — Fax 623-5958
www.columbus.k12.wi.us
Columbus HS — 400/9-12
1164 Farnham St 53925 — 920-623-5956
Jeffrey Mastin, prin. — Fax 623-5959
Columbus MS — 400/4-8
400 S Dickason Blvd 53925 — 920-623-5954
David DeGuire, prin. — Fax 623-5742

Wisconsin Academy — 100/9-12
N2355 Du Borg Rd Bldg 1 53925 — 920-623-3300

Combined Locks, Outagamie, Pop. 3,308
Kimberly Area SD — 4,600/PK-12
425 S Washington St 54113 — 920-788-7900
Bob Mayfield Ed.D., supt. — Fax 788-7919
www.kimberly.k12.wi.us
Other Schools – See Kimberly

Cornell, Chippewa, Pop. 1,446
Cornell SD — 500/PK-12
PO Box 517 54732 — 715-239-6577
Paul Schley, supt. — Fax 239-6587
www.cornell.k12.wi.us
Cornell JSHS — 200/7-12
PO Box 517 54732 — 715-239-6464
David Elliott, prin. — Fax 239-6587

Cottage Grove, Dane, Pop. 6,069
Monona Grove SD
Supt. — See Monona
Glacial Drumlin MS — 5-8
801 Damascus Trl 53527 — 608-839-8437
Renee Tennant, prin. — Fax 839-8984

Crandon, Forest, Pop. 1,853
Crandon SD — 700/PK-12
9750 US Highway 8 W 54520 — 715-478-3339
Jim Asher, supt. — Fax 478-5130
www.crandon.k12.wi.us

Crandon HS 200/9-12
9750 US Highway 8 W 54520 715-478-6125
Andy Space, prin. Fax 478-5570
Crandon MS 200/6-8
9750 US Highway 8 W 54520 715-478-6124
Andy Space, prin. Fax 478-5130

Crivitz, Marinette, Pop. 971
Crivitz SD 600/PK-12
400 South Ave 54114 715-854-2721
Patrick Mans, supt. Fax 854-3755
www.crivitz.k12.wi.us
Crivitz HS 200/9-12
400 South Ave 54114 715-854-2721
Jeff Baumann, prin. Fax 854-3755

Cross Plains, Dane, Pop. 3,510
Middleton-Cross Plains Area SD
Supt. — See Middleton
Glacier Creek MS 700/6-8
2800 N Military Rd 53528 608-829-9420
Tim Keeler, prin. Fax 798-5425

Cuba City, Grant, Pop. 2,077
Cuba City SD 700/PK-12
101 N School St 53807 608-744-2847
Roger Kordus, supt. Fax 744-2324
www.cubacity.k12.wi.us
Cuba City HS 300/9-12
101 N School St 53807 608-744-8888
James Boebel, prin. Fax 744-2324

Cudahy, Milwaukee, Pop. 17,945
Cudahy SD 2,700/PK-12
2915 E Ramsey Ave 53110 414-294-7400
James Heiden, supt. Fax 294-4083
www.cudahy.k12.wi.us/
Cudahy HS 800/9-12
4950 S Lake Dr 53110 414-294-2700
Christopher Haeger, prin. Fax 769-2379
Cudahy MS 400/7-8
5530 S Barland Ave 53110 414-294-2830
Mike Carolan, prin. Fax 489-3010

Cumberland, Barron, Pop. 2,141
Cumberland SD 1,000/PK-12
1010 8th Ave 54829 715-822-5124
Barry Rose, supt. Fax 822-5136
www.csdmail.com
Cumberland HS 300/9-12
1000 8th Ave 54829 715-822-5121
Ritchie Narges, prin. Fax 822-5138
Cumberland MS 300/5-8
980 8th Ave 54829 715-822-5122
Colin Green, prin. Fax 822-5132

Darlington, Lafayette, Pop. 2,431
Darlington Community SD 800/PK-12
11630 Center Hill Rd 53530 608-776-2006
Dr. Denise Wellnitz, supt. Fax 776-3407
www.darlington.k12.wi.us
Darlington HS 300/9-12
11838 Center Hill Rd 53530 608-776-4001
Douglas McArthur, prin. Fax 776-2378

Deerfield, Dane, Pop. 2,294
Deerfield Community SD 800/PK-12
300 Simonson Blvd 53531 608-764-5431
Michelle Jensen, supt. Fax 764-2556
www.deerfield.k12.wi.us
Deerfield HS 300/9-12
300 Simonson Blvd 53531 608-764-5431
Brad Johnsrud, prin. Fax 764-5433
Deerfield MS 100/7-8
300 Simonson Blvd 53531 608-764-5431
Brad Johnsrud, prin. Fax 764-5433

De Forest, Dane, Pop. 8,802
De Forest Area SD 3,200/PK-12
520 E Holum St 53532 608-842-6500
Jon Bales, supt. Fax 842-6576
www.deforest.k12.wi.us
De Forest Area HS 1,000/9-12
815 Jefferson St 53532 608-842-6600
Machell Schwarz, prin. Fax 842-6615
De Forest Area MS 1,000/5-8
404 Yorktown Rd 53532 608-842-6000
Paul Herrick, prin. Fax 842-6015

Delafield, Waukesha, Pop. 7,026

St. Johns Northwestern Military Academy 300/7-12
1101 Genesee St 53018 262-646-3311
Jack Albert, pres. Fax 646-7128

Delavan, Walworth, Pop. 8,369
Delavan-Darien SD 2,600/PK-12
324 Beloit St 53115 262-728-2642
Dr. Robert Crist, supt. Fax 728-5954
www.ddschools.org
Delavan-Darien HS 800/9-12
150 Cumming St 53115 262-728-2642
Mark Schmitt, prin. Fax 728-9713
Phoenix MS 500/6-8
414 Beloit St 53115 262-728-2642
Mark Weerts, prin. Fax 728-0359

Wisconsin School for the Deaf Post-Sec.
309 W Walworth Ave 53115

Denmark, Brown, Pop. 2,098
Denmark SD 1,500/PK-12
450 N Wall St 54208 920-863-4000
Tony Klaubauf, supt. Fax 863-4015
www.denmark.k12.wi.us
Denmark HS 500/9-12
450 N Wall St 54208 920-863-4200
Oran Nehls, prin. Fax 863-8856
Denmark MS 300/6-8
450 N Wall St 54208 920-863-4100
Joe Koch, prin. Fax 863-3184

De Pere, Brown, Pop. 23,399
De Pere SD 3,900/PK-12
1700 Chicago St 54115 920-337-1032
Benjamin Villarruel, supt. Fax 337-1033
www.depere.k12.wi.us
De Pere HS 1,300/9-12
1700 Chicago St 54115 920-337-1020
Annette Deuman, prin. Fax 337-1041
De Pere MS 600/7-8
700 Swan Rd 54115 920-337-1024
Tammy Woulf, prin. Fax 337-1049

West De Pere SD 2,900/PK-12
400 Reid St Ste W 54115 920-337-1393
John Zegers, supt. Fax 337-1398
www.wdpsd.com
West De Pere HS 800/9-12
665 Grant St 54115 920-338-5200
Dr. Russell Gerke, prin. Fax 338-5310
West De Pere MS 600/6-8
1177 S 9th St 54115 920-337-1099
James Finley, prin. Fax 337-1380

St. Norbert College Post-Sec.
100 Grant St 54115 920-337-3181

De Soto, Vernon, Pop. 286
De Soto Area SD 500/PK-12
615 Main St 54624 608-648-0102
James Kuchta, supt. Fax 648-3959
www.desoto.k12.wi.us
De Soto HS 200/9-12
615 Main St 54624 608-648-0100
Linzi Gronning, prin. Fax 648-0117
De Soto MS 100/6-8
615 Main St 54624 608-648-0104
Linzi Gronning, prin. Fax 648-0117

Dodgeville, Iowa, Pop. 4,656
Dodgeville SD 1,400/PK-12
307 N Iowa St 53533 608-935-3307
Diane Messer, supt. Fax 935-3021
www.dsd.k12.wi.us/
Dodgeville HS 400/9-12
912 W Chapel St 53533 608-935-3307
Jeff Athey, prin. Fax 935-9540
Dodgeville MS 200/6-8
951 W Chapel St 53533 608-935-3307
Jacque Goetzke, prin. Fax 935-9643

Dousman, Waukesha, Pop. 2,279
Kettle Moraine SD
Supt. — See Wales
Kettle Moraine MS 1,000/6-8
301 E Ottawa Ave 53118 262-965-6500
Theresa Gonnerman, prin. Fax 965-6506

Drummond, Bayfield, Pop. 153
Drummond Area SD 400/PK-12
PO Box 40 54832 715-739-6669
John Knight, supt. Fax 739-6345
www.dasdk12.net
Drummond HS 100/9-12
PO Box 40 54832 715-739-6231
Ellen Nelson, prin. Fax 739-6345
Drummond MS 100/7-8
PO Box 40 54832 715-739-6231
Ellen Nelson, prin. Fax 739-6345

Dunbar, Marinette, Pop. 48

Northland International University Post-Sec.
W10085 Pike Plains Rd 54119 715-324-6900

Durand, Pepin, Pop. 1,916
Durand SD 900/PK-12
PO Box 190 54736 715-672-8919
Greg Doverspike, supt. Fax 672-8930
www.durand.k12.wi.us
Durand MSHS 500/6-12
PO Box 190 54736 715-672-8917
Bill Clouse, prin. Fax 672-8930

Assumption Catholic MS 100/4-8
901 W Prospect St 54736 715-672-5617
Mary Lansing, prin. Fax 672-3931

Eagle River, Vilas, Pop. 1,377
Northland Pines SD 1,400/PK-12
1800 Pleasure Island Rd 54521 715-479-6487
Mike Richie Ed.D., supt. Fax 479-7633
www.npsd.k12.wi.us/
Northland Pines HS 500/9-12
1800 Pleasure Island Rd 54521 715-479-4473
Jim Brewer, prin. Fax 479-5808
Northland Pines MS 300/6-8
1700 Pleasure Island Rd 54521 715-479-6479
Jacqueline Coghlan, prin. Fax 479-7303

East Troy, Walworth, Pop. 4,231
East Troy Community SD 1,700/PK-12
2043 Division St 53120 262-642-6710
Dr. Christopher Hibner, supt.
www.easttroy.k12.wi.us
East Troy HS 600/9-12
3128 Graydon Ave 53120 262-642-6760
Rick Penniston, prin. Fax 642-6776
East Troy MS 300/6-8
3143 Graydon Ave 53120 262-642-6740
Peter Synes, prin. Fax 642-6743

Eau Claire, Eau Claire, Pop. 64,812
Eau Claire Area SD 10,100/PK-12
500 Main St 54701 715-852-3000
Dr. Mary Ann Hardebeck, supt. Fax 852-3004
www.ecasd.k12.wi.us
Delong MS 900/6-8
2000 Vine St 54703 715-852-4900
Dr. Tim O'Reilly, prin. Fax 852-4904

Memorial HS 1,700/9-12
2225 Keith St 54701 715-852-6300
David Oldenberg, prin. Fax 852-6304
North HS 1,400/9-12
1801 Piedmont Rd 54703 715-852-6600
Dave Valk, prin. Fax 852-6604
Northstar MS 500/6-8
2711 Abbe Hill Dr 54703 715-852-5100
Michelle Golden, prin. Fax 852-5104
South MS 800/6-8
2115 Mitscher Ave 54701 715-852-5200
Mike Erickson, prin. Fax 852-5204

Chippewa Valley Technical College Post-Sec.
620 W Clairemont Ave 54701 715-833-6200
Eau Claire Academy 100/4-12
PO Box 1168 54702 715-834-6681
Globe University Post-Sec.
4955 Bullis Farm Rd 54701 715-855-6600
Immanuel Lutheran HS 100/9-12
501 Grover Rd 54701 715-836-6621
Jeffrey Schierenbeck, prin. Fax 836-6634
Professional Hair Design Academy Post-Sec.
3408 Mall Dr 54701 715-835-2345
Regis HS 200/9-12
2100 Fenwick Ave 54701 715-830-2271
Todd Fischer, prin. Fax 830-5461
Regis MS 100/7-8
2100 Fenwick Ave 54701 715-830-2272
Todd Fischer, prin. Fax 830-5461
Sacred Heart Hospital Post-Sec.
900 W Clairemont Ave 54701 715-839-4131
University of Wisconsin Post-Sec.
PO Box 4004 54702 715-836-2637

Edgar, Marathon, Pop. 1,476
Edgar SD 700/PK-12
PO Box 196 54426 715-352-2351
Dave Brandvold, supt. Fax 352-3198
www.edgar.k12.wi.us
Edgar HS 200/9-12
PO Box 196 54426 715-352-2352
Jordan Sinz, prin. Fax 352-3198
Edgar MS 200/6-8
PO Box 198 54426 715-352-2727
Jordan Sinz, prin. Fax 352-3022

Edgerton, Rock, Pop. 5,394
Edgerton SD 1,800/PK-12
200 Elm High Dr 53534 608-561-6100
Dr. Dennis Pauli, supt. Fax 884-9327
www.edgerton.k12.wi.us
Edgerton HS 600/9-12
200 Elm High Dr 53534 608-561-6020
Dr. Mark Coombs, prin. Fax 884-7969
Edgerton MS 400/6-8
300 Elm High Dr 53534 608-561-6030
Phill Klamm, prin. Fax 884-2279

Oaklawn Academy 100/6-9
432 Liguori Rd 53534 608-884-3425
Javier Valenzuela, prin. Fax 884-8175

Elcho, Langlade, Pop. 333
Elcho SD 300/PK-12
PO Box 800 54428 715-275-3225
William Fisher, supt. Fax 275-4388
www.elcho.k12.wi.us
Elcho HS 100/6-12
PO Box 800 54428 715-275-3707
Shawn Rude, prin. Fax 275-4388

Elkhart Lake, Sheboygan, Pop. 964
Elkhart Lake - Glenbeulah SD 500/PK-12
PO Box 326 53020 920-876-3381
Ann Buechel-Haack, supt. Fax 876-3511
www.elgs.k12.wi.us/
Elkhart Lake - Glenbeulah HS 100/9-12
PO Box 326 53020 920-876-3381
Todd Timm, prin. Fax 876-3511

Elkhorn, Walworth, Pop. 9,969
Elkhorn Area SD 3,000/K-12
3 N Jackson St 53121 262-723-3160
Gregory Wescott, supt. Fax 723-4652
www.elkhorn.k12.wi.us
Elkhorn Area HS 900/9-12
482 E Geneva St 53121 262-723-4920
Tina Bosworth, prin. Fax 723-8092
Elkhorn Area MS 700/6-8
627 E Court St 53121 262-723-6800
Sam Santacroce, prin. Fax 723-4967

Gateway Technical College Post-Sec.
400 County Road H 53121 262-741-8200

Elk Mound, Dunn, Pop. 858
Elk Mound Area SD 1,100/PK-12
405 University St 54739 715-879-5066
Ronald Walsh, supt. Fax 879-5846
www.elkmound.k12.wi.us
Elk Mound HS 300/9-12
405 University St 54739 715-879-5521
Paul Weber, prin. Fax 879-5846
Elk Mound MS 300/5-8
302 University St 54739 715-879-5595
Eric Wright, prin. Fax 879-5886

Ellsworth, Pierce, Pop. 3,234
Ellsworth Community SD 1,700/PK-12
300 Hillcrest St 54011 715-273-3900
Barry Cain, supt. Fax 273-5775
www.ellsworth.k12.wi.us
Ellsworth HS 600/9-12
323 Hillcrest St 54011 715-273-3904
Mark Stoesz, prin. Fax 273-6824
Ellsworth MS 500/5-8
312 Panther Dr 54011 715-273-3908
Paul Uhren, prin. Fax 273-6834

Elm Grove, Waukesha, Pop. 5,869
Elmbrook SD
Supt. — See Brookfield
Pilgrim Park MS 800/6-8
1500 Pilgrim Pkwy 53122 262-785-3920
Michael Sereno, prin. Fax 785-3933

Elmwood, Pierce, Pop. 815
Elmwood SD 300/PK-12
213 S Scott St 54740 715-639-2711
Paul Blanford Ed.D., supt. Fax 639-3110
www.elmwood.k12.wi.us
Elmwood HS 100/9-12
213 S Scott St 54740 715-639-2721
Fax 639-3110
Elmwood MS 100/6-8
213 S Scott St 54740 715-639-2721
Fax 639-3110

Elroy, Juneau, Pop. 1,424
Royall SD 500/PK-12
1501 Academy St 53929 608-462-2600
Mark Gruen, supt. Fax 462-2618
www.royall.k12.wi.us
Royall MSHS 200/7-12
1501 Academy St 53929 608-462-2600
Scott Uppena, prin. Fax 462-2618

Evansville, Rock, Pop. 4,947
Evansville Community SD 1,800/PK-12
340 Fair St 53536 608-882-5224
Jerry Roth, supt. Fax 882-6564
www.evansville.k12.wi.us
Evansville HS 500/9-12
640 S 5th St 53536 608-882-4600
Scott Everson, prin. Fax 882-6157
McKenna MS 400/6-8
307 S 1st St 53536 608-882-4780
Robert Flaherty, prin. Fax 882-5744

Fall Creek, Eau Claire, Pop. 1,306
Fall Creek SD 800/PK-12
336 E Hoover Ave 54742 715-877-2123
Joseph Sanfelippo, supt. Fax 877-2911
www.fallcreek.k12.wi.us
Fall Creek HS 300/9-12
336 E Hoover Ave 54742 715-877-2809
Brian Schulner, prin. Fax 877-2911
Fall Creek MS 200/6-8
336 E Hoover Ave 54742 715-877-2511
Brad LaPoint, prin. Fax 877-2911

Fall River, Columbia, Pop. 1,685
Fall River SD 500/PK-12
PO Box 116 53932 920-484-3333
Jeff Tortomasi, supt. Fax 484-3600
www.fallriver.k12.wi.us
Fall River HS 300/6-12
PO Box 116 53932 920-484-3333
Dan Dowden, prin. Fax 484-3600

Fennimore, Grant, Pop. 2,489
Fennimore Community SD 800/PK-12
1397 9th St 53809 608-822-3243
Jamie Nutter, supt. Fax 822-3250
www.fennimore.k12.wi.us
Fennimore JSHS 300/7-12
510 7th St 53809 608-822-3245
Dan Bredeson, prin. Fax 822-3247

Southwest Wisconsin Technical College Post-Sec.
1800 Bronson Blvd 53809 608-822-3262

Fish Creek, Door
Gibraltar Area SD 600/PK-12
3924 State Highway 42 54212 920-868-3284
Tina Van Meer, supt. Fax 868-2714
www.gibraltar.k12.wi.us
Gibraltar HS 200/9-12
3924 State Highway 42 54212 920-868-3284
Kirk Knutson, prin. Fax 868-2714
Gibraltar MS 100/6-8
3924 State Highway 42 54212 920-868-3284
Kirk Knutson, prin. Fax 868-2714

Fitchburg, Dane, Pop. 24,633
Verona Area SD
Supt. — See Verona
Savanna Oaks MS 500/6-8
5890 Lacy Rd 53711 608-845-4000
Steve Penne, prin. Fax 845-4020

Florence, Florence, Pop. 589
Florence SD 500/PK-12
PO Box 440 54121 715-528-3217
Ben Niehaus, supt. Fax 528-5338
www.florence.k12.wi.us
Florence HS 200/9-12
PO Box 440 54121 715-528-3215
Brandon Jerue, admin. Fax 528-5330
Florence MS 100/7-8
PO Box 440 54121 715-528-3215
Brandon Jerue, admin. Fax 528-5338

Fond du Lac, Fond du Lac, Pop. 42,372
Fond du Lac SD 6,700/K-12
72 W 9th St 54935 920-929-2900
James Sebert Ed.D., supt. Fax 929-6804
www.fonddulac.k12.wi.us
Fond du Lac HS 2,100/9-12
801 Campus Dr 54935 920-929-2740
Jon Wiltzius, prin. Fax 929-6964
Sabish MS 500/6-8
100 N Peters Ave 54935 920-929-2800
Torrie Rochon-Luft, prin. Fax 929-2807
Theisen MS 500/6-8
525 E Pioneer Rd 54935 920-929-2850
Brad Nerat, prin. Fax 929-2854
Woodworth MS 500/6-8
101 Morningside Dr 54935 920-929-6900
Steven Hill, prin. Fax 929-6944

Fond du Lac Christian S 100/K-12
720 Rienzi Rd 54935 920-924-2177
Wendy Lundberg, admin. Fax 322-9459
Marian University Post-Sec.
45 S National Ave 54935 920-923-7600
Moraine Park Technical College Post-Sec.
235 N National Ave 54935 920-922-8611
St. Mary's Springs HS 200/9-12
255 County Road K 54937 920-921-4870
Kevin Shaw, pres. Fax 921-2786
University of Wisconsin Fond du Lac Post-Sec.
400 University Dr 54935 920-929-1100
Winnebago Lutheran Academy 400/9-12
475 E Merrill Ave 54935 920-921-4930
Justin Gregorius, prin. Fax 921-4280

Fort Atkinson, Jefferson, Pop. 12,238
Fort Atkinson SD 2,800/PK-12
201 Park St 53538 920-563-7807
James Fitzpatrick, supt. Fax 563-7809
www.fortschools.org
Fort Atkinson HS 1,000/9-12
925 Lexington Blvd 53538 920-563-7811
Jeff Zaspel, prin. Fax 563-7810
Fort Atkinson MS 600/6-8
310 S 4th St E 53538 920-563-7833
Robert Abbott, prin. Fax 563-7838

Fountain City, Buffalo, Pop. 848
Cochrane-Fountain City SD 700/PK-12
S2770 State Road 35 54629 608-687-7771
Thomas Hiebert, supt. Fax 687-3312
www.cfc.k12.wi.us
Cochrane-Fountain City JSHS 300/7-12
S2770 State Road 35 54629 608-687-4391
Steve Stoppelmoor, prin. Fax 687-6412

Fox Point, Milwaukee, Pop. 6,600
Fox Point Bayside SD 900/PK-8
7300 N Lombardy Rd 53217 414-247-4167
Dr. Vance Dalzin, admin. Fax 351-7164
www.foxbay.k12.wi.us
Other Schools – See Bayside

Maple Dale-Indian Hill SD 500/PK-8
8377 N Port Washington Rd 53217 414-351-7380
Mary Dean, supt.
www.mapledale.k12.wi.us
Maple Dale S 300/3-8
8377 N Port Washington Rd 53217 414-351-7380
Mary Dean, prin.

Franklin, Milwaukee, Pop. 34,981
Franklin SD 4,200/PK-12
8255 W Forest Hill Ave 53132 414-529-8220
Steve Patz, supt. Fax 529-8230
www.franklin.k12.wi.us
Forest Park MS 700/7-8
8225 W Forest Hill Ave 53132 414-529-8250
Theresa West, prin. Fax 529-8249
Franklin HS 1,400/9-12
8222 S 51st St 53132 414-423-4640
Michael Nowak, prin. Fax 421-0558

Frederic, Polk, Pop. 1,124
Frederic SD 500/PK-12
1437 Clam Falls Dr 54837 715-327-5630
Josh Robinson, supt. Fax 327-5609
www.frederic.k12.wi.us/
Frederic JSHS 200/6-12
1437 Clam Falls Dr 54837 715-327-4223
Josh Robinson, prin. Fax 327-8655

Fredonia, Ozaukee, Pop. 2,138
Northern Ozaukee SD 1,500/PK-12
401 Highland Dr 53021 262-692-2489
Blake Peuse, supt. Fax 692-6257
www.nosd.edu
Ozaukee HS 200/9-12
401 Highland Dr 53021 262-692-2453
Jeff Sauer, prin. Fax 692-6257
Ozaukee MS 200/6-8
401 Highland Dr 53021 262-692-2463
Jeff Sauer, prin. Fax 692-2313

Freedom, Outagamie
Freedom Area SD 1,600/PK-12
N4021 County Rd E, Kaukauna WI 54130
920-788-7944
Kevin Kilstofte, supt. Fax 788-7949
www.freedomschools.k12.wi.us
Freedom HS 500/9-12
N4021 County Rd E, Kaukauna WI 54130
920-788-7940
Kurt Erickson, prin. Fax 788-7700
Freedom MS 400/6-8
N4021 County Rd E, Kaukauna WI 54130
920-788-7945
Ken Fisher, prin. Fax 788-7701

Friendship, Adams, Pop. 720
Adams-Friendship Area SD 1,800/PK-12
201 W 6th St 53934 608-339-3213
Steven Lavallee, supt. Fax 339-6213
www.af.k12.wi.us/pages/index.cfm
Other Schools – See Adams

Galesville, Trempealeau, Pop. 1,463
Galesville-Ettrick-Trempealeau SD 1,400/PK-12
PO Box 4000 54630 608-582-4657
Kevin Shetler Ed.D., supt. Fax 582-4961
www.getschools.k12.wi.us
Coulee Region HS Alt
16935 N Main St 54630 608-582-2200
Fax 582-4263
Gale-Ettrick-Tremp HS 400/9-12
PO Box 4000 54630 608-582-2291
Troy White, prin. Fax 582-4263
Gale-Ettrick-Tremp MS 300/6-8
19650 Prairie Ridge Ln 54630 608-582-3500
Matt Wenthe, prin. Fax 582-3501

Genoa City, Walworth, Pop. 3,006
Genoa City J2 SD 500/K-8
PO Box 250 53128 262-279-1051
Bill Lehner, supt. Fax 279-1052
Brookwood MS 300/4-8
PO Box 250 53128 262-279-1053
Kellie Bohn, prin. Fax 279-1052

Germantown, Washington, Pop. 19,491
Germantown SD 4,000/PK-12
N104W13840 Donges Bay Rd 53022 262-253-3900
Jeff Holmes, supt. Fax 251-6999
www.germantown.k12.wi.us
Germantown HS 1,500/9-12
W180N11501 River Ln 53022 262-253-3400
Joel Farren, prin. Fax 253-3494
Kennedy MS 900/6-8
W160N11836 Crusader Ct 53022 262-253-3450
Susan Climer, prin. Fax 253-3499

ITT Technical Institute Post-Sec.
W177N9886 Rivercrest # 200 53022 262-257-7100

Gillett, Oconto, Pop. 1,370
Gillett SD 700/PK-12
PO Box 227 54124 920-855-2137
Kyle Ransom, supt. Fax 855-1557
www.gillett.k12.wi.us
Gillett HS 200/9-12
PO Box 227 54124 920-855-2137
Jeremy Pach, prin. Fax 855-6600
Gillett MS 100/6-8
PO Box 227 54124 920-855-2137
Jeremy Pach, prin. Fax 855-6600

Gilman, Taylor, Pop. 409
Gilman SD 400/PK-12
325 N 5th Ave 54433 715-447-8211
Mark Heyerdahl, supt. Fax 447-8731
www.gilman.k12.wi.us
Gilman JSHS 200/7-12
325 N 5th Ave 54433 715-447-8211
Georgia Kraus, prin. Fax 447-8731

Gilmanton, Buffalo
Gilmanton SD 200/PK-12
PO Box 28 54743 715-946-3158
Glen Denk, supt. Fax 946-3474
www.ghs.k12.wi.us
Gilmanton HS 100/9-12
PO Box 28 54743 715-946-3158
Kory Rud, prin. Fax 946-3474
Gilmanton MS 50/5-8
PO Box 28 54743 715-946-3158
Kory Rud, prin. Fax 946-3174

Glendale, Milwaukee, Pop. 12,578
Glendale-River Hills SD 1,000/PK-8
2600 W Mill Rd 53209 414-351-7170
Larry Smalley, supt. Fax 434-0109
www.glendale.k12.wi.us
Glen Hills MS 500/4-8
2600 W Mill Rd 53209 414-351-7160
Haydee Smith, prin. Fax 351-8100

Nicolet UNHSD 1,100/9-12
6701 N Jean Nicolet Rd 53217 414-351-7520
Richard Monroe, supt. Fax 351-7526
nicolet.k12.wi.us/
Nicolet Union HS 1,100/9-12
6701 N Jean Nicolet Rd 53217 414-351-7524
Greg DePue, prin. Fax 351-7526

Bryant & Stratton College Post-Sec.
500 W Silver Spring Dr K340 53217 414-961-9600
Columbia College of Nursing Post-Sec.
4425 N Port Washington Rd 53212 414-326-2330

Glenwood City, Saint Croix, Pop. 1,234
Glenwood City SD 700/PK-12
850 Maple St 54013 715-265-4757
Timothy Emholtz, supt. Fax 265-4214
www.gcsd.k12.wi.us/
Glenwood City HS 200/9-12
850 Maple St 54013 715-265-4266
Timothy Johnson, prin. Fax 265-7129
Glenwood City MS 200/6-8
850 Maple St 54013 715-265-4266
Timothy Johnson, prin. Fax 265-7129

Glidden, Ashland, Pop. 505
Chequamegon SD
Supt. — See Park Falls
Chequamegon MS 200/6-8
370 Grant St 54527 715-264-2141
Diana Rein, prin. Fax 264-3413

Goodman, Marinette, Pop. 271
Goodman-Armstrong Creek SD 100/PK-12
PO Box 160 54125 715-336-2575
Ben Niehaus, supt. Fax 336-2576
www.goodman.k12.wi.us
Goodman JSHS 100/7-12
PO Box 160 54125 715-336-2575
Ben Niehaus, prin. Fax 336-2576

Grafton, Ozaukee, Pop. 11,349
Grafton SD 2,200/PK-12
1900 Washington St 53024 262-376-5400
Mel Lightner, supt. Fax 376-5599
www.grafton.k12.wi.us
Grafton HS 800/9-12
1950 Washington St 53024 262-376-5500
Ken McCormick, prin. Fax 376-5510
Long MS 500/6-8
700 Hickory St 53024 262-376-5800
Michael Leach, prin. Fax 376-5810

Granton, Clark, Pop. 353
Granton Area SD 100/K-12
217 N Main St 54436 715-238-7292
Charles Buckel, supt. Fax 238-7288
www.granton.k12.wi.us
Granton HS 100/6-12
217 N Main St 54436 715-238-7175
Rhonda Opelt, prin. Fax 238-7827

Grantsburg, Burnett, Pop. 1,314
Grantsburg SD 1,500/PK-12
480 E James Ave 54840 715-463-5499
Joni Burgin, supt. Fax 463-2534
www.gk12.net/
Grantsburg HS 300/9-12
480 E James Ave 54840 715-463-2531
Stan Marczak, prin. Fax 463-5068
Grantsburg MS 300/4-8
480 E James Ave 54840 715-463-2455
Brad Jones, prin. Fax 463-3209

Green Bay, Brown, Pop. 101,558
Ashwaubenon SD 3,200/PK-12
1055 Griffiths Ln 54304 920-492-2900
Brian Hanes, supt. Fax 492-2911
www.ashwaubenon.k12.wi.us
Ashwaubenon HS 1,000/9-12
2391 S Ridge Rd 54304 920-492-2950
Brian Nelsen, prin. Fax 492-2912
Parkview MS 700/6-8
955 Willard Dr 54304 920-492-2940
Kris Hucek, prin. Fax 492-2944

Green Bay Area SD 20,300/PK-12
PO Box 23387 54305 920-448-2000
Michelle Langenfeld, supt. Fax 448-3562
www.greenbay.k12.wi.us
Bay View S 100/Alt
200 S Broadway 54303 920-448-7356
Kathy Kops, prin. Fax 272-7051
East HS 1,300/9-12
1415 E Walnut St 54301 920-448-2090
Ed Dorff, prin. Fax 448-2166
Edison MS 1,200/6-8
442 Alpine Dr 54302 920-391-2450
Jonathon Wiebel, prin. Fax 391-2531
Franklin MS 700/6-8
1233 Lore Ln 54303 920-492-2670
Sandra Beyer, prin. Fax 492-5563
Lombardi MS 800/6-8
1520 S Point Rd 54313 920-492-2625
Ann Barszcz, prin. Fax 492-5564
Preble HS 2,200/9-12
2222 Deckner Ave 54302 920-391-2400
Natasha Rowell, prin. Fax 391-2530
Southwest HS 1,300/9-12
1331 Packerland Dr 54304 920-492-2650
Rod Bohm, prin. Fax 492-5561
Washington MS 900/6-8
314 S Baird St 54301 920-448-2095
Lori Frerk, prin. Fax 448-3551
West HS 1,000/9-12
966 Shawano Ave 54303 920-492-2600
Mark Flaten, prin. Fax 492-2641

Howard-Suamico SD 5,400/K-12
2700 Lineville Rd 54313 920-662-7878
Damian LaCroix, supt. Fax 662-9777
www.hssd.k12.wi.us
Bay Port HS 1,700/9-12
2710 Lineville Rd 54313 920-662-7000
Michael Frieder, prin. Fax 662-7291
Bay View MS 800/7-8
1217 Cardinal Ln 54313 920-662-8196
Steve Meyers, prin. Fax 662-7979

Bellin College Post-Sec.
3201 Eaton Rd 54311 920-433-6699
Bellin Hospital Post-Sec.
PO Box 23400 54305 920-433-3497
Empire Beauty School Post-Sec.
2575 W Mason St 54303 920-494-1430
Globe University Post-Sec.
2620 Development Dr 54311 920-264-1600
Green Bay Adventist Jr. Academy 50/K-10
1422 Shawano Ave 54303 920-494-2741
Kiana Binford, prin. Fax 494-6507
ITT Technical Institute Post-Sec.
470 Security Blvd 54313 920-662-9000
Northeastern Wisconsin Lutheran HS 100/9-12
1311 S Robinson Ave 54311 920-469-6810
Chris Nelson, dir. Fax 469-2200
Northeast Wisconsin Technical College Post-Sec.
PO Box 19042 54307 920-498-5400
Notre Dame De La Baie Academy 700/9-12
610 Maryhill Dr 54303 920-429-6100
Robert Pauley, prin. Fax 429-6168
Rasmussen College Post-Sec.
904 S Taylor St Ste 100 54303 920-593-8400
St. Vincent Hospital Post-Sec.
PO Box 13508 54307 920-433-8155
University of Wisconsin Post-Sec.
2420 Nicolet Dr 54311 920-465-2000
Wisconsin College of Cosmetology Post-Sec.
PO Box 28257 54324 920-336-8888

Greendale, Milwaukee, Pop. 13,859
Greendale SD 2,700/PK-12
6815 Southway 53129 414-423-2700
John Tharp Ed.D., supt. Fax 423-2723
www.greendale.k12.wi.us
Greendale HS 1,000/9-12
6801 Southway 53129 414-423-0110
Steven Lodes, prin. Fax 423-1667
Greendale MS 600/6-8
6800 Schoolway 53129 414-423-2800
John Weiss, prin. Fax 423-2806

Luther HS 300/9-12
5201 S 76th St 53129 414-421-4000
Dr. Wayne Jensen, prin. Fax 421-4071

Greenfield, Milwaukee, Pop. 36,124
Greenfield SD 3,700/PK-12
4850 S 60th St 53220 414-855-2050
Lisa Elliott, supt. Fax 855-2051
www.greenfield.k12.wi.us
Greenfield HS 1,300/9-12
4800 S 60th St 53220 414-281-6200
Paul Thusius, prin. Fax 281-8860
Greenfield MS 800/6-8
3200 W Barnard Ave 53221 414-282-4700
Brad Iding, prin. Fax 282-1017

Whitnall SD 2,300/PK-12
5000 S 116th St 53228 414-525-8400
Dr. Lowell Holtz, supt. Fax 525-8401
www.whitnall.com
Whitnall HS 900/9-12
5000 S 116th St 53228 414-525-8500
Jacquelyn Winter, prin. Fax 525-8501
Whitnall MS 500/6-8
5025 S 116th St 53228 414-525-8650
Lynn Davies, prin. Fax 525-8651

Green Lake, Green Lake, Pop. 956
Green Lake SD 300/PK-12
PO Box 369 54941 920-294-6411
Ken Bates, supt. Fax 294-6589
www.glsd.k12.wi.us
Green Lake JSHS 100/7-12
PO Box 369 54941 920-294-6411
Mary Allen, prin. Fax 294-6589

Greenville, Outagamie
Hortonville SD
Supt. — See Hortonville
Greenville MS 600/5-8
N1450 Fawn Ridge Dr 54942 920-757-7140
Travis Lawrence, prin. Fax 757-7141

Greenwood, Clark, Pop. 1,021
Greenwood SD 400/PK-12
PO Box 310 54437 715-267-6101
Jennifer Vogler, supt. Fax 267-6113
www.greenwood.k12.wi.us/
Greenwood MSHS 200/7-12
PO Box 310 54437 715-267-6101
Todd C. Fischer, prin. Fax 267-6113

Gresham, Shawano, Pop. 545
Gresham SD 200/PK-12
501 Schabow St 54128 715-787-3211
Keary Mattson, supt. Fax 787-3951
www.gresham.k12.wi.us/
Gresham HS 100/9-12
501 Schabow St 54128 715-787-3211
Keary Mattson, prin. Fax 787-3951

Hales Corners, Milwaukee, Pop. 7,616

Sacred Heart School of Theology Post-Sec.
PO Box 429 53130 414-425-8300

Hammond, Saint Croix, Pop. 1,895
St. Croix Central SD 1,400/PK-12
PO Box 118 54015 715-796-2256
David Bradley, supt. Fax 796-2460
www.scc.k12.wi.us
St. Croix Central HS 400/9-12
1751 Broadway St 54015 715-796-5383
Dr. Glenn Webb, prin. Fax 796-5662
St. Croix Central MS 400/5-8
PO Box 118 54015 715-796-2256
Scott Woodington, prin. Fax 796-2460

Hartford, Washington, Pop. 14,070
Hartford J1 SD 1,800/PK-8
675 E Rossman St 53027 262-673-3155
Dr. Mark Smits, admin. Fax 673-3548
www.hartfordjt1.k12.wi.us
Central MS 500/6-8
1100 Cedar St 53027 262-673-8040
Bob Kieckhefer, prin. Fax 673-7596

Hartford UNHSD 1,500/9-12
805 Cedar St 53027 262-670-3200
Dr. Lisa Olson, supt. Fax 673-8943
www.huhs.org
Hartford Union HS 1,500/9-12
805 Cedar St 53027 262-670-3200
Chad Ellefson, prin. Fax 673-8943

Hartland, Waukesha, Pop. 8,992
Arrowhead UNHSD 2,300/9-12
700 North Ave 53029 262-369-3611
Craig Jefson, supt. Fax 367-7406
www.arrowheadschools.org
Arrowhead Union HS 2,300/9-12
700 North Ave 53029 262-369-3611
Gregg Wieczorek, prin. Fax 367-4693

Hartland-Lakeside J3 SD 1,300/PK-8
800 N Shore Dr 53029 262-369-6700
Dr. Glenn Schilling, supt. Fax 369-6755
www.hartlake.org
North Shore MS 400/6-8
800 N Shore Dr 53029 262-369-6767
Michele Schmidt, prin. Fax 369-6766

Lake Country Lutheran HS 200/9-12
401 Campus Dr 53029 262-367-8600
Dwayne Jobst, prin. Fax 367-0611
University Lake S 300/PK-12
4024 Nagawicka Rd 53029 262-367-6011
Paul Atkinson, head sch Fax 367-3146

Hayward, Sawyer, Pop. 2,245
Hayward Community SD 1,800/PK-12
15930 W 5th St 54843 715-634-2619
Craig Olson, supt. Fax 634-3560
www.hayward.k12.wi.us
Hayward HS 600/9-12
15930 W 5th St 54843 715-634-2619
Todd Johnson, prin. Fax 634-2761
Hayward MS 400/6-8
15930 W 5th St 54843 715-634-2619
Hugh Duffy, prin. Fax 634-9953

Lac Courte Oreilles Ojibwa Comm College Post-Sec.
13466 W Trepania Rd 54843 715-634-4790

Hazel Green, Grant, Pop. 1,238
Southwestern Wisconsin SD 600/PK-12
PO Box 368 53811 608-854-2261
James Egan, supt. Fax 854-2305
www.swsd.k12.wi.us
Southwestern Wisconsin HS 200/9-12
PO Box 368 53811 608-854-2261
Cynthia Lacey, prin. Fax 854-2315

Hilbert, Calumet, Pop. 1,124
Hilbert SD 500/PK-12
PO Box 390 54129 920-853-3558
Anthony Sweere, supt. Fax 853-7030
www.hilbert.k12.wi.us
Hilbert HS 200/9-12
PO Box 390 54129 920-853-3558
Dennis Kaczor, prin. Fax 853-7030
Hilbert MS 100/5-8
PO Box 390 54129 920-853-3558
Anthony Sweere, prin. Fax 853-7030

Hillsboro, Vernon, Pop. 1,405
Hillsboro SD 500/PK-12
PO Box 526 54634 608-489-2221
Curt Bisarek, supt. Fax 489-2811
www.hillsboro.k12.wi.us
Hillsboro MSHS 300/6-12
PO Box 526 54634 608-489-2221
Greg Zimmerman, prin. Fax 489-2811

Holcombe, Chippewa, Pop. 266
Lake Holcombe SD 100/PK-12
27331 262nd Ave 54745 715-595-4241
Thomas Goulet, supt. Fax 595-6383
lakeholcombe.k12.wi.us
Holcombe S 100/PK-12
27331 262nd Ave 54745 715-595-4241
Mark Porter, prin. Fax 595-6383

Holmen, LaCrosse, Pop. 8,875
Holmen SD 3,700/PK-12
1019 McHugh Rd 54636 608-526-6610
Dale Carlson, supt. Fax 526-1333
www.holmen.k12.wi.us
Holmen HS 1,000/9-12
1001 McHugh Rd 54636 608-526-3372
Robert Baer, prin. Fax 526-9446
Holmen MS 800/6-8
502 N Main St 54636 608-526-3391
Ryan Vogler, prin. Fax 526-6716

Horicon, Dodge, Pop. 3,609
Horicon SD 800/PK-12
611 Mill St 53032 920-485-2898
Gary Berger, supt. Fax 485-3601
www.horicon.k12.wi.us
Horicon HS 300/9-12
841 Gray St 53032 920-485-4441
Teresa Graven, prin. Fax 485-3244
Van Brunt MS 200/6-8
611 Mill St 53032 920-485-4423
Aaron Olson, prin. Fax 485-4318

Hortonville, Outagamie, Pop. 2,685
Hortonville SD 3,400/PK-12
PO Box 70 54944 920-779-7900
Dr. Heidi Schmidt, supt. Fax 779-7903
www.hasd.org
Hortonville HS 1,100/9-12
211 E Towne Dr 54944 920-779-7933
Todd Timm, prin. Fax 779-7935
Hortonville MS 500/5-8
220 Warner St 54944 920-779-7922
Steven Gromala, prin. Fax 779-7923
Other Schools – See Greenville

Howards Grove, Sheboygan, Pop. 3,170
Howards Grove SD 900/K-12
403 Audubon Rd 53083 920-565-4454
Christopher Peterson, supt. Fax 565-4461
www.hgsd.k12.wi.us
Howards Grove HS 300/9-12
401 Audubon Rd 53083 920-565-4450
Scott Fritz, prin. Fax 565-4451
Howards Grove MS 300/5-8
506 Kennedy Ave 53083 920-565-4452
Andy Hansen, prin. Fax 565-4460

Hudson, Saint Croix, Pop. 12,505
Hudson SD 5,500/PK-12
644 Brakke Dr 54016 715-377-3700
Mary Bowen-Eggebraaten, supt. Fax 377-3726
www.hudson.k12.wi.us
Hudson HS 1,700/9-12
1501 Vine St 54016 715-377-3800
Peg Shoemaker, prin. Fax 377-3801
Hudson MS 1,200/6-8
1300 Carmichael Rd 54016 715-377-3820
Dan Koch, prin. Fax 377-3821

Hurley, Iron, Pop. 1,529
Hurley SD 300/PK-12
5503 W Range View Dr 54534 715-561-4900
Christopher Patritto, supt. Fax 561-4953
www.hurley.k12.wi.us

Hurley S — 300/PK-12
5503 W Range View Dr 54534 — 715-561-4900
Jeffrey Gulan, prin. — Fax 561-4157

Hustisford, Dodge, Pop. 1,121
Hustisford SD — 400/PK-12
PO Box 326 53034 — 920-349-8109
Douglas Keiser Ph.D., supt. — Fax 349-3716
www.hustisford.k12.wi.us
Hustisford JSHS — 200/6-12
PO Box 326 53034 — 920-349-3261
Chad Schraufnagel, prin. — Fax 349-8495

Independence, Trempealeau, Pop. 1,329
Independence SD — 400/PK-12
23786 Indee Blvd 54747 — 715-985-3172
Paul Vine, supt. — Fax 985-2303
www.indps.k12.wi.us
Independence HS — 100/9-12
23786 Indee Blvd 54747 — 715-985-3172
Barry Schmitt, prin. — Fax 985-2303

Iola, Waupaca, Pop. 1,297
Iola-Scandinavia SD — 700/PK-12
450 Division St 54945 — 715-445-2411
David Dyb Ed.D., admin. — Fax 445-4468
www.iola.k12.wi.us
Iola-Scandinavia MSHS — 400/7-12
540 S Jackson St 54945 — 715-445-2411
Sara Anderson, prin. — Fax 445-5119

Jackson, Washington, Pop. 6,685

Kettle Moraine Lutheran HS — 400/9-12
3399 Division Rd 53037 — 262-677-4051
David Bartelt, supt. — Fax 677-4290
Living Word Lutheran HS — 100/9-12
2230 Living Word Ln 53037 — 262-677-9353
Dr. Cary Stelmachowicz, dir. — Fax 677-8357

Janesville, Rock, Pop. 62,455
Janesville SD — 9,800/PK-12
527 S Franklin St, — 608-743-5000
Dr. Karen Schulte, supt. — Fax 743-5110
www.janesville.k12.wi.us/sdj
Craig HS — 1,600/9-12
401 S Randall Ave 53545 — 608-743-5200
Dr. Alison Bjoin, prin. — Fax 743-5150
Edison MS — 700/6-8
1649 S Chatham St 53546 — 608-743-5900
James Lemire, prin. — Fax 743-5910
Franklin MS — 600/6-8
450 N Crosby Ave, — 608-743-6000
Charles Urness Ph.D., prin. — Fax 743-6010
Marshall MS — 900/6-8
25 S Pontiac Dr 53545 — 608-743-6200
Synthia Taylor, prin. — Fax 743-6210
Parker HS — 1,500/9-12
3125 Mineral Point Ave, — 608-743-5600
Chris Laue, prin. — Fax 743-5550

Blackhawk Technical College — Post-Sec.
PO Box 5009 53547 — 608-758-6900
Oakhill Christian S — 100/K-12
1650 S Oakhill Ave 53546 — 608-754-2759
Jim Eaker, prin. — Fax 754-2159
University of Wisconsin Rock County — Post-Sec.
2909 Kellogg Ave 53546 — 608-758-6565
WI School for Visually Handicapped — Post-Sec.
1700 W State St 53546 — 608-758-6100

Jefferson, Jefferson, Pop. 7,891
Jefferson SD — 1,900/PK-12
206 S Taft Ave 53549 — 920-675-1000
Craig Gerlach, supt. — Fax 675-1020
www.jefferson.k12.wi.us
Jefferson HS — 600/9-12
700 W Milwaukee St 53549 — 920-675-1100
Mark Rollefson, prin. — Fax 675-1120
Jefferson MS — 400/6-8
501 S Taft Ave 53549 — 920-675-1300
David Wallace, prin. — Fax 675-1320

St. Coletta School, RR 1 Box 43 53549 — Post-Sec.

Johnson Creek, Jefferson, Pop. 2,707
Johnson Creek SD — 600/PK-12
PO Box 39 53038 — 920-699-2811
Michael Garvey Ph.D., supt. — Fax 699-2801
www.johnsoncreek.k12.wi.us/
Johnson Creek HS — 300/6-12
PO Box 39 53038 — 920-699-3481
Eric Ranzen, prin. — Fax 699-3566

Juda, Green, Pop. 357
Juda SD — 300/PK-12
N2385 Spring St 53550 — 608-934-5251
Phillip Updike, supt. — Fax 934-5254
www.judaschool.com
Juda HS — 100/9-12
N2385 Spring St 53550 — 608-934-5251
Phillip Updike, prin. — Fax 934-5254

Juneau, Dodge, Pop. 2,802
Dodgeland SD — 800/PK-12
401 S Western Ave 53039 — 920-386-4404
Annette Thompson, supt. — Fax 386-4498
www.dodgeland.k12.wi.us
Dodgeland HS — 300/9-12
401 S Western Ave 53039 — 920-386-4404
Christopher Weiss, prin. — Fax 386-2601
Dodgeland MS — 200/6-8
401 S Western Ave 53039 — 920-386-4404
Marcia Modaff, prin. — Fax 386-0345

Kaukauna, Outagamie, Pop. 15,244
Kaukauna Area SD — 3,400/PK-12
1701 County Road CE 54130 — 920-766-6100
Mark Duerwaechter, admin. — Fax 766-6104
www.kaukauna.k12.wi.us
Kaukauna HS — 1,200/9-12
1701 County Road CE 54130 — 920-766-6113
Mike Werbowsky, prin. — Fax 766-6157
River View MS — 500/5-8
101 Oak St 54130 — 920-766-6111
Dan Joseph, prin. — Fax 766-6109

Holy Cross S — 200/3-8
220 Doty St 54130 — 920-766-0186
Larry Konetzke, prin. — Fax 759-2428

Kenosha, Kenosha, Pop. 96,606
Kenosha SD — 21,500/PK-12
3600 52nd St 53144 — 262-359-6300
Dr. Michele Hancock, supt. — Fax 359-7672
www.kusd.edu/
Bradford HS — 2,000/9-12
3700 Washington Rd 53144 — 262-359-6200
Dr. Kurt Sinclair, prin. — Fax 359-5948
Bullen MS — 800/6-8
2804 39th Ave 53144 — 262-359-4460
Kim Fischer, prin. — Fax 359-4487
Hillcrest S — 50/Alt
4616 24th St 53144 — 262-359-6118
Terry Ehiorobo, prin. — Fax 359-7870
Indian Trail Academy — 1,300/9-12
6800 60th St 53144 — 262-359-8700
Bethany Ormseth, prin. — Fax 359-8756
Lance MS — 900/6-8
4515 80th St 53142 — 262-359-2240
Chad Dahlk, prin. — Fax 359-2184
Lincoln MS — 600/6-8
6729 18th Ave 53143 — 262-359-6296
Ernest Llanas, prin. — Fax 359-5966
Mahone MS — 1,000/6-8
6900 60th St 53144 — 262-359-8100
Terri Huck, prin. — Fax 359-6851
Reuther Central HS — 500/Alt
913 57th St 53140 — 262-359-6160
Karen Walters, prin. — Fax 359-6281
Tremper HS — 2,200/9-12
8560 26th Ave 53143 — 262-359-2200
Richard Aiello, prin. — Fax 359-2187
Washington MS — 600/6-8
811 Washington Rd 53140 — 262-359-6291
Sharon Miller, prin. — Fax 359-6056
Other Schools – See Pleasant Prairie

Carthage College — Post-Sec.
2001 Alford Park Dr 53140 — 262-551-8500
Christian Life S — 700/PK-12
10700 75th St 53142 — 262-694-3900
Susan Nelson, admin. — Fax 694-3312
Gateway Technical College — Post-Sec.
3520 30th Ave 53144 — 262-564-2200
St. Joseph Catholic Academy — 300/6-12
2401 69th St 53143 — 262-654-8651
Edward Kovochich, prin. — Fax 654-1615
University of Wisconsin — Post-Sec.
PO Box 2000 53141 — 262-595-2345

Keshena, Menominee, Pop. 1,238
Menominee Indian SD — 800/PK-12
PO Box 1330 54135 — 715-799-3824
Wendell Waukau, supt. — Fax 799-4659
www.misd.k12.wi.us
Menominee Indian HS — 300/9-12
PO Box 850 54135 — 715-799-3846
Leslie Shawanokasic, prin. — Fax 799-5558
Other Schools – See Neopit

College of Menominee Nation — Post-Sec.
PO Box 1179 54135 — 715-799-5600

Kewaskum, Washington, Pop. 3,967
Kewaskum SD — 2,000/PK-12
PO Box 37 53040 — 262-626-8427
James Smasal, supt. — Fax 626-2961
www.kewaskumschools.org
Kewaskum Career Academy — Vo/Tech
PO Box 426 53040 — 262-626-8427
Anne Ignatowski, prin. — Fax 626-4702
Kewaskum HS — 700/9-12
PO Box 426 53040 — 262-626-8427
Kristine Dreher, prin. — Fax 626-4214
Kewaskum MS — 400/6-8
PO Box 432 53040 — 262-626-8427
Julie Skelton, prin. — Fax 626-4214

Kewaunee, Kewaunee, Pop. 2,918
Kewaunee SD — 800/PK-12
915 2nd St 54216 — 920-388-3230
Joe Innis, supt. — Fax 388-5174
www.kewaunee.k12.wi.us
Kewaunee HS — 300/9-12
911 3rd St 54216 — 920-388-2951
Michael Holtz, prin. — Fax 388-5165
Kewaunee MS — 200/6-8
921 3rd St 54216 — 920-388-2458
Karen Treml, prin. — Fax 388-5696
Lakeshore Alternative S — 50/Alt
915 2nd St 54216 — 920-388-3230
Michael Holtz, prin. — Fax 388-5174

Kiel, Manitowoc, Pop. 3,708
Kiel Area SD — 1,400/PK-12
PO Box 201 53042 — 920-894-2266
Louise Blankenheim Ed.D., supt. — Fax 894-5100
www.kiel.k12.wi.us/
Kiel HS — 500/9-12
210 Raider Hts 53042 — 920-894-2263
Dario Talerico, prin. — Fax 894-5101
Kiel MS — 400/5-8
PO Box 197 53042 — 920-894-2264
David Slosser, prin. — Fax 894-5121

Kimberly, Outagamie, Pop. 6,394
Kimberly Area SD
Supt. — See Combined Locks
Gerritts MS — 700/7-8
545 S John St 54136 — 920-788-7905
Eric Brinkmann, prin. — Fax 788-7914
Kimberly HS — 1,300/9-12
1662 E Kennedy Ave 54136 — 920-687-3024
Michael Rietveld, prin. — Fax 687-3029

Kohler, Sheboygan, Pop. 2,103
Kohler SD — 600/PK-12
333 Upper Rd 53044 — 920-803-7201
Quynh Trueblood, supt. — Fax 459-2930
www.kohlerpublicschools.org/
Kohler HS — 200/9-12
333 Upper Rd 53044 — 920-803-7201
Quynh Trueblood, prin. — Fax 459-2930

La Crosse, LaCrosse, Pop. 50,284
La Crosse SD — 6,900/PK-12
807 East Ave S 54601 — 608-789-7600
Randy Nelson, supt. — Fax 789-7960
www.lacrosseschools.org/
Central HS — 1,200/9-12
1801 Losey Blvd S 54601 — 608-789-7900
Jeffrey Fleig, prin. — Fax 789-7931
Lincoln MS — 400/6-8
510 9th St S 54601 — 608-789-7780
Larry Myhra, prin. — Fax 789-7181
Logan HS — 900/9-12
1500 Ranger Dr 54603 — 608-789-7700
Scott Mihalovic, prin. — Fax 789-7711
Logan MS — 500/6-8
1450 Avon St 54603 — 608-789-7740
Jay Pica, prin. — Fax 789-7754
Longfellow MS — 500/6-8
1900 Denton St 54601 — 608-789-7670
Penny Reedy, prin. — Fax 789-7975

Aquinas HS — 300/9-12
315 11th St S 54601 — 608-784-0287
Ted Knutson, prin. — Fax 782-8851
Aquinas MS South Campus — 200/7-8
315 11th St S 54601 — 608-784-0156
P. Gallagher-Kosmatka, prin. — Fax 784-0229
Gunderson Medical Foundation — Post-Sec.
1836 South Ave 54601 — 608-782-7300
University of Wisconsin — Post-Sec.
1725 State St 54601 — 608-785-8000
Viterbo University — Post-Sec.
900 Viterbo Dr 54601 — 608-796-3000
Western Technical College — Post-Sec.
400 7th St N 54601 — 608-785-9200

Ladysmith, Rusk, Pop. 3,376
Ladysmith SD — 900/PK-12
1700 Edgewood Ave E 54848 — 715-532-5277
Kurt Lindau, supt. — Fax 532-7445
ladysmith.k12.wi.us
Ladysmith HS — 300/9-12
1700 Edgewood Ave E 54848 — 715-532-5531
Robert Lecheler, prin. — Fax 532-5961
Ladysmith MS — 200/5-8
115 E 6th St S 54848 — 715-532-5252
Chris Poradish, prin. — Fax 532-7455

La Farge, Vernon, Pop. 740
La Farge SD — 300/PK-12
301 W Adams St 54639 — 608-625-0107
Shawn Donovan, supt. — Fax 625-0118
www.lafarge.k12.wi.us/
La Farge HS — 100/9-12
301 W Adams St 54639 — 608-625-2400
Shawn Donovan, prin. — Fax 625-0152
La Farge MS — 100/6-8
301 W Adams St 54639 — 608-625-2400
Shawn Donovan, prin. — Fax 625-0152

Lake Geneva, Walworth, Pop. 7,583
Lake Geneva J1 SD — 2,000/PK-8
208 E South St 53147 — 262-348-1000
James Gottinger, supt. — Fax 248-9704
www.lakegenevaschools.com
Lake Geneva MS — 700/6-8
600 N Bloomfield Rd 53147 — 262-348-3000
Anne Heck, prin. — Fax 348-3092

Lake Geneva-Genoa City UHSD — 1,400/9-12
208 E South St 53147 — 262-348-1000
James Gottinger, supt. — Fax 248-9704
www.lakegenevaschools.com
Badger HS — 1,400/9-12
220 E South St 53147 — 262-348-2000
Bob Kopydlowski, prin. — Fax 248-6178

Lake Mills, Jefferson, Pop. 5,657
Lake Mills Area SD — 1,400/PK-12
120 E Lake Park Pl 53551 — 920-648-2215
Dean Sanders, supt. — Fax 648-5795
www.lakemills.k12.wi.us
Lake Mills HS — 400/9-12
615 Catlin Dr 53551 — 920-648-2355
Pamela Streich, prin. — Fax 648-2357
Lake Mills MS — 400/5-8
318 College St 53551 — 920-648-2358
Jennifer Nicholson, prin. — Fax 648-8928

Lakeside Lutheran HS — 400/9-12
231 Woodland Beach Rd 53551 — 920-648-2321
James Grasby, prin. — Fax 648-5625

Lancaster, Grant, Pop. 3,854
Lancaster Community SD — 900/PK-12
925 W Maple St 53813 — 608-723-2175
Rob Wagner, supt. — Fax 723-6397
www.lancastersd.k12.wi.us

Lancaster HS 300/9-12
806 E Elm St 53813 608-723-2173
Mark Uppena, prin. Fax 723-2441
Lancaster MS 200/6-8
802 E Elm St 53813 608-723-6425
Mark Uppena, prin. Fax 723-6731

Land O Lakes, Vilas

Conserve S 50/10-11
5400 N Black Oak Lake Rd 54540 715-547-1300
Stefan Anderson, hdmstr. Fax 547-1386

Laona, Forest, Pop. 574
Laona SD 200/PK-12
PO Box 100 54541 715-674-2143
Laurie Asher, supt. Fax 674-5904
www.laona.k12.wi.us
Laona JSHS 100/7-12
PO Box 100 54541 715-674-2143
David Bardo, prin. Fax 674-5904

Lena, Oconto, Pop. 558
Lena SD 400/PK-12
304 E Main St 54139 920-829-5703
David Honish, supt. Fax 829-5122
www.lena.k12.wi.us
Lena HS 100/9-12
304 E Main St 54139 920-829-5244
David Honish, prin. Fax 829-5122
Lena MS 100/6-8
304 E Main St 54139 920-829-5244
David Honish, prin. Fax 829-5122

Little Chute, Outagamie, Pop. 10,339
Little Chute Area SD 1,300/PK-12
325 Meulemans St Ste A 54140 920-788-7605
David Botz, supt. Fax 788-7603
www.littlechute.k12.wi.us
Little Chute HS 500/9-12
1402 Freedom Rd 54140 920-788-7600
Daniel Valentyn, prin. Fax 788-7841
Little Chute MS 200/7-8
325 Meulemans St Ste B 54140 920-788-7607
Lori Van Handel, prin. Fax 788-7615

Livingston, Iowa, Pop. 663
Iowa-Grant SD 800/PK-12
498 County Road IG 53554 608-943-6311
Linda Erickson, supt. Fax 943-8438
www.igs.k12.wi.us
Iowa-Grant HS 200/9-12
462 County Road IG 53554 608-943-6312
Chris Gotto, prin. Fax 943-8707

Lodi, Columbia, Pop. 3,022
Lodi SD 1,700/PK-12
115 School St 53555 608-592-3851
Charles Pursell, supt. Fax 592-3852
www.lodi.k12.wi.us
Lodi HS 500/9-12
1100 Sauk St 53555 608-592-3853
Vincent Breunig, prin. Fax 592-1045
Lodi MS 400/6-8
900 Sauk St 53555 608-592-3854
David Dyb, prin. Fax 592-1035

Lomira, Dodge, Pop. 2,408
Lomira SD 900/PK-12
PO Box 919 53048 920-269-4396
Robert Lloyd, admin. Fax 269-4996
www.lomira.k12.wi.us/
Lomira HS 300/9-12
PO Box 919 53048 920-269-4396
Debra Janke, prin. Fax 269-4128
Lomira MS 200/6-8
PO Box 919 53048 920-269-4396
Robert Lloyd, prin. Fax 269-4996

Loyal, Clark, Pop. 1,258
Loyal SD 600/PK-12
PO Box 10 54446 715-255-8552
Cale Jackson, supt. Fax 255-8553
www.loyalschools.org
Loyal HS 200/9-12
PO Box 10 54446 715-255-8511
Christopher Lindner, prin. Fax 255-8553
Loyal JHS 100/7-8
PO Box 10 54446 715-255-8511
Christopher Lindner, prin. Fax 255-8553

Luck, Polk, Pop. 1,101
Luck SD 500/PK-12
810 S 7th St 54853 715-472-2151
Rick Palmer, supt. Fax 472-2159
www.lucksd.k12.wi.us
Luck JSHS 200/7-12
810 S 7th St 54853 715-472-2152
Mark Gobler, prin. Fax 472-2159

Luxemburg, Kewaunee, Pop. 2,502
Luxemburg-Casco SD 1,900/PK-12
PO Box 70 54217 920-845-2391
Patrick Saunders, supt. Fax 845-5871
www.luxcasco.k12.wi.us/
Luxemburg-Casco HS 600/9-12
PO Box 410 54217 920-845-2336
Steve Okoniewski, prin. Fax 845-2280
Other Schools – See Casco

Mc Farland, Dane, Pop. 7,692
Mc Farland SD 3,000/PK-12
5101 Farwell St 53558 608-838-3169
Scott Brown, admin. Fax 838-3074
www.mcfarland.k12.wi.us
Indian Mound MS 500/6-8
6330 Exchange St 53558 608-838-8980
Erin Tarnutzer, prin. Fax 838-4588
Mc Farland HS 600/9-12
5103 Farwell St 53558 608-838-3166
James Hickey, prin. Fax 838-4562

Madison, Dane, Pop. 226,807
Madison Metro SD 24,300/PK-12
545 W Dayton St 53703 608-663-1879
Daniel Nerad, supt. Fax 204-0342
www.madison.k12.wi.us
Black Hawk MS 400/6-8
1402 Wyoming Way 53704 608-204-4360
Sean Storch, prin. Fax 204-0368
Cherokee Heights MS 500/6-8
4301 Cherokee Dr 53711 608-204-1240
David Watkins, prin. Fax 204-0378
East HS 1,600/9-12
2222 E Washington Ave 53704 608-204-1600
Mary Kelley, prin. Fax 204-0388
Hamilton MS 700/6-8
4801 Waukesha St 53705 608-204-4620
Henry Schmelz, prin. Fax 204-0417
Jefferson MS 600/6-8
101 S Gammon Rd 53717 608-663-6403
Anne Fischer, prin. Fax 442-2193
LaFollette HS 1,600/9-12
702 Pflaum Rd 53716 608-204-3600
Chad Wiese, prin. Fax 204-0435
Memorial HS 1,900/9-12
201 S Gammon Rd 53717 608-663-5990
Bruce Dahmen, prin. Fax 442-2197
O'Keeffe MS 400/6-8
510 S Thornton Ave 53703 608-204-6820
Kay Enright, prin. Fax 204-0561
Sennett MS 600/6-8
502 Pflaum Rd 53716 608-204-1920
Tremayne Clardy, prin. Fax 204-0495
Shabazz-City HS 100/Alt
1601 N Sherman Ave 53704 608-204-2440
Aric Soderbloom, prin. Fax 204-0503
Sherman MS 400/6-8
1610 Ruskin St 53704 608-204-2100
Michael Hernandez, prin. Fax 204-0501
Spring Harbor MS 300/6-8
1110 Spring Harbor Dr 53705 608-204-1100
Leia Esser, prin. Fax 204-0509
Toki MS 500/6-8
5606 Russett Rd 53711 608-204-4740
Nicole Schaefer, prin. Fax 204-0523
West HS 2,100/9-12
30 Ash St 53726 608-204-4100
Ed Holmes, prin. Fax 204-0529
Whitehorse MS 400/6-8
218 Schenk St 53714 608-204-4480
Deborah Ptak, prin. Fax 204-0538

Abundant Life Christian S 300/K-12
4901 E Buckeye Rd 53716 608-221-1520
Diann Cook, prin. Fax 221-8572
Edgewood College Post-Sec.
1000 Edgewood College Dr 53711 608-663-4861
Edgewood HS 700/9-12
2219 Monroe St 53711 608-257-1023
Robert Growney, prin. Fax 257-9133
Empire Beauty School Post-Sec.
6414 Odana Rd 53719 608-270-0188
Globe University Post-Sec.
4901 Eastpark Blvd 53718 608-216-9400
Herzing University Post-Sec.
5218 E Terrace Dr 53718 608-249-6611
Herzing University - Madison West Post-Sec.
3 Point Pl 53719 608-620-2200
ITT Technical Institute Post-Sec.
2450 Rimrock Rd Ste 100 53713 608-288-6301
Madison Area Technical College Post-Sec.
1701 Wright St 53704 608-246-6100
Madison Media Institute Post-Sec.
2702 Agriculture Dr 53718 608-663-2000
St. Ambose Academy 100/6-12
602 Everglade Dr 53717 608-827-5863
Scott Schmiesing, prin.
University of Wisconsin Post-Sec.
500 Lincoln Dr 53706 608-262-1234

Manawa, Waupaca, Pop. 1,362
Manawa SD 700/PK-12
800 Beech St 54949 920-596-2525
Ed Dombrowski, supt. Fax 596-5308
www.manawa.k12.wi.us
Little Wolf JSHS 300/7-12
515 E 4th St 54949 920-596-2524
Duane Braun, prin. Fax 596-2655

Manitowoc, Manitowoc, Pop. 33,258
Manitowoc SD 5,500/PK-12
PO Box 1657 54221 920-686-4777
Marcia Flaherty, supt. Fax 686-4780
www.manitowocpublicschools.com
Lincoln SHS 1,300/10-12
1433 S 8th St 54220 920-683-4861
Luke Valitchka, prin. Fax 683-4845
Washington JHS 600/7-9
2101 Division St 54220 920-683-4857
Kathleen Lemberger, prin. Fax 683-7989
Wilson JHS 600/7-9
1201 N 11th St 54220 920-683-4859
Eric Johnson, prin. Fax 683-7988

Empire Beauty School Post-Sec.
1034 S 18th St 54220 920-684-3028
Manitowoc Lutheran HS 200/9-12
4045 Lancer Cir 54220 920-682-0215
Dennis Steinbrenner, prin. Fax 682-2363
Roncalli HS 400/9-12
2000 Mirro Dr 54220 920-682-8801
Tim Olson, prin. Fax 686-8110
St. Francis of Assisi MS 200/6-8
2109 Marshall St 54220 920-683-6884
James Clark, prin. Fax 683-6882
Silver Lake College of the Holy Family Post-Sec.
2406 S Alverno Rd 54220 920-684-6691

University of Wisconsin Manitowoc Post-Sec.
705 Viebahn St 54220 920-683-4700

Maple, Douglas
Maple SD 1,500/PK-12
PO Box 188 54854 715-363-2431
Gregg Lundberg, supt. Fax 363-2191
www.maple.k12.wi.us
Northwestern HS 400/9-12
PO Box 218 54854 715-363-2434
Steve High, prin. Fax 363-2523
Other Schools – See Poplar

Marathon, Marathon, Pop. 1,520
Marathon City SD 700/PK-12
PO Box 37 54448 715-443-2226
Richard Parks, supt. Fax 443-2611
www.marathon.k12.wi.us
Marathon HS 200/9-12
PO Box 37 54448 715-443-2226
David Beranek, prin. Fax 443-2611

Marinette, Marinette, Pop. 10,850
Marinette SD 2,100/PK-12
2139 Pierce Ave 54143 715-735-1400
Tim Baneck, supt. Fax 732-7930
www.marinette.k12.wi.us
Marinette HS 700/9-12
2135 Pierce Ave 54143 715-735-1300
Corry Lambie, prin. Fax 732-7929
Marinette MS 600/5-8
1011 Water St 54143 715-735-1500
Shawn Limberg, prin. Fax 732-7939

Northeast Wisconsin Technical College Post-Sec.
1601 University Dr 54143 715-735-9361
St. Thomas Aquinas Academy 50/PK-PK, 1-
1200 Main St 54143 715-735-7460
Peter Mayhew, admin. Fax 735-3375
University of Wisconsin Marinette Post-Sec.
750 W Bay Shore St 54143 715-735-4300

Marion, Waupaca, Pop. 1,253
Marion SD 500/PK-12
1001 N Main St 54950 715-754-2511
Michael Gaunt, supt. Fax 754-4508
www.marion.k12.wi.us
Marion JSHS 200/7-12
105 School St 54950 715-754-5273
Daniel Breitrick, prin. Fax 754-1350

Markesan, Green Lake, Pop. 1,472
Markesan SD 600/PK-12
PO Box 248 53946 920-398-2373
Duane Bark, supt. Fax 398-3281
www.markesan.k12.wi.us
Markesan HS 200/9-12
PO Box 248 53946 920-398-2373
Pamela Waite, prin. Fax 398-3281
Markesan MS 100/6-8
PO Box 248 53946 920-398-2373
Pamela Waite, prin. Fax 398-3281

Marshall, Dane, Pop. 3,813
Marshall SD 1,200/PK-12
PO Box 76 53559 608-655-3466
Barb Sramek, supt. Fax 655-4481
www.marshall.k12.wi.us
Marshall HS 400/9-12
PO Box 76 53559 608-655-1310
Brian Sniff, prin. Fax 655-3046
Marshall MS 200/7-8
PO Box 76 53559 608-655-1571
Lisa Blochwitz, prin. Fax 655-1591

Marshfield, Wood, Pop. 18,924
Marshfield SD 3,800/PK-12
1010 E 4th St 54449 715-387-1101
Peg Geegan, supt. Fax 387-0133
www.marshfield.k12.wi.us/
Marshfield HS 1,300/9-12
1401 E Becker Rd 54449 715-387-8464
Steve Sukawaty, prin. Fax 384-3589
Marshfield MS 500/7-8
900 E 4th St 54449 715-387-1249
David Schoepke, prin. Fax 384-9269

Columbus HS 100/9-12
710 S Columbus Ave 54449 715-387-1177
Steven VanWhye, prin. Fax 384-4535
Columbus MS 100/6-8
710 S Columbus Ave 54449 715-387-1177
Steven VanWyhe, prin. Fax 384-4535
Marshfield Clinic/St. Josephs Hospital Post-Sec.
1000 N Oak Ave 54449 715-221-6332
Mid-State Technical College Post-Sec.
2600 W 5th St 54449 715-387-2538
St. Joseph Hospital/Marshfield Clinic Post-Sec.
611 N Saint Joseph Ave 54449 715-387-1713
Univ. of Wisconsin - Marshfield/Wood Co. Post-Sec.
2000 W 5th St 54449 715-389-6530

Mauston, Juneau, Pop. 4,366
Mauston SD 1,500/PK-12
510 Grayside Ave 53948 608-847-5451
Dr. Christine M. Weymouth, supt. Fax 847-4635
www.maustonschools.org
Mauston HS 500/9-12
800 Grayside Ave 53948 608-847-4410
Jim Dillin, prin. Fax 847-4802
Olson MS 300/6-8
508 Grayside Ave 53948 608-847-6603
Michael Gonzalez, prin. Fax 847-4925

Mayville, Dodge, Pop. 5,113
Mayville SD 1,200/PK-12
234 N John St 53050 920-387-7963
Dr. Patricia Antony, supt. Fax 387-7979
www.mayvilleschools.com

Mayville HS 400/9-12
500 N Clark St 53050 920-387-7960
Lee Zarnott, prin. Fax 387-7977
Mayville MS 500/3-8
445 N Henninger St 53050 920-387-7970
Robert Clark, prin. Fax 387-7974

Mazomanie, Dane, Pop. 1,638
Wisconsin Heights SD 800/PK-12
10173 US Highway 14 53560 608-767-2595
Mark Elworthy Ed.D., supt. Fax 767-3579
www.wisheights.k12.wi.us
Wisconsin Heights HS 300/9-12
10173 US Highway 14 53560 608-767-2586
Asta Sepetys, prin. Fax 767-2062
Wisconsin Heights MS 200/6-8
10173 US Highway 14 53560 608-767-2586
Asta Sepetys, prin. Fax 767-2062

Medford, Taylor, Pop. 4,279
Medford Area SD 2,200/PK-12
124 W State St 54451 715-748-4620
Patrick Sullivan, supt. Fax 748-6839
www.medford.k12.wi.us
Medford Alternative HS Alt
624 College St 54451 715-748-1520
Kellie Keene, lead tchr.
Medford HS 700/9-12
1015 W Broadway Ave 54451 715-748-5951
Jill Lybert, prin. Fax 748-6438
Medford MS 600/5-8
509 Clark St 54451 715-748-2516
Al Leonard, prin. Fax 748-1213

Mellen, Ashland, Pop. 725
Mellen SD 300/PK-12
PO Box 500 54546 715-274-3601
Melissa Nigh, admin. Fax 274-3715
www.mellendiggers.org
Mellen HS 100/9-12
PO Box 500 54546 715-274-3601
Melissa Nigh, admin. Fax 274-3715

Melrose, Jackson, Pop. 499
Melrose-Mindoro SD 700/PK-12
N181 State Hwy 108 54642 608-488-2201
Del DeBerg, supt. Fax 488-2805
www.mel-min.k12.wi.us
Melrose-Mindoro HS 200/9-12
N181 State Hwy 108 54642 608-488-2201
Jeff Arzt, prin. Fax 488-2805

Menasha, Winnebago, Pop. 17,081
Menasha JSD 3,700/PK-12
PO Box 360 54952 920-967-1400
Robert Kobylski, supt. Fax 751-5038
www.mjsd.k12.wi.us
Maplewood MS 700/6-8
1600 Midway Rd 54952 920-967-1600
Bev Sturke, prin. Fax 832-5837
Menasha HS 1,000/9-12
420 7th St 54952 920-967-1800
Lawrence Haase, prin. Fax 751-5223

Seton Catholic MS 200/6-8
312 Nicolet Blvd 54952 920-727-0279
Sandy Ehlers, prin. Fax 727-1215
University of Wisconsin Fox Valley Post-Sec.
1478 Midway Rd 54952 920-832-2600

Menomonee Falls, Waukesha, Pop. 35,186
Menomonee Falls SD 4,400/PK-12
W156N8480 Pilgrim Rd 53051 262-255-8440
Patricia Greco, supt. Fax 255-8461
www.sdmf.k12.wi.us
Menomonee Falls HS 1,500/9-12
W142N8101 Merrimac Dr 53051 262-255-8444
Corey Golla, prin. Fax 255-8377
North MS 1,000/6-8
N88W16750 Garfield Dr 53051 262-255-8450
Lynn Grimm, prin. Fax 255-8475

Bethlehem Lutheran S - South 100/5-8
N84W15252 Menomonee Ave 53051 262-251-3120
Daryl Weber, prin. Fax 251-4679
Calvary Baptist S 200/PK-12
N84W19049 Menomonee Ave 53051 262-251-0328

Menomonie, Dunn, Pop. 15,977
Menomonie Area SD 3,000/K-12
215 Pine Ave NE 54751 715-232-1642
Chris Stratton, supt. Fax 232-1317
msd.k12.wi.us
Menomonie HS 1,000/9-12
1715 5th St W 54751 715-232-2606
David Munoz, prin. Fax 232-2629
Menomonie MS 700/6-8
920 21st St SE 54751 715-232-1673
Stacey Everson, prin. Fax 232-5486

University of Wisconsin Post-Sec.
712 Broadway St S 54751 715-232-1122

Mequon, Ozaukee, Pop. 22,848
Mequon-Thiensville SD 3,700/PK-12
5000 W Mequon Rd 53092 262-238-8500
Demond Means, supt. Fax 238-8520
www.mtsd.k12.wi.us
Homestead HS 1,400/9-12
5000 W Mequon Rd 53092 262-238-5646
Brett Bowers, prin. Fax 238-5633
Lake Shore MS 400/6-8
11036 N Range Line Rd 53092 262-238-7613
Michael Harris, prin. Fax 238-7650
Steffen MS 400/6-8
6633 W Steffen Dr 53092 262-238-4706
Deborah Anderson, prin. Fax 238-4740

Concordia University Post-Sec.
12800 N Lake Shore Dr 53097 262-243-5700
Lumen Christi MS 200/4-8
11300 N Saint James Ln 53092 262-242-7960
Kelly Fyfe, prin. Fax 512-8986
Milwaukee Area Technical College Post-Sec.
5555 W Highland Rd 53092 262-238-2200

Mercer, Iron, Pop. 516
Mercer SD 100/PK-12
2690 W Margaret St 54547 715-476-2154
Erik Torkelson, supt. Fax 476-2587
www.mercer.k12.wi.us
Mercer S 100/PK-12
2690 W Margaret St 54547 715-476-2154
Erik Torkelson, prin. Fax 476-2587

Merrill, Lincoln, Pop. 9,553
Merrill Area SD 2,900/PK-12
1111 N Sales St 54452 715-536-4581
Don Stevens, supt. Fax 536-1788
www.maps.k12.wi.us
Merrill HS 1,100/9-12
1201 N Sales St 54452 715-536-4594
Shannon Murray, prin. Fax 536-5504
Prairie River MS 700/6-8
106 N Polk St 54452 715-536-9593
Gerald Beyer, prin. Fax 536-6378

Merton, Waukesha, Pop. 3,309
Merton Community SD 1,000/PK-8
PO Box 15 53056 262-538-2227
Ronald Russ, supt. Fax 538-3937
www.merton.k12.wi.us
Merton IS 600/4-8
PO Box 15 53056 262-538-1130
Jay Posick, prin. Fax 538-4978

Middleton, Dane, Pop. 17,031
Middleton-Cross Plains Area SD 6,100/PK-12
7106 South Ave 53562 608-829-9000
Donald Johnson, supt. Fax 836-1536
www.mcpasd.k12.wi.us
Kromrey MS 700/6-8
7009 Donna Dr 53562 608-829-9530
Steve Soeteber, prin. Fax 831-8388
Middleton HS 1,900/9-12
2100 Bristol St 53562 608-829-9660
Denise Herrmann, prin. Fax 831-1995
Other Schools – See Cross Plains

Globe University Post-Sec.
1345 Deming Way 53562 608-830-6900

Milton, Rock, Pop. 5,493
Milton SD 3,200/PK-12
448 E High St 53563 608-868-9200
Theresa Rusch, supt. Fax 868-9215
www.milton.k12.wi.us
Milton HS 1,000/9-12
114 W High St 53563 608-868-9300
Jeremy Bilhorn, prin. Fax 868-9399
Milton MS 500/7-8
20 E Madison Ave 53563 608-868-9350
Tim Schigur, prin. Fax 868-9269

Milwaukee, Milwaukee, Pop. 580,512
Milwaukee SD 74,000/PK-12
PO Box 2181 53201 414-475-8393
Gregory Thornton Ed.D., supt. Fax 475-8595
www.milwaukee.k12.wi.us
ASSATA 100/Alt
2023 W Wisconsin Ave 53233 414-345-6113
Carlotta Pritchett, prin. Fax 345-9893
Banner Prep HS Alt
5460 N 64th St 53218 414-461-9561
Theresa Yeldell Ed.D., admin. Fax 461-9846
Bay View MSHS 1,100/6-12
2751 S Lenox St 53207 414-294-2400
Jonathan Leinfelder, prin. Fax 294-2415
Bradley Tech & Trade HS Vo/Tech
700 S 4th St 53204 414-212-2400
Jody Bloyer, prin. Fax 212-2415
Career Youth Development S 100/Alt
3517 W Courtland Ave 53209 414-449-5960
Lawrence Roth, admin. Fax 449-5971
Centro Hispano HS 100/Alt
1645 S 36th St 53215 414-672-6868
Amy Crumble, admin. Fax 672-6871
Grandview HS 200/Alt
615 W Washington St 53204 414-672-1168
Debi Harry, admin. Fax 672-1273
Groppi HS 400/Alt
1312 N 27th St 53208 414-934-8200
Joel Eul, prin. Fax 934-8215
Hamilton HS 1,900/9-12
6215 W Warnimont Ave 53220 414-327-9300
Rosana Mateo, prin. Fax 327-9315
King International HS 1,700/6-12
1801 W Olive St 53209 414-267-0700
Peter Samaranayake, prin. Fax 267-0715
Lad Lake Synergy MSHS 100/Alt
2820 W Grant St 53215 414-332-2675
Lincoln MS of the Arts 900/6-8
820 E Knapp St 53202 414-212-3300
Ramon Evans, prin. Fax 212-3315
MacDowell Montessori S 600/PK-12
6415 W Mount Vernon Ave 53213 414-935-1400
Andrea Corona, prin. Fax 935-1415
Meir S 400/3-8
1555 N Martin Luther King 53212 414-212-3200
Michelle Morris, prin. Fax 212-3215
Milwaukee HS of the Arts 900/9-12
2300 W Highland Ave 53233 414-934-7000
Barry Applewhite, prin. Fax 934-7015
Milwaukee S of Languages 1,100/6-12
8400 W Burleigh St 53222 414-393-5700
Jennifer Smith, admin. Fax 393-5715
Morse-Marshall S for Gifted and Talented 1,200/6-12
4141 N 64th St 53216 414-393-2300
Larry Farris, prin. Fax 393-2315
New School for Community Services 200/Alt
609 N 8th St 53233 414-298-9390
Hector Rosales, lead tchr. Fax 298-9395
NOVA HS 100/Alt
2320 W Burleigh St 53206 414-874-0283
Scott Campbell, dir. Fax 874-0284
Project Excel 50/Alt
1300 S Layton Blvd Stop 1 53215 414-383-5966
Jamilia Burton, admin. Fax 383-8152
Project STAY 100/Alt
609 N 8th St 53233 414-298-9300
Diane Rosado, admin. Fax 298-9315
Pulaski HS 1,500/9-12
2500 W Oklahoma Ave 53215 414-902-8900
Darrell Williams, prin. Fax 902-8915
Reagan Preparatory HS 1,100/9-12
4965 S 20th St 53221 414-304-6100
Michael Roemer, prin. Fax 304-6115
Riverside University HS 1,600/9-12
1615 E Locust St 53211 414-906-4900
Daniel Donder, prin. Fax 906-4915
Roosevelt Creative Arts MS 800/6-8
800 W Walnut St 53205 414-267-8800
Floyd Williams, prin. Fax 267-8815
Shalom HS 100/Alt
1749 N 16th St 53205 414-933-5019
Gwendolyn Spencer, admin. Fax 933-5433
South Division HS 1,200/9-12
1515 W Lapham Blvd 53204 414-902-8300
Maurice Turner, prin. Fax 902-8315
Southeastern Education Center 50/Alt
4050 N 34th St 53216 414-875-9452
Barry Schwartz, admin. Fax 875-9004
Vincent HS 1,300/9-12
7501 N Granville Rd 53224 262-236-1200
Matthew Boswell, prin. Fax 236-1254
Washington HS of Info Technology 400/9-12
2525 N Sherman Blvd 53210 414-875-5900
Tanya Adair, prin.
Wedgewood Park International S 700/6-8
6506 W Warnimont Ave 53220 414-604-7800
Suzanne Kirby, prin. Fax 604-7815
WI Consrv Lifelong Learning S 700/Alt
1017 N 12th St 53233 414-304-6800
Rae Ellen Sena, prin. Fax 304-6815

West Allis SD 8,900/PK-12
1205 S 70th St Ste 600 53214 414-604-3000
Kurt Wachholz, supt. Fax 546-5795
www.wawm.k12.wi.us
Other Schools – See West Allis, West Milwaukee

Alverno College Post-Sec.
PO Box 343922 53234 414-382-6000
Atlas Preparatory Academy 700/K-12
2911 S 32nd St 53215 414-385-0771
Aurora Health Care Post-Sec.
3000 W Montana St 53215 414-647-3000
Believers in Christ Christian Academy 300/PK-12
4065 N 25th St 53209 414-444-1146
Candace Covington, prin. Fax 444-5378
Blood Center of SE Wisconsin Post-Sec.
1701 W Wisconsin Ave 53233 414-937-6338
Bryant & Stratton College Post-Sec.
310 W Wisconsin Ave Ste 500 53203 414-276-5200
Bufkin Christian Academy 100/PK-12
827 N 34th St 53208 414-934-8885
Texas Bufkin, admin. Fax 934-8886
Cardinal Stritch University Post-Sec.
6801 N Yates Rd 53217 414-410-4000
Catholic East S Sts. Peter & Paul Campus 100/3-8
2461 N Murray Ave 53211 414-964-1770
Gail Kraig, prin. Fax 964-6578
Columbia Hospital Post-Sec.
2025 E Newport Ave 53211 414-961-3800
Destiny HS 300/9-12
7210 N 76th St 53223 414-353-4430
Kristen Reed, prin. Fax 353-0637
DeVry University Post-Sec.
411 E Wisconsin Ave Ste 300 53202 414-278-7677
Divine Savior-Holy Angels HS 700/9-12
4257 N 100th St 53222 414-462-3742
Dan Quesnell, prin. Fax 466-0590
Early View Academy of Excellence 300/PK-10
7132 W Good Hope Rd 53223 414-431-0001
Fax 431-0046
Eastbrook Academy 400/PK-12
5375 N Green Bay Ave 53209 414-228-7905
Jay Wriedt, head sch Fax 228-9854
Everest College Post-Sec.
1311 N 6th St 53212 414-831-8400
Froedtert Memorial Lutheran Hospital Post-Sec.
PO Box 26099 53226 414-259-2606
Holy Redeemer Christian Academy 500/PK-12
3500 W Mother Daniels Way 53209 414-466-1800
Hope Christian HS 300/9-12
3215 N Dr Martin L King Dr 53212 414-264-4476
Paul Becker, dir. Fax 264-4592
ITT Technical Institute Post-Sec.
6300 W Layton Ave 53220 414-282-9494
Kaplan College Post-Sec.
111 W Pleasant St Ste 101 53212 414-225-4610
Marquette University Post-Sec.
PO Box 1881 53201 414-288-7700
Marquette University HS 1,100/9-12
3401 W Wisconsin Ave 53208 414-933-7220
Jeff Monday, prin. Fax 937-8588
Medical College of Wisconsin Post-Sec.
8701 W Watertown Plank Rd 53226 414-955-8296
Messmer HS 700/9-12
742 W Capitol Dr 53206 414-264-5440
Bob Smith, pres. Fax 264-0672
Milwaukee Area Technical College Post-Sec.
700 W State St 53233 414-297-6282

Milwaukee Institute of Art & Design Post-Sec.
273 E Erie St 53202 414-847-3200
Milwaukee Lutheran HS 600/9-12
9700 W Grantosa Dr 53222 414-461-6000
Matthew Pankow, prin. Fax 461-2733
Milwaukee School of Engineering Post-Sec.
1025 N Broadway 53202 414-277-7300
Milwaukee SDA S 100/K-10
10900 W Mill Rd 53225 414-353-3520
Daniel Kuntz, admin. Fax 353-1451
Mt. Mary College Post-Sec.
2900 N Menomonee River Pkwy 53222 414-258-4810
Nativity Jesuit MS 100/6-8
1515 S 29th St 53215 414-645-1060
Jim Wilkinson, prin. Fax 645-0505
Noach S 100/PK-12
222 E Burleigh St 53212 414-431-0146
Dr. Brenda Noach, pres. Fax 431-2171
Northwest Catholic S - West Campus 100/4-8
8202 W Denver Ave 53223 414-352-6927
Diana Erlandson, prin. Fax 352-7258
Notre Dame MS 100/5-8
1420 W Scott St 53204 414-671-3000
Sr. Jean Ellman, prin. Fax 671-3170
Pius XI HS 1,000/9-12
135 N 76th St 53213 414-290-7000
Dr. Melinda Skrade, admin. Fax 290-7001
Prince of Peace S 200/PK-K, 6-8
1646 S 22nd St 53204 414-645-4922
Judy Birlem, prin. Fax 645-4940
St. Anthony HS, 4807 S 2nd St 53207 9-12
Julia D'Amato, prin. 414-763-6352
St. Anthony MS 300/6-8
1747 S 9th St 53204 414-384-1730
Ramon Cruz, prin. Fax 384-1733
St. Francis Hospital Post-Sec.
3237 S 16th St 53215 414-647-5106
St. Joan Antida HS 300/9-12
1341 N Cass St 53202 414-272-8423
Maria Schram, hdmstr. Fax 272-3135
St. Luke's Medical Center Post-Sec.
2900 W Oklahoma Ave 53215 414-649-7500
St. Thomas More HS 400/9-12
2601 E Morgan Ave 53207 414-481-8370
Dr. Mark Joerres, prin. Fax 481-3382
Salam S 800/PK-12
4707 S 13th St 53221 414-282-0504
Wanis Shalaby, prin. Fax 282-6959
The Art Institute of Wisconsin Post-Sec.
320 E Buffalo St Ste 100 53202 414-978-5000
Torah Academy of Milwaukee 50/9-12
6800 N Green Bay Ave 53209 414-352-6789
Sora Rauch, admin. Fax 352-6646
Travis Academy 400/K-12
2733 W Wisconsin Ave 53208 414-342-1671
Wilnekia Brinson, admin. Fax 342-4953
Travis Technology HS 200/9-12
8350 N Steven Rd 53223 414-354-7440
Junior Gentry, admin. Fax 354-7420
University of Wisconsin Post-Sec.
PO Box 413 53201 414-229-1122
University S 1,100/PK-12
2100 W Fairy Chasm Rd 53217 414-352-6000
Laura Fuller, admin. Fax 352-8076
Vici Beauty School Post-Sec.
11010 W Hampton Ave 53225 414-464-5002
Wisconsin Conservatory of Music Post-Sec.
1584 N Prospect Ave 53202 414-276-5760
Wisconsin Institute for Torah Study 100/9-12
3288 N Lake Dr 53211 414-963-9317
Wisconsin Lutheran College Post-Sec.
8800 W Bluemound Rd 53226 414-443-8800
Wisconsin Lutheran HS 800/9-12
330 Glenview Ave 53213 414-453-4567
Ned Goede, prin. Fax 453-3001
WI School of Professional Psychology Post-Sec.
9120 W Hampton Ave Ste 212 53225 414-464-9777
Zablocki VA Medical Center Post-Sec.
5000 W National Ave 53295 414-384-2000

Mineral Point, Iowa, Pop. 2,475
Mineral Point SD 700/PK-12
705 Ross St 53565 608-987-0740
Luke Francois, supt. Fax 987-3766
www.mp.k12.wi.us
Mineral Point HS 200/9-12
705 Ross St 53565 608-987-0730
Mitch Wainwright, prin. Fax 987-3766
Mineral Point MS 200/6-8
705 Ross St 53565 608-987-0720
Vickie Dahl, prin. Fax 987-3766

Minocqua, Oneida, Pop. 440
Lakeland UNHSD 800/9-12
9573 State Highway 70 54548 715-356-5252
Todd Kleinhans, supt. Fax 356-1892
www.luhs.k12.wi.us
Lakeland HS 800/9-12
9573 State Highway 70 54548 715-356-5252
James Bouche, prin. Fax 356-1892

Minong, Washburn, Pop. 520
Northwood SD 400/PK-12
N14463 Highway 53 54859 715-466-2297
Dr. Jean Serum, supt. Fax 466-5149
northwood.k12.wi.us/
Northwood S 400/PK-12
N14463 Highway 53 54859 715-466-2297
Joshua Tomesh, prin. Fax 466-5149

Mishicot, Manitowoc, Pop. 1,424
Mishicot SD 900/PK-12
PO Box 280 54228 920-755-4633
Colleen Timm, supt. Fax 755-4068
www.mishicot.k12.wi.us
Mishicot HS 300/9-12
PO Box 280 54228 920-755-2311
Thomas Ellenbecker, prin. Fax 755-2390
Mishicot MS 200/6-8
PO Box 280 54228 920-755-2808
Colleen Timm, prin. Fax 755-2390

Mondovi, Buffalo, Pop. 2,751
Mondovi SD, 337 N Jackson St 54755 1,200/PK-12
Cheryl Gullicksrud, supt. 715-926-3684
www.mondovi.k12.wi.us/
Mondovi HS 300/9-12
337 N Jackson St 54755 715-926-3656
Mike Bruning, prin. Fax 926-3617
Mondovi MS, 337 N Jackson St 54755 200/6-8
Mike Bruning, prin. 715-926-3656

Monona, Dane, Pop. 7,407
Monona Grove SD 2,500/PK-12
5301 Monona Dr 53716 608-221-7660
Daniel Olson, supt. Fax 221-7688
www.mononagrove.org
Monona Grove HS 900/9-12
4400 Monona Dr 53716 608-221-7666
Paul Brost Ph.D., prin. Fax 221-7690
Other Schools – See Cottage Grove

Monroe, Green, Pop. 10,726
Monroe SD 2,800/PK-12
925 16th Ave Ste 3 53566 608-328-7171
Cory Hirsbrunner, supt. Fax 328-7214
www.monroeschools.com
Monroe HS 700/9-12
1600 26th St 53566 608-328-7117
Chris Medenwaldt, prin. Fax 328-7230
Monroe MS 600/6-8
1510 13th St 53566 608-328-7120
Lynn Wheeler, prin. Fax 328-7224

Paul Mitchell The School Post-Sec.
1015 18th Ave Ste 212 53566 608-329-7004

Montello, Marquette, Pop. 1,476
Montello SD 700/PK-12
222 Forest Ln 53949 608-297-7617
Jeff Holmes, supt. Fax 297-7726
www.montello.k12.wi.us
Montello JSHS 300/7-12
222 Forest Ln 53949 608-297-2126
Chuck Harsh, prin. Fax 297-9390

Monticello, Green, Pop. 1,208
Monticello SD 400/PK-12
334 S Main St 53570 608-938-4194
Allen Brokopp, supt. Fax 938-1062
www.monticello.k12.wi.us/
Monticello HS 100/9-12
334 S Main St 53570 608-938-4194
Mark Gustafson, prin. Fax 938-1062
Monticello MS 100/6-8
334 S Main St 53570 608-938-4194
Mark Gustafson, prin. Fax 938-1062

Mosinee, Marathon, Pop. 3,964
Mosinee SD 2,100/PK-12
591 W State Highway 153 54455 715-693-2530
Dr. Ann Schultz, supt. Fax 693-7272
www.mosineeschools.org
Mosinee HS 700/9-12
1000 High St 54455 715-693-2550
Nathan Lehman, prin. Fax 693-1152
Mosinee MS 800/4-8
700 High St 54455 715-693-3660
Ronald Mueller, prin. Fax 693-6655

Northland Lutheran HS 100/9-12
2107 Tower Rd 54455 715-359-3400
Rick Grundman, prin. Fax 241-9203
WI Valley Lutheran HS 100/9-12
601 Maple Ridge Rd 54455 715-693-2693
Dave Beringer, admin. Fax 693-5962

Mount Calvary, Fond du Lac, Pop. 757

St. Lawrence Seminary HS 200/9-12
301 Church St 53057 920-753-7500
Fr. Dennis Druggan, pres. Fax 753-7507

Mount Horeb, Dane, Pop. 6,889
Mount Horeb Area SD 2,300/PK-12
1304 E Lincoln St 53572 608-437-2400
Debra Klein, supt. Fax 437-5597
www.mhasd.k12.wi.us
Mount Horeb HS 700/9-12
305 S 8th St 53572 608-437-2400
Stephanie Spoehr, prin. Fax 437-4926
Mount Horeb MS 500/6-8
900 E Garfield St 53572 608-437-2400
Jeff Rasmussen, prin. Fax 437-6227

Mukwonago, Waukesha, Pop. 7,291
Mukwonago SD 5,000/PK-12
385 County Road NN E 53149 262-363-6300
Paul Strobel, supt. Fax 363-6272
www.masd.k12.wi.us
Mukwonago HS 1,700/9-12
605 W School Rd 53149 262-363-6200
Shawn McNulty, prin. Fax 363-6239
Park View MS 800/7-8
930 N Rochester St 53149 262-363-6292
Mark Doome, prin. Fax 363-6320

Norris SD 100/6-12
W247S10395 Center Dr 53149 262-662-5911
Sara Trampf, supt. Fax 662-5502
www.norriscenter.org/
Norris JSHS 100/6-12
W247S10395 Center Dr 53149 262-662-5911
Christopher Fountain, prin. Fax 662-5502

Muscoda, Grant, Pop. 1,294
Riverdale SD 700/PK-12
PO Box 66 53573 608-739-3832
Bryce Bird, supt. Fax 739-3751
www.riverdale.k12.wi.us/
Riverdale HS 200/9-12
PO Box 66 53573 608-739-3116
Fax 739-4486
Riverdale MS 200/5-8
800 N 6th St 53573 608-739-3101
Shari Hougan, prin. Fax 739-9118

Muskego, Waukesha, Pop. 23,915
Muskego-Norway SD 4,900/PK-12
S87W18763 Woods Rd 53150 262-971-1800
Dr. Kelly Thompson, supt. Fax 679-5790
www.muskegonorway.org/
Bay Lane MS 700/5-8
S75W16399 Hilltop Dr 53150 262-971-1810
Erik Olson, prin. Fax 422-2204
Lake Denoon MS 800/5-8
W216S10586 Crowbar Dr 53150 262-971-1820
Linda O'Bryan, prin. Fax 662-1588
Muskego HS 1,700/9-12
W183S8750 Racine Ave 53150 262-971-1790
Ryan Oertel, prin. Fax 679-3534

Nashotah, Waukesha, Pop. 1,378

Nashotah House Post-Sec.
2777 Mission Rd 53058 262-646-6500

Necedah, Juneau, Pop. 904
Necedah Area SD 800/PK-12
1801 S Main St 54646 608-565-2256
Larry Gierach, supt. Fax 565-3201
www.necedahschools.org
Necedah MSHS 400/6-12
1801 S Main St 54646 608-565-2256
Mark Becker, prin. Fax 565-7044

Neenah, Winnebago, Pop. 25,158
Neenah SD 6,300/PK-12
410 S Commercial St 54956 920-751-6800
Mary Pfeiffer Ph.D., supt. Fax 751-6809
www.neenah.k12.wi.us
Neenah HS 2,100/9-12
1275 Tullar Rd 54956 920-751-6900
Brian Wunderlich, prin. Fax 751-7001
Shattuck MS 900/7-8
600 Elm St 54956 920-751-6850
Stephanie Phernetton, prin. Fax 751-6899

St. Mary Central HS 200/9-12
1050 Zephyr Dr 54956 920-722-7796
Patrick Batey, prin. Fax 722-5940
Theda Clark Regional Medical Center Post-Sec.
130 2nd St 54956 920-729-2004

Neillsville, Clark, Pop. 2,446
Neillsville SD 400/PK-12
614 E 5th St 54456 715-743-3323
John Galer, supt. Fax 743-8718
www.neillsville.k12.wi.us
Neillsville MSHS 300/7-12
401 Center St 54456 715-743-8738
Craig Ruskin, prin. Fax 743-8714

Nekoosa, Wood, Pop. 2,530
Nekoosa SD 1,200/K-12
600 S Section St 54457 715-886-8000
Terry Whitmore, supt. Fax 886-8012
www.nekoosasd.net
Alexander MS 500/4-8
540 Birch St 54457 715-886-8040
Jon Sprehn, prin. Fax 886-8097
Nekoosa Academy Alt
310 1st St 54457 715-886-8190
Terry Whitmore, prin. Fax 886-8191
Nekoosa HS 400/9-12
500 Cedar St 54457 715-886-8060
Michael Kumm, prin. Fax 886-8087

Neopit, Menominee, Pop. 682
Menominee Indian SD
Supt. — See Keshena
Menominee Indian MS 100/6-8
PO Box 9 54150 715-756-2324
Stephanie Feldner, prin. Fax 756-2496

Neosho, Dodge, Pop. 566

Lake Country Victory Christian HS 50/9-12
112 Hale Rd 53059 920-625-3995
Bruce Dickman, prin. Fax 625-3995

New Auburn, Chippewa, Pop. 537
New Auburn SD 300/PK-12
PO Box 110 54757 715-237-2202
Brian Henning, supt. Fax 237-2350
www.newauburn.k12.wi.us
New Auburn JSHS 100/7-12
PO Box 110 54757 715-237-2505
Cory Martens, prin. Fax 237-2350

New Berlin, Waukesha, Pop. 39,208
New Berlin SD 4,400/PK-12
4333 S Sunnyslope Rd 53151 262-789-6200
Joe Garza, supt. Fax 786-0512
www.nbexcellence.org/
Eisenhower MSHS 1,200/7-12
4333 S Sunnyslope Rd 53151 262-789-6300
Michael Fesenmaier, prin. Fax 789-6313
New Berlin West MSHS 1,200/7-12
18695 W Cleveland Ave 53146 262-789-6400
John Budish, prin. Fax 789-6442

New Glarus, Green, Pop. 2,162
New Glarus SD 800/PK-12
PO Box 7 53574 608-527-2410
Dr. Jennifer Thayer, supt. Fax 527-5101
www.ngsd.k12.wi.us
New Glarus HS 300/9-12
PO Box 7 53574 608-527-2410
Jeff Eichelkraut, prin. Fax 527-5101
New Glarus MS 100/5-8
PO Box 67 53574 608-527-2410
Mark Stateler, prin. Fax 527-5101

New Holstein, Calumet, Pop. 3,214
New Holstein SD 1,100/PK-12
1715 Plymouth St 53061 920-898-5115
William Van Meer, supt. Fax 898-4112
www.nhsd.k12.wi.us
New Holstein HS 400/9-12
1715 Plymouth St 53061 920-898-4256
Rodney Figuero, prin. Fax 898-4112
New Holstein MS 200/6-8
1717 Plymouth St 53061 920-898-4769
Richard Amundson, prin. Fax 898-4810

Divine Savior S 100/5-8
1814 Madison St 53061 920-898-4210
Ben Pfiffner, prin. Fax 898-4220

New Lisbon, Juneau, Pop. 2,524
New Lisbon SD 700/PK-12
500 S Forest St 53950 608-562-3700
Dennis Birr, supt. Fax 562-5333
www.newlisbon.k12.wi.us
New Lisbon JSHS 300/7-12
500 S Forest St 53950 608-562-3700
Gary Syftestad, prin. Fax 562-5333

New London, Waupaca, Pop. 7,241
New London SD 2,500/PK-12
901 W Washington St 54961 920-982-8530
Dr. Kathleen Gwidt, supt. Fax 982-8551
www.newlondon.k12.wi.us
New London HS 800/9-12
1700 Klatt Rd 54961 920-982-8420
Joe Pomrening, prin. Fax 982-8440
New London IS / MS 700/5-8
1000 W Washington St 54961 920-982-8532
Pete Schulz, prin. Fax 982-8605

New Richmond, Saint Croix, Pop. 8,254
New Richmond SD 3,100/PK-12
701 E 11th St 54017 715-243-7411
Jeff Moberg, supt. Fax 246-3638
www.newrichmond.k12.wi.us
New Richmond HS 800/9-12
701 E 11th St 54017 715-243-7451
Tom Wissink, prin. Fax 243-7464
New Richmond MS 600/6-8
701 E 11th St 54017 715-243-7472
Doug Hatch, prin. Fax 246-0580

Wisconsin Indianhead Technical College Post-Sec.
1019 S Knowles Ave 54017 715-246-6561

Niagara, Marinette, Pop. 1,609
Niagara SD 400/PK-12
700 Jefferson Ave 54151 715-251-1330
Dan Nett, supt. Fax 251-4544
www.niagara.k12.wi.us
Niagara JSHS 200/7-12
700 Jefferson Ave 54151 715-251-4541
Kipp Beaudoin, prin. Fax 251-3715

North Fond du Lac, Fond du Lac, Pop. 4,969
North Fond Du Lac SD 1,200/PK-12
225 McKinley St 54937 920-929-3750
Aaron Sadoff, supt. Fax 929-3696
www.nfdl.k12.wi.us
Allen MS 300/6-8
305 Mckinley St 54937 920-929-3754
William Paris, prin. Fax 929-3747
Mann HS 400/9-12
325 Mckinley St 54937 920-929-3740
Samantha Freimund, prin. Fax 929-3664

Oak Creek, Milwaukee, Pop. 33,834
Oak Creek-Franklin SD 5,900/PK-12
7630 S 10th St 53154 414-768-5886
Sara Burmeister, supt. Fax 768-6172
www.oakcreek.k12.wi.us
Oak Creek East MS 900/6-8
9330 S Shepard Ave 53154 414-768-6260
Annalee Bennin, prin. Fax 768-6293
Oak Creek HS 2,000/9-12
340 E Puetz Rd 53154 414-768-6100
Michael Read, prin. Fax 768-6130
Oak Creek West MS 500/6-8
8401 S 13th St 53154 414-768-6250
Michael Maxson, prin. Fax 768-6296

Milwaukee Area Technical College Post-Sec.
6665 S Howell Ave 53154 414-571-4500

Oakfield, Fond du Lac, Pop. 1,057
Oakfield SD 500/PK-12
PO Box 99 53065 920-583-4117
Pam Yoder, supt. Fax 583-4671
www.oakfield.k12.wi.us/
Oakfield JSHS 200/7-12
PO Box 39 53065 920-583-3141
Joseph Heinzelman, prin. Fax 583-4673

Oconomowoc, Waukesha, Pop. 15,586
Oconomowoc Area SD 4,600/K-12
W360N7077 Brown St 53066 262-560-1115
Dr. Roger Rindo, supt.
www.oasd.k12.wi.us
Nature Hill IS 800/4-8
850 N Lake Rd 53066 262-569-4945
Michael O'Connor, prin. Fax 569-4958
Oconomowoc HS 1,400/9-12
641 E Forest St 53066 262-560-3100
Joseph Moylan, prin. Fax 567-8960
Silver Lake IS 700/5-8
555 Oconomowoc Pkwy 53066 262-560-4305
Ellyn Helberg, prin. Fax 560-4318

Oconto, Oconto, Pop. 4,472
Oconto USD 1,000/PK-12
400 Michigan Ave 54153 920-834-7814
Dr. Sara Croney, supt. Fax 834-9884
www.oconto.k12.wi.us
Oconto HS 300/9-12
1717 Superior Ave 54153 920-834-7812
Bill Slough, prin. Fax 834-7804
Oconto MS 300/5-8
400 Michigan Ave 54153 920-834-7806
Aaron Malczewski, prin. Fax 834-9884

Oconto Falls, Oconto, Pop. 2,850
Oconto Falls SD 1,800/PK-12
200 N Farm Rd 54154 920-848-4471
David Polashek, supt. Fax 848-4474
www.ocontofalls.k12.wi.us
Oconto Falls HS 600/9-12
PO Box 988 54154 920-848-4467
Bruce Russell, prin. Fax 846-4444
Washington MS 400/6-8
102 S Washington St 54154 920-846-4463
Lou Hobyan, prin. Fax 846-4453

Omro, Winnebago, Pop. 3,492
Omro SD 1,300/PK-12
455 Fox Trl 54963 920-685-5666
Fax 685-5757
www.omro.k12.wi.us/
Omro HS 400/9-12
455 Fox Trl 54963 920-685-7405
Bret Steffen, prin. Fax 685-7040
Omro MS 300/6-8
455 Fox Trl 54963 920-685-7403
Paul Williams, prin. Fax 685-5757

Onalaska, LaCrosse, Pop. 17,449
Onalaska SD 3,000/PK-12
1821 E Main St 54650 608-781-9700
Dr. Francis Finco, supt. Fax 781-9712
www.onalaska.k12.wi.us
Onalaska HS 900/9-12
700 Hilltopper Pl 54650 608-783-4561
Jared Schaffner, prin. Fax 783-0102
Onalaska MS 700/6-8
711 Quincy St 54650 608-783-5366
Jed Kees, prin. Fax 781-8030

Globe University Post-Sec.
2651 Midwest Dr 54650 608-779-2600
Luther HS 300/9-12
1501 Wilson St 54650 608-783-5435
Paul Wichmann, prin. Fax 783-4758
The Salon Professional Academy Post-Sec.
566 Theater Rd 54650 608-781-8772

Ontario, Vernon, Pop. 550
Norwalk-Ontario-Wilton SD 700/PK-12
PO Box 130 54651 608-337-4403
Dr. Kelly Burhop, supt. Fax 337-4348
www.now.k12.wi.us/
Brookwood JSHS 300/7-12
PO Box 130 54651 608-337-4401
Brad Pettit, prin. Fax 337-4348

Oostburg, Sheboygan, Pop. 2,866
Oostburg SD 1,000/PK-12
PO Box 700100 53070 920-564-2346
Kevin Bruggink, supt. Fax 564-6138
oostburg.k12.wi.us
Oostburg HS 300/9-12
PO Box 700100 53070 920-564-2346
Scott Greupink, prin. Fax 564-6138
Oostburg MS 200/6-8
PO Box 700100 53070 920-564-2383
Steve Harder, prin. Fax 564-6138

Oregon, Dane, Pop. 9,079
Oregon SD 3,500/K-12
123 E Grove St 53575 608-835-4000
Brian Busler, supt. Fax 835-9509
www.oregonsd.org
Oregon HS 1,100/9-12
456 N Perry Pkwy 53575 608-835-4300
Kelly Meyers, prin. Fax 835-7894
Oregon MS 500/7-8
601 Pleasant Oak Dr 53575 608-835-4800
Jim Pliner, prin. Fax 835-3849

Orfordville, Rock, Pop. 1,432
Parkview SD 700/PK-12
PO Box 250 53576 608-879-2717
Steve Lutzke, supt. Fax 879-2732
www.parkview.k12.wi.us
Parkview JSHS 300/7-12
PO Box 247 53576 608-879-2994
William Trow, prin. Fax 879-2732

Osceola, Polk, Pop. 2,529
Osceola SD 1,900/PK-12
PO Box 128 54020 715-294-4140
Mark Luebker, supt. Fax 294-2428
www.osceola.k12.wi.us
Osceola HS 600/9-12
PO Box 128 54020 715-294-2127
Michael McMartin, prin. Fax 755-2068
Osceola MS 400/6-8
PO Box 128 54020 715-294-4180
Rebecca Styles, prin. Fax 294-2428

Oshkosh, Winnebago, Pop. 65,117
Oshkosh Area SD 9,600/PK-12
PO Box 3048 54903 920-424-0395
Stan Mack, supt. Fax 424-0466
www.oshkosh.k12.wi.us
Merrill MS 400/6-8
108 W New York Ave 54901 920-424-0177
Cindy Olson, prin. Fax 424-7512
Oshkosh North HS 1,300/9-12
1100 W Smith Ave 54901 920-424-7000
Jacqueline Schleicher, prin. Fax 424-4054
Oshkosh West HS 1,800/9-12
375 N Eagle St 54902 920-424-4090
Erin Kohl, prin. Fax 424-4950
South Park MS 400/6-8
1551 Delaware St 54902 920-424-0431
Lisa McLaughlin, prin. Fax 424-7513
Stanley MS 400/6-8
915 Hazel St 54901 920-424-0442
Philip Marshall, prin. Fax 424-7515
Tipler MS 400/6-8
325 S Eagle St 54902 920-424-0320
Jay Jones, prin. Fax 424-7514
Traeger MS 500/6-8
3000 W 20th Ave 54904 920-424-0065
Jill Pascarella, prin. Fax 424-7511

Fox Valley Technical College Post-Sec.
150 N Campbell Rd 54902 920-233-9191
Lourdes HS 200/6-12
110 N Sawyer St 54902 920-235-5670
Mike Mauthe, prin. Fax 235-7453
Mercy Medical Center Post-Sec.
PO Box 3370 54903 920-233-5110
Oshkosh Christian S Valley Christian HS 200/PK-12
3450 Vinland St 54901 920-231-9704
John Davis, admin. Fax 231-9804
University of Wisconsin Post-Sec.
800 Algoma Blvd 54901 920-424-1234

Osseo, Trempealeau, Pop. 1,691
Osseo-Fairchild SD 900/PK-12
50851 East St 54758 715-597-3141
William Tourdot, supt. Fax 597-3606
www.ofsd.k12.wi.us
Osseo-Fairchild HS 300/9-12
50900 Francis St 54758 715-597-3141
Bill Tourdot, prin. Fax 597-3647
Osseo MS 200/6-8
50900 Francis St 54758 715-597-3141
Bill Tourdot, prin. Fax 597-3647

Owen, Clark, Pop. 936
Owen-Withee SD 500/PK-12
PO Box 417 54460 715-229-2151
Robert Houts, supt. Fax 229-4322
www.owen-withee.k12.wi.us
Owen-Withee HS 200/9-12
PO Box 417 54460 715-229-2151
Robert Houts, prin. Fax 229-4322
Owen-Withee JHS 100/7-8
PO Box 417 54460 715-229-2151
Robert Houts, prin. Fax 229-4322

Palmyra, Jefferson, Pop. 1,774
Palmyra-Eagle Area SD 1,100/PK-12
PO Box 901 53156 262-495-7101
Glenn Schlender, supt. Fax 495-7151
www.palmyra.k12.wi.us
Palmyra-Eagle HS 300/9-12
PO Box 901 53156 262-495-7101
Nicholas Schultek, prin. Fax 495-7146
Palmyra-Eagle MS 200/7-8
PO Box 901 53156 262-495-7101
Nicholas Schultek, prin. Fax 495-7146

Pardeeville, Columbia, Pop. 2,095
Pardeeville Area SD 800/PK-12
PO Box 130 53954 608-429-2153
Earl Knitt, supt. Fax 429-2277
www.pardeeville.k12.wi.us
Pardeeville HS 300/9-12
PO Box 130 53954 608-429-2153
Jason Lemay, prin. Fax 429-2277
Pardeeville MS 200/5-8
PO Box 130 53954 608-429-2153
Fax 429-2277

Park Falls, Price, Pop. 2,367
Chequamegon SD 800/PK-12
420 9th St N 54552 715-762-2474
David Anderson, admin. Fax 762-5469
www.csdk12.net
Chequamegon HS 300/9-12
400 9th St N 54552 715-762-2474
Timothy Kief, prin. Fax 762-5674
Other Schools – See Glidden

Patch Grove, Grant, Pop. 198
River Ridge SD 500/PK-12
PO Box 78 53817 608-994-2715
Lee Pritzl, supt. Fax 994-2891
www.rrsd.k12.wi.us
River Ridge HS 200/9-12
PO Box 78 53817 608-994-2715
Rodney Lewis, prin. Fax 994-2891
Other Schools – See Bloomington

Pembine, Marinette, Pop. 189
Beecher-Dunbar-Pembine SD 300/PK-12
PO Box 247 54156 715-324-5314
Robert Berndt, supt. Fax 324-5282
www.pembine.k12.wi.us/
Pembine JSHS 100/7-12
PO Box 247 54156 715-324-5314
Robert Berndt, prin. Fax 324-5282

Pepin, Pepin, Pop. 835
Pepin Area SD 200/PK-12
PO Box 128 54759 715-442-2391
Bruce Quinton, supt. Fax 442-3607
pepin.k12.wi.us
Pepin HS 100/9-12
PO Box 128 54759 715-442-2391
Bruce Quinton, prin. Fax 442-3607

Peshtigo, Marinette, Pop. 3,466
Peshtigo SD 1,200/PK-12
341 N Emery Ave 54157 715-582-3677
Kim Eparvier, supt. Fax 582-3850
www.peshtigo.k12.wi.us
Peshtigo MSHS 500/7-12
380 Green St 54157 715-582-3711
Chad Sodini, prin. Fax 582-0740

Pewaukee, Waukesha, Pop. 8,065
Pewaukee SD 2,500/PK-12
404 Lake St 53072 262-691-2100
JoAnn Sternke Ed.D., supt. Fax 691-1052
pewaukeeschools.schoolfusion.us
Clark MS 400/7-8
472 Lake St 53072 262-691-2100
Randy Daul, prin. Fax 695-5004
Pewaukee HS 700/9-12
510 Lake St 53072 262-691-2100
Marty Van Hulle, prin. Fax 695-5006

Trinity Academy 100/PK-12
W225N3131 Duplainville Rd 53072 262-695-2933
Robin Mitchell Ph.D., hdmstr. Fax 695-2934
Waukesha County Technical College Post-Sec.
800 Main St 53072 262-691-5566

Phelps, Vilas
Phelps SD 100/K-12
4451 Old School Rd 54554 715-545-2724
Delnice Hill, supt. Fax 545-3728
www.phelps.k12.wi.us
Phelps HS 50/9-12
4451 Old School Rd 54554 715-545-2724
Jason Pertile, dean Fax 545-3728

Phillips, Price, Pop. 1,454
Phillips SD 800/PK-12
PO Box 70 54555 715-339-2419
Rick Morgan, supt. Fax 339-2416
www.phillips.k12.wi.us/
Phillips HS 300/9-12
PO Box 70 54555 715-339-2141
Colin Hoogland, prin. Fax 339-2144
Phillips MS 200/6-8
PO Box 70 54555 715-339-3393
Colin Hoogland, prin. Fax 339-2416

Pittsville, Wood, Pop. 868
Pittsville SD 600/PK-12
5459 Elementary Ave Ste 2 54466 715-884-6694
Terry Reynolds, supt. Fax 884-5210
www.pittsville.k12.wi.us
Pittsville HS 200/9-12
5407 1st Ave 54466 715-884-6412
Mark Weddig, prin. Fax 884-2870

Plainfield, Waushara, Pop. 852
Tri-County Area SD 500/PK-12
409 S West St 54966 715-335-6366
Tony Marinack, supt. Fax 335-6365
www.tricounty.k12.wi.us
Tri-County HS 200/7-12
409 S West St 54966 715-335-6366
Nicholas Marti, prin. Fax 335-6322

Platteville, Grant, Pop. 11,124
Platteville SD 1,500/PK-12
780 N 2nd St 53818 608-342-4000
Connie Valenza, supt. Fax 342-4412
www.platteville.k12.wi.us
Platteville HS 500/9-12
710 E Madison St 53818 608-342-4020
Jeffrey Jacobson, prin. Fax 342-4427
Platteville MS 500/4-8
40 E Madison St 53818 608-342-4010
Lisa Finnegan, prin. Fax 342-4497

University of Wisconsin Post-Sec.
1 University Plz 53818 608-342-1491

Pleasant Prairie, Kenosha, Pop. 19,418
Kenosha SD
Supt. — See Kenosha
Lakeview Technology Academy Vo/Tech
9449 88th Ave 53158 262-947-8155
William Hittman, prin. Fax 947-8159

Plum City, Pierce, Pop. 598
Plum City SD 300/PK-12
907 Main St 54761 715-647-2591
Stephen LaFave, supt. Fax 647-3015
www.plumcity.k12.wi.us
Plum City JSHS 200/6-12
907 Main St 54761 715-647-2591
Paul Churchill, prin. Fax 647-3015

Plymouth, Sheboygan, Pop. 8,357
Plymouth SD 2,200/PK-12
125 S Highland Ave 53073 920-892-2661
Clark Reinke, supt. Fax 892-6366
www.plymouth.k12.wi.us
Plymouth HS 800/9-12
125 S Highland Ave 53073 920-893-6911
Dan Mella, prin. Fax 892-6366
Riverview MS 500/6-8
300 Riverside Cir 53073 920-892-4353
Chris Scudella, prin. Fax 892-5072

Poplar, Douglas, Pop. 589
Maple SD
Supt. — See Maple

Northwestern MS 300/6-8
PO Box 46 54864 715-364-2218
Ken Bartelt, prin. Fax 364-2540

Portage, Columbia, Pop. 10,179
Portage Community SD 2,300/PK-12
305 E Slifer St 53901 608-742-4879
Charles Poches, supt. Fax 742-4950
www.portage.k12.wi.us
Bartels MS 300/6-8
2505 New Pinery Rd 53901 608-742-2165
Robert Meicher, prin. Fax 745-4884
Portage HS 800/9-12
301 E Collins St 53901 608-742-8545
Robin Kvalo, prin. Fax 742-0617

Port Edwards, Wood, Pop. 1,802
Port Edwards SD 400/K-12
801 2nd St 54469 715-887-9000
Patricia Sullivan, supt. Fax 887-9040
www.pesd.k12.wi.us
Edwards HS 200/9-12
801 2nd St 54469 715-887-9000
Kyle Cronan, prin. Fax 887-9040
Edwards MS 100/6-8
801 2nd St 54469 715-887-9000
Kyle Cronan, prin. Fax 887-9040

Port Washington, Ozaukee, Pop. 11,098
Port Washington-Saukville SD 2,700/PK-12
100 W Monroe St 53074 262-268-6000
Michael Weber Ph.D., supt. Fax 268-6020
www.pwssd.k12.wi.us
Jefferson MS 800/5-8
1403 N Holden St 53074 262-268-6100
Arlan Galarowicz, prin. Fax 268-6120
Port Washington HS 800/9-12
427 W Jackson St 53074 262-268-5500
Eric Burke, prin. Fax 268-5520

Port Washington Catholic MS 100/5-8
1802 N Wisconsin St 53074 262-284-2682
Rick Goeden, prin. Fax 284-4168

Port Wing, Bayfield, Pop. 160
South Shore SD 200/PK-12
PO Box 40 54865 715-774-3500
Clendon Gustafson, supt. Fax 774-3569
www.sshore.k12.wi.us
South Shore JSHS 100/7-12
PO Box 40 54865 715-774-3500
Clendon Gustafson, prin. Fax 774-3569

Potosi, Grant, Pop. 686
Potosi SD 300/PK-12
128 US Highway 61 N 53820 608-763-2162
Dr. Steven Lozeau, supt. Fax 763-2035
www.potosisd.k12.wi.us
Potosi HS 100/9-12
128 US Highway 61 N 53820 608-763-2161
Terry Mengel, prin. Fax 763-2035
Potosi MS 100/6-8
128 US Highway 61 N 53820 608-763-2162
Terry Mengel, prin. Fax 763-2035

Poynette, Columbia, Pop. 2,497
Poynette SD 1,100/PK-12
PO Box 10 53955 608-635-4347
Matt Shappell, supt. Fax 635-9200
www.poynette.k12.wi.us
Poynette HS 300/9-12
PO Box 10 53955 608-635-4347
Mark Hoernke, prin. Fax 635-9201
Poynette MS 300/6-8
PO Box 10 53955 608-635-4347
Brian Sutton, prin. Fax 635-9233

Prairie du Chien, Crawford, Pop. 5,867
Prairie du Chien Area SD 1,100/PK-12
800 E Crawford St 53821 608-326-3700
Drew Johnson, supt. Fax 326-0000
www.pdc.k12.wi.us
Prairie du Chien HS 400/9-12
800 E Crawford St 53821 608-326-3700
Andy Banasik, prin. Fax 326-3709

St. John Nepomucene MS 100/6-8
720 S Wacouta Ave 53821 608-326-4400
Wade Marlow, prin. Fax 326-4876

Prairie du Sac, Sauk, Pop. 3,923
Sauk Prairie SD
Supt. — See Sauk City
Sauk Prairie HS 800/9-12
105 9th St 53578 608-643-5900
Chris Grinde, prin. Fax 643-5419

Prairie Farm, Barron, Pop. 472
Prairie Farm SD 400/PK-12
630 River Ave S 54762 715-455-1683
Craig Broeren, supt. Fax 455-1056
www.prairiefarm.k12.wi.us
Prairie Farm HS 100/9-12
630 River Ave S 54762 715-455-1861
Patrick Olson, prin. Fax 455-1869
Prairie Farm MS 100/6-8
630 River Ave S 54762 715-455-1841
Patrick Olson, prin. Fax 455-1869

Prentice, Price, Pop. 653
Prentice SD 300/PK-12
PO Box 110 54556 715-428-2811
Randall Bergman, supt. Fax 428-2815
www.prentice.k12.wi.us
Prentice MSHS 200/5-12
PO Box 110 54556 715-428-2811
Melissa Pilgrim, prin. Fax 428-2815

Prescott, Pierce, Pop. 4,176
Prescott SD 1,200/PK-12
1220 Saint Croix St 54021 715-262-5782
Roger Hulne, supt. Fax 262-5091
www.prescott.k12.wi.us
Prescott HS 400/9-12
1220 Saint Croix St 54021 715-262-5010
David Vortherms, prin. Fax 262-4888
Prescott MS 300/6-8
125 Elm St N 54021 715-262-5054
Lyle Nolt, prin. Fax 262-3965

Princeton, Green Lake, Pop. 1,208
Princeton SD 400/PK-12
PO Box 147 54968 920-295-6571
Jeff McCartney, supt. Fax 295-4778
www.princeton.k12.wi.us
Princeton S 400/PK-12
PO Box 147 54968 920-295-6571
Jeff McCartney, prin. Fax 295-4778

Pulaski, Brown, Pop. 3,500
Pulaski Community SD 3,800/PK-12
PO Box 36 54162 920-822-6000
Milton Thompson, supt. Fax 822-6005
www.pulaskischools.org
Pulaski Community MS 800/6-8
911 S Saint Augustine St 54162 920-822-6500
Patrick Fullerton, prin. Fax 822-6505
Pulaski HS 1,200/9-12
1040 S Saint Augustine St 54162 920-822-6700
Dan Slowey, prin. Fax 822-6707

Racine, Racine, Pop. 76,696
Racine USD 20,600/PK-12
3109 Mount Pleasant St 53404 262-635-5600
Ann Laing, supt. Fax 631-7121
www.racine.k12.wi.us
Case HS 2,000/9-12
7345 Washington Ave 53406 262-619-4200
Jeff Eben, prin. Fax 619-4259
Gilmore MS 800/6-8
2330 Northwestern Ave 53404 262-619-4260
Kevin Brown, prin. Fax 619-4272
Horlick HS 2,000/9-12
2119 Rapids Dr 53404 262-619-4300
Angela Apmann, prin. Fax 619-4390
Jerstad-Agerholm MS 800/6-8
3601 Lasalle St 53402 262-664-6075
Doug Clum, prin. Fax 664-6120
Mack Achievement Center 100/Alt
1325 Park Ave 53403 262-664-6600
Robert Holzem, dir. Fax 664-6644
McKinley MS 900/6-8
2340 Mohr Ave 53405 262-664-6150
Cheri Kulland, prin. Fax 664-6196
Mitchell MS 700/6-8
2701 Drexel Ave 53403 262-664-6400
Soren Gajewski, prin. Fax 664-6444
Park HS 1,900/9-12
1901 12th St 53403 262-619-4400
Dan Thielen, prin. Fax 619-4490
Starbuck MS 800/6-8
1516 Ohio St 53405 262-664-6500
Janet Colvin, prin. Fax 664-6510
Walden III MSHS 300/6-12
1012 Center St 53403 262-664-6250
Robert Holzem, dir. Fax 664-6255

All Saints Healthcare System Post-Sec.
1320 Wisconsin Ave 53403 262-636-2846
Gateway Technical College Post-Sec.
1001 Main St 53403 262-619-6200
Lutheran HS 200/9-12
251 Luedtke Ave 53405 262-637-6538
Randy Baganz, prin. Fax 637-6601
Midwest College of Oriental Medicine Post-Sec.
6232 Bankers Rd 53403 262-554-2010
Prairie S 700/PK-12
4050 Lighthouse Dr 53402 262-260-3845
Mark Murphy, hdmstr. Fax 260-3790
St. Catherine HS 400/6-12
1200 Park Ave 53403 262-632-2785
Dr. Thomas Noonan, prin. Fax 632-5144

Randolph, Columbia, Pop. 1,798
Randolph SD 600/PK-12
110 Meadowood Dr 53956 920-326-2427
Steve Huebbe, supt. Fax 326-2439
www.randolph.k12.wi.us
Randolph HS 200/9-12
110 Meadowood Dr 53956 920-326-2425
Thomas Erdmann, prin. Fax 326-2430

Random Lake, Sheboygan, Pop. 1,574
Random Lake SD 900/PK-12
605 Random Lake Rd 53075 920-994-4342
Thomas Malmstadt, supt. Fax 994-4820
www.randomlake.k12.wi.us
Random Lake HS 300/9-12
605 Random Lake Rd 53075 920-994-9193
Scott Schultz, prin. Fax 994-4820
Random Lake MS 300/5-8
605 Random Lake Rd 53075 920-994-2498
David Farnham, prin. Fax 994-4820

Reedsburg, Sauk, Pop. 9,120
Reedsburg SD 2,600/PK-12
501 K St 53959 608-524-2016
Thomas Benson, supt. Fax 524-6818
www.rsd.k12.wi.us
Reedsburg Area HS 900/9-12
1100 S Albert Ave 53959 608-524-4327
Rob Taylor, prin. Fax 524-1373
Webb MS 600/6-8
707 N Webb Ave 53959 608-524-2328
Casey Campbell, prin. Fax 524-1161

Reedsville, Manitowoc, Pop. 1,195
Reedsville SD 600/PK-12
PO Box 340 54230 920-754-4341
Dennis Raabe, supt. Fax 754-4344
www.reedsville.k12.wi.us
Reedsville HS 200/9-12
PO Box 340 54230 920-754-4341
Tony Butturini, prin. Fax 754-4344
Reedsville MS 100/7-8
PO Box 340 54230 920-754-4345
Pat Popp, prin. Fax 754-4577

Rhinelander, Oneida, Pop. 7,686
Rhinelander SD 2,400/K-12
665 Coolidge Ave Ste B 54501 715-365-9700
Dr. Roger Erdahl, supt. Fax 365-9713
www.rhinelander.k12.wi.us
Rhinelander HS 900/9-12
665 Coolidge Ave Ste B 54501 715-365-9500
David Ditzler, prin. Fax 365-9568
Williams MS 500/6-8
915 Acacia Ln 54501 715-365-9220
Paul Johnson, prin. Fax 365-9296

Nicolet Area Technical College Post-Sec.
PO Box 518 54501 715-365-4410

Rib Lake, Taylor, Pop. 905
Rib Lake SD 500/PK-12
PO Box 278 54470 715-427-3222
Lori Manion, supt. Fax 427-3221
www.riblake.k12.wi.us
Rib Lake HS 200/9-12
PO Box 278 54470 715-427-3220
Rick Cardey, prin. Fax 427-5022
Rib Lake MS 100/6-8
PO Box 278 54470 715-427-5446
Rick Cardey, prin. Fax 427-3221

Rice Lake, Barron, Pop. 8,342
Rice Lake Area SD 2,100/PK-12
700 Augusta St 54868 715-234-9007
Larry Brown, supt. Fax 234-4552
www.ricelake.k12.wi.us
Rice Lake HS 800/9-12
30 S Wisconsin Ave 54868 715-234-2181
Chad Harnisch, prin. Fax 234-6679
Rice Lake MS 600/5-8
204 Cameron Rd 54868 715-234-8156
Drew Goeldner, prin. Fax 234-9439

Univ. of Wisconsin Center-Barron County Post-Sec.
1800 College Dr 54868 715-234-8024
Wisconsin Indianhead Technical College Post-Sec.
1900 College Dr 54868 715-234-7082

Richfield, Washington, Pop. 11,239
Richfield J1 SD 400/PK-8
PO Box 127 53076 262-628-1032
Tara Villalobos, admin. Fax 628-3013
www.richfield.k12.wi.us
Richfield ES 200/3-8
PO Box 127 53076 262-628-1032
Tara Villalobos, admin. Fax 628-3013

Richland Center, Richland, Pop. 5,137
Ithaca SD 300/K-12
24615 State Hwy 58 53581 608-585-2512
Dr. Anthony Kujawa, supt. Fax 585-2505
www.ithaca.k12.wi.us/
Ithaca HS 100/9-12
24615 State Hwy 58 53581 608-585-2311
Robert Smudde, prin. Fax 585-2505
Ithaca MS 100/6-8
24615 State Hwy 58 53581 608-585-2311
Robert Smudde, prin. Fax 585-2505

Richland SD 1,400/PK-12
1996 US Hwy 14 W 53581 608-647-6106
Rachel Schultz, supt. Fax 647-8454
www.richland.k12.wi.us
Richland Center HS 500/9-12
1996 US Hwy 14 W 53581 608-647-6131
Jon Bosworth, prin. Fax 647-8734
Richland MS 300/6-8
1801 State Hwy 80 S 53581 608-647-6381
David Guy, prin. Fax 647-4735

University of Wisconsin Richland Post-Sec.
1200 US Hwy 14 W 53581 608-647-6186

Rio, Columbia, Pop. 1,045
Rio Community SD 500/PK-12
411 Church St 53960 920-992-3141
Mark McGuire, supt. Fax 992-3157
www.rio.k12.wi.us
Rio MSHS 200/6-12
411 Church St 53960 920-992-3141
Mark McGuire, prin. Fax 992-3157

Ripon, Fond du Lac, Pop. 7,674
Ripon Area SD 1,600/PK-12
PO Box 991 54971 920-748-4600
Richard Zimman, supt. Fax 748-2715
www.ripon.k12.wi.us
Ripon HS 500/9-12
PO Box 991 54971 920-748-4616
Dan Tjernagel, prin. Fax 748-4622
Ripon MS 400/6-8
PO Box 991 54971 920-748-4638
Thomas Hoh, prin. Fax 748-4653

Ripon College Post-Sec.
PO Box 248 54971 920-748-8115

River Falls, Pierce, Pop. 14,778
River Falls SD 3,000/PK-12
852 E Division St 54022 715-425-1800
Jamie Benson, supt. Fax 425-1804
www.rfsd.k12.wi.us
Meyer MS 600/6-8
230 N 9th St 54022 715-425-1820
Mark Chapin, prin. Fax 425-1823
River Falls HS 1,000/9-12
818 Cemetery Rd 54022 715-425-1830
Kit Luedtke, prin. Fax 425-1827

University of Wisconsin Post-Sec.
410 S 3rd St 54022 715-425-3911

Rosendale, Fond du Lac, Pop. 1,054
Rosendale-Brandon SD 900/PK-12
300 W Wisconsin St 54974 920-872-2851
Gary Hansen, supt. Fax 872-2647
www.rbsd.k12.wi.us
Laconia HS 300/9-12
301 W Division St 54974 920-872-2161
Wayne Weber, prin. Fax 872-2777
Rosendale IS 200/4-8
200 S Main St 54974 920-872-2126
John Hokenson, prin. Fax 872-2061

Rosholt, Portage, Pop. 506
Rosholt SD 600/PK-12
PO Box 310 54473 715-677-4542
Marc Christianson, supt. Fax 677-3543
www.rosholt.k12.wi.us
Rosholt HS 200/9-12
PO Box 310 54473 715-677-4541
James Grygleski, prin. Fax 677-6767
Rosholt MS 100/6-8
PO Box 310 54473 715-677-4541
James Grygleski, prin. Fax 677-6767

Rothschild, Marathon, Pop. 5,209

Globe University Post-Sec.
1480 County Road XX 54474 715-301-1300

Saint Croix Falls, Polk, Pop. 2,110
St. Croix Falls SD 1,100/PK-12
PO Box 130 54024 715-483-2507
Glenn Martin, supt. Fax 483-3695
www.scf.k12.wi.us
St. Croix Falls HS 400/9-12
PO Box 130 54024 715-483-2507
Peggy Ryan, prin. Fax 483-3695
St. Croix Falls MS 300/5-8
PO Box 130 54024 715-483-2507
Joe Connors, prin. Fax 483-3695

Saint Francis, Milwaukee, Pop. 9,213
St. Francis SD 1,300/PK-12
4225 S Lake Dr 53235 414-747-3900
John Thomsen, supt. Fax 482-7198
www.stfrancisschools.org
Deer Creek IS 400/4-8
3680 S Kinnickinnic Ave 53235 414-482-8400
Mary Garcia-Velez, prin. Fax 482-8406
Saint Francis HS 600/9-12
4225 S Lake Dr 53235 414-747-3600
Fax 747-3605

St. Francis Seminary Post-Sec.
3257 S Lake Dr 53235 414-747-6400

Salem, Kenosha
Central HSD of Westosha 1,200/9-12
PO Box 38 53168 262-843-2321
Dr. Scott Pierce, admin. Fax 843-4069
www.westosha.k12.wi.us
Central-Westosha HS 1,200/9-12
PO Box 38 53168 262-843-2321
Lisa Albrecht, prin. Fax 843-4069

Sauk City, Sauk, Pop. 3,378
Sauk Prairie SD 2,800/PK-12
213 Maple St 53583 608-643-5990
Cliff Thompson, supt. Fax 643-6216
www.saukpr.k12.wi.us
Sauk Prairie MS 600/6-8
207 Maple St 53583 608-643-5500
Ted Harter, prin. Fax 643-5503
Other Schools – See Prairie du Sac

Seneca, Crawford
Seneca SD 300/PK-12
PO Box 34 54654 608-734-3411
David Boland, supt. Fax 734-3430
www.seneca.k12.wi.us
Seneca HS 100/9-12
PO Box 34 54654 608-734-3411
David Boland, prin. Fax 734-3430
Seneca JHS 50/5-8
PO Box 34 54654 608-734-3411
David Boland, prin. Fax 734-3430

Seymour, Outagamie, Pop. 3,392
Seymour Community SD 2,400/PK-12
10 Circle Dr 54165 920-833-2304
Peter Ross, supt. Fax 833-6037
www.seymour.k12.wi.us/
Seymour Community HS 800/9-12
10 Circle Dr 54165 920-833-2306
Michael Flaherty, prin. Fax 833-7608
Seymour MS 400/6-8
10 Circle Dr 54165 920-833-7199
Judy Schenk, prin. Fax 833-9376

Shawano, Shawano, Pop. 9,050
Shawano SD 2,600/PK-12
218 County Road B 54166 715-526-3194
Todd Carlson, supt. Fax 526-6072
www.shawanoschools.com
Shawano Community HS 900/9-12
220 County Road B 54166 715-526-2175
Scott Zwirschitz, prin. Fax 524-8414
Shawano Community MS 500/6-8
1050 S Union St 54166 715-526-2192
Daniel Labby, prin. Fax 526-5037

Sheboygan, Sheboygan, Pop. 48,427
Sheboygan Area SD 9,900/PK-12
830 Virginia Ave 53081 920-459-3500
Joseph Sheehan Ph.D., supt. Fax 459-6487
www.sheboygan.k12.wi.us
Farnsworth MS 600/6-8
1017 Union Ave 53081 920-459-3655
Todd DeBruin, prin. Fax 459-3660
Mann MS 600/6-8
2820 Union Ave 53081 920-459-3666
Vicki Ritchie, prin. Fax 459-3669
North HS 1,600/9-12
1042 School Ave 53083 920-459-3600
Jason Bull, prin. Fax 459-3601
South HS 1,300/9-12
3128 S 12th St 53081 920-459-3637
Mike Trimberger, prin. Fax 459-6733
Urban MS 700/6-8
1226 North Ave 53083 920-459-3680
Susan Nennig, prin. Fax 459-4065

Lakeland College Post-Sec.
PO Box 359 53082 920-565-1000
Sheboygan Area Lutheran HS 200/9-12
3323 University Dr 53081 920-452-3323
Allen Holzheimer, prin. Fax 452-1310
Sheboygan County Christian HS 100/9-12
929 Greenfield Ave 53081 920-458-9981
Corey Navis M.Ed., head sch Fax 458-9957
University of Wisconsin Sheboygan Post-Sec.
1 University Dr 53081 920-459-6600

Sheboygan Falls, Sheboygan, Pop. 7,719
Sheboygan Falls SD 1,800/PK-12
220 Amherst Ave 53085 920-467-7893
Jean Born, supt. Fax 467-7899
www.sheboyganfalls.k12.wi.us
Sheboygan Falls HS 600/9-12
220 Amherst Ave 53085 920-467-7890
Luke Goral, prin. Fax 467-7825
Sheboygan Falls MS 500/5-8
101 School St 53085 920-467-7880
Meloney Markofski, prin. Fax 467-7885

Shell Lake, Washburn, Pop. 1,340
Shell Lake SD 600/K-12
271 Highway 63 S 54871 715-468-7816
James Connell, supt. Fax 468-7812
www.shelllake.k12.wi.us
Shell Lake JSHS 300/7-12
271 Highway 63 S 54871 715-468-7814
Don Peterson, prin. Fax 468-7989

Wisconsin Indianhead Technical College Post-Sec.
505 Pine Ridge Dr 54871 715-468-2815

Shiocton, Outagamie, Pop. 910
Shiocton SD 700/PK-12
PO Box 68 54170 920-986-3351
Chris VanderHeyden, supt. Fax 986-3291
www.shiocton.k12.wi.us
Shiocton HS 200/7-12
PO Box 68 54170 920-986-3351
Kelly Zeinert, prin. Fax 986-3291

Shorewood, Milwaukee, Pop. 12,886
Shorewood SD 2,000/PK-12
1701 E Capitol Dr 53211 414-963-6901
Martin Lexmond Ph.D., supt. Fax 963-6904
www.shorewoodschools.org
Shorewood HS 600/9-12
1701 E Capitol Dr 53211 414-963-6921
Matthew Joynt, prin. Fax 961-2819
Shorewood IS 300/7-8
3830 N Morris Blvd 53211 414-963-6951
Anthony Strancke, prin. Fax 963-6946

Shullsburg, Lafayette, Pop. 1,223
Shullsburg SD 400/PK-12
444 N Judgement St 53586 608-965-4427
Loras Kruser, admin. Fax 965-3794
www.shullsburg.k12.wi.us
Shullsburg HS 100/9-12
444 N Judgement St 53586 608-965-4427
Melissa Emler, prin. Fax 965-3794
Shullsburg JHS 100/6-8
444 N Judgement St 53586 608-965-4427
Melissa Emler, prin. Fax 965-3794

Siren, Burnett, Pop. 776
Siren SD 500/PK-12
24022 4th Ave 54872 715-349-2290
Scott Johnson, supt. Fax 349-7476
www.siren.k12.wi.us
Siren HS 200/7-12
24022 4th Ave 54872 715-349-2277
Peggy Ryan, prin. Fax 349-7476

Slinger, Washington, Pop. 5,014
Slinger SD 2,900/PK-12
207 Polk St 53086 262-644-9615
Robert Reynolds, supt. Fax 644-7514
www.slinger.k12.wi.us
Slinger HS 900/9-12
209 Polk St 53086 262-644-5261
Philip Ourada, prin. Fax 644-0479
Slinger MS 700/6-8
521 Olympic Dr 53086 262-644-5226
Dean Goneau, prin. Fax 644-7353

Soldiers Grove, Crawford, Pop. 590
North Crawford SD 500/PK-12
47050 County Road X 54655 608-735-4318
Dr. Daniel Davies, supt. Fax 735-4317
www.northcrawford.com
North Crawford HS 200/9-12
47050 County Road X 54655 608-735-4311
Dr. Daniel Davies, prin. Fax 624-6269

Solon Springs, Douglas, Pop. 597
Solon Springs SD 300/PK-12
8993 E Baldwin Ave 54873 715-378-2263
Michael Cox, supt. Fax 378-2073
eyrie3.solonk12.net/school
Solon Springs S 300/PK-12
8993 E Baldwin Ave 54873 715-378-2263
Sue Chandler, prin. Fax 378-2073

Somers, Kenosha

Shoreland Lutheran HS 300/9-12
PO Box 295 53171 262-859-2595
Paul Scriver, prin. Fax 859-2783

Somerset, Saint Croix, Pop. 2,588
Somerset SD 1,700/PK-12
PO Box 100 54025 715-247-3313
Randal Rosburg, supt. Fax 247-5588
www.somerset.k12.wi.us
Somerset HS 500/9-12
PO Box 100 54025 715-247-3355
Shawn Madden, prin. Fax 247-3864
Somerset MS 500/5-8
PO Box 100 54025 715-247-4400
Sara Eichten, prin. Fax 247-4437

South Milwaukee, Milwaukee, Pop. 20,823
South Milwaukee SD 3,300/PK-12
901 15th Ave 53172 414-766-5000
Dr. Rita Olson, supt. Fax 766-5005
www.sdsm.k12.wi.us/
South Milwaukee HS 1,200/9-12
801 15th Ave 53172 414-766-5100
Beth Kaminski, prin. Fax 766-5131
South Milwaukee MS 700/6-8
1001 15th Ave 53172 414-766-5800
James Hendrickson, prin. Fax 766-5803

South Wayne, Lafayette, Pop. 489
Black Hawk SD 300/PK-12
PO Box 303 53587 608-439-5400
William Chambers, supt. Fax 439-1022
www.blackhawk.k12.wi.us
Black Hawk HS 100/6-12
PO Box 303 53587 608-439-5371
Cory Milz, prin. Fax 439-1022

Sparta, Monroe, Pop. 9,396
Sparta Area SD 2,600/PK-12
201 E Franklin St 54656 608-269-3151
John Hendricks, supt. Fax 366-3526
www.spartan.org
Sparta HS 700/9-12
506 N Black River St 54656 608-366-3504
Samuel Russ, prin. Fax 366-3506
Sparta Meadowview MS 500/6-8
1225 N Water St 54656 608-366-3497
Mike Crneckiy, prin. Fax 366-3500

Spencer, Marathon, Pop. 1,903
Spencer SD 800/PK-12
PO Box 418 54479 715-659-5347
Michael Endreas, supt. Fax 659-5470
www.spencer.k12.wi.us
Spencer JSHS 400/6-12
PO Box 418 54479 715-659-4211
Jerry Zanotelli, prin. Fax 659-5470

Spooner, Washburn, Pop. 2,637
Spooner Area SD 1,300/PK-12
801 County Highway A 54801 715-635-2171
Dr. Donald Haack, supt. Fax 635-7174
www.spooner.k12.wi.us
Spooner HS 400/9-12
801 County Highway A 54801 715-635-2172
Jennifer Peterson, prin. Fax 635-7074
Spooner MS 400/5-8
500 College St 54801 715-635-2173
Lynnea Lake, prin. Fax 635-7074

Spring Green, Sauk, Pop. 1,601
River Valley SD 1,300/PK-12
660 W Daley St 53588 608-588-2551
Jamie Benson, supt. Fax 588-2558
www.rvschools.org
River Valley HS 500/9-12
660 Varsity Blvd 53588 608-588-2554
Kim Kaukl, prin. Fax 588-2827
River Valley MS 300/6-8
660 W Daley St 53588 608-588-2556
James Radtke, prin. Fax 588-2026

Spring Valley, Pierce, Pop. 1,346
Spring Valley SD 700/PK-12
PO Box 249 54767 715-778-5551
David Wellington, supt. Fax 778-4761
www.springvalley.k12.wi.us
Spring Valley MSHS 200/7-12
PO Box 249 54767 715-778-5554
Gretchen Cipriano, prin. Fax 778-5556

Stanley, Chippewa, Pop. 3,592
Stanley-Boyd Area SD 1,000/PK-12
507 E 1st Ave 54768 715-644-5534
James Jones, supt. Fax 644-5584
www.stanleyboyd.k12.wi.us
Stanley-Boyd HS 300/9-12
507 E 1st Ave 54768 715-644-5534
Dave Ludy, prin. Fax 644-6701
Stanley-Boyd MS 100/7-8
507 E 1st Ave 54768 715-644-5715
Dave Ludy, prin. Fax 644-5584

Stevens Point, Portage, Pop. 26,351
Stevens Point Area SD 6,800/PK-12
1900 Polk St 54481 715-345-5444
Attila Weninger Ph.D., supt. Fax 345-7302
www.pointschools.net
Fernandez Ctr for Alternative Learning 100/Alt
1025 Clark St 54481 715-345-5592
Elizabeth Fulton, prin. Fax 345-7374
Franklin JHS 800/7-9
2000 Polk St 54481 715-345-5413
Connie Negaard, prin. Fax 345-5696
Jacobs JHS 700/7-9
2400 Main St 54481 715-345-5422
Dan Dobratz, prin. Fax 345-7340
Stevens Point Area SHS 1,500/10-12
1201 Northpoint Dr 54481 715-345-5400
Mike Devine, prin. Fax 345-5408

Mid-State Technical College Post-Sec.
933 Michigan Ave 54481 715-344-3063
Pacelli HS 200/9-12
1301 Maria Dr 54481 715-341-2442
Jeffrey Brengman, prin. Fax 341-6779
St. Peter MS 200/6-8
708 1st St 54481 715-344-1890
Ellen Lopas, prin. Fax 342-2005
University of Wisconsin Post-Sec.
2100 Main St 54481 715-346-0123

Stockbridge, Calumet, Pop. 630
Stockbridge SD 200/PK-12
PO Box 188 53088 920-439-1158
David Moscinski, supt. Fax 439-1150
www.stockbridge.k12.wi.us/
Stockbridge HS 100/9-12
PO Box 188 53088 920-439-1158
Chad Marx, prin. Fax 439-1150
Stockbridge MS 50/6-8
PO Box 188 53088 920-439-1158
Chad Marx, prin. Fax 439-1150

Stoughton, Dane, Pop. 12,430
Stoughton Area SD 3,200/K-12
320 North St 53589 608-877-5000
Tim Onsager, admin. Fax 877-5028
www.stoughton.k12.wi.us
River Bluff MS 800/6-8
235 N Forrest St 53589 608-877-5501
Trish Gates, prin. Fax 877-5508
Stoughton HS 1,100/9-12
600 Lincoln Ave 53589 608-877-5601
Mike Kruse, prin. Fax 877-5619

Stratford, Marathon, Pop. 1,570
Stratford SD 900/PK-12
PO Box 7 54484 715-687-3130
Scott Winch, supt. Fax 687-4074
www.stratford.k12.wi.us
Stratford JSHS 400/6-12
PO Box 7 54484 715-687-4311
Janeen LaBorde, prin. Fax 687-4652

Strum, Trempealeau, Pop. 1,111
Eleva-Strum SD 600/PK-12
W23597 US Highway 10 54770 715-695-2696
Craig Semingson, admin. Fax 695-3519
www.esschools.k12.wi.us/
Eleva-Strum MSHS 300/7-12
W23597 US Highway 10 54770 715-695-2696
Cory Kulig, prin. Fax 695-3938

Sturgeon Bay, Door, Pop. 9,041
Sevastopol SD 500/PK-12
4550 State Highway 57 54235 920-743-6282
Dr. Linda Underwood, supt. Fax 743-4009
www.sevastopol.k12.wi.us
Sevastopol HS 200/9-12
4550 State Highway 57 54235 920-743-6282
Adam Baier, prin. Fax 743-4009
Sevastopol MS 100/6-8
4550 State Highway 57 54235 920-743-6282
Adam Baier, prin. Fax 743-4009

Sturgeon Bay SD 1,200/PK-12
1230 Michigan St 54235 920-746-2800
Joe Stutting, supt. Fax 746-3888
www.sturbay.k12.wi.us
Sturgeon Bay HS 400/9-12
1230 Michigan St 54235 920-746-2800
Robert Nickel, prin. Fax 746-3888
Walker MS 200/6-8
19 N 14th Ave 54235 920-746-2810
Randy Watermolen, prin. Fax 746-3885

Northeast Wisconsin Technical College Post-Sec.
229 N 14th Ave 54235 920-746-4900

Sun Prairie, Dane, Pop. 28,546
Sun Prairie Area SD 5,500/PK-12
501 S Bird St 53590 608-834-6500
Tim Culver, supt. Fax 834-6555
www.spasd.k12.wi.us
Cardinal Heights Upper MS 8-9
220 Kroncke Dr 53590 608-318-8000
Ryan Ruggles, prin. Fax 318-8192
Prairie Phoenix Academy 100/Alt
160 South St 53590 608-834-6900
Wendi Tavs, prin. Fax 834-6992
Sun Prairie HS 1,400/10-12
888 Grove St 53590 608-834-6700
Lisa Heipp, prin. Fax 834-6792

Diesel Truck Driver Training School Post-Sec.
7190 Elder Ln 53590 608-837-7800

Superior, Douglas, Pop. 26,443
Superior SD 4,600/PK-12
3025 Tower Ave 54880 715-394-8700
Janna Stevens, supt. Fax 394-8708
www.superior.k12.wi.us
Superior HS 1,400/9-12
2600 Catlin Ave 54880 715-394-8720
Kent Bergum, prin. Fax 394-8760
Superior MS 1,000/6-8
3626 Hammond Ave 54880 715-394-8740
Richard Flaherty, prin. Fax 395-8483

Maranatha Academy 100/PK-12
4916 S State Road 35 54880 715-399-8757
Keith Russell, admin. Fax 399-8758
University of Wisconsin Post-Sec.
PO Box 2000 54880 715-394-8101
Wisconsin Indianhead Technical College Post-Sec.
600 N 21st St 54880 715-394-6677

Suring, Oconto, Pop. 532
Suring SD 500/PK-12
PO Box 158 54174 920-842-2178
Robert Ray, supt. Fax 842-4570
www.suring.k12.wi.us
Suring HS 200/9-12
PO Box 158 54174 920-842-2182
Fax 842-4570

Sussex, Waukesha, Pop. 10,416
Hamilton SD 4,600/PK-12
W220N6151 Town Line Rd 53089 262-246-1973
Dr. Kathleen Cooke, supt. Fax 246-6552
www.hamilton.k12.wi.us/
Hamilton HS 1,400/9-12
W220N6151 Town Line Rd 53089 262-246-6471
Candis Mongan, prin. Fax 246-1885
Templeton MS 1,000/6-8
N59W22490 Silver Spring Dr 53089 262-246-6477
Patricia Polczynski, prin. Fax 246-0465

Thorp, Clark, Pop. 1,612
Thorp SD 500/PK-12
PO Box 429 54771 715-669-5548
James Montgomery, admin. Fax 669-5403
www.thorp.k12.wi.us/
Thorp HS 200/6-12
PO Box 449 54771 715-669-5401
Brad Ceranski, prin. Fax 669-5403

Three Lakes, Oneida, Pop. 604
Three Lakes SD 600/PK-12
6930 W School St 54562 715-546-3496
Dr. George Karling, supt. Fax 546-8125
www.3lks.net
Three Lakes HS 300/7-12
6930 W School St 54562 715-546-3321
Dr. William Greb, prin. Fax 546-2828

Tigerton, Shawano, Pop. 725
Tigerton SD 300/PK-12
PO Box 10 54486 715-535-4000
Fax 535-4010
www.tigerton.k12.wi.us
Tigerton MSHS 200/6-12
PO Box 40 54486 715-535-4001
David Battenberg, prin. Fax 535-1355

Tomah, Monroe, Pop. 8,916
Tomah Area SD 3,100/PK-12
129 W Clifton St 54660 608-374-7004
Cindy Zahrte, supt. Fax 372-5087
www.tomah.k12.wi.us
Kupper Learning Center 100/Alt
1310 Townline Rd 54660 608-374-7011
Paul Skofronick, admin. Fax 374-8710
Tomah HS 1,000/9-12
901 Lincoln Ave 54660 608-374-7358
David Hay, prin. Fax 374-7290
Tomah MS 600/6-8
612 Hollister Ave 54660 608-374-7882
Steven Buss, prin. Fax 374-7303

Tomahawk, Lincoln, Pop. 3,356
Tomahawk SD 1,400/PK-12
1048 E King Rd 54487 715-453-5551
Dr. Roger Rindo, supt. Fax 453-6736
www.tomahawk.k12.wi.us
Tomahawk HS 500/9-12
1048 E King Rd 54487 715-453-2106
Scott Swenty, prin. Fax 453-1437
Tomahawk MS 300/6-8
1048 E King Rd 54487 715-453-5371
Nathan Hanson, prin. Fax 453-9630

Tony, Rusk, Pop. 113
Flambeau SD 300/PK-12
PO Box 86 54563 715-532-3183
William Pfalzgraf, supt. Fax 532-5405
www.flambeau.k12.wi.us
Flambeau S 300/PK-12
PO Box 86 54563 715-532-3183
Connie Gasior, prin. Fax 532-5405

Turtle Lake, Barron, Pop. 1,031
Turtle Lake SD 500/PK-12
205 Oak St 54889 715-986-2597
Maurice Veilleux, admin. Fax 986-2444
www.turtlelake.k12.wi.us
Turtle Lake HS 100/9-12
205 Oak St 54889 715-986-4470
Kent Kindschy, prin. Fax 986-2444

Two Rivers, Manitowoc, Pop. 11,594
Two Rivers SD 1,700/K-12
4521 Lincoln Ave 54241 920-793-4560
Randy Fredrikson, supt. Fax 793-4014
www.trschools.k12.wi.us
Clarke MS 500/5-8
4608 Bellevue Pl 54241 920-794-1614
Lisa Quistorf, prin. Fax 793-1819

Two Rivers HS 600/9-12
4519 Lincoln Ave 54241 920-793-2291
Larry Schlosser, prin. Fax 793-5068

Union Grove, Racine, Pop. 4,851
Union Grove UNHSD 900/9-12
3433 S Colony Ave 53182 262-878-4427
Alan Mollerskov, supt. Fax 878-3291
www.ug.k12.wi.us
Union Grove HS 900/9-12
3433 S Colony Ave 53182 262-878-2434
Thomas Hermann, prin. Fax 878-4056

Union Grove Christian S 100/PK-12
PO Box 87 53182 262-878-1264

Valders, Manitowoc, Pop. 958
Valders Area SD 1,000/PK-12
138 E Wilson St 54245 920-775-9500
Debra Hunt, supt. Fax 775-9509
www.valders.k12.wi.us
Valders HS 400/9-12
201 E Wilson St 54245 920-775-9530
Julie Laabs, prin. Fax 775-9509
Valders MS 300/5-8
138 Jefferson St 54245 920-775-9520
Derrick Krey, prin. Fax 775-9509

Verona, Dane, Pop. 10,419
Verona Area SD 4,900/PK-12
700 N Main St 53593 608-845-4300
Dean Gorrell, supt. Fax 845-4321
www.verona.k12.wi.us
Badger Ridge MS 500/6-8
740 N Main St 53593 608-845-4100
David Jennings, prin. Fax 845-4120
Verona Area HS 1,500/9-12
300 Richard St 53593 608-845-4400
Pam Hammen, prin. Fax 845-4420
Other Schools – See Fitchburg

Viola, Vernon, Pop. 694
Kickapoo Area SD 400/PK-12
S6520 State Highway 131 54664 608-627-0101
Douglas Olsen, supt. Fax 627-0118
www.kickapoo.k12.wi.us
Kickapoo MSHS 200/6-12
S6520 State Highway 131 54664 608-627-0100
Aaron Mithum, prin. Fax 627-0132

Viroqua, Vernon, Pop. 4,314
Viroqua Area SD 1,200/PK-12
115 N Education Ave 54665 608-637-1186
Dr. Robert Knadle, supt. Fax 637-8554
www.viroqua.k12.wi.us
Viroqua HS 400/9-12
100 Blackhawk Dr 54665 608-637-3191
Katherine Klos, prin. Fax 637-8034
Viroqua MS 300/5-8
100 Blackhawk Dr 54665 608-637-3171
John Schneider, prin. Fax 637-8034

Cornerstone Christian Academy 50/PK-12
S3655 Duncan Ln 54665 608-634-4102
Ben Marx, admin. Fax 634-4162
Youth Initiative HS 50/9-12
500 E Jefferson St Ste 302 54665 608-637-6445

Wabeno, Forest, Pop. 550
Wabeno Area SD 500/PK-12
PO Box 460 54566 715-473-2592
Kimberly Odekirk Ph.D., supt. Fax 473-5201
www.wabeno.k12.wi.us
Wabeno JSHS 200/7-12
PO Box 460 54566 715-473-5122
Matthew Paulsen, prin. Fax 473-3406

Wales, Waukesha, Pop. 2,532
Kettle Moraine SD 4,200/PK-12
563 A J Allen Cir 53183 262-968-6300
Patricia Deklotz, supt. Fax 968-6390
www.kmsd.edu/
Kettle Moraine HS 1,500/9-12
349 N Oak Crest Dr 53183 262-968-6200
Jeffrey Walters, prin. Fax 968-6217
Other Schools – See Dousman

Walworth, Walworth, Pop. 2,799
Big Foot UNHSD 500/9-12
PO Box 99 53184 262-275-2116
Dorothy Kaufmann, admin. Fax 275-5117
www.bigfoot.k12.wi.us
Big Foot Union HS 500/9-12
PO Box 99 53184 262-275-2116
Michael Hinske, prin. Fax 275-5117

Washburn, Bayfield, Pop. 2,031
Washburn SD 500/PK-12
PO Box 730 54891 715-373-6188
Dr. Thomas Wiatr, supt. Fax 373-5877
www.washburn.k12.wi.us
Washburn HS 200/9-12
PO Box 730 54891 715-373-6188
Dr. Thomas Wiatr, prin. Fax 373-5877
Washburn MS 100/6-8
PO Box 730 54891 715-373-6199
Al Krause, prin. Fax 373-0586

Washington Island, Door
Washington SD 100/K-12
888 Main Rd 54246 920-847-2507
Timothy Raymond, supt. Fax 847-2865
www.island.k12.wi.us
Washington Island HS 50/9-12
888 Main Rd 54246 920-847-2507
Timothy Raymond, prin. Fax 847-2865

Waterford, Racine, Pop. 5,327
Waterford Graded JSD 1 1,600/K-8
819 W Main St 53185 262-514-8250
Christopher Joch, supt. Fax 514-8251
www.waterford.k12.wi.us
Fox River MS 400/7-8
921 W Main St 53185 262-514-8240
Darlene Markle, prin. Fax 514-8241

Waterford UNHSD 1,100/9-12
507 W Main St 53185 262-534-9059
Keith Brandstetter, supt. Fax 534-6871
www.waterforduhs.k12.wi.us
Waterford Union HS 1,100/9-12
100 Field Dr 53185 262-534-3189
Eric Blake, prin. Fax 534-4971

Waterloo, Jefferson, Pop. 3,304
Waterloo SD 700/PK-12
813 N Monroe St 53594 920-478-3633
Connie Schiestl, supt. Fax 478-3821
www.waterloo.k12.wi.us
Waterloo HS 300/9-12
865 N Monroe St 53594 920-478-2171
Brad Donner, prin. Fax 478-9539
Waterloo MS 100/5-8
865 N Monroe St 53594 920-478-2696
Susan Piazza, prin. Fax 478-3987

Watertown, Jefferson, Pop. 23,579
Watertown Unified SD 3,900/PK-12
111 Dodge St 53094 920-262-1460
Cassandra Schug, supt. Fax 262-1469
www.watertown.k12.wi.us
Riverside MS 800/6-8
131 Hall St 53094 920-262-1480
Kent Jacobson, prin. Fax 262-1468
Watertown HS 1,400/9-12
825 Endevour Dr 53098 920-262-7500
Scott Bostwick, prin. Fax 262-7545

Luther Preparatory S 300/9-12
1300 Western Ave 53094 920-261-4352
Rev. Matthew Crass, pres. Fax 262-8118
Maranatha Baptist Bible Coll & Seminary Post-Sec.
745 W Main St 53094 920-261-9300
Trinity-St. Luke's Lutheran S 100/5-8
303 Clark St 53094 920-206-1844
James Moeller, prin. Fax 206-1750

Waukesha, Waukesha, Pop. 69,639
Waukesha SD 13,000/PK-12
222 Maple Ave 53186 262-970-1000
Todd Gray, supt. Fax 970-1021
www.waukesha.k12.wi.us
Butler MS 1,000/6-8
310 N Hine Ave 53188 262-970-2900
Jason Sadowski, prin. Fax 970-2920
Central MS 700/6-8
400 N Grand Ave 53186 262-970-3100
Rob Bennett, prin. Fax 970-3120
Horning MS 800/6-8
2000 Wolf Rd 53186 262-970-3300
Mark Wegner, prin. Fax 970-3320
North HS 1,200/9-12
2222 Michigan Ave 53188 262-970-3500
Jody Landish, prin. Fax 970-3520
South HS 1,100/9-12
401 E Roberta Ave 53186 262-970-3705
Timothy Joynt, prin. Fax 970-3720
West HS 1,300/9-12
3301 Saylesville Rd 53189 262-970-3900
David Towers, prin. Fax 970-3920

Carroll University Post-Sec.
100 N East Ave 53186 262-547-1211
Catholic Memorial HS 800/9-12
601 E College Ave 53186 262-542-7101
Robert Hall, prin. Fax 542-1633
DeVry University Post-Sec.
N14W23833 Stone Ridge Dr 53188 262-347-2911
St. Joseph MS 200/6-8
818 N East Ave 53186 262-896-2930
Lisa Kovaleski, prin. Fax 896-2935
University of Wisconsin Waukesha Post-Sec.
1500 N University Dr 53188 262-521-5200

Waunakee, Dane, Pop. 11,963
Waunakee Community SD 3,700/PK-12
905 Bethel Cir 53597 608-849-2000
Randy Guttenberg, supt. Fax 849-2350
www.waunakee.k12.wi.us
Waunakee HS 1,200/9-12
301 Community Dr 53597 608-849-2100
Brian Kersten, prin. Fax 849-2164
Waunakee MS 500/7-8
1001 South St 53597 608-849-2060
Marcy Peters-Felice, prin. Fax 849-2088

Madison Country Day S 300/PK-12
5606 River Rd 53597 608-850-6000
Luke Felker, hdmstr. Fax 850-6006

Waupaca, Waupaca, Pop. 6,011
Waupaca SD 2,200/PK-12
515 School St 54981 715-258-4121
David Poeschl, supt. Fax 258-4125
www.waupaca.k12.wi.us/
Waupaca HS 800/9-12
E2325 King Rd 54981 715-258-4131
Robert Becker, prin. Fax 258-4135
Waupaca MS 500/5-8
1149 Shoemaker Rd 54981 715-258-4140
Ben Rayome, prin. Fax 256-5681

Waupun, Dodge, Pop. 11,240
Waupun Area SD 1,700/PK-12
950 Wilcox St 53963 920-324-9341
Tonya Gubin, supt. Fax 324-2630
www.waupun.k12.wi.us
Waupun Area JSHS 600/7-12
801 E Lincoln St 53963 920-324-5591
Jeff Finstad, prin. Fax 324-6980

Central Wisconsin Christian S 300/PK-12
301 Fox Lake Rd 53963 920-324-4233
Mark Buteyn, admin. Fax 324-5036

Wausau, Marathon, Pop. 38,312
Wausau SD 8,300/PK-12
PO Box 359 54402 715-261-0500
Dr. Kathleen Williams, supt. Fax 261-2503
www.wausauschools.org/
Mann MS 800/6-8
3101 N 13th St 54403 715-261-0725
Julie Sprague, prin. Fax 261-2035
Muir MS 900/6-8
1400 Stewart Ave 54401 715-261-0100
Dean Hess, prin. Fax 261-2461
Wausau East HS 1,200/9-12
2607 N 18th St 54403 715-261-0650
Bradley Peck, prin. Fax 845-2913
Wausau West HS 1,400/9-12
1200 W Wausau Ave 54401 715-261-0850
Jeb Steckbauer, prin. Fax 261-3260

Faith Christian Academy 100/PK-12
225 S 28th Ave 54401 715-842-0797
Dave Wysong, admin. Fax 842-1042
Newman Catholic MSHS 200/6-12
1130 W Bridge St 54401 715-845-8274
James Delikowski, prin. Fax 842-1302
Northcentral Technical College Post-Sec.
1000 W Campus Dr 54401 715-675-3331
Rasmussen College Post-Sec.
1101 Westwood Dr 54401 715-841-8000
State College of Beauty Culture Post-Sec.
1930 Grand Ave 54403 715-849-5368
University of Wisconsin Marathon County Post-Sec.
518 S 7th Ave 54401 715-261-6235
Wausau Hospital Center Post-Sec.
333 Pine Ridge Blvd 54401 715-847-2117

Wausaukee, Marinette, Pop. 563
Wausaukee SD 500/PK-12
PO Box 258 54177 715-856-5153
Jan Dooley, supt. Fax 856-6592
www.wausaukee.k12.wi.us
Wausaukee HS 200/9-12
PO Box 258 54177 715-856-5151
Jared Deschane, prin. Fax 856-6592
Wausaukee JHS 100/7-8
PO Box 258 54177 715-856-5151
Jared Deschane, prin. Fax 856-6592

Wautoma, Waushara, Pop. 2,182
Wautoma Area SD 1,500/PK-12
PO Box 870 54982 920-787-7112
Jeff Kasuboski, supt. Fax 787-1389
www.wautomasd.org
Parkside MS 500/4-8
PO Box 870 54982 920-787-4577
Tom Rheinheimer, prin. Fax 787-7336
Wautoma HS 400/9-12
PO Box 870 54982 920-787-3354
Todd Lindstrom, prin. Fax 787-1513

Wauwatosa, Milwaukee, Pop. 45,454
Wauwatosa SD 7,200/PK-12
12121 W North Ave 53226 414-773-1000
Phil Ertl, supt. Fax 773-1019
www.wauwatosaschools.org
East HS 1,200/9-12
7500 Milwaukee Ave 53213 414-773-2000
Nick Hughes, prin. Fax 773-2020
Longfellow MS 800/6-8
7600 W North Ave 53213 414-773-2400
Jason Galien, prin. Fax 773-2420
Plank Road S 100/Alt
9501 W Watertown Plank Rd 53226 414-257-7128
Tom Seidl, prin. Fax 257-6620
River Hills S Alt
9455 W Watertown Plank Rd 53226 414-257-7537
Tom Seidl, prin. Fax 257-6297
West HS 1,000/9-12
11400 W Center St 53222 414-773-3000
Frank Calarco, prin. Fax 773-3020
Whitman MS 600/6-8
11100 W Center St 53222 414-773-2600
Jeff Keranen, prin. Fax 773-2620

Bryant & Stratton College Post-Sec.
10950 W Potter Rd 53226 414-302-7000
Institute of Kings and Priests 50/9-12
12201 W Burleigh St Ste 14 53222 414-699-1962
Dr. Shone Bagley, admin.

Wauzeka, Crawford, Pop. 697
Wauzeka-Steuben SD 200/PK-12
301 E Main St 53826 608-875-5311
Roger Kordus, supt. Fax 875-5100
www.wauzeka.k12.wi.us
Wauzeka-Steuben S 200/PK-12
301 E Main St 53826 608-875-5311
Robert Sailer, prin. Fax 875-5100

Webster, Burnett, Pop. 634
Webster SD 700/PK-12
PO Box 9 54893 715-866-4391
Jim Erickson, supt. Fax 866-4283
www.webster.k12.wi.us

Webster HS 200/9-12
PO Box 9 54893 715-866-4281
Tim Widiker, prin. Fax 866-4377
Webster MS 200/5-8
PO Box 9 54893 715-866-4282
Tim Widiker, prin. Fax 866-4377

West Allis, Milwaukee, Pop. 59,182
West Allis SD
Supt. — See Milwaukee
Central HS 1,400/9-12
8516 W Lincoln Ave 53227 414-604-3110
Paul Mielke, prin. Fax 546-5536
Hale HS 1,600/9-12
11601 W Lincoln Ave 53227 414-604-3210
Matthew Lesar, prin. Fax 546-5734
Lincoln IS 400/6-8
7815 W Lapham St 53214 414-604-4210
Diane Ulezelski, prin. Fax 777-7256
Wright IS 900/6-8
9501 W Cleveland Ave 53227 414-604-3410
Beth Koehler, prin. Fax 546-5785

Grace Christian Academy 200/PK-12
8420 W Beloit Rd 53227 414-327-4200
Cynthia Hummitzsch, admin. Fax 327-4386
Milwaukee Area Technical College Post-Sec.
1200 S 71st St 53214 414-456-5500
Sanford-Brown College Post-Sec.
6737 W Washington St # 2355 53214 414-771-2200

West Bend, Washington, Pop. 30,669
West Bend SD 6,800/PK-12
735 S Main St 53095 262-335-5435
Ted Neitzke, supt. Fax 335-5470
www.west-bend.k12.wi.us
Badger MS 900/6-8
727 S 6th Ave 53095 262-335-5456
Kurt Becker, prin. Fax 306-4380
East HS 1,100/9-12
1305 E Decorah Rd 53095 262-335-5532
James Curler, prin. Fax 335-8242
Rolfs Education Center Alt
737 S 3rd Ave 53095 262-335-5471
Cassie Martin, prin. Fax 335-6182
Silverbrook MS 500/6-8
120 N Silverbrook Dr 53095 262-335-5499
Lance Roell, prin. Fax 335-5610
West HS 1,200/9-12
1305 E Decorah Rd 53095 262-335-5587
Jim Curler, prin. Fax 335-8251

Moraine Park Technical College Post-Sec.
2151 N Main St 53090 262-335-5706
University of Wisconsin Washington Co Post Sec.
400 S University Dr 53095 262-335-5200

Westby, Vernon, Pop. 2,182
Westby Area SD 1,100/PK-12
206 West Ave S 54667 608-634-0101
Charles Norton, supt. Fax 634-0118
www.westby.k12.wi.us
Westby Area HS 300/9-12
206 West Ave S 54667 608-634-3101
Ken Manning, prin. Fax 634-0123
Westby Area MS 300/5-8
206 West Ave S 54667 608-634-0200
Clarice Kammel, prin. Fax 634-0218

Westfield, Marquette, Pop. 1,241
Westfield SD 1,100/PK-12
N7046 County Road M 53964 608-296-2107
John Eyerly, supt. Fax 296-2938
www.westfield.k12.wi.us
Westfield Area HS 400/9-12
N7046 County Road M 53964 608-296-2141
David Moody, prin. Fax 296-2293
Westfield Area MS 200/7-8
N7046 County Road M 53964 608-296-2141
David Moody, prin. Fax 296-2293

West Milwaukee, Milwaukee, Pop. 4,109
West Allis SD
Supt. — See Milwaukee
West Milwaukee IS 500/6-8
5104 W Greenfield Ave 53214 414-604-3310
Jeffery Taylor, prin. Fax 389-3815

Weston, Marathon, Pop. 12,921
D.C. Everest Area SD 5,400/PK-12
6300 Alderson St 54476 715-359-4221
Kristine Gilmore, supt. Fax 359-2056
www.dce.k12.wi.us
D.C. Everest HS 1,400/10-12
6500 Alderson St 54476 715-359-6561
Thomas Johanson, prin. Fax 355-7220
D.C. Everest JHS 900/8-9
1000 Machmueller St 54476 715-359-0511
Steven Pophal, prin. Fax 359-9395

West Salem, LaCrosse, Pop. 4,740
West Salem SD 1,800/PK-12
405 Hamlin St E 54669 608-786-0700
Troy Gunderson, supt. Fax 786-2960
www.wsalem.k12.wi.us
West Salem HS 600/9-12
490 Mark St N 54669 608-786-1220
Mark Carlson, prin. Fax 786-1273
West Salem MS 400/6-8
450 Mark St N 54669 608-786-2090
Dean Buchanan, prin. Fax 786-1081

Coulee Christian S 100/PK-12
230 Garland St W 54669 608-786-3004
Cindy Moses, admin. Fax 786-3005

Weyauwega, Waupaca, Pop. 1,882
Weyauwega-Fremont SD 900/PK-12
PO Box 580 54983 920-867-8800
Scott Bleck, supt. Fax 867-8815
www.wegafremont.k12.wi.us
Weyauwega-Fremont HS 300/9-12
PO Box 580 54983 920-867-8950
Matt Wilbert, prin. Fax 867-8975
Weyauwega-Fremont MS 200/6-8
PO Box 580 54983 920-867-8850
Matt Wilbert, prin. Fax 867-8875

Whitefish Bay, Milwaukee, Pop. 13,847
Whitefish Bay SD 3,000/PK-12
1200 E Fairmount Ave 53217 414-963-3921
Mary Gavigan, supt. Fax 963-3959
www.wfbschools.com
Whitefish Bay HS 900/9-12
1200 E Fairmount Ave 53217 414-963-3928
William Henkle, prin. Fax 963-3870
Whitefish Bay MS 600/6-8
1144 E Henry Clay St 53217 414-963-6800
Amy Levek, prin. Fax 963-6808

Dominican HS 300/9-12
120 E Silver Spring Dr 53217 414-332-1170
Leanne Giese, hdmstr. Fax 332-4101

Whitehall, Trempealeau, Pop. 1,550
Whitehall SD 700/PK-12
PO Box 37 54773 715-538-4374
Michael Beighley, supt. Fax 538-4639
www.whitehallsd.k12.wi.us
Whitehall HS 300/9-12
PO Box 37 54773 715-538-4364
Mike Beighley, prin. Fax 538-4639
Whitehall MS 200/6-8
PO Box 37 54773 715-538-4364
Mike Beighley, prin. Fax 538-4639

White Lake, Langlade, Pop. 352
White Lake SD 200/PK-12
PO Box 67 54491 715-882-8421
William Fisher, supt. Fax 882-2914
www.whitelake.k12.wi.us
White Lake JSHS 100/7-12
PO Box 67 54491 715-882-2361
Glenda Boldig, prin. Fax 882-2914

Whitewater, Walworth, Pop. 14,180
Whitewater USD 1,900/K-12
419 S Elizabeth St 53190 262-472-8700
Eric Runez, supt. Fax 472-8710
www.wwusd.org
Whitewater HS 600/9-12
534 S Elizabeth St 53190 262-472-8100
Doug Parker, prin. Fax 472-8181
Whitewater MS 400/6-8
401 S Elizabeth St 53190 262-472-8300
Dan Foster, prin. Fax 472-8310

University of Wisconsin Post-Sec.
800 W Main St 53190 262-472-1234

Wild Rose, Waushara, Pop. 719
Wild Rose SD 700/PK-12
PO Box 276 54984 920-622-4203
Claude Olson, supt. Fax 622-4604
www.wildrose.k12.wi.us
Wild Rose MSHS 400/6-12
PO Box 276 54984 920-622-4201
Craig Hayes, prin. Fax 622-4801

Williams Bay, Walworth, Pop. 2,540
Williams Bay SD 600/PK-12
PO Box 1410 53191 262-245-1575
Vance Dalzin, supt. Fax 245-5877
www.williamsbayschool.org
Williams Bay HS 100/9-12
PO Box 1410 53191 262-245-6224
Barry Butters, prin. Fax 245-5877
Williams Bay JHS 100/7-8
PO Box 1410 53191 262-245-6224
Barry Butters, prin. Fax 245-5877

Faith Christian S 200/PK-12
PO Box 1230 53191 262-245-9404
Craig Skrede, admin. Fax 245-0128

Wilmot, Kenosha, Pop. 442
Wilmot UNHSD 1,100/9-12
PO Box 8 53192 262-862-9005
Daniel S. Kopp, admin. Fax 862-6413
www.wilmothighschool.com
Wilmot HS 1,100/9-12
PO Box 8 53192 262-862-2351
Chris Trottier, prin. Fax 862-6929

Winneconne, Winnebago, Pop. 2,364
Winneconne Community SD 1,500/PK-12
PO Box 5000 54986 920-582-5802
Margaret Larson, supt. Fax 582-5816
www.winneconne.k12.wi.us
Winneconne HS 500/9-12
PO Box 5000 54986 920-582-5810
Terry Wetzel, prin. Fax 582-5813
Winneconne MS 300/6-8
PO Box 5000 54986 920-582-5800
Todd Schroeder, prin. Fax 582-5812

Winter, Sawyer, Pop. 305
Winter SD 300/PK-12
PO Box 310 54896 715-266-3301
Dr. Penny Boileau, admin. Fax 266-2216
www.winter.k12.wi.us/
Winter HS 100/9-12
PO Box 310 54896 715-266-3301
Adam Zopp, prin. Fax 266-9221
Winter MS 100/6-8
PO Box 310 54896 715-266-6701
Dr. Penny Boileau, prin. Fax 266-2216

Wisconsin Dells, Columbia, Pop. 2,648
Wisconsin Dells SD 1,800/PK-12
811 County Road H 53965 608-254-7769
Terrance Slack, supt. Fax 254-8058
www.sdwd.k12.wi.us
Spring Hill MS 400/6-8
300 Vine St 53965 608-253-2468
Brian Grove, prin. Fax 254-6397
Wisconsin Dells HS 600/9-12
520 Race St 53965 608-253-1461
Randy Kuhnau, prin. Fax 254-6288

Wisconsin Rapids, Wood, Pop. 18,141
Wisconsin Rapids SD 5,500/PK-12
510 Peach St 54494 715-424-6700
Colleen Dickmann, supt. Fax 422-6070
www.wrps.org
East JHS 800/8-9
311 Lincoln St 54494 715-424-6730
Kevin Yeske, prin. Fax 422-6270
Lincoln SHS 1,300/10-12
1801 16th St S 54494 715-424-6750
Ronald Rasmussen, prin. Fax 422-6097
River Cities HS 100/Alt
2390 48th St S 54494 715-424-6798
Kathi Stebbins Hintz, prin. Fax 422-6370

Assumption HS 200/9-12
445 Chestnut St 54494 715-422-0910
Martin Gibbons, prin. Fax 422-0912
Assumption MS 100/7-8
440 Mead St 54494 715-422-0950
Martin Gibbons, prin. Fax 422-0955
Mid-State Technical College Post-Sec.
500 32nd St N 54494 715-422-5300

Wittenberg, Shawano, Pop. 1,064
Wittenberg-Birnamwood SD 1,200/PK-12
400 W Grand Ave 54499 715-253-2213
Garrett Rogowski, supt. Fax 253-3588
www.wittbirn.k12.wi.us/
Wittenberg-Birnamwood HS 400/9-12
400 W Grand Ave 54499 715-253-2211
Jill Sharp, prin. Fax 253-3588

Wonewoc, Juneau, Pop. 810
Wonewoc-Union Center SD 400/PK-12
101 School Rd 53968 608-464-3165
Arthur Keenan, supt. Fax 464-3325
www.theclasslist.com/wcschools
Wonewoc HS 100/9-12
101 School Rd 53968 608-464-3165
Michelle Noll, prin. Fax 464-3325
Wonewoc JHS 50/7-8
101 School Rd 53968 608-464-3165
Michelle Noll, prin. Fax 464-3325

Woodville, Saint Croix, Pop. 1,320
Baldwin-Woodville Area SD
Supt. — See Baldwin
Viking MS 400/5-8
500 Southside Dr 54028 715-698-2456
Jason Dachel, prin. Fax 698-3315

Wrightstown, Brown, Pop. 2,803
Wrightstown Community SD 1,300/PK-12
PO Box 128 54180 920-532-5551
Carla Buboltz, supt. Fax 532-4664
www.wrightstown.k12.wi.us
Wrightstown HS 500/9-12
PO Box 128 54180 920-532-0525
Scott Thompson, prin. Fax 532-0860
Wrightstown MS 400/5-8
PO Box 128 54180 920-532-5553
Lee Mierow, prin. Fax 532-3869

WYOMING

WYOMING DEPARTMENT OF EDUCATION
2300 Capitol Ave, Cheyenne 82001-3644
Telephone 307-777-7673
Fax 307-777-6234
Website http://www.k12.wy.us

Superintendent of Public Instruction Richard Crandall

WYOMING BOARD OF EDUCATION
2300 Capitol Ave, Cheyenne 82001-3644

Chairperson Gerald "Joe" Reichardt

BOARDS OF COOPERATIVE EDUCATIONAL SERVICES (BOCES)

Carbon Co. Higher Education Center BOCES
David Throgmorton, dir. 307-328-9204
705 Rodeo St, Rawlins 82301 Fax 324-3338
www.cchec.org
Central Wyoming BOCES 307-268-3309
, 125 College Dr, Casper 82601 Fax 268-2731
www.caspercollege.edu/boces/index.html
Douglas BOCES
Sue McBride, dir. 307-358-5622
203 N 6th St, Douglas 82633 Fax 358-5629
Fremont County BOCES
Sandy Barton, dir. 307-856-2028
320 W Main St, Riverton 82501 Fax 856-4058
www.fcboces.org

Northeast Wyoming BOCES
Julie Cudmore, dir. 307-682-0231
410 N Miller Ave, Gillette 82716 Fax 686-7628
www.newboces.com/
Northwest Wyoming BOCES
Carolyn Connor, dir. 307-864-2171
PO Box 112, Thermopolis 82443 Fax 864-9463
www.nwboces.com/
Oyster Ridge BOCES
Heidi Lively, dir. 307-877-6958
20 Adaville Dr, Diamondville 83116 Fax 828-9040
www.kemmereroutreach.com
Region V BOCES
Kevin Garvey, dir. 307-733-8210
PO Box 240, Wilson 83014 Fax 733-8462
boces5.org

Sublette BOCES
Donna Lozier, dir. 307-367-6873
PO Box 977, Pinedale 82941 Fax 367-6634
www.subletteboces.com/
Sweetwater BOCES
Bernadine Craft Ph.D., dir. 307-382-1607
PO Box 428, Rock Springs 82902 Fax 382-1875
www.wwcc.wy.edu/boces/
Uinta BOCES
Michael Williams, dir. 307-789-5742
1013 W Cheyenne Dr Unit A Fax 789-7975
Evanston 82930
www.uintaeducation.org
Uinta County SD #4 & #6 BOCES
Karla Behunin, dir. 307-782-6401
PO Box 130, Mountain View 82939 Fax 782-7410

PUBLIC, PRIVATE AND CATHOLIC SECONDARY SCHOOLS

Afton, Lincoln, Pop. 1,881
Lincoln County SD 2 2,600/K-12
PO Box 219 83110 307-885-3811
Jon Abrams, supt. Fax 885-9562
www.lcsd2.org
Star Valley HS 700/9-12
PO Box 8000 83110 307-885-7847
Richard Woodford, prin. Fax 885-3299
Star Valley MS 400/7-8
PO Box 8001 83110 307-885-5208
Kem Cazier, prin. Fax 885-0472
Swift Creek HS 50/Alt
PO Box 219 83110 307-885-7139
Russell Gardner, prin. Fax 885-9562
Other Schools – See Cokeville

Baggs, Carbon, Pop. 438
Carbon County SD 1
Supt. — See Rawlins
Little Snake River Valley S 200/K-12
PO Box 9 82321 307-383-2185
Joel Thomas, prin. Fax 383-2184

Basin, Big Horn, Pop. 1,274
Big Horn County SD 4 300/PK-12
PO Box 151 82410 307-568-2684
Mary Fisher, supt. Fax 568-2654
www.bgh4.k12.wy.us/
Riverside HS 100/9-12
PO Box 151 82410 307-568-2416
Tony Anson, prin. Fax 568-2415
Other Schools – See Manderson

Big Horn, Sheridan, Pop. 487
Sheridan County SD 1
Supt. — See Ranchester
Big Horn HS 100/9-12
PO Box 490 82833 307-674-8190
George Mirich, prin. Fax 672-5306
Big Horn MS 100/6-8
PO Box 490 82833 307-674-8190
George Mirich, prin. Fax 672-5306

Big Piney, Sublette, Pop. 550
Sublette County SD 9 700/K-12
PO Box 769 83113 307-276-3322
Gerry Chase, supt. Fax 276-3731
sublette9.org
Big Piney HS 200/9-12
PO Box 769 83113 307-276-3324
Bill Schlepp, prin. Fax 276-3480
Big Piney MS 200/6-8
PO Box 769 83113 307-276-3315
Stanley Dodds, prin. Fax 276-5209

Buffalo, Johnson, Pop. 4,536
Johnson County SD 1 1,200/K-12
601 W Lott St 82834 307-684-9571
Rod Kessler, supt. Fax 684-5182
www.jcsd1.k12.wy.us
Buffalo HS 400/9-12
29891 Old Highway 87 82834 307-684-2269
Chad Bourgeois, prin. Fax 684-9481
Clear Creek MS 200/6-8
361 W Gatchell St 82834 307-684-5594
Darren Schmidt, prin. Fax 684-9096
Other Schools – See Kaycee

Burlington, Big Horn, Pop. 287
Big Horn County SD 1
Supt. — See Cowley
Burlington HS 100/9-12
PO Box 9 82411 307-762-3334
Matt Davidson, prin. Fax 762-3604
Burlington JHS 50/7-8
PO Box 9 82411 307-762-3334
Matt Davidson, prin. Fax 762-3604

Burns, Laramie, Pop. 295
Laramie County SD 2
Supt. — See Pine Bluffs
Burns JSHS 300/7-12
PO Box 160 82053 307-245-4100
Jerry Becking, prin. Fax 547-3583

Casper, Natrona, Pop. 54,284
Natrona County SD 1 11,700/PK-12
970 N Glenn Rd 82601 307-253-5200
Dr. Joel Dvorak, supt. Fax 253-5333
www.natronaschools.org/
Casper Classical Academy 200/6-8
920 S Beverly St 82609 307-253-3160
Marie Puryear, prin. Fax 253-2286
Centennial JHS 500/6-8
1421 Waterford 82609 307-253-2900
Michael Jennings, prin. Fax 253-2891
CY MS 600/6-8
2900 Cyclone Blvd 82604 307-253-2700
Valerie Braughton, prin. Fax 253-2683
Frontier MS 200/6-8
900 S Beverly St 82609 307-253-2300
Tommy Ray, prin. Fax 253-2286
Morgan JHS 800/6-8
1440 S Elm St 82601 307-253-2500
Walter Wilcox, prin. Fax 253-2411
Natrona County SHS 1,600/9-12
930 S Elm St 82601 307-253-1700
Dean Kelly, prin. Fax 253-1507
ProStart, 500 S Wolcott St 82601 Vo/Tech
Calvin Colling, prin. 307-234-9612
Roosevelt HS 100/Alt
140 E K St 82601 307-253-1400
Shawna Trujillo, prin. Fax 253-1450
Star Lane Center 9-12
1400 S Fairdale Ave 82601 307-253-3100
Marie Puryear, prin. Fax 253-3117
Transitions Learning Center Alt
2000 Casper St 82604 307-253-4350
Rick Porter, prin. Fax 253-4321
Walsh HS 1,500/9-12
3500 E 12th St 82609 307-253-2000
Brad Diller, prin. Fax 253-2066
Other Schools – See Midwest

Casper College Post-Sec.
125 College Dr 82601 307-268-2110
Paradise Valley Christian S 100/PK-12
3041 Paradise Dr 82604 307-234-2450
Jeanne Boyd, prin. Fax 577-0763
SAGE Technical Service Truck Driving Sch Post-Sec.
2368 Oil Dr 82604 800-307-0242
Wyoming School for the Deaf Post-Sec.
539 Payne Ave 82609

Cheyenne, Laramie, Pop. 58,048
Laramie County SD 1 12,800/K-12
2810 House Ave 82001 307-771-2100
Mark Stock, supt. Fax 771-2364
www.laramie1.org/
Carey JHS 1,000/7-9
1780 E Pershing Blvd 82001 307-771-2580
Tory Richey, prin. Fax 771-2578
Central HS 1,100/9-12
5500 Education Dr 82009 307-771-2680
Steve Newton, prin. Fax 771-2699
East HS 1,400/10-12
2800 E Pershing Blvd 82001 307-771-2663
Sam Mirich, prin. Fax 771-2679
Johnson JHS 600/7-8
1236 W Allison Rd 82007 307-771-2640
John Balow, prin. Fax 771-2660
McCormick JHS 700/7-8
6000 Education Dr 82009 307-771-2650
Jeff Conine, prin. Fax 771-2661
South HS, 1213 W Allison Rd 82007 500/9-12
Phil Thompson, prin. 307-771-2140
Triumph HS 200/Alt
1250 W College Dr 82007 307-771-2500
Michael Helenbolt, prin. Fax 771-2508

Cheeks Intl Academy of Beauty Culture Post-Sec.
207 W 18th St 82001 307-637-8700
CollegeAmerica Post-Sec.
6101 Yellowstone Rd Ste 101 82009 307-632-7048
Institute of Business & Medical Careers Post-Sec.
1854 Dell Range Blvd 82009 307-433-8363
Laramie County Community College Post-Sec.
1400 E College Dr 82007 307-778-5222
Webster Christian S 100/PK-12
PO Box 21239 82003 307-635-2175
DeAnn Gomez, admin. Fax 773-8523

Chugwater, Platte, Pop. 210
Platte County SD 1
Supt. — See Wheatland
Chugwater HS 50/9-12
406 5th St 82210 307-422-3501
George Kopf, prin. Fax 422-3433
Chugwater JHS 50/7-8
406 5th St 82210 307-422-3501
George Kopf, prin. Fax 422-3433

Clearmont, Sheridan, Pop. 141
Sheridan County SD 3 100/PK-12
PO Box 125 82835 307-758-4412
John Baule, supt. Fax 758-4444
www.sheridan3.com

Arvada-Clearmont HS 50/9-12
PO Box 125 82835 307-758-4412
Charles Auzqui, prin. Fax 758-4444
Arvada-Clearmont JHS 50/7-8
PO Box 125 82835 307-758-4412
Charles Auzqui, prin. Fax 758-4444

Cody, Park, Pop. 9,367
Park County SD 6 2,200/K-12
919 Cody Ave 82414 307-587-4253
Bryan Monteith, supt. Fax 527-5762
www.park6.org/
Cody HS 700/9-12
919 Cody Ave 82414 307-587-4251
Brandon Jensen, prin. Fax 587-9369
Cody MS 500/6-8
919 Cody Ave 82414 307-587-4273
Tim Foley, prin. Fax 587-3547

West Park Hospital Post-Sec.
707 Sheridan Ave 82414 307-527-7501

Cokeville, Lincoln, Pop. 533
Lincoln County SD 2
Supt. — See Afton
Cokeville JSHS 100/7-12
PO Box 220 83114 307-279-3273
Keith Harris, prin. Fax 279-3221

Cowley, Big Horn, Pop. 654
Big Horn County SD 1 700/PK-12
PO Box 688 82420 307-548-2254
Shon Hocker, supt. Fax 548-7610
bighorn1.com
Rocky Mountain HS 100/9-12
PO Box 280 82420 307-548-2723
Tim Winland, prin. Fax 548-6452
Rocky Mountain MS 100/6-8
PO Box 280 82420 307-548-2723
Tim Winland, prin. Fax 548-6452
Other Schools – See Burlington

Dayton, Sheridan, Pop. 749
Sheridan County SD 1
Supt. — See Ranchester
Tongue River HS 200/9-12
PO Box 408 82836 307-655-2236
Mark Fritz, prin. Fax 655-9798

Diamondville, Lincoln, Pop. 720
Lincoln County SD 1 600/K-12
PO Box 335 83116 307-877-9095
Teresa Chaulk, supt. Fax 877-9638
www.lcsd1.k12.wy.us
Other Schools – See Kemmerer

Douglas, Converse, Pop. 6,039
Converse County SD 1 1,700/K-12
615 Hamilton St 82633 307-358-2942
Dr. Dan Espeland, supt. Fax 358-3934
converse1schools.org
Douglas HS 500/9-12
615 Hamilton St 82633 307-358-2940
Dan Edwards, prin. Fax 358-2737
Douglas MS 400/6-8
615 Hamilton St 82633 307-358-9771
Eric Pingrey, prin. Fax 358-5315

Dubois, Fremont, Pop. 957
Fremont County SD 2 200/K-12
PO Box 188 82513 307-455-5545
Gerald Nolan, supt. Fax 455-2178
www.fremont2.org/
Dubois HS 100/9-12
PO Box 188 82513 307-455-2279
Gerald Nolan, prin. Fax 455-3015
Dubois MS 50/6-8
PO Box 188 82513 307-455-5524
Brandon Farris, prin. Fax 455-2654

Encampment, Carbon, Pop. 445
Carbon County SD 2
Supt. — See Saratoga
Encampment S 100/K-12
PO Box 277 82325 307-327-5442
Mike Erickson, prin. Fax 327-5142

Ethete, Fremont, Pop. 1,530
Fremont County SD 14 600/PK-12
638 Blue Sky Hwy 82520 307-332-3904
Michelle Hoffman, supt. Fax 332-7567
www.fremont14.k12.wy.us
Wyoming Indian HS 100/9-12
636 Blue Sky Hwy 82520 307-332-9765
Phil Garhart, prin. Fax 335-7739
Wyoming Indian MS 100/6-8
638 Blue Sky Hwy 82520 307-332-2992
Pam Frederick, prin. Fax 335-7318

Evanston, Uinta, Pop. 12,128
Uinta County SD 1 2,900/K-12
PO Box 6002 82931 307-789-7571
James Bailey, supt. Fax 789-6225
www.uinta1.com
Davis MS 400/6-8
PO Box 6002 82931 307-789-8096
Jim Harrell, prin. Fax 789-3386
Evanston HS 800/9-12
PO Box 6002 82931 307-789-0757
Doug Rigby, prin. Fax 789-7447
Evanston MS 300/6-8
PO Box 6002 82931 307-789-5499
Eric Christenot, prin. Fax 789-7972
Horizon Alternative S 100/Alt
PO Box 6002 82931 307-789-0122
Doug Rigby, prin. Fax 789-2522

Farson, Sweetwater, Pop. 309
Sweetwater County SD 1
Supt. — See Rock Springs
Farson-Eden HS 100/9-12
PO Box 400 82932 307-273-9301
Dr. Charles Cook, prin. Fax 273-9313
Farson-Eden MS 50/6-8
PO Box 400 82932 307-273-9301
Dr. Charles Cook, prin. Fax 273-9313

Fort Washakie, Fremont, Pop. 1,730
Fremont County SD 21 500/PK-12
90 Ethete Rd 82514 307-332-5983
H. Terry Ebert, supt. Fax 332-7267
www.fortwashakieschool.com
Fort Washakie HS 50/9-12
90 Ethete Rd 82514 307-332-0142
Shad Hamilton, prin. Fax 332-7267
Fort Washakie MS 100/7-8
90 Ethete Rd 82514 307-332-2380
Elberta Monroe, prin. Fax 332-3597

Gillette, Campbell, Pop. 28,659
Campbell County SD 1 7,900/K-12
PO Box 3033 82717 307-682-5171
Dr. Richard Strahorn, supt. Fax 682-6619
www.campbellcountyschools.net/
Campbell County HS 1,500/10-12
1000 Camel Dr 82716 307-682-7247
Kirby Eisenhauer, prin. Fax 686-7274
Sage Valley JHS 900/7-9
1000 W Lakeway Rd 82718 307-682-2225
Terry Quinn, prin. Fax 687-7614
Twin Spruce JHS 800/7-9
100 E 7th St 82716 307-682-3144
Dave Foreman, prin. Fax 686-1969
Westwood HS 100/Alt
601 Rohan Ave 82716 307-682-9809
Kelly Morehead, prin. Fax 686-7566
Other Schools – See Wright

Gillette College Post-Sec.
300 W Sinclair St 82718 307-686-0254
Heritage Christian S 100/PK-12
510 Wall Street Ct 82718 307-686-1392
George Haines, admin. Fax 682-6515

Glendo, Platte, Pop. 203
Platte County SD 1
Supt. — See Wheatland
Glendo HS 50/9-12
305 N Paige Ave 82213 307-735-4471
Stanetta Twiford, prin. Fax 735-4220
Glendo JHS 50/7-8
305 N Paige Ave 82213 307-735-4471
Stanetta Twiford, prin. Fax 735-4220

Glenrock, Converse, Pop. 2,551
Converse County SD 2 600/K-12
PO Box 1300 82637 307-436-5331
Kirk Hughes, supt. Fax 436-8235
www.cnv2.k12.wy.us/
Glenrock HS 200/9-12
PO Box 1300 82637 307-436-9201
Christopher Gray, prin. Fax 436-8517
Glenrock Intermediate MS 100/5-8
PO Box 1300 82637 307-436-9258
Scott Gion, prin. Fax 436-7507

Green River, Sweetwater, Pop. 12,356
Sweetwater County SD 2 2,600/K-12
320 Monroe Ave 82935 307-872-5500
Donna Little-Kaumo, supt. Fax 872-5518
www.sw2.k12.wy.us
Expedition Academy 100/10-12
351 Monroe Ave 82935 307-872-4800
John Poole, prin. Fax 872-4797
Green River HS 700/9-12
1615 Hitching Post Dr 82935 307-872-4747
Jason Fuss, prin. Fax 872-4758
Lincoln MS 400/7-8
350 Monroe Ave 82935 307-872-4400
Mark Rose, prin. Fax 872-4477

Greybull, Big Horn, Pop. 1,834
Big Horn County SD 3 500/K-12
636 14th Ave N 82426 307-765-4756
Barry Bryant, supt. Fax 765-4617
gps.bgh3.k12.wy.us
Greybull HS 200/9-12
636 14th Ave N 82426 307-765-2537
Ty Flock, prin. Fax 765-2870
Greybull MS 100/6-8
636 14th Ave N 82426 307-765-4492
Scott McBride, prin. Fax 765-2586

Guernsey, Platte, Pop. 1,136
Platte County SD 2 200/K-12
PO Box 189 82214 307-836-2735
Dave Barker, supt. Fax 836-2450
www.plt2.k12.wy.us
Guernsey-Sunrise HS 100/9-12
PO Box 189 82214 307-836-2745
Troy Lake, prin. Fax 836-2729
Guernsey-Sunrise JHS 50/7-8
PO Box 189 82214 307-836-2745
Troy Lake, prin. Fax 836-2729

Hanna, Carbon, Pop. 829
Carbon County SD 2
Supt. — See Saratoga
Hanna-Elk Mountain-Medicine Bow JSHS 100/7-12
PO Box 810 82327 307-325-6545
Dale Kari, prin. Fax 325-9223

Hulett, Crook, Pop. 375
Crook County SD 1
Supt. — See Sundance
Hulett S 200/K-12
PO Box 127 82720 307-467-5231
Darlene Hartman-Hallman, prin. Fax 467-5280

Jackson, Teton, Pop. 9,432
Teton County SD 1 2,500/K-12
PO Box 568 83001 307-733-2704
Dr. Pam Shea, supt. Fax 733-6443
www.tcsd.org/
Jackson Hole HS 600/9-12
PO Box 568 83001 307-732-3700
Dr. Scott Crisp, prin. Fax 732-3720
Jackson Hole MS 500/6-8
PO Box 568 83001 307-733-4234
Bo Miller, prin. Fax 733-4254
Summit HS 50/9-12
PO Box 568 83001 307-733-9116
Beth Auge, prin. Fax 739-8922

Journeys S 200/PK-12
700 Coyote Canyon Rd 83001 307-733-3729
Jack Shea, dir. Fax 733-7560

Kaycee, Johnson, Pop. 260
Johnson County SD 1
Supt. — See Buffalo
Kaycee K-12 S 200/K-12
PO Box 6 82639 307-738-2573
Andrea Gilbert, prin. Fax 738-2495

Kemmerer, Lincoln, Pop. 2,635
Lincoln County SD 1
Supt. — See Diamondville
Kemmerer Alternative S 50/Alt
1004 Elk St 83101 307-877-5819
David Gardner, prin. Fax 877-5644
Kemmerer HS 200/9-12
1525 3rd West Ave 83101 307-877-6991
Orlen Zempel, prin. Fax 877-4117
Kemmerer MS 200/5-8
1310 Antelope St 83101 307-877-2286
Chris Leathers, prin. Fax 877-3365

Lander, Fremont, Pop. 7,311
Fremont County SD 1 1,300/K-12
400 Baldwin Creek Rd 82520 307-332-4711
Dr. Mike Bowman, supt. Fax 332-6671
www.landerschools.org
Lander MS 300/6-8
755 Jefferson St 82520 307-332-4040
Brian Janish, prin. Fax 332-0435
Lander Valley HS 500/9-12
350 Baldwin Creek Rd 82520 307-332-4433
Lisa Hafer, prin. Fax 332-2861
Pathfinder HS 50/Alt
PO Box 1259 82520 307-335-7050
Kathy Hitt, prin. Fax 335-8695

Wyoming State Training School Post-Sec.
8204 State Highway 789 82520 307-332-5302

Laramie, Albany, Pop. 30,183
Albany County SD 1 3,300/PK-12
1948 E Grand Ave 82070 307-721-4400
Dr. Brian Recht, supt. Fax 721-4408
www.acsd1.org
Laramie JHS 700/6-9
1355 N 22nd St 82072 307-721-4430
Kelly Carroll, prin. Fax 721-4435
Laramie SHS 800/10-12
1275 N 11th St 82072 307-721-4420
Kim Sorenson, prin. Fax 721-4419
Whiting HS 50/Alt
801 S 24th St 82070 307-721-4449
Ursula Harrison, prin. Fax 721-4461
Other Schools – See Rock River

University of Wyoming Post-Sec.
1000 E University Ave 82071 307-766-1121
WyoTech Post-Sec.
4373 N 3rd St 82072 307-742-3776

Lingle, Goshen, Pop. 467
Goshen County SD 1
Supt. — See Torrington
Lingle-Ft. Laramie HS 100/9-12
PO Box 379 82223 307-837-2296
Jerry Vandersloot, prin. Fax 837-3025
Lingle-Fort Laramie MS 100/6-8
PO Box 379 82223 307-837-2283
Jerry Vandersloot, prin. Fax 837-2057

Lovell, Big Horn, Pop. 2,347
Big Horn County SD 2 700/K-12
502 Hampshire Ave 82431 307-548-2259
Dan Coe, supt. Fax 548-7555
www.bgh2.k12.wy.us/
Lovell HS 200/9-12
502 Hampshire Ave 82431 307-548-2256
Scott O'Tremba, prin. Fax 548-9452
Lovell MS 200/6-8
325 W 9th St 82431 307-548-6553
Sherie Monk, prin. Fax 548-6136

Lusk, Niobrara, Pop. 1,541
Niobrara County SD 1 600/PK-12
PO Box 629 82225 307-334-3793
Richard Luchsinger, supt. Fax 334-0126
www.lusk.k12.wy.us/
Niobrara County HS 300/9-12
PO Box 1050 82225 307-334-3320
Stuart Larson, prin. Fax 334-2331

Lyman, Uinta, Pop. 2,090
Uinta County SD 6 700/K-12
PO Box 1090 82937 307-786-4100
Kent Stokes, supt. Fax 787-3241
www.uinta6.k12.wy.us/
Lyman HS 200/9-12
PO Box 1090 82937 307-787-6197
Todd Limoges, prin. Fax 787-6193

Lyman MS 200/5-8
PO Box 1090 82937 307-786-4100
Christy Campbell, prin. Fax 786-6949

Manderson, Big Horn, Pop. 112
Big Horn County SD 4
Supt. — See Basin
Cloud Peak MS 100/6-8
PO Box 97 82432 307-568-2846
Shane Schaffner, prin. Fax 568-3885

Meeteetse, Park, Pop. 325
Park County SD 16 100/K-12
PO Box 218 82433 307-868-2501
Jay Curtis, supt. Fax 868-9264
www.park16.k12.wy.us/
Meeteetse S 100/K-12
PO Box 218 82433 307-868-2501
Jay Curtis, prin. Fax 868-9264

Midwest, Natrona, Pop. 395
Natrona County SD 1
Supt. — See Casper
Midwest S 200/PK-12
PO Box 368 82643 307-253-3500
Chris Tobin, prin. Fax 253-3520

Moorcroft, Crook, Pop. 998
Crook County SD 1
Supt. — See Sundance
Moorcroft JSHS 200/7-12
PO Box 129 82721 307-756-3446
Jeffrey Rieckman, prin. Fax 756-3724

Mountain View, Uinta, Pop. 1,273
Uinta County SD 4 700/K-12
PO Box 130 82939 307-782-3377
Jeffrey Newton, supt. Fax 782-6879
www.uinta4.com
Mountain View HS 200/9-12
PO Box 130 82939 307-782-6340
Ben Carr, prin. Fax 782-6967
Mountain View MS 200/6-8
PO Box 130 82939 307-782-6338
Lane Stratton, prin. Fax 782-6876

Newcastle, Weston, Pop. 3,468
Weston County SD 1 800/K-12
116 Casper Ave 82701 307-746-4451
Brad LaCroix, supt. Fax 746-3289
www.weston1.k12.wy.us
Newcastle HS 200/9-12
116 Casper Ave 82701 307-746-2713
Tracy Ragland, prin. Fax 746-2350
Newcastle MS 200/6-8
116 Casper Ave 82701 307-746-2746
Scott Shoop, prin. Fax 746-4983

Pavillion, Fremont, Pop. 225
Fremont County SD 6 200/PK-12
PO Box 10 82523 307-856-7970
Diana Clapp, supt. Fax 856-3385
www.fre6.k12.wy.us/
Wind River HS 100/9-12
PO Box 10 82523 307-856-7970
Ceatriss Wall, prin. Fax 856-8641
Wind River MS, PO Box 10 82523 4-8
Jeff Verosky, prin. 307-856-7970

Pine Bluffs, Laramie, Pop. 1,114
Laramie County SD 2 900/K-12
PO Box 489 82082 307-245-4050
Jack Cozort, supt. Fax 245-3561
laramie2.org
Pine Bluffs JSHS 200/7-12
PO Box 520 82082 307-245-4000
Todd Sweeter, prin. Fax 245-3144
Other Schools – See Burns

Pinedale, Sublette, Pop. 1,999
Sublette County SD 1 1,000/K-12
PO Box 549 82941 307-367-2139
Jay Harnack, supt. Fax 367-4626
www.pinedaleschools.org/
Pinedale HS 300/9-12
PO Box 549 82941 307-367-2137
Fletcher Turcato, prin. Fax 367-2611
Pinedale MS 200/6-8
PO Box 549 82941 307-367-2821
Jeryl Fluckiger, prin. Fax 367-4217

Powell, Park, Pop. 6,232
Park County SD 1 1,700/K-12
160 N Evarts St 82435 307-764-6186
Kevin Mitchell, supt. Fax 764-6156
www.park1.net
Powell HS 500/9-12
160 N Evarts St 82435 307-764-6181
Jim Kuhn, prin. Fax 764-6151
Powell MS 400/6-8
160 N Evarts St 82435 307-764-6185
Jason Sleep, prin. Fax 764-6155
Shoshone Learning Center 50/Alt
160 N Evarts St 82435 307-764-6187
Ginger Sleep, prin. Fax 764-6157

Northwest College Post-Sec.
231 W 6th St 82435 307-754-6000

Ranchester, Sheridan, Pop. 853
Sheridan County SD 1 900/K-12
PO Box 819 82839 307-655-9541
Marty Kobza, supt. Fax 655-9477
www.sheridan.k12.wy.us/
Tongue River MS 100/6-8
PO Box 879 82839 307-655-9533
Matt Spring, prin. Fax 655-9894
Other Schools – See Big Horn, Dayton

Rawlins, Carbon, Pop. 9,144
Carbon Co. Higher Education Center BOCES
705 Rodeo St 82301 307-328-9204
David Throgmorton, dir. Fax 324-3338
www.cchec.org
Vocational Campus Vo/Tech
812 E Murray St 82301 307-328-9274
Fax 328-9273

Carbon County SD 1 1,300/K-12
615 Rodeo St 82301 307-328-9200
M. Neil Terhune, supt. Fax 328-9258
www.crb1.k12.wy.us/
Cooperative HS 50/Alt
615 Rodeo St 82301 307-328-9250
Ryan Searle, prin. Fax 328-9258
Rawlins HS 500/9-12
1401 Colorado St 82301 307-328-9280
Dan Hadden, prin. Fax 328-9286
Rawlins MS 400/6-8
1001 Brooks St 82301 307-328-9201
Traci Blaize, prin. Fax 328-9226
Other Schools – See Baggs

Riverton, Fremont, Pop. 10,330
Fremont County SD 25 2,300/K-12
121 N 5th St W 82501 307-856-9407
Terry Snyder, supt. Fax 856-3390
www.fremont25.k12.wy.us
Riverton HS 700/9-12
121 N 5th St W 82501 307-856-9491
JoAnne Flanagan, prin. Fax 856-2333
Riverton MS 600/6-8
121 N 5th St W 82501 307-856-9443
Cheryl Mowry, prin. Fax 857-1695

Central Wyoming College Post-Sec.
2660 Peck Ave 82501 307-855-2000

Rock River, Albany, Pop. 236
Albany County SD 1
Supt. — See Laramie
Rock River S 50/K-12
PO Box 128 82083 307-378-2271
Ron Leathers, prin. Fax 378-2505

Rock Springs, Sweetwater, Pop. 22,670
Sweetwater County SD 1 5,100/K-12
PO Box 1089 82902 307-352-3400
Mathew Neal, supt. Fax 352-3411
www.sweetwater1.org
Independence HS 50/Alt
PO Box 1089 82902 307-352-3290
Dr. Randal Wendling, prin. Fax 503-3192
Rock Springs HS 1,200/9-12
PO Box 1089 82902 307-352-3440
Darrin Peppard, prin. Fax 315-2632
Rock Springs JHS 800/7-8
PO Box 1089 82902 307-352-3474
Tina Johnson, prin. Fax 316-5634
Other Schools – See Farson, Wamsutter

Western Wyoming Community College Post-Sec.
2500 College Dr 82901 307-382-1600

Saratoga, Carbon, Pop. 1,658
Carbon County SD 2 600/K-12
PO Box 1530 82331 307-326-5271
Robert Gates, supt. Fax 326-8089
www.crb2.k12.wy.us
Saratoga MSHS 100/7-12
PO Box 1710 82331 307-326-5246
Larry Uhling, prin. Fax 326-9607
Other Schools – See Encampment, Hanna

Sheridan, Sheridan, Pop. 17,182
Sheridan County SD 2 3,100/K-12
PO Box 919 82801 307-674-7405
Craig Dougherty, supt. Fax 674-5041
www.scsd2.com/
Fort Mackenzie HS 50/Alt
620 Lewis St 82801 307-673-8730
Laurien Alangi, prin. Fax 673-8732
Sheridan HS 900/9-12
1056 Long Dr 82801 307-672-2495
Dirlene Wheeler, prin. Fax 672-8071
Sheridan JHS 700/6-8
500 Lewis St 82801 307-674-9745
Mitch Craft, prin. Fax 672-5311
Wright Place 50/Alt
620 Lewis St 82801 307-673-8730
Laurien Alangi, prin. Fax 673-8732

Sheridan College Post-Sec.
PO Box 1500 82801 307-674-6446

Shoshoni, Fremont, Pop. 645
Fremont County SD 24 300/PK-12
112 W 3rd St 82649 307-876-2583
Tammy Cox, supt. Fax 876-2469
www.fremont24.com/
Shoshoni HS 100/9-12
112 W 3rd St 82649 307-876-2576
Dan Martin, prin. Fax 876-9325
Shoshoni JHS 50/7-8
112 W 3rd St 82649 307-876-2576
Dan Martin, prin. Fax 876-9325

Sundance, Crook, Pop. 1,174
Crook County SD 1 1,100/K-12
PO Box 830 82729 307-283-2299
Byron Stutzman, supt. Fax 283-1810
www.crook1.com
Bear Lodge HS, PO Box 1160 82729 50/Alt
Jason Moss, prin. 307-283-2144
Sundance JSHS 200/7-12
PO Box 850 82729 307-283-1007
Mark Broderson, prin. Fax 283-2300
Other Schools – See Hulett, Moorcroft

Ten Sleep, Washakie, Pop. 257
Washakie County SD 2 100/K-12
PO Box 105 82442 307-366-2223
Jerry Erdahl, supt. Fax 366-2304
www.wsh2.k12.wy.us
Ten Sleep HS 50/9-12
PO Box 105 82442 307-366-2233
Russell Budmayr, prin. Fax 366-2304
Ten Sleep MS 50/7-8
PO Box 105 82442 307-366-2233
Russell Budmayr, prin. Fax 366-2304

Thermopolis, Hot Springs, Pop. 2,973
Hot Springs County SD 1 700/K-12
415 Springview St 82443 307-864-6515
Dustin Hunt, supt. Fax 864-6615
www.hotsprings1.org
Hot Springs County HS 200/9-12
415 Springview St 82443 307-864-6511
Travis Anderson, prin. Fax 864-3970
Thermopolis MS 200/5-8
415 Springview St 82443 307-864-6551
Breez Daniels, prin. Fax 864-6608

Torrington, Goshen, Pop. 6,432
Goshen County SD 1 1,800/K-12
626 W 25th Ave 82240 307-532-2171
Jean Chrostoski, supt. Fax 532-7085
www.goshen1.org
Torrington HS 400/9-12
2400 W C St 82240 307-532-7101
Jim English, prin. Fax 532-2696
Torrington MS 300/6-8
2742 W E St 82240 307-532-7014
Marvin Haiman, prin. Fax 532-8402
Other Schools – See Lingle, Yoder

Eastern Wyoming College Post-Sec.
3200 W C St 82240 307-532-8200

Upton, Weston, Pop. 1,090
Weston County SD 7 300/K-12
PO Box 470 82730 307-468-2461
Summer Stephens, supt. Fax 468-2797
bobcat.weston7.k12.wy.us
Upton HS 100/9-12
PO Box 470 82730 307-468-2361
Pete Wilson, prin. Fax 468-2459
Upton MS 100/6-8
PO Box 470 82730 307-468-9331
Clark Coberly, prin. Fax 468-2832

Wamsutter, Sweetwater, Pop. 442
Sweetwater County SD 1
Supt. — See Rock Springs
Desert MS 50/6-8
PO Box 10 82336 307-324-7811
Kenneth Dietz, prin. Fax 589-1164

Wheatland, Platte, Pop. 3,590
Platte County SD 1 1,000/K-12
1350 Oak St 82201 307-322-3175
Dennis Fischer, supt. Fax 322-2084
platte1.org
Wheatland HS 300/9-12
1350 Oak St 82201 307-322-2075
Tracy de Ryk, prin. Fax 322-9739
Wheatland MS 200/6-8
1350 Oak St 82201 307-322-1518
Steven Loyd, prin. Fax 322-1560
Other Schools – See Chugwater, Glendo

Worland, Washakie, Pop. 5,424
Washakie County SD 1 1,400/K-12
1900 Howell Ave 82401 307-347-9286
David Nicholas, supt. Fax 347-8116
www.wsh1.k12.wy.us
Worland HS 400/9-12
801 S 17th St 82401 307-347-2412
Randy Durr, prin. Fax 347-8549
Worland MS 300/6-8
2150 Howell Ave 82401 307-347-3233
Richard Schaal, prin. Fax 347-3710

Wright, Campbell, Pop. 1,786
Campbell County SD 1
Supt. — See Gillette
Wright JSHS 300/7-12
PO Box 490 82732 307-464-0140
Hal Johnson, prin. Fax 464-0154

Yoder, Goshen, Pop. 151
Goshen County SD 1
Supt. — See Torrington
Southeast HS 100/9-12
PO Box 160 82244 307-532-7176
Randy Epler, prin. Fax 532-5771
Southeast JHS 100/7-8
PO Box 160 82244 307-532-7176
Randy Epler, prin. Fax 532-5771

CHARTER SCHOOLS

School	Address	City,State	Zip code	Telephone	Fax	Grade	Contact
Alaska							
Academy Charter S	801 E Arctic Ave	Palmer, AK	99645-6179	907-746-2358	746-2368	K-8	Barbara Gerard
Alaska Native Cultural Charter S	110 Muldoon Rd	Anchorage, AK	99504-1403	907-742-1370	742-1373	K-7	Patsy Shaha
American Charter Academy	244 S Sylvan Rd Ste 110	Wasilla, AK	99623	907-352-0150	352-0180	2-12	Becky Huggins
Anvil City Science Academy	PO Box 131	Nome, AK	99762-0131	907-443-6207	443-5144	5-8	Todd Hindman
Aquarian Charter S	1705 W 32nd Ave	Anchorage, AK	99517-2002	907-742-4900	742-4919	K-6	Lucas Saltzman
Aurora Borealis Charter S	705 Frontage Rd Ste A	Kenai, AK	99611-7740	907-283-0292	283-0293	K-8	Larry Nauta
Birchtree Charter S	7107 E Palmer Wasilla Hwy	Palmer, AK	99645	907-745-1831	745-1843	K-8	Cathey Busbey
Chinook Charter S	3002 International St	Fairbanks, AK	99701-7391	907-452-5020	452-5048	K-8	Paul Fontes
Eagle Academy Charter S	10901 Mausel St Ste 101	Eagle River, AK	99577-8065	907-742-3025	742-3035	K-6	Kitty Logan
Family Partnership Charter S	401 E Fireweed Ln Ste 100	Anchorage, AK	99503-2100	907-742-3700	742-3710	K-12	Reed Whitmore
Fireweed Academy	995 Soundview Ave	Homer, AK	99603-8318	907-235-9728	235-8561	K-6	Kiki Abrahamson
Fronteras Spanish Immersion S	PO Box 871433	Wasilla, AK	99687-1433	907-745-2223	745-6132	K-8	Jennifer Schmidt
Frontier Charter S	400 W Northern Lights Blvd	Anchorage, AK	99503	907-742-1180	742-1188	K-12	Tim Scott
Highland Tech Charter S	5530 E Northern Lights Blvd	Anchorage, AK	99504	907-742-1700	742-1711	6-12	Dr. Ginger Blackmon
Juneau Community Charter S	10014 Crazy Horse Dr	Juneau, AK	99801-8529	907-586-2526	586-3543	K-8	Marjorie Hamburger
Kaleidoscope S	549 N Forest Dr	Kenai, AK	99611-7410	907-283-0804	283-3786	K-6	Robin Dahlman
Ketchikan Charter S	410 Schoenbar Rd	Ketchikan, AK	99901-6218	907-225-8568	247-8568	K-8	Robert Marshall
Kokrine Charter S	601 Loftus Rd	Fairbanks, AK	99709-3430	907-474-0958	479-2104	7-12	Linda Evans
Midnight Sun Family Learning Center	7275 W Midnight Sun Cir	Wasilla, AK	99654	907-357-6786	373-6786	K-8	John Weetman
Rilke Schule German Schl of Arts & Sci	2511 Sentry Dr Ste 100	Anchorage, AK	99507-4469	907-742-7455	742-7456	K-8	Dean Ball
Soldotna Montessori Charter S	162 E Park Ave	Soldotna, AK	99669-7552	907-260-9221	260-9032	K-6	Mary Jo Sanders
Star of the North Secondary S	2945 Monk Ct	North Pole, AK	99705-6129	907-490-9025	490-9021	7-12	Bao Do
Tongass S of Arts & Sciences	410 Schoenbar Rd Ste 202	Ketchikan, AK	99901-6218	907-225-5720	225-8822	PK-6	Marion Gonzales
Twindly-Bridge Charter S	141 E Seldon Rd Ste C	Wasilla, AK	99654-3358	907-376-6680	746-6683	K-12	Gerald Finkler
Watershed S	4975 Decathlon Ave	Fairbanks, AK	99709-4514	907-374-9350	374-9360	K-8	John Carlson
Winterberry Charter S	4802 Bryn Mawr Ct	Anchorage, AK	99508-4720	907-742-0139		K-8	Shanna Mall
Arizona							
AAEC - Estrella Mountain HS	3400 N Dysart Rd	Avondale, AZ	85392-1003	623-535-0754	535-1210	9-12	Mona Ramirez Ed.D.
AAEC - Paradise Valley	17811 N 32nd St	Phoenix, AZ	85032-1201	602-569-1101	243-8001	9-12	Dennis Gray
AAEC - Prescott Valley	7500 E Civic Cir	Prescott Valley, AZ	86314-6800	928-775-3200		9-12	C.J. Williams
AAEC - Red Mountain	2165 N Power Rd	Mesa, AZ	85215-2971	480-854-1504	854-3564	9-12	Dr. C. Ybarra
AAEC - South Mountain	2002 E Baseline Rd	Phoenix, AZ	85042-6906	602-323-9890		9-12	Linda LaFontain
Acacia ES	12955 E Colossal Cave Rd	Vail, AZ	85641-9091	520-879-2200	879-2201	K-5	Jerry Wood
Academy Adventures Midtown ES	3025 N Winstel Blvd	Tucson, AZ	85716-1740	520-777-3757	207-6489	K-5	John Penczar
Academy Adventures PS	3902 N Flowing Wells Rd	Tucson, AZ	85705-2403	520-407-1200	407-1201	K-5	Mindy Griffith
Academy Del Sol - Hope	6740 S Santa Clara Ave	Tucson, AZ	85756-6450	520-325-2800	325-2811	K-8	Jason Riegert
Academy Del Sol - Midtown	4525 E Broadway Blvd	Tucson, AZ	85711-3509	520-325-2800	325-2812	K-8	Jason Riegert
Academy Del Sol - Star Valley	7102 W Valley Crest Pl	Tucson, AZ	85705	520-325-2800		K-8	Jason Reigert
Academy of Building Industries	1547 E Lipan Blvd	Fort Mohave, AZ	86426-6031	928-788-2601	788-2610	9-12	Jean Thomas
Academy of Excellence	425 N 36th St	Phoenix, AZ	85008-6303	602-389-4271	389-4278	K-8	Dr. Eula Dean
Academy of Math & Science	1557 W Prince Rd	Tucson, AZ	85705-3023	520-293-2676	888-1732	K-12	Tatyana Chayka
Academy of Tucson ES	9209 E Wrightstown Rd	Tucson, AZ	85715-5514	520-886-6076	886-6575	K-5	David Allardice
Academy of Tucson HS	10720 E 22nd St	Tucson, AZ	85748-7029	520-733-0096	733-0097	9-12	Jose Garcia
Academy of Tucson MS	7310 E 22nd St	Tucson, AZ	85710-6427	520-749-1413	749-2824	6-8	Larry Speta
Academy With Community Partners	433 N Hall	Mesa, AZ	85203-7407	480-833-0068	833-8966	9-12	Margaret Williamson
Accelerated Learning Center	4105 E Shea Blvd	Phoenix, AZ	85028-3525	602-485-0309	485-9356	9-12	Frank Canady Ed.D.
Accelerated Learning Center Laboratory	5245 N Camino De Oeste	Tucson, AZ	85745-8925	520-743-2256	743-2417	K-12	David Jones
Accelerated Learning Charter S	320 S Main St	Cottonwood, AZ	86326-3905	928-634-0650	634-0672	K-8	Susan Pluff
ACCLAIM Academy	7624 W Indian School Rd	Phoenix, AZ	85033-3009	623-691-0919	691-6091	K-8	Melanie Powers
ACE Charter HS	1929 N Stone Ave	Tucson, AZ	85705-5642	520-623-5843	701-0803	9-12	Arnold Palacios
ACE Charter HS - South	1915 E 36th St	Tucson, AZ	85713-3810	520-628-8316	628-2820	9-12	Arnold Palacios
A Child's View S	2846 W Drexel Rd Ste 100	Tucson, AZ	85746-3824	520-578-2075	578-2076	K-5	Dona Jones
Acorn Montessori Charter S	8556 E Loos Dr	Prescott Valley, AZ	86314-6455	928-772-5778	775-8654	2-8	Cynthia Johnson
Acorn Montessori Charter S - West	7555 E Long Look Dr	Prescott Valley, AZ	86314-5507	928-775-0238	775-8654	PK-1	Dawn Grantham
Adams Traditional Academy	2323 W Parkside Ln	Phoenix, AZ	85027-1256	602-938-5517	938-1179	K-8	Sharon Malone
Adventure S	5757 E Pima St	Tucson, AZ	85712-5609	520-296-0656	721-4472	K-5	Maryann Penczar
All Aboard Charter S	5827 N 35th Ave	Phoenix, AZ	85017-1915	602-433-0500	973-8208	K-5	Rhonda Newton
Allsport Academy	6211 E Speedway Blvd	Tucson, AZ	85712-5128	520-731-2150	731-2160	5-9	Moses Montoya
Alta Vista Charter HS	5040 S Campbell Ave	Tucson, AZ	85706-1510	520-294-4922	294-4933	9-12	Alicia Alvarez
Ambassador Academy	3820 E Ray Rd Ste 8	Phoenix, AZ	85044-7159	480-961-2214	993-3222	K-5	Dr. Elba Reyes
American Heritage Academy	2030 E Cherry St	Cottonwood, AZ	86326-6963	928-634-2144	634-9053	K-12	Ron Miller
American Heritage Academy	132 W General Crook Trl	Camp Verde, AZ	86322-8575	928-567-0462	567-0464	K-8	Colleen Kerr
American Leadership Academy	23908 S Hawes Rd	Queen Creek, AZ	85142-9505	480-987-4500	882-1330	9-12	Richard Morley
American Leadership Academy	3155 S San Tan Village Pkwy	Gilbert, AZ	85295-0857	480-988-3204	988-3280	K-8	Robert Brown
Amerischools Academy - Camelback	1333 W Camelback Rd	Phoenix, AZ	85013-2106	602-532-0100	532-9964	K-8	Alejandra Abrams
Amerischools Academy - Country Club	1150 N Country Club Rd	Tucson, AZ	85716-3942	520-620-1100	624-4376	K-8	Jordan Krause
Amerischools Academy - Yuma	2098 S 3rd Ave	Yuma, AZ	85364-6425	928-329-1100	329-9177	K-8	Ashley Fox
Amerischools Academy - Yuma North	1220 S 4th Ave	Yuma, AZ	85364-4624	928-919-7203	919-7205	K-6	Bill Wachunas
Anthem Preparatory Academy	42101 N 41st Dr	Anthem, AZ	85086-3816	623-465-4776	465-4832	3-11	Bryan Smith
Apache Trail HS	945 W Apache Trl	Apache Junction, AZ	85120-5409	480-288-0337	288-0340	9-12	Greg Garland
Archway Classical Academy - Anthem	42112 N 41st Dr Ste 10	Anthem, AZ	85086	623-465-4776	465-4832	3-11	Bryan Smith
Archway Classical Academy - Chandler	1951 N Alma School Rd	Chandler, AZ	85224-2840	480-855-6474	855-7475	K-5	Leanne Fawcett
Archway Classical Academy - N Phoenix	13613 N Cave Creek Rd Ste C	Phoenix, AZ	85022-5137	602-996-4355	889-0187	K-5	Kevin Topper
Archway Classical Academy - Scottsdale	7496 E Tierra Buena Ln	Scottsdale, AZ	85260-1613	480-776-0413	889-7014	K-4	Robby Kuhlman
Archway Classical Academy - Trivium	14130 W McDowell Rd	Goodyear, AZ	85395-2514	623-414-4883	889-6286	K-5	Dave Beskar
Archway Classical Academy - Veritas	3102 N 56th St Ste 100	Phoenix, AZ	85018-6606	602-263-1128	263-7997	K-5	Erik Twist
Arizona Academy of Leadership - South	PO Box 22046	Tucson, AZ	85734-2046	520-887-5863	887-5869	K-7	Kelvin Strozier
Arizona Academy of Science & Technology	1875 N Central Ave	Phoenix, AZ	85004-1507	602-253-1199	595-8693	K-8	Joan Miller
AZ Call-A-Teen Center of Excellence	649 N 6th Ave	Phoenix, AZ	85003-1659	602-252-6721	252-2952	9-12	
Arizona Charter Academy	16011 N Dysart Rd	Surprise, AZ	85374-4062	623-974-4959	974-4931	K-12	Heather Henderson
Arizona College Prep Academy	7444 E Broadway Blvd	Tucson, AZ	85710-1411	520-722-1200	722-0052	K-8	Charlene Mendoza
AZ Compass Prep S	2020 N Arizona Ave	Chandler, AZ	85225	480-779-2000	779-2100	7-12	Kellyn Wines
AZ Connections Academy	335 E Germann Rd Ste 140	Gilbert, AZ	85297-2920	480-782-5842	782-5845	K-12	Brian Rosta
AZ Conservatory for Arts & Academics	16454 N 28th Ave	Phoenix, AZ	85053-7534	623-878-0986	776-7956	K-5	Christopher Lalley
AZ Conservatory for Arts & Academics	2820 W Kelton Ln	Phoenix, AZ	85053-3028	602-266-4278	978-2764	6-12	Christopher Lalley
Arizona School for the Arts	1410 N 3rd St	Phoenix, AZ	85004-1608	602-257-1444	252-7795	5-12	Dr. Leah Roberts
Arizona Virtual Academy	99 E Virginia Ave Ste 200	Phoenix, AZ	85004-1195	866-339-4946	595-6874	K-12	Cindy Carter
Arts Academy at Estrella Mountain	2504 S 91st Ave	Tolleson, AZ	85353-8921	623-474-2120	936-5337	PK-8	Kimberly Steele-Haynes
Arts Academy at Scottsdale	7214 E Jenan Dr	Scottsdale, AZ	85260-5416	480-951-3190	998-4029	K-4	Charles Boebinger
ASU Preparatory Academy	735 E Fillmore St	Phoenix, AZ	85006-3324	602-257-4843	257-4852	K-8	
Athlos Traditional Academy	3201 S Gilbert Rd	Chandler, AZ	85286-5193	480-270-5422	237-5780	K-8	Dana Croatt Ed.D.
Avalon ES	1045 S San Marcos Dr	Apache Junction, AZ	85120-6337	480-671-4584	671-4586	K-8	Michael McCord
AZTEC HS	2330 W 28th St	Yuma, AZ	85364-6954	928-314-1900	726-2826	9-12	Linda Munk
BASIS Flagstaff	1700 N Gemini Dr	Flagstaff, AZ	86001-1600	928-774-5502	774-5503	5-11	Kara Kelty
BASIS HS - Tucson	3434 E Broadway Blvd	Tucson, AZ	85716-5406	520-326-3444		8-12	Jason Shorbe
BASIS MS - Tucson	3825 E 2nd St	Tucson, AZ	85716-4368	520-326-6367	326-6359	5-7	Jason Shorbe
BASIS Oro Valley	11155 N Oracle Rd	Oro Valley, AZ	85737-5606	520-308-5220	308-5078	5-12	Sean Aiken
BASIS Peoria	25950 N Lake Pleasant Pkwy	Peoria, AZ	85383-1434	623-215-4920	566-9109	5-11	Ashley Brown
BASIS Phoenix	11850 N 32nd St	Phoenix, AZ	85028-1200	602-595-9870	595-9820	5-10	Petra Pajtas
Basis S - Chandler	1800 E Chandler Blvd	Chandler, AZ	85225-5109	480-907-6072	907-6624	5-11	Stephanie Terrell
BASIS - Scottsdale	11440 N 136th St	Scottsdale, AZ	85259-3812	480-451-7500	451-4555	5-12	Hadley Ruggles M.A.
BASIS Tucson North	5740 E River Rd	Tucson, AZ	85750	520-326-3444		5-10	Julia Toews
Benchmark S	4120 E Acoma Dr	Phoenix, AZ	85032-4753	602-765-3582	765-1932	K-6	Barbara Darroch
Bennett Academy	2930 W Bethany Home Rd	Phoenix, AZ	85017-1615	602-943-1317		K-8	Nancy Bennett
Berean Academy	1169 Colombo Ave	Sierra Vista, AZ	85635-2391	520-459-4113	459-4121	K-12	Mark Bennett
Blueprint HS	670 N Arizona Ave Ste 1	Chandler, AZ	85225-6742	480-892-0235	892-0236	9-12	Anthony Scanio
Bradley Academy of Excellence	16060 W Lower Buckeye Rd	Goodyear, AZ	85338-3633	623-932-9902	932-9904	K-8	
Bright Beginnings MS	2716 N Dobson Rd	Chandler, AZ	85224-1803	480-634-8867		5-8	
Bright Beginnings S	400 N Andersen Blvd	Chandler, AZ	85224-8273	480-821-1404	821-1463	K-4	Karen Edris
Burke Basic S	131 E Southern Ave	Mesa, AZ	85210-5355	480-964-4602	964-6566	K-6	
Calibre Academy	4744 W Grovers Ave	Glendale, AZ	85308-3453	602-439-5026	547-2841	K-8	
Calibre Academy Surprise	15688 W Acoma Dr	Surprise, AZ	85379-5652	623-556-2179	547-2806	K-8	Curtis Gardner
Cambridge Academy - Mesa Campus	9412 E Brown Rd	Mesa, AZ	85207-4338	480-641-2828	325-2365	K-6	Amy Monarrez
Cambridge Academy - Queen Creek	20365 E Ocotillo Rd	Queen Creek, AZ	85142-9584	480-987-3577	987-4281	K-8	Kaylee Gonzalez
Camelback Academy	7634 W Camelback Rd	Glendale, AZ	85303-5627	623-247-2204	247-1113	K-8	Karen Kordon
Candeo Schools	9965 W Calle Lejos	Peoria, AZ	85383-1117	623-979-6500	979-6510	K-6	Stephanie Musser

School	Address	City,State	Zip code	Telephone	Fax	Grade	Contact
Canyon Pointe Academy	4941 W Union Hills Dr	Glendale, AZ	85308-1486	602-896-1166	896-1164	K-6	Amy Rhone
Canyon Rose Academy	3686 W Orange Grove Rd #192	Tucson, AZ	85741	520-797-4884	797-8868	9-12	Michael Baun
Carden of Tucson S	5260 N Royal Palm Dr	Tucson, AZ	85705-1148	520-293-6661	408-7366	K-8	Bette Jeppson
Career Success HS - Duffy Campus	2550 E Jefferson St	Phoenix, AZ	85034-2637	602-393-4200	393-4205	9-12	Lisa Carr
Career Success HS - Main Campus	3816 N 27th Ave	Phoenix, AZ	85017-4703	602-285-5525	285-0026	9-12	Kimberly White-Grundy
Career Success HS - Mesa	1455 S Stapley Dr	Mesa, AZ	85204-5849	480-833-7470	833-7480	9-12	Steve Myers
Career Success JSHS - North Phoenix	2321 E Bell Rd	Phoenix, AZ	85022-2901	602-687-8282	687-8283	7-12	Maureen Racz
Career Success S - Sage Campus	3120 N 32nd St	Phoenix, AZ	85018-6202	602-955-0355	508-0682	K-8	Hector Placencia
Carpe Diem E-Learning Community S	3777 W 22nd Ln	Yuma, AZ	85364-5905	928-317-3113	317-0828	7-12	Rick Ogston
Casa Verde Charter HS	1362 N Casa Grande Ave	Casa Grande, AZ	85122-2648	520-876-0661	876-0667	9-12	James Simmons
Caurus Academy	41900 N 42nd Ave	Anthem, AZ	85086-1595	623-551-5083	551-5679	K-8	Rhonda Rides
Center for Academic Success #1	900 Carmelita Dr	Sierra Vista, AZ	85635-1927	520-458-4200	458-6396	9-12	Stephen Huff
Center for Academic Success #2	510 N G Ave	Douglas, AZ	85607-2822	520-364-2616	417-0973	7-12	Marcela Munguia
Center for Academic Success #3	1415 F Ave	Douglas, AZ	85607-1655	520-805-1558	458-1409	K-4	Marcela Munguia
Center for Academic Success #4	1415 F Ave	Douglas, AZ	85607-1655	520-805-1558	805-1549	5-8	Marcela Munguia
Center for Academic Success #5	900 Carmelita Dr	Sierra Vista, AZ	85635-1927	520-458-4200	458-1409	K-6	Linda Denno
Center for Educational Excellence	1700 E Elliot Rd Ste 9	Tempe, AZ	85284-1631	480-632-1940	632-1398	K-8	Stacey Cochran
Challenge Charter S	5801 W Greenbriar Dr	Glendale, AZ	85308-3847	602-938-5411	938-5393	K-6	Gregory Miller
Challenger Basic S	1315 N Greenfield Rd	Gilbert, AZ	85234-2813	480-830-1750	830-1763	K-6	
Champion Schools	7900 S Jesse Owens Pkwy	Phoenix, AZ	85042-6523	602-341-6527	341-6529	K-8	Carolyn Sawyer
Chandler Preparatory Academy	1951 N Alma School Rd	Chandler, AZ	85224-2840	480-855-5410	855-7789	6-12	Helen Hayes
Children First Academy - Phoenix	374 N 6th Ave	Phoenix, AZ	85003-1510	602-712-0500	712-0506	K-8	Bob Meko
Children First Academy - Tempe	1938 E Apache Blvd	Tempe, AZ	85281-6008	480-557-6211	557-6249	K-8	Dan Cooper
Children Reaching for the Sky Prep	1844 S Alvernon Way	Tucson, AZ	85711-5607	520-790-8400	620-6570	K-5	Lee Griffin
Childrens Success Academy	PO Box 11368	Tucson, AZ	85734-1368	520-799-8403	799-8427	K-8	Nanci Aiken
City HS	PO Box 2608	Tucson, AZ	85702-2608	520-623-7223	547-0680	9-12	Carrie Brennan
Civano Community S	10625 E Drexel Rd	Tucson, AZ	85747-6120	520-879-1700	879-1701	K-5	Connie Erickson
Civano MS	10620 E Drexel Rd	Tucson, AZ	85747-6119	520-879-1704	879-1705	6-8	Connie Erickson
Compass HS	PO Box 17810	Tucson, AZ	85731-7810	520-296-4070	296-4103	9-12	John Ferguson
Concordia Charter S	142 N Date	Mesa, AZ	85201-6419	480-461-0555	461-0556	K-5	Margaret Roush-Meier
Concordia Charter S - Navajo Mission	PO Box 354	Rock Point, AZ	86545-0354	928-659-4201	659-4255	K-6	Margaret Roush-Meier
Copper Canyon Academy	7785 W Peoria Ave	Peoria, AZ	85345-5922	623-930-1734	930-8709	K-8	Paul Taylor
Cornerstone Charter S	7107 N Black Canyon Hwy	Phoenix, AZ	85021-7619	602-595-2198	242-2398	9-12	Casey Weiss
Country Gardens Charter S	6313 W Southern Ave	Laveen, AZ	85339-2916	602-237-3741	237-3892	K-12	Goldie Burge
Crestview College Prep HS	2616 E Greenway Rd	Phoenix, AZ	85032-4320	602-765-8470	765-8471	9-12	Kristin Schaefer
Crown Charter S	PO Box 363	Litchfield Park, AZ	85340-0363	623-535-9300	535-5410	K-6	
Deer Valley Academy	18424 N 51st Ave	Glendale, AZ	85308-1443	602-467-6874	467-6955	9-12	Barbara Dalicandro
Desert Heights Charter S	5821 W Beverly Ln	Glendale, AZ	85306-1801	602-896-2900	467-9540	K-8	Katie Fjell
Desert Hills HS	1515 S Val Vista Dr	Gilbert, AZ	85296-3854	480-813-1151	813-1161	9-12	Art Madden
Desert Marigold S	6210 S 28th St	Phoenix, AZ	85042-4715	602-243-6909	243-6933	K-12	Charles Burkum
Desert Mosaic S	5757 W Ajo Hwy	Tucson, AZ	85735-9334	520-578-2022	578-0834	K-12	Thomas Dean
Desert Pointe Academy	7785 W Peoria Ave	Peoria, AZ	85345-5922	623-930-1734	930-8709	9-12	Jinny Ludwig
Desert Rose Academy	3686 W Orange Grove Rd #192	Tucson, AZ	85741	520-797-4884	797-8868	9-12	John Sills
Desert Sky Community S	1350 N Arcadia Ave	Tucson, AZ	85712-4706	520-745-3888	745-5110	K-5	Shelly Adrian
Desert Springs Academy	10129 E Speedway Blvd	Tucson, AZ	85748-1921	520-321-1709	321-9316	K-8	Mary Spatola
Desert Star Community S	1240 S Recycler Rd	Cornville, AZ	86325-5224	928-282-0171	284-9565	K-8	
Desert Sun Academy	27880 N 64th Street	Scottsdale, AZ	85262	480-575-2900	502-2364	K-6	Donald Wood Ed.D.
Desert View Academy	2363 S Kennedy Ln	Yuma, AZ	85365-2416	928-314-1102	314-1086	K-6	Rick Ogston
Desert Willow ES	4322 E Desert Willow Dr	Phoenix, AZ	85044	480-575-2800	419-7265	PK-6	Mark Culbertson
Destiny S	798 E Prickly Pear Dr	Globe, AZ	85501-2395	928-425-0925	425-0927	K-8	Scott Williamson
Digital Technology Academy	1250 W Continental Rd	Green Valley, AZ	85614	520-219-4383			
DINE Southwest HS	HC 63 Box 303	Winslow, AZ	86047-9424	928-657-3272	657-3272	9-12	Leah Claw
Discovery Plus Academy	PO Box 1089	Pima, AZ	85543-1089	928-485-2498	485-2508	K-6	
Dobson Academy	PO Box 6070	Chandler, AZ	85246-6070	480-855-6325	855-6323	K-8	Dr. Taime Bengochea
Doby MS	8632 W Northern Ave	Glendale, AZ	85305-1308	623-776-2069	878-8175	5-8	
EAGLE College Prep S	2450 W South Mountain Ave	Phoenix, AZ	85041-7601	602-323-5400	323-5401	K-8	
EAGLE Harmony S	2435 E Pecan Rd	Phoenix, AZ	85040-3632	602-885-7333		K-8	
Eastpointe HS	8495 E Broadway Blvd	Tucson, AZ	85710-4009	520-731-8180	731-8179	9-12	Donnie Houston
East Valley Academy	855 W 8th Ave	Mesa, AZ	85210-3401	480-981-2008	641-4473	9-12	Timothy Keilty
Edge Charter S - Himmel Park	2555 E 1st St	Tucson, AZ	85716-4152	520-881-1389	881-0852	9-12	Rob Pecharich
Edge Charter S - Northwest	2555 E 1st St	Tucson, AZ	85716-4152	520-877-9179	881-0852	9-12	Rob Pecharich
Edge Charter S - Sahuarita	15500 S Sahuarita Park Rd	Sahuarita, AZ	85629	520-393-1690	881-1381	9-12	Rob Pecharich
EdOptions HS	2150 E Southern Ave	Tempe, AZ	85282-7504	480-621-3365		9-12	Dr. David Reed
Educational Opportunity Center	3818 W 16th St	Yuma, AZ	85364-4107	928-329-0990	783-0886	9-12	Brian Grossenburg
EduPreneurship Student Center	7801 N 27th Ave	Phoenix, AZ	85051-6675	602-973-8998	973-5510	K-8	Deborah Salas
Edu-Prize S	4567 W Roberts Rd	Queen Creek, AZ	85142-7511	480-888-1610		1-6	
Edu-Prize S	580 W Melody Ave	Gilbert, AZ	85233-1418	480-813-9537	813-6742	K-8	Dr. Robbie McCamman
E-Institute at Avondale	1035 E Van Buren St	Avondale, AZ	85323-1552	623-760-9061	760-9068	9-12	Patricia Dowd
E-Institute at Metro	9201 N 29th Ave	Phoenix, AZ	85051-3468	602-439-5026	889-0351	9-12	Eric Luthi
E-Institute at Surprise	16578 W Greenway Rd Ste 204	Surprise, AZ	85388-2184	623-556-2179	547-2841	9-12	J.D. Corey
E-Institute Charter HS at Grovers	4744 W Grovers Ave	Glendale, AZ	85308-3453	602-621-4398	889-0351	11-12	Charlene Shores
E-Institute HS at Buckeye	6213 S Miller Rd	Buckeye, AZ	85326-1256	623-505-7118	505-3594	9-12	Tisha Jones
El Dorado HS	2200 N Arizona Ave Ste 17	Chandler, AZ	85225-3452	480-726-9536	726-9543	9-12	Dave Miller
Empower College Prep	5757 N Central Ave	Phoenix, AZ	85012-1315	602-283-5720		9-12	Brian Holman
Esperanza Community Collegial Academy	2507 E Bell Rd	Phoenix, AZ	85032-2413	602-996-1125	996-4238	9-12	Sylvia Herrera
Esperanza Montessori Academy	4848 S 2nd St	Phoenix, AZ	85040-2122	602-243-7788	243-7799	K-3	Adrian Ruiz
Estrella HS	510 N Central Ave	Avondale, AZ	85323-1909	623-932-6561	932-1263	9-12	Casey Zordani
Excalibur Charter S	1045 S San Marcos Dr	Apache Junction, AZ	85120-6337	480-671-4584	671-4586	9-12	M. Sheen
Flagstaff Arts and Leadership Academy	3401 N Fort Valley Rd	Flagstaff, AZ	86001-8388	928-779-7223	779-7041	7-12	Becky Daggett
Flagstaff Junior Academy	306 W Cedar Ave	Flagstaff, AZ	86001-1413	928-774-6007	774-7268	PK-8	Jen Conway
Foothills Academy	7191 E Ashler Hills Dr	Scottsdale, AZ	85266-9300	480-488-5583	488-6902	K-12	Dr. Donald Senneville
Fountain Hills Charter S	PO Box 18419	Fountain Hills, AZ	85269-8419	480-837-0046	837-0024	K-8	Michael Bashaw
Franklin Charter S	320 E Warner Rd	Gilbert, AZ	85296-2976	480-632-0722	632-8716	PK-6	Terry Nicoll
Franklin Charter S	21151 S Crismon Rd	Queen Creek, AZ	85142-8957	480-987-0722	987-3517	PK-6	Mark Mcafee
Franklin Charter S	2345 N Horne	Mesa, AZ	85203-1823	480-649-0712	649-8716	PK-6	Rebekah Baker
Franklin Charter S	22951 S Power Rd	Queen Creek, AZ	85142-4500	480-677-8400	677-8555	PK-8	Thomas Lee
Franklin Phonetic S	6116 E State Route 69	Prescott Valley, AZ	86314-2806	928-775-6747	775-6740	K-8	Kristen Goode
Freedom Academy North	28700 N Pima Rd	Scottsdale, AZ	85266-9008	602-424-0771	424-0773	K-6	Barbara Guenther
Freedom Academy South	15014 N 56th St Ste 1	Scottsdale, AZ	85254-2407	602-424-0771	424-0773	K-8	Linda Hoffman
Freire Freedom S	300 E University Blvd	Tucson, AZ	85705-7899	520-906-7552	624-7518	6-8	JoAnn Groh
Friendly House Academia Del Pueblo S	201 E Durango St	Phoenix, AZ	85004-2913	602-258-4353	416-7375	K-8	Ed Hendricks
Future Investment MS	1854 S Alvernon Way	Tucson, AZ	85711-5607	520-747-3733	745-2848	6-8	
GateWay Early College HS	108 N 40th St	Phoenix, AZ	85034-1795	602-286-8762	286-8752	9-12	Lisa Smith
GEM Charter S	1704 N Center St	Mesa, AZ	85201-2223	480-833-2622	833-2655	K-6	Nelleke van Savooyen
Genesis Academy	525 E McDowell Rd	Phoenix, AZ	85004-1537	602-254-8090	254-8094	9-12	Karen Callahan
Gilbert Arts Academy	862 E Elliot Rd	Gilbert, AZ	85234-6912	480-325-6100	632-2077	K-6	Cathie Hirsch
Gilbert Early College HS	415 N Gilbert Rd	Gilbert, AZ	85234-4702	480-545-8011	558-7038	7-12	Vicky Hallam
Girls Leadership Academy	715 W Mariposa St	Phoenix, AZ	85013-2449	602-274-7318	274-7549	6-12	Pam Duty
Glendale Preparatory Academy	7151 W Beardsley Rd	Glendale, AZ	85308-5643	623-889-0822	889-0825	6-11	David Williams
Glendale Preparatory Academy	7201 W Beardsley Rd	Glendale, AZ	85308-5673	602-889-0822	889-0825	6-12	David Williams
Grand Canyon College Prep Charter S	5301 S McClintock Dr	Tempe, AZ	85283-2234	480-233-3622	491-7096	6-12	David Gordon
Great Expectations Academy	1466 W Camino Antigua	Sahuarita, AZ	85629-9720	520-399-2121	399-2123	K-8	Mark Phillips
Greenhouse Charter S	3335 E Baseline Rd	Gilbert, AZ	85234-2633	480-635-0386		PK-2	
Guerrero MS	2797 N Introspect Dr	Tucson, AZ	85745	520-807-5892	807-2120	3-8	Richard Montano
Ha:San Prep & Leadership Charter S	1333 E 10th St	Tucson, AZ	85719-5808	520-882-8826	882-8651	9-12	Robin Kauakahi
Happy Valley S	7140 W Happy Valley Rd	Peoria, AZ	85383-3255	623-376-2900	376-9030	K-6	Roger McCurley
Happy Valley S East	22721 S Ellsworth Rd	Queen Creek, AZ	85142-7577	480-560-5540		K-6	
Harvest Preparatory Academy	350 E 18th St	Yuma, AZ	85364-5723	928-782-2052	819-5976	K-12	Deborah Ybarra
Harvest Preparatory Academy - San Luis	1044 N 10th Ave	San Luis, AZ	85349	928-782-2052	819-5976	K-5	Alicia Schroeder
Havasu Preparatory Academy	3155 Maricopa Ave	Lk Havasu Cty, AZ	86406-8635	928-854-4011		K-8	Julia Angel
Haven Montessori S	621 W Clay Ave	Flagstaff, AZ	86001-6221	928-522-0985	774-7412	K-K	Elisa McKnight
Hayes HS	PO Box 10899	Bapchule, AZ	85121-0105	520-315-5100	315-5115	9-12	Dr. Wendy Ong
Hearn Academy	17606 N 7th Ave	Phoenix, AZ	85023-1567	602-896-9160	896-1997	K-8	Gaye Leo
Heritage Academy	32 S Center St	Mesa, AZ	85210-1306	480-969-5641	969-6972	7-12	Earl Taylor
Heritage ES	6805 N 125th Ave	Glendale, AZ	85307-2402	623-935-1909	935-1931	K-8	Justin Dye
Heritage ES - Williams Campus	790 E Rodeo Rd	Williams, AZ	86046-9653	928-635-3998	635-3999	K-5	Kaytie Thies
Hermosa Montessori Charter S	12051 E Fort Lowell Rd	Tucson, AZ	85749-9702	520-749-5518	749-6087	K-8	Sheila Stolov
Hiaki HS	4747 W Calle Vicam	Tucson, AZ	85757-8860	520-883-5051		9-12	Theresa Carino
Highland Free S	510 S Highland Ave	Tucson, AZ	85719-6427	520-623-0104	903-1318	K-6	Nicholas Sofka
Hillcrest Academy	4710 E Baseline Rd	Mesa, AZ	85206-4602	480-325-8950	452-0911	K-8	
Holsteiner Agricultural S	44400 W Honeycutt Rd	Maricopa, AZ	85138-2944	520-568-8620		K-6	Tanya Graysmark
Hope HS	7620 W Lower Buckeye Rd	Phoenix, AZ	85043	623-772-8013	772-8021	9-12	Jennifer Blackstone
Hope HS Online	5651 W Talavi Blvd Ste 170	Glendale, AZ	85306-1893	602-674-8344	943-9700	7-12	Jennifer Blackstone
Horizon Community Learning Center	16233 S 48th St	Phoenix, AZ	85048-0801	480-659-3000	659-3022	K-12	Betsy Fera
Horseshoe Trails ES	5405 E Pinnacle Vista Dr	Phoenix, AZ	85085	480-272-8500	907-6643	PK-6	Janiene Marlow
Humanities & Sciences Academy	1105 E Broadway Rd	Tempe, AZ	85282-1505	480-317-5900	829-4999	9-12	Michael Curd
Humanities & Sciences Institute	5201 N 7th St	Phoenix, AZ	85014-2802	602-650-1333	650-1881	9-12	Sue Durkin

School	Address	City,State	Zip code	Telephone	Fax	Grade	Contact
Imagine Avondale ES	950 N Eliseo Felix Jr Way	Avondale, AZ	85323-1202	602-344-1730	344-1740	PK-8	Kim Agnew
Imagine Charter S at Bell Canyon	18052 N Black Canyon Hwy	Phoenix, AZ	85053-1715	602-547-7920	547-7923	K-8	Dr. Lynnette Harris-Scott
Imagine Charter S at Camelback	5050 N 19th Ave	Phoenix, AZ	85015-3205	602-344-4620	344-4630	K-8	Freddie Villalon
Imagine Charter S at Cortez Park	3535 W Dunlap Ave	Phoenix, AZ	85051-5303	602-589-9840	589-9841	K-8	Jason Archuleta
Imagine Charter S at Desert West	6738 W McDowell Rd	Phoenix, AZ	85035-4642	602-344-7150	344-7160	K-8	Bill Heintz
Imagine Charter S at East Mesa	9701 E Southern Ave	Mesa, AZ	85209-3769	480-355-6830	355-6840	K-9	April Blatzheim
Imagine Charter S at Rosefield	12050 N Bullard Ave	Surprise, AZ	85379-6325	623-344-4300	344-4310	K-8	James Mecca
Imagine Charter S at Tempe	1538 E Southern Ave	Tempe, AZ	85282-5687	480-355-1640	355-1650	K-6	Stacey Boyd
Imagine Charter S at West Gilbert	2061 S Gilbert Rd	Gilbert, AZ	85295-4620	480-855-2700	855-2701	K-8	Linda Horner
Imagine Coolidge ES	1290 W Vah Ki Inn Rd	Coolidge, AZ	85128-9314	520-723-5391	723-5491	K-8	Michele Stout
Imagine Prep at Surprise	14850 N 156th Ave	Surprise, AZ	85379-5653	623-344-1770	214-1083	7-12	Chris McComb
Imagine Prep - Superstition	1843 W 16th Ave	Apache Junction, AZ	85120-6967	480-355-0530	355-0540	6-12	Kerry Clark
Imagine Sierra Vista S	1000 E Wilcox Dr	Sierra Vista, AZ	85635-2622	520-224-2500	224-2511	K-8	Dr. David Snyder
Integrity Education Centre	515 E Continental Dr	Scottsdale, AZ	85257	480-731-4829	945-2008	K-12	Holly Mullan
Intelli School - Glendale	13806 N 51st Ave	Glendale, AZ	85306-4834	602-564-7210	564-7301	9-12	Patricia Shaw
Intelli School - Main	1727 N Arizona Ave Ste 5	Chandler, AZ	85225-7084	480-855-5318	855-5904	9-12	Jonathan Owen
Intelli School - Metro Center	3327 W Peoria Ave	Phoenix, AZ	85029-4605	602-564-7240	564-7241	9-12	Patricia Shaw
Intelli School - Paradise Valley	1427 E Bell Rd Ste 102	Phoenix, AZ	85022-2712	602-564-7280	564-7281	9-12	Patricia Shaw
International Commerce Institute	5201 N 7th St	Phoenix, AZ	85014-2802	602-650-1116	650-1881	9-12	Sue Durkin
International Commerce Institute - Tempe	1105 E Broadway Rd	Tempe, AZ	85282-1505	480-317-5900	829-4999	9-12	Ana Kennedy
International Commerce Institute-Tsaile	1 Circle Dr	Tsaile, AZ	86556-9998	800-762-0010	650-1777	9-12	
iSchool 2020	3777 W 22nd Ln	Yuma, AZ	85364-5905	928-317-3113	783-3473	9-12	Ryan Hackmann
Jefferson Academy of Advanced Learning	40 S 11th St	Show Low, AZ	85901-6001	928-537-5432	537-0440	K-12	Sandy Stewart
Kestrel HS	325 N Washington Ave	Prescott, AZ	86301-2639	928-541-1090	541-9939	9-12	Jana Truman
Keystone Montessori Charter S	1025 E Liberty Ln	Phoenix, AZ	85048-8462	480-460-7312	283-8402	K-9	Sherri Sampson
Khalsa Montessori S	2536 N 3rd St	Phoenix, AZ	85004-1308	602-252-3759	252-1890	K-6	Keerat Giordano
Khalsa Montessori S	3701 E River Rd	Tucson, AZ	85718-6633	520-529-3611	615-0625	K-8	Keerat Giordano
Kingman Academy of Learning HS	3420 N Burbank St	Kingman, AZ	86409-3105	928-681-2900	681-2424	9-12	Jeff Martin
Kingman Academy of Learning IS	3419 Harrison St	Kingman, AZ	86409-3604	928-681-3200	681-2424	3-5	Dean Colvig
Kingman Academy of Learning MS	3269 Harrison St	Kingman, AZ	86409-3679	928-692-5265	681-2424	6-8	Dawn Day
Kingman Academy of Learning PS	3400 N Burbank St	Kingman, AZ	86409-3105	928-692-2500	692-2505	K-2	Trudi Bradley
La Paloma Academy	2050 N Wilmot Rd	Tucson, AZ	85712-3039	520-721-4205	721-4263	K-8	Raena Janes
La Paloma Academy - Lakeside	8140 E Golf Links Rd	Tucson, AZ	85730-1229	520-733-7373	733-7392	K-8	Steve Leininger
La Paloma Academy South	5660 S 12th Ave	Tucson, AZ	85706-3102	520-807-9668		K-8	Paul Bummer
La Puerta HS	5757 W McDowell Rd	Phoenix, AZ	85035-4947	623-878-8059	878-8175	9-12	Jimmie Daniels
La Tierra Community S	124 N Virginia St	Prescott Valley, AZ	86314	928-445-5100		K-6	Jennifer Roderick
Leading Edge Academy	415 N Gilbert Rd Ste 102	Gilbert, AZ	85234-4703	480-545-8011	558-7038	K-12	Victoria Hallam
Leading Edge Academy at East Mesa	10115 E University Dr	Mesa, AZ	85207-7210	480-984-5645	627-3634	K-6	Derrick Jamerson
Leading Edge Academy -ES	919 E Guadalupe Rd	Gilbert, AZ	85234-4705	480-545-6646		K-5	Arnie Ziegler
Leading Edge Academy - Maricopa	18700 N Porter Rd	Maricopa, AZ	85138-4220	520-568-7800		K-6	Mathew Reese
Leading Edge Academy - Queen Creek	4815 W Hunt Hwy	Queen Creek, AZ	85142-3271	480-655-6787	655-6788	K-12	Dr. Jonathan Johnson
Learning Foundation & Performing Arts	5761 E Brown Rd	Mesa, AZ	85205-4400	480-807-1100	807-1190	K-12	Nicki Triggs
Learning Foundation & Performing Arts S	1120 S Gilbert Rd	Gilbert, AZ	85296-3465	480-635-9400	635-1907	K-12	Robert Villa
Learning Foundation Performing Arts S	851 N Stapley Dr	Mesa, AZ	85203-5644	480-834-6202	834-3991	K-12	Jeannine Rucker
Legacy S	7618 E University Dr	Mesa, AZ	85207-6601	480-981-1500	641-4473	K-8	Isaac Perez
Legacy Traditional S	17760 Regent Dr	Maricopa, AZ	85138-7804	520-423-9999	423-9997	K-8	Nicole Mangum
Legacy Traditional S - Avondale Campus	12320 W Van Buren St	Avondale, AZ	85323-5238	623-344-0330	932-7848	K-8	Kristen Smith M.Ed.
Legacy Traditional S - Casa Grande	1274 E ONeil Dr	Casa Grande, AZ	85122	520-421-2323	421-4443	K-8	Jennifer Hackett M.Ed.
Legacy Traditional S - Laveen Campus	7900 S 43rd Ave	Laveen, AZ	85339-3023	623-344-0472	237-0477	K-8	Kimberly Allison M.Ed.
Legacy Traditional S - Maricopa	17760 Regent Dr	Maricopa, AZ	85138-7804	520-423-9999	423-9997	K-8	Nicole Mangum M.Ed.
Legacy Traditional S - Northwest Tucson	3500 W Cortaro Farms Rd	Tucson, AZ	85742-7808	520-505-3640	579-6833	K-8	Christine Fitzsimmons
Legacy Traditional S - Queen Creek	41800 N Barnes Pkwy	San Tan Valley, AZ	85140-6638	480-655-5553	655-5558	K-8	Claudia McKim M.Ed.
Liberty Arts Academy	3015 S Power Rd	Mesa, AZ	85212-3000	480-830-3444	830-4335	K-6	Cheri Wasiel
Liberty HS	PO Box 2343	Globe, AZ	85502-2343	928-402-8024	402-8358	9-12	Colleen DeRose
Liberty Traditional Charter S	4027 N 45th Ave	Phoenix, AZ	85031-2840	602-442-8791	353-9270	K-8	Raena Janes
Liberty Traditonal S - Saddleback	3715 N Washington Ave	Douglas, AZ	85607-3602	520-364-6311		K-4	Raena Janes
Lifelong Learning Academy	3295 W Orange Grove Rd	Tucson, AZ	85741-2937	520-219-4383	544-0220	K-8	Mary Lou Klem
Life Skills Center of Arizona	8123 N 35th Ave Ste 2	Phoenix, AZ	85051-9403	602-242-6400	242-6823	9-12	
Lone Mountain ES	PO Box 426	Cave Creek, AZ	85327-0426	480-437-3000	595-1312	K-6	Nancy Shaver
Luz Guerrero Early College	2797 N Introspect Dr	Tucson, AZ	85745	520-807-5892	623-9291	9-12	Ricardo Robles
Madison Preparatory S	5815 S Mcclintock Dr	Tempe, AZ	85283-3227	480-345-2306	345-0050	7-12	Paul Grant
Maryvale Preparatory Academy	6301 W Indian School Rd	Phoenix, AZ	85033-3326	602-247-6095	889-6282	K-3	Mac Esau
Masada Charter S	PO Box 2277	Colorado City, AZ	86021-2277	928-875-2525	875-2526	K-9	Le Anne Timpson
Math & Science Success Academy	434 W Lerdo Rd	Tucson, AZ	85756-6655	520-751-2783	888-1732	K-12	Adriana Rodriguez
Maya HS	3660 W Glendale Ave	Phoenix, AZ	85051-8335	602-242-3442	242-5255	9-12	John Anderson
Mesa Arts Academy	221 W 6th Ave	Mesa, AZ	85210-2446	480-844-3965	844-0205	K-8	David Crummey
Mesa Preparatory Academy	1303 S Lindsay Rd	Mesa, AZ	85204-6228	480-222-4233	222-4234	6-12	Robert Wagner
Mesquite ES	9455 E Rita Rd	Tucson, AZ	85747-6300	520-879-2100	879-2101	K-5	Katie Dabney
Metropolitan Arts Institute	1700 N 7th Ave Ste 100	Phoenix, AZ	85007-1760	602-258-9500	258-9504	9-12	Matthew Baker
Mexicayotl Charter S	338 N Morley Ave	Nogales, AZ	85621-2801	520-287-6790	287-0037	K-8	Baltizar Garcia
Midtown HS	7318 W Lynwood St	Phoenix, AZ	85035-4542	623-936-8682	936-8559	9-12	
Midtown PS	4735 N 19th Ave	Phoenix, AZ	85015-3725	602-265-5133	604-2337	K-5	Judy White
Milestones Charter S	4707 E Robert E Lee St	Phoenix, AZ	85032-9529	602-404-1009	404-5456	K-8	Tara Cabardo
Mingus Springs Charter S	3600 Sunset Dr	Chino Valley, AZ	86323-5054	928-636-4766	636-5149	K-8	Dawn Gonzales
Mission Academy HS	4301 W Fillmore St	Phoenix, AZ	85043-2908	602-944-2097	944-0252	9-12	
Mission Charter S	1118 W Glendale Ave	Phoenix, AZ	85021-8635	602-943-4986	943-5936	K-8	Jayne Shaw
Mission Heights Prep HS	1376 E Cottonwood Ln	Casa Grande, AZ	85122-2971	520-836-9383		9-12	Matthew Chesney
Mission Montessori Academy	12990 E Shea Blvd	Scottsdale, AZ	85259-5305	480-860-4330	657-3715	K-7	
Mohave Accelerated ES	625 Marina Blvd	Bullhead City, AZ	86442-5414	928-704-9345	704-4977	K-5	Casey Mulligan
Mohave Accelerated ES East	2850 Silver Creek Rd	Bullhead City, AZ	86442-8309	928-704-9345	704-4977	K-5	Casey Mulligan
Mohave Accelerated Learning Center	PO Box 21288	Bullhead City, AZ	86439-1288	928-704-9345	704-4977	6-12	Vickie Christensen
Montage Academy	32619 N Scottsdale Rd	Scottsdale, AZ	85266-1521	480-488-0215	488-0241	K-8	
Montessori Academy	6050 N Invergordon Rd	Paradise Valley, AZ	85253-5248	480-945-1121	874-2928	K-8	Juli Newman
Montessori Charter S of Flagstaff	850 N Locust St	Flagstaff, AZ	86001-3343	928-226-1212	774-0337	K-8	Marina Smith
Montessori Childrens House	2400 W Datsi St	Camp Verde, AZ	86322-8412	928-567-1878	567-2107	K-K	Janet Taylor
Montessori Day Charter S - Mountainside	9215 N 14th St	Phoenix, AZ	85020-2713	602-943-7672	395-0271	K-8	Pat Freeman
Montessori Day S - Chandler Lakeshore	1700 W Warner Rd	Chandler, AZ	85224-2676	480-730-8886	730-9072	K-8	Theresa Averill
Montessori de Santa Cruz Charter S	PO Box 4706	Tubac, AZ	85646-4706	520-398-0536	398-0776	K-8	
Montessori Education Center Charter S	2834 E Southern Ave	Mesa, AZ	85204-5517	480-926-8375	503-0515	PK-6	
Montessori Education Ctr - Charter S N	815 N Gilbert Rd	Mesa, AZ	85203-5805	480-964-1381	668-5457	PK-10	
Montessori House Charter S	2415 N Terrace Cir	Mesa, AZ	85203-1220	480-464-2800	464-2836	K-6	Sheryl Richardson
Montessori Schoolhouse	1301 E Fort Lowell Rd	Tucson, AZ	85719-2239	520-319-8668	881-4096	K-5	Michael Ebner
Mosaica Prepatory Academy of Chandler	5835 W Ray Rd	Chandler, AZ	85226-1800	480-763-5101	763-5107	K-9	Howard Brown
Mountain Oak Charter S	1455 Willow Creek Rd	Prescott, AZ	86301-1438	928-541-7700	445-1301	K-8	Cynthia Roe
Mountain Rose Academy	3686 W Orange Grove Rd #192	Tucson, AZ	85741	520-797-4884	797-8868	9-12	Chari Taber
Mountain S	311 W Cattle Drive Trl	Flagstaff, AZ	86005-7060	928-779-2392	773-3246	K-6	Renee Fauset
Mt. Turnbull Academy	PO Box 28	Fort Thomas, AZ	85536-0028	928-475-3050	475-3051	9-12	Jayson Stanley
New Destiny Leadership Charter S	2454 E Broadway Rd	Phoenix, AZ	85040-2622	602-268-2234	268-1622	K-5	
New Horizon S for the Performing Arts	446 E Broadway Rd	Mesa, AZ	85204-2020	480-655-7444	655-8220	K-6	Jim Wyler
New School for the Arts	1216 E Apache Blvd	Tempe, AZ	85281-6005	480-481-9235	970-6625	6-12	Katy Cardenas
Newton Montessori & Charter S	PO Box 2166	Camp Verde, AZ	86322-2166	928-567-2363	567-5374	PK-5	Loretta Donovan
New Visions Academy	125 S 6th St	Cottonwood, AZ	86326-4239	928-634-7320	634-7494	9-12	Ann Shaw
New Visions Academy - St. John's Campus	PO Box 791	Saint Johns, AZ	85936-0791	928-337-3268	337-3383	9-12	Ann Shaq
New Visions Academy - Star Valley S	166 Ezell Ln	Payson, AZ	85541	928-468-1401	468-1402	9-12	
New West S	98 N Oak Dr	Benson, AZ	85602-7732	520-586-1976	586-1655	K-8	Michael Payton
New World Educational Center Charter S	5818 N 7th St	Phoenix, AZ	85014-5806	602-238-9577	238-9210	K-12	Jesus Armenta
NFL YET College Prep Academy	4848 S 2nd St	Phoenix, AZ	85040-2122	602-243-7788	243-7799	7-12	
Northern AZ Academy for Career Dev.	PO Box 125	Taylor, AZ	85939-0125	928-536-4222	536-4441	9-12	Cindy Johnson
Northern AZ Academy for Career Dev.	502 Airport Rd	Winslow, AZ	86047-5400	928-289-3329	289-4485	9-12	Thomas Drumm
Northland Preparatory Academy	3300 E Sparrow Ave	Flagstaff, AZ	86004-6703	928-214-8776	214-8778	7-12	Bob Lombardi
North Phoenix Preparatory Academy	13613 N Cave Creek Rd Ste F	Phoenix, AZ	85022-5137	602-996-4355	889-0161	6-9	David Denton
North Pointe Preparatory S	10215 N 43rd Ave	Phoenix, AZ	85051-1025	623-209-0017	209-0021	7-12	Richard Gow
Northpoint Expeditionary Learning Acad	551 1st St	Prescott, AZ	86301-2599	928-717-3272	717-2316	9-12	Geneva Saint-Amour
North Star Charter S	10720 W Indian School Rd	Phoenix, AZ	85037-5721	623-907-2661	907-2501	9-12	Caroline Birney
Nosotros Academy	440 N Grande Ave	Tucson, AZ	85745-2703	520-624-1023	624-7999	3-12	Paul Felix
Oasis HS	8632 W Northern Ave	Glendale, AZ	85305-1308	623-878-8059	878-8175	9-12	
Odyssey Institute	1495 S Airport Rd	Buckeye, AZ	85326-9214	623-402-4090		6-9	
Odyssey Preparatory Academy	6500 S Apache Rd	Buckeye, AZ	85326-1528	623-327-3111	327-0554	K-6	
Odyssey Preparatory Academy	17532 W Harrison St	Goodyear, AZ	85338-8000	623-882-1140	882-1196	K-6	
Old Pueblo Children's Academy	165 N Sarnoff Dr	Tucson, AZ	85710-2933	520-296-1600	298-0558	K-8	Ronda McCarthy
Ombudsman Charter S - Central	1525 N Oracle Rd	Tucson, AZ	85705	520-624-2260	882-2160	6-12	Emily Langfeldt
Ombudsman Charter S - East	3943 E Thomas Rd	Phoenix, AZ	85018-7511	602-840-2997	840-1402	6-12	Emily Langfeldt
Ombudsman Charter S - East II	4041 E Thomas Rd Ste 106	Phoenix, AZ	85018-7528	602-667-7759	667-7793	9-12	
Ombudsman Charter S - Metro	4220 W Northern Ave	Phoenix, AZ	85051-5753	602-840-2997	842-6157	6-12	
Ombudsman Charter S - Northeast	3242 E Bell Rd	Phoenix, AZ	85032-2727	602-485-9872	367-0367	6-12	
Ombudsman Charter S - Northwest	9516 W Peoria Ave	Peoria, AZ	85345-6100	602-840-2997	840-1402	6-12	Emily Langfeldt
Ombudsman Charter S - Valencia	1686 W Valencia Rd Ste 100	Tucson, AZ	85746-6065	520-573-5858	807-9333	6-12	Emily Langfeldt

School	Address	City,State	Zip code	Telephone	Fax	Grade	Contact
Ombudsman Charter S - West	3618 W Bell Rd	Glendale, AZ	85308-4338	602-840-2997	840-1402	6-12	Emily Langfeldt
Omega Alpha Academy	1402 N San Antonio Ave	Douglas, AZ	85607-2434	520-805-1261	805-1272	K-12	Jose Frisby
PACE Preparatory Academy	155 S Montezuma Castle Hwy	Camp Verde, AZ	86322-7392	928-237-1272	567-3943	9-12	Bill Sakelarios
PACE Preparatory Academy	6650 E 2nd St Ste B	Prescott Valley, AZ	86314-2596	928-227-3090	282-3776	9-12	Bill Sakelarios
Paideia Academy of South Phoenix	7777 S 15th Ter	Phoenix, AZ	85042-6754	602-343-3040	381-9029	PK-6	
Painted Rock Academy	14841 N Black Canyon Hwy	Phoenix, AZ	85023-5068	602-466-8855		K-8	
Pan-American Charter ES	3001 W Indian School Rd	Phoenix, AZ	85017-4168	602-266-3989	266-3979	K-8	Marta Pasos
Paradise Education Center	15533 W Paradise Ln	Surprise, AZ	85374-5851	623-975-2646	975-2841	K-8	Allison Gonzales
Paradise Honors HS	12775 N 175th Ave	Surprise, AZ	85388-5088	623-546-7215	975-4380	9-12	Tim Gonzales
Paragon Science Academy Campus I	2975 W Linda Ln	Chandler, AZ	85224-7340	480-814-1600	814-1661	K-3	Selimhan Tanyeri
Paragon Science Academy Campus II	5580 W Chandler Blvd	Chandler, AZ	85226-3697	480-753-3889	763-3385	4-12	Selimhan Tanyeri
Paramount Academy	11039 W Olive Ave	Peoria, AZ	85345-9200	623-977-0614	977-0615	K-8	
Park View MS	9030 E Florentine Rd	Prescott Valley, AZ	86314-8973	928-775-5115	775-6253	6-8	Jeannette Bray
Patagonia Montessori S	PO Box 628	Patagonia, AZ	85624-0628	520-394-9530	394-2864	PK-8	Jessi Beebe
Pathfinder Academy	2542 N 76th Pl	Mesa, AZ	85207-1252	480-986-7071	986-9858	K-8	Susan Stradling
Patriot Academy	19011 E San Tan Blvd	Queen Creek, AZ	85142	480-279-4780	807-1209	K-8	Jay Brown
Paulden Community S	24850 N Naples St	Paulden, AZ	86334-2839	928-636-1430	636-3087	K-8	James Sexton
Payson Center for Success	PO Box 919	Payson, AZ	85547-0919	928-472-2011	472-2039	9-12	Linda Gibson
Peak S	2016 N 1st St Ste A	Flagstaff, AZ	86004-4241	928-779-0771	779-0774	K-8	Paula Drossman
Peoria Accelerated HS	8885 W Peoria Ave	Peoria, AZ	85345-6442	623-979-0031	979-0113	9-12	Marcus Englund
Phoenix Advantage Charter S	3738 N 16th St	Phoenix, AZ	85016-5915	602-263-8777	263-8822	K-8	Jim Mosley
Phoenix Collegiate Academy	5610 S Central Ave	Phoenix, AZ	85040	602-268-9900	268-9911	6-12	Rachel Bennett Yanof
Pillar Academy of Business & Finance	1589 E Plantation Rd	Mohave Valley, AZ	86440	928-346-3925	346-3930	9-12	
Pima Partnership S	1346 N Stone Ave	Tucson, AZ	85705-7338	520-326-2528	326-2527	7-12	
Pima Rose Academy	1690 W Irvington Rd	Tucson, AZ	85746-4174	520-797-4884	797-8868	9-12	
Pima Vocational HS - Downtown	97 E Congress St	Tucson, AZ	85701	520-243-1745		9-12	
Pima Vocational HS - Main	1550 S 6th Ave	Tucson, AZ	85713-2801	520-243-1740	903-0753	9-12	Gloria Proo
Pima Vocational HS Northwest	5025 W Ina Rd	Tucson, AZ	85743-9751	520-443-6469		9-12	Gloria Proo
Pine Forest Charter S	1120 W Kaibab Ln	Flagstaff, AZ	86001-6217	928-779-9880	779-9792	K-8	Michael Heffernan
Pinnacle HS - Casa Grande	409 W McMurray Blvd	Casa Grande, AZ	85122-2314	520-423-2380	423-2383	9-12	Tami Powell
Pinnacle HS - Mesa	151 N Centennial Way	Mesa, AZ	85201-6734	480-668-5003	668-5005	9-12	Bob Asadi
Pinnacle HS - Nogales	2055 N Grand Ave	Nogales, AZ	85621-1038	520-281-5109	281-5132	9-12	Valerie Bridges
Pinnacle HS - Tempe E	1712 E Guadalupe Rd Ste 101	Tempe, AZ	85283-3983	480-785-7776	785-7778	9-12	Michael Epperson
Pinnacle HS - Tempe W	2224 W Southern Ave Ste 2	Tempe, AZ	85282-4345	602-414-0950	414-0927	9-12	Dr. Gerae Peten
Pinnacle Pointe Academy	6753 W Pinnacle Peak Rd	Glendale, AZ	85310-5301	623-537-3535	537-4433	K-6	Suzanne Smailagic
Pinnacle Virtual HS	3225 S Hardy Dr	Tempe, AZ	85282-3394	480-755-8222	755-8111	7-12	
Pioneer Preparatory S	6510 W Clarendon Ave	Phoenix, AZ	85033-4001	623-933-3733		K-8	Tony Best
Polytechnic ES	6950 E Williams Field Rd	Mesa, AZ	85212-6033	480-727-5700	727-5701	K-6	Donna Bullock
PPEP TEC - Chavez Learning Center	1233 N Main St Ste B	San Luis, AZ	85349	928-627-8550	627-8980	9-12	Angelica Sanchez
PPEP TEC - Fernandez Learning Center	1840 E Benson Hwy	Tucson, AZ	85714-1770	520-889-8276	741-4369	9-12	Randy Kempton
PPEP TEC - Paul Learning Center	220 E Florence Blvd	Casa Grande, AZ	85122-4031	520-836-6549	836-0290	9-12	Leticia Lujan
PPEP TEC - Powell Learning Center	4116 Avenida Cochise Ste F	Sierra Vista, AZ	85635-5843	520-458-8205	458-8293	9-12	Lynn Buckmaster
PPEP TEC - Raul H. Castro Learning Ctr	530 E 12th St	Douglas, AZ	85607-1925	520-364-4405	364-1405	9-12	Raul Torrez
PPEP TEC - Soltero Learning Center	8677 E Golf Links Rd	Tucson, AZ	85730-1315	520-290-9167	290-9220	9-12	Randy Kempton
PPEP TEC - Yepez Learning Center	115 N Columbia Ave	Somerton, AZ	85350	928-627-9648	627-9197	9-12	Gloria Rodriguez
Precision Academy	7318 W Lynwood St	Phoenix, AZ	85035-4542	623-936-8682	936-8559	9-12	Dr. Caroline White
Precision Academy System Charter S	3906 E Broadway Rd	Phoenix, AZ	85040-2996	602-453-3661	453-3667	9-12	Daniel Martinez
Premier Charter HS	7544 W Indian School Rd	Phoenix, AZ	85033-3030	623-245-1500	245-1506	9-12	Elisha Madden
Prescott Valley S	PO Box 27348	Prescott Valley, AZ	86312-7348	928-772-8744	775-4457	K-12	
Presidio de las Sierras S	240 N Highway 90 Byp	Sierra Vista, AZ	85635-2238	520-335-2898	335-6025	K-8	Patricia Gale
Presidio S	1695 E Fort Lowell Rd	Tucson, AZ	85719-2319	520-881-5222	881-5522	K-12	Mindy White
Primavera Online HS	2471 N Arizona Ave Ste 1	Chandler, AZ	85225-1394	480-456-6678	355-2100	7-12	Debra Bender
Quest HS	5040 S Price Rd	Tempe, AZ	85282-7445	480-831-6057	831-6095	9-12	
RCB Medical Arts Academy	6049 N 43rd Ave	Phoenix, AZ	85019-1641	602-973-6018	589-1349	9-12	Mark Hebert
Reyes Maria Ruiz Leadership Academy	4848 S 2nd St	Phoenix, AZ	85040-2122	602-243-7788	243-7799	4-6	Adrian Ruiz
Ridgeline Academy	33625 N North Valley Pkwy	Phoenix, AZ	85085-4229	623-223-1335		K-6	Keven Barker
Rimrock Public HS	PO Box 248	Rimrock, AZ	86335-0248	928-567-9213	567-9304	9-12	Kathleen McCabe
Riverbend Preparatory S	5625 S 51st Ave	Laveen, AZ	85339-6300	602-285-3003	285-5560	K-6	Joseph Hattrick
RSD Charter HS	12814 N 28th Dr	Phoenix, AZ	85029-1357	602-993-5225	993-0506	9-12	
SABIS International	1903 E Roeser Rd	Phoenix, AZ	85040-3341	602-305-8865	323-5526	K-8	Will Henry
Sage Academy	1055 E Hearn Rd	Scottsdale, AZ	85254	602-485-3402	485-7874	K-8	
Sandoval Preparatory HS	4802 N 59th Ave	Phoenix, AZ	85033-1702	623-845-0781	849-2840	9-12	Ken Turer
San Pedro Valley HS	360 S Patagonia St	Benson, AZ	85602-6533	520-720-6725	720-6702	9-12	Richard Connet
San Tan Learning Center	1475 S Higley Rd	Gilbert, AZ	85296	480-222-0811	539-1028	K-8	Colleen Campbell
Satori Charter S	3727 N 1st Ave	Tucson, AZ	85719-1609	520-293-7555	293-7020	2-8	Jesse Ramos
Scholars' Academy	PO Box 3475	Quartzsite, AZ	85359-3475	928-927-9420	927-9425	7-12	
School for Integrated Academics & Tech	518 S 3rd St	Phoenix, AZ	85004-2506	602-258-3927	340-1965	9-12	Nicole Biggs
School for Integrated Academics & Tech	901 S Campbell Ave	Tucson, AZ	85719-6519	520-791-3016	791-3582	9-12	David Gerber
Scottsdale Preparatory Academy	16537 N 92nd St	Scottsdale, AZ	85260-1528	480-776-1970	776-1975	5-12	Dr. Peter Bezanson
Sedona Charter S	165 Kachina Dr	Sedona, AZ	86336-4303	928-204-6464	204-6486	K-8	Alice Madar
Self Development Charter S	1709 N Greenfield Rd	Mesa, AZ	85205-3103	480-641-2640	641-2678	K-8	Anjie Majeed
Sequoia Academics & Arts Charter	1460 S Horne	Mesa, AZ	85204-5760	480-446-9288	890-4103	K-12	Lori Graham
Sequoia Charter ES	1460 S Horne	Mesa, AZ	85204-5760	480-890-4002		K-6	Amy Fraser
Sequoia Charter Secondary S	1460 S Horne	Mesa, AZ	85204-5760	480-649-7737	649-0711	9-12	David Blakeley
Sequoia Choice S - AZ Distance Learning	323 N Gilbert Rd Ste 104	Mesa, AZ	85203-8262	480-655-7005	655-7911	K-12	David Hamblin
Sequoia Choice - Star Academy	323 N Gilbert Rd Ste 108	Mesa, AZ	85203-8262	480-834-7400	834-7402	K-12	
Sequoia Pathway Academy	19265 N Porter Rd	Maricopa, AZ	85138-4053	520-568-9333	568-9444	K-12	Jonathan Gentile
Sequoia Redwood Charter S	6810 W Thunderbird Rd	Peoria, AZ	85381-5025	623-878-0986		K-5	Ron Palmer
Sequoia S for the Deaf & Hard of Hearing	1460 S Horne	Mesa, AZ	85204-5760	480-890-4001	890-4113	K-12	Heather Lane
Sequoia School - Sequoia Village S	982 Full House Ln	Show Low, AZ	85901-4042	928-537-1208	537-4275	K-12	Mindy Savoia
Shelby S	249 W Standage Dr	Payson, AZ	85541	928-478-4706	478-0681	K-10	Ezra Stuyvesant
Sierra Oaks S	650 W Linda Vista Rd	Oracle, AZ	85623-6039	520-896-3100	896-3101	K-8	Nancy Davis
Sky Islands S	3101 N Sabino Canyon Rd	Tucson, AZ	85715-2610	520-382-9210	382-5888	9-12	Dr. Shari Popen
Skyline District 5 S	PO Box 10858	Bapchule, AZ	85121-0104	520-315-3237	315-3233	5-8	Robert Grace
Skyline Prep HS	7500 S 40th St	Phoenix, AZ	85042-6353	602-343-4980	343-4996	9-12	Keith Brown
Skyview HS	7820 E Wrightstown Rd	Tucson, AZ	85715-4339	520-722-4721	722-4785	9-12	Marianne Goodwin
Skyview S	125 S Rush St	Prescott, AZ	86303-4432	928-776-1730	776-1742	K-8	Scott McCreery
Sonoran Desert S	6724 S Kings Ranch Rd	Gold Canyon, AZ	85118	480-396-5463	396-4980	9-12	Patricia Dalman
Sonoran Science Academy - Ahwatukee	14647 S 50th St Ste 125	Phoenix, AZ	85044-6500	480-961-5730	961-5397	K-5	Fethiye Ozis Ph.D.
Sonoran Science Academy - Broadway	6880 E Broadway Blvd	Tucson, AZ	85710-2818	520-751-2401	751-2451	K-8	Erdal Kocak
Sonoran Science Academy - Davis Monthan	5741 E Ironwood St	Tucson, AZ	85708-1217	520-300-5699	207-7698	6-12	Peggy Fontenot M.Ed.
Sonoran Science Academy - Peoria	17667 N 91st Ave	Peoria, AZ	85382-3019	623-776-9344		K-8	Arif Akpinar
Sonoran Science Academy - Phoenix	4837 E McDowell Rd	Phoenix, AZ	85008-4225	602-244-9855	244-9856	K-12	Ismail Ozis M.S.
Sonoran Science Academy - Tucson	2325 W Sunset Rd	Tucson, AZ	85741-3809	520-665-3430	665-3440	K-12	Bilal Dogan
Sonoran West Academy	17667 N 91st Ave	Peoria, AZ	85382-3019	623-875-3175	875-9261	K-12	
Southern Arizona Community Academy	2470 N Tucson Blvd	Tucson, AZ	85716-2469	520-319-6113	319-6115	9-12	Abelardo Cubillas
Southgate Academy	850 W Valencia Rd	Tucson, AZ	85706-7619	520-741-7900	741-7901	K-12	Sherry Matyjasik
South Pointe Charter ES	2033 E Southern Ave	Phoenix, AZ	85040-3344	602-276-1943	276-2726	K-6	Nadine Taylor
South Pointe HS	8325 S Central Ave	Phoenix, AZ	85042-6576	602-243-0600	243-0800	9-12	Larry McGill
South Pointe JHS	217 E Olympic Dr	Phoenix, AZ	85042-6564	602-268-3782	268-4863	6-8	Jenni Kincaid
South Ridge HS	1122 S 67th Ave	Phoenix, AZ	85043-4417	623-247-0106	247-0527	9-12	Melissa Rivers
Southside Community S	2701 S Campbell Ave	Tucson, AZ	85713-5080	520-623-7102	623-7125	6-12	Janet Dougherty
South Valley Prep & Arts Academy	7500 S 40th St	Phoenix, AZ	85042-6353	877-225-2118	437-2901	K-8	Debra Coleman
South Verde MSHS	410 Camp Lincoln Rd	Camp Verde, AZ	86322-7494	928-567-8076	567-8093	6-12	Steve King
STAR Charter S	145 Leupp Rd	Flagstaff, AZ	86004-8501	928-415-3533	606-9965	K-8	Mark Sorenson
StarShine Academy Creative Community	3535 E McDowell Rd	Phoenix, AZ	85008-3847	602-957-9557	956-0065	K-12	Sean Diana
Starshine Fay Landrum Academy	1902 W Roeser Rd	Phoenix, AZ	85041-3736	602-237-6030		K-12	
Stellar Prep	8632 W Northern Ave	Glendale, AZ	85305-1308	623-878-8059	878-8175	K-4	Jimmie Daniels
Stepping Stones Academy	35812 N 7th St	Phoenix, AZ	85086-7410	623-465-4910	587-8514	K-8	
Student Choice HS	1833 N Scottsdale Rd	Tempe, AZ	85281-1563	480-947-9511	947-9624	9-12	Peggy Lynam
Student Choice HS - Paradise Valley	4645 E Marilyn Rd	Phoenix, AZ	85032-4839	602-334-4101	493-0033	9-12	Jennifer Willcutt
Student Choice HS - Peoria	8194 W Deer Valley Rd	Peoria, AZ	85382-2127	623-242-2722	566-1634	9-12	Jaime Claros
Sturgeon MS	5757 W McDowell Rd	Phoenix, AZ	85035-4947	602-269-1007	269-1073	5-8	
Successful Beginnings Charter S	841 E McNeil	Show Low, AZ	85901-6006	928-537-2365	537-2365	K-5	
Summit HS	728 E Mcdowell Rd	Phoenix, AZ	85006-2592	602-258-8959	258-8953	9-12	James Sigman
Sunnyside Charter & Montessori S	PO Box 2166	Camp Verde, AZ	86322-2166	928-567-2363	567-5374	6-9	Keven Chester
Sun Valley Charter S	5806 S 35th Pl	Phoenix, AZ	85040-2844	602-692-4914	612-2196	K-6	Tanae Morrison M.Ed.
Sun Valley HS	1143 S Lindsay Rd	Mesa, AZ	85204-6298	480-497-4800	497-1314	9-12	Joe Procopio
TAG S	10129 E Speedway Blvd	Tucson, AZ	85748-1921	520-296-0006	296-0046	K-8	Ron Hom
Taylion Virtual Academy	4744 W Grovers Ave	Glendale, AZ	85308-3453	855-297-2466	889-7806	7-12	
Teacher Preparation Charter HS	1202 W Thomas Rd	Phoenix, AZ	85013-4208	602-285-7998	285-7697	9-12	David Singer
Teleos Preparatory Academy	1401 E Jefferson St	Phoenix, AZ	85034-2315	602-275-5455	275-5954	1-8	Brian Taylor
Telesis Preparatory Academy	2598 Starlite Ln	Lk Havasu Cty, AZ	86403-4946	928-855-8661	855-9302	K-12	Sandra Breece Ed.D.
Tempe Preparatory Academy	1251 E Southern Ave	Tempe, AZ	85282-5605	480-839-3402	755-0546	6-12	
Thoman Air and Space Academy	730 W Calle Arroyo Sur	Green Valley, AZ	85614-5883	520-219-4383		K-8	Mary Lou Klem
Toltecali Academy	200 N Stone Ave	Tucson, AZ	85701-1208	520-882-3029	882-3041	9-12	
Tri-City College Prep HS	5522 Side Rd	Prescott, AZ	86301-8483	928-777-0403	777-0402	9-12	Dr. Mary Ellen Halvorson

School	Address	City,State	Zip code	Telephone	Fax	Grade	Contact
Triumphant Learning Center	201 E Main St	Safford, AZ	85546-2051	928-348-8422	348-8423	K-8	Robin Dutt
Trivium Preparatory Academy	14140 W McDowell Rd	Goodyear, AZ	85395-2512	623-414-4883	889-6286	6-12	Dave Beskar
Tucson Country Day S	9239 E Wrightstown Rd	Tucson, AZ	85715-5514	520-296-0883	290-1521	K-8	Dr. Mark Saliba
Tucson International Academy	1230 E Broadway Blvd	Tucson, AZ	85719-5821	520-792-3255	792-3245	K-12	Jennifer Herrera
Tucson International Academy East Campus	450 N Pantano Rd	Tucson, AZ	85710-2309	520-792-3255	792-3245	K-10	Jennifer Herrera
Tucson International Academy - Midvale	1625 W Valencia Rd Ste 109	Tucson, AZ	85746-6022	520-792-3255	792-3245	K-12	Jennifer Herrera
Tucson International Academy West Campus	2700 W Broadway Blvd	Tucson, AZ	85745-1715	520-792-3255	792-3245	K-12	Jennifer Herrera
Tucson Preparatory S	104 E Prince Rd	Tucson, AZ	85705-3666	520-622-4185	622-4755	9-12	Jody Sullivan
Vail Academy and HS	7762 E Science Park Dr	Tucson, AZ	85747	520-879-1900	879-1901	K-12	Dennis Barger
Valley Academy - Charter S	1520 W Rose Garden Ln	Phoenix, AZ	85027-3529	623-516-7747	516-2703	K-8	Victoria Wilber
Vechij Himdag Mashchamakud	168 S Skill Center Rd	Sacaton, AZ	85147	520-562-3286		7-12	
Vector Prep and Arts Academy	2020 N Arizona Ave	Chandler, AZ	85225	480-779-2002	779-2100	K-6	Rodney James
Verde Valley Montessori Charter S	215 S Main St	Cottonwood, AZ	86326-3908	928-634-3288	634-9781	PK-6	Heather Basham
Veritas Preparatory Academy	3102 N 56th St Ste 200	Phoenix, AZ	85018-6606	602-263-1128	263-7997	6-12	Andrew Ellison
Victory HS	PO Box 8374	Phoenix, AZ	85066-8374	602-243-7583	243-7563	9-12	Dr. Shirley Branham
Villa Montessori - Phoenix	4535 N 28th St	Phoenix, AZ	85016-4998	602-955-2210	381-4017	K-8	Margo O'Neill
Vision Charter S	5901 S Santa Cruz Calle	Tucson, AZ	85709-6000	520-444-0241	741-8123	9-12	
Visions Unlimited Academy	1275 E Barney Ln	Benson, AZ	85602-7955	520-586-8691	586-3074	K-8	Richard Valentine
Vista Grove Preparatory Academy	2929 E McKellips Rd	Mesa, AZ	85213-3128	480-924-1500	924-0552	PK-9	Abelardo Batista
Webster Basic S	7301 E Baseline Rd	Mesa, AZ	85209-4907	480-986-2335	373-9176	PK-6	Kelly Wade
Westland S	4141 N 67th Ave	Phoenix, AZ	85033-3314	623-247-6456	247-6520	K-12	
West Phoenix HS	3835 W Thomas Rd	Phoenix, AZ	85019-4434	602-269-1110	269-1112	9-12	Romona Gonzales
Westwind Preparatory Academy	2045 W Northern Ave	Phoenix, AZ	85021-5157	602-864-7731	864-7720	6-12	Debra Slagle
Wildcat S	42 E Adams St	Tucson, AZ	85705-6647	520-294-5473	294-5475	K-8	Vivien Sessums
Willow Creek Charter S	2100 Willow Creek Rd	Prescott, AZ	86301-5391	928-776-1212	776-0009	K-8	Terese Soto
Young Scholars Academy	1501 E Valencia Rd	Bullhead City, AZ	86426-5218	928-704-1100	704-1177	K-8	Tonnie Smith
Youngtown Charter S	8632 W Northern Ave	Glendale, AZ	85305-1308	623-974-0355	815-8902	K-8	Jacob Duran
Youth Works Charter HS	1915 E 36th St	Tucson, AZ	85713-3810	520-623-5843		9-12	
Arkansas							
Academic Center of Excellence	21 Funtastic Dr	Cabot, AR	72023-6005	501-743-3520	843-0283	7-12	Michele Evans
Academics Plus Charter ES	900 Edgewood Dr	Maumelle, AR	72113-6275	501-803-0666	851-2599	K-6	Rachel Wheeler
Academics Plus Charter HS	900 Edgewood Dr	Maumelle, AR	72113-6275	501-851-3333	851-2599	7-12	Sharon Walker
Academy of Technology	PO Box 160	Vilonia, AR	72173-0160	501-796-2018	796-4322	2-4	Susan Loyd
Arkansas Virtual Academy	4702 W Commercial Dr Ste B3	No Little Rock, AR	72116-7073	866-339-4951	664-4226	K-8	Scott Sides
Benton County HS of the Arts	8 Halsted Cir Ste 5	Rogers, AR	72756-3144	479-631-2787	899-6479	9-12	Barbara Padgett
Benton County School of the Arts	8 Halsted Cir Ste 5	Rogers, AR	72756-3144	479-636-2272	636-5447	K-8	Julia Rice
Brunson New Vision Charter S	PO Box 1210	Warren, AR	71671-1210	870-226-2351	226-8541	4-5	Regina Scroggins
Cloverdale Magnet MS	6300 Hinkson Rd	Little Rock, AR	72209-4712	501-447-2500	447-2501	6-8	Wanda Ruffins
Covenant Keepers College Preparatory S	8300 Geyer Springs Rd	Little Rock, AR	72209-4946	501-682-7550	682-7577	6-12	Kasey Porchia
Cross County Elementary Technology Acad	2622 Highway 42	Cherry Valley, AR	72324-8674	870-588-3337	588-4454	K-6	Stephen Prince
Cross County HS A New Tech S	21 County Road 215	Cherry Valley, AR	72324-8957	870-588-3337	588-4606	7-12	Jennifer McFarland
Eastside New Vision Charter S	PO Box 1210	Warren, AR	71671-1210	870-226-6761	226-8538	K-3	Sara Weaver
eStem Public Charter ES	112 W 3rd St	Little Rock, AR	72201-2702	501-748-9200	975-4092	K-4	Cindy Barton
eStem Public Charter HS	123 W 3rd St	Little Rock, AR	72201	501-748-9335	748-9370	9-12	Ruthie Walls
eStem Public Charter MS	112 W 3rd St	Little Rock, AR	72201-2702	501-748-9200	975-4092	5-8	Cindy Barton
Haas Hall Academy	3155 N College Ave Ste 108	Fayetteville, AR	72703-3500	479-966-4930	966-4932	8-12	Dr. Martin Schoppmeyer
Imboden Area Charter S	PO Box 297	Imboden, AR	72434-0297	870-869-3015	869-3016	K-8	Judy Warren
Jacksonville Lighthouse Charter S	251 N 1st St	Jacksonville, AR	72076-4462	501-985-1200	985-1201	K-6	Norman Whitfield
Jacksonville Lighthouse Coll Prep Acad	251 N 1st St	Jacksonville, AR	72076-4462	501-985-1200	985-1201	7-12	Chris Carter
Jacksonville Lighthouse Flightline S	Bldg 1030 Cannon Dr	Jacksonville, AR	72099	501-988-1085	988-1090	5-8	Evan McGrew
KIPP Blytheville College Preparatory S	1200 Byrum Rd	Blytheville, AR	72315-8119	870-780-6333	780-6310	5-8	Maisie Wright
KIPP Delta College Preparatory S	514 Missouri	Helena, AR	72342-3751	870-753-9444	753-9450	5-8	Marcus Nelson
KIPP Delta Collegiate High School	320 Missouri	Helena, AR	72342-3709	870-338-8138	338-8623	9-12	Todd Dixon
KIPP Delta Elementary Literacy Academy	215 Cherry St	Helena, AR	72342	870-753-9800	753-9801	K-4	Amanda Johnson
Lincoln Middle Academy of Excellence	149 N Water St	Forrest City, AR	72335-3156	870-261-1810	261-1838	5-6	Shirley Taylor
Lisa Academy	21 Corporate Hill Dr	Little Rock, AR	72205-4537	501-227-4942	227-4952	6-12	Luanne Baroni
Lisa Academy-North Little Rock	5410 Landers Rd	No Little Rock, AR	72117-1935	501-945-2727	945-2728	K-12	
Little Rock Prep Academy	1205 S Schiller St	Little Rock, AR	72202-5239	501-683-1855	683-1847	K-8	Ben Lindquist
Pine Bluff Lighthouse S	708 W 2nd Ave	Pine Bluff, AR	71601-4002	870-534-0277	534-0263	K-5	Sandra Smith-Jones
SIATech Little Rock	6900 Scott Hamilton Dr	Little Rock, AR	72209-3144	501-618-2500	570-0410	9-12	Katie Tatum
California							
Abraxis Charter HS	PO Box 2587	Santa Rosa, CA	95405-0587	707-568-4492	568-3762	9-12	Carley Moore
Academia Avance Charter S	PO Box 42095	Los Angeles, CA	90042-0095	213-230-7270	652-0994	6-12	Ricardo Mireles
Academia Moderna	2410 Broadway	Walnut Park, CA	90255-6342	323-923-0383	923-0380	K-8	Barry Baxter
Academic/Vocational Charter Institute	112 Diamond Dr	Watsonville, CA	95076-3184	831-728-6225	728-6233	11-12	Bruce White
Academies of the Antelope Valley	6300 W Avenue L	Lancaster, CA	93536-4540			7-12	Robert Dutton
Academy for Academic Excellence	17500 Mana Rd	Apple Valley, CA	92307-2181	760-242-3514	946-9193	K-12	Gordon Soholt
Academy of Alameda	401 Pacific Ave	Alameda, CA	94501-1837	510-214-2460	523-5801	6-8	Matt Huxley
Academy of Business Law & Education	6515 Inglewood Ave	Stockton, CA	95207-3871	209-478-1600	235-2986	9-12	Matthew George
Academy of Careers & Exploration	PO Box 249	Helendale, CA	92342-0249	760-952-2396	952-1178	K-12	Diana Green
Academy of Personalized Learning	2195 Larkspur Ln	Redding, CA	96002-0629	530-945-2892		K-12	Patricia Dougherty
Academy of Science and Engineering	4126 Arlington Ave	Los Angeles, CA	90008-4028	323-545-1100	545-1102	9-12	Nick Nichols
Accelerated Achievement Academy	1059 N State St	Ukiah, CA	95482-3413	707-463-7080	463-7085	4-12	Selah Sawyer
Accelerated Charter ES	119 E 37th St	Los Angeles, CA	90011-2603	323-846-6694	846-6695	K-5	Susan Raudry
Accelerated S	4000 S Main St	Los Angeles, CA	90037-1022	323-235-6343	235-6346	K-8	Lenita Lugo
ACE Charter HS	570 Airport Way	Camarillo, CA	93010-8500	805-437-1410	437-1491	9-12	Ron Fisher
ACE Charter S	625 S Sunset Ave	San Jose, CA	95116-3442	408-729-3920	729-3952	5-8	Elena Luna
ACE Elementary Charter S	2000 Kammerer Ave	San Jose, CA	95116-3016	408-729-3920		5-8	
ACEL Fresno	1713 Tulare St	Fresno, CA	93721	559-408-7077	408-7078	9-12	John Minkler
Achieve Academy	303 Hegenberger Rd Ste 301	Oakland, CA	94621-1419	510-904-6440	904-6761	4-5	Stephen Cilono
Achieve Charter S of Paradise	771 Elliott Rd	Paradise, CA	95969-3913	530-872-4100	872-4105	K-8	Casey Taylor
Adelante Charter S	1102 E Yanonali St	Santa Barbara, CA	93103-2704	805-966-7392	966-7243	K-6	Juanita Hernandez
Alameda Community Learning Center	210 Central Ave	Alameda, CA	94501-3246	510-521-7123	521-7350	7-12	Lora Lewis
Alder Grove Charter S	433 M St	Eureka, CA	95501-0540	707-268-0854	268-0813	K-12	J. Allen-San Giovanni
Alexander Science Center	3737 S Figueroa St	Los Angeles, CA	90007-4366	213-746-1995	746-7443	K-5	Barbara Lake
Alianza Charter S	115 Casserly Rd	Watsonville, CA	95076-9740	831-728-6333	728-6947	K-8	Michael Jones
All Tribes American Indian Charter S	PO Box 1432	Valley Center, CA	92082-1432	760-749-5982	749-4153	K-12	Mary Ann Donohue
Alpaugh Achievement Academy	PO Box 9	Alpaugh, CA	93201-0009	559-949-8644	949-8173	K-12	Robert Hudson
Alpha Blanca Alvarado MS	1601 Cunningham Ave	San Jose, CA	95122-2314	408-455-1223		6-7	John Glover
Alta Vista Charter S	12100 Palmdale Rd Ste B3	Adelanto, CA	92301-6709	760-904-0533	949-5876	K-12	Ken Larson
Alternative Coop Education Charter S	400 Hemlock St	Vacaville, CA	95688-2616	707-453-6245	448-7933	K-6	Luci DelRio
Alvarado Academy	26247 Ellis St	Madera, CA	93638-0813	559-675-2070	675-2074	K-8	Dr. Nicolas Retana
Alvina Charter ES	295 W Saginaw Ave	Caruthers, CA	93609-9710	559-864-9411	864-1808	K-8	Mike Iribarren
American Indian Charter HS	PO Box 12063	Oakland, CA	94604-2363	510-482-6000	482-6002	9-12	Claudia Walker
American Indian Charter S	3637 Magee Ave	Oakland, CA	94619-1427	510-482-6000	482-6002	5-8	Claudia Walker
American Indian Charter S II	171 12th St	Oakland, CA	94607-4900	510-893-8701	893-0345	5-8	John Glover
American River Charter S	6620 Wentworth Springs Rd	Georgetown, CA	95634-9701	530-333-8340	333-8346	K-12	Susan Whittington
Americas Finest Charter S	4001 El Cajon Blvd	San Diego, CA	92105-1110	619-546-4176		K-8	Jan Perry
Anahuacalmecac Intl University Prep HS	4736 Huntington Dr S	Los Angeles, CA	90032-1942	323-352-2070	987-1240	9-12	Marcos Aguilar
Anchor Academy Charter S	2385 S Fairview Ave	Fresno, CA	93706-4811	559-286-7680	266-4764	K-8	Paula DeGross
Anderson New Technology HS	2098 North St	Anderson, CA	96007 3477	530-365-3100	365-2957	9-12	Pat Allison
Animo Alain Leroy Locke HS #3	325 E 111th St	Los Angeles, CA	90061-3003	323-420-2100	420-2199	9-12	Damon Hands
Animo Charter MS #3	12226 S Western Ave	Los Angeles, CA	90047-5240	323-600-6000	652-1849	6-8	Silke Bradford
Animo Charter MS #4	12226 S Western Ave	Los Angeles, CA	90047-5240	323-600-6099		6-8	Nathaniel Pickering
Animo College Preparatory Academy	2265 E 103rd St	Los Angeles, CA	90002-3132	323-568-4136	568-4190	9-12	Veronica Coleman
Animo Inglewood Charter HS	3425 W Manchester Blvd	Inglewood, CA	90305-2101	323-565-2100	565-2109	9-12	Leilani Abulon
Animo Jackie Robinson Charter HS	3500 S Hill St	Los Angeles, CA	90007-4333	323-846-5800	846-8760	9-12	Lori Pawinski
Animo Jefferson Charter MS	1655 E 27th St	Los Angeles, CA	90011-2202	323-232-1857	232-6505	6-8	Damon Hands
Animo Leadership Charter HS	11044 S Freeman Ave	Inglewood, CA	90304-2418	323-565-4420	565-4421	9-12	Julio Murcia
Animo Locke HS #1	325 E 111th St	Los Angeles, CA	90061-3093	323-420-2067	420-2180	9-12	Dr. Peggy Gutierrez
Animo Locke HS #2	325 E 111th St	Los Angeles, CA	90061-3093	323-420-2150	420-2197	9-12	Rachelle Alexander
Animo Locke Technology HS	820 E 111th Pl	Los Angeles, CA	90059-1520	323-568-8613	568-8617	9-12	Blain Watson
Animo-Oscar De La Hoya S	1114 S Lorena St	Los Angeles, CA	90023-2915	323-780-1259	780-4862	9-12	Harris Luu
Animo Pat Brown Charter HS	8255 Beach St	Los Angeles, CA	90001-4014	323-585-3312	585-8985	9-12	Joshua Hartford
Animo Ralph Bunche Charter HS	1655 E 27th St	Los Angeles, CA	90011-2202	323-232-9436	232-9440	9-12	Xochil Avellan
Animo South Los Angeles HS	11100 S Western Ave	Los Angeles, CA	90047-4845	323-779-0544	779-0565	9-12	Sabrina Ayala
Animo Venice HS	820 Broadway St	Venice, CA	90291-3408	310-392-8751	392-8752	9-12	Sabrina Ayala
Animo Watts Charter HS	12628 Avalon Blvd	Los Angeles, CA	90061-2728	323-756-3930	756-3947	9-12	Sabrina Ayala
Animo Westside Charter MS	7615 Cowan Ave	Los Angeles, CA	90045-1206	323-565-3251	227-9739	6-8	Lemuel Mossett
Annenberg HS	4000 S Main St	Los Angeles, CA	90037-1022	323-235-6343	235-6346	9-12	Katherine Aguirre
Antecello Preparatory Academy	2320 W Martin Luther King	Los Angeles, CA	90008	323-290-9200		6-7	
Antelope Valley Learning Academy	1601 E Palmdale Blvd Ste C	Palmdale, CA	93550-4840	661-266-2044	945-2430	K-8	Erin Wade
Antelope View Charter S	3243 Center Court Ln	Antelope, CA	95843-9111	916-339-4690	339-4693	6-12	Doug Hughey

School	Address	City,State	Zip code	Telephone	Fax	Grade	Contact
Antioch Charter Academy	3325 Hacienda Way	Antioch, CA	94509-5407	925-755-7311	755-7313	K-8	Todd Heller
Antioch Charter Academy II	1201 W 10th St	Antioch, CA	94509-1406	925-755-1252	755-7527	K-8	Todd Heller
Apple Academy Charter S	4900 S Western Ave	Los Angeles, CA	90062-2326	323-348-4276		K-5	Laurie Inman
Ararat Charter S	6555 Sylmar Ave	Van Nuys, CA	91401-6202	818-994-2904	994-8096	K-5	Vahe Boujekian
ARISE HS	3301 E 12th St Ste 205	Oakland, CA	94601-2940	510-436-5487	436-5493	9-12	Romeo Garcia
Arroyo Paseo Charter HS	3773 El Cajon Blvd	San Diego, CA	92105	619-677-3017		9-12	Brian Thurman
Arroyo Vista Charter S	2491 School House Rd	Chula Vista, CA	91915-2534	619-656-9676	656-1858	K-6	Patricia Roth
Arts in Action Community Charter S	1241 S Soto St	Los Angeles, CA	90023-2652	323-266-4371	266-4371	K-5	Terry Phillips
Arundel ES	200 Arundel Rd	San Carlos, CA	94070-1999	650-508-7311	508-7314	K-4	Adam Paulson
ASA Charter S	3512 N E St	San Bernardino, CA	92405-2110	909-475-3322	883-2708	K-12	Melissa Campbell
Aspire Alexander Twilight College Prep S	2360 El Camino Ave	Sacramento, CA	95821-5611	916-979-1788	979-1796	K-5	Paris Williams
Aspire Alexander Twilight Secondary Acad	2360 El Camino Ave	Sacramento, CA	95821-5611	916-979-1788	979-1796	6-12	Robert Spencer
Aspire APEX Academy	444 N American St	Stockton, CA	95202-2129	209-466-3861	466-4290	K-5	Kat Ellison
Aspire Capitol Heights Academy	2520 33rd St	Sacramento, CA	95817-1943	916-739-8520	739-8529	K-8	Kristin Murphy
Aspire College Academy	8030 Atherton St	Oakland, CA	94605-3430	510-562-8030	562-8013	6-12	Tina Hernandez
Aspire East Palo Alto Phoenix Academy	1039 Garden St	East Palo Alto, CA	94303-1748	650-325-1460	325-1327	9-12	Thomas Madson
Aspire Eres Academy	1936 Courtland Ave	Oakland, CA	94601-4614	510-436-9760	436-9765	K-8	Emily Murphy
Aspire Firestone Academy	8929 Kauffman Ave	South Gate, CA	90280-3422	323-249-5740	568-2017	K-5	Marcie Jones
Aspire Gateway Academy	8929 Kauffman Ave	South Gate, CA	90280-3422	323-249-5750	249-5759	K-5	Stefan Bean
Aspire Golden State College Prep Academy	1009 66th Ave	Oakland, CA	94621-3535	510-567-9631	632-1569	6-12	Thomas Kadelbach
Aspire Huntington Park Charter S	6005 Stafford Ave	Huntington Park, CA	90255-3006	323-584-9033	584-0735	K-5	Stephanie Schulman
Aspire Inskeep Academy	123 W 59th St	Los Angeles, CA	90003-1103	323-235-8400	232-8030	K-6	Adam Rand
Aspire Junior Collegiate Academy	6724 S Alameda St	Huntington Park, CA	90255-3617	323-583-5421		K-5	Bonnie Brimecombe
Aspire Langston Hughes Academy	2050 West Ln	Stockton, CA	95205-3358	209-943-2389	943-2901	6-12	Anthony Solina
Aspire Lugo Academy	2665 Clarendon Ave	Huntington Park, CA	90255-4138	323-585-1153	585-1283	K-5	Sarah Ali
Aspire Pacific College Prep Academy	2565 E 58th St	Huntington Park, CA	90255-2606	323-589-2800	589-2802	6-12	Matthew Seigel
Aspire Port City Academy	2040 West Ln	Stockton, CA	95205-3358	209-943-2389	943-2901	K-5	Shelby Scheideman
Aspire River Oaks Charter S	1801 Pyrenees Ave	Stockton, CA	95210-5207	209-956-8100	956-8102	K-5	Kim Whitehead
Aspire Slauson Academy	123 W 59th St	Los Angeles, CA	90003-1103	323-235-8400	232-8030	K-6	Barbara Harris
Aspire Tate Academy	123 W 59th St	Los Angeles, CA	90003-1103	323-235-8400	583-7271	K-6	Ana Martinez
Aspire Titan Academy	6724 S Alameda St	Huntington Park, CA	90255-3617	323-583-5421	588-7342	K-5	Kim Chai Benaraw
Aspire University Charter S	3313 Coffee Rd	Modesto, CA	95355-1534	209-544-8722	544-8864	K-6	Laura Thompson
Aspire Vanguard College Prep Acad	5255 1st St	Empire, CA	95319	209-269-9977	538-1620	6-12	Wesley Frakes
Aspire Vincent Shalvey Academy	10038 N Highway 99	Stockton, CA	95212-2127	209-931-5399	931-5185	K-6	Karla Fachner
Audeo Charter S	10170 Huennekens St	San Diego, CA	92121-2964	858-678-2050	552-9394	6-12	Tim Tuter
Aveson Global Leadership Acadmey	1919 Pinecrest Dr	Altadena, CA	91001-2116	626-797-1440	797-1918	6-12	Kate Bean
Aveson School of Leaders	1919 Pinecrest Dr	Altadena, CA	91001-2116	626-797-1440	797-1918	K-5	Kate Bean
Bachrodt Charter Academy	102 Sonora Ave	San Jose, CA	95110-1499	408-535-6211	535-6588	K-5	Rigo Palacios
Ballington Academy for the Arts/Sciences	1525 W Main St	El Centro, CA	92243-2211	760-353-0140	353-0745	K-5	Grace Jimenez
Banks Charter S	PO Box 80	Pala, CA	92059-0080	760-742-3300	742-3102	K-5	Eric Kosch
Barona Indian Charter S	1095 Barona Rd	Lakeside, CA	92040-1516	619-443-0948	443-7280	K-8	Bill Adams
Bay Area S of Enterprise	1900 3rd St	Alameda, CA	94501-1851	510-748-4314	748-4326	9-12	Jason Gardner
Bay Area Technology S	8251 Fontaine St	Oakland, CA	94605-4109	510-382-9932	382-9934	6-12	Hayri Hatipoglu
Bayshore Prep Charter S	1175 Linda Vista Dr	San Marcos, CA	92078-3811	760-471-0847	736-0275	K-12	Nancy Spencer
Bay View Academy	222 Casa Verde Way	Monterey, CA	93940-3753	831-751-3142		K-5	John Favero
Beckford Charter S for Enriched Studies	19130 Tulsa St	Northridge, CA	91326-2698	818-360-1924	832-9831	K-5	Shelly Brower
Bellevue-Sante Fe Charter S	1401 San Luis Bay Dr	San Luis Obispo, CA	93405-8007	805-595-7169	595-9013	K-6	Brian Getz
Berkley Maynard Academy	6200 San Pablo Ave	Oakland, CA	94608-2228	510-658-2900	658-1013	K-8	Melissa Granetz
Big Picture HS - Fresno	1207 S Trinity St	Fresno, CA	93706-2611	559-420-1234		7-12	Pasquale Catanzarite
Big Sur Charter S	PO Box 138	Big Sur, CA	93920-0138	831-667-0203	667-2237	K-12	Shawna Garritson
Binkley ES	4965 Canyon Dr	Santa Rosa, CA	95409-3204	707-539-6060	539-4862	PK-6	Mike Herfurth
Birmingham Community HS	17000 Haynes St	Van Nuys, CA	91406-5499	818-758-5200	342-5877	9-12	Doris Lasiter
Bitney College Prep HS	135 Joerschke Dr	Grass Valley, CA	95945-5249	530-477-1235	272-1091	9-12	Bruce Herring
Blue Oak Charter Montessori ES	2391 Merrychase Dr	Cameron Park, CA	95682-9094	530-676-0164	676-0758	K-4	Paul Stewart
Blue Oak Charter S	450 W East Ave	Chico, CA	95926-7238	530-879-7483	879-7490	K-8	Laurie Kopping
Bowling Green Chacon Language & Science	6807 Franklin Blvd	Sacramento, CA	95823-1846	916-433-7321	433-7388	K-6	Elizabeth Aguirre
Bowling Green McCoy Academy	4211 Turnbridge Dr	Sacramento, CA	95823-1929	916-433-5426	433-5429	K-6	Elizabeth Aguirre
Bowman Charter S	13777 Bowman Rd	Auburn, CA	95603-3196	530-885-1974	888-8175	K-8	Gary Yee
Bridges Academy	1702 McLaughlin Ave	San Jose, CA	95122-2936	408-283-6400	283-6419	7-8	Paul de Ayora
BRIDGES Charter S	1335 Calle Bouganvilla	Thousand Oaks, CA	91360-6604	805-492-3560		K-8	Nancy Carroll
Bright Star Secondary Academy	2636 S Mansfield Ave	Los Angeles, CA	90016-3512	424-789-8337		9-12	Monique Bonilla
Brittan Acres ES	2000 Belle Ave	San Carlos, CA	94070-3798	650-508-7307	508-7310	K-4	John Triska
Buckingham Magnet Charter S	188 Bella Vista Rd Ste B	Vacaville, CA	95687-5413	707-453-7300	453-7303	9-12	Jeff Erickson
Bullis Charter S	102 W Portola Ave	Los Altos, CA	94022-1210	650-947-4939	947-4989	K-8	Wanny Hersey
Burton Pathways Charter Academy	1414 W Olive Ave	Porterville, CA	93257-3062	559-782-4748	782-4708	9-12	Troy Hayes
Burton Technology Academy HS	10101 S Broadway	Los Angeles, CA	90003-4534	323-920-6125	920-6950	9-12	Robert Pambello
Butterfield Charter HS	600 W Grand Ave	Porterville, CA	93257-2029	559-782-7057	782-7090	9-12	Fernando Carrera
Cain MS	150 Palm Ave	Auburn, CA	95603-3712	530-823-6106	823-0943	6-8	Randy Ittner
Cali Calmecac Language Academy	9491 Starr Rd	Windsor, CA	95492-9460	707-837-7747	837-7752	K-8	Jeanne Acuna
California Academy for Liberal Studies	7350 N Figueroa St	Los Angeles, CA	90041-2547	213-239-0063	239-9008	9-12	Connie Rivas
California Academy for Liberal Studies	7350 N Figueroa St	Los Angeles, CA	90041-2547	323-254-4427	254-4099	6-8	Nancy Villagomez
California College Prep Academy	2125 Jefferson Ave	Berkeley, CA	94703-1414	510-486-8133	486-2385	9-12	Javier Cabra
California Heritage Youthbuild Academy	451 Sierra Park Rd	Mammoth Lakes, CA	93546	760-034-0031		9-12	Cathy Taylor
California Military Institute	755 N A St	Perris, CA	92570-1958	951-443-2731	943-0473	6-12	Richard Wallis
California Montessori Project-Capitol	2635 Chestnut Hill Dr	Sacramento, CA	95826-2912	916-325-0910	325-0912	K-8	Bernie Evangelista
California Montessori Project-Elk Grove	8828 Elk Grove Blvd Ste 4	Elk Grove, CA	95624-1875	916-714-9699	714-9703	K-8	Kathleen Merz
California Montessori Project-Shingl Spr	4645 Buckeye Rd	Shingle Springs, CA	95682-9505	530-672-3095	672-3097	K-8	Kim Zawilski
California Virtual Academies	2360 Shasta Way Ste A	Simi Valley, CA	93065-1800	805-581-0202	581-0330	K-12	Katrina Abston
Camarillo Academy of Progressive Educ	777 Aileen St	Camarillo, CA	93010-2959	805-384-1415	385-1473	K-8	MaryEllen Lang
Camino Nuevo Academy - Cisneros	1018 Mohawk St	Los Angeles, CA	90026-3131	213-353-5300	596-3878	K-8	Shannon Leonard
Camino Nuevo Charter Academy	635 S Harvard Blvd	Los Angeles, CA	90005-2511	213-736-5542	736-5664	PK-8	Heather McManus
Camino Nuevo Charter HS	3500 W Temple St	Los Angeles, CA	90004-3620	213-736-5566	736-5066	9-12	Julie Jhun
Camino Nuevo Charter S Burlington Campus	697 S Burlington Ave	Los Angeles, CA	90057-3743	213-413-4245	413-8553	K-8	Sean Holiday
Camino Nuevo ES - Jose Castellanos	1723 Cordova St	Los Angeles, CA	90007-1114	323-730-7165	737-5626	K-5	Yvonne Carrillo
Camino Science & Natural Rsrcs Charter S	3060 Snows Rd	Camino, CA	95709-9578	530-644-2204	644-5412	K-8	Daylin Boyd
Camptonville Academy	922 G St	Marysville, CA	95901-5122	530-742-2786	742-6067	K-12	Christopher Mahurin
Canyon ES	421 Entrada Dr	Santa Monica, CA	90402-1303	310-454-7510	454-7543	K-5	Joyce Dara
Capistrano Connections Academy	26800 Aliso Viejo Pkwy #120	Aliso Viejo, CA	92656	949-492-9131	492-9140	K-12	Richard Savage
Capitol Collegiate Academy	2118 Meadowview Rd	Sacramento, CA	95832-1212	916-476-5796		K-8	Penny Schwinn
Capitol Heights Academy	2520 33rd St	Sacramento, CA	95817-1943	916-739-8520	739-8529	K-8	Kristen Murphy
Career & Technical HS	2829 Transworld Dr	Stockton, CA	95206-3950	209-468-5940	468-9000	9-12	Kathleen Focacci
Carpenter Community Charter S	3909 Carpenter Ave	Studio City, CA	91604-3793	818-761-4363	508-6724	K-5	Joseph Martinez
Carver S of Arts & Sciences	10101 Systems Pkwy	Sacramento, CA	95827-3007	916-228-5751	228-5760	9-12	Allegra Alessandri
Casa Ramona Academy for Technology	1524 W 7th St	San Bernardino, CA	92411-2508	909-888-3132		K-12	Esther Ramos Estrada
Castle Rock Charter S	1260 Glenn St	Crescent City, CA	95531	707-464-0390	464-9606	K-12	Jeff Napier
Cecil Avenue Math & Science Academy	1430 Cecil Ave	Delano, CA	93215-1444	661-721-5030	721-5097	6-8	Darrell Hennessee
Ceiba College Preparatory Academy	280 Main St	Watsonville, CA	95076-5047	831-345-6056	464-3213	6-8	Heidy Shinn
Celerity Cardinal Charter S	7330 Bakman Ave	Sun Valley, CA	91352-4914	323-479-8842	688-3835	K-5	Wilbur Estrada
Celerity Dyad Charter S	4501 Wadsworth Ave	Los Angeles, CA	90011-3637	323-231-1202	231-1255	K-8	Vielka McFarlane
Celerity Nascent Charter S	4231 4th Ave	Los Angeles, CA	90008-3903	323-732-6613	733-2977	K-8	Angela Beck
Celerity Nascent Charter S	3417 W Jefferson Blvd	Los Angeles, CA	90018-3235	323-732-6613	733-2977	K-8	Angela Beck
Celerity Octavia Charter S	3010 Estara Ave	Los Angeles, CA	90065-2205	310-904-2012	843-9912	K-8	Nadia Shaiq
Celerity Palmati Charter S	6501 Laurel Canyon Blvd	North Hollywood, CA	91606-1520	323-459-7661	301-2278	K-6	Titchamroeun Son
Celerity Sirius Charter S	900 E Rosecrans Ave	Los Angeles, CA	90059-3513	310-764-1234		K-5	Autrillia Gillis
Celerity Troika Charter S	1495 Colorado Blvd	Los Angeles, CA	90041-2366	323-344-0160	344-0165	K-8	Megan McNamara
Centennial College Preparatory Academy	2079 Saturn Ave	Huntington Park, CA	90255-3635	323-826-9616	588-7342	6-8	Jennifer Garcia
Center for Advanced Learning	4016 S Central Ave	Los Angeles, CA	90011-2708	323-232-0245	233-3675	K-5	Brooke Jackson
Center for Advanced Research Technology	2555 Clovis Ave	Clovis, CA	93612-3901	559-248-7400	248-7423	11-12	Devin Blizzard
Central California Connections Academy	4020 S Demaree St Ste B	Visalia, CA	93277-9476	559-713-1324	713-1330	K-12	Bill Crocket
Central City Value S	221 N Westmoreland Ave	Los Angeles, CA	90004-4815	213-471-4686	471-4693	9-12	David Doyle
Century Academy for Excellence	2400 W 85th St	Inglewood, CA	90305-1816	323-752-8834	752-8874	6-8	Giselle Edman
Century Community Charter S	901 Maple St	Inglewood, CA	90301-3823	310-412-2286	412-4085	6-8	Teri Delahousie-Norris
Charter Alternatives Academy	28050 Road 148	Visalia, CA	93292-9297	559-730-7491	730-7490	7-12	Scott Braden
Charter Alternative S	6520 Oak Dell Rd	El Dorado, CA	95623-4322	530-622-6984	621-2543	K-8	David Publicover
Charter Community S and Home Study Acad	6767 Green Valley Rd	Placerville, CA	95667-8984	530-295-2259	642-0492	7-12	David Publicover
Charter HS of Arts Multimedia/Performing	6842 Van Nuys Blvd	Van Nuys, CA	91405-4650	818-994-4744	994-0099	9-12	John Biroc Ph.D.
Charter Home School Academy	31411 Road 160	Visalia, CA	93292-9019	559-730-7916	735-8060	K-8	Christine Fischer
Charter S of Morgan Hill	9530 Monterey Rd	Morgan Hill, CA	95037-9356	408-463-0618	463-0267	K-8	Paige Cisewski
Charter S of San Diego	10170 Huennekens St	San Diego, CA	92121-2964	858-678-2020	552-6660	7-12	Ginese Quann
Chicago Park Community Charter S	15725 Mount Olive Rd	Grass Valley, CA	95945-7906	530-346-2153	346-8559	K-8	Dan Zeisler
Chico Country Day S	102 W 11th St	Chico, CA	95928-6006	530-895-2650	895-9159	K-8	
Children of Promise Preparatory Academy	3130 W 111th Pl	Inglewood, CA	90303-2315	310-677-3014	677-1599	K-3	Carleton Lincoln
Children's Community Charter S	6830 Pentz Rd	Paradise, CA	95969-2902	530-877-2227	872-1396	K-8	Sharon Norris
CHIME Institute's Schwarzenegger Cmnty S	19722 Collier St	Woodland Hills, CA	91364-3618	818-346-5100	346-5120	K-8	Jennifer Lockwood
Choice 2000 On-Line S	755 N A St	Perris, CA	92570-1958	951-940-5700	940-5706	7-12	Rick Wallis
Chrysalis Charter S	PO Box 709	Palo Cedro, CA	96073-0709	530-547-9726	547-9734	K-8	Paul Krafel
Chula Vista Learning Community Charter S	590 K St	Chula Vista, CA	91911-1118	619-426-2885	426-3048	K-6	Dr. Jorge Ramirez

School	Address	City,State	Zip code	Telephone	Fax	Grade	Contact
Cielo Vista Charter S	650 S Paseo Dorotea	Palm Springs, CA	92264-1499	760-416-8250	416-8253	K-6	Lynda Lake
Circle of Independent Learning	4700 Calaveras Ave	Fremont, CA	94538-1124	510-797-0100	797-0118	K-12	Lisa Cole
Citizens of the World Charter S	5482 Wilshire Blvd Ste 149	Los Angeles, CA	90036-4218	323-634-7113	634-7115	K-3	Amy Dresser-Held
Citizens of the World Charter S	1316 N Bronson Ave	Hollywood, CA	90028-8415	323-464-4292	464-8292	K-8	Marissa Berman
City Arts & Technology HS	325 La Grande Ave	San Francisco, CA	94112-2866	415-841-2200	695-5326	9-12	Daniel Allen
City Heights Preparatory Academy	3770 Altadena Ave	San Diego, CA	92105-3007	619-795-3137		6-12	Dr. Marnie Nair
City Honors Charter HS	155 W Kelso St	Inglewood, CA	90301-2237	310-680-4880	680-5144	9-12	Joy Bramlette
City S	1518 S Robertson Blvd	Los Angeles, CA	90035-4232	310-273-2489	273-2499	6-8	Sheri Werner
Civicorps Academy	101 Myrtle St	Oakland, CA	94607-2543	510-992-7800	992-7950	9-12	Tessa Nicholas
Classical Academy	2950 Bear Valley Pkwy S	Escondido, CA	92025-7446	760-546-0101	739-8289	K-8	Cameron Curry
Classical Academy HS	144 Woodward Ave	Escondido, CA	92025-2637	760-480-9845	739-8289	9-12	Dana Moen
Clayton Valley Charter HS	1101 Alberta Way	Concord, CA	94521-3747	925-682-7474	825-7859	9-12	David Linzey
Clovis Online S	1655 David E Cook Way	Clovis, CA	93611-0581	559-327-4400	327-4490	7-12	Kevin Cookingham
Coastal Academy Charter	4183 Avenida de la Plata	Oceanside, CA	92056-6037	760-631-4020	739-8289	K-8	Marcy Cashin
Coastal Grove Charter S	PO Box 510	Arcata, CA	95518-0510	707-825-8804	825-1761	K-8	Bettina Eipper
Cole Academy	333 E Walnut St	Santa Ana, CA	92701-5928	714-836-9023	836-9041	K-5	John Norton
Coleman Tech HS	3540 Aero Ct	San Diego, CA	92123-1711	858-874-4338	874-5645	9-12	Dr. Nicole Wahab
Colfax Charter ES	11724 Addison St	North Hollywood, CA	91607-3202	818-761-5115	985-6017	K-5	Susana Gomez
College Preparatory MS	5150 Jackson Dr	La Mesa, CA	91942-9001	619-303-2782	303-3759	5-8	Christina Callaway
College Ready Academy HS #5	4610 S Main St	Los Angeles, CA	90037-2736	323-342-2874	342-2875	9-12	Dean Marolla
College Ready Academy HS #16	1575 W 2nd St	Los Angeles, CA	90026-5701	213-427-4837	943-4931	9-12	Carmen Vasquez-Mancini
College Ready Middle Academy #4	9719 S Main St	Los Angeles, CA	90003-4135	323-451-3009	249-6784	6-8	Leticia Vallejo
College Ready Middle Academy #5	211 S Avenue 20	Los Angeles, CA	90031-2508	323-987-1680	987-1687	6-8	Judy Burton
College Ready Middle Academy #7	2941 W 70th St	Los Angeles, CA	90043-4420	323-920-4388		6-8	Luis Ramirez
Collins School at Cherry Valley	1001 Cherry St	Petaluma, CA	94952-2065	707-778-4740	778-4839	K-8	Chad Carvey
Community Charter Early College HS	11500 Eldridge Ave	Lake View Ter, CA	91342-6522	818-485-0951	485-0952	9-12	Brian Wagner
Community Charter MS	11500 Eldridge Ave	Lake View Ter, CA	91342-6522	818-485-0933	485-0940	6-8	Dr. Ron Alatorre
Community Collaborative Charter S	9880 Jackson Rd	Sacramento, CA	95827-9706	916-369-5533	369-3959	K-8	Joi Tikoi
Community Collaborative Charter S	5715 Skvarla Ave	McClellan, CA	95652-2424	916-286-5161	643-2031	K-12	Jon Campbell
Community Magnet ES	11301 Bellagio Rd	Los Angeles, CA	90049-1705	310-476-2281	472-6391	K-5	Carla Cretaro
Community Outreach Academy	5637 Skvarla Ave	McClellan, CA	95652-2439	916-286-5170	640-0227	4-6	Larissa Gonchar
Community Outreach Academy	3800 Bolivar Ave	North Highlands, CA	95660-4370	916-286-1908	286-1992	7-8	Anjam Khan
Community Outreach Academy	5800 Skvarla Ave	McClellan, CA	95652-2418	916-286-5170	640-0227	K-2	Larissa Gonchar
Community S for Creative Education	8755 Fontaine St	Oakland, CA	94605-4141	510-517-0331		K-8	Ida Oberman
Competitive Edge Charter Academy	34450 Stonewood Dr	Yucaipa, CA	92399-6852	909-790-3207	790-8364	K-8	Jeff Litel
Connecting Waters Charter S	12420 Bentley St	Waterford, CA	95386-9158	209-874-9463	874-9531	K-12	Sherri Nelson
Connections VPA Academy	17555 Tuolumne Rd	Tuolumne, CA	95379-9701	209-928-4228	928-1422	7-12	Diana Hardford
Conservatory of Vocal/Instrumental Arts	3800 Mountain Blvd	Oakland, CA	94619-1630	510-285-7511		K-8	Valerie Abad
Constellation Charter S	620 Olive Ave	Long Beach, CA	90802-1546	562-435-7181		6-8	
CORE Butte Charter S	260 Cohasset Rd Ste 120	Chico, CA	95926-2282	530-894-3952	566-9819	K-12	Jonelle Pena
CORE Placer Charter S	1033 S Auburn St	Colfax, CA	95713-9703	530-346-8340	346-2446	K-12	Kathryn Peak
Cornerstone Academy Preparatory	1598 Lucretia Ave	San Jose, CA	95122	408-361-3876		K-6	Shara Hegde
Corona Charter S	9400 Remick Ave	Pacoima, CA	91331-4223	818-834-5805	834-8075	6-8	Ruben Duenas
Cottonwood Creek Charter S	3425 Brush St	Cottonwood, CA	96022	530-347-7200	347-9375	K-8	Mark Boyle
Cox Academy	9860 Sunnyside St	Oakland, CA	94603-2750	510-904-6300	904-6730	K-5	Julia Nowlin
Creative Arts Charter S	1601 Turk St	San Francisco, CA	94115-4527	415-749-3509	749-3437	K-8	Paul Greenwood
Creative Connections Art Academy	6444 Walerga Rd	North Highlands, CA	95660-3945	916-566-3470	566-3505	6-11	Joe Breault
Creative Connections Arts Academy	7201 Arutas Dr	North Highlands, CA	95660-2809	916-566-1870	331-2959	K-5	Joe Breault
Creekside Cooperative Charter S	PO Box 5369	Tahoe City, CA	96145-5369	530-581-1036	581-2012	K-8	Camille Taylor
Crenshaw Arts-Technology Charter HS	4120 11th Ave	Los Angeles, CA	90008-3712	323-778-7700	778-7712	9-12	Ginger Stemnock
Crescent Valley Public Charter S	309 W Main St Ste 110	Visalia, CA	93291-6257	559-970-5894	243-9102	K-12	Abigail Sipes
Crescent View Charter West HS	1901 E Shields Ave	Fresno, CA	93726	559-225-1106	225-1205	9-12	Rafael Aguilar
Crescent View South Charter S	1901 E Shields Ave	Fresno, CA	93726-5313	559-222-8439	222-8430	K-12	Demitri Gonos
Crossroads Charter S	418 W 8th St	Hanford, CA	93230-4536	559-585-7295	585-7298	K-12	Laurie Blue
Crown Preparatory Academy	2055 W 24th St	Los Angeles, CA	90018-1925	213-448-9747	410-2271	5-8	Laura McGowan
Culture & Language Academy of Success	4400 Coliseum St	Los Angeles, CA	90016-5734	310-294-0782	294-5763	K-8	Janis Bucknor
Culture & Language Academy of Success	6550 W 80th St	Los Angeles, CA	90045-1127	310-665-0214	665-2914	2-8	Anthony Jackson
Cypress Charter HS	2039 Merrill St	Santa Cruz, CA	95062-4176	831-477-0302	477-7659	9-12	Les Forster
Dailey Charter ES	3135 N Harrison Ave	Fresno, CA	93704-5299	559-248-7060	227-5530	K-5	Melissa Dutra
Dantzler Preparatory Charter ES	1260 W 36th Pl	Los Angeles, CA	90007-3947	323-290-6968		K-5	Glenetta Pope
Dantzler Preparatory Charter HS	7400 W Manchester Ave	Los Angeles, CA	90045-2399	323-290-0935	783-4011	9-12	Germaine Decree
Dantzler Preparatory Charter MS	5029 S Vermont Ave	Los Angeles, CA	90037-2907	323-290-6930	460-9606	6-8	Candice Waters
Darnall Charter S	6020 Hughes St	San Diego, CA	92115-6520	619-582-1822	287-4732	K-6	Leslie Dahab
DaVinci Academy JSHS	1400 E 8th St	Davis, CA	95616-2404	530-757-7154	759-2178	7-12	Rody Boonchouy
DaVinci Design S	12501 Isis Ave	Hawthorne, CA	90250-4149	310-725-5800	643-7659	K-12	Matthew Wunder
DaVinci Health Sciences Charter S	PO Box 8830	Chula Vista, CA	91912-8830	619-420-0066	420-0677	K-6	Amber Goslee
DaVinci Science S	13500 Aviation Blvd	Hawthorne, CA	90250-6462	310-725-5800	643-3013	K-12	Matthew Wunder
Dearborn ES	9240 Wish Ave	Northridge, CA	91325-2533	818-349-4381	886-2149	K-5	Debra Hirsch
Dehesa Charter S	1441 Montiel Rd Ste 143	Escondido, CA	92026-2242	760-743-7880	743-7919	K-12	Terri Novacek
Delta Charter ES	PO Box 127	Clarksburg, CA	95612-0127	916-744-1200	744-1246	K-6	Steve Lewis
Delta Charter S	343 Soquel Ave	Santa Cruz, CA	95062-2355	831-477-5213	479-6173	9-12	Mary Gaukel Forster
Delta Charter S	31400 S Koster Rd	Tracy, CA	95304-8824	209-830-6363	830-9707	K-12	Stephanie Lytle
Del Vista Math & Science Academy	710 Quincy St	Delano, CA	93215-3044	661-721-5040	721-5087	K-5	Rosa Montes
Denair Academic Avenues	3460 Lester Rd	Denair, CA	95316-9502	209-632-6906	632-6908	1-5	Carol Hammond
Denair Charter Academy	3460 Lester Rd	Denair, CA	95316-9502	209-634-0917	669-9282	K-12	Michelle Bush
Desert Sands Charter HS	44130 20th St W	Lancaster, CA	93534-4045	661-942-3357	944-4857	9-12	Cheri Tuinstra Ed.D.
Diego Hills Charter S	4585 College Ave	San Diego, CA	92115-4011	619-286-0312	286-0791	K-12	Armando Martinez
Discovery Charter Preparatory S	12550 Van Nuys Blvd	Pacoima, CA	91331-1354	818-897-1187	897-1295	9-12	Karen Smith
Discovery Charter S	1100 Camino Biscay	Chula Vista, CA	91910-7737	619-656-0797	656-3899	K-6	Dr. Patricia Maruca
Discovery Charter S	51 E Beverly Pl	Tracy, CA	95376-3191	209-831-5240	831-5243	5-8	Virginia Stewart
Discovery Charter S	4021 Teale Ave	San Jose, CA	95117-3433	408-243-9800	243-9812	K-8	Dale Jones
Dixie Canyon Community Charter S	4220 Dixie Canyon Ave	Sherman Oaks, CA	91423-3904	818-784-6283	788-3340	K-5	Lea Moche
Dixon Montessori Charter S	355 N Almond St	Dixon, CA	95620-2702	707-678-8953	676-5215	K-8	Joanne Green
Doris Topsy-Elvord Academy	5951 Downey Ave	Long Beach, CA	90805-4518	562-630-6096	630-6038	6-8	Karla Smith
Douglass Academy ES	2400 S Western Ave	Los Angeles, CA	90018-2607	323-290-6997	415-9130	K-5	Kazuki Uema
Douglass Academy HS	3200 W Adams Blvd	Los Angeles, CA	90018-1832	323-290-6992	317-2841	9-12	Dr. Luther Waters
Douglass Academy MS	3200 W Adams Blvd	Los Angeles, CA	90018-1832	323-290-6940	540-3749	6-8	Karen Anderson
Downtown College Prep - Alum Rock	1250 S King Rd	San Jose, CA	95122-2146	408-942-7000	942-7007	6-8	
Downtown College Preparatory	1460 The Alameda	San Jose, CA	95126-2652	408-271-1730	271-1734	9-12	Ruth Schriver
Downtown Value S	950 W Washington Blvd	Los Angeles, CA	90015-3312	213-748-8062	748-8868	K-8	Gerry Jacoby
Dunham Charter S	4111 Roblar Rd	Petaluma, CA	94952-9202	707-795-5050	795-5166	K-6	Adam Schaible
Dunlap Leadership Academy	39500 Dunlap Rd	Dunlap, CA	93621	559-305-7320	338-2026	9-12	Gary Willems
Eagle Peak Montessori S	800 Hutchinson Rd	Walnut Creek, CA	94598-4505	925-946-0994	946-9409	K-6	Michelle Hammons
Early College Acad for Leaders/Scholars	2050 N San Fernando Rd	Los Angeles, CA	90065-1267	323-276-5525	276-5534	9-12	Mara Simmons
East Oakland Leadership Academy	2614 Seminary Ave	Oakland, CA	94605-1570	510-562-5238	562-5239	K-8	Dr. Laura Armstrong
East Palo Alto Academy	475 Pope St	Menlo Park, CA	94025-2800	650-329-2811	321-6628	9-12	Larry Vilaubi
East Palo Alto Charter S	1286 Runnymede St	East Palo Alto, CA	94303-1332	650-614-9100	614-9183	K-8	Sharon Johnson
eCademy Charter S	1100 Cahill Ave	Turlock, CA	95380-4102	209-669-3410	669-0180	K-12	Robin Swartz
Edison-Bethune Charter Academy	1616 S Fruit Ave	Fresno, CA	93706-2819	559-457-2530	498-0711	K-6	Rodolfo Garcia
Edison Charter Academy	3531 22nd St	San Francisco, CA	94114-3405	415-970-3330	285-0527	K-8	Adrienne Morrell
Educational Outreach Academy	PO Box 1507	Red Bluff, CA	96080-1507	530-529-8755	529-8709	7-12	Julian Howell
Eel River Charter S	PO Box 218	Covelo, CA	95428-0218	707-983-6946	983-6197	K-6	Betty Tuttle
Einstein Academy	3035 Ash St	San Diego, CA	92102-1718	619-795-1190	795-1180	K-5	Jeannette Vaughn
Einstein Academy MS	3035 Ash St	San Diego, CA	92102-1718	619-795-1190	795-1180	6-8	David Sciarretta
Einstein Acad Letters Arts Sci	28141 Kelly Johnson Pkwy	Santa Clarita, CA	91355-5003	661-702-0755	775-0321	7-12	Edward Gika
EJE Academy Charter ES	851 S Johnson Ave	El Cajon, CA	92020-5811	619-401-4150	401-4151	K-8	Delia Pacheco
El Camino Real Charter HS	5440 Valley Circle Blvd	Woodland Hills, CA	91367-5996	818-595-7500	710-9023	9-12	David Fehte
Elk Grove Charter S	10065 Atkins Dr	Elk Grove, CA	95757-4309	916-714-1653	714-1721	K-12	Marc Levine
El Oro Way Charter S	12230 El Oro Way	Granada Hills, CA	91344-1600	818-360-2288	360-3264	K-5	SooJoon Choi
El Rancho Charter S	181 S Del Giorgio Rd	Anaheim, CA	92808-1307	714-997-6238	281-8791	7-8	John Besta
El Sol Santa Ana Science & Arts Academy	1010 N Broadway	Santa Ana, CA	92701-3408	714-543-0023	543-0026	K-6	Alberto Hananel
Emerson Parkside Academy	2625 Josie Ave	Long Beach, CA	90815-1511	562-420-2631	420-7642	K-5	Margaret Kerns
Enadia ES	22944 Enadia Way	West Hills, CA	91307-2206	818-595-3900	716-7738	K-5	Vivian Cordoba
Encino Charter ES	16941 Addison St	Encino, CA	91316-3433	818-784-1762	995-7110	K-5	Marcia Koff
Encore HS for Performing & Visual Arts	16955 Lemon St	Hesperia, CA	92345-5139	760-956-2632	956-7052	7-12	Denise Griffin
Endeavor College Prep Charter S	126 Bloom St	Los Angeles, CA	90012-1902	323-947-7311	843-9502	4-8	Michelle Jasso
Environmental Charter HS	16315 Grevillea Ave	Lawndale, CA	90260-2858	310-214-3400	214-3410	9-12	Alison Diaz
Environmental Charter MS	3600 W Imperial Hwy	Inglewood, CA	90303-2714	310-425-1605	680-9843	6-8	Kami Cotler
Environmental Science & Technology HS	2930 Fletcher Dr	Los Angeles, CA	90065-1407	323-739-0560	739-0565	9-12	Melissa Chew
Envision Academy for Arts & Technology	1515 Webster St	Oakland, CA	94612-3355	510-596-8901	596-8905	9-12	Kirsten Grimm
Equitas Academy Charter S	1740 N New Hampshire Ave	Los Angeles, CA	90027-4208	213-201-0440	652-4444	K-5	Malka Borrego
Equitas Academy Charter S	1700 W Pico Blvd	Los Angeles, CA	90015-2412	213-201-0440	652-4444	K-5	Malka Borrego
eScholar Academy	715 Jackson St Ste B	Red Bluff, CA	96080-3771	530-527-0188	527-0273	6-12	Dr. Harold Vietti
Escondido Charter HS	1868 E Valley Pkwy	Escondido, CA	92027-2525	760-737-3154	738-8996	9-12	Denny Snyder
Escuela Popular Accelerated Family Lrng	467 N White Rd	San Jose, CA	95127-1441	408-275-7190	275-7192	K-12	Patricia Reguerin
Escuela Popular/Ctr Training & Careers	467 N White Rd	San Jose, CA	95127-1441	408-275-7193	259-7473	9-12	Patricia Reguerin
Everest Public HS	455 5th Ave	Redwood City, CA	94063-3727	650-366-1050	366-1892	9-12	Kelly Garcia

School	Address	City,State	Zip code	Telephone	Fax	Grade	Contact
Excel Academy	2720 Transworld Dr	Stockton, CA	95206-3947	209-227-2300		7-12	Lonnie Cox
Excel Charter Academy	1855 N Main St	Los Angeles, CA	90031-3227	323-222-5010	222-5148	6-8	Zenzontl Kuauhtzin
Excel Prep Charter S	1672 Palm Ave	Highland, CA	92346-2502	909-864-6000	864-6100	K-8	Antoinette Sims
Excelsior Education Center Charter S	18422 Bear Valley Rd # 11	Victorville, CA	92395-5850	760-245-4262	245-4009	7-12	Michael Hayhurst
Explorer ES	2230 Truxtun Rd Ste A	San Diego, CA	92106-6128	619-795-3600	795-3090	K-5	Mike Seal
Extera Public School	2226 E 3rd St	Los Angeles, CA	90033-3906	323-454-2430	319-2025	K-6	Jim Kennedy Ed.D.
Fairmont Charter ES	1355 Marshall Rd	Vacaville, CA	95687-5519	707-453-6240	447-0759	K-6	Deanna Brownlee
FAME Public Charter S	39899 Balentine Dr Ste 335	Newark, CA	94560-5359	510-687-9111	687-9145	K-12	Maram Alaiwat
Family Partnership Home Study Charter S	545 Alisal Rd	Solvang, CA	93463-2606	805-686-5339	686-4658	K-12	Todd Mitchell
Fammatre Charter ES	2800 New Jersey Ave	San Jose, CA	95124-1556	408-377-5480	377-8751	K-5	Kristi Schwiebert
Farnham Charter S	15711 Woodard Rd	San Jose, CA	95124-2697	408-377-3321	377-7237	K-5	Linh Nguyen
Feaster Charter S	670 Flower St	Chula Vista, CA	91910-1399	619-422-8397	422-4780	K-6	Francisco Velasco
Fenton Avenue Charter S	11828 Gain St	Sylmar, CA	91342-7132	818-896-7482	890-9986	2-5	Michelle Rappino
Fenton Primary Center	11828 Gain St	Sylmar, CA	91342-7132	818-896-7482	890-9986	K-1	Richard Parra
Film and Theatre Arts	3801 S Broadway	Los Angeles, CA	90037-1411	323-231-3915	231-7232	9-12	Steve Bachrach
Finch S	451 S Villa Ave	Willows, CA	95988-2964	530-934-6320	934-6325	K-12	Susan Domenighini
Five Keys Charter S	70 Oak Grove St	San Francisco, CA	94107-1019	415-734-3310	734-3314	9-12	Steve Good
Folsom Cordova Community Charter S	715 Riley St	Folsom, CA	95630-3053	916-985-2239	985-3665	K-8	Wayne Edney
Forest Charter S	470 Searls Ave	Nevada City, CA	95959-3030	530-265-4823	265-5037	K-12	Peter Sagebiel
Forest Ranch Charter S	15815 Cedar Creek Rd	Forest Ranch, CA	95942	530-891-3154	891-3155	K-6	Christia Marasco
Forestville ES	6321 Hwy 116	Forestville, CA	95436-9614	707-887-2279	887-2185	PK-1	Talin Tamzarian
Fortune S	6829 Stockton Blvd Ste 380	Sacramento, CA	95823-2396	916-287-4470		K-8	Odisa Nyong
Fremont Charter S	1120 W 22nd St	Merced, CA	95340-3540	209-385-6627	385-6301	K-5	Trisha Wylie
Freshwater Charter MS	75 Greenwood Heights Dr	Eureka, CA	95503-9441	707-442-2969	442-9527	7-8	Thom McMahon
Frontier ES	1854 Mustang Dr	Hanford, CA	93230-9811	559-585-2430	585-2440	K-5	John Raven
Fuenta Nueva Charter S	1897 S St	Arcata, CA	95521-5474	707-822-3348	822-5862	K-5	Beth Wylie
Futures HS	3701 Stephen Dr	North Highlands, CA	95660-4532	916-286-1902	263-6059	7-12	Nataliya Burko
Futuro College Prep ES	1314 S Dacotah St	Los Angeles, CA	90023-2707	323-397-1440	221-1311	K-5	Edward Morris
Gabriella Charter S	1435 Logan St	Los Angeles, CA	90026-3307	213-413-5741	413-5874	K-8	Lisa Rooney
Garfield ES	3600 Middlefield Rd	Menlo Park, CA	94025-3010	650-369-3759	367-4358	K-8	Michelle Griffith
GARR Academy of Math & Entrepreneurial	5101 S Western Ave	Los Angeles, CA	90062-2333	323-294-2008	295-3936	K-5	William Green
Gates ES	23882 Landisview Ave	Lake Forest, CA	92630-5199	949-837-2260	837-5013	K-6	Yvonne Estling
Gateway HS	1430 Scott St	San Francisco, CA	94115-3510	415-749-3600	749-2716	9-12	Sharon Olken
Gateway MS	2340 Jackson St	San Francisco, CA	94115-1323	415-922-1001	922-1055	6-8	Aaron Watson
Gateway to College Early College HS	4800 Magnolia Ave	Riverside, CA	92506-1201	951-222-8931	222-8975	10-12	Jill Marks
Germain Charter Academy	20730 Germain St	Chatsworth, CA	91311-2418	818-341-5821	882-3599	K-5	Sonia Ugarte
Gertz-Ressler HS-College Ready HS 1	2023 S Union Ave	Los Angeles, CA	90007-1326	213-745-8141	745-8142	9-12	James Waller
Glacier Charter HS	41267 Highway 41	Oakhurst, CA	93644-9403	559-642-1422	642-1592	9-12	Michael Cox
Global College Prep Charter HS	3243 Center Court Ln	Antelope, CA	95843-9111	916-339-4680	339-4684	9-12	Doug Hughey
Global Education Academy	4141 S Figueroa St	Los Angeles, CA	90037-2038	310-232-9588	232-9587	K-5	Craig Merrill
Goethe International Charter S	12500 Braddock Dr	Los Angeles, CA	90066-6808	310-306-3484	306-3245	K-8	Nancy Marorelli
Golden Eagle Charter S	2226 S Mount Shasta Blvd #C	Mount Shasta, CA	96067	530-926-5800	926-5826	K-12	Shelly Adams
Golden Lakes Charter S	3191 El Prado Rd	La Grange, CA	95329-9761	209-852-9563	852-9646	K-12	Mari Brabbin
Golden Oak Montessori S of Hayward	951 Palisade St	Hayward, CA	94542-1048	510-931-7868		1-8	Deirdre Fennesey
Golden State Virtual Academy	800 W Elm St	Bishop, CA	93514-2524	760-872-3680	872-6016	9-12	Randy Cook
Golden Valley Charter S	2421 Portola Rd Ste C	Ventura, CA	93003-8048	805-642-3435	642-3468	K-12	Terri Adams
Golden Valley Charter S	9601 Lake Natoma Dr	Orangevale, CA	95662-5099	916-987-6141	987-6741	K-8	Deborah Lenny
Gold Rush Charter HS	14683 Mono Way	Sonora, CA	95370-9220	209-533-8644	532-9234	9-12	Kathleen Hansen
Gold Rush Charter S	10304 Fiske Rd	Coulterville, CA	95311-9502	209-878-3481		K-8	Kathleen Hansen
Gompers Preparatory Academy	1005 47th St	San Diego, CA	92102-3626	619-263-2171	264-4342	6-12	Vince Riveroll
Gorman Learning Center	1826 Orange Tree Ln	Redlands, CA	92374-2821	909-307-6312	793-5964	K-12	Ambler Moss
Granada Hills Charter HS	10535 Zelzah Ave	Granada Hills, CA	91344-5999	818-360-2361	363-9504	9-12	Brian Bauer
Grass Valley Charter S at Hennessy	225 S Auburn St	Grass Valley, CA	95945-7229	530-273-8723	271-0557	PK-8	Brian Martinez
Gratton ES	4500 S Gratton Rd	Denair, CA	95316-9762	209-632-0505	632-7810	K-8	Shannon Sanford-Rice
Grayson Charter S	PO Box 7	Westley, CA	95387-0007	209-892-4725	894-3393	K-5	Arturo Duran
Greater San Diego Academy	13881 Campo Rd Ste A-5	Jamul, CA	91935-3208	619-669-3050	669-3066	K-12	Gail Levine
Great Valley Academy	486 Button Ave	Manteca, CA	95336-8596	209-824-5400	239-3436	K-8	Russell Howell
Great Valley Academy	3200 Tully Rd	Modesto, CA	95350-0811	209-576-2283	576-2838	K-4	
Green Valley Charter S	PO Box 1311	Los Banos, CA	93635-1311	209-587-4150		K-3	Tisha Blackwood-Freitas
Grimmway Academy	11001 River Run Boulevard	Arvin, CA	93203	661-855-8200		K-6	Jose Salas
Grizzly ChalleNGe Charter S	PO Box 3209	San Luis Obispo, CA	93403-3209	805-782-6882	594-6341	10-12	Paul Piette
Grove S	200 Nevada St	Redlands, CA	92373-5385	909-798-7831	307-6464	7-12	Gena Engelfried
Guajome Park Academy	2000 N Santa Fe Ave	Vista, CA	92083-1534	760-631-8500	631-8504	K-12	Bob Hampton
Guidance Charter S	1125 E Palmdale Blvd Ste B	Palmdale, CA	93550-4867	661-272-1701	272-1728	K-8	Kamal Al-Khatib
HAAAT	26400 Dartmouth St	Hemet, CA	92544-6302	951-925-5155	929-9017	9-12	Frank Green
Hale Charter Academy	23830 Califa St	Woodland Hills, CA	91367-2922	818-313-7400	346-7517	6-8	Neal Siegel
Hallmark Charter S	2445 9th St	Sanger, CA	93657-2780	559-524-7170	875-3573	K-12	Alfred Sanchez
Hamlin Charter Academy	22627 Hamlin St	West Hills, CA	91307-3603	818-348-4741	348-3506	K-5	Bette Kaplan
Hardy Brown College Prep	295 Carousel Mall Ste 190	San Bernardino, CA	92401-1505	909-884-1410	889-5002	K-8	Susan Nisonger
Harmony Magnet Academy	19429 Road 228	Strathmore, CA	93267	559-568-0347	568-1929	9-12	Jeff Brown
Hart-Ransom Academic Charter S	3920 Shoemake Ave	Modesto, CA	95358-8577	209-523-0401	523-1064	K-12	David Cline
Harvest Ridge Cooperative Charter S	9050 Old State Hwy	Newcastle, CA	95658-9515	916-259-1425	259-1428	K-8	Janet Sutton
Hawthorne Math & Science Academy	4467 W Broadway	Hawthorne, CA	90250-3819	310-973-8620	973-8167	9-12	Esau Berumen
Haynes Charter for Enriched Studies	6624 Lockhurst Dr	West Hills, CA	91307-3135	818-716-7310	716-7249	K-5	Barbara Meade
Healdsburg Charter S @ Fitch Mountain	520 Monte Vista Ave	Healdsburg, CA	95448-3543	707-473-4449	473-4483	3-5	Amber Stringfellow
Healdsburg Charter S @ Healdsburg ES	400 1st St	Healdsburg, CA	95448-3939	707-431-3440	431-3592	K-2	Stephanie Feith
Health Careers Academy	1540 N Lincoln St	Stockton, CA	95204-5617	209-933-7360		9-12	Traci Miller
Health Sciences HS & Middle College	3910 University Ave Ste 100	San Diego, CA	92105-7302	619-528-9070	528-9084	9-12	Sheri North
Health Services Academy HS	12226 S Western Ave	Los Angeles, CA	90047-5240	213-943-4930	943-4931	9-12	Judy Burton
Heather ES	2757 Melendy Dr	San Carlos, CA	94070-3604	650-508-7303	508-7306	K-4	Pam Jasso
Helix HS	7323 University Ave	La Mesa, CA	91942-0592	619-466-4194	462-9257	9-12	Mike Lewis
Heritage Charter S	1855 E Valley Pkwy	Escondido, CA	92027-2517	760-737-3111	737-9322	K-8	Dennis Snyder
Heritage Peak Charter S	6450 20th St	North Highlands, CA	95660	866-992-9033	348-4325	K-12	Dr. Paul Keefer
Hesby Oaks Leadership Charter S	15530 Hesby St	Encino, CA	91436-1519	818-528-7000	907-0788	K-8	David Hirsch
Hickman Charter S	13306 4th St	Hickman, CA	95323-9634	209-874-9070	874-1457	K-8	Paul Gardner
Hickman ES	13306 4th St	Hickman, CA	95323-9634	209-874-1816	874-3721	K-5	Candetta Holdren
Hickman MS	13306 4th St	Hickman, CA	95323-9634	209-556-6540	874-3721	6-8	Candetta Holdren
Higher Learning Academy	2625 Plover St	Sacramento, CA	95815-2712	916-286-5183	643-9893	K-7	Ana Gutierrez
High Tech ES Chula Vista	1949 Discovery Falls Dr	Chula Vista, CA	91915-2037	619-591-2550	591-2553	K-5	Anne Worrall
High Tech High Media Arts	2230 Truxtun Rd Ste B	San Diego, CA	92106-6128	619-398-8640	758-9568	9-12	Robert Kuhl
High Tech HS Chula Vista	1945 Discovery Falls Dr	Chula Vista, CA	91915-2037	619-591-2500	591-2503	9-12	Lillian Hsu
High Tech HS North County	1420 W San Marcos Blvd	San Marcos, CA	92078-4017	760-759-2700	759-2799	9-12	Isaac Jones
High Tech International HS	2855 Farragut Rd	San Diego, CA	92106-6029	619-398-4900	758-1960	9-12	Colleen Green
HighTech LA	17111 Victory Blvd	Van Nuys, CA	91406-5455	818-609-2640	881-1754	9-12	Marsha Rybin
High Tech Middle Media Arts	2230 Truxtun Rd Ste B	San Diego, CA	92106-6128	619-398-8640	758-9568	6-8	Steven Elizondo
High Tech MS	2291 Truxtun Rd	San Diego, CA	92106-6040	619-814-5060	243-5050	6-8	Janie Griswold
High Tech MS Chula Vista	1949 Discovery Falls Dr	Chula Vista, CA	91915-2037	619-591-2530	591-2533	6-8	Melissa Daniels
High Tech MS North Country	1460 W San Marcos Blvd	San Marcos, CA	92078-4017	760-759-2750	759-2779	6-8	Susan Battistuz
Holly Drive Leadership Academy	4801 Elm St	San Diego, CA	92102-1354	619-266-7333	266-7330	K-8	Alysia Smith
Holt College Prep Academy	3201 Morada Ln	Stockton, CA	95212-3110	209-955-1477	955-1472	6-12	Gretchen Salvetti
HomeTech Charter S	7126 Skyway	Paradise, CA	95969-3271	530-872-1171	872-1172	K-12	Michael Ervin
Horizon Charter S	PO Box 489000	Lincoln, CA	95648-9000	916-408-5200	408-5223	K-12	Craig Heimbichner
Hume Lake Charter S	64144 Hume Lake Rd	Hume, CA	93628-9600	559-305-7565	305-7707	K-12	Michael Stockdale
Huntington Park College Ready Academy	2071 Saturn Ave	Huntington Park, CA	90255-3635	323-923-1588	923-1589	9-12	Laura Galvan
ICEF Inglewood Elementary Charter Academ	434 S Grevillea Ave	Inglewood, CA	90301-2300	323-298-6420	293-9092	K-5	Shuron Owens-Lincoln
ICEF Inglewood Middle Charter Academy	304 E Spruce Ave	Inglewood, CA	90301-2711	323-298-6425	293-9092	6-8	Michael Flores
ICEF Vista Academy	4471 Inglewood Blvd	Los Angeles, CA	90066-6209	323-298-6400	317-2839	K-5	Ryan Gomez
ICEF Vista Middle Academy	4471 Inglewood Blvd	Los Angeles, CA	90066-6209	323-298-6400	317-2839	6-8	Ryan Gomez
Iftin Charter HS	730 45th St	San Diego, CA	92102-3619	619-583-7234	583-7223	9-12	Wilson Nacario
IFTIN Charter S	5465 El Cajon Blvd	San Diego, CA	92115-3620	619-265-2411	265-2484	K-8	Abdulkadir Mohamed
Imagine School at Imperial Valley	1150 N Imperial Ave	El Centro, CA	92243-1740	760-592-7250	592-7251	K-8	Susan Castro
Impact Academy of Arts & Technology	2560 Darwin St	Hayward, CA	94545-3451	510-300-1560	300-1565	9-12	David Hoopes
Imperial Beach Charter S	650 Imperial Beach Blvd	Imperial Beach, CA	91932-2794	619-628-5600	628-5680	K-8	Pamela Reichert-Montiel
Independence Charter S	3920 Blue Bird Dr	Modesto, CA	95356-0254	209-545-4415	545-2682	K-8	
Ingenium Charter S	22250 Elkwood St	Canoga Park, CA	91304-5501	818-456-4590		K-6	Brandy Price
Inland Leaders Charter S	13456 Bryant St	Yucaipa, CA	92399-5441	909-446-1100	446-1125	K-8	Michael Gordon
Innovations Academy	10380 Spring Canyon Rd	San Diego, CA	92131-3699	619-271-1414	271-1418	K-8	Christine Kuglen
Innovative Horizons Charter S	1461 N A St	Perris, CA	92570-1968	951-657-0728	940-5103	K-8	Jason Archard
Insight S of California	2360 Shasta Way Ste B	Simi Valley, CA	93065-1876	800-670-5391	884-9671	9-12	Sheila Shiebler
Insight School of California - North Bay	8733 Lakewood Dr Ste B	Windsor, CA	95492-9554	707-837-8789	884-9671	9-12	Sheila Shiebler
Inspire School of Arts and Sciences	901 Esplanade	Chico, CA	95926-3908	530-891-3090	891-3089	9-12	Eric Nilsson
Integrity Charter S	701 National City Blvd	National City, CA	91950-1123	619-336-0808	336-1526	K-8	
International S of Monterey	1720 Yosemite St	Seaside, CA	93955-3914	831-583-2165	899-7653	K-5	Sean Madden
Ipakanni Early College Charter S	PO Box 6119	Oroville, CA	95966-1119	530-589-1810		K-12	Freedom Cheteni
IQ Academy California Los Angeles	1830 Nogales St	Rowland Heights, CA	91748-2945	888-997-4722	398-5515	K-12	Carol Henson
Island Community Day S	1776 6th Avenue Dr	Kingsburg, CA	93631-1701	559-897-1046	897-1265	4-8	Lori Willson
Island S	7799 21st Ave	Lemoore, CA	93245-9694	559-924-6424	924-0247	K-8	Charlotte Hines

School	Address	City,State	Zip code	Telephone	Fax	Grade	Contact
Ivy Academia	7335 Lubao Ave	Winnetka, CA	91306-3670	818-312-3168	914-3674	3-3	Jennifer Lyons
Ivy Academia	6051 De Soto Ave	Woodland Hills, CA	91367-3707	818-716-0771	914-3662	3-7	Jennifer Lyons-Urbach
Ivy Academia HS	20920 Knapp St	Chatsworth, CA	91311-5906	818-885-1052	914-3674	8-12	Steven Thompson
Ivy Academia - Sunny Brae	20620 Arminta St	Winnetka, CA	91306-2109	818-998-3753	998-3746	K-2	Jennifer Lyons-Urbach
Ivy Bound Academy	15355 Morrison St	Sherman Oaks, CA	91403-1514	818-808-0158	808-0157	5-8	Kiumars Arzani
Jacobs High Tech HS	2861 Womble Rd	San Diego, CA	92106-6025	619-243-5000	243-5050	9-12	Brett Peterson
Jacoby Creek Charter S	1617 Old Arcata Rd	Bayside, CA	95524-9324	707-822-4896	822-4898	K-8	Catherine Stone
Jardin De la Infancia	611 S Lorena St	Los Angeles, CA	90023-1666	213-614-1745	614-2046	K-K	Alice Callaghan
Jew Academies	1944 Flint Ave	San Jose, CA	95148	408-223-3750	223-7346	K-8	Laurie Aknin
Johnson JHS	1300 Stroud Ave	Kingsburg, CA	93631-1000	559-897-1091	897-6867	7-8	Laura North
Jordan MS	20040 Parthenia St	Northridge, CA	91324-3222	818-882-2496	882-1798	6-8	Dr. Myranda Marsh
Journey S	27102 Foxborough	Aliso Viejo, CA	92656-3377	949-448-7232	448-7256	K-5	Shaheer Faltas
Juan Bautista de Anza S	2101 S Marina Dr Ste 4	Thermal, CA	92274-8509	760-767-5850	759-1221	6-12	Dr. Sandra Thorpe
Julian Charter S	PO Box 1780	Julian, CA	92036-1780	866-853-0003	765-3849	K-12	Jennifer Cauzza
Juniperidge Virtual Academy	PO Box 99	Ravendale, CA	96123-0099	530-251-8938	251-8940	K-12	Pam Auld
Justice Street Academy Charter	23350 Justice St	West Hills, CA	91304-4402	818-346-4388	346-4649	K-5	Cynthia Morrison Hernand
Kawana Academy of Arts and Sciences	2121 Moraga Dr	Santa Rosa, CA	95404-6114	707-545-4283	573-9065	K-8	Carolina Castro
Keegan Academy	28780 Single Oak Dr Ste 210	Temecula, CA	92590-5515	951-595-9095		K-8	Sonja Clause
Keiller Leadership Academy MS	7270 Lisbon St	San Diego, CA	92114-3007	619-263-9266	262-2217	K-8	Joel Christman
Kenny Charter S	3525 M L King Blvd	Sacramento, CA	95817	916-277-6500	277-6507	K-8	Gail Johnson
Kenter Canyon ES	645 N Kenter Ave	Los Angeles, CA	90049-1999	310-472-5918	472-9738	K-5	Dr. Terry Moren
Kern Workforce 2000 Academy	5801 Sundale Ave	Bakersfield, CA	93309-2924	661-827-3224	827-3320	9-12	Fuchsia Ward
Keyes To Learning Charter S	PO Box 519	Keyes, CA	95328-0519	209-634-6467	669-7121	K-12	Rusty Wynn
Kid Street Learning Center	PO Box 6784	Santa Rosa, CA	95406-0784	707-525-9223	525-9432	K-6	Linda Conklin
King-Chavez Academy of Excellence	2850 Logan Ave	San Diego, CA	92113-2412	619-232-2825	232-2943	K-8	Tim Wolf
King/Chavez Arts Academy	415 31st St	San Diego, CA	92102-4236	619-525-7320	696-7459	3-5	Scott Worthing
King/Chavez Athletics Academy	415 31st St	San Diego, CA	92102-4236	619-525-7320	744-3817	3-5	Tim Wolf
King/Chavez Community HS	201 A St	San Diego, CA	92101-4003	619-704-1020		9-12	Jeb Hubbs M.Ed.
King/Chavez Preparatory Academy	500 30th St	San Diego, CA	92102-3090	619-744-3828	744-3829	6-8	Tim Wolf
King/Chavez Primary Academy	415 31st St	San Diego, CA	92102-4236	619-525-7320	696-7459	K-2	Tim Wolf
King City Arts Magnet S	415 Pearl St	King City, CA	93930-2919	831-385-5473	385-1016	K-5	Brad Smith
Kings River-Hardwick S	10300 Excelsior Ave	Hanford, CA	93230-9794	559-584-4475	585-1422	K-8	Cathlene Anderson
KIPP Academy of Opportunity	7019 S Van Ness Ave	Los Angeles, CA	90047-1659	323-778-0125	778-0162	5-8	Archana Patel
KIPP Adelante Preparatory Academy	1475 6th Ave Ste 100	San Diego, CA	92101-3245	619-233-3242	233-3212	5-8	Christa Coleman
KIPP Bayview Academy	1060 Key Ave	San Francisco, CA	94124-3563	415-467-2522	467-9522	5-8	Kerianne Ryan
KIPP Bridge Charter S	991 14th St	Oakland, CA	94607-3230	510-874-7255	874-6796	5-8	Lolita Jackson
KIPP Comienza Community Prep S	6410 Rita Ave	Huntington Park, CA	90255-4126	323-589-1450	589-1716	K-4	Margarita Florez
KIPP Empower Academy	7511 Raymond Ave	Los Angeles, CA	90044-2430	323-750-2279	750-7902	K-4	Mike Kerr
KIPP Heartwood Academy	1250 S King Rd	San Jose, CA	95122-2146	408-926-5477	926-5478	K-5	Judy Tang
KIPP King Collegiate HS	2005 Via Barrett	San Lorenzo, CA	94580-1315	510-828-9509	317-2333	9-12	Kate Belden
KIPP Los Angeles College Preparatory	2814 Whittier Blvd	Los Angeles, CA	90023-1527	323-264-7737	264-7730	5-8	Carlos Lanuza
KIPP Philosophers Academy	8300 S Central Ave	Los Angeles, CA	90001-3707	323-584-6664	584-6666	5-8	Reginald Greene
KIPP Raices Academy	668 S Atlantic Blvd	Los Angeles, CA	90022-3212	323-780-3900	780-3939	K-4	Amber Young Medina
KIPP San Francisco Bay Academy	1430 Scott St	San Francisco, CA	94115-3510	415-440-4306	440-4308	5-8	Kyle Shaffer
KIPP San Jose Collegiate Charter S	1790 Educational Park Dr	San Jose, CA	95133-1703	408-937-3752	937-3755	9-12	Tom Ryan
KIPP Scholar Academy	1729 W MLK Jr Blvd	Los Angeles, CA	90062	323-292-2272	292-2555	5-8	Tiffany Moore
KIPP Summit Academy	2005 Via Barrett	San Lorenzo, CA	94580-1315	510-258-0106	258-0097	5-8	Ric Zappa
Klamath River Early College of Redwoods	PO Box 849	Klamath, CA	95548-0849	707-482-1737	482-1738	9-12	Danielle Carmesin
LACC Charter HS - South Central	2824 S Main St	Los Angeles, CA	90007-3334	213-749-3601	745-8890	9-12	Noel Trout
Lake County International Charter S	PO Box 984	Middletown, CA	95461-0984	707-987-3063	825-9344	K-8	Gwendolyn Maupin-Ahern
Lakeview Charter Academy	11465 Kagel Canyon St	Lake View Ter, CA	91342-6505	818-485-0340	485-0342	6-8	Manuel Ponce
Lakeview Charter HS	919 8th St	San Fernando, CA	91340-1312	818-356-2591	356-2581	9-12	Michael Kinnaman
Language Academy	2850 49th St	Sacramento, CA	95817-2303	916-277-7137	277-7141	K-8	Eduardo De Leon
Larchmont Charter ES	815 N El Centro Ave	Los Angeles, CA	90038-3805	323-836-0860	755-3301	K-5	Dolores Patton
Larchmont Charter MS	668 S Catalina St	Los Angeles, CA	90005-1708	213-384-0040	755-3301	6-8	Rick Esquivel
Larchmont Charter S West Hollywood	1265 N Fairfax Ave	West Hollywood, CA	90046-5205	323-656-6418	656-6407	K-6	Dr. Kristin Droege
La Sierra Academy	1735 E Houston Ave	Visalia, CA	93292-2349	559-733-6963	733-6845	7-12	Anjelica Zermeno
La Tijera S	1415 N La Tijera Blvd	Inglewood, CA	90302-1078	310-680-5260	419-2537	K-8	Ugema James
Latino College Preparatory Academy	1966 Flint Ave	San Jose, CA	95148-1213	408-729-2281	285-5324	9-12	Priscilla Reza
Laverne Elementary Preparatory Academy	PO Box 400880	Hesperia, CA	92340-0880	760-948-4333	948-9333	K-8	Debbie Tarver
LaVerne Science & Technology Charter S	250 W La Verne Ave	Pomona, CA	91767-2375	909-397-4004	392-0191	PK-6	Delores Lobaina
La Vida Charter S	16201 N Highway 101	Willits, CA	95490-8724	707-459-6344	459-6377	K-12	Ann Kelly
Lazear Charter Academy	824 29th Ave	Oakland, CA	94601-2205	510-689-2000		K-8	Andy West
Leadership HS	241 Oneida Ave Ste 301	San Francisco, CA	94112-3228	415-841-8910	841-8925	9-12	Anita Sufi
Leadership Public S - Hayward	28000 Calaroga Ave	Hayward, CA	94545-4600	510-300-1340	372-0396	9-12	Lauren Klaffky
Leadership Public S - Richmond	251 S 12th St	Richmond, CA	94804-2411	510-235-4522	588-4593	9-12	Shawn Benjamin
Leadership Public S - San Jose	1881 Cunningham Ave	San Jose, CA	95122-1712	408-937-2700	937-2705	9-12	Vanessa Sifuentes
Learning Choice Academy	4215 Spring St Ste 321	La Mesa, CA	91941-7985	619-463-6801	463-8339	K-12	Debi Gooding
Learning Community Charter S	1859 Bird St	Oroville, CA	95965-4854	530-532-5644	532-5794	K-12	Kim Guzzetti
Learning for Life Charter S	330 Reservation Rd Ste F	Marina, CA	93933-3286	831-582-9820	582-9825	7-12	Cindy Dotson
Learning Works!	88 N Daisy Ave	Pasadena, CA	91107-3704	626-564-2871	564-2870	7-12	Mikala Rahn
Lemoore Middle College HS	555 College Dr	Lemoore, CA	93245-9248	559-925-3552	925-6059	9-12	Victor Rosa
Lemoore University Charter S	100 Vine St	Lemoore, CA	93245-3418	559-924-6890	924-6839	5-8	Crescenciano Camarena
Lennox Math Science & Technology Academy	10319 Firmona Ave	Lennox, CA	90304-1419	310-680-5600	671-5029	9-12	Armando Mena
Liberty ES	170 Liberty School Rd	Petaluma, CA	94952	707-795-4380	795-6468	K-6	Chris Rafanelli
Life Learning Academy	651 8th St	San Francisco, CA	94130-1901	415-397-8957	397-9274	9-12	Teri Delane
Lifeline Education Charter S	357 E Palmer St	Compton, CA	90221-2610	310-605-2510	764-4890	6-12	Paula DeGroat
Lighthouse Community Charter S	444 Hegenberger Rd	Oakland, CA	94621-1418	510-271-8801	271-8803	K-12	Stephen Sexton
Lincoln ES	1900 Mariposa St	Kingsburg, CA	93631-2044	559-897-5141	897-3537	2-3	Jennifer DuPras
Linscott Charter S	220 Elm St	Watsonville, CA	95076-5025	831-728-6301	761-5478	K-8	Robin Higbee
Literacy First Charter S	799 E Washington Ave	El Cajon, CA	92020-5327	619-579-7232	579-5730	K-12	Debbie Beyer
Live Oak Charter S	PO Box 2054	Petaluma, CA	94953-2054	707-762-9020	762-9019	K-8	Matthew Morgan
Livermore Valley Charter HS	2451 Portola Ave	Livermore, CA	94551-1756	925-456-9000	456-9009	9-12	Lauren Kelly
Livermore Valley Charter S	543 Sonoma Ave	Livermore, CA	94550-4045	925-443-1690	443-1692	K-8	Tara Aderman
Lockhurst Drive ES	6170 Lockhurst Dr	Woodland Hills, CA	91367-1299	818-888-5280	346-0283	K-5	Aleta Johnson
Loma Vista Charter S	467 E Honolulu St	Lindsay, CA	93247-2116	559-562-5111	562-4637	K-12	Dennis Doane
Loma Vista Immersion Academy	207 Maria Dr	Petaluma, CA	94954-2301	707-765-4302	765-4343	PK-5	Carlos Ulloa Ph.D.
Long Valley Charter S	PO Box 7	Doyle, CA	96109-0007	530-827-2395	827-3562	K-12	Cindy Henry
Loomis Basin Charter S	5438 Laird Rd	Loomis, CA	95650-8916	916-652-2642	652-1809	K-8	Erika Sloane
Los Angeles Academy of Arts & Enterprise	600 S La Fayette Park Pl	Los Angeles, CA	90057-3243	213-487-0600	487-0500	6-12	Elizabeth Oberreiter
Los Angeles Big Picture HS	700 Wilshire Blvd Ste 400	Los Angeles, CA	90017-3837	323-231-3915	231-7232	9-12	Steve Bachrach
Los Angeles International Charter S	625 Coleman Ave	Los Angeles, CA	90042-4903	323-257-1499	257-1497	9-12	Clifford Moseley
Los Angeles Leadership Academy	2670 Griffin Ave	Los Angeles, CA	90031-2311	323-381-8484	381-8489	K-8	Mercedes Ibarra
Los Angeles Leadership Academy - HS	234 E Avenue 33	Los Angeles, CA	90031-1937	323-227-7719	227-7721	6-12	Brooke Soles
Los Feliz Charter S for the Arts	2709 Media Center Dr	Los Angeles, CA	90065-1700	323-539-2810	539-2815	K-6	Staci Block
LPS College Park Charter S	344 Thomas L Berkley Way	Oakland, CA	94612-3577	510-633-0750	291-9783	9-12	David Chamberlain
Luskin Academy	2941 W 70th St	Los Angeles, CA	90043-4420	213-905-1210	905-1215	9-12	Rosalio Medrano
MAAC Community Charter S	1385 3rd Ave	Chula Vista, CA	91911-4302	619-476-0749	476-0913	9-12	Marisol Rerucha
Madera County Independent Academy	1105 S Madera Ave	Madera, CA	93637-5576	559-662-4636	675-8313	K-12	Steve Carney
Magnolia Science Academy	18238 Sherman Way	Reseda, CA	91335-4550	818-609-0507	609-0534	6-12	Mustafa Sahin
Magnolia Science Academy 2	17125 Victory Blvd	Van Nuys, CA	91406-5455	818-758-5290	462-9222	6-12	Suat Acar
Magnolia Science Academy 3	1254 E Helmick St	Carson, CA	90746-3164	310-637-3806	637-3809	6-12	Steven Selcuk Keskinturk
Magnolia Science Academy 4	11330 Graham Pl	Los Angeles, CA	90064-3725	310-473-2464	473-2416	6-12	Omar Polat
Magnolia Science Academy 5	929 N Las Palmas Ave	Los Angeles, CA	90038-2422	323-871-4258	871-8658	6-12	Ismail Ozkay
Magnolia Science Academy 6	3754 Dunn Dr	Los Angeles, CA	90034-5805	310-842-8555	842-8558	6-8	John Terzi
Magnolia Science Academy 7	18355 Roscoe Blvd	Northridge, CA	91325-4104	818-886-0585	975-5215	K-8	Irina Erangey-Millard
Magnolia Science Academy 8	6411 Orchard Ave	Bell, CA	90201-2222	310-826-3925	826-3926	6-8	Alfredo Rubalcava
Magnolia Science Academy - San Diego	6365 Lake Atlin Ave	San Diego, CA	92119-3206	619-644-1300	644-1600	6-9	Hakki Karaman
Magnolia Science Academy Santa Clara	2720 Sonoma Pl	Santa Clara, CA	95051-4806	408-244-2620	244-2666	6-12	Tim Saka
Making Waves Academy	4123 Lakeside Dr	Richmond, CA	94806-1942	510-262-1511	262-1518	5-12	Alton Nelson
Mandarin Language Academy	9308 Winter Gardens Blvd	Lakeside, CA	92040-4539	619-390-2662	390-2668	K-8	Olympia Kyriakidis
Manzanita Charter MS	2925 Technology Ct	Richmond, CA	94806-1952	510-524-5500	524-5550	6-8	Jim Trombley
Manzanita Public Charter S	991 Mountain View Blvd	Vandenberg AFB, CA	93437	805-734-5600	734-3572	K-6	Lynnda Palmer
Mare Island Technology Academy HS	2 Positive Pl	Vallejo, CA	94589-1825	707-552-6482	552-0288	6-12	Matt Smith
Maria Montessori Charter Academy	1850 Wildcat Blvd	Rocklin, CA	95765-5471	916-630-1510	624-7305	K-8	Brent Boothby
Marquez Charter S	16821 Marquez Ave	Pacific Plsds, CA	90272-3294	310-454-4019	573-1532	K-5	Anna Feig
Marshall Charter MS	3500 S Normandie Ave	Los Angeles, CA	90007-3427	323-290-6940	279-9323	6-8	Didi Watts
Marysville Charter Academy for the Arts	1917 B St	Marysville, CA	95901-3731	530-749-6157	741-7892	7-12	Tim Malone
Mattole Valley Charter S	PO Box 211	Petrolia, CA	95558-0211	707-629-3634	629-3649	K-12	Richard Graey
McGill School of Success	3025 Fir St	San Diego, CA	92102-1123	619-239-0632	239-1318	K-3	Deborah Huggins
Meadows Arts & Technology ES	2000 La Granada Dr	Thousand Oaks, CA	91362-2016	805-495-7037	374-1160	K-5	Brenda Priske
Media Arts and Entertainment HS	5156 Whittier Blvd	Los Angeles, CA	90022-3932	323-859-0750	859-0758	9-12	Judy Burton
Merced Scholars Charter S	808 W 16th St	Merced, CA	95340-4600	209-381-5165	381-5166	6-12	Lori Gattuso
Mercury On-Line Academy	34862 Monte Vista Dr # 108	Wildomar, CA	92595	800-246-6024	566-1649	K-10	Jason Erdmann
Merkin MS	2023 S Union Ave	Los Angeles, CA	90007-1326	213-748-0141	748-0142	6-8	Donna Jacobson
Metropolitan Arts & Technology HS	1195 Hudson Ave	San Francisco, CA	94124-2488	415-550-5920	206-1444	9-12	Nick Kappelhof
MET Sacramento Charter HS	810 V St	Sacramento, CA	95818-1330	916-264-4700	264-4701	9-12	Allen Young

School	Address	City,State	Zip code	Telephone	Fax	Grade	Contact
Mid Valley Alternative Charter S	9895 7th Ave	Hanford, CA	93230-8802	559-583-1149	582-7565	K-8	Todd Barlow
Milagro Charter S	1855 N Main St	Los Angeles, CA	90031-3227	323-223-1786	223-8593	K-5	Sascha Robinett
Milestones Cooperative Charter S	24750 Main St	Foresthill, CA	95631-9216	530-367-2966	367-2470	K-8	Jim Roberts
Millennium Charter HS	51 E Beverly Pl	Tracy, CA	95376-3191	209-831-5240	831-5243	9-12	Virginia Stewart
Millsmont Academy	3200 62nd Ave	Oakland, CA	94605-1614	510-638-9445	638-0744	K-5	Jessica Chacon
Minarets Charter HS	PO Box 208	O Neals, CA	93645-0208	559-868-8659	868-8686	9-12	Jon Corippo
Mirus Secondary S	14073 Main St Ste 103	Hesperia, CA	92345-4675	760-947-7100	947-7135	7-12	Mary Bixby
Mission View Charter S	20655 Soledad Canyon Rd #12	Santa Clarita, CA	91351	661-272-1225	945-2430	7-12	Steve Gocke
Miwok Valley Language Academy	1010 Saint Francis Dr	Petaluma, CA	94954-5322	707-765-4304	765-4380	K-6	
Mohan High School	644 W 17th St	Los Angeles, CA	90015-3400	213-342-2870	342-2871	9-12	Janette Rodriguez
Mojave River Academy	16519 Victor St	Victorville, CA	92395	760-245-3222	245-3774	K-12	Jared Mecham
Monarch Academy	1445 101st Ave	Oakland, CA	94603-3207	510-568-3101	655-1222	K-5	Jill Tabachnick
Monarch Learning Center	PO Box 992418	Redding, CA	96099-2418	530-247-7307	243-4819	K-8	Chris Johnson M.A.
Montague Charter Academy	13000 Montague St	Pacoima, CA	91331-4146	818-899-0215	834-9782	K-5	Dr. Ariana Goldring-Ravin
Monterey Bay Charter S	1004B David Ave	Pacific Grove, CA	93950-5443	831-655-4638	655-4815	K-8	Cassandra Gallup-Bridge
Monterey County Home Charter S	PO Box 80851	Salinas, CA	93912-0851	831-755-0331	755-0837	K-12	Amy Ish
Moreno Valley Community Learning Center	13911 Perris Blvd	Moreno Valley, CA	92553-4306	951-571-7895	571-7892	6-12	Henry Herreras
Mountain Home Charter S	41267 Highway 41	Oakhurst, CA	93644-9403	559-642-1422	642-1592	K-8	Michael Cox
Mountain Oaks S	PO Box 1209	San Andreas, CA	95249-1209	209-754-0532	754-3556	K-12	Anne Colman
Mountain Peak Charter S	3220 Executive Rdg Ste 160	Vista, CA	92081-8572	760-727-7980	727-7295	K-12	Elmer Lee
Mountain View Montessori Charter S	15579 8th St	Victorville, CA	92395-3399	760-843-3303	843-1074	K-6	Laurien Dusharme
Mueller Charter S	715 I St	Chula Vista, CA	91910-5199	619-422-6192	422-0356	K-8	Dr. Kevin Riley
Muir Charter S	9845 Horn Rd Ste 150	Sacramento, CA	95827-1948	916-366-7319	366-7349	9-12	Richard Guess
Multicultural Learning Center	7510 De Soto Ave	Canoga Park, CA	91303-1430	818-716-5783	716-1085	K-8	Gayle Nadler
Museum S	211 Maple St	San Diego, CA	92103-6527	619-236-8712	236-8906	K-8	Phil Beaumont
Napa Valley Language Academy	2700 Kilburn Ave	Napa, CA	94558-5623	707-253-3678	259-8427	K-6	Deborah Wallace
National University Academy	2030 University Dr	Vista, CA	92083-7736	760-631-5842	631-6201	9-12	Bernard Hanlon
National University Academy	3530 S Cherry Ave	Fresno, CA	93706-5615	559-237-0437	237-9380	K-12	Bernard Hanlon
Natomas Charter S	4600 Blackrock Dr	Sacramento, CA	95835-1250	916-928-5353	928-5333	PK-12	Ting Sun Ph.D.
Natomas-Pacific Pathways Prep	3700 Del Paso Rd	Sacramento, CA	95834-9606	916-567-5740	567-5749	9-12	Tom Rutten
Natomas Pacific Pathways Prep MS	3700 Del Paso Rd	Sacramento, CA	95834-9606	916-567-5740	567-5749	6-8	David Hunt
Nea Community Learning Center	401 Pacific Ave	Alameda, CA	94501-1837	510-995-8885		K-5	Annalisa Moore
Nea Community Learning Center	500 Pacific Ave	Alameda, CA	94501-2125	510-748-4008	864-4281	6-12	Annalisa Moore
Nestle Avenue ES	5060 Nestle Ave	Tarzana, CA	91356-4399	818-342-6148	609-9864	K-5	Jeffrey Gerson
Nestor Language Academy Charter S	1455 Hollister St	San Diego, CA	92154-4063	619-628-0900	628-0980	K-8	Guadalupe Avilez
Nevada City Charter S	625 Zion St	Nevada City, CA	95959-2918	530-265-1885	265-1889	K-8	Joe Limov
Nevada City S for the Arts	13032 Bitney Springs Rd # 8	Nevada City, CA	95959-9017	530-273-7736	273-1378	K-8	Holly Pettitt
NEW Academy Canoga Park	21425 Cohasset St	Canoga Park, CA	91303-1450	818-710-2640	710-2654	K-5	Christina Duran
NEW Academy of Science & Arts	379 Loma Dr	Los Angeles, CA	90017-1149	213-413-9183	413-9187	K-5	Eric Todd Ed.D.
Newcastle Charter S	8951 Valley View Dr	Newcastle, CA	95658-9723	916-663-3307	663-3524	PK-8	Kathleen Daugherty
Newcastle Virtual Learning Academy	8951 Valley View Dr	Newcastle, CA	95658-9723	916-663-3307	663-3524	K-12	Kathleen Daugherty
New City S	1637 Long Beach Blvd	Long Beach, CA	90813-1929	562-599-6404	218-5620	K-8	Sabrina Bow
New Day Academy	PO Box 1536	Alturas, CA	96101-1536	530-233-3861	233-3864	K-12	Laura Van Acker
New Designs Charter S	2303 Figueroa Way	Los Angeles, CA	90007-2504	213-765-9084	765-0214	6-12	Yaw Adutwum
New Designs Charter S - Watts	12714 Avalon Blvd	Los Angeles, CA	90061-2730	323-418-0600	418-1600	6-12	Hazel Rojas
New Heights Charter S	3989 S Hobart Blvd	Los Angeles, CA	90062-1124	323-508-0155	508-0156	4-8	Amy Berfield
New Heights Charter S	2202 W Martin Luther King	Los Angeles, CA	90008	323-508-0155	508-0156	K-8	Amy Berfield
New Jerusalem S	31400 S Koster Rd	Tracy, CA	95304-9543	209-835-2597	835-2613	K-8	Donald Patzer
New Los Angeles Charter S	1919 S Burnside Ave	Los Angeles, CA	90016-1114	323-939-6400	939-6411	6-8	Brooke Merryfield
Newman Leadership Academy	1314 E Date St	San Bernardino, CA	92404-4234	909-522-4461		K-6	Jessica Miller
New Millenium Secondary S	20700 Avalon Blvd Ste 285	Carson, CA	90746-3701	310-999-6162	999-6163	9-12	Kim Irons
New Millennium Charter S	830 Fresno St	Fresno, CA	93706-3117	559-497-9331	497-9109	7-12	Kim Reed-Irons
New Spirit Charter Academy	3973 E Cedar Ave	Fresno, CA	93726	559-221-6300		PK-5	Kathy Brown
New Technology HS	1400 Dickson St	Sacramento, CA	95822-3437	916-433-2839	433-2840	9-12	Paula Hanzel
New Village Charter HS	147 N Occidental Blvd	Los Angeles, CA	90026-4601	213-385-4015	385-4020	9-12	Javier Guzman
New Vision MS	2050 Pacific St	San Bernardino, CA	92404-6179	909-888-8390	888-8470	6-8	Alex Lucero
New West Charter S	1905 Armacost Ave	Los Angeles, CA	90025-5210	310-943-5444	231-3399	6-10	Dr. Sharon Weir
Nightingale S	1721 Carpenter Rd	Stockton, CA	95206-3809	209-933-7260	234-1850	K-8	Myra Machuca
Nobel MS	9950 Tampa Ave	Northridge, CA	91324-1142	818-773-4700	701-9480	6-8	Derek Horowitz
Nord Country Charter S	5554 California St	Chico, CA	95973-9795	530-891-3138	891-3273	K-6	Kathleen Dahlgren
Northcoast Prep and Performing Arts Acad	PO Box 276	Arcata, CA	95518-0276	707-822-0861	822-0878	9-12	Michael Bazemore
North County Trade Tech HS	1126 N Melrose Dr	Vista, CA	92083-3467	760-598-0782	598-0895	9-12	Doreen Quinn
North Oakland Community Charter S	1000 42nd St	Oakland, CA	94608-3621	510-655-0540	655-1222	K-8	Carolyn Gramstorff
North Valley Charter Academy	16551 Rinaldi St Ste A	Granada Hills, CA	91344	818-368-1557	368-1935	6-12	Diane French
North Valley Pivot Charter School	2550 Lakewest Dr	Chico, CA	95928-8419	877-544-1423		6-12	Jayna Gaskill
Northwest Prep Charter S	2590 Piner Rd	Santa Rosa, CA	95401-4035	707-522-3320	522-3101	7-12	Tony Harris
North Woods Discovery S	14732 Bass Dr	Redding, CA	96003-7303	530-275-5480	275-5416	K-8	John Husome
Norton Space and Aeronautics Academy	503 E Central Ave	San Bernardino, CA	92408-2313	909-386-2300	386-7855	K-12	Guadalupe Girard
Nova Academy Early College HS	2609 W 5th St	Santa Ana, CA	92703-1818	714-569-0948	569-1693	9-12	Erin Craig
Novato Charter S	940 C St	Novato, CA	94949-5060	415-883-4254	883-1859	K-8	Nikki Lloyd
Nubia Leadership Academy	6134 Benson Ave	San Diego, CA	92114-4204	619-262-0050	262-0084	K-6	Harvey Curry
Nueva Esperanza Charter Academy	1218 4th St	San Fernando, CA	91340-2314	818-256-1951	256-2397	6-8	Adriana Abich
Nueva Vista Language Academy	120 Garces Hwy	Delano, CA	93215-3328	661-721-5070	721-3638	K-8	Nora Tapia
Nuview Bridge Early College HS	30401 Reservoir Ave	Nuevo, CA	92567-9361	951-928-8498	928-0186	9-12	Jeff Simmons
Oakdale Charter HS	250 Hinkley Ave	Oakdale, CA	95361-3609	209-848-4361	848-4363	9-12	Amy Simons
Oak Grove ES	8760 Bower St	Sebastopol, CA	95472-2450	707-823-5225	829-2614	K-5	Paige Gardner
Oakland Charter Academy	3001 International Blvd	Oakland, CA	94601-2203	510-532-6751	532-6753	6-8	Jorge Lopez
Oakland Charter HS	345 12th St	Oakland, CA	94607-4217	510-893-8700	893-8705	9-12	Jorge Lopez
Oakland Military Institute College Prep	3877 Lusk St	Oakland, CA	94608-3822	510-594-3900	597-9886	6-12	Mark Ryan
Oakland S for the Arts	530 18th St	Oakland, CA	94612-1512	510-873-8800	873-8816	9-12	Donn Harris
Oakland Unity HS	6038 Brann St	Oakland, CA	94605-1544	510-635-7170	635-3830	9-12	David Castillo
Oak Park Prep S	2315 34th St	Sacramento, CA	95817-1211	916-533-4861		7-8	Paul Schwinn
Oasis Charter S	1135 Westridge Pkwy	Salinas, CA	93907-2529	831-424-9003	424-9005	K-8	Dr. Juanita Perea
Obama Charter S	PO Box 72028	Los Angeles, CA	90002-0028	323-566-1965	566-1418	K-6	Chaleese Norman
Ocean Charter S	12606 Culver Blvd	Los Angeles, CA	90066-6506	310-827-5511	827-2012	K-8	Stephanie Edwards
Ocean Charter S	13150 Bluff Creek Dr	Los Angeles, CA	90094-2520	310-862-9751	862-9755	3-5	Stephanie Edwards
Ocean Grove Charter S	1166 Broadway Ste Q	Placerville, CA	95667-5745	800-979-4436	295-3583	K-12	Randy Gaschler
O'Donovan Middle Academy	5355 4th Ave	Los Angeles, CA	90043-2619	323-294-3172	596-2698	6-8	Sundar Dhillon
Odyssey Charter S	725 W Altadena Dr	Altadena, CA	91001-4103	626-229-0993	229-0586	K-8	Lauren O'Neill
O'Farrell Charter S	6130 Skyline Dr	San Diego, CA	92114-5620	619-263-3009	263-4339	K-12	Jonathan Dean
Old Adobe ES	2856 Old Adobe Rd	Petaluma, CA	94954-9546	707-765-4301	765-4334	K-6	Jeff Williamson
Old Town Academy	2120 San Diego Ave	San Diego, CA	92110-2901	619-574-6225		K-8	Tom Donahue
Olive Grove Charter S	PO Box 208	Los Olivos, CA	93441-0208	805-693-5933	688-4885	K-12	Dr. Thomas Littlefair
Olivet Elementary Charter S	1825 Willowside Rd	Santa Rosa, CA	95401-3923	707-522-3045	522-3047	K-6	Kaesa Enemark
one.Charter	800 Douglas Rd	Stockton, CA	95207-3607	209-468-9079	468-4651	7-12	James Mousalimas
100 Black Men of the Bay Area Comm S	3400 Malcolm Ave	Oakland, CA	94605-5353	510-995-7949		K-12	Mark Alexander
Open Charter Magnet S	5540 W 77th St	Los Angeles, CA	90045-3214	310-568-0735	568-0904	K-5	Antoinette Cass
Opportunities for Learning Charter S	18523 Soledad Canyon Rd	Canyon Country, CA	91351-3722	661-424-1337	424-1129	7-12	Bill Toomey
Opportunities for Learning S	33621 Del Obispo St Ste E	Dana Point, CA	92629-2100	949-248-1282	248-2450	K-12	Norma Vijeila
Opportunities Unlimited Charter HS	5100 S Broadway	Los Angeles, CA	90037-3837	323-234-8500	234-8506	9-12	A. Jacques-Marcoulis
Options for Youth	3542 A St	North Highlands, CA	95660-4600	916-338-2375	338-2417	7-12	Christopher Timpson
Options for Youth	11088 Olson Dr	Rancho Cordova, CA	95670-5650	916-631-8113	631-8121	K-12	Christopher Timpson
Options for Youth - Arden	2627 Alta Arden Expy	Sacramento, CA	95825-1306	916-971-3175	971-3186	K-12	Christopher Timpson
Options for Youth Charter S	405 S San Gabriel Blvd	San Gabriel, CA	91776-1965	626-685-9300		7-12	Chris Hodge
Options for Youth Charter S	1610 W Burbank Blvd	Burbank, CA	91506-1311	818-566-7525	566-7712	K-12	Valerie Brennan
Options for Youth Charter S	6110 Fair Oaks Blvd Ste E	Carmichael, CA	95608-4819	916-485-5155	485-5484	K-12	Christopher Timpson
Options for Youth - Fontana 1	16981 Foothill Blvd	Fontana, CA	92335-3581	909-357-3168	357-2875	7-12	Brian Albright
Options for Youth - Fontana 2	17216 Slover Ave	Fontana, CA	92337-7580	909-429-0482	429-9212	7-12	Brian Albright
Options for Youth San Bernardino I	985 S E St Ste A	San Bernardino, CA	92408-1941	909-381-6260	381-6230	7-12	Brock McCorkle
Options for Youth San Bernardino II	1181 E Highland Ave	San Bernardino, CA	92404-4605	909-882-8500		7-12	Heather Barnhart
Options for Youth Van Nuys	7335 Van Nuys Blvd	Van Nuys, CA	91405-1998	818-781-9059	781-9067	7-12	Valeria Brennan
Options for Youth Victorville - 1	14725 7th St Ste 400	Victorville, CA	92395-4025	760-955-5525	955-1107	7-12	Kathy Lento
Options for Youth Victorville - 2	16932 Bear Valley Rd	Victorville, CA	92395-4790	760-955-5900	955-5919	7-12	Kathy Lento
Options for Youth Victorville - 3	14196 Amargosa Rd Ste C	Victorville, CA	92392-2429	760-241-6546	241-7698	7-12	Kathy Lento
Options for Youth Victorville - 4	15048 Bear Valley Rd Ste E	Victorville, CA	92395-9235	626-685-9300	685-9316	7-12	Kathy Lento
Options for Youth Victorville - 5	13801 Rodeo Dr Ste B	Victorville, CA	92395-5622	760-843-0066	843-6675	7-12	Kathy Lento
Orange County Arts Academy	825 N Broadway	Santa Ana, CA	92701-3423	714-558-2787	558-2775	K-8	Linda Hardman-Greene
Orange County HS of the Arts	1010 N Main St	Santa Ana, CA	92701-3602	714-560-0900	664-0463	7-12	Benjamin Wolf
Orchard View Charter S	700 Watertrough Rd	Sebastopol, CA	95472-3917	707-823-4709	823-6187	K-12	Carol Rogers
Orcutt Academy	3491 Point Sal Rd	Orcutt, CA	93457	805-937-6515	937-9108	K-8	Joe Dana
Orcutt Academy	610 Pinal Ave	Orcutt, CA	93455-5302	805-938-8550	938-8995	9-12	Joe Dana
Ouchi HS	5356 5th Ave	Los Angeles, CA	90043-2622	323-596-2290	596-2295	9-12	Ena LaVan
Our Community Charter S	10045 Jumilla Ave	Chatsworth, CA	91311-3507	818-920-5285	920-5383	K-8	Chris Ferris
Oxford Preparatory Academy	23000 Via Santa Maria	Mission Viejo, CA	92691-1827	949-305-6111	297-4747	K-8	Sue Roche
Pacific American Academy	4260 54th St	San Diego, CA	92115-6009	619-229-9508		K-5	Margaret Sanborn
Pacific Coast Charter S	294 Green Valley Rd	Watsonville, CA	95076-1300	831-761-6021	786-2192	K-12	Suzanne Smith
Pacific Collegiate Charter S	PO Box 1701	Santa Cruz, CA	95061-1701	831-479-7785	427-5254	7-12	Archie Douglas

School	Address	City,State	Zip code	Telephone	Fax	Grade	Contact
Pacific Community Charter S	PO Box 984	Point Arena, CA	95468-0984	707-882-4131	882-4132	K-12	Sigrid Hillscan
Pacific Law Academy	1621 Brookside Rd	Stockton, CA	95207-7804	209-933-7445		9-12	Carol Sanderson
Pacific Technology S - Orangevale	6550 Filbert Ave	Orangevale, CA	95662-4112	916-293-8611	293-8609	6-12	Zafer Sipahioglu
Pacific Technology S Santa Ana	102 Baker St E	Costa Mesa, CA	92626-4503	714-557-7002	557-7003	6-12	Emrah Erduran
Pacific View Charter S	3670 Ocean Ranch Blvd	Oceanside, CA	92056-2669	760-757-0161	435-2666	K-12	Gina Campbell
Pacific View Charter S	2937 Moore Ave	Eureka, CA	95501-3316	707-269-9490	269-9491	K-12	James Malloy
Pacoima Charter S	11016 Norris Ave	Pacoima, CA	91331-2598	818-899-0201	890-3812	K-5	Sylvia Fajardo
Palisades Charter ES	800 Via De La Paz	Pacific Plsds, CA	90272-3617	310-454-3700	459-5627	K-5	Joan Ingle
Palisades Charter HS	15777 Bowdoin St	Pacific Plsds, CA	90272-3586	310-230-6623	454-6076	9-12	Dr. Pamela Magee
Palmdale Aerospace Academy	38060 20th St E	Palmdale, CA	93550-4903	661-273-3680	266-7201	7-9	Dr. Laura Herman
Palm Desert Charter MS	74200 Rutledge Way	Palm Desert, CA	92260-2646	760-862-4320	862-4327	6-8	Sallie Fraser
Paradise Charter MS	6473 Clark Rd	Paradise, CA	95969-3501	530-872-7277	872-2924	6-8	Chris Reid
Paradise Charter S	3361 California Ave	Modesto, CA	95358-9213	209-524-0184	524-0363	K-8	Heath Thomason
Paradise eLearning Academy	5911 Maxwell Dr	Paradise, CA	95969-4023	530-872-6425	872-6418	9-12	Kathleen Blacklock
Paragon Collegiate Academy	1608 Sampson St	Marysville, CA	95901-4314	530-742-2505	763-5772		Lisa Reese
Para Los Ninos Charter S	1617 E 7th St	Los Angeles, CA	90021-1207	213-239-6605		K-5	Titus Campos
Para Los Ninos - Gratts ECC	474 Hartford Ave	Los Angeles, CA	90017-1306	213-481-3200	977-5449	PK-2	Dr. Andrea Purcell
Para Los Ninos MS	1617 E 7th St	Los Angeles, CA	90021-1207	213-239-6605	239-9821	6-8	Titus Campos
Paramount Bard Academy	1942 Randolph St	Delano, CA	93215-1527	661-454-3000	454-3099	6-12	Joanna Kendrick-Miranda
Pasadena Rosebud Academy	3544 Canon Blvd	Altadena, CA	91001-4008	626-797-7704		K-1	Shawn Brumfield Ed.D.
Pathways Charter S	150 Professional Center Dr	Rohnert Park, CA	94928	707-585-6510	585-6515	K-12	Dr. Robert Tavonatti
Pathways icare Charter S	1020 Sundown Way	Roseville, CA	95661-4473	916-784-6107	771-0893	K-8	Debby Lum
Pathways to College Charter S	PO Box 402672	Hesperia, CA	92340-2672	760-949-8002	947-9648	K-8	Joe Williams
Peabody Charter S	3018 Calle Noguera	Santa Barbara, CA	93105-2899	805-563-1172	569-7042	K-6	Demian Barnett
Penngrove ES	365 Adobe Rd	Penngrove, CA	94951	707-778-4755	778-4831	K-6	Amy Fadeji
Phillips Charter S	1210 Shetler Ave	Napa, CA	94559-4205	707-253-3481	259-8425	K-6	Theresa Manzanedo
Phoenix Academy	PO Box 4925	San Rafael, CA	94913-4925	415-491-0581	491-0981	9-12	Raquel Rose
Piner-Olivet Charter S	2707 Francisco Ave	Santa Rosa, CA	95403-1869	707-522-3310	522-3317	6-8	Diana Drew-Ingham
Pioneer ES	1888 Mustang Dr	Hanford, CA	93230-9811	559-584-8831	584-7049	PK-5	Lisa Horne
Pioneer MS	101 W Pioneer Way	Hanford, CA	93230-9489	559-584-0112	584-0118	6-8	Greg Henry
Pioneer Technical Center	1105 S Madera Ave	Madera, CA	93637-5576	559-664-1600	673-5569	9-12	Steve Carney
Pittman S	701 E Park St	Stockton, CA	95202-2207	209-933-7496	942-2769	K-8	Adrienne Machado
Pivot Online Charter - North Bay	1577 Farmers Ln	Santa Rosa, CA	95405	707-843-4676	544-2908	K-12	Jayna Gaskell
Pivot Online Charter S	1030 La Bonita Dr	San Marcos, CA	92078	760-591-0217		9-12	Jayna Gaskell
Plainview Academic Charter Academy	10819 Plainview Ave	Tujunga, CA	91042-1633	818-353-1730	353-6658	K-5	Kenneth Johnson
Plumas Charter S	175 N Mill Creek Rd	Quincy, CA	95971-9678	530-283-3851	283-3841	K-12	Taletha Washburn
Pomelo Community Charter S	7633 March Ave	West Hills, CA	91304-5233	818-887-9700	887-1744	K-5	Marsha Gardner
Port of Los Angeles HS	250 W 5th St	San Pedro, CA	90731-3304	310-832-9201	832-1605	9-12	James Cross
Preuss S	9500 Gilman Dr	La Jolla, CA	92093-5004	858-658-7404	658-0988	6-12	Scott Barton
Price Charter MS	2650 New Jersey Ave	San Jose, CA	95124-1520	408-377-2532	377-7406	6-8	Debra Negrete
Primary Charter S	51 E Beverly Pl	Tracy, CA	95376-3191	209-831-5240	831-5243	K-4	Virginia Stewart
Primary Years Academy	1540 N Lincoln St	Stockton, CA	95204-5617	209-933-7470	469-3681	K-5	
Provisional Accelerated Learning Academy	PO Box 7100	San Bernardino, CA	92411-0100	909-887-7002	887-8942	9-12	Dr. Mildred Henry
Public Safety Academy	1482 E Enterprise Dr	San Bernardino, CA	92408-0161	909-382-4574		6-12	Kathy Toy
Puente Charter S	10000 S Western Ave	Los Angeles, CA	90047-4254	323-756-4921		K-K	Jerome Greening
Puente Charter S	501 S Boyle Ave	Los Angeles, CA	90033-3816	323-780-8900		K-K	Jerome Greening
Quail Lake Charter S	4087 N Quail Lake Dr	Clovis, CA	93619-4646	559-524-6720	292-1276	K-8	Amy Williams
R. A. A. M. P. Charter Academy	PO Box 2175	Antioch, CA	94531-2175	925-754-9800	754-9801	K-9	Karla Branch
RAI Online Charter	5253 5th St	Fallbrook, CA	92028-9795	760-728-4305	728-7712	K-12	Jarom Luedtke
REACH	708 Gravenstein Hwy N	Sebastopol, CA	95472-2808	707-823-8618	829-6285	4-8	Goldie Currie
Reagan ES	1180 Diane Ave	Kingsburg, CA	93631-2830	559-897-6986	897-6987	4-6	Greg Sansom
REALM Charter HS	2023 8th St	Berkeley, CA	94710-2026	510-809-9800	809-9809	7-12	Victor Diaz
Redding School of the Arts II	955 Inspiration Pl	Redding, CA	96003-8297	530-243-7145	243-4318	K-8	Margaret Johnson
Redwood Academy of Ukiah	PO Box 1383	Ukiah, CA	95482-1383	707-467-0500	467-4942	7-12	Kim Logan
Reems Academy of Technology & Art	8425 MacArthur Blvd	Oakland, CA	94605-3553	510-729-6635	562-9539	K-8	Lisa Blair
Renaissance Arts Academy	1800 Colorado Blvd	Los Angeles, CA	90041-1340	323-259-5700	259-5718	6-12	P. Candaux
Revere Charter MS	1450 Allenford Ave	Los Angeles, CA	90049-3614	310-917-4800	576-7957	6-8	Forn Somoza
Richmond Charter Academy	3200 Barrett Ave	Richmond, CA	94804-1718	510-235-2465	235-2469	6-8	Jorge Lopez
Richmond College Prep S	PO Box 2814	Richmond, CA	94802-2814	510-232-4004	232-4023	K-6	Peppina Chang
Ridgecrest Charter S	325 S Downs St	Ridgecrest, CA	93555-4531	760-375-1010	375-7766	K-8	Tina Ellingsworth
Riebli ES	315 Mark West Springs Rd	Santa Rosa, CA	95404-1101	707-524-2900	524-2986	K-6	Fran Hansell
Rincon Valley Charter S	5305 Dupont Dr	Santa Rosa, CA	95409-3843	707-539-3410	537-1791	7-8	Matt Reno
Rio Valley Charter S	1530 W Kettleman Ln Ste A	Lodi, CA	95242-9220	209-368-4934	368-4953	K-12	Joy Groen
Rise Kohyang MS	631 S Commonwealth Ave	Los Angeles, CA	90005-4003	424-789-8338	256-3074	6-8	Eliza Kim
Riverbank Language Academy Charter S	2400 Stanislaus St	Riverbank, CA	95367-2233	209-869-8093	869-0430	K-8	Rosie Ramos
River Charter MS	2447 Old Sonoma Rd	Napa, CA	94558-6006	707-253-6813	258-2800	6-8	Linda Inlay
River Montessori Charter S	3880 Cypress Dr	Petaluma, CA	94954-5613	707-778-6414	778-6493	1-6	Kelly Mannion
River Oak Charter S	555 Leslie St	Ukiah, CA	95482-5507	707-467-1855	467-1857	K-8	Rima Meechan
River Oaks Academy	880 Hampshire Rd	Westlake Vlg, CA	91361-2811	805-777-7999	777-7998	K-12	Resa Brown
Riverside Drive ES	13061 Riverside Dr	Sherman Oaks, CA	91423-2199	818-990-4525	789-4835	K-5	Jennifer Kessler
Riverside Preparatory S	PO Box 455	Oro Grande, CA	92368-0455	760-243-5884	843-3766	K-12	Joseph Andreasen
River Springs Charter S	43466 Business Park Dr	Temecula, CA	92590-5526	951-252-8800	252-8801	K-12	Kathleen Hermsmeyer
River Valley Charter S	9707 1/2 Marilla Dr	Lakeside, CA	92040-2868	619-390-2579	390-2581	7-12	Cheryl Bloom
Roberts Ferry Charter School Academy	101 Roberts Ferry Rd	Waterford, CA	95386-9502	209-874-2331	874-4625	K-8	George Johnson
Roberts Institute of Learning Charter S	6785 Imperial Ave	San Diego, CA	92114-4317	619-674-6019	546-0274	K-6	Shelia Malveaux
Rocketship Discovery Prep S	370 Wooster Ave	San Jose, CA	95116-1095	408-217-8951	217-9251	K-6	Jaya Deutsch
Rocketship Los Suenos Academy	331 S 34th St	San Jose, CA	95116-2905	877-806-0920	935-6084	K-5	Drew Sarratore
Rocketship Mateo Sheedy ES	950 Owsley Ave	San Jose, CA	95122-3109	408-899-2607	899-2613	K-5	Adam Nadeau
Rocketship Si Se Puede Academy	2249 Dobern Ave	San Jose, CA	95116-3405	408-286-3344	286-3331	K-12	Andrew Elliott-Chandler
Rocklin Academy	6532 Turnstone Way	Rocklin, CA	95765-5865	916-632-6580	784-3034	K-6	Robin Stout
Rocklin Academy at Meyers Street	5035 Meyers St	Rocklin, CA	95677-2811	916-632-6580	784-3034	K-6	Jillayne Antoon
Rocky Point Charter S	3500 Tamarack Dr	Redding, CA	96003-1747	530-225-0456	225-0499	K-8	Deborah Stierli
Romero Charter S	2900 W Temple St	Los Angeles, CA	90026-4516	213-413-9600	381-0884	6-8	Yvette King-Berg
Roosevelt Community Learning Center	31191 Road 180	Visalia, CA	93292-9585	559-592-9160	592-2927	K-12	Frank Murphy
Roosevelt ES	1185 10th Ave	Kingsburg, CA	93631-2100	559-897-5193	897-6865	1-1	Lori Willson
Rosa Parks Academy	1930 S D St	Stockton, CA	95206-2489	209-944-5590	465-2690	K-5	Natalie June
Roseland Accelerated MS	1777 West Ave	Santa Rosa, CA	95407-7449	707-546-7050	546-0434	7-8	Jenny Young
Roseland Collegiate Prep	80 Ursuline Rd	Santa Rosa, CA	95403	707-528-1764		7-8	Amy Jones-Kerr
Roseland University Preparatory S	100 Sebastopol Rd	Santa Rosa, CA	95407-6928	707-566-9990	566-9992	9-12	Aubin Giampaoli
Sacramento HS	PO Box 5038	Sacramento, CA	95817-0038	916-277-6200	277-6370	9-12	Dwan Jordan
Sacramento River Discovery Charter	1660 Monroe St	Red Bluff, CA	96080-2694	530-529-1650	529-1694	6-12	Larry Newman
Sacramento Valley Charter S	2301 Evergreen Ave	West Sacramento, CA	95691-3009	916-596-6422	564-5764	K-8	Jane Egashira
St. Hope Public School 7	5201 Strawberry Ln	Sacramento, CA	95820-4815	916-649-7850	277-7039	K-8	
Salmon Creek S	1935 Bohemian Hwy	Occidental, CA	95465-9100	707-874-1205	874-1226	2-8	Rene McBride
San Carlos Charter Learning Center	750 Dartmouth Ave	San Carlos, CA	94070-1769	650-508-7343	508-7341	K-8	Christopher Mahoney
San Diego Cooperative Charter S	7260 Linda Vista Rd	San Diego, CA	92111-6128	858-496-1613	467-9741	K-8	Dr. Wendy Ranck-Buhr
San Diego Global Vision Academy	3430 School St	San Diego, CA	92116-3423	619-600-5321	550-3637	K-5	Dena Harris
San Diego Neighborhood Homeschools	3548 Seagate Way Ste 140	Oceanside, CA	92056-2676	760-295-1117	509-4691	K-12	Salvador Leon
San Francisco Flex Academy	555 Post St	San Francisco, CA	94102-1228	415-762-8800	674-7748	9-12	Royce Conner
Sanger Academy Charter S	2207 9th St	Sanger, CA	93657-2711	559-524-6840	875-8045	K-8	Christy Platt
San Jacinto Valley Academy	480 N San Jacinto Ave	San Jacinto, CA	92583-2729	951-654-6113	644-5083	K-9	Penny Harrison
San Joaquin Building Futures Academy	3100 Monte Diablo Ave	Stockton, CA	95203-1108	209-468-9107	468-4951	9-12	Sheilah Goulart
San Joaquin Valley HS	900 S Newmark Ave	Parlier, CA	93648-2034	559-646-2723	888-0210	7-12	Esperanza Zendejas
San Jose Charter Academy	2021 W Alwood St	West Covina, CA	91790-3259	626-856-1693	480-7126	K-8	Dr. Denise Patton
San Jose Conservation Corps Charter S	1560 Berger Dr	San Jose, CA	95112-2703	408-595-3131		9-12	Gina Ortiz
San Juan Choices Charter S	4425 Laurelwood Way	Sacramento, CA	95864-0881	916-979-8378		7-12	Marie Pflugrath
San Lorenzo Valley USD Charter S	325 Marian Ave	Ben Lomond, CA	95005	831-336-8527	336-0131	K-12	Rhonda Schlosser
Santa Barbara Charter S	6100 Stow Canyon Rd	Goleta, CA	93117-1705	805-967-6522	967-6382	K-8	Bev Abrams
Santa Clarita Valley International S	28060 Hasley Canyon Rd	Castaic, CA	91384-4572	661-705-4820	607-0295	K-12	
Santa Monica Blvd Community Charter S	1022 N Van Ness Ave	Los Angeles, CA	90038-3252	323-469-0971	462-4093	K-6	Vahe Markarian
Santa Rosa Academy	28237 La Piedra Rd	Menifee, CA	92584-8947	951-672-2400	672-6060	K-12	Laura Badillo
Santa Rosa Accelerated Charter	4650 Badger Rd	Santa Rosa, CA	95409-2633	707-528-5319	528-5644	5-6	Matt Marshall
Santa Rosa Charter Academy	3838 Eagle Rock Blvd	Los Angeles, CA	90065-3638	323-254-1703	254-0958	6-8	Shirley Aragon
Santa Rosa Charter S for the Arts	756 Humboldt St	Santa Rosa, CA	95404-3717	707-522-3170	522-3172	K-8	Elizabeth Evans
Santa Rosa French-American Charter S	1350 Sonoma Ave	Santa Rosa, CA	95405-6623	707-522-3161		K-6	Pascal Stricher
Santa Ynez Valley Charter S	PO Box 59	Santa Ynez, CA	93460-0059	805-686-7360	686-7383	K-8	Colleen Million
Santiago Charter MS	515 N Rancho Santiago Blvd	Orange, CA	92869-2724	714-997-6366	532-4758	7-8	James D'Agostino
Sartorette Charter S	3850 Woodford Dr	San Jose, CA	95124-3736	408-264-4380	264-1758	K-5	Scott Johnson
SAVA: Sacramento Academic and Vocational	3141 Dwight Rd Ste 400	Elk Grove, CA	95758-6473	916-428-3200	428-3232	7-12	Paul Haas
SAVA: Sacramento Academic and Vocational	5330 Power Inn Rd Ste D	Sacramento, CA	95820-6757	916-286-5102	387-0139	7-12	Paul Haas
Schaefer Charter S	1370 San Miguel Rd	Santa Rosa, CA	95403-1986	707-522-3015	522-3017	K-6	Joe Hamp
School of Arts and Enterprise	295 N Garey Ave	Pomona, CA	91767-5429	909-622-0699	620-1018	9-12	Lucille Berger
School of Extended Educational Options	1460 E Holt Ave Ste 100	Pomona, CA	91767	909-397-4900	622-2496	7-12	Susan Williams
School of Unlimited Learning	2336 Calaveras St	Fresno, CA	93721-1104	559-498-8543	237-0956	9-12	Dr. Mark Wilson
Science and Technology Charter S	PO Box 458	Knights Landing, CA	95645-0458	530-735-6435	735-6155	K-6	Barbara Herms
Sebastopol Independent Charter S	PO Box 1170	Sebastopol, CA	95473-1170	707-824-9700	824-1432	K-8	Susan Olson
Sequoia Charter S	21445 Centre Pointe Pkwy	Santa Clarita, CA	91350-2684	661-259-0033	286-2120	7-12	Dr. Pete Getz

School	Address	City,State	Zip code	Telephone	Fax	Grade	Contact
Serna Charter S	19 S Central Ave	Lodi, CA	95240-2901	209-331-7809	331-7997	K-6	Maria Cervantes
Serrania Charter for Enriched Studies	5014 Serrania Ave	Woodland Hills, CA	91364-3350	818-340-6700	592-0565	K-5	Theresa Wedaa
Shasta Secondary Home S	1401 Gold St	Redding, CA	96001-1937	530-245-2600	245-2611	6-12	Ben Claassen
Shearer Charter S	1590 Elm St	Napa, CA	94559-3924	707-253-3508	253-3847	K-5	Olivia McCormick
Shenandoah HS	6540 Koki Ln	El Dorado, CA	95623-4328	530-622-6212	622-1071	9-12	Debby Hanson
Sherman Oaks Charter S	14755 Greenleaf St	Sherman Oaks, CA	91403-4199	818-784-8283	981-8258	K-5	Paula Denen
Sherwood Montessori S	746 Moss Ave	Chico, CA	95926-2900	530-513-2296		K-8	Michelle Yezbick
SIATech Charter S	2611 Temple Heights Dr # A	Oceanside, CA	92056	760-945-1227	631-3411	9-12	Dr. Linda Dawson
Sierra Charter S	1931 N Fine Ave	Fresno, CA	93727-1534	559-490-4290	490-4292	K-12	Lisa Marasco
Sierra Expeditionary Learning	11603 Donner Pass Rd	Truckee, CA	96161-4953	530-414-5326	448-8115	K-8	David Manahan
Sierra Hills Arts & Science Charter Acad	16505 Placer Hills Rd	Meadow Vista, CA	95722-9550	530-878-9475	878-9473	K-3	Fred Adam
Sierra Montessori Academy	16229 Duggans Rd	Grass Valley, CA	95949-8520	530-268-9990	268-0613	K-8	Henry Bietz
Silicon Valley Flex Academy	305 W Main Ave	Morgan Hill, CA	95037-4530	408-659-0088		9-12	Jean Southland
Simon Technology Acad HS	10720 Wilmington Ave	Los Angeles, CA	90059-1236	213-744-2122	744-2123	9-12	Dr. Clarence Miller
Six Rivers Charter HS	1720 M St	Arcata, CA	95521-5741	707-825-2428	825-2034	9-12	Nic Collart
Sixth Grade Academy	700 Bantam Way	Petaluma, CA	94952-1709	707-778-4724		6-6	Renee Semik
Sixth Street Prep S	15579 8th St	Victorville, CA	92395-3399	760-241-0962	241-0967	K-6	Linda Rueter
Skirball MS	603 E 115th St	Los Angeles, CA	90059-2322	323-905-1377	905-1378	6-8	Joy May-Harris
Sky Mountain Charter S	4535 Missouri Flat Rd	Placerville, CA	95667-6846	530-295-3566	295-3583	K-12	Shana Fisk
Smidt Technology HS	211 S Avenue 20	Los Angeles, CA	90031-2508	323-352-3206		9-12	Dr. Lori Rhodes
Smythe Academy of Arts & Sciences	2781 Northgate Blvd	Sacramento, CA	95833-2208	916-566-2740	263-8465	PK-6	Linda Bean
Smythe Academy of Arts & Sciences	700 Dos Rios St	Sacramento, CA	95811-0434	916-566-3430	449-8634	7-8	Will Brown
SOAR Charter Academy	198 W Mill St	San Bernardino, CA	92408-1402	909-888-3300		K-7	Trisha Lancaster
Sol Aureus College Prep Charter S	6620 Gloria Dr	Sacramento, CA	95831-1655	916-421-0600	421-0601	K-8	Norman Hernandez
Soledad Enrichment Action Charter S	222 N Virgil Ave	Los Angeles, CA	90004-3622	213-480-4200	480-4199	9-12	Margaret Godinez
Sonoma Charter S	17202 Highway 12	Sonoma, CA	95476-3667	707-935-4232	935-4207	K-8	Paula Hunter
Sonoma Mountain ES	1900 Rainier Cir	Petaluma, CA	94954-2543	707-765-4305	765-4385	K-6	Michele Gochborg
Southern California Online Academy	1405 Education Way	Lake Elsinore, CA	92530-2809	951-253-7777	253-7080	K-12	Ryan Mulvanny
South Sutter Charter S	1166 Broadway Ste Q	Placerville, CA	95667-5745	800-979-4436	295-3583	K-12	Becky Cote
Spring Creek Matanzas Charter S	1687 Yulupa Ave	Santa Rosa, CA	95405-7778	707-546-6183	528-8027	3-6	Kelly Lister
Spring Creek Matanzas Charter S	4675 Mayette Ave	Santa Rosa, CA	95405-7399	707-545-1771	545-6926	PK-2	Emily Davis
Stallworth Charter S	1610 E Main St	Stockton, CA	95205-5521	209-948-4511	943-5218	K-12	Alice Stallworth
Stanford New S	475 Pope St	Menlo Park, CA	94025-2826	650-847-1203	847-1232	K-8	
Steele Canyon HS	12440 Campo Rd	Spring Valley, CA	91978-2331	619-660-3500	660-7198	9-12	Eileen Poole
Stella Middle Charter Academy	2636 S Mansfield Ave	Los Angeles, CA	90016-3512	323-954-9957	954-6415	5-8	Eliza Kim
Stella Middle Charter Academy	5431 W 98th St	Los Angeles, CA	90045-5715	310-954-9957	954-6415	7-8	Eliza Kim
Stellar Charter School	5885 E Bonnyview Rd	Redding, CA	96001-4535	530-245-7730	245-7731	K-12	Patti Furnari
Stern Math and Science S	5151 State Univ Dr Lot 7	Los Angeles, CA	90032	323-987-2144	987-2149	9-12	Judy Burton Ph.D.
Stockton Alternative HS	22 S Van Buren St	Stockton, CA	95203-3118	209-933-7365	469-3740	9-12	Maryann Santella
Stockton Alternative IS	975 N D St	Stockton, CA	95205-4367	209-933-7375		4-8	Maryann Santella
Stockton Collegiate International ES	PO Box 2286	Stockton, CA	95201-2286	209-390-9861	390-9862	K-5	Scott Luhn
Stockton Collegiate International S	PO Box 2286	Stockton, CA	95201-2286	209-390-9861	390-9862	6-12	Scott Luhn
Stockton Early College Academy	349 E Vine St	Stockton, CA	95202-1107	209-933-7370	939-9504	9-12	Essa Allred
Stone Bridge S	1680 Los Carneros Ave	Napa, CA	94559-9741	707-252-5522	251-9767	K-8	Darryl Centers
Stony Point Academy	3223 Primrose Ave	Santa Rosa, CA	95407-7723	707-568-7504		K-7	Lisa Katimbang
Summit Charter Academy	175 S Mathew St	Porterville, CA	93257-2710	559-782-5902	782-5907	K-6	Timothy Mofhitz
Summit Charter Academy	2036 E Hatch Rd	Modesto, CA	95351-5142	209-538-8082	538-1620	K-5	Jamey Olney
Summit Charter Academy-Lombardi Campus	15550 Redwood St	Porterville, CA	93257-2530	559-788-6445		K-6	Treasure Weisenberger
Summit Charter Collegiate Academy	15550 Redwood St	Porterville, CA	93257-2530	559-782-5902		7-12	Krista Gaines-Herrera
Summit Leadership Academy High Desert	12850 Muscatel St	Hesperia, CA	92344-5566	760-949-9202	949-9257	9-12	Shannon Brandner
Summit Preparatory Charter HS	890 Broadway St	Redwood City, CA	94063-3105	650-556-1110	556-1121	9-12	Brian Johnson
SunRidge Charter S	7285 Hayden Ave	Sebastopol, CA	95472-4359	707-824-2844	824-2861	K-8	Mark Rice
Sunset Charter S	1755 S Crystal Ave	Fresno, CA	93706-2797	559-457-3310	495-1334	K-8	Juan Silva
Sycamore Academy Science & Cultural Arts	32326 Clinton Keith Rd	Wildomar, CA	92595-7317	951-678-5217	678-5932	K-6	Barbara Hale
Synergy Charter Academy	PO Box 78999	Los Angeles, CA	90016-0999	323-235-7960	235-7970	K-5	Jennifer Epps
Synergy Kinetic Academy	PO Box 78999	Los Angeles, CA	90016-0999	323-846-2225	846-2234	6-8	Russell Lawton
Synergy Quantum Academy	PO Box 78999	Los Angeles, CA	90016-0999	323-846-4716	846-4729	9-12	Dr. Barbara Shannon
Taylion Virtual Academy	1184 W 2nd St Ste 101	San Bernardino, CA	92410-1735	909-889-5152		K-12	Will Griffin
TEACH Academy of Technologies	8477 S Normandie Ave	Los Angeles, CA	90044-2246	323-777-2068	777-7143	5-8	Dr. Raul Carranza
Temecula Preparatory S	35777 Abelia St	Winchester, CA	92596-8450	951-926-6776	926-6797	K-12	Scott Phillips
Temecula Valley Charter S	35755 Abelia St	Winchester, CA	92596-8450	951-294-6775	294-6780	K-8	JoAnne Burnett
Tennenbaum Family Technology HS	2050 N San Fernando Rd	Los Angeles, CA	90065-1267	213-276-5545		9-12	Dr. Michelle Tubbs
Thomas Charter HS	101 W Adell St	Madera, CA	93638-0877	559-675-6626	675-6612	9-12	Tera Napier
Thomas Charter S	101 W Adell St	Madera, CA	93638-0877	559-674-1192	674-8955	K-8	Tera Napier
Tierra Linda MS	750 Dartmouth Ave	San Carlos, CA	94070-1769	650-508-7370	508-7341	5-8	John Nazar
Tierra Pacifica Charter S	986 Bostwick Ln	Santa Cruz, CA	95062-1756	831-462-9404	477-0936	K-8	Linda Lambdin
Today's Fresh Start Charter S	4514 Crenshaw Blvd	Los Angeles, CA	90043-1221	323-293-9826	293-9202	K-8	Dr. Jeanette Parker
Topanga Charter ES	22075 Topanga School Rd	Topanga, CA	90290-3835	310-455-3711	455-3517	K-6	Nicole Sheard
Topeka Charter S for Advanced Studies	9815 Topeka Dr	Northridge, CA	91324-1800	818-886-2266	885-7682	K-5	Temika Dixon
Tree of Life Montessori S	PO Box 966	Ukiah, CA	95482-0966	707-462-0913	462-0914	1-8	Celeste Beck
Trillium Charter S	1464 Spear Ave	Arcata, CA	95521-4882	707-822-4721	822-7054	PK-5	Marianne Keller
Triumph Academy	14600 Tyler St	Sylmar, CA	91342-2826	818-837-6221	837-6222	6-8	Karman Mak
Triumph Center for Early Childhood Ed	4104 Martin Luther King Jr	Sacramento, CA	95820	916-731-8200		PK-PK	Cristin Fiorelli
Triumph Charter HS	9171 Telfair Ave	Sun Valley, CA	91352-1844	818-356-2795	979-6579	9-12	James Pasto
Trivium Charter S	4949 Foxen Canyon Rd	Santa Maria, CA	93454-9145	805-291-1303		K-12	Trisha Vais
Tubman Village Charter S	6880 Mohawk St	San Diego, CA	92115-1728	619-668-8635	668-2480	K-8	Lidia Scinski
Twin Hills Charter MS	1685 Watertrough Rd	Sebastopol, CA	95472-4647	707-823-7446	823-6470	6-8	Catherine Bosch
Twin Ridges Home Study Charter S	111 New Mohawk Rd	Nevada City, CA	95959-3270	530-478-1815	478-0266	K-8	Jenny Travers
Twin Rivers Charter S	840 Cooper Ave	Yuba City, CA	95991-3849	530-755-2872	673-1847	K-8	Bob Loretelli
Uncharted Shores Academy	330 E St	Crescent City, CA	95531-3945	707-464-9828	464-1428	K-8	Margie Rouge
Union Hill Charter S	11638 Colfax Hwy	Grass Valley, CA	95945-8899	530-273-2461		K-8	Susan Barry
Union Street Charter S	470 Union St	Arcata, CA	95521-6429	707-822-4845	825-9025	K-5	John Schmidt
University HS	2611 E Matoian Way MS/UH134	Fresno, CA	93740-0001	559-278-8263	278-0447	9-12	Dr. James Bushman
University Preparation S	550 Temple Ave	Camarillo, CA	93010-4833	805-482-4608	388-5814	K-5	Charmon Evans
University Preparatory Academy	2315 Canoas Garden Ave	San Jose, CA	95125-2005	408-723-1839	779-0519	7-12	Daniel Ordaz
University Preparatory HS	915 S Mooney Blvd	Visalia, CA	93277-2214	559-730-2529	737-4378	9-12	John Kelly
University Preparatory S	2200 Eureka Way	Redding, CA	96001-0337	530-245-2790	245-2791	6-12	Kathy Malain
Urban Discovery Academy	2850 6th Ave Ste 110	San Diego, CA	92103-6309	619-788-4668	688-9796	K-8	Cynthia Moser
Urban Montessori Charter S	5328 Brann St	Oakland, CA	94619-3312	510-842-1181		K-8	Peter Laub
Vallejo Charter S	436 Del Sur St	Vallejo, CA	94591-8226	707-556-8850	556-8859	K-8	Marilyn Abelon
Valley Arts & Science Academy	735 N Glenn Ave	Fresno, CA	93728-3714	559-497-8272	497-5621	K-6	Sandy Fuerte
Valley Charter ES	16514 Nordhoff St	North Hills, CA	91343-3724	818-810-6713	810-9667	K-5	Leslie Lainer
Valley Charter HS	108 Campus Way	Modesto, CA	95350-5803	209-238-6800	238-6897	9-12	Susan Nisan
Valley Charter MS	9229 Haskell Ave	North Hills, CA	91343-3114	818-830-7562	830-7672	6-8	Blanca Alves
Valley Life Charter S	3737 W Walnut Ave	Visalia, CA	93277-3947	559-761-1299		K-12	Lori Lackey
Valley Oak Charter S	PO Box 878	Ojai, CA	93024-0878	805-640-4421	646-4700	K-10	Laura Fulmer
Valley Oaks Charter S	1300 17th St	Bakersfield, CA	93301-4504	661-852-6750	633-5287	K-12	Blanca Cavazos
Valley Preparatory Academy	4221 N Hughes Ave	Fresno, CA	93705-1611	559-225-7737	225-0976	K-12	Shelley Melton
Valor Academy Charter S	8755 Woodman Ave	Arleta, CA	91331-6506	818-830-1700	830-1799	5-8	Hrag Hamalian
Van Gogh Charter S	17160 Van Gogh St	Granada Hills, CA	91344-1299	818-360-2141	831-9081	K-5	Susan Gunderson
Vantage Point Charter S	10862 Spenceville Rd	Penn Valley, CA	95946-9625	530-432-5312	432-8744	K-12	Thomas Bivens
Vaughn Next Century Learning Center	13330 Vaughn St	San Fernando, CA	91340-2216	818-896-7461	834-9036	PK-12	Anita Zepeda
Ventura S of Arts & Global Education	PO Box 392	Ventura, CA	93002-0392	805-648-5503	648-5539	K-8	Mary Galvin
Venture Academy	PO Box 213030	Stockton, CA	95213-9030	209-468-5940	468-9000	K-12	Kathleen Focacci
View Park Accelerated MS	5749 Crenshaw Blvd	Los Angeles, CA	90043-2409	323-290-6970	290-9271	6-8	Kenya Jackson
View Park Prep Accelerated Charter ES	3751 W 54th St	Los Angeles, CA	90043-2356	323-290-6950	298-4935	K-5	Kenneth Wheeler
View Park Prep Accelerated HS	5701 Crenshaw Blvd	Los Angeles, CA	90043-2409	323-290-6975	881-4924	9-12	Dr. Darnise Williams
Village Charter S	50 Mark West Springs Rd	Santa Rosa, CA	95403	707-591-9262	591-9275	K-8	Rebecca Ivanoff
Village ES	900 Yulupa Ave	Santa Rosa, CA	95405-7099	707-545-5754	573-0951	K-6	Maria McCormick
Vincent Academy	1911 Union St	Oakland, CA	94607-2316	510-452-2100		K-5	Jean Driscoll
Visalia Charter Independent Study	1821 W Meadow Ave	Visalia, CA	93277-2247	559-735-8055	622-3170	9-12	Heather Rocha
Visalia Technology Educational Center	2049 S Linwood St	Visalia, CA	93277-5749	559-622-3212	322-6214	10-12	Victoria Porter
Visions in Education Charter S	4800 Manzanita Ave	Carmichael, CA	95608-0891	916-971-5331	971-5590	K-12	Jody Graf
Vista Charter MS	2900 W Temple St	Los Angeles, CA	90026-4516	213-201-4000	201-5861	6-8	Roger Avila
Vista Real Charter HS	401 S A St Ste 3	Oxnard, CA	93030-5278	805-486-5449	486-5455	9-12	Corrine Manley
Voices College-Bound Language Academy	4075 Sacramento Ave	San Jose, CA	95111-1584	408-361-1960		K-8	Frances Teso
Walden Academy	408 Pacific Academy	Willows, CA	95988	530-361-6480		PK-5	
Washington Charter S	45768 Portola Ave	Palm Desert, CA	92260-4861	760-862-4350	862-4356	K-5	Allan Lehmann
Washington ES	1501 Ellis St	Kingsburg, CA	93631-1896	559-897-2955	897-6863	PK-K	Shirley Esau
Watsonville Charter S of the Arts	115 Casserly Rd	Watsonville, CA	95076-8645	831-728-8123	728-6286	K-8	Trish Hucklebridge
Watts Learning Center	310 W 95th St	Los Angeles, CA	90003-4012	323-754-9900	754-0935	K-5	Cordiya Butler
Watts Learning Ctr Charter MS	8800 S San Pedro St	Los Angeles, CA	90003-3541	323-750-5058		6-8	
W.E.B. DuBois Charter S	2604 Martin Luther King Blv	Fresno, CA	93706	559-486-1166	486-1199	K-12	Linda Washington
Weimar Hills Charter S	PO Box 255	Weimar, CA	95736-0255	530-637-4121	637-4054	6-8	Steve Schaumleffel
Welby Way Charter ES & Gifted Magnet Ctr	23456 Welby Way	West Hills, CA	91307-3328	818-348-1975	704-8726	K-5	Jungun Yoo
West Charter S	5350 Faught Rd	Santa Rosa, CA	95403-1205	707-524-2741	524-2782	K-8	Pam Carpenter
West County Community HS	777 Sonoma St	Richmond, CA	94805-1534	510-230-4105	230-4127	9-12	Kristin Kirkman

School	Address	City,State	Zip code	Telephone	Fax	Grade	Contact
Western Center Academy	2345 Searl Pkwy	Hemet, CA	92543	951-791-0033	791-0032	6-8	Paul Bailey
Western Sierra Collegiate Academy	660 Menlo Dr	Rocklin, CA	95765-3713	916-778-4544	626-5540	7-12	Gregg Moses
Westlake Charter S	3800 Del Paso Rd	Sacramento, CA	95834-2599	916-567-5760	567-5769	K-5	Robert Capp
West Park Charter Academy	2695 S Valentine Ave	Fresno, CA	93706-9042	559-485-0727	485-0682	K-12	Stacy Nicol-Stefano
West Sacramento Early College Prep S	1504 Fallbrook St	West Sacramento, CA	95691-3622	916-375-7680		6-12	Yolanda Falkenberg
Westside Innovative School House	8820 Sepulveda Eastway	Los Angeles, CA	90045-4811	310-642-9474	642-9475	K-5	Shawna Draxton
Westside Prep Charter S - Eastside	6469 Guthrie St	North Highlands, CA	95660-3944	916-566-1860	339-2033	7-8	Julie Struckmeyer
Westside Prep Charter S - Frontier	6691 Silverthorne Cir	Sacramento, CA	95842-2654	916-566-1840	344-8932	7-8	Ellen Giffin
Westside Prep Charter S - Westside	6537 W 2nd St	Rio Linda, CA	95673-3231	916-566-1990	991-5842	7-8	Janelle Scheftner
Westwood Charter ES	2050 Selby Ave	Los Angeles, CA	90025-6397	310-474-7788	475-1295	K-5	Phyllis Scadron
Westwood Charter S	PO Box 56	Westwood, CA	96137-0056	877-256-2994	256-2964	K-12	Marty Growdon
Wheatland Charter Academy	123 Beale Hwy	Beale AFB, CA	95903	530-788-0248	788-0518	K-5	Jodie Jacklett
White Oaks ES	1901 White Oak Way	San Carlos, CA	94070-4799	650-508-7317	508-7320	K-4	Allison Liner
Whitmore Charter HS	PO Box 307	Ceres, CA	95307	209-556-1617	538-7931	9-12	David Viss
Whitmore Charter S	PO Box 307	Ceres, CA	95307	209-556-1610	538-7931	K-8	David Viss
Wilbur Charter S for Enriched Academics	5213 Crebs Ave	Tarzana, CA	91356-4010	818-345-1090	881-8128	K-5	Deborah Plat
Wilder's Preparatory Academy Charter S	830 N La Brea Ave	Inglewood, CA	90302-2206	310-671-5578	671-2424	K-8	Raymond Wilder
Willits Charter S	1431 S Main St	Willits, CA	95490-4309	707-459-5506	459-5576	6-12	John Kirchero
Willow Creek Academy	33 Buchanan Dr	Sausalito, CA	94965-1650	415-331-7530	331-1622	K-8	Carol Cooper
Willowside MS	5285 Hall Rd	Santa Rosa, CA	95401-7304	707-542-3322	525-4439	6-8	Brian Howard
Wilson College Prep S	400 105th Ave	Oakland, CA	94603-2968	510-635-7737	635-7727	6-12	Michelle Cortez
Wisdom Academy for Young Scientists	706 E Manchester Ave	Los Angeles, CA	90001-3633	323-752-6655	752-6344	K-5	Alake Watson
Woodlake ES	23231 Hatteras St	Woodland Hills, CA	91367-3199	818-347-7097	883-3953	K-5	Jaqueline Shehab
Woodland Hills Charter S	22201 San Miguel St	Woodland Hills, CA	91364-3039	818-347-9220	347-2365	K-5	Antoinette Brusca
Woodland Polytechnic Academy	1280 Santa Anita Ct	Woodland, CA	95776-6127	530-219-2542		9-12	Steve Marks
Woodland Star Charter S	17811 Arnold Dr	Sonoma, CA	95476-4019	707-996-3849	996-4369	K-8	Sheila Reilly
Woodson Charter S	3333 N Bond Ave	Fresno, CA	93726-5712	559-229-3529	229-0459	7-12	Eric Smyers
Woodward Leadership Academy	1777 W Base Line St	San Bernardino, CA	92410	909-266-1762		K-6	Veronica Godinez
Workforce Investment Act Charter S	6767 Green Valley Rd	Placerville, CA	95667-8984	530-295-2271	621-1395	9-12	David Publicover
World Academy	303 Hegenberger Rd Ste 301	Oakland, CA	94621-1419	510-904-6400	904-6763	K-5	Susan Sperber
Wright Charter S	4389 Price Ave	Santa Rosa, CA	95407-6500	707-542-0556	542-0418	K-8	Terrena Rodebaugh
Xinaxcalmecac Acad Semillas del Pueblo	4736 Huntington Dr S	Los Angeles, CA	90032-1942	323-352-2070	987-1240	K-8	Minnie Ferguson
Yav Pem Suab Academy	7555 S Land Park Dr	Sacramento, CA	95831-3863	916-433-5057	433-5289	K-6	Vince Xiong
Youth Opportunities Unlimited S	915 W Manchester Ave	Los Angeles, CA	90044-4915	323-789-4731	778-4612	9-12	Maisha James-McIntosh
Yuba City Charter S	256 Wilbur Ave	Yuba City, CA	95991-5536	530-822-9667	822-9629	K-12	James Ferreira
Yuba County Career Prep Charter S	1104 E St	Marysville, CA	95901-4825	530-741-6025	741-6032	K-12	Carol Holtz
Yuba Environmental Science Charter Acad	9841 Texas Hill Rd	Oregon House, CA	95962	530-692-2210	692-2210	PK-8	Kathy Smith
Yuba River Charter S	505 Main St	Nevada City, CA	95959-2218	530-265-6060	265-6070	K-8	Caleb Buckley
Yu Ming Charter S	1086 Alcatraz Ave	Emeryville, CA	94608-1265	415-452-2063	452-2095	K-8	Gloria Lee
Colorado							
Academy Charter S	1551 Prairie Hawk Dr	Castle Rock, CO	80109-7900	303-660-4881	660-6385	K-8	Yvette Brown
Academy for Advanced & Creative Learning	2510 N Chestnut St	Colorado Spgs, CO	80907-5912	719-434-6566	434-9696	K-8	Nikki Myers
Academy of Charter S	11800 Lowell Blvd	Westminster, CO	80031-5097	303-289-8088	289-8087	K-12	David Floodeen
Academy of Urban Learning Charter S	2417 W 29th Ave	Denver, CO	80211-3709	303-282-0900	282-0902	9-12	David Brown
Ace Community Challenge Charter S	948 Santa Fe Dr	Denver, CO	80204-3937	303-436-9588	436-0919	8-10	Eloy Chavez
Alta Vista Charter ES	PO Box 449	Lamar, CO	81052-0449	719-336-2154	336-0170	K-6	Talara Coen
American Academy Charter S	6971 Mira Vista Ln	Castle Pines, CO	80108-9511	720-292-5200		K-8	Erin Kane
Animas HS	3206 Main Ave	Durango, CO	81301-4205	970-247-2474		9-12	Michael Ackerman
Aspen Community Charter S	PO Box 336	Woody Creek, CO	81656-0336	970-923-4080	923-7380	K-8	Jim Gilchrist
Aspen Ridge Prep S	705 Austin Ave	Erie, CO	80516-2424	720-242-6225	294-0573	K-5	Pam Richau
Atlas Preparatory S	1602 S Murray Blvd	Colorado Spgs, CO	80916-4501	719-358-7196	355-1819	5-8	Zachary McComsey
Aurora Academy Charter S	10251 E 1st Ave	Aurora, CO	80010-4308	303-367-5983	367-5820	K-8	Stephen Garretson
Axl Academy	14100 E Jewell Ave	Aurora, CO	80012	303-377-0758	597-1547	K-5	Audria Philippon
Banning Lewis Ranch Academy	7094 Cottonwood Tree Dr	Colorado Spgs, CO	80927-5000	719-570-0075	522-2900	K-8	Andrew Franko
Battle Rock Charter S	11351 Road G	Cortez, CO	81321-9569	970-565-3237	564-1140	K-6	Michael Canzona
Belle Creek Charter S	9290 E 107th Ave	Henderson, CO	80640-8964	303-468-0160	468-0164	K-8	Irene German
Blair Edison Charter S	4905 Cathay St	Denver, CO	80249-8376	303-371-9570	371-8348	K-8	Deborah Blair-Minter
Boulder Prep Charter HS	5075 Chaparral Ct	Boulder, CO	80301-3589	303-545-6186	545-6187	9-12	Andre Adeli
Bromley East Charter S	356 Longspur Dr	Brighton, CO	80601-8700	720-685-3297	685-9513	K-8	Roberta Harrell
Caprock Academy	714 24 1/2 Rd	Grand Junction, CO	81505-9628	970-243-1771	243-3612	K-12	Kristin Trezise
Carbondale Community Charter S	PO Box 365	Carbondale, CO	81623-0365	970-963-9647	704-0501	K-8	Tom Penzel
Carbon Valley Charter S	4040 Coriolis Way	Frederick, CO	80504-5449	303-774-9555	774-9592	PK-8	Lisa Gjellum
Cardinal Community Academy	3101 County Road 65	Keenesburg, CO	80643-8604	303-732-9312	732-9314	K-8	April Dowdy
Challenge to Excellence Charter S	16995 Carlson Dr	Parker, CO	80134-8000	303-841-9816	840-3246	K-8	Linda Parker
Chavez Academy	2500 W 18th St	Pueblo, CO	81003-1152	719-295-1623	295-1625	K-8	Arlen Arguello
Chavez Academy	3752 Tennyson St	Denver, CO	80212-1914	303-455-0848	855-7252	K-8	Kamini Patel
Cherry Creek Academy Charter	6260 S Dayton St	Englewood, CO	80111-5203	303-779-8988	779-8817	K-8	Jay Cerny
Cheyenne Mountain Charter Academy	1832 S Wahsatch Ave	Colorado Spgs, CO	80905-2341	719-471-1999	471-4949	K-8	Ward Barr
CIVA Charter S	4635 Northpark Dr	Colorado Spgs, CO	80918-3813	719-633-1306	633-1691	9-12	Randy Zimmerman
Classical Academy Central	1655 Springcrest Rd	Colorado Spgs, CO	80920-1545	719-265-9766	265-1751	K-6	Don Stump
Classical Academy East	12201 Cross Peak Vw	Colorado Spgs, CO	80921-3438	719-282-1181	260-9743	K-6	Veronica Wolken
Classical Academy HS	975 Stout Rd	Colorado Spgs, CO	80921-3801	719-484-0091	484-0085	9-12	Paul Dellacroce
Classical Academy JHS	975 Stout Rd	Colorado Spgs, CO	80921-3801	719-484-0091	487-2339	7-8	Hugh DiPretore
Classical Academy North	975 Stout Rd	Colorado Spgs, CO	80921-3801	719-484-0081	484-0078	K-6	Rachel O'Donnell
Collegiate Academy of Colorado	8420 Sangre De Cristo Rd	Littleton, CO	80127-4201	303-972-7433	932-0695	K-12	Stephen Higgins
Colorado Calvert Academy	155 Boardwalk Dr Ste 547	Fort Collins, CO	80525-3040	970-232-3317		K-8	Elizabeth Davis
Colorado Charter HS	1175 Osage St Ste 100	Denver, CO	80204-3445	303-892-8475	825-3011	10-12	Cyndi Bush-Luna
Colorado Early Colleges Fort Collins	4800 Wheaton Dr	Fort Collins, CO	80525-9483	970-377-0044		9-12	Keith King
Colorado Springs Charter Academy	2577 N Chelton Rd	Colorado Spgs, CO	80909-1345	719-636-2722	636-2726	K-8	Jacob Murphy
Colorado Springs Early Colleges	4435 N Chestnut St	Colorado Spgs, CO	80907-3812	719-955-4675	528-7006	9-12	Keith King
Colorado Virtual Academy	11990 Grant St Ste 402	Northglenn, CO	80233-1136	303-255-4650	255-7044	K-12	Heidi Magri
Community Leadership Academy	6880 Holly St	Commerce City, CO	80022-2536	303-288-2711	288-2714	PK-8	Ron Jajdelski
Community Prep Charter S	332 E Willamette Ave	Colorado Spgs, CO	80903-1116	719-227-8836	227-8897	9-12	Marty Schneider
Compass Montessori Charter S	10399 W 44th Ave	Wheat Ridge, CO	80033-2701	303-420-8288	420-0139	PK-6	Tracy McIlrath
Compass Montessori Charter S	4441 Salvia St	Golden, CO	80403-1698	303-271-1977	271-1984	PK-12	Tracy McIlrath
Connect Charter S	104 W 7th St	Pueblo, CO	81003	719-542-0224	583-9799	6-8	Jeff Hawkins
Corridor Community Academy	420 7th St	Bennett, CO	80102-8124	303-644-5180	644-4918	K-8	Natalie Polcyn
Crest Academy	220 W 12th St	Salida, CO	81201-2306	719-539-2977	530-5234	5-8	Karen Lundberg
Crestone Charter S	PO Box 400	Crestone, CO	81131-0400	719-256-4907	256-4908	K-12	Kathryn Brady
Crown Pointe Academy	2900 W 86th Ave	Westminster, CO	80031-3849	303-428-1882	428-1938	K-8	Keith Ouweneel
DCS Montessori Charter S	311 E Castle Pines Pkwy	Castle Rock, CO	80108-8101	303-387-5625	387-5626	PK-7	Jeromy Johnson
Denver Language S	451 Newport St	Denver, CO	80220-6019	303-557-0852	393-6805	K-8	Dr. Sara Baird Amodio
Denver S of Science and Technology	2000 Valentia St	Denver, CO	80238-2785	303-320-5570	377-5101	9-12	Mark Heffron
Denver S of Science and Technology	2000 Valentia St	Denver, CO	80238-2785	303-320-5570		6-8	Stefan McVoy
Denver S of Science and Technology-Cole	3240 Humboldt St	Denver, CO	80205-3934	303-524-6310		6-12	Jeff Osborne
Denver S of Science and Technology CV MS	3001 S Federal Blvd	Denver, CO	80236-2711	720-524-6374		6-8	Heather Newton
Denver S of Science and Technology - GVR	4800 Telluride St	Denver, CO	80249-6803	303-524-6300		6-8	Jessica Degenhart
Denver S of Science and Technology - GVR	4800 Telluride St	Denver, CO	80249-6803	303-524-6300		9-12	Rochelle Bell
Eagle County Charter Academy	PO Box 2108	Edwards, CO	81632-2108	970-926-0656	926-0786	K-8	Kim Walter
Eagle Ridge Academy	3551 E Southern St	Brighton, CO	80601-0015	303-655-0773	655-9155	9-12	Ben Ploeger
Early College of Arvada	4905 W 60th Ave	Arvada, CO	80003-6916	720-473-4400		6-12	Eric Covington
Excel Academy	11500 W 84th Ave	Arvada, CO	80005-5272	303-467-2295	467-2291	K-8	Holly Hensey
Flagstaff Academy	2040 Miller Dr	Longmont, CO	80501-6748	303-651-7900	651-7922	PK-8	Andrew Moore
Foundations Academy	340 S 45th Ave	Brighton, CO	80601-4652	303-659-9519	835-7151	K-5	Joe Hammond
Franklin Academy	2270 Plaza Dr	Highlands Ranch, CO	80129-1501	720-383-4519		PK-8	Bob Barber
Free Horizon Montessori S	581 Conference Pl	Golden, CO	80401-5615	303-231-9801	231-9983	PK-8	Gerald Gabbard
Frontier Academy Charter S	2560 W 29th St	Greeley, CO	80631-8507	970-330-1780	330-4334	K-5	Rebecca Dougherty
Frontier Academy Charter S	6530 W 16th St	Greeley, CO	80634-8675	970-339-9153	339-5631	6-12	Mary Meersman
Frontier Charter Academy	418 Yoder St	Calhan, CO	80808	719-347-3156	347-3054	K-8	
Georgetown Community S	PO Box 74	Georgetown, CO	80444-0074	303-569-3277	569-2761	PK-6	Sharon Warren
Girls Athletic Leadership S	200 S University Blvd	Denver, CO	80209-3270	303-282-6437		6-12	Liz Wolfson
Global Village Academy	403 S Airport Blvd Unit A	Aurora, CO	80017-3900	303-309-6657	317-6538	K-8	Christina Burton
Global Village Academy	550 W 112th Ave	Northglenn, CO	80234	303-248-4300		K-8	John Kaufman
Global Village Academy Colorado Springs	1702 N Murray Blvd	Colorado Spgs, CO	80915	719-645-8063	694-8506	K-4	Sherman Fuller
Global Village Academy Fort Collins	8005 Highland Meadows Pkwy	Fort Collins, CO	80528	970-682-9242		K-4	Russ Spicer
GLOBE Charter S	3302 Alpine Pl	Colorado Spgs, CO	80909-2100	719-630-0577	630-0395	K-9	Jan Songer
GOAL Academy	107 W 11th St	Pueblo, CO	81003	719-776-4625	746-2874	9-12	Ken Crowell
Guffey Community Charter S	PO Box 147	Guffey, CO	80820-0147	719-689-2093	689-3407	K-8	Pam Moore
Highline Academy	2170 S Dahlia St	Denver, CO	80222-5106	303-759-7808	759-7809	K-8	Gregg Gonzales
High Point Academy	6750 N Dunkirk St	Aurora, CO	80019-2107	303-217-5152	217-5153	PK-8	Dr. Terry Croy-Lewis
Hope Online Learning Academy	373 Inverness Pkwy Ste 205	Englewood, CO	80112-5898	303-989-3539	675-3013	K-12	Heather O'Mara
Horizons K-8 School	4545 Sioux Dr	Boulder, CO	80303-3732	720-561-5580	561-5580	K-8	Sonny Zinn
Huerta Preparatory HS	2727 W 18th St	Pueblo, CO	81003-1185	719-583-1030	583-1031	9-12	Rose Benitez
Imagine Charter S at Firestone	5753 Twilight Ave	Firestone, CO	80504-6481	303-772-3711	772-3977	PK-8	Nancy Box
Imagine Classical Academy - Indigo Ranch	6464 Peterson Rd	Colorado Spgs, CO	80923-3565	719-495-7360	495-4239	PK-8	Tina Leone

School	Address	City,State	Zip code	Telephone	Fax	Grade	Contact
Independence Academy	600 N 14th St	Grand Junction, CO	81501-4402	970-254-6850	241-2064	K-8	Damon Lockhart
Indian Peaks Charter S	PO Box 1819	Granby, CO	80446-1819	970-887-3805	887-3829	K-8	Polly Gallagher
Irwin Charter Academy	1801 Howard Ave	Colorado Spgs, CO	80909	719-302-9000		K-5	Cindee Will
Irwin Charter ES	5525 Astrozon Blvd	Colorado Spgs, CO	80916-4226	719-302-9107	884-0992	K-5	Elizabeth Berg
Irwin Charter HS	5525 Astrozon Blvd	Colorado Spgs, CO	80916-4226	719-302-9109	576-8071	9-12	Alex Marquez
Irwin Charter MS	5525 Astrozon Blvd	Colorado Spgs, CO	80916-4226	719-302-9108	591-9993	6-8	Holly Varnum
Jefferson Academy	9955 Yarrow St	Broomfield, CO	80021-4048	303-887-1992	887-2435	7-12	Tammy Stringari
Jefferson Academy	9955 Yarrow St	Broomfield, CO	80021-4048	303-438-1011	438-1046	K-6	Michael Nolan
Juniper Ridge Charter S	640 24 1/2 Rd	Grand Junction, CO	81501	970-639-0884		K-6	Patrick Ebel
Justice HS	4760 Shoshone St	Denver, CO	80211-1260	303-480-5610	480-5613	7-12	Gary Losh
Justice HS	805 Excalibur St	Lafayette, CO	80026-1909	720-328-4864	328-4865	9-12	Jeremy Jimenez
KIPP Denver Collegiate HS	451 S Tejon St	Denver, CO	80223-1928	303-623-5772	922-9910	9-12	Kaye Taavialma
KIPP Montbello College Prep	5290 Kittredge St	Denver, CO	80239-5628	720-934-3245		5-8	Nick Bucy
KIPP Sunshine Peak Academy	375 S Tejon St	Denver, CO	80223-1961	303-623-5772	623-0410	5-8	Kurt Pusch
Knowledge Quest Academy	705 School House Dr	Milliken, CO	80543-3154	970-587-5742	587-5750	K-8	Linda Spreitzer
Lake George Charter S	PO Box 420	Lake George, CO	80827-0420	719-748-3911	748-8151	PK-6	Pat Lewis
Landmark Academy at Reunion	10566 Memphis St	Commerce City, CO	80022-6236	303-287-2901	287-4196	K-8	Matt Carlton
Legacy Academy	1975 Legacy Cir	Elizabeth, CO	80107-8330	303-646-2636	646-2635	K-8	Jason Cross
Liberty Common HS	2745 Minnesota Dr	Fort Collins, CO	80525-6794	970-672-5500	672-5499	7-12	Bob Shaffer
Liberty Common S	1725 Sharp Point Dr	Fort Collins, CO	80525-4424	970-482-9800	482-8007	K-8	Casey Churchill
Life Skills Center of Colorado Springs	1810 Eastlake Blvd	Colorado Spgs, CO	80910-3422	719-471-0684	471-4392	9-12	Kim Caplan
Lincoln Academy	6980 Pierce St	Arvada, CO	80003-3646	303-467-5363	467-5367	PK-8	Janelle Johnson
Littleton Charter Academy	1200 W Mineral Ave	Littleton, CO	80120-4536	303-798-5252	798-0298	K-8	Shelly Russell
Littleton Preparatory Charter S	5151 S Federal Blvd Ste 1	Littleton, CO	80123-8590	303-734-1995	734-3620	K-8	Kimberly Ash
Lotus S for Excellence	11001 E Alameda Ave Ste A	Aurora, CO	80012-1034	303-360-0052	360-0071	6-12	Dr. Adnan Doyuran
Loveland Classical Charter S	3835 14th St SW	Loveland, CO	80537-6075	970-670-0527	237-4829	K-12	David Yu
Maclaren Charter S	303 Austin Bluffs Pkwy	Colorado Spgs, CO	80918-3922	719-313-4488	313-4491	6-12	Mary Faith Hall
Madison Charter Academy	660 Syracuse St	Colorado Spgs, CO	80911-2546	719-391-3977	391-1744	K-6	Dr. Anne Shineman
Magon Academy	5301 Lowell Blvd	Denver, CO	80221	303-412-7610	412-7658	K-8	Kaye Taavialma
Marble Charter S	412 W Main St	Marble, CO	81623-9396	970-963-9550	963-8435	K-10	Amy Rusby
Monarch Montessori of Denver	11200 E 45th Ave	Denver, CO	80239-3018	720-746-2140		K-5	Nancy Radkiewicz
Montessori del Mundo	15503B E Mississippi Ave	Aurora, CO	80017			PK-1	Karen Farquharson
Montessori Peaks Academy	9904 W Capri Ave	Littleton, CO	80123-3535	303-972-2627	933-4182	PK-6	Char Weaver
Monument Academy	1150 Village Ridge Pt	Monument, CO	80132-8992	719-481-1950	481-1948	PK-8	Dr. Don Griffin
Mountain MS	108 W 31st St	Durango, CO	81301	970-828-5600		6-8	Shane Voss
Mountain Phoenix Community S	4725 Miller St	Wheat Ridge, CO	80033-2824	303-728-9100	728-9801	PK-7	Donna Newberg-Long
Mountain Phoenix Community S Coal Creek	11398 Ranch Elsie Rd	Golden, CO	80403-7309	303-642-7634	642-2455	PK-8	Donna Newberg-Long
Mountain Song Community S	2904 W Kiowa St	Colorado Spgs, CO	80904	719-344-5770	375-0180	PK-6	Neah Douglas
Mountain View Core Knowledge S	890 Field Ave	Canon City, CO	81212-9250	719-275-1980	275-1998	K-8	Karen Sartori
New America HS	500 Red Table Dr	Gypsum, CO	81637	970-328-8990	328-8995	9-12	Wade Hill
New America S - Aurora	9125 E 7th Pl	Denver, CO	80230-7111	303-320-9854	320-9304	9-12	Annie Trujillo
New America S - Jeffco	5806 W Alameda Ave	Lakewood, CO	80226-3533	303-894-3171	237-4119	9-12	Jon Berninzoni
New Vision Charter S	2366 E 1st St	Loveland, CO	80537-5906	970-593-6827	461-1947	K-8	Carmella Schroeder
Northeast Academy	4895 Peoria St	Denver, CO	80239-2847	303-307-8837	307-8867	K-8	Jere Pearcy
North Routt Charter S	26990 Eagle Ln	Clark, CO	80428-9702	970-871-6062	871-6067	K-8	Colleen Poole
North Star Academy	16700 Keystone Blvd	Parker, CO	80134-3544	720-851-7827	851-0976	K-8	Kendra Hossfeld
Odyssey Charter S	6550 E 21st Ave	Denver, CO	80207-3961	303-316-3944	316-4016	K-8	Marcia Fulton
Paradox Valley Charter S	PO Box 420	Paradox, CO	81429-0420	970-859-7236	859-7235	PK-8	Jon Orris
Parker Core Knowledge Charter S	11661 N Pine Dr	Parker, CO	80138-8022	303-840-7070	840-9785	PK-8	Teri Aplin
Passage Charter S	703 S 9th St	Montrose, CO	81401-4409	970-249-8066	249-3497	9-12	Corinne Vogenthaler
Paul Academy of Arts & Knowledge	4512 McMurry Ave	Fort Collins, CO	80525-3400	970-226-2800	226-2806	K-8	Phyllis Nakagawa
Peak to Peak Charter S	800 Merlin Dr	Lafayette, CO	80026-2146	303-453-4600	453-4613	K-12	Noelle Roni
Pikes Peak Prep S	525 E Costilla St	Colorado Spgs, CO	80903-3764	719-570-7575	475-0831	K-12	Dr. Dawn Nelson
Pikes Peak S of Expeditionary Learning	11925 Antlers Ridge Dr	Falcon, CO	80831-8658	719-522-2580		PK-8	Don Knapp
Pinnacle Charter S	1001 W 84th Ave	Federal Heights, CO	80260-4717	303-450-3985	255-6305	K-12	Dr. William Wiener
Pioneer Charter S	3230 E 38th Ave	Denver, CO	80205-3726	303-329-8412	468-1133	PK-6	Richard Barrett
Platte River Academy	4085 Lark Sparrow St	Highlands Ranch, CO	80126-5209	303-221-1070	221-1069	K-8	Dr. Gary Stueven
Prairie Creeks Charter S	56729 Colorado Ave	Strasburg, CO	80136-7809	303-622-6328	622-6327	9-12	Jeffrey Rasp
Prospect Ridge Academy	2555 Preble Creek Pkwy	Broomfield, CO	80023-8096	720-399-0300	545-2163	K-12	April Wilkin
Provost Academy	7730 E Belleview Ave # AG9	Greenwood Vlg, CO	80111	303-770-1240	771-1210	9-12	Ian Jones
Pueblo S for the Arts & Sciences	2415 Jones Ave	Pueblo, CO	81004-2689	719-404-2680	404-2681	K-8	Natalie Allen
Ridge View Academy	28101 E Quincy Ave	Watkins, CO	80137-9502	303-214-1139	766-2151	9-12	Ed Cope
Ridgeview Classical S	1800 S Lemay Ave	Fort Collins, CO	80525-1240	970-494-4620	494-4625	K-12	Florian Hild
Rocky Mountain Academy of Evergreen	2959 Royale Elk Way	Evergreen, CO	80439-8689	303-670-1070	670-1253	PK-8	J. Daniel Cohen
Rocky Mountain Classical Academy	1710 Piros Dr	Colorado Spgs, CO	80915-4307	719-622-8000	622-8004	K-8	Christianna Fogler
Rocky Mountain Deaf S	1921 Youngfield St	Golden, CO	80401-6301	303-984-5749	984-7290	PK-12	Nancy Bridenbaugh
Rocky Mountain Prep	7808 Cherry Creek South Dr	Denver, CO	80231	720-608-0219		PK-8	James Cryan
Roosevelt-Edison Charter S	205 Byron Dr	Colorado Spgs, CO	80910-2599	719-637-0311	380-0176	K-5	Lance Howard
Ross Montessori Charter S	407 Merrill Ave	Carbondale, CO	81623-1643	970-963-7199	963-7342	K-8	Sonya Hemmen
St. Vrain Montessori Charter S	1055 Delaware Ave	Longmont, CO	80501-6143	303-682-4339	682-8925	PK-5	Katie Torres
Scholars to Leaders Academy	3115 Larkspur Dr	Colorado Spgs, CO	80907-5719	719-575-9380	575-9385	K-8	Dr. Carolyn Gery
Sims-Fayola International Academy	6850 Argonne St	Denver, CO	80249-8650	720-515-7342	836-3142	6-12	Dedrick Sims
SkyView Academy	6161 Business Center Dr	Highlands Ranch, CO	80130-3605	303-471-8439	470-1903	PK-12	Merlin Holmes
SOAR Green Valley Ranch	4800 Telluride St	Denver, CO	80249-6803	720-287-5100		K-5	Reed Dyer
Southwest Early College Charter S	3001 S Federal Blvd	Denver, CO	80236-2711	303-935-5473	935-5591	9-12	Rudy Lucero
Southwest Open Charter S	PO Box DD	Cortez, CO	81321-0870	970-565-1150	565-8770	9-12	Jennifer Carter
STAR Academy	2520 Airport Rd	Colorado Spgs, CO	80910-3120	719-638-6554	638-2246	K-8	Joseph Torrez
Stargate Charter S	3951 Cottonwood Lakes Blvd	Thornton, CO	80241-2187	303-450-3936	450-3941	K-8	Josh Cochran
Stone Creek Charter S	33520 Highway 6	Edwards, CO	81632	970-569-3327	569-3492	K-8	John Brendza
STRIVE Prep - Federal Campus	1825 S Federal Blvd	Denver, CO	80219-4905	303-573-2017	935-5004	6-8	Katie Holz-Russell
STRIVE Prep - GVR	4800 Telluride St	Denver, CO	80249-6803	303-630-0360		6-8	Ken Greenbaum
STRIVE Prep - Harvey Park	3201 W Arizona Ave	Denver, CO	80219-3941	303-962-9880	962-9886	6-8	Joshua Smith
STRIVE Prep - Highland Campus	2960 N Speer Blvd	Denver, CO	80211-3795	303-962-9880		6-8	Betsy Peterson
STRIVE Prep - Lake Campus	1820 Lowell Blvd	Denver, CO	80204-1549	303-551-7200		6-8	Ryan Kockler
STRIVE Prep - Montbello	11200 E 45th Ave	Denver, CO	80239-3018	720-630-0360		6-8	Jennifer Troy
STRIVE Prep - SMART	3201 W Arizona Ave	Denver, CO	80219-3941	303-630-0360		9-12	Antonio Vigil
Summit MS	4655 Hanover Ave	Boulder, CO	80305-6036	720-561-3900	561-3901	6-8	James Bagen
Swallows Charter Academy	278 S McCulloch Blvd	Pueblo West, CO	81007-2844	719-547-1627	547-2509	K-8	Dr. Cindy Compton
TCA College Pathways	12201 Cross Peak Vw	Colorado Spgs, CO	80921-3438	719-494-0631	484-0087	7-12	Steve Wright
Twin Peaks Charter Academy	340 S Sunset St	Longmont, CO	80501-6107	720-772-7286	485-0394	K-11	B.J. Buchmann
Two Roads HS	7180 Oak St	Arvada, CO	80004-1416	303-423-3377	467-6955	PK-12	Terry Johns
Union Colony Prep ES	1051 29th Street Rd	Evans, CO	80620	970-673-4997	353-2271	K-5	Pat Gilliam
Union Colony Prep S	2000 Clubhouse Dr	Greeley, CO	80634-3643	970-673-4546	330-7604	6-12	Pat Gilliam
University Preparatory Academy	2409 Arapahoe St	Denver, CO	80205-2614	303-292-0463	296-2844	K-5	David Singer
University Schools	6525 W 18th St	Greeley, CO	80634-8674	970-506-7000	506-7070	K-12	Sherry Gerner
Vanguard Classical S	801 Yosemite St	Denver, CO	80230-6087	303-691-2384	226-5529	K-8	Robert Miller
Vanguard S	1605 S Corona Ave	Colorado Spgs, CO	80905	719-471-1999	634-4180	9-12	Colin Mullaney
Venture Prep Charter S	2540 Holly St	Denver, CO	80207-3228	303-893-0805	320-7665	6-12	Ken Burdette
Vista Charter S	PO Box 10000	Montrose, CO	81402-9701	970-249-4470	252-3354	9-12	Beth Sass
Westgate Community S	11700 Irma Dr	Northglenn, CO	80233-2198	303-425-0967	452-4519	K-8	Christine Johnston
West Ridge Academy	6200 W 20th St	Greeley, CO	80634-9675	970-330-3671	330-3679	K-9	Victoria Martino
Wilson Academy	8300 W 94th Ave	Westminster, CO	80021-4590	303-431-3694	423-4388	PK-8	Tim Matlick
Windsor Charter Academy	680 Academy Ct	Windsor, CO	80550-3101	970-674-5020	674-5017	K-8	Rebecca Teeples
Wyatt-Edison Charter S	3620 Franklin St	Denver, CO	80205-3325	303-292-5515	292-5111	K-8	David Trajtenberg
Youth & Family Academy Charter S	1920 Valley Dr	Pueblo, CO	81008-1764	719-546-1740	542-1335	7-12	Molly Melendez

Connecticut

School	Address	City,State	Zip code	Telephone	Fax	Grade	Contact
Achievement First Bridgeport Academy	529 Noble Ave	Bridgeport, CT	06608-1803	203-333-9128	333-9142	5-8	Morgan Barth
Achievement First Bridgeport Academy	655 Stillman St	Bridgeport, CT	06608-1331	203-338-0593	338-0714	K-8	Katherine Baker
Achievement First Hartford Academy	305 Greenfield St	Hartford, CT	06112-1826	860-695-6560	242-6457	K-4	Liz Ferguson
Achievement First Hartford Academy MS	305 Greenfield St	Hartford, CT	06112-1826	860-695-6760	242-6457	5-8	Jeff House
Achievement First Hartford HS	305 Greenfield St	Hartford, CT	06112-1826	860-695-6685	722-8138	9-12	Claire Shin
Amistad Academy ES	130 Edgewood Ave	New Haven, CT	06511-4520	203-772-2166	772-2520	K-4	Amanda Alonzy
Amistad Academy MS	130 Edgewood Ave	New Haven, CT	06511-4520	203-772-7000	773-0170	5-8	Sarah White
Amistad-Elm City HS	49 Prince St	New Haven, CT	06519-1603	203-772-1092	772-1784	9-12	Jeff Sudmeyer
Bridge Academy	401 Kossuth St	Bridgeport, CT	06608-2318	203-336-9999	336-9852	7-12	Timothy Dutton
Common Ground HS	358 Springside Ave	New Haven, CT	06515-1024	203-389-4333	389-7458	9-12	Lizanne Cox
Community Connections HS	12 Railroad Ave	Plainfield, CT	06374-1215	860-319-9733		9-12	Dr. KellyAnn Graves
Elm City College Preparatory ES	407 James St	New Haven, CT	06513-3016	203-772-7010		K-4	Andrew Poole
Elm City College Preparatory MS	794 Dixwell Ave	New Haven, CT	06511-1035	203-772-5332	772-3641	5-8	Rebecca Good
Explorations Charter S	71 Spencer St	Winsted, CT	06098-1128	860-738-9070	738-9092	10-12	Gail Srebnik
Highville Charter S	130 Leeder Hill Dr	Hamden, CT	06517-2730	203-287-0528	287-0693	PK-8	Bill Troy
Integrated Day Charter S	68 Thermos Ave	Norwich, CT	06360-6943	860-892-1900	892-1902	PK-8	Anna James
Interdistrict S for Arts & Communication	190 Governor Winthrop Blvd	New London, CT	06320-6633	860-447-1003	447-0470	6-8	Gina Fafard
Jumoke Academy	339 Blue Hills Ave	Hartford, CT	06112-1505	860-527-0575	525-7758	PK-K,	Dr. Michael Sharpe
Jumoke Academy @ Milner	104 Vine St	Hartford, CT	06112-2271	860-695-4380	278-4694	PK-8	Doreen Crawford

School	Address	City,State	Zip code	Telephone	Fax	Grade	Contact
Museum Academy	11 Turkey Hill Rd	Bloomfield, CT	06002-3046	860-231-7800	231-7236	PK-5	Shandra Brown
New Beginnings Family Academy	184 Garden St	Bridgeport, CT	06605-1213	203-384-2897	384-2898	K-8	Paul Whyte
Odyssey Community S	579 Middle Tpke W	Manchester, CT	06040-2728	860-645-1234	533-0324	4-8	Elaine Stancliffe
Park City Prep Charter S	510 Barnum Ave Ste 2	Bridgeport, CT	06608-2400	203-953-3766	953-3771	6-8	Bruce Ravage
Side by Side Community S	10 Chestnut St	Norwalk, CT	06854-2928	203-857-0306	838-2666	PK-8	Matthew Nittoly
Stamford Academy	229 North St	Stamford, CT	06901-1112	203-324-6300	324-6310	9-12	Clark Callahan
Trailblazers Academy	83 Lockwood Ave	Stamford, CT	06902-4201	203-977-5690	977-5688	6-8	Mike McGuire

Delaware

School	Address	City,State	Zip code	Telephone	Fax	Grade	Contact
Academy of Dover Charter S	104 Saulsbury Rd	Dover, DE	19904-2705	302-674-0684	674-3894	K-4	Noel Rodriguez
Campus Community S	350 Pear St	Dover, DE	19904-3016	302-736-0403	736-5330	K-8	Trish Hermance
Charter S of Wilmington	100 N DuPont Rd	Wilmington, DE	19807-3199	302-651-2727	652-1246	9-12	Charles Baldwin
Delaware Acad of Pub Safety & Security	179 Stanton Christiana Rd	Newark, DE	19702-1619	302-731-2777		9-12	Chuck Hughes
Delaware College Preparatory Academy	510 W 28th St	Wilmington, DE	19802-3022	302-762-7424	762-7426	K-5	Howard Johnson
Delaware Military Academy	112 Middleboro Rd	Wilmington, DE	19804-1621	302-998-0745	998-3521	9-12	Jack Wintermantel
East Side Charter S	3000 N Claymont St	Wilmington, DE	19802-2807	302-762-5834	762-3864	K-8	Dr. Lamont Browne
Edison Charter S	2200 N Locust St	Wilmington, DE	19802-4429	302-778-1101	778-2232	K-8	Salome Thomas-El
Family Foundations Academy	1101 Delaware St	New Castle, DE	19720-6033	302-324-8901	324-8908	K-8	Dr. Tennell Brewington
Gateway Lab S	2501 Centerville Rd	Wilmington, DE	19808-1603	302-633-4091	633-5680	1-8	Pam Draper
Kuumba Academy Charter S	519 N Market St	Wilmington, DE	19801-3004	302-472-6450	472-6452	K-5	Sally Maldonado
Las Americas Aspira Academy	326 Ruthar Dr	Newark, DE	19711-8017	302-292-1463	292-1291	K-8	Margaret Lopez Waite
MOT Charter S	1156 Levels Rd	Middletown, DE	19709-7700	302-376-5125	376-5120	K-8	Linda Jennings
Moyer Academy	610 E 17th St	Wilmington, DE	19802-5031	302-428-9501	428-9506	6-12	Glenn Clarke
Newark Charter S	2001 Patriot Way	Newark, DE	19711-1809	302-369-2001	368-3460	K-8	Greg Meece
Odyssey Charter S	3821 Lancaster Pike	Wilmington, DE	19805-1512	302-994-6490	994-6915	K-5	Dr. Nick Manolakos
Pencader Business & Finance Charter HS	170 Lukens Dr	New Castle, DE	19720-2727	302-472-0794	472-0796	9-12	Steve Quimby
Positive Outcomes Charter S	3337 S Dupont Hwy	Camden, DE	19934-1378	302-697-8805	697-8813	7-12	Edward Emmett
Prestige Academy	1121 Thatcher St	Wilmington, DE	19802-5135	302-762-3240	762-4782	5-8	Jack Perry
Providence Creek Academy Charter S	PO Box 265	Clayton, DE	19938-0265	302-653-6276	653-5238	K-8	Audrey Erschen
Reach Academy for Girls	3210 Philadelphia Pike	Claymont, DE	19703-3103	302-792-6400	792-6402	K-8	Tara Allen
Sussex Academy of Arts and Sciences	21777 Sussex Pines Rd	Georgetown, DE	19947-3901	302-856-3636	856-3376	6-8	Patricia Oliphant Ed.D.

District Of Columbia

School	Address	City,State	Zip code	Telephone	Fax	Grade	Contact
Achievement Preparatory Academy	908 Wahler Pl SE	Washington, DC	20032-4098	202-562-1214	562-1219	4-8	Shantelle Wright
Angelou Charter HS-Evans Campus	5600 E Capitol St NE	Washington, DC	20019-6732	202-232-2885	315-3995	9-Adu	Corey Carter
Angelou Charter MS	5600 E Capitol St NE Fl 1	Washington, DC	20019-6735	202-232-2885	315-3995	6-8	La'Mont Geddis
Angelou Charter S - Young Adult	5600 E Capitol St NE	Washington, DC	20019-6732	202-232-2885	315-3995	9-Adu	Jose de Olivares
AppleTree Early Learning - Columbia Hts	2750 14th St NW	Washington, DC	20009-6909	202-667-9490	667-9493	PK-PK	LaRon Martin
AppleTree Early Learning-Douglass Knoll	2017 Savannah Ter SE	Washington, DC	20020-2127	202-629-4525	629-2548	PK-PK	Shannon Anderson
AppleTree Early Learning - Lincoln Park	138 12th St NE	Washington, DC	20002-6471	202-621-6581	621-6584	PK-PK	Eneida Thomas
AppleTree Early Learning - Oklahoma Ave	330 21st St NE	Washington, DC	20002-6713	202-525-7807	629-2189	PK-PK	Nazo Burgy
AppleTree Early Learning - Parkland	2011 Savannah St SE	Washington, DC	20020-7574	202-506-1890	506-1894	PK-PK	Shannon Anderson
AppleTree Early Learning - Riverside	680 I St SW	Washington, DC	20024-2432	202-646-0500	646-0510	PK-PK	LaRon Martin
AppleTree Early Learning S - Amidon	401 I St SW	Washington, DC	20024-4438	202-646-0094	646-0095	PK-PK	LaRon Martin
Arts & Technology Academy	5300 Blaine St NE	Washington, DC	20019-6665	202-398-6811	388-8467	PK-5	Marva McClure
Basis DC Charter S	412 8th St NW	Washington, DC	20004	202-393-5437	803-5764	5-8	Paul Morrissey
Bethune Day Academy	1404 Jackson St NE	Washington, DC	20017-2951	202-459-4710	536-2670	PK-8	Dr. Linda McKay
Bridges Public Charter S	1250 Taylor St NW	Washington, DC	20011-5600	202-545-0515	545-0517	PK-K	Olivia Smith
Capital City Public Charter S	100 Peabody St NW	Washington, DC	20011	202-387-0309	387-7074	PK-12	Karen Dresden
Center City Pub Charter S - Brightwood	6008 Georgia Ave NW	Washington, DC	20011-5104	202-723-3322	291-0219	PK-8	Shavone Gibson
Center City Pub Charter S - Capitol Hill	1503 E Capitol St SE	Washington, DC	20003-1508	202-547-7556	547-5686	PK-8	Sharise Deal
Center City Pub Charter S - Congress Hts	220 Highview Pl SE	Washington, DC	20032-1581	202-562-7070	547-5829	PK-8	Niya White
Center City Public Charter S - Petworth	510 Webster St NW	Washington, DC	20011-4758	202-726-9212	726-3378	PK-8	LaShada Ham
Center City Public Charter S - Shaw	711 N St NW	Washington, DC	20001-3505	202-234-1093	462-6875	PK-8	Demetria Gartrell
Center City Public Charter S - Trinidad	1217 W Virginia Ave NE	Washington, DC	20002-3817	202-397-1614	398-4832	PK-8	Travis Bouldin
Chavez - Capitol Hill HS	709 12th St SE	Washington, DC	20003-2962	202-547-3424	547-3449	9-12	Daneen Keaton
Chavez - Parkside MSHS	3701 Hayes St NE	Washington, DC	20019-1702	202-398-2230	398-2535	6-12	Yvonne Waller
Chavez Prep MS	770 Kenyon St NW	Washington, DC	20010-1522	202-723-3795	547-3449	6-9	Bryan Eberwein
Clark Public Charter S	2501 M L K Jr Ave SE	Washington, DC	20020	202-563-6556	563-6605	PK-8	Jenny DuFresne
Community Academy Pub Charter - Amos I	1300 Allison St NW	Washington, DC	20011-4441	202-723-4100	723-6867	PK-5	Bryan Lewallen
Community Academy Pub Charter - Amos II	33 Riggs Rd NE	Washington, DC	20011-2463	202-723-5136	723-5139	PK-K	Tanya Clark-Morgan
Community Academy Pub Charter - Amos III	1400 1st St NW	Washington, DC	20001-1763	202-234-2122	234-2166	PK-8	Kevin Walston
Community Academy Pub Charter - Butler	5 Thomas Cir NW	Washington, DC	20005-4104	202-332-6565	332-1073	PK-5	William Thomas
Community Academy Pub Charter - Online	1351 Nicholson St NW	Washington, DC	20011-2813	202-234-5437		K-8	John Sloane
Creative Minds International Charter S	3324 16th St NW	Washington, DC	20010	202-588-0370	588-0263	PK-2	Golnar Abedin Ph.D.
DC Bilingual Public Charter S	1420 Columbia Rd NW	Washington, DC	20009-4779	202-332-4200	745-2562	PK-5	Wanda Perez
DC Prep Charter ES - Edgewood	707 Edgewood St NE	Washington, DC	20017-3341	202-635-4411	635-4412	PK-3	Nicole Bryan
DC Prep Charter ES - Benning	100 41st St NE	Washington, DC	20019-3310	202-398-2838	398-2839	PK-3	Raymond Weeden
DC Prep Charter MS - Edgewood	701 Edgewood St NE	Washington, DC	20017-3341	202-832-5700	832-5701	4-8	Cassie Pergament
DC Scholars Charter S	5601 E Capitol St SE	Washington, DC	20019-6772	202-559-6138	618-9396	PK-3	Rebecca Crouch
Doar Charter S for Performing Arts	705 Edgewood St NE Fl 2	Washington, DC	20017-3341	202-269-4646	403-3222	PK-8	Dr. Barbara Smith
Eagle Academy at New Jersey Ave	1017 New Jersey Ave SE	Washington, DC	20003-3339	202-459-6825	479-6796	PK-3	Kimberly Jackson
Eagle Academy Charter S - Wheeler Road	3400 Wheeler Rd SE	Washington, DC	20032-4137	202-544-2646	544-0187	PK-3	Jeffrey Cline
Early Childhood Academy Johenning Campus	4025 9th St SE	Washington, DC	20032-6051	202-373-0035	373-5586	PK-3	Thann Ingraham
Early Childhood Academy - Washington	4031 9th St SE	Washington, DC	20032	202-373-0035	373-0096	1-3	Thann Ingraham
Education Strengthens Families Charter S	1755 Newton St NW	Washington, DC	20010-1823	202-232-7777	797-8470	PK-12	Christie McKay
Education Strengthens Families Charter S	3912 Georgia Ave NW	Washington, DC	20011-5861	202-545-2020	797-8470	PK-12	Christie McKay
Education Strengthens Families Charter S	2333 Ontario Rd NW	Washington, DC	20009-2627	202-797-7337	797-8470	PK-12	Christie McKay
Excel Academy Public Charter S	2501 M L K Jr SE	Washington, DC	20020	202-373-0097	373-0477	PK-4	Kaye Savage
Friendship Charter S - Blow-Pierce	725 19th St NE	Washington, DC	20002-4713	202-572-1070	399-6157	PK-8	Mya Baker
Friendship Charter S - Chamberlain	1345 Potomac Ave SE	Washington, DC	20003-4411	202-547-5800	547-4554	PK-8	Maurita Scranton
Friendship Charter S - Southeast Academy	645 Milwaukee Pl SE	Washington, DC	20032-2606	202-562-1980	562-0726	PK-5	Joseph Speight
Friendship Charter S - Tech Prep	620 Milwaukee Pl SE	Washington, DC	20032-2605	202-562-1681	562-1817	6-10	Doranna Tindle
Friendship Charter S - Woodridge	2959 Carlton Ave NE	Washington, DC	20018-2615	202-635-6500	635-6481	PK-8	Rictor Craig
Friendship Collegiate Academy	4095 Minnesota Ave NE	Washington, DC	20019-3541	202-396-5500	396-8229	9-12	Peggy Jones
Haynes Public Charter S	4501 Kansas Ave NW	Washington, DC	20011	202-706-5838		PK-12	Michelle Molitor
Haynes Public Charter S	3600 Georgia Ave NW	Washington, DC	20010-1621	202-667-4446	667-8811	4-8	Towanda Pierre-Floyd
Hospitality Public Charter HS	4301 13th St NW Fl 3	Washington, DC	20011-5629	202-737-4150	737-4151	9-12	Rodney McBride
Howard Road Academy	2405 M L K Jr SE	Washington, DC	20020	202-610-5780	610-5784	7-8	Dr. Nicole Garcia
Howard Road Academy	701 Howard Rd SE	Washington, DC	20020-7101	202-610-4193	610-2845	PK-6	Dr. Marva Tutt
Howard Road Academy	3000 Pennsylvania Ave SE	Washington, DC	20020-3718	202-582-3322	582-1204	PK-K	Allen Blessing
Howard University MS of Math & Science	405 Howard Pl NW	Washington, DC	20059-0001	202-806-7725	865-0271	6-8	Yohance Maqubela
Ideal Academy - North Capitol	6130 N Capitol St NW	Washington, DC	20011-1405	202-729-6660	729-6677	PK-8	George Rutherford Ph.D.
IDEA Public Charter HS	1027 45th St NE	Washington, DC	20019-3802	202-399-4750	399-4387	7-12	Alcine Mumby
Imagine Hope Community Charter - Lamond	6200 Kansas Ave NE	Washington, DC	20011-1508	202-722-4421	722-4431	PK-6	Danah Telfaire
Imagine Hope Community Charter - Tolson	2917 8th St NE	Washington, DC	20017-1669	202-832-7370	832-7644	PK-8	Dr. Chloe Marshall
Imagine Southeast Public Charter S	3100 Martin Luther King Jr	Washington, DC	20032	202-561-1622	561-1644	PK-6	Stacey Scott
Inspired Teaching S	1328 Florida Ave NW	Washington, DC	20009-4824	202-248-6825	248-6939	PK-4	Zoe Duskin
KIPP DC: AIM Academy	2600 Douglass Pl SE	Washington, DC	20020-4419	202-678-5477	678-4383	5-8	Kristy Ochs
KIPP DC: College Preparatory	2600 Douglass Pl SE	Washington, DC	20020-4419	202-678-2527	678-0082	9-12	Jessica Cunningham
KIPP DC: Discover Academy	2600 Douglass Pl SE	Washington, DC	20020-4419	202-678-7735	678-0085	PK-K	Philonda Johnson
KIPP DC: Heights Academy	2600 Douglass Pl SE	Washington, DC	20020-4419	202-610-5323	610-6555	1-2	Cherese Brauer
KIPP DC: KEY Academy	4801 Benning Rd SE	Washington, DC	20019-6145	202-582-5477	582-0152	5-8	David Ayala
KIPP DC: LEAD Academy	421 P St NW	Washington, DC	20001-2417	202-223-4505	223-4504	1-1	Mekia Love
KIPP DC: LEAP Academy	4801 Benning Rd SE	Washington, DC	20019-6145	202-582-5327	582-4680	PK-K	Abraham Clayman
KIPP DC: Promise Academy	4801 Benning Rd SE	Washington, DC	20019-6145	202-265-7766	582-4686	1-4	Casey Fullerton
KIPP DC: WILL Academy	421 P St NW	Washington, DC	20001-2417	202-328-9455	328-9457	5-8	Kate Finley
KIPP DC : Grow Academy	421 P St NW	Washington, DC	20001-2417	202-986-4769	986-1625	PK-K	Stacie Kossoy
Latin American Montessori Bilingual S	1375 Missouri Ave NW	Washington, DC	20011-1807	202-726-6200	722-4125	PK-5	Cristina Encinas
Latin American Montessori Bilingual S	1600 Taylor St NE	Washington, DC	20017-3035	202-726-6200	722-4125	PK-K	Cristina Encinas
LAYC Career Academy	3047 15th St NW	Washington, DC	20009-4211	202-319-2225	462-5696	9-Adu	Angela Stepancic
Marshall Academy	2427 M L K Jr Ave SE	Washington, DC	20020	202-563-6862	563-6946	9-12	Alexandra Pardo
Meridian Public Charter S	2120 13th St NW	Washington, DC	20009	202-387-9830	387-7605	PK-8	Robinette Breedlove
Mundo Verde Public Charter S	3220 16th St NW	Washington, DC	20010-3356	202-630-8373	667-4811	PK-1	Dahlia Aguilar
National Collegiate Preparatory S	4600 Livingston Rd SE	Washington, DC	20032	202-832-7737	832-7736	9-12	Jennifer Ross
Next Step Public Charter S	3047 15th St NW	Washington, DC	20009-4211	202-319-2249	332-0398	9-12	Susan Evans-Espinoza
Options Academy	702 15th St NE	Washington, DC	20002-4508	202-232-4627	232-4502	6-12	Amos Pierre
Options Public Charter S	1375 E St NE	Washington, DC	20002-5429	202-547-1028	547-1272	6-12	Michelle Pianim
Paul Charter S	5800 8th St NW	Washington, DC	20011-1900	202-291-7499	291-7495	6-9	Jami Dunham
Perry Street Preparatory S	1800 Perry St NE	Washington, DC	20018-2742	202-529-4400	526-2214	PK-12	Shadwick Jenkins
Potomac Lighthouse Public Charter S	4401 8th St NE	Washington, DC	20017-2200	202-526-6003	526-6005	PK-7	Ramon Richardson
Roots Public Charter S	15 Kennedy St NW	Washington, DC	20011-5201	202-882-8073	882-8075	PK-8	Dr. Bernida Thompson
Rosario International Public Charter S	1100 Harvard St NW	Washington, DC	20009-5356	202-797-4700	232-6442	10-Ad	Sonia Gutierrez
St. Coletta Special Education Charter S	1901 Independence Ave SE	Washington, DC	20003-1733	202-350-8680	350-8699	PK-12	Janice Corazza
SEED Public Charter S	4300 C St SE	Washington, DC	20019-4100	202-248-7773	248-3021	6-12	Charles Adams

School	Address	City,State	Zip code	Telephone	Fax	Grade	Contact
Shining Stars Montessori Academy	1328 Florida Ave Annex	Washington, DC	20009	202-319-2307	319-2309	PK-1	Rhonda Lucas-Sabater
Stokes Charter S	3700 Oakview Ter NE	Washington, DC	20017-2521	202-265-7237	265-4656	PK-6	Linda Moore
Tree of Life Community Charter S	2315 18th Pl NE	Washington, DC	20018-3610	202-832-1108	832-1113	PK-8	Patricia Williams
Two Rivers Public Charter S	1234 4th St NE	Washington, DC	20002-3432	202-543-8477	543-8479	6-8	David Philhower
Two Rivers Public Charter S	1227 4th St NE	Washington, DC	20002-3431	202-546-4477	546-0869	PK-5	Maggie Bello
Washington Charter S for Technical Arts	1346 Florida Ave NW	Washington, DC	20009-4838	202-232-6090	232-6282	9-12	Dr. G. Hope Asterilla
Washington Latin Public Charter HS	4715 16th St NW	Washington, DC	20011-4330	202-541-1591	541-1594	9-12	Martha Cutts
Washington Latin Public Charter MS	4115 16th St NW	Washington, DC	20011-7003	202-223-1111	450-6047	5-8	Martha Cutts
Washington MST Public Charter HS	1920 Bladensburg Rd NE	Washington, DC	20002-1812	202-636-8011	636-3493	9-12	N'Deye Diagne
Washington Yu Ying Public Charter S	220 Taylor St NE	Washington, DC	20017-1009	202-635-1950	635-1960	PK-5	Maquita Alexander
Wright Charter S	770 M St SE	Washington, DC	20003-3609	202-388-1011	388-5197	8-10	Dr. Marco Clark
Youth Build Public Charter S	3014 14th St NW	Washington, DC	20009-6819	202-319-0141	518-0618	9-Adu	Andrea Henson

Florida

School	Address	City,State	Zip code	Telephone	Fax	Grade	Contact
AcadeMir Charter MS	10601 SW 48th St	Miami, FL	33165-5665	305-485-9911	485-9944	6-8	Albert Mancebo
AcadeMir Charter S West	14880 SW 26th St	Miami, FL	33185-5929	305-485-9911	485-9944	K-5	Dr. Carolina Claro
Academy at the Farm	9500 Alex Lange Way	Dade City, FL	33525-8213	352-588-9737	588-0508	K-8	Ray Polk
Academy Da Vinci	1060 Keene Rd	Dunedin, FL	34698-6300	727-298-2778	298-2780	K-5	Susan Ray
Academy for Positive Learning Charter S	1200 N Dixie Hwy	Lake Worth, FL	33460-2123	561-585-6104	585-7849	K-8	Renatta Adan-Espinoza
Academy of Arts & Minds	3138 Commodore Plz	Miami, FL	33133-5814	305-448-1100	448-9737	9-12	Jorge Suarez
Academy of Business & Leadership Ed	7 Williams St	Saint Augustine, FL	32084-2878	904-826-1606	794-4119	5-8	Scott Beebe
Academy of Environmental Science	12695 W Fort Island Trl	Crystal River, FL	34429-5290	352-795-8793	794-0065	9-12	Ben Stofcheck
Access Charter S	1100 Lee Rd	Orlando, FL	32810-5847	321-319-0640	319-0643	6-12	Roger Watkins
ACE Charter S	710 E Bella Vista St	Lakeland, FL	33805-3009	863-686-3189	682-1348	PK-PK	Gay Ratcliff
Achievement Academy - Bartow	695 E Summerlin St	Bartow, FL	33830-4848	863-533-0690	534-0798	PK-PK	Paula Sullivan
Achievement Academy - Lakeland	716 E Bella Vista St	Lakeland, FL	33805-3009	863-683-6504	688-9292	PK-PK	Paula Sullivan
Achievement Academy - Winter Haven	2211 28th St NW	Winter Haven, FL	33881-1807	863-965-7586	968-5016	PK-PK	Paula Sullivan
Adler ES	4515 38th Ave N	St Petersburg, FL	33713-1126	727-329-9545	525-6636	K-3	Greg Decosmo
Advanced Learning Charter S	5855 NW 171st St	Miami, FL	33015-4607	305-231-4888	231-4881	K-5	Carlos Gonzalez
Advantage Academy	304 W Prosser Dr	Plant City, FL	33563-6975	813-567-0801	441-0272	K-8	Todd Haughey
Advantage Academy Santa Fe	9790 SW 107th Ct	Miami, FL	33176-2701	786-228-5309	718-1921	K-5	Yesenia Cantillo
Alachua Learning Center	11100 W State Road 235	Alachua, FL	32615-4965	386-418-2080	418-4116	K-8	Tom Allin
Alee Academy Charter S	1705 E County Road 44	Eustis, FL	32736-2500	352-357-9426	357-8426	9-12	Jennings Neeld
Allen Leadership Academy	16001 Bunche Park Dr	Miami Gardens, FL	33054	305-623-3174	624-1668	K-5	Frances Young
Aloma Charter HS	495 N Semoran Blvd Ste 8	Winter Park, FL	32792-3802	407-657-4343	657-4317	9-12	Chuck Finch
Alpha Charter S of Excellence	1217 SW 4th St	Miami, FL	33135	305-643-2132	642-3717	K-5	Isabel Navas
Alpha International Academy	520 NW 5th St	Hallandale Bch, FL	33009-3314	754-816-7965	846-7135	K-5	Tamara Gammon
Altoona S	42630 State Road 19	Altoona, FL	32702-9638	352-669-3444	669-3407	K-5	Jerry Hatfield
Apalachicola Bay Charter S	98 12th St	Apalachicola, FL	32320-2003	850-653-1222	653-1857	K-8	Chimene Johnson
Archimedean Academy	12425 SW 72nd St	Miami, FL	33183-2513	305-279-6572	675-8448	K-5	Susan Simpson
Archimedean Middle Conservatory	12425 SW 72nd St	Miami, FL	33183-2513	305-279-6572	675-8448	6-8	Vasiliki Moysidis
Archimedean Upper Conservatory	12425 SW 72nd St	Miami, FL	33183-2513	305-279-6572	675-8448	9-12	Demetrios Demopoulos
ASPIRA De Hostos Charter S	1 NE 19th St	Miami, FL	33132-1030	305-576-1512	576-0810	6-8	
ASPIRA Raul Martinez Charter S	13300 Memorial Hwy	North Miami, FL	33161-3940	305-893-8050	891-6055	6-9	
ASPIRA South Youth Leadership	13330 SW 288th St	Homestead, FL	33033-1928	305-246-1111	246-1433	6-8	
Aspire Charter Academy	5015 Goddard Ave	Orlando, FL	32804-1169	407-297-9955		K-3	Pam Schenkel
Athenian Academy of Pasco	3118 Seven Springs Blvd	New Port Richey, FL	34655-3340	727-372-0200	376-1916	K-8	Dr. Fern Aefsky
Athenian Academy	2817 Saint Marks Dr	Dunedin, FL	34698-1920	727-298-2718	298-2719	K-8	Kathy Manrique
Atlantic Montessori Charter S	9893 Pines Blvd	Pembroke Pines, FL	33024-6164	754-263-2700	263-2596	K-3	Juana Garcia
Aventura City of Excellence Charter S	3333 NE 188th St	Aventura, FL	33180-2933	305-466-1499	466-1339	K-8	Julie Alm
Babson Park ES	815 N Scenic Hwy	Babson Park, FL	33827-9795	863-678-4664	678-4669	PK-5	Ken Hensen
Bay Haven Charter Academy	2501 Hawks Landing Blvd	Panama City, FL	32405-6658	850-248-3500	248-3514	K-8	Larry Bolinger
Believers Academy	5840 Corporate Way Ste 100	West Palm Beach, FL	33407-2040	561-340-2507	340-2510	9-12	Lori Dyer
Bellalago Charter Academy	3651 Pleasant Hill Rd	Kissimmee, FL	34746-2935	407-933-1690	933-2143	K-8	Wendy Honeycutt
Berkley Accelerated MS	5316 Berkley Rd	Auburndale, FL	33823-8493	863-968-2400	968-2411	6-8	Jill Bolender
Berkley ES	5240 Berkley Rd	Auburndale, FL	33823-8491	863-968-5024	968-5026	PK-5	Gayle Thomas
Beulah Academy of Science	8633 Beulah Rd	Pensacola, FL	32526-5203	850-944-2822	941-0702	6-8	Sherry Bailey
Big Pine Academy	30220 Overseas Hwy	Big Pine Key, FL	33043-3357	305-872-1266	872-1265	PK-7	Cathy Hoffman
Boca Raton Charter S	269 NE 14th St	Boca Raton, FL	33432-1821	561-750-0437	750-7880	K-5	Louise Nelson
Bok Academy	13895 Hwy 27	Lake Wales, FL	33859-2549	863-638-1010	638-1212	6-8	Damien Moses
Bonita Springs Charter S	25380 Bernwood Dr	Bonita Springs, FL	34135-7850	239-992-6932	992-7359	K-8	Deborah Tracy
Bonita Springs Preparatory\Fitness Acad	28011 Performance Ln	Bonita Springs, FL	34135-6850	239-989-2807	495-7178	K-8	Gwen Dapore
Boston Avenue Charter S	340 N Boston Ave	DeLand, FL	32724-4441	386-624-6982	734-5617	PK-5	Douglas Jackson
Bradenton Charter S	2615 26th St W	Bradenton, FL	34205-3731	941-739-6100	752-3250	3-8	Richard Donnelly
Bridgepoint Academy	10700 SW 56th St	Miami, FL	33165-7044	305-271-3109	271-5315	K-5	Dr. Maria Saunders
Bridgepoint Academy Greater Miami	137 NE 19th St	Miami, FL	33132-1010	786-477-4372	446-8714	K-8	Maria Cedeno
Bridgepoint Academy Interamerican	621 Beacom Blvd	Miami, FL	33135-2931	305-643-4833	643-4832	K-5	Maria Cedeno
Bridgepoint Academy of Village Green	4707 SW 127th Ave	Miami, FL	33175-4603	305-290-4246		K-8	Dr. Maria Saunders
Bright Futures Academy	10350 Riverside Dr	Palm Bch Gdns, FL	33410-4216	561-253-7504	622-3335	K-8	Kendall Artusi
Brooks-DeBartolo Collegiate HS	10948 N Central Ave	Tampa, FL	33612-6604	813-971-5600	971-5656	9-12	Kristine Bennett
Broward Charter S of Science\Technology	1800 N Douglas Rd	Pembroke Pines, FL	33024-3200	954-885-4040	441-6490	K-8	Dr. Ron Hunter
Broward Community Charter S	11421 NW 56th Dr	Coral Springs, FL	33076-3122	954-345-6500	345-1199	K-8	John Drag
Broward Community Charter S West	11421 NW 56th Dr	Coral Springs, FL	33076-3122	954-345-6500	345-1199	K-5	John Drag
Burns Science & Technology Charter S	160 Ridge Rd	Oak Hill, FL	32759-9773	386-210-4915	210-4922	K-8	Dr. Janet McGee
Byrneville Charter S	1600 Byrneville Rd	Century, FL	32535-3640	850-256-6350	256-6357	K-5	Dee Wolfe-Sullivan
Campus Charter S	3815 Curtis Blvd	Port Saint John, FL	32927-3942	321-633-8234	633-8234	K-4	Trisha Leitem
Canoe Creek Charter S	3600 Canoe Creek Rd	Saint Cloud, FL	34772-9132	407-891-7320	891-7330	PK-8	Julie Ramirez
Cape Coral Charter S	76 Mid Cape Ter	Cape Coral, FL	33991-2008	239-995-0904	995-0369	K-8	Dr. Deborah Nauss
Cape Coral Preparatory & Fitness Academy	2107 Santa Barbara Blvd	Cape Coral, FL	33991-4335	239-989-1458	242-0477	K-8	Mandy Rice
Capstone Academy	4901 W Fairfield Dr	Pensacola, FL	32506-4111	850-458-7735	455-7754	PK-K	Nancy Wolfe
Capstone Academy Milton Charter S	5308 Stewart St	Milton, FL	32570-4736	850-626-3091	626-3093	PK-K	Kathy Mueller
Caring & Sharing Charter S	PO Box 5936	Gainesville, FL	32627-5936	352-372-1004	372-0894	K-5	Curtis Peterson
Central Charter S	4525 N State Road 7	Laud Lakes, FL	33319-5855	954-735-6295	735-6232	K-6	Dr. Tonya Dix
Central Florida Leadership Academy	427 N Primrose Dr	Orlando, FL	32803-5012	407-480-2352		6-9	Tiffany Ward
Chain of Lakes Collegiate HS	999 Avenue H NE	Winter Haven, FL	33881-4256	863-298-6800	298-6801	11-12	Bridget Fetter
Chancery High Charter	7001 S Orange Blossom Trl	Orlando, FL	32809-5714	407-850-9791	850-9856	9-12	Evelyn Chandler
Channelside Academy of Math & Science	1029 E Twiggs St	Tampa, FL	33602-3527	813-579-9649	463-2439	K-8	Tiffani Richmond
Charter ES of Boynton Beach	1425 Gateway Blvd	Boynton Beach, FL	33426-8313	561-374-8989	374-6153	K-5	Wayne Owens
Charter HS of Boynton Beach	1325 Gateway Blvd	Boynton Beach, FL	33426-8304	561-374-8989	536-2056	6-12	Wayne Owens
Charter HS of the Americas	970 W Flagler St	Miami, FL	33130-1140	305-325-1001	324-9934	9-12	Nataly Parra
Charter S at Waterstone	855 Waterstone Way	Homestead, FL	33033-5941	305-248-6206	248-6208	K-8	Melissa Aguilar
Charter S of Excellence - Davie	2801 N University Dr	Pembroke Pines, FL	33024-2547	954-433-8838	433-8702	K-5	Jennifer Jaynes
Charter S of Excellence - Ft Lauderdale	1217 SE 3rd Ave	Fort Lauderdale, FL	33316-1905	954-522-2997	522-3159	K-5	Lisa Castro
Charter S of Excellence Riverland	3550 Davie Blvd	Fort Lauderdale, FL	33312-3438	954-581-0167	522-3159	K-5	Ruth Kalinsky
Charter School of Excellence Tamarac 1	7595 NW 61st St	Tamarac, FL	33321-6043	954-721-8902	721-8908	K-5	Mary Travers
Chautauqua Learn & Serve Charter S	1118 Magnolia Ave	Panama City, FL	32401-2815	850-785-5056	785-5071	9-Adu	Cynthia McCauley
Children's Reading Center	7901 Saint Johns Ave	Palatka, FL	32177-1730	386-328-9990	328-9949	K-5	Dr. Geri Melosh
Chiles Academy	868 George W Engram Blvd	Daytona Beach, FL	32114-1859	386-322-6102	258-4681	6-12	Anne Ferguson
Choices in Learning Charter S	1100 E State Road 434	Winter Springs, FL	32708-2715	407-331-8477	331-5075	K-5	
City of Coral Springs Charter S	3205 N University Dr	Coral Springs, FL	33065-4115	954-340-4100	340-4111	6-12	Gary Springer
City of Hialeah Education Academy	2590 W 76th St	Hialeah, FL	33016-6888	305-362-4006	362-7006	6-12	Carlos Alvarez
City of Palms Charter HS	2830 Winkler Ave Ste 201	Fort Myers, FL	33916-9301	239-561-6611	561-6230	9-12	Sarah White
City of Pembroke Pines Charter HS	17189 Sheridan St	Pembroke Pines, FL	33331-1934	954-538-3700	538-3714	9-12	Peter Bayer
City of Pembroke Pines ES - Central	12350 Sheridan St	Pembroke Pines, FL	33026-3813	954-322-3330	322-3383	K-5	Kenneth Bass
City of Pembroke Pines-ES East	10801 Pembroke Rd	Pembroke Pines, FL	33025-1707	954-443-4800	443-4811	K-5	Sean Chance
City of Pembroke Pines-ES West	1680 SW 184th Ave	Pembroke Pines, FL	33029-6120	954-450-6990	443-4820	K-5	Devarn Flowers
City of Pembroke Pines MS - Central	12350 Sheridan St	Pembroke Pines, FL	33026-3813	954-322-3300	322-3383	6-8	Kenneth Bass
City of Pembroke Pines-MS West	18500 Pembroke Rd	Pembroke Pines, FL	33029-6108	954-443-4847	447-1691	6-8	Devarn Flowers
Clark Advanced Learning Center	2400 SE Salerno Rd	Stuart, FL	34997-6505	772-419-5750	419-5760	10-12	Maria Mosley
C.O.A.S.T. Charter S	PO Box 338	Saint Marks, FL	32355-0338	850-925-6344	925-6396	PK-8	Alyssa Higgins
Collegiate HS at NW FL State College	100 College Blvd E	Niceville, FL	32578-1347	850-729-4949	729-4950	10-12	Anthony Boyer
Community Charter S of Excellence	10948 N Central Ave	Tampa, FL	33612-6604	813-931-5100	931-1333	K-8	Charles Malatesta M.Ed.
Compass Middle Charter S	550 E Clower St	Bartow, FL	33830-6403	863-519-8701	519-8704	5-8	Anita Fine
Coral Reef Montessori Academy	10853 SW 216th St	Cutler Ridge, FL	33170-3146	305-255-0064	255-4085	K-8	Lucy Canzoneri-Golden
Cornerstone Academy Charter S	5903 Randolph Ave	Orlando, FL	32809-4241	407-608-7171		K-12	
Coronado HS	3057 Cleveland Ave	Fort Myers, FL	33901-7002	239-337-9140	337-9141	9-12	Arthur Nauss
Countryside Montessori Academy	5852 Ehren Cutoff	Land O Lakes, FL	34639-3428	813-996-0991	996-0993	1-6	Dennise Ondina
Crossroad Academy Charter S	470 Strong Rd	Quincy, FL	32351-6006	850-875-9626	875-1403	PK-8	Kevin Forehand
Dayspring Academy ES	8911 Timber Oaks Ave	Port Richey, FL	34668-2426	727-862-8600	868-5175	K-5	Gayle Barr
Dayspring Academy MS	9509 Palm Ave	Port Richey, FL	34668-4647	727-847-9003	848-8774	6-8	Sara Calleja
DayStar Academy of Excellence	970 N Seacrest Blvd	Boynton Beach, FL	33435-4702	561-369-2323	369-2642	K-5	Francene King
Discovery Academy at Lake Alfred	1000 N Buena Vista Dr	Lake Alfred, FL	33850-2031	863-295-5955	295-5978	6-8	Kevin Warren
Discovery MS	11421 NW 56th Dr	Coral Springs, FL	33076-3122	954-345-6500	345-1199	6-8	John Drag
Dixon Charter S of Excellence	1201 N H St	Pensacola, FL	32501-2448	850-435-0511	466-2185	K-6	Kathy Colbert
Doctors Charter S of Miami Shores	11301 NW 5th Ave	Miami Shores, FL	33168-3343	305-754-2381	751-5833	6-12	Dr. Gary Meredith
Dolphin Park HS	3206 S University Dr	Miramar, FL	33025-3007	954-433-1573	433-1589	9-12	Carlos Flores

School	Address	City,State	Zip code	Telephone	Fax	Grade	Contact
Doral Academy	2450 NW 97th Ave	Doral, FL	33172-2308	305-597-9999	591-2669	K-5	Eleonora Cuesta
Doral Academy HS	11100 NW 27th St	Doral, FL	33172-5001	305-597-9950	477-6762	9-12	Douglas Rodriguez
Doral Academy MS	2601 NW 112th Ave	Doral, FL	33172-1804	305-591-0020	591-9251	6-8	Douglas Rodriguez
Downtown Miami Charter S	305 NW 3rd Ave	Miami, FL	33128-1606	305-579-2112	579-2115	K-6	Dr. Rebecca Dinda
Duval Charter School at Arlington	100 Bell Tel Way	Jacksonville, FL	32216	904-724-1536	721-5381	K-8	Dr. Sylvia Hall
Duval Charter S at Baymeadows	7510 Baymeadows Way	Jacksonville, FL	32256-6818	904-638-7947	466-4901	K-12	Teresa Brown
Eagles Nest ES	201 N University Dr	Coral Springs, FL	33071-7323	954-344-7144	344-7148	K-5	Christine Mentis
Eagles Nest MS	201 N University Dr	Coral Springs, FL	33071-7323	954-344-7144	344-7148	6-8	Christine Mentis
Early Beginnings Academy-Civic Center	1411 NW 14th Ave	Miami, FL	33125-1616	305-325-1080	325-1044	PK-2	Barbara Penkosky
Early Beginnings Academy-North Shore	985 NW 91st St	Miami, FL	33150-2350	305-835-9006	696-1688	PK-K	Barbara Penkosky
Easter Seals Charter S	1219 Dunn Ave	Daytona Beach, FL	32114-2405	386-255-4568	258-7677	PK-PK	Kristal Barringer
Edison Collegiate HS	8099 College Pkwy	Fort Myers, FL	33919-5566	239-432-6767		9-12	Dr. Brian Botts
Edison Collegiate HS	26300 Airport Rd	Punta Gorda, FL	33950-5748	941-637-5673	637-3508	9-12	Diane Juneau
Educational Horizons Charter S	1281 S Wickham Rd	West Melbourne, FL	32904-2450	321-729-0786	729-8403	1-5	Aileen Tapp
Ed Venture Charter S	117 E Coast Ave	Lantana, FL	33462-5316	561-582-1454	547-9682	10-12	Barbara Fitz
Einstein Montessori Orlando East	10301 E Colonial Dr	Orlando, FL	32817-4333	321-631-9876	446-5505	K-8	Zach Osbrach
Einstein Montessori S	5910 SW Archer Rd	Gainesville, FL	32608-4702	352-335-4321	335-1575	2-8	Christine Aurelio
Emerald Coast Marine Institute	207 4th St SE	Ft Walton Bch, FL	32548-5636	850-244-2711	244-2171	6-12	Bernard Williams
Escambia Charter S	391 90 9 Ranch Rd	Cantonment, FL	32533-9098	850-937-0500	968-5605	9-12	Jerome Chisholm
Everest Charter S	10054 W McNab Rd	Tamarac, FL	33321-1894	954-726-5227	772-9702	K-8	Raul Baez
Everglades Preparatory Academy	360 E Main St Bldg C	Pahokee, FL	33476-1800	561-924-3002	924-3013	9-12	Edna Stevens
Everglades Preparatory Academy	2251 E Mowry Dr	Homestead, FL	33033-4913	786-601-1969	377-5759	6-12	Dr. Margaret Fahringer
Excel Leadership Academy	1310 N Congress Ave Ste A	West Palm Beach, FL	33409-6314	561-697-8050	697-8082	9-12	Angela Kemp
Excelsior Charter Academy	3490 NW 191st St	Miami Gardens, FL	33056-2936	786-565-9188	623-0900	K-8	Janell Wyartt
Excelsior Charter S of Broward	10046 W McNab Rd	Tamarac, FL	33321-1894	954-726-5227	726-5228	K-5	Raul Baez
Excelsior Language Academy of Hialeah	600 W 20th St	Hialeah, FL	33010-2428	305-883-8359	883-5279	PK-11	Brenda Cruz
Expressions Learning Arts Academy	5408 SW 13th St	Gainesville, FL	32608-5038	352-373-5223	373-6327	K-5	Cheryl Valantis
Florida Autism Center of Excellence	6400 E Chelsea St	Tampa, FL	33610-5628	813-621-3223	622-7139	PK-12	Heather Brace-Duncan
Florida Intercultural Academy	1704 Buchanan St	Hollywood, FL	33020-4030	954-924-8006	924-8044	K-5	Tammy Lara
Florida Intercultural Academy West	3367 N University Dr	Davie, FL	33328	954-362-3415	640-9678	K-8	Tammy Lara
Florida International Academy	13400 NW 28th Ave	Opa Locka, FL	33054-4842	305-685-8190	688-1745	K-8	Sonia Mitchell
Florida SIA Tech at Gainesville	7022 NW 10th Pl	Gainesville, FL	32605-3147	352-371-4424	371-4426	9-12	Christal Blue
Florida State University School	3000 School House Rd	Tallahassee, FL	32311-7855	850-245-3700	245-3997	K-12	Neal Trafford
Fort Myers Preparatory & Fitness Academy	4740 S Cleveland Ave	Fort Myers, FL	33907-1311	239-333-0766	333-0768	K-8	Susanne Bisplinghoff
Four Corners Charter S	9100 Teacher Ln	Davenport, FL	33897-6212	407-787-4300	787-4331	K-8	Denise Thompson
Franklin Academy Charter S	18800 Pines Blvd	Pembroke Pines, FL	33029-1310	954-703-2294	436-2861	K-8	Brenda Cummings
Gamla Charter S	1685 S Belcher Rd	Clearwater, FL	33764-6561	727-642-1593		K-5	Jayme Joslyn
Gamla Charter S	8600 S Jog Rd	Boynton Beach, FL	33472-2966	561-742-8017	742-8018	K-5	Elanit Weizman
Gamla Charter S	11155 SW 112th Ave	Miami, FL	33176-3251	305-596-6266	596-6964	K-8	Jose Baca
Gamla Charter S North Broward	2620 Hollywood Blvd	Hollywood, FL	33020-4807	954-342-4064	342-4107	K-8	Sharon Miller
Gamla Charter School South Broward	6501 W Sunrise Blvd	Sunrise, FL	33313-6036	954-587-8348	587-8347	K-12	Toni Weissberg
Gardens S of Technology Arts	9153 Roan Ln	Palm Bch Gdns, FL	33403-1029	561-290-7661	449-3470	K-8	Lana Thormodsgaard
GATES SHS	15316 N Florida Ave	Tampa, FL	33613-1257	813-961-8701	969-4107	9-12	Robert Craven
Gateway Charter HS	12770 Gateway Blvd	Fort Myers, FL	33913-8654	239-768-3350	768-3874	9-12	Sara Abraham
Gateway Charter S	12850 Commonwealth Dr	Fort Myers, FL	33913-8039	239-768-5048	768-5710	K-8	Sara Abraham
Genesis Preparatory S	207 NW 23rd Ave	Gainesville, FL	32609-3604	352-379-1188	379-1142	K-3	Charmaine Henry
Gibson Charter S	1698 NW 4th Ave	Miami, FL	33136-1507	305-438-0895	438-0896	K-8	Fareed Khan
Glades Academy	7368 State Road 15	Pahokee, FL	33476-1700	561-924-9402	924-9279	K-5	Dr. Don Zumpano
Global Outreach Charter Academy	9570 Regency Square Blvd	Jacksonville, FL	32225-9103	904-551-7104	551-7120	K-8	Tangia Anderson
Goodwill L.I.F.E. Academy	3365 Seminole Ave Ste D	Fort Myers, FL	33916-1429	239-334-4434	334-4439	6-12	Lynn Pottorf
Green Springs HS	3555 NW 7th St	Miami, FL	33125-4015	305-720-2996	541-5559	9-12	Daniel Fernandez
G-STAR School of the Arts	2065 Prairie Rd Bldg J	Palm Springs, FL	33406-7700	561-967-2023	963-8975	9-12	Kim Collins M.Ed.
Gulf Coast Acad of Science & Technology	10444 Tillery Rd	Spring Hill, FL	34608-3706	352-688-5092	688-5095	6-8	Nevin Siefert
Gulfstream Goodwill LIFE Academy	3800 S Congress Ave	Boynton Beach, FL	33426-8424	561-259-1000	259-1011	9-12	Cindy Maunder
Harris Preparatory Academy	1408 E Blount St	Pensacola, FL	32503-5620	850-432-2273	432-4624	K-5	Celestine Lewis
Hartridge Academy	1400 US Highway 92	Winter Haven, FL	33881-8137	863-956-4434	956-3267	K-5	Debra Richards
Hawn Charter School of the Arts	565 S Lakeview Dr Unit 110	Lake Helen, FL	32744-3520	386-228-3900	228-3901	K-8	Dr. Carol Kelley
Healthy Learning Academy	13505 W Newberry Rd	Newberry, FL	32669-2752	352-372-2279	372-1665	K-2	Ann Egan
Hillcrest ES	1051 State Road 60 E	Lake Wales, FL	33853-4258	863-678-4216	678-4086	PK-5	Jennifer Barrow
Hoggetowne MS	1717 NE 9th St Ste A	Gainesville, FL	32609-3719	352-367-4369	335-4775	6-8	Gaspar Nichols
Hollywood Academy of Arts & Science	1705 Van Buren St	Hollywood, FL	33020	954-925-6404	925-8123	K-8	Donte Fulton
Hope Center for Autism Charter S	1695 SE Indian St	Stuart, FL	34997-4962	772-334-3288	334-2203	PK-2	Staci Routt
Hope Charter S	1550 E Crown Point Rd	Ocoee, FL	34761-3722	407-656-4673	264-6960	K-8	Crystal Yoakum
Humanities and Fine Arts Charter S	213 Lee St	Leesburg, FL	34748-4914	352-315-4322	315-4326	K-3	Dr. Shelia Smalley
iGeneration Academy	3970 RCA Blvd	Palm Bch Gdns, FL	33410-4253	561-420-0614	420-0616	6-12	Nancy Sokoloff
Imagine Charter S at Broward	9001 Westview Dr	Coral Springs, FL	33067-2069	954-255-0020	255-1336	K-5	Erin Kelly
Imagine Charter S at Evening Rose	3611 Austin Davis Ave	Tallahassee, FL	32308-7402	850-877-5187	877-6463	K-8	Linda Williams
Imagine Charter S at Lakewood Ranch	10535 Portal Xing	Bradenton, FL	34211	941-750-0900	750-0966	PK-8	Stephen Sajewski
Imagine Charter S at Land O' Lakes	2940 Sunlake Blvd	Land O Lakes, FL	34638-0001	813-428-7444	428-7445	K-7	Kathy Helean
Imagine Charter S at North Lauderdale	1395 S State Road 7	N Lauderdale, FL	33068-4023	954-973-8900	974-5588	K-8	Rebecca Dahl
Imagine Charter S at North Manatee	9275 49th Ave E	Palmetto, FL	34221-8932	941-981-5345	981-5349	PK-8	Jennifer Lucas
Imagine Charter S at North Port	1000 Innovation Ave	North Port, FL	34289-9308	941-426-2050	423-8252	K-5	Justin Matthews
Imagine Charter S at St. Petersburg	1950 1st Ave N	St Petersburg, FL	33713-8928	727-821-7100	821-7171	PK-8	Angela Prince
Imagine Charter S at South Vero	6000 4th St	Vero Beach, FL	32968-9563	772-567-2728	410-0329	PK-8	Chris Rock
Imagine Charter S at Town Center	775 Town Center Blvd	Palm Coast, FL	32164-2520	386-586-0100	586-2784	PK-8	Lisa O'Grady
Imagine Charter S at West Melbourne	3355 Imagine Way	West Melbourne, FL	32904-9112	321-768-6200	768-6300	K-12	Shannon Gerbi
Imagine Charter S at Weston	2500 Glades Cir	Weston, FL	33327-2253	954-659-3600	659-3620	K-5	Nadine Laham
Imagine MS West	2500 Glades Cir	Weston, FL	33327-2253	954-659-3600	659-3620	6-8	Nadine Laham
Imagine MSHS at North Port	2757 Sycamore St	North Port, FL	34289-9511	941-426-2050	423-8252	6-12	Justin Matthews
Imagine S at Palmer Ranch	6220 McIntosh Rd	Sarasota, FL	34238-2965	941-257-1124	923-1124	K-7	Alisa Wright
Imagine S at South Lake	2750 Hartwood Marsh Rd	Clermont, FL	34711-5201	352-243-2960	243-2697	K-8	Mary Briggs
Imagine S - Chancellor Campus	3333 High Ridge Rd	Boynton Beach, FL	33426-8745	561-585-1189	585-1166	K-8	Susan Onori
Imagine S Plantation Campus	8200 Peters Rd	Plantation, FL	33324-3201	954-358-4200	472-1994	K-8	Jean Reilly
Immokalee Community S	123 N 4th St	Immokalee, FL	34142-3721	239-867-3223	867-3224	K-5	James McDevitt
Indian River Charter HS	6055 College Ln	Vero Beach, FL	32966-1285	772-567-6600	567-2288	9-12	Cynthia Trevino-Aversa
Inlet Grove Community HS	600 W 28th St	Riviera Beach, FL	33404-4309	561-881-4600	881-4668	9-12	Emma Banks
Innovations MS	2768 N Hiawassee Rd	Orlando, FL	32818-3319	407-429-7901		6-8	Dr. Patricia Lightner
Integrated Science and Asian Culture	5876 SW 68th St	South Miami, FL	33143-3693	305-740-0509	740-0510	K-8	Kim Guilarte
International S of Broward	3100 NW 75th Ave	Hollywood, FL	33024-2355	954-987-2026	987-7261	6-12	Michelle Garay
International Studies Charter S	2480 SW 8th St	Miami, FL	33135-3016	305-643-2955	643-2956	6-12	Victoriano Rodriguez
Island S	PO Box 1090	Boca Grande, FL	33921-1090	941-964-8016	964-8017	K-5	Jean Thompson
Island Village Montessori S	11011 Clark Rd	Sarasota, FL	34241	941-954-4999	484-2150	K-8	Jennifer Ocana
Island Village Montessori S	2001 Pinebrook Rd	Venice, FL	34292-1560	941-484-4999	484-2150	K-8	Jennifer Ocana
Island Village Montessori S	11011 Clark Rd	Sarasota, FL	34241	941-954-4999	342-6502	K-5	Jennifer Ocana
Jackson Preparatory S	546 Mary Esther Blvd	Ft Walton Bch, FL	32548	850-833-3321	833-3292	K-8	Mary Gunter
JFK Charter S	4696 Davis Rd	Lake Worth, FL	33461-5204	561-868-6100	963-4697	K-5	Stephen Sills
Just Arts and Management Charter MS	2450 NW 97th Ave	Doral, FL	33172-2308	305-597-9999	591-2669	K-5	Eleonara Cuesta
Keys Gate Charter HS	2355 SE 28th Ave	Homestead, FL	33035-2280	305-230-5630	230-1347	9-12	David McKnight
Keys Gate Charter S	2000 SE 28th Ave	Homestead, FL	33035-2102	305-230-1616	230-1347	K-8	David McKnight
Key West Collegiate Charter S	5901 College Rd Ste A130	Key West, FL	33040-4315	305-296-5927	809-3191	9-12	C. Plantada
Kids Community College Charter MS	6528 US Highway 301 S # 114	Riverview, FL	33578	813-699-4600		6-8	Karen Seder
Kids Community College Charter S	1450 Citrus Oaks Ave	Gotha, FL	34734-5027	407-982-2421		K-5	Cynthia Schaefer
Kids Community College - Riverview South	10030 Mathog Rd	Riverview, FL	33578-5433	813-671-1440	511-7193	K-8	Karen Seder
Kids Community College SE Campus	6528 US Highway 301 S # 114	Riverview, FL	33578	813-699-4600	511-7193	K-2	Martha Caballero
Kidz Choice Charter S	9063 Taft St	Pembroke Pines, FL	33024-4650	954-251-2419	450-6482	K-5	Lilly Swanson
Kings Kids Academy of Health Sciences	1924 E Comanche Ave	Tampa, FL	33610-8226	813-238-4900	238-6700	K-5	Lillia Stroud
KIPP Impact MS	1440 McDuff Ave N	Jacksonville, FL	32254-2035	904-683-6643	683-9895	K-K,	Ashley Ferguson
Kissimmee Charter Academy	2850 Bill Beck Blvd	Kissimmee, FL	34744-4073	407-847-1400	847-1401	PK-8	Lori McCarley
Lake Eola Charter S	135 N Magnolia Ave	Orlando, FL	32801-2301	407-246-0900	246-6334	K-8	Ronnie DeNoia
Lakeland Montessori MS	800 E Palmetto St	Lakeland, FL	33801-5529	863-688-7743	812-4689	7-8	Heather Manrow
Lakeland Montessori Schoolhouse	1124 N Lake Parker Ave	Lakeland, FL	33805-4725	863-413-0003	413-0006	PK-6	Josie Zinninger
Lakeside Academy	716 S Main St	Belle Glade, FL	33430-4202	561-993-5000	993-5001	K-6	Barbara Litinski
Lake Wales HS	1 Highlander Way	Lake Wales, FL	33853-8517	863-678-4222	678-4064	9-12	Donna Dunson
Lauderhill HS	4131 NW 16th St	Lauderhill, FL	33313-5810	954-731-2585	731-2587	9-12	Merceda Stanley
Lawrence Academy	713 W Palm Dr	Florida City, FL	33034-3223	305-247-4800	247-4895	K-12	Iliana Valdes
LBA Academy	13835 NW 97th Ave	Hialeah, FL	33018-1213	305-827-3022	827-3023	9-12	Gyovania Marante
Leadership Academy West	1760 N Congress Ave	West Palm Beach, FL	33409	561-434-0996	434-0575	9-12	Tiphanie Forbes-Mitchell
Learning Gate Community S	16215 Hanna Rd	Lutz, FL	33549-5701	813-948-4190	948-7587	K-8	Patricia Girard
Lee Alternative Charter HS	1201 Taylor Lane Ext	Lehigh Acres, FL	33936-6104	239-303-2834	303-1373	9-12	Dr. Tim Butts
Lee Charter Academy	3348 Edgewood Ave	Fort Myers, FL	33916-1418	239-334-2235	334-2241	K-8	Dr. Shirley Chapman
Legacy HS	1550 E Crown Point Rd	Ocoee, FL	34761-3722	407-656-4673	264-6960	9-12	Crystal Yoakum
Lehigh Charter S of Excellence	235 Joel Blvd Ste A	Lehigh Acres, FL	33936-5229	239-674-9624	674-9632	K-8	Bernadette Athime
Lincoln-Marti Charter S	3500 W 84th St	Hialeah, FL	33018-4945	305-827-8080	827-8004	K-8	Charity Moreno
Lincoln-Marti Charter S	970 W Flagler St	Miami, FL	33130-1140	305-325-1001	324-9934	K-8	Nataly Parra
Lincoln-Marti Charter S - International	103 E Lucy St	Florida City, FL	33034-2501	305-242-3330	242-3331	K-8	Mairelys Llorente
Literacy/Leadership Technology Academy	6771 Madison Ave	Tampa, FL	33619-6836	813-234-0940	234-0946	6-8	Lesley Logan
Littles-Nguzo Saba Charter S	1601 N Tamarind Ave	West Palm Beach, FL	33407-6231	561-803-9001	803-9096	K-8	Helen Byrd

School	Address	City,State	Zip code	Telephone	Fax	Grade	Contact
Lone Star HS	8050 Lone Star Rd Ste 1	Jacksonville, FL	32211-6227	904-725-5998		9-12	
Lutz Preparatory S	17951 N US Highway 41	Lutz, FL	33549-4503	813-428-7100		K-5	Diane Farmer
Manatee S for the Arts	700 Haben Blvd	Palmetto, FL	34221-4173	941-721-6800	721-6805	6-12	Dr. Bill Jones
Manatee S of Arts/Science	3700 32nd St W	Bradenton, FL	34205-2708	941-755-5012	755-7934	PK-6	Miriam Jolly
Marco Island Academy	1450 Winterberry Dr	Marco Island, FL	34145-5051	239-393-5133	393-5143	9-12	George Andreozzi
Marco Island Charter MS	1401 Trinidad Ave	Marco Island, FL	34145-3949	239-377-3200	377-3201	6-8	George Abounader
Marion Charter S	39 Cedar Rd	Ocala, FL	34472-8331	352-687-2100	687-2700	K-5	Gina Evers
Marion Military Academy	2091 NE 35th St	Ocala, FL	34479-2909	352-291-6600	291-6601	9-12	Bill Archibald
Mascotte Charter ES	460 Midway Ave	Mascotte, FL	34753-8800	352-429-2294	429-5166	PK-5	Wayne Cockcroft
Mater Academy	7700 NW 98th St	Hialeah Gardens, FL	33016-2403	305-698-9900	698-3822	K-5	Cecilia Bermeosolo
Mater Academy	8625 Byron Ave	Miami Beach, FL	33141-4834	305-864-2889	864-2890	K-8	Marisol Gomez
Mater Academy at Mount Sinai	4300 Alton Rd	Miami Beach, FL	33140-2948	305-604-1453	604-1454	K-5	Ileana Gomez
Mater Academy Charter HS	7901 NW 103rd St	Hialeah Gardens, FL	33016-2419	305-828-1886	828-6175	9-12	Judith Marty
Mater Academy Charter MS	7901 NW 103rd St	Hialeah Gardens, FL	33016-2419	305-828-1886	828-6175	6-8	Judith Marty
Mater Academy East Charter HS	998 SW 1st St	Miami, FL	33130-1112	305-324-6963	324-6966	9-12	Alex Tamargo
Mater Academy East Charter MS	998 SW 1st St	Miami, FL	33130-1112	305-324-6963	324-6966	6-9	Alejandro Tamargo
Mater Academy East Charter S	450 SW 4th St	Miami, FL	33130-1410	305-324-4667	324-6580	K-5	Beatrice Riera
Mater Academy HS International Studies	795 NW 32nd St	Miami, FL	33127-3645	305-634-0445	634-0446	9-12	Ofelia Alvarez
Mater Academy Lakes HS	17300 NW 87th Ave	Hialeah, FL	33015-3516	305-512-3917	512-3912	9-12	Rene Rovirosa
Mater Academy Lakes MS	17300 NW 87th Ave	Hialeah, FL	33015-3516	305-512-3917	512-3912	6-8	Frank Jimenez
Mater Academy of International Studies	795 NW 32nd St	Miami, FL	33127-3645	305-634-0445	634-0446	K-8	Betty Perez
Mater Gardens Academy	9010 NW 178th Ln	Hialeah, FL	33018-6548	305-512-9775	512-3708	K-8	Lourdes Isla-Marrero
Mater Performing Arts Academy	7901 NW 103rd St	Hialeah Gardens, FL	33016-2419	305-828-1886	828-6175	9-12	Judith Marty
Mavericks High Central Broward	424 W Sunrise Blvd	Fort Lauderdale, FL	33311-6211	954-446-9234	804-6712	9-12	Nadine Leblanc
Mavericks HS	1100 N Main St	Kissimmee, FL	34744	321-250-1871	846-0816	9-12	Carl Martin
Mavericks HS at Palm Springs	3525 S Congress Ave	Palm Springs, FL	33461-3767	561-623-6935	641-6370	9-12	DeeEtte Naukana
Mavericks HS of North Broward County	3500 North Andrews Ave	Pompano Beach, FL	33064	954-944-4123	784-3850	9-12	
Mavericks HS of North Miami-Dade County	16150 NE 17th Ave	N Miami Beach, FL	33162-4744	786-629-7053	949-5604	9-12	Alejandro Madrigal
Mavericks HS of South Miami-Dade County	698 N Homestead Blvd	Homestead, FL	33030-6207	305-909-6307	248-2913	9-12	Alejandro Madrigal
Mavericks North in Education	1197 E Bay Dr	Largo, FL	33770-2556	727-474-8836	581-9557	9-12	Greg Clark
Mavericks South in Education	4901 Central Ave	St Petersburg, FL	33710-8239	727-471-2811	321-1230	9-12	Zema Florence
McAuliffe Charter ES	2817 SW 3rd Ln	Cape Coral, FL	33991-1151	239-283-4511	282-0376	PK-5	Jacquelin Collins
Mc Intosh Area Charter S	PO Box 769	Mc Intosh, FL	32664-0769	352-591-9797	591-9747	K-5	Andrea Arnow
McKeel Academy	1810 W Parker St	Lakeland, FL	33815-1243	863-499-2818	603-6339	6-12	Dr. Linda Acocelli
McKeel ES	411 N Florida Ave	Lakeland, FL	33801-4803	863-499-1287	688-1607	K-5	Michele Spurgeon
Miami Arts Charter S	3900 Biscayne Blvd	Miami, FL	33137-3721	305-763-6257	740-5670	6-12	Alfredo de la Rosa
Miami Childrens Museum Charter S	980 MacArthur Cswy	Miami, FL	33132-1604	305-329-3758	329-3767	K-5	Nina Cortina
Miami Community Charter HS	18720 SW 352nd St	Florida City, FL	33034-4580	305-245-2552	245-2527	9-12	Dr. Jila Rezaie
Miami Community Charter MS	18720 SW 352nd St	Florida City, FL	33034-4580	305-245-2552	245-2527	6-8	Jacqueline Sera-Sirven
Miami Community Charter S	101 S Redland Rd	Florida City, FL	33034-4630	305-245-2552	245-2527	K-5	Dr. Jila Rezaie
Micanopy Area Cooperative S	802 NW Seminary Ave	Micanopy, FL	32667-8500	352-466-0990	466-4090	PK-5	Anne Thompson
Micanopy MS	PO Box 109	Micanopy, FL	32667-0109	352-466-1090	466-1030	6-8	Bobby Johnson
Milburn Academy - Daytona Beach	1031 Mason Ave	Daytona Beach, FL	32117-4611	386-304-0086	304-0087	6-12	Sam Smith
Milburn Academy - Deland	913 E New York Ave	DeLand, FL	32724-5663	386-738-9150	738-9151	6-12	Earl Barnett
Milestones Community School of Lake Co.	10516 Treadway School Rd	Leesburg, FL	34788-4669	352-742-7007	383-0744	K-8	Sharen Jackson
Minneola Charter ES	320 E Pearl St	Minneola, FL	34715-9001	352-394-2600	394-2079	K-5	Sandra Reaves
Montessori Academy of Early Enrichment	6300 Lake Worth Rd	Greenacres, FL	33463-3006	561-649-0004	649-0964	PK-5	Jean Ranck
Montessori Charter ES	1400 United St	Key West, FL	33040	305-294-4910	294-1404	1-6	Lynn Barras
Montessori of Winter Garden	855 E Plant St Ste 600	Winter Garden, FL	34787-3164	407-654-2045	654-2046	K-5	Kimberly Riggins M.Ed.
Mount Pleasant MS	1906 N Rome Ave	Tampa, FL	33607-4424	813-253-0053	253-0182	6-8	Yolanda Capers
Murray Hill HS	929 McDuff Ave S Ste 101	Jacksonville, FL	32205-5753	904-866-4516	388-8297	9-12	Ernest Woodard
My Choice Academy	1345 Watertower Rd	Lake Park, FL	33403	561-842-3220		K-7	Fred Weitz
MYcroSchool Pinellas HS	840 3rd Ave S	St Petersburg, FL	33701-4010	727-825-3710	825-3751	9-12	Martina Green
Nap Ford Community Charter S	648 W Livingston St	Orlando, FL	32801-1418	407-245-8711	245-8712	PK-5	
Nature Coast MS	6830 NW 140th St	Chiefland, FL	32626-8271	352-490-0700	490-0702	6-8	Charles Bowe
Nau Charter S	4402 SW Yamada Dr	Port St Lucie, FL	34953-6756	772-237-8600	237-8620	K-8	Mary Karnetsky
New Beginnings HS	3425 Lake Alfred Rd	Winter Haven, FL	33881-1492	863-298-5666	298-5675	6-12	Ashlee Wright
New Dimensions HS	4900 Old Pleasant Hill Rd	Kissimmee, FL	34759-3430	407-870-9949	870-8976	9-12	Dr. Jacqueline Grimm
Newpoint Bay Academy	700 W 23rd St Bldg H	Panama City, FL	32405-3936	850-215-0770	763-7613	6-8	John Graham
Newpoint Bay HS	700 W 23rd St Bldg H	Panama City, FL	32405-3936	850-215-0770	763-7613	9-12	John Graham
Newpoint Charter S	21810 US Highway 19 N # 10	Clearwater, FL	33765-2837	727-475-1256		9-12	John Selover
New Point HS of Tampa	2584 E State Road 60	Valrico, FL	33594-3816	813-413-4800		9-12	Christopher Wiand
New Springs S	2410 E Busch Blvd	Tampa, FL	33612-8410	813-933-5025	933-5009	K-8	Emre Akbaba
NewStart Pinellas North S	2461 N McMullen Booth Rd	Clearwater, FL	33759-1312	727-474-1237	725-3470	9-12	Donna Hulbert
Next Generation Charter S	4850 N State Road 7	Laud Lakes, FL	33319-5869	954-739-0571	739-9664	K-5	Daniel Sandberg
North Bay Haven Charter S	1104 Balboa Ave	Panama City, FL	32401-2017	850-248-0205	215-0644	K-9	Meredith Higgins
North Broward Academy of Excellence	8200 SW 17th St	N Lauderdale, FL	33068-4101	954-718-2211	718-2215	K-5	Jackson Self
North Broward Academy of Excellence MS	8200 SW 17th St	N Lauderdale, FL	33068-4101	954-718-2211	718-2215	6-8	Jackson Self
North County Charter S	6640 Old Dixie Hwy	Vero Beach, FL	32967-5913	772-794-1941	794-1945	K-5	Beth Miller
North Gardens HS	4692 NW 183rd St	Miami Gardens, FL	33055-3054	786-528-6308	621-1611	9-12	Dr. Robert Martin
North Nicholas HS	428 SW Pine Island Rd	Cape Coral, FL	33991-1916	239-242-4230	242-4231	9-12	Carol Taylor
North Park HS	3400 NW 135th St	Opa Locka, FL	33054-4708	305-720-2995	953-3289	9-12	Carlos del Cuadro
North University HS	4800 N University Dr	Sunrise, FL	33351-5746	954-746-4483	746-5031	9-12	Laurel Suarez
Oakland Avenue Charter S	456 E Oakland Ave	Oakland, FL	34760-8844	407-877-2039	877-6222	K-5	Marcia Cason
Oasis Charter ES	3415 Oasis Blvd	Cape Coral, FL	33914-4924	239-542-1577	549-7662	K-5	Steven Hook
Oasis Charter HS	3519 Oasis Blvd	Cape Coral, FL	33914-4914	239-541-1167	541-1590	9-12	Kimberly Lunger
Oasis Charter MS	3507 Oasis Blvd	Cape Coral, FL	33914-4914	239-945-1999	540-7677	6-8	Kevin Beckman
Oasis MS	202 13th Ave E	Bradenton, FL	34208-3246	941-749-1979	714-7333	6-8	Edna Bailey
Obama Academy for Boys	404 NW 7th Ter	Fort Lauderdale, FL	33311-8139	954-330-8371	200-6970	K-8	Jessica Rojas
Ocean Studies Charter S	92295 Overseas Hwy	Tavernier, FL	33070	305-852-7700		K-3	Jennifer Flores
Odyssey Charter Lower S	1755 Eldron Blvd SE	Palm Bay, FL	32909-6832	321-733-0442	733-1178	K-6	Wendi Nolder M.Ed.
Odyssey Charter Upper S	1350 Wyoming Dr SE	Palm Bay, FL	32909-5757	321-345-4117		7-12	Brent Christensen
Okaloosa Academy	2053 S Ferdon Blvd	Crestview, FL	32536-8424	850-689-7688	689-0799	6-12	Bill Eddins
Okaloosa Academy FWB	81 Roberts Blvd	Ft Walton Bch, FL	32547-5118	850-864-3133	864-4305	6-12	Christol Jarrett
One Room S House Project	4180 NE 15th St	Gainesville, FL	32609-2011	352-376-4014	376-3345	K-5	Brett Beckett
Orlando Science Charter S	2427 Lynx Ln	Orlando, FL	32804-4720	407-253-7304	253-7305	6-12	Necati Sahin
Our Children's Academy	555 Burns Ave	Lake Wales, FL	33853-3335	863-679-3338	679-3944	PK-5	Sharon McManus
Our Children's Middle Academy	16 N 3rd St	Lake Wales, FL	33853-3715	863-679-7500		6-8	Wendy Borden
Oxford Academy of Miami	10870 SW 113th Pl	Miami, FL	33176-3227	305-598-4494	598-4475	K-8	Angela Klinedinst
Palm Bay Academy	2112 Palm Bay Rd NE	Palm Bay, FL	32905-2915	321-984-2710	984-0799	K-5	Madhu Longani
Palm Bay Charter MS	635 Community College SE	Palm Bay, FL	32909	321-726-9005	726-3938	6-8	Irving Rashkover
Palm Bay Language Immersion S	1464 Troutman Blvd NE	Palm Bay, FL	32905-4101	321-723-4218	953-5160	K-4	Madhu Longani
Palm Beach Maritime Academy	1518 Lantana Rd	Lantana, FL	33462-1538	561-547-3775	540-5177	K-8	Marie Turchiaro
Palm Beach S for Autism	1199 Lantana Rd Ste 19	Lantana, FL	33462-1514	561-533-9917	533-9918	PK-8	Nancy Frank
Palmetto Charter S	1601 17th St W	Palmetto, FL	34221-6151	941-723-3711	729-5805	K-8	Brian Bustle
Palm Glades Preparatory Academy	22655 SW 112th Ave	Miami, FL	33170	786-272-2269	446-8956	K-12	Minelli Duclerc
Palm Harbor Academy	95 Old Kings Rd N	Palm Coast, FL	32137-8227	386-447-9692		K-5	Dr. Hortense Evans
Palm Pointe Educ Research S at Tradition	10680 SW Academic Way	Port St Lucie, FL	34987-2361	772-345-3245	468-3250	K-8	Debra Snyder
Paragon Academy of Technology	502 N 28th Ave	Hollywood, FL	33020-3811	954-925-0155	925-0209	6 8	Dr. Steven Montes
Paragon ES	2210 Pierce St	Hollywood, FL	33020-4414	954-943-0471	943-0473	K-5	
Parkway Academy	7451 Riviera Blvd	Miramar, FL	33023-6530	954-961-2911	961-2451	9-12	Dr. Clarissa Wright
Passport S	5221 Curry Ford Rd	Orlando, FL	32812-8741	407-658-9900	658-9911	K-8	Dr. Osvaldo Garcia
Pathways Academy	101 State St W	Jacksonville, FL	32202-3099	904-633-8125	633-8364	9-12	Erica Trent
Pemayetv Emahakv Charter S	100 E Harney Pond Rd NE	Okeechobee, FL	34974-2867	863-467-2501	467-8610	K-8	Brian Greseth
Pembroke Pines FSU Charter ES	601 SW 172nd Ave	Pembroke Pines, FL	33029-4003	954-499-4244	499-3016	K-5	Dr. Lisa Libidinsky
Pensacola Beach ES	900 Via De Luna Dr	Pensacola Beach, FL	32561-2262	850-934-4020	934-4040	K-5	Jeff Castleberry
Pepin ES	3916 E Hillsborough Ave	Tampa, FL	33610-4542	813-236-1462	231-5049	K-5	Celeste Kellar
Pepin HS	3916 E Hillsborough Ave	Tampa, FL	33610-4542	813-237-1239	236-1195	9-12	Monika Perez
Pepin HS	3916 E Hillsborough Ave	Tampa, FL	33610-4542	813-231-4893	236-1195	9-12	George Shaw
Pepin MS	3916 E Hillsborough Ave	Tampa, FL	33610-4542	813-239-2092	232-9680	6-8	Geri Henry
Phillips Learning Academy	2506 S Parsons Ave	Seffner, FL	33584-5748	813-685-7551	681-3333	K-5	Zenobia Cann
Pinecrest Academy MS	14901 SW 42nd St	Miami, FL	33185-4535	305-559-8583	559-8584	6-8	Maria Nunez
Pinecrest Academy - North Campus	10207 W Flagler St	Miami, FL	33174-1743	305-553-9762	553-9763	PK-8	Victoria Larrauri
Pinecrest Academy - South Campus	15130 SW 80th St	Miami, FL	33193-1302	305-386-0800	386-6298	K-5	Carmen Cangemi
Pinecrest Creek Charter S	3032 Monte Carlo Trl	Orlando, FL	32805-4354	407-435-6716		K-5	Dr. Ron Large
Pinecrest Preparatory Academy	14301 SW 42nd St	Miami, FL	33175-7832	305-207-1027	207-1897	K-5	Dr. Susie Dopico
Pinecrest Preparatory Academy HS	14901 SW 42nd St	Miami, FL	33185-4535	305-559-8583	559-8584	9-12	Maria Nunez
Pinecrest Preparatory S Orlando	8503 Daetwyler Dr	Orlando, FL	32827-5018	407-856-8359	856-8361	K-12	Jon Chace
Pinellas Academy of Math and Science	1775 S Highland Ave	Largo, FL	33756-1847	727-330-9449	213-0581	K-8	Glenn Piros
Pinellas Preparatory Academy	2300 Belcher Rd S Ste 100	Largo, FL	33771-4257	727-536-3600	536-3661	4-8	Joel Ramsdell
Pinellas Primary Academy	2300 Belcher Rd S	Largo, FL	33771-4257	727-536-3600	536-3661	PK-4	Nancy Walker
Pivot Charter S	2675 Winkler Ave Ste 200	Fort Myers, FL	33901-9328	239-243-8266	280-0387	6-12	Dr. Kelsey Johnson
Pivot Charter S	3020 S Falkenburg Rd	Riverview, FL	33578-2562	813-626-6724		6-12	Elizabeth Bretz
Plato Academy	2795 Keystone Rd	Tarpon Springs, FL	34688-7425	727-940-5232	940-5247	K-5	Danielle Turro
Plato Academy	401 S Old Coachman Rd	Clearwater, FL	33765-4410	727-793-2400	793-2405	PK-8	Dawn Parker
Plato North Academy	1601 Curlew Rd	Palm Harbor, FL	34683-6515	727-286-6249	286-6253	K-8	Janet Hurst
Plato Seminole Academy	10888 126th Ave	Largo, FL	33778-2710	727-400-6885	400-6890	K-8	

School	Address	City,State	Zip code	Telephone	Fax	Grade	Contact
Plato South Academy	7100 142nd Ave	Largo, FL	33771-4603	727-286-6244	286-6247	K-8	Amy Hayes
Polk Avenue ES	110 E Polk Ave	Lake Wales, FL	33853-4199	863-678-4244	678-4680	PK-5	Gail Quam
Polk Pre-Collegiate Academy	5316 Berkley Rd	Auburndale, FL	33823-8493	863-984-2443	984-2411	9-12	Cathy Carver
Polk State College Collegiate HS	3425 Winter Lake Rd	Lakeland, FL	33803-9765	863-669-2322	669-2944	11-12	Sallie Brisbane
Pompano Charter MS	2210 Pierce St	Hollywood, FL	33020-4414	954-943-0471	943-0473	6-8	
Potentials Charter S	1201 Australian Ave	Riviera Beach, FL	33404-6635	561-842-3213	863-4352	PK-5	Dr. Tiffany North
Princeton House Charter S	1166 Lee Rd	Orlando, FL	32810-5847	407-523-7121	523-7187	PK-5	Kim Gelalia
Prosperitas Leadership Academy Charter	4526 S Orange Blossom Trl	Orlando, FL	32839-1704	407-816-3566	855-7269	9-12	Nadia Pierre
Putnam Academy of Arts and Sciences	113 Putnam County Blvd	East Palatka, FL	32131-4020	386-326-4212	326-6235	6-7	Carla Aycock
Quantum HS	1275 Gateway Blvd	Boynton Beach, FL	33426-8302	561-293-2971	742-5716	9-12	Joy Hicks
RAMZ Academy Miami	2609 NW 7th St	Miami, FL	33125-3022	786-445-5697	642-8624	K-8	David Diaz
RCMA Leadership Academy	18236 S US Highway 310	Wimauma, FL	33598	813-672-5159	633-6119	6-8	Mark Haggett
RCMA Wimauma Academy	18236 S US Highway 310	Wimauma, FL	33598	813-672-5159	633-6119	K-5	Mark Haggett
Reading Edge Academy	2975 Enterprise Rd	DeBary, FL	32713-2708	386-668-8911	668-8443	K-5	Margaret Comardo
Reading Star Academy	2700 Enterprise Rd	Orange City, FL	32763-8312	386-775-3856	624-6450	K-5	
Red Shoe Charter S for Girls	404 NW 7th Ter	Fort Lauderdale, FL	33311-8139	954-330-8371	200-6970	K-8	Corey Alston
Renaissance Charter S	300 NW Cashmere Blvd	Port St Lucie, FL	34986-1969	772-344-5982	344-5985	K-8	Rachel Windler-Freitag
Renaissance Charter S	1889 Palm Beach Lakes Blvd	West Palm Beach, FL	33409-3501	561-839-1994	839-1995	K-8	Raymond Collum
Renaissance Charter S at Chickasaw Trail	8203 Valencia College Ln	Orlando, FL	32825-3242	321-206-0662	206-0664	K-8	Thomas Wheeler
Renaissance Charter S at Cooper City	2800 N Palm Ave	Cooper City, FL	33026-3500	954-668-2500	668-2980	K-8	Daniel Verdier
Renaissance Charter S at University	8399 N University Dr	Tamarac, FL	33321-1711	954-414-0996	414-0998	K-8	Robin Sandler
Renaissance Charter S of Coral Springs	6250 W Sample Rd	Coral Springs, FL	33067-3176	954-369-1179	780-5411	K-7	Mark Hage
Renaissance Charter S of Plantation	6701 W Sunrise Blvd	Plantation, FL	33313-6039	954-556-9700	556-9701	K-6	Elinav Cabrera
Renaissance Elementary Charter S	10651 NW 19th St	Doral, FL	33172-2536	305-591-2225	591-2984	K-8	Ana Cordal
Renaissance Learning Academy	1310 N Congress Ave	West Palm Beach, FL	33409	561-296-1776	296-1791	9-12	Toby Honsberger
Renaissance Learning Center	5800 Corporate Way	West Palm Beach, FL	33407-2004	561-640-0270	640-0272	K-5	Debra Johnson
Richardson Montessori S	6815 N Rome Ave	Tampa, FL	33604-5839	813-930-2988	930-2929	K-6	Tommie Brumfield
Ridgeview Global Studies Academy	1000 Dunson Rd	Davenport, FL	33896-8383	863-419-3171	419-3172	PK-5	Ralph Frier
Rio Grande Charter S	2210 S Rio Grande Ave	Orlando, FL	32805-5262	407-649-9122	649-8151	PK-5	
RISE Academy S of Science and Technology	3698 NW 15th St	Lauderhill, FL	33311-4133	954-585-4671	585-4871	K-8	Tal Hinkins
RISE Academy S of Science and Technology	6101 NW 31st St	Margate, FL	33063-7015	954-404-0192	585-4871	K-8	Sharon Smith
River Cities Community Charter S	3405 NW 27th Ave	Miami, FL	33142-5206	305-634-6090	638-9480	6-8	Connie Rodriguez
River City Science Academy	7565 Beach Blvd	Jacksonville, FL	32216-3003	904-855-8010	855-8014	6-12	Adem Dokmeci
River City Science Elementary Academy	7555 Beach Blvd	Jacksonville, FL	32216-3000	904-565-0065	997-9613	K-5	Deborah Dodd
Riviera Beach Maritime Academy	251 W 11th St	Riviera Beach, FL	33404-7534	561-841-7600	841-7626	9-12	Tonya Hicks
Round Lake Conversion Charter ES	31333 Round Lake Rd	Mount Dora, FL	32757-9599	352-385-4399	735-1860	PK-5	Linda Bartberger
Royal Palm Charter S	7145 Babcock St SE	Palm Bay, FL	32909-5462	321-723-0650	722-1117	K-2	Shannon Shupe
St. Johns Community Campus	62 Cuna St	Saint Augustine, FL	32084-3684	904-209-6842		9-12	Lynne Funcheon
Saint Peter's Academy	4250 38th Ave	Vero Beach, FL	32967-1711	772-562-1963	562-8920	PK-6	Ruth Jefferson
St. Petersburg Collegiate HS	PO Box 13489	St Petersburg, FL	33733-3489	727-341-4610	341-4226	10-12	Starla Metz
Samsula Academy	248 N Samsula Dr	New Smyrna, FL	32168-8762	386-423-6650	423-6651	K-5	Peggy Comardo
Sarasota Military Academy	801 Orange Ave	Sarasota, FL	34236-4116	941-926-1700	926-1701	9-12	Daniel Kennedy
Sarasota S of Arts & Sciences	645 Central Ave	Sarasota, FL	34236-4016	941-330-1855	330-1835	6-8	Tara Tahmosh M.Ed.
Sarasota Suncoast Academy	8084 Hawkins Rd	Sarasota, FL	34241-9300	941-924-4242	924-8282	K-5	Steve Crump
School of Arts & Sciences	3208 Thomasville Rd	Tallahassee, FL	32308-7904	850-386-6566	386-8183	K-8	Julie Fredrickson
School of Success Academy	6974 Wilson Blvd	Jacksonville, FL	32210-3663	904-573-0880	573-0889	6-8	Genell Mills
Sculptor Charter S	1301 Armstrong Dr	Titusville, FL	32780-7907	321-264-4000	264-4011	PK-8	Patricia O'Sullivan
Seacoast Charter Academy	9100 Regency Square Blvd N	Jacksonville, FL	32211-8103	904-562-4780	726-0249	K-5	Marla Stremmel
Seagull Academy for Independent Living	1801 12th Ave S	Lake Worth, FL	33461-5771	561-540-8110	540-8331	9-Adu	Linda Moore
Seaside Neighborhood S	PO Box 4610	Santa Rsa Bch, FL	32459-4610	850-231-0396	231-4725	6-9	Cathy Brubaker
Sebastian Charter JHS	782 Wave St	Sebastian, FL	32958-5049	772-388-8838	388-8815	6-8	Martha McAdams
Seminole Heights Charter HS	4006 N Florida Ave	Tampa, FL	33603-3816	813-234-0809	236-2406	9-12	Dr. Bobby Smith
Sheeler Charter HS	875 E Semoran Blvd	Apopka, FL	32703-5516	407-886-1825	886-7482	9-12	Tom Hanley
Shiloh Charter S	905 W Terrace Dr	Plant City, FL	33563-8903	813-707-1060	707-8060	K-8	Shirley Sanchez
SIA Tech	4811 Payne Stewart Dr	Jacksonville, FL	32209-9208	904-360-8200	768-8618	9-12	Michael LaRoche
SIA Tech Greater Miami	810 NW 28th St	Miami, FL	33127-4046	305-636-3446	636-3447	9-12	Catherine Bonnewell
SIATech - North	3050 NW 183rd St	Miami Gardens, FL	33056-3536	305-624-1144	624-9172	9-12	Catherine Bonnewell
SIATech - South	12350 SW 285th St	Homestead, FL	33033-1251	305-258-9477	258-9584	9-12	Catherine Bonnewell
Sigsbee Charter S	939 Felton Rd	Key West, FL	33040-6798	305-294-1861	292-6869	PK-6	Elisa Jannes
Six Mile Charter Academy	6851 Lancer Ave	Fort Myers, FL	33912-4334	239-768-9375	225-2477	K-8	Eric Lewis
Sky Academy	701 Center Rd	Venice, FL	34285-4808	941-492-9622		6-7	Dr. Oleh Bula
Somerset Academy	20801 Johnson St	Pembroke Pines, FL	33029-1916	954-442-0233	442-0813	K-5	Bernardo Montero
Somerset Academy	300 SE 1st Dr	Homestead, FL	33030-7307	305-245-6108	245-6109	K-12	Christina Cruz-Ortiz
Somerset Academy	18491 SW 134th Ave	Miami, FL	33177-2923	305-969-6074	969-6077	K-5	Suzette Ruiz
Somerset Academy Boca	333 SW 4th Ave	Boca Raton, FL	33432-5700	561-393-1091	393-1092	K-5	Bonnie May
Somerset Academy Central Miramar Campus	9300 Pembroke Rd	Miramar, FL	33025-1640	954-435-1570	435-1571	K-12	Athena Guillen
Somerset Academy Charter HS	23255 SW 115th Ave	Homestead, FL	33032-4505	305-257-3737	257-3751	9-12	Kerri Maysonet
Somerset Academy - Davie	3788 Davie Rd	Davie, FL	33312	954-584-5528	584-5598	K-5	Dina Miller
Somerset Academy Eagle Campus	8985 Lone Star Rd	Jacksonville, FL	32211-5195	904-854-0990	854-0917	6-8	Olatunji Williams
Somerset Academy Eagle Campus	8711 Lone Star Rd	Jacksonville, FL	32211-5123	904-551-3292	240-0228	K-5	Olatunji Williams
Somerset Academy East Preparatory	2000 S State Road 7	Miramar, FL	33023-6740	954-987-7890	987-7891	K-8	Dr. Mary Stuart
Somerset Academy ES	5876 SW 68th St	South Miami, FL	33143-3693	305-740-0509	740-0510	K-8	Kim Guilarte
Somerset Academy HS	20805 Johnson St	Pembroke Pines, FL	33029-1916	954-442-0233	442-1762	9-12	Bernardo Montero
Somerset Academy MS	18491 SW 134th Ave	Miami, FL	33177-2923	305-969-6074	969-6077	6-8	Suzette Ruiz
Somerset Academy MS	20803 Johnson St	Pembroke Pines, FL	33029-1916	954-442-0233	442-1762	6-8	Bernardo Montero
Somerset Academy Miramar	12601 Somerset Blvd	Miramar, FL	33027-5898	305-829-2406	829-4477	PK-8	Alexandra Prieto
Somerset Academy Pompano	3311 NW 9th Ave	Pompano Beach, FL	33064-2036	954-946-4144	946-4005	K-5	Dr. Donna Kaye
Somerset Academy Silver Palms	23255 SW 115th Ave	Homestead, FL	33032-4505	305-257-3737	257-3751	PK-8	Kerri Maysonet
Somerset Arts Academy	1700 N Krome Ave	Homestead, FL	33030	305-246-4949	249-4919	K-8	Idalia Suarez
Somerset Conservatory	20807 Johnson St	Pembroke Pines, FL	33029-1916	954-442-0233	442-1762	9-12	Bernardo Montero
Somerset Gables Academy	624 Anastasia Ave	Coral Gables, FL	33134-6404	305-442-8626	442-8627	K-8	Suzette Ruiz
Somerset Miramar South S	12425 SW 53rd St	Miramar, FL	33027-5493	305-829-2406	829-4477	K-5	Alexandra Prieto
Somerset Pines Academy	901 NE 33rd St	Pompano Beach, FL	33064-5231	954-786-5980	786-5981	K-8	Donna Kaye
Somerset Preparatory Academy	7101 Kimberly Blvd	N Lauderdale, FL	33068-2388	954-718-5065	718-5066	K-12	James Griffin
Somerset Village Academy	225 NW 29th St	Wilton Manors, FL	33311-2427	954-390-0971	390-0972	K-8	Shannie Sadesky
South Florida Autism Charter S	13835 NW 97th Ave	Hialeah, FL	33018-1213	305-823-2700	823-2705	K-11	Dr. Tamara Ramdeen
South McKeel Elementary Academy	2222 Edgewood Dr S	Lakeland, FL	33803-3631	863-510-0044	510-0021	K-7	Judith Morris
South Tech Academy	1300 SW 30th Ave	Boynton Beach, FL	33426-9099	561-369-7004	369-7024	9-12	Myron Cost
Sports Leadership Academy of Miami	998 SW 1st St	Miami, FL	33130-1112	305-324-6963	324-6966	9-12	Alex Tamargo
Spring Creek ES	44440 Spring Creek Rd	Paisley, FL	32767-9063	352-669-3275	669-3762	PK-6	Robert Curry
Stars MS	1500 Miccosukee Rd	Tallahassee, FL	32308-5164	850-681-7827	827-1263	6-8	Ahmet Temel
State College of Florida Collegiate S	5840 26th St W	Bradenton, FL	34207-3522	941-752-5491	758-4801	6-12	Kelly Monod
Steele/Collins Charter MS	412 N Bronough St	Tallahassee, FL	32301-1120	850-681-1929	224-1663	6-8	Tisa Jones
Stellar Leadership Academy	7900 NW 27th Ave Ste F-1	Miami, FL	33147-4909	305-693-2273	693-8016	9-12	Dr. Angel Chaisson
Student Leadership Academy	200 Field Ave E	Venice, FL	34285-3936	941-485-5551	485-2694	6-8	Vickie Marble
Success Leadership Academy	1237 NE 4th Ave	Fort Lauderdale, FL	33304-1924	954-735-6970	735-6022	9-12	Dana Ligocki-Vignale
Summerville Advantage Academy	11575 SW 243rd St	Homestead, FL	33032-7163	305-253-2123	253-4304	K-8	Breezy Leza
Suncoast S for Innovative Studies	845 S School Ave	Sarasota, FL	34237-8039	941-953-4433	953-4435	PK-8	Stephen Evans
SunEd HS	2360 W Oakland Park Blvd	Oakland Park, FL	33311-1410	954-678-3939	485-6243	9-12	Derek Stein
Sunshine ES	502 N 28th Ave	Hollywood, FL	33020-3811	954-925-0155	925-0209	K-5	Dr. Steven Montes
Sunshine High Charter	6600 Old Winter Garden Rd	Orlando, FL	32835-1218	407-641-4156	886-7482	9-12	
Sweetwater Branch Academy	1000 NE 16th Ave Bldg C	Gainesville, FL	32601-4541	352-375-8838	241-5125	K-10	Ugur Baslanti
Tampa Charter S	5429 Beaumont Center # 800	Tampa, FL	33634	813-887-3800	885-9626	3-8	Sheila Thomley
Team Success S of Excellence	202 13th Ave E	Bradenton, FL	34208-3246	941-714-7260	714-7333	K-8	Fredrick Spence
Terrace Community Charter S	11734 Jefferson Rd	Thonotosassa, FL	33592-2101	813-987-6555	987-6565	6-8	Tahvia Shaw
Therapeutic Learning Center	2109 ARC Dr	Saint Augustine, FL	32084-0512	904-824-8932	824-8063	PK-PK	Paulette Hudson
Tiger Academy	6079 Bagley Rd	Jacksonville, FL	32209-1805	904-309-6840	309-6867	PK-4	Charles McWhite
Tomorrows Promise Community S	601 N Congress Ave Ste 110	Delray Beach, FL	33445-4625	561-266-2206	266-2208	9-12	Marjorie Waldo
Touchdowns4Life Charter S	10044 W McNab Rd	Tamarac, FL	33321-1894	954-726-8785	726-9590	6-8	Latoya Almonord
Toussaint L'Ouverture HS	301 SW 14th Ave	Delray Beach, FL	33444-1455	561-266-1200	266-1286	9-12	Mandy Freeman
Treasure Village Montessori Charter S	86731 Old Hwy	Islamorada, FL	33036-3129	305-852-3482	852-2432	PK-8	Kelly Astin-Wix
Trinity S for Children	2402 W Osborne Ave	Tampa, FL	33603-1434	813-874-2402	874-2412	K-5	Madeline O'Dea
Trinity Upper S	4807 N Armenia Ave	Tampa, FL	33603-1427	813-874-2402	874-2412	6-8	Madeline O'Dea
Turner Learning Academy	2201 SW 42nd Ave	West Park, FL	33023-3456	954-463-8404	463-3566	K-5	Maxine Spence
UCP Charter S Downtown Campus	3305 S Orange Ave	Orlando, FL	32806-6125	407-852-3300	852-3334	PK-K	Lillian Flores
UCP Charter S West Orange Campus	630 S Dillard St	Winter Garden, FL	34787-3903	407-905-0531	905-0532	PK-K	Marilyn Martinez
UCP East Orlando/Bailes Campus	12702 Science Dr	Orlando, FL	32826-3016	407-852-3300	281-0422	PK-K	Anna O'Connor-Morin
UCP Kissimmee/Osceola Campus	448 W Donegan Ave	Kissimmee, FL	34741-2335	407-852-3300	932-3480	PK-PK	Ana Velez
UCP Lake Mary/Seminole Campus	3590 N US Highway 17/92	Lake Mary, FL	32746-4510	407-322-6222	322-5596	PK-1	Marife Gomez
UCP Pine Hills Charter S	5800 Golf Club Pkwy	Orlando, FL	32808-4800	407-299-5553	299-5520	PK-1	Brenda Korpi
UCP Transitional Learning Academy	8291 Curry Ford Rd	Orlando, FL	32822-7890	407-852-3300	852-3334	6-8	Dr. Jonathan McIntire
University Academy	4750 Collegiate Dr	Panama City, FL	32405-1000	850-770-2422		K-5	Judy Vandegrift
Valrico Lake Advantage Academy	13306 Boyette Rd	Riverview, FL	33569-5741	813-699-5049	413-5191	K-5	Bonnie Guertin
Village of Excellence Academy	8718 N 46th St	Temple Terrace, FL	33617-6002	813-988-8632	983-0683	K-5	Cametra Edwards
Villages Charter HS	251 Buffalo Trl	Lady Lake, FL	32162-7176	352-259-3777	259-3850	9-12	Dr. Bill Zwick
Villages Charter Intermediate Center	521 Old School Rd	Lady Lake, FL	32162-7170	352-259-2300	259-2056	2-3	LeAnne Yerk
Villages Charter MS	450 Village Campus Cir	Lady Lake, FL	32162-7169	352-259-0044	753-1113	6-8	Dr. Peggy Irwin

School	Address	City,State	Zip code	Telephone	Fax	Grade	Contact
Villages Charter Primary Center	420 Village Campus Cir	Lady Lake, FL	32162-7169	352-259-7700	259-7707	K-1	LeAnne Yerk
Walton Academy	389 Dorsey Ave	Defuniak Spgs, FL	32435-3013	850-892-3999	892-7854	6-12	Steve Ruder
Walton Academy of the Performing Arts	PO Box 7578	Tampa, FL	33673-7578	813-231-9272	231-9271	K-5	Tanika Walton
Waverly Academy	4200 Georgetown Dr	Jacksonville, FL	32210-4705	904-206-7836	551-4212	6-8	Fernette Moore
Wayman Academy of the Arts	1176 Labelle St	Jacksonville, FL	32205-6487	904-695-9995	695-9992	K-5	Renee Robinson
Wells Charter S	2426 Remington Blvd	Kissimmee, FL	34744-8467	407-697-1020	697-1021	K-8	Bonnie Brett
West Broward Academy at Excelsior	10038 W McNab Rd	Tamarac, FL	33321-1815	954-726-5227	772-9702	K-8	Raul Baez
Western Academy Charter S	650 Royal Palm Blvd Ste 300	Ryl Palm Bch, FL	33411	561-792-4123	422-0674	K-8	Linda Terranova
Westminister Academy Charter S	830 29th St	Orlando, FL	32805-6219	407-841-6560	841-7311	K-12	Janice Clausen
West Orange Montessori S	855 E Plant St Ste 600	Winter Garden, FL	34787-3164	407-654-2045		K-8	Kimberly Riggins Ed.D.
West University HS	11602 N 15th St	Tampa, FL	33612-6086	813-774-4396	833-7216	9-12	Cloty Davis
Whispering Winds Charter S	PO Box 506	Chiefland, FL	32644-0506	352-490-5799	490-7242	K-8	Dr. J. Suzann Cornell
Wilson ES	306 Florida Ave	Lake Wales, FL	33853-3121	863-678-4211	678-4217	PK-5	Steve Whitaker
Windsor Preparatory Academy	5175 45th St N	St Petersburg, FL	33714-2266	727-475-1297		K-5	Jessica Clements
Winthrop Charter S	6204 Scholars Hill Ln	Riverview, FL	33578-4298	813-235-4811	315-4403	K-8	Terry Johnson
Woodmont Charter S	10402 N 56th St	Temple Terrace, FL	33617-3637	813-708-1596	739-7301	K-8	Jason Lewis
Workforce Advantage Academy	2113 E South St	Orlando, FL	32803-6502	407-898-7228	898-6448	11-12	Belinda Jones
Worthington HS	1711 Worthington Rd	West Palm Beach, FL	33409-6407	561-537-5696	697-4366	9-12	Victor Frias
Wright Leadership Academy	2099 W Prospect Rd	Tamarac, FL	33309-3624	954-306-2041	533-1285	K-8	Dewanda Chambers
Youth Co-Op Charter S	12051 W Okeechobee Rd	Hialeah Gardens, FL	33018-2933	305-819-8855	819-8455	K-8	Maritza Aragon
Youth Co-Op Preparatory HS	7700 W 20th Ave	Hialeah Gardens, FL	33016-1859	305-821-8277	819-8455	9-12	Kenneth Feria
		Georgia					
Addison ES	3055 Ebenezer Rd	Marietta, GA	30066-4542	770-578-2700	578-2702	PK-5	Karen Crowder
Amana Academy	285 S Main St	Alpharetta, GA	30009-1937	678-624-0989	624-0892	K-8	Ehab Jaleel
Athens Community Career Academy	240 Mitchell Bridge Rd	Athens, GA	30606-2043	706-357-5244	353-3877	9-12	Dr. Lynn Johns
Atlanta Heights Charter S	3712 Martin Luther King Jr	Atlanta, GA	30331	404-472-3003	264-2132	K-8	Melissa Clarke
Atlanta Neighborhood Charter MS	820 Essie Ave SE	Atlanta, GA	30316-2425	678-904-0051	904-0052	6-8	Matt Underwood
Atlanta Neighborhood Charter S	688 Grant St SE	Atlanta, GA	30315-1420	404-624-6226	627-8922	K-5	Lara Zelski
Baconton Community Charter S	260 E Walton St	Baconton, GA	31716-7782	229-787-9999	787-0077	PK-12	Lynn Pinson
Baldwin College and Career Academy	155 GA Highway 49 W	Milledgeville, GA	31061-3600	478-453-6429	453-5060	9-12	Dr. Jessica Swain
Berrien Academy Performance Learning Ctr	1015 Exum Rd	Nashville, GA	31639-2730	229-686-6576	686-6580	9-12	Ted Folsom
Bishop Hall Charter S	1819 E Clay St	Thomasville, GA	31792-4736	229-227-1397	558-9420	9-12	Rich Johnson
Brighten Academy	3264 Brookmont Pkwy	Douglasville, GA	30135-2108	770-615-3675	615-3677	K-8	Lisa McDonald
Carroll County College and Career Acad	1075 Newnan Rd	Carrollton, GA	30116-6435	770-832-8380	830-5037	10-12	Cindy Clanton
Central Educational Center	160 Martin Luther King Dr	Newnan, GA	30263-2331	678-423-2000	423-2008	9-12	Mark Ballou
Chamblee Charter HS	3688 Chamblee Dunwoody Rd	Chamblee, GA	30341-2185	678-676-6902	676-6910	9-12	Rochelle Lowery
Charter Conservatory Liberal Arts/Tech.	149 Northside Dr E	Statesboro, GA	30458-1089	912-764-5888	489-8493	5-12	Corliss Reese
Cherokee Charter Academy	2126 Sixes Rd	Canton, GA	30114-8162	678-385-7322	385-7323	K-8	Vanessa Suarez
Chesnut Charter ES	4576 N Peachtree Rd	Dunwoody, GA	30338-5892	678-676-7102	676-7110	PK-5	Veronica Williams
Chestatee Academy	2740 Fran Mar Dr	Gainesville, GA	30506-1136	770-297-6270	297-6275	6-8	Dr. David Robles
Chestnut Mountain Creative S of Inquiry	4841 Union Church Rd	Flowery Branch, GA	30542-5202	770-967-3121	967-4891	K-5	Dr. Sabrina May
Clubview ES	2836 Edgewood Rd	Columbus, GA	31906-1298	706-565-3017	565-3022	PK-5	Lorrie Watt
Coastal Empire Montessori Charter S	301 Buckhalter Rd	Savannah, GA	31405-6111	912-238-1973	388-2317	PK-5	Christina Placek
Coweta Charter Academy	6675 Highway 16	Senoia, GA	30276-3345	770-599-0228	599-0556	K-6	Tiffany Pollock
Da Vinci Academy at South Hall MS	3215 Poplar Springs Rd	Gainesville, GA	30507-8659	770-533-4004	533-4018	6-8	Paula Stubbs
Dekalb Academy of Tech & Environment	1492 Kelton Dr	Stone Mountain, GA	30083-1918	678-999-9290	999-9294	K-12	Dr. Maury Wills
DeKalb PATH Academy	3007 Hermance Dr NE	Atlanta, GA	30319-2627	404-846-3242	846-3243	K-12	Suttiwan Cox
DeKalb Prepatory Academy	1402 Austin Dr	Decatur, GA	30032-3838	404-937-2000	937-2020	K-4	Michael Daly
Destiny Academy of Excellence	3595 Linecrest Rd	Ellenwood, GA	30294-1839	404-328-0898	328-1294	9-12	Dr. Charles Maxwell
Douglas Co. College & Career Institute	4600 Timber Ridge Dr	Douglasville, GA	30135-1225	770-947-7690	947-3896	9-12	Mandy Johnson
Drew Charter S	301 E Lake Blvd SE	Atlanta, GA	30317-3152	404-687-0001	687-0480	PK-9	Don Doran
Effingham Career Academy	2940 GA Highway 21 S	Rincon, GA	31326-3337	912-754-5610	754-5611	10-12	Travis Nesmith
Elite Scholars Academy	137 Spring St	Jonesboro, GA	30236-3558	770-515-7684		6-12	Dr. Shonda Shaw
Fargo Charter S	PO Box 267	Fargo, GA	31631-0267	912-637-5466	637-5242	K-3	
Flowery Branch HS	6603 Spout Springs Rd	Flowery Branch, GA	30542-5529	770-967-8000	967-1218	9-12	Dr. Mark Coleman
Floyd County College and Career Academy	100 Tom Poe Dr	Rome, GA	30161	706-236-1860	236-1862	9-12	Eric Waters
Forsyth County Academy	1130 Dahlonega Hwy	Cumming, GA	30040-4536	770-781-3141	888-1193	9-12	Brad Smith
Fulton Leadership Academy	4141 Old Fairburn Rd	Atlanta, GA	30349-1747	404-472-3529	472-3520	6-12	Dr. Gavin Samms
Fulton Science Academy HS	4100 Old Milton Pkwy	Alpharetta, GA	30005-4442	770-475-3223	475-8870	9-12	Namik Sercan
Fulton Sunshine Academy	1335 Northmeadow Pkwy	Roswell, GA	30076-4949	770-410-1500	410-1551	K-5	Murat Cetin
Futral Road ES	180 Futral Rd	Griffin, GA	30224-7454	770-229-3735	233-6001	PK-5	Larry Jones
Gateway to College Academy	555 N Indian Creek Dr	Clarkston, GA	30021-2361	678-891-3220	891-3610	9-12	Robert Wigfall
Golden Isles Career Academy	4404 Glynco Pkwy	Brunswick, GA	31525-6852	912-280-4000	261-2285	10-12	Rick Townsend
Gwinnett County Online Campus	2595 Beaver Ruin Rd	Norcross, GA	30071-4124	770-326-8082	326-8064	6-12	Dr. Christopher Ray
Gwinnett S of Math Science and Tech	970 McElvaney Ln	Lawrenceville, GA	30044-2300	678-518-6700	518-6702	9-12	Dr. Jeff Mathews
Hapeville Career Academy	6045 Buffington Rd	College Park, GA	30349-3602	404-766-0101	941-1102	9-12	Jannard Rainey
Hapeville Charter MS	3535 S Fulton Ave	Hapeville, GA	30354-1701	404-767-7730	767-7706	6-8	Marcia Lowe
Harris Elementary Charter S	2300 Danielsville Rd	Athens, GA	30601-1038	706-357-5203	357-5209	PK-5	Xernona Thomas
Heart of Georgia College & Career Acad	720 Industrial Blvd	Dublin, GA	31021-1775	478-689-4774	689-6593	9-12	Dr. Howard Abney
Heritage Preparatory Academy	3350 Greenbriar Pkwy SW	Atlanta, GA	30331-2610	678-399-2810		6-8	Dr. Natilee Brown-Van
Hillcrest ES	1100 Edgewood Dr	Dublin, GA	31021-5599	478-277-9833	277-9809	K-5	Demme McManus
Houston County Career Academy	1311 Corder Rd	Warner Robins, GA	31088-7117	478-322-3280	322-3294	9-12	Sabrina Phelps
Imagine International Academy of Smyrna	2144 S Cobb Dr SE Ste A	Smyrna, GA	30080-1322	678-370-0980	370-0981	K-8	
International Community S	2418 Wood Trail Ln	Decatur, GA	30033-4849	404-499-8969	499-8968	K-5	Laurent Dittman
International Studies Magnet ES	2237 Cutts Dr	Albany, GA	31705-3899	229-431-3384	431-3381	K-5	Zeda George
Intown Academy Charter S	386 Pine St NE	Atlanta, GA	30308-2500	404-892-7733	870-0086	K-8	Lola Burse
Ivy Preparatory Academy	3705 Engineering Dr	Norcross, GA	30092-2878	770-342-0089	342-0088	6-12	Victoria Hudson
Ivy Preparatory Academy at Kirkwood	1807 Memorial Dr SE	Atlanta, GA	30317-2103	404-622-2727	622-2725	6-12	Sherry Miller
Jenkins-White Charter ES	800 15th Ave	Augusta, GA	30901-4145	706-737-7320	731-7651	PK-5	Janie Norris
Kennesaw Charter Science & Math Academy	3010 Cobb Pkwy NW	Kennesaw, GA	30152-2502	678-290-9628	290-9638	K-6	Kay Frey
Kindezi S	1890 Detroit Ave NW	Atlanta, GA	30314-1638	404-671-4900	671-4901	K-5	Dean Leeper
Kingsley ES	2051 Brendon Dr	Dunwoody, GA	30338-4599	678-874-8902	874-8910	PK-5	Dr. Jasmine Smith
KIPP Atlanta Collegiate S	98 Anderson Ave NW	Atlanta, GA	30314-1820	404-574-5126		9-12	David Howland
KIPP South Fulton Academy	1286 Washington Ave	East Point, GA	30344-3537	678-278-0160	278-0165	5-8	Jondre Pryor
KIPP STRIVE Academy	1444 Lucile Ave SW	Atlanta, GA	30310-1217	404-753-1530	753-1532	5-8	Edwin Chang
KIPP STRIVE Primary Academy	1444 Lucile Ave SW	Atlanta, GA	30310-1217	404-753-1530	753-1532	K-4	Mini'imah Shaheed
KIPP Vision Charter S	660 McWilliams Rd SE	Atlanta, GA	30315-7544	404-537-5252	671-4882	5-7	Steven Jones
KIPP WAYS Academy	80 Joseph E Lowery Blvd NW	Atlanta, GA	30314-3421	404-475-1941	475-1946	5-8	Dwight Ho-Sang
Lake Oconee Academy	1021 Titan Cir	Greensboro, GA	30642-6047	706-454-1562	453-1773	K-8	Otho Tucker Ph.D.
Lamar County College and Career Academy	1 Trojan Way	Barnesville, GA	30204-1544	770-358-8641	358-8649	9-12	Derek Austin
Lanier Charter Career Academy	2719 Tumbling Creek Rd	Gainesville, GA	30504-5863	770-532-3161	532-3156	9-12	Dr. Cindy Blakley
Latin Academy	2050 Tiger Flowers Dr NW	Atlanta, GA	30314-1326	404-314-7354		5-5	Chris Clemons
Leadership Preparatory Academy	6400 Woodrow Rd	Lithonia, GA	30038-2437	404-665-3103		K-7	Dr. Frankie Callaway
Liberty College and Career Academy	245 Darsey Rd	Hinesville, GA	31313	912-876-4904		9-12	Tom Alexander
Main Street Academy - Lower	3480 Main St	College Park, GA	30337-2064	404-763-3900		K-1	Raine Hackler
Main Street Academy - Upper	1805 Harvard Ave	College Park, GA	30337-3703	404-768-0081		2-6	Raine Hackler
Martin Technology Academy	4216 Martin Rd	Flowery Branch, GA	30542-3509	770-965-1578	965-1668	K-5	Tamara Etterling
Maxwell HS of Technology	990 McElvaney Ln	Lawrenceville, GA	30044-2303	770-963-6838	338-4612	10-12	Jeff Hall
McEver Arts Academy	3265 Montgomery Dr	Gainesville, GA	30504-5515	770-534-7473	531-3055	K-5	Dr. Catherine Rosa
Morgan County ES	1640 Buckhead Rd	Madison, GA	30650	706-342-5040	342-5050	3-5	Jean Triplett
Morgan County HS	1231 College Dr	Madison, GA	30650-1499	706-342-2336	342-5046	9-12	Jim Malanowski
Morgan County MS	920 Pearl St	Madison, GA	30650-1021	706-342-0556	342-5048	6-8	Lydia Norburg
Morgan County PS	993 East Ave	Madison, GA	30650-1498	706-342-3475	342-9184	PK-2	Dr. Betsy Short
Mountain Education Charter HS	901 Fairview School Rd	Demorest, GA	30535-3017	706-754-4461	754-5181	9-12	Wayne Lovell
Mountain Education Charter HS	218 School St	Blairsville, GA	30512-3690	706-745-9575	745-3588	9-12	John Hill
Mountain Education Charter HS	4560 Old Highway 76	Blue Ridge, GA	30513-4756	706-632-6100	632-0461	9-12	Lori Chastain
Mountain Education Charter HS	175 Primary School Rd	Ellijay, GA	30540-3666	706-276-5002	276-5008	9-12	Timothy Mount
Mountain Education Charter HS	123 Mountain View Dr	Dahlonega, GA	30533-0307	706-864-0229	864-9391	9-12	Tracy Sanford
Mountain Education Charter HS	191 Old Big A School Rd	Toccoa, GA	30577	706-886-3114	886-3127	9-12	Debbie Gurley
Mountain Education Charter HS	328 Old Blairsville Rd	Cleveland, GA	30528	706-865-0727	348-4498	9-12	Joe Cash
Mountain Education Charter HS	121 D B Carrol	Jasper, GA	30143-1522	706-253-1750	253-1755	9-12	Ron Hunter
Mount Vernon Exploratory S	4844 Jim Hood Rd	Gainesville, GA	30506-2834	770-983-1759	983-1663	K-5	Connie Daniels
Murphey Middle Charter S	2610 Milledgeville Rd	Augusta, GA	30904-5181	706-737-7350	737-7353	6-8	Veronica Bolton
Museum S of Avondale Estates	923 Forrest Blvd	Decatur, GA	30030-4730	404-292-9760		PK-8	Katherine Kelbaugh
New Life Academy of Excellence	3159 Campus Dr Ste 100	Norcross, GA	30071-1492	770-248-3032	248-3037	K-8	Alphonsa Forward
New Life Academy of Excellence	4725 River Green Pkwy	Duluth, GA	30096-2567	678-720-9870	720-9875	K-8	Alphonsa Forward
Newton College & Career Academy	144 Ram Dr	Covington, GA	30014-1956	678-625-6769	625-6041	10-12	James Woodard
North Springs HS of Arts & Sciences	7447 Roswell Rd	Sandy Springs, GA	30328-1026	770-551-2490	551-2498	9-12	Lisa Stueve
Northwest Georgia College & Career Acad	2300 Maddox Chapel Rd NE	Dalton, GA	30721-6645	706-876-3600	876-3602	9-12	Jay Williams
Odyssey Charter S	14 Saint John Cir	Newnan, GA	30265-1020	770-251-6111	251-6606	K-8	Andy Geeter
Oglethorpe Charter S	7202 Central Ave	Savannah, GA	31406-4203	912-395-5075	201-7626	6-8	Kevin Wall
Pataula Charter Academy	PO Box 332	Edison, GA	39846-0332	229-835-3322	835-2233	K-8	Kylie Holley
Peachtree Charter MS	4664 N Peachtree Rd	Atlanta, GA	30338-5898	678-676-7702	676-7710	6-8	Brian Heptinstall
P.R.E.P. Academy	4685 US Highway 84 Byp W	Thomasville, GA	31792-2607	229-225-5050		9-12	Beth Adams
Provost Academy of Georgia	100 Edgewood Ave NE Ste 915	Atlanta, GA	30303-3070	404-577-8593	669-2303	9-12	

School	Address	City,State	Zip code	Telephone	Fax	Grade	Contact
Putnam County ES	314 S Washington Ave	Eatonton, GA	31024-1126	706-485-5312	923-2808	3-5	Raymond Braziel
Putnam County HS	300 War Eagle Rd	Eatonton, GA	31024-2304	706-485-9971	485-3128	9-12	Barry Lollis
Putnam County MS	140 Sparta Hwy	Eatonton, GA	31024-8493	706-485-8547	485-7090	6-8	Dr. Susan Usry
Putnam County PS	162 Old Glenwood Springs Rd	Eatonton, GA	31024-6525	706-485-5141	485-4147	PK-2	Fernando Aker
Reese Road Leadership Academy	3100 Reese Rd	Columbus, GA	31907-1610	706-569-3684	569-3688	PK-5	Jeanella Pendleton
Ridgeview Charter MS	5340 Trimble Rd	Sandy Springs, GA	30342-1413	404-843-7710	847-3292	6-8	Lisa Hastey
Riverwood HS	5900 Raider Dr	Sandy Springs, GA	30328-4706	404-847-1980	255-8709	9-12	Christopher Triolo
Rockdale Career Academy	1064 Culpepper Dr SW	Conyers, GA	30094-5985	770-388-5677	388-5678	9-12	Dr. Miki Edwards
Sandy Springs MS	8750 Colonel Dr	Sandy Springs, GA	30350-2505	770-552-4970	643-3334	6-8	Kay Walker
Sardis Enrichment School	2805 Sardis Rd	Gainesville, GA	30506-2228	770-532-0104	531-3057	K-5	Neil Yarrington
Sawyer Road ES	840 Sawyer Rd	Marietta, GA	30062-2263	770-429-9923	429-9936	K-5	Jill Sims
Scholars Academy Charter S	6449 Church St	Riverdale, GA	30274-2004	770-756-9710	629-4755	K-5	Carlotta Blatch
Sedalia Park ES	2230 Lower Roswell Rd	Marietta, GA	30068-3359	770-509-5162	509-5342	K-5	Jennifer Lawson
Smoke Rise ES	1991 Silver Hill Rd	Stone Mountain, GA	30087-1699	678-874-3602	874-3610	PK-5	Aaron Moore
South Eastern Early College & Career Acd	3001 E 1st St	Vidalia, GA	30474-8817	912-538-3177		9-12	Dr. Barbara Christmas
Spalding Drive Charter ES	130 W Spalding Dr	Sandy Springs, GA	30328-1999	770-551-5880	673-4090	PK-5	Christine Young
Spout Springs S of Enrichment	6640 Spout Springs Rd	Flowery Branch, GA	30542-5575	770-967-4860	967-4883	K-5	Steve McDaniel
Taliaferro County S	557 Broad St NW	Crawfordville, GA	30631-2918	706-456-2575	456-2689	PK-12	Jemessyn Foster
Tybee Island Maritime Academy	PO Box 1519	Tybee Island, GA	31328-1519	912-484-0083	786-9803	K-8	
Unidos Dual Language Charter S	4475 Hendrix Dr	Forest Park, GA	30297-1244	404-361-3494	362-2498	K-4	Nancy Said
Walton HS	1590 Bill Murdock Rd	Marietta, GA	30062-5999	770-578-3225	578-3227	9-12	Judith McNeill
Wauka Mtn Multiple Intelligences Academy	5850 Brookton Lula Rd	Gainesville, GA	30506-2909	770-983-3221	983-1019	PK-5	Dr. Jo Dinnan
Webster County HS	7168 Washington St	Preston, GA	31824-5232	229-828-3315	828-3206	9-12	Janie Downer
Wesley International Academy	1049 Custer Ave SE	Atlanta, GA	30316-3100	678-904-9137	904-9138	K-8	Duke Bradley
Woodland Charter ES	1130 Spalding Dr	Sandy Springs, GA	30350-5013	770-551-5890	673-4091	PK-5	Amy Gamble
World Language Academy	4670 Winder Hwy	Flowery Branch, GA	30542-3611	770-967-5856	967-3496	K-5	David Moody
Wynnton Arts Academy	2303 Wynnton Rd	Columbus, GA	31906-2540	706-748-3147	748-3151	K-5	Carolyn Mull

Hawaii

School	Address	City,State	Zip code	Telephone	Fax	Grade	Contact
Connections New Century Charter S	174 Kamehameha Ave	Hilo, HI	96720-2865	808-961-3664	961-2665	K-12	John Thatcher
Education Laboratory	1776 University Ave	Honolulu, HI	96822-2447	808-956-7833	956-7260	K-12	Keoni Jeremiah
Hakipuu Learning Center	PO Box 1159	Kaneohe, HI	96744-1159	808-235-9155	235-9160	4-12	Charlene Hoe
Halau Ku Mana Charter S	2101 Makiki Heights Dr	Honolulu, HI	96822-2520	808-945-1600	945-1604	6-12	Mahina Duarte
Halau Lokahi Charter S	401 Waiakamilo Rd Ste A1	Honolulu, HI	96817-4955	808-832-3594	842-9800	K-12	Laara Allbrett
Hawaii Academy of Arts & Science	PO Box 1494	Pahoa, HI	96778-1494	808-965-3730	965-3733	K-12	Steve Hirakami
Hawaii Technology Academy	94-810 Moloalo St	Waipahu, HI	96797	808-676-5444	676-5470	K-12	Jeff Piontek
Innovations Public Charter S	75-5815 Queen Kaahumanu Hwy	Kailua Kona, HI	96740-2013	808-327-6205	327-6209	1-8	Jennifer Hiro
Kamaile Academy	85-180 Ala Akau St	Waianae, HI	96792-2323	808-697-7110	697-7115	PK-12	Emma Weiss
Kanuikapono Charter S	PO Box 12	Anahola, HI	96703-0012	808-822-9032	823-9140	K-10	Ku'uipo Torio
Kanu O Ka 'Aina New Century Charter S	PO Box 398	Kamuela, HI	96743-0398	808-887-8144	887-8146	K-12	Allyson Tamura
Ka 'Umeke Ka'eo Public Charter S	222 Desha Ave	Hilo, HI	96720-4815	808-933-3482	933-3488	K-9	L. Makekau-Whittaker
Ka Waihona O Ka Na'auao Charter S	89-195 Farrington Hwy	Waianae, HI	96792-4102	808-620-9030	620-9036	K-8	Alvin Parker
Kawaikini Charter S	PO Box 662014	Lihue, HI	96766-7014	808-632-2032	246-4635	K-12	Leialoha Kauahi
Ke Ana La'ahana Public Charter S	1500 Kalanianaole Ave	Hilo, HI	96720-4914	808-961-6228	961-6229	7-12	Dr. Russell Ili
Ke Kula Ni'ihau Kekaha Public Charter S	PO Box 129	Kekaha, HI	96752-0129	808-337-0481	337-1289	PK-12	Haunani Seward
Ke Kula 'O Nawahiokalani'opu'u Charter S	16-120 Opukahaia St	Keaau, HI	96749-8135	808-982-4260	966-7821	K-8	Kauanoe Kamana
Ke Kula O Samuel Kamakau Lab S	45-037 Kaneohe Bay Dr	Kaneohe, HI	96744-2417	808-235-9174	235-9173	K-12	Keahilahila Kelling
Kihei Charter S	PO Box 1098	Kihei, HI	96753-1098	808-875-0700	874-6745	K-12	Mark Christiano
Kona Pacific Charter S	PO Box 115	Kealakekua, HI	96750-0115	808-322-4900	322-4906	K-8	Usha Kotner
Kualapu'u Charter ES	PO Box 260	Kualapuu, HI	96757-0260	808-567-6900	567-6906	K-6	Lydia Trinidad
Kua O Ka La Public Charter S	PO Box 1413	Pahoa, HI	96778-1413	808-965-5098	965-9618	K-12	Susan Osborne
Kula Aupuni Niihau A Kahelelani Aloha	8315 Kekaha Rd	Kekaha, HI	96752	808-337-2022	337-2033	K-12	Hedy Sullivan
Lanikai ES	140 Alala Rd	Kailua, HI	96734-3199	808-266-7844	266-7848	PK-6	Ed Noh
Thompson Academy	629 Pohukaina St Ste 3	Honolulu, HI	96813-5004	808-441-8000	586-3640	K-12	Diana Oshiro
Volcano S of Arts & Sciences	PO Box 845	Volcano, HI	96785-0845	808-985-9800	985-9898	K-8	Dr. David Rizor
Voyager Charter S	547 Halekauwila St Ste 203	Honolulu, HI	96813-5029	808-521-9770	521-9772	K-8	Susan Lee Deuber
Wai'alae ES	1045 19th Ave	Honolulu, HI	96816-4699	808-733-4880	733-4886	K-5	Wendy Lagareta
Waimea Charter MS	67-1229 Mamalahoa Hwy	Kamuela, HI	96743-8429	808-887-6090	887-6087	6-8	Matt Horne
Waters of Life Charter S	181355 Volcano Hwy	Mountain View, HI	96771	808-966-6175	968-0778	K-8	Daniel Caluya
West Hawaii Explorations Academy	73-4460 Queen Kaahumanu Hwy	Kailua Kona, HI	96740-2632	808-327-4751	327-4750	6-12	Heather Nakakura

Idaho

School	Address	City,State	Zip code	Telephone	Fax	Grade	Contact
Academy	240 E Maple St	Pocatello, ID	83201-4647	208-232-1447	232-1448	K-8	Joel Lovstedt
American Heritage Charter S	1240 S 35th W	Idaho Falls, ID	83402-5538			K-8	Debra Infanger
Another Choice Virtual Charter S	1014 W Hemingway Blvd	Nampa, ID	83651-1733	208-475-4255	475-4274	K-12	Kelsey Williams
ANSER Charter S	202 E 42nd St	Garden City, ID	83714-6315	208-426-9840	426-9863	K-8	Dr. Suzanne Gregg
ARTEC Charter S	1070 Elkhorn Cir N	Twin Falls, ID	83301-8355	208-732-6346	736-4770	7-12	Michael Gibson
Blackfoot Charter Community Learning Ctr	2801 Hunters Loop	Blackfoot, ID	83221-6206	208-782-0744	782-1330	K-5	Dr. Fred Ball
Chief Tahgee Elementary Academy	PO Box 217	Fort Hall, ID	83203-0217	208-478-4024	478-4005	K-6	Joel Weaver
Coeur D'Alene Charter Academy	4904 N Duncan Dr	Coeur d Alene, ID	83815-8329	208-676-1667	676-8667	6-12	Dan Nicklay
Compass Charter S	2511 W Cherry Ln	Meridian, ID	83642-1135	208-855-2802	895-0197	K-12	Kelly Trudeau
Falcon Ridge Charter S	278 S Ten Mile Rd	Kuna, ID	83634-1768	208-922-9228	922-4198	K-8	Mark Green
Heritage Academy	500 S Lincoln Ave	Jerome, ID	83338-3027	208-595-1617		K-8	Christine Ivie
Heritage Community Charter S	1803 E Ustick Rd	Caldwell, ID	83605-6607	208-453-8070		K-8	Javier Castaneda
Idaho Arts Charter S	1220 5th St N	Nampa, ID	83687-3416	208-463-4324	468-0572	K-12	Jackie Collins
Idaho Connects Online S	12639 W Explorer Dr Ste 185	Boise, ID	83713-1889	208-287-3668	287-3671	6-12	Vickie McCullough
Idaho Distance Education Academy	PO Box 338	Deary, ID	83823-0338	208-877-1513	877-1713	K-12	Jason Bransford
Idaho Science and Technology Charter S	21 N 550 W	Blackfoot, ID	83221-5562	208-785-7827	785-9913	6-8	Gary Larsen
Idaho Virtual Academy	1965 S Eagle Rd Ste 190	Meridian, ID	83642-9246	866-339-9065	322-3688	K-12	Desiree Laughlin
Inspire Virtual Charter S	600 N Steelhead Way Ste 164	Boise, ID	83704-9620	208-332-4002	332-4008	K-12	Gerald Chouinard
iSucceed Virtual HS	6148 N Discovery Way # 120	Boise, ID	83713	208-375-3116	375-3117	9-12	Aaron Ritter
Jefferson Charter S	1209 Adam Smith Ave	Caldwell, ID	83605-5487	208-455-8772	455-8713	K-12	Chuck Ward
Kootenai Bridge Academy	637 N Park Dr	Coeur D Alene, ID	83814-2133	208-930-4515	930-4791	11-12	Charles Kenna
Legacy Charter S	4015 Legacy Way	Nampa, ID	83686-5801	208-467-0947	467-0948	K-6	Seth Stallcop
Liberty Charter S	9955 Kris Jensen Ln	Nampa, ID	83686-4742	208-466-7952	466-7961	K-12	Becky Stallcop
McKenna Charter HS	675 S Haskett St	Mountain Home, ID	83647-3375	208-580-2449	580-2450	9-12	Larry Slade
Meridian Medical Arts Charter HS	1789 E Heritage Park Ln	Meridian, ID	83646-4855	208-855-4075	855-4081	9-12	Scott Hill
Meridian Technical Charter HS	3800 N Locust Grove Rd	Meridian, ID	83646-5510	208-288-2928	288-5685	9-12	Christian Housel
Monticello Montessori Charter S	4707 Sweetwater	Ammon, ID	83406-7546	208-419-0742	419-0765	K-6	Randy Crisler
Moscow Charter S	1723 E F St	Moscow, ID	83843-9571	208-883-3195	892-3855	K-6	Dr. Marie Axman
North Idaho STEM Charter Academy	PO Box 434	Rathdrum, ID	83858-0434	208-687-8002		K-8	Scott Thomson
North Star Charter S	839 N Linder Rd	Eagle, ID	83616-4427	208-939-9600	939-6090	K-12	Lawrence Rogien Ph.D.
North Valley Academy	906 Main St	Gooding, ID	83330-1625	208-934-4567	934-4522	K-12	Keelie Campbell
Palouse Prarie S	PO Box 9511	Moscow, ID	83843-0120	208-882-3684	882-3689	K-8	Anthony Warn
Payette River Technical Academy	721 W 12th St Ste A	Emmett, ID	83617-3827	208-365-0985	365-7800	9-12	William Knickrehm
Pocatello Community Charter S	995 S Arthur Ave	Pocatello, ID	83204-3400	208-478-2522	478-2622	K-8	Dr. Martha Martin
Rolling Hills Charter S	8900 Horseshoe Bend Rd	Boise, ID	83714-3859	208-939-5400	939-5401	K-8	Dr. John Montgomery
Sage International S of Boise	457 E Parkcenter Blvd	Boise, ID	83706-6501	208-343-7243	388-3429	K-9	Don Keller
Sandpoint Charter S	614 S Madison Ave	Sandpoint, ID	83864-8724	208-255-7771	263-9441	6-8	Alan Millar
Taylors Crossing Charter S	1445 Wood River Rd	Idaho Falls, ID	83401-5095	208-552-0397	529-2755	K-12	Jared Emfield
Upper Carmen Charter S	PO Box 33	Carmen, ID	83462-0033	208-756-4590	756-1594	K-6	Sue Smith
Victory Charter S	9779 Kris Jensen Ln	Nampa, ID	83686-4741	208-442-9400	442-9401	K-12	Dr. Marianne Saunders
Village Charter S	219 N Roosevelt St	Boise, ID	83706-1850	208-336-2000		K-8	Teresa England
Vision Charter S	19291 Ward Ln	Caldwell, ID	83605-7936	208-455-9220	455-9121	K-12	Wendy OldenKamp
White Pine Charter S	2959 John Adams Pkwy	Ammon, ID	83406-4508	208-522-4432	522-4452	K-8	Jeremy Clarke
Wings Charter S	771 N College Rd	Twin Falls, ID	83301-3382	208-734-2902	734-2907	6-8	Letha Blick
Xavier Charter S	1218 N College Rd W	Twin Falls, ID	83301-5651	208-734-3947	733-1348	K-12	Thad Biggers

Illinois

School	Address	City,State	Zip code	Telephone	Fax	Grade	Contact
Academy for Global Citizenship	4647 W 47th St	Chicago, IL	60632-4847	773-582-1100	582-6504	K-5	Anne Gillespie
Academy of Scholastic Achievement S	4651 W Madison St	Chicago, IL	60644-3646	773-921-1315	921-8324	9-12	Gladys Simpson
ACE Technical Charter HS	5410 S State St	Chicago, IL	60609-6382	773-548-8705	548-8706	9-12	Marvin Talley
Addams Alternative HS	1814 S Union Ave	Chicago, IL	60616-1045	312-563-1746	563-1701	9-12	Theresa Comparini
Albizu Campos HS	2739 W Division St	Chicago, IL	60622-2854	773-342-8022	342-6609	9-12	Matthew Rodrguez
Amandla Charter S	6800 S Stewart Ave	Chicago, IL	60621-2441	773-535-7150	535-7151	5-9	Erin Ferguson
Aspira - Antonia Pantoja Alternative HS	3121 N Pulaski Rd	Chicago, IL	60641-5447	773-252-0970	427-0872	9-12	Hugo Campuzano
ASPIRA at Haugan MS	3729 W Leland Ave	Chicago, IL	60625-5706	773-252-0970	267-3568	6-8	Michelle Garcia-Jones
ASPIRA Early College S	3986 W Barry Ave	Chicago, IL	60618-6524	773-252-0970	739-2350	9-12	Yolanda Mijangos
ASPIRA - Mirta Ramirez Computer Science	1711 N California Ave	Chicago, IL	60647-5103	773-252-0970	252-0094	9-12	Gabriela Reyes
Austin Business & Entrepreneurship S	231 N Pine Ave	Chicago, IL	60644-2333	773-534-6316	534-6267	9-12	Wayne Issa
Austin Career Education Center	5352 W Chicago Ave	Chicago, IL	60651-2857	773-626-6988	626-2641	9-12	Debra Williams
Beardstown Charter School Learning Acad	515 Canal St	Beardstown, IL	62618-2150	217-323-4529	323-4918	9-12	Carrie Martin
Bronzeville Lighthouse Charter S	8 W Root St	Chicago, IL	60609-2931	773-535-1460	535-1459	K-8	Ashleigh Plauche
Cambridge Lakes S	900 Wester Blvd	Pingree Grove, IL	60140-2050	847-464-4300	464-0318	PK-8	Kathleen Poole
Catalyst Charter S - Circle Rock	5608 W Washington Blvd	Chicago, IL	60644-3009	773-945-5025	626-2345	K-8	Michael Kasang

School	Address	City,State	Zip code	Telephone	Fax	Grade	Contact
Catalyst Charter S- Howland	1616 S Spaulding Ave	Chicago, IL	60623-2653	773-534-1753	534-1727	K-8	Chaun Johnson
Catalyst Charter S - Maria	6727 S California Ave	Chicago, IL	60629-1816	773-993-1770	993-1701	K-5	Katherine List
Chatham Academy	9035 S Langley Ave	Chicago, IL	60619-7596	773-651-1500	651-1523	9-12	
Chicago Bulls College Prep S	2040 W Adams St	Chicago, IL	60612-3052	773-534-7599	850-0192	9-10	Tyson Kane
Chicago International Charter S - Avalon	1501 E 83rd Pl	Chicago, IL	60619-6501	773-721-0858	731-0142	K-8	Brandon Kimble
Chicago International Charter S - Basil	1816 W Garfield Blvd	Chicago, IL	60609-5606	773-778-9455	778-9456	K-8	Victoria Jackson
Chicago International Charter S - Bond	13300 S Langley Ave	Chicago, IL	60827-1396	773-468-1300	253-0988	K-6	Linda Martin
Chicago International Charter S Bucktown	2235 N Hamilton Ave	Chicago, IL	60647-3360	773-645-3321	645-3327	K-8	Christy Krier
Chicago International Charter S Hawkins	801 E 133rd Pl	Chicago, IL	60827-1494	773-264-0505	651-5001	7-12	Eric Mitchell
Chicago International Charter S - Irving	3820 N Spaulding Ave	Chicago, IL	60618-4413	773-433-5000	433-5009	K-8	Karin Breo
Chicago International Charter S Longwood	1309 W 95th St	Chicago, IL	60643-1496	773-238-5330	238-5350	3-12	Kenyatta Stansberry
Chicago International Charter S - Loomis	9535 S Loomis St	Chicago, IL	60643-1374	773-429-8955	429-8441	K-2	Lindsey Girard
Chicago International Charter S Prairie	11530 S Prairie Ave	Chicago, IL	60628-5691	773-928-0480	928-6971	K-8	Andy Parker
Chicago International Charter S - Quest	1443 N Ogden Ave	Chicago, IL	60610-1007	773-565-2100	951-2906	6-9	Michael Donhost
Chicago International Charter S Rockford	615 S 5th St	Rockford, IL	61104-3021	815-316-0093	316-0170	K-6	Amanda Rychel
Chicago International Charter S W Belden	2245 N McVicker Ave	Chicago, IL	60639-2766	773-637-9430	637-9791	K-8	Lisa Meyer
Chicago Intl Charter S Northtown	3900 W Peterson Ave Ste 1	Chicago, IL	60659-3162	773-478-3655	478-6029	9-12	Andrew Reuland
Chicago Intl Charter S Ralph Ellison	1817 W 80th St	Chicago, IL	60620-4557	773-478-4434	478-4494	9-12	Kimberly Hinton
Chicago Intl Charter S Washington Park	110 E 61st St	Chicago, IL	60637-2116	773-347-0200	324-3302	K-8	Jessica Beasley
Chicago Intl Charter S Wrightwood	8130 S California Ave	Chicago, IL	60652-2716	773-434-4575	434-2026	K-8	Dr. David Lewis
Chicago Math and Science Academy	7212 N Clark St	Chicago, IL	60626-2416	773-761-8960	761-8961	6-12	Aydin Kara
Chicago Talent Development Charter HS	2245 W Jackson Blvd	Chicago, IL	60612-2999	773-345-8768	345-8779	9-12	Kirby Callam
Chicago Virtual Charter S	38 S Peoria St	Chicago, IL	60607-2628	312-267-4486	676-3689	K-12	Dr. Craig Butz
Comer College Prep S	7131 S South Chicago Ave	Chicago, IL	60619-1230	773-729-3969	729-3960	9-12	James Troupis
Community Services West - CCA	1231 S Pulaski Rd	Chicago, IL	60623-1234	773-762-2272	762-2065	9-12	
Community Youth Development Institute	7836 S Union Ave	Chicago, IL	60620-2409	773-224-2273	224-2214	9-12	
DuSable Leadership Academy	4934 S Wabash Ave	Chicago, IL	60615-2115	773-535-1170	535-1912	9-12	Venesa Woods-Andrews
8 Points Charter S	630 E State St	Jacksonville, IL	62650	217-271-1000	271-1001	5-8	Josh Slaughterback
El Cuarto Ano - Association House	1116 N Kedzie Ave	Chicago, IL	60651-4152	773-772-7170	772-8617	9-12	Edward Peacock
EPIC Academy	8255 S Houston Ave	Chicago, IL	60617-2191	773-535-7930	535-7934	8-12	Matthew King
Erie Charter S	1405 N Washtenaw Ave	Chicago, IL	60622-1632	773-486-7161	486-7234	K-8	Velia Soto
Ford Academy: Power House Charter HS	931 S Homan Ave	Chicago, IL	60624-4108	773-533-7600	533-7601	9-12	Tom Mulder
Galapagos Charter ES	3814 W Iowa St	Chicago, IL	60651-3708	773-384-9400	384-4866	K-8	Tasha Gray
Galapagos Charter S	2605 School St	Rockford, IL	61101-5264	815-708-7946	708-7966	K-5	Michael Lane
Golder College Prep S	1454 W Superior St	Chicago, IL	60642-5255	312-265-9925	243-8402	9-12	Rosa Alanis
Harvey Middle College S	10001 S Woodlawn Ave	Chicago, IL	60628-1696	773-291-6518	291-6131	9-12	Rita Pietrzak
Houston HS	4701 S King Dr	Chicago, IL	60615-1309	773-723-9630	665-8357	9-12	
Howard Area Alternative S	7647 N Paulina St	Chicago, IL	60626-1017	773-381-0366	338-7693	9-12	
Innovation HS	17 N State St Fl 3	Chicago, IL	60602-3047	312-999-9306	999-9361	9-12	LaShaun Jackson
Instituto Health Sciences Career Academy	2520 S Western Ave	Chicago, IL	60608	312-890-0055	843-9116	9-12	Patricia Munoz-Rocha
Johnson College Prep S	6350 S Stewart Ave	Chicago, IL	60621-3138	312-348-1888	278-0449	9-12	Dr. Garland Thomas
Johnston S of Art & Design	1551 W 95th St	Chicago, IL	60643-1329	773-341-2260	341-2922	9-12	Carol Levystein
KIPP Ascend Charter S	1616 S Avers Ave	Chicago, IL	60623-2401	773-521-4399	521-4766	5-8	Amy Pouba
Latino Youth Alternative HS	2001 S California Ave	Chicago, IL	60608-2486	773-648-2130	648-2098	9-12	
LEARN 6 in North Chicago	3131 Sheridan Rd	Great Lakes, IL	60088-1600	847-473-3845	473-2988	K-7	Anik Zampini
LEARN Charter S Campbell Campus	212 S Francisco Ave	Chicago, IL	60612-3618	773-826-0370	826-0109	K-6	Nicole Laskov
LEARN Charter S Excel Campus	2401 W Congress Pkwy	Chicago, IL	60612-3534	312-243-7001	432-7160	K-6	Sekou Robertson
LEARN Charter S Hunter Perkins Campus	1700 W 83rd St	Chicago, IL	60620-4621	773-488-1634	488-1753	PK-4	Jenny Micon
LEARN Charter S - Romano Butler Campus	1132 S Homan Ave	Chicago, IL	60624-4344	773-722-0200	826-0015	PK-8	Robin Johnson
LEARN Charter S - South Chicago Campus	8914 S Buffalo Ave	Chicago, IL	60617-3416	773-722-8577		K-5	Brandy Reeves
Legacy Academy for Excellence Charter S	4029 Prairie Rd	Rockford, IL	61102-4501	815-961-1100		K-12	Barbara Forte
Legacy Charter ES	4217 W 18th St	Chicago, IL	60623-2325	773-542-1640	542-1699	PK-8	Lisa Kenner
Legal Prep Charter Academy	1901 W Carroll Ave	Chicago, IL	60612-2401	312-401-6889		9-12	Deth Dulgeron
Locke Charter Academy	3141 W Jackson Blvd	Chicago, IL	60612-2729	773-265-7232	265-7258	PK-8	Patrick Love
McKinley Lakeside Campus	2920 S Wabash Ave	Chicago, IL	60616-3197	773-949-5010	602-2677	9-12	
Muchin College Prep S	1 N State St Ste 700	Chicago, IL	60602-3311	312-445-4680	332-0058	9-12	Kimberly Neal
Namaste ES	3737 S Paulina St	Chicago, IL	60609-2047	773-715-9558	376-6495	K-8	Allison Slade
Noble Street College Prep	2710 E 89th St	Chicago, IL	60617-3192	773-862-1449	278-0421	9-12	William Olsen
North Lawndale College Prep at Collins	1313 S Sacramento Dr	Chicago, IL	60623-2297	773-542-6766	542-6995	9-12	Tim Bouman
North Lawndale College Prep Charter HS	1616 S Spaulding Ave	Chicago, IL	60623-2653	773-542-1490	542-1492	9-12	Nicole Howard
Options Laboratory S	1060 E 47th St	Chicago, IL	60653-3600	773-690-5500	690-5518	9-12	
Passages Charter ES	1643 W Bryn Mawr Ave	Chicago, IL	60660-4106	773-433-3530	769-3229	PK-8	Nicole Feinberg
Perspectives Charter MS	8131 S May St	Chicago, IL	60620-3007	773-358-6300	358-6399	6-8	Sauda Porter
Perspectives Charter S - Joslin Campus	1930 S Archer Ave	Chicago, IL	60616-6505	312-225-7400	225-7411	6-12	Angela Brooks-Rallins
Perspectives HS of Technology	8131 S May St	Chicago, IL	60620-3007	773-358-6120	358-6129	9-12	Heather Haines
Perspectives/IIT Math & Science Academy	3663 S Wabash Ave	Chicago, IL	60653-1032	773-358-6800	358-6055	6-12	Julie Puzon
Perspectives Leadership Academy	8131 S May St	Chicago, IL	60620-3007	773-358-6100	358-6199	9-12	Heather Haines
Plato Learning Academy	5545 W Harrison St	Chicago, IL	60644-5367	773-413-3090	413-3095	K-8	Vanesa Scott-Thompson
Polaris Charter Academy	620 N Sawyer Ave	Chicago, IL	60624-1598	773-534-0820	534-6645	K-7	Michelle Navarre
Prairie Crossing Charter S	1571 Jones Point Rd	Grayslake, IL	60030-3536	847-543-9722	543-9744	K-8	Nigel Whittington
Pritzker College Prep Campus	4131 W Cortland St	Chicago, IL	60639-4923	773-394-2848	394-2931	9-12	Pablo Sierra
Prologue Early College HS	1135 N Cleaver St	Chicago, IL	60642-4002	773-935-9925	935-8357	9-12	Pa Joof
Providence Englewood Charter S	6515 S Ashland Ave	Chicago, IL	60636-3003	773-434-0202	434-0196	K-8	Angela Johnson-Williams
Quest Charter Academy	2503 N University St	Peoria, IL	61604-2601	309-402-0030	685-3001	5-7	Ali Kuran
Rauner College Prep Campus	1337 W Ohio St	Chicago, IL	60642-6430	312-226-5345	226-3552	9-12	Mindy Sjoblom
Robertson Charter S	2240 E Geddes Ave	Decatur, IL	62526-5127	217-428-7072	428-9214	K-8	Cordell Ingram
Rowe - Clark Math & Science Academy	3645 W Chicago Ave	Chicago, IL	60651-3934	773-242-2212	826-6936	9-12	Joseph Tenbusch
Shabazz International Charter S	7823 S Ellis Ave	Chicago, IL	60619-3213	773-651-1221	651-0302	K-8	Shannon Mason
SIU East St. Louis Charter S	601 James R Thompson Blvd	E Saint Louis, IL	62201-1129	618-482-8370	482-8372	9-12	Veronica Washington
Sizemore Academy of B Shabazz	6936 S Hermitage Ave	Chicago, IL	60636-3333	773-535-9144	779-5668	K-8	Soyini Walton
Southland College Prep	3718 213th St	Matteson, IL	60443-2513	708-748-8105	850-3111	9-12	Dr. Blondean Davis
Springfield Ball Charter S	2530 E Ash St	Springfield, IL	62703-5600	217-525-3275	525-3316	PK-8	Dr. Nicole Gales
Sullivan House Alternative HS	8164 S South Chicago Ave	Chicago, IL	60617-1041	773-978-8680	375-1482	9-12	
Truman Middle College HS	1145 W Wilson Ave	Chicago, IL	60640-5691	773-907-4840	907-4844	9-12	
UCCS - Donoghue Campus	707 E 37th St	Chicago, IL	60653-1406	773-285-5301	285-5389	PK-5	Elizabeth Meyers
UCCS - North Kenwood/Oakland Campus	1119 E 46th St	Chicago, IL	60653-4403	773-536-2399	536-2435	PK-5	Tanika Island-Smith
UCCS - Woodlawn Campus	6420 S University Ave	Chicago, IL	60637-3608	773-752-8101	324-0653	6-12	Assata Moore
UCCS - Woodson Campus	4444 S Evans Ave	Chicago, IL	60653-3519	773-624-0700	624-0707	6-8	Jared Washington
UIC College Prep S	1231 S Damen Ave	Chicago, IL	60608-1145	312-768-4858	496-7149	9-12	Tressie McDonough
UNO Charter Garcia Campus HS	4248 W 47th St Fl 3	Chicago, IL	60632-4402	773-579-3480	376-5785	9-12	Brian Chelmecki
UNO Charter S - Bartolome De Las Casas	1641 W 16th St	Chicago, IL	60608-2039	312-432-3224	432-1066	K-8	Kaycie Carr
UNO Charter S - Carlos Fuentes Campus	2845 W Barry Ave	Chicago, IL	60618-7015	312-279-9826	279-9852	K-8	Joann Tanner
UNO Charter S - Esmeralda Santiago	2510 W Cortez St	Chicago, IL	60622-3422	312-455-5410	455-5411	PK-8	Melissa Sweazy
UNO Charter S - Galewood	2050 N Natchez Ave	Chicago, IL	60707-3420	312-455-5425	455-5456	K-8	Erin Neubert
UNO Charter S - Octavio Paz Campus	2651 W 23rd St	Chicago, IL	60608-3609	773-890-1054	890-1069	K-8	Martin Masterson
UNO Charter S - Officer Donald Marquez	2916 W 47th St	Chicago, IL	60632-1907	773-321-2200	321-2250	K-8	Stephanie Medina
UNO Charter S - Omar Torres	4248 W 47th St	Chicago, IL	60632-4402	773-579-3475	376-5645	K-8	Jill Bousson
UNO Charter S - Rogers Park	7416 N Ridge Blvd	Chicago, IL	60645-1919	312-455-5440	455-5441	K-8	John Keith
UNO Charter S - Rufino Tamayo Campus	5135 S California Ave	Chicago, IL	60632-2124	773-434-6355	434-5036	K-8	Katherine Reing
UNO Charter S - Sandra Cisneros	2744 W Pershing Rd	Chicago, IL	60632-1631	312-376-8830	376-8825	K-8	Molly Robinson
UNO Charter S - SPC Daniel Zizumbo	4248 W 47th St	Chicago, IL	60632-4402	773-579-3470	376-5605	K-8	Christopher Allen
UNO Soccer Academy	5050 S Homan Ave	Chicago, IL	60632-3059	312-455-5450	455-5451	PK-8	Thomas Denneen
Urban Prep Academy Charter S - Englewood	6201 S Stewart Ave	Chicago, IL	60621-3247	773-535-9724	535-0012	9-12	Dennis Lacewell
Urban Prep - Bronzeville	2710 S Dearborn St	Chicago, IL	60616-2684	773-624-3444	624-3405	9-12	Ben Blakeley
Urban Prep - West	1326 W 14th Pl	Chicago, IL	60608-2106	773-534-8860	534-8914	9-12	Theartris Childress
Westside Holistic Alternative HS	4909 W Division St	Chicago, IL	60651-3161	773-261-0944	261-1029	9-12	
West Town Academy	534 N Sacramento Blvd	Chicago, IL	60612-1024	312-563-9044	563-9672	9-12	
YCCS Virtual HS	1900 W Van Buren St Rm 2417	Chicago, IL	60612-3145	312-429-0027	243-5733	9-12	
Young Womens Leadership S	2641 S Calumet Ave	Chicago, IL	60616-2901	312-949-9400	949-9142	7-12	Deniece Fields
YouthBuild McLean County Charter S	502 S Morris Ave Unit D	Bloomington, IL	61701-4891	309-261-1780	827-9035	10-12	Suzanne Fitzgerald
Youth Connection Leadership Academy	3424 S State St Fl 2	Chicago, IL	60616-5000	312-225-4668	225-4862	9-12	

Indiana

School	Address	City,State	Zip code	Telephone	Fax	Grade	Contact
Anderson Preparatory Academy	3205 W 25th St	Anderson, IN	46011-4601	765-649-8472	649-2071	K-12	Robert Gillaume
Aspire Charter Academy	4900 W 15th Ave	Gary, IN	46406-2308	219-944-7400	944-7474	K-8	Rasheeda Green
Beacon Academy	620 Cumberland Ave	West Lafayette, IN	47906-1522	765-838-2045	838-2034	7-12	Deb Lukens
Bloomington Project S	349 S Walnut St	Bloomington, IN	47401-3568	812-558-0041	334-5873	K-9	Catherine Diersing
Bowman Leadership Academy	975 W 6th Ave	Gary, IN	46402-1708	219-883-4826	883-1331	K-12	Gwendolyn Griffith-Adell
Brown Charter Academy	3600 N German Church Rd	Indianapolis, IN	46235-8504	317-891-0730	891-0908	K-8	Thelma Wyatt
Campagna Academy Charter S	7403 Cline Ave	Schererville, IN	46375-2645	219-322-8614	322-8436	9-12	Elena Dwyre
Canaan Community Academy	8775 N Canaan Main St	Canaan, IN	47224	812-839-0003		K-6	Deena Schafer
Carpe Diem - Meridian	2220 N Meridian St	Indianapolis, IN	46208-5728	317-673-2733		6-12	Robert Sommers
Challenge Foundation Academy	3980 Meadows Dr	Indianapolis, IN	46205-3114	317-803-3182	803-2367	K-5	Dr. Charles Schlegel
Charter School of the Dunes	860 N Lake St	Gary, IN	46403-1070	219-939-9690	939-9031	K-10	Christine Pepa
Christel House Academy	2717 S East St	Indianapolis, IN	46225-2104	317-783-4690	783-4693	K-12	Carey Dahncke
Community Montessori S	4102 Saint Joseph Rd	New Albany, IN	47150-9750	812-948-1000	948-0441	PK-12	Barbara Burke-Fondren

School	Address	City,State	Zip code	Telephone	Fax	Grade	Contact
Damar Charter Academy	6067 Decatur Blvd	Indianapolis, IN	46241-9606	317-455-7121	455-7220	K-12	Dwight Ashley
Decatur Discovery Academy	5106 S High School Rd	Indianapolis, IN	46221-3606	317-856-0900	856-0143	7-12	Kevin Leineweber
Discovery Charter S	800 Canonie Dr	Chesterton, IN	46304-1100	219-983-9800	929-5723	K-8	Ernesto Martinez
East Chicago Lighthouse Charter S	3916 Pulaski St	East Chicago, IN	46312-2420	219-378-7450	378-7460	K-7	Kristen Ivy-Wendell
East Chicago Urban Enterprise Academy	1402 E Chicago Ave	East Chicago, IN	46312-3587	219-392-3650	392-3652	K-8	Charlotte Jackson
Excel Center - Anderson	630 Nichol Ave	Anderson, IN	46016-1247	888-959-9062	524-4003	9-12	Joe White
Fall Creek Academy	2540 N Capitol Ave	Indianapolis, IN	46208-5628	317-536-1026	921-9453	K-12	Rick Hunt
Faulkner Academy	1111 W 2nd St	Marion, IN	46952-3674	765-662-9910	662-9918	K-6	Janice Adams
Flanner House ES	2424 Dr Mrtn Lthr Kng Jr St	Indianapolis, IN	46208	317-925-4231	923-9632	K-6	Latika Warthaw
Fountain Square Academy	1615 Barth Ave	Indianapolis, IN	46203-2743	317-536-1028	423-2507	7-12	Gerald McGee
Galileo Charter S	855 N 12th St	Richmond, IN	47374-2477	765-983-3709	983-3735	K-6	Kevin Handley
Gary Lighthouse Charter S	1775 W 41st Ave	Gary, IN	46408-2464	219-880-1762	884-4858	K-7	Kristina Shultz
Gary Middle College	556 Washington St	Gary, IN	46402-1915	219-888-7120		9-12	James Joiner
Geist Montessori S	13942 E 96th St Ste 100	Mc Cordsville, IN	46055-9811	317-335-1158	335-1265	K-8	Trisha Armstrong
Hammond Academy of Science & Tech	33 Muenich Ct	Hammond, IN	46320-1706	219-852-0500	852-4153	6-12	Dr. Sean Egan
Herron Charter HS	110 E 16th St	Indianapolis, IN	46202-2404	317-231-0010	231-3759	9-12	Janet Harmon McNeal
Hoosier Academy	5640 Caito Dr	Indianapolis, IN	46226-1346	317-547-1400	547-1500	K-6	Lynn Black
Hoosier Academy	2801 E 16th St	Muncie, IN	47302-4719	765-288-9633	288-9655	K-8	Shannon Hare
Hoosier Academy HS	2855 N Franklin Rd	Indianapolis, IN	46219-1347	317-495-6494	495-6020	7-12	Heather Holly
Hope Academy	8102 Clearvista Pkwy	Indianapolis, IN	46256-1661	317-572-9356	849-1455	9-12	Gale Stone
Imagine Indiana Life Sciences Academy E	4352 N Mitthoefer Rd	Indianapolis, IN	46235-1224	317-890-9100	890-9109	K-8	Brian Dinkins
Imagine Indiana Life Sciences Academy W	4950 W 34th St	Indianapolis, IN	46224-1646	317-297-9100	297-9460	K-8	Keith Marsh
Imagine MASTer Academy	2000 N Wells St Bldg 6	Fort Wayne, IN	46808-2495	260-420-8395	423-3508	K-8	James Huth
Imagine Schools on Broadway	2320 Broadway	Fort Wayne, IN	46807-1104	260-458-8395	458-8355	K-5	Ra'Chelle Spearman
Indiana Connections Academy	6640 Intech Blvd	Indianapolis, IN	46278	317-818-5590	818-6000	K-12	Melissa Brown
Indiana Cyber Charter S	746 E US Highway 30	Schererville, IN	46375-2616	888-427-2863		K-12	Dr. Jean Aldrich
Indiana Math and Science Academy	7435 N Keystone Ave	Indianapolis, IN	46240	317-259-7300	259-7363	K-12	John Aytekin
Indiana Math and Science Academy	4575 W 38th St	Indianapolis, IN	46254-3313	317-298-0025	282-0505	K-12	Mustafa Yazici
Indianapolis Lighthouse Charter S	1780 Sloan Ave	Indianapolis, IN	46203-3640	317-351-1534	351-1804	PK-8	Amanda Koth
Indianapolis Metropolitan HS	1635 W Michigan St	Indianapolis, IN	46222-3852	317-524-4638	524-4002	9-12	Patrick Fassnacht
Indiana Virtual S	2206 E 96th St	Indianapolis, IN	46240-3712	317-581-5355	581-5399	6-12	David Stashevsky
International S of Columbus	3136 N National Rd Ste E	Columbus, IN	47201-3153	812-314-7078	314-7079	7-12	Jonah Sims
Irvington Community S	6705 Julian Ave	Indianapolis, IN	46219-6642	317-357-5359	357-9752	K-12	David Nidiffer
Johnson Academy	4615 Werling Dr	Fort Wayne, IN	46806-3410	260-441-8727	441-9357	K-5	Dr. Steve Bollier
Joshua Academy	1230 E Illinois St	Evansville, IN	47711-5745	812-401-6300	401-6307	K-6	Pamela Decker
KIPP Indianapolis College Prep	3202 E 42nd St	Indianapolis, IN	46205-3014	317-547-5477	547-5499	5-8	Aleesia Johnson
KIPP LEAD College Preparatory S	6070 Miller Ave	Gary, IN	46403-2467	219-979-9236	979-2611	5-11	Nehemiah Thomas
Marshall Leadership Academy	2310 Weisser Park Ave	Fort Wayne, IN	46803-3462	260-745-3100	745-0405	K-8	Nicole Chisley
Monument Lighthouse Charter S	4002 N Franklin Rd	Indianapolis, IN	46226-5297	317-897-2472	897-2460	K-10	Jamie Brady
Neighbors New Vistas HS	5391 Central Ave	Portage, IN	46368-2854	219-850-4448		9-12	Donald Knotts
New Community S	710 North St	Lafayette, IN	47901-1158	765-420-9617	420-9672	K-8	Misty Ndiritu
Options Charter S	PO Box 3790	Carmel, IN	46082-3790	317-815-2098	846-3806	9-12	Barbara Maschino
Options Charter S - Noblesville	9945 Cumberland Pointe Blvd	Noblesville, IN	46060-4905	317-773-8659	773-9017	9-12	Mike Gustin
Paramount S of Excellence	3020 Nowland Ave	Indianapolis, IN	46201-1422	317-775-6660	778-9334	K-8	Tommy Reddicks
Renaissance Academy	4093 W US Highway 20	La Porte, IN	46350-8269	219-878-8711	311-6038	PK-8	Kieran McHugh
Rock Creek Community Academy	11525 Highway 31	Sellersburg, IN	47172-9618	812-246-9271	246-0722	PK-12	Sara Hauselman
Rural Community Academy	2385 N State Road 63	Sullivan, IN	47882-7152	812-382-4500	382-4055	K-8	Susie Pierce
Signature S	610 Main St	Evansville, IN	47708-1618	812-421-1820	421-9189	9-12	Vicki Snyder
Smith Academy for Excellence	6806 Embers Ct	Fort Wayne, IN	46815-7983	260-749-5832	749-5832	6-9	Thomas Smith
South Bend Career Academy	3801 Crescent Cir	South Bend, IN	46628-6136	574-299-9800	288-6125	7-12	Yolanda Turner-Smith
Southeast Neighborhood S of Excellence	1601 Barth Ave	Indianapolis, IN	46203-2743	317-423-0204	631-4401	K-6	Dr. Kristie Sweeney
Tindley Accelerated S	3960 Meadows Dr	Indianapolis, IN	46205-3114	317-545-1745	547-4415	9-12	Marcus Robinson
Tindley Preparatory Academy	4010 Sherman Dr	Indianapolis, IN	46205	317-777-6290	546-7198	6-8	Patrick Jones
21st Century Charter S	556 Washington St	Gary, IN	46402-1915	219-886-9339	886-9333	K-12	Angela West
Veritas Academy	530 E Ireland Rd	South Bend, IN	46614-2660	574-287-3230	287-2643	K-8	Germaine Smith
West Gary Lighthouse Charter S	725 Clark Rd	Gary, IN	46406-1822	219-977-9583	977-9725	K-8	Kenneth McCants
Xavier S of Excellence	3423 S Michigan St	South Bend, IN	46614-1719	574-231-6600	231-6640	K-8	Tania Grimes

Iowa

School	Address	City,State	Zip code	Telephone	Fax	Grade	Contact
Elma ES	PO Box 298	Elma, IA	50628-0298	641-393-2280	547-5973	PK-5	Todd Knobloch
Northeast Iowa Charter HS	PO Box 54	Maynard, IA	50655-0054	563-637-2283	637-2294	11-12	Stuart Fuhs
Prescott ES	1151 White St	Dubuque, IA	52001-6005	563-552-4200	552-4201	PK-5	Christine McCarron
Vista Early College S	621 Tornado Dr	Storm Lake, IA	50588-2277	712-732-8065	732-8068	9-12	Beau Ruleaux

Kansas

School	Address	City,State	Zip code	Telephone	Fax	Grade	Contact
Abilene Virtual S	213 N Broadway St	Abilene, KS	67410-2648	785-263-2630		6-12	B. Roth
Caney Valley Charter Academy	601 E Bullpup Blvd	Caney, KS	67333-2543	620-879-9232	879-9232	10-12	Ron Oyler
Erie HS	1400 N Main St	Erie, KS	66733-5006	620-244-3287	244-3290	9-12	Noah Francis
Greeley County HS	400 W Lawrence St	Tribune, KS	67879-9636	620-376-4265	376-2465	6-12	Ken Bockwinkel
Hope Street Charter Academy	1900 SW Hope St	Topeka, KS	66604-3984	785-438-4280	271-3684	9-12	Dale Noll
Hugoton Learning Academy	529 S Main St	Hugoton, KS	67951-2432	620-428-6374	428-6378	7-12	Jan Kilbourne
Humboldt ES	1100 Central St	Humboldt, KS	66748-1899	620-473-2461	473-2642	K-5	Kay Bolt
Insight S of Kansas	16740 W 175th St	Olathe, KS	66062-8984	800-260-0438	664-2796	1-12	Cassandra Barton
Kansas Career & Technical Virtual S	PO Box 218	Little River, KS	67457-0218	620-897-6325	897-6788	7-12	Dawn Johnson
Kinsley-Offerle JSHS	716 Colony Ave	Kinsley, KS	67547-1155	620-659-2126	659-2180	7-12	William King
Lawrence Virtual HS	1104 E 1000 Rd	Lawrence, KS	66047-9409	785-832-5620	832-5621	9-12	Sarah Berger
Lawrence Virtual S	1104 E 1000 Rd	Lawrence, KS	66047-9409	785-832-5620	832-5621	K-8	Keith Wilson
Mulvane Academy	PO Box 130	Mulvane, KS	67110-0130	316-777-3070	777-3072	9-12	Barbie Hamlin
Pleasantview Academy	5013 S Dean Rd	Hutchinson, KS	67501-9123	620-662-5516	662-5031	PK-12	Terry Fehrenbach
Service Valley Charter Academy	PO Box 129	Oswego, KS	67356-0129	620-421-3449	421-3640	K-8	Ray Huff
Smoky Valley Virtual Charter S	121 S Main St	Lindsborg, KS	67456-2417	785-227-4292	227-2982	K-12	Cody Whetstone
Turning Point Learning Center	315 S Market St	Emporia, KS	66801-4731	620-341-2455	341-2456	K-12	Tell Kirk
21st Century Learning Academy	PO Box 7	Mullinville, KS	67109-0007	620-548-2289	548-2389	K-12	Susan Staats
Walton Rural Life ES	PO Box 140	Walton, KS	67151-0140	620-837-3161	837-5669	K-4	Natise Vogt
West Franklin Learning Center	1966 California Rd	Pomona, KS	66076-9309	785-746-5766		9-12	Robert Allen
Yoder Charter S	PO Box 78	Yoder, KS	67585-0078	620-465-2605	465-2307	K-8	Delon Martens

Kentucky

School	Address	City,State	Zip code	Telephone	Fax	Grade	Contact
Taylor County Virtual Charter Academy	300 Ingram Ave	Campbellsville, KY	42718-1625	270-465-4431	465-5731	5-12	Dr. Bill Mattingly

Louisiana

School	Address	City,State	Zip code	Telephone	Fax	Grade	Contact
Akili Academy of New Orleans	1700 Pratt Dr	New Orleans, LA	70122-2408	504-355-4172	355-4176	K-8	Julie MacFetters
Algiers Technology Academy	6501 Berkley Dr	New Orleans, LA	70131-5513	504-302-7071	324-6998	9-12	Tomika Washington
Arise Academy	3819 Saint Claude Ave	New Orleans, LA	70117-5735	504-615-6354	456-2087	PK-5	Andrew Shahan
Ashe Charter S	1456 Gardena Dr	New Orleans, LA	70122-1914	504-373-6267	896-4003	K-8	Sabrina Pence
Audubon Charter S	6101 Chatham Dr	New Orleans, LA	70122-2743	504-862-5135	866-1691	PK-8	Janice Dupuy
Avoyelles Charter S	201 Longfellow Rd	Mansura, LA	71350-4292	318-240-9991	253-4198	K-12	Julie Roy
Batiste Cultural Arts Academy	3128 Constance St	New Orleans, LA	70115-2337	504-367-3307	315-2672	PK-8	Cicily Devezin
Bayou Community Academy	800 E 7th St	Thibodaux, LA	70301-3607	985-446-3011		PK-5	Dr. Melanie Becnel
Beekman S	15190 A M Baker Rd	Bastrop, LA	71220-6408	318-281-1743	283-5100	PK-9	Roy McCoy
Behrman S	715 Opelousas Ave	New Orleans, LA	70114-2499	504-302-7090	309-8174	PK-8	Rene Lewis-Carter
Belle Chase Academy	100 5th St	Belle Chasse, LA	70037-1002	504-433-5850	433-5590	K-8	Jane Dye
Capdau Charter S	4621 Canal St	New Orleans, LA	70119-5807	504-872-9257	872-0393	PK-8	J'Vann Martin
Career Acadmey	4375 E Brookstown Dr	Baton Rouge, LA	70805-4616	225-388-5252	388-5253	9-12	Pamela Mackie
Carver Collegiate Academy	5552 Read Blvd	New Orleans, LA	70127-3143	504-308-3660	324-0258	9-12	Jerel Bryant
Carver Preparatory Academy	5552 Read Blvd	New Orleans, LA	70127-3143	504-484-9721	324-0107	9-12	Benjamin Davis
Children's Charter S	1143 North St	Baton Rouge, LA	70802-4547	225-387-9273	387-9272	PK-5	Michael Eskridge
Clark Prep HS	1301 N Derbigny St	New Orleans, LA	70116-2213	504-373-6202	827-4538	9-12	Reginald Coleman
Cohen College Prep HS	3520 Dryades St	New Orleans, LA	70115-5399	504-335-0400	910-1045	7-12	Noell Lugay
Community S for Apprenticeship Learning	1555 Madison Ave	Baton Rouge, LA	70802-3460	225-336-1410	336-1414	6-8	Dujan Johnson
Crescent Leadership Academy	4300 Almonaster Ave	New Orleans, LA	70126-5439	504-940-2701	940-2214	6-12	Dr. Chauncey Nash
Crestworth Learning Academy	10650 Avenue F	Baton Rouge, LA	70807-2501	225-775-6845	775-0051	6-8	Robert Marks
Crocker Arts and Technology ES	2300 General Taylor St	New Orleans, LA	70115-5899	504-367-2669	367-2669	PK-5	Charmaine Roberts
Dalton ES	3605 Ontario St	Baton Rouge, LA	70805-5800	225-239-7502	357-1171	PK-5	Marilyn Taylor
D'Arbonne Woods Charter S	1002 Sterlington Hwy	Farmerville, LA	71241-3810	318-368-8051	368-8053	K-12	Pam Schooler
Delhi Charter S	6940 Highway 17	Delhi, LA	71232-7021	318-878-0433	878-0434	K-12	Brett Raley
Dibert S	4217 Orleans Ave	New Orleans, LA	70119-4605	504-373-6205	488-4091	PK-8	Diana Archuleta
Downsville Charter S	PO Box 8	Downsville, LA	71234-0008	318-982-5318	982-5737	PK-12	Rosemary Parnell
Easton Charter HS	3019 Canal St	New Orleans, LA	70119-6305	504-324-7400	324-7946	9-12	Alexina Medley
Einstein Charter S	5100 Cannes St	New Orleans, LA	70129-1203	504-324-7450	254-4121	PK-8	Shawn Toranto
Eisenhower S	3700 Tall Pines Dr	New Orleans, LA	70131-8499	504-302-7109	398-7129	PK-8	Deanna Rogers
Encore Charter S	2301 Marengo St	New Orleans, LA	70115-6253	504-444-2224		PK-5	Terri Smith
Esperanza Charter S	4407 S Carrollton Ave	New Orleans, LA	70119-6823	504-373-6272	488-1813	K-8	Nicole Saulny
Fischer S	1801 L B Landry Ave	New Orleans, LA	70114-6166	504-302-7111	363-1013	PK-8	Dr. Wylene Sorapuru

School	Address	City,State	Zip code	Telephone	Fax	Grade	Contact
Franklin HS	2001 Leon C Simon Dr	New Orleans, LA	70122-3525	504-286-2600	286-2642	9-12	Dr. Timothy Rusnak
Gentilly Terrace S	4720 Painters St	New Orleans, LA	70122-5099	504-708-2053	284-5847	PK-8	Tracy Guillory
Glencoe Charter S	4491 Highway 83	Franklin, LA	70538-7500	337-923-6900	923-0982	K-8	Michael Parrie
Glen Oaks MS	5300 Monarch Ave	Baton Rouge, LA	70811-5628	225-239-7501	302-7953	6-8	Dr. Staughton Jennings
Green Charter S	2319 Valence St	New Orleans, LA	70115-5959	504-304-3532	896-4147	K-8	Ava Lee
Harney S	2503 Willow St	New Orleans, LA	70113-3234	504-373-6230	891-6919	PK-8	Eileen Williams
Harte Elementary Charter S	4422 General Meyer Ave	New Orleans, LA	70131-3588	504-302-7121		K-8	Jamar McKneely
Harte ES	4422 General Meyer Ave	New Orleans, LA	70131-3588	504-373-6281	398-7103	K-8	Jamar McKneely
Haynes Charter ES	8600 Elmgrove Pl W	Baton Rouge, LA	70807	225-774-1311	774-1323	PK-5	Diana Haynes
Hughes Academy	3519 Trafalgar St	New Orleans, LA	70119-2041	504-373-6251	267-9760	K-8	Mark Martin
Hynes Charter S	990 Harrison Ave	New Orleans, LA	70124-3800	504-324-7160	488-0213	PK-8	Michelle Douglas
Inspire Charter Academy	5454 N Foster Dr	Baton Rouge, LA	70805-3031	225-356-3936		K-8	Philip Price
Intercultural Charter S	5316 Michoud Blvd	New Orleans, LA	70129-1435	504-662-0220	662-0019	PK-5	Pamela Randall
Jeff Community S	2239 Poydras St	New Orleans, LA	70119-7561	504-373-6258	308-3620	PK-2	Patricia Perkins
Jefferson Chamber Foundation Academy	475 Manhattan Blvd	Harvey, LA	70058-4441	504-410-3121		10-12	Millie Harris
Karr Charter HS	3332 Huntlee Dr	New Orleans, LA	70131-7046	504-302-7135		9-12	John Hiser
Karr HS	3332 Huntlee Dr	New Orleans, LA	70131-7046	504-302-7135	301-2721	9-12	John Hiser
Kenilworth Science & Technology Charter	7600 Boone Ave	Baton Rouge, LA	70808-6716	225-766-8111	767-9061	6-8	Hasan Suzuk
Kenner Discovery Health Sciences Academy	2504 Maine Ave	Kenner, LA	70062	504-233-4720		K-12	Patty Glaser Ph.D.
King Charter S for Science & Tech	1617 Caffin Ave	New Orleans, LA	70117-2909	504-940-2243	940-2276	PK-12	Dr. Doris Hicks
KIPP Believe College Prep S	1607 S Carrollton Ave	New Orleans, LA	70118-2825	504-304-8857	304-8862	5-8	Adam Meinig
KIPP Believe PS	1700 Pratt Dr	New Orleans, LA	70122-2408	504-266-2050	264-9363	K-4	Sarah Beth Greenberg
KIPP Central City Academy	2625 Thalia St	New Orleans, LA	70113-2843	504-609-2283	708-5334	5-8	Alex Jarrell
KIPP Central City PS	2625 Thalia St	New Orleans, LA	70113-2843	504-373-6290	302-9737	K-4	Korbin Johnson
KIPP McDonogh 15 MS	5500 Piety Dr	New Orleans, LA	70126-2308	504-609-2280	264-5598	5-8	Deanna Reddick
Kipp McDonogh 15 PS	721 Saint Philip St	New Orleans, LA	70116-2795	504-566-1706	592-8515	PK-4	Mark Burton
KIPP New Orleans Leadership Academy	2300 Saint Claude Ave	New Orleans, LA	70117-8307	504-373-6256	322-3924	5-7	Jared Lamb
KIPP New Orleans Leadership PS	2300 Saint Claude Ave	New Orleans, LA	70117-8307	504-592-8520	322-3924	K-1	Colin Smith
KIPP Renaissance HS	5316 Michoud Blvd	New Orleans, LA	70129-1435	504-373-3924	322-3924	9-12	Cody Yocum
Lafayette Academy	2727 S Carrollton Ave	New Orleans, LA	70118-4387	504-861-8370	861-8369	PK-8	Monica Boudouin
Lagniappe Academies of New Orleans	1501 Saint Louis St	New Orleans, LA	70112-3253	504-355-0950	355-0959	K-5	Kendall Petri
Lake Area New Tech Early College HS	6026 Paris Ave	New Orleans, LA	70122-2726	504-267-8811	267-8833	7-8	Chad Broussard
Lake Forest Charter S	12000 Hayne Blvd	New Orleans, LA	70128-1127	504-826-7140	248-7020	PK-8	Mardele Early
Lanier ES	4705 Lanier Dr	Baton Rouge, LA	70812-4020	225-239-7503	663-2950	PK-5	Alicia Franklin
Linwood MS	401 W 70th St	Shreveport, LA	71106-3034	318-865-4800	865-0542	6-8	Vickie Carroll
Louisiana S for Agricultural Sciences	5303 Highway 115	Bunkie, LA	71322-4301	318-346-8029	346-4479	8-12	Blaine Dauzat
Lusher Charter S	5624 Freret St	New Orleans, LA	70115-6547	504-304-3960	861-1839	6-12	Kathleen Riedlinger
Lusher Charter S	7315 Willow St	New Orleans, LA	70118-5232	504-862-5110	866-4292	K-5	Kathleen Riedlinger
MAX Charter S	PO Box 2072	Thibodaux, LA	70310-0001	985-227-9500	227-9515	1-8	Linda Musson Ed.D.
Mays Preparatory S	3059 Higgins Blvd	New Orleans, LA	70126-5422	504-613-4171	613-4111	PK-6	Shanda Gentry
McDonogh 32 S	800 De Armas St	New Orleans, LA	70114-4414	504-302-7144	363-1057	PK-8	Andre DuVoisin
McDonogh 42 S	1651 N Tonti St	New Orleans, LA	70119-2540	504-942-3660	309-9031	PK-8	Fran Trujillo
McDonogh City Park Academy	2733 Esplanade Ave	New Orleans, LA	70119-3332	504-940-1740	940-1780	K-8	Christine Mitchell
McDonogh HS	2426 Esplanade Ave	New Orleans, LA	70119-2405	504-373-6211	301-2179	9-12	Marvin Thompson
Mentorship Academy	339 Florida St	Baton Rouge, LA	70801-1721	225-346-5180		9-12	Dr. Brian Dixon
Miller-McCoy Academy for Math & Business	7301 Dwyer Rd	New Orleans, LA	70126-4215	504-373-6215	222-1046	5-12	Janice Bailey-Walker
Moton ES	3774 Gentilly Blvd	New Orleans, LA	70122-6128	504-245-4400	248-7300	PK-7	Paulette Bruno
Nelson Charter S	3121 Saint Bernard Ave	New Orleans, LA	70119-1916	504-943-1311	943-9824	PK-8	Deidra Denis-Bradley
NET Charter HS	1614 Oretha Castle Haley Bl	New Orleans, LA	70113	504-267-9060	267-9059	9-12	Elizabeth Ostberg
New Orleans Accelerated HS City Park	3649 Laurel St	New Orleans, LA	70115-2549	504-267-3882		6-12	Dr. Jean Pinney
New Orleans Accelerated HS Westbank	3649 Laurel St	New Orleans, LA	70115-2549	504-267-3882		9-12	Jean Pinney
New Orleans Science and Math HS	5625 Loyola Ave	New Orleans, LA	70115-5014	504-324-7061	309-4178	9-12	Chana Benenson
New Vision Learning Academy	507 Swayze St	Monroe, LA	71201-8130	318-338-9995	338-9987	PK-6	Rev. Andrew Mansfield
Pointe Coupee Central HS	8434 Pointe Coupee Rd	Morganza, LA	70759-3320	225-638-3096	638-9595	9-12	William McInnis
Prescott MS	3730 Winbourne Ave	Baton Rouge, LA	70805-5947	225-239-7504	239-7513	6-8	Rodney Coates
Reed S	10200 Curran Blvd	New Orleans, LA	70127-1304	504-373-6217		PK-8	
Sci Academy	5552 Read Blvd	New Orleans, LA	70127-3143	504-373-6264	324-0171	6-12	Rhonda Dale-Hart
SciTech Academy @ Laurel	820 Jackson Ave	New Orleans, LA	70130-4940	504-367-3307	315-2672	K-8	Jennie Aleshire
Singleton Charter S	2220 Oretha C Haley Blvd	New Orleans, LA	70113-1508	504-568-3466	569-3378	PK-8	Debra Robertson
Success Preparatory Academy	2011 Bienville St	New Orleans, LA	70112-3313	504-909-6275	571-6317	K-6	Niloy Gangopadhyay
Tubman S	2013 General Meyer Ave	New Orleans, LA	70114-1533	504-227-3800	227-3801	PK-8	Julie Lause
Walker HS	2832 General Meyer Ave	New Orleans, LA	70114-3097	504-302-7170	309-2960	9-12	Mary Laurie
Williams ES	11755 Dwyer Rd	New Orleans, LA	70128-3454	504-373-6228	245-2796	PK-8	Kelly Batiste
Wilson Charter S	3617 General Pershing St	New Orleans, LA	70125-4530	504-373-6274	373-3615	K-8	Logan Crowe
Wright Charter S	1426 Napoleon Ave	New Orleans, LA	70115-3980	504-304-3915	896-4095	6-12	Sharon Clark

Maine

School	Address	City,State	Zip code	Telephone	Fax	Grade	Contact
Cornville Regional Charter S	1192 W Ridge Rd	Cornville, ME	04976-6214	207-474-3944	474-0665	K-6	William Crumley
Maine Academy of Natural Sciences	PO Box 159	Hinckley, ME	04944-0159	207-238-4200	238-4207	9-12	Troy Frost

Maryland

School	Address	City,State	Zip code	Telephone	Fax	Grade	Contact
Academy for College & Career Exploration	1300 W 36th St	Baltimore, MD	21211-2303	410-396-7607	396-0432	6-12	Quinhon Goodlowe
AFYA Charter MS	2800 Brendan Ave	Baltimore, MD	21213-1213	410-485-2102		6-8	Katie Marts
Baltimore Freedom Academy	1601 E Lombard St	Baltimore, MD	21231-1718	443-642-2158	537-5141	6-12	
Baltimore International Academy	4410 Frankford Ave	Baltimore, MD	21206-5133	410-426-3650	426-3651	K-8	Grace Yador
Baltimore IT Academy	900 Woodbourne Ave	Baltimore, MD	21212-4027	443-642-2067		6-8	Faith Kandil
Baltimore Montessori Charter S	1600 Guilford Ave	Baltimore, MD	21202-2823	410-528-5393	528-8126	PK-8	Allison Shecter
Baltimore Talent Development HS	1500 Harlem Ave	Baltimore, MD	21217-2103	443-984-2744	669-7519	9-12	Laura Schulz
Browne S	1000 N Montford Ave	Baltimore, MD	21213-3542	410-396-9239	396-9328	PK-8	Tetra Jackson
Carroll Creek Montessori Charter S	7215 Corporate Ct	Frederick, MD	21703-8488	301-663-7970	663-6107	PK-4	Giuseppe DiMonte
Chesapeake Charter S	20945 Great Mills Rd	Lexington Park, MD	20653-4370	301-863-9585	863-9586	K-8	Angela Funya
Chesapeake Math and IT Charter S	6100 Frost Pl	Laurel, MD	20707-2928	301-350-6052	350-6029	6-12	Ali Gurbuz
Chesapeake Science Point Charter S	7321 Parkway Dr	Hanover, MD	21076-1159	410-757-5277	757-5280	6-12	Mehmet Gurbuz
City Neighbors Charter S	4301 Raspe Ave	Baltimore, MD	21206-1913	410-325-2627	325-2489	K-8	Michael Chalupa
City Neighbors Hamilton S	5609 Sefton Ave	Baltimore, MD	21214-2342	443-642-2052	426-0190	K-8	Obidimma Okobi
City Neighbors HS	5609 Sefton Ave	Baltimore, MD	21214-2342	443-642-2119		9-12	Danique Dolly
City Springs S	100 S Caroline St	Baltimore, MD	21231-1798	410-396-9165	396-9113	PK-8	Rhonda Richetta
Collington Square S	1409 N Collington Ave	Baltimore, MD	21213-3418	410-396-9198	396-8632	PK-8	
ConneXions Leadership Academy	2801 N Dukeland St	Baltimore, MD	21216-2808	410-984-1418	669-4418	6-12	Helen Atkinson
Coppin Academy	2500 W North Ave	Baltimore, MD	21216-3633	410-951-2602	951-2610	9-12	Marian Peck
Crossroads S	802 S Caroline St	Baltimore, MD	21231-3332	410-685-0295	752-8433	6-8	Dan Schochor
Empowerment Academy	851 Braddish Ave	Baltimore, MD	21216-4723	443-984-2381	362-2454	PK-8	Carolyn Smith
Excel Academy	7910 Scott Rd	Landover, MD	20785-2744	301-925-2320		K-8	Diane Kanu
Green S	2851 Kentucky Ave	Baltimore, MD	21213-1215	410-488-5312	488-5314	K-5	Kate Primm
Hampstead Hill Academy	500 S Linwood Ave	Baltimore, MD	21224-3800	410-396-9146	396-3637	PK-8	Matthew Hornbeck
Imagine Andrews Charter S	4798 Yuma Cir	Andrews AFB, MD	20762-5720	301-350-6000	599-5620	K-5	Marquis Dwarte
Imagine Discovery Charter S	1726 Whitehead Rd	Baltimore, MD	21207-4003	410-887-3338	277-0085	K-6	Robert Harris
Imagine - Foundations at Leeland	14111 Oak Grove Rd	Upper Marlboro, MD	20774-8424	301-808-4003	952-8708	K-8	Erika McCoy
Imagine Foundations at Morningside	6900 Ames St	Suitland, MD	20746-3504	301-817-0544	817-0956	K-3	Peter Thompson
Imagine - Lincoln Public Charter S	4207 Norcross St	Temple Hills, MD	20748-1624	301-808-5600	808-5611	K-8	Danielle Goddard
Independence S Local I HS	1250 W 36th St	Baltimore, MD	21211-2301	410-467-1090	467-1091	9-12	Helen Atkinson
Inner Harbor East Academy	200 N Central Ave	Baltimore, MD	21202-5005	410-537-5890		PK-8	Pedro Cartegena
Jemison STEM Academy	1130 N Caroline St	Baltimore, MD	21213-2844	410-276-3095	276-3096	6-8	Kelvin Bridgers
Jemison STEM Academy West	2000 Edgewood St	Baltimore, MD	21216-2537	443-642-2110	984-2774	6-11	Audrey Freeman
KIPP Harmony	4701 Greenspring Ave	Baltimore, MD	21209-4704	443-642-2027		K-3	Natalia Walter
KIPP Ujima Village Academy	4701 Greenspring Ave	Baltimore, MD	21209-4704	410-545-3669	664-6865	5-8	Natalia Walter
Maryland Acad of Technology & Health Sci	2801 N Dukeland St	Baltimore, MD	21216-2808	410-545-0955	396-0338	6-12	
Midtown Academy	1398 W Mount Royal Ave	Baltimore, MD	21217-4134	410-225-3257	225-3514	K-8	Kathleen O'Hanlon
Monarch Academy	1200 N Fremont Ave	Baltimore, MD	21217-2729	443-642-2402	254-0201	K-8	Sundai Riggins
Monarch Academy Charter S	6730 Baymeadow Dr	Glen Burnie, MD	21060-6412	410-760-2072	760-1321	K-8	Maurine Larkin
Monocacy Valley Montessori S	217 Dill Ave	Frederick, MD	21701-4905	301-668-5013	668-5015	K-8	Felacita King
New Era Academy	2700 Seamon Ave	Baltimore, MD	21225-1117	443-984-2415	355-1130	6-12	Rhonda Drayton
New Song Academy	1530 Presstman St	Baltimore, MD	21217-2312	410-728-2091	728-0829	PK-8	Nancy Neilson
Northwood Appold Community Academy	4417 Loch Raven Blvd	Baltimore, MD	21218-1554	410-323-9546	323-1836	K-5	
Patterson Park S	27 N Lakewood Ave	Baltimore, MD	21224-1155	410-558-1230	558-1003	K-8	Dr. Charles Kramer
REACH Partnership S	2815 Saint Lo Dr	Baltimore, MD	21213-1325	443-642-2291		6-12	Michael Frederick
Renaissance Academy	1301 McCulloh St	Baltimore, MD	21217-3044	443-984-3164	947-2968	9-12	
Roots and Branches S	1807 Harlem Ave	Baltimore, MD	21217-1411	443-642-2320		K-3	Anne Rossi
Rosemont S	2777 Presstman St	Baltimore, MD	21216-4025	410-396-0574	545-3298	PK-8	Dwayne Wheeler
Southwest Baltimore Charter S	1300 Herkimer St	Baltimore, MD	21223-3523	443-984-3385	685-3492	K-8	Jamie Stone
Turning Point Academy	7800 Good Luck Rd	Lanham Seabrook, MD	20706-3505	301-552-0164	552-7307	K-8	Rhonda Clomax
Wolfe Street Academy	245 S Wolfe St	Baltimore, MD	21231-2622	410-396-9140	396-8064	PK-5	Mark Gaither

Massachusetts

School	Address	City,State	Zip code	Telephone	Fax	Grade	Contact
Academy of Pacific Rim Charter S	1 Westinghouse Plz	Hyde Park, MA	02136-2075	617-361-0050	361-0045	5-12	Rene Dickhaut

School	Address	City,State	Zip code	Telephone	Fax	Grade	Contact
Advanced Math & Science Academy	201 Forest St	Marlborough, MA	01752-3012	508-597-2400	597-2499	6-12	Joseph Sweeney
Alma del Mar Charter S	26 Madeira Ave	New Bedford, MA	02746-2345	774-206-6827	206-6833	K-3	William Gardner
Amesbury Academy	67 Friend St	Amesbury, MA	01913-2723	978-388-8037	388-8073	7-12	Donna Georges
Atlantis Charter S	37 Park St	Fall River, MA	02721-1712	508-672-3537	672-2474	K-8	Robert Beatty
Banneker Charter S	21 Notre Dame Ave	Cambridge, MA	02140-2505	617-497-7771	497-4223	K-6	Sherley Bretous-Carre
Barnstable Comm Horace Mann Charter S	165 Bearses Way	Hyannis, MA	02601-3830	508-790-6485	790-6432	K-3	Marilee Cantelmo
Berkshire Arts & Technology Charter S	PO Box 267	Adams, MA	01220-0267	413-743-7311	743-7327	6-12	Ben Klompus
Boston Collegiate Charter S	11 Mayhew St	Dorchester, MA	02125-1628	617-265-1172	265-1176	5-12	Shannah Varon
Boston Day & Evening Academy	20 Kearsarge Ave	Roxbury, MA	02119-2318	617-635-6789	635-6380	9-12	Beatriz Zapater
Boston Green Academy	95 G St	South Boston, MA	02127-2920	617-635-9860	635-1504	9-12	Jeffrey Liberty
Boston Preparatory Charter S	1286 Hyde Park Ave	Hyde Park, MA	02136-2714	617-333-6688	333-6689	6-12	Sharon Liszanckie
Boston Renaissance Charter S	1415 Hyde Park Ave	Hyde Park, MA	02136	617-357-0900	357-0949	K-6	Roger Harris
Bridge Boston Charter S	2 McLellan St	Dorchester, MA	02121-4011	857-229-1601	674-0861	PK-1	Jennifer Daly
Brook Charter S 2	7 Elkins St	South Boston, MA	02127-1601	617-325-7977		K-6	Kimberly Steadman
Brooke Charter S 3	189 Paris St	East Boston, MA	02128-3058	617-268-1006		K-5	Mary C. Cole
Brooke Charter S	190 Cummins Hwy	Roslindale, MA	02131-3722	617-325-7977	325-2260	K-8	Kimberly Steadman
Cape Cod Lighthouse Charter S	195 Route 137	Harwich, MA	02645-1320	508-240-2800	240-3583	6-8	Paul Niles
City on a Hill Charter S	58 Circuit St	Roxbury, MA	02119-1925	617-445-1515	445-9153	9-12	Paul Hays
Codman Academy	637 Washington St	Dorchester, MA	02124-3510	617-287-0700	287-9064	9-12	Thabiti Brown
Community Charter S of Cambridge	245 Bent St	Cambridge, MA	02141-2001	617-354-0047	354-3624	7-12	Caleb Hurst-Hiller
Community Day Arlington ES	150 Arlington St	Lawrence, MA	01841-1604	978-722-8311	722-8514	K-1	Brent Merten
Community Day Charter S	190 Hampshire St	Lawrence, MA	01840-1251	978-722-2538	681-5838	K-8	Kennedy Hilario
Conservatory Lab Charter S	25 Arlington St	Brighton, MA	02135-2124	617-254-8904	254-8909	PK-5	Diana Lam
Dorchester Collegiate Academy	131 Hancock St	Dorchester, MA	02125-2136	617-379-3029		4-7	Robert Flynn
Dudley Street Neighborhood S	6 Shirley St	Roxbury, MA	02119-2726	617-635-8507	635-6320	K-5	Christine Landry
Excel Academy Charter S	1150 Saratoga St	East Boston, MA	02128-1228	617-561-1371	963-7162	5-12	Nina Keough
Excel Academy - Chelsea	180 2nd St	Chelsea, MA	02150-1806	617-895-8029		5-6	Stephanie Morgan
Foster Charter S	10 New Bond St	Worcester, MA	01606-2699	508-854-8400	854-8484	K-12	Kathleen Greenwood
Four Rivers Charter S	248 Colrain Rd	Greenfield, MA	01301-9701	413-775-4577	775-4578	7-12	Peter Garbus
Foxborough Regional Charter S	131 Central St	Foxboro, MA	02035-2458	508-543-2508	543-7982	K-12	Ronald Griffin
Franklin Classical Charter S	201 Main St	Franklin, MA	02038-1933	508-541-3434	541-5396	K-8	Heather Zolnowski
Global Learning Charter S	190 Ashley Blvd	New Bedford, MA	02746-1752	508-991-4105	991-4110	5-12	Lena Pires
Hampden Charter S of Science	20 Johnson Rd	Chicopee, MA	01022-1065	413-593-9090	294-2648	6-12	Harun Celik
Hilltown Cooperative Charter S	PO Box 147	Haydenville, MA	01039-0147	413-268-3421	268-3185	K-8	Amy Aaron
Hill View Montessori Charter S	75 Foundation Ave	Haverhill, MA	01835-6926	978-521-2616	521-2656	K-8	Ruthann Goguen
Holyoke Community Charter S	2200 Northampton St	Holyoke, MA	01040-3430	413-533-0111	536-5444	K-8	Sonia Pope
Innovation Academy Charter S	72 Tyng Rd	Tyngsboro, MA	01879-2044	978-649-0432	649-6337	5-12	Walter Landberg
Kennedy Academy for Health Careers	110 Fenway	Boston, MA	02115-3782	617-373-8576	373-7850	9-12	Dr. Caren Walker-Gregory
King Charter S of Excellence	285 Dorset St	Springfield, MA	01108-2821	413-214-7806	214-7838	K-5	Lan Katz
KIPP Academy Boston Charter S	215 Forest Hills Ave	Boston, MA	02130	617-500-6774		5-5	Christine Barford
KIPP Academy Lynn Charter S	90 High Rock St	Lynn, MA	01902-3851	781-598-1609	598-1639	5-12	Anna Breen
Lawrence Family Development Charter S	34 West St	Lawrence, MA	01841-3426	978-689-9863	689-8133	K-8	Patricia Karl
Lowell Community Charter S	206 Jackson St	Lowell, MA	01852-2106	978-323-0800	323-4600	K-6	Kathy Egmont
Lowell Middlesex Academy Charter S	67 Middle St	Lowell, MA	01852-1868	978-656-3165	459-0456	9-12	Margaret McDevitt
Mann New Leadership Charter S	37 Alderman St	Springfield, MA	01108-2120	413-782-9111	782-9991	6-12	
Marblehead Community Charter S	17 Lime St	Marblehead, MA	01945-2530	781-631-0777	631-0500	4-8	Helena Cullen-Hamzeh
Martha's Vineyard Charter S	PO Box 1150	West Tisbury, MA	02575-1150	508-693-9900	696-9008	K-12	Robert Moore
MATCH Charter HS	1001 Commonwealth Ave	Boston, MA	02215-1308	617-232-0300	232-2838	6-12	Megan McDonough
MATCH Community Day Charter S	86 Wachusett St	Jamaica Plain, MA	02130-4141	617-983-0300	983-0332	PK-3	Katherine Bernier
McAuliffe Regional Charter S	25 Clinton St	Framingham, MA	01702-6702	508-879-9000	879-1066	6-8	Kristin Harrison
Mystic Valley Regional Charter S	770 Salem St	Malden, MA	02148-4415	781-388-0222	321-5688	K-12	Martin Trice
Neighborhood House Charter S	21 Queen St	Dorchester, MA	02122-2509	617-825-0703	825-1829	PK-8	Kevin Andrews
New Leadership Charter S	37 Alderman St	Springfield, MA	01108-2120	413-782-9111	782-9991	6-12	Andrew Marshall
North Central Essential Charter S	171 South St	Fitchburg, MA	01420-5484	978-345-2701	345-9127	7-12	Patricia May
Parker Charter Essential S	49 Antietam St	Ayer, MA	01434-5230	978-772-3293	772-3295	7-12	Todd Sumner
Phoenix Academy	526 Lowell St	Lawrence, MA	01841-4414	978-722-8410	686-3613	9-12	Olivia Lahann
Phoenix Charter Academy	59 Nichols St	Chelsea, MA	02150-1225	617-889-3100	889-3144	9-12	Sarah Miller
Pioneer Charter S of Science	51 Summer St	Everett, MA	02149-3741	617-389-7277	389-7270	7-12	Barish Icin
Pioneer Valley Chinese Immrsn Charter S	317 Russell St	Hadley, MA	01035-3535	413-582-7040	582-7068	K-9	Kathleen Wang
Pioneer Valley Performing Arts Charter S	15 Mulligan Dr	South Hadley, MA	01075-7511	413-552-1580	552-1594	7-12	Laura Davis
Prospect Hill Academy Charter S	50 Essex St	Cambridge, MA	02139-2602	617-284-7800	284-7980	K-12	Jed Lippard
Rising Tide Charter S	6 Resnik Rd	Plymouth, MA	02360-4873	508-747-2620	830-9441	5-10	Jill Crafts
River Valley Charter S	2 Perry Way	Newburyport, MA	01950-4001	978-465-0065	465-0119	K-8	Jeanne Schultz
Roxbury Preparatory Charter S	120 Fisher Ave	Roxbury, MA	02120-3320	617-566-2361	566-2373	5-8	Will Austin
SABIS International Charter S	160 Joan St	Springfield, MA	01129-1530	413-783-2600	783-2555	K-12	Karen Reuter
Salem Academy Charter S	45 Congress St	Salem, MA	01970-5579	978-744-2105	744-7246	6-12	Rachel Hunt
Salem Community Charter S	1 Museum Pl	Salem, MA	01970	978-825-3470	825-3475	9-12	Jessica Yurwitz
Seven Hills Charter S	51 Gage St	Worcester, MA	01605-3014	508-799-7500	753-9679	K-8	Michael Barth
Silver Hill Horace Mann Charter S	675 Washington St	Haverhill, MA	01832-4500	978-374-3448	374-3461	K-5	Christopher Jayne
Smith Leadership Academy Charter S	23 Leonard St	Dorchester, MA	02122-2718	617-474-7950	474-7957	6-8	Karmala Sherwood
South Shore Charter S	100 Longwater Cir	Norwell, MA	02061-1650	781-982-4202	982-4201	K-12	Angie Pepin
Spirit of Knowledge Charter S	19 Chatham St	Worcester, MA	01609-2424	508-252-7321	562-4552	7-12	Paula Bailey
Sturgis Charter S	427 Main St	Hyannis, MA	02601-3905	508-778-1782	771-6785	9-12	Paul Marble
UP Academy	215 Dorchester St	South Boston, MA	02127-2876	617-635-8819	635-8820	6-8	Amanda Gardner
Veritas Preparatory Charter S	370 Pine St	Springfield, MA	01105-1931	413-539-0055		5-5	Rachel Romano

Michigan

School	Address	City,State	Zip code	Telephone	Fax	Grade	Contact
Abney Academy	1435 Fulton St E	Grand Rapids, MI	49503-3853	616-454-5541	454-5598	K-6	Markeith Large
Academic and Career Education Academy	884 E Isabella Rd	Midland, MI	48640-8326	989-631-5202	631-4541	9-12	Michelle Zielinski
Academy of Business and Technology	19625 Wood St	Melvindale, MI	48122-2201	313-382-3422	382-3906	6-12	John Kirk
Academy of Business and Technology ES	5277 Calhoun St	Dearborn, MI	48126-3203	313-581-2223	581-2247	K-5	Dr. Paul Merritt
Academy of Flint	PO Box 310716	Flint, MI	48531-0716	810-789-9484	789-9483	K-8	Elnora Crutchfield
Academy of Southfield	18330 George Washington Dr	Southfield, MI	48075-2785	248-557-6121	557-2915	K-8	Carolyn Mosley
Academy of Warren	13943 E 8 Mile Rd	Warren, MI	48089-3351	586-552-8010	552-8014	K-8	Patricia Eggleston
Academy of Waterford	3000 Sashabaw Rd	Waterford, MI	48329-4040	248-674-1649	674-3173	K-8	Robert Hooper
Achieve Charter Acadmey	3250 Denton Rd	Canton, MI	48188-2110	734-397-0960	397-0968	K-7	Jen Conley
Advanced Technology Academy	4801 Oakman Blvd	Dearborn, MI	48126-3755	313-625-4700	582-9407	K-12	Cynthia Anderson
A.G.B.U. Alex & Marie Manoogian S	22001 Northwestern Hwy	Southfield, MI	48075-4081	248-569-2988	569-1346	K-12	Dyana Kezelian
Aisha Shule/W.E.B. Dubois Prep Academy	20119 Wisconsin St	Detroit, MI	48221-1132	313-345-6050	345-1059	6-12	Hasina Murphy
Allen Academy	8666 Quincy St	Detroit, MI	48204-2306	313-898-6444	898-6555	K-12	Georgia Burrell
American Montessori Academy	14800 Middlebelt Rd	Livonia, MI	48154-4031	734-525-7100	525-8952	K-2	Amy Pogorzelski
American Montessori Academy Upper ES	17175 Olympia	Redford, MI	48240-2137	313-533-0000	533-0005	3-6	Jennifer Wilkins
Ann Arbor Learning Community	3980 Research Park Dr	Ann Arbor, MI	48108-2220	734-477-0340	929-6505	K-8	Dr. Wayne Millette
Arbor Academy	55 Arbor St	Battle Creek, MI	49015-2903	269-963-5851	964-2643	K-6	Paul Doersam
Arts Academy in the Woods	32101 Caroline	Fraser, MI	48026-3209	586-294-0391	294-0617	9-12	Maxwell Spayde
Arts & Technology Academy of Pontiac	48980 Woodward Ave	Pontiac, MI	48342-5034	248-452-9309	452-9312	PK-8	Septembra Williams
Bahweting Charter S	1301 Marquette Ave	Sault S Marie, MI	49783-9533	906-635-5055	635-3805	K-8	Dr. Theresa Kallstrom
Battle Creek Area Learning Center	15 Arbor St	Battle Creek, MI	49015-2903	269-565-4782	565-4784	10-12	John Wemlinger
Bay-Arenac Community HS	1608 Hudson St	Essexville, MI	48732-1387	989-893-8811	895-7749	9-12	Ryan Donlan
Bay County Public School Academy	1110 State St	Bay City, MI	48706-3699	989-684-6484	684-6202	PK-6	Jennifer Parrish
Benton Harbor Charter S	455 Riverview Dr	Benton Harbor, MI	49022-5080	269-925-3807	927-3673	PK-8	Tim Harris
Bingham Arts Academy	555 S 5th Ave	Alpena, MI	49707-2744	989-358-2500	358-2503	PK-8	Robin Benson
Black River Public S	491 Columbia Ave	Holland, MI	49423-4838	616-355-0055	355-0057	K-12	Shannon Brunink
Blue Water Learning Academy	5202 Taft Rd	Algonac, MI	48001-4701	810-794-8067	794-8888	7-12	James Lenore
Bradford Academy	24218 Garner St	Southfield, MI	48033-2900	248-351-0000	356-4770	K-12	Cheryll Paull
Bridge Academy	9600 Buffalo St	Hamtramck, MI	48212-3323	313-887-8100	887-8101	K-8	Dr. Nagi Jaber
Burton Glen Charter Academy	4171 E Atherton Rd	Burton, MI	48519-1435	810-744-2300	744-2400	PK-8	Denesha Rawls-Smith
Byron Center Charter S	9930 Burlingame Ave SW	Byron Center, MI	49315-8631	616-878-4852	878-7196	PK-12	Tom Kruzel
Canton Charter Academy	49100 Ford Rd	Canton, MI	48187-5415	734-453-9517	453-9551	K-8	Cathy Henkenberns
Capitol Area Academy	5525 S Pennsylvania Ave	Lansing, MI	48911-4013	517-882-1400	882-0400	PK-8	Dan Laabs
Carleton Academy	2001 W Hallett Rd	Hillsdale, MI	49242-1959	517-437-2000	437-2919	K-12	Colleen Gadwood
Carver Academy	14510 2nd Ave	Highland Park, MI	48203-5715	313-865-6024	865-6658	K-8	Celestine Sanders
Casa Richard Academy	2635 Howard St	Detroit, MI	48216-2058	313-963-7757	963-7768	9-12	Angela Johnson
CASMAN Alternative Academy	225 9th St	Manistee, MI	49660-3109	231-723-4981	723-1555	7-12	Sarah Bailey
Center for Literacy & Creativity	18401 W McNichols Rd	Detroit, MI	48219-4113	313-537-9400	537-9410	K-8	Kimistri Hall
Central Academy	2459 S Industrial Hwy	Ann Arbor, MI	48104-6129	734-822-1100	822-1101	PK-12	Dr. Luay Shalabi
Chandler Park Academy ES	20200 Kelly Rd	Harper Woods, MI	48225-1203	313-884-8830	884-9130	K-5	Dr. Wilhelmina Hall
Chandler Park Academy HS	20234 Kelly Rd	Harper Woods, MI	48225	313-499-3010	499-3052	9-12	Diane Tinsley Fisher
Chandler Park Academy MS	20100 Kelly Rd	Harper Woods, MI	48225-1201	313-839-9886	839-3221	6-8	Kenneth Williams
Chandler Woods Charter Academy	6895 Samrick Ave NE	Belmont, MI	49306-8844	616-866-6000	866-6001	PK-8	Barbara Lindquist
Chatfield S	231 Lake Dr	Lapeer, MI	48446-1661	810-667-8970	667-8983	K-8	Matt Young
Chavez HS	1761 Waterman St	Detroit, MI	48209-2194	313-551-0611	552-0552	9-12	Juan Martinez
Chavez Lower Academy	8126 W Vernor Hwy	Detroit, MI	48209-1524	313-843-9440	297-6948	K-2	Gabriela Jaime
Chavez MS	6782 Goldsmith St	Detroit, MI	48209-2089	313-842-0006	842-0167	6-8	Tiffany von Keltz
Chavez Upper ES	4100 Martin St	Detroit, MI	48210-2806	313-361-1083	361-1095	3-5	David Meloche
Cole Academy	1915 W Mount Hope Ave	Lansing, MI	48910-2434	517-372-0038	372-1446	K-6	Brian Shaughnessy

School	Address	City,State	Zip code	Telephone	Fax	Grade	Contact
Commonwealth Community Development Acad	13477 Eureka St	Hamtramck, MI	48212-1754	313-366-9470	366-9471	K-8	Angela Moore
Concord Academy - Boyne	401 E Dietz Rd	Boyne City, MI	49712-9653	231-582-0194	582-4214	PK-12	Rebekah Leist
Concord Academy-Petoskey	2468 Atkins Rd	Petoskey, MI	49770-9003	231-439-6800	439-6803	K-12	Denise Sanidson
Conner Creek Academy East	16911 Eastland St	Roseville, MI	48066-2078	586-779-8055	498-8734	K-6	Karen Smith
Consortium College Preparatory HS	4366 Military St	Detroit, MI	48210-2452	313-964-2339	964-3922	7-12	Rod Atkins
Countryside Academy	4800 Meadowbrook Rd	Benton Harbor, MI	49022-9629	269-944-3319	944-0242	K-12	Lyn Sperry
Covenant House Academy Central	2959 Martin Luther King Jr	Detroit, MI	48208	313-899-6900	899-6910	9-12	Anna West
Covenant House Academy East	7600 Goethe St	Detroit, MI	48214-1762	313-267-4315	267-4320	9-12	Michael Springs
Covenant House Academy SW	1450 25th St	Detroit, MI	48216-1404	313-297-8720	297-8730	9-12	Raymond Alverado
Creative Montessori Academy	15100 Northline Rd	Southgate, MI	48195-2408	734-284-5600	281-2637	PK-8	Carol Hutton
Creative Technologies Academy	350 Pine St	Cedar Springs, MI	49319-8680	616-696-4905	696-4920	K-12	Daniel George
Crescent Academy	17570 W 12 Mile Rd	Southfield, MI	48076-1905	248-423-4581	423-1027	PK-12	Cherise Cupidore
Crockett Academy	4851 14th St	Detroit, MI	48208-2204	313-896-6078	896-1363	K-12	Mary Lou Van Antwerp
Cross Creek Charter Academy	7701 Kalamazoo Ave SE	Byron Center, MI	49315-9534	616-656-4000	656-4001	PK-8	Joe Nieuwkoop
Crossroads Charter Academy	215 N State St	Big Rapids, MI	49307-1444	231-796-6589	796-9874	K-6	Kendall Schroeder
Crossroads Charter Academy	215 Spruce St W	Big Rapids, MI	49307-1471	231-796-9041	796-9790	7-12	Ross Meads
da Vinci Institute	559 Murphy St	Jackson, MI	49202-1622	517-780-9980	780-9747	K-8	Kristi Rydjord
da Vinci Institute	2255 Emmons Rd	Jackson, MI	49201-8335	517-796-0031	796-0320	9-12	Sandy Maxson
Dearborn Academy	19310 Ford Rd Ste 2	Dearborn, MI	48128-2403	313-982-1300	982-9087	K-8	Waseem Younis
Detour Arts & Technology Academy	PO Box 24	De Tour Village, MI	49725-0024	906-297-2011	297-3403	K-6	David Rhinard
Detroit Academy of Arts & Sciences	2985 E Jefferson Ave	Detroit, MI	48207-4288	313-259-1744	393-0460	K-6	Bob Thomas
Detroit Academy of Arts & Sciences	3100 E Jefferson Ave	Detroit, MI	48207-4221	313-259-1704		6-8	Turquoise Neal
Detroit Community ES	12675 Burt Rd	Detroit, MI	48223-3314	313-537-3570	537-6904	K-8	Sean Waters
Detroit Community HS	12675 Burt Rd	Detroit, MI	48223-3314	313-537-3570	537-6904	9-12	Walter Esaw
Detroit Edison Academy	1903 Wilkins St	Detroit, MI	48207-2112	313-833-1100	833-8653	PK-9	Ralph Bland
Detroit Enterprise Academy	11224 Kercheval St	Detroit, MI	48214-3323	313-823-5799	823-0342	K-8	Rodney Deal
Detroit Leadership Academy	13550 Virgil St	Detroit, MI	48223-3051	313-242-1500	241-1527	K-6	
Detroit Merit Academy	1091 Alter Rd	Detroit, MI	48215-2861	313-331-3328	331-3270	PK-8	Sandra Terry-Martin
Detroit Premier Academy	7781 Asbury Park	Detroit, MI	48228-3685	313-945-1472	945-1744	K-8	Vondra Glass
Detroit Service Learning Academy	21605 W 7 Mile Rd	Detroit, MI	48219-1810	313-541-7619	541-7656	K-8	Robert Davis
Detroit West Preparatory Academy	23749 Elmira	Redford, MI	48239-1405	313-387-9238	387-9261	K-6	Thomas White
Discovery Arts & Technology Academy	27355 Woodsfield St	Inkster, MI	48141-1242	313-827-0762	827-0763	PK-8	Shawn Hurt
Dove Academy of Detroit	8210 Rolyat St	Detroit, MI	48234-3358	313-366-9110	366-9130	K-8	Brandon Slone
Dream Academy	248 9th St	Benton Harbor, MI	49022-4723	269-926-1587	926-2371	9-12	Lacey James
Drew Academy	50 W Josephine St	Ecorse, MI	48229-1748	313-383-7501	383-7502	K-8	Scott Morgan
Eagle Crest Charter Academy	11950 Riley St	Holland, MI	49424-8553	616-786-2400	786-4692	K-8	Tracy Murray
Eaton Academy	21450 Universal Ave	Eastpointe, MI	48021-2969	586-777-1519	777-1527	K-12	Jamie Nord
El-Hajj Malik El-Shabazz Academy	1028 W Barnes Ave	Lansing, MI	48910-1377	517-267-8474	484-0095	PK-6	Dr. Eugene Cain
Ellis Academy	18977 Schaefer Hwy	Detroit, MI	48235-1762	313-927-5395	927-5376	K-6	Sylvia Green
Ellis Academy West	19800 Beech Daly Rd	Redford, MI	48240-1348	313-450-0300	450-0305	K-8	Dr. Ticheal Jones
EMAN Hamilton Academy	14223 Southampton St	Detroit, MI	48213-3744	313-866-4505	866-4493	K-8	Dr. Tammy Anderson
Endeavor Charter Academy	380 Helmer Rd N	Springfield, MI	49037-7776	269-962-9300	962-9393	K-8	Russ Ainslee
Excel Charter Academy	4201 Breton Rd SE	Grand Rapids, MI	49512-3857	616-281-9339	281-6707	K-8	Daniel Bartels
Flagship Charter Academy	13661 Wisconsin St	Detroit, MI	48238-2356	313-933-7933	933-9061	K-8	Krystal Bell
Ford Academy	PO Box 1148	Dearborn, MI	48121-1148	313-982-6200	982-6195	9-12	Cora Christmas
Ford Academy/Schl for Creative Studies	485 W Milwaukee St	Detroit, MI	48202-3220	313-481-4000	481-4001	6-12	Rashid Faisal
Fortis Academy	3875 Golfside Dr	Ypsilanti, MI	48197-3726	734-572-3623	572-5792	K-8	Ira Kleiman
Four Corners Montessori Academy	1075 E Gardenia Ave	Madison Heights, MI	48071-3433	248-542-7001	542-7901	PK-8	Chris Schoenherr
Frontier International Academy	2619 Florian St	Hamtramck, MI	48212-3452	313-887-7500	887-7501	6-12	Adan Aabed
Gaudior Academy	27100 Avondale St	Inkster, MI	48141-1816	313-792-9444	792-9445	PK-8	Curtis Warren
GEE Edmonson Academy	1300 W Canfield St	Detroit, MI	48201-1097	313-228-0910	447-2533	PK-8	Daria Neal
GEE White Academy	5161 Charles St	Detroit, MI	48212-2462	313-866-3595	866-3476	PK-8	Felicia Jones M.Ed.
Global Heights Academy	23713 Joy Rd	Dearborn Hts, MI	48127-1408	313-730-9035	730-9045	K-5	Jaleelah Ahmed
Global Preparatory Academy	26200 Ridgemont St	Roseville, MI	48066-3270	586-575-9500	491-2556	PK-8	Timothy Green
Grand Blanc Academy	5135 E Hill Rd	Grand Blanc, MI	48439-7637	810-953-3140	953-3165	K-8	Patty Wood
Grand Rapids Child Discovery Center	409 Lafayette Ave SE	Grand Rapids, MI	49503-5329	616-459-0330	732-4437	K-5	Erin Melcher
Grand River Prep HS	624 52nd St SE	Kentwood, MI	49548-5837	616-261-1800	261-1853	9-12	Jason Bannister
Grand Traverse Academy	1245 Hammond Rd E	Traverse City, MI	49686-9000	231-995-0665	995-0880	K-12	Allyson Apsey
Grattan Academy ES	12047 Old Belding Rd NE	Belding, MI	48809-9367	616-691-8999	691-9857	K-5	Tom Kreiner
Grattan Academy HS	9481 Jordan Rd	Greenville, MI	48838-9437	616-754-9360	754-9363	6-12	Tom Kreiner
Great Lakes Academy	46312 Woodward Ave	Pontiac, MI	48342-5006	248-334-6434	334-6457	K-8	Michelle Parham
Great Oaks Academy	4257 Bart Ave	Warren, MI	48091-1977	586-427-4540	427-4541	K-8	Ricky Fountain
Hamtramck Academy	11420 Conant St	Hamtramck, MI	48212-3134	313-368-7312	368-7376	K-8	Crystal Byse
Hanley International Academy	2400 Denton St	Hamtramck, MI	48212-3616	313-875-8888	872-9113	K-8	Carolyn Boyer
HEART Academy	19800 Anita St	Harper Woods, MI	48225-1109	313-882-4631	882-4761	9-12	Rosalind Brathwaite
Hillsdale Preparatory S	160 Mechanic Rd	Hillsdale, MI	49242-1053	517-437-4625	437-3830	K-8	Stephen Philipp
Holly Academy	820 Academy Rd	Holly, MI	48442-1546	248-634-5554	634-5564	K-8	Julie Kildee
Honey Creek Community S	PO Box 1406	Ann Arbor, MI	48106-1406	734-994-2636	994-2341	K-8	Al Waters
Hope Academy	12121 Broadstreet Ave	Detroit, MI	48204-1550	313-934-0054	934-0074	K-6	Veneda Fox Sanders
Hope of Detroit Academy	4443 N Campbell St	Detroit, MI	48210-2520	313-897-8720	897-5142	K-12	Ali Abdel
Huron Academy	11401 Metropolitan Pkwy	Sterling Hts, MI	48312-2937	586-446-9170	446-9173	K-6	Mark Talbot
International Academy of Flint	2820 S Saginaw St	Flint, MI	48503-5708	810-600-5000	600-5300	K-12	Traci Cormier
International Academy of Saginaw	1944 Iowa Ave	Saginaw, MI	48601-5213	989-921-1000	921-1001	K-6	Christopher Matheson
International Prep Academy	4201 W Outer Dr	Detroit, MI	48221-1457	313-494-7310		PK-7	Dr. Grayson Walles
Island City Academy	6421 S Clinton Trl	Eaton Rapids, MI	48827-9698	517-663-0111	663-0167	PK-8	William Warren
Japanese American S of SE Michigan	9101 Hillcrest St	Livonia, MI	48150	734-266-0611	266-0611	K-1	Ted Delphia
Joy Preparatory Academy	1129 Oakman Blvd	Detroit, MI	48238-2950	313-867-7828	867-7831	K-2	Delores Jones-Bell
Joy Preparatory Academy	15055 Dexter Ave	Detroit, MI	48238-2124	313-340-0023	340-0678	3-8	Frances Gardulescu
Kensington Woods HS	3700 Cleary Dr	Howell, MI	48843-6614	517-545-0828	545-7588	7-12	James Perry
Keystone Academy	47925 Bemis Rd	Belleville, MI	48111-9760	734-697-9470	697-9471	K-8	Keturah Godfrey
King Education Center	16827 Appoline St	Detroit, MI	48235-4205	313-341-4944	341-7014	K-8	Dr. Constance Price
Knapp Charter Academy	1759 Leffingwell Ave NE	Grand Rapids, MI	49525-4531	616-364-1100	364-9780	PK-8	Dave Turcotte
Landmark Academy	4800 Lapeer Rd	Kimball, MI	48074-1517	810-982-7210	982-0679	K-12	Travis Gostinger
Lansing Charter Academy	3300 Express Ct	Lansing, MI	48910-4370	517-882-9585	882-9587	K-6	Marcus Puccioni
Laurus Academy	24590 Lahser Rd	Southfield, MI	48033-6040	248-799-8401	799-8404	K-8	Dr. Raul Calderon
Leaders Preparatory Academy	27700 Southfield Rd	Lathrup Village, MI	48076-7901	248-569-0089	569-4944	K-8	Jerome Townsend
Leelanau Montessori Academy	PO Box 838	Suttons Bay, MI	49682-0838	231-271-8609	271-8605	PK-6	Connie Laufersky
Legacy Charter Academy	4900 E Hildale St	Detroit, MI	48234-2225	313-368-2215	432-2807	K-5	John Cogley
Life Skills Center of Pontiac	142 Auburn Ave	Pontiac, MI	48342-3008	248-322-1163	322-1164	9-12	Damian Perry
Linden Charter Academy	3244 N Linden Rd	Flint, MI	48504-1753	810-720-0515	720-0626	K-8	Corinne Weaver
Macomb Academy	39092 Garfield Rd	Clinton Twp, MI	48038-2790	586-228-2201	228-2210	12-12	Andrew Wise
Madison Academy	6170 Torrey Rd	Flint, MI	48507-5954	810-655-2949	655-2931	K-12	Brigitte Jackson
Marshall Academy	18203 Homer Rd	Marshall, MI	49068-8718	269-781-6330	781-8749	K-12	Brent Swan
Merritt Academy	59900 Havenridge Rd	New Haven, MI	48048-1915	586-749-6000	749-8582	PK-12	Nathan Seiferlein
Metro Charter Academy	34800 Ecorse Rd	Romulus, MI	48174-1642	734-641-3200	641-6530	K-8	Shelli Wildfong
Michigan Collegiate MSHS	31300 Ryan Rd	Warren, MI	48092-1354	586-777-5792	698-0392	7-12	Erica Walsh
Michigan Connections Academy	2140 University Park Dr	Okemos, MI	48864	517-507-5390	507-5389	K-12	Bryan Klochack
Michigan Math & Science Academy	8155 Ritter	Center Line, MI	48015-1452	586-920-2163	920-2164	K-12	Cafer Cengiz
Michigan Technical Academy	19940 Mansfield St	Detroit, MI	48235-2332	313-272-1649	272-1849	PK-4	Charla Ross
Michigan Technical Academy	19900 Evergreen Rd	Detroit, MI	48219-2044	313-538-4927	538-8396	PK-1	Sue Soborowski
Michigan Technical Academy	23750 Elmira St	Redford, MI	48239	313-537-9311	537-9312	5-8	James Abercrombie
Michigan Virtual Academy	678 Front Ave NW	Grand Rapids, MI	49504-5325	877-794-9427	843-5871	K-12	Stephanie Hargens
Midland Acad Advanced & Creative Studies	4653 E Bailey Bridge Rd	Midland, MI	48640-8542	989-496-2404	496-2466	K-12	Betsy Haigh
Mid-Michigan Leadership Academy	730 W Maple St	Lansing, MI	48906-5086	517-485-5379	485-5892	K-8	Aimee LeTarte
Morey Public School Academy	418 W Blanchard Rd	Shepherd, MI	48883-8544	989-866-6741	866-6737	PK-8	Brad Henry
Mt. Clemens Montessori Academy	1070 Hampton Rd	Mount Clemens, MI	48043-2955	586-465-5545	465-2283	PK-5	Genie P'Sachoulias
Multicultural Academy	5550 Platt Rd	Ann Arbor, MI	48108-9762	734-677-0732	677-0740	K-12	Randa Furrha
Nataki Talibah Schoolhouse of Detroit	19176 Northrop St	Detroit, MI	48219-1857	313-531-3720	531-3779	K-8	Melita Smith
New Bedford Academy	6315 Secor Rd	Lambertville, MI	48144-9411	734-854-5437	854-1573	K-8	Greg Sauter
New Beginnings Academy	211 E Michigan Ave	Ypsilanti, MI	48198-5677	734-481-9001	544-2706	K-5	Marlene Kukuzke
New Branches S	3662 Poinsettia Ave SE	Grand Rapids, MI	49508-5546	616-243-4763	243-0305	K-7	Pamela Duffy
New Paradigm Glazer Academy	2001 La Belle St	Detroit, MI	48238-2941	313-852-1500	852-1499	PK-6	Eddie Thomas
New Paradigm Loving Academy	1000 Lynn St	Detroit, MI	48211-1081	313-252-3028	866-0989	PK-6	Ronald Newton
North Central Academy	5055 Corey Rd	Mancelona, MI	49659-9467	231-584-2080	584-2082	K-12	Patrick Cleland
Northpointe Academy	53 Candler St	Highland Park, MI	48203-2827	313-868-2916	868-0443	K-8	Thomas Goodley
Northridge Academy	530 W Pierson Rd	Flint, MI	48505-3114	810-785-8811	785-9844	K-8	Latricia Brown-Coates
North Saginaw Charter Academy	2332 Trautner Dr	Saginaw, MI	48604-9593	989-249-5400	249-5800	K-8	Kathy Williams
North Star Academy	3030 Wright St	Marquette, MI	49855-9649	906-226-0156	226-0167	K-12	Karen Anderson
Northwest Academy	115 W Hurlbut St	Charlevoix, MI	49720-1510	231-547-9000	547-9464	K-12	Matt Saunders
Nsoroma Institute	20045 Joann St	Detroit, MI	48205-1136	248-521-0400	521-0401	K-8	Eliabeth Whittaker
Oakland Academy	6325 Oakland Dr	Portage, MI	49024-2589	269-324-8951	324-8974	PK-6	Henry Winter
Oakland International Academy	6111 Miller St	Detroit, MI	48211-1552	313-925-1000	925-1133	4-6	Dr. Amanda Magnuson
Oakland International Academy	8228 Conant St	Detroit, MI	48211-1407	313-347-0246	347-0250	7-12	Dale Bernard
Oakland International Academy	4001 Miller St	Detroit, MI	48211-1554	313-923-0790	923-0927	PK-3	Ahmed Saber
Ojibwe Charter S	11507 W Industrial Dr	Brimley, MI	49715-9087	906-248-2530	248-2532	K-12	Stephanie Vittitow
Old Redford Academy ES	17195 Redford St	Detroit, MI	48219-3259	313-532-7510	543-2055	PK-5	Aaron Williams
Old Redford Academy MS	22122 W McNichols Rd	Detroit, MI	48219-3245	313-653-3888	412-2162	6-8	Amelia Norwood

School	Address	City,State	Zip code	Telephone	Fax	Grade	Contact
Old Redford Academy Prep HS	8001 W Outer Dr	Detroit, MI	48235-3293	313-543-3080	543-3129	9-12	Zetia Hogan
Pansophia Academy	52 Abbott Ave	Coldwater, MI	49036-1430	517-279-4686	279-0089	K-12	Steve Palmer
Paragon Charter Academy	3750 McCain Rd	Jackson, MI	49201-7675	517-750-9500	750-9501	K-8	Zacary Perfitt
Paramount Charter Academy	3624 S Westnedge Ave	Kalamazoo, MI	49008-2969	269-553-6400	553-6401	PK-8	Kathleen Grinwis
Plymouth Educational Center	1460 E Forest Ave	Detroit, MI	48207-1000	313-831-3280	831-5766	PK-8	Dr. Jessie Kilgore
Plymouth Educational Ctr Prep HS	7375 Woodward Ave	Detroit, MI	48202-3158	313-309-1630	309-1631	9-12	Diane Murg
Pollack Academic Center of Excellence	23777 Southfield Rd	Southfield, MI	48075-3458	248-569-1060	569-1403	K-8	Damian Perry
Pontiac Academy for Excellence	196 Cesar E Chavez Ave	Pontiac, MI	48342	248-745-9420	745-1275	K-12	Alonzo Terry
Presque Isle Academy	21045 M 68 Hwy	Onaway, MI	49765-8694	989-733-6708	733-6701	9-12	Rick Bongard
Prevail Academy	353 Cass Ave	Mount Clemens, MI	48043-2112	586-783-0173	783-0179	K-8	Nicole Young
Quest Charter Academy	24745 Van Born Rd	Taylor, MI	48180-1221	734-299-0534	299-0577	K-8	Ralph Garza
Reach Academy	25275 Chippendale St	Roseville, MI	48066-3960	586-498-9171	498-9173	K-6	Julie Breakiron
Reh Academy	2201 Owen St	Saginaw, MI	48601-3466	989-753-2349	753-1819	PK-8	Kate Scheid
Renaissance Public S Academy	2797 S Isabella Rd	Mount Pleasant, MI	48858-2067	989-773-9889	772-4503	K-8	Holly Adcox
Richfield Public School Academy	3807 N Center Rd	Flint, MI	48506-2642	810-736-1281	736-2326	PK-8	Pamela Haldy
Ridge Park Charter Academy	4120 Camelot Ridge Dr SE	Grand Rapids, MI	49546-2432	616-222-0093	222-0138	K-8	Bob Morgenstein
Riverside Academy East	7124 Miller Rd	Dearborn, MI	48126-1918	313-586-0200	586-0201	K-5	Eman Radha
Riverside Academy West	6409 Schaefer Rd	Dearborn, MI	48126-2212	313-624-3600	624-3601	6-12	Ramzi Saab
Ross Hill Academy - Elmwood	3111 Elmwood St	Detroit, MI	48207-2418	313-922-8088	922-2015	K-8	Phyllis Ross
Rutherford Winans Academy	16411 Curtis St	Detroit, MI	48235-3202	313-852-0709		PK-5	Karen Abbott
Saginaw County Transition Academy	1000 Tuscola St	Saginaw, MI	48607-1421	989-399-8775	399-9801	7-12	Brad Gomoluch
Saginaw Learn to Earn Academy	PO Box 5679	Saginaw, MI	48603-0679	989-399-7400	399-7484	10-12	
Saginaw Preparatory Academy	5173 Lodge St	Saginaw, MI	48601-6829	989-752-9600	752-9618	PK-8	Debra Jones
St. Clair County Academy of Style	1100 Michigan Rd	Port Huron, MI	48060	810-364-3661	364-4448	11-12	Patrick Yanik
St. Clair County Intervention Academy	1170 Michigan Rd	Port Huron, MI	48060-4658	810-966-1649	966-4312	6-12	Joann Murphy
St. Clair County Learning Academy	1238 Michigan Rd	Port Huron, MI	48060-4658	810-364-8990	364-5315	6-12	Denice Lapish
Schools of Choice HS	G2138 W Carpenter Rd	Flint, MI	48505-1997	810-760-1780	760-6809	9-12	Cheryl Adkins
South Arbor Charter Academy	8200 Carpenter Rd	Ypsilanti, MI	48197-9800	734-528-2821	528-2829	K-8	Kim Bondy
Star International Academy	24425 Hass St	Dearborn Hts, MI	48127-3275	313-724-8990	724-8994	PK-12	Nawal Hamadeh
Stockwell Academy	9758 E Highland Rd	Howell, MI	48843-9098	810-632-2200	632-2201	K-8	Josh McDowell
Stockwell Preparatory Academy	1032 Karl Greimel Dr	Brighton, MI	48116-9471	810-225-9940	225-9941	9-12	James Reese
Summit Academy	PO Box 310	Flat Rock, MI	48134-0310	734-379-6810	379-6745	K-8	Leann Hedke
Summit Academy HS	18601 Middlebelt Rd	Romulus, MI	48174-9290	734-955-1730	955-1737	9-12	Erin Avery
Summit Academy MS	18601 Middlebelt Rd	Romulus, MI	48174-9290	734-955-1712	955-1729	6-8	Leann Hedke
Summit Academy North ES	28697 Sibley Rd	Romulus, MI	48174-9736	734-789-1428	789-1431	K-5	Leann Hedke
Taylor Exemplar Academy	26727 Goddard Rd	Taylor, MI	48180-3912	734-941-7742	941-9641	K-8	Walter Reese
Taylor International Academy	26555 Franklin Rd	Southfield, MI	48033-5340	248-354-1500	354-1501	K-5	Frederick Borowski
Three Lakes Academy	PO Box 159	Curtis, MI	49820-0159	906-586-6631	586-6573	K-7	Susan Pann
Three Oaks Public School Academy	1212 Kingsley St	Muskegon, MI	49442-4025	231-767-3365	777-9815	PK-8	Monecia Vasbinder
Threshold Academy	5827 Orleans Rd	Orleans, MI	48865-8603	616-761-2296	761-2298	K-5	Victoria Simon
Timberland Charter Academy	2574 McLaughlin Ave	Muskegon, MI	49442-4439	231-767-9700	767-9710	K-8	Angelia Coleman
Timbuktu Academy of Science & Technology	10800 E Canfield St	Detroit, MI	48214-1601	313-823-6000	823-9748	K-6	ChaRhonda Edgerson
Timbuktu Academy of Science & Technology	5221 Montclair St	Detroit, MI	48213-3432	313-267-4000	267-4949	7-12	Brenda Parker
Toussaint Academy	2450 S Beatrice St	Detroit, MI	48217-1631	313-383-1485	383-6532	K-8	Stephen Turk
Traverse City College Prep Academy	1402 Carlisle Rd	Traverse City, MI	49696-8375	231-929-4539	929-4763	9-12	Cameron Owens
Trillium Academy	15740 Racho Blvd	Taylor, MI	48180-5211	734-374-8222	374-5025	K-12	Angela Romanowski
Triumph Academy	3000 Vivian Rd	Monroe, MI	48162-8600	734-240-2610	240-2785	K-8	Tim Lenahan
Universal Academy	4612 Lonyo St	Detroit, MI	48210-2105	313-581-5006	581-5514	K-12	Nawal Hamadeh
Universal Learning Academy	28015 Joy Rd	Westland, MI	48185	734-402-5900	402-5901	PK-7	Nawal Hamadeh
University Prep Academy Murray ES	435 Amsterdam St	Detroit, MI	48202-3407	313-309-0552	309-0487	PK-5	Kimberly Llorens
University Preparatory Academy HS	600 Antoinette St	Detroit, MI	48202-3457	313-874-4340	874-4510	9-12	Eric Redwine
University Preparatory Academy MS	5310 Saint Antoine St	Detroit, MI	48202-4131	313-831-0100	831-4197	6-8	Nigena Livingston
University Preparatory Acad Thompson ES	957 Holden St	Detroit, MI	48202-3443	313-874-9800	874-9822	K-5	Tamara Johnson
University Prep Science & Math HS	2664 Franklin St	Detroit, MI	48207-4423	313-393-9166	393-9165	9-12	Dr. Gabriela Gui
University Prep Science & Math MS	5100 John R St	Detroit, MI	48202-4061	313-832-8400	833-4816	6-8	Margaret Trimer-Hartley
Vanderbilt Charter Academy	301 W 16th St	Holland, MI	49423-3329	616-820-5050	820-5051	PK-8	Holly Hillary
Vanguard Charter Academy	1620 52nd St SW	Wyoming, MI	49519-9629	616-538-3630	538-3646	K-8	Daryl Vriesenga
Victory Academy Charter S	1715 E Forest Ave	Ypsilanti, MI	48198-4160	734-217-1000	217-1007	K-5	Kevin Whelan
Virtual Learning Academy of St. Clair	499 Range Rd	Marysville, MI	48040-2220	810-364-8990	364-7474	9-12	Denice Lapish
Vista Charter Academy	711 32nd St SE	Grand Rapids, MI	49548-2307	616-246-6920	246-6930	K-8	Joe Grandy
Vista Meadows Academy	20651 W Warren St	Dearborn Hts, MI	48127-2698	313-240-4347	441-9169	9-12	Christopher Lindsay
Voyageur Academy	4321 Military St	Detroit, MI	48210-2451	313-361-4180	361-4770	K-6	Rod Adkins
Walden Green Montessori S	17339 Roosevelt Rd	Spring Lake, MI	49456-1253	616-842-4523	842-4522	K-8	Barbara Koning
Walker Charter Academy	1801 3 Mile Rd NW	Grand Rapids, MI	49544-1445	616-785-2700	785-0894	K-8	Steve Bagley
Walton Charter Academy	744 E Walton Blvd	Pontiac, MI	48340-1361	248-371-9300	371-1642	K-8	Amy Ebling
Warrendale Charter Academy	19400 Sawyer St	Detroit, MI	48228-3330	313-240-4200	240-4203	K-8	Christine Harwood
Washington-Parks Academy	11685 Appleton	Redford, MI	48239-1445	313-592-6061	242-5156	K-8	Tom Willis
Washtenaw Technical Middle College	4800 E Huron River Dr	Ann Arbor, MI	48105-4800	734-973-3410	973-3464	10-12	Dr. Karl Covert
Wavecrest Career Academy	633 Apple Ave	Holland, MI	49423-5434	616-393-7662	393-7633	9-12	Eryn Sluiter
WayPoint Academy	2900 E Apple Ave	Muskegon, MI	49442-4504	231-777-4972	767-8488	6-12	Reedell Holmes
Wells Academy	281 S Fair Ave	Benton Harbor, MI	49022-7219	269-926-2885	926-2923	K-7	Raymond Gant
Wellspring Preparatory HS	1031 Page St NE	Grand Rapids, MI	49505-5544	616-235-9500	235-2526	9-9	Koree Woodward
West MI Academy Environmental Science	4463 Leonard St NW	Grand Rapids, MI	49534-2138	616-791-7454	791-7453	PK-12	Scott Morgan
West Michigan Acad of Arts & Academics	17350 Hazel St	Spring Lake, MI	49456-1222	616-844-9961	844-9941	PK-8	Travis Thomsen
West Michigan Aviation Academy	5363 44th St SE	Grand Rapids, MI	49512-4093	616-446-8886	957-0491	9-9	Patrick Cwayna
Weston Preparatory Academy	22930 Chippewa St	Detroit, MI	48219-1161	313-387-6038	387-6180	K-8	Philip Yaccick
West Village Academy - South Campus	3530 Westwood St	Dearborn, MI	48124-3100	313-274-9200	274-0062	K-8	Donita White
White Pine Academy	510 Russell St	Leslie, MI	49251-9478	517-589-8961	589-9194	K-8	Jared Vickers
Winans Academy of Performing Arts ES	9740 McKinney St	Detroit, MI	48224-2503	313-640-4610	640-4611	K-5	Dr. Shelley McIntosh
Winans Academy Performing Arts MSHS	7616 E Nevada St	Detroit, MI	48234-3284	313-365-5578	365-5684	6-12	Lindsberg Pettway
Windemere Park Charter Academy	3100 W Saginaw St	Lansing, MI	48917-2307	517-327-0700	327-0800	PK-8	Yvonne Thomas
Windover HS	919 Smith Rd	Midland, MI	48640-4164	989-832-0852	839-7699	9-12	Gina Wilson
Woodland Park Academy	2083 E Grand Blanc Rd	Grand Blanc, MI	48439-2700	810-695-4710	695-1658	K-8	Jeremy Brown
Woodland S	7224 Supply Rd	Traverse City, MI	49696-9416	231-947-7474	947-7667	K-8	Nathan Tarsa
Woodmont Academy	25175 Code Rd	Southfield, MI	48033-5805	248-352-1805	352-1810	K-7	Zakia Gibson
Woodward Academy	951 E Lafayette St	Detroit, MI	48207-2999	313-961-2108	963-3501	PK-8	William Jackson
Woodward Collegiate Preparatory Academy	8904 Woodward Ave	Detroit, MI	48202-1821	313-285-9246		9-12	
Young Early College Academy	8100 W Davison	Detroit, MI	48238-3130	313-646-6438	491-0252	6-8	Tim Daniel

Minnesota

School	Address	City,State	Zip code	Telephone	Fax	Grade	Contact
Academia Cesar Chavez	1800 Ames Ave	Saint Paul, MN	55119-4898	651-778-2940	778-2942	K-6	Ramona de Rosales
Academic Arts HS	60 Marie Ave E	West Saint Paul, MN	55118-5910	651-457-7427	554-7611	9-12	Jane Davin
Achieve Language Academy	2169 Stillwater Ave E	Saint Paul, MN	55119-3508	651-738-4875	738-8268	K-5	Mary Apuli
AFSA HS	100 Vadnais Blvd	Vadnais Heights, MN	55127-4036	651-209-3910	209-3911	9-12	Becky Meyer
Arcadia Charter S	1719 Cannon Rd	Northfield, MN	55057-1680	507-663-8806	663-8802	6-12	Ryan Krominga
Aspen Academy	14825 Zinran Ave	Savage, MN	55378-4557	952-226-5940	226-5949	K-8	Cynthia Sherar
Augsburg Fairview Academy /Health Career	2504 Columbus Ave	Minneapolis, MN	55404-4432	612-333-1614	339-2229	9-12	Bart Johnson
Aurora Charter S	2520 Minnehaha Ave	Minneapolis, MN	55404-4118	612-870-3891	870-4287	K-3	Cheryl Avina
Avalon Charter S	700 Glendale St	Saint Paul, MN	55114-1782	651-649-5495	649-5462	7-12	Carrie Bakken
Beacon Academy	9060 Zanzibar Ln N	Maple Grove, MN	55311-1261	763-546-9999	416-3682	K-5	Jordan Ford
Beacon Preparatory S	8600 Bloomington Ave	Minneapolis, MN	55425-1920	952-426-6000	426-6020	6-8	Carl Schlueter
Best Academy	1300 Olson Memorial Hwy	Minneapolis, MN	55411-3968	612-221-8901		K-6	Eric Mahmoud
Birch Grove Community S	PO Box 2242	Tofte, MN	55615-2242	218-663-0170	663-7904	PK-5	Diane Blanchette
Bluesky Online Charter S	33 Wentworth Ave E Ste 300	West Saint Paul, MN	55118-3482	651-642-0888	642-0435	7-12	Amy Larsen
Bluffview Montessori S	1321 Gilmore Ave	Winona, MN	55987-2459	507-452-2807	452-6869	K-8	Stephanie Wehman
Bright Water ES	5140 Fremont Ave N	Minneapolis, MN	55430-3419	612-302-3410	302-5911	K-6	Ann Luce
Cannon River STEM S	1800 14th St NE	Faribault, MN	55021-2508	507-331-7836		K-8	Nalani McCutcheon
Cedar Riverside Community Charter S	1610 S 6th St Ste 100	Minneapolis, MN	55454-1102	612-339-5767	339-2951	K-8	Walt Stull
City Academy	958 Jessie St	Saint Paul, MN	55130-4058	651-298-4624	292-6511	9-12	Milo Cutter
Clarkfield Charter S	301 13th St	Clarkfield, MN	56223-1218	320-669-1995	669-1997	K-8	Kathy Koetter
College Prep Elementary S	1355 Pierce Butler Rte	Saint Paul, MN	55104-1359	651-605-2360	605-2369	K-6	Michael Raimondi
Cologne Academy	1221 Village Pkwy	Cologne, MN	55322-9248	952-466-2276	466-4030	K-8	Lynn Gluck-Peterson
Community of Peace Academy	471 Magnolia Ave E	Saint Paul, MN	55130-3849	651-776-5151	771-4841	K-12	Cara Quinn
Community School of Excellence	170 Rose Ave W	Saint Paul, MN	55117-4437	651-917-0073	917-3717	K-8	Mo Chang
Concordia Creative Learning Academy	930 Geranium Ave E	Saint Paul, MN	55106-2610	651-793-6624	793-6633	PK-8	Myla Johnson
Crosslake Community Charter S	36974 County Road 66	Crosslake, MN	56442-2527	218-692-5437	692-5437	K-8	Tami Martin
Cyber Village Academy	768 Hamline Ave S	Saint Paul, MN	55116-2224	651-523-7170	523-7113	2-12	Dave Glick
Dakota Area Community Charter S	220 Golden Rule Rd	Dakota, MN	55925-7103	507-643-6869	643-6953	K-5	Lisa Kent
DaVinci Academy	13001 Central Ave NE	Blaine, MN	55434-4150	763-754-6577	754-6578	K-12	Debra Lach
Discovery Public S	126 8th St NW	Faribault, MN	55021-4241	507-331-5423	331-2618	6-12	Jim Severson
Dugsi Academy	1091 Snelling Ave N	Saint Paul, MN	55108-2705	651-642-0667	642-0668	K-5	Mohamed Osman
Eagle Ridge Academy Charter S	7255 Flying Cloud Dr	Eden Prairie, MN	55344-3549	952-746-7760	746-7765	6-12	Jason Ulbrich
East Range Academy of Tech & Science	2000 Siegel Blvd	Eveleth, MN	55734-8642	218-744-7965	744-2349	10-12	Judy Youso
E.C.H.O. Charter S	PO Box 158	Echo, MN	56237-0158	507-925-4143	925-4165	K-8	Steve Blacker
Edvisions Off Campus S	PO Box 307	Henderson, MN	56044-0307	800-617-7857	665-2752	9-12	Doug Thomas
El Colegio Charter S	4137 Bloomington Ave	Minneapolis, MN	55407-3332	612-728-5728	728-5790	9-12	Norma Garces

School	Address	City,State	Zip code	Telephone	Fax	Grade	Contact
Excell Academy for Higher Learning	6510 Zane Ave N	Brooklyn Park, MN	55429-1559	763-533-0500	533-0508	PK-3	Sabrina Williams
Fraser Academy	1534 6th St NE	Minneapolis, MN	55413-1319	612-465-8600	465-8603	K-5	Linda Silrum
Friendship Acad of Fine Arts Charter S	2600 E 38th St	Minneapolis, MN	55406-3022	612-879-6703	879-6707	K-4	Nell Collier
Glacial Hills ES	PO Box 189	Starbuck, MN	56381-0189	320-239-3840	239-2803	K-6	Deb Mathias
Global Academy	4065 Central Ave NE	Columbia Hts, MN	55421-2917	763-404-8200	781-5260	K-6	Helen Fisk
Goodridge-Grey Accelerated S	300 Industrial Blvd NE	Minneapolis, MN	55413-4507	612-238-0788	238-0795	K-6	Dimitri Russell
Great Expectations S	PO Box 310	Grand Marais, MN	55604-0310	218-387-9322	387-9344	K-8	Peter James
Great River S	1326 Energy Park Dr	Saint Paul, MN	55108-5202	651-305-2780	305-2781	7-12	Christina Beck
Green Isle Community S	PO Box 277	Green Isle, MN	55338-0277	507-326-7144	326-5434	K-6	Kirsten Kinzler
Harbor City International S	332 W Michigan St Ste 300	Duluth, MN	55802-1644	218-722-7574	625-6068	9-12	John Haire
Harvest Prep S - Seed Academy	1300 Olson Memorial Hwy	Minneapolis, MN	55411-3968	612-381-9743	381-0748	PK-6	Eric Mahmoud
Hiawatha Leadership Academy	3810 E 56th St	Minneapolis, MN	55417-2218	612-987-5688	825-4777	PK-2	Eli Kramer
Higher Ground Academy	1381 Marshall Ave	Saint Paul, MN	55104-6353	651-645-1000	645-2100	K-12	Bill Wilson
High School for Recording Arts	550 Vandalia St	Saint Paul, MN	55114-1833	651-287-0890	287-0891	9-12	Anthony Simmons
Hmong Academy	1515 Brewster St	Saint Paul, MN	55108-2612	612-209-8002	209-8003	9-12	Christianna Hang
Hope Community Academy	720 Payne Ave	Saint Paul, MN	55130-4127	651-796-4500	796-4599	K-6	MayChy Vu
International Spanish Language Academy	5959 Shady Oak Rd S	Minnetonka, MN	55343-8969	952-746-6020	746-6023	K-4	Karen Terhaar
Jeffrey Academy	1550 Summit Ave	Saint Paul, MN	55105-2274	651-414-6000	414-6006	5-8	Brenda Natala
Jennings Community Learning Center	2455 University Ave W	Saint Paul, MN	55114-1507	651-649-5403	649-5490	9-12	Bill Zimneiwicz
Kaleidoscope Charter S	7525 Kalland Ave NE	Otsego, MN	55301-9690	763-428-1890	428-1691	K-8	Paula Higgins
KIPP Stand Academy	1601 Laurel Ave	Minneapolis, MN	55403-1205	612-287-9700	287-9702	5-8	Alvin Abraham
La Crescent Montessori Academy	1116 S Oak St	La Crescent, MN	55947-1560	507-895-4054	895-4064	PK-9	Tammy Stremcha
Lafayette Public Charter S	PO Box 125	Lafayette, MN	56054-0125	507-228-8943	228-8288	K-8	Andrea Harder
Lakes Area Charter S	601 W Nokomis St	Osakis, MN	56360-8203	320-859-5302	859-5342	7-12	Phil Grant
Lakes International Language Academy	246 11th Ave SE	Forest Lake, MN	55025	651-464-0771	464-4429	K-6	Cameron Hedlund
Learning for Leadership Charter	3300 5th St NE	Minneapolis, MN	55418-1117	612-789-9598	789-0547	K-12	Steve Dess
Lighthouse Academy of Nations	2600 E 26th St	Minneapolis, MN	55406-1201	612-722-2555	720-2274	9-12	Farhan Hussein
Lincoln International S	2123 Clinton Ave	Minneapolis, MN	55404-2650	612-872-8690	879-9557	9-12	Abdimalik Askar
Lionsgate Academy	3420 Nevada Ave N	Crystal, MN	55427	763-486-5359	390-0012	7-12	Diane Halpin
Loveworks Academy for Arts	2225 Zenith Ave N	Golden Valley, MN	55422-3852	952-522-6830	522-6840	K-8	April Harrison
Main Street S of Performing Arts	1320 Mainstreet	Hopkins, MN	55343-7497	952-224-1340	224-2955	9-12	Barbara Wornson
Math & Science Academy	8430 Woodbury Xing	Woodbury, MN	55125-9433	651-353-2317	578-7532	6-12	Paul Simone
Metro Deaf S	1471 Brewster St	Saint Paul, MN	55108-2612	651-224-3995	222-0939	PK-12	Dyan Sherwood
Metro Tech Career Academy	1704 Dupont Ave N	Minneapolis, MN	55411-3219	612-746-2700	377-4313	9-12	Benito Matias
Milroy Area Charter S	PO Box 129	Milroy, MN	56263-0129	507-336-2563	336-2568	PK-6	Jeff Hansen
Minisinaakwaang Leadership Academy	20930 367th Ln	McGregor, MN	55760-5968	218-768-5301	768-3357	K-12	Noah Johnson
Minneapolis Academy Charter S	5011 31st Ave S	Minneapolis, MN	55417-1405	612-455-1340	455-1345	5-8	Leon Cooper
Minnesota International MS	277 12th Ave N	Minneapolis, MN	55401-1026	612-465-8465	465-8411	5-8	Abdirashid Warsame
Minnesota Internship Center	2507 Fremont Ave N	Minneapolis, MN	55411	612-722-5416	722-1503	9-12	Kevin Byrne
Minnesota New Country S	PO Box 488	Henderson, MN	56044-0488	507-248-3353	248-3604	7-12	Dee Grover Thomas
Minnesota Online HS	2314 University Ave W	Saint Paul, MN	55114	800-764-8166	586-2870	9-12	Elissa Raffa
Minnesota Transitions Charter S	2872 26th Ave S	Minneapolis, MN	55406-1529	612-722-9013	722-0013	K-12	Shelia Casey
Natural Science Academy	920 Holley Ave Ste 3	Saint Paul Park, MN	55071-1558	651-925-5050	925-5051	K-5	Kirsten Kinzler
Naytahwaush Community S	PO Box 8	Naytahwaush, MN	56566-0008	218-935-5025	935-5263	K-6	Terri Anderson
Nerstrand Charter S	PO Box 156	Nerstrand, MN	55053-0156	507-333-6850	333-6870	K-5	Bonnie Jean Flom
New Century Charter S	1000 5th Ave SE	Hutchinson, MN	55350-7028	320-234-3660	234-3668	7-12	Jason Vold
New City S	229 13th Ave NE	Minneapolis, MN	55413-1117	612-623-3309	623-3319	K-6	Jitendrapal Kundan
New Discoveries Montessori Academy	1000 5th Ave SE	Hutchinson, MN	55350-7028	320-234-6362	234-6300	K-6	Dave Conrad
New Heights Charter S	614 Mulberry St W	Stillwater, MN	55082-4858	651-439-1962	439-0716	K-12	Thomas Kearney
New Millenium Academy	1203 Bryant Ave N	Minneapolis, MN	55411-4087	612-377-6260	377-6261	K-8	Yee Yang
New Visions Charter S	1800 2nd St NE	Minneapolis, MN	55418-4306	612-706-5566	706-5599	K-8	Jennifer Geraghty
Noble Academy	4021 Thomas Ave N	Minneapolis, MN	55412-1503	763-592-7706	592-7707	K-5	Neal Thao
Northern Lights Community S	PO Box 2829	Warba, MN	55793-2829	218-492-4400	492-4402	6-12	David Hagman
North Lakes Academy	308 15th St SW Ste 130	Forest Lake, MN	55025-1380	651-982-2688	464-6409	9-12	Jackie Saunders
North Lakes Academy	255 7th Ave NW Ste B	Forest Lake, MN	55025-1177	651-982-2773	464-6409	5-8	Caroline Little
North Shore Community S	5926 Ryan Rd	Duluth, MN	55804-9672	218-525-0663	525-0024	K-6	Susan Rose
North Star Academy	3301 Technology Dr	Duluth, MN	55811-4115	218-728-9556	728-2075	K-8	Danielle Perich
Northwest Passage HS	11345 Robinson Dr NW	Coon Rapids, MN	55433-4061	763-862-9223	862-9250	9-12	Jamie Steckart
Nova Classical Academy	1455 Victoria Way	Saint Paul, MN	55102-4213	651-209-6320	209-6325	K-12	Brian Bloomfield
Odyssey Academy	6201 Noble Ave N	Brooklyn Center, MN	55429-2483	763-971-8200	549-2380	K-9	John Sedey
Oshki Ogimaag Charter S	PO Box 320	Grand Portage, MN	55605-0320	218-475-2112	475-2119	K-6	Anna Deschampe
PACT Charter S	7250 E Ramsey Pkwy	Ramsey, MN	55303-6902	763-712-4200	712-4201	K-12	Shirley Delich
Paideia Academy Charter S	7200 147th St W	Apple Valley, MN	55124-9008	952-953-6200	432-2130	K-8	Marci Levy Maguire
Paladin Academy	308 Northtown Dr NE	Blaine, MN	55434-1039	763-786-4799	786-4798	9-12	Kathleen Mortensen
Partnership Academy	305 E 77th St	Richfield, MN	55423-4312	612-866-3630	866-3640	K-5	Lisa Hendricks
Pillager Area Charter S	PO Box 130	Pillager, MN	56473-0130	218-746-3875	746-3876	9-12	Mark Wolhart
Prairie Creek Community S	27695 Denmark Ave	Northfield, MN	55057-5333	507-645-9640	645-8234	K-5	Simon Tyler
Prairie Seeds Academy	6200 W Broadway Ave	Minneapolis, MN	55428-2826	763-450-1388	450-1389	K-8	Choua Yang
Quest Academy	3946 Wooddale Ave S	St Louis Park, MN	55416-2915	952-285-4100	285-4114	5-12	Suzi Splinter
Raleigh Academy	5905 Raleigh St	Duluth, MN	55807-2343	218-628-0697	628-2264	K-5	Danielle Perich
Ridgeway Community S	35564 County Road 12	Houston, MN	55943-4006	507-454-9566	454-9567	K-6	Jodi Dansingburg
RiverBend Academy	110 N 6th St	Mankato, MN	56001-4443	507-387-5524	387-5680	7-12	Don Johannsen
River's Edge Academy	188 Plato Blvd W	Saint Paul, MN	55107-2021	651-234-0150	234-0159	9-12	Meghan Cavalier
Riverway Learning Community Charter S	1733 W Service Dr Ste 18	Winona, MN	55987-2286	507-474-6120	474-6190	PK-12	Katey Wadewitz
Rochester Math and Science Academy	415 16th St SW	Rochester, MN	55902-2125	507-252-5995		K-8	Abdulkadir Abdulle
Rochester Off Campus Charter HS	2364 Valleyhigh Dr NW	Rochester, MN	55901-7641	507-282-3325	282-0976	9-12	Jay Martini
Sage Academy Charter S	3900 85th Ave N	Brooklyn Park, MN	55443-1908	763-315-4020	315-4028	9-12	Diane Scholten
St. Croix Preparatory Academy	4260 Stagecoach Trl N	Stillwater, MN	55082-1197	651-395-5900	395-5901	K-12	Jon Gutierrez
Saint Paul City S	260 Edmund Ave	Saint Paul, MN	55103-1783	651-225-9177	487-7551	K-8	Nancy Dana
Saint Paul Conservatory Performing Art	75 5th St W Ste 522	Saint Paul, MN	55102-1439	651-290-2225	290-9000	9-12	Callie Jacobs
Schoolcraft Learning Community S	PO Box 1685	Bemidji, MN	56619-1685	218-586-3284	586-3285	K-8	Scott Anderson
Seven Hills Classical Academy	8600 Bloomington Ave	Bloomington, MN	55425-1920	952-426-6000	426-6020	K-8	Alice Woog
Sojourner Truth Academy	3820 Emerson Ave N	Minneapolis, MN	55412-2039	612-588-3599	588-0217	K-8	Julie Guy
Southside Family Charter S	4500 Clinton Ave	Minneapolis, MN	55419-5143	612-872-8322	872-0612	K-8	Toni Wilcox
Spectrum HS	17796 Industrial Cir NW	Elk River, MN	55330-4754	763-241-8703	633-1380	9-12	Vanessta Spark
Stonebridge Community S	4530 Lyndale Ave S	Minneapolis, MN	55419	612-877-7400	877-7444	K-6	Barbara Novy
Stride Academy	1025 18th St N	Saint Cloud, MN	56303-1205	320-230-5340	253-0006	K-6	Lowell Haagenson
Swan River Montessori Charter S	500 Maple St	Monticello, MN	55362-8878	763-271-7926	295-0075	K-6	Sandra Morrow
TEAM Academy	220 17th Ave NE	Waseca, MN	56093-2753	507-833-8326	833-8327	K-6	Jill Ladwig
Treknorth HS	2520 Hannah Ave NW	Bemidji, MN	56601-2110	218-444-1888	444-1893	7-12	Dan McKeon
Trio Wolf Creek Distance Learning	10363 Liberty Ln	Chisago City, MN	55013-5418	651-213-2017	257-0576	4-12	Tracy Quarnstrom
Twin Cities Academy	835 5th St E	Saint Paul, MN	55106-5260	651-205-4797	205-4799	6-8	Betsy Lueth
Twin Cities Academy HS	835 5th St E	Saint Paul, MN	55106-5260	651-284-4797	205-4799	9-12	Betsy Lueth
Twin Cities German Immersion S	1745 University Ave W	Saint Paul, MN	55104-3632	651-492-7106	789-0117	K-8	Ann Jurewicz
Twin Cities International ES	277 12th Ave N	Minneapolis, MN	55401-1026	612-821-6470	821-6477	K-4	Randal Eckart
Ubah Medical Academy Charter S	1600 Mainstreet	Hopkins, MN	55343-7409	952-540-2942	540-2950	9-12	Musa Farah
Urban Academy Charter S	133 7th St E	Saint Paul, MN	55101-3377	651-215-9419	215-9571	K-6	Mongsher Ly
Voyageurs Expeditionary HS	3724 Bemidji Ave N	Bemidji, MN	56601-4335	218-444-3130	444-3126	9-12	Julie Johnson-Willborg
Watershed HS	4544 4th Ave S	Minneapolis, MN	55419-5145	612-871-4363	871-1004	9-12	Destiny Sparks
Woodson Institute for Excellence	1501 Aldrich Ave N	Minneapolis, MN	55411-3335	612-522-4022	522-4012	K-8	LaTanya Washington
World Learner Charter S	112050 Hundertmark Rd	Chaska, MN	55318-2817	952-368-7398	368-6094	K-6	Deana Siekmann
Yinghua Academy	1616 Buchanan St NE	Minneapolis, MN	55413-1609	612-788-9095	788-9079	K-8	Susan Berg
Mississippi							
Hayes Cooper Center for Math & Science	500 N M L K	Merigold, MS	38759	662-748-2734	748-2735	PK-6	Beverly Hardy
Missouri							
Academie Lafayette S	6903 Oak St	Kansas City, MO	64113-2530	816-361-7735	361-5788	K-8	Elimane Mbengue
Academy for Integrated Arts	5604 Troost Ave	Kansas City, MO	64110-2824	816-844-1720	844-1721	K-1	Dana McMillan
Allen Village S	706 W 42nd St	Kansas City, MO	64111-3120	816-931-0177	561-4640	K-8	Phyllis Washington
Alta Vista Charter HS	1722 Holly St	Kansas City, MO	64108-2217	816-471-2582	471-2139	9-12	Eduardo Mendez
Alta Vista ES - Academia Los Ninos	3201 Southwest Trfy	Kansas City, MO	64111-2727	816-604-4140	472-1735	K-K	Janna Cooper
Alta Vista MS	1711 Broadway St	Kansas City, MO	64108-1209	816-472-4120	472-1471	6-8	Melody Stutzman
Banneker Charter Academy Technology	6401 Rockhill Rd	Kansas City, MO	64131-1122	816-926-9110	363-8721	PK-8	Dr. Marion Brown
Better Learning Communities Academy	2153 Salisbury St Ste C	Saint Louis, MO	63107-3129	314-436-2603		K-3	Coralyn Vandermay
Brookside Charter Academy	1815 E 63rd St	Kansas City, MO	64130-3436	816-531-2192	756-3055	K-8	Millie Krna
Carondelet Leadership Academy	7604 Michigan Ave	Saint Louis, MO	63111-3332	314-802-8744	802-8721	K-8	Patrice Coffin
City Garden Montessori Charter S	2109 S Spring Ave	Saint Louis, MO	63110-3768	314-664-7646	664-4997	PK-8	Christie Huck
Confluence Academy-Old North St. Louis	3017 N 13th St	Saint Louis, MO	63107-3924	314-241-1110	241-1115	K-8	Sonya Murray
Confluence Academy-South City Campus	4235 S Compton Ave	Saint Louis, MO	63111-1129	314-481-4700		K-8	Pam Davenport
Confluence Academy-Walnut Park Campus	5421 Thekla Ave	Saint Louis, MO	63120-2513	314-383-8900		K-8	Mary Davis
Confluence Prep Academy	310 N 15th St	Saint Louis, MO	63103-2378	314-588-1247		9-12	Chester Bluette
Construction Careers Center	1224 Grattan St	Saint Louis, MO	63104-2922	314-588-9991	588-1982	9-12	Todd Williams
Crossroads Academy of Kansas City	1015 Central St	Kansas City, MO	64105-1619	816-221-2600	221-2601	K-5	Dean Johnson
DeLaSalle Charter S	3737 Troost Ave	Kansas City, MO	64109-2658	816-561-4445	561-6106	9-12	Mark Williamson

School	Address	City,State	Zip code	Telephone	Fax	Grade	Contact
Frontier S of Innovation	6700 Corporate Dr Ste 150	Kansas City, MO	64120-2102	816-363-1907	363-1165	K-8	Sean Isik
Gateway Science Academy	6576 Smiley Ave	Saint Louis, MO	63139-2425	314-932-7513	932-7514	K-8	Ali Tekin
Genesis S	3800 E 44th St	Kansas City, MO	64130-2183	816-921-0775	921-4268	K-8	Pamela Pearson
Grand Center Arts Academy	620 N Grand Blvd	Saint Louis, MO	63103-1009	314-533-1791	371-4630	6-9	Lynne Glickert
Hogan Preparatory Academy	6409 Agnes Ave	Kansas City, MO	64132-1154	816-444-4479	444-4268	6-8	Will McDowell
Hogan Preparatory Academy	1221 E Meyer Blvd	Kansas City, MO	64131-1207	816-444-3464	363-0473	9-12	Danny Tipton
Hope Academy - Bennington	1001 Bennington Ave	Kansas City, MO	64126-2219	816-595-0800	595-0801	9-12	Michael Graham
Hope Academy - Zion Grove	2801 Swope Pkwy	Kansas City, MO	64130-2710	816-877-8570	877-8571	9-12	Michael Jones
Hope Leadership Academy	2800 E Linwood Blvd	Kansas City, MO	64128-1544	816-921-1213	931-6142	K-3	Sean Saunders
Jamaa Learning Center	7220 N Lindbergh Blvd # 13	Saint Louis, MO	63042-2019	314-329-8507		K-8	Kimberley Townsend
Kauffman S	4251 Bridger Rd	Kansas City, MO	64111-3116	816-268-5660	268-5645	5-6	Hannah Lofthus
KIPP Endeavor Academy	PO Box 22624	Kansas City, MO	64113-0624	816-241-3994	241-3339	5-8	Jake Schmitz
KIPP Inspire S	2647 Ohio Ave	Saint Louis, MO	63118-1533	314-865-2535		5-8	Jeremy Esposito
Lamb ES	1000 Charlotte St	Kansas City, MO	64106-3051	816-842-8040	842-7727	K-8	Judy Akers
Lift for Life Academy	1731 S Broadway	Saint Louis, MO	63104-4050	314-231-2337	231-1299	6-12	Marshall Cohen
North Side Community S	3033 N Euclid Ave	Saint Louis, MO	63115-1632	314-385-9502	385-9538	K-5	John Grote
Parks ES	3715 Wyoming St	Kansas City, MO	64111-3945	816-753-6700	753-3436	K-5	Rierson Clark
Pathway Academy	2015 E 72nd St	Kansas City, MO	64132-1756	816-960-7290	333-6197	K-6	Jennifer Fleming
Preclarus Mastery Academy	620 N Grand Blvd	Saint Louis, MO	63103-1009	314-454-0815	338-7435	5-7	Daryl McAdoo
St. Louis Charter S	5279 Fyler Ave	Saint Louis, MO	63139-1300	314-645-9600	645-9700	K-8	Julie Frugo
St. Louis Language Immersion S	4011 Papin St	Saint Louis, MO	63110-1731	314-533-0975	533-0974	K-4	Rhonda Broussard
Scuola Vita Nuova	544 Wabash Ave	Kansas City, MO	64124-1747	816-231-5788	231-5181	K-8	Nicole Goodman
South City Preparatory Academy	2900 S Grand Blvd	Saint Louis, MO	63118-1005	314-561-3440	667-3477	5-7	Mike Malone
Tolbert Community Academy	3400 Paseo Blvd	Kansas City, MO	64109-2429	816-561-0114	561-1015	K-8	Mark Tolbert
University Academy	6801 Holmes Rd	Kansas City, MO	64131-1382	816-412-5900	410-0322	K-12	Tony Kline

Nevada

School	Address	City,State	Zip code	Telephone	Fax	Grade	Contact
Academy for Career Education	2800 Vassar St	Reno, NV	89502-3214	775-324-3900	324-3901	9-12	Bob DeRuse
Agassi Academy	1201 W Lake Mead Blvd	Las Vegas, NV	89106-2411	702-948-6000	948-6002	K-12	Mike Piscal
Alpine Academy	605 Boxington Way Ste 112	Sparks, NV	89434-6918	775-356-1166	356-1168	9-12	Jill Petersen
Bailey Charter ES	210 Gentry Way	Reno, NV	89502-4209	775-323-6767	323-6799	K-6	Michelle Engebretson
Beacon Academy of Nevada	7360 W Flamingo Rd	Las Vegas, NV	89147-5404	702-726-8600	538-9500	9-12	Susan Waters
Carson Montessori S	2263 Mouton Dr	Carson City, NV	89706-0446	775-887-9500	887-9502	K-6	Jessica Daniels
Coral Academy of Science Charter S	1701 Valley Rd	Reno, NV	89512-2239	775-322-0274	322-1378	K-4	Seyzi Tandogan
Coral Academy of Science Charter S	1350 E 9th St	Reno, NV	89512-2904	775-323-2332	323-2366	5-12	Seyzi Tandogan
Coral Academy of Science - Las Vegas	8185 Tamarus St	Las Vegas, NV	89123-2464	702-269-8512	269-3258	K-12	Feyzi Tandogan
Delta Academy	4075 N Rancho Dr	Las Vegas, NV	89130-3416	702-396-2252	396-0848	7-12	Dr. Kyle Konold
Discovery Charter S	3883 E Mesa Vista Ave	Las Vegas, NV	89120-2036	702-547-5682	547-5685	K-8	Dr. David Price
Elko Institute for Academic Achievement	1031 Railroad St Ste 107	Elko, NV	89801-3975	775-738-3422	738-3488	K-8	Connie Zeller
Explore Knowledge Academy	5871 Mountain Vista St	Las Vegas, NV	89120-2308	702-870-5032	871-5032	K-5	Abbe Mattson
Explore Knowledge HS	5871 Mountain Vista St	Las Vegas, NV	89120-2308	702-730-2933	730-2934	6-12	Abbe Mattson
High Desert Montessori Charter S	PO Box 5908	Reno, NV	89513-5908	775-624-2800	624-2801	PK-8	Tammie Stockton
I Can Do Anything Charter HS	1195 Corporate Blvd Ste C	Reno, NV	89502-2363	775-857-1544	857-6825	9-12	Dr. Carol White
Imagine S at Mountain View	7885 W Rochelle Ave	Las Vegas, NV	89147-6227	702-631-3925	253-0254	K-4	Tiffani Curtis
Innovations International Charter S	1600 E Oakey Blvd	Las Vegas, NV	89104-3334	702-216-4337	216-4353	K-12	Dr. Connie Malin
Mariposa Dual Language Academy	3875 Glen St	Reno, NV	89502-4803	775-826-4040	826-4030	K-5	Neil Schott
Nevada Connections Academy	175 Salomon Cir Ste 201	Sparks, NV	89434-4300	775-826-4200	826-4288	K-12	Jennifer Dukek
Nevada State HS	233 N Stephanie St	Henderson, NV	89074-8060	702-953-2600	953-2608	11-12	Dr. John Hawk
Nevada Virtual Academy	8965 S Eastern Ave Ste 330	Las Vegas, NV	89123-4893	702-407-1825	407-5055	K-12	Mike Kazek
Oasis Academy	PO Box 6322	Fallon, NV	89407-6322	775-423-5437	423-5433	K-8	Melissa Mackedon
Odyssey Charter S	2251 S Jones Blvd	Las Vegas, NV	89146-3161	702-257-0578	259-7793	K-12	Dr. Michelle Guthrie
One Hundred Academy of Excellence	2341 Comstock Dr	North Las Vegas, NV	89032-3512	702-636-2551	636-9475	K-8	
Quest Academy	6610 Grand Montecito Pkwy	Las Vegas, NV	89149-0210	702-631-4751	586-0836	K-12	Deb Roberson
Rainbow Dreams Academy	950 W Lake Mead Blvd	Las Vegas, NV	89106-2339	702-638-0222	638-0220	K-5	Billie Rayford
Rainshadow Community Charter HS	121 Vesta St	Reno, NV	89502-2913	775-322-5566	322-5509	9-12	Steve West Ph.D.
Sierra Nevada Academy	13880 Stead Blvd	Reno, NV	89506-1579	775-677-4500	677-4441	K-8	Kim Regan
Silver Sands Montessori Charter S	1841 Whitney Mesa Dr	Henderson, NV	89014-2070	702-522-6220	522-6218	K-8	
Silver State Charter S	788 Fairview Dr	Carson City, NV	89701	775-883-7900	883-9130	7-12	Steve Knight
Somerset Academy of Las Vegas	385 W Centennial Pkwy	North Las Vegas, NV	89084-5801	702-633-5616	633-5628	K-8	Gayle Jefferson
Somerset Academy of Las Vegas	2525 Emerson Ave	Las Vegas, NV	89121-4012	702-998-0500	998-0503	K-6	Reggie Farmer
Somerset Academy of Las Vegas	600 W Oakey Blvd	Las Vegas, NV	89146	702-636-5577	636-5570	K-6	Bridget Bilbray-Phillips
Washoe Online Learning for the Future	785 W 6th St	Reno, NV	89503-4315	775-333-6100	333-5189	K-12	Sandi Foster

New Hampshire

School	Address	City,State	Zip code	Telephone	Fax	Grade	Contact
Academy for Science & Design	486 Amherst St Unit 1	Nashua, NH	03063-1282	603-595-4705	262-9163	9-12	Jennifer Cava
Cocheco Arts and Technology Academy	1 Washington St Ste 555	Dover, NH	03820-3851	603-742-0700	742-7207	9-12	Christy Holmes
CSI Charter S	26 Washington St	Penacook, NH	03303-1519	603-753-0199	753-6429	9-12	James Gorman
Great Bay eLearning Charter S	30 Linden St	Exeter, NH	03833-2622	603-775-8638	775-8528	8-12	Peter Stackhouse
Ledyard Charter Academy	PO Box 327	Lebanon, NH	03766-0327	603-727-4772		9-12	Lynne Grigelevich
North Country Charter Academy	260 Cottage St Ste A	Littleton, NH	03561-4137	603-444-1535	444-9843	9-12	Lisa Lavoie
Seacoast Charter S	13 Church St	Kingston, NH	03848-3074	603-642-8400	642-8404	K-8	Roberta Mantione
Strong Foundations Charter S	715 Riverwood Dr	Pembroke, NH	03275-3701	603-225-2715	225-2738	K-8	Beth McClure
Surry Village Charter S	449 Route 12A	Surry, NH	03431-8106	603-357-9700	357-9701	K-8	Dr. Matora Fiorey
Virtual Learning Academy	30 Linden St	Exeter, NH	03833-2622	603-778-2500	651-5038	6-12	Steve Kossakoski

New Jersey

School	Address	City,State	Zip code	Telephone	Fax	Grade	Contact
Academy Charter HS	1725 Main St	South Belmar, NJ	07719-3051	732-681-8377	681-8375	9-12	Mary Jo McKinley
Academy for Urban Leadership HS	612 Amboy Ave	Perth Amboy, NJ	08861-2578	848-203-3742	203-3948	9-12	Deborah Egan
Banneker Preparatory Charter S	PO Box 128	Willingboro, NJ	08046-0128	609-531-0158		6-8	Richard Wilson
BelovED Community Charter S	508 Grand St	Jersey City, NJ	07302-4103	201-744-9775		K-3	Kelly Convery
Bergen Arts and Science Charter HS	43 Maple Ave	Hackensack, NJ	07601-4501	201-968-5039	968-5044	7-12	
Bergen Arts and Science Charter S	200 MacArthur Ave	Garfield, NJ	07026-1214	973-253-0002	253-0110	K-6	
Burch Charter S of Excellence	100 Linden Ave	Irvington, NJ	07111-2560	973-373-3223	373-3228	PK-5	Dr. Dorian Dorsey
Camden Academy Charter HS	879 Beideman Ave	Camden, NJ	08105-4227	856-365-1000	365-8179	9-12	Dr. Joseph Conway
Camden's Pride Charter S	879 Beideman Ave	Camden, NJ	08105-4227	856-365-1000	965-5358	K-4	Dr. Joseph Conway
Camden's Promise Charter S	879 Beideman Ave	Camden, NJ	08105-4227	856-365-1000	365-1005	5-8	Dr. Joseph Conway
Central Jersey Arts Charter S	1225 South Ave	Plainfield, NJ	07062-1919	908-753-0030	753-0032	K-5	Doug Dresher
Central Jersey College Prep Charter S	17 Schoolhouse Rd	Somerset, NJ	08873-4245	732-302-9991	302-9992	6-12	Tarkan Topcuoglu
ChARTer-TECHnical HS for Performing Arts	413 New Rd	Somers Point, NJ	08244-2143	609-926-7694	926-8472	9-12	Arthur Tubbs
City Invincible Charter S	832 S 4th St	Camden, NJ	08103-2047	856-342-9500		K-5	John Frangipani
Classical Academy Charter S of Clifton	20 Valley Rd	Clifton, NJ	07013-1030	973-278-7707	277-7720	6-8	Vincent DeRosa
Community Charter S of Paterson	75 Spruce St	Paterson, NJ	07501-1720	973-413-2057	345-7623	K-5	Marnie McKoy
Discovery Charter S	303 Washington St	Newark, NJ	07102-2738	973-623-0222	623-0024	4-8	Barbara Weiland
D.U.E. Season Charter S	1000 Atlantic Ave	Camden, NJ	08104-1132	856-225-0511	668-2196	K-8	Dr. Doris Carpenter
East Orange Community Charter S	99 Washington St	East Orange, NJ	07017-1006	973-996-0400	996-0398	K-4	Harvin Dash
Edison Energysmart Charter S	17 Schoolhouse Rd	Somerset, NJ	08873-4245	732-412-7643	412-7645	K-5	Oguz Yildiz
Edwards Academic Charter S	509 Bramhall Ave	Jersey City, NJ	07304-2730	201-433-5300		K-8	Mona Lisa Kalina
Elysian Charter S	301 Garden St Ste 5	Hoboken, NJ	07030-5895	201-876-0102	876-9576	K-8	Harry Laub Ph.D.
Englewood on the Palisades Charter S	65 W Demarest Ave	Englewood, NJ	07631-2316	201-569-9765	568-9576	K-5	Anthony Barckett M.Ed.
Environment Comm Opportunity Charter S	817 Carpenter St	Camden, NJ	08102-1132	856-963-2627	963-2628	K-5	Dr. Antoinette Dendtler
Ethical Community Charter S	95 Broadway	Jersey City, NJ	07306-6304	201-984-4151	200-9931	K-4	Marta Bergamini
Foundation Academy Charter IS	363 W State St	Trenton, NJ	08618-5705	609-920-9200	920-9205	3-8	Graig Weiss
Foundation Collegiate Academy	22 Grand St	Trenton, NJ	08611-2416	609-920-9200	920-9205	9-12	Nicole Falconer
Freedom Academy Charter S	1400 Collings Rd	Camden, NJ	08104-3113	856-962-0766	962-0769	5-8	Bridgit Cusata-Rosa
Freire Charter S	PO Box 120	Newark, NJ	07101-0120	973-733-9393	733-9377	9-9	Tauhhedah Baker-Jones
Galloway Community Charter S	112 S New York Rd	Galloway, NJ	08205-9608	609-652-7118	652-3640	K-8	Deborah Nataloni
Golden Door Charter S	3044 John F Kennedy Blvd	Jersey City, NJ	07306-3604	201-795-4400	795-3308	K-8	Brian Stiles
Gray Charter S	55 Liberty St	Newark, NJ	07102-4815	973-824-6661	824-2296	K-8	Verna Gray
Greater Brunswick Charter S	429 Joyce Kilmer Ave	New Brunswick, NJ	08901-3322	732-448-1052	448-1055	K-8	Patrick Mulhern
Greater Newark Charter S	72 Central Ave	Newark, NJ	07102-1905	973-242-3543	242-5792	5-8	Christopher Pringle
Great Oaks Charter MSHS	21 Eagle St	Newark, NJ	07102-2103	973-917-4286	917-4287	6-12	Jared Taillefer
Hatikvah International Academy Charter S	367 Cranbury Rd	East Brunswick, NJ	08816-3084	732-640-5850	917-7555	K-8	Marcia Grayson
Hoboken Charter S	255 Congress St	Jersey City, NJ	07307-3420	201-963-0222	963-0880	PK-12	Deirdra Grode
Hoboken Dual Language Charter S	123 Jefferson St	Hoboken, NJ	07030-1808	201-427-1458	706-4491	K-6	Elizabeth Willaum
Holland Charter S	190 Oliver St	Paterson, NJ	07501-1816	973-345-2212	345-2233	K-8	Christina Scano
Hope Academy Charter S	601 Grand Ave	Asbury Park, NJ	07712	732-988-4227	988-9125	K-8	Alexis Harris
Institute for Excellence Charter S	41 S Route 73 Ste 205	Hammonton, NJ	08037-9448	609-561-9414	561-9418	K-2	Diane Osbourne
International Charter S of Trenton	105 Grand St	Trenton, NJ	08611-2417	609-394-3111	394-3116	K-4	Melissa Benford
Jersey City Community Charter S	128 Danforth Ave	Jersey City, NJ	07305-2626	201-433-2288	433-5803	K-8	Eugene Harris
Kingdom Charter S of Leadership	121 W Church St	Blackwood, NJ	08012-3971	856-232-0100		K-6	Wandria McCall-Hampton
Knowledge A to Z Charter S	1725 Park Blvd	Camden, NJ	08103	856-292-3255		K-4	Chifonda Henry
Lady Liberty Academy Charter S	115 Frank E Rodgers Blvd S	Harrison, NJ	07029	973-623-9005	483-0807	K-8	Chris Finn
LEAP Academy University Charter S	549 Cooper St	Camden, NJ	08102-1210	856-614-0400	342-7900	K-12	Janice Strigh
Learning Community Charter S	2495 John F Kennedy Blvd	Jersey City, NJ	07304-2007	201-332-0900	332-4981	K-8	Colin Hogan
Liberty Academy Charter S	211 Sherman Ave	Jersey City, NJ	07307-2040	201-217-6771	217-6772	K-8	Gregory Cooper

School	Address	City,State	Zip code	Telephone	Fax	Grade	Contact
Merit Prepartory Charter S	909 Broad St	Newark, NJ	07102-2622	973-642-4400	367-7706	6-6	Ben Rayer
M.E.T.S. Charter S	211 Sherman Ave	Jersey City, NJ	07307-2040	201-526-8500	526-7630	6-12	Walter Goodwin
Millville Public Charter S	1101 Wheaton Ave Ste 220	Millville, NJ	08332-2003	856-506-8143		K-3	Yvonne Cribbs
Newark Educators Community Charter S	17 Crawford St	Newark, NJ	07102-2411	973-732-3848	732-3847	K-5	Xiania Foster
Newark Prep Charter S	570 Broad St	Newark, NJ	07102-4532	862-307-7010	307-7107	9-9	Patrick Byrne
New Horizons Community Charter S	45 Hayes St	Newark, NJ	07103-3019	973-848-0400	596-0984	K-5	Andre Hollis
New Legacy Charter S	460 Lyons Ave	Newark, NJ	07112-1028	973-642-7000	556-1250	K-1	Paula White Bradley
North Star Academy Charter S	10 Washington Pl	Newark, NJ	07102-3106	973-642-0101	642-5800	K-12	Michael Ambriz
Obama Green Charter HS	35 Watchung Ave	Plainfield, NJ	07060-1207	877-643-4064		9-12	Safiyah Satterwhite
Oceanside Charter S	1750 Bacharach Blvd	Atlantic City, NJ	08401-4308	609-348-3485	348-5951	PK-8	Jeanine Middleton
100 Legacy Academy Charter S	75 Morton St	Newark, NJ	07103-3752	973-732-9180	367-8250	6-8	Cheryl LeBeof
PACE Charter School of Hamilton	1949 Hamilton Ave	Hamilton, NJ	08619-3736	609-587-2288	587-8483	K-3	Debbie Pontoriero
Paterson Charter S for Science and Tech	276 Wabash Ave	Paterson, NJ	07503-1612	973-345-4400	345-4636	K-6	Riza Gurcanli
Paterson Charter S for Science and Tech	764 11th Ave	Paterson, NJ	07514-1001	973-247-0600	247-9924	7-12	Riza Gurcanli
People's Preparatory HS	321 Bergen St	Newark, NJ	07103-2639	973-622-1790	622-1453	9-12	Jess Rooney
Philips Academy Charter S	342 Central Ave	Newark, NJ	07103-2808	973-624-0644	624-0102	K-8	Mark Shultz
Pride Academy Charter S	117 Elmwood Ave	East Orange, NJ	07018-2420	973-672-3200	672-3207	5-8	Fiona Thomas
Princeton Charter S	100 Bunn Dr	Princeton, NJ	08540-2821	609-924-0575	924-0282	K-8	Lawrence Patton
Queen City Academy Charter S	815 W 7th St	Plainfield, NJ	07063-1449	908-753-4700	753-4816	K-8	Theresa Radline
Red Bank Charter S	58 Oakland St	Red Bank, NJ	07701-1104	732-450-2092	936-1923	K-8	Meredith Pennotti
Renaissance Regional Leadership S	PO Box 247	Wrightstown, NJ	08562-0247	609-283-0794		K-6	Lorna Hassel
Ridge & Valley Charter S	1234 State Route 94	Blairstown, NJ	07825-4115	908-362-1114	362-6680	K-8	Rowena McNulty
Riverbank Charter S of Excellence	1300 Hornberger Ave	Roebling, NJ	08554-1313	609-499-4321	447-0350	K-3	Beth Kelley
Robeson Charter S for the Humanities	643 Indiana Ave	Trenton, NJ	08638-3821	609-394-7721	394-7720	4-8	Megan Lane
Roseville Community Charter S	11 Gray St	Newark, NJ	07107-1529	973-908-8057	733-9555	K-1	
Sanford Charter S	53 Lincoln Park	Newark, NJ	07102-2390	973-297-1275	297-1120	K-6	DeLacy Davis
Soaring Heights Charter S	1 Romar Ave	Jersey City, NJ	07305-1713	201-434-4800	434-7474	K-8	Claudia Zuorick
Sussex Co. Charter S for Technology	385 N Church Rd	Sparta, NJ	07871-3307	973-383-3250	383-2901	6-8	Jill Eckel
TEAM Academy Charter S	60 Park Pl Ste 802	Newark, NJ	07102-5508	973-705-8326	556-1238	K-12	Ryan Hill
Teaneck Community Charter S	563 Chestnut Ave	Teaneck, NJ	07666-2424	201-833-9600	833-9225	K-8	Billy Bowie
Thomas Charter MS	308 S 9th St	Newark, NJ	07103-2111	973-792-0060	792-0066	5-8	John Gamble
Thomas Charter S	370 S 7th St	Newark, NJ	07103-2047	973-621-0060	621-0061	PK-4	Remi Dabney
Treat Academy Charter S - North	443 Clifton Ave	Newark, NJ	07104-1339	973-482-8811	482-7681	K-8	Theresa Adubato
Treat Academy Chartr S - Central	180 William St	Newark, NJ	07103-3004	973-286-1020	286-1050	K-8	Theresa Adubato
Union County TEAMS Charter S	515 W 4th St	Plainfield, NJ	07060-4225	908-754-9043	754-7790	K-12	Sheila Thorpe
Unity Charter S	1 Evergreen Pl	Morristown, NJ	07960-4012	973-292-1808	267-9288	K-8	Carolyn Mungo
University Academy Charter HS	275 W Side Ave	Jersey City, NJ	07305-1130	201-200-3200	200-3262	9-12	Erie Lugo
University Heights Charter S	74 Hartford St	Newark, NJ	07103-2832	973-623-1965	623-8511	K-5	Misha Simmonds B.A.
Varisco-Rogers Charter S	233 Woodside Ave	Newark, NJ	07104-3113	973-481-9001	481-9009	K-8	Teresa Segarra
Village Charter S	101 Sullivan Way	Trenton, NJ	08628-3425	609-695-0110	695-1880	K-8	Keoke Wooten-Johnson
Vineland Public Charter S	610 E Montrose St	Vineland, NJ	08360-4660	856-691-1004	691-1005	K-5	Dr. Ann Garcia
Visions Academy Charter HS	88 Shipman St	Newark, NJ	07102	973-230-0605	643-4982	9-12	Fred Givens

New Mexico

School	Address	City,State	Zip code	Telephone	Fax	Grade	Contact
Academia De Lengua Y Cultura	1900 Randolph Rd SE	Albuquerque, NM	87106-4247	505-563-4242	563-4260	6-8	
Academy for Technology and the Classics	74 A Van NU PO	Santa Fe, NM	87508-1465	505-473-4282	467-6513	7-12	Susan Lumley
Academy of Trades & Technology	2551 Karsten Ct SE	Albuquerque, NM	87102-5083	505-765-5517	244-0341	9-12	Arlene Trujillo
ACE Leadership HS	800 20th St NW	Albuquerque, NM	87104-2043	505-242-4733	242-2220	9-12	Tony Monfiletto
Albuquerque Institute of Math & Science	933 Bradbury Dr SE	Albuquerque, NM	87106-4374	505-559-4249	243-9235	6-12	Kathy Sandoval-Snider
Albuquerque School of Excellence	13201 Lomas Blvd NE	Albuquerque, NM	87112-7001	505-312-7711	312-7712	1-12	Ahmet Cetinkaya
Albuquerque Sign Language Academy	620 Lomas Blvd NW	Albuquerque, NM	87102-2080	505-247-1701	247-1704	K-8	Rafe Martinez
Albuquerque Talent Development Charter S	1900 Atrisco Dr NW	Albuquerque, NM	87120-1146	505-503-2465	831-7031	9-12	
Alma D Arte Charter HS	505 S Main St Ste 249	Las Cruces, NM	88001-1243	575-541-0145	541-0146	9-12	Mark Harshorne
Anansi Charter S	PO Box 1709	El Prado, NM	87529-1709	575-776-2256	776-5561	K-5	Michele Hunt
Anthony Charter S	PO Box 355	Anthony, NM	88021-0355	575-882-0600	882-0603	7-12	Colleen Adolph
ASK Academy	1380 Rio Rancho Dr SE # 361	Rio Rancho, NM	87124-1006	505-891-0757	891-2115	8-12	Pamela Correa
Bataan Military Academy	8001 Mountain Road Pl NE	Albuquerque, NM	87110-7808	505-292-5588	232-3230	9-12	
Bernell Charter S	100 John Dantis Rd SW	Albuquerque, NM	87151-0100	505-468-7701	468-7711	9-12	Greta Roskom
Biehl Charter HS	123 4th St SW	Albuquerque, NM	87102-3201	505-299-9409	299-9493	9-12	Mike May
Carinos De Los Ninos S	PO Box 130	Espanola, NM	87532	505-753-1128	753-1130	K-8	Vernon Jaramillo
Chavez Community S	1325 Palomas Dr SE	Albuquerque, NM	87108-4718	505-877-0558	242-1466	9-12	Caryl Thomas
Cien Aguas International S	3501 Campus Blvd NE	Albuquerque, NM	87106-1311	505-255-0001	255-0400	K-8	Michael Rodriguez
Coral Community Charter S	PO Box 11494	Albuquerque, NM	87192-0494	505-292-6725		K-3	Donna Eldredge
Corrales International S	3821 Singer Blvd NE	Albuquerque, NM	87109-5804	505-344-9733	338-1409	K-10	Dr. Elsy Fierro Diaz
Cottonwood Classical Preparatory S	1776 Montano Rd NW Bldg 3	Los Ranchos, NM	87107-3248	505-998-1021	341-9510	6-12	Sam Obenshain
Cottonwood Valley Charter S	PO Box 1829	Socorro, NM	87801-1829	575-838-2026	838-2420	K-8	Karin Williams
Creative Education Prep Institute #1	4801 Montano Rd NW	Albuquerque, NM	87120-2428	505-314-2374	314-2377	9-12	Jeff Arthur
Deming Cesar Chavez Charter HS	315 E 1st St	Deming, NM	88030-3104	575-544-8404	544-8755	9-12	Paul Reeves
Digital Arts and Technology Academy	1011 Lamberton Pl NE	Albuquerque, NM	87107-1641	505-341-0888	341-0749	9-12	
Dorn Community Charter S	1119 Edith Blvd SE	Albuquerque, NM	87102-4486	505-764-8867	217-3835	K-2	Dr. Elisabeth Valenzuela
Duncan Heritage Academy	816 Broadway Blvd SE	Albuquerque, NM	87102-4210	505-839-4971	831-9027	K-5	
East Mountain HS	PO Box 340	Sandia Park, NM	87047-0340	505-281-7400	281-4173	9-12	Doug Wine
El Camino Real Charter S	3713 Isleta Blvd SW	Albuquerque, NM	87105-5990	505-314-2212	314-2216	K-12	Gene Johnson
Estancia Valley Classical Academy	PO Box 2340	Moriarty, NM	87035-2340	505-832-2223		K-12	Larry Miller
GREAT Academy	6001A San Mateo Blvd NE	Albuquerque, NM	87109	505-792-0306	792-0225	9-12	Jasper Matthews
Gutierrez MS	PO Box 1437	Roswell, NM	88202-1437	575-347-9703	347-9707	6-8	Joe Andreis
Health Leadership HS	800 20th St NW Ste B	Albuquerque, NM	87104-2043	505-750-4547		9-12	Gabriella Blakey
Horizon Academy - West	1900 Atrisco Dr NW	Albuquerque, NM	87120-1146	505-998-0459	998-0463	K-6	Amie Duran
International S at Mesa del Sol	2660 Eastman Ave SE	Albuquerque, NM	87106-9716	505-508-3295	508-3328	K-8	Dr. Sean Joyce
Jefferson Montessori Academy	500 W Church St	Carlsbad, NM	88220-5135	575-234-1703	887-9391	K-12	Cindy Holguin
Kennedy HS	4300 Blake Rd SW	Albuquerque, NM	87121-5179	505-873-1165	242-7444	9-12	
King Community S	1905 Mountain Rd NW	Albuquerque, NM	87104-1452	505-344-0746	344-0789	K-6	
La Academia de Esperanza	5200 Sequoia Rd NW	Albuquerque, NM	87120-1208	505-764-5500	764-5501	6-12	Steve Woods
La Academia Dolores Huerta	505 S Main St Ste 249	Las Cruces, NM	88001-1243	575-526-2984	523-2924	6-8	Gilbert Gutierrez
La Jicarita Community S	PO Box 552	Penasco, NM	87553-0552	575-692-3200		K-5	Frank Fastwolf
La Promesa Early Learning Center	5201 Central Ave NW	Albuquerque, NM	87105-1970	505-268-3274	268-3276	K-8	Dr. Analee Maestas
La Resolana Leadership Academy	1718 Yale Blvd SE	Albuquerque, NM	87106-4246	505-243-8114	243-8385	6-8	Justina Montoya
Las Montanas Charter S	505 S Main St Ste 249	Las Cruces, NM	88001-1243	575-636-2100	527-7686	9-10	Richard Robinson
La Tierra Montessori S of the Arts & Sci	State Road 68 Building 854	Alcalde, NM	87511	505-852-0200	852-0326	K-8	Sandy Beerry
Learning Community Charter S	5555 McLeod Rd NE	Albuquerque, NM	87109-2408	505-332-3200	332-8780	6-12	Ken Lairsey
Leopold Charter S	1422 Highway 180 E	Silver City, NM	88061-7837	575-538-2547	388-4970	9-12	Eric Ahner
Lindrith Area Heritage Charter S	PO Box 119	Lindrith, NM	87029-0119	575-774-6669	774-6669	K-8	Rebecca Gibson
Los Puentes Charter S	4012 4th St NW	Albuquerque, NM	87107-3551	505-342-5959	341-0836	7-12	Ellen Moore
MASTERS Program	6401 S Richards Ave	Santa Fe, NM	87508-4887	505-428-7320	428-7322	10-12	Anne Salzmann
McCurdy Charter S	PO Box 2250	Espanola, NM	87532-2250	505-692-6090	692-6095	K-12	Janette Archuleta
Media Arts Collaborative S	4401 Central Ave NE	Albuquerque, NM	87108-1209	505-243-1957	268-1651	6-12	Glenna Voigt
Middle College HS	200 College Rd Ste 9	Gallup, NM	87301-5603	505-722-9945	722-9946	10-12	Wally Feldman
Mission Achievement & Success Charter S	1718 Yale Blvd SE	Albuquerque, NM	87106-4286	505-242-3118	243-3062	6-7	JoAnn Myers
Monte Del Sol Charter S	PO Box 4068	Santa Fe, NM	87502-4068	505-982-5225	982-5321	7-12	Dr. James Ledyard
Montessori ES	3831 Midway Pl NE	Albuquerque, NM	87109-5864	505-796-0149	796-0147	K-8	Mary Jane Besante
Montessori of the Rio Grande Charter S	1650 Gabaldon Dr NW	Albuquerque, NM	87104-2761	505-842-5993	242-2907	K-6	
Moreno Valley HS	PO Box 1037	Angel Fire, NM	87710-1037	575-377-3100	377-7263	9-12	Jacque Boyd
Mosaic Academy	450 Llano St	Aztec, NM	87410-2201	505-334-6364	334-6364	K-8	Bonnie Braden
Mountain Mahogany Community S	5014 4th St NW	Albuquerque, NM	87107-3908	505-341-1424	341-1428	K-8	
Native American Community Academy	1100 Cardenas Dr SE	Albuquerque, NM	87108-4809	505-266-0992	266-2905	6-12	
New America S - Las Cruces	PO Box 16680	Las Cruces, NM	88004-6680	575-527-9085		9-12	
New America School	1734 Isleta Blvd SW	Albuquerque, NM	87105-4636	505-222-4360	873-2602	9-12	Margarita Porter
New Mexico International School	4261 Balloon Park Rd NE	Albuquerque, NM	87109-5802	505-433-3250		K-5	LaTricia Mathis
New Mexico School for the Arts	275 E Alameda St	Santa Fe, NM	87501-2113	505-310-4194	629-4108	9-12	Dr. Carlos Pagan
New Mexico Virtual Academy	PO Box 1679	Farmington, NM	87499-1679	505-436-2383	258-4080	6-12	Cindy Montoya
North Valley Academy	7939 4th St NW	Los Ranchos, NM	87114-1008	505-998-0501	998-0505	K-8	Ashley Barr
Nuestros Valores Charter S	1021 Isleta Blvd SW	Albuquerque, NM	87105-3934	505-873-7758	873-3567	9-12	Stephanie Belmore
Public Academy for Performing Arts	3000 Adams St NE	Albuquerque, NM	87110-8051	505-830-3128	830-9930	6-12	
Red River Valley Charter S	PO Box 742	Red River, NM	87558-0742	575-754-6117	754-3258	PK-8	Karen Phillips
Rio Gallinas S	301 Socorro St	Las Vegas, NM	87701-3353	505-454-8687	454-8688	1-8	Tom Goss
Roots & Wings Community S	HC 81 Box 22	Questa, NM	87556-9712	575-586-2076	586-2087	K-8	Al Spungen
Sage Montessori Charter S	5120 Masthead St NE	Albuquerque, NM	87109-4366	505-797-4305	797-4294	K-8	Algene Herrick
SAMS Academy	4100 Aerospace Pkwy NW	Albuquerque, NM	87120-8792	505-338-8601	296-0510	7-12	Dr. Scott Glasrud
San Diego Riverside S	PO Box 99	Jemez Pueblo, NM	87024-0099	575-834-7419	834-9167	K-8	Arlene Lorreto
School for Integrated Academics & Tech	1500 Indian School Rd NW	Albuquerque, NM	87104-2306	505-242-6640	242-6872	9-12	
School of Dreams Academy	1800 Main St NE	Los Lunas, NM	87031	505-866-7632	866-0780	7-12	Michael Ogas
Sena Charter HS	69 Hotel Cir NE	Albuquerque, NM	87123-1202	505-237-2373	237-2380	9-12	Nadine Torres
South Valley Academy	3426 Blake Rd SW	Albuquerque, NM	87105-5009	505-452-3132	452-3133	9-12	
South Valley Preparatory S	2813 Gun Club Rd SW	Albuquerque, NM	87105-6333	505-222-5642	222-5647	6-8	Charlotte Trujillo
Southwest Intermediate Learning Center	10301 Candelaria Rd NE	Albuquerque, NM	87112-1504	505-296-7677	296-0510	7-8	Scott Glasrud Ph.D.
Southwest Primary Learning Center	10301 Candelaria Rd NE	Albuquerque, NM	87112-1504	505-296-7677	296-0510	4-6	Scott Glasrud Ph.D.

School	Address	City,State	Zip code	Telephone	Fax	Grade	Contact
Southwest Secondary Learning Center	10301 Candelaria Rd NE	Albuquerque, NM	87112-1504	505-296-7677	296-0510	7-12	Scott Glasrud
Taos Academy	110 Paseo Del Canon W	Taos, NM	87571-6743	575-751-3109	751-3394	5-12	Traci Filiss
Taos Integrated School of the Arts	PO Box 668	Taos, NM	87571-0668	575-758-7755	758-7766	K-8	Sandy Beery
Taos Municipal Charter S	1303 Paseo Del Canon	Taos, NM	87571-6738	575-751-7222	751-7546	K-8	Dr. Deidre McAdam
Taylor Academy	3900 Del Rey Blvd	Las Cruces, NM	88012-7992	575-652-4006	652-4621	K-8	Cynthia Risner
Tierra Adentro - NM Sch Acedemics/Art	1511 Central Ave NE	Albuquerque, NM	87106-4408	505-967-4720	967-4721	6-12	Veronica Torres
Tierra Encantada Charter HS	551 Alarid St Ste A	Santa Fe, NM	87501-3733	505-983-3337	983-6637	7-12	Daniel Benavidez
Turqoise Trail ES	13a San Marcos Loop	Santa Fe, NM	87508-7083	505-467-1700	474-7862	PK-6	Sandra Davis
Twenty-First Century Public Academy	6805 Academy Pkwy West NE	Albuquerque, NM	87109	505-254-0280	254-8507	5-8	Donna Eldredge
Uplift Community S	406 Highway 564	Gallup, NM	87301	505-863-4333		K-4	Jennifer Mercer
Village Academy	PO Box 279	Bernalillo, NM	87004-0279	505-867-9094	867-0594	6-8	Karen Mayhew
Vista Grande HS	213 Paseo Del Canon E	Taos, NM	87571-6239	575-758-5100	758-5102	9-12	C.J. Grace
Walatowa Charter HS	PO Box 669	Jemez Pueblo, NM	87024-0669	575-834-0443	834-0449	9-12	Arrow Wilkinson

New York

School	Address	City,State	Zip code	Telephone	Fax	Grade	Contact
Academic Leadership Charter S	677 E 141st St	Bronx, NY	10454-2410	718-585-4215	585-4837	K-5	Norma Figueroa-Hurwitz
Academy Charter S	117 N Franklin St	Hempstead, NY	11550-1314	516-408-2200	292-2329	K-5	Clarence Williams
Academy of the City Charter S	3614 12th St	Astoria, NY	11106	718-487-9857	785-9592	K-2	Richard Lee
Achievement Academy Charter S	75 Park Ave	Albany, NY	12202-1742	518-533-1601	694-3666	5-8	O'Rita Swan
Achievement First Apollo Charter S	350 Linwood St	Brooklyn, NY	11208-2116	718-235-2647	235-2649	K-4	Jabari Sims
Achievement First Aspire Charter S	1137 Herkimer St	Brooklyn, NY	11233-3109	718-774-0906			
Achievement First Brooklyn HS	1485 Pacific St	Brooklyn, NY	11216-3204	718-363-2260	363-2262	9-12	Paul Adler
Achievement First Brownsville Charter S	2021 Bergen St	Brooklyn, NY	11233-4801	718-342-4302	346-3270	K-8	Keith Brooks
Achievement First Bushwick Charter S	1300 Greene Ave	Brooklyn, NY	11237-4502	718-453-0425	453-0428	K-12	Amy D'Angelo
Achievement First Crown Heights Charter	790 E New York Ave	Brooklyn, NY	11203-1212	718-774-0762	774-0830	K-12	Camilla Lopez
Achievement First East New York ES	557 Pennsylvania Ave	Brooklyn, NY	11207-5727	718-485-4924	342-5194	K-8	Hilary Cymrot
Achievement First Endeavor S	510 Waverly Ave	Brooklyn, NY	11238-2702	718-622-4786	789-1649	K-12	Tom Kaiser
Albany Community Charter S	65 Krank St	Albany, NY	12202-1150	518-433-1500	433-1501	K-4	S. Neal Currie
Albany Leadership Charter HS for Girls	19 Hackett Blvd	Albany, NY	12208-3407	518-694-5300	694-5307	9-12	Melissa Cedeno
Amani Charter S	PO Box 3022	Mount Vernon, NY	10553-3022	914-668-6450	699-0839	5-8	Debra Stern
Amber Charter S	220 E 106th St	New York, NY	10029-4020	212-534-9667	534-6225	K-6	Dr. Vasthi Acosta
Ark Community Charter S	762 River St	Troy, NY	12180-1231	518-274-6312	274-3615	K-6	Mary Streck
Bedford Stuyvesant Collegiate Charter S	800 Gates Ave	Brooklyn, NY	11221-2203	718-669-7460	669-7771	5-12	Mabel Lajes-Guiteras
Bed-Stuy New Beginnings Charter S	82 Lewis Ave	Brooklyn, NY	11206-7013	718-453-1001	452-2090	K-5	Joshua Morales
Beginning With Children Charter S	11 Bartlett St	Brooklyn, NY	11206-5001	718-388-8847	388-8936	K-8	Les King
Beginning With Children Charter S II	215 Heyward St	Brooklyn, NY	11206-2966	718-302-7700		PK-1	Esosa Ogbahon
Believe Northside Charter HS	198A Varet St	Brooklyn, NY	11206-3703	347-390-1273	390-1274	9-12	Reshma Baig
Brighter Choice Charter MS for Boys	395 Elk St	Albany, NY	12206-2707	518-703-6100	694-5551	5-8	Darryl Williams
Brighter Choice Charter MS for Girls	395 Elk St	Albany, NY	12206-2707	518-694-5550	694-5551	5-8	Darryl Williams
Brighter Choice Charter S for Boys	116 N Lake Ave	Albany, NY	12206-2710	518-694-8200	694-8201	K-4	Darryl Williams
Brighter Choice Charter S for Girls	250 Central Ave	Albany, NY	12206-2639	518-694-4100	694-4123	K-4	Darryl Williams
Brilla College Preparatory Charter S	354 E 91st St Apt 2006	New York, NY	10128-0090	212-402-4621		K-5	Scott Hamilton
Bronx Academy of Promise Charter S	1166 River Ave	Bronx, NY	10452-8305	718-681-8275	681-8225	K-8	Catherine Jackvony
Bronx Charter S for Better Learning	3740 Baychester Ave	Bronx, NY	10466-5031	718-655-6660	655-5555	K-5	Shubert Jacobs
Bronx Charter S for Children	388 Willis Ave	Bronx, NY	10454-1303	718-402-3300	402-3258	K-5	Doreen Land
Bronx Charter S for Excellence	1960 Benedict Ave	Bronx, NY	10462-4402	718-828-7301	828-7302	K-6	Charlene Reid
Bronx Charter S for the Arts	950 Longfellow Ave	Bronx, NY	10474-4809	718-893-1042	893-7910	K-5	Christina Brown
Bronx Community Charter S	2348 Webster Ave	Bronx, NY	10458	718-584-1400	584-2800	K-5	Martha Andrews
Bronx Global Learning Institute	750 Concourse Vlg W	Bronx, NY	10451-3865	718-993-1740	993-1965	K-5	Celia Domenich
Bronx Lighthouse Charter S	1001 Intervale Ave	Bronx, NY	10459-3151	646-915-0025	915-0037	K-10	Meghan Kimpton
Bronx Preparatory Charter S	3872 3rd Ave	Bronx, NY	10457-8222	718-294-0841	294-2381	5-12	Jacqueline Robinson
Brooklyn Ascend Lower S	205 Rockaway Pkwy	Brooklyn, NY	11212-3444	718-240-9162	240-9140	K-6	Brandon Sorlie
Brooklyn Charter S	545 Willoughby Ave	Brooklyn, NY	11206-6815	718-302-2085	302-2426	K-5	Omigbade Escayg
Brooklyn Dreams Charter S	259 Parkville Ave	Brooklyn, NY	11230-1310	718-859-8400	586-0347	K-6	Letta Belle
Brooklyn East Collegiate Charter S	80 Underhill Ave	Brooklyn, NY	11238-3509	718-250-5760	250-5761	5-8	Eric Green
Brooklyn Excelsior Charter S	856 Quincy St	Brooklyn, NY	11221-3612	718-246-5681	246-5864	K-8	Dr. Tom Demarco
Brooklyn Prospect Charter S	3002 Fort Hamilton Pkwy	Brooklyn, NY	11218-1608	347-889-7041	889-7083	6-12	LaNolia Omowanile
Brooklyn Scholars Charter S	2635 Linden Blvd	Brooklyn, NY	11208-4907	718-348-9360	348-9362	K-8	Desiree Kirton
Brooklyn S of Inquiry	50 Avenue P	Brooklyn, NY	11204-6105	718-621-5730	621-5735	K-8	Donna Taylor
Brooklyn Urban Garden S	111 Broadway Rm 604	New York, NY	10006-1975	212-437-8318		6-8	Linda Rosenbury
Broome Street Academy	121 Avenue of the Americas	New York, NY	10013-1510	212-453-0295	966-7253	9-12	Jeremy Kaplan
Brownsville Ascend Charter S	1501 Pitkin Ave	Brooklyn, NY	11212-4181	718-240-9162	240-9140	K-6	Kelli Bowers
Brownsville Collegiate Charter S	364 Sackman St	Brooklyn, NY	11212-7614	718-636-0370	296-8321	5-9	Jessica Simmons
Buffalo Academy of Science Charter S	190 Franklin St	Buffalo, NY	14202-2407	716-854-2490	854-5039	7-12	Mustafa Ersoy
Buffalo United Charter S	325 Manhattan Ave	Buffalo, NY	14214-1809	716-835-9862	835-6272	K-8	Tammy Messmer
Bushwick Ascend Charter S	751 Knickerbocker Ave	Brooklyn, NY	11221-5336	718-240-9162	484-0498	K-3	Dellianna Burrows
Canarsie Ascend Charter S	9719 Flatlands Ave	Brooklyn, NY	11236-3729	718-907-0153		K-1	Brenda Daniels
Central Queens Academy Charter S	5530 Junction Blvd	Elmhurst, NY	11373-4622	718-271-6200		5-5	Jesse Tang
Challenge Preparatory Charter S	710 Hartman Ln	Far Rockaway, NY	11691-1849	347-634-1634	634-1637	K-3	Latoiya Tolliver-Revell
Charter S for Applied Technologies	2303 Kenmore Ave	Buffalo, NY	14207-1311	716-876-7505	876-9758	K-12	Andrew Lyle
Charter S of Educational Excellence	260 Warburton Ave	Yonkers, NY	10701-2226	914-476-5070	476-2858	K-7	Catalina Castillo
Child Dev. Center / Hamptons Charter S	110 Stephen Hands Path	East Hampton, NY	11937	631-324-0207	324-4112	K-8	Robert Budd
Children's Aid Society Charter S	1919 Prospect Ave	Bronx, NY	10457-6506	347-871-9002		K-1	Lenard Ife
City Polytechnic HS	105 Johnson St	Brooklyn, NY	11201-2915	718-875-1473	875-1947	9-12	Christopher Aguirre
Community Charter S	404 Edison Ave	Buffalo, NY	14215-2936	716-833-5967	833-5985	K-6	Denise Luka
Community Partnership Charter S	241 Emerson Pl	Brooklyn, NY	11205-3808	718-399-3824	399-2149	K-5	Anna Sathe
Community Roots Charter S	51 Saint Edwards St	Brooklyn, NY	11205-2932	718-858-1629	858-1754	K-6	Allison Keil
Coney Island Prep Public Charter S	501 West Ave	Brooklyn, NY	11224-4220	718-513-6951	513-6955	6-8	Jacob Mnookin
Cultural Arts Academy at Spring Creek	1400 Linden Blvd	Brooklyn, NY	11212-5149	718-683-3300	272-1330	K-3	Laurie Midgette
de Hostos Charter S	938 Clifford Ave	Rochester, NY	14621-4808	585-544-6170	544-3848	K-8	Jeffrey Halsdorfer
Democracy Preparatory Harlem Charter S	222 W 134th St	New York, NY	10030-3002	212-281-3061	281-3064	6-8	Emmanuel George
Democracy Prep Charter S	207 W 133rd St	New York, NY	10030-3201	212-281-1248	283-4202	6-8	Emmanuel George
Democracy Prep Endurance Charter S	250 W 127th St	New York, NY	10027-2957	212-212-1248		6-8	Margaret Marrer
Democracy Prep MSHS	2230 5th Ave	New York, NY	10037-2102	212-281-1248	283-4202	6-12	Lisa Friscia
Discovery Charter S	125 Kings Hwy S	Rochester, NY	14617-5502	585-342-4032	342-4003	K-2	Joseph Saia
DREAM Charter S	232 E 103rd St	New York, NY	10029-5458	212-722-0232	348-5979	K-8	Eva Colavito
Eagle Academy for Young Men III	17110 Linden Blvd	Jamaica, NY	11434-1327	718-723-4703	723-4709	6-8	Kenyatte Reid
East Harlem Scholars Academy	1573 Madison Ave	New York, NY	10029-3819	212-348-2518	831-7967	K-2	Cheyenne Sao Roque
Elmwood Village Charter S	40 Days Park	Buffalo, NY	14201-2008	716-886-4581	348-3707	K-8	John Sheffield
Enterprise Charter S	275 Oak St	Buffalo, NY	14203-1638	716-855-2114	855-2967	K-8	Jill Norton
Equality Charter S	4140 Hutchinson River Pkwy	Bronx, NY	10475	718-320-3032	320-3721	6-8	Caitlin Franco
Equity Project Charter S	549 Audubon Ave	New York, NY	10040-3401	646-254-6451	202-3584	5-8	Zeke Vanderhoek
Ethical Community Charter S	700 Park Ave	Brooklyn, NY	11206-5269	718-599-2176	599-2814	K-4	Annette Keane
Evergreen Charter S	605 Peninsula Blvd	Hempstead, NY	11550-5424	516-292-2060		K-5	Rosa Escoto
Excellence Charter S	239 Patchen Ave	Brooklyn, NY	11233	718-638-1830	638-2548	K-9	Kevin Hall
Excellence Charter S for Girls	794 Monroe St	Brooklyn, NY	11221-3501	718-638-1875	228-6670	K-4	Celestina De La Garza
Explore Charter S	655 Parkside Ave	Brooklyn, NY	11226-1505	718-703-4484	703-8550	K-8	Rod Bowen
Explore Empower Charter S	188 Rochester Ave	Brooklyn, NY	11213-3102	718-771-2090	771-2128	K-5	Beth Doyle
Explore Exceed Charter S	443 Saint Marks Ave	Brooklyn, NY	11238-3707	718-989-6702		K-8	Curtis Palmore
Explore Excel Charter S	1077 Remsen Ave	Brooklyn, NY	11236-3451	347-902-1758	272-1827	K-4	Dana Bogle
Fahari Academy Charter S	72 Veronica Pl	Brooklyn, NY	11226-4122	718-282-5139	282-5397	5-8	Dirk Tillotson
Family Life Academy Charter S	14 W 170th St	Bronx, NY	10452-3227	718-410-8100	410-8800	K-8	Angel Rodriguez
Family Life Academy Charter S II	296 E 140th St	Bronx, NY	10454-1125	718-665-2808	665-2811	K-1	Lourdes Arroyo
Future Leaders Institute	134 W 122nd St	New York, NY	10027-5501	212-678-2868	666-2749	K-8	Ismael Colon
Genesee Community Charter S	657 East Ave	Rochester, NY	14607-2101	585-697-1960	271-5904	K-6	Lisa Wing
Girls Preparatory Charter S	442 E Houston St	New York, NY	10002-1122	212-388-0241	388-1086	K-8	Anne Lackritz
Girls Preparatory Charter S of the Bronx	681 Kelly St Rm 205	Bronx, NY	10455-3410	718-292-2113	292-5586	K-4	Josie Carbone
Global Community Charter S	421 W 145th St	New York, NY	10031-5203	888-717-9993		K-1	Phyllis Siwiec
Global Concepts Charter S	1001 Ridge Rd	Lackawanna, NY	14218-1755	716-821-1903	821-9563	K-11	Richard Fill
Grand Concourse Charter S	116 E 169th St	Bronx, NY	10452-7704	718-590-1300	590-1065	K-5	Ira Victor
Great Oaks Charter S	PO Box 845	New York, NY	10274-0845	212-437-8332		6-6	Kristin Levine
Green Dot NY Charter S	600 Saint Anns Ave	Bronx, NY	10455-2800	718-585-0560	585-0563	9-12	Ashish Kapadia
Green Tech High Charter S	321 Northern Blvd	Albany, NY	12210-2635	518-694-3400	694-3401	9-12	Dr. Paul Miller
Growing Up Green Charter S	3927 28th St	Long Is City, NY	11101-3728	347-642-4306	642-4310	K-4	Matthew Greenberg
Hahn Expeditionary Learning S	5800 Tilden Ave	Brooklyn, NY	11203-4824	718-629-1204	629-1076	9-12	Matt Brown
Harbor Science & Arts Charter S	1 E 104th St	New York, NY	10029-4418	212-427-2244	360-7429	K-8	Joanne Hunt
Harlem Childrens Zone Promise Academy I	35 E 125th St	New York, NY	10035-1816	212-534-0700	289-0661	K-12	Tonya White
Harlem Childrens Zone Promise Academy II	2005 Madison Ave	New York, NY	10035-1215	917-492-1481	492-1576	K-8	Kathy Fernald
Harlem Hebrew Language Academy Charter S	6 E 39th St Fl 10	New York, NY	10016-0112	646-801-2427	537-0280	K-1	Robin Natman
Harlem Link Charter S	20 W 112th St	New York, NY	10026-3902	212-289-3249	289-3686	K-5	Steven Evangelista
Harlem Prep Charter S	240 E 123rd St Frnt 1	New York, NY	10035-2068	212-876-9953	876-9926	K-6	Lindsay Malanga
Harlem Village Academy Charter S	244 W 144th St	New York, NY	10030-1202	646-812-9300	548-9576	5-12	Laurie Warner
Harlem Village Acad Ldrshp Charter S	2351 1st Ave	New York, NY	10035-3422	646-812-9400	996-1626	5-12	Lisa Fromelt
Health Sciences Charter S	1140 Ellicott St	Buffalo, NY	14209-1934	716-549-4157	464-7623	9-12	Dr. Hank Stopinski
Hebrew Language Academy Charter S	1340 E 29th St	Brooklyn, NY	11210-5315	718-377-7200	377-7220	K-4	Laura Silver
Heketi Community Charter S	423 E 138th St	Bronx, NY	10454-3041	347-361-0211		K-8	Cythia Rosario

School	Address	City,State	Zip code	Telephone	Fax	Grade	Contact
Hellenic Classical Charter S	646 5th Ave	Brooklyn, NY	11215-5401	718-499-0957	499-0959	K-8	Christine Tettonis
Hyde Leadership Charter S	730 Bryant Ave	Bronx, NY	10474-6006	718-991-5500	842-8617	K-12	Betsy Olney
Hyde Leadership Charter S	330 Alabama Ave	Brooklyn, NY	11207-4005	718-495-5620	495-5827	K-5	Sandra DuPree
Icahn Charter S 1	1525 Brook Ave	Bronx, NY	10457-8005	718-716-8105	214-6596	K-8	Daniel Garcia
Icahn Charter S 2	1640 Bronxdale Ave	Bronx, NY	10462-3302	212-828-6107	828-7308	K-7	Brenda Carrasquillo
Icahn Charter S 3	1500 Pelham Pkwy S	Bronx, NY	10461-1100	718-294-4827	294-4952	K-6	Midga Agosto
Icahn Charter S 4	1500 Pelham Pkwy S	Bronx, NY	10461-1100	718-828-0034	828-0664	K-5	Michelle Allen
Icahn Charter S 5	1500 Pelham Pkwy S	Bronx, NY	10461-1100	718-828-0034	828-0664	K-3	Lawford Cunningham
Icahn Charter S 6	1701 Fulton Ave	Bronx, NY	10457-7546	718-716-8105		K-2	Brian Geelan
Icahn Charter S 7	1535 Story Ave	Bronx, NY	10473-4555	718-828-0034	828-0664	K-2	
Imagine Me Leadership Charter S	818 Schenck Ave	Brooklyn, NY	11207-7904	347-985-2140	985-2145	K-3	Dennis McKesey
Innovate Manhattan Charter S	38 Delancey St Fl 3	New York, NY	10002-4195	212-374-2301		6-8	Gayla Thompson
International Leadership Charter S	2900 Exterior St	Bronx, NY	10463-7103	212-562-2300	562-2335	9-12	Elaine Lopez
Invictus Preparatory Charter S	370 Fountain Ave	Brooklyn, NY	11208-4304	718-235-1682	235-1685	5-8	Cliff Thomas
Inwood Academy for Leadership Charter S	93 Nagle Ave	New York, NY	10040-1438	212-942-1450	942-2740	5-7	Christina Reyes
Izquierdo Health and Science Charter S	800 Home St	Bronx, NY	10456-5443	718-378-0490	378-0492	6-8	Anthony Lopez
Johnson Charter S	30 Watervliet Ave	Albany, NY	12206-1983	518-432-4300	432-4311	K-4	Kathleen O'Brien
Johnson Fruit Belt Community Charter S	833 Michigan Ave	Buffalo, NY	14203-1207	716-856-4390	856-4391	K-4	Elaine Hayes
King Center Charter S	938 Genesee St	Buffalo, NY	14211-3025	716-891-7912	895-2058	K-5	Dr. Claity Massey
King's Collegiate Charter S	1084 Lenox Rd	Brooklyn, NY	11212-1930	718-342-6047	342-6727	5-12	Scott Schuster
KIPP Academy Charter S	250 E 156th St	Bronx, NY	10451-4796	718-665-3555	585-7982	K-12	Natalie Webb
KIPP A.M.P. Charter S	1224 Park Pl	Brooklyn, NY	11213-2703	718-943-3710	774-3673	5-12	Natalie Webb
KIPP Infinity Charter S	625 W 133rd St	New York, NY	10027-7303	212-991-2600	234-8396	K-12	Alison Holley
KIPP S.T.A.R College Prep Charter S	433 W 123rd St	New York, NY	10027-5002	212-991-2650	666-4723	K-12	Orpheus Williams
KIPP Tech Valley Charter S	1 Dudley Hts	Albany, NY	12210-2601	518-694-9494	694-9411	5-8	Dustin Mitchell
KIPP Washington Heights MS	21 Jumel Pl	New York, NY	10032-4316	212-991-2620		5-5	Danny Swersky
La Cima Charter S	800 Gates Ave	Brooklyn, NY	11221-2203	718-443-2136	443-7291	K-5	Andrea Zayas
Launch Expeditionary Learning Charter S	1580 Dean St	Brooklyn, NY	11213-1713	718-221-1064		6-8	Geoffrey Roehm
Lavelle Preparatory Charter S	1 Teleport Dr	Staten Island, NY	10311	347-630-1760		6-9	Evelyn Finn
Leadership Preparatory Charter S	141 Macon St	Brooklyn, NY	11216-2206	718-636-0360	636-0747	K-7	Sultana Noormuhammad
Leadership Preparatory Ocean Hill S	51 Christopher Ave	Brooklyn, NY	11212-8014	718-250-5767	250-5768	K-3	Nikeya Bridges
Leadership Prep Brownsville Charter S	985 Rockaway Ave	Brooklyn, NY	11212-5152	718-669-7461	228-6496	K-4	Darcy Richie
Lefferts Gardens Charter S	601 Parkside Ave	Brooklyn, NY	11226-1509	718-284-1480	284-2162	K-3	Karen Palmer
Lindsay Wildcat Academy Charter S	17 Battery Pl	New York, NY	10004-1207	212-209-6006	635-3874	9-12	Ronald Tabano
Manhattan Charter S	100 Attorney St	New York, NY	10002-3405	212-533-2743	533-2820	K-5	Genie Depolo
Manhattan Charter S II	220 Henry St	New York, NY	10002-4815	212-533-2743		K-1	Joanne Mejias
Merrick Academy-Queens Public Charter S	20701 Jamaica Ave	Queens Village, NY	11428-1544	718-479-3753	479-8108	K-6	Tonya Johnson
MESA Charter HS	231 Palmetto St	Brooklyn, NY	11221-4712	917-257-6876		9-12	Arthur Samuels
Metropolitan Lighthouse Charter S	1535 Story Ave	Bronx, NY	10473-4555	718-893-0640	893-0675	K-5	Courtney Russell
Middle Village Prep Charter S	6802 Metropolitan Ave	Middle Village, NY	11379-1622	718-869-2933		6-8	
Mott Hall Charter S	1260 Franklin Ave	Bronx, NY	10456-3502	917-526-2746		6-6	Geovanti Steward
Mott Haven Academy Charter S	170 Brown Pl	Bronx, NY	10454-4140	718-292-7015	292-7823	K-5	Jessica Nauiokas
Neighborhood Charter S of Harlem	132 W 124th St	New York, NY	10027-4919	646-701-7117		K-1	Brett Gallini
New American Academy Charter S	60 E 94th St	Brooklyn, NY	11212-2349	845-570-3217		K-1	Matt Harrington
Newburgh Preparatory Charter HS	471 Broadway	Newburgh, NY	12550-5332	845-541-3432		9-12	Thomas Fitzgerald
New Dawn Charter HS	242 Hoyt St	Brooklyn, NY	11217-2913	347-505-9103		9-12	Sarah Asmussen
New Heights Academy Charter S	1818 Amsterdam Ave	New York, NY	10031-1715	212-283-5400	507-9314	5-12	Robert Parkes
New Hope Academy Charter S	475 E 57th St	Brooklyn, NY	11203-6010	718-337-8303		K-5	Keishea Allen
New Roots Charter S	PO Box 936	Ithaca, NY	14851-0936	607-882-9220	882-9230	9-12	Tina Nilsen-Hodges
New Visions Charter HS for Humanities	99 Terrace View Ave	Bronx, NY	10463-5079	718-817-7686		9-12	Seth Levin
New Visions Charter HS Humanities II	455 Southern Blvd	Bronx, NY	10455-4911	718-665-5380		9-12	Richard Gonzlez
New Visions Charter HS II	900 Tinton Ave	Bronx, NY	10456-7411	718-665-3671		9-12	Stacey King
New Visions Charter HS Math & Science	99 Terrace View Ave	Bronx, NY	10463-5079	718-817-7683		9-12	Julia Chun
New World Preparatory Charter S	26 Sharpe Ave	Staten Island, NY	10302-1234	718-705-8990	442-1583	6-8	Jamie Esperon
NY Center for Autism Charter S	433 E 100th St	New York, NY	10029-6606	212-860-2580	860-2960	K-8	Julie Fisher
New York City Montessori Charter S	423 E 138th St Ste 201	Bronx, NY	10454-3041	347-226-9094	226-9097	K-5	Gina Sardi
New York French American Charter S	311 W 17th St	New York, NY	10011-5071	212-666-4134	666-4138	K-12	Marie Bernard
Niagara Charter S	2077 Lockport Rd	Niagara Falls, NY	14304-1109	716-297-4520	297-4617	K-6	Karen Marchioli
NYC Charter HS for AECI	838 Brook Ave	Bronx, NY	10451-4620	646-400-5566	585-4780	9-12	Eugene Foley
Ocean Hill Collegiate Charter S	1137 Herkimer St	Brooklyn, NY	11233-3109	718-250-5765	250-5766	5-6	Hannah Solomon
Opportunity Charter S	240 W 113th St	New York, NY	10026-3306	212-866-6137	665-7436	6-12	Marya Baker
Oracle Charter S	888 Delaware Ave	Buffalo, NY	14209-2008	716-362-3188	362-3187	9-12	John Ashwood
Our World Neighborhood Charter S	3612 35th Ave	Astoria, NY	11106-1227	718-392-3405	392-2840	K-8	Brian Ferguson
PAVE Academy	71 Sullivan St	Brooklyn, NY	11231-1600	718-858-7813	858-7814	K-5	Spencer Robertson
Peninsula Prep Academy Charter S	611 Beach 19th St	Far Rockaway, NY	11691	347-403-9231	318-4561	K-5	Ruth Peets-Butcher
Pinnacle Charter S	115 Ash St	Buffalo, NY	14204-1452	716-842-1244	842-1242	K-8	Linda Marszalek
Professional Preparatory Charter S	616 Quincy St	Brooklyn, NY	11221-1812	718-285-3787	919-0486	K-5	Rafiq Kalam Id-Din
Renaissance Charter HS for Innovation	410 E 100th St	New York, NY	10029-6604	212-722-5871	430-8555	9-12	Nicholas Tishuk
Renaissance Charter S	3559 81st St	Jackson Heights, NY	11372-5033	718-803-0060	803-3785	K-12	Stacey Gauthier
Riverhead Charter S	3685 Middle Country Rd	Calverton, NY	11933-1807	631-369-5252	369-6687	K-6	Dorothy Porteus
Riverton Street Charter S	11834 Riverton St	Saint Albans, NY	11412-4024	718-481-8200	923-3315	K-5	Verone Kennedy
ROADS Charter S I	1495 Herkimer St	Brooklyn, NY	11233-3491	718-280-9819		9-12	Travis Brown
ROADS Charter S II	1010 Rev James A Polite Ave	Bronx, NY	10459-3053	718-861-7515		9-12	Seth Litt
Rochdale Early Advantage Charter S	12205 Smith St	Jamaica, NY	11434-2522	718-978-0075	978-0110	K-3	Lena Richarson
Rochester Academy Charter S	841 Genesee St	Rochester, NY	14611-3817	585-235-4141	232-1357	7-12	Mehmet Demirtas
Rochester Career Mentoring Charter S	30 Hart St Ste 3	Rochester, NY	14605-1100	585-232-1045		9-12	Jennifer Borsa
Rochester Prep ES	899 Jay St	Rochester, NY	14611-1219	585-235-0008	235-0014	K-4	Jaimie Brillante
Rochester Prep MS - Brooks Campus	630 Brooks Ave	Rochester, NY	14619-2255	585-436-8629	436-5985	5-8	David McBride
Rochester Prep MS - West Campus	1020 Maple St	Rochester, NY	14611-1614	585-368-5090	368-5091	5-7	Kelli Ragin
Roosevelt Childrens Academy Charter S	55 Mansfield Ave	Roosevelt, NY	11575-1414	516-771-4870	771-4875	6-8	Dr. Sheila Maxwell
Roosevelt Childrens Academy Charter S	201 Debevoise Ave	Roosevelt, NY	11575-1715	516-442-2147	442-5430	K-1	Reshma Persad
Roosevelt Childrens Academy Charter S	105 Pleasant Ave	Roosevelt, NY	11575-2126	516-867-6202	867-6206	2-5	Chesika McNeil
St. Hope Leadership Academy	222 W 134th St	New York, NY	10030-3002	212-283-1204	283-1207	5-8	Constance Bond
Sisulu-Walker Charter S	125 W 115th St	New York, NY	10026-2908	212-663-8216	866-5793	K-5	Michelle Haynes
South Bronx Charter S Intl Culture/Arts	383 E139th St	Bronx, NY	10454	718-401-9216	401-9219	K-5	Evelyn Hay
South Bronx Classical Charter S	977 Fox St	Bronx, NY	10459-3320	718-860-4340	860-4125	K-5	Lester Long
South Buffalo Charter S	2219 S Park Ave	Buffalo, NY	14220-2202	716-826-7213	826-7168	K-8	Carrie Dzierba
Southside Academy Charter S	2200 Onondaga Creek Blvd	Syracuse, NY	13207-2300	315-476-3019	476-6639	K-8	Delvin Vick
Staten Island Community Charter S	309 Saint Pauls Ave	Staten Island, NY	10304-2217	347-857-6981	861-0601	K-3	Dr. Michael Courtney
Success Academy Charter Harlem 1	34 W 118th St	New York, NY	10026-1937	646-747-7170	457-5659	K-7	Jacqui Albers
Success Academy Charter Harlem 2	144 E 128th St Ste 3	New York, NY	10035-1329	646-442-6600	281-4638	K-8	Noah Green
Success Academy Charter Harlem 3	141 E 111th St	New York, NY	10029-2641	646-747-6700	478-9492	K-5	Richard Seigler
Success Academy Charter Harlem 4	240 W 113th St	New York, NY	10026-3306	646-442-6500	478-9493	K-5	Danique Loving
Success Academy Charter Harlem 5	301 W 140th St	New York, NY	10030-1406	646-380-2590	961-4731	K-3	Stacey Apatov
Success Academy Charter S Bed-Stuy 2	211 Throop Ave	Brooklyn, NY	11206-5701	718-704-1439		K-1	Beth David-Dillard
Success Academy Charter S Bed-Stuy 1	70 Tompkins Ave	Brooklyn, NY	11206-5616	718-635-3294	964-6598	K-2	Monica Burris
Success Academy Charter S Bronx 1	510 E 141st St	Bronx, NY	10454-2753	347-286-7950	479-1192	K-5	Michele Caracappa
Success Academy Charter S Bronx 2	968 Cauldwell Ave	Bronx, NY	10456-6804	347-286-7965	479-1194	K-8	Vanessa Bangser
Success Academy Charter S Cobble Hill	284 Baltic St	Brooklyn, NY	11201-6402	718-704-1460		K-1	Kerri Tabarcea
Success Academy Charter S Harlem Central	21 W 111th St Fl 2	New York, NY	10026-4328	646-569-5900		5-5	Jim Manly
Success Academy Charter S Harlem West	215 W 114th St Fl 5	New York, NY	10026-2802	646-569-5920		5-7	Andrea Klein
Success Academy Charter S Upper West	145 W 84th St Fl 2	New York, NY	10024-4614	646-274-1580		K-2	Carrie Roby
Success Academy Charter S Williamsburg	183 S 3rd St Fl 4	Brooklyn, NY	11211-5311	718-704-1419		K-1	Abigail Johnson
Summit Academy Charter S	27 Huntington St	Brooklyn, NY	11231-1824	718-875-1403	875-1891	6-9	Natasha Campbell
Syracuse Academy of Science Charter S	1001 Park Ave	Syracuse, NY	13204-2125	315-428-8997	428-9109	6-12	Tolga Hayali
Tapestry Charter S	65 Great Arrow Ave	Buffalo, NY	14216-3203	716-204-5883	204-5887	K-12	Lynn Bass
Tech International Charter S	3120 Corlear Ave	Bronx, NY	10463-3938	646-678-1934		6-6	Adjowah K. Scott
True North Troy Preparatory S	2 Polk St	Troy, NY	12180-5512	518-445-3100	445-3101	K-8	Bill Sherman
Tubman Charter S	3565 3rd Ave	Bronx, NY	10456-3403	718-537-9912	537-9858	K-8	Cleveland Person
UFT Charter S	300 Wyona St	Brooklyn, NY	11207-3522	718-922-0438	922-0543	K-12	Michelle White
Unity Prep S of Brooklyn	432 Monroe St	Brooklyn, NY	11221-1111	212-437-8372		6-12	Joshua Beauregard
University Preparatory Charter S	180 Raines Park	Rochester, NY	14613-1451	585-730-5135	730-5134	7-8	Joseph Munno
Urban Choice Charter S	545 Humboldt St	Rochester, NY	14610-1221	585-288-5702	654-9882	K-8	Christina Schermerhorn
Urban Dove Charter S	600 Lafayette Ave	Brooklyn, NY	11216-1020	718-783-8232		9-10	Marianne Rossant
Utica Academy of Science Charter S	1214 Lincoln Ave	Utica, NY	13502			6-12	Fehmi Damkaci
VOICE Charter S of NY	3715 13th St	Long Is City, NY	11101-6024	718-786-6213	537-1703	K-5	Frank Headley
West Buffalo Charter S	113 Lafayette Ave	Buffalo, NY	14213-1481	716-923-1534	768-0980	K-4	Andrea Todoro
Western NY Maritime Charter S	266 Genesee St	Buffalo, NY	14204-1453	716-842-6289	842-4241	9-12	Lawrence Astyk
Westminster Community Charter S	24 Westminster Ave	Buffalo, NY	14215-1614	716-816-3450	838-7458	K-8	Ayinde Rudolph
Williamsburg Charter S	198 Varet St	Brooklyn, NY	11206-3703	718-782-9830	464-7604	9-12	Marsha Spampinato
Williamsburg Collegiate Charter S	157 Wilson St	Brooklyn, NY	11211-7706	718-302-4018	302-4641	5-12	J. T. Leaird
Young Women's College Prep Charter S	1001 Lake Ave	Rochester, NY	14613-1720	585-627-1590	672-5680	7-12	Jennifer Gkourlias Ed.D.

North Carolina

School	Address	City,State	Zip code	Telephone	Fax	Grade	Contact
Academy of Moore County	12588 US Highway 15 501	Aberdeen, NC	28315-4955	910-757-0401	757-0403	K-5	Allyson Schoen
Alpha Academy	PO Box 35476	Fayetteville, NC	28303-0476	910-223-7711	678-9011	K-8	Eugene Slocum

School	Address	City,State	Zip code	Telephone	Fax	Grade	Contact
American Renaissance ES	132 E Broad St	Statesville, NC	28677-5852	704-924-8870	873-1398	K-5	Stephen Gay
American Renaissance MS	132 E Broad St	Statesville, NC	28677-5852	704-878-6009	878-9350	6-8	Stephen Gay
Arapahoe Charter S	9005 NC Highway 306 S	Arapahoe, NC	28510-9699	252-249-2599	249-1316	K-8	Tom McCarthy
Arts Based ES	1380 N Martin Luther King	Winston Salem, NC	27101	336-748-4116	748-4117	K-5	Robin Hollis
ArtSpace Charter S	2030 US 70 Hwy	Swannanoa, NC	28778-8211	828-298-2787	298-6221	K-8	Lori Cozzi
Bear Grass S	6344 E Bear Grass Rd	Williamston, NC	27892-8434	252-789-1010	789-1014	6-12	Donna Moore
Bethany Community MS	181 Bethany Rd	Reidsville, NC	27320-7464	336-951-2500	951-0087	6-8	Vicky Bethel
Bethel Hill Charter S	401 Bethel Hill School Rd	Roxboro, NC	27574-7503	336-599-2823	599-9299	K-6	John Betterton
Brevard Academy	299 Andante Ln	Brevard, NC	28712-9125	828-885-2665	862-3497	K-8	Anthony Helton
Bridges Charter S	2587 Pleasant Ridge Rd	State Road, NC	28676-9318	336-874-2721	874-3804	K-8	Paul Welborn
Cape Fear Center for Inquiry	2525 Wonder Way	Wilmington, NC	28401-8014	910-362-0000	362-0048	K-8	Lori Roy
Cape Lookout Marine Science HS	1108 Bridges St	Morehead City, NC	28557-3799	252-726-1601	726-5245	9-12	Teresa Parker
Carolina International S	8810 Hickory Ridge Rd	Harrisburg, NC	28075-7659	704-455-3847	455-4672	K-10	Mystica Nelmes
Carter Community S	4100 N Roxboro St	Durham, NC	27704-2122	919-797-2340	797-2343	K-8	Gail Taylor
Casa Esperanza Montessori S	2600 Sumner Blvd Ste 130	Raleigh, NC	27616-5146	919-855-9811	855-9813	PK-8	Diana Bush
Central Park S for Children	724 Foster St	Durham, NC	27701-2111	919-682-1200	683-1261	K-5	John Heffernan
Charlotte Secondary S	8310 McAlpine Park Dr	Charlotte, NC	28211-6247	704-295-0137	295-0156	6-8	Beth Warshauer
Charter Day S	7055 Bacons Way NE	Leland, NC	28451-7960	910-655-1214	655-1549	K-8	Mark Cramer
Chatham Charter S	PO Box 245	Siler City, NC	27344-0245	919-742-4550	742-2518	K-8	John Eldridge
Childrens Village Academy	PO Box 2206	Kinston, NC	28502-2206	252-939-1958	939-1242	K-8	Gloria Carr-Battle
CIS Academy	818 W 3rd St	Pembroke, NC	28372-7307	910-521-1669	521-1670	6-8	Billy Higgans
Clover Garden S	2454 Altamahaw Union Ridge	Burlington, NC	27217	336-586-9440	586-9477	K-12	Walter Finnigan
College Preparatory & Leadership Academy	300 NC Highway 68 S	Greensboro, NC	27409-9638	336-264-5573		K-4	Dr. Michelle Johnson
Columbus Charter S	35 Bacons Way	Whiteville, NC	28472-6225	910-641-4042	641-4043	K-5	Steven Smith
Community Charter S	510 S Torrence St	Charlotte, NC	28204-3160	704-377-3180	377-3182	K-5	Anissa Miller
Community S of Davidson	565 Griffith St	Davidson, NC	28036-9326	704-896-6262	896-2025	K-12	Joy Warner
Cornerstone Charter Academy	2535 New Garden Rd E	Greensboro, NC	27455-1822	336-482-3855	482-3857	K-6	Brent Smith
Corvian Community School	9501 David Taylor Dr	Charlotte, NC	28262-2360	704-717-7550	717-7558	K-4	Stacey Haskell
Crosscreek Charter S	306 Sandalwood Ave	Louisburg, NC	27549-2650	919-497-3198	497-0232	K-8	Robin Jackson
Crossnore Academy	PO Box 309	Crossnore, NC	28616-0309	828-733-5241	737-7915	K-12	Cyndi Austin Ed.D.
Crossroads Charter HS	5500 N Tryon St	Charlotte, NC	28213-7120	704-597-5100	597-3941	9-12	Gentry Campbell
Delany New S	119 Brevard Rd	Asheville, NC	28806-2922	828-236-9441	236-9442	K-8	Buffy Fowler
Dillard Academy	PO Box 1188	Goldsboro, NC	27533-1188	919-581-0166	581-0122	K-4	Hilda Hicks
East Wake Academy	400 NMC Dr	Zebulon, NC	27597-2759	919-404-0444	404-2377	K-12	Stephen Gay
Endeavor Charter S	9400 Forum Dr	Raleigh, NC	27615-2971	919-848-0333	848-8716	K-8	Steve McAdams
Evergreen Community Charter S	50 Bell Rd	Asheville, NC	28805-1538	828-298-2173	298-2269	K-8	Dr. Susan Gottfried
Exploris MS	401 Hillsborough St	Raleigh, NC	27603	919-715-3690	715-2042	6-8	Summer Clayton
Forsyth Academy	5426 Shattalon Dr	Winston Salem, NC	27106-1919	336-922-1121	922-1033	K-8	Wendy Watkins
Franklin Academy	604 S Franklin St	Wake Forest, NC	27587-2276	919-554-4911	554-2340	K-12	Denise Kent
Gaston College Preparatory S	320 Pleasant Hill Rd	Gaston, NC	27832-9511	252-308-6932	308-6936	5-12	Tammi Sutton
Global Scholars Academy	311 Dowd St	Durham, NC	27701-2443	919-682-5903	956-8535	K-4	Agatha Brown
Grandfather Academy	PO Box 98	Banner Elk, NC	28604-0098	828-897-4563	898-8513	K-12	Stephanie Knowles
Gray Stone Day S	PO Box 650	Misenheimer, NC	28109-0650	704-463-0567	463-0569	9-12	Helen Nance
Greensboro Academy	4049 Battleground Ave	Greensboro, NC	27410-8410	336-286-8404	286-8403	K-8	Rudy Swofford
Guilford Preparatory Charter S	2210 E Cone Blvd	Greensboro, NC	27405-4857	336-954-1344	954-1965	K-8	John Brown
Haliwa-Saponi Tribal S	130 Haliwa Saponi Trl	Hollister, NC	27844-9390	252-257-5853	257-1093	K-12	Marjorie Barber
Hawbridge S	PO Box 162	Saxapahaw, NC	27340-0162	336-376-1122	376-6996	6-12	Dr. Marcia Huth
Healthy Start Academy	807 W Chapel Hill St	Durham, NC	27701-3112	919-956-5599	688-9027	K-8	James McCormick
Henderson Collegiate Charter S	906 Health Center Rd	Henderson, NC	27536-5479	252-598-1038	598-1037	4-5	Eric Sanchez
Hope Elementary Charter S	1116 N Blount St	Raleigh, NC	27604-1302	919-834-0941	834-9338	K-5	Clarissa Fleming
Howard S	1004 Herring Ave E	Wilson, NC	27893-3311	252-293-4150	293-4151	K-8	Dr. Jo Anne Woodard
Jefferson Classical Academy	2527 US 221A Hwy	Mooresboro, NC	28114-7698	828-657-9998	657-9012	K-12	Joseph Maimone
Joy Charter S	1955 W Cornwallis Rd	Durham, NC	27705-5707	919-493-6056	402-4263	K-8	Alex Quigley
Kennedy Charter S	1717 Sharon Rd W	Charlotte, NC	28210-5663	704-688-2939	688-2962	K-12	William Stubbs
Kestrel Heights S	4700 S Alston Ave	Durham, NC	27713-4419	919-484-1300	484-1355	K-12	Tim Dugan
Kinston Charter Academy	2000 Martin L King Jr Blvd	Kinston, NC	28501	252-522-0210	527-7785	K-8	Ozzie Hall
KIPP Academy Charlotte	931 Wilann Dr	Charlotte, NC	28215-2147	704-537-2044	537-2855	5-8	Donna Rogers
Lake Lure Classical Academy	PO Box 6	Lake Lure, NC	28746-0006	828-625-9292		K-8	Caroline Upchurch
Lake Norman Charter S	12435 S Old Statesville Rd	Huntersville, NC	28078-7252	704-948-8600	948-8778	5-12	Shannon Stein
Learning Center	945 Connahetta St	Murphy, NC	28906-3524	828-835-7240	835-9471	K-8	Mary Jo Dyre
Lincoln Charter S Denver	7834 Galway Ln	Denver, NC	28037-8600	704-483-6611	489-4343	K-12	Dave Machado
Lincoln Charter S Lincolnton	133 Eagle Nest Rd	Lincolnton, NC	28092-7383	704-736-9888	736-1166	K-8	Rachel Greer
Magellan Charter S	9324 Baileywick Rd	Raleigh, NC	27615-1909	919-844-0277	844-3882	3-8	Mary Griffin
Metrolina Regional Scholars Academy	5225 77 Center Dr	Charlotte, NC	28217-0708	704-503-1112	503-1183	K-8	Dr. Michael Postma
Millennium Charter Academy	500 Old Springs Rd	Mount Airy, NC	27030-3034	336-789-7570	789-8445	K-8	Kirby McCrary
Mountain Community S	613 Glover St	Hendersonville, NC	28792-5451	828-696-8480	696-8451	K-8	Denise Pesce
Mountain Discovery Charter S	890 Jenkins Branch Rd N	Bryson City, NC	28713-4514	828-488-1222	488-0526	K-8	Carter Petty
Mountain Island Charter S	14516 Lucia Riverbend Hwy	Mount Holly, NC	28120-9703	704-827-8840	831-5285	K-9	Linda Bratcher
Neuse Charter S	PO Box 30	Smithfield, NC	27577-0030	919-938-1077	938-1079	K-12	Joel Erby
New Dimensions S	550 Lenoir Rd	Morganton, NC	28655-2697	828-437-5753	437-2980	K-6	Larry Wilkerson
North East Carolina Prep S	PO Box 8	Tarboro, NC	27886-0008	252-641-0464	641-0463	K-8	John Westburg
Orange Charter S	920 Corporate Dr	Hillsborough, NC	27278-8557	919-644-6272	644-6275	K-8	Jarrod Dennis
PACE Academy	308 NC 54	Carrboro, NC	27510-1952	919-933-7699	967-9905	9-12	Rhonda Franklin
Phoenix Academy	4020 Meeting Way St	High Point, NC	27265-8233	336-869-0079	869-3399	K-5	Kim Norcross
Piedmont Community S	PO Box 3706	Gastonia, NC	28054-0038	704-853-2428	853-3689	K-12	Audene Scarlett
Pine Lake Preparatory S	PO Box 5185	Mooresville, NC	28117-5185	704-237-5300	237-5398	K-12	Christopher Terrill
PreEminent Charter S	3815 Rock Quarry Rd	Raleigh, NC	27610-5123	919-235-0511	235-0514	K-8	Melanie Butler-Williams
Quality Education Academy	5012 Lansing Dr Ste C	Winston Salem, NC	27105-3026	336-744-7138	744-1538	K-12	Simon Johnson
Queens Grant Community S	6400 Matthews Mint Hill Rd	Mint Hill, NC	28227-9323	704-573-6611	573-0995	K-12	Christy Morrin
Quest Academy	10908 Strickland Rd	Raleigh, NC	27615-1873	919-841-0441	841-0443	K-8	Dr. Charles Watson
Raleigh Charter HS	1307 Glenwood Ave	Raleigh, NC	27605-1216	919-715-1155	715-1766	9-12	Dr. Thomas Humble
Research Triangle Academy	2418 Ellis Rd	Durham, NC	27703-5543	919-957-7108	957-9698	K-8	Dr. Devon Carson
Research Triangle Charter Academy	PO Box 13453	Durham, NC	27709-3453	919-998-6757	998-3402	9-12	Eric Grunden
River Mill Academy	PO Box 1450	Graham, NC	27253-1450	336-229-0909	229-9975	K-12	Jeff Dishmon
Rocky Mount Prep S	3334 Bishop Rd	Rocky Mount, NC	27804-7639	252-443-9923	443-9932	K-12	Douglas Haynes
Roxboro Community S	115 Lake Dr	Roxboro, NC	27573-5672	336-597-0020	597-3152	6-12	Sam Kennington
Sandhills Theatre Arts Renaissance S	140 Southern Dunes Dr	Vass, NC	28394-9218	910-695-1004	695-7322	K-8	Wesley Graner
Socrates Academy	3909 Weddington Rd	Matthews, NC	28105-6673	704-321-1711	321-1714	K-8	Janis Dellinger-Holton
Southern Wake Academy	5108 Old Powell Rd	Holly Springs, NC	27540-9200	919-567-9955	567-9956	9-12	Caroll Reed
STEAM Academy	280 S Liberty St	Winston Salem, NC	27101-5211	336-748-3838	748-3359	5-8	Susan Willis
Sterling Montessori Academy	202 Treybrooke Dr	Morrisville, NC	27560-9300	919-462-8889	462-8890	K-8	Bill Zajic
Success Institute	PO Box 1332	Statesville, NC	28687-1332	704-881-0441	881-0870	K-8	Tenna Williams
Sugar Creek Charter S	4101 N Tryon St	Charlotte, NC	28206-2066	704-509-5470	921-1004	K-8	Cheryl Turner
Summit Charter S	PO Box 1339	Cashiers, NC	28717-1339	828-743-5755	743-9157	K-8	Dr. Jack Talmadge
Tiller S	1950 US Highway 70 E	Beaufort, NC	28516-7836	252-728-1995	728-3711	K-5	Virginia Jones
Torchlight Academy	3211 Bramer Dr	Raleigh, NC	27604-1603	919-850-9960	850-9961	K-5	Dr. Cynthia McQueen
Triad Math & Science S	700 Creek Ridge Rd	Greensboro, NC	27406-4802	336-621-0061	621-0072	K-12	Hakan Orak
Triangle Math & Science Academy	207 E Hargett St	Raleigh, NC	27601-1437	919-297-8709	651-1418	K-6	Alper Tekten
Two Rivers Community S	1018 Archie Carroll Rd	Boone, NC	28607-8506	828-262-5411	262-5412	K-8	Jessica Gilway
Union Academy	675 N M L King Jr Blvd	Monroe, NC	28110-8119	704-283-8883	283-8823	K-12	Joe Delaney
Vance Charter S	1227 Dabney Dr	Henderson, NC	27536-3558	252-431-0440	436-0688	K-8	Sean Connolly
Voyager Academy	PO Box 71567	Durham, NC	27722-1567	919-433-3301	433-3305	K-12	Carl Forsyth
Washington Montessori S	2330 Old Bath Hwy	Washington, NC	27889-7779	252-946-1977	946-5938	K-8	Jen Hales
Water's Edge Village S	PO Box 215	Corolla, NC	27927-0215	252-455-9449		K-6	Meghan Agresto
Wilmington Preparatory Academy	4905 S College Rd	Wilmington, NC	28412-2203	910-799-6776	338-1834	K-8	Kevin Johnson
Woods Charter S	160 Woodland Grove Ln	Chapel Hill, NC	27516-4085	919-960-8353	960-0133	K-12	Harrell Rentz
Woodson S of Challenge	437 Goldfloss St	Winston Salem, NC	27127-3125	336-723-6838	723-6425	K-12	Ruth Hopkins

Ohio

School	Address	City,State	Zip code	Telephone	Fax	Grade	Contact
A+ Arts Academy	270 S Napoleon Ave	Columbus, OH	43213-4235	614-338-0767	338-0787	K-8	Carolyn Berkley
Academic Acceleration Academy	1990 Jefferson Ave	Columbus, OH	43211-2175	614-298-4742	298-9107	9-12	Brian Terrell
Academy of Arts & Sciences	201 W Erie Ave	Lorain, OH	44052-1651	440-244-0156	244-3935	K-12	Joell Mullen-Liscano
Academy of Columbus	4656 Heaton Rd	Columbus, OH	43229-6612	614-433-7510	433-7515	K-8	Robert Palmer
Achieve Career Preparatory Academy	301 Collingwood Blvd	Toledo, OH	43604-8600	419-243-8559	243-8583	9-12	Kerry Gordon-Keese
Akron Digital Academy	335 S Main St	Akron, OH	44308-1203	330-237-2200	237-2207	K-12	LaShawn Terrell
Akros MS	265 Park St	Akron, OH	44304-1305	330-374-6704	374-6713	6-8	
Allen Academy III	1206 Shuler Ave	Hamilton, OH	45011-4566	513-868-2900	868-0498	K-6	Aleta Benson
Allen Academy II	184 Salem Ave	Dayton, OH	45406-5804	937-586-9756	586-9764	2-6	Novea Jackson
Allen Academy	700 Heck Ave	Dayton, OH	45417-4641	937-586-9815	586-0271	7-9	Aundray Brooks
Allen Preparatory S	627 Salem Ave	Dayton, OH	45406-5822	937-278-4201	278-4229	K-1	Yolanda Clark
Alliance Academy of Cincinnati	1712 Duck Creek Rd	Cincinnati, OH	45207-1644	513-751-5555	751-5072	K-8	Bryan Cannon
Alternative Education Academy	1830 Adams St	Toledo, OH	43604-4428	330-253-8680	514-8227	K-12	Margaret Ford
Apex Academy	16005 Terrace Rd	East Cleveland, OH	44112-2001	216-451-1725	451-1765	K-8	LaDondra Howell
Arts Academy	4125 Leavitt Rd	Lorain, OH	44053-2341	440-960-0470	960-0475	K-12	
Arts Academy West S	1881 E 71st St	Cleveland, OH	44103-4005	216-344-9191		K-12	
Arts & College Preparatory Academy	4401 Hilton Corporate Dr	Columbus, OH	43232-4161	614-986-9974	986-9976	9-12	Anthony Gatto

School	Address	City,State	Zip code	Telephone	Fax	Grade	Contact
Arts and Science Prep Academy	2711 Church Ave	Cleveland, OH	44113-2909	216-344-2081	344-2312	K-8	Cheryl Tibai
Ashland County Community Academy	2011 Baney Rd S	Ashland, OH	44805	419-903-0295	903-0341	9-12	Donne Copenhaver
Auglaize County Educational Academy	1130 E Albert St	Lima, OH	45804-1614	419-738-4572	738-4591	K-12	Deborah Munis
Aurora Academy	541 Utah St	Toledo, OH	43605-2299	419-693-6841	693-4799	K-8	Cindy Wilson
Autism Academy of Learning	219 Page St	Toledo, OH	43620-1430	419-865-7487	865-8360	K-12	Mark Lafferty
Autism Model S	3020 Tremainsville Rd	Toledo, OH	43613-1901	419-897-4400	897-4403	K-12	Mary Walters
Bennett Venture Academy	5130 Bennett Rd	Toledo, OH	43612-3422	419-269-2247	269-2257	K-8	Xavier Owens
Bridges Community Academy	190 Saint Francis Ave	Tiffin, OH	44883-3475	419-455-9295	455-9296	K-12	Dona Kaufman
Buckeye On-Line School for Success	119 E 5th St	East Liverpool, OH	43920-3030	330-385-1987	385-4535	K-12	
Cardington Lincoln Digital Academy	121 Nichols St	Cardington, OH	43315-1121	419-864-4566	864-9515	K-12	Jennifer Zierden
Center for Student Achievement	21 Tropic St	Jackson, OH	45640-1966	740-286-6442	286-7827	9-12	James Pope
Central Academy of Ohio	2727 Kenwood Blvd	Toledo, OH	43606-3216	419-475-6620	205-9899	K-12	Tiffany Adamski
Charles S at Ohio Dominican	1270 Brentnell Ave	Columbus, OH	43219-2017	614-258-8588	258-8584	9-12	Gregory Brown
Chavez College Prep ES	1533 Cleveland Ave	Columbus, OH	43211-2743	614-351-1774	299-3684	K-5	Jameica Shoultz
Cincinnati College Prep Academy	1425 Linn St	Cincinnati, OH	45214-2605	513-684-0777	684-8888	K-12	Guyton Mathews
Cincinnati Leadership Academy	7243 Eastlawn Dr	Cincinnati, OH	45237-3515	513-351-5737	351-5740	K-8	Kimberly Euler
Cincinnati Speech & Reading Center	1812 Central Pkwy	Cincinnati, OH	45214-2304	513-651-9624	618-0272	K-8	
Citizens' Academy	1827 Ansel Rd	Cleveland, OH	44106-4107	216-791-4195	791-3013	K-8	Jennifer Taylor
City Day Community S	318 S Main St	Dayton, OH	45402-2716	937-223-8130	223-8136	K-8	Shonise Carr
Clay Avenue Community S	1030 Clay Ave	Toledo, OH	43608-2167	419-727-9900	727-9902	K-12	
Cleveland Art & Social Science Academy	10701 Shaker Blvd	Cleveland, OH	44104-3752	216-229-3000	229-3182	K-8	Deborah Mays
Cleveland College Preparatory S	4906 Fleet Ave	Cleveland, OH	44105-3328	216-341-1347	341-4466	K-8	Tyler Roberts
College Hill Leadership Academy	1540 W North Bend Rd	Cincinnati, OH	45224-2506	513-541-3274	541-3317	K-8	
Columbus Arts & Tech Academy	2255 Kimberly Pkwy E	Columbus, OH	43232-7210	614-577-0900	888-0300	K-12	Derrick Shelton
Columbus Bilingual Academy	35 Midland Ave	Columbus, OH	43223-1064	614-324-1492	324-1060	K-8	Donray Bennett
Columbus Bilingual Academy - North	1507 Loretta Ave	Columbus, OH	43211-1507	614-525-0309		K-8	Donray Bennett
Columbus Collegiate Academy	1469 E Main St	Columbus, OH	43205-2152	614-299-5284	299-5303	6-8	John Dues
Columbus Humanities Arts & Tech Academy	1333 Morse Rd	Columbus, OH	43229-6322	614-261-1200	261-1201	K-8	Julieta Dinkins
Columbus Performance Academy	2 Easton Oval Ste 525	Columbus, OH	43219-7008	614-318-0720	238-3184	K-8	Joan Pammer
Columbus Prep & Fitness Academy	1258 Demorest Rd	Columbus, OH	43204-7003	614-318-0606	351-9804	K-8	Jessica Hursey
Columbus Preparatory Academy	3330 Chippewa St	Columbus, OH	43204-1653	614-275-3600	275-3601	K-8	Chad Carr
Cornerstone Academy	6015 E Walnut St	Westerville, OH	43081-9620	614-775-0615	775-0633	K-12	Natalee Long
Coshocton Opportunity S	1205 Cambridge Rd	Coshocton, OH	43812-2741	740-622-3600	623-6860	9-12	
Crittenton Community S	1418 E Broad St	Columbus, OH	43205-1505	614-372-2401	372-2416	6-9	Norbert Tate
Cruiser Academy	2751 Winchester Pike	Columbus, OH	43232-4827	614-237-8756	237-9308	9-12	Bill Young
Dayton Business Technology HS	348 W 1st St	Dayton, OH	45402-3006	937-225-3989	225-3998	9-12	Philitia Charlton
Dayton Early College Academy	300 College Park Ave	Dayton, OH	45469-0001	937-229-5780	229-5786	7-12	David Taylor
Dayton Liberty Campus	4401 Dayton Liberty Rd	Dayton, OH	45417-5903	937-262-4080	262-4091	K-8	Channey Goode
Dayton View Academy	1416 W Riverview Ave	Dayton, OH	45402-6217	937-567-9426	567-9446	K-8	Channey Goode
Dixon Early Learning Center	333 N Middle St	Columbiana, OH	44408-1001	330-482-5355	482-5361	PK-3	Kimberly Sharshan
Dohn Community HS	608 E McMillan St	Cincinnati, OH	45206-1926	513-281-6100	281-6103	9-12	Leando Davenport
Eagle Academy	2014 Consaul St	Toledo, OH	43605-1412	419-691-4876	691-5184	K-12	Mitchel Bean
Eagle Learning Center HS	2665 Navarre Ave	Oregon, OH	43616-3245	419-720-2003	720-2007	9-12	Loren Dirr
East End Community Heritage S	7030 Reading Rd Ste 106	Cincinnati, OH	45237-3890	513-281-3900	281-0818	K-12	John Sowinsky
Edge Academy	92 N Union St	Akron, OH	44304-1347	330-535-4581	535-5074	K-6	Chris Burchfield
Educational Academy at Linden	PO Box 12579	Columbus, OH	43212-0579	614-252-7611	299-3680	3-5	Jameica Shoultz
Electronic Classroom of Tomorrow	3700 S High St Ste 95	Columbus, OH	43207-4083	614-492-8884	492-8894	K-12	
Elyria Community S	300 Abbe Rd N	Elyria, OH	44035-3724	440-366-5225	366-6280	K-9	Tracey Frierson
Emerson Academy of Dayton	501 Hickory St	Dayton, OH	45410-1232	937-223-2889	223-3757	K-8	Ronald Albino
E Prep & Village Prep Charter S	1417 E 36th St	Cleveland, OH	44114-4116	216-456-2070	361-9717	K-8	John Dues
E Prep & Village Prep Charter S	9201 Crane Ave	Cleveland, OH	44105-1627	216-298-1164	341-0106	K-8	Robert Dues
Fairborn Digital Academy	700 Black Ln	Fairborn, OH	45324-5844	937-879-0511	879-8160	9-12	Erik Tritsch
Falcon Academy of Creative Arts	1473 Saxe Rd	Mogadore, OH	44260	330-673-4514		3-7	Margo Snider
FCI Academy	2177 Mock Rd	Columbus, OH	43219-1258	614-471-4527	471-4943	K-12	
Findlay Digital Academy	1219 W Main Cross St # 206	Findlay, OH	45840	419-425-3598	425-3588	9-12	Lawrence Grove
Focus Learning Academy East	4480 Refugee Rd	Columbus, OH	43232-4459	614-269-0150	269-0151	9-12	
Focus Learning Academy North	4807 Evanswood Dr	Columbus, OH	43229-6285	614-310-0430	310-0469	K-12	Eugene Greenfield
Focus Learning Academy Southwest	190 Southwood Ave	Columbus, OH	43207-1133	614-545-2000	545-1995	9-12	
Foundation Academy	1050 Wyandotte Ave	Mansfield, OH	44906-1939	419-526-9540	526-9542	K-8	Joann Hipsher
Fox Academy	1505 Jefferson Ave	Toledo, OH	43604-5722	419-720-4503	720-4502	7-12	Craig Cotner
Foxfire Center for Student Success	PO Box 1818	Zanesville, OH	43702-1818	740-453-4509	455-4084	5-12	
Franklin Local Community S	PO Box 95	Roseville, OH	43777-0095	740-697-7317	697-0793	7-12	Frank VanKirk
Gahanna Community S	160 S Hamilton Rd	Gahanna, OH	43230-2919	614-478-5515	337-3762	9-12	Robin Murdock
Glass City Academy	1000 Monroe St	Toledo, OH	43604	419-720-6311	720-6315	11-12	Stewart Jesse
Goal Digital Academy	890 W 4th St Ste 400	Mansfield, OH	44906-2561	419-521-9008	529-2976	K-12	
Graham Academy	370 E Main St	Saint Paris, OH	43072-9200	937-663-0370	663-0373	K-12	Scott Howell
Graham Expeditionary MS	140 E 16th Ave	Columbus, OH	43201-1617	614-253-4000	253-4002	5-8	Gregory Brown
Graham S	3950 Indianola Ave	Columbus, OH	43214-3167	614-262-1111	262-5878	9-12	Gregory Brown
Grant Leadership Academy	2030 Leonard Ave	Columbus, OH	43219-2105	614-252-2087	252-2311	K-8	Mary Cann
Greater Ohio Virtual S	1879 Deerfield Rd Ste 1	Lebanon, OH	45036-8602	513-695-2924	695-2588	9-12	Brian Barot
Greater Summit County Early Learning Ctr	2141 Pickle Rd	Akron, OH	44312-4221	330-945-5600		K-3	Teresa Graves
Great Western Academy	310 N Wilson Rd	Columbus, OH	43204-6221	614-276-1028	276-1049	K-8	Jason Knight
Groveport Community S	4485 S Hamilton Rd	Groveport, OH	43125-9334	614-574-4100	574-4107	K-8	Michelle Brown
Hamilton Alternative Academy	775 Rathmell Rd	Columbus, OH	43207-4737	614-491-8044		K-12	
Hamilton County Math & Science S	2675 Civic Center Dr	Cincinnati, OH	45231-1311	513-728-8620	728-8623	K-8	Dwan Moore
Harrisburg Pike Community S	680 Harrisburg Pike	Columbus, OH	43223-2100	614-223-1510	223-1584	K-8	Stefanie Lowery
Harvard Avenue Community S	12000 Harvard Ave	Cleveland, OH	44105-5444	216-283-5100	283-5762	K-8	Kathleen Young
Heir Force Community S	PO Box 180	Lima, OH	45802-0180	419-228-9241	228-1555	K-8	Darwin Lofton
Hollingsworth S for Talented & Gifted	824 6th St	Toledo, OH	43605-4008	419-705-3411	720-4923	K-8	Lois Fuller
Hope Academy Brown Street Campus E	1035 Clay St	Akron, OH	44301-1517	330-785-0180	785-0681	K-8	Frederick Cardinal
Hope Academy Chapelside Campus	3845 E 131st St	Cleveland, OH	44120-4661	216-283-6589	283-3087	K-8	Nathan Richards
Hope Academy Cuyahoga Campus	12913 Bennington Ave	Cleveland, OH	44135-3761	216-251-5450	251-6410	K-8	William Byrd
Hope Academy East Campus	15720 Kipling Ave	Cleveland, OH	44110-3105	216-383-1214		K-8	Julio Alarcon
Hope Academy Lincoln Park	3185 W 41st St	Cleveland, OH	44109-1275	216-271-7008	263-7007	K-3	Holly Williams
Hope Academy Northcoast Campus	4310 E 71st St	Cleveland, OH	44105-5759	216-429-0232	429-0249	K-8	Willie Banks
Hope Academy Northwest	1441 W 116th St	Cleveland, OH	44102-2301	216-226-6800	226-6805	K-12	Brian Willmott
Hope Academy University Campus	107 S Arlington St	Akron, OH	44306-1328	330-535-7728	535-7864	K-8	Veronica Fly
Horizon Science Academy Cincinnati	1055 Laidlaw Ave	Cincinnati, OH	45237-5005	513-242-0099	242-2467	K-12	
Horizon Science Academy Cleveland ES	6150 S Marginal Rd	Cleveland, OH	44103-1043	216-432-9576	432-9801	K-5	
Horizon Science Academy Cleveland HS	6150 S Marginal Rd	Cleveland, OH	44103-1043	216-432-9576	432-9801	9-12	Cengiz Karatas
Horizon Science Academy Cleveland MS	6100 S Marginal Rd	Cleveland, OH	44103-1043	216-432-9940	432-9941	K-12	Aydin Kara
Horizon Science Academy Columbus ES	2835 Morse Rd	Columbus, OH	43231-6033	614-475-4585	475-4587	K-5	
Horizon Science Academy Columbus HS	1070 Morse Rd	Columbus, OH	43229-6290	614-846-7616	846-7696	9-12	Onder Sechen M.Ed.
Horizon Science Academy Columbus MS	2350 Morse Rd	Columbus, OH	43229-5801	614-428-6564	428-6574	6-8	
Horizon Science Academy Dayton	4751 Sue Anne Blvd	Dayton, OH	45405	937-277-1177	277-3090	K-6	
Horizon Science Academy Dayton Downtown	121 S Monmouth St	Dayton, OH	45403-2127	937-281-1980	281-1979	K-6	
Horizon Science Academy Dayton HS	250 Shoup Mill Rd	Dayton, OH	45415-3517	937-281-1480	281-1481	5-12	Ugur Zengince
Horizon Science Academy - Denison	1700 Denison Ave	Cleveland, OH	44109-2945	216-739-9911	739-9913	K-8	Mustafa Ada
Horizon Science Academy Denison ES	2261 Columbus Rd	Cleveland, OH	44113-4230	216-661-8840	661-8850	K-5	Nuh Celik
Horizon Science Academy Lorain	760 Tower Blvd	Lorain, OH	44052-5223	440-282-4277	282-4278	K-9	Dr. Osman Arslan
Horizon Science Academy Springfield	630 S Reynolds Rd	Toledo, OH	43615-6314	419-535-0524	535-0525	K-8	
Horizon Science Academy Toledo	2600 W Sylvania Ave Ste 109	Toledo, OH	43613-4332	419-474-3350	474-3351	K-12	
Horizon Science Academy Youngstown	3403 Southern Blvd	Youngstown, OH	44507-2044	330-782-3003	782-3356	K-8	Hasan Akkaya
IMAC HS	445 Bowman St	Mansfield, OH	44903-1201	419-525-0105	525-0106	9-12	
Imagine Bella Academy	19114 Bella Dr	Cleveland, OH	44119-3007	216-481-1500	481-4515	K-8	
Imani Learning Academy	728 Parkside Blvd	Toledo, OH	43607-3858	419-535-7078		K-8	Thomas Gladieux
Intergenerational S	12200 Fairhill Rd	Cleveland, OH	44120-1058	216-721-0120	721-0126	K-8	Dr. Cathy Whitehouse
International Academy of Columbus	1201 Schrock Rd	Columbus, OH	43229-1117	614-844-5539	844-5857	K-8	Dr. Mouhamed Tarazi
Invictus HS	3122 Euclid Ave	Cleveland, OH	44115-2508	216-539-7200	361-3090	9-12	Vernon Fawcett
James Leadership Academy	120 Knox Ave	Dayton, OH	45417-7823	937-835-3580	835-3576	9-12	Kecia Williams
Kessler S	118 E Wood St	Youngstown, OH	44503-1625	330-746-3095	746-4272	1-8	Lydia Brown-Payton
King Academy Community S	933 Bank St	Cincinnati, OH	45214-2103	513-421-7519	421-1770	K-8	Andrea Martinez
KIPP Journey Academy	1406 Myrtle Ave	Columbus, OH	43211-1445	614-263-6137	263-6207	5-8	Hannah Powell
Klepinger Road Community S	3650 Klepinger Rd	Dayton, OH	45416-1919	937-610-1710	610-1730	K-8	Melissa McManaway
Knight Academy	110 Arco Dr	Toledo, OH	43607	419-720-4444		5-8	
Lake Erie Academy	2740 W Central Ave	Toledo, OH	43606-3452	419-475-3786	475-6048	K-5	Dr. Steven Rios
Lakewood City Academy	1470 Warren Rd	Lakewood, OH	44107-3918	216-529-4037	227-5975	6-12	Terrilynn Bornino-Elwell
Lakewood Digital Academy	PO Box 70	Hebron, OH	43025-0070	740-404-7586	928-3152	K-12	Eva Pound-Bickle
Lancaster Digital Academy	111 S Broad St Ste 201	Lancaster, OH	43130-4383	740-277-7450	277-7452	K-12	Steven Scott
Lancaster Fairfield Community S	320 E Locust St	Lancaster, OH	43130-4437	740-652-7200	687-7178	7-12	Jeffrey Graf
Legacy Academy for Leaders & Arts	1812 Oak Hill Ave	Youngstown, OH	44507-1053	330-747-1620	747-1753	K-8	
LifeLinks Community S	205 W Crawford St	Van Wert, OH	45891-1903	419-623-5380	238-3974	6-12	Shawn Deitemeyer
LifeSkills Center Columbus North	1900 E Dublin Granville Rd	Columbus, OH	43229-3553	614-891-9041	891-8571	9-12	Joseph Buckalew
Life Skills Center Middleton	631 S Breiel Blvd	Middletown, OH	45044-5113	513-423-1800	423-1818	9-12	Charles Hall
Life Skills Center of Cincinnati	2612 Gilbert Ave	Cincinnati, OH	45206-1205	513-475-0222	475-0444	9-12	
Life Skills Center of Dayton	1721 N Main St	Dayton, OH	45405-4143	937-274-2841	274-2873	9-12	James Brown
Life Skills Center of Elyria	2015 W River Rd N	Elyria, OH	44035-2309	440-324-1755	324-1723	9-12	Crystal Garmon

School	Address	City,State	Zip code	Telephone	Fax	Grade	Contact
Life Skills Center of Hamilton County	7710 Reading Rd	Cincinnati, OH	45237-6800	513-821-6695	821-8755	9-12	Arnez Booker
Life Skills Center of North Akron	1458 Brittain Rd	Akron, OH	44310-3641	330-633-5990	633-7005	9-12	Steven Garton
Life Skills Center of Northeast OH	12201 Larchmere Blvd	Shaker Heights, OH	44120-1101	216-421-7587	421-8189	9-12	Jennifer Minor
Life Skills Center of Springfield	1637 Selma Rd	Springfield, OH	45505-4245	937-322-2940	322-2944	9-12	Karl Perkins
Life Skills Center of Summit County	2168 Romig Rd	Akron, OH	44320-3879	330-745-3678	753-1506	9-12	Jennifer Ciptak
Life Skills Center of Toledo	1830 Adams St	Toledo, OH	43604-4428	419-241-5504	241-9176	9-12	Brian Burden
Life Skills Center of Trumbull County	458 Franklin St SE	Warren, OH	44483-5715	330-392-0231	392-0253	9-12	Jason Cooper
Life Skills Center of Youngstown	3405 Market St	Youngstown, OH	44507-2009	330-743-6698	743-6702	9-12	Ruth Harris
LifeSkills Columbus Southeast	2400 S Hamilton Rd	Columbus, OH	43232-4963	614-863-9175	863-9185	9-12	Eunique Seifullah
Lighthouse Community S	6100 Desmond St	Cincinnati, OH	45227-1897	513-561-7888	561-7818	6-12	Amy Shrock
Lion of Judah Academy	1468 E 55th St	Cleveland, OH	44103-1307	216-881-9200	881-9201	K-8	Monroe Kennedy
London Academy	40 S Walnut St	London, OH	43140-1246	740-852-5700	852-3078	9-12	Adelle Faulkner
Lorain Community ES	1110 W 4th St	Lorain, OH	44052-1408	440-204-2130	204-2134	K-4	Melisa Shady
Lorain Community MS	1110 W 4th St	Lorain, OH	44052-1408	440-242-2023	244-0857	5-9	Deborah Thoren
Lorain Preparatory Academy	3038 Leavitt Rd	Lorain, OH	44052-4112	440-282-3127	282-3179	3-8	Patricia Jannuzzi
Madison Ave School of the Arts	1511 Madison Ave	Toledo, OH	43604-4433	419-259-4000	243-1513	K-5	Daphne Williams
Madison Community S	2015 W 95th St	Cleveland, OH	44102-3791	216-651-5212	651-9040	K-8	Melissa Rice
Mahoning Unlimited S	100 Debartolo Pl Ste 170	Youngstown, OH	44512-6066	330-965-7828	965-7901	4-12	
Mahoning Valley Opportunity S	496 Glenwood Ave Ste 112	Youngstown, OH	44502-1509	330-744-7656	743-9757	9-12	
Mansfield Community ES	215 N Trimble Rd	Mansfield, OH	44906-2630	419-522-4578	522-0045	K-3	Bethany Young
Mansfield Community MS	1033 Larchwood Rd	Mansfield, OH	44907-2424	419-522-3563	522-2705	4-8	Bethany Young
Mansfield Elective Academy	445 Bowman St	Mansfield, OH	44903-1201	567-247-4475	247-3392	K-8	
Marion City Digital Academy	910 E Church St	Marion, OH	43302-4317	740-223-4417	223-4569	K-12	Raymond Haines
Maritime Academy of Toledo	803 Water St	Toledo, OH	43604-1831	419-244-9999	244-9898	5-12	Leah Williams
Massillon Digital Academy	207 Oak Ave SE	Massillon, OH	44646-6790	330-830-3900	830-0953	K-12	Jennifer Fischer
Meadows Choice Community S	1853 South Ave	Toledo, OH	43609-2086	419-385-5730	385-5781	K-9	
Menlo Park Academy	14440 Triskett Rd	Cleveland, OH	44111-2263	440-925-6365	925-0698	K-8	Paige Baublitz-Watkins
Miamisburg Secondary Academy	540 Park Ave	Miamisburg, OH	45342-2854	937-866-3381	865-5250	7-12	Greg Whitehead
Miami Valley Academies	5656 Springboro Pike	Dayton, OH	45449-2806	937-294-4522	294-4545	K-12	Jennifer Claypool
Middletown Prep & Fitness Academy	816 2nd Ave	Middletown, OH	45044-4201	513-424-6110	424-6121	K-8	Elizabeth Kelliher
Midnimo Cross Cultural Community S	PO Box 24816	Columbus, OH	43224-0816	614-261-7480	261-7481	6-9	Karen Carson
Millenium Community ES	3500 Refugee Rd	Columbus, OH	43232-4862	614-255-5585	255-5580	K-8	Tijuana Russell
Mound Street Health Careers Academy	354 Mound St	Dayton, OH	45402-8325	937-223-3041	223-5867	9-12	Ron Cothran
Mound Street IT Careers Academy	354 Mound St	Dayton, OH	45402-8325	937-223-3041	223-5867	9-12	Ron Cothran
Mound Street Military Careers Academy	354 Mound St	Dayton, OH	45402-8325	937-223-3041	223-5867	9-12	Ron Cothran
Mt. Auburn International Academy	244 Southern Ave	Cincinnati, OH	45219-3023	513-241-5500	241-5501	K-12	Wissam Sabbagh
Mt. Healthy Prep & Fitness Academy	7601 Harrison Ave	Mount Healthy, OH	45231-3107	513-587-6280	521-4509	K-8	Dr. Peter DeDominici
Newark Digital Academy	255 Woods Ave	Newark, OH	43055-4436	740-328-2022	328-2270	K-12	
New Choices Community S	601 S Keowee St	Dayton, OH	45410-1168	937-224-8201	224-8209	7-12	
New Day Academy	8566 Barbara Dr	Mentor, OH	44060-1917	216-797-1602	797-1604	K-12	
Noble Academy - Cleveland	1200 E 200th St	Euclid, OH	44117-1172	216-486-8866	486-2846	K-12	Hakan Bagcioglu
Noble Academy - Columbus	1329 Bethel Rd	Upper Arlington, OH	43220-2611	614-326-0687	326-0691	K-8	
North Central Academy	928 W Market St Ste B	Tiffin, OH	44883-2529	419-448-5786	448-5789	6-12	
North Dayton S of Discovery	3901 Turner Rd	Dayton, OH	45415-3654	937-278-6671	278-6964	K-8	Jacqueline Robbeloth
Northeast Ohio College Preparatory S	2357 Tremont Ave	Cleveland, OH	44113-4633	216-965-0580	393-0059	K-10	Sydney Gruhin
Northland Prep & Fitness ES	1875 Morse Rd	Columbus, OH	43229-6603	614-318-0600	262-9111	K-8	Ashley Graver
Northpointe Academy	3248 Warsaw St	Toledo, OH	43608-1852	419-244-4202	244-4205	K-8	Andre Fox
Notten S for Science Tech Engrng Math	2972 E 10th Ave	Columbus, OH	43219-3709	614-252-3722	252-5122	K-12	
Oakstone Community S	5747 Cleveland Ave	Columbus, OH	43231-2831	614-865-9643	865-9649	K-12	
Ohio Connections Academy	5181 Natorp Blvd Ste 410	Mason, OH	45040-5907	513-533-3230	533-3260	K-12	Sara Deaterla
Ohio Virtual Academy	1655 Holland Rd Ste F	Maumee, OH	43537-1656	419-482-0948	482-0954	K-12	Dr. Kristin Stewart
Old Brooklyn Community ES	4430 State Rd	Cleveland, OH	44109	216-661-7888	661-5975	K-4	Cherie Kaiser
Old Brooklyn Community MS	4430 State Rd	Cleveland, OH	44109-4705	216-351-0280	661-5975	5-8	Amy Mobley
Orion Academy	1798 Queen City Ave	Cincinnati, OH	45214-1427	513-251-6000	251-3851	K-8	Jarome Farley
Outreach Academy-Students w/Disabilities	3727 Bosworth Rd	Cleveland, OH	44111-6037	216-688-1244	732-2497	K-12	
P.A.C.E. S	1601 California Ave	Cincinnati, OH	45237-5603	513-751-7223	482-3322	9-12	
Par - Excellence Academy	96 Maholm St	Newark, OH	43055-3994	740-344-7279	344-7272	PK-6	Gisele James
Parma Community ES	7667 Day Dr	Parma, OH	44129-5603	440-888-5490	888-5890	K-3	Linda Geyer
Parma Community HS	5983 W 54th St	Parma, OH	44129-3854	440-887-0319	845-2834	9-12	Linda Geyer
Parma Community MS	5983 W 54th St	Parma, OH	44129-3854	440-845-2587	845-2834	4-8	Linda Geyer
Pathway S of Discovery	173 Avondale Dr	Dayton, OH	45404-2123	937-235-5498	235-5569	K-8	Keith Colbert
Patriot Preparatory Academy	4938 Beatrice Dr	Columbus, OH	43227-2113	614-864-5332	864-5381	K-12	Michael Cosgrove
Performance Academy of Eastland	2220 S Hamilton Rd	Columbus, OH	43232-4304	614-318-1037	577-1933	K-8	Megan Larsen
Phoenix Academy Community S	2238 Jefferson Ave	Toledo, OH	43604-7120	419-720-4500		7-12	Craig Cotner
Phoenix Community Learning Center	3595 Washington Ave	Cincinnati, OH	45229-2017	513-351-5001	351-5000	K-8	Elaine Wilson
Phoenix Village Academy S1	12601 Shaker Blvd	Cleveland, OH	44120-2041	216-812-0244	812-0234	K-12	
Pinnacle Academy	860 E 222nd St	Euclid, OH	44123-3317	216-731-0127	731-0688	K-8	Lorianne DiDomenico
Pleasant Community Digital S	1107 Owens Rd W	Marion, OH	43302-8421	740-389-4476	389-6985	K-12	
Premier Academy of Ohio	1555 Elaine Rd	Columbus, OH	43227-2347	614-501-3820		7-12	Hydia Green
Project Rebuild Community HS	1731 Grace Ave NE	Canton, OH	44705-2261	330-452-8414	452-8452	9-12	Joseph Cole
Promise Academy	1701 E 13th St	Cleveland, OH	44114-3227	216-443-0500	443-0506	9-12	Dr. Cordelia Harris
Pschtecin S	985 Mediterranean Ave	Columbus, OH	43229-2541	614-985-3428	985-3115	8-12	Cynthia Bronson
Puritas Community ES	15204 Puritas Ave	Cleveland, OH	44135-2716	216-688-0680	688-0609	K-4	Margaret Colwell
Puritas Community MS	15204 Puritas Ave	Cleveland, OH	44135-2716	216-251-1596	251-3540	4-8	Donald Disantis
QDA HS	248 Front Ave SW	New Phila, OH	44663-2150	330-364-0618	364-0680	K-12	Steve Eckert
Quest Academy Community S	190 E 8th St	Lima, OH	45804-2302	419-227-7730	227-7515	K-8	Andrea Guice
RASE MS	75 N Walnut St	Mansfield, OH	44902-1211	419-522-8224		5-8	
Ridgedale Community S	3103 Hillman Ford Rd	Morral, OH	43337-9302	740-382-6065	383-6538	K-12	
Rittman Academy	100 Saurer St	Rittman, OH	44270-1259	330-927-7401		K-12	
Riverside Academy	3280 River Rd	Cincinnati, OH	45204-1214	513-921-7777	921-7704	K-12	Vallrey Crump
Romig Road Community S	2405 Romig Rd	Akron, OH	44320-3826	330-848-1100	848-1130	K-8	Christopher Haynes
Roosevelt Public Community S	1550 Tremont St	Cincinnati, OH	45214-1432	513-471-7323	244-6037	K-12	
Rushmore Academy	910 E Church St	Marion, OH	43302-4317	740-387-2043		6-12	
Schnee Learning Center	2222 Issaquah St	Cuyahoga Falls, OH	44221-3704	330-922-1966	945-4059	9-12	Dona Cardone
Scholarts Preparatory S	907 Lexington Ave	Columbus, OH	43201-3076	614-224-1610	443-1499	K-12	Dr. Cheryl Parchia
Sciotoville Elementary Academy	5540 3rd St	Sciotoville, OH	45662-5402	740-776-2916		K-4	
Sciotoville HS	224 Marshall St	Sciotoville, OH	45662-5549	740-776-6777	776-6812	5-12	Michael Yeagle
South Scioto Academy	707 E Jenkins Ave	Columbus, OH	43207-1318	614-445-7684	445-7688	K-6	Courtney Watters
Southside Academy	1833 Market St	Youngstown, OH	44507-1137	330-742-9090	743-1998	K-12	Stephanie Groscost
Southwest Licking Digital Academy	927 South St Unit A	Pataskala, OH	43062-6014	740-927-3941	927-4648	K-12	Jeffrey Severino
Springfield Academy of Excellence	623 S Center St	Springfield, OH	45506-2209	937-325-0933	325-0962	K-6	Edna Chapman
Springfield Prep & Fitness Academy	1615 Selma Rd	Springfield, OH	45505-4245	937-323-6250	323-6252	K-8	Darren Fansler
Stambaugh Charter Academy	2420 Donald Ave	Youngstown, OH	44509-1306	330-792-4806	792-4860	K-8	Alan Harper
Star Academy of Toledo	1850 Airport Hwy	Toledo, OH	43609-2069	419-720-6330	385-1083	K-12	Cheryl Flynn
Stockyard Community ES	3200 W 65th St	Cleveland, OH	44102-5510	216-651-5143	651-9515	K-6	Amber Edmisten
Stockyard Community MS	3200 W 65th St	Cleveland, OH	44102-5510	216-961-5052	651-9515	7-8	Gregory Cek
Sullivant Avenue Community S	3435 Sullivant Ave	Columbus, OH	43204-1103	614-308-5991	308-5622	K-5	Jamie Lama
Summit Academy Akron ES	88 Kent St	Akron, OH	44305-2544	330-253-7441	253-7457	K-5	
Summit Academy Akron HS	464 S Hawkins Ave	Akron, OH	44320-1228	330-434-2343	434-5295	9-12	Heather Barone
Summit Academy Akron MS	2791 Mogadore Rd	Akron, OH	44312-1504	330-252-1510	784-8347	6-8	
Summit Academy - Canton HS	2400 Cleveland Ave NW	Canton, OH	44709-3613	330-453-8547	453-8924	9-12	
Summit Academy - Canton S	1620 Market Ave S	Canton, OH	44707	330-458-0393	458-0518	K-8	
Summit Academy Columbus	1850 Bostwick Rd	Columbus, OH	43227	614-237-5497	237-6519	K-8	
Summit Academy Community S Cincinnati	1660 Sternblock Ln	Cincinnati, OH	45237-3005	513-321-0561	321-0795	K-8	
Summit Academy Community S Dayton	4128 Ceder Ridge Rd	Dayton, OH	45414	937-278-4298	278-4613	K-7	
Summit Academy Community S for Alt Lrnrs	2140 E 36th St	Lorain, OH	44055-2756	440-277-4110	277-4112	K-5	Jody Wessler
Summit Academy Community S Warren	2106 Arbor Ave SE	Warren, OH	44484-5296	330-369-4233	369-4299	K-4	
Summit Academy Community S Xenia	1694 Pawnee Dr	Xenia, OH	45385-4126	937-372-5210	372-5250	K-8	
Summit Academy Lorain	1051 E St	Lorain, OH	44052	440-288-0448	288-0997	9-12	Joshua Preece
Summit Academy - Middletown	4700 Central Ave	Middletown, OH	45044-5354	513-422-8540	423-6352	1-8	Megan Bockelman
Summit Academy Middletown HS	7 S Marshall Rd	Middletown, OH	45044-5375	513-420-9767	727-1520	9-12	Beth Varley
Summit Academy Painesville	268 N State St	Painesville, OH	44077-4009	440-358-0877	358-0397	K-9	Frank Cheraso
Summit Academy Parma	5868 Stumph Rd	Parma, OH	44130-1736	440-888-5407	888-5417	K-12	Eric Johnson
Summit Academy S for Alt Learners	1461 Moncrest Dr NW	Warren, OH	44485-1928	330-399-1692	399-1768	5-12	
Summit Academy Secondary S Toledo	703 Phillips Ave	Toledo, OH	43612-1332	419-476-7859	476-7763	9-12	
Summit Academy Toledo	703 Phillips Ave	Toledo, OH	43612-1332	419-476-0784	476-0763	K-8	
Summit Academy Transition HS - Cinci	5800 Salvia Ave	Cincinnati, OH	45224-3029	513-541-4000	541-4075	9-12	
Summit Academy Transition HS Columbus	1855 E Dublin Granville Rd	Columbus, OH	43229-3516	614-880-0714	880-0732	9-12	Trina Moore
Summit Academy Transition HS Dayton	1407 E 3rd St	Dayton, OH	45403-1818	937-223-3154	223-3229	9-12	Gary Miller
Summit Academy - Youngstown	1400 Oak Hill Ave	Youngstown, OH	44507-1018	330-747-0950	747-0957	9-12	
Summit Academy Youngstown	144 N Schenley Ave	Youngstown, OH	44509-2041	330-259-0421	259-0424	K-7	
T.C.P. World Academy	6000 Ridge Ave	Cincinnati, OH	45213-1624	513-531-9500	531-2406	K-6	Karen French
TechCon Institute HS	501 E Main St Unit C	Dayton, OH	45426-2947	937-277-0117	837-4083	9-12	
Toledo Prep & Fitness Academy	20 Arco Dr	Toledo, OH	43607-2901	419-535-3700	535-3701	K-8	Stephanie Widner
Toledo S for the Arts	333 14th St	Toledo, OH	43604-5459	419-246-8732	244-3979	6-12	Nicholas Mariano
Tomorrow Center	PO Box 216	Edison, OH	43320-0216	419-946-1900	947-9551	K-12	
TRECA Digital Academy	100 Executive Dr	Marion, OH	43302-6306	740-389-4798	389-6695	K-12	Adam Clark

School	Address	City,State	Zip code	Telephone	Fax	Grade	Contact
Trotwood Preparatory & Fitness Academy	3100 Shiloh Springs Rd	Trotwood, OH	45426-2247	937-854-4100	837-9759	K-8	Alison Foreman
Urbana Community S	711 Wood St	Urbana, OH	43078-1498	937-653-1478	652-3845	K-12	Larry Nickels
Victory Academy of Toledo	3319 Nebraska Ave	Toledo, OH	43607-2819	419-534-2304	534-2379	K-8	
Villaview Lighthouse Community S	1701 E 12th St	Cleveland, OH	44114-3236	216-523-1133	523-1134	K-9	
Virtual Community S of Ohio	4480 Refugee Rd	Columbus, OH	43232-4459	614-501-9473	501-9470	K-12	Ron Thornton
Virtual Schoolhouse	736 Lakeview Rd	Cleveland, OH	44108-2608	216-541-2048	541-2018	K-12	Kenneth Schmiesing
V L T Academy	1100 Sycamore St	Cincinnati, OH	45202-1321	513-421-1129	421-1464	K-12	Ravine Hubbard
Washington Park Community S	4000 Washington Park Blvd	Newburgh Hts, OH	44105-3211	216-271-6055	271-6099	K-8	
Wesley-Taylor Preparatory S	30 E Main St	Chillicothe, OH	45601-2503	740-772-5437	773-2427	K-12	Beverly Yoakum
West Central Learning Academy	522 W North St	Lima, OH	45801-4215	419-227-9252	227-2511	7-12	Connie Houser
Westpark Community ES	16210 Lorain Ave	Cleveland, OH	44111-5521	216-688-0271	688-0273	K-4	Sheila Delzani
Westpark Community MS	16210 Lorain Ave	Cleveland, OH	44111-5521	216-251-7200	251-0355	5-8	
Westside Academy	4330 Clime Rd N	Columbus, OH	43228-3439	614-272-9392		K-8	
Westside Community S of the Arts	3727 Bosworth Rd	Cleveland, OH	44111-6037	216-688-1900	688-1902	K-6	Deborah Kilbane
Whitehall Prep & Fitness S	3474 E Livingston Ave	Columbus, OH	43227-2219	614-324-4585	238-3184	K-8	Ryan Young
Wildwood Environmental Academy	1546 Dartford Rd	Maumee, OH	43537-1374	419-868-9885	868-9981	K-8	Elizabeth Lewin
Winterfield Venture Academy	305 Wenz Rd	Toledo, OH	43615-6244	419-531-3285	531-3637	K-8	Amy Kramer
Youngstown Academy of Excellence	1408 Rigby St	Youngstown, OH	44506-1617	330-746-3970	746-3965	K-12	Melissa Wheatley M.Ed.
Youngstown Community S	50 Essex St	Youngstown, OH	44502-1838	330-746-2240	746-6618	K-6	Lydia Hammar
YouthBuild Columbus Comm S	1183 Essex Ave	Columbus, OH	43201-2925	614-291-0805	291-0890	9-12	Derek Steward
Zanesville Community S	968 Pine St	Zanesville, OH	43701-5362	740-588-5685	455-4331	9-12	
Zenith Academy	8210 Havens Rd	Blacklick, OH	43004-8630	614-419-6753	888-3290	K-9	
Zenith Academy East	2261 S Hamilton Rd	Columbus, OH	43232-4301	614-577-0999	577-0995	K-8	

Oklahoma

School	Address	City,State	Zip code	Telephone	Fax	Grade	Contact
ASTEC Charter S	2401 NW 23rd St Ste 3	Oklahoma City, OK	73107-2431	405-947-6274	947-0035	6-12	Dr. Freda Deskin
Brown Community S	2 S Elgin Ave	Tulsa, OK	74120-1808	918-425-1407	425-6693	K-5	Deborah Brown
Discovery School of Tulsa	4821 S 72nd East Ave	Tulsa, OK	74145-6502	918-960-3131	960-3130	K-8	Barbaros Aslan
Dove Science Academy	919 NW 23rd St	Oklahoma City, OK	73106-5691	405-524-9762	524-9471	6-12	Barbaros Aslan
Dove Science Academy	280 S Memorial Dr	Tulsa, OK	74112-2202	918-834-3936	834-3352	6-12	Abidin Erez
Dove Science Academy	4901 N Lincoln Blvd	Oklahoma City, OK	73105-3322	405-605-5566	605-5578	K-5	Hasan Suzuk
Epic One on One S	11911 N Pennsylvania Ave	Oklahoma City, OK	73120-7826	405-749-4550		PK-12	David Chaney
Garvey S	1537 NE 24th St	Oklahoma City, OK	73111-3212	405-427-7616	425-4632	PK-8	Caletta McPherson
Harding Charter Preparatory HS	3333 N Shartel Ave	Oklahoma City, OK	73118-7277	405-528-0562	556-5063	9-12	Justin Hunt
Harding Fine Arts Center	PO Box 18895	Oklahoma City, OK	73154-0895	405-702-4322	601-0904	9-12	Sherry Rowan Ph.D.
Hupfeld Academy at Western Village	1508 NW 106th St	Oklahoma City, OK	73114-5214	405-751-1774	752-6833	PK-5	Ruthie Rayner
Independence Charter MS	3232 NW 65th St	Oklahoma City, OK	73116-3512	405-767-3000	767-3007	6-8	Vanna Baker
KIPP Reach College Preparatory	PO Box 776	Oklahoma City, OK	73101-0776	405-425-4622	425-4624	5-8	Tracy McDaniel
KIPP Tulsa Academy	1661 E Virgin St	Tulsa, OK	74106-5552	918-794-8652	794-8712	5-8	John Wolfkill
Oklahoma Virtual Charter Academy	7508 Dripping Springs Ln	Oklahoma City, OK	73150-8314	405-386-3018		K-12	Kristi Gifford
Santa Fe South ES	301 SE 38th St	Oklahoma City, OK	73129-3099	405-681-7480	681-7484	K-5	Chris Brewster
Santa Fe South HS	301 SE 38th St	Oklahoma City, OK	73129-3099	405-631-6100	681-6993	9-12	Chris Brewster
Santa Fe South MS	4712 S Santa Fe Ave	Oklahoma City, OK	73109-7545	405-635-1053	635-0423	6-8	Michael Figueroa
SeeWorth Academy	12600 N Kelley Ave	Oklahoma City, OK	73131-1869	405-475-6400	475-8566	3-12	Stacey Golden
Tsunadeloquasdi Cherokee Immersion S	PO Box 520	Tahlequah, OK	74465-0520	918-453-5400	467-4746	PK-5	Holly Davis
Tulsa S of Arts and Sciences	5155 E 51st St Ste 200	Tulsa, OK	74135-7458	918-828-7727	828-7747	9-12	Dennis Shoemaker

Oregon

School	Address	City,State	Zip code	Telephone	Fax	Grade	Contact
Academy of Arts and Academics	615 Main St	Springfield, OR	97477-4764	541-746-0372	746-5712	9-12	Mike Fisher
Acad for Character Education Charter S	PO Box 1652	Cottage Grove, OR	97424-0067	541-942-9707	942-7884	K-12	Starr Sahnow
ACE Academy	4222 NE 158th Ave	Portland, OR	97230-5084	503-546-9928	546-9708	11-12	Mike Bryant
Alliance Charter Academy	16075 Front St	Oregon City, OR	97045-1273	503-785-8556	722-4113	K-12	Lara Fabrycki
Arlington ES	PO Box 10	Arlington, OR	97812-0010	541-454-2727	454-2335	K-8	Travis Reeser
Arlington HS	PO Box 10	Arlington, OR	97812-0010	541-454-2632	454-2137	9-12	Travis Reeser
Armadillo Technical Institute	PO Box 1560	Phoenix, OR	97535-1560	541-535-3287		4-12	Josh Bald
Arthur Academy	13717 SE Division St	Portland, OR	97236-2841	503-252-3753	760-1204	K-5	Stephani Walker
Bethany Charter S	11824 Hazelgreen Rd NE	Silverton, OR	97381-9611	503-873-4300	873-0143	K-8	Kathy Frank
Bridges Charter HS	7654 N Delaware Ave	Portland, OR	97217-6417	503-916-2000		9-12	
Burnt River S	PO Box 9	Unity, OR	97884-1000	541-446-3336	446-3581	K-12	Lorrie Andrews
Butte Falls Charter S	PO Box 228	Butte Falls, OR	97522-0228	541-865-3563	865-7810	K-12	David Courtney
Camas Valley S	PO Box 57	Camas Valley, OR	97416-0057	541-445-2131	445-2041	K-12	Wayne Gallagher
Career Technical HS	801 SW Highway 101 Ste 404	Lincoln City, OR	97367-2752	541-351-8551	994-7592	9-12	Sean Larson
Cascade Heights Charter S	13515 SE Rusk Rd	Milwaukie, OR	97222-3243	503-653-3996	653-1026	K-8	Holly Denman
Center for Advanced Learning	1484 NW Civic Dr	Gresham, OR	97030-5564	503-667-4978	492-1572	11-12	Carol Eagan
Childs Way Charter S	37895 Row River Rd	Dorena, OR	97434-9610	541-946-1821	946-2007	6-12	Michael Kerns
City View Charter S	PO Box 1808	Hillsboro, OR	97123-1808	503-844-9424	844-9425	K-8	Jeffrey Hays
Clackamas Academy of Industrial Science	995 S End Rd	Oregon City, OR	97045-3469	503-785-7860		9-10	Kyle Laier
Clackamas Middle College HS	12021 SE 82nd Ave	Happy Valley, OR	97086-7713	503-518-5925	518-5928	9-12	Brian Sien
Clackamas Web Academy	8740 SE Sunnybrook Blvd	Clackamas, OR	97015-5737	503-659-4664	659-4994	1-12	Brad Linn
Coburg Community Family Charter S	91274 N Coburg Rd	Coburg, OR	97408	541-344-4113	344-4120	K-5	Laura Ralls
Columbia County Education Campus	474 N 16th St	Saint Helens, OR	97051-1340	503-366-3207	397-2723	9-12	Colleen Grogan
Community Roots S	330 N James St	Silverton, OR	97381-1029	503-874-4107	874-4108	1-6	Miranda Traegar
Corbett Charter S	35800 E Historic Colmb Riv	Corbett, OR	97019	503-261-4221		K-12	Robert Dunton
Cove S	PO Box 68	Cove, OR	97824-0068	541-568-4424	568-4231	K-12	Bruce Neil
Days Creek Charter S	PO Box 10	Days Creek, OR	97429-0010	541-825-3296	825-3052	6-12	Laurie Newton
EAGLE Charter S	999 Locust St NE	Salem, OR	97301-0687	503-339-7114		K-5	Cliff Monroe
EagleRidge Charter HS	677 S 7th St	Klamath Falls, OR	97601	541-884-7627	871-7054	9-12	Donald Peterson
Eddyville Charter S	PO Box 68	Eddyville, OR	97343-0068	541-875-2942	875-2491	K-12	Dennis Schultz
Emerson Charter S	105 NW Park Ave	Portland, OR	97209-3315	503-525-6124	223-4875	K-5	Tara O'Neil
Estacada All Prep Early College	PO Box 2631	Estacada, OR	97023-2631	503-630-5001	630-5206	9-12	Joni Tabler
Estacada Web Academy	PO Box 2631	Estacada, OR	97023-2631	503-630-5001	630-5206	K-12	Joni Tabler
Forest Grove Community S	1914 Pacific Ave	Forest Grove, OR	97116-2326	503-359-4600	359-4622	1-9	Vanessa Gray
Fossil S	PO Box 287	Fossil, OR	97830-0287	541-763-4155	763-4010	K-8	Brad Sperry
Four Rivers Community S	2449 SW 4th Ave	Ontario, OR	97914-1829	541-889-3715	889-3718	K-5	Chelle Robins
Goodall Environmental MS	999B Locust St NE	Salem, OR	97301	503-399-3215	399-4070	6-8	Joe Grant
Gresham Arthur Academy	1890 NE Cleveland Ave	Gresham, OR	97030-4210	503-667-4900	667-4933	K-5	Amber Sparks
Harper Charter S	2987 Harper Westfall Rd	Harper, OR	97906-2008	541-358-2473	358-2488	K-12	Ron Talbot
Howard Street Charter S	710 Howard St SE	Salem, OR	97302-3098	503-399-3408	375-7861	6-8	Christina Tracy
Ione S	PO Box 167	Ione, OR	97843-0167	541-422-7131	422-7555	K-12	Jerry Archer
Ivy S	4212 NE Prescott St	Portland, OR	97218-1632	503-288-8820	288-8894	1-8	Mary Zigman
Joseph Charter S	PO Box 787	Joseph, OR	97846-2023	541-432-7311	432-1100	K-12	Sherri Kilgore
Kings Valley Charter S	38840 Kings Valley Hwy	Philomath, OR	97370-9750	541-929-2134	929-8179	K-12	Mark Hazelton
KNOVA Learning Oregon	18201 SE Stark St	Portland, OR	97233-4862	503-907-1023	907-1024	K-6	Dennis Tiede
Leadership & Entrepreneurship Charter HS	2044 E Burnside St	Portland, OR	97214-1674	503-254-2537	236-6783	9-12	Lorna Fast Buffalo Horse
Lewis & Clark Montessori Charter S	14151 SE 242nd Ave	Damascus, OR	97089-7341	503-427-0803	855-3017	PK-3	Melissa Harbert
Lighthouse S	93670 Viking Ln	North Bend, OR	97459-8623	541-751-1649		K-8	Wade Lester
Logos Public Charter S	400 Earhart St	Medford, OR	97501-7828	541-842-3658	842-1927	K-12	Joe VonDoloski
Lourdes Charter S	39059 Jordan Rd	Scio, OR	97374-9330	503-394-3340		K-8	Linda Duman
Luckiamute Valley Charter S	17475 Bridgeport Rd	Dallas, OR	97338-9458	503-838-1933	606-9879	K-8	Dan Austin
Madrone Trail Charter S	3070 Ross Ln	Central Point, OR	97502-1325	541-842-3657	842-1966	K-7	Joe Frodsham
Metro East Web Academy	1394 NW Civic Dr	Gresham, OR	97030-5569	503-258-4790	258-4791	6-12	David Gray
Milwaukie Academy of the Arts	11300 SE 23rd Ave	Milwaukie, OR	97222-7753	503-353-5843	353-5845	9-12	Tim Taylor
M.I.T.C.H. Charter S	19550 SW 90th Ct	Tualatin, OR	97062-7505	503-639-5757		K-8	Melissa Meyer
Molalla River Academy	16897 S Callahan Rd	Molalla, OR	97038-8606	503-829-6672	759-6672	K-8	Shelley Urben
Mosier Community S	PO Box 307	Mosier, OR	97040-0307	541-478-3321	478-2536	K-6	Carole Schmidt
Muddy Creek Charter S	30252 Bellfountain Rd	Corvallis, OR	97333-9524	541-752-0377	752-9481	K-5	Dan Hays
Multisensory Learning Academy	22565 NE Halsey St	Fairview, OR	97024-2642	503-405-7868	405-7869	K-6	Sheri Fitzsimmons
Network Charter S	2550 Portland St	Eugene, OR	97405-3127	541-344-1229	344-5118	7-12	Mary Leighton
Nixyaawi Community S	PO Box 638	Pendleton, OR	97801-0638	541-966-2240	276-6543	9-12	Ronda Smith
North Columbia Academy	28168 Old Rainier Rd	Rainier, OR	97048-3017	503-556-3777	556-3778	9-12	Jack Correia
North Powder Charter S	PO Box 10	North Powder, OR	97867-0010	541-898-2244	898-2046	PK-12	Lance Dixon
Opal School of Portland Childrens Museum	4015 SW Canyon Rd	Portland, OR	97221-2759	503-471-9917	223-6600	K-5	Tara Papandrew
Optimum Learning Environments Charter S	7905 June Reid Pl NE	Keizer, OR	97303-2559	503-399-5548	399-3469	1-5	Gary Etchemendy
Oregon City Service Learning Academy	995 S End Rd	Oregon City, OR	97045-3469	503-785-8220	650-5483	9-12	Tim Graham
Oregon Coast Technology S	1913 Meade St	North Bend, OR	97459-3432	541-756-8341	756-1313	6-12	Ralph Brooks
Oregon Connections Academy	PO Box 1160	Scio, OR	97374-1160	503-394-4315	394-4320	K-12	Todd Miller
Oregon Virtual Academy	400 Virginia Ave Ste 210	North Bend, OR	97459-3444	541-751-8060	751-8016	K-12	James Moyer
Paisley S	PO Box 97	Paisley, OR	97636-0097	541-943-3111	943-3129	K-12	Donna Howard
Phoenix S of Roseburg	3131 NE Diamond Lake Blvd	Roseburg, OR	97470-3632	541-673-3036	957-5906	7-12	Ron Breyne
Pine Eagle Charter S	375 N Main St	Halfway, OR	97834-8153	541-742-2811	742-2422	K-12	Cammie de Castro
Portland Arthur Academy	7507 SE Yamhill St	Portland, OR	97215-2284	503-257-3936	257-3929	K-5	Ryan Hull
Portland Village S	7654 N Delaware Ave	Portland, OR	97217-6417	503-445-0056	445-0058	K-8	Jackie Jaffe
Powell Butte Community Charter S	13650 SW Highway 126	Powell Butte, OR	97753-1604	541-548-1166	548-7635	K-7	
Prospect Charter S	PO Box 40	Prospect, OR	97536-0040	541-560-3653	560-3644	PK-12	Jennifer Pettit
REALMS	63175 O B Riley Rd	Bend, OR	97701-9003	541-322-5323	322-5473	6-8	Roger White

School	Address	City,State	Zip code	Telephone	Fax	Grade	Contact
Redmond Proficiency Academy	657 SW Glacier Ave	Redmond, OR	97756-2710	541-526-0882	516-1160	9-12	Jon Bullock
Reedsport Community Charter S	2260 Longwood Dr	Reedsport, OR	97467-1195	541-271-2141	271-2143	7-12	Laura Davis
Renaissance Public Academy	PO Box 208	Molalla, OR	97038-0208	503-759-7002	759-7004	5-12	Randle Brown
Resource Link Charter S	1255 Hemlock Ave	Coos Bay, OR	97420-1298	541-267-1499	266-7314	K-12	Shelly McKnight
Reynolds Arthur Academy	123 SW 21st St	Troutdale, OR	97060-3300	503-465-8882	465-8883	K-5	Chris Arnold
Riddle Education Center	PO Box 45	Riddle, OR	97469-0045	541-874-3202		7-12	William Starkweather
Ridgeline Montessori Charter S	4500 W Amazon Dr	Eugene, OR	97405-4652	541-681-9662	681-4394	K-8	
Sage Community S	PO Box 655	Chiloquin, OR	97624-0655	541-783-2533	783-2544	K-8	Sandra Girdner
Saint Helens Arthur Academy	33035 Pittsburg Rd	Saint Helens, OR	97051-3305	503-366-7030		K-8	Michael Arthur
Sand Ridge Charter S	30581 Sodaville Mtn Home Rd	Lebanon, OR	97355-9008	541-258-2416	258-1898	K-12	Jay Jackson
SEI Academy Charter S	3920 N Kerby Ave	Portland, OR	97227-1255	503-249-1721	548-1450	6-8	Carl Reinhold
Sheridan Japanese S	PO Box 446	Sheridan, OR	97378-0446	503-843-3400	843-7438	4-12	Kathryn Mueller
Sherwood Charter S	PO Box 1342	Sherwood, OR	97140-1342	503-925-8007	925-8172	K-8	Fred Puhl
Siletz Valley S	PO Box 247	Siletz, OR	97380-0247	541-444-1100	444-2368	K-12	Sam Tupou
Silvies River Charter S	550 N Court Ave	Burns, OR	97720-1525	541-573-6811	573-7557	K-12	Katie Baltzor
South Columbia Family S	34555 Berg Rd	Warren, OR	97053-9611	503-366-9009	366-9010	K-8	Anita Ott-Veile M.Ed.
Southwest Charter S	PO Box 19816	Portland, OR	97280-0816	503-244-1697	244-1709	K-8	Anne Gurnee
Springwater Environmental Sciences S	PO Box 3010	Oregon City, OR	97045-0301	503-631-7700	631-7720	K-8	Dawn Bolotow
Sunny Wolf Charter S	PO Box 438	Wolf Creek, OR	97497-0438	541-866-2735	866-2738	K-5	Sarah McNamara
Sweet Home Charter S	28721 Liberty Rd	Sweet Home, OR	97386-9776	541-367-1833	367-1839	K-6	Scott Richards
Three Rivers Charter S	4975 Willamette Falls Dr	West Linn, OR	97068-3348	503-723-6019	723-6407	4-8	Katherine Holtgraves
Triangle Lake Charter S	20264 Blachly Grange Rd	Blachly, OR	97412-9714	541-925-3262	925-3062	K-12	William Beaudoin
Trillium Charter S	5420 N Interstate Ave	Portland, OR	97217-4569	503-285-3833	249-0348	K-12	Genevieve Bouwes
Valley Inquiry Charter S	5774 Hazelgreen Rd NE	Salem, OR	97305-9576	503-399-4120	364-4050	K-5	Manuel Palacio
Village S	2855 Lincoln St	Eugene, OR	97405-2737	541-345-7285	242-6874	K-8	Martha Collins
West Lane Technology Learning Center	24936 Fir Grove Ln	Elmira, OR	97437-9751	541-935-2101	935-8345	9-12	Ken Woody
Wheeler HS	PO Box 266	Fossil, OR	97830-0266	541-763-4146	763-4010	9-12	Brad Sperry
Woodburn Arthur Academy	575 Gatch St	Woodburn, OR	97071-4927	503-981-5746	981-5742	K-5	Brittany Lopez
Pennsylvania							
Academy Charter S	900 Agnew Rd	Pittsburgh, PA	15227-3902	412-885-5200		8-12	
Achievement House Charter S	600 Eagleview Blvd Ste 1	Exton, PA	19341-1121	484-615-6200	458-1204	7-12	Dr. Timothy Daniels
Ad Prima Charter S	5901 Woodbine Ave	Philadelphia, PA	19131-1206	215-452-5580	452-5588	K-8	Meghan Allhouse
Agora Cyber Charter S	995 Old Eagle School # 315	Wayne, PA	19087	866-548-9452	529-0166	K-12	Sharon Williams
Allen Preparatory Charter S	2601 S 58th St	Philadelphia, PA	19143-6146	215-878-1544	727-0711	5-9	Lawrence Jones
Alliance for Progress Charter S	1630 N 16th St	Philadelphia, PA	19121	215-232-4892	232-4894	4-8	Maria Snipe
Alliance for Progress Charter S	1821 Cecil B Moore Ave	Philadelphia, PA	19121-3135	215-232-4892	232-4893	K-3	Tina Lloyd
Architecture & Design Charter HS	105 S 7th St	Philadelphia, PA	19106	215-351-2900	351-9458	9-12	Dr. Peter Kountz
ARISE Academy Charter HS	1108 Market St	Philadelphia, PA	19107-3601	215-563-1656		9-12	Gabriel Kuriloff
ASPIRA Bilingual Cyber Charter S	4101 N American St	Philadelphia, PA	19140-2606	215-329-2733	329-2433	K-12	Dr. Lucila Paramo
ASPIRA Olney HS	100 W Duncannon Ave	Philadelphia, PA	19120-3598	215-456-3014	456-3064	9-12	Jose Lebron
ASPIRA Stetson Charter S	3200 B St	Philadelphia, PA	19134-2202	215-291-4720	291-4168	5-8	Renato Lajara
Attucks Youth Build Charter S	605 S Duke St	York, PA	17401-3111	717-848-3610	843-3914	K-6	Jacquie Martino
Avon Grove Charter S	110 State Rd	West Grove, PA	19390-8908	484-667-5000		K-12	Dr. Kevin Brady
Bear Creek Community Charter S	2000 Bear Creek Blvd	Wilkes Barre, PA	18702-9684	570-820-4070	270-6149	K-7	Brian Dugas
Beaver Area Academic Charter S	Gypsy Glen Rd	Beaver, PA	15009	724-774-4022		9-12	Carrie Rowe
Belmont Academy Charter S	907 N 41st St	Philadelphia, PA	19104-1278	215-386-5768	386-5769	K-K	Jennifer Faustman
Belmont Charter S	4030 Brown St	Philadelphia, PA	19104-4899	215-823-8208	823-8209	1-8	Jennifer Faustman
Birney Charter S	900 Lindley Ave	Philadelphia, PA	19141-3999	215-456-3000	457-6695	K-8	Bernard James
Boys Latin of Philadelphia Charter S	5501 Cedar Ave	Philadelphia, PA	19143-1929	215-387-5149	387-5159	9-12	Noah Tennant
Bracetti Academy Charter S	2501 Kensington Ave	Philadelphia, PA	19125-1321	215-291-4436	291-4985	6-12	Angela Villani
Bucks County Montessori Charter S	219 Tyburn Rd	Fairless Hills, PA	19030-4403	215-428-6700	428-6702	K-6	Brian Long
Byers Charter S	1911 Arch St	Philadelphia, PA	19103-1403	215-972-1700	972-1701	PK-6	Anna Hadgis
Career Connections Charter HS	4412 Butler St	Pittsburgh, PA	15201-3012	412-682-1816	682-6559	9-12	Peter Simpson
Center for Student Learning Charter S	345 Lakeside Dr	Levittown, PA	19054-3933	215-269-7390	269-7395	6-12	Thomas Reiley
Central Pennsylvania Digital Charter S	1500 4th Ave	Altoona, PA	16602-3616	814-940-6989	946-8526	K-12	Jill Daloisio
Centre Learning Community Charter S	2643 W College Ave	State College, PA	16801-2604	814-861-7980	861-8030	5-8	Kosta Dusslas
Chester Community Charter S	214 E 5th St	Chester, PA	19013-4510	610-447-0400	876-5716	K-6	Dr. David Clark
Chester County Family Academy	323 E Gay St Ste B7	West Chester, PA	19380-2755	610-696-5910	696-6324	K-2	Lorraine Anderson
City Charter HS	201 Stanwix St	Pittsburgh, PA	15222-1350	412-600-2480	600-2316	9-12	Dr. Ron Sofo
Clemente Charter S	136 S 4th St	Allentown, PA	18102-5445	610-439-5181	435-4731	6-12	Dr. Maritza Robert
Collegium Charter S	535 James Hance Ct	Exton, PA	19341-2560	610-903-1300	903-1317	K-12	Bill Winters
Columbus Charter S	1242 S 13th St	Philadelphia, PA	19147-4597	215-389-6000	389-3332	5-8	Rosemary Dougherty
Columbus Charter S	916 Christian St	Philadelphia, PA	19147-3808	215-925-7400	925-6851	K-8	Rosemary Dougherty
Commonwealth Connections Charter S	4050 Crums Mill Rd	Harrisburg, PA	17112-2827	717-651-7200	651-0670	K-12	Dr. Maurice Flurie
Community Academy of Philadelphia	1100 E Erie Ave	Philadelphia, PA	19124-5424	215-533-6700	533-6722	K-12	Joe Proietta
DeHostos Charter S	4322 N 5th St	Philadelphia, PA	19140-2302	215-455-2300	455-6312	K-8	Diana Garcia
Delaware Valley Charter HS	5201 Old York Rd	Philadelphia, PA	19141-2985	215-455-2550	455-5701	9-12	Ernest Holiday
Discovery Charter S	5070 Parkside Ave Unit 6200	Philadelphia, PA	19131-4750	215-879-8182	879-9510	K-8	Jacquelyn Kelley
Eastern University Academy Charter S	3300 Henry Ave Ste 2	Philadelphia, PA	19129-1121	215-769-3131	769-3112	7-12	Omar Barlow
Environmental Charter S at Frick Park	829 Milton St	Pittsburgh, PA	15218-1005	412-247-7970	247-7971	K-6	Jon McCann
Evergreen Community Charter S	PO Box 523	Mountainhome, PA	18342-0523	570-595-6355	595-6038	6-12	Jill Shoesmith
Fell Charter S	27 Farview St Ste 33	Carbondale, PA	18407-1518	570-282-5199	282-0930	K-8	Mary Jo Walsh
First Philadelphia Charter S	4300 Tacony St	Philadelphia, PA	19124-4134	215-743-3100	743-9877	K-8	Josephine Arcaro
Folk Arts-Cultural Treasures Charter S	1023 Callowhill St	Philadelphia, PA	19123-3704	215-569-2600	569-3985	K-8	Susan Stengel
Franklin Towne Charter ES	4259 Richmond St	Philadelphia, PA	19137-1930	215-289-3389	288-4041	K-8	Patrick Field
Franklin Towne Charter HS	PO Box 310	Philadelphia, PA	19105-0310	215-289-5000	535-8910	9-12	Joseph Venditti
Freire Charter HS	2027 Chestnut St	Philadelphia, PA	19103-3301	215-592-4252	557-9051	9-12	Dr. Kelly Davenport
Freire Charter S	1026 Market St	Philadelphia, PA	19107-4205	215-592-4252	557-9051	5-8	Dr. Kelly Davenport
Gettysburg Montessori Charter S	120 E Broadway	Gettysburg, PA	17325-1512	717-334-1120		PK-6	Robin Kirkpatrick
Global Leadership Academy	4601 W Girard Ave	Philadelphia, PA	19131-4615	267-295-5700	295-5701	K-8	Dr. Naomi Johnson-Booker
Graystone Academy Charter S	139 Modena Rd	Coatesville, PA	19320-4036	610-383-4311		K-6	Marita Barber
Green Woods Charter S	119 Rector St	Philadelphia, PA	19127-1523	215-482-6337	482-9135	K-8	Jean Wallace
Harambee Institute of Science Technology	640 N 66th St	Philadelphia, PA	19151-3606	215-472-8770	472-9611	K-8	Damaas Stephens
Hope Charter S	2116 E Haines St	Philadelphia, PA	19138-2800	267-336-2730	336-2740	9-12	Eric Worley
Imani Education Circle Charter S	5612 Greene St Fl 2	Philadelphia, PA	19144-2808	215-713-9240	713-9243	K-8	Adrienne Davis
Imhotep Institute Charter HS	6201 N 21st St	Philadelphia, PA	19138	215-438-4140	438-4160	9-12	Christine Wiggins
Independence Charter S	1600 Lombard St	Philadelphia, PA	19146-1507	215-238-8000	545-2924	K-8	Richard Trzaska
Infinity Charter S	51 Banks St Ste 1	Penbrook, PA	17103-2067	717-238-1880		K-6	Suzanne Gausman
Ketterer Charter S	1133 Village Way	Latrobe, PA	15650-5201	724-537-9110	537-9114	1-12	Eric Guldin
Keystone Education Center Charter S	425 S Good Hope Rd	Greenville, PA	16125-8629	724-588-2511	588-2545	6-12	Mike Gentile
Khepera Charter S	144 Carpenter Ln	Philadelphia, PA	19119-2563	215-843-1700	843-3530	6-8	Verna Holmes
Khepera Charter S	6641 Ardleigh St	Philadelphia, PA	19119	215-843-1700	843-3530	K-5	Verna Holmes
KIPP Dubois Collegiate Academy	2601 W Cumberland St	Philadelphia, PA	19132-3540	267-687-4297	717-2054	9-12	Aaron Bass
KIPP Philadelphia Charter S	2709 N Broad St	Philadelphia, PA	19132-2722	215-227-1728	827-5942	5-8	Meredith Mehra
KIPP Philadelphia ES	2409 W Westmoreland St	Philadelphia, PA	19129-1309	267-687-7283	687-7295	K-1	Ben Speicher
KIPP West Philadelphia Prep Charter S	5900 Baltimore Ave	Philadelphia, PA	19143-3129	215-294-2973	294-8707	5-7	Shawna Wells
La Academia Charter S	30 N Ann St	Lancaster, PA	17602-3063	717-295-7763	399-6456	6-12	Thomas Scheid
Laboratory Charter S	5339 Lebanon Ave	Philadelphia, PA	19131	215-877-9880	877-9882	2-8	Kimberly O'Rourke
Laboratory Charter S	5901 Woodbine Ave	Philadelphia, PA	19131-1206	215-452-5580	452-5588	K-1	Katherine Makar
Laboratory Charter S	800 N Orianna St	Philadelphia, PA	19123-2250	215-574-1680	574-0622	K-8	Elizabeth Bonner
Lehigh Valley Academy	1560 Valley Center Pkwy	Bethlehem, PA	18017	610-866-9660		K-12	Aldo Cavalli
Lehigh Valley Charter HS	675 E Broad St	Bethlehem, PA	18018-6332	610-868-2971	868-1446	9-12	Diane LaBelle
Lehigh Valley Dual Language Charter S	551 Thomas St	Bethlehem, PA	18015-3447	610-419-3120	419-3968	K-6	Lisa Pluchinsky
Lincoln Charter S	559 W King St	York, PA	17401-3776	717-699-1573	846-4031	K-5	George Fitch
Lincoln Leadership Academy Charter S	1414 E Cedar St	Allentown, PA	18109-2308	484-860-3300		K-12	Sandra Figueroa-Torres
Lincoln Park Performing Arts Charter S	1 Lincoln Park	Midland, PA	15059-1535	724-643-9004	643-0769	K-12	Rebecca Manning
Manchester Academic Charter S	1214 Liverpool St	Pittsburgh, PA	15233-1309	412-322-0585	322-2176	K-8	Vasilios Scoumis
Maritime Academy Charter S	2275 Bridge St	Philadelphia, PA	19137-2307	215-535-4555	535-4398	4-12	Edward Poznek
MAST Community Charter S	1800 Byberry Rd	Philadelphia, PA	19116-3012	215-348-1100	348-1217	K-12	John Swoyer
Mastery Charter S -Hardy Williams Campus	1712 S 56th St	Philadelphia, PA	19143-5308	215-724-2343	724-2374	K-8	
Mastery Charter S Harrity Campus	5601 Christian St	Philadelphia, PA	19143-2899	215-471-2908	471-3807	PK-8	Debi Durso
Mastery Charter S - Lenfest	35 S 4th St	Philadelphia, PA	19106-2710	215-922-1902	922-1903	7-12	Scott Gordon
Mastery Charter S Mann Campus	5376 W Berks St	Philadelphia, PA	19131-3198	215-581-5616	581-5610	K-6	Stan Bobowski
Mastery Charter S - Pickett	5700 Wayne Ave	Philadelphia, PA	19144-3314	215-866-9000	866-9001	7-12	Scott Gordon
Mastery Charter S - Shoemaker Campus	5301 Media St	Philadelphia, PA	19131-4035	267-296-7111	296-7112	7-12	Scott Gordon
Mastery Charter S Smedley Campus	1790 Bridge St	Philadelphia, PA	19124-1395	215-537-2523	537-2860	K-6	Brian McLaughlin
Mastery Charter S - Thomas Campus	927 Johnston St	Philadelphia, PA	19148-5016	267-236-0036	236-0030	7-12	Scott Gordon
Math Civics & Sciences Charter S	447 N Broad St	Philadelphia, PA	19123-3643	215-923-4880	923-4859	1-12	Frank Devine
Memphis Street Academy Charter S	2950 Memphis St	Philadelphia, PA	19134-4314	215-291-4709	291-4754	5-8	Michael Silverman
Montessori Regional Charter S	2910 Sterrettania Rd	Erie, PA	16506-2646	814-833-7771	833-1838	K-6	Anthony Pirrello
Multi-Cultural Academy Charter S	3821 N Broad St	Philadelphia, PA	19140-3609	215-227-0513	227-0415	8-12	James Higgins
New Day Charter S	256 S 5th St	Huntingdon, PA	16652-1285	814-643-7112	643-7116	7-12	Julia Cigola Ph.D.
New Foundations Charter S	8001 Torresdale Ave	Philadelphia, PA	19136-2917	215-624-8100	624-0600	K-8	Paul Stadelberger
New Foundations Charter S	6701 Calvert St	Philadelphia, PA	19149-2427	215-624-8100	624-0600	9-12	Paul Stadelberger
New Hope Academy Charter S	459 W King St	York, PA	17401-3801	717-845-4046	845-4057	5-12	Karen Schoonover

School	Address	City,State	Zip code	Telephone	Fax	Grade	Contact
New Media Technology Charter S	8034 Thouron Ave	Philadelphia, PA	19150-2423	267-286-6900	286-6904	6-12	DonnaMaria Parker
Nittany Valley Charter S	1612 Norma St	State College, PA	16801-6228	814-867-3842	231-0795	1-8	Kara Martin
Northwood Academy	4621 Castor Ave	Philadelphia, PA	19124-3097	215-289-5606	289-5464	K-8	Amy Hollister
Nueva Esperanza Academy Charter HS	301 W Hunting Park Ave	Philadelphia, PA	19140-2625	215-457-3667	457-4381	9-12	David Rossi
Palmer Leadership Learning Partners HS	5502 Harbison Ave	Philadelphia, PA	19124	215-341-9830		5-12	Daira Hinson
Palmer Leadership Learning Partners S	910 N 6th St	Philadelphia, PA	19123-1496	215-627-7434	627-9375	K-4	Daira Hinson
Pan American Academy Charter S	2830 N American St	Philadelphia, PA	19133-3517	215-425-1212	423-0871	K-8	Dr. Darcy Russotto
Pantoja Community Charter S	4101 N American St	Philadelphia, PA	19140-2606	215-329-2733	329-2433	K-8	Evelyn Nunez
Pennsylvania Cyber Charter S	652 Midland Ave	Midland, PA	15059-1433	724-643-1180	643-2845	K-12	Dr. Michael Conti
Pennsylvania Distance Learning Charter S	2100 Corporate Dr Ste 500	Wexford, PA	15090-7647	724-933-7300	933-7655	K-12	Dr. James Hoover
Pennsylvania Leadership Charter S	1332 Enterprise Dr	West Chester, PA	19380-5970	610-701-3333		K-12	Dr. James Hanak
Pennsylvania Virtual Charter S	1 W Main St Ste 400	Norristown, PA	19401-4766	610-275-8501	275-1719	K-12	Joanne Jones Barnett
People for People Charter S	800 N Broad St	Philadelphia, PA	19130-2202	215-763-7060	763-6210	K-8	Andre Williams
Perseus House Charter S of Excellence	1511 Peach St	Erie, PA	16501-2104	814-480-5914	454-9859	7-12	Dr. Robert Oliver
Philadelphia Academy Charter S	1700 Tomlinson Rd	Philadelphia, PA	19116-3848	215-673-3990	673-3341	9-12	Larry Sperling
Philadelphia Academy Charter S	11000 Roosevelt Blvd	Philadelphia, PA	19116-3961	215-676-8320	676-8340	K-8	Larry Sperling
Philadelphia Electrical & Tech Charter S	1420 Chestnut St	Philadelphia, PA	19102-2505	267-514-1823	514-1834	9-12	Jeffrey Taylor
Philadelphia Montessori Charter S	2227 Island Rd	Philadelphia, PA	19142-1009	215-365-4011	365-4367	PK-6	Carrie Kries
Philadelphia Performing Arts Charter S	2600 S Broad St	Philadelphia, PA	19145-4616	215-551-4000	551-1113	K-8	Dr. Gail Avicolli
Philadelphia Performing Arts Charter S	2407 S Broad St	Philadelphia, PA	19148-3508	215-551-4000	551-1113	K-8	Dr. Gail Avicolli
Planet Abacus Charter S	6649 Tulip St	Philadelphia, PA	19135-2835	215-332-2111	332-2840	K-8	John Goulding
Pocono Mountain Charter S	1110 Carriage Ln	Tobyhanna, PA	18466-8278	570-894-5108	894-2788	K-12	
Preparatory Charter S	1928 Point Breeze Ave	Philadelphia, PA	19145-2612	215-334-6144	334-6147	9-12	Patricia Sack
Propel Charter HS - Andrew Street	605 E 10th Ave	Munhall, PA	15120-1911	412-462-4625	462-6980	9-12	Angela Allie
Propel Charter HS - Braddock Hills	1500 Yost Blvd	Pittsburgh, PA	15221-4822	412-271-4929	271-4905	9-12	J. Oliphant
Propel Charter S - Braddock Hills	1500 Yost Blvd	Braddock Hills, PA	15221-4822	412-271-3061	271-0865	K-8	Marsha Burleson
Propel Charter S - East	1611 Monroeville Ave	Turtle Creek, PA	15145-1652	412-823-0347		K-8	Sandra Gough
Propel Charter S - Homestead	129 E 10th Ave	Homestead, PA	15120-1608	412-464-2604		K-8	Frank Brettschneider
Propel Charter S - Mc Keesport	2412 Versailles Ave	McKeesport, PA	15132-2037	412-678-7215		K-8	Hampton Conway
Propel Charter S - Montour	340 Bilmar Dr	Pittsburgh, PA	15205-4620	412-539-0100		K-8	Diane Mooney
Propel Charter S - Northside	1805 Buena Vista St	Pittsburgh, PA	15212-3914	412-325-1412	325-1428	K-8	Ariane Watson
Propel Charter S - Pitcairn	435 Agatha St	Pitcairn, PA	15140-1310	412-457-0020		K-8	Robert Bischoff
Renaissance Academy	40 Pine Crest Ave	Phoenixville, PA	19460-2955	610-983-4080	983-4096	K-12	Gina Guarino-Buli
Sankofa Academy	446 W Gay St	West Chester, PA	19380-2851	610-696-0333	696-0620	5-12	Dr. LaMont McKim
Sankofa Freedom Academy	4256 Paul St	Philadelphia, PA	19124-4610	215-228-2001	228-2099	K-12	Dr. Ayesha Imani
School Lane Charter S	2400 Bristol Pike	Bensalem, PA	19020-5293	215-245-6055	245-6058	K-8	Karen Schade
Seven Generations Charter S	154 E Minor St	Emmaus, PA	18049-4103	610-421-8844		K-5	Susan Pfeil
Souderton Charter S Collaborative	110 E Broad St	Souderton, PA	18964-1276	215-721-4560	721-4071	K-8	Jennifer Arevalo
Southwest Leadership Academy	7101 Paschall Ave	Philadelphia, PA	19142-1031	215-729-1939	729-1976	K-8	Alphonso Evans
Spectrum Charter S	4369 Northern Pike	Monroeville, PA	15146-2807	412-374-8130	374-9629	9-12	Michelle Johnson
Stream Academy	201 Penn Center Blvd	Pittsburgh, PA	15235-5435	855-478-7326	394-4604	K-12	Dr. David Martin
String Theory Edmunds ES	1197 Haworth St	Philadelphia, PA	19124-2505	215-537-2520	537-2861	K-8	Leta Johnson
Sugar Valley Rural Charter S	236 E Main St	Loganton, PA	17747-9502	570-725-7822	725-7825	K-12	Logan Coney
SusQ-Cyber Charter S	240 Market St	Bloomsburg, PA	17815	866-370-1226	245-0246	9-12	Karin Shipman
Sylvan Heights Science Charter S	915 S 13th St	Harrisburg, PA	17104-3402	717-232-9220	232-9221	K-4	Dr. Kevin Moran
Tacony Academy Charter S	1330 Rhawn St	Philadelphia, PA	19111-2802	215-742-5100	742-5200	K-8	Sterling Garris
Tacony Academy Charter S	6283 Rising Sun Ave	Philadelphia, PA	19111	215-742-5100	742-5200	9-12	Sterling Garris
Thackston Charter MS	625 E Philadelphia St	York, PA	17403-1625	717-846-6160	848-2856	5-8	Jamy Jackson
Tidioute Community Charter S	241 Main St	Tidioute, PA	16351-1299	814-484-3550	484-3977	K-12	Dr. Doug Allen
Truebright Science Academy	926 W Sedgley Ave	Philadelphia, PA	19140-5439	215-225-3437	225-3439	7-12	Bekir Duz
21st Century Cyber Charter S	805 Springdale Dr	Exton, PA	19341-2843	484-875-5400	875-5404	6-12	Jon Marsh
Universal Audenried Charter HS	3301 Tasker St	Philadelphia, PA	19145-1021	215-952-4801	952-4805	9-12	Robert Rouse
Universal Bluford Charter S	5801 Media St	Philadelphia, PA	19131-3824	215-581-5502	581-5725	K-6	Ray Ragland
Universal Creighton Charter S	5401 Tabor Ave	Philadelphia, PA	19120-2130	215-537-2531	537-8398	K-8	
Universal Daroff Charter S	5630 Vine St	Philadelphia, PA	19139-1301	215-471-2905	471-3159	K-8	Anna Smith
Universal Institute Charter S	801 S 15th St	Philadelphia, PA	19146-2215	215-732-2876	732-8066	K-8	Bruce Frazier
Universal Vare Charter MS	2100 S 24th St	Philadelphia, PA	19145-3222	215-952-8611	952-8520	5-8	Sharon Nurse
Urban League of Pittsburgh Charter S	327 N Negley Ave	Pittsburgh, PA	15206-2851	412-361-1008	361-1042	K-5	Dr. Gail Edwards
Urban Pathways Charter S	914 Penn Ave	Pittsburgh, PA	15222-3713	412-392-4601	392-4602	K-12	Linda Clautti
Vida Charter S	120 E Broadway	Gettysburg, PA	17325-1512	717-334-3643	334-9806	K-6	Dr. April Yetsko
Wakisha Charter S	900 W Jefferson St	Philadelphia, PA	19122-3515	267-256-0950	256-0953	6-8	Nina Smith
West Oak Lane Charter S	7115 Stenton Ave	Philadelphia, PA	19138-1136	215-927-7995	927-7980	K-8	Dr. Debbera Peoples-Lee
West Philadelphia Achievement Charter S	111 N 49th St	Philadelphia, PA	19139-2718	215-476-6471	476-6481	K-5	
Widener Partnership Charter S	1450 Edgmont Ave	Chester, PA	19013-3944	610-872-1358	872-1794	K-7	Rose Sampson
Wiley Community Charter S	1446 E Lake Rd	Erie, PA	16507-1936	814-461-9600	461-0226	K-8	Peter Russo
Wissahickon Charter S	4700 Wissahickon Ave	Philadelphia, PA	19144	267-338-1020	338-1030	K-8	Kristi Littell
Wonderland Charter S	2112 Sandy Dr	State College, PA	16803-2282	814-234-5886		K-K	Harold Ohnmeis
World Communications Charter S	512 S Broad St	Philadelphia, PA	19146-1695	215-735-3198	735-3824	6-12	Janet Middleton
Young Scholars Charter S	900 N Marshall St	Philadelphia, PA	19123-1307	215-232-9727	232-4542	6-8	John Amenda
Young Scholars Douglass Charter S	2118 W Norris St	Philadelphia, PA	19121	215-684-5063	684-8916	K-8	Onome Pela
Young Scholars of Central PA Charter S	1530 Westerly Pkwy	State College, PA	16801-2848	814-237-9727	237-1517	K-8	Levent Kaya
YouthBuild Charter S	1231 N Broad St Fl 3	Philadelphia, PA	19122-4023	215-627-8671	763-5774	12-12	Simran Sidhu

Rhode Island

School	Address	City,State	Zip code	Telephone	Fax	Grade	Contact
Academy for Career Exploration	130 Broadway	Providence, RI	02903-3003	401-456-1738	521-0653	9-12	Lawrence DeSalvatore
Ph.D.							
BEACON Charter S	320 Main St	Woonsocket, RI	02895-3138	401-671-6261	671-6264	9-12	Michael Skeldon
Blackstone Academy	334 Pleasant St	Pawtucket, RI	02860-5288	401-726-1750	726-1753	9-12	Kyleen Carpenter
Blackstone Valley Prep ES	291 Broad St	Cumberland, RI	02864-7802	401-335-3133	303-3185	K-3	Lidsey Tavares
Blackstone Valley Prep ES 2	7 Fatima Dr	Cumberland, RI	02864-8226	401-335-3133	305-3185	K-1	Colleen Colarusso
Blackstone Valley Prep MS	3 Fairlawn Way	Lincoln, RI	02865-3122	401-335-3287	475-2415	5-7	Joy Souza
Compass S	537 Old North Rd	Kingston, RI	02881-1220	401-788-8322	788-8326	K-8	Allen Zipke
Cuffee S	459 Promenade St	Providence, RI	02908-5601	401-453-2711	453-4964	K-12	Nancy Cresser
Greene S	94 John Potter Rd	West Greenwich, RI	02817-2099	401-397-8601	397-8700	9-12	Deanna Duncan
Highlander Charter S	42 Lexington Ave	Providence, RI	02907-1716	401-277-2600	277-2603	K-8	Rose Grant
International Charter S	334 Pleasant St	Pawtucket, RI	02860-5288	401-721-0824	721-0976	K-5	Darlene Pugnali Ph.D.
Kingston Hill Academy	850 Stony Fort Rd	Saunderstown, RI	02874-1003	401-783-8282	783-5656	K-5	Stephen Panikoff
Learning Community S	21 Lincoln Ave	Central Falls, RI	02863-2012	401-722-9998	722-0990	K-8	Sarah Friedman
NEL/CPS Construction Career Academy	4 Sharpe Dr	Cranston, RI	02920-4410	401-270-8692	270-8697	9-12	Dennis Curran
Providence Mayoral Academy	370 Hartford Ave	Providence, RI	02909-5104			K-1	Morgan Carter
RI Nurses Institute Charter HS	150 Washington St	Providence, RI	02903-3300	401-680-4900	331-5646	10-12	Robert Pilkington
Segue Institute for Learning	325 Cowden St	Central Falls, RI	02863-2145	401-721-0964	721-0984	6-8	Denise Boule
Times2 Academy	50 Fillmore St	Providence, RI	02908-3105	401-272-5094	272-0555	K-12	Jerry Kowalczyk
Trinity Academy for the Performing Arts	158 Messer St	Providence, RI	02909-1741	401-484-2630	432-7882	7-12	Steven Olsen
Village Green Virtual Charter S	175 Broad St	Providence, RI	02903-4026			9-10	Robert Pilkington

South Carolina

School	Address	City,State	Zip code	Telephone	Fax	Grade	Contact
Academy for Teaching and Learning	109 Hinton St	Chester, SC	29706-2022	803-385-6334	385-6335	PK-8	Robyn Welborn
Academy of Hope Charter S	504 Church St	Conway, SC	29526-4822	843-995-4861		K-8	Natasha Butler
Aiken Performing Arts Academy	130 Avery Ln	Aiken, SC	29801-1902	803-644-4824	641-1155	9-12	Keisha Lloyd-Kennedy
Anderson V Charter S	1225 S McDuffie St	Anderson, SC	29624-2746	864-260-5538	260-5911	9-12	Katie Brown
Apple Charter S	1101 Camp Rd	Charleston, SC	29412-8832	843-795-6877	795-6844	K-8	Patricia Williams
Brashier Middle College HS	1830 W Georgia Rd	Simpsonville, SC	29680-7212	864-757-1800	757-1850	9-12	Michael Sinclair
Bridgewater Academy	2601 Fantasy Harbour Blvd	Myrtle Beach, SC	29579	843-236-3689	236-4921	K-8	Steve Wilson
Calhoun Falls Charter S	205 Edgefield St	Calhoun Falls, SC	29628-1018	864-418-8014	418-9379	6-12	Deirdre McCullough
Cape Romain Environmental Educ Charter S	1011 Old Cemetery Rd	Mc Clellanville, SC	29458-9735	843-887-3323	887-3525		Dr. Sally I'Anson
Carolina School for Inquiry	PO Box 2484	Columbia, SC	29202-2484	803-691-1250	691-1247	K-5	LaQuisha Chester
Charleston Charter S for Math & Science	1002 King St	Charleston, SC	29403-4182	843-720-3085	720-3196	6-12	Dr. Michael Stagliano
Charleston Development Academy	233 Line St	Charleston, SC	29403-5145	843-722-2689	722-2694	PK-8	Cecelia Gordon Rogers
CHOiCES Charter S	PO Box 15386	Florence, SC	29506-0386	843-664-8993	664-8881	6-12	Ralph Porter
Coastal Montessori Charter S	247 Wildcat Way	Pawleys Island, SC	29585	843-235-0413	235-0418	1-6	Dr. Nathalie Hunt
Discovery S	302 W Dunlap St	Lancaster, SC	29720-2405	803-285-8430	416-8907	K-5	Tom McDuffie
East Cooper Montessori Charter S	250 Ponsbury Rd	Mount Pleasant, SC	29464-6601	843-216-2883	216-8880	1-8	Jody Swanigan
East Point Academy	1340 Knox Abbott Dr	Cayce, SC	29033-3328	803-739-4992	739-4977	K-3	D. Renee Mathews
Fox Creek HS	165 Shortcut Rd	North Augusta, SC	29860-9123	803-613-9435	613-1533	9-12	Dr. Tim Murph
Greenville Technical Charter HS	PO Box 5616	Greenville, SC	29606-5616	864-250-8845	250-8846	9-12	Bob Bayne
Greer Middle College Charter HS	138 W McElhaney Rd	Taylors, SC	29687-5843	864-469-7571	469-7573	9-12	William Roach Ph.D.
Imagine Columbia Leadership Academy	3810 N Main St	Columbia, SC	29203-6443	803-929-1140	929-1145	K-5	Suezan Turknett
James Island Charter HS	1000 Fort Johnson Rd	Charleston, SC	29412-8898	843-762-2754	762-5228	9-12	Dr. Robert Bohnstengel
Kennedy Charter S	130 Avery Ln	Aiken, SC	29801-1902	803-644-4824	641-1155	5-8	Keisha Lloyd-Kennedy
Lake City College Preparatory Academy	1310 N Matthews Rd	Lake City, SC	29560-7015	843-374-0128	374-9029	K-12	Dr. Deloris Brown
Langston Charter MS	1950 Woodruff Rd	Greenville, SC	29607-5937	864-286-9700	286-9699	6-8	Gregory Abel
LEAD Academy	29 Ridgeway Dr	Greenville, SC	29605-2454	864-770-1790	281-1512	5-8	Rodney Johnson
Legacy Charter S Fuller Campus	PO Box 1832	Greenville, SC	29602-1832	864-214-1600	451-7023	K-4	Virginia Burrows
Legacy Charter S Parker Campus	PO Box 1832	Greenville, SC	29602-1832	864-248-0646	283-6444	5-12	Ed Roman

School	Address	City,State	Zip code	Telephone	Fax	Grade	Contact
Mathis HS	2872 Azalea Dr	N Charleston, SC	29405-8216	843-557-1611	747-5810	9-12	Eleanor Hardy
Meyer Center for Special Children	1132 Rutherford Rd	Greenville, SC	29609-3927	864-250-0005	250-0028	PK-PK	Louise Anthony
Midlands Math & Business Academy	2638 Two Notch Rd Ste 204	Columbia, SC	29204-1454	803-799-5101	799-5318	4-8	
Midland Valley Preparatory S	2432 Jefferson Davis Hwy	Graniteville, SC	29829-3828	803-594-1000	594-0511	PK-8	Bette Jean Doggett
OCSD5 HS for Health Professions	3720 Magnolia St	Orangeburg, SC	29118-1404	803-536-4473	535-1664	9-9	Angel Hightower
Orange Grove Charter S	1225 Orange Branch Rd	Charleston, SC	29407-3336	843-763-1520	769-2245	K-5	John Clendaniel
Palmetto Academy of Learning and Success	PO Box 15432	Myrtle Beach, SC	29587-5432	843-839-1725	839-1726	K-8	Courtney Fancher
Palmetto Scholar's Academy	2415 Avenue F	N Charleston, SC	29405-1941	843-300-4118	300-4123	6-12	Dr. Marty Hale
Palmetto S at Children's Attention Home	PO Box 2892	Rock Hill, SC	29732-4892	803-328-6555	327-8618	K-8	Dr. Hugh Wilson
Palmetto State E-cademy	115 Atrium Way Ste 200	Columbia, SC	29223-6383	803-227-6670	935-0071	9-12	Dr. Barbara Stoops
Palmetto Youth Academy	1209 N Douglas St	Florence, SC	29501-0600	843-679-7070	679-7046	3-6	Yvonne Burgess
Pattison's Academy for Comprehensive Ed.	2014 Bees Ferry Rd	Charleston, SC	29414-6603	843-556-1070	556-6742	K-8	Carol Kozlowski
Phoenix Charter HS	PO Box 170	Alcolu, SC	29001-0170	803-505-6800	505-6801	9-12	Elease Fulton
Provost Academy of South Carolina	400 Arbor Lake Dr Ste B800	Columbia, SC	29223-4567	803-735-9110	801-8040	9-12	Stephanie Cagle
Richland One Middle College S	316 Beltline Blvd	Columbia, SC	29205-3624	803-738-7114	738-7117	11-12	Audrey Breland
Richland Two Charter HS	750 Old Clemson Rd	Columbia, SC	29229-4205	803-419-1348		11-12	Henry Lovett
Riverview Charter S	81 Savannah Hwy	Beaufort, SC	29906-6284	843-379-0123	379-0133	K-5	Alison Thomas
Royal Live Oaks Academy Arts & Sciences	PO Box 528	Hardeeville, SC	29927-0528	843-784-2630	784-2623	K-8	Karen Wicks
South Carolina Calvert Academy	100 Summit Pkwy	Columbia, SC	29229-9000	803-462-0254	462-0326	K-8	Laura Blackmore
SC Connections Academy	220 Stoneridge Dr Ste 403	Columbia, SC	29210-8018	803-212-4712	212-4946	K-12	Allison Reaves
SC Virtual Charter School	140 Stoneridge Dr Ste 420	Columbia, SC	29210-8020	803-253-6222	253-6279	K-12	Dr. Cherry Daniel
South Carolina Whitmore S	PO Box 1054	Chapin, SC	29036-1054	866-476-6416	476-1646	9-12	Ellen Ray
Spartanburg Charter S	PO Box 3343	Spartanburg, SC	29304-3343	864-621-3882	804-6404	K-9	Dr. John von Rohr
York Preparatory Academy	1047 Golden Gate Ct	Rock Hill, SC	29732-8878	803-324-4400	496-2083	K-12	Jan Lee
Youth Academy Charter S	711 Tomlinson St	Kingstree, SC	29556-3723	843-355-5424	355-5425	7-12	Stephanie Tisdale
Youth Leadership Academy	698 Concord Church Rd	Pickens, SC	29671-9167	864-878-1103	878-5985	6-8	Patsy Wood Smith

Tennessee

School	Address	City,State	Zip code	Telephone	Fax	Grade	Contact
Aurora Collegiate Academy	3804 Given Ave	Memphis, TN	38122-3535	901-297-0657	274-4019	K-5	Ciji Pittman
Boys Preparatory S	1460 McGavock Pike	Nashville, TN	37216-3225	615-352-1253		7-7	Robert Deckard
Brick Church College Prep S	2835 Brick Church Pike	Nashville, TN	37207-3903	615-262-6665		5-5	Edon Katz
Cameron College Prep S	PO Box 331088	Nashville, TN	37203-7508	615-291-6365		5-6	Tait Danhausen
Chattanooga Girls Leadership Academy	1802 Bailey Ave	Chattanooga, TN	37404	423-702-7230		6-12	Elaine Swafford Ed.D.
Circles of Success Learning Academy	867 S Parkway E	Memphis, TN	38106-5605	901-322-7978	322-7993	K-5	Sheri Catron-Cooper
City University S Boys Prep	1500 Dunn Ave	Memphis, TN	38106-7318	901-775-2219	775-2044	6-8	William Greenwood
City University S of Liberal Arts	1500 Dunn Ave	Memphis, TN	38106-7318	901-775-2219	775-2044	9-12	Victoria Shields
Cornerstone Prep - Lester Campus	320 Carpenter St	Memphis, TN	38112-4002	901-416-5969	416-5971	PK-3	
Drexel Preparatory Academy	4481 Jackson Rd	Whites Creek, TN	37189-9201	615-724-1670	246-2602	K-5	Dr. Sheryl Bowman
East End Preparatory S	1460 McGavock Pike	Nashville, TN	37216-3225	615-630-7470		K-1	Jim Leckrone
Freedom Preparatory Academy	5132 Jonetta St	Memphis, TN	38109-7061	901-259-5959	259-5950	6-12	Sundiata Salaam
Gordon Science Art Academy	815 Breedlove St	Memphis, TN	38107-2708	901-264-0636		6-6	Julia Callaway
Ivy Academy	8443 Dayton Pike	Soddy Daisy, TN	37379-4204	423-305-7494	305-7496	9-12	Angie Markum
KIPP Academy	3410 Knight Dr	Nashville, TN	37207-2306	615-226-4484	226-4401	5-8	Laura Miguez-Howarth
KIPP Memphis Academy MS	2110 Howell Ave	Memphis, TN	38108-2268	901-292-9618	791-9394	5-8	Andy Bobowski
KIPP Memphis Collegiate ES	230 Henry Ave	Memphis, TN	38107-2483	901-791-9391	791-9394	K-4	Grace Williams
KIPP Memphis Collegiate HS	2110 Howell Ave	Memphis, TN	38108-2268	901-791-9792	791-9796	9-10	Richard Bailey
KIPP Memphis Collegiate MS	230 Henry Ave	Memphis, TN	38107-2483	901-791-9390	791-9394	5-8	Michelle Lyons
Knowledge Academies	5380 Hickory Hollow Pkwy	Antioch, TN	37013-3117	615-810-8370		5-6	Art Fuller
LEAD Academy	1015 Davidson Dr	Nashville, TN	37205-1042	615-352-1253	327-5425	5-8	Mike Risen
LEAD Academy HS	1704 Heiman St	Nashville, TN	37208-2406	615-327-5422		9-11	LaVoe Mulgrey
Liberty Collegiate Academy	217 S 10th St	Nashville, TN	37206-2946	615-564-1965		5-6	Linda Lentz
Memphis Academy of Health Sciences	3925 Chelsea Avenue Ext	Memphis, TN	38108-2612	901-382-1441	382-1944	6-12	Curtis Weathers
Memphis Academy of Science & Engineering	1254 Jefferson Ave	Memphis, TN	38104-7229	901-333-1580	333-1582	6-12	Harold Wingood
Memphis Business Academy	2450 Frayser Blvd	Memphis, TN	38127-5823	901-353-1475	308-1430	K-5	Marsharee Shaw
Memphis Business Academy HS	3306 Overton Crossing St	Memphis, TN	38127-6549	901-357-8680	357-8681	9-12	Dr. Menthia Clark
Memphis Business Academy MS	3306 Overton Crossing St	Memphis, TN	38127-6549	901-357-2708	357-2442	6-8	Toya Venable-Rubin
Memphis College Prep S	278 Greenlaw Ave	Memphis, TN	38105-1861	901-620-6475	620-6476	K-5	Michael Whaley
Memphis Grizzlies Prep Charter S	168 Jefferson Ave	Memphis, TN	38103-2219	901-474-0955	474-9049	9-12	Elizabeth Simpson
Memphis School of Excellence	4450 S Mendenhall Rd	Memphis, TN	38141-6701	901-367-7814	367-7816	6-9	Ali Gumus
Nashville Prep Academy	330 10th Ave N	Nashville, TN	37203-3401	615-538-7284		5-8	Ravi Gupta
New Consortium of Law & Business	110 N Court Ave Ste 100	Memphis, TN	38103-2217	901-214-5298	531-8127	6-12	Tommie Henderson
Now Vision Academy	297 Plus Park Blvd	Nashville, TN	37217-1003	615-360-1115		5-8	Tim Malone
Omni Prep North Pointe Lower S	3333 Old Brownsville Rd	Memphis, TN	38134-8419	901-828-4912	828-4902	K-1	Cary Booker
Omni Prep North Pointe MS	3333 Old Brownsville Rd	Memphis, TN	38134-8419	901-828-4912		5-6	Brian Rentzsch
Power Center Academy HS	6120 Winchester Rd	Memphis, TN	38115-4014	901-333-6874	922-6028	9-12	Dr. Steevon Hunter
Power Center Academy MS	6120 Winchester Rd	Memphis, TN	38115-4014	901-333-6874	922-6028	6-8	Kimberly Hopkins-Clark
Promise Academy	1346 Bryan St	Memphis, TN	38108-2401	901-324-4456	324-4457	K-4	Talitha Smith
Smithson-Craighead Academy	3307 Brick Church Pike	Nashville, TN	37207-2301	615-228-9886	228-9799	K-4	Janelle Glover
Smithson-Craighead Academy MS	730 Neelys Bend Rd	Madison, TN	37115-4927	615-868-0882	868-0327	5-8	Deaundra Jenkins-Holder
Soulsville Charter S	1115 College St	Memphis, TN	38106-2203	901-261-6366	261-6398	6-12	NeShante Brown
Southern Avenue Charter S	2221 Democrat Rd	Memphis, TN	38132-1802	901-743-7335	743-7677	K-5	Toby Finley
Southern Avenue MS	2185 Democrat Rd	Memphis, TN	38132-1802	901-744-6644	744-6645	6-8	Dr. Stanley Ellis
STAR Academy Charter S	3260 James Rd	Memphis, TN	38128-5351	901-387-5050	387-0798	K-5	Angela Holloway
STEM Prep Academy	3748 Nolensville Pike	Nashville, TN	37211-3322	615-921-2200		K-5	Dr. Kristen McGraner
Veritas College Preparatory Charter S	690 Mississippi Blvd	Memphis, TN	38126-3902	901-526-1900	526-1988	6-8	Tim Ware

Texas

School	Address	City,State	Zip code	Telephone	Fax	Grade	Contact
A+ Academy	10327 Rylie Rd	Dallas, TX	75217-8240	972-557-5578	557-4128	PK-12	Dr. Shala Flowers
Academy of Accelerated Learning	6025 Chimney Rock Rd	Houston, TX	77081-4011	713-773-4766	666-2532	PK-5	Doris Robins
Academy of Accelerated Learning	6711 Bellfort St	Houston, TX	77087-6456	713-645-0336	640-2435	PK-5	Doris Robins
Academy of Careers & Technologies	PO Box 681866	San Antonio, TX	78268-1866	210-226-7568	226-8548	9-12	Akenese Iosefo
Academy of Dallas	1030 Oak Park Dr	Dallas, TX	75232-1238	214-371-9600	371-1053	PK-8	Conrad Hargest
Accelerated Interdisciplinary Academy	901 E Belt Line Rd	Lancaster, TX	75146-3600	713-667-1184	667-9181	PK-8	LaShawn Hoskins
Accelerated Intermediate Adademy	PO Box 20589	Houston, TX	77225-0589	713-728-9330	283-6190	PK-8	LaShawn Hoskins
Accelerated Learning Center	721 Omaha Dr	Corpus Christi, TX	78408-2839	361-887-7766	887-6035	PK-12	Maria Garza
Advanced Virtual Academy	4141 Costa Rica Rd	Houston, TX	77092-5502	713-957-7710	613-2205	9-12	Alan Summers
Advantage Academy - Grand Prairie	955 Freetown Rd	Grand Prairie, TX	75051-3802	214-451-2119	602-2212	K-12	Herbert Fitzpatrick
Advantage Academy - North Duncanville	4009 Joseph Hardin Dr	Dallas, TX	75236-1507	214-276-5880	467-9131	K-8	Shedrick Hay
Advantage Academy - Rowlett	8200 Schrade Rd	Rowlett, TX	75088-4716	214-451-2138	412-2320	K-8	Lisa Hiatt
Advantage Academy - Waxahachie	701 W Highway 287 Byp	Waxahachie, TX	75165-5163	972-451-2104	937-9876	K-12	Tom Close
AIM College & Career Prep	1110 21st St	Galveston, TX	77550-4625	409-761-6302	770-0918	5-12	Jean Fullen
Alief Montessori Community S	12013 6th St	Houston, TX	77072-5308	281-530-9406	530-2233	PK-5	Nancy Chieu
Allen Charter S	5220 Nomas St	Dallas, TX	75212-3229	972-794-5100	794-5101	PK-5	Connie Hovseth
Alpha Academy	502 E Southcross Blvd	San Antonio, TX	78214-2044	210-798-1792	798-1829	9-12	Evonne Murillo
Alpha Charter S	701 W State St	Garland, TX	75040-6310	972-272-2173	205-9050	PK-12	
Ambassadors Preparatory Academy	5001 Avenue U	Galveston, TX	77551-6007	409-762-1115	762-1114	PK-6	Dr. Patricia Williams
American Youth Works Charter S	1901 E Ben White Blvd	Austin, TX	78741-7840	512-744-1900	916-4708	9-12	Terence Gahan
Amigos Por Vida-Friends for Life Charter	5500 El Camino Del Rey St	Houston, TX	77081-1867	713-349-9945	349-0671	PK-8	Lucille Maggi
Annunciation Home	3610 Shell Rd	Georgetown, TX	78628-9246	512-864-7755		6-12	Holly Engleman
Aristoi Classical Academy	5618 11th St	Katy, TX	77493-1971	281-391-5003	391-5010	K-8	Brenda Davidson
Arlington Classics Academy	2800 W Arkansas Ln	Arlington, TX	76016-5819	817-274-2008	274-8768	K-2	Barry Parker
Arlington Classics Academy Intermediate	5200 S Bowen Rd	Arlington, TX	76017-3756	817-303-1553	549-0246	3-5	Aaron Daffern
Arlington Classics Academy Middle	5200 S Bowen Rd	Arlington, TX	76017-3756	817-987-1819	549-0246	6-8	Kurtis Flood
Arrow Academy	8600 Sweetwater Ln	Houston, TX	77037-2729	979-703-8820		K-12	
Austin Academy	621 W Euclid Ave	San Antonio, TX	78212-5128	210-226-5441	226-6192	PK-8	Alexandro Flores
Austin Achieve Public S	6510 Berkman Dr	Austin, TX	78723-1939	512-887-2709	727-3788	6-12	John Armbrust
Austin Can Academy Charter S	2406 Rosewood Ave	Austin, TX	78702-2408	512-477-4226	931-8034	9-12	Frank Oakes
Austin Discovery S	8509 FM 969 Ste 200	Austin, TX	78724-5771	512-674-0700	674-3133	K-6	Cinnamon Henley
Austin State University Charter S	PO Box 6072	Nacogdoches, TX	75962-0001	936-468-5899	468-7015	K-5	Lysa Hagan
Azleway Charter S	15892 County Road 26	Tyler, TX	75707-2728	903-566-8444	566-2053	K-12	Lacey Hogue
Azleway Charter S Pine Mountain	Azleway Wilderness Camp	Palestine, TX	75801	903-549-3194	549-2227	7-12	
Baker-Ripley Charter S	6500 Rookin St	Houston, TX	77074-5019	713-779-4856		K-5	
Barkley/Ruiz ES	1111 S Navidad St	San Antonio, TX	78207-5813	210-978-7940	227-4029	PK-5	Belinda Hernandez
Bay Area Charter ES	2600 Humble Dr	El Lago, TX	77586-5900	281-326-4555	326-4888	PK-5	Karen Lawley
Bay Area Charter MS	PO Box 2126	League City, TX	77574-2126	281-332-7788	316-8866	6-8	Kendra Persohn
Bethel's Learning Center	14442 Fondmeadow	Houston, TX	77035	713-728-5076	728-5079	K-6	Darlene Breaux
Bexar County Academy	1485 Hillcrest Dr	San Antonio, TX	78228-3900	210-432-8600	432-8667	PK-8	Linda Sleeper
Bonham Academy	925 S Saint Marys St	San Antonio, TX	78205-3410	210-228-3300	223-3899	PK-8	Patricia Ortiz
Branch Park Academy	13605 Webb Chapel Rd	Farmers Branch, TX	75234-3727	972-243-2462	243-2684	6-8	Janet Epstein
Brazos River Charter S	PO Box 949	Nemo, TX	76070-0949	254-898-9226	898-2297	K-12	Mike Thames
Brazos S for Inquiry & Creativity	5900 Pinemont Dr	Houston, TX	77092-2606	713-691-9500	691-9502	PK-K	Barry Ward
Brazos S for Inquiry & Creativity	6400 Southwest Fwy Ste S	Houston, TX	77074-2213	713-270-4500	270-4510	6-12	Tiffany Rock
Brazos S for Inquiry & Creativity	410 Bethel Ln	Bryan, TX	77802-1005	979-774-5032	774-5039	PK-8	Christopher Osgood
Briarmeadow Charter S	3601 Dunvale Rd	Houston, TX	77063-5707	713-458-5500	458-5506	PK-8	Peter Heinze
Bright Ideas Charter S	2507 Central Fwy E	Wichita Falls, TX	76302-5802	940-767-1561	767-1239	K-12	Lynda Plummer

School	Address	City,State	Zip code	Telephone	Fax	Grade	Contact
Briscoe ES	2015 S Flores St	San Antonio, TX	78204-1990	210-228-3305	222-0822	PK-6	Lanore Cantu
Brooks Academy of Science & Engineering	3803 Lyster Rd	San Antonio, TX	78235-5152	210-633-9006	633-9990	6-12	Ixchell Gonzalez
Brown-Fellowship Leadership Academy	5701 Red Bird Center Dr	Dallas, TX	75237-1917	972-709-4700	709-6605	K-7	Paula Brown
Brown-Fellowship Leadership Preschool	6901 S Westmoreland Rd	Dallas, TX	75237-2431	972-709-4700	709-6605	PK-PK	Paula Brown
Brune Charter S	PO Box 399	Leakey, TX	78873-0399	830-232-7101	232-4279	1-12	Albert Hernandez
Burch Charter S	5703 Blanco Rd	San Antonio, TX	78216-6616	210-431-9881	432-8467	4-6	Eric Davis
Burnham ES	7310 Bishop Flores Dr	El Paso, TX	79912-1429	915-584-9499	585-8814	K-4	
Cage ES	4528 Leeland St	Houston, TX	77023-3095	713-924-1700	924-1704	PK-5	Jose Covarrubia
Cailloux-Najim S	PO Box 609	Ingram, TX	78025-0609	830-367-6100	367-2611	1-12	Maria De La Cruz
Canyon Lakes S	5502 58th St Ste 600	Lubbock, TX	79414-2087	806-762-5782	762-0838	6-12	Jessica Crabb
Cedar Hill Collegiate HS	1515 W Belt Line Rd	Cedar Hill, TX	75104-1603	469-272-2021	293-2652	9-12	Jackie Fagan
Cedars International Academy	8416 N Interstate 35	Austin, TX	78753-6438	512-419-1551	419-1581	PK-8	Heather Rauls
Challenge Early College HS	5601 West Loop S	Houston, TX	77081-2221	713-664-9712	664-9780	9-12	Tonya Miller
Chaparral Star Academy	14046 Summit Dr	Austin, TX	78728	512-989-2672	251-9799	PK-12	Marsha Hagin
Chapel Hill Academy	4640 Sycamore School Rd	Fort Worth, TX	76133-7356	817-289-0242	289-3657	PK-5	Victoria Sendejo M.Ed.
Chavez Academy	3701 Mueller St	Corpus Christi, TX	78408-3139	361-561-5651	561-5654	9-12	Sandra Valencia
Children First Academy of Dallas	315 E Wheatland Rd	Dallas, TX	75241-5314	214-371-2545	371-0283	PK-7	
Children First Academy of Houston	7803 Little York Rd	Houston, TX	77016-2436	713-491-9030	491-9032	PK-7	Charlene McGarter
Children of the Sun Charter S	5324 E US Highway 83 Ste 2	Rio Grande City, TX	78582-9408	956-488-8883	488-0889	PK-12	Dr. Abelardo Mendieta
Children of the Sun Charter S	1205 S 7th St	Raymondville, TX	78580-3302	956-689-3300	292-0371	PK-12	Myrna Woods
City Center Health Careers	1114 Willow	San Antonio, TX	78208-1343	210-255-8265	255-8270	6-12	Bernice Hinnant
Clay Academy	3303 Potters House Way	Dallas, TX	75236-3037	214-467-4143	467-4066	PK-7	Misty Cannon
Clear Horizons Early College HS	13735 Beamer Rd Box 913	Houston, TX	77089-6009	281-929-4657	284-9960	9-12	Dr. Jennifer Morrow
Collegiate HS	101 Baldwin Blvd	Corpus Christi, TX	78404-3805	361-698-2425	698-2427	9-12	Tracie Rodriguez
Compass Academy Charter S	1111 Pagewood Ave	Odessa, TX	79761-3440	432-300-2067	332-8667	PK-12	Debra Stewart
Conquest Academy	207 Peach St	Tomball, TX	77375-4733	281-516-0611	290-6524	9-12	Tanis Stanfield
Copeland ES	6500 N Interstate 35 Ste N1	San Antonio, TX	78218-3702	210-599-2473	590-0376	PK-3	Angel Perez
Cornerstone Academy	9016 Westview Dr	Houston, TX	77055-4602	713-251-1600	365-5787	6-8	Jill Wright
Corpus Christi College Prep HS	3401 Santa Fe St	Corpus Christi, TX	78411-1441	361-225-4240	225-4021	9-12	Stephen Mora
Corpus Christi Montessori Charter S	3530 Gollihar Rd	Corpus Christi, TX	78415-2759	361-852-0707	852-0640	PK-8	Minerva Salazar
Creekview Academy	405 S 2nd St	Killeen, TX	76541-7113	254-690-3962	690-8376	K-9	Amy Dickson
Crockett ES	2112 Crockett St	Houston, TX	77007-3923	713-802-4780	802-4783	PK-5	Claudia Chavez-Pinto
Crosstimbers Academy	PO Box 1327	Weatherford, TX	76086-1327	817-594-6220	594-6227	9-12	
Crutch's - Life Support Center	7115 Clarewood Dr	Houston, TX	77036-4401	713-779-9990	779-3047	6-12	Debra Gaddis
Cumberland Academy	1340 Shiloh Rd	Tyler, TX	75703-1523	903-581-2890	581-1476	K-5	James Moyers
Cumberland Academy MS	1040 Shiloh Rd	Tyler, TX	75703	903-581-2890	581-1476	6-8	James Moyers
Dallas Can Academy	325 W 12th St	Dallas, TX	75208-6502	214-943-2244	946-4427	9-12	Faustino Rivas
Dallas Can Academy Carrollton/Farmers	2720 Hollandale Ln	Farmers Branch, TX	75234-2035	972-243-2178	243-2669	9-12	Tony Swafford
Dallas Can Academy Charter S	4621 Ross Ave	Dallas, TX	75204-4994	214-824-4226	841-7951	9-12	Rawly Sanchez
Dallas Can Academy - Pleasant Grove	1227 N Masters Dr	Dallas, TX	75217-3722	972-225-1194	225-1164	9-12	Mene Khepera
DaVinci S for Science and the Arts	7310 Bishop Flores Dr	El Paso, TX	79912-1429	915-584-4024	581-9840	5-12	
DePelchin - Elkins Campus	4950 Memorial Dr	Houston, TX	77007-7440	713-802-6260	802-6261	7-12	Erin Resch
DePelchin - Richmond Campus	710 S 7th St	Richmond, TX	77469-3445	281-342-4906		7-12	Erin Resch
Draw Academy	3920 Stoney Brook Dr	Houston, TX	77063-6406	713-706-3729	706-3711	PK-8	Lisa Newton
Early College HS	3939 Valley View Ln	Farmers Branch, TX	75244-4906	972-968-6200	968-6210	9-12	Michael Arreola
East Austin College Prep Academy	6002 Jain Ln	Austin, TX	78721-3104	512-287-5000	462-2028	6-8	James Cuellar
East Early College HS	220 N Milby St	Houston, TX	77003-1933	713-847-4809	847-4813	9-12	Tamera Bolden
East Fort Worth Montessori Academy	501 Oakland Blvd	Fort Worth, TX	76103-1014	817-496-3003	496-3004	PK-5	Joyce Brown
East Texas Charter S Chadwick Campus	2402 Alpine Rd	Longview, TX	75601-3407	903-753-9400	753-0285	9-12	Terry Lapic
East Texas Charter S - Nelms Campus	2402 Alpine Rd	Longview, TX	75601-3407	903-753-9400	753-0285	7-12	Terry Lapic
Eastwood Academy	1315 Dumble St	Houston, TX	77023-1902	713-924-1697	923-3157	9-12	Paula Fendley
Eden Park Academy	6215 Manchaca Rd Bldg D	Austin, TX	78745-4927	512-383-0613	383-0665	K-6	Johnnie Smith
Education Center International Academy 1	302 N Town East Blvd	Sunnyvale, TX	75182-9284	214-628-9152	628-9124	K-6	Bob Densmore
Education Center International Academy 2	302 N Town East Blvd	Sunnyvale, TX	75182-9284	214-628-9152	628-9124	7-8	Bob Densmore
Ehrhart S	PO Box 7733	Beaumont, TX	77726-7733	409-839-8200	839-8242	PK-8	Teresa Richard
El Paso Academy East	11000 Argal Ct	El Paso, TX	79935-3712	915-590-8589	590-0052	9-12	Ofelia Jiminez
El Paso Academy West	201 W Redd Rd	El Paso, TX	79932-1903	915-845-7997	845-7522	9-12	Barbara Duggar
Empowerment College Preparatory HS	7414 St Lo Rd	Houston, TX	77033-2732	713-732-3623	732-3425	10-12	Traci Stewart-Jones
Energized for Excellence Academy ES	6201 Bissonnet St	Houston, TX	77081-6809	713-773-3600	773-3630	PK-5	Lois Bullock
Energized for Excellence Academy MS	3703 Sampson St	Houston, TX	77004-4741	713-749-8876	749-8887	6-8	Arlen Kho
Energized for STEM Academy Central MSHS	9220 Jutland Rd	Houston, TX	77033-3905	713-773-3600	773-3630	6-12	Dr. Shavon Clark
Energized for STEM Academy West MSHS	7419 Ashcroft Dr	Houston, TX	77081-6801	713-773-3600	773-3630	6-12	Tamicha Jackson
Evolution Academy Charter S	1101 S Sherman St	Richardson, TX	75081-4852	972-907-3755	907-3765	9-12	Cynthia Jones Trigg
Excellence in Leadership Academy	915 W Expressway 83	Mission, TX	78572-6133	956-424-9504	585-4673	PK-12	Elizabeth Lopez
Faith Family Academy of Oak Cliff	300 W Kiest Blvd	Dallas, TX	75224-3402	214-375-7682	375-7681	PK-12	Brenda Mcgeorge
Fallbrook College Preparatory Academy	12512 Walters Rd	Houston, TX	77014-2784	281-880-1360	880-1362	K-12	Tarla Crumb
Focus Learning Academy	2524 W Ledbetter Dr	Dallas, TX	75233	214-467-7751	339-6908	PK-9	Leroy McClure
Ford Academy Alameda S for Art & Design	439 Arbor Pl	San Antonio, TX	78207-1728	210-226-4031	271-0125	9-12	Jeffrey Flores
Fort Worth Academy of Fine Arts	3901 S Hulen St	Fort Worth, TX	76109-3321	817-924-1482	926-9932	K-12	Craig Schreckengast
Fort Worth Can Academy	4301 Campus Dr	Fort Worth, TX	76119-5535	817-431-4226	531-0443	9-12	Ku-Masi Lewis
Fort Worth Can Academy	5508 Black Oak Ln	River Oaks, TX	76114	817-735-1515	735-1465	9-12	Rudy Mendoza
Founders Classical Academy in Lewisville	1010 Bellaire Blvd	Lewisville, TX	75067-5650	469-464-3415		K-12	Jason Caros
Galaviz Academy	1507 Little York Rd	Houston, TX	77093-3223	832-300-6010	300-6013	5-12	Luis Cano
Garza-Gonzales Charter S	4129 Greenwood Dr	Corpus Christi, TX	78416-1841	361-881-9988	881-9994	PK-12	Adolfo Chapa
Gateway Academy Sierra Vista	4620 S Lucy	Laredo, TX	78046-7786	956-723-0345	712-1112	9-12	
Gateway Academy Townlake	PO Box 3129	Laredo, TX	78044-3129	956-722-0747	722-0767	9-12	Aida Ponce
Gateway Charter Academy	6103 Houston School Rd	Dallas, TX	75241-2516	214-375-2039	375-1842	PK-12	Robbie Moore
Gateway College Prep S	3360 Westinghouse Rd	Georgetown, TX	78626-7658	512-868-4947	868-4946	6-12	Steve Werlein
Gateway Tech HS	1313 W Washington St	Levelland, TX	79336-3921	512-868-5299	868-3744	9-12	Annette Stevenson
GCCLR Institute of Technology	4125 Greenwood Dr	Corpus Christi, TX	78416	361-881-9988	814-1687	PK-12	Adolfo Chapa
Gervin Academy	6944 S Sunbelt Dr	San Antonio, TX	78218-3335	210-568-8800	568-8897	PK-12	Jesse Villanueva
Gervin Technology Center	3030 E Commerce St	San Antonio, TX	78220-1013	210-587-3576	587-3587	10-12	Dorothy Wendorf
Girls & Boys Prep Academy	8415 W Bellfort St	Houston, TX	77071-2205	713-270-2006	270-2046	6-8	Joseph Cuillier
Girls & Boys Prep Academy	8282 Bissonnet St Ste 400	Houston, TX	77074-3904	713-270-2006	270-2046	PK-5	Tyra Ross
Girls & Boys Prep Academy	8415 W Bellfort St	Houston, TX	77071-2205	713-270-5994	270-1302	9-12	Joseph Cuillier
Golden Rule Charter S Cockrell Hill	2602 W Illinois Ave	Dallas, TX	75233-1002	214-333-9330	333-9325	PK-8	Irma Pizarro
Golden Rule Charter S DeSoto	135 W Wintergreen Rd	DeSoto, TX	75115-2315	469-248-4463	248-4471	PK-2	Constance Douglas
Golden Rule Charter S Grand Prairie	1729 Avenue B	Grand Prairie, TX	75051-3416	214-333-9330	333-9325	PK-1	
Golden Rule Charter S Oak Cliff	2602 W Illinois Ave	Dallas, TX	75233-1002	214-333-9330	333-9325	PK-12	Vicente Delgado
Golden Rule Charter S Pleasant Grove	2602 W Illinois Ave	Dallas, TX	75233-1002	214-333-9330	333-9325	PK-2	Vashti Gonzalez
Hampton Preparatory S	8915 S Hampton Rd	Dallas, TX	75232-6002	972-421-1982	421-1986	K-12	Corey Harris
Harbach-Ripley Charter S	6225 Northdale St	Houston, TX	77087-5821	713-640-7150		K-5	Cecilia Randall
Harlingen Leadership Academy	4501 W Expressway 83	Harlingen, TX	78552-3604			PK-3	
Harmony S of Advancement	3171 N Sam Houston Pkwy W	Houston, TX	77038-1219	281-741-8899	741-8006	9-12	
Harmony S of Arts and Technology	9115 Kirby Dr	Houston, TX	77054-2505	832-433-7001	433-7083	K-9	
Harmony S of Business-Dallas	8080 President George Bush	Dallas, TX	75252	214-321-0100	919-4352	K-12	
Harmony S of Discovery	6270 Barker Cypress Rd	Houston, TX	77084-1628	281-861-5105	656-8525	K-10	Alpaslan Uzgoren
Harmony School of Excellence	7340 Gessner Rd	Houston, TX	77040-3144	713-983-8668	983-8667	K-12	
Harmony S of Excellence - Austin	2100 E Saint Elmo Rd	Austin, TX	78744-1050	512-693-0000	693-0008	K-12	
Harmony S of Excellence-Endeavor	5668 W Little York Rd	Houston, TX	77091-1116	281-999-8400	999-8804	K-12	
Harmony S of Ingenuity	10555 Stella Link Rd	Houston, TX	77025-5631	713-664-1020	664-1025	K-12	
Harmony S of Innovation	9421 W Sam Houston Pkwy S	Houston, TX	77099-1898	713-541-3030	541-3032	PK-8	
Harmony S of Innovation - Dallas	1024 W Rosemeade Pkwy	Carrollton, TX	75007-6250	469-892-5556	892-5667	K-12	
Harmony S of Innovation - El Paso	5210 Fairbanks Dr	El Paso, TX	79924-3907	915-757-2929	757-2202	K-12	
Harmony S of Innovation-Fort Worth	8100 S Hulen St	Fort Worth, TX	76123-2764	817-386-5505	977-1727	6-12	Salih Aykac
Harmony S of Innovation - San Antonio	8125 Glen Mont	San Antonio, TX	78239-3499	210-265-1715	265-5364	K-8	
Harmony S of Nature & Athletics	8120 W Camp Wisdom Rd	Dallas, TX	75249-4402	972-296-1000	296-2125	K-12	Hakan Yagci
Harmony S of Political Science & Comm	13415 Ranch Road 620 N	Austin, TX	78717-1020	512-284-9880	284-9632	K-8	
Harmony S of Science	13415 W Bellfort Ave	Sugar Land, TX	77478-3184	713-265-2525	265-2565	PK-8	
Harmony S of Science HS	13522 W Airport Blvd	Sugar Land, TX	77498-6313	281-302-6445	302-6745	9-12	Huseyin Sari
Harmony Science Academy	5435 S Braeswood Blvd	Houston, TX	77096-4001	713-729-4400	729-6600	6-12	
Harmony Science Academy - Austin	930 E Rundberg Ln	Austin, TX	78753-4826	512-835-7900	835-7901	6-12	Gina Gregory
Harmony Science Academy - Austin	11800 Stonehollow Dr # 100	Austin, TX	78758	512-821-1700	821-1702	K-8	Erdal Caglar
Harmony Science Academy - Beaumont	4055 Calder Ave	Beaumont, TX	77706-4925	409-838-4000	838-4009	PK-12	
Harmony Science Academy - Brownsville	1124 Central Blvd	Brownsville, TX	78520-7513	956-574-9555	574-9558	PK-12	
Harmony Science Academy - Bryan	2031 S Texas Ave	Bryan, TX	77802-1834	979-779-2100	779-2110	PK-12	Ali Teckin
Harmony Science Academy - Dallas	12005 Forestgate Dr	Dallas, TX	75243-5442	214-954-7277	954-7993	PK-12	Fatih Ay
Harmony Science Academy - El Paso	9405 Betel Dr	El Paso, TX	79907-3457	915-859-4620	859-4630	K-12	Fatih Ay
Harmony Science Academy - Euless	701 S Industrial Blvd # 115	Euless, TX	76040	817-354-3000	354-3008	K-12	
Harmony Science Academy - Fort Worth	5651 Westcreek Dr	Fort Worth, TX	76133-2248	817-263-0700	263-0705	K-12	Fatih Oner
Harmony Science Academy - Garland	2302 Firewheel Pkwy	Garland, TX	75040-4054	972-212-4777	212-4778	K-8	
Harmony Science Academy - Grand Prairie	1102 NW 7th St	Grand Prairie, TX	75050-3468	972-642-9911	642-9922	K-12	Hakan Yagci
Harmony Science Academy HS	9431 W Sam Houston Pkwy S	Houston, TX	77099-1849	713-492-0214	640-5581	9-12	Edip Ercetin Ph.D.
Harmony Science Academy - Houston NW	16200 State Highway 249	Houston, TX	77086-1014	281-444-1555	444-1015	K-8	
Harmony Science Academy - Laredo	4401 San Francisco Ave	Laredo, TX	78041-4663	956-712-1177	712-1188	K-12	
Harmony Science Academy - Lubbock	1516 53rd St	Lubbock, TX	79412-2916	806-747-1000	747-1005	K-12	
Harmony Science Academy - North Austin	1421 Wells Branch Pkwy #200	Pflugerville, TX	78660	512-251-5000	251-5001	6-12	

School	Address	City,State	Zip code	Telephone	Fax	Grade	Contact
Harmony Science Academy - Odessa	2755 N Grandview Ave	Odessa, TX	79762-6952	432-363-6000	363-6001	K-12	Emin Cavusoglu
Harmony Science Academy - San Antonio	8505 Lakeside Pkwy	San Antonio, TX	78245-2481	210-674-7788	674-7766	K-12	
Harmony Science Academy - Waco	1900 N Valley Mills Dr	Waco, TX	76710-2559	254-751-7878	751-7877	PK-12	
Harmony Science Academy - West Houston	22400 Grand Corner Dr	Katy, TX	77494-5718	832-437-3926	437-3927	K-9	Mehet Dogan
Harris MS	325 Pruitt Ave	San Antonio, TX	78204-2598	210-228-1220	226-9448	6-8	Lourdes Correa
Harvest Preparatory Academy	17770 Imperial Valley Dr	Houston, TX	77060-6100	281-872-5201	872-5206	K-6	Cassandra Dyson
Hawkins HS	1826 Basse Rd	San Antonio, TX	78213-4606	210-431-9881	432-8467	9-12	James Cuellar
Hawthorne S	115 W Josephine St	San Antonio, TX	78212-4125	210-738-9795	733-1495	PK-8	G. Rodriguez-Pollock
Heights Preparatory Charter S	2650 Canada Dr	Dallas, TX	75212-1517	469-621-8553		6-8	Shawn Stover
Helping Hands Charter S	PO Box 7667	Austin, TX	78713-7667	512-538-0177	232-9177	K-5	Wendy Riney
Higgs Carter King Gifted & Talented S	PO Box 18854	San Antonio, TX	78218-0854	210-735-2341	733-6434	PK-12	Claudette Yarbrough
Highland Heights ES	865 Paul Quinn St	Houston, TX	77091-4154	713-696-2920	696-2922	PK-5	Kettisha Jones
Highland Park ES	635 Rigsby Ave	San Antonio, TX	78210-3099	210-228-3335	533-8132	PK-5	Manuel Caballero
Highland Park Gifted & Talented Academy	901 E Drexel Ave	San Antonio, TX	78210-3105	210-293-4206	337-2357	PK-6	Geneva Rico
Hope Academy Charter S	3015 N MacGregor Way	Houston, TX	77004-7628	832-217-3240	217-3272	9-12	Raymond Whitley
Hope S	2849 9th Ave	Port Arthur, TX	77642-3961	409-983-6659	983-6408	6-12	Bobby Lopez
Horizon Montessori III - Harlingen	801 N 13th St Ste 5	Harlingen, TX	78550-5073	956-423-8200	423-8207	PK-6	Linda Cantu
Horizon Montessori II - Weslaco	1222 W Sugar Cane Dr	Weslaco, TX	78599-3892	956-969-0044	969-0065	PK-8	Romeo Benavides
Horizon Montessori I - Mc Allen	221 N Main St	McAllen, TX	78501-4630	956-668-1400	668-1404	PK-8	Sandra Naranjo
Houston Acad for International Studies	1810 Stuart St	Houston, TX	77004-3043	713-942-1430	942-1433	9-12	Melissa Jacobs
Houston Can Academy - Hobby	9020 Gulf Fwy	Houston, TX	77017-7007	832-379-4226	944-6736	9-12	James Troutman
Houston Can Academy - North	3401 Hardy St	Houston, TX	77009-5928	713-659-4226	651-1493	9-12	Trenn Russell
Houston Gateway Academy	1020 Coral St	Houston, TX	77012-2906	713-923-5060	923-9070	PK-12	Francisco Penning
Houston Gateway Academy	3400 Evergreen Dr	Houston, TX	77087-3715	713-649-2706	649-8165	PK-12	Francisco Penning
Houston Heights HS	1125 Lawrence St	Houston, TX	77008-6651	713-868-9797	868-9750	9-12	Richard Mik
Houston Heights Learning Academy	902 W 8th St	Houston, TX	77007-1408	713-869-9453	869-0785	PK-5	Yvette East
Huston Academy	680 Peach Orchard Rd	Stephenville, TX	76401-4938	254-965-8883	965-8654	7-12	Valarie Harvick
IDEA Academy Alamo	325 State Highway 495	Alamo, TX	78516-6877	956-588-4005	588-4006	K-12	Ana Garza
IDEA Academy Allan	4900 Gonzales St	Austin, TX	78702-5028	512-414-6120	385-2512	K-2	Angie Arismendi
IDEA Academy Brownsville	4395 Paredes Line Rd	Brownsville, TX	78526	956-832-5150	832-5716	K-5	Erica Matamoros
IDEA Academy Carver	217 Robinson Pl	San Antonio, TX	78202-2751	210-223-8885	223-8970	K-5	Mackee Mason
IDEA Academy Donna	401 S 1st St	Donna, TX	78537-3055	956-464-0203	464-8532	PK-5	Rebecca Saldana
IDEA Academy Edinburg	2553 N Roegiers Rd	Edinburg, TX	78541-8602	956-287-6100	287-6101	PK-5	Nora Perez
IDEA Academy Frontier	2800 S Dakota Ave	Brownsville, TX	78521-6133	956-541-2002	541-5561	K-5	Dora Villegas
IDEA Academy McAllen	201 N Bentsen Rd	McAllen, TX	78501-8297	956-429-4100	429-4126	K-5	Cassandra Flores
IDEA Academy Mission	1600 S Schuerbach Rd	Mission, TX	78572-1217	956-583-8315	424-3248	K-5	Marissa Falcon
IDEA Academy Pharr	600 E Las Milpas Rd	Pharr, TX	78577-9864	956-283-1515	783-1557	K-5	Sonia Aguilar
IDEA Academy San Benito	2151 Russell Ln	San Benito, TX	78586-8969	956-399-5252	361-9478	K-5	Stephanie Ramirez
IDEA Academy San Juan	200 N Nebraska Ave	San Juan, TX	78589-3038	956-702-5150	702-4497	K-3	Hilda Helsing
IDEA Academy South Flores	6919 S Flores St	San Antonio, TX	78221	210-239-4150		K-5	Angie Arismendi
IDEA Academy Weslaco	2931 E Sugar Cane Dr	Weslaco, TX	78599-2723	956-351-4100	351-4101	K-5	Jayne Pocquette
IDEA College Prep Alamo	325 State Highway 495	Alamo, TX	78516-6877	956-588-4005	588-4006	6-12	Israel Ybarra
IDEA College Prep Allan	4900 Gonzales St	Austin, TX	78702-5028	512-414-6120	385-2512	6-6	Amanda Marquez
IDEA College Prep Brownsville	4395 Paredes Line Rd	Brownsville, TX	78526	956-832-5150	832-5716	6-12	Marco Lopez
IDEA College Prep Donna	401 S 1st St	Donna, TX	78537-3055	956-464-0203	464-8532	6-12	Christina Escamilla
IDEA College Prep Edinburg	2553 N Roegiers Rd	Edinburg, TX	78541-8602	956-287-6100	287-6101	6-12	Frankie Gray
IDEA College Prep Frontier	2800 S Dakota Ave	Brownsville, TX	78521-6133	956-541-2002	541-5561	6-12	Michael Hardy
IDEA College Prep McAllen	201 N Bentsen Rd	McAllen, TX	78501-8297	956-429-4100	447-4126	6-12	Jon Alvarez
IDEA College Prep Mission	1600 S Schuerbach Rd	Mission, TX	78572-1217	956-583-8315	424-3248	6-12	Diana Aguilar
IDEA College Prep Pharr	600 E Las Milpas Rd	Pharr, TX	78577-9864	956-283-1515	783-1557	6-12	Ernesto Cantu
IDEA College Prep San Benito	2151 Russell Ln	San Benito, TX	78586-8969	956-399-5252	361-9478	6-12	Joel Garcia
IDEA College Prep San Juan	600 E Sioux Rd	San Juan, TX	78589-3491	956-588-4021	588-4030	6-12	Andrea Lopez
IDEA College Prep South Flores	6919 S Flores St	San Antonio, TX	78221	210-239-4150		6-12	Constantine Polites
IDEA College Prep Weslaco	2931 E Sugar Cane Dr	Weslaco, TX	78599-2723	956-351-4100	351-4101	6-12	John Nguyen
IDEA Quest Academy	14001 N Rooth Rd	Edinburg, TX	78541-4194	956-287-1003	287-2737	K-5	Rosy Chapa
IDEA Quest College Prep S	14001 N Rooth Rd	Edinburg, TX	78541-4194	956-287-1003	287-2737	6-12	Jose De Leon
Ignite Charter S	1205 S 7th St	Haymondville, TX	78580-3302	956-689-3300	292-0371	PK-12	Myrna Wood
Ignite Charter S	1352 E 1st St	Mission, TX	78572-5951	956-519-2227	687-6062	PK-12	Daniel Flores
Ignite Charter S	4737 S Sugar Rd	Edinburg, TX	78539-7012	956-380-6616	292-0371	PK-12	Hector Ortiz
Ignite Charter S	615 S International Blvd	Weslaco, TX	78596-9141	956-969-2600	969-1191	PK-12	Ramiro Vela
Ignite Charter S	508 E Elizabeth St	Brownsville, TX	78520-5367	956-542-3363	292-0371	PK-12	Jimmy Padilla
Ignite Charter S	5324 E US Highway 83	Rio Grande City, TX	78582-9412	956-488-8883	292-0371	PK-12	Abelardo Mendieta
Imagine International Academy	2860 Virginia Pkwy	Mc Kinney, TX	75071-3444	972-838-8921	540-1424	K-12	Julia Brady
Infinity Preparatory S	1401 S MacArthur Blvd	Irving, TX	75060-5848	469-621-9200		K-7	Nina Bhatia
Innovation Academy	3900 University Blvd	Tyler, TX	75799-6600	903-565-5669	565-5867	3-12	
Innovation Academy	3201 N Eastman Rd	Longview, TX	75605-5026	903-705-4330	617-6814	3-6	Angela Ladine
Innovation Academy	1820 W Spring St	Palestine, TX	75803-7900	903-705-4330	617-6814	3-6	Becky Rutledge
Inspired for Excellence Academy West	4103 Brisbane St	Houston, TX	77047-1701	713-772-2200	773-3630	5-6	Letha Gilmore
Inspired Vision Academy ES	8421 Bohannon Dr	Dallas, TX	75217-1917	214-391-7964	391-7954	PK-5	Lana Sprayberry-King
Inspired Vision Academy MS	8501 Bruton Rd	Dallas, TX	75217-1909	972-285-5758	285-0061	6-9	Lucy Simpkins
Irving MS	1300 Delgado St	San Antonio, TX	78207-1467	210-738-9740	734-0941	6-8	Michael Jordan
iSchoolHigh Amarillo	3242 Hobbs Rd Ste F	Amarillo, TX	79109-3213	806-387-5447		9-12	Michael Griffin
iSchool Media Arts Academy	1301 Waters Ridge Dr	Lewisville, TX	75057-6022	972-316-4160	262-8996	9-12	
iSchool STEM	1800 Lakeway Dr Ste 100	Lewisville, TX	75057-6438	972-317-2470	397-1633	9-12	Elaine Marchant
iSchool University Park	20515 State Highway 249	Houston, TX	77070-2607	281-546-2295		9-12	Mike Laird
Jamie's House Charter S	PO Box 681183	Houston, TX	77268-1183	281-866-9777	880-9919	6-12	
Jubilee Academy	4434 Roland Rd	San Antonio, TX	78222-2830	210-333-6227	337-2357	PK-8	
Kandy Stripe Academy	8701 Delilah St	Houston, TX	77033-1797	713-734-4909	731-2780	PK-8	Cassandra Anderson
Kelley Charter S	802 Oblate Dr	San Antonio, TX	78216-7330	210-431-9881	432-8467	K-3	Alma Garza
King S	3501 Martin Luther King Dr	San Antonio, TX	78220-2325	210-978-7935	223-6907	PK-8	Derrick Cade
Kingsway Leadership Academy	1727 Senator Carlos Truan	Kingsville, TX	78363	210-333-6227		PK-8	
KIPP 3D Academy	4610 E Crosstimbers St	Houston, TX	77016-6337	713-636-6082	636-6084	5-8	Alison Cumbley
KIPP Academy MS	10711 Kipp Way	Houston, TX	77099-2675	832-328-1051	879-1308	5-8	Andrew Rubin
KIPP Aspire Academy	735 Fredericksburg Rd	San Antonio, TX	78201-6348	210-735-7300	735-7305	5-8	Roy Feliciano
KIPP Austin Academy of Arts & Letters	8509 FM 969 Ste A	Austin, TX	78724-5702	512-501-3640	501-3641	5-8	Kevin Newman
KIPP Austin College Prep S	8509 FM 969 Ste 627	Austin, TX	78724-5710	512-637-6870	637-6899	5-8	Freddy Gonzalez
KIPP Austin Collegiate	8509 FM 969 Ste 676	Austin, TX	78724-5701	512-501-3586	501-3587	9-12	Carrie Donovan
KIPP Camino Academy	128 S Audubon Dr	San Antonio, TX	78212-1520	210-279-5166		5-7	Brennecke Hinojosa
KIPP Coastal Village	721 10th St	Galveston, TX	77550-5115	409-465-5401		PK-4	Lynn Barnes
KIPP DREAM Prep	4610 E Crosstimbers St	Houston, TX	77016-6337	713-636-6082	636-6084	PK-4	Olive Moore
KIPP Explore Academy	5402 Lawndale St	Houston, TX	77023-3743	832-230-0547	924-5046	PK-5	Frank Cush
Kipp Generations Collegiate S	500 Tidwell Rd	Houston, TX	77022-2122	832-230-0566	328-0178	9-12	Denise Rodriguez
KIPP Houston HS	10711 Kipp Way	Houston, TX	77099-2675	832-328-1051	838-4293	9-12	Lara Wheatley
KIPP Intrepid Preparatory S	5402 Lawndale St	Houston, TX	77023-3743	281-879-3100	463-7318	6-8	Steven Khadam
KIPP Legacy Preparatory S	9616 Mesa Dr	Houston, TX	77078-3024	832-230-0567	491-7311	PK-2	Tresha Francis
KIPP Liberation College Preparatory S	5400 Martin Luther King Jr	Houston, TX	77021	832-230-0565	842-6689	5-8	Tai Ingram
Kipp PEACE ES	5400 Martin Luther King Jr	Houston, TX	77021	832-230-0565		PK-4	Aundrea Johnson
KIPP Polaris Academy for Boys	9636 Mesa Dr	Houston, TX	77078-3024	832-230-0567	633-4783	6-8	Simone Senior
KIPP SHARP College Preparatory Lower S	8430 Westglen Dr	Houston, TX	77063-6312	281-879-3000	915-0074	PK-4	Alma Salman
KIPP Sharpstown College Prep	8440 Westpark Dr	Houston, TX	77063-5808	281-879-3005	915-0074	5-8	Karina Wilson
KIPP Shine Prep	10711 Kipp Way	Houston, TX	77099-2675	832-328-1051	328-0178	PK-5	Deborah Shifrine
KIPP Spirit College Preparatory S	11000 Scott St	Houston, TX	77047-1500	832-230-0562	731-1644	5-8	Charles King
KIPP Sunnyside HS	11000 Scott St	Houston, TX	77047-1500	832-230-0570		9-12	John Allen
KIPP Truth Academy	3200 S Lancaster Rd # 230A	Dallas, TX	75216	214-375-8326	375-2990	4-8	Michael Horne
KIPP University Prep HS	319 E Mulberry Ave	San Antonio, TX	78212-3024	210-290-8729	290-9427	9-12	
KIPP Voyage Academy for Girls	9616 Mesa Dr	Houston, TX	77078-3024	832-230-0567	491-7311	6-8	Tasha Ginn
KIPP ZENITH Academy	11000 Scott St	Houston, TX	77047-1500	832-230-0562		PK-4	Tiffany George
Kometzky S	PO Box 7667	Austin, TX	78713-7667	512-471-5280	232-9177	PK-8	Wendy Riney
La Academia de Estrellas	111 S Beckley Ave	Dallas, TX	75203-2610	214-946-8908	946-8777	PK-5	Lorraine Mantei M.Ed.
La Amistad Love & Learning Academy	10860 Rockley Rd	Houston, TX	77099-3416	281-498-2477	988-9201	PK-3	Rev. Fredrick Nixon
La Amistad Love & Learning Academy	10860 Rockley Rd	Houston, TX	77099-3416	713-541-1057	988-9201	PK-2	Rev. Fredrick Nixon
La Amistad Love & Learning Academy	10860 Rockley Rd	Houston, TX	77099-3416	281-988-9201	988-9201	PK-5	Rev. Fredrick Nixon
La Fe Preparatory S	616 E Father Rahm Ave	El Paso, TX	79901-2912	915-533-4560	533-4175	PK-4	Amy O'Rourke
Landmark S	101 Brushy Creek Rd	Palestine, TX	75803-8619	903-729-4208	729-1389	6-12	Mike Anderson
Lanier MS	2600 Woodhead St	Houston, TX	77098-1615	713-942-1900	942-1907	6-8	Linda Smith
Laredo Early College HS	5201 University Blvd	Laredo, TX	78041-1920	956-273-7700	795-8185	9-12	Jose Cerda
Las Americas Learning Center	5909 Glenmont Dr	Houston, TX	77081-1692	713-703-8820		K-5	
Laureate Preparatory S	2020 N Lamar St	Dallas, TX	75202	214-442-7882		K-4	Karen Aikman
Laureate Preparatory S	2625 Elm St	Dallas, TX	75226-1400	214-445-3300		6-9	Scott Hudnor
Laurel Ridge	17720 Corporate Woods Dr	San Antonio, TX	78259-3509	210-957-8964	232-9177	PK-12	Sally Arnold
Lawson Institute	3100 Cleburne St	Houston, TX	77004-4501	713-225-1551	225-1561	6-8	
Leadership Prep S	8500 Teel Pkwy	Frisco, TX	75034-0525	972-294-6921	294-3416	K-12	Michelle Holland
Lee Academy	1826 Basse Rd	San Antonio, TX	78213-4606	210-431-9881	435-0896	9-12	Valarie Walker
Legacy Park Preparatory Academy	601 S Washington St	Kaufman, TX	75142-2407	972-932-3814	962-2265	6-9	Cerone Lacey
Legacy Preparatory Academy	8510 Military Pkwy	Dallas, TX	75227-4401	214-680-8869	329-1665	K-12	Mary Davis
Legacy Preparatory Academy	790 Windbell Cir	Mesquite, TX	75149-3116	214-680-8869	329-1665	K-12	Rebecca Good
Legacy Preparatory Academy	1515 Blake Dr	Richardson, TX	75081-2504	214-680-8869	329-1665	K-12	Dr. Rebecca Good

School	Address	City,State	Zip code	Telephone	Fax	Grade	Contact
Liberation Academy	401 Present St	Missouri City, TX	77489-1109	281-969-7766	969-7762	K-6	Audrey Sanders
Liberty HS	6400 Southwest Fwy Ste A	Houston, TX	77074-2213	713-458-5555	458-5567	9-12	Monico Rivas
Life S - Cedar Hill	129 W Wintergreen Rd	Cedar Hill, TX	75104-5007	972-293-2825	291-2877	K-6	Joy Shepherd
Life S - Lancaster	950 S Interstate 35 E	Lancaster, TX	75146-3304	972-274-7950	274-7991	K-6	DeWayne Parker
Life S - Mt. Creek	5525 W Illinois Ave	Dallas, TX	75211-6612	214-623-0012		K-1	Stephanie Colwell
Life S - Oak Cliff	4400 S R L Thornton Fwy	Dallas, TX	75224-5110	214-376-8200	371-0193	K-12	Byron Mason
Life S - Red Oak	777 S Interstate 35 Rd	Red Oak, TX	75154-6221	469-552-9200	617-5767	K-6	Anne Beckman
Life S - Red Oak HS	3295 N Highway 77	Waxahachie, TX	75165-5735	972-938-1001	937-0503	7-12	Rick Pinson
Lighthouse Charter S	2718 Frontier Dr	San Antonio, TX	78227-4069	210-674-4100	674-4108	PK-7	Mary Salinas
Lindsley Park Community S	7130 Lindsley Ave	Dallas, TX	75223	214-321-9155	321-0702	PK-3	Tom Loew
LivingWay Leadership Academy	350 Ruben M Torres Blvd	Brownsville, TX	78520-8148	210-333-6227		PK-8	
Lowell MS	919 Thompson Pl	San Antonio, TX	78226-1494	210-228-1225	223-6248	6-8	Claudio Garcia
Mainland Preparatory Academy	319 Newman Rd	La Marque, TX	77568-3440	409-934-9100	934-9130	PK-8	Wilma Green
Manara Academy	8201 Tristar Dr	Irving, TX	75063-2816	972-304-1155	304-1150	K-8	Michelle Alkhatib
Massieu Academy	823 N Center St	Arlington, TX	76011-5859	817-460-0396	460-4762	PK-12	Karina Boyles
Mayes Institute	5807 Calhoun Rd	Houston, TX	77021-3301	713-747-5629	747-5683	K-8	Beatrice Mayes
MeadowLand Charter S	121 Old San Antonio Rd	Boerne, TX	78006-3415	830-331-4094		7-12	
Medical Center Charter S	10420 Mullins Dr	Houston, TX	77096-4927	713-726-0223	726-0225	PK-8	Margot Heard
Meridell Achievement Center	12550 W State Highway 29	Liberty Hill, TX	78642-4733	512-528-2462	515-5875	K-12	Wendy Rollins
Meridian Preparatory S	1801 S Beach St	Fort Worth, TX	76105-2122			K-12	April Knox
Meridian S	2555 N Interstate 35	Round Rock, TX	78664-2015	512-660-5230	660-5231	K-12	Rick Fernandez
Methodist Children's Home	1111 Herring Ave	Waco, TX	76708-3696	254-750-1298	750-1307	7-12	Cristy Cunningham
Meyer HS	1020 Elm St Bldg 100	Waco, TX	76704-2277	254-754-2288	754-8002	9-12	Dr. Matthew Polk
Meyerpark Charter S	PO Box 35616	Houston, TX	77235-5616	713-729-9712	729-9720	K-5	Julia Hutcherson
Midland Academy Charter S	500 N Baird St	Midland, TX	79701-4704	432-686-0003	686-0845	K-12	Janet Wallace
MId-Valley Academy	1785 W US Highway 77	San Benito, TX	78586-4153	956-276-9906	276-9943	9-12	Dr. Daniel Garcia
Mid-Valley Academy	200 N 17th St	McAllen, TX	78501-4743	956-618-2303	618-2323	9-12	Dr. Daniel Garcia
Mid-Valley Academy	103 E 2nd St	Mercedes, TX	78570-2701	956-565-5417	565-8439	9-12	Dr. Daniel Garcia
Mighty Preparatory S	3700 Wichita St	Fort Worth, TX	76119-2866	817-288-3800	276-0363	K-7	April Knox
Milburn Academy - Amarillo	4106 SW 51st Ave	Amarillo, TX	79109-6132	806-463-2284	463-2231	9-12	Becky Pinson
Milburn Academy-Corpus Christi	5333 Everhart Rd Bldg C	Corpus Christi, TX	78411-4835	361-225-4424	225-4945	9-12	Alys Williams
Milburn Academy - Fort Worth	6785 Camp Bowie Blvd	Fort Worth, TX	76116	817-731-7627	731-7628	9-12	Holly Tarter
Milburn Academy - Houston	713 E Airtex Dr	Houston, TX	77073	281-209-3505	209-9475	9-12	Verlean West
Milburn Academy - Killeen	802 N 2nd St Bldg G	Killeen, TX	76541-4711	254-634-4444	634-4044	9-12	Kim Sheppard
Milburn Academy - Lubbock	2333 50th St	Lubbock, TX	79412-2501	806-740-0811	740-0804	9-12	Starlette Gill
Milburn Academy - Midland	3303 W Illinois Ave Ste 14	Midland, TX	79703-6232	432-522-7200	522-5201	9-12	Kim Blackketter
Milburn Academy - Odessa	2525 N Grandview Ave	Odessa, TX	79761-1600	432-550-7833	550-7884	9-12	D.J. Hittinger
Mount Carmel Academy	7155 Ashburn St	Houston, TX	77061-2611	713-643-2008	645-0078	9-12	Rodney Takacs
Nelms Charter HS	20625 Clay Rd	Katy, TX	77449-5593	281-398-8031	398-8032	9-12	Michael Dean
Nelms Charter MS	20625 Clay Rd	Katy, TX	77449-5593	281-398-8031	398-8032	5-8	David Dean
New Frontiers Charter S	4018 S Presa St	San Antonio, TX	78223-1005	210-533-3655	533-5077	K-8	Melissa Holguin
New Horizons S	850 Highway 574 W	Goldthwaite, TX	76844	325-938-5513	935-5512	1-12	Suzanne Goen
Newman International Academy Arlington	2011 S Fielder Rd	Arlington, TX	76013-6255	817-459-8555	563-0312	PK-12	Donna Hart
North Hills S	606 E Royal Ln	Irving, TX	75039-3503	972-501-0645	501-9439	K-12	Richard Young
Northwest Early College HS	6701 S Desert Blvd	El Paso, TX	79932-8501	915-877-1700	877-7033	9-12	Ivette Savina
Northwest Preparatory S	4705 Lyons Ave	Houston, TX	77020-4306	713-674-2105	676-1940	PK-8	Steve Roberts
Northwest Preparatory S	600 Charles St	Humble, TX	77338-3847	713-672-1959	676-1940	PK-8	Erik Singleton
Nova Academy	PO Box 170127	Dallas, TX	75217-0127	214-381-3422	381-3499	PK-3	Donna Houston-Woods
Nova Academy Southeast - Bruton	PO Box 170127	Dallas, TX	75217-0127	214-309-9030	398-6363	K-6	Donna Houston-Woods
Nova Academy Southeast - Prichard	PO Box 170127	Dallas, TX	75217-0127	972-808-7470	808-7471	1-8	Donna Houston-Woods
NYOS Charter S	12301 N Lamar Blvd	Austin, TX	78753-1320	512-583-6967	583-6973	4-12	Julie Atchley
NYOS Magnolia McCullough Campus	1605 Kramer Ln	Austin, TX	78758-4284	512-275-1593	287-5258	PK-3	Terry Berkenhoff
Odyssey Academy	2412 61st St	Galveston, TX	77551-1802	409-750-9289	740-3310	PK-8	Jennifer Goodman
Odyssey Preparatory S	8787 N Houston Rosslyn Rd	Houston, TX	77088-6430	713-983-0165	983-0294	PK-8	Venora Goodie
Olive Tree Montessori Academy	614 Hiett Ave	Arlington, TX	76010-2523	817-460-5000		K-5	Angela Clemmer
Olympic Hills Charter S	PO Box 7667	Austin, TX	78713-7667	512-444-4835	232-9177	2-12	Dottie Goodman
One Stop Multiservice Charter S	4705 S Sugar Rd	Edinburg, TX	78539-3564	956-380-6616	292-0371	PK-12	Hector Ortiz
One Stop Multiservice Charter S	615 S International Blvd	Weslaco, TX	78596-9141	956-969-2600	969-1191	PK-12	Ramiro Vela
One-Stop Multiservice Charter S	101 1st Blvd	Mission, TX	78572	956-519-2227	687-6062	PK-12	Velma Vela
Osborne ES	800 Ringold St	Houston, TX	77088-6337	281-405-2525	405-2528	PK-5	Jacqueline Parnell
Outreach Academy Charter S	71 Galveston Dr	Victoria, TX	77904	361-579-6922	573-5788	PK-5	Lorrine Hernandez
Panola Charter S	PO Box 610	Carthage, TX	75633-0610	903-693-6355	693-6391	8-12	Keith Koonce
Panola Early College HS	1109 W Panola St	Carthage, TX	75633-2397	903-694-4028	694-4030	8-12	Keith Koonce
Paso Del Norte Academy	400 S Zaragoza Rd Ste 230	El Paso, TX	79907-6672	915-298-3637	298-3644	9-12	Lee Clay
Paso Del Norte Academy - Ysleta	711 N Mesa St	El Paso, TX	79902-3925	915-532-7216	532-2251	9-12	Maria Baquera
Pathfinder Camp	20800 FM 150 W	Driftwood, TX	78619-9202	512-858-4258	858-4960	6-12	Christee Jackson
Pathways 3H Ranch	110 Youth Ranch Rd # 3H	Mountain Home, TX	78058	830-866-3761	866-3705	6-12	Sonja Herrington
Peak Academy	4600 Bryan St	Dallas, TX	75204	214-276-0879	276-0856	PK-5	Teno Sigmon
Pegasus Campus	5299 South Highway 183	Lockhart, TX	78644	512-432-1651	398-2731	5-12	Jason Hybner
Pegasus Charter HS	601 N Akard St Ste 203	Dallas, TX	75201-3303	214-740-9991	740-9799	K-12	Virginia Hart
Phoenix Charter S	8501 Jack Finney Blvd	Greenville, TX	75402-3018	903-454-7153	455-0604	PK-12	Mary Kahama
Pineywoods Community Academy	602 S Raguet St	Lufkin, TX	75904-3936	936-634-5515	634-5518	PK-6	Bruce Marchand
Pineywoods Community Academy	602 S Raguet St	Lufkin, TX	75904-3936	936-634-5515	634-5518	7-12	Monica Gnter
Pinnacle Academy	5006 James Ave	Fort Worth, TX	76115-3818	817-735-8527	735-1910	K-8	Linda Eikenberry
Pinnacle Preparatory S	2510 S Vernon Ave	Dallas, TX	75224-1803	214-442-6100		K-2	Karen Salerno
Porter S	PO Box 2053	Wimberley, TX	78676-6953	512-847-6867	847-0737	9-12	Jon Batson
Por Vida Academy	1135 Mission Rd	San Antonio, TX	78210-4505	210-532-9161	533-5612	9-12	Joseph Rendon
Positive Solutions Charter S	1325 N Flores St	San Antonio, TX	78212-4900	210-299-1025	299-1052	9-12	Steven Langseth
Premier HS of Austin	1701 W Ben White Blvd	Austin, TX	78704	512-444-8442	444-1266	9-12	Elizabeth Camarena
Premier HS of Beaumont	209 N 11th St	Beaumont, TX	77702-2213	409-835-4303	835-2882	6-12	Dr. Jeannie Atkinson
Premier HS of Brenham	10602 FM 2621	Brenham, TX	77833-0163	979-838-0901		7-12	Caty Pabon
Premier HS of Brownsville	955 Paredes Line Rd	Brownsville, TX	78521-2659	956-550-0084	554-0890	6-12	Norma Sorola
Premier HS of Brownwood/Early	819 Early Blvd	Early, TX	76802-2130	325-643-3735	643-9028	9-12	Joe Branham
Premier HS of Comanche	1008 S Austin St	Comanche, TX	76442-3022	325-356-9673	356-9674	6-12	Vicky Cavitt B.S.
Premier HS of Dayton	1709 County Road 611	Dayton, TX	77535-8561	936-257-8017		6-12	Kevin Nichols
Premier HS of Del Rio	4300 E Highway 90	Del Rio, TX	78840-8878	830-298-2100	298-2122	6-12	Berta Martinez
Premier HS of Dublin	112 S Grafton St	Dublin, TX	76446-2318	254-445-4844	445-4907	6-12	Marsha Grissom
Premier HS of El Paso	1035 Belvidere St Ste 116	El Paso, TX	79912-2433	915-581-4300	581-4378	6-12	Mimi Allen
Premier HS of Granbury	919 E Highway 377 Ste 1	Granbury, TX	76048-1436	817-573-0435	895-9616	9-12	Marsha Grissom
Premier HS of Huntsville	2407 Sam Houston Ave	Huntsville, TX	77340-5862	936-439-5204	622-9113	7-12	Raymond Moore
Premier HS of Irving South	1081 W Shady Grove Rd	Irving, TX	75060-5868	972-264-1016		9-12	Dave Sammon
Premier HS of Irving West	1401 W Royal Ln	Irving, TX	75063	972-456-3004		9-12	L. Waite
Premier HS of Lanier	1201 Payton Gin Rd	Austin, TX	78758-6699	855-866-6878		9-12	Rachel Stevens
Premier HS of Laredo	2201 Chihuahua St	Laredo, TX	78043-3737	956-723-7788	284-0175	9-12	Ethel Monroy
Premier HS of Lindale	17141 State Highway 110 N	Lindale, TX	75771-5933	903-881-9940	882-0183	6-12	M. Parker
Premier HS of Lubbock	2002 W Loop 289 Ste 121	Lubbock, TX	79407-7701	806-763-1518	763-9310	6-12	Thomas Martin
Premier HS of Midland	1900 N Big Spring St	Midland, TX	79705-8817	432-682-0384	682-0897	6-12	Rhonda Gibbs
Premier HS of Mission	1203 St Claire Blvd	Mission, TX	78572-8465	956-424-9290	424-7661	6-12	Laura Thatcher
Premier HS of New Braunfels	1928 S Seguin Ave	New Braunfels, TX	78130-3910	830-609-6606	319-4382	9-12	Richard Ramirez
Premier HS of North Austin	1835 Kramer Ln Ste A600	Austin, TX	78758-4259	512-832-0965	832-0986	6-12	Amanda Marlin
Premier HS of Palmview	406 W Veterans Blvd	Palmview, TX	78572-8327	956-584-8458	584-9807	6-12	Selma Femat
Premier HS of Pharr	200 E Expressway 83 Ste E	Pharr, TX	78577-6506	956-781-8800	781-7464	6-12	Rosie Zamora
Premier HS of Richardson	1111 Digital Dr	Richardson, TX	75081-1948	972-479-9002		9-12	Shaina Tackett-Cox
Premier HS of San Antonio	502 E Ramsey Rd	San Antonio, TX	78216-4639	210-524-8103		9-12	C. Timmons
Premier HS of San Juan	1200 E Business 83	San Juan, TX	78589-4758	956-961-4721	961-4724	6-12	Alma Prado
Premier HS of Travis	1211 E Oltorf St	Austin, TX	78704-5799	855-809-2819		9-12	Anne Warren
Premier HS of Tyler	1106 N Glenwood Blvd	Tyler, TX	75702-5059	903-592-5222	592-0324	6-12	Tabatha Ervin
Premier HS of Waco	4720 N 19th St	Waco, TX	76708-1213	254-752-0441	752-0445	6-12	Lisa Linton
Premier Leadership Academy	1630 Goliad Rd	San Antonio, TX	78223-2722	210-333-6227		PK-4	Trina A.Cardenas
Premier Learning Academy	5130 Casey St	La Marque, TX	77568-2707	409-935-8369	935-3337	K-12	Travis Witherspoon
Preparatory Academy of Houston	12525 Fondren Rd Ste M	Houston, TX	77035-5226	713-271-6905	729-5308	PK-12	Betty Montgomery
Prime Prep Academy	4400 Panola Ave	Fort Worth, TX	76103-3701	214-473-5504	840-5999	PK-12	Cleveland Starr
Prime Prep Academy	330 E Ann Arbor Ave	Dallas, TX	75216-6717	214-473-5504	840-5999	6-12	Clyde Pikes
Project Chrysalis MS	4528 Leeland St	Houston, TX	77023-3047	713-924-1700	924-1704	6-8	Jose Covarrubia
Pro-Vision Academy Charter S	4590 Wilmington St	Houston, TX	77051-3332	713-748-0030	748-0037	5-12	Carrie Tate
Quest Academy	1404 Walnut Hill Ln	Dallas, TX	75203	972-753-6165	550-1425	6-12	Cerone Lacey
Quest MS	1301 Waters Ridge Dr	Lewisville, TX	75057-6022	972-316-6700	316-6705	6-8	Glenda Simons
Quest MS of Coppell	1615 W Belt Line Rd	Carrollton, TX	75006-6633	972-242-5864	245-2820	6-8	Derrick Graves
Quinn Campus MS	1020 Elm St Bldg 100	Waco, TX	76704-2277	254-754-8000	754-8009	5-8	Nancy Grayson
Radiance Academy of Learning - Abndnt Lf	7431 S Presa St	San Antonio, TX	78223-3535	210-531-9026	531-9912	K-5	Emma Alexander
Radiance Academy of Learning - Daystar	413 Kitty Hawk Rd	Universal City, TX	78148-3826	210-659-1928	659-1974	PK-6	Kerry Armstead
Radiance Academy of Learning - Del Rio	709 Kings Way	Del Rio, TX	78840-2029	830-774-6230	774-6235	6-12	Manuel Polanco
Radiance Academy of Learning - Intl	4151 Culebra Rd	San Antonio, TX	78228-4557	210-967-3206	637-9264	K-8	Dorothy Scott
Radiance Academy of Learning - Lttl Lion	13118 El Sendero St	San Antonio, TX	78233-5816	210-599-1005	599-1808	PK-2	Valerie VanRogue
Ramirez Charter S	702 Avenue T	Lubbock, TX	79401-2303	806-766-1833	766-1825	K-5	Nancy Parker
Ranch Academy	3120 VZ County Road 2318	Canton, TX	75103-4671	903-479-3601	479-1161	6-12	Melissa Pardue
Ranch Academy - Tyler Campus	14023 State Highway 155 S	Tyler, TX	75703-6635	903-479-3601	479-1161	1-12	Melissa Vonsenden

School	Address	City,State	Zip code	Telephone	Fax	Grade	Contact
Rapoport Academy	1020 Elm St Bldg 100	Waco, TX	76704-2277	254-799-4191	799-4525	PK-4	Bonnie Luft
Raven S	PO Box 515	New Waverly, TX	77358-0515	936-344-6677	344-7236	9-12	Dale Underwood
Reach Charter S	520 Mercury Dr	Houston, TX	77013-5217	713-675-1118	671-3612	11-12	Bertie Simmons
Real Learning Academy	220 Foremost Dr	Austin, TX	78745-7324	512-571-7999	383-0665	PK-4	Michelle Stahl
Reconciliation Academy	4311 Bryan St	Dallas, TX	75204-6738	214-821-9192	824-4447	PK-12	Carol Thorne
Rhodes MS	3000 Tampico St	San Antonio, TX	78207-6498	210-978-7925	433-7299	6-8	Edward Garcia
Rhodes S	12822 Robert E Lee Rd	Houston, TX	77044-2411	281-458-4334	458-7595	PK-6	Michelle Bonton
Richland Collegiate HS	12800 Abrams Rd	Dallas, TX	75243-2199	972-761-6888	761-6890	11-12	Kristyn Edney
Ripley House Charter S	4410 Navigation Blvd	Houston, TX	77011-1036	713-315-6429	547-8201	K-8	Karen Elsen
Riverside Park ES	202 School St	San Antonio, TX	78210-3940	210-228-3355	534-6987	PK-5	Homer Rivera
Saenz JHS	1830 Basse Rd	San Antonio, TX	78213-4606	210-431-9881	435-0896	7-8	James Cuellar
St. Anthony Academy	3732 Myrtle St	Dallas, TX	75215-3849	214-421-3645	421-7416	PK-8	David Ray
St. Mary's Academy Charter S	507 N Filmore St	Beeville, TX	78102-5000	361-358-5601	358-5704	K-8	Stan Simonson
San Antonio Can Academy	1807 Centennial Blvd	San Antonio, TX	78211-1205	210-923-1226	928-3366	9-12	Mark Peters
San Antonio S for Inquiry & Creativity	4618 San Pedro Ave	San Antonio, TX	78212-1411	210-738-0020	738-0033	K-12	Dr. Debbie De Leon
San Antonio Technology Academy	2507 Fredericksburg Rd	San Antonio, TX	78201-3784	210-527-9250	225-7282	9-12	Earl Costley
Sanchez HS	6001 Gulf Fwy	Houston, TX	77023-5423	713-926-1112	926-1346	7-12	Eduardo Lopez
Sanchez HS	201 Meredith Dr	San Antonio, TX	78228-3231	210-270-8567	886-0816	8-12	Diana Perez
Save Our Streets Learning Center	1700 Groesbeck St	Bryan, TX	77803-4416	979-703-1810	703-1834	4-8	Dr. Freema Ervin
School of Science and Technology	4737 Saratoga Blvd	Corpus Christi, TX	78413-2117	361-851-2450	851-2475	K-12	Ekrem Demirci
School of Science and Technology Alamo	12200 Crownpoint Dr	San Antonio, TX	78233-5371	210-657-6400	657-6401	K-8	Mehmet Nalcaci
School of Science & Technology Discovery	5707 Bandera Rd	Leon Valley, TX	78238-1918	210-543-1111	543-1112	K-8	Mustafa Kililioglu
School of Science and Technology HS	1450 NE Loop 410	San Antonio, TX	78209-1513	210-804-0222	822-3422	6-12	Atila Akyurek
Scott Collegiate Academy	4116 Avenue N 1/2	Galveston, TX	77550-6957	409-761-6100	765-5946	5-8	Debra Owens
Seashore Learning Center	14493 S Padre Isl PMB 307A	Corpus Christi, TX	78418	361-949-1222	949-6762	PK-4	
Seashore Middle Academy	14493 S Padre Isl PMB 307A	Corpus Christi, TX	78418	361-654-1134	654-1139	5-8	Barbara Beeler
Sentry Technology Prep S	508 E Elizabeth St	Brownsville, TX	78520-5367	956-542-3363	292-0371	PK-12	Paul Rudnik
SER-Ninos Charter S	5815 Alder Dr	Houston, TX	77081-2708	713-667-6145	667-0645	PK-8	Charmaine Constantine
Settlement Home	PO Box 7667	Austin, TX	78713-7667	512-695-6596	836-2159	K-12	Mayola Toliver
Shekinah Radiance Academy - Dallas Ctr	201 N Erby Campbell Blvd	Royse City, TX	75189-8299	972-636-0055	635-0055	K-6	Rusty Mitchell
Shekinah Radiance Academy - Garland	10715 Garland Rd Ste 100	Dallas, TX	75218-2608	214-320-2500	320-2502	K-6	Richard Mitchell
Shekinah Radiance Academy - Live Oak	13069 N Interstate 35	San Antonio, TX	78233-2615	210-590-0838	590-0856	PK-5	Derrick Love
Shekinah Radiance Academy - Pearsall	5203 Old Pearsall Rd	San Antonio, TX	78242-1918	210-623-3030	623-3046	PK-5	Javier Arredondo
Shekinah Radiance Academy - Tomball	612 Malone St	Tomball, TX	77375-4642	281-516-0993		K-6	
Shekinah Radiance Academy - Villg S Park	9133 Scott St	Houston, TX	77051-2763	713-734-7989	734-7990	K-6	Claudette Edwards
Shekinah Radiance Academy - Walzem	6663 Walzem Rd	San Antonio, TX	78239-3612	210-967-6933	967-6280	PK-12	Emma Alexander
Shekinah Radiance Academy - W Columbia	719 W Brazos Ave	West Columbia, TX	77486-2617	979-345-2434	345-5134	K-12	Michael Blackshire
Shoreline Academy	1220 Gregory St	Taft, TX	78390-3044	361-528-3959	528-2143	7-12	Deann Phillips
South Plains Academy	4008 Avenue R	Lubbock, TX	79412-1603	806-744-0330	741-1089	9-12	Michael Carothers
Southwest ES	8440 Bissonnet St	Houston, TX	77074-3908	713-988-5839	270-0076	PK-5	
Southwest HS	6400 Westpark Dr Ste 200	Houston, TX	77057-7408	713-954-9528	953-0119	9-12	Rosalinda Mercado-Garza
Southwest MS	6400 Westpark Dr Ste 200	Houston, TX	77057-7408	713-954-9528	953-0119	6-8	Rosalinda Mercado-Garza
Southwest Preparatory S NE Campus	1258 Austin Hwy Ste 220	San Antonio, TX	78209-4820	210-829-8017	829-8514	6-12	Sherry Head
Southwest Preparatory S NW Campus	6535 Culebra Rd	San Antonio, TX	78238-4910	210-432-2634	432-5482	6-12	Brooks Green
Southwest Preparatory S SE Campus	735 S WW White Rd	San Antonio, TX	78220-2524	210-333-1403	333-3024	6-12	Javier Garcia
Southwest Prep S New Directions Campus	1258 Austin Hwy Bldg 2	San Antonio, TX	78209-4891	210-828-2161	826-9962	9-12	Sherry Head
Stepping Stones Charter S	11250 S Wilcrest Dr	Houston, TX	77099-4313	281-988-7797	988-7736	PK-8	William Clark
Storm ES	435 Brady Blvd	San Antonio, TX	78207-8099	210-978-8005	224-1998	PK-5	Jackie Ibarra-Lanford
Summit International Preparatory S	1100 Roosevelt St	Arlington, TX	76011-4837	817-287-5121	287-0532	K-12	Priscilla Parhms
Tafolla Charter S	PO Box 1709	Uvalde, TX	78802-1709	830-278-1471	278-2225	PK-12	Richard Juarez
Tekoa Academy	326 Thomas Blvd	Port Arthur, TX	77640-5242	409-982-5400	982-8498	PK-12	Dr. Paula Richardson
Tekoa Academy of Accelerated Studies	1704 14th St	Orange, TX	77630-3300	409-982-5400	982-9711	PK-6	Dr. Paula Richardson
Temple Charter Academy	7177 Airport Rd	Temple, TX	76502-7142	254-778-8682	778-8690	PK-12	Jason Osburn
Texas Connections Academy at Houston	10550 Richmond Ave Ste 140	Houston, TX	77042-5112	281-661-8293	496-4697	3-8	Lea Ann Lockard
Texas Early College HS	2400 E End Blvd S	Marshall, TX	75672-7402	903-935-4109	935-4067	8-12	Robert Bruce
Texas Education Centers at Aubrey	5411 US Highway 377 S	Aubrey, TX	76227-6212	940-440-9580	440-9581	K-12	Samie Shelby
Texas Education Centers at Denton	4420 Country Club Rd	Denton, TX	76210-3222	940-383-1972	383-7655	K-12	Susan Taraba
Texas Education Centers at Little Elm	5901 Crestwood Pl	Little Elm, TX	75068-3754	972-292-3562	292-3563	K-12	Clarrisa Figueroa
Texas Education Centers in Lewisville	968 Raldon St	Lewisville, TX	75067-5229	972-221-3564	292-2373	K-12	Donica Hill
Texas Elementary School of the Arts	6025 Village Pkwy	Fort Worth, TX	76134-3430	817-732-8372	732-8373	K-8	Natalie Texada
Texas Empowerment Academy	6414 N Hampton Dr	Austin, TX	78723-2043	512-494-1076	494-1009	K-4	David Nowlin
Texas Empowerment Academy	3613 Bluestein Dr	Austin, TX	78721-2900	512-494-1076	494-0199	5-12	David Nowlin
Texas NeuroRehabilitation Center	PO Box 7667	Austin, TX	78713-7667	512-444-4835	462-6665	K-12	Dottie Goodman
Texas Preparatory S	PO Box 1643	San Marcos, TX	78667-1643	512-805-3000	805-7739	K-8	Mark Torry
Texas Serenity Academy	8500 Sweetwater Ln	Houston, TX	77037-2816	281-820-9540	820-6204	K-12	Michelle Foreman
Texas Virtual Academy	1800 Lakeway Dr Ste 100	Lewisville, TX	75057-6438	866-360-0161		3-12	Sherri Remington
TLC Academy	PO Box 61726	San Angelo, TX	76906-1726	325-652-3200	942-6795	K-12	Ron Ledbetter
Transformative Charter Academy	802 N 8th St	Killeen, TX	76541-4819	254-628-8989	628-8981	9-12	Claudette Morgan-Scott
Travis Early College HS	1915 N Main Ave	San Antonio, TX	78212-3900	210-733-1911	733-5486	9-12	Orlando Vera
Treetops School International	12500 S Pipeline Rd	Euless, TX	76040-5853	817-283-1771	684-0892	K-12	Lou Blanchard
Trinity Basin ES	831 W 10th St	Dallas, TX	75208-4912	214-296-9302	296-9306	3-5	Jennifer Masten
Trinity Basin Preparatory S	808 N Ewing Ave	Dallas, TX	75203-1524	214-942-8846	946-9194	PK-12	Alicia Dunson
Trinity Charter - Krause Center Campus	25752 Kingsland Blvd	Katy, TX	77494-2086	281-392-7505	392-7560	6-12	Jacqueline Thomas
Trinity Charter - New Life Campus	650 Scarbourough	Canyon Lake, TX	78133-4529	830-964-4390	964-4376	4-12	Kellie Ragland
TSU Charter Lab S	3100 Cleburne St	Houston, TX	77004-4501	713-313-6754	747-0672	K-5	Debbra Collins
Two Dimensions Preparatory Academy	12121 Veterans Memorial Dr	Houston, TX	77067-5237	281-227-4700	232-0032	PK-5	Shirley Harris
Two Dimensions Preparatory Academy	901 E 10th Ave	Corsicana, TX	75110-6726	281-227-4700	872-2858	PK-1	Shirley Harris
Two Dimensions Preparatory Academy	12330 Vickery St	Houston, TX	77039-3608	281-227-4700	987-7306	PK-4	Shirley Harris
UME Preparatory Academy	3838 Spur 408	Dallas, TX	75236-3294	972-400-1771	692-7005	K-12	Randy Horton
Universal Academy	2616 N MacArthur Blvd	Irving, TX	75062-5401	972-255-1800	255-6122	PK-12	Sheraton Duffey
Universal Academy - Flower Mound	1001 E Sandy Lake Rd	Coppell, TX	75019-3112	972-393-5834	255-6122	PK-12	Lisa Davis
University Charter S	2200 E 6th St	Austin, TX	78702-3457	512-495-9705	499-4240	PK-5	Melissa Chavez
University of Houston Charter S of Tech	3855 Holman St	Houston, TX	77204-6056	713-743-9111	743-9121	K-5	Dr. Carolyn Black
Vanguard Academy Charter School	1200 E Kelly Ave	Pharr, TX	78577-5033	956-781-1701	781-8055	PK-12	Robert Olivarez
Vanguard Academy II	901 S Athol	Pharr, TX	78577	956-702-0134	702-0166	PK-5	Patricia Cardoza
Varnett S - East	PO Box 1457	Houston, TX	77251-1457	713-637-6574	637-8319	PK-5	Gayle Voltz
Varnett S - Northeast	PO Box 1457	Houston, TX	77251-1457	713-631-4396	491-3597	PK-5	Dora Morrow
Varnett S - Southwest	PO Box 1457	Houston, TX	77251-1457	713-723-4699	283-1728	PK-5	Twilett Alexander
Victory Preparatory Academy	2903 Jensen Dr	Houston, TX	77026-6019	713-229-0560	250-7072	PK-12	
Vision Academy HS	4590 Wilmington St	Houston, TX	77051-3332	713-748-0030	748-0037	9-12	Carrie Tate
Vista Academy of Amarillo	3242 Hobbs Rd Ste F	Amarillo, TX	79109-3213	806-367-5447	367-5449	K-8	Michael Griffin
Vista Academy of Austin	1504 E 51st St	Austin, TX	78723-3012	512-371-0933		K-4	Miriam Troilo
Vista Academy of Beaumont	10255 Eastex Fwy Ste 100	Beaumont, TX	77708-1061	409-434-4549		K-4	Sherry Hanson
Vista Academy of Carrollton	2400 N Josey Ln	Carrollton, TX	75006-1617	972-245-2900	245-2999	K-5	Stephanie Scott
Vista Academy of Coppell	140 S Heartz Rd	Coppell, TX	75019-5812	972-393-3077		K-5	Chris Sisk
Vista Academy of Crockett	1303 E Houston Ave	Crockett, TX	75835-1749	936-546-0493		K-6	Deborah Kelly
Vista Academy of Dallas	7300 Bruton Rd	Dallas, TX	75217-1447	214-792-9331	792-9334	K-6	Yvette Iglinsky
Vista Academy of DeSoto	1121 E Pleasant Run Rd	DeSoto, TX	75115-4201	214-954-7075		K-4	Camille Penny
Vista Academy of Edinburg	2110 S McColl Rd	Edinburg, TX	78539-8831	956-720-4361		K-4	Norma McDaniel
Vista Academy of Elgin	2418 FM 1704	Elgin, TX	78621-5565	855-809-2813		K-4	Jenness LaPage
Vista Academy of Garland	3024 Anita Dr	Garland, TX	75041-2708	972-840-1100	840-1105	K-8	Campbell Gillis
Vista Academy of Hickory Creek	800 Point Vista Dr Ste 518	Hickory Creek, TX	75065-7639	940-321-1144	321-1116	K-5	Kimberly Powell
Vista Academy of Huntsville	2407 Sam Houston Ave	Huntsville, TX	77340-5862	936-291-0203	293-8096	K-6	Robbie Harris
Vista Academy of Jasper	1501 S Wheeler St	Jasper, TX	75951-5103	409-489-9222	489-9272	K-8	Laura McMillon
Vista Academy of North Garland	1600 W Campbell Rd	Garland, TX	75044-2300	855-290-0505		K-4	Stephanie Scott
Vista Academy of San Antonio	2235 Thousand Oaks Dr # 130	San Antonio, TX	78232	210-402-0253		PK-2	Rheatha Miller
Vista Academy of The Woodlands	6565 Research Forest Dr	The Woodlands, TX	77381-6030	936-242-1541		K-8	Timm Petersen
Vista Academy of Tyler	3105 University Blvd Ste B	Tyler, TX	75701-6614	903-504-5690		K-4	Keith Garcia
Vista Academy of Willis	202 S Thomason St	Willis, TX	77378-8987	936-890-0100	890-0110	K-8	Robert Riggs
Vista del Futuro Charter S	7310 Bishop Flores Dr	El Paso, TX	79912	915-855-8143	855-8179	K-5	
Waco Charter S	615 N 25th St	Waco, TX	76707-3443	254-754-8169	754-7389	PK-5	Sabrina Gray
Walker IS	6500 N Interstate 35	San Antonio, TX	78218-3702	210-654-4411	599-3546	4-6	Pamela Tankerson
Wallace Accelerated HS	149 S State Highway 208	Colorado City, TX	79512-6603	325-728-2392	728-1025	8-12	Melinda Alexander
Washington Tyrannus S of the Arts	8410 E FM 1518 N	Schertz, TX	78154-4520	210-659-0329	566-5912	7-12	Emma Alexander
Waxahachie Faith Family Academy	701 Ovilla Rd	Waxahachie, TX	75167-9430	972-937-3704	937-5806	PK-12	Eric Lejeune
Wesley ES	800 Dillard St	Houston, TX	77091-2301	713-696-2860	696-2866	PK-5	Dr. Kimberly Borders
Westchester Academy International Study	901 Yorkchester Dr	Houston, TX	77079-3446	713-251-1800	365-5686	6-12	Nancy Bertin
Westlake Academy	2600 J T Ottinger Rd	Westlake, TX	76262-8012	817-490-5757	490-5758	K-12	Rod Harding
White Memorial HS	PO Box 2126	League City, TX	77574-2126	281-316-0001	316-0018	9-12	Dr. Rosalind Perez
Whittier MS	2101 Edison Dr	San Antonio, TX	78201-3499	210-738-9755	735-0704	6-8	Janet Perez
Williams Charter MS	6100 Knox St	Houston, TX	77091-4143	713-696-2600	696-2604	6-8	Corey Seymour
Williams House S	108 E Main St	Lometa, TX	76853-2105	512-752-7501	752-7503	K-12	Cathy Ramirez
Williams Preparatory S	1750 Viceroy Dr	Dallas, TX	75235-2308	214-276-0352	637-6393	K-12	Paul Fulce-Ewing
Wilmer Academy	211 S Dallas Ave	Wilmer, TX	75172-1133	972-525-3051	525-3246	K-8	Dr. Kitt Square-Johnson
Winfree Academy Charter S	2985 S State Highway 360	Grand Prairie, TX	75052-7615	214-204-2034	204-2034	9-12	Eric Dillie
Winfree Academy Charter S	518 Acme St	Denton, TX	76205-5802	940-243-0486	243-0219	9-12	Emily Keating
Winfree Academy Charter S	1661 Gateway Blvd	Richardson, TX	75080-3530	972-234-9855	234-9975	9-12	Madge Ennis

School	Address	City,State	Zip code	Telephone	Fax	Grade	Contact
Winfree Academy Charter S	3110 Skyway Cir S	Irving, TX	75038-4207	972-251-2010	251-4301	9-12	Maritza Olivarez
Winfree Academy Charter S	341 Bennett Ln	Lewisville, TX	75057-4801	214-222-2200	222-0201	9-12	Mike Quinlan
Winfree Academy Charter S	6311 Boulevard 26 Ste 300	N Richlnd Hls, TX	76180-1595	817-590-2240	590-8724	9-12	Holly Gregg
Wood Charter S at Afton Oaks	620 E Afton Oaks Blvd	San Antonio, TX	78232-1236	210-638-5000	638-5575	5-12	Chris Skipper
Wood Charter S at Garza	800 N Avenue F	Post, TX	79356-9300	210-638-5800	638-5875	5-12	Carlton Johnson
Wood Charter S at Granbury	1300 Crossland Rd	Granbury, TX	76048-5208	210-638-5600	638-5675	4-12	Marc Malloy
Wood Charter S at Hays County	2250 Clovis R Barker Rd	San Marcos, TX	78666-9716	210-638-5400	638-5475	5-12	Jessica Raney
Wood Charter S at Rockdale	696 N FM 487	Rockdale, TX	76567-6005	210-638-5700	638-5775	4-12	Raymon Puente
Wood Charter S at San Marcos	120 Bert Brown St	San Marcos, TX	78666-5803	210-638-5300	638-5375	3-12	Wade Cherry
Yes Prep S - Brays Oaks	9000 W Bellfort St	Houston, TX	77031-2410	713-967-8400	778-0917	6-12	Chris Claflin
Yes Prep S - East End	8329 Lawndale St	Houston, TX	77012-3707	713-967-7800		6-12	Leah Peters
Yes Prep S - Fifth Ward	1305 Benson St	Houston, TX	77020-4044	713-924-0602	670-0032	6-12	Luz Navarro
Yes Prep S - Gulfton	6565 De Moss Dr	Houston, TX	77074-5099	713-967-9800	774-1808	6-12	Andrew Goldin
Yes Prep S - Northbrook	3030 Rosefield Dr	Houston, TX	77080-2610	713-251-4200		6-12	Cendie Stanford
Yes Prep S - North Central	13703 Aldine Westfield Rd	Houston, TX	77039-2001	281-227-2044	227-2090	6-12	Bryan Reed
Yes Prep S - North Forest	6602 Winfield Rd	Houston, TX	77050-4704	713-967-8600	636-7895	6-12	Eldridge Gilbert
Yes Prep S - Northside	5215 Jensen Dr	Houston, TX	77026-2514	713-924-0400		6-12	Carlos Anguiano
Yes Prep S - Southeast	353 Crenshaw Rd	Houston, TX	77034-1543	713-967-9400	910-2350	6-12	Philip Wright
Yes Prep S - Southwest	4411 Anderson Rd	Houston, TX	77053-2307	713-967-9200	413-0003	6-12	Eric Newcomer
Yes Prep S - West	10535 Harwin Dr	Houston, TX	77036-1505	713-967-8200	541-8518	6-12	Andrew Goldin
Young Learners Charter S	8432 Bissonnet St	Houston, TX	77074-3908	713-772-7100	772-7104	PK-PK	Kristina Troutman
Young Scholars Academy of Excellence	1809 Louisiana St	Houston, TX	77002-8013	713-654-1404	654-1401	PK-8	Anella Coleman
Young Womens Leadership Academy	2123 W Huisache Ave	San Antonio, TX	78201-4809	210-244-0300	732-7999	6-12	Delia McLerran
Young Women's Leadership Academy	1066 W Magnolia Ave	Fort Worth, TX	76104-4401	817-815-2400	815-2450	6-7	Mia Hall
Yzaguirre S for Success	2950 Broadway St	Houston, TX	77017-1706	713-640-3784	644-6232	6-8	Philip Cano
Yzaguirre S for Success	2950 Broadway St	Houston, TX	77017-1706	713-649-6201	641-1853	PK-12	Carlos Rodriguez
Yzaguirre S for Success	2255 N Coria St	Brownsville, TX	78520-8731	956-542-2404	542-2667	PK-5	Raul Yzaguirre
Zoe Learning Academy	515 W Center St	Duncanville, TX	75116-3211	972-296-3335		PK-6	
Zoe Learning Academy	6701 Cullen Blvd	Houston, TX	77021-5005	713-748-4228	748-7833	PK-6	Lonnie Reynolds

Utah

School	Address	City,State	Zip code	Telephone	Fax	Grade	Contact
Academy for Math Engineering & Science	5715 S 1300 E	Salt Lake City, UT	84121-1023	801-278-9460	277-3527	9-12	Brian McGill
Alianza Academy	420 E South Temple Ste 200	Salt Lake City, UT	84111-1330	801-953-1157	953-1196	K-8	Robert Ralphs
American Leadership Academy	898 W 1100 S	Spanish Fork, UT	84660-5654	801-794-2226	794-2246	K-12	Kenna Marrelli
American Prep Academy - Accelerated S	3636 W 3100 S	West Valley, UT	84120-2149	385-351-3090	351-3089	K-9	Cindy Barrs
American Preparatory Academy	12892 S Pony Express Rd	Draper, UT	84020-9273	801-553-8500	576-9300	K-9	Carolyn Sharette
American Preparatory Academy - W Valley	1255 W Crystal Ave	West Valley, UT	84119-2105	801-839-3613	839-3626	K-9	Debra Davies
Aristotle Academy	704 S 600 E	American Fork, UT	84003-2405	801-763-7286	756-7037	K-8	Mark Peterson
Bear River Charter S	75 S 400 W	Logan, UT	84321-4445	435-753-8811	755-7082	K-8	Anne Desjardins
Beehive Science & Tech Academy	830 E 9400 S	Sandy, UT	84094-3653	801-576-0070	618-4115	7-12	Hanifi Oguz
Bowen Laboratory ES	6700 Old Main Hl	Logan, UT	84322-6700	435-797-3085	797-3668	K-5	Dan Johnson
Canyon Rim Academy	3005 S 2900 E	Salt Lake City, UT	84109-2108	801-474-2066	474-2085	K-6	Merry Fusselman
Channing Hall Charter S	13515 S 150 E	Draper, UT	84020-8602	801-572-2709	571-8786	K-8	Heather Shepherd
City Academy	555 E 200 S	Salt Lake City, UT	84102-2007	801-596-8489	521-4181	8-12	Sonja Woodbury
DaVinci Academy of Science and the Arts	2033 Grant Ave	Ogden, UT	84401-0409	801-409-0700	866-1311	7-12	Jessie Kidd
Dual Immersion Academy	1155 S Glendale Dr	Salt Lake City, UT	84104-3317	801-972-1425	972-9482	PK-8	Michael Westover
Early Light Academy	11709 S Vadania Dr	South Jordan, UT	84095-5835	801-302-5988	727-0773	K-9	Wade Glathar
East Hollywood HS	2185 S 3600 W	West Valley, UT	84119-1121	801-886-8181	972-9585	9-12	Eric Lindsay
Edison Charter S - North	180 E 2600 N	North Logan, UT	84341-1551	435-787-2820	787-0299	K-8	Scott Jackson
Edison Charter S - South	1275 W 2350 S	Nibley, UT	84321-6181	435-752-0123	787-4350	K-8	Eldon Budge
Endeavor Hall Charter S	PO Box 70568	West Valley, UT	84170-0568	801-972-1153		K-6	Jennifer Perry
Entheos Academy	2606 S 7200 W	Magna, UT	84044-1426	801-250-5233	250-5240	K-9	Kevin Baron
Entheos Academy	4710 W 6200 S	Kearns, UT	84118-6702	801-417-5444	417-5448	K-9	Eric Robins
Esperanza ES	854 E Elm Ave	Salt Lake City, UT	84106-1808	801-305-1450		K-6	Barbara Lovejoy
Excelsior Academy	124 E Erda Way	Tooele, UT	84074-9735	435-882-3062	882-4997	K-9	Keri Stoddard
Fast Forward Charter S	875 W 1400 N	Logan, UT	84321-6804	435-713-4255	753-9615	9-12	Stephanie Sorenson
Freedom Academy	1190 W 900 N	Provo, UT	84604-3171	801-437-3100	437-3149	K-8	Lynne Herring
Gateway Preparatory Academy	201 E Thoroughbred Way	Enoch, UT	84721-7217	866-867-5558	867-5497	K-8	Rob Lee
Good Foundations Academy	5101 S 1050 W	Riverdale, UT	84405-3732	801-393-2950	393-2953	K-6	Peggy Downs
Guadalupe S	340 S Goshen St	Salt Lake City, UT	84104-1216	801-531-6100	531-6106	K-4	Vicki Mori
Hancock Charter S	125 N 100 E	Pleasant Grove, UT	84062-2355	801-796-5646	785-4934	K-8	Julie Adamic
Hawthorn Academy	9062 S 2200 W	West Jordan, UT	84088-5564	801-282-9066	727-0836	K-9	Dr. Debra Swenson
HighMark Charter S	2467 E South Weber Dr	South Weber, UT	84405-9621	801-476-4676	476-5803	K-9	Kent Fuller
Intech Collegiate HS	1787 Research Park Way	North Logan, UT	84341-5600	435-753-7377	753-3775	9-12	Jason Stanger
Itineris Early College HS	9301 S Wights Fort Rd	West Jordan, UT	84088-8850	801-256-5970	256-5992	11-12	Stephen Jolley
Lakeview Academy	527 W 400 N	Saratoga Spgs, UT	84045-3101	801-331-6788	331-6792	K-9	Rick Veasey
Leadership Learning Academy	100 W 2675 N	Layton, UT	84041-7460	801-593-9552		K-6	Heidi Bauerle
Legacy Preparatory Academy	1375 W Center St	North Salt Lake, UT	84054-2952	801-936-0555	936-1038	K-12	David Stohel
Lewis Academy	364 N State Road 198	Santaquin, UT	84655-5537	801-754-3376	754-3102	K-8	Vickie Peterson
Liberty Academy	1195 Elk Ridge Dr	Salem, UT	84653-5521	801-465-4434	465-7808	K-12	Rick Clark
Lincoln Academy	1582 W 3300 N	Pleasant Grove, UT	84062-9041	801-756-2039	785-2109	K-9	Jake Hunt
Maeser Prep Academy	320 W 600 S	Lindon, UT	84042-1756	801-235-9000	235-9010	7-12	Robyn Ellis
Maria Montessori Academy	2505 N 200 E	Ogden, UT	84414-2215	801-827-0150	827-0145	K-6	Nancy Lindeman
Merit College Prep Academy	1440 W Center St	Springville, UT	84663-3029	801-491-7600	491-7650	9-12	Todd Powell
Moab Charter S	358 E 300 S	Moab, UT	84532-2624	435-259-2277	259-6652	K-6	Joe Heywood
Monticello Academy	2782 S Corporate Park Dr	Salt Lake City, UT	84120-5549	801-417-8040	417-8041	K-9	Michael Westover
Mountain Heights Academy	9067 S 1300 W Ste 303	West Jordan, UT	84088-5582	801-721-6329	670-0032	7-12	DeLaina Tonks
Mountainville Academy	195 S Main St	Alpine, UT	84004-1630	801-756-9805	763-9823	K-8	Emma Bullock
Navigator Pointe Academy	6844 S Navigator Dr	West Jordan, UT	84084-4405	801-840-1210	840-1236	K-9	Judy Farris
North Davis Preparatory Academy	1765 W Hill Field Rd	Layton, UT	84041-7323	801-547-1809	547-1649	K-9	Deborah Gomberg
Northern Utah Acad for Math Engnrg & Sci	2750 University Park Blvd	Layton, UT	84041-9099	801-402-5920	402-5921	10-12	Alan Stokes
North Star Academy	2920 W 14010 S	Bluffdale, UT	84065-5331	801-302-9579	302-9578	K-9	Charne Adams
Odyssey Charter S	738 Quality Dr	American Fork, UT	84003-3309	801-492-8105	763-8743	K-8	Russell Schellhous
Ogden Preparatory Academy	170 15th St	Ogden, UT	84404-5661	801-334-4255	334-4259	K-4	Kathleen Thornburg
Ogden Preparatory Academy	2221 Grant Ave	Ogden, UT	84401-1405	801-627-2066	394-2267	5-6	Kathleen Thornburg
Ogden Preparatory Academy	215 E 22nd St	Ogden, UT	84401-2646	801-627-3066	395-2267	7-10	Kathleen Thornburg
Open Classroom	134 D St	Salt Lake City, UT	84103-2610	801-578-8144	578-8218	PK-8	Martin Yablonovsky
Oquirrh Mountain Charter S	1425 S Angel St	Kaysville, UT	84037-6838	801-593-8200	660-6996	K-9	Dr. Gregory Cox
Pacific Heritage Academy	1755 W 1100 N	Salt Lake City, UT	84116-4675	801-363-1892		K-8	Ofa Moea'i
Paradigm HS	11577 S 3600 W	South Jordan, UT	84095-8018	801-676-1018	676-1036	9-12	Scott Jones
Pinnacle Canyon Academy	210 N 600 E	Price, UT	84501-2613	435-613-8102	613-8105	K-12	Mark Stuckenschneider
Pioneer HS for the Performing Arts	4421 Thanksgiving Way	Lehi, UT	84043-2951	801-768-8787		9-12	Darren Hensley
Promontory S of Expeditionary Learning	1051 W 2700 S	Perry, UT	84302	435-919-1900	919-1902	K-9	Bryce Passey
Providence Hall	4795 W Mount Ogden Peak Dr	Herriman, UT	84096-3497	801-432-7866	446-3952	K-6	Erin Preston
Quail Run Primary S	588 W 3300 N	Pleasant Grove, UT	84062-9136	801-785-9300	785-8997	K-8	Mike Moffett
Quest Academy	4862 W 4000 S	West Haven, UT	84401-9633	801-731-9859	731-9860	K-8	Lani Rounds
Ranches Academy	7789 Tawny Owl Cir	Eagle Mountain, UT	84005-4308	801-789-4000	789-4001	K-6	Susie Scherer
Reagan Academy	1143 W Center St	Springville, UT	84663-3028	801-489-7828	491-2829	K-8	Brian Myrup
Renaissance Academy	3435 N 1120 E	Lehi, UT	84043-6538	801-768-4202	768-4295	K-9	Brenda Hedden
Rockwell Charter HS	3435 Stonebridge Ln	Eagle Mountain, UT	84005-5807	801-789-7625	789-7628	7-12	Darren Beck
Salt Lake Arts Academy	844 S 200 E	Salt Lake City, UT	84111-4203	801-531-1173	531-7726	5-8	Amy Wadsworth
Salt Lake Center for Science Education	1400 W Goodwin Ave	Salt Lake City, UT	84116-1629	801-578-8226	578-8677	6-12	Larry Madden
Salt Lake Charter S	4393 S Riverboat Rd	Taylorsville, UT	84123-2503			K-12	Angela Aiono
Salt Lake School for the Performing Arts	2291 S 2000 E	Salt Lake City, UT	84106-4138	801-466-6700	485-1707	9-12	Sheldon Worthington
Soldier Hollow S	2002 Olympic Dr	Midway, UT	84049-6216	435-654-1347	654-1349	K-8	Brendan McGinn
Spectrum Academy	665 Cutler Dr	North Salt Lake, UT	84054-2970	801-936-0318	936-0209	7-12	Jaime Christensen
Spectrum Academy	575 Cutler Dr	North Salt Lake, UT	84054-2953	801-936-0318	936-0568	K-6	Rebecca Peterson
Success Academy at Dixie	225 S 700 E	Saint George, UT	84770-3875	435-652-7830	656-4149	10-12	John Tripp
Success Academy at SUU	351 W University Blvd	Cedar City, UT	84720-2415	435-865-8790	865-8795	9-12	John Tripp
Summit Academy	1285 E 13200 S	Draper, UT	84020-9000	801-572-4166	572-4169	K-8	Steve Crandall
Summit Academy HS	14942 S 550 W	Bluffdale, UT	84065-5640	801-495-3272	495-3275	9-12	Steve Crandall
Syracuse Arts Academy	2893 W 1700 S	Syracuse, UT	84075-9838	801-779-2066	779-2087	K-9	Jan Whimpey
Timpanogos Academy	70 S 100 E	Lindon, UT	84042-2058	801-785-4979	785-9690	K-8	Errol Porter
Tuacahn HS for the Performing Arts	1100 Tuacahn	Ivins, UT	84738-4700	435-652-3201	652-3306	9-12	Bill Fowler
Uintah River HS	PO Box 235	Fort Duchesne, UT	84026-0235	435-725-4088	722-0811	9-12	Byron Richardson
Utah Connections Academy	596 W 750 S Ste 110	Woods Cross, UT	84010-7261	801-298-6660	298-6670	K-12	Linda Harless
Utah County Academy of Sciences	940 W 800 S	Orem, UT	84058-5915	801-863-2222	225-2214	10-12	Clark Baron
Utah International Charter S	350 E Baird Cir	Salt Lake City, UT	84115-4633	801-448-6414		7-10	Angela Rowland
Utah Virtual Academy	310 E 4500 S Ste 290	Murray, UT	84107-4251	801-262-4922	262-5086	K-12	Stacey Hutchings
Valley Academy	539 N 870 W	Hurricane, UT	84737-1646	435-635-0772		K-7	Ed Woodd
Venture Academy	495 N 1500 W	Ogden, UT	84404-4746	801-393-3900	393-2006	K-12	Dr. Mark Child
Vista Charter S	585 E Center St	Ivins, UT	84738-5114	435-673-4110	256-6433	K-8	Mike Webb
Voyage Academy	1891 N 1500 W	Clinton, UT	84015			K-6	Stacee Phillips
Walden S of Liberal Arts	4230 N University Ave	Provo, UT	84604-4928	801-374-1545	374-3397	K-12	Diana West
Wasatch Peak Academy	414 Cutler Dr	North Salt Lake, UT	84054-2951	801-936-3066	936-0887	K-6	Sandra Shepard
Washington Academy	2277 S 3000 E	Saint George, UT	84790-8510	435-673-2232	673-0142	K-8	Don Fawson

School	Address	City,State	Zip code	Telephone	Fax	Grade	Contact
Weber State University Charter Academy	1305 University Cir	Ogden, UT	84408-0001	801-626-6343		K-K	Dr. Jack Rasmussen
Webster Academy	205 E 400 S	Orem, UT	84058-6311	801-426-6624	426-6645	K-6	Rick Kempton
Weilenmann S of Discovery	4199 Kilby Rd	Park City, UT	84098-5466	435-575-5411	575-5412	K-8	Mary Kimball

Virginia

School	Address	City,State	Zip code	Telephone	Fax	Grade	Contact
Community Public Charter S	901 Rose Hill Dr	Charlottesville, VA	22903-5239	434-972-1607	984-4975	6-8	Ashby Kindler
Henry S of Science and Arts	611 W 31st St	Richmond, VA	23225-3518	804-888-7061		K-5	Pamela Boyd
Murray Charter HS	1200 Forest St	Charlottesville, VA	22903-5264	434-296-3090	979-6479	9-12	Ashby Kindler
York River Academy	11201 George Washington Mem	Yorktown, VA	23690	757-898-0516	890-1045	9-12	Walter Cross

Wisconsin

School	Address	City,State	Zip code	Telephone	Fax	Grade	Contact
Advanced Learning Academy of WI	100 W River Ave	Barron, WI	54812-1052	715-537-5612	637-5161	K-12	Craig Broeren
A L A S	1515 W Lapham Blvd	Milwaukee, WI	53204-3236	414-902-8460		9-12	Marisol Alvarado-Patten
A L B A	1712 S 32nd St	Milwaukee, WI	53215-2104	414-902-7525	902-7526	K-5	Brenda Martinez
Alliance Charter ES	215 E Forest Ave	Neenah, WI	54956-2765	920-751-6970	751-6861	K-5	Philip Johnson
Alliance HS	850 W Walnut St	Milwaukee, WI	53205-1717	414-227-5400	227-5415	7-12	Tina Owen
ALPS Charter S	108 W New York Ave	Oshkosh, WI	54901-3760	920-424-0349	424-7596	5-8	Sarah Poquette
Andrews Academy	26 Eclipse Ctr	Beloit, WI	53511-3550	608-361-3360	361-3350	6-12	Tina Goecks
Appleton Bilingual S	913 N Oneida St	Appleton, WI	54911-4910	920-832-6232	832-6355	K-2	Jennifer Dordel
Appleton Career Academy	5000 N Ballard Rd	Appleton, WI	54913-8942	920-832-4309	832-4301	9-12	Patrick Lee
Appleton Central HS	PO Box 2019	Appleton, WI	54912-2019	920-832-6136	993-7074	6-12	Katherine Peckham
Appleton eSchool	2121 E Emmers Dr	Appleton, WI	54915-3802	920-832-1744	832-4880	9-12	Matt Mineau
Appleton Public Montessori S	2725 E Forest St	Appleton, WI	54915-3332	920-832-6265	832-6199	1-6	Dom Ferrito
Audubon Technology & Communication Ctr	3300 S 39th St	Milwaukee, WI	53215-4019	414-902-7800	902-7815	6-8	Jesse Mazur
Audubon Technology & Communication HS	3300 S 39th St	Milwaukee, WI	53215-4099	414-902-7800		9-12	Jesse Mazur
Badger Rock MS	501 E Badger Rd	Madison, WI	53713-2120	608-663-1633		6-8	Timothy Bubon
Barron Area Montessori S	808 E Woodland Ave	Barron, WI	54812-1759	715-537-5621	637-9353	PK-4	Nancy Weise
Birchwood Blue Hills Charter HS	201 E Birch Ave	Birchwood, WI	54817-8800	715-354-9809	354-3469	7-12	Jeffrey Stanley
Birchwood Discovery Center	201 E Birch Ave	Birchwood, WI	54817-8800	715-354-9809	354-3469	K-6	Jeffrey Stanley
Black River Area Green S	333 S 7th St	Blk River Fls, WI	54615-1678	715-284-4324	284-4081	11-12	Thomas Chambers
Bridges Virtual S	1201 N Sales St	Merrill, WI	54452-3171	866-537-2743		K-12	John Hagemeister
Brompton S	7951 36th Ave	Kenosha, WI	53142-2119	262-359-2191	359-2194	K-5	Suzanne Loewen
Bruce - Guadalupe Community S	1028 S 9th St	Milwaukee, WI	53204-1335	414-643-6441	649-9022	K-8	Pascual Rodriguez
Business & Economics Acad of Milwaukee	3620 N 18th St	Milwaukee, WI	53206-2362	414-615-3915	988-6704	PK-8	Alisha Birtha
Capitol West Academy	3939 N 88th St	Milwaukee, WI	53222-2748	414-465-1302	465-1319	PK-8	Donna Niccolai-Weber
C.A.R.E. Charter S	2000 Polk St	Stevens Point, WI	54481-5876	715-345-5260	345-5696	7-9	Connie Negaard
Carmen HS of Science & Tech - Northwest	5496 N 72nd St	Milwaukee, WI	53218-2820			6-12	Dr. Patricia Hoben
Carmen HS of Science and Tech - South	1712 S 32nd St	Milwaukee, WI	53215-2104	414-384-4444	384-4455	9-12	Dr. Patricia Hoben
Catalyst Charter S	PO Box 991	Ripon, WI	54971-0991	920-748-4638	748-4653	6-8	Thomas Hoh
CAVE	PO Box 378	Cameron, WI	54822-0378	715-458-4560	458-4236	K-12	Tamara Sharp
Central Cities Health Institute	1801 16th St S	Wisc Rapids, WI	54494-5413	715-424-6750	422-6097	11-12	Ronald Rasmussen
Central City Cyberschool	4301 N 44th St	Milwaukee, WI	53216-1473	414-444-2330	444-2435	K-8	Christine Faltz
Central HS	621 S Water St	Sheboygan, WI	53081-4431	920-459-3540		9-12	Jacob Konrath
CEO Leadership Academy	3222 W Brown St	Milwaukee, WI	53208-1950	414-873-4014	873-4344	9-12	Rashida Evans
Chippewa Valley Montessori Charter S	400 Cameron St	Eau Claire, WI	54703-5101	715-852-6950	852-6995	PK-5	Todd Johnson
Clark Street Community S	2429 Clark St	Middleton, WI	53562-2619	608-829-9640		9-12	Jill Gurtner
Classical Charter S	3310 N Durkee St	Appleton, WI	54911-1215	920-832-4968	997-1390	K-8	Nancy Fischer
Community HS	6700 N 80th St	Milwaukee, WI	53223-5506	414-256-8200	256-8215	9-12	Roxane Mayeur
Connects Learning Center	6201 S Barland Ave	Cudahy, WI	53110-2951	414-766-5090	766-5095	9-12	Stacey Adamczyk
CORE4	5000 S 116th St	Greenfield, WI	53228-3128	414-525-8414	525-8401	PK-PK	Lori Komas
CORE Charter S	1662 E Kennedy Ave	Kimberly, WI	54136-2362	920-687-3024	687-3029	9-12	Tim Fosshage
Coulee Montessori Charter S	1307 Hayes St	La Crosse, WI	54603-1949	608-789-7760	789-7080	PK-8	Laura Huber
Crandon Alternative Resource S	9750 US Highway 8 W	Crandon, WI	54520-8499	715-478-6125	478-5570	9-12	Andy Space
CRE8 Charter S	PO Box 227	Gillett, WI	54124-0227	920-855-2137	855-6600	K-5	Sarah VandeCorput
Creative Minds Charter S	7450 Titus Dr	Minocqua, WI	54548-9139	715-356-5206	356-1626	3-5	Rob Way
Crossroads Charter S	PO Box 991	Ripon, WI	54971-0991	920-748-4805	748-4805	6-12	Dan Tjernagel
Daniels University Preparatory Academy	4834 N Mother Daniels Way	Milwaukee, WI	53209-5981	414-466-1650		K-9	Karen Huff
Denmark Community Charter S	450 N Wall St	Denmark, WI	54208-8000	920-863-4153	863-4036	7-12	Mark Meisner
Dewey Academy of Learning	1420 Harvey St	Green Bay, WI	54302-1918	920-272-7074	492-5565	9-12	Matt Draheim
Dimensions of Learning Academy	6218 25th Ave	Kenosha, WI	53143-4370	262-359-6849	359-3134	K-8	Diana Pearson
Discovery Charter S	200 Fuller St	Columbus, WI	53925-1647	920-623-5952	623-6026	K-3	Sue Sewell
Downtown Montessori Academy	2507 S Graham St	Milwaukee, WI	53207-1609	414-744-6005	744-6007	K-8	Virginia Flynn
eAchieve Academy of Wisconsin	222 Maple Ave	Waukesha, WI	53186-4725	262-970-1074	970-1148	6-12	Rick Nettesheim
Eagleville Charter S	S101W34511 County Road LO	Eagle, WI	53119-1860	262-363-6258	594-5495	1-6	John Steib
Early Learning Academy	3871 E Bluestem Dr	Oak Creek, WI	53154-6640	414-768-6220		PK-PK	Christopher Gabrhel
ES for the Arts and Academics	1528 N 5th St	Sheboygan, WI	53081-2834	920-459-3626	459-3719	K-5	Ted Hamm
Enrich Excel Achieve Learning Academy	2607 N 18th St	Wausau, WI	54403-3176	715-261-0636	845-2913	6-12	Joy Trollop
Escuela Verde	126 E Mineral St	Milwaukee, WI	53204-1840	414-988-7960		7-12	Bobbi Aguero
Fairview S	6500 W Kinnickinnic River	Milwaukee, WI	53219	414-546-7700	546-7715	PK-8	Joseph Hartlaub
Flambeau Charter S	PO Box 86	Tony, WI	54563-0086	715-532-5559	532-9040	7-12	Connie Gasior
Fond du Lac STEM Academy	401 S Military Rd	Fond du Lac, WI	54935-4822	920-906-6700		3-5	Donald Smith
Fond du Lac STEM Institute	401 S Military Rd	Fond du Lac, WI	54935	920-906-6700		6-8	Donald Smith
Forest Lane Community S	222 Forest Ln	Montello, WI	53949-9390	608-297-2128	297-8075	PK-6	Jeff Fimreite
Foster ES	305 W Foster St	Appleton, WI	54915-1515	920-832-6288	832-4831	PK-6	Matt Zimmerman
Fox River Academy	1000 S Mason St	Appleton, WI	54914-5457	920-832-6260	993-1390	3-8	Lori Leschisin
Fox West Academy	220 Warner St	Hortonville, WI	54944-8559	920-779-7929	779-7923	6-8	Steven Gromala
Gibraltar Charter S	1100 Sauk St	Lodi, WI	53555-1446	608-592-3853	592-1045	9-12	Paula Tonn
Glidden Class ACT Charter S	400 9th St N	Park Falls, WI	54552-1384	715-762-2474	762-5674	9-12	Timothy Kief
GOAL Academy	PO Box 227	Gillett, WI	54124-0227	920-855-2137	855-6600	6-12	Gary Kohl
Green Lake Global & Environmental Acad	PO Box 369	Green Lake, WI	54941-0369	920-294-6411	294-6589	7-8	Ken Bates
HACIL	15930 W 5th St	Hayward, WI	54843-7181	715-934-2112	934-8080	K-12	Crystal Hexum
Harborside Academy	714 49th St	Kenosha, WI	53140-3353	262-359-8400	359-8450	9-12	William Haithcock
Hartland S of Community Learning	651 E Imperial Dr	Hartland, WI	53029-2615	262-369-6720	369-6722	3-5	David Risch
Hawley Environmental S	5610 W Wisconsin Ave	Milwaukee, WI	53213-4200	414-256-8500	256-8515	PK-5	Cynthia Dismuke
Health Care Academy	115 E 6th St S	Ladysmith, WI	54848-1910	715-532-5531	532-7899	7-12	Robert King
Highland Community MS	1030 Cardinal Dr	Highland, WI	53543-9791	608-929-4525	929-4527	6-8	Josh Tarrell
Highland Community S	1706 W Highland Ave	Milwaukee, WI	53233-1132	414-342-1412	342-1408	PK-3	Kathy Ronco
Highland ES	1030 Cardinal Dr	Highland, WI	53543-9791	608-929-4525	929-4527	PK-5	Josh Tarrell
Highland HS	1030 Cardinal Dr	Highland, WI	53543-9791	608-929-4525	929-4527	9-12	Josh Tarrell
High Marq Environmental Charter S	383 E Montello St	Montello, WI	53949-9603	608-297-2499	297-7726	7-12	Chuck Harsh
Hines Academy	7151 N 86th St	Milwaukee, WI	53224-4861	414-358-3542	760-4364	PK-8	Barbara Horton
Hmong American Peace Academy	4601 N 84th St	Milwaukee, WI	53225-4958	414-383-4944	383-4950	PK-8	Chris Her-Xiong
Honey Creek Continuous Progess ES	6701 W Eden Pl	Milwaukee, WI	53220-1335	414-604-7900	604-7915	PK-5	Gitanjali Chawla
Humboldt Park ES	3230 S Adams Ave	Milwaukee, WI	53207-2700	414-294-1700	294-1715	PK-8	Georgia Becker
IDEA Charter S	4704 Camp Phillips Rd	Weston, WI	54476-1573	715-359-6561		6-11	Steven Pophal
IDEAL Charter S	4965 S 20th St	Milwaukee, WI	53221-2860	414-304-6200	304-6215	K-8	Jennifer Carter
IDEAS Academy	830 Virginia Ave	Sheboygan, WI	53081-4427	920-459-0950		9-12	Ted Hamm
IForward: Wisconsin's Online Charter S	480 E James Ave	Grantsburg, WI	54840-7959	855-447-4723	463-2534	6-12	Billy Beesley
iLEAD Charter S	510 Grayside Ave	Mauston, WI	53948-1921	608-847-5451	847-4635	7-12	Gil Saylor
International Peace Academy	4601 N 84th St	Milwaukee, WI	53225-4958	414-383-4031		9-12	Chris Her-Xiong
Island City Academy	980 8th Ave	Cumberland, WI	54829-9188	715-822-5122	822-5132	7-12	Colin Green
Island City Virtual Academy	1010 8th Ave	Cumberland, WI	54829-9174	715-822-5124	822-5136	K-12	Barry Rose
Janesville Academy for Intl Studies	2909 Kellogg Ave	Janesville, WI	53546-5606	608-758-6512	314-1172	9-12	Karen Schulte
Janesville Virtual Academy	1831 Mount Zion Ave	Janesville, WI	53545-1236	608-743-5146	743-5130	9-12	Mary Ann Kahl
JEDI Virtual HS	1221 Innovation Dr	Whitewater, WI	53190-1482	262-473-1469	472-2269	9-12	Leslie Steinhaus
Jefferson S for the Arts	1800 East Ave	Stevens Point, WI	54481-3799	715-345-5418	345-7352	K-6	Dave Lockett
Juneau County Charter S	N11003 17th Ave	Necedah, WI	54646-7618	608-565-7494	565-7559	7-12	Michele Yates-Wickus
Kaleidoscope Academy	318 E Brewster St	Appleton, WI	54911-3702	920-832-6294	832-4605	6-8	Al Brant
Kenosha e-School	6121 Green Bay Rd Ste 100	Kenosha, WI	53142-2931	262-359-7715	359-5933	9-12	Andrew Lattimore
Kenosha Schl of Enhanced Tech/Curriculum	6811 18th Ave	Kenosha, WI	53143-4932	262-359-3800	359-3850	K-8	Angela Andersson
Kiel eSchool	PO Box 201	Kiel, WI	53042-0201	920-894-2266	894-5100	7-12	Heidi Dorner
Kings Academy	7798 N 60th St	Milwaukee, WI	53223-4153	414-371-9100	371-9200	PK-8	Mondell Mayfield
KM Global S	349 N Oak Crest Dr	Wales, WI	53183-9711	262-968-6273	968-6390	9-12	Valerie Schmitz
Kornerstone S	217 E Kimberly Ave	Kimberly, WI	54136-1404	920-423-4128	788-7919	9-12	Josh Zimmers
Kosciuszko Montessori S	971 W Windlake Ave	Milwaukee, WI	53204-3822	414-902-7200	902-7215	PK-3	Yolanda Hernandez-Garcia
La Causa S	PO Box 4188	Milwaukee, WI	53204-0188	414-902-1660	902-1676	K-8	Maria Ayala-Smith
La Crosse Design Institute	1900 Denton St	La Crosse, WI	54601-5816	608-789-7670	789-7975	6-8	Penny Reedy
LaCrossroads Charter HS	1801 Losey Blvd S	La Crosse, WI	54601-6866	608-789-7700	789-7711	9-12	Debra Markos
Lake Country Academy	4101 Technology Pkwy	Sheboygan, WI	53083-6049	920-208-3020	208-3022	PK-8	Carla Koepp
Lakeview Montessori S	711 Pine St	Sparta, WI	54656-1947	608-366-3468	366-3473	PK-6	Patrick Olbert
Laurel HS	100 Blackhawk Dr	Viroqua, WI	54665-1399	608-637-3191	637-8034	9-12	Katherine Klos
LEADS Primary Charter S	1410 Waukechon Rd	Shawano, WI	54166-3168	715-524-2134	526-4372	PK-2	Troy Edwards
LEAN Alternative Charter S	304 E Main St	Lena, WI	54139-9488	920-829-5703	829-5122	9-12	David Honish
LIFE Charter S	800 N Shore Dr	Hartland, WI	53029-2713	262-369-6767	369-3766	6-8	Michele Schmidt
Lincoln Inquiry Charter S	242 S Prince St	Whitewater, WI	53190-1777	262-472-8500	472-8510	K-5	Dr. Mary Jo Bernhardt

School	Address	City,State	Zip code	Telephone	Fax	Grade	Contact
Link2Learn Virtual Charter S	PO Box 6	Chetek, WI	54728-0006	715-924-2226	924-2376	PK-12	Cali Kohlmeyer
Little Chute Career Pathways	325 Meulemans St Ste A	Little Chute, WI	54140-3300	920-788-7600	788-7841	9-12	Dan Valentyn
Lumen Charter HS	PO Box 991	Ripon, WI	54971-0991	920-748-4616	748-4622	9-12	Dan Tjernagel
Madison Academic Campus	8135 W Florist Ave	Milwaukee, WI	53218-1745	414-393-6100	393-6222	9-12	Lonnie Anderson
Magellan Charter MS	225 N Badger Ave	Appleton, WI	54914-3832	920-832-6226	832-4857	7-8	Debra Moreland
Manitowoc County Comprehensive Charter S	1010 Huron St	Manitowoc, WI	54220-3314	920-683-4780	683-4782	1-8	Kristen Lee
Maple Grove Charter S	290 County Road F	Hamburg, WI	54411-9141	715-536-7684	536-4221	K-5	Russ Noland
Marathon Venture Academy	100 Spring Valley Dr	Marathon, WI	54448	715-443-2538		6-8	Jeffrey Reiche
Marshall Charter S	PO Box 76	Marshall, WI	53559-0076	608-655-1310	655-3046	11-12	Brian Sniff
McDill Academies	2516 School St	Stevens Point, WI	54481-6100	715-345-5420	345-7345	K-6	Jeanne Koepke
McKinley Academy	1010 Huron St	Manitowoc, WI	54220-3314	920-683-4780	683-4782	9-12	Kristin Lee
McKinley Center	2926 Blaine St	Stevens Point, WI	54481-4799	715-345-5421	345-7350	PK-6	John Blader
McKinley Charter S	1266 McKinley Rd	Eau Claire, WI	54703-2220	715-852-6900	852-6904	6-12	Peter Riley
Mead Charter S	241 17th Ave S	Wisc Rapids, WI	54495-2401	715-424-6777	422-6333	PK-6	Margie Dorshorst
Meeme LEADS Charter S	12121 County Road XX	Newton, WI	53063-9732	920-693-8255	693-8730	PK-4	Chad Ramminger
Mellen Technology Charter S	PO Box 500	Mellen, WI	54546-0500	715-274-3601	274-3715	9-12	Melissa Nigh
Mercer Environmental Tourism S	2690 W Margaret St	Mercer, WI	54547-9181	715-476-2154	476-2587	9-12	Erik Torkelson
Merrill Adult Diploma Academy	1101A N Mill St	Merrill, WI	54452-1179	715-536-1431	539-2769	9-12	Shannon Murray
Merrimac Community Charter S	360 School St	Merrimac, WI	53561-9584	608-493-2217	493-2895	PK-5	Sid Malek
Milwaukee Academy of Chinese Language	2430 W Wisconsin Ave	Milwaukee, WI	53233-1828	414-934-4340	934-4345	PK-8	James Sayavong
Milwaukee Academy of Science	2000 W Kilbourn Ave	Milwaukee, WI	53233-1625	414-933-0302	933-1426	PK-12	Judy Merryfield
Milwaukee College Prep - 38th St	2623 N 38th St	Milwaukee, WI	53210-2502	414-445-1000	445-1005	K-5	Maggy Olson
Milwaukee College Prep - Lloyd St	1248 W Lloyd St	Milwaukee, WI	53205	414-264-6000	264-2004	K-8	Andy Vitrano
Milwaukee College Prep S - 36th St	2449 N 36th St	Milwaukee, WI	53210-3040	414-445-8020	445-8167	K-8	Kristen Foster
Milwaukee Community Cyber HS	131 S 1st St	Milwaukee, WI	53204-1404	414-308-1230	308-1231	9-12	Jan Dahlman
Milwaukee Excel HS	1236 S Layton Blvd	Milwaukee, WI	53215-1653	414-847-0632		9-12	Nicole Johnson
Milwaukee Math & Science Academy	110 W Burleigh St	Milwaukee, WI	53212-2046	414-263-6400	263-6403	K-6	Ergun Sevilmis
Milwaukee Scholars Charter S	7000 W Florist Ave	Milwaukee, WI	53218-1855	414-393-0197		K-8	Tamika Draper
Monona Grove Liberal Arts Charter S	5301 Monona Dr	Monona, WI	53716-3126	608-221-7660	221-7688	10-12	Rebecca Fox-Blair
Monroe Alternative Charter S	1600 26th St	Monroe, WI	53566-3692	608-328-7122	328-7230	9-12	Chris Medenwaldt
Monroe Independent Virtual Charter S	1600 26th St	Monroe, WI	53566-3692	608-328-7122	328-7230	9-12	Chris Medenwaldt
Montessori ES	211 N Fremont St	River Falls, WI	54022	715-425-7645	425-5380	PK-6	Nate Schurman
Mosaic S	830 Virginia Ave	Sheboygan, WI	53081-4427	920-459-0946		6-8	Ted Hamm
New Century Charter S	420 Church Ave	Verona, WI	53593-1803	608-845-4900	845-4920	K-5	Lynn Berge
New Directions Learning Community	2601 Sullivan Ave	Kaukauna, WI	54130-3564	920-766-6116	766-6122	K-5	Sharon Rath
New Horizons for Learning	1701 E Capitol Dr	Shorewood, WI	53211-1911	414-963-6921	961-2819	9-12	Matthew Joynt
New Path Charter S	512 Caldwell Ave	Oconto Falls, WI	54154-1138	920-848-4455	848-3899	7-12	Michelle Desterheft
Next Door Charter S	2545 N 29th St	Milwaukee, WI	53210-3155	414-562-2929	562-1979	PK-K	Kate Linscott
Next Generation Academy	1700 Klatt Rd	New London, WI	54961	920-982-8420	982-8440	6-12	Colleen Berry
Niikuusara Community S	540 Birch St	Nekoosa, WI	54457-1318	715-886-8040	886-8097	5-7	Jon Sprehn
North Division Charter HS	1011 W Center St	Milwaukee, WI	53206-3299	414-267-4900	267-5015	9-12	Stanley McWilliams
Northeast Wisconsin Montessori S	411 E Washington Ave	Cleveland, WI	53015-1517	920-693-8241	693-8357	1-6	Deb Streblow
Northern Lakes Regional Academy	33 Ann St	Rice Lake, WI	54868-2265	715-234-9007		9-12	Curt Pacholke
Northern Waters Environmental S	15930 W 5th St	Hayward, WI	54843-7181	715-634-2619	634-9953	6-8	Brittany Roberts
North Point Lighthouse Charter S	4200 W Douglas Ave	Milwaukee, WI	53209-3529	414-461-5339	461-5482	K-4	Jazmeka Crain
North Star Academy	207 N 1st St	Cameron, WI	54822-9703	715-537-5612	637-5161	9-12	Monti Hallberg
NorthStar Community Charter S	N14463 Highway 53	Minong, WI	54859-9483	715-466-2297	466-5149	4-8	Joshua Tomesh
Northwoods Community ES	9086 County K	Harshaw, WI	54529-9731	715-282-8200	282-8218	K-5	Kelli Jacobi
Northwoods Community Secondary S	665 Coolidge Ave	Rhinelander, WI	54501-2898	715-365-9660	365-9687	6-12	David Ditzler
NR4Kids Charter S	701 E 11th St	New Richmond, WI	54017-2399	715-243-7403	246-4278	PK-PK	Mike Ballard
Nuestro Mundo Community S	902 Nichols Rd	Monona, WI	53716-2565	608-663-1079	204-0364	K-5	Silvia Romero-Johnson
Oakwood Environmental Educ Charter S	1225 N Oakwood Rd	Oshkosh, WI	54904-8456	920-424-0315	424-7591	PK-5	Kirby Schultz
Oconto Falls Alternative Learning Site	320 E Central Ave	Oconto Falls, WI	54154-1456	920-848-4455	848-3899	10-12	Becky Spengler
Oconto Literacy Charter S	810 Scherer Ave	Oconto, WI	54153-1110	920-834-7808	834-9883	K-2	Chad Collier
Odyssey Charter S	2037 N Elinor St	Appleton, WI	54914-2255	920-832-6250	832-4389	3-6	Kristin Comerford
Osceola Charter Preschool	PO Box 128	Osceola, WI	54020-0128	715-294-3457	294-2428	PK-PK	Peggy Weber
Ouisconsing S of Collaboration	101 School St	Lodi, WI	53555-1046	608-592-3842	592-1025	3-5	Lyle Hendricson
Park Community Charter S	509 Lawe St	Kaukauna, WI	54130-2099	920-766-6129	766-6544	K-4	Kenneth Kortens
Phantom Knight S of Opportunity	400 Reid St Ste W	De Pere, WI	54115-2164	920-425-1915	429-1919	7-12	Dr. Jason Lau
Philip Alternative Charter S	621 W College Ave	Waukesha, WI	53186-4505	262-970-4355	970-4380	9-12	Sharon Thiede
Portage Academy of Achievement	117 W Franklin St	Portage, WI	53901-1755	608-742-8545	745-0887	9-12	Seth Meinel
Portage Virtual S	301 E Collins St	Portage, WI	53901-3424	608-742-8545	742-0617	6-12	Lindsey Heselbarth
Professional Learning Institute	2430 W Wisconsin Ave	Milwaukee, WI	53233-1828	414-934-4200	934-4215	9-12	Andrew Lazzari
Project Change Alt Recovery Charter Schl	222 Maple Ave	Waukesha, WI	53186-4725	262-524-8677	524-8653	9-12	Jennifer Wimmer
Promethean Charter S	312 W Wisconsin St	Butternut, WI	54514-9109	715-769-3434	769-3712	9-12	
Quest ES	PO Box 991	Ripon, WI	54971-0991	920-748-4695	748-4698	3-5	Randy Hatlen
REAL Charter S	5915 Erie St	Racine, WI	53402-1925	262-664-8100	664-8110	6-12	Robert Holzem
Red Cedar Environmental Institute	PO Box 6	Chetek, WI	54728-0006	715-924-2226	924-2376	6-8	Mike Steiner
Renaissance Charter Alternative Academy	211 N Fremont St	River Falls, WI	54022-2148	715-425-7687	425-7693	9-12	Linda Berg
Renaissance S for the Arts	610 N Badger Ave	Appleton, WI	54914-3405	920-832-5708	832-5798	9-12	Greg Hartjes
Rhinelander Environmental Steward Acad	511 S Pelham St	Rhinelander, WI	54501-3316	715-365-3660	365-9687	7-12	David Ditzler
River Valley Studio S	830 W Daley St	Spring Green, WI	53588-8813	608-588-2559	588-2550	K-5	Tom Wermuth
Rock River Charter S	31 W Milwaukee St	Janesville, WI	53548-2911	608-743-5070	752-8430	9-12	Dr. Lisa Peterson
Roosevelt IDEA	2200 Wisconsin Ave	Plover, WI	54467-2981	715-345-5425	345-7347	K-6	Rob Greenwood
Rural Virtual Academy	509 Clark St	Medford, WI	54451-1567	715-748-2400		PK-8	Charlie Heckel
S for Agricultural & Environmental Study	200 S Depot St	Fox Lake, WI	53933-9625			K-6	Lisa Grosz
School for Arts and Performance	349 N Oak Crest Dr	Wales, WI	53183-9711	262-968-6273	968-6217	9-12	Kevin Erickson
School for Early Developmnt & Achievmnt	2020 W Wells St	Milwaukee, WI	53233-2720	414-937-2024	937-2021	K-2	Tracey Sparrow
School of Career and Technical Education	5075 N Sherman Blvd	Milwaukee, WI	53209-5246	414-393-4900		9-12	
School of Enterprise Marketing	1700 Klatt Rd	New London, WI	54961-8603	920-982-8420	982-8440	10-12	Joseph Pomrening M.Ed.
School of Sci Engineering & Technology	PO Box 125	Blair, WI	54616-0125	608-989-9835	989-2451	K-6	Mike Thomley
School of Technology & Arts I	1111 7th St S	La Crosse, WI	54601-5474	608-789-7695	789-7030	K-5	Steve Michaels
School of Technology & Arts II	510 9th St S	La Crosse, WI	54601-4703	608-789-7780	789-7181	6-8	Larry Myhra
Shapiro ES	1050 W 18th Ave	Oshkosh, WI	54902-6688	920-424-0164	424-7594	PK-5	Lynn Brown
Shared Journeys Charter S	9004 W Lincoln Ave	West Allis, WI	53227-2452	414-604-3070		7-12	Lisa Colla
Sheboygan Leadership Academy	1305 Saint Clair Ave	Sheboygan, WI	53081-3233	920-208-5930		K-8	Peggy Henseler
Sparta Area Independent Learning S	201 E Franklin St	Sparta, WI	54656-1803	608-366-3430	366-3526	9-12	Dale Stafslien
Sparta Charter Preschool	201 E Franklin St	Sparta, WI	54656-1803	608-269-3151	366-3529	PK-PK	Diane Everson-Riley
Sparta High Point Charter S	201 E Franklin St	Sparta, WI	54656-1803	608-366-3151	366-3529	6-12	Peggy Jadack
Spooner Area Virtual Academy	801 County Highway A	Spooner, WI	54801-7429	715-635-2171	635-7174	K-12	Donald Haack
TAGOS Leadership Academy	1350 N Parker Dr	Janesville, WI	53545-0720	608-743-5071	743-5095	7-12	Dr. Kim Ehrhardt
Tenor High S	840 N Jackson St	Milwaukee, WI	53202-3807	414-431-4371	431-4376	9-12	Tyson Tlachac
Tesla Engineering Charter S	2121 E Emmers Dr	Appleton, WI	54915-3802	920-997-1399	832-4880	9-12	Paul Weisse
THINK Academy	6950 Knowledge Ave	Rudolph, WI	54475-9729	715-424-6784	435-2070	K-5	Tina Wallner
Time 4 Learning Charter S	5900 S 51st St	Greendale, WI	53129-2634	414-423-2750	423-0592	PK-PK	Leni Dietrich
Transformation Learning Community	2610 W North Ave	Milwaukee, WI	53205-1026	414-212-2671		11-12	Monique Hall
Transitional Skills Center	850 Maple St	Glenwood City, WI	54013-4346	715-265-4266	265-7129	10-12	Tim Johnson
21st Century eSchool	2429 Clark St	Middleton, WI	53562-2619	608-829-9027	831-5160	K-12	Jill Gurtner
21st Century Prep S	1220 Mound Ave	Racine, WI	53404-3350	262-598-0026	598-0031	PK-8	Arletta Tucker
United Public Montessori S	610 N Badger Ave	Appleton, WI	54914-3405	920-832-6219	832-4198	7-12	Todd Kadolph
Urban Day S	1441 N 24th St	Milwaukee, WI	53205-1899	414-937-8400	937-8406	PK-8	S. Hendricks-Williams.
Valley New S	10 E College Ave Ste 228	Appleton, WI	54911-5756	920-993-7037	832-1725	7-12	Judy Baseman
Veritas HS	3025 W Oklahoma Ave	Milwaukee, WI	53215-4347	414-389-5575	389-5576	9-12	Sherry Tolkan
Vernon County Area Better Futures HS	100 Blackhawk Dr	Viroqua, WI	54665-1399	608-637-3191	637-8034	10-12	Katherine Klos
Verona Area Core Knowledge Charter S	740 N Main St	Verona, WI	53593-1153	608-845-4130	845-4961	K-8	Brett Stousland
Verona Area International S	5830 Devoro Rd	Fitchburg, WI	53711-5015	608-845-4200	845-4220	K-1	Amanda Mayo
Vesper Community Academy	6443 Virginia St	Vesper, WI	54489-9460	715-424-6786	569-5300	PK-5	Tina Wallner
Waadookodaading Charter S	15930 W 5th St	Hayward, WI	54843-7181	715-634-8924	934-2246	PK-4	Brooke Ammann
Walworth County Education Alternative HS	400 County Road H	Elkhorn, WI	53121-2035	262-741-8138	741-8131	9-12	Kelly Demerath
Warriner MSHS for Personalized Learning	712 Riverfront Dr Ste 101	Sheboygan, WI	53081-4665	920-459-0950	459-0950	6-12	Jake Konrath
Washington S for Comprehensive Literacy	1238 Geele Ave	Sheboygan, WI	53083-4797	920-459-3661	459-3180	K-5	Karl Bekkum
Waukesha Academy of Health Professions	401 E Roberta Ave	Waukesha, WI	53186-6637	262-970-3710	970-3720	9-12	Richard Lehman
Waukesha Engineering Preparatory Academy	401 E Roberta Ave	Waukesha, WI	53186-6637	262-970-3880	970-3720	9-12	Timothy Joynt
Waukesha STEM Academy	114 S Charles St	Waukesha, WI	53186-6202	262-970-2300	970-2320	K-5	Chris Kluck
Waukesha STEM Academy	130 Walton Ave	Waukesha, WI	53186-5904	262-970-2500	970-2520	6-8	Michael Leach
Waupaca County Charter S	PO Box 457	Weyauwega, WI	54983-0457	920-867-4744		6-12	Michele Yates-Wickus
Wausau Area Montessori Charter S	3101 N 13th St	Wausau, WI	54403-2317	715-261-0795	261-2035	K-6	Michael Wridt
Wausau EGL Academy	2607 N 18th St	Wausau, WI	54403-3176	715-261-0625	845-5341	9-12	
Wauwatosa STEM	1060 Glenview Ave	Wauwatosa, WI	53213-3034	414-773-1900	773-1920	K-5	Mike Heun
Westside Academy	1940 N 36th St	Milwaukee, WI	53208-1927	414-934-4400	934-4415	K-8	Zannetta Walker
Whitetail Academy Charter S	PO Box 86	Tony, WI	54563-0086	715-532-5559	532-9040	9-12	Connie Gasior
Whittier ES	4382 S 3rd St	Milwaukee, WI	53207-4999	414-294-1400	294-1415	PK-5	Peggy Mystrow
Wildlands Research Charter S	E19320 Bartig Rd	Augusta, WI	54722-7501	715-877-2292	877-2234	7-12	Paul Tweed
Windlake ES-Seeds of Health	2433 S 15th St	Milwaukee, WI	53215-3132	414-643-9052	643-0162	K-8	Karen Rutt
Wisconsin College Prep Academy	4801 S 2nd St	Milwaukee, WI	53207-5919	414-483-2117	483-2152	6-12	Yasar Bora
Wisconsin Connections Academy	PO Box 2019	Appleton, WI	54912-2019	920-832-4800	832-6284	K-12	Michelle Mueller
Wisconsin River Academy	1201 Northpoint Dr	Stevens Point, WI	54481-1114	715-345-5400	345-5408	11-12	Mike Devine

School	Address	City,State	Zip code	Telephone	Fax	Grade	Contact
Wisconsin Virtual Learning	401 Highland Dr	Fredonia, WI	53021-9491	262-692-3988	692-3952	PK-12	Melissa Horn
WIVA	4709 Dale Curtin Dr	Mc Farland, WI	53558-8958	608-838-9482	838-9483	K-12	Dr. Leslye Moraski Erickson
Woodland Progressive Charter S	7450 Titus Dr	Minocqua, WI	54548-9139	715-356-5206	358-2649	6-8	Rob Way
Woodlands S	5510 W Blue Mound Rd	Milwaukee, WI	53208-3012	414-475-1600	475-9575	PK-8	Maureen Sullivan
Wright Charter MS	1717 Fish Hatchery Rd	Madison, WI	53713-1244	608-204-1340	204-0547	6-8	Angela Crawford
YMCA Young Leaders Academy	1350 W North Ave	Milwaukee, WI	53205-1264	414-374-9400	374-9459	K-8	Trina Gandy
Wyoming							
Arapaho Charter HS	189 Lefthand Ditch Rd	Riverton, WY	82501-9135	307-856-9333	857-4327	9-12	Mel Miller

BUREAU OF INDIAN AFFAIRS SCHOOLS

BUREAU OF INDIAN AFFAIRS
1849 C St NW, Washington, DC 20240-0001
Telephone 202-208-6123
Fax 208-3312
Website http://www.bie.edu/Schools/index.htm

BUREAU OF INDIAN AFFAIRS SCHOOLS

Agency/School	Address	City,State	Zip code	Telephone	Fax	Grade	Enr	Superintendent/Principal
Arizona Navajo Central Agency	**PO Box 6003**	**Chinle, AZ**	**86503-6003**	**928-674-5130**	**674-5134**	**K-12**	**50**	**Gloria Hale-Showalter**
Black Mesa Community S	PO Box 97	Pinon, AZ	86510-0097	928-674-3632	659-8187	K-8		Marie Rose
Cottonwood Day S	Navajo Route 4	Chinle, AZ	86503	928-725-3256	725-3243	K-8		Ronald Thompson
Jeehdeez'a ES	PO Box 1073	Pinon, AZ	86510-1073	928-725-3308	725-3306	K-5		
Lukachukai Community S	PO Box 230	Lukachukai, AZ	86507-0230	928-787-4418	787-4435	K-8		Stanley Kedelty
Many Farms Community S	PO Box 70	Many Farms, AZ	86538-3070	928-781-6221	781-6376	K-8		Dr. Elvia Largie
Many Farms HS	PO Box 307	Many Farms, AZ	86538-3307	928-781-6226	781-6355	9-12		Brian Dillon
Nazlini Community S	HC 58 Box 35	Ganado, AZ	86505-9704	928-755-6125	755-3729	K-6	50	Loren Joseph
Pinon Community S	PO Box 159	Pinon, AZ	86510-0159	928-725-3234	725-3232	K-12		Oscar Tso
Rock Point Community S	PO Box 560	Rock Point, AZ	86545-0560	928-659-4221	659-4235	K-12		Roger Benally
Rough Rock Community S	HC 61 Box 5050PTT	Chinle, AZ	86503	928-728-3550	728-3502	K-12		Dr. Marc Space
BIE-Arizona Navajo North Agency	**PO Box 746**	**Tuba City, AZ**	**86045-0746**	**928-283-2218**	**283-2286**	**K-12**	**100**	**John McIntosh**
Chilchinbeto Community S	PO Box 740	Kayenta, AZ	86033-0740	928-697-3800	697-3448	K-8		Eugene Charley
Dennehotso Boarding S	PO Box 2570	Dennehotso, AZ	86535-2570	928-658-3201	658-3221	K-8		James Brown
Greyhills Academy HS	PO Box 160	Tuba City, AZ	86045-0160	928-283-6271	283-6604	9-12		Marie Morales
Kaibeto Boarding S	PO Box 1420	Kaibeto, AZ	86053-1420	928-673-3480	673-3489	K-8		Phyllis N. Yazzie
Kayenta Community S	PO Box 188	Kayenta, AZ	86033-0188	928-697-3637	697-3490	K-8		Brian Dixon
Kinlani Bordertown Dormitory	901 N Kinlani Dr	Flagstaff, AZ	86001-1585	928-774-5270	556-9683	9-12		Lolita Paddock
Leupp S	Highway 99	Leupp, AZ	86035	928-686-6211	686-6216	K-12		Emma Yazzie
Little Singer Community S	PO Box AQ	Winslow, AZ	86047-1541	928-686-6108	686-6439	K-6		Etta Shirley
Naa Tsis 'Aan Community S	PO Box 10010	Tonalea, AZ	86044-5010	928-672-2335	672-2609	K-8		Lenora Shirley
Richfield Residential Hall	765 W 1st Ave	Richfield, UT	84701-2436	435-896-5101	896-6157	9-12		Cody Workman
Rocky Ridge Boarding S	PO Box 299	Kykotsmovi, AZ	86039-0299	928-725-3650	725-3655	K-8		Ernestine Singer
Shonto Preparatory S	PO Box 7900	Shonto, AZ	86054-7900	928-672-3528	672-3505	K-12	100	Lemual Adson
Tonalea Day S	PO Box 39	Tonalea, AZ	86044-0039	928-283-6325	283-5158	K-8		Dr. Deborah Holgate
Tuba City Boarding S	PO Box 187	Tuba City, AZ	86045-0187	928-283-2330	283-2362	K-8		Donald Coffland
Billings Area Office	**316 N 26th St Ste 3051**	**Billings, MT**	**59101-1373**	**406-247-7953**	**247-7965**	**K-12**	**100**	**Barbara Parisian**
Blackfeet Dormitory	PO Box 627	Browning, MT	59417-0627	406-338-7441	338-5725	1-12		Lyle MacDonald
Northern Cheyenne Tribal S of Busby	PO Box 150	Busby, MT	59016-0150	406-592-3646	592-3645	K-12		Dr. Elvira Bitsoi Largie
St. Stephens Indian S	PO Box 345	Saint Stephens, WY	82524-0345	307-856-4147	856-3742	K-12		Mike Hejtmanek
Shoshone Bannock S	PO Box 790	Pocatello, ID	83204-0790	208-238-4200	238-2628	7-12	100	Francine Hall
Two Eagle River S	PO Box 160	Pablo, MT	59855-0160	406-675-0292	675-0294	7-12		
Bureau of Indian Education Arizona South	**2901 N Central Ave Ste 970**	**Phoenix, AZ**	**85012-2729**	**602-265-1592**	**265-0293**	**K-12**	**300**	**Jim Hastings**
Blackwater Community S	3652 E Blackwater School Rd	Coolidge, AZ	85128-6609	520-215-5859	215-5862	K-2		Jacquelyn Power
Casa Blanca Community S	PO Box 10940	Bapchule, AZ	85121-0105	520-315-3489	315-3505	K-4		Eric James
Dishchii'bikoh Community S	PO Box 80068	Cibecue, AZ	85911-0068	928-332-2480	332-2341	K-12		Juan Aragon
Gila Crossing S	4665 W Pecos Rd	Laveen, AZ	85339-9009	520-550-4834	550-4252	K-8		Ryan LoMonaco
Kennedy S, John F.	PO Box 130	Whiteriver, AZ	85941-0130	928-338-4593	338-4592	K-8		Dr. Rea Goklish
Roosevelt S, Theodore	PO Box 567	Fort Apache, AZ	85926-0567	928-338-4464	338-1009	6-8		Michael Brock
Salt River ES	10005 E Osborn Rd	Scottsdale, AZ	85256-4019	480-362-2400	362-2401	K-6		Jacque Bradley
San Simon S	HC 1 Box 8292	Sells, AZ	85634-9711	520-362-2231	362-2405	K-8		Frank Rogers
Santa Rosa Day S	HC 1 Box 8400	Sells, AZ	85634-9713	520-361-2276	361-2511	K-8		Louis Barajas
Santa Rosa Ranch S	HC 2 Box 7570	Sells, AZ	85634-9741	520-383-2359	383-3960	K-8		Delbert Ortiz
Tohono O'Odham HS	HC 1 Box 8513	Sells, AZ	85634-9735	520-362-2400	362-2265	9-12		Michael Krug
Cheyenne River Agency	**PO Box 2020**	**Eagle Butte, SD**	**57625-2020**	**605-964-8723**	**964-1155**	**K-12**		**Jane Azure**
Cheyenne-Eagle Butte S	PO Box 672	Eagle Butte, SD	57625-0672	605-964-8777	964-8776	K-12		Dr. Nadine Eastman
Pierre Indian Learning Center	3001 E Sully Ave	Pierre, SD	57501-4403	605-224-8661	224-8465	1-8		Darrell Jeanotte
Takini S	HC 77 Box 537	Howes, SD	57748-9511	605-538-4399	538-4315	K-12		Ted Rowland
Tiospaye Topa S	PO Box 300	Ridgeview, SD	57652-0300	605-733-2290	733-2299	K-12		Don Farlee
Crow Creek/Lower Brule Educ Line Office	**PO Box 245**	**Lower Brule, SD**	**57548-0245**	**605-473-0216**	**473-0217**	**K-12**		
Crow Creek Sioux Tribal S	101 Crow Creek Loop	Stephan, SD	57346-6120	605-852-2455	852-2791	K-12		Silas Blaine
Enemy Swim S	13525 446th Ave	Waubay, SD	57273-5715	605-947-4605	947-4188	K-8		Virginia Donley
Lower Brule Day S	PO Box 245	Lower Brule, SD	57548-0245	605-473-0216	473-0217	PK-6		John Beheler
Lower Brule HS	PO Box 245	Lower Brule, SD	57548-0245	605-473-5510	473-5207	7-12		Tara Thomas
Tiospa Zina Tribal S	PO Box 719	Agency Village, SD	57262-0719	605-698-3953	698-7686	K-12		Ted Hamilton
Fort Defiance Agency	**PO Box 110**	**Fort Defiance, AZ**	**86504-0110**	**928-729-7255**	**729-7286**	**K-12**		**Jacqueline Wade**
Crystal Boarding S	Navajo Route 12	Navajo, NM	87328	505-777-2385	777-2648	K-6		Lorraine Dodge
Dilcon Community S	HC 63 Box G	Winslow, AZ	86047-9414	928-657-3485	657-3213	K-8		Dr. Tommy Lewis
Greasewood Springs Community S	HC 58 Box 60	Ganado, AZ	86505-9706	928-654-3383	654-3384	K-8		Johanson Phillips
Hunters Point Boarding S	PO Box 99	Saint Michaels, AZ	86511-0099	928-871-4439	871-4435	K-5		Theresa Kedelty
Kin Dah Lichi'i Olta	PO Box 800	Ganado, AZ	86505-0800	928-755-3439	755-3448	K-6		Ora James
Pine Springs Day S	PO Box 4198	Houck, AZ	86506-4198	928-871-4311	871-4341	K-4		Lou Ann Jones
Seba Dalkai Boarding S	HC 63 Box H	Winslow, AZ	86047-9415	928-657-3208	657-3224	K-8		Esther Frejo
Tiyaatin Residential Hall	1100 W Buffalo St	Holbrook, AZ	86025-2330	928-524-6222	524-2231	9-12		Maye Bigboy
Wide Ruins Community S	PO Box 309	Chambers, AZ	86502-0309	928-652-3251	652-3252	K-6		Teresa Lang-Tsinagine
Winslow Residential Hall	600 N Alfred Ave	Winslow, AZ	86047-3130	928-289-4483	289-2821	7-12		Holona Botone
Hopi Agency	**PO Box 568**	**Keams Canyon, AZ**	**86034-0519**	**928-738-2262**	**738-5139**	**K-12**	**500**	**John McIntosh**
First Mesa ES	PO Box 750	Polacca, AZ	86042-0750	928-737-2581	737-2323	K-6		Lorrie Harding
Havasupai S	PO Box 40	Supai, AZ	86435-0040	928-448-2901	448-2108	K-8		Gregory Mooring
Hopi Day S	PO Box 42	Kykotsmovi, AZ	86039-0042	928-734-2468	734-2470	K-6		Dr. John Thomas
Hopi JSHS	PO Box 337	Keams Canyon, AZ	86034-0356	928-738-5111	738-5333	7-12	500	Dr. Paul Reynolds
Hotevilla-Bacavi Community S	PO Box 48	Hotevilla, AZ	86030-0048	928-734-2462	734-2225	K-8		Margarito Uranga
Keams Canyon ES	PO Box 397	Keams Canyon, AZ	86034-0385	928-738-2385	738-5519	K-6		Rachel Maho
Moencopi Day S	PO Box 185	Tuba City, AZ	86045-0185	928-283-5361	283-4662	K-6		Donald Harvey
Second Mesa Day S	PO Box 98	Second Mesa, AZ	86043-0098	928-737-2571	737-2565	K-6		Alma Sinquah-Ashley
Minneapolis Agency	**5600 American Blvd W**	**Minneapolis, MN**	**55437-1274**	**612-725-4591**	**713-4438**	**K-12**	**600**	**Lynn Lafferty**
Bug-O-Nay-Ge-Shig S	15353 Silver Eagle Dr NW	Bena, MN	56626-1012	218-665-3000	665-3024	K-12		Jeff Lindstrom
Circle of Life S	PO Box 447	White Earth, MN	56591-0447	218-983-4180	983-3767	K-12		Mitch Vogt
Circle of Nations Indian Boarding S	832 8th St N	Wahpeton, ND	58075-3642	701-642-3796	642-1984	1-8		David Keehn
Fond du Lac Ojibwe S	105 University Rd	Cloquet, MN	55720-8520	218-878-7571	878-7573	K-12		Mike Rabideaux
Lac Courte Oreilles Ojibwa S	8875 N Round Lake School Rd	Hayward, WI	54843	715-634-8924	634-6058	K-12		Dennis White
Lumsden Bahweting Anishinabe S, J.K.	1301 Marquette Ave	Sault S Marie, MI	49783-9533	906-635-5055	635-3805	K-8	500	Susan Palmer
Menominee Tribal S	PO Box 39	Neopit, WI	54150-0039	715-756-2354	756-2364	K-8		Robert Tucker
Meskwaki Settlement S	1610 310th St	Tama, IA	52339	641-484-4990	484-3264	K-12		Jerry Stephens
Nah Tah Wahsh Public S Academy	N14911 Hannahville Road B 1	Wilson, MI	49896-9612	906-466-2952	466-2556	K-12	200	Tom Miller
Nay Ah Shing S	43651 Oodena Dr	Onamia, MN	56359-2320	320-532-4695	532-4675	K-12		
Oneida Nation ES	PO Box 365	Oneida, WI	54155-0365	920-869-1676	869-1684	K-12		Sharon Mousseau

Agency/School	Address	City,State	Zip code	Telephone	Fax	Grade	Enr	Superintendent/Principal
New Mexico Navajo Central Agency	**PO Box 328**	**Crownpoint, NM**	**87313-0328**	**505-786-6152**	**786-6112**	**K-12**	**4,500**	**Charlotte Garcia**
Dibe Yazhi Habitiin Olta S	PO Box 679	Crownpoint, NM	87313-0679	505-786-5237	786-7078	K-8		Dr. Glenn Whiteeagle
Dzilth-Na-O-Dith-Hle Comm. S	35 Road 7585 Ste 5003	Bloomfield, NM	87413-4936	505-632-1697	632-8563	K-12		Kathryn Coleman
Lake Valley Navajo S	PO Box 748	Crownpoint, NM	87313-0748	505-786-5392	786-5956	K-8		Geraldine Thomason
Mariano Lake Community S	PO Box 787	Crownpoint, NM	87313-0787	505-786-5265	786-5203	K-6		Delores Bitsilly
NaNeel Zhiin Ji'olta S	HC 79 Box 9	Cuba, NM	87013-9701	575-731-2272	731-2252	K-8		Kenneth Toledo
Ojo Encino S	HC 79 Box 7	Cuba, NM	87013-9701	505-731-2333	731-2361	K-8		Yolanda Denny
Pueblo Pintado Community S	HC 79 Box 80	Cuba, NM	87013-9600	575-655-3341	655-3342	K-8		Notah Benally
T'iists'oozi Bi'olta S	PO Box 178	Crownpoint, NM	87313-0178	505-786-6159	786-6163	K-8		Virginia Jumbo
Tse'ii'ahi' Community S	PO Box 828	Crownpoint, NM	87313-0828	505-786-5389	726-5635	K-4		Rebecca Vesely
New Mexico Navajo South Educ Line Office	**301 W Hill Ave Rm 118**	**Gallup, NM**	**87301-6310**	**505-863-8395**	**863-8363**	**K-12**		**John McIntosh**
Alamo S	PO Box 5907	Alamo, NM	87825-5907	575-854-2635	854-2545	K-12		Dr. Tamarah Pfeiffer
Baca Community S	PO Box 509	Prewitt, NM	87045-0509	505-972-2769	972-2310	K-6		Timothy Nelson
Bread Springs Day S	PO Box 1117	Gallup, NM	87305-1117	505-778-5665	778-5692	K-3		Carl Granfors
Chi-Chil Tah/Jones Ranch S	PO Box 278	Vanderwagen, NM	87326-0278	505-778-5574	778-5575	K-8		Marlene Tsosie
Ch'ooshgai Community S	PO Box 321	Tohatchi, NM	87325-0321	505-733-2707	733-2703	K-8		Lester Hudson
Tohaali' Community S	PO Box 9857	Newcomb, NM	87455-9857	505-789-3201	789-3202	K-8		Dr. Loretta Wheeler
To'Hajiilee'He S	PO Box 3438	Canoncito, NM	87026-3438	505-908-2174	908-2914	K-12		Jane Pitts
Wingate ES	PO Box 1	Fort Wingate, NM	87316-0001	505-488-6300	488-6312	K-8		Dr. Edie Morris
Wingate HS	PO Box 2	Fort Wingate, NM	87316-0002	505-488-6400	488-6444	9-12		Gloria Arviso
New Mexico North Agency	**661 Roadrunner Dr**	**San Juan Pueblo, NM**	**87566-3700**	**505-753-1465**	**753-1475**	**K-12**	**200**	**Dr. Benjamin Atencio**
Jicarilla Dormitory	PO Box 1009	Dulce, NM	87528-1009	575-759-3101	759-3338	1-12		David Montoya
Ohkay Owingeh Community S	PO Box 1077	San Juan Pueblo, NM	87566-1077	505-852-2154	852-4305	K-6		Patricia Archuleta
San Ildefonso Day S	36 Tunyo Po	Santa Fe, NM	87506-7258	505-455-2366	455-2155	K-6		Dolores Guzman
Santa Clara Day S	2 Kee Rd	Espanola, NM	87532-8920	505-753-4406	753-8866	K-6		David Nex
Santa Fe Indian S	PO Box 5340	Santa Fe, NM	87502-5340	505-989-6300	989-6317	7-12		Everette Chavez
Taos Day S	PO Box 1850	Taos, NM	87571-1850	575-758-3652	758-1566	K-8	200	Patricia Kessler
Te Tsu Geh Oweenge S	RR 42 Box 2	Santa Fe, NM	87506-8368	505-982-1516	982-2090	K-6		
New Mexico South Education Line Office	**1001 Indian School NW # 149**	**Albuquerque, NM**	**87104**	**505-563-3690**	**563-3078**	**K-12**	**2,800**	**Casey Sovo**
Isleta ES	1000 Moonlight Dr SW	Albuquerque, NM	87105-8124	505-869-2321	869-1625	K-6		Gweneth Toriveo
Jemez Day S	PO Box 139	Jemez Pueblo, NM	87024-0139	575-834-7304	834-7081	K-6		Freddie Cardenas
Laguna ES	PO Box 191	Laguna, NM	87026-0191	505-552-9200	552-7294	K-5		Yolanda Batrez
Laguna MS	PO Box 268	Laguna, NM	87026-0268	505-552-9091	552-6466	6-8		David Jiron
Mescalero Apache S	PO Box 230	Mescalero, NM	88340-0230	575-464-4431	464-4822	K-12		Maria Saenz
Pine Hill S	PO Box 220	Pinehill, NM	87357-0220	505-775-3242	775-3241	K-12		Sam Alonzo
San Felipe Pueblo S	PO Box 4343	San Felipe Pb, NM	87001-4343	505-867-3364	867-6253	K-7		Cynthia Luna
Sky City Community S	PO Box 349	Pueblo of Acoma, NM	87034-0349	505-552-6671	552-6672	K-8		Pauline Villegas
T'siya S, Zia	1000 Borrego Canyon Rd	Zia Pueblo, NM	87053-6104	505-867-3553	867-5079	K-8		Robin Rodar
Northern Navajo Agency	**PO Box 3239**	**Shiprock, NM**	**87420-3239**	**505-368-3400**	**368-3409**	**K-12**		**Dr. Joel Longie**
Aneth Community S	PO Box 600	Montezuma Creek, UT	84534-0600	435-651-3271	651-3272	K-6		Brenda Whitehorse
Atsa'biya'a'zh Community S	PO Box 1809	Shiprock, NM	87420-1809	505-368-2100	368-2076	K-6		
Beclabito Day S	PO Box 1200	Shiprock, NM	87420-1200	928-656-3555	656-3557	K-4		Tanya Amrine
Cove Day S	PO Box 2000	Red Valley, AZ	86544-2000	928-653-4457	653-4415	K-6		Perfilliea Charlie
Navajo Prep S	1220 W Apache St	Farmington, NM	87401-3886	505-326-6571	564-8099	9-12		John Tohtsoni
Nenahnezad Community S	PO Box 337	Fruitland, NM	87416-0337	505-598-6922	598-0970	K-6		Dean Cunningham
Red Rock Day S	PO Box 2007	Red Valley, AZ	86544-2007	928-653-4456	653-5711	K-8		Susanna Gaddy
Sanostee Day S	PO Box 159	Sanostee, NM	87461-0159	505-723-2476	723-2425	K-3		
Shiprock Alternative Dormitory Program	PO Box 1809	Shiprock, NM	87420-1809	505-368-2074	368-2076	9-12		Melissa Culler
T'iisNazbas Community S	PO Box 102	Teec Nos Pos, AZ	86514-0102	928-656-3252	656-3486	K-8		Delphina John
Oklahoma Education Office	**200 NW 4th St Ste 4049**	**Oklahoma City, OK**	**73102-3072**	**405-605-6051**	**605-6057**	**K-12**	**100**	**Joy Martin**
Chickasaw Children's Village	1185 Village Rd	Kingston, OK	73439-1017	580-564-3060	564-3605	1-12		Sallie Wallace
Eufaula Dormitory	716 Swadley Dr	Eufaula, OK	74432-2201	918-689-2522	689-2438	1-12		Greg Anderson
Jones Academy	909 Jones Academy Rd	Hartshorne, OK	74547-5119	918-297-2518	297-2364	1-12	100	Brad Spears
Kickapoo Nation S	PO Box 106	Powhattan, KS	66527-0106	785-474-3550	474-3530	K-12		Dr. Neil Trottier
Riverside Indian S	100 Riverside Dr	Anadarko, OK	73005-9772	405-247-6673	247-5529	4-12		Tony Dearman
Sequoyah HS	PO Box 948	Tahlequah, OK	74465-0948	918-453-5400	456-0634	9-12		Rita Bunch
Pacific Regional Office	**2800 Cottage Way Ste W2820**	**Sacramento, CA**	**95825-1886**	**916-978-6057**	**978-6056**	**K-12**	**1,100**	
Duckwater Shoshone S	PO Box 140068	Duckwater, NV	89314-0068	775-863-0180	863-0199	K-8		Stacey Norcutt
Noli S	PO Box 700	San Jacinto, CA	92581-0700	951-654-5596	654-7198	6-12		Donovan Post
Pyramid Lake HS	PO Box 256	Nixon, NV	89424-0256	775-574-1016	574-1037	7-12		Randy Melendez
Sherman Indian HS	9010 Magnolia Ave	Riverside, CA	92503-3972	951-276-6332	276-6336	9-12		Roland Doepner
Pine Ridge Agency	**PO Box 333**	**Pine Ridge, SD**	**57770-0333**	**605-867-1306**	**867-5610**	**K-12**		**Norma Tibbitts**
American Horse S	PO Box 660	Allen, SD	57714-0660	605-455-6750	455-2249	K-8		Gloria Kitsopoulas
Crazy Horse S	PO Box 260	Wanblee, SD	57577-0260	605-455-6800	462-6510	K-12		Dena Bogay
Little Wound S	PO Box 500	Kyle, SD	57752-0500	605-455-6175	455-2703	K-12		Linda Hunter
Loneman S	PO Box 50	Oglala, SD	57764-0050	605-455-6882	867-5109	K-8		Deborah Bordeaux
Pine Ridge S	PO Box 1202	Pine Ridge, SD	57770-1202	605-867-5198	867-5482	K-12		Victoria Sherman
Porcupine S	PO Box 180	Porcupine, SD	57772-0180	605-455-6450	867-5480	K-8		Jerry Lessert
Wounded Knee S	PO Box 350	Manderson, SD	57756-0350	605-455-6363	867-2051	K-8		Marnee White Wolf
Portland Area Office	**911 NE 11th Ave**	**Portland, OR**	**97232-4128**	**503-872-2743**	**231-6219**	**PK-12**	**200**	
Chemawa Indian S	3700 Chemawa Rd NE	Salem, OR	97305-1199	503-399-5721	399-5870	9-12		Donald Tomin
Chief Leschi S	5625 52nd St E	Puyallup, WA	98371-3610	253-445-6000	445-2350	K-12		Raymond Lorton
Couer D'Alene Tribal S	PO Box 338	Desmet, ID	83824-0338	208-686-5808	686-5080	K-8	100	Bob Sobotta
Lummi HS	2334 Lummi View Dr	Bellingham, WA	98226-9277	360-758-4330	758-3152	9-12		Heather Leighton
Lummi Tribal S	2334 Lummi View Dr	Bellingham, WA	98226-9277	360-758-4300	758-3160	K-8		Heather Leighton
Muckleshoot Tribal S	38811 172nd Ave SE	Auburn, WA	98092-9763	253-931-6709	939-5568	K-12		
Paschal Sherman Indian S	169 N End Omak Lake Rd	Omak, WA	98841-9477	509-422-7590	422-7538	K-9		Debbie Simpson
Quileute Tribal S	PO Box 39	La Push, WA	98350-0039	360-374-5648		K-12		Al Zantua
Wa He Lut Indian S	11110 Conine Ave SE	Olympia, WA	98513-9603	360-456-1311	456-1319	K-8		Harvey Whitford
Yakima Tribal S	601 Linden Ln	Toppenish, WA	98948	509-865-5121	865-6092	9-12	100	Shelley Sonnabend
Rosebud Agency	**PO Box 669**	**Mission, SD**	**57555-0669**	**605-856-4478**	**856-4487**	**K-12**		**Neva Sherwood**
Marty Indian S	PO Box 187	Marty, SD	57361-0187	605-384-2212	384-5933	K-12		Tony Garcia
St. Francis Indian S	PO Box 379	Saint Francis, SD	57572-0379	605-747-2299	747-2379	K-12		Gorgeous Paulhamus
Sicangu Owaye Oti	PO Box 669	Mission, SD	57555-0669	605-856-4486	856-4490	1-12		Nancy Hernandez
South & Eastern States Agency	**545 Marriott Dr Ste 720**	**Nashville, TN**	**37214-5081**	**615-564-6630**	**564-6631**	**PK-12**	**400**	
Ahafachkee S	HC 61 Box 40	Clewiston, FL	33440	863-983-6348	983-6535	K-12		Lucy Dafoe
Bogue Chitto S	13241 Highway 491 N	Philadelphia, MS	39350-5463	601-389-1000	389-1002	K-8		Linda Dick
Cherokee Central ES	1582 Ravensford Dr	Cherokee, NC	28719	828-554-5022	497-4351	K-5		Paula Coker
Cherokee Central HS	1582 Ravensford Dr	Cherokee, NC	28719	828-497-5511	497-4372	9-12		Jason Ormsby
Cherokee MS	1582 Ravensford Dr	Cherokee, NC	28719	828-554-5027		6-8		Mike Rogers
Chitimacha Day S	3613 Chitimacha Trl	Jeanerette, LA	70544-8317	337-923-9960	923-7346	K-8	100	Tanya Rosamond
Choctaw Central HS	150 Recreation Rd	Choctaw, MS	39350-7180	601-663-7777	656-7077	9-12		Greg Carlyle
Choctaw Central MS	150 Recreation Rd	Choctaw, MS	39350-7180	601-656-8938	656-1558	7-8		Rodney Tadlock
Conehatta S	851 Tushka Rd	Conehatta, MS	39057-2804	601-775-8254	775-9229	K-8		Sylvia Johnson
Indian Island S	10 Wabanaki Way	Indian Island, ME	04468-1259	207-827-4285	827-3599	PK-8	100	Linda McLeod
Indian Township S	13 School Dr	Princeton, ME	04668-5000	207-796-2362	796-2726	PK-8	100	Terry Lux
Miccosukee Indian S	PO Box 440021	Miami, FL	33144-0021	305-894-2364	894-2365	K-12		Manuel Varela
Pearl River ES	470 Industrial Rd	Choctaw, MS	39350-4256	601-656-9051	656-9054	K-6		Suzanne Hyatt
Rafferty S, Beatrice	22 Bayview Dr	Pleasant Point, ME	04667-4111	207-853-6085	853-2483	PK-8	100	Mike Chadwick
Red Water S	106 Braves Blvd	Carthage, MS	39051	601-267-8500	267-5193	K-8		Bobby Boone
Standing Pine ES	538 Highway 487 E	Carthage, MS	39051-6031	601-267-9225	267-9129	K-6		Jackie Harpole
Tucker S	126 E Tucker Cir	Philadelphia, MS	39350-8351	601-656-8775	656-9341	K-8		Brooke Sibley
Standing Rock Agency	**PO Box E**	**Fort Yates, ND**	**58538-0523**	**701-854-3497**	**854-7280**	**K-12**	**200**	**Emma Blue Earth**
Jamerson S, Theodore	3315 University Dr	Bismarck, ND	58504-7565	701-255-3285	530-0601	K-8		Francis Azure
Rock Creek Grant S	PO Box 127	Bullhead, SD	57621-0127	605-823-4971	823-4350	K-8		Linda Lawrence
Sitting Bull Day S	PO Box 26	Little Eagle, SD	57639-0026	605-823-4235	823-2292	K-8		Davie Archambault
Standing Rock Community S	PO Box 377	Fort Yates, ND	58538-0377	701-854-3461	854-2078	K-12	200	Robert Taken Alive
Tate Topa Tribal S	PO Box 199	Fort Totten, ND	58335-0199	701-766-1400	766-1457	K-8		Mark Mindt
Turtle Mountain Education Line Office	**PO Box 30**	**Belcourt, ND**	**58316-0030**	**701-477-3463**	**477-9364**	**PK-12**	**100**	**Rose-Marie Davis**
Dunseith Day S	PO Box 759	Dunseith, ND	58329-0759	701-263-4636	263-4200	K-8		Yvonne St. Claire
Mandaree S	PO Box 488	Mandaree, ND	58757-0488	701-759-3311	759-3112	K-12	50	Carolyn Bluestone
Ojibwa Indian S	PO Box 600	Belcourt, ND	58316-0600	701-477-3108	477-6039	K-8		Michael Blue
Turtle Mountain ES	PO Box 440	Belcourt, ND	58316-0440	701-477-6471	477-8835	K-5		Dave Gourneau
Turtle Mountain HS	PO Box 440	Belcourt, ND	58316-0440	701-477-6471	477-8821	9-12		Melvin Laducer
Turtle Mountain MS	PO Box 440	Belcourt, ND	58316-0440	701-477-6471	477-3973	6-8		Louis Dauphinais
Twin Buttes S	7997 7A St NW	Halliday, ND	58636-4004	701-938-4396	938-4398	K-8	50	Chad Dahlen
White Shield S	2 2nd Ave W	Roseglen, ND	58775-6009	701-743-4350	743-4501	K-12	100	Travis Frank

DEPARTMENT OF DEFENSE DEPENDENT SCHOOLS

DEPT. OF DEFENSE DEPENDENT SCHOOLS
4040 Fairfax Dr Fl 9, Arlington, VA 22203-1613
Telephone 703-588-3104
Website http://www.dodea.edu

DEPARTMENT OF DEFENSE DEPENDENT SCHOOLS

District/School	Address	City,State	Zip code	Telephone	Fax	Grade	Enr	Superintendent/Principal
Fort Campbell Dependent SD	**77 Texas Ave**	**Fort Campbell, KY**	**42223-5127**	**270-439-1927**	**439-6992**	**PK-12**	**4,900**	**Dr. Frank Calvano**
Barkley ES	4720 Polk Rd	Fort Campbell, KY	42223-1900	270-439-1951	439-1901	PK-5	600	Rhonda Pawlawski
Barsanti ES	7409 McAuliffe Loop	Fort Campbell, KY	42223-6025	270-640-1213	431-0519	PK-5	600	Jennifer Halley
Fort Campbell HS	1101 Bastogne Ave	Fort Campbell, KY	42223-5133	270-640-1219	431-9386	9-12	600	Mohan Vaswani
Jackson ES	675 Mississippi Ave	Fort Campbell, KY	42223-5353	931-431-6211	431-4453	PK-5	700	Linda Shelton
Lincoln ES	4718 Polk Rd	Fort Campbell, KY	42223-1400	270-640-1212	439-2335	PK-5	600	Dr. Renee Butler
Lucas ES, Andre	2115 Airborne St	Fort Campbell, KY	42223-5333	270-640-1208	431-5842	PK-5	500	Ted Turnipseed
Mahaffey MS	585 S Carolina Ave	Fort Campbell, KY	42223-5134	270-640-1215	439-3472	6-8	400	Hugh McKinnon
Marshall ES	75 Texas Ave	Fort Campbell, KY	42223-5135	270-640-1214	439-4382	PK-5	500	Dr. Suzanne Jones
Wassom MS	3066 Forest Rd	Fort Campbell, KY	42223-5272	270-640-1218	439-0249	6-8	300	Kimberly Butts
Fort Knox Community SD	**281 Fayette Ave**	**Fort Knox, KY**	**40121-6201**	**502-624-2345**	**624-3969**	**PK-12**	**2,300**	**Dr. Frank Calvano**
Fort Knox HS	266 Maine St	Fort Knox, KY	40121-6800	502-624-6647	624-6171	9-12	400	Dr. Gregg Mowen
Kingsolver ES	427 3rd Ave	Fort Knox, KY	40121-7023	502-624-8650	624-6977	PK-3	300	Laura Gibson
MacDonald IS	128 McCracken St	Fort Knox, KY	40121-2706	502-624-5650	624-2108	4-6	200	Dr. Youlanda Washington
Mudge ES	360 S Tulip St	Fort Knox, KY	40121-3126	502-624-8345	624-2439	PK-3	200	Talisha Thompson
Pierce ES	174 Maine St	Fort Knox, KY	40121-2290	502-624-7449	624-5274	PK-3	200	Dr. Wanda Bradley
Scott MS	266 Mississippi St	Fort Knox, KY	40121-6814	502-624-2236	624-5433	7-8	300	Linda Haberman
Van Voorhis ES	120 Folger St	Fort Knox, KY	40121-6086	502-624-5854	624-7267	PK-3	500	Andrea McClain
Walker IS	114 Conroy Ave	Fort Knox, KY	40121-2276	502-624-8348	624-6759	4-6	200	Dr. Todd Kreider
Georgia / Alabama Dependent SD	**7441 Custer Rd Bldg 2670**	**Fort Benning, GA**	**31905-9647**	**706-545-7276**	**545-8227**	**PK-8**	**2,600**	**Dr. Christy Cavezas**
Dexter ES, Herbert J.	99 Yeager Ave	Fort Benning, GA	31905-9699	706-545-3424	545-9106	PK-5		Dr. Ronald Knight
Faith MS, Don C.	1375 Ingersoll St	Fort Benning, GA	31905-7200	706-545-0310	545-7800	6-8		Jeff Herron
Fort Rucker ES	PO Box 620279	Fort Rucker, AL	36362-0279	334-255-1607	268-7482	2-6		Dr. Vicki Gilmer
Fort Rucker PS	PO Box 620279	Fort Rucker, AL	36362-0279	334-255-2822	268 7483	PK-1		Dr. Deborah Deas
Loyd ES, Frank R.	5701 Santa Fe Rd	Fort Benning, GA	31905-2724	706-544-8964	544-8972	PK-5		Julita Martinez
Maxwell AFB ES	800 Magnolia Blvd	Maxwell AFB, AL	36112-5922	334-953-7804	953-4339	PK-8		Robbie Swint
McBride ES, Morris R.	700 Custer Rd	Fort Benning, GA	31905-7402	706-544-9411	544-9299	PK-5		Phyllis Parker
Stowers ES, Freddie	7791 Stowers Dr	Fort Benning, GA	31905-3130	706-544-2312	544-2349	PK-5		Scott Sterry
White ES, Edward A.	300 1st Division Rd	Fort Benning, GA	31905-6627	706-545-4623	545-5469	PK-5		Glenn Hughes
Wilson ES, Richard G.	112 Lavoie Ave	Fort Benning, GA	31905-7523	706-545-5723	545-9505	PK-5		Dr. Renee Mallory
NY/VA Domestic Dependent School System	**3308 John Quick Rd Ste 201**	**Quantico, VA**	**22134-1752**	**703-784-3100**	**784-3100**	**PK-12**	**1,200**	**Michael Gould**
Ashurst ES	4320 Dulaney Rd	Quantico, VA	22134-2248	703-630-7040	784-2694	PK-3		Janice Weiss
Burrows ES, W.W.	3308 John Quick Rd	Quantico, VA	22134-1702	703-630-7050	784-1353	4-5		Randy Ekanger
Dahlgren S	6117 Sampson Rd Ste 206	Dahlgren, VA	22448-5121	540-653-8822	653-4591	PK-8		Alice Herring
Quantico MSHS	3307 Purvis Rd	Quantico, VA	22134-2198	703-630-7055	784-4851	6-12		Michael Hollier
Russell ES, John H.	3301 Purvis Rd	Quantico, VA	22134-2199	703-630-7065	784-4870	PK-3		Donna Kacmarski
West Point ES	705A Barry Rd	West Point, NY	10996-1196	845-938-2313	938-3352	PK-4		Nadine Sapiente
West Point MS	705 Barry Rd	West Point, NY	10996-1110	845-938-2923	938-2568	5-8		David Rudy
North Carolina Dependent SD	**PO Box 70089**	**Fort Bragg, NC**	**28307-0089**	**910-907-0220**	**907-1405**	**PK-9**	**4,600**	**Dr. Emily Marsh**
Albritton JHS	PO Box 70089	Fort Bragg, NC	28307-0089	910-907-0201	432-4072	6-8	600	Pat Schob
Bitz IS	2028 Bevin St	Camp Lejeune, NC	28547-1436	910-451-2575	451-1475	3-5		Michelle Allen
Bowley ES	PO Box 70089	Fort Bragg, NC	28307-0089	910-907-0202	907-3513	PK-5	300	Andrea Mial
Brewster MS	883 Stone St	Camp Lejeune, NC	28547-2501	910-451-2561	451-2600	6-8		Emilio Garza
Butner PS	PO Box 70089	Fort Bragg, NC	28307-0089	910-907-0203	432-8400	PK-2	500	Priscilla Joiner
Delalio ES	1500 Curtis Rd	Jacksonville, NC	28540-3406	910-449-0601	449-0677	PK-5		Wyonia Chevis
Devers ES	PO Box 70089	Fort Bragg, NC	28307-0089	910-907-0204	396-7374	PK-5	500	Miriam Breece
Gordon ES	4200 Percy Blvd	Cameron, NC	28326	910-907-1300	908-3504	PK-5	500	Joel Grim
Heroes ES	100 Barnett Way	Camp Lejeune, NC	28547-2552	910-449-8000		PK-5		Dewanda Sholar
Holbrook ES	PO Box 70089	Fort Bragg, NC	28307-0089	910-907-0205	432-8385	PK-5		Wanda McKinzy
Irwin IS	PO Box 70089	Fort Bragg, NC	28307-0089	910-907-0206	907-1247	3-5	500	Charlie Council
Johnson PS	2027 Stone St	Camp Lejeune, NC	28547-2506	910-451-2431	451-2433	PK-2		Scott Tefft
Lejeune HS	835 Stone St	Camp Lejeune, NC	28547-2520	910-451-2451	451-3130	9-12		Eric Steimel
Murray PS	PO Box 70089	Fort Bragg, NC	28307-0089	910-907-0208	907-2889	PK-2	300	Cassandra White
Pope ES	PO Box 70089	Fort Bragg, NC	28307-0089	910-907-0209	907-0901	PK-5	300	Dr. Kim McBroom
Shugart ES	PO Box 70089	Fort Bragg, NC	28307-0089	910-907-0210		PK-5	600	Dr. Carolyn Carr
Shugart MS	PO Box 70089	Fort Bragg, NC	28307-0089	910-907-0211		6-8	500	Mary Leinard
Tarawa Terrace ES	84 Iwo Jima Blvd	Tarawa Terrace, NC	28543-1231	910-450-1635	450-1637	PK-5		Leigh Kapiko
South Carolina / Fort Stewart SD	**376 Davis Ave**	**Fort Stewart, GA**	**31315-1033**	**912-369-6691**	**876-4339**	**PK-6**	**5,900**	**Dr. Samantha Ingram**
Bolden S, Charles Frank	1523 Laurel Bay Blvd	Beaufort, SC	29906-3675	843-846-6112	846-9283	3-8	4,000	Vicky Parr
Brittin ES	2772 Hero Rd	Fort Stewart, GA	31315-1713	912-368-3324	368-3412	PK-6	600	Shelia Cary
Diamond ES	482 Davis Ave	Fort Stewart, GA	31315-1015	912-876-5797	876-8350	PK-6		Brenda Gilchrist
Elliott ES, Middleton Stuart	1635 Albacore St	Beaufort, SC	29906-3570	843-846-6982	846-6720	PK-2	300	Latonya Leeks
Galer ES, Robert Edward	1516 Cardinal Ln	Beaufort, SC	29906-3486	843-846-6100	846-1860	PK-2	300	Carol Kipp-Caldwell
Kessler ES, Patrick	1127 Austin Rd	Fort Stewart, GA	31315-5792	912-368-3958	368-5048	PK-6	100	Dr. Djuna Underwood
Pierce Terrace ES	5715 Adams Ct	Columbia, SC	29206-5379	803-782-1772	738-8895	PK-2	300	Brian Perry
Pinckney ES, Charles C.	5900 Chesnut Rd	Columbia, SC	29206-5365	803-787-6815	790-2169	3-6	200	Annie Crandle

CATHOLIC SCHOOL SUPERINTENDENTS

NATIONAL CATHOLIC EDUCATIONAL ASSOC.
1005 N Glebe Rd Ste 525, Arlington, VA 22201-5792
Telephone 800-711-6232
Fax 243-0025
Website ncea.org

CATHOLIC SCHOOL SUPERINTENDENTS

Archdiocese/Diocese	Address	City,State	Zip code	Telephone	Fax	Grade	Enr	Superintendent
Diocese of Albany	40 N Main Ave	Albany, NY	12203-1481	518-453-6602	453-6667	PK-12	6,900	Michael Pizzingrillo
Diocese of Alexandria	PO Box 7417	Alexandria, LA	71306-0417	318-445-6424	448-6121	PK-12	2,800	Thomas Roque
Diocese of Allentown	2145 Madison Ave	Bethlehem, PA	18017-4698	610-866-0581	867-8702	PK-12	13,100	Philip Fromuth
Diocese of Altoona-Johnstown	933 S Logan Blvd	Hollidaysburg, PA	16648-3035	814-693-1401	696-6725	PK-12	4,400	Sr. Donna Leiden
Diocese of Amarillo	1800 N Spring St	Amarillo, TX	79107-7252	806-383-2243	383-8452	PK-12	600	Fr. Robert A. Busch Ph.D.
Archdiocese of Anchorage	225 Cordova St	Anchorage, AK	99501-2409	907-297-7790	297-7758	PK-12	500	Sr. Ann Fallon
Diocese of Arlington	200 N Glebe Rd Ste 614	Arlington, VA	22203-3728	703-841-2519	524-8670	PK-12	16,700	Sr. Bernadette McManigal
Archdiocese of Atlanta	2401 Lake Park Dr SE	Smyrna, GA	30080	404-920-7700	920-7701	PK-12	11,700	Diane Starkovich Ph.D.
Diocese of Austin	6225 E Highway 290	Austin, TX	78723-1025	512-949-2400	949-2520	PK-12	5,000	Dr. Ned Vanders
Diocese of Baker	PO Box 5999	Bend, OR	97708-5999	541-388-4004	388-2566	PK-8	500	Dr. Dennis Dempsey
Archdiocese of Baltimore	320 Cathedral St	Baltimore, MD	21201-4421	410-547-5555	539-5566	PK-12	28,700	Dr. Barbara Edmondson
Diocese of Baton Rouge	PO Box 2028	Baton Rouge, LA	70821-2028	225-336-8735	336-8711	PK-12	16,000	Dr. Melanie Verges
Diocese of Beaumont	PO Box 3948	Beaumont, TX	77704-3948	409-924-4322	838-4511	PK-12	1,600	Marcia Stevens
Diocese of Belleville	2620 Lebanon Ave	Belleville, IL	62221-3002	618-235-9601	235-7115	PK-12	6,100	Thomas Posnanski
Diocese of Biloxi	1790 Popps Ferry Rd	Biloxi, MS	39532-2118	228-702-2130	702-2178	PK-12	3,500	Dr. Mike Ladner
Diocese of Birmingham	PO Box 12047	Birmingham, AL	35202-2047	205-838-8303	838-8330	PK-12	6,200	Frances Lawlor
Diocese of Bismarck	218 1st St SE	Minot, ND	58701-3920	701-838-4603		PK-12	2,300	Fr. Justin Waltz
Diocese of Boise	1501 S Federal Way Ste 400	Boise, ID	83705-2591	208-342-1311	342-0224	PK-12	2,800	Bob Sobotta
Archdiocese of Boston	66 Brooks Dr	Braintree, MA	02184-3839	617-779-3604	746-5702	PK-12	40,700	Dr. Mary Grassa O'Neill
Diocese of Bridgeport	238 Jewett Ave	Bridgeport, CT	06606-2892	203-416-1375	372-1961	PK-12	11,700	Dr. Margaret Dames
Diocese of Brooklyn	310 Prospect Park W	Brooklyn, NY	11215-6214	718-965-7300	965-7353	PK-12	45,800	Dr. Thomas Chadzutko
Diocese of Brownsville	700 Virgen de San Juan	San Juan, TX	78589-3030	956-784-5051	784-5081	PK-12	3,900	Lisette Allen M.Ed.
Diocese of Buffalo	795 Main St	Buffalo, NY	14203-1250	716-847-5512	847-5593	PK-12	17,100	Carol Kostyniak
Diocese of Burlington	PO Box 2226	S Burlington, VT	05407-2226	802-658-6110	658-6112	PK-12	2,200	Mona Faulkner
Diocese of Camden	631 Market St	Camden, NJ	08102-1103	856-756-7900	756-0225	PK-12	15,000	Mary Boyle
Diocese of Charleston	1662 Ingram Rd	Charleston, SC	29407-4242	843-402-9115	402-5464	PK-12	7,000	Sandra Leatherwood
Diocese of Charlotte	1123 S Church St	Charlotte, NC	28203-4003	704-370-3214	370-3291	PK-12	7,600	Janice Ritter Ed.D.
Diocese of Cheyenne	PO Box 1468	Cheyenne, WY	82003-1468	307-638-1530	637-7936	PK-12	1,000	Vernon Dobelmann
Archdiocese of Chicago	PO Box 1979	Chicago, IL	60690-1979	312-534-5200	534-5295	PK-12	87,900	Sr. Mary McCaughey
Archdiocese of Cincinnati	100 E 8th St	Cincinnati, OH	45202	513-421-3131	421-6271	PK-12	45,800	Jim Rigg Ph.D.
Diocese of Cleveland	1404 E 9th St	Cleveland, OH	44114-1740	216-696-6525	579-9655	PK-12	48,200	Margaret Lyons
Diocese of Colorado Springs	228 N Cascade Ave	Colorado Spgs, CO	80903-1324	719-636-2345	866-6453	PK-12	1,800	Holly Goodwin
Diocese of Columbus	197 E Gay St	Columbus, OH	43215	614-221-5829	241-2563	PK-12	17,500	Lucia McQuaide
Diocese of Corpus Christi	PO Box 2620	Corpus Christi, TX	78403-2620	361-882-6191	693-6798	PK-12	3,500	Rene Gonzalez
Diocese of Covington	PO Box 15550	Covington, KY	41015-0550	859-392-1500	392-1537	K-12	10,800	Michael Clines
Diocese of Crookston	PO Box 610	Crookston, MN	56716-0610	218-444-4262	444-1381	PK-12	1,400	Al Foley
Diocese of Dallas	PO Box 190507	Dallas, TX	75219-0507	214-528-2360	522-1753	PK-12	14,900	Sr. Gloria Cain
Diocese of Davenport	780 W Central Park Ave	Davenport, IA	52804-1901	563-324-1911	324-5811	PK-12	4,900	Lee Morrison
Archdiocese of Denver	1300 S Steele St	Denver, CO	80210-2599	303-715-3200	715-2042	PK-12	14,800	Richard Thompson
Diocese of Des Moines	601 Grand Ave	Des Moines, IA	50309-2501	515-237-5013	237-5070	PK-12	6,400	Luvern Gubbels Ed.D.
Archdiocese of Detroit	305 Michigan Ave	Detroit, MI	48226	313-237-4661	237-5857	PK-12	33,100	Kimberly Young
Diocese of Dodge City	PO Box 137	Dodge City, KS	67801-0137	620-227-1535	227-1570	PK-8	1,100	Trina Delgado
Archdiocese of Dubuque	1229 Mount Loretta Ave	Dubuque, IA	52003-8787	563-556-2580	556-5464	PK-12	11,500	Dr. Jeff Henderson
Diocese of Duluth	2830 E 4th St	Duluth, MN	55812-1501	218-724-9111	724-1056	PK-8	1,600	Cynthia Zook
Diocese of El Paso	499 Saint Matthews St	El Paso, TX	79907-4214	915-872-8426	872-8434	PK-12	4,100	Sr. Elizabeth Swartz
Diocese of Erie	PO Box 10397	Erie, PA	16514-0397	814-824-1241	824-1247	PK-12	9,000	Patricia McLaughlin
Diocese of Evansville	PO Box 4169	Evansville, IN	47724-0169	812-424-5536	424-0973	PK-12	7,100	Daryl Hagan
Diocese of Fairbanks	615 Monroe St	Fairbanks, AK	99701-2936	907-456-4574	456-7481	K-12	500	Nancy Hanson
Diocese of Fall River	423 Highland Ave	Fall River, MA	02720-3718	508-678-2828	674-4218	PK-12	7,400	Dr. Michael Griffin
Diocese of Fargo	5600 25th St S	Fargo, ND	58104-7123	701-893-3305		PK-12	2,000	David Haney
Diocese of Fort Worth	800 W Loop 820 S	Fort Worth, TX	76108-2936	817-560-3300	244-8839	PK-12	6,300	Donald Miller
Diocese of Fresno	1510 N Fresno St	Fresno, CA	93703-3711	559-488-7420	488-7422	PK-12	6,400	Richard Sexton
Diocese of Ft. Wayne-South Bend	PO Box 390	Fort Wayne, IN	46801-0390	260-422-4611	426-3077	PK-12	12,300	Dr. Mark Myers
Diocese of Gallup	PO Box 1338	Gallup, NM	87305-1338	505-863-4406	722-6644	PK-12	1,400	Fr. James Walker
Archdiocese of Galveston-Houston	2403 Holcombe Blvd	Houston, TX	77021-2023	713-741-8704	741-7379	PK-12	17,900	Sr. Kevina Keating
Diocese of Gary	9292 Broadway	Merrillville, IN	46410-7088	219-769-9292	738-9034	PK-12	6,500	Barbara O'Block Ed.D.
Diocese of Gaylord	611 W North St	Gaylord, MI	49735-8349	989-732-5147	705-3589	PK-12	3,000	Charles Taylor
Diocese of Grand Island	PO Box 996	Grand Island, NE	68802-0996	308-382-6565	382-6569	PK-12	1,400	Rev. Thomas Ryan
Diocese of Grand Rapids	360 Division Ave S Ste 3A	Grand Rapids, MI	49503-4501	616-246-0590	551-5650	PK-12	6,400	David Faber
Diocese of Great Falls-Billings	121 23rd St S	Great Falls, MT	59401-3997	406-594-1461	454-3480	PK-12	2,500	Patrick Haggarty Ed.D.
Diocese of Green Bay	PO Box 23825	Green Bay, WI	54305-3825	920-437-7531	272-8430	PK-12	10,600	Dr. Joseph Bound
Diocese of Greensburg	723 E Pittsburgh St	Greensburg, PA	15601-2697	724-837-0901	837-0857	PK-12	3,800	Trent Bocan
Diocese of Harrisburg	4800 Union Deposit Rd	Harrisburg, PA	17111-3710	717-657-4804	657-3790	PK-12	12,000	Livia Riley
Archdiocese of Hartford	467 Bloomfield Ave	Bloomfield, CT	06002-2903	860-242-4362	242-8683	PK-12	16,300	Dale Hoyt
Diocese of Helena	515 N Ewing St	Helena, MT	59601-4002	406-594-1461		PK-12	1,400	Patrick Haggarty Ed.D.
Diocese of Honolulu	6301 Pali Hwy	Kaneohe, HI	96744-5224	808-263-8844	262-6126	PK-12	10,200	Michael Rockers Ed.D.
Diocese of Houma-Thibodaux	PO Box 505	Schriever, LA	70395-0505	985-850-3113	850-3225	PK-12	5,900	Marian Fertitta
Archdiocese of Indianapolis	1400 N Meridian St	Indianapolis, IN	46202-2305	317-236-1430	261-3364	PK-12	21,900	Gina Kuntz Fleming
Diocese of Jackson	PO Box 2248	Jackson, MS	39225-2248	601-969-2742	960-8469	PK-12	4,300	Catherine Cook
Diocese of Jefferson City	PO Box 104900	Jefferson City, MO	65110-4900	573-635-9127	635-2286	PK-12	7,100	Rev. Joseph Corel
Diocese of Joliet	101 Airport Rd	Romeoville, IL	60446-6527	815-838-2181	838-2182	PK-12	21,800	Fr. John Belmonte Ph.D.
Diocese of Juneau	415 6th St Ste 300	Juneau, AK	99801-1091	907-586-2227	463-3237	PK-6	100	
Diocese of Kalamazoo	215 N Westnedge Ave	Kalamazoo, MI	49007-3760	269-349-8714	349-0166	PK-12	3,400	Margaret Erich
Archdiocese of Kansas City	12615 Parallel Pkwy	Kansas City, KS	66109-3748	913-721-1570	721-5598	PK-12	15,500	Dr. Kathleen O'Hara
Diocese of Kansas City-Saint Joseph	PO Box 419037	Kansas City, MO	64141-6037	816-756-1850	756-1571	PK-12	11,900	Dr. Dan Peters
Diocese of Knoxville	805 S Northshore Dr	Knoxville, TN	37919	865-584-3307	584-4319	PK-12	3,400	Sr. Mary Marta Abbott
Diocese of La Crosse	PO Box 4004	La Crosse, WI	54602-4004	608-788-7707	788-7709	PK-12	7,600	Dr. Susan Holman
Diocese of Lafayette	1408 Carmel Dr	Lafayette, LA	70501-5215	337-261-5529	261-5572	PK-12	15,100	Anna Larriviere
Diocese of Lafayette-in-Indiana	2300 S 9th St	Lafayette, IN	47909-2400	765-269-4670	269-4671	PK-12	5,000	Marie Williams
Diocese of Lake Charles	1112 Bilbo St	Lake Charles, LA	70601-5226	337-433-9640	433-9685	PK-12	2,500	Kimberlee Gazzolo
Diocese of Lansing	228 N Walnut St	Lansing, MI	48933-1122	517-342-2482	342-2515	PK-12	9,600	Rev. Steven Mattson
Diocese of Laredo	1201 Corpus Christi St	Laredo, TX	78040-5354	956-753-5208	753-5203	K-12	2,100	Dr. Rosa Maria Vida
Diocese of Las Cruces	1280 Med Park Dr	Las Cruces, NM	88005-3239	575-523-7577	524-3874	PK-8	600	Ben Trujillo
Diocese of Las Vegas	PO Box 18316	Las Vegas, NV	89114-8316	702-697-3903	735-8941	K-12	3,900	Rev. Robert Stoecki
Diocese of Lexington	1310 W Main St	Lexington, KY	40508-2048	859-253-1993	253-0939	PK-12	4,200	Tim Weaver
Diocese of Lincoln	PO Box 80328	Lincoln, NE	68501-0328	402-488-2040	488-6525	K-12	7,000	Rev. John Perkinton
Diocese of Little Rock	PO Box 7565	Little Rock, AR	72217-7565	501-664-0340	603-0518	K-12	7,100	Vernell Bowen M.Ed.
Archdiocese of Los Angeles	3424 Wilshire Blvd	Los Angeles, CA	90010-2241	213-637-7300	637-6140	PK-12	81,600	Dr. Kevin Baxter
Archdiocese of Louisville	1935 Lewiston Dr	Louisville, KY	40216-2523	502-448-8581	448-5518	PK-12	20,800	Leisa Schulz
Diocese of Lubbock	PO Box 98700	Lubbock, TX	79499-8700	806-792-3943	792-8109	PK-12	400	Christine Wanjura
Diocese of Madison	PO Box 44983	Madison, WI	53744-4983	608-821-3180	821-3181	PK-12	7,600	Michael Lancaster
Diocese of Manchester	PO Box 310	Manchester, NH	03105-0310	603-669-3100	669-0377	PK-12	7,400	Rev. Dennis Audet
Diocese of Marquette	1004 Harbor Hills Dr	Marquette, MI	49855-8897	906-227-9127	225-0437	PK-8	1,300	Mark Salisbury
Diocese of Memphis	5825 Shelby Oaks Dr	Memphis, TN	38134-7316	901-373-1219	373-1223	PK-12	7,100	Dr. Mary McDonald
Diocese of Metuchen	146 Metlars Ln	Piscataway, NJ	08854-4303	732-562-1990	562-1016	PK-12	12,100	Ellen Ayoub
Archdiocese of Miami	9401 Biscayne Blvd	Miami Shores, FL	33138-2970	305-762-1076	762-1115	PK-12	34,200	Kim Pryzbylski Ph.D.
Archdiocese of Milwaukee	PO Box 070912	Milwaukee, WI	53207-0912	414-758-2256	769-3408	PK-12	30,100	Dr. Kathleen Cepelka
Archdiocese of Mobile	PO Box 129	Mobile, AL	36601-0129	251-438-4611	438-4612	PK-12	6,300	Gwen Byrd
Diocese of Monterey	485 Church St	Monterey, CA	93940-3207	831-373-1608	373-0173	PK-12	5,000	Kathleen Radecke
Diocese of Nashville	30 White Bridge Rd	Nashville, TN	37205-1401	615-352-7218	353-7972	PK-12	6,200	Dr. Therese Williams
Archdiocese of Newark	PO Box 9500	Newark, NJ	07104-0500	973-497-4260	497-4249	PK-12	33,300	Dr. Margaret Dames
Archdiocese of New Orleans	7887 Walmsley Ave	New Orleans, LA	70125-3496	504-866-7916	861-6260	PK-12	39,900	Dr. Jan Lancaster
Diocese of New Ulm	1400 6th St N	New Ulm, MN	56073-2099	507-359-2966	354-3667	PK-12	2,300	Karla Cross
Archdiocese of New York	1011 1st Ave Fl 6	New York, NY	10022-4112	212-371-1000	317-9236	PK-12	72,200	Dr. Timothy McNiff

Archdiocese/Diocese	Address	City,State	Zip code	Telephone	Fax	Grade	Enr	Superintendent
Diocese of Norwich	43 Perkins Ave	Norwich, CT	06360-3643	860-887-4086	887-9371	PK-12	4,600	Dr. John Shine
Diocese of Oakland	2121 Harrison St	Oakland, CA	94612	510-628-2154	451-5331	PK-12	17,600	Sr. Barbara Bray
Diocese of Ogdensburg	PO Box 369	Ogdensburg, NY	13669-0369	315-393-2920	314-7296	PK-12	2,300	Sr. Ellen Coughlin
Archdiocese of Oklahoma City	PO Box 32180	Oklahoma City, OK	73123-0380	405-721-5651	709-2811	PK-12	4,900	Dr. Cristiana Carter
Archdiocese of Omaha	3300 N 60th St	Omaha, NE	68104-3402	402-554-8493	827-3792	PK-12	19,400	Msgr. James Gilg
Diocese of Orange	PO Box 14195	Orange, CA	92863-1595	714-282-3065	282-5059	PK-12	19,800	Gregory Dhuyvetter
Diocese of Orlando	PO Box 1800	Orlando, FL	32802-1800	407-246-4900	246-4940	PK-12	14,100	Henry Fortier
Diocese of Owensboro	600 Locust St	Owensboro, KY	42301-2130	270-683-1545	683-6883	PK-12	3,900	Jim Mattingly
Diocese of Palm Beach	9995 N Military Trl	West Palm Beach, FL	33410-5497	561-775-9547	775-9545	PK-12	6,600	Gary Gelo
Diocese of Paterson	777 Valley Rd	Clifton, NJ	07013-2297	973-777-8818	779-0083	PK-12	12,300	Br. William Dygert Ph.D.
Diocese of Pensacola-Tallahassee	11 N B St	Pensacola, FL	32502-4601	850-435-3500	436-6424	PK-12	2,800	Kevin Vickery
Diocese of Peoria	419 NE Madison Ave	Peoria, IL	61603	309-671-1579	671-1595	PK-12	11,200	Sharon Weiss Ed.D.
Archdiocese of Philadelphia	222 N 17th St	Philadelphia, PA	19103-1295	215-587-3700	587-5644	PK-12	72,500	Mary Rochford
Diocese of Phoenix	400 E Monroe St	Phoenix, AZ	85004-2336	602-354-2345	354-2436	PK-12	14,300	MaryBeth Mueller
Diocese of Pittsburgh	111 Blvd of the Allies	Pittsburgh, PA	15222-1618	412-456-3090	456-3098	PK-12	19,900	Michael Latusek Ed.D.
Archdiocese of Portland	2838 E Burnside St	Portland, OR	97214-1895	503-233-8300	236-3683	PK-12	13,900	Robert Mizia
Diocese of Portland	510 Ocean Ave	Portland, ME	04103-4900	207-773-6471	773-0182	PK-12	3,300	Sr. Rosemary Donohue
Diocese of Providence	1 Cathedral Sq	Providence, RI	02903-3695	401-278-4550	278-4596	PK-12	14,500	Daniel Ferris
Diocese of Pueblo	101 N Greenwood St	Pueblo, CO	81003-3164	719-561-1121	561-2251	PK-8	900	John Brainard M.Ed.
Diocese of Raleigh	715 Nazareth St	Raleigh, NC	27606-2187	919-821-9749	522-1695	PK-12	8,900	Dr. Michael Fedewa
Diocese of Rapid City	300 Fairmont Blvd	Rapid City, SD	57701-5423	605-343-8484	343-1315	K-12	1,000	Barb Honeycutt
Diocese of Reno	290 S Arlington Ave Ste 200	Reno, NV	89501-1713	775-326-9430	348-8619	PK-12	1,700	Karen Barreras
Diocese of Richmond	7800 Carousel Ln	Richmond, VA	23294-4201	804-359-5661	358-9159	PK-12	9,100	Annette Parsons
Diocese of Rochester	1150 Buffalo Rd	Rochester, NY	14624-1890	585-328-3228	328-3149	PK-12	8,200	Anne Willkens Leach
Diocese of Rockford	PO Box 7044	Rockford, IL	61125-7044	815-399-4300	399-6278	PK-12	14,400	Michael Kagan
Diocese of Rockville Centre	PO Box 9023	Rockville Ctr, NY	11571-9023	516-678-5800	678-7362	PK-12	30,300	Sr. Joanne Callahan
Diocese of Sacramento	2110 Broadway	Sacramento, CA	95818-2518	916-733-0110	733-0120	PK-12	13,900	Rick Maya
Diocese of Saginaw	5800 Weiss St	Saginaw, MI	48603-2762	989-799-7910	399-2257	PK-12	3,200	Mary Ann Deschaine
Diocese of St. Augustine	11625 Old St Augustine Rd	Jacksonville, FL	32258	904-262-3200	596-1042	PK-12	10,500	Patricia Bronsard
Diocese of St. Cloud	305 7th Ave N Ste 201	Saint Cloud, MN	56303-3633	320-251-0111	251-0259	PK-12	4,900	Linda Kaiser
Archdiocese of St. Louis	4445 Lindell Blvd	Saint Louis, MO	63108-2403	314-792-7300	792-7350	PK-12	44,200	George Henry
Archdiocese of St. Paul	328 Kellogg Blvd W	Saint Paul, MN	55102-1900	651-291-4500	290-1628	PK-12	33,100	
Diocese of St. Petersburg	PO Box 40200	St Petersburg, FL	33743-0200	727-347-5539	341-6848	PK-12	13,100	Alberto Vazquez Matos
Diocese of Salina	PO Box 825	Salina, KS	67402-0825	785-827-8746	827-6133	PK-12	2,300	Dr. Nick Compagnone
Diocese of Salt Lake City	27 C St	Salt Lake City, UT	84103-2302	801-328-8641	328-8643	PK-12	5,500	Sr. Catherine Kamphaus
Diocese of San Angelo	499 Saint Matthews St	El Paso, TX	79907-4214	915-872-8426	872-8423	PK-8	700	Sr. Elizabeth Ann Swartz
Archdiocese of San Antonio	2718 W Woodlawn Ave	San Antonio, TX	78228-5195	210-734-2620	734-9112	PK-12	12,800	Patricia Davis
Diocese of San Bernardino	1201 E Highland Ave	San Bernardino, CA	92404-4641	909-475-5437	475-5477	PK-12	7,300	Patricia Vesely
Diocese of San Diego	PO Box 85728	San Diego, CA	92186-5728	858-490-8240	490-8272	PK-12	14,400	Tom Beecher
Archdiocese of San Francisco	1 Peter Yorke Way	San Francisco, CA	94109-6602	415-614-5660	614-5664	PK-12	24,900	Maureen Huntington
Diocese of San Jose	1150 N 1st St Ste 100	San Jose, CA	95112-4966	408-983-0100	983-0295	PK-12	16,100	Kathy Almazol
Archdiocese of Santa Fe	4000 Saint Josephs Pl NW	Albuquerque, NM	87120-1714	505-831-8173	831-8107	PK-12	5,100	Susan Murphy
Diocese of Santa Rosa	PO Box 1297	Santa Rosa, CA	95402-1297	707-566-3311	566-3382	PK-12	4,300	Dr. John Collins
Diocese of Savannah	601 E Liberty St	Savannah, GA	31401-5118	912-201-4121	201-4101	K-12	5,400	Sr. Rose Mary Collins
Diocese of Scranton	300 Wyoming Ave	Scranton, PA	18503-1243	570-207-2251	207-2261	PK-12	5,900	Dr. Kathleen Hanlon
Archdiocese of Seattle	710 9th Ave	Seattle, WA	98104-2017	206-382-4861	654-4651	PK-12	23,100	Stephen Rowan Ph.D.
Diocese of Shreveport	3500 Fairfield Ave	Shreveport, LA	71104-4108	318-219-7253	868-5057	PK-12	1,800	Sr. Carol Shively
Diocese of Sioux City	PO Box 3379	Sioux City, IA	51102-3379	712-255-7933	233-7598	PK-12	6,200	Dan Ryan
Diocese of Sioux Falls	523 N Duluth Ave	Sioux Falls, SD	57104-2714	605-988-3766	988-3795	PK-12	5,200	Katie Mellor
Diocese of Spokane	PO Box 1453	Spokane, WA	99210-1453	509-358-7330	358-7302	PK-12	4,700	Duane Schafer Ph.D.
Diocese of Springfield-Cape Girardeau	601 S Jefferson Ave	Springfield, MO	65806-3107	417-866-0841	866-1140	PK-12	4,300	Leon Witt
Diocese of Springfield	1615 W Washington St	Springfield, IL	62702-4757	217-698-8500	698-8620	PK-12	10,800	Jean Johnson
Diocese of Springfield	PO Box 1730	Springfield, MA	01102-1730	413-452-0830	452-0555	PK-12	4,700	Sr. M. Andrea Ciszewski
Diocese of Steubenville	PO Box 969	Steubenville, OH	43952-5969	740-282-3631	282-3327	PK-12	1,800	Paul Ward
Diocese of Stockton	212 N San Joaquin St	Stockton, CA	95202-2409	209-466-0636	463-5937	PK-12	4,200	Tom Butler
Diocese of Superior	PO Box 280	Haugen, WI	54841-0280	715-234-5044	234-5241	PK-8	2,400	Peggy Schoenfuss
Diocese of Syracuse	240 E Onondaga St	Syracuse, NY	13202-2668	315-470-1450	470-1470	PK-12	5,900	Christopher Mominey
Diocese of Toledo	1933 Spielbusch Ave	Toledo, OH	43604-5360	419-244-6711	244-4791	PK-12	20,000	Christopher Knight
Diocese of Trenton	PO Box 5147	Trenton, NJ	08638-0147	609-406-7145	406-7429	PK-12	21,100	JoAnn Tier
Diocese of Tucson	PO Box 31	Tucson, AZ	85702-0031	520-792-3410	838-2589	PK-12	7,400	Sr. Rosa Maria Ruiz
Diocese of Tulsa	820 S Boulder Ave	Tulsa, OK	74119-1624	918-582-9177	582-1851	PK-12	4,500	Jim Pohlman
Diocese of Tyler	1015 E Southeast Loop 323	Tyler, TX	75701-9656	903-534-1077	534-1370	PK-12	1,000	Dr. James Klassen
Diocese of Venice in Florida	1000 Pinebrook Rd	Venice, FL	34285-6426	941-484-9543	484-1121	PK-12	4,400	Dr. Kathleen Schwartz
Diocese of Victoria	PO Box 4070	Victoria, TX	77903-4070	361-573-0828	573-5725	PK-12	3,100	John Quary
Archdiocese of Washington DC	5001 Eastern Ave	Hyattsville, MD	20782-3447	301-853-4500	853-7670	PK-12	27,700	Bert L'Homme
Diocese of Wheeling-Charleston	PO Box 230	Wheeling, WV	26003-0010	304-232-0444	233-8551	PK-12	5,700	Vincent Schmidt M.A.
Diocese of Wichita	424 N Broadway St	Wichita, KS	67202-2310	316-269-3950	269-2486	PK-12	10,500	Bob Voboril
Diocese of Wilmington	1626 N Union St	Wilmington, DE	19806-2540	302-573-3133	573-6945	PK-12	12,500	Catherine Weaver
Diocese of Winona	PO Box 588	Winona, MN	55987-0588	507-858-1269	454-8106	PK-12	5,500	Marsha Stenzel
Diocese of Worcester	49 Elm St	Worcester, MA	01609-2514	508-929-4317	929-4386	PK-12	7,900	Delma Josephson Ph.D.
Diocese of Yakima	5301 Tieton Dr Ste B	Yakima, WA	98908-3479	509-965-7117	966-8334	PK-12	1,800	Rev. Thomas Kuykendall
Diocese of Youngstown	144 W Wood St	Youngstown, OH	44503-1081	330-744-8451	744-5099	K-12	8,400	Dr. Nicholas Wolsonovich

LUTHERAN SCHOOL SUPERINTENDENTS

LUTHERAN CHURCH MISSOURI SYNOD
1333 S Kirkwood Rd, Saint Louis, MO 63122-7295
Telephone 314-965-9000
Fax 996-1016
Website http://www.lcms.org

LUTHERAN SCHOOL SUPERINTENDENTS

Region	Address	City,State	Zip code	Telephone	Fax	Superintendent
Atlantic	171 White Plains Rd	Bronxville, NY	10708-1923	914-337-5700	337-7471	Dr. David Benke
California-Nevada-Hawaii	2772 Constitution Dr Ste A	Livermore, CA	94551-7571	925-245-4000	245-1107	Dr. Robert Newton
Central Illinois	1850 N Grand Ave W	Springfield, IL	62702-1626	217-793-1802	793-1822	Rev. Mark Miller
Eastern	5111 Main St	Williamsville, NY	14221-5203	716-634-5111	634-5452	Dr. Chris Wicher
English	33100 Freedom Rd	Farmington, MI	48336-4030	248-476-0039	476-0188	Rev. David Stechholz
Florida-Georgia	5850 T G Lee Blvd Ste 500	Orlando, FL	32822-4410	407-857-5556	857-5665	Mark Brink
Indiana	1145 Barr St	Fort Wayne, IN	46802-3135	260-423-1511	423-1514	Daniel May
Iowa East	1100 Blairs Ferry Rd	Marion, IA	52302-3093	319-373-2112	373-9827	Brian Saunders
Iowa West	409 Kenyon Rd Ste B	Fort Dodge, IA	50501-5718	515-576-7666	576-2323	Rev. Paul Sieveking
Kansas	1000 SW 10th Ave	Topeka, KS	66604-1104	785-357-4441	357-5071	Keith Kohlmeier
Michigan	3773 Geddes Rd	Ann Arbor, MI	48105-3028	734-665-3791	665-0255	Rev. David Maier
Mid-South	1675 Wynne Rd	Cordova, TN	38016-4905	901-373-1343	373-4826	Dr. Roger Paavola
Minnesota North	PO Box 604	Brainerd, MN	56401-0604	218-829-1781	829-0037	Rev. Donald Fondow
Minnesota South	14301 Grand Ave	Burnsville, MN	55306-5790	952-435-2550	435-2581	Dr. Dean Nadasdy
Missouri	660 Mason Ridge Center Dr	Saint Louis, MO	63141-8557	314-590-6215	590-6202	Dennis Gehrke
Montana	30 Broadwater Ave	Billings, MT	59101-1826	406-259-2908	259-1305	Rev. Terry Forke
Nebraska	PO Box 407	Seward, NE	68434-0407	888-643-2961	643-2990	Russ Sommerfeld
New England	400 Wilbraham Rd	Springfield, MA	01109-2723	413-783-0131	783-0909	Tim Yeadon
New Jersey	1168 Springfield Ave	Mountainside, NJ	07092-2906	908-233-8111	233-3883	Rev. Anthony Steinbronn
North Dakota	PO Box 9029	Fargo, ND	58106-9029	877-293-9001	293-9022	Dr. James Baneck
Northern Illinois	2301 S Wolf Rd	Hillside, IL	60162-2211	708-449-3020	449-3026	Rev. Dan Gilbert
Northwest	1700 NE Knott St	Portland, OR	97212-3301	503-288-8383	284-2785	Paul Linnemann
North Wisconsin	3103 Seymour Ln	Wausau, WI	54401-4049	715-845-8241	845-3836	Rev. Paul Weber
Ohio	PO Box 38277	Olmsted Falls, OH	44138-0277	440-235-2297	235-1970	Gordon Stuckert
Oklahoma	308 NW 164th St	Edmond, OK	73013-2006	405-348-7600	384-7601	Rev. Barrie Henke
Pacific Southwest	1540 Concordia	Irvine, CA	92612-3203	949-854-3232	854-8140	Rachel Klitzing
Rocky Mountain	14334 E Evans Ave	Aurora, CO	80014-1408	303-695-8001	695-4047	Rev. Allen Anderson

Region	Address	City,State	Zip code	Telephone	Fax	Superintendent
SELC	4850 S Lake Dr	Cudahy, WI	53110-1743	414-698-7208	481-0736	Rev. Carl Krueger
South Dakota	PO Box 89110	Sioux Falls, SD	57109-9110	605-361-1514	361-7959	Rev. Dale Sattgast
Southeastern	6315 Grovedale Dr	Alexandria, VA	22310-2501	703-971-9371	922-6047	Rev. John Denninger
Southern	100 Mission Dr	Slidell, LA	70460-5221	504-282-2632	871-9696	Rev. Kurtis Schultz
Southern Illinois	2408 Lebanon Ave	Belleville, IL	62221-2529	618-234-4767	234-4830	Roger Sprengel
South Wisconsin	8100 W Capitol Dr	Milwaukee, WI	53222-1981	414-464-8100	464-0602	John Wille
Texas	7900 E Highway 290	Austin, TX	78724-2402	512-926-4272	926-1006	Ken Hennings
Wyoming	2400 S Hickory St	Casper, WY	82604-3471	307-265-9000	234-6629	Rev. Richard Boche

GENERAL CONFERENCE OF SEVENTH-DAY ADVENTISTS SUPERINTENDENTS

NORTH AMERICAN DIV. OFFICE OF EDUCATION
12501 Old Columbia Pike, Silver Spring, MD 20904-6601
Telephone 301-680-6400
Fax 680-6464
Website http://www.nadadventist.org

GENERAL CONFERENCE OF SEVENTH-DAY ADVENTISTS SUPERINTENDENTS

Conference	Address	City,State	Zip code	Telephone	Fax	Superintendent
Atlantic Union	**PO Box 1189**	**South Lancaster, MA**	**01561-1189**	**978-368-8333**	**368-7948**	**Astrid Thomassian**
Greater New York Conference	PO Box 5029	Manhasset, NY	11030-5029	516-627-9350	627-9272	David Cadavero
New York Conference	4930 W Seneca Tpke	Syracuse, NY	13215-2225	315-469-6921	469-6924	Kim Kaiser
Northeastern Conference	11550 Merrick Blvd	Jamaica, NY	11434-1852	718-291-8006	739-5133	Viola Chapman
Northern New England Conference	479 Main St	Westbrook, ME	04092-4330	207-797-3760	797-2851	Trudy Wright M.A.
Southern New England Conference	PO Box 1169	South Lancaster, MA	01561-1169	978-365-4551	365-3838	Pat Giese
Columbia Union Conference	**5427 Twin Knolls Rd**	**Columbia, MD**	**21045-3200**	**410-997-3414**	**997-7420**	**Hamlet Canosa**
Allegheny East Conference	767 Douglass Dr	Boyertown, PA	19512-7775	610-326-4610	326-3946	Judy Dent
Allegheny West Conference	1339 E Broad St	Columbus, OH	43205-1588	614-252-5271	252-3246	William Cox
Chesapeake Conference	6600 Martin Rd	Columbia, MD	21044-3999	410-995-1910	995-1434	Carole Smith Ed.D.
Mountain View Conference	1400 Liberty St	Parkersburg, WV	26101-4124	304-422-4581	422-4582	Larry Boggess
New Jersey Conference	2303 Brunswick Ave	Lawrenceville, NJ	08648-4410	609-802-0840	396-9273	Sadrail Saint-Ulysse
Ohio Conference	PO Box 1230	Mount Vernon, OH	43050-8230	740-397-4665	397-1648	Alison Jobson
Pennsylvania Conference	720 Museum Rd	Reading, PA	19611-1429	610-374-8331	374-9331	Ray Hartwell
Potomac Conference	606 Greenville Ave	Staunton, VA	24401-4881	540-886-0771	886-5734	Keith Hallam
Lake Union Conference	**PO Box 287**	**Berrien Springs, MI**	**49103-0287**	**269-473-8200**	**473-8209**	**Don Livesay**
Illinois Conference	619 Plainfield Rd Ste 200	Willowbrook, IL	60527-8438	630-856-2890	734-0929	Bill Reinke
Indiana Conference	PO Box 1950	Carmel, IN	46082-1950	317-844-6201	571-9281	Mark Haynal M.A.
Lake Region Conference	8517 S State St	Chicago, IL	60619-5697	773-846-2661	846-5309	Dr. Ruth Horton
Michigan Conference	PO Box 19009	Lansing, MI	48901-9009	517-316-1500	316-1559	Linda Fuchs
Wisconsin Conference	PO Box 100	Fall River, WI	53932-0100	920-484-6555	484-6550	Linda Rosen
Mid-America Union Conference	**PO Box 6128**	**Lincoln, NE**	**68506-0128**	**402-484-3000**	**483-4453**	**John Kriegelstein**
Central States Conference	3301 Parallel Pkwy	Kansas City, KS	66104-4354	913-371-1071	371-1609	Judith Mason
Dakota Conference	7200 N Washington St	Bismarck, ND	58503-6301	701-751-6177	751-6178	Neil Biloff
Iowa-Missouri Conference	PO Box 65665	West Des Moines, IA	50265-0665	515-223-1197	223-5692	Dr. Joseph Allison
Kansas-Nebraska Conference	3440 SW Urish Rd	Topeka, KS	66614-4601	785-478-4726	478-1000	Gary Kruger
Minnesota Conference	7384 Kirkwood Ct	Maple Grove, MN	55369-5200	763-424-8923	424-9576	Connie McCormick
Rocky Mountain Conference	2520 S Downing St	Denver, CO	80210-5818	303-282-3650	733-1843	Lonnie Hetterle
North Pacific Union Conference	**5709 N 20th St**	**Ridgefield, WA**	**98642-7724**	**360-857-7000**	**857-7001**	**Alan Hurlbert M.Ed.**
Alaska Conference	6100 OMalley Rd	Anchorage, AK	99507-6958	907-346-1004	346-3279	Tom Maher
Idaho Conference	7777 W Fairview Ave	Boise, ID	83704-8418	208-375-7524	375-7526	
Montana Conference	175 Canyon View Rd	Bozeman, MT	59715-0607	406-587-3101	587-1598	Archie Harris
Oregon Conference	19800 Oatfield Rd	Gladstone, OR	97027-2564	503-850-3500	654-5657	Wayne Wentland
Upper Columbia Conference	3715 S Grove Rd	Spokane, WA	99224-6090	509-838-2761	838-4882	Larry Marsh
Washington Conference	32229 Weyerhaeuser Way S	Federal Way, WA	98001-9347	253-681-6008	681-6009	Kelly Bock Ph.D.
Pacific Union Conference	**PO Box 5005**	**Westlake Vlg, CA**	**91359-5005**	**805-413-7314**	**413-7319**	**Berit von Pohle**
Arizona Conference	PO Box 12340	Scottsdale, AZ	85267-2340	480-991-6777	991-4833	Ivan Weiss M.A.
Central California Conference	PO Box 770	Clovis, CA	93613-0770	559-347-3000	347-3120	Ramiro Cano
Hawaii Conference	2728 Pali Hwy	Honolulu, HI	96817-1485	808-595-7591	595-2345	Teryl Loeffler M.Ed.
Nevada-Utah Conference	10475 Double R Blvd	Reno, NV	89521-8905	775-322-6929	322-9371	Larry Unterseher
Northern California Conference	PO Box 23165	Pleasant Hill, CA	94523-0165	925-685-4300	685-4380	Berit vonPohle
Southeastern California Conference	PO Box 8050	Riverside, CA	92515-8050	951-509-2200	509-2390	Donald Dudley
Southern California Conference	PO Box 969	Glendale, CA	91209-0969	818-546-8400	546-8454	Harold Crook
Southern Union Conference	**PO Box 849**	**Decatur, GA**	**30031-0849**	**404-299-1832**	**299-9726**	**Debra Fryson**
Carolina Conference	PO Box 44270	Charlotte, NC	28215-0043	704-596-3200	596-5775	Gary Rouse
Florida Conference	PO Box 2626	Winter Park, FL	32790-2626	407-644-5000	644-7550	Frank Runnels Ed.D.
Georgia-Cumberland Conference	PO Box 12000	Calhoun, GA	30703-7001	706-629-7951	625-3684	Cynthia Gettys Ph.D.
Gulf States Conference	PO Box 240249	Montgomery, AL	36124-0249	334-272-7493	272-7987	Gary Swinyar
Kentucky-Tennessee Conference	PO Box 1088	Goodlettsville, TN	37070-1088	615-859-1391	859-2120	Chris Juhl
South Atlantic Conference	PO Box 92447	Atlanta, GA	30314-0447	404-792-0535	792-7817	James Lamb
South Central Conference	PO Box 78767	Nashville, TN	37207-8767	615-226-6500	262-9141	Dr. Eunice Warfield
Southeastern Conference	1701 Robie Ave	Mount Dora, FL	32757-6339	352-735-3142	735-3562	Carol Byrd
Southwestern Union Conference	**PO Box 4000**	**Burleson, TX**	**76097-1630**	**817-295-0476**	**447-2443**	**Larry Moore**
Arkansas-Louisiana Conference	PO Box 31000	Shreveport, LA	71130-1000	318-631-6240	631-6247	Steve Burton
Oklahoma Conference	PO Box 32098	Oklahoma City, OK	73123-0298	405-721-6110	721-7594	Jack Francisco
Southwest Region Conference	PO Box 226289	Dallas, TX	75222-6289	214-943-4491	946-2528	Samuel Green
Texas Conference	PO Box 800	Alvarado, TX	76009-0800	817-790-2255	783-5266	Carlos Craig
Texico Conference	PO Box 1366	Corrales, NM	87048-1366	505-244-1611	244-1811	James Stevens